DIRECTORY
OF
AMERICAN
SCHOLARS

DIRECTORY

OF

AMERICAN

SCHOLARS

SIXTH EDITION

VOLUME II
ENGLISH,
SPEECH
& DRAMA

EDITED BY JAQUES CATTELL PRESS

R. R. BOWKER COMPANY
New York & London, 1974
A Xerox Education Company

XEROX

Published by R. R. Bowker Comapny (a Xerox Education Company)
1180 Avenue of the Americas, New York, N.Y. 10036

International Standard Book Number: 0-8352-0648-3
International Standard Serial Number: 0070-5101
Library of Congress Catalog Card Number: 57-9125

Printed and bound in the United States of America

CONTENTS

PREFACE

The Sixth Edition of the *Directory of American Scholars* is the culmination of a year's work and nearly 70 years' experience in producing biographical directories by the Jaques Cattell Press. More than 38,000 scholars are profiled in the four-volume set: I. History; II. English, Speech and Drama; III. Foreign Languages, Linguistics and Philology; and IV. Philosophy, Religion and Law. This, the English, Speech and Drama volume, has increased by over 800 entries since the previous edition and contains research and publication information on subject specialties as diverse as Piers Plowman, speech education in Japan and the rhetoric of graffiti.

Special features designed to facilitate research and increase the usefulness of the directory include the listing of cross-references for scholars with major involvement in several fields, a geographic index, including disciplines, in each volume and an alphabetic index of all scholars at the end of Volume IV.

From the gathering of information to the final pagination, the many phases in the production of the *Directory of American Scholars* have been completed by a cooperative staff, dedicated to sustaining quality. Their accomplishments are deeply appreciated. Gratitude is expressed also to the American Council of Learned Societies for their continued interest in this project and to the many societies, colleges and universities that were so generous with their help.

The staff has made a concerted effort to reproduce the material submitted by biographees as accurately and completely as possible within the confines of format and scope. However, the publishers do not assume and hereby disclaim any liability to any party for any loss or damage caused by errors or omissions in the *Directory of American Scholars,* whether such errors or omissions result from negligence, accident or any other cause.

Reader's comments and suggestions are invited and should be addressed to The Editors, Directory of American Scholars, Jaques Cattell Press, P.O. Box 25001, Tempe, Arizona 85282.

Renee Lautenbach, *Supervising Editor*
Anne Rhodes, *Administrative Managing Editor*
Dorothy Hancock, *Executive Editor*
Fred Scott, *General Manager,*
THE JAQUES CATTELL PRESS

Elizabeth A. Geiser, *Senior*
Vice President and Publisher
Book Division, R. R. Bowker Company

CRITERIA

Criteria for inclusion in the *Directory of American Scholars:*

> Achievement, by reason of experience and training, of a stature
> in scholarly work equivalent to that associated with the doctorate
> degree, coupled with presently continued activity in such work;

or

> Achievement as evidenced by publication of scholarly works;

or

> Attainment of a position of substantial responsibility by reason
> of achievement as outlined in (1) and (2).

Construction of a sample biography:

[1] CUNNINGHAM, RICHARD NELSON, b. [2] Kingston, Ont. [3] Nov. 2, 21; [4] U.S. citizen; [5] m. 48; [6] c. 3. [7] ENGLISH & AMERICAN LITERATURE. [8] A.B, Brooklyn Col, 46; M.A, Columbia Univ, 47, Ford Found. fel, 47-48; Ph.D. (Eng), Yale Univ, 50; hon. Dr, Duke Univ, 65. [9] Instr. ENG, Yale Univ, 48-50; asst. prof, DUKE UNIV, 50-57, assoc. prof, 57-62, PROF, 62- [10] Smith-Mundt vis. prof, Univ. Geneva, 58-59 & Univ. Lausanne, Switz, 63-64; mem. comt. Eng, Col. Entrance Exam. Bd, 65-70. [11] O. Henry award, 53. [12] U.S.A, 42-45, Lt. [13] MLA; NCTE; Col. Eng. Asn; Conf. Col. Compos. & Commun. [14] The American short story; 20th century English literature; the novel. [15] Publ: Handbook of short story writing, Ronald, 62; Symbolism in English literature, Mod. Fiction Stud, 8/68; Patterns in literature, Mod. Lang. Notes, 4/71. [16] Add: Dept. of English, Duke University, Durham, NC 27706.

[1] Name, [2] birthplace & [3] date	[11] Honors, awards and decorations
[4] Citizenship	[12] Military service (optional)
[5] Marriage date & [6] children	[13] Current memberships in national professional societies
[7] Discipline	[14] Chief fields of research interest
[8] Education	[15] Major publications
[9] Professional experience, past and present	[16] Mailing address
[10] Concurrent appointments	

ABBREVIATIONS

AAAS—American Association for the Advancement of Science
AAUP—American Association of University Professors
abnorm—abnormal
abstr—abstract(s)
acad—academia, academic, academica, académie, académique, academy
accad—accademia
acct—account, accountant, accounting
acoust—acoustical
adj—adjunct, adjutant
adjust—adjustment
Adm—Admiral
admin—administration, administrative
adminr—administrator(s)
admis—admissions
adv—adviser(s), advisory
advan—advance(d), advancement
advert—advertisement, advertising
aerodyn—aerodynamic(s)
aeronaut—aeronautic(s), aeronautical
aesthet—aesthetics
affil—affiliate(s), affiliation
agr—agricultural, agriculture
AFB—Air Force Base
AHA—American Historical Association
akad—akademi, akademia
Ala—Alabama
algem—algemeen, algemen
allergol—allergological, allergology
allgem—allgemein, allgemeine, allgemeinen
Alta—Alberta
Am—America, Americain, American, Americana, Americano, Amerika, Amerikaansch, Amerikaner, Amerikanisch, Amerikansk
anal—analysis, analytic, analytical
analog—analogue
anat—anatomic, anatomy
ann—annal(s)
anthrop—anthropological, anthropologist, anthropology
anthropom—anthropometric, anthropometricol, anthropometry
antiq—antiquaire(s), antiquarian, antiquary(ies), antiquities
App—appoint, appointed, appointment
appl—applied
appln—application
Apr—April
apt—apartment(s)
arbit—arbitration
arch—archiv, archiva, archive(s), archivio, archivo
archaeol—archaeological, archaeology
archäol—archäologie, archäologisch
archeol—archeological, archéologie, archéologique, archeology
archit—architect(s), architectural, architecture
Arg—Argentina, Argentine
Ariz—Arizona
Ark—Arkansas
asn—association
asoc—asociación
assoc—associate(s), associated
asst—assistant
Assyriol—Assyriology
astrodyn—astrodynamics
astron—astronomical, astronomy
astronaut—astronautical, astronautics
astronr—astronomer
attend—attending

atty—attorney
audiol—audiology
Aug—August
auth—author(s)
AV—audiovisual
ave—avenue

b—born
B.C—British Columbia
bd—board
behav—behavior, behavioral
Belg—Belgian, Belgica, Belgie, Belgique, Belgish, Belgium
Bibl—Biblical, Biblique
bibliog—bibliografía, bibliographical, bibliography
bibliogr—bibliographer
bibliot—biblioteca, bibliotek, bibliotheca, bibliothek, bibliothéque
biog—biographical, biography
biol—biology
bk(s)—book(s)
bldg—building
blvd—boulevard
bol—boletim, boletín
boll—bollettino
bot—botany
br—branch
Brig. Gen—Brigadier General
Brit—Britain, British
Bro(s)—Brother(s)
bull—bulletin
bur—bureau
bus—business
B.W.I—British West Indies

c—children
Calif—California
Can—Canada, Canadian, Canadien, Canadienne
cand—candidate
Capt—Captain
cartog—cartografic, cartographical, cartography
cartogr—cartographer
Cath—Catholic, Catholique
CBS—Columbia Broadcasting System
cent—central
Cent. Am—Central America
cert—certificat, certificate, certified
chap—chapter
chem—chemical, chemistry
chg—charge
Cie—Compagnie
chmn—chairman
Cie—Compagnie
cient—científica, científico
class—classical
clin—clinic(s), clinical
Co—Companies, Company, County
co-auth—co-author
co-ed—co-editor
Col—Colonel
col(s)—colegio, college(s), collegiate
collab—collaborator
Colo—Colorado
Comdr—Commander
commun—communication(s)
comn—commission(s)
comnr—commissioner
comp—comparative, comparée
compos—composition(s)
comput—computer, computing
comt—committee(s)
conf—conference

congr—congress
Conn—Connecticut
conserv—conservación, conservation, conservatoire, conservatory
consol—consolidated, consolidation
const—constitution, constitutional
construct—construction
consult—consultant, consulting
contrib—contributor
coop—cooperation, cooperative
coord—coordinating, coordination, coordinator
cor—corresponding
Corp—Corporation
counc—council
counr—councillor, counselor
criminol—criminology
Ct—Court
ctr—center
cult—cultura, cultural, culturale, culture
cur—curator
cybernet—cybernetics
C.Z—Canal Zone
Czech—Czechoslovakia

D.C—District of Columbia
Dec—December
Del—Delaware
deleg—delegate, delegation
demog—demographic, demography
demonstr—demonstrator
dent—dental, dentistry
dep—deputy
dept—department
Deut—Deutsch, Deutschland
develop—development
diag—diagnosis, diagnostic
dialectol—dialectology
dig—digest
dipl—diplom, diploma, diplomate, diplôme
dir—director(s), directory
Diss. Abstr—Dissertation Abstracts
dist—district
distrib—distributive
div—division, divorced
doc—document, documentation
Dom—Dominion
Dr—Doctor, Drive
Drs—Doctorandus

e—east
east—eastern
ecol—ecological, ecology
econ—economic(s), economical, economy
ed—edición, edition, editor, editorial, edizione
educ—education, educational
educr—educator(s)
Egyptol—Egyptology
elec—electric, electrical, electricity
elem—elementary
emer—emeriti, emeritus
encour—encouragement
encycl—encyclopedia
employ—employment
Eng—England, English
Ens—Ensign
environ—environment, environmental
EPDA—Education Professions Development Act
ERIC—Educational Resources Information Center
ESEA—Elementary & Secondary Education Act
espec—especially
estab—established, establishment

estud—estudante, estudas, estudiante, estudio(s)
    estudo(s)
ethnog—ethnographical, ethnography
ethnol—ethnological, ethnology
Europ—European
eval—evaluation
evangel—evangelical
eve—evening
exam—examination
examr—examiner
except—exceptional
exec—executive(s)
exeg—exegesis(es), exegetic, exegetical, exegetics
exhib—exhibition(s)
exp—experiment, experimental, experimentation
exped—expedition(s)
explor—exploration(s)
expos—exposition
exten—extension

fac—faculties, faculty
Feb—Febuary
fed—federal, federation
fel(s)—fellow(s), fellowship(s)
filol—filología, filológico
filos—filosofía, filosófico
Fla—Florida
FLES—Foreign Languages in the Elementary
    Schools
for—foreign
forsch—forschung, forschungen
found—foundation
Fr—Francais(e), French
Ft—Fort

Ga—Georgia
gen—general, générale
geneal—genealogical, genealogy
genoot—genootschap
geod—geodesy, geodetic
geog—geografía, geográfico, geographer(s),
    geographic, geographie, geograph-
    ical, geography
geogr—geographer
geol—geologic, geological, geology
geophys—geophysical
Ger—German, Germanic, Germanisch, Germany
ges—gesellschaft
gov—governing, governor(s)
govt—government, governmental
grad—graduate
Gt. Brit—Great Britain
guid—guidance
gym—gymnasium

handbk(s)—handbook(s)
Hisp—Hispanic, Hispánico, Hispano
hist—histoire, historia, historial, historian(s),
    historic, historica, historical, his-
    torique, historische, history
Hochsch—Hochschule
hon—honorable, honorary
hosp(s)—hospital(s)
hq—headquarters
HumRRO—Human Resources Research Office
hwy—highway

Ill—Illinois
illum—illuminating, illumination
illus—illustrate, illustration
illusr—illustrator
imp—imperial
improv—improvement
Inc—Incorporated
Ind—Indiana
indust(s)—industrial, industry(ies)
inform—information
inst—institut, institute(s), institution(s), instituto
instnl—institutional
instr—instruction, instructor(s)
instruct—instructional
int—internacional, international, internazionale
intel—intelligence
introd—introduction
invest—investigación, investiganda, investigation,
    investigative
investr—investigator
ist—istituto
Ital—Italia, Italian, Italiana, Italiano, Italica,
    Italien, Italienisch, Italienne, Italy

J—Journal
Jan—January
jour—journal, journalism
jr—junior
jurisp—jurisprudence

Kans—Kansas
koninkl—koninklijk
Ky—Kentucky

La—Louisiana
lab—laboratoire, laboratorio, laboratorium,
    laboratory(ies)

lang—language(s)
lect—lecture(s)
lectr—lecturer
legis—legislación, legislatief, legislation, legis-
    lative, legislativo, legislature,
    legislazione
lett—letter(s), lettera, letteraria, let-
    teratura, lettere
L.I—Long Island
lib—liberal
libr—library(ies), librerio
librn—librarian(s)
lic—license, licencia
ling—linguistic(s), lingüística, linguistique
lit—literary, literatur, literatura, literature,
    littera, litterature
Lt—Lieutenant
Ltd—Limited

m—married
mach—machine(s), machinery
mag—magazine
Maj—Major
Man—Manitoba
Mar—March
Mariol—Mariological, Mariology
Mass—Massachusetts
mat—matemãtica, matematiche, matematico,
    matematik
math—matematica, mathematical, mathematics,
    mathematik, mathématique(s),
    mathematisch
Md—Maryland
mech—mechanical
med—medical, medicine
Mediter—Mediterranean
mem—member, memoirs, memorial
ment—mental, mentally
metrop—metropolitan
Mex—Mexican, Mexicano, Mexico
mfg—manufacturing
mfr—manufacture, manufacturer
mgr—manager(s)
mgt—management
Mich—Michigan
mid—middle
mil—military
Minn—Minnesota
Miss—Mississippi
mitt—mitteilung
mkt—market, marketing
MLA—Modern Language Association of America
Mo—Missouri
mod—modern, moderna, moderne, moderno
monatsh—monatsheft(e)
monatsschr—monatsschrift
monogr—monograph
Mont—Montana
morphol—morphologica, morphologie, morphol-
    ogy
Msgr—Monsignor
mt—mount, mountain(s)
munic—municipal
mus—museum(s)
musicol—musicological, musicology

n—north
nac—nacional
NASA—National Aeronautics & Space Adminis-
    tration
nat—nationaal, national, nationale, nationalis,
    naturalized
NATO—North Atlantic Treaty Organization
naz—nazionale
N.B—New Brunswick
N.C—North Carolina
NCTE—National Council of Teachers of English
N.Dak—North Dakota
NDEA—National Defense Education Act
NEA—National Education Association
Nebr—Nebraska
Ned—Nederland, Nederlandsch
Nev—Nevada
Neth—Netherlands
Nfld—Newfoundland
N.H—New Hampshire
N.J—New Jersey
N.Mex—New Mexico
no—number
nonres—nonresident
norm—normal, normale
north—northern
northeast—northeastern
northwest—northwestern
Norweg—Norwegian
Nov—November
N.S—Nova Scotia
N.S.W—New South Wales
numis—numismatic, numismático, numismatique
N.Y—New York
N.Y.C—New York City
N.Z—New Zealand

occup—occupation, occupational
Oct—October
OEEC—Organization for European Economic
    Cooperation
off—office, officer(s), official(s)
Okla—Oklahoma
Ont—Ontario
oper—operation(s), operational
ord—ordnance
Ore—Oregon
orgn—organization, organizational
orient—oriental, orientale, orientalist, orientalia
ornithol—ornithological, ornithology

Pa—Pennsylvania
Pac—Pacific
paleontol—paleontological, paleontology
Pan-Am—Pan-American
pedag—pedagogía, pedagogic, pedagogical,
    pedagogico, pédagogie, pedagogik,
    pédagogique, pedagogy
P.E.I—Prince Edward Island
penol—penological, penology
phenomenol—phenomenological, phenomenologie,
    phenomenology
Phila—Philadelphia
Philippines—Philippine Islands
philol—philologica, philological, philologie,
    philologisch, philology
philos—philosophia, philosophic, philosophical,
    philosophie, philosophique, philos-
    ophisch, philosophy, philoszophia
photog—photographic, photography
phys—physical
pkwy—parkway
pl—place
polit—politica, political, politicas, politico,
    politics, politiek, politike, politique,
    politisch, politisk
polytech—polytechnic
pop—population
Pontif—Pontifical
Port—Portugal, Portuguese
postgrad—postgraduate
P.Q—Province of Quebec
P.R—Puerto Rico
pract—practice
prehist—prehistoric
prep—preparation, preparatory
pres—president
Presby—Presbyterian
preserv—preservation
prev—prevention, preventive
prin—principal(s)
prob—problem(s)
proc—proceedings
prod—production
prof—professional, professor, professorial
prog—program(s), programmed, programming
proj—project, projective
prom—promotion
Prov—Province
psychiat—psychiatria, psychiatric, psychiatrica,
    psychiatrie, psychiatrique, psy-
    chiatrisch, psychiatry
psychol—psychological, psychology
pt—point
pub—public, publique
publ—publication(s), published, publisher(s),
    publishing
pvt—private

qm—quartermaster
quad—quaderni
qual—qualitative, quality
quart—quarterly

R.A.F—Royal Air Force
R.A.F.V.R—Royal Air Force Voluntary Reserve
R.A.M.C—Royal Army Medical Corps
R.A.O.C—Royal Army Ordnance Corps
R.A.S.C—Royal Army Service Corps
R.C.A.F—Royal Canadian Air Force
R.C.A.F.V.R—Royal Canadian Air Force
    Volunteer Reserve
R.C.A.M.C—Royal Canadian Army Medical
    Corps
R.C.A.O.C—Royal Canadian Army Ordnance
    Corps
R.C.A.S.C—Royal Canadian Army Service Corps
R.C.E—Royal Canadian Engineers
R.C.E.M.E—Royal Canadian Electrical & Me-
    chanical Engineers
R.C.N—Royal Canadian Navy
R.C.N.R—Royal Canadian Naval Reserve
R.C.N.V.R—Royal Canadian Naval Volunteer
    Reserve
rd—road
R.D—Rural Delivery, Rural Free Delivery
R.E—Royal Engineers
rec—record(s), recording
rech—recherche
ref—reference

registr—registrar, registration
rehabil—rehabilitation
relac—relación
relat—relation(s), relative
relaz—relazione
relig—religion, religious
R.E.M.E—Royal Electrical & Mechanical
      Engineers
rep—representative
repub—republic
res—research, reserve
Rev—Reverend
rev—review, revised, revista, revue
rhet—rhetoric, rhetorical
R.I—Rhode Island
R.M—Royal Marines
R.N—Royal Navy
R.N.R—Royal Naval Reserves
R.N.V.R—Royal Naval Volunteer Reserves
R.R—Rural Route
Rt—Right
Rte—Route
Russ—Russian

s—south
S.Africa—South Africa
S.Am—South America, South American
Sask—Saskatchewan
S.C—South Carolina
Scand—Scandinavian
sch(s)—school(s)
scholar—scholarship
sci—science(s), scientia, scientific, scientifico,
      scientifique, scienza
S.Dak—South Dakota
SEATO—Southeast Asia Treaty Organization
sec—secondary
sect—section
secy—secretary
sem—séminaire, seminar, seminario, seminary
sen—senator, senatorial
Sept—September
ser—serial, series
serv—service(s)
Sgt—Sergeant
soc—social, sociedad, sociedade, societa, so-
      cietas, societate, société, societet,
      society(ies)
soc. sci—social science(s)
sociol—sociological, sociology
south—southern
southeast—southeastern
southwest—southwestern
Span—Spanish
spec—special
sq—square
sr—senior
St—Saint, Street
sta—station
statist—statistical, statistics
Ste—Sainte

struct—structural, structure(s)
stud—studencheskii, studencheskikh, student,
      studentov, studentship, studi(e),
      studie(n), studja, study(ies)
subcomt—subcommittee
subj—subject
substa—substation
super—supérieur, superior, superiore
suppl—supplement, supplementary
supt—superintendent
supv—supervising, supervision
supvr—supervisor
supvry—supervisory
surg—surgical, surgery
surv—survey
Swed—Swedish
Switz—Switzerland
symp—symposium
syst—system, systematic

tech—technic(s), technica, technical, technicky,
      techniczny, techniek, technik, tech-
      nika, technikum, technique, technisch
technol—technologic, technological, technol-
      ogicke, technologico, technol-
      ogiczny, technologie, technologika,
      technologique, technologisch, tech-
      nology
tecnol—tecnología, tecnológico
tel—telegraph(y), telephone
temp—temporary
Tenn—Tennessee
Terr—Terrace
teol—teología, teológico
Tex—Texas
textbk—textbook(s)
theol—theological, théologie, théologique,
      theologisch, theology
theoret—theoretical, theoretis
ther—therapy
trans—transactions
transl—translation, translator(s)
treas—treasurer, treasury
trop—tropical
TV—television
twp—township

u—und
U.A.R—United Arab Republic
U.K—United Kingdom
UN—United Nations
unemploy—unemployment
UNESCO—United Nations Educational, Scientific
      & Cultural Organization
UNICEF—United Nations Children's Fund
univ(s)—universidad, université, university(ies)
UNRRA—United Nations Relief & Rehabilitation
      Administration
UNRWA—United Nations Relief and Works
      Agency

U.S—United States
U.S.A—United States Army
U.S.A.A.F—United States Army Air Force
U.S.A.A.F.R—United States Army Air Force
      Reserve
U.S.A.F—United States Air Force
U.S.A.F.R—United States Air Force Reserve
U.S.A.R—United States Army Reserve
U.S.C.G—United States Coast Guard
U.S.C.G.R—United States Coast Guard Reserve
U.S.M.C—United States Marine Corps
U.S.M.C.R—United States Marine Corps Reserve
U.S.N—United States Navy
U.S.N.A.F—United States Navy Air Force
U.S.N.R—United States Naval Reserve
U.S.P.H.S—United States Public Health Service
U.S.S.R—Union of Soviet Socialist Republics
U.S.W.M.C—United States Women's Marine Corps

Va—Virginia
var—various
veg—vegetable(s), vegetation
ver—vereeniging, verein, vereinigt, vereinigung
vet—veteran, veterinarian, veterinary
V.I—Virgin Islands
vis—visiting
voc—vocational
vocab—vocabulary
vol(s)—volume(s), voluntary, volunteer(s)
v.chmn—vice chairman
v.pres—vice president
Vt—Vermont

w—west
W.A.C—Women's Army Corps
Wash—Washington
Wash, D.C—Washington, D.C.
W.A.V.E.S—Women Accepted for Voluntary
      Emergency Service
west—western
wetensch—wetenschappelijk, wetenschappen
WHO—World Health Organization
W.I—West Indies
wid—widow, widowed, widower
Wis—Wisconsin
wiss—wissenschaft(en), wissenschaftliche(e)
W.R.C.N.S—Woman's Royal Canadian Naval
      Service
W.R.N.S—Woman's Royal Naval Service
W.Va—West Virginia
Wyo—Wyoming

yearbk—yearbook(s)
YMCA—Young Men's Christian Association
YMHA—Young Men's Hebrew Association
YWCA—Young Women's Christian Association
YWHA—Young Women's Hebrew Association

z—zeitschrift

DIRECTORY OF AMERICAN SCHOLARS

VOLUME II
ENGLISH,
SPEECH & DRAMA

A

AARON, DANIEL, b. Chicago, Ill, Aug. 4, 12; m. 37; c. 3. AMERICAN STUD-IES. A.B, Univ. Mich, 33; fel, Harvard, 37-39, Ph.D, 43; hon. Dr.Let, Union Col, 68. Instr. Eng, Harvard, 36-39, counsel. Am. civilization, 37-39; from instr. to prof. Eng, Smith Col, 39-61, Jordan Prof. Eng. Lang. & Lit, 61-71; PROF. ENG, HARVARD UNIV, 71- Guggenheim fel, 47; vis. lectr, Benning-ton Col, 50-51; Smith-Mundt fel, 51-52; vis. prof, Univ. Helsinki, 51-52; Am-herst Col, 54-55; Fund for the Republic grant, 55; fel, Ctr. Advan. Stud. Be-hav. Sci, 58-59; vis. prof, Univ. Warsaw, 62-63; fel, Huntington Libr, 64, summer 68; Am. specialist lectr, Montivideo, Uruguay, summer 66; mem. adv. comt. Am. stud, Comt. Int. Exchange Persons, 66-; Fulbright prof, Univ. Sussex, 68-69; lectr, Kyoto Am. Stud. Summer Sem, 73. MLA; Am. Acad. Arts & Sci; Am. Antiq. Soc; Am. Stud. Asn.(v.pres, 67-68, pres, 71-73). American literature and history. Publ: Men of good hope, Oxford; co-auth, Ralph Waldo Emerson: a modern anthology, Houghton, 59; auth, Writ-ers on the left, 61 & ed, Paul Elmer More's Shelbourne essays, 63, Har-court; co-auth, The United States: a history of the republic, Prentice-Hall; ed, The memoirs of an American citizen, Harvard, 63; co-ed, The strenuous decade: a social and intellectual record of the 1930's, Doubleday, 70; auth, The unwritten war: American writers and the Civil War, Knopf, 73. Add: Warren House Five, Harvard University, Cambridge, MA 02138.

AARSLEFF, HANS, b. Denmark, July 19, 25. ENGLISH. B.A, Univ. Copen-hagen, 45; M.A, Univ. Minn, 54, Ph.D, 60. Instr. ENG, Univ. Minn, 52-56; PRINCETON, 56-60, asst. prof, 60-65, assoc. prof, 65-72, PROF, 72- Jr. fel. counc. humanities, Princeton, 62; Am. Counc. Learned Soc. fel, 64-65 & 72-73. MLA; Gottfried-Wilhelm-Leibniz-Gex; Lärdomshistoriska Sam-fundet. History of doctrines concerning the nature and study of language since the Renaissance; Locke; Leibniz. Publ: The study of language in En-gland, 1780-1860, Princeton, 67; co-ed. & contrib, Historiography of lin-guistics & co-ed, Biographical dictionary of linguistics, Mouton, The Hague, 74; contrib, John Locke: problems and perspectives, Cambridge Univ, 69; Dictionary of scientific biography, Scribner's, 70; Studies in the history of linguistics, Ind. Univ, 73; plus others. Add: Dept. of English, Princeton University, Princeton, NJ 08540.

ABBE, GEORGE, b. Somers, Conn, Jan. 28, 11; m. 34. ENGLISH. B.A, Univ. N.H, 33; M.A, Univ. Iowa, 38. Instr. Eng, Mt. Holyoke Col, 39-43; Yale, 45-46; asst. prof, Univ. Pittsburgh, 47-48; lectr. short story, Columbia Univ, 48-49; asst. prof. ENG, Wayne Univ, 49-50; instr, Univ. Maine, 52-53; Teachers Col, Conn, 55-57; Springfield Col, 54-55; from asst. prof. to assoc. prof, Russell Sage Col, 58-66; PROF. & WRITER-IN-RESIDENCE, STATE UNIV. N.Y. COL, PLATTSBURGH, 66- State Univ. N.Y. Awards Found. grant, 70. Shelley Mem. Award, 54. Poetry Soc. Am. Poetry; fic-tion; non-fiction. Publ: Voices in the square, Coward, 38; Wait for these things, 40 & Dreamer's clay, 40, Henry Holt; Mr. Quill's crusade, Island, 48; The winter house, Doubleday, 57; Collected poems, 62, You and con-temporary poetry, 65 & Dreams and dissent (poetry), 72, William Bauhan; Stephen Vincent Benet on writing, Stephen Greene, 64; The larks, Regnery, 65; The non-conformist: autobiography of a conscience, 66 & Yonderville (novel), 68, Branden; The funeral, Horizon, 67; Shatter the day, Poet Lore, 70; Abbe and Benet, Rat & Mole Press, 73; Horizon thong, Atlantic monthly, 55; The adomatic man, Whetstone, 59; Day of rest, Trace, 67-68; plus others. Add: State University of New York College at Plattsburgh, Platts-burgh, NY 12901.

ABBICK, JOHN F, S.J, b. Kansas City, Kans, Sept. 16, 12. ENGLISH. A.B, St. Louis Univ, 37, A.M, 39, Ph.L, 39, S.T.L, 46; Ph.D.(Eng), Univ. N.C, 67. Asst. prof. ENG, Marquette Univ, 52-70; ASSOC. PROF, ROCKHURST COL, 70- Mem, Renaissance Inst, Sophia Univ, Japan. MLA; NCTE; Midwest Mod. Lang. Asn; Renaissance Soc. Am; Hopkins Soc, Eng. Shakespeare; Medieval and Renaissance drama; Hopkins. Add: Dept. of English, Rock-hurst College, Kansas City, MO 64110.

ABBOTT, ANTHONY S, b. San Francisco, Calif, Jan. 7, 35; m. 60; c. 3. EN-GLISH. A.B, Princeton, 57; Ph.D.(Eng), Harvard, 61. Instr. ENG, Bates Col, 61-64; asst. prof, DAVIDSON COL, 64-67, ASSOC. PROF, 67- MLA;

Soc. Relig. Higher Educ. Modern drama; history of English drama; Ameri-can literature. Publ: Shaw and Christianity, Seabury, 65. Add: Dept. of En-glish, Davidson College, Davidson, NC 28036.

ABBOTT, CRAIG STEPHENS, b. Washington, D.C, Nov. 23, 41. AMERICAN LITERATURE. B.A, Tex. A&M Univ, 64, M.A, 66; Ph.D.(Eng), Univ. Tex, Austin, 73. ASST. PROF. ENG, NORTH. ILL. UNIV, 73- Modern poetry; bibliography; Marianne Moore. Add: Dept. of English, Northern Illinois University, DeKalb, IL 60115.

ABBOTT, H. PORTER, b. Baltimore, Md, Nov. 21, 40; m. 66; c. 2. ENGLISH LITERATURE. B.A, Reed Col, 62; M.A, Univ. Toronto, 64, Ph.D.(Eng), 68. Asst. prof. ENG. LIT, UNIV. CALIF, SANTA BARBARA, 66-73, ASSOC. PROF, 73- MLA. The novel; literary theory; 19th and 20th century English litera-ture. Publ: The fiction of Samuel Beckett: form and effect, Univ. Calif, 73; Farewell to incompetence: Beckett's How it is & Imagination dead imagine, Contemporary Lit, winter 70; The journals of W.N.P. Barbellion, J. Mod. Lit, 2/73; A poetics of radical displacement: Samuel Beckett coming up to seventy, Tex. Stud. Lit. & Lang, 74; plus others. Add: Dept. of English, University of California, Santa Barbara, CA 93106.

ABBOTT, JOHN L, b. Lansing, Mich, May 5, 37; m. 59; c. 2. ENGLISH. Woodrow Wilson fel. & B.A, Mich. State Univ, 59, Ph.D.(Eng), 63; M.A, Ohio State Univ, 60. Instr. Am. thought & lang, Mich. State Univ, 63-64; asst. prof, ENG, UNIV. CONN, 64-68, ASSOC. PROF, 68-, COORD, GRAD. STUD, 73-, res. found. grant, 66-67 & 70-71, asst. dir. honors prog, 68-68, assoc. dir, 68-70. Am. Philos. Soc. grants, 66-67 & 70-71. Am. Soc. 18th Cen-tury Stud; MLA; fel. Royal Soc. Arts. Eighteenth century English literature; Johnson, Johnson Circle and John Hawkesworth. Publ: Dr. Johnson and the making of the Life of Father Paul Sarpi, Bull. John Rylands Libr, spring 66; No dialect of France: Dr. Johnson's translations from the French, Univ. To-ronto Quart, 1/67; Dr. Johnson and the society, J. Royal Soc. Arts, 4-5/67. Add: Dept. of English, University of Connecticut, Storrs, CT 06268.

ABBOTT, JOHN PAUL, b. Nashville, Tenn, July 16, 04; m. 31. ENGLISH, AMERICAN LITERATURE. B.A, Vanderbilt Univ, 25; Ph.D.(Eng), Univ. Iowa, 39. Instr. Eng, TEX. A&M UNIV, 26-28, asst. prof, 29-38, assoc. prof, 39-40, prof, 40-56, dean arts & sci, 49-53, dean col, 53-56, distin-guished prof. ENG, 57-72, EMER. PROF, 72- S-Cent. Mod. Lang. Asn. Publ: Co-auth, A manual for college English, Ronald, 47; auth, Modern en-gineering physics from the viewpoint of administration, J. Engineering Educ, 54. Add: 701 Hereford S, College Station, TX 77840.

ABCARIAN, RICHARD, b. Reedley, Calif, Jan. 29, 29; m. 51; c. 4. ENGLISH. B.A, Univ. Calif, Berkeley, 52, M.A, 55, Ph.D.(Eng), 61. Asst. prof. ENG, CALIF. STATE UNIV, NORTHRIDGE, 59-64, assoc. prof, 64-68, PROF, 68- Fulbright lectr. Am. lit, Univ. Pau, 67-68. Publ: Ed, Richard Wright's Native son: a critical handbook, 70 & Words in flight: an introduction to po-etry, 72, Wadsworth; co-ed, Literature: the human experience, St. Martins, 73; auth, The world of love and the spheres of fright: Melville's Bartleby the scrivener, Stud. Short Fiction, spring 64; Cooper's critics and the realistic novel, Tex. Stud. Lit. & Lang, spring 66; Innocence and experience in Wines-burg, Ohio, Univ. Rev. Add: Dept. of English, California State University, Northridge, 18111 Nordhoff St, Northridge, CA 91324.

ABEGGLEN, HOMER N, b. Albia, Iowa, Apr. 5, 01. SPEECH. A.B, Grinnell Col, 23; Univ. Wash, 26-27; Yale, 27-28; A.M, Columbia Univ, 32; Ph.D, West. Reserve Univ, 44; hon. Litt.D, Wilmington Col.(Ohio), 66. Asst. prof. SPEECH, MIAMI UNIV, 28-40, assoc. prof, 40-46, prof, 46-68, dir. theatre, 59-68, EMER. PROF, 68- Speech Commun. Asn; Am. Theatre Asn; Nat. Theatre Conf. Theatre. Add: Dept. of Speech, Miami University, Oxford, OH 45056.

ABEL, DARREL, b. Lost Nation, Iowa, Aug. 25, 11; m. 35; c. 6. ENGLISH. A.B, State Univ. Iowa, 36, A.M, 37; Ph.D, Univ. Mich, 49. Instr, S.Dak. State Col, 37-42; Purdue Univ, 42-44, 46-47; teaching fel, Univ. Mich, 44-46; asst. prof, Franklin & Marshall Col, 47-50; ENG, PURDUE UNIV, WEST LAFAYETTE, 50-52, assoc. prof, 52-57, PROF, 57- Fulbright sr. lectr. Am. lit, Univ. Freiburg, 64-65. Emerson Soc; Am. Stud. Asn. American literature. Publ: Colonial and early national writing, Literature of the At-lantic culture & Masterworks of American realism, Barron's, 63. Add: Dept. of English, Purdue University, West Lafayette, IN 47906.

ABEL, JAMES WALDEN, b. Monroe Co, Ind, May 10, 10; m. 38. SPEECH. A.B, Ind. Univ, 31, M.A, 36; Ph.D.(speech), La. State Univ, 49. Tutor Eng, Anatolia Col, Greece, 31-34; instr. speech, Univ. Hawaii, Manoa, 40-42, 45-46; censor & regulation off, Off. Cable & Radio Censorship, Hawaii, 42-45; instr. speech, Brooklyn Col, 49-58, asst. prof, 58-65, assoc. prof, 65-74; RETIRED. Vis. prof, Anatolia Col, 54-55; vis. asst. prof, Univ. Hawaii, Manoa, 58. Speech Commun. Asn; Phonetic Soc. Japan; Int. Phonetic Asn; Int. Soc. Phonetic Sci. Phonetics; foreign language teaching. Publ: Monosyllables, 60 & Vowel-r symbolization, 3/72, Speech Monogr; Syllabic /1/ ?, Quart. J. Speech, 10/66; plus one other. Add: 193 Los Arcos, Green Valley, AZ 85614.

ABEL, RICHARD OWEN, b. Canton, Ohio, Aug. 20, 41; m. 70. COMPARATIVE LITERATURE, CINEMA. B.A, Utah State Univ, 63; M.A, Univ. South. Calif, 65, Ph.D.(comp. lit), 70. Teaching asst. comp. lit, Univ. South. Calif, 65, Eng, 65-66, 66-67, lectr, summers 66, 67, instr. ENG, 67-68; DRAKE UNIV, 68-70, ASST. PROF, 70-, res. fel, 72-73, summer stipend, 73. MLA; Midwest Mod. Lang. Asn.(secy, film-lit. sect, 73-74); Am. Comp. Lit. Asn; Am. Fedn. Film. Soc; Am. Film Inst; Brit. Film Inst. Developments in European poetry, 1900-1930; relationship between film, literature, and art, 1900-1930; stylistic, thematic and structural studies of individual films. Publ: The influence of Saint-John Perse on T. S. Eliot, Contemporary Lit, spring 73; Saint-John Perse encounters T.S. Eliot, Rev. Lit. Comp., 74. Add: Dept. of English, Drake University, Des Moines, IA 50311.

ABELSETH, MURIEL, b. Minot, N.Dak, Oct. 2, 24; m. 62, 72. ENGLISH JOURNALISM. B.A, Minot State Teachers Col, 45; M.A, Univ. Minn, 59. Teacher Eng, high sch, Roseau, Minn, 45-47; Troy, Mont, 47-48, Culbertson, 48-51; ENG. & JOUR, Williston, N.Dak, 51-55; ASST. PROF, MINOT STATE COL, 55- Asn. Educ. Jour; Nat. Counc. Col. Pub. Advs; Nat. Educ. Asn. Foreign news content of North Dakota daily newspapers; writings of F. Scott Fitzgerald; handbooks and stylebooks for high school and college publication staffs. Add: Dept. of Journalism & English, Minot State College, Minot, ND 58701.

ABERNATHY, ELTON, b. Brady, Tex, Apr. 4, 13; c. 2. SPEECH. B.A, Abilene Christian Col, 32; M.A, State Univ. Iowa, 37; Ph.D, 40. Asst. prof. SPEECH, La. Polytech. Inst, 38-42; PROF, SOUTHWEST TEX. STATE UNIV, 46-, chmn. dept, 46-73. Dir. binat. cult. ctr, U.S. Inf. Agency, Rosario, Arg, 64-66. U.S.N.R, 43-, Lt. Comdr. South. Speech Asn.(pres, 58); Speech Asn. Am. Public address; speech education. Publ: Fundamentals of speech communication, Brown, 60, 64 & 70; The advocate, McKay, 64; Directing speech activities, Univ. Press, 70. Add: Dept. of Speech, Southwest Texas State University, San Marcos, TX 78666.

ABERNETHY, CECIL EMORY, b. Charleston, S.C, Apr. 8, 08; m. 40; c. 1. ENGLISH. A.B, Birmingham-South. Col, 30; A.M, Univ. N.C, 35; Ph.D, Vanderbilt Univ, 40. Instr. Eng, high sch, Ala, 31-35; teaching fel, Vanderbilt Univ, 35-37; instr. ENG, Univ. Ala, 37-38; from instr. to assoc. prof, BIRMINGHAM-SOUTH. COL, 39-47, PROF, 47- S.Atlantic Mod. Lang. Asn. Literary history; 17th century London; Samuel Pepys. Publ: Mr. Pepys of Seething Lane, McGraw; Mr. Pepys at the Coronation, Sat. Rev. Add: Dept. of English, Birmingham-Southern College, Birmingham, AL 35204.

ABERNETHY, FRANCIS EDWARD, b. Altus, Okla, Dec. 3, 25; m. 48; c. 5. ENGLISH. B.A, Stephen F. Austin State Col, 49; M.A, La. State Univ, 51, Ph.D, 56. Asst. prof. ENG, Lamar State Col. Tech, 56-59, assoc. prof, 59-65; PROF, STEPHEN F. AUSTIN STATE UNIV, 65- Lamar State Col. Tech. res. grant, 59-63; resident grants res. folklore, 59-68. U.S.N, 43-46. Am. Folklore Soc; S-Cent. Renaissance Conf; S.Cent. Mod. Lang. Asn; Asn. Mex. Cave Stud. Folklore; Renaissance drama; east Texas history. Publ: Social protest literature, 1485-1558, La. State, 62; Tales from the big thicket, Univ. Tex, 66; J. Frank Dobie, Steck-Vaughn Co, 67; ed. & contrib, Observations and reflections, Encino Press, 72; auth, The east Texas communal hunt, Publ. Tex. Folklore Soc, 71; plus two others. Add: Dept. of English, Stephen F. Austin State University, Nacogdoches, TX 75961.

ABLER, LAWRENCE ANTHONY, b. Mount Calvary, Wis, Dec. 22, 20. ENGLISH, COMPARATIVE LITERATURE. B.A, Univ. Wis, Madison, 48, M.A, 49; Lafrentz fel, Univ. Zurich, 49-50; Fund Advan. Educ. fel. & Ph.D. (comp. lit), Occidental Col, 58. Instr. Eng. & comp. lit, Occidental Col, 55-59, vis. assoc. prof. comp. lit, 63-65; asst. prof. Eng, North. Ariz. Univ, 59-62, assoc. prof, 62-63; vis. assoc. prof. comp. stud, Juniata Col, 65-68; assoc. prof. COMP. LIT, SUSQUEHANNA UNIV, 68-73, PROF, 73-, CHMN. DEPT, 70- C.Eng, A.U.S, 42-45. MLA; Am. Comp. Lit. Asn; Asn. Gen. & Lib. Stud. Romanticism; 20th century European literature. Publ: Transl, Three Rilke poems, Monument, winter 60; co-auth, A role for aesthetics in the teaching process, J. Teacher Educ, winter 67. Add: Dept. of English, Susquehanna University, Selinsgrove, PA 17870.

ABOOD, EDWARD FRANCIS, b. Erie, Pa, Nov. 29, 25. ENGLISH & COMPARATIVE LITERATURE. B.A, Univ. Chicago, 49, M.A, 55, Ph.D.(Eng), 62; B.A, Univ. Calif, Berkeley, 51. Asst. prof. ENG, Chicago Jr. Col, 55-63; PROF, CALIF. STATE UNIV, LOS ANGELES, 63- Lectr. drama, KPFK Radio, Los Angeles, 66-67. U.S.N.R, 44-46. Literature and psychology. Publ: Underground man, Chandler & Sharp, 73; Some observations on Yvor Winters, Chicago Rev, fall 57; Jung's concept of individuation in Hesse's Steppenwolf, South. Humanities Rev, winter 68; Genet: an underground man, Psychol. Perspectives, fall 71. Add: Dept. of English, California State University, Los Angeles, 5151 State University Dr, Los Angeles, CA 90032.

ABRAHAMS, ROGER DAVID, b. Philadelphia, Pa, June 12, 33; m. 59; c. 2. FOLKLORE. B.A, Swarthmore Col, 55; M.A, Columbia Univ, 59; Ph.D.(lit. & folklore), Univ. Pa, 61. Instr. Eng, UNIV. TEX, AUSTIN, 60-63, asst. prof, 63-66, assoc. prof, 66-69, PROF. ENG. & ANTHROP, 69-, assoc. dir, Ctr. Intercult. Stud. Folklore & Oral Hist, 67-69, dir, African & Afro-Am. Res. Inst, 69-73. Seven Tex. Res. Inst. grants; Guggenheim fel, 65-66; vis. fac, Folklore Inst, Ind. Univ, summer 67; mem, Comt. Afro-Am. Soc. & Cult, Soc. Sci. Res. Counc, 68-; assoc. ed, J. Am. Folklore, 68-; vis. fac, Carleton Col, spring,69; mem, Nat. Humanities Fac, 70-; vis. fac, Univ. Pa, summer 71; mem, Smithsonian Inst. Counc, 71-72. Deleg, Am-Yugoslav Sem, Novi Sad, Yugoslavia, summer 65; Cong. Americanists, Mar del Plata, Arg, 66; Conf. Folklife, Smithsonian Inst, summer 67; Conf. Folklore & Soc. Sci, Soc. Sci. Res. Counc. & Wenner-Gren Found, 67 & Conf. Continuties & Discontinuties Afro-Am. Soc. & Cult, Mona, Jamaica, 70; Symp. Urban Experience & Folk Tradition, Wayne State Univ, summer 68; Anglo-Am. Folklore Conf, Ditchley, Eng, fall 69; Conf. Educ. & Training in Nat. Interest, Role of Lang. Variety, Wash, D.C, winter 70; Issues Community & Res. Group Relat, Nat. Insts. Health, New Orleans, spring 70; Conf. African Folklore, Folklore Inst, Ind. Univ, summer 70; Conf. Traditional African Archit, Joint Comt. African Stud, Am. Counc. Learned Soc. & Soc. Sci. Res. Counc, Belmont, Md, fall 70; Conf. Black Stud. & Univ, South. Regional Educ. Bd, Atlanta, Ga, spring 71; Appl. Folklore, Fourth Annual Mid. Am. Conf. Folk Cult, Pittsburgh, summer 71; Georgetown Round Table Ling, spring 72; Conf. Ethnog. of Commun, Comt. Socioling, Soc. Sci. Res. Counc, Univ. Tex, spring 72; Question of Authority, Nat. Humanities Fac, Durham, summer 72; Conf. Black Commun, Univ. Pittsburgh, fall 72. Fel. Am. Folklore Soc; Am. Anthrop. Asn. Folklore of the Negro in the new world; folklore and folklore theory; anthropology of performance. Publ: Deep down in the jungle, Negro narratives from the streets of Philadelphia, Folklore Assocs, 64, rev. ed, Aldine, 70; co-auth, Anglo-American folklore style, 68, auth, Positively Black, 70 & co-ed, Language and cultural diversity in American education, 72, Prentice-Hall; auth, Jump-rope rhymes: a dictionary, 69, Deep the water, shallow the shore, (in press) & co-ed, Afro-American folklore: an annotated bibliography, (in press), Univ. Tex; ed, A singer and her songs, La. State Univ, 70; auth, Talking Black, Newberry, (in press); Introductory remarks to a rhetorical theory of folklore, J. Am. Folklore, 68; contrib, Afro-American anthropology; contemporary perspectives, Free Press, 70 & Rappin' and stylin' out, Univ. Ill, 72; plus many others. Add: Dept. of English, University of Texas at Austin, Austin, TX 78712.

ABRAHAMSON, IRVING, b. Chicago, Ill, Dec. 21, 25. ENGLISH LANGUAGE & LITERATURE. B.A, Roosevelt Univ, 48; M.A, Univ. Chicago, 49, Ph.D, 56. Mem. fac. ENG, KENNEDY-KING COL, 56-62, asst. prof, 62-64, ASSOC. PROF, 64- Lectr, Roosevelt Univ, 49-56; Univ. Ill, Navy Pier, 55-56. U.S.N.R, 44-46. NCTE. American drama; contemporary fiction and poetry. Publ: Rachel Crothers, In: Encycl. Britannica, 60. Add: 888 Bob-o-link Rd, Highland Park, IL 60035.

ABRAMS, MEYER HOWARD, b. Long Branch, N.J, July 23, 12; m. 37; c. 2. ENGLISH LITERATURE. A.B, Harvard, 34, A.M, 37, Ph.D, 40; Henry fel. from Harvard, Cambridge, 34-35. Instr, Harvard, 38-42, res. assoc, 42-45; asst. prof. ENG, CORNELL UNIV, 45-47, assoc. prof, 47-53, prof, 53-61, Whiton Prof, 61-73, CLASS OF 1916 PROF, 73- Rockefeller Found. fel, 46-47; Ford Found. fel, 53; Fulbright scholar, Malta & Cambridge, 54; hon. mem. fac, Royal Univ. Malta, 54-; Guggenheim fels, 58, 60; Roache lectr, Ind. Univ, 63; Alexander lectr, Univ. Toronto, 64; adv. ed, W.W. Norton & Co; mem, Eng. Inst; mem. exec. counc, MLA, 61-64; fel, Ctr. Advan. Stud. Behav. Sci, 67-68; mem. bd. ed, Cornell Stud. Eng. & Cornell Concordances. Gauss Prize, 53. MLA (James Russell Lowell Prize, 72); fel. Am. Philos. Soc; fel. Am. Acad. Arts & Sci. History of literature; literary criticism; European romanticism. Publ: The milk of paradise, Harvard, 34 & Octagon, 70; The mirror and the lamp: romantic theory and the critical tradition, 53, & The Romantic poets: modern essays in criticism, 60, Oxford; co-auth. & ed, Literature and belief, Columbia Univ, 58; co-auth, The Norton anthology of English literature, 62, rev. ed, 74 & auth, Natural supernaturalism: tradition and revolution in Romantic literature, 71, Norton; A glossary of literary terms, 57 & 70 & co-auth. & ed, The poetry of Pope, 58, Holt; auth, Coleridge, Baudelaire, and modernist poetics, Poetik Hermanentik, 65; co-auth. & ed, Wordsworth: a collection of critical essays, Prentice-Hall, 72; auth, What's the use of theorizing about the arts, In: In search of literary theory, 72. Add: Dept. of English, Cornell University, Ithaca, NY 14850.

ABRAMSON, ARTHUR SEYMOUR, Linguistics. See Volume III, Foreign Languages, Linguistics & Philology.

ABRAMSON, DORIS E, b. Northampton, Mass, May 6, 25. THEATRE. B.A, Univ. Mass, 49; M.A, Smith Col, 51; Danforth grants, 59-60 & 62-63; Ph.D. (theatre), Columbia Univ, 67. Instr. SPEECH & DRAMA, Wheaton Col, 51-53; UNIV. MASS, AMHERST, 53-59, asst. prof, 59-68, ASSOC. PROF, 68- Speech Commun. Asn; Am. Theatre Asn. American theatre history; oral interpretation. Publ: Negro playwrights in the American theatre 1925-1959, Columbia Univ, 69; It'll be me: the voice of Langston Hughes, Mass. Rev, autumn 63. Add: Dept. of Theatre, University of Massachusetts, Amherst, MA 01002.

ABRASH, MERRITT, Modern History. See Volume I, History.

ABU-SHAWAREB, HASSAN MUHAMMAD, b. Yasour, Palestine, Jan. 1, 36; m. 55; c. 7. ENGLISH. A.B, Univ. Riyadh, Saudi Arabia, 62; M.A, Ind. Univ. Bloomington, 68; Ph.D.(Eng), Univ. S.C, 70. Instr. ENG, Sch. Lang, Mil. Acad. Riyadh, Saudi Arabia, 62-65; asst. prof, S.C. STATE COL, 70-72, ASSOC. PROF, 73- MLA; Col. Lang. Asn; Col. Eng. Asn. The English romantic movement; the Victorian age; Shakespeare. Publ: A simplified English grammar, Dar Al Asfahani, 65; Shakespeare's The two gentlemen of Verona: a question of authorship, spring 72 & An interpretation of Keats's La belle dame sans mercy, spring 73, Explorations in Educ. Add: Dept. of English, South Carolina State College, Box 1893, Orangeburg, SC 29115.

ACHTERT, WALTER SCOTT, b. Yeadon, Pa, May 23, 43. ENGLISH LITERATURE. A.B, Drew Univ, 65; M.A, N.Y. Univ, 66, Ph.D.(Eng. lit), 72. Intern instr. Eng, State Univ. N.Y. Maritime Col, 67-68; asst. to exec. secy, MLA, 67-72, DIR. RES. & SPEC. PUBL, 72- MLA. History of scholarship in English language and literature; Victorian prose and prose fiction. Publ: Ed, MLA abstracts, MLA, annually, 70-; auth, MLA group projects, 1955-68, PMLA, 9/68; Universities and legislatures, Bull. Asn. Dept. Eng, 5/71; Scholarly journals in the seventies, Scholarly Publ, 10/73. Add: Modern Language Association of America, 62 Fifth Ave, New York, NY 10011.

ACHURCH, ROBERT WALLER, b. Charleston, S.C, July 16, 05; m. 30; c. 2. ENGLISH. A.B, Col. of Charleston, 27; A.M, Univ. N.C, 30, Ph.D, 43. Asst. prof. ENG, THE CITADEL, 30-43, assoc. prof, 43-50, prof, 50-70, head dept, 60-70, EMER. PROF, 70- Lectr, Med. Col. S.C, 49-; vis. lectr, Univ.

N.C, summer, 50; chmn, Dept. of Eng, Col. Charleston, 70-72, vis. prof, 73- MLA; S.Atlantic Mod. Lang. Asn. The literary periodical during the age of Anne; the literary periodical in the 18th century. Publ: Richard Steele, Gazetteer and Bickerstaff, In: Studies in the early English periodical, Univ. N.C, 57. Add: 2 Battery Pl, Charleston, SC 29401.

ACKERMAN, ROBERT WILLIAM, b. Swanton, Ohio, Feb. 1, 10; m. 62; c. 2. ENGLISH. A.B, Univ. Mich, 31, A.M, 33, Ph.D, 38. Instr. ENG, Univ. Mich, 38; State Col. Wash, 38-41; Ill. Inst. Technol, 41-42; asst. prof, Stanford Univ, 46-50, assoc. prof, 50-55, prof, 55-73; RETIRED. U.S.A, 42-46. MLA; Int. Arthurian Soc; fel. Mediaeval Acad. Am. Arthurian names in Middle English; Middle English literature. Publ: An index of the Arthurian names in Middle English, Stanford Univ, 52; co-auth, Ywain the Knight of the Lion, Ungar, 57; auth, Backgrounds to Medieval English literature, Random, 66; The English rimed and prose romances, In: Arthurian literature in the Middle Ages, Oxford, 59; Middle English literature to 1400, In: The medieval literature of western Europe, N.Y. Univ, 66. Add: P.O. Box 26, Walpole, NH 03608.

ACZEL, TAMAS, b. Budapest, Hungary, Dec. 16, 21; Brit. citizen; m. 60; c. 1. CREATIVE WRITING, HISTORY OF IDEAS. B.A, Pázmány Peter Univ, Budapest, 48; M.A, Eötvös Lorand Univ, Budapest, 50. Lectr. Hungarian lit, Eötvös Lorand Univ, Budapest, 50-53; mod. drama, Hungarian Acad. Dramatic Art, 53-55; sr. res. fel. relig, Ctr. Stud. & Res. Relig. Insts, Geneva, Switz, 66-70; lectr. ENG, UNIV. MASS, AMHERST, 66-67, PROF, 68- Kossuth Prize Poetry, Hungary, 49; Stalin Prize Lit, 52. AAUP; MLA; Am. Asn. Advan. Slavic Stud; PEN Club. History of heretical thought; psychology of creative writing; modern drama. Publ: A song on the ship (poems), Officina, Budapest, 41; Vigilance and faith (poems), Hungaria, 48; In the shadow of liberty, Szikra, 49; In lieu of a report (poems), 50, In the wake of the tremor, 54 & Flames and ashes, 55, Szépirodalmi; co-auth, The revolt of the mind, Praeger, 59; ed. & co-auth, Ten years after, Holt, 66; auth, The ice age, Simon & Schuster, 66; co-auth, Poetry of the Russian underground, Harper & Row, 73. Add: Dept. of English, University of Massachusetts, Amherst, MA 01002.

ADAIR, VIRGINIA H, b. New York, N.Y, Feb. 28, 13; m. 37; c. 3. LITERATURE. A.B, Mt. Holyoke Col, 33; scholar. & M.A, Radcliffe Col, 36; teaching fel, Univ. Wis, 35-37; Univ. Wash. Instr. Eng. & hist, Miss Fine's Sch, Princeton, N.J, 42; bibliotherapist, East. State Hosp, Va, 52-55; from asst. prof. to PROF. ENG, CALIF. STATE POLYTECH. UNIV, 57- Nat. Found. Arts & Humanities grant, 67. Glascock Poetry Award, 32, 33; Atlantic Monthly Col. Essay Contest Prize, 33. Col. Eng. Asn. Seventeenth century poetry, especially Marvell and Lovelace; Wordsworth and Coleridge. Publ: Contrib. to: Atlantic; Poetry Magazine; Explicator; Am. Notes & Queries; plus others. Add: Dept. of English & Modern Languages, California State Polytechnic University, Pomona, Pomona, CA 91766.

ADAM, IAN WILLIAM, b. Cabri, Sask, Nov. 14, 32; m. 57; c. 3. ENGLISH LITERATURE. B.A, Univ. Alta, 55; Imp. Order Daughters of Empire W.W.I. Mem. scholarship, Univ. London, 56, Can. Counc. fels, 58, 59, M.A, 60; Can. Counc. fel, 67-68. Asst. prof. ENG, UNIV. CALGARY, 60-67, ASSOC. PROF, 67- Asn. Can. Univ. Teachers Eng; Victorian Stud. Asn. West. Can.(pres, 73-). George Eliot; theory of fiction; contemporary Canadian literature. Publ: George Eliot, Routledge & Kegan Paul, 69; Character and destiny in George Eliot's fiction, Nineteenth Century Fiction, 9/65; Society as novelist, J. Aesthetics & Art Criticism, summer 67; Lawrence's anti-symbol, J. Narrative Tech, 5/73. Add: Dept. of English, University of Calgary, Calgary, Alta, T2N 1N4, Can.

ADAMANY, RICHARD G, b. Janesville, Wis, June 15, 30. ENGLISH LITERATURE & LANGUAGE. B.A, Univ. Wis, 52, M.A, 57, Knapp fel, 59-60, Ph.D, 63. Asst, Univ. Wis, 56-60; Fulbright teaching & res. grant, Univ. Florence, Italy, 60-62; instr. ENG, Kans. State Univ, 62-63, asst. prof, 63-64; assoc. prof, UNIV. WIS-WHITEWATER, 64-66, PROF, 67- Renaissance studies; Latin literature; Italian Renaissance literature. Add: Dept. of English, University of Wisconsin-Whitewater, Whitewater, WI 53190.

ADAMS, ALBERT C, b. Oklahoma City, Okla, July 27, 25; m. 45; c. 3. ENGLISH. A.B, Baylor Univ, 47, M.A, 57; B.D, Univ. of the South, 50; Ph.D. (Eng), Univ. Mo, 61. Instr. Eng, Univ. Mo, 57-61; asst. prof. Eng. & coord. freshman Eng, NORTH. ARIZ. UNIV, 61-63, assoc. prof. Eng. & dir. freshman Eng, 63-64, PROF. ENG. & CHMN. DEPT, 64- U.S.N, 42-45. Composition; Milton. Add: Dept. of English, Northern Arizona University, Flagstaff, AZ 86001.

ADAMS, ANTHONY ANDREW, b. Los Angeles, Calif, Apr. 13, 37; m. 70. ELECTRONIC MASS MEDIA. B.A, Gonzaga Univ, 61, M.A, 62; M.S.T, Santa Clara Univ, 69; Ph.D.(speech, mass commun), Ohio State Univ, 71. ASST. PROF. BROADCASTING, SPEECH & DRAMATIC ART DEPT, UNIV. IOWA, 71- Broadcast Educ. Asn; Nat. Asn. Educ. Broadcasters; Speech Commun. Asn. Broadcast history; broadcast regulation; media criticism. Publ: Broadcasters' attitudes toward public responsibility: an Ohio case study, J. Broadcasting, fall 72. Add: Div. of Broadcast-Film, University of Iowa, Iowa City, IA 52240.

ADAMS, BARRY BANFIELD, b. Boston, Mass, Aug. 31, 35; m. 62; c. 2. ENGLISH. B.A, Boston Col, 57; M.A, Univ. N.C, 59, Ph.D.(Eng), 63. Instr. ENG, CORNELL UNIV, 63-65, asst. prof, 65-69, ASSOC. PROF, 69-, CHMN. DEPT, 70-, Henry E. Huntington Libr. summer res. grant, 64. MLA; Renaissance Soc. Am. Middle and Renaissance English literature. Publ: Ed, John Bale's King Johan, Huntington Libr, 68; auth, The prudence of Prince Escalus, ELH, 3/68; The audiences of the Spanish tragedy, JEGP, 69. Add: Dept. of English, Cornell University, Ithaca, NY 14850.

ADAMS, BESS PORTER, b. Morgan, Utah, Apr. 2, 02; m; c. 3. ENGLISH. A.B, Univ. Redlands, 37, A.M, 38; Univ. Calif. Teacher elem. schs, Calif, 37-38; instr. ENG, UNIV. REDLANDS, 38-40, asst. prof, 40-52, assoc. prof, 52-72, EMER. ASSOC. PROF, 72- Lectr, exten. div, Univ. Calif, 49-; chief grading ed, Am. Educ. Encycl, United Educators, Inc, 60; lectr. Eng. lit, Calif. Baptist Col, 66- NCTE; MLA. Juvenile literature; Italian Renaissance; Language and culture of the Congo. Publ: About books and children, Holt, 53; Books for children, Vogue, 3/55; Books to grow on, Nat. Counc. Social Stud, 1/56. Add: Dept. of English, University of Redlands, Redlands, CA 90723.

ADAMS, CHARLES CLINTON, b. Tulsa, Okla, Dec. 11, 27; m. 48; c. 4. ENGLISH. B.A, Chico State Col, 55; M.A, Univ. Wash, 59, Ph.D.(Eng), 67. Teacher, Pub. Schs, Calif, 48-58; from instr. to PROF. ENG, CALIF. STATE UNIV, CHICO, 59-, chmn. dept, 70-72. NDEA consult. Eng. ling, Various Schs. & Sch. Dist, Calif, 65-; chmn. statewide acad. senate, Calif. State Univ. & Cols, 72-74. American dialectology; linguistics in the teaching of English; English literature before 1500. Publ: Boontling: an American lingo, Univ. Tex, 71; A wee deek on Boont Harpin's Boontlinger Club, 67. Add: 38 Arroyo Way, Chico, CA 95926.

ADAMS, CHARLES L, b. Joliet, Ill, May 11, 29; m. 53; c. 2. ENGLISH. B.A, Mich. State Univ, 51; M.A, Univ. Ill, 52; Ph.D.(Eng), Univ. Ore, 59. Instr. ENG, Univ. Ore, 59-60; asst. prof, UNIV. NEV, LAS VEGAS, 60-65, assoc. prof, 65-67, PROF, 67-, grad. sch. rep, 64-66, coord. grad. stud, 66-68, dean grad. stud, 68-71. Rocky Mountain Mod. Lang. Asn; AAUP; Philol. Asn. Pac. Coast; NCTE; MLA. Comparative experimental poetry, 1900 to 1940; Shelley; Chaucer. Publ: Notes on Lolita, Northwest Rev, spring 59; The structure of The Cenci, Drama Surv, summer 65. Add: Dept. of English, University of Nevada, Las Vegas, NV 89154.

ADAMS, DONALD KNAPP, b. Can, Nov. 1, 24; U.S. citizen. ENGLISH. A.B. & B.Comm, Univ. B.C, 46; M.A, Northwest. Univ, 52, Ph.D.(Eng), 53. Instr. Eng, Univ. South. Calif, 53-54; from instr. to PROF. ENG. & COMP. LIT. & CHMN. DEPT, OCCIDENTAL COL, 55- Ford Found. grant, 54-55; Haynes fel, summer 60; Fulbright lectr, Univ. Dacca, 61-62 & Univ. Baghdad, 65-66. MLA; Jane Austen Soc. Poe Soc; Asiatic Soc. Bangladesh. Publ: Ed. & publ, Mystery & Detection Annual, 72 & 73; auth, Critical biography of Dr. John Polidori, In: The vampyre, Dahlstrom, 68; plus articles in scholarly jour. Add: Dept. of English & Comparative Literature, Occidental College, Los Angeles, CA 90041.

ADAMS, ELSIE B, b. Atoka, Okla, Aug. 11, 32; m. 59; c. 2. ENGLISH. B.S, Univ. Okla, 53, M.A, 59, Ph.D.(Eng), 66. Instr. Eng, Northeast. Okla. A&M Jr. Col, 53-54; teacher, high sch, Okla, 55-56; asst. prof. ENG, Wis. State Univ, Whitewater, 66-67, assoc. prof, 67-71; ASST. PROF, SAN DIEGO STATE UNIV, 71- Bernard Shaw; female studies; Victorian literature. Publ: Co-ed, Up against the wall, mother . . . : on women's liberation, Glencoe, 71; auth, Israel Zangwill, Twayne, 71; Bernard Shaw and the aesthetes, Ohio State Univ, 71; Bernard Shaw's pre-Raphaelite drama, PMLA, 10/66; No exit: an exploration of Kipling's A wayside comedy, Eng. Lit. Transition, 68; Gissing's allegorical House of cobwebs, Stud. Short Fiction, spring 70; plus others. Add: School of Literature, San Diego State University, San Diego, CA 92102.

ADAMS, EZRA JOHN, b. Darnell, La. JOURNALISM, MODERN HISTORY. B.A, Northeast La. Univ, 56; M.A, La. State Univ, 64; Northwest. State Univ, 68-69. News reporter & ed, Monroe Morning World, La, 53-56; pub. relat. dir, East Baton Rouge Parish Recreation & Parks Comn, 56-57; news reporter & ed, WJBO Radio, Baton Rouge, 57-58; Baton Rouge Morning Advocate, 58; reporter & ed, La. Elec. Coop. Asn, 59-63; pub. inform. off, La. Dept. Agr, 63-64; asst. prof. jour. & dir. publ, Southeast. La. Univ, 64-66; pub. relat. rep, Int. Paper Co, 66-68; ASSOC. PROF. JOUR, NORTHWEST. STATE UNIV, 69- Ed, La. Stud, Northwest. State Univ, 69-72. U.S.A.F, 42-46, 51-53, S/Sgt. Asn. Educ. in Jour. American history. Publ: Ed, A Louisiana Confederate: diary of Felix Pierre Poche, Northwest. State Univ, 72. Add: Division of Journalism, Northwestern State University, Natchitoches, LA 71457.

ADAMS, FRANCIS RAYMOND, JR, b. Watsontown, Pa, Aug. 19, 16; m. 42, 50; c. 3. AMERICAN LITERATURE; A.B, Williams Col, 38; M.A, Univ. Md, 47, Ph.D.(Am. civilization, lit), 55. Instr. ENG, Susquehanna Univ, 43-44; Yale, 44-45; Univ. Md, 45-57; Am. Univ.(D.C), 57-58; assoc. prof, E E.Carolina Col, 58-61, PROF, 61-68; MADISON COL.(VA), 68- U.S.A.A.F, 42-43. Col. Eng. Asn; MLA; Am. Stud. Asn; S.Atlantic Mod. Lang. Asn; AAUP. Robert E. Lee; 19th and 20th century American literature; literary criticism. Publ: Robert E. Lee and the concept of democracy, Am. Quart, fall 60; Relevance, Forum, 2/71. Add: Dept. of English, Madison College, Harrisonburg, VA 22801.

ADAMS, GEORGE ROY, b. Lime Springs, Iowa, Nov. 23, 28; m. 59; c. 3. ENGLISH, LINGUISTICS. B.A, Univ. Okla, 52, Fulbright grant, 57-58, South. Fel. Fund fel, 60-61, Ph.D, 61. Instr. ENG, Boston Univ, 61-63; asst. prof, Harpur Col, State Univ. N.Y. Binghamton, 63-66; ASSOC. PROF, UNIV. WIS-WHITEWATER, 66- Qm.C, 52-54, 1st Lt. MLA; Mediaeval Acad. Am. Medieval literary esthetic; medieval drama; history of the English language. Publ: Paul Goodman, Twayne; Chaucer's Shipman's tale, Explicator, 66; co-auth, Good and bad Fridays and May 3 in Chaucer, Eng. Lang. Notes, 66 & Chauntecleer's paradise lost and regained, Mediaeval Stud, 67. Add: Dept. of English, University of Wisconsin-Whitewater, Whitewater, WI 53190.

ADAMS, HARLEN MARTIN, b. Provo, Utah, Mar. 15, 04; m. 38; c. 3. ENGLISH, SPEECH, DRAMA. A.B Brigham Young Univ, 25; A.M, Harvard, 28; Princeton, 31-32; D.Ed, Stanford Univ, 38. Instr. Eng, Brigham Young Univ, 24; Eng, French & speech, high sch, Utah, 24-26, head dept. Eng, 28-31; instr. Eng. & speech, high sch, N.J, 32-35; chmn. Eng. & dir. speech, Menlo Jr. Col, Calif, 35-39; head dept. speech arts, Chico State Col, 39-43; asst. prof. speech & drama, Stanford Univ, 43-46; dean, Sch. Arts & Sci, Calif. State Univ, Chico, 46-47, Sch. Educ, 47-50, exec. dean, 50-57, prof. Eng. & speech, 67-74; RETIRED. NCTE (pres, 53); Speech Asn. Am. Language study for teachers; oral study of literature. Publ: Junior college library program, Stanford; Language arts and skills & Speak up, Macmillan. Add: Apt. 43, 555 Vallombrosa Ave, Chico, CA 95926.

ADAMS, HAZARD, b. Cleveland, Ohio, Feb. 15, 26; m. 49; c. 2. ENGLISH. B.A, Princeton, 48; M.A, Univ. Wash, 49, Ph.D, 53. Instr. ENG, Cornell Univ, 52-55, asst. prof, 56; Univ. Tex, 56-59; assoc. prof, Mich. State Univ, 59-62, prof, 62-64; PROF, UNIV. CALIF, IRVINE, 64-, V.CHANCELLOR ACAD. AFFAIRS, 72-, chmn. dept. Eng. & comp. lit, 64-69, dean sch. humanities, 70-72. Vis. prof, Wash. Univ, 59; Fulbright res. scholar & exchange lectr, Trinity Col, Dublin Univ, 62-63. U.S.M.C, 43-45, 51, Lt. MLA; Am. Soc. Aesthetics. Literary criticism; modern Anglo-Irish literature; romanticism. Publ: Blake and Yeats: the contrary vision, Cornell, 55; The contexts of poetry, 63 & ed, Poetry: an introductory anthology, 68, Little; William Blake: a reading of the shorter poems, Univ. Wash, 63; The horses of instruction, 68, The interests of criticism, 68, The truth about dragons: an antiromance, 71 & ed, Critical theory since Plato, 71, Harcourt; co-auth. & ed, Fiction as process, Dodd, 68; ed, William Blake: Jerusalem? selected poems and prose, Rinehart, 70; auth, Lady Gregory, Bucknell, 73. Add: Dept. of English & Comparative Literature, University of California, Irvine, CA 92664.

ADAMS, HENRY HITCH, b. Ann Arbor, Mich, Mar. 26, 17; m. 43; c. 2. ENGLISH LITERATURE, NAVAL HISTORY. A.B, Univ. Mich, 39; A.M, Columbia Univ, 40, Ph.D, 42. Instr. Eng, Cornell Univ, 45-51; from asst. prof. to prof. Eng. & hist, U.S. Naval Acad, 51-68; prof. Eng. & head dept, Ill. State Univ, 68-73; RES. & WRITING, 73- U.S.N.R, 43-, Capt. MLA; Col. Eng. Asn.(pres, 67-68); AHA; Mid. Atlantic Col. Eng. Asn.(pres, 55). Drama. Publ: Co-auth, Sea power, Prentice-Hall, 60; auth, English domestic or homiletic tragedy, 1575-1642, Blom; 1942: the year that doomed the Axis, 67, Years of deadly peril, 69, Years of expectation, 73 & Years to victory, 73, McKay; Submarine, In: Encycl. Britannica, 65; plus others. Add: Ferry Farms, Annapolis, MD 21402.

ADAMS, HENRY WELCH, b. Bonham, Tex, Apr. 2, 98; m. 26; c. 2. AMERICAN & ENGLISH LITERATURE. A.B, South. Methodist Univ, 21; A.M, Columbia Univ, 49. Instr, South. Methodist Univ, 21-23, asst. prof, 23-28; assoc. prof. ENG, Auburn Univ, 28-46; GA. INST. TECHNOL, 46-57, prof, 58-65, EMER. PROF, 65- Asst, Columbia Univ, 27-28. S.Atlantic Mod. Lang. Asn. Southern literature and theatrical history; 19th century English literature. Publ: Elements of sentence structure, Prentice-Hall, 37; Organization, logic and style; The Montgomery, Alabama, theatre from 1822-1835, Univ. Ala, 55. Add: 2032 McLendon Ave. N.E, Atlanta, GA 30307.

ADAMS, JOHN FESTUS, b. Zillah, Wash, June 30, 30. ENGLISH LITERATURE. B.A, Univ. Wash, 52, M.A, 57, Ph.D, 60. Asst, Univ. Wash, 55-58, assoc, 58-59, acting instr. ENG, 59-60; asst. prof, Univ. Denver, 60-63; ASSOC. PROF, Univ. Calif, Irvine, 63-68; WASH. STATE UNIV, 68- U.S.A, 52-54, Capt. MLA; Philol. Asn. Pac. Coast. Piers Plowman; Chaucer; Anglo-Saxon poetry. Publ: Two plus two equals minus seven, Macmillan, 69; The art of brewing, 69 & Beekeeping: the gentle craft, 72, Doubleday; Piers Plowman and the three ages of man, J. Eng. & Germanic Philol, 1/62; All's well that ends well; paradox, Shakespeare Quart, 63; Leda and the swan: the aesthetics of rape, Bucknell,Rev, 12/64. Add: Dept. of English, Washington State University, Pullman, WA 99163.

ADAMS, JOHN HOWARD, b. Chicago, Ill, Jan. 7, 39; m. 63; c. 2. AMERICAN LITERATURE. B.A, Kalamazoo Col, 60; M.A, Univ. Ala, 62; fel, Univ. Denver, 63-65, Ph.D.(Eng), 67. Asst. ENG, Univ. Ala, 60-62; instr, West. Ky. Univ, 62-63; ASSOC. PROF, MURRAY STATE UNIV, 67- AAUP. American poetry; modern novel. Publ: Co-auth, Motivation in freshman English, Improving Col. & Univ. Teaching, 62; auth, Rebellion and conformity in five modern novels, Murray State Univ. Rev, 69. Add: Dept. of English, Murray State University, Murray, KY 42071.

ADAMS, JOHN R, b. Cincinnati, Ohio, July 22, 00; m. 23. ENGLISH. A.B, Univ. Mich, 20, A.M, 22; Ph.D, Univ. South. Calif, 40. Instr. rhetoric, Univ. Mich, 20-25; assoc. ENG, Univ. Wash, 25-28; from instr. to assoc. prof, SAN DIEGO STATE UNIV, 28-40, prof, 40-68, chmn, Div. Lang. & Lit, 46-56, Div. Humanities, 56-68, COL. ARCHIVIST, 68- Instr, Exten. Div, Univ. Calif, 35. MLA; NCTE; Philol. Asn. Pac. Coast. Nineteenth century American literature in its international setting; local literary history. Publ: Harriet Beecher Stowe, Twayne, 63; Books and authors of San Diego, San Diego State Col, 66; ed, Regional sketches of Harriet Beecher Stowe, Col. & Univ, 72. Add: 4131 Marlborough Ave, San Diego, CA 92105.

ADAMS, JOSEPH DOMENIC, b. New York, N.Y, July 25, 31; m. 53; c. 2. AMERICAN LITERATURE, ENGLISH AS A FOREIGN LANGUAGE. B.A, Franklin & Marshall Col, 52; M.Ed, Shippensburg State Col, 66; Ph.D.(Eng), Lehigh Univ, 72. Teacher Eng. & art, Mercersburg Acad, Pa, 61-67; teaching asst. ENG, Lehigh Univ, 67-68; instr, Rider Col, 68-69; ASSOC. PROF. & DIR. ENG. SPEAKERS OTHER LANGS. PROG, CENT. MO. STATE UNIV, 69- Proj. dir, Nat. Endowment for Arts prof. artists workshop, 72-73; mem. visual arts adv. comt, Mo. State Counc. on Arts, 72-; proj. dir, Mo. State Comt. for Humanities grant, 73; state chmn, Alliance for Arts Educ, Mo, 73- Ord.C, U.S.A, 53-55. MLA. Hawthorne; Melville; English for speakers of other languages. Publ: Co-auth, Nathaniel Hawthorne: a reference bibliography, 72 & Herman Melville: a reference bibliography, 73, G.K. Hall; ed, Open for discussion: a humanities handbook, Cent. Mo. State Univ, 73; auth, The hard-luck artist of the Renaissance, Cent. Mo. State Univ. Publ, 4/71; Social control through education: dream or nightmare?, In: Open for discussion, 73. Add: Dept. of English, Central Missouri State University, Warrensburg, MO 64093.

ADAMS, LEONIE, (MRS. WILLIAM TROY), b. Brooklyn, N.Y, Dec. 9, 99; wid. ENGLISH. A.B, Columbia Univ; Guggenheim fel, 28-30; hon. D.Litt, Rutgers Univ, 50. Instr. lit, N.Y. Univ, 30-32; writing, Sarah Lawrence Col, 33-34; Bennington Col, 35-37, 41-45; lectr, N.J. Col. Women, Rutgers Univ, 46-48; Eng, Columbia Univ, 47-68; RETIRED. Lectr, Olivet Writers Conf, 31; fel, Libr. Congr, 48-55, consult, 48-49; instr, N.Y. Univ, 53-54; Fulbright lectr, France, 55-56; lectr, Bread Loaf Writers Conf, 56-58; vis. prof. poetry, Univ. Wash, 61 & 68-69; Nat. Found. Arts grant, 66-67; vis. prof. poetry, Purdue Univ, 71-72; Mark Rothko Found. grant, 73. Shelley Mem. Award; Harriet Monroe Award; Bollingen Prize, 54; fel, Acad. Am. Poets, 59; medal & award for poetry, Brandeis Univ. Arts Counc, 69. Nat. Inst. Arts & Lett.(award, 49, secy, 59-61). English and American poetry and poetic technique. Publ: Those not elect, McBride, 25; High Falcon, Day, 29; Poems, a selection, Funk, 53, Noonday, 59; Contemporary poet, In: Artist & critic, Little, 64; Problems of form, Nat. Poetry Festival, Libr. Congr, 62. Add: R.R. 2, New Milford, CT 06776.

ADAMS, MARJORIE, b. Jena, La, Apr. 13, 22. ENGLISH. B.A, La. Polytech. Inst, 41; M.A, Univ. Tex, 47, Ph.D.(Eng), 51. Instr. ENG, South. Methodist Univ, 51-53; Univ. Tenn, 53-54; asst. prof, KANS. STATE UNIV, 54-61, ASSOC. PROF, 61-, ASST. DEAN ARTS & SCI. & DIR. HONORS PROG, 60-, dir. arts & sci. 3 year M.A. prog, 63. W.A.C, 43-45, Sgt. MLA; Renaissance Soc. Am; Mediaeval Acad. Am; Cent. Renaissance Conf.(secy, 56). Anglo-French Renaissance literary relations, especially Edmund Spenser and Pierre de Ronsard. Publ: Spenser and Ronsard, In: Renaissance Papers, Duke Univ. Add: Dept. of English, Kansas State University, Manhattan, KS 66502.

ADAMS, MARTHA LOU LATIMER, b. Shaw, Miss, Dec. 13, 22; c. 2. ENGLISH. B.A, Delta State Col, 63; M.A, Univ. Miss, 65, Ph.D.(Eng), 68. Teaching asst. ENG, Univ. Miss, 64-68; asst. prof, NORTHEAST LA. UNIV, 68-71, ASSOC. PROF, 73- Vis. asst. prof. Eng, Univ. Miss, summer 71; Renaissance manuscript evaluator, Univ. Miss. Press, 71. Renaissance. Publ: Ed, Selected bibliography of Northeast Louisiana University faculty research and publications, Northeast La. Univ, 73; auth, William Shakespeare and the Greek romance, Univ. Miss. Stud. Eng, 67. Add: Dept. of English, Northeast Louisiana University, DeSiard St, Monroe, LA 71201.

ADAMS, MAURIANNE SCHIFREEN, b. Philadelphia, Pa, May 30, 38; m. 61. ENGLISH LITERATURE. B.A, Swarthmore Col, 59; Ph.D.(Eng), Ind. Univ, 67. Instr. ENG, Smith Col, 64-67, asst. prof, 67-73; LECTR. & ACAD. COORD. SOUTHWEST RESIDENTIAL COL, UNIV. MASS, AMHERST, 73- Co-researcher, Nat. Endowment for Humanities Proj. grant, 67-74; lectr, NDEA Summer Inst. Advan. Stud. Eng, 67-68; dir. spec. prog. for minority students, Smith Col, 68-71. MLA; Eng. Inst; Res. Soc. Victorian Periodicals (secy, 71-73). Nineteenth century poetry and criticism; Victorian periodicals; women in literature. Publ: Auth. & ed, Autobiography, Bobbs, 68; auth, Ocular proof in Othello and its source, PMLA, 64. Add: 19 Tyler Ct, Northampton, MA 01060.

ADAMS, MILDRED DAVIS, b. Jacksonville, Fla, Oct. 2, 16; m. 39, 68; c. 2. COMPARATIVE LITERATURE. B.A, Agnes Scott Col, 38; M.A, Columbia Univ, 39, Ph.D.(Eng), 60; Univ. Chicago, 40-42. Instr. Eng, N.J. Col. Women, 43-44; lit, Stephens Col, 45-46; lectr. ENG, Wash. Univ, 46-47; asst. prof, Shurtleff Col, 47-49; Am. Univ. Cairo, 52-54; assoc. prof, Queen Aliyya Col, Baghdad, 55-56; asst. prof, Am. Univ. Beirut, 56-60; instr, Shimer Col, 61-62; asst. prof, Univ. South Fla, 62-67; ASSOC. PROF, KEENE STATE COL, 67- Instr, Univ. Md. Overseas Prog, Ger, autumn 66. MLA. English novel, especially George Moore; 19th century civilization; Roman civilization, especially Virgil. Add: Dept. of English, Keene State College, Keene, NH 03431.

ADAMS, PERCY GUY, b. Beeville, Tex, Dec. 16, 14. ENGLISH. A.B, Tex. Col. Arts & Indust, 33; A.M, Univ. Tex, 37, Ph.D, 46; Sorbonne, 53-54. Tutor ENG, Univ. Tex, 41-43; instr, Ohio State Univ, 46-48; asst. prof, Univ. Tenn, 48-55, assoc. prof, 55-62, PROF, 62-66; La. State Univ, Baton Rouge, 66-72; UNIV. TENN, KNOXVILLE, 72- Summer res. grants, Duke Univ, 54; Newberry Libr, 58; Fulbright lectr, Univs. Aix-Marseille & Grenoble, France, 58-59; Am. Counc. Learned Soc. summer res. grants, 60, 62, 66 & 73; vis. prof, Univ. South. Calif, summer 64; gen. ed, Great travel books, Dover Publ, Inc, 65-; La. State Univ. summer res. grants, 67 & 68. U.S.N.A.F, 43-46, Lt. Southeast. Soc. 18th Century Stud.(pres, 74); Am. Comp. Lit. Asn; Soc. Hist. Discoveries; Soc. South. Lit; MLA; NCTE; S.Cent. Mod. Lang. Asn; S.Atlantic Mod. Lang. Asn. Eighteenth century and comparative literature. Publ: Travelers and travel liars: 1660-1800, Univ. Calif, 62; Historical importance of assonance to poets, PMLA, 73; Epic tradition and the novel, South. Rev, 73; Faulkner and French literature, Proc. Comp. Lit. Symp, 73; plus others. Add: Dept. of English, University of Tennessee, Knoxville, TN 37916.

ADAMS, PHILLIP DUANE, b. Grand Rapids, Mich, Dec. 21, 34; m. 55; c. 2. COMPARATIVE ARTS, ENGLISH. B.A, West. Mich. Univ, 59; M.A, Ohio Univ, 61, Ph.D, 71. Grad. intern Eng, Ohio Univ, 59-61; asst. prof. & acting head dept, Lakeland Col, 61-63; teaching fel. fine arts, Ohio Univ, 63-64; asst. prof. Eng, West. Mich. Univ, 64-68; chmn. div. humanities, Kalamazoo Valley Community Col, 68-69; teaching asst. comp. arts, Ohio Univ, 69-70; asst. prof. humanities, WEST. MICH. UNIV, 70-72, ASSOC. PROF. HUMANITIES & CHMN. HUMANITIES AREA, 72- Martin Luther King Tutorial Award, 72. Fel. Royal Soc. Arts. Publ: David Hostetler, the carver from Coolville Ridge, West. Mich. Univ, 67; Bring down the Jolly Roger! (poems), Olivant, 70; A letter of celebration by way of introduction, Introd. to A birdness Flown, Hors Commerce, 66; The integrity of the line in Haiku, Mod. Haiku, spring-summer 72; The nude in the doorway, Mich. Academician, winter 70; plus over one hundred poems and short stories in Motive, Am. Haiku & Human Voice. An eighteenth-century panorama (thirty-minute TV prog), 62; Sculpture (forty-minute TV prog), West. Mich. Univ, 66. Add: Humanities Area, 201 Moore, Western Michigan University, Kalamazoo, MI 49001.

ADAMS, RAYMOND, b. Elgin, Ill, May 7, 98; m. 27. ENGLISH. A.B, Beloit Col, 20; A.M, Univ. N.C, 21, Ph.D, 28. Asst. prof. ENG, UNIV. N.C, CHAPEL HILL, 29-35, assoc. prof, 35-39, prof, 39-68, EMER. PROF, 68-, acting chmn. dept, 66-67. Gen. Educ. Bd. fel, 34-35; Alumni Distinguished Serv. award, Beloit Col, 60. MLA; Am. Stud. Asn; Bibliog. Soc. Am; Emerson Soc; Thoreau Soc.(pres, 40-51). American transcendentalism; American utopias; Thoreau. Add: P.O. Box 762, Chapel Hill, NC 27514.

ADAMS, RICHARD PERRILL, b. Mound City, Kans, Aug. 17, 17; m. 41; c. 3. ENGLISH. A.B, Univ. Ill, 39, M.A, 40; Ph.D.(Eng), Columbia Univ, 51. Instr. ENG, Univ. Ky, 40-42; L.I. Univ, 47; Rutgers Univ, 47-49; Lafayette Col, 49-53; asst. prof, TULANE UNIV, 53-56, assoc. prof, 56-59, PROF, 59- Fulbright lectr, Univ. Lyon, 58-59, Univ. Lille, 65-66 & Debrecen Univ, spring 73. U.S.A.F, 42-45, Res, 45-, Maj. MLA; Col. Eng. Asn; Am. Stud. Asn; AAUP. American literature; Hawthorne; the Romantic tradition in American literature. Publ: Romanticism and the American Renaissance, Am. Lit; Emerson and the organic metaphor, PMLA; Whitman: a brief revaluation, Tulane Stud. Eng. Add: Dept. of English, Tulane University, New Orleans, LA 70118.

ADAMS, ROBERT MARTIN, b. New York, N.Y, Nov. 27, 15; m. 58; c. 1. ENGLISH. A.B, Columbia Univ, 35, M.A, 37, Ph.D.(Eng), 42. Instr. ENG, Columbia Univ, 38-41; Univ. Wis, 42-43; from instr. to asst. prof, Rutgers

Univ, 47-50; from asst. prof. to prof, Cornell Univ, 50-68; PROF, UNIV. CALIF, LOS ANGELES, 68- Hudson Rev. fel, lit. criticism, 56-57; Guggenheim fel, 60-74. U.S.A.A.F, 43-46, Capt. English literature of the 17th and 20th centuries. Publ: Ikon, John Milton and the modern critics, Cornell, 55; Stendhal, notes on a novelist, Noonday, 59; Surface and symbol, 62 & Nil, 66, Oxford; James Joyce: common sense and beyond, Random, 66; auth. & transl, Voltaire, Candide, 66, Stendhal, Red and black, 68 & auth, Proteus, 73, Norton; The Roman stamp, Univ. Calif, 74. Add: Dept. of English, University of California, Los Angeles, CA 90024.

ADAMS, ROBERT PARDEE, b. Detroit, Mich, Apr. 21, 10; m. 32, 61; c. 2. ENGLISH LITERATURE & LANGUAGE. A.B, Oberlin Col, 31; Ph.D, Univ. Chicago, 37. Instr. ENG, Cornell Univ, 36; Parsons Col, 36-37; from instr. to assoc. prof, Mich. State Univ, 37-47; assoc. prof, UNIV. WASH, 47-67, PROF, 67- Fel, Folger Shakespeare Libr, 53, 56, sr. fel, 71-72; sr. fel, Newberry Libr, 64-65; grant-in-aid res, Huntington Libr, summer 64; ed. consult, Northwest. Univ. Press, 66; Duke Univ. Press, 67. MLA; Renaissance Soc. Am; Am. Civil Liberties Union; AAUP. Tudor Christian humanism; Elizabethan drama; literature and social reconstruction. Publ: The better part of valor: More, Erasmus, Colet, and Vives on humanism, war, and peace, 62, Shakespeare, 67, Shakespeare's comedies and histories, 67, Shakespeare's tragedies, 67, Utopias and social ideas, 67, Shakespeare for independent study, 70 & Shakespeare to 1603, Univ. Wash; The social responsibilities of sciences in Utopia, New Atlantis and after, J. Hist. Ideas, 49; Shakespeare's tragic vision, In: Pacific Coast studies in Shakespeare, Univ. Ore, 66; Critical myths and Chapman's original Bussy d'Ambois, In: Renaissance drama IX, Northwest. Univ, 67; plus others. Add: Dept. of English, University of Washington, Seattle, WA 98195.

ADAMS, RUTH MARIE, b. New York, N.Y, July 10, 14. ENGLISH. B.A, Adelphi Col, 35; M.A, Columbia Univ, 43; Ph.D.(Eng), Radcliffe Col, 51; hon. L.H.D, Adelphi Col, 61, Northeast. Univ, 67, Bates Col, 70, St. Lawrence Univ, 71, Union Col, 72; hon. Litt.D, Russell Sage Col, 61; hon. LL.D, Rutgers Univ, 66, Univ. Mass, 70. Teacher, high sch, 38-43; teaching fel. & tutor Eng, Harvard Col, 44-46; from instr. to assoc. prof, Univ. Rochester, 46-60; prof. Eng. & dean col, Douglass Col, Rutgers Univ, 60-66; pres, Wellesley Col, 66-72; PROF. ENG. & V.PRES. COL, DARTMOUTH COL, 66- Ford Found. award, 53-54. MLA. Victorian novel; Victorian biography; journal articles. Add: Dept. of English, Dartmouth College, Hanover, NH 03755.

ADAMS, THEODORE S, b. Watsontown, Pa, July 11, 22; m. 47; c. 2. ENGLISH & AMERICAN LITERATURE. B.A, Univ. Rochester, 47; M.A, Ohio State Univ, 49, Ph.D, 60. Instr. Eng, Univ. Buffalo, 49-56, chmn. comt. remedial Eng, 52-56; instr. ENG, Ohio State Univ, 56-57; from asst. prof. to ASSOC. PROF, STATE UNIV. N.Y. ALBANY, 57- Instr. lit. & accent correction, Niagara Falls Adult Educ. Ctr, 53-54; N.Y. State Res. Found. grant, summer 62. MLA. Add: Dept. of English, State University of New York at Albany, Albany, NY 12222.

ADAMSON, ARTHUR H, b. Winnipeg, Man, Jan. 8, 26; m. 58; c. 2. ENGLISH, FRENCH. B.A, Univ. Man, 49, M.A, 60; Ph.D, Univ. Wis, 62. Asst. prof. French, St. John's Col, UNIV. MAN, 62-69, ASSOC. PROF. ENG, 69- Res. fel, Univ. Wis, 62. Can. Army, 44-46. Add: Dept. of English, University of Manitoba, Winnipeg, Man. R3T 2N2, Can.

ADDINGTON, DAVID W, b. Los Angeles, Calif, Mar. 9, 33; m. 54; c. 2. SPEECH, DRAMA. B.A, Palos Verdes Col, 54; M.A, Univ. Calif, Los Angeles, 60; Ph.D, State Univ. Iowa, 63. Asst. speech, State Univ. Iowa, 58-60; asst. prof. speech & drama, Okla. State Univ, 60-67; vis. lectr. drama, San Jose State Col, 67-68; PROF. SPEECH & DRAMA, BOWLING GREEN STATE UNIV, 68- Co-ed, Empirical research in theatre, Ctr. Commun. Res, Bowling Green State Univ, 71- U.S.A, 54-56. Speech Asn. Am; Cent. States Speech Asn. Theatre, especially experimental research and paralanguage. Publ: Voice and the perception of personality: an experimental study, Okla. State Univ. Monogr, 68; The relationship of selected vocal characteristics to personality perception, 11/68 & The effect of vocal variations on ratings of source credibility, 8/71, Speech Monogr; Games as an aid to playscript interpretations, Proc. Nat. Gaming Conf, 12/72; plus one other. Add: Dept. of Speech & Drama, Bowling Green State University, Bowling Green, OH 43403.

ADDISON, MICHAEL, C. b. South Africa, June 23, 37; U.S. citizen; m. 58; c. 2. DRAMA. B.A, Pomona Col, 58; M.F.A, Tulane Univ, 60; Ph.D.(theatre), Stanford Univ, 68. Asst. prof. drama, Univ. California, Riverside, 64-67; assoc. prof. dramatic art, Univ. Calif, Santa Barbara, 67-72; dean sch. of theatre & dance, Calif. Inst. of Arts, 72-73; ASSOC. PROF. DRAMA & GRAD. ADV, UNIV. CALIF, SAN DIEGO, 73- Assoc. producer, Utah Shakespearean Festival, 63-69; vis. fel. in theatre, Univ. West. Australia, 69-70; mem, Humanities Inst, Univ. Calif, 71. Am. Theatre Asn. Directing; acting; Shakespeare. Publ: Unloose this tied up justice: Measure for measure and the Elizabethan stage, Callboard, 4/67; co-auth, Actor training in Australia, Educ. Theatre J, 12/70; Towards a new Australian theatre, Masque, 3/71; plus three others. Add: Dept. of Drama, University of California, San Diego, La Jolla, CA 92037.

ADELMAN, GARY, b. Brooklyn, N.Y, July 1, 35; m. 65; c. 5. ENGLISH. B.A, Univ. Mich, 57; M.A, Columbia Univ, 58, Ph.D.(Eng), 62. Instr. ENG, Brooklyn Col, 58-63; asst. prof, UNIV. ILL, URBANA, 63-71, ASSOC. PROF, 71- Contemporary British literature; 19th century Russian and American literature; modern British and American poetry. Publ: Political poems, Depot Press, 68; Honey out of stone, Doubleday, 70; A reading of The Rainbow, 3/70, The tyranny of the will: a reading of Women in Love, 10/71 & Hermitage, 10/72, Karamu; plus two others. Add: 125 English Bldg, University of Illinois, Urbana, IL 61801.

ADELMAN, JANET ANN, b. Mt, Kisco, N.Y, Jan. 28, 41. ENGLISH LITERATURE. B.A, Smith Col, 62; Fulbright fel, Oxford, 62-63; M.A, Yale, 66, M.Phil, 67, Ph.D.(Eng), 69. Acting asst. prof. ENG, UNIV. CALIF, BERKELEY, 68-70, asst. prof, 70-72, ASSOC. PROF, 72- MLA; Shakespeare Asn. Am. Shakespeare; English Renaissance narrative poetry. Publ: The common liar: an essay on Antony and Cleopatra, Yale, 73; That we may leere som wit, In: Twentieth century interpretation of The pardoner's tale, Prentice-Hall, 73. Add: Dept. of English, University of California, Berkeley, CA 94720.

ADELSBERGER, JANE, C.S.J, b. St. Louis, Mo, Apr. 8, 27. ENGLISH. B.A, Fontbonne Col, 55; M.A, Univ. Notre Dame, 61, Ph.D.(Eng), 66. Teacher elem. schs, 49-55, sec. schs, 55-61; instr. Eng, AVILA COL, 66-68, ASSOC. PROF. ENG. & CHMN. DEPT. MOD. LANG, 68- Vis. scholar ling, Univ. Mich, summer 67; Kansas City Regional Counc. Higher Educ. grant summer stud. tour Gt. Brit, 68. MLA; NCTE; Ling. Soc. Am. Linguistics; teaching English as foreign language. Publ: Concept of nature as unifying principle underlying aesthetics and moral judgments in the works of Alexander Pope, Univ. Microfilms, 67. Add: Avila College, 11901 Wornall Rd, Kansas City, MO 64145.

ADELSTEIN, MICHAEL E, b. Nov. 21, 22; U.S. citizen; m. 45; c. 2. ENGLISH. B.S, Univ. Pa, 43; M.A, Univ. Mich, 47, Ph.D.(Eng), 58. Instr. ENG, Col. William & Mary, 47-49; Univ. Mich, 55-57; UNIV. KY, 58-60, asst. prof, 60-67, ASSOC. PROF, 67- U.S.A, 43-45, M/Sgt. MLA; NCTE; S.Atlantic Lang. Asn; Am. Bus. Commun. Asn; AAUP. Eighteenth century English literature; freshman English; business writing. Publ: Fanny Burney, Twayne, 68; Contemporary business writing, Random, 71; co-ed, Ecocide and population, 71, Women's liberation, 72 & Drugs, 72, St. Martin; auth, Duality of theme in The vicar of Wakefield, Col. Eng, 2/61. Add: Dept. of English, University of Kentucky, Lexington, KY 40506.

ADEN, JOHN M, b. Atlanta, Ga, Feb. 24, 18; m. 42; c. 2. ENGLISH. A.B, Univ. Tenn, 40; M.A, Cornell Univ, 41, fel, Univ. N.C, 44-45, Ph.D.(Eng), 50. Asst, Univ. N.C, 42-45; instr. Eng, Ga. Sch. Tech, 45-46; asst. prof, Centre Col, 46-49, assoc. prof, 50-53, Carnegie grant, 52; asst. prof. ENG, VANDERBILT UNIV, 53-57, assoc. prof, 57-63, PROF, 63-, dir. grad. stud, 67-70. MLA; NCTE; S.Atlantic Mod. Lang. Asn. Restoration and 18th century English literature. Publ: The critical opinions of John Dryden, 63 & Something like Horace ... studies in Pope's Horatian satires, 69, Vanderbilt; Bethel's sermon and Pope's Exemplum: towards a critique, Stud. Eng. Lit, 69; chap, In: Writers and their background: Alexander Pope, Bell & Sons, London, 72; chap, In: Quick springs of sense, Univ. Ga, 72; plus many others. Add: Dept. of English, Vanderbilt University, Nashville, TN 37203.

ADERMAN, RALPH MERL, b. Malinta, Ohio, May 27, 19; m. 42; c. 1. ENGLISH. B.Ed, Univ. Toledo, 41, M.A, 45; Ph.D, Univ. Wis, 51. Teacher, pub. schs, Ohio, 41-43, prin, 43-45; grad. asst. ENG, Univ. Wis, 45-47; instr, UNIV. WIS-MILWAUKEE, 47-56, assoc. prof, 56-59, PROF, 59-, chmn. dept, 59-61, res. grants, 57, 61, 63 & 66. Am. Philos. Soc. grants-in-aid, 54, 57 & summer 70; Fulbright lectr. Am. lit, Univ. Bucharest, 65-66; Am. Coun. Learned Soc. grant-in-aid, summer 70. MLA; Am. Stud. Asn; NCTE; Manuscript Soc; Emerson Soc; Melville Soc; Thoreau Soc. James Kirke Paulding; Washington Irving; 19th century American fiction. Publ: Letters of James Kirke Paulding, Univ. Wis, 62; co-auth, Aspects of American English, Harcourt, 63, rev. ed, 71; ed, Ion, Twayne, 67, The Negro in Milwaukee, Milwaukee County Hist. Soc, 68 & Washington Irving reconsidered, Transcendental, 69; auth, James Kirke Paulding as social critic, Papers Lang. & Lit, summer 65; The reactions of Rumanians to American literature, Wis. Stud. Lit, 67. Add: Dept. of English, University of Wisconsin-Milwaukee, Milwaukee, WI 53201.

ADES, JOHN I, b. Cincinnati, Ohio, July 14, 25; m. 50; c. 3. ENGLISH. B.S, Univ. Cincinnati, 49, A.M, 50, Ph.D.(Eng), 63; Johns Hopkins Univ, 51-53. Instr. ENG, Col. Wooster, 50-51, 53-55; jr. instr, Johns Hopkins Univ, 51-53; instr, Univ. Cincinnati, 55-56, 57-58; South. Ill. Univ, Alton Campus, 58-63, asst. prof, 63-66; ASSOC. PROF. & CHMN. DEPT, SOUTH. ILL. UNIV, EDWARDSVILLE, 66- Drama & music critic, Alton Evening Tel, 58-68. U.S.N, 43-46. MLA; Charles Lamb Soc. Literary criticism; late eighteenth and early nineteenth centuries in England, Charles Lamb; Milton, the Bible as literature. Publ: D.H. Lawrence and Cezanne: a study in the psychology of critical intuition, J. Aesthet. & Art Criticism, summer 70; auth, The pizza plot, Class. Outlook, 6/72; Criticus Redivivus: the history of Charles Lamb's critical reputation, Charles Lamb Soc. Bull, 7/72; plus four others. Add: Dept. of English, Southern Illinois University, Edwardsville, IL 62025.

ADEY, HARVEY LEE, b. Clifton Mills, W.Va, Feb. 11, 28; m. 50; c. 4. THEATRE. B.A, Allegheny Col, 52; M.A, Univ. Minn, Minneapolis, 56. Instr. theatre & speech, Cornell Univ, 56-57; ASSOC. PROF. THEATRE, Univ. Minn, Minneapolis, 59-71; South. Colo. State Col, 71-72; UNIV. MINN, MINNEAPOLIS, 72- Dir. & mgr, Paul Bunyan Playhouse, Bemidji, Minn, 57-63; dir, Oberlin Col. Summer Theatre, 64; critic & judge, Minn. State High Sch. League, 65-; artistic dir, Stage Coach Players, Inc, Shakopee, Minn, 72- U.S.A, 53-55. Am. Theatre Asn. Stage direction; melodrama; scene design. Add: 216 Middlebrook Hall, University of Minnesota, Minneapolis, MN 55455.

ADEY, LIONEL, b. Wednesbury, Eng, Jan. 4, 25; m. 53; c. 3. ENGLISH. B.A, Birmingham Univ, 49, Grant-Robertson scholar, 50-52, M.A, 53; cert. educ, Univ. London, 55; fel, Univ. Nottingham, summer 63; Ph.D.(Eng. lit), Univ. Leicester, 64. Master Eng, King Edward VII Sch, Sheffield, 50-52; Nicholas Chamberlaine Sch, Coventry, 52-55; Gateway Sch, Leicester, 56-63, head dept. gen. stud, 58-63; head dept. Eng, Longslade Sch, Birstall, 64-67; ASST. PROF. ENG, UNIV. VICTORIA (B.C), 67- Can. Counc. res. grants, summers 69 & 70. R.N, 43-46. West. Can. Victorian Stud. Asn. Victorian poetry; letters of C.S. Lewis; C.S. Lewis and Owen Barfield, especially relationship of their ideas. Publ: Tennyson's Sorrow & her lying lip, Victorian Poetry, Vol. VIII, No. 3; A reading of Hopkin's Epithalamion, Victorian Newslett, fall 72; The light of holiness: some comments on William Morris in letters of C.S. Lewis, J. William Morris Soc, 73. Add: Dept. of English, University of Victoria, Victoria, B.C. V8W 2Y2, Can.

ADICKS, RICHARD R, b. Lake City, Fla, Aug. 19, 32; m. 59; c. 1. ENGLISH. B.A.E, Univ. Fla, 54, M.A, 59; Ph.D.(Eng), Tulane Univ, 65. Teacher, high schs, Fla, 56-58, 59-61; instr. ENG, Rollins Col, 61-63; asst. prof, Ga. Inst. Technol, 65-68; FLA. TECHNOL. UNIV, 68-70, ASSOC. PROF, 70- U.S.A, 54-56. Col. Eng. Asn; NCTE; AAUP. Victorian literature; American literature. Publ: The lily maid and the scarlet sleeve, Univ. Rev, 10/67; The unconsecrated Eucharist in Dubliners, Stud. in Short Fiction, spring 68;

Conrad and the politics of morality, Bull. Asn. Can. Humanities, fall 72; plus one other. Add: Dept. of English, Florida Technological University, Orlando, FL 32816.

ADIX, VERN, b. Boone, Iowa, May 3, 12. SPEECH. A.B, Univ. Iowa, 35; A.M, Univ. Minn, 45. Teaching asst, Univ. Minn, 41-43; from teaching asst. to PROF. & DESIGNER THEATRE & SUPV. DIR. YOUNG PEOPLE'S THEATRE, UNIV. UTAH, 43- Am. Educ. Theatre Asn; Children's Theatre Conf. Revolving stage in America. Publ: Theatre scenecraft; plus numerous plays for children. Add: Dept. of Theatre, University of Utah, Salt Lake City, UT 84112.

ADKINS, GALE ROY, b. Murray, Iowa, Oct. 21, 18; m. 44. JOURNALISM, SPEECH & DRAMA. B.S, Univ. Tex, 40, M.Ed, 41, Counc. South. Univs. fel, 56-57; Northwest. Univ, 47; Univ. Ill, 53; Univ. Denver, 55. Teacher pub. schs, Tex, 41-43; instr. speech, Univ. Tex, 46-48, asst. dir. radio, 48-51, asst. prof. educ. admin, 51-53, educ. psychol, 53-57, dir. radio-TV res, 52-57; asst. prof. speech & jour, Univ. Kans, 57-62, assoc. prof, 62-70, dir. radio-TV res, 57-70; PROF. SPEECH, IND. STATE UNIV, TERRE HAUTE, 70- Rockefeller Found. grant, 50; Nat. Asn. Educ. Broadcasters TV scholars, 53, 54, 55; consult, nat. stud. use of recorded TV instr. & proj. develop. instr. TV demonstration materials, NDEA, 59-61; Great Plains Regional Instr. TV Libr, 62-; Nat. Tape Repository, 62- Nat. Asn. Educ. Broadcasters; Am. Educ. Res. Asn; Speech Commun. Asn.(ed, Radio-TV-Film Newslett, 60-62); Asn. Educ. Jour; Radio-TV News Dir. Asn; Asn. Prof. Broadcasting Educ; Nat. Soc. Stud. Commun; Dept. Audio-visual Instr; Am. Asn. Pub. Opinion Res. Requirements for employment success in radio and television broadcasting; educational utilization of radio and television; effective radio and television news broadcasting. Publ: A handbook for the radio workshop, Univ. Tex, 47; What is important for success in television?, Univ. Kans, 59; plus others. Add: Dept. of Speech, Indiana State University, Terre Haute, IN 47809.

ADKINS, NELSON FREDERICK, b. Hartford, Conn, Feb. 3, 97; m. 50. ENGLISH. A.B, Trinity Col.(Conn), 20, A.M, 21; Ph.D, Yale, 25. Instr. ENG, N.Y. UNIV, 25-31, asst. prof, 31-47, assoc. prof, 47-52, prof, 52-70, EMER. PROF, 70- MLA; Bibliog. Soc. Am; Emerson Soc; Mark Twain Res. Found. American literature; bibliography. Publ: Fitz-Greene Halleck, Yale, 30; Philip Freneau and the cosmic enigma, N.Y. Univ, 49; The early projected works of Nathaniel Hawthorne, second quarter, 45 & Chapter on American cribbage: Poe and plagiarism, third quarter 48, Papers Bibliog. Soc. Am; Emerson and the Bardic tradition, Publ. Mod. Lang. Asn, 6/48. Add: 19 Christopher St, New York, NY 10014.

ADKINS, PATRICIA G, b. Paris, Tex, Aug. 23, 25; m. 44; c. 2. SPEECH PATHOLOGY, LINGUISTICS. B.A, Univ. Tex, El Paso, 60; M.A, Tex. Woman's Univ, 61; Ph.D.(ling), Univ. Colo, 66. Asst. prof. speech path, Univ. Tex, El Paso, 60-64; teaching assoc. Eng. as second lang, Univ. Colo, 64-65; assoc. prof. speech path. & ling, Univ. Tex, El Paso, 65-69, fac. res. grant, 67-68; DIR. EDUC. PROF. DEVELOP. & DIR. EARLY CHILDHOOD LEARNING CTR, REGION XIX EDUC. CTR, EL PASO, 69- Trainee, H.K. Cooper Inst, 66; lectr, NDEA Insts, 67 & 68; U.S. presentor, World Cong. Inst. Asn. Logopedics & Phoniatrics, Buenos Aires, summer 71. Am. Speech & Hearing Asn; Am. Asn. Ment. Deficiency; Asn. Children Learning Disabilities; Int. Asn. Logopedics & Phoniatrics. Linguistics; special education; early childhood education. Publ: Co-auth, Speech for the bilingual Spanish-speaking student, Univ. Tex, El Paso, 67; auth, Structured experiences for developmental learning, Learning Resources Pres, 73; The speech pathologist and early childhood education, Actas Logopedia & Foniatria, Buenos Aires, 7/72; Sociocultural factors in educating disadvantaged children, Educ, 9/72; The IRS and the learning disabled child, J. Learning Disabilities, 5/73; plus two others. Add: 609 La Cruz Dr, El Paso, TX 79902.

ADLER, JACOB HENRY, b. Evansville, Ind, Mar. 26, 19; m. 52; c. 2. ENGLISH. M.A, Univ. Fla, 46; M.A, Harvard, 47, univ. fel, 48-49, Ph.D.(Eng), 51. Instr. ENG, UNIV. KY, 49-50, 51-53, asst. prof, 53-59, assoc. prof, 59-65, prof, 65-69, chmn. dept, 64-69; PROF. & HEAD DEPT, PURDUE UNIV, W.LAFAYETTE, 69- Fulbright lectr, India, 60-61. U.S.A, 42-46. MLA; NCTE; Am. Soc. 18th Century Stud. Eighteenth century English literature; contemporary drama; literary criticism. Publ: The reach of art: a study in the prosody of Pope, Univ. Fla, 64; Lillian Hellman, In: Southern Writers Series, Steck, 69; Pope and the rules of prosody, PMLA, 6/61; Rose and the fox: notes on the southern drama, In: South, Doubleday, 61; Two Hamlet plays: The wild duck and The seagull, J. Mod. Lit, 10/70; plus others. Add: Dept. of English, Purdue University, West Lafayette, IN 47907.

ADLER, RICHARD RAYMOND, b. Madison, Wis, Oct 1, 35; m. 58; c. 2. ENGLISH EDUCATION, HEALTH & PHYSICAL EDUCATION. B.S, Mont. State Univ, 57; M.Ed, Univ. Ill, Urbana, 68, Ph.D.(Eng. Educ), 71. Teacher Eng, Sheridan High Sch, Wyo, 60-66, chmn. dept, 63-66; staff asst, NCTE, 66-67, asst. to exec. secy, 67-68, convention coord, 68-71; ASST. PROF. ENG. & DIR. TEACHER TRAINING, UNIV. MONT, 71- Chmn. comt. creative drama in schs, NCTE, 68-70, mem. curriculum eval, 71- U.S.A, 58-60; Nat. Guard, 60-66, Capt. NCTE; Conf. Eng. Educ; Conf. Col. Compos. & Commun. Response to literature; composing process, composition. Publ: Ed, Humanities programs today, Citation, 71; Alternatives in creative dramatics, Scholastic Mag, 69; Dreams for English curriculum, Ariz. Eng. Bull, 73. Add: Dept. of English, University of Montana, Missoula, MT 59801.

ADLER, THOMAS PETER, b. Cleveland, Ohio, Jan. 3, 43; m. 68; c. 2. ENGLISH & AMERICAN LITERATURE. A.B, Boston Col, 64, A.M, 66; Ph.D. (Eng), Univ. Ill, Urbana, 70. ASST. PROF. ENG, PURDUE UNIV, WEST LAFAYETTE, 70- AAUP; MLA; Cath. Renascence Soc. Modern British and American drama; Victorian literature; Renaissance literature. Publ: Who's afraid of Virginia Woolf?: a long night's journey into day, Educ. Theatre J, 3/73; The search for God in the plays of Tennessee Williams, Renascence, fall 73; Religious ritual in Arden's Serjeant Musgrave's dance, Mod. Drama, 9/73. Add: Dept. of English, Purdue University, West Lafayette, IN 47907.

ADOLPH, ROBERT, b. Cambridge, Mass, Feb. 15, 36; m. 58; c. 3. ENGLISH. B.A, Williams Col, 57; M.A, Univ. Mich, 58; Woodrow Wilson fel, Harvard, 58, univ. fel, 59-60, Ph.D.(Eng), 64. Instr. Eng, Mass. Inst. Technol, 61-63, asst. prof, 63-67; ASSOC. PROF. HUMANITIES & ENG, YORK UNIV, 68- Co-ed, Can. Rev. Am. Stud, 72- MLA; Can. Asn. Univ. Teachers; Can. Asn. Am. Stud.(treas, 71-73). Seventeenth century English literature; nineteenth and twentieth century prose fiction. Publ: The rise of modern prose style, M.I.T, 68; auth, Reflections of a new Canadian professor, Can. Dimension, 70. Add: Div. of Humanities, York University, 4700 Keele St, Downsview, Ont. M3J 1P3, Can.

ADRIAN, ARTHUR ALLEN, b. Moundridge, Kans, Apr. 24, 06; m. 47. ENGLISH LITERATURE. B.S, Kans. State Teachers Col, 29; A.M, Univ. Kans, 35; Univ. Chicago, 39-40; fel, West. Reserve Univ, 44-46, Ph.D, 46. Teacher, High Schs, Kans, 29-36; instr. ENG, Univ. Kans, 36-39; Ore. State Col, 40-44; asst. prof, CASE WEST. RESERVE UNIV, 46-49, assoc. prof, 50-62, PROF, 62- Am. Philos. Soc. grants, 54, 62 & 64; Henry E. Huntington Libr. grant, 55; Am. Counc. Learned Soc. grant, 62. Dickens Fel; Int. Asn. Univ. Prof. Eng; MLA. Biography; literature and art; Victorian literature. Publ: Georgina Hogarth and the Dickens circle, 57 & Mark Lemon: first editor of Punch, 66, Oxford; Dickens on American slavery: a Carlylean slant, 6/52 & The Rossetti-Browning friendship: some unpublished letters, 12/58, PMLA; Charles Dickens as verse editor, Mod. Philol, 11/60. Add: 1099 Mt. Vernon Blvd, Cleveland Heights, OH 44112.

ADRIAN, DARYL B, b. Hutchinson, Kans, Sept. 24, 33; m. 53; c. 3. ENGLISH. A.B, Tabor Col, 55; M.A, Kans. State Teachers Col, 61; Ph.D.(Eng), Univ. Mo, Columbia, 67. Educ. therapist, Menninger Found, Topeka, Kans, 57-63, supvr. educ. unit, 62-63; lectr. Eng, Washburn Univ, 62-63; instr, Univ. Mo, Columbia, 61-62, 63-67, coord. Brit. lit. surv. sect, 64-67; asst. prof. ENG, BALL STATE UNIV, 67-71, ASSOC. PROF, 71-, ADMIN. ASST. CHMN. DEPT, 69- Consult, Field Oper. Off, Educ. Commun. Asn, Indianapolis, 70-73. Alternative mil. serv, Psychiat. aide, Menninger Clinic, Topeka, Kans, 55-57. MLA; Conf. Christianity & Lit; Midwest Mod. Lang. Asn; John Steinbeck Soc. Am; Milton Soc. Am; Johnson Soc. Cent. Region; Am. Soc. 18th Century Stud. Seventeenth and eighteenth century British literature, especially Milton; religion and literature; John Steinbeck. Publ: Ed, John Bunyan's Pilgrim's progress, Airmont, 69; auth, Humanities and the arts: non-fiction before 1900, In: Encounter with books; A guide to reading, Intervarsity, 70; Steinbeck's new image of America and Americans, Steinbeck Quart, fall 70; A comparative school curriculum and the study of religion, Religious Educ, 7-8/72; plus two others. Add: Dept. of English, Ball State University, Muncie, IN 47306.

AGEE, WARREN KENDALL, b. Sherman, Tex, Oct. 23, 16; m. 41; c. 2. JOURNALISM. B.A, Tex. Christian Univ, 37; M.A, Univ. Minn, 49, Gen. Educ. Bd. fel, 51-52, Ph.D, 55. Mem. ed. staff, Star-Telegram, Ft. Worth, Tex, 37-48; instr. jour, Tex. Christian Univ, 48-49; asst. prof, 49-55, assoc. prof, 55-57, prof, 57-58, chmn. dept, 50-58; dean sch. jour, W.Va. Univ, 58-60; nat. exec. off, Sigma Delta Chi, Chicago, Ill, 60-62; prof. jour. & dean evening col, Tex. Christian Univ, 62-65; prof. jour. & dean William Allen White Sch. jour. & dir. found, Univ. Kansas 65-69; PROF. JOUR. & DEAN HENRY W. GRADY SCH. JOUR, UNIV. GA, 69- Mem. adv. screening comt, jour, Comt. Int. Exchange of Persons, U.S. Dept. State, 58-62; trustee William Allen White Found, 69- Carl Towley Award, Jour. Educ. Asn, 69; Outstanding Achievement Award, Univ. Minn, 73. U.S.C.G, 42-45. Am. Soc. Jour. Sch. Adminr.(pres, 56); Asn. Educ. Jour.(v.pres, 55, pres, 58-59, mem. Jour. Counc, 72-); Am. Stud. Asn; Am. Counc. Educ. Jour. Journalism; American studies; mass communication and society. Publ: Co-auth, Introduction to mass communications, Dodd, 60, rev. eds, 65, 70 & 73; ed, The press and the public interest, Pub. Affairs, 68; Mass media in a free society, Univ. Kans, 69; auth, Cross-channel ownership of communication media, Jour. Quart, 12/49. Add: 130 Highland Dr, Athens, GA 30601.

AGEE, WILLIAM HUGH, b. Petersburg, Va, July 8, 33; m. 58; c. 2. ENGLISH, ENGLISH EDUCATION. B.S, E.Carolina Univ, 59, M.A, 60; Ph.D. (Eng. educ), Fla. State Univ, 66. Asst. Eng, E.Carolina Univ, 59-60; instr, West. Ky. Univ, 60-63; asst. Eng. educ. & Eng, Fla. State Univ, 63-66; ASSOC. PROF. Eng, West. Ky. Univ, 66-71; LANG. EDUC, UNIV. GA, 71- U.S.A.F, 52-56. NCTE; MLA. American literature; contemporary fiction; English linguistics. Publ: Co-auth, Existential heroes: Frank Alpine and Rabbit Angstrom, Ball State Univ. Forum, winter 68. Add: Dept. of Language Education, University of Georgia, Athens, GA 30601.

AGGELER, GEOFFREY DONOVAN, b. Berkeley, Calif, Sept. 26, 39; m. 62; c. 3. ENGLISH. B.A, Univ. Calif, Davis, 61, M.A, 63, Ph.D.(Eng), 66. Lectr. ENG, Calif. State Polytech. Col, 63-64; asst. prof, Canadian Serv. Col. Royal Rds, 66-69; UNIV. UTAH, 69-71, ASSOC. PROF, 71- Philol. Asn. Pac. Coast; MLA; Shakespeare Asn. Am. English Renaissance drama; twentieth century British fiction; history of ideas. Publ: Stoicism and revenge in Marston, Eng. Stud, 12/70; Incest and the artist: Anthony Burgess's MF as summation, Mod. Fiction Stud, winter 72-73; Between God and notgod: Anthony Burgess's Tremor of intent, Malahat Rev, 1/71; plus others. Add: Dept. of English, University of Utah, Salt Lake City, UT 84112.

AGGERTT, OTIS J, b. Ashland, Ill, May 31, 16; m. 38; c. 4. SPEECH. B.Ed, West. Ill. State Col, 38; M.A, Univ. Ill, 48; Ed.D, Mich. State Univ, 60. Teacher high schs, Ill, 38-44, 46-49; assoc. prof. speech, Albion Col, 49-56; PROF. SPEECH & CHMN. PUB. ADDRESS AREA, IND. STATE UNIV, TERRE HAUTE, 56- Speech Asn. Am; Cent. States Speech Commun. Asn; Am. Forensic Asn. Oratory of R.W. Emerson; teaching of oral interpretation; English and American poetry. Publ: Co-auth, Communicative reading, Macmillan, 56, 2nd ed, 63; auth, The case for the speech festival, Speech Notes, 4/68. Add: Dept. of English, Indiana State University, Terre Haute, IN 47809.

AHEARN, EDWARD J, French & Comparative Literature. See Volume III, Foreign Languages, Linguistics & Philology.

AHL, FREDERICK MICHAEL, Classics, Comparative Literature. See Volume III, Foreign Languages, Linguistics & Philology.

AHO, GARY L, b. Portland, Ore, May 27, 35; m. 59; c. 2. ENGLISH. B.S, Portland State Col, 59; Ph.D.(Eng), Univ. Ore, 66. ASST. PROF. ENG, UNIV. MASS, AMHERST, 66- U.S.A, 55-56. Ling. Soc. Am; MLA; Am-Scand. Found. Old English and Old Norse literatures. Publ: Nifrstigningarsaga: an Old Norse version of Christ's harrowing of hell, Scand. Stud, (in press). Add: Dept. of English, University of Massachusetts, Amherst, MA 01003.

AHRENDTS, HAROLD L, b. Loretto, Nebr, Aug. 4, 14; m. 42; c. 1. SPEECH. A.B, Nebr. Wesleyan Univ, 38; M.A, Univ. Mich, 42; Ph.D.(speech), Univ. Denver, 62. Prin, High Sch, Nebr, 38-39, teacher, 39-43; head dept. speech, KEARNEY STATE COL, 43-51, CHMN. DIV. FINE ARTS, 51-, PROF. SPEECH, 58- Guest lectr, Univ. Denver, 62. The life and times of William Jennings Bryan; speech education; the field of education generally. Add: Dept. of Speech, Kearney State College, Kearney, NE 68847.

AHSAN, SYED MOHAMMAD, b. Lucknow, Uttar Pradesh, India; Pakistani citizen; m. 52; c. 2. ENGLISH LITERATURE. B.A, Univ. Lucknow, 46; M.A, Univ, Karachi, 54; A.M, Ind. Univ, Bloomington, 62; fel, Univ. Ottawa, 67-69, Ph.D.(Eng. lit), 69. Lectr. ENG, Govt. Col, Karachi, Pakistan, 56-63, prof. & chmn. dept, 63-67; asst. prof, NORTH. STATE COL, 69-71, assoc. prof, 71-74, PROF, 74- MLA; AAUP. Renaissance; romantic period; metaphysical poetry. Add: 1423 S. Eighth St, Aberdeen, SD 57401.

AID, FRANCES MARY, Spanish, Linguistics. See Volume III, Foreign Languages, Linguistics & Philology.

AITKEN, DAVID, b. Gordonsville, Va, July 31, 33; m. 67. ENGLISH. B.A, Univ. Wis, 55; Ph.D.(Eng), Princeton, 62. Instr. ENG, Pomona Col, 59-62; ASST. PROF. UNIV. CALIF, SANTA BARBARA, 67- Prose style. Publ: Dramatic archetypes in Joyce's Exiles, Mod. Fiction Stud, spring 58; A kind of felicity: some notes about Trollope's style, Nineteenth Century Fiction, 3/66. Add: Dept. of English, University of California, Santa Barbara, CA 93106.

AKIN, JOHNNYE, b. Haynesville, La, Nov. 17, 05. SPEECH. B.L.I, Emerson Col, 27; cert, Am. Acad. Dramatic Arts, 29; B.S, Huntingdon Col, 33; M.A, La. State Univ, 35, Ph.D, 38; M.S, Univ. Mich, 36; Univ. Wis, summer, 39. Instr. SPEECH & head dept, Maryville Col, 38-44; vis. prof, La. State Univ, 44; asst. & head speech clinic, Univ. Ill, 44-46; asst. prof, UNIV. DENVER, 46-52, assoc. prof, 52-61, PROF, 61- Teaching fel, Huntingdon Col, 31-33; La. State Univ, 33-38; vis. prof. speech, Univ. Hawaii, 50-51; speech & ling, C.W. Post Col, summers, 60-61. Speech Commun. Asn; MLA; Am. Speech & Hear. Asn; West. Speech Commun. Asn.(2nd v.pres, 55-56, 1st v.pres, 58-59, pres, 59-60); Polynesian Soc, N.Z; Am. Dialect Asn. Linguistics; theatre. Publ: And so we speak: voice and articulation, Prentice-Hall, 58; co-auth, Helping the Bible speak, Assoc. Press, 56; co-ed, Language behavior: readings in communication, Mouton, 70. Add: Dept. of Speech Communication, University of Denver, Denver, CO 80210.

AKMAJIAN, ADRIAN, Theoretical Linguistics. See Volume III, Foreign Languages, Linguistics & Philology.

AKRIGG, GEORGE PHILIP VERNON, b. Calgary, Alta, Aug. 13, 13; m. 44; c. 3. ENGLISH. B.A, Univ. B.C, 37, M.A, 40; Ph.D, Univ. Calif, 44. Instr. ENG, UNIV. B.C, 41-44, asst. prof, 44-47, assoc. prof, 47-58, PROF, 58-, grant to Eng, 52. Res. fel, Folger Shakespeare Libr, Wash, D.C, 46-47; Can. Counc. fel, 70-71. Fel. Royal Hist. Soc; MLA; Asn. Can. Univ. Teachers Eng; Shakespeare Asn. Am. English literature and history; Shakespeare; Jacobean court and the drama. Publ: Jacobean pageant: the court of King James I, 62 & Shakespeare and the Earl of Southampton, 68, Harvard; co-auth, 1001 British Columbia name places, Discovery Press, 69 & 73; The marginalia of Charles, second Lord Stanhope; England in 1609. Add: Dept. of English, University of British Columbia, Vancouver 8, B.C, Can.

ALAYA, FLAVIA M, b. New Rochelle, N.Y, May 16, 35. ENGLISH & COMPARATIVE LITERATURE. B.A, Barnard Col, Columbia Univ, 56; Fulbright & Ital. govt. scholar, Univ. Padua, 57-58; M.A, Columbia Univ, 60, Ph.D. (Eng. & comp. lit), 65. Instr. Eng, Univ. N.C, Greensboro, 59-60; lectr, Hunter Col, 62-66; instr, N.Y. Univ, 66-67, asst. prof, 67-71; assoc. prof. ENG. & COMP. LIT, SCH. INTERCULT. STUD, RAMAPO COL. N.J, 71-73, PROF, 73-, dir, Sch, 71-73. Eng. Inst; MLA; Victorian Soc. Am; Res. Soc. Victorian Periodicals; Am. Asn. Higher Educ. Nineteenth century literature; feminism; literature of national and cultural consciousness. Publ: Wm. Sharp (Fiona MacLeod): a study in later Victorian cosmopolitanism, Harvard, 70; Two worlds revisited: Arnold, Renan, the monastic life, and the Stanzas from the Grande Chartreuse, 1/68 & Tennyson's Lady of Shalot: the triumph of art, winter 70, Victorian Poetry; Victorian science and the genius of woman, J. Hist. Ideas, (in press); plus one other. Add: School of Intercultural Studies, Ramapo College of New Jersey, Mahwah, NJ 07430.

ALBAUGH, RALPH M, b. Mingo Junction, Ohio, June 7, 09; m. 45. ENGLISH. A.B, Miami Univ, 40, M.A, 42; Ph.D.(Eng), Ohio State Univ, 48. Instr. ENG, Ohio State Univ, 44-48; asst. prof, Ohio Univ, 48-51; Univ. Md, 51-56; IND. STATE UNIV, TERRE HAUTE, 57-60, assoc. prof, 60-64, PROF, 64- MLA; Mod. Humanities Res. Asn, Gt. Brit; NCTE; Conf. Col. Compos. & Commun. Restoration and 18th century English literature; English grammar; linguistics. Publ: Thesis writing, Littlefield, 51; English: a dictionary of grammar and structure, Chandler, 64. Add: Dept. of English, Indiana State University, Terre Haute, IN 47809.

ALBERT, LEONARD, b. New York, N.Y, Jan. 30, 18; m. 64; c. 2. ENGLISH, COMPARATIVE LITERATURE. B.A, City Col. New York, 50; M.A, Columbia Univ, 52, Ph.D.(Eng, comp. lit), 57; M.S.Ed, Hunter Col, 74. Lectr, City Col. New York, 48-54; vis. asst. prof. Eng, Univ. Rochester, 54-55; instr, HUNTER COL, 55-66, asst. prof, 67-71, ASSOC. PROF. ENG, 71-, PROG. RELIG, 73- Instr, Columbia Univ, 52-54; lectr, Brooklyn Col, 55-56; instr. mod. Greek & hon. dean stud, Case Inst. Lang, 65-66; mem. prof. staff congr, City Univ. New York; mem. relig. sch. comt. & chmn. adult educ, Temple Emanu-El, 73- James Joyce. Publ: Joyce and the new psychology, Univ. Microfilms, 58; Ulysses, cannibals and freemasons, A.D. Quart, autumn 51; transl, Horace: Odes, I, i, In: Latin poetry in verse translation, Houghton, 57; auth, A pastor's pupil bull, In: The Celtic bull: essays on Joyce's Ulysses, Benjamin, 66. Add: Dept. of English, Hunter College, 695 Park Ave, New York, NY 10021.

ALBERT, SIDNEY PAUL, Philosophy. See Volume IV, Philosophy, Religion & Law.

ALBERTINI, VIRGIL, b. Frontenac, Kans, Apr. 1, 32; m. 60. ENGLISH. B.S.Ed, Kans. State Col. Pittsburg, 53, M.S, 60; Univ. Kans, 61-63. Teacher, high schs, Kans, 54-60; prep. sch, Calif, 60-61; ASST. PROF. ENG, NORTHWEST MO. STATE UNIV, 65-, sabbatical leave, 70-71. NCTE; Conf. Col. Compos. & Cummun. Nineteenth century American literature; Frank Norris. Publ: James Thurber and the short story, 8/64 & Chaucer's artistic accomplishment in molding the Wife of Bath's tale, 11/64; Northwest Mo. State Col. Stud; Samuel Johnson's Life of Gray, 5/68 & Two images: Belinda and Prufrock, 1/69, Mo. Eng. Bull; Hepzibah & prayer, Am. Notes & Queries, 73. Add: R.R. 3, Maryville, MO 64468.

ALBERTSON, CLINTON EDWARD, S.J, b. Los Angeles, Calif, Nov. 11, 18. ENGLISH LITERATURE. B.A, Santa Clara Univ, 42; M.A, Gonzaga Univ, 43; S.T.L, Alma Col, 50; M.A, Oxford, 57. Lectr. ENG. LIT, LOYOLA MARYMOUNT UNIV, 43-45, asst. prof, 54-60, assoc. prof, 60-70, PROF, 70- AAUP; MLA; Col. Eng. Asn. Anglo-Saxon literature; medieval literature and art. Publ: Anglo-Saxon saints and heroes, Fordham Univ, 67. Add: Dept. of English, Loyola Marymount University, Los Angeles, CA 90045.

ALBRECHT, ALFRED J, b. Middlebury, Ind, Jan. 22, 24; m. 51; c. 2. SPEECH. B.A, Goshen Col, 50; M.S, Purdue Univ, 56; Ph.D.(speech), Ind. Univ, 66. Instr. SPEECH, Univ. Vt, 57-60; PROF, GOSHEN COL, 64- Speech Commun. Asn. Rhetoric, public address and history. Add: Dept. of Communication, Goshen College, Goshen, IN 46526.

ALBRECHT, ROBERT CHARLES, b. Aurora, Ill, Sept. 27, 33. AMERICAN LITERATURE. B.A, Univ. Ill, 55; M.A, Univ. Mich, 57; univ. fel, Univ. Minn, 61-62, Ph.D.(Am. stud), 62. Instr. ENG, Univ. Chicago, 62-64, asst. prof, 64-67; assoc. prof, UNIV. ORE, 67-74, PROF, 74-, ASSOC. DEAN COL. LIB. ARTS, 72- U.S. Steel fac. fel, 66; consult, Free Press, 66-73. U.S.A, 57-58, Res, 58-68, Capt. MLA; Am. Stud. Asn. New England transcendentalism; American novel; psychology and literature. Publ: The world of short fiction, Free Press, 68; Theodore Parker, Twayne, 71; Content and style in The red badge of courage, Col. Eng, 66; Conflict and resolution: slavery in Massachusetts, Emerson Soc. Quart, 73; Thematic unity of Melville's The encantadas, Tex. Stud. Lit. & Lang, 73; plus three others. Add: Dept. of English, University of Oregon, Eugene, OR 97403.

ALBRECHT, WILLIAM PRICE, b. Wilkinsburg, Pa, June 25, 07; m. 31; c. 3. ENGLISH. B.S, Carnegie Inst. Technol, 29; A.M, Univ. Pittsburgh, 34; fel, Univ. Chicago, 38-39, Ph.D, 43. Tech. writer, Westinghouse Electric Corp, 29-32 & 43; from instr. to asst. prof. ENG, Carnegie Inst. Technol, 34-37, 46; asst, Univ. Chicago, 38-39; instr, Univ. Pittsburgh, 39-42; asst. prof, Jr. Col, Bucknell Univ, 42-43; from asst. prof. to prof. & acting chmn. dept. Univ. N.Mex, 46-57; PROF, UNIV. KANS, 57-, chmn. dept. Eng, 57-63, dean, Grad. Sch, 63-72. Ford fac. fel, Oxford, 52-53; consult. doctorate prog. Eng, South. Ill. Univ, 60 & 73, consult. master's prog, 65; consult. summer insts, U.S. Off. Educ, 62-63, consult, Off, 65-67; doctorate prog. in Eng, Univ. Wyo, 64; consult-exam, N.Cent. Asn, 64-; consult, Counc. Grad. Schs. U.S, 66; dept. stud. proj, Mich. State Univ, 68- U.S.N.R, 43-63, Comdr. MLA; Midwest Mod. Lang. Asn.(pres, 59-60); NCTE; Int. Asn. Univ. Profs. Eng; Mod. Humanities Res. Asn. Romantic period. Publ: William Hazlitt and the Malthusian Controversy, 50 & The loathly lady in Thomas of Erceldoune, 54, Univ. N.Mex; co-auth, The American technical writer, Am. Bk. Co, 60; Hazlitt and the creative imagination, Univ. Kans, 65; War and fraternity: a study of some recent American war novels, N.Mex, Quart, winter, 51; Hazlitt's preference for tragedy, 12/56 & Hazlitt on the poetry of wit, 6/60, PMLA. Add: 1633 University Dr, Lawrence, KS 66044.

ALBRIGHT, DANIEL, b. Chicago, Ill, Dec. 7, 16; m. 46. ENGLISH, LINGUISTICS. A.M, Univ. Chicago, 49, Ph.D.(Eng), 56. Instr. Eng, Ind. Univ, Gary, 49-56; teacher high sch, Ill, 55-57, chmn. dept, Eng, 57-65; assoc. prof, Wis. State Univ, Platteville, 65-67; assoc. prof. Eng. & dir. freshman compos, Point Park Col, 67-70; ASST. PROF. ENG, UNIV. VA, 70- U.S.A, 40-45. MLA; NCTE; Conf. Col. Compos. & Commun; Col. Eng. Asn. Linguistics; high school curriculum; 19th century American literature. Publ: Approach to programing, Clearing House, 12/61; A test on John Hersey's Hiroshima, Exercise Exchange, 11/62; An organic curriculum for English, Eng. J, 1/63. Add: Dept. of English, University of Virginia, Charlottesville, VA 22903.

ALBRIGHT, HARRY DARKES, b. Lebanon, Pa, July 24, 07; m. 36; c. 2. THEATRE ARTS. A.B, Lebanon Valley Col, 28; A.M, Cornell Univ, 31, Ph.D, 36. Instr, high sch, Pa, 28-30; Eng, Iowa State Teachers Col, 34-36; THEATRE ARTS, CORNELL UNIV, 36-39, asst. prof, 40-46, assoc. prof, 46-58, prof, 58-72, EMER. PROF, 72-, chmn. dept, 49-57, 65-66. Gen. ed, Bks of the Theatre, 62- Am. Educ. Theatre Asn.(v.pres, 47, pres, 48, assoc. ed, jour, 49-51, ed, 52-54); Speech Commun. Asn.(assoc. ed, Quart. J. Speech, 44-46). Drama and the theatre; dramatic production; theatre history and aesthetics. Publ: Working up a part, 47 & co-auth, Principles of theatre art, 55, Houghton; transl, Appia's The work of living art, 60, ed, The story of the Meininger, 63, Memories of the Theatre libre, 64 & Meyerhold's theatre of the grotesque, 71, Univ. Miami. Add: Dept. of Theatre Arts, Cornell University, Ithaca, NY 14850.

ALDEN, DONALD HITT, b. Los Angeles, Calif, Nov. 24, 05; m. 29; c. 3. ENGLISH. A.B, Stanford Univ, 27, M.A, 28; Ph.D, Yale, 33. Instr, Sacramento Jr. Col, 28-30; teacher, Los Angeles City Col, 33-46; from asst. prof. to prof. ENG, CALIF. STATE UNIV, SAN JOSE, 46-70, EMER. PROF, 70- U.S.N.R, 43-46, Lt. Ling. Soc. Am; Philol. Asn. Pac. Coast. Modern English language; 18th century English and American language and literature. Publ: The first pronouncing dictionary, Quart. J. Speech; Los Angeles City College pronunciation test. Add: Dept. of English, California State University, San Jose, CA 95114.

ALDEN, (HOWEL) HENRY, b. Topeka, Kans, Aug. 12, 07. ENGLISH. A.B, Washburn Col, 26; A.M, Univ. Kans, 28; M.S. in L.S, Columbia Univ, 50; Sorbonne. Instr. Eng, Univ. Kans, 27-28; GRINNELL COL, 34-46, asst. prof, 46-52, assoc. prof. ENG. & librn, 52-72, EMER. PROF. & EMER. LIBRN, 72- Transportation C, A.U.S, 42-45, Master Sgt. MLA; AAUP. The novels of Joseph Conrad. Add: 833 East St, Grinnell, IA 50112.

ALDERMAN, WILLIAM ELIJAH, b. Glouster, Ohio, Oct. 13, 88; m. 12; c. 4. ENGLISH LITERATURE. Ph.B, Ohio Univ, 09, LL.D, 54; A.M, Hiram Col, 10; Harvard, 12-14; Ph.D, Univ. Wis, 20; LL.D, Beloit Col, 58, Miami Univ, 59. Instr. Eng, Univ. Wis, 14-20; assoc. prof, Beloit Col, 20-21, prof, 21-35, dean col. & men, 25-35; prof. ENG. & dean COL. ARTS & SCI, MIAMI UNIV, 35-59, EMER. PROF. & EMER. DEAN, 59- MLA. English literature of the 18th century, especially Shaftesbury. Publ: English editions of Shaftesbury's Characteristics, 67 & Pope's Essay on man and Shaftesbury's Moralist, 73, Papers Bibliog. Soc. Am. Add: 215 Ridge Ave, Oxford, OH 45056.

ALDRICH, RUTH ISABELLE, b. Milwaukee, Wis. BRITISH LITERATURE, DRAMA. M.A, Univ. Wis-Madison, 48, Ph.D.(19th century Brit. lit), 61. Asst. prof. ENG, UNIV. WIS-MILWAUKEE, 61-69, ASSOC. PROF, 69- MLA; Popular Cult. Asn. British romantic poets; Walter Scott; British utopias. Publ: Ed, Thomas Holcroft, The road to ruin, Univ. Nebr, 68; auth, John Galt, Twayne, 74; The Wordsworths and Coleridge: three persons' but not one soul, Studies Romanticism, autumn 62. Add: Dept. of English, University of Wisconsin-Milwaukee, Milwaukee, WI 53201.

ALDRIDGE, ALFRED OWEN, b. Buffalo, N.Y, Dec. 16, 15; div; c. 1. ENGLISH. B.S, Ind. Univ, 37; A.M, Univ. Ga, 38; Ph.D, Duke Univ, 42; D.Univ, Paris, 55. Instr. Eng, N.C. State Col, 42; Univ. Buffalo, 42-45, asst. prof, 45-47, assoc. prof, 47; PROF, Univ. Md, 47-67, dir. prog. comp. lit, 63-67; COMP. LIT, UNIV. ILL, URBANA, 67-, ED, COMP. LIT. STUD, 63- Fulbright lectr, Univ. Toulouse, 52 & Univ. Clermont-Ferrand, France, 53. MLA; Int. Comp. Lit. Asn.(mem. adv. bd, 68-73); Soc. Am. Hist; Am. Comp. Lit. Asn.(mem. adv. bd, 65-71); Am. Soc. 18th Century Stud; Inst. Iberoam. Lit; Am. Soc. Teachers Span. & Port. Eighteenth century English and American literature; literary criticism; polygamy in early fiction. Publ: Shaftesbury and the Deist Manifests, Am. Philos. Soc; Benjamin Franklin and his French contemporaries, N.Y. Univ; Man of reason; Life of Thomas Paine, 59 & Benjamin Franklin: philosopher and man, 65, Lippincott; Benjamin Franklin et ses contemporains Français, Didier, Paris, 63; Jonathan Edwards, Wash. Sq. Press, 64; Benjamin Franklin and nature's God, Duke Univ, 67; ed, Comparative literature: matter & method, 69 & The Ibero-American enlightenment, 71, Univ. Ill; A religious hoax by Benjamin Franklin, Am. Lit, 64; Thomas Paine and the classics, 18th Century Stud, 1/68; The cloudy Spanish Enlightenment, Mod. Lang. J, 68; plus others. Add: Dept. of Comparative Literature, 2054 Foreign Language Bldg, University of Illinois, Urbana, IL 61801.

ALDRIDGE, JOHN WATSON, b. Sioux City, Iowa, Sept. 26, 22; div; c. 5. ENGLISH. B.A, Univ. Calif, Berkeley, 47. Lectr. lit. criticism, Univ. Vt, 48-50, asst. prof. Eng, 50-53, 54-55; lectr. Christian Gauss sem. in lit. criticism, Princeton, 53-54; prof. Eng, Sarah Lawrence Col, 56-57; Henry A. & Albert W. Berg prof, N.Y. Univ, 57-58; Fulbright prof, Univ. Munich, 58-59; writer-in-residence, Hollins Col, 60-62; Fullbright prof. ENG, Univ. Copenhagen, 62-63; PROF, UNIV. MICH, ANN ARBOR, 64- Staff mem. Bread Loaf Writers' Conf, Middlebury Col, 66-; chief regional judge, Bk-of-the-Month Club Writing Fel. Prog, 67-68; spec. adv. Am. Stud, U.S. Inform. Agency, Bonn, 72-73. U.S.A, 43-45. MLA; Authors League Am; PEN Club. American and British literature 1900 to the present. Publ: After the lost generation, 51 & In search of heresy, 56, McGraw; ed, Critiques and essays on modern fiction, Ronald, 52 & Selected stories by P.G. Wodehouse, Random, 58; auth, The party at Cranton & Time to murder and create, 66, McKay; In the country of the young, 70 & The devil in the fire: retrospective essays on American literature and culture, 1951-1971, 72, Harper's Mag. Press; plus others. Add: Dept. of English, University of Michigan, Ann Arbor, MI 48104.

ALDRIDGE, JUNE McDONALD; U.S. citizen. ENGLISH & AMERICAN LITERATURE. B.A, Spelman Col, 53; M.A. & Lasker fel, Mt. Holyoke Col, 54; Columbia Univ, 57; Ph.D.(Eng), Univ. Conn, 65. Asst. prof. ENG, South. Univ, Baton Rouge, 54-61; PROF, SPELMAN COL, 64- Vis. prof, NDEA Summer Inst. Sec. Teachers Eng, S.C. State Col, 65 & 66; dir, Nat. Endowment for Humanities Planning Grant, Spelman Col, 74-75. NCTE; Col. Lang. Asn. Women's studies; Southern and Afro-American literature. Add: Dept. of English, Spelman College, P.O. Box 100, Atlanta, GA 30314.

ALEXANDER, AIMEE H, b. Mill Springs, Ky, May 1, 19; wid; c. 1. ENGLISH. A.B, Transylvania Col, 40; M.A, Univ. Ky, 54; Columbia Univ, 57; George Peabody Col. Teachers, 60. Teacher, high sch, Ky, 43-61, chmn. dept. Eng, 5 years; ASST. PROF. ENG, EAST. KY. UNIV, 61- Liaison off, NCTE, 55-57, mem. stud. group on teaching writing, 66; prepared proposals for NDEA grants, East. Ky. Univ, 67-68. NCTE; Conf. Col. Compos. & Commun; S.Atlantic Mod. Lang. Asn; NEA; Soc. Stud. South. Lit. Improvements of reading institutes; American literature, especially short fiction and Southern literature; Carson McCullers. Publ: Contrib, Principles and standards in composition, fall 56 & The teaching of literature, grades 7-12, fall 67, Ky. Eng. J. Add: Dept. of English, Eastern Kentucky University, Richmond, KY 40475.

ALEXANDER, EDWARD, b. Brooklyn, N.Y, Dec. 28, 36; m. 58; c. 2. ENGLISH. B.A, Columbia Univ, 57, Henry Evans traveling fel, 57-58; M.A, Univ. Minn, 59, fel, 59-60, Ph.D.(Eng), 63; Fulbright fel, London, 61-62. Instr. ENG, UNIV. WASH, 60-64, asst. prof, 64-67, assoc. prof, 67-69, PROF, 69- Am. Counc. Learned Soc. fel, 66-67. Victorian literature; nineteenth century English literature; modern Jewish literature. Publ: Matthew Arnold and John Stuart Mill, Columbia Univ, 65; John Stuart Mill: literary essays, Bobbs, 67; John Morley, Twayne, 72; Matthew Arnold, John Ruskin and the modern temper, Ohio State Univ, 73; Roles of the Victorian critic: Matthew Arnold and John Ruskin, In: Literary criticism and historical understanding, Columbia Univ, 67; Thomas Carlyle and D.H. Lawrence: a parallel, Univ. Toronto Quart, 4/68; Ruskin and science, Mod. Lang. Rev, 7/69; plus one other. Add: Dept. of English, University of Washington, Seattle, WA 98105.

ALEXANDER, JEAN A, b. Forest Grove, Ore, May 4, 26. COMPARATIVE LITERATURE. B.A, Univ. Ore, 47; M.A, Univ. Wash, 55, Ph.D.(comp. lit), 60; Fulbright fel, France, 57-58. Instr. ENG, La. State Univ, 58-61; asst. prof, UNIV. CALGARY, 61-68, ASSOC. PROF, 68- Asn. Can. Univ. Teachers Eng; Int. Asn. Stud. Anglo-Irish Lit. Irish Renaissance writers; comparative Renaissance studies; the modern novel. Publ: Affidavits of genius; Edgar Allan Poe and the French critics, 1847-1924, Kennikat, 71; Yeats and the rhetoric of defilement, Rev. Eng. Lit, 7/65; contrib, Sunshine & the moon's delight; a centenary tribute to J.M. Synge, Colin Smythe, 72; plus one other. Add: Dept. of English, University of Calgary, Calgary, Alta, T2N 1N4, Can.

ALEXANDER, MARGARET ABIGAIL WALKER, b. Birmingham, Ala, July 7, 15; m. 43; c. 4. ENGLISH. B.A, Northwest. Univ, 35; M.A, Univ. Iowa, 40, Ph.D.(Eng), 65. Instr. ENG, Livingstone Col, 41-42, 45-46; W.Va. State Col, 42-43; JACKSON STATE COL, 49-54, assoc. prof, 54-64, PROF, 64-, DIR, INST. STUD. HIST, LIFE & CULT, BLACK PEOPLE, 68- Lectr. platform, Nat. Concert & Artists Corp, 43-48; asst, Univ. Iowa, 62-64; instr, Cape Cod Writers Conf, summer 67; vis. prof. creative writing, Northwest. Univ, 69. MLA; NEA; NCTE; AAUP; Poetry Soc. Am. Publ: For my people (verse), Yale, 42; Jubilee (novel), Houghton, 66; Prophets for a new day (poems), 70 & October journey (poems), 73, Broadside; How I wrote Jubilee, Third World Press, 72; A brief introduction to Southern literature, Miss. Arts Festival, 71; Richard Wright, Univ. Mo. New Lett, Vol. 38, No. 2. Add: Dept. of English, Jackson State College, P.O. Box 17315, Jackson, MS 39217.

ALEXANDER, ROBERT JOSEPH, b. Cambridge, Mass, Sept. 2, 44. ENGLISH LITERATURE. A.B, Bowdoin Col, 66; M.A, Univ. Wis-Madison, 68, Ph.D.(Eng), 73. ASST. PROF. ENG, POINT PARK COL, 72- MLA; Medieval Acad. Am. Anglo-Saxon homiletics. Add: Dept. of English, Point Park College, Wood St. & Blvd. of the Allies, Pittsburgh, PA 15232.

ALEXANDER, ROBERT RITCHIE, b. Calcutta, India, Feb. 15, 13; m. 46; c. 2. ENGLISH. B.A, St. Xavier's Col, 36; B.T, Univ. Calcutta, 36; dipl. educ, Univ. N.Z, 42, M.A, 50; Ph.D, Univ. Minn, 65. Sr. lectr. ENG, cols. & teachers cols, N.Z, 40-63; asst. prof, Macalester Col, 63-65; Trinity Univ. (Tex), 66-67; assoc. prof, West. State Col.(Colo), 67-68; UNIV. WIS-EAU CLAIRE, 68-70, PROF, 70- N.Z. govt. grant to assist publ. History of Te Aute Col, N.Z. Armed Forces, 40. MLA. Race relations in New Zealand; British Romantic poetry; 20th century British and American poetry. Publ: The history of Te Aute College, Reed, Wellington, 51; articles, In: An encyclopedia of New Zealand, N.Z. Govt, 65. Add: Dept. of English, University of Wisconsin-Eau Claire, Eau Claire, WI 54701.

ALEXANDER, RODNEY WILSON, b. Spokane, Wash, Apr. 23, 19; m. 42; c. 2. DRAMA. B.A, Whitman Col, 41; M.A, Columbia Univ, 53. Prof. drama, Whitman Col, 48-67, dir, Whitman Theatre, 50-67; PROF. DRAMA, DARTMOUTH COL. & DIR. THEATRE, HOPKINS CTR, 67- Guest dir. & actor, Ore. Shakespearean Festival, summers, 62, 63, 64; Regent's lectr. & guest dir, Univ. Calif, Santa Barbara, 65-66; guest dir, Univ. Mo, Kansas City Repertory Co, 66, Center Stage Repertory Co, Baltimore, Md, 66 & Syracuse Repertory Co, N.Y, 66-67; producer & dir, Dartmouth Repertory Theatre, summers, 67, 68. U.S.N, 41-45, Lt. Am. Nat. Theatre & Acad; Am. Theatre Asn. Add: Dept. of Drama, Dartmouth College, Hanover, NH 03755.

ALEXANDER, STANLEY GERALD, b. Roscoe, Tex, Nov. 24, 28; m. 56; c. 1. ENGLISH. B.A, Univ. Tex, 56, M.A, 59, Ph.D.(Eng), 65. Instr. ENG, Univ. Tex, 62-63; N.Tex. State Univ, 63-65, asst. prof, 65-66; assoc. prof, Tarleton State Col, 66-72, PROF, STEPHEN F. AUSTIN STATE UNIV, 72- U.S.A, 50-52. MLA. American literature; the novel; modern poetry. Publ: George Sessions Perry, Southwest Writers Ser, Steck, 67; The conflict of form in Tortilla Flat, Am. Lit, 3/68; Cannery Row: Steinbeck's pastoral poem, West. Am. Lit, spring 68. Add: Dept. of English, Stephen F. Austin State University, Nacogdoches, TX 75962.

ALEXIS, GERHARD T, b. St. Paul, Minn, Jan. 20, 18; m. 47; c. 2. AMERICAN LITERATURE. A.B, Univ. Minn, 37, Ph.D, 47. Instr. ENG, Univ. Minn, 46-47; asst. prof, GUSTAVUS ADOLPHUS COL, 47-51, assoc. prof, 51-56, PROF, 56- Summers, vis. prof, Winona State Col, 64 & 67; St. Olaf Col, 66; staff mem, Nat. Defense Educ. Act Eng. Inst, Augustana Col.(S.Dak), 68. A.U.S, 42-45, Lt. Am. Stud. Asn; MLA. Puritanism, religion and literature; American fiction. Publ: Farrell since our days of anger, Col. Eng, 12/65; Sweden to Minnesota: Vilhelm Moberg's fictional reconstruction, Am. Quart, spring, 66; Jonathan Edwards and the theocratic ideal, Church Hist, 9/66. Add: 809 S. Seventh St, St. Peter, MN 56082.

ALFONSI, FERDINANDO PETER, Comparative Literature, Italian. See Volume III, Foreign Languages, Linguistics & Philology.

ALFONSO, ROBERT J, b. New York, N.Y, Dec. 17, 28; m. 56; c. 2. ENGLISH, EDUCATION. B.A, Wesleyan Col.(N.Y), 52; M.A, N.Y. Univ, 53; Syracuse Univ, 56-57; Ph.D.(educ), Mich. State Univ, 62. Teacher pub. schs, N.Y. & Mont, 56-59; asst. to dean. col. educ, Mich. State Univ, 59-60, instr, 60-62; asst. prof. Eng. educ, Queens Col.(N.Y), 62-64; assoc. exec. secy, Asn. Supv. & Curriculum Develop, Nat. Educ. Asn, 64-67; assoc. prof. educ, Univ. Ala, 67-68; PROF. EDUC, KENT STATE UNIV, 68-, DEAN COL. EDUC. & GRAD. SCH. EDUC, 71-, asst. dean instr. & grad. stud, 68-71. Asst. ed, Mich. J. Sec. Educ, Mich. State Univ, 60-62; mem. bd. dirs, Nat. Interagency Counc. Smoking & Health, 64-67; consult, Nat. Stud. Eng. Teacher Prep, 65-66; chmn. comt. improving subj. supv, NCTE, 65-67; mem, Task Force on Supv. Theory, 67-70; Asn. Supv. & Curriculum Develop. Comn. on Prob. of Supvrs. & Curriculum Workers, 67-69; chmn. distinguished achievement award comt, Am. Asn. Cols. Teacher Educ, 72. U.S.M.C, 53-56, U.S.M.C.R, 56-, Lt. Col. NCTE; NEA; Asn. Supv. & Curriculum Develop.(ed, News Exchange, 64-67); Am. Asn. Sch. Adminr. Teaching of English to disadvantaged; instructional supervisory behavior. Publ: Co-auth, Administrative responsibility for school mathematics programs, Am. Asn. Sch. Adminr, 65; auth, What is creative leadership?, Sch.

Libr, 67; Collective negotiation in curriculum instruction, NEA Negotiation Res. Digest, 5/69. Add: College of Education, Kent State University, Kent, OH 44240.

ALFORD, NORMAN WILLIAM, b. Croydon, Surrey, Eng, Sept. 2, 29; m. 67. ENGLISH. B.A, Univ. London, 62; fel, Univ. Tex, 64-66, Ph.D.(Eng), 66. ASST. PROF. ENG, UNIV. VICTORIA (B.C), 66- Can. Counc. summer res. grant, 68. English literature in transition: 1890-1914; the modern novel: Conrad to the present day. Publ: The Rhymer's Club, Skilton, London, 74; Seven note-books of Ronald Firbank, Libr. Chronicle, Tex, spring 67; Oscar Wilde in Texas, Tex. Quart, summer 67. Add: Dept. of English, University of Victoria, Victoria, B.C, Can.

ALFRED, WILLIAM, b. New York, N.Y, Aug. 16, 22. ENGLISH. B.A, Brooklyn Col, 48; M.A, Harvard, 49, Ph.D, 54. Instr. ENG, HARVARD, 54-57, asst. prof, 57-59, assoc. prof, 59-63, PROF, 63- John Harvard fel, 49-50; Amy Lowell traveling poetry fel, 56-57. Brandeis Univ. Creative Arts Award, 59. A.U.S, 43-46. MLA; Mediaeval Acad. Am; Dramatists Guild. Old English poetry; Middle English poetry; drama. Publ: Co-ed, The complete proseworks of John Milton, Yale, Vol. I, 53; auth, Agamemnon, Knopf, 54; Hogan's goat (play), Farrar, Straus, 65; co-auth, Beowolf translations, In: Medieval epics, Mod. Lib, 63. Add: Dept. of English, Harvard University, Cambridge, MA 02138.

ALGEO, JOHN THOMAS, b. St. Louis, Mo, Nov. 12, 30; m. 58; c. 2. ENGLISH. B.Ed, Univ. Miami, 54; M.A, Univ. Fla, 56, Ph.D.(Eng), 60. Instr. Eng, Fla. State Univ, 59-61; asst. prof, Univ. Fla, 61-66, assoc. prof, 66-70, asst. dean grad. sch, 69-71, PROF. ENG. & LING, 70-71; ENG, UNIV. GA, 71- Am. Counc. Learned Soc. grant, summer 56; Univ. Fla. grant, summers 65 & 68. U.S.A, 51-54, Sgt. MLA; Ling. Soc. Am; Am. Dialect Soc.(ed, Am. Speech, 71-); Int. Phonetic Asn; Early Eng. Text Soc; S.Atlantic Mod. Lang. Asn; Int. Ling. Asn; NCTE; Am. Name Soc; Southwest. Conf. Ling.(pres, 70-71). English linguistics; mediaeval literature. Publ: Co-auth, English: an introduction to language, 70 & auth, Problems in the origins and development of the English language, 66 & 72, Harcourt; ed, Spelling: sound to letter, Macmillan, 71; auth, On defining the proper name, Univ. Fla, 73; Stratificational grammar, J. Eng. Ling, 69; The vogue uses of non, Am. Speech, 73; plus several others. Add: Dept. of English, Park Hall, University of Georgia, Athens, GA 30602.

ALKON, PAUL KENT, b. Portsmouth, N.H, May 1, 35; m. 57; c. 3. ENGLISH LITERATURE. A.B, Harvard, 57; Ph.D.(Eng. lit), Univ. Chicago, 62. Instr. ENG. LIT, Univ. Calif, Berkeley, 62-63, asst. prof, 63-70; assoc. prof, Univ. Md, 70-71; UNIV. MINN, MINNEAPOLIS, 71-73, PROF, 73- MLA; Am. Soc. 18th Century Stud. Eighteenth century English literature; Samuel Johnson; time. Publ: Samuel Johnson and moral discipline, Northwest. Univ, 67; Boswell's control of aesthetic distance, Univ. Toronto Quart, 1/69; Critical and logical concepts of method from Addison to Coleridge, Eighteenth-Century Stud, fall 71; Boswellian time, Stud. Burke & His Time, spring 73; plus five others. Add: Dept. of English, University of Minnesota, Minneapolis, MN 55455.

ALLABACK, STEVEN LEE, b. Burbank, Calif, Jan. 24, 39; m. 61; c. 3. ENGLISH. B.A, Univ. Calif, Santa Barbara, 60; Ph.D.(Eng), Univ. Wash, 66. ASST. PROF. ENG, Univ. Conn, 66-70; UNIV. CALIF, SANTA BARBARA, 70- American literature; British fiction; creative writing. Publ: Voices of Longfellow: Kavanagh, Emerson Soc. Quart, 70; Mrs. Clemm and Henry W. Longfellow, Harvard Libr. Bull, 70; contrib, Watching out for the other guy, Prairie Schooner, 71. Add: Dept. of English, University of California, Santa Barbara, CA 93106.

ALLEE, JOHN GAGE, JR, Philology, English. See Volume III, Foreign Languages, Linguistics & Philology.

ALLEMAN, GELLERT SPENCER, b. Swarthmore, Pa, June 24, 13; m. 53; c. 1. ENGLISH. A.B, Lehigh Univ, 34; A.M, Univ. Pa, 37, Ph.D, 42. Instr. ENG, Lehigh Univ, 38-40, 42-47; asst. prof, RUTGERS UNIV, NEWARK, 47-56, assoc. prof, 56-61, PROF, 61-, acting chmn. dept, 62-66. U.S.A.F, 42-46, U.S.A.R, 49-57, Warrant Off.(jg). MLA; Mod. Humanities Res. Asn; Col. Eng. Asn; NCTE. Restoration comedy; English marriage law to 1754. Publ: Matrimonial law and the materials of restoration comedy, privately publ, 42; co-ed, English literature, 1660-1800: a current bibliography, Philol. Quart, 54-64. Add: 86 Vreeland Ave, Nutley, NJ 07110.

ALLEN, CHARLES A, b. Indianapolis, Ind, Jan. 1, 13; m. 43; c. 1. AMERICAN LITERATURE. A.B, DePauw Univ, 35; Ph.D, State Univ. Iowa, 42. Instr. Eng, Purdue Univ, 39-45; asst. prof, Univ. Ariz, 45-47, ed, Quart, 46-47; univ. press, Univ. N.Mex, 47-48, 'Pubs,' 48-49, acting ed, Quart. Rev, 48; asst. prof. Eng, Stanford Univ, 49-57, ed. univ. press, 49-56; asst. prof. ENG, CALIF. STATE UNIV, LONG BEACH, 57-60, assoc. prof, 60-64, PROF, 64- MLA. American literature; satire. Publ: Little magazine, Princeton, 46; Satire: theory and practice, Wadsworth, 62. Add: Dept. of English, California State University, Long Beach, Long Beach, CA 90801.

ALLEN, DICK, b. Troy, N.Y, Aug. 8, 39; m. 60; c. 2. ENGLISH. A.B, Syracuse Univ, 61; M.A, Brown Univ, 63. Teaching asst. ENG, Brown Univ, 62-63, teaching assoc, 63-64; instr, Wright State Univ, 64-68; asst. prof, UNIV. BRIDGEPORT, 68-71, ASSOC. PROF. & DIR. CREATIVE WRITING, 71- Ed-in-chief, Mad River Rev, 66-68; Robert Frost fel, 72; contrib. ed, Am. Poetry Rev, 72-; contrib. ed. & mem. adv. bd, Dictics, 73- Sci. Fiction Res. Asn. Contemporary American poetry; science and speculative fiction; modern criticism. Publ: Anon and various time machine poems, Delacorte, 71; ed, Science fiction: the future, 71, co-ed, Detective fiction: crime and compromise, 74 & Science fiction: the future continued, 74, Harcourt; auth, Science-space-speculative fiction, Yale Alumni J, 71; The village of contemporary poets, Poetry, 72; The poet in the gray flannel suit, Am. Poetry Rev, spring 74; plus others. Add: Dept. of English, University of Bridgeport, Bridgeport, CT 06602.

ALLEN, DONALD S, b. Clairton, Pa, Jan. 29, 05; m. 31; c. 1. THEATER ARTS. A.B, Ohio Wesleyan Univ, 28, A.M, 33. Tech. dir, Little Theater, Ohio Wesleyan Univ, 30-32; prof. THEATER ARTS, ROLLINS COL, 34-66, EMER. PROF, 66- Rollins Medal, 45. Southeast. Theatre Conf. Add: Dept. of Theater Arts, Rollins College, Winter Park, FL 32789.

ALLEN, GAY WILSON, b. Lake Junaluska, N.C, Aug. 23, 03; m. 29. ENGLISH. A.B, Duke Univ, 26, A.M, 28; legislative scholar, Univ. Wis, 33-34, Ph.D, 34. Asst. prof. ENG, Lake Erie Col, 29-31; Ala. Polytech. Inst, 31-32; assoc. prof, Shurtleff Col, 34-35; Bowling Green State Univ, 35-46; N.Y. UNIV, 46-47, prof, 47-69, EMER. PROF, 69-, PART-TIME TEACHER, 73- Rockefeller Found. fel, 44-45; Guggenheim fels, 52-53, 59-60; U.S. Dept. State lectr, Japan, summer 55; prof. Am. lit, Harvard, summer 57; Univ. Hawaii, summer 63; mem. bd. ed, Am. Lit, 67-69; vis. prof, Harvard Univ, 69-70. Tamiment Award, 55. MLA; Am. Stud. Asn; Int. Asn. Univ. Prof. Eng; PEN Club; Auth. Guild. Ralph Waldo Emerson; poetics; theory of biography. Publ: American prosody, Am. Bk. Co, 35; Walt Whitman handbook, Packard, 46, Hendricks, 58, 63; The solitary singer: a critical biography of Walt Whitman, Macmillan, 55, N.Y. Univ. 67; Walt Whitman as man, poet, and legend, South. Ill. Univ, 61; co-ed, Collected writings of Walt Whitman (9 vols), N.Y. Univ, 64-; auth, William James, a biography, Viking, 67; William James, 70 & Carl Sandburg, 72, Univ. Minn; A reader's guide to Walt Whitman, Noonday, 70; ed, A William James reader, Houghton, 71. Add: Dept. of English, New York University, 19 University Pl, New York, NY 10003.

ALLEN, JAMES GEORGE, b. Denison, Tex, Jan. 7, 02; m. 28; c. 1. ENGLISH LITERATURE. A.B, South. Methodist Univ, 24; A.M, Harvard, 28. Instr. ENG, TEX. TECH UNIV, 27-31, asst. prof, 31-37, assoc. prof, 37-40, prof, 40-72, EMER. PROF, 72-, EMER. DEAN STUD. LIFE, 72-, acting dean men, 37-38, dean, 38-50, dean stud. life, 59-72. Dir, Tex. Tech Dads Asn, 56-72. Distinguished Teaching Award, Standard Oil Ill, 71-72. MLA. Add: 3110 21st St, Lubbock, TX 79410.

ALLEN, JAMES LOVIC, b. Atlanta, Ga, Jan. 2, 29; m. 53; c. 2. ENGLISH. B.A, Tulane Univ, 53, M.A, 54; South. Fel. Fund fels, Univ. Fla, 56, 57, Ph.D, 59. Instr. ENG, Univ. Tenn, 54-56; asst. prof, Stephen F. Austin State Col, 59-60; assoc. prof, Univ. South. Miss, 60-63; UNIV. HAWAII, HILO, 63-69, PROF, 69-, ed, South. Quart, 62-63, chmn. div. humanities, 66-69. Summer vis. assoc. prof, West. Wash. State Col, 68; vis. prof. Eng, Hartwick Col, summer 69; Stephen F. Austin State Univ, 70-71. U.S.N, 46-49. MLA. Modern literature, especially work of Yeats and Faulkner. Publ: Yeat's phase in the system of A vision, Eire-Ireland winter 73; A bibliography of scholarship and criticism on Yeats' Byzantium poems, 1935-1970, Bull. New York Pub. Libr, winter 73; New light on Yeats' last years, Sewanee Rev, winter 74; plus others. Add: Dept. of English, University of Hawaii at Hilo, Box 1357, Hilo, HI 96720.

ALLEN, JAMES STEWART, b. Henrietta, Tex, Jan. 26, 21; m. 46; c. 2. ENGLISH RENAISSANCE, PHILOSOPHY. B.A, Univ. Tex, Austin, 42, M.A, 46; Ph.D.(Eng), Vanderbilt Univ, 54. Instr. Eng, Parkville, Mo, 46-47; assoc. prof, Arlington State Col, 47-50; teaching fel, Vanderbilt Univ, 50-52; prof, Arlington State Col, 52-56; Sam Houston State Col, 56-60, grad. dean & acting dean students, 61-63; asst. dir. acad. progs, Tex. Comn. Higher Educ, 63-65; v.pres. acad. affairs, Marshall Univ, 65-67; exec. dir. & pres, Asn. Tex. Cols. & Univs, 67-71; DEAN HUMANITIES, SAM HOUSTON STATE UNIV, 71- Carnegie fel, Ctr. Stud. Higher Educ, Univ. Mich, 60-61; admin. secy, Independent Cols. & Univs. Tex, Inc, 67-71. Am. Asn. Higher Educ.(mem. Southwest Regional Adv. Comt, 70-71). Renaissance drama; academic administration. Publ: Legal education in Texas: a curriculum study, 64, ed, A study of private higher education in Texas and its place in the statewide system, 68, ed, Pluralism and partnership: the case for the dual system of higher education, 68 & ed, Private higher education in profile: Texas colleges and universities report of their current position, 68, Austin, Tex; auth, By their fruits, a study of small college faculties, Forum, fall 63; Systems in transition, Proc. Tex. Asn. Educ. Data Systs, 67. Add: Office of the Dean of Humanities, Sam Houston State University, Huntsville, TX 77340.

ALLEN, JEREMIAH M, JR, b. Boston, Mass, Sept. 3, 19; m. 41; c. 5. ENGLISH. A.B, Duke Univ, 47; M.A, Tufts Univ, 48; Ph.D, Univ. Colo, 56. Instr. ENG, Col. Engineering, Univ. Colo, 48-56, asst. prof, 56-60, assoc. prof, 60-62, prof, 62-68, acting dean grad. sch, 63-64, dir. engineering honors prog, 63-67, coord. educ. opportunity prog, 68; PROF. ENG, UNIV. MASS, AMHERST, 68-, DEAN FAC. HUMANITIES & FINE ARTS, 70-, assoc. provost, 68-70. Mem. steering comt. new access routes to med. careers, Am. Found. Negro Affairs, 73-; mem. bd. dir, Counc. Cols. & Arts & Sci, 73- English literature; 19th century; Shakespeare. Publ: Co-auth, Writing clinical reports, 63 & Curricula in solid mechanics, 61, Prentice-Hall; co-auth, Honors programs in engineering, Allyn & Bacon, 64. Add: Office of the Dean, Faculty of Humanities & Fine Arts, South College, University of Massachusetts, Amherst, MA 01002.

ALLEN, JOHN ALEXANDER, b. Chevy Chase, Md, Apr. 25, 22; m. 51; c. 2. ENGLISH. B.A, Swarthmore Col, 43; A.B, Oxford, 48, A.M, 52; Ph.D.(Eng), Univ. N.C, Chapel Hill, 54. Instr. ENG, Univ. Rochester, 52-55; asst. prof, HOLLINS COL, 55-60, assoc. prof, 60-67, PROF, 67-, chmn. dept, 67-70. Vis. prof. Eng. & Am. lit, Univ. E.Anglia, 70-71. U.S.N, 43-46, Lt.(jg.) MLA. Myth and literature; Shakespearian comedy. Publ: Co-auth, The Hollins poets, Univ. Va, 67; ed, Hero's way: contemporary poems in the mythic tradition, Prentice-Hall, 71; auth, The lean divider, Golden Quill, 68; Bottom and Titania, Shakespeare Quart, spring 67; Dogberry, Shakespeare Quart, winter 73. Add: Dept. of English, Hollins College, Hollins College, VA 24020.

ALLEN, JUDSON BOYCE, b. Louisville, Ky, Mar. 15, 32; m. 56; c. 2. MEDIEVAL ENGLISH & LATIN. B.A, Baylor Univ, 53; M.A, Vanderbilt Univ, 54; Oxford, 60-62; Ph.D.(Eng), Johns Hopkins Univ, 63. Res. asst, South. Baptist Hist. Comn, 54, assoc. ed, Encycl. South. Baptists, 54-57; instr. ENG, Wake Forest Univ, 62-63, asst. prof, 63-69; ASSOC. PROF, MARQUETTE UNIV, 69- Fel, Southeast. Inst. Medieval & Renaissance Stud, summer 65; Coop. Prog. in Humanities fel, Duke Univ. & Univ. N.C, 65-66; secy, Ecumenical Inst, Wake Forest Univ, 68-69; Nat. Endowment for Humanities younger scholar fel, Rome, 69-70. MLA; Mediaeval Acad. Am; AAUP. Medieval English and Latin; literary theory. Publ: The friar as critic: literary attitudes in the later Middle Ages, Vanderbilt Univ, 71; A twelfth century De natura deorum in the Bodleian Library, Traditio, 26: 352-364; Commentary as criticism: formal cause, discursive form, and the late Medieval Accessus, In: Acta Conventus Neo-Latinus Lovaniensis, Fink, 73; plus others. Add: Dept. of English, Marquette University, 635 N. 13th St, Milwaukee, WI 53233.

ALLEN, LOURIE STRICKLAND, b. Kossuth, Miss, Jan. 12, 15; m. 48; c. 1. NINETEENTH CENTURY ENGLISH & AMERICAN LITERATURE. B.A, Blue Mountain Col, 37; M.A, Univ. Ala, 48, Ph.D.(Eng), 72. Teacher Eng. & hist, Holcut High Sch, Miss, 37-38; teacher & librn, Fifth Dist. Spec. Consolidated High Sch, Belmont, 38-42; teacher & prin, Ackerman High Sch, 42-45; teacher & chmn. dept, Amory High Sch, 45-50, 55-62; instr. ENG, MISS. STATE COL. WOMEN, 62-65, asst. prof, 65-72, ASSOC. PROF, 72- MLA; NCTE. Milton; 19th century fiction; 19th century poetry. Publ: W.C. Falkner: writer of romance and realism, Univ. Miss, (in prep). Add: Dept. of English, Mississippi State College for Women, College St, Columbus, MS 39701.

ALLEN, MARGARET VANDERHAAR, b. Louisville, Ky, Jan. 14, 34. ENGLISH & AMERICAN LITERATURE. B.A, Ursline Col.(Ky), 55; M.A, Univ. Chicago, 61; Ph.D.(Eng), Tulane Univ, 66. Asst. prof. Eng, Loyola Univ. (La), 61-69; Wilkes Col, 69-72. MLA. Modern poetry; modern fiction; American literature. Publ: Margaret Fuller's writing revisited, Southwest Rev, spring 73; The political and social criticism of Margaret Fuller, S.Atlantic Quart, autumn 73; Autocracy and rebellion in Hawthorne's Lady Eleanor's mantle, Junction, winter 73; plus others. Add: Box 158B, Old Philadelphia Pike, Bethlehem, PA 18015.

ALLEN, MICHAEL JOHN B, b. Lewes, Eng, Apr. 1, 41; m. 72. RENAISSANCE LITERATURE & PHILOSOPHY. b.A, Oxford, 64, M.A, 68; Ford fel, Univ. Mich, 68-69, Rackham fel, 69-70, Ph.D.(Eng), 70. Instr. ENG, Ohio Univ, 66-67; asst. prof, UNIV. CALIF, LOS ANGELES, 70-74, ASSOC. PROF, 74- Mem, Humanities Inst, 72-73; mem. Am. bd, World Ctr. Shakespeare Stud, 73-; secy. Neo-Latin sem, MLA, 73, leader, 74. MLA; Renaissance Soc. Am. Renaissance neoplatonism; Shakespeare. Publ: Marsilio Ficino: the Philebus commentary, Univ. Calif, 75; The chase: the development of a Renaissance theme, Comp. Lit, fall 68; The absent angel in Ficino's philosophy, J. Hist. Ideas, (in press). Add: Dept. of English, University of California, Los Angeles, CA 90024.

ALLEN, RALPH GILMORE, b. Philadelphia, Pa, Jan. 7, 34; m. 57. THEATRE ARTS. B.A, Amherst Col, 55; John Golden fels, Yale, 57-59, D.F.A, 60. Asst. prof. speech & theatre arts, Univ. Pittsburg, 60-65, assoc. prof, 65-68; chmn. div. theatre, Univ. Victoria (B.C), 68-72; PROF. SPEECH & THEATRE & HEAD DEPT, UNIV. TENN, KNOXVILLE, 72- Charles E. Merrill fel, 62; managing ed, Theatre Surv, 63-65, ed, 65-; Guggenheim fel, 65; artistic dir, Victoria Fair Theatre, 69-71. Am. Theatre Asn.(admin. v.pres, 69-71, v.pres, res, 71-72); Am. Soc. Theatre Res; Int. Fed. Theatre Res. English theatre, 1660-1900; stage directing; American popular comedy. Publ: Co-auth, Theatre and drama in the making, Houghton, 63, auth, Turcaret, (adapter of Le Sage's play) Victoria Fair Drama Ser. No. 1, 70; Topical scenes for pantomime, Educ. Theatre J, 65; Capon's scenes for melodrama, Theatre Res, 66; contrib, Our native theatre, In: The American theatre: a sum of its parts, French, 72; plus one other. Add: Dept. of Speech & Theatre, University of Tennessee, Knoxville, TN 37916.

ALLEN, RICHARD EILERS, b. St. Louis, Mo, Dec. 7, 26, m. 50; c. 3. ENGLISH. A.B, Wash. Univ, 48, M.A, 49, Ph.D.(Eng), 56. Instr. ENG, Univ. Md, Europe, 56-57; Bates Col, 57-59; asst. prof, Univ. Omaha, 59-63; ASSOC. PROF, ILL. STATE UNIV, 63- U.S.N, 44-46, 52-54, Lt.(jg). MLA; Renaissance Soc. Am; Mediaeval Acad. Am. Renaissance and 17th century; medieval. Publ: The voices of the owl and the nightingale, Stud. Medieval Cult, 70. Add: 1309 N. Clinton, Bloomington, IL 61701.

ALLEN, ROBERT JOSEPH, b. Indianapolis, Ind, Mar. 9, 02. ENGLISH LITERATURE. A.B, Univ. Ill, 23; A.M, Harvard, 28, Ph.D, 29. Asst. prof, Univ. Kans, 29-30; instr, Harvard, 30-37; asst. prof. ENG, WILLIAMS COL, 37-43, assoc. prof, 43-48, prof, 48-72, chmn. dept, 48-65, EMER. PROF, 72- Prof. humanities, Calif. Inst. Tech, 59-60. MLA; Col. Eng. Asn. English literature of the 18th century. Publ: The clubs of Augustan London, Harvard Univ, 33; Life in 18th century England, Boston Mus. Fine Arts, 41; Addison and Steele: selections, Holt, 57. Add: Cluett Dr, Williamstown, MA 01267.

ALLEN, ROBERT RANDOLPH, b. Boston, Mass, Aug. 10, 33; m. 61. ENGLISH. B.A, Amherst Col, 55; M.A, Harvard, 59, Ph.D.(Eng), 63. Asst. prof. Eng, Univ. Ill, Urbana, 63-70; UNIV. SOUTH. CALIF, 70-73, SR. LECTR. BIBLIOG, 73- Gen. ed, The eighteenth century: a current bibliography, 73- Bibliog. Soc. Am; Am. Soc. 18th Century Stud.(bibliogr, 73-); MLA. English literature, 1500-1800; bibliography and rare books; 20th century American literature. Publ: Ed, Erasmus, Funus and The epicure, Univ. Chicago, 69; Variant readings in Johnson's London Papers, Bibliog. Soc. Am, 66. Add: Dept. of English, 404 Founders Hall, University of Southern California, Los Angeles, CA 90007.

ALLEN, RONALD ROYCE, b. Horicon, Wis, Dec. 8, 30; m. 57; c. 2. SPEECH. B.S, Wis. State Col, Eau Claire, 52; M.S, Univ. Wis, 57, Ph.D. (speech), 60. Asst. prof. pub. speaking & chmn. dept, Amherst Col, 60-63; asst. prof. speech educ, UNIV. WIS-MADISON, 63-66, assoc. prof. speech & curriculum, 66-69, PROF. COMMUN. ARTS & CURRICULUM & INSTR, 69- U.S.N.R, 52-56, Lt. Speech Commun. Asn. Teaching of speech; theory of argument; American public address. Publ: Co-auth, Contemporary American speeches, Wadsworth, 65 & 72, Speech in American society, 68 & Communication: interacting through speech, 74, Merrill & Speech communication in the secondary school, Allyn & Bacon, 72; co-auth, Research in speech education, In: The communicative arts and science of speech, Merrill, 67; plus others. Add: Dept. of Communication Arts, University of Wisconsin-Madison, Madison, WI 53706.

ALLEN, SAMUEL WASHINGTON, b. Columbus, Ohio, Dec. 9, 17; m. 53; c. 1. LITERATURE. A.B, Fisk Univ, 38; J.D, Harvard, 41; New Sch. Soc. Res, 47-48; Sorbonne, 49-50. Deputy asst. dist. atty, Off. Dist. Atty. County of N.Y, Manhattan, 46-47; atty, Armed Forces Europe, 51-55; pvt. pract, N.Y.C, 56-58; assoc. prof. law, Tex. South. Univ, 58-60; asst. gen. counsel, U.S. Inform. Agency, 61-64; chief counsel, Community Relat. Serv, Dept. Commerce & Dept. Justice, 65-68; Avalon prof. humanities, Iuskegee Inst, 68-70; PROF. ENG, BOSTON UNIV, 71- Vis. prof, Wesleyan Univ, 69-70; v.pres. & mem. bd. dirs, South. Educ. Found, 69-; vis. prof, Duke Univ, 72-73, 73-74. Adj.Gen.C, U.S.A, 42-46. African Stud. Asn; African Heritage Stud. Asn; NCTE; Col. Eng. Asn. Afro-American and African literature. Publ: Elfenbein Zahne (Ivory tusks) (bilingual vol. poetry), Wolfgang Rothe, Heidelberg, 56; co-ed. & auth, Introd, Pan Africanism reconsidered, Univ. Calif, 62; auth, Ivory tusks and other poems, Poets Press, 68; transl, Jean Paul Sartre, Black Orpheus, Presence Africaine, London, 60; ed, Poems from Africa, Crowell, 73; auth, Introd, Enemy of the sun: poetry of the Palestinian resistance, Drum & Spear Press, 70; transl, Aimee Cesaire's Africa (poem), In: Voices in the whirlwind and other essays, Hill & Wang, 72 & Leopold Senghor's Elegy for Martin Luther King (poem), Black Orpheus, (in press); plus numerous others. Add: Dept. of English, Boston University, 236 Bay State Rd, Boston, MA 02215.

ALLEN, SHIRLEY SEIFRIED, b. Oak Park, Ill, May 25, 21; m. 42, 71; c. 3. ENGLISH LITERATURE, THEATRE HISTORY. B.A, Carleton Col, 42; M.A, Bryn Mawr Col, 44, Ph.D.(Eng), 49. Asst. prof. ENG, UNIV. CONN, HARTFORD, 69-72, ASSOC. PROF, 72- AAUP; MLA; Soc. Theatre Res, Eng; Am. Soc. Theatre Res. Shakespearean stage history; women in literature; the novel. Publ: Samuel Phelps and Sadler's Wells Theatre, Wesleyan Univ, 71; Samuel Phelps, last of a dynasty, Theatre Annual, 50. Add: University of Connecticut, Hartford Branch, Asylum Ave. & Trout Brook Dr, West Hartford, CT 06117.

ALLEN, WALTER POWELL, b. Chicago, Ill, May 13, 17; m; c. 1. ENGLISH. B.A, Pomona Col, 39; M.A, Univ. Calif, 40; Ed.D.(Eng. as for. lang), Teachers Col, Columbia Univ, 48; Univ. Wis. Teacher Eng. & hist, St. John's Univ. Mid. Sch, Shanghai, China, 40; Eng, Hankow Union Diocesan Mid. Sch, 40-41; instr, Huachung Univ, 41-44, asst. prof, 48-50, head dept, 50; asst. prof, Mission House Col, 51-55; asst. prof. Eng. for foreigners & counsel. for. stud, Miami Univ, 55-62; ASSOC. PROF. ENG, UNIV. HOUSTON, 62-, dir. int. stud. serv, 62-68. U.S.A, 44-45. NCTE; Nat. Asn. For. Stud. Affairs; Teachers Eng. to Speakers Other Lang; MLA; S.Cent. Mod. Lang. Asn. Second language learning; teaching of English as a foreign language. Publ: Selecting reading materials for foreign students, Easy crossword puzzles for people learning English, More easy crossword puzzles, 70 & A cultural checklist, 73, Eng. Lang. Serv; Interesting the intermediate level learner, Teaching Eng. Speakers Other Lang, 65; Pronoun chart, T.E.S.O.L. Reporter, 72; A cease-fire proposal, Eng. in Tex, 73. Add: Dept. of English, University of Houston, Houston, TX 77004.

ALLEN, WARD SYKES, b. Nashville, Tenn, July 10, 22; m. 51; c. 4. ENGLISH. B.A, Vanderbilt Univ, 47, M.A, 49, Ph.D.(Eng. & Greek), 63. Asst. prof. Eng, Miss. State Col. Women, 57-62; instr, Vanderbilt Univ, 62-64; assoc. prof, AUBURN UNIV, 64-70, prof, 70-74, HARGIS PROF. ENG. LIT, 74- John Simon Guggenheim Mem. Found. fel, 72-73. U.S.A.F, 42-46, Sgt. MLA; Renaissance Soc. Am; Early Eng. Text Soc; Milton Soc. Am; Amici Thomae Mori; Bibliog. Soc. Am. English translations of the Bible. Publ: Ed, Translating for King James, Vanderbilt Univ, 69; auth, Speculations on St. Thomas More's use of Hesychius, Philol. Quart, 4/67; Hythloday and the root of all evil, Moreana, 11/71. Add: Dept. of English, Auburn University, Auburn, AL 36830.

ALLENTUCK, MARCIA EPSTEIN, b. Manhattan, N.Y, June 8, 28; m. 49; c. 1. ENGLISH. B.A, N.Y. Univ, 48, univ. scholar, 44-47; Cornell Univ, 47; Kenyon Sch, Eng, 48; univ. grant, Columbia Univ, 48-49, Ph.D, 64. Lectr. ENG, Columbia Univ, 55-57; Hunter Col, 57-59; from lectr. to ASSOC. PROF, CITY COL. NEW YORK, 59- Am. Asn. Univ. Women Morrison fel, Huntington Libr, 58-59; Howard fel, Brown Univ, 66-67; Am. Philos. Soc. res. grant, 66-67; Am. Counc. Learned Soc. travel grant, summer 67; Huntington Libr. fel, 68; Nat. Transl. Ctr. fel, Univ. Tex, 68-69; Chapelbrook Found. fel, 70-71; sr. res. fel, Dumbarton Oaks, Harvard, 72-73; sr. res. fel, Nat. Endowment for Humanities, 73-74; vis. fel, Wolfson Col, Oxford, spring 74. Fischel Award, N.Y. Univ, 45-48, Sussman Mem. Medal, 46. Brit. Soc. Aesthet; MLA; Milton Soc. Am; Augustan Reprint Soc; Renaissance Soc. Am; Am. Soc. Aesthet; NCTE; Col. Art Asn. Am; Int. Comp. Lit. Asn; Hist. Sci. Soc; Mod. Humanities Res. Asn; Soc. Archit. Hist, Gt. Brit. History of ideas; comparative literature; aesthetics. Publ: The works of Henry Needler, Augustan Reprint Soc, 61; Isaac Bashevis Singer, South. Ill. Univ, 69; John Graham's System in modern art, Johns Hopkins Univ, 71; Expression, aesthetic science and information theory, Proc. Fifth Int. Cong. Aesthet, Amsterdam, 64; Fuseli and Lavater: physiognomonical theory and the Enlightenment, In: Studies on Voltaire and the eighteenth century, Lounz, 67; Fuseli and Herder, J. Hist. Ideas, 1/74. Add: 5 W. 86th St, Apt. 12B, New York, NY 10024.

ALLISON, ALEXANDER W, b. Kuling, China, Aug. 4, 19; U.S. citizen; m. 53; c. 5. ENGLISH LITERATURE. A.B, Hampden-Sydney Col, 41; Ph.D, Univ. Va, 49. Instr. ENG, Univ. Mich, 49-54, asst. prof, 54-58; vis. lectr, Kalamazoo Col, 58-59; lectr, UNIV. MICH, ANN ARBOR, 59-64, assoc. prof, 64-71, PROF, 71- U.S.N.R, 42-46, Lt. MLA. Seventeenth and 18th century poetry; intellectual history. Publ: Toward an Augustan poetic, Univ. Ky, 62; co-ed, Masterpieces of the drama, Macmillan, 57. Add: Dept. of English, University of Michigan, Ann Arbor, MI 48104.

ALLISON, LUTHER WILLIAM, b. Petersburg, Pa, Dec. 12, 11; m. 35; c. 4. ENGLISH LITERATURE & EDUCATION. A.B, Juniata Col, 32; A.M, Pa. State Univ, 39; Ed.D.(sec. educ), 59. Teacher & prin. high schs, 32-69; assoc. prof. Eng, FRAMINGHAM STATE COL, 69-72, PROF. ENG. EDUC. & EXTERNAL DEGREE PROG, 72- NCTE; MLA. Open education, all levels; the quest in English literature; literary criticism. Add: Dept. of English, Framingham State College, Framingham, MA 01701.

ALLISON, RALPH ROBERT, b. Sosua, Dominican Republic, Mar. 6, 46; U.S. citizen; m. 68. THEATRE. B.A, Univ. Calif, Riverside, 67; M.A, Univ. Calif, Davis, 69; Ph.D.(theatre), Fla. State Univ, 72. Instr. THEATRE, Fla. State Univ, 70-72; ASST. PROF, TEMPLE UNIV, 72- Am. Theatre Asn. Contemporary British theatre; professional actor training. Publ: England's

National theatre, Performance, 10/72 & Southern Theatre, 6/73; co-auth, Rhapsody in an anechoic chamber: Pinter's Landscape, Educ. Theatre J, 5/73. Add: Dept. of Theatre, School of Communications & Theatre, Temple University, Broad St, Philadelphia, PA 19122.

ALLMAN, WILLIAM ARTHUR, b. Tiffin, Ohio, June 10, 24; m. 50; c. 2. THEATRE ARTS, SPEECH. B.A, Heidelberg Col, 49; M.A, Ohio Univ, 51; summers, Ohio State Univ, 53, 54. Teacher & dir. drama, High Sch, Ohio, 51-53; asst. prof. Eng. & theatre arts, Ohio North. Univ, 53-55; asst. prof. SPEECH, BALDWIN-WALLACE COL, 55-71, ASSOC. PROF, 71-, DIR. DRAMA, 55- U.S.A.A.F, 43-46. Speech Commun. Asn; Am. Theatre Asn; Nat. Theatre Conf. Interpretative reading; religious drama. Add: Dept. of Speech, Baldwin-Wallace College, Berea, OH 44017.

ALLRED, GORDON THATCHER, b. Iowa City, Iowa, Dec. 27, 30; m. 56; c. 8. CREATIVE WRITING, MODERN LITERATURE. B.S, Univ. Utah, 57, M.S, 58, NDEA fel. & Ph.D.(creative writing, mod. lit), 72. Assoc. ed, Improvement Era, 56-58; publ. writer, U.S. Forest Serv, Intermt. Region, 59-63; ASSOC. PROF. ENG, WEBER STATE COL, 63- U.S.A, 54-56. Contemporary literature. Publ: Kamikaze, Ballantine, 57; If a man die, 64 & The valley of tomorrow (novel), 66, Bookcraft; Old Crackfoot (novel), Obolensky, 65; Dori the mallard (novel), Astor Bks, 68; Lonesome coyote (novel), Lantern, 69; The hungry journey, 73, Starfire (novel), 74 & ed. & auth, Introd, Immortality, 74, Hawkes Publ; auth, A practical religion, Instructor, 6/65; co-auth, For women only, tri-weekly column, Nat. News Syndicate; Fujiyama & Resurrection (poems), In: Japan-theme and variations, Charles E. Tuttle; plus numerous others. Add: Dept. of English, Weber State College, 3800 Harrison Blvd, Ogden, UT 84403.

ALM, RICHARD S, b. Minneapolis, Minn, Aug. 26, 21; m. 48; c. 2. ENGLISH EDUCATION, READING. B.S, Univ. Minn, 42, M.A, 48, Ph.D.(Eng. educ, reading), 54. Instr, univ. high sch, Univ. Minn, 46-48; teacher, high sch, Wash, 49-51; instr. Eng. educ, UNIV. HAWAII, MANOA, 51-54, asst. prof. educ, 54-58, assoc. prof, 58-62, prof, 62-68, dir. reading clin, 55-68, chmn, Curriculum & Instr. Dept, 68-71, CHMN. GRAD. STUD, SEC. EDUC, 68- Vis. lectr, Univ. Colo, summers, 49-52 & 58; Univ. Minn, summer 54; consult, A basic bk. for high schs, 6th ed, Am. Libr. Asn, 55-57; vis. prof. & dir. reading clin, Univ. Wis, summer 62; vis. lectr, Univ. Calif, Berkeley, summer 64; ed, Eng. J, 64-; vis. lectr, Teachers Col, Columbia Univ, summer 65. U.S.A, 42-46, Tech. Sgt. NCTE (dir, 55-57, 59-73); Conf. Res. Eng; Int. Reading Asn. English language arts, especially curriculum, instruction and materials; developmental and remedial reading. Publ: Co-auth, Social understanding through literature, Nat. Counc. Soc. Study, 54; ed, Books for you, Wash. Sq, 64; co-auth, Insights, Encounters, American literature & Western literature, In: Themes and writer ser.(4 vols), Webster Div, McGraw, 67; auth, What is a good unit in English?, In: Teaching English in today's schools, Holt, 70; Causes of reluctance, In: Remedial reading, Allyn & Bacon, 72; Goose flesh and glimpses of glory, In: Teaching reading for human values in high school, Merrill, 72; plus one other. Add: College of Education, University of Hawaii, 1776 University Ave, Honolulu, HI 96822.

ALMON, BERT LYNN, b. Port Arthur, Tex, July 29, 43; m. 65; c. 2. ENGLISH. B.A, Univ. Tex, El Paso, 65; Woodrow Wilson fel. & M.A, Univ. N.Mex, 67; Ph.D.(Eng), 71. ASST. PROF. ENG, UNIV. ALTA, 68- Asn. Can. Univ. Teachers Eng; Johnson Soc. Pac. Northwest. Modern poetry; prosody; North American Indian literature. Publ: The return, San Marcos Press, 68; Keeping sane: four poets, Cafe Solo, 1/69; Gary Snyder and communal art, White Pelican, 2/72. Add: Dept. of English, University of Alberta, Edmonton, Alta. T6G 2G2, Can.

ALPERS, PAUL JOEL, b. Philadelphia, Pa, Oct. 16, 32; m. 58; c. 2. ENGLISH. A.B, Harvard, 53, A.M, 55, Ph.D.(Eng), 59. Instr. ENG, Harvard, 59-61; asst. prof, UNIV. CALIF, BERKELEY, 62-68, assoc. prof, 68-71, PROF, 71- Am. Counc. Learned Soc. grant-in-aid, 61-62, stud. fel, 66-67, fel, 72-73; Univ. Calif. jr. fac. summer fel, 66. Explicator Prize, 68. MLA; Renaissance Soc. Am. Nondramatic poetry of the English Renaissance; pastoral poetry. Publ: The poetry of The faerie queene, Princeton, 67; ed, Elizabethan poetry: modern essays in criticism, Oxford Univ, 67 & Edmund Spenser, Penguin, 70; auth, The Milton controversy, Harvard Eng. Stud, 71; The eclogue tradition and the nature of pastoral, Col. Eng, 72; co-auth, Ut pictura noesis? criticism in literary studies and art history, New Lit. Hist, 72; plus three others. Add: Dept. of English, 322 Wheeler Hall, University of California, Berkeley, CA 94720.

ALSPACH, RUSSELL KING, b. Philadelphia, Pa, Feb. 22, 01; m. 25; c. 2. IRISH LITERATURE. A.B, Univ. Pa, 24, A.M, 31, Ph.D, 32. Mem. fac, Dept. Eng, Univ. Pa, 24-42, 46-47; prof. ENG, U.S. Mil. Acad, 47-65, head dept, 61-65; prof, UNIV. MASS, AMHERST, 65-67, EMER. PROF, 71-, acting head dept, 67-68, head, 68-71. Vis. prof, Grad. Sch. Arts & Sci, Univ. Pa, 62-63; mem, Eng. Inst. U.S.N.R, 42-46, Lt. Comdr; U.S.A, 51-65, Brig. Gen. MLA; Am. Folklore Soc; NCTE. Irish poetry in English; Shakespearean criticism; modern literature. Publ: Irish poetry to 1798, Univ. Pa, 43 & 57; co-auth, Variorum edition of Yeats' poems, 57 & Variorum edition of Yeats's plays, 66, Macmillan; Yeats and Innisfree, Dolmen, 67; ed, Wade's bibliography of Yeats, Hart-Davis, 68. Add: 324 Pomeroy Lane, Amherst, MA 01002.

ALSSID, MICHAEL WILLIAM, b. Buenos Aires, Arg, Aug. 25, 27; U.S. citizen; m. 56; c. 2. ENGLISH LITERATURE. A.B, N.Y. Univ, 51, A.M, 53; Sorbonne, France, 49-50; Ph.D, Syracuse Univ, 59. Asst, N.Y. Univ, 51-53; lectr. & instr, Syracuse Univ, 53-58; instr. ENG, BOSTON UNIV, 59-61, asst. prof, 61-66, assoc. prof, 66-71, PROF, 71- U.S. Maritime Serv, 45-46; U.S.A, 46-47. MLA. Restoration poetry and drama, especially Dryden & Shadwell. Publ: Co-auth, The world of ideas: essays for study, Holt, 64; auth, Thomas Shadwell, Twayne, 67; co-auth, The unity of literature, Addison-Wesley, 68; auth, Dryden's rhymed heroic tragedies: a critical study of the plays and of their place in Dryden's poetry, Univ. Salzburg, 74; The perfect conquest: a study of theme, structure and characters in Dryden's The Indian Emperor, Stud. Philol, 62; The design of Dryden's Aureng-Zebe, J. Eng. & Germanic Philol, 65; Shadwell's MacFlecknoe, Stud. Eng. Lit, 67. Add: Dept. of English, Boston University, Boston, MA 02215.

ALTAFFER, CLARA BELLE, b. Hobart, Okla, Jan. 10, 10; m. 34; c. 1. ENGLISH, SECONDARY EDUCATION. B.A, Bethany Nazarene Col, 31; M.A, Univ. Okla, 43, Ed.D.(sec. educ, Eng), 60. Teacher elem. & high sch, Okla, 31-42 & 46-58; Eng. & math, Poteau Jr. Col, 42-46; PROF. ENG, CENT. STATE UNIV.(OKLA), 58- NEA; NCTE; Conf. Eng. Educ; S.Cent. Mod. Lang. Asn; Am. Asn. Univ. Women. Romantic period of English literature; preparation of teachers of English in the secondary schools. Add: Dept. of English, Central State University, 100 N. University Dr, Edmond, OK 73034.

ALTENBERND, A. LYNN, b. Cleveland, Ohio, Feb. 3, 18; m. 41; c. 3. AMERICAN LITERATURE. B.Sc, Ohio State Univ, 39, M.A, 49, Ph.D.(Eng), 54. Teacher, high sch, Ohio, 42-44; asst. buyer spec. aircraft, U.S. Army Air Force, Wright Field, Ohio, 46-48; asst. ENG, Ohio State Univ, 49-51; instr, 51-54; UNIV. ILL, URBANA, 54-57, asst. prof, 57-61, assoc. prof, 61-65, PROF, 65-, head dept, 66-71. Spec. adv. col. Eng, Macmillan Co, 63- A.U.S, 44-46, 2nd Lt. MLA; NCTE; AAUP. American fiction, 1865-1920; history of ideas; aesthetics of fiction. Publ: Co-auth, Introduction to literature: stories, poems, plays, 63 & 69 & ed, Exploring literature, 70, Macmillan; On Pope's horticultural romanticism, J. Eng. & Ger. Philol, 55; Huck Finn, emancipator, Criticism, 59. Add: Dept. of English, University of Illinois, Urbana, IL 61801.

ALTER, ROBERT, b. Bronx, N.Y, Apr. 2, 35; m. 61, 73; c. 3. ENGLISH LITERATURE. B.A, Columbia Col, 57; Woodrow Wilson fel. & M.A, Harvard, 58, Danforth fel. & Ph.D, 62. Instr. Eng, Columbia Univ, 62-64, asst. prof, 64-67. assoc. prof. HEBREW & COMP. LIT, UNIV. CALIF, BERKELEY, 67-69, PROF, 69-, chmn. dept. comp. lit, 70-72. Guggenheim fel, 66-67; Meier Segals vis. lectr, Sir George Williams Univ, 68; Roland vis. lectr. Jewish stud, Stanford Univ, 71; Nat. Endowment for Humanities sr. fel, 71-72; Harry Kaplan scholar in residence, Ohio State Univ, 72; contrib, ed, Commentary, 73- Eng. Inst. Essay Prize, 65. Am. Comp. Lit. Asn; Asn. Jewish Stud. Modern Hebrew literature; modern novel; 18th century. Publ: Rogue's progress: studies in the picaresque novel, 64 & Fielding and the nature of the novel, 68, Harvard; After the tradition, Dutton, 69; Nabokov and the art of politics, Triquart, winter 70; Literature and crisis, Commentary, 10/71; The modernity of Don Quixote, South. Rev, spring 73. Add: Dept. of Comparative Literature, University of California, Berkeley, CA 94720.

ALTICK, RICHARD DANIEL, b. Lancaster, Pa, Sept. 19, 15; m. 42; c. 2. ENGLISH LITERATURE. A.B, Franklin & Marshall Col, 36, hon. Litt.D, 64; Ph.D, Univ. Pa, 41. Instr. ENG, Franklin & Marshall Col, 41-45; asst. prof, OHIO STATE UNIV, 45-47, assoc. prof, 47-50, prof, 50-68, REGENTS' PROF, 68- Vis. prof, Grad. Sch, N.Y. Univ, 50; Stanford Univ, 56; Am. Counc. Learned Soc. fel, 59-60; consult, Nat. Endowment for Humanities, 70- PEN Club; MLA; Conf. Brit. Stud; Int. Asn. Univ. Prof. Eng. Literary biography; bibliography; 19th century English literature and social history. Publ: The Cowden Clarkes, Oxford, 48; Scholar adventurers, Macmillan, 50; English common reader, 57 & co-auth, Browning's Roman murder story, 68, Univ. Chicago; auth, Art of literary research, 63, To be in England, 69, Victorian studies in scarlet, 70 & Victorian people and ideas, 73, Norton; Lives and letters, Knopf, 65; ed, Carlyle: Past and present, Houghton, 65; & Browning: The ring and the book, Penguin, 71. Add: Dept. of English, Ohio State University, Columbus, OH 43210.

ALTIERI, CHARLES F, b. New York, N.Y, Nov. 11, 42; m. 67; c. 2. ENGLISH. A.B, Le Moyne Col, 64; Ph.D.(Eng), Univ. N.C, Chapel Hill, 69. ASST. PROF. ENG, STATE UNIV. N.Y. BUFFALO, 68- MLA; AAUP. Modern poetry; post Kantian philosophy; 19th century literature. Publ: Northrop Frye and the problem of spiritual authority, PMLA, 72; From symbolist thought to immanence: the logic of post-modernist poetics, Boundary 2, spring 73; The significance of Frank O'Hara, Iowa Rev, spring 73. Add: Dept. of English, State University of New York at Buffalo, Buffalo, NY 14214.

ALTIERI, JOANNE SMITH, b. Worcester, Mass, Feb. 12, 40; m. 66; c. 2. RENAISSANCE DRAMA. A.B, Boston Univ, 62; M.A, Univ. N.C, 64, Ph.D. (Eng), 69. Instr. ENG, Univ. N.C, 67-68; ASST. PROF, CANISIUS COL, 69- MLA; Renaissance Soc. Am. Shakespeare; Renaissance drama. Publ: Style and purpose in M. Edgeworth's fiction, Nineteenth Century Fiction, 12/68; Style and social disorder in Measure for measure, Shakespeare Quart, 74. Add: Dept. of English, Canisius College, Buffalo, NY 14208.

ALWORTH, E. PAUL, b. Cleveland, Okla, Dec. 18, 17; m. 47; c. 1. ENGLISH & AMERICAN LITERATURE. B.A, Univ. Mo, 39, M.A, 40, Ph.D.(Eng), 58. Instr. ENG, Okla. Mil. Acad, 40-42; UNIV. TULSA, 46-48, asst. prof, 48-54, assoc. prof, 54-62, PROF, 62-, chmn. dept, 62-71. U.S.A, 42-46, Capt. MLA; NCTE; S.Cent. Mod. Lang. Asn. Romantic period; American humor; semantics. Publ: Co-auth, A semantics workbook, Feron, 54, Classics in semantics, 65 & Classics in linguistics, 68, Philos. Libr; auth, Semantics as communication, Park Col. Bull, 59; Spenser: theory of nature, Monogr. Ser, 67. Add: Dept. of English, University of Tulsa, Tulsa, OK 74104.

ALY, BOWER, b. Crystal City, Mo, Feb. 20, 03. RHETORIC, PUBLIC ADDRESS. B.S, Southeast Mo. State Col, 25; A.M, Univ. Mo-Columbia, 26, hon. L.H.D, 73; Univ. Calif, 29; scholar, Columbia Univ, 37-38, Ph.D, 41. Prof. Eng, Southeast Mo. State Col, 26-30; instr, Univ. Mo, 30-35, asst. prof, 35-39, assoc. prof. SPEECH, 39-41, prof, 41-57; UNIV. ORE, 57-73, EMER. PROF, 73- Speech Commun. Asn.(v.pres, 43, pres, 44, ed, Quart. J. Speech, 51-53); West Speech Commun. Asn. History and criticism of American oratory; rhetoric of Alexander Hamilton; public speaking. Publ: The rhetoric of Alexander Hamilton, 41, co-auth, The fundamentals of speaking, 63 & co-ed, American short speeches, 68, Macmillan; ed, Alexander Hamilton: essays, Lib. Arts, 57 & co-ed, Speeches in English, Random, 68; co-auth, A rhetoric of public speaking, McGraw, 73; auth, Alexander Hamilton, In: The history and criticism of American public address, Longmans, Vol. III, 54. Add: 1138 22nd Ave. E, Eugene, OR 97403.

ALY, LUCILE F, b. Kansas City, Mo, July 31, 13; m. 43; c. 6. ENGLISH. B.S, Univ. Mo, Columbia, 35, Ph.D.(speech, rhetoric), 59; M.A, Columbia Univ, 42. Teacher high sch, Mo, 36-41; univ. lab. sch, Columbia, Mo, 42-43; instr. ENG, Univ. Mo, 45-58; UNIV. ORE, 60-63, asst. prof, 63-71, ASSOC. PROF, 71- Instr. speech, Univ. Hawaii, summer 55; consult, NDEA Ore. Curriculum Stud. proj. Eng, 64-67. MLA; NCTE; Speech Commun. Asn. John G. Neihardt life and work; George Meredith life and work; rhetoric, metaphor enthymeme. Publ: Co-auth, Speeches in English, Random, 68 & American short speeches, Macmillan, 68; auth, The word sender; John G. Neihardt and his audiences, Quart. J. Speech, 4/57; John G. Neihardt, poet of the west, Focus/Midwest, 2/64; John G. Neihardt and rhetorical poetry, In: Rhetoric of the people, Rodop, Amsterdam. Add: Dept. of English, University of Oregon, Eugene, OR 97403.

AMABILE, GEORGE N, b. Jersey City, N.J. CREATIVE WRITING, CONTEMPORARY POETRY. A.B, Amherst Col, 57; M.A, Univ. Minn, 61; Ph.D. (Eng), Univ. Conn, 69. Lectr. Eng, Univ. Man, 63-65, asst. prof, 66-69; vis. writer in residence, Univ. B.C, 69-70; ASSOC. PROF. ENG, UNIV. MAN, 70- Asn. Can. Univ. Teachers Eng; MLA; Can. Asn. Univ. Teachers. Poetic theory; Blake; 20th century literature. Publ: Ed, The far point, Univ. Man, bi-annually, 68-; auth, Blood ties, Sono Nis Press, 72; contrib, numerous journals & poetry anthologies. Add: Dept. of English, University of Manitoba, Winnipeg, Man, Can.

AMACHER, RICHARD EARL, b. Ridgway, Pa, Dec. 13, 17; m. 53. AMERICAN LITERATURE. A.B, Ohio Univ, 39; Univ. Chicago, 39-42; Ph.D, Univ. Pittsburgh, 47. Instr. ENG, Carnegie Inst. Technol, 44: Yale, 44-45; Rensselaer Polytech. Inst, 45; Rutgers Univ, 45-47, asst. prof, 47-54; prof. & chmn. dept, Henderson State Teachers Col, 54-57; assoc. prof, AUBURN UNIV, 57-65, PROF, 65- Fulbright prof. Am. lit, Univ. Wurzburg, 61-62; Univ. Konstanz, 69-70; Am. Counc. Learned Soc. grant, 71-72. S.Atlantic Mod. Lang. Asn; AAUP; Am. Lit. Group, MLA; Am. Stud. Asn. Literary criticism. Publ: Franklin's wit and folly, Rutgers, 53; Practical criticism Henderson State Col, 56; Benjamin Franklin, Twayne, 62; Edward Albee, Twayne, 68, Span. transl, Fabril Ed, Buenos Aires, 72; co-auth, Edward Albee at home and abroad, AMS Press, 73 & J.G. Baldwin's the flush times of California, Univ. Ga. Monogr, 66; auth, A new Franklin satire?, Early Am. Lit, fall 72. Add: Dept. of English, Auburn University, Auburn, AL 36830.

AMATO, PHILIP P, b. Boston, Mass, Sept. 23, 35; m. 66. EUDCATION, SPEECH. A.B, Emerson Col, 60, M.A, 61; Ph.D.(speech), Mich. State Univ, 63. Asst.prof. educ. & speech, EMERSON COL, 63-66, assoc. prof, 66-68, PROF. EDUC. & CHMN. DEPT, 69- Consult. & book reviewer, Choice: Books for Col. Libr, 65-; consult, Nat. Educr. Prog. Asn. Speech Commun. Asn; East. Commun. Asn.(1st v.pres, pres. elect, 73-74); Programmed instruction and automated learning; public speaking. Publ: A comparative study of programed instruction and videotaped lectures in public speaking, Speech Monogr, 11/64; P.I. and speech—part I: history, principles and theories of programed instruction, Today's Speech, 11/65; co-auth, The effect of audience feedback on the beginning public speaker, Speech Teacher, 1/67. Add: Dept. of Education, Emerson College, 148 Beacon St, Boston, MA 02116.

AMBERG, GEORGE H, b. Halle, Ger, Dec. 28, 01; m. 43. ART. Ph.D, Univ. Cologne, 29. Cur, N.Y. Mus. Mod. Art, 43-48; lectr. art, N.Y. Univ, 47-52; prof, Univ. Minn, 52-66, dir, La. Story Film Stud. Proj, 60-63; PROF. FILM & DIR. GRAD. PROG. CINEMA, N.Y. UNIV, 66- Mem, Am. Fed. Film Soc; trustee, Int. Film Seminars, Inc. Col. Art Asn. Am; Am. Soc. Aesthet; Am. Soc. Theatre Res; Soc. Cinematologists (pres, 68); Brit. Film Inst; Benjamin Franklin fel. Royal Soc. Arts. Film; theater; visual perception. Publ: Art in modern ballet, Pantheon, 46; The theatre of Eugene Berman, Mus. Mod. Art, 47; Ballet in America, Duell, Sloan & Pearce, 49 & New Am. Libr, 50; The ambivalence of realism, Wesleyan Univ, 60; The rationale of the irrational, Minn. Rev, 63; Pop avant-garde, Arts & Soc, 65. Add: Dept. of Cinema, Graduate School, New York University, New York, NY 10003.

AMBLE, KJELL, b. Sarpsborg, Norway, Feb. 26, 28; m. 61; c. 3. DRAMA. B.A, Denison Univ, 54; M.A, Northwest. Univ, 60; Ph.D.(theatre), 64. From asst. to assoc. prof. THEATRE, SAN DIEGO STATE UNIV, 62-69, PROF, 69- Supply C, Norwegian Army, 48-49. Am. Educ. Theatre Asn; Speech Commun. Asn. Directing; acting; translation. Publ: Transl, The master builder by Henrik Ibsen, Chandler, 68. Add: Dept. of Drama, San Diego State University, San Diego, CA 92115.

AMBRESTER, MARCUS LaROY, b. Scottsboro, Ala, Oct. 21, 35; m. 56; c. 2. ORAL COMMUNICATION. B.A, Samford Univ, 56; M.A, Univ. Ala, 59; Ph.D.(rhetorical theory), Ohio Univ, 72. Asst. prof. debate & debate dir, Montevallo Univ, 61-62; asst. prof. readers theatre & debate dir, Samford Univ, 62-66; Univ. South. Ala, 67-68; Ouachita Univ, 68-70; Miss. State Col. Women, 70-71; PROF. ORAL COMMUN. & CHMN. DEPT, HOWARD PAYNE COL, 71- Speech Commun. Asn; South. Speech Commun. Asn; Cent. State Speech Commun. Asn. Rhetorical theory; interpretation theory; phenomenological communication theory. Publ: Co-auth, The effect of the complement in persuasive communication, Ohio Speech J, spring 66; auth, Project Camelot, Ohio Univ, Publ, summer 71; Identification within: Kenneth Burke's view of the unconscious, Philos. & Rhet, 74. Add: Dept. of Oral Communication, Howard Payne College, Austin Ave, Brownwood, TX 76801.

AMEND, VICTOR EARL, b. Kans, Oct. 14, 16; m. 46; c. 2. ENGLISH. A.B, Univ. Kans, 39, M.A, 42; fel. & Ph.D.(Eng), Univ. Mich, 53. Teacher, pub. schs, Kans, 40-41; instr. ENG, Knox Col, 52-53; asst. prof, BUTLER UNIV, 53-57, assoc. prof, 57-69, PROF, 69- U.S.A, 42-46. NCTE; MLA. Modern drama and fiction. Publ: Co-ed, Ten contemporary thinkers, 64 & Readings from left to right, 69, Free Press. Add: Dept. of English, Butler University, Indianapolis, IN 46208.

AMES, KENNETH JOHN, b. Wakefield, Eng, Aug. 1, 25; U.S. citizen. ENGLISH. B.A, Univ. London, 45; A.L.A, Libr. Asn, Eng, 50; NDEA fel, Univ. South. Calif, 62-65, M.A, 63, Ph.D.(Eng), 67. Head librn, Pub. Libr, Normanton, Eng, 50-55; sr. librn, Akron Pub. Libr, Ohio, 55-56; librn. & cur, Hudson Libr. & Hist. Soc, 58-60; head dept, Col. Libr, Calif. State Univ, Los Angeles, 60-62; lectr. ENG, Univ. South. Calif, 65-66; Univ. Calif, Los Angeles, 66-68; asst. prof, CALIF. STATE UNIV, LONG BEACH, 68-73, ASSOC. PROF, '73- Seventeenth century English literature; 20th century fiction and poetry. Publ: Elements of mock heroic in Virginia Woolf's Mrs. Dalloway, Mod. Fiction Stud, autumn 72. Add: Dept. of English, California State University, Long Beach, 6101 E. Seventh St, Long Beach, CA 90840.

AMOR, EDWARD, b. Brooklyn, N.Y, Dec. 13, 33. DRAMA. A.B, Univ. Fla, 55; M.A, Ind. Univ, 60, Ph.D.(drama), 66. Instr. speech & drama, Russell Sage Col, 61-64; asst. prof. drama, UNIV. WIS-MADISON, 65-69, ASSOC. PROF. THEATRE & DRAMA, 69- Lectr. drama, Univ. Wyo, summer 62. Am. Theatre Asn. Dramatic literature; stage production. Add: Dept. of Theatre & Drama, University of Wisconsin, Madison, WI 53706.

AMOS, GEORGE, b. Montgomery, Ala, Aug. 23, 37. ENGLISH. B.A, Ark. State Col, 59; M.A, Univ. Ark, 60, Ph.D.(Eng), 68; Univ. Kiel, 64-65. Instr. ENG, Ark. State Teachers Col, 60-63, asst. prof, 63-68; La. Polytech. Inst, 68-70; PROF. & CHMN. DEPT, LA. COL, 70- Teaching asst, Univ. Ark, 59-60 & 63-64. MLA; NCTE. Add: Box 827, Louisiana College, Pineville, LA 71360.

ANAPOL, MALTHON M, b. Atlantic City, N.J, Nov. 15, 26; m. 49; c. 3. SPEECH, COMMUNICATION. B.S, Rutgers Univ, 49; M.A, Temple Univ, 53; Ph.D.(speech), Ohio State Univ, 63; Univ. Conn, 67-68. Instr. speech & debate, W.Va. Univ, 52-55; speech, Denison Univ, 55-57; dir. forensics speech, Univ. Md, 57-61; dir. forensics speech & commun, Univ. Pa, 61-64; assoc. prof. speech, Univ. Hartford, 64-69; ASSOC. PROF. & DIR. GRAD. STUD. SPEECH-COMMUN, UNIV. DEL, 69- Vincent Coffin fac. res. grant, 67-68; assoc. ed, Speaker & Gavel, 70-72; Univ. Del. res. grant, 72-74. Speech Commun. Asn; Am. Forensic Asn.(assoc. ed, Register, 57-59); Int. Commun. Asn; Law & Soc. Asn; Tri-State Speech Asn.(pres, 71-73). Research in graduate study in speech; communication and law & legal aspects of communication; mass communication: audiences and effects. Publ: Auth, Rhetoric and law: an overview, Today's Speech, 11/70; Graduate study in speech, Speech Teacher, 1/73; Communication, law, and justice, Educ. Resources Inform. Ctr. Speech Commun. Module, 3/73; plus several others. Add: Dept. of Speech Communication, University of Delaware, 203 Elliot Hall, Newark, DE 19711.

ANCKER, SIDNEY LOUIS, b. San Francisco, Calif, Dec. 23, 12; m. 47. ENGLISH, HUMANITIES. A.B, Univ. Calif, Berkeley, 34, M.A, 37; Ed.D, Stanford Univ, 54. Teaching asst, Univ. Calif, Berkeley, 36-37; teacher, high sch, Calif, 38-41; INSTR. ENG. & HUMANITIES, CITY COL. SAN FRANCISCO, 46- U.S.A, 41-43; U.S.A.F, 43-45. NCTE. Implications of experimentalist philosophy for teaching of college English; courses in humanities that cut across department lines. Add: 234 Currey Lane, Sausalito, CA 94965.

ANDEREGG, MICHAEL ALAIN, b. Paris, France, Nov. 19, 42; U.S. citizen; m. 73. ENGLISH LITERATURE, FILM HISTORY. B.A, Univ. Calif, Los Angeles, 68; Ph.D.(Eng), Yale, 72. ASST. PROF. ENG, UNIV. N.DAK, 72- MLA. Prose and poetry of the Tudor period; biography as a literary form; Thomas More. Publ: Utopia and early More biography: another view, 2/72 & The anecdotal tradition of Thomas More: a note, 9/72, Moreana. Add: Dept. of English, University of North Dakota, Grand Forks, ND 58201.

ANDERSEN, KENNETH ELDON, b. Harlan, Iowa, Dec. 28, 33. PUBLIC ADDRESS, RHETORIC. B.A, Univ. North. Iowa, 54, M.A, 55; Knapp fel, Univ. Wis, 60-61, Ph.D.(speech), 61. Instr. speech, Univ. Colo, 55-56, Univ. Mich, 61-63, asst. prof, 63-67, assoc. prof, 67-70; UNIV. ILL, URBANA, 70-73, PROF. SPEECH COMMUN, 73-, ASSOC. HEAD DEPT, 70- Instr. speech, N.Mex. State Univ, 57-58; Iowa State Teachers Col. Merchant scholar. advan. stud, 58-59; teaching asst, Univ. Wis, 58-60; vis. assoc. prof, Univ. South. Calif, 68. U.S.A, 56-58. Speech Commun. Asn; Am. Forensic Asn; Cent. States Speech Asn.(award, 62, exec. secy, 69-72, v.pres, 72-73, pres. elect, 73-74, pres, 74-75); AAUP; Int. Commun. Asn; Am. Asn. Pub. Opinion Res. Experimental persuasion; ethos; communication theory. Publ: Co-auth, Speech communication: analysis and readings, 68 & auth, Persuasion theory and practice, 71, Allyn & Bacon; Introduction to communication theory and practice, Cummings Publ, 72; A summary of experimental research in ethos, Speech Monogr, 6/63; plus others. Add: Dept. of Speech Communication, 244 Lincoln Hall, University of Illinois, Urbana, IL 61801.

ANDERSEN, MARTIN PERRY, b. Minneapolis, Minn, Aug. 22, 04; m. 39; c. 2. SPEECH. A.B, Univ. Wis, 28, A.M, 36, Ph.D, 47. Instr. speech & rural sociol, Univ. Wis, 35-43, asst. prof, 46-47, exten. group discussion specialist, 35-47; asst. prof. speech & head dept. confs. & spec. activities, Univ. Calif, Los Angeles, 47-53, assoc. prof. SPEECH, 53-59, prof, 59-65; CALIF. STATE UNIV, FULLERTON, 65-70, EMER. PROF. SPEECH COMMUN, 70- Consult. discussion methods, Great Lakes Regional Soil Conserv. Serv. Conf, 43; West. States Am. Hosp. Asn. & U.S. Pub. Health Serv. Conf, 47; UN Conf, San Francisco, 48; ed. consult, indust. & community orgns, South. Calif, 47-; mem. staff, West. Training Lab. Group Develop, Idyllwild, Calif, 52-55; Fund Adult Educ. scholar, Teachers Col, Columbia Univ, 54-55; consult. commun. & conf. methods, Credit Unions, Calif, 60-68; commun. consult, Syst. Develop. Corp, Calif, 63-65; dir, NDEA Inst. Speech, summer, 68. U.S.N.R, 43-46, Res, 48-58, Lt. Comdr. Speech Commun. Asn; Nat. Soc. Stud. Commun; West. Speech Asn. Historical and current applications of discussion methodology to group work, social action, teaching, and scientific problem solving; techniques for implementing adult education in a democracy. Publ: Co-auth, Understanding and being understood & Discussion: a guide to effective practice, Wadsworth, 63, 70; The speaker and his audience, Harper, 64, 74; Visual aids handbook, Syst. Develop. Corp, Calif, 66; From thought to speech, Heath, 69; auth, Discussion in agriculture, Quart. J. Speech; A mid-century survey of books on communication, J. Commun, 64; A model of group discussion, South. Speech J, 65. Add: Dept. of Speech Communication, California State University, Fullerton, 800 N. State College Blvd, Fullerton, CA 92631.

ANDERSON, A. EDWIN, b. Mayfield, Ky, Dec. 15, 05; m. 68; c. 3. LITERATURE, LANGUAGE. A.B, Vanderbilt Univ, 28, M.A, 29, Ph.D, 53; M.A, George Peabody Col, 34; Harvard, 32-33; Univ. Munich, Ger, 37-38. Instr. Eng. & Ger, Jr. Col. Augusta, 34-42; PROF. ENG. & WORLD LIT, GEORGE PEABODY COL, 45-, acting chmn. dept. Eng, 67-68, chmn. dept, 68-72. Fund Advan. Educ. study grant humanities, 51-52; South. Regional Educ. Bd. humanities study proj, 59-60. NCTE; Col. Eng. Asn. Humanities in higher education; comparative and world literature; English language and literature. Publ: The humanities in the colleges and universities of the South, South. Regional Educ. Bd, 61. Add: 718 Westview Ave, Nashville, TN 37205.

ANDERSON, CARL LENNART, b. Philadelphia, Pa, Dec. 3, 19; m. 52; c. 2. ENGLISH. A.B, Univ. Pa, 48, Harrison fel, 50-51, M.A, 51, Ph.D.(Eng), 55; exchange scholar, Univ. Uppsala, 49-50. Instr. ENG, Norwich Univ, 51-54; asst. prof, 54-55; instr, DUKE UNIV, 55-57, asst. prof, 57-64, assoc. prof, 64-71, PROF, 71-, chmn. acad. counc, 73-75. Fulbright lectr, Univ. Oslo, 61-62; Am. Philos. Soc. res. grant, Scand, 63; vis. prof, Wake Forest Univ, summer 65; Am-Scand. Found. Bernadotte fel, 68-69. U.S.N.R, 44-46. MLA; Am. Stud. Asn; Soc. Advan. Scand. Stud; S.Atlantic Mod. Lang. Asn. American literature, comparative literature. Publ: Swedish acceptance of American literature, Univ. Pa, 57; transl, Knut Hamsun's, On overgrown paths, Eriksson, 67; auth, Poe in Northlight: the Scandinavian response to his life and work, Duke Univ, 73; Fredrika Bremer's Spirit of the new world, New Eng. Quart, 6/65; Strindberg's translations of American humor, Am. Norvegica III, Universitetsforlaget (Oslo), 71. Add: Dept. of English, Duke University, Durham, NC 27706.

ANDERSON, CHARLES ROBERTS, b. Macon, Ga, Oct. 17, 02; m. 63. AMERICAN & ENGLISH LITERATURE. A.B, Univ. Ga, 24, A.M, 28; Mercer Univ, 24-26; Ph.D.(Eng), Columbia Univ, 36. Instr. Eng, Univ. Ga, 27-30; Duke Univ, 30-35, asst. prof, 35-39, assoc. prof, 39-41; Johns Hopkins Univ, 41-46, prof, 46-56, Caroline Donovan prof, 56-69, chmn. dept, 50-56; RETIRED. Managing ed, Am. Lit, 32-33; Rosenwald fel, 38-39; lectr, Carolina Poetry Soc, 40 & 42; assoc. ed, Mod. Lang. Notes, 42-62; Am. Philos. Soc. res. scholar, 43; Barrow Ser. lectr, Univ. Ga, 47; vis. prof, Univ. Heidelberg, 49; res. scholar, Huntington Libr, 50, fel, summer 52; Fulbright lectr, Univ. Rome, 52-53; Nagano Seminar, Japan, 54; Univ. Turin, 60; Guggenheim fel, 65-66; Dept. State vis. lectr, Japan & Southeast Asia, 65-66; vis. prof, Kyoto Univ, summer 69; vis. prof. Am. lit, Yugoslavia, 72. Christian Gauss Bk. Award, Nat. Phi Beta Kappa, 61. Fel. Soc. Am. Stud; MLA; Melville Soc.(pres, 46); Thoreau Soc.(pres-elect, 69). American autobiography; 19th and 20th century American literature; Henry James. Publ: Ed, Journal of a cruise in the frigate United States with notes on Melville, Duke Univ, 37; auth, Melville in the South Seas, Columbia Univ, 39; gen. ed, Centennial edition of Sidney Lanier (10 vols), 46 & ed, Selected poetry and prose of Sidney Lanier, 69, Johns Hopkins; auth, Emily Dickinson's poetry: stairway of surprise, Holt, 60 & Heinemann, 63; gen. ed, American literary masters (2 vols), 65 & auth, The magic circle of Walden, 68, Holt; ed, Thoreau's world: miniatures from his journal, 71 & Thoreau's vision: the major essays, 73, Prentice-Hall; auth, Hayne and Gayerré: the last literary cavaliers, In: Studies in honor of W.K. Boyd, Duke Univ, 40; Wit and metaphor in Walden, In: USA in focus, Oslo, 65; James' Portrait of a lady, In: Studies in honor of Jay Hubbell, Duke Univ, 67; plus others. Add: 4 Legare St, Charleston, SC 29401.

ANDERSON, CHESTER GRANT, b. River Falls, Wis, Dec. 8, 23; m. 45; c. 3. ENGLISH. M.A, Univ. Chicago, 48; Ph.D, Columbia Univ, 62. Instr, Creighton Univ, 48-50, asst. prof. ENG, 54-57; lectr, Fordham Univ, 51-52; assoc. prof, Danbury State Col, 57-63; asst. prof, Columbia Univ, 64-68; PROF, UNIV. MINN, MINNEAPOLIS, 68- Fulbright lectr, Univ. Helsinki, 63-64. U.S.N, 42-45. MLA. James Joyce. Publ: Word index to Stephen Hero, Ridgebury Press; James Joyce and his world, Thames & Hudson & Viking, 67; ed, James Joyce, A portrait of the artist as a young man, Viking Critical Libr, 68; auth, On the sublime and its anal origins in Pope, Eliot and Joyce, In: Modern Irish literature, Iona Col. & Twayne, 72; Leopold Bloom as Dr. Sigmund Freud, Mosaic, fall 72; The sacrificial butter, Accent; plus one other. Add: Dept. of English, University of Minnesota, Minneapolis, MN 55455.

ANDERSON, COLENA MICHAEL, b. Buffalo, N.Y, May 30, 91; wid; c. 3. ENGLISH. A.B, Cornell Univ, 14; A.M, Univ. Chicago, 17; Columbia Univ; Honnold scholar, Claremont Grad. Sch, 45, Ph.D, 54. Teacher, high sch, N.Y, 14-16; Shanghai Univ, China, 17-19; Eng, Shanghai-Am. Sch, China, 28-29, 31-32; assoc. prof. ENG. & HIST, LINFIELD COL, 46-58, EMER. ASSOC. PROF, 58- Far East studies; study of two contemporary Chinese women writers, Ping Hsin, Ting Ling. Publ: Handbook for Christian writers. 66, Don't put on your slippers yet, 71, 72 & 73 & Joy beyond grief, 74, Zondervan. Add: 345 S. Baker St, McMinnville, OR 97128.

ANDERSON, DAVID DANIEL, b. Lorain, Ohio, June 8, 24; m. 53. AMERICAN & SOUTH ASIAN LITERATURE. B.S, Bowling Green State Univ, 51, M.A, 52; Ph.D.(Am. lit), Mich. State Univ, 60. From instr. to PROF. AM. THOUGHT & LANG, MICH. STATE UNIV, 56- Fulbright lectr, Univ. Karachi, Pakistan, 63-64; Am. del, Int. Fed. Mod. Lang. & Lit, 69-; Int. Congr. Orient, 73-; sr. instr, Gen. Motors Inst. U.S.N, 42-45; U.S.A, 52-53, 1st. Lt; Silver Star. MLA; Midwest Mod. Lang. Asn; AAUP; Soc. Stud. Midwest. Lit.(founder; pres, 71-73). Modern American fiction; South Asian literature and culture; American studies. Publ: Critical studies in American literature, Univ. Karachi, 64; Louis Bromfield, 64, Brand Whitlock, 68, Abraham Lincoln, 70 & Robert Ingersoll, 72, Twayne; Sherwood Anderson, Holt, 67. Add: Dept. of American Thought & Language, Michigan State University, East Lansing, MI 48824.

ANDERSON, DONALD K, JR, b. Evanston, Ill, Mar. 18, 22; m. 49; c. 2. ENGLISH. A.B, Yale, 43; M.A, Northwest. Univ, 47; Ph.D.(Eng), Duke Univ, 57. Instr. ENG, Geneva Col, 47-49; Rose Polytech. Inst, 52-53, asst. prof, 53-57, assoc. prof, 57-58; asst. prof, Butler Univ, 58-62, assoc. prof, 62-65; UNIV. MO-COLUMBIA, 65-67, PROF, 67-, ASSOC. DEAN GRAD. SCH, 70- Folger Shakespeare Libr. summer grant, 65. U.S.N.R, 43-46, Lt.(jg). MLA; Malone Soc. Elizabethan drama; Shakespeare. Publ: Ed, Ford's Perkin Warbeck, 65 & Ford's The broken heart, 68, Univ. Nebr; auth, John Ford, Twayne, 72; Kingship in Ford's Perkin Warbeck, ELH, 9/60; The banquet of love in English drama, 1595-1642, JEGP, 7/64; Donne's Hymne to God my God, in my sicknesse and the T-in-O maps, S.Atlantic Quart, autumn 72. Add: 1309 Ridge Rd, Columbia, MO 65201.

ANDERSON, DOROTHY IOLA, b. North Liberty, Iowa, Dec. 21, 07. SPEECH. A.B, State Univ. Iowa, 28, A.M, 31, Ph.D, 44. Supvr. speech correction, Green Bay, Wis. 31-36; instr, Univ. Ill, 36-41, 42-43; asst. prof, UNIV. COLO, BOULDER, 45-49, assoc. prof. Eng. & speech, 49-72, prof. COMMUN, 72-73, EMER. PROF, 73- Am. Speech & Hearing Asn; Speech Commun. Asn. History of rhetorical theory. Publ: Ed. & introd, Lectures read to the seniors in Harvard College, South. Ill. Univ, 68; auth, Edward T. Channing's definition of rhetoric & Edward T. Channing's teaching of rhetoric, Speech Monogr; The public speeches of Justice Oliver Wendell Holmes, In: American public address, Univ. Mo, 61. Add: Dept. of Communications, University of Colorado, Boulder, CO 80302.

ANDERSON, EDWARD L, b. Tryon, N.C, June 12, 14; m. 63. ENGLISH. B.A, Univ. Mich, 39, M.A, 40; Ph.D.(Eng. educ), N.Y. Univ, 50. Instr. ENG, N.Y. Univ, 45-52; Brooklyn Col, 52-55; test specialist, Educ. Testing Serv, 55-58; prof. & chmn. dept, Mansfield State Col, 62-66; PROF, INDIANA UNIV. PA, 66- Creative writing; linguistics. Publ: Co-auth, Your English, book three, McGraw, 56; auth, The nature of our grammar, Col. Eng, 6/55; Literary censorship past and present, PCTE Bull, 2/68. Add: Dept. of English, Indiana University of Pennsylvania, Indiana, PA 15701.

ANDERSON, EWING, b. Tallahassee, Fla, Dec. 27, 04; m. 38. ENGLISH LANGUAGE & LITERATURE. A.B, Univ. Fla, 25; scholar, Duke, 28-31, A.M, 29, summers, Univ. Fla, 26, 27, Univ. Mich, 37. Teacher, high schs, Fla, 25-28, 33-37; asst, Duke Univ, 28-31, instr, 32; head dept, Palm Beach Jr. Col, 33-37; instr, Ala. Polytech. Inst, 37-41; asst. prof, Ga. Inst. Technol, 41-44; instr. Ore. State Col, 44-45; asst. prof, Wofford Col, 46; ENG, UNIV. MIAMI, 46-70, EMER. ASST. PROF, 70- S.Atlantic Mod. Lang. Asn; Int. Soc. Gen. Semantics. American literature; personal relations of Whitman and Emerson. Add: 809 W. Christina Lane, Port Richey, FL 33568.

ANDERSON, FRANK W, JR, American Literature. See Volume I, History.

ANDERSON, FREEMAN BURKET, b. Washington, D.C, May 30, 22; div. ENGLISH. A.B, Bucknell Univ, 48; Ph.D.(Eng. philol), Stanford Univ, 52. Asst. ed, etymology, G. & C. Merriam Co, Mass, 52-53, 57; vis. prof. ENG, N.Mex. Highlands Univ, 54; asst. prof, Col. Puget Sound, 55-56; instr, PORTLAND STATE UNIV, 56-59, asst. prof, 59-63, assoc. prof, 63-69, PROF, 69- Mem, Metrop. Youth Comn, 62-71, v.chmn, 69-70; vis. prof, Reed Col, 63-66; instr. ling, NDEA Inst, East. Ore. Col, summer 65; consult. ling, Off. Econ. Opportunity pre-sch. project, Portland, 65-66; dir. & instr, ESEA Inst, Hermiston, 66; mem, Ore. Teacher Standards & Practices Comn, 66-69, chmn, 68; mem. educ. policies comn, Ore. Educ. Asn, 66-69; mem, Ore. Bd. Educ. Lang. Arts Norm. Rev. Comt, 71. U.S.A.A.F, 41-45. NCTE; Conf. Col. Compos. & Commun; Am. Asn. Col. Teachers Educ.(univ. rep, 71-). Middle English, language and literature; modern American English linguistics; preparation of teachers of English. Publ: Co-auth, New directions in English, Harper, 69. Add: 4405 S.W. Condor, Portland, OR 97201.

ANDERSON, GEORGE KUMLER, b. Springfield, Ill, Oct. 20, 01; m. 33; c. 2. ENGLISH LITERATURE. A.B, Harvard, 20, A.M, 21, Ph.D, 25; hon. Litt.D, Middlebury Col, 66; hon. L.H.D, R.I. Col, 73. Instr. ENG, George Washington Univ, 24-27; asst. prof, BROWN UNIV, 27-30, assoc. prof, 30-47, PROF, 47-, chmn. dept, 50-60. Vis. prof, Bread Loaf Sch, Middlebury Col, Eng, 31-; Guggenheim fel, 45. MLA; Mediaeval Acad. Am; Ling. Soc. Am; Renaissance Soc. Am; Col. Eng. Asn.(pres, New Eng. br, 67-68). Medieval literature; 19th century English literature; Germanic linguistics. Publ: This generation, 38 & 49, co-auth, The world in literature, 49, 57, 59 & 63 & auth, The literature of England (2 vols), 36, 41, 47, 53, 58 & 66, Scott; English literature, beginnings to 1485, Oxford, 50 & Collier, 62; The legend of the wandering Jew, Brown Univ, 65; The literature of the Anglo-Saxons, Princeton, 49 & 66; The first 50 years: a history of the Bread Loaf School of English, Middlebury Col, 69; Old English, In: The medieval literatures of western Europe, N.Y. Univ, 66. Add: Dept. of English, Brown University, Providence, RI 02912.

ANDERSON, GEORGE LINCOLN, b. Palmyra, N.J, Apr. 21, 20; m. 69. ENGLISH, COMPARATIVE LITERATURE. A.B, Univ. Pa, 46, M.A, 48, Ph.D, 53. Instr. Eng, Univ. Md, 48-53; from asst. prof. to assoc. prof. ENG, N.Y. Univ, 55-67; PROF, UNIV. HAWAII, MANOA, 67- Ed, Lit. East & West, 54-63; Fund Advan. Educ. fel, 54-55; Fulbright lectr, Kanazawa Univ, Japan, 61-62. MLA (assoc. exec. secy. & treas, 63-67); Am. Soc. 18th Century Stud; Asn. Asian Stud; Asia Soc; Japan Soc; Mod. Humanities Res. Asn. Eighteenth century English literature; drama; Oriental-Western literary relations. Publ: Co-ed. & co-auth, Papers of the Indiana conference on Oriental-Western literary relations; ed, Masterpieces of the Orient & Genius of the Asian theater. Add: 2533 Malama Pl, Honolulu, HI 96822.

ANDERSON, (WILLIAM) HILTON, b. Rembert, S.C, Mar. 22, 32; m. 59; c. 1. ENGLISH. A.B, Wofford Col, 54; M.A, Univ. S.C, 62, Ph.D.(Eng), 66. Instr. ENG, Hampden-Sydney Col, 62-64; asst. prof, UNIV. SOUTH. MISS, 66-69, ASSOC. PROF, 69- Ed, Notes on Mississippi Writers, 68- Intel.C, U.S.A, 54-56. Am. Stud. Asn; S.Atlantic Mod. Lang. Asn; Soc. Stud. South. Lit. Modern American literature. Publ: Americans in Europe before the Civil War, 4/67 & The rich bunch in The great Gatsby, 1/68, South. Quart. Add: Dept. of English, Box 433, Southern Station, University of Southern Mississippi, Hattiesburg, MS 39401.

ANDERSON, HOWARD PETER, b. Duluth, Minn, Dec. 10, 32; m. 59; c. 3. ENGLISH. B.B.A, Univ. Minn, 55, M.A, 60, Ph.D.(Eng), 64. Lectr. ENG, Ind. Univ, 63-64, asst. prof, 64-68; assoc. prof, MICH. STATE UNIV, 68-71, PROF, 71- U.S.A, 55-57. MLA. Eighteenth century literature. Publ: Co-ed, The familiar letter in the 18th century, Univ. Kans, 66 & Studies in criticism and aesthetics 1660-1800, Univ. Minn, 67; ed, The monk, Oxford, 73; auth, Associationism and wit in Tristram Shandy, 1/69 & Answers to the author of Clarissa: theme and narrative technique in Tom Jones and Tristram Shandy, 4/72, Philos. Quart; Tristram Shandy and the reader's imagination, PMLA, 10/71. Add: Dept. of English, Michigan State University, East Lansing, MI 48823.

ANDERSON, HURST ROBINS, b. Cleveland, Ohio, Sept. 16, 04; m. 32; c. 3. SPEECH. A.B, Ohio Wesleyan Univ, 26, hon. LL.D, 49; Univ. Mich, 27-28; M.A, Northwest. Univ, 34; Gen. Educ. Bd. fel, 40-41; hon. L.H.D, W.Va. Wesleyan Col, 55, DePauw Univ, 63, Nebr. Wesleyan Univ, 66; hon. LL.D, Birmingham-South Col, 56, Albright Col, 65; hon. Litt.D, Simpson Col, 58; hon. Ed.D, Univ. Chattanooga, 60; hon. D.P.S, Ohio North. Univ, 66. Instr. Eng. & debate, Allegheny Col, 28-31, asst. prof, 31-39, assoc. prof, 39-40, prof. speech, registr, admin. coord. & dean summer sessions, 40-43; pres, Centenary Jr. Col, 43-48; Hamline Univ, 48-52; AM. UNIV.(D.C), 52-68, HON. CHANCELLOR, 68- Trustee, China Int. Found, Inc, 54-; chmn. adv.

corrections counc, U.S. Dept. Justice, 55; chmn. comt. profess. staffing, White House Conf. Educ, 56; v.chmn. & mem. bd. for. scholar, U.S. Dept. State, 58-62; mem. dist. selections comt, Rhodes Scholar. Trust, 59-61; v.chmn. & mem. exec. comt, White House Conf. Children & Youth, 60; mem. President's Adv. Comt, Inst. Int. Educ, 61-; mem, Am. Counc. Educ; Sino-Am. Cult. Comt. Asn. Am. Col.(treas, 61, v.pres, 62, pres, 63). Practical speaking. Add: American University, Washington, DC 20016.

ANDERSON, JARVIS LYNN, b. Ogden, Utah, Feb. 12, 32; m. 62; c. 2. MODERN DRAMA, THEATRE HISTORY. B.A, Utah State Univ, 58, M.A, 59; Ph.D.(theatre), Univ. Minn, 71. Instr. Eng, Yuba Col, 61-63; rhet. & drama, Univ. Minn, 64-66; asst. prof. theatre, Okla. State Univ, 66-68; ASSOC. PROF. ENG. & THEATRE, UTAH STATE UNIV, 68- Med.C, U.S.N, 55-57. AAUP. Modern drama; Elizabethan drama. Add: Dept. of English, Utah State University, Logan, UT 84322.

ANDERSON, JERRY MAYNARD, b. Deronda, Wis, Sept. 16, 33; m. 59; c. 1. SPEECH. B.S, Wis. State Univ, River Falls, 58; M.S, North. Ill. Univ, 59; Ph.D.(speech), Mich. State Univ, 64. Instr. speech, Univ. Maine, 59-61; Mich. State Univ, 63-65, asst. prof, 65-68, dir. forensics, 62-67, speech area, Commun. Arts Inst, 62-67, undergrad. educ. speech, 67-68, speech area, dept. speech & theater, 67-68; prof. speech & dramatic arts & chmn. dept, Cent. Mich. Univ, 68-72, prof. speech, 73, spec. asst. to provost, 72, acting v.provost, 72-73; V. PRES. ACAD. AFFAIRS, WEST. WASH. STATE COL, 73- All-univ. res. grants, Mich. State Univ, 63-68; Harry S Truman Libr. Found. res. grant, 65; Cent. Mich. Univ. res. grants, 68-71; Am. Counc. Educ. fel. acad. internship, 71-72. Sr. Distinguished Prof. Award, Cent. Mich. Univ, 70. U.S.N, 52-54. Midwest Forensic Asn.(secy-treas, 65-67, v.pres, 67-69, pres, 69-72); Am. Forensic Asn.(pres, 72-); Cent. States Speech Asn.(pres, 73-); AAUP; Am. Civil Liberties Union; Am. Asn. Higher Educ; Am. Counc. Educ; Int. Commun. Asn; Speech Commun. Asn. Interpersonal and public communication; higher education administration; political campaigning. Publ: Co-auth, Readings in argumentation, Allyn & Bacon, 68; co-ed, Essays in forensics, Am. Forensic Asn, 70; auth, Student congress on trial, Speaker & Gavel, 11/65; contrib, Discussion and debate, Mich. High Sch. Forensic Asn, 69. Add: Office of the Vice-President for Academic Affairs, Western Washington State College, Bellingham, WA 98225.

ANDERSON, JOHN QUINCY, b. Wheeler, Tex, May 30, 16; m. 46. AMERICAN LITERATURE. A.B, Okla. State Univ, 39; M.A, La. State Univ, 48; Ph.D.(Am. lit), Univ. N.C, 52. Teaching fel, Univ. Tex, 48-49; instr. ENG, Univ. N.C, 51-52; asst. prof, McNeese State Col, 52-53; instr, Tex. A&M, Univ, 53-54, asst. prof, 54-56, assoc. prof, 56-59, prof, 59-66, head dept, 62-66, fac. award, 61; PROF, UNIV. HOUSTON, 66- Spec. lectr, Am. Stud. Sem, Miss. Col, 61, 62, 63; mem. ed. bds, Miss. Quart, 64-, Computer Stud. in Humanities & Verbal Behav, 66-, Paisano Bks, Tex. Folklore Soc, 67- & Southwest. Am. Lit. Asn, 70- U.S.A, 40-46, Capt. MLA; Am. Folklore Soc; Am. Stud. Asn; S.Cent. Mod. Lang. Asn; Emerson Soc; West. Lit. Asn. American literature; Southern literature and history; folklore. Publ: A Texas surgeon in the C.S.A, Confederate Publ. Co, 57; Louisiana swamp doctor: the life and writings of Henry Clay Lewis, 62 & ed, Brokenburn: the journal of Kate Stone, 1861-1868, 55 & 72, La. State Univ; auth, Tales of frontier Texas, 1830-1860, South. Methodist Univ, 66; With the bark on: popular humor of the Old South, 1830-1860, Vanderbilt Univ, 67; Campaigning with Parson's Texas Cavalry Brigade, C.S.A, Hill Jr. Col, 67; ed, Texas folk medicine, Encino Press, 70; auth, The liberating gods: Emerson on poets and poetry, Univ. Miami, 71; Lowell's The washers of the shroud and the Celtic legend of the washer of the ford, Am. Lit, 63; Emily Dickinson's Butterflies and tigers, Emerson Quart, 67; Emerson's Young American as democratic nobleman, Am. Transcendental Quart, 70. Add: Dept. of English, University of Houston, Houston, TX 77004.

ANDERSON, JOHN RICHARD, b. New Orleans, La, Nov. 5, 42; m. 65; c. 2. RHETORIC, COMMUNICATION STUDIES. B.S, Pac. Univ, 64; M.A, Wash. State Univ, 65, Carpenter fel, 70-72, Ph.D.(rhet, commun), 73. Teaching asst. speech, Wash. State Univ, 64-65, 70-72; instr, Univ. Wash, 65-67; SOUTH. ORE. COL, 67-69, ASST. PROF. RHET. & COMMUN. STUD, 70- Speech Commun. Asn; West. Speech Commun. Asn. The rhetorical use of language by social movements and other forms of collective behavior; the philosophy of rhetoric; persuasion and attitude change. Publ: Mental attitude and the speaker, In: Speaker's guide, U.S. Navy, 68; The audience as a concept in the philosophic rhetoric of Perelman, Johnstone, Natanson, South. Speech Commun. J, fall 72. Add: Dept. of Speech Communication, Southern Oregon College, Ashland, OR 97520.

ANDERSON, JUDITH HELENA, b. Worcester, Mass, Apr. 21, 40. ENGLISH. B.A, Radcliffe Col, 61; Woodrow Wilson fels, Yale, 61 & 63, M.A, 62, Ph.D, 65. Asst. prof. ENG, Cornell Univ, 66-72; vis. lectr, Yale, 73; vis. asst. prof, Univ. Mich, Ann Arbor, 73-74; ASSOC. PROF, IND. UNIV, BLOOMINGTON, 74- MLA; AAUP; Renaissance Soc. Am. Renaissance literature and intellectual history; Spenser. Publ: The knight and the palmer in the Faerie queene, Book II, Mod. Lang. Quart, 70; Nat worth a boterflye: Muiopotmos and The nun's priest's tale, J. Medieval & Renaissance Stud, 71; contrib, Nor man it is: the knight of justice in Book V of Spenser's Faerie queene, In: Essential articles for the study of Edmund Spenser, Archon Bks, 72; plus four others. Add: Dept. of English, Indiana University, Bloomington, IN 47401.

ANDERSON, KARL OSCAR EMANUEL, b. Cambridge, Mass, Dec. 25, 05. ENGLISH & AMERICAN LITERATURE. A.B, Harvard, 27, A.M, 28, Ph.D, 42; Upsala Univ, Sweden, 33-34. Instr. ENG, Cornell Univ, 39-45; PROF, CLARK UNIV, 45- MLA; Soc. Advan. Scand. Stud; Col. Eng. Asn. Literary relations between Scandinavia and England. Add: Dept. of English, Clark University, Worcester, MA 01610.

ANDERSON, LOREN JAMES, b. Rugby, N.Dak, July 6, 45; m. 68. SPEECH COMMUNICATION. B.A, Concordia Col, 67; M.A, Mich. State Univ, 68; Ph.D.(speech), Univ. Mich, Ann Arbor, 71. ASST. PROF. SPEECH, Wayne State Univ, 69-72; CONCORDIA COL, 72- Speech Commun. Asn; Asn. Inst. Res; Am. Forensics Asn; Cent. States Speech Commun. Asn. Persuasive communications; classroom communication and instructional effectiveness. Publ: Co-auth, Communication as identification, Harper, 75 & The dimensions of teacher credibility, Speech Teacher, 73; contrib, Concepts in communication, Allyn & Bacon, 73. Add: Dept. of Speech Communication & Theatre Arts, Concordia College, Moorhead, MN 56560.

ANDERSON, NORMAN ARTHUR, b. San Diego, Calif, June 28, 23; m. 64; c. 4. ENGLISH LITERATURE. B.A, Principia Col, 49; M.A, Univ. Calif, Berkeley, 51; Ph.D.(Eng. lit), Univ. Wis, 62. Instr. ENG, Principia Col, 49-55; asst. prof, U.S. Naval Acad, 57-63, assoc. prof, 63-65; WEST. ILL. UNIV, 65-69, PROF, 69-, acting dir, Black Stud, 68-69. Pub. ed, U.S. Forest Products Lab, Wis, 55-57; asst. prof, Anne Arundel Community Col, 61-65; lectr, George Washington Univ, 62; tech. ed. & writer, U.S. Dept. Agr, 64; sessional lectr, Carleton Univ.(Can), summer 68. U.S.A, 43-45, Sgt. MLA; Midwest Mod. Lang. Asn; Keats-Shelley Asn. Am; AAUP. Keats: romance and mythology; Romantic poetic theory; American Romanticism. Publ: Rappaccini's daughter: a Keatsian analogue?, PMLA, 5/68; A pair of ragged claws, Tidewater Times, 8/71; Faulkner's Sanctuary: death is life and life is death, Miss. Valley Rev, winter 72. Add: Dept. of English, Western Illinois University, Macomb, IL 61455.

ANDERSON, PATRICIA DAVIS, b. New York, N.Y. ENGLISH. B.L.S, Univ. Okla, 66, M.A, 68, Ph.D.(Eng), 70. Christian educ. dir, Church of the Holy Spirit, Lake Forest, Ill, 57-60; St. Mark's Church, Evanston, Ill, 60-62; secy, Nat. Counc. Protestant Episcopal Church, 63-65; teaching asst. ENG, Univ. Okla, 71; ASST. PROF, MADISON COL, 71- MLA. Literature as an interdisciplinary subject; the function of literature in the education of students of average or below average scholastic aptitude. Add: Dept. of English, Madison College, Harrisonburg, VA 22801.

ANDERSON, PAUL BUNYAN, b. Osakis, Minn, Apr. 28, 04; m. 36; div. 56; m. 62. ENGLISH, AMERICAN LITERATURE. A.B, Univ. Minn, 25; A.M, Harvard, 27, Ph.D. 31. Instr. Eng. & speech, Mass. State Col, 27-29; prof. Eng. lang. & lit, Parsons Col, 31-36; assoc. prof. Eng, Tusculum Col, 36-37; prof. Eng. lang. & lit, Otterbein Col, 37-55, dir. debate, 37-46, acad. dean, 46-54; prof. Eng. & acad. dean, Nat. Col. Christian Workers, 55-56; asst. prof. Eng & speech, Calif. State Polytech. Col, 56-58, assoc. prof, 59-69; RETIRED. Vis. scholar, Univ. Tex, 64. Linguistics; American, English and comparative literature. Publ: Mistress Delariviere Manley, a cavalier's daughter in Grubstreet; Bernard Mandeville on gin, PMLA. Add: 2438 Tulare Ave, El Cerrito, CA 94530.

ANDERSON, QUENTIN, b. Minnewaukan, N.Dak, July 21, 12; m. 33, 47; c. 3. ENGLISH. A.B, Columbia Univ, 37, Ph.D.(philos), 53; M.A, Harvard, 45; Evans traveling fel. From instr. to assoc. ENG, COLUMBIA UNIV, 39-53, asst. prof, 53-55, assoc. prof, 55-61, PROF, 61-, dept. rep, Columbia Col, 63-69. Fulbright lectr, France, 62-63; vis. prof, Univ. Sussex, 66-67; Nat. Endowment for Humanities sr. fel, 73-74. MLA. Nineteenth century American literature; general education; Victorian literature. Publ: The American Henry James, Rutgers, 57; co-ed, Proper study, essays on western classics, St. Martins, 62; auth, The imperial self, Knopf, 71; George Eliot in Middlemarch, In: Pelican guide to English literature, Vol. VI, Penguin, 58. Add: 422 Hamilton Hall, Columbia University, New York, NY 10027.

ANDERSON, RAYMOND E, b. Buffalo, Minn, Dec. 12, 24; m. 49; c. 3. SPEECH. B.S, Univ. Minn, 46, M.A, 50, Ph.D.(speech), 59. Instr. SPEECH, Univ. Vt, 49; PROF, AUGSBURG COL, 49- U.S.N.R, 43-46, Ens. Speech Commun. Asn; Nat. Col. Honors Counc. Public address; philosophy and rhetoric. Publ: Kierkegaard's theory of communication, Speech Monogr, 2/63. Add: Augsburg College, Minneapolis, MN 55414.

ANDERSON, ROBERT GENE, b. Denver, Colo, Dec. 4, 30; m. 63. ORAL INTERPRETATION OF LITERATURE. B.A, Colo. State Col, 55, M.A, 57; Ph.D.(speech), Univ. Mo, 65. Producer & dir. instructional TV, Univ. Mo, 63-65; asst. prof. speech, Univ. Houston, 65-67; MISS. STATE UNIV, 67-69, ASSOC. PROF. COMMUN, 69- U.S.M.C, 50-52, Sgt. Speech Commun. Asn; U.S. Inst. Theatre Technol; Asn. Brit. Theatre Tech; Am. Theatre Asn; South. Speech Asn. History and theory of oral interpretation; theatre architecture; video tape recording as an aid to actor-director communications. Publ: Instructional television in theatrical production, Dramatics, 3/66; James Rush, his legacy to interpretation, South. Speech J, fall 67. Add: Dept. of Communication, Mississippi State University, Drawer NJ, Mississippi State, MS 39762.

ANDERSON, ROBERT L, Religion. See Volume IV, Philosophy, Religion & Law.

ANDERSON, ROLAND FRANK, b. London, Eng, Mar. 19, 28; m. 55; c. 1. ENGLISH. B.A, Univ. B.C, 57; M.A, Univ. Wis, 58; univ. open fel, Univ. Toronto, 58-59, Can. Counc. fel, 59-60, Ph.D.(Eng), 63. Teaching fel. ENG, Univ. Toronto, 60-61; asst. prof, Univ. Alta, 61-65; sr. lectr, Massey Univ, N.Z, 65-68; asst. prof, UNIV. ALTA, 68-69, ASSOC. PROF, 69- R.N, 45-48. Can. Asn. Univ. Teachers; Asn. Can. Univ. Teachers Eng; Australasian Univs. Lang. & Lit. Asn; Asn. Commonwealth Lit. & Lang. Stud. George Eliot; Victorian novel; Commonwealth literature. Publ: George Eliot provoked: John Blackwood and chapter seventeen of Adam Bede, Mod. Philol, 8/73. Add: Dept. of English, University of Alberta, Edmonton, Alta, Can.

ANDERSON, RUTH LEILA (MRS. D.C. MAXWELL), b. Albia, Iowa, Oct. 7, 97; m. 43. ENGLISH LITERATURE. A.B, State Univ. Iowa, 18, A.M, 23, Ph.D, 27. Teacher, high sch, 18-22; asst. Eng, State Univ. Iowa, 24-26, instr, 26-29; head dept, Penn Col.(Iowa), 29-30; prof. Eng. & dean women, Cent. Col.(Mo), 30-43; assoc. prof. Eng, Millikin Univ, 45-48, prof. & chmn. dept, 48-63, EMER. PROF, 63-, dean women, 45-48, chmn, Humanities Div, 48-63. Prof. Eng, Carthage Col, 63-70. Col. Eng. Asn. Literature of the English Renaissance; Elizabethan psychology and Shakespeare's plays; the mirror concept and its relation to the drama of the Renaissance and aspects of kingship. Publ: Elizabethan psychology and Shakespeare's plays, Russell, 65; The pattern of conduct culminating in Macbeth, Stud. Eng. Lit, 64; plus others. Add: 310 N. Clinton St, Iowa City, IA 52240.

ANDERSON, VALBORG, b. Colton, Ore, Mar. 10, 11. ENGLISH LITERATURE. B.A, Univ. Ore, 35, fel, 35-38, M.A, 38; univ. fel, Brown Univ, 44-45, Miss Abbotts Sch. Alumnae fel, 45-46, Ph.D, 46. Instr. ENG, Univ. Ore,

38-43; Temple Univ, 46-47; BROOKLYN COL, 47-57, asst. prof, 57-63, assoc. prof, 63-70, PROF, 70- Bollingen fel, 63-64; mem, Eng. Inst. MLA. Spenser; Wordsworth, Strindberg. Publ: My students wear a mask, Atlantic Monthly Press, 61; transl. & ed, The father, a dream play by August Strindberg, Appleton, 64. Add: Dept. of English, Brooklyn College, Brooklyn, NY 11210.

ANDERSON, WALLACE LUDWIG, b. Hartford, Conn, Sept. 9, 17; m. 43; c. 2. ENGLISH. B.A, Trinity Col, 39, M.A, 45; Ph.D.(Eng), Univ. Chicago, 48. Instr. Eng, Litchfield Sch. Boys, 39-40; William Hall High Sch, 41-42; asst. prof, Univ. North. Iowa, 48-54, assoc. prof, 54-58, prof, 58-72, assoc. dean. instr, 63-64, dean undergrad. stud, 65-71; PROF. ENG. & ACAD. DEAN, BRIDGEWATER STATE COL, 72- Fulbright teacher, Netherlands, 57-58; Guggenheim fel, 67-68; participant, Educ. & World Affairs Comt. Intercult. Educ, 67- U.S.A.A.F, 42-46. NCTE; MLA; AAUP. Literary forms; American literature; English language. Publ: Collab, Poetry as experience, Am. Bk. Co, 52; co-auth, Introductory readings on language, Holt, 62, rev. ed, 66; auth, Edwin Arlington Robinson, a critical introduction, Houghton, 67 & Harvard, 68; A world view for undergraduates, Saturday Rev, 8/66; E.A. Robinson's Scattered lives, Am. Lit, 1/67; contrib, The young Robinson as critic and self-critic, In: Edwin Arlington Robinson centenary essays, Univ. Ga, 69; plus one other. Add: Office of Academic Dean, Bridgewater State College, Bridgewater, MA 02324.

ANDERSON, WALTER ELDON, b. Detroit, Mich, Mar. 30, 34; m. 61; c. 1. ENGLISH. Woodrow Wilson fel. & B.A, Univ. Mich, 61; M.A, Univ. Calif, Berkeley, 63, Ph.D.(Eng), 68. ASST. PROF. ENG, UNIV. CALIF, LOS ANGELES, 68- U.S.A, 57-58. MLA. Criticism and English fiction. Add: Dept. of English, University of California, Los Angeles, CA 90024.

ANDERSON, WARREN DEWITT, Comparative Literature. See Volume III, Foreign Languages, Linguistics & Philology.

ANDERSON, WILLIAM DAVIS, b. Dallas, Tex, Sept. 25, 38. ENGLISH. B.A, Univ. Tex, 60, M.A, 62, Ph.D.(Eng), 66. Asst. prof. Eng, King Col, 62-63; instr. for. lang, Univ. Tex, Arlington, 63-65; asst. prof. ENG, CALIF. STATE UNIV, NORTHRIDGE, 66-70, ASSOC. PROF, 70- U.S. Off. Educ. fel, Tri-Univ. Proj. Elem. Educ, Univ. Nebr, 67-68; co-dir, NDEA Inst. Elem. Eng, San Fernando Valley State Col, summer 68. MLA; NCTE. Romantic period; children's literature; psycholinguistics. Publ: A new look at children's literature, Wadsworth, 72; Children and poetry, Top of the News Am. Libr. Asn, 6/68. Add: Dept. of English, California State University, Northridge, 18111 Nordhoff St, Northridge, CA 91324.

ANDREACH, ROBERT J, b. Newark, N.J, Aug. 19, 30; m. 58; c. 2. ENGLISH. A.B, Rutgers Univ, 53; M.A, N.Y. Univ, 58, Ph.D.(Eng), 63. Instr. ENG, Univ. Toledo, 61-63; Univ. R.I, 63-65; asst. prof, State Univ. N.Y. Binghamton, 65-69; ASSOC. PROF, MONMOUTH COL.(N.J), 71- U.S.A, 53-55. MLA; James Joyce Soc. Medieval and modern literature. Publ: Studies in structure, Fordham Univ. & Burns & Oates, 64; The slain and resurrected God, N.Y. Univ. & Univ. London, 70; Henry James' The sacred fount, Nineteenth-century Fiction 12/62; Nathanael West's Miss lonely-hearts, Mod. Fiction Stud, summer 66; Eugene O'Neill's The hairy ape, Mod. Drama, 5/67. Add: Dept. of English, Monmouth College, West Long Branch, NJ 07764.

ANDRESEN, OLIVER S, b. Duluth, Minn, Jan. 8, 22. READING SPECIALIZATION. B.A, Univ. Minn, 45, M.A, 50; Ph.D.(reading), Univ. Chicago, 67. Instr. hist, reading & Eng, Northwest. Mil. & Naval Acad, 46-54; Eng. & Reading, Valley Forge Mil. Acad, 54-60; res. assoc. reading, Univ. Chicago, 60-65; asst. prof. ENG. & READING, CHICAGO STATE UNIV, 65-67, ASSOC. PROF, 67- Am. Educ. Res. Asn; Int. Reading Asn; NCTE. Reading comprehension at secondary level. Publ: The evaluation of profundity in literature, J. Reading, 6/65; Evaluating the author's theme in literature, In: Perspectives in reading, Int. Reading Asn, 66; co-auth, Developing competence in reading comprehension, In: Reading instruction: an international forum, Int. Reading Asn, 67. Add: 1450 E. 55th Pl, Chicago, IL 60637.

ANDREW, GEOFFREY CLEMENT, b. Bayfield, N.S, Can, July 3, 06. ENGLISH. B.A, Dalhousie Univ, 29; B.A, Oxford, 35, M.A, 47; D.C.L, Univ. King's Col, 62; D ès L, Laval Univ, 68; hon. D.C.L, Bishops Univ, 70; hon. LL.D, Univ. N.B, Fredericton, 71. Asst. master, Rothesay Col. Sch, N.B, Can, 29-30; Upper Can. Col, 30-33, sr. housemaster & teacher Eng, 35-42; secy, War Indust. Bd, Ottawa, 43-45; dir, Can. Inform. Serv, 45-47; chief inform. div, Can. Dept. External Affairs, 47; prof. Eng. & exec. asst. to pres, Univ. B.C, 48-53, dean & dep. to pres, 53-62; exec. dir, Asn. Univs. & Cols. Can, 62-71; RETIRED. Mem. Comn. Post-Sec. Educ. Kootenay Area, B.C, 73; mem. counc, Univ. Botswana, Lesotho & Swaziland, 73- Add: 4633 W. 13th Ave, Vancouver, B.C. V6R 2V6, Can.

ANDREWS, CLARENCE ADELBERT, b. Waterloo, Iowa, Oct. 24, 12; m. 37; c. 3. ENGLISH. B.A, Univ. Iowa, 54, M.A, 60, Ph.D.(Eng), 63. Instr. advan. compos, Univ. Iowa, 58-60; asst. prof. tech. jour, Colo. State Univ, 60-61; instr. Eng. & jour, Univ. Iowa, 61-63, asst. prof, 63-67, assoc. prof. Eng, 67-69; PROF. LANG. & LIT. & DIR. SCI. & TECH. COMMUN, MICH. TECHNOL. UNIV, 72- Vis. summer prof, Naval Ord. Test Sta, China Lake, Calif, 59; summer consult, Measurement Res. Corp, Iowa City, 60; ed, The Personnel Adminr, 60-61; vis. prof. lang. & lit, Mich. Technol. Univ, 71-72; vis. prof. Eng, Univ. Iowa, summer 74. Outstanding Educr. 73, Mich. Technol. Univ. U.S.A.F, 44-46, 47-53, 1st Sgt. Midwest Mod. Lang. Asn; NCTE; Conf. Col. Compos. & Commun; Soc. Study Midwest. Lit. Technical and scientific writing; Midwestern literature; advanced composition. Publ: Co-auth, Technical and scientific writing, Univ. Iowa, 63, 65; Writing: growth through structure, Glencoe, 72; A literary history of Iowa, Univ. Iowa, 72; Technical software, Houghton, 74; Le comte du Cedar Rapids, spring 71 & Man of the midland, fall 71, The Iowan; Big Annie and the 1913 copper strike, Mich. Hist, spring 73; plus three others. Add: Dept. of Humanities, Michigan Technological University, Houghton, MI 49931.

ANDREWS, JAMES ROBERTSON, b. Atlantic City, N.J, Dec. 8, 36. SPEECH. B.A, N.J. State Teachers Col, Montclair, 58; M.A, Pa. State Univ, 60, Ph.D.(speech), 66. Instr. SPEECH, Pa. State Univ, 62-65; asst. prof, Univ. Calif, Santa Barbara, 65-67; Teachers Col, Columbia Univ, 67-72; ASSOC. PROF, IND. UNIV, BLOOMINGTON, 72- Speech Commun. Asn; AHA; Am. Acad. Polit. & Soc. Sci. Rhetorical aspects of historical movements; rhetoric in British history and politics; rhetorical criticism. Publ: The ethos of pacifism, Quart. J. Speech, 2/67; Rhetorical aspects of the British peace movement, Speech Monogr, 11/67; The rhetoric of a lobbyist, Cent. States Speech J, 11/67; plus others. Add: Dept. of Speech, Indiana University, Bloomington, IN 47401.

ANDREWS, JOHN FRANK, b. Carlsbad, N.Mex, Nov. 2, 42; m. 66; c. 2. RENAISSANCE ENGLISH LITERATURE. A.B, Princeton, 65; M.A.T, Harvard, 66; Ph.D.(Eng), Vanderbilt Univ, 70. Instr. ENG, Univ. Tenn, Nashville, 69-70; ASST. PROF. & DIR. GRAD. STUD, FLA. STATE UNIV, 70-, fac. res. grant, summer 73. Asst. ed, Shakespeare Stud, 71-73, assoc. ed, Shakespeare Stud, 74-; fel, Folger Shakespeare Libr, 72. AAUP; MLA; S.Atlantic Mod. Lang. Asn; Shakespeare Asn. Am. Shakespeare criticism; editorial problems in Shakespeare; Renaissance literature. Publ: The Pavier quartos of 1619—evidence for two compositors, Shakespeare Newsletter, 2/72; The Ipsissima verba in My diary?, review article, Shakespeare Stud, 1/75. Add: Dept. of English, 330 Williams Bldg, Florida State University, Tallahassee, FL 32306.

ANDREWS, MICHAEL CAMERON, b. Hanover, N.H, July 22, 38; m. 70; c. 2. ENGLISH. B.A, Dartmouth Col, 61; M.A, Harvard, 62; Ph.D.(Eng), Duke Univ, 66. Instr. ENG, Univ. N.C, 66; Princeton, 66-68; asst. prof, Univ. Ky, 68-70; ASSOC. PROF, OLD DOM. UNIV, 70- Fel, Medieval & Renaissance Inst, summer 66. MLA; Renaissance Soc. Am; Shakespeare Soc. Am. Shakespeare; Elizabethan drama; Renaissance poetry. Publ: The double death of Claudius in Hamlet, Renaissance Papers, 71; Sweetness in The changeling, Yearbk. Eng. Stud, 71; Honest Othello: the handkerchief once more, Stud. Eng. Lit, 73; plus others. Add: 500 Massachusetts Ave, Norfolk, VA 23508.

ANDREWS, S. GENE, b. Memphis, Tenn, Apr. 25, 25; m. 51; c. 2. ENGLISH LITERATURE. B.S, Univ. S.C, 46, M.A, 48; Ph.D, 53; fel, Univ. Fla, 48-50. Assoc. prof. ENG, Ark. Agr. & Mech. Col, 50-55; asst. prof, Ball State Teachers Col, 55-58; assoc. prof, Wis. State Col, Superior, 58-62; from asst. prof. to PROF, BALL STATE UNIV, 62- Res. grant, Asn. Col. & Ref. Libr, 56-57; Fulbright fel, 67-68. U.S.N, 43-46, Lt.(jg). MLA. Shakespeare; English romanticism. Publ: Contrib, Explicator; Mod. Lang. Notes. Add: Dept. of English, Ball State University, Muncie, IN 47306.

ANDREWS, WILLIAM DAVID, b. Johnstown, Pa, Apr. 26, 45; m. 70; c. 1. AMERICAN LITERATURE & CULTURAL HISTORY. B.A, Univ. Pittsburgh, 66; M.A, Ohio State Univ, 67; M.A, Univ. Pa, 70, Ph.D.(Am. civilization), 71. Instr. ENG, OHIO STATE UNIV, 70-71, ASST. PROF, 71- Nat. Endowment for Humanities younger humanist fel, 72-73. MLA; Soc. Archit. Hist; Am. Stud. Asn. Nineteenth century and early American literature; 19th century American architectural and cultural history. Publ: The printed funeral sermons of Cotton Mather, 70 & The literature of the 1727 New England earthquake, 73, Early Am. Lit; William T. Coggeshall: booster of western literature, Ohio Hist, 72. Add: Dept. of English, Ohio State University, 164 W. 17th Ave, Columbus, OH 43210.

ANGEL, D. DUANE, b. Detroit, Mich, Dec. 23, 39; m. 65. COMMUNICATIONS, POLITICAL SCIENCE. B.S, Wayne State Univ, 61, 63; David Ross fel. & Ph.D.(commun), Purdue Univ, 65. Asst. speech, Purdue Univ, 62-65; asst. prof, Univ. Del, 65-66; asst. prof. speech & dir. forensics, Albion Col, 66-73, dir. exp. relevance & continuing educ, 69-72; STATE REP, 49th DIST. STATE OF MICH, 73- Instr, Wayne State Univ, summer 63; vis. lectr, Queens Col.(N.Y), summers 67 & 68; spec. asst. to Sen. Robert P. Griffin(R-Mich), Washington, D.C, summer 69. Speech Commun. Asn. Political communication. Publ: Romney, a political biography, Exposition, 67; William G. Milliken: a touch of steel, Public Affairs Press, 70; The G.I. and the GOP, Mich. Republican Quart, 5/68. Add: State Capitol, Lansing MI 48901.

ANGELESCU, VICTOR, b. Detroit, Mich, Apr. 2, 22; m. 68. EIGHTEENTH CENTURY ENGLISH LITERATURE. B.S, Wayne State Univ, 58, M.A, 60, Ph.D.(Eng), 68. Instr. Eng, Wayne State Univ, 62-64, asst. prof, 64-68; PROF. ENG. & SOCIOL, LAWRENCE INST. TECHNOL, 69-, CHMN. DEPT. HUMANITIES, 69- Sect. head Romanian lit, MLA Annual Bibliog, 65- MLA; AAUP. Literary criticism; Romanian literature; sociology, modern sociological problems. Add: Dept. of Humanities, Lawrence Institute of Technology, 21000 W. Ten Mile Rd, Southfield, MI 48075.

ANGELL, JOSEPH WARNER, JR, b. Atkinson, Nebr, May 29, 08; m. 35; c. 3. LITERATURE, HISTORY. A.B, Col. Wooster, 30; M.A, Univ. Ore, 34; Yale, 35-37, 38-39. Instr. Eng, Albertus Magnus Col, 37-39; Pomona Col, 39-42, asst. prof, 46-48, assoc. prof, 48-51; mil. hist, Air Univ, 51-53, prof, 53-65; spec. asst. for policy, Off. Comdr, U.S. Air Force Syst. Command, 65-68; prof. Eng, COLO. STATE UNIV, 68-73, dir. univ. serv, 68-70, dir. cult. prog, univ. & assoc. dir. spec. resources, libr, 71-73, EMER. PROF. ENG, 73- Asst. prof, Claremont Grad. Sch, 46-48, assoc. prof, 48-51; spec. consult, U.S. Dept. War & Defense, 46-51; adv. to Thomas Mann Collection, Yale Univ. Libr, 47-; asst. chief, hist. off, hq, U.S. Air Force, 51-59, chief, 59-63; mem. bd. adv, Humanities Ctr. Lib. Educ. Indust. Soc, 58; chmn. final reports group, U.S. Air Force Proj. Forecast, 63-64, dir. task force, U.S. Air Force Syst. Command, 65-66, w.coast stud. facility, 66-68, spec. consult, 68- U.S.A.A.F, 42-46, Maj. MLA. Life and works of Thomas Mann; literature and culture of English romantic period; 20th century European literature and literary theory. Publ: Thomas Mann reader, Knopf, 50, Universal Libr, 54 & Bk. of the Month Club, 61; Guided missiles could have won, Atlantic Monthly & Van Nostrand; chaps, In: Army Air Forces in World War II, Univ. Chicago. Add: 421 S. Howes St, Apt. 1003, Ft. Collins, CO 80521.

ANGELL, RICHARD CHURCHILL, b. Seattle, Wash, July 15, 11; m. 37. ENGLISH LITERATURE. A.B, Univ. N.Mex, 59, M.A, 62, Ph.D.(Eng), 71. Asst. ed, Univ. N.Mex. Press, 60-65; asst. prof. ENG, IND. STATE UNIV, 65-72, ASSOC. PROF, 72- Rev. ed, N.Mex. Quart, 60-65. MLA. Comparative literature, especially Iberian; English prose seventeenth century; twentieth century criticism. Publ: The long swim, Putnam, 47; Better for the birds, Atlantic monthly, 12/56; Eastlake at home and abroad, N.Mex.

Quart, fall 64; Latin American short stories, Stud. Short Fiction, fall 63; plus others. Add: Dept. of English, Indiana State University, Terre Haute, IN 47809.

ANGELL, RUTH SPEER, b. Bowie, Tex, Jan. 1, 01; wid. ENGLISH. B.S, Tex. State Col. Women, 21; B.A, Univ. Tex, 22; M.A, Columbia Univ, 37; Univ. Calif; Univ. London. Teacher, High Sch, Tex, 22-24; instr. ENG, TEX. CHRISTIAN UNIV, 37-46, asst. prof, 46-63, assoc. prof, 63-71, EMER. PROF, 71- S.Cent. Mod. Lang. Asn; Am. Stud. Asn. Texas ballads and folksongs; American literary scene. Add: Dept. of English, Texas Christian University, Ft. Worth, TX 76129.

ANGOFF, CHARLES, b. Russia, Apr. 22, 02; nat. ENGLISH, JOURNALISM. A.B, Harvard, 23; hon. Litt.D, Fairleigh Dickinson Univ, 66. PROF. ENG, FAIRLEIGH DICKINSON UNIV, 55- Adj. prof, N.Y. Univ, 50-66; lectr, Columbia Univ, Fordham Univ, Jewish Theol. Sem. & Univ. N.H, 50-; Hunter Col, 52-60; Wayne State Univ, 55; adj. prof, Wagner Col, 56-57; ed, Lit. Rev, 57-; chief ed, Fairleigh Dickinson Univ. Press, 67-; novelist in residence, Los Angeles State Col, 70. Daroff Award, Jewish Bk. Counc. Am, 55 & 69; N.J. Asn. Teachers Eng. Awards, 70, 71 & 72. Poetry Soc. Am. (pres, 69-72); Auth. League Am; fel, Jewish Acad. Arts & Sci; PEN Club. American literature and journalism; Jewish-American literature and culture. Publ: H.L. Mencken: a portrait from memory, Summer storm, 64, Memory of autumn, 68 & Seasons of mists, 71, Yoseloff; The tone of the twenties, 66 & George Sterling: a centenary memoir, 71, A.S. Barnes; The bell of time, 66, ed, Modern stories from many lands, 71 & auth, Prayers at midnight, 72, Manyland; ed, The humanities in the age of science, Fairleigh Dickinson Univ, 68; co-ed, The rise of American-Jewish literature, Simon & Schuster, 71; plus others. Add: 140 W. 86th St, New York, NY 10024.

ANGOTTI, VINCENT L, b. Kansas City, Mo, Mar. 5, 41; m. 62. THEATRE, DRAMA. B.S, St. Louis Univ, 62; M.A, Univ. Kans, 65, Ph.D.(theatre, drama), 67. Asst. prof. theatre & drama, Fla. State Univ, 67-73, Stud. Ctr, Florence, Italy, 68-69; vis. prof. drama, Univ. Birmingham, 71-72; ASSOC. PROF. THEATRE & DRAMA & CHMN. DEPT. THEATRE, UNIV. S.DAK, VERMILLION, 73- Asst. prof. drama, London Stud. Ctr. for Soc. Sci, 71-72. Speech Commun. Asn; Soc. Theatre Res, Eng; Int. Fed. Theatre Res; Univ. & Col. Theatre Asn. Theatre history; dramatic theory and criticism; dramatic literature. Publ: Source materials in the field of theatre, Xerox Educ. Div, 67; Return to man: Jacques Copeau and the actor, Cent. States Speech J, 73; Introduction to theatre; or, what you will, Educ. Theatre J, 73. Add: Dept. of Theatre, University of South Dakota, Vermillion, SD 57069.

ANGUS, DOUGLAS ROSS, b. Amherst, N.S, July 6, 09; nat; m. 41; c. 2. ENGLISH. B.A, Acadia Univ, 34; scholar. & M.A, Univ. Maine, 35; Ph.D, Ohio State Univ, 40. Instr. ENG, George Washington Univ, 40-41; Va. Polytech. Inst, 42-43; chmn. dept, Univ. Tampa, 43-46; asst. prof, Case Inst. Technol, 46-47; assoc. prof, ST. LAWRENCE UNIV, 47-59, prof, 59-73, DANA PROF, 73- Fulbright lectr, Univ. Istanbul, Turkey, 63-64. MLA. Modern literature; cultural implications of the new physics and evolutionary theories; novel; short story anthology and criticism. Publ: The lions fed the tigers, Houghton, 58; The ivy trap, Bobbs, 59; The green and the burning, Hodder & Stoughton, 59; Death on Jerusalem road, Random, 63; ed, The best short stories of the modern age, 62, co-auth, Great modern European short stories, 67, Contemporary American short stories, 67 & ed, Love is the theme (short story anthology), 71, Fawcett; Antievolution, Tex. Rev, winter 67; Quantum physics and the creative imagination, Am. Scholar, spring 61; Modern art and the new physics, West. Humanities Rev, spring 62. Add: 31 W. Main St, Canton, NY 13617.

ANISMAN, MARTIN JAY, b. Brooklyn, N.Y, Nov. 4, 42; m. 64; c. 2. VICTORIAN LITERATURE. B.A, Syracuse Univ, 63; M.A, N.Y. Univ, 64, Ph.D. (Eng), 70. ASSOC. PROF. ENG, SOUTH. CONN. STATE COL, 68- MLA (mem. bibliog. comt, 69-). Victorian novel; Victorian literature; Thackeray. Publ: Ed, William Makepeace Thackeray: The luck of Barry Lyndon: a critical edition, N.Y. Univ, 70. Add: Dept. of English, Southern Connecticut State College, 501 Crescent St, New Haven, CT 06515.

ANNUNZIATA, ANTHONY W, b. Brooklyn, N.Y, Mar. 5, 31; m. 59; c. 1. ENGLISH. B.S, Manhattan Col, 53; M.A, N.Y, Univ, 59, Ph.D.(Eng), 66. Instr. ENG, St. John's Univ, 60-62; asst. prof, STATE UNIV. N.Y. COL. OSWEGO, 62-67, ASSOC. PROF, 67-, asst. dean arts & sci, 67-70. State Univ. N.Y. grants-in-aid, 66-68. U.S.A, 54-56. MLA; Early Eng. Text Soc. Medieval literature; historical linguistics; literature by Tolkien, Lewis and Williams. Add: Dept. of English, State University of New York College at Oswego, Oswego, NY 13126.

ANSDELL, (ORA) JOYE, b. Jamestown, Kans, Oct. 17, 10. ENGLISH. Univ. fel, Univ. Colo, 54-55, Ph.D.(Eng. lit), 56. Instr. ENG, KANS. STATE UNIV, 47-57, asst. prof, 57-66, ASSOC. PROF, 66- MLA; NCTE. Eighteenth century English literature; James Boswell. Add: Dept. of English, Kansas State University, Manhattan, KS 66502.

ANSHUTZ, HERBERT LEO, b. Boville, Idaho, Jan. 17, 15. ENGLISH. A.B, Univ. Wash, 37, Ph.D, 49. Teaching fel, Univ. Wash, 40-42, assoc, 46-47, instr, 48-49; asst. prof, Valparaiso Univ, 49-50; from asst. prof. to PROF. ENG. CENT. WASH. STATE COL, 50- MLA; NCTE. Nineteenth century English and American literature; Coleridge; Hardy; Melville. Add: Dept. of English, Central Washington State College, Ellensburg, WA 98926.

ANSON, JOHN S, b. San Francisco, Calif, Sept. 26, 36; m. 61; c. 2. ENGLISH. B.A, Univ. Calif, Berkeley, 57, M.A, 59, Ph.D.(Eng), 64. Acting instr. ENG, Univ. Wis, Madison, 62-63; instr, Harvard, 63-64; asst. prof, UNIV. CALIF, BERKELEY, 64-71, ASSOC. PROF, 71- Shakespeare. Publ: Julius Caesar: the politics of the hardened heart, Shakespeare Stud, 66; The hunt of love: Gottfried von Strassburg's Tristan as tragedy, Speculum, 10/70. Add: Dept. of English, University of California, 322 Wheeler Hall, Berkeley, CA 94720.

ANTIPPAS, ANDY PETER, b. New York, N.Y, July 22, 41. ENGLISH. B.A, N.Y. Univ, 62; Gilman fel. & M.A, Johns Hopkins Univ, 63; Nat. Univ. Athens, 63-64; fel, Univ. Wis, Madison, 64-68, grant & Ph.D.(Eng), 68. ASSOC. PROF. ENG, TULANE UNIV, 67-, summer res. grant, 68. Vis. asst. prof, La. State Univ. Baton Rouge, summer 68. MLA; Keats-Shelley Asn. Am. English pre-romantic and romantic poetry; Victorian poetry. Publ: Sidney Lanier's unpublished letters to Mary Clare de Graffenreid, Am. Lit, 73; Browning's The guardian angel: a possible early reference to Ruskin, Victorian Poetry, 73; Four new Southey letters, Wordsworth Circle, 74; plus four others. Add: 534 Esplanade, New Orleans, LA 70125.

ANTONAKES, MICHAEL, b. Waltham, Mass, Feb. 25, 26; m. 55; c. 3. ENGLISH. A.B, Tufts Col, 49; M.A, Boston Univ, 57; Fulbright scholar, Univ. Athens, 63-64; Ph.D.(comp. lit), N.Y. Univ, 64. Teacher, high sch, Mass, 50-51, pub. sch, 52-55, N.Y, 57-61; asst. prof. ENG, Jersey City State Col, 61-63, assoc. prof, 64-65; SALEM STATE COL, 65-66, PROF. & CHMN. DEPT, 66- U.S.M.C, 44-46. Counc. Basic Educ; MLA; NCTE; AAUP; Mod. Lang. Asn; Mod. Greek Stud. Asn. Modern Greek literature; poetry and criticism. Publ: A comment on Gerard Manley Hopkins, Concern, fall 69; transl, Antonio Samarakis, Post Office Street, Charioteer, 71; auth, Kazantzakis and Christ as hero, Salem State Col. Eng. Rev, 12/72. Add: Dept. of English, Salem State College, Lafayette St, Salem, MA 01970.

ANTRIM, HARRY T, b. Richmond, Va, Feb. 17, 36; m. 57; c. 2. ENGLISH, LINGUISTICS. A.B, Davidson Col, 57; M.A, Univ. Fla, 62, Ph.D.(Eng), 67. Asst. cur, John & Mabel Ringling Mus. Art, 57-59; instr. ENG, Univ. Fla, 62-65; asst. prof, Univ. Va, 65-71; ASSOC. PROF, FLA. INT. UNIV, 71-, CHMN. DEPT, 73-, asst. dean, Col. Arts & Sci, 71-73. Consult, Eng. Exten, Univ. Va, 66-71; chmn, First Novel Award Comt, William Faulkner Found, 69-71; adv. ed, Film J, 69-71. U.S.A, 59-61, 1st Lt. MLA; Southeast. Mod. Lang. Asn; Mod. Humanities Res. Asn. Twentieth century British poetry; recent theoretical linguistics; film. Publ: T.S. Eliot's concept of language, Univ. Fla, 71; Faulkner's suspended style, Univ. Rev, winter 66. Add: Dept. of English, Florida International University, Tamiami Trail, Miami, FL 33157.

ANTUSH, JOHN VINCENT, b. Tacoma, Wash, Nov. 5, 32; m. 68; c. 2. ENGLISH. A.B, Gonzaga Univ, 56, M.A, 60; Ph.D.(Eng, Am. lit), Stanford, 67. Instr. Eng, FORDHAM UNIV, 64-67, ASST. PROF. ENG. & AM. LIT, 67- MLA; AAUP; Am. Stud. Asn. Nineteenth century American novel; 20th century American novel and poetry. Publ: Realism in the Catholic novel, Cath. World, 7/57; Money as myth and reality in the world of Henry James, Ariz. Quart, summer 69; The much finer complexity of history in Henry James' The American, J. Am. Stud, 4/72. Add: Dept. of English, Fordham University, Bronx, NY 10458.

APPEL, ALFRED, JR, b. New York, N.Y, Jan. 31, 34; m. 57; c. 2. ENGLISH. B.S, Columbia Univ, 59, M.A, 60, Ph.D, 63. Asst. prof. Eng, Stanford Univ, 63-68, co-dir. freshman Eng, 65-66; asst. prof. ENG, NORTHWEST. UNIV, EVANSTON, 68-70, ASSOC. PROF, 70-, DIR. INTROD. STUD. PROG, 68- U.S.A, 55-57. MLA; Philol. Asn. Pac. Coast. American literature; contemporary literature; art and literature, comparative studies. Publ: A season of dreams: the fiction of Eudora Welty, La. State Univ, 65; ed, Witching times, Col. & Univ. Press, 67, The annotated Lolita, McGraw, 69 & Vladimir Nabokov: a collection of critical essays, Prentice-Hall, 69; auth, An interview with Vladimir Nabokov & Lolita: the springboard of parody, In: Nabokov: the man and his work, Univ. Wis, 67; The art of Nabokov's artifice, Denver Quart, summer 68. Add: Dept. of English, Northwestern University, Evanston, IL 60201.

APPLBAUM, MORRIS J, b. Hungary, July 29, 12; U.S. citizen; m. 45; c. 2. ENGLISH. B.S.S, City Col. New York, 36; M.A, N.Y. Univ, 38; Ed.D, Columbia Univ, 58. Teacher Eng, Torah Vodaath High Sch, Brooklyn, N.Y, 36-42, teacher & chmn. dept, 46-48; supvr, Ramaz Upper Sch, New York, N.Y, 48-57; TEACHER ENG, ERASMUS HALL HIGH SCH, BROOKLYN, 57- Instr, Brooklyn Col, 46-52; City Col. New York, 47-51; mem. vis. fac. speech & commun, grad. sch. educ, Yeshiva Univ, 59-; mem. adj. fac. Eng, New York City Community Col, 69- U.S.A.A.F, 42-46. NCTE; Nat. Asn. Sec. Sch. Prin; Am. Asn. Sch. Adminr. Merit certificate winners. Add: 1488 E. 19th St, Brooklyn, NY 11218.

APPLBAUM, RONALD LEE, b. Charleroi, Pa, Dec. 14, 43; m. 68; c. 1. SPEECH COMMUNICATION. A.B, Calif. State Univ, Long Beach, 65, M.A, 66; Ph.D.(speech), Pa. State Univ, 69. Asst. prof. SPEECH, CALIF. STATE UNIV, LONG BEACH, 69-73, ASSOC. PROF, 73- Long Beach State Univ. Found. grant, 72, fel, 73, innovative teaching grant, 73. Speech Commun. Asn; Int. Commun. Asn; West. Speech Commun. Asn.(chmn. speech educ, 69-); AAUP. Persuasion; group communication; speech education. Publ: Co-auth, Fundamental concepts in human communication, Canfield, 73, Process of group communication, Sci. Res. Assocs, 74 & PERT: a tool for communication research, J. Commun, 12/71; co-auth, The factor structure of source credibility as a function of the speaking situation, 8/72 & Source credibility: the reproducibility of measurement, 8/73, Speech Monogr. Add: Dept. of Speech Communication, California State University, Long Beach, 6101 E. Seventh St, Long Beach, CA 90840.

APPLE, MAX ISAAC, b. Grand Rapids, Mich, Oct. 22, 41; m. 70; c. 1. RENAISSANCE LITERATURE, CREATIVE WRITING. B.A, Univ. Mich, Ann Arbor, 63, Ph.D.(Eng), 70; Stanford Univ, 64. ASST. PROF. lit. & humanities, Reed Col, 70-71; ENG. LIT, RICE UNIV, 72- Nat. Endowment for Humanities Younger Humanists fel, 71. MLA. Seventeenth century literature; 20th century literature; Yiddish literature. Publ: The oranging of America, Bantam & Am. Rev, 73; History and case history in Day of the locust and Red Cavalry, In: Nathanael West: the cheaters and the cheated, Everett Edwards, 72. Add: Dept. of English, Rice University, Houston, TX 77001.

APPLEBEE, ROGER KENYON, b. Olean, N.Y, Feb. 8, 25; m. 50; c. 5. ENGLISH LITERATURE. A.B, Western Reserve Univ, 50; Ed.M, Univ. Buffalo, 54; John Hay fel, Yale, 59-60. Teacher Eng, Rochester Pub. Schs, N.Y, 52-62; assoc. dir, Nat. Stud. High Sch. Eng. Progs, 63-66; lectr, ENG, UNIV. ILL, URBANA, 65-70, ASSOC. PROF, 70-, ASSOC. DEAN COL. LIB. ARTS & SCI, 66-, assoc. dean students, 66-67, acting head div. gen. stud, 67-69. Lectr, Univ. Rochester, 56-60; co-dir, Stud. Eng. Teaching in Selected British Schs, 67. U.S.N, 43-46. NCTE; MLA. Teaching of English; undergraduate education. Publ: Co-auth, High school English instruction today, Appleton, 68 & Teaching English in the United Kingdom, Nat. Counc. Teachers Eng, 69; auth, A record of English teaching today, Eng. J, 66; National aims in using and learning the mother tongue, In: Mother tongue practice in the schools UNESCO Inst. Educ, Hamburg, 72; The Transatlantic dialogue, In: New movements in the study of teaching of English, Maurice Temple Smith, London, 73. Add: College of Liberal Arts & Sciences, University of Illinois, Urbana, IL 61801.

APPLEBY, BRUCE C, b. Monticello, Iowa, June 19, 36. ENGLISH, EDUCATION. B.A, State Univ. Iowa, 58, M.A, 64, Ph.D.(Eng, educ), 67. Teacher Eng, high sch, Iowa, 58-63; high sch, Univ. Iowa, 63-66; instr. Eng. educ, Univ. Iowa, 66-67; asst. prof, Eng, SOUTH. ILL. UNIV, CARBONDALE, 67-68, ENG. & EDUC, 68-70, ASSOC. PROF, 70- Summers, vis. prof. Eng, Cent. Wash. State Col, 65, curriculum consult. Eng, NDEA Inst. High Sch. Teachers, Univ. Ky, 67 & NDEA Inst. Col. Eng, Fla. State Univ, 68; nat. chmn. convention newslett, NCTE, 67-; mem. adv. bd. consult, Am. Educ. Publ, 69-72; chmn. prog. comt, nat. convention, Conf. Eng. Educ, 70-71. NCTE; MLA. Teaching of literature; preparation of English teachers. Publ: Ed, Journeys, Ginn, 73; auth, Everybody is talking about it, Media & Methods, 1/70; co-auth, Growing up Black, Negro Am. Lit. Forum, summer 71; plus others. Add: Dept. of English, Southern Illinois University, Carbondale, IL 62901.

APPLEBY, JANE, b. Elberton, Ga, Dec. 20, 21. ENGLISH LANGUAGE. A.B, Piedmont Col, 41; M.A, Univ. Ga, 51; Sarah Moss fels, 56-58, E.B, Fred fel, 63-64; Ph.D.(Eng), Univ. Wis, 67. Ed. asst, Off. War Inform, 43-45; instr. ENG, UNIV. GA, 47-53, asst. prof, 53-69, ASSOC. PROF, 69-, DIR. LING. CURRICULUM, 73- Instr, Ling. Soc. Am. Inst, 72. MLA; Ling. Soc. Am; Am. Dialect Soc; Am. Name Soc; AAUP. American dialectology, especially Southern United States. Add: Dept. of English, University of Georgia, Athens, GA 30602.

APPLEGATE, JAMES EARL, b. Mt. Ayr, Ind, Sept. 16, 23; m. 53. ENGLISH. B.A, Johns Hopkins Univ, 43, Ph.D, 54. Instr. Eng, Univ. Rochester, 50-54, asst. prof, 55-56; instr, Exten, Univ. Md, 54-55; from asst. prof. to assoc. prof, Elmira Col, 56-65; PROF. ENG. & CHMN. DEPT, WILSON COL, 65- Southeast. Inst. Medieval & Renaissance Stud. fel, summer 68. U.S.A, 43-45, Staff Sgt. MLA; Col. Eng. Asn; Renaissance Soc. Am. Henry Lawes. Publ: Co-auth, Adventures in world literature, Harcourt, 71; auth, Sidney's classical meters, Mod. Lang. Notes; The classical learning of Robert Greene, Bibliot. d'Humanisme et Renaissance, 66. Add: Dept. of English, Wilson College, Chambersburg, PA 17201.

APPLEMAN, PHILIP DEAN, b. Kendallville, Ind, Feb. 8, 26; m. 50. ENGLISH. B.S, Northwest. Univ. 50, Ph.D, 55; A.M, Univ. Mich, 51; Fulbright scholar, Univ. Lyon, France, 51-52. Instr. ENG, IND. UNIV, BLOOMINGTON, 55-58, asst. prof, 58-62, assoc. prof, 62-67, PROF, 67- Co-ed, Victorian Stud, 57-62; instr. world lit. & philos, Int. Sch. Am, 60-61, field dir, 62-63; mem. adv. comt, Int. Honors Prog, 65-; vis. prof. lit, State Univ. N.Y. Col. Purchase, 73; vis. prof. Eng, Columbia Univ, 74. U.S.A.F, 44-45; U.S. Merchant Marine, 46, 48-49. MLA; NCTE; Poetry Soc. Am; AAUP. Creative writing in poetry; creative writing in fiction; Darwin studies. Publ: The silent explosion, Beacon, 65; Kites on a windy day, Byron, Univ. Nottingham, 67; Summer love and surf, Vanderbilt Univ, 68; co-auth, 1859: entering an age of crisis, Ind. Univ, 59; ed. & contrib, Darwin, Norton, 70; auth, In the twelfth year of the war, Putnam, 70; plus others. Dept. of English, Indiana University, Bloomington, IN 47401.

APPLEYARD, JOSEPH A, S.J, b. Malden, Mass, May 9, 31. ENGLISH. A.B, Boston Col, 53; Ph.L, Weston Col, 58; Ph.D, Harvard, 64; S.T.L, Theol. Faculteit S.J, Maastricht, Netherlands, 67. ASST. PROF. ENG, BOSTON COL, 67- Nineteenth and 20th century English literature; literary criticism and theory. Publ: Coleridge's philosophy of literature, Harvard, 65. Add: Dept. of English, Boston College, Chestnut Hill, MA 02167.

APROBERTS, RUTH, b. Vancouver, B.C; U.S. citizen. ENGLISH LITERATURE. B.A, Univ. B.C, 41; M.A, Univ. Calif, Berkeley, 50; Ph.D.(Eng), Univ. Calif, Los Angeles, 66. Lectr. ENG, Univ. Calif, Los Angeles, 66-69; Hacettepe Univ, Turkey, 69-70; Univ. Calif, Los Angeles, 70-71; asst. prof, UNIV. CALIF, RIVERSIDE, 70-73, ASSOC. PROF, 73- MLA; Philol. Asn. Pac. Coast; Am. Class. League. Victorian literature; aesthetics; English Bible. Publ: The moral Trollope, Ohio Univ, 71; Frank Kermode and the invented world, Novel, winter 68; Trollope's Cousin Henry, 19th Century Fiction, 6/69; The novel as self-evident sham: Flann O'Brien's At Swim-Two-Birds, Eire-Ireland, summer 71. Add: Dept. of English, University of California, Riverside, Riverside, CA 92502.

APTEKAR, JANE, b. Prestwick, Scotland, June 9, 35; m. 59; c. 2. ENGLISH. B.A, Oxford, 56, M.A, 60; Ph.D.(Eng), Columbia Univ, 67. ASST. PROF. Eng, Queens Col.(N.Y), 67-69; comp. lit, Rutgers Univ, 69-72; LIT, STATE UNIV. N.Y. COL. PURCHASE, 72- Publ: Icons of justice: iconography and thematic imagery in book V of The faerie queene, Columbia Univ, 69. Add: 645 Water St, New York, NY 10002.

ARCHER, JEROME WALTER, b. Milwaukee, Wis, May 23, 07; m; c. 1. ENGLISH. A.B, Marquette Univ, 30, A.M, 32; univ. fel, Northwest. Univ, 39-40, Ph.D, 42. Instr. ENG. & head dept, high sch, Wis, 30-36; instr, Marquette Univ, 36-39, 40-44, asst. prof, 44-45, assoc. prof, 45-52, prof, 52-63, chmn. dept, 48-63; PROF, ARIZ. STATE UNIV, 63-, chmn. dept, 63-71. Consult, U.S. Off. Educ, 66-71. MLA; NCTE; Mediaeval Acad. Am; Am. Dialect Soc; Conf. Col. Compos. & Commun.(chmn, 55). English language; Chaucer; English composition. Publ: Co-auth, A reader for writers, 62, 66 & 71 & Exposition, 66 & 71, McGraw; auth, Latin-loan words in early Middle English & Chaucer, PMLA. Add: Dept. of English, Arizona State University, Tempe, AZ 85281.

ARCHER, LEONARD COURTNEY, b. Atlanta, Ga, Aug. 17, 11; m. 40. ENGLISH. A.B, Morehouse Col, 34; M.A, Univ. Toronto, 40; Ph.D, Ohio State Univ, 58. Head dept. Eng, Albany State Col, 38-43; Alcorn Agr. & Mech. Col, 43-45; Ark. Agr. & Mech. Col, 45-47; dept. speech, Cent. State Col. (Ohio), 47-57; PROF. SPEECH & ENG, TENN. STATE UNIV, 58- Dr. Christian Award, 43. Natl. Asn. Dramatic & Speech Arts (v.pres, 46); Am. Theatre Asn. The Negro in the American theatre; the African Methodist Episcopal Church; ancient literature of the world. Publ: A study of world literature: from Confucius to Dante, workbook, W.C. Brown, 63; Black images in the American theatre, Pageant-Poseidon, 73; Frederick Douglass, testament of freedom, 3/49 & Ethiopian romance, 1 & 2/56, Negro Hist. Bull. Add: Dept. of English & Speech, Tennessee State University, Nashville, TN 37203.

ARCHER, LEWIS FRANKLIN, b. Salt Lake City, Utah, July 15, 35; m. 60; c. 1. THEOLOGY & LITERATURE. A.B, Univ. Denver, 57; B.D, Pac. Sch. Relig, 64; Ph.D.(relig. & Lit), Drew Univ, 67. Asst. prof, humanities, Oxford, Col, Emory Univ, 66-68; ENG, WHITWORTH COL.(WASH), 68-70, ASSOC. PROF, 70-, CHMN. DEPT, 73- Fac. lectr, Oxford Col, 67, res. grant, 67. MLA; Am. Acad. Arts & Sci; AAUP. Computer assisted instruction in the humanities using PDP-11 and BASIC plus author language; Romantic poets and novelists of 19th century England and America. Publ: Teles holy week drama in Mozambique, Int. J. Relig. Educ, 4/62. Add: Dept. of English, Whitworth College, Spokane, WA 99251.

ARCHER, STANLEY LOUIS, b. Tyler, Tex, Apr. 6, 35; m. 55; c. 1. ENGLISH. B.A, Tex. A&M Univ, 59; Woodrow Wilson fel, Univ. Miss, 59, M.A, 61, NDEA fel, 59-62, Ph.D.(Eng), 65. Teacher, High Sch, Tex, 59; asst. ENG, Univ. Miss, 61; instr, TEX. A&M UNIV, 62-65, asst. prof, 65-67, assoc. prof, 67-70, PROF, 70- MLA; NCTE. Seventeenth and 18th century English literature and restoration literature. Publ: Meditation and the structure of Donne's Holy sonnets, ELH, 61; The persons in An essay of dramatic poesy, Papers on Lang. & Lit, 66; Benaiah in Absalom and Achitophel II, Eng. Lang. Notes, 66. Add: 1219 Westover, College Station, TX 77840.

ARCHIBALD, DOUGLAS NELSON, b. New York, N.Y, Apr. 20, 33; m. 61; c. 5. ENGLISH LITERATURE. B.A, Dartmouth Col, 55; M.A, Univ. Mich, 59, Ph.D.(Eng), 66. From instr. to asst. prof. Eng. & asst. dean, Cornell Univ, 64-73; PROF. ENG. & CHMN. DEPT, COLBY COL, 73- Res. fel, Cornell Univ, summer 67-70; Soc. for Humanities jr. fel, 68. U.S.A.F, 55-58, Capt. Am. Comt. Irish Stud; Can. Asn. Irish Stud. Irish studies; literary history; literature and politics. Publ: John Butler Yeats, Bucknell Univ, 73; Yeats' encounters: observations on literary history, New Lit. Hist, 70; Father and son: J.B. and W.B. Yeats, Mass. Rev, 73; Yeats' encounter with Jonathan Swift, Yeats Stud, 74. Add: Dept. of English, Colby College, Waterville, ME 04901.

ARDEN, EUGENE, b. New York, N.Y, June 25, 23; m. 48; c. 2. ENGLISH. B.A, N.Y. Univ, 44; M.A, Columbia Univ, 47; Ph.D.(Eng), Ohio State Univ, 53. Instr, Ohio State Univ, 47-50; Queens Col.(N.Y), 50-52; Eng, Hofstra Col, 52-57; asst. prof, C.W. Post Col, L.I. Univ, 57-59, assoc. prof, 59-61, prof, 61-62, dean, 62-64, dean grad. fac, Univ, 64-70, exec. dean, Brooklyn Ctr, 70-72; DEAN ACAD. AFFAIRS, UNIV. MICH-DEARBORN, 72-, PROVOST, 74- U.S.A, 43-46. MLA; NEA. Naturalism in fiction; literary uses of urbanism; American literature. Publ: The evil city in American history, N.Y. Hist, 7/54; What college students read, Sat. Rev, 11/61; Great scholars, great teacher, J. Higher Educ, 3/64; plus others. Add: Office of Academic Affairs, University of Michigan-Dearborn, Dearborn, MI 48128.

ARENDS, ROBERT LOWELL, b. Alexander, Iowa, Mar. 12, 20; m. 59; c. 2. ENGLISH, PHILOSOPHY. A.B, North. Iowa Univ, 41; M.A, Northwest. Univ, 44; Ph.D.(philos, relig), Yale, 48. Instr. Eng, Cornell Univ, 46-49; asst. prof. philos, Fla. State Univ, 49-53; Eng, Heidelberg Col, 54-56; Ky. Wesleyan Col, 56-60; assoc. prof, Memphis State Univ, 60-62; philos, North. Ariz. Univ, 62-66; Eng, Morehead State Univ, 66-68; Ball State Univ, 68-70; PROF. LANG. & LIT. & CHMN. DEPT, NORTH. MONT. COL, 70- Consult. CHOICE, Asn. Col. & Res. Librs, 68. NEA. World literature; the philosophy of history and culture; an integrative approach to the arts. Publ: The humanities: medieval, Renaissance, Baroque, 51 & The humanities: the modern world, 52, Tampa Grower; Helping the less-competent student to write, Ky. Eng. Bull, winter 59. Add: Dept. of Language & Literature, Northern Montana College, Havre, MT 59501.

ARGO, IRIS STEWART, b. Leslie, Ga, Aug. 22, 14; m. 33; c. 2. ELIZABETHAN DRAMA, AMERICAN ROMANTICISM. A.B, Ga. Col. Milledgeville, 50; M.Ed, Mercer Univ, 57; Delta Kappa Gamma int. scholar, Univ. Ga, 61, Ph.D.(Eng), 66. Teacher, pub. schs, Ga, 45-57; asst. prof. ENG, Ga. Southwest. Col, 57-59; teaching asst, Univ. Ga, 61-62; assoc. prof, GA. SOUTHWEST. COL, 63-66, PROF, 66-, CHMN. DIV. ENG. & HUMANITIES, 63- MLA. Elizabethan drama, especially Shakespeare; American literature, especially the Romantic period. Publ: Simms and the Elizabethans, Lithographed Ed, 66; Maiden aunts, Am. Bard, 59; Ask again, Poetry Digest, 59; Bargain, Ga. Mag, 59; plus several poems in various publ. Add: Macon Rd, Americus, GA 31709.

ARIAS, BOGDANKA, b. Pampa, Argentina, Oct. 4, 30; m. 54; c. 1. ENGLISH, SPANISH. B.A, Bahia Blanca Col, Argentina, 47, M.A, 49; Univ. Buenos Aires, 53; Ph.D.(comp. lit), Univ. Ark, 67. PROF. Spanish & lit, Nat. Col. Gen. Roca, Argentina, 53-57; Spanish, Univ. Ark, 64-65; ENG. Ark. State Univ, Jonesboro, 66-67; Delta State Col, 66-67; Cent. Mo. State Col, 67-68; NORTHEAST. STATE COL, 68- Argentina Ministery Educ. fel, 61-62; lectr, Univ. Ecuador, 73. Am. Asn. Teachers Span. & Port; MLA. Comparative literature; Argentine literature; drama. Publ: Co-auth, In the Colón, no, Hispania, 9/68; auth, Sailor's reveries, Costerus, Amsterdam, 71. Add: 1224 Stephens, Fayetteville, AR 72701.

ARMATO, PHILIP MICHELE, b. Chicago, Ill, Oct. 28, 43. MODERN DRAMA, ENGLISH LITERATURE. B.A, Univ. Wis-Madison, 65; M.A, Purdue Univ, West Lafayette, 66, Ph.D.(Eng), 70. Instr. ENG, Univ. Cincinnati, 68-70; ASST. PROF, NORTH. ILL. UNIV, 70- MLA. Modern drama; American drama; English literature 1880-1920. Publ: Good and evil in Lillian Hellman's The children's hour, Educ. Theatre J, 12/73. Add: Dept. of English, Northern Illinois University, De Kalb, IL 60115.

ARMENS, SVEN MAGNUS, b. Cambridge, Mass, Aug. 11, 21; m. 42; c. 2. ENGLISH. A.B, Tufts Univ, 43; M.A, Harvard, 47, fel. & Ph.D.(Eng), 51. Teaching fel. ENG, Harvard, 49-50; instr, UNIV. IOWA, 50-54, asst. prof, 54-61, assoc. prof, 61-66, PROF, 66- U.S.A, 44-45. MLA; Renaissance Soc. Am; Int. Asn. Univ. Prof. Eng. Eighteenth century English literature;

English literature of the Renaissance; modern poetry. Publ: John Gay: social critic, Columbia Univ, 54; Archetypes of the family in literature, Univ. Wash, 66. Add: 617 S. Dodge St, Iowa City, IA 52240.

ARMOLD, BENJAMIN, b. York, Pa, Dec. 6, 07; m. 47. ENGLISH, ADMINISTRATION. A.B, Gettysburg Col, 29; A.M, Univ. N.C, 36; M.S, Univ. Pa, 41. Teacher, Somerville High Sch, N.J, 29-31; Hun Sch, N.J, 31-34; prin, N.York High Sch, Pa, 35-41; ASSOC. PROF. ENG, WIDENER COL, 46-, DEAN EVENING DIV, 54- U.S.A.F, 43-46, Maj. Asn. Univ. Evening Cols; Am. Soc. Engineering Educ. Old English. Add: Dept. of English, Widener College, Chester, PA 19013.

ARMOUR, RICHARD (WILLARD), b. San Pedro, Calif, July 15, 06; m. 32; c. 2. ENGLISH LITERATURE. A.B, Pomona Col, 27, Litt.D, 72; A.M, Harvard, 28, Dexter scholar, 31, Ph.D, 33; Litt.D, Col. of Ozarks, 44; hon. L.H.D, Whittier Col, 68, South. Calif. Col. Optom, 72; LL.D, Col. of Idaho, 69. Instr. Eng, Tex, 28-29; Northwest. Univ, 30-31; prof, Col. of Ozarks, 32-33; Am. lectr, Univ. Freiburg, 33-34; from asst. prof. to prof. ENG, Wells Col, 34-45; prof, SCRIPPS COL, 45-66, dean fac, 61-63, EMER. PROF. & DEAN FAC, 66- Prof. Claremont Grad. Sch, 45-66; Fund Advan. Educ. fel, 53-54; Carnegie vis. prof, Univ. Hawaii, 57; Am. specialist for State Dept, Europe & Asia, 64, & 66-70; chancellor's lectr, Calif. State Cols, 65, 67, 69 & 70; writer-in-residence, Univ. Redlands, 74. U.S.A, 42-46, Res, 27-53, Col; Legion of Merit & Oak Leaf. MLA. Light verse; early 19th century English literature; literary criticism. Publ: Co-ed, Coleridge the talker, 40; auth, Yours for the asking, 42; Golf bawls, 46; Writing light verse, 47; For partly proud parents, 50; It all started with Columbus, 53; Light armour 54; It all started with Europa, 55; It all started with Eve, 56; Twisted tales from Shakespeare, 57; Nights with armour, 58; It all started with Marx, 58; Drug Store days, 59; The classics reclassified, 60; Safari into satire, 61; Golf is a four-letter word, 62; Armour's almanac, 62; The medical muse, or what to do until the patient comes, 63; Through darkest adolescence, 63; The year Santa went modern, 64; American lit relit, 64; An armoury of light verse, 64; Our presidents, 64; The adventures of Egbert the Easter egg, 65; Going around in academic circles, 65; Animals on the ceiling, 66; It all started with Hippocrates, 66; Punctured poems, 66; Dozen dinosaurs, 67; It all started with stones and clubs, 67; My life with women: confessions of a domesticated male, 68; Odd old mammals, 68; English lit relit, 69; On your marks, 69; A diabolical dictionary of education, World, 70; A short history of sex, 70, All sizes and shapes of monkeys and apes, 70, Who's in holes?, 71, Out of my mind, 72, All in sport, 72, The strange dreams of Rover Jones, 73, It all started with freshman English, 73, Going like sixty: a lighthearted look at the later years, 74 & Sea full of whales, 74, McGraw; Writing light verse and prose humor, Writer, 71; plus syndicated weekly newspaper column & numerous poems & articles. Add: 460 Blaisdell Dr, Claremont, CA 91711.

ARMOUR, ROBERT ALEXANDER, b. Richmond, Va, Mar. 23, 40; m. 65. AMERICAN & ENGLISH LITERATURE. B.A, Randolph-Macon Col, 62; M.A, Vanderbilt Univ, 63; Ph.D.(Am. lit), Univ. Ga, 68. Instr. ENG, VA. COMMONWEALTH UNIV, 63-68, ASST. PROF, 68- Nat. Endowment for Arts grants, 73, 74. Religious satire of 18th century England and America; film and literature. Publ: Student filmmaking in English courses, 71 & TV commercials and the teaching of English, 72, Va. Eng. Bull, 72; Deliverance: four variations on the American Adam, Lit. Film Quart, 73. Add: Dept. of English, Virginia Commonwealth University, 901 W. Franklin St, Richmond, VA 23220.

ARMS, GEORGE (WARREN), b. La Grande, Ore, Feb. 1, 12; m. 36. ENGLISH LITERATURE. A.B, Princeton, 33; Univs. Zurich & Munich, 34-35; Ph.D, N.Y. Univ, 39. Teacher, Bennett Jr. Col, 39; asst. prof. ENG, Mary Washington Col, Va, 39-44; PROF, UNIV. N.MEX, 44-, chmn. dept, 51-56, Ford fac. fel, 54-55. Co-ed, Explicator, 42-; Am. Counc. Learned Soc. grant-in-aid, 64; mem. exec. comt, Howells Edition ed. bd, 64-; Am. Philos. Soc. grant, 68; mem. adv. bd, ESQ, 71-; mem. ed. bd, Ariel, 73- MLA; NCTE; Am. Stud. Asn; Rocky Mt. Mod. Lang. Asn.(co-pres, 67-68). Nineteenth century American literature; contemporary criticism; pragmatism and realism. Publ: The fields were green, Stanford, 53; co-auth, Twelve American writers, Macmillan, 62 & co-ed, TLE six: options for the 1970's, Holt, 72; plus others. Add: Dept. of English, University of New Mexico, Albuquerque, NM 87131.

ARMSTRONG, CHLOE, b. Pauls Valley, Okla, Jan. 4, 07. SPEECH. A.B, Okla. E.Cent. State Col, 36; M.A, Northwest. Univ, 41; fel, Univ. Okla, 41-43. Instr. SPEECH, Univ. Okla, 41-43; asst. prof, Univ. Miss, 47-49; assoc. prof, BAYLOR UNIV, 49-59, PROF, 60- Vis. prof, Wayne State Univ, 59-60; summer guest prof, Univ. N.C, 67. Speech Commun. Asn; South. Speech Commun. Asn. Oral interpretation and communication; oral interpretation of Bible. Publ: Co-auth, Oral interpretation of literature, McGraw, 63; contrib, Perspective in oral interpretation, 66 & auth, Oral interpretation of Biblical literature, 68, Burgess; contrib, The communicative arts and sciences of speech, Merrill, 67; auth, Editor of news and notes, South. Speech J, 53; Book review Literature as experience—Bacon and Breen, Speech Teacher, 1/60. Add: Dept. of Speech, College of Arts & Sciences, Baylor University, Waco, TX 76703.

ARMSTRONG, ELIZABETH P, b. Baltimore, Md, Mar. 14, 33; m. 56. ENGLISH. A.B, Ind. Univ, 57, fel, 63-64, Ph.D.(comp. lit), 66. Lectr. ENG, Queens Col.(N.Y), 64-66; ASST. PROF, McMICKEN COL, UNIV. CINCINNATI, 66- Mediaeval Acad. Am; MLA. Middle English; Mediaeval Latin; Old French. Publ: Heinrich Suso's Horologium: a newly discovered excerpt, Manuscripta, 68. Add: Dept. of English, McMicken College, University of Cincinnati, Cincinnati, OH 45221.

ARMSTRONG, RAY LIVINGSTONE, b. Brooklyn, N.Y, June 20, 10. ENGLISH. A.B, Williams Col, 30; B.A, Oxford, 32, M.A, 36; univ. fel, Columbia Univ, 37-38, Ph.D, 41. Master, Asheville Sch, 33-34; Mt. Hermon Sch, 34-35; instr, Carnegie Inst. Tech, 38-41; Pine Manor Jr. Col, 41-43; asst. prof. ENG, LEHIGH UNIV, 46-58, assoc. prof, 58-70, PROF, 70- English literature; poems of James Shirley. Add: Dept. of English, Lehigh University, Bethlehem, PA 18015.

ARNER, ROBERT DAVID, b. Lehighton, Pa, Jan. 17, 43. AMERICAN LITERATURE. B.S. in Ed, Kutztown State Col, 64; M.A, Pa. State Univ, 66, Ph.D. (Eng), 70. Instr. ENG, Cent. Mich. Univ, 68-69, asst. prof, 69-71; UNIV. CINCINNATI, 71-72, ASSOC. PROF, 72- Mem. int. bibliog. comt, MLA, 68-; fel, John Carter Brown Libr, Providence, R.I, summer 70. MLA; Soc. Stud. South. Lit. Early American literature; 19th century American literature; American humor. Publ: Hawthorne and Jones Very: two dimensions of satire in Egotism: or, the bosom serpent, New Eng. Quart, 6/69; Ebenezer Cooke's The sot-weed factor: the structure of satire, South. Lit. J, fall 71; Pastoral patterns in William Bartram's Travels, Tenn. Stud. Lit, 73. Add: Dept. of English, University of Cincinnati, Cincinnati, OH 45221.

ARNOLD, AEROL, b. Chicago, Ill, May 30, 11. ENGLISH. Ph.B, Univ. Chicago, 31, A.M, 33, Ph.D, 37. Mem. fac. Eng. & comp. lit, Univ. Tex, 35; Univ. Minn, 36-37; Northwest. Univ, 37-38; asst. prof. Eng. & humanities, Univ. Louisville, 38-39; chmn. dept. ENG, Englewood Evening Jr. Col, 39-41; asst. prof, UNIV. SOUTH. CALIF, 46-51, assoc. prof, 51-56, PROF, 56- Mem. fac, Ill. Inst. Technol, 39-41. U.S.A.A.F, 43-45. MLA; Col. Eng. Asn. Elizabethan literature. Publ: The character of Brabantio in Othello, Shakespeare Quart; Why structure in fiction, Am. Quart. 58; Picture, scene, and social criticism in The Great Gatsby, Univ. Rev, 63. Add: Dept. of English, University of Southern California, Los Angeles, CA 90007.

ARNOLD, CARROLL CLYDE, b. Lake Park, Iowa, Apr. 29, 12; m. 36. SPEECH. A.B, Sioux Falls Col, 33; A.M, State Univ. Iowa, 40, Ph.D.(hist. & criticism of pub. address), 42. Teacher elem. schs, S.Dak, 33-34, sec. schs, 34-39; asst, State Univ. Iowa, 39-41; instr, Univ. Akron, 41-42; Pa. Col. Women, 42-43; speech & drama, Cornell Univ, 46, asst. prof, 46-52, assoc. prof, 52-60, PROF, 60-63, chmn. dept, 57-63; SPEECH, PA. STATE UNIV, 63- Assoc. ed, Philos. & Rhetoric, 68- U.S.A.A.F, 43-46. Speech Commun. Asn.(ed, Speech Monogr, 66-68); Speech Asn. East. States (pres, 63-64). Rhetorical criticism; philosophy of rhetoric. Publ: Co-auth, Public speaking as a liberal art, Allyn & Bacon, 64, 68 & 74; Handbook of group discussion, Houghton, 2nd ed, 65; Select British speeches, Ronald, 67; auth, Criticism of oral rhetoric, Merrill, 74; George William Curtis, In: History & criticism of American public address, Vol. 3, Longmans; Oral rhetoric, rhetoric and literature, Philos. & Rhetoric, fall 68; co-auth, An analysis of Logos: a methodological inquiry, Quart. J. Speech, 2/70; plus others. Add: 492 Sierra Lane, State College, PA 16801.

ARNOLD, JAMES ALDEN, b. New York, N.Y, Sept. 27, 18; m. 38; c. 5. LITERATURE, NAVAL HISTORY. A.B, Princeton Univ, 39, A.M, 49, Ph.D. (Eng), 51. Half-time instr. Eng, Princeton Univ, 47-48, 50-51, asst. naval sci, 48-50; asst. prof. ENG, LIT. & HIST, U.S. NAVAL ACAD, 51-58, ASSOC. PROF, 58- Lectr, George Washington Univ, 53, tech. writing, 54, 56, 57; consult. pub. standards, tech. pub. sect, Aerospace Div, Westinghouse Electric Corp, Friendship, Md, 56-70; tech. writer & ed, Trident Eng. Assocs, Annapolis, 70- U.S.N.R, 41-46, 48-50, Comdr. Mediaeval Acad. Am; MLA; Milton Soc. Am. English literature, mediaeval and renaissance; Joseph Conrad. Publ: Co-auth, The United States and world sea power, 55, Sea power: a naval history, 60 & The great sea war, 63, Prentice-Hall. Add: Dept. of English, U.S. Naval Academy, Annapolis, MD 21402.

ARNOLD, JUDD B, b. New York, N.Y, Sept. 11, 35; m. 57; c. 3. ENGLISH. B.A, Univ. Conn, 57, Ph.D.(Eng), 65; Nat. Defense fel, 59-62. Asst. prof. ENG, PA. STATE UNIV, UNIVERSITY PARK, 62-72, ASSOC. PROF, 72- Assoc. ed. & reviewer, Seventeenth Century News, 65- Intel.C, U.S.A. MLA; Milton Soc. Am. Renaissance and 17th century poetry and drama. Publ: A grace peculiar: Ben Jonson's cavalier heroes, Pa. State Univ, 72; The double plot in Volpone, Seventeenth Century News, winter 65; Lovewit's triumph: a note on Jonsonian morality, spring 72 & How do we judge King Lear? spring 72, Criticism. Add: Dept. of English, Pennsylvania State University, University Park, PA 16802.

ARNOLD, LIONEL ATWELL, Religion, Literature. See Volume IV, Philosophy, Religion & Law.

ARNOLD, LOIS VIRGINIA, b. Buffalo, N.Y, Apr. 3, 18. ENGLISH, EDUCATION. A.B, Shorter Col.(Ga), 39; M.Ed, Univ. Va, 55; Ed.D.(Eng. & educ), Fla. State Univ, 63. Teacher, jr. & sr. high schs, Fla, 39-59; supvr, Pinellas County pub. schs, Fla, 59-68; INSTRUCT. CONSULT. READING, SAN DIEGO CITY SCHS, 68- Mem, Comn. Eng. Curriculum, NCTE, 65-66, 68-70; regional counc, Southeast. Educ. Lab, 66-68; Fla. State Textbook Comt, 67-68. NCTE; Int. Reading Asn; NEA. Written composition; secondary reading. Publ: Co-auth, Effects of frequency of writing and intensity of teacher evaluation upon students' performance in written composition, U.S. Off. Educ, 63; auth, Writer's cramp and eyestrain—are they paying off?, Eng. J, 1/64. Add: 6544 Belle Glade Ave, San Diego, CA 92119.

ARNOLD, MARC HADLEY, b. Seattle, Wash, Feb. 21, 41; m. 63; c. 2. ENGLISH LITERATURE. B.A, Univ. Wash, 63; M.A, Johns Hopkins Univ, 64; Ph.D.(Eng), Univ. Wis-Madison, 73. ASST. PROF. ENG, Colby Col, 69-73; UNIV. ARK, LITTLE ROCK, 73- MLA. Renaissance literature and religion. Publ: The logos metaphor in Milton's epic poetry, Diss. Abstr, 73. Add: Dept. of English, University of Arkansas at Little Rock, Little Rock, AR 72204.

ARNOLD, RICHARD LEE, b. Ames, Iowa, June 2, 28; m. 51; c. 3. DRAMATIC ART. B.A, State Univ. Iowa, 50, M.A, 51; Ph.D.(drama), Northwest. Univ, 62. Instr. speech & drama, Iowa State Teachers Col, 51-53; Fresno State Col, 53-56, assoc. prof. theatre, 56-65; THEATRE ART, NORTH. ILL. UNIV, 65-70, PROF, 70-, CHMN. DEPT, 72- Vis. instr, State Univ. Iowa, summer 53, 55; grad. asst, Northwest. Univ, 60-61. U.S. Inst. Theatre Technol; Am. Theatre Asn; Sec. Sch. Theatre Conf; Speech Commun. Asn; West. Speech Commun. Asn; U.S. Inst. Theatre Technol.(v.pres, 71-73, pres, 73-). Technical theatre production; theatrical history; scenography. Publ: A study of the comic techniques in the farces of John Maddison Morton, West. Speech, winter 65; Progressive intensification in design, Educ. Theatre J, fall 68; The great chariot race: scenic effects at the turn of the century, Theatre Design & Technol, 12/70; plus one other. Add: Dept. of Theatre Arts, Northern Illinois University, DeKalb, IL 60115.

ARNOLD, ROBERT L, b. Bangor, Maine, Aug. 15, 26; m. 48; c. 3. BROADCASTING, SPEECH. B.A, Univ. Maine, 50; M.A, Ohio Univ, 61, Ph.D.(radio & TV), 64. Asst. prof. radio-TV & speech, West. Ill. Univ, 63-68; assoc. prof. radio-TV & commun, FLA. TECHNOL. UNIV, 68-71, PROF. COMMUN. & DIR. GRAD. PROG, 71- West. Ill. Univ. Res. Coun. grant, summer 66; vis. prof, Univ. Maine, summer 67. U.S.A, 44-46, T/Sgt. Asn. Prof. Broadcasting Educ; Nat. Asn. Educ. Broadcasting; Speech Commun. Asn; Broadcast Educ. Asn.(chmn. Course & Curricula Comt, 73-74). Cablevision; communication instruction; auto-tutorial methods. Publ: Co-auth, Radio-television-film composite course outlines, Asn. Prof. Broadcasting Educ, 9/68. Add: Dept. of Communications, Florida Technological University, Box 25,000, Orlando, FL 32816.

ARNOLD, WILLIAM E, b. Tecumseh, Mich, Nov. 23, 40; m. 63; c. 2. COMMUNICATION, SPEECH. B.S, North. Ill. Univ, 62, M.A, 63; univ. res. grant, Pa. State Univ, 65, Ph.D.(speech), 66. Instr. speech, Pa. State Univ, 63-66; asst. prof. commun, Univ. Conn, 66-68; Case West. Reserve Univ, 68-70; assoc. prof. speech, Ill. State Univ, 70-73, chmn. dept. speech commun, 71-72; PROF. SPEECH & CHMN. DEPT. SPEECH & THEATRE, ARIZ. STATE UNIV, 73- U.S. Off. Educ. grant, 66; vis. asst. prof. speech, Univ. Mass, summer 67; mem, U.S. Off. Educ-Speech Asn. Am. Res. Conf. Speech Commun, 68; summer fel, Fla. State Univ, 68. Am. Psychol. Asn; Int. Commun. Asn; Am. Asn. Suicidology; Cent. States Speech Asn; Am. Asn. Pub. Opinion Res. Jury size and satisfaction; political communication; teacher evaluation. Publ: Co-auth, Communication behavior, Xerox Corp, 72 & Attitude intensity and the neutral point on the semantic differential scales, Pub. Opinion Quart, winter 67; auth, Jefferson Davis—forgotten statesman, J. Miss. Hist, 71; co-auth, The intensity component of semantic differential scores for measuring attitude, West. Speech, 72; plus others. Add: Dept. of Speech & Theatre, Arizona State University, Tempe, AZ 85281.

ARNOTT, PETER D, b. Ipswich, Eng, Nov. 21, 31; m. 58; c. 2. FOREIGN LANGUAGES, DRAMATIC ARTS. B.A, Univ. Col. N.Wales, 52; B.A, Oxford, 54; M.A, Univ. Wales, 56, Ph.D, 58. Vis. lectr. classics, Univ. Iowa, 58-59, asst. prof, 59-60, classics & dramatic art, 60-61, assoc. prof, 61-68, PROF, 68-69; DRAMA, TUFTS UNIV, 69-, DIR. GRAD. STUD, DRAMA DEPT, 70- Can. Counc. touring lectr, 60, 62; vis. prof, Univ. Miss, 61; Monmouth Col, 63; summer vis. prof, Univ. Colo, 60, 62; Hill Family Found. res. prof, Japan, 67. Hellenic Soc; Class Asn. Mid.W. & S; Educ. Theatre Asn. Oriental and Greek theatre; puppetry; Greek theatre history. Publ: An introduction to the Greek theatre, 59, The theatres of Japan, 69, The Romans and their world, 70 & The Byzantine world, 73, Macmillan, London & St. Martin's, N.Y; Three Greek plays for the theatre, Ind. Univ, 61; Greek scenic conventions in the fifth century B.C, Oxford, 62; An introduction to the Greek world, 67 & Ballet of comedians, 72, Macmillan; The ancient Greek and Roman theatre, Random, 71. Add: 6 Herrick St, Winchester, MA 01890.

ARNQUIST, JAMES, b. Hoffman, Minn, Jan. 29, 32; m. 62; c. 2. AMERICAN HISTORY & LITERATURE. B.A, Hamline Univ, 54; Ph.D.(Am. stud), Univ. Minn, Minneapolis, 68. Asst. prof. Eng, State Univ. N.Y. Plattsburgh, 64-66; instr. Eng. & Am. lit, Wayne State Univ, 66-68; ASST. PROF. AM. STUD, UNIV. MD, BALTIMORE COUNTY, 68- U.S.A, 54-56. Am. Stud. Asn. Utopian studies, literature and experimental communities; New England transcendentalism; science fiction. Add: Division of Humanities & Arts, University of Maryland, Baltimore County, 5401 Wilkens Ave, Baltimore, MD 21228.

ARNTSON, HERBERT EDWARD, b. Tacoma, Wash, Apr. 8, 11; m. 46; c. 3. ENGLISH. B.A, Univ. Puget Sound, 37, M.A, 40, Univ. Wash, 43-45, summers, 48 & 52. Instr. ENG, WASH. STATE UNIV, 46-50, asst. prof, 50-58, assoc. prof, 58-65, PROF, 65-, MEM. GRAD. FAC, 69-, coord. creative writing prog, 69-72. MLA; Authors Guild. Old English; romantic poets; creative writing. Publ: Caravan to Oregon, Binfords, 57; Adam Gray; stowaway, 61 & Two guns in old Oregon, 63, Watts; Frontier boy, 67, Mountain boy, 68 & River boy, 69, Ives Washburn. Add: Dept. of English, Washington State University, Pullman, WA 99163.

ARNTZ, MARY LUKE, S.N.D, b. Stark Co, Ohio, July 6, 11. ENGLISH. A.B, Notre Dame Col.(Ohio), 35; M.A, Univ. Notre Dame, 44; Ph.D.(Eng), Fordham Univ, 61. Instr. Eng. & Latin, Notre Dame Acad, Cleveland, Ohio, 35-48, prin, 48-53; Notre Dame Acad, Los Angeles, Calif, 53-57; prof. Eng, NOTRE DAME COL.(OHIO), 61-66, v.pres, 66-67, PRES, 67- NCTE; MLA. Medieval literature; history of English language, especially linguistics. Publ: Co-auth, The holy boke gratia Dei, Univ. Microfilms, 61; auth, That fol of whos folie men ryme, Am. Notes & Queries, 6/65. Add: Notre Dame College, 4545 College Rd, Cleveland, OH 44121.

ARONS, PETER L, b. New York, N.Y, Dec. 16, 34; m. 64; c. 1. ENGLISH. A.B, N.Y. Univ, 57; M.A, Yale, 59, Ph.D.(Eng), 64. Instr. ENG, Univ. Ky, 62-65; asst. prof, UNIV. DAYTON, 65-69, ASSOC. PROF, 69- Consult. prog. for self-directed learning, Univ. Dayton, 71- AAUP; Am. Asn. Higher Educ. Contemporary American novel; 20th century American fiction; small group dynamics applied to college teaching methods. Publ: Romanticism in the modern era, Genre, 3/70. Add: Dept. of English, University of Dayton, Dayton, OH 45469.

ARPAD, JOSEPH JOHN, b. Randolph, Ohio, Mar. 9, 37; m. 62. AMERICAN STUDIES, FOLKLORE. B.A, Univ. Calif, Los Angeles, 62; M.A, Univ. Iowa, 64; Ph.D.(Am. lit), Duke Univ, 68. ASST. PROF. ENG. & FOLKLORE, UNIV. CALIF, LOS ANGELES, 68- MLA; Am. Lit. Group, Mod. Lang. Asn; Philol. Asn. Pac. Coast (secy. folklore, 73-74, chmn, 74-75); Popular Cult. Asn.(chmn. folklore, 70-); Orgn. Am. Hist; Am. Folklore Soc. American folklore and literature, especially of the 19th century; American cultural and intellectual history; literary criticism. Publ: Co-ed, Buffalo Bill's Wild West, Filter Press, 71; ed, Narrative of the life of David Crockett, Col. & Univ, 72; co-ed, Essays mostly on periodical publishing in America: a collection in honor of Clarence Gohdes, Duke Univ, 73; auth, Hart Crane's Platonic myth: the Brooklyn Bridge, Am. Lit, 67; William Faulkner's legendary novels: the Snopes trilogy, Miss. Quart, 69; The fight: quotation and originality in native American humor, J. Folklore Inst, 74. Add: Dept. of English, University of California, Los Angeles, CA 90024.

ARRENDELL, ODES CHARLES, b. Baytown, Tex, Jan. 13, 37; m. 60; c. 2. COMMUNICATION. B.A, Wayland Col, 59; M.A, Univ. Iowa, 65; Ph.D.(commun) & univ. fel, Univ. Tex, Austin, 69. Pub. relat, dir. & tutor commun, New Orleans Baptist Seminary, 61-64; press rep, Baptist Gen. Convention of Tex, 64-65; publ. relat. dir. & instr. jour, Wayland Col, 65-67; reporter, Lubbock Avalanche-Journal, 67; asst. prof. JOUR, UNIV. ALA, 69-73, ASSOC. PROF, 73- Ed. Byliner Mag, Nat. Editorial Found, 73-74. Asn. Educ. Jour. Content analysis; political communication; public opinion. Publ: Baptist public relations directors, South. Baptist Educ, 66; Predicting the completeness of newspaper election coverage, Jour. Quart, 72; U.S. agencies look better to J-students after capital visit, Jour. Educr, 73. Add: School of Communication, University of Alabama, Box 1448, University, AL 35486.

ARRINGTON, RUTH MOZELLE, b. Tulsa, Okla, Oct. 15, 24. SPEECH. B.A, Okla. Col. Women, 46; M.A, Univ. Mich, Ann Arbor, 51; Ph.D.(speech), La. State Univ, Baton Rouge, 71. TEACHER SPEECH, Northeast. Okla. A&M Col, 46-56; NORTHEAST. STATE COL, 56- Actress, Horn in the West, Boone, N.C, summers 55-59, 62; The Trail of Tears, Tahlequah, Okla, summer 69; mem. ed. bd, Speech Teacher, 72- Speech Commun. Asn. American Indian literature; interpretation; drama. Add: 208 S. Mission, Tahlequah, OK 74464.

ARROWSMITH, WILLIAM AYRES, b. Orange, N.J, Apr. 13, 24; m. 45; c. 2. CLASSICS. A.B, Princeton, 47, Woodrow Wilson fel, 47-48, Ph.D.(classics), 54; Rhodes scholar, Oxford, 48-51, B.A, 51, M.A, 58; hon. LL.D, Loyola Univ.(Ill), 68; hon. D.L.H, St. Michael's Col, 68, Dickinson Col, 71, Grand Valley State Col, 73, Carnegie-Mellon Univ, 74; hon. D.Litt, Westminster Col.(Mo), 69, Dartmouth Col, 70, Univ. Detroit, 73 & Lebanon Valley Col, 73. Instr. classics, Princeton, 51-53; classics & humanities, Wesleyan Univ, 53-54; asst. prof. classics, Univ. Calif, Riverside, 54-56; assoc. prof, Univ. Tex, Austin, 58-59, prof, 59-70, Univ. Prof. arts & lett, 66-70, chmn. dept. classics, 66-67; vis. prof. humanities, Mass. Inst. Technol, 71; PROF. CLASSICS & UNIV. PROF, BOSTON UNIV, 72- Ed, Chimera, 42-44; Hudson Rev, 48-60; res. fel, Am. Acad. Rome, 56-57; Bollingen fel, 57; Guggenheim fel, 57-58; adv. ed, Tulane Drama Rev, 59-60; honors prof, Univ. Mich, summer 62; ed, Arion, J. Classics & Humanities, 62-; nat. Phi Beta Kappa vis. scholar, 64-65; mem. exec. bd, Nat. Transl. Ctr, 65-69; consult, Off. Educ, Mass. Inst. Technol, Ford Found, York Col, Kirkland Col. & Univ. Mass, 65-; mem. jury, Nat. Bk. Awards, 67 & 72; fel, Ctr. Advan. Stud, Wesleyan Univ, 67-68; fel, Battelle Mem. Inst, 68; ed, Delos, 68-70; adv. ed, Mosaic, 68-; mem. bd, Nat. Prof. Found, 70-; contrib. ed, Change, 70-72; Am. specialist Mid.E, U.S. Dept. State, 71-; comnr, Nat. Stud. Comn. Undergrad. Educ, 72-73; mem. comt. lib. learning, Asn. Am. Cols, 72-; contrib. ed, Am. Poetry Rev, 72-; mem. bd, Nat. Humanities Fac, 72- Bromberg Award for Excellence in Teaching, 59; Longview Award in Criticism, 60; Morris I. Ernst Award for Excellence in Teaching, 62; Piper Prof, 66; E. Harris Harbison Award for Distinguished Teaching, 71. Mil.Intel, U.S.A, 43-46. PEN Club. Film criticism; American Indian and Italian literature; educational reform. Publ: Transl, The Satyricon, 59, transl. & ed, The complete Greek comedies (12 vols), 60- & co-auth. & transl, Cesare Pavese: dialogues with Leuco, 65, Univ. Mich; transl, Euripides' Bacchae, Heracles, Cyclops, Hecuba & Orestes, 60; ed, Image of Italy, Univ. Tex, 61; co-auth, Craft and context of translation, 61; transl, Aristophanes' Birds, 61 & Clouds, 62; auth, The shame of the graduate schools, Harper, 66; The future of teaching, Pub. Interest, 67; The idea of a new university, 70; Notes toward an old frontier: teaching and the liberal arts, 70; gen. ed, The new Greek tragedy (33 vols), 73; plus others. Add: Box 311, R.D. 1, Lincoln, VT 05443.

ARSCOTT, JOHN R, b. Lorain, Ohio, Mar. 2, 06; m. 38; c. 2. ENGLISH. A.B, Col. Wooster, 28; M.A, Princeton, 30; Ph.D.(Eng. & educ), N.Y. Univ, 48. Teacher, jr. high sch, Ohio, 28-29; instr. Eng, Monmouth Col.(N.J), 34-36; teacher, Hubbard Sch, N.J, 36-37; high sch. N.J, 37-45; instr. Eng, N.Y. Univ, 45-47; chmn. Eng. dept, High Sch, N.J, 47-53; head dept, Anatolia Col, 53-54; chmn. dept, high schs, N.J, 54-61; dir. Eng, 61-62; coord. sr. div, 62-65; PROF. ENG, CLARION STATE COL, 65- Mem. comt, Mid. States Asn. Sec. Schs. & Cols, 50-51, 53 & 64; consult. Warriner Ser. Eng. grammar & compos, Harcourt, 65; sabbatical leave, Eng, fall 73. NCTE; NEA. Publ: Introduction to nonfiction, 65 & co-auth, New dimensions in literature (18 vols), 67, McCormick-Mathers; auth, William Torrey Harris: philosopher of freedom, 11/49 & Two philosophies of freedom, 11/51, Sch. & Soc; auth, Macbeth and the Idylls of the king (filmstrips), Audio-Visual Div, Popular Sci, 68. Add: Dept. of English, Clarion State College, Clarion, PA 16214.

ARTHOS, JOHN, b. Wilmington, Del, July 18, 08; m. 52; c. 5. ENGLISH PHILOLOGY. A.B, Dartmouth Col, 30; A.M, Harvard, 33, Ph.D, 37; Sheldon traveling fel, Harvard, 37-38. Instr. ENG, UNIV. MICH, ANN ARBOR, 38-42, asst. prof, 42-48, assoc. prof, 48-54, PROF, 54-, Henry Russell lectr, 70, Hereward T. Price univ. prof. Eng, 72. Fulbright res. scholar, Univ. Florence, 49-50; Guggenheim fel, 56-57; vis. prof, Univ. Wash, summer, 63; Am. Counc. Learned Soc. fel, 63-64; res. prof, Univ. Rome, 72-73. U.S.A, 42-45. MLA; Renaissance Soc. Am; Dante Soc. Renaissance; 18th century; modern literature. Publ: The language of natural description in eighteenth century poetry, Univ. Mich, 49, Octagon, 67; On a mask presented at Ludlow-Castle by John Milton, Univ. Mich, 54; On the poetry of Spenser and the form of romances, Allen & Unwin, 56; The art of Shakespeare, 63, Milton and the Italian cities, 68 & Shakespeare: the early writings, 72, Bowes & Bowes; Dante, Michelangelo and Milton, Routledge & Kegan Paul, 62; ed, Love's labor lost, Signet Shakespeare, New Am. Libr, 65; co-ed, The life of Adam, Scholar's Facsimiles, 68. Add: Dept. of English, University of Michigan, Ann Arbor, MI 48104.

ARTHURS, MARIE, b. Fayetteville, Ark, Jan. 25, 13; m. 33; c. 2. ENGLISH. B.A, Univ. Ark, 34, M.A, 37; Ed.D, Univ. Tulsa, 54; Univ. Chicago, 36; Univ. Minn, 48. Prin. elem. pub. schs, Ark, 31-34; teacher ENG, Bristow High Sch, Okla, 34-40, 46-57; assoc. prof, NORTHWEST. STATE COL, 57-60, PROF, 60-, CHMN. DEPT, 57, 63- Fund Advan. Educ. res. grant world lit, 54-55. NEA; NCTE. World literature, especially in the American high school; recent American novel. Add: Dept. of English, Northwestern State College, Alva, OK 73717.

ARTIN, THOMAS, b. Bloomington, Ind, Nov. 12, 38; m. 60; c. 2. ENGLISH, COMPARATIVE LITERATURE. B.A, Princeton, 60, M.A, 65, Ph.D.(comp. lit), 68. Instr. ENG, Swarthmore Col, 66-68, ASST. PROF, 68-70; Lowell Technol. Inst, 71; ROCKLAND COMMUNITY COL, 71- Mediaeval Acad. Am. Arthurian romance; Wagnerian studies; environmental politics. Publ: Earth talk—independent voices on the environment, Grossman, 73; The allegory of adventure—reading Chretien's Erec and Yvain, Bucknell Univ, 74. Add: 132 Grandview Ave, Monsey, NY 10952.

ARYANPUR, MANOOCHER, b. Tehran, Iran, Sept. 2, 29; m. 58; c. 3. ENGLISH. B.A, Tehran Univ, 53; Univ. Kans, 55; Int. Inst. Educ. scholar, Univ. Colo, 55-57, M.A, 56, fel, 56-58, Ph.D, 58. Asst. prof. Eng, Wartburg Col, 58-59; Tehran Teachers Col, 59-61; ASSOC. PROF, Buena Vista Col, 61-64, RENAISSANCE LIT, UNIV. MO-KANSAS CITY, 64- NCTE; MLA. Comparative literature; Elizabethan literature; English travellers of the 17th century in the Middle East. Publ: Co-auth, The English-Persian collegiate dictionary, Amir Kahir, 67; auth, Introduction to Omar, In: The Rubayyat of Omar Khayyam, Hallmark Ed, 67; Paradise lost and the oddyssey, Tex. Stud. Lang. & Lit, summer 67; Fitzgerald and the other English translators of the Rubaiyat, Lit. East & West, 68. Add: Dept. of English, University of Missouri-Kansas City, Kansas City, MO 64110.

ARZOOMANIAN, RALPH SARKIS, b. Providence, R.I, Jan. 23, 37; m. 57; c. 4. DRAMA. B.A, Boston Univ, 61; M.A, Iowa Univ, 63, Ph.D.(drama), 65. Fel, Yale, 65-66; instr. theatre, Hunter Col, 66-71; ASST. PROF. SPEECH & THEATRE, LEHMAN COL, 71- U.S.A.F, 55-58. Publ: The coop (play), Prompt Theatre Mag, London, 6/68. Add: Dept. of Speech & Theatre, Lehman College, Bronx, NY 10468.

ASALS, FREDERICK JOHN, b. Philadelphia, Pa, May 12, 35; m. 62; c. 1. ENGLISH. B.A, Col. William & Mary, 57; M.A, Middlebury Col, 61; Ph.D, (Am. lit), Brown Univ, 67. Instr. ENG, Brown Univ, 67-68; ASST. PROF, UNIV. TORONTO, 68- U.S.A.R, 55-63. MLA. American literature. Publ: Emily Dickinson's Two butterflies went out at noon, Emerson Soc. Quart, 71; Jeremy Taylor and Hawthorne's early tales, Am. Transcendental Quart, spring 72; Hawthorne, Mary Ann, and The lame shall enter first, Flannery O'Conner Bull, 73; plus five others. Add: New College, University of Toronto, Toronto 181, Ont, Can.

ASALS, HEATHER ROSS, b. New York, N.Y, Sept. 7, 40; m. 62; c. 2. ENGLISH LITERATURE. A.B, Smith Col, 62; Ph.D.(Eng), Brown Univ, 68. Teacher Eng. & math, Marg C. Wheeler Sch, 62-64; teaching asst. ENG, Brown Univ, 64-68; asst. prof, YORK UNIV, 68-73, ASSOC. PROF, 73- MLA; Asn. Can. Univ. Teachers Eng; Renaissance Soc. Am. Seventeenth century poetry; Shakespeare. Publ: The voice of George Herbert's The church, ELH, 69; Venus and Adonis: the education of a goddess, Stud. Eng. Lit, 73; In defense of Delila: Samson Agonistes and the Reformation theology of the word, J. Eng. & Ger. Philol, (in press). Add: Dept. of English, York University, Toronto 12, Ont, Can.

ASCHENBRENNER, DUANE LEO, b. Dysart, Iowa, Nov. 20, 30; m. 55; c. 3. FORENSICS, PUBLIC ADDRESS. B.A, Westmar Col, 55; M.A, Univ. North. Colo, 61. Instr. SPEECH, Cent. Community Schs, Iowa, 55-56; Durant Community Schs, 56-57; Muscatine Community Schs, 57-60; Newton Community Schs, 60-63; UNIV. NEBR. AT OMAHA, 63-66, asst. prof, 66-72, ASSOC. PROF, 72- Dir, Nat. Col. Debate Workshop, 66-; chmn, Int. Debate Tournament of Champions Comt, 66- Ronald Regan Debate Coach of the Year Award, 72. Interstate Oratorical Asn.(exec. secy, 71-); Am. Forensic Asn; Speech Commun. Asn. American oratory; accountability in forensics. Publ: Ed, National college debate handbook, 2nd, 69, 3rd, 70 & 6th, 73, Univ. Nebr. at Omaha; ed, Winning orations, 71, 72, & 73, Interstate Oratorical Asn. Add: Dept. of Speech, University of Nebraska, at Omaha, Box 688 Downtown Station, Omaha, NE 68101.

ASH, LEE, Bibliography. See Volume I-History.

ASHBROOK, WILLIAM SINCLAIR, b. Philadelphia, Pa, Jan. 28, 22; m. 42; c. 2. ENGLISH, HUMANITIES. A.B, Univ. Pa, 46; M.A, Harvard, 47. Teaching fel. Eng, Harvard, 47-49; asst. prof. humanities, Stephens Col, 49-55; Eng, Ind. State Univ, 55-59, assoc. prof, 59-63, PROF. Eng. & humanities, 63-73; OPERA, PHILA. MUSICAL ACAD, 73 Ital. govt. summer stud. grant, 62. Ind. Auth. Day Award, 65. U.S.A, 42-45, Sgt. MLA. Publ: Donizetti, Cassell, 65; The operas of Puccini, Oxford-Cassell, 68. Add: 310 Barberry Lane, Wayne, VA 19087.

ASHBURN, WILLIAM ALWYN, b. Reno, Ohio, Apr. 25, 11. ENGLISH. A.B, Baldwin-Wallace Col, 34; A.M, West. Reserve Univ, 47. Supvr, Gen. Motors Corp, 42-46; from asst. prof. to ASSOC. PROF. ENG, BALDWIN-WALLACE COL, 46- NCTE. Publ: Mediaeval literature; Manual of middle eastern literature; History of the English language; plus others. Add: Dept. of English, Baldwin-Wallace College, Berea, OH 44017.

ASHBY, CLIFFORD, b. Effingham, Ill, June 11, 25; m. 50; c. 2. DRAMA. B.A, State Univ. Iowa, 50; M.A, Univ. Hawaii, 53; Ph.D, Stanford Univ, 63. Asst. prof. drama, Univ. Pac, 53-54; instr, Univ. Fla, 54-57; asst. prof, Univ. Nebr, 61-63; assoc. prof, TEX. TECH UNIV, 63-67, PROF. THEATRE, 67-, res. grant, 68. Theatre history; history of acting; scene design. Publ: Lighting control: is something wrong with simplicity?, Theatre Crafts, 10/72; Alla Nazimova, In: Dictionary of American Biography, suppl. 3, 73; Fanny Kemble's vulgar journal, Pa. Mag. Hist. & Biog, 1/74; plus three others. Add: 2711 24th St, Lubbock, TX 79410.

ASHE, DORA JEAN, b. Leesburg, Va, Mar. 19, 25. ENGLISH. B.A, Emory & Henry Col, 45; M.A, Univ. Va, 48, Du Pont fel, Ph.D.(Eng), 53. Instr. ENG, Am. Univ.(D.C), 48-49; Univ. Tenn, 49-51; asst. prof, E.Carolina Col, 53-56; assoc. prof, LYNCHBURG COL, 56-64, PROF, 64-, CHMN. DEPT, 65- MLA; Col. Eng. Asn; Malone Soc; Southeast Renaissance Conf; Bibliog. Soc. Univ. Va; AAUP; Am. Asn. Univ. Women. Renaissance literature, especially drama; textual criticism. Publ: Ed, Beaumont & Fletcher's Philaster, Univ. Nebr, 74. Add: Dept. of English, Lynchburg College, Lynchburg, VA 24504.

ASHIN, MARK, b. New York, N.Y, Mar. 1, 17; m. 49; c. 1. ENGLISH. A.B, Univ. Chicago, 37, A.M, 38, univ. fel, 41-42, Ph.D.(Eng), 50. Instr. ENG, Mich. State Col, 38-41; UNIV. CHICAGO, 47-51, asst. prof, 51-57, assoc. prof, 57-67, PROF, 67-, assoc. chmn. dept, 66-72. U.S.A, 43-46. Shakespeare Asn. Am; MLA. Shakespeare; 17th century drama; modern drama. Publ: Co-auth, Reading literature, Scott, 55; auth, The argument of Madison's Federalist No. 10, Col. Eng. Add: 5541 Dorchester Ave, Chicago, IL 60637.

ASHLEY, LEONARD R. N, b. Miami, Fla, Dec. 5, 29. ENGLISH. B.A, McGill Univ, 49, M.A, 50; A.M, Princeton, 53, Gordon Macdonald & univ. fels. & Ph.D.(Eng), 56. Instr. Eng, Univ. Utah, 53-55; geopolit, 1 Off. Sch, Royal Can. Air Force, London, 55-56, second asst. to air historian, 56-58; instr. ENG, Univ. Rochester, 58-61; BROOKLYN COL, 61-65, asst. prof, 65-68, assoc. prof, 68-72, PROF, 72- Res. grants, Univ. Utah, 55; Univ. Rochester, 60; lectr, New Sch. Soc. Res, 61-; Brooklyn Col. fac. res. grant, 68; contrib. ed, Papertexts, Simon & Schuster & Wash. Sq. Press; consult. publ. Shakespeare Gold Medal, 49. R.C.A.F, 56-58, Flying Off. MLA; NCTE; Am. Name Soc; Int. Conf. Gen. Semantics; Int. Asn. Stud. Anglo-Irish Lit. English drama; English language, especially onomastics and semantics; English nondramatic literature. Publ: Colley Cibber, 65 & George Peele, 69, Twayne; Nineteenth Century British drama, Scott, 68; co-auth, British short stories: classics and criticism, Prentice-Hall, 68; ed, The picture of Dorian Gray, Wash. Sq, 68; Other people's lives: 34 short stories, Houghton, 69; A narrative of the life of Mrs. Charlotte Clarke, 69, Reliques of Irish poetry, 71 & Ballad poetry of Ireland, 73, Scholar's Facsimilies; auth, Shakespeare's jest book, AMS Pub, 72; ed, Mirrors for man: 26 plays of the world drama, Winthrop, 74; auth, A guided tour of gobbledygook, In: Classical rhetoric for the modern student, Oxford Univ, 65 & 71; Changing times and changing names, 9/71 & You pays yer money and you takes yer choice: British slang for pounds and pennies, old and new, 3/73, Names; plus numerous others. Add: Dept. of English, Brooklyn College, Brooklyn, NY 11210.

ASHLEY, ROBERT PAUL, JR, b. Baltimore, Md, Apr. 15, 15; m. 39; c. 5. ENGLISH. A.B, Bowdoin Col, 36; A.M, Harvard, 37, Dexter traveling fel, Eng, 48, Ph.D, 49. Instr. Eng. & coach tennis, Portland Jr. Col, Maine, 38-39; instr. Eng, Colby Jr. Col, 39-43; training instr, Boston Qm. Depot, 44; coach tennis & teaching fel. Eng, Harvard, 46-48; asst. prof. Eng, coach tennis & asst. dean, Washington & Jefferson Col, 48-51; asst. prof. Eng, U.S. Mil. Acad, 51-55; PROF. ENG, RIPON COL, 55-, dean, 55-67, acting pres, 66, v.pres, 67-74. Consult. & exam, N.Cent. Asn. Cols. & Sec. Sch, 63-; mem, Wis. Comn. Higher Educ. Aids, 64-67, chmn, 65-66; chmn, Nat. Summer Conf. Acad. Deans, 68; distinguished vis. prof, U.S. Naval Acad, 68-69. U.S.N.R, 44-46; U.S.A.R, 51-55, Col. MLA; Midwest Mod. Lang. Asn; AAUP. The novel; Victorian literature; the American Civil War. Publ: Wilkie Collins, Roy Publ, 52; co-auth, Elizabethan fiction, Holt, 53; auth, The stolen train, 53 & Rebel raiders, 56, Winston; co-ed, Tales of suspense, Libr. Publ, 54 & Faulkner at West Point, Random, 64; ed, Civil War poetry: an anthology, U.S. Naval Acad, 70; auth, Understanding the novel, Walch, 73; Let no such man be trusted: advice on hiring faculty, N.Cent. Asn. Quart, spring 64; The St. Albans raid, Civil War Times, 11/67; What make a good novel?, Eng. Lang, Notes, 12/70; plus one other. Add: Ripon College, Ripon, WI 54971.

ASHLIMAN, DEE L, German Language & Literature, Comparative Literature. See Volume III, Foreign Languages, Linguistics & Philology.

ASHMEAD, JOHN, JR, b. New York, N.Y, Aug. 22, 17. ENGLISH LITERATURE. A.B, Harvard, 38, univ. fel. & A.M, 39; Ph.D, 51. Instr. ENG, HAVERFORD COL, 47-50, asst. prof, 50-55, assoc. prof, 56-62, PROF, 62-, CHMN. DEPT, 73- Instr, Bryn Mawr Col, 49; Fulbright lectr. Am. lit, Osaka Univ, Japan, 55-56, Am. stud, Nat. Chengchi Univ. & Taiwan Provincial Norm. Univ, 60-61; lectr. Eng. & hist, Athens Col, Greece, 56-57; Am. Counc. Learned Soc. res. grant, Japan, summer 60; deleg. conf, Brit. Counc. Teaching Eng. Lit. Overseas, 62; Ford Found. res. grant, 63 & grant stud. film theory, Europe, 70-71; Fulbright lectr, Banaras Hindu Univ, 64-65; fel. Indian lit, Am. Inst. Indian Stud, summer 65; chmn, Sch. & Col. Conf. Eng, 66-68; consult, Ctr. Applied Ling, 63-67; mem. lib. arts comt, Phila. Col. Art & Phila. Col. Music, summer 68; pres, Fels. in Am. Stud, 68-69. MLA; fel. Am. Stud. Asn; Authors Guild; Conf. Col. Compos. & Commun. American and English literature; theory and language of film; Greek revival in American literature and art. Publ: Mountain and the feather, Houghton, 61; co-auth, English 12, Ginn, 68; auth, Man with only one suit, Harper's Mag, 4/63; New theories of film and their significance for the seventies, NCTE Distinguished Lect, 72; The language of movies and Kubrick's Clockwork orange, The Alternative, 72; plus one other. Add: Dept. of English, Haverford College, Haverford, PA 19041.

ASHMORE, CHARLES DeLOACH, b. Atlanta, Ga, May 21, 16; m. 46; c. 5. ENGLISH. A.B, Harvard, 38; M.A, George Washington Univ, 49; Ph.D, Emory Univ, 57. Instr. ENG, Emory Univ, 55-58; assoc. prof, CONVERSE COL, 58-61, chmn. dept, 60-61, PROF, 61-, DEAN COL. ARTS & SCI, 62-, V.PRES. ACAD. AFFAIRS, 72-, acting dean, 61-62. U.S.M.C.R, 42-46, 47-49, Maj. MLA; S.Atlantic Mod. Lang. Asn; South. Lit. Festival Asn.(pres, 61-62). The ethical thought in the novels of Henry Fielding. Add: Office of Vice President for Academic Affairs, Converse College, Spartanburg, SC 29301.

ASHTON, THOMAS L, b. New York, N.Y, Apr. 21, 41; m. 63; c. 2. ENGLISH & AMERICAN LITERATURE. B.A, City Col. New York, 63; M.A, Columbia Univ, 64, Ph.D.(Eng), 69. Instr. ENG, City Col. New York, 64-67; asst. prof, UNIV. MASS, AMHERST, 67-73, ASSOC. PROF, 73- Henry E. Huntington Libr. fels, 70 & 72; fel, Grad. Inst, Univ. Tulsa, 71. MLA; Keats-Shelley Asn. Am; Northeast Mod. Lang. Asn. Romanticism; modern literature; creative writing. Publ: Byron's Hebrew melodies, Univ. Tex. & Routledge, Kegan, Paul, 73; The thorn: Wordsworth's insensitive plant, 72 & The censorship of Byron's Marino faliero, 73, Huntington Libr. Quart; C.P. Snow's Cinéma vérité, S.Atlantic Quart, 73. Add: Dept. of English, University of Massachusetts, Amherst, MA 01002.

ASPIZ, HAROLD, b. St. Louis, Mo, June 19, 21; m. 52; c. 1. ENGLISH, AMERICAN LITERATURE. B.A, Univ. Calif, Los Angeles, 43, M.A, 44,

Will Rogers fel, 46-47, Ph.D.(Eng), 49. Asst. prof. Eng, Lewis & Clark Col, 50-51; res. technician & statistician, Div. Hwy, State Bd. Equalization, Calif, 52-58; from asst. prof. to PROF. ENG, CALIF. STATE UNIV, LONG BEACH, 58-, res. fel, 65. Am. Stud. Asn; MLA; Philol. Asn. Pac. Coast. Nineteenth century literature and popular culture; Walt Whitman; literary realism. Publ: Educating the Kosmos: There was a child went forth, Am. Quart, winter 66; Phrenologizing the whale, Nineteenth-Century Fiction, 6/68; A reading of Whitman's Faces, Walt Whitman Rev, 6/73; plus others. Add: Dept. of English, California State University, Long Beach, 6101 E. Seventh St, Long Beach, CA 90840.

ASSAD, THOMAS JOSEPH, b. Worcester, Mass, Feb. 21, 22; m. 50; c. 4. LITERATURE. B.A, Col. Holy Cross, 47; M.A, Boston Col, 53; Ph.D, Univ. Wis, 54. Instr. ENG, Boston Col, 48-50; TULANE UNIV, 54-58, asst. prof, 58-62, assoc. prof, 62-64, PROF, 64- U.S.A.A.F, 42-46, 1st Lt. MLA. Victorian literature; influence of Arabic on English. Publ: Three Victorian travellers, Routledge & Kegan Paul, 64; Hopkins' Carrion comfort, 59, Browning's My last duchess, 60 & On the major poems of Tennyson's Enoch Arden volume, 65, In: Tulane studies in English. Add: Dept. of English, Tulane University, New Orleans, LA 70118.

ATCHISON, RAY M, b. Shelby, Ala, Oct. 8, 21; m. 48. ENGLISH. A.B, Howard Col, 43; M.A, George Peabody Col, 47; South. Fels. Fund grant, Duke Univ, 55-56, Ph.D.(Am. & South. lit), 56. Instr. lit, George Peabody Col, 46-47; instr. ENG, SAMFORD UNIV, 47-49, asst. prof, 53-56, assoc. prof, 56-57; PROF, 58- U.S.A, 43-45. American literature, especially Civil War poetry; southern literature, especially southern literary magazines; Alabama Baptist publications. Publ: Southern literary magazines, 1865-1887; Baptists of Shelby County, Alabama, 64 & co-auth, Richard Hopkins Pratt and the Six Mile Academy, 65, Banner; contrib, Essays on American literature in honor of Jay B. Hubbell, Duke Univ, 67; auth, The land we love: a Southern post-bellum magazine of agriculture, literature, and military history, N.C. Hist. Rev, 10/60; plus others. Add: Dept. of English, Samford University, Birmingham, AL 35209.

ATCHITY, KENNETH JOHN, b. Eunice, La, Jan. 16, 44; c. 2. COMPARATIVE LITERATURE, ENGLISH. A.B, Georgetown Univ, 65; Cambridge, summer 64; Woodrow Wilson fel, Yale, 66-67, cert. Ital, 68, NDEA fel. & M.Phil, 69, Ph.D.(comp. lit), 70. ASST. PROF. ENG. & COMP. LIT, OCCIDENTAL COL, 70- Consult, Res. & Teacher Educ. Proj, Pasadena, Calif, 70-73; Nat. Endowment for Humanities summer stipend, 72; Am. Counc. Learned Soc. grant-in-aid, Florence, Italy, summer 73; consult, South. Calif. Res. Counc, 73; Fulbright-Hays jr. lectr, Italy, 74-75. MLA; Dante Soc. Am; Am. Comp. Lit. Asn; Renaissance Soc. Am; Am. Asn. Teachers Ital. The epic; medieval Renaissance literature; Homer and Dante. Publ. Ed, Eterne in mutabilitie: the unity of the Faerie Queene, Archon, 72; auth, Achilles' Sidonian bowl, Class. Outlook, 73; Wallace Stevens: of ideal time and choice, Res. Stud, 73; Skelton's Collyn Clout: visions of perfectibility, Philol. Quart, 74; plus others. Add: Dept. of English & Comparative Literature, Occidental College, Los Angeles, CA 90041.

ATHERTON, JOHN WILLIAM, b. Minneapolis, Minn, Oct. 17, 16; m. 41; c. 3. ENGLISH LITERATURE. A.B, Amherst Col, 39; A.M, Univ. Chicago, 40, Ph.D, 52; hon. LL.D, MacMurray Col, 66, Amherst Col, 68; hon. L.H.D, Pitzer Col, 70. Instr. Eng, Iowa State Col, 40-43; Eng. & humanities, Univ. Chicago, 46-49; from asst. prof. to assoc. prof, Claremont Men's Col, 49-60, prof. Eng. list, 60-63, dean fac, 61-63; pres, PITZER COL, 63-70, EMER. PRES, 70-; PROF. ENG. & CHMN. DEPT, STATE UNIV. N.Y. COL. BROCKPORT, 70- Fulbright lectr, Univ. Tokyo, 55-56; vis. prof, Amherst Col, 60-61. U.S.N.R, 43-46, Lt. Comdr. Victorian and American literature; creative writing. Add: 1462 Covell Rd, Brockport, NY 14420.

ATKINS, GEORGE DOUGLAS, b. Greenville, S.C, May 16, 43; m. 67; c. 1. ENGLISH LITERATURE. A.B, Wofford Col, 65; M.A, Univ. Va, 66, Woodrow Wilson fel, 65-66, Danforth fel, 65-69, Ph.D.(Eng. lit), 69. Asst. prof. ENG, UNIV. KANS, 69-73, ASSOC. PROF, 73- William Andrews Clark Mem. Libr. fel, summer 72. Am. Soc. 18th Century Stud; MLA; AAUP; Soc. Relig. Higher Educ; Midwest Mod. Lang. Asn; S.Atlantic Mod. Lang. Asn; Rocky Mt. Mod. Lang. Asn; Johnson Soc. Cent. Region. Restoration and 18th century poetry and prose; the history of ideas; literature and religion. Publ: The function and significance of the priest in Dryden's Troilus and Cressida, Tex. Stud. Lit. & Lang, spring 71; Pope and deism: a new analysis, Huntington Libr. Quart, 5/72; The Eve of St. Agnes reconsidered, Tenn. Stud. Lit, 73. Add: Dept. of English, University of Kansas, Lawrence, KS 66045.

ATKINS, PAUL ALEXANDER, b. Portsmouth, Va, Jan. 8, 24; m. 52; c. 1. JOURNALISM. B.S, W.Va. Univ, 49; M.A, Univ. Va, 50. Reporter, Lynchburg, Va. News, 50-51; Richmond Times-Dispatch, 51-53; instr. JOUR, W.VA. UNIV, 53-59, asst. prof, 59-61, assoc. prof, 61-71, PROF, 71- U.S.A, 42-45, Sgt. Publ: Gathering and writing the news, W.Va. Univ, 73; Women are invading newsrooms, The Quill, 2/65; co-auth, chap, In: Freedom and censorship of the college press, W.C. Brown, 66; co-auth, J schools sever ties with campus newspapers, Jour. Educr, fall 70. Add: School of Journalism, West Virginia University, Morgantown, WV 26506.

ATKINSON, BENJAMIN PETER, b. Cynthiana, Ky, Apr. 8, 17; m. 40; c. 3. LITERATURE. A.B, Amherst Col, 38; A.M, Syracuse Univ, 41. Instr. ENG, Syracuse Univ, 40-47; HOBART & WILLIAM SMITH COLS, 47-50, asst. prof, 50-54, assoc. prof, 54-62, PROF, 62-, asst. dean, Hobart Col, 55-58, dean, 59-66. Old and Middle English literature; literary criticism; linguistics. Publ: Literature for our times, Holt. Add: Dept. of English, Hobart & William Smith Colleges, Geneva, NY 14456.

ATKINSON, JAMES BLAKELY, b. Honolulu, Hawaii, Nov. 24, 34; m. 70; c. 1. ENGLISH & COMPARATIVE LITERATURE. A.B, Swarthmore Col, 56; Fulbright travel grant & Fr. Govt. award, Univ. Paris, 58-59; M.A, Columbia Univ, 61, N.Y. State Regents fel, 64-65, univ. fel, 65-66, Ph.D. (Eng. & comp. lit), 68. Asst. prof. Eng, Dartmouth Col, 66-73, fac. fel, 71; ASST. PROF. ENG, EARLHAM COL, 73- MLA; Renaissance Soc. Am; AAUP. Literature of the Renaissance in Europe and England; the novel. Publ: Transl, Mandrou Duby's A history of French civilization, Random, 65; ed. & transl, Machiavelli's The prince, Bobbs-Merrill, 75; auth, Montaigne and naivete, Romanic Rev, 73; Naivete and modernity: the French Renaissance battle for a literary vernacular, J. Hist. Ideas, 74. Add: Dept. of English, Earlham College, Richmond, IN 47374.

ATKINSON, JENNIFER ELIZABETH, b. Joliet, Ill, Nov. 17, 37. DRAMA, AMERICAN LITERATURE. B.A, Columbia Col, 59; M.A, Univ. S.C, 67, Ph.D.(Eng), 71. Instr. ENG, UNIV. S.C, 66-68, ADJ. ASST. PROF, 71-; ASST. TO DIR, CTR. EDS. AM. AUTH, MOD. LANG. ASN, 71- MLA; S.Atlantic Mod. Lang. Asn; Am. Soc. Theatre Res. American drama. Publ: Co-ed, As ever, Scott Fitz—, Lippincott, 72; ed, Children of the sea and three other unpublished plays by Eugene O'Neill, Microcard Eds, 72; auth, Fitzgerald's marked copy of The great Gatsby, 70 & F.Scott Fitzgerald's unpublished short fiction, 71, Fitzgerald/Hemingway Annual. Add: Dept. of English, University of South Carolina, Columbia, SC 29208.

ATNALLY, RICHARD FRANCIS, b. New York, N.Y, Dec. 24, 35; m. 60; c. 2. ENGLISH. B.A, St. John's Univ.(N.Y), 62; Ph.D.(Eng), Univ. Fla, 67. Instr. ENG, Yale, 66-68, asst. prof, 68-72; ASSOC. PROF, QUEENS COL.(N.C), 72-, chmn. dept, 72-73. MLA. Eighteenth century English literature; 20th century poetry. Add: Dept. of English, Queens College, 1900 Selwyn Ave, Charlotte, NC 28207.

ATTEBERRY, JAMES L, b. Springfield, Mo, Sept. 30, 23; m. 43; c. 2. ENGLISH LITERATURE. B.A, Abilene Christian Col, 46; M.A, Univ. Tex, 48, Ph.D, 61. Instr. ENG, Colo. Sch. Mines, 48-51, asst. prof, 51-53; Harding Col, 53-60, assoc. prof, 60-63, prof. & chmn. dept, 63-69; PROF, PEPPERDINE UNIV, MALIBU, 69- Danforth Found. teacher grant, 58-59; South. Fel. Found fel, 59-60. U.S.A.F, 43-45, 1st Lt. NCTE; MLA. The use of the sleeping potion in Renaissance drama; Bartholomew the Englishman and Edmund Spenser, medieval platonists. Publ: The story of Harding College, Harding Col, 66; Thomas: faith and doubt in the disciple's life, Twentieth Century Christian, 5/65; The freedom of scholarship, Alpha Chi Recorder, spring 68. Add: Box 1247, Pepperdine University at Malibu, 24255 Pacific Coast Hwy, Malibu, CA 90265.

ATTEBERY, LOUIE WAYNE, b. Weiser, Idaho, Aug. 14, 27; m. 47; c. 2. ENGLISH & AMERICAN LITERATURE. B.A, Col. Idaho, 50; M.A, Mont. State Univ, 51; Ph.D, Univ. Denver, 61. Teacher ENG, Middleton High Sch, Idaho, 49-50; Payette High Sch, 51-52; Nyssa High Sch, Ore, 52-55; East High Sch, Denver, Colo, 55-61, chmn. dept, 61; asst. prof, COL. OF IDAHO, 61-64, assoc. prof, 64-69, PROF, 69-, CHMN. DEPT, 68-, prin. lectr, Summer Inst. Am. Stud, 63-70, dir, 66-70. Bruern fel, Univ. Leeds, 71-72. U.S.N, 45-46. West. Lit. Asn; West. Hist. Asn. The epistemology of Western American literature; the cement truck urban belief tale; the Oregon cowboy: a continuing search for authenticity. Publ: Governor jokes, South. Folklore Quart, 12/69; The American West and the archetypal orphan, West. Am. Lit, fall 70; It was a DeSoto, J. Am. Folklore, 10-12/70; plus three others. Add: Dept. of English, College of Idaho, Caldwell, ID 83605.

ATWATER, ELIZABETH AMANDA, b. McKeesport, Pa, Sept. 6, 12. JOURNALISM, SPEECH. A.B, Duquesne Univ, 35; M.A, Univ. Pittsburgh, 36, Ph.D.(classics), 38; Cornell Univ, summer 41. Asst. classics, Univ. Pittsburgh, 36-38; instr. hist, St. Mary-of-the-Woods Col, 38-39; from mem. staff to PROF. JOUR. & SPEECH, POTOMAC STATE COL, W.VA. UNIV, 39-, dir. pub. relat, 39-72. Mem, W.Va. Arts & Humanities Counc, 67- Nat. Educ. Asn; Speech Asn. Am. Classics. Add: Dept. of Journalism, Potomac State College of West Virginia University, Keyser, WV 26726.

ATWOOD, LYNN ERWIN, b. Sioux Falls, S.Dak, Aug. 27, 32; m. 54; c. 1. JOURNALISM. B.S, S.Dak. State Univ, 54; M.A, Univ. Iowa, 62, Ph.D.(mass commun), 65. Reporter, Miller Press, S.Dak, 54; ed, Clearwater Tribune, Orofino, Idaho, 56-59; instr. JOUR, Univ. Iowa, 62-66, asst. prof, 66-67; SOUTH. ILL. UNIV, CARBONDALE, 67-71, ASSOC. PROF, 71- U.S.A, 54-56. Asn. Educ. in Jour; Int. Commun. Asn.(secy. polit. commun. div, 73-74). Information selection; attitudes and attitude change; political communication. Publ: How newsmen and readers perceive each others' story preferences, summer 70 & co-auth, Effects of community press councils: real and imagined, summer 72, Jour. Quart; co-auth, Changes in faculty attitudes toward university role and governance, J. Exp. Educ, summer 73. Add: School of Journalism, Southern Illinois University, Carbondale, IL 62901.

AUBURN, MARK STUART, b. Cincinnati, Ohio, Dec. 9, 45; m. 69; c. 2. ENGLISH & AMERICAN LITERATURE, DRAMA. B.S. & A.B, Univ. Akron, 67; univ. fel, Univ. Chicago, 68-71, A.M, 68, Danforth fel, 70, Ph.D.(Eng), 71. ASST. PROF. ENG, OHIO STATE UNIV, 71- MLA. Restoration and eighteenth century literature; the novel; drama. Add: Dept. of English, Ohio State University, 164 W. 17th St, Columbus, OH 43210.

AUER, JOHN JEFFERY, b. Aurora, Ill, May 8, 13; m. 38; c. 3. RHETORIC, PUBLIC ADDRESS. A.B, Wabash Col, 34; A.M, Univ. Wis, 35, Ph.D, 47. Instr. speech, Hanover Col, 35-37; polit. sci, 36-37; prof. pub. speaking, Oberlin Col, 37-52; from prof. speech & chmn. dept. to PROF. SPEECH & THEATRE & CHMN. DEPT, IND. UNIV, BLOOMINGTON, 52- U.S.N.R, 43-46, Lt. Am. Stud. Asn; Speech Commun. Asn.(asst. ed, Quart. Jour, 51-54, ed, Speech Monogr, 54-56, exec. v.pres, 58-60). History of American public address; communication and persuasion. Publ: Discussion and debate; Essentials of parliamentary procedure; Handbook for discussion leaders. Add: Dept. of Speech & Theatre, Indiana University, Bloomington, IN 47401.

AUGHTRY, CHARLES EDWARD, b. Okla. City, Okla, May 7, 25; m. 49; c. 2. ENGLISH & AMERICAN LITERATURE. B.A, Univ. Okla, 49, M.A, 51; Ph.D, Brown Univ, 59. Instr. ENG, Univ. Conn, 55-56; Wheaton Col, 56-59, asst. prof, 59-61; master, Kent Sch, 61-62; asst. prof, WHEATON COL.(MASS), 62-63, assoc. prof, 63-68, PROF, 68-, assoc. dean, 69-72, acting dean, 72. C.Eng, U.S.A, 43-46. New Eng. Col. Eng. Asn. Modern drama; American literature; Christian writers. Publ: Ed, Landmarks in modern drama, Houghton, 63. Add: Dept. of English, Wheaton College, Norton, MA 02766.

AUGUST, EUGENE R, b. Jersey City, N.J, Oct. 19, 35; m. 64; c. 2. ENGLISH. A.B, Rutgers Univ, 58; M.A, Univ. Conn, 60; Ph.D.(Eng), Univ. Pittsburgh, 65. Asst. ENG, Univ. Conn, 58-60; instr, Carnegie-Mellon Univ, 62-64, asst. prof, 64-66; Univ. Dayton, 66-71, assoc. prof, 71-74; VIS. ASSOC. PROF, UNIV. HAWAII, MANOA, 74- Nat. Endowment for Humanities younger humanist fel, 73-74. MLA; Tennyson Soc; Hopkins Soc. Victorian literature; John Stuart Mill. Publ: Ed, The Nigger question, 71 & The Negro question, 71, AHM Publ; The growth of the windhover, 10/67 & Mill as sage: the essay on Bentham, 1/74, PMLA; Mill's autobiography as philosophic commedia, Victorian Poetry, summer 73. Add: Dept. of English, University of Hawaii at Manoa, Honolulu, HI 96822.

AULT, DONALD DUANE, b. Canton, Ohio, Oct. 5, 42; m. 65; c. 1. ENGLISH LITERATURE, PHILOSOPHY OF SCIENCE. B.A, Kent State Univ, 64, M.A, 65; Ph.D.(Eng), Univ. Chicago, 68. ASST. PROF. ENG, UNIV. CALIF, BERKELEY, 68- English romantic poetry, especially William Blake; popular culture studies, phenomenological approach to film and comics. Publ: Visionary physics: Blake's response to Newton, Univ. Chicago, 74. Add: Dept. of English, University of California, Berkeley, CA 94720.

AUNGST, RONALD LEE, b. Findlay, Ohio, Sept. 28, 34; m. 60; c. 2. SPEECH. B.S.J, Ohio Univ, 56, M.S, 61; Findlay Col, 58-59; Ph.D.(speech), Ind. Univ, Bloomington, 73. Teacher, Montgomery Local Sch, 56-57; off. mgr, Hubbard Press, 58-59; instr. spech & dir. forensics, Carthage Col, 62-64; asst. prof. SPEECH, MANCHESTER COL, 64-67, ASSOC. PROF, 67-, DIR. FORENSICS, 64- Speech Commun. Asn; Am. Asn. Univ. Prof; Cent. States Speech Asn; Am. Forensic Asn. Effects of culture on public speaking practices; intercollegiate speech activities; historical research in speech education. Add: 1008 N. Wayne St, North Manchester, IN 46962.

AUSMUS, MARTIN RUSSEY, b. Garvin, Okla, Oct. 29, 32. ENGLISH LITERATURE. B.S, Okla. Baptist Univ, 54; M.A, Univ. Okla, 59, Ph.D.(Eng), 69. Asst. prof. ENG, Ark. State Univ, 62-66; instr, Univ. Okla, 66-67; ASSOC. PROF, CENT. STATE UNIV, 67-, CHMN. DEPT, 71- U.S.A, 54-56, Sgt. MLA; NCTE; Conf. Col. Compos. & Commun; S.Cent. Mod. Lang. Asn. Twentieth century British novel; modern sequence novel; metaphysical poetry, especially Donne. Publ: Sinclair Lewis, Dodsworth, and the fallacy of reputation, Bks. Abroad, autumn 60. Add: Dept. of English, Central State University, Edmond, OK 73034.

AUSTER, HENRY, b. Stanislavov, Poland, Feb. 18, 38; Can. citizen; m. 60. ENGLISH. B.A, McGill Univ, 60; Commonwealth scholar & B.A, St. Catharine's Col, Cambridge, 62, M.A, 67; Can. Counc. fel, Harvard, 62-64, Ph.D. (Eng), 66. Teaching fel. hist. & lit, Harvard, 64-66, instr. ENG, 66-68, asst. prof, 68-69; UNIV. TORONTO, 69-70, ASSOC. PROF, 70- MLA; Can. Asn. Univ. Teachers; Asn. Can. Univ. Teachers Eng. George Eliot—Victorian fiction; 19th century poetry and criticism; early modern English literature. Publ: Local habitations: regionalism in the early novels of George Eliot, Harvard, 70. Add: Dept. of English, University College, University of Toronto, Toronto, Ont, M5S 1A1, Can.

AUSTIN, ALLEN CLETUS, b. Mayfield, Ky, May 24, 22; m. 49; c. 2. ENGLISH. A.B, Wayne Univ, 44; M.A, Columbia Univ, 50; Ph.D, N.Y. Univ, 56. Instr. ENG, Long Island Univ, 49; grad. asst, N.Y. Univ, 51-55; instr, Calumet Campus, IND. UNIV, 55-59, asst. prof, 59-63; assoc. prof, IND. UNIV. NORTHWEST, 63-68, PROF, 68- U.S.N, 43-46, Lt.(jg). MLA; NCTE. American literature; literary criticism. Publ: T.S. Eliot: the literary and social criticism, Ind. Univ, 71; An interview with Sinclair Lewis, 3/58 & T.S. Eliot's Objective correlative, 12/59, Univ. Kans City Rev; T.S. Eliot's theory of personal expression, PMLA, 6/66; plus others. Add: Dept. of English, Indiana University Northwest, 3400 Broadway, Gary, IN 46408.

AUSTIN, ALVIN E, b. Grand Forks, N.Dak; m. 46; c. 2. JOURNALISM, COMMUNICATIONS. B.A, Univ. N.Dak, 46. Night ed, Grand Forks Herald, N.Dak, 31-46, columnist, 31-58; PROF. JOUR, UNIV. N.DAK, 46- Consult, Wall St. Jour, 57-58; Minneapolis Star & Tribune, 59-; vis. prof. jour, Univ. Vt, 68-69. U.S.A, 42-45; Bronze Star Medal. Am. Soc. Jour. Sch. Adminr. (pres, 55-56); Asn. Educ. in Jour; Inter-Am. Press Asn. Newspaper opportunities; Latin American freedom of information; communications law. Publ: Co-auth, Modern journalism, Pitman, 60. Add: Dept. of Journalism, University of North Dakota, Grand Forks, ND 58201.

AUSTIN, JAMES CLAYTON, b. Kansas City, Mo, Nov. 27, 23; m. 45; c. 2. ENGLISH. B.A, West. Reserve Univ, 44, M.A, 45, Ph.D.(Eng), 52. Instr. ENG, Univ. Nebr, 46-48; teaching fel, West. Reserve Univ, 48-50; instr, Waynesburg Col, 50-51; Ohio Univ. 51-54; prof. & chmn. dept, Yankton Col, 54-60; assoc. prof, SOUTH. ILL. UNIV, EDWARDSVILLE, 60-63, PROF, 63-, acting head humanities div, 63-64. Fulbright lectr, Philippines, 57-58; Eng, 65-66; U.S. State Dept. Am. specialist, Romania, summer 66; exchange prof. Am. stud, Univ. Provence, 72-73. U.S.A, 42-43. MLA; AAUP; Am. Dialect Soc; Popular Cult. Asn; Fr. Asn. Am. Stud; Am. Stud. Asn; West. Lit. Asn. Popular literature; American literature; American studies. Publ: Fields of the Atlantic Monthly, letters to editor, 1861-1870, 53; Artemus Ward, 63, Petroleum V. Nasby, 65 & Bill Arp, 69, Twayne; ed, Popular literature in America, Bowling Green Univ. Popular Press, 72. Add: Dept. of English, Southern Illinois University, Edwardsville, IL 62025.

AUSTIN, JESSIE GARDNER, b. Passaic, N.J, Sept. 28, 13; m. 44; c. 1. ENGLISH. B.A, Wellesley Col, 34; M.A, Univ. Chicago, 37; Ph.D.(Eng), Univ. Ala, 69. Instr. ENG, SHORTER COL.(GA), 34-41, 58-59, asst. prof, 59-62, assoc. prof, 62-69, PROF, 69- W.A.C, 41-45, Capt. Am. Dialect Soc. English language; substandard dialects. Add: Dept. of English, Shorter College, Rome, GA 30161.

AUSTIN, LETTIE JANE (MRS. LEWIS H. FENDERSON), b. Joplin, Mo, Mar. 21, 25; m. 65. ENGLISH, EDUCATION. B.A, Lincoln Univ.(Mo), 46; M.A, Kans. State Univ, 47; Ed.D.(Eng), Stanford Univ, 52; M.A, Univ. Nottingham, 54; M.S, Howard Univ, 63. Instr. ENG, HOWARD UNIV, 47-50, asst. prof, 54-57, assoc. prof, 57-68, PROF, 68- Lectr, Univ. Md. Overseas Prog, Eng, 52-53; Fulbright grant, 52-54; consult. annual reading conf, Temple Univ, 55; curriculum preparation specialists in Eng, Educ. Serv, Inc, 64-65; asst. dir, NDEA Insts, 65-67; reader, Educ. Testing Serv, Princeton, 66; Nat. Assessment Educ. Progress, 69-70; consult. teaching Eng. as for. lang, Peace Corps, Togo & Senegal, summer 71; consult. commun. skills prog, Norfolk State Col, 71-72; consult, Phelps-Stokes Found, 72- NCTE; Col. Asn. Reading Teachers; Am. Psychol. Asn. English; education; psychology. Publ: Co-auth, College reading skills, Knopf, 66 & Black man in the United States, Scott, 69; auth, Teaching English to underprivileged college students, CLA Jour, winter 62; co-auth, Stereotypes in group-linked personality traits, Personality & Social Psychol, 3/65; auth, Reading: a dimension of creative power, J. Reading, spring 72; plus one other. Add: Box 954, Howard University, Washington, DC 20001.

AUSTIN, WARREN BARKER, b. New York, N.Y, Jan. 22, 10; m. 33; c. 3. ENGLISH. B.A, City Col. New York, 31, fel, 31-32; univ. traveling fel, Columbia Univ, 38-39, Ph.D.(Eng), 51. Tutor Eng, City Col. New York, 32-38, instr, 38-40, asst. prof, 40-57; asst. ed, Webster's Third New Int. Dictionary, 58-63; assoc. prof. ENG, STEPHEN F. AUSTIN STATE UNIV, 63-65, PROF, 65-, coord. Eng. grad. prog, 67-71. Res. Oxford, Cambridge & Brit. Mus, 38-39, 52-53; U.S. Off. Educ. res. grant, 67-68. MLA; NCTE; Shakespeare Asn. Am; Renaissance Soc. Am; Milton Soc. Am; Int. Shakespeare Asn. Milton; Shakespeare; Elizabethan and Renaissance literature. Publ: A computer-aided technique for stylistic discrimination: the authorship of Greene's Groatsworth of wit, U.S. Off. Educ, 69; William Withie's notebook: lampoons on Lyly and Harvey, Rev. Eng. Stud; Supposed contemporary allusion to Shakespeare as a plagiarist, Shakespeare Quart; Thomas Nashe's authorship of a sonnet attributed to Shakespeare, Shakespeare in the Southwest, 69. Add: Dept. of English, Stephen F. Austin State University. Nacogdoches, TX 75961.

AUSTON, JOHN T, b. Pueblo, Colo, June 8, 16; m. 45; c. 1. SPEECH, RESEARCH METHODOLOGY. B.A, Univ. Denver, 39, M.A, 40, Ph.D.(speech & res. methods), 50; fel, Purdue Univ, 47-48. Instr. speech, Univ. Minn, 40-42; asst. prof, Marshall Univ, 46-47; Purdue Univ, 47-50; assoc. prof, speech path, Mich. State Univ, 51-59; SPEECH, Univ. Denver, 59-62; Univ. Akron, 62-68; PROF, APPALACHIAN STATE UNIV, 68- Fel, Univ. Mich, 50-51; all-univ. res. grant, Mich. State Univ, 55-57; gen. chmn, Nat. Speech Tournament, 63-64. U.S.A, 43-46. Speech Commun. Asn; NEA; Nat. Soc. Stud. Commun. Measurement; research methodology; public address. Publ: Co-auth, Introduction to graduate work in speech and theatre, Mich. State Univ, 62, Argumentation and debate, Holt, 62 & Guidelines for effective speaking, W.C. Brown, 66; auth, Speech disorders at Michigan State, Mich. Educ. J, 2/53; Methods and levels of measurement in speech, J. Educ. & Psychol. Measurement, summer 53; Rationale for reorienting educational research, J. Educ. Res, 1/54. Add: Dept. of Speech, Appalachian State University, Boone, NC 28607.

AUTREY, MAX L, b. Newberry, Ind, Nov. 17, 28. ENGLISH. B.S, Ind. State Univ, 51, M.S, 55; Ph.D.(Eng), Wayne State Univ, 65. Instr, High Schs, Mich, 53-57; teaching fel. ENG, Wayne State Univ, 57-60; instr, DRAKE UNIV, 60-65, asst. prof, 65-68, assoc. prof, 68-72, PROF, 72- U.S.A.F, 51-53, Res, 53-65, 1st Lt. NCTE; MLA. Eighteenth century and romantic period English. Publ: Hawthorne and the beautiful impulse, Am. Transcendental Quart, spring 72; Hawthorne's study in clay, Xavier Univ. Stud, 73. Add: Dept. of English, Drake University, Des Moines, IA 50311.

AVERY, LAURENCE GREEN, b. Birmingham, Ala, Dec. 7, 34; m. 57. ENGLISH. B.A, Baylor, 57; M.A, Univ. Mich, 58; summer fel, Harvard, 59; Ph.D.(Eng), Univ. Tex, 66. Instr. ENG, Howard Col, 58-61; asst. prof, UNIV. N.C, CHAPEL HILL, 66-70, ASSOC. PROF, 70-, Smith Fund grant, 66-68, fac. summer stud. fel, 68. Nat. Endowment for Humanities fel, 71-72. MLA. Drama; bibliography. Publ: Maxwell Anderson: a catalogue, 68 & ed, Maxwell Anderson, Notes on a dream, 71, Univ. Tex; Addenda to the Maxwell Anderson bibliography: The measure, 63: 31-36 & Addenda to the Maxwell Anderson bibliography: Monro's Chapbook, 65: 408-411, Papers Bibliog. Soc. Am; Maxwell Anderson and Both your houses, N.Dak. Quart, 38: 5-24; plus two others. Add: Dept. of English, University of North Carolina, Chapel Hill, NC 27514.

AVIS, WALTER SPENCER, English, Linguistics. See Volume III, Foreign Languages, Linguistics & Philology.

AVNI, ABRAHAM ALBERT, b. Brno, Czech, Sept. 6, 21; m. 48; c. 1. ENGLISH, COMPARATIVE LITERATURE. M.A, Hebrew Univ, Israel, 49; Ph.D.(comp. lit), Univ. Wis, Madison, 63. Instr. Hebrew & Bible, Univ. Wis, Madison, 63-64; asst. prof. ENG. & COMP. LIT, CALIF. STATE UNIV, LONG BEACH, 64-67, assoc. prof, 67-72, PROF, 72-, res. grant, 67. Brit. Army, 41-46; Israeli Army, 48-49. MLA; Am. Comp. Lit. Asn. Romantic poetry, French, English, and German; influence of the Old Testament on European literatures. Publ: The Bible and romanticism, Mouton, The Hague, 69; The influence of the Bible on American literature: a review of research from 1955 to 1965, Bull. Bibliog, 10-12/70; A reevaluation of Baudelaire's Le Vin: its originality and significance for Les Fleurs du mal, French Rev, 12/70; The Bible and Les Fleurs du mal, PMLA, 3/73; plus others. Add: Dept. of English, California State University, Long Beach, 6101 Seventh St, Long Beach, CA 90840.

AXELRAD, ARTHUR MARVIN, b. New York, N.Y, Aug. 26, 34. ENGLISH LITERATURE. B.A, Brooklyn Col, 55; M.A, N.Y. Univ, 57, Ph.D, 62. Asst, Sch. Commerce, N.Y. Univ, 55-57; asst. prof. ENG, Utah State Univ, 61-64; from assoc. prof. to PROF, CALIF. STATE UNIV, LONG BEACH, 64- Assoc. ed, in charge abstr, Seventeenth-Century News, 57-65; Woodrow Wilson rep, 68-; Danforth Fel. liaison off, 68- Andiron Club Award, N.Y. Univ, 62, Founders' Day Distinguished Scholar Award, 63. Milton Soc. Am; Int. Arthurian Soc. English Renaissance, especially Milton; medieval, especially Arthurian literature. Publ: Co-ed, The prose of John Milton, N.Y. Univ, 67; contrib, Milton encyclopedia, Univ. Wis, (in press). Add: Dept. of English, California State University, Long Beach, CA 90801.

AXELROD, STEVEN GOULD, b. Los Angeles, Calif, May 15, 44; m. 66; c. 1. ENGLISH & AMERICAN LITERATURE. A.B, Univ. Calif, Los Angeles, 66, Regents fel, 67-68, M.A, 69, NDEA fel, 69-71, Ph.D.(Eng), 72. ASST. PROF. ENG, Univ. Mo-St. Louis, 72-73; UNIV. CALIF, RIVERSIDE, 73-, res. grant, 73-74. MLA; Philol. Asn. Pac. Coast; Am. Stud. Asn. Modern literature; poetry. Publ: Baudelaire and the poetry of Robert Lowell, Twentieth Century Lit, 10/71; Colonel Shaw in American poetry, Am. Quart, 10/72; The private and public worlds of Robert Lowell's For the Union dead, Bucknell Rev, 74. Add: Dept. of English, University of California, Riverside, CA 92502.

AXTON, WILLIAM F, b. Louisville, Ky, Sept. 24, 26; m. 51; c. 3. ENGLISH LITERATURE. A.B, Yale, 48; M.A, Univ. Louisville, 51; Scribner fel, Princeton, 55-56, Proctor fel, 56-57, Ph.D, 61. Instr. ENG, Miami Univ, 52-53; Brown Univ, 57-61; asst. prof, Univ. Ky, 61-66, assoc. prof, 66-67; UNIV. LOUISVILLE, 67-69, PROF, 69-, CHMN. DEPT, 71- Assoc. ed, Dickens Stud. Annual, 68-; rev. ed, Dickens Newslett, 69-71; pres, Dickens Soc, 72. U.S.N.R, 44-46, Lt.(jg). MLA; Victorian Soc.(dir, 69-71); AAUP; NCTE; Browning Soc; Tennyson Soc; Byron Soc. Nineteenth century art and architecture; Dickens; Victorian aesthetics. Publ: Circle of fire, Univ. Ky, 66; Keystone structure in Dickens' novels, Univ. Toronto Quart, fall 67; Religious and scientific imagery in Bleak House, Nineteenth Century Fiction, 3/68; Great Expectations once again, Dickens Stud. Annual, 72; plus others. Add: Dept. of English, University of Louisville, Louisville, KY 40208.

AYCOCK, ANDREW LEWIS, b. Elberon, N.C, Nov. 24, 00; m. 29; c. 2. ENGLISH. B.A, Wake Forest Col, 26; M.A, Tulane Univ, 28; Carnegie scholar, Harvard, 29, 30; Johns Hopkins Univ, 32-33; Carnegie grants-in-aid, 49, 51. Teacher, pub. schs, Ala, 26-27; Sharpe teaching fel, Tulane Univ, 27-28; instr. ENG, WAKE FOREST UNIV, 28-31, asst. prof, 31-51, assoc. prof, 51-70, prof, 70-71, EMER. PROF, 71-, CUR. MUS. ART, 41-, DIR, ORAL HIST. PROJ, 71-, lectr. art hist, 29-71. Seventeenth century English literature; art history. Add: Box 7222 Reynolda Station, Winston-Salem, NC 27109.

AYCOCK, ROY E, b. Greenville, S.C, Apr. 11, 26. ENGLISH. B.A, Furman Univ, 49; M.A, Univ. N.C, 52, Ph.D, 60. Instr. ENG, Auburn Univ, 52-54; Ga. Inst. Tech, 54-57; assoc. prof, OLD DOMINION UNIV, 60-64, PROF, 64- MLA; Renaissance Soc. Am; Shakespeare Asn. Am. Shakespeare, Milton and Donne; 16th and 17th centuries; metaphysical poetry. Publ: Gray's-Inn journal, Yearbook Eng. Stud, 72; Shakespeare, Boito, and Verdi, Musical Quart, 10/72; Dual progression in Richard III, S.Atlantic Bull.(in press); plus three others. Add: Dept. of English, Old Dominion University, Norfolk, VA 23508.

AYERS, ROBERT WEAVER, b. Chanute, Kans, July 17, 17; m. 44; c. 3. ENGLISH LANGUAGE & LITERATURE. A.B, Butler Univ, 39; M.A, Univ. Mich, 40; Princeton, 46-48; Ph.D, Rutgers Univ, 55. Instr. ENG, Hofstra Col, 50-52, 53-55; Rutgers Univ, 56-58; PROF, GEORGETOWN UNIV, 58- Am. Philos. Soc. grant & fel, 50-60. U.S.N.A.F, 42-45, Lt. MLA; Eng. Asn, Gt. Brit; Mediaeval Acad. Am; Milton Soc. Am. Chaucer and the middle ages; Milton and the 17th century; Defoe and the 18th century. Publ: Co-ed, Complete prose works of John Milton, Vol. IV, Yale, 67; auth, Milton's Letter to a friend and the anarchy of 1659, 68 & Major-General Thomas Harrison: herald of the fifth monarchy, 68-69, J. Hist. Stud; Brief notes upon a late sermon, In: The complete prose works of John Milton, Vol. VII, Yale Univ, 74; plus others. Add: Dept. of English, Georgetown University, Washington, DC 20007.

AYLING, RONALD FREDERICK, b. Epsom, Gt. Brit, May 29, 32; m. 62; c. 1. ENGLISH & AMERICAN LITERATURE. B.A, Nottingham Univ, 56; fel, Univ. Bristol, 64-68, Ph.D.(Eng), 68. Lectr. ENG, Rhodes Univ. S.Africa, 58-64; fel, UNIV. ALTA, 69-70, ASSOC. PROF, 70- Mem. ed. bd, Nineteenth Century Theatre Res, 72- Mod. Humanities Res. Asn, Gt. Brit; MLA; Am. Comt. Irish Stud; Int. Asn. Anglo-Irish Lit. Anglo-Irish literature; modern drama. Publ: Ed, Blasts and benedictions: articles and stories by Sean O'Casey, Macmillan, London & St. Martin's, 67 & Sean O'Casey: modern judgments, Macmillan, London, 69, Aurora, 70; auth, O'Casey's manuscripts and working methods, Bull. N.Y. Pub. Libr, 69; O'Casey and the Abbey Theatre, Dublin, Dalhousie Rev, spring 72; Sean O'Casey's Dublin trilogy, J. Mod. Lit, 11/72. Add: Dept. of English, University of Alberta, Edmonton, Alta. T6G 2E1, Can.

AYO, NICHOLAS RICHARD, b. Elizabeth, N.J, Apr. 3, 34. AMERICAN LITERATURE. A.B, Univ. Notre Dame, 56, M.A, 62; S.T.L, Gregorian Univ. 60; Ph.D.(Am. lit), Duke Univ, 66. Asst. prof. ENG, UNIV. PORTLAND, 66-71, ASSOC. PROF, 71- Roman Cath. Priest, Congregation Holy Cross, 59-; mem. state appeal bd, Selective Serv. Syst, Ore, 70-; mem. bd. regents, Univ. Portland, 72- American literature; Roman Catholic theology. Publ: Robinson's use of the Bible, Colby Libr. Quart, 69; The secular heart: the achievement of Edward Lewis Wallant, Critique, 70; Bartleby's lawyer on trial, Ariz. Quart, 72. Add: 5000 N. Willamette Blvd, Portland, OR 97203.

AYORA, JORGE RODRIGO, Spanish-American Literature. See Volume III, Foreign Languages, Linguistics & Philology.

AYRES, JAMES BERNARD, b. Kansas City, Mo, Mar. 25, 33; m. 58; c. 5. ENGLISH LITERATURE, SHAKESPEARE. A.B, Baylor Univ, 58; A.M, Fla. State Univ, 60; Ph.D.(Eng. lit), Ohio State Univ, 64. Asst. ENG, Fla. State Univ, 58-60, instr, 60; asst. instr, Ohio State Univ, 60-64; asst. prof, UNIV. TEX, AUSTIN, 64-69, ASSOC. PROF, 69-, DIR, SHAKESPEARE AT WINDALE, 70-, ASST. DEAN, COL. HUMANITIES, 73-, dean stud, 68-69. Chief consult, Commun. Ctr, Huston-Tillotson Col, 67-69; asst. to dir, Shakespeare Inst, Bridgeport, Conn, summers 69 & 70. Bromberg Award, 67. U.S.A, 53-55, Sgt. MLA. Shakespeare; Elizabethan drama; dramatic history, performance. Add: College of Humanities, University of Texas at Austin, WMOB 203, Austin, TX 78712.

B

BABB, HOWARD SELDEN, b. Portland, Maine, May 14, 24; m. 52. ENGLISH. B.A, Kenyon Col, 48; Ph.D, Harvard, 55. Instr. ENG, Kenyon Col, 51-52; asst. instr, Ohio State Univ, 52-54, instr, 54-56, asst. prof, 56-62, assoc. prof, 62-65; UNIV. CALIF, IRVINE, 65-67, PROF, 67-, chmn. dept. Eng. & comp. lit, 69-72. U.S.N.R, 43-46, Lt.(jg). MLA; AAUP. The English novel; stylistics. Publ: Jane Austen's novels: the fabric of dialogue, 62 & The novels of William Golding, 70, Ohio State Univ; ed, Essays in stylistic analysis, Harcourt, 72; auth, Setting and theme in Far from the madding crowd, ELH, 6/63; The great Gatsby and the grotesque, Criticism, fall 63; A reading of Sherwood Anderson's The man who became a woman, PMLA, 9/65. Add: Dept. of English and Comparative Literature, University of California, Irvine, CA 92664.

BABB, LAWRENCE, b. Columbia, Mo, Dec. 1, 02. ENGLISH LITERATURE. A.B, Univ. Mo, 23, A.M, 26; Ph.D, Yale, 34. Instr, Ore. State Col, 25-27; Univ. Wis, 27-29; Northwest. Univ, 31-36; asst. prof, Okla. Agr. & Mech. Col, 36-38; instr. ENG, MICH. STATE UNIV, 39-43, asst. prof, 43-47, assoc. prof, 47-51, prof, 51-72, EMER. PROF, 72- English literature of the 17th century. Publ: The Elizabethan malady, 51, Sanity in bedlam, 59, ed, The anatomy of melancholy, 65 & auth, The moral cosmos of Paradise lost, 70, Mich. State Univ. Add: 632 Kedzie Dr, East Lansing, MI 48823.

BABBITT, SAMUEL FISHER, b. New Haven, Conn, Feb. 22, 29; m. 54; c. 3. AMERICAN STUDIES, AMERICAN LITERATURE. B.A, Yale, 53, M.A, 57; Ph.D.(Am. stud), 65; hon. LL.D, Hamilton Col, 69. Asst. to dir. admis, Yale Col, 53-55, asst. to dean, 55-57; lectr. Eng. & dean men, Vanderbilt Univ, 57-62; chief col. & univ. div, Off. Pub. Affairs, Peace Corps, Wash, D.C, 62-63; asst. dean, Yale Col, 63-64; asst. dean grad. sch. & lectr. Am. stud, Yale Col, 64-66; PROF. AM. LIT. & PRES, KIRKLAND COL, 66- Mem. N.Y. State adv. comt, U.S. Comn. Civil Rights, 70- U.S.A, 48-51, M/Sgt. Am. Stud. Asn; Am. Asn. Cols. Literature as historical source material. Add: Office of the President, Kirkland College, Clinton, NY 13323.

BABCOCK, CLARENCE MERTON, b. Duluth, Minn, Mar. 9, 08; m. 42; c. 2. AMERICAN THOUGHT. A.B, Union Col.(Nebr), 38; M.A, Univ. Denver, 46, Ed.D, 48. Chmn. dept. Eng, Doane Col, 48-49; from assoc. prof. communication skills to PROF. AM. THOUGHT, MICH. STATE UNIV, 49- Distinguished Fac. Award, Mich. State Univ, 72. U.S.A, 42-46. Melville Soc; Am. Dialect Soc. Mark Twain's social criticism; Herman Melville's language; H.L. Mencken's criticism. Publ: Ordeal of American English, 61 & Focus: a book of college prose, 63, Houghton; The American frontier, Holt, 65; Mark Twain, Mencken and the higher goofyism, Am. Quart, winter 64; Mark Twain's adventures in art, Art in Am, 3-4/67; Poe and Mencken, Tex. Quart, autumn 70; plus others. Add: 1252 Ivanhoe Dr, East Lansing, MI 48823.

BABEY-BROOKE, ANNA (MARY), b. New York, N.Y, July 16, 11; m. 45; c. 1. ENGLISH, MEDICINE. B.A, Hunter Col, 31; M.A, Columbia Univ, 32, Ph.D.(Eng), 38; Dr. Acupuncture, Taipei, Taiwan, 64. Lectr ENG, New Col, Teachers Col, Columbia Univ, 32-36, from instruct. asst. to lectr, Teachers Col, 36-38; from tutor to ASSOC. PROF, BROOKLYN COL, 36- Am. Counc. Learned Soc. fel, 44; Fulbright sr. grantee, sr. prof. in charge grad. prog. & chmn, Lady Doak Col, Madras State Univ, Madurai S.India, 63-64; lectr, Int. Cong. Acupuncture & Moxibustion, Tokyo, 65. English and medicine. Publ: Americans in Russia 1776-1917—American travelers in Russia from American Revolution to Russian Revolution, 38; Vocations for majors in English, Part II, 51 & 56 & co-auth, English and your career, 54 & 56, Brooklyn Col; co-auth, The pulse in Occident and Orient—its philosophy and practice in India, China, Iran and the West, Santa Barbara Press & Dawsons Pall Mall, 66; auth, The pulse: Ayurvedic, Chinese and Western allopathic views, J. Int. Cong. Acupuncture & Moxibustion Revue Cong. Int. D'Acupuncture Moxibustion, Tokyo, 65. Add: Dept. of English, Brooklyn College, Brooklyn, NY 11210.

BABINSKI, HUBERT F, b. Hempstead, N.Y, Nov, 2, 36; m. 70. COMPARATIVE LITERATURE. B.S, Tufts Univ, 58; M.A, Columbia Univ, 63, Ph.D.(comp. lit), 70; Polish Acad. Arts & Sci. grant, Inst. Lit. Res, Warsaw, 64-65. Instr. Eng, St. John's Univ.(N.Y), 62-65; ASST. PROF, Long Island Univ, 66-70; COMP. LIT, COLUMBIA UNIV, 70- Nat. Endowment for Humanities grant, summer 71; Columbia Univ. grant for humanities, summer 72. U.S.N, 58-61, Lt.(jg). MLA. European Romanticism; Byron in European Romanticism; 19th century European Messianism. Publ: The Mazeppa legend in European Romanticism, Columbia Univ, 74; contrib. & transl, K.A. Jelenski's Some contradictions in modern art, In: Kultura essays, Free Press, 70; Juliusz Stowacki's Mazepa, Pamiętnik Literacki, 73-74. Add: Dept. of English,& Comparative Literature, 603 Lewisohn Hall, Columbia University, New York, NY 10025.

BABULA, WILLIAM, b. Stamford, Conn, May 19, 43; m. 65; c. 1. ENGLISH LITERATURE. B.A, Rutgers Univ, New Brunswick, 65; M.A, Univ. Calif, Berkeley, 67, Ph.D.(Eng), 69. ASST. PROF. ENG, UNIV. MIAMI, 69- MLA; Shakespeare Asn. Am. Elizabethan drama; Renaissance literature; modern drama. Publ: Fortune or fate: ambiguity in Robert Greene's Orlando Furioso, Mod. Lang. Rev, 7/72; The play-life metaphor in Shakespeare and Stoppard, Mod. Drama, 12/72; Shylock's dramatic function, Dalhousie Rev, spring 73; plus others. Add: Dept. of English, University of Miami, Coral Gables, FL 33124.

BACCUS, JOSEPH HAROLD, b. Kewanee, Ill, July 30, 02; m. 29. SPEECH. A.B, Univ. Ill, 25, M.S, 27; Ph.D, Univ. Wis, 41. Asst. prof. speech, Hastings Col, 26-30; assoc. prof, Univ. Redlands, 30-63; lectr, Calif. State Col, Fullerton, 68-70; RETIRED. Pasadena Soc. Gen. Semantics scholar, 50. Speech Asn. Am; Nat. Soc. Stud. Commun.(secy. & 2nd v.pres); West. Speech Asn.(past pres, past ed, pres. exec. club, 67-68). Listening; communication; teaching of communication in elementary grades. Publ: Modern debating; Arms and munitions; Minimum wages and maximum hours. Add: 1640 Dwight, Redlands, CA 92373.

BACH, BERT COATES, b. Jenkins, Ky, Dec. 14, 36; m. 57; c. 2. ENGLISH. A.B, East. Ky. State Col, 58; M.A, George Peabody Col, 59; Ph.D, N.Y. Univ, 66. Asst. prof. Eng, W.Ga. Col, 59-61; instr, Manhattan Col, 61-63, asst. prof, 63-66; assoc. prof. Eng. & chmn. dept. Eng. compos, East. Ky. Univ, 66-68, PROF. ENG, 68-70; MILLIKIN UNIV, 70-, chmn. dept, 70-73. Mem. bd. trustees, Community Col. Decatur, 71-; Am. Counc. Educ. fel, 72-73. MLA; NCTE; Conf. Col. Compos. & Commun; Am. Asn. Higher Educ. Nineteenth century American literature; 18th century English literature. Publ: Co-auth, Fiction for composition, 68 & ed, Drama for composition, 73, Scott; The liberating form, Dodd, 72; plus others. Add: Dept. of English, Millikin University, W. Main St, Decatur, IL 62522.

BACHMAN, FERDINAND FRANCIS, b. Brooklyn, N.Y, Dec. 2, 13. ENGLISH. A.B, St. John's Col.(N.Y), 36, A.M, 38, Ph.D, 45. Teaching fel, ST. JOHN'S UNIV.(N.Y), 36-38, teacher Eng, prep sch, 36-39, prof, teachers col, 39-58, PROF. ENG, GRAD. SCH. & SUPVR. STUD. TEACHING, SCH. EDUC, 58-, head dept. Eng, 49-58. Mem, Am. Lit. Group, MLA. Outstanding teacher award, St. John's Univ.(N.Y), 64. MLA; Nat. Cath. Educ. Asn. Elizabethan drama; 19th century English literature; American literature. Add: Dept. of English, Graduate School, St. John's University, Grand Central & Utopia Pkwy, Jamaica, NY 11432.

BACHMANN, JAMES KEVIN, English As a Foreign Language, Linguistics. See Volume III, Foreign Languages, Linguistics & Philology.

BACKES, JAMES GLENN, b. Peoria, Ill, July 22, 32; m. 53; c. 4. RHETORIC & PUBLIC ADDRESS. B.S, Ill, State Univ, 56, M.S, 57; Univ. Ill, 58; Ph.D. (speech), South. Ill. Univ, 62. Instr. pub. address, Ill. State Univ, 56-57; Lincoln Col, 57-59; asst. prof, South. Ill. Univ, 61-63; assoc. prof. & chmn. dept. speech, Idaho State Univ, 63-65, head div. humanities, 64-65; asst. to pres, Univ. Iowa, 65-66; prof. speech & chmn. dept, Idaho State Univ, 66-69; prof. rhetoric & dept. head, Univ. Ariz, 69-71; PROF. RHETORIC & DIR. GRAD. STUD. SPEECH, IND. STATE UNIV. TERRE HAUTE, 71- Ellis L. Phillips internship acad. admin, 65-66. U.S.A, 52-53. Speech Commun. Asn; West. Speech Asn. British public address; American public address: rhetorical criticism. Publ: J.S. Mill and his preposterous motion, West. Speech, spring 70; The visual mode, In: Project text in interpersonal communication, Univ. Ariz, 71; co-auth, A call for revolution, Speech Teacher, 9/72; plus four others. Add: Dept. of Speech, Indiana State University, Terre Haute, IN 47809.

BACKMAN, MELVIN ABRAHAM, b. Lynn, Mass, Feb. 12, 19; m. 46, 71; c. 1. ENGLISH. B.S, Mass. State Teachers Col, 41; M.A, Columbia Univ, 47, Ph.D, 60. Instr. Eng, Richmond Prof. Inst, 48-51; instr. humanities & Eng, Clarkson Col. Technol, 53-56, asst. prof, 56-60, assoc. prof, 60-62, PROF, 62-67; ENG, C.W. POST COL, L.I. UNIV, 67-, CHMN. DEPT, 73- Teaching award, Clarkson Col. Technol, 63; consult, CHOICE, Am. Libr. Asn, 65- U.S.A.A.F, 43-46, S/Sgt. NCTE; MLA; AAUP. William Faulkner; American literature; modern literature. Publ: Hemingway: the matador and the crucified, Mod. Fiction Stud, 55, Hill & Wang, 61, Scribner, 62 & Oxford, 63; Faulkner: the major years, Ind. Univ, 66; Fr. transl, William Faulkner: De Sartoris à Descends, Moise, M.J. Minard, Paris, 68; auth, Absalom, Absalom!, In: Twentieth century interpretations of Absalom, Absalom!, Prentice-Hall, 71 & In: The American novel, background readings and criticism, Free Press, 72; The bear and Go down, Moses, In: William Faulkner, a collection of criticism, McGraw, 73; plus five others. Add: Dept. of English, C.W. Post College, Long Island University, Greenvale, NY 11548.

BACKSCHEIDER, PAULA RICE, b. Brownsville, Tenn, Mar. 31, 43; m. 64; c. 2. ENGLISH & AMERICAN LITERATURE. B.A, Purdue Univ, West Lafayette, 64, Ph.D.(Eng), 72; M.S, South. Conn. State Col, 67. Fel. Eng, Purdue Univ, West Lafayette, 72-73; ASST. PROF. ENG. & MINORITY STUD, ROLLINS COL, 73-, curriculum develop. grant, 73-74. William Andrews Clark Libr. summer sem. fel, Univ. Calif, Los Angeles, 74. MLA; Am. Soc. 18th Century Stud; S.Atlantic Mod. Lang. Asn. Restoration and 18th century; early English periodicals; contemporary minority literature. Publ: Punctuation for the reader—a teaching approach, Eng. J, 9/72; Introduction to Defoe's Life of Marlborough, Augustan Reprints, 74; co-auth, Updike's Couples: squeak in the night, Mod. Fiction Stud, 74. Add: Dept. of English, Box 33, Rollins College, Winter Park, FL 32789.

BACKUS, JOSEPH MOORHEAD, b. North East, Pa, Mar. 11, 25. LITERATURE. A.B, Allegheny Col, 49; M.S, Columbia Univ, 54; M.A, Univ. Calif, Berkeley, 57, Ph.D, 61. Instr. Eng, Am. Univ. Beirut, 49-50; resettlement off, Int. Refugee Orgn, Ger, 50-51; ed, North East Breeze, Pa, 54-55; reporter, San Francisco Exam, 55-56; assoc, Univ. Calif, Berkeley, 60-61; asst. prof. ENG, UNIV. HAWAII, MANOA, 61-66, assoc. prof, 66-72, PROF, 72- Assoc. prof, World Campus Afloat, 68. U.S.A, 51-53, Sgt. Am. Name Soc; Am. Soc. Psychical Res. English and American literature; psychism in literature; creative writing. Publ: Co-auth, Behind the scenes, Bk. Club Calif, 68; auth, Names of characters in Faulkner's The sound and the fury, Names, 12/58; co-auth, Each in its ordered place; structure and narrative in Benjy's section of The sound and the fury, Am. Lit, 1/58; auth, Non-sequential sequence-signals in short story openings, Lang. Learning, 65; plus others. Add: Dept. of English, University of Hawaii at Manoa, Honolulu, HI 96822.

BACON, ROGER LEE, b. Boise, Idaho, Oct. 23, 39; m. 65; c. 2. ENGLISH, CINEMA. B.A, Univ. Ore, 64, M.A, 65; fel, Univ. Utah, 69-72, Ph.D.(Eng), 72. ASST. PROF. ENG, South. Ore. Col, 65-69; NORTH. ARIZ. UNIV, 72- NCTE; Soc. Tech. Commun; Conf. Col. Compos. & Commun; AAUP. Education; technical writing. Publ: Geriatrics or obstetrics?, Interchange, 2/72; Why movies move us, summer 72 & co-auth, Do opposites attract?, winter 73, Rocky Mt. Mod. Lang. Asn. Bull; plus others. Add: Dept. of English, Northern Arizona University, Flagstaff, AZ 86001.

BACON, WALLACE ALGER, b. Bad Axe, Mich, Jan. 27, 14. SPEECH. A.B, Albion Col, 35, hon. Litt.D, 67; A.M, Univ. Mich, 36, Ph.D, 40. Lloyd fel, Univ. Mich, 40-41, instr. Eng, 41-42, 46-47; asst. prof. Eng. & speech, NORTHWEST. UNIV, EVANSTON, 47-50, assoc. prof, 50-55, PROF. INTERPRETATION, 55-, chmn. dept. interpretation. Rockefeller Found. fel, 48-49; Ford Found. fel, 54-55; assoc. ed, Quart. J. Speech, 57-59, 63-65; Fulbright lectr, Univ. Philippines, 61-62; Fulbright-Hays lectr, Univ. Philippines & Univ. Santo Tomas, 64-65; assoc. ed, Speech Monogr, 66-68, 69-71, 75-77; consult-panelist Off. Fels. & Stipends, Nat. Endowment for Humanities, 72-74. Sig.C, A.U.S, 42-46, Capt; Legion of Merit. Malone Soc; Speech Commun. Asn; Cent. States Speech Asn. Literature of the English Renaissance; oral interpretation. Publ: Savonarola, Bookman Assoc, 49; William Warner's Syrinx, Northwest. Univ, 50; co-auth, Literature as experience, McGraw, 59 & Literature for interpretation, 61 & auth, The art of interpretation, 66 & 72, Holt; co-auth, Spoken English, 62 & The art of oral interpretation, 65, Phoenix; auth, The structure of Jonson's comedies, Huntington Libr. Quart, 56; The elocutionary career of Thomas Sheridan, 64 & The diseased world of Henry IV, part two, and the disordered world of Troilus and Cressida: the Margery Bailey Memorial Lectures at the Ashland (Oregon) Shakespeare Festival, 6/73, Speech Monogr; plus others. Add: School of Speech, Northwestern University, Evanston, IL 60201.

BADEN, ROBERT C, b. Wewoka, Okla, Sept. 10, 36; m. 59; c. 4. ENGLISH. B.S, Concordia Teachers Col.(Nebr), 58; M.A, Univ. Nebr, 63, Ph.D.(Eng), 73. Instr, high sch, Nebr, 58-66; consult. Eng, State Dept. Educ, Nebr, 66-69; ASSOC. PROF. ENG, CONCORDIA TEACHERS COL.(NEBR), 69- Conf. Col. Compos. & Commun; NCTE; Lutheran Educ. Asn. Freshman English, novels of Henry Green; reading interests of adolescents. Add: Dept. of English, Concordia Teachers College, 800 N. Columbia, Seward, NE 68434.

BADER, ARNO L, b. Grand Rapids, Mich, Jan. 12, 02; m. 27; c. 2. ENGLISH. A.B, Univ. Mich, 24, A.M, 25, Ph.D, 34. Instr. rhetoric, UNIV. MICH, ANN ARBOR, 25-30, ENG, 30-38, asst. prof, 38-45, assoc. prof, 45-51, prof, 51-72, EMER. PROF, 72- Exchange prof, Nat. Cent. Univ.(China), 36-37. MLA; NCTE; English and American literature; Victorian literature; contemporary poetry. Publ: Co-ed, Prose patterns, Harcourt, Essays of three decades & Essays for our time, Harper. Add: Dept. of English, University of Michigan, Ann Arbor, MI 48104.

BADESSA, RICHARD PAUL, b. Pawtucket, R.I, Sept. 3, 34; m. 60; c. 1. MEDIEVAL LITERATURE, LINGUISTICS. B.A. & M.A, Univ. R.I, 60; Ph.D. (Eng), Ind. Univ, 67. Instr. ENG, UNIV. LOUISVILLE, 64-67, asst. prof, 67-72, ASSOC. PROF, 72-, DIR. GRAD. STUD. ENG, 67- Consult. sci. writing seminar in Louisville, U.S. Civil Serv. Comn, Chicago, 66, sci. writing seminar in Cincinnati, 67. U.S.A, 50-55. MLA. Medieval courtly love literature; generative-trans-formational grammar. Add: Dept. of English, University of Louisville, Louisville, KY 40208.

BADY, DAVID MICHAEL, b. New York, N.Y, Jan. 26, 39; m. 63; c. 1. ENGLISH & DRAMATIC LITERATURE. A.B, Columbia Univ, 59, A.M, 63, traveling fel, 65-66, Ph.D.(Eng. lit), 72. Instr. ENG, Rutgers Univ, 64-65; lectr, Hunter Col. & Lehman Col, 67-72; ASST. PROF, LEHMAN COL, 72- MLA; Renaissance Soc. Am. English Renaissance drama; modern European drama; film aesthetics. Publ: In defense of formalism, N.Y. Film Bull, 1/60; From Hitchcock to Hitler, Second Coming Mag, 1/61; weekly film reviews, New York Westside News, 67-68. Add: Dept. of English, Herbert H. Lehman College, Bedford Park Blvd, Bronx, NY 10468.

BAENDER, PAUL, b. Alameda, Calif, Dec. 1, 26; m. 57; c. 3. AMERICAN LITERATURE. A.B, Univ, Calif, Berkeley, 49, M.A, 52, univ. fel, 55-56, Ph.D, 56. Instr. ENG, Univ. Chicago, 56-60; asst. prof, UNIV. IOWA, 60-64, assoc. prof, 64-68, PROF, 68- Secy. ed. bd, Iowa-Calif. Ed. of Mark Twain, 62- Midwest Mod. Lang. Asn. Nineteenth century American literature; Mark Twain; bibliography. Publ: Co-ed, Mark Twain's Roughing it, 72, ed, What is man? and other philosophical writings of Mark Twain, 73 & co-ed, Mark Twain's The innocents abroad, 74, Univ. Calif; plus others. Add: Dept. of English, University of Iowa, Iowa City, IA 52242.

BAER, EVELYN ESTHER, b. Cleveland, Ohio, Jan. 18, 15. COMMUNICATION DISORDERS. B.A, Univ. Chicago, 36; M.A, Univ. Akron, 48. Teacher, High Schs, Ohio, 36-45, 57-66; rehabil. dir, Stark County Tuberc. & Health Asn, 45-47; vis. teacher, Child Stud. Dept, Akron Pub. Schs, Ohio, 47-57; asst. prof. SPEECH, UNIV. AKRON, 66-69, ASSOC. PROF, 69-, dir, comprehensive serv. for deaf & assoc. dir. speech & hearing ctr, 71-74. Nat. Asn. Soc. Workers; Acad. Cert. Soc. Workers. English as a second language for foreign university students and the culturally deprived. Add: 874 Westgrove Rd, Akron, OH 44303.

BAERGEN, JOHN DARREL, b. Villa Park, Ill, Mar. 4, 35; m. 65; c. 1. DRAMA, SPEECH. B.A, Okla. Baptist Univ, 57; M.A, Baylor Univ, 60; State Univ. Iowa, 62-63; Tex. Baptist fel. & Ph.D, Univ. Denver, 64. Instr. SPEECH & DRAMA, Okla. Baptist Univ, 59-62; asst. prof, Hardin-Simmons Univ, 63-66; SOUTHWEST. TEX. STATE UNIV, 66-68, ASSOC. PROF, 68- Air Nat. Guard, 58-64. Religious mass communication; religious drama, performance and writing. Add: 17 Timbercrest Dr, San Marcos, TX 78666.

BAETZHOLD, HOWARD GEORGE, b. Buffalo, N.Y, Jan. 1, 23; m. 50; c. 2. ENGLISH. A.B, Brown Univ, 44, A.M, 48; Ph.D.(Eng. & Am. lit), Univ. Wis, 53. From asst. dir. to dir. veterans col, Brown Univ, 47-49, admis. off, 48-50; asst. to the assoc. dean, Col. Lett. & Sci, Univ. Wis, 51-53; asst. prof. ENG, BUTLER UNIV, 53-57, assoc. prof, 57-67, PROF, 67- Am. Philos. Soc. grant, Univ. Calif, Berkeley, summer 58; vis. prof, Univ. Del, summer 63; Univ. Iowa & U.S. Off. Educ. res. grant for work on Iowa-Calif. Ed. of Writings of Mark Twain, Univ. Calif, Berkeley, N.Y. Pub. Libr, Yale, Princeton & Univ. Va, 65-66; Am. Counc. Learned Soc. grant-in-aid, Univ. Calif, Berkeley & Yale, summer 67. U.S.A.A.F, 43-46, Lt. MLA; Am. Lit. Group, MLA; Midwest Mod. Lang. Asn; Am. Stud. Asn; Ohio-Ind. Am. Stud. Asn.(v.pres, 65-66, pres, 66-67); AAUP; Soc. Stud. Midwest. Lit. Late 19th century American literature, especially works of Mark Twain; 19th century Anglo-American literary relations; twentieth century American literature. Publ: Mark Twain and John Bull: The British connection, Ind. Univ, 70; Course of composition of Mark Twain's A Connecticut Yankee, 5/61 & Found: Mark Twain's lost sweetheart, 11/72, Am. Lit; What was the model for Martin Chuzzlewit's Eden?, Dickensian, 9/59. Add: 6723 Riverview Dr, Indianapolis, IN 46220.

BAGG, ROBERT ELY, b. Orange, N.J, Sept. 21, 35; m. 57; c. 5. ENGLISH. A.B, Amherst Col, 57; Harvard, 60; NDEA fel, Univ. Conn, 60-63, Ingram-Merrill grant & M.A, 61, Ph.D.(Eng), 65. Instr. ENG, Univ. Wash, 63-65; asst. prof, UNIV. MASS, AMHERST, 65-70, ASSOC. PROF, 70- Lectr. Eng, Smith Col, 67; fac. growth grant, Univ. Mass, Amherst, summer 68. transl-in-residence, Nat. Transl. Ctr, Austin, Tex, 69; vis. assoc. prof. classics, Univ. Tex, Austin, 71. Prix de Rome, Am. Acad. Arts & Lett, 58-59. MLA. English Romantic literature, critical theory; classical literature. Publ: Madonna of the Cello, Wesleyan Univ, 61; Liberations: three one act plays, Spiritus Mundi Press, 69; transl, Euripides' Hippolytos, Oxford Univ, 73; auth, The scrawny sonnets and other narratives, Ill. Univ, 73; Love, ceremony and daydream in Sappho's lyrics, autumn 64 & Some versions of lyric impasse in Shakespeare and Catullus, spring 65, Arion; The rise of Lady Lazarus, Mosaic, summer 69. Add: 32 Barrett Pl, Northampton, MA 01060.

BAGLEY, CAROL LENORE, b. Cleveland, Ohio, May 12, 19; wid; c. 1. AMERICAN LITERATURE & HISTORY. B.A, Wash. State Univ, 60, M.A, 63, Ph.D.(Am. stud), 66. Asst. ENG, Wash. State Univ, 60-64, assoc, 64-65; instr, IDAHO STATE UNIV, 65-66, asst. prof, 66-70, ASSOC. PROF,

70-, acting chmn. dept, 67-68, dir. Am. stud. prog, 70-71. Coe Found. & Lincoln Univ. grant, Am. Stud. Inst, Lincoln Univ, summer 68; Newberry Libr. sr. fel, Ctr. Hist. Am. Indian, Chicago, 73-74. MLA; Am. Stud. Asn; Melville Soc. Am. Herman Melville; Sigmund Freud; Samuel L. Clemens (Mark Twain). Publ: Young man river, Wash. State Univ, 64; co-ed, Preparation for college English, Idaho State Univ, 71; auth, Early American views of Coleridge as poet, Res. Stud, 12/64; A psychological view of Henry Adams' Virgin and dynamo concepts, Rocky Mt. Soc. Sci. J, 4/67; Can popular culture save American studies?, In: Popular culture and curricula, Bowling Green State Univ, 70 & 72. Add: Dept. of English, Idaho State University, Pocatello, ID 83201.

BAGLEY, HENRY L, b. Greenville, Tex, Aug. 16, 09; m. 30; c. 2. ENGLISH, JOURNALISM. B.S, Kans. State Col. Pittsburg, 35; M.A, Colo. State Col. Educ, 41; Ed.D, Univ. Colo, 59. Teacher, High Sch, Tex. 37-47; assoc. prof. Eng, Sul Ross State Col, 47-51; prof. jour, Okla. City Univ. & Hardin Simmons Univ, 54-56; assoc. prof, Eng, Kans. State Col. Pittsburg, 56-61; prof. educ, Grand Canyon Col, 62-64; assoc. dir. sec. educ, Ariz. State Dept. Educ, 64-65, 65; PROF. ENG, METROP. STATE COL, 66- Lectr. Eng, Ariz. State Univ, 61-62; vis. prof. educ, Univ. Tex, El Paso, summer, 68; mem. code of ethics comt, Nat. Counc. Col. Pub. Adv, 60- U.S.A, 30-35. Nat. Educ. Asn; Am. Col. Pub. Relat. Asn. Publications in public relations; school and college public relations. Publ: Co-auth, Freedom of the college press, W.C. Brown, 61; auth, State college public relations (textbk), Am. Press, 69; ed, The bounty-hunter's Bible, Golden Bell, 73; Grammar and the spoken word, 4/61 & Journalism and speech, they need each other, winter 73, Kans. Speech J; Debators need grammatical accuracy, Tex. Interscholastic Leaguer, 10/61; plus others. Add: 1581 Holly St, Denver, CO 80220.

BAGSTER-COLLINS, JEREMY FELIX, b. New York, N.Y, Nov. 12, 06; m. 39. ENGLISH. A.B, Brown Univ, 27; A.M, Columbia Univ, 29, Ph.D, 42. Instr. ENG, Union Univ.(N.Y), 30-31, 32-33; lectr, Columbia Col, 31-32; instr, Lafayette Col, 35-37; FINCH COL, 38-72, chmn. dept, 48-72, educ. dir, intercontinental stud. plan, 63-64, EMER. PROF, 72- MLA; Am. Soc. Theatre Res; NCTE. English drama. Publ: George Colman the younger, King's Crown Press, 46. Add: 63 Barrow St, New York, NY 10014.

BAHLKE, GEORGE WILBON, b. Chicago, Ill, June 20, 34; m. 55; c. 3. ENGLISH & AMERICAN LITERATURE. A.B, Univ. Chicago, 53, M.A, 56; B.A, Swarthmore Col, 55; Ph.D, Yale, 60. Instr. ENG, Mary Washington Col, 58-60; Rutgers Univ, 60-61; asst. prof, Middlebury Col, 61-69; ASSOC. PROF, KIRKLAND COL, 69- Eng. Inst; MLA. Twentieth century British and American literature; English novel; literature and painting; literary criticism. Publ: The later Auden: from New Year Letter to About the House, Rutgers Univ, 70. Add: Div. of Humanities, Kirkland College, Clinton, NY 13323.

BAHN, EUGENE, b. Cape Girardeau, Mo, Nov. 23, 06; m. 39. SPEECH. B.A, Univ. Wis, 29, M.A, 30, Ph.D, 35; Salzburg Mozarteum, 35. Asst. instr. speech, Univ. Wis, 30-32; instr, State Univ. Iowa, 32-34; Colgate Univ, 34-37; asst. prof, Ohio State Univ, 37-43; off. historian, Am. Red Cross, Gt. Brit. & West. Europe, 43-46; mil. govt. cult. & educ. off, U.S. State Dept, 46-52; PROF. SPEECH, WAYNE STATE UNIV, 52- Lectr, Univ. Wis, 37; dean, Anatolia Col, Thessaloniki, Greece, 59-60. Nat. Col. Players (2nd v.pres, 40); Speech Commun. Asn. Oral reading of literature; history of reading of literature; theatre and acting. Publ: Co-auth, The communicative act of oral interpretation, 67 & An oral interpreter's anthology, 68, Allyn & Bacon; co-auth, History of the oral interpretation of literature, Burgess, 70; auth, Epochs in the history of oral interpretation, In: The communicative arts & sciences of speech, C.E. Merrill, 67; co-auth, Speech education in Greece, In: International studies of national speech educational systems, Burgess, 70; plus others. Add: Dept. of Speech, Room 70, Old Main Bldg, Wayne State University, Detroit, MI 48202.

BAHR, GISELA ELISE, Modern German Literature & European Drama. See Volume III, Foreign Languages, Linguistics & Philology.

BAHR, HOWARD W, b. New Matamoras, Ohio, July 4, 12; m. 39. ENGLISH LITERATURE. A.B, Oberlin Col, 38; Ohio State Univ, 38-39; Ph.D.(Eng. lit), Univ. N.C, 60. Instr. ENG, Valparaiso Univ, 47-49; asst. prof, Ark. State Col, 54-58, coord. humanities, Ford Found. Ark. Expt. in Teacher Educ, 54-57; asst. prof, UNIV. SOUTH. MISS, 58-60, assoc. prof, 60-62, PROF, 62- U.S.A, 43-46. S.Cent. Mod. Lang. Asn. Seventeenth and 18th century literature, especially the philosophical writings of those authors influenced by Bacon and the New Science Movement and the ancients versus moderns controversy; 19th century American literature. Publ: The misery of Florimell: the ladder of temptation, 10/65 & Spenser and the painted female beauty of conventional sonnetteers, 10/70, South. Quart; John Stuart Mill's philosophy of education, South. J. Educ. Res, 4/67. Add: University of Southern Mississippi, Box 162, Southern Station, Hattiesburg, MS 39401.

BAIER, LEE STANLEY, b. Portland, Ore, May 7, 24; m. 59; c. 2. ENGLISH. B.A, Reed Col, 48; M.A, Columbia Univ, 52, Ph.D.(Eng), 66. Instr. ENG, Colby Col, 55-57, Polytech. Inst. Brooklyn, 58-59; Univ. N.H, 60-65, asst. prof, 65-66; UNIV. MAINE, PORTLAND, 66-70, ASSOC. PROF, 70- U.S.A, 43-46. MLA; Milton Soc. Am. Seventeenth century English. Publ: An early instance of daydreams, N&Q, 11/70; Praise-as-power in Marvell and Davenant, Am. N&Q, (in press). Add: Dept. of English, University of Maine at Portland, 96 Falmouth St, Portland, ME 04103.

BAILEY, DOROTHY DEE, b. San Antonio, Tex. ENGLISH. B.A, Our Lady Lake Col, 34; M.A, Univ. Tex, 36; summers, Northwest. Univ, 38, Am. Univ, 42; Ph.D, Univ. Wis, 50. Teacher, San Antonio Pub. Sch. Syst, Tex, 34-43; asst. prof. ENG, Trinity Univ, 45-47; prof, Sul Ross State Col, 50-54; assoc. prof, Wis. State Col, Superior, 54-58; PROF, W.CHESTER STATE COL, 58- Fulbright prof, Tsuda-Juku Women's Col, Japan, 52-53; Cordoba Nat. Univ, 57; consult, dept. Eng, Upper Merion Twp, Pa, 68. U.S.N.R, 43-45, Lt.(jg). MLA; NCTE; Conf. Eng. Educ; AAUP. George Meredith; Catharine Beecher and Harriet Beecher Stowe; development of the Argentine Normal School System under Sarmiento. Publ: Growth in English, Steck, 49; Teaching English to the culturally different—a research project, W.Chester State Col, 67 & Educ. Resources Inform. Ctr. microfiche, 69-70; Harriet's big sister, TORCH, spring 66; A Beecher sister comes to Elmira, Chemung Hist. J. 12/70; The new teacher is not so new, Delta Kappa Gamma Bull, spring 71; plus one other. Add: Dept. of English, West Chester State College, West Chester, PA 19380.

BAILEY, DUDLEY, b. Lamoni, Iowa, Feb. 7, 18; m. 45; c. 3. ENGLISH LANGUAGE & LITERATURE. A.B, Univ. Kansas City, 42, A.M, 44; Ph.D.(Eng), Univ. Ill, 54. Instr. ENG, Univ. Nebr, 43-44, 45-46; Univ. Kansas City, 46-48; asst. prof, UNIV. NEBR, LINCOLN, 54-58; assoc. prof, 58-63, PROF, 63-, dir. freshman Eng, 56-62, chmn. dept, 62-72. Mem, Int. Adv. Comt. Barnhart Dictionaries, 61-; Woods fel, 62-63; mem, Nat. Counc. Accreditation of Teacher Educ, 66-68. MLA; NCTE; Conf. Col. Compos. & Commun.(chmn. 67-68); Col. Eng. Asn; Rhetoric Soc. Am. Modern English grammar; rhetoric; English Romantic movement. Publ: Co-auth, Form in modern English, 58 & auth, Essays on rhetoric, 65, Oxford; Introductory language essays, Norton, 65; The obvious content of freshman English, Col. Compos. & Commun, 58; Coleridge's revisions of The friend, Mod. Philol, 61. Add: Dept. of English, 212 Andrews Hall, University of Nebraska, Lincoln, NE 68508.

BAILEY, FREDERICK, b. Princeton, W.Va, May 22, 30; m. 52; c. 1. ENGLISH. A.B, Concord Col, 52; M.A, W.Va. Univ, 56; South. Fel. Fund fel, Univ. Tenn, 62-63, Ph.D, 63. Teacher ENG, Mercer County Bd. Educ, 52-55; asst, Univ. Tenn, 56-60; instr, CONCORD COL, 60-61, from asst. prof. to ASSOC. PROF, 61- U.S.N, 50. Traditions of historical ballads in Britain and America. Add: Div. of Language & Literature, Concord College, Athens, WV 24712.

BAILEY, JAMES OSLER, b. Raleigh, N.C, Aug. 12, 03. ENGLISH LITERATURE. A.B, Univ. N.C, 24, A.M, 27, Ph.D, 34. Teacher high sch, N.C, 24-25; teaching fel. ENG, Univ. N.C, 26-26; asst. prof, Wofford Col, 26-27; instr, UNIV. N.C, CHAPEL HILL, 27-34, asst. prof, 34-42, assoc. prof, 42-52, prof, 52-68, alumni distinguished prof, 68-71, EMER. PROF, 71- Textwriter, U.S. Qm. Sch, 42-43; lectr, Robert Col. & Istanbul Univ, Turkey, 56 56-57; Coop. Prog. in Humanities res. grant, summer 65. MLA; S.Atlantic Mod. Lang. Asn; South. Humanities Conf.(secy, 47-49). Victorian literature; poetry of Thomas Hardy. Publ: Thomas Hardy and the cosmic mind, 56 & The poetry of Thomas Hardy: a handbook and commentary, 70, Univ. N.C; co-auth, Victorian poetry, Ronald, 62; auth, British plays of the nineteenth century, Odyssey, 66; Hardy's Mephistophelian visitants, PMLA, 46; Evolutionary meliorism in the poetry of Thomas Hardy, Stud. in Philol, 63; What happens in the fall of the House of Usher?, Am. Lit, 64; plus others. Add: 801 Woodland Ave, Chapel Hill, NC 27514.

BAILEY, JAMES ROSS, b. Martinsville, Ind, Mar. 13, 38. AMERICAN LITERATURE, VICTORIAN FICTION. A.B, Franklin Col, 60; M.A, Duke Univ, 63; Ph.D.(Eng), Ind. Univ, Bloomington, 71. Teacher ENG, Franklin Jr. High Sch, Ind, 60-62; Ben Davis High Sch, Indianapolis, 63-64; ASST. PROF, OTTERBEIN COL, 67-, CHMN. DEPT, 73- MLA; Soc. Stud. Midwest. Lit. American fiction; Victorian fiction. Add: Dept. of English, Otterbein College, Westerville, OH 43081.

BAILEY, JAMES W, b. Detroit, Mich, June 5, 27; m. 49. ENGLISH. B.S, L.I. Univ, 52; M.A, Wayne State Univ. 56, Ph.D.(Eng), 63. Instr. ENG, Wayne State Univ, 58-60; Univ. Akron, 60-63, asst. prof, 63-66; assoc. prof, CENT. CONN. STATE COL, 66-70, PROF, 70- CHMN. DEPT, 69- U.S.A, 46-47. MLA. Eighteenth and 19th century English novel; Victorian literature. Add: Dept. of English, Central Connecticut State College, New Britain, CT 06050.

BAILEY, JOE ALLEN, b. Amarillo, Tex, Apr. 25, 29. COMMUNICATIONS, ADULT EDUCATION. B.S, West Tex. State Univ, 50, M.A, 51; Ph.D.(jr. col. admin), Univ. Tex, Austin, 60. Teacher, Pub. Schs, Tex, 50-52; instr. speech & coord. dept. pub. serv, West Tex. State Univ, 52-54; instr. speech, Mary Hardin-Baylor Col, Ft. Hood, 55-56; teaching asst. speech, Univ. Tex, Austin, 58-60, asst. prof, dir. bus. & prof. speaking & group discussion courses, asst. dean, sch. commun. & lang. coord, for. stud. prog, 60-68; COORD. EDUC. DEVELOP, MKT. EDUC. CTR, EASTMAN KODAK CO, 68-; ASST. PROF. SPEECH, STATE UNIV. N.Y. COL. BROCKPORT, 71- Dept. Health Educ. & Welfare & Fund for Advan. Educ. grant, 60-63; Nat. Asn. Broadcasters res. grant, 66-67; commun. consult, Off. Econ. Opportunity, 67-68. U.S.A, 53-56, 1st Lt. Speech Commun. Asn; Nat. Social Stud. Commun. Business and professional communications; legibility study—visual aids; photographic history. Publ: Co-auth, Glass, brass and chrome, the American 35 mm camera, Univ. Okla, 72, Collecting vintage cameras, Vol. I, Am. Photog. Publ, 72, Photographic equipment restoration, 73 & Peterson's guide to architectural photography, 73, Peterson Publ; plus articles in Photog. Mag, 72-73. Add: 120 Dorking Rd, Rochester, NY 14610.

BAILEY, MABEL DRISCOLL, b. Sycamore, Ill, Apr. 29, 04; m. 48. ENGLISH. B.A, Wheaton Col, 30; M.A, Univ. Ill, 33; Ph.D.(Eng), Univ. Iowa, 55. Prof. Eng, William Penn Col, 45-51; instr, Scattergood Sch, Iowa, 53-56; asst. prof. Eng. & humanities, Eureka Col, 57-61, assoc. prof, 61-66, prof, 66-69; RETIRED. Nat. Asn. Blind Teachers (corresp. secy, 71-75); Col. Eng. Asn; MLA. English romantic authors; 20th century American drama. Publ: Maxwell Anderson: The playwright as prophet, Schuman, 57; Maxwell Anderson, Collier's Encycl, 63; Literature as sustenance, Col. Eng. Asn. Critic, 1/66. Add: 610 S. Darst, Eureka, IL 61530.

BAILEY, RAYMOND HAMBY, Church History, Rhetoric. See Volume IV, Philosophy, Religion & Law.

BAILEY, RICHARD WELD, b. Pontiac, Mich, Oct. 26, 39; m. 60; c. 2. ENGLISH. A.B, Dartmouth Col, 61; M.A, Univ. Conn, 63, Ph.D.(Eng), 66; Int. Ctr. Semiotics & Ling, Urbino, summer 71. Asst. prof. ENG, UNIV. MICH, ANN ARBOR, 65-71, ASSOC. PROF, 71- Fel, Inst. Advan. Stud. Humanities, Univ. Edinburgh, 71. NCTE; MLA; Ling. Soc. Am; Am. Dialect Soc. Stylistics; dialectology; computational lexicography. Publ: Co-ed, English Stylistics; a bibliography, M.I.T, 68; An annotated bibliography of statistical stylistics, Mich. Slavic Contrib, 68; Statistics and style, Am. Elsevier, 69; The computer and literary studies, Univ. Edinburgh, 73; Varieties of present-day English, Macmillan, 73; ed, Computer poems, Potagannissing, 73. Add: Dept. of English, University of Michigan, Ann Arbor, MI 48104.

BAILLIE, WILLIAM MAYAN, b. Boston, Mass, Nov. 4, 40; m. 62; c. 2. ENGLISH LITERATURE. A.B, Ball State Univ, 62; M.A, Univ. Chicago, 64, Ph.D.(Eng), 67. ASST. PROF. ENG, OHIO STATE UNIV, COLUMBUS, 67- MLA; AAUP. Elizabethan drama; bibliography. Publ: Gratiae theatrales: three seventeenth century English plays, Mouton, 74; Printing of privileged books at Cambridge 1630-34, Trans. Cambridge Bibliog. Soc, 71; Authorship attribution in Jacobean dramatic texts, Papers Int. Conf. Computers in Humanities, 74. Add: Dept. of English, Ohio State University, 164 W. 17th St, Columbus, OH 43210.

BAIM, JOSEPH, b. Brooklyn, N.Y, Apr. 27, 38; m. 63. ENGLISH. B.A, Alfred Univ, 59; M.A, Syracuse Univ, 61, Ph.D.(Eng), 67. Instr. ENG, CARNEGIE-MELLON UNIV, 66-67, asst. prof, 67-72, ASSOC. PROF, 72- Nat. Endowment for Humanities summer stipend, 69. MLA. Modern British and American literature; D.H. Lawrence. Publ: Escape from intellection: Saul Bellow's Dangling man, Univ. Rev, 70; Past and present in D.H. Lawrence's A fragment of stained glass, Stud. Short Fiction, 71; D.H. Lawrence's social vision, Carnegie Ser. Eng, 72; plus others. Add: Dept. of English, Carnegie-Mellon University, Pittsburgh, PA 15213.

BAIN, CARL EDWIN, b. Jackson, Miss, Feb. 9, 30; m. 69; c. 1. ENGLISH. B.A, Baylor Univ, 52, M.A, 53; Ph.D, Johns Hopkins Univ, 61. Instr. ENG, EMORY UNIV, 60-62, asst. prof, 62-65, ASSOC. PROF, 65-, asst. dean, Grad. Sch, 66-69, acting dean, 69-70. U.S.N, 53-56, Res, 56-58, Lt. MLA. Modern drama. Publ: Co-ed, Introduction to literature, Norton, 73; auth, A valentine for Queen Joanne, 61 & W.H. Auden, 65, Emory Univ. Quart; plus others. Add: Dept. of English, Emory University, Atlanta, GA 30322.

BAIN, ROBERT ADDISON, b. Marshall, Ill, Sept. 20, 32; m. 51; c. 3. ENGLISH. B.S, East. Ill. Univ, 54; A.M, Univ. Ill, 59, Ph.D.(Eng), 64. ASSOC. PROF. ENG, UNIV. N.C, CHAPEL HILL, 64- MLA; S.Atlantic Mod. Lang. Asn; Conf. Col. Compos. & Commun; Col. Eng. Asn. American fiction; Colonial & Federalist American writing; nineteenth century American literature. Publ: Co-ed, Colonial and Federalist American writing, Odyssey, 66. Add: Dept. of English, University of North Carolina, Chapel Hill, NC 27514.

BAINE, RODNEY MONTGOMERY, b. Kosciusko, Miss, July 1, 13; m. 40, 68; c. 4. ENGLISH LITERATURE. A.B, Southwest. at Memphis, 35; Vanderbilt Univ, 35-36; Rhodes scholar. & B.A, Oxford, 38, B.Litt, 39, M.A, 51; Ph.D, Harvard, 51. Instr, Univ. Mo, 39-41; Mass. Inst. Technol, 41-44; assoc. prof. Eng, Univ. Richmond, 46-54; head div. langs. & lit, Delta State Col, 54-57; chmn, Dept. Eng, Ala. Col, 57-62; assoc. prof. ENG, UNIV. GA, 62-66, PROF, 66- U.S.A, 44-46. MLA; S.Atlantic Mod. Lang. Asn. Daniel Defoe; 18th century novel; William Blake. Publ: Thomas Holcroft and the revolutionary novel, 65, Robert Munford: America's first comic dramatist, 67 & Daniel Defoe and the supernatural, 68, Univ. Ga; Blake's Tyger: the nature of the beast, Philol. Quart, 10/67. Add: Dept. of English, University of Georgia, Athens, GA 30601.

BAINES, BARBARA JOAN HURST, b. Cheyenne, Wyo, Feb. 6, 39; m. 69; c. 1. ENGLISH LITERATURE. B.A, Univ. Okla, 61, M.A, 68; Ph.D.(Eng), Ohio Univ, 71. ASST. PROF. ENG, N.C. STATE UNIV, 71- MLA; Southeast. Renaissance Conf. English Renaissance drama; women's studies. Publ: The lust motif in the plays of Thomas Middleton, Univ. Salzburg, 73. Add: Dept. of English, North Carolina State University, Box 5308, Raleigh, NC 27607.

BAIRD, ALBERT CRAIG, b. Vevay, Ind, Oct. 20, 83; m. 23; c. 1. SPEECH, RHETORIC. A.B, Wabash Col, 07, hon. D.Litt, 32; B.D, Union Theol. Sem, 10; A.M, Columbia Univ, 12; hon. L.H.D, South. Ill. Univ, 70; hon. LL.D, Bates Col, 73. Instr. Eng, Ohio Wesleyan Univ, 10-11; Dartmouth Col, 11-13; prof. rhetoric, Bates Col, 13-25; assoc. prof. SPEECH, UNIV. IOWA, 25-28, prof, 28-52, EMER. PROF, 52- Speech Commun. Asn.(pres, 39, outstanding bk. award, 71). American public address; speech criticism; general speech. Publ: Co-auth, Speech criticism, Ronald, 71. Add: 200 Ferson Ave, Iowa City, IA 52240.

BAIRD, CLARIBEL, b. Van Alstyne, Tex, Dec. 9, 04; m. 29, 52; c. 1. SPEECH, THEATRE. B.A, Okla. Col. Women, 25; M.A, Univ. Mich, 36; Univ. London, 56. Instr. speech & drama, Okla. Col. Women, 26-28, 32-35, asst. prof, 35-38, assoc. prof, 38-40, prof, 40-47; assoc. prof. SPEECH & THEATRE, UNIV. MICH, ANN ARBOR, 48-60, prof, 60-71, EMER. PROF, 71- Lectr. theatre, Univ. Mich, Ann Arbor, summers 37-47. Hon. life mem, Am. Theatre Asn; Am. Nat. Theatre & Acad; Speech Asn. Am. Dramatic literature; theatre production. Publ: European festivals, Theatre Arts Mag, 5/57; A flexible theatre plant, Mannheim, Germany, Players Mag, 11/61; contrib, The theatre restored, Accent, 59. Add: 2409 Vinewood Blvd, Ann Arbor, MI 48104.

BAIRD, JAMES RICHARD, b. Tenn, Nov. 2, 10. AMERICAN LITERATURE. A.B, Univ. Tenn, 31, A.M, 35; Yale, 42, Ph.D.(Eng), 47; A.M, Columbia Univ, 44. Asst. prof. ENG, Univ. Tenn, 47-48; assoc. prof, Univ. Hawaii, 49-50; asst. prof, CONN. COL, 50-57, assoc. prof, 57-63, PROF, 63- Rockefeller Found. fel, France & Eng. 48-49; Fund Advan. Educ. fel, Yale, 55-56; summer vis. prof, Univ. Hawaii, 60; Wesleyan Univ, 63, 66, 67; chmn, Sch. & Col. Conf. Eng, 63-64; vis. lectr. Am. lit, U.S.Educ. Comn, Tokyo, Japan, 70; vis. prof. Eng, Brown Univ, 71-72. U.S.N.R, 43-46, Lt. MLA; Am. Stud. Asn. American romanticism, 1830-1890; contemporary American poetry; the contemporary Japanese novel. Publ: Ishmael, Johns Hopkins, 56 & Harper, 60; co-ed, American literary masters (2 vols), Holt, 65; auth, The dome and the rock: structure in the poetry of Wallace Stevens, Johns Hopkins, 68. Add: Dept. of English, Connecticut College, New London, CT 06320.

BAIRD, JOHN D, b. Glasgow, Scotland, May 9, 41. ENGLISH LITERATURE. M.A, Univ. St. Andrews, 63; M.A, McMaster Univ, 64; M.A, Princeton, 67, Ph.D.(Eng), 70. Lectr. ENG, VICTORIA COL, UNIV. TORONTO, 67-68, asst. prof, 68-73, ASSOC. PROF, 73- Can. Counc. res. grants, 71, 72, leave fel, 73-74; vis. fel, Princeton, 73-74. Am. Soc. 18th Century Stud. Eighteenth century literature; William Cowper; fiction. Publ: Ed, Editing texts of the romantic period, Hakkert, Toronto, 72. Add: Dept. of English, Victoria College, University of Toronto, Toronto, Ont. M5S 1K7, Can.

BAIRD, JOHN E, b. Eugene, Ore, Feb. 3, 22; m. 47; c. 3. SPEECH. B.Th, Northwest Christian Col, 44; B.A, Univ. of the Pac, 47, M.A, 48; Ph.D. (speech), Columbia Univ, 59. Instr. speech, Univ. Ore, 47-48; asst. lib. arts exten, Univ. N.H, 48-51; instr. SPEECH, Columbia Univ, 51-53; teacher, Manhattan Bible Col, 53-55; Modesto Jr. Col, 55-63; assoc. prof, Phillips Univ, 63-67; ASSOC. PROF, CALIF. STATE UNIV, HAYWARD, 67- U.S.A, 45-46. Speech Commun. Asn. Religious speech. Publ: A guide to conducting meetings, 65, co-auth, Funeral meditations, 66 & auth, Preparing for platform and pulpit, 68, Abingdon. Add: Dept. of Speech, California State University at Hayward, 25800 Hillary St, Hayward, CA 94542.

BAIRD, JOSEPH LEE, b. Gastonia, N.C, Apr. 15, 33; m. 61; c. 3. ENGLISH. B.S, Appalachian State Univ, 57, M.A, 60; Ph.D, Univ. Ky, 66. Instr. ENG, KENT STATE UNIV, 64-66, asst. prof, 66-68, ASSOC. PROF, 68- MLA; Mediaeval Acad. Am. English literature, especially medieval. Publ: Grendel the exile, Neuphilol. Mitteilungen, 66; Unferth the Thyle, Medium Aevum, 70; the Nor-clause in Beowulf 1084-85a, Mod. Philol, 71; plus two others. Add: Dept. of English, Kent State University, Kent, OH 44240.

BAIRD, JULIAN THOMPSON, JR, b. Harlingen, Tex, Jan. 28, 38; m. 61. ENGLISH LITERATURE. A.B, Harvard, 60, Ph.D.(Eng. lit), 68; B.A, Oxford, 63, M.A, 67. Instr. HUMANITIES, BOSTON UNIV, 67-68, asst. prof, 68-70, ASSOC. PROF. & CHMN. DEPT, 70- Myth and symbol in the arts; Blake and Swinburne; comparative history of criticism and aesthetics. Publ: Principles of violence in Inferno XIII, Italian Quart, winter-spring 66; Swinburne, Sade, and Blake: the pleasure-pain paradox, Victorian Poetry, spring-summer 71; Anna Hempstead branch, In: Notable American women, 1607-1950, Harvard Univ, 71. Add: Dept. of Humanities, Boston University, 855 Commonwealth Ave, Boston, MA 02215.

BAIRD, REED M, b. Pittsburgh, Pa, June 25, 32; m. 58; c. 2. ENGLISH. B.A, Dartmouth Col, 54; M.A, Univ. Mich, 60, Rackham fel, 65, Ph.D.(Am. cult), 66. Asst, Univ. Mainz, 60-61; teaching fel. Eng, Univ. Mich, 63-65; asst. prof. AM. THOUGHT & LANG, MICH. STATE UNIV, 66-71, ASSOC. PROF, 71- U.S.A.F, 55-59, Res, 59-67, Capt. Am. Stud. Asn; MLA. American literature and American intellectual history. Publ: Section IV, In: General liberal education, Mich. State Univ, 68; Articles in American studies-1970: mass culture, 8/71 & Articles in American studies-1971: mass culture, 8/72, Am. Quart. Add: 204 Kedzie St, East Lansing, MI 48823.

BAIRD, RUSSELL NORMAN, b. Joffre, Pa, June 14, 22; m. 42; c. 6. JOURNALISM. B.A, Kent State Univ, 42; M.A, Univ. Wis, 46. Instr. JOUR, Bowling Green State Univ, 47-48, asst. prof, 48-52; OHIO UNIV, 52-56, assoc. prof, 56-62, PROF, 62- U.A.S, 43-46. Asn. Educ. in Jour. Publ: Co-auth, Industrial and business journalism, Chilton, 61, Graphics of communication, 64, 2nd ed, 68 & Practical exercises in typography, design and layout, 68, Holt; auth, The penal press, Northwest. Univ, 68; co-auth, Magazine editing and production, W.C. Brown, 74. Add: School of Journalism, Ohio University, Athens, OH 45701.

BAISLER, PERRY, b. Winnipeg, Man, May 11, 09; U.S. citizen; m. 32; c. 1. SPEECH. B.A, Univ. Wash, 32, M.A, 38; Ph.D.(speech), Northwest. Univ, 50. Instr. Eng, speech & math, High Sch, Wash, 32-35; SPEECH, Univ. Wash, 35-39; asst. prof, 46-52; asst, Northwest. Univ, 39-41; PROF, STATE UNIV. N.Y. COL. NEW PALTZ, 52-, CHMN. SPEECH, 69-, acting chmn. humanities, 63-64; chmn. speech & theatre arts, 64-69. Prof, Univ. Hawaii, 61-62. U.S.N.R, 41-46, Lt. Comdr. Speech Commun. Asn; Am. Speech & Hearing Asn.(cert. clin. competence); Int. Phonetic Asn. Speech science and phonetics; speech correction. Add: Dept. of Speech, State University of New York College at New Paltz, New Paltz, NY 12561.

BAIZER, ASHUR, b. Philadelphia, Pa, Dec. 23, 19; m. 43; c. 2. ENGLISH. B.A, Univ. Pa, 40; M.A, Columbia Univ, 49; Ph.D, N.Y. Univ, 60. Tutor ENG, City Col. New York, 48-50; instr, Brooklyn Col, 50-56; from asst. prof. to PROF, ITHACA COL, 56- Mem, Eng. Inst. Sig.C, 41-46, S/Sgt. MLA; Milton Soc. Am; NCTE. Eighteenth century English literature; Victorian literature; 20th century American novel. Publ: Living amoeba, New Repub, 47; The proposition, Commentary, 51; co-auth, Complete prose works of Milton, Vol. I, Tale, 53. Add: Dept. of English, Ithaca College, Ithaca, NY 14850.

BAKELESS, JOHN (EDWIN), b. Carlisle, Pa, Dec. 30, 94; m. 20. ENGLISH. Pa. State Norm. Sch, 13; A.B, Williams Col.(Mass), 18; A.M, Harvard, 20, Ph.D.(Eng), 36. RES. & WRITING, 21- Lit. ed, Living Age, 21-23, managing ed, 23-25, ed, 28-29; lit. adv, Independent, 25-26; managing ed, Forum, 26-28; lectr. jour, N.Y. Univ, 27-29, instr, 29-30, asst. prof, 30-40, assoc. prof, 40-47, lectr, 47-54, grad. fac, 48-54; Guggenheim fel, 36-37, 46-47; asst. mil. attache, Turkey, 44; chief mil. sect, Am. deleg, Allied Control Comn, Bulgaria, 45; Trumbull lectr, Yale, 48, Gray lectr, 64; Adams lectr, Univ. Mich, 60; vis. instr, Writers' Conf, Univ. Colo, 62; Spahr lectr, Dickinson Col, 68; Huntington Libr. grant, 68. David A. Wells Prize, Williams Col, 20; Harvard Club of N.China Prize, 20; Helen Choate Bell Prize, Harvard; Bowdoin Prize, 22, 23. U.S.A, 18-19, 40-46, U.S.A.R, 20-39, 47-53, Col; Bronze Star Medal. Lepidopterists Soc; fel. Co. Mil. Hist. History of military intelligence. Publ: Magazine making, 31; Daniel Boone, 39; Tragicall history of Christopher Marlowe, Harvard & Oxford, 42; Lewis and Clark, partners in discovery, Morrow, 47; Turncoats, traitors and heroes, 59 & Spies of the Confederacy, 71, Lippincott; plus others. Add: Elbowroom Farm, Great Hill, Seymour, CT 06483.

BAKER, CARLOS, b. Biddeford, Maine, May 5, 09; m. 32; c. 3. ENGLISH & AMERICAN LITERATURE. A.B, Dartmouth Col, 32, hon. Litt.D, 57; A.M, Harvard, 33; Ph.D, Princeton, 39. Instr. ENG, PRINCETON, 38-42, asst. prof, 42-46, assoc. prof, 46-51, PROF, 51-, HEAD DEPT, 74-, WOODROW WILSON PROF. LIT, 53- Guggenheim fels, 65-66 & 67-68. MLA. English romantic literature; modern fiction and poetry. Publ: Shelley's major poetry; Hemingway, the writer as artist; Ernest Hemingway: a life story, Scribner, 69. Add: 34 Allison Rd, Princeton, NJ 08540.

BAKER, DONALD C, b. Jonesboro, Ark, Dec. 12, 28; m. 52; c. 4. ENGLISH MEDIAEVAL LITERATURE. A.B, Ark. State Col, 49; M.A, Univ. Miss, 50; Ph.D, Univ. Okla, 54. Instr. Eng. compos, Univ. Okla, 52-53; Agr. &

Mech. Col. Tex, 53-55; asst. prof. Eng. lit, State Univ. S.Dak, 55-57; assoc. prof, Univ. Miss, 57-62; UNIV. COLO, BOULDER, 62-68, PROF. ENG, 68- Fulbright lectr, Finland, 61-62. MLA; Mediaeval Acad. Am; Renaissance Soc. Am. Middle English; Old English; Renaissance literature. Publ: The dreamer again in Chaucer's Book of the duchess, PMLA, 3/55; Gold coins in Mediaeval English literature, Speculum, 4/61; Gentilesse in the Clerk's tale and the Wife of Bath's tale, Stud. Philol, 10/62. Add: Dept. of English, University of Colorado, Boulder, CO 80302.

BAKER, DONALD WHITELAW, b. Boston, Mass, Jan. 30, 23; m. 45; c. 2. ENGLISH LITERATURE. A.B, Brown Univ, 47, A.M, 49, Ph.D.(Eng), 55. Instr. ENG, Brown Univ, 48-52; asst. prof, WABASH COL, 53-57, assoc. prof, 57-67, PROF, 67-, POET IN RESIDENCE, 63-, dir. drama, 54-59. Mem. nat. adv. comt, NCTE achievement awards, 67- U.S.A.A.F, 42-45, Lt. MLA; NCTE. English novel; modern fiction; creative writing. Publ: Three poets, 7/67, Five poets, 12/67 & The poetry of James Dickey, 3/68, Poetry. Add: 16 Mills Pl, Crawfordsville, IN 47933.

BAKER, ELMER E, JR, b. Hagerstown, Md, Apr. 15, 22; m. 45. SPEECH. B.S, N.Y. Univ, 48, M.A, 49, Ph.D, 54; hon. Litt.D, Emerson Col, 69. Suprv. speech ther, Dept. Phys. Med. & Rehabil, Bellevue Med. Ctr, N.Y. UNIV, 48-50, instr. speech educ, SCH. EDUC, 50-54, asst. prof, 54-58, assoc. prof, 58-61, PROF. ENG. & SPEECH EDUC, 61-, ASSOC. DEAN INSTR, 72-, chmn. dept. Eng. & speech educ, 61-72, dir. summer sessions, Sch. Educ, 62-65, clin. prof, Col. Dent, 63-72, acting dir. univ. summer sessions, 66, 68, acting v.dean, Sch. Educ, 66, 68, 69, head, Div. Eng. Educ, Speech & Educ. Theatre, 66-72. Consult. speech path, St. Vincent's Hosp, New York, 66- & Vet. Admin. Hosp, 67-68. U.S.A.A.F, 43-46, Staff Sgt. Am. Speech & Hearing Asn.(clin. cert. speech); Speech Commun. Asn; East. States Speech Asn. Speech pathology. Publ: Co-auth, Bibliography of speech and allied areas, Chilton, 62; co-ed, Listening and speaking in the English classroom, Macmillan, 71; co-auth, The survey approach, In: An introduction to graduate study in speech and theatre, Mich. State Univ, 61. Add: Press 42, School of Education, New York University, Washington Sq, New York, NY 10003.

BAKER, FRANK SHEAFFER, b. Findlay, Ohio, May 20, 10; m. 35; c. 3. ENGLISH JOURNALISM. A.B, Col. Wooster, 30; Ball State Teachers Col, 32-33; A.M, Harvard, 43; summers, Ind. Univ, 47-53, Univ. Mo, 60-61. Supvr. Pubs, sr. high sch, Ind, 37-46; ASSOC. PROF. ENG. & JOUR, HANOVER COL, 46-, COL. ED, 68- Asn. Educ. Jour; Am. Col. Pub. Relat. Asn; Nat. Counc. Col. Pub. Adv; Nat. Press Photographers Asn. English language; photojournalism; magazine editing. Publ: Co-auth, Guide to writing term papers, W.C. Brown, 59; ed, Christian perspectives in contemporary culture, Twayne, 62; auth, The Hanover Presbyterian Church 1820-1970, Superior Printing Co, 70. Add: Dept. of Journalism, Hanover College, Hanover, IN 47243.

BAKER, HERSCHEL, b. Cleburne, Tex, Nov. 8, 14. ENGLISH LITERATURE. A.B. & Mus.B, South. Methodist Univ, 35, hon. D.Litt, 65; A.M, Harvard, 36, Ph.D, 39; hon. D.Litt, Univ. Vt, 67. Instr. Eng, Univ. Tex, 39-44, asst. prof, 44-46; HARVARD, 46-49, assoc. prof, 49-56, prof, 56-67, HENRY LEE HIGGINSON PROF. ENG. LIT, 67-, chmn. dept, 52-57. Alexander lectr, Univ. Toronto, 66. Intellectual history; Renaissance literature; English stage history. Publ: John Philip Kemble, 42, The dignity of man, 47, The wars of truth, 51 & William Hazlitt, 62, Harvard; co-auth, The Renaissance in England, Heath, 54; auth, The race of time, Univ. Toronto, 67. Add: 117 Widener Library, Cambridge, MA 02138.

BAKER, HOUSTON A, JR, b. Louisville, Ky, Mar. 22, 43; m. 66; c. 1. VICTORIAN & BLACK AMERICAN LITERATURE. B.A, Howard Univ, 65; M.A, Univ. Calif, Los Angeles, 66, Ph.D.(Eng. & Am. lit), 68; Univ. Edinburgh, 67-68. Inst. ENG, Howard Univ, 66; Yale, 68-69, asst. prof, 69-70; assoc. prof, UNIV. VA, 70-73, PROF, 73- Mem. screening comt. Am. lit, Fulbright Comt. Int. Exchange of Persons, 73-76. MLA. Victorian literature; Black American literature; American literature. Publ: Ed, Black literature in America, McGraw, 71; Twentieth century interpretations of Native Son, Prentice-Hall, 72; auth, Long black song: essays in Black American literature and culture, Univ. Va, 72; A decadent's nature: the poetry of Ernest Dawson, Victorian Poetry, 68; Completely well: one view of Black American culture, In: Key issues in the Afro-American experience, Harcourt, 71; A forgotten prototype: The autobiography of an ex-colored man and Invisible man, Va. Quart. Rev, 72. Add: Dept. of English, Wilson Hall, University of Virginia, Charlottesville, VA 22901.

BAKER, IRA L, b. Fairwood, Va, Sept. 5, 14. JOURNALISM, ENGLISH. B.A, Wake Forest Col, 36; M.A, Columbia Univ, 52; M.S.J, Univ. Ill, 63. Instr. Eng, N.C. State Col, 46-50, asst. exten. ed, Exten. Serv, 50-51; from asst. prof. to assoc. prof. jour. & head dept, Furman Univ, 51-65; assoc. prof. Eng. & jour, High Point Col, 65-68; ASST. PROF. ENG. & COORD, JOUR. PROF, E.CAROLINA UNIV, 68- Adv. ed, Scholastic Ed, 60-; Stud. Writer, 61-; mem, Comn. Freedoms & Responsibilities of Col. Stud. Press, 67; ed, Col. Journalist, 70-72. Pioneer Award, Nat. Scholastic Press Asn, 70. U.S.A.A.F, 42-44. Asn. Educ. in Jour; Nat. Counc. Col. Publ. Adv.(award, 67, honor role col. & univ. adv, 69); Baptist Pub. Relat. Asn; Pub. Relat. Soc. Am. History of press and scholastic journalism; graphics and communications; financial gimmicks for sound papers. Publ: Elizabeth Timothy: America's first woman editor; Modern journalism, Pitman, 63; Behind the lines—Hanoi, 4/67, The best of Harry Golden, 2/68 & A D.H. Lawrence miscellany, 4/68, Greensboro Daily News; plus others. Add: Box 2707, East Carolina University, Greenville, NC 27834.

BAKER, JAMES RUPERT, b. Freeport, Ill, May 18, 25; m; c. 1. ENGLISH. Ph.D, Univ. Denver, 54. Instr. ENG, Colo. State Univ, 51; Univ. Idaho, 54-56; asst, CALIF. STATE UNIV, SAN DIEGO, 56-61, assoc, 61-67, PROF, 67- Mem. ed. bd, Twentieth Century Lit, 55-; adv. ed, James Joyce Quart, 66-; vis. prof, Univ. Mo, 67-68. U.S.M.C.R, 43. MLA. Contemporary literature. Publ: Co-ed, Casebook edition of Golding's Lord of the flies, Putnam, 64; William Golding: a critical study, St. Martin's, 65; James Joyce, esthetic freedom and dramatic art, West. Humanities Rev; Ibsen, Joyce and the living dead, In: A James Joyce miscellany, 3rd ser, South. Ill, 62; plus others. Add: Dept. of English, California State University, San Diego, CA 92115.

BAKER, JAMES VOLANT, b. Reading, Eng, July 20, 03; U.S. citizen; m. 47, 51; c. 1. ENGLISH. M.A, Oxford, 29; Ph.D.(Eng), Univ. Mich, 54. Lectr. ENG, Edwardes Col, India, 24-26; teacher, Egyptian sec. schs, 27-30; assoc. prof, Westminster Col, 33-45; instr, Univ. Nebr, 47-50; assoc. prof, UNIV. HOUSTON, 50-55, prof, 55-73, EMER. PROF, 73- Major Hopwood Award Poetry, Univ. Mich, 47. MLA. English romanticism; contemporary English and American poetry; phenomenology and existentialism. Publ: The sacred river: Coleridge's theory of imagination, La. State Univ, 57; A fresh look at Prufrock, J. Existential Psychiat, fall 64; T.S. Eliot, In: American winners of Nobel prize for literature, 68 & W.B. Yeats, In: British winners of the Nobel prize for literature, 74, Univ. Okla. Add: 4369 Fiesta Lane, Houston, TX 77004.

BAKER, JOSEPH ELLIS, b. Sullivan, Ill, Aug. 24, 05; m. 32; c. 3. ENGLISH LITERATURE. A.B, Univ. Ill, 27, A.M, 28; Ph.D, Princeton, 31. Instr. ENG, Princeton, 29; Northwest. Univ, 31-35, UNIV. IOWA, 35-38, asst. prof, 38-46, assoc. prof, 46-52, prof, 52-73, EMER. PROF, 73-, chmn. interdept. Europ. lit. & thought, 58-73. Fulbright prof, France, 54-55; William James Lemon prof. lit, Clemson Univ, 74-75. MLA. Victorian literature; literary criticism; regional arts. Publ: The novel and the Oxford movement, 32 & ed, Reinterpretation of Victorian literature, 50, Princeton; Browning: Pippa Passes and shorter poems, Odyssey, 47; Shelley's Platonic answer to a Platonic attack on poetry, Univ. Iowa, 65. Add: 30 S. Governor, Iowa City, IA 52240.

BAKER, PAUL, b. Hereford, Tex, July 24, 11; m. 36; c. 3. DRAMA. A.B, Trinity Univ, Tex. & Univ. Wis, 32; M.F.A, Yale, 39. Prof. drama & chmn. dept, Baylor Univ, 45-63; PROF. SPEECH & DRAMA & CHMN. DEPT, TRINITY UNIV, 63-, DIR. DALLAS THEATER CTR, 59- Margo Jones Award, 68. U.S.A, 43-45, Maj. Nat. Theatre Conf.(pres. elect, 58); Southwest Theatre Conf.(pres, 50). Experimental theater. Publ: Ten talents in the American theatre; Integration of abilities: exercises for creative growth, Trinity Univ, 72. Add: Dept. of Speech & Drama, Trinity University, 715 Stadium Dr, San Antonio, TX 78284.

BAKER, RICHARD T, b. Coggon, Iowa, Mar. 27, 13; m. 37; c. 1. JOURNALISM. B.A, Cornell Col, 34, hon. D.D, 46; M.S, Columbia Univ, 37; B.D, Union Theol. Sem, 41. Mem. ed. staff, Christian Advocate & Epworth Herald, 34-36; dir. publicity, Methodist Bd. Missions, 38-39; assoc. ed, World Outlook, 39-43, correspondent in Orient, 45-46; assoc. prof. & acting dean, Grad. Sch. Jour, Chungking, China, 43-45; assoc. prof. JOUR, GRAD. SCH. JOUR, COLUMBIA UNIV, 47-52; PROF, 52-, assoc. dean, 61-68, dean, 68-70. Pulitzer traveling fel, 37-38; summer consult, relig. affairs br, Off. High Comnr. Ger, 50; mem. staff, New York Times, 53-54. Victory medal, Repub. China, 47; Columbia Jour. Alumni award, 67. Asn. Educ. Jour. Religious journalism; Far Eastern affairs. Publ: The seed and the soil, Friendship Press, 41; Darkness of the sun, Abingdon, 47; The graduate school of journalism, Columbia Univ, 54; The Christian as a journalist, Asn. Press, 61; American journalism, In: Encyclopedia Americana, 48- & Newspapers, Americana Annual, 65-69, Grolier. Add: 709 Journalism, Columbia University, New York, NY 10027.

BAKER, ROBERT SAMUEL, b. Weed, Calif, Sept. 30, 26; div; c. 3. ENGLISH. B.A, Pac. Univ, 53; M.A, Univ. Chicago, 56. Instr, HUMANITIES, ORE. COL. EDUC, 57-60, ASST. PROF, 60. Fulbright teachers grant, Univ. Trieste, 64-66. Sig.C, U.S.A, 46-49. NCTE; MLA. Contemporary and comparative literature; translation theory. Publ: Co-ed, The wor(l)d on wheels: reading/thinking/writing about the automobile in America, Allyn & Bacon, 72. People get hooked, Commentary, 3/63; Italo Svevo and the limits of marriage, In: Essays on Italo Svevo, Univ. Tulsa, 68; plus others. Add: Dept. of Humanities, Oregon College of Education, Monmouth, OR 97361.

BAKER, ROBERT SAMUEL, b. St. Catharines, Ont, Jan. 11, 40; m. 68. ENGLISH LITERATURE. B.A, Univ. West. Ont, 67, M.A, 69; Ph.D.(Eng), Univ. Ill, Urbana, 72. Instr. ENG, Univ. West. Ont, 68-69; ASST. PROF, UNIV. WIS-MADISON, 72- Can. Counc. doctoral fel, 69-72. R.C.A.F, 58-61. MLA. Victorian novel; Romantic and Victorian poetry; modern British literature. Publ: Gabriel Nash's house of strange idols: aestheticism in The tragic muse, Tex. Stud. Lit. & Lang, spring, 73; The ordeal of Richard Feverel: a psychological approach to structure; Stud. Novel, 9/74; Spandrell's Lydian heaven: moral masochism and the centrality of Spandrell in Huxley's Point counter point, Criticism, spring 74. Add: Dept. of English, Helen C. White Hall, University of Wisconsin-Madison, Madison, WI 53706.

BAKER, ROBERTA HARDY, b. Manhattan, Ill, May 21, 25; m. 63. DRAMA. B.A, Beloit Col, 47; M.A, Univ. Wis, 48; Ph.D, Northwest. Univ, 62. Instr. speech & drama, Beloit Col, 48-50, 53-55; Tex. Christian Univ, 50-51; DRAMA, UNIV. MIAMI, 57-59, asst. prof, 59-62, assoc. prof, 62-72, PROF, 72- Southeast Theatre Conf; Am. Theatre Asn. Add: Dept. of Drama, University of Miami, Coral Gables, FL 33124.

BAKER, RONALD JAMES, b. London, Eng, Aug. 24, 24; Can. citizen; m. 49; c. 5. ENGLISH, LINGUISTICS. B.A, Univ. B.C, 51, M.A, 53; Humanities Res. Counc. fel, Sch. Orient. & African Stud, Univ. London, 55, Royal Soc. Can. fel, Univ. London, 56; hon. LL.D, Univ. N.B, 70. Lectr. Eng, Univ. B.C, 53-54, instr, 56-57, asst. prof, 57-62, assoc. prof, 63-64; prof. & head dept, Simon Fraser Univ, 65-69, dir. acad. planning, 64-66; SPEC. LECTR. ENG. & FIRST PRES, UNIV. PRINCE EDWARD ISLAND, 69- Mem. Prov. Comt. on Higher Educ, 62; cor. mem, Humanities Res. Counc. Can, 62; mem, Can. Counc, 70. R.A.F, 43-47, Flight Lt. Ling. Soc. Am; Can. Ling. Asn; Philol. Soc, Eng; NCTE; MLA; Can. Counc. Teachers Eng; Asn. Can. Univ. Teachers Eng.(pres, 67-68); Conf. Col. Compos. & Commun. Modern English language; American Indian linguistics. Contrib. to J. Can. Ling. Asn; Can. Lit; J. Educ. Add: University of Prince Edwward Island, Charlottetown, P.E.I. C1A 4P3, Can.

BAKER, RONALD LEE, b. Indianapolis, Ind, June 30, 37; m. 60; c. 2. FOLKLORE. B.S, Ind. State Univ, Terre Haute, 60, M.A, 61; Univ. Ill, Urbana, 63-65; Ford Found. fel, Ind. Univ, Bloomington, 65-66, Ph.D.(folklore), 69. Instr. Eng, Univ. Ill, Urbana, 63-65; teaching assoc, Eng. & Folklore, Ind. Univ, Ft. Wayne, 65-66; instr. ENG, IND. STATE UNIV, TERRE HAUTE, 66-69, asst. prof, 69-71, ASSOC. PROF, 71- Vis. lectr. Eng, Univ. Ill, Urbana, 72-73; mem. exec. comt, Place-Name Survey of U.S, 72- U.S.A.F.R, 60-66. Am. Folklore Soc; Am. Name Soc; Int. Soc. Ethnol. & Folklore; MLA; Popular Cult. Asn. American folk legend; place names; folklore in American literature. Publ: Folklore in the writings of Rowland E. Robinson, Bowling Green Univ, 73; Folklore courses and programs in American colleges and universities, 4-6/71 & The role of folk legends in place-name research, 10-12/72, J. Am. Folklore; Monsterville: a traditional place-name and its legends, Names: J. Am. Name Soc, 9/72. Add: Dept. of English, Indiana State University, Terre Haute, IN 47809.

BAKER, S. ORVILLE, b. Chicago, Ill, Jan. 21, 12. ENGLISH DRAMA. Ph.B, Univ. Chicago, 34; Ph.D, Harvard, 48. Instr, Carnegie Inst. Tech, 37-40; asst. prof, Simmons Col, 46-47; lectr, Wellesley Col, 48-49; asst. prof, Carnegie Inst. Technol, 49-50; assoc. prof. ENG, NORTH. ILL. UNIV, 50-55, PROF, 55-, COORD. FOR. STUD. PROG, 68-, head dept. Eng, 55-68. MLA; NEA; NCTE. Add: Dept. of English, Northern Illinois University, DeKalb, IL 60115.

BAKER, SHERIDAN (WARNER, JR), b. Santa Rosa, Calif, July 10, 18. ENGLISH LITERATURE. A.B, Univ. Calif, 39, A.M, 46, Ph.D, 50. Teaching asst, Univ. Calif, 46-49, lectr, 49-50; instr. ENG. LIT, UNIV. MICH, ANN ARBOR, 50-57, asst. prof, 57-61, assoc. prof, 61-64, PROF, 64-, Rackham Fac. Res. Fund grant, 50-51, 69 & 72. Ed. Papers, Mich. Acad. Sci, Arts & Lett, 54-61; Fulbright lectr, Univ. Nagoya, 61-62; ed, Mich. Quart. Rev, 64-71; judge, Explicator Prize, 65-; vis. prof, Univ. Calif, Berkeley, winter 71. Named One of Top Fifty Living Am. Poets, Epoch, 66. U.S.N.R, 40-46, Lt. Comdr. MLA; AAUP. Fielding; 18th-century literature; rhetoric. Publ: The practical stylist, 62, The complete stylist, 66 & ed, Joseph Andrews and Shamela, 72, Crowell; auth, Hemingway: an introduction and interpretation, Holt, 67; Paton's Cry the beloved country, Scribner, 68; co-auth, The written word, Newbury House, 71; ed, Tom Jones, Norton, 73; auth, The new English, Occasional papers no. 12, Counc. Basic Educ, 2/67; The sociology of dictionaries and the sociology of words, In: New aspects of lexicography, South. Ill. Univ, 72; Buckingham's permanent rehearsal, Mich. Quart. Rev, spring 73; plus others. Add: 2866 Provincial Dr, Ann Arbor, MI 48104.

BAKER, STEWART ADDISON, b. Houston, Tex, Oct. 5, 38; div; c. 2. ENGLISH. B.A, Columbia Univ, 60; Woodrow Wilson fel, Yale, 60-61, M.A, 61, Lewis-Farmington fel, 61-62, Ph.D.(Eng), 64. Asst. prof. ENG, RICE UNIV, 64-71, ASSOC. PROF, 71- Eng. Inst; MLA. Milton and the seventeenth century. Publ: Sannazaro and Milton's brief epic, Comp. Lit, spring 68. Add: Dept. of English, Rice University, Houston, TX 77001.

BAKER, WILLIAM CALVIN, b. Youngstown, Ohio, Sept. 7, 06; m. 42. AMERICAN LITERATURE. A.B, Mt. Union Col, 29; M.A, Univ. Pittsburgh, 41, univ. scholar, 40-41. Teacher Eng. & hist, Salem Pub. Schs, Ohio, 29-46; instr. Eng, Univ. Pittsburgh, 46-52; YOUNGSTOWN STATE UNIV, 52-56, ASST. PROF. ENG, 56-, coord. commun. courses, 56-66. U.S.A.A.F, 42-45. MLA; NCTE; Thoreau Soc; Am. Stud. Asn. Bradford Torrey; Henry D. Thoreau; nature in American literature. Add: 559 Euclid St, Salem, OH 44460.

BAKER, WILLIAM DeGROVE, b. Buffalo, N.Y. Mar. 5, 24; m. 46, 72; c. 3. AMERICAN LITERATURE, COMPOSITION. B.A, Hobart Col, 47; M.A, Univ. Chicago, 48; Ph.D.(Am. lit), Northwest. Univ, 50. Instr. Eng, Hobart Col, 46-47; Wayne State Univ, 50-51; asst. prof. commun. skills, Mich. State Univ, 51-56; prof. & dir. gen. stud, State Univ. N.Y. Col. Buffalo, 56-62; dir. Ctr. Am. Stud, Milan, Italy, 62-63; v.pres. & dean, Rockford Col, 63-68; dean lib. arts, WRIGHT STATE UNIV, 68-71, PROF. ENG, 71- V.pres, Nat. Counc. of Communities Serving Int. Visitors, 59-62. U.S.N, 43-45, Lt.(jg). Gertrude Stein; 19th and 20th century American literature; creative writing. Publ: Reading skills, 53, 74, co-auth, University spelling book, 55, auth, The sound of English, 55, co-auth, The experience of writing, 58, 70 & auth, Focus on prose, 60, 72, Prentice-Hall; A guide to clear writing, Mich. State Univ, 55; co-auth, Reading and writing skills, McGraw, 58, 64, 72; Language lab, McMillan, 72. Add: Dept. of English, Wright State University, Dayton, OH 45431.

BAKER, WILLIAM PRICE, b. Clarendon, Tex, Mar. 7, 14. ENGLISH. B.A, Tex. Christian Univ, 36; M.A, Tulane Univ, 40; Rockefeller Found. grant, 45-46, Ph.D, 49. From instr. to asst. prof. Eng, Tex. Christian Univ, 40-43; Rutgers Univ, 46-50; asst. librn, Ft. Worth Pub. Libr, Tex, 50-54; asst. prof. ENG, Univ. Houston, 54-58; assoc. prof, Willamette Univ, 58-61, prof, 61-67; assoc. prof, UNIV. CALGARY, 67-72, PROF, 72- U.S.C.G, 44. MLA; Milton Soc. Publ: The Faerie Queene, Book III: an Elizabethan synthesis of ethical theory; co-ed, Animadversions. Add: Dept. of English, University of Calgary, Calgary, Alta, Can.

BALCH, MARSTON (STEVENS), b. Detroit, Mich, Nov. 21, 01; m. 27; c. 1. DRAMATICS, BIOGRAPHY. A.B, Kalamazoo Col, 23, hon. L.H.D, 60; A.M, Harvard, 25, Ph.D, 31. Instr. Eng, Williams Col, 25-27; instr. Eng. & tutor, Div. Mod. Langs, Harvard & Radcliffe Col, 28-33; instr. Eng, Phillips Exeter Acad, 33-34; asst. prof, TUFTS UNIV, 34-37, prof. dramatic lit, 37-41, Fletcher Prof. oratory, 37-71, prof. drama, 41-71, EMER. FLETCHER PROF. ORATORY & EMER. PROF. DRAMA, 71-, dir. univ. theater, 35-66, head dept. drama & speech, 41-66. Algiers correspondent, UN Radio & chief cable desk, psychol. warfare br, Allied Force Hdqrs, 43-44; chief French press & radio anal. sect, U.S. Inform. Serv, Paris, 44-45, cult. relat. sect, 45-46; co-founder & off, Fr. Libr. in Boston, 46- Medaille de la Reconnaissance Francaise, 47; Chevalier, Legion d'Honneur; Margo Jones Award, 66. Nat. Theatre Conf.(exec. secy, 61-67); New Eng. Theatre Conf; Am. Theatre Asn; Am. Soc. Theatre Res; Dramatists Guild. Drama; theatre; playdirecting and translations. Publ: Modern short biography, 35, You and college & ed, Modern short biographies and autobiographies, 40, Harcourt; co-auth, Theater in America: appraisal and challenge, Dembar, 68; auth, 15 biogs, In: World book encyclopedia, Field, 58, 67-68; Profile of the successful playwright, Dramatists Guild Quart, 1/65; Off-Broadway theater, In: Encyclopaedia Britannica, 65. Add: 50 Sawyer Ave, Medford, MA 02155.

BALDANZA, FRANK, b. Cleveland, Ohio, Nov. 17, 24. ENGLISH. B.A, Oberlin Col, 49; M.A, Univ. Chicago, 50; Ph.D, Cornell Univ, 54. Instr. ENG, Ga. Inst. Technol, 50-52; asst. prof, La. State Univ, 54-57; PROF, BOWLING GREEN STATE UNIV, 57- U.S.A, 43-45, T/Sgt. MLA. Modern British novel. Publ: Mark Twain: an introduction and interpretation, Barnes & Noble, 61; Ivy Compton-Burnett, 64 & Iris Murdoch, 74, Twayne. Add: Dept. of English, Bowling Green State University, Bowling Green, OH 43402.

BALDERSON, JAY RUSSELL, b. Omaha, Nebr, Nov. 26, 41; m. 63; c. 2. EARLY AMERICAN LITERATURE. A.B, Grinnell Col, 63; William Robertson Coe fel, Univ. Wyo, 63-64, M.A, 65; Ph.D.(Eng), Univ. Iowa, 72. Instr. ENG, WEST. ILL. UNIV, 64-65, ASST. PROF, 71- MLA. Early American literature; bibliography and textual criticism; American studies. Add: Dept. of English, Western Illinois University, Macomb, IL 61455.

BALDERSTON, KATHARINE CANBY, b. Boise, Idaho, Jan. 2, 95. ENGLISH LITERATURE. A.B, Wellesley Col, 16; A.M, Radcliffe Col, 20; Ph.D, Yale, 25. Instr, South. Methodist Univ, 16-19; from instr. to prof. Eng. lit, Wellesley Col, 20-60, EMER. PROF, 60- Vis. scholar, Huntington Libr, Calif, 34-35. Brit. Acad. Rose Mary Crawshay Prize, 42. MLA. Literature of Oliver Goldsmith; 18th century English literature; Dr. Johnson and Mrs. Thrale. Publ: History and sources of Percy's Memoir of Goldsmith, 26 & Collected letters of Oliver Goldsmith, 28, Cambridge; Thraliana, the diary of Mrs. Hester Lynch Thrale, Clarendon, 42; Johnson's vile melancholy, In: Age of Johnson, Yale, 49; Dr. Johnson and William Law, PMLA, 9/60. Add: 49 Cottage St, Wellesley, MA 02181.

BALDESHWILER, EILEEN MARY, b. Stanley, Wis, Apr. 23, 20. ENGLISH. B.A, Col. St. Scholastica, 43; M.A, Univ. Minn, 47; Ph.D.(Eng), Fordham Univ, 54. Instr. ENG, Col. St. Scholastica, 47-50, asst. prof, 54-60, assoc. prof, 60-65, pres, 58-60; assoc. prof, LOYOLA UNIV.(ILL), 66-73, PROF, 73- Asst. prof, Albertus Magnus Col, summer 56; Mt. Mercy Col.(Pa), summer 58; Danforth summer sem. fel, Univ. Chicago, 59; Am. Asn. Univ. Women fel, 65-67. MLA; NCTE. Literary criticism and theory; prose fiction. Publ: Katherine Mansfield's theory of fiction, Stud. Short Fiction, summer 70; Fénéon and the minimal story, Critique, winter 72; The structure of Katherine Anne Porter's fiction, S.Dak. Rev, summer 73; plus four others. Add: Dept. of English, Loyola University, 6525 N. Sheridan Rd, Chicago, IL 60660.

BALDWIN, ARMINTA TUCKER, b. West Union, W.Va, Feb. 15, 39; m. 62. ENGLISH LITERATURE. B.A, Glenville State Col, 60; M.A, W.Va. Univ, 62. Asst. ENG, W.Va. Univ, 60-62; instr, Alderson-Broaddus Col, 62-66; ASSOC. PROF. & CHMN. DEPT, W.VA. WESLEYAN COL, 66- Teacher-humanities fed. grant, 73. AAUP; NCTE; Nat. Counc. Publ. Adv. Add: Dept. of English, Div. of Humanities, West Virginia Wesleyan College, Box 94, Buckhannon, WV 26201.

BALDWIN, BENJAMIN HARRISON, b. St. Louis, Mo, Mar. 1, 19; m. 55; c. 2. JOURNALISM. B.Ed, South. Ill. Univ, 40; M.S.J, Northwest. Univ, 46. In private indust, 46-56; assoc. prof. jour, MEDILL SCH. JOUR, NORTHWEST. UNIV, EVANSTON, 56-65, PROF. JOUR, 65-, chmn. ed. dept, 65-73. Dir, Nat. High Sch. Jour. Inst, Northwest. Univ, 58-67; consult, Comn. Church Papers, Lutheran Church in Am, 67-70; consult. ed. content, Cahners Publ. Co, 70- U.S.A.A.F, 42-46, 1st Lt. Asn. Educ. in Jour; Radio-TV News Dir. Asn; Nat. Asn. Sci. Writers. Editorial journalism; science writing. Publ: Co-auth, Teaching about smoking and health, State of Ill, 64; auth, What about equipment for teaching TV news, Jour. Quart, summer 57; The State Department and the grass roots, Add 1, spring 61; plus others. Add: Medill School of Journalism, Northwestern University, Evanston, IL 60201.

BALDWIN, DAVID, b. Cambridge, Mass, Feb. 9, 22; m. 47; c. 4. ENGLISH, AMERICAN STUDIES. A.B, Harvard, 47; Kenyon Sch. Eng, 48; M.A, Columbia Univ, 53; Harrison fel, Univ. Pa, 55-56, Ph.D.(Am. civilization), 61. Instr. Eng, Rensselaer Polytech. Inst, 49-53; inst. Am. stud, Rutgers Univ, 56-57; ed, Arthur D. Little, Inc, 57-58; instr. Eng, Northeast. Univ, 58-61; chmn. div. humanities, Dean Jr. Col, 61-64; assoc. prof. ENG, HARTWICK COL, 64-68, PROF, 68-, chmn. dept, 65-68. U.S.N, 44-46. MLA; Col. Eng. Asn. American literature, 1830-1860; the English romantic writers; American literature since 1890. Add: Dept. of English, Hartwick College, Oneonta, NY 13820.

BALDWIN, JOSEPH BURKETTE, b. New Tazewell, Tenn, May 18, 18; m. 42; c. 3. SPEECH, DRAMATIC ARTS. B.A, Univ. Tex, 40, M.A, 46; M.F.A, State Univ. Iowa, 48, Ph.D, 50. Teacher, Baker Jr. Sch, Tex, 40-41; instr, Hardin-Simmons Univ, summer, 46; asst. speech, State Univ. Iowa, 48-49; instr. Eng, Univ. Tenn, 49-50; asst. prof. speech, Stephen F. Austin State Col, 50-52; assoc. prof, Univ. Miss, 52-58; asst. prof. SPEECH & DRAMATIC ART, UNIV. NEBR-LINCOLN, 58-59, assoc. prof, 59-62, PROF, 62- U.S.A.F, 41-45, Res, 45-, Maj. Am. Educ. Theatre Asn; Speech Asn. Am. Playwriting and experimental theatre production. Publ: Committees forever, 63 & I married Irene (one-act play), 66, French; The wind in the willows (dramatization of the novel), Dramatic Publ, 66. Add: Dept. of Speech & Dramatic Art, University of Nebraska-Lincoln, Lincoln, NE 68508.

BALDWIN, MARILYN AUSTIN, b. Richmond, Ind, Nov. 10, 35; m. 57; c. 3. ENGLISH. B.S, Ind. Univ, 57; Univ. Mich, 58-59; M.A, Rutgers Univ, 61, Ph.D.(Eng), 63. Teacher ENG, Bloomington High Sch, Ind, 57-58; instr, Augusta Col, 61-63; lectr, DARTMOUTH COL, 67-69, 70-71, asst. provost, 71-72, acting provost, 72, ADJ. ASST. PROF, 72-, ASST. V.PRES, 72-, ACTING DEAN STUDENT SERV, 73- Partic, Inst. Educ. Mgt, summer 73; mem. Comt. Concerns of Women in New Eng. Cols. & Univs. MLA. W.D. Howells and psychological realism. Publ: Ed, Annotated edition: My Mark Twain, La. State Univ, 67; auth, Emerson's Brahma, Explicator, 12/61; The transcendental phase of William Dean Howells, Emerson Soc. Quart, 69. Add: 209 Parkhurst Hall, Dartmouth College, Hanover, NH 03755.

BALDWIN, ROBERT GEORGE, b. Vancouver, B.C, Jan. 13, 27; m. 48; c. 3. ENGLISH. B.A, Univ. B.C, 48; M.A, Univ. Toronto, 49, Ph.D, 57. Lectr. ENG, UNIV. ALTA, 51-54, asst. prof, 54-58, assoc. prof, 58-63, PROF, 63-, DEAN ARTS, 72-, chmn. dept. Eng, 67-71, assoc. dean arts, 71-72. Can. Counc. sr. fel, 66-67. Int. Asn. Univ. Prof. Eng; Asn. Can. Univ. Teachers Eng.(v.pres, 70-72). Seventeenth century poetry and prose; 18th and 19th century English novel. Publ: Phineas Fletcher: his modern readers and his

Renaissance ideas, Philol. Quart, 10/61; The yeoman's canons: a conjecture, J. Eng. & Ger. Philol, 4/62; Great expectations, In: Studies of major works in English, Oxford, Toronto, 68; plus one other. Add: Faculty of Arts, University of Alberta, Edmonton, Alta, Can.

BALDWIN, THOMAS WHITFIELD, b. Laurens Co, S.C, Jan. 28, 90; m. 17; c. 3. ELIZABETHAN LITERATURE. A.B, Erskine Col, 09; A.M, Princeton, 14, Ph.D.(Eng), 16; hon. Dr. Lit, Univ. Ill, 59; hon. Dr.Let, Univ. Waterloo, 62. Prin. & supt. schs, S.C, 09-12; asst, Erskine Col, 12-13; prof. ENG. & head dept, Muskingum Col, 15-18; S.Dak. State Col, 18-20; Reed Col, 20-23; asst. prof, Goucher Col, 23-25; UNIV. ILL, URBANA-CHAMPAIGN, 25-27, assoc. prof, 27-28, prof, 28-58, EMER. PROF, 58- Guggenheim fel, 31-32; Fulbright res. scholar, U.K, 53-54; vis. prof, South. Ill. Univ, 58-72. MLA; Shakespeare Asn. Am. Early English drama; Shakespeare; 16th century textbooks, education and literature. Publ: William Shakespeare's small Latine and lesse Greeke, 44, William Shakespeare's five-act structure, 47, On the literary genetics of Shakspere's plays 1592-1594, 59 & On the compositional genetics of the Comedy of errors, 65, Univ. Ill; On act and scene division in the Shakspere first folio, South. Ill. Univ, 65. Add: 807 W. Schwartz St, Carbondale, IL 62901.

BALES, ALLEN, b. Birmingham, Ala, July 9, 20; m. 44; c. 1. SPEECH, DRAMA. A.B, Univ. Ala, 43, M.A, 47; Ph.D, Northwest. Univ, 59. Instr. speech, Univ. Ala, 47-51; asst. oral interpretation, Northwest. Univ, 51-52; asst. prof. SPEECH, UNIV. ALA, 52-59, assoc. prof, 59-60, PROF, 60-, CHMN. DEPT, 69-, area chmn. theatre arts, 64-68. Mem. State Comn. Alliance Art Educ, U.S. Off. Educ. & John F. Kennedy Ctr. Performing Arts, 74-75. U.S.A, 43-46, Sgt. South. Speech Commun. Asn; Speech Commun. Asn.(assoc. ed, Speech Monogr, 63-); Southeast. Theatre Conf.(v.pres, 72-73, pres, 73-74). Phonetics; point of view in the novels of Nathanial Hawthorne; aesthetics of the theatre. Add: Dept. of Speech, University of Alabama, University, AL 35486.

BALES, KENT R, b. Anthony, Kans, June 19, 36; m. 58; c. 2. ENGLISH. B.A, Yale, 58; M.A, San Jose State Col, 63; Ph.D.(Eng), Univ. Calif, Berkeley, 67. Instr. ENG, Menlo Sch. & Col, 58-63; acting instr, Univ. Calif, Berkeley, 67; asst. prof, UNIV. MINN, MINNEAPOLIS, 67-71, ASSOC.PROF, 71- U.S.A.R, 59-65, MLA. Nineteenth century American literature; eighteenth and nineteenth century aesthetic theory. Add: Dept. of English, University of Minnesota, Minneapolis, MN 55455.

BALICE, VINCENT JOSEPH, b. Rocky River, Ohio, Mar. 11, 37. ENGLISH LITERATURE, PSYCHOLOGY. B.A, Univ. Dayton, 60; Ph.D.(Eng. lit), Purdue Univ, West Lafayette, 71. Counr, Cath. Charities, Detroit, Mich, 64-65; instr. ENG, ST. JOSEPH'S COL.(IND), 65-66, ASST. PROF, 71- Mod. Humanities Res. Asn. Modern British and American poetry; Ibsen dramas; modern British fiction. Publ: Ibsen's feminine mystique, Vantage, (in press). Add: Dept. of English, St. Joseph's College, Box 816, Rensselaer, IN 47978.

BALIO, AGATINO THOMAS, b. Nov. 12, 37; U.S. citizen; m. 60; c. 2. FILM, THEATRE. A.B, Wabash Col, 59; Univ. Exeter, 57-58; M.A, Ind. Univ, 61, Ph.D.(theatre), 64. Asst. prof. speech, Oberlin Col, 64-66; asst. prof, COMMUN. ARTS, UNIV. WIS-MADISON, 66-71, assoc. prof, 71-73, PROF, 73-, DIR, WIS. CTR. THEATRE RES, 66-, summer salary support, 66-68. Am. Theatre Asn; Speech Commun. Asn; Nat. Theatre Conf. American theatre history; film history. Publ: Co-auth, The history of the National Theatre Conference, Nat. Theatre Conf, 68; auth, Sam Hume at the Detroit Arts and Crafts Theatre, Quart. J. Speech, 4/67; The public confrontation of Herman Joseph Muller, Bull. Atomic Scientists, 11/67. Add: Wisconsin Center for Theatre Research, 6041 Vilas Hall, University of Wisconsin-Madison, Madison, WI 53706.

BALL, DAVID RAPHAEL, French & Comparative Literature. See Volume III, Foreign Languages, Linguistics & Philology.

BALL, DONALD LEWIS, b. Baltimore, Md, Oct. 25, 22; m. 50; c. 4. ENGLISH. B.A, Univ. Richmond, 48; M.A, Univ. Del, 51; Ph.D.(Eng), Univ. N.C, Chapel Hill, 65. Instr. ENG, Va. Mil. Inst, 53-57; COL. WILLIAM & MARY, 60-65, asst. prof, 65-69, ASSOC. PROF, 69- U.S.N.R, 42-46, Lt. Col. Eng. Asn; S.Atlantic Mod. Lang. Asn; MLA; NCTE. Eighteenth century English novel; English language. Publ: Samuel Richardson's theory of fiction, Mouton, The Hague, 71; Eastern shore of Maryland literature, In: The eastern shore of Maryland and Virginia, Lewis Hist. Publ, 50; Pamela II: a primary link in Richardson's development as a novelist, Mod. Philol, 5/68; ETS's English composition test, Va. Eng. Bull, 5/70. Add: 201 Matoaka Ct, Williamsburg, VA 23185.

BALL, LEE HAMPTON, JR, b. New York, N.Y, June 15, 26; m. 51; c. 2. AMERICAN LITERATURE. A.B, Syracuse Univ, 47, A.M, 48; Univ. Tex, 48-49; Ph.D.(Eng-Am. lit), Univ. Wis, 58. Mem. fac, ENG, Caney Jr. Col, 53-54; Pikeville Col, 54-58; asst. prof, Simpson Col, 58-60; SOUTHEAST. STATE COL, 69-64, ASSOC. PROF, 64- Assoc. prof, Univ. N.Dak, 66-67; travel, Paris, France, 68. S.Cent. Mod. Lang. Asn. James Fenimore Cooper; Sidney Lanier. Publ: An explication of Donne's The computation, Explicator, 4/50; Leather-Stocking's simplicity of mind as a key to his psychological character, S.Cent. Bull, winter 62. Add: Dept. of English, Southeastern State College, Durant, OK 74701.

BALL, LEWIS FRANKLIN, b. Havre de Grace, Md, July 7, 08; m. 46; c. 1. ENGLISH LITERATURE. A.B, Johns Hopkins Univ, 28, Ph.D, 33. Instr. ENG, Johns Hopkins Univ, 33-35; Univ. Tex, 35-37; asst. prof, UNIV. RICHMOND, 37-52, ASSOC. PROF, 52-62, PROF, 62- U.S.A, 43-45. Col. Eng. Asn. Literature of the English Renaissance. Add: Box 172, University of Richmond, VA 23173.

BALL, ROBERT HAMILTON, b. New York, N.Y, May 21, 02; m. 28; c. 1. ENGLISH. A.B, Princeton, 23, A.M, 24, Ph.D 28. Instr. Eng. & dramatic art, Princeton, 27-31, asst. prof, 31-38; ENG, QUEENS COL.(N.Y), 39-43, assoc. prof, 44-51, prof, 51-71, EMER. PROF, 71-, chmn. dept, 41-47, 60-64, chmn. div. lang, lit. & arts, 48-55. Guggenheim fel, 46-47; vis. assoc. prof, Grad. Sch, N.Y. Univ, 48-49; vis. prof, Univ. Ankara, 55-56. MLA; Shakespeare Asn. Am; Mod. Humanities Res. Asn, Gt. Brit; Malone Soc; Am. Soc. Theatre Res. Drama; stage history; Shakespeare. Publ: The amazing career of Sir Giles Overreach, Princeton, 39 & Octagon, 68; co-auth, A short view of Elizabethan drama, Scribner, 43, 58 & 60; Theatre language, Theatre Arts, 61; auth, Shakespeare on silent film, Allen & Unwin, London & Theatre Arts, 68. Add: 11 N. Washington St, Port Washington, NY 11050.

BALLARD, EMERALD GARRETT, b. Liberty, Miss, Feb. 18, 12; m. 35; c. 3. ENGLISH. B.A, Univ. Miss, 31, M.A, 31; M.A, Univ. Ill, 35, Ph.D.(Eng), 39. Asst. prof. ENG, Miss. State Teachers Col, Delta, 31-34; asst, Univ. Ill, 35-39; from asst. prof. to PROF, N.TEX. STATE UNIV, 39-, CHMN. DIV. HUMANITIES, 65- Dir, NDEA Inst. Eng, 66 & Experienced Teacher Fel. Prog, 68- U.S.N.R, 42-46, Comdr. NCTE; Conf. Col. Compos. & Commun; S.Cent. Mod. Lang. Asn; MLA; Conf. Eng. Educ. English novel; literary criticism; English education. Publ: A workbook for English composition. Add: Dept. of English, North Texas State University, Denton, TX 76203.

BALLARD, FRANK WILLARD, b. Alton, Ill. Dec. 7, 29; m. 53; c. 2. PUPPETRY, SCENE DESIGN. B.A, Shurtleff Col, 51; M.A, Univ. Ill, Urbana, 53; Univ. Iowa, 53-56. PROF. THEATRE, UNIV. CONN, 56- Puppeteers Am.(pres, 71-74); Union Int. Marionette; Am. Theatre Asn. Puppetry in education and theatre. Publ: Developing theatrical effectiveness, 9-10/72, The challenge of our times, 5-6/72 & Artistic persuasion, 9-10/73, Puppetry J; plus one other. Add: Dept. of Dramatic Arts, University of Connecticut, Storrs, CT 06268.

BALLARD, LOU ELLEN, b. Covington Co, Ala, Oct. 19, 32. ENGLISH. B.A, Troy State Col, 53; fel, Auburn Univ, 56-57, M.A, 57. Teacher, High Sch, Ala, 53-56; instr. ENG, Univ. South. Miss, 57-60; from instr. to ASST. PROF, SOUTHEAST. LA. UNIV, 60-, DIR. FRESHMAN ENG, 68- S.Cent. Mod. Lang. Asn; Am. Stud. Asn; NCTE; Conf. Col. Comp. & Commun. Folktales from southeast Alabama. Publ: Some tales of local color from southeast Alabama: an original collection, La. Folklore Miscellany, 8/61; Collecting folk materials, Miss. Folklore Register, summer 67. Add: Box 286 University Station, Southeastern Louisiana University, Hammond, LA 70401.

BALLEW, LEIGHTON MILTON, b. Des Arc, Ark, Feb. 17, 16; m. 49. THEATRE. B.S, Memphis State Col, 37; fel, West. Reserve Univ, 40-41, M.A, 41; Gen. Educ. Bd. fel, Univ. Ill, 53-54; Ph.D, 55. Asst. prof. Eng, S.Dak. State Col, 45-46; assoc. prof. DRAMA & THEATRE, UNIV. GA, 46-56, PROF, 56-, HEAD DEPT, 46-, DIR. UNIV. THEATRE, 46- U.S.A.A.F, 43-45. Speech Commun. Asn; Am. Theatre Asn. Nat. Theatre Conf; Am. Nat. Theatre & Acad; Southeast. Theatre Conf; South. Speech Commun. Asn. Drama; theatre. Add: Dept. of Theatre & Drama, University of Georgia, Athens, GA 30602.

BALLIET, CONRAD A, b. Hazleton, Pa, June 3, 27; m. 50; c. 4. ENGLISH, AMERICAN LITERATURE. A.B, Muhlenberg Col, 51; M.A, Lehigh Univ, 53; Danforth grant, Cornell Univ, 58-59, Ph.D, 61. Teacher high sch, Pa, 52-55; asst. prof. ENG, Edinboro State Col, 55-58; WITTENBERG UNIV, 61-66, assoc. prof, 66-71, PROF, 71- Fulbright teaching award, Innsbruck, Austria, 66-67. U.S.A, 45-47, S/Sgt. MLA. Nineteenth century English and American literature. Publ: History and rhetoric of the triplet, PMLA, 12/65; To sleep, to die, tis a consummation, Res. Stud, Wash, 5/68; White on black: a checklist of poetry by white Americans about the Black experience, 1708-1970, Bull. N.Y. Pub. Libr, 11/71. Add: Dept. of English, Wittenburg University, Springfield, OH 45501.

BALLIN, MICHAEL GERALD, b. Newport, Eng, Dec. 23, 39; Brit. & Can. citizen. ENGLISH LANGUAGE & LITERATURE. B.A, Oxford, 61, M.A, 64; cert. educ, Univ. London, 62; M.A, McMaster Univ, 64; Ont. fel, Univ. Toronto, 65-68, Can. Counc. fel, 68, Ph.D.(Eng), 72. Asst. master ENG, North Romford Comprehensive Sch, Eng, 62-63; lectr, Mt. Allison Univ, 64-65; WILFRID LAURIER UNIV, 68-72, ASST. PROF, 72- Can. Asn. Univ. Teachers; Asn. Can. Univ. Teachers Eng; MLA. Modern Romanticism; Shakespeare and Elizabethan drama; 17th century poetry and prose. Add: Dept. of English, Wilfrid Laurier University, Waterloo, Ont, Can.

BALLINGER, RICHARD HENRY, b. Dallas, Tex, Feb. 1, 13; m. 44; c. 3. AMERICAN LITERATURE. A.B, & A.M, Univ. Tex, 36; Ph.D, Harvard, 53. Tutor Eng, Univ. Tex, 36-38; asst. Harvard, 39-40; teacher Eng. & hist, U.S. Naval Acad, 40-42; asst. prof. Eng, Univ. Tex, 47-51; educ. adv, basic div, TEX. A&M UNIV, 54, assoc. prof. ENG, 54-57, PROF, 57- U.S.N.R, 40-46, 51-54, Capt. MLA. Publ: Origins of James Fenimore Cooper's The two admirals, Am. Lit; Establishing an honors program at Texas A&M University, Proc. South. Honors Symposium, 5/68. Add: Dept. of English, Texas A&M University, College Station, TX 77843.

BALLOWE, JAMES C, b. Carbondale, Ill, Nov. 28, 33; m. 53; c. 2. LITERATURE. B.A, Millikin Univ, 54; M.A, Univ. Ill, 56, fel, 57, Ph.D, 63. Asst. ENG, Univ. Ill, 55-61; asst. prof, Millikin Univ, 61-63; BRADLEY UNIV, 63-67, assoc. prof, 67-71, PROF. & CHMN. DEPT, 71- MLA; Am. Stud. Asn; Midcontinent Am. Stud. Asn. American cultural criticism; poet; George Santayana. Publ: George Santayana's America: essays on literature and culture, Univ. Ill, 67; Initiation (short story), Discourse, spring 70; co-auth, Thoreau and Etzler: alternative views of economic reform, Mid-continent Am. Stud. J, spring 70; auth, The intellectual traveller: an essay on George Santayana, Dalhousie Rev, summer 70; plus other articles & poems. Add: Dept. of English, Bradley University, Peoria, IL 61606.

BALSON, CARL GEORGE, b. Buffalo, N.Y, June 1, 32; m. 59; c. 2. SPEECH. B.S, Bowling Green State Univ, 54; fel, Syracuse Univ, 56-57, M.S, 57. Instr. speech & radio-TV, Beloit Col, 57-61; asst. prof. radio-TV, Col. William & Mary, 61-63; assoc. educ, TV, N.Y. State Educ. Dept, 63-64; PROF. COMMUN, BELOIT COL, 64-, DIR. AV SERV, 68- U.S.A, 54-55, 1st Lt. Speech Commun. Asn; South. Speech Asn; Nat. Asn. Educ. Broadcasters. Educational television; voice science; electronics. Add: 1239 Porter Ave, Beloit, WI 53511.

BALTZELL, JANE L, English. See Kopp, Jane Baltzell.

BAMBAS, RUDOLPH CHARLES, b. Chicago, Ill, June 15, 15; m. 42; ENGLISH. B.A, Wabash Col, 37; M.A, Northwest. Univ, 39, Ph.D.(Eng), 41. Instr. ENG, Okla. Col. Women, 41-42; Univ. Mo, spring 46; from instr. to PROF, UNIV. OKLA, 46- U.S.A, 42-46, 1st Lt. MLA; Am. Dialect Soc. English linguistics; Old English literature; history of the English language. Publ: Verb forms in -s and -th in early modern English, 47 & Another view of the Old English Wife's lament, 63, J. Eng. & Ger. Philol. Add: Dept. of English, University of Oklahoma, Norman, OK 73069.

BAMBERG, ROBERT DOUGLAS, b. Buenos Aires, Arg, Feb. 6, 28; U.S. citizen; m. 52; c. 3. ENGLISH & AMERICAN LITERATURE. B.A, Cornell Univ, 51, M.A, 58, John L. Senior fel. & Ph.D.(Eng), 61. Teaching asst, Cornell Univ, 58, instr. Eng, 59-61; Univ. Pa, 61-64, asst. prof, 64-68, assoc. prof. & undergrad. chmn, 68-70, asst. chmn. dept, 65-68, spec. asst, v.provost stud. affairs, 67-68; Charles A. Dana Prof. Eng. & chmn. dept, BATES COL, 70-72, PROF. ENG. & DEAN FAC, 72- U.S.A.F, 46-47, Sgt. MLA. British and American fiction; American literature; twentieth century literature. Publ: Ed, Confession of Jereboam O Beauchamp, Univ. Pa, 66. Add: Dept. of English, Bates College, Lewiston, ME 04240.

BANDEEN, BETTY ISOBELLE, b. Rodney, Ont, Mar. 10, 29. ENGLISH. B.A, Univ. West. Ont, 49; A.M, Radcliffe Col, 50, Ph.D.(Eng), 58. Teacher, Bishop Strachan Sch, 51-53; instr. ENG, Smith Col, 55-57; UNIV. WEST. ONT, 57-58, lectr, 58-59, asst. prof, 59-65, ASSOC. PROF, 65- Ed, Can. Asn. Univ. Teachers Bull, 63-65. Asn. Can. Univ. Teachers Eng; MLA; Mediaeval Acad. Am. Old and Middle English. Publ: Geoffrey Chaucer: prologue to the Canterbury tales, In: Studies of major works in English, Oxford, 68. Add: Dept. of English, University College, University of Western Ontario, London, Ont. N6A 3K7, Can.

BANDEL, BETTY, b. Washington, D.C, July 28, 12. ENGLISH. B.Mus, Univ. Ariz, 33; M.A, Columbia Univ, 47, Ph.D.(Eng), 51. Newspaper reporter & women's page ed, Ariz. Daily Star, Tucson, 35-42; PROF. ENG, UNIV. VT, 47- U.S.A.A.F, 42-46, Lt. Col. MLA: NCTE; Col. Eng. Asn. Shakespeare; social position of women; 18th and 19th century Vermont history, especially psalmody. Publ: Ed, Walk into my parlor: chapters from inviting books, Tuttle, 72; auth, English chroniclers' attitude toward women, J. Hist. Ideas; Thaddeus Stevens, playwright, Vt. Hist, spring 72; Ellen Terry's foul papers, Theatre Survey, X: 43-52; plus others. Add: Dept. of English, University of Vermont, Burlington, VT 05401.

BANDY, WILLIAM THOMAS, French Literature. See Volume III, Foreign Languages, Linguistics & Philology.

BANE, CLARENCE LAVERNE, b. Ankeny, Iowa, June 7, 03; m. 24; c. 2. SPEECH. A.B, State Univ. Iowa, 24, A.M, 30; D.Ed, Stanford Univ, 40. Head dept. speech, Sterling Col, 26-27; Col. Emporia, 27-29; dir. debate & forensics, Univ. Utah, 29-42; adult educ, War Relocation Authority, Utah, 42-45; prin, Muskogee Jr. Col, 45-47; assoc. prof. SPEECH, UNIV. UTAH, 47-56, prof, 56-71, EMER. PROF, 71- Contrib, Minaret, 71- History of education in Utah 1870-1896; critical evaluation of Senator Borahs speeches; fundamentals of speech. Publ: Dramatizing parliamentary usage, Clearing House; The people speak, West. Speech; A pattern of discussion, Speech Teacher. Add: Dept. of Speech, University of Utah, Salt Lake City, UT 84112.

BANERJEE, (RON) DIBYENDU KUMAR, b. Calcutta, Bengal, India, July 29, 34; U.S. citizen; m. 61. ENGLISH & COMPARATIVE LITERATURE. M.A, Univ. Edinburg, 55; Ital. Inst. Mid. & Far East fel, Univ. Rome, 57-61; univ. fel, Harvard, 62-65, Ph.D.(comp. lit), 71; Ford Found. grant, 70-71. Lectr. ENG, SMITH COL, 66-70, ASST. PROF, 70- Modern poetry, especially Pound and Eliot; Renaissance drama, English and continental; Dante and the Provencaux. Publ: Dante through the looking glass: Rossetti, Pound and Eliot, Comp. Lit, spring 72; The Dantian overview: the epigraph to Prufrock, Mod. Lang. Notes, 12/72; Formality and intimacy in the Cantos of Ezra Pound, Indian J. Am. Stud, 12/72. Add: 17 Henshaw Ave, Northampton, MA 01060.

BANGHAM, P. JERALD, b. Dayton, Ohio, Jan. 12, 36. THEATRE. B.A, Ohio State Univ, 57, M.A, 59, Ph.D.(speech), 65. Asst. prof. drama, Morehead State Univ, 61-68; assoc. prof. speech, Miss. State Col. Women, 68-70; tech. asst. zool, Ohio State Univ, 72-73; ASSOC. PROF. SPEECH & THEATRE & DIR. THEATRE, ALCORN A&M COL, 73- Int. Fed. Theatre Res; Speech Commun. Asn; Am. Theatre Asn; Am. Soc. Theatre Res; U.S. Inst. Theatre Technol; Theatre Libr. Asn. Nineteenth century theatre history; play direction. Publ: Samuel Phelps; producer of Shakespeare at Sadler's Wells, Ohio State Univ. Theatre Collection Bull, 59. Add: Box 59, Dept. of Fine Arts, Alcorn A&M College, Lorman, MS 39096.

BANKOWSKY, RICHARD JAMES, b. Wallington, N.J, Nov. 25, 28; m. 52; c. 3. CREATIVE WRITING. B.A, Yale, 52; M.A, Columbia Univ, 54; State Univ. Iowa, 57-58. Instr. ENG, CALIF. STATE UNIV, SACRAMENTO, 59-61, asst. prof, 61-64, assoc. prof, 64-67, PROF, 67- Nat. Inst. Arts & Lett. grant, 63; Rockefeller Found. grant, 68. U.S.A, 54-56. Writing novels. Publ: A glass rose, 58, After Pentecost, 61, On a dark night, 64 & The pale criminals, 67, Random; The barbarians at the gates, Little, 72. Add: Dept. of English, California State University, Sacramento, 6000 Jay St, Sacramento, CA 95819.

BANKS, LANDRUM, b. Shady Dale, Ga, Nov. 28, 40. ENGLISH. A.B, Mercer Univ, 61; M.A, Univ. Tenn, 63, Ph.D.(Eng), 67; Sorbonne, 71-73. Instr. ENG, La. State Univ, Baton Rouge, 64-65, asst. prof, 67-71; ASSOC. PROF, XAVIER UNIV. LA, 73- Lectr, Europ. div, Univ. Md, 65-66; ed, Xavier Univ. Stud, 74- S.Cent. Mod. Lang. Asn; MLA; AAUP. Restoration and 18th century literature; Shakespeare. Publ: Dryden's Baroque drama, In: Essays in honor of Esmond Linworth Marilla, La. State Univ, 70. Add: Dept. of English, Xavier University of Louisiana, New Orleans, LA 70125.

BANKS, WILLIAM STEPHEN, b. Lancaster, Pa, Dec. 7, 12; m. 39; c. 2. SPEECH, DRAMA. B.A, Hobart Col, 35; M.F.A, Yale, 48; N.Y. Univ, 55. Asst. prof. speech & drama, UNIV. BRIDGEPORT, 48-70, ASSOC. PROF. SPEECH & THEATRE ARTS, 70-, STAGE DIR, DEPT. SPEECH & THEATRE ARTS, 65-, coord, 64, interim chmn, 67-68, chmn. dept, 70-73. Lectr, White Barn Theatre, Westport, Conn, 51-54; newslett. ed, Yale Drama Alumni Asn, 67-69. U.S.N.R, 43-45. Am. Theatre Asn; Speech Commun. Asn; AAUP. Modes in drama; theatre production and history; voice and diction. Publ: Mennonite, In: Yale one act plays, Vol. II, French, 37; Reaching your audience, Educators Publ. Serv, 64; Educational implications of regional speech differences, Clearing House, 12/61. Add: 290 Carol Rd, Stratford, CT 06497.

BANKSON, DOUGLAS HENNECK, b. Valley, Wash, May 13, 20; m. 43; c. 3. DRAMA. B.A, Univ. Wash, 43, M.A, 48, Ph.D.(Eng), 54. Teaching fel, Eng, Univ. Wash, 49-50; dir. res, Frye Art Mus, Seattle, Wash, 50-51; instr. Eng. & jour, Univ. Idaho, 55-57; asst. prof, Eng, Univ. Mont, 57-59, assoc. prof, drama & playwright in residence, 59-65, assoc. dir. theatre, 59-65, dir. summer theater, 60-65; PROF. PLAYWRITING, UNIV. B.C, 65- Auth. & dir, Shellgame, 60, Fallout, 63, Many happy returns, Pratt, 65; Music Corp. Am. scholar-fel. in screenwriting, Universal Studios, summer 66; gov, Theatre Can, 69-71; pres, New Play Ctr, 70-; mem. bd. dirs, Tamahnous Theatre Workshop, 73- U.S.N.R, 43-46, Lt.(jg). Can. Theatre Ctr. Publ: Auth. plays, The ball, 61, Nature in the raw is seldom, 62, Mr. Magoo, 62; The waterwitch, 62, Shootup, 63, The ants go marching one by one, hurrah!, 66, Lenore nevermore, 72 & Signore lizard, 73. Add: Dept. of Creative Writing, University of British Columbia, Vancouver, B.C. V6T 1B9, Can.

BANNINGA, JERALD LYLE, b. Hesperia, Mich. SPEECH. B.S, Bowling Green State Univ, 58, M.A, 59; Ph.D.(speech), Ind. Univ, 63. Instr. SPEECH, Univ. Conn, 62-64; ASST. PROF, Mt. Union Col, 64-66; WEST. ILL. UNIV, 66- U.S.A, 54-56. Speech Commun. Asn; Cent. States Speech Commun. Asn. History and criticism of American public address. Publ: Co-auth, A speaker's guide to syllogistic reasoning, W.C. Brown, 67 & The genesis of John Quincy Adams' lectures on rhetoric and oratory, Quart. J. Speech, 63; auth, John Quincy Adams as a contemporary critic, Cent. States Speech J, 65; John Quincy Adams' address of July 4, 1821, Quart J. Speech, 67. Add: Dept. of Speech, Western Illinois University, Macomb, IL 61455.

BANNON, PETER LAURENCE, b. Dublin, Ireland, May 7, 12; nat; m. 38; c. 1. ENGLISH. B.A, State Univ. Iowa, 36, M.A, 37, Ph.D.(Eng), 43. Asst. Eng, State Univ. Iowa, 35-37, instr, 43-45; asst. prof, Nanking Univ, 37-42; Morningside Col, 45-46, assoc. prof. & chmn. div. arts, 46-47; PROF. ENG, MEMPHIS STATE UNIV, 47- Civilian instr. communs. prog, U.S.A.A.F, 44- MLA; Nat. Asn. Standard Med. Vocab. Eighteenth century literature; romantic movement; composition. Publ: Elementary exposition, & ed, Graded readings, Nanking Univ, 42. Add: Dept. of English, Memphis State University, Memphis, TN 38111.

BANSEN, NORMAN CLARENCE, b. Ferndale, Calif, Nov. 26, 20. AMERICAN & SCANDINAVIAN LITERATURE. B.A, Dana Col, 47; Copenhagen, 49; M.A, Univ. Minn, 54; summers, Univ. Calif, 54-55, 60-61. From asst. prof. Eng. & chmn. dept. to PROF. ENG. & DANISH, DANA COL, 53- Vis. assoc. prof. Scand, Univ. Calif, Berkeley, 64; participant, ScanPresence Sem, Univ. Minn, 73. Knight, Order of Dannebrog, 70. U.S.A, 42-46. Soc. Advan. Scand. Stud; Am-Scand. Found; Midwest. Mod. Lang. Asn. Publ: My Danish West Indies, Dansk Nytaar, 59; Four Danish poems by Ole Wivel, Midwest Rev, spring 60; plus others. Add: Dana College, Blair, NE 68008.

BANTA, MARTHA, b. Muncie, Ind, May 11, 28. ENGLISH. A.B, Ind. Univ, 50, Ph.D.(Eng), 64. ASSOC. PROF. ENG, UNIV. WASH, 70-, summer res. grant, 71. MLA. 19th century painting and literature in England and America; success and failure in American literature; literary imagery of creation and destruction based on theological, aesthetic and philosophical theories. Publ: Rebirth or revenge, Huckleberry Finn and The American, Mod. Fiction Stud, summer 69; Quality of experience in What Maisie knew, New Eng. Quart, 12/69; Benjamin, Edgar, Humbert and Jay, Yale Rev, summer 71. Add: Dept. of English, University of Washington, Seattle, WA 98105.

BAPTISTE, HERMAN C, b. São Miguel, Portugal, Dec. 18, 12; U.S. citizen; m. 42; c. 2. ENGLISH. B.S, Mass. State Col, Bridgewater, 36; M.A, Columbia Univ, 43. TEACHER, ENG, New Bedford High Sch, Mass, 41-45; Briarcliff Manor High Sch, N.Y, 45-47; Peekskill High Sch, N.Y, 47-59; FOX LANE SCH, BEDFORD, N.Y, 60- John Hay fel, grad. faculties, Columbia Univ, 59-60; participant summer inst. comn. on Eng, col. entrance exam. bd, N.Y. Univ, summer 62; v.pres, N.Y. State Eng. Counc, 64-65; mem. comn. lit, NCTE, 65-68; consult. N.Y-New Eng. conf. Eng. in two-year col, NCTE-Conf. Col. Compos. & Commun, Cazenovia Col, N.Y, 66. NCTE (dir-at-large, 65-68). Philosophy considered as literature; world literature; study and the teaching of literature in the secondary school. Add: 191 Frederick St, Peekskill, NY 10566.

BARAM, ROBERT, b. Newark, N.J, Feb. 8, 19; m. 43; c. 2. JOURNALISM. B.S, Boston Univ, 48, M.Ed, 63. ASSOC. PROF. JOUR. & DIR. GRAD. STUD. BROADCAST JOUR, SCH. PUB. COMMUN, BOSTON UNIV, 52- Exec. secy, N.E. Press Asn, 52-63; exec. dir, N.E. Scholastic Press Asn, 53-; news analyst & commentator, TV & radio stations, 58-; spec. guest lectr, many cols. & univs, 58-; polit. columnist, Mass newspapers, 63-67; exec. dir, N.E. Col. Press Asn, 66-; auth-photographer-narrator, New Eng. Vignettes, WGBH-TV, Boston & other sta, 70- U.S.A, 42-45, Res, 45-, Lt. Col. Polit. Sci. Asn; Acad. Polit. Sci; Newspaper Asn. Mgr; Asn. Educ. in Jour. Publ: The shiny penny, 68, I remember, 70 & I search for peace, 72 (poetry), Branden; The integration-segregation story, Boston Globe, fall 56; The press and civil rights, Negro Digest, 62; The Presidential primary hoax, Hadassah Mag, 68; plus others. Add: 1530 Beacon St, Brookline, MA 02146.

BARASCH, FRANCES K, b. New York, N.Y, Apr. 10, 28; m. 52; c. 3. ENGLISH. B.A, Brooklyn Col, 49; M.A, N.Y. Univ, 52, Ph.D.(Eng), 64. Teacher, common branches, New York Bd. Educ, 50-56; asst. Eng, N.Y. Univ, 57-59, asst. to dir. stud. activities, 59-60, instr, 59-61; asst. prof. ENG, Long Island Univ. 64-65; BARUCH COL, 65-72, ASSOC. PROF, 72- Adj. asst. prof, Pace Col, 61-67, adj. assoc. prof, 67-; consult, Adult Educ. Commun. Skills Eval. Team, Region II, U.S. Off. Educ, 72-73, Regional Equal Opportunity Task Force, 73-74. AAUP; NEA; Am. Fed. Teachers.

MLA. Medieval, Renaissance, and Romantic literature. Publ: Shakespeare's second part of Henry IV, Simon & Schuster, 64; Bibliographies for A library of literary criticism: modern British literature, Ungar, 66; The grotesque, Mouton, The Hague, 71; ed, Home life, Macmillan, 71; co-auth, Teaching composition, Eng. Rec. & Lang. & Lang. Behavior Abstracts, winter 73; auth, CUNY's collective bargaining, Change, 7/73; HEW, the university, and the women, Dissent, summer 73; plus others. Add: Dept. of English, City University of New York, 17 Lexington Ave, New York, NY 10010.

BARBA, HARRY, b. Bristol, Conn, June 17, 22; m. 56; 65; c. 1. ENGLISH & CREATIVE WRITING. A.B, Bates Col, 44; Yaddo fel, Harvard, 50, M.A, 51; M.F.A, Univ. Iowa, 60, fel, 61-62, Ph.D.(Eng. & creative writing), 63. Instr. Eng, Wilkes Col, 47; Univ. Conn, Hartford Campus, 47-49; Univ. Iowa, 59-63; asst. prof. Eng. & creative writing, Skidmore Col, 63-68, fac. res. fels, 65-67; prof. & dir. writing, Marshall Univ, 68-70; RES. & WRITING, 70- Fulbright prof, Damascus Univ, 63-64; ed. consult, Bantam Bks, Inc, 67; mem. staff, Writers Confs; publ, Harian Press, N.Y. & W.Va; dir. & consult, Spa Writers & Educ. Conf, 67-73; Benedum res. grant, Marshall Univ, 69; HEA grant, 69-70; residence fel, MacDowell Colony, 70; speaker & reader, N.Y. State Counc. on Arts, 71. Auth. League Am; MLA; Col. Eng. Asn. Creative and expository writing, interdiscipline; interdisciplinary studies, creative and liberal arts; innovative and traditional education, interanimating and adjusted to each other. Publ: For the grape season, Macmillan, 60; The bulbul bird, Univ. Microfilm, 63; Three by Harry Barba, 67, How to teach writing, 69, Teaching in your own write, 70 & The case for socially functional education, 73, Harian; Joyce Cary's image of the African in transition, Part I & II, Univ. Res, spring & summer 63; The ikon (former title, And gladly teach?), Southwest Rev, 71; plus others. Add: 47 Hyde Blvd, Ballston Spa, NY 12020.

BARBATO, LOUIS RICHARD, b. Jersey City, N.J, Apr. 3, 37. ENGLISH LITERATURE. B.S, St. Peter's Col.(N.J), 59; M.S, Purdue Univ, W. Lafayette, 61; Marie Christine Kohler fel, Univ. Wis-Madison, 64-65, Ph.D.(Eng), 71. Instr. ENG, Univ. Del, 65-67; res. asst, Univ. Wis-Madison, 67-68; asst. prof, Univ. Cincinnati, 68-70; CLEVELAND STATE UNIV, 70-74, ASSOC. PROF, 74- Am. Soc. Theatre Res; Renaissance Soc. Am; Int. Shakespeare Soc; AAUP; MLA. Renaissance drama and dramatic theory; contemporary drama; Renaissance literature. Publ: Marino, Crashaw, and Sospetto d'Herode, Philol. Quart, fall 74. Add: Dept. of English, Cleveland State University, Cleveland, OH 44115.

BARBER, CESAR LOMBARDI, b. Berkeley, Calif, June 3, 13; m. 36; c. 3. ENGLISH. A.B, Harvard, 35, Soc. Fels, jr. fel, 36-39; Henry fel, Magdalene Col, Cambridge, 35-36; fel, Folger Shakespeare Libr, 49, 54. Instr. & tutor hist. & lit, Harvard, 39-41, 42-43; asst. to dir, Oceanog. Inst, Woods Hole, 43-44; asst. prof. Eng, Amherst Col, 46-51, assoc. prof, 51-56, prof, 56-62; prof. & chmn. dept, Ind. Univ, 62-66; vis. prof, Smith Col, 66-67; prof, State Univ. N.Y. Buffalo, 67-70; PROF. LIT, UNIV. CALIF, SANTA CRUZ, 70-, v.chancellor humanities, 70-73. Vis. prof, Princeton, 60-61; trustee, Sarah Lawrence Col, 65-69; fel, Ctr. Advan. Stud. Behav. Sci, 69-70. George Jean Nathan Prize, 59. U.S.N.R, 43-45, Lt. MLA. Renaissance and modern English literature; English drama and folk custom; 20th century literature. Publ: Co-auth, The new college plan, 58; auth, Shakespeare's festive comedy, Princeton, 59; co-auth, The lyric and dramatic Milton, Columbia Univ, 65; auth, The form of Faustus' fortunes, Tulane Drama Rev, 64. Add: College VIII, University of California, Santa Cruz, CA 95060.

BARBER, DAVID SPEAR, b. Schenectady, N.Y, June 17, 40; c. 1. ENGLISH, AMERICAN STUDIES. A.B, Hamilton Col, 62; M.A, Univ. Mich, Ann Arbor, 63, Ph.D.(Eng), 68. ASST. PROF. ENG, UNIV, IDAHO, 68- MLA; AAUP; NCTE. Later 19th century American fiction; Henry Adams; D.H. Lawrence. Publ: Can a radical interpretation of Women in love be adequate, D.H. Lawrence Rev, summer 70; Community in Women in love, Novel, fall 71; Henry Adams' Esther: the nature of individuality and immortality, New Eng. Quart, 6/72. Add: Dept. of English, University of Idaho, Moscow, ID 83843.

BARBER, EDDICE BELLE, b. Graham, Mo, Oct. 26, 20. ENGLISH. B.S, Northwest Mo. State Univ, 42; Univ. Iowa, summer 44; M.A, Univ. Colo, 48; Ford Found. fel, Univ. Chicago, summer 55; Ph.D.(Eng), Univ. Minn, Minneapolis, 72. Supvr. ENG, Nebr. State Teachers Col, Peru, 48-49; instr, Parson Jr. Col, Kans, 49-56; MANKATO STATE COL, 56-62, asst. prof, 64-65, assoc. prof, 66-73, PROF, 73- MLA; Midwest Mod. Lang. Asn; AAUP; Am. Asn. Univ. Women; Early Am. Lit. Asn; Am. Stud. Asn. Colonial American literature; nineteenth century American literature. Add: Dept. of English, Mankato State College, Mankato, MN 56001.

BARBER, GEORGE BRADFORD, b. Hamilton, Ill, June 29, 06; m. 32. SPEECH. B.Ed, West. Ill. Univ, 28; M.A, State Univ. Iowa, 35 & 42; Univ. South. Calif, summer, 40; Ph.D, Ohio State Univ, 53. Teacher speech & soc. stud, Pittsfield High Sch, 28-36; SPEECH, Muscatine High Sch, Iowa, 36-44; asst. prof, ILL. STATE UNIV, 44-54, assoc. prof, 54-60, prof, 60-70, EMER. PROF, 70- Cent. States Speech Asn.(v.pres, 60-61, pres. elect, 61-62, pres, 62-63); Am. Inst. Parliamentarians. Speech education. Publ: Analysis and evaluation of forensic contests as conducted in the secondary schools within the area of the North Central Association, N.Cent. Asn, 54; co-auth, Speech status in Illinois, Ill. J. Educ, 2/67. Add: 103 W. Vernon Ave, Normal, IL 61761.

BARBER, GEORGE S, b. June 29, 23; U.S. citizen; m. 56; c. 3. ENGLISH. B.A, Pa. State Univ, 46, M.A, 47, Ph.D.(Eng), 52. Instr. Eng, Butler Univ, 47-53; asst. prof, Chatham Col, 53-56; assoc. prof. Eng. & music, Ohio Northern Univ, 56-59; assoc. prof. Eng. & head dept. & dir. Eng. lang. inst, Park Col, 59-62; prof. Eng. & head dept, Ky. Wesleyan Col, 62-63; prof. Eng. & head dept. & head humanities div, Frostburg State Col, 63-66; dean, Alliance Col, 66-67; PROF. ENG, CLARION STATE COL, 67- Shaw; Shakespeare; 19th century American literature. Publ: Bernard Shaw's contributions to music criticism, PMLA, 12/57. Add: Dept. of English, Clarion State College, Clarion, PA 16214.

BARBER, LAIRD H, b. Greenwich, Conn, May 13, 30; m. 60. ENGLISH LITERATURE. B.A, Williams Col, 52; Fulbright scholar, Cambridge, 52-53; M.A, Univ. Mich, 56, Ph.D, 62; fel, Univ. Mainz, 58-59. Instr. ENG, Univ. Mich, 61-62; asst. prof, Grinnell Col, 62-64; UNIV. MINN, MORRIS, 64-66, assoc. prof, 66-72, PROF, 72- U.S.A, 53-55. MLA; Renaissance Soc. Am. English Renaissance drama. Add: Dept. of English, University of Minnesota, Morris, MN 56267.

BARBOUR, ALTON BRADFORD, b. San Diego, Calif, Oct. 13, 33; m. 61; c. 4. INTERPERSONAL COMMUNICATION. A.B, Univ. North. Colo, 56; M.A, Univ. Denver, 61, Ph.D.(commun), 68. Spec. lectr. humanities, Colo. Sch. Mines, 64-65; instr. SPEECH COMMUN, UNIV. DENVER, 65-68, asst. prof, 68-71, ASSOC. PROF. & DIR. GRAD. STUD, 71- Affiliate dir, Inst. Gen. Semantics, Conn, 70-; staff assoc, Colo. Ctr. Psychodrama, 72- Speech Commun. Asn; Am. Soc. Group Psychother. & Psychodrama; Rocky Mountain Asn. Humanistic Psychol.(pres, 70-72). Psychological dimensions of free speech attitudes; psychodrama; interpersonal and non-verbal behavior. Publ: Ed, Free speech yearbook, Speech Commun. Asn, 73; co-ed, Interpersonal communication: teaching resources and strategies, Eric, 74; contrib, Speech: science-art, Bobbs, 69, Sightings: essays in humanistic psychology, Shields, 73 & Language thought and behavior, Nan'un-do, Japan, 73. Add: Dept. of Speech Communication, University of Denver, Denver, CO 80210.

BARBOUR, BRIAN MICHAEL, b. Lorain, Ohio, July 26, 43; m. 68; c. 2. ENGLISH & AMERICAN LITERATURE. B.A, Univ. Notre Dame, 65; M.A, Kent State Univ, 66, Ph.D.(Eng), 69. ASST. PROF. ENG, PROVIDENCE COL, 69- Melville Soc. Am. Nineteenth and 20th century American literature; English novel; modern criticism. Publ: Ed, American transcendentalism: an anthology of criticism, Univ. Notre Dame, 73; auth, The great Gatsby, and the American past, South. Rev, 73; Emerson's poetic prose, Mod. Lang. Quart, 74. Add: Dept. of English, Providence College, Providence, RI 02918.

BARCHEK, JAMES R, b. South Norwalk, Conn, May 24, 35; m. 56; c. 3. ENGLISH. B.S, Portland State Col, 59; M.Ed, Univ. Ore, 62, Dr. Arts(Eng), 68. Teacher, pub. schs, Ore, 59-65; res. assoc, Ore. Curriculum Stud. Ctr, 65-67; instr. Eng, Univ. Ore, 66-68; asst. prof, West. Wash. State Col, 68-72; COORD. ENG. LANG. ARTS, KENT SCH. DIST, WASH, 72- Asst. dir, NDEA summer inst. teachers Eng, Univ. Ore, 66. NCTE(dir, 72-73); Int. Arthurian Soc. Medieval literature; Arthurian romance; teacher education and curriculum. Publ: Co-auth, The private I, on purpose, Holt, 74; auth, English course structures: approaches to more effective teaching, In: Individualizing learning through modular flexible scheduling, McGraw, 68. Add: Kent School District 415, Kent, WA 98031.

BARCUS, JAMES E, b. Alliance, Ohio, Oct. 29, 38; m. 61; c. 1. ENGLISH LITERATURE. B.A, Houghton Col, 59; univ. fel, Univ. Ky, 59-61, M.A, 61; John Louis Haney fel, Univ. Pa, 61-64, Ph.D.(Eng), 68. Vis. prof. ENG, Nyack Col, 63-64; assoc. prof, HOUGHTON COL, 64-68, PROF, 68-, CHMN. DEPT. ENG. & SPEECH, 69- Vis. prof, Univ. Ky, summer 66; Danforth Found. assoc, 66-70; ed. humanities, Christian Scholar Rev, 70-72, mem. ed. bd, 70-; consult. humanities, Rushford Cent. Sch, 73-74; mem, Eng. Inst. MLA; NCTE; Conf. Christianity & Lit.(treas, 71-73). Nineteenth century poetry, periodicals and aesthetics. Publ: The literary correspondence of Bernard Barton, Univ. Pa, 66; Shelley, Routledge & Kegan Paul, London, 74; Pulling for prime, Seventeenth Century News, 74; Recapturing the music of the spheres, J. Aesthet. Educ, 74. Add: Dept. of English, Houghton College, Houghton, NY 14744.

BARD, ISAIAH S, b. Boston, Mass, Oct. 29, 19. COMMUNICATIONS, JOURNALISM. B.A, Yeshiva Univ, 40; M.A, N.Y. Univ, 52, Kaltenborn Found. fel, 53, Ph.D.(commun), 57. Writer & producer radio & TV, N.C. & N.Y, 47-49; free-lance writer & producer, 49-56; asst. to v.pres, Radio Liberty Comt, N.Y, 56-66; vis. lectr, Fairfield Univ. Grad. Sch. Corporate & Polit. Commun, 67; ASST. PROF. JOUR, UNIV. BRIDGEPORT, 70- Sr. researcher commun. stud, H.W. Land Corp, N.Y.C, 68-; adj. asst. prof, Sch. Gen. Stud, Queens Col.(N.Y), 70-72. U.S.A, 43-46. Am. Asn. Pub. Opinion Res; Speech Commun. Asn. Mass communication; broadcasting public opinion. Add: 11 E. Seventh St, New York, NY 10003.

BAREFIELD, PAUL ACTON, b. Mobile, Ala, Sept. 3, 38; m. 63; c. 3. SPEECH. B.A, Samford Univ, 60; M.A, La. State Univ, 62, Ph.D.(speech), 66. Asst. prof. speech & dir. Forensics, Moorhead State Col, 64-66; UNIV. OKLA, 66-70, ASSOC. PROF. SPEECH COMMUN. & DIR. FORENSICS, 70- Univ. Okla. Found. fel. grant, 69; sr. assoc. & consult, Situation Dynamics, Inc, 72-73. Am. Stud. Asn; Am. Forensic Asn; Cent. States Speech Asn; South. Speech Asn; Am. Soc. Training & Develop; Speech Commun. Asn; Mid-continent Am. Stud. Asn. American political conventions; criminal justice system; Reconstruction Negro congressmen. Publ: Competitive individual speaking in rhetorical criticism, Speech Teacher, 3/67; Speech and specialization: world enough and time, Vital Speeches, 2/68; Republican keynoters, Speech Monogr, 11/70. Add: Dept. of Speech Communication, University of Oklahoma, Norman, OK 73069.

BARISH, JONAS A, b. New York, N.Y, Mar. 22, 22. ENGLISH. A.B, Harvard, 42, M.A, 47, Ph.D.(Eng), 52; Fulbright fel, Paris, 52-53. Instr. ENG, Yale, 53-54; asst. prof, UNIV. CALIF, BERKELEY, 54-60, assoc. prof, 60-66, PROF, 66-, chmn. dept. French, 71-72. Fulbright res. fel, Paris, 61-62; Am. Counc. Learned Soc. fel, 61-62. Sig.C, U.S.A, 43-45. MLA; Renaissance Soc. Am; Am. Acad. Arts & Sci. Elizabethan drama. Publ: Ben Jonson and the language of prose comedy, Harvard, 60; ed, Ben Jonson's Sejanus, Yale, 65; auth, Exhibitionism and the antitheatrical prejudice, Eng. Lit. Hist, spring 69; Yvor Winters and the antimimetic prejudice, New Lit. Hist, 71; Antitheatrical prejudice in the nineteenth century, Univ. Toronto Quart, 72; plus many others. Add: Dept. of English, University of California, Berkeley, CA 94720.

BARKER, ARTHUR EDWARD, b. Toronto, Ont, Jan. 21, 11; m. 38; c. 2. ENGLISH LITERATURE. B.A, Univ. Toronto, 33, fel, 33-35, M.A, 34; fel, Univ. London, 35-37, Ph.D.(Eng), 37. Lectr. ENG, Trinity Col, Univ. Toronto, 37-39, assoc. prof, col. & Sch. Grad. Stud, 39-42, prof, 42-61, head dept, 42-57; prof, Assoc. Ctr. Adv. Stud, Univ. Ill, 61-70; PROF. RENAISSANCE LIT, UNIV. WEST. ONT, 70- Imp. Order Daughters Empire Can. Overseas War-Mem. fel, 35-37; Guggenheim fel, Can, 44-45; vis. prof,

Adams House, Harvard, 45; Columbia Univ, 45-46, 60-61; Univ. Wis, 49; Univ. Toronto, 62; Univ. Calif, Los Angeles, 66; Folger Libr. fel, 57-58. Can. Army, 40-44, Lt. MLA; Mod. Humanities Res. Asn, Gt. Brit; Renaissance Soc. Am; Milton Soc. Am; Can. Asn. Univ. Prof; Asn. Can. Univ. Teachers Eng. Renaissance; John Milton; history of criticism. Publ: Milton and the Puritan dilemma, 1641-1660, Univ. Toronto, 42, 55, 64 & 71; ed, Milton, modern essays in criticism, Oxford, 65. Add: Dept. of English, University of Western Ontario, London, Ont, N6A 3K7, Can.

BARKER, LARRY LEE, b. Wilmington, Ohio, Nov. 22, 41; m. 61; c. 2. SPEECH, COMMUNICATION. A.B, Ohio Univ, 62, M.A, 63, univ. fel, 63-65, Ph.D.(speech), 65. Asst. prof. speech, South. Ill. Univ, 65-66; Purdue Univ, 66-69; assoc. prof. COMMUN, FLA. STATE UNIV, 69-71, PROF, 71- South, Ill. Univ. grant, 65-66; U.S. Off. Educ. grants, 65-67; asst. ed, Conf. Res. & Develop. Speech, under grant from U.S. Off. Educ. & Speech Commun. Asn, 67-68. Speech Commun. Asn; Nat. Soc. Stud. Commun; Am. Educ. Res. Asn. Speech and language instructional strategies; computerized information retrieval; nonverbal communication. Publ: Co-auth, Speech—interpersonal communication, 67 & Speech—interpersonal communication workbook, Chandler, 67; co-ed, Speech communication behavior, 71 & auth, Listening behavior, 71, Prentice-Hall; Irrelevant factors and speech evaluation, South. Speech J, fall 66; co-auth, Effect of perceived mispronunciation on speech effectiveness ratings and retention, Quart. J. Speech, 2/68 & An experimental study to assess the effects of three levels of mispronunciation on comprehension for three different populations, Speech Monogr, 3/68. Add: Dept. of Communication, Florida State University, Tallahassee, FL 32303.

BARKER, ROSALIND ALLEN, b. Lumberton, N.C, Nov. 5, 35; m. 59; c. 3. ENGLISH. B.A, Univ. Richmond, 57; Fulbright scholar, Univ. Southampton, 57-58; M.A, Yale, 59, Woodrow Wilson & univ. fels, 60-61, Lewis-Farmington fel, 61-62, Sterling fel. & Ph.D.(Eng), 63. Lectr. ENG, Victoria Col, Univ. Toronto, 63-67; Rice Univ, 67-71; VICTORIA COL, UNIV. TORONTO, 71-72, ASST. PROF, 72- Can. Counc. fel, 66; trustee, Univ. Richmond, 71-; mem, Inter-univ. Ctr. Europ. Stud, Montreal. Asn. Can. Univ. Teachers Eng; Am. Soc. 18th Century Stud. Restoration and 18th century English literature; Anglo-French literary relationships, 17th and 18th centuries. Add: Dept. of English, Victoria College, University of Toronto, Toronto 181, Ont, Can.

BARKER, THOBURN VAIL, b. Scott, Ohio, Oct. 31, 21; m. 46; c. 2. SPEECH, LINGUISTICS. B.A, Ohio Wesleyan Univ, 43; M.A, Columbia Univ, 51. Instr. SPEECH, Hampton Inst, 51-53; LEHIGH UNIV, 53-57, asst. prof, 57-62, ASSOC. PROF, 62- East. States Speech Commun. Asn.(exec. secy, 60-63); Speech Commun. Asn. Origination of grouping by sound method of phonetically presenting the English language; phonetics; public speaking. Publ: The speech, its structure and composition, Am. Bk. Co, 68; Training aids for the classroom teacher, Pa. Speech Annual, 6/55; Are we becoming non-communicatore?, 2/64 & Lincoln: rhetorical copycat?, 2/67, Today's Speech. Add: Div. of Speech, Lehigh University, Bethlehem, PA 18015.

BARKER, WALTER L, b. Newport, R.I, Oct. 1, 33; m. 61; c. 2. ENGLISH. B.A, Univ. R.I, 60, M.A, 62; Ph.D.(Eng), Univ. Conn, 66. Instr. ENG, Northeast. Univ, 62-63; asst. prof, UNIV. R.I, 66-72, ASSOC. PROF, 72- U.S.A, 53-55. MLA; Renaissance Soc. Am. Shakespeare; Elizabethan drama; Renaissance literature. Add: Dept. of English, University of Rhode Island, Kingston, RI 02881.

BARKSDALE, RICHARD KENNETH, b. Winchester, Mass, Oct. 31, 15; m. 60; c. 4. ENGLISH. A.B, Bowdoin Col, 37, hon. L.H.D, 72; A.M, Syracuse Univ, 38; Gen. Educ. Bd. fel, 42-43, 51; Ph.D, Harvard, 51. Instr. Eng, South. Univ, 37-38; asst. prof, Tougaloo Col, 38-42; prof, N.C. Col, Durham, 49-58, vice-dean grad. sch, 49-53, dean, 53-58; chmn. dept. Eng, Morehouse Col, 58-62, prof, Atlanta Univ, 62-71, dean, Grad. Sch. Arts & Sci, 68-71; PROF. ENG, UNIV. ILL, URBANA-CHAMPAIGN, 71-, DIR, UNDERGRAD. STUD. ENG, 72- Consult, Nat. Endowment for Humanities & Ford Found, 70; mem, Comn. Higher Educ, N.Cent. Asn. Cols. & Sec. Schs, 73- U.S.A, 43-46. MLA; S.Atlantic Mod. Lang. Asn; NCTE (dir, 72-); Col. Lang. Asn. (pres, 73-). English literature of the 19th century. Publ: Co-ed, Black writers of America, Macmillan, 72; auth, Urban crisis and Black poetic avant garde, 68 & Symbolism and irony in McKay's Home to Harlem, 3/72, CLA Jour, contrib, Humanistic protest in recent Black poetry, In: Modern Black poetry, 73. Add: Dept. of English, University of Illinois, Urbana, IL 61801.

BARNARD, ANN W, b. Kansas City, Mo, Feb. 17, 30. ENGLISH & AMERICAN LITERATURE. B.A, Univ. Kansas City, 50, univ. fel, 50-52, M.A, 52, teaching fel, 57-60, Ph.D, 63. MEM. FAC. ENG, BLACKBURN COL, 60-, CHMN. DEPT, 64- Storck Mem. Award, 51-52. NCTE; MLA. Modern American literature; 19th century novel; women's studies. Add: Dept. of English, Blackburn College, Carlinville, IL 62626.

BARNARD, DEAN STANTON, JR, b. Chicago, Ill, Dec. 8, 25; m. 56; c. 1. ENGLISH. A.B, Univ. Mich, 51, M.A, 55, fel, 56, Ph.D.(Eng. lang. & lit), 61. Instr. ENG, East. Mich. Univ, 57-58, asst. prof, 58-62; Humboldt State Col, 62-63; Parsons Col, 63-64, assoc. prof, 64-66; prof. & dean, Lea Col, 66-70; PROF. ENG, YORK COL. PA, 70- U.S.A, 43-46. MLA; NCTE; Northeast Mod. Lang. Asn; Col. Eng. Asn; Am. Asn. Higher Educ. Publ: Holland's Leaguer: a critical edition, Mouton, 69. Add: Dept. of English, York College of Pennsylvania, York, PA 17405.

BARNARD, ELLSWORTH, b. Shelburne Falls, Mass, Apr. 11, 07; m. 36. ENGLISH. B.S, Univ. Mass, 28, hon. L.H.D, 69; M.A, Univ. Minn, 29, Ph.D, 35. Instr. Eng, Univ. Mass, 30-33; asst. prof, Univ. Tampa, 36-37; instr, Williams Col, 37-40; lectr, Univ. Wis, 40-41; assoc. prof, Alfred Univ, 41-46, prof, 46-50; lectr. libr. arts, Univ. Chicago, 52-55; vis. lectr, Bowdoin Col, 55-57; assoc. prof. Eng, North. Mich. Univ, 57-62, prof, 62-68; vis. prof, UNIV. MASS, AMHERST, 68-69, prof. ENG, 69-73, EMER. PROF, 73- MLA; Col. Eng. Asn; NCTE. Nineteenth century British literature; twentieth century British and American literature. Publ: Shelley's religion, Russell, 37; ed, Shelley: representative poems, essays and letters, Odyssey, 44; auth, Wendell Wilkie: fighter for freedom, North. Mich. Univ, 66; Edward Arlington Robinson: a critical study, Octagon, 69; co-auth. & ed, Edwin Arlington Robinson: centenary essays, Univ. Ga, 69; co-auth, E.A. Robinson, In: Fifteen American authors, Duke Univ, 69. Add: 86 Leverett Rd, R.D. 3, Amherst, MA 01002.

BARNELLE, VIRGINIA MARIE, b. Covington, Ky. THEATRE ARTS, EDUCATIONAL PSYCHOLOGY. B.A, Univ. Calif, Los Angeles, 47, M.S, 49. Instr. theatre arts, Marymount Col.(Calif), 49-57; counr. & teacher Eng, U.S. Dependents' Schs, Europe, 57-58; asst. prof. theatre arts, Marymount Col. (Calif), 58-60, assoc. prof, 60-63, prof, 63-65, chmn. dept, 60-65, asst. to pres. & dir. int. educ, 65-73, PROF. THEATRE ARTS, LOYOLA MARYMOUNT UNIV, 73- Mem, Inst. Int. Educ, 70-; secy, Int. Counc. Acad. Inst, 73- AAUP; Coun. Int. Educ. Exchange. International education; classical theatre; psychology of acting. Add: Dept. of Theatre Arts, Loyola Marymount University, 7101 W. 80th St, Los Angeles, CA 90045.

BARNES, DANIEL RAMON, b. Fillmore, N.Y, May 16, 40; m. 63; c. 2. AMERICAN LITERATURE, FOLKLORE. B.A, St. Bonaventure Univ, 62; M.A, Univ. Kans, 66; Ph.D.(Eng), Univ. Ky, 70. Instr. ENG, OHIO STATE UNIV, COLUMBUS, 68-69, asst. prof, 69-73, ASSOC. PROF, 73- Ohio State Univ. fac. summer fel, 70 & 73; consult, Smithsonian Inst. Festival of Am. Folklife, 71. MLA; Am. Folklore Soc; Am. Stud. Asn. Nineteenth century American literature; folklore and literature; 20th century fiction. Publ: Ford and the slaughtered saints: a new reading of The good soldier, Mod. Fiction Stud, summer 68; Folktale morphology and the structure of Beowulf, Speculum, 4/70; Physical fact and folklore: Hawthorne's egotism, or the bosom serpent, Am. Lit, 3/71. Add: Dept. of English, Ohio State University, 164 W. 17th Ave, Columbus, OH 43210.

BARNES, JIM WEAVER, b. Summerfield, Okla, Dec. 22, 33. COMPARATIVE LITERATURE, CREATIVE WRITING. B.A, Southeast. State Col, 64; M.A, Univ. Ark, Fayetteville, 66, Ph.D.(comp. lit), 72. Instr. Eng, Northeast. Okla. State Col, 65-68; ASST. PROF. COMP. LIT, NORTHEAST MO. STATE UNIV, 70- Consult. poetry, Wesley Found, Northeast. Okla. State Col, 73. Nat. Guard, 50-51. MLA; Conf. Col. Compos. & Commun. Comparative literature; 20th century fiction and poetry; creative writing. Publ: Myth of Sisyphus in Under the volcano, Prairie Schooner, 68/69; Reflections on Faust: Goethe, Marlowe, Valery, Fine Arts Discovery, 72; The trees in the middle of the field, Snowy Egret, 73; plus others. Add: Division of Language & Literature, Northeast Missouri State University, Kirksville, MO 63501.

BARNES, REY LEROY, b. Provo, Utah, Apr. 17, 33; m. 56; c. 8. TELECOMMUNICATIONS, BROADCASTING. B.S, Utah State Univ, 60, M.S, 62; Stanford Univ, 60; Found. Econ. Educ. fel, 66; Nat. Asn. Broadcasters res. grant, 67-70; Ph.D.(speech), Univ. Iowa, 70. Mgr. KUSU-FM, Utah State Univ, 58-62, prod-dir. production ctr, 60-62; dir. in-sch. serv, KUSU-FM-TV, 63-65, instr. radio-TV, 64-65; telecommun. & area adv, Univ. Utah, 65-70, asst. prof. & coord. stud, 70-73; ASSOC. PROF. BROADCAST STUDIES & DIR. AREA, UNIV. SOUTHWEST; LA, 73- Consult, Bonneville Int. Corp. prog. serv, 65-73; Utah Network for Instr. TV, 67-73; Burroughs Corp, La Jolla Interactive Res. Lab, 72; adv, KBYU-TV, 73. Broadcast Educ. Asn.(publ. comt, 72-73). Decision making parameters; institutional image building; curriculum building. Publ: Teachers and television, Impressors de Los Reyes, 66; Shattering the shiboleths, Feedback, 12/71; ed, Broadcasting and society, Broadcast. Educ. Asn, 73; auth, The consultant and the industry, West Newslett, 2/73. Add: Dept. of Speech, University of Southwestern Louisiana, Lafayette, LA 70501.

BARNES, RICHARD G, b. San Bernardino, Calif, Nov. 5, 32; m. 53, 72; c. 5. ENGLISH. B.A, Pomona Col, 54; A.M, Harvard, 59; Ph.D, Claremont Grad. Sch, 60. Acting instr. ENG, Univ. Calif, Riverside, 58-59; instr, POMONA COL, 61-62, asst. prof, 62-65, assoc. prof, 65-73, PROF, 73- Auth. play, The death of Buster Quinine, produced by Pomona Col, 72. U.S.N.R, 50-54. MLA; Renaissance Soc. Am. Chaucer; Joyce, film maker. Publ: Plays and fugitive essays 1963-1966, Barnes, 66; The cotton gnomic poem 68 & The complete poems of R.G. Barnes, 72, Grabhorn-Hoyem; transl, Three Spanish sacramental plays, 69 & auth, Episodes in five poetic traditions, 72, Chandler. Add: Dept. of English, Pomona College, Claremont, CA 91711.

BARNES, ROBERT JAY, b. Hutchinson, Kans, July 7, 25; m. 48; c. 2. ENGLISH. B.A, Univ. Kans, 47, M.A, 50; Ph.D, Univ. Tex, 55. Instr. ENG, Univ. Tex, 53-55; asst. prof, Univ. South. Miss, 55-57, assoc. prof, 57-60; LAMAR UNIV, 60-61, PROF, 61-, head dept, 66-69. State of Tex. res. grants, 60-62 & 69-71; consult, Beaumont Independent Sch. Dist, Tex, 62-63; vis. prof. Eng, Tex. Tech Univ, summer 70. AAUP; NCTE; MLA. Publ: Co-auth, Mechanics of English, Appleton, 60; A concordance to Byron's Don Juan, Cornell Univ, 67; Two modes of fiction: Hemingway and Greene, Renascence, 62; auth, Conrad Richter, In: Southwest writers series, Steck, 68; Oil field fiction, Southwest. Am. Lit, fall 72; plus one other. Add: Dept. of English, Lamar University, Beaumont, TX 77710.

BARNES, RONALD EDGAR, b. Minneapolis, Minn, Mar. 12, 30; m. 52. DRAMATIC LITERATURE, THEATRE HISTORY. B.S, Univ. Minn, 51; Ph.D. (drama), Stanford Univ, 63. Instr. DRAMA, Mills Col, 57-61, asst. prof, 61-65; assoc. prof, CALIF. STATE COL, SAN BERNARDINO, 65-69, PROF. & CHMN. DEPT, 70- U.S.N.R, 52-55, Lt.(jg). U.S. Inst. Theatre Technol; Am. Theatre Asn. Dramatic analysis; theatre architecture. Publ: The dramatic comedy of William Somerset Maugham, Mouton, 68. Add: Dept. of Drama, California State College, San Bernardino, 5500 State College Parkway, San Bernardino, CA 92407.

BARNES, SAMUEL GILL, b. Kans. City, Mo, Aug. 5, 13; m. 47; c. 4. ENGLISH. B.S, Okla. Agr. & Mech. Col, 36; M.A, Univ. N.C, 46, Ph.D.(Eng), 53. Instr. ENG, Va. Mil. Inst, 39-41, 46-50; Washington & Lee Univ, 46-47; lectr, UNIV. N.C, CHAPEL HILL, 53-56, asst. prof, 56-66, ASSOC. PROF, 66- U.S.N.R, 41-45. MLA. Nineteenth century British and American transcendentalism; Victorian prose; Thomas Carlyle. Publ: Learning composition skill by means of a controlled-source book, Odyssey, 62; Ready, wrestle!, Farrar, Straus, 65. Add: Dept. of English, University of North Carolina, Chapel Hill, NC 27514.

BARNES, WARNER J, b. Waco, Tex, Nov. 25, 34; m. 58; c. 3. ENGLISH. A.B, Harvard, 59; Ph.D, Univ. Tex, 63. Spec. instr. ENG, Univ. Tex, 62-63;

instr, Univ. Iowa, 63-64, asst. prof, 64-66, assoc. prof, 67-68; vis. prof, UNIV. TEX, AUSTIN, 68-70, ASSOC. PROF, 70- Am. Counc. Learned Soc. grant-in-aid, 64; founding ed, Bks. at Iowa, 64-66; U.S. Off. Educ. grant, dir. textual stud. Iowa-Calif. ed. Mark Twain, 65-68; Piper Found. award, publ. E.B. Browning bibliog, 65; Nat. Endowment for Humanities fel, 67-68; ed, Browning Newslett, 68- Bibliog. Soc, London; Bibliog. Soc. Am. Analytical bibliography; the Brownings; the Bible as literature. Publ: The Browning collection at the University of Texas, 67 & A bibliography of Elizabeth Barrett Browning, 68, Univ. Tex; co-auth, Bibliography and textual criticism; English and American literature, 1700 to the present, Univ. Chicago, 69; co-ed, The Ohio Browning edition (Vols. III & IV), Ohio Univ; contrib, A drama of exile, In: A new introduction to bibliography, Oxford, 72. Add: Dept. of English, University of Texas at Austin, Austin, TX 78712.

BARNES, WESLEY, b. Providence, R.I, Jan. 3, 16; m. 41; c. 1. RENAISSANCE, MODERN NOVEL. B.Sc, La. State Univ, 38; B.P.H.E, Univ. Toronto, 49, B.A, 51; M.A, Univ. Ottawa, 52, Ph.D.(Eng), 54; D.Litt, Univ. Manchester, 64; Univ. London, 65-68. Asst. prof. ENG, Brescia Col, 50-52; State Univ. N.Y. Albany, 52-55; assoc. prof, Adelphi Univ, 55-58; sr. lectr, Univs. Manchester & Leeds, 58-60; PROF, St. Mary's Dominican Col, 60-62; MOREHEAD STATE UNIV, 63- Argyll & Sutherland grant, 64; state & regional consult. ling, 65-68; Collection Adjectives All Educ. Levels res. grant, 70; ed, Bull. Appl. Ling, Morehead State Univ. Royal Can. Artillery & Argyll & Sutherland Highlanders, 39-45, 1st Lt. NEA; NCTE; MLA; Int. Soc. Gen. Semantics; Am. Dialect Soc; Ling. Soc. Am. Emotive theories and language; computational analysis of the poetry of Milton; programming texts for semantics. Publ: Existentialism, Barron, 68; plus 35 articles in Bull. Appl. Ling. & TV credit courses. Add: Box 681, Morehead State University, Morehead, KY 40351.

BARNET, SYLVAN, b. New York, N.Y, Dec. 11, 26. ENGLISH. B.A, N.Y. Univ, 48; M.A, Harvard, 50, Ph.D.(Eng), 54. Teaching fel. gen. educ, Harvard, 51-54; instr. ENG, TUFTS UNIV, 54-57, asst. prof, 57-60, assoc. prof, 60-63, FLETCHER PROF, 63-, chmn. dept, 62-67. U.S.A, 45-46, Sgt. Malone Soc; MLA; Shakespeare Asn. Am. Romanticism; theory of tragedy; Shakespeare. Publ: Co-auth, Dictionary of literary terms, 60, Introduction to literature, 61, auth, Short guide to writing about literature, 68 & 71, co-ed, Types of drama, 72 & Nine modern classics, 73, Little; ed, Complete Signet classic Shakespeare, 72 & auth, Short guide to Shakespeare 74, Harcourt; gen. ed, The Signet Shakespeare, (40 vols), New Am. Libr, 63-68. Add: Dept. of English, East Hall, Tufts University, Medford, MA 02155.

BARNETT, GEORGE LEONARD, b. Caldwell, N.J, Jan. 18, 15; m. 40; c. 2. ENGLISH LITERATURE. A.B, Randolph-Macon Col, 36; A.M, Princeton, 39, Ph.D, 42. Instr. Eng, French & Latin, Randolph-Macon Col, 39-41; Eng. & naval correspondence, U.S. Naval Training Sch, IND. UNIV, BLOOMINGTON, 42-43, supvr, 43-44, instr. ENG, UNIV, 44-46, asst. prof, 46-56, assoc. prof, 56-63, PROF, 63- Vis. lectr, Univ. Colo, summer, 62. MLA; Charles Lamb Soc. English essay and novel; biography; Romantic period. Publ: Co-auth, The English romantic poets and essayists: a review of research and criticism, 57, rev. ed, 68, Eighteenth-century British novelists on the novel & ed, Nineteenth-century British novelists on the novel, 71, Appleton; An unpublished review by Charles Lamb, 56 & Charles Lamb's part in an edition of Hogarth, 59, Mod. Lang. Quart; A disquisition on Punch and Judy attributed to Charles Lamb, Huntington Lib. Quart, 62. Add: Dept. of English, Indiana University, Bloomington, IN 47401.

BARNETT, HOWARD ALBERT, b. Dallas, Tex, June 14, 20; m. 47; c. 2. ENGLISH. B.A, Ind. Univ, 47, M.A, 48, Ph.D, 59; Univ. Chicago, summers, 50, 51. Asst. prof. ENG, Bridgewater Col, 48-50; Wash. Col, 50-52; Wis. State Col, Whitewater, 57-59; Marshall Evans assoc. prof, Morris Harvey Col, 59-61, Marshall Evans prof, 61-65, chmn. dept, 63-65; Alice Parker Prof. & chmn. dept, LINDENWOOD COLS, 65-69, PROF, DEAN FAC. & V.PRES, 69-, asst. to pres. acad. planning, 66-68. U.S.N, 41-45. Am. Conf. Acad. Deans; NCTE; MLA. Victorian Age, especially Browning; criticism and aesthetics; linguistics. Publ: A time of the year for Milton's Ad Patrem, Mod. Lang. Notes, 2/58; Christian art forms and the miracle play, Episcopal News W.Va, 5/63; Romeo and Juliet: Myth and tragic form, Proc. 4th Marshall Univ. Eng. Inst, 4/64. Add: office of the Vice President, Lindenwood Colleges, St. Charles, MO 63301.

BARNETT, LLOYD, JR, b. Montgomery, Ala, Feb. 9, 22; m. 48; c. 6. CREATIVE WRITING, MEDIEVAL ENGLISH LITERATURE. B.S, U.S. Mil. Acad, 44; Stanford Univ, 55-56; M.A, Univ. Denver, 65, Ph.D.(creative writing), 71. Instr. ENG, U.S. Air Force Acad, 56-60; Univ. Denver, 67-68; asst. prof, WEST. STATE COL. COLO, 68-71, ASSOC. PROF, 71- U.S.A.F, 44-64, Lt. Col. NEA. World myths; Western United States folklore; creative writing. Add: Div. of Arts & Humanities, Western State College of Colorado, Gunnison, CO 81230.

BARNHILL, JAMES ORRIS, b. Sumner, Miss, May 23, 22. THEATER, SPEECH. B.A, Yale, 47, M.F.A, 54; M.A, N.Y. Univ, 49; hon. M.A, Brown Univ, 61. Instr. speech, Univ. Dubuque, 49-50; ENG, BROWN UNIV, 54-56, asst. prof, 56-61, assoc. prof, 61-69, PROF, 69-, DIR. THEATRE, 68- Mem, Inst. Advan. Stud. Theatre Arts & Rockefeller grant in directing, 63; Ford Found. grant, 66-68; vis. prof. theatre, Univ. Baroda, 72; vis. director, Darpana Acad, India, 73. U.S.N, 40-46, Lt.(jg). New Eng. Theatre Conf.(v.pres, 58-60); U.S. Inst. Theatre Tech; Am. Soc. Theatre Res; Speech Commun. Asn; Am. Educ. Theatre Asn; Am. Nat. Theatre & Acad. Acting theory; directing; Asian theatre. Add: 81 Transit St, Providence, RI 02906.

BARNOUW, ERIK, b. The Hague, Holland, June 23, 08, nat; m. 39; c. 3. DRAMATIC ARTS. A.B, Princeton, 29. Writer, dir. & producer, 31-42; script ed, Nat. Broadcasting Co, 42-44; consult, Secy. War, 44; supvr. ed. unit, armed forces radio serv, U.S. War Dept, 44-45; asst. prof. Eng, COLUMBIA UNIV, 46-53, assoc. prof. DRAMATIC ARTS, 53-64, prof, 64-73, EMER. PROF, 73-, in charge courses in TV, radio & film, 46-69, ed, Ctr. for Mass Commun, Univ. Press, 49-72. Consult, U.S. Pub. Health Serv, 48-51; Fulbright grant, India, 61-62; Guggenheim fel, 67; J.D. Rockefeller III Fund fel, Asia, 72. Gavel Award, Am. Bar Asn, 59; Bancroft Prize, Columbia Univ, 71; Preceptor Award, San Francisco State Col, 71; George Polk Award, L.I. Univ, 72. Auth. League Am. (secy, 49-53); Soc. Am. Hist; Soc. Cinema Stud. Documentary film; television. Publ: Mass communication: television, radio, film, press, Holt, 56; Television writer, Hill & Wang, 62; co-auth, Indian film, Columbia Univ, 63; auth, A tower in Babel, 66, The golden web, 68 & The image empire, 70, Oxford. Add: 39 Claremont Ave, New York, NY 10027.

BARON, DENNIS E, b. New York, N.Y, May 9, 44. ENGLISH LITERATURE, LINGUISTICS. B.A, Brandeis Univ, 65; N.Y. State Regents fel, Columbia Univ, 65-67, M.A, 68; Rackham fel, Univ. Mich, 70-71, Ph.D.(Eng), 71. Res. asst, Early Mod. Eng. Dict. Proj, 71; ASST. PROF. ENG, East. Ill. Univ, 71-73; CITY COL. NEW YORK, 73- Mediaeval Acad. Am; Ling. Soc. Am; Am. Dialect Soc; MLA; Early Eng. Text Soc; Popular Cult. Asn. Medieval English; stylistics; historical linguistics. Publ: Case grammar and diachronic English syntax, Mouton, 74; The syntax of perception in Richard Wright's Native son, Lang. & Style, (in press); Against interpretation: the linguistic structure of television drama, J. Popular Cult, (in press); Role structure and the language of literature, J. Lit. Semantics (in press). Add: Dept. of English, City College of New York, New York, NY 10031.

BARON, F. XAVIER, b. Springfield, Mo, July 29, 41. MEDIEVAL & ENGLISH LITERATURE. B.A, Mo. State Univ, 63; M.A, Univ. Iowa, 65, Ph.D.(Eng), 69. ASST. PROF. ENG, UNIV. WIS-MILWAUKEE, 69- Nat. Endowment for Humanities younger humanist fel, 71-72. Int. Arthurian Soc; MLA; Midwest Mod. Lang. Asn; Int. Courtly Lit. Soc. Medieval Arthurian literature; Chaucer and Middle English literature. Publ: Co-auth, Amour Courtors, The medieval ideal of love: a bibliography, Univ. Louisville, 73; auth, Visual presentation in Bévoul's Tristan, 72 & Love in Chretien's Charrette: reversed values and isolation, 73, Mod. Lang. Quart; Chaucer's Troilus and self-renunciation in love, Papers Lang. & Lit, 74. Add: Dept. of English, 321 Garland, University of Wisconsin-Milwaukee, Milwaukee, WI 53201.

BAROODY, WILSON GEORGE, b. Geneva, N.Y, Apr. 27, 31. LITERATURE & HUMANITIES. A.B, Grand Canyon Col, 53; M.A, Univ. Ariz, 55; Univ. N.Mex, 55-57, 59. Teaching fel, Univ. Ariz, 53-55; Univ. N.Mex, 55-57; instr. ENG, ARIZ. STATE UNIV, 57-61, ASST. PROF, 61-, FAC. MEM, RELIG. CONF. SCH. RELIG, 68-, vis. lectr. relig. & humanities. Consult. teaching lang, NEA, 62-63; Lilly Endowment stud. pre-sem. educ, 62-63; Fine Arts Relig. & Humanities grants, 72 & 73. Rocky Mountain Mod. Lang. Asn.(ed, Bull, 63-64); Renaissance Soc. Am; Philol. Asn. Pac. Coast; NEA. Biblical and theological backgrounds for literatures and Western thought; integrated humanities and inter-disciplinary programs; comparative literature and religion. Publ: New Testament in modern English, N.Mex. Quart, fall 59; The late Wordsworth and childhood, 8/60 & Donne's struggle for religious assurance, 2/62, Rocky Mountain Mod. Lang. Asn. Bull. Add: Dept. of English, Arizona State University, Tempe, AZ 85281.

BARR, ALAN PHILIP, b. Brooklyn, N.Y, Nov. 25, 38; m. 65; c. 2. ENGLISH. B.A, Mass. Inst. Technol, 59; Ph.D, Univ. Rochester, 63. Instr. ENG, Wayne State Univ, 63-65, asst. prof, 65-68; IND. UNIV. NORTHWEST, 68-72, ASSOC. PROF, 72- Victorian literature; modern drama. Publ: Victorian stage pulpiteer: Bernard Shaw's crusade, 73; Diabolonian pundit: G.B.S. as critic, Shaw Rev, 68; The paradise behind 1984, Eng. Miscellany, 68; Cervantes' probing of reality & psychological realism in Don Quixote, Lit. & Psychol, 68; plus one other. Add: Dept. of English, Indiana University Northwest, Gary, IN 46408.

BARRACLOUGH, ELMER DAVIES, b. Columbus, Wis, July 23, 20; m. 45. THEATRE ARTS. B.A, Beloit Col, 47; M.F.A, Cath. Univ. Am, 64. Instr. speech & drama, Univ. Md, College Park, 47-51; managing dir. community theatre, Madison Theatre Guild, Wis, 51-62; ASSOC. PROF. THEATRE ARTS, BELOIT COL, 63- U.S.A.A.F, 42-45, 2nd Lt. Am. Theatre Asn. Add: Dept. of Theatre Arts, Beloit College, Beloit, WI 53511.

BARRADA, MOHAMED AMR, b. Cairo Egypt, Oct. 9, 38. ENGLISH, LINGUISTICS. B.A, Cairo Univ, 59; M.A, Am. Univ. Cairo, 63; Ph.D.(Eng), Univ. Minn, 73. Instr. ENG, Cairo Univ, 61-62; teaching asst, Univ. Minn, 63-66, teaching assoc, 66-70; instr, WILLIAMS COL, 70-71, ASST. PROF, 71- Ling. Soc. Am. Medieval English literature; literary theory. Add: Dept. of English, Williams College, Williamstown, MA 01267.

BARRANGER, MILLY SLATER, b. Birmingham, Ala, Feb. 12, 37; m. 61; c. 1. DRAMA & LITERATURE. B.A, Univ. Montevallo, 58; M.A, Tulane Univ, 59, Ph.D.(theatre), 64. Spec. lectr. Eng, La. State Univ, New Orleans, 64-69; asst. prof. THEATRE, TULANE UNIV, 69-73, ASSOC. PROF, 73-, CHMN. DEPT, 71-, acting chmn, 71. Am. Theatre Asn; Speech Commun. Asn; Southwest Theatre Conf. Modern drama and theatre; Renaissance drama. Publ: Henrik Ibsen's major plays: Peer Gynt, A doll's house, An enemy of the people, 69 & Henrik Ibsen's major plays: Ghosts, The wild duck, Hedda Gabler, 69, Barron's; co-ed, Generations: an introduction to drama, Harcourt, 71; auth, The cankered rose: a consideration of the Jacobean tragic heroine, Col. Lang. Asn. J, 70; Ibsen's strange story in The master builder: a variation in technique, 72 & Ibsen's endgame: a reconsideration of When we dead awaken, 74, Mod. Drama; plus four others. Add: Dept. of Theatre & Speech, Tulane University, New Orleans, LA 70118.

BARRETT, ALBERTA GREGG, b. Glenarm, Md, Jan. 12, 26; m. 60; c. 1. ENGLISH. A.B, Howard Univ, 47, A.M, 48; Ph.D.(Eng. lit), Univ. Pa, 65. Substitute instr. ENG, Morgan State Col, 48-50, instr, 62-63; Bennett Col, 52; Va. State Col, 56-60, asst. prof, 60-61; assoc. prof, TENN. STATE UNIV, 64-66, PROF, 66- NCTE; Col. Lang. Asn. Renaissance through 19th century English literature. Add: Dept. of English, Tennessee State University, Nashville, TN 37203.

BARRETT, EDWARD WARE, b. Birmingham, Ala, July 3, 10; m. 39; c. 2. JOURNALISM. B.A, Princeton, 32; hon. LL.D, Bard Col, 50. Mem. publicity dept, CBS, 32-33; researcher & writer, Newsweek, 33-35, Wash. correspondent, 35-36, nat. affairs ed, 36-37, assoc. ed, 37-42, ed. dir, 46-50; asst. secy. state for pub. affairs, U.S. Dept. State, 50-52; pres, Edward W. Barrett & Assocs, New York, N.Y, 52-56; dean, Grad. Sch. Jour, Columbia Univ, 56-68; V.PRES, ACAD. EDUC. DEVELOP, INC. & DIR. COMMUN. INST, Asst. ed, Today Mag, 37; overseas news & features div, Off. War Inform, 42-45, acting deputy chief psychol. warfare, Allied Force Hqs, 43-44, exec. dir. overseas oper, 44, dir, 44-45; exec. v.pres, Hill. & Knowlton, Inc, New

York, 54-56; dir, Atlantic Counc, 57-; trustee, Correspondents' Fund, Overseas Press Club, 59-; dir, Pub. Affairs Press, 61-; consult. scholar. comt, Inter Am. Press Asn, 62-; juror, Nat. Mag. Awards, 65-; dir, Race Relat. Inform. Ctr, 69-, chmn. bd, 73-; mem, Presidential Comn. Int. Radio Broadcasting, 72- Am. Polit. Sci. Asn. Publ: Truth is our weapon, Funk, 53; ed, This is our challenge, Assoc. Col. Presses, 58 & Journalists in action, Meredith, 63; co-auth, Educational TV: who should pay?, Am. Enterprise Inst. Pub. Policy, 68. Add: Academy for Educational Development, Inc, 680 Fifth Ave, New York, NY 10019.

BARRETT, EDWIN BLOIS, b. Browns Valley, Minn, Feb. 3, 22; m. 44; c. 3. ENGLISH LITERATURE. A.B, Macalester Col, 43; A.M, Univ. Minn, 47; Danforth Found. grant, 57-58; Ph.D, Columbia Univ, 61. Instr. ENG, Hamline Univ, 46-47; HAMILTON COL, 50-52, asst. prof, 52-61, assoc. prof, 61-67, PROF, 67- U.S.A, 43-46. MLA; AAUP; Shakespeare Asn. Am. American literature; Elizabethan and Jacobean drama; Charles Dickens. Add: Dept. of English, Hamilton College, Clinton, NY 13323.

BARRETT, HAROLD, b. Healdsburg, Calif, Mar. 20, 25; m. 48; c. 5. RHETORIC. B.A, Univ. of the Pac, 49, M.A, 52; Ph.D.(rhetoric, pub. address), Univ. Ore, 62. Teacher speech & Eng, High Sch, Calif, 50-54; SPEECH, Compton Col, 54-59; instr, Univ. Ore, 59-61; asst. prof, South. Ore. Col, 61-63; from asst. prof. to PROF, CALIF. STATE UNIV, HAYWARD, 63- U.S.N, 43-46. Speech Commun. Asn; West. Speech Commun. Asn. Rhetorical criticism and theory; public address. Publ: Practical methods in speech, Holt, 59 & 68, Rinehart, 73; Scott of the Oregonian vs. Wm. Jennings Bryan, Quart. J. Speech, 62; The rhetorician and the enthymeme, South. Ore. Rev, 63; John F. Kennedy before the Greater Houston Ministerial Association, Cent. States Speech J, 11/64; The rhetoric of a possible infidel, West. Speech, winter 68. Add: 5126 Crane Ave, Castro Valley, CA 94542.

BARRETT, RALPH P, Linguistics, English Language. See Volume III, Foreign Languages, Linguistics & Philology.

BARROLL, JOHN LEEDS, III, b. Lausanne, Switz, July 20, 28; m. 51; c. 3. ENGLISH. B.A, Harvard, 50; M.A, Princeton, 55, Ph.D, 56. Teacher classics, Asheville Sch. Boys, 50-52; Eng, Riverdale Country Sch, New York, N.Y, 52-53; instr. Eng, Douglass Col, Rutgers Univ, 55-56; Univ. Tex, 56-59, asst. prof, 59-60; assoc. prof, Univ. Cincinnati, 60-64, prof, 64-68, asst. dean grad. sch, 66-67, assoc. dean, 67-68; prof. Eng, Vanderbilt Univ, 68-69; dean, Arts & Sci, William Paterson Col. N.J, 69-70; PROF. ENG, UNIV. S.C, 70-, DIR, CTR. SHAKESPEARE STUD, 72- Summer grants-in-aid, Huntington Libr, 57, 59 & Folger Shakespeare Libr, 58; vis. assoc. prof, Wash. Univ, 62; ed, Shakespeare Stud, 65-; vis. prof. Eng. lit, Univ. Newcastle, 67-68; gen. ed, S.C. Shakespeare, 71- U.S.A, 46-48. MLA; Malone Soc; Shakespeare Asn. Am.(exec. secy, 72-); Int. Asn. Univ. Prof. & Lectr; Mod. Humanities Res. Asn, Gt. Brit. Shakespeare; Elizabethan drama; 18th century English. Publ: Artificial persons, Univ. S.C, 74; The historical study of Shakespeare, Univ. Ky, 75; Gulliver and the Struldbruggs, PMLA; plus others. Add: Center for Shakespeare Studies, University of South Carolina, Columbia, SC 29208.

BARRON, LEON OSER, b. Boston, Mass, May 23, 23. ENGLISH LITERATURE. B.A, Univ. Mass, Amherst, 47; M.A, Univ. Minn, Minneapolis, 47; Ph.D.(Eng), Harvard, 60. Instr. ENG, UNIV. MASS, AMHERST, 49-52, asst. prof, 53-65, ASSOC. PROF, 65-, fel, Orchard Hill Residential Col, 64-68, master, 68-72. Teacher, Writers Workshop, Chatauqua Inst, N.Y, 59, 72; mem. ed. bd, Mass. Rev, 62- Neoclassic and modern literature; modern poetry. Publ: Poetry of Leon Barron (record), Harvard, 63; Co-ed. & ed, Masterpieces of western literature (2 vols), Brown, 66; contrib, Curious Quire (poems), Univ. Mass, 61, 67. Add: Dept. of English, University of Massachusetts, Amherst, MA 01002.

BARROWS, HERBERT C, b. Jan. 2, 14; U.S. citizen. ENGLISH. A.B, Harvard Col, 35; A.M, Harvard Univ, 36, Ph.D.(Eng), 48. Instr. ENG, UNIV. MICH, ANN ARBOR, 47-49, asst. prof, 49-55, assoc. prof, 55-64, PROF, 64- Fulbright res. fel, Italy, 53-54. U.S.A, 43-46. MLA. English travelers' experience of Italy; 18th and 19th centuries. Publ: Ed, Observations and reflections made in the course of a journey through France, Italy and Germany, Univ. Mich, 67; Convention and novelty in the romantic generation's experience of Italy, In: Literature as a mode of travel, N.Y. Pub. Libr, 63. Add: Dept. of English, Haven Hall, University of Michigan, Ann Arbor, MI 48104.

BARRS, JAMES THOMAS, Philology. See Volume III, Foreign Languages, Linguistics & Philology.

BARRY, JACKSON GRANVILLE, b. Boston, Mass, Nov. 4, 26; m. 56; c. 1. ENGLISH. B.A, Yale, 50; M.A, Columbia Univ, 51; M.F.A, West. Reserve Univ, 62, Ph.D.(drama-aesthet), 63. Instr. drama, DeCordova Mus, 53-56; Smith Col, 58-61; asst. prof. humanities, Univ. Miami, 63-64; drama, Villanova Univ, 64-67; ASSOC. PROF. theatre arts, State Univ. N.Y. Stony Brook, 67-70; ENG, UNIV. MARYLAND, COLLEGE PARK, 70- U.S.N, 45-46. Am. Soc. Aesthet; MLA; Shakespeare Soc. Am. Shakespeare; theory of literature. Publ: Dramatic structure; the shaping of experience, Univ. Calif, 70; José Quintero: the director as image maker, 3/62 & Form or formula: comic theory in Northrup Frye and Susanne Langer, 12/64, Educ. Theatre J; Shakespeare's deceptive cadence: a study in the structure of Hamlet, Shakespeare Quart, 9/73; plus one other. Add: Dept. of English, University of Maryland, College Park, MD 20742.

BARRY, JAMES DONALD, b. Oak Park, Ill, Feb. 28, 26; m. 51; c. 5. ENGLISH. Ph.B, Loyola Univ.(Ill), 48, A.M, 51; Ph.D, Northwest. Univ, 55. Teaching fel, LOYOLA UNIV. CHICAGO, 49-53, instr. ENG, 53-55, asst. prof, 55-61, assoc. prof, 61-66, PROF, 66-, CHMN. DEPT, 73- U.S.A, 44-46. MLA; Col. Eng. Asn; NCTE; Conf. Col. Compos. & Commun.(asst. chmn, 70-71, assoc. chmn, 71-72, chmn, 72-73); Dickens Soc; Conf. Eng. Educ. Victorian fiction, especially George Eliot. Publ: Co-auth, Language into literature, Sci. Res. Assoc, 65; ed, The future of the English curriculum, Mod. Lang. Asn, 67; auth, Elizabeth Gaskell; Charles Kingsley, Victorian Fiction, 64. Add: 6739 N. Newgard Ave, Chicago, IL 60626.

BARRY, M. MARTIN, O.P, b. San Francisco, Calif, Apr. 11, 03. ENGLISH. A.B, Dominican Col. San Rafael, 25; A.M, Cath. Univ. Am, 38, Ph.D, 48. PROF. ENG, DOMINICAN COL. SAN RAPHAEL, 48-, dean grad. dept, 50-72. Col. Eng. Asn. Conrad; modern poetry. Publ: Prosodic analysis of selected poems of T.S. Eliot, Cath. Univ. Am, rev. ed, 69. Add: Dept. of English, Dominican College of San Rafael, San Rafael, CA 94901.

BARTEL, ROLAND, b. Hillsboro, Kans, Feb. 17, 19; m. 43; c. 2. ENGLISH. B.A, Bethel Col, 47; Strauss fel, Ind. Univ, 50-51, Ph.D.(Eng), 51. Teacher, pub. sch, Kans, 38-41; instr. ENG, UNIV. ORE, 51-54, asst. prof, 55-59, assoc. prof. & asst. dean, Col. Lib. Arts, 59-64, PROF, 64-, HEAD DEPT, 69- Ersted Distinguished Teaching Award, 65. MLA; Philol. Asn. Pac. Coast; NCTE. English romantic literature; English education, especially, training high school English teachers. Publ: Ed, Johnson's London, 56, London in plague and fire, 57 & Liberty and terror in England: reactions to the French Revolution, 65, Heath; auth, Public fast days in England, Anglican Theol. Rev; Byron's respect for language, Papers Eng. Lang. & Lit, autumn 65; Proportioning in fiction, Eng. J, 4/67. Add: 2660 Baker Blvd, Eugene, OR 97403.

BARTER, ALICE KNAR, b. Sivas, Turkey, Nov. 11, 18; U.S. citizen; div; c. 1. ENGLISH EDUCATION. B.A, East. Mich. Univ, 39; M.A, Univ. Mich, 44; Ph.D.(educ), 57. Teacher Eng, Mich. schs, 39-55; asst. prof. educ, Univ. Detroit, 57-60; from asst. prof. to assoc. prof. educ. & Eng, Miami Univ, 60-67; PROF. ENG, CHICAGO STATE UNIV, 67- NCTE; Nat. Soc. Stud. Educ; Midwest Mod. Lang. Asn. Spelling and grammar; reading abilities of prospective teachers; status of women in school administration. Publ: Status of women in school administration, Educ. Horizons, spring 59 & Educ. Digest, Oct. 59; co-auth, Reading improvement and the prospective teacher, Peabody J, 3/65; auth, The provisional teacher, Ill. Sch. J, fall 69. Add: Dept. of English, Chicago State University, 95th & King Dr, Chicago, IL 60628.

BARTH, JOHN ROBERT, S.J, b. Buffalo, N.Y, Feb. 23, 31. ENGLISH. A.B, Fordham Univ, 54, M.A, 56; Ph.L, Bellarmine Col.(N.Y), 55; S.T.L, Woodstock Col, 62; Ph.D.(Eng), Harvard, 67. Asst. prof. ENG, Canisius Col, 67-70; Harvard, 70-74, fac. res. grant, 73-74; ASSOC. PROF, UNIV. MO-COLUMBIA, 74- Dexter travelling fel. from Harvard, summer 67; Nat. Endowment for Humanities summer stipend, 69; Am. Counc. Learned Soc. grant, summer 70. Howard Mumford Jones Prize, Harvard, 67. MLA; Mod. Humanities Res. Asn; Eng. Inst; AAUP. Romantic and Victorian literature; S.T. Coleridge; literature and theology. Publ: Coleridge and Christian doctrine, Harvard Univ, 69; ed, Religious perspectives in Faulkner's fiction: Yoknapatawpha and beyond, Univ. Notre Dame, 72; auth, T.S. Eliot's image of man: thematic study of his drama, Renascence, spring 62; Symbol as sacrament in Coleridge's thought, Stud. Romanticism, fall 72; A newer criticism in America: the religious dimension, Harvard Eng. Stud. 4, 73; plus others. Add: Dept. of English, 231 Arts & Science, University of Missouri-Columbia, Columbia, MO 65201.

BARTH, JOHN SIMMONS, b. Cambridge, Md, May 27, 30; m. 50; c. 3. ENGLISH. B.A, Johns Hopkins Univ, 51, M.A, 52; hon. Litt.D, Univ. Md, 69; hon. L.H.D, West. Md. Col, 73. Jr. instr. writing, Johns Hopkins Univ, 51-53; instr. Eng, Pa. State Univ, 53-57, asst. prof, 57-61, assoc. prof, 61-65; PROF, State Univ. N.Y. Buffalo, 65-73; ENG. & CREATIVE WRITING, JOHNS HOPKINS UNIV, 73- Rockefeller Found. grant fiction-writing, 65-66; Nat. Inst. Arts & Lett. grant lit, 66. Brandeis Univ. Creative Arts Citation Fiction, 65; Nat. Bk. Award Fiction, 73. Fiction writing. Publ: The floating opera, Appleton, 56; The end of the road, 58, The sot-weed factor, 60, Giles goat-boy, 66 & Lost in the funhouse, 68, Doubleday; Chimera, Random, 72. Add: Writing Seminars, Johns Hopkins University, Baltimore, MD 21218.

BARTH, LEWIS M, b. Los Angeles, Calif, Apr. 21, 38; m. 62; c. 2. MIDRASHIC LITERATURE. B.A, Univ. Calif, Los Angeles, 59; B.H.L, Hebrew Union Col.(Calif), 60; M.A, Hebrew Union Col.(Ohio), 64, fel, 67-68, Ph.D. (Midrash), 70; M.A, Univ. Chicago, 65. Instr. MIDRASH & RELATED LIT, Hebrew Union Col.(Ohio), 68-69; asst. prof, HEBREW UNION COL.(CALIF), 69-72, ASSOC. PROF, 72-, DEAN, 71-, asst. dean, 70-71, acting dean, 71. Am. Acad. Relig; AAUP; Asn. Jewish Stud; Cent. Conf. Am. Rabbis; Soc. Bibl. Lit. Midrashic literature and manuscript; apocrypha and pseudepigrapha; Jewish history Rabbinic period. Publ: An analysis of Vatican 30, Hebrew Union Col, 73. Add: Office of Dean, 3077 University Mall, Hebrew Union College-Jewish Institute of Religion, Los Angeles, CA 90007.

BARTLETT, LYNN CONANT, b. Bethlehem, Pa, Dec. 14, 21; m. 46. ENGLISH. B.A, Lehigh Univ, 43; A.M, Harvard, 47, Ph.D.(Eng), 57; B.Litt, Oxford, 52. Instr. ENG, Lehigh Univ, 46; teaching fel, Harvard, 48-50; instr, VASSAR COL, 52-57, asst. prof, 57-62, assoc. prof, 62-70, PROF, 70-, SECY. COL, 66-, asst. dean, 58-61, fac. fel, 61-62. George Moore; history of the short story; 19th century English and American literature. Publ: Co-ed, The English novel: background readings, Lippincott, 67. Add: Office of the Secretary, Vassar College, Poughkeepsie, NY 12601.

BARTON, FRED JACKSON, b. Lynn, Ala, Oct. 7, 11; m. 41; c. 2. SPEECH. B.A, Abilene Christian Col, 37; M.A, Univ. Iowa, 39, Ph.D, 49. Teacher, pub. schs, Ala, 33-35; Tex, 37-38; from instr. to PROF. SPEECH, ABILENE CHRISTIAN COL, 38-, DEAN RES, 72-, head dept. speech, 46-57, dean, Grad. Sch, 57-72. U.S.A.A.F, 41-46, Lt. Col. Speech Commun. Asn; South. Speech Asn; Am. Acad. Relig. Homiletics and preaching. Publ: Co-auth, American public address, Univ. Mo, 61. Add: 681 College Dr, Abilene, TX 79601.

BARTON, JAMES GABRIEL, b. Ayr, Nebr, Oct. 31, 14; m; c. 2. THEATRE, SPEECH. B.F.A, Nebr. State Col, Kearney, 39; M.A, Univ. Mich, 40. Instr. SPEECH & THEATRE, Baylor Univ, 40; Sterling Col, 40; Univ. Kans, 40-42; from instr. to asst. prof, Okla. Agr & Mech. Col, 42-47; dir. theatre & assoc. prof, SOUTHWEST TEX. STATE UNIV, 47-67, PROF, 67- U.S.N, 44-46, Lt.(jg). Am. Theatre Asn; Am. Speech Asn; Southwest Theatre Conf. (pres, 69). Add: Dept. of Speech & Drama, Southwest Texas State University, San Marcos, TX 78666.

BARTON, LUCY (ADALADE), b. Ogden, Utah, Sept. 26, 91. THEATRE ARTS. B.A, Carnegie Inst. Technol, 17; M.A, N.Y. Univ, 43. Mem. fac. hist. of costume & stage costume design, State Univ. Iowa, 29-30; head dept. drama, Univ. Ariz, 42-45; assoc. prof. DRAMA, UNIV. TEX, AUSTIN, 45-61, EMER. PROF, 61- Consult, Carnegie Study in Am. Art, 56; Southwest Theatre Conf. Annual Award, 57; Carnegie Inst. Technol. Alumni Fed. Award of Merit, 61. Am. Theatre Asn.(Eaves Senior Award, 60). Costume in the court spectacles of the Renaissance; regional dress in America; art history. Publ: Historic costume for the stage; Costuming the Biblical play; Costumes by you; Appreciating costume, Baker Co, 69; Why not costume Shakespeare according to Shakespeare, Educ. Theatre J. Add: Drama Bldg, University of Texas at Austin, Austin, TX 78712.

BARTON, MIKE ALAN, b. Wichita, Kans, Sept. 30, 40; m. 64; c. 1. THEATRE HISTORY, DRAMATIC LITERATURE. B.A, Kans. State Teachers Col, 61, M.S, 66; Ph.D.(theatre hist), Ind. Univ, 71. Prof. actor, New York, N.Y, 61-62; instr. speech, Kans. State Teachers Col, 65-66; THEATRE, Univ. Omaha, 66-68; asst, Ind. Univ, Bloomington, 68-71; ASST. PROF, DRAKE UNIV, 71- U.S.A, 62-64. Nineteenth century theatre history; film history. Publ: Silent films; high camp or genuine art, Advance, 11/72. Add: Dept. of Theatre Arts, Drake University, 25th & University, Des Moines, IA 50311.

BARTOS, MICHAEL WILLIAM, b. Chicago, Ill, Sept. 24, 30; m. 56; c. 7. ENGLISH, LITERATURE. Ph.B, DePaul Univ, 55, M.Ed, 59; M.A, Northwest. Univ, 63; NDEA grant, Univ. Chicago, 68. Teacher Latin, Notre Dame High Sch. Boys, Ill, 56-58; ENG, E.Leyden High Sch, 58-59; W.Leyden High Sch, 59-67; ASSOC. PROF, WILLIAM RAINEY HARPER COL, 67- Mem. bd. educ, Maine Twp. High Sch. Dist, 70-73; part-time teacher, DePaul Univ, Maine Twp. High Sch, Triton Col. MLA; NCTE; Col. Eng. Asn. Teenagers with heart, Ill. Educ, 1/66. Add: Div. of Communication, William Rainey Harper College, Roselle & Algonquin Rds, Palatine, IL 60067.

BARUSHOK, JAMES WILLIAM, b. Chicago, Ill, Feb. 26, 29; m. 52; c. 3. SPEECH, DRAMA. B.S, Northwest. Univ, 51, M.A, 52; Ph.D.(theatre), Mich. State, 66. Instr. SPEECH, Wright Jr. Col, 54-56; Univ. Maine, 56-59, asst. prof, 59-62, assoc. prof, 62-68; CHMN. DEPT, NORTHEAST. ILL. UNIV, 68- Maine fine arts rep, New Eng. Ctr. Continuing Educ, 66-68. U.S.A, 53-54. Speech Commun. Asn; Am. Educ. Theatre Asn; Am. Acad. Polit. & Soc. Sci. History of theatre; sociology of the community theatre; dramatic theory. Publ: Lost prodigy: community theatre, Players, 9/69. Add: Dept. of Speech, Northeastern Illinois University, Chicago, IL 60625.

BARZAK, ROBERT WILLIAM, b. Waco, Tex, June 17, 28; m. 50; c. 4. ENGLISH. B.A, Agr. & Mech. Col. Tex, 49; M.A, Univ. Ill, 51, Ph.D, 59. Asst. Univ. Ill, 49-55; instr. ENG, TEX. A&M UNIV, 55-58, asst. prof, 58-62, ASSOC. PROF, 62- Renaissance Soc. Am. Elizabethan drama; 16th century literature; Chaucer. Add: Dept. of English, Texas A&M University, College Station, TX 77843.

BARZUN, JACQUES, History. See Volume I, History.

BASCOM, MARION, R.S.C.J, b. St. Louis, Mo, Apr. 11, 03. ENGLISH. A.B, Maryville Col.(Mo), 25; A.M, Wash. Univ, 26; B.A, Oxford, 37, M.A, 40. Instr. ENG, MARYVILLE COL.(MO), 30-37, asst. prof, 37-42, assoc. prof, 42-48, prof, 48-71, chmn. honors prog, 39-71, EMER. PROF, 71- Libr. staff, Maryville Col.(Mo), 71-73; asst. archivist, Soc. Sacred Heart, 72- MLA; NCTE; Col. Eng. Asn; Cath. Renascence Soc. Publ: Blessed Rose Philippine Duchesne, Manhattanville Col, 46. Add: 13550 Conway Rd, St. Louis, MO 63141.

BASH, JAMES RICHARD, b. Ft. Wayne, Ind, June 12, 15; m. 41; c. 2. ENGLISH. A.B, Ind. State Teachers Col, 37, M.A, 40; Ph.D.(Eng), Univ. Ill, 54. From instr. to PROF. ENG, IND. STATE UNIV, TERRE HAUTE, 40- Dir, U.S. Agency Int. Develop. Eng. Prog, Rabat, Morocco, 61-63. U.S.N.R, 42-45, Lt. MLA; Midwest Eng. Conf. Contemporary American literature; literature of protest. Publ: Willa Cather: a study in primitivism. Add: 152 Monterey St, Terre Haute, IN 47803.

BASKERVILLE, BARNET, b. Strasburg, Pa, Sept. 14, 16; m. 42; c. 2. SPEECH. A.B, Univ. Wash, 40, A.M, 44; Ph.D, Northwest. Univ, 48. Asst. prof. SPEECH, UNIV. WASH, 48-54, assoc. prof, 54-60, PROF, 60-, CHMN. DEPT, 64-, dir. honors, Col. Arts & Sci, 61-64. Fund Advan. Educ. fel, Harvard, 55-56. Sig.C, U.S.A, 42-46. Speech Commun. Asn. Rhetoric; history and criticism of American public address. Publ: Co-auth, American forum, 60 & Contemporary forum, 62, Harper; Some American critics of public address: 1850-1900, Speech Monogr, 3/50; The dramatic criticism of oratory, Quart. J. Speech, 2/59; Joe McCarthy, brief-case demogogue, In: The rhetoric of the speaker, D.C. Heath, 67. Add: Dept. of Speech, University of Washington, Seattle, WA 98105.

BASKERVILLE, EDWARD J, b. Paterson, N.J, Oct. 7, 27; m. 56; c. 1. ENGLISH LANGUAGE & LITERATURE. B.S, Lehigh Univ, 50; M.A, Columbia Univ, 53, Ph.D.(Eng, hist), 67; Univ. London, 59-60. From instr. to asst. prof. ENG, GETTYSBURG COL, 56-68, assoc. prof, 68-73, PROF, 73- Nat. Endowment for Humanities younger scholar fel, 69. U.S.A.F, 46-47, 50-51, Sgt. Renaissance Soc. Am; Mediaeval Acad. Am; Soc. Stud. Mediaeval Lang. & Lit; Conf. Brit. Stud. English Renaissance literature and history; mediaeval literature and history; polemic and propaganda during Edwardian and Marian reigns, 1547-1558. Add: Dept. of English, Gettysburg College, Gettysburg, PA 17325.

BASKETT, HELEN WHEELER, b. Lamar, Mo, July 21, 09; m. 54. ENGLISH. B.S. in Ed, Southwest Mo. State Col, 31; summers, Univ. Colo; M.A, Univ. Mo, 43. Teacher ENG, Trenton Jr. Col, 43-45; instr, Univ. Mo, 45-48; from asst. prof. to ASSOC. PROF, CENT. METHODIST COL, 48- NCTE; Midwest Mod. Lang. Asn. Early literature of the United States of America. Add: Dept. of English, Central Methodist College, Fayette, MO 65248.

BASKETT, SAM S, b. Fayette, Mo, Apr. 4, 21; m. 53; c. 3. AMERICAN LITERATURE. A.B, Cent. Col.(Mo), 41; M.A, Univ. Calif, Berkeley, 48, Ph.D, 51. Asst. prof, ENG, Cent. Mo. State Col, 51-53; instr, MICH. STATE UNIV, 53-57, asst. prof, 57-61, assoc. prof, 61-65, PROF, 65-, exec. asst, 60-66, acting chmn. dept, 66-67, v.chmn, 67-69. Fulbright prof, Nat. Univ. Mex, 64; Hacettepe Univ, Turkey, 70-71. U.S.N.R, 42-46, Lt. MLA; Am. Stud. Asn. Nineteenth and twentieth century American literature. Publ: Ed, Martin Eden, Holt, 56; co-ed, The American identity, Heath, 62. Add: Dept. of English, Michigan State University, East Lansing, MI 48823.

BASKETTE, FLOYD KENNETH, b. Chama, N.Mex, July 2, 10. JOURNALISM. B.J, Univ. Mo, 32, A.M, 36; Univ. Wis, 38-39, 44-45. Asst. prof. social stud, Adams State Col, 32-38; asst. JOUR, Univ. Wis, 38-39; asst. prof, Syracuse Univ, 40-41; assoc. prof, Emory Univ, 41-50; from assoc. prof. to PROF, UNIV. COLO, BOULDER, 50- Lectr, Univ. Wis, 44-45; assoc. ed, Jour. Quart, 45-48; dir. dept. jour, Hislop Col, India, 53-54; dir, Jour. Training Ctr, Univ. Rangoon, Burma, 59-60. Counc. Radio-TV Jour.(pres, 49-). American journalism; journalism in the Methodist Church. Publ: Colorado place name pronunciation guide; co-auth, Editing the days news, 4th ed; co-auth, The art of editing, Macmillan, 71. Add: School of Journalism, University of Colorado, Boulder, CO 80302.

BASS, EBEN E, b. Willimantic, Conn, June 12, 24; m. 57. ENGLISH. B.A, Univ. Conn, 48, M.A, 50; Ph.D.(Eng), Univ. Pittsburgh, 61. Asst. instr. ENG, Ohio State Univ, 54-56; asst. prof, Geneva Col, 56-62, assoc. prof, 62-65, prof, 65-72, PROF. & CHMN. DEPT, SLIPPERY ROCK STATE COL, 72- MLA; NCTE. Henry James and modern novel; English Romantic and Victorian writers. Publ: Dramatic scene and The awkward age, PMLA, 3/64; The verbal failure of Lord Jim, Col. Eng, 3/65; The fourth element in Ode to the west wind, Papers on Lang. & Lit, fall 67. Add: Dept. of English, Slippery Rock State College, Slippery Rock, PA 16051.

BASS, WILLIAM WILSON, b. McMinnville, Tenn, July 7, 08; m. 38; c. 2. ENGLISH. B.S, Univ. Tenn, 31, A.M, 33, Ph.D, Univ. N.C, 54. Teaching fel, Univ. Tenn, 31-34; assoc. prof. ENG, CARSON-NEWMAN COL, 34-55, prof, 55-73, head dept, 56-73, EMER. PROF, 73- S.Atlantic Mod. Lang. Asn. Add: 108 W. Ellis St, Jefferson City, TN 37760.

BASSAN, MAURICE, b. New York, N.Y, Apr. 22, 29; m. 60; c. 2. AMERICAN LITERATURE. B.A, New York Univ, 51, M.A, 52; Ph.D, Univ. Calif, Berkeley, 61. Instr. ENG, Univ. Ariz, 58-60; Univ. N.C, 61-63; asst. prof, SAN FRANCISCO STATE UNIV, 63-67, assoc. prof, 67-72, PROF, 72- Lectr, Univ. Calif, Exten, Japan, 53-54; asst, Univ. Calif, Berkeley, 55-58; Fulbright lectr, Univ. Valladolid, 67-68. U.S.A, 52-54, Res, 54- MLA; Am. Stud. Asn. Stephen Crane; late 19th century American fiction; American poetic traditions. Publ: Ed, Stephen Crane's Maggie: text and context, Wadsworth, 66 & Stephen Crane: a collection of critical essays, Prentice-Hall, 67; auth, Hawthorne's son, Ohio State Univ, 69; Chaucer's Cursed monk, Mediaeval Stud, 62; Flannery O'Connor's way, Renascence, 63; Some new perspectives on Stephen Crane's fiction, Studia Neophilologica, 63. Add: Dept. of English, San Francisco State University, San Francisco, CA 94132.

BASSEIN, BETH ANN, b. North Kansas City, Mo, Mar. 22, 25; m. 57; c. 2. ENGLISH LITERATURE. B.A, Tarkio Col, 47; M.A, Univ. Mo, 52, Ph.D. (Eng), 61. Instr. ENG, Cent. Col.(Iowa), 53-54; Univ. Mo, 54-58; ASSOC. PROF, SOUTH. COLO. STATE COL, 66- Hon. fel, Univ. Wis-Madison, 72-73. Social problems reflected in novels of 18th century England; Milton; 19th century rationalism as reflected in literature. Add: Dept. of English, Southern Colorado State College, Pueblo, CO 81001.

BASSETT, ABRAHAM,JOSEPH; b. W.Va, Sept. 27, 30; m. 59; c. 2. THEATRE. B.A, Bowling Green State Univ, 52; M.A, Ohio State Univ, 57, Ph.D, 62. Asst. prof. speech & dir. broadcasting, Cent. Mo. State Col, 60-63; dir. theatre, William Woods Col, 63-64; asst. prof. & dir. theatre, Pac. Lutheran Univ, 64-68; prof. speech & theatre arts & chmn. div, Dickinson State Col, 68-70; PROF. THEATRE & CHMN. DEPT. THEATRE ARTS, WRIGHT STATE UNIV, 70- U.S.A, 52-54. Speech Commun. Asn; Am. Theatre Asn. Acting; theatre administration; theatre history. Publ: The capitol scene in Julius Caesar, 59 & William C. Macready's contributions to the modern theatre, 67, Ohio State Univ. Theatre Collection Bull. Add: 4085 Danern Dr, Dayton, OH 45430.

BASSETT, CHARLES WALKER, b. Aberdeen, S.Dak, July 7, 32; m. 56; c. 2. ENGLISH, AMERICAN LITERATURE. A.B, Univ. S.Dak, 54, M.A, 56; S.L. Whitcomb fel, Univ. Kans, 61-62, univ. fel, 62-63, Ph.D.(Eng), 64. Instr. ENG, Univ. Pa, 64-66, asst. prof, 66-69; asst. prof, COLBY COL, 69-74, DIR. AM. STUD, 70- Summer res. fel, Univ. Pa, 67, fac. res. grant, 68; summer humanities grants, Colby Col, 70, 71 & 73. U.S.A, 56-58, Capt. Am. Stud. Asn.(asst. exec. secy, 67-69); MLA; Popular Cult. Asn; AAUP. Popular culture—American studies; American satire. Publ: American studies programs in the U.S.—a survey, Am. Quart, summers 67-73; Katahdin, Wachusett, and Kilimanjaro: the symbolic mountains of Thoreau and Hemingway, Thoreau J, 4/71; plus three others. Add: Dept. of English, Colby College, Waterville, ME 04901.

BASSETT, CLYDE H, b. Purcell, Okla, Oct. 5, 30; m. 57; c. 3. THEATRE. B.F.A, Univ. Okla, 52; M.A, N.Y. Univ, 60; Ph.D.(theatre), Univ. Wis, 65. Asst. prof. THEATRE, Lesley Col, 62-66; PROF, CENT. CONN. STATE COL, 66-, CHMN. DEPT, 69- U.S.A, 52-54, Res, 54-60, 1st Lt. Am. Theatre Asn. Theatre management; American theatre; acting and directing. Add: Dept. of Theatre, Central Connecticut State College, New Britain, CT 06050.

BASSETT, JOHN EARL, b. Washington, D.C, May 12, 42; m. 64; c. 2. AMERICAN LITERATURE. B.A, Ohio Wesleyan Univ, 63, M.A, 66; Ph.D.(Eng), Univ. Rochester, 70. Instr. ENG, Univ. Rochester, 69-70; ASST. PROF, WAYNE STATE UNIV, 70- MLA; Orgn. Am. Hist. Publ: William Faulkner: an annotated checklist of criticism, David Lewis, 72; William Faulkner: the critical heritage, Routledge & Kegan Paul, London, 74. Add: Dept. of English, Wayne State University, Detroit, MI 48202.

BASSETT, SHARON MARIE, b. Red Creek, N.Y, Dec. 28, 41. NINETEENTH & TWENTIETH CENTURY LITERATURE. B.A, Elmira Col, 64; scholarship, London Sch. Econ, 62-63; M.A, Univ. Rochester, 66, fel. & Ph.D.(Eng), 72. Asst. prof. ENG, CALIF. STATE UNIV, LOS ANGELES, 67-73, ASSOC.

PROF, 73- MLA. Walter Pater; psychoanalysis and literature; criticism. Publ: Pater and Freud on Leonardo, Lit. & Psychol, summer 73. Add: Dept. of English, California State University, Los Angeles, 5151 State University Dr, Los Angeles, CA 90032.

BATAILLE, ROBERT RAYMOND, b. Newark, N.J, Sept. 13, 40; m. 72; c. 2. BRITISH LITERATURE. B.A, Rutgers Univ, 62; M.A, Univ. Kans, 65, Ph.D. (Eng. lit), 70. Asst. prof. ENG, IOWA STATE UNIV, 69-72, ASSOC. PROF, 72- Midwest Mod. Lang. Asn; MLA; AAUP. General satire and 18th century literature American agrarians. Add: Dept. of English, 421 Ross Hall, Iowa State University, Ames, IA 50010.

BATCHELLER, DAVID R, b. Buffalo, N.Y, Aug. 4, 30; m. 54; c. 1. DRAMA. A.B, Col. Wooster, 54; A.M, Univ. Ill, Urbana, 55; Ph.D.(theatre), Ohio State Univ, 61. Instr. speech & theatre, Col. Wooster, 57-61, asst. prof, 61-62, ASSOC. PROF, N.C. Wesleyan Col, 63-67; DRAMA, UNIV. N.C, GREENSBORO, 67-, DIR. THEATRE, 68-, DIR, DRAMA DIV, 70- U.S.A, 52-54. Am. Educ. Theatre Asn; Speech Commun. Asn; U.S. Inst. Theatre Technol. Publ: 16mm films for use in teaching drama and theatre, Am. Educ. Theatre Asn, 67; Designing with levels, Player's Mag, 5/61; Status of the technical director in American education theatre, Quart. J. Speech, 12/62; A colorimetric study of stage lighting filters, Theatre Design & Technol, 10/72. Add: Dept. of Drama & Speech, University of North Carolina at Greensboro, Greensboro, NC 27412.

BATCHELLER, JOSEPH DONALD, b. Portland, Maine, Mar. 7, 15; m. 37; c. 2. SPEECH. A.B, Carnegie Inst. Technol, 36; A.M, Univ. Minn, 38, Ph.D, 42. Tech. asst, Univ. Minn, 36-37, teaching asst, 38-39; instr. speech educ, Occidental Col, 39-41; dramatics, Ohio Univ, 41-44; asst. prof. SPEECH, UNIV. N.H, 44-50, ASSOC. PROF, 50-, chmn. dept. speech & drama, 60-72. Am. Theatre Asn; Am. Nat. Theatre & Acad; New Eng. Theatre Conf.(pres, 56); Speech Commun. Asn; New Eng. Speech Commun. Asn. American theatre; David Belasco. Add: Dept. of Speech & Drama, University of New Hampshire, Durham, NH 03824.

BATE, WALTER JACKSON, b. Mankato, Minn, May 22, 18. ENGLISH. A.B, Harvard, 39, A.M, 40, Ph.D, 42; Litt.D, Ind. Univ, 69, Merrimac Col, 70, Univ. Chicago, 73; L.H.D, Boston Col, 71. Asst. prof. Eng, HARVARD, 46-49, assoc. prof, 49-56, prof, 56-62, LOWELL PROF. HUMANITIES, 62- Christian Gauss Prizes, 56, 64 & 70; Putitzer Prize, 64; Harvard Faculty Prize, 64. Am. Acad. Arts & Sci; Am. Philos. Soc. Eighteenth and 19th century English literature. Publ: Negative capability, 39, From classic to romantic, 46, John Keats, 63 & The burden of the past and the English poet, 70, Harvard; Criticism: major texts, Harcourt, 52; Achievement of Samuel Johnson, Oxford, 55; Prefaces to criticism, Doubleday, 59; Yale edition of Johnson, Vols. 2-5, Yale, 60-68; Coleridge, Macmillan, 68. Add: 3 Warren House, Harvard University, Cambridge, MA 02138.

BATEMAN, JAMES LaVAR, b. West Jordan, Utah, June 6, 20; m. 45; c. 5. SPEECH. B.A, Brigham Young Univ, 41; M.S, Univ. Wis, 47, Ph.D, 50. Asst. prof. SPEECH, BRIGHAM YOUNG UNIV, 49-54, assoc. prof, 54-58, PROF, 59- Vis. prof, Territorial Col. Guam, 54-56; vis. prof, Mich. State Univ, 58; George Washington Univ, 59; asst. to Utah senator, Wash, D.C, 59; prof, Col. V.I, 66-67. U.S.N.R, 41-46, Lt. Speech Commun. Asn; West. Speech Commun. Asn. General speech; public address. Publ: Speaking in the Mormon missionary system. Add: Dept. of Speech, Brigham Young University, Provo, UT 84601.

BATES, ALLAN, b. Cleveland, Ohio, May 20, 29; m. 65; c. 5. ENGLISH. B.A, Ohio Wesleyan, 51; M.A, Univ. Chicago, 55, Ph.D.(Eng), 68. Instr. ENG, Lake Forest Col, 57-62; asst. prof, Chicago State Col, 62-68; ASSOC. PROF, NORTHEAST. ILL. STATE UNIV, 68- Mark Twain. Publ: The Quintus Curtius Snodgrass letters: a clarification of the Mark Twain canon, 3/64 & Sam Clemens pilot—humorist of a tramp steamboat, 3/67, Am. Lit. Add: Dept. of English, Northeastern Illinois University, 5500 St. Louis Ave, Chicago, IL 60625.

BATES, ARTHENIA JACKSON, b. Sumter, S.C, June 1, 20; m. 50. AMERICAN & ENGLISH LITERATURE, COMPOSITION. A.B, Morris Col, 41; M.A, Atlanta Univ, 48; South. Fel. Fund grant, La. State Univ, 67-68, Ph.D.(Eng), 72. Instr. Eng, Westside High Sch, Kershaw, S.C, 42-44; civics, Butler High Sch, Hartsville, 45-46; chmn. dept. ENG, Morris Col, 47-49; instr, Mary Bethune High Sch, Halifax, Va, 49-55; Miss. Voc. Col, 55-56; SOUTH. UNIV, 56-59, asst. prof, 59-64, assoc. prof, 64-72, PROF, 72- Col. Lang. Asn; NCTE; Conf. Col. Comp. & Commun. Negro American literature, especially James Welson Johnson. Publ: Seeds beneath the snow, Greenwich, 69; The deity nodded, Harlo, 73; Wake me mama (short story), In: Black World, 7/71; Metamorphosis (poem), In: National Poetry Anthology, 72; The second stone (short story), In: The last cookie, 72; plus others. Add: P.O. Box 9267, Southern University, Baton Rouge, LA 70813.

BATES, PAUL ALLEN, b. Sioux City, Iowa, June 22, 20; m. 41; c. 4. ENGLISH. B.A, State Univ. Iowa, 41; fel. & M.A, Univ. Mich, 48; Ph.D.(Eng), Univ. Kans, 55. Teaching fel. ENG, Univ. Mich, 47-48; instr, Univ. Kans, 49-55; from asst. prof. to prof, Colo. State Univ, 55-68; chmn. dept, Pershing Col, 68-71; PROF, COLO. STATE UNIV, 71- Summer grant-in-aid, Folger Shakespeare Libr, 56; Colo. State Univ. Res. Found. grant-in-aid, Bodleian Libr, Oxford, 64-65; vis. prof, Univ. Kans, summer 66. U.S.A.A.F, 43-45. MLA; Renaissance Soc. Am; Am. Fed. Teachers. Renaissance poetry; Shakespeare. Publ: Faust: sources, works and criticism, Harcourt, 68; Shakespeare's portrayal of women, Eleusis, 11/66; Shakespeare's sonnets in relation to pastoral poetry, Shakespeare Jahrbuch, 67. Add: 609 Duke Lane, Ft. Collins, CO 80521.

BATES, RONALD GORDON NUDELL, b. Regina, Sask, Apr. 3, 24; m. 48; c. 3. ENGLISH. B.A, Univ. Toronto, 48, M.A, 49, Ph.D, 60. Lectr. ENG, Univ. Uppsala, Sweden, 51-54; instr, Univ. Col, Univ. Toronto, 54-56; lectr, Univ. Col, UNIV. WEST. ONT, 56-59, asst. prof, 59-60, Middlesex Col, 60-65, assoc. prof, UNIV. COL, 65-69, PROF, 69- Can. Army, 43-45, Sgt. Humanities Asn. Can.(pres, London br, 68-69); Asn. Promotion Scand. Stud. Modern literature; literary criticism; theory of poetry and translation. Publ: The wandering world, Macmillan, Can, 59; Changes, Macmillan, 68; Northrop Frye, McClelland & Stewart, 72; A topic in The waste land, Wis. Stud. Contemporary Lit, 64; The feast is a flyday, James Joyce Quart, 65; Downdolphinry, Univ. Toronto Quart, 67. Add: Dept. of English, University College, University of Western Ontario, London, Ont, Can.

BATES, STEVEN LATIMER, b. Midland, Tex, Feb. 22, 40. ENGLISH & AMERICAN LITERATURE. B.A, Dartmouth Col, 61; M.A, Univ. Minn, 64; Ph.D.(Eng), Princeton, 71. ASST. PROF. ENG, UNIV. CALIF, LOS ANGELES, 69- MLA; Renaissance Soc. Am; Milton Soc. Am. Renaissance English literature. Add: Dept. of English, University of California, Los Angeles, CA 90024.

BATTAGLIA, FRANCIS JOSEPH, b. Yeadon, Pa, Dec. 18, 41; m. 63; c. 2. ENGLISH, AMERICAN LITERATURE. B.A, La Salle Col, 63, Woodrow Wilson fel, James B. Duke fel. & M.A, 64; Ph.D.(Eng), Univ. Calif, Davis, 66. Asst. prof. Eng, Univ. Wis-Madison, 66-72, ASSOC. PROF. ENG. & SPEECH, STATEN ISLAND COMMUNITY COL, 72- Mem. Am. lit. group, MLA. Midwest Mod. Lang. Asn; MLA. Contemporary literature; old English. Publ: Anglo-Saxon chronical for 755: the missing evidence for a traditional reading, 6/66 & The house of the seven gables: new light on old problems, 12/67, PMLA; Spurious Armageddon: Joyce Cary's Not honour more, Mod. Fiction Stud, winter 67-68. Add: Dept. of English & Speech, Staten Island Community College, Staten Island, NY 10301.

BATTEN, CHARLES LINWOOD, JR, b. Norfolk, Va, Dec. 31, 42; m. 72. EIGHTEENTH CENTURY ENGLISH LITERATURE. B.A, Univ. Va, 65; A.M, Univ. Chicago, 66, Ph.D.(Eng), 71. ASST. PROF. ENG, UNIV. CALIF, LOS ANGELES, 69- MLA; Am. Soc. 18th Century Stud. Eighteenth century non-fiction travel literature; Restoration and 18th century poetry, drama and novel. Publ: Philip Freneau's newly discovered poem on the death of General Moreau, Am. Lit, 72. Add: Dept. of English, University of California, 405 Hilgard Ave, Los Angeles, CA 90024.

BATTENHOUSE, ROY WESLEY, b. Nevinville, Iowa, Apr. 9, 12; m. 52; c. 1. ENGLISH LITERATURE. A.B, Albion Col, 33; B.D, Yale, 36, Ph.D, 38; hon. Litt.D, Ripon Col, 64, St. Michael's Col, 74. Instr. Eng, Ohio State Univ, 38-40; asst. prof. church hist, Vanderbilt Univ, 40-43, assoc. prof, 43-46; Episcopal Theol. Sch, 46-49; res, Folger Libr, 49-50; assoc. prof. ENG, IND. UNIV, BLOOMINGTON, 50-56, PROF, 56- Vis. prof, Berkeley Divinity Sch, 48; N.Y. Univ, 53; Ford fel, Princeton, 54-55; Guggenheim fel, 58-59; vis. prof, Univ, 53; Ford fel, Princeton, 54-55; Guggenheim fel, 58-59; vis. prof, Univ. West. Ont, 63-64; Univ. Notre Dame, 68; Univ. Wash, 74; mem. ed. bd, Shakespeare Stud, 65- Shakespeare Soc. Am; MLA; Soc. Relig. Higher Educ; Renaissance Soc. Am. Shakespeare; Elizabethan literature; history of Christian thought. Publ: Ed, A companion to the study of St. Augustine, Oxford, 55; auth, Marlowe's Tamburlaine, Vanderbilt Univ, 64; Shakespearean tragedy, Ind. Univ, 69. Add: 1216 E. Second St, Bloomington, IN 47401.

BATTERSBY, JAMES L, b. Pawtucket, R.I, Aug. 24, 36; m. 57; c. 1. EIGHTEENTH CENTURY ENGLISH LITERATURE. B.S.Ed, Univ. Vt, 61; Woodrow Wilson fels, 61-62 & 64-65, M.A, 62, Samuel S. Fels fel, 64-65, Ph.D. (Eng. lit), 65. Asst. prof. ENG. LIT, Univ. Calif, Berkeley, 65-70, summer fac. fel, 66; ASSOC. PROF, OHIO STATE UNIV, 70- U.S.A, 54-57. MLA; Am. Soc. 18th Century Stud. Samuel Johnson; 18th century literature; modern critical theory. Publ: Patterns of significant action in Samuel Johnson's Life of Addison, Genre, 1/69; Johnson and Shiels; biographers of Addison, Stud. Eng. Lit, summer 69; Typical folly: evaluating student performance in higher education, Nat. Counc. Teachers Eng, 73; plus other articles on 18th century lit. Add: Dept. of English, Ohio State University, 164,W. 17th Ave, Columbus, OH 43210.

BATTESTIN, MARTIN CAREY, b. New York, N.Y, Mar. 25, 30; m. 52, 63; c. 2. ENGLISH LITERATURE. B.A, Princeton, 52, univ. fel, 53, Scribner fel, 54, Frelinghuysen fel, 55, Ph.D.(Eng), 58. Instr. ENG, Wesleyan Univ, 56-58, asst. prof, 58-61; UNIV. VA, 61-63, assoc. prof, 63-67, PROF, 67- Am. Counc. Learned Soc. fel, 60-61 & 67; Guggenheim fel, 64-65; adv. ed, Eighteenth Century Stud. & Stud. in the Novel, 67-; vis. prof, Rice Univ, 67-68; adv. ed, Stud. in Eng. lit, 68-; hon. res. fel, Univ. Col, Univ. London, 70-71; Counc. Humanities sr. fel, Princeton, 71; assoc. Clare Hall, Cambridge, 72; fel, Am. Counc. Learned Socs, 72. MLA; S.Atlantic Mod. Lang. Asn; Acad. Lit. Stud. Eighteenth century literature and the arts; the British novel, especially Henry Fielding. Publ: The moral basis of Fielding's art, Wesleyan Univ, 59; ed, Fielding's Joseph Andrews and Shamela, Houghton, 61; Fielding's Joseph Andrews, 67 & co-ed, Fielding's Tom Jones, 74, Clarendon & Wesleyan Univ; ed, Tom Jones: a collection of critical essays, Prentice-Hall, 68; auth, The providence of wit: aspects of form in Augustan literature and the arts, Clarendon, 74, Tom Jones and his Egyptian majesty: Fielding's parable of government, PMLA, 3/67; Fielding and master punch in Panton Street, Philol. Quart, 66; Henry Fielding, In: New Cambridge bibliography of English literature, Cambridge, 71. Add: Dept. of English, University of Virginia, Charlottesville, VA 22901.

BATTIN, TOM C, b. Marietta, Ohio, July 20, 09; m. 48. TELEVISION. B.S, Ohio Univ, 35; M.A, Univ. Mich, 40, Ph.D.(educ. TV), 51. Teacher, pub. sch, Ohio, 37-42; instr, Univ. Mich, 45-51; asst. prof, Univ. Fla, 51-54; assoc. prof. RADIO & TV, UNIV. HOUSTON, 54-62, PROF, 62-, CHMN. GRAD. STUD. COMMUN. ARTS & PRODUCER-DIR. UNIV. EDUC. TV STA. Mem. prod. staff, WRGB-TV, New York, N.Y, 49; TV consult, State of Fla, 52-53; writer-producer, Target: delinquency, TV ser, Houston Youth Proj, 63; exec. producer-dir, Col. News Conf, also News on Campus, weekly TV ser, produced on local sta, Houston, Tex; exec. dir, Campus Workshop, weekly TV ser, Houston. Honored by Nat. Commun. Asn, 73. Speech Commun. Asn; South. Speech Asn; Nat. Asn. Educ. Broadcasters. Impact of educational television; influence of television on children; creative drama in television. Publ: Co-auth, Understanding television, Hastings, 63; auth, A study of the televiewing in education, South. Speech J; Television: the world's largest blackboard, J. Educ. Radio & TV. Add: Dept. of Communications, University of Houston, A110 Cullen Bldg, Houston, TX 77004.

BATTLE, GUY ARTHUR, b. Ft. Wayne, Ind, Sept. 8, 18; m. 50; c. 4. ENGLISH. A.B, Duke Univ, 40, M.A, 47, Ph.D.(Eng), 51. Instr. Eng, Univ. Ky, 49-50; Duke Univ, 51; assoc. prof, Mid. Tenn. State Col, 51-56; PROF. ENG. & HEAD DEPT, MURRAY STATE UNIV, 56- U.S.A, 41-46, Capt. MLA; AAUP. Add: 1103 Main St, Murray, KY 42071.

BATZER, HAZEL MARGARET, English, Criticism. See POLLARD, HAZEL M. (BATZER).

BAUER, NEIL STEPHEN, b. Cincinnati, Ohio, July 2, 43. ENGLISH LITERATURE. A.B, Hamilton Col, 65; M.A, Columbia Univ, 66, Ph.D.(Eng. & comp. lit), 71. Instr. ENG, COL. WILLIAM & MARY, 69-72, ASST. PROF, 72- MLA; S.Atlantic Mod. Lang. Asn; Rydal Mt. Summer Sch. Asn.(secy, 72-); Romantic poetry; Romantic and Victorian periodicals. Publ: Wordsworth and early anthologies, Libr, 3/72. Add: Dept. of English, College of William & Mary, Williamsburg, VA 23185.

BAUER, OTTO FRANK, b. Elgin, Ill, Dec. 1, 31; m. 56; c. 2. SPEECH, SEMANTICS. B.S, Northwest. Univ, 53, M.A, 55, Ph.D.(pub. address), 59. Instr. Eng, U.S. Air Force Acad, 59-60, asst. prof, 60-61; instr. speech, Bowling Green State Univ, 61-63, asst. prof, 63-66, assoc. prof, 66-68, prof, 68-71, dir. grad. admis. & fels, 65-69, asst. dean grad. sch, 67-69; PROF. COMMUN. & V.CHANCELLOR, UNIV. WIS-PARKSIDE, 71- Midwest forensic Asn. res. grant, 66-67; mem, Inst. Gen. Semantics; Am. Counc. Educ. fel, Univ. Calif, Berkeley, 69-70; Fac. man of year, Bowling Green State Univ, 67. U.S.A.F, 56-61, 1st Lt. Am. Forensic Asn; Speech Commun. Asn; Int. Soc. Gen. Semantics. Semantics; debate; political campaigning. Publ: Fundamentals of debate: theory and practice, Scott, 66; Student trust at Berkeley, Educ. Rec, fall 71; Relational abstracting and the structural differential, In: Research designs in general semantics, Gordon & Breach, 72; plus five others. Add: Office of the Vice Chancellor, University of Wisconsin-Parkside, Kenosha, WI 53140.

BAUER, ROBERT VanAKIN, b. Naperville, Ill, Dec. 13, 14. ENGLISH & AMERICAN LITERATURE. A.B, N.Cent. Col, 37; A.M, Univ. Ill, 38, Ph.D, 48. Asst. Eng, Univ. Ill, 39-42, 46-47; instr. Eng. lit, Pa. State Univ, 47-49, asst. prof, 49-61, assoc. prof. Eng, 61-63; staff writer, Centre Daily Times, 66-74. Ed, Accent, 40-50. MLA. Seventeenth century English comedy; 20th century American poetry and drama. Publ: Amy Bonner, poet and friend of poets, Pa. State Univ, 59; co-auth, American drama, In: College and adult reading list, NCTE & Wash. Sq, 61. Add: 425 Waupelani Dr, Apt. 220, State College, PA 16801.

BAUER, WALTER JOHN, JR, b. Trenton, N.J, Nov. 16, 36; m. 71. ENGLISH & AMERICAN LITERATURE. A.B, Rutgers Col, 59; M.A, N.Y. Univ, 60, Ph.D.(Eng), 73; cert. educ, Newark State Col, 62-63; Seton Hall Univ, 62-63; Drew Univ, 64-65. Teacher, Edison High Sch, N.J, 63; Westfield High Sch, 63-64; instr. ENG, KEAN COL. N.J, 65-68, asst. prof, 68-72, ASSOC. PROF, 72-, COORD. FRESHMAN ENG, 73- Lectr. Eng, City Col. New York, summers, 63 & 64; honors scholar, N.Y. Univ, 73-74. Sig.C, U.S.A, 60-62, 1st Lt. MLA; NCTE; Conf. Col. Compos. & Commun; Col. Eng. Asn; AAUP. Realism and naturalism; novel; Frank Norris. Add: Dept. of English, Kean College of New Jersey, Union, NJ 07083.

BAUER, WILLIAM ALFRED, b. Portland, Maine, May 10, 32; m. 56; c. 3. ENGLISH LITERATURE. B.A, Amherst Col, 54; M.A.T, Wesleyan Univ, 56; Ph.D.(Eng), Univ. N.C, Chapel Hill, 70. ASSOC. PROF. ENG, UNIV. N.B, FREDERICTON, 65- U.S.A.F, 56-57. MLA; Asn. Can. Univ. Teachers Eng; Can. Soc. 18th Century Stud. English literary journalism of the 18th century; modern Canadian poetry. Add: Dept. of English, University of New Brunswick, Fredericton, N.B, Can.

BAUERLE, RICHARD F, Linguistics. See Volume III, Foreign Languages, Linguistics & Philology.

BAUGH, ALBERT CROLL, b. Philadelphia, Pa, Feb. 26, 91. ENGLISH LANGUAGE & LITERATURE. A.B, Univ. Pa, 12, A.M, 14, Ph.D, 15, hon. Litt.D, 61; hon. LL.D, Ursinus Col, 39; hon. Litt.D, Franklin & Marshall Col, 56. Asst. ENG, UNIV. PA, 12-13, instr, 13-20, asst. prof, 20-28, from prof. to SCHELLING MEM. PROF, 28- Pres, Int. Fed. Mod. Langs. & Lit, 60-63. Fel. Mediaeval Acad. Am.(pres, 63-); MLA (pres, 52); Ling. Soc. Am; Mod. Humanities Res. Asn. Gt. Brit.(pres, 49-50). Publ: History of the English language, 2nd ed, 57, co-auth, Literary history of England, 60, rev. ed, 67 & ed, Chaucer's major poetry, 63, Appleton. Add: 4220 Spruce St, Philadelphia, PA 19104.

BAUGHAN, DENVER EWING, b. Henderson, Tenn, Dec. 24, 96; m. 27; c. 3. ENGLISH. A.B, Vanderbilt Univ, 23, A.M, 24; Ph.D, Yale, 34. Prof. ENG, Memphis State Univ, 25-30; instr, Univ. N.H, 34-36; prof, E.Carolina Univ, 36-44; asst. prof, Mary Washington Col, 44-46; assoc. prof, UNIV. FLA, 46-57, prof, 57-67, EMER. PROF, 67- Prof, Baptist Col. Charleston, 67-70. MLA; Col. Eng. Asn; S.Atlantic Mod. Lang. Asn; Southeast Renaissance Conf. Publ: Ed. & introd, The traveller, Scholars' Facsimiles, 51; Sir Philip Sidney and the matchmakers, Mod. Lang. Rev, 10/38; Swift and Gentillet, Stud. in Philol, 1/40. Add: 2201 N.W. 21st St, Gainesville, FL 32605.

BAUGHMAN, ERNEST WARREN, b. Manson, Iowa, Sept. 10, 16; m. 40. ENGLISH, FOLKLORE. A.B, Ball State Teachers Col, 38; M.A, Univ. Chicago, 39; Ph.D.(Eng), Ind. Univ, 53. Teacher, high sch, Ind, 39-42; teaching asst, Ind. Univ, 42-46, instr, 46-48; ENG, UNIV. N.MEX, 48-51, asst. prof, 51-56, assoc. prof, 56-64, PROF, 64- Panelist, N.Y. Hist. Asn. Seminars, 53; spec. lectr, Folklore Inst. Am, summer, 58. MLA; Am. Folklore Soc; NCTE. The folktale, especially American and English; American literature and studies. Publ: Type and motif index of folktales of England and North America, Ind. Univ, 64 & Mouton, The Hague, 66; co-ed, Sticks in the knapsack, Columbia Univ, 58; auth, Folklore to the fore, Eng. J, 42; Public confession and The scarlet letter, New Eng. Quart, 12/67. Add: Dept. of English, University of New Mexico, Albuquerque, NM 87106.

BAULAND, PETER MAX, b. Ulm, Ger, Dec. 19, 32; U.S. citizen; m. 61; c. 2. ENGLISH, DRAMA. B.A, Univ. Pa, 53, Harrison scholar, 53-54, Harrison fels, 54-55, 58-59, M.A, 55, Ph.D.(Eng), 64. Instr. ENG, Lafayette Col, 57-58; Drexel Inst, 59-63, asst. prof, 63-64; UNIV. MICH, ANN ARBOR, 64-69, ASSOC. PROF, 69-, chmn. comp. lit, 70-71. Nat. Endowment for Humanities fel, 69; Rackham res. grant, 69; Fulbright lectr. & vis. prof. drama, Univ. Munich, 71-72. U.S.A, 55-57. Midwest Mod. Lang. Asn. (chmn. comp. lit, 72). Modern drama; film; comparative literature, especially German and English. Publ: The hooded eagle; modern German drama on the New York stage, Syracuse Univ, 68; co-ed, The tradition of the theatre, Allyn & Bacon, 71; chap, In: Modernes Amerikanisches drama/Modern American drama, Vandenhoeck & Ruprechet, for Univ. Tübingen, Göttingen, & Zürich, 73. Add: Dept. of English, University of Michigan, Ann Arbor, MI 48104.

BAUMBACH, JONATHAN, b. New York, N.Y, July 5, 33; m. 68; c. 3. ENGLISH, FILM STUDIES. A.B, Brooklyn Col, 55; M.F.A, Columbia Univ, 56; Ph.D.(Eng. & Am. lit), Stanford Univ, 61. Asst. prof. ENG, Ohio State Univ, 61-64; dir. writing, N.Y. Univ, 64-66; assoc. prof, BROOKLYN COL, 66-70, PROF, 71- Mem. bd. dirs, Teachers & Writers Collaborative, 66-; vis. prof. Eng, Tufts Univ, 70-71; movie critic, Partisan Rev, 73- Sig.C, U.S.A, 56-58. PEN Club. American novel; cinema. Publ: The landscape of nightmare: studies in contemporary American novel, N.Y. Univ. & Peter Owen, London, 65; A man to conjure with, 65 & co-ed, Modern and contemporaries: nine masters of the story, 68, Random; auth, What comes next, Harper, 68; ed. & contrib, Writers as teachers/teachers as writers, Holt, 70; plus numerous others. Add: Dept. of English, Brooklyn College, Brooklyn, NY 11210.

BAUMGARTNER, ALEX MILLER, b. Wilmington, Del, Nov. 5, 37; m. 63. ENGLISH. B.A, Brown Univ, 60; M.A, Univ. Pa, 62, fel, 62-65, Ph.D.(Eng), 71. Mem. fac, Pennington Sch, 61-62; asst. prof. ENG, Washington Col, 66-68; asst. prof, W. Chester State Col, 70-71; LECTR, PHILA. COL. TEXTILES & SCI, 71- Univ. Pa. res. grant, summers 65 & 66. MLA; NCTE; Am. Stud. Asn. American romanticism; American prose style. Publ: Co-ed, The early lectures of Ralph Waldo Emerson, Harvard, 73; Dryden's Caleb and Agag, Rev. Eng. Stud, 12/62; The lyceum is my pulpit: homiletics in Emerson's early lectures, Am. Lit, 1/63; Illusion and role in The scarlet letter, Papers Lang. & Lit, spring 71. Add: 101 W. Harvey St, Philadelphia, PA 19144.

BAUMWOLL, DENNIS, b. New York, N.Y, July 8, 32; m. 56; c. 4. ENGLISH. B.A, Univ. Okla, 54, M.A, 58, South. fel, 60, Ph.D.(Eng), 64. Instr. ENG, Boston Univ, 62-65; BUCKNELL UNIV, 65-66, asst. prof, 66-72, ASSOC. PROF, 72- Instr. Boston Univ. For. Stud. Inst, summers 63, 64, 65; ed. consult, Bucknell Rev, 65-; consult, Pa. Dept. Pub. Instr, 67-; mem. ed. bd, D.H. Lawrence Rev, 67-; coord. acad. enrichment prog, U.S. Penitentiary, Lewisburg, 67- MLA; Teachers of Eng. to Speakers of Other Lang. The novel as genre; modern fiction; English as a second language. Publ: Co-auth, Advanced reading and writing, Holt, 65. Add: Dept. of English, Bucknell University, Lewisburg, PA 17837.

BAXTER, ANNETTE KAR, American Civilization. See Volume I, History.

BAXTER, MARY RUTH, b. Mishawaka, Ind, July 20, 30; m. 52; c. 3. ENGLISH. A.B, Oberlin Col, 52; M.A.T, Radcliffe Col, 53; Ph.D.(Eng), Ohio State Univ, 72. ASST. PROF. ENG, CAPITAL UNIV, 72- MLA; AAUP. Samuel Johnson and James Boswell. Add: Dept. of English, Capital University, Columbus, OH 43209.

BAXTER, RALPH CLAYTON, b. Detroit, Mich, Aug. 2, 35; m. 61. ENGLISH. A.B, Univ. Detroit, 58; M.A, Wayne State Univ, 59, fel, 59-64, Ph.D.(Eng), 64. Asst. prof. Eng, Ind. Univ, Northwest Campus, 64-69, fac. fel, summer 68; chmn. div. humanities, St. Mary's Col. Md, 69-73, col. dean fac, 71-72, dean acad. develop, 72-73; PROF. ENG. & ASSOC. PROVOST, GEORGE MASON UNIV, 73- S.Atlantic Mod. Lang. Asn; MLA; Nat. Audubon Soc. Thomas Warton, Jr, as poet, historiographer and historian; genres, forms and rhetoric of literary natural history; implications of the use of popular American bird names as slang. Publ: Latin moments: translations from T. Warton, Arion, winter 67; Shakespeare's Dauphin and Hopkins' Windhover, Victorian Poetry, spring 69; A sonnet wrongly ascribed to Thomas Warton, Jr, Ball State Univ. Forum, autumn 70; plus others. Add: Office of Associate Provost, George Mason University, 4400 University Dr, Fairfax, VA 22030.

BAYARD, SAMUEL PRESTON, b. Pittsburgh, Pa, Apr. 10, 08; m. 42. MUSIC. A.B, Pa. State Col, 34; A.M, Harvard, 36. From instr. to prof. ENG, PA. STATE UNIV, 45-73, EMER. PROF, 73- Am. Folklore Soc. Folk music; mythology; Celtic material. Publ: Hill country tunes. Add: 220 Osmond St, State College, PA 16801.

BAYES, RONALD HOMER, b. Milton, Ore, July 19, 32. ENGLISH. B.S, East. Ore. Col, 55, M.S, 56; Woodrow Wilson fel, Univ. Pa, 59-60; summers, Colo. State Col, 55, 62, Univ. B.C, 63, Trinity Col.(Dublin), 66. Lectr. Eng. speech & lit, Univ. Md, 58-59; asst. prof. Eng. & speech, East. Ore. Col, 55-56, 60-67, assoc. prof. Eng, 67-68; ASSOC. PROF. ENG. & WRITER IN RESIDENCE, ST. ANDREWS PRESBY. COL, 68- Lectr, Far East Div, Univ. Md, 66-67; ed, St. Andrews Rev, 69-; consult. creative writing, Nat. Endowment for Arts, 69-70; chmn. creative writing, N.C. Writers' Conf, 72-73; Piedmont Univ. Ctr. grant in writing, summer 72; St. Andrews Col. grant in writing, summer 73. U.S.A, 56-58. MLA; NCTE; Mod. Poetry Asn; Poetry Soc. Japan; AAUP. John Reed; Ezra Pound; William Carlos Williams. Publ: Dust and desire, Stockwell, 62; co-auth, Paint the window purple, Palmer, 63; auth, An evening with Ezra Pound, New Directions; History of the turtle, Grande Ronde, 66; Ejection, 67 & History of the turtle I-IV, 70, Olivant Constructions in English and Japanese, Novakast, Tokyo, 68; X-ing warm, Wine Press, 68; co-ed, Humane learning in a changing world, St. Andrews, 72; auth, The casketmaker (poems), John Blair, 73; Porpoise I-IV, Red Clay, 73; Charles Olson's Selected writings & The truth is whips and sweets: Mme De Sade, West Coast Rev, 68; James Merrill's poetry, Nights and days, South & West, 68. Add: Dept. of English, St. Andrews Presbyterian College, Laurinburg, NC 28352.

BAYLESS, OVID LYNDAL, b. Duncan, Okla, July 20, 31; m. 53; c. 3. SPEECH COMMUNICATION. B.A, Baylor Univ, 53, M.A, 59; Ph.D.(speech), Univ. Denver, 65. U.S. AIR FORCE, 54-, instr, broadcasting workshop, Baylor Univ, 59; Eng, U.S. AIR FORCE ACAD, 62-63, asst. prof. tech. writing & speech, 65-67, ASSOC. PROF. ADVAN. COMPOS. & SPEECH, 67-, DEPUTY DIR. INSTRUCT. TECHNOL, 68- Deputy dir. plans div, stud. & observations group, Mil. Assistance Command, Vietnam, 70. U.S.A.F, 54-, Lt. Col; Bronze Star Medal. Speech Commun. Asn; Nat. Soc. Stud. Commun; Am. Forensic Asn; Int. Commun. Asn; Broadcast Educ. Asn. Group problem-solving; persuasion; broadcasting. Publ: The American

Forces Vietnam Network, J. Broadcasting, 69; The oral history program, 69 & Television as a demonstration tool, 69, Educ. TV; plus others. Add: Directorate of Instructional Technology, U.S. Air Force Academy, CO 80840.

BAYLEY, RICHARD BENNETT, Russian Cultural History, Mass Communications. See Volume III, Foreign Languages, Linguistics & Philology.

BAYM, NINA, b. Princeton, N.J, June 14, 36; m. 58, 71; c. 2. ENGLISH. B.A, Cornell Univ, 57; M.A, Harvard, 58, Ph.D.(Eng), 63. Asst. ENG, Univ. Calif, Berkeley, 62-63; instr, UNIV. ILL, URBANA, 63-66, asst. prof, 66-69, assoc. prof, 69-72, PROF, 72-, ASSOC. HEAD DEPT, 71- Mem. ed. bd, Am. Quart, 73- MLA; Am. Stud. Asn; Women's Caucus Mod. Lang. Women in literature; American literature. Publ: Hawthorne's women: the tyranny of social myths, Centennial Rev, 71; The marble faun: Hawthorne's elegy for art, New Eng. Quart, 71; The women of Cooper's Leatherstocking tales, Am. Quart, 71; plus many others. Add: 100 English Bldg, University of Illinois, Urbana, IL 61801.

BAZERMAN, CHARLES, b. Brooklyn, N.Y, June 30, 45; m. 72. ENGLISH & AMERICAN LITERATURE. B.A, Cornell Univ, 67; M.A, Brandeis Univ, 68, Ph.D.(Eng), 71. Teacher elem. sch, N.Y.C. Bd. Educ, 68-70; instr. ENG, Union Col.(N.J), 71-72; ASST. PROF, BARUCH COL, 72- MLA; NCTE; Northeast Mod. Lang. Asn; Col. Eng. Asn. Renaissance English literature; modern fiction; pedagogy of composition. Publ: Building the new Jerusalem, 4/73 & Victories of happy madness, 9/73, Nation; contrib, The contemporary novel: essays in criticism, Everett Edwards, 74. Add: Dept. of English, Baruch College, 17 Lexington Ave, New York, NY 10010.

BAZIN, NANCY TOPPING, b. Pittsburgh, Pa, Nov. 5, 34; m. 58; c. 2. BRITISH LITERATURE. B.A, Ohio Wesleyan Univ, 56; M.A, Middlebury Col, 58; Ph.D.(Eng), Stanford Univ, 69. ASST. PROF. ENG, RUTGERS COL, RUTGERS UNIV, NEW BRUNSWICK, 70- MLA. Twentieth century British literature; Victorian literature; women's studies. Publ: Virginia Woolf and the androgynous vision, Rutgers Univ, 73; Virginia Woolf's quest for equilibrium, Mod. Lang. Quart, 9/71. Add: Dept. of English, Scott Hall, Rutgers University, College Ave, New Brunswick, NJ 08903.

BEACH, D. M, b. Lincoln, Nebr, Oct. 15, 32; m. 60; c. 2. ENGLISH LITERATURE. B.A, Reed Col, 54; Woodrow Wilson fel, 54-55; M.A, Cornell Univ, 55, univ. fel, 55-56, Ph.D, 59. Instr. ENG, Univ. Wash, 58-60; asst. prof, UNIV. B.C, 60-67, ASSOC. PROF, 67- Asn. Can. Univ. Teachers Eng. Elizabethan literature; English poetry. Publ: Love and rhetoric in euphuistic fiction, Asn. Can. Univ. Teachers Eng. Report, 62. Add: Dept. of English, University of British Columbia, Vancouver, B.C, Can.

BEACH, LEONARD B, b. Bridgeport, Conn, Jan. 14, 05; m. 36; c. 3. AMERICAN LITERATURE. A.B, Wesleyan Univ, 25; A.M, Yale, 30, Ph.D, 33; LL.D, Univ. Chattanooga, 64; hon. Litt.D, Manhattan Col, 71. Instr. classics, Tilton Sch, N.H, 25-28; from asst. to instr. ENG, Yale, 30-34; instr. Northwest. Univ, 34-39; asst. prof, Ohio State Univ, 39-45; prof, Univ. Okla, 45-51, chmn. dept, 49-51; prof, VANDERBILT UNIV, 51-72, dean grad. sch, 51-64, dean univ. for inst. relat, 64-72, EMER. PROF. ENG. & EMER. DEAN UNIV, 72- Consult, NDEA, 58-; exec. dir, South. Col. Univ. Union, 68-73. MLA; S.Cent. Mod. Lang. Asn.(pres, 50); Asn. Grad. Schs.(pres, 57-58); Conf. Deans South. Grad. Schs.(pres, 57-58). English poetry; graduate education; Knickerbocker period in American literature. Add: 412 Ellendale Dr, Nashville, TN 37205.

BEACHAM, EUGENE WALTON, b. Greenville, S.C, Dec. 30, 43; m. 67; c. 1. CREATIVE WRITING, CRITICISM. World Stud. Fund scholar, Hanover, Ger, 64-65; B.S, Ga. Inst. Technol, 67; B.A, Ga. State Univ, 68; M.A. & M.F.A, Univ. Ark, Fayetteville, 70. Instr. physics, Atlanta Pub. Schs, Ga, 66-67; physics & Eng, Arlington Sch, Atlanta, 67-68; asst. prof. Eng, Univ. Richmond, 70-73; ASST. PROF. ENG. & DIR. CREATIVE WRITING, VA. COMMONWEALTH UNIV, 73- Bk. ed, Richmond Times-Dispatch, 71-72; dir, Boatwright Lit. Festival, 71, 73; mem. bd. dirs, Assoc. Writing Progs, 71- MLA. History of prosody; original data for novels set in Syria and Lebanon. Publ: Ed, Intro. four, 73 & Intro five, 74, Univ. Va; auth, The meaning of poetry: a guide to explication, Allyn & Bacon, 74. Add: Dept. of English, Virginia Commonwealth University, Richmond, VA 23220.

BEAL, DENTON, b. Urbana, Ill, July 30, 17; m. 41; c. 2. ENGLISH. B.A, Univ. Pittsburgh, 39, Ph.D.(Eng), 47. Instr. Eng. & jour, Univ. Pittsburgh, 46-53, dir. stud. publ, 52-53, asst. prof. Eng, Johnstown Ctr, 54-58; ed, Carnegie Alumnus, Carnegie-Mellon Univ, 58-62, dir. dept. pub. relat, 62-70; v.pres, C.W. Post Col, L.I. Univ, 70-73; DIR. PUB. RELAT, UNIV. BRIDGEPORT, 73- V.pres. bd. trustees, Ed. Proj. Educ, Inc, 61-63, pres. & chmn. bd, 63-67; consult, Gov. Comt. Transportation, Pa, 68- Med.C, 43-44, Med.Admin.C, 44-46, Lt. Am. Alumni Counc; Am. Col. Pub. Relat. Asn. Criticism; poetry; communications. Add: 35 Point Beach Dr, Milford, CT 06460.

BEAL, RICHARD S, b. Whitman, Mass, June 14, 15; m. 41; c. 1. ENGLISH. A.B, Tufts Col, 37, A.M, 39; Univ. Wis, 39-40 & summers, 41, 47. Instr. ENG, Tufts Col, 40-42; Simmons Col, 46-47; BOSTON UNIV, 47-52, asst. prof, 52-56, assoc. prof, 56-63, PROF, 63-, ASSOC. DEAN, 67- Chmn. comt. jr. col. eng, NCTE-Conf. Col. Compos. & Commun, 65-66, mem. steering comt. northeast regional conf. of two year cols, 66-69. U.S.N.R, 42-46, Lt. Comdr. NCTE; Col. Conf. Compos. & Commun. Publ: Co-auth, Thought in prose, 3rd ed, 66 & The complete reader, 2nd ed, 67, Prentice-Hall; auth, Rhetoric and composition, Holt, 67. Add: College of Liberal Arts, Boston University, 725 Commonwealth Ave, Boston, MA 02215.

BEALE, WALTER HENRY, b. Roseboro, N.C, Jan. 15, 45; m. 68; c. 1. ENGLISH LANGUAGE & LITERATURE. B.A, Wake Forest College, 67; M.A, Univ. Mich, 68, Ph.D.(Eng), 71. ASST. PROF. ENG, UNIV. N.C, GREENSBORO, 71- MLA; Mediaeval Acad. Am; Ling. Soc. Am. Old and Middle English literature; English linguistics. Add: Dept. of English, University of North Carolina at Greensboro, Greensboro, NC 27412.

BEARD, JAMES FRANKLIN, b. Memphis, Tenn, Feb. 14, 19; m. 45; c. 2. ENGLISH & AMERICAN LITERATURE. A.B, Columbia Univ, 40, M.A, 41; Ph.D, Princeton, 49. Instr. ENG, Princeton, 43-48; Dartmouth Col, 48-51, asst. prof, 51-55; CLARK UNIV, 55-57, assoc. prof, 57-62, PROF, 62- Guggenheim fel, 52-53, 58-59; Nat. Endowment for Humanities sr. fel, 67-68, grant 71-72; gen. ed, Writings of James Fenimore Cooper, Ctr. Ed. Am. Authors. MLA; Am. Stud. Asn; Col. Eng. Asn; Am. Antiq. Soc. American literature and studies; James Fenimore Cooper. Publ: The letters and journals of James Fenimore Cooper, 6 vols, Belknap, 60, 64 & 68. Add: 108 Winifred Ave, Worcester, MA 01602.

BEARD, RAYMOND S, b. East Liverpool, Ohio, Aug. 17, 18; m. 54; c. 3. SPEECH. B.A, West. Reserve Univ, 41, M.A, 46; Ph.D, Northwest. Univ, 54. Instr. speech & assoc. dir. debate, Wayne Univ, 48-52; instr. speech, N.Y. Univ, 54-55, asst. prof, 55-58, dir. debate, 54-58; assoc. prof. SPEECH, STATE UNIV. N.Y. COL. CORTLAND, 58-61, PROF, 61-, DIR. DEBATE, 58- NDEA grant, Fac. Develop. Inst, Cornell Univ, 68-69. U.S.A, 41-45. East. Forensic Asn.(pres, 62-64); Am. Forensic Asn; Speech Commun. Asn; AAUP. Argumentation and debate, especially cross-examination; parliamentary procedure. Publ: A comparison of classical dialectic, legal cross-examination and cross-question debate, 5/66 & Legal cross-examination and academic debate, spring 69, J. Am. Forensic Asn. Add: Dept. of Speech & Theatre Arts, State University of New York College at Cortland, Cortland, NY 13045.

BEARDS, RICHARD DOUGLAS, b. New York, N.Y, Oct. 21, 36; m. 62; ENGLISH LITERATURE. B.A, Dartmouth Col, 58; Ph.D.(Eng), Univ. Wash, 65. Teaching asst. ENG, Univ. Wash, 59-61, assoc, 61-62; instr, Univ. Maine, 63-64; TEMPLE UNIV, 64-65, ASST. PROF, 65- Fulbright prof. Am. lit, Odense, Denmark, 71-72. Fulbright-Hays lectr. Am. Stud, Univ. Lund, 66-67. Victorian fiction; modern British literature; American literature. Publ: D.H. Lawrence: ten years of criticism, 1959-1968, a checklist, D.H. Lawrence Rev, fall 68; Teaching Sons and lovers as a Bildungsroman, Col. Lit. (in press); Parody as tribute: William Melvin Kelley's A different drummer and Faulkner, Stud. Black Lit, (in press). Add: Dept. of English, Temple University, Philadelphia, PA 19122.

BEASLEY, JERRY CARR, b. Nashville, Tenn, Sept. 15, 40; m. 66; c. 2. ENGLISH LITERATURE. B.A, George Peabody Col, 63; M.A, Univ. Kans, 67; Ph.D.(Eng), Northwest. Univ, 71. ASST. PROF. ENG, UNIV. DEL, 69- MLA. English novel, 18th and 19th centuries. Publ: Check list of prose fiction published in England 1740-1749, Univ. Va, 72; Fanny Burney and Jane Austen's Pride and prejudice, Eng. Miscellany, 73; English fiction in the 1740's: some glances at the major and minor novels, Stud. Novel, fall 73; The role of Tom Pinch in Martin Chuzzlewit, Ariel, 74. Add: Dept. of English, University of Delaware, Newark, DE 19711.

BEASLEY, MARY FOWLER, b. Ruston, La, Nov. 24, 42; m. 64. SPEECH, ENGLISH LITERATURE. B.A, La. Tech. Univ, 64, M.A, 66; univ. fel, Purdue Univ. W. Lafayette, 67, David Ross res. grant, 69-70, Ph.D.(speech), 70. Instr. speech, LA. TECH UNIV, 65-67, Eng, 69-71, asst. prof. SPEECH, 71-73, ASSOC. PROF, 73- Am. Asn. Univ. Women Educ. Found. fel, 72-, mem. nat. dymanic learning topic comt, 72-74. Nat. Recognition Award, Phi Beta Speech & Music Nat. Hon, 70-71; Nat. Writers Award, New Dramatists Asn, 73. Speech Commun. Asn; South. Speech Commun. Asn; Am. Forensic Asn; AAUP. Rhetoric and public address; oral interpretation; speech education. Publ: Programmed study guide for leadership-communication training, Gen. Fed. Women's Clubs, 73, co-auth, Dynamic learning: releasing human potential, 73 & Model community-influence education projects, 73, Am. Asn. Univ. Women Educ. Off; auth, The development of a critical evaluation form for readers theatre, 4/72 & Audience-role considerations in writing for readers theatre, 11/72; Educ. Resources Inform. Ctr, It's what you don't say: omissio in Cicero's speeches, South. Speech Commun. J, fall 72; plus others. Add: Dept. of Speech, Box 4505 Tech Station, Louisiana Tech University, Ruston, LA 71270.

BEASLEY, WILLIAM MADISON, b. Nashville, Tenn, Sept. 9, 24; m. 48; c. 3. ENGLISH & AMERICAN LITERATURE. B.S, Mid. Tenn. State Univ, 47; M.A, Vanderbilt Univ, 49, Ph.D.(Eng), 57. Instr. ENG, Marion Inst, 49-51; Vanderbilt Univ, 52-53; Troy State Col, 53-55; MID. TENN. STATE UNIV, 55-57; asst. prof, 57-60, assoc. prof, 60-64, PROF, 64- U.S.A.F, 43-46, Lt. MLA; NCTE; Col. Eng. Asn. Nineteenth century American literature. Add: Dept. of English, Middle Tennessee State University, Murfreesboro, TN 37130.

BEATTIE, ALEXANDER MUNRO, b. Brockville, Ont, Oct. 1, 11; m. 40; c. 2. ENGLISH LITERATURE. B.A, Univ. Toronto, 33; A.M, Columbia Univ, 48, Ph.D, 52. Lectr, ENG. LIT, CARLETON UNIV, 42-48, asst. prof, 49-52, assoc. prof, 53-57, PROF, 58-, chmn. dept, 50-69. Can. Counc. sr. res. fel, 60-61 & 67-68. MLA; Asn. Can. Univ. Teachers Eng.(pres, 64-65). Modern Canadian poetry; Henry James and the modern novel. Publ: Co-auth, Composition for Canadian Universities, Macmillan, Can, 64; Chaps. 37-40, In: Literary history of Canada, 65 & Patterns of commitment in American literature, 67, Univ. Toronto, Add: Dept. of English, Carleton University, Ottawa,1, Ont. K1S 5B6, Can.

BEATTIE, THOMAS CHARLES, b. St. Johns, Mich, Feb. 7, 38; m. 62. ENGLISH LANGUAGE & LITERATURE. B.A, Mich. State Univ, 60; Woodrow Wilson fel, Univ. Pa, 60-61, M.A, 61; Rackham fel, Univ. Mich, Ann Arbor, 61-63, Ph.D.(Eng), 68. Teaching fel. ENG, Univ. Mich, 63-68; ASST. PROF, HARTWICK COL, 68- Instr. Eng, Westmar Col, summer 64. MLA; Col. Eng. Asn. Novel; Jane Austen; 18th century English literature. Add: Dept. of English, Hartwick College, Oneonta, NY 13820.

BEATY, FREDERICK L, b. New Braunfels, Tex, Oct. 22, 26; m. 55; c. 2. ENGLISH. B.A, Univ. Tex, 46; A.M, Harvard, 48, Ph.D, 52; Rhodes scholar, Oxford, 48-50, B.Litt, 50. Instr. ENG, Cornell Univ, 54-55; IND. UNIV, BLOOMINGTON, 55-58, asst. prof, 58-62, assoc. prof, 62-69, PROF, 69- Intel.C, U.S.A, 52-54. MLA; Keats-Shelley Asn. Am. Romatic period of English literature; Romantic writers and Romanticism. Publ: Ed, The Lloyd-Manning letters, Ind. Univ, 57; auth, Light from heaven: love in British Romantic literature, North Ill. Univ, 71; Harlequin Don Juan, J. Eng. & Ger. Philol, 8/68; Bryon on Malthus and the population problem,

Keats-Shelley J, 69; Bryon's longbow and strongbow, Stud. Eng. Lit, autumn 72; plus three others. Add: Dept. of English, Indiana University, Bloomington, IN 47401.

BEATY, JEROME, b. Baltimore, Md, Oct. 12, 24; m. 47, 70; c. 3. ENGLISH. B.A, Johns Hopkins Univ, 47, Pres. scholar & M.A, 48; resid. fel, Univ. Ill, 50, traveling fel, 51-52, Ph.D.(Eng), 56. Asst. prof. ENG, Va. Mil. Inst, 53-56; instr. Univ. Wash, 56-58, asst. prof, 58-60; assoc. prof, EMORY UNIV, 60-64, PROF, 64- Guggenheim fel, 62-63; vis. prof, Univ. Wis, Madison, 65-66; mem, Eng. Inst; mem. ed. bd, Victorian Poetry. U.S.M.C, 43-44; U.S.N.R, 44-46. MLA; S.Atlantic Mod. Lang. Asn. Victorian and modern literature; the novel as genre. Publ: Middlemarch from notebook to novel, Univ. Ill, 60; co-auth, Poetry: from statement of meaning, Oxford, N.Y, 65; ed, Norton introduction to fiction, 73 & co-ed, Norton introduction to literature, 73, Norton; History by indirection: the era of reform in Middlemarch, Victorian Stud, 12/57; The text of the novel; a study of the proof, In: Middlemarch: critical approaches to the novel, Athlone Press, 67; All Victoria's horses, and all Victoria's men, New Lit. Hist, winter 70. Add: Dept. of English, Emory University, Atlanta, GA 30322.

BEAUCHAMP, GEORGE E, b. Andrews, Ind, Dec. 8, 06; m. 30; c. 2. ENGLISH & SPEECH. A.B, Ind. Univ, 28; M.A, Univ. Mich, 32; Ph.D.(Eng), Northwest. Univ, 42. Teacher Eng, Latin & speech, High Schs, Andrews & Warsaw, Ind, 26-29; asst. prof. speech & Eng, Manchester Col, 29-34, prof. speech & chmn. dept, 36-42; instr. speech & coach men's debate, Northwest. Univ, 34-36; with Off. Civilian Defense, Off. War Inform. & Bur. Budget, Wash, D.C, 42-48; assoc. dir. comn. occupied areas, Am. Counc. Educ, 48-51; consult. & dir. patient educ, Vet. Admin, Wash, D.C, 51-54; assoc. prof. Eng. & speech, Univ. S.Fla, 60-71; RETIRED. Pres, Kokomo Jr. Col, 32-36; chmn. div. pub. speaking, Grad. Sch, Wash, D.C, 44-57; mem, Teacher-Training Mission, Korea, 48; pres, Orange Gardens, Inc, Kissimmee, Fla, 54-; trustee, Fla. Counc. Aging, 57-67; mem, Gov's. Adv. Comt. Aging, 58-60, 61-64; mem. Fla. deleg, White House Conf. Aging, 61. Speech Commun. Asn; South. Speech Asn; MLA; Col. Eng. Asn. Add: Dept. of English, University of South Florida, Tampa, FL 33620.

BEAUCHAMP, VIRGINIA WALCOTT, b. Sparta, Mich, June 28, 20; m. 54; c. 3. ENGLISH LITERATURE, WOMEN'S STUDIES. A.B, Univ. Mich, 42, M.A, 48; Univ. London, 48; Ph.D.(Eng), Univ. Chicago, 54. Teacher Eng, Bad Axe High Sch, Mich, 42-44; Grosse Pointe High Sch, 44-45; recreation worker, Am. Nat. Red Cross, Philippines & Japan, 45-47; teacher Eng, Ypsilanti High Sch, Mich, 48-49; instr. commun. skills, Stephens Col, 51-53; instr. ENG, UNIV. MD, COLLEGE PARK, 61-62, 65-68, ASST. PROF, 68- COORD. WOMEN'S STUDIES, 74- MLA; S.Atlantic Mod. Lang. Asn. Women in the Tudor period; Mary Sidney Herbert, Countess of Pembroke. Publ: An empathic perception, Chicago Rev, summer 55; Sidney's sister as translator of Garnier, Renaissance News, spring 57; A feminist looks at Tom and Huck, Md. Eng. J, fall 73. Add: Dept. of English, University of Maryland, College Park, MD 20742.

BEAUDRY, HARRY RICHARD, b. Ft. Worth, Tex, Jan. 23, 30; m. 58; c. 5. ENGLISH LITERATURE. A.B, Rice Univ, 52; Harvard, summers 51, 55, 57, 58; M.A, Boston Univ, 56; Ph.D.(Eng), Duke Univ, 68. Master Eng, Vt. Acad, 56-58; Eng. & hist, Ft. Worth Country Day Sch, 64-66; instr, ENG, UNIV. TEX, ARLINGTON, 66-68, asst. prof, 68-72, ASSOC. PROF, 72- U.S.N, 52-54, Res, 65-66, Lt.(jg). MLA; AAUP. John Keats and dramas; early 19th century London theater. Publ: The English Theatre and John Keats, Salzburg Stud. Eng. Lit, 73. Add: Dept. of English, University of Texas at Arlington, Arlington, TX 76010.

BEAUMONT, CHARLES ALLEN, b. Bristol, Va, July 8, 26. ENGLISH LITERATURE. A.B, Univ. Ga, 49, M.A, 53; Ph.D, Vanderbilt Univ, 58, Instr. ENG, UNIV. GA, 49-56, asst. prof, 56-63, assoc. prof, 63-69, PROF, 69- U.S.A, 44-46. S.Atlantic Mod. Lang. Asn; MLA. Early 18th century literature; the satire of Swift. Publ: Swift's classical rhetoric, 61 & Swift's use of the Bible, 65, Univ. Ga; Rising & falling metaphor in Pope's Essay on man, Style, 67. Add: Dept. of English, University of Georgia, Athens, GA 30602.

BEAURLINE, LESTER ALBERT, b. St. Paul, Minn, Apr. 25, 27; m. 50; c. 3. ENGLISH & AMERICAN LITERATURE. A.B, Univ. Mo, 50; A.M, Univ. Chicago, 51, Ph.D.(Eng), 60; Fulbright fel, King's Col, Univ. London, 56-57. Instr. ENG, Augustana Col, 51-53; asst. prof, N.Cent. Col, 55-60; UNIV. VA, 60-64, assoc. prof, 64-68, PROF, 69- Assoc. ed, Stud. Bibliog, 63-73; fel, coop. prog. humanities, Univ. N.C-Duke Univ, 68-69; mem. ed. bd, New Lit. Hist, 69- & Eng. Lit. Renaissance, 73-; fel, Huntington Libr, 73-74. MLA; Malone Soc; Renaissance Soc. Am. English drama; Renaissance literature. Publ: Ed, Ben Jonson's Epicoene, Univ. Nebr, 66 & Beaumont and Fletcher's Captain, Love's pilgrimage & The noble gentleman, Cambridge, 66-73; co-ed, John Dryden: four comedies & John Dryden: four tragedies, Univ. Chicago, 67; ed, The works of Sir John Suckling: the plays, Clarendon, 71; auth, The selective principle in Jonson's poems, Criticism, 66; Ben Jonson and the illusion of completeness, PMLA, 68; Gorgeous speech in Volpone, Stud. Lit. Imagination, 73; plus one other. Add: 115 Wilson Hall, University of Virginia, Charlottesville, VA 22901.

BEAVEN, WINTON H, b. Binghamton, N.Y, Jan. 26, 15. SPEECH. A.B, Atlantic Union Col, 37; M.A, Clark Univ, 38; fel. & Ph.D, Univ. Mich, 50. Instr. hist, Madison Col.(Tenn), 38-40; instr. speech & dean men, Atlantic Union Col, 40-43; prof. & asst. to pres, Union Col.(Nebr), 43-50; asst. prof, Univ. Mich, 50-53; educ. dir, Int. Comn. Prev. Alcoholism, 53-56; prof. commun, Seventh Day Adventist Theol. Sem, 56-59, dean sch. grad. stud, 57-59; acad. dean, Columbia Union Col, 59-65, pres, 65-70; DEAN, KETTERING COL. MED. ARTS, 70-, V.PRES. EDUC, MED. CTR, 72- V.pres, Int. Comn. Prev. Alcoholism, 72- Nat. Educ. Asn; Speech Commun. Asn. Narcotics education; rhetorical criticism. Publ: Toward prevention, Am. Businessmen's Res. Found, summer 73. Add: Kettering College of Medical Arts, 3737 Southern Blvd, Kettering, OH 45429.

BECK, EVELYN TORTON, German Comparative Literature. See Volume III, Foreign Languages, Linguistics & Philology.

BECK, HORACE PALMER, b. Newport, R.I, Sept. 27, 20; m. 43; c. 1. ENGLISH. M.A, Univ. Pa, 47, Ph.D.(Eng), 52. Instr. Eng, Temple Univ, 48-54; asst. prof, 54-56; from asst. prof. to PROF. AM. LIT, MIDDLEBURY COL, 56- Fulbright grant, Australia, 66-67. U.S.N.R, 43-46, Lt.(jg). Am. Folklore Soc; Midwest Folklore Soc; New Eng. Folklore Soc.(pres, 65-66). Colonial literature; folklore; marine history. Publ: Folklore of Maine, Lippincott, 57; American Indian as a colonial sea-fighter, Mystic Seaport, 60; co-auth, Folklore in action, Am. Folklore Soc, 64; Gluskup the liar, Bond Wheelwright, 67; auth, America's maritime heritage, Am. Neptune, 64; Sea love, Northwest Folklore, 67; Where the workers of the world unite, In: Our living traditions, Basic Bks, 68. Add: Dept. of American Literature, Middlebury College, Middlebury, VT 05753.

BECK, RONALD JAMES, b. Bad Axe, Mich, Aug. 20, 32; m. 57; c. 1. ENGLISH & AMERICAN LITERATURE. B.A, Univ. Mich, 58, M.A, 59; Ed.D.(humanities), Wayne State Univ, 66. From instr. to asst. prof. Eng, Detroit Inst. Technol, 59-66; asst. prof. humanities, Ore. Col. Educ, 66-69; ASSOC. PROF. ENG, OHIO NORTH. UNIV, 69- Vis. scholar, Univ. Mich, summer 70. U.S.A, 52-54. MLA; Am. Soc. Aesthet; NCTE (state chmn. writing awards, 70-71). Literary theory; 18th century British literature; modern Icelandic literature. Publ: The structure of Song of myself and the critics, Walt Whitman Rev, 3/69; James' The beast in the jungle: theme and metaphor, Markham Rev, 2/70; Art and life in the novel, J. Aesthet. & Art Criticism, fall 72. Add: Dept. of English, Ohio Northern University, Ada, OH 45810.

BECK, WARREN, b. Richmond, Ind; m. 30; c. 1. ENGLISH. A.B, Earlham Col, hon. Litt.D, 55; A.M, Columbia Univ, 26. From instr. to prof. ENG, LAWRENCE COL, 26-68, EMER. PROF, 68- Mem. fac, U.S. Army Univ, Eng, 45; Bread Loaf Sch. Eng, Middlebury Col, summers, 47-55; vis. prof, Conn. Col, 46; Univ. Minn, 56; Univ. Colo, summer, 57; Rockefeller Found. grant-in-aid, 48, Ford fel, 52-53; fel, Am. Counc. Learned Soc, 63; mem, Eng. Inst. Nineteenth century English literature; modern fiction; theory of fiction. Publ: The blue sash, 41, The first fish, 47 & The far whistle, 51, Antioch; Final score, 44 & Into thin air, 51, Knopf; Pause under the sky, Morrow, 47; Man in motion: Faulkner's trilogy, Univ. Wis, 61; The rest is silence, Swallow, 63; Joyce's Dubliners: substance, vision & art, Duke Univ, 69. Add: 207 N. Park Ave, Appleton, WI 54911.

BECKELHYMER, (PAUL) HUNTER, Religion. See Volume IV, Philosophy, Religion & Law.

BECKER, GEORGE JOSEPH, b. Aberdeen, Wash, Apr. 19, 08. ENGLISH LITERATURE. A.B, Univ. Wash, 29, A.M, 30, Ph.D, 37. Mem. fac, Immaculate Heart Col, 34-39; Los Angeles City Col, 39-42; prof. ENG, Swarthmore Col, 45-61, Alexander G. Cummings prof, 61-70, chmn. dept, 53-70; PROF, WEST. WASH. STATE COL, 70-, acting chmn. dept, 73. Mem. lit. comt, Sch. & Col. Study Advan. Standing, 52-55; Fulbright lectr. Am. lit, Bordeaux-Lille, France, 56-57, Pau, France, summer 63; Fulbright res. grant, Spain, 63-64. U.S.A, 42-45. Modern comparative literature; modern realism as a literary movement. Publ: Documents of modern literary realism, Princeton Univ, 63; ed. & transl, Paris under siege 1870-1871 from the Goncourt Journal, 69 & co-ed. & transl, Paris and the arts 1851-1896 from the Goncourt Journal, 71, Cornell Univ; auth, John Dos Passos, Ungar, 74. Add: 2225 Niagara Dr, Bellingham, WA 98225.

BECKER, HONORA E, b. Junction City, Ore, Dec. 10, 99. ENGLISH. A.M, Univ. Colo, 38; Univ. Minn, 45; hon. Litt.D, Bethel Col.(Kans), 72. Teacher, High Schs, Kans, 24-39; from asst. prof. to prof. ENG. & chmn. dept, BETHEL COL.(KANS), 39-68, EMER. PROF, 68- MLA; NCTE; Col. Eng. Asn. Modern drama. Add: 2519 College, North Newton, KS 67117.

BECKER, ISIDORE HERMAN, b. Fleming, Colo, Feb. 4, 20; m. 72; c. 3. ENGLISH & AMERICAN LITERATURE. A.B, St. Mary's Univ.(Tex), 43; M.A, La. State Univ, Baton Rouge, 55; Ph.D.(Eng), Univ. N.Mex, 70. Instr. ENG, Col. Santa Fe, 60-63, asst. prof, 64-67, ASSOC. PROF, 68-70; LOCK HAVEN STATE COL, 70- World short story; Romantic period in American literature; contemporary literature. Publ: The ironic dimension in Hawthorne's short fiction, Carlton, 71; Thoreau's princely leisure, 5/70 & Tragic irony in Rappaccini's daughter, 5/71; Husson Rev; The genial side of Jonathan Swift, Lock Haven Rev, 73. Add: Dept. of English & Philosophy, Lock Haven State College, N. Fairview, Lock Haven, PA 17745.

BECKER, JOHN EDWARD, b. Kansas City, Mo, Nov. 4, 30; m. 70. AMERICAN LITERATURE. B.A, St. Louis Univ, 54, Ph.L. & M.A, 58, S.T.L, 63; univ. fel, Yale, 64-67, Ph.D.(Eng), 68. Teacher, St. Louis Univ. High Sch, 55-56; Kapaun Mem. High Sch, Wichita, 56-57; asst. ed, Rev. for Relig, 58-62; ASST. PROF. ENG, FAIRLEIGH DICKINSON UNIV, TEANECK, 70- Ed. consult, Dept. Ministry, Nat. Counc. Churches, 70; ed, IDOC-N.Am, 70-71. Eng. Inst; MLA. Fictional form in 19th and 20th century American literature; Bible and literature. Publ: Hawthorne's historical allegory, Kennikat, 71; We have seen His glory, 61 & Nat Turner and the secular humanist, 68, Rev. for Relig; Morality and expertise, IDOC-N.Am, 71. Add: Dept. of English, Fairleigh Dickinson University, Teaneck, NJ 07666.

BECKER, SAMUEL LEO, b. Quincy, Ill, Jan. 5, 23; m. 53; c. 3. SPEECH, MASS MEDIA. B.A, Univ. Iowa, 47, M.A, 49, Ph.D.(speech), 53. Dir. radio, Univ. Wyo, 49-50; instr. TV, radio & speech, UNIV. IOWA, 50-55, asst. prof. speech & exec. secy. TV ctr, 55-56, PROF. SPEECH & DIR. DIV. TV, RADIO & FILM, 56-, CHMN. DEPT. SPEECH & DRAMATIC ART, 68- Fund Adult Educ. mass media fel. sociol, Columbia Univ, 58-59; media res. consult, U.S. Dept. Educ, 60-; Fulbright lectr, Nottingham Univ, Eng, 63-64; ed, Speech Monogr, 69-72. U.S.A, 42-45. Int. Commun. Asn; Speech Commun. Asn.(pres, 74); Cent. St. Speech Asn; Nat. Asn. Educ. Broadcasters; Asn. Prof. Broadcasting Educ; Communications research. Publ: Co-auth, Television: techniques for planning and performance, Holt, 58 & A bibliographical guide to research in speech and dramatic art, Scott, 63; co-auth, General speech communication, 71 & Essentials of general speech communication, 73, McGraw; Broadcasting's role in Presidential political campaigns, In: The great debates, Ind. Univ, 62; auth, The impact of mass media, In: Educational media: theory into practice, C.E. Merrill, 69; Rhetorical studies for the contemporary world, In: The prospect of rhetoric, Prentice-Hall, 71; plus others. Add: 521 W. Park Rd, Iowa City, IA 52240.

BECKERMAN, BERNARD, b. New York, N.Y, Sept. 24, 21; m. 40; c. 2. DRAMA. B.S.S, City Col. New York, 42; M.F.A, Yale, 43, fel. summer, 43; Ph.D, Columbia Univ, 56. Instr. Eng, Hofstra Univ, 47-50, asst. prof. drama, 50-60, prof, 60-65, dir. Shakespeare Festival, 50-65, chmn. dept. drama & speech, 57-65; PROF. DRAMATIC ARTS & CHMN. THEATRE ARTS, COLUMBIA UNIV, 65-, DEAN SCH. ARTS, 72- Lectr, Grad. dept. Eng, Columbia Univ, 57-58, thesis adv, Grad. dept. drama, 58-60; Fulbright lectr, Tel-Aviv Univ, 60-61; mem. ed. bd, Shakespeare Quart, 73- Award, Am. Shakespeare Festival & Acad, 62. U.S.A, 43-46, Sgt. Am. Educ. Theatre Asn; Am. Soc. Theatre Res. Shakespeare; forms of dramatic art; stage direction. Publ: Shakespeare at the Globe, 1599-1609, Macmillan,62; Dynamics of drama, Knopf, 70; co-ed, On stage: selected theatre reviews from New York Times, Quadrangle, 73; Shakespeare's theatre, In: Complete works of William Shakespeare, Pelican, 68; Theatre, In: Encycl. Americana, Grolier, 73; plus others. Add: Office of the Dean, School of the Arts, Columbia University, New York, NY 10027.

BECKETT, ROBERT D, b. Detroit, Mich, June 16, 34; m. 56; c. 8. ENGLISH. A.B, Univ. Mich, 57, A.M, 61; Ph.D.(Eng), Univ. Colo, 67. Instr. ENG, SOUTHWEST MO. STATE COL, 63-66, asst. prof, 66-70, ASSOC. PROF, 70- U.S.A, 53-55. MLA; AAUP; NCTE; Renaissance Soc. Am; Mod. Humanities Res. Asn; Midwest Mod. Lang. Asn. English Renaissance drama and non-dramtic literature; 17th century Scots-British literature. Publ: Themes in Tamburlaine, Part 2, Univ. Colo. Publ, fall 64; A series of assignments: prewriting and writing, Mo. Eng. Bull, 3/68. Add: Dept. of English, Southwest Missouri State College, Springfield, MO 65802.

BECKMAN, RICHARD, b. New York, N.Y, Jan. 11, 32; m. 52; 62; c. 2. ENGLISH LITERATURE. B.A, Columbia Univ, 53; M.A, Univ. Rochester, 54; Ph.D, Johns Hopkins Univ, 62. Instr. ENG, Univ. Md, 57-62; asst. prof, TEMPLE UNIV, 62-68, ASSOC. PROF, 68- MLA. English Romantic and Victorian literature. Publ: A character typology for Hardy's novels, ELH, 63. Add: Dept. of English, Temple University, Philadelphia, PA 19122.

BECKMAN, VERNON E, b. Appleton, Wis, June 4, 15; m. 40; c. 4. SPEECH. B.A, Lawrence Col, 36; M.S, Univ. Wis, 49; Ph.D.(speech), Univ. Minn, 56. Teacher high schs, 37-49; instr. SPEECH, MANKATO STATE COL, 49-53, asst. prof, 53-56, assoc. prof, 56-59, PROF, 59-, CHMN. DEPT, 64- Speech Commun. Asn. Debate; discussion; public address. Add: Dept. of Speech, Mankato State College, Mankato, MN 56001.

BECKSON, KARL, b. New York, N.Y, Feb. 4, 26; m. 57; c. 2. ENGLISH. B.A, Univ. Ariz, 49; M.A, Columbia Univ, 52, Ph.D.(Eng), 59. Instr. ENG, Fairleigh Dickinson Univ, 60-61; BROOKLYN COL, 61-66, asst. prof, 66-70, ASSOC. PROF, 70- City Univ. New York summer res. grant, 67. U.S.N.R, 43-46. MLA; Col. Eng. Asn. Late 19th and 20th century British literature. Publ: Co-auth, A reader's guide to literary terms, 61 & ed, Great theories in literary criticism, 63, Farrar, Straus; Aesthetes & decadents of the 1890's, Random, 66; Oscar Wilde: the critical heritage, Routledge & Kegan Paul, 70; co-ed, The ex-Arcadians: letters of William Rothenstein and Max Beerbohm, 1893-1945, Harvard Univ, 75 & Spiritual and unspiritual adventures: selected letters of Arthur Symons, 1880-1935, Colin Smythe Ltd, 75; co-auth, Symons, Browning and the development of the modern aesthetic, Stud. Eng. Lit, 69; auth, Yeats and the Rhymers' Club, Yeats Stud, 71 & Moore's Untilled Field and Joyce's Dubliners, Eng. Lit. in Transition, 72; plus others. Add: Dept. of English, Brooklyn College, Bedford Ave. & Ave. H, Brooklyn, NY 11210.

BECKWITH, CHARLES EMILIO, b. Oberlin, Ohio, June 8, 17; m. 51, 71; c. 3. ENGLISH. M.A, Univ. Calif, Berkeley, 48; Ph.D, Yale, 56. Lectr. ENG, Univ. Calif, Berkeley, 52-54; instr, Cornell Univ, 56-57; asst. prof, CALIF. STATE UNIV, LOS ANGELES, 57-62, assoc. prof, 62-64, PROF, 64-, found. res. grant, 62, chmn. div. lang. arts, 63-64, dept. Eng, 64-67. U.S.A, 42-44, Qm.C, 44-45, Med.Admin.C, 45-46, Lt. Am. Fed. Teachers; Am. Stud. Asn. Renaissance; American studies; Augustan age. Publ: Ed, Twentieth century interpretations of A Tale of Two Cities, Prentice-Hall, 72; co-ed, John Gay poetry and prose, Clarendon, 74. Add: Dept. of English, California State University, Los Angeles, 5151 State University Dr, Los Angeles, CA 90032.

BEDARD, BERNARD JOHN, b. Detroit, Mich, May 27, 28; m. 62; c. 4. ENGLISH. A.B, Univ. Notre Dame, 49; M.A, Univ. Mich, 50, fel, 51-55, Ph.D, 59. Instr. ENG, Univ. Notre Dame, 50-51; asst. prof, Villanova Univ, 55-62; assoc. prof, UNIV. DAYTON, 62-67, PROF, 67-, CHMN. DEPT, 62- MLA; NCTE; Milton Soc. Seventeenth century literature; Shakespeare; Milton. Add: Dept. of English, University of Dayton, Dayton, OH 45409.

BEDFORD, ALLEN GERALD, b. Isabella, Man, Feb. 28, 25; m. 54; c. 3. ENGLISH. B.A, Univ. Man, 48, M.A, 50; fel, Univ. Toronto, 50-51, Ph.D. (Eng), 57. Lectr. math, UNITED COL, UNIV. WINNIPEG, 46-49, ENG, 51-53, asst. prof, 53-61, assoc. prof, 61-67, PROF, 67-, registr, 59-66, acting chmn. dept. Eng, 71-72. Asn. Can. Univ. Teachers Eng; Can. Counc. Teachers Eng.(nat. treas, 71-); Can. Asn. Univ. Teachers; Victorian Stud. Asn. West. Can. Victorian thought; 17th-century poetry, especially metaphysicals; English humanism. Add: Dept. of English, University of Winnipeg, Winnipeg, Man. R3B 2E9, Can.

BEDFORD, EMMETT GRUNER, b. Columbia, Mo, Oct. 30, 22; m. 46; c. 3. ENGLISH LITERATURE. A.B. & B.J, Univ. Mo-Columbia, 47; Univ. Md, College Park, 62-63; univ. fels, South. Ill. Univ, Carbondale, 65-67 & 69, M.A, 69, Ph.D.(Eng), 70. Copy ed, Salt Lake Tribune, Utah, 47-48; reporter, St. Joseph Gazette, Mo, 48-49; writer, Congr. Quart, Wash, D.C, 49-53, asst. managing ed, 53-54; asst. city ed, Wash. Post, Wash, D.C, 54-55; copy ed, Wash. Star, Wash. D.C, 55-62, asst. chief copy desk, 62-63; instr. jour, South. Ill. Univ, Carbondale, 63-65; ASST. PROF. ENG. WIS-PARKSIDE, 70-, Wis. Alumni Res. Found. grant, summer 71. U.S.A.A.F, 43-45, 2nd Lt. MLA; Am. Soc. 18th Century Stud. Restoration and 18th century literature; Alexander Pope; religious symbolism. Publ: Co-ed, A concordance to the poems of Alexander Pope (2 vols), Gale, (in press); auth, Review of Pope's couplet art, Style, spring 72. Add: Div. of Humanistic Studies, University of Wisconsin-Parkside, Kenosha, WI 53140.

BEDFORD, JIMMY BERTCH, b. Columbia, Mo, June 10, 27. JOURNALISM, PHOTOGRAPHY. A.B, Univ. Mo, 50, B.J, 51, M.A.(jour, econ), 52. Assoc. ed, Memphis Democrat, Mo, 52-54; instr. JOUR, Univ. Kans, 54-58; asst. prof, Univ. Md, 60-64; Fulbright prof, Kabul Univ, Afghanistan, 64-65; PROF. & HEAD DEPT, UNIV. ALASKA, FAIRBANKS, 65- Photographer, Vancouver Sun, B.C, summer 57; Sunday Pictorial, London, summer 58; free lance writer-photographer, 58-60; correspondent for Afghanistan, United Press Int, 64. U.S.N, 45-46. Nat. Press Photographers Asn; Explorers Club; Asn. Educ. in Jour; Soc. Prof. Jour. Photojournalism; free lance and travel writing. Publ: Around the world on a nickel, Assoc. Publ. House, New Delhi, 67; co-auth, Concise English-Afghan Dari dictionary, Univ. Kabul, 73. Add: Dept. of Journalism, University of Alaska, Fairbanks, AK 99701.

BEDFORD, RICHARD COLBERT, b. Brooklyn, N.Y, Jan. 25, 23; m. 56. ENGLISH. B.A, Olivet Col, 47; M.A, State Univ, Iowa, 51, Ph.D.(Eng. & Am. civilization), 60. Res. asst. Eng, State Univ. Iowa, 52-53; instr, Wayne State Univ, 53-54, 56-59; guest prof, Osaka Univ, Japan, 54-56; asst. prof, Univ. Alaska, 59-60; assoc. prof. Eng. & chmn. dept, Sault. Ste. Marie Br, Mich. Col. Mining & Technol, 60-61; asst. prof. Eng, Wayne State Univ, 61-71; PROF. AM. LIT, DOSHISHA WOMEN'S COL, DOSHISHA UNIV, JAPAN, 71- Am. Counc. Learned Soc. grant ling, Univ. Mich, summer 61; Ford Found. lang. consult. Eng, Upgrading in Indonesia, 68. U.S.A, 42-46. Apocatastasis of Henry Miller; applied linguistics; Japanese-American literary relations. Publ: English experienced, Wayne State Univ, 72; The rule and function of the native teacher, Lang. Learning, 6/69; Steinbeck's bank robbery motif, Asphodel, 7/72; The genesis and consolation of our discontent, Criticism, summer 72. Add: Dept. of English, Doshisha Women's College, Doshisha University, Kyoto, Japan 602.

BEDFORD, WILLIAM CHARLES, b. Pittsfield, Mass, July 11, 10; m. 40; c. 2. ENGLISH, AMERICAN STUDIES. Mus.B, Syracuse Univ, 34; A.M, Univ. Mo, Columbia, 42, Ph.D.(Am. stud), 64. Asst. dir. music, Hoosac Sch, N.Y, 36-37; instr. hist, music & organ, Christian Col, 37-58, dean fac, 58-63; dir. residence ctr, SOUTHWEST MO. STATE UNIV, West Plains, 63-66, PROF. ENG, SPRINGFIELD, 66- Am. Stud. Asn; Mid-continent Am. Stud. Asn. Elizabeth Sprague Coolidge, patron of chamber music; patronage, philanthropy, related to music; American literature. Publ: A musical apprentice: Amy Lowell to Carl Engel, Musical Quart, 10/72. Add: Dept. of English, Southwest Missouri State University, Springfield, MO 65802.

BEEBE, MAURICE, b. Anacortes, Wash, Jan. 26, 26; m. 46, 62; c. 6. ENGLISH. B.A. & M.A, Univ. Wash, 47; Ph.D.(Eng), Cornell Univ, 52. Teaching fel. ENG, Cornell Univ, 48-51; instr, Univ. Kans, 51-52; Purdue Univ, 52-55, asst. prof, 55-59, assoc. prof, 59-63, PROF, 63-68; TEMPLE UNIV, 68- Ed, Mod. Fiction Stud, 55-; summer vis. prof, Univ. Va, 59; Trinity Col.(Conn), 61; State Univ. N.Y. Buffalo, 64; Univ. Tulsa, 70, 72; Univ. Maine, 72; gen. ed, Wadsworth Guides to Lit. Stud; ed, J. Mod. Lit, 70- MLA; NCTE; Am. Comp. Lit. Asn; Am. Soc. Aesthet; Mod. Humanities Res. Asn; Col. Eng. Asn; Am. Stud. Asn; Am. Comt. Irish Stud; James Joyce Found. Modern literary history; literature and fine arts; bibliography. Publ: Literary symbolism, 60 & co-auth, Robert Penn Warren's All the king's men: a critical handbook, 66, Wadsworth; auth, Ivory towers and sacred founts: the artist as hero from Goethe to Joyce, N.Y. Univ, 64; ed, Ernest Hemingway: configuration critique, Lett. Mod, 59; Ulysses and age of modernism, James Joyce Quart, fall 72. Add: P.O. Box 45, Temple University, Philadelphia, PA 19122.

BEECHHOLD, HENRY FRANK, English, Linguistics. See Volume III, Foreign Languages, Linguistics & Philology.

BEEKMAN, ERIC MONTAGUE, Germanic Languages, Comparative Literature. See Volume III, Foreign Languages, Linguistics & Philology.

BEGNAL, MICHAEL HENRY, b. Washington, D.C, Oct. 17, 39; m. 65; c. 2. MODERN ENGLISH & COMPARATIVE LITERATURE. B.A, Univ. Conn, 61; M.A, Pa. State Univ, 63; Ph.D.(Eng), Univ. Wash, 68. Instr. Eng, Colgate Univ, 63-65; ASSOC. PROF. ENG. & COMP. LIT, PA. STATE UNIV, 68- Prof. Am. lit, Charles Univ. Prague, 73-74. James Joyce; Irish literature; modern literature. Publ: Joseph Sheridan LeFanu, 71 & Dream voices of Finnegans Wake, 74, Bucknell Univ; co-ed. & contrib, A conceptual guide to Finnegans Wake, Pa. State Univ, 74. Add: Dept. of English, Pennsylvania State University, University Park, PA 16802.

BEHARRIELL, STANLEY ROSS, b. Toronto, Ont, June 15, 22; m. 48; c. 3. ENGLISH. B.A, Univ. Toronto, 44, M.A, 51; Ph.D, Univ. Wis, 54. Instr. Eng, Univ. West. Ont, 47-48; Univ. Toronto, 48-49; teaching fel, Univ. Wis, 49-52; asst. prof, Wabash Col, 52-54; ENG, Niagara Univ, 54-58; asst. prof, ROYAL MIL. COL. CAN, 58-61, ASSOC. PROF, 61- R.C.N, 42-46, Lt. MLA; Humanities Asn. Can; Melville Soc; Asn. Can. Univ. Teachers Eng; Can. Asn. Am. Stud. American and Canadian literature, especially 19th century; Shakespeare and Elizabethan drama. Publ: Ralph Connor, 60 & Stephen Leacock, 63, McLelland & Stewart; co-auth, Literary history of Canada, Univ. Toronto, 65. Add: R.R. 1, Kingston, Ont, Can.

BEHEN, DOROTHY MARGARET FORBIS, United States History & Literature. See Volume I, History.

BEHLER, DIANA IPSEN, Germanics, Comparative Literature. See Volume III, Foreign Languages, Linguistics & Philology.

BEHRENS, RALPH, b. Malvern, Ark, Oct. 10, 16. ENGLISH. B.S.E, Ark. State Teachers Col, 39; M.A, Univ. Colo, 49; Fulbright grantee, King's Col, London, 49-50. Prin. & teacher, High Sch, 39-49; asst. prof. ENG, STATE COL. ARK, 49-53, assoc. prof, 53-60, PROF, 60-, CHMN. DEPT, 70- Instr. ling, Nat. Defense Educ. Act summer inst. Eng, State Col. Ark, summer 67. U.S.A.A.F, 42-45. MLA; NCTE; Keats-Shelley Asn. Am. Keats andthe romantics; symbolists and decadents. Publ: John Gould Fletcher and Rimbaud's Alchimie du verbe, Comp. Lit; Existential character ideas in Camus' The misunderstanding, Mod. Drama, 9/64; Merimee, Hemingway, and the bulls, Costerus: Essays in Eng. & Am. Lang. & Lit, 2: 1-8; plus one other. Add: Dept. of English & Journalism, State College of Arkansas, Conway, AR 72032.

BEHRINGER, CLARA MARIE, b. Beaver Falls, Pa, Aug. 8, 15. THEATRE. B.S. Ed, Edinboro State Col, 37; M.A, Univ. Mich, 44, Ph.D.(speech), 51. Instr. speech & theatre, Geneva Col, 40-41; teacher, High Sch, Pa, 42-47; instr. THEATRE, UNIV. ILL, URBANA, 50-53, asst. prof, 53-60, assoc. prof, 60-67, PROF, 67- Ford Found. Fund grant adult educ, 53. Am. Theatre Asn; Am. Nat. Theatre & Acad; Am. Soc. Theatre Res; Int. Fed. Theatre Res; Theatre Libr. Asn; Speech Commun. Asn. American theatre history; current German theatre production. Publ: Jeanne Eagels, Gertrude Elliot & Maxine Elliott, In: Notable American Women, Harvard, 71 plus four others. Add: 4-121B Krannert Center for Performing Arts, University of Illinois, Urbana, IL 61801.

BEICHNER, PAUL EDWARD, C.S.C, b. Franklin, Pa, July 23, 12. ENGLISH. A.B, Univ. Notre Dame, 35; A.M, 41; Holy Cross Col, 35-39; Ph.D, Yale, 44. Res. fel, Yale, 44-45; asst. head dept. Eng, UNIV. NOTRE DAME, 47-50, asst. dean, col. arts & let, 49-50, asst. to v.pres. in charge acad. affairs, 50-52, dean grad. sch, 52-71, chmn. bd, Univ. Press, 52-74, PROF. MEDIEVAL STUD, 71- Mem. nat. selection comt, Woodrow Wilson Fel. Prog, 58-67; mem. exec. comt, Midwest Conf. Grad. Stud. & Res. 65-68, chmn, 66-67; mem. exec. comt, Counc. Grad. Schs. U.S, 66-69. MLA; Mediaeval Acad. Am. Middle English; Medieval Latin. Publ: Aurora, Petri Rigae Biblia Versificata: A verse commentary on the Bible (2 vols), Univ. Notre Dame, 65; Baiting the summoner, Mod. Lang. Quart, 12/61; Chaucer's Pardoner as entertainer, Mediaeval Stud, 63; The allegorical interpretation of medieval literature, PMLA, 3/67. Add: Mediaeval Institute, University of Notre Dame, Notre Dame, IN 46556.

BEIGHLEY, KENNETH CLARE, b. East McKeesport, Pa, Sept. 8, 14. SPEECH. A.B, Muskingum Col, 36; A.M, Ohio State Univ, 37, Ph.D, 52. Teacher, high sch, Ohio, 36-41; Calif, 41-43; from asst. prof. to PROF. COUNSELING & SPEECH, STOCKTON VOL, 46- U.S.A, 43-46. Public address area of speech. Publ: Effect of four variables upon the comprehension of prose and Effect of three variables on the comprehension of prose, Speech Monogr; A summary of experimental studies on the effect of skill of the speaker and organization on audience comprehension, J. Commun. Add: 2237 Polk Way, Stockton, CA 95207.

BEIRNE, RAYMOND MICHAEL, b. New Haven, Conn, Oct. 2, 22. ENGLISH. B.A, Trinity Col.(Conn), 50; Russell fel, 50-52; M.A, Columbia Univ, 51. Instr. ENG, Rutgers Univ, 52-54; UNIV. FLA, 54-63, asst. prof, 63-69, ASSOC. PROF, 69- U.S.N, 43-44; U.S.M.C, 44-46. MLA; S.Atlantic Mod. Lang. Asn; Eng-Speaking Union. Contemporary drama; 20th century literary criticism; film history and appreciation. Add: Dept. of English, University of Florida, Gainesville, FL 32601.

BEJA, MORRIS, b. New York, N.Y, July 18, 35; m. 57; c. 2. ENGLISH. B.A, City Col. New York, 57; M.A, Columbia Univ, 58; Ph.D.(Eng), Cornell Univ, 63. Instr. ENG, OHIO STATE UNIV, 61-63, asst. prof. 63-68, assoc. prof, 68-71, PROF, 71- Ohio State Univ. res. grants, 65 & 68, Develop. Fund fac. fel, 68; Fulbright lectr. Am. lit, Univ. Thessaloniki, 65-66; Fulbright vis. prof. Eng, Univ. Col, Dublin, 72-73; Guggenheim fel, 72-73. MLA; Am. Comt. Irish Stud; James Joyce Found. Modern English, American and Irish literature. Publ: Virginia Woolf's To the lighthouse, 70 & ed, James Joyce's Dubliners and A portrait of the artists as a young man, 73, Macmillan, London: Epiphany in the modern novel, Univ. Wash, 71; ed, Psychological fiction, Scott, 71; It must be important: Negroes in contemporary American fiction, Antioch Rev, fall 64; The wooden sword: threatener and threatened in the fiction of James Joyce, James Joyce Quart, fall 64; Felons of ourselves: the fiction of Aidan Higgins, Irish Univ. Rev, fall 73; plus one other. Add: Dept. of English, Ohio State University, 164 W. 17th Ave, Columbus, OH 43210.

BELCHER, WILLIAM FRANCIS, JR, b. Abilene, Tex, Nov. 16, 19; m. 46; c. 2. ENGLISH. B.A, Tex. Technol. Col, 42; M.A, Univ. N.C, 47, Ph.D. (Eng), 50. Asst. prof. ENG, N.TEX. STATE UNIV, 50-53, assoc. prof, 53-55, PROF, 55- U.S.A, 43-46. MLA; NCTE. Eighteenth century English literature; contemporary poetry and fiction. Publ: Co-auth, Reading and writing, Rinehart, 54 & J.D. Salinger and the critics, Wadsworth, 62; auth, The sale and distribution of the British Apollo, In: Studies in the early English periodical, Univ. N.C, 57. Add: Box 5965, North Texas State University Station, Denton, TX 76203.

BELKIN, ROSLYN K, b. Montreal, P.Q; c. 1. ENGLISH, DRAMA. B.A, Sir George Williams Univ, 52; M.A, Univ. Montreal, 64, Ph.D.(Eng), 73. Lectr. ENG, CONCORDIA UNIV, 59-61, asst. prof, 61-67, ASSOC. PROF, 67- Asn. Can. Univ. Teachers Eng. Criticism; rhetoric. Add: Dept. of English, Concordia University, de Maisonneuve St. W, Montreal, P.Q, Can.

BELKIND, ALLEN J, b. Milwaukee, Wis, Mar. 27, 27; m. 59; c. 1. ENGLISH. B.A, Univ. Calif, Los Angeles, 56, M.A, 61; Ph.D.(Eng), Univ. South. Calif, 66. Asst. prof. ENG, Univ. Nev, Reno, 64-71; ASSOC. PROF, CALIF. STATE COL, BAKERSFIELD, 71- Fulbright lectr, Helsinki Sch. Econ, 69-70, Univ. Haiti, 74-75. U.S.N.R, 45-47. MLA; Philol. Asn. Pac. Coast; AAUP. American literature; modern literature; comparative literature. Publ: Jean-Paul Sartre and existentialism in English: a bibliographical guide, 70 & John Dos Passos: an international checklist, 74, Kent State Univ; Dos Passos, the critics and the writer's intention, Crosscurrent Critiques Series, South. Ill. Univ, 71; contrib, J. Mod. Lit. Add: Dept. of English, California State College, Bakersfield, Bakersfield, CA 93309.

BELL, ALEXANDER ROBERT LUNDRIGAN, b. Rock Island, Ill, Aug. 9, 36. OLD ENGLISH LANGUAGE & LITERATURE. B.S, Univ. Miami, 60; Ford Found fel, 60-62, M.A, 62; NDEA fel, 67-69, Univ. Md, Ph.D.(Medieval stud), 71. Instr. Eng. & comp. lit, Calif. State Univ. Long Beach; Univ. Md, 67-69, ASST. PROF. ENG, CALIF. STATE UNIV, LONG BEACH, 69-, DIR. CTR. MEDIEVAL & RENAISSANCE STUD, 73- Ed, Comp. Lit. Newsl, 65-; co-ed, Conradiana, 67-70; vis. prof. Eng, George Mason Col, 68; Bowie State Col, 68-69. Philol. Asn. Pac. Coast; MLA; Mediaeval Acad. Am; Early English Text Soc; Mediaeval Asn. Pac. Mediaeval comparative literature; Old English; Mediaeval studies. Publ: Ed, Mediaeval thesis bibliography, Perian, (in prep); auth, Folklore and mythology: an introductory course, Calif. State Univ, 66 & English literature from 1798, 67, Calif. State Univ. World literature: a course guide, Univ. Md, 68; Folklore and mythology in La Celestina, Univ. South. Calif. Publ. Comp. Lit, 68. Add: Dept. of English, California State University, Long Beach, 6101 E. Seventh St, Long Beach, CA 90840.

BELL, BERNARD WILLIAM, b. Washington, D.C, Feb. 7, 36; m. 58; c. 3. AMERICAN & AFRO-AMERICAN LITERATURE. B.A, Howard Univ, 62, M.A, 66; Ph.D.(Eng), Univ. Mass, Amherst, 70. Teaching asst. ENG, Howard Univ, 62-63; teacher, Coolidge High Sch, Wash, D.C, 63-67; teaching asst, UNIV. MASS, AMHERST, 67-68, NDEA fel, 68-69, lectr-asst. prof, 69-70, ASST. PROF, 70- Vis. prof, Clark Univ, 70; acting head, Univ. Mass, 70; Nat. Endowment Humanities Young Humanist fel, 72-73; lectr, Smith Col, 73. U.S.M.C, 53-57, Sgt. MLA; Col. Lang. Asn; NCTE. Afro-American literature; novel; 19th and 20th century American literature. Publ: Ed, Modern and contemporary Afro-American poetry, Allyn & Bacon, 72; The folk roots of contemporary Afro-American poetry, 74 & Jean Toomer: a portrait of the modern Black artist, 74, Broadside; A key to the poems in cane, 3/71 & New black poetry: a double edged sword, 12/71, Col. Lang. Asn. J; Contemporary Afro-American poetry as folk art, Black World, 3/73; plus others. Add: Dept. of English, University of Massachusetts, Amherst, MA 01002.

BELL, CHARLES GREENLEAF, b. Greenville, Miss, Oct. 31, 16; m. 39; 49; c. 5. HUMANITIES. B.S, Univ. Va, 36; Rhodes scholar, Oxford, 36-39, B.A, 38, B.Litt, 39, M.A, 66. Instr. Eng, Blackburn Col, 39-40; from instr. to asst. prof, Iowa State Col, 40-43, physics, 43-45; res. asst, Palmer Lab, Princeton, 45, asst. prof, Eng, 45-49; humanities, Univ. Chicago, 49-56; TUTOR, St. John's Col.(Md), 56-67, ST. JOHN'S COL.(N.MEX), 67-, dir, Integrative Grad. Preceptorial, 72-73. Rockefeller Found. grant, 48; lectr, Black Mt. Col, 48; guest prof, Univ. Frankfort, 52; Ford grant, 52-53; prof. & head honors Eng, Univ. P.R, 55-56; Fulbright lectr, Munich, Ger, 58-59; guest prof. & writer-in-residence, Univ. Rochester, 67. Problems of organic philosophy and cultural history, with a correlation of the arts; Edward Fairfax and the evolution of English verse. Publ: Songs for a new America, Ind. Univ, 53, rev. ed, Norman S. Berg, 66; Delta return, Ind. Univ, 56, Norman Berg, 68; The married land, 62 & The half gods, 68, Houghton. Add: 1260 Canyon Rd, Sante Fe, NM 87501.

BELL, HANEY H, b. Petersburg, Va, Aug. 25, 17; m. 42; c. 2. ENGLISH. A.B, Randolph-Macon Col, 39; Univ. N.C, 40-41; Johns Hopkins Univ, 52-53; M.A, Univ. Md, 65. Instr. ENG, Staunton Mil. Acad, 41-44; U.S. NAVAL ACAD, 44-47, asst. prof, 47-52, ASSOC. PROF, 52- Part-time assoc. prof, Anne Arundel Col, 66-67. NCTE; Col. Eng. Asn. Genealogy in Faulkner's works. Publ: Sam Fathers and Ike McCaslin and the world in which Ike matures, Costerus, 73; The masque of the red death: an interpretation, S.Atlantic Bull, 73; The relative maturity of Lucious Priest and Ike McCaslin, Aegis, 73. Add: Dept. of English, U.S. Naval Academy, Annapolis, MD 21401.

BELL, (F) KENNETH, b. Birmingham, Ala, Jan. 23, 04; m. 29; c. 2. JOURNALISM. B.J, Univ. Mo, 28, A.M, 36. Advertising mgr, Brunswick News, Ga, 28-30; from instr. to asst. prof. jour, Univ. Mo, 30-38; ed. & pub, Alexander City Outlook, Ala, 41-44; asst. prof. JOUR, W.Va. Univ, 44-47; assoc. prof, UNIV. ALA, 47-57, PROF, 57- Asn. Educ. Jour. Newspaper readership. Add: Dept. of Journalism, University of Alabama, University, AL 35486.

BELL, MICHAEL DAVITT, b. Pittsburgh, Pa, Mar. 30, 41; m. 67; c. 2. ENGLISH & AMERICAN LITERATURE. B.A, Yale, 63; M.A, Harvard, 68, Ph.D.(Eng), 69. Teaching fel. ENG, Harvard, 64-68; instr, PRINCETON, 68-69, ASST. PROF, 69-, ASST. DIR. AM. STUD. PROG, 72- MLA; Am. Stud. Asn. American literature; novel. Publ: Hawthorne and the historical romance of New England, Princeton, 71; co-auth, Blacks in America: bibliographical essays, Doubleday, 71; auth, Pamela's wedding the marriage of the lamb, Philol. Quart, 9/70; History and romance convention in Catherine Sedgwick's Hope Leslie, Am. Quart, 5/70. Add: Dept. of English, McCosh 22, Princeton University, Princeton, NJ 08540.

BELL, ROBERT HUNTLEY, b. Cambridge, Mass, Feb. 21, 46; m. 67. ENGLISH & AMERICAN LITERATURE. B.A. & Woodrow Wilson fel, Dartmouth Col, 67; Danforth Found. fel, 67-72; M.A, Harvard, 68, fel, 69-72, Ph.D.(Eng), 72. ASST. PROF. ENG, WILLIAMS COL, 72- Soc. Relig. Higher Educ. Eighteenth century literature; autobiography; the modern literature. Add: Dept. of English, Williams College, Williamstown, MA 01267.

BELL, VEREEN McNEILL, b. Cairo, Ga, Oct. 31, 34; m. 55; c. 3. ENGLISH. B.S, Davidson Col, 55; M.A, Duke Univ, 56, Ph.D, 59. Instr. ENG, La. State Univ, 59-61; asst. prof, VANDERBILT UNIV, 61-65, ASSOC. PROF, 65- MLA; S.Atlantic Mod. Lang. Asn. English fiction; modern British and American fiction and poetry. Publ: Wuthering Heights as epos, Col. Eng, 12/63; Comic seriousness in A passage to India, S.Atlantic Quart, fall 67; plus others. Add: Dept. of English, Vanderbilt University, Nashville, TN 37235.

BELL, WAYNE EDWARD, b. Lakeland, Fla, Nov. 29, 35; m. 60; c. 2. LITERATURE, RELIGION. A.B, Stetson Univ, 57; Danforth Sem. inter, Univ. Minn, 59-60; B.D, Southeast. Baptist Theol. Sem.(N.C), 61; Ph.D.(lit. & relig), Emory Univ, 66. Instr. Eng. & interdisciplinary stud, Ky. South. Col, 64-65, asst. prof, 65-67, assoc. prof, 67-68; Eng, Valdosta State Col, 68-72; PROF. ENG. & ACAD. DEAN, DALTON JR. COL, 72- Conf. Acad. Deans South. States. Literature and religion; American literature, 1850 to the present. Add: Dalton Junior College, Dalton, GA 30720.

BELLAMY, JOE DAVID, b. Cincinnati, Ohio, Dec. 29, 41; m. 64; c. 2. CONTEMPORARY AMERICAN FICTION & POETRY. B.A, Antioch Col, 64; M.F.A, Univ. Iowa, 69. Asst. col. ed, Antioch Col, 65-67; instr. ENG, Mansfield State Col, 69-70, ASST. PROF, 70-72; ST. LAWRENCE UNIV, 72- Chmn. symp. writing courses & acad. growth, Col.Eng. Asn, 71-72; publ. & ed, Fiction Int, 72-; Breadloaf scholar, Bridgman Award, Middlebury Col, 73; mem, Coord. Counc. Lit. Mag. MLA (chmn. contemp. lit. sect, Northeast Mod. Lang. Asn, 70-71); AAUP. Formal innovation in contemporary fiction. Publ: Ed, Apocalypse: dominant contemporary forms, Lippincott, 72; auth, The new fiction: interviews with innovative American writers,

Univ. Ill, 74; The dark lady of American letters, Atlantic Monthly, 2/72; Having it both ways: a conversation between John Barth and Joe David Bellamy, New Am. Rev, 72; contrib, The Vonnegut statement, Delacorte, 73. Add: Dept. of English, St. Lawrence University, Canton, NY 13617.

BELLAS, RALPH A, b. Hazleton, Pa, Sept. 22, 24; m. 49; c. 6. ENGLISH. A.B, Cath. Univ. Am, 50; M.A, Univ. Pa, 52; Ph.D.(Eng), Univ. Kans, 60. Instr. ENG, Univ. Kans, 53-58; asst. prof, Villanova Univ, 58-65; ASSOC. PROF, ILL. STATE UNIV, 65- U.S.A, 44-46. NCTE; MLA. Victorian literature; 19th century English literature. Add: Dept. of English, Illinois State University, Normal, IL 61761.

BELLI, ANGELA, b. Brooklyn, N.Y, Oct. 8, 35. ENGLISH, COMPARATIVE LITERATURE. B.A, Brooklyn Col, 57; M.A, Univ. Conn, 59; Ph.D.(comp. lit), N.Y. Univ, 65. Asst. ENG, Univ. Conn, 57-59; lectr, Brooklyn Col, 59-66; asst. prof, ST. JOHN'S UNIV.(N.Y), 66-69, ASSOC. PROF, 69- MLA. Contemporary drama; comparative literature. Publ: Ancient Greek myths and modern drama: a study in continuity, N.Y. Univ, 69; Lenormand's Asie and Anderson's The wingless victory, Comp. Lit, summer 67; The rugged individualists of Henry de Montherlant, Mod. Drama, 9/70. Add: Dept. of English, St. John's University, Grand Central & Utopia Pkwys, Jamaica, NY 11439.

BELLMAN, SAMUEL IRVING, b. El Paso, Tex, Sept. 28, 26; m. 52; c. 2. ENGLISH. B.A, Univ. Tex, 47; M.A, Wayne Univ, 51; fel, Ohio State Univ, 53, Ph.D, 55. Teaching asst, Ohio State Univ, 53-54, asst. instr, 54-55; instr. ENG, Fresno State Col, 55-57; asst. prof, Calif. State Polytech. Col, San Luis Obispo, 57-59, CALIF. STATE POLYTECH. UNIV, POMONA, 59-62, assoc. prof, 62-66, PROF, 66- Vis. prof, Univ. South. Calif, summer 68. Col. Eng. Asn; Philol Asn. Pac. Coast. Modern American literature; poetics; literary criticism. Publ: Ed, College experience, 62 & Survey and forecast, 66, Chandler Publ; auth, The transformation psychology of Bernard Malamud, Critique, 65; Domestic relations and social vision in the modern novel, Calif, Eng. J, 67; Apocalyptic criticism, 73 & Sleep, pride and fantasy in the American novel, 73, Costerus; plus numerous others. Add: 1012 Lake Forest Dr, Claremont, CA 91711.

BELLMAN, WILLARD F, b. Tacoma, Wash, May 4, 20; m. 49; c. 2. DRAMA. B.A, Univ. Puget Sound, 46; M.A, Northwest. Univ, 47, Ph.D.(drama), 49. Instr. speech & drama, Univ. Wyo, 50-51; asst. prof. Eng. & drama, Wash. Univ, 51-56, assoc. prof, 56; asst. prof. theater, Univ. Calif, Los Angeles, 56-57; speech drama, CALIF. STATE UNIV, NORTHRIDGE, 57-61, assoc. prof, 61-67, PROF. DRAMA, 67- U.S. del. educ. comn, Orgn. Int. Scenographers & Techniciens Theatre, 71- U.S.A.A.F, 41-46. Am. Educ. Theatre Asn; U.S. Inst. Theatre Technol. Theatre lighting and aesthetics; theatrical scenic projection. Publ: Lighting the stage—art and practice, Chandler Publ, 67; plus others. Add: Dept. of Drama, California State University, Northridge, 18111 Nordhoff St, Northridge, CA 91324.

BELLOW, SAUL, b. Lachine, P.Q, June 10, 15; m; c. 3. ENGLISH. B.S, Northwest. Univ, 37; D.Litt. from several insts. Asst. prof. Eng, Univ. Minn, Minneapolis, 46-48; fel. creative writing, Princeton, 52-53; Bard Col, 53-54; assoc. prof, Univ. Minn, 57-59; PROF. LETT. & ENG. & MEM. COMT. SOC. THOUGHT, UNIV. CHICAGO, 63- Guggenheim fels, 48-49, 55-56; Ford Found. grant, 59-61; fel. Brandford Col, Yale; adv, Guggenheim Found, Rockefeller Found. & Nat. Inst. Arts & Lett. Nat. Inst. Arts & Lett. Award, 52; Nat. Bk. Award, 53, 64; Friends of Lit. Fiction Award, 60; James L. Dow Award, 64; Int. Lit. Prize, 65; Chevalier, Legion d'honneur, France. U.S. Merchant Marine. Nat. Inst. Arts & Lett. Publ: Dangling man, New Am. Libr. & Vanguard, 44; The victim, New Am. Libr. & Vanguard, 47, Viking, 56; Adventures of Augie March, Mod. Libr. & Fawcett, 53, Viking, 60; Henderson, the rain king, 59, Seize the day, 61 & Last analysis (play), 66, Viking; co-ed, Noble savage, 5 vols, Meridian, 62; auth, Herzog, Fawcett & Viking, 64; Mosby's memoirs, Viking, 68. Add: Dept. of English, University of Chicago, Chicago, IL 60637.

BELOOF, ROBERT, b. Wichita, Kans, Dec. 30, 23; div; c. 4. LITERATURE, SPEECH, DRAMA. M.A, Middlebury Col, 48; M.A, Northwest. Univ, 48, Fund Advan. Educ. fel. & Ph.D.(speech), 54. Lectr. oral interpretation of lit, UNIV. CALIF, BERKELEY, 48-54, asst. prof, 54-58, assoc. prof. SPEECH, 58-64, PROF, 64-, chmn. dept, 64-68. Fulbright prof. Am. lit, Orient. Inst, Naples, 59-60. MLA; Speech Commun. Asn. English prosody; dramatic structure. Publ: The one-eyed gunner, Villiers Publ, London, 57; The performing voice in literature, Little, 66; Good poems, Sampler Bks, 73; Prosody and tone: the mathematics of Marianne Moore, Kenyon Rev, 58; Strength in the exquisite: a study of John Crowe Ransom's prosody, Annali Dell 'Istituto Universitario Orientale, Naples, 61. Add: Dept. of Rhetoric, University of California, Berkeley, CA 94720.

BELSON, JOEL J, b. New York, N.Y, Mar. 6, 33; m. 56; c. 1. ENGLISH. B.A, Columbia Univ, 54, M.A, 55, Ph.D.(Eng), 64. Instr. ENG, STATE UNIV. N.Y. MARITIME COL, 58-61, asst. prof, 61-64, assoc. prof, 64-69. PROF, 69- H.C. Bunner Medal Am. Lit, Columbia Univ, 54. MLA. Sixteenth century English literature. Publ: Escaped faults in the Spenser concordance, Am. Notes & Queries, 1/70; The nature and consequences of the loneliness of Huckleberry Finn, Ariz. Quart, 26: 243-248; Whitman's Overstaid fraction, Walt Whitman Rev, 6/71; plus one other. Add: Dept. of Humanities, State University of New York Maritime College at Ft. Schuyler, Bronx, NY 10465.

BELTRAN, LUIS, Comparative Literature. See Volume III, Foreign Languages, Linguistics & Philology.

BELVEDERE, JOSEPH F, b. New York, N.Y, Feb. 22, 14. ENGLISH LITERATURE. B.S, Fordham Univ, 35, A.M, 37. Instr. Fordham Univ, 37-42, 46; asst. prof. ENG, Univ. Scranton, 46-52; ST. PETER'S COL.(N.J), 52-68, ASSOC. PROF, 68-, chmn. dept, 66-69. MLA. Dante Gabriel Rossetti; poems. Add: Dept. of English, St. Peter's College, Jersey City, NJ 07306.

BENARDETE, JANE, b.Columbus, Ohio, Nov. 6, 30; m. 61; c. 1. ENGLISH & AMERICAN LITERATURE. A.B, Radcliffe Col, 52, A.M, 54, Ph.D.(hist. Am. civilization), 58. Instr. hist. & lit, Harvard, 58-61; asst. prof, ENG, Northeast. Univ. 61-65; HUNTER COL, 65-71, ASSOC. PROF, 71- Am. Stud. Asn. American literature, especially colonial and 19th century. Publ: Ed, Crumbling idols, Harvard, 60 & American realism, Putnam, 72; auth, Huckleberry Finn and the nature of fiction, Mass. Rev, spring 68. Add: 405 Bleecker St, New York, NY 10014.

BENBOW, R. MARK, b. Sioux City, Iowa, May 25, 25; m. 48; c. 4. ENGLISH LITERATURE. B.A, Univ. Wash, 47; M.A, Yale, 49, Ph.D, 50. Instr. Eng, COLBY COL, 50-52, asst. prof, 52-55, assoc. prof, 55-62, prof, 62-71, ROBERTS PROF. ENG. LIT, 71-, CHMN. DEPT, 66- Folger fel, 57 & 65. U.S.N.R, 43-47, Ens. MLA. Elizabethan-Jacobean drama and literature: Reformation theology. Publ: The plays of W. Wager, Univ. Nebr, 67; Providential theory of historical causation in Holinshed's chronicles, Univ. Tex. Stud. Lang. & Lit, 59. Add: Dept. of English, Colby College, Waterville, ME 04901.

BENCE, EUGENE, b. Memphis, Tenn, Dec. 29, 11; m. 62; c. 1. SPEECH, DRAMA. B.S, Memphis State Col, 33; M.A, Northwest. Univ, 49. Instr. SPEECH & DRAMA, MEMPHIS STATE UNIV, 49-53, asst. prof, 53-58, assoc. prof, 58-63, PROF, 63- Speech Commun. Asn; Southeast. Theatre Conf. Drama. Add: Dept. of Speech & Drama, Memphis State University, Memphis, TN 38152.

BENDER, COLEMAN C, b. Coalport, Pa, Mar. 30, 21; m. 47; c. 2. SPEECH, EDUCATION. B.A, Pa. State Univ, 46, M.A, 47; fel, Univ. Ill, 50-51, 55, Ph.D.(speech), 55. Instr. speech, Pa. State Univ, 46-48; Univ. Ill, 48-51; educ. specialist instr. training, Chanute AFB, 51; PROF. SPEECH, CHMN. DEPT. & CHMN. GRAD. STUD, EMERSON COL, 51- Consult, Sch. Pub. Health, Harvard, 69-73; staff, New Eng. Inst. Law Enforcement Mgt, 69-; mem, Munic. Police-Sci. Inst. U.S.A, 42-46. Speech Commun. Asn; East. States Speech Asn; New Eng. Speech Asn; Int. Commun. Asn. Communication problems; group dynamics advertising. Publ: Co-auth, Speaking is a practical matter, 68, auth, Guidebook to speech communication, 69, co-auth, Words in context, 70 & Issues and problems in relevance, 70, Holbrook. Add: 81 Bromfield St, Watertown, MA 02172.

BENDER, JACK E, b. Grand Rapids, Mich, Dec. 6, 18; m. 49; c. 1. DRAMA. A.B, Univ. Mich, 41, M.A, 42, Ph.D, 54. Instr. speech, N.Y. Univ, 42-46; teaching fel, UNIV. MICH, ANN ARBOR, 46, from lectr. to instr. SPEECH & DRAMA, 46-54, asst. prof, 54-60, assoc. prof, 60-65, PROF, 65- Am. Theatre Asn. Theatre criticism; history of the American theatre. Publ: Brander Matthews: critic of the theatre, 60 & Criterion Independent Theatre, 66, Educ. Theatre J. Add: 1620 Hillridge Blvd, Ann Arbor, MI 48103.

BENDER, JOHN BRYANT, b. Tulsa, Okla, July 19, 40; m. 67. ENGLISH LITERATURE. A.B, Princeton, 62; Yale, 62-63; Ph.D.(Eng), Cornell Univ, 67. Asst. prof. ENG, STANFORD UNIV, 67-73, ASSOC. PROF, 73- Renaissance Soc. Am; MLA. Renaissance and eighteenth-century English literature; interaction of literature and the visual arts. Publ: Spenser and literary pictorialism, Princeton, 72. Add: Dept. of English Stanford University, Stanford, CA 94305.

BENDER, ROBERT MORTON, b. Chicago, Ill, Mar. 15, 36; m. 63; c. 3. ENGLISH. B.S, Ill. Inst. Technol, 57; M.A, Univ. Mich, 58, Ph.D.(Eng), 63. Instr. ENG, Univ. Mich, 62-63; Brooklyn Col, 63-66, asst. prof, 67-68; UNIV. MO-COLUMBIA, 68-69, ASSOC. PROF, 70- Am. Counc. Learned Soc. study fel, 64-65. Shakespeare Asn. Am. Shakespeare; modern drama; opera. Publ: Co-auth, The sonnet, 65, auth, Five courtier poets of the English Renaissance, 67 & ed, The shaping of fiction, 70, Washington Sq. Add: Dept. of English, University of Missouri-Columbia, Columbia, MO 65201.

BENDER, TODD K, b. Stark Co, Ohio, Jan. 8, 36; m. 58; c. 2. ENGLISH, CLASSICAL LANGUAGES. B.A, Kenyon Col, 58; Fulbright fel, Univ. Sheffield, 58-59; Ph.D.(class. lang. & Eng), Stanford Univ, 62. Instr. ENG, Stanford Univ, 61-62; Dartmouth Col, 62-63; asst. prof, Univ. Va, 63-65; assoc. prof, UNIV. WIS-MADISON, 65-73, PROF, 73- Am. Counc. Learned Soc. grant-in-aid, Oxford, 63 & fel, Bibliot. Nat, Paris, 65-66; Am. Philos. Soc. grant, Paris, 69; vis. prof, World Campus Prog, 73. MLA. Nineteenth century English and European literature; Homeric Greek; computational linguistics. Publ: Gerard Manley Hopkins: the critical reception and classical background of his work, Johns Hopkins Univ, 66; co-auth, A Hopkins concordance, Univ. Wis, 70; Concordance to Conrad's Heart of darkness, South. Ill. Univ, 73; auth, The sad tale of Dowell, Criticism, fall 62; The plantan in Donne, Theocritus, Virgil, etc, Time Lit. Suppl, London, 8/12/65. Add: Dept. of English, University of Wisconsin-Madison, Madison, WI 53706.

BENEDETTI, ROBERT LAWRENCE, b. Chicago, Ill, Feb. 27, 39; m. 65; c. 3. THEATRE. B.S, Northwest. Univ, Evanston, 60, M.A, 62, Ph.D.(interpretation), 69; fel, Ind. Univ, Bloomington, 65-66. Lectr. fine arts & dir. theatre, Univ. Chicago, 60-64; dir-in-residence, Univ. Wis-Milwaukee, 65-66, asst. prof. theatre, 66-68; Carnegie-Mellon Univ, 68-70; assoc. prof. theatre & chmn. acting prog, Sch. Drama, Yale, 70-71; assoc. prof. theatre & chmn. dept, York Univ, 71-73; assoc. prof, Univ. Calif, Riverside, 73-74; DEAN SCH. THEATRE, CALIF. INST. ARTS, 74- Guest prof. & dir, Univ. Colo, 67-71. Am. Theatre Asn. Acting; social interaction; directing. Publ: The actor at work, Prentice-Hall, 72; Seeming, being, and becoming, Scott, 74; contrib, Actor training number 1, Drama Bk. Specialists, 73; auth, The director as gardener, Southeast. Educ. Theatre J, 73; What we need to learn from the Asian actor, Educ. Theatre J, 74; plus others. Add: School of Theatre, California Institute of the Arts, Valencia, CA 91355.

BENEDICT, TED W, b. Hinsdale, Ill, Nov. 25, 19; m. 45; c. 3. SPEECH & COMMUNICATION. B.A, Pac. Union Col, 42; M.A, Univ. South. Calif, 47, Ph.D, 58. Asst. prof. speech, Pac. Union Col, 47-50, assoc. prof, 51-58, prof, 59-64; assoc. prof. SPEECH & COMMUN, SAN JOSE STATE UNIV, 64-67, PROF, 68-, DEAN ACAD. PLANNING, 71-, acting assoc. dean grad. stud. & res, 69, chmn. dept. speech commun. & spec. asst. to pres, 69-71. Teaching asst, Univ. South. Calif, 46, 53; vis. prof, Andrews Univ, summer 59; assoc. dir. ctr. interdisciplinary stud. & dir. commun. & media res. group, San Jose State Univ, 66-; internship, Am. Counc. Educ. Acad. Admin, 68-69. U.S.A, 42-45, Sgt. Speech Commun. Asn; West. Speech Commun. Asn; Nat. Soc. Stud. Commun. Communication theory; persuasion; sociology. Publ: An essay on information metabolism, Perspective, fall 66. Add: Academic Planning, San Jose State University, 125 S. Seventh St, San Jose, CA 95192.

BENJAMIN, EDWIN BONETTE, b. Salem, Mass, Dec. 18, 16; m. 52. ENGLISH LITERATURE. A.B, Bowdoin Col, 37; A.M, Harvard, 38, Ph.D, 46. Instr. ENG, Hamilton Col, 41-42; Yale, 46-47; asst. prof, Wesleyan Univ, 47-51; Bowdoin Col, 53-59; assoc. prof, TEMPLE UNIV, 59-65, PROF, 65- Vis. prof, Kyushu Univ, 51-53. MLA; Renaissance Soc. Am; Col. Eng. Asn. English novel; Renaissance historigraphy; Renaissance classicism. Publ: Province of poetry, Am. Bk. Co, 66; Patterns of morality in The white devil, Eng. Stud, 65; Bacon and Tacitus, J. Class. Philol, 65; Milton and Tacitus, Milton Stud, 72. Add: Dept. of English, Temple University, Philadelphia, PA 19122.

BENKOVITZ, MIRIAM, b. Chattanooga, Tenn, Nov. 16, 11. ENGLISH LITERATURE. A.B, Vanderbilt Univ, 32; A.M, George Peabody Col, 41; A.M, Yale, 47, Ph.D, 51. PROF. ENG, SKIDMORE COL, 45- Vis. prof, State Univ. N.Y. Albany, 69. MLA; Bibliog. Soc. Am; Manuscript Soc. English novel of 1920's, Richard Aldington, Frederick Rolfe and Baron Corvo. Publ: Bibliography of Ronald Firbank, Hart-Davis, 63; ed, Edwy and Elgiva, Shoestring, 58; auth, Chronology in Ronald Firbank: two novels, New Dir, 62; co-auth, Nancy Cunard, Chilton, 68; auth, Ronald Firbank, a biography, Knopf, 69; A passionate prodigality, 74. Add: 17 Ten Springs Dr, Saratoga Springs, NY 12866.

BENNETT, ALVIN LOWELL, b. Osage, Tex, Jan. 26, 05; m. 30; c. 4. ENGLISH. B.A, Tex, 27, Ph.D, 52; M.A, Univ. Wash, 31. Instr. ENG, Univ. Tex, 47-52; asst. prof, Tex. A&M Univ, 54-57, ASSOC. PROF, 57-66; SOUTHWEST TEX. STATE UNIV, 66- U.S.N.R, 43-45. MLA; Renaissance Soc. Am. English Renaissance; Texas folklore. Publ: The sanctified sisters, 64, Tex. Folklore Annual; The moral tone of Massinger's plays, 66, Papers Lang. & Lit; The sources of Shakespeare's Merry wives, Renaissance Quart, winter 70; plus others. Add: 5814 Trailridge Dr, Austin, TX 78731.

BENNETT, CARL DOUGLAS, b. Waycross, Ga, July 22, 17; m. 42; c. 3. ENGLISH, CHRISTIANITY & CULTURE. A.B, Emory Univ, 40, A.M, 44, Ph.D, 62. Instr. Eng, W.Ga. Col, 41-42; asst. prof, Wesleyan Col, 44-47; assoc. prof, 47-59, chmn. humanities div, 56-59; PROF. ENG, ST. ANDREWS PRESBY. COL, 59-, CHMN. LANG. & LIT. DIV, 73-, chmn. Afro-Asian Cult, 63-67. Vis. prof, Mercer Univ, 48; Carnegie Found. res. grant, 47; Danforth Found. grant, 50; Fulbright-Hays grant, Inst. Indian Civilization, New Delhi & Mysore, India, summer 64. Assignee, Quaker work camps, Civilian Pub. Serv, 42-44. S.Atlantic Mod. Lang. Asn; Am. Civil Liberties Union; Asn. Asian Stud. English and American literature; Joseph Conrad; ethics and the novel. Add: St. Andrews Presbyterian College, Laurinburg, NC 28352.

BENNETT, CLEON VERNON, b. Sapulpa, Okla, Nov. 16, 31; m. 54; c. 3. SPEECH & DRAMA, THEATRE HISTORY. B.S, Murray State Univ, 55; M.A, South. Ill. Univ, 59; Ph.D.(theatre arts), Univ. Wis-Madison, 71. Dir. speech & drama, Harrisburg Township High Sch, Ill, 55-56; instr. speech & theatre arts & tech. dir, ORE. STATE UNIV, 58-63, from asst. prof. to ASSOC. PROF. THEATRE ARTS, 66- Instr. stage craft & tech. div, Univ. B.C, summer 60. U.S.A, 50-52. Am. Soc. Theatre Res; AAUP; Am. Theatre Asn; Speech Commun. Asn; Univ. & Col. Theatre Asn; Am. Community Theatre Asn. Nineteenth century British theatre; American theatre; theatre history. Add: Dept. of Speech Communications, Mitchell Playhouse, Oregon State University, Corvallis, OR 97331.

BENNETT, FORDYCE JUDSON, b. Corning, N.Y, May 8, 21; m. 41; c. 4. ENGLISH. A.B, Greenville Col, 45; M.A, Univ. Ill, 60, Ph.D, 64. Asst. prof. Eng, Olivet Nazarene Col, 62-64, prof. & chmn. dept, 64-69, chmn. div. lang. & lit, 65-69; PROF. ENG. & CHMN. DIV. LETT, POINT LOMA COL, 69- MLA; NCTE. Add: 105 Taylor Hall, Point Loma College, 3900 Lomaland Dr, San Diego, CA 92106.

BENNETT, GEORGE NEIL, b. Holyoke, Mass, Dec. 18, 21; m. 42; c. 1. AMERICAN LITERATURE. B.A, Mass. State Col, 42; M.A, Univ. Okla, 48; Edward G. Selden fel, Yale, 52-53, Ph.D.(Eng), 54. Instr. ENG, Univ. Okla, 48-49, VANDERBILT UNIV, 53-54, asst. prof, 54-59, assoc. prof, 59-70, PROF, 70- U.S.A, 42-46, 50-52, 1st Lt. American literature; 19th century novel. Publ: William Dean Howells: the development of a novelist, Univ. Okla, 59; The realism of William Dean Howells, 1889-1920, Vanderbilt Univ, 73. Add: Box 1657, Vanderbilt University, Nashville, TN 37235.

BENNETT, HOMER DOUGLAS, b. Opelika, Ala, Mar. 6, 25; m. 44; c. 2. SPEECH, THEOLOGY. B.A, South. Missionary Col. 51; B.D, Andrews Univ, 64, M.A, 62; Ph.D.(speech), Bowling Green State Univ, 72. Pastor, Seventh-day Adventist Church, 51-62; asst. prof. RELIG, SOUTH. MISSIONARY COL, 62-73, PROF, 73- Preaching; apocalyptic studies; Old Testament studies. Add: Southern Missionary College, Collegedale, TN 37315.

BENNETT, JACOB, b. Mansfield, Mass, Mar. 12, 16; m. 56; c. 2. MEDIEVAL LITERATURE, LINGUISTICS. A.B, Boston Univ, 49, fel, 54-55, Ph.D, 60; M.A, Columbia Univ, 50. Instr. Eng, Univ. Mo, 55-57; assoc. prof, East. Ill. Univ, 57-63; asst. prof, UNIV. MAINE, ORONO, 63-64, assoc. prof, 64-66, PROF. ENG. & LING, 66- Vis. prof, Boston Univ, summers, 58-60, Grad. Sch, 62. U.S.A, 42-45, Sgt. Mediaeval Acad. Am; Ling. Soc. Am; Am. Dialect Soc. Middle English dialectology; history of medieval drama; American dialects. Publ: The Castle of perseverance: redactions, place and date, Mediaeval Stud, 62; The Middle English dialect of the northeast midlands, 6/70 & The language and the home of the Ludus Coventriae, 6/73, Orbis. Add: Dept. of English, 215C Stevens Hall, University of Maine at Orono, Orono, ME 04473.

BENNETT, JAMES RICHARD, b. Harrison, Ark, Mar. 15, 32; m. 51; c. 2. ENGLISH LITERATURE, HUMANITIES. B.A, Univ. Ark, 53, M.A, 54; Ph.D.(Eng, humanities), Stanford Univ, 61. Instr. ENG, Mont. State Univ, 60-61, asst. prof, 61-62; West. Wash. State Col, 62-65; UNIV. ARK, FAYETTEVILLE, 65-66, assoc. prof, 66-69, PROF, 69- Fulbright lectr, Yugoslavia, 68-69; co-ed, Style, 67- U.S.A.F, 54-56, 1st Lt. NCTE; MLA. Nineteenth century literature; style; literature and film. Publ: English prose style, Chandler, 69; Style, S.Atlantic Mod. Lang. Bull, 71; Shelley, Keats-Shelley J, 74; Tzvetan Todorov, Bucknell Rev, 74. Add: Dept. of English, University of Arkansas, Fayetteville, AR 72701.

BENNETT, JOHN, b. Pittsfield, Mass, Mar. 12, 20; m. 60; c. 2. ENGLISH & AMERICAN LITERATURE. B.A, Oberlin Col, 47; M.A, Univ. Wis, 50, Adams fel, 52, Ph.D, 56. Instr. ENG, Ind. Univ, 53-58; asst. prof, Beloit Col, 58-59; assoc. prof, Rockford Col, 59-62, prof, 62-68, chmn. dept, 60-68; prof, ST. NORBERT COL, 68-70, BERNARD H. PENNINGS DISTINGUISHED PROF, 70- Consult. commun, Air War Col, Maxwell AFB, Ala, 51; ed, Beloit Poetry J, 58-72; mem. fac. adv. comt, Ill. Bd. Higher Educ, 62-68. Devins Mem. Award, 70; Soc. Midland Auth. Poetry Award, 71. U.S.A, 42-46, 1st Lt. Melville Soc. Herman Melville; modern poetry; creative writing. Publ: Melville's humanitarian thought, Univ. Microfilms, 56; The zoo manuscript, Sydon, 68; The struck Leviathan, Univ. Mo, 70; Griefs and exultations, 70 & Knights and squires, 72, St. Norbert. Add: Dept. of English, St. Norbert College, West de Pere, WI 54178.

BENNETT, JOSEPH THOMAS, b. Syracuse, N.Y, Dec. 18, 33; m. 68; c. 2. VICTORIAN LITERATURE. B.A, New Sch. Soc. Res, 64; M.A, N.Y. Univ, 65, Ph.D.(Eng), 68. ASSOC. PROF. ENG. LIT, STATE UNIV. N.Y. STONY BROOK, 67- MLA; AAUP; Res. Soc. Victorian Periodicals. Victorian novel; 19th century social history; letters and papers of Edward Bulwer-Lytton. Publ: Co-ed, An introduction to fiction, Wiley, 74; auth, A note on Lord Acton's view of Charles Dickens, Eng. Lang. Notes, 70; Devil in the flesh: Samuel Butler's Confessional novel, Victorian Newslett, spring 71. Add: Dept. of English, State University of New York at Stony Brook, Stony Brook, NY 11790.

BENNETT, KENNETH CHISHOLM, JR, b. Highland Park, Ill, Mar. 28, 27; m. 50; c. 2. ENGLISH. A.B, Univ. Wis, 47; M.A, Univ. Ill, 49; Ph.D.(Eng), Ind. Univ, 61. Ed. col. Eng. texts, Scott, Foresman & Co, 50-56; instr. ENG, N.Cent. Col.(Ill), 56-58; asst. prof, LAKE FOREST COL, 61-68, ASSOC. PROF, 68- U.S.N, 44-46, Ens. MLA; NCTE. George Bernard Shaw; 19th century literature; modern drama. Add: Dept. of English, Lake Forest College, Lake Forest, IL 60045.

BENNETT, PAUL LEWIS, b. Gnadenhutten, Ohio, Jan. 10, 21; m. 41; c. 2. AMERICAN LITERATURE. A.B, Ohio Univ, 42; M.A, Harvard, 47. Instr. ENG, Univ. Maine, 46-47; DENISON UNIV, 47-52, asst. prof, 52-55, assoc. prof, 55-60, PROF, 60- Teaching asst, Harvard, 45-46; instr, Samuel Adams Sch. Soc. Study, 46-47; Nat. Endowment for Arts writing fel, 73. U.S.N.R, 42-45, Lt.(jg). Writing poetry, film scripts and fiction. Publ: Robbery on the highway, Abelard, 61. Add: Dept. of English, Denison University, Granville, OH 43023.

BENNETT, ROBERT A, b. Albert Lea, Minn, May 31, 27; m. 49; c. 4. ENGLISH, EDUCATION. A.B, Univ. Calif, Los Angeles, 49; B.S, Univ. Minn, 51, M.A, 53; Ed.D.(Eng. educ), Fla. State Univ, 64. Teacher & chmn. dept. Eng, Marshall High Sch, Minn, 51-56; head dept. lang. arts, Fla. State Univ. Sch, 56-57; consult. in curriculum, Minneapolis Pub. Schs, 57-63; lang. arts specialist, SAN DIEGO CITY SCHS, 63-74, DIR. PROG. DEVELOP, 74- Prog. dir, Individualized Lit. Prog, Am. Bk. Co, 72. NCTE (pres, 70-71); Int. Reading Asn. Publ: Mirrors, Scholastic Mag. Inc, 60, rev, 66; co-auth, Types of literature, Ginn, 64, rev, 67, 70; gen. ed, The world of language, Bks. S & H, Follett, 72; auth, English to be real, Elem. Eng, 10/72; Survival: society, schools, students, Eng. J, 11/72; The undiscovered, Col. Eng, 4/72. Add: San Diego City Schools Education Center, 4100 Normal St, San Diego, CA 92103.

BENNETT, ROBERT BEALE, b. Washington, D.C, Dec. 18, 41; m. 66; c. 1. RENAISSANCE DRAMA. B.A, Univ. N.C, 64; M.A, Stanford Univ, 67, Ph.D. (Eng), 70. ASST. PROF. ENG, UNIV. DEL, 69- MLA; Shakespeare Asn. Am. Shakespeare; Elizabethan and Jacobean drama. Publ: Reform of a malcontent: Jaques and the meaning of As you like it, Shakespeare Stud, (in press). Add: Dept. of English, College of Arts & Science, University of Delaware, Newark, DE 19711.

BENNETT, SCOTT BOYCE, b. Kansas City, Mo, July 22, 39; m. 60; c. 3. ENGLISH. A.B, Oberlin Col, 60; Woodrow Wilson fel, Ind. Univ, 60-61, univ. fel, 66-67, Haskell fel, 66-67, M.A, 66, Ph.D.(Eng), 67. Woodrow Wilson intern. ENG, St. Paul's Col.(Va), 64-65; ASST. PROF, UNIV. ILL, URBANA-CHAMPAIGN, 67- Mem. ed. bd, Selected Ed. W.D. Howells, 68-70. MLA; Res. Soc. Victorian Periodicals. Victorian literature and history; textual criticism. Publ: Co-ed, W.D. Howells, Altrurian Romances, 68, Art and error: modern textual editing, 70 & ed, W.D. Howells, Indiana summer, 71, Ind. Univ; auth, Catholic Emancipation, The Quarterly Review and Britain's Constitutional Revolution, Victorian Stud, 3/69; The profession of authorship: some problems for descriptive bibliography, In: Research methods in librarianship, Univ. Ill, 71; David Douglas and the British publication of W.D. Howells' works, Stud. Bibl, 72; plus one other. Add: Dept. of English, University of Illinois, Urbana-Champaign, Urbana, IL 61801.

BENNETT, STEPHANIE MITCHELL, b. Albuquerque, N.Mex; m. 66; c. 1. AMERICAN STUDIES. B.A, Univ. N.Mex, 63, Ford Found. fel, 63, M.A, 66; Ph.D.(Am. stud), Univ. Iowa, 73. Instr. ENG, Loretto Heights Col, 67-68; ASST. PROF. & DIR. PROG. AM. STUD, ALBION COL, 68- Commun. skills coord, Upward Bound, Greeley, Colo, 68. Am. Stud. Asn; Popular Cult. Asn; MLA. American novel; American Civil War; urban history and literature. Add: Dept. of English, Albion College, Albion, MI 49224.

BENNETT, STEPHEN JOHN, Philosophy. See Volume IV, Philosophy, Religion & Law.

BENOIST, HOWARD, III, b. St. Louis, Mo, Apr. 12, 43; m. 70; c. 1. ENGLISH LITERATURE. A.B, Wash. Univ, 64; A.M, Univ. Pa, 65, Ph.D.(Eng), 68. ASST. PROF. ENG, OUR LADY OF THE LAKE COL, 70- Med.Serv.C, U.S.A, 68-70, Capt. MLA; AAUP; NCTE; S.Cent. Renaissance Conf. Eighteenth century British novel and literature; composition and communication. Publ: An unpublished letter of Samuel Richardson, Libr. Chronicle, 70. Add: Humanities Div, Our Lady of the Lake College, 411 S.W. 24th St, San Antonio, TX 78285.

BENOIT, RAYMOND PAUL, b. Yakima, Wash, Apr. 17, 36; m. 65. ENGLISH. B.A, Gonzaga Univ, 59; NDEA & Woodrow Wilson fels. & Ph.D. (Eng), Univ. Ore, 65. Asst. prof. ENG, ST. LOUIS UNIV, 65-68, assoc. prof, 68-70, PROF, 71-, CHMN. DEPT, 73- British and American romanticism; American literature; contemporary American poetry. Publ: Single nature's double name: the collectedness of the conflicting in British and American romanticism, Mouton, The Hague, 73; Hawthorne's psychology of death: The minister's black veil, Stud. Short Fiction, 71; Theology and literature: The scarlet letter, Bucknell Rev, 72; In dear detail by ideal light: Ode on a Grecian urn, Costerus, 72; plus five others. Add: Dept. of English, St. Louis University, St. Louis, MO 63103.

BENSEN, ALICE RHODUS, b. Charlotte, Mich. ENGLISH. Ph.D.(Eng), Univ. Chicago, 43. Instr. ENG, Valparaiso Univ, 38-40, 42-45, asst. prof, 45-47; assoc. prof, EAST. MICH. UNIV, 47-57, PROF, 57- Ford Found. fel, 52-53. Int. Asn. Univ. Prof. Eng; MLA; Col. Eng. Asn; Mod. Humanities Res. Asn; NCTE. Twentieth century literature. Publ: Rose Macaulay, Twayne, 69; Problems of poetic diction in twentieth-century criticism, PMLA, 45; E.M. Forster's dialectic: Howards end, Mod. Fiction Stud, 55; The ironic aesthete and the sponsoring of causes, Eng. Lit. in Transition, 66. Add: Dept. of English, Eastern Michigan University, Ypsilanti, MI 48197.

BENSKY, ROGER DANIEL, Avant-Garde & French Theatre. See Volume III, Foreign Languages, Linguistics & Philology.

BENSMAN, MARVIN ROBERT, b. Two Rivers, Wis, Sept. 18, 37; m. 65; c. 2. MASS COMMUNICATIONS, SPEECH & DRAMA. B.A, Univ. Wis-Madison, 60, M.S, 64, Ph.D.(speech), 69. Teacher speech, West High Sch, Green Bay, Wis, 60-62; North High Sch, Sheboygan, Wis, 62-63; instr. MASS COMMUN, Univ. Vt, 67-69; asst. prof, MEMPHIS STATE UNIV, 69-73, ASSOC. PROF, 73- Speech Commun. Asn; Broadcast Educ. Asn.(chmn. hist. comt, 73-75); Univ. Film Asn; South. Speech Commun. Asn.(chmn. mass media div, 73); Radio Hist. Soc. Am. History of broadcasting; archival audio-visual materials; survey research. Publ: Co-ed, History of radio-television collection, Arno, 71; auth, WJAZ-Zenith case and the chaos of 1926, fall 70 & co-auth, Broadcasting-film academic budgets 1971-1972, summer 71, J. Broadcasting. Add: Dept. of Speech & Drama, Memphis State University, Memphis, TN 38152.

BENSMILLER, MILDRED, b. Brighton, Iowa, Sept. 19, 23; m. 45; c. 3. ENGLISH. M.A, Nebr. State Col, Kearney, 60; summers, Univ. Iowa, 65 & 66. Teacher ENG, Sec. Schs, 45-47; asst. prof, IOWA WESLEYAN COL, 61-66, ASSOC. PROF, 66-, DIR. FRESHMAN ENG, 65- Mem, Nat. Creative Writing fraternity; Nat. Endowment for Humanities fel, Univ. Mass, Amherst, summer 73. Poetry Prizes, 63, 64-68. NCTE. Shakespeare's comedies; composition and rhetoric; poetry. Publ: Poem, Rectangle, spring 66; plus others. Add: 1007 Lucas St, Mt. Pleasant, IA 52641.

BENSON, CARL, b. Camden, Ark, Feb. 19, 16; m. 41; c. 2. ENGLISH. B.A, Univ. Tex, 37, M.A, 38; Ph.D.(Eng), Univ. Ill, 48. Asst. prof. ENG, Ark. Agr. & Mech. Col, 39-41; asst, Univ. Ill, 41-43, 46-47; asst. prof, AUBURN UNIV, 47-52, assoc. prof, 52-63, PROF, 63- Ford Found. Advan. Educ. fel, Harvard, 55-56; Fulbright lectr, Erlangen Univ, Ger, 60-61; vis. prof, N.Y. Univ, summer, 64. A.U.S, 43-46. MLA; S.Atlantic Mod. Lang. Asn; Am. Stud. Asn. Contemporary English and American literature. Publ: Co-auth, The idea of tragedy, Scott, 66. Add: Dept. of English, Auburn University, Auburn, AL 36830.

BENSON, DONALD ROBERT, b. Kansas City, Mo, Mar. 30, 27; m. 49; c. 3. ENGLISH. A.B, Univ. Kansas City, 49; M.A, Colgate Univ, 51; Ph.D, Univ. Kans, 59. Preceptor, Colgate Univ, 49-51; instr. ENG, Univ. Kans, 51-58; IOWA STATE UNIV, 58-59, asst. prof, 59-63, assoc. prof, 63-67, PROF, 67-, CHMN. DEPT, 72- Fulbright teacher, Holland, 56-57; fac. fel, Episcopal Theol. Sch, summer 60; Eng. Reader, Col. Entrance Exam. Bd, Princeton, N.J, 61, 62; ed, Iowa English yearbk, Iowa.Counc. Teachers Eng, 62-64; Iowa State Univ. Res. Found. res. grant, Brit. Mus. & Kunsthistorisch Instituut, Utrecht, 64-65. U.S.N.R, 45-46. MLA. Seventeenth century English literature; science and imagination; modern British and American literature. Publ: Halifax and the trimmers, Huntington Libr. Quart, 2/64; Ideas and the problem of knowledge in 17th-century English aesthetics, Eng. Miscellany, 68; Platonism and Neoclassic metaphor: Dryden's Eleonora and Donne's Anniversaries, Stud. Philol, 71. Add: Dept. of English, Iowa State University, Ames, IA 50010.

BENSON, FREDERICK R, b. New York, N.Y, June 26, 34; div; c. 2. COMPARATIVE LITERATURE, ENGLISH. B.A, South. Methodist Univ, 55; M.A, N.Y. Univ, 62, Ph.D.(comp. lit), 66. Asst. prof. Eng, Rider Col, 62-65; comp. lit. & Eng, City Col. New York, 65-70; ASSOC. PROF. ENG, BRIARCLIFF COL, 70- Mod. for. lang. consult, NDEA, 63; mem, N.Y. Comp. Lit. Colloquium, 70- U.S.A, 56-58. Am. Comp. Lit. Asn; MLA. Literary criticism; European Romanticism; modern political novel. Publ: Writers in arms: the literary impact of the Spanish Civil War, 67 & co-auth, Western literature: a historical approach, 74, N.Y. Univ; auth, Ernest Hemingway and the Spanish Civil War, Cahier de l'Herne, winter 73; Critical studies of major American, English and European film directors (21), In: World biography, McGraw, 73. Add: 156 E. 64th St, New York, NY 10021.

BENSON, JACKSON J, b. San Francisco, Calif, Sept. 2, 30; m. 60; c. 2. CONTEMPORARY AMERICAN LITERATURE. A.B, Stanford Univ, 52; M.A, San Francisco State Univ, 56; Ph.D.(Eng), Univ. South. Calif, 66. Assoc. prof. Eng, Orange Coast Col, 56-66; asst. prof. AM. LIT, SAN DIEGO STATE UNIV, 66-69, assoc. prof, 69-72, PROF, 72- Consult, San Diego City Schs, 67-68; Nat. Endowment for Humanities grant, 70; Am. Philos. Soc. grant, 71. U.S.A, 52-54. MLA; Am. Stud. Asn. William Faulkner; Ernest Hemingway; John Steinbeck. Publ: Hemingway: the writer's art of self-defense, Univ. Minn, 69; co-ed, Hemingway in our time, Ore. State Univ, 73; ed, Essays on the short stories of Ernest Hemingway, Duke Univ, 74; auth, Quentin Compson: self-portrait of a young artist's emotions, Twentieth Century Lit, 8/71. Add: School of Literature, San Diego State University, San Diego, CA 92115.

BENSON, JAMES ALLEN, b. River Falls, Wis, Apr. 4, 38. SPEECH. B.S, Univ. Wis-Eau Claire, 60; M.S, Purdue, 62, Ph.D.(speech), 69. Instr. SPEECH, Univ. Wis-Superior, 6266; asst. prof, BALL STATE UNIV, 68-72, ASSOC. PROF, 72-, DIR. DEBATE & FORENSIC PROG, 68- Am. Forensic Asn; Speech Commun. Asn; Cent. States Speech Asn. Intercollegiate debate and forensics; rhetorical theory. Publ: James Otis and the writs of assistance speech—fact and fiction, South. Speech J, summer 69; Use of evidence in intercollegiate debate, J. Am. Forensic Asn, spring 71; How should finalists be chosen in individual events, Speaker & Gavel, 11/71. Add: Dept. of Speech, Ball State University, Muncie, IN 47306.

BENSON, LARRY DEAN, b. S.Dak, June 20, 29; m. 51; c. 4. ENGLISH. A.B, Univ. Calif, Berkeley, 54, M.A, 56, Ph.D, 59; hon. M.A, Harvard, 65. Instr. ENG, HARVARD, 59-61, asst. prof, 61-65, assoc. prof, 65-69, PROF, 69- U.S.M.C, 46-48, 50-51. MLA; Mediaeval Acad. Am.(assoc. exec. secy, 72-). Old and middle English literature. Publ: Art and tradition in Sir Gawain and the Green Knight, Rutgers Univ, 65; co-ed, The literary context of Chaucer's Fabliaux, 71 & ed, King Arthur's death, the middle English alliterative Morte Arthure and stanzaic Morte Arthur, 74, Bobbs; The literary character of Anglo-Saxon formulaic verse, PMLA, 10/66; The pagan coloring of Beowulf, In: Old English poetry, Brown Univ, 67; The originality of Beowulf, In: The interpretation of narrative: theory and practise, Harvard, 70. Add: 271 Widener Library, Harvard University, Cambridge, MA 02138.

BENSON, LaVONN MARCEIL, b. Neshoba County, Miss. ENGLISH. A.B, Anderson Col, 52; M.S, Fla. State Univ, 59; Ed.S, George Peabody Col, 62, Ph.D.(Eng), 71. Teacher ENG, Fla. Pub. Schs, 52-61; asst. prof, West. Ky. Univ, 62-65; Morehead State Univ, 66-67; ASSOC. PROF. & HEAD DEPT, MOTLOW STATE COMMUNITY COL, 72- Nat. Endowment for Humanities grant, summer 73. NCTE; Col. Eng. Asn; AAUP. The teaching of English; study of the novel. Add: Dept. of English, Motlow State Community College, Tullahoma, TN 37388.

BENSON, MERRITT ELIHU, b. Sabetha, Kans, July 17, 02; m. 29; c. 1. COMMUNICATIONS, JOURNALISM. J.D, Univ. Minn, 30; A.B, Univ. Wash, 42. Reporter & news exec, metrop. newspapers, 21-29; instr. jour. writing & editing & law, Univ. Minn, 29-30; from asst. prof. to prof, UNIV. WASH, 31-67, acting dir. sch. commun, 51, EMER. PROF. COMMUN, 68- Acting prof, Stanford Univ, 35, 37, 57; adv. Off. Secy. Defense, 49; admin. asst, Governor of Wash, 50-51; lectr, Univ. Minn, 54; pres, Ranger Publ. Co, Inc, 63- U.S.N.R, 43-45, Lt. Comdr. Asn. Educ. Jour. Communication law. Publ: The right to demand scholars. Add: 5700 Ann Arbor Ave, Seattle, WA 98105.

BENSON, MORRIS, b. Bombay, India, Dec. 1, 27; wid; c. 1. ENGLISH LITERATURE. B.A, Univ. Bombay, 47, M.A, 49; M.A, Agra Univ, 51, M.C, 52; Ph.D.(Eng), Syracuse Univ, 73. Chmn. humanities, Nat. Defence Acad, India, 49-53; sr. lectr. Eng, French & Ger. & head dept. Eng, Sch. Mines, Agra Univ, 53-57; sr. master Eng. & French, Lister County Tech. Sch, Eng, 57-58; lectr. Eng, French & Ger, Univ. Saarland, 58-60; prof. Eng. & Ger, Al-Tahrir Col, Univ. Baghdad, 60-63; assoc. prof. Eng, Stephens Col, 63-64; head dept. Eng, Dept. Educ, Saudi Arabia, 64-65; sr. lectr. Eng. & French, Medway Col. Technol. & Watford Col. Technol, Eng, 65-67; PROF. ENG, STATE UNIV. N.Y. AGR. & TECH. COL, MORRISVILLE, 67- AAUP; MLA. Renaissance; 20th century post-Ibsenian existentialist literature; economic determinism and cultural change. Publ: The champagne of comedy, 47, A critical study of Galsworthy's Man of property 49 & How to become a master of English, 50, Browne Publ, Poona, India; Erring Othello, Coleman, London, 71. Add: Div. of Liberal Arts, State University of New York Agricultural & Technical College at Morrisville, Morrisville, NY 13408.

BENSON, RICHARD LEE, b. Brawley, Calif, Dec. 12, 30; m. 58; c. 5. DRAMA, SPEECH. B.A, Univ. Calif, Los Angeles, 58; M.A, Univ. Ill, Urbana, 62, Ph.D.(theatre), 68. From instr. to asst. prof. drama, Beloit Col, 62-69; PROF. SPEECH & DRAMA & CHMN. DEPT, EAST. KY. UNIV, 69- U.S.A.F, 50-54, S/Sgt. Speech Commun. Asn. Shakespearean promptbooks; American theatre history. Add: Dept. of Drama & Speech, Eastern Kentucky University, Richmond, KY 40475.

BENSON, THOMAS W, b. Abington, Pa, Jan. 25, 37; m. 60; c. 2. SPEECH COMMUNICATION. A.B, Hamilton Col, 58; M.A, Cornell Univ, 61, Ph.D. (speech), 66. Instr. speech, State Univ. N.Y. Buffalo, 63-66, asst. prof, 66-70, ASSOC. PROF. photog. stud, 70-71; SPEECH, PA. STATE UNIV, UNIVERSITY PARK, 71- State Univ. N.Y. summer fac. res. fel, 68; vis. asst. prof. rhetoric, Univ. Calif, Berkeley, 69-70. Speech Commun. Asn; Soc. Cinema Stud; Am. Film Inst; Rhetoric Soc; Am. Anthrop. Asn. Rhetorical criticism, rhetorical theory; cinema. Publ: Readings in classical rhetoric, 69, 72 & Readings in medieval rhetoric, 73, Ind. Univ; Rhetoric of resistance, Today's Speech, 9/68; Inaugurating peace, FDR's last speech, Speech Monogr, 69; Rhetoric and autobiography: the case of Malcolm X, Quart. J. Speech, 74; plus five others. Add: Dept. of Speech, 227 Sparks Bldg, Pennsylvania State University, University Park, PA 16802.

BENSTOCK, BERNARD, b. New York, N.Y, Mar. 23, 30; m. 59, 73; c. 2. ENGLISH, COMPARATIVE LITERATURE. A.B, Brooklyn Col, 50; M.A, Columbia Univ 54; Ph.D.(Eng), Fla. State Univ, 57. Instr. ENG, La. State Univ, 57-61, asst. prof, 61-65; assoc. prof, KENT STATE UNIV, 65-67, PROF, 67- Fulbright lectr. Am. lit, Univ. Tabriz, 61-62; vis. summer prof. Eng. & comp. lit, Columbia Univ, 68; vis. summer prof, Grad. Inst, Univ. Tulsa, 70 & State Univ. N.Y. Buffalo, 72. U.S.A, 51-53. MLA; (chmn. Irish stud. sem, 73); Am. Comt. Irish Stud; James Joyce Found.(pres, 71-) Int. Asn. Stud. Anglo-Irish Lit; Midwest Mod. Lang. Asn. Modern British and Irish literature, particularly James Joyce and Sean O'Casey; Flann O'Brien. Publ: Joyce-again's wake, Univ. Wash, 66; Sean O'Casey, Bucknell Univ, 70; co-ed, Approaches to Ulysses: ten essays, Univ. Pittsburgh, 70; auth, The James Joyce industry, South. Rev, winter 66; L. Boom as dreamer in Finnegans wake, PMLA, 3/67; Every telling has a taling: the narrative of Finnegans wake, Mod. Fiction Stud, spring 69; plus one other. Add: Dept. of English, Kent State University, Kent, OH 44240.

BENTHUL, HERMAN FORREST, b. Celeste, Tex, Dec. 22, 11; m. 32; c. 2. ENGLISH CURRICULUM & INSTRUCTION. B.A, E.Tex. State Univ, 35; M.A, South. Methodist Univ, 42; Ph.D.(curriculum, Eng), Univ. Tex, 54; Columbia Univ, 63. Teacher & prin, Bellefonte Rural Sch, 33-35; Lindale Pub. Schs, 35-40; supt, Covington Pub. Schs, 40-42; prin, Hillsboro Jr-Sr. High Schs, 42-43; Tyler Pub. Schs, 43-47; Dallas Pub. Schs, 47-50, instructional consult, coord. & asst, 50-73; VIS. PROF. ENG, E. TEX. STATE UNIV, 73- Teacher, sem. & summer courses, South. Methodist Univ, 47-

57; summer courses, Univ. Colo, 53; teacher & dir, summer workshop, Univ. Tex, 57; summer courses, Univ. Md, 62. NEA; Asn. Supv. & Curriculum Develop; NCTE. Backgrounds in ethnic groups; word origins, particularly as related to ethnic groups and the teaching of language arts. Publ: Co-auth, Holiday reader, 57, auth, Literature of the old Southwest, 58 & co-auth, Texas roundup: American heroes all, 65, Noble; sr. auth, Spell correctly, Silver, 65; Oral reading and linguistics (suppl. readers), Benefic, 73; Various reviews of language arts materials, Curriculum Adv. Serv, 60; Upgrading the substitute, The Instr, 9/63; Teaching the language arts in the elementary school, J. Tex. Counc. Teachers Eng, 71; plus one other. Add: Box 433, Golden, TX 75444.

BENTLEY, ERIC, b. Eng, 16, nat; m. DRAMA, COMPARATIVE LITERATURE. B.A, Oxford, 38, B.Litt, 39; Ph.D, Yale, 41. Matthews prof. dramatic lit, Columbia Univ, 54-69; RES. & WRITING, 69- Guggenheim fel, 48-49 & 67-68; Charles Eliot Norton prof. poetry, Harvard, 60-61; ed, Grove Press ed. Works of Brecht, 60-67; Ford Found. artist in residence, Berlin, 64-65. Longview Award, 60; George Nathan Prize, 67. Literary record albums; poetry and songs. Publ: A century of hero worship, 44; The play wright as thinker, 46; In search of theatre, 53; The dramatic event, 54; What is theatre?, 56; The life of the drama, 64; The theatre of commitment, 67; Theatre of war, 72; The recantation, 72; Are you now or have you ever been, 72. Add: 711 West End Ave, New York, NY 10025.

BENTLEY, GERALD EADES, b. Brazil, Ind, Sept. 15, 01. ENGLISH. A.B, DePauw Univ, 23, hon. D.Litt, 49; A.M, Univ. Ill, 25; Ph.D, Univ. London, 29; hon. Litt.D, Univ. Birmingham, Eng, 59; hon. L.H.D, Ind. Univ, 70. Instr. ENG, N.Mex. Mil. Inst, 26-27; Univ. Chicago, 29-31, asst. prof, 31-39, assoc. prof, 39-43, prof, 43-45; PRINCETON, 45-50, MURRAY PROF, 50-, asst. librn, rare bks. & spec. collection, 71-73. Rector scholar, DePauw; res. fel, Huntington Libr, 38-39; lectr, Calif. Inst. Technol, 42; Guggenheim fel, 44-45; lectr, Shakespeare Inst, Eng, 47, 53, 57, 59, 62 & 66; Cambridge, 52; Fulbright res. fel, 52-53; lectr, Harvard, 56. Mod. Humanities Res. Asn, Gt. Brit; Malone Soc.(pres, 72-); Shakespeare Asn. Am. (pres, 72-74). English drama; Shakespeare. Publ: Jacobean and Caroline stage (7 vols), Clarendon, 42-68; Shakespeare and Jonson (2 vols), 45 & The seventeenth-century stage, 68, Univ. Chicago; Shakespeare: a biographical handbook, Yale, 61; Shakespeare and his theatre, Univ. Nebr, 64; A book of masques, Cambridge, 67; The profession of dramatist in Shakespeare's time, Princeton, 71. Add: 22 McCosh Hall, Princeton University, Princeton, NJ 08540.

BENTLEY, GERALD EADES, JR, b. Chicago, Ill, Aug. 23, 30; m. 52; c. 2. ENGLISH LITERATURE. B.A, Princeton, 52; B.Litt, Oxford, 54, D.Phil, 56. Instr. ENG, Univ. Chicago, 56-60; from asst. prof. to PROF, UNIV. TORONTO, 60- Guggenheim fel, Eng, 58-59; Can. Counc. fel, Eng, 63-64 & 70-71; Fulbright lectr, Algiers, 67-68. MLA; Bibliog. Soc; Oxford Bibliog. Soc; Int. Asn. Univ. Prof. Eng; Conf. Ed. Probs.(chmn, 72-). William Blake; John Flaxman. Publ: Ed, William Blake's Four zoas, Clarendon, 63; co-auth, A Blake bibliography, Univ. Minn, 64; auth, The early editions of Flaxman's Classical designs, New York Pub. Libr, 64; ed, William Blake, Tiriell & Blake records, 69, Clarendon; The Blake collection of Mrs. Landon K. Thorne, Pierpont Morgan, 71; plus others. Add: Dept. of English, University College, University of Toronto, Toronto 7, Ont, Can.

BENTLEY, H. WILDER, b. San Francisco, Calif, Nov. 19, 00; m. 27; c. 2. ENGLISH, HUMANITIES. Ph.B, Yale, 23; M.A, Univ. Mich, 29. Instr. Eng, Okla. Agr. & Mech. Col, 26-27; Italian, Univ. Mich, 28-30; Eng, Carnegie Inst. Tech, 30-31, French, 31-32, lab. asst, press, 32-33; sales mgr, Univ. Press, Univ. Calif, 33-35; master, Archetype Press, Berkeley, Calif, 35-40; ed. & typographer, Gillick Press, 40-44; instr. Eng. & philos, Stockton Col, 46-56; assoc. prof. ENG, SAN FRANCISCO STATE COL, 56-67, prof, 67-71, EMER. PROF, 71- Publ. lectr, Fine Arts Dept, Univ. Pittsburgh, 33; lectr, Exten. Div, Univ. Calif, 33-35; Col. Pac, 49-52. Am. Fed. Teachers; Am. Inst. Graphic Arts. History of printing and of books in manuscript; culture of China and Japan; world literature. Publ: The art of Laurence Pickett Williams: The communication of Utopian thought: its history, forms, and use, Part I, Bibliog, 62, Part II, Syllabus & Anthol: Gandhian theory and practice and the literature of non-violence, East and West: a selective, partially annotated and classified check list of instructional materials in the Bay-Area libraries, 69, San Francisco State Col. Bookstore; The Pestalozzi sequence, privately publ, 71; The XXIV canons of the T'ang Dynasty, Hudson Rev. A bilingual recording of the Divina commedia of Dante, Carnegie-Mellon Univ, 73. Add: 2683 Le Conte Ave, Berkeley, CA 94709.

BENTLEY, HAROLD WOODMANSEE, b. Colonia Juarez, Mex, June 5, 99; m. 25; c. 3. ENGLISH, SPANISH. Teacher Eng. & Spanish, Brigham Young Univ, 22-25; Schs, New York, N.Y, 25-26; Columbia Univ, 30-49; prof. ENG. & dean, summer sch. & exten. div, UNIV. UTAH, 49-64, EMER. PROF. & EMER. DEAN DIV. CONTINUING EDUC, 64- Dir, Benjamin Franklin Libr, Mex. City, Mex, 44-46; Eng. Lang. Inst, 45-46; acad. v.pres. & acting pres, Haile Sellassie I Univ, 61-62; pres, Park City Inst. Arts & Sci, 70-; Fulbright Award, Mex, 70-72. Knight Comdr, Order of Aztec Eagle. MLA; Adult Educ. Asn. English language and idiom; place names liberal adult education. Publ: Dictionary of Spanish terms in English, Octagon, 73. Add: Dept. of English, University of Utah, Salt Lake City, UT 84114.

BENTLEY, JOHN ALBERT, b. Halifax, N.S. Sept. 10, 97. ENGLISH PHILOLOGY. A.M, Dalhousie Univ, 21; A.M, Harvard, 22, Townsend scholar, Austin fel. & Parker traveling fel, 22-25, Ph.D, 30; M.A, Univ. Sask, 26. Asst. prof. ENG, UNIV. SASK, 25-49, from assoc. prof. to prof, 49-61, EMER. PROF, 61- Humanities Asn. Can. Ruskin as a literary critic; the trend towards decadence in Western civilization; the artistic achievement of the past. Add: 389 Levis St, St. Johns, P. Q. Can.

BENTLEY, JOSEPH GOLDRIDGE, b. Atlanta, Ga, Sept. 2, 32; m. 64; c. 2. ENGLISH. B.A, Fla. State Univ, 54, M.A, 58; Ph.D.(Eng), Ohio State Univ, 61. Instr. ENG, Ohio State Univ, 60-61; UNIV. S.FLA, TAMPA, 61-63, asst. prof, 63-66, assoc. prof, 66-71, PROF, 71- Vis. summer lectr, West. Ill. Univ, 65. U.S.A, 54-56, Res, 56-62. Literature of the 20th century; history and theory of satire; aestehtics. Publ: Satire and the rhetoric of sadism, Centennial Rev, summer 67; Aldous Huxley's ambivalent attitudes toward D.H. Lawrence, Twentieth Century Lit, 10/67; Semantic gravitation: an essay on satiric reduction, Mod. Lang. Quart, 3/69. Add: Dept. of English, University of South Florida, Tampa, FL 33620.

BENTLEY, NORMA ELIZABETH, b. Syracuse, N.Y, Sept. 17, 16. ENGLISH. A.B, Radcliffe Col, 38; M.A, Syracuse Univ, 40, Ph.D, 44, M.S, 57. Asst, Syracuse Univ, 38-40, instr. Eng, 40-45, asst. librn, bus. libr, 55-57; asst. prof. Eng, Lake Erie Col, 45-47; Earlham Col, 47-51; dir. adult educ, YWCA, 51-55; PROF. ENG, CAZENOVIA COL, 57-, CHMN. DEPT. LANG. & LIT, 66-, chmn. div. lib. arts, 60-66. Mem. exec. comt, Jr. Col. Counc. Mid. Atlantic States, 68-70; assoc. ed. poetry, Blackbird Circle, 72- MLA; NCTE; Conf. Col. Compos. & Commun; AAUP; Japan Soc. Modern novel; poetry; comparative literature. Publ: Hudibras Butler abroad, Mod. Lang. Notes, 45; Another Butler manuscript, Mod. Philol, 48; Cultivated flexibility, Conf. Report N.Y. State Asn. Jr. Cols, 65. Add: Dept. of Language & Literature, Cazenovia College, Cazenovia, NY 13035.

BENTLEY, WARNER, b. Bradley, S.Dak, Dec. 3, 01. DRAMA. A.B, Pomona Col, 26; Yale, 26-28; A.M, Dartmouth Col, 37; hon. D.F.A, New Eng. Col, 72. Instr. Eng, DARTMOUTH COL, 28-30, asst. prof, 30-36, dir. drama prod, 36-60, dir, HOPKINS CTR. CREATIVE & PERFORMING ARTS, 60-69, EMER. DIR, 69-, Dartmouth players, 28-36, grad. mgr. counc. stud. orgn, 40-60. Comnr, N.H. Comn. Arts. Am. Nat. Theatre & Acad; Am. Theatre Asn; Int. Asn. Concert Mgr. Add: Main St, Norwich, VT 05055.

BENTMAN, RAYMOND, b. Philadelphia, Pa, July 9, 25; m. 62; c. 2. ENGLISH LITERATURE. B.A, Kenyon Col, 50; M.A, Univ. Pa, 51; Fulbright fel, Univ. Rome, 51-52; Ph.D, Yale, 61. Instr. ENG, Univ. Mich, 59-60, Univ. N.C, 60-61; TEMPLE UNIV, 61-62, asst. prof, 62-66, assoc. prof, 66-70, PROF, 70- Am. Philos. Soc. grant-in-aid, 68. Sig.C, U.S.A, 43-46, Sgt. MLA; Nat. Col. Honors Counc. Satire; 18th century British literature; Shakespeare. Publ: Ed, The Methodist, ARS, 72 & The poetry of Robert Burns, Houghton, 72; auth, Robert Burn's use of Scottish diction, In: From sensibility to romanticism, Oxford, 66; Satiric structure and tone in the conclusion of Gulliver's travels, SEL, 71; Robert Burn's declining fame, SIR, 72; plus two others. Add: Dept. of English, Temple University, Philadelphia, PA 19118.

BENTON, RICHARD PAUL, b. Everett, Pa, Aug. 24, 14; m. 41. ENGLISH. B.S, Johns Hopkins Univ, 52, M.A, 53, Ph.D.(aesthet. of lit), 55. Draftsman-engineer, Pa. Railroad Co, 40-52; jr. instr. writing, Johns Hopkins Univ, 53-54; instr. ENG, TRINITY COL.(CONN), 55-57, asst. prof, 57-71, ASSOC. PROF, 71- NCTE; MLA; Int. Soc. Gen. Semantics; Keats-Shelley Asn. Am. British romantics; Victorians; Chinese literature. Publ: Tennyson and Lao Tzu, 62 & Keats and Zen, 66, Philos. East & West; The works of N.P. Willis as a catalyst of Poe's criticism, Am. Lit, 67. Add: Dept. of English, Trinity College, Hartford, CT 06106.

BENTON, ROBERT MILTON, b. Braidwood, Ill, July 6, 32; m. 56. ENGLISH. B.A, Trinity Univ, 54; M.A, Univ. Colo, 63, Ph.D.(Eng), 67. Teaching assoc. ENG, Univ. Colo, 63-66, instr, 66-67; asst. prof, CENT. WASH. STATE COL, 67-71, ASSOC. PROF, 71- MLA; John Steinbeck Soc. Am. Colonial American literature; John Steinbeck; science and American literature. Publ: The biological naturalism of John Steinbeck, 72 & Realism, growth and contrast in The gift, 72, Steinbeck Quart; The John Winthrops and developing scientific thought in New England, Early Am. Lit, 73; plus three others. Add: Dept. of English, Central Washington State College, Ellensburg, WA 98926.

BENTON, VERA LOUISE, b. Covington, Ga, Apr. 21, 26. ENGLISH LANGUAGE & LITERATURE. A.B, Morris Brown Col, 46; M.A, Univ. Mich, 53; Univ. South. Calif, 56; Rockefeller Found. grants, Ind. Univ, 64, Wesleyan Univ, summers 65-69. From instr. to ASSOC. PROF. ENG, MORRIS BROWN COL, 50-, LECTR. BUS. REPORT WRITING, 69-, coord. freshman Eng, 65-69, coord. acad. affairs, Stud. Assistance Prog, 70-73, coord. lectr. Eng, Proj. Upward Bound, 71-73. Consult, Col. Educ. Achievement Proj, 69; teacher Eng, Metrop. Atlanta Trio Prog, summer 73, suprv. teacher, 73-74. NCTE; Conf. Col. Compos. & Commun. Oral and written expression of black students from low income families; interdisciplinary study of literature and science and other humanistic disciplines; William Faulkner and Herman Melville. Add: Dept. of English, Morris Brown College, 643 Hunter St. S.W, Atlanta, GA 30314.

BENVENUTO, RICHARD ERCOLE, b. Detroit, Mich, May 28, 38; m. 61; c. 3. ENGLISH. A.B, Univ. Detroit, 61; Woodrow Wilson fel, Hollins Col, 61-62, M.A, 62; Ph.D.(Eng), Ohio State Univ, 68. Asst. ENG, Ohio State Univ, 62-65, assoc, 65-68; asst. prof, MICH. STATE UNIV, 68-73, ASSOC. PROF, 73- MLA. Nineteenth century English literature. Add: Dept. of English, Michigan State University, East Lansing, MI 48823.

BENZIE, WILLIAM, b. Aberdeen, Scotland, July 10, 30. ENGLISH. M.A, Aberdeen Univ, 55, M.Ed, 57, Ph.D.(Eng), 67. Asst. prof. ENG, UNIV. VICTORIA (B.C), 58-72, ASSOC. PROF, 72- R.A.F, 48-50. Eighteenth century rhetoric and belles lettres; F.J. Furnivall. Publ: The Dublin orator, Scolar Press, Eng, 72; Thomas Sheridan and 18th century rhetoric and belles lettres, Leeds Stud. Eng, 5/69. Add: Dept. of English, Victoria University, Victoria, B.C, Can.

BENZIGER, JAMES GEORGE, b. New York, N.Y, Mar. 31, 14; m. 44; c. 3. ENGLISH LITERATURE. B.A, Princeton, 36, Ph.D, 40. Instr. ENG, Northwest. Univ, 40-41; N.Y. Univ, 46; from asst. prof. to assoc. prof, Carleton Col, 46-50; from assoc. prof. to PROF. SOUTH. ILL. UNIV, CARBONDALE, 50- Mem, Ill-Ind. selection comt, Wilson Nat. Fel. Found, 62-68. U.S.A.A.F, 41-46, Capt. MLA. English romantics; 19th and 20th century poetry; history of criticism. Publ: Images of eternity: studies in the poetry of religious vision from Wordsworth to T.S. Eliot, South. Ill. Univ, 63; Tintern Abbey revisited, 3/50 & Organic unity: Liebniz to Coleridge, 3/51, PMLA. Add: Dept. of English, Southern Illinois University, Carbondale, IL 62903.

BERCOVITCH, SACVAN, b. Montreal, Ont, Oct. 4, 33; m. 56; c. 1. ENGLISH. B.A, Sir George Williams Univ, 61; Ph.D.(Eng), Claremont Grad. Sch, 65. Instr. ENG, Columbia Univ, 64-66; asst. prof, Brandeis Univ, 66-68; assoc. prof, Univ. Calif, San Diego, 68-70; PROF, COLUMBIA UNIV,

70- Fels, Columbia Humanities Res. Counc, 65, Am. Counc. Learned Soc, 66 & 72, Huntington Libr, summer 68; ed. consult, Early Am. Lit, 68-71; Am. Philos. Soc. fel, 69; mem. ed. bd, Twentieth Century Lit, 69-71; Guggenheim fel, 70; Am. Counc. Learned Soc. fel, 72; mem. ed. bd, William & Mary Quart, 72-75; mem. adv. counc, Inst. Early Am. Hist. & Cult, 72-75; ed. consult, Columbia Encycl, 72- Award for Excellency in Teaching, Brandeis Univ, 68. MLA; Northeast Mod. Lang. Asn; Renaissance Soc. Am. New England Puritanism; Renaissance English Drama; 19th century American literature. Publ: Horologicals to chronometricals: the rhetoric of the Jeremiad, Univ. Wis, 70; ed, Typology and Early American literature, Univ. Mass, 72 & The American puritan imagination, Cambridge, 74; auth, Cotton Mather, In: Major writers of Early American literature, Univ. Wis, 72; plus three others. Add: Dept. of English, Columbia University, New York, NY 10027.

BEREK, PETER, b. Brooklyn, N.Y, June 20, 40, m. 62; c. 3. ENGLISH. B.A, Amherst Col, 61; M.A, Harvard, 63, Ph.D.(Eng), 67. Instr. ENG, Hamilton Col, 65-67; asst. prof, WILLIAMS COL, 67-72, ASSOC. PROF, 72- Nat. Endowment for Humanities younger humanist fel, 71-72. MLA; AAUP. English literature of the 16th and 17th centuries. Publ: The transformations of allegory from Spenser to Hawthorne, Amherst Col, 62; Plain and ornate styles and the structure of Paradise lost, PMLA, 3/70; The voices of Marvell's lyrics, Mod. Lang. Quart, 6/71. Add: Dept. of English, Williams College, Williamstown, MA 01267.

BERESFORD-HOWE, CONSTANCE (MRS. CHRISTOPHER PRESSNELL), b. Montreal, Que, Nov. 10, 22; c. 1. ENGLISH LITERATURE. Dodd fel. & B.A, McGill Univ, 45, M.A, 46; Prov. Que. fel, 46-48; Ph.D.(Eng), Brown Univ, 50. Lectr. Eng, McGill Univ, 48-49, asst. prof, 49-66, assoc. prof, 66-70; INSTR. ENG. LIT. & CREATIVE WRITING, RYERSON POLYTECH. INST, 70- PEN Club. Canadian literature, French and English; modern British and American fiction; creative writing and French-English translation. Publ: The unreasoning heart, Of this day's journey & The invisible gate, Dodd; My lady Greensleeves, Ballantine; The book of Eve, Macmillan, Toronto & Little, 73. Add: 16 Cameron Crescent, Toronto, Ont. M4G 1Z8, Can.

BERETS, RALPH ADOLPH, b. Amersfoort, Netherlands, Dec. 5, 39; U.S. citizen; m. 63; c. 2. MODERN FICTION, FILM. B.A. & M.A, Univ. Mich, 63, Ph.D.(Eng), 69; Univ. Calif, Berkeley, 64-65. Instr. Eng, Univ. Mich, 69-70; ASST. PROF. NOVEL & FILM, UNIV. MO-KANSAS CITY, 70- Instr. film, Kansas City Art Inst, 71- MLA; Midwest Mod. Lang. Asn. Comparative literature; film and literature. Publ: Ed, A technical survey of the tool and die industry in Michigan, 67, Technological change in Michigan's tool and die industry, 68, A prototype structural system integrating mechanical services, 69, Constraints to the development and marketing of medical electronic equipment, 69 & Manufactured housing in the 1970's, 70, Univ. Mich; auth, The magus: study in the creation of a personal myth, Twentieth Century Lit, 4/73. Add: Dept. of English, University of Missouri at Kansas City, 5315 Holmes, Kansas City, MO 64110.

BERG, DAVID MERLEN, b. Minneapolis, Minn, Dec. 4, 32; m. 55; c. 1. SPEECH, COMMUNICATION. B.A, St. Olaf Col, 54; M.A, Univ. Minn, 62, Ph.D.(speech), 63. Instr. SPEECH, Hamline Univ, 62-63; asst. prof, Univ. Okla, 63-66; UNIV. KANS, 66-68, assoc. prof, 68-72, PROF, 72- U.S.N, 54-59, Res, 59-, Lt. Comdr. Speech Commun. Asn. (Golden Anniversary Award, 73); Cent. States Speech Commun. Asn.(exec. secy, 72-). Small group communication theory; persuasion and public opinion formation during time of war. Publ: Co-auth, A time to speak, Wadsworth, 70; auth, The rhetoric of war preparation: the New York press in 1898, Jour. Quart, winter 68; Communicating with the people: the relationship of government and the press, 10/71 & Rhetoric, reality and mass media, 10/72, Quart. J. Speech. Add: Dept. of Speech & Drama, University of Kansas, Lawrence, KS 66044.

BERGAMO, RALPH, b. Newark, N.J, Nov. 30, 09; div; c. 2. ENGLISH. A.B, DePaul Univ, 42; A.M, Columbia Univ, 47; Univ. Pisa, summer 68; Soc. Dante Alighieri, Rome, Italy, summer 72. Instr, Univ. Ky, 47-49; lectr, Rutgers Univ, 49-53; asst. prof. ENG, GA. INST. TECHNOL, 53-73, ASSOC. PROF, 74- Copy reader, Atlanta Constitution, 68-72. U.S.A, 42-45; Bronze Star Medal & Oak Leaf Cluster. NCTE; S.Atlantic Mod. Lang. Asn. World literature; contemporary fiction. Add: Dept. of English, Georgia Institute of Technology, Atlanta, GA 30332.

BERGBUSCH, MARTIN LUTHER THEODORE, b. Edmonton, Alta, Apr. 8, 40; m. 63; c. 4. ENGLISH. B.A, Univ. Victoria (B.C), 62; M.A, Univ. B.C, 64; Ph.D.(Eng), Cornell Univ, 70. Instr. ENG, UNIV. SASK, REGINA, 64-67, lectr, 67-70, ASST. PROF, 70-, CHMN. DEPT, 73- Can. Asn. Univ. Teachers; Asn. Can. Univ. Teachers Eng; Humanities Asn. Can; Can. Asn. Chmn. Eng. Non-dramatic literature of Renaissance, especially the works of Sir Philip Sidney; novels and poetry of Thomas Hardy. Publ: Rebellion in Sidney's Arcadia, Philol. Quart, (in press). Add: Dept. of English, University of Saskatchewan, Regina, Sask. S4S 0A2, Can.

BERGEN, MARY JEANELLE, B.V.M, b. Chicago, Ill, Jan. 7, 12. THEATRE, TELEVISION. A.B, Mundelein Col, 45; M.A, State Univ. Iowa, 49; summers, Mich. State Univ, 58; Northwest. Univ, 63, 65; Ind. Univ, Bloomington, 64. Instr. speech, MUNDELEIN COL, 42-45, speech & drama, 45-50, asst. prof, drama, 50-60, ASSOC. PROF. THEATRE & TV, 60-, CHMN. DEPT. THEATRE, 71- Am. Theatre Asn; Nat. Asn. Educ. Broadcasters; Am. Women Radio & TV. Educational and closed-circuit television; theatre criticism. Add: Dept. of Theatre, Mundelein College, 6363 Sheridan Rd, Chicago, IL 60626.

BERGER, HARRY, JR, b. New York, N.Y, Dec. 18, 24; m. 47; c. 3. ENGLISH. B.A, Yale, 48, Ph.D.(Eng), 55. Asst. in instr, ENG, Yale, 49-50, 51-52, instr, 54-58, asst. prof, 58-62, assoc. prof, 62-65; UNIV. CALIF, SANTA CRUZ, 65-66, PROF, 67- Vis. prof, Univ. N.C, Chapel Hill, 67. U.S.M.C.R, 43-46, S/Sgt. Renaissance Soc. Am; Col. Art Asn; MLA. Spenser and the Renaissance; theory and practice of literary interpretation; cultural ecology—literary interpretation as intellectual history. Publ: The allegorical temper, Yale, 57; ed. & contrib, Spenser: a collection of critical essays, Prentice-Hall, 68; auth, Paradise lost evolving: books I-VI toward a new view of the poem as the speaker's experience, Centennial Rev, fall 67; Poetry as revision: interpreting Robert Frost, Criticism, Quart. Lit. & Arts, winter 68; Theatre, drama, and the second world: a prologue to Shakespeare, Comp. Drama, spring 68. Add: Dept. of English, University of California, Santa Cruz, CA 95060.

BERGER, IRWIN, b. New York, N.Y, Aug. 31, 29; m. 58; c. 2. ENGLISH, SEMANTICS. B.S.E, City Col. New York, 51, M.A, 52; Ph.D.(Eng), Yeshiva Univ, 65. Teacher, High Sch, N.Y, 52-61, acting chmn. dept. Eng, 61-64; curriculum consult. Eng. & lang. arts, Bur. Curriculum Res, New York Bd. Educ, 65-66; from asst. prof. to PROF. ENG. & DEP. CHMN. DEPT, BRONX COMMUNITY COL, 66- Mem. adv. bd, Gen. Semantics Found. Non-a-Award, N.Y. Soc. Gen. Semantics, 63; Irving J. Lee Award, Int. Conf. Gen. Semantics, 68. Ist. Soc. Gen. Semantics; NCTE. Improving composition through semantics and critical thinking; curriculum development, English language arts; evolution and increasing role of the community college. Publ: Activities in the English class based on the covers of the S.E.P, High Points, 55; Eleven common sense principles about language, 65 & Student writings examined for logic and clarity, 65, In: A guide for evaluating student composition, NCTE. Add: 7 Lake Shore Dr, Brookfield, CT 06804.

BERGER, MARSHALL DANIEL, Linguistics. See Volume III, Foreign Languages, Linguistics & Philology.

BERGER, SIDNEY E, b. Brooklyn, N.Y, Apr. 8, 44; m. 67; c. 1. MEDIEVAL & RENAISSANCE LITERATURE. B.A, Univ. Calif, Berkeley, 65; M.A, Univ. Iowa, 67, Ph.D.(Eng), 71. ASST. PROF. ENG, UNIV. CALIF, DAVIS, 71- Leopold Schepp Found. fel, 72-73. Mediaeval Acad. Am; MLA; Early Eng. Text. Soc; Philol. Asn. Pac. Coast. Medieval literature; bibliography and textual criticism; Renaissance literature. Publ: Thrymskvitha, Windhover, 70; ed, Pudd'nhead Wilson and Those extraordinary twins, Univ. Calif, 74; auth, A method for compiling a computer assisted concordance for a Middle English text, Stud. Bibliog, 73; New Mark Twain items, Bibliog. Soc. Am. Publ, 74; Dante's use of Venantius Fortunata's Vexilla regis prodeunt hymn, Ital. Quart. Add: Dept. of English, University of California, Davis, CA 95616.

BERGER, SIDNEY LOUIS, b. New York, N.Y, Jan. 25, 36; m. 63; c. 1. THEATRE, DRAMA. B.A, Brooklyn Col, 57; M.A, Univ. Kans, 60, Ph.D. (drama), 64. Asst. instr. speech & theatre, Univ. Kans, 58-64; asst. prof. theatre, Mich. State Univ, 64-68, assoc. prof. theatre & dir. grad. stud, 68-69, assoc. dir. theatre, 67-68; PROF. DRAMA & CHMN. DEPT, UNIV. HOUSTON, 69- Am. Educ. Theatre Asn-U.S. Dept. Defense summer travel grants, Asia, 60, Iceland & Greenland, 66; U.S. Dept. State summer lectrs. & Am. specialist in theatre, Europe, 63-64; Nat. Found. Jewish Cult. grant, 63-64; mem, Mich. Counc. Arts, 68-; rep, Conf. Group Big Ten Heads of Theatre, 67-68; dir, Houston Grand Opera Previews, 72-73; mem. bd. dirs, Tex. Opera Theatre, 73-; mem. cult. affairs comt, Houston Chamber of Commerce, 73-; mem. screening comt, Fulbright-Hays Int. Exchange of Persons, 73- Am. Theatre Asn. Acting; directing; East European theatre. Publ: The musical play, Bull. Educ, 4/62; The musical theatre before 1850, Players Mag, 1/66; The Jew in contemporary American drama, Jewish Bk. Annual, 10/72. Add: Dept. of Drama, University of Houston, Cullen Blvd, Houston, TX 77004.

BERGER, THOMAS LELAND, b. Oak Park, Ill, Mar. 26, 41; m. 64; c. 3. ENGLISH LITERATURE. B.A, Dartmouth Col, 63; M.A, Duke Univ, 67, Ph.D.(Eng), 69. Instr. ENG, Univ. N.C. Chapel Hill, 69-70; post-doctoral fel, Macalester Col, 70-71; ASST. PROF, ST. LAWRENCE UNIV, 71- MLA. English Renaissance drama; bibliography and textual criticism. Publ: Petrarchan fortress of The changeling, Renaissance Papers, 69; Notes on the text of Chapman's Caesar and Pompey, Papers Bibliog. Soc. Am, 71. Add: Dept. of English, St. Lawrence University, Canton, NY 13617.

BERGERON, DAVID MOORE, b. Alexandria, La, Feb. 8, 38; m. 66. ENGLISH. B.A, La. Col, 60; Woodrow Wilson fel, Vanderbilt Univ, 60-61, M.A, 62, Ph.D.(Eng), 64. Asst. prof. ENG, Univ. Louisville, 64-68; ASSOC. PROF, UNIV. NEW ORLEANS, 68- Folger Shakespeare libr. fels, summers 65, 68, 70 & 73; Southeast. Inst. Medieval Renaissance Stud. fel, summer 66; Am. Counc. Learned Soc. fel, 68-69; asst. ref. librn. & asst. ed, Folger Shakespeare Libr, Wash, D.C, 71-72; assoc. ed, Shakespeare Quart, 72-; ed, Res. Opportunities in Renaissance Drama, 73- MLA; Malone Soc.(hon. Am. treas, 69-); Shakespeare Asn. Am; Renaissance Soc. Am. English Renaissance civic pageantry; Shakespeare; Renaissance drama. Publ: English civic pageantry 1558-1642, Edward Arnold, London, 71 & Univ. S.C, 71; Twentieth-century criticism of English masques, pageants and entertainments, 1558-1642, Trinity Univ, 72; Medieval drama and Tudor-Stuart civic pageantry, J. Medieval & Renaissance Stud, 72; King Lear and John Hall's casebook, Shakespeare Quart, 72; The mythical structure of All's well that ends well, Tex. Stud. Lit. & Lang, 73. Add: Dept. of English, University of New Orleans, New Orleans, LA 70122.

BERGGREN, PAULA S, b. New York, N.Y, July 10, 42; m. 68. ENGLISH RENAISSANCE LITERATURE, ENGLISH POETRY & DRAMA. A.B, Barnard Col, 63; M.A, Yale, 64, Ph.D.(Eng), 67. ASST. PROF. ENG, Yale, 67-72; BARUCH COL, 72- Jacobean drama; female image in English and American literature. Add: Dept. of English, Baruch College, 17 Lexington Ave, New York, NY 10010.

BERGHUIS, MELVIN E, b. Clare City, Minn, Oct. 19, 15; m. 40; c. 3. SPEECH. A.B, Calvin Col, 36; A.M, Univ. Mich, 49; Ph.D.(speech), Mich. State Univ, 64. Teacher, Allendale Christian Sch, 37-39; Baxter Christian Sch, 39-41; Chicago Christian High Sch, 41-45; Grand Rapids Christian High Sch, 46-48; PROF. SPEECH, CALVIN COL, 48-58 & 71-, registr, 58-61, dir. stud. serv, 61-64, v.pres. stud. affairs, 64-71. U.S.N, 45-46. Speech Commun. Asn; Cent. States Speech Asn. Add: 1718 Radcliff Ave. S.E, Grand Rapids, MI 49506.

BERGMAN, HERBERT, b. New York, N.Y, June 11, 25. ENGLISH. B.S.S, City Col. New York, 46; M.A, Duke Univ, 47; Ph.D, Univ. Wis, 53. Acting instr. ENG, Ohio Univ, 48-49; instr, Univ. Tex, 51-57; asst. prof, West. Mich. Univ, 57-58; from asst. prof. to PROF. AM. THOUGHT & LANG, MICH. STATE UNIV, 58- Grants, Am. Counc. Learned Soc, Am. Philos.

Soc, MLA & Educ. Develop. Prog. MLA; Am. Stud. Asn; NCTE; Col. Eng. Asn; Conf. Col. Compos. & Commun; Am. Film Inst; Brit. Film Inst; Univ. Film Asn. American literature, especially Walt Whitman; American culture, especially film. Publ: Co-ed, The black experience, 69 & auth, Fiction and film, 74, Mich. State Univ; auth, Walt Whitman as a journalist, 71 & Whitman on editing, newspapers and journalism, 71, Jour. Quart. Add: Dept. of American Thought & Language, Michigan State University, East Lansing, MI 48824.

BERGMANN, FREDRICK LOUIS, b. Tecumseh, Kans, Sept. 27, 16; m. 41; c. 2. ENGLISH. A.B, Washburn Univ, 37; fel, State Col. Wash, 37-39, A.M, 39; Columbia Univ, 42; fel, George Washington Univ, 49-50, Ph.D.(Eng), 53; fel, Folger Shakespeare Libr, 51. From instr. to prof. Eng, DePAUW UNIV, 40-69, JAMES WHITCOMB RILEY PROF. ENG. LIT, 69-, CHMN. DEPT. ENG, 40-, DIR, CONF. AM. STUD, 57- Ford humanities grant res. & travel in Europe, 71. MLA; Johnson Soc. Great Lakes Region; Am. Soc. 18th Century Stud; Soc. Fr. Etude XVIIIe Siècle. David Garrick; 18the century English literature; rhetoric. Publ: Co-auth, Writing craftsmanship, Norton, 56; auth, Paragraphy rhetoric, 67, Sentence rhetroic, 69 & Essays, 70, Allyn & Bacon; David Garrick and the clandestine marriage, PMLA; Shakespeare in Indiana, Shakespeare Quart; plus others. Add: Dept. of English, DePauw University, Greencastle, IN 46135.

BERGMANN, JOHANNES DIETRICH, b. New Haven, Conn, Dec. 3, 41; m. 64; c. 1. AMERICAN LITERATURE. A.B, Amherst Col, 63; M.A, Univ. Conn, 64, Ph.D.(Eng), 69. From instr. to asst. prof. ENG, N.Y. Univ, 67-71; ASST. PROF, STATE UNIV. N.Y. ALBANY, 71- Consult, N.Y. State Educ. Dept, 69-; regional dir, Am. Lit. Manuscripts Revision Proj, 71- MLA; Am. Stud. Asn; Melville Soc. Herman Melville; American urban literature; American literature 1815-1865. Publ: The original confidence man, Am. Quart, fall 69. Add: Dept. of English, State University of New York at Albany, Albany, NY 12222.

BERGQUIST, BARBARA EDITH, b. Ft. Benning, Ga, Aug. 10, 35. ENGLISH. B.A, Dickinson Col, 58; M.A, Univ. Pa, 60, 64-68. Instr. ENG, UNIV. P.R, 60-68, ASSOC. PROF, 68- MLA; AAUP. British literature of the 17th century. Add: Dept. of English, College of Humanities, University of Puerto Rico, Rio Piedras, PR 00931.

BERINGAUSE, ARTHUR F, b. New York, N.Y, Jan. 15, 19; m. 48; c. 2. ENGLISH. B.A, City Col, 39, M.S, 46; M.A, N.Y. Univ, 51, Ph.D, 54. Teacher Eng, pub. sch, N.Y, 46-49; Brooklyn Tech. High Sch, 49-54; chmn, Evander Childs High Sch, Bronx, 54-61; prof. Eng, Queens Col.(N.Y) & supvr. dept, Sch. Gen. Stud, 61-64; CHMN. DEPT. ENG, BRONX COMMUNITY COL, 64- Lectr, Brooklyn Col, 46-53, Grad. Sch, Hunter Col, 56 & Queens Col.(N.Y), 59-61; instr, N.Y. Univ, 53-56; mem, NCTE Comt. All-Sch. Learning, 55; prof, Yeshiva Univ, 57-59; ed, The New Lang, Am. Bk. Co, 68-; State Univ. N.Y. grant stud. Hebrew names, Israel, 70. U.S.A, 42-46, Lt. MLA; fel. Am. Stud. Asn; NCTE; Col. Eng. Asn. Modern and American literature; linguistics; Hebrew and Jewish names. Publ: Brooks Adams, Knopf, 55; James Joyce's philosophy, Cresset, 63; English literature since 1945, McCormick-Mathers, 67; co-auth, The range of college reading, Houghton, 67; auth, Faulkner's Yoknapatawpha register, Bucknell Rev, 63; plus others. Add: Dept. of English, Bronx Community College, 120 E. 184th St, Bronx, NY 10453.

BERKELEY, DAVID SHELLEY, b. Pittsburgh, Pa; m. 43. ENGLISH LITERATURE. A.B, Juniata Col, 38; A.M, Harvard, 41, Ph.D, 49. Instr. ENG, OKLA. STATE UNIV, 48-49, asst. prof, 49-54, assoc. prof, 54-60, PROF, 60-, CHMN, GRAD. ENG. STUD, 69- Vis. prof, Univ. Okla, 65. MLA; S.Cent. Mod. Lang. Asn; Milton Soc. Am. Milton; Shakespeare; Restoration drama. Publ: Inwrought with figures dim: a reading of Milton's Lycidas, Mouton, 74; The penitent rake in Restoration comedy, Mod. Philol; co-auth, The theme of Henry IV, part I, Shakespeare Quart, winter 68; plus others. Add: Dept. of English, Oklahoma State University, Stillwater, OK 74074.

BERKMAN, LEONARD, b. New York, N.Y, July 21, 38; m. 62; c. 2. THEATRE, SPEECH. B.A, Columbia Univ, 60; M.F.A, Yale, 63, D.F.A.(Dramatic lit. & criticism), 70. Instr. Eng, Univ. Tex, El Paso, 63-64; playwrighting, Univ. Mass, 68-69; ASST. PROF. THEATRE & SPEECH, SMITH COL, 69- Nineteenth and 20th century European drama; American drama; Afro-American and African drama. Publ: Really, now (play), Publ. Broadcasting Syst, 71; Two demon plays, Can. Broadcasting Corp, 73; Blanche DuBois: the tragic downfall, Mod. Drama, 12/67; Four books on rock, Mass. Rev, spring 71. Add: Dept. Theatre & Speech, Smith College, Ctr. for Performing Arts, Northampton, MA 01060.

BERKOBEN, LAWRENCE D, b. McKeesport, Pa, May 6, 30; m. 62. ENGLISH LITERATURE. B.A, Pa. State Univ, 57; M.A, Ohio Univ, 58; Ph.D, Univ. Wash, 63. Asst, Ohio Univ, 57-58; instr. Eng, Univ. Ariz, 58-60; asst, Univ. Wash, 60-62, instr. ENG, 62-63; asst. prof, CALIF. STATE UNIV, STANISLAUS, 63-66, ASSOC, PROF, 66- U.S.A.F, 50-54. MLA. English literature of the 18th and 19th century. Publ: Image and theme in Christabel, Mod. Lang. Quart, 12/64; The composition of Coleridge's Hymn before sunrise: some mitigating circumstances, Eng. Lang. Notes, 9/66. Add: Dept. of English, California State University, Stanislaus, Turlock, CA 95380.

BERKOVE, LAWRENCE IVAN, b. Rochester, N.Y, Jan. 8, 30. ENGLISH. LITERATURE. A.B, Univ. Ill, 51; M.A, Univ. Minn, 53; Ph.D, Univ. Pa, 62. Asst. instr, Univ. Pa, 57-58 & 60-61; instr. Eng, Skidmore Col, 58-60; De-Paul Univ, 61-62; Colo. Col, 62-63, asst. prof. ENG. LIT, 63-64; UNIV. MICH, DEARBORN, 64-67, ASSOC. PROF, 67- Nat. Fac. Res. grant, 68. Mil.Intel, U.S.A, 53-56. MLA; Midwest Mod. Lang. Asn; NCTE. American literature of the 19th century. Publ: Biblical influence on Whitman's concept of creatorhood, Emerson Soc. Quart, 2nd Quart, 67; The poor players of Huckleberry Finn, Papers Mich. Acad. Sci, Arts & Lett, 68; Arms and the man: Ambrose Bierce's response to war, Mich. Academician, winter 69. Add: Dept. of English, University of Michigan, 4901 Evergreen Rd, Dearborn, MI 48128.

BERKOWITZ, MORTON SELIG, b. New York, N.Y. AMERICAN LITERATURE, MILTON. B.A, N.Y. Univ, 63; Hebrew Univ. Jerusalem, 64-67; Ph.D.(Eng), Univ. Mass, 70. ASST. PROF. ENG. & AM. LIT, TRENT UNIV, 70- Nineteenth century American literature; myth. Add: Dept. of English, Trent University, Peterborough, Ont, Can.

BERLIN, NORMAND, b. New York, N.Y, Dec. 6, 31; m. 56; c. 2. ENGLISH. B.A, N.Y. Univ, 53; Woodrow Wilson fel, Columbia Univ, 55-56, M.A, 56; Ph.D.(Eng), Univ. Calif, Berkeley, 64. Instr. ENG, McGill Univ, 61-64, asst. prof, 64-65; UNIV. MASS, AMHERST, 65-68, assoc. prof, 68-74, PROF, 74- U.S.A, 53-55. Shakespeare; Elizabethan and Jacobean drama; modern drama. Publ: The base string: the underworld in Elizabethan drama, Fairleigh Dickinson Univ, 68; Thomas Dekker: a partial reappraisal, Stud. Eng. Lit, spring 66; Beckett and Shakespeare, Fr. Rev, 4/67; The Duchess of Malfi: act V and genre, Genre, 12/70; plus ten others. Add: Dept. of English, University of Massachusetts, Amherst, MA 01002.

BERLIND, BRUCE, b. Brooklyn, N.Y, July 17, 26; m. 54; c. 5. ENGLISH. B.A, Princeton, 47; M.A, Johns Hopkins Univ, 50, Ph.D, 58. Instr. ENG, COLGATE UNIV, 54-58, asst. prof, 58-63, assoc. prof, 63-66, PROF, 66-, chmn. dept, 67-72. U.S. Inform. Serv. lectr, Ger, 63; vis. assoc. prof, Univ. Rochester, 66. U.S.A, 44-46, 50-52, Lt. MLA. Contemporary American poetry. Publ: Ways of happening, Chenango Ed, 50; Companion pieces, Penyeach Press, 71. Add: 62 Broad St, Hamilton, NY 13346.

BERLY, CHARLSIE ELIZABETH, b. Leesville, La, July 27, 03. ENGLISH. B.A, Randolph-Macon Col, 23; M.A, South. Methodist Univ, 41; summers, Univ. Tex, 51-54. Teacher, high sch, Tex, 23-45; asst. prof. Eng, Univ. Southwest. La, 45-47; assoc. prof, Lamar Univ, 47-66, prof, 66-69; RETIRED. MLA; Renaissance Soc. Am; Shakespeare Asn. Am. Renaissance literature. Add: 135 Seventh St, Beaumont, TX 77702.

BERMAN, ALBERT ANATOLE, b. Newport, R.I, Oct. 14, 28. ENGLISH, CLASSICS. A.B, Harvard, 49, fel, 53-57, Ph.D.(comp. lit), 60; M.A, Haverford Col, 51. Instr. Eng. & humanities, Brandeis Univ, 57-58; from asst. prof. to ASSOC. PROF. ENG. & COMP. LIT, L.I. UNIV, 60- The epic; symbolism in literature; classical and Renaissance drama. Publ: The realistic imagination, Cambridge Rev, 55; Readings and translations from Greek, Latin, Anglo-Saxon, In: Sounds of world poetry, Delta Records, 63. Add: Dept. of English, Long Island University, Brooklyn Center, Flatbush Ave. Extension, Brooklyn, NY 11201.

BERMAN, MORTON, b. Syracuse, N.Y, Mar. 21, 24. ENGLISH. A.B, Univ. Ill, 48; A.M, Harvard, 50, summer, Dexter traveling fel, 54, Ph.D.(Eng), 57. Teaching fel. gen. educ, Harvard, 51-54; instr. ENG, BOSTON UNIV, 54-58, asst. prof, 58-61, assoc. prof, 61-64, PROF, 64-, CHMN. DEPT, 62- Ruskin Prize, 54. U.S.A, 44-46. MLA; AAUP. Victorian literature; drama. Publ: Collab, Eight great tragedies, 57, Eight great comedies, 58, The genius of the Irish theater, 60 & co-ed, The genius of the English theatre (2 vols), 62, Mentor Bks; co-auth, Study of literature, 60, Aspects of the drama, 62, An introduction to literature: fiction, poetry, drama, 67, 71, 73; Tragedy and comedy: an anthology of drama, 67, A dictionary of literary, dramatic and cinematic terms, 71, co-ed, Types of drama: plays and essays, 72 & Nine modern classics: an anthology of short novels, 73, Little; auth, Afterword to George Eliot's The mill on the floss, Signet Classic, 65. Add: Dept. of English, Boston University, Boston, MA 02215.

BERMAN, RONALD S, b. New York, N.Y, Dec. 15, 30; m. 53; c. 3. ENGLISH LITERATURE. A.B, Harvard, 52; M.A, Yale, 57, Ph.D, 59. Instr. Eng. Lit, Columbia Univ, 59-61, asst. prof, 61-62; assoc. prof. Eng. lit. & assoc. ed, Kenyon Rev, Kenyon Col, 62-65; PROF. ENG, UNIV. CALIF, SAN DIEGO, 65-, CHMN. HUMANITIES, NAT. ENDOWMENT FOR HUMANITIES, 71- U.S.N.R, 52-56, Lt.(jg). MLA; Renaissance Soc. Am. Shakespeare; 17th and 20th centuries; Renaissance. Publ: Henry King and the seventeenth century, Chatto & Windus & Oxford, 64; Reader's guide to Shakespeare's plays, Scott, 65; Henry V, Prentice-Hall, 68; America in the sixties, Free Press, 68; Notes on the motives of Marcus Brutus, Shakespeare Quart, spring 72; Science and values: National Endowment for the Humanities, Science, 11/72; An unquiet quiet on campus, New York Times, 2/74; plus others. Add: National Endowment for the Humanities, 806 15th St. N.W, Washington, DC 20506.

BERMEL, ALBERT (CYRIL), b. London, Eng, Dec. 20, 27; U.S. citizen; m. 56; c. 2. THEATRE HISTORY. B.Sc, Univ. London, 51. Guggenheim fel, Columbia Univ, 65-66, assoc. prof. THEATRE, 66-71, adj. prof, 71-72; ASSOC. PROF, LEHMAN COL, 72- Consult. ed, Arts in Soc, Univ. Wis, 64-; theatre critic, New Leader, 64-; vis. prof. comp. lit, Rutgers Univ, 66-67; drama, Juillard Sch, 71-72; contrib. ed, Performance Mag, 71-; mem. ed. bd, Twentieth Century Lit, 74- Brit. Army, 46-48. Dramatists Guild; Authors League Am. Theatrical analysis; dramatic criticism. Publ: Ed, The plays of Courteline, Theatre Arts Bks, 61, Genius of the French theatre, Mentor, New Am. Libr, 61, Horatius, Chandler, 62 & The one-act comedies of Moliere, World, 64; auth, Contradictory characters: an interpretation of the modern theatre, Dutton, 73; contrib, The infernal machine and other plays by Jean Cocteau, New Directions, 63. Add: 5 Pershing Ave, New Rochelle, NY 10801.

BERNARD, JULES (EUGENE), Comparative Literature. See Volume III, Foreign Languages, Linguistics & Philology.

BERNARD, KENNETH, b. Brooklyn, N.Y, May 7, 30; m. 52; c. 3. ENGLISH. B.A, City Col. New York, 53; M.A, Columbia Univ, 56, Ph.D, 62. Instr. ENG, L.I. UNIV, 59-62, asst. prof, 62-66, assoc. prof, 66-71, PROF, 71- Off. Advan. Drama Res. grant, Univ. Minn, summer 71; Guggenheim Found. fel. playwriting, 72-73; N.Y. State Creative Artists pub. serv. grant playwriting, 73-74. U.S.A, 53-55. Dramatic writing. Publ: Night club and other plays, Winter House, 71; King Kong: a meditation, New Am. Rev, 5/72; Two stories, Perishable Press, 73; plus three others. Add: 788 Riverside Dr, New York, NY 10032.

BERNARDIN, CHARLES WILHELM, b. Lawrence, Mass, July 26, 17. AMERICAN LITERATURE. A.B, Assumption Col, 39; A.M, Boston Col, 42; Ph.D, Univ. Wis, 49. Res. asst, Univ. Wis, 42-43, teaching asst, 46-48; instr. ENG, grad. sch, Fordham Univ, 48-54; CHMN. DEPT, VILLANOVA UNIV,

54-, PROF, 60- A biographical and critical study of John Dos Passos; Chaucer; modern poetry. Add: Dept. of English, Villanova University, Villanova, PA 19085.

BERND, DANIEL W, b. Omaha, Nebr, Nov. 12, 22; m. 42; 71; c. 3. ENGLISH, DRAMA. B.A, Stanford Univ, 49; M.A, Univ. Nebr, 57, Ph.D.(Eng), 62. Instr. ENG, Univ. Nebr, 58-60, Univ. Mich, 60-62; asst. prof, San Fernando Valley State Col, 62-66, assoc. prof, 66-68, prof, 68-70; UNIV. PROF, GOVERNORS STATE UNIV, 70-, CHMN. UNIV. ASSEMBLY 71-, asst. dean col. of cult. stud, 70-72, acting dean, 72. Rhetoric consult, Nebr. Curriculum Develop. Ctr, summer 62; dir. Nat. Defense Educ. Act. Inst. Eng, San Fernando Valley State Col, 64-67, experienced teacher fel. prog, 66 & 67; chief mod. lang. br, Div. Educ. Personnel Training, U.S. Off. Educ, 67-68, Prog. Planning & Develop. Br, Div. Prog. Admin, 68-69, chief, Trainers of Teacher Trainers Br, 69; ed. consult, Consortium of Prof. Asns. for Stud. Speech Teacher Improvement Progs, 69-70. U.S.A.F, 42-45 & 50-53, 1st Lt. MLA; NCTE; Int. Reading Asn. Dramatic literature; literary criticism; interdisciplinary studies. Publ: Co-auth, Plays: classic and contemporary, Lippincott, 67; contrib, Project Impact: A pilot study evaluating the NDEA summer Institute program, Am. Inst. Res, 10/67; auth, Prologomenon to a definition of interdisciplinary studies: the experience at Governors State University, Bull. Assoc. Depts. Eng, 12/71. Add: College of Cultural Studies, Governors State University, Park Forest South, IL 60466.

BERNE, STANLEY, b. New York, N.Y, June 8, 23; m. 52. ENGLISH. B.S, Rutgers Univ, 51; M.A, N.Y. Univ, 52; fel, La. State Univ, 58-62. Asst. prof. ENG, EAST. N.MEX. UNIV, 63-67, ASSOC. PROF, 68-, res. grants, 66-73. Cult. affairs div. Dept. State & U.S. Embassy, Mexico City lect. tour, summer 65; guest lectr, Univ. of the Americas, 65; Univ. S.Dak, 68. U.S.A.A.F, 42-45. MLA. Contemporary novel and short story; aesthetics and criticism. Publ: Co-auth, A first book of the neo-narrative, 54 & Cardinals and saints, 58, auth, The dialogues, 62 & The multiple modern gods and other stories, 64, Wittenborn; The unconscious victorious and other stories, Wittenborn, 68, Horizon, 73; Breakthrough fictioneers, Something Else Press, 73; The new rubaiyat of Stanley Berne (poems), Am. Can. Publ, 73. Add: Dept. of English, Eastern New Mexico University, Portales, NM 88130.

BERNER, ROBERT LESLIE, b. Bloomfield, Nebr, July 4, 28; m. 54; c. 6. LITERATURE, AMERICAN STUDIES. B.A, Univ. Wash, 53, M.A, 56, Ph.D, 60. Teaching asst, Univ. Wash, 54-56; instr. ENG, Everett Jr. Col, 56-59; Univ. B.C, 60-63, asst. prof, 63-64; assoc. prof, Frostburg State Col, 64-66; head dept, Alliance Col, 66-68; ASSOC. PROF, UNIV. WIS-OSHKOSH, 68- MLA; Am. Stud. Asn; West. Lit. Asn. Western American literature; American Indian history; modern literature. Publ: The required past: world enough and time, Mod. Fiction Stud, spring 60; Charles L. McNichols and Crazy weather: a reconsideration, West. Am. Lit, spring 71. Add: Dept. of English, University of Wisconsin-Oshkosh, Oshkosh, WI 54901.

BERNHARD, FRANK JAMES, JR, b. Beaumont, Tex, Oct. 20, 37; m. 61; c. 3. ENGLISH LITERATURE. B.A, Rice Univ, 59; Marshall scholar, 59-61; M.A, Univ. Birmingham, Eng, 61. Copy ed, Houston Press, 61-62, drama critic, 62-63, asst. city ed, 62-63; asst. prof, Eng, Muhlenberg Col, 63-64; asst. mgr. & creative dir, Commercial Lett. Serv, Tex, 64-68; MGR, SOC. PERFORMING ARTS, 68- Modern British and American drama. Publ: English theatre 1963: in the wake of the new wave, Bks Abroad, spring 64; Beyond realism: the plays of Harold Pinter, Mod. Drama, 9/65. Add: Jones Hall for the Performing Arts, 615 Louisiana St, Houston, TX 77002.

BERNHARDT-KABISCH, ERNEST, b. Chemnitz, Ger, Nov. 15, 34; U.S. citizen; m. 56; c. 1. ENGLISH. B.A, Univ. Calif, Berkeley, 57, Loewy fel, 57-58, univ. fel, 58-59, M.A, 59, Ph.D.(Eng), 62. Instr. ENG, IND. UNIV, BLOOMINGTON, 62-64, asst. prof, 64-66, ASSOC. PROF, 66- MLA. Wordsworth; Romantic movement; history of ideas in 18th and early 19th century. Publ: Robert Southey, Twayne, (in prep); Wordsworth: the monumental poet, Philol. Quart, 65; The epitaph and the Romantic poets, Huntington Libr; Quart, 67; Southey in the tropics, Wordsworth Circle, 74. Add: Dept. of English, Indiana University, Bloomington, IN 47401.

BERNHEIMER, CHARLES CLARENCE, b. Bryn Mawr, Pa, Aug. 16, 42. COMPARATIVE LITERATURE. B.A, Haverford Col, 63; Univ. Göttingen, 63-64; M.A, Harvard, 65, Ph.D.(comp. lit), 73. ASST. PROF. ENG. & COMP. LIT, STATE UNIV. N.Y. BUFFALO, 70- MLA. Nineteenth and 20th century novel; novel theory. Publ: Linguistic realism in Flaubert's Bouvard et Pécuchet, Novel, winter 74. Add: Dept. of English, State University of New York at Buffalo, Buffalo, NY 14214.

BERNSTEIN, CAROL L, b. New York, N.Y, Feb. 9, 33; m. 55; c. 4. ENGLISH. B.A, Swarthmore Col, 54; M.A, Yale, 56, Ph.D.(Eng), 61. Instr. Eng, Hebrew Univ, Israel, 57-58; lectr, Albertus Magnus Col, 65; vis. lectr. Eng. & Am. lit, Hebrew Univ, Israel, 65-66; lectr. ENG, Univ. Pa, 67-69, asst. prof, 69-74; LECTR, BRYN MAWR COL, 74- MLA. Victorian literature; 19th and 20th century British and American literature. Add: Dept. of English, Bryn Mawr College, Bryn Mawr, PA 19010.

BERNSTEIN, JOHN ALBERT, b. Miami, Fla, Apr. 4, 36. ENGLISH LITERATURE. B.A, Haverford Col, 57; Libr. Serv. scholar, Univ. Pa, 57-58, univ. scholar, 58-59, Harrison scholar, 59-60, Ph.D, 61. Instr. Eng, Haverford Col, 59-60; Princeton, 61-65; Fulbright prof. Am. lit, Norweg. Advan. Teachers Col, Trondheim, 65-66; lectr. ENG, Univ. Pa, 66-67; asst. prof, MACALESTER COL, 67-69, ASSOC. PROF, 69- MLA. American literature; modern British literature; movies. Publ: Pacifism and rebellion in the writings of Herman Melville, Mouton, Netherlands, 64; Benito Cereno and the Spanish Inquisition, Nineteenth Century Fiction, 3/62; Literature in the Great Society, Under Dusken, Norway, 11/65; Protest and pain, Bowering's Mirror on the floor, Minn. Rev, 68. Add: Dept. of English, Macalester College, St. Paul, MN 55105.

BERNSTEIN, MELVIN HERBERT, b. New York, N.Y, Apr. 21, 14; m. 37; c. 1. ENGLISH. A.B, City Col. New York, 36; A.M, N.Y. Univ, 41, Ph.D, 51. Tutor, City Col. New York, 39-43, 46-49; asst. prof. ENG, ALFRED UNIV, 49-54, assoc. prof, 54-57, PROF, 57-, OMBUDSMAN, 71-, chmn. civilization panel, 50-69. Lectr, Salzburg Sem. Am. Stud, Austria, 61. MLA. Short story; Gerard Manley Hopkins and John Jay Chapman; Dr. James Rush (1786-1869). Add: Dept. of English, Alfred University, Alfred, NY 14802.

BERQUIST, GOODWIN F, JR, b. Rockville Center, N.Y, June 29, 30; m. 53. SPEECH. B.A, Ohio Wesleyan Univ, 52; M.A, Pa. State Univ, 54, Ph.D. (Brit. pub. address), 58; summer, Inst. Hist. Res, Univ. London, 56. Instr. speech, Pa. State Univ, 56-57; Ohio State Univ, 57-60; asst. prof, Univ. Wis-Milwaukee, 60-64, assoc. prof, 64-68, PROF. COMMUN, 68-69, chmn. dept, 67-69; OHIO STATE UNIV, 69- Res. grant, grad. sch, Univ. Wis, summer 61, Kiekhofer award, 64; lectr. commun, Peace Corps Training Prog, 64-67; vis. prof. speech, Univ. Hawaii, 65; Huntington Libr. & Art Gallery res. fel, 71. Speech Commun. Asn; Cent. States Speech Asn.(teaching award, 57); AAUP. Rhetoric and public address: historiography; Anglo-American culture. Publ: Ed, Speeches for illustration and example, Scott, 65; auth, Revolution through persuasion: John Pym's appeal to the moderates in 1640, Quart J. Speech, 2/63; co-auth, A study of context content and meaning in school board deliberations, J. Educ. Res, 1/66; auth, The rhetorical heritage of Frederick Jackson Turner, Trans. Wis. Acad. Sci, Arts & Lett, annual issue, 71; plus one other. Add: Dept. of Communication, Ohio State University, 154 N. Oval Dr, 205 Derby, Columbus, OH 43210.

BERRY, CAROLYN FISCHER, b. Cambridge, Mass, July 7, 09; m. 33; c. 3. ENGLISH. B.A, Mt. Holyoke Col, 30; fel, Wash. State Col, 32-33, M.A, 35. Instr. ENG, Intermountain Union Col, 30-31; N.CENT. COL, 36-58, asst. prof, 58-67, ASSOC. PROF, 67-72, EMER. ASSOC. PROF, 72- NCTE; Conf. Col. Compos. & Commun. Walt Whitman as literary critic; contemporary English and American poets. Add: 153 N. Brainard, Naperville, IL 60540.

BERRY, EDWARD I, b. Camden, N.J, Nov. 30, 40; m. 61; c. 2. ENGLISH LITERATURE. A.B, Wesleyan Univ, 62; M.A, Univ. Calif, Berkeley, 66, Ph.D. (Eng), 69. ASST. PROF. ENG, Univ. Conn, 69-70; UNIV. VA, 70- Shakespeare; Renaissance historical literature. Publ: History and rhetoric in Bacon's Henry VII, In: Seventeenth century prose, Oxford Univ, 71. Add: Dept. of English, University of Virginia, Charlottesville, VA 22901.

BERRY, HERBERT, b. New York, N.Y, May 9, 22; m. 48; c. 4. ENGLISH. B.A, Furman Univ, 47; M.A, Univ. Nebr, 48, Johnson fel, 48, 49, Ph.D. (Eng), 53; Univ. Colo. Instr. ENG, Univ. Nebr, 50-51; asst. prof, Univ. Omaha, 51-55; assoc. prof. & head dept, Doane Col, 55-58; asst. prof, Univ. West. Ont, 59-61, assoc. prof, 61-67; PROF, UNIV. SASK, 67- Can. Counc. stud. grant, summers, 62 & 68. MLA; Renaissance Soc. Am. English literature of the 16th and 17th centuries. Publ: Sir John Suckling's poems and letters from manuscript, Univ. West. Ont, 60; The Playhouse in the Boar's Head Inn, Whitechapel, In: Vol. I, 69 & The Boar's Head again, In: Vol. III, 73, The Elizabethan theatre, Macmillan, Toronto; The Playhouse in the Boar's Head Inn, Whitechapel III, In: Shakespeare 1971, Univ. Toronto, 72; plus others. Add: 1405 Ewart Ave, Saskatoon, Sask, Can.

BERRY, J. WILKES, b. Ft. Worth, Tex, Feb. 9, 38; m. 60; c. 2. ENGLISH. B.A, Abilene Christian Col, 60; M.A, Rice Univ, 62, Woodrow Wilson fel, NDEA fel. & Ph.D.(Eng), 64. Asst. prof. ENG, TEX. TECH UNIV, 64-68, assoc. prof, 68-73, PROF, 73- MLA. English Renaissance literature; southwestern American literature. Publ: Thomas May's Tragedy of Cleopatra, Discourse, winter 68; The conclusion of Lucrece, McNeese Rev, winter 72; Two hoops in Shakespeare's Antony and Cleopatra, CEA Critic, 3/73. Add: Dept. of English, Texas Tech University, Lubbock, TX 79409.

BERRY, LLOYD EASON, b. Houston, Tex, Aug. 1, 35; m. ENGLISH LITERATURE. B.A, Univ. N.C, 57, spec. grad. scholar & univ. scholar, 57-58, M.A, 58; Marshall scholar, 58-60; Ph.D, Cambridge, 60. Asst. prof. ENG, Univ. Ill, Urbana, 60-63, assoc. prof, 63-66, PROF, 66-72, fac. fel, 62, assoc. mem, Ctr. Adv. Stud, 68-69; PROF. & DEAN GRAD. SCH. & DIR. RES, UNIV. MO-COLUMBIA, 72- Am. Philos. Soc. grant-in-aid, 63 & 65; Folger Libr. fel, 65; Huntington Libr. fel, 66; John Simon Guggenheim fel, 66-67; chmn. Marshall Scholar. Comn, 72- Cambridge Bibliog. Soc.(secy. for U.S. & Can, 60-); Milton Soc. Am.(exec. comt, 64-); Renaissance Eng. Text Soc.(exec. comt, 65-); Mod. Humanities Res. Asn; MLA; NCTE; Bibliog. Soc. Eng; Malone Soc; Renaissance Soc. Am; Cent. Renaissance Conf; AHA; Asn. Grad. Schs; Nat. Conf. Res. Adminr. Non dramatic literature and history of the 16th and 17th centuries. Publ: The English works of Giles Fletcher, the Elder, 64, A bibliography of studies in metaphysical poetry, 1939-1960, 64, The Geneva Bible: a facsimile of the 1560 edition, 69 & co-auth, Rude and barbarous kingdom: Russia in the accounts of sixteenth-century English voyagers, 68, Univ. Wis; auth, John Stubbs' Gaping gulf with letters and other relevant documents, Univ. Va, 68; co-auth, The dramatic works of George Chapman, Univ. Ill, 69; auth, Giles Fletcher, the Elder, and Milton's A brief History of Moscovia, Rev. Eng. Stud, 5/60; Phineas Fletcher's account of his father, J. Eng. & Ger. Philol, 4/61; Five Latin poems by Giles Fletcher the Elder, Anglia, 9/62. Add: 202 Jesse Hall, University of Missouri-Columbia, Columbia, MO 65201.

BERRY, MARGARET, b. Greensboro, N.C. ENGLISH, SOUTH ASIAN STUDIES. B.A, St. Joseph Col, 44; M.A, Cath. Univ. Am, 50; Ph.D.(Eng), St. Johns Univ.(N.Y), 56; M.A, Univ. Pa, 68. Instr. ENG, St. Joseph Col, 54-58, asst, 58-62, ASSOC. PROF, 62-65; JOHN CAROLL UNIV, 65-, fac. fel, 73. Ford Found. Asian stud. grant, 63-64; Univ. Pa, summer grants S.Asian regional stud, 64 & 65; Duke Univ. consortium S.Asian stud, summer, 66; participant, Fulbright Summer Inst, India, 66; NDEA fel. S.Asia stud, 67-68; Danforth assoc, 72; vis. res. scholar, Univ. Mysore, fall 73; vis. lectr, Univ. Madurai, fall 73. Asn. Asian Stud; AAUP. Literary criticism of the English Catholic revival; Indian fiction in English. Publ: Mulk Raj Anand, the man and the novelist, 71, gen. ed. ser, Indian writers of fiction in English, 72- & auth, Narayan, man and novelist, vol, In: Indian writers of fiction in English, 74, Oriental Press, Amsterdam; Purpose in the novels of Mulk Raj Anand, Mahfil, 3/69; Chinese mythology and the Chinese mystique, Carroll Quart, 4/69; The Equal Rights Amendment: the case for the defense, Cath. Univ. Bull, 5/73; plus many others. Add: Dept. of English, John Carroll University, Cleveland, OH 44118.

BERRY, WILLIAM RAY, b. Waco, Tex, Jan. 23, 32; m. 52; c. 2. SPEECH, BROADCASTING. B.A, Baylor Univ, 55, M.A, 59; M.R.E, Southwest. Baptist Theol. Sem.(Tex), 58; Univ. Denver, 60; Ph.D, Syracuse Univ, 69. Minister,

Tex. Baptist churches, 54-59; instr. SPEECH, N.Tex. State Univ, 59-61; ASSOC. PROF, STATE UNIV. N.Y. COL. GENESEO, 61- Guest lectr, Onondaga Community Col, N.Y, 66 & 68; vis. prof. pub. address, Utica Col, Syracuse Univ, 68-69. Speech Commun. Asn; Nat. Asn. Educ. Broadcasters. Homiletics; communication theory; communicology. Publ: Speech education and the minister, Baylor Press, 59; Rewards of college radio, Col. Radio Mag, 66; The college broadcasting clinic, Speech Teacher, 69; On-the-job training in broadcasting, J. Broadcasting, 69. Add: Speech Division, State University of New York College at Geneseo, Geneseo, NY 14454.

BERRYMAN, CHARLES BEECHER, b. New York, N.Y, Dec. 14, 39; m. 67; c. 2. ENGLISH LITERATURE. B.A, Amherst Col, 61; M.A, Yale, 62, Ph.D.(Eng), 65. Asst. prof. ENG, UNIV. SOUTH. CALIF, 64-67, ASSOC. PROF, 67- MLA. American and Renaissance literature. Publ: W.B. Yeats: design of opposites, Exposition, 67; Ironic design of fortune in Troilus and Criseide, Chaucer Rev, summer 67. Add: Dept. of English, University of Southern California, Los Angeles, CA 90007.

BERRYMAN, ERIC J, b. Berlin, Ger, Aug. 3, 40; U.S. citizen; m. 62; c. 3. ENGLISH LITERATURE. B.A, Hofstra Univ, 66; M.A, Univ. N.Mex, 68, univ. fel, 69-70, D.H. Lawrence grad. fel, 69, Ph.D.(Eng), 71. ASST. PROF. SHAKESPEARE, FITCHBURG STATE COL, 71- Proj. consult, Bicentennial Coord. Off, Dept. of Navy, 74-77. U.S.A, 58-64; Air Medal & Oak Leaf Cluster. AAUP; MLA. The ballad forgeries of John Payne Collier. Publ: Punch and Judy: the old man's first forgery, Scarab, 74. Add: Dept. of English, Fitchburg State College, Fitchburg, MA 01420.

BERST, CHARLES A, b. Seattle, Wash, Sept. 30, 32; m. 62; c. 2. ENGLISH. B.A, Univ. Wash, 55, Ph.D.(Eng), 65. Asst. prof. ENG, Univ. Alta, 65-67; UNIV. CALIF, LOS ANGELES, 67-73, ASSOC. PROF, 73- MLA; Philol. Asn. Pac. Coast. Modern drama. Publ: Bernard Shaw and the art of drama: Univ. Ill, 73; Propaganda and art in Mrs. Warren's profession, ELH, 9/66; The devil and Major Barbara, PMLA, 3/68; The anatomy of greatness in Caesar and Cleopatra, JEGP, 1/69; plus one other. Add: Dept. of English, University of California, Los Angeles, CA 90024.

BERTHELOT, JOSEPH A, b. Detroit, Mich, Jan. 3, 27. ENGLISH. B.A, Univ. West. Ont, 49; M.A, Univ. Tex, El Paso, 55; Ph.D.(Eng. lit), Univ. Denver, 62. Instr. Eng, U.S. Air Force Acad, 58-60, asst. prof, 62-64, assoc. prof, 64-71, prof, 71-72; RETIRED. U.S.A.F, 52-72, Lt. Col. (Ret); Distinguished Flying Cross; Bronze Star Medal; Air Medal & 4 Oak Leaf Clusters; Air Force Commendation Medal. MLA; Mod. Humanities Res. Asn. Renaissance English literature; Graeco-Roman classics. Publ: Michael Drayton, Twayne, 68; contrib. ed, Annual bibliography of English language and literature, Mod. Humanities Res. Asn, 64-72. Add: 2115 W. Chalet Ave, Anaheim, CA 92804.

BERTHOFF, WARNER BEMENT, b. Oberlin, Ohio, Jan. 22, 25; m. 49; c. 2. ENGLISH. B.A, Harvard, 47, M.A, 49, Ph.D, 54. Teaching fel, ENG, Harvard, 49-51; asst. prof, Bryn Mawr Col, 51-57, assoc. prof, 57-65, PROF, 65-67; HARVARD, 67- Fulbright fel. & vis. prof, Univ. Catania, 57-58, Univ. Warsaw, 63 & var. univs, Italy, 72; vis. prof, Univ. Minn, 61; Univ. Calif, Berkeley, 62-63; Guggenheim fel, 68-69. U.S.N.R, 43-46, Ens. MLA. Publ: American literature: traditions and talents, Press of the Times, 60; Example of Melville, Princeton, 62; The ferment of realism: American literature 1884-1919, Free Press, 65; Emerson's nature, Chandler, 68; Edmund Wilson, Univ. Minn, 68; Great short works of Herman Melville, Harper, 70; Fictions and events, Dutton, 71. Add: Widener 446, Harvard University, Cambridge, MA 02138.

BERTHOLD, DENNIS ALFRED, b. Los Angeles, Calif, Oct. 29, 42; m. 66; c. 2. AMERICAN LITERATURE. B.A, Univ. Calif, Riverside, 64; M.A, 66; Ph.D.(Eng), Univ. Wis-Madison, 72. Instr. ENG, Savannah State Col, 66-68; Univ. Wis-Stevens Point, 71-72; ASST. PROF, TEX. A&M UNIV, 72- MLA; S.Cent. Mod. Lang. Asn; AAUP. American romanticism; American cultural and intellectual history; 20th century American literature. Publ: Ong, McLuhan, and the function of the literary message, Savannah State Col. Bull, 12/67; Hawthorne, Ruskin, and the gothic revival: transcendent gothic in The marble faun, ESQ, 1/74; The concept of merit in Paradise lost, Stud. Eng. Lit, 75. Add: Dept. of English, Texas A&M University, College Station, TX 77843.

BERTONASCO, MARC F, b. Valperga, Italy, Feb. 26, 34; U.S. citizen. ENGLISH. B.S, St. Paul Sem, 56; M.A, Univ. Mich, 60; Ph.D.(Eng), Univ. Wis, 64. Instr. ENG, CALIF. STATE UNIV, SACRAMENTO, 64-65, asst. prof, 65-68, ASSOC. PROF, 68- MLA. Seventeenth century. Publ: Crashaw and the Baroque; A new look at The weeper, Tex. Stud. Lang. & Lit, fall 68; Crashaw and the emblem, Eng. Stud, 12/68. Add: Dept. of English, California State University, Sacramento, Sacramento, CA 95819.

BERTRAM, JEAN DE SALES, b. Burlington, Iowa; m. 60; c. 1. THEATRE ARTS, HISTORY. B.A, Univ. N.C, Greensboro; Towzer Found. fel. & M.A, Univ. Minn, 51; Stanford-Wilson fel. & Ph.D, Stanford Univ, 63. Reporter, Greensboro News-Record Co, N.C, 42-43; founder and organizer, pub. relat. dept, Burlington Industs, 43-49; asst. to dean educ, Univ. N.C, Greensboro, 49-50; dir. radio workshop, Minneapolis Voc. High Sch, 51-52; instr. drama, SCH. CREATIVE ARTS, SAN FRANCISCO STATE UNIV, 52-62, asst. prof, 63-65, assoc. prof, 66-71, PROF. THEATRE ARTS, 72- Spec. res. ear training & listening, 64, sabbatical leave, Japan & Eng, 67; founder & dir, Readers' Repertory, San Francisco State Univ, 68- & Jean De Sales Bertram Players, 72- Speech Commun. Asn; AAUP. Phonetics; theatre speech; oral interpretation. Publ: The oral experience of literature, Chandler Publ, 67; California cameos & American cameos, Am. Revolution Bicentennial Comn, 73-; plus others. Add: Dept. of Theatre Arts, School of Creative Arts, San Francisco State University, Holloway at 19th Ave, San Francisco, CA 94132.

BERTRAM, PAUL BENJAMIN, b. Buffalo, N.Y, Jan. 26, 28. ENGLISH. A.B, N.Y, Univ, 48; M.A, Harvard, 52, Ph.D.(Eng), 60. Instr. ENG, Mt. Holyoke Col, 55-56; RUTGERS UNIV, NEW BRUNSWICK, 56-61, asst. prof, 61-64, assoc. prof, 64-69, PROF, 69-, assoc. dean, Grad. Sch, 66-72. Publ: Shakespeare and The two noble kinsmen, Rutgers Univ, 65; The date of The two noble kinsmen, Shakespeare Quart, winter 61; Henry VIII; the conscience of the king, In: In defense of reading, Dutton, 62. Add: 100 Memorial Pkwy, New Brunswick, NJ 08901.

BESSER, MILTON, b. Denver, Colo, Jan. 12, 11; m. 37; c. 6. JOURNALISM. B.A, Univ. Colo, 33. City ed, Scottsbluff Star-Herald, Nebr, 33-37; state ed, Assoc. Press, 37-44, foreign news desk ed, 44-57, UN correspondent, 51-71; ASSOC. PROF. JOUR, WICHITA STATE UNIV, 71- Asn. Educ. in Jour. History of Black homesteaders in Kansas. Add: 2672 N. Pershing, Wichita, KS 67220.

BESSINGER, JESS BALSOR, JR, b. Detroit, Mich, Sept. 25, 21; m. 56. ENGLISH. B.A, Rice Inst, 43; M.A, Harvard, 47, Ph.D.(Eng), 52; Fulbright scholar, U.K, 50-52. Hon. res. assoc, Univ. Col, Univ. London, 51-52; asst. prof. ENG, Brown Univ, 52-56; assoc. prof, Univ. Col, Univ. Toronto, 56-61, PROF, 61-63; GRAD. SCH. ARTS & SCI, N.Y. UNIV, 63- Can. Counc. fel, 60; Guggenheim fel, 63-64 & 73-74; ed, Harvard Old Eng. Ser, 66-; co-ed, Old Eng. Newslett, 67- Mil. Intel, U.S.A, 43-45. MLA; Mediaeval Acad. Am; Am. Folklore Soc; Int. Asn. Univ. Prof. Eng. Medieval language and literature; comparative heroic poetry. Publ: A short dictionary of Anglo-Saxon poetry, Univ. Toronto, 60; co-auth, Franciplegius: medieval studies in honor of Francis P. Magoun, Jr, N.Y. Univ, 65 & Essential articles for the study of Old English poetry, Archon, 68; auth, A concordance to Beowulf, Cornell Univ, 68; Maldon and the Olafsdrapa: an historical caveat, Comp. Lit, 62; Robin Hood: folklore and historiography, Tenn, Stud. Lit, 66; The Sutton Hoo Harp replica and Old English musical verse, In: Old English poetry, Brown Univ, 67. Add: Dept. of English, New York University, 19 University Pl, New York, NY 10003.

BEST, MICHAEL R, b. Adelaide, S.Australia, May 26, 39; m. 68. ENGLISH. B.A, Univ. Adelaide, 60, Ph.D, 66. Teacher, Beckenham & Penge Grammar Sch. for Boys, London, 65-67; ASSOC. PROF. ENG, UNIV. VICTORIA (B.C), 67- Tudor drama; Elizabethan popular culture; magic and the Renaissance mind. Publ: Co-ed, The book of secrets of Albertus Magnus, Clarendon, 73; A theory of the literary genesis of Lyly's Midas, Rev. Eng. Stud, 5/66; Lyly's static drama, Renaissance Drama, 68; The staging and production of the plays of John Lyly, Theatre Res, 68. Add: Dept. of English, University of Victoria, Victoria, B.C, Can.

BESTON, JOHN B, b. Australia, Jan. 16, 30; m. 56, 70; c. 1. ENGLISH. A.M, Sydney Univ, 50, M.Ed, 51; univ. scholar, Harvard, 56-57, A.M, 57, Ph.D.(Eng), 66. Lectr. ENG, Univ. New Eng, Australia, 54-55; Newcastle Univ. Col, 58-60; instr, Col. William & Mary, 61-62; assoc. prof, Fordham Univ, 62-66; asst. prof, City Col. New York, 66-70; LECTR, Univ. Queensland, 70-73; UNIV. WEST. AUSTRALIA, 73- Fulbright travel grant, 55-58; Salstonstall scholar, Harvard, 60-61. Mediaeval Acad. Am. The Breton Lai in Old French and Middle English. Publ: The hero's fear of freedom in Keneally, Australian Lit. Stud, 10/72; Fire imagery, In: The aunt's story, Ariel, 72; Keneally as a dramatist, Southerly, 72. Add: Dept. of English, University of Western Australia, Nedlands, Western Australia, 6009.

BESTUL, THOMAS HOWARD, b. Evanston, Ill, Oct. 30, 42; m. 65; c. 1. ENGLISH. B.A, Univ. Wis-Madison, 64; Woodrow Wilson fel, Harvard, 64-65, Danforth fel, 64-68, A.M, 66, Ph.D.(Eng), 70. Asst. prof. ENG, UNIV. NEBR, LINCOLN, 68-73, ASSOC. PROF. & V.CHMN. DEPT, 73- MLA; Mediaeval Acad. Am; NCTE; AAUP. Medieval literature. Publ: Satire and allegory in Wynnere and Wastoure, Univ. Nebr, 73; The Old English resignation and the Benedictine reform, Neuphilologische Mitt, (in press); The Man of law's tale and the rhetorical foundations of Chaucerian pathos, Chaucer Rev, (in press); The Saturnalia of Macrobius and the Praecepta artis rhetoricae of Julius Severianus, Class. J, (in press). Add: Dept. of English, University of Nebraska, Lincoln, NE 68508.

BETHURUM, (FRANCES) DOROTHY (MRS. R.S. LOOMIS), b. Franklin, Tenn, Apr. 5, 97. ENGLISH LANGUAGE & LITERATURE. A.B, Vanderbilt Univ, 19, A.M, 22; Ph.D, Yale, 30; hon. D.Litt, Lawrence Col, 47; hon. L.H.D, Colby Col, 59. Instr. Randolph-Macon Woman's Col, 22-24, asst. prof, 24-25; assoc. prof, Lawrence Col, 27-29, prof, 29-40; prof. ENG. & chmn. dept, CONN. COL, 40-62, EMER. PROF, 62- Guggenheim fel, 37-38; Fulbright fel, Oxford, 54-55; Am. Counc. Learned Soc. fel, 62-63; vis. scholar, Phi Beta Kappa, 65-66; vis. prof, Vanderbilt Univ, 68; chmn. bd, Nat. Humanities Fac, 68-69; Drew Vis. Prof. Eng, Smith Col, 70. AAUP (1st v.pres, 60-63); MLA; Mediaeval Acad. Am; Int. Asn. Prof. Eng. Stylistic features of the Old English laws; the form of Alfric's lives of saints; the connection of the Katherine group with Old English prose. Publ: The homilies of Wulfstan, 57 & Chaucer: The squire's tale, 65, Clarendon; Masterpieces of English literature, Scott; Critical approaches to mediaeval literature, Columbia Univ; Saturn in Chaucer's Knight's tale, In: Chaucer und Seine Zeit: Symposium für Walter Schirmer, 69; The Venus of Alonus de Insulis and the Venus of Chaucer, In: Philosophical essays in honor of Herbert Dean Meritt, 70; Regnuum and Sacerdotium in the early eleventh century, In: England before the conquest: studies presented to Dorothy Whitelace, 71; plus ten others. Add: 76 Great Neck Rd, Waterford, CT 06385.

BETTENBENDER, JOHN I, b. Chicago, Ill, Apr. 18, 21. THEATER ARTS. Ph.B, Loyola Univ. Chicago, 43; M.F.A, Cath. Univ. Am, 48. Asst. prof. speech & drama & chmn. dept, Loyola Univ, 48-55; asst. prof, Jersey State Col, 59-64; assoc. prof. speech & theater & chmn. dept, St. Joseph's Col, Calumet Campus, 64-69; prof. theater & chmn. dept, Oberlin Col, 69-70; PROF. THEATER ARTS & CHMN. DEPT, DOUGLASS COL, RUTGERS UNIV, 70- U.S.N, 43-46, Lt. Am. Theatre Asn; AAUP. Creative work. Publ: Ed, Three English comedies, Poetry festival, co-ed, Famous battles, contrib, West Side story & Romeo and Juliet & Man of La Mancha, Dell. Add: Dept. of Theater Arts, Douglass College, Rutgers University, New Brunswick, NJ 08903.

BETTRIDGE, WILLIAM E, b. Toledo, Ohio, Sept. 14, 34; m. 59; c. 1. ENGLISH. B.A, Capital Univ, 59; M.A, Ohio State Univ, 60, Ph.D.(Eng), 66. Asst. prof. ENG, UNIV. MD. BALTIMORE COUNTY, 66-73, ASSOC. PROF, 68-, chmn. dept, 71-74. MLA; Medieval Acad. Am; Int. Arthurian Soc; Col. Eng. Asn. Chaucer; history of English. Publ: American borrowings of British motoring terms, Am. Speech, 2/67; New light on the origin of the

Griselda story, Tex. Stud. Lit. & Lang, summer 71. Add: Dept. of English, University of Maryland, Baltimore County, 5401 Wilkens Ave, Baltimore, MD 21228.

BETTS, WILLIAM WILSON, JR, b. Clearfield, Pa, July 25, 26; m. 51; c. 2. ENGLISH. A.B, Dickinson Col, 49; Univ. Minn; A.M, Pa. State Univ, 50, Ph.D, 54. Instr. ENG, Ohio Univ, 54-55; assoc. prof, INDIANA UNIV. PA, 55-57, PROF, 57-, asst. dean, Grad. Sch, 67-71. Assoc. ed, Crosscurrents, 57- U.S.N, 44-46. Comparative literature, especially Anglo-German and American German literary relations; American literature; modern poetry. Publ: Lincoln and the poets, Univ. Pittsburgh, 65; A docketful of wry, Park Press, 70; George Meredith, The Saxon in the Celt & The relations of William Dean Howells to German life and letters, Crosscurrents; Moby Dick: Melville's Faust, Lock Haven Bull, 59. Add: R.D. 2, Box 243, Indiana, PA 15701.

BETZ, PAUL FREDRICK, b. Philadelphia, Pa, June 11, 39; m. 63. ENGLISH LITERATURE. B.A, La Salle Col, 61; scholar, Cornell Univ, 61-62, Danforth fel, 61-65, M.A, 63, Ph.D.(Eng), 65. Asst. prof. ENG, GEORGETOWN UNIV, 65-71, ASSOC. PROF, 71-, summer res. grant, 66. Danforth postdoctoral fel, 69-70. MLA; Soc. Relig. Higher Educ. William Wordsworth; S.T. Coleridge; English poetry. Add: Dept. of English, Georgetown University, Washington, DC 20007.

BETZ, SIEGMUND ALFRED EDUARD, b. Cincinnati, Ohio, Dec. 12, 11. ENGLISH, CLASSICS. A.B, Univ. Cincinnati, 31, univ. scholar, 31-34, A.M, 32, Ph.D, 34; summers, Harvard, 40, Univ. Chicago, 47; Xavier Univ, 54; Univ. Heidelberg, 63-64. Instr. ENG, Univ. Cincinnati, 34-35; assoc. prof, Lindenwood Col, 35-46, prof, 46-56; lectr, Wash. Univ, 53-56; PROF, EDGECLIFF COL, 56-, CHMN. DEPT, 71-, chmn. fac. senate, 68-70, 71-72. Brit-Am. Assoc. lectr. fel, Gt. Brit, 55, 57, 60, 65, 67, 71 & 73. U.S.A.A.F, 42-46, Capt. MLA; Am. Philol. Asn. Seventeenth century literature; romantic literature; interdisciplinary studies. Publ: Francis Osborn's Advice to a son, In: Seventeenth century studies, Princeton Univ. Press for Univ. Cincinnati, 2nd ser, 37; The operatic criticism of the Tatler and Spectator, Musical Quart, 7/45. Add: 2413 Ohio Ave, Cincinnati, OH 45219.

BEUM, ROBERT, b. Mt. Vernon, Ohio, Aug. 20, 29; m. 54; c. 3. ENGLISH. B.A, Ohio State Univ, 52, M.A, 58; Univ. Nebr, 58-62. Instr. ENG, Univ. Nebr, 59-62; asst. prof, Creighton Univ, 62-65; Nebr. Wesleyan Univ, 65-68; ASSOC. PROF, St. Dunstan's Univ, 68-69; Univ. Prince Edward Island, 69-70; Univ. Lethbridge, 70-71; UNIV. PRINCE EDWARD ISLAND, 71- Milton Soc. Am; Renaissance Eng. Text Soc. Sixteenth and 17th century poetry; prosody and prose style; late victorian and early modern English literature. Publ: Poems and epigrams, Henry Regnery, 64; co-auth, A prosody handbook, Harper, 64; Some observations on Spenser's verse forms, Neuphilol. Mitt, 63; Spenser's Epithalamion, Merrill, 68; The poetic art of W.B. Yeats, Ungar, 69; co-auth, Papers on literature: models and methods, Holt, 70; auth, Modernity and the left: an equivalence, Ga. Rev, 73. Add: Dept. of English, University of Prince Edward Island, Charlottetown, P. E. I, Can.

BEUTNER, HARVEY FREMONT, b. Springfield Twp, Ind, May 3, 22. ENGLISH LITERATURE, JOURNALISM. B.A, Valparaiso Univ, 49; M.S.J, Northwest. Univ, Evanston, 51, M.A, 55, scholar, 59-60, Ph.D.(Eng), 67. Asst. prof. Eng, Stetson Univ, 57-59; ed. social stud, Follett Publ. Co, Ill, 60-64; asst. prof. Eng, ILL. WESLEYAN UNIV, 64-68, assoc. prof, 68-74, PROF. ENG. & JOUR, 74- Ill. Wesleyan Univ. stud. & res. leave, Sheffield Cent. Libr, Eng, 66-67; ed, Iris, 71- Med.C, U.S.N, 42-46, 51-52. NCTE; Nat. Counc. Col. Publ. Adv; Conf. Col. Compos. & Commun. Nineteenth century English literature; James Montgomery, poet, editor, critic, journalist; 19th century American newspapers. Add: Dept. of English, Illinois Wesleyan University, Bloomington, IL 61701.

BEVAN, ALLAN REES, b. Druid, Sask, May 25, 13; m. 41; c. 3. ENGLISH. B.A, Univ. Saks, 39; M.A, Univ. Man, 47; Ph.D.(Eng), Univ. Toronto, 53. Asst. prof. ENG, DALHOUSIE UNIV, 49-55, assoc. prof, 55-59, PROF, 59-, head dept, 58-69. Royal Soc. Can. grant, 56-57; Can. Counc. grants, 59, 67 & 70; ed, Dalhousie Rev, 70- R.C.A, 43-45, Sgt. Asn. Can. Univ. Prof. Eng.(pres, 68-70); Int. Asn. Prof. Eng; Humanities Asn. Can. Restoration and early eighteenth century; the novel; Canadian literature. Add: Dept. of English, Dalhousie University, Halifax, N.S, Can.

BEVILACQUA, VINCENT MICHAEL, b. Haverhill, Mass, Sept. 25, 35; m. 60. SPEECH. B.A, Emerson Col, 57, M.A, 58; Ph.D, Univ. Ill, 61. Instr. SPEECH, Univ. N.Mex, 61-62; asst. prof, Univ. Va, 62-66; Cornell Univ, 66-68; assoc. prof, UNIV. MASS, AMHERST, 68-71, PROF, 71- Am. Philos. Soc. grant, 66. MLA; Speech Commun. Asn. Eighteenth century rhetoric, aesthetics, and art theory. Publ: Co-ed, A course of lectures on oratory and criticism, South. Ill. Univ, 65; auth, Baconian influences in the development of Scottish rhetorical theory, Proc. Am. Philos. Soc, 8/67; Philosophical influences in the development of English rhetorical theory: 1748 to 1783, Leeds Philos. & Lit. Soc, 4/68; Adam Smith and some philosophical origins of eighteenth-century rhetorical theory, Mod. Lang. Rev, 7/68. Add: Dept. of Speech, Bartlett Hall, University of Massachusetts, Amherst, MA 01002.

BEVINGTON, DAVID M, b. New York, N.Y, May 13, 31; m. 53; c. 3. ENGLISH. B.A, Harvard, 52, M.A, 57, Ph.D, 59. Instr. ENG, Harvard, 59-61; asst. prof, Univ. Va, 61-64, assoc. prof, 64-66, PROF, 66-68; UNIV. CHICAGO, 68- Guggenheim fel, 64-65. U.S.N, 52-55, Lt.(jg). MLA; Mediaeval Acad. Am; Renaissance Soc. Am. Late medieval and Renaissance English drama. Publ: From Mankind to Marlowe, Harvard, 62; ed, Shakespeare's 1 Henry VI, Penguin, 67 & Twentieth-century interpretations of Hamlet, Prentice-Hall, 68; auth, Tudor drama and politics, Harvard, 68; co-ed, The complete works of Shakespeare, 73. Add: Dept. of English, University of Chicago, Chicago, IL 60637.

BEVINGTON, HELEN, b. Afton, N.Y, Apr. 2, 06; m. 28; c. 2. ENGLISH. Ph.B, Univ. Chicago, 26; M.A, Columbia Univ, 28, 28-31. Instr. ENG, DUKE UNIV, 43-47, asst. prof, 47-56, assoc. prof, 56-70, PROF, 70- Roanoke-Chowan Award, 56, 62. English and American twentieth century poetry. Publ: Dr. Johnson's waterfall, 46, Nineteen million elephants, 50 & A change of sky, 56, Houghton; When found, make a verse of, 61 & Charley Smith's girl, 65, Simon & Schuster; A book and a love affair, 68, The house was quiet and the world was calm, 71 & Beautiful lofty people, 74, Harcourt; contrib, New Yorker, Atlantic Monthly, Am. Scholar, Saturday Rev. Lit, 46- Add: 4428 Guess Rd, Durham, NC 27705.

BEVIS, RICHARD WADE, b. New York, N.Y, June 4, 37; m. 60; c. 1. ENGLISH LITERATURE. B.A, Duke Univ, 59; M.A, Univ. Calif, Berkeley, 62, Ph.D.(Eng), 65. ASST. PROF. ENG, Am. Univ. Beirut, 65-70; UNIV. B.C, 70- Eighteenth century English stage comedy; English literature of Near and Middle East; changing attitudes toward nature in 19th and 20th century English and American literature. Publ: Ed, Eighteenth century drama: afterpieces, Oxford, 70; Bibliotheca Cisorientalia: annotated checklist of early English books on Middle East, G.K. Hall, 73; auth, Spiritual geology: C.M. Doughty and the Land of the Arabs, Victorian Stud, 72. Add: Dept. of English, University of British Columbia, Vancouver 8, B.C, Can.

BEYER, WERNER WILLIAM, b. Laporte, Ind, Mar. 22, 11; m. 54; c. 2. ENGLISH. A.B, Columbia Col, 34; A.M, Columbia Univ, 36, Lydig fel, 41-42, Cutting fel, 42-43, Ph.D, 45. Sr. Eng. master, Englewood Sch, N.J, 36-40; instr. Eng, Drew Univ, 43-44; asst. prof, Rutgers Univ, 45-48; assoc. prof, BUTLER UNIV, 48-50, prof, 50-68, R.C. READE PROF. ENG, 68-, HEAD DEPT. ENG, 67- Vis. asst. prof, Columbia Univ, 48; Ford fel, 51-52; vis. prof. grad. sch, Ind. Univ, 64-65. MLA; Col. Eng. Asn. Romantic period, 18th and 19th century English; comparative literature. Publ: Enchanted forest, Basil Blackwell, 63; Keats and the daemon king, Oxford; Prestige of C.M. Wieland in England, Columbia Univ. Add: Dept. of English, Butler University, Indianapolis, IN 46208.

BEYETTE, THOMAS KENT, b. Houston, Tex, June 25, 39; m. 65; c. 1. ENGLISH & AMERICAN LITERATURE. B.A, Univ. Tex, Austin, 61, M.A, 68, Ph.D.(Eng. lit), 69. ASST. PROF. ENG. LIT, UNIV. FLA, 69- U.S.N.R, 61-65, Res, 65-, Lt. Comdr. MLA; S.Atlantic Mod. Lang. Asn; NCTE; Col. Eng. Asn; Res. Soc. Victorian Periodicals. Victorian literature; literary symbolism; popular culture. Publ: Hopkins' phenomenology of art in The shepherd's brow, Victorian Poetry, fall 73. Add: Dept. of English, University of Florida, Gainesville, FL 32611.

BEZANKER, ABRAHAM, b. Hartford, Conn, Mar. 6, 19; m. 52. ENGLISH. B.A, Kalamazoo Col, 41; M.A, Univ. Mich, 47, Ph.D.(Eng), 54. Instr. ENG, Wayne State Univ, 51-52; asst. prof, CALIF. STATE UNIV, SAN JOSE, 62-68, assoc. prof, 68-71, PROF, 71- U.S.A, 43-46, Staff Sgt. Allegory-Symbolism; contemporary fiction; Renaissance literature. Publ: The odyssey of Saul Bellow, Yale Rev; I.B. Singer's crises of identity, Critique: Stud. Mod. Fiction, Vol. 14, No. 2. Add: Dept. of English, California State University, San Jose, 125 S. Seventh St, San Jose, CA 95114.

BEZANSON, WALTER EVERETT, b. Needham, Mass, June 19, 12; m. 40; c. 2. AMERICAN STUDIES. A.B, Dartmouth Col, 33; Ph.D, Yale, 43. Instr. Eng, Dartmouth Col, 41-42; Harvard, 42-43, 46-47; asst. prof. Eng. & hist, RUTGERS UNIV, NEW BRUNSWICK, 47-54, assoc. prof. AM. CIVILIZATION, 54-60, PROF, 60- Tutor hist, Yale, 40-41; summer vis. prof, Ohio State Univ, 49, Univ. Minn, 50, Ind. Univ, 61; lectr, Princeton, 51; fac. fel, Fund Advan. Educ, 52-53; Fulbright Chair, Am. civilization & lit, Univ. Liège, 57-58; textual consult, Ctr. Ed. Am. Authors, MLA, 68- Medals from Univs. Liege, Brussels & Ghent, 57-58. U.S.N.R, 43-46, Lt. MLA; Am. Stud. Asn; Melville Soc. Am.(pres, 54, 67). American civilization, literature and history; literary criticism. Publ: Ed, Melville's Clarel: a poem and pilgrimage in the Holy Land, Hendricks, 60; auth, Moby-Dick: work of art, In: Moby-Dick centennial essays, South. Methodist Univ, 53; Melville's reading of Arnold's poetry, PMLA, 54. Add: Dept. of English, Rutgers University, New Brunswick, NJ 08903.

BEZANSON, WARREN B, b. Athol, Mass, Apr. 25, 12; m. 40. ENGLISH, AMERICAN STUDIES. B.A, Guilford Col, 34; B.E, Cent. Conn. State Col, 37; M.A, Univ. N.C, 38; Ph.D.(Am. stud), Univ. Md, 53. Teacher, high sch, N.C, 38-43; instr. Eng, Univ. N.C, 43-44; teacher, St. Christopher's Sch, Va, 44-46; asst. prof, Wash. Col, 46-47; instr, Univ. Md, 47-54; asst. ed, G. & C. Merriam Co, Mass, 54-56; ed. supvr, United Aircraft Corp, Conn, 56-64; assoc. prof. ENG, E.CAROLINA UNIV, 64-68, PROF, 68- S.Atlantic Mod. Lang. Asn. Editing of university catalogues, faculty manual & technical publications. Publ: Co-auth, Private secondary education in the South, In: Secondary education in the South, Univ. N.C, 45; auth, A method of conducting the technical writing course, Col. Compos. & Commun, 54; A timetable for report writing, Soc. Tech. Writers & Ed, 58. Add: Dept. of English, East Carolina University, Greenville, NC 27834.

BICKET, ZENAS J, b. Hartford, Ill, Oct. 14, 32; m. 54; c. 3. ENGLISH. B.Ed, Wis. State Univ, Whitewater, 54; Th.B, Cent. Bible Col, 57; NDEA fel. & M.A, Univ. Ark, 63, NDEA fel. & Ph.D.(Eng), 65. PROF. ENG, EVANGEL COL, 64-, ACAD. DEAN, 73-, chmn. humanities div, 64-66, acad. dean, 66-70, chmn. commun. & art dept, 70-73. Chmn. accreditation comt, Midwest div. Counc. Advan. Small Cols, 66-67. NCTE. Seventeenth century literature, Thomas Traherne's Centuries of Meditations; the Bible as literature. Add: 2257 Claiborne, Springfield, MO 65804.

BICKLEY, ROBERT BRUCE, JR, b. New Rochelle, N.Y, Aug. 20, 42; m. 66; c. 1. AMERICAN LITERATURE. B.A, Univ. Va, 64; M.A, Duke Univ, 65, Ph.D.(Eng), 69. Teaching asst. ENG, Duke Univ, 66-68; ASST. PROF, FLA. STATE UNIV, 69- Compiler, Am. Lit. Manuscripts Proj, MLA, spring 73. MLA; Am. Stud. Asn; NCTE. Nineteenth century American literature; the short story; the novel. Publ: Contrib, A guide to critical reviews of United States fiction, 1870-1910, Scarecrow, 71; auth, Humorous portraiture in Twain's news writing, Am. Lit. Realism, fall 70; The minor fiction of Hawthorne and Melville, Am. Transcendental Quart, spring 72. Add: Dept. of English, Florida State University, Tallahassee, FL 32306.

BICKNELL, JOHN W, b. Mansfield, Mass, Jan. 22, 13; m. 36; c. 7. ENGLISH. B.S, Hamilton Col, 35, M.A, 36; Columbia Univ, 36-37; Martin Sampson teaching fel, Cornell Univ, 49-50, Ph.D, 50. Instr. ENG, St. Lawrence Univ, 37-43; Cornell Univ, 50-54; assoc. prof, DREW UNIV, 54-57, PROF, 57-, CONVENOR, GRAD. PROF. ENG, 62-, chmn. dept, 59-71, acting dean, Grad. Sch, 67-69. U.S.N.R, 43-46, Lt.(jg). MLA; Col. Eng. Asn; Conf. Brit. Stud. Victorian literature; the history of intellectual history; Sir

Leslie Stephen. Publ: Virginia Woolf in homage and remembrance, J. Mod. Lit, 6/73; The unbelievers, In: Victorian prose writers: a guide to research, Mod. Lang. Asn, fall 73; co-auth, Who was Mrs. Morley?, Victorian News Lett, fall 73. Add: Dept. of English, Drew University, Madison, NJ 07940.

BIDDLE, PHILLIPS R, b. Sioux City, Iowa, Dec. 17, 33; m. 58; c. 2. RHETORIC, PSYCHOLOGY. A.B, Portland State Col, 61; A.M, Univ. Ill, 63, Ph.D. (rhetoric, psychol), 66. Asst. speech, Univ. Ill, 61-63; instr, Univ. Mass, 63-65; asst, Univ. Ill, 65-66; ASSOC. PROF. COMMUN. STUD, CALIF. STATE UNIV, SACRAMENTO, 66- U.S.A, 53-55. Int. Commun. Asn. Interpersonal communication. Publ: Co-auth, Essentials of discussion, 68 & Essentials of debate, 72, Holt. Add: Dept. of Communication Studies, California State University, Sacramento, 6000 Jay St, Sacramento, CA 95819.

BIDDLE, STEPHEN PIERCE, b. Westfield, Mass, July 22, 44; m. 67. CONTEMPORARY THEATRE. B.A, Baker Univ, 65; M.A, Univ. Kans, 67, Ph.D. (theatre), 72. Instr. Eng. & drama, Baker Univ, 67-68; INSTR. SPEECH & DRAMA & DIR. THEATRE, OTTAWA UNIV, 72- Auth, The canteen, produced by Topeka Community Theatre, 67; Young Goodman Brown, 69; co-auth, Quantrill!, 70 & auth, Pigskin!, 71, produced by Univ. Kans. Experimental Theatre; Sam. S. Shubert Found. fel, 70-71, 71-72. Am. Theatre Asn; Speech Commun. Asn. Contemporary drama; contemporary dramatic theory; theatre history 1870-1970. Add: 2620 W. 24th St. Terrace, Lawrence, KS 66044.

BIDERMAN, SOL, b. Dallas, Tex, Nov. 10, 36; m. 67; c. 2. ENGLISH & AMERICAN LITERATURE. B.A, Univ. Colo, Boulder, 60; M.A, Stanford Univ, 62; NDEA grant, Univ. Wis-Madison, 62-63; Orgn. Am. States grant & Ph.D.(sociol. of lit), Univ. São Paulo, 70. Instr. Eng, Univ. Genoa, 63-64; prof. Am. lit, Am. Stud. Ctr, Naples, Italy, 64-65; CHMN. DEPT. ENG, FAC. PHILOS, SCI. & LETT, MARILIA, BRAZIL, 66- Mem. selection comt, Fulbright Fels, Italy, 63; Ford Found. fel, 68-70; Organizer, Brazilian Chapbook Collection, Libr. Cong, 70; asst. prof. Eng, Calif. State Univ, San Jose, 71-72. Borestone Mountain Poetry Awards, 68. Twentieth century English literature; the novel; Chicano and Latin-American literature. Publ: Bring me to the banqueting house, Macmillan, London & Viking, N.Y, 69, Pyramid, 71; Charlemagne on a string, Americas, 3/67; Mount Abiegnos and the masks, Luso-Brazilian Rev, summer 68; contrib, Best poems of 1968, Pac. Press, 69. Add: Faculty of Philosophy, Science & Letters of Marilia, C.P. 420, Marilia, São Paulo, Brazil 17500.

BIDNEY, MARTIN PAUL, b. New York, N.Y, Apr. 21, 43. ENGLISH & COMPARATIVE LITERATURE. A.B, Ind. Univ, 63, Ph.D.(Eng. lit), 71; A.M, Harvard, 65. Instr. ENG. & GEN. LIT, STATE UNIV. N.Y. BINGHAMTON, 69-71, ASST. PROF, 71- Nineteenth century poetry and fiction; Anglo-Russian literary relations. Add: Dept. of English, 48 Library Wing, State University of New York at Binghamton, Binghamton, NY 13901.

BIEBER, MARGARETE, Classical Archaeology. See Volume I, History.

BIEN, PETER ADOLPH, b. New York, N.Y, May 28, 30; m. 55; c. 3. ENGLISH. B.A, Haverford Col, 52; M.A, Columbia Univ, 57, fels, 57-58, 59-60, Fulbright fel, 58-59, Ph.D, 61. Lectr. ENG, Columbia Univ, 59-60; instr, DARTMOUTH COL, 61-63, asst. prof, 63-65, assoc. prof, 65-68, PROF, 69-, fac. fel, 64. Hon. fel. Greek, Univ. Birmingham, 70-71. E. Harris Harbison Award, Danforth Found, 67. MLA; Mod. Greek Stud. Asn. Modern British and Greek literature. Publ: Transl, Nikos Kazantzakis: The last temptation of Christ, 60, Saint Francis, 62 & Report to Greco, 65, Simon & Schuster & Cassirer, Eng; auth, L.P. Hartley, Chatto & Windus, Eng. & Pa. State Univ, 63; Constantine Cavafy, 64 & Nikos Kazantzakis, 72, Columbia Univ; co-auth, Demotic Greek, Univ. Press New Eng, 72; auth, Kazantzakis and the linguistic revolution in Greek literature, 72 & co-ed, Modern Greek writers, 72, Princeton Univ; auth, Zorba the Greek, Nietzsche and the perennial Greek predicament, Antioch Rev, spring 65; The politics of Kazantzakis, In: The politics of twentieth century novelists, Hawthorne, 72; Kazantzakis' Nietzschianism, J. Mod. Lit, 71-72. Add: Dept. of English, Dartmouth College, Hanover, NH 03755.

BIER, JESSE, b. Hoboken, N.J, July 18, 25; m. 50; c. 3. ENGLISH. A.B, Bucknell Univ, 49; Hunt fel, Princeton, 51-52, A.M, 52, Ph.D.(Eng), 56. Instr. Eng. lang. & lit, Univ. Colo, 52-55; ENG, UNIV. MONT, 55-56, asst. prof, 56-59, assoc. prof, 59-63, PROF, 63- Fulbright prof. Am. lit. & civilization, Univs. Lyon & Clermont, 57-58; vis. lectr. Eng, Bucknell Univ, 65-66; vis. prof. humanities, Calif. State Univ, San Diego, summer 71; chair in Am. Lit, Univ. Lausanne, 71-72. Native Son Writer award in fiction, N.J. State Teachers Asn, 65. U.S.A, 43-46. MLA; Philol. Asn. Pac. Coast. American literature; creative writing; education. Publ: Trial at Bannock, Harcourt; A hole in the lead apron, Harcourt, 64; The rise and fall of American humor, 68; No vacancy, 4/72 & The man on zero-four, 11/72, Fantasy & Sci. Fiction; Melville's The fiddler, Am. Transcendental Quart, 8/72; plus three others. Add: Wildcat Rd, Missoula, MT 59801.

BIERK, JOHN CASHION, b. Perryville, Mo, Oct. 2, 31. AMERICAN LITERATURE. B.S, Southeast Mo. State Univ, 55; M.A, Northwest. Univ, 57, Ph.D, (Am. lit), 68. Assoc. prof. ENG, SOUTHEAST MO. STATE UNIV, 57-69, PROF, 69- U.S.A, 55-57. MLA; NCTE; Am. Stud. Asn. American studies. Publ: College guide to library research: style sheet, Missourian Litho & Printing Co, 62; Three poems, fall 64 & Four poems, fall 65, Cape Rock Quart. Add: Dept. of English, Southeast Missouri State University, Cape Girardeau, MO 63701.

BIERLY, CHARLES E, b. Yakima, Wash, Aug. 25, 09; m. 51; c. 2. ENGLISH. B.A, Univ. Wash, 36, fel, 52, Ph.D, 57; M.A, Univ. Chicago, 41; Univ. Paris. Instr. Eng, Univ. Nebr, 46-47; State Col. Wash, 47-49; U.S. Army, Supreme Hq. Allied Powers Europe, Paris, 51; Eng. & French, Wenatchee Valley Col, 53-59; asst. prof. ENG, Univ. Santa Clara, 59-60, assoc. prof, Gen. Beadle State Col, 60-61; UNIV. WIS-OSHKOSH, 61-65, PROF, 65- U.S.A, 42-45. MLA. American literature; the British and American novel; Shakespeare. Add: 1715 Algoma Blvd, Oshkosh, WI 54901.

BIERMAN, JAMES HENRY, b. New York, N.Y, July 10, 42. DRAMATIC ARTS, HUMANITIES. B.A, Princeton, 64; dipl. Fr. lit, Univ. Paris, 67; Ph.D.(drama, humanities), Stanford Univ, 68. Asst. prof. dramatic arts, Amherst Col, 68-73; ASST. PROF. THEATRE ARTS & FEL. COWELL COL, UNIV. CALIF, SANTA CRUZ, 73- Dramatic literature. Publ: Ed, Alfred Jarry's Caesar antichrist, Omen Press, 72. Add: Cowell College, University of California, Santa Cruz, CA 95064.

BIERMAN, JUDAH, b. New York, N.Y, Feb. 4, 17; m. 48; c. 2. ENGLISH, HUMANITIES. A.B, Univ. Wash, 39; fel, Univ. Calif, Los Angeles, 49, Ph.D, 51. Instr. Eng, PORTLAND STATE UNIV, 49-51, asst. prof, 51-56, assoc. prof. Eng. & humanities, 56-67, PROF. ENG, 67-, DIR, HONORS PLANNING, 68-, DIR, UNIV. SCH. PROG, 70- Folger Libr. fel, summer 56; Fund for Repub. grant, summer 57; E.C. Brown Trust res. grant, 60-61; George A. Weyerhauser Mem. Found. res. grant, 61-62. Am. Civil Liberties Union; MLA; Philol. Asn. Pac. Coast. Utopian literature; 17th century history of ideas; censorship and literary theory. Publ: Co-auth, Dramatic experience, 58 & The play and the reader, 66, Prentice-Hall, auth, Discovery and response, Winthrop, 71; Bacon's utopia of science, Papers Eng. Lang. & Lit, 67; New Atlantis revisited, Stud. Lit. Imagination, 71; The next steps, Report of Comn. Instnl. Goals, 71; plus two others. Add: Office of Experimental Honors Program, Portland State University, Portland, OR 97207.

BIGELOW, GORDON ELLSWORTH, b. Springfield, Mass, July 26, 19; m. 44; c. 4. AMERICAN LITERATURE. M.A, Johns Hopkins Univ, 47, Ph.D, 50. Jr. instr. ENG, Johns Hopkins Univ, 45-49; instr, Univ. Ky, 49-51; asst. prof, UNIV. FLA, 51-61, assoc. prof, 61-67, PROF, 67- Am. Philos. Soc. res. grant, 61; Fulbright lectr, Univ. Vienna, 61-62. U.S.A.F, 41-45, Res, 45-, Lt. Col. S.Atlantic Mod. Lang. Asn; MLA. Relationship of rhetoric and poetic; Faulkner; the kinds and means of literary symbolism. Publ: Rhetoric and American poetry of the early national period & Frontier Eden: the literary career of Marjorie Kinnan Rawlings, 66, Univ. Fla; co-auth, The U.S.A: readings of English as a second language, Holt, 60; A primer of existentialism, Col. Eng, 12/61; auth, Marjorie Kinnan Rawlings' Wilderness, Sewanee Rev, spring 65. Add: Dept. of English, University of Florida, Gainesville, FL 32601.

BIGGS, BERNICE PRINCE, b. Alliance, Nebr, Jan. 3, 23; m. 52; c. 4. ENGLISH, READING, SECONDARY EDUCATION. B.Sc, Univ. Nebr, 44; M.A, Univ. Denver, 48, Ph.D.(speech), 54. Instr. commun. skills, Stephens Col, 48-49; teaching fel. basic communs, Univ. Denver, 49-50; PROF. ENG. & SEC. EDUC, SAN FRANCISCO STATE UNIV, 50-, COORD. GEN. STUD, 70- Vis. asst. prof, Univ. Minn, 56-57; Fulbright prof, Univ. Navarra, 66-68. Speech Commun. Asn; Am. Bus. Writing Asn; Nat. Soc. Stud. Communs. Communication; secondary education; listening. Publ: Co-auth, A focus on rebellion, Chandler, 62. Add: Dept. of English, San Francisco State University, San Francisco, CA 94132.

BIGGS, WALLACE ROBERT, b. Forsyth, Mo, Feb. 17, 05. JOURNALISM. A.B, Drury Col, 26; A.M, Wash. Univ. 27; M.S.J, Northwest. Univ, 42. Instr. Eng, Ore. State Col, 27-28; jour, DePauw Univ, 28-29; Eng, Northwest. Univ, 29-33; Drury Col, 33-35; head dept. jour. & dir. publicity, Westminster Col.(Pa), 35-41; head dept. jour, Lehigh Univ, 41-44; mem. dept. advertising & prom, Armstrong Cork Co, Lancaster, Pa, 44-46; prof. jour, Univ. Wyo, 46-69, head dept, 46-47; RETIRED. Exec-mgr, Wyo. Press Asn, 51-, owner, Wyo Newspaper Clipping Serv, 51- Am. Soc. Jour. Sch. Adminr.(ed, Roundtable, 56-). Add: Dept. of Journalism, University of Wyoming, Laramie, WY 82071.

BILDER, JOHN RABAN, b. Burlington, N.C, Jan. 1, 30; m. 56; c. 1. ENGLISH. B.S, Georgetown Univ, 51; M.A, Univ. Pa, 59, Ph.D.(Eng), 64. Instr. Eng, Pa. State Univ, Ogontz, 59-61; asst. prof, Georgetown Univ, 61-65; assoc. prof, Univ. P.R, 65-68; PROF, Edinboro State Col, 68-69; ENG. LIT. & HUMANITIES, UNIV. P.R, RIO PIEDRAS, 69- Vis. prof, Schiller Col-London Stud. Centre & Richmond Col, Eng, 73-74. MLA; Col. Eng. Asn; AAUP. Modern comparative literature; Milton; Shakespeare. Publ: Meredith's experiments with ideas, Victorian Newslett, fall 70; Cabrera Infante's Three trapped tigers, Caribbean Rev, 7/72; Guillermo Cabrera Infante, In: Encycl. World Lit. in 20th Century, Ungar, 74. Add: P.O. Box BG, University of Puerto Rico, Rio Piedras, PR 00931.

BILES, JACK I, b. Atlanta, Ga, Nov. 17, 20; m. 44; c. 1. ENGLISH. B.S, Ga. Teachers Col, 49; M.A, Emory Univ, 51, fel, 53-54, Ph.D.(Eng), 54. Asst. prof. ENG, GA. STATE UNIV, 54-57, assoc. prof, 57-62, PROF, 62-, ASST. DEPT. HEAD, 67- U.S.A.F, 40-45. MLA; S.Atlantic Mod. Lang. Asn. English novel; William Golding; contemporary fiction. Publ: Ed, A William Golding miscellany, 10/69 & Aspects of utopian fiction, fall 73, spec. issues of Stud. Lit. Imagination; auth, Talk: conversations with William Golding, Harcourt, 70; An interview in London with Angus Wilson, Stud. in Novel, spring 70; A William Golding checklist, Twentieth Century Lit, 4/71; Literary sources and William Golding, S.Atlantic Bull, 5/72; plus others. Add: Dept. of English, Georgia State University, Atlanta, GA 30303.

BILLINGS, ALAN GAILEY, b. June 29, 29; m. 57; c. 1. THEATRE HISTORY & DESIGN. B.F.A, Univ. Ga, 55; M.F.A, Carnegie Inst. Technol, 58; Ph.D. (theatre), Univ. Ill, 67. Instr. theatre, Univ. Louisville, 58-60; SPEECH & THEATRE, Univ. Del, 60-63; Univ. Ill, 63-66; ASSOC. PROF, UNIV. MICH, ANN ARBOR, 66- Sig.C, U.S.A, 51-53. U.S. Inst. Theatre Technol; Am. Theatre Asn. Scenic design and technology. Publ: Touring the educational theatre, Educ. Theatre J, 10/64; The use of plastic film, 10/69 & Form casting with flexible foam, 10/69, Theatre crafts; plus two others. Add: Dept. of Speech & Theatre, Room 2020 Frieze Bldg, University of Michigan, Ann Arbor, MI 48104.

BILLINGS, ROBERT S, b. South Berwick, Maine, Apr. 8, 20; div; c. 2. ENGLISH. B.A, Univ. N.H, 42; M.A, Boston Univ, 48; Ph.D.(Eng), State Univ, Iowa, 52. Instr. ENG, N.Dak. Agr. Col, 50-54, asst. prof, 54-56; Univ. Denver, 56-57; instr, CALIF. STATE UNIV. FRESNO, 57-59, asst. prof, 59-64, assoc. prof, 64-68, PROF, 68-, CHMN. DEPT, 66-69, 72- Field Artillery, U.S.A, 42-46, Lt. MLA. Modern American literature; the short story; war fiction. Add: 134 Poppy Lane, Clovis, CA 93610.

BILSBORROW, ELEANOR J, b. Yuma, Colo, June 9, 15. RHETORIC, PUBLIC ADDRESS. A.B, Colo. State Col. Educ, 37; M.A, Stanford Univ, 42; Ph.D, Univ. Denver, 57. Instr. Eng, speech, drama & music, Peetz High Sch, Colo, 37-40; Eng. & music, Carpinteria High Sch, Calif, 42-45; music,

Eng. & speech, Kauai High Sch, Hawaii, 45-47; Eng, UNIV. HAWAII, 47-55, from asst. prof. to assoc. prof. SPEECH, 55-68, PROF, 68-, ACAD. ADV. COL. LIB. ARTS, 66- Delta Kappa Gamma scholar, 54. Speech Teacher of the Year, Hawaii, 67. Speech Commun. Asn; West. Speech Commun. Asn; Pac. Speech Asn.(pres, 62-63). Philosophy of social reform in the speeches of Eleanor Roosevelt. Add: Dept. of Speech, University of Hawaii, Honolulu, HI 96822.

BILSLAND, JOHN WINSTANLEY, b. Vancouver, B.C, May 30, 22; m. 57; c. 5. ENGLISH. B.A, Univ. B.C, 49, M.A, 51; Ph.D.(Eng), Univ. Toronto, 57. Lectr. ENG, Univ. Alta, 55-57, asst. prof, 57; lectr, Univ. Col, Univ. Toronto, 57-59; asst. prof, UNIV. ALTA, 59-62, assoc. prof, 62-70, PROF, 70- R.C.A.F, 41-45. Asn. Can. Univ. Teachers Eng. Romantics; history of literary criticism. Publ: De Quincey on literary power, Univ. Toronto Quart, 57; De Quincey on poetic genius, Dalhousie Rev, 68; On the teaching of the drama, Eng. J, 68. Add: Dept. of English, University of Alberta, Edmonton, Alta, Can.

BINDRUP, JEWEL JACOBSEN, b. Wallsburg, Utah, Jan. 27, 15; m. 31; c. 1. ENGLISH, SPEECH. B.S, Utah State Univ, 40, M.S, 47; John Hay fel, Northwest. Univ, 60-61 & Williams Col, summer 63. Teacher high schs, Idaho & Utah, 45-47; asst. speech, Utah State Univ, 47-48; teacher, Weber High Sch, 57-63, coord. advan. placement, Weber Dist, 61-63; teacher, Salt Lake City Schs, 64-65; ENG. & EDUC. SPECIALIST, UTAH STATE BD. EDUC, 65- Mem. comn. Eng. workshop, Univ. Nev, summer 62; Asn. State Eng. & Reading Specialists, 65-; state adv. for gifted & talented. Nat. Asn. Humanities Educ; NCTE. Curriculum; teacher education; creativity. Publ: We like team teaching, La. Eng. J, spring 61; co-auth, The library curriculum center, Audiovisual Instr, 10/62. Add: 1400 University Bldg, 136 E.S. Temple, Salt Lake City, UT 84111.

BINGHAM, SYLVESTER HINCKLEY, b. Manchester, N.H, May 22, 01. ENGLISH. A.B, Dartmouth Col, 22; A.M, Harvard, 29; Ph.D, Yale, 37. Master, Taft Sch, Watertown, Conn, 26-28; instr, Rollins Col, 28-30, asst. prof, 30-33; ENG, UNIV. N.H, 36-45, assoc. prof, 45-47, prof, 47-70, chmn. dept, 45-66, EMER. PROF, 70- MLA. Eighteenth century English literature; publishing business in 18th century England. Add: Dept. of English, University of New Hampshire, Durham, NH 03824.

BINKLEY, WILLIAM O, b. Bayshore, N.Y, Sept. 27, 30; m. 53; c. 2. ENGLISH. B.A, State Univ, N.Y. Albany, 57, N.Y. War Serv. scholar & M.A, 57; fel, Univ. Wis, 57-58, & 60-61, Ph.D.(Eng), 61. Instr. Eng. lit, Univ. Va, 61-64; asst. prof, UNIV. OF THE PAC, 64-66, ASSOC. PROF. ENG, 66-, DEAN COL, 68-, dir, freshman Eng, 65-66, coord. fac. res. & dean grad. sch, 66-68, Dir, NDEA Inst. Advan. Stud. Eng, Univ. of the Pac, summers 65-66. U.S.A, 51-53. MLA; NCTE; Nat. Counc. Univ. Res. Adminr. Add: College of the Pacific, University of the Pacific, Stockton, CA 95204.

BINNICK, ROBERT IRA, Linguistics. See Volume III, Foreign Languages, Linguistics & Philology.

BIRD, DONALD ARTHUR, b. Beloit, Wis, July 12, 19; wid. ENGLISH LANGUAGE. A.B, Univ. Wis, 40, A.M, 41, Ph.D, 50. Instr. ENG, Ohio State Univ, 46-49; Univ. Calif, Los Angeles, 49-51, asst. prof, 51-56; CALIF. STATE UNIV, LOS ANGELES, 56-59, assoc. prof, 59-63, PROF, 63-, dean grad. stud, 64-67. Mem. adv. bd, Am. Speech, 65-66; mem, Calif. State Curriculum Comn, 65-67. MLA; Mediaeval Acad. Am; Am. Dialect Soc; Ling. Soc. Am. History of English pronunciation; current English structure. Publ: Co-auth, Patterns of thinking and writing, Wadsworth, 59. Add: Dept. of English, California State University, Los Angeles, Los Angeles, CA 90032.

BIRDSALL, ESTHER KATHERINE, b. Mich; m. 48; c. 1. LITERATURE. A.B, Cent. Mich. Col, 47; M.A, Univ. Ariz, 50; Johns Hopkins Univ, 51-52; Ph.D, Univ. Md, 58. Asst. prof. Eng, Hood Col, 57-60; instr, UNIV. MD, COLLEGE PARK, 60-64, asst. prof. folklore, 64-69, ASSOC. PROF. ENG, 69- Mediaeval Acad. Am; Am. Folklore Soc. Medieval literature; Middle English romances. Add: Dept. of English, University of Maryland, College Park, MD 20742.

BIRENBAUM, HARVEY, b. Philadelphia, Pa, July 8, 36; m. 63; c. 1. ENGLISH LITERATURE. B.A, Antioch Col, 58; M.A, Yale, 59, Ph.D.(Eng), 63. Asst. prof. ENG, SAN JOSE STATE UNIV, 65-69, ASSOC. PROF, 69- Vis. lectr, Univ. E.Anglia, 72-73. Shakespeare; tragic theory and myth; Blake. Add: Dept. of English, San Jose State University, 125 S. Seventh St, San Jose, CA 95114.

BIRKY, WILBUR J, b. Oct. 23, 35; U.S. citizen; m. 60; c. 2. AMERICAN & ENGLISH LITERATURE. B.A, Goshen Col, 63; M.A, Univ. Iowa, 64, fels, 67-70, Ph.D.(Eng), 70. Instr. ENG, GOSHEN COL, 64-66, asst. prof, 66-67, ASSOC. PROF, 70-, chmn. dept, 70-74. MLA. Short story; 19th century British novel. Add: Dept. of English, Goshen College, Goshen, IN 46526.

BIRNBAUM, MILTON, b. Poland, June 6, 19. ENGLISH. A.B, City Col. New York, 42; Cambridge, 43; A.M, N.Y. Univ, 48, Ph.D.(Eng), 56. Instr. ENG, AM. INT. COL, 48-49, asst. prof, 50-57, assoc. prof, 57-62, prof. & chmn. dept, 62-73; DEAN, SCH. ARTS & SCI, 73- Lectr, Univ. Conn; prof, Holyoke Jr. Col, 61-64; vis. prof. Shakespeare, St. Hyacinth Col. & Sem, 72-73. U.S.A, 42-45, Tech. Sgt. MLA; NCTE; Col. Eng. Asn; AAUP. British novel between the world wars; American romanticism; literature, philosophy and religion. Publ: The CEA critic; The new Christianity; Jewish parent; Aldous Huxley's quest for values, Univ. Tenn, 71; introd, An encyclopedia of pacifism, Garland Publ, 72, Professor Scylla & Professor Charybdis, 2/72 & Higher education, eh?, column, 72-, Chronicle Higher Educ; plus five others. Add: Office of the Dean, School of Arts & Sciences, American International College, Springfield, MA 01109.

BIRNEY, EARLE, b. Calgary, Alta, May 13, 04; m. 37; c. 1. ENGLISH. B.A, Univ. B.C, 26; Leonard fel, Univ. Toronto, 26-27, M.A, 27, Ph.D, 36; univ. fel, Univ. Calif, 27-30; Royal Soc. Can. fel, Univ. London, 34-35; hon. LL.D, Univ. Alta, 65. Instr. Eng, Univ. Utah, 30-34; lectr, Univ. Toronto, 36-40, asst. prof, 40-45; supvr. for. lang. broadcasts, int. short wave serv, Can. Broadcasting Corp, 45-46; prof. Eng, Univ. B.C, 46-63, creative writing, 63-65, faculty arts rep, univ. senate, 56-57 & 63-65; writer-in-residence, Univ. Toronto, 65-67; Univ. Waterloo, 67-68; regents prof. Eng. & comp. lit, Univ. Calif, Irvine, 68; LECTR. & WRITER, 68- Gov. Gen. Award, 42-45; Leacock Medal, 50; Can. Govt. overseas fel, France, 53; ed. consult, Can. Arts Counc, 56-59; Nuffield Found. res. fel, Brit. Mus, London, 58-59; vis. prof, Univ. Ore, 61; Can. Counc. sr. lectr, Latin Am. & W.Indies, 62-63; poetry rep, Nat. Adv. Panel, Can. Counc, 66-68; Can. Counc. spec. travelling lectr, Australia & N.Z, 68-69, Brit. Isles, spring 71, fall 73 & Africa & Asia, spring 72. Can. Army, 40-45, Maj. Chaucer; Malcolm Lowry; Canadian and Commonwealth literature. Publ: Ed, Twentieth century Canadian poetry, Ryerson, Toronto, 53; auth, Turvey, a picaresque novel, Abelard-Schuman, N.Y. & London, 58; ed. & co-auth, Creative writing in Canada, Dent, Toronto, 58; auth. & ed, Selected poems of Malcolm Lowry, City Lights Press, 62; auth, Ice, cod, bell or stone, 62, Near False Creek mouth, 64, Selected poems of Earle Birney, Rag and bone shop, 70, What's so big about green?, 73 & Collected poems, 74, McClelland & Stewart, Toronto; The creative writer, Can. Broadcasting Corp, Toronto, 66; The cow jumped over the moon, Holt, Toronto, 72; Bear on the Delhi road, Chatto & Windus, London, 73; Is Chaucer's irony a modern discovery?, J. Eng. & Ger. Philol, XLI: 303-319; After His Ymage: the central ironies of the Friar's tale, Medieval Stud, XXI: 17-35; Structural irony within the Summoner's tale, Anglia, LXXVIII: 204-218. Add: McClelland & Stewart Publishers, 25 Hollinger Rd, Toronto, Ont. M4B 3G2, Can.

BISCHOFF, ANTHONY D, S.J, b. Walla Walla, Wash, Nov. 30, 10. ENGLISH LITERATURE. B.A, Gonzaga Univ, 34, M.A, 35; Ph.D, Yale, 52. Lectr. philos. & Eng. lit, Seattle Col, 35-38; assoc. prof. Eng. lit, Gonzaga Univ, 49-53, assoc. prof, 55-56, chmn. Eng. dept, 49-53; assoc. prof. ENG. LIT, Seattle Univ, 58-62; VIS. PROF, GEORGETOWN UNIV, 62- Vis. asst. prof, George Washington Univ, 68-69. MLA; NCTE. Publ: Poet in black: Gerard Manley Hopkins, Farrar, Straus; G.M. Hopkins as literary critic, Univ. Microfilms, 68; Manuscripts of Gerard Manley Hopkins, Thought, 52. Add: Georgetown University, Washington, DC 20007.

BISHOP, ALLAN RICHARD, b. Muskegon, Mich, Apr. 17, 36; m. 58; c. 4. ENGLISH LITERATURE. B.A, Calvin Col, 58; M.A, Northwest. Univ, 59, univ. fel, 62, Ph.D.(Eng), 69. Instr. ENG, Univ. Wis-Milwaukee, 63-70; ASST. PROF, UNIV. WIS-SUPERIOR, 70- AAUP; Conf. Christianity & Lit; Midwest Mod. Lang. Asn; MLA; Res. Soc. Victorian Periodicals. Nineteenth century British literature; Victorian periodicals; religion and literature. Publ: Nathan Scott's The unquiet vision, fall 70 & contrib, Annotated bibliography of religion and literature, quart. 70-, Christianity & Lit. Add: Dept. of English, University of Wisconsin-Superior, Superior, WI 54880.

BISHOP, CONRAD JOY, b. Denver, Colo, Oct. 8, 41; m. 61. THEATRE, DRAMA. B.S, Northwest. Univ, 62, M.A, 63; Ph.D.(drama), Stanford Univ, 67. Teaching asst. acting & directing, Stanford Univ, 64-66; asst. prof. Eng. & assoc. dir, Univ. Theatre, Univ. S.C, 66-68; asst. prof. theatre art, Univ. Wis-Milwaukee, 68-71; CO-MGR, THEATRE X, INC, 69- Commissioned playwright, Wis. Counc. Criminal Justice, 73; Wis. Arts Counc. grant, 74. Am. Theatre Asn; AAUP; Union Int. Marionettes. Community uses of theatre; puppetry; 19th century stage techniques. Publ: 4 plays from Theatre X, Hyde Parker, 10/72; Theatre as communicator, Mil. Press Club Annual, 72. Prod: Ten plays, Theatre X, 69-74; Halfway to somewhere, Wis. Counc. Criminal Justice, 73; Songs of Passers-by, Shakerag Players/Wis. Arts Counc, 74. Add: 3077 N. Newhall, Milwaukee, WI 53211.

BISHOP, DAVID RAND, JR, b. Lansing, Mich, Feb. 3, 33. COMPARATIVE LITERATURE, AFRICAN STUDIES. B.A, Univ. Mich, Ann Arbor, 54, M.A, 61; cert. African stud. & French, For. Serv. Inst, Wash, D.C, 63; Ph.D.(comp. lit), Mich. State Univ, 70. Copyboy, N.Y. Times, 56-57; col. rep, Henry Holt & Co, Inc, 57-59; cult. affairs & Eng. teaching off, U.S. Inform. Agency, 63-66; Am. Embassy, Lome, Togo, 64-66; asst. prof. Eng, Calif. State Univ, Sacramento, 66-69; ling. & orient. & African lang, Mich. State Univ, 70-71; ASSOC. PROF. ENG, STATE UNIV. N.Y. COL. OSWEGO, 71- Mem. staff, Eng. Teaching Sem, U.S. Agency Int. Develop, Bamako, Mali, summer 65; coord. teaching Eng. as for. lang, Peace Corps Training Proj, Dartmouth Col, summer 66; mem. African lit. comt, MLA Int. Bibliog, 72-; vis. assoc. prof, Case West. Reserve Univ, summer 73; vis. prof, McGill Univ, summer 74; Fulbright lectr, Nat. Univ. Gabon, 74-75. MLA; African Stud. Asn; Teachers Eng. to Speakers Other Lang; Am. Comp. Lit. Asn; Int. Comp. Lit. Asn. African literature; prose fiction; comparative literature. Publ: On identifying a standard of African literary criticism: characterization in the novel, J. New African Lit. & Arts, summer-fall 71; A bibliography of African literary criticism, 1947-1966, Africana Libr. J, summer 73. Add: Dept. of English, State University of New York College at Oswego, Oswego, NY 13126.

BISHOP, FERMAN, b. Landrum, S.C, May 4, 22; m. 48; c. 2. ENGLISH. B.A, Wofford Col, 42; M.A, Univ. Wis, 48, Ph.D.(Eng), 55. Instr. ENG, Univ. Wis, Milwaukee, 46-47; Univ. Colo, 51-55; asst. prof. Univ. Wichita, 55-58; assoc. prof, 58-60; ILL. STATE UNIV, 60-64, PROF, 64- U.S.N, 42-46, Lt. MLA; Midwest Mod. Lang. Asn.(secy-treas, 59-66). The mind and art of Sarah Orne Jewett. Publ: Allen Tate, Twayne, 67; Henry James criticizes the Tory lover, Am. Lit; Sarah Orne Jewett's ideas of race, New Eng. Quart, 60. Add: Dept. of English, Illinois State University, Normal, IL 61761.

BISHOP, JIMMY DEAN, b. Ladonia, Tex, Oct. 10, 33. ENGLISH. B.A, E.Tex. State Univ, 54, M.A, 58; Ph.D.(Eng), La. State Univ, 68. Instr. ENG, Schreiner Inst, 55-56; asst. prof, Nicholls State Col, 58-63; instr, La. State Univ, 65-68; ASSOC. PROF, TEX. WOMAN'S UNIV, 68- Vis. instr, NDEA Inst. Adv. Stud. Eng, Northwest. State Col.(La), summer 66. Nineteenth and twentieth century British and American literature; modern poetry. Add: Dept. of English, Texas Woman's University, Denton, TX 76204.

BISHOP, JONATHAN (PEALE), b. Paris, France, Oct. 27, 27; m. 48; c. 2. ENGLISH. A.B, Harvard, 50, A.M, 52, Ph.D.(Eng), 56. Instr. Eng, Amherst Col, 54; assoc. prof. ENG, CORNELL UNIV, 66-72, PROF, 72- MLA. American literature. Publ: Emerson on the soul, Harvard, 64; Something else, Braziller, 72. Add: Dept. of English, Cornell University, Ithaca, NY 14850.

BISHOP, ROBERT LEE, b. Cincinnati, Ohio, Aug. 17, 31; m. 52; c. 4. MASS COMMUNICATIONS. B.S, Okla. Baptist Univ, 52; M.R.E, South. Baptist Theol. Sem, 56, D.R.E, 60; Ph.D.(mass commun), Univ. Wis-Madison, 66. Reporter, News-Star, Shawnee, Okla, 50-52; from instr. to asst. prof. jour. & dir. pub. relat, Okla. Baptist Univ, 58-63; from asst. prof. to ASSOC. PROF. JOUR, UNIV. MICH, ANN ARBOR, 65- Copy ed, Free Press, Detroit, Mich, 66. U.S.N.R, 52-54, Res, 54-72, Comdr. Asn. Educ. in Jour. (div. res. comt. chmn, 68-70); Int. Asn. Mass Commun. Res; AAUP. Relation of media, economic, and political systems; media systems of western Europe; computer assisted instruction in journalism. Publ: Co-auth, Mysterious silence, lyrical scream: government information in World War II, Asn. Educ. in Jour, 71; auth, Cable TV: last hope for a free press?, New Republic, 3/70; co-auth, Computer-assisted instruction in English composition and advanced writing skills, Proc. Int. Fed. Inform. Processing, 8/71; auth, Media barons—the rush to chain ownership, Columbia Jour. Rev, 11-12/72. Add: Dept. of Journalism, University of Michigan, Ann Arbor, MI 48104.

BISHOP, THOMAS W, French & Comparative Literature. See Volume III, Foreign Languages, Linguistics & Philology.

BISIGNANO, DOMINIC J, b. Brooklyn, N.Y, July 27, 30; m. 67. ENGLISH. B.A, St. Benedict's Col.(Kans), 54; M.A, Niagara Univ, 58; Ph.D.(Eng), N.Y. Univ, 64. Teacher, pub. schs, N.Y, 59-60; ENG, U.S. Inform. Agency, Torino, Italy, 61-63; asst. prof, Marshall Univ, 63-65; West. Ill. Univ, 66-67; assoc. prof. & chmn. dept, McMurry Col, 67-69; ASSOC. PROF, IND. UNIV-PURDUE UNIV, INDIANAPOLIS, 69- Fulbright travel grant & Ital. govt. grant, 60-61. MLA. Translations of major critical works by Italian scholars; Anglo-Italian literary and cultural relations in the 19th century; computer research. Publ: Enrico Nencioni and Robert Browning, Eng. Miscellany, 63; Towards a computerized analysis of Joseph Conrad's style, Comput. & Humanities, 5/73. Add: Dept. of English, Indiana University-Purdue University at Indianapolis, 925 W. Michigan, Indianapolis, IN 46202.

BISWANGER, RAYMOND ADAM, JR, b. Philadelphia, Pa, Aug. 8, 22; m. 50; c. 3. ENGLISH. A.B, Univ. Pa, 43, M.S, 48, A.M, 50, Ph.D.(Eng), 51. Asst. instr. ENG, Univ. Pa, 46-51; instr, State Univ. N.Y. Teachers Col, Cortland, 51-54, asst. prof, 54; Univ. Ga; 54-61, PROF, SLIPPERY ROCK STATE COL, 61-, chmn. dept, 61-66. Folger fel, 59; mem, Eng. Inst. U.S.N.R, 40-46, Lt. MLA; Bibliog. Soc. Univ. Va. Restoration and early 18th century English drama. Publ: Thomas D'Urfey's Richmond heiress, a bibliographical study, Stud. Bibliog; More seventeenth century allusions to Shakespeare, Notes & Queries; Several words first employed in D'Urfey's The Richmond heiress, Mod. Lang. Notes. Add: 233 E. Cooper St, Slippery Rock, PA 16057.

BITTNER, JOHN ROBERT, b. Greensburg, Pa, May 4, 43; m. 72. COMMUNICATION. B.A, Dakota Wesleyan Univ, 67; M.A, Purdue Univ, 70, Ph.D. (commun), 72. Instr. commun, Purdue Univ, 69-71; asst. prof. commun. & dir, Ctr. Media Rev, Univ. Ore, 72-73; DIR. BROADCAST COMMUN, DePAUW UNIV, 73- Mem. ed. bd, Col. Stud. J, 72-; dir. news media rels, Int. Commun. Asn, 73. Int. Commun. Asn.(mem. nat. stud. publ. comt, 73-); Broadcast Educ. Asn.(mem. res. comt, 72-); West. Speech Asn. Mass media effects; telecommunications policy; computer analysis of mass media messages. Publ: Mass media: responsibilities of senders and receivers, In: Speech communication, W.C. Brown, 71; auth, News media and campus unrest & co-auth, Kennedy on King: the rhetoric of control, In: On Speech communication, Holt, 72. Add: Dept. of Speech, DePauw University, Greencastle, IN 46135.

BITTRICH, LOUIS EDWARD, b. Omaha, Nebr, Nov. 4, 37; m. 61; c. 2. COMPARATIVE LITERATURE. B.A, Gustavus Adolphus Col, 59; M.A, Bowling Green State Univ, 60; Ph.D.(comp. lit), Univ. N.C, 67. Instr. Eng. & dir. theatre, Tex. Lutheran Col, 60-62. instr. ENG, Gustavus Adolphus Col, 62-63; asst. prof, Winthrop Col, 65-66; Gustavus Adolphus Col, 66-67; ASSOC. PROF. & CHMN. DEPT, TEX. LUTHERAN COL, 67- Exchange prof. humanities, Winthrop Col, 65-66. MLA. Modern Roman elegies; contemporary mythology; Romantic poetry. Publ: Alchemy vindicated in our age, Cresset, 4/72. Add: Dept. of English, Texas Lutheran College, Seguin, TX 78155.

BITZER, LLOYD FRANK, b. Wapakoneta, Ohio, Jan. 2, 31; m. 53; c. 4. SPEECH. B.S, South. Ill. Univ, 55, M.A, 57; Univ. N.C, 57-58; Ph.D, State Univ. Iowa, 62. Instr. commun. skills, State Univ. Iowa, 60-61; from asst. prof. to PROF. SPEECH, UNIV. WIS-MADISON, 61- U.S.N, 52-54. Speech Commun. Asn.(1st v.pres, 75); AAUP; Cent. States Speech Asn. Rhetorical theory; 18th century philosophy and criticism. Publ: George Campbell's philosophy of rhetoric, South. Ill. Univ, 63; co-auth, The prospect of rhetoric, Prentice-Hall, 71. Add: Dept. of Communication Arts, 6142 Vilas Hall, University of Wisconsin-Madison, Madison, WI 53706.

BIVENS, WILLIAM PATTERSON, III, b. Camden, Tenn, Sept. 28, 43; m. 66; c. 1. STYLISTICS, ENGLISH LINGUISTICS. A.B, Univ. Tenn, Chattanooga, 65; M.A, Univ. Calif, Santa Barbara, 67, Ph.D.(Eng. ling. & lit), 70; Ohio State Univ, summer 70. Teaching asst. Eng, Univ. Calif, Santa Barbara, 65-69, assoc. remedial Eng, 69; ASST. PROF. ENG, HUMBOLDT STATE UNIV, 70-, COORD. LANG. STUD. PROG, 72-, univ. res. grant, summer 71, univ-Nat. Sci. Found. grant, summer 72. Nat. Sci. Found-Am. Counc. Learned Soc. summer stipend, 70, Nat. Endowment for Humanities summer stipend, 74. Ling. Soc. Am; MLA; NCTE; Rhet. Soc. Am; Conf. Col. Compos. & Commun. Linguistics stylistics; rhetorical invention and style; linguistics and the teaching of English. Publ: Verbs of remembering, Working Papers in Ling, 8/71; Preliminaries to composition, Freshman Eng. News, fall 73; NP case schema in the deep structure of poems, In: Meaning: a common ground of linguistics and literature, Mouton, (in press). Add: Dept. of English, Humboldt State University, Arcata, CA 95521.

BJORNSTAD, WILLIAM BERNARD, b. La Crosse, Wis, Feb. 22, 07; m. 36; c. 1. ENGLISH. A.B, Univ. Minn, 29, Comt. Educ. Res. fel, 29-31, A.M, 30, Ph.D, 45. Instr. Eng, Colo. Agr. & Mech. Col, 35-42, asst. prof, 42-46; prof. Eng. & head dept. langs, Union Col.(Ky), 46-48; assoc. prof. ENG, DRAKE UNIV, 48-59, PROF, 59- MLA; Malone Soc; NCTE; Col. Eng. Asn; Renaissance Soc. Am; Am. Soc. 18th Century Stud. Restoration and 18th century English literature; Jonathan Swift; political satire in Restoration poetry, 1660-1689. Add: Dept. of English, Drake University, Des Moines, IA 50311.

BLACK, EDWIN, b. Houston, Tex, Oct. 26, 29. RHETORIC & PUBLIC ADDRESS. B.S, Univ. Houston, 51; M.A, Cornell Univ, 53, Ph.D, 62. Instr. speech, Wash. Univ, 56-60, asst. prof, 60-61; Univ. Pittsburgh, 61-63, assoc. prof. speech & admin. off. dept. speech & theatre arts, 63-66, PROF. speech, 66-67; COMMUN. ARTS, UNIV. WIS-MADISON, 67-, CHMN. DEPT, 70- Vis. assoc. prof, Univ. Calif, Berkeley, 64-65; vis. prof, Univ. Minn, 67; Calif. State Univ, Los Angeles, summer 72. Speech Commun. Asn.(distinguished book award, 66); AAUP. History of public address; criticism; rhetorical theory. Publ: Co-auth, American issues, Harcourt, 61; auth, Rhetorical criticism: a study in method, Macmillan, 65; co-ed, The prospect of rhetoric, Prentice-Hall, 71; auth, Plato's view of rhetoric, 58 & The second persona, 4/70, Quart. J. Speech; Frame of reference in rhetoric and fiction, Papers Rhetoric & Poetic, 65; plus one other. Add: Dept. of Communication Arts, University of Wisconsin-Madison, Madison, WI 53706.

BLACK, JAMES, b. Belfast, Ireland, Mar. 29, 32; Can. citizen; m. 58; c. 1. ENGLISH. B.A, Univ. Alta, 60, M.A, 62; Ph.D.(Eng), Univ. Birmingham, 64. Asst. prof. ENG, UNIV. CALGARY, 64-72, ASSOC. PROF, 72- Asn. Can. Univ. Teachers Eng. Shakespeare; 18th century studies, especially 18th century drama. Publ: The influence of Hobbes on Nahum Tate's King Lear, Stud. Eng. Lit, 67; An Augustan stage history: Nahum Tate's King Lear, Restoration & 18th Century Theatre Res, 5/67. Add: Dept. of English, University of Calgary, Calgary, Alta, Can.

BLACK, LAURENCE NORMAN, b. Houston, Tex, Sept. 10, 18; m. 50; c. 4. ENGLISH. B.A, Univ. Houston, 51, M.A, 52; South. Fac. fel, 58; Ph.D(Eng), Univ. Tex, 59. Instr. ENG, Univ. Houston, 51-52, 53-54; teaching asst, Univ. Tex, 54-56; asst. prof, E.Cent. State Col, 56-58; SAM HOUSTON STATE UNIV, 59-61, assoc. prof, 61-65, PROF, 65- U.S.A.A.F, 42-46. MLA; Col. Eng. Asn. Works of Samuel Butler, 1835-1902; 19th century English literature. Add: Dept. of English, Sam Houston State University, Huntsville, TX 77340.

BLACK, MATTHEW WILSON, b. Altoona, Pa, Apr. 14, 95. ENGLISH LITERATURE. A.B, Pa. State Col, 15; A.M, Univ. Pa, 16, Ph.D, 28. Instr. ENG, UNIV. PA, 16-18, 19-23; asst. prof, 23-33, assoc. prof, 33-39, prof, 39-65, EMER. PROF, 65- Dir. drama sect, Eng. inst, Columbia Univ, 39; exam. Elizabethan lit, Swarthmore Col, 51; vis. prof, South. Ill. Univ, 65-66, 67; Univ. Pa. res. grant, 65-; Am. Philos. Soc. res. grants, 66-68. U.S.A, 18-19. MLA (ed. consult, 65-). Publ: Co-auth, Typical Elizabethan plays, Harper; Shakespeare's seventeenth-century editors, 35 & Richard II; auth, a variorum edition, 55, MLA; Elizabethan and seventeenth-century lyrics, Lippincott, 38; A midsummer night's dream: an outline-guide to the play, Barnes & Noble, 65; ed, New variorum edition of Shakespeare's Titus Andronicus (in prep); plus others. Add: 1143 Edgewood Rd, Berwyn, PA 19312.

BLACK, MICHAEL LAWRENCE, b. Alton, Ill, Jan. 7, 40; m. 64. ENGLISH. A.B, Middlebury Col, 62; M.A, Columbia Univ, 63, Ph.D.(Eng), 67. Asst. prof. ENG, City Col. New York, 67-68; BARUCH COL, 68-73, ASSOC. PROF, 73- MLA; Am. Stud. Asn; NCTE; Am. Folklore Soc; Col. Eng. Asn. Early national literature, especially Washington Irving; Knickerbocker writers; folklore. Publ: Bibliographical problems in Washington Irving's early works, Early Am. Lit, 68-69; A history of New York: significant revision in 1848, Am. Transcendental Quart, 70; Irving's A history of New York, In: The Knickerbocker tradition and Washington Irving, Sleepy Hollow Restorations, 74. Add: Dept. of English, Baruch College, 17 Lexington Ave, New York, NY 10010.

BLACK, SIDNEY J, b. Cambridge, Mass, Aug. 11, 24; m. 46; c. 3. ENGLISH LITERATURE, HUMANITIES. B.S, Harvard, 46; A.M, Univ. Chicago, 48; Ph.D.(Eng. novel), Boston Univ, 55. Instr. Eng. compos, Univ. Nebr, 49-50; HUMANITIES, COL. BASIC STUD, BOSTON UNIV, 52-56, asst. prof, 56-59, assoc. prof, 59-64, PROF, 64- U.S.N.R, 43-45. English novel; modern drama; curricular relationships of philosophy and literature. Publ: Co-auth, Critical thinking and the humanities, Boston Univ, 55 & Humanities at Boston University, In: The humanities in general education, W.C. Brown, 60; auth, Utopias in class, Boston Univ. Lit. Currents, 4/71; Utopia as reality, Col. Eng, 12/71; plus two others. Add: Dept. of Humanities, College of Basic Studies, Boston University, 871 Commonwealth Ave, Boston, MA 02215.

BLACK, STEPHEN AMES, b. Los Angeles, Calif, Aug. 31, 35; m. 65; c. 1. AMERICAN LITERATURE. B.A, Calif. State Col. Los Angeles, 60, M.A, 61; Ph.D.(Eng), Univ. Wash, 64. ASST. PROF. ENG, Monmouth Col, 64-66; SIMON FRASER UNIV, 66- MLA; Philol. Asn. Pac. Coast; Asn. Can. Univ. Teachers Eng. Whitman; psychoanalysis and literature; the creative process. Publ: James Thurber: his masquerades, Mouton, The Hague, 68; The claw of the sea-puss: James Thurber's sense of experience, Wis. Stud. Contemporary Lit, fall 65; The symbolic narrative of The scarlet letter, introd. to Perennial Classics Ed, Harper, 68; Radical utterances from the soul's abysms: toward a new sense of Whitman, PMLA, 1/73; plus one other. Add: Dept. of English, Simon Fraser University, Burnaby 2, B.C, Can.

BLACKALL, JEAN FRANTZ, b. Washington, D.C, July 8, 28; m. 60; c. 1. ENGLISH LITERATURE. B.A, Mt. Holyoke Col, 50; Mary E. Woolley fel. from Mt. Holyoke Col, Radcliffe Col, 52-53, 55-56, M.A, 55, Ph.D.(Eng), 61. Ed. asst, Am. Nat. Red Cross, 50-51, ed, 51-52; instr. ENG, CORNELL UNIV, 58-63, asst. prof, 63-64, 69-71, lectr, 64-69, ASSOC. PROF, 71-, DIR. GRAD. STUD. ENG, 74- MLA; Am. Asn. Univ. Women. Nineteenth century English and American prose fiction. Publ: Jamesian ambiguity and The sacred fount, Cornell Univ, 65; James's In the cage: an approach through the figurative language, Univ. Toronto Quart, 1/62; Perspectives on Harold Frederic's Marketplace, PMLA, 5/71; Frederic's Gloria mundi as a novel of education, Markham Rev, 5/72; plus five others. Add: 811 Triphammer Rd, Ithaca, NY 14850.

BLACKBURN, CHARLES EDWIN, b. Elberton, Wash, Aug. 2, 15; m. 41; c. 3. ENGLISH. B.A, Univ. Wash, 41; Ph.D.(Am. stud), Yale, 52. Instr. Eng, Wash. State Col, 51-55, asst. prof, 55-59; tech. writer, Indust. Prod. Div,

Boeing Co, Wash, 59-60, mkt. adminr, 60-62, admin. asst, contract admin, 62-64; assoc. prof. ENG. & AM. STUD, WASH. STATE UNIV, 64-69, PROF, 69- MLA; Am. Stud. Asn; NCTE; AAUP. American literature, 1800-1860; American drama; America in the 1930's. Publ: Self-study report—Washington State University, Wash. State Univ, 70; Some new light on The western messenger, Am. Lit, 11/54; The honor English program at Washington State College, Col. Compos. & Commun, 11/56. Add: Dept. of English, Washington State University, Pullman, WA 99163.

BLACKBURN, THOMAS HAROLD, b. N.J, May 28, 32; m. 63. ENGLISH LITERATURE. B.A, Amherst Col, 54; Rhodes scholar & B.A, Oxford, 56, M.A, 60; Ph.D, Stanford Univ, 63. Acting instr. Eng, Stanford Univ, 60-62; instr, SWARTHMORE COL, 62-63, asst. prof, 63-69, ASSOC. PROF. ENG. LIT, 69- Am. Counc. Learned Soc. fel, 65-66; vis. lectr, Bryn Mawr Col, 68; vis. tutor, St. Edmund Hall, Oxford, 70. MLA; Renaissance Soc. Am; Milton Soc. Am. Milton; Shakespeare; science and literature. Publ: Edmund Bolton's The cabanet royal: a belated reply to Sidney's Apology for poetry, Stud. Renaissance, 67; Uncloister'd virtue: Adam and Eve in Milton's paradise, 71 & Paradises lost and found: the meaning and function of the paradise within in Paradise lost, 73, Milton Stud; plus two others. Add: Dept. of English, Swarthmore College, Swarthmore, PA 19081.

BLACKFORD, PAUL WELDON, b. Jacksonville, Ill, Aug. 12, 16. ENGLISH. B.S, West. Ill. State Col, 38; M.A, Bradley Univ, 48; Ph.D, Northwest. Univ, 50. Instr. ENG, Bradley Univ, 47-48; asst. prof, Drury Col, 50-51; assoc. prof, West. Ill. State Col, 51-57; asst. prof, DePauw Univ, 57-60; assoc. prof, WEST. ILL. UNIV, 60-63, PROF, 63- Am. Philos. Soc. grant & Folger Shakespeare Libr. fel, 60; co-ed, Neo-Latin News Renaissance Soc. Am; Milton Soc. Am. Neo-Latin lexicography; Renaissance Latin polemic; Milton. Publ: A Neo-Latin lexicon; Stratocracy, a seventeenth century Greek coinage. Add: Dept. of English, Western Illinois University, Macomb, IL 61455.

BLACKMAN, EUGENE J, b. Malden, Mass, Nov. 8, 22; m. 45; c. 2. THEATRE ARTS, ENGLISH. B.S, Boston Univ, 44, M.A, 47, 47-56. Instr. Eng. & speech, NORTHEAST. UNIV, 47-52, asst. prof, 52-56, assoc. prof. speech & drama, 56-59, PROF. DRAMA, 59- U.S.A, 43-46, Sgt. Maj. Am. Theatre Asn; Nat. Theatre Conf; Speech Asn. Am; Am. Nat. Theatre & Acad; Children's Theatre Conf; New Eng. Theatre Conf; Speech Asn. East. States. Publ: Co-ed, The actor in America, 66 & The playwright in America, 67, New Eng. Theatre Conf. Add: Dept. of Drama, Northeastern University, Boston, MA 02115.

BLACKMON, JENNINGS MASON, b. Junction City, Ark, Aug. 5, 35; m. 54; c. 3. ENGLISH. B.A, La. Polytech. Inst, 57; M.A, Univ. Ark, 60, Ph.D. (Eng), 67. Asst. prof. ENG, Nicholls State Col, 62-64; KANS. STATE COL. PITTSBURG, 66-67, assoc. prof, 67-72, PROF, 72- MLA. Earlier 17th century English literature; English Romantism. Publ: A review of Joyce and the Bible, Midwest Quart, winter 68. Add: Dept. of English, Kansas State College of Pittsburg, Pittsburg, KS 66764.

BLACKMORE, ROBERT LONG, b. Akron, N.Y, Sept. 13, 19; m. 41; c. 2. ENGLISH. B.A, Colgate Univ, 41, M.A, 61; Ph.D.(Eng), Syracuse Univ, 65. Instr. ENG, COLGATE UNIV, 60-63, asst. prof, 63-66, assoc. prof, 66-70, PROF, 70-, CHMN. DEPT, 72- Dir, Colgate Univ. Press, 64-; ed, Powys Newslett, 70- R.A.F, 42-43; U.S.N.A.F, 43-45, Lt. MLA. Nineteenth-century British literature; Georgian literature; creative writing. Publ: Introduction to Blackmore's Lorna Doone, Everyman's Libr, London, 66; Introduction to John Cowper Powys' Autobiography, Macdonald, London, 67; ed, Introduction to Blackmore's Springhaven, Everyman's Libr, 69, ed, Advice to a young poet: Llewelyn Powys, Farleigh Dickinson, 69 & John Cowper Powys' An Englishman upstate, Village, London, 74. Add: Dept. of English, Colgate University, Hamilton, NY 13346.

BLACKSTOCK, WALTER, b. Atlanta, Ga, Jan. 22, 17; div; m. 46; c. 3. ENGLISH, AMERICAN LITERATURE. B.A, Univ. Ga, 42; M.A, Vanderbilt Univ, 44; Ph.D.(Am. lit), Yale, 52. Instr. ENG, Ga. Inst. Technol, 46-48, from instr. to asst. prof, Fla. State Univ, 48-56; vis. prof, N.E. Mo. State Teachers Col, 57-58; prof, High Point Col, 58-62; Lander Col, 63-65; assoc. prof, E.Carolina Univ, 65-66; prof. & chmn. dept, Methodist Col, 66-72; PROF, ELIZABETH CITY STATE UNIV, 72- Ford Found. fel, Harvard, 54-55. MLA; Poetry Soc. Am; S.Atlantic Mod. Lang. Asn. American, modern & world literature. Publ: Poems, Quest for beauty, Dorrance, 42; A creed for darkness, 46, Delirium and drums, 47, Dreamer's clay, 48, The west wind blowing, 50, Call back the swallows, 52 & The deeper bond, 55, Wings Press; Miracle of flesh, Golden Quill, 60; Leaves before the wind: new and selected poems from two decades, Methodist Col, 66; ed, Selected poems of James Larkin Pehrson, Rand McNally, 60 & Word-gatherers: poems of the East Carolina University Poetry Forum, E.Carolina Univ, 66; Dreiser's dramatizations of art, the artist, and the beautiful in American life, South. Quart, 10/62; The fall and rise of Eugene Witla: Dreiser's dramatic vision of artistic integrity in The genius, fall-winter, 66 & The existentialist quest for an authentically human existence in contemporary literature, spring-summer 68, Univ. S.Fla. Lang. Quart. Add: Dept. of English, Elizabeth City State University, Elizabeth City, NC 27909.

BLACKWELDER, JAMES RAY, b. Kannapolis, N.C, Sept. 8, 41. AMERICAN LITERATURE. B.A, Wake Forest Univ, 63, fel. & M.A, 64; fel. & Ph.D. (Eng), 68. Teaching asst. ENG, Emory Univ, 65-66; instr, N.C. State Univ, 66-68; asst. prof, WEST. ILL. UNIV, 68-72, ASSOC. PROF, 72- AAUP; MLA; Midwest Mod. Lang. Asn; S.Atlantic Mod. Lang. Asn. Modern American fiction, novel; 19th century American literature; American drama. Publ: The human extremities of emotion in Cat on a hot tin roof, Res. Stud, 3/70 & Am. Lit. Abstr, 12/70. Add: Dept. of English, Western Illinois University, Macomb, IL 61455.

BLACKWELL, HERBERT R, b. Ft. Monroe, Va, Aug. 20, 27; m. 57. ENGLISH. B.A, Univ. Richmond, 50, M.A, 55; Ph.D.(Eng), Univ. Va, 67. Asst. prof. ENG, Delta State Col, 55-59; instr, Univ. Va, 61-63; asst. prof, Millsaps Col, 63-64; assoc. prof. Eng, LONGWOOD COL, 64-68, PROF. ENG. & DEAN, 68- U.S.A, 45-47, 50-53, 1st Lt. MLA; NCTE. Shakespeare; the 18th century. Add: Office of the Dean, Longwood College, Farmville, VA 23901.

BLACKWOOD, BYRNE DAVID, b. Chanute, Kans, Mar. 6, 30; m. 55; c. 2. SPEECH, DRAMA. B.S.Ed, Kans. State Teachers Col, 52; M.A, Univ. Ark, 55; Northwest. Univ, 56-57; Ph.D.(speech theatre), Univ. Kans, 66. Instr. speech & tech. dir. theatre, Univ. Miss, 55-56; Univ. Ark, 57-58; Stetson Univ, 58-59; asst. prof. SPEECH, SOUTHWEST MO. STATE UNIV, 59-66, PROF, 66-, DESIGNER & TECH. DIR. THEATRE, 59- Designer & Tech. dir. speech & theatre, Perry-Mansfield Sch. Dance, summer 56. Am. Theatre Asn; Speech Commun. Asn. Theatre architecture; stage lighting and design. Add: Dept. of Speech, Southwest Missouri State University, Springfield, MO 65802.

BLACKWOOD, ROBERT JAMES, b. Detroit, Mich, Nov. 21, 42; m. 66; c. 1. ENGLISH DRAMA. B.A, St. Joseph's Col.(Ind), 64; Ph.D.(Eng. lit), Loyola Univ. Chicago, 73. ASSOC. PROF. ENG, WILBUR WRIGHT COL, CITY COLS. CHICAGO, 67- MLA; Col. Conf. Compos. & Commun.(chmn. learning skills ctr. comt, 73-74); Col. Eng. Asn; Rhetoric Soc. Am; Screen Educr. Soc. Shakespeare; American film; European film. Publ: Coriolanus: in Shakespeare and the historians, Diss. Abstracts, 72; Umberto B. Reviews, Chicago Seed, 67-68; Woody Allen, Cozmozodiac, 1/73. Add: Dept. of English, Wilbur Wright College, 3400 N. Austin Ave, Chicago, IL 60634.

BLAIR, ARTHUR HADFIELD, b. Washington, D.C, Dec. 2, 27; m. 52; c. 2. ENGLISH & AMERICAN LITERATURE. B.S, U.S. Mil. Acad, 50; M.S, Calif. Inst. Technol, 56; M.A, Univ. Pa, 61; Univ. N.C, Chapel Hill, 68-70. Instr. ENG, U.S. MIL. ACAD, 57-58, asst. prof, 58-61, ASSOC. PROF, 65-, DIR. FRESHMAN ENG, 70-, asst. dean, 65-67. C.Eng, U.S.A, 50, Col; Legion of Merit; Bronze Star Medal. MLA; NCTE; Conf. Col. Compos. & Commun; Soc. Stud. South. Lit. William Faulkner; composition; Southern American literature. Add: Dept. of English, United States Military Academy, West Point, NY 10996.

BLAIR, CAROLINE COUCH, b. Snyder, Tex, Feb. 17, 10; m; c. 1. SPEECH & DRAMA. B.A, McMurry Col, 30, B.S, 31; M.A, Hardin Simmons Univ, 32; summers, Univ. South. Calif, 31 & Northwest. Univ, 32; Int. Acad. Fine Arts, Salzburg, Austria, 59. Mem. fac, McMurry Col, 30-36; prof. speech, private studio speech, 38-57; asst. prof. SPEECH, McMURRY COL, 57-58, ASSOC. PROF, 58-, chmn. dept, 58-65, dir. speech, drama, educ. & social welfare stud, Jan. term, 70- Participant, Mozartieum, Salzburg, Austria, 58 & Harvard, 70, Baalbeck Drama Festival, Lebanon, 67; critic, Flint Hills Oral Interpretation Festival, Emporia, Kans, 72 & Univ. Interscholastic League Finals, Austin, Tex, 72; deleg. & regional off, Int. Interpretative Conf, 71, southwest region rep, 72. Speech Commun. Asn; Poetry Soc, Eng; Am. Inst. Parliamentarians. Education; social welfare; rhetoric in Japan. Publ: Ed, Documentary film, Film Dir, 72; auth, Costerus essays in English, literature and philology, Editions Rodopi, Amsterdam, 72. Add: 601 Sayles Blvd, Abilene, TX 79605.

BLAIR, JOEL M, JR, b. Groveton, Tex, Nov. 3, 34; ENGLISH. B.A, Univ. Tex, 59; M.A, Harvard, 60, fel, 60-62, Ph.D.(Eng), 65, ASST. PROF. ENG, Univ. Calif, Santa Barbara, 65-66; UNIV. MASS, BOSTON, 66-, summer growth grant, 67. Dexter summer traveling fel, 65. U.S.A, 55-58. MLA. Restoration and eighteenth century literature; the novel. Publ: Dryden's ceremonial hero, Stud. Eng. Lit, summer 69; Dryden and the writing of fanciful poetry, Criticism, spring 70; Defoe's art in A journal of the plague year, S.Atlantic Quart, spring 73. Add: Dept. of English, University of Massachusetts, Boston, MA 02116.

BLAIR, JOHN GEORGE, b. Brooklyn, N.Y, Dec. 3, 34; m. 61; c. 1. ENGLISH, AMERICAN STUDIES. A.B, Brown Univ, 56, fel, 57-58, Ph.D.(Eng), 62; M.A, Columbia Univ, 57. Part-time instr. ENG, R.I. Sch. Design, 58-62; instr, Oakland Univ, 62-63, asst. prof, 63-66, assoc. prof, 66-70, PROF, UNIV. GENEVA, 70- Nat. Humanities Found. summer stipend, 67; Fulbright lectr. Am. lit, Univ. Strasbourg, 67-68. MLA; Am. Stud. Asn; Europ. Am. Stud. Asn. American literature and civilization, especially romanticism in America. Publ: The poetic art of W.H. Auden, Princeton, 65 & 66; co-auth, Thoreau on Katahdin, Am. Quart, 60; auth, W.H. Auden: the poem as performance, Shenandoah, 65; Puns and ambiguity in Melville's The confidence man, Transcendental Quart, 74. Add: Dept. of English, Faculty of Letters, University of Geneva, Geneva, Switz.

BLAIR, ROBERT LEE, b. Mt. Vernon, Ohio, May 18, 06. ENGLISH. A.B, Ohio State Univ, 28, A.M, 29; Ph.D, Univ. Ill, 36. Instr. ENG, 36-39; asst. prof, Univ. S.Dak, 39-42; assoc. prof, Youngstown Col, 44-45; instr, Morgan Park Mil. Acad, 45-46; assoc. prof, EAST. ILL. UNIV, 46-55, prof, 55-67, EMER. PROF, 67- Supvr. Eng. instr, air corps cadet detachment, Wittenberg Col, 43-44. U.S.A, 42-43. Elizabethan drama; romantic comedy in Tudor England. Publ: On teaching Shakespeare, Ill. Eng. Bull, 1/56. Add: 1025 Fourth St, Charleston, IL 61920.

BLAIR, THOMAS MARSHALL HOWE, b. Pittsburgh, Pa, Oct. 23, 01; m. 26, 70; c. 2. ENGLISH. A.B, Univ. Pittsburgh, 24, A.M, 25; Univ. London, 25-26; Johns Hopkins Univ, 31-34. Instr. Eng, Carnegie Inst. Tech, 26-28; West. Reserve Univ, 28-31; asst, main reading room, Libr. Congr, 34-35; instr. Eng. comp, Pa. State Col, 35-39; from asst. prof. to prof. ENG, KENT STATE UNIV, 39-73, EMER. PROF, 73- Vis. asst. prof, U.S. Mil. Acad. Prog, Cornell Univ, 44-45. MLA; Col. Eng. Asn. English drama of the Restoration period; creative writing; the short story. Publ: Ed, Unhappy favourite or the Earl of Essex, Columbia Univ, 39; auth, Teachers handbook, 60 & ed, Fifty modern stories, 60, Harper; auth, How an anthology is made, Writer, 3/67. Add: 520 Crain Ave, Kent, OH 44240.

BLAIR, WALTER, b. Spokane, Wash, Apr. 21, 00; m. 25; c. 1. ENGLISH. Ph.B, Yale, 23; Univ. Chicago, M.A, 26, Ph.D, 31. Asst. prof. ENG, Univ. Minn, 28-29; instr, UNIV. CHICAGO, 29-30, asst. prof, 30-39, assoc. prof, 39-44, prof, 44-68, chmn. dept, 51-60, EMER. PROF, 68- Ed, Am. Lit, 43-51; PMLA, 45-51; Col. Eng, 45-48, 52; fac. adv, Encycl. Britannica, 51-; Beckman lectr, Univ. Calif, Berkeley, 72. Thormod Monsen Award, 60. MLA; Am. Stud. Asn. American literature; American humor; Mark Twain. Publ: Native American humor, Chandler Publ, 37, 60; Horse sense in American humor, Russell, 42, 61; Mark Twain and Huck Finn, 60 & Mark Twain's Hannibal, Huck & Tom, 69, Univ. Calif; co-ed, Herman Melville, Omoo, Hendricks, 72; auth, A man's voice, speaking: a continuum in American humor, Veins of humor, Harvard Eng. Stud, 72. Add: Dept. of English, University of Chicago, Chicago, IL 60637.

BLAKE, CAESAR ROBERT, b. Charlotte, N.C, Oct. 5, 25. ENGLISH LANGUAGE & LITERATURE. A.B, Johnson C. Smith Univ, 45; M.A, Univ. Mich, 46, univ. fel, 56-57, Ph.D, 58; Rockefeller Found fel, 51-53. Instr. ENG, Bennett Col, 46-48; Johnson C. Smith Univ, 48-50, asst. prof, 50-51, assoc. prof, 54-56; instr, Univ. Mich, 57-59, asst. prof, 59-64, assoc. prof, 64-67; PROF, UNIV. TORONTO, 67- MLA. American poetry; 18th and 20th century English novel. Publ: Dorothy Richardson, 60 & co-auth, The recognition of Emily Dickinson, 64, Univ. Mich; co-ed, The Norton anthology of poetry, Norton, 70; plus one other. Add: Dept. of English, University College, University of Toronto, Toronto, Ont, Can.

BLAKE, HOWARD E, b. Fairfield, N.C, May 6, 22; m. 43; c. 2. ENGLISH EDUCATION. A.B, Atlantic Christian Col, 43; M.Ed, Univ. N.C, 52; Ed.D, Columbia Univ, 54. Teacher & prin, Leaksville Twp. Schs, N.C, 46-53; curriculum consult. & supvr. res, Pinellas County Schs, Fla, 54-55; asst. prof. EDUC, TEMPLE UNIV, 55-58, assoc. prof, 58-62, PROF, 62-, CHMN. DIV. CURRICULUM & INSTR, 66- Consult, Solomon Schecter Day Sch, Pa, 63-; Sch. Dist. Phila, 66-; Polyfax, Inc, 67-; Res. for Better Schs, Inc, 70-; Scott Paper Co, 72- Recipient, Christian R. & Mary F. Lindback Award, 65. U.S.N.R, 43-46, Lt. NCTE.(ed, JM Newslett, 61-66, mem. comn. compos, 70-); Nat. Conf. Res. Eng; NEA. Oral expression; written composition; spelling. Publ: Shoestring cameras and what to do with them, K-eight, 9/71; Written composition in British primary schools, Elem. Eng, 10/71; contrib, What children write about, In: Language arts in the elementary school: a forum for focus, Nat. Conf. Teachers Eng, 73; plus six others. Add: Div. of Curriculum & Instruction, Temple University, Broad & Montgomery, Philadelphia, PA 19122.

BLAKE, JAMES JOSEPH, b. New York, N.Y, Apr. 29, 39. ENGLISH & IRISH LITERATURE. B.A, Manhattan Col, 62; N.Y. State Regents fel, N.Y. Univ, 62-64, M.A, 64, univ. fel, 64-65; Fulbright fel, Trinity Col.(Dublin), 69-70. Instr. ENG, NASSAU COMMUNITY COL, 65-69, ASST. PROF, 71- Co-ed, An Féinics, 70-72. MLA; Am. Comt. Irish Stud; Int. Asn. Study Anglo-Irish Lit. William Butler Yeats; the Irish literary revival; Anglo-Irish literature. Publ: Materials available for the study of modern Irish, 70, Frank O'Connor's art of translation and criticism, 70 & Irish language and literature, 72, An Féinics. Add: Dept. of English, Nassau Community College, Garden City, NY 11530.

BLAKE, KATHLEEN ANN, b. Vernon, Tex, Oct. 4, 44; m. 67. ENGLISH LITERATURE. A.B, San Diego State Col, 66; M.A, Univ. Calif, Los Angeles, 67; Ph.D.(lit), Univ. Calif, San Diego, 71. ASST. PROF. ENG, UNIV. WASH, 71- MLA; Women's Caucus Mod. Lang. Asn; Victorian Stud. Asn. West. Can. Seventeenth century English and American metaphysical poets; Lewis Carroll; play and Victorianism. Publ: Play, games and sport: the literary works of Lewis Carroll, Cornell Univ, 74; Edward Taylor's protestant poetic: non-transubstantiating metaphor, Am. Lit, 3/71; Order and noble life in Chaucer's Knight's tale?, Mod. Lang. Quart, 3/73; The whispering gallery and structural coherence in DeQuincey's revised Confessions of an English opium-eater, Stud. Eng. Lit, fall 73. Add: Dept. of English, University of Washington, Seattle, WA 98195.

BLAKE, LESLIE M, b. Glasco, Kans, June 9, 13; m. 42; c. 4. SPEECH, DRAMA. B.S, Kans. State Univ, 37, M.S, 39; univ. scholar, Univ. Colo, 39-40, summers, 41, 47, 48, 49; dipl, Strategic Intel. Sch, Wash, D.C, 52; dipl, Command & Gen. Staff Col, Ft. Leavenworth, 62. Rural teacher, Kans, 31-35; prin, high sch, Oakley, Kans, 38-39; instr. SPEECH, WICHITA STATE UNIV, 40-42, asst. prof, 46-48, dir. div. adult educ. & exten, 48-51, from assoc. prof. to PROF, 53-, CHMN. DEPT. SPEECH & DRAMA, 60- Ed, Kans. Speech Jour, 53-55. Mil.Intel, U.S.A, 42-46, 51-53, Col. Speech Commun. Asn; Cent. St. Speech Asn. Fundamentals of speech; forensics; speech education. Publ: Co-auth, Chinese communist armed forces, U.S. Dept. Army, 53. Add: Dept. of Speech & Drama, Wichita State University, Wichita, KS 67208.

BLAKE, LINCOLN CARLYLE, b. Merzifon, Turkey, Aug. 10, 32; U.S. citizen; m. 55; c. 1. ENGLISH, AMERICAN STUDIES. A.B. & B.S, Tufts Univ, 55; Danforth fel, Univ. Chicago, 59, M.A, 61, Ph.D.(Am. stud), 66. ASSOC. PROF. ENG, EARLHAM COL, 64- U.S.N. Civil Eng.C, 55-59, Lt.(jg). NCTE; Soc. Relig. Higher Educ. Melville; Afro-American literature. Publ: E.Curmie Price, a Black odyssey, Earlham Rev, fall 71. Add: 295 Earlham Dr, Richmond, IN 47374.

BLAKE, ROBERT GRADY, b. Charlotte, N.C, Mar. 6, 34; m. 65; c. 2. ENGLISH. A.B, Harvard, 56; Johns Hopkins Univ, 56-57; M.A, Duke Univ, 59, Ph.D.(Eng), 68. Asst. prof. ENG, Stetson Univ, 59-62; assoc. prof, Morris Harvey Col, 64-68, acting chmn. dept, 65-68; WILLIAM S. LONG PROF. & CHMN. DEPT, ELON COL, 68- MLA; S.Atlantic Mod. Lang. Asn. Periodicals of the 19th century; Victorian literature, especially poetry; 19th century poetry reviews. Add: Dept. of English, Elon College, Elon College, NC 27244.

BLAKE, ROBERT WILLIAM, b. Springfield, Vt, Jan. 25, 30; m. 53; c. 3. ENGLISH, EDUCATION. A.B, Am. Int. Col, 52; A.M, Boston Univ, 54; Ed.D, Univ. Rochester, 64. Instr. Eng, Univ. Md. Overseas Prog, 56; teacher jr. & sr. high schs, Mass, 57-58; Acad, Canandaigua, N.Y, 58-60, chmn. dept, Eng, 60, supv. v.prin, 60-62; assoc. prof. ENG. EDUC, STATE UNIV. N.Y. COL. BROCKPORT, 63-64, PROF, 64-, chmn. dept. curriculum & instr, 70-72. Ed, Eng. Rec, 67-70; N.Y. State Eng. Counc. fel, 72. U.S.A, 55-56. NCTE; Conf. Eng. Educ. Applied linguistics; English education; American literature. Publ: Co-auth, English for meaning 7, Houghton, 66; auth, The effect of special instruction on the ability of seventh and eighth grade pupils to write compositions and understand poetry and short fiction, U.S. Off. Educ. Res. Proj. S-312, 66; The new English: hot stuff or cool, man, cool?, Eng. J, 9/71; Behavioral objectives—yes!, fall 71 & Behavioral objectives and teaching English, winter 71, Eng. Educ; plus others. Add: Dept. of Curriculum & Instruction, State University of New York College at Brockport, Brockport, NY 14420.

BLANAR, MICHAEL, b. Montreal, Can, Apr. 26, 33; m. 55; c. 3. ENGLISH LITERATURE. B.A, Loyola Col.(Can), 54; B.Ed, St. Joseph's Teachers Col, 55; M.A, Univ. Montreal, 56, Ph.D, 60; Univ. London, Eng, 58-59. Teacher, Eng. & Latin, Loyola High Sch, Montreal, 55-58, 59-60; asst. prof. Restoration & 18th century Eng. lit, Loyola Col.(Que), 60-63, assoc. prof. ENG, 63-70, asst. dean arts, 67-70; assoc. prof, Mt. St. Vincent Univ, 70-72, head dept, 71-72; PROF. & DEAN ARTS, BRANDON UNIV, 72- Can. Counc. summer travel grant, 62. MLA; NCTE; Can. Asn. Univ. Teachers Eng; Can. Counc. Teachers Eng. Jonathan Swift; 18th century British and Canadian travel journals and journalists; 18th century novel and development of novel form. Add: Office of the Dean of Arts, Brandon University, Brandon, Man. R7A 6A9, Can.

BLANCH, MAE, b. Ogden, Utah, May 11, 28. ENGLISH LITERATURE. A.B, Brigham Young Univ, 50; Ph.D.(Eng), Univ. Colo, Boulder, 66. ASSOC. PROF. ENG, BRIGHAM YOUNG UNIV, 66- Add: Dept. of English, Brigham Young University, Provo, UT 84601.

BLANCH, ROBERT JAMES, b. Brooklyn, N.Y, Feb. 17, 38; m. 61; c. 5. ENGLISH. A.B, Col. Holy Cross, 59; fel, Northeast. Univ, 59-61, M.A, 61; Ph.D.(Eng), State Univ. N.Y. Buffalo, 67. Instr. ENG, Northeast. Univ, 61-62; Newman Prep. Sch, Boston, 62-63; State Univ. N.Y. Buffalo, 63-66; asst. prof, Canisius Col, 66-67; Bentley Col. Acct. & Finance, 67-68; ASSOC. PROF, NORTHEAST. UNIV, 68- MLA. The works of the Pearl Poet; Chaucer; courtly love literature. Publ: Sir Gawain and Pearl: critical essays, Ind. Univ, 66; Style and symbolism in Piers plowman: a modern critical anthology, Univ. Tenn, 69; ed, Casebook on Chaucer's Merchant's tale, C.E. Merrill, 70; auth, Precious metal and gem symbolism in Pearl, 12/65 & Irony in Chaucer's Merchant's tale, 12/66, Lock Haven Rev; The symbolic gifts of the shepherds in the Secunda pastorum, Tenn. Stud. Lit, 10/72; plus one other. Add: Dept. of English, Northeastern University, Boston, MA 02115.

BLANCHARD, CARLENE BAGNALL, b. Battle Creek, Mich, June 4, 24; c. 3. AMERICAN STUDIES. B.A, West. Mich. Univ, 46; M.A, Univ. Mich, 50, fel, 67, Ph.D.(Am. stud), 69. Teacher Eng. & soc. stud, Lakeview High Sch, Battle Creek, Mich, 46-47; vol, Am. Friends Serv. Comt. & Le Serv. Civil Int, 47-48; teacher, Wayneflete Sch, Portland, Maine, 49; Eng. & soc. stud, Ypsilanti Pub. Schs, Willow Run, Mich, 50-51; Northwest. High Sch, Clark County, Ohio, 52-53; instr. & supvr. stud. teachers, Cent. State Univ. (Ohio), 66; ASST. PROF. AM. STUD. & ENG, Miami Univ, 69-70; BOWLING GREEN STATE UNIV, 70- Am. Women Biog. Proj. grantee, Bowling Green State Univ, 72-73. Am. Stud. Asn.(comn. status women, 70-71); AAUP. Social change in American culture; biographies of American women. Publ: Ramparts Magazine: social change in the sixties, Univ. Mich, 69; co-auth, American women and American studies, 71 & The status of women faculty at Bowling Green State University, 72, Know; Heroes of the non-violent revolution, Fel. Mag, 7/64; Zazen in Ohio, Camerica Mag, 65; American lit survey, New Directions in Teaching, winter 71. Add: American Studies Program, Bowling Green State University, Bowling Green, OH 43403.

BLANCHARD, ELIZABETH SHEILA, b. New York, N.Y, Mar. 13, 37. ENGLISH. B.A, Col. New Rochelle, 58; M.A, N.Y. Univ, 60; NDEA fel. & Ph.D. (Eng), Univ. Rochester, 66. Asst. lectr. ENG, Univ. Rochester, 63-64; instr, Coe Col, 64-66; ASST. PROF, Wayne State Univ, 66-69; North. Ill. Univ, 69-73; WILLIAM PATERSON COL. & QUEENSBOROUGH COMMUNITY COL, 73- Milton Soc. Am; Renaissance Soc. Am; MLA. Milton; the English Renaissance. Publ: Milton's foothill, Genre, 3/71. Add: 49-17 Overbrook St, Douglaston, NY 11362.

BLANKMAN, EDWARD JAMES, b. Canton, N.Y, Mar. 15, 08; m. 42; c. 4. ENGLISH, HISTORY. A.B, St. Lawrence Univ, 29; Hervey fel, Harvard, 29-31, A.M, 30. Teacher high sch, N.Y, 31-36; from instr. to EMER. PROF. ENG, ST. LAWRENCE UNIV, 36-, ARCHIVIST & HISTORIAN, 65- U.S.A, 42-44. Col. Eng. Asn; Am. Stud. Asn; AAUP. American literature; journalism; New York state and area history. Publ: Contrib, Candle in the wilderness, Appleton, 58; contrib, Adirondack life, York State Tradition, New York History and others, Add: Herring-Cole, St. Lawrence University, Canton, NY 13617.

BLANSETT, BARBARA NIEWEG, b. Owensville, Mo, Sept. 13, 26; m. 46; c. 2. AMERICAN LITERATURE. B.S, Univ. Houston, 57, M.A, 58; Ph.D. (Eng), Univ. Tex, 63. Asst. ENG, Univ. Houston, 58; Univ. Tex, 58-61; asst. prof, Univ. South. Miss, 61-63; Del Mar Col, 63-65; assoc. prof, Adams State Col, 64-67; METROP. STATE COL, 67-69, PROF, 69-, COORD. WOMEN'S STUD. PROG, 72- Rocky Mountain Mod. Lang. Asn; AAUP; Am. Asn. Univ. Women. Melville; Emerson; women's studies. Publ: From dark to dark: Melville's Mardi as a fore-shadow of Pierre, South. Quart, spring 63; Overcoming traditions and negative attitudes about women, Fed. Women's Prog. Publ, 72. Add: Dept. of English, Box 40, Metropolitan State College, 250 W. 14th Ave, Denver, CO 80204.

BLANSHARD, RUFUS ANDERSON, b. Rochester, N.Y, Aug. 30, 21; m. 52; c. 3. ENGLISH. B.A, Swarthmore Col, 43; Fulbright fel, Univ. London, 51-52; Ph.D.(Eng), Harvard, 52. Teaching fel, Harvard, 48-51; instr. ENG, Univ. Wis, 52-55; UNIV. CONN, 55-59, asst. prof, 59-63, ASSOC. PROF, 63- Fulbright lectr, Univ. Zagreb, 68-69. U.S.A, 43-45. Seventeenth and 18th century literature; modern literature. Publ: Ed, A reviewer's ABC: Collected criticism of Conrad Aiken, Meridian, 58 & Discussions of Alexander Pope, Heath, 60. Add: Dept. of English, University of Connecticut, Storrs, CT 06268.

BLANTON, RAYMOND EUGENE, b. Gaffney, S.C, Sept. 15, 43; m. 66; c. 1. EIGHTEENTH CENTURY ENGLISH LITERATURE. B.A, Univ. S.C, 66, M.A, 69, Ph.D.(Eng), 71. ASSOC. PROF. ENG, JACKSONVILLE STATE UNIV, 71- MLA; Am. Soc. 18th Century Stud. Satire; world literature. Add: Dept. of English, Jacksonville State University, Jacksonville, AL 36265.

BLATCHFORD, CHARLES H, English As A Second Language. See Volume III, Foreign Languages, Linguistics & Philology.

BLATT, MURIEL R, b. Chicago, Ill, Aug. 10, 30; m. 57; c. 2. ENGLISH, AMERICAN LITERATURE. B.A, Univ. Calif, Los Angeles, 52, M.A, 55; Univ. Calif, Irvine, 71- Teacher ENG, Los Angeles Pub. Schs, 55-57; asst. prof, Pierce Col.(Calif), 57-68; ASSOC. PROF, HARBOR COL, 68- MLA; NCTE (mem. comt. promoting student growth in reading of lit, 73-). California literature and culture; ethnic literature; teaching of literature and composition. Publ: Co-ed, A various collection, 66 & co-ed, A lively collection, 66, Aegeus; co-ed, Reader's choice, 70 & co-ed, Like it is, 70, Canfield; contrib, American English today, 70, 2nd ed, 74, McGraw. Add: 29225 Stonecrest Rd, Rolling Hills Estates, CA 90274.

BLATT, STEPHEN JOSEPH, b. Huntington, W.Va, Nov. 2, 41; m. 64; c. 1. COMMUNICATION. B.A, Morehead State Univ, 64; M.A, Ohio Univ, 67, Ph.D.(interpersonal commun), 69. Teacher hist. & speech, Shawnee High Sch, Ohio, 64-66; lectr. speech, Europ. Div, Univ. Md, 69-71; ASST. PROF. COMMUN, UNIV. DAYTON, 71- Evaluator, Criminal Justice Prog, Dayton Police Dept, 71-74; consult. police commun, Dayton Criminal Justice Ctr, 72-74; instr. inserv. training, Columbus Police Dept, 74. Speech Commun. Asn; Int. Commun. Asn; Cent. States Speech Asn; AAUP. Radio dispatching communications; political communications; organizational communications. Publ: Co-auth, Brown-Carlsen listening comprehension test, Form BM: report for 52 police dispatchers, Harcourt, 73, Community centered team policing: a second year evaluation, Dayton-Montgomery County Criminal Justice Ctr, 73 & Evaluating instructional films, J. Law Enforcement Educ. & Training, 4/73. Add: Dept. of Communication Arts, University of Dayton, Dayton, OH 45409.

BLAU, SHERIDAN D, b. Trenton, N.J, Mar. 10, 39; m. 60; c. 3. ENGLISH LITERATURE & EDUCATION. B.A, Rutgers Univ, 60; M.A, Brandeis Univ, 64, Ph.D.(Eng. & Am. lit), 67. Asst. prof. ENG, Univ. Mich, 66-70; UNIV. CALIF, SANTA BARBARA, 70-73, ASSOC. PROF, 73- Milton Soc. Am; NCTE. Seventeenth century English literature; teacher preparation. Publ: Co-ed, The house we live in: an environment reader, Macmillian, 71; auth, Milton's salvational aesthetic, J. Relig, 66; Pope's Chain of being: and the modern ecological vision, C.E.A. Critic, 1/71; The poet as casuist: Herbert's Church-porch, Genre, 6/71. Add: Dept. of English, University of California, Santa Barbara, CA 93106.

BLAYDES, SOPHIA BOYATZIES, b. Rochester, N.Y, Oct. 16, 33; m. 61; c. 2. ENGLISH & AMERICAN LITERATURE. B.A, Univ. Rochester, 55; M.A, Ind. Univ, Bloomington, 58, Ph.D.(Eng), 62. Instr, Am. lit, Mich. State Univ, 62-63, asst. prof, 63-65; ENG. & AM. LIT, W.VA. UNIV, 66-73, ASSOC. PROF, 73- Am. Soc. 18th Century Stud; MLA; Eng. Inst; S.Atlantic Mod. Lang. Asn. Eighteenth-century poetry; Restoration and eighteenth-century drama; modern drama. Publ: Christopher Smart as a poet of his time: a re-appraisal, Mouton, The Hague, 66; Poor Kit Smart, Bull. W.Va. Asn. Col. Eng. Teachers, 73; co-auth, Modern theater on film, Notes Teaching Eng, 73; auth, The McCarthy-Army Hearings: history as drama, Improving Col. & Univ. Teaching, 74. Add: Dept. of English, Armstrong Hall, West Virginia University, Morgantown, WV 26506.

BLAYNEY, GLENN HAMMOND, b. Washington, Pa, Mar. 27, 27; div; c. 1. ENGLISH. B.A, Lafayette Col, 47; M.A, Brown Univ, 48; Rotary Int. fel. & B.Litt, Oxford, 53. Instr. ENG, Univ. Colo, 48-50; Oberlin Col, 53-56; asst. prof, Wayne State Univ, 56-60; E.Stroudsburg State Teachers Col, 60-61; Point Park Col, 64-66; CALIF. STATE COL.(PA), 66-71, ASSOC. PROF, 71- Folger Shakespeare fel, 63. MLA. English Renaissance literature; fourteenth and fifteenth century French prose; American drama from its beginnings through 1860. Publ: A diplomatic facsimile of G. Wilkin's Miseries of enforced marriage, Malone Soc, Oxford, 64; Variants in Q1 of A Yorkshire tragedy, Library, 56; City life in the American drama, 1825-1860, Stud. John Wilcox Detroit, 58; Convention, plot, and structure in The broken heart, Mod. Philol, 58. Add: Dept. of English, California State College, California, PA 15419.

BLECHNER, MICHAEL HARRY, b. Brooklyn, N.Y, May 16, 44. MEDIEVAL & RENAISSANCE ENGLISH LITERATURE. B.S, Mass. Inst. Technol, 66; Woodrow Wilson fel, Princeton, 66-67, Ph.D.(Eng), 71. ASST. PROF. ENG, UNIV. TULSA, 70- Medieval Acad. Am; Renaissance Soc. Am; MLA; Mod. Humanities Res. Asn; Mod. Lang. Soc, Finland. Old English literature; Middle English literature; Chaucer. Add: Dept. of English, University of Tulsa, Tulsa, OK 74104.

BLEETH, KENNETH ALAN, b. New York, N.Y, Mar. 12, 43. MEDIEVAL LITERATURE. A.B, Harvard, 63, A.M, 65, Ph.D.(Eng), 69. ASST. PROF. ENG, BOSTON UNIV, 69- Asst. prof. Eng, Harvard Univ. summer sch, 72. Nat. Endowment for Humanities younger humanist fel, 73-74. MLA; Medieval Acad. Am. Middle English poetry, especially Chaucer. Publ: Juliana, 647-652, Medium Aevum, 69; Narrator and landscape in the Commedia, Dante Stud, 70; The image of paradise in the Merchant's tale, Harvard Eng. Stud, 74. Add: Dept. of English, Boston University, 236 Bay State Rd, Boston, MA 02215.

BLEHL, VINCENT FERRER, b. New York, N.Y, July 31, 21. ENGLISH LITERATURE. A.B, Woodstock Col, 45, Ph.L, 46, S.T.L, 53; M.A, Fordham Univ, 51; Ph.D.(Eng), Harvard, 59. Instr. ENG, Univ. Scranton, 46-47, asst. prof, 47-48; Canisius Col, 59-62; FORDHAM UNIV, 62-64, assoc. prof, 64-67, PROF, 67- Lectr, Inst. Philos. & Let, Univ. Namur, Belgium, 53-54; Am. Philos. Soc. res. grants, Newman Arch, Birmingham, Eng, 61-62, summer 63. MLA; Conf. Christianity & Lit. John Henry Newman; Victorian literature & art. Publ: The essential Newman, New Am. Libr, 63; Realizations, Darton, Longman & Todd, 64; co-auth, The letters and diaries of John Henry Newman, Nelson, Vol. XIV, 63, Vol. XV, 64 & Newman's Apologia, Harcourt, 64; auth, Newman's Delation, Dublin Rev, winter 60-61; Newman, the Fathers, and education, Thought, summer 70; Newman, the Bishops and The rambler, Downside Rev, 1/72. Add: Dept. of English, Fordham University, Bronx, NY 10458.

BLEICH, DAVID, b. New York, N.Y, Jan. 17, 40. ENGLISH, BEHAVIORAL SCIENCE. B.S, Mass. Inst. Technol, 60; M.A, N.Y. Univ, 62, Ph.D.(Eng), 68. Lectr. ENG, IND. UNIV, BLOOMINGTON, 66-68, asst. prof, 68-72, ASSOC. PROF, 72- Am. Counc. Learned Soc. stud. fel, Res. Ctr. Ment. Health, N.Y. Univ, 70-71. MLA. Literature and psychology; psycholinguistics. Publ: More's Utopia: confessional modes, Am. Imago, spring 71; Artistic form as defensive adaptation: Henry James and The golden bowl, Psychoanal. Rev, summer/fall 71; The psychological bases of learning from literature, Col. Eng, fall 71; plus others. Add: Dept. of English, Ballantine Hall, Indiana University, Bloomington, IN 47401.

BLENKNER, LOUIS, b. Broadus, Mont, Apr. 29, 22. ENGLISH. B.S, Mont. State Col, 47; M.A, Univ. N.C, Chapel Hill, 51, Ph.D.(Medieval Eng. lit), 64. Instr. ENG, Univ. Mo, 52-54; East. Mont. Col, 54-57; ASST. PROF, ST. JOHN'S UNIV.(MINN), 65- Pres, Am. Benedictine Acad, 71-73. Med. Admin.C, U.S.A, 42-46, 1st Lt. MLA; NCTE. Middle English literature. Publ: The theological structure of Pearl, Traditio, 68; Redemption in chaos: Brecht's Caucasian chalk circle, Am. Benedictine Rev, 12/70; The pattern of traditional images in Pearl, Stud. in Philol, 1/71. Add: Dept. of English, St. John's University, Collegeville, MN 56321.

BLESI, MARIUS, b. Cincinnati, Ohio, July 21, 08; m. 47; c. 1. ENGLISH. A.B, Harvard, 30, A.M, 32; Ph.D.(Eng), Univ. Va, 38. Instr. ENG, Syracuse Univ, 30-31; Univ. Louisville, 32-36; Univ. Va, 37-38; PROF, Marshall Univ. 38-47; EMORY & HENRY COL, 47-, HENRY CARTER STUART CHAIR, 64-, traveling grant Univ. Birmingham, summer 54. MLA. Elizabethan drama; 19th century American literature. Publ: Our Mr. Edwards, Watauga Rev, winter 67. Add: Dept. of English, Emory & Henry College, Emory, VA 24327.

BLESSING, JAMES H, b. Philadelphia, Pa, June 13, 28; m. 55. ENGLISH. B.A, Princeton Univ, 49; M.A, Harvard, 57; Ph.D.(Eng), Stanford Univ, 59. Instr. ENG, Univ. Colo, 54-55; res. asst, div. higher ed, U.S. Off. Educ, 58-61, asst. dir, NDEA Title IV Grad. Fel. Prog, 61-66; DIR. DIV. FELS. & STIPENDS, NAT. ENDOWMENT FOR THE HUMANITIES, 66- Middle English literature. Publ: Co-auth, Graduate general humanities programs, 60 & auth, Graduate education: an annotated bibliography, 61, U.S. Off. Educ. Add: 2331 49th St. N.W, Washington, DC 20007.

BLESSINGTON, FRANCIS CHARLES, b. Boston, Mass, May 21, 42. ENGLISH LITERATURE, CLASSICS. A.B, Boston Col, 63; fel, Northeast. Univ, 64-66, M.A, 66; fel, Boston Univ, 66-67; fel, Brown Univ, 68-69, Ph.D.(Eng), 72, A.M, 73. Instr. ENG, NORTHEAST. UNIV, 69-72, ASST. PROF, 72- MLA. Milton; Renaissance English literature; classics. Add: Dept. of English, Northeastern University, Boston, MA 02115.

BLINDERMAN, CHARLES S, b. New York, N.Y, Oct. 31, 30; m. 54. ENGLISH. B.A, N.Y. Univ, 52, scholar & M.A, 53; Ph.D, Ind. Univ, 57. Asst. prof. ENG, South. Ill. Univ, 56-63; PROF, CLARK UNIV, 63- Fulbright award, 55-56; Am. Philos. Soc. award, 62; prog. off, Nat. Endowment Humanities, 67-68. Victorian literature. Publ: Huxley's theory of aesthetics, J. Aesthet. & Art Criticism; The great bone case, Perspectives in Biol. & Med, spring 71; The servility of dependence, In: Images of women in fiction, Bowling Green Popular Press, 72; plus two others. Add: Dept. of English, Clark University, Worcester, MA 01610.

BLISS, EDWARD L, b. Foochow, China, July 30, 12; U.S. citizen; m. 40; c. 2. BROADCAST JOURNALISM. B.A, Yale, 35. Reporter, Bucyrus Telegraph-Forum, Ohio, 35-36; reporter & state ed, Columbus Citizen, Ohio, 36-43; news ed. & producer, CBS News, N.Y, 43-68; assoc. prof. COMMUN, AM. UNIV, 68-73, PROF, 73- Asn. Educ. in Jour; Nat. Acad. TV Arts & Sci. Publ: Ed, In search of light, Knopf, 67; co-auth, Writing news for broadcast, Col. & Univ, 71. Add: Dept. of Communication, American University, Washington, DC 20016.

BLISS, FRANK WALKER, JR, b. Minneapolis, Minn, July 27, 25; m. 53; c. 3. ENGLISH. Ph.D.(Eng), Univ. Minn, 54. Instr. ENG, Univ. Ore; Univ, Minn; Princeton, 54-57, asst. prof, 57-60; assoc. prof, St. Olaf Col, 60-63; DAVIDSON COL, 63-66, PROF, 66- Fulbright vis. prof. Am. lit, Univ. Poona, 71-72. AAUP; Am. Soc. Aesthet; Shakespeare Asn. Am; NCTE. Shakespeare; modern poems. Add: Dept. of English, Davidson College, Davidson, NC 28036.

BLISS, ISABEL ST. JOHN, b. Fredericton, N.B, Sept. 29, 95; nat. ENGLISH LITERATURE. B.A, Univ. N.B, 17, M.A, 21, LL.D, 62; A.M, Univ. Chicago, 22, Ph.D, 31; hon. Litt.D, West. Col. Women, 66. Instr. Eng. lit, WEST. COL, 28-31, asst. prof, 31-33, assoc. prof, 33-35, prof. Eng. lit. & head dept. lit, 35-42, prof. Eng. lang. & lit. & head dept, 42-62, prof. ENG, 62-65, EMER. PROF, 65- MLA; NCTE; Col. Eng. Asn. Shakespeare; Canadian poetry; 18th century English literature. Publ: Edward Young, Twayne, 69. Add: 611 E. Chestnut St, Oxford, OH 45056.

BLISSETT, WILLIAM FRANK, b. Sask, Oct. 11, 21. ENGLISH LITERATURE. B.A, Univ. B.C, 43; M.A, Univ. Toronto, 47, Ph.D, 50. Teaching fel, Univ. Toronto, 46-47, instr, 47-48, lectr, 48-50; assoc. prof. Eng. lit, Univ. Sask, 50-57, prof. ENG, 57-60; prof. & head dept, Huron Col, 60-65; PROF, UNIV. COL, UNIV. TORONTO, 65- Can. Counc. sr. fel, 58-59; ed, Univ. Toronto Quart, 65- English Renaissance; modern literature; Richard Wagner and literature. Publ: Ed, A celebration of Ben Jonson, 74; auth, In parenthesis among the war books, Univ. Toronto Quart, 73; Recognition in King Lear, In: Some facets of King Lear, 74; Your majesty is welcome to a fair, In: The Elizabethan theatre IV, 74; plus three others. Add: Dept. of English, University College, University of Toronto, Toronto, Ont. M5S 1A1, Can.

BLISTEIN, ELMER MILTON, b. Pawtucket, R.I, Sept. 17, 20; m. 46; c. 2. ENGLISH. A.B, Brown Univ, 42, A.M, 47, Ph.D.(Eng), 53. Instr. ENG, BROWN UNIV, 46-53, asst. prof, 53-59, assoc. prof, 59-65, PROF, 65- U.S.A, 42-45. MLA; Am. Arbit. Asn; Renaissance Soc. Am; Malone Soc. Shakespeare; comedy; drama. Publ: Co-auth, The order of poetry, 61 & The variety of poetry, 64, Odyssey; auth, Comedy in action, Duke Univ, 64; ed, George Peele's David and Bethsabe, Yale, 70 & The drama of the Renaissance: essays for Leicester Bradner, Brown Univ, 70; plus others. Add: Dept. of English, Brown University, Providence, RI 02912.

BLITCH, ALICE FOX, b. Trenton, N.J, July 29, 28; div; c. 2. SIXTEENTH & SEVENTEENTH CENTURY ENGLISH. A.B, Univ. Mo, 50; M.A, Univ. Tenn, 57; fel, Mich. State Univ, 58-59, Ph.D.(Eng), 65. Instr. ENG, Wash. State Univ, 59-60; WEST. COL, 61-64, asst. prof, 64-67, assoc. prof, 67-68, PROF, 68-, summer grant-in-aid, 68, chmn. dept, 68-70. Fel, Southeast. Inst. Medieval & Renaissance Stud, Duke Univ, summer 68; Nat. Endowment for Humanities grant, summer 73. MLA. Spenser; Shakespeare; 17th century English literature. Publ: The mutability cantos in meet order ranged, Eng. Lang. Notes, 3/70; O'Casey's Shakespeare, Mod. Drama,

12/72; Proserpina preserved: Book VI of the Faerie queene, Stud. Eng. Lit, winter 73; plus three others. Add: Dept. of English, Western College, Oxford, OH 45056.

BLOCK, HASKELL M, Comparative Literature. See Volume III, Foreign Languages, Linguistics & Philology.

BLOCK, RAPHAEL HERMAN, b. Memphis, Tenn, Nov. 9, 12; m. 34; c. 3. ENGLISH LITERATURE. B.Phil, Univ. Chicago, 33; M.A, Miami Univ, 62; Ph.D.(Eng), Univ. Denver, 72. Instr. ENG, UNIV. S.DAK, 62-64, asst. prof, 64-73, ASSOC. PROF, 73- U.S.A.F, 42-46, Res, 46-63, Lt. Col. MLA; NCTE. Eighteenth century British drama. Publ: The viewless theatre, S.Dak. Rev, 12/63; Frank Waters in the atomic age, Denver Quart, 3/67. Add: Dept. of English, University of South Dakota, Vermillion, SD 57069.

BLODGETT, EDWARD DICKINSON, Mediaeval & Canadian Literature. See Volume III, Foreign Languages, Linguistics & Philology.

BLODGETT, HAROLD WILLIAM, b. Corning, N.Y, Mar. 24, 00; m. 24; c. 3. AMERICAN LITERATURE. A.B, Cornell Univ, 21, A.M, 23, Ph.D, 29. Instr. Eng, Cornell Univ, 21-23; asst, Univ. Ill, 24-26; instr. Eng. & hist, Keuka Col, 26-28, prof. Eng, 34-36; instr, Dartmouth Col, 29-34; asst. prof, UNION COL.(N.Y), 36-45, chmn. dept. ENG. LIT, 45-63, Thomas Lamont prof, 45-65, EMER. PROF, 65- Fulbright scholar, Holland, 52-53; Iran, 58-59; Guggenheim fel, 55-56; vis. prof, Univ. Bombay, 65-66; Univ. N.Mex, 66-67; Univ. Pa, 67. MLA; Am. Stud. Asn; Thoreau Soc. Whitman manuscripts; American literature in Europe; American humor. Publ: Walt Whitman in England, Cornell Univ, 34; Samson Occom: the biography of an Indian preacher, Dartmouth Col. Manuscript Series, 35; The best of Whitman, Ronald, 53; An 1855-56 notebook toward the second edition of Leaves of grass, South. Ill. Univ, 59; co-auth, Collected writings of Walt Whitman, 60 & Reader's edition of Leaves of grass, 65, N.Y. Univ; co-ed, Norton critical edition of Leaves of grass, Norton, 73. Add: 1086 Gillespie St, Schenectady, NY 12308.

BLOMQUIST, ALLEN P, b. Pocatello, Idaho, Jan. 15, 28; m. 54; c. 2. THEATRE ARTS. B.A, Idaho State Col, 50; fel, Univ. Wis, 50, out-of-state scholar. & M.S, 51; Univ. Stockholm, Sweden; univ. theatre scholar, Univ. Minn, 57, Ph.D.(theatre arts), 67. Instr. drama, West. State Col, 53-54; instr, Sch. Agr, Univ. Minn, 54-55, speech, 57-58; drama, Univ. Wyo, 55-56; IDAHO STATE UNIV, 58-61, asst. prof, 62-68, ASSOC. PROF. THEATRE ARTS, 68- Instr, Univ. Wis, summer, 51; scene tech, Royal Opera, Stockholm, Sweden, 51-52, Europa Film A.B, 52, King Gustaf V fel. & instr. Eng, Swed. Adult Educ. Prog, 52-53; Tozer Found. fel, 58; assoc. dir. exhibits, Am-Swed. Inst, Minneapolis, Minn, 58-59; dir, Pocatello City Musical, 68-73; producer, Summer Theatre, 68-73. Am. Theatre Asn; Rocky Mt. Theatre Conf.(ed, Newslett, 60-, secy, 63, pres, 63-65). Scandinavian theatre; modern dramatic literature; stage direction. Publ: Co-auth, Projects and procedures in oral communication, Univ. Minn, 58; Report from Sweden, Univ. Wis. Quart, 52; Scandinavian roots of our state, Am-Swed. Inst. Bull, summer 58. Add: Dept. of Speech & Drama, Idaho State University, Pocatello, ID 83201.

BLOMQUIST, GRACE ELEANOR, b. North Branch, Minn, Apr. 10, 13. LITERATURE, COMPOSITION. B.A, Concordia Col, 34; M.A, Syracuse Univ, 39; summers, Univ. Minn, 48 & Johann Wolfgang Goethe Univ, Ger, 55. Teacher Eng. & Latin, Mohall High Sch, N.Dak, 34-37; asst. in pers. admin, Syracuse Univ, 37-39; mem. fac. Eng. & from asst. dean of women to dean, PAC. LUTHERAN UNIV, 39-47, assoc. prof. ENG, 47-54, PROF, 55- Counselor, Frankfurt Am. High Sch, Ger, 54-55. NCTE; Nat. Counc. Admin. Women Educ. Greek and Roman literature; children's literature. Publ: Let your speech be seasoned with salt, Augsburg, 44. Add: Dept. of English, Pacific Lutheran University, Tacoma, WA 98447.

BLOODSTEIN, OLIVER, Speech Pathology. See 12th Edition, American Men & Women of Science, Social & Behavioral Sciences Section.

BLOODWORTH, BERTHA ERNESTINE, b. Tallahassee, Fla, Feb. 10, 16. ENGLISH, LINGUISTICS. A.B, Fla. State Col. Women, 40; M.A, Univ. Fla, 55, Ph.D.(Eng), 59. Exam. ed, Univ. Fla, 44; publicity dir, Fla. State Col. Women, 44-46; exam. ed, Univ. Fla, 46-55; ASST. PROF. ENG, Florence State Col, 59-61; UNIV. FLA, 61- Am. Name Soc; S.Atlantic Mod. Lang. Asn. Place-names; folklore. Publ: Co-auth, The place-names of Florida: a romance, Univ. Fla, 74. Add: Dept. of Comprehensive English, University of Florida, Gainesville, FL 32611.

BLOOM, ARTHUR WILLIAM, b. New York, N.Y, Oct. 17, 39. DRAMA, THEATRE HISTORY. A.B, Dartmouth Col, 61; Ph.D.(theatre hist), Yale, 66. Instr. Eng, Quinnipiac Col, 64-66, asst. prof, 66; assoc. prof. dramatics, Fisk Univ, 66-70; head dept. theatre arts & drama, Wash. State Univ, 70-72; ASSOC. PROF. THEATRE & CHMN. DEPT, LOYOLA UNIV. CHICAGO, 72- Lectr. Eng, Univ. Bridgeport, summer 66; vis. prof, Vanderbilt Univ, summer 67; speech & Eng, Aquinas Jr. Col, 67-70; vis. assoc. prof. drama, Scarritt Col, 68-70; regional judge, Am. Col. Theatre Festival, 71-72. Am. Theatre Asn; MLA; Am. Soc. Theatre Res; Int. Fed. Theatre Res. History of the theatre in New Haven, Connecticut. Publ: Peter Weiss: the revolution from despair, Motive Mag, 3/68; The gradual emergence of theatrical entertainment in New Haven, Connecticut, New Haven Colony Hist. Soc. J, 68; The theatre of non-mimetic propaganda, Xavier Univ. Stud, 71. Add: 731 Laurel Ave, Wilmette, IL 60091.

BLOOM, EDWARD ALAN, b. Michigan City, Ind, May 24, 14; m. 47. ENGLISH & AMERICAN LITERATURE. B.S, Univ. Ill, 36, A.M, 39, Ph.D, 47. hon. M.A, Brown Univ, 57. Instr. ENG, Univ. Ill, 46-47; BROWN UNIV, 47-50; asst. prof, 50-55, assoc. prof, 55-59, PROF, 59-, Nicholas Brown prof. oratory & belles lettres & chmn. dept. Eng, 60-67. Huntington Libr. fel, 63-64, grant, 67-68; consult. ed, Blaisdell Publ. Col, 64-70; J.S. Guggenheim fel, 69-70; Huntington Libr. grant, 72. U.S.A, 42-46, Capt; Bronze Star Medal. MLA; AAUP. Satiric theory; studies in eighteenth and twentieth century literature; literary criticism. Publ: Samuel Johnson in Grub Street, 57, ed, Shakespeare: 1564-1964, 64 & co-auth, Joseph Addison's sociable animal, 72, Brown Univ; co-auth, The order of poetry, 61, auth, The order of fiction, 64, co-ed, The variety of poetry, 64 & The variety of fiction, 69, Odyssey; co-auth, Willa Cather's gift of sympathy, South. Ill. Univ, 62; ed, Evelina, 68 & co-ed, Camilla, 72, Oxford; ed, Novel: a forum on fiction, 67-; co-auth, Johnson's Mournful narrative: rhetoric of London, Grolier Club, 70; ed, Fanny Burney's journals and letters, Vol. VII, 74 & co-ed, The journals and letters of Mme. d'Arblay, Vol. VII, 74, Clarendon; auth, The vatic temper in literary criticism, Criticism, 64; co-auth, Steele in 1719: additions to the canon, Huntington Libr. Quart, 68; auth, Sacramentum militiae: dynamics of religious satire, Stud. Lit. Imagination, 72. Add: Dept. of English, Brown University, Providence, RI 02912.

BLOOM, HAROLD, b. New York, N.Y, July 11, 30; m. 58; c. 1. ENGLISH & AMERICAN LITERATURE. B.A, Cornell Univ, 51; Fulbright fel, Cambridge, 54-55; Ph.D, Yale, 55; hon. Litt.D, Boston Col, 73. Instr. Eng, YALE, 55-60, asst. prof, 60-63, assoc. prof, 63-65, prof, 65-74, WILLIAM CLYDE DeVANE PROF. HUMANITIES, 74- Morse fel, Yale, 58-59; lectr, Hebrew Univ, 59; Guggenheim fel, 62-63; mem, Eng. Inst; sr. vis. fel, Cornell Soc. Humanities, 68-69. John Addison Porter Prize, 56; Melville Cane Award, Poetry Soc. Am, 71. MLA. English Romantic and Victorian poetry; theory of poetic influence; British and American poetry from the later 18th century to the present day. Publ: Shelley's mythmaking, Yale, 59; The visionary company, Doubleday, 61, Anchor Bks, 63, rev. ed, Cornell Univ, 71; Blake's apocalypse, Doubleday, 63; Yeats, 70 & 72, The anxiety of influence, 73, co-ed, Oxford anthology of English literature, 73 & auth, Kabbalah and criticism, 74, Oxford; The ringers in the tower, Univ. Chicago, 71. Add: Dept. of English, Linsey Chittenden Hall, Yale University, New Haven, CT 06520.

BLOOM, LILLIAN DORIS, b. New York, N.Y, July 17, 20; m. ENGLISH. B.A, N.Y. Univ, 41, univ. fel, 41-42, M.A, 42; univ. fel, Yale, 42-45, Donald Grant Mitchell fel, 43-45, Ph.D.(Eng), 46. Asst. ENG, Univ. Ill, 45-46; instr, Queens Col.(N.Y), 46-47; asst. prof, Univ. R.I, 47-50; R.I. COL, 56-60, assoc. prof, 60-64, PROF, 64- Am. Counc. Learned Soc. grant-in-aid, 67-68. MLA. Eighteenth century English journalism; American fiction; 18th century English letter writers. Publ: Co-auth, Willa Cather's gift of sympathy, South. Ill. Univ, 62 & An edition of Anthony Collin's Essay on Ridicule, Augustan Reprint, Soc, 70; co-ed, The variety of fiction, Odyssey, 69; co-auth, Joseph Addison's Sociable animal, Brown Univ, 71; co-ed, Fanny Burney's Camilla, Oxford Univ, 72 & Journals and letters of Fanny Burney, Clarendon, Vol. 7, 74; co-auth, Steele in 1719, Huntington Libr. Quart, 68 & The case for Mr. Addison, Scriblerian, 72; auth, They all cried Woolf, Novel, 73; plus others. Add: Dept. of English, Rhode Island College, Providence, RI 02908.

BLOOM, LYNN ZIMMERMAN, b. Ann Arbor, Mich, July 11, 34; m. 58; c. 1. ENGLISH LANGUAGE & LITERATURE. B.A, Univ. Mich, 56, M.A, 57; Alumnae fel, 57, dean women's off. grant-in-aid, 58-62, Ph.D.(Eng. lang. & lit), 63. Teaching fel. Eng, Ohio State Univ, 57-58; Univ. Mich, 58-61; lectr, Case West. Reserve Univ, 62-63, instr, 63-65, assoc, 65-67; auth, 67-70; asst. prof. ENG, Butler Univ, 70-73, assoc. prof, 73-74, fac. fel, spring 74; LECTR, WASH. UNIV, 74- MLA; NCTE (abstractor, Abstr. Eng. Stud, 61-68, judge, Creative Writing Contest, 73); Midwest Mod. Lang. Asn; Conf. Col. Compos. & Commun; AAUP. English composition; biography; research methodology. Publ: Bear, man and God: seven approaches to William Faulkner's The bear, 63 & co-ed, Bear, man and God: eight approaches to William Faulkner's The bear, 71, Random; co-auth, Symposium, 69 & co-ed, Symposium on love, 70, Houghton; auth, Doctor Spock: biography of a conservative radical, Bobbs, 72; Biography for book collectors, Am. Bk. Collector, 12/65; co-auth, The teaching and learning of argumentative writing, 11/67 & But will they answer?, 11/69, Col. Eng; plus poetry in var. periodicals. Add: 96 Arundel Pl, Clayton, MO 63105.

BLOOM, ROBERT, b. Brooklyn, N.Y, May 28, 30; m. 53; c. 3. ENGLISH LITERATURE. B.A, N.Y. Univ, 51; M.A, Columbia Univ, 52; Univ. Wis, 54-55; fel, Univ. Mich, 55-58, Ph.D, 60. Instr. ENG, Univ. Mich, 58-60; asst. prof, UNIV. CALIF, BERKELEY, 60-66, assoc. prof, 66-73, PROF, 73- Bruern fel. Am. lit, Univ. Leeds & Fulbright travel grant, Eng, 63-64; humanities res. fel, Univ. Calif, Berkeley, 67-68. U.S.C.G, 52-54, Res, 54-, Lt.(jg). MLA. Modern British and American literature; literary criticism. Publ: The indeterminate world: a study of the novels of Joyce Cary, Univ. Pa, 62; Irving Babbitt's Emerson, New Eng. Quart, 57; Allan Seager: some versions of disengagement, critique, Stud. Mod. Fiction, 63; The humanization of Auden's early style, PMLA, 5/68. Add: 2340 Vine St, Berkeley, CA 94708.

BLOOMFIELD, MORTON WILFRED, b. Montreal, P.Q, May 19, 13; nat; m. 52; c. 3. ENGLISH, HISTORY OF IDEAS. B.A, McGill Univ, 34, M.A, 35; Moyse traveling fel, Univ. London, 35-36; Ph.D, Univ. Wis, 38; hon. A.M, Harvard, 61. Instr, Univ. Wis, 38-39; ENG, Univ. Akron, 39-41, asst. prof, 41-46; Ohio State Univ, 46-51, assoc. prof, 51-54, PROF, 54-61; HARVARD, 61-, chmn. dept, 68-72. Guggenheim fel, 49-50, 64-65; Howald fel. & hon. res. assoc, Univ. London, 53-54; Berg prof, N.Y. Univ, 55-56; Am. Counc. Learned Soc. grant-in-aid, 58, fel, 64-65; lectr. summer schs, Columbia Univ, 58 & Mich. State Univ, 60; mem. bd. trustees, Ctr. Appl. Ling, Wash, 66-68; fel, Ctr. Advan. Stud. Behav. Sci, 67-68; fel, Inst. Advan. Stud, Princeton, fall 72; vis. prof. Eng, Hebrew Univ, Jerusalem, 73. Mil.Intel, U.S.A, 42-45, M/Sgt; Bronze Star Medal, 46. MLA; Am. Dialect Soc; fel. Mediaeval Acad. Am.(Haskins Medal, 64); Renaissance Soc. Am; Can. Ling. Asn; Ling. Soc. Am; Dante Soc. Am; Int. Soc. Stud. Medieval Philos; Int. Asn. Univ. Prof. Eng; Am. Acad. Arts & Sci.(v.pres, 72-); Mod. Humanities Res. Asn. Gt. Brit. Mediaeval literature and civilization; history of the English language; stylistics. Publ: The seven deadly sins, Mich. State Univ, 52; Piers Plowman as a fourteenth century apocalypse, Rutgers Univ, 62; co-auth, A linguistic introduction to the history of English, Knopf, 63; ed, Narrative theory and practice & auth, Essays and explorations, Harvard, 70; ed, In search of literary theory, Cornell, 72; Sir Gawain and the Green Knight: an appraisal, PMLA, 61; A grammatical approach to personification allegory, Mod. Philol, 62-63; Authenticating realism and the realism of Chaucer, Thought, 64. Add: Dept. of English, Warren House, Harvard University, Cambridge, MA 02138.

BLOOMGARDEN, IRA LEWIS, b. New York, N.Y, Sept. 15, 41; m. 66; c. 2. MEDIEVAL ENGLISH, COMPARATIVE LITERATURE. A.B, Columbia Univ, 62; M.A, Hunter Col, 65; Ph.D.(Eng), City Univ. New York, 71. Instr.

ENG, JOHN JAY COL. CRIMINAL JUSTICE, 67-70, asst. prof, 71-72, ASSOC. PROF, 73-, CHMN. DEPT, 71- MLA; Int. Arthurian Soc. Middle English Arthurian romances; Icelandic family sagas. Add: Dept. of English, John Jay College of Criminal Justice, 445 W. 59th St, New York, NY 10019.

BLOTNER, JOSEPH LEO, b. Plainfield, N.J, June 21, 23; m. 46; c. 3. ENGLISH. B.A, Drew Univ, 47; M.A, Northwest. Univ, 47; Ph.D.(Eng), Univ. Pa, 51. Instr, ENG, Univ. Idaho, 53-55; asst. prof, Univ. Va, 55-61, dept. exec. secy, 61-63, assoc. prof, 61-68; PROF, Univ. N.C, Chapel Hill, 68-71; UNIV. MICH, ANN ARBOR, 72- Fulbright lectr. Am. lit, Univ. Copenhagen, 58-59 & 63-64; Guggenheim fels, 64-65 & 67-68. U.S.A.A.F, 43-45, Lt. MLA; Am. Lit. Group; Soc. Stud. South. Lit. Contemporary American and British literature; the novel. Publ: The political novel, Doubleday, 55; co-auth, Faulkner in the university, 59 & auth, William Faulkner's library: a catalogue, 64, Univ. Va; Fiction of J.D. Salinger, Univ. Pittsburgh, 59; The modern American political novel: 1900-1960, Univ. Tex, 66; Faulkner: a biography (2 vols), Random, 74. Add: Dept. of English Language & Literature, University,of Michigan, Ann Arbor, MI 48104.

BLOUNT, PAUL GROVES, b. Fulton, Mo, Jan. 20, 19; m. 42; c. 1. VICTORIAN LITERATURE. A.B, Westminster Col, 41; M.A, Emory Univ, 42; Ph.D, Cornell Univ, 61. From instr. to asst. prof. ENG, Ga. Inst. Technol, 46-50; PROF. & HEAD DEPT, GA. STATE UNIV, 51- U.S.N.R, 42-46, Lt. S.Atlantic Mod. Lang. Asn. Victorian literature. Publ: Henry Bellaman and Lonesome waters: a novel that was never published, summer 61 & George Sand and the victorians, fall 64, Emory Univ. Quart. Add: Dept. of English, Georgia State University, 33 Gilmer St, S.W, Atlanta, GA 30303.

BLOW, SUZANNE KATHERINE, b. Ocala, Fla, Jan. 24, 32. ENGLISH. B.A, Stetson Univ, 53, univ. fel. & M.A, 54; Am. Asn. Univ. Women fel. & Ph.D, Fla. State Univ, 62. Instr. ENG, Jacksonville Univ, 57-59; asst. prof, Southeast. La. Col, 61-64; assoc. prof, MISS. STATE COL. WOMEN, 64-68, PROF, 68- MLA; Renaissance Soc. Am; AAUP. Renaissance drama and poetry; modern poetry. Publ: Rhetoric in the plays of Thomas Dekker, Vol. III, In: Jacobean drama series, Inst. Englische Sprache & Lit, 72; Pre-Raphaelite allegory in The marble faun, Am. Lit, 3/72. Add: Dept. of English, Mississippi State College for Women, Columbus, MS 39701.

BLUBAUGH, JON ALFRED, b. Electra, Tex, Dec. 7, 38; m. 59; c. 5. COMMUNICATION, EDUCATION. B.A, Wichita State Univ, 61; M.A, Univ. Kans, 63, Nat. Inst. Neurol. Diseases & Blindness fel, 64-66, Ph.D.(speech commun), 66. Instr. speech, Bowling Green State Univ, 65-67; asst. prof. commun, Univ. Wis-Milwaukee, 67-69; ASSOC. PROF. SPEECH COMMUN. & HUMAN RELAT. & DIR. COMMUNITY DEVELOP, UNIV. KANS, 69- Commun. consult, Ohio Bur. Voc. Rehabil, 66-68. Air Nat. Guard, 59-65. Speech Commun. Asn; Int. Commun. Asn; Nat. Univ. Exten. Asn; Community Develop. Soc. Intercultural communication; minority relations; interpersonal communication. Publ: Co-ed, Approaches to community development, Am. Col. Testing & Nat. Univ. Exten, 73; auth, Effects of positive and negative audience behavior on selected variables, Speech Monogr, 9/69; co-auth, The black experience in speech communication courses: a survey, Speech Teacher, 9/73; plus others. Add: Dept. of Speech & Drama, University of Kansas, Lawrence, KS 66044.

BLUEFARB, SAMUEL, b. London, Eng, Apr. 21, 19; U.S. citizen; m. 55. ENGLISH. B.A, Univ. Calif, Los Angeles, 51; M.S, Univ. South. Calif, 54, M.A, 61; fel, Univ. N.Mex, 65-66, Ph.D.(Eng), 67. Librn, Calif. State Libr, 54-55; San Bernardino Pub. Libr, 55-57; teacher, High Sch, Calif, 57-62; instr. ENG, LOS ANGELES HARBOR COL, 62-67, asst. prof, 67-69, ASSOC. PROF, 69- Instr. Eng, Exten, Univ. Calif, Los Angeles, fall 71 & 72. C.Eng, U.S.A, 41-45. MLA; Rocky Mountain Mod. Lang. Asn. Fiction; drama. Publ: The escape motif in the American novel: Mark Twain to Richard Wright, Ohio State Univ, 72; The radicalism of the Princess Casamassima, Bara Rev, spring 71; John Wayne and the anti-anti-hero, New Orleans Rev, spring-summer 72; plus others. Add: Dept. of English, Los Angeles Harbor College, 1111 S. Figueroa Pl, Wilmington, CA 90744.

BLUES, THOMAS, b. Detroit, Mich, June 16, 36; m. 58; c. 2. ENGLISH. B.A, Univ. Mich, 58; M.A, Univ. Iowa, 60, Ph.D.(Eng), 66; Mich. State Univ, 60-61. Asst. prof. ENG, UNIV. KY, 65-70, ASSOC. PROF, 70- Fulbright lectr, Univ. Warsaw, 71-72. MLA; Am. Stud. Asn. American literature 1860 to present; Black literature. Publ: Mark Twain and the community, Univ. Ky, 70; The strategy of compromise in Mark Twain's boy books, Mod. Fiction Stud, spring 68; The moral structure of Catch-22, Stud. in Novel, spring 71. Add: Dept. of English, University of Kentucky, Lexington, KY 40506.

BLUESTEIN, GENE, b. Bronx, N.Y, May 1, 28; m. 49; c. 4. AMERICAN STUDIES, FOLKLORE. B.A, Brooklyn Col, 50; M.A, Univ. Minn, 53, Ph.D. (Am. stud), 60. From instr. to asst. prof. ENG, Mich. State Univ, 59-63; from asst. prof. to PROF, CALIF. STATE UNIV, FRESNO, 63- Carnegie Found. fel, 57-58; James J. Hill Family Found. fel, 58; Calif. State Cols. & Univs. fel, 67; Fulbright-Hays lectr, Helsinki Univ, 67-68. Philol. Asn. Pac. Coast. American studies; folklore; American literature. Publ: The voice of the folk, Univ. Mass, 72; The advantages of barbarism: Herder and Whitman's nationalism, J. Hist. Ideas, 1/63; Emerson's epiphanies, New. Eng. Quart, 12/66; The blues as a literary theme, Mass. Rev, autumn 67. Add: Dept. of English, Sch. of Humanities, California State University, Fresno, Shaw & Cedar Ave, Fresno, CA 93710.

BLUESTONE, GEORGE, b. New York, N.Y, Aug. 25, 28; m. 54. AMERICAN LITERATURE, FILM AESTHETICS. B.A, Harvard, 49; univ. fel, State Univ. Iowa, 49-52, M.F.A, 51; univ. fel, Johns Hopkins Univ, 52-56, Ph.D, 56. Jr. instr, Johns Hopkins Univ, 52-56; assoc. prof. Eng, Univ. Wash, 57-66; film writing & producing, 66-72; FILM-MAKER IN RESIDENCE, BOSTON UNIV, 72- JDR III Fund grant documentary film, The Monkey and the Fox, 65. Atlantic Prize, 52; Va. Quart. Rev. Balch Prize, 61. MLA; Am. Stud. Asn. Film-making and fiction. Publ: Novels into film, Hopkins Univ, 57; Private world of Cully Powers, Doubleday, 60; The send-off, Secker & Warburg, 68; auth. & producer, The walking stick (film), Winkast Film, MGM, 70. Add: 90 Babcock St, Brookline, MA 02146.

BLUM, IRVING D, b. Baltimore, Md, May 9, 06; m. 42. ENGLISH. A.B, Univ. Minn, 48, M.A, 49; Ph.D, Rutgers Univ, 53. Instr. ENG, Univ. Mo, 50-54; asst. prof, Univ. Ill, Chicago Circle, 54-60, assoc. prof, 60-74; RETIRED. U.S.A, 43-46. MLA; Am. Dialect Soc; Col. Eng. Asn; Conf. Col. Compos. & Commun. English satire; the business man as a literary figure. Publ: English Utopias, 1550-1649; English Utopias from 1551-1699, Bull. Bibliog, 55; The paradox of money imagery in English Renaissance poetry, Stud. Renaissance, 61. Add: 716 South Blvd, Evanston, IL 60202.

BLUMBERG, NATHAN BERNARD, b. Denver, Colo, Apr. 8, 22; div; c. 3. JOURNALISM. B.A, Univ. Colo, 47, M.A, 48; Rhodes scholar, Oxford, 48-50, D.Phil.(mod. hist), 50. From asst. to assoc. prof. jour, Univ. Nebr, 50-55; assoc. prof, Mich. State Univ, 55-56; PROF. JOUR, UNIV. MONT, 56-, dean, 56-68. Am. specialist, U.S. State Dept, Thailand, 61; Caribbean area, 64; vis. prof, Pa. State Univ, 64; Northwest. Univ, 66-67; Univ. Calif, Berkeley, fall 70. U.S.A, 43-46. Nat. Conf. Ed. Writers; Asn. Educ. Jour. News editorial; political campaign coverage. Publ: One-party press?, Univ. Nebr. Add: School of Journalism, University of Montana, Missoula, MT 59801.

BLYTON, GIFFORD, b. Clarkston, Wash, Sept. 18, 09; m. 38; c. 2. SPEECH. A.B, Univ. Wash, 35, A.M, 36; Univ. La, 37; Ph.D, Ohio State Univ, 41. Dir. speech clin, Ohio Univ, 37-40; men's debate, West. Mich. Univ, 41-48; from assoc. prof. to PROF. SPEECH & DIR. FORENSICS, UNIV. KY, 48- Establisher & adminr. prog. to teach Eng, U.S. Dept. State, Damascus, Syria, 52-53; chmn. bd. stud. publ, Univ. Ky, 67-; secy-treas, Counc. Commun. Soc, 69-; stud. grant ling, Ohio State Univ, summer 70. Great Teacher of Year Award, Univ. Ky, 70. Am. Forensic Asn.(pres, 68). Function of speech education in a democracy; speech education in Kentucky; famous Kentucky speakers. Publ: Co-auth, Argumentation and debate, Holt, 63; auth, History of American Forensic Association, winter 70 & American Forensic Association presidents, winter 70, J. Am. Forensic Asn; Common misconceptions about speech education in Kentucky, J. Ky. Asn. Commun. Arts, winter 71; plus two others. Add: 625 Blue Ash Dr, Lexington, KY 40503.

BOASE, PAUL HENSHAW, b. Topeka, Ind, July 13, 15; m. 47; c. 3. SPEECH. A.B, Manchester Coll, 37; M.S, Univ. Wis, 47, Ph.D, 52. Teacher, pub. schs, Ind, 37-41; instr. speech, Oberlin Col, 48-50, asst. prof, 50-53, assoc. prof, 53-64; PROF. INTERPERSONAL COMMUN, OHIO UNIV, 64- U.S.A.A.F, 41-46, Capt. Speech Commun. Asn; Cent. States Speech Asn. (exec. secy, 63-66, v.pres, 66-67, pres, 68-69). Rhetoric; American history; communication. Publ: Co-auth, Basic speech, Macmillan, 64; auth, The rhetoric of Christian socialism, Random, 69; The education of a circuit rider, Quart. J. Speech; Philip Gatch, preacher, pioneer, public servant, Ohio Hist. & Philos. Soc. Bull; Romance rides the circuit, Ohio Hist. Quart. Add: 2 Canterbury Dr, Athens, OH 45701.

BOATWRIGHT, JAMES, III, b. Augusta, Ga, Sept. 28, 33. ENGLISH. A.B, Univ. Ga, 54, M.A, 56; Duke Univ, 56-60. Instr. ENG, Univ. Ga, 54-56; tutor Duke Univ, 56-60; instr, WASHINGTON & LEE UNIV, 60-64, asst. prof, 64-66, ASSOC. PROF, 66-, ED, SHENANDOAH, 62- Mem. Adv. Lit. Panel, Nat. Endowment for Arts; v.chmn, Coord. Counc. Lit. Mag. PEN Club. Contemporary literature; 17th century. Add: Dept. of English, Washington & Lee University, Lexington, VA 24450.

BOAZ, JOHN KNOX, b. Enid, Okla, June 7, 38; m. 61; c. 2. SPEECH COMMUNICATION. B.S, Northwest. Univ, 60; M.A, Wayne State Univ, 61, Ph.D. (speech), 69. Instr. speech, Wayne State Univ, 62-65; ASST. PROF. SPEECH COMMUN, ILL. STATE UNIV, NORMAL, 65- Guest instr, Univ. Vt, summer 69. Speech Commun. Asn.(chmn. forensics div, 70-71); Am. Forensic Asn.(pres, 70-72); Cent. States Speech Asn; Midwest Forensic Asn.(pres, 65-67). Argumentation and debate; 20th century American public address; presidential press conference. Publ: Co-auth, An audience debate tournament, Speech Teacher, 11/64; auth, Analysis of Final Road: Harvard debate tournament 1966, Harvard Radio Recordings, 66; contrib, A bibliography of argumentation and debate, J. Am. Forensic. Asn, fall 68- Add: Dept. of Information Sciences, Illinois State University, Normal, IL 61761.

BOCHIN, HAL WILLIAM, b. Cleveland, Ohio, Feb. 23, 42. SPEECH COMMUNICATION. B.A, John Carroll Univ, 64; M.A, Univ. Wis-Madison, 67; Ph.D.(speech), Ind. Univ, Bloomington, 70. ASST. PROF. SPEECH. COMMUN. & DIR. FORENSICS, CALIF. STATE UNIV, FRESNO, 69- Am. Forensics Asn; Speech Commun. Asn. History of American public address; argumentation; rhetorical criticism. Publ: Caleb B. Smith's opposition to the Mexican War, Ind. Mag. Hist, 6/73. Add: Dept. of Speech Communication, California State University, Fresno, CA 93710.

BOCK, DARILYN WINIFRED, b. Chicago, Ill, Apr. 7, 46. AMERICAN & ENGLISH LITERATURE. B.A, Univ. Chicago, 67, M.A, 68, Ford Found. fel, 70-71, Ph.D.(Eng), 72. ASST. PROF. ENG, ILL. WESLEYAN UNIV, 71- MLA. Henry James; fiction; 19th century poetry. Add: 1350 North Astor St, Chicago, IL 60610.

BODDY, MARGARET PEARSE, b. Ont, Apr. 10, 09; U.S. citizen. ENGLISH. B.A. & M.A, Univ. Minn, Ph.D.(Eng), 35. Instr. Eng, Duchesne Col, 36-37; asst. prof, N.Mex. State Col, 37-39; instr, Mont. State Univ, 40; mem. fac, Eng. dept, Winsor Sch, Mass, 40-43; head Eng. dept, Kent Sch, Colo, 43-44; Park Sch, N.Y, 44-46; Columbia Sch, N.Y, 46-50; mem. fac, WINONA STATE COL, 50-57, PROF. ENG, 57- Am. Asn. Univ. Women Atkinson fel, 35-36; mem. bd, Minn. Br, Am. Civil Liberties Union, 57-; chmn, Comt. Employ. Women, Minn. State Dept. Human Rights, 71-, mem. women's adv. comt, 73- MLA; Vergilian Soc; Milton Soc. Am; Renaissance Eng. Text Soc; Renaissance Soc. Am; Mod. Humanities Res. Asn; Virgil Soc, U.K. English verse translation; classical backgrounds of English literature; Renaissance. Publ: The 1692 fourth book of Virgil, Rev. Eng. Stud, 11/64; The MSS and printed editions of the translation of Virgil made by Richard Maitland, 4th Earl of Lauderdale and the connexion with Dryden, Notes & Queries, 4/65; Milton's translation of Psalms, 80-88, Mod. Philol, 8/66. Add: Dept. of English, Winona State College, Winona, MN 55987.

BODE, CARL, b. Milwaukee, Wis, Mar. 14, 11; m. 38, 72; c. 3. AMERICAN LITERATURE & CULTURE. Ph.B, Univ. Chicago, 33; A.M, Northwest.

Univ, 38, fel, 40-41, Ph.D, 41. Teacher, Milwaukee Voc. Sch, Wis, 33-37; asst. prof. ENG, Univ. Calif, Los Angeles, 46-47; PROF, UNIV. MD, COLLEGE PARK, 47-, exec. secy, Am. Civilization Prog, 50-57. Ford Found. fel, 52-53; Newberry Libr. fel, summer 54; Guggenheim Found. fel, 54-55; cult. attaché, Am. Embassy, London, 57-59; chmn, U.S. Educ. Comn. U.K, 57-59; mem. adv. counc, Marshall Comn, 60-69; deleg, Am. Counc. Learned Soc, 63-; mem, Md. Arts Counc, 71-, chmn, 72-; vis. prof, Calif. Inst. Technol, Claremont Cols, Northwest. Univ, Stanford Univ. & Univ. Wis. U.S.A, 44-45. AAUP; Am. Stud. Asn.(first pres, 52); AHA; Col. Eng. Asn.(dir, 55-57); MLA; Thoreau Soc.(dir, 55-57, pres, 60-61); Emerson Soc; Eng-Speaking Union; hon. fel. Royal Soc. Lit. U.K; Popular Cult. Asn.(v.pres, 72-); Am. Civilization Conf.(secy, 50-51). Mid-19th and mid-20th century American cultural history; New England transcendentalism; life of H.L. Mencken. Publ: Ed, Collected poems of Henry Thoreau, 43, rev. ed, 64 & The portable Thoreau, 47, rev. ed, 64; auth, The sacred seasons (poems), 53; co-ed, American heritage (2 vols), 55; auth, The American lyceum, Oxford, 56 & 68; co-ed, The correspondence of Henry David Thoreau, 58; ed. & contrib, The young rebel in American literature, 59; auth, The man behind you (poems), 59; The anatomy of American popular culture, 1840-1861, Univ. Calif, 59; ed. & contrib, The great experiment in American literature, 61; co-ed, American literature (3 vols), 66; auth, The half-world of American culture, South. Ill. Univ, 66; ed, American life in the 1840's, 67 & The selected journals of Henry David Thoreau, 67; auth, Mencken, 69; ed, Ralph Waldo Emerson: a profile, 69; auth, Antebellum culture, 70; ed, The best of Thoreau's journals, 71, Midcentury America: life in the 1850's, 72 & The young Mencken, 73; contrib, Encycl. Britannica and Encycl. Americana; plus others. Add: Dept. of English, University of Maryland, College Park, MD 20741.

BODE, ROBERT FRANCIS, b. Baltimore, Md, Oct. 14, 44. ENGLISH LITERATURE. B.S, Loyola Col.(Md), 66; M.A, Univ. S.C, 69, Ph.D.(Eng), 70. ASST. PROF. ENG, TENN TECH. UNIV, 70- S.Atlantic Mod. Lang. Asn. Seventeenth century British drama; metaphysical poetry; Chaucer. Publ: Co-auth, Shakespeare's use of verse form as social dialect to stratify characters in A midsummer night's dream, Tenn. Philol. Asn. Bull, 73. Add: Dept. of English, Tennessee Technological University, Cookeville, TN 38501.

BODTKE, RICHARD A, b. Peoria, Ill, Dec. 8, 20; m. 47; c. 1. ENGLISH LITERATURE. B.A, Bradley Univ, 42; M.A, Columbia Univ, 47, Ph.D, 57. Instr. ENG. LIT, ADELPHI UNIV, 47-53, asst. prof, 53-58, assoc. prof, 58-63, PROF, 63-, CHMN. DEPT, 71- Lectr, Columbia Univ, 57-58, 59-69. Sig.C, U.S.A, 42-45, Sgt. English Renaissance drama; modern drama; modern poetry. MLA; AAUP. Publ: World of undisguise (poems), Nauset, 68; Tragedy and the Jacobean temper: the major plays of John Webster, Univ. Salzburg, 72. Add: Dept. of English, Adelphi University, Garden City, NY 11530.

BOE, KAREN ELIZABETH, b. Sioux Falls, S.Dak, Dec. 3, 02. ENGLISH, LANGUAGE & LITERATURE. B.A, St. Olaf Col, 25; M.A, Univ. Wis, 30. Teacher, high sch. & jr. col, Minn, 30-35; high sch, Wis, 38-46; asst. prof. ENG, S.Dak. State Univ, 46-49; Yankton Col, 49-50; instr, Univ. Minn, Duluth, 52-53; asst, Univ. Wis, 53-54; assoc. prof, Sioux Falls Col, 56-62; Hastings Col, 62-63; asst. prof, University Wis-Stout, 64-73; RETIRED. Midwest Mod. Lang. Asn. Medicine as revealed in Shakespeare's plays; frontier mythical heroes in American folklore; the personality of grammar. Publ: Over the coffee cups, Mod. Lang. J, 1/45; Frustration, S.Dak. Educ. J, 3/58; What's in a word (poem), Pasque Petals, 7/60. Add: 504 S. Duluth Ave, Sioux Falls, SD 57104.

BOENING, JOHN, b. New York, N.Y, June 15, 42; m. 68. COMPARATIVE LITERATURE. B.A, Pace Col, 64; M.A, Univ. Md, 66; univ. fel, Ind. Univ, 66-68, Ph.D.(comp. lit), 71. Teaching asst. ENG, Univ. Md, 66-68; instr, UNIV. TOLEDO, 69-71, ASST. PROF, 71- Vis. lectr, Univ. Hamburg, 68-69. MLA; Am. Soc. Aesthet; Am. Comp. Lit. Asn. Literature and society; Anglo-German literary relations; modern poetry. Publ: Literature, language frontiers, and cultural thanatology, Proc. VII Int. Congr. Aesthet, 73. Add: 2017 Bretton Pl, Toledo, OH 43606.

BOERCKER, MARGUERITE JEANNE, b. Chicago, Ill, Oct. 18, 26; m. 48; c. 3. LINGUISTICS, READING. B.S, Northwest. Univ, 47; Wash. Univ, 48; M.A, West. Ky. State Univ, 62; NDEA fel, Univ. Ky, 66-67, Ph.D.(ling, reading), 67. Teacher, Lowell High Sch, Ind, 47; Belleview Sch, Clayton, Mo, 49; Kirkwood Pub. Schs, 52-53; Heege Sch, Afton, 56-57; instr. elem. Ger, West. Ky. State Univ, 60-62; Eng, Georgetown Col, 64-65; suprv. Eng. lang. arts & reading, Montgomery County Pub. Schs, Md, 67-70; PROF. EDUC. & ENG, AUSTIN PEAY STATE UNIV, 70-, ASSOC. DIR. PREDISCHARGE EDUC. PROG, 73- Participant, Invitational Fac. Sem. Socioling. & Reading, Georgetown Univ, summer 73. Int. Reading Asn; NCTE; Am. Dialect Soc. Dialect samples; adult remedial reading instruction. Publ: Co-auth, Look, look, find George & auth, Look at me, teach! Montgomery County Pub. Schs, Md, 69-70; auth, What every single teacher should know about language, Univ. Ala, (in press); co-auth, The influence of a Head Start program on reading achievement, In: Forging ahead in reading, Proc. Convention Int. Reading Asn, 68; auth, Behavioral statements: comprehension, Educ. Catalyst, spring 73. Add: Dept. of Education, Austin Peay State University, Clarksville, TN 37040.

BOGARD, MORRIS R, b. St. Louis, Mo, Oct. 26, 26; m. 48; c. 4. SPEECH, THEATRE. Ph.B, Ill. Wesleyan Univ, 50; M.A, Univ. Ill, 52, Ph.D, 62; Cornell Univ, 54, Inst. Educ. Media, 68-69. Asst. speech, Univ. Ill, 52-53, summer rural drama adv. theatre, 52-53; instr. SPEECH & THEATRE, STATE UNIV. N.Y. COL. CORTLAND, 53-54, asst. prof, 54-57, assoc. prof, 57-63, PROF, 63-, DIR. THEATRE, 62-, CHMN. DEPT, SPEECH & THEATRE ARTS, 64-, ASSOC. V.PRES, FOR ACAD. AFFAIRS, 71-, acting chmn. dept. speech, 57-58, dir. col. centennial year, 67-68. Consult, Choice mag, 65-; Theatre ed, Reports, 66-; U.S. Off. Educ. fel, 70; consult, U.S. Off. Agr, 72-; mem. comt, Nat. Counc. Accreditation Teacher Educ, 72- U.S.A.A.F, 46-47. Am. Nat. Theatre & Acad; Am. Theatre Asn. Theatre history and aesthetics. Publ: American theatre: 1900-1930, Nat. Thespian Soc, 67; Play production in the secondary schools, Int. Thespian Soc, 69; A summer theatre in your town, Nat. Recreation J, 5/60; Contributions of the Drama League of America, Cath. Theatre, 12/64; The Drama League of America, Dramatics Mag, 11/65. Add: 15 Cowance St, Cortland, NY 13045.

BOGARD, TRAVIS MILLER, b. San Francisco, Calif, Jan. 25, 18; m. 47; c. 2. ENGLISH. A.B, Univ. Calif, 39, M.A, 40; Ph.D, Princeton, 47. Instr. ENG, Yale, 42-43; UNIV. CALIF, BERKELEY, 47-49, asst. prof, 49-55, from assoc. prof. to prof, 55-66, PROF. DRAMATIC ART, 66-, v.chmn. dept, 66-73. Guggenheim fel, 58-59; dir, Univ. Calif. Study Ctr. for Classical Drama, Delphi, Greece, 66-67. U.S.A, 41-46. MLA; Am. Theatre Asn. Elizabethan-Jacobean drama; Shakespeare; British and American drama since 1850, especially Eugene O'Neill. Publ: The tragic satire of John Webster, Russell, 55; co-ed, Modern drama, essays in criticism, 65 & auth, Contour in time: the plays of Eugene O'Neill, 72, Oxford; ed, The later plays of Eugene O'Neill, Mod. Libr, Random, 67; International conference in theatre education and development: report, Educ. Theatre J, 68. Add: Dept. of Dramatic Art, University of California, Berkeley, CA 94720.

BOGEN, NANCY, b. New York, N.Y, Apr. 24, 32. ENGLISH. B.A, N.Y. Univ, 54; M.A, Columbia Univ, 62, pres. fel, 64-66, Ph.D.(Eng), 68. Instr. ENG, Adelphi Univ, 63-64; preceptor, Columbia Univ, 66-67; ASST. PROF, RICHMOND COL.(N.Y), 67- Am. Philos. Soc. grant, summer 68. MLA; Eng-Speaking Union. William Blake; late 18th century studies. Publ: An early listing of William Blake's poetical sketches, Eng. Lang. Notes, 3/66; Blake's Island in the moon revisited, Satire Newslett, spring 68; The problem of William Blake's early religion, Personalist, fall 68. Add: Div. of Humanities, Richmond College, 130 Stuyvesant Pl, Staten Island, NY 10301.

BOGLE, EDRA CHARLOTTE, b. Des Moines, Iowa, Jan. 4, 34. COMPARATIVE LITERATURE, BIBLIOGRAPHY. B.A, Univ. North. Iowa, 56; M.S, Columbia Univ, 57; Ph.D, Univ. South. Calif, 69. Asst. librn, Ore. Col. Educ, 57-59; Frostburg State Teachers Col, 59-60; educ. librn, Univ. South Calif, 60-65, asst. librn. for pub. serv, 65-68; asst. prof. ENG, N.TEX. STATE UNIV, 68-72, ASSOC. PROF, 72- MLA; Mod. Humanities Res. Asn; S.Cent. Mod. Lang. Asn. The novel; English literature 1870-1920; symbolism. Publ: Co-ed, Dictionary of anonymous and pseudonymous English literature, Oliver & Boyd, 74-; contrib, Modern Humanities Research Association Annual Bibliography, 68-. Add: Dept. of English, North Texas State University, Denton, TX 76203.

BOGORAD, SAMUEL NATHANIEL, b. New Bedford, Mass, Apr. 7, 17; m. 44. ENGLISH. A.B, Brown Univ, 39, A.M, 41; fel, Northwest. Univ, 41-42, 45-46, Ph.D, 46. Instr. eng, Northwest. Univ, 42-45; UNIV. VT, 46-47, asst. prof, 47-52, assoc. prof, 52-57, prof, 57-68, FREDERICK CORSE PROF. ENG. LANG. & LIT, 68-, chmn. dept, 61-69. Vis. asst. prof, Brown Univ, 48-49; summer vis. prof, Col. William & Mary, 51; Univ. Colo, 58; mem. comt. insts. higher educ, New Eng. Asn. Cols. & Sec. Schs, 63-70; comnr, New Eng. Bd. Higher Educ, 73- MLA; Col. Eng. Asn.(pres, 73-74); NCTE; New Eng. Col. Eng. Asn.(pres, 66-67). Milton; English restoration and 18th century literature; modern fiction and poetry. Publ: Co-auth, College miscellany, Rinehart, 52, Atlantic essays, Heath, 58 & Samuel Foote's piety in pattens, Theatre Surv. Monogr, 73. Add: Dept. of English, University of Vermont, Burlington, VT 05401.

BOHLKEN, ROBERT LEO, b. Nebraska City, Nebr, Jan. 14, 35; m. 58; c. 2. SPEECH COMMUNICATION & THEATRE. B.S, Peru State Col, 56-59; M.A, Univ. Nebr, 63; Ph.D.(speech commun), Univ. Kans, 69. Instr. Eng. & speech, Stanton High Sch, Iowa, 59-60; Nebraska City High Sch, 60-63; from instr. to assoc. prof, Peru State Col, 63-69; from assoc. prof. to PROF. SPEECH & THEATRE, NORTHWEST MO. STATE UNIV, 69- Res. stud. dir, Continuing Educ. Grant, Northwest Mo. State Univ, 72-73, Mo. State Comt. for Humanities, 73-. Med.C, U.S.A, 53-56. Speech Commun. Asn. Speech education; community communication. Publ: The speech concept test, Speech Teacher, fall 70; co-auth, The micro inductive approach to teaching, Educ, spring 71; auth, Ethos of an author and its influence on philosophical message's effectiveness and believability, Mo. State Speech J, spring 72. Add: Dept. of Speech & Theatre, Northwest Missouri State University, Administration Bldg, Maryville, MO 64468.

BOHMAN, GEORGE VROOM, b. Princeton, Ill, Sept. 24, 08; m; c. 2. SPEECH. A.B, Monmouth Col, 29; A.M, Univ. Wis, 34, Ph.D, 47. Asst. prof. speech & head dept, Dakota Wesleyan Univ, 30-37; instr. pub. speaking, Dartmouth Col, 37-39, asst. prof, 39-47, chmn. dept, 41-45; PROF. SPEECH, WAYNE STATE UNIV, 47-, chmn. dept, 55-73. Speech Commun. Asn. Add: Dept. of Speech Communication & Theatre, Wayne State University, Detroit, MI 48202.

BOHN, ROSHNI RUSTOMJI, Comparative Literature. See Volume III, Foreign Languages, Linguistics & Philology.

BOHNER, CHARLES HENRY, b. Wilmington, Del, Nov. 23, 27; m. 61; c. 3. AMERICAN LITERATURE; B.A, Syracuse Univ, 50; M.A, Univ. Pa, 52, Ph.D, 57. Instr. Eng. Syracuse Univ, 52-54; UNIV. DEL, 55-58, asst. prof, 58-62, assoc. prof, 62-66, PROF. AM. LIT, 66-, CHMN. DEPT, 69-, res. fels, 58, 61. Assoc, Am. Counc. Learned Soc, 62-64; U.S. Dept. State Am. specialist grantee, lecturing in Germany, Ireland, Yugoslavia, Finland & Norway, 65. Eng.C, U.S.A, 46-47. MLA; Col. Eng. Asn. American literature. Publ: John Pendleton Kennedy: gentleman from Baltimore, Johns Hopkins, 61; Robert Penn Warren, Twayne, 65. Add: 61 Kells Ave, Newark, DE 19711.

BOHRINGER, KENNETH CHARLES, b. St. Louis, Mo, Sept. 15, 40. ENGLISH LITERATURE. A.B, William Jewell Col, 62; M.A, Univ. Tenn, Knoxville, 64, NDEA fel, 68-71, Ph.D.(Eng), 73. Instr. Eng, William Jewell Col, 64-67, asst. prof, 67-68; ASST. DIR. CTR. EXTENDED LEARNING, UNIV. TENN, KNOXVILLE, 73- U.S.M.C.R, 66-72. Renaissance drama; Medieval English and French history; Victorian novel. Add: 447 Communications & University Extension Bldg, University of Tennessee, Knoxville, TN 37916.

BOIES, JACK J, b. Leon, Iowa, Nov. 26, 26; m. 55; c. 4. ENGLISH & DRAMA. B.A, Univ. N.Mex, 50; M.A, Miami Univ, 51; Ph.D.(Eng), Univ. Wis, 59. Instr. Eng, Univ. Wis, Green Bay Ctr, 55-58, asst. prof, 58-62, dir, Green Bay Ctr, 60-62; assoc. prof, ENG, WAGNER COL, 62-67, PROF, 67-, dean

Grad. Sch, 66-68. U.S.N.R, 44-46. Nat. Endowment for Humanities summer grant stud. sublit. Am. West, 72. Melville Soc. Am; MLA. Mid-nineteenth century American literature; modern drama; comparative literature. Publ: Circular imagery in Thoreau's Week, Col. Eng, 2/65; The Calvinist obsession in American letters, J. Gen. Educ, 4/67; Existential exchange in the novels of Charles Williams, Renascence, 74; plus one other. Add: Dept. of English, Wagner College, Staten Island, NY 10301.

BOJARSKI, EDMUND ANTONI, b. Milwaukee, Wis, Apr. 25, 24; m. 58. ENGLISH & AMERICAN LITERATURE. B.S, Univ. Wis-Madison, 49, M.A, 50; Johns Hopkins Univ. Sch. Advan. Int. Stud, D.C, 56-58; M.A, Univ. S.Africa, 59, D.Litt. et Phil, 74. Teacher Eng, Shullsburg High Sch, Wis, 50-51; res. analyst, U.S. Dept. State, 52-65; lectr. Eng, Univ. Md, 65-69; assoc. prof, McMURRY COL, 69-73, MGR. RARE BKS, CONRADIANA BOOKSHOP, 73- Co-ed. & regional rep. in S.Africa, Chrysallys, 59-61; gen. ed. & founder, Conradiana, 67-72, ed-at-large, 72-; founder & gen. ed, Thesis Bibliog. Ser, 69-; Conrad Collector, 70-; mem. bd. dirs, Int. Inst. Maritime Cult, 70- Med.C, U.S.A, 43-46. AAUP; MLA; Fed. Ling. Soc; Col. Eng. Asn; Int. Joseph Conrad Soc.(pres. & ed, Newslett, 73-); Polish Inst. Arts & Sci. Am; Polish Am. Hist. Asn. Life and work of Joseph Conrad; international bibliography of theses and dissertations on world literature; Henryk Sienkiewicz in Africa. Add: Conradiana Bookshop, McMurry College, Abilene, TX 79605.

BOKLUND, K. GUNNAR, b. Kramfors, Sweden, Feb. 14, 19; m. 45; c. 3. ENGLISH LITERATURE. B.A, Univ. Uppsala, 42, M.A, 44, Ph.D.(Eng), 51 & 57. Lectr. Swed, Harvard, 53-56; asst. prof. ENG, Univ. Uppsala, 57-63, PROF, 68-72; UNIV. DENVER, 63-68, 72- Fel. Folger Shakespeare Libr, 58, 60; vis. lectr. Swed, Harvard, 60; vis. prof. Eng, Univ. Wash, 64; fel, Huntington Libr, 68; co-ed, Studia Neophilologica, 70. Royal Soc. Arts & Lett, Uppsala; Royal Soc. Arts & Sci, Uppsala. Renaissance literature and civilization; the drama; Shakespeare. Publ: The sources of the White devil, 57 & The Duchess of Malfi, 62, Harvard Univ; ed, Swift: prose works (in Swed), Natur & Kultur, Stockholm, 62 & Shakespeare: works (in Swed), Bonniers, Stockholm, 62-67; auth, Judgment in Hamlet, Princeton Univ, 64; The devil's law-case, G. Benn, 70. Add: Dept. of English, University of Denver, Denver, CO 80210.

BOLEN, FRANCES E, b. Randolph, Miss, Feb. 13, 32. ENGLISH & AMERICAN LITERATURE. B.A.E, Univ. Miss, 53, M.A, 54, Ph.D.(Eng), 63. Instr. ENG, Univ. Miss, 59-62; asst. prof, Univ. Ala, 63-64; assoc. prof, MISS. STATE COL. WOMEN, 64-67, PROF, 67-, assoc. dean fac, 64-67. AAUP; MLA; Renaissance Soc. Am. Shakespeare; Elizabethan drama. Publ: Irony and self-knowledge in the creation of tragedy, Univ. Salzburg, 73. Add: 209 Eastwood Dr, Columbus, MS 39701.

BOLEY, TOMMY J, b. Paducah, Tex, Jan. 28, 35. ENGLISH. B.B.A, N.Tex. State Univ, 56; M.A, Univ. Tex, Austin, 63, Ph.D.(educ), 72. Instr. Eng, Ector County Sch. Dist, Tex, 59-61, 62-66; Tex. Southmost Col, 66-67; Univ. Tex, El Paso, 67-70; teaching asst. curriculum & instr, Univ. Tex, Austin, 70-72, ASST. PROF. ENG, CURRICULUM & INSTR, UNIV. TEX, EL PASO, 73- U.S.A, 58; Nat. Guard, 58-64, Sgt. NCTE; Am. Dialect Soc; Conf. Col. Compos. & Commun; Conf. Eng. Educ. Rhetoric and composition; English education. Publ: The true life story of Ella Bird Dumont, Univ. Tex, Austin, 63 & Rhetorical invention: a synthesis of contemporary concepts, 72, Univ. Tex, Austin. Add: Dept. of English, University of Texas at El Paso, El Paso, TX 79968.

BOLGAN, ANNE (CATHERINE), b. Buffalo, N.Y, Aug. 22, 23. ENGLISH. B.A, D'Youville Col, 45; M.A, Univ. Toronto, 50, Ph.D, 60; Humanities Res. Can. Counc. grant, 57. Instr. Eng, D'Youville Col, 46-50; asst. dean women, St. Mary's Col.(Ind), 53-54; instr. ENG, Univ. Col, Univ. Toronto, 54-59; asst. prof, Univ. Alaska, 59-60, assoc. prof, 60-64; UNIV. WEST. ONT, 64-73, PROF, 73- Am. Asn. Univ. Women fel, 63-64; Can. Counc. fel, 68-69. The study of the philosophical postulates that often mediate concepts in poetry and literary criticism of T.S. Eliot. Publ: Ed, Knowledge and experience in the philosophy of F.H. Bradley—the Ph.D. dissertation of T.S. Eliot completed by him in 1916, Faber & Faber, London & Farrar, Straus, 64; auth, What the thunder really said: a retrospective essay on the making of The waste land, McGill-Queens Univ. Montreal & London, 73; The philosophy of F.H. Bradley and the mind and art of T.S. Eliot: an introduction, In: English literature and British philosophy, Univ. Chicago, 71. Add: Dept. of English, University of Western Ontario, London, Ont, Can.

BOLGER, STEPHEN GARRETT, b. Philadelphia, Pa, Apr. 27, 27; m. 51; c. 6. ENGLISH. A.B, Univ. Notre Dame, 50; M.A, Univ. Pa, 51, Ph.D.(Am. civilization), 71. Instr, St. Joseph's High Sch, Phila, Pa, 50-53; ENG, Georgetown Univ, 53-58; asst. prof, ROSEMONT COL, 58-62, ASSOC. PROF, 62- U.S.N, 45-46. Am. Stud. Asn. 19th century American popular novel. Add: Dept. of English, Rosemont College, Rosemont, PA 19010.

BOLIN, JOHN SEELYE, b. Ft. Bragg, N.C, Sept. 20, 43; m. 65; c. 1. DRAMATIC LITERATURE, THEATRE HISTORY. B.A, Kalamazoo Col, 65; M.A, Univ. Mich, Ann Arbor, 67, Ford. Found. Rackham fel, 67-68, Ph.D. (theatre), 70. ASST. PROF. THEATRE HIST, BEREA COL, 70- Nat. Endowment for Humanities summer stipend, 73. Speech Commun. Asn; Can. Speech Asn; Am. Soc. Theatre Res; Popular Cult. Asn; AAUP. Theatre history; drama criticism; oral interpretation. Add: Dept. of English, Berea College, Berea, KY 40403.

BOLL, THEOPHILUS ERNEST MARTIN, b. New York, N.Y, Jan. 6, 02. ENGLISH LITERATURE. A.B, Univ. Pa, 22, A.M, 24, Ph.D.(Eng), 30. Instr. ENG, UNIV. PA, 22-36, asst. prof, 36-46, assoc. prof, 46-72, EMER. PROF, 72- ; secy. col. fac, 47-60. Am. Philos. Soc. res. grant, 20th century novelists, 59. Int. Asn. Univ. Prof. Eng; Mod. Humanities Res. Asn, Gt. Brit. English fiction since 1800; Dickens and Dickens manuscripts; May Sinclair. Publ: Miss May Sinclair: novelist, Fairleigh Dickinson Univ, 73; Social causation in the English novel of the armistice interval, Psychiatry, 11/46; May Sinclair and the Medico-Psychological Clinic of London, Proc. Am. Philos, Soc, 8/62. Add: Dept. of English, 314 Bennett Hall, University of Pennsylvania, Philadelphia, PA 19104.

BOLLIER, ERNEST PHILLIP, b. Allentown, Pa, June 20, 22; m. 51. ENGLISH. Ph.B, Muhlenberg Col, 43; M.A, Columbia Univ, 48, Ph.D, 59. Instr. ENG, Muhlenberg Col, 46-47; tutor, Hunter Col, 48-51; instr, Univ. Colo, 51-55; NEWCOMB COL, TULANE UNIV, 55-61, assoc. prof, 61-64, PROF, 64-, ASSOC. DEAN, GRAD. SCH, 69-, head Newcomb dept. Eng, 67-69. Planning fel, Comn. Eng. Summer Inst. Prog, summer 61, instr, summer 62, evaluation consult, winter 63; Newcomb rep, Danforth Found. Workshop Lib. Arts Educ, summer 66; mem. serv. comt, Grad. Rec. Exam. Bd, 72-75; mem. task force on internal prog. eval, Counc. Grad. Schs, 73. U.S.A.A.F, 43-45. MLA; AAUP; S.Cent. Mod. Lang. Asn. Contemporary literature, especially British; poetry, novel and criticism. Publ: A broken Coriolanus: a note on T.S. Eliot's Coriolan, South. Rev, summer 67; T.S. Eliot's 'Lost' Ode, Bucknell Rev, spring 68; La poesie pure: the ghostly dialogue between T.S. Eliot and Paul Valery, Forum, winter-spring 70; plus others. Add: Graduate School, Tulane University, New Orleans, LA 70118.

BOLLINGER, EVANGELINE GRACE, b. Detroit, Mich, Nov. 30, 22. ENGLISH. A.B, Madison Col, 44; M.A, Univ. Mich, 45, fel, 49-50, Ph.D.(Eng), 51. Instr. ENG, Stephens Col, 45-46; Univ. Mich, 50-51; St. Joseph Col.(Conn), 51-54; Univ. Dayton, 54-55, asst. prof, 55-57; ST. XAVIER COL, 57-58, PROF, 58-, DEAN, 67-, V.PRES. ACAD. AFFAIRS, 70-, head dept. Eng, 58-66, chmn. div. lib. arts & humanities, 61-66. MLA; NCTE; Col. Eng. Asn. Literary criticism; Dante. Publ: Dante's divine comedy in English and American criticism since 1910. Add: St. Xavier College, 103rd & Central Park Ave, Chicago, IL 60655.

BOLTON, (HAROLD) PHILIP, b. Jacksonville, Ill, Aug. 11, 44. ENGLISH LITERATURE. B.A, Brown Univ, 66; M.A, Univ. Chicago, 67, Ph.D, 72. ASST. PROF. ENG. & AM. LIT, WICHITA STATE UNIV, 70- MLA. Theory of fiction; temporal dimensions of fiction and theater; theory of literature. Add: 530 N. Ash, Wichita, KS 67214.

BOLTON, WHITNEY FRENCH, b. New York, N.Y, Oct. 15, 30; m. 62; c. 1. ENGLISH LANGUAGE & LITERATURE. B.A, Bard Col, 51; Charles Scribner fel, Princeton, 52, Fulbright scholar & M.A, 53, Ph.D.(Eng), 55. Res. fel. ENG, Univ. Reading, 57-59, from lectr. to prof, 61-70; from instr. to asst. prof, Univ. Calif, Berkeley, 59-61; PROF, DOUGLASS COL, RUTGERS UNIV, 70-, chmn. dept, 71-74. Sellers vis. prof. Eng, Simon Fraser Univ, 68-69. U.S.N, 55-57. MLA; AAUP; Early Eng. Text Soc; Eng. Inst; Mediaeval Acad. Am; Philol. Soc, Eng; Soc. Advan. Scand. Stud; fel. Royal Hist. Soc; fel. Soc. Antiq, London. Medieval literary history; history of the English language. Publ: Ed, An Old English anthology, Northwest. Univ, 63, rev. ed, 65; ed, The English language: essays, Vol. I, 66, 73 & co-ed, Vol. II, 69, Cambridge Univ; ed. & auth, Introd, Ben Jonson's Sejanus his fall, Hill & Wang, 66; ed, A short history of literary English, Edward Arnold, 67, 72, Crane Russak, 72, Littlefield, 73, Japanese ed, Eihosha, 69; ed, A history of Anglo-Latin literature, 597-1066, Vol. I, 67, 68 & co-ed, Vol. II, (in prep), Princeton Univ; ed. & auth. chap. in, Vol. I, The Middle Ages, 70 & ed, Vol. XI, The English language, (in press), In: A history of literature in the English language, Barrie & Jenkins; co-ed, Beowulf, St. Martin's, 73; co-ed. & auth, Introd, Ben Jonson's Catiline his conspiracy, Univ. Nebr, 73; co-ed, A study of Old English literature, George G. Harrap, (in prep); auth, The Alfredian Boethius in Aelfric's Lives of Saints I, Notes & Queries, 72; The Conybeare copy of Thorkelin, Eng. Stud, (in press); A further echo of the Old English Genesis in Milton's Paradise lost, Rev. Eng. Stud, (in press); plus several others. Add: Dept. of English, Douglass College of Rutgers University, New Brunswick, NJ 08903.

BOMBERGER, JAMES ROHRER, b. Mt. Joy, Pa, Mar. 15, 33; m. 56; c. 2. ENGLISH, LINGUISTICS. B.A, East. Mennonite Col, 55; M.S, Temple Univ, 60; Eng. courses, Madison Col, 61-68; Ed.D, Columbia Univ, 66. Instr. & head dept. Eng, Lancaster Mennonite Sch, Pa, 57-61; asst. prof. ENG, EAST. MENNONITE COL, 61-63, assoc. prof, 64-72, PROF, 72- Part-time instr, Teachers Col, Columbia Univ, 64; participant NDEA Eng. Inst, A&T State Univ, summer 68; Fulbright prof. Eng, Cuttington Col, Liberia, 71-73. Alternative mil. serv, 55-57. NCTE. Communication theory; linguistics. Add: Dept. of English, Eastern Mennonite College, Harrisonburg, VA 22801.

BOMBERGER, RICHARD WATSON, b. Boonsboro, Md, Oct. 13, 96; m. 23; c. 1. ENGLISH. A.B, Franklin & Marshall Col, 20; A.M, Univ. Va, 26, Instr. Eng, Donaldson Sch, Md, 20-28, headmaster, 28-31; dean, FRANKLIN & MARSHALL COL, 31-46, prof. ENG, 46-62, EMER. PROF, 62-; ELIZABETHTOWN COL, 73-, prof. & chmn. dept, 62-73. U.S.A, 18-19. Col. Eng. Asn; MLA. College administration. Add: Dept. of English, Elizabethtown College, Elizabethtown, PA 17022.

BONAZZA, BLAZE ODELL, b. Hancock, N.Y, Aug. 20, 21; m. 45; c. 2. ENGLISH, COMPARATIVE LITERATURE. A.B, Cornell Univ, 43; M.A, Los Angeles State Col, 52; Ph.D.(Eng), Univ. S.C, 61. Instr. ENG, Fullerton Jr. Col, 57-59; div. chmn, Cerritos Jr. Col, 58-64; coord. grad. stud, Calif. State Col. Fullerton, 64-66; assoc. prof, CALIF. STATE UNIV, LONG BEACH, 66-71, PROF, 71- Renaissance Soc. Am; MLA. Shakespearean comedy. Publ: Co-auth, Studies in fiction, 65, Read and write, 66 & Studies in drama, 68, Harper; auth, Shakespeare's early comedies, Mouton, 66. Add: Dept. of English, California State University, Long Beach, Long Beach, CA 90804.

BOND, CHARLES ALVIN, b. Chillicothe, Tex, June 16, 22. ENGLISH, JOURNALISM. A.B, Stanford Univ, 47; M.A, Univ. Detroit, 64; Mich. State Univ, 66-67; Ed.D.(Eng. educ), Wayne State Univ, 69. Ed, Glendale News, Ariz, 53-55; ed. & publ, Peoria Times, Ariz, 55-58; instr. jour, Cullman Col, 62-63; instr. & publ. adv, Margrove Col, 63-65; instr. Eng. & jour. & publ. adv, Mercy Col.(Mich), 65-66, asst. prof, 67-69; asst. prof. ENG, FERRIS STATE COL, 66-67, ASSOC. PROF, 69- Innovative teaching award, Ferris State Col, 70. U.S.A.A.F, 43-46, 1st Lt; Air Medal & 3 Oak Leaf Clusters. NCTE. English composition; folklore; industrial editing. Publ: A new approach to freshman composition: a trial of the Christensen method, Col. Eng, 3/72. Add: Dept. of English, Ferris State College, Big Rapids, MI 49307.

BOND, DONALD FREDERIC, b. Frankfort, Ind, Nov. 27, 98; m. 27; c. 2. ENGLISH LITERATURE. Ph.B, Univ. Chicago, 22, A.M, 23, fel, 28-30, Ph.D, 34. Instr. ENG, Wash. Univ, 23-24, asst. prof, 24-28; instr, UNIV. CHICAGO, 30-40, asst. prof, 40-47, assoc. prof, 47-52, prof, 52-67, William H. Colvin res. prof, 61-62, EMER. PROF, 67- Guggenheim fel, 58-59, 67-68; ed, Mod. Philol, 59-67; vis. prof, North. Ill. Univ, 69-71. MLA; Mod. Humanities Res. Asn; Int. Asn. Univ. Profs. Eng. Anglo-French literary relations; 18th century English literature. Publ: Co-auth, Critical bibliography of French literature, Syracuse Univ, Vol. IV, 51; auth, Reference guide to English studies, Univ. Chicago, 62, 2nd ed, 71; The Spectator: a critical edition, Clarendon, 65; plus others. Add: 501 Balra Dr, El Cerrito, CA 94530.

BOND, DONOVAN HINER, b. Mt. Clare, W.Va, Feb. 9, 21; m. 46; c. 1. JOURNALISM. B.S.J, W.Va. Univ, 42, A.M, 48; Ohio State Univ, 43. Instr. JOUR, W.VA. UNIV, 46-49, asst. prof, 49-56, assoc. prof, 56-60, PROF, 60-, DIR. DEVELOP, 59-, EXEC. DIR, W.VA. UNIV. FOUND, INC, 59- East. States Archeol. Fed; Am. Col. Pub. Relat. Asn.(Nat. trustee, 70-). Journalistic history; local history; frontier forts. Add: West Virginia University, 1549 University Ave, Morgantown, WV 26506.

BOND, HAROLD LEWIS, b. Newton, Mass, July 19, 20; m. 46; c. 4. ENGLISH LITERATURE. A.B, Dartmouth Col, 42; M.A, Harvard, 49, Ph.D, 55. Instr. ENG, Mass. Inst. Technol, 46-47; Dartmouth Col, 47-48, 50-52; Wellesley Col, 52-53; asst. prof, DARTMOUTH COL, 55-58, assoc. prof, 58-61, prof, 61-72, HENRY WINKLEY PROF. ANGLO-SAXON & ENG. LANG. & LIT, 72-; fac. fel, 61-62, chmn. dept, 63-67. U.S.A, 42-45, Capt. MLA. English renaissance; 18th century. Publ: Literary art of Edward Gibbon, Oxford, 60; Return to Cassino, Doubleday, 64. Add: Dept. of English, Dartmouth College, Hanover, NH 03755.

BOND, RICHMOND PUGH, b. Magnolia, Miss, Sept. 16, 99. ENGLISH. A.B, Vanderbilt Univ, 20; A.M, Harvard, 23, Ph.D, 29. Instr. ENG, Baylor Univ, 21-22; Hollins Col, 23-24; Ind. Univ, 24-26; asst. prof, UNIV. N.C, CHAPEL HILL, 29-34, assoc. prof, 34-39, prof, 39-55, Kenan prof, 56-70, EMER. KENAN PROF, 70- Spec. univ. lectr, Univ. London, 50, hon. lectr, univ. col, 50-51; resident fel, Newberry Libr, Chicago, Ill, 63; prof. in residence, Louisburg Col, 67-68. U.S.N.R, 42-44, Lt. Comdr. MLA; Mod. Humanities Res. Asn; Eng. Asn, Gt. Brit. Eighteenth century English literature. Publ: English burlesque poetry, 1700-1750, 32 & The Tatler: the making of a literary periodical, 71, Harvard Univ; Queen Anne's American kings, Clarendon, 52; co-auth, Studies in the early English periodical, Univ. N.C, 57; ed, New letters to the Tatler and Spectator, Univ. Tex, 59. Add: 101 Pine Lane, Chapel Hill, NC 27514.

BONE, ROBERT A, b. New Haven, Conn, Aug. 12, 24; m. 45; c. 2. ENGLISH LITERATURE. B.A, Yale, 45, M.A, 48, Am. Counc. Learned Soc. fel, 52-53, Ph.D.(Am. stud), 55. Instr. Eng. lit, Yale, 54-59; asst. prof. Am. lit, Univ. Calif, Los Angeles, 59-64; assoc. prof. ENG. LIT, TEACHERS COL, COLUMBIA UNIV, 65-67, PROF, 67- Fulbright lectr, Univ. Grenoble, 67-68; vis. fel, Ctr. Twentieth Century Stud, Univ. Wis-Milwaukee, 73-74. MLA; Am. Stud. Asn; NCTE. American Negro literature. Publ: The Negro novel in America, Yale, 58; Richard Wright, Univ. Minn, 69; Ralph Ellison and the uses of imagination, 66 & William Demby's dance of life, winter 69, Tri-Quart; plus one other. Add: Dept. of Languages & Literature, Teachers College, Columbia University, New York, NY 10027.

BONFIELD, JUNE McKENNA, b. Washington, D.C. MEDIEVAL LITERATURE. B.S, Univ. South Calif, 49; M.A, Church Divinity Sch. of the Pac, 61; Ph.D.(Eng), Univ. Tex, Austin, 69. Instr. Bible & relig, Southwest Tex. State Univ, 61-65; ASST. PROF. ENG, N.DAK. STATE UNIV, 69- Nat. Endowment for Humanities summer stipend, 72. Mediaeval Acad. Am; MLA; Folklore Soc, London; Int. Arthurian Soc. Medieval Christianity; epic and saga; Arthurian romance. Add: Dept. of English, North Dakota State University, University Station, Fargo, ND 58102.

BONGIORNO, ANDREW, b. Palermo, Italy, Aug. 5, 00; nat; m. 33. ENGLISH LITERATURE. A.B, Oberlin Col, 23, A.M, 24; Ph.D, Cornell Univ, 35. Instr. ENG, Univ. Mo, 24-25; OBERLIN COL, 25-36, asst. prof, 36-42, assoc. prof, 42-48, prof, 48-67, chmn. dept, 49-52, 58-64, EMER. PROF, 67-, distinguished vis. prof, 71- Vis. prof, Scripps Col, 67-68 & 69-70; Univ. Ariz, 68-69. MLA; Renaissance Soc. Am; Dante Soc. Am. History of literary criticism; Milton; Dante. Add: 19 N. Park St, Oberlin, OH 44074.

BONHAM, HILDA, I.H.M, b. Geneva, Ala, Sept. 14, 11. ENGLISH. B.A, Agnes Scott Col, 32; M.A, St. Louis Univ, 54; Ph.D.(Eng), Univ. Mich, 64. Instr. Eng, Marygrove Col, 38-42, 55-57, asst. prof, 57-59, assoc. prof. & head dept, 59-67, prof, 67-72; ASST. TO HOPWOOD COMT, UNIV. MICH, ANN ARBOR, 72- MLA; Milton Soc. Am. John Milton, Paradise Lost; Nathaniel Hawthorne, The Scarlet Letter; literary criticism in the 20th century. Publ: Hawthorne's symbols Sotto voce, Col. Eng, 1/59; John Erskine's Hester of Troy, 64 & The anthropomorphic God of Paradise Lost, 68, Papers Mich. Acad. Sci, Arts & Lett. Add: Hopwood Room, 1006 Angell Hall, University of Michigan, Ann Arbor, MI 48104.

BONHEIM, HELMUT W, b. Danzig, Jan. 6, 30; U.S. citizen; m. 51; c. 1. LITERATURE. B.A, Cornell Univ, 51; M.A, Columbia Univ, 52; Fulbright scholar, Univ. Vienna, 56-58; Ph.D, Univ. Wash, 59. Asst. prof. Eng, Univ. Calif, Santa Barbara, 58-63; vis. prof, Univ. Munich, 63-65; PROF. & DIR. ENG. SEM, UNIV. COLOGNE, 65- MLA; Conf. Col. Compos. & Commun; Int. Asn. Univ. Prof. Eng. Modern British literature; 17th century fiction. Publ: The King Lear perplex, Wadsworth, 60; Joyce's benefictions, 63 & A lexicon of the German in Finnegans wake, 67, Univ. Calif; Two dozen beasts, Hueber, Munich, 65; Objective testing methods in English studies, Pedag. Inst, Cologne, 69; The English novel before Richardson, Scarecrow, 71; James Joyce: nation versus world, In: Proceedings of the fourth congress of the International Comparative Literature Association, Mouton, The Hague, 66; Emanuel Forde: Ornatus and Artesia, Anglia, 72; Hawthorne: the birthmark, Am. Kurzgeschichte, 72; plus others. Add: English Seminar, University of Cologne, 5 Cologne, Germany.

BONIN, HELEN, D.H.S, b. Pittsfield, Mass, Dec. 16, 25. ENGLISH. B.A, Annhurst Col, 55; M.A, Fordham Univ, 57, Ph.D.(Eng), 62. Instr. ENG, ANNHURST COL, 59-64, ASST. PROF, 64-, ACAD. DEAN, 70-, chmn. dept, 59-70, asst. dean stud, 68-70. NCTE; Am. Asn. Higher Educ; Am. Conf. Acad. Deans; East. Asn. Deans; Am. Film Inst; Am. Asn. Univ. Adminr. Linguistics; the novel; Chaucer and the 18th century. Add: Office of Academic Dean, Annhurst College, R.R. 2, Woodstock, CT 06281.

BONNER, FRANCIS WESLEY, b. Lanett, Ala, Jan. 28, 17; m. 41; c. 2. ENGLISH. A.B, Univ. Ala, 39, A.M, 40; Ph.D, Univ. N.C, 49; Harvard, 52-53. Instr. Eng, Univ. Ala, 39-40, teacher, high sch, Ga, 40-42, assoc. prof. ENG, FURMAN UNIV, 49-54, PROF, 54- V.PRES, 64-, PROVOST, 72-, dean men's col, 53-61, head dept. Eng, 54-60, dean univ, 61-72. Mem. staff, Off. Strategic Serv, 45-46. U.S.A.A.F, 42-45, Capt. MLA; Mediaeval Acad. Am; Col. Eng. Asn; S.Atlantic Mod. Lang. Asn. Middle English literature; Chaucer's reputation during the 19th century; Wordsworth's philosophy of education. Add: Furman University, Greenville, SC 29613.

BONNER, WILLARD HALLAM, b. Lynn, Mass, May 13, 99. ENGLISH & AMERICAN LITERATURE. A.B, Col. Pac, 20; A.M, Stanford Univ, 21; Ph.D, Yale, 31. Instr. ENG, Mich. State Col, 21-22; from instr. to prof, STATE UNIV. N.Y. BUFFALO, 22-55, McNulty prof, 55-68, dir. grad. stud. in Eng, 55-66, EMER. PROF, 68- MLA. Travel books of the 18th century; the legend of Captain Kidd; H.D. Thoreau. Publ: Captain William Dampier, buccaneer-author, Stanford Univ, 34; DeQuincey at work, 36 & Journals and letters of Sarah and William Hazlitt, 59, Univ. Buffalo; Pirate laureate, the life and legends of Captain Kidd, Rutgers Univ, 47; var. articles, papers, newspaper bk. rev. column, encycl. articles. Add: 11 Meadowbrook Rd, Brunswick, ME 04011.

BOONE, LALIA PHIPPS, b. Tehuacana, Tex, Apr. 19, 07. ENGLISH PHILOLOGY. A.B, E.Tex. State Teachers Col, 38; A.M, Univ. Okla, 47; Ph.D, Univ. Fla, 51. Teacher pub. schs, Tex, 25-32, 39-46; teaching asst. & instr, Univ. Okla, 46-49; instr. ENG, Univ. Fla, 49-52, asst. prof, 52-60, assoc. prof, 60-65, mem. res. staff grad. sch, summer 63; PROF. UNIV. IDAHO, 65-, res. grant, 66-67. Havor fel, Am. Counc. Learned Soc, 48; Am. Philos. Soc. grant, summer 66. MLA; Am. Dialect Soc; Am. Name Soc; Rocky Mountain Mod. Lang. Asn; NCTE; NEA. Present day English; folklore and dialect; linguistics. Publ: Petroleum dictionary, Univ. Okla, 52; Communicative arts, vols. 9-12, Randall, 60; Names of Idaho counties, Names, 3/68; plus others. Add: Dept. of Humanities, University of Idaho, Moscow, ID 83843.

BOOS, FLORENCE SAUNDERS, b. Santa Barbara, Calif, Nov. 11, 43; m. 65; c. 1. ENGLISH LITERATURE, WOMEN'S STUDIES. B.A, Univ. Mich, 64; A.M, Harvard, 65; Univ. Ill, spring 66; Queen's Univ, 66-67; Ph.D.(Eng), Univ. Wis, 72. Instr. ENG, Univ. Sask, 70-71; ASST. PROF, UNIV. IOWA, 73- Midwest Mod. Lang. Asn; MLA; Women's Caucus Mod. Lang; AAUP; Res. Soc. Victorian Periodicals; Hopkins Soc; William Morris Soc. & Kelmscott Fel. Victorian poetry; women in 19th century British literature. Publ: The poetry of Dante Rossetti: a critical and source study, Mouton, 74; co-auth, Check list for Mary Wollstonecraft, 4/73 & auth, The biographies of Mary Wollstonecraft, 4/73, Mary Wollstonecraft Newslett; Mary Wollstonecraft's A vindication of the rights of woman, J. Int. Inst. Women Stud, (in press). Add: Dept. of English, English Philosophy Bldg, University of Iowa, Iowa City, IA 52240.

BOOTH, MARCELLA JOYCE (SPANN), b. Aubrey, Tex, June 21, 32; m. 72. AMERICAN LITERATURE. B.A. E.Tex. State Univ, 55, M.Ed, 56; Ph.D. (Eng), Univ. Tex, Austin, 69. Instr. ENG, Majorie Webster Jr. Col, 57-58; teacher, pub. schs, Tex, 60-65; ASST. PROF, UNIV. CONN, 69- AAUP. Modern poetry. Publ: Co-ed, Confucius to Cummings: an anthology of poetry, New Directions, 64; auth, A catalogue of the Louis Zukofsky collection at the University of Texas at Austin, Humanities Res. Ctr, 74; The Zukofsky papers, Libr. Chronicle Univ. Tex. Austin, 11/70; Beauty in fragments: Ezra Pound's Cantos CX-CXVII, Agenda, 70; Ezra Pound: drafts and fragments of Cantos CX-CXVII, Sou'Wester, 10/70. Add: Dept. of English, University of Connecticut, Storrs, CT 06268.

BOOTH, MARK WARREN, b. Mt. Vernon, Wash, Mar. 17, 43; m. 65; c. 2. ENGLISH LITERATURE. B.A, Rice Univ, 65; Danforth fel, Harvard, 65-71, M.A, 66, Woodrow Wilson teaching intern, 68-69, Ph.D.(Eng), 71. Instr. humanities, Norfolk State Col, 68-69; ASST. PROF. ENG, LEHMAN COL, 71- Eighteenth century English literature; song lyrics. Publ: Johnson's critical judgments in the Lives of the poets, Stud. Eng. Lit, summer 74. Add: Dept. of English, Herbert H. Lehman College, Bedford Park Blvd, Bronx, NY 10468.

BOOTH, MICHAEL RICHARD, b. Shanghai, China, Mar. 24, 31; Can. citizen; m. 58. ENGLISH, DRAMA. B.A, Univ. B.C, 52; M.A, Univ. London, 54, Ph.D.(Eng), 58. Instr. Eng, Univ. B.C, 54-60; from asst. to assoc. prof, Royal Mil. Col. Can, 60-67; from assoc. prof. to prof, UNIV. GUELPH, 67-69, PROF. DRAMA & CHMN. DEPT, 69- Can. Counc. sr. fel, 66-67, leave, fel, 70-71. Am. Soc. Theatre Res; Soc. Theatre Res, Eng; Int. Fed. Theatre Res; Asn. Can. Univ. Teachers Eng. Nineteenth century English drama and theatre; Canadian theatre history. Publ: Hiss the villain, Eyre, 64; Eighteen century tragedy, Oxford, 65; English melodrama, Jenkins, 65; ed, English plays of the nineteenth century, Vols. I & II, 68 & Vols. III & IV, 73, Clarendon; The acting of melodrama, 10/64 & Queen Victoria and the theatre, 4/67, Univ. Toronto Quart; plus others. Add: College of Arts, University of Guelph, Guelph, Ont, Can.

BOOTH, PHILIP, b. Hanover, N.H, Oct. 8, 25; m. 46; c. 3. ENGLISH. A.B, Dartmouth Col, 48; A.M, Columbia Univ, 49; D.Litt, Colby Col, 68. Instr. Eng, Bowdoin Col, 49-50; asst. to dir. admis, Dartmouth Col, 51-52, instr. ENG, 53; Wellesley Col, 54-57, asst. prof, 57-61; assoc. prof, SYRACUSE UNIV, 61-66, PROF, 66- Guggenheim fel, 58-59; 65; Rockefeller Found. fel, 68. Hokin Prize, 55; Lamont Prize, 56; Saturday Rev. poetry award, 57; Phi Beta Kappa poet, Columbia Univ, 62; co-recipient, Emily Clark Balch Prize, 64; Nat. Inst. Arts & Lett. Award, 67; Theodore Roethke Prize, 70. U.S.A.A.F, 44-45. PEN Club; Acad. Am. Poets. Contemporary poetry; poetry workshops; the novel. Publ: Letter from a distant land, 57, The Islanders, 61, Weathers and edges, 66 & Margins, new and selected poems, 70, Viking; North by east, Impression Workshop, Boston, 67; ed, Syracuse poems, 65, 70 & 73, Syracuse Univ; auth, On directive, In: Master poems of the English language, Trident, 66; Image and idea, In: Teaching literature to adolescents, Scott, 66; Jarrell's lost world, In: Randall Jarrell 1914-1965, Farrar, Strauss, 67. Add: Dept. of English, Syracuse University, Syracuse, NY 13210.

BOOTH, THORNTON YOUNG, b. Provo, Utah, Mar. 14, 18; m. 45; c. 2. ENGLISH LITERATURE. A.B, Brigham Young Univ, 41; Ph.D, Stanford Univ, 51. Acting instr, Stanford Univ, 46-50; asst. prof. ENG. LIT, Brigham Young Univ, 50-51; PROF, UTAH STATE UNIV, 53-, head dept. Eng. & jour. 66-70. Dir, Nat. Endowment for Humanities-Utah State Univ. presentation & discussion series, Utah, 72-73. U.S.A, 41-46, 51-53, Capt. NCTE; MLA. English literature of the Victorian writers: the novel. Publ: Moby Dick: standing up to God, Nineteenth-Century Fiction, 6/62; Mastering the event: commitment to fact in George Meredith's fiction, Utah State Univ. Monogr. Ser, 5/67; The supreme organ of the mind's self-ordering growth, In: Essay on I.A. Richards, Utah State Univ, 73. Add: Dept. of English & Journalism, Utah State University, Logan, UT 84322.

BOOTH, WAYNE CLAYSON, b. American Fork, Utah, Feb. 22, 21; m. 46; c. 3. ENGLISH LITERATURE. A.B, Brigham Young Univ, 44; A.M, Univ. Chicago, 47, Ph.D, 50; hon. LL.D, Rockford Col, 65, St. Ambrose Col, 70. Instr, Univ. Chicago, 47-50; asst. prof. ENG, Haverford Col, 50-53; prof. & head dept, Earlham Col, 53-62; PULLMAN PROF, UNIV. CHICAGO, 62-, CHMN. COM. IDEAS & METHODS, 73-, dean. col, 64-69. Ford fac. fel, 52-53; Guggenheim fel, 56-57, 69-70; fel, Ind. Univ, 62; vis. consult, U.S-S.Africa Leader Exchange Prog, 63; consult, Danforth Found, 63-; mem. bd, trustees, Earlham Col; mem. ed. bd, Novel & Philos. & Rhet; co-ed, Critical Inquiry, 74- Christian Gauss Award, Phi Beta Kappa, 62. U.S.A, 44-46. MLA; NCTE (David H. Russell Award, 66); Conf. Col. Compos. & Commun; fel. Am. Acad. Arts & Sci. Theory of literary criticism; 18th century English literature; theory and practice of rhetoric. Publ: The rhetoric of fiction, 61, ed, The knowledge most worth having, 67, auth, Now don't try to reason with me, 70 & A rhetoric of irony, 74, Univ. Chicago; auth, Modern dogma and the rhetoric of assent, Univ. Notre Dame, 74; The rhetoric of fiction and the poetics of fictions, Novel, 68. Add: Dept. of English, University of Chicago, Chicago, IL 60637.

BOOTH, WILLARD CLAUDE, b. Chefoo, Shantung, China, Apr. 4, 26; U.S. citizen; m. 71; c. 1. COMMUNICATIONS, DRAMA EDUCATION. B.A, Univ. Mich, Ann Arbor, 49, M.A, 51; Ford Found fel, Claremont Col, 53; Danforth Found grant & Ph.D.(commun), Univ. South. Calif, 69. Teacher drama & student asst, Whittier Col, 49-50; teacher elem. childrens theatre, Whittier City Schs, 52-56; asst. prof. speech & drama, Southwest Tex. State Univ, 56-60; teacher, Whittier Union High Sch, Calif, 60-64; asst. prof. speech educ, Calif. State Univ, Chico, 64-69; ASSOC. PROF. SPEECH & DRAMA EDUC, GEORGE PEABODY COL, 69- Dir, Personal commun. Res. & Anal, 68-73. Intel.C, U.S.A, 43-47, Res, 49-52, Capt. Speech Commun. Asn. Personal communications; discussion; drama education. Publ: Co-auth, Improvising stories with children, Peabody J. Educ, 5/70; auth, The knockout's a dame, Gent, 4/71; Historical uses of projected scenery, Speech Commun. Asn. Abstracts, 12/71; plus others. Add: 1806 Ashwood Ave, Nashville, TN 37212.

BORAM, WILLIAM, b. Weston, W.Va, Nov. 14, 31; m. 54; c. 3. ENGLISH. B.A, Glenville State Col, 53; M.A, W.Va. Univ, 58; Univ. Cincinnati, 58-59; Ph.D.(Eng. educ), Univ. Pittsburgh, 63. Instr. Eng. & jour, St. Albans High Sch, W.Va, 53-54; Montreat Col, 54-55; Marietta Col, 55-58; Univ. Cincinnati, 58-59; asst. prof, Calif. State Col.(Pa), 59-62, assoc. prof, 62-63; assoc. prof. Eng, Fairmont State Col, 63-65, prof. & chmn. dept, 65-67; dir. Chillicothe campus, Ohio Univ, 67-69, asst. dean fac, 69-70; PROF. ENG. & DEAN ACAD. AFFAIRS, FAIRMONT STATE COL, 70- Int. Soc. Gen. Semantics; Asn. Higher Educ. English teaching methods; mass communication and education; general semantics. Publ: Improving scholastic journalism, Clearing House, 12/62; Mass media as extra-school educative force, J. Educ. Sociol, 5/63; Teachers should administrate, Today's Educ, 9/68. Add: Office of Academic Affairs, Fairmont State College, Fairmont, WV 26554.

BORCHARDT, DONALD ARTHUR, b. St. Paul, Minn, June 4, 31; m. 57. SPEECH & DRAMA. B.A, Univ. Minn, 53, M.A, 58; Ph.D.(theatre arts), Univ. Utah, 60. Instr, Univ. Minn, 56-57; consult, drama adv. serv, Univ. Minn. Concerts & Lect. Dept, 57-58; asst, Univ. Utah, 58-60; asst. prof. speech & theatre, Wis. State Col, River Falls, 60-61; Macalester Col, 61-64; theatre, Univ. Fla, 64-67; RUTGERS UNIV, NEWARK, 67-73, ASSOC. PROF. THEATRE ARTS & SPEECH, 73- Chmn. northeast region, Am. Col. Theatre Festival, 72- Sig.C, U.S.A, 53-55. Speech Commun. Asn; Am. Nat. Theatre & Acad; Am. Theatre Asn.(dir. region 2, univ-col. div, 70-). Contemporary theatre; television; film. Publ: Co-auth, History through drama, Univ. Minn, 57; auth, Creative dramatics U.S.A, Theatre: Children & Youth, 71-72; A revised theatre curriculum, Theatre J, 71-72; Idea, medium and manner, Playbill, fall 72; plus others. Add: Dept. of Theatre Arts & Speech, Rutgers University, 31 Fulton St, Newark, NJ 07102.

BORCHERS, GLADYS LOUISE, b. La Valle, Wis, July 4, 91. SPEECH. A.B, Univ. Wis, 21, A.M, 25, Ph.D, 27. Chmn. teachers training, Jefferson, Wis, 18-19; instr, Rockford Col, 21-23, assoc. prof, 23-24; asst. prof. SPEECH, UNIV. WIS-MADISON, 27-34, assoc. prof, 34-47, prof, 47-62, EMER. PROF, 62- Vis. prof, La. State Univ, 46-47; Univ. Hawaii, 49-50; ed, Speech Teacher, 61-64; vis. prof, Univ. Colo, 62-63; lab. sch, Univ. Wis, 63-64; vis. prof. & distinguished consult, Taylor Univ, 64-65, 66-67, distinguished prof, 67-68; vis. prof, Brigham Young Univ, 65 & 69; vis. lectr, West. Wash. State Col, 65-66; vis. prof, Ill. State Univ, 66; summers, Wash. State Univ, 66, 67 & 68, Univ. Minn, 68. Speech Commun. Asn.(v.pres, 32); NCTE; Ger. Speech Asn. Differences between oral and written style; speech education in Germany; speech education methods. Publ: Living speech; The new better speech, 39, Speech, 46 & co-auth, Modern speech, 49, Harcourt; co-auth, Teaching of speech, 52 & Speaking and listening, 56, Prentice-Hall; Women in America, Univ. Halle, Ger, 63, The communicative arts and sciences in speech, C.E. Merrill, 67 & Volume in honor of Harry Caplan, Cornell Univ, 67. Add: The Normandy, 4715 Sheboygan Ave, Madison, WI 53705.

BORCK, JIM SPRINGER, b. New Orleans, La, Aug. 16, 41; m. 64. ENGLISH LITERATURE. B.A, Univ. Fla, 63, M.A, 65; regents' fel, Univ. Calif, Riverside, 65-66, Ph.D.(Eng), 69. ASST. PROF. ENG, LA. STATE UNIV, BATON ROUGE, 69- MLA; South Cent. Mod. Lang. Asn. Late 18th and early 19th century English literature. Publ: Wordsworth's The Prelude and the failure of language, Stud. Eng. Lit, fall 73. Add: Dept. of English, Louisiana State University, Baton Rouge, LA 70803.

BORDEN, ARTHUR ROSS, JR, b. Boston, Mass, Feb. 22, 17. ENGLISH. A.B, Harvard, 39; M.A, Harvard, 41; Ph.D.(Eng. philol), 50. Instr. Eng, Lafayette Col, 46-47; asst. dean, Harvard, 47-50; instr. Eng, Wash. Sq. Col, N.Y. Univ, 50-52; asst. prof, Washington & Lee Univ, 52-55, assoc. prof, 55-59, prof, 59-64; PROF. ENG, NEW COL, FLA, 64-, dean div. humanities, 64-70. Consult. Eng. & advan. placement, Col. Eng. Exam. Bd, 63-64. Order of Brit.Empire. U.S.A, 41-44; Off. Strategic Serv, 44-46, Maj; Bronze Star Medal. MLA; Col. Eng. Asn. Elizabethan literature; contemporary literature; Old and Middle English. Publ: On the reading of poetry in relation to testing, In: Reflections on high school English, Univ. Tulsa, 66; New College, Christian Scholar, 67. Add: Division of Humanities, New College, Sarasota, FL 33578.

BORDINAT, PHILIP, b. Toledo, Ohio, May 31, 22; m. 46; c. 4. ENGLISH. B.A, Hillsdale Col, 49; M.A, Wayne State Univ, 50; Ph.D.(Eng), Univ. Birmingham, Eng, 52. Instr. Eng, Dartmouth Col, 52-53; Miami Univ, 53-55, asst. prof, 55-58, assoc. prof, 58-64; prof, Wright State Univ, 64-69, dir. gen. col, 64-66, dean lib. arts, 66-68; PROF. ENG, W.VA. UNIV, 69- Sr. lectr. Eng. & head dept, Univ. Nigeria, 60-62. Can. Army, 42-46, Capt. Eng. Inst; MLA. Jacobean and Caroline drama; modern drama; English Renaissance literature. Publ: Ed, Readings in criticism, Univ. Nigeria, 61; co-ed, Revealer of secrets: folk stories from Nigeria, Ginn, 74; auth, The poetic image in D.H. Lawrence's The Captain's doll, W.Va. Univ. Philol. Papers, 7/72; The dramatic function of Aunt Rina in Ibsen's Hedda Gabler, Stud. Humanities, 74; Chekhov's two great American directors, Midwest Quart, 74; plus others. Add: Dept. of English, West Virginia University, Morgantown, WV 26506.

BOREN, ROBERT REED, b. Burley, Idaho, Nov. 8, 36; m. 58; c. 4. COMMUNICATION. B.A, Brigham Young Univ, 58, M.A, 64; Ph.D.(rhet, speech educ), Purdue Univ, 65. Instr. speech, Brigham Young Univ, 61-64, asst. prof, 64-67; vis. prof, Univ. Utah, 67; assoc. prof. speech commun, Univ. Mont, 67-71; PROF. COMMUN. & CHMN. DEPT, BOISE STATE UNIV, 71- Forest naturalist, U.S. Forest Serv, summers 60-70; assoc. dir, Orgn. Assocs, 71- West. Forensic Asn.(v.pres, 66-68; pres, 68-70); Am. Forensic Asn.(treas, 68-70; v.pres, 70-72); West. Speech Commun. Asn.(1st v.pres, 71-72; pres, 72-); Speech Commun. Asn; Int. Commun. Asn; Nat. Univ. Exten. Asn. Communication theory; contemporary communication practices and public address; interpersonal communication. Publ: Co-auth, The human transaction, Scott, 73. Add: Dept. of Communication, Boise State University, Boise, ID 83725.

BORKAT, ROBERTA FRIEDMAN SARFATT, b. Cleveland, Ohio, July 12, 42; m. 73. ENGLISH LITERATURE. B.A, Cornell Univ, 64; Ph.D.(lit), Univ. Calif, San Diego, 69. Asst. humanities, Univ. Calif, San Diego, 65-69; ASST. PROF. ENG, SAN DIEGO STATE UNIV, 69- MLA; AAUP; Augustan Reprint Soc. Jonathan Swift; 18th century English literature; satire and fantasy. Publ: Co-auth, I hate English but . . . , San Diego State Univ, 73. Add: School of Literature, San Diego State University, 5402 College Ave, San Diego, CA 92115.

BORMANN, DENNIS ROBERT, b. Mitchell, S.Dak, Nov. 7, 35; m. 62; c. 2. SPEECH COMMUNICATION, GERMAN. B.A, Univ. S.Dak, 57; Fulbright scholar, Univ. Frankfurt, 57-58; M.A, Univ. Iowa, 59, Ph.D, (speech, drama), 68. Asst. prof. SPEECH, Mankato State Col, 64-66; instr, UNIV. NEBR-LINCOLN, 66-68, asst. prof, 68-72, ASSOC. PROF, 72- Woods fac. res. fel, Univ. Marburg, 73. U.S.A, 59-61. Speech Commun. Asn; AAUP. Rhetorical theory; German rhetoric and poetic; public address. Publ: A rhetoric of the German Enlightenment: J.C. Gottsched's Ausführliche Redekunst, Speech Monog, 6/71; The uncontested term contested: an analysis of Weaver on Burke, Quart. J. Speech, 10/71; The willing suspension of disbelief: Kames as a forerunner of Coleridge, Cent. States Speech J, spring 72. Add: Dept. of Speech Communication, University of Nebraska-Lincoln, Lincoln, NE 68508.

BORMANN, ERNEST GORDON, b. Mitchell, S.Dak, July 28, 25; m. 52. SPEECH. B.A, Univ. S.Dak, 49; M.A, Iowa State Univ, 51, Ph.D.(speech), 53. Instr. SPEECH, Univ. S.Dak, 49-50; asst. prof, East. Ill. State Col, 53-55, assoc. prof, 55-56; Fla. State Univ, 56-59; asst. prof. UNIV. MINN, MINNEAPOLIS, 59-61, assoc. prof, 62-65, PROF, 65- U.S.A, 43-46. Speech Commun. Asn; Cent. States Speech Asn. American public address and rhetorical theory; small group communication; history of religious and reform speaking. Publ: Theory and research in the communicative arts, Holt, 65; Discussion and group methods, 69, co-auth, Presentational speaking for business and the professions, 71 & Speech communication, 72, Harper; Interpersonal communication in the modern organization, 69 & ed, Forerunners of Black power, 71, Prentice-Hall. Add: Dept. of Speech Communication, University of Minnesota, Minneapolis, MN 55455.

BORNSTEIN, DIANE D, b. New York, N.Y, Apr. 22, 42. MEDIEVAL & RENAISSANCE LITERATURE, LINGUISTICS. B.A, Hunter Col, 66, M.A, 67; NDEA fel, N.Y. Univ, 68-70, Ph.D.(Eng), 70. Lectr. Eng, Hunter Col, 70-71; instr. QUEENS COL.(N.Y), 71-73, ASST. PROF. ENG. & LING, 73- Am. Counc. Learned Soc. grant-in-aid, 73. MLA; NCTE; Mediaeval Acad. Am. Historical linguistics; editing. Publ: Ed, The Scottish prose version of Vegetius' De re militari: introduction and text, Stud. Scottish Lit, 71 & Captan Perse and his coragios company, Am. Antiq. Soc, 73; co-auth, In forme of speche is chaunge, Prentice-Hall, 74; auth, Military strategy in Malory and Vegetius' De re militari, Comp. Lit. Stud, 72; Trial by combat and official irresponsibility in Richard II, Shakespeare Stud, 73; Military manuals in fifteenth century England, Mediaeval Stud, 73. Add: Dept. of English, Queens College, Flushing, NY 11367.

BORNSTEIN, GEORGE JAY, b. St. Louis, Mo, Aug. 25, 41; m. 67. ENGLISH & AMERICAN LITERATURE. B.A, Harvard, 63; Woodrow Wilson fel, Princeton, 63, Ph.D.(Eng), 66. Asst. prof. lit, Mass. Inst. Technol, 66-69; ENG, Rutgers Univ, 69-70; ASSOC. PROF, UNIV. MICH, ANN ARBOR,

70- Old Dom. fel, fall 68; Am. Counc. Learned Soc. fel, 72-73. MLA. Nineteenth and 20th century poetry; 19th century periodicals; literary theory. Publ: Yeats and Shelley, Univ. Chicago, 70; co-auth, British periodicals of the 18th & 19th centuries, Xerox, 72 & From villain to visionary; Pound and Yeats on Villon, Comp. Lit, fall 67; auth, Keats's concept of the ethereal, Keats-Shelley J, 69; Miscultivated field and corrupted garden: imagery in Hard times, Nineteenth century fiction, 71. Add: Dept. of English, University of Michigan, Ann Arbor, MI 48104.

BOROS, DONALD MICHAEL, b. Little Falls, Minn, Sept. 12, 43. THEATRE. B.S, St. Cloud State Col, 66, M.A, 67; U.S. Steel Found. fel, Fla. State Univ, 67-70, Ph.D.(theatre), 70. ASST. PROF. THEATRE, Grinnell Col, 70-71; UNIV. MICH, ANN ARBOR, 71-, Rackham fac. res. spec. proj. grant, 74. Creator & coord, Univ. Mich. Invitational Festival of Exp. Theatre, 73; host, Exp. Theatre, Univ. Mich. TV Ctr, 74. Am. Theatre Asn. American experimental theatre; stage directing; improvisation in actor-training. Add: Theatre Programs, Mendelssohn Theatre, University of Michigan, Ann Arbor, MI 48104.

BORROFF, MARIE, b. New York, N.Y, Sept. 10, 23. ENGLISH LANGUAGE & LITERATURE. Ph.B, Univ. Chicago, 43, M.A, 46; Sterling fel, Yale, 54-55, Ph.D, 56. Instr. ENG, Smith Col, 48-51, asst. prof, 56-59; vis. assoc. prof, YALE, 59-60, assoc. prof, 60-65, prof, 65-71, WILLIAM LAMPSON PROF, 71- Margaret Lee Wiley fel, Am. Asn. Univ. Women, 55-56; vis. asst. prof. Eng, Yale, 57-58; Guggenheim fel, 69-70; Phi Beta Kappa vis. scholar, 73-74. John Billings Fiske Mem. Poetry Prize, Univ. Chicago, 43; Eunice Tietjens Mem. Prize, Poetry Mag, 45. MLA; Mediaeval Acad. Am; NCTE. The relationship between language and literary style; stylistic studies in modern and medieval poetry; translation into modern verse of Sir Gawain and the Green Knight. Publ: Sir Gawain and the Green Knight: a stylistic and metrical study, Yale, 62; ed, Wallace Stevens: a collection of critical essays, Prentice-Hall, 63; auth, Sir Gawain and the Green Knight: a new verse-translation, Norton, 67; Creativity, poetic language and the computer, Yale Rev, summer 71; Robert Frost's new testament: language and the poem, Mod. Philol, 8/71; Words, language and form, In: Literary theory and structure: essays in honor of William K. Wimsatt, 73. Add: Dept. of English, Yale University, New Haven, CT 06520.

BORT, BARRY DAVIS, b. Dixon, Ill, Sept. 30, 32; m. 54; c. 3. ENGLISH. B.A, DePauw Univ, 54; univ. fel, Brown Univ, 55-56, M.A, 56, Ph.D, 60. Instr. ENG, Wheaton Col.(Mass), 58-60; asst. prof, Cent. Mich. Univ, 60-65; assoc. prof, STATE UNIV. N.Y. COL. NEW PALTZ, 65-70, PROF, 70- Victorian; modern British and American; literature and film. Publ: Co-auth, Guide to Japanese prose, Twayne & Asia Soc, 74; auth, Frost and the deeper vision, Midwest Rev, 10/63; Dove or serpent: the imposter in Vanity Fair, Discourse, antumn 66; The good soldier: comedy or tragedy?, Twentieth Century Lit, 1/67. Add: Dept. of English, State University of New York College at New Paltz, New Paltz, NY 12561.

BOS, WILLIAM HERMAN, b. Muskegon, Mich, Feb. 18, 16; m. 42, 61. SPEECH, ENGLISH. A.B, Wheaton Col, 39; dipl, West. Theol. Sem, 42; A.M, Wash. Univ, 50; Ph.D.(speech), Univ. Mich, 55. Minister, Presby. Church, 42-49; teaching fel. speech, Wash. Univ, 50-51; Univ. Mich, 51-54; asst. prof. speech & relig, Detroit Inst. Technol, 54-56; Eng. & speech, East. Mich. Univ, 56-63; prof. speech & head dept, Calif. State Col. Pa, 63-66; Hope Col, 66-68; ASSOC. PROF. SPEECH, STEPHEN F. AUSTIN STATE UNIV, 68- Speech Commun. Asn. Speech for ministers; educational television. Add: Dept. of Communications, Stephen F. Austin State University, Nacogdoches, TX 75962.

BOSCH, L. ALAN, b. Chicago, Ill, July 20, 39; m. 63; c. 2. AMERICAN LITERATURE. B.A, Univ. Notre Dame, 61; M.A, Ind. Univ, 66, Ph.D.(Eng), 71. Resident lectr. ENG, IND. UNIV, KOKOMO, 66-71, ASST. PROF, 71- AAUP; MLA. Henry James; relations between novels and drama; American political novels. Add: Div. of Humanities, Indiana University at Kokomo, 2300 S. Washington, Kokomo, IN 46901.

BOSMAJIAN, HAIG ARAM, b. Fresno, Calif, Mar. 26, 28; m. 57; c. 1. SPEECH. A.B, Univ. Calif, Berkeley, 49; A.M, Univ. Pac, 51; Ph.D.(Nazi rhet), Stanford Univ, 60. Instr. pub. speech & Parliamentary proc, Univ. Idaho, 59-61; asst. prof. Am. pub. address & pub. speech, Univ. Conn, 61-65; assoc. prof. PARLIAMENTARY PROC, RHET. & FREEDOM OF SPEECH, UNIV. WASH, 65-72, PROF, 72- Speech Commun. Asn; West. Speech Asn. Rhetoric of social movements; freedom of speech; language and behavior. Publ: Readings in speech, 65 & Readings in Parliamentary procedure, 68, Harper; The rhetoric of the speaker, Heath, 67; The rhetoric of the civil rights movement, Random, 69; The principles and practice of freedom of speech, Houghton, 71; The rhetoric of nonverbal communication, Scott, 71; Dissent: symbolic behavior and rhetorical strategies, Allyn & Bacon, 72; This great argument: the rights of women, Addison-Wesley, 72; The magic word in Nazi persuasion, ETC, 3/66; The language of white racism, Col. Eng, 12/69; Speech and the First Amendment, Today's Speech, fall 70; plus others. Add: Dept. of Speech, University of Washington, Seattle, WA 98195.

BOSSONE, RICHARD M, b. Philadelphia, Pa, Aug. 8, 24. ENGLISH EDUCATION. B.A, Univ. Calif, Berkeley, 48; M.A, San Francisco State Col, 51; Ph.D.(educ), Univ. South. Calif, 58. Teacher, Jr. High, Calif, 51-53; high sch, 53-54; instr. Eng, El Camino Jr. Col, 54-59; assoc. prof. Eng. educ, Univ. Calif, Riverside, 61-67; Richmond Col.(N.Y), 67-70, PROF. ENG, BARUCH COL, 70- Eng. consult, Riverside City & County Schs, Calif, 62-66; ed. consult, Addison-Wesley Pub. Co, 65-68. U.S.A.F, 42-45. NCTE; Am. Asn. Jr. Cols; Nat. Soc. Stud. Educ. Training of English teachers; reading-study skills problems of community college students; teaching remedial English. Publ: The training and work of California junior college English teachers, Riverside County Schs. & NCTE, 64; Remedial English in California public junior colleges: an analysis and evaluation, State Dept. Educ, Calif. & Addison-Wesley, 66; ed, Teaching basic English courses, Van Nostrand, 71; co-auth, Handbook of basic English skills, Xerox, 71; auth, Disadvantaged teachers in disadvantaged schools, Contemporary Educ, 70; Open admissions: one year later, 71 & Teaching composition to open admission students, 72, Eng. Rec; plus others. Add: Dept. of English, Baruch College, 17 Lexington Ave, New York, NY 10010.

BOSTETTER, EDWARD EVERETT, b. Hagerstown, Md, Aug. 13, 14. ENGLISH LITERATURE. A.B, Franklin & Marshall Col, 35; A.M, Princeton, 37, Ph.D, 38. Instr, Univ. Minn, 38-40; asst. prof. ENG, UNIV. WASH, 40-47, assoc. prof, 47-59, PROF, 59- Mem. ed. comt, PMLA, 67-71. MLA; NCTE. Early 19th century English literature; modern criticism; thematic patterns in Romantic poetry; Byron: selected poetry and prose, Publ: The Romantic ventriloquists, Univ. Wash, 63. Add: Dept. of English, University of Washington, Seattle, WA 98105.

BOSTICH, JUNE MARIE, b. Loma Linda, Calif, Jan. 4, 37; m. 69; c. 1. ENGLISH. B.A, Univ. Calif, Riverside, 64, M.A, 67, Ph.D.(Eng), 71. ASST. PROF. ENG, PURDUE UNIV, N.CENT. CAMPUS, 69- MLA; Milton Soc. Am. Eighteenth century and Restoration literature; John Milton. Publ: Influence of Milton on Alexander Pope, In: Milton Encyclopedia, 74. Add: Dept. of English, Purdue University, North Central Campus, Westville, IN 46391.

BOSTROM, ROBERT N, b. Kearney, Nebr, Nov. 2, 30; m. 52; c. 3. COMMUNICATION. A.B, Morningside Col, 55; A.M, State Univ. Iowa, 58, Ph.D, 61. Instr. speech, Sacramento State Col, 60-61; asst. prof, West. Ill. Univ, 61-66; assoc. prof. COMMUN, Ohio Univ, 66-70; PROF. & CHMN. DEPT, UNIV. KY, 70- Mil. Intel, A.U.S, 52-54. Speech Commun. Asn; Nat. Soc. Study Commun. Scientific study of the process of communication; attitude and opinion change. Publ: Co-auth, Communication for everyday use, Holt, 68. Add: Dept. of Speech, University of Kentucky, Lexington, KY 40506.

BOSWELL, GEORGE WORLEY, b. Nashville, Tenn, Mar. 29, 19; m. 51; c. 4. LITERATURE, ENGLISH. B.A, Vanderbilt Univ, 39, M.A, 40; Ph.D, George Peabody Col, 51. Instr. Eng, Vanderbilt Univ, 46-48; assoc. prof, Austin Peay State Col, 50-53, prof, 53-60; prof. Eng. & chmn. div. lang. & lit, Morehead State Col, 60-66; PROF. ENG, UNIV. MISS, 66-, res. grants, 66-69 & 71-73. Jo Stafford Prize in Am. Folklore & Algernon Sydney Sullivan Medallion, George Peabody Col, 50. Sig.C, 41-46, 1st Lt. MLA; NCTE; Am. Folklore Soc; Col. Eng. Asn; S.Atlantic Mod. Lang. Asn; Southeast. Folklore Soc.(pres, 54-55); S.Cent. Mod. Lang. Asn; Keats-Shelley Asn. Am; Int. Folk Music Counc. Literature of the English Romantic period; folklore; folksongs of the South, especially of Tennessee. Publ: Co-auth, Tennessee folk songs, Tenn. State Dept. of Educ, 50 & Fundamentals of folk literature, Anthrop. Publ, 62; auth, Study of the Bible as literature, 58, 2nd. ed, privately publ, 65; Traditional ballads and folk-songs of West Virginia, Am. Folklore Soc, 64; Verse and music in The sacred harp, South. Folklore Quart, 70; Metrical alteration in folksinging, J. Am. Folklore, 72; Tolkien as littérateur, S.Cent. Bull, 72; plus several others. Add: 1225 Beanland Dr, Oxford, MI 38655.

BOSWELL, GRACE HADAWAY, b. Buford, Ga, Dec. 19, 25; m. 52; c. 2. ENGLISH. A.B, La Grange Col, 49; M.A, Univ. Ga, 52, Alumni Found. fel, 54-55, Ph.D, 60. Instr. ENG, Reinhardt Col, 49-53; Univ. Ga, 54, 55-57; Miss. State Univ, 57-60, asst. prof, 60-62; MONMOUTH COL.(ILL), 62-74, ASSOC. PROF, 74- MLA; Col. Eng. Asn. English literature of the Victorian Period; Romantic movement in English literature. Add: Dept. of English, Monmouth College, Monmouth, IL 61462.

BOSWELL, JACKSON CAMPBELL, b. Whiteville, N.C, Oct. 2, 34; m. 69. ENGLISH LITERATURE, AMERICAN STUDIES. A.B, Univ. N.C, Chapel Hill, 60, M.A, 62; Univ. Aix-Marseilles, 60-61; fel, George Washington Univ, 65-68, M.Phil, 73, Ph.D.(Am. stud), 74. Instr. ENG, Col. William & Mary, 62-63; Randolph-Macon Woman's Col, 63-65; ASST. PROF, D.C. TEACHERS COL, 68- Fel, Folger Shakespeare Libr, summer 73; contrib. critic, Washington Star-News. U.S.N, 54-58. MLA (mem. comt. bibliog, 68-); Am. Stud. Asn; Milton Soc. Am; Col. Lang. Asn; Southeast. Renaissance Conf. Milton; American thought and culture; North Atlantic civilization. Publ: Shylock's turquoise ring, Shakespeare Quart, 63; Navigation of James V, Bibliotheck, 72; A lost book, Milton Quart, 73. Add: 365 N. Granada St, Arlington, VA 22203.

BOSWORTH, RAYMOND FRANCIS, b. New Haven, Conn, July 19, 04; m. 34; c. 1. ENGLISH. B.S, Middlebury Col, 29, A.M, 32; dipl, Univ. London, 30. Teacher, sec. schs, 30-35; from instr. to prof. Eng. & dir. sch. publ, SIMMONS COL, 35-71, EMER. PROF. ENG, 71- Instr, Bread Loaf Sch. Eng, 32-41; univ. exten, Harvard, 46-58. U.S.N.R, 42-45, Capt. Col. Eng. Asn; Asn. Educ. in Jour; Soc. Tech. Writers & Publ; Int. Graphic Arts Educ. Asn. English composition; one-act plays and articles. Add: 549 High Rock St, Needham, MA 02197.

BOTKIN, BENJAMIN ALBERT, b. Boston, Mass, Feb. 7, 01; m. 25; c. 2. FOLKLORE. A.B, Harvard, 20; univ. fel, Columbia Univ, 20-21, M.A, 21; Ph.D.(Eng. & anthrop), Univ. Nebr, 31, hon. Litt.D, 56. Instr. Eng, Univ. Okla, 21-31, asst. prof, 31-38, assoc. prof, 38-40; from asst-in-charge to chief, Arch. Am. Folksong, Libr. Congr, 42-45. Asst. instr. Eng, Univ. Nebr, 30-31; summers, asst. prof, Mont. State Univ, 32 & N.Mex. Norm. Univ, 33; comt. population problems, Nat. Resources Comn, 36; Julius Rosenwald fel, 37; consult. folklore, Fed. Writers Proj, 38, nat. folklore ed, 38-39; chief ed, writers unit, Libr. Congr. Proj, Work Projs. Admin, 39-41; assoc. fel, Libr. Congr, 40-41; resid. fel, 41-42, hon. fel, 42-55; Guggenheim fel, 51; Louis M. Rabinowitz Found. grant, 65; consult. games, Random House Dictionary of the English Language, 66; ed-in-chief, Rediscovering America & Folklore & Society, Johnson Reprint Corp, 66-; mem. adv. subcomt. folk music, music panel, cult. presentations prog, Bur. Educ. & Cult. Affairs, Dept. of State, 67-; Nat. Endowment for Humanities sr. fel, 68. Folklore and Society, Essays in Honor of Benjamin A. Botkin, 66. Fel. Am. Folklore Soc.(pres, 44); Manuscript Soc; Int. Folk Music Counc; Int. Soc. Ethnol. & Folklore; Nat. Folk Festival Asn.(hon. pres, 73-). American popular culture, folklore and folk music. Publ: Ed, Folk-say, a regional miscellany, Univ. Okla, 29, 30, 31, 32; The southwest scene, Economy, 31; auth, The American play-party song, Univ. Nebr, 37, Ungar, 63; ed, A treasury of American folklore, 44, A treasury of New England folklore, 47, rev. ed, 65, A treasury of Southern folklore, 49, A treasury of Western folklore, 51, co-ed, A treasury of railroad folklore, 53 & ed, A treasury of Mississippi River folklore, 55, Crown; Lay my burden down: a folk history of slavery, Univ. Chicago, 45, Phoenix Bks, 58, German version, Die Stimme des Negers, Nannen, Hamburg, 63; Sidewalks of America, Bobbs, 54; New York City folklore, 56, A treasury of American anecdotes,

57 & A Civil War reasury of tales, legends, and folklore, 60, Random; co-ed, The illustrated book of American folklore, Grosset, 58; auth, A sampler of Western folklore and songs, In: The book of the American West, Messner, 63; The folksong revival: cult or culture?, In: The American folk scene, Dell, 67; Automobile humor, J. Popular Cult, 68. Add: 45 Lexington Dr, Croton-on-Hudson, NY 10520.

BOTTKOL, JOSEPH McGRATH JAMES, b. Menominee, Mich, July 14, 09; m. 37; c. 2. ENGLISH LITERATURE. A.B, Harvard, 32, A.M, 34, Ph.D, 37. Asst. ENG, Harvard, 33-37; instr, Yale, 37-39; asst. prof, Col. William & Mary, 39-45; MT. HOLYOKE COL, 45-48, assoc. prof, 48-54, PROF, 54- Fulbright scholar, Univ. Rome, 51-53, lectr, Univ. Thessaloniki, 59-60; vis. prof, Amherst Col, 59; Four Col. Asia-Africa Stud. travel grant, Japan, summers 67, 68. Off. Strategic Servs, 43-45. Classical influence in the English Renaissance: Dryden and Milton; contemporary fiction, including Japanese. Add: Dept. of English, Mt. Holyoke College, South Hadley, MA 01075.

BOTTMAN, PHILIP NATHANIEL, b. Lake Bronson, Minn, July 11, 16. ENGLISH, COMPARATIVE LITERATURE. B.A, Univ. Wash, 51, M.A, 64, Ph.D.(comp. lit), 69. Asst. Norweg. lang. & lit, Univ. Wash, 64-66; instr. Eng, UNIV. WIS-SUPERIOR, 66-69, asst. prof, 69-73, ASSOC. PROF. ENG. & COMP. LIT, 73- Lectr. Eng. & Scand. lit, Wis. State Univs. Lib. Arts Stud. Ctr, Copenhagen, Denmark, 72. U.S.N.R, 42-45. MLA; Philol. Asn. Pac. Coast; AAUP; Am-Scand. Found; Norweg-Am. Hist. Asn; Soc. Advan. Scand. Stud. Nineteenth century English literature, especially drama and the novel; 20th century English and American literature, especially the drama; 19th and 20th century Norwegian, Danish and Swedish literature, especially the drama and the novel. Publ: Quentin's quest: Arthur Miller's move into expressionism, Wis. Stud. Lit, 68; Ibsen's Apollonian-Dionysian dialectic: a reconsideration, In: Germanistiches Forschungsketten, Univ. Ky, (in press). Add: Dept. of English, University of Wisconsin-Superior, Superior, WI 54880.

BOTTORFF, WILLIAM KENNETH, b. Toledo, Ohio, July 28, 31; m. 58; c. 2. ENGLISH, AMERICAN STUDIES. A.B, Bowling Green State Univ, 58; Woodrow Wilson Found. fel. & A.M, West. Reserve Univ, 59; univ. fel. & Ph.D. (Am. poetry), Brown Univ, 64. Instr. ENG, Boston Univ, 61-63; asst. prof, State Univ. N.Y. Col. Geneseo, 63-65; Ohio Univ, 65-68; ASSOC. PROF, UNIV. TOLEDO, 68-, DIR. AM. STUD. PROF, 71- U.S.N, 51-55. Am. Stud. Asn; Mid-Continent Am. Stud. Asn; MLA; Thoreau Soc. Thomas Jefferson; American poetry, especially 18th century; American culture. Publ: James Lane Allen, Twayne, 64; American poems, 1793, 66, The Anarchiad, 1786-1787, 67, Miscellaneous works of David Humphreys (1804), 68, co-ed, Major poems of Timothy Dwight, 69 & Works of Joel Barlow, 70, Scholars' Facsimiles; A Kentucky cardinal, Aftermath, and other selected works of James Lane Allen, Col. & Univ, 67; Challenges in American culture, Popular, 70, auth, Whatever inly rejoices me: paradox of Self-reliance, Emerson Soc. Quart, 72, Hindu and Buddhist usages in the poetry of T.S. Eliot, In: From Irving to Steinbeck, Univ. Fla, 72; Emerson's power, Explicator, 2/73; plus three others. Add: Dept. of English, University of Toledo, Toledo, OH 43606.

BOUCHARD, DONALD F, b. Manchester, N.H, Nov. 20, 37; m. 63; c. 2. ENGLISH LITERATURE. B.A, Univ. N.H, 63; Ph.D.(Eng), State Univ. N.Y. Buffalo, 68. ASST. PROF. ENG, McGILL UNIV, 68- Can. Counc. leave fel, 74-75. Seventeenth century English literature; critical theory, French structuralism; Shakespeare. Publ: Milton: a structural interpretation, Edward Arnold, 74; ed, The literary and philosophical essays of Michel Foucault, Cornell Univ, 74; auth, Samson as medecine man, Genre, 72. Add: Dept. of English, McGill University, Montreal, P.Q, Can.

BOUCHER, WAYNE IRVING, b. Bay City, Mich, Dec. 12, 34; div; c. 2. ENGLISH, PHILOSOPHY. B.A, Univ. Mich, 56, M.A, 60; Univ. Mo, 59-61. Teacher jr. high sch, Mich, 58; instr. Eng, Univ. Mo, 58-63; asst. to pres, Rand Corp, 63-69; res. assoc, Inst. For Future, 69-71; SECY. & SR. PROJ. MGR, FUTURES GROUP, 71- Instr. Eng, exten. div, Univ. Mo, 63; exten. div, Univ. Calif, Los Angeles, 64-65; consult. many pvt. corp. & govt. agencies, 71-; prof. bus, Univ. Conn, 72-73. Nat. Asn. Sci. Writers; Policy Stud. Orgn. Systems analysis; futures research and technology assessment; corporate planning and forecasting. Publ: Co-ed, Systems analysis and policy planning: applications in defense, Am. Elsevier, 68; plus numerous articles. Add: Futures Group, 124 Hebron Ave, Glastonbury, CT 06033.

BOUDREAU, GORDON V, b. Marshall, Minn, May 17, 29; m. 60; c. 7. ENGLISH. B.A, St. Mary's Col.(Minn), 51; M.A, Marquette Univ, 57; Univ. Minn, summer 59; Ph.D.(Eng), Ind. Univ, 67. Instr. ENG, Marquette Univ, 57-60; LE MOYNE COL.(N.Y), 63-64; asst. prof, 64-69, ASSOC. PROF, 69-; dir. honors prog, 68-72. U.S.A.F, 51-55, S/Sgt. MLA; Thoreau Soc; Melville Soc. Am. Herman Melville; Henry David Thoreau; Hawthorne. Publ: Of pale ushers and Gothic piles: Melville's architectural symbology, Emerson Soc. Quart, 72; The summons of Young Goodman Brown, Greyfriar, 72; H.D. Thoreau and William Gilpin: the metaphysical ground of the picturesque, Am. Lit, 11/73. Add: Dept. of English, Le Moyne College, Syracuse, NY 13214.

BOUGHTON, CHARLES R, b. Danville, Ill, June 19, 32; m. 56; c. 1. SPEECH. A.B, Univ. Ill, 53, M.A, 54; summer, Univ. Mich, 55; Ph.D.(theatre, Eng), Northwest. Univ, 60. Teacher high sch, Ill, 54-56; instr. SPEECH, Ill. State Norm. Univ, 56-58; asst. prof, Univ. Minn, Duluth, 60-61; ASSOC. PROF, BOWLING GREEN STATE UNIV, 61- Speech Commun. Asn; Am. Theatre Asn. Dramatic theory and criticism; Greek and Elizabethan-Jacobean stage production; non-realistic modern styles of play production. Add: Dept. of Speech, Bowling Green State University, Bowling Green, OH 43402.

BOUISE, OSCAR ADONIS, b. New Orleans, La, Mar. 3, 08; m. 38; c. 2. ENGLISH. B.S. & Ph.G, Xavier Univ.(La), 30, hon. Litt.D, 60; A.M, Univ. Mich, 37, 47-50. Instr. Eng, Latin & math, Xavier Univ.(La), 33-41, registr, 41-42, asst. prof. Eng, 42-48, assoc. prof, 48-65; South. Univ, 65-68, dir. freshman Eng, 65-68; COORD. AFRO-AM. STUD, XAVIER UNIV.(LA), 68-, GRAD. STUD. ADV, 69-, HEALTH PROF. & MED. ADV, 71-, PROF. BLACK HIST, BLACK & AFRICAN LIT, 72- Judge, Nat. Achievement Awards, NCTE, 59-67, state chmn. of judges, 67-69, mem. comt. on relating compos. & lit, 64-69; mem, Lang. Arts Work Conf, La, 63; Conf. Eng. Educ, 64, 66, 68; Forest Park Community Col, 67; asst. dir. NDEA Eng. Inst, summer 67; mem. comt. Eng. compos. examr, Col. Entrance Exam. Bd-Educ. Testing Serv, 69-; consult, test construct, Nat. Assessment Educ. Progress-Comn. of States, 70- NCTE; Asn. Stud. Afro-Am. Life & Hist; AHA; Asn. Am. Med. Cols; Asn. Health Prof. Adv. Rhetoric and composition; teaching of English in secondary schools; history of English language and of modern American grammar, structural and transformational. Publ: The Negro and his idea of rights, 1780 to 1840, Negro Hist. Bull, 11/62; Jacques Maritain's theory of art: an introduction, Xavier Univ. Stud, 12/62; Generating a composition, Eng, J, 10/67 & Educ. Digest, 1/68; plus others. Add: 2707 Havana St, New Orleans, LA 70119.

BOULGER, JAMES DENIS, b. North Adams, Mass, June 9, 31; m. 57; c. 4. ENGLISH. A.B, Col. Holy Cross, 53; M.A, Yale, 54, Ph.D.(Eng), 57. Instr. Eng, Yale, 57-61; Morse jr. fac. fel. from Yale, St. Catherine's Col, Cambridge, 61-62; asst. prof. ENG, Yale, 62-64; assoc. prof, BROWN UNIV, 64-69, PROF, 69-, Bronson fel, 70-71. Am. Philos. Soc. fel, 71. MLA. Romanticism in England; S.T. Coleridge as a major figure; religious backgrounds of Romanticism. Publ: Coleridge as religious thinker, Yale, 61; ed. & auth, Twentieth century interpretations of Rime of ancient mariner, Prentice-Hall, 69; Imagination and speculation in Coleridge's conversation poems, J. Eng. & Ger. Philol, 10/65; Yeats and Irish identity, Thought, summer 67; Coleridge: Marginalia, myth-making and the later poetry, Stud. Romanticism, fall 72; plus many others. Add: Horace Mann House, Dept. of English, Brown University, Providence, RI 02912.

BOUSLOG, CHARLES SCOTT, b. Shirley, Ind, Sept. 17, 11; m. 51; c. 2. ENGLISH LITERATURE. A.B, Ind. Univ, 34; A.M, Harvard, 48, Ph.D, 51. Acting instr, Ind. Univ, 34-36; instr. Eng. lit, UNIV. HAWAII, MANOA, 39-42, 47-48, asst. prof, 48-52, assoc. prof, 52-57, PROF. ENG, 57-, chmn. dept, 56-59, 64-66, acting dir, Inst. Am. Stud, E-W Ctr, 60-61. Summer vis. prof, Univ. Colo, 60; San Francisco State Col, 64; Fulbright Smith-Mundt Act lect, Doshisha & Kobe Univs, Japan, 66-67. U.S.A.A.F, 42-46, Capt. MLA; Philol. Asn. Pac. Coast. Romantic and contemporary period in English and American literature. Publ: Coleridge's Marginalia, Bull. N.Y. Pub. Libr, 61; Structure and theme in Coleridge's Dejection, Mod. Lang. Quart, 63. Add: Dept. of English, 1733 Donaghho Rd, University of Hawaii at Manoa, Honolulu, HI 96822.

BOVEE, WARREN GILLES, b. Billings, Mont, Jan. 2, 22; m. 47; c. 6. JOURNALISM. A.B, Marquette Univ, 47, M.A, 49; Columbia Univ, 49-53. Instr. Eng. & jour, Col. New Rochelle, 48-53; asst. prof. JOUR, MARQUETTE UNIV, 53-59, assoc. prof, 59-64, PROF, 64-, DIR. JOUR. GRAD. PROG, 72-, acting dean, Col. Jour, 70-71. Mem, Mag. Publ. Asn, mag. fel, 63-64; mem. counc, Ctr. Res. Libr, 64- Andrew Hamilton Award, 61. U.S.A.A.F, 43-46. Asn. Educ. in Jour; Nat. Conf. Ed. Writers; Int. Commun. Asn. Magazine journalism; editorial persuasion; microform publishing. Publ: The mythology of editorial anonymity, Pt. I, fall 72, Pt. II, winter 72-73, Masthead; Scientific and technical journals on microfiche, IEEE Trans. on Prof. Commun, 9/73; plus others. Add: College of Journalism, Marquette University, 1135 W. Kilbourn Ave, Milwaukee, WI 53233.

BOWDEN, EDWIN TURNER, JR, b. Milledgeville, Ga, June 5, 24; m. 48; c. 3. ENGLISH. B.A, Harvard, 48; Fulbright fel, Cambridge Univ, 49-50; M.A. & Ph.D.(Eng), Yale, 52. Instr. ENG, Yale, 52-56; asst. prof, UNIV. TEX, AUSTIN, 56-59, assoc. prof, 59-66, PROF, 66- Eng. Inst, secy, 55; text. ed, Complete Works of Washington Irving, Univ. of Wis. Press, 68- U.S.A.A.F, 43-46. MLA. American and colonial literature; American bibliography. Publ: Themes of Henry James, Yale, 56; Dungeon of the heart; human isolation and the American novel, Macmillan, 61; ed, Satiric poems of John Trumbull, Univ. Tex, 62; ed, A history of New York, Twayne, 64; auth, James Thurber: a bibliography, Ohio State Univ, 69. Add: Dept. of English, University of Texas, Austin, TX 78712.

BOWDEN, JAMES HENRY, b. Louisville, Ky, Oct. 28, 34; m. 64; c. 3. AMERICAN LITERATURE. B.A, Univ. Minn, Minneapolis, 55, Ph.D.(Am. stud), 70; M.A, Univ. Louisville, 59; Rockefeller scholarship, Seabury-West. Theol. Sem, 64-65; Louisville Presyby. Theol. Sem, 66-70. Instr. ENG, Univ. Ky, 60-61; Univ. Mont, 62-64; Colgate Univ, 65-66; ASST. PROF, IND. UNIV. SOUTHEAST, 66- U.S.A.F, 55-57, 1st Lt. AAUP; MLA. Peter de Vries; study of the religious significance of the Oneida community; Amway soap as an evangelical endeavor. Publ: You can take Salem out of the country, but..., Christian Century, 12/70; Courtly love is alive and well in America, Living Church, 10/71; No redactor, no redeemer, In: The cheaters and the cheated, Everett Edwards, 73; plus others. Add: 419 Wood Rd, Louisville, KY 40222.

BOWDEN, ROBERT JOHN, Religion, English. See Volume IV, Philosophy, Religion & Law.

BOWDEN, WILLIAM ROBERT, b. Dunbar, Pa, May 18, 14; m. 45; c. 2. ENGLISH. A.B, Haverford Col, 35; A.M, Duke Univ, 37; Ph.D, Yale, 48. Instr. ENG, W.Nottingham Acad, 37-38; Ga. Sch. Technol, 38-41; from asst. prof. to assoc. prof, DICKINSON COL, 48-59, PROF, 59- Mem, Comn. Higher Educ, Mid. States Asn. Cols. & Sec. Schs, 73- U.S.A.A.F, 42-46. MLA; Col. Eng. Asn. Shakespeare; history and structure of English language. Publ: English dramatic lyric, 1603-1642, Yale Univ, 51; contrib, Col. Eng; Shakespeare Quart; plus others. Add: 227 Parker St, Carlisle, PA 17013.

BOWDRE, PAUL H, JR, b. Memphis, Tenn, Jan. 3, 26; m. 51; c. 2. ENGLISH. B.S, U.S. Naval Acad, 47; Southwest. at Memphis, 50-51; M.A, Univ. Miss, 60; Ph.D.(Eng), Univ. Fla, 64. Instr. ENG, Univ. Fla, 61-62; assoc. prof, W.GA. COL, 62-64, PROF. & HEAD DEPT, 64- Consult. Eng. lang, State of Ga, 64-; dir, NDEA Eng. Inst, 68. U.S.N, 47-50, Res, 51-53, Lt. Comdr. MLA. English curriculum development; dialect studies; transformational grammar. Publ: The new grammar, Ga. Asn. Curriculum Develop, 66; The structure of English as defined for the development of an English curriculum, Ga. Dept. Educ, 66. Add: Dept. of English, West Georgia College, Carrollton, GA 30117.

BOWEN, ELBERT RUSSELL, b. Lynn, Ind, June 21, 18; m. 41; c. 3. SPEECH & DRAMA. A.B, DePauw Univ, 41; M.A, Univ. Denver, 46; Mich. State Univ, 46; Ph.D, Univ. Mo, 50. Instr. SPEECH, Univ. Mo, 46-50; assoc.

prof, CENT. MICH. UNIV, 50-54, PROF, 54-, chmn. dept, 67-68. Univ. Mich. study grant, summer 56. U.S.A, 42-45. Speech Commun. Asn; Cent. States Speech Asn. Interpretative reading; general speech; American theatre history. Publ: Co-auth, Communicative reading, Macmillan, 56, rev. ed, 63 & 72; auth, Theatrical entertainments in early rural Missouri, Univ. Mo, 59; Report from eerywhere I, Today's Speech, 67; A gap in the Peter Principle, 7/71 & The manner of memory, 1/72, World J. Psychosyntheses; plus others. Add: Dept. of Speech & Dramatic Arts, Central Michigan University, Mt. Pleasant, MI 48858.

BOWEN, HARRY W, b. New Castle, Pa, Sept. 20, 30; m. 57; c. 2. RHETORIC. B.A, Westminster Col.(Pa), 53; M.A, Ohio State Univ, 54; Ph.D, Univ. Pittsburgh, 62. Radio-TV announcer, Sta. WKBN, Youngstown, Ohio, 54; mgt. trainee, Bell Telephone Co, Pa, 57-58; instr. speech, Geneva Col, 58-59, instr. asst. prof. speech, West. Mich. Univ, 62-67; assoc. prof. SPEECH & DRAMATIC ARTS, EAST. MICH. UNIV, 67-72, PROF, 72- Adj.Gen.C, U.S.A, 54-56. Speech Commun. Asn; Cent. States Speech Commun. Asn. Rhetoric. Publ: Liberalization of the stifling category, Cent. States Speech J, 5/66; A reassessment of speech delivery, 11/66 & A realistic view of non-violent assumptions, 9/67, Today's Speech. Add: Dept. of Speech & Dramatic Arts, Eastern Michigan University, Ypsilanti, MI 48197.

BOWEN, HOYT EDWIN, b. Gainesville, Ga, Mar. 13, 19; m. 51. ENGLISH. A.B, Piedmont Col, 39; M.A, Columbia Univ, 52; Ph.D.(Eng), Fla. State Univ, 55. Teacher Eng, Piedmont Col, 46-52; instr, Fla. State Univ, 55; S.C. Univ, 55-56; prof. & head dept, Pfeiffer Col, 56-67, acad. dean, 67-69; prof. Eng. & dean col, Huntington Col, 69-71; PROF. ENG, WEST. KY. UNIV, 72- U.S.N.R, 40-46, Lt. Comdr. MLA; Col. Eng. Asn; Southeast. Renaissance Conf; S.Atlantic Mod. Lang. Asn. Shakespeare; drama; English renaissance. Publ: Ed, Thomas Heywood's Troia Britanica; Coleridge's Rime of the ancient mariner, Explicator; I break my staff . . . I'll drown my book, Renaissance Papers, 61. Add: Dept. of English, Western Kentucky University, Box U 356, Bowling Green, KY 42101.

BOWEN, JAMES KEITH, b. Chicago, Ill, Apr. 18, 32; m. 59; c. 2. AMERICAN LITERATURE. B.A, Univ. Nev, 63, M.A, 65; Univ. of the Pac, 67-68. Instr. ENG, SOUTH. ORE. COL, 65, asst. prof, 68-70, ASSOC. PROF, 70- Dunbar Carpender res. fel, 67-68; lectr, Univ. of the Pac, summer 68; co-ed, Am. Lit. Abstr. U.S.A, 52-54, Capt. Col. Eng. Asn; MLA; Melville Soc. Am. Hegelian philosophy and Herman Melville; existentialism and American literature. Publ: Confrontations, 69, co-ed, An edition of Huckleberry Finn, 71 & A critical guide to Herman Melville, 72, Scott; co-auth, American short fiction, 70 & co-ed, International short fiction, 72, Bobbs; Drama: a critical collection, Harper, 70; auth, Crazy Ahab & Kierkegaard's Melancholy fantastic, Res. Stud, spring 70; Alienation and withdrawal are not the absurd: preference and renunciation in Bartleby, Stud. Short Fiction, fall 72; To build a fire: epistemology and the white wilderness, West. Am. Lit, winter 72; plus others. Add: Dept. of English, Southern Oregon College, Ashland, OR 97520.

BOWEN, MERLIN S, b. Eureka, Calif, Aug, 7, 10; m. 41; c. 2. AMERICAN LITERATURE, HUMANITIES. A.B, Univ. Chicago, 36, M.A, 47, Ph.D, 57. Teacher Eng, Francis W. Parker Sch, Chicago, Ill, 40-46; instr. humanities, UNIV. CHICAGO, 47-50, asst. prof, 50-57, from assoc. prof. to PROF. ENG. & HUMANITIES, 57-, von der Marwitz fel, div. humanities, 56. Fulbright lectr. Am. lit, Univ. Athens, Greece, 60-61, Univ. Bucharest, 71-72. American literature, 1800-1865; 20th century English and American poetry. Publ: The long encounter: self and experience in the writings of Herman Melville, Univ. Chicago, 60; ed, Herman Melville: Redburn: his first voyage, Holt, 71. Add: Dept. of English, University of Chicago, 1050 E. 59th St, Chicago, IL 60637.

BOWEN, ZACK RHOLLIE, b. Philadelphia, Pa, Aug. 10, 34; m. 58; c. 3. ENGLISH. B.A, Univ, Pa, 56; M.A, Temple Univ, 60; univ. res. fel, Univ. Buffalo, 61, univ. scholar, 61, 62; Ph.D.(Eng), State Univ. N.Y. Buffalo, 64. Asst, Temple Univ, 58-60, instr. ENG, 60; ASST. PROF, State Univ. N.Y. Col. Fredonia, 60-64; STATE UNIV. N.Y. BINGHAMTON, 64-, CHMN. DEPT, 73- Lectr. poetry, drama & Eng. res, Phila. Mus. Col. Art, 60; grants-in-aid, State Univ. N.Y. Res. Found, 60-63, 64-67, summer res. fels, 62, 63; Am. Philos. Soc. grant-in-aid, 67. MLA; James Joyce Soc. Music in the works of James Joyce; descriptive linguistics. Publ: Padraic Colum: a biographical-critical introduction, South. Ill. Univ, 70; The bronze-gold sirensong, In: Literary monographs I, Univ. Wis, 67. Producer-dir, James Joyce's Lestrygonians, 61, Calypso, 63, Lotus Eaters, 63, Hades, 64 & Sirens, 65, Folkways Records. Add: Dept. of English, State University of New York at Binghamton, Binghamton, NY 13901.

BOWER, WARREN, b. Elkhart, Ind, July 24, 98. ENGLISH. A.B, Hillsdale Col, 20; A.M, Univ. Mich, 23. Instr. rhet, Univ. Mich, 22-28; Eng. Ala. Polytech. Inst, 28-29; N.Y. UNIV, 30-45, asst. prof, 45-50, assoc. prof, 50-60, prof, 60-, 70, asst. dean, 51-70, EMER. PROF. ENG, 70- Mem. nat. comt. on writing awards, Scholastic Mag, 65-; consult. ed, Funk & Wagnalls, 67- George Foster Peabody broadcasting award, 62. Nat. Asn. Educ. Broadcasters. Modern literature and criticism; methods of teaching creative writing. Publ: How to write for pleasure and profit, Lippincott; co-auth, Short story craft, Macmillan. Add: Room 43, School of Continuing Education, New York University, 2 University Pl, New York, NY 10003.

BOWERS, ANTHONY ROBIN, b. Iver, Eng, Apr. 17, 40; m. 69; c. 1. ENGLISH LITERATURE. B.A, Mich. State Univ, 61; M.A, Princeton, 64, Ph.D. (Eng), 68. Asst. prof. ENG, Univ. B.C, 64-65; UNIV. NEBR, LINCOLN, 65-72, ASSOC. PROF, 72- Univ. Nebr. summer res. fel, 68; Frank H. Woods Found. fel, 71-72. MLA; Renaissance Soc. Am; Shakespeare Asn. Am. John Milton's rhetoric; Renaissance literature; medieval literature. Publ: Milton and Salmasius: the rhetorical imperatives, Philol. Quart, 73. Add: Dept. of English, University of Nebraska, Lincoln, NE 68508.

BOWERS, EDGAR, b. Rome, Ga, Mar. 2, 24. ENGLISH. B.A, Univ. N.C, 47; Jones fel, Stanford Univ, 48, M.A, 49, Ph.D.(Eng), 53; Fulbright fel, France, 50. Instr. ENG, Duke Univ, 52-55; asst. prof, Harpur Col, State Univ. N.Y, 55-58; UNIV. CALIF, SANTA BARBARA, 58-61, assoc. prof, 61-67, PROF, 67- Sewanee Rév. fel, 54; Guggenheim fels, 59 & 69. U.S.A, 43-46. English, American and French lyric poetry and literary criticism. Publ: The form of loss, 56 & The astronomers, 65, Swallow; Living together, new and selected poems, David R. Godine, 73. Add: 1502 Miramar Beach, Santa Barbara, CA 93103.

BOWERS, FRANCIS R, F.S.C, b. New York, N.Y, May 4, 20. ENGLISH. B.A, Cath. Univ. Am, 46, Ph.D, 59; M.A, Fordham Univ, 52. Asst. prof. Eng, De La Salle Col, 53-59; from asst. prof. to ASSOC. PROF. ENG. & WORLD LIT, MANHATTAN COL, 59-, CHMN. GRAD. ENG. DEPT, 61-, CHMN. UNDERGRAD. ENG. & WORLD LIT. DEPT, 67-, DEAN ARTS & SCI, 70- Bd. Trustees fel, Cath. Univ. Am, 53-58; Finn Fund grant, Oxford, summer 62; Manhattan Col. summer proj. grant, Cambridge, 66. Am. Conf. Acad. Deans; East. Asn. Deans; Am. Asn. Higher Educ. Restoration period; 18th century English literature; English novel. Publ: Characterization in narrative poetry of George Crabbe, Catholic Univ. Am, 59. Add: Manhattan College, Bronx, NY 10471.

BOWERS, FREDSON, b. New Haven, Conn, Apr. 25, 05. ENGLISH LITERATURE. Ph.B, Brown Univ, 25, hon. Litt.D, 71; Ph.D, Harvard, 34; hon. Litt.D, Clark Univ, 71; hon. L.H.D, Univ. Chicago, 73. Instr, Harvard, 26-36; Princeton, 37-38; asst. prof. ENG, UNIV. VA, 39-42, assoc. prof, 46-49, PROF, 49-68, LINDEN KENT PROF, 69-, dean fac. arts & sci, 68-70. Prof. lectr, Univ. Chicago, 50-65; Fulbright advan. res. fel, U.K, 52-53; regional chmn, Woodrow Wilson Nat. Fel. Found, 56-59; Sandars reader bibliog, Cambridge, 59; Guggenheim fel, 58-59, 72-73; James Lyell reader bibliog, Oxford, 59, vis. fel, All Souls Col, 72 & 74; Phi Beta Kappa vis. scholar, 62-63; resident res. fel, Villa Serbelloni Res. Ctr, 71 & 73; adv. ed, Va. Quart Rev. U.S.N.R, 42-45, Comdr. Bibliog. Soc, Eng.(Gold Medal, 69); Grolier Club; fel. Am. Acad. Arts & Sci; MLA (mem. Eng. adv. comt, 66-68); S.Atlantic Mod. Lang. Asn.(pres, 69); Oxford Bibliog. Soc; Bibliog. Soc. Am; Bibliog. Soc. Univ. Va; Cambridge Bibliog. Soc; Am. Antiq. Soc; cor. fel, Brit. Acad. Bibliographical and textual problems in 16th and 17th century literature, especially drama, and in 19th century American literature. Publ: Ed, Studies in bibliography, annually, 48-, auth, On editing Shakespeare, 66 & ed, Works of Stephen Crane (10 vols), 69-75, Univ. Va; auth, Principles of bibliographical description, 49 & Russell, 62; ed, Dramatic works of Thomas Dekker (4 vols), 53-58, auth, Textual and literary criticism, 59 & ed, The complete works of Christopher Marlowe (2 vols), 73, Cambridge Univ; Whitman's manuscripts: Leaves of grass, 1860, Univ. Chicago, 55; Bibliography and textual criticism, Oxford Univ, 64; plus others. Add: Woodburn, Rte. 8, Charlottesville, VA 22901.

BOWERS, JOHN WAITE, b. Alton, Iowa, Nov. 28, 35; m. 56; c. 3. SPEECH, DRAMA. B.S, Univ. Kans, 58, M.A, 59; Ph.D.(speech & drama), Univ. Iowa, 62. Asst. prof, SPEECH & DRAMA, UNIV. IOWA, 62-65, assoc. prof, 65-69, PROF, 69-, speech supvr. rhet, 62-67. Old Gold Res. fel, summer 64; vis. lectr, Univ. Wis, summer 66; assoc. ed, Speech Monogr, 66-69, sr. assoc. ed, 69-72. Speech Commun. Asn.(mem. res. bd, 73-76); Int. Commun. Asn. Language and communication; rhetorical criticism. Publ: Designing the communication experiment, Random, 70; co-auth, The rhetoric of agitation and control, Addison-Wesley, 71; auth, Content analysis, In: Methods of research in communication, Houghton, 70; plus others. Add: Dept. of Speech, University of Iowa, Iowa City, IA 52240.

BOWERS, ROBERT HOOD, JR, b. New York, N.Y, June 29, 06. ENGLISH. A.B, Yale, 27, Ph.D, 35. From assoc. prof. to PROF. ENG, UNIV. FLA, 46- MLA. Renaissance. Add: Dept. of English, 207 Anderson, University of Florida, Gainesville, FL 32601.

BOWLER, NED W, b. Shoshone, Idaho, Apr. 17, 19; m. 47; c. 2. PHONETICS, SPEECH PATHOLOGY. B.A, Univ. Idaho, 47; M.A, N.Y. Univ, 48; Ph.D. (speech), Stanford Univ, 57. Asst. prof. speech & drama, Col. Idaho, 47-50; SPEECH, Calif. State Col. Long Beach, 54-59; assoc. prof, UNIV. COLO, BOULDER, 59-70, PROF, 70- Sig.C, 41-43; U.S.A.F, 43-45, 50-51. Am Speech & Hearing Asn. Experimental phonetics; voice. Publ: Co-auth, Improve your speech, W.C. Brown, 65; auth, Fundamental frequency analysis of harsh vocal quality, Speech Monogr, 6/64; A comparison of conventional and audiolingual methods in teaching the IPA, J. Colo. Speech & Hearing Asn, fall 69. Add: Dept. of Speech Pathology & Audiology, University of Colorado, Boulder, CO 80301.

BOWLING, LAWRENCE EDWARD, b. Ashland, Ky, Apr. 2, 16; m. 38; c. 1. ENGLISH. A.B, Berea Col, 38; A.M, Vanderbilt Univ, 39; scholoar, Univ. Iowa, 42-43, fel, 43-44, Ph.D, 46. Instr, sec. schs, Ky, 39-41; instr. Eng. & critic teacher, Berea Col, 41-42; res. asst, Univ. Iowa, 44-45; instr. Eng, Yale, 45-47; prof. & head dept, King Col, 47-48; lectr, Univ. Ky, 50-51; res. fel, Am. Counc. Learned Soc, 51-52; PROF. ENG, Tex, Technol. Col, 52-64; UNIV. ALA, 64-, res. grant, 65-66. Tex. State res. grants, summers, 54-64; fac. fel, Ford Found. Fund Advan. Educ, 55-56; mem. Eng. Inst; chmn. Am. lit. prog, S.Cent. Mod. Lang. Asn, 59; secy. Shakespeare prog, S.Atlantic Mod. Lang. Asn, 66. MLA; S.Cent. Mod. Lang. Asn; S.Atlantic Mod. Lang. Asn. Shakespeare; American literature; literary criticism. Publ: The thematic framework of Romeo and Juliet, PMLA, 3/49; Faulkner and the theme of innocence, Kenyon Rev, summer 58; Thoreau's social criticism as poetry, Yale Rev, winter 66; plus others. Add: P.O. Box 3001, University of Alabama, University, AL 35486.

BOWMAN, ELIZABETH, Linguistics, English. See Volume III, Foreign Languages, Linguistics & Philology.

BOWMAN, FRANCIS EZRA, b. Cleveland, Ohio, Sept. 18, 02. ENGLISH & AMERICAN LITERATURE. A.B, Harvard, 24, A.M, 26, Ph.D, 34. Instr. Eng, col. lib. arts & pure sci, N.Y. Univ, 26-30; chmn. freshman compos. 28-30; instr. Eng. & tutor div. mod. langs, Harvard, 30-34; instr. Eng, Univ. Rochester, 35-39, asst. prof, 39-43, dir. debate, 38-43; assoc. prof. Eng, DUKE UNIV, 46-63, prof, 63-72, supvr. freshman instr, 46-56, asst. dean, grad. sch, 57-62, assoc. dean, 62-66, acting dean, 66-67, EMER. PROF. ENG, 72- Ed, Col. Compos. & Commun. U.S.N.R, 43-45, Lt. Comdr. MLA; NCTE; Col. Eng. Asn; S.Atlantic Mod. Lang. Asn. Seventeenth century English literature; modern rhetoric; life and correspondence of John Evelyn. Add: 2114 Woodrow St, Durham, NC 27705.

BOWMAN, GEORGE WILLIAM, b. Muncie, Ind, Sept. 1, 15; m. 42; c. 3. ENGLISH. A.B, Ashland Col, 37; M.A, Ind. Univ, 42, Ph.D.(Eng), 54; hon.

D.Litt, Wilmington Col, 69. Asst. ENG, Ind. Univ, 39-42; asst. prof, Gogebic Col, 46; prof, Wilmington Col, 46-69; PROF. & CHMN. DIV. HUMANITIES, UNIV. MAINE, PRESQUE ISLE, 69- U.S.A, 42-46, Capt. Col. Eng. Asn; MLA; Asn. Depts. Eng. Hawthorne; Chaucer; Swift. Add: Div. of Humanities, University of Maine at Presque Isle, Presque Isle, ME 04769.

BOWMAN, GEORGIA B, b. Bonne Terre, Mo, May 20, 14. SPEECH, JOURNALISM. A.B, William Jewell Col, 34; B.J, Univ. Mo, 34; M.A, Univ. Iowa, 41, Ph.D.(rhet), 56. Teacher, high sch, Mo, 34-40; instr. jour, Univ. Mo, 42-44; lectr. speech, Brooklyn Col, 46-47; instr. speech & jour, William Jewell Col, 47-50, asst. prof, 50-55; instr. commun. skills, Univ. Iowa, 55-56; assoc. prof. SPEECH & JOUR, WILLIAM JEWELL COL, 56-63, PROF, 63-, CHMN. DEPT, 65- Ed, Forensic, 71- William Jewell Col. citation for achievement, 45; Liberty Chamber Commerce teacher of the year award, 62. Speech Commun. Asn; Cent. States Speech Asn; Nat. Counc. Col. Publ. Adv. Add: William Jewell College, Liberty, MO 64068.

BOWMAN, LEONARD JOSEPH, Religion, Literature. See Volume IV, Philosophy, Religion and Law.

BOWMAN, NED ALAN, b. Lyons, Ind, Apr. 6, 32; m. 57; c. 4. THEATER ARTS. B.A, State Univ. Iowa, 53, M.A, 56; Univ. Veracruz, Mex, 57; Ph.D, Stanford Univ, 63. Instr. SPEECH & THEATER, Univ. N.Dak, 56-58; acting instr, Stanford Univ, 59; ASSOC. PROF, UNIV. PITTSBURGH, 60- Consult, theater bldg. design, 58-; Field-Hoteling grant, Stanford Univ, 60; compiler, recent publ. on theater archit, 60-70; ed, Theatre Design & Technol, 65-70; Fulbright lectr, Colombia, 67; Int. Dimensions Prog. grantee, E.Europe & U.S.S.R, 68; chmn. publ. comn, Orgn. Int. Scenographs & Tecniciens Theatre, 71- U.S.A, 53-55, Sgt. Am. Educ. Theatre Asn; U.S. Inst. Theatre Technol.(pres, 72-73). Theater architecture and technology; stage scenery design. Publ: Co-auth, Theatre architecture, N.Y. Pub. Libr, 65 & Planning for the theatre, Univ. Pittsburgh, 66; ed, Handbook of technical practice for the performing arts, Scenographic Media, 73. Add: Dept. of Speech & Theatre Arts, University of Pittsburgh, Pittsburgh, PA 15260.

BOWMAN, RICHARD STEARNS, b. White Plains, N.Y, June 4, 17; m. 48; c. 2. COMPARATIVE LITERATURE. B.S, Haverford Col, 38; Columbia Univ, 38-39. Instr. Eng. & German, COOPER UNION, 39-49, asst. prof. COMP. LIT, 49-57, assoc. prof, 57-70, PROF, 70- DIR. DRAMATICS, 48-, LECTR. ADULT EDUC, 53-, res. asst. to pres, 46-51. Shell Assist Award, 58; Fulbright lectr. Am. stud, Int. People's Col, Denmark, 62-63. U.S.N, 41-46. Col. Eng. Asn; Am. Stud. Asn; NCTE. Scientific travel-literature of the naturalists; a focus on the interplay of science and romanticism in English, French and German literature. Publ: Darwin's bulldog and the voyage of the Rattlesnake, Cooper Union Centennial Symposium Paper, 4/60; co-auth, The general education movement... in engineering, J. Engineering Educ, 11/60. Add: Cooper Union, Cooper Square, New York, NY 10003.

BOWMAN, SYLVIA E, b. Advance, Ind, June 19, 14. ENGLISH. B.S, Cent. Norm. Col, 39; M.A, Univ. Chicago, 43; Am. Asn. Univ. Women scholar, 52; Ph.D.(comp. lit), Univ. Paris, France, 52; hon. LL.D, St. Mary's Col. (Ind), 72. Instr. elem. schs, 35-44, dir. pubs, 44-47; instr. ENG. IND. UNIV, FT. WAYNE CAMPUS, 47-53, asst. prof, 53-63, PROF, 63-, CHANCELLOR REGIONAL CAMPUS ADMIN, 72-, acting chmn. dept, 64-72, chmn. div. arts & sci, 70-72, Consult, N.Am. Van Lines, 54-72; ed-in-chief, U.S. Auth. Series, Eng. Auth. Series, Am. Classics Series & gen. ed, World Auth. Series, Twayne Pubs; mem. N.Cent. Asn. Cols. & Sec. Schs. Frederich Bachman Leiber Award, Ind. Univ, 62; medal of honor, Ctr. Stud. Scambi Int, Rome, 65; cert. merit, Dictionary Int. Biog, 67; Prof. Achievement Award, Univ. Chicago, 73. MLA; Am. Stud. Asn; Am. Asn. Higher Educ. Novel; utopian fiction. Publ: English manual: The year 2000; A critical biography of Edward Bellamy; Edward Bellamy abroad: an America prophet's influence, Twayne, 62. Add: 6767 N. Meridian, Indianapolis, IN 46260.

BOWMAN, WALTER PARKER, b. New Haven, Conn, Nov. 13, 10; m. 46; c. 1. COMPARATIVE LITERATURE. A.B, Bowdoin Col, 31; A.M, Columbia Univ, 33, Ph.D.(comp. lit), 42; Clare Col, Cambridge; Sorbonne, France. Teacher private sch. & col, 33-42; asst. prof. Eng. & French, Marietta Col, 46-47; assoc. prof. Eng, West. Reserve Univ, 47-50; prof. Eng. & chmn. dept. commun, Am. Univ.(D.C), 50-53; auth, 53-56; dir, Am. Lang. Inst, Baghdad, Iraq, 57-58; lectr. Eng, lang. ctr, Am. Univ.(D.C), 58-61; supvr. res. & for. lang, pub. schs, Montgomery County, Md, 61-63; PROF. ENG, STATE UNIV. N.Y. COL. BROCKPORT, 63- U.S.A.A.F, 42-46, Capt. MLA; Milton Soc. Am.(treas, 52-62; NCTE; Am. Name Soc; Am. Soc. Theatre Res. Franco-British literary relations; studies in John Milton. Publ: Co-auth, Theatre language, Theatre Arts, 61; contrib. to Fr. Rev, Mod. Lang. Notes; plus others. Add: Dept. of English, State University of New York College at Brockport, Brockport, NY 14420.

BOWMAN, WAYNE, b. Rouses Point, N.Y, July 28, 14; m. 44; c. 3. ENGLISH. A.B, Elon Col, 37; A.M, Univ. N.C, 40, 47. Teacher, high sch, N.C, 37-40; instr. Eng. & dir. dramatics, N.Ga. Col, 40-41; asst. dramatic arts, Univ. N.C, 46-47, asst. prof. Eng. & tech. dir. Playlikers, Woman's Col, 47-54; lectr. ENG, OLD DOMINION UNIV, 54-55, asst. prof, 55-62, ASSOC. PROF, 62- U.S.N.R, 41-45, Lt. AAUP. Dramatic literature; theatre. Publ: Modern theatre lighting, Harper, 57. Add: Dept. of English, Old Dominion University, Norfolk, VA 23508.

BOWRON, BERNARD ROY, JR, b. Berkeley, Calif, May 19, 13. ENGLISH. A.B, Univ. Calif, 35; Heller traveling fel. from Univ. Calif, Harvard, 39-40, A.M, 41, Sheldon traveling fel, 46-47, Ph.D, 48. Teaching fel. hist, Harvard, 43-45, tutor hist. & lit, 42-46; asst. prof. ENG, UNIV. MINN, MINNEAPOLIS, 48-51, assoc. prof, 51-61, PROF, 61-, secy, 50-61, chmn. Am. stud. prog, 60-68. AHA; MLA; Am. Stud. Asn. American literature, 1865-1917; American civilization; Latin American biography. Publ: Henry B. Fuller of Chicago: the ordeal of a genteel realist in ungenteel America, 74. Add: Dept. of English, University of Minnesota, Minneapolis, MN 55455.

BOX, TERRY JOE, b. Brady, Tex, Aug. 10, 43; m. 67; c. 2. ENGLISH & AMERICAN LITERATURE. B.A, Sam Houston State Univ, 65, M.A, 67; Ph.D.(Eng), Tex. Tech Univ, 72. Instr. ENG, STEPHEN F. AUSTIN STATE UNIV, 67-70, ASST. PROF, 72- English Renaissance drama; Victorian novel. Add: Dept. of English, Stephen F. Austin State University, Box 3007 SFA Sta, Nacogdoches, TX 75961.

BOXILL, ROGER, b. Sydney, Australia, Mar. 27, 28; U.S. citizen; m. 65. ENGLISH. A.B, Columbia Univ, 53, univ. fel. & Ph.D.(Eng), 66; Fulbright fel. & cert, Royal Acad. Dramatic Art, 54; univ. scholar. & M.A, Hunter Col, 59. Lectr. ENG, CITY COL. NEW YORK, 65-66, instr, 66-67, asst. prof, 67-72, ASSOC. PROF, 72- City Univ. New York res. grant, 67. U.S.A.F, 46-48, Sgt. MLA. Shaw; Shakespeare. Publ: Shaw and the doctors, Basic Bks, 69. Add: Dept. of English, City College of New York, 138th St. & Convent Ave, New York, NY 10031.

BOYCE, BENJAMIN, b. Lansing, Mich, Nov. 26, 03; m. 39. ENGLISH, LITERATURE. A.B, Univ. Mich, 26; A.M, Harvard, 27, Ph.D, 33. Instr. Eng, Northwest. Univ, 27-30; asst. prof, Munic. Univ. Omaha, 33-35, prof. Eng. & head dept. Eng. & Comp. lit, 35-46; prof. ENG, Univ. Neb, 46-50; DUKE UNIV, 50-69, EMER. PROF, 69- Mem. ed. bd, Stud. Eng. Lit, 63- English prose fiction of 17th and 18th centuries. Publ: Tom Brown of facetious memory, 39; Theophrastan character in England to 1642, 47 & The benevolent man: a life of Ralph Allen of Bath, 67, Harvard Univ; ed, The adventures of Lindamira, Univ. Minn, 49; auth, The Polemic character 1640-1661, Univ. Nebr, 55; Character-sketches in Pope's poems, Duke Univ, 62; ed, Paul, Scarron: the comical romance, Blom, 68. Add: Dept. of English, Duke University, Durham, NC 27706.

BOYD, BEVERLY, b. Brooklyn, N.Y, Mar. 27, 25. ENGLISH. A.B, Brooklyn Col, 46; Bryn Mawr Col, 46-47; A.M, Columbia Univ, 48, Fisher fel, 54-55, Ph.D.(Eng), 56. Instr. ENG, Univ. Tex, 55-59; prof, Radford Col, Va. Polytech. Inst, 59-62; asst. prof, UNIV. KANS, 62-64, assoc. prof, 64-69, PROF, 69- Summer res. grants, Huntington Libr, 60 & Am. Philos. Soc, 61; Guggenheim Found. fel, 69-70. MLA; Mediaeval Acad. Am. Middle English. Publ: The Middle English miracles of the Virgin, 64 & Chaucer and the Medieval book, 73, Huntington Libr; Chaucer and the liturgy, Dorrance, 67; Chaucer's Prioress: her green gauds, Mod. Lang. Quart; Hoccleve's miracle of the Virgin, Tex. Stud. Eng. Add: Dept. of English, University of Kansas, Lawrence, KS 66044.

BOYD, ELIZABETH FRENCH, b. Princeton, N.J, May 24, 05. ENGLISH. A.B, Wells Col, 28; Univ. Vienna, 28-29; A.M, Columbia Univ, 33, Ph.D, 44; Univ. Ariz, 33-34. Instr. ENG, Briarcliff Jr. Col, 35-36; N.J. Col. Women, Rutgers Univ, 36-39; Lawrence Col, 43-44; asst. prof, DOUGLASS COL, RUTGERS UNIV, NEW BRUNSWICK, 44-50, assoc. prof, 50-57, prof, 57-70, chmn. dept, 62-68, EMER. PROF, 70- MLA. English and American literature; contemporary fiction and poetry. Publ: Byron's Don Juan, Rutgers Univ, Humanities & Routledge. Add: 7 Redcliffe Ave, Highland Park, NJ 08904.

BOYD, ERNEST LEE, b. Parke Co, Ind, Apr. 20, 11; m. 37; c. 3. SPEECH, ENGLISH. A.B, Wabash Col, 32; M.A, Univ. Toronto, 34; Ph.D.(speech), Northwest. Univ, 54. Lectr. bus. Eng. & advert, Northwest. Univ, 48-54; ASSOC. PROF. SPEECH, South. Ill. Univ, 57-58; W.GA. COL, 68- U.S.N.R, 43-46, Lt. Speech Commun. Asn. Rhetorical theory; public address. Add: Dept. of Fine Arts, West Georgia College, Carrollton, GA 30117.

BOYD, EVELYN MAE, b. Oelwein, Iowa. MEDIEVAL LITERATURE. A.B, Grinnell Col, 18; A.M, Univ. Chicago, 20; Roberts fel, Columbia Univ, 29-31, 33-34; Danforth Found. scholar, summer, 56. Asst. prof. Eng. North. Ill. State Teachers Col, 20-22; instr, Grinnell Col, 23-27, asst. prof, 27-54, assoc. prof, 54-56, prof, 56-59; asst. prof, Waterloo Univ. Col, 59-61, dir, Workshop Creative Writing, 61; assoc. prof, Mansfield State Col, 63; PROF. OLD ENG, UNIV. WATERLOO, 63- Asst. prof, Kobe Col, 26-27; mem. exec. comt, Columbia in Toronto Lect. Series, 67-68. Presidential Citation, 46, Am. Red Cross, 42-46. MLA; Col. Eng. Asn; Mediaeval Acad. Am. Masters of English literature; Old English; creative writing. Publ: Dante Gabriel Rossetti's The house of life and its Italian backgrounds. Add: 225 Lourdes St, Waterloo, Ont. Can.

BOYD, GEORGE WILSON, b. Water Valley, Ky, Jan. 4, 18; m. 50; c. 4. ENGLISH LANGUAGE & LITERATURE. A.B, Murray State Univ, 39; A.M, Univ. Ky, 41; Danforth Found. study grant, 56-57; Ph.D.(Eng), Columbia Univ, 57. Instr. ENG, Univ. Ky, 41-42, 46; lectr, Hunter Col, 47-48; asst. prof, Memphis State Univ, 48-50; Miss. State Univ, 52-56, assoc. prof, 57-58; Univ. Southwest. La, 58-59; PROF. & CHMN. DEPT, MILLSAPS COL, 59- Vis. prof, Tulane Univ, 65-66; fels, Southeastern Inst. Medieval & Renaissance Stud, Univ. N.C, summer 67 & Duke Univ., summer 68. U.S.A.F, 42-46, Maj. MLA; S.Cent. Mod. Lang. Asn.(chmn, 70-71); S.Cent. Renaissance Conf.(pres, 68-69); AAUP. Milton studies; English lyric from high Renaissance to present; religious dimensions in contemporary literature. Publ: Herbert's language: curling with metaphor a plain intention?, Southwest. La. J, summer 58; What is metaphysical poetry?, Miss. Quart, winter 59. Add: Dept. of English, Millsaps College, Jackson, MS 39210.

BOYD, JOHN ALLEN, b. Springfield, Mo, June 13, 15; m. 39; c. 2. JOURNALISM. A.B, DePauw Univ, 37; M.A, Ind. Univ, 41, Ed.D, 60. Teacher Eng. & jour, Bosse High Sch, Evansville, Ind, 39-48; asst. prof, Evansville Col, 48-52; IND. STATE UNIV, TERRE HAUTE, 52-55, assoc. prof. JOUR, 55-64, PROF, 65-, DIR. JOURNALISTIC STUD, 70- Nat. Counc. Col. Publ. Adv.(nat. chmn, 61-63, exec. dir, 65-). High school journalism programs; school newspaper and yearbook layout. Publ: The statesman manual, Ind. State Col, 57; The Sycamore manual, Moore-Langen, 63, 68; contrib, Teacher's guide to high school journalism, Ind. State Dept. Pub. Instr, 65. Add: Dept. of English & Journalism, Indiana State University, Terre Haute, IN 47809.

BOYD, JOHN DOMINIC, S.J, b. New York, N.Y, Aug. 4, 16. ENGLISH. A.B, Georgetown Univ, 40; Ph.L, Woodstock Col, 41, S.T.L, 48; M.A, Fordham Univ, 51; Ph.D, Harvard, 58. Instr. Latin & Eng, St. Peter's Prep. Sch, 41-42; teacher, high sch, D.C, 42-44; N.Y, 51; instr. ENG, Bellarmine Col, 55-60; FORDHAM UNIV, 60-68, assoc. prof, 68-71, PROF. & CHMN. DEPT, 71-, dir, col. honors prog, 62-67, fac. fel, 66-67, rector, Murray-Weigel Hall, 69-73. Mem, Eng. Inst. MLA. History of English criticism; critical theory and aesthetics; 18th century English literature. Publ: The function of mimesis and its decline, Harvard Univ, 68; Poetry, In: New Catholic encyclopedia, McGraw, 67; The dry salvages: topography as symbol, Renascence, 68; Earth imagery in Graham Greene's The potting shed, Mod. Drama, 6/73. Add: Dept. of English, Fordham University, New York, NY 10458.

BOYD, JOHN DOUGLAS, b. Cedar Rapids, Iowa, Mar. 28, 41; m. 66. ENGLISH. B.A, Carleton Col, 63, Woodrow Wilson fel, 63; fel, Cornell Univ, 64, M.A, 65, Ph.D, 68. ASST. PROF. ENG, CORNELL UNIV, 67- MLA. English and American lyric poetry; Victorian prose fiction. Add: Dept. of English, Cornell University, Ithaca, NY 14850.

BOYD, JOHN HARVEY, JR, b. Martinsville, Ind, Sept. 4, 22; m. 47; c. 2. JOURNALISM. B.S,Ind. Univ, 48, M.A, 55. Instr. jour, Univ. Ala, 50-53; news ed, Pensacola J. & Sunday News J, Fla, 53-54; tri-state ed, Evansville Press, Ind, 54-61; asst. prof. JOUR, Univ. Evansville, 61-65; Mich. State Univ, 65-68; ASSOC. PROF, Univ. Mo, 68-71; IND. STATE UNIV, TERRE HAUTE, 71-, DIR. JOUR, 74- Copy ed, Evansville Press, Ind, 52; city ed, Columbia Missourian, 68-71; adv, Ind. Statesman, 71- U.S.A.A.F, 43-46, Sgt. Asn. Educ. in Jour. Add: Dept. of English & Journalism, Indiana State University, Terre Haute, IN 47809.

BOYD, KATHARINE, b. Miss, Nov. 7, 09. DRAMA & SPEECH. Chambers fel, Columbia Univ, 44, Rowe scholar, 45, Ph.D.(drama), 46; Univ. London, 51; Univ. Florence, 63; hon. Litt.D, William Carey Col, 63. Instr. speech, Miss. Woman's Col, 31-37; PROF. SPEECH & DRAMA, Hardin Simmons Univ, 37-55; SUL ROSS STATE UNIV, 55- Am. Educ. Theatre Asn. History of the theater; play directing and acting; theatre criticism and research. Publ: Interchange of plays between London and New York, 1910-1939, King's Crown, 48. Add: Dept. of Speech & Drama, Sul Ross State University, Alpine, TX 79830.

BOYD, LESLIE EMERSON, b. Kimball, S.Dak, July 21, 04; m. 31. ENGLISH. A.B, Huron Col, 30; Univ. Colo, summers, 35, 36, 38, 39; M.E, Mont. State Univ, 53. Teacher high sch, S.Dak, 30-45; instr. ENG. & SOC. SCI, S.DAK. SCH. MINES & TECHNOL, 42-44, asst. prof, 45-54, assoc. prof, 54-62, prof, 62-71, dir. dept. Eng, 66-71, EMER. PROF, 71- Judge, state declamatory & debate contests, S.Dak, 49. NCTE; Am. Soc. Engineering Educ. Add: Dept. of English, South Dakota School of Mines & Technology, Rapid City, SD 57701.

BOYER, DALE KENNETH, b. Baker, Ore, Apr. 6, 36; m. 59; c. 3. ENGLISH & AMERICAN LITERATURE. B.A, Univ. Ore, 58, M.A, 63; Ph.D.(Eng), Univ. Mo, Columbia, 69. Instr. ENG, Univ. Mo, Columbia, 63-68; BOISE STATE UNIV, 68-69, asst. prof, 69-72, ASSOC. PROF, 72- Consult. reader, Boise State Col. West. Writers Ser, 73. U.S.A, 58-60, Res, 60-64. MLA. British Romantic poetry; 20th century American poetry; the novel. Add: Dept. of English, Boise State University, 1910 College Blvd, Boise, ID 83725.

BOYER, ROBERT DOWNER, b. Washington, D.C, Sept. 23, 39. THEATRE STUDIES, DRAMATIC LITERATURE. B.A, Univ. Md, 61, M.A, 63; Ph.D. (theatre), Ohio State Univ, 70. Lectr. theatre, OHIO STATE UNIV, 68-71, ASST. PROF, COMP. LIT, 71- Theatre history; 20th century dramatic literature. Publ: Co-auth, The international seminar in a program of graduate theatre studies, Speech J, 70; auth, No offense intended: W.S. Gilbert and the Victorian public, Theatre Studies, 71-72; co-auth, The National Theatre of Washington, D.C, 1835-1972: audiences and buildings, Records Columbia Hist. Soc, 73. Add: Division of Comparative Literature, Ohio State University, Columbus, OH 43210.

BOYER, ROBERT HORACE, b. Philadelphia, Pa, Oct. 9, 37; m. 64; c. 4. ENGLISH LITERATURE, HUMANITIES. B.A, La Salle Col, 59, M.A, 60; Nat. Sci. Found. grant, summer 61; M.A, Marquette Univ, 64; Ph.D.(Eng), Univ. Pa, 69. Teacher biol, Cent. Cath. High Sch, Canton, Ohio, 60-62; ENG, Phoenix Union High Sch. Syst, Ariz, 64-66; ASST. PROF, ST. NORBERT COL, 68- Nat. Endowment for Humanities jr. fel, 71-72. MLA. W. H. Auden, his use of Anglo-Saxon poetry; science fiction and fantasy in modern literature; Soviet Russian literature. Publ: Anglo-Saxon and Middle English influences in the poetry of W.H. Auden, Univ. Microfilms, 70. Add: Division of Humanities & Fine Arts, St. Norbert College, De Pere, WI 54115.

BOYERS, WILLIAM HAYDEN, b. Woodsfield, Ohio, Sept. 4, 00; m. 27; c. 1. ROMANCE LANGUAGES. A.B, Ohio Wesleyan Univ, 22, M.A, 24; Ph.D, Univ. Chicago, 29. Instr. Latin & Greek, Ohio Wesleyan Univ, 22-23, Romance lang, 23-25; Univ. Chicago, 27-28; from instr. to assoc. prof. French & Italian, OBERLIN COL, 28-55, prof, 55-67, dir. summer stock, Oberlin Col. players, 53-67, EMER. PROF. ROMANCE LANG, 67-; PROF. ENG. & DIR. DRAMA, ST. PAUL'S COL.(VA), 67-, CHMN. DEPT. ENG, 68- U.S.A, 18. MLA; Am. Asn. Teachers Fr; NEA. Dante; French drama of the 18th and 19th centuries; Gilbert and Sullivan opera. Publ: Transl. & ed, The Economic Harmonies, Van Nostrand, 64. Add: Box 22, St. Paul's College, Lawrenceville, VA 23868.

BOYETT, WOODROW WILSON, b. Rockford, Ala, Dec. 12, 18. ENGLISH. B.A, Univ. Ala, 39, M.A, 47; Ph.D.(Eng), Univ. Mich, 54. Instr. ENG, UNIV. ALA, 47-50, from asst. prof. to PROF, 50- U.S.A, 42-46, Capt. MLA. Old English; Chaucer; Renaissance. Add: Dept. of English, Box 1721, University of Alabama, University, AL 35486.

BOYETTE, PURVIS ELTON, b. Johnston Co, N.C, Dec. 10, 37. ENGLISH. A.B, East Carolina Col, 59; M.A, Univ. Kans, 61; Ph.D.(Milton), Vanderbilt Univ, 66. Teaching fel, Univ. Kans, 59-61; asst. prof. ENG, Newberry Col, 61-64; TULANE UNIV, 66-69, ASSOC. PROF, 69-, DIR. GRAD. STUD, 70-71, 72- Founder & assoc. ed, Stud. in Short Fiction; fel, Southeast. Inst. Medieval & Renaissance Stud, summer 67; ed, Tulane Stud. Eng, 67-; prof-in-charge, Tulane-Newcomb Jr. Yr. in Gt. Brit, 71-72. MLA; Milton Soc; Southeast Renaissance Conf; S.Atlantic Mod. Lang. Asn; S.Cent. Mod. Lang. Asn. Milton; 17th century English literature. Publ: Milton and the sacred fire: sex symbolism in Paradise Lost, 73 & co-ed, Milton encyclopedia, 75, Univ. Wis; auth, The songs of George Etherege, Stud. Eng. Lit, summer 66; Milton's abstracted sublimities: the structure of meaning in A Mask, Tulane Stud. Eng, 70; Myra Breckinridge and imitative form, Mod. Fiction Stud, summer 71; plus others. Add: Dept. of English, Tulane University, New Orleans, LA 70118.

BOYLE, CHARLES J, b. Bristol, Pa, Nov. 25, 24. ENGLISH. A.B, Spring Hill Col, 50; M.A, Marquette Univ, 52; Ph.D, Univ. Wis, 57. Asst, Marquette Univ, 50-52; instr. Eng, Spring Hill Col, 52-53; asst, Univ. Wis, 53-57; asst. prof. ENG, SPRING HILL COL, 57-60, assoc. prof, 60-62, PROF, 62-, ACAD. DEAN, 69- MLA. Nineteenth century American drama and fiction. Publ: Institutional self-study program of Spring Hill College, 63 & Faculty manual of Spring Hill College, 63, Spring Hill Col. Add: Dept. of English, Spring Hill College, Mobile, AL 36608.

BOYLE, ELDRIDGE ROGER, b. Washington, D.C, May 10, 07. DRAMA. B.S, Univ. Va, 30; Yale, 30-31; A.M, Univ. N.C, 39. From asst. prof. to ASSOC. PROF. DRAMA, UNIV. VA, 30-, DIR. THEATRE, 60- Dir, The Common Glory, Williamsburg, Va, 48. Sig.C, U.S.A, 43-45. Am. Theatre Asn; Southeast. Theatre Asn. Add: Dept. of Drama, University of Virginia, Culbreth Rd,Charlottesville, VA 22903.

BOYLE, HARRY HERBERT, b. San Francisco, Calif, Jan. 6, 28; m. 55; c. 4. ENGLISH, NEO-LATIN PHILOLOGY. B.A, Univ. Calif, Los Angeles, 55, M.A, 60, Ph.D.(Eng), 66. Instr. Eng, Univ. Ariz, 64-66, asst. prof, 66-69; community health worker Eng. compos. & social stud, Dept. Psychiat, Drug Abuse Ctr, Univ. Calif, San Diego, 71-72; TRAINER & PROG. DESIGNER INTERPERSONAL COMMUN, EDUC. DEVELOP. CTR, CLAREMONT COLS, 72- Commun. specialist res. pilot prog, Stud. Develop. Ctr, Mt. St. Mary's Col.(Calif), 70-71. U.S.A, 46-47. Am. Asn. Humanistic Psychol. The experiential mode in liberal arts curricula; Spenser; neo-Latin studies. Publ: Elizabeth's entertainment at Elvetham: war policy in pageantry, Stud. Philol, 71; co-auth, The student-development center: a ten-week experience in re-education, Calif. State Col, Long Beach, 71 & Creating a holistic learning environment: an experiential classroom, Col. Stud. J, 73. Add: Educational Development Ctr, Claremont Colleges, Ninth & Amherst Sts, Claremont, CA 91711.

BOYLE, ROBERT RICHARD, S.J, b. Clinton, Ill, June 13, 15. ENGLISH. B.A, Univ. Ill, 38; M.A, St. Louis Univ, 45, Ph.L, 46, Th.L, 51; Ph.D, Yale, 55. Instr. ENG, Regis Col.(Colo), 55-57, asst. prof, 58-60, assoc. prof, 61-64, PROF, 64-66; MARQUETTE UNIV, 68- MLA; NCTE. Philosophy of metaphor; techniques of criticism; James Joyce. Publ: Metaphor in Hopkins, Univ. N.C, 61; The priesthoods of Stephen and Buck; In: Approaches to Ulysses, Univ. Pittsburgh, 70; Joyce's eucharistic image, James Joyce Quart, fall 72; Mystery in Ulysses, Etudes Anglaises, fall 73; plus others. Add: Dept. of English, Marquette University, Milwaukee, WI 53233.

BOYLE, TED E, b. Strang, Nebr, Nov. 26, 33; m. 59; c. 1. ENGLISH. B.A, Univ. Nebr, 55, M.A, 59, Ph.D, 62. Asst. prof. ENG, Kans. State Col, 62-63; SOUTH. ILL. UNIV, CARBONDALE, 63-66, assoc. prof, 66-71, PROF, 71- U.S.A, 55-57, Res, 57-62, Sgt. MLA; NCTE. English and American fiction; Victorian poetry. Publ: Symbol and meanings in the writings of Joseph Conrad, Mouton, 65; Brendan Behan, Twayne, 69; The serious side of Lucky Jim, Critique, 67; plus others. Add: Dept. of English, Southern Illinois University, Carbondale, IL 62903.

BOYLE, THOMAS E, b. Chicago, Ill, Nov. 27, 29; m. 51; c. 3. ENGLISH. A.B, Univ. Richmond, 52; M.A, Univ. Ill, 58, Ph.D.(Eng), 64. Teaching fel, ENG, Univ. Ill, 57-61; asst. prof, South. Colo. State Col, 62-64; Albion Col, 64-66; assoc. prof, UNIV. NORTH. COLO, 68-70, PROF, 70-, ASSOC. DEAN COL. ARTS & SCI, 72-, acting dean, 70-72. Great Lakes Col. Asn. grant, 64; mem. ed. bd, West. Rev, 71-73; chmn. bd. trustees, Colo. Assoc. Univ. Press, 73-74. U.S.A, 48-49. MLA. American literature; literary criticism. Publ: Thomas Wolfe: theme through imagery, Mod. Fiction Stud, autumn 65; The tenor in the organic metaphor: a view of American romanticism, Discourse, Rev. Lib. Arts, 4/68; The frontier in history and in literature, West. Am. Lit, winter 70. Add: 1834 Reservoir Rd, Greeley, CO 80631.

BOYNTON, ROBERT WHITNEY, b. New York, N.Y, June 19, 21; m. 48; c. 4. ENGLISH. A.B, Princeton, 43; M.A.T, Harvard, 47; Columbia Univ, 51-55. Head dept. Eng, Newark Acad, Newark, N.J, 48-54; mem. fac, Germantown Friends Sch, 54-59, head dept. Eng, 59-61, prin. sr. high sch, 60-68, planning & develop, 68-70. Consult. ed, Hayden Bk. Co, 63- U.S.A.A.F, 43-46. NCTE. English literature; linguistics. Publ: Co-auth, Images of man: readings in English literature, Prentice-Hall, 63; co-auth, Introduction to the play, 68, Introduction to the short story, 72 & Introduction to the poem, 73, Hayden. Add: Stamford, NY 12167.

BOYS, RICHARD CHARLES, b. Kalamazoo, Mich, Nov. 13, 12; m. 35; c. 4. ENGLISH. Univ. Col. Southwest Eng, 30-31; A.B, Harvard, 35; Ph.D, Johns Hopkins Univ, 39. Instr. ENG, UNIV. MICH, ANN ARBOR, 39-44, asst. prof. 44-50, from assoc. prof. to PROF, 50- Nat. dir, Wilson Fel. Found, 56-58; co-ed, Augustan Reprint Soc. MLA; AAUP. Eighteenth century and Neo-classical literature: the history of the novel; poetical miscellanies. Publ: Studies in the literature of the Augustan Age; Grongar Hill; Sir Richard Blackmore and the wits, Univ. Mich, 49. Add: Dept. of English, 7616 Haven Hall, University of Michigan, Ann Arbor, MI 48104.

BOYUM, JOY GOULD, b. New York, N.Y, Dec. 8, 34; m. 60; c. 2. ENGLISH. B.A, Barnard Col, Columbia Univ, 55; M.A, N.Y. Univ, 57, Ph.D.(Eng), 62. Asst. prof. ENG, Jersey City State Col, 59-60; instr, N.Y. UNIV, 60-62, asst. prof, 62-68, assoc. prof, 68-73, PROF, 73- Film critic, Wall Street J, 71-; mem, N.Y. Film Critics. NCTE; MLA; Nat. Soc. Film Critics. Interrelationships between arts; contemporary literature; film. Publ: Co-auth, Film as film: critical approaches to film art, Allyn & Bacon, 71 & Film: a share in the great tradition, Scholastic Teacher, 11/70; auth, Motion pictures, In: The world book year book, Field, 72, 73; Heroes in black and white, In: The great ideas today, Encycl. Britannica, 73. Add: 45 Remsen St, Brooklyn, NY 11201.

BOZORTH, RICHARD (GROTH), b. New York, N.Y, Nov. 8, 20. ENGLISH. A.B, Univ. Pa, 42; Hunt fel. & Ph.D.(Eng. lang. & lit), Princeton, 51. Instr.

Eng, Princeton, 45-47; from instr. to asst. prof, Univ. Pa, 47-69, asst. dean col, 54-55; ASSOC. PROF. ENG, URSINUS COL, 69-, DEAN COL, 70- U.S. Dept. State specialist, India, 57-58. Col. Eng. Asn; Mod. Humanities Res. Asn; Am. Counc. Acad. Deans. Victorian literature; contemporary literature; criticism. Add: Office of the Dean, Ursinus College, Collegeville, PA 19426.

BRACE, GERALD WARNER, b. New York, N.Y, Sept. 23, 01; m. 27; c. 3. ENGLISH LITERATURE. A.B, Amherst Col, 22, hon. Litt.D, 70; A.M, Harvard, 24; Ph.D, 30; hon. Litt.D, Southeast. Mass. Technol. Inst, 65, Univ. Maine, 72. Instr, Williams Col, 24-26; instr. & tutor, Radcliffe Col, 27-30; instr. ENG, Dartmouth Col, 30-34; asst. prof, Mt. Holyoke Col, 35-39; prof, BOSTON UNIV, 39-67, EMER. PROF, 67- Instr, Amherst Col, 38; vis. prof, Harvard, 56. Modern novels. Publ: The islands, 38, The wayward pilgrims, 38, Light on a mountain, 41; The Garretson Chronicle, 47 & 64, A summer's tale, 49, The spire, 52, Bell's landing, 55, The world of Carrick's Cove, 57, Winter solstice, 60, The wind's will, 64, Between wind and water, 66, The department, 68 & The stuff of fiction, 69, Norton. Add: 123 Pinehurst Rd, Belmont, MA 02178.

BRACHER, FREDERICK (GEORGE), b. Monohan, Wash, Mar. 28, 05; m. 37; c. 2. ENGLISH LITERATURE. B.S, Ore. State Univ, 27; A.M, Univ. Calif, 29, Ph.D, 34. Instr, Univ. Calif, 35-36; Univ. Wis, 36-37; City Col. San Francisco, 37-42; asst. prof. ENG, POMONA COL, 43-46, assoc. prof, 46-52, prof, 52-70, EMER. PROF, 70- Assoc. instr. & dept. head, pilots preflight sch, Santa Ana Army Airbase, Calif, 42-43; Am. Counc. Learned Soc. grant for res. in England, summer 66. MLA; Philol. Asn. Pac. Coast; Asn. Depts. Eng. English and American literature; linguistics. Publ: Exercises in the craft of writing, Houghton, 46; College handbook of composition, 58 & co-auth, Heath handbook of composition, 8th ed, 72, Heath; Novels of James Gould Cozzens, Harcourt, 59; ed, Letters of Sir George Etherege, Univ. Calif, 74; auth, Sir George Etherege and his secretary, 67 & Etherege as diplomat, 69, Harvard Libr. J. Add: 284 Central Ave, Pacific Grove, CA 93950.

BRACHER, PETER SCHOLL, b. La Grande, Ore, May 20, 32; m. 53; c. 3. ENGLISH. B.A, Wittenberg Univ, 54; M.A, Univ. Wash, 56; Ph.D.(Eng), Univ. Pa, 66. Instr. ENG, Univ. Colo, 59-64; asst. prof, WRIGHT STATE UNIV, 64-68, ASSOC. PROF, 68-, acting chmn. dept, 65-67. MLA; NCTE; AAUP. Dickens; Victorian literature; Bible and literature. Publ: The New York Herald and American notes, Dickens Stud, 69; The Lea and Blanchard edition of Dickens' American notes, 1842, Papers Bibliog. Soc. Am, 69; The Bible and literature, Eng. J, 72. Add: Dept. of English, Wright State University, Col. Glenn Highway, Dayton, OH 45431.

BRACK, HAROLD ARTHUR, b. East Moline, Ill, Oct. 8, 23; m. 52; c. 3. SPEECH. B.A, Augustana Col, 48; B.D, Garrett Bibl. Inst, 51; M.A, Northwest. Univ, 51, Ph.D, 53. Asst. prof. speech, DREW UNIV, 53-58, assoc. prof, 58-59, SPEECH & HOMILETICS, 59-68, PROF, 68- V.chmn, Speech for Relig. Workers Interest Group, Speech Asn. Am, 68-69, chmn, 69-70; vis. prof. homiletics, Immaculate Conception Sem, 71- A.U.S, 43-46, T/Sgt. Speech Commun. Asn.(assoc. ed. preaching & homiletics, Quart. J. Speech, 63-65). Public speaking; discussion; oral interpretation. Publ: Co-auth, Public speaking and discussion for religious leaders, 61 & auth, Effective oral interpretation for religious leaders, 64, Prentice-Hall; Neo-orthodoxy and the American pulpit, In: Preaching in American history, Abingdon, 69; Needed—a new language for communicating religion, In: Costerus, Rodopi, Netherlands, 3/72; Contextual communication therapy for stuttering, Speech Teacher, 1/73; plus others. Add: Dept. of Speech & Homiletics, Drew University, Madison, NJ 07940.

BRACK, O. M, JR, b. Houston, Tex, Nov. 30, 38; m. 68. ENGLISH. A.B, Baylor Univ, 60, A.M, 61; Ph.D.(Eng), Univ. Tex, 65. Asst. prof. ENG, William Woods Col, 64-65; Univ, Iowa, 65-68, assoc. prof, 68-73, dir, ctr, textual stud, 67-73; PROF. ENG, ARIZ. STATE UNIV, 73- Am. Philos. Soc. grant, summer 66; chmn, 18th Century Short-title Catalogue Comt, 70-73. Am. Soc. 18th Century Stud; NCTE; Printing Hist. Soc; Bibliog. Soc. Univ. Va; AAUP; MLA; Bibliog. Soc, Eng; Bibliog. Soc. Am. Bibliography and textual criticism; English literature of the 18th century. Publ: Ed, The bicentennial edition of the works of Tobias Smollett, Univ. Iowa Ctr. Textual Stud,(in prep); co-ed, Bibliography and textual criticism, Univ. Chicago, 69; co-auth, Samuel Johnson's early biographers, 71 & co-ed, The early biographies of Samuel Johnson, 74, Univ. Iowa; ed, John Hoole's Death of Dr. Johnson, Windhover, 72; co-auth, A catalogue of the Leigh Hunt manuscripts in the University of Iowa Libraries, Friends Univ. Iowa Libr, 73. Add: Dept. of English, Arizona State University, Tempe, AZ 85281.

BRACKER, JON, b. New York, N.Y, Oct. 10, 36; m. 65. AMERICAN LITERATURE, MODERN ENGLISH. B.A, Univ. Tex, 58, M.A, 60. Res. assoc. manuscript cataloger, Christopher Morley Manuscript Collection, Humanities Res. Ctr, Univ. Tex, 60-62; instr, Amarillo Col, 63-64; ASST. PROF, ENG, Midwest. Univ, 64-67; Slippery Rock State Col, 67-68; IND. STATE UNIV, TERRE HAUTE, 68- Ed, Penny Poems From Amarillo Col, 63-64; Penny Pems From Midwestern Univ, 64-67; poet-in-residence, Ind. State Arts Comn, 73. MLA; NCTE. Writings of Marianne Moore, Longfellow and Byron. Publ: Ed, Bright cages, the selected poems of Christopher Morley, Univ. Pa, 65; auth, Constellations of clover (poems), Prickly Pear Press, 73; Notes on two poems by Dante Gabriel Rossetti, Libr. Chronicle, Univ. Tex, summer 63; The conslusion of Song of myself, Walt Whitman Rev, 3/64; The love song of J. Alfred Prufrock, Explicator, 11/66. Add: Dept. of English, Indiana State University, Terre Haute, IN 47809.

BRACY, WILLIAM, b. Rich Square, N.C, Mar. 25, 15; m. 62; c. 2. ENGLISH. A.B, Univ. N.C, Chapel Hill, 36, fels, 39-42, M.A, 39, Ph.D.(Eng), 49. Asst, Univ. N.C, Chapel Hill, 39-42, part-time instr, 46-48, instr. Eng, 48-49; asst. prof, Univ. Mo, Columbia, 49-54; asst. ed. humanities, Collier's Encycl, New York, 55-57, humanities ed, 57-58; humanities ed. & consult, Encycl. Americana, 58-64; lectr. ENG, City Col. New York, 64-65; assoc. prof, BEAVER COL, 65-68, PROF, 69-, acting chmn. dept, 67-68, chmn, 69-71. Foyle res. fel, Shakespeare Inst, Stratford-on-Avon, Eng, 53. Med.Dept, U.S.A, 42-45, S/Sgt. MLA; Northeast Mod. Lang. Asn; Renaissance Soc. Am; Shakespeare Asn. Am. Shakespeare; renaissance; English and modern drama. Publ: The merry wives of Windsor: the history and transmission of Shakespeare's text, Univ. Mo, 52; Doctor Faustus . . . analysis with critical commentary, 65 & co-auth, Early English drama . . . Middle Ages to the early 17th century, 66, Stud. Master. Add: Dept. of English, Beaver College, Glenside, PA 19038.

BRADDOCK, RICHARD REED, b. Glenridge, N.J, June 14, 20. ENGLISH, RHETORIC. B.A, N.J. State Teachers Col, Montclair, 42; M.A, Columbia Univ, 47, Ed.D, 56. Teacher, high sch, N.J, 47-48; instr. Eng, Iowa State Teachers Col, 48-53, asst. prof, 53-55; rhet, UNIV. IOWA, 55-61, assoc. prof. ENG. & RHET, 61-65, PROF, 65- U.S. Off. Educ. grants, 62-68; vis. assoc. prof. Eng. & educ, Harvard, summer 63; vis. prof. Eng, Univ. Ore, summer 68; chmn. comt. res, NCTE, 65-68, trustee, Res. Found, 67-69; ed, Res. in Teaching of Eng, 67-72; vis. lectr, New South Wales Inst. Technol, 74. U.S.A.A.F, 42-45, 2nd Lt. NCTE; Conf. Col. Compos. & Commun.(secy, 61-62, asst. chmn, 65, assoc. chmn, 66, chmn, 67). Teaching of written composition. Publ: Introductory readings on the English language, 62 & A little casebook in the rhetoric of writing, 71, Prentice-Hall; co-auth, Research in written composition, NCTE, 63; auth, English composition, In: Encyclopedia of educational research, Macmillan, 69; plus others. Add: Dept. of English, University of Iowa, Iowa City, IA 52242.

BRADDY, HALDEEN, b. Fairlie, Tex, Jan. 22, 08; m. 27. ENGLISH. B.A, E.Tex. State Univ, 28; M.A, Univ. Tex, 29; Ph.D, N.Y. Univ, 34. Instr. Eng, N.Y. Univ, 29-35, 36-38; prof. & head dept, Sul Ross Col, 35-36; prof, Tex. Christian Univ, 38-42; supvr. mil. Eng, Tex. Tech. Col, 43-44; assoc. prof, Univ. Kans, 44-45; lectr, Tulane Univ, 46; from assoc. prof. to PROF. ENG, UNIV. TEX, EL PASO, 46-50, 50-, fac. res. award, 73. U.S.A.A.F, 43, Lt. MLA; Am. Folklore Soc; Shakespeare Asn. Am; Rocky Mt. Mod. Lang. Asn. (pres, 72-73, hon. pres, 73-74). Creative writing; English literature; American folklore; King Alfred, Edgar Allan Poe, and Pancho Villa. Publ: Chaucer and French poet Graunson, La. State Univ, 47; Glorious incense, fulfillment of E.A. Poe, Scarecrow, 53; Cock of the walk, N.Mex. Univ, 55; Hamlet's wounded name, 64 & Pershing's mission in Mexico, 66, Univ. Tex, El Paso; Pancho Villa rides again, Paisano, 67; Chaucer's Parlement of foules, Octagon, 69; Geoffrey Chaucer, 71 & Mexico and the Old Southwest, 71, Kennikat; Three dimensional Poe, Tex. Western, 73; England and English before Alfred, Costerus, 73. Add: 2109 Arizona St, El Paso, TX 79930.

BRADEN, WALDO WARDER, b. Ottumwa, Iowa, Mar. 7, 11; m. 38; c. 1. SPEECH. A.B, William Penn Col, 32; A.M, Univ. Iowa, 38, Ph.D, 42. Teacher, high schs, Iowa, 33-38; prof. & dean, Iowa Wesleyan Col, 38-40, 42-43, 46; from assoc. prof. to prof. SPEECH, LA. STATE UNIV, BATON ROUGE, 46-73, BOYD PROF, 73-, CHMN. DEPT, 58- U.S.A, 42-45. Speech Commun. Asn.(exec. secy, 54-57, pres, 62, ed, Speech Teacher, 67-69); South. Speech Commun. Asn.(pres, 69); Am. Stud. Asn. Southern public address; American public address. Publ: Co-auth, Oral decision making, 55, co-auth. & ed, Speech methods and resources, 61 & 72, co-auth, Public speaking, 2nd ed, 63 & auth, Public speaking: the essentials, 66, Harper; co-auth, Speech criticism, Ronald, 70; ed, Oratory in the Old South 1828-1869, La. State Univ, 70; ed, Representative American speeches, 1970-1971, 1971-1972 & 1972-1973, Wilson, 71-73. Add: Dept. of Speech, Louisiana State University, University Station, Baton Rouge, LA 70803.

BRADEN, WILBUR SPRONG, b. Frankfort, Ky, Jan. 7, 40; m. 65; c. 3. ENGLISH & AMERICAN LITERATURE. B.A, Wash. State Univ, 62, M.A, 64; M.Litt, Trinity Col.(Dublin), 65; Ph.D.(Eng), Univ. Va, 71. Asst. prof. ENG, WILLAMETTE UNIV, 70-74, ASSOC. PROF, 74-, coord. study prog. Eng, 72-73. Johnson Soc, London. Restoration drama; 18th century prose style; contemporary poetry. Publ: A musical history of limerick, Dublin Grand Opera Soc, 65. Add: Dept. of English, Willamette University, 900 State St, Salem, OR 97301.

BRADFORD, CLINTON WILLIAM, b. Grapevine, Ark, Nov. 5, 09; m. 46; c. 1. SPEECH & DRAMA. B.A, Univ. Ark, 38; M.A, State Univ. Iowa, 41; Ph.D. (speech), La. State Univ, 51. Teacher pub. schs, Ark, 29-33, 35-37 & 38-40; Iowa, 41-42; asst. prof. Eng. & speech, Ark. State Teachers Col, 46; asst, LA. STATE UNIV, BATON ROUGE, 46-49, asst. prof. SPEECH, 50-57, ASSOC. PROF, 57- Auth. & producer, Always Acadia, St. Martinville, La, 55. U.S.A, 42-45, M/Sgt. Am. Counc. Better Broadcasts (pres, 61-64); Speech Commun. Asn; Am. Theatre Asn. Non-professional theater history; history of pioneer period of broadcasting in the United States. Publ: Teaching radio and television, In: Speech methods and resources, Harper, 61; co-auth, Teaching a unit on television in high school, Speech Teacher, 10/67. Add: Dept. of Speech, Louisiana State University, Baton Rouge, LA 70803.

BRADFORD, MELVIN EUSTACE ADONIS, b. Ft. Worth, Tex, May 8, 34; m. 55; c. 1. AMERICAN LITERATURE. B.A, Univ. Okla, 55, M.A, 56, fel, Vanderbilt Univ, 59-62, Ph.D.(Eng), 68. Instr. Eng, U.S. Naval Acad, 57-59; Vanderbilt Univ, 59-62; asst. prof, Hardin Simmons Univ, 62-64; Northwest. State Col.(La), 64-67; UNIV. DALLAS, 67-70, ASSOC. PROF. ENG. LIT, 70-, chmn. dept, 70-73. Nat. Humanities Found. fel, summer 70; mem. ed. bd, Mod. Age, 70- U.S.N.R, 56-59, Lt. S.Cent. Mod. Lang. Asn; MLA. Southern literature; American political rhetoric; criticism. Publ: Co-ed, The southern tradition at bay, Arlington, 68; auth, Allen Tate, Argus, 69; ed, The form discovered: essays on the achievement of Andrew Lytle, Univ. & Col. Miss, 73; Faulkner's tall men, S.Atlantic Quart, 62; Faulkner, James Baldwin, and the South, Ga. Rev, winter 66; A durable fire: Donald Davidson and the profession of letters, South. Rev, summer 68; plus others. Add: Dept. of English, Box 54, University of Dallas, Irving, TX 75060.

BRADFORD, ROBERT WHITMORE, b. Melrose, Mass, Oct. 14, 18; m. 44; c. 3. ENGLISH. A.B, Dartmouth Col, 47; A.M, Columbia, 48; Ph.D, Syracuse Univ, 57. Instr. ENG, Syracuse Univ, 48-53; LAFAYETTE COL, 53-57, asst. prof, 57-63, ASSOC. PROF, 63-, res. grant, 58. Thomas Roy & Lura Jones fac. lectr. award, 66-67. MLA; Col. Eng. Asn. Henry D. Thoreau; English and American romanticism. Publ: Co-auth, An E.B. White reader, Harper, 66. Add: Dept. of English, Lafayette College, Easton, PA 18042.

BRADLEY, BERT E, JR, b. Birmingham, Ala, June 2, 26; m. 48; c. 2. SPEECH. A.B, Birmingham-South. Col, 50; M.A, Univ. Ala, 51; Ph.D. (speech), Fla. State Univ, 55. Instr. SPEECH, Fla. State Univ, 54-55; asst. prof, Univ. Richmond, 55-58, assoc. prof, 58-66, prof, 66-67; assoc. prof,

Univ. N.C, Chapel Hill, 67-70, PROF, 70-73; AUBURN UNIV, 73- Summer assoc. prof, Birmingham-South. Col, 55-58, Ohio Univ, 63; speech consult, Chesapeake & Potomac Tel. Co, 65-67. U.S.N.R, 44-46. Am. Forensic Asn; Speech Commun. Asn; South. Speech Asn. Rhetorical theory; history of American public address; communication theory. Publ: Speech performance, 67 & Fundamentals of speech communication: the credibility of ideas, 74, W.C. Brown; co-auth, Forms of debate, In: Argumentation and debate, Holt, 63; auth, North Carolina newspaper accounts of Lincoln's first inaugural, N.C. Hist. Rev, 66: 271-280; An experimental study of the effectiveness of the video-recorder in teaching the basic speech course, Speech Teacher, 19: 161-167; plus two others. Add: Dept. of Speech Communication, Auburn University, Auburn, AL 36830.

BRADLEY, EARL EDSEL, b. Marshall, Ark, Jan. 29, 07; m. 27; c. 2. SPEECH. A.B, Cent. State Col.(Okla), 30; Ed.M, Univ. Okla, 39; Ph.D. (speech), Northwest. Univ, 50. Teacher, high sch, Okla, 30-37; mem. fac. SPEECH, Panhandle Agr. & Mech. Col, 37-50; assoc. prof, Univ. Denver, 50-58; PROF, ASST. CHMN. DEPT. & DIR. GRAD. STUD, SOUTH. ILL. UNIV, 58- Distinguished Alumni Award, Cent. State Col.(Okla), 56. Speech Commun. Asn; Cent. States Speech Asn; West. Speech Asn. Rhetorical criticism; classical and medieval rhetoric. Publ: Ed. & contrib, Argumentation and debate; auth, The laboratory theatre, Playbill Mag; What I consider good debating, West. Speech; Field trial reports, Am. Field, 12/67. Add: 701 Skyline Dr, Carbondale, IL 62901.

BRADLEY, JOHN LEWIS, b. London, Eng, Aug. 5, 17; m. 43; c. 1. ENGLISH LITERATURE. B.A, Yale, 40, Ph.D, 50; M.A, Harvard, 46. Instr. ENG, Wellesley Col, 48-51; Univ. Md, 52-53; asst. prof, Clark Univ, 53-55; Mt. Holyoke Col, 55-58, assoc. prof, 58-64; PROF, Ohio State Univ, 64-65; Univ. S.C, 65-69; UNIV. DURHAM, 69-, CHMN. DEPT, 72- Am. Philos. Soc. grants, 57, 59, 64; Guggenheim fel, 61-62; vis. lectr, Smith Col, 62-63; vis. assoc. prof, Ohio State Univ, 63-64. R.C.A.F, 43-46, Flying Off. MLA. Victorian literature. Publ: Ruskin's Letters from Venice 1851-1852, Yale, 55; ed, Letters of John Ruskin to Lord & Lady Mount-Temple, Ohio State Univ, 65, Selections from Henry Mayhew's London labour and the London poor, Oxford, 66 & Unto this last and traffic, Appleton, 67; co-ed, Masterworks of English prose, Holt, 68; Samuel Smiles' Self-help: forgotten centenary, Victorian Newslett, fall 59; Ruskin's advice to an amateur artist: some new letters to Louisa, Marchioness of Waterford, Stud. Eng. Lit, autumn 61. Add: Dept. of English, University of Durham, Durham, Eng.

BRADLEY, RITAMARY, S.F.C.C, b. Stuart, Iowa, Jan. 30, 16. ENGLISH. Ph.B, Marygrove Col, 38; M.A, St. Louis Univ, 45, Ph.D.(Eng), 53; hon. LL.D, Marquette Univ, 60; hon. L.H.D, Fordham Univ, 60. Head dept. Eng, Marycrest Col, 45-56; asst. exec. secy, Sister Formation Conf, 61-64, ed, Sister Formation Bull, 54-64; distinguished res. fel, Univ. Minn, 64-65; PROF. ENG, ST. AMBROSE COL, 65- Mem. staff, Sister Formation Workshop, Marquette Univ, summers 59, 60, 61, 63; workshop philos. in a tech. cult, Cath. Univ. Am, 63; travel & res. grant ecumenical & medieval stud, John XXIII Found, Eng, summer 67; vis. lectr, Englewood Cliffs Col, summer 68; instr. Eng, Black Hawk Col, summers 70- MLA; Mediaeval Acad. Am; Relig. Educ. Asn. Women in literature; medieval literature; women in religious history. Publ: Ed, The mind of the Church in the formation of sisters, 55 & The juniorate in sister formation, 60, Fordham Univ; auth, The challenge of renewal to sisters today (pamphlet), Liturgical Press, 66; Backgrounds of the title, Speculum, in medieval literature, Speculum, 54; co-auth, Motivation and religious behavior, In: Research on religious development, Hawthorn, 71. Add: Dept. of English, St. Ambrose College, 518 W. Locust, Davenport, IA 52803.

BRADLEY, ROBERT HARLOW, b. Clarksville, Tenn, Mar. 9, 36. THEATRE. B.A, Austin Peay State Univ, 57; M.S, Univ. Ill, Urbana, 59, Ph.D.(theatre), 64. Instr. theatre, Southwest Mo. State Univ, 63-64, asst. prof, 64-67, assoc. prof, 67-72, PROF. THEATRE & HEAD DEPT, SPEECH & THEATRE, 72- Am. Theatre Asn; Speech Commun. Asn; Cent. State Speech Asn. Modern theatre, 1875 to present; directing. Add: Dept. of Speech & Theatre, Southwest Missouri State University, Springfield, MO 65802.

BRADSHAW, JAMES PHILIP, b. Gainesville, Fla, May 22, 19. LINGUISTICS, LIBRARY SCIENCE. B.A, Univ. Fla, 39, M.A, 40; M.S.L.S, Columbia Univ, 51. Chmn. dept. ENG, Hernando High Sch, Brooksville, Fla, 40-41; ASSOC. PROF, UNIV. FLA, 46- Consult, Col. Entrance Exam. Bd, Educ. Testing Serv, 65-70. U.S.A, 41-46, M/Sgt. NCTE; Conf. Col. Compos. & Commun; S.Atlantic Mod. Lang. Asn; Eng-Speaking Union. Linguistics; drama; library science. Publ: Co-auth, Word study 9, Colonial Press, 61; co-ed. & co-auth, The meaning in reading, 60, 64, College English: the first year, 64, 68, 73, The modern essay, 65, 68 & Imaginative literature, 68, 72, Harcourt; co-ed, Annual bibliography, S.Atlantic Bull, 63-70. Add: Depts. of English, University of Florida, Gainesville, FL 32611.

BRADSHAW, JAMES STANFORD, b. Campbell, Mo, Dec. 6, 21; m. 53; c. 4. JOURNALISM, MODERN HISTORY. A.B, Univ. Mich, Ann Arbor, 46, fel, 46-47, M.A, 47; Ph.D.(hist), Mich. State Univ, 72. Ed. writer, Ann Arbor News, Mich, 47-49; ed. & correspondent, Assoc. Press, Detroit & Lansing, Mich, Buenos Aires, Arg, Rio de Janeiro, Brazil & Wash, D.C, 49-61; press. adv. to secy. gen, Orgn. Am. States, 61-62; deputy pub. affairs adv, Bur. Latin Am. Agency Int. Develop, 62-65, reports & Food for Peace off, USAID to Chile, Santiago, 65-67; from asst. prof. to ASSOC. PROF. JOUR, CENT. MICH. UNIV, 69- U.S.A, 42-45; Bronze Star Medal. Asn. Educ. in Jour. Inter-American relations; journalistic history. Publ: Political avalanche in Chile, 70 & An end to inter-Americanism, 73, Christian Century; Prognosis of Allende, 71, New Leader; plus several others. Add: 324 Hiawatha Dr, Mt. Pleasant, MI 48858.

BRADSHAW, LARRY LEE, b. Wichita, Kans, May 5, 43; m. 65; c. 2. SPEECH COMMUNICATION. B.A, Abilene Christian Col, 65; M.A, Univ. Ariz, 66; Ph.D.(speech), South. Ill. Univ, Carbondale, 70. ASST. PROF. SPEECH. UNIV. TULSA, 68- Consult, Am. Airlines, summer 69; Okla. Natural Gas Co, summer 71; Tulsa Police Dept, 73- Cent. States Speech Asn; Speech Commun. Asn. Interpersonal communication; public address; small group communication. Publ: Genesis of dissent, South. Speech Commun. J, winter 73; co-auth, Glossolalia and speech-event communication, Mission, 2/74. Add: Dept. of Communication, University of Tulsa, 600 S. College, Tulsa, OK 74104.

BRADY, CHARLES ANDREW, b. Buffalo, N.Y, Apr. 15, 12; m. 37; c. 6. ENGLISH. A.B, Canisius Col, 33; A.M, Harvard, 35; L.H.D, Le Moyne Col, 54. From instr. to PROF. ENG, CANISIUS COL, 38-, chmn. dept, 38-59, dean grad. dept, 38-40. Bk. columnist, Buffalo Evening News, 45-; ed. adv, Desmond & Stapleton, 48-50; lectr, Boston Col, 49; Univ. Notre Dame, 54. Archbishop Cushing Poetry Award, 49; Cecil Hemley Mem. Award, Poetry Soc. Am, 70. Poetry Soc. Am.(first prize, 68); Gallery Living Cath. Auth. Nineteenth and twentieth century English and American literature; medieval literature. Publ: Sword of Clontarf, 60, The king's thane, 67 & St. Thomas of London Town, 69, St. Anthony; First Century: Canisius College 1870-1970, Canisius Col, 69; plus others. Add: 371 Deerhurst Park Blvd, Buffalo P.O, Kenmore, NY 14223.

BRADY, DONALD VINCENT, b. Brooklyn, N.Y, May 20. THEATRE, SPEECH. B.A, Tex. West. Col, 58; M.A, Tulane Univ, 60, Ph.D.(theatre), 65. Instr. speech, Tex. West. Col, 62-64; asst. prof. THEATRE & SPEECH, LOYOLA UNIV.(LA), 64-67, ASSOC. PROF, 67-, CHMN. DEPT, 64- U.S.A.F, 54-58. Am. Theatre Asn; Speech Commun. Asn. Southwest theatre history; mass communications; propaganda. Add: Dept. of Drama & Speech, Loyola University, 6363 St. Charles Ave, New Orleans, LA 70118.

BRADY, FRANK, b. Brookline, Mass, Nov. 3, 24. ENGLISH. B.A, Dartmouth Col, 48; M.A, Yale, 49, Ph.D.(Eng), 52. Instr. ENG, Yale, 51-56, asst. prof, 56-60; assoc. prof, Dartmouth Col, 60-63; PROF, Pa. State Univ, 63-67; CITY UNIV. NEW YORK, 67-, exec. off. Ph.D. prog, 69-72. Morse fel, Yale, 55-56; Guggenheim fel, 66-67; mem. exec. comt, Yale Ed. Private Papers of James Boswell, 72- Qm.C, A.U.S, 43-46, 1st Lt. MLA; AAUP. James Boswell; 18th century literature; modern critical theory. Publ: Co-ed, Boswell on the grand tour, Vol. II, 55 & Boswell in search of a wife, 56, McGraw; co-auth, English prose and poetry: 1660-1800, Holt, 61; auth, Boswell's political career, 65 & co-ed, Literary theory and structure, 73, Yale Univ; ed, Pope's Essay on man, Bobbs, 65 & Twentieth century interpretations of Gulliver's travels, Prentice-Hall, 68; Structure and meaning in Gray's Elegy, In: From sensibility to romanticism, Oxford Univ, 65; Tristram Shandy: sexuality, morality, and sensibility, ECS, 70; Boswell's self-presentation and his critics, Stud. Eng. Lit, 72. Add: 562 West End Ave, New York, NY 10024.

BRADY, LEO, b. Wheeling, W.Va, Jan. 23, 17; m. 45; c. 8. DRAMA. A.B, Cath. Univ. Am, 41, M.A, 42. From assoc. prof. to PROF. SPEECH & DRAMA, CATH. UNIV. AM, 46- U.S.A, 42-46. Am. Theatre Asn. Dramatic criticism; history of drama; aesthetics. Publ: Brother Orchid; The edge of doom; Signs and wonders. Add: Dept. of Speech & Drama, Catholic University of America, Washington, DC 20017.

BRADY, MARY WILLIAM, C.S.J, b. Fall River, Mass, Mar. 4, 06. ENGLISH & AMERICAN LITERATURE. Ph.D, Univ. Chicago, 47. Mem. fac. Eng, COL. ST. CATHERINE, 37-55, pres, 55-61, PROF. AM. LIT, 61- MLA. Teacher education; humanities of the Far East; world literature in English. Publ: Certain revisions in Coventry Patmore's Angel in the house; Whitman's revisions of the Song of myself; Improving the professional education of teachers, Bull. Nat. Counc. Educ. Admin. Add: College of St. Catherine, 2004 Randolph St, St. Paul, MN 55105.

BRADY, PATRICK, French & Comparative Literature. See Volume III, Foreign Languages, Linguistics & Philology.

BRADY, WILLIAM E, b. Newark, N.J, Dec. 24, 26; m. 59; c. 3. ENGLISH LITERATURE. B.A, Hobart Col, 50; M.A, Brown Univ, 53, univ. fel. & Ph.D, 58. Asst. ENG, Hobart Col, 50, instr, 50-51; Brown Univ, 52-56; Univ. Chicago, 57-59, asst. prof, 59-63; PROF, KNOX COL, 63- Vis. prof. Eng, Hobart Col, 64-65, trustee, Hobart & William Smith Cols, 67-; vis. prof. Eng, Colo. Col, 71. U.S.N, 44-46. MLA; Renaissance Soc. Am. Renaissance literature; Shakespeare. Add: Dept. of English, Knox College, Galesburg, IL 61401.

BRAKE, ROBERT JOHN, b. Jamestown, N.Dak, Sept. 21, 37; m. 72; c. 1. SPEECH, DRAMATIC ARTS. B.S, N.Dak. State Univ, 60; M.A, Univ. S.Dak, 61; Ph.D.(speech & hist), Mich. State Univ, 65. Instr. speech, Iowa State Univ, 61-62; asst. prof, John Carroll Univ, 64-66; speech & dramatic arts, Univ. S.Dak, 66-68; ASSOC. PROF. SPEECH & COMMUN, ILL. STATE UNIV, 68- Speech Commun. Asn; Cent. States Speech Asn.(outstanding young teacher award, 68). Rhetoric; interpersonal communication; contemporary public address. Publ: Pedants, professors and the law of the excluded middle: on sophists and sophistry, Cent. States Speech J, summer 69; The porch and the stump: campaign strategies in the 1920 Presidential election, 10/69 & On Speechifiers well snubbed: some rhetorical viewpoints of Montaigne, 4/70, Quart. J. Speech; plus others. Add: Dept. of Information Sciences, Illinois State University, Normal, IL 61761.

BRAMER, GEORGE ROBERT, b. Springfield, Mo, July 12, 31; m. 54; c. 7. ENGLISH, RHETORIC. A.B, Drury Col, 54; M.A, Univ. Notre Dame, 58, fel, 56-60, Ph.D.(Eng), 66. Instr. ENG, St. Ambrose Col, 60-61, North. Ill. Univ, 61-62; resident lectr, Ind. Univ, 62-66; assoc. prof, Creighton Univ, 66-71; ASSOC. PROF. ENG. & COORD. WRITING PROG, W.VA. UNIV, 71- Dir, NDEA Summer Inst. Eng, 68. Sig.C, U.S.A, 54-56. MLA; NCTE; Conf. Col. Compos. & Commun; Conf. Eng. Educ; Rhetoric Soc. Am; AAUP. Discourse theory; the ethics of rhetoric; the teaching of writing. Publ: Truth and harmony as rhetorical goals, Eng. J, 9/70; Like it is: discourse analysis for a new generation, Col. Compos. & Commun, 12/70; Communication at school: truth or myth?, Can. Speech Commun. J, fall 71; plus others. Add: 112 S. Walnut St, Morgantown, WV 26505.

BRANAM, GEORGE CURTIS, b. Amarillo, Tex, July 15, 23. ENGLISH. B.A, Univ. Calif, 47, M.A, 49, Ph.D.(Eng), 52. Teacher ENG, Univ. Calif, 50-52; instr, UNIV. NEW ORLEANS, 52-54, asst. prof, 54-58, assoc. prof, 58-63, PROF, 63-, V.CHANCELLOR, 69-, dir. humanities div, 58-62, dean col. lib. arts, 62-64, dean acad. affairs, 64-69. U.S.A, 43-46. MLA. Drama; 18th century literature; literary criticism. Publ: Eighteenth century adaptations of Shakespearean tragedy, Univ. Calif, 56. Add: Office of Academic Affairs, University of New Orleans, New Orleans, LA 70122.

BRANCACCIO, PATRICK, b. New York, N.Y, Aug. 13, 34; m. 57; c. 3. ENGLISH, AMERICAN STUDIES. B.A, Brooklyn Col, 56; M.A, Ohio State Univ, 58; Ph.D.(Eng), Rutgers Univ, 67. Instr. Eng, COLBY COL, 63-66, asst. prof, 66-70, ASSOC. PROF. ENG. & AM. STUD, 70- Am. Philos. Soc. res. grant, 69-70. MLA; Am. Stud. Asn. Nineteenth century American literature and society. Publ: Studied ambiguities: Arthur Mervyn and the problem of the unreliable narrator, Am. Lit, 3/70. Add: Dept. of English, Colby College, Waterville, ME 04901.

BRANCH, EDGAR MARQUESS, b. Chicago, Ill, Mar. 21, 13; m. 39; c. 3. AMERICAN LITERATURE, A.B, Beloit Col, 34; Brown Univ, 34-35; A.M, Univ. Chicago, 38, Ph.D, Univ, Iowa, 41. Instr. ENG, MIAMI UNIV, 41-43, asst. prof, 43-46, assoc. prof, 49-57, prof, 57-64, RES. PROF, 64-, chmn. dept, 59-64. Vis. assoc. prof, Univ. Mo, 49; Nat. Endowment for Humanities sr. fel, 71-72. Soc. Stud. South. Lit; MLA; Am. Stud. Asn; NCTE; West. Lit. Asn. Mark Twain; 19th century American literature; contemporary American novel. Publ: The literary apprenticeship of Mark Twain, Univ. Ill, 50; James T. Farrell, Univ. Minn, 63; Clemens of the Call, Univ. Calif, 69; James T. Farrell, Twayne, 71; co-auth, The great landslide case, Friends of Bancroft Libr, Calif, 72; auth, Mark Twain and J.D. Salinger: a study in literary continuity, Am. Quart, 57; Freedom and determinism in James T. Farrell's fiction, In: Essays on determinism in American literature, Kent State Univ, 64; My voice is still for Setchell: a background study of Jim Smiley and his jumping frog, PMLA, 12/67. Add: Dept. of English, Miami University, Oxford, OH 45056.

BRAND, RICHARD CLYDE, b. Morgantown, W.Va, June 14, 08; m. 37; c. 3. SPEECH. A.B, W.Va. Univ, 30, A.M, 39; Northwest. Univ, 31-32; summers, Univ. Wis, 35, 36, 37; N.Y. Univ, 48; summer, Fla. State Univ, 55. Asst. prof, Morris Harvey Col, 39-41; Va. Intermont Col, 41-42; instr, Univ. Ala, 42-45; assoc. prof, Sam Houston State Teachers Col, 45-46; prof. speech, Stetson Univ, 46-51; col. rep, Pub. Bus, 51-55; assoc. prof, speech, E.Tenn. State Univ, 55-69; RETIRED. Speech Commun. Asn. Debate; public address. Add: 816 W. Locust St, Johnson City, TN 37601.

BRANDABUR, EDWARD, b. Cleveland, Ohio, Oct. 19, 30; m. 56; c. 7. ENGLISH. A.B, Xavier Univ.(Ohio), 52, M.A, 57; Ph.D.(Eng), Univ. Cincinnati, 61. Teaching fel. ENG, Univ. Cincinnati, 58-61; instr, UNIV. ILL, URBANA-CHAMPAIGN, 61-63, asst. prof, 63-67, assoc. prof, 67-71, PROF, 71-, fac. fels, 63, 65. Sem. chmn, MLA, 68; Guggenheim fel, 72-73; ed. consult, PMLA, 72- U.S.A, 53-55. Am. Comt. Irish Stud; MLA; Midwest Mod. Lang. Asn; Int. Asn. Stud. Anglo-Irish Lit; AAUP; James Joyce Found. Modern British and American literature; literature and psychoanalysis; literature and the graphic arts. Publ: A scrupulous meanness: a study of Joyce's early work, Univ. Ill, 71; Eliot and the myth of mute speech, Renascence, spring 70; The pilgrimage of Curleyman, New Lett, 3/72; Pound and Kandinsky: a language in form and color, J. Aesthetic Educ, 4/73; plus others. Add: Dept. of English, University of Illinois at Urbana-Champaign, Urbana, IL 61801.

BRANDENBURG, ALICE STAYERT, b. Jersey City, N.J, Nov. 10, 15; m. 58. ENGLISH LITERATURE. A.B, Goucher Col, 36; A.M, Radcliffe Col, 37, Ph.D.(Eng), 40. Instr. Eng. & Latin, Fairfax Hall Jr. Col, 40-42; instr. ENG, South. Methodist Univ, 42-44; Wilson Col, 44-48; from asst. prof. to assoc. prof, Mary Washington Col, 48-62; assoc. prof, Pembroke State Col, 55-67; PROF, LIVINGSTON UNIV, 67- Col. Eng. Asn. English literature of the 17th and 18th centuries. Publ: The dynamic image in metaphysical poetry, PMLA, 42; English education and neo-classical taste in the 18th century, 46 & The theme of The mysterious mother, 48, Mod. Lang. Quart. Add: Station 22, Livingston University, Livingston, AL 35470.

BRANDES, PAUL DICKERSON, b. Ft. Thomas, Ky, Aug. 3, 20; m. 48; c. 1. RHETORIC. A.B, East. Ky. State Col, 42; M.A, Univ. Wis, 47, Ph.D.(rhet), 53. Asst. prof. speech, Univ. Miss, 46-54; chmn. dept, Univ. South. Miss, 53-58; prof. speech & dir. persuasion lab, Ohio Univ, 58-66; PROF. ENG, UNIV. N.C, CHAPEL HILL, 66- Ohio Univ. Baker Grant, France, 64-65. Sig.C, U.S.A, 43-46, Sgt. Speech Commun. Asn; South. Speech Commun. Asn.(exec. secy, 55-58); Cent. States Speech Asn. Ancient and French rhetoric; social dialects. Publ: Co-auth, Building better speech, Noble, 62; auth, The oral interpretation of literature, McGraw, 63; co-auth, Research manual for the performance course in speech, Harper, 67; Rhetoric of revolt, Prentice-Hall, 71. Add: 402 Morgan Creek Rd, Chapel Hill, NC 27514.

BRANDON, JAMES R, b. St. Paul, Minn, Apr. 10, 27; m. 61; c. 1. DRAMA. Ph.B, Univ. Wis, 48, M.S, 49, Ph.D, 55. Instr. drama & speech, Univ. Conn, 50; asst. cult. attaché, U.S. Inform. Agency, Djakarta, 55-56, radio off, 56-57, Japanese lang. off, Tokyo, 58-59, asst. cult. attaché, 59-61; assoc. prof. drama, Mich. State Univ, 61-67, PROF. THEATER, 67-68; UNIV. HAWAII, 68- Int. Prog. Mich. State Univ-Ford Found. res. grant, Southeast Asia, 63-64; Fulbright Res. Scholar grant, Japan, 66-68; Nat. Endowment for Humanities sr. fel, 71-72. U.S.A, Sgt. Asia Soc; Japan Soc; Am. Theatre Asn. Asian theatre. Publ: Co-auth, Kabuki plays, French, 66; auth, Theatre in Southeast Asia, 67, On thrones of gold: three Javanese shadow plays, 69 & Five classic Kabuki plays, 74, Harvard; co-ed, The performing arts in Asia, UNESCO, 71; Traditional Asian plays, Hill & Wang, 72; plus others. Add: Dept. of Drama & Theatre, University of Hawaii, Honolulu, HI 96822.

BRANHAM, MARY EDITH, b. Joplin, Mo, Sept. 8, 09; m. 47. ENGLISH COMPOSITION & LITERATURE. A.B, Univ. Kans. City, 40, M.A, 41; Ph.D, Columbia Univ, 49. Asst. ed, Chicago Hy-Lites, 34-38; free-lance writer, New York, N.Y, 41-47; res. asst, State Univ. Iowa, 48-50; teacher Eng. & hist, St. Paul's Sch, Walla Walla, Wash, 54-58; ed, Univ. Wash. Press, 58-60; INSTR. ENG, EVERETT JR. COL, 61- William Volker scholar, 36-42; lectr, Whitman Col, 55-56; Nat. Endowment for Humanities fel, 72-73. NCTE; NEA; Am. Asn. Univ. Women. Mediaeval literature; legends of the South Pacific. Publ: Medieval skepticism and Chaucer, William-Frederick, 50. Add: 3518 Upland Ave, Everett, WA 98203.

BRANMAN, IRVING, b. New York, N.Y, May 26, 23; m. 49; c. 3. SPEECH, ENGLISH. B.S.Ed, City Col. New York, 46; M.A, Columbia Univ, 47, Ed.D, 56. Tutor SPEECH, CITY COL. NEW YORK, 46-51, lectr, 51-56, instr, 56-58, asst. prof, 58-67, chmn. dept, 66-67, assoc. prof, 67-71, PROF, 71-, CHMN. DEPT. SPEECH & THEATRE, 72- Fulbright prof. & chmn. dept. Eng. lang. training, Am. Col. Girls, Istanbul, 59-61; Fulbright prof, Cent. Univ. Ecuador & coord. Fulbright Eng. lang. prog. Ecuador, 62-63; vis. lectr, summers, Bennington Col, 59, 61, Univ. Colo, 62, 65 & Sch. Law, South. Methodist Univ, 63; consult, VISTA training prog, Univ. Colo, 65, 66 & 67; dir, Univ. Ctr. Pre-baccalaureate Prog, City Univ. N.Y, 67-69. U.S.A.A.F, 43-46. Speech Commun. Asn; Teachers Eng. Speakers of Other Lang. Teaching of English as a second language; administration of teacher training programs abroad; providing educational services for the educationally disadvantaged. Add: Dept. of Speech & Theatre, City College of New York, New York, NY 10031.

BRANNAN, ROBERT L, b. Mineral Wells, Tex, May 10, 27; m. 52; c. 5. ENGLISH. B.A, Univ. Tex, 48, M.A, 52; Danforth grant, 61-62; Ph.D.(Eng), Cornell Univ, 65. Teaching asst. ENG, Cornell Univ, 54-56, instr, 56-58; Univ. Notre Dame, 58-61, asst. prof, 61-66; ASSOC. PROF, Hiram Col, 66-67; BENEDICTINE COL, 67- Med.C, U.S.A, 46-47. MLA; NCTE. English literature of the 19th century; prose fiction. Publ: Under the management of Mr. Charles Dickens, Cornell Univ, 66. Add: Dept. of English, Benedictine College, Atchison, KS 66002.

BRANSON, VIRGINIA MARIE, b. Columbus, Ohio, Jan. 3, 20. SPEECH PATHOLOGY. B.A, Marietta Col, 52; M.A, Ohio Univ, 55, Ph.D.(speech path. & audiol), 61. Teacher jr. high sch, Calif, 52-54; instr. speech, Marietta Col, 55-57; teacher & speech therapist, Pub. Sch, Ohio, 57-59; PROF. SPEECH, SOUTH. CONN. STATE COL, 61- W.A.V.E.S, 44-45. Speech Commun. Asn; Am. Speech & Hearing Asn; Int. Asn. Logopedics & Phoniatrics. Use of television in teaching graduate students in speech and hearing and in therapeutic work in speech. Publ: To see ourselves, Speech J, South. Conn. State Col, fall 66; Television as a medium for training and therapy, J. N.J. Speech & Hearing Asn, spring 67. Add: Dept. of Speech, Southern Connecticut State College, New Haven, CT 06515.

BRANTLEY, JOHN D, b. Yancey, Tex, Dec. 29, 28; m. 51; c. 2. ENGLISH. B.A, Southwest Tex. State Col, 53; M.A, Trinity Univ.(Tex), 54; Ph.D.(Am. civilization), Univ. Tex, Austin, 61. Teacher, San Antonio Independent Sch. Dist, 53-57; from instr. to assoc. prof. ENG, San Antonio Col, 57-65; asst. prof, TRINITY UNIV. (TEX), 65-68, assoc. prof, 68-72, PROF, 72-, CHMN. DEPT, 67-, asst. to chmn. dept, 66-67. Mem. Nat. Am. Stud. fac. vis. team, Bethune-Cookman Col, 71 & Rust Col, 72. U.S.A.F. & U.S.A, 46-49, 50-51, Sgt. MLA; Am. Stud. Asn; S-Cent. Mod. Lang. Asn; AAUP. American fiction 1918-1945 and 45-present. Publ: The fiction of John Dos Passos, Mouton, The Hague, 68; Reminiscences of a Texas pioneer, Tex. Folklore Soc, 58. Add: Dept. of English, Trinity University, 715 Stadium Dr, San Antonio, TX 78284.

BRANTON, CLARENCE LEROY, b. Baxley, Ga, Feb. 2, 22; m. 56; c. 2. ENGLISH. B.A, Univ. Fla, 43, M.A, 47; A.M, Harvard, 48, Ph.D, 51. Instr. ENG, Rutgers Univ, 51-55; asst. prof, WASHINGTON & JEFFERSON COL, 55-57, assoc. prof, 57-71, PROF, 71- U.S.A.R, 43-, Col. Nineteenth century English novel: the church in English literature; Dr. Samuel Johnson. Add: Dept. of English, Washington & Jefferson College, Washington, PA 15301.

BRASHER, THOMAS LOWBER, b. Roswell, N.Mex, Dec. 16, 12; m. 47; c. 1. ENGLISH. B.A, Hardin-Simmons Univ, 49, fel, 49-51, M.A, 51; fel, La. State Univ, 52-53, Ph.D, 56. Instr. ENG, La. State Univ, 53-56; asst. prof, SOUTHWEST. TEX. STATE UNIV, 56-58, assoc. prof, 58-62, PROF, 62-, Piper Prof, 70. Air Intel, 42-46, 1st Lt. MLA. Walt Whitman; American poetry; 19th century American literature. Publ: Ed, Early poems and fiction of Walt Whitman: the collected writings of Walt Whitman, N.Y. Univ, 63; auth, Whitman as editor of the Brooklyn Daily Eagle, Wayne State Univ, 70; plus others. Add: Dept. of English, Southwest Texas State University, San Marcos, TX 78666.

BRASHERS, HOWARD CHARLES, b. Martin Co, Tex, Dec. 11, 30; m. 59; c. 3. CREATIVE WRITING, AMERICAN LITERATURE. B.A, Univ. Calif, Berkeley, 56; M.A, San Francisco State Col, 60; Ph.D.(Eng), Univ. Denver, 62. Instr. Eng, Univ. Denver, 61-62; Fulbright lectr. Am. stud, Univ. Stockholm, 62-65; asst. prof. Eng, Univ. Mich, 65-68; SAN DIEGO STATE UNIV, 68-70, ASSOC. PROF. LIT, 70- A.U.S, 53-55. West. Lit. Asn. Creative writing; American culture; aesthetics. Publ: The other side of love (two novellas), Swallow, 63; An introduction to American literature for European students, Svenska Bokförlaget, Stockholm, 65; The life of America, Natur Och Kultur, Stockholm, 66; Creative writing: fiction, drama, poetry, essay, Am. Bk. Co, 68; Creative writing for high school students, Univ. Mich. Bur. Sch. Serv, 68; The structure of essays, Prentice-Hall, 72; The cowboy story from stereotype to art, Modern Sprak, fall 63; Teaching descriptive style, J. Eng. Teaching Tech, summer 68; Aesthetic form in familiar essays, Col. Compos. & Commun, 5/71; plus others. Add: School of Literature, San Diego State University, San Diego, CA 92115.

BRASMER, WILLIAM OTTO, JR, b. Evanston, Ill, Oct. 22, 21; m. 48. THEATRE ARTS. B.S, Northwest. Univ, 46, M.A, 48. From assoc. prof. to PROF. THEATRE ARTS, DENISON UNIV, 48-, CHMN. DEPT. THEATRE & FILM, 64-, chmn. fine arts comt, 65-70. U.S.A, 42-46. Am. Theatre Asn. Dramatic production; theatre history; dramatic literature. Add: Dept. of Theatre & Film, Denison University, Granville, OH 43023.

BRASWELL, LAUREL ANNE, b. Chicago, Ill. ENGLISH, COMPARATIVE MEDIEVAL LITERATURE. B.A, Univ. Ark, 54, M.A, 55; Grad. en phil. et lett, Univ. Louvain, 56; M.A, Univ. Toronto, 58, Ph.D.(Eng), 64. Lectr. ENG, Univ. Toronto, 60-63, asst. prof, 64-67; guest lectr, Free Univ. Berlin, 68-69; ASSOC. PROF, McMASTER UNIV, 70- Can. Counc. res. fel, 67-68, fel, 69-70. Asn. Can. Univ. Teachers Eng; Can. Asn. Univ. Teachers; Early Eng. Text Soc. Medieval English; Old Norse; linguistics. Publ: The horn at Grendel's mere: Beowulf, 1417-41, Neuphilologische Mitteilungen, 73; The Middle Dutch prose legendary in the McMaster University Library, Mediaeval Stud, 74; contrib, A Middle English lunary, Pontif. Inst. Mediaeval Stud, 74; plus others. Add: 2153 Bellwood Ave, Burlington, Ont. L7R 1P9, Can.

BRASWELL, WILLIAM, b. Demopolis, Ala, June 26, 07; m. 45; c. 2. AMERICAN LITERATURE. Howard Col, 25-27; A.B, Duke Univ, 29, A.M, 31; Ph.D, Univ. Chicago, 34. Instr, Ala. Polytech. Inst, 34-35; ENG, PURDUE UNIV, 35-38, asst. prof, 38-46, assoc. prof, 46-48, prof, 48-73, EMER. PROF, 73- Fulbright prof, Univ. Athens, Greece, 54-55. U.S.N, 42-46, Lt. Comdr. MLA; Col. Eng. Asn; Melville Soc.(pres, 48). Herman Melville; American humor; literature of social criticism. Publ: Melville's religious thought, Duke Univ, 43; co-ed, Thomas Wolfe's Purdue speech: Writing and living, Purdue Univ. Stud, 64. Add: 1306 Sunset Lane, West Lafayette, IN 47906.

BRATCHER, JAMES TERRY, b. Dallas, Tex, Jan. 30, 34; m. 59; c. 2. ENGLISH. B.A, Tex. Christian Univ, 59, M.A, 62; Woodrow Wilson fel, Harvard, 59-60; Ph.D.(Eng), Univ. Tex, Austin, 74. Instr. Eng, Tex. Christian Univ, 62-63; teaching asst, Univ. Tex, 63-66; asst. prof, Sul Ross State Col, 66-69. U.S.M.C, 52-55. English studies; bibliography; folklore. Publ: Co-auth, Wise's Swinburne transactions: addendum to An enquiry, Univ. Tex, 70; auth, Analytical index to publications of the Texas Folklore Society, South. Methodist Univ, 73; The Lorenzo-Jessica subplot and Genesis XXXIV, In: Shakespeare 1964, Tex. Christian Univ, 65; co-auth, Two further footnotes to An enquiry, Tex. Stud. Lit. & Lang, spring 65; Peele's Old wives' tale and tale-type 425A, In: Studies in medieval, Renaissance and American literature: a festschrift, Tex. Christian Univ, 71; plus others. Add: 2805 N. Florence, El Paso, TX 79902.

BRATER, ENOCH, b. New York, N.Y, Oct. 1, 44; m. 73. ENGLISH & AMERICAN LITERATURE. B.A, N.Y. Univ, 65; A.M, Harvard, 67, Ph.D.(Eng), 71. Managing dir, Loeb Drama Ctr, Harvard, 70-71; ASST. PROF. ENG, UNIV. PA, 71-, COORD. UNDERGRAD. PROG. THEATER, 73-, fel, 72. Am. Philos. Soc. grant-in-aid, 73; vis. lectr, Summer Inst. Arts. Admin, Harvard, 73. MLA; Northeast Mod. Lang. Asn; Univ. & Col. Theater Asn; Am. Soc. Theater Res. Samuel Beckett; modern drama; 20th century novels. Publ: The empty can: Andy Warhol and Samuel Beckett, 11/73 & W.B. Yeats: the poet as critic, J. Mod. Lit; The absurd actor in the theater of Samuel Beckett, Educ. Theatre J; plus others. Add: Dept. of English, University of Pennsylvania, Philadelphia, PA 19174.

BRATSET, RICHARD, b. Alameda, Calif, Mar. 12, 24. ENGLISH & COMPARATIVE LITERATURE. A.B, Univ. Calif, Berkeley, 49, M.A, 53, Ph.D.(Educ), 61. Instr. Eng, Athens Col, Greece, 53-56; lang. arts, SAN FRANCISCO STATE UNIV, 56-61, from asst. prof. ENG. & WORLD LIT. to assoc. prof, 61-70, PROF, 70-, chmn. dept. comp. lit, 70-72. C.Eng, U.S.A, 43-46. Am. Comp. Lit. Asn; MLA. Comparative literature; English. Add: Dept. of Comparative Literature, San Francisco State University, San Francisco, CA 94132.

BRAUDY, LEO, b. Philadelphia, Pa, June 11, 41. ENGLISH. B.A, Swarthmore Col, 63; M.A, Yale, 64, Ph.D.(Eng), 67. Instr. ENG, Yale, 66-68; asst. prof, COLUMBIA UNIV, 68-70, assoc. prof, 70-73, PROF, 73- Fel, Huntington Libr, 71-72; Guggenheim fel, 71-72; Am. Counc. Learned Soc. grant-in-aid, 71. MLA (regional del, 70-74); Am. Soc. 18th Century Stud. Novel; film; 18th century. Publ: Auth, Narrative form in history and fiction: Hume, Fielding and Gibbon, Princeton, 70; Jean Renoir: the world of his films, Doubleday, 72; ed, Norman Mailer: a collection of critical essays, 72 & Focus on Shoot the piano player, 72, Prentice-Hall. Add: Dept. of English, 420 Hamilton Hall, Columbia University, New York, NY 10027.

BRAUER, GEORGE C, JR. b. Cleveland, Ohio, Aug. 7, 25. ENGLISH. B.A, Princeton, 47, M.A, 49, Ph.D, 52. Instr. ENG, Univ. Tex, 52-56; asst. prof, UNIV. S.C, 56-62, assoc. prof, 62-70, PROF, 70- Russell Award, 61. MLA; Inst. Studi Romani; Am. Sch. Oriental Res. Eighteenth century English literature; Roman history; classical numismatics. Publ: The education of a gentleman, Bookman Assoc, 59; The young emperors: Rome, A.D. 193-244, 67 & Judaea weeping: the Jewish struggle against Rome from Pompey to Masada, 63 B.C. to A.D. 73, 70, Crowell; Good breeding in the eighteenth century, Univ. Tex. Stud. Eng, 53; Recommendations of the Spectator for students during the eighteenth century, Notes & Queries, 55; Johnson and Boswell, CEA Critic, 1/65. Add: Dept. of English, University of South Carolina, Columbia, SC 29208.

BRAUN, RICHARD EMIL, Classics, Literature. See Volume III, Foreign Languages, Linguistics & Philology.

BRAUN, SHIRLEY WORCESTER, Linguistics, English As A Second Language. See Volume III, Foreign Languages, Linguistics & Philology.

BRAUNMULLER, ALBERT RICHARD, b. Plainfield, N.J, Nov. 25, 45. ENGLISH LITERATURE. B.A, Stanford Univ, 67; NDEA fel, Yale, 67-70; Folger Shakespeare Libr. fel, summer 70; Thomas Eastman fel, Yale, 70-71, M.Phil, 70, Ph.D.(Eng), 71. ASST. PROF. ENG, UNIV. CALIF, LOS ANGELES, 71- Nat. Endowment for Humanities fel, summer 72; Folger Shakespeare Libr, fel, 73-74; mem. adv. bd. dir, World Ctr. Shakespeare Stud. MLA; Renaissance Soc. Am. Renaissance drama and poetry; modern drama. Publ: The natural course of light inverted: an impresa in Chapman's Bussy d'Ambois, J. Warburg & Courtauld Insts, 71; The serious comedy of Greene's James IV, Eng. Lit. Renaissance, 73. Add: Dept. of English, University of California, 405 Hilgard Ave, Los Angeles, CA 90024.

BRAWER, ROBERT ALLEN, b. New York, N.Y, Mar. 22, 38; m. 62; c. 2. MEDIEVAL ENGLISH LANGUAGE & LITERATURE. B.A, Univ. Md, 59; M.A, Univ. Pa, 62; Ph.D.(Eng), Univ. Chicago, 70. Instr. ENG, Fieldston Sch, Riverdale, N.Y, 63-65; ASST. PROF, UNIV. WIS-MADISON, 68- Eng.C, U.S.A, 60-61, U.S. Nat. Guard, 61-66. Medieval Acad. Am; MLA. Medieval drama; medieval lyric poetry; Chaucer. Publ: The dramatic function of the ministry group in the Towneley cycle, Comp. Drama, fall 70; Dramatic technique in the Corpus Christi creation and fall, Mod. Lang. Quart, 12/71; The form and function of the procession of prophets in the Middle English cycle plays, Annuale Mediaevale, 72. Add: Dept. of English, University of Wisconsin-Madison, 600 N. Park St, Madison, WI 53706.

BRAWNER, JAMES PAUL, b. Magazine, Ark, Aug. 10, 02. ENGLISH & AMERICAN LITERATURE. A.B, Washington & Lee Univ, 24, A.M, 25; Ph.D, Univ. Ill, 35. Assoc. prof. ENG, Ark. State Teachers Col, Conway, 25-29; from asst. to instr, Univ. Ill, 29-35; instr. W.VA. UNIV, 35-36, asst. prof, 36-45, assoc. prof, 45-52, prof, 52-72, chmn. dept, 49-67, EMER. PROF, 72- Mem. fac, U.S. Army Advan. Stud. Ctr, Univ. Florence, 45. MLA; Int. Asn. Univ. Prof. Eng. Early Tudor Drama; Shakespeare; English and American romanticism. Publ: The wars of Cyrus, Univ. Ill, 42. Add: 311 Laurel St, Morgantown, WV 26505.

BRAY, WILLIAM ALBERT, b. Bethany, Mo, Dec. 4, 24; m. 53; c. 2. JOURNALISM. B.J, Univ. Mo, 48. Ed-publ, Odessa Odessan, 48-53; ASSOC. PROF. NEWSPAPER PUBL, UNIV. MO-COLUMBIA, 53- Ed, Mo. Press News. U.S.A, 43-46, Sgt. Inst. Newspaper Controllers & Finance Off; Nat. Newspaper Asn.(bd. dir, Nat. Ed. Asn, 58-60); Newspaper Asn. Mgr.(pres, 58-59). Newspaper organization and management; community newspapers. Add: Missouri Press Bldg, Eighth & Locust, Columbia, MO 65201.

BRAZELL, JAMES REID, b. Canton, Ohio, July 7, 34; m. 61; c. 2. ENGLISH LITERATURE. A.B, Princeton, 56; M.A, Univ. Mich, 61, Ph.D.(Eng), 67. ASST. PROF. ENG, Briarcliff Col, 64-69; TRENTON STATE COL, 69- Lectr, Doshisha Univ, Japan, 67-68 & 72-73; Kyoto Univ, 72-73. U.S.A.F, 56-59, 1st Lt. MLA; NCTE. English Romantic poetry; contemporary American poetry; Oriental-Western literary relations. Publ: Shelley and the concept of humanity, Univ. Salzburg, 72; Shelley's Alastor and the hazards of an expanded consciousness, Wascana Rev, 73; Poetry and words: their relationship in contemporary American poetry, Study English, Tokyo, 73. Add: 31 Colonial Lake Dr, Trenton, NJ 08638.

BREAUX, ELWYN ELLISON, b. Guthrie, Okla; m. 43; c. 2. ENGLISH. B.A, Fisk Univ, 39; M.S, Okla. State Univ, 57, Ed.D,(Eng. & higher educ), 71. Teacher ENG, Booker T. Washington Sch, Sand Springs, Okla, 42-46; PROF, LANGSTON UNIV, 55-, CHMN. DEPT, 66- NCTE; Col. Conf. Compos. & Commun. Black literature; dialects of Afro-Americans; extra sensory perception. Publ: Co-auth, Inman E. Page, outstanding educator, Negro Hist. Bull, 5/69; auth, The students' image: a by-product, In: Classroom practices 1970-1971, NCTE, 71. Add: Dept. of English, Langston University, Langston, OK 73050.

BREDAHL, A. CARL, JR, b. Washington, D.C, July 27, 40; m. 66; c. 3. AMERICAN LITERATURE. B.A, Princeton, 62; Ph.D.(Am. lit), Univ. Pittsburgh, 69. Instr. lit, Univ. Pittsburgh, 69-70; ASST. PROF. AM. LIT, UNIV. FLA, 70- MLA. American literature, philosophy and visual arts. Publ: Melville's angles of vision, Univ. Fla, 72; The artist in The damnation of Theron Ware, Stud. Novel, 72; Look homeward, angel: individuation and articulation, South. Lit. J, 73; The drinking image in The grapes of wrath, Steinbeck Quart, 73. Add: Dept. of English, 200 Anderson Hall, University of Florida, Gainesville, FL 32601.

BREDE, ALEXANDER, b. Detroit, Mich, Nov. 25, 90; m. 22; c. 3. ENGLISH. A.B, Univ. Mich, 18; A.M, Stanford Univ, 31. Instr, Marietta Col, 18-19; Detroit Jr. Col, 19-21; Stanford Univ, 21-22; prof. Eng. & head dept, Univ. Nanking, China, 22-27; from asst. prof. to assoc. prof, WAYNE STATE UNIV, 27-61, EMER. ASSOC. PROF. ENG. & EMER. CHIEF ED, UNIV. PRESS, 61-, ed, 41-61. MLA; Col. Eng. Asn. Linguistics; China; fine printing. Add: 2301 Shankin, Walled Lake, MI 48088.

BREGLIO, LOUIS ANTHONY, b. New York, N.Y, Jan. 16, 15; m. 46; c. 3. ENGLISH. B.A, N.Y. Univ, 34; M.A, Columbia Univ, 35, Ph.D, 41. Pub. inform. off, Ford Found, 49-51; assoc. prof. ENG, BROOKLYN COL, 57-69, PROF, 69-, dean stud, 68-71. Lectr. sch. gen. stud, Columbia Univ, 46-51; Marymount Col, 49-51; sch. gen. stud, Brooklyn, 51-57. Med.C, U.S.A, 42-46, 1st Lt. Nat. Counc. Col. Publ. Adv. Creative writing; advanced exposition. Publ: Francesco De Sanctis, Vanni, 41; Standards for college newspapers, Col. Press Rev, 63; Shakespeare's poetry in the development of De Sanctis' criticism, Italica, 2/64. Add: Dept. of English, Brooklyn College, Brooklyn, NY 11210.

BREITROSE, HENRY S, b. Brooklyn, N.Y, July 22, 36; m. 68; c. 1. FILM, COMMUNICATION RESEARCH. B.A, Univ. Wis-Madison, 58; M.A, Northwest. Univ, Evanston, 59; Ph.D.(commun. res), Stanford Univ, 66. From instr. to ASSOC. PROF. COMMUN, STANFORD UNIV, 60- Rockefeller Found. travel grant, 65-66; consult, Stanford Res. Inst, 66; Nat. Film Bd. Can, 68; mem. steering comt, Univ. Adv. Counc, Am. Film Inst, 72-; Stanford Univ. fel, 72-74. Soc. Cinema Stud; Am. Asn. Pub. Opinion Res; Univ. Film Asn.(co-chmn. res. comt, 68-70); Broadcast Educ. Asn. Film aesthetics and criticism; non-verbal communication; attitude formation and change. Publ: On the search for the real nitty-gritty: problems and possibilities in cinema-verite, Film Quart, summer 64; co-auth, Teacher accuracy in assessing cognitive visual feedback, J. Appl. Psychol, 12/64; auth, Film, In: Handbook of Communication, Rand, 73. Add: Dept. of Communication, Stanford University, Stanford, CA 94305.

BREMBECK, WINSTON LAMONT, b. Urbana, Ind, Sept. 28, 12. SPEECH. A.B, Manchester Col, 36; A.M, Univ. Wis, 38, Ph.D, 47. Instr, West. Union Col, 37-39; tutor, Brooklyn Col, 39-42; instr, UNIV. WIS-MADISON, 46-47, asst. prof. PUB. ADDRESS, 47-54, assoc. prof, 54-58, PROF, 58- Am. Forensic Asn; Cent. States Speech Asn.(pres, 64-65); Speech Commun. Asn. Rhetoric; public address. Publ: Co-auth, Persuasion: a means of social control, 52 & Persuasion: a means of social influence, 74, Prentice-Hall; auth, The effects of a course in argumentation on critical thinking ability, Speech Monogr, 9/49; Teaching the course in persuasion, 9/60 & The content of the college course in persuasion, 11/64, Speech Teacher. Add: Dept. of Communication Arts, University of Wisconsin-Madison, Madison, WI 53713.

BRENGELMAN, FREDERICK HENRY, Linguistics, English Language Studies. See Volume III, Foreign Languages, Linguistics & Philology.

BRENIMAN, LESTER, b. Brooklyn, Iowa, Jan. 15, 05; m. 34. SPEECH. A.B, Parsons Col, 27, M.A, Northwest. Univ, 41; Ph.D, Ohio State Univ, 53. Instr. soc. sci, Geneseo Twp. High Sch, Ill, 29-31; speech, Eveleth Sr. High Sch, Minn, 31-40; Hutchinson Jr. Col, Kans, 40-43; civilian training adminr, Midwest Dist, Air Tec. Serv. Command, 43-45; assoc. prof. speech, Oklahoma City Univ, 48-50; asst, Ohio State Univ, 51-53; asst. prof. speech, Univ. Ark, 53-54; assoc. prof. SPEECH EDUC, SOUTH. ILL. UNIV, CAR-

BONDALE, 54-73, EMER. ASSOC. PROF, 73- Distinguished Serv. Award, Nat. Forensic League, 36. Speech Commun. Asn. Speech education; basic speech; Mark Twain. Publ: Co-auth, Oral communication of ideas: a study-guide, Stipes, 65; Principles and objectives common to the major speech areas, Speech Teacher, 9/58; The problem of class size, West. Speech, summer 63. Add: R.D. 7, Carbondale, IL 62901.

BRENNAN, JOHN PATRICK, b. Melrose, Mass, July 2, 42; m. 66, 72; c. 2. ENGLISH. B.S, Boston Col, 63; M.A, Univ. Calif, Davis, 65; Ph.D.(Eng), 67. Assoc. ENG, Univ. Calif, Davis, 66-67; ASST. PROF, IND. UNIV, FT. WAYNE, 67- MLA; Mediaeval Acad. Am. Medieval English literature; speculative fiction; critical theory. Publ: Co-auth, Medieval manuscripts of Jerome Adversus Jovinianum, Manuscripta, 69; auth, Reflections on a gloss to the Prioress's tale..., Stud. Philol, 73. Add: Dept. of English, Indiana University at Ft. Wayne, Ft. Wayne, IN 46805.

BRENNAN, JOSEPH XAVIER, b. Providence, R.I, June 24, 24. ENGLISH. A.B, Providence Col, 45; M.A, Brown Univ, 49; Ph.D.(Eng), Univ. Ill, 53. Instr. ENG, Providence Col, 46-50; teaching asst, Univ. Ill, 51; asst. prof, UNIV. NOTRE DAME, 55-62, assoc. prof, 62-68, PROF, 68- Instr, Georgetown Univ, 47; Fulbright fel, Univ. Florence, 53-54. MLA. Elizabethan and American literature. Publ: Joannes Susenbrotus: a forgotten humanist, PMLA, 12/60; Ironic and symbolic structure in Crane's Maggie, Nineteenth-Century Fiction, 62; Willa Cather and music, Univ. Rev, spring-summer 65. Add: Dept. of English, University of Notre Dame, Notre Dame, IN 46556.

BRENNAN, NEIL F, b. Savannah, Ga, Mar. 1, 23; m. 49; c. 4. MODERN BRITISH LITERATURE. Ann Watkins fel, 48; M.A, Univ. Chicago, 49; Ph.D, Univ. Ill, 59. Instr. ENG, Auburn Univ, 50-53; Cornell Univ, 57-60; asst. prof, VILLANOVA UNIV, 60-63, ASSOC. PROF, 63- U.S.A, 43-46, Capt. MLA; NCTE; AAUP. Modern British novel; publications on Graham Greene and Anthony Powell. Add: Dept. of English, Villanova University, Villanova, PA 19085.

BRENNER, GERRY, b. Seattle, Wash, Oct. 7, 37; m. 60; c. 3. LITERATURE. B.A, Univ. Wash, 61, M.A, 62, Ph.D.(Eng), 65. Asst. ENG, Univ. Wash, 61-64, instr, 64-65; asst. prof, Univ. Idaho, 65-67; assoc. prof, Boise Col, 67-68; asst. prof, UNIV. MONT, 68-71, ASSOC PROF, 71- U.S.A, 55-57. MLA; Philol. Asn. Pac. Coast; Rocky Mt. Mod. Lang. Asn. Twentieth century Anglo-American literature; the novel; Hemingway. Publ: Frank O'Connor's imprudent hero, Tex. Stud. Lit. & Lang, 68; Cooper's composite order: The pioneers as structured art, Stud. Novel, 70; Epic machinery in Hemingway's For whom the bell tolls, Mod. Fiction Stud, 71; plus others. Add: Dept. of English, University of Montana, Missoula, MT 59801.

BRENTLINGER, W. BROCK, b. Flora, Ill, Aug. 21, 26; m; c. 6. SPEECH. B.A, Greenvillé Col, 50; M.A, Ind. State Teachers Col, 51; Ph.D, Univ. Ill, 59. From instr. to assoc. prof. speech, Greenville Col, 51-63, dean, 63-69; PROF. SPEECH & DEAN COL. FINE & APPL. ARTS, LAMAR UNIV, 69- Danforth Found. teacher stud. grant, 57. U.S.N, 44-46. Speech Commun. Asn; Int. Counc. Fine Arts Deans. Public address. Add: College of Fine Arts, Box 10197, Lamar University, Beaumont, TX 77710.

BRESLIN, JAMES E, b. New York, N.Y, Dec. 12, 35; m. 63; c. 2. ENGLISH. B.A, Brooklyn Col, 57; M.A, Univ. N.C, 59; fel, Univ. Minn, 63-64, Ph.D. (Eng), 64. Instr. ENG, Univ. Minn, 61-63; asst. prof, UNIV. CALIF, BERKELEY, 64-71, ASSOC. PROF, 71-, summer fac. fel, 65, humanities res. prof, 69. MLA. American poetry; modern literature. Publ: William Carlos Williams: an American artist, Oxford Univ, 69; William Carlos Williams and the Whitman tradition, In: Literary criticism and historical understanding, Columbia Univ, 67; Whitman and the early development of William Carlos Williams, PMLA, 12/67. Add: Dept. of English, University of California, Berkeley, CA 94720.

BREWER, FREDRIC ALDWYN, b. Andrews, Ind, Dec. 20, 21; m. 56; c. 3. MASS COMMUNICATIONS. B.Sc. & M.Sc, Ind. Univ, 50. Asst. prof. broadcasting, Ithaca Col, 50-53; mass commun, Ore. State Syst. Higher Educ, Portland, Ore, 53-54; ed. newspapers, R.I, Calif. & Wash, 54-58; mem. staff pub. relat, Columbia Univ, 58-60; exec. ed, Thorpe & Porter Ltd, London, Eng, 60-62; assoc. ed, Scholastic Mag, Inc, New York, 62-64; ASSOC. PROF. TELECOMMUN, IND. UNIV, BLOOMINGTON, 64- Consult, Empire State Sch. of the Air, N.Y, 50-53, Gilberton World Wide Publ. Co, New York, 58-62 & Curtis Publ. Co, 72-; mem. hist. comt, Broadcast Educ. Asn, 71-73. Sigma Delta Chi medal distinguished pub. serv. broadcast news, 49. Ord.C, U.S.A, 42-45, 1st Sgt. Fel. AAAS; Astron. Soc. Pac; Brit. Astron. Asn; Overseas Press Club Am. Communication in science. Publ: Co-auth, Creative broadcasting, Prentice-Hall, 50; auth, Challengers of the unknown, Four Winds, 66; The solar system (AV rec. album), H. Wilson, 72; plus others. Add: Dept. of Telecommunications, Radio-Television Bldg, Indiana University, Bloomington, IN 47401.

BREWER, GWENDOLYN, WHITEHEAD, b. Provo, Utah, Nov. 18, 28; m. 63; c. 2. EIGHTEENTH CENTURY ENGLISH LITERATURE, ENGLISH EDUCATION. B.A, Brigham Young Univ, 55, M.A, 57; Ford Found. fel, Claremont Grad. Sch, 58-61, Ph.D.(Eng. lit), 68. Instr. Eng, Brigham Young Univ, 56-57; res. asst. 18th century Eng, Claremont Grad. Sch, 59-60; instr. ENG, Citrus Col.(Calif), 60-63; from instr. to ASSOC. PROF, CALIF. STATE UNIV, NORTHRIDGE, 65- Consult. & speaker, var. educ. orgn, Calif, 67-; mem. Eng. lang. assessment adv. comt, Calif. Dept. Educ, 73; consult, Conejo Elem. Sch, Thousand Oaks, 73; mem. steering comt. Eng. & reading, Calif. Curriculum Develop. & Suppl. Materials Comn, 74- Am. Soc. 18th Century Stud; NCTE; Philol. Asn. Pac. Coast. Children's and adolescent literature. Publ: Co-auth, Language arts curriculum, Enterprise City Sch. Dist, 68 & Literature-based language arts units, Calif. State Univ, Northridge, 74. Add: Dept. of English, California State University, 18111 Nordhoff St, Northridge, CA 91324.

BREWER, HELENE MAXWELL, b. San Francisco, Calif, Nov. 20, 07; m. 40, 58. AMERICAN LITERATURE & STUDIES. A.B, Santa Barbara State Col, 30; M.A, Stanford Univ, 34; Ph.D, Johns Hopkins Univ, 40. Instr. Eng, QUEENS COL.(N.Y), 52-60, assoc. prof. ENG, 60-69, PROF, 69- Am. Counc. Learned Soc. grant-in-aid, 47, mem. Am. Stud. adv. comt, 72-; Guggenheim fel, 49-50; Fulbright vis. lectr, Japan, 66-68. MLA; Am. Stud. Asn; Emerson Soc; Oral Hist. Asn; Eng. Lit. & Lang. Soc, Japan. American literature, political and social movements, 1900-1925; the Progressive Movement and Party, 1900-1920. Publ: Ed, History of the Progressive Party, 1912-1916, N.Y. Univ, 58; co-auth, Emma Moffat McLaughlin: a life in community service, Univ. Calif, 70; A man and two books: Frances Heney, J. Allen Smith and Frederic C. Howe, Pac. Hist. Rev, 8/62; Francis J Heney, (Suppl. 1) & Amos R. E. Pinchot, (Suppl. 2), In: Dictionary of American Biography, Scribners, 72. Add: Dept. of English, Queens College, Flushing, NY 11367.

BREWER, JOHN MOTSINGER, b. Marion, Ill, Aug. 20, 09; m. 38; c. 2. ENGLISH, SPEECH. B.Ed, South. Ill. Univ, 35; M.A, Univ. Ill, Urbana, 42. Prin, grade sch, Marion, Ill, 30-32, high sch, 42-47; asst. prof. ENG, UNIV. MO-ROLLA, 56-60, assoc. prof, 60-67, PROF, 67- Pres, Esperanto Asn. Am, 55-63. U.S.N, 44-46, Lt. Am. Soc. Eng. Educ; Speech Commun. Asn. Technical writing. Publ: Speech manual for engineers, 55 & Readings in technical writing, 59, Lucas Publ. Add: Dept. of English, University of Missouri-Rolla, Rolla, MO 65401.

BREWER, JOSEPH E, b. Paducah, Ky, May 8, 21; m. 45; c. 3. ENGLISH, LINGUISTICS. B.A, Univ. Akron, 47; fel, Univ. Ill, 47-48; M.A, Univ. Cincinnati, 48; Ph.D.(Eng), West. Reserve Univ, 54. Asst. prof. ENG, Baldwin-Wallace Col, 48-54, assoc. prof, 54-58; asst. prof, Calif. State Col. Long Beach, 58-61; prof, Simpson Col, 61-67, acting head dept, 66-67; assoc. prof, CALIF. STATE COL, STANISLAUS, 67-73, PROF, 73- Fulbright prof, Philippines, 55-56. Victorian literature; descriptive linguistics; modern literature. Publ: Poetry: an anthology, Anderson, 65; The anti-hero in contemporary literature, Iowa Eng. Bull, 67. Add: Dept. of English, California State College, Stanislaus, Turlock, CA 95380.

BREWER, JUNE HARDEN, b. Austin, Tex, Sept. 5, 25; m. 49; c. 1. ENGLISH. A.B, Huston-Tillotson Col, 44; M.A, Howard Univ, 46; Cornell Univ, 48; South. Educ. Found. fel, 57-58; United Negro Col. Fund fel, 60; Ph.D, Univ. Tex, 63. Instr. ENG, Morgan State Col, 46; asst. prof, Huston-Tillotson Col, 47-72, chmn. dept, 67-72; assoc. prof, Southern Univ, 72-73. Vis. lectr, Macalester Col, 66-67; Nat. Endowment for Humanities res. fel, 73-74. MLA; NCTE; Conf. Col. Compos. & Commun; S.Cent. Mod. Lang. Asn.(chmn. African & Afro-Am. lit. section, 72-73). Student ecology; Afro-American literature; African literature. Add: 2006 Leona St, Austin, TX 78722.

BREWER, RICHARD E, b. Trenton, N.J, Apr. 7, 31; m. 63. ENGLISH, COMPARATIVE RELIGION. A.B, Drew Univ, 54; Th.M, Princeton Theol. Sem, 58; M.A, Rutgers Univ, 60; N.Y. Univ, 62. Asst. comp. relig, Princeton Theol. Sem, 59; from instr. to ASST. PROF. ENG. & PHILOS, MONMOUTH COL, 60- NCTE. Dante; 18th century English literature; religious literature. Publ: Perspectives on Ocean Grove, Shoreline Press, 69; co-ed, A short account of a long journey, Tract Asn. Friends, 70; Tide winds, In: College anthology of poetry, 51; Letter on Dante, Time Mag, 7/65. Add: Dept. of English, Monmouth College, West Long Branch, NJ 07764.

BREWER, WILMON, b. Hingham, Mass, Apr. 1, 95; m. 22. COMPARATIVE LITERATURE, A.B, Harvard, 17, A.M, 20, Ph.D, 25; hon. D.Sc. (oratory), Curry Col, 59. Instr. Eng, Harvard, 23-24; LECTR, LIT. SOC, 25-; AUTHOR, 25- Dir, Hingham Pub. Libr, 36-, secy, 37-43. U.S.A, 18-19, 2nd Lt. Fel. Int. Inst. Arts & Lett; Poetry Soc. Am.(treas, 35-38, 41-47, pres, 39-41); MLA; London Auth. Club; Shakespeare Asn. Am; Dante Soc. Am. Poetry; biography. Publ: Ovid's metamorphoses in European culture, Dante's eclogues, Sonnets and sestimas, Adventures in verse, New adventures, Adventures further, 58 & Still more adventures, 66, Marshall Jones. Add: Great Hills, Hingham, MA 02043.

BREWINGTON, ARTHUR W, b. Brooklyn, N.Y, Nov. 10, 06; m. 55. ENGLISH LANGUAGE & LITERATURE. A.B, Asbury Col, 24; M.A, Cornell Univ, 31; fel, George Peabody Col, 34-37, Ph.D, 41. Teacher, high sch, Md, 28-29; Massanutten Mil. Acad, 29-30; Cascadilla Sch, Ithaca, N.Y, 30-31; prof. Eng. & speech, Rider Col, 31-32; prof. & head dept. Eng, Tenn. Wesleyan Col, 32-34; assoc. prof. Eng. & speech, Memphis State Col, 37-41; inspector quality control, Martin Aircraft Co, 42-45; prof. ENG. & SPEECH, TOWSON STATE COL, 44-71, EMER. PROF, 71- Fulbright grant & consult. Eng. lang. teaching, Indian Ministry Educ, New Delhi, 57-58; Danforth Found. grant, Ling. Inst, Univ. Wash, 63. Speech Commun. Asn; Speech Asn. East. States; Col. Eng. Asn; NCTE; Ling. Asn. Am. Speech education; English language; phonetics. Publ: Survey of speech education in the American junior college, Peabody, 41; English language in India, CEA Critic, 58. Add: 230 Los Jardines, Green Valley, AZ 85614.

BREWSTER, DOROTHY, b. St. Louis, Mo, Sept. 8, 83. CONTEMPORARY LITERATURE. A.B, Columbia Univ, 06, A.M, 07, spec. fel, 11-12, Ph.D, 13. Asst, Barnard Col, Columbia Univ, 08-11; reader Eng, Bryn Mawr Col, 14-15; instr, Columbia Univ, 15-23, asst. prof, 23-44, assoc. prof, 44-50; RES. & WRITING, 50- MLA. Publ: East-West passage, Allen & Unwin, London; Virginia Woolf's London, 59 & 60 & Virginia Woolf, 62 & 63, N.Y. Univ. & Allen & Unwin, London; Doris Lessing, Twayne, 65; William Brewster of the Mayflower: portrait of a pilgrim, N.Y. Univ, 70. Add: 310 Riverside Dr, New York, NY 10025.

BREYER, BERNARD R, b. Nashville, Tenn, July 25, 19; m. 47; c. 3. ENGLISH LITERATURE. B.A, Vanderbilt Univ, 39; M.A, La. State Univ, 40; Ph.D, Univ. Va, 48. Instr. ENG, Univ. Ariz, 47-49; asst. prof, AUBURN UNIV, 49-56, assoc. prof, 56-64, PROF, 66- Ford fel, 54-55; Fulbright lectr, Univ. Innsbruck, Austria, 61-62. U.S.A, 42-45. S.Atlantic Mod. Lang. Asn. The Romantic movement; contemporary literature. Publ: Towards an interpretation of Kubla Khan, Univ. Va, 53; A new look at Julius Caesar, Vanderbilt Univ, 55; Violence in recent southern fiction, Miss. Quart, 62; Wordsworth's pleasure: an approach to his poetic theory, South. Humanities Rev, spring 72. Add: Dept. of English, Auburn University, Auburn, AL 36830.

BRIAN, GEORGE C, b. Baton Rouge, La, July 16, 19; m. 53; c. 1. SPEECH, DRAMA. Ph.D.(speech), La. State Univ, 65. PROF. SPEECH, NORTHEAST LA. UNIV, 53- Sig.C, U.S.A, 41-46. Am. Speech Asn; Am. Theatre Asn; Children's Theatre Asn. Drama—children's theatre; motion pictures. Add: Dept. of Speech, Northeast Louisiana University, Monroe, LA 71201.

BRIAND, PAUL L, JR, b. Cambridge, Mass, Oct. 29, 20; m. 52; c. 8. ENGLISH. B.A, Univ. N.H, 48; M.A, Columbia Univ, 52; Ph.D.(mod. lit, creative writing), Univ. Denver, 59. Instr, U.S. Mil. Acad, 52-55; ENG, U.S. Air Force Acad, 55-57, asst. prof, 59-60, assoc. prof, 60-63, tenure assoc. prof, 63-67; assoc. prof, STATE UNIV. N.Y. COL. OSWEGO, 67-71, PROF, 71- Consult, Colo. State Bd. Educ, 62; electronics syst. div, U.S. Air Force Syst. Command, Hanscom Field, Mass, 65-66. U.S.A.F, 45-67, Lt. Col; Air Medal. MLA; NCTE. Modern literature; biography; instructional technology. Publ: Co-auth, The sound of wings, Holt, 57; auth, Daughter of the sky, 60 & In search of paradise, 66, Duell; Turning students on through multimedia, In: New teaching, new learning, Jossey-Bass, 71; Nonverbal literacy and verbal communication, AV Instr, 6-7/72; Dear Ben, on the wall, who is the loyalest of them all?, New Hampshire, 10/72; plus five others. Add: Dept. of English, State University of New York College at Oswego, Oswego, NY 13126.

BRICE, MARSHALL MOORE, b. White Oak, S.C, Aug. 30, 98; m. 23; c. 2. ENGLISH. B.S, Clemson Univ, 17; Columbia Univ, 19, 22; M.A, Univ. Wis, 27; Ed.D, Univ. Va, 56. Asst. prin, high sch, Ga, 17-19, prin, 19-20; head dept. ENG, Staunton Mil. Acad, 20-56; prof, MARY BALDWIN COL, 56-68, EMER. PROF, 68- U.S.A.R, 24-58, Col. NCTE; Conf. Col. Compos. & Commun. The Civil War; methods of study; American revolution. Publ: Co-auth, How to study with success and satisfaction, Anderson Bk, 54; auth, Conquest of a valley, Univ. Va, 65; The Stonewall Brigade Band, 67 & Daughter of the stars, 73, McClure; Comparison of subjective predictions with objective predictions of college achievement, Col. & Univ, spring 57; Lincoln and rhetoric, Col. Compos. & Commun, 2/66. Add: Dept. of English, Mary Baldwin College, Staunton, VA 24401.

BRICKER, HERSCHEL LEONARD, b. Earlham, Iowa, May 22, 05; m. 44; c. 1. THEATRE. A.B, Coe Col, 28; Rockefeller Found. fel, 36-37. From asst. prof. to prof. speech, UNIV. MAINE, ORONO, 28-70, dir. theatre, 37-70, EMER. PROF. THEATRE, 70-; VIS. PROF, UNIV. MAINE, FARMINGTON, 70- Head theatre br, U.S. Army Univ, Eng, 45-46; theatre consult, U.S. Forces Europ. Theater, 46; founder & dir-mgr, Camden Hills Theatre Sch, 48-54; dir, Maine Masque Theatre Tour, U.S. Dept. Defense, Europe, 59-60, U.S. Dept. State, India & Pakistan, 62; mem, Maine State Comn. Arts & Humanities, 65-70; mem. bd. dirs, New World Mime Theatre Sch, 72- & Maine State Ballet. Am. Educ. Theatre Asn.(pres, 43-45); Nat. Theatre Conf; Am. Nat. Theatre & Acad. Our theatre today. Add: Dept. of Fine Arts, University of Maine at Farmington, 86 Main St, Farmington, ME 04938.

BRIDGES, LLOYD, b. Brandsville, Mo, Feb. 18, 33; m. 73; c. 2. ENGLISH, AMERICAN LITERATURE. B.A, Harding Col, 53; M.A, South. Ore. Col, 65; Ph.D.(Eng), Univ. Utah, 71. Minister, Church of Christ, 53-65; instr. ENG, South. Ore. Col, 66-69; PROF, ABILENE CHRISTIAN COL, 71- NDEA fel, Univ. Utah, 69-71. Rocky Mountain Mod. Lang. Asn; AAUP. Ethnic literature; flight in Western novels. Publ: Co-auth, Do opposites attract? an experiment in college team teaching, Rocky Mountain Mod. Lang. Asn, 12/73. Add: Dept. of English, Abilene Christian College, Abilene, TX 79601.

BRIDGES, WILLIAM EMERY, b. Boston, Mass, Nov. 24, 33; m. 59; c. 3. ENGLISH, AMERICAN CIVILIZATION. A.B, Harvard, 55; A.M, Columbia Univ, 56; Ph.D.(Am. civilization), Brown Univ, 63. Dir. admis, Pine Manor Jr. Col, 58-60; teaching assoc. Am. civilization, Brown Univ, 61-62; chmn. dept. Eng, Pine Manor Jr. Col, 62-66; asst. prof, MILLS COL, 66-69, AURELIA HENRY REINHART ASSOC. PROF. AM. LIT, 69- U.S.A, 56-58. MLA; Am. Stud. Asn; Asn. Humanistic Psychol.(educ. coord, 70-). Literature and psychology; humanistic education. Publ: Ed, Spokesmen for the self, Chandler Publ, 71; auth, Three faces of humanistic education, Liberal Educ, 73; Transcendentalism and psychotherapy, Am. Lit, 69; Warm hearth, cold world: social perspectives on the household poets, Am. Quart, 69; Thoughts on humanistic education, J. Humanistic Psychol, 72; plus others. Add: Dept. of English, Mills College, Oakland, CA 94613.

BRIDGMAN, RICHARD, b. Toledo, Ohio, Aug. 24, 27; m. 54; c. 3. ENGLISH. B.A, Univ. Calif, 56, M.A, 57, Ph.D, 60. Lectr. ENG, Univ. Calif, Berkeley, 59-60; instr, Dartmouth Col, 60-62; asst. prof, UNIV. CALIF, BERKELEY, 62-66, assoc. prof, 66-71, PROF, 71- Fulbright lectr, Copenhagen Univ, 65-66; Guggenheim fel, 68-69. U.S.N, 45-46. MLA. American and French 19th century literature. Publ: The colloquial style in America, 66 & Gertrude Stein in pieces, 71, Oxford Univ. Add: Dept. of English, University of California, Berkeley, CA 94720.

BRIER, PETER A, b. Vienna, Austria, Mar. 5, 35; U.S. citizen. ENGLISH LITERATURE. B.A, Yale, 56; Fulbright scholarship, Univ. Mainz, 56-57; M.A, Harvard, 58; Ph.D.(Eng), Claremont Grad. Sch. & Occidental Col, 71. Instr. ENG, Ark. A&M State Col, 58-60; Occidental Col, 65-68; CALIF. STATE UNIV, LOS ANGELES, 69-70, ASST. PROF, 70- Asst. prof. Eng, Pitzer Col, 70-71. MLA; Philol. Asn. Pac. Coast (chmn. Eng. sect. II, 73-74). English romantic writers; Charles Lamb. Publ: Charles Lamb in the Huntington Library, 1796-1833, Wordsworth Circle, spring 72; Acrostic to E.B—an unpublished poem by Charles Lamb, Eng. Lang. Notes, 9/72; Dramatic characterization in the essays of Charles Lamb, Coranto, spring & summer 73. Add: Dept. of English, University of California, Los Angeles, CA 90024.

BRIER, WARREN J, b. Seattle, Wash, Apr. 25, 31; m. 53; c. 2. JOURNALISM. B.A, Univ. Wash, 53; M.S, Columbia Univ, 54; Ph.D, State Univ. Iowa, 57. Reporter, Seattle Post-Intelligencer, 57-58; mem. staff pub. relat, U.S. Air Force, 58-59; asst. prof. JOUR, San Diego State Col, 59-60; Univ. South. Calif, 60-62; assoc. prof, UNIV. MONT, 62-67, PROF, 67-, DEAN SCH. JOUR, 68- Newsman, Assoc. Press, summers 60-66 & 70. U.S.A.F, 58-59, Res, 59-68, Capt. Asn. Educ. in Jour. History of the Pacific Northwest press. Add: School of Journalism, University of Montana, Missoula, MT 59801.

BRIGGS, AUSTIN EUGENE, JR, b. Highland Park, Mich, May 4, 31; m. 56; c. 1. ENGLISH. A.B, Harvard, 54; M.A, Columbia Univ, 55, Danforth fel, 62-63, Ph.D.(Eng), 63. Instr. ENG, HAMILTON COL, 57-64, asst. prof, 64-68, assoc. prof, 68-72, PROF, 72- MLA. Nineteenth century American and modern British literature. Publ: The novels of Harold Frederic, Cornell Univ, 69. Add: Dept. of English, Hamilton College, Clinton, NY 13323.

BRIGGS, EDWIN STUART, b. Waltham, Mass, Jan. 10, 24. ENGLISH. A.B, Bowdoin Col, 44; A.M, Harvard, 48, Ph.D, 56. Teaching fel, Bowdoin Col, 47; instr. ENG, WHEATON COL.(MASS), 50-54, asst. prof, 54-59, assoc. prof, 59-64, PROF, 64- Vis. lectr, Bowdoin Col, 61-62. U.S.N.R, 43-46. Chaucer; Milton; poetry and poetic theory. Add: Dept. of English, Wheaton College, Norton, MA 02766.

BRIGGS, F. ALLEN, b. Superior, Nebr, Apr. 23, 16; m. 41; c. 4. ENGLISH. B.S, Cent. Mo. State Col, 37; M.A, Baylor Univ, 41; Ph.D, Ind. Univ, 53. Assoc. prof. Eng, Hardin-Simmons Univ, 47-53; prof. Eng. & dir. reading, Sul Ross State Col, 53-67; prof. Eng. & educ. & chmn. dept. lang. & lit. in col. educ, Univ. S.Fla, 67-70; PROF. ENG, TEX. A&I UNIV, LAREDO, 70- Fulbright lectr, Grad. Sch. Econ, Nat. Polytech. Univ, Greece, 57; guest lectr, Ore. Shakespeare Festival, 61. NCTE; Southwest. Conf. Col. Teachers Reading; Int. Reading Asn. English language; Shakespeare; programmed instruction. Publ: Tricks of the trade in language arts, Cathedral, 61; The play of words, Harcourt, 72; Knowing the news, Tex. Counc. Teachers Eng. & Houston Post, 73; Sunday school library in the 19th century, Libr. Quart, 4/61; Programming in the language arts, Nat. Soc. Prog. Instr. Yearbk, 63. Add: Texas A&I University at Laredo, Box 537, Laredo, TX 78040.

BRIGGS, NANCY ELAINE, b. Huron, S.Dak, July 28, 44; m. 66. SPEECH COMMUNICATION. B.A, Augustana Col.(S.Dak), 66; NDEA fel, Univ. South. Calif, 66-70, M.A, 68, Ph.D.(speech commun), 70. Asst. debate coach, Augustana Col.(S.Dak), 65-66; teaching asst. SPEECH, Univ. South. Calif, 66-67, debate asst, 67-68; instr, Calif. State Univ, Los Angeles, 69-70; Calif. State Univ, Dominguez Hills, 70-71; ASST. PROF, CALIF. STATE UNIV, LONG BEACH, 70- Nat. Sci. Found. grant, 70-71; consult, Intraleisure, Inc, Redondo Beach, Calif, 70-71; Torrance Libr. Syst, 72- Speech Commun. Asn.(mem. women's rhet. bd, 68-); West. Speech Commun. Asn; Am. Forensic Asn. Speech arts for children; rhetoric of the women's movement; systems approach in communication studies. Publ: Co-ed, Speech abstracts, Speech Commun. Asn, 72-73; auth, Speech arts for children, Mini Publ, 73; A survey of story favorites of pupils from kindergarten to grade six, 72 & The rhetoric of nursery rhymes, 73, Speech Teacher; contrib, Clement Attlee's advocacy of democratic socialism: reasonable rhetoric of revolution, Diss. Abstr. Int, 73; plus others. Add: Dept. of Speech Communications, California State University, Long Beach, 6101 E. Seventh St, Long Beach, CA 90801.

BRIGGS, WALLACE NEAL, b. Meridian, Miss, Mar. 1, 15. ENGLISH, SPEECH. A.B, Univ. Ky, 37, A.M, 45. Teacher high sch, Ky, 38-41; Eng. & speech, Univ. High Sch, UNIV. KY, 41-43, from asst. prof. Eng. & dir. Guignol Theatre to ASSOC. PROF. THEATRE ARTS, 43-66, chmn. dept, 66-71. Play directing; principles of acting; speech correction. Add: Dept. of English, Fine Arts Bldg, University of Kentucky, Lexington, KY 40506.

BRIGHT, ELIZABETH SWEET, English, Linguistics. See Volume III, Foreign Languages, Linguistics & Philology.

BRIGHT, JEAN MARIE, b. Rutherfordton, N.C, Sept. 23, 15. AMERICAN LITERATURE, AFRO-AMERICAN STUDIES. B.S, N.C. A&T State Univ, 39; M.A, Columbia Univ, 53. Ed. clerk, Publ. Div, Adj. Gen. Off, Dept. Defense, 43-44; staff asst, Am. Red Cross, New Guinea, Philippines, Japan, 44-46; social investr, N.Y.C. Dept. Welfare, 51; ASSOC. PROF. ENG. & AM. LIT, N.C. A&T STATE UNIV, 51- AAUP; NCTE; Col. Lang. Asn. African literature and folklore; American folklore. Publ: Co-ed, Images of the negro in America, D.C. Heath, 65 & Voices from the black experience, Ginn, 72. Add: 1008 S. Benbow Rd, Greensboro, NC 27406.

BRIGNANO, RUSSELL CARL, b. Hartford, Conn, June 26, 35, m. 69. ENGLISH. B.A, Dartmouth Col, 57; M.S, Univ. Wis, 63, Ph.D.(Eng), 66. Asst prof. ENG, CARNEGIE-MELLON UNIV, 66-70, ASSOC. PROF, 70- Vis. asst. prof. Eng, Univ. Pittsburgh, summer 70; Nat. Endowment for Humanities younger humanist fel, 70-71. U.S.A, 57-59. MLA; AAUP. Modern literature; Afro-American literature. Publ: Richard Wright: an introduction to the man and his works, Univ. Pittsburgh, 70; Black American in autobiography: an annotated bibliography of autobiographies and autobiographical books written since the Civil War, Duke Univ, 74; Richard Wright: a bibliography of secondary sources, Stud. Black Lit, 71; The racial problem, American romantic style, CEA Form, 12/73. Add: Dept. of English, Carnegie-Mellon University, Schenley Park, Pittsburgh, PA 15213.

BRILHART, BARBARA L, Speech, Education. See LIEB-BRILHART, BARBARA.

BRILHART, JOHN K, b. Johnstown, Pa, Feb. 23, 29; m. 46; c. 4. SPEECH. B.A, David Lipscomb Col, 52; M.A, Pa. State Univ, 57, Ph.D.(speech), 62. Teacher speech & sci, high sch, Ky, 52-55; instr. speech, Pa. State Univ, 57-59, res. asst. adult educ, Ctr. Continuing Lib. Educ, 59-60, asst. prof. SPEECH, 60-65; PROF, UNIV. NEBR. AT OMAHA, 65-, head dept, 65-72. Mem, Inst. Gen. Semantics. Speech Commun. Asn.(mem. comn. professions & soc, 72-); Cent. States Speech Asn. General semantics; small group discussion procedures; organizational communication. Publ: Leading study-discussion programs, Ctr. Continuing Lib. Educ, 59; Effective group discussion, W.C. Brown, 67 & 74; co-auth, Effects of different patterns on outcomes of problem-solving discussions, J. Appl. Psychol, 6/64; auth, An experimental comparison of three techniques for communicating a problem-solving pattern to members of a discussion group, Speech Mongr, 6/66; Gifford Pinchot: conservation crusader and political reformer, In: History of public speaking in Pennsylvania, Pa. Speech Asn, 70. Add: Dept. of Speech, University of Nebraska at Omaha, Omaha, NE 68101.

BRINEY, MARTHA M, b. Brackenridge, Pa, June 26, 13. ENGLISH LITERATURE. A.B, Hood Col, 35, fac. fel, 52-53; A.M, Univ. Mich, 36; alumnae fel, Mich. State Univ, 52-53, Ph.D, 56. Instr. ENG. LIT, HOOD COL, 45-48, asst. prof, 48-54, assoc. prof, 54-57, PROF, 57-, CHMN. DEPT. ENG, 64-, COORD, AEGEAN INST. SUMMER PROG, GREECE, 70- MLA; NCTE; Col. Eng. Asn; Mod. Greek Stud. Asn. American Southern fiction; 19th century English poetry; 17th century English poetry, especially Milton. Add: Dept. of English, Hood College, Frederick, MD 21701.

BRINKMAN, ELIZABETH ABELL, b. Westfield, N.Y, Jan. 14, 35. ENGLISH. B.A, Univ. Rochester, 56; M.A, Univ. Wis, 57, summer fels, 64, 66, Ph.D. (Eng), 66. Instr. ENG, Augustana Col.(Ill), 58-60; St. Lawrence Univ, 64-66; WITTENBERG UNIV, 66-67, asst. prof, 67-72, ASSOC. PROF, 72- MLA. Add: Dept. of English, Wittenberg University, Springfield, OH 45501.

BRINNIN, JOHN MALCOLM, b. Halifax, N.S, Sept. 13, 16; U.S. citizen. ENGLISH. A.B, Univ. Mich, 41; Harvard, 41-42. Instr. ENG, Vassar Col, 42-47; from asst. prof. to prof, Univ. Conn, 51-61; PROF, BOSTON UNIV, 61- U.S. State Dept. specialist Am. lit. lectr, Europe, 54, 57 & 61; adv, Ford Found, 58; Nat. Inst. Arts & Lett. grant, 68. Publ: Dylan Thomas in America, 55, The third rose: Gertrude Stein and her world, 58 & The selected poems of John Malcolm Brinnin, 63, Atlantic-Little; The sway of the Grand Saloon: a social history of the North Atlantic, Delacorte, 71. Add: King Caesar Rd, Duxbury, MA 02332.

BRIODY, DAVID MATHEW, b. Olean, N.Y, Oct. 20, 42. COMMUNICATION THEORY. B.S, State Univ. N.Y. Col. Geneseo, 64; M.A, Univ. Ariz, 65; Ph.D.(commun), Univ. Utah, 71. Instr. speech, DePauw Univ, 65-66; Millikin Univ, 66-69; ASST. PROF. COMMUN, UNIV. PUGET SOUND, 71- Speech Commun. Asn. Nonverbal communication; physiological communication; attitude change. Publ: Internal feedback theory and communication behavior: a theoretical view, Interchange, 71. Add: Dept. of Speech Communication, University of Puget Sound, 15th & Warner Sts, Tacoma, WA 98416.

BRISCOE, MARY LOUISE, b. Hutchinson, Kans, May 24, 37. MEDIEVAL LITERATURE, LITERARY CRITICISM. B.A, Kans. State Univ, 59; M.A, Bowling Green State Univ, 61; Ph.D.(Eng), Univ. Wis, 68. Asst. prof. Eng, Univ. Wis-Whitewater, 67-68, ASSOC. PROF, 68-71; ENG. & WOMEN'S STUD, UNIV. PITTSBURGH, 71- MLA; NCTE. The rhetoric of narration in medieval literature; the literature of Arthurian tradition; literary criticism as a history of perception. Add: Dept. of English, University of Pittsburgh, Pittsburgh, PA 15213.

BRISTOW, EUGENE KERR, b. Birmingham, Ala, Feb. 12, 27; m. 50; c. 4. THEATRE, DRAMA. A.B, Ind. Univ, 50, fel, 51-52, M.A, 52; Ph.D, Univ. Iowa, 56. Instr. Eng, speech & drama, New Albany High Sch, Ind, 50-51, Reitz High Sch, Evansville, 52-54; res. fel. theatre hist, Univ. Iowa, 55-56; asst. prof speech & theatre, MacMurray Col. Women, 56-57; instr, IND. UNIV, BLOOMINGTON, 57-60, asst. prof, 60-68, ASSOC. PROF. THEATRE & DRAMA, 68-, RUSSIAN & E.EUROP. INST, 72- Dir, Ind. Speech & Theatre Inst, 59-64; Ind. Univ. Found. res. grant, 64-65; vis. assoc. prof. dramatic art, Univ. Calif, Santa Barbara, 68-69. Award, Cent. States Speech Asn, 57. U.S.A.A.F, 45-46. MLA; Am. Theatre Asn.(news ed, Educ. Theatre J, 60-62); Speech Commun. Asn; Int. Fed. Theatre Res; Soc. Theatre Res, Eng; Am. Soc. Theatre Res; AAUP; Theatre Libr. Asn. Russian drama 19th century; Russian theatre and drama 20th century; American variety and vaudeville, 19th century, Publ: Ed. & transl, Five plays of Alexander Ostrovsky, Pegasus, 69; auth, Directory of long plays for high school, Nat. Thespian Soc, Cincinnati, Ohio, 61; On translating Chekhov, Quart. J. Speech, 66; co-auth, Box office, U.S.A, 1864-1870: regional profile, Theatre Surv, 67; The making of a regisseur: V.E. Meyerhold, the early years 1874-1895, Theatre Annual, 69; plus others. Add: Dept. of Theatre & Drama, Indiana University, Bloomington, IN 47401.

BRITSCH, RALPH A, b. Ephraim, Utah, Jan. 30, 12; m. 36; c. 5. ENGLISH, HUMANITIES. A.B, Brigham Young Univ, 33, M.A, 51; Univ. Wis, 38; Univ. Wash, 41; Univ. Okla, 50-51. Instr. ENG, BRIGHAM YOUNG UNIV, 38-44, asst. prof, 44-52, assoc. prof, 52-63, PROF, 63-, CHMN. DEPT. HUMANITIES & COMP. LIT, 69-, chmn. dept. Eng, 57-60, acting dean. col. humanities & soc. sci, 63-64. NCTE; Am. Soc. Aesthetics. Victorian literature; comparative humanities. Publ: A humanities reader, 65 & co-ed, Literature as art: a reader, 72, Brigham Young Univ. Add: Dept. of Humanities and Comparative Literature, Brigham Young University, Provo, UT 84101.

BRITTAIN, JOAN TUCKER, b. Manchester, Ga, Dec. 13, 28; m. 47; c. 4. ENGLISH. B.A, Ky. South. Col, 65; fel, Univ. Louisville, 65-66, M.A, 66, Ph.D.(Eng), 70. Instr. ENG, Ky. South. Col, 66-67; BELLARMINE COL, (KY), 67-68, asst. prof, 68-70, ASSOC. PROF, 70-, DIR. PHOENIX PROG, 71- Nat. Endowment for Humanities younger humanist fel, 72-73. American literature, specifically Flannery O'Connor. Publ: Laurence Stallings, Twayne, (in prep); The fictional family of Flannery O'Connor, Renascence, fall 66; Flannery O'Connor's A good man is hard to find, The Explicator, 9/67; Flannery O'Connor: a bibliography, I and II, Bull. Bibliog, 12/67 & 1-4/68. Add: Dept. of English, Bellarmine College, 2000 Norris Pl, Louisville, KY 40205.

BRITTIN, NORMAN AYLSWORTH, b. Syracuse, N.Y, Sept. 9, 06; m. 29; wid; c. 2; m. 51. ENGLISH LITERATURE. A.B, Syracuse Univ, 27, A.M, 30; Univ. Calif, 34-36; Ph.D, Univ. Wash, 47. Res. assoc. character educ, Univ. South. Calif, 31-34; instr. Eng, Univ. Utah, 37-45, asst. prof, 47; acting instr, Univ. Wash, 46; vis. asst. prof. humanities, Univ. Chicago, 47-48; assoc. prof. Eng, Auburn Univ, 48-54, prof, 54-61; from lectr. to prof. Eng, Univ. P.R, 62-66; HOLLIFIELD PROF. ENG. LIT, AUBURN UNIV, 66- Ford fel, Columbia Univ. & Harvard, 52-53; Fulbright lectr, Univ. La Laguna, Canary Islands, 68-69; co-ed, South. Humanities Rev, 67- Warshaw prize, 53. MLA; Renaissance Soc. Am; Shakespeare Asn. Am; AAUP; NCTE. Elizabethan drama, especially Thomas Middleton and Shakespeare. Publ: A writing apprenticeship, 63, 68 & 72, Writing description and narration, 69 & ed, A reading apprenticeship: literature, 71, Holt; Edna St. Vincent Millay, 67 & Thomas Middleton, 72, Twayne; Coriolanus, Alceste, and dramatic genres, PMLA, 56; plus others. Add: Dept. of English, Auburn University, Auburn, AL 36830.

BRITTON, JOE S, b. Cedar Hill, Tenn, Nov. 23, 35; m. 55; c. 2. ENGLISH & DRAMATIC LITERATURE. A.B, Ky. Wesleyan Col, 56; fel. & M.A, South. Ill. Univ, 57, 62-64 & 67. Instr. Eng. & speech, Cumberland Univ, 57-58; ENG, KY. WESLEYAN COL, 58-60, asst. prof, 60-64, ASSOC. PROF, 64-, acting chmn. depts. Eng. & speech-drama, 64-68, chmn, 68-70. MLA; NCTE; AAUP. American literature and drama; modern continental drama. Add: Dept. of English, Kentucky Wesleyan College, Owensboro, KY 43201.

BRITTON, JOHN, b. Burlington, N.J, Dec. 8, 29. ENGLISH LITERATURE. A.B, Univ. Pa, 51; Ph.L, West Baden Col, 57; Ph.D, Loyola Univ.(Ill), 60. Lectr. ENGLISH, City Col. New York, 60-61; instr, FORDHAM UNIV, 61-62, ASST. PROF, 62- Secy-treas, Col. Counc. on English, Cent. Atlantic States, 63-67. MLA; Shakespeare Asn. Am. Shakespeare critics and criticism; Shakespeare and theatre; Renaissance occult. Publ: Pied beauty and the glory of God, Renascence, 58-59; Cummings, In: Pity this busy monster, manunkind, Explicator, 59; A.C. Bradley and those children of Lady Macbeth, Shakespeare Quart, 61. Add: Dept. of English, Fordham University, Bronx, NY 10458.

BRITTON, ROBERT GRUBBS, b. Winston-Salem, N.C, Apr. 29, 36; m. 73; c. 2. THEATRE HISTORY, ACTING. B.A, Pfeiffer Col, 58; M.A, Univ. Miss, 60; Ph.D.(theatre arts), Fla. State Univ, 69. Dept. chmn. theatre, Pfeiffer Col, 60-64; prof. actor, 64-70; chmn. dept. theatre arts, Tex. Christian Univ, 70-72; ASSOC. PROF. SPEECH & DRAMA & DIR. SUMMER THEATER, TRINITY UNIV, 72- Am. Theatre Asn. Acting techniques; directing; writing for the stage. Publ: Co-auth, MLL: a new base for scene paint, Educ. Theater J, 64; auth, Piedmont University Center theatre, South. Theatre J, 64. Add: Dept. of Speech & Drama, Trinity University, 715 Stadium Dr, San Antonio, TX 78284.

BRITTON, WEBSTER EARL, b. Petersburg, Va, Oct. 15, 05; m. 38; c. 1. ENGLISH LITERATURE. A.B, Randolph-Macon Col, 27; Univ. Va, 28; A.M, Syracuse Univ, 30; Ph.D, Univ. Mich, 45. Instr. ENG, Randolph-Macon Col, 25-27; head dept, Norfolk Acad, 27-29; asst, Syracuse Univ, 29-30, instr, 30-36; teaching fel, ENGINEERING COL, UNIV. MICH, ANN ARBOR, 36-38, instr, 38-45, asst. prof, 45-48, assoc. prof, 48-51, PROF, 51-, dir. written sci. commun, summer conf, 58-73. Consult, Caterpillar Tractor Co, Upjohn Co, Community Syst. Found, Gen. Motors, Ford, & Tex. Instruments; mem, Inst. Sci. & Tech. Communicators, 72- MLA; Augustan Reprint Soc; fel, Soc. Tech. Commun; fel, AAAS. Smollett; patterns and perspectives; scientific and technical written communications. Publ: Technical reporting, In: On writing by writers, Ginn, 66; Some effects of science and technology upon our language, Col. Compos. & Commun, 12/70; Personality in scientific writing, Tech. Commun, 73. Add: Dept. of Humanities, College of Engineering, University of Michigan, Ann Arbor, MI 48103.

BROADRICK, KING WOODARD, b. Granite, Okla, July 17, 18; m. 45; c. 4. LANGUAGE COMMUNICATION, LAW. A.B, Ariz. State Col, 40; J.D, Univ. Va, 48; M.A, Univ. Ill, 50; LL.M, Columbia Univ, 57. Dir. debate, Univ. Va, 46-47; UNIV. ILL, URBANA, 48-50, asst. prof. SPEECH, 50-58, assoc. prof, 58-71, PROF, DIR. HONORS PROG. & DIR. 3 YR BACCALAUREATE STUD, 71- U.S.A.F, 41-45. Speech Commun. Asn. History of forensic rhetoric; philosophy of law and language in society; history and policy of higher education. Publ: Relationship of argument to syllogistic and experimental logic, Quart J. Speech, 12/50; co-auth, TV teacher's report, Speech Teacher, 3/62. Add: Dept. of Speech Communication, University of Illinois, Urbana, IL 61801.

BROCK, DEWEY HEYWARD, b. Greenville, S.C, June 2, 41; m. 63; c. 3. ENGLISH & AMERICAN LITERATURE. A.B, Newberry Col, 63; M.A, Univ. Kans, 65, Ph.D.(Eng), 69. Instr. ENG, UNIV. DEL, 68-69, ASST. PROF, 69-, asst. to dean, col. arts & sci, 69, fac. res. grant, summer 71. Am. Counc. Learned Soc. & Nat. Sci. Found. fel, Summer Inst. Humanistic Computation, 70. MLA; Renaissance Soc. Am. Seventeenth century English literature; American literature; comparative literature. Publ: Co-auth, Ben Jonson: a quadricentennial bibliography, 1947-1972, Scarecrow, 74; auth, Linguistics and the teaching of literature, Univ. Kans. Bull. Educ, 5/66; co-auth, Percy MacKaye: community drama and the masque tradition, Comp. Drama, 72; auth, The portrait of Abbot Samson in past and present: Carlyle and Jocelin of Brakelond, Eng. Miscellany, 72. Add: Dept. of English, University of Delaware, Newark, DE 19711.

BROCK, ELIZABETH, b. Decatur, Ala, Jan. 1, 08. ENGLISH. B.A, Birmingham-South. Col, 28; M.A, Univ. Va, 35, Ph.D, 56. Teacher, Phillips High Sch, 34-46; instr. ENG, BIRMINGHAM CTR, UNIV. ALA, 46-56, asst. prof, 56-57, assoc. prof, 57-70, prof, 70-72, EMER. PROF, 72- MLA; S.Atlantic Mod. Lang. Asn; Shakespeare Soc. Am; Bibliog. Soc. Univ. Va. Shakespeare; textual criticism. Add: 2 Oakwood Ct, Tuscaloosa, AL 35401.

BROCK, JAMES W, b. Greensfork, Ind, May 23, 19; m. 41, 56, 69; c. 3. DRAMA. A.B, Manchester Col, 41; M.A, Northwest. Univ, 42, Ph.D.(theatre), 50. Instr. speech, Albion Col, 45-46, asst. prof, 46-48, assoc. prof, 48-55; asst. prof. commun. skills, Mich. State Univ, 55-56; speech, Univ. Mich, 56-57; assoc. prof, Fla. State Univ, 57-58; asst. prof. DRAMA, CALIF. STATE UNIV, NORTHRIDGE, 58-61, assoc. prof, 61-66, PROF. & CHMN. DEPT, 66-, fac. res. grants, 63-64, 65-68. Church Soc. Col. Work fel, 64-65. U.S.A.A.F, 42-45, Sgt. Speech Commun Asn; Nat. Theatre Conf; Am. Educ. Theatre Asn. Elizabethan, religious and contemporary drama. Publ: Modern chancel drama, Bakers Plays, 64. Add: Dept. of Drama, California State University, Northridge, CA 91324.

BROCK, MARIANNE, b. Winnipeg, Man, Oct. 9, 05. ENGLISH LITERATURE. B.A, McGill Univ, 28; B.A, Oxford, 30, M.A, 35; Ph.D, Bryn Mawr Col, 44. Instr, MT. HOLYOKE COL, 30-37, asst. prof. ENG, 38-49, assoc. prof, 49-53, prof, 53-71, EMER. PROF, 71- Instr, Univ. Colo, 37-38. MLA. Jacobean drama; contemporary poetry. Add: 31 Woodbridge, South Hadley, MA 01075.

BROCK, VANDALL KLINE, b. Thomas County, Ga, Oct. 31, 32; m. 61; c. 2. TWENTIETH CENTURY LITERATURE, CREATIVE WRITING. A.B, Emory Univ, 54; M.A, Univ. Iowa, 53, M.F.A, 64, Ph.D.(Am. lit. & mod. poetry), 70. ASST. PROF. humanities, Oglethorpe Col, 64-68; ENG. FLA. STATE UNIV, 70- Fla. State Univ. fac. res. grant, summer 71; consult. poets-in-the-schs. prog, Ga. Arts Counc, spring 72; coord. poets-in-the-schs. prog, Leon County, Fla. Pilot Proj, 72-74; founder & dir, Apalachee Poetry Ctr, 73- Borestone Mountain Best Poems of 1971 Award; Kans. City Heart of Am. Poetry Contest 1st Prize. Literature and psychology; Apalachee region of Northern Florida; creativity and poetry writing. Publ: Final belief (poems), Back door, 72; ed. & contrib, Lime tree prism (poems), Apalachee Poetry Ctr, 73; Rouault, New Yorker, 1/72; In the zebra, Prairie Schooner, summer 72; The Nazi innocents, South. Rev, spring 73; plus poems in

Shenandoah, South. Poetry Rev, N.Am. Rev. and other journals. Add: Dept. of English, Florida State University, Tallahassee, FL 32306.

BROCKETT, OSCAR GROSS, b. Hartsville, Tenn, Mar. 18, 23; m. 51; c. 1. SPEECH & DRAMA. B.A, George Peabody Col, 47; M.A, Stanford Univ, 49, Ph.D, 53. Instr. Eng, speech & drama, Univ. Ky, 49-50; asst. prof. speech & drama, Stetson Univ, 52-56; dramatic art, Univ. Iowa, 56-59, assoc. prof, 59-63; PROF. THEATRE & DRAMA, IND. UNIV, BLOOMINGTON, 63- Vis. assoc. prof. drama, Univ. South. Calif, summer 59; vis. prof. speech & theatre, Univ. Ill, 63; Fulbright lectr. drama, Bristol Univ, Eng, 63-64; Guggenheim fel, 70-71. U.S.N.R, 43-46, Lt.(jg). Fel. Am. Theatre Asn. (ed, Educ. Theatre J, 60-63; v.pres. prog, 73-74); Speech Commun. Asn; Am. Soc. Theatre Res; Cent. States Speech Asn; Int. Fed. Theatre Res; MLA. Theatre history of the 18th and 19th centuries; modern theatre. Publ: Co-auth, A bibliographical guide to research in speech and dramatic art, Scott, 63; auth, An introduction to the theatre 64, 69 & 74 & co-auth, Plays for the theatre, 67 & 74; Holt; auth, A history of the theatre, Allyn & Bacon, 68 & 74; Perspectives on contemporary theatre, La. State Univ, 71; ed. & contrib, Studies in theatre and drama, Mouton, 72; co-auth, Century of innovation, Prentice-Hall, 73. Add: Dept. of Theatre & Drama, Indiana University, Bloomington, IN 47401.

BROCKHAUS, HERMAN HENRY, b. Antigo, Wis, May 20, 07; m. 30. SPEECH. B.A, N. Cent. Col.(Ill), 29; M.A, Univ. Wis, Madison, 37; Ph.D. (speech), 49. Teacher, high sch, Wis, 29-38; prof. speech, Pac. Univ, 38-41; instr, Oberlin Col, 41-42; lectr, UNIV. WIS-MADISON, 47-49, asst. prof, 49-52, assoc. prof, 52-56, prof, 56-72, EMER. PROF. COMMUN. ARTS, 72- Med.C, U.S.A, 42-45, S/Sgt. Speech Commun. Asn. Co-curricular speech activities in secondary schools; audience analysis. Publ: Co-auth, The Wisconsin sequential sampling audience analyzer, 3/58 & The teletalk project: a study of the effectiveness of two public relations speeches, 11/63, Speech Monogr; auth, Summer high school speech institutes, Speech Teacher, 1/64. Add: 3914 Priscilla Lane, Madison, WI 53705.

BROCKI, MARY DAMASCENE, C.S.S.F, b. Detroit, Mich. ENGLISH. B.A, Madonna Col, 48; M.A, Univ. Notre Dame, 49, Ph.D, 59. INSTR. ENG, MADONNA COL, 58- NCTE; Conf. Col. Compos. & Commun. Medieval and American literature; North American Indian literature and culture. Publ: Teaching the appreciation of poetry, Cath. Educr, 69; Making writing relevant and meaningful, Res. & Develop, 70; Irony in Browning's Bishop orders his tomb?, Mark Twain J, 72; plus others. Add: Dept. of English, Madonna College, 36600 Schoolcraft, Livonia, MI 48150.

BROCKMAN, BENNETT ALBERT, b. Greer, S.C, Oct. 14, 42; m. 65; c. 1. ENGLISH MEDIEVAL & CHILDREN'S LITERATURE. B.A, Fuman Univ, 64; M.A, Vanderbilt Univ, 65, univ. fel, & Ph.D, 69. ASST. PROF. ENG, UNIV. CONN, 68- Assoc. ed, Children's Literature: The Great Excluded, 72- Mediaeval Acad. Am; MLA (co-chmn. sem. children's lit, 73-); AAUP; Children's Literature Asn. Old and Middle English literature; medieval drama; children's literature. Publ: Medieval songs of innocence and experience, Children's Lit, 73; Heroic and Christian in the Genesis A, Mod. Lang, Quart, 6/74; The law of man and the peace of God: judicial process as satiric theme in the Wakefield Mactacio Abel, Speculum, 74; plus others. Add: Dept. of English, University of Connecticut, Storrs, CT 06268.

BROCKRIEDE, WAYNE ELMER, b. Evansville, Ind, July 24, 22; m. 48; c. 6. COMMUNICATION. B.S, Ind. State Teachers Col, 47, M.S, 47; Ph.D. (speech), Univ. Ill, 54. Instr. speech, Univ. Miami, 47-50; asst, Univ. Ill, 50-52, instr, 53-56, asst. prof, 56-60; assoc. prof, Carthage Col, 52-53; Univ. Okla, 60-65; PROF. COMMUN, UNIV. COLO, BOULDER, 65- Ed, Quart. J. Speech, 69-71. Speech Commun. Asn. Rhetoric; communication; argumentation. Publ: Co-auth, Decision by debate, Dodd, 63, The rhetoric of black power, Harper, 69 & Moments in the rhetoric of the Cold War, Random, 70; auth, Dimensions of the concept of rhetoric, Quart. J Speech, 2/68. Add: Dept. of Communication, University of Colorado, Boulder, CO 80302.

BRODERICK, JAMES H, b. Holyoke, Mass, June 8, 25; m. 51; c. 4. ENGLISH LITERATURE. B.A, Harvard, 47; M.A, Univ. Chicago, 49; Ph.D, Harvard, 61. Instr. Latin & Eng, Dean Acad. & Jr. Col, 47-48; ENG, Conn. Col, 55-60; asst. prof, Bryn Mawr Col, 60-64; assoc. prof, Univ. Rochester, 65-67; UNIV. MASS, BOSTON, 67-72, PROF, 72- Teaching fel. humanities, Harvard, 51-55; Am. Philos. Soc. grant, 61-63; mem. Eng. Inst, 63; Am. Counc. Learned Soc. fel, 64-65. U.S.A.A.F, 43-46, 2nd Lt. Nineteenth century English literature; early Victorian literature. Publ: Dr. Johnson's impossible doubts, S.Atlantic Quart, 57; A study of freshman English at Amherst, Harvard Educ. Rev, 58; co-auth, The identity of Esther Summerson, Mod. Philol, 58. Add: Dept. of English, University of Massachusetts, Boston, MA 02116.

BRODERICK, JOHN CARUTHERS, b. Memphis, Tenn, Sept. 6, 26; m. 49; c. 2. ENGLISH. A.B, Southwest. at Memphis, 48; M.A, Univ. N.C, 49, Ph.D.(Eng), 53. Instr. Eng, Univ. N.C, 49-52; Univ. Tex, 52-56, spec. instr, 56-57; asst. prof, Wake Forest Col, 57-58, assoc. prof, 58-63, prof, 63-65; specialist Am. cult. hist, MANUSCRIPT DIV, LIBR. CONGR, 64-65, ASST. CHIEF, 65-, acting chief, 68. Vis. prof, Univ. Va, 59; Am. Counc. Learned Soc. grant-in-aid, 62-63; adj. prof. Eng, George Washington Univ, 64-; adv, Calendars Am. Lit. Manuscripts, 66-; vis. prof. Eng, Univ. N.C, 68; gen. ed, The journal of Henry D. Thoreau, Princeton Univ. Press, 74; mem. adv. bd, Resources for Am. Lit. Stud, 70-; Counc. Libr. Resources fel, 71. U.S.A, 45-46. MLA (assoc. ed, Thoreau Ed, 67-); Am. Stud. Asn; Manuscript Soc; Soc. Am. Archivists; Bibliog. Soc. Am. Literature of 19th century New England; Thoreau's essays on government and society. Publ: Whitman the poet, Wadsworth, 62; The movement of Thoreau's prose, 61 & Emerson and Moorfield Storey: a lost journal found, 66, Am. Lit; Emerson, Thoreau and transcendentalism, In: American literary scholarship (1967-1971): an annual, Duke Univ, 69-73; plus others. Add: Manuscript Division, Library of Congress, Washington, DC 20540.

BRODERICK, JOHN PATRICK, English & General Linguistics. See Volume III, Foreign Languages, Linguistics & Philology.

BRODTKORB, PAUL, JR, b. Ossining, N.Y, Sept. 6, 30; m. 58; c. 2. ENGLISH & AMERICAN STUDIES. B.A, Yale, 52, Coe fel. & Ph.D.(Am. stud), 63; Univ. Heidelberg, 54-55. Instr. ENG, Univ. Conn, 60-65; asst. prof, HUNTER COL, 65-70, ASSOC. PROF, 70-, chmn. dept, 70-72. U.S.A, 52-54. MLA. Nineteenth century American literature. Publ: Ishmael's white world, Yale Univ, 65; Art allegory in The marble faun, 6/62 & The definitive Billy Budd, 12/67, PMLA; The con-man as hero, Stud. in Novel, winter 69. Add: Dept. of English, Hunter College, Box 153, 695 Park Ave, New York, NY 10021.

BRODWIN, LEONORA LEET, b. New York, N.Y, Mar. 24, 29; m. 60. ENGLISH LITERATURE. B.A, Univ. Mich, 50; M.A, Yale, 52, Jr. Sterling fel, 53-55, Ph.D, 60; Fulbright fel, Bedford Col, Univ. London, Eng, 55-56. Teaching asst, Univ. Calif, Berkeley, 52-53; instr. ENG, Hofstra Col, 57-60; Queens Col.(N.Y), 60-63; asst. prof, ST. JOHN'S UNIV.(N.Y), 65-66, assoc. prof, 66-71, PROF, 71- MLA. Elizabethan drama; Milton; seventeenth century literature. Publ: Elizabethan love tragedy: 1587-1625, N.Y. Univ, 71; Edward II: Marlowe's culminating treatment of love, ELH, 6/64; Authorship of the second maiden's tragedy: a reconsideration of the manuscript attribution to Chapman, Stud. Philol, 1/66; Miltonic allusion in Absalom and Achitophel: its function in the political satire, J. Eng. & Ger. Philol, 1/69; plus others. Add: 110 Irving Ave, Freeport, NY 11520.

BRODY, SAUL NATHANIEL, b. Bronx, N.Y, Mar. 6, 38; m. 60; c. 2. ENGLISH, COMPARATIVE MEDIEVAL LITERATURE. A.B, Columbia Univ, 59, M.A, 60, Ph.D.(Eng, comp. Medieval lit), 68. Lectr. ENG, Hunter Col, 64-65; CITY COL. NEW YORK, 65-67, instr, 68, asst. prof, 68-73, ASSOC. PROF, 74- MLA; Int. Arthurian Soc; Int. Courtly Lit. Soc. Middle English literature; history of medicine. Publ: The disease of the soul: leprosy in medieval literature, Cornell Univ, 73; contrib, In pursuit of perfection: courtly love in medieval literature, Kennikat, 74. Add: Dept. of English, City College of New York, New York, NY 10031.

BROEKER, HARRIET DURKEE, b. Laramie, Wyo, Sept. 25, 26; m. 48. ENGLISH. B.A, Univ. Wyo, 50; M.A, Univ. Ore, 52; Ph.D, Univ. Minn, 57. Instr. ENG, Univ. Md, Eng, 55-56; Univ. Minn, 56-57; Univ. Tenn, 57-58; assoc. prof, KNOXVILLE COL, 58-64, PROF, 64-, CHMN. DEPT, 58-, asst. to pres. acad. oper, 71-72. MLA; NCTE; Col. Conf. Compos. & Commun; Col. Eng. Asn; S.Atlantic Mod. Lang. Asn; Renaissance Soc. Am. Tudor-Stuart drama; Elizabethan lyric. Add: Dept. of English, Knoxville College, Knoxville, TN 37921.

BROER, LAWRENCE R, U.S. citizen. ENGLISH. B.A, Fla. State Univ, 60, assistantship, 60-63, M.A, 63; fel, Bowling Green State Univ, 63-65, Ph.D, 68. Instr. ENG, UNIV. S.FLA, TAMPA, 65-68, asst. prof, 68-73, ASSOC. PROF, 73-, Res. Counc. awards, 69 & 72. Publ: Counter currents: an introduction to current literature, Kendall/Hunt, 73; Hemingway's Spanish tragedy, Univ. Ala, 73; Patterns of perception in Crane's The open boat & Biographical introductions, In: The art of fiction, Holt, 2nd ed, 74; plus others. Add: Dept. of English, University of South Florida, Tampa, FL 33620.

BROGAN, HOWARD OAKLEY, b. Thornton, Iowa, Dec. 7, 12; m. 38; c. 3. ENGLISH LITERATURE. A.B, Grinnell Col, 36; A.M, Univ. Iowa, 38; Ph.D, Yale, 41. Instr, Ill. Col, 37-39; Sterling res. fel, Yale, 41-42; asst. prof, The Citadel, 42-44; lectr, Princeton, 44-46; assoc. prof, Franklin & Marshall Col, 46-47; assoc. prof, Syracuse Univ, 47-53; prof. ENG, Bowling Green State Univ, 53-62, chmn. dept, 56-62; COMMONWEALTH PROF, UNIV. MASS, AMHERST, 62-, head dept, 62-67. Carnegie intern, Yale, 52-53. MLA; Col. Eng. Asn.(v.pres, 71-72 dir, 72-73); NEA; AAUP; Int. Asn. Univ. Prof. Eng. Poetry, novel, and satire of the English romantics. Publ: Co-auth, Bibliography of the Ranke manuscripts, Syracuse, 52; Faculty power: pretense and reality, J. Higher Educ, 2/69; Some conservative thoughts on current college education; CEA Critic, 10/71; Satirist Burns and Lord Byron, Costerus/Essays in Eng. & Am. Lit, fall 72; plus others. Add: 10 Dana St, Amherst, MA 01002.

BROGUNIER, JOSEPH EDWARD, b. Hagerstown, Md, Aug. 23, 35; m. 59; c. 4. ENGLISH & AMERICAN LITERATURE. A.B, Brown Univ, 58; M.A, Purdue Univ, West Lafayette, 64; Ph.D.(Eng), Univ. Minn, Minneapolis, 69. ASST. PROF. ENG, UNIV. MAINE, ORONO, 69- Northeast Mod. Lang. Asn. Twentieth and late 19th century American novel; 20th century British literature. Publ: Expiation in Yeat's late plays, Drama Surv, spring 66; A Housman source in The sound and the fury, Mod. Fiction Stud, summer 72; A source for the commissary entries in Go down, Moses, Tex. Stud. Lit. & Lang, fall 72; plus others. Add: Dept. of English, University of Maine, Orono, ME 04473.

BROMAN, WALTER ERIC, b. Eureka, Utah, Nov. 21, 20; m. 46; c. 4. ENGLISH. M.A, Univ. Chicago, 49, Ph.D.(Eng), 51. Asst. prof. ENG, Drury Col, 51-57; WHITMAN COL, 57-64, assoc. prof, 64-69, PROF, 69- U.S.A, 42-45. Late 18th century British literature; modern Scandinavian literature. Publ: Factors in Crabbe's eminence, Mod. Philol, 9/53. Add: Dept. of English, Whitman College, Walla Walla, WA 99362.

BROMBERGER, FREDERICK S, b. El Paso, Tex, Mar. 5, 18; m. 44; c. 5. ENGLISH LITERATURE. A.B, Knox Col, 40; A.M, Univ. Cincinnati, 41; Univ. Mo, 46-47; Harvard, 47-48; Ph.D.(Eng), Univ. South. Calif, 64. Instr, Kemper Mil. Sch, 41-42; Univ. Mo, 46-47; asst. prof. ENG, UNIV. REDLANDS, 48-56, assoc. prof, 56-64, PROF, 64-, CHMN. DEPT, 66-, coord. able stud. prog, 57-67, res. grants, 67, 68 & 71, acting div. dir, 69-70. Intercol. Prog. Grad. Stud. fel, 58-; Ford grad. prog. fels, Claremont Col, Occidental Col. & Whittier Col; initiator, Redlands in London Prog, 69- U.S.A.F, 42-46, Res, 52-, Maj. MLA; NCTE; Col. Eng. Asn; Philol. Asn. Pac. Coast; AAUP. Use of the computer as a teaching device for analyzing literary works. Publ: Medievalist of the future, 58 & Glimpse of Carl Sandburg, 59, Redlands Fac. Rev; Poetic techniques in the writing of prose, Spectrum, 6/62. Add: Dept. of English, University of Redlands, Redlands, CA 92373.

BROMMEL, BERNARD J, b. Des Moines, Iowa, Aug. 13, 30; m. 50; c. 6. SPEECH, HISTORY. B.A, Iowa North. Univ, 51; M.A, State Univ. Iowa, 55; Danforth summer grant, 61, 62; Ph.D.(speech, drama), Ind. Univ, 63.

Teacher, High Sch, Iowa, 51-54; Keokuk Sr. High & Community Col, 54-59; assoc. prof. SPEECH, Ind. State Univ, 59-67; prof. & chmn. dept, Univ. N.Dak, 67-71. PROF, NORTHEAST. ILL. UNIV, 71- Ind. State Univ. res. grant & leave, spring 64; mem. bd. dir, Eugene V. Debs Found, 68-73; scholar in residence, Newberry Libr, 71-73. Speech Commun. Asn; Cent. States Speech Commun. Asn; Int. Commun. Asn. History; speech; communication. Publ: Pacifist speechmaking of Eugene V. Debs, Quart. J. Speech, 4/66; Debs' cooperative commonwealth movement, Labor Hist, fall 71; co-auth, Vocalic communication in persuasion, Quart. J. Speech, 10/72; plus others. Add: Dept. of Speech, Northeastern Illinois University, Bryn Mawr at St. Louis Ave, Chicago, IL 60625.

BRONSON, BERTRAND HARRIS, b. Lawrenceville, N.J, June 22, 02; m. 27. ENGLISH LITERATURE. A.B, Univ. Mich, 21, hon. L.H.D, 70; A.M, Harvard, 22; Rhodes scholar, Oxford, 22-25, B.A, 24, M.A, 29; Ph.D, Yale, 27; hon. D.ès L, Laval Univ, 61; L.H.D, Univ. Chicago, 68; hon. LL.D, Univ. Calif, Berkeley, 71. Instr, Univ. Mich, 25-26; ENG, UNIV. CALIF, BERKELEY, 27-29, asst. prof, 29-38, assoc. prof, 38-45, prof, 45-69, EMER. PROF, 69- Guggenheim fel, 43, 44, 48; Berg prof, N.Y. Univ, 73. Am. Counc. Learned Soc. Humanities Award, 59; Medal of Honor, Rice Univ, 62; Wilbur Cross Medal, Yale, 70. MLA; Am. Folklore Soc; Am. Musicol. Soc; Soc. Ethnomusicol; Philol. Asn. Pac. Coast; Int. Folk Music Counc; cor. fel, Brit. Acad; Am. Acad. Arts & Sci. The popular ballad; 18th century literary history and criticism; Chaucer. Publ: Joseph Ritson: scholar-at-arms, 38, Johnson Agonistes and other essays, 65 & Facets of the Enlightenment, 68, Univ. Calif; ed, Traditional tunes of the Child ballads, Vol. I, 59, Vol. II, 62, Vol. III, 66 & Vol. IV, 72, Princeton Univ: auth, In search of Chaucer, Univ. Toronto, 60; ed, Samuel Johnson: Rasselas, poems and selected prose, Holt, 71. Add: 927 Oxford St, Berkeley, CA 94707.

BRONSON, LARRY LAWRENCE, b. Plainwell, Mich, Aug. 28, 38. MIDDLE ENGLISH POETRY. B.A, West. Mich. Univ, 60; M.A, Rutgers Univ, 62, NDEA fel. & Ph.D.(Eng), 70. Instr. ENG, Russell Sage Col, 64-66, asst. prof, 66-67; CENT. MICH. UNIV, 67-71, ASSOC. PROF, 71- MLA; Midwest Mod. Lang. Asn; Mediaeval Acad. Am; Mod. Humanities Res. Asn. Works of Geoffrey Chaucer; medieval English drama; Arthurian legends. Add: Dept. of English, Central Michigan University, Mt. Pleasant, MI 48859.

BRONTE, DIANA LYDIA, b. Memphis, Tenn, Dec. 27, 38. COMPARATIVE LITERATURE. Nat. Merit Scholarship, Hendrix Col, 56-60, B.A, 60; Fulbright scholarship, Univ. Aix-Marseilille, 60-61; Woodrow Wilson fel, Univ. N.C, 61-62, career teaching fel, 62-63, assistantship, 64-65, Ph.D.(comp. lit), 69. From instr. to asst. prof. French, George Washington Univ, 65-70, asst. prof. Eng, 69-71; spec. asst. to dir, Folger Shakespeare Libr, 70-71; dir. res. & publ, Nat. Humanities Series, 71-73; consult. HUMANITIES, ROCKEFELLER FOUND, 73, ASST. DIR, 74- Co-ed, Acad. Forum, 69-70. MLA; Am. Comp. Lit. Asn; S.Atlantic Mod. Lang. Asn.(chairperson found. comt, 72-); Asn. Amis Andre Gide; Am. Asn. Teachers Fr; Shakespeare Asn. Am.(coord. dir, 73-). French; English. Publ: A sense of place, Nat. Humanities Series, 72; Andre Gide et le symbolisme, Cahiers Andre Gide, fall 69. Add: 59 Wiggins St, Princeton, NJ 08540.

BROOKES, STELLA BREWER, b. Fannin, Tex, Jan. 22, 03; m. 28. ENGLISH. A.B, Wiley Col, 23; A.M, Univ. Mich, 30; Ph.D, Cornell Univ, 46. Prof. ENG, Walden Col, 23-24; prof. & chmn. dept, Clark Col, 24-69; RETIRED. NCTE; Am. Soc. African Cult; Asn. Depts. Eng. American folklore. Publ: Joel Chandler Harris: folklorist, Univ. Ga, 50, 2nd ed, 67; 3rd ed, 72; Harris, Joel Chandler, In: Encycl. Britannica, 58; introd, Joel Chandler Harris Uncle Remus stories, Schocken, 65; Master trickster: Brer Rabbit, Atlanta Const. Centennial Ed, 4/68. Add: 1120 Chicon St, Austin, TX 78702.

BROOKHOUSE, JOHN CHRISTOPHER, b. Cincinnati, Ohio, Jan. 6, 38; m. 59; c. 2. ENGLISH. A.B, Stanford Univ, 59; M.A, Harvard, 60, Ph.D.(Eng), 64. Instr. ENG, Harvard, 64-66; ASST. PROF, UNIV. N.C, CHAPEL HILL, 66- Mediaeval Acad. Am. Middle English; American poetry. Publ: Sir Amadace and the avowing of Arthur, Rosenkilde, 68; Chaucer's Imposibilia, Medium Aevum, 65; The confessions of three pilgrims, Laurel Rev, 68. Add: Dept. of English, Bingham Hall, University of North Carolina, Chapel Hill, Chapel Hill, NC 27515.

BROOKING, JACK THOMAS, b. Galesburg, Ill, July 10, 27; m. 56. SPEECH, DRAMA. B.A, State Univ. Iowa, 51; M.A, West. Reserve Univ, 54, M.F.A, 54, Ph.D.(drama), 56. Instr. speech, UNIV. KANS, 55-56, asst. prof, 56-60, assoc. prof, 60-65, PROF. SPEECH & DRAMA, 65-, ASST. DIR. UNIV. THEATRE, 55- Res, France, 62; mem. Carnegie Found. prog, Costa Rica, summers, 63 & 64; E.Europ. acting tour dir, 64; Fulbright lectr, Guatemala, 66. Speech Commun. Asn; Am. Theatre Asn. Joan of Arc as a dramatic figure; international theatre; actor training. Publ: Jeanne d'Arc, the trial notes and Anouilh, Theatre Annual, 59; Directing 'Summer and smoke,' an existentialist approach, Mod. Drama, 2/60; The declamatory theatre of France, parts I & II, Players Mag, 11-12/60; plus others. Add: Dept. of Speech & Drama, University of Kansas, Lawrence, KS 66044.

BROOKS, ALFRED GLENN, b. Chicago, Ill, Mar. 30, 27; m. 54; c. 1. THEATRE. B.A, Univ. Ill, 50, summer fel, 61, Ph.D, 62; M.A, Univ. Calif, Los Angeles, 51; Fulbright grant, Univ. Vienna, Austria, 52-53. Asst. prof. THEATRE, West. Ill. Univ, 61-63; STATE UNIV. N.Y. BINGHAMTON, 63-67, assoc. prof, 67-70, PROF, 70-, DIR. MAX REINHARDT ARCH, 66-, DIR. INT. STUD, 67-, CHMN. DEPT, 68- Ed, Max Reinhardt Publ, 68-; managing ed, Modern Int. Drama series, 70-; guest prof, Univ. Vienna, 71; pres, Max Reinhardt Found, 72- U.S.A.A.F, 44-46. Am. Theatre Asn; Speech Commun. Asn; Int. Soc. Theatre Res. European theatre history, especially 19th and 20th centuries; propaganda and political control in theatre and related areas; history of directing. Publ: Buhnewelt-Weltbühne, Weltschau, 53; Die Entwicklung eines amerikanischen Nationaltheaters, Burgtheater Almanach, 66. Add: Dept. of Theatre, State University of New York at Binghamton, Binghamton, NY 13901.

BROOKS, ALFRED RUSSELL, b. Montgomery, Ala, May 19, 06. ENGLISH LITERATURE. A.B, Morehouse Col, 31; A.M, Univ. Wis, 34, Ph.D, 58; Univ. Edinburgh, 38-39; Rosenwald fel, 39-40. Instr. ENG, univ. high sch, Univ. Atlanta, 32-33; prof, Agr. & Tech. Col. N.C, 34-44; Morehouse Col, 46-60; prof. & head dept, Ky. State Col, 60-72; RETIRED. MLA; NCTE; Col. Lang. Asn. James Boswell; Afro-American literature. Publ: James Boswell, Twayne, 71. Add: 415 College Park Dr, Frankfort, KY 40601.

BROOKS, CHARLES BENTON, b. Okolona, Miss, Jan. 19, 21; m. 51. ENGLISH. A.B, Univ. Calif, 42, M.A, 49, Ph.D.(Eng), 54. Lectr. Eng, Univ. Calif, 54-55; asst. prof. Eng. & humanities, Lewis & Clark Col, 55-57; ENG, CALIF. STATE UNIV, LONG BEACH, 57-61, assoc. prof, 61-65, PROF, 65-, chmn. dept, 68-70. La. Literary Award, 61. Med.Admin.C, U.S.A, 42-46, 2nd Lt. MLA; Philol. Asn. Pac. Coast; Shakespeare Asn. Am; Renaissance Soc. Am. Elizabethan literature; Shakespeare; drama. Publ: Siege of New Orleans, Univ. Wash, 61; The multiple set in American drama, Tulane Drama Rev, 12/58; Shakespeare's heroine actresses, Shakespeare Jahrbuch, 60. Add: Dept. of English, California State University, Long Beach, 6101 E. Seventh St, Long Beach, CA 90840.

BROOKS, CLEANTH, b. Murray, Ky, Oct. 16, 06; m. 34. ENGLISH. B.A, Vanderbilt Univ, 28; M.A, Tulane Univ, 29, hon. D.Litt, 69; Rhodes scholar & B.A, Oxford, 31, B.Litt, 32; hon. D.Litt, Upsala Col, 63, Univ. Ky, 63, Univ. Exeter, 66, Washington & Lee Univ, 68; hon. L.H.D, St. Louis Univ, 68. Prof. Eng, La. State Univ, 32-47; YALE, 47-60, GRAY PROF. RHETORIC, 60- Libr. Congr. fel; co-ed, South. Rev, 35-42; fel, Ind. Sch. Lett, 48- Am. Acad. Arts & Sci; Nat. Inst. Arts & Sci; Am. Philos. Soc; MLA. Criticism; mid-eighteenth century literature; contemporary literature. Publ: The well wrought urn, 47 & A shaping joy, 72, Harcourt; William Faulkner: the Yoknapatawpha country, 63 & co-ed, Percy letters, 7 vols, Yale; co-auth, American literature: the makers and the making, St. Martin's, 73. Add: Forest Rd, Northford, CT 06472.

BROOKS, ELMER LEROY, b. Rush Springs, Okla, May 16, 17; m. 52; c. 3. ENGLISH. B.A, Cent. State Col.(Okla), 41; M.A, Univ. Okla, 48; Ph.D.(Eng), Harvard, 54. Instr. ENG, Panhandle Agr. & Mech. Col, 48-49; Duke Univ, 53-56; from asst. prof. to assoc. prof, East. Ill. Univ, 56-63; lectr, Univ. Calif, Los Angeles, 63-64; PROF, East. Ill. Univ, 64-69; IND. STATE UNIV, TERRE HAUTE, 69- U.S.N.R, 42-46, Lt.(jg). Col. Eng. Asn. Romantic period, especially 1800-1825; Victorian period; mid-20th century. Publ: Co-auth, Correlated grammar & composition, Ill. Asn. Teachers Eng, 62; auth, In lieu of wit, Prairie, 67; The poet—an error in the Keats canon?, Mod. Lang. Notes, 11/52; Byron in the London Magazine, Keats-Shelley J, 55; A restoration satire on the court ladies, Eng. Lang. Notes, 3/73; plus others. Add: Dept. of English, Indiana State University, Terre Haute, IN 47809.

BROOKS, JOHN BRADBURY, b. Hampton, N.H, July 4, 30; m. 54; c. 3. ENGLISH. B.A, Univ. N.H, 53; M.A, Univ. Pa, 59, Ph.D.(Eng), 65. Instr. ENG, Pa. State Univ, 59-60; Univ. N.Dak, 60-62; asst. prof, Univ. Alta, Calgary, 62-65; UNIV. WIS-OSHKOSH, 65-67, assoc. prof, 67-70, PROF, 70-, chmn. dept, 68-71, Chancellor's res grant, 72-73. U.S.A.F, 52-56, S/Sgt. MLA; Popular Cult. Asn. Jacobean and Caroline drama; restoration drama; American popular literature and culture. Publ: Middleton's stepfather and the captain of the Phoenix, Notes & Queries, 10/61; College student reading preferences, Reading Improvement, winter 67; Improvised classroom drama, Wis. Eng. J, 4/69; plus one other. Add: Dept. of English, University of Wisconsin-Oshkosh, Oshkosh, WI 54901.

BROOKS, KEITH, b. Tigerton, Wis, May 14, 23; c. 2. COMMUNICATION, ORAL INTERPRETATION. B.S. & M.S, Univ. Wis, 49; Ph.D, Ohio State Univ, 55. Instr, East. Ky. State Univ, 49-53; OHIO STATE UNIV, 53-56, asst. prof. SPEECH COMMUN, 56-61, assoc. prof, 61-65, PROF, 65-, CHMN. DEPT, 68- Consult, Men in Govt. Insts, Ohio State Univ, 67-68; Ohio Trade Asn. Exec, 73; Ohio Funeral Dir. Asn; Procter & Gamble Co; vis. prof, Calif. State Univ, Los Angeles, summer 70. Speech Commun. Asn; Int. Commun. Asn; Cent. State Speech Commun. Asn. Publ: Co-auth, Practical speaking for the technical man, Prentice-Hall, 58; auth, The communicative arts and sciences of speech, C.E. Merrill, 67; co-auth, The communicative act of oral interpretation, 67 & co-auth, Literature for listening, 68, Allyn & Bacon. Add: Dept. of Communication, Ohio State University, 154 N. Oval Dr, Columbus, OH 43210.

BROOKS, PETER PRESTON, French, Comparative Literature. See Volume III, Foreign Languages, Linguistics & Philology.

BROOKS, RICHARD ALBERT EDWARD, b. Karachi, India, May 14, 04. ENGLISH LITERATURE. A.B, Wesleyan Univ, 26, Olin fel, 26-27, A.M, 27, univ. fel. at Yale, 29-30; univ. scholar, Yale, 31-32, Ph.D, 36. Instr. ENG, Wesleyan Univ, 27-29, Weeks vis. prof, 52-53; instr, Yale, 32-33; VASSAR COL, 33-37, asst. prof, 37-43, assoc. prof, 43-49, prof, 49-63, Henry Noble MacCracken prof, 63-69, chmn. dept, 58-60, EMER. PROF, 69- Fac. fel. from Vassar Col, Harvard, 39-40, stud. in Eng, 61-62; trustee, Poughkeepsie Day Sch, 44-45, 46-48. U.S.A, 45-46. MLA. Victorian literature and development of the historical mind; Thomas Carlyle; British literature 1880-1930. Publ: Ed, Thomas Carlyle: journey to Germany, autumn 1858, 40 & The diary of Michael Floy, Junior, Bowery Village, 1833-1837, 41, Yale; co-ed, The sad shepherd of Ben Jonson, Day, 44; auth, The development of the historical mind, In: The reinterpretation of Victorian literature, Princeton, 50; co-auth, John Galsworthy: an annotated checklist of writings about him, 58 & E.M. Forster: an annotated checklist of writings about him, 59, Eng. Fiction in Transition. Add: 493-B Heritage Village, Southbury, CT 06488.

BROOKS, ROBERT D, b. St. Louis, Mo, Oct. 24, 34; m. 57; c. 5. COMMUNICATION. A.B, Wash. Univ, 59; M.A, Cornell, 61, Ph.D, 65. Instr. speech, Cornell Univ, 62-63, asst. prof, San Diego State Col, 63-64; SPEECH & VERBAL COMMUN, Univ. Ill, Urbana, 64-71, ASSOC. PROF, NORTHWEST. UNIV, EVANSTON, 71- Assoc. ed, Speech Monographs, 73-75. Speech Commun. Asn; Nat. Soc. Stud. Commun. Communication processes; communication in social movements; Nazi propaganda. Publ: Co-auth, Speech as process: a case study, Speech Monogr, 3/68; auth, Black power, West. Speech, 5/70; The playmate of the month, J. Pop. Culture, 74. Add: Dept. of Communication Studies, Northwestern University, Evanston, IL 60201.

BROOKS, ROBERT SCOTT, b. Kansas City, Mo, July 17, 28; m. 52; c. 3. SPEECH. B.A, Ottawa Univ, 52; M.S, Univ. Kans, 54, Ph.D.(speech), 64. Speech pathologist, Salina Pub. Schs, Kans, 54-59, dir. spec. educ, 61-64; asst. prof. speech, Kans. State Univ, 64-67, assoc. prof, 67-69; PROF.

SPEECH PATH, MANKATO STATE COL, 69- Consult, Veterans Hosp, Topeka, Kans, 65-; Irwin Army Hosp, Ft. Riley, 65-67; Mem. Hosp, Manhattan, 66- U.S.M.C, 46-48, Sgt. Am. Speech & Hearing Asn. Speech; hearing; special education. Publ: Co-auth, Filming speed in cinefluorographic speech study, J. Speech & Hearing Res, 63; auth, Vocabulary variables and language skills in the PB discrimination of children, J. Auditory Res, 66; A tool for clinical supervision, J. Speech & Hearing Disorders, 66. Add: Dept. of Speech, Mankato State College, Mankato, MN 56001.

BROOKS, ROGER L, b. El Dorado, Ark, Apr. 14, 27; m. 50; c. 5. ENGLISH. B.A, Baylor Univ, 49; M.A, Univ. Ill, 50; Ph.D, Univ. Colo, 59. Instr. Eng, Univ. Colo, 55-57, 58-60; asst. prof, Tex. Technol. Col, 60-62, assoc. prof, 62-64, prof. Eng. & assoc. dean grad. sch, 64-67; prof. eng. & dean arts & sci, E.Tex. State Univ, 67-73; PROF. ENG. & PRES, HOWARD PAYNE COL, 73- Univ. Colo. fel, Brit. Mus, 57-58; summer grants, Univ. Colo. Counc. Creative Work & Res, 59, Am. Philos. Soc, 63, Tex. Technol. Col, 64-66. U.S.N.R, 45-51. MLA; Mod. Humanities Res. Asn, Gt. Brit; Bibliog. Soc. Am. Matthew Arnold; Victorian literature. Publ: The letters of Matthew Arnold, Stud. Philol, 1/66; Matthew Arnold's A few words about the Education Act, Mod. Philol, 2/69; Some additions to Matthew Arnold's library, Papers Bibliog. Soc. Am, 71; plus others. Add: Office of the President, Howard Payne College, Brownwood, TX 76801.

BROOKS, WILLIAM DEAN, b. Bucklin, Kans, Sept. 10, 29; m. 48; c. 4. SPEECH COMMUNICATION & EDUCATION. A.B, Southwest. Col.(Kans), 50; M.A, Univ. Colo, 60; Ph.D.(speech commun), Ohio Univ, 65. Teacher, high sch, Kans, 50-54; instr. speech & debate, Garden City Jr. Col, 54-61; assoc. prof. speech & chmn. dept, McPherson Col. 61-63; instr. Ohio Univ, 63-64, dir. listening res. lab, 64-65; asst. prof. speech commun, Univ. Kans, 65-66, asst. chmn. dept, 66-67; assoc. prof. speech, PURDUE UNIV, LAFAYETTE, 67-73, PROF. COMMUN. & EDUC, 73-, DIR, TEACHER TRAINING IN SPEECH, 67- Consult, polit. cand, Campaign Comn, 66-68; mem. adv. comt. undergrad. speech instr, Speech Asn. Am, 67-68, nat. comt. to stud. basic speech course, 68-70. Speech Asn. Am; Nat. Soc. Stud. Commun.(consult, ed, 67); Cent. States Speech Asn; Am. Educ. Res. Asn. Political campaign communication; speech education; communication for the aged. Publ: Introduction to debate, Univ-Exposition, 66; co-auth, Quantitative methods of communication research, 69 & Teaching speech communication in the secondary school, 73, Houghton; auth, Speech communication, W.C. Brown, 71; co-auth, Public communication, Harper, 74; plus three arts. Add: 5715 N. 225 W, West Lafayette, IN 47906.

BROPHY, ELIZABETH BERGEN, b. New York, N.Y, Jan. 28, 29; m. 51; c. 5. EIGHTEENTH CENTURY ENGLISH LITERATURE. B.A, Smith Col, 59; M.A, Sarah Lawrence Col, 64; Fulbright fel. & Columbia Univ. travelling fel, Univ. London, 66-67; Ph.D.(Eng), Columbia Univ, 70. Instr. ENG, COL. NEW ROCHELLE, 68-70, ASST. PROF, 70- MLA; AAUP. Eighteenth century literature; the early novel; satire. Publ: Samuel Richardson, the triumph of craft, Univ. Tenn, 74; Dr. Johnson operatically preserv'd, Opera, 67; A clockwork orange: English and Nadsat, Notes Contemporary Lit, 72. Add: Dept. of English, College of New Rochelle, New Rochelle, NY 10801.

BROPHY, JAMES DAVID, JR, b. Mt. Vernon, N.Y, Oct. 5, 26; m. 51; c. 5. ENGLISH. B.A, Amherst Col, 49; M.A, Columbia Univ, 50, Ph.D.(Eng), 65; Fulbright grant, Univ. Dijon, 50-51. Instr. ENG, IONA COL, 51-58, asst. prof, 58-64, assoc. prof, 64-68, PROF. & CHMN. DEPT, 68- N.Y. State Russian stud. sem. grant, 62; Ford Found-N.Y. State Russian lang. grant, 63-64; N.Y. State Fac. scholar, 65; N.Y. State fac. res. grant, 68. U.S.N, 45-46. MLA. Modern poetry, English, American, French and Russian; Edith Sitwell; science and modern poetry. Publ: Co-ed, The achievement of Galileo, Twayne, 62; auth, Edith Sitwell: the symbolist order, South. Ill. Univ, 68; W.H. Auden, Columbia Univ, 70; co-ed, Modern Irish literature, Iona Col. & Twayne, 72; auth, Edith Sitwell: modern metaphysical, Renascence, spring 63; Shakespeare's Saucy jacks, Eng. Lang. Notes, 9/63; John Montague's Restive Sally-Switch, In: Modern Irish literature, Iona Col. & Twayne, 72; plus one other. Add: Dept. of English, Iona College, New Rochelle, NY 10801.

BROPHY, ROBERT JOSEPH, b. San Francisco, Calif, Feb. 6, 28. MODERN AMERICAN & BRITISH LITERATURE. B.A, Gonzaga Univ, 52, Ph.L, 53; M.A, Loyola Univ.(Calif), 56; S.T.L, Alma Col, 60; M.A, Univ. Santa Clara, 60; Ph.D.(Eng), Univ. N.C, Chapel Hill, 66. Instr, St. Ignatius High Sch, 53-55; Eng. lit, Univ. San Francisco, 65-66, asst. prof, 66-68; ENG, CALIF. STATE UNIV, LONG BEACH, 68-72, ASSOC. PROF, 72- Ed, Robinson Jeffers Newslett, 68-; host & moderator, Carmel Poetry Festival: Robinson Jeffers, summers 69, 70, 71. West. Am. Lit. Asn.(mem. bibliog. staff, 72-); Conf. Christianity & Lit; MLA. Robinson Jeffers studies; myth criticism; theology and literature. Publ: Robinson Jeffers: a checklist, Lawton Kennedy, 67; Robinson Jeffers: myth, ritual, and symbol in his narrative poems, Case West. Reserve Univ, 73; Textual note on Robinson Jeffers' The beginning and the end, Publ. Bibliog. Soc. Am, 3rd quart/66; Tamar, The Cenci and incest, Am. Lit, 5/70; Jeffers' Cawdor and the Hippolytus story, West. Am. Lit, fall 72; plus others. Add: Dept. of English, California State University, Long Beach, 6101 E. Seventh St, Long Beach, CA 90840.

BROSNAHAN, LEGER, b. Kansas City, Mo, Dec. 11, 29; m. 67; c. 2. ENGLISH LITERATURE & LINGUISTICS. B.A, Georgetown Univ, 51; M.A, Harvard, 52, Dexter scholar, 55, John Harvard fel, 55-57, Ph.D, 58. Instr. Eng, Northwest. Univ. 57-61; asst. prof, Univ. Hawaii, Manoa, 61-63; Fulbright res. grant, 63-64; asst. prof. ENG, Univ. Md, 65-68; ASSOC. PROF, ILL. STATE UNIV, 68- Fulbright vis. lectr, Univ. Lyon, 64-65, Japan, 68-70. U.S.A, 52-54. MLA; Mediaeval Acad. Am; AAUP. Mediaeval English literature; history and structure of English language; English as a foreign language. Publ: Does the NPT epilogue contain a link?, Stud. Philol, 61; Wace's use of proverbs, Speculum, 64; Apropos de ligne 3 de la 2e partie de La Geste des Normanz, Romania, 66. Add: Dept. of English, Illinois State University, Normal, IL 61761.

BROSS, ADDISON CLEM, b. Birmingham, Ala, Jan. 1, 37; m. 64; c. 2. ENGLISH & AMERICAN LITERATURE. B.A, Davidson Col, 59; M.A, Duke Univ, 60; Ph.D.(Eng), La. State Univ, Baton Rouge, 67. Instr. ENG, Univ. N.C, Greensboro, 60-62; Xavier Univ. La, 65-66; asst. prof, LEHIGH UNIV, 67-73, ASSOC. PROF, 73- Fulbright Hays lect. Am. lit, Jagiellonian Univ, 71-72, Kosciuszko Found. Stud. fel, 74; vis. fel, Slavic lang, Ohio State Univ, summer 72. MLA. Victorian literature; Joseph Conrad; American literature. Publ: Soldier's pay and the art of Aubrey Beardsley, Am. Quart, 67; The unextinguishable light of belief: Conrad's attitude toward women, Conradiana, 70; Beerbohm's The feast and Conrad's early fiction, Nineteenth century Fiction, 71. Add: Dept. of English, Lehigh University, Bethlehem, PA 18017.

BROSTOWIN, PATRICK RONALD, b. Brooklyn, N.Y, Jan. 27, 31; m. 52; c. 7. ENGLISH. B.A, St. John's Univ.(N.Y), 51; M.A, N.Y. Univ, 53, Ph.D.(Eng), 69. Teacher high schs, N.Y, 51-61; assoc. prof. ENG, NASSAU COMMUNITY COL.(N.Y), 61-68, PROF. & SUPVR. EVENING DIV, 69- Chmn. workshop prep. of Eng. teachers for two year col, NCTE annual conf. Col. Compos. & Commun, 68; dir. convocation on lit. & sci. State Univ. N.Y. grant, 69, convocation on the role of Afro-Am. writers, 70. MLA; NCTE. Relations of science and literature; Utopian societies and literature in early 19th century America; 19th century American literature. Publ: Co-auth, Science and literature; a reader, Heath, 64; auth, Survey of English literature from early time to 1066 (filmstrips accompanied by records), Eye Gate House, 65; co-auth, Relations of literature and science: select bibliography for 1965-66, winter 67 & for 1966-67, winter 68, Symposium, Syracuse Univ; Pragmatists and prophets: George Rapp and J.A. Roebling vs. J.A. Etzler and Count Leon, West. Pa. Hist. Mag, 10/68. Add: 356 East Rd, Garden City, NY 11530.

BROUGHTON, BRADFORD BROWNE, b. Allentown, Pa, Feb. 6, 26; m. 50; c. 2. ENGLISH. A.B, Allegheny Col, 47; M.A, Univ. Pa, 49, Ph.D.(Eng), 61. Asst. instr. Eng, Univ. Pa, 47-49, 53-55; instr, Utica Col, Syracuse Univ, 49-50; lib. stud, CLARKSON COL. TCHNOL, 55-57, asst. prof, 57-61, assoc. prof, 61-66, PROF. HUMANITIES, 66-, CHMN. DEPT, 73- U.S.N,R, 43-46, 50-52, Lt. MLA; Soc. Rencesvals; Int. Arthurian Soc. Medieval romances; French chansons de gestes. Publ: The legends of Richard I; a study in sources and variations to 1600, Mouton, The Hague, 66; transl, Richard the Lion-Hearted and other Medieval English romances, Dutton, 66; ed, Twenty-seven to one, Clarkson Col, 70. Add: Dept. of Humanities, Clarkson College of Technology, Potsdam, NY 13676.

BROUGHTON, PANTHEA REID, b. Birmington, Ala, Sept. 11, 40; m. 62; c. 1. TWENTIETH CENTURY LITERATURE, HISTORY OF IDEAS. B.A, Univ. Ala, 62, M.A, 63; Ph.D.(Eng), Univ. N.C, 71. Instr. ENG, Univ. Ala, 64-65; Montreat-Anderson Col, 65-66; VA. POLYTECH. INST. & STATE UNIV, 67-69, ASST. PROF, 70- Vis. scholar, C.W. Post Col, 72. MLA (secy, South. Am. Lit. Sem, 74); Women's Caucus Modern Lang; S.Atlantic Mod. Lang. Asn; AAUP; Soc. Study South. Lit. Literary theory; 20th century novel; Henry Adams. Publ: William Faulkner: the abstract and the actual, La. State Univ, 74; Requiem for a Nun: no part in rationality, South. Rev, fall 72; The modifying metaphor in Dejection: an ode, Wordsworth Circle, fall 73; Faulkner's fancy-work, Saturday Rev/World, 1/74. Add: Dept. of English, Virginia Polytechnic Institute & State University, Blacksburg, VA 24061.

BROUSE, ALBERT JOSEPH, b. Cleveland, Ohio, June 23, 23. ENGLISH. B.A, West. Reserve Univ, 44, Ph.D, 56; M.A, Duke Univ, 47, fel, 49; fel, Stanford Univ, 49-50. Instr. ENG, Duke Univ, 47-49; asst. prof, Case Inst. Tech, 57-62; ASSOC. PROF, ILL. INST. TECH, 62-, DIR. SCI. INFORM. PROG, 70- Consult, U.S. Steel Co. & Cleveland Electric Illuminating Co, 53-58; Ford Found. exchange prof, Rensselaer Polytech. Inst, 57-58; adv, Engineering & Sci. Rev, 58-62; dir. training, Nat. Reading & Res. Found, 61, dir. Nat. Inst. Health grant for sci. inform. training prog, 70. U.S.A, 50-53, 1st Lt. Int. Commun. Asn; Soc. Tech. Commun; Health Sci. Commun. Asn; Am. Soc. Inform. Sci. Charles Reade as a dramatist; information systems as applied to literature, specifically systems analysis. Publ: James Russell Lowell in Spain, Duke; Clarity in science writing is not enough, J. Tech. Writing & Commun, 1/71; What really happened to Holden Caulfield, Col. Compos. & Commun, 12/72; Science information: new academic discipline, Technol. & Human Affairs, 71-72. Add: Dept. of Humanities, Life Science Bldg, Illinois Institute of Technology, Chicago, IL 60616.

BROUSSARD, ALTON E, b. St. Martinville, La, Mar. 16, 11; m. 39; c. 3. JOURNALISM. B.A, La. State Univ, 35, M.A, 53; summers, Univ. Mo, 59-61. Ed, Harper Newspapers, 35-36; staff correspondent, Beaumont, Tex, Enterprise, 36-42; inform. exec, Off. War Inform, 42-44; city, ed, Lake Charles Am. Press, La, 44-47; dir. pub. relat, UNIV. SOUTHWEST. LA, 47-53, ASST. PROF. JOUR, 53-, DIR. COLD TYPE LAB, 67- Ed. consult, Southwest. La. Electric Membership Corp, 54-62; consult, Lafayette Guide, 62-64; feature writer, Lafayette Daily Advertiser, 69- Asn. Educ. in Jour; Nat. Counc. Col. Publ. Adv. Reducing newspaper production costs; cold type composition for small newspapers; history and bibliography of the newspapers of St. Martinville, Louisiana. Add: 124 Duclos St, Lafayette, LA 70501.

BROUSSARD, LOUIS, b. Breaux Bridge, La, Dec. 27, 22. ENGLISH. B.A, Univ. Southwest. La, 42; M.A, Univ. Calif, Los Angeles, 45; Ph.D.(Eng), N.Y. Univ, 63. Asst. prof. ENG, Univ. Ill, 46-52, 62-65; lectr, Hunter Col, 57-61; assoc. prof, ST. JOHN'S UNIV. (N.Y), 65-70, PROF, 70- American literature. Publ: American drama: contemporary allegory from O'Neill to Williams, 62 & The measure of Poe, 69, Univ. Okla; Hemingway as a critic, Ariz. Quart, fall 64. Add: Dept. of English, St. John's University, Jamaica, NY 11432.

BROWER, REUBEN ARTHUR, b. Lanesboro, Pa, May 5, 08; m. 34; c. 3. ENGLISH, CLASSICS. B.A, Amherst Col, 30; B.A, Cambridge, 32, M.A, 36. Tutor Eng. & classics, Harvard, 32-36, instr. Eng, 36-39; asst. prof. Greek & Eng, Amherst Col, 39-44, assoc. prof, 44-48, Class of 1880 prof, 48-53; prof. ENG, HARVARD, 53-70, HENRY B. & ANNE M. CABOT PROF, 70-, SR. FEL, SOC. FELS, 67-, master, Adams House, 54-68. John Woodruff Simpson stud. fel, England; Guggenheim stud. fels, Italy, 56-57 & England, 65-66; fel, Ctr. Advan. Stud. Behavioral Sci, 61-62; Fulbright sr. vis. prof, Oxford, 68-69; fel, Churchill Col, 74; Nat. Endowment for Humanities fel, 74. Harvard Univ. Press fac. prize, hon. mention, 59; Phi Beta Kappa Christian Gauss bk. award, 60; Explicator bk. award, 63. MLA. Greek and English; translation; 18th century poetry. Publ: The fields of light, 51, The poetry of Robert Frost—constellations of intention, 63 & Hero and saint: Shakespeare and the Graeco-Roman heroic tradition, 71, Oxford; Alexander Pope: the poetry of allusion, Clarendon, 59; co-auth, In defence of reading, Dutton, 62; co-ed, Pope's translation of The Iliad, Macmillan, 65; ed, Coriolanus, New Am. Libr, 66; ed, Forms of lyric, 70 & co-ed, I.A. Richards: essays in his honor, 73, Columbia Univ; Twentieth century literature in retrospect, Harvard Univ, 71. Add: Dept. of English, Harvard University, Cambridge, MA 02138.

BROWN, ALAN KELSEY, b. San Francisco, Calif, Dec. 21, 33; m. 71; c. 1. MEDIEVAL ENGLISH. A.B, Hamilton Col, 56; Ph.D.(Eng. philol), Stanford Univ, 69. Instr. & lectr. ENG, Univ. Ariz, 63-69; ASSOC. PROF, OHIO STATE UNIV, 70- Res. assoc, San Mateo County Hist. Asn, 64- U.S.A, 56-58. MLA (bibliogr, Eng. group 1, 71-); Am. Name Soc; Ling. Soc. Am; Am. Dialect Soc. Publ: Co-auth, Who discovered the Golden Gate?, San Mateo County Hist. Asn, 69; auth, Heifer, Neophilologus, 72; Neorxnawong, Neuphilol. Mitt, 73; The English compass terms, Medium AEvum, 74. Add: Dept. of English, Ohio State University, 164 W. 17th Ave, Columbus, OH 43210.

BROWN, ALAN WILLARD, b. New York, N.Y, Oct. 3, 10; m. 33; c. 2. ENGLISH & COMPARATIVE LITERATURE, INTELLECTUAL HISTORY. A.B, Harvard, 30, A.M, 32; Univ. Paris, 30-31; Am. Sch. Class. Stud, Athens, 30-31; cert, Univ. München, Ger, 31; Ph.D.(Eng), Columbia Univ, 45. Teacher Millbrook Sch, 32-33; instr. Eng, Columbia Col, Columbia Univ, 34-45, asst. to dean, 38-48, asst. prof, 45-48; pres, Hobart & William Smith Col, 48-55; provost & prof, Union Col.(N.Y), 55-57; pres, Metrop. Educ. TV Asn, 57-59; PROF. ENG, UNIV. P.R, MAYAGUEZ, 60-, dir. dept. Eng. & humanities, 60-62, acad. asst. to dean arts & sci, 62-66. Mem. comt. acad. freedom & acad. tenure, Asn. Am. Cols, 49-51; Mid. State Asn. Col. & Sec. Schs. Comts, 51-58; mem. comt. pre-prof. educ, Am. Med. Asn, Markle Found, 51-61; pres, N.Y. State Citizen's Counc, 52-54; Asn. Col. & Univ. State N.Y, 54-56; Ford Found. summer fel, England & France, summer 59; resident fel. ctr. adv. stud, Wesleyan Univ, 59-60; res. in Europe, Univ. P.R, 66-67. MLA; Grolier Club. Victorian cultural and intellectual history; mannerism, baroque and neo-classicism: relation to the rise of romanticism; the Greek revival in literature, art, and architecture, 1720-1850. Publ: Auth. & ed, Classics of the Western world, Am. Libr. Asn, 43; auth, The Metaphysical society: Victorian minds in crisis 1869-1880, Columbia Univ, 47; A history of Hobart College, Newcomen Soc, 58; Education in an open society, Atenea, Univ. P.R, Mayagüez, 60; The future of educational television, In, Preparation for medical education: a restudy, McGraw, 61; plus others. Add: Dept. of English, University of Puerto Rico, College Station, Mayagüez, PR 00708.

BROWN, ANNE MARIE, O.P, b. Chicago, Ill, Nov. 16, 13. ENGLISH. A.B, Siena Heights Col, 40; M.A, Univ. Detroit, 47; Univ. Mich, 57-58, summers 58, 59. Prin, St. Paul Elem. & High Sch, Grosse Pointe, Mich, 51-57; instr. ENG, SIENA HEIGHTS COL, 58-62, from asst. prof. to assoc. prof, 62-69, asst. dean, 61-63, acad. dean, 63-69, DIR. ADMIS, 69- Add: Siena Heights College, Adrian, MI 49221.

BROWN, ANTHONY EUGENE, b. Rocky Mount, N.C, July 22, 37; m. 73; c. 9. ENGLISH LITERATURE. B.A, Univ. S.C, 60, M.A, 62; Ph.D.(Eng), Vanderbilt Univ, 71. Asst. prof. ENG, WEST. CAROLINA UNIV, 64-71, ASSOC. PROF, 71- Am. Philos. Soc. grant-in-aid, summer 71; Am. Counc. Learned Soc. fel, 72-73. S.Atlantic Mod. Lang. Asn. Age of Johnson; contemporary reputation of James Boswell; Boswell bibliography. Publ: Boswellian studies, a bibliography, 2nd ed, Archon, 72; Boswellian studies: a bibliography, In: Cairo studies in English, 1963-1966, 66; contrib, The virgin's lottery, Satire Newslett, spring 73. Add: Dept. of English, Western Carolina University, Cullowhee, NC 28723.

BROWN, ARTHUR WAYNE, b. Sheshequin, Pa, Apr. 20, 17; m. 38; c. 8. ENGLISH. B.A, Univ. Scranton, 37, L.H.D, 65; fel. & M.A, Cornell Univ, 38; Ph.D.(Eng), Syracuse Univ, 50; L.L.D, Hofstra Univ, 66. Instr. Latin, Univ. Scranton, 36-37; chmn. dept. Eng, Monmouth Col, 40-45, asst. dean, 45-46; instr, Utica Col, Syracuse Univ, 46-48, asst. prof, 48-51, assoc. prof, 51-55, prof, 55-63; chmn. dept. & dir. inst. humanities, Adelphi Univ, 63-65, pres, 65-67; dean grad. sch, Fordham Univ, 67-69, v.pres, acad. affairs, 68-69; pres, Marygrove Col, 69-72; PROF. ENG. & DEAN SCH. LIB. ARTS & SCI, BARUCH COL, 72- Mem. evaluation teams, Mid. States Asn. Cols. & Sec. Sch, 65-; consult. Eng, Counc. Grad. Schs, U.S, 68. MLA; Col. Eng. Asn; Am. Lit. Asn; AAUP; Cath. Comn. Intellectual & Cult. Affairs (secy, 60-70). Modern American novel; 19th century American literature; Renaissance pre-Shakespearean drama. Publ: Always young for liberty, Syracuse Univ, 56; William Ellery Channing, 61 & Margaret Fuller, 63, Twayne; co-ed, Great American thinkers, (16 vols), Washington Square, 63-68; Ralph Waldo Emerson, 73, Henry George, 73, Felix Adler 74 & Thomas H. Green, 74, In: World Thinkers Series, Twayne. Add: Office of the Dean, School of Liberal Arts & Sciences, Baruch College, 17 Lexington Ave, New York, NY 10010.

BROWN, ASHLEY, b. Louisville, Ky, Dec. 19, 23. ENGLISH & AMERICAN LITERATURE. A.B, Univ. Louisville, 45; M.A, Vanderbilt Univ, 46, Ph.D. (Eng), 58; Yale, 50-51. Instr. Eng, Washington & Lee Univ, 46-53; Univ. Calif, Santa Barbara, 56-59; asst. prof, UNIV. S.C, 59-65, assoc. prof, 65-71, PROF. ENG. & COMP. LIT, 71- Fulbright prof, Univ. Rio de Janeiro, 64-65 & 71-72. S.Atlantic Mod. Lang. Asn; MLA. Modern British and American poetry; satire; Brazilian literature. Publ: Co-auth, The achievement of Wallace Stevens, Lippincott, 62, Satire: a critical anthology, World Publ, 67 & Modes of literature, C.E. Merrill, 68; auth, The early fiction of Peter Taylor, autumn 62 & Landscape into art: Henry James and John Crowe Ransom, spring 71; Sewanee Rev; The novel as Christian comedy, In: Reality and myth, Vanderbilt Univ, 64. Add: Dept. of English, University of South Carolina, Columbia, SC 29208.

BROWN, BENJAMIN EARL, b. Pittsburgh, Pa, Sept. 4, 23. ENGLISH. B.A, Univ. Pittsburgh, 48, M.Litt, 50. Teacher, jr. high sch, Pa, 51-52; ASST. PROF. ENG, ALBRIGHT COL, 52- NCTE; Nat. Educ. Asn. English Renaissance literature; philosophical trends in literature; problems of written communication. Add: Dept. of English, Albright College, Reading, PA 19604.

BROWN, CALVIN SMITH, Comparative Literature. See Volume III, Foreign Languages, Linguistics & Philology.

BROWN, CAROLE ANN, b. New York, N.Y, May 26, 36; m. 56; c. 2. ENGLISH. B.A, Univ. Minn, 56, Tozer fel. & M.A, 61, Ph.D.(Eng), 65; Yale, 56-57. Teaching asst. ENG, Univ. Minn, 57-60, instr, 61-66; asst. prof. HAMLINE UNIV, 66-74, ASSOC. PROF, 74- MLA; NCTE; Conf. Col. Compos. & Commun. Eighteenth century English literature; English Renaissance literature. Add: Dept. of English, Hamline University, St. Paul, MN 55101.

BROWN, CHARLES THOMAS, b. Mar. 22, 12; m. 36; c. 2. SPEECH. B.B.A, Westminster Col.(Pa), 34; M.A, Univ. Wis, 40, Ph.D.(speech), 49. PROF. SPEECH, Fla. South. Col, 40-44; WEST. MICH. UNIV, 48-, DIR, CTR, COMMUN. RES, 58-, CHMN. DEPT. COMMUN. ARTS & SCI, 66- U.S.N.R, 44-46, Lt. Speech Commun. Asn. Psychology of speech; discussion; learning theory. Publ: Introduction to speech, Houghton, 55; co-auth, Speech and man, 66 & Monologue to dialogue: an exploration of interpersonal communication, 73, Prentice-Hall; co-auth, Communication in human relationships, Nat. Textbk, 73, An interpersonal ethic for communication, 3/68 & The physiological response to the communication modes: writing, speaking, listening and evaluating, 9/70, J. Commun; co-auth, Repeated self-viewings on closed circuit television as it affects changes in the self-concept and personality needs of student speakers, Speech Teacher, 71; plus others. Add: 1828 Hillsdale, Kalamazoo, MI 49007.

BROWN, CLARENCE ARTHUR, b. Janesville, Wis, Sept. 4, 11; m. 52; c. 4. ENGLISH, EDUCATION. B.A, Univ. Wis, 32, M.A, 38, Ph.D.(Eng), 41. Asst. prof. Eng, Univ. Mo, 44-45; Marquette Univ, 47-52, assoc. prof, 52-60, prof, 60-63; vis. prof, Univ. Minn, 63-64; PROF, Marquette Univ, 64-65; ENG. & EDUC, Wis. State Univ, Eau Claire, 65-68; MARQUETTE UNIV, 68- MLA; NCTE; Conf. Eng. Educ; Am. Stud. Asn. Literary criticism; rhetoric; teaching of English. Publ: Achievement of American criticism, 57 & co-auth, The strategy of composition, 68, Ronald; co-auth, American literature: a college survey, McGraw, 61; auth, Whitman and Lincoln, Lincoln Herald, 59; Whitman and the new critics, Am. Lit, 62; Huckleberry Finn: a study in structure, Mark Twain Quart, 63. Add: Dept. of English, Marquette University, Milwaukee, WI 53233.

BROWN, DANIEL RUSSELL, b. Litchfield, Ill. AMERICAN LITERATURE. Ph.B, Univ. Detroit; M.A, Kent State Univ; Ph.D.(Am. lit), Wayne State Univ, 69. Instr. ENG, Univ. Detroit, Wayne State Univ; LECTR, UNIV. MD. FAR EAST DIV, 72- MLA. Writing fiction; poetry; creative writing. Publ: Something you do in the dark, Putnam, 71, Lancer, 72, Edition Spéciale (French), 72 & Dutch ed, 72; Swift's scatology, Books & Bookmen, 71; Swift and the limitations of satire, Dublin Mag, 73; The war within Nathanael West, Mod. Fiction Stud, 74. Add: Far East Div, University of Maryland, APO San Francisco 96525.

BROWN, DENNIS EDWARD, b. Marshalltown, Iowa, Feb. 4, 33; m. 63; c. 2. JOURNALISM, MASS COMMUNICATION. A.B, Harvard, 55; Rockefeller Brothers Theol. fel, Union Theol. Sem, 55-56; M.A, Univ. Iowa, 61; U.S. Steel Found. fel, Univ. Mo, 67-68, Ph.D.(jour), 70. Reporter, Des Moines Register & Tribune, 59-60; periodicals ed. & ed. assoc, Off. Pub. Inform, Univ. Iowa, 60-65; assoc. dir, Off. Pub. Inform, Univ. Mo, 66-67; asst. prof, JOURN, SAN JOSE STATE UNIV, 68-71, assoc. prof, 71-72, PROF, 73-, CHMN. DEPT, 70- Asst. dir, Freedom of Inform. Ctr, 67-68. U.S.A, 57-58, 2nd Lt. Asn. Educ. in Jour; Am. Soc. Jour. Sch. Adminr; Am. Asn. Schs. & Dept. Jour. International communications; press law; mass communication and society. Publ: Co-auth, Regulatory pluralism in the press?, 10/67 & auth, S.1312: the failing newspaper bill, 2/68, Freedom Inform. Ctr. Report; Trust in international relations: a mass media perspective, Jour. Quart, winter 69. Add: Dept. of Journalism & Advertising, San Jose State University, San Jose, CA 95192.

BROWN, DOROTHY S, b. Montgomery, Ala, Mar. 1, 14; div; c. 2. ENGLISH. A.B, Univ. Hawaii, Manoa, 34; M.A, Stanford Univ, 36; Ph.D, Univ. Wash, 56. Instr. ENG, Univ. Hawaii, Manoa, 47-56, asst. prof, 56-69; ASSOC. PROF, BEREA COL, 69- NCTE; Teachers Eng. Speakers Other Lang; Conf. Col. Compos. & Commun; Am. Dialect Soc. Negro literature; linguistics. Publ: Some of my best friends, Dramatic Publ, 68; The English lexicon, Philippine J. Lang. Teaching, 5/69; Thesis and theme in Uncle Tom's cabin, Eng. J, 12/69. Add: Dept. of English, Berea College, Berea, KY 40403.

BROWN, DOUGLAS MITCHELL, b. Woodland, Calif, June 2, 37; m. 57; c. 4. HUMANITIES. B.S, Univ. Idaho, 62; M.A, Univ. Maine, Orono, 66; Seigfred Award, NDEA fel. & Ph.D.(comp. arts), Ohio Univ, 71. Teacher Eng, High Sch, Flathead County Schs, Mont, 62-64; Bishop Lehr Sch, Colo. & Univ. North. Colo, 66-68; ASST. PROF. HUMANITIES, CHADRON STATE COL, 71- Consult, Total Educ. in Total Environment, 73- U.S.N, 55-58, Res, 58-62. Nat. Asn. Humanities Educ. Add: Div. of Humanities, Chadron State College, Chadron, NE 69337.

BROWN, E. ALLAN, b. Charleston, S.C, Sept, 17, 19. LITERATURE. A.B, Univ. N.C, 41, M.A, 47, Ph.D, 52. PROF. ENG, VA. COMMONWEALTH UNIV, 51-, chmn. dept, 51-70. U.S.A, 41-46, Maj. Renaissance Soc. Am; Shakespeare Asn. Am; MLA; Col. Eng. Asn; NCTE. English Renaissance literature. Add: Dept. of English, Virginia Commonwealth University, Richmond, VA 23220.

BROWN, EMERSON, JR, b. Champaign, Ill, July 25, 34; m. 56; c. 2. ENGLISH LITERATURE. A.B, Hamilton Col, 56; A.M, Syracuse Univ, 58; Ph.D.(Eng), Cornell Univ, 67. Instr. ENG, Inter-Am. Univ. P.R, 58-61; asst. prof, Univ. P.R, Rio Piedras, 61-68, assoc. prof, 68-69; ASST. PROF, STANFORD UNIV, 69- Vis. asst. prof, Cornell Univ, summer 68, vis. prof, summer 71; Carnegie-Mellon fel, 74. MLA; Mediaeval Acad. Am; Dante Soc. Am; Am. Name Soc; Medieval Asn. Pac.(mem. adv. bd, 73-75). Medieval English literature, with special attention to Chaucer; medieval French and Italian literature. Publ: Allusion in Chaucer's Merchant's tale, Cornell Univ, 67; Proserpina, Matelda, and the Pilgrim, Dante Stud, 71; The Merchant's tale: Januarie's Unlikly Elde, Neuphilol. Mitt, 73; Biblical women in the Merchant's tale: feminism, anti-feminism, and beyond, Viator, 74; plus others. Add: Dept. of English, Stanford University, Stanford, CA 94305.

BROWN, ERIC DONALD, b. Palmyra, Pa, May 13, 44; m. 69; c. 1. ENGLISH & AMERICAN LITERATURE. A.B, Lebanon Valley Col, 66; M.A, Pa. State Univ, 68, Ph.D.(Eng. & art hist), 72. Instr. humanities, Univ. S.Fla, 68-69; career educ. & eng, Pa. State Univ, 71-72; ASST. PROF. ENG, NORTHEAST LA. UNIV, 72- MLA. Jung and literature; Chaucer; bibliography. Add: Dept. of English, Northeast Louisiana University, Monroe, LA 71201.

BROWN, GEORGE HARDIN, b. Denver, Colo, Feb. 14, 31; m. 71. MEDIEVAL ENGLISH, PHILOLOGY. B.A, St. Louis Univ, 55, Ph.L, 56, M.A, 59; B.D, Innsbruck Univ, 63; Dexter fel, Harvard, 68, Ph.D.(Eng), 71. Instr. Greek, Latin & Eng, Regis High Sch, 56-58; ASST. PROF. ENG, St. Louis Univ, 69-71; STANFORD UNIV, 71- MLA; Midwest Mod. Lang. Asn.(chmn. Medieval stud. sect, 70-71); Mediaeval Acad. Am; Medieval Asn. Pac; Am. Philol. Asn; Philol. Asn. Pac. Coast. Old and Middle English; patristics; palaeography. Publ: Codex Vaticanus Latinus 13025: Cassian's institutes, Manuscripta, 73; Yvain's sin of neglect, Symposium, 73; The ascent-descent motif in Christ II of Cynewulf, J. Eng. & Ger. Philol, 74; plus others. Add: Dept. of English, Stanford University, Stanford, CA 94305.

BROWN, HAROLD CLIFFORD, JR. b. Cape Girardeau, Mo, Jan. 15, 44. EIGHTEENTH CENTURY ENGLISH LITERATURE. B.A, Duke Univ, 65; M.A, Univ. Va, 67, Ph.D.(Eng), 70. Instr. ENG, Washington & Lee Univ, 69-70; ASST. PROF, Murray State Univ, 70-71; UNIV. AKRON, 71- MLA; Am. Soc. Aesthetics. Later eighteenth century British literature; later nineteenth century comparative European literature. Publ: Etherege and comic shallowness, Tex. Stud. Lit. & Lang, 75. Add: Dept. of English, University of Akron, Buchtel Ave, Akron, OH 44325.

BROWN, HARRY MATTHEW, b. Newark, Ohio, Jan. 24, 21; m. 51; c. 4. ENGLISH. Th.B, Cleveland Bible Col, 45; A.B, Baldwin-Wallace Col, 46; M.A, West. Reserve Univ, 48, Ph.D.(Eng), 55. Instr. ENG, Baldwin-Wallace Col, 46-50; teaching fel, West. Reserve Univ, 50-53; asst. prof, Shepherd Col, 53-56; La. Polytech. Inst, 56-58, assoc. prof, 58-63; intermediate instr, Calif. State Polytech. Col, 63-66; PROF, MIDWESTERN UNIV, 66-, DEAN HUMANITIES & SOC. SCI, 68- MLA; Nat. Educ. Asn; NCTE. American literature; poetry; literature and religion. Publ: Sea-rock and coral; co-auth, A workbook for writers, Am. Bk. Co, 60 & Van Nostrand, 70, Readings for writers, Ronald, 62, Patterns in poetry, 68 & What the poem means, 70, Scott; auth, The contemporary college writer, Van Nostrand, 71. Add: Dept. of English, Midwestern University, Wichita Falls, TX 76308.

BROWN, HELEN E, b. Auburn, Mich, Dec. 14, 02; m. 25. SPEECH, DRAMA. B.A, Univ. Mich, 41, M.A, 47; Mich. State Univ. Coach speech & drama, Cent. High Sch, 26-50; producer-dir, FM radio, Bd. Educ, Flint, 50-53, dir-coord. radio theatre, Mott Prog, 53-54, coord-consult. speech & drama, 54-70; RETIRED. Summer, teacher directing interpretation, Mich. State Univ, 52; lectr, Province Ont. Counc. Arts, 68. Am. Nat. Theatre Asn; Nat. Educ. Asn; Am. Educ. Theatre Asn; Children's Theatre Conf; Am. Theatre Asn; Children's Theatre Asn; Am. Community Theatre Asn; Am. Asn. Univ. Women. Creative dramatics and puppetry as a therapeutic activity; children's theatre; outline for speech art teachers. Publ: Drama curriculum in the secondary schools, Speech Teacher; co-auth, The curtain rises, Mich. Educ. J, 53; auth, Puppetry in Flint, Michigan, Puppetry J, 6/68. Add: 2012 Stoney Brook Ct, Flint, MI 48507.

BROWN, HERBERT ROSS, b. Allentown, Pa, Feb. 9, 02. AMERICAN LITERATURE. B.S, Lafayette Col, 24, D.Litt, 49; A.M, Harvard, 28; Ph.D, Columbia Univ, 39; hon. L.H.D, Bucknell Univ, 50; hon. Litt.D, Bowdoin Col, 63; hon. LL.D, Univ. Maine, 65. Instr. ENG, Lafayette Col, 24-25; BOWDOIN COL, 25-29, asst. prof, 29-33, assoc. prof, 33-39, PROF, 39- Vis. prof, Duke Univ, summer 39; Columbia Univ, summers 40, 41, 45; managing ed, New Eng. Quart, 45-; vis. prof, Univ. Minn, summers 47, 63; chmn, Am. Lit. Group, MLA, 61; vis. prof, Univ. Maine, summer 65; Harvard, summer 68; trustee, Univ. State Maine, 68-72, Samuel Harris lectr. lit, Bangor Theol. Sem, 73. Duke Univ. Centennial Award, 39. MLA; cor. mem. Colonial Soc. Mass. American fiction; Shakespeare. Publ: American fiction; the sentimental novel in America, 1789-1860, Duke Univ; The heritage of American literature, Ginn; Sills & Bowdoin, Columbia Univ, 64; contrib, Essays mostly on periodical publishing in America, Duke Univ, 73. Add: Dept. of English, Hubbard Hall, Bowdoin College, Brunswick, ME 04011.

BROWN, IRBY BLAND, b. Richmond, Va, Apr. 30, 32; m. 56; c. 2. ENGLISH LITERATURE. B.A, Univ. Richmond, 54; M.A, Univ. Va, 57, Ph.D.(Eng), 67. Instr. ENG, UNIV. RICHMOND, 59-65, 66-67, asst. prof, 67-68, assoc. prof, 68-73, PROF, 73- MLA; S.Atlantic Mod. Lang. Asn; NCTE. Modern drama; film; 19th century novel. Add: Dept. of English, Box 314, University of Richmond, Richmond, VA 23173.

BROWN, IRVING M, b. Cambridge, Mass, Apr. 15, 22; m. 46; c. 2. THEATRE & FINE ARTS. A.B, Antioch Col, 48; M.A, Univ. Iowa, 50; Ph.D. (theatre & fine arts), Ohio State Univ, 61. Asst, Univ. Iowa, 49; tech. dir, univ. theatre, Univ. Conn, 50-51, acting dir, 51-52; assoc. dir, theatre arts prog, Lake Erie Col, 54-55, dir, 55-66; theatre & dance educ. specialist, arts & humanities prog, U.S. Off. Educ, 66-68, prof. fine arts & dir. fine arts prog, Univ. Md, Baltimore County, 68-70; dir. arts prog, Antioch Col, Washington-Baltimore Campus, 70-73; DEAN FINE & PERFORMING ARTS, STATE UNIV. N.Y. COL. NEW PALTZ, 73- Asst. univ. theatre & speech, Ohio State Univ, 52, 53, 54; Fulbright lectr-consult. theatre arts, U.S. Educ. Found, Cyprus, 62-63; consult. arts & humanities prog, U.S. Off. Educ, 66; co-auth, Carlo Goldoni's The Servant of Two Masters, transl. produced McCarter Theatre, Princeton, 67; mem. dance & theatre panels, Md. Arts Counc, 70-72; pres, Greater Baltimore Arts Counc, 71-72; mem. bd. dirs, Md. Dance Theatre, 72-73; consult. arts, Wash. Univ, 73. Citation Outstanding Serv, Nat. Asn. Mental Health, 60; distinguished serv. award, North. Ohio Counc. Little Theatres, 60. U.S.N.R, 43-46, Lt.(jg). Am. Theatre Asn; Comt. Res. Dance; Int. Counc. Fine Arts Deans; Nat. Theatre Conf; Am. Dance Guild; AAUP. Arts in higher education. Publ: Co-auth, Help wanted, Family Plays Ser, Am. Theatre Wing, 62; auth, The effervescent Egyptian theatre, Theatre Annual, 64. Add: Office of Dean Fine & Performing Arts, State University of New York College at New Paltz, New Paltz, NY 12561.

BROWN, JACK A. ENGLISH, LINGUISTICS. B.A, Univ. Miami, 56, M.A, 58; Ph.D.(Eng), Univ. Fla, 62. Teacher, Normandy Prep. Sch, 58-59; from assoc. prof. to PROF. ENG. & CHMN. DIV. LANG, COLUMBUS COL, 62- U.S.A.F, 42-45, S/Sgt. MLA. Historic linguistics; Beowulf text and scribal influence; Medieval English lyrics. Add: Division of Language, Columbus College, Columbus, GA 31907.

BROWN, JACK RICHARD, b. St. Louis, Mo, Mar, 6, 11. ENGLISH & AMERICAN LITERATURE. A.B, Ohio Wesleyan Univ, 32; A.M, Northwest. Univ, 33, Ph.D, 37. From instr. to assoc. prof. ENG, Roanoke Col, 35-46; assoc. prof, Baldwin-Wallace Col, 46-48; PROF, MARSHALL UNIV, 48-, CHMN. DEPT, 67- Benedum Found. res. grant, summer 63; mem, Nat. Comt. Shakespeare Birthplace Trust, 68. Writer, U.S. War Dept, Camp Lee, Va, 43-46. MLA; NCTE. Eightennth century English literature; contemporary English and American literature; Shakespeare. Add: Dept. of English, Marshall University, Huntington, WV 25701.

BROWN, JAMES ANTHONY, S.J, b. Cleveland, Ohio, May 10, 32. RADIO & TELEVISION COMMUNICATIONS. A.B, Loyola Univ.(Ill), 55, Ph.L, 57, M.A, 59, St.L, 67; fel, Univ. Detroit, 57-58; KNXT/CBS-TV scholar, Univ. South. Calif, 59, Ph.D.(telecommun), 70. Asst. prof. radio-TV & chmn. dept, Univ. Detroit, 67-70; resident consult. broadcast prog. practices, CBS-TV, 71; ASST. PROF. TELECOMMUN. & CHMN. DEPT, UNIV. SOUTH. CALIF, 71- Consult, N.Am. Comn. Mass. Media, Soc. Jesus, 61-68; dir, U.S. Off. Educ. Educ. Media Inst, Univ. Detroit, summers 67 & 68; chmn. minority educ. subcomt, Commun. Dept, U.S. Cath. Conf, 69-73. Broadcast Educ. Asn. (chmn. minority training comt, 69-73); Nat. Asn. Educ. Broadcasters; UNDA-USA. Roman Catholic Church policies regarding commercial broadcasting in the United States, 1920-1972; commercial radio-television station and network broadcasting vis-a-vis public interest and the Federal Communications Commission; training collegians—including emphasis on minorities—for responsible professional broadcasting. Publ: Are better programs shown only during non-prime time?, Nat. Asn. Educ. Broadcasters J, 7-8/61; Mass media of communications: church philosophy, radio and television, 67 & Catholic schools of communication arts, 67, In: New Catholic encyclopedia, McGraw. Add: Dept. of Telecommunications, University of Southern California, University Park, Los Angeles, CA 90007.

BROWN, JAMES ISAAC, b. Tarkio, Mo, Dec. 15, 08; m; c. 2. RHETORIC. A.B, Tarkio Col, 30; A.M, Univ. Chicago, 33; State Univ, Iowa, 43-44; Ph.D, Univ. Colo, 49. Instr. Eng, Monmouth Col, 33-34; RHETORIC, UNIV. MINN, ST. PAUL, 34-46, asst. prof, 46-49, assoc. prof, 49-54, PROF, 54- Mem. automation comt, Int. Reading Asn, 68-69. Hall of Fame Award, Tarkio Col, 65. NCTE; Nat. Soc. Stud. Commun.(exec. secy, 51, 1st v.pres, 63, pres, 64); Int. Reading Asn. Reading; listening; vocabulary. Publ: Efficient reading, alternate ed, 56, rev. ed, 62, Explorations in college reading, 59, co-auth, Effective writing and reading, 62, auth, Guide to effective reading, 66, Efficient reading, rev. form A, 71 & co-auth, Better spelling, 71, Heath; co-auth, Listening comprehension test, Harcourt, 53; auth, Nelson-Denny reading test, rev. ed, 58 & Forms C and D of the Nelson-Denny reading test, 73, Houghton; co-auth, Building a better vocabulary, Ronald, 59; auth, Programed vocabulary, Appleton, 64, Lyons & Carnahan, 65 & New Century, 71; Visual-linguistic reading series, Minn. Mining, 66; The Look 20-day course in quick reading, Look Mag, 70; You can read faster, Readers Digest, 70. Add: Dept. of Rhetoric, University of Minnesota, St. Paul, MN 55101.

BROWN, JAMES MONTGOMERY, b. Dallas, Tex, May 21; m. 42; c. 4. ENGLISH. B.A, Rice Univ, 42; M.S, Calif. Inst. Technol, 43; M.A, State Univ. Iowa, 48, Ph.D.(Eng), 51. Assoc. prof. Eng, East. Mont. Col. Educ, 50-54; N.Tex. State Univ, 54-56, prof, 56-63; tech. publ. specialist, Gen. Dynamics, Ft. Worth, Tex, 63-65; prof. Eng. & lit, South. Ill. Univ, Edwardsville, 65-69, asst. to v.pres, acad. affairs, 66-68, asst. to chancellor, 68-69, exec. dean acad. affairs, 69; spec. asst. to pres, South. Ill. Univ, Carbondale, 69-70; CHIEF OF BD. STAFF, BD. TRUSTEES, SOUTH. ILL. UNIV. SYST, 70- U.S.A.A.F, 42-46, Capt. MLA; Midwest. Mod. Lang. Asn. Literary criticism; linguistics; fiction writing. Publ: Casebook for technical writers, 61 & Cases for business communications, 62, Wadsworth; Introductory technical writing, Britannica Schs, 62; Swift and moralist, Philol. Quart, 10/54; Eight types of puns, PMLA, 3/56; Head downhill to home, Va. Quart. Rev, summer 56. Add: Office of Board of Trustees, Southern Illinois University, Carbondale, IL 62901.

BROWN, JARED ALLEN, b. New York, N.Y, Dec. 3, 36; m. 58; c. 2. DRAMA, SPEECH. B.F.A, Ithaca Col, 60; M.A, San Francisco State Col, 62; Ph.D. (theatre), Univ. Minn, 67. Asst. prof. speech & dramatic art, WEST. ILL. UNIV, 65-72, ASSOC. PROF. THEATRE, 72-, coord. summer music theatre, 72, 74. Regional adminr. & judge, Ill. Sesquicentennial one-act play competition, 68. Speech Commun. Asn; Am. Theatre Asn. Theatre history; dramatic theory. Add: Dept. of Theatre, Western Illinois University, Macomb, IL 61455.

BROWN, JESSIE LEMON, b. Columbia, S.C, May 15, 11; m. ENGLISH. B.S, Hampton Inst, 34; M.A, Columbia Univ, 45, gen. educ. bd. fel, 45-46, Ed.D. (Eng), 55. Teacher high sch, Va, 35-44; instr. ENG, HAMPTON INST, 44-46, asst. prof, 46-53, assoc. prof, 53-55, prof, 55-70, OLD DOM. PROF. & DIR. FRESHMAN COMMUN. CTR, 70-; dir. spec. proj. upgrading & remediation, 65-70, dir. div. lang. & lit, 67-70. Dir. in-service teacher training inst, Virgin Islands, summer 55; consult. teaching Eng, Va. Sec. Schs, 58-63; dir. South. Educ. Found. Inst. for Elem. Sch. Teachers, summers 64 & 65. Lindback Distinguished Teaching Award, 63-64. Col. Eng. Asn; Asn. Higher Educ.(mem. planning comt, 68, conf, 67, mem. comt. undergrad. educ, 68-). Publ: Contrib, Communication in general education, W.C, Brown, 60; auth, Identifying academic achievement, Va. Teachers Asn. Bull, 12/61; The road less traveled by—a message to college students, Negro Hist. Bull, 3/64. Add: Dept. of English, Box 6007, Hampton Institute, Hampton, VA 23368.

BROWN, JOHN L, b. Ilion, N.Y, Apr. 29, 14; m. 41; c. 2. COMPARATIVE LITERATURE, FRENCH. B.A, Hamilton Col, 35; M.A, Cath. Univ. Am, 36; Ph.D.(French, Medieval Latin), 39; Ecole des chartes Paris & Univ. Paris, 37-38. Asst. prof. French, Cath. Univ. Am, 39-42; asst. chief publ. sect, Off. War Inform, 42-43; correspondent Sunday ed, N.Y. Times, Paris, 45-48; cult. attaché, U.S. Embassies, Paris, Brussels, Rome, Mexico City, 48-68; PROF. COMP. LIT, CATH. UNIV. AM, 68- Mem, Cath. Comn. on Intellectual & Cult. Affairs, 60-; fel, Ctr. Advan. Stud, Wesleyan Univ, 62-63; vis. prof. French & Eng, Univ. Louisville, 66-67; prof. Am. lit. & civilization, Inst. Anglo-Am. Stud, Nat. Univ. Mex, 66-68; lectr, Cath. Inst. Paris, 69; Univs. Laval, McGill, Montreal & Toronto, 70; Harvard, summer 73. MLA; Am. Stud. Asn; Am. Comp. Lit. Asn; Mediaeval Acad. Am; Dante Soc. European, especially Franco, American literary relations in the 19th and 20th centuries; Europe avant-garde movement of the 20th century; the problem of expatriation in American literature. Publ: The methodus of Jean Bodin: a critical study, Cath. Univ. Am, 39; Panorama de la littérature contemporaine aux Etats-Unis, 54 & Hemingway, 61, Gallimard, Paris, Il Gigantesco Teatro, Opera nuove, Rome, 63; Dialogos transatlanticos, Limusa Wiley, Mexico, 66; contrib. chap. on France, In: Public opinion and foreign policy, Harper, 49; plus numerous others. Add: 3024 Tilden St. N.W, Washington, DC 20008.

BROWN, JOYCE COMPTON, b. Statesville, N.C. June 8, 42; m. 62; c. 2. AMERICAN LITERATURE. B.S, Appalachian State Univ, 63, M.A, 65; Ph.D.(Am. lit), Univ. South. Miss, 71. Teacher Eng. & French, Queen Anne's County Schs, Md, 64-66; instr. ENG, GARDNER WEBB COL, 66-68, ASST. PROF, 70- MLA. American fiction of 1930's and 1920's. Add: Box 856, Boiling Springs, NC 28017.

BROWN, KENNETH LEE, b. Camp Hill, Pa, Apr. 8, 33; m. 58; c. 2. SPEECH, DRAMA. B.S, Syracuse Univ, 55; M.A, Northwest. Univ, 60, Ph.D.(speech educ), 65. Instr. speech educ, Northwest. Univ, 60-65, asst. prof. & chmn. dept, 65-67; asst. prof, Univ. Colo, Boulder, 68-71; ASSOC. PROF. SPEECH, UNIV. MASS, AMHERST, 71- Speech consult, Indust. Mgt. Inst, Lake Forest Col, Ill, 60-67; U.S. Naval Reserve Off. Training Corps, 62; Bank Pub. Relat. & Marketing Asn, Chicago, Ill, 63-67; dir, Nat. High Sch. Inst. Speech, Northwest. Univ, 65-67; speech educ. consult, Elem. Sch. Dist. 65, Evanston, Ill, 65-67; Bur. Speech Serv, Univ. Colo, 67-71. U.S.A.F, 55-58, 1st Lt. Speech Commun. Asn.(interest group off, 66-68; NCTE; East. Commun. Asn; Nat. Asn. Educ. Young Children. Speech education in the elementary school; reading and psychology; speech education in the secondary school. Publ: Speech education in the elementary school, Ill. J. Educ, 2/67; Speech in the language arts institute, Arts of Lang, 2/67; Speech and listening in language arts textbooks, Elem. Eng, 4-5/67. Add: Dept. of Speech, University of Massachusetts, Amherst, MA 01002.

BROWN, LeROY, b. Velpen, Ind, May 29, 08; m. 43; c. 2. SPEECH, EDUCATION. A.B, Greenville Col, 47; M.A, Univ. Ill, 49; Ed.D, Bradley Univ, 53. Asst. prof. SPEECH, Olivet Nazarene Col, 51-71, ASSOC. PROF, 71-72; POINT LOMA COL, 73- U.S.A, 42-45. Speech. Publ: Speaking to persuade, Naylor, 60; Christian go-givers, Review & Herald, 61; How to make a good speech, 65 & How to acquire a million-dollar personality, 68, Fell. Add: Dept. of Speech, Point Loma College, San Diego, CA 92106.

BROWN, LORRAINE ANNE, b. Grand Rapids, Mich, Apr. 3, 29; m. 51, 69; c. 1. ENGLISH, AMERICAN LITERATURE. B.A, Univ. Mich, 52, M.A, 61; Ph.D.(Am. lit), Univ. Md, 68. ASST. PROF. ENG, GEORGE MASON UNIV, 65- MLA; S.Atlantic Mod. Lang. Asn; Am. Stud. Asn; Am. Soc. 18th Century Stud; Women's Caucus Mod. Lang. Henrik Ibsen; Adrienne Kennedy; contemporary drama, American, English and continental. Add: Dept. of English, George Mason University, 4400 University Dr, Fairfax, VA 22030.

BROWN, LOUISE STEPHENS, b. Ft. Worth, Tex; m. 28; c. 1. ENGLISH. B.A, Columbia Col, 52; M.A, Univ. S.C, 54; Ph.D.(Eng), Duke Univ, 66. Asst. prof. Eng, Columbia Col, 55-61; assoc. prof, Erskine Col, 66-68, PROF, 68-72; PROF. ENG. & CHMN. INTEGRATED STUD, SACRED HEART COL, 72- Eng. Inst; MLA; Col. Eng. Asn; NCTE; Southeast. Renaissance Conf. Eighteenth century English literature; renaissance drama. Add: Dept. of Integrated Studies, Sacred Heart College, Belmont, NC 82012.

BROWN, M. ROSE ELLEN, O.P, English. See BROWN, ANNE MARIE.

BROWN, MARION MARSH, b. Brownville, Nebr, July 22, 08; m. 37; c. 1. ENGLISH. A.B, Nebr. State Teachers Col, Peru, 27; M.A, Univ. Nebr, 31; Univ. Minn. Teacher Eng, High Sch, Auburn, Nebr, 27-29; Nebr. Sch. Agr, Curtis, Nebr, 29-31; high sch, Wayne, Nebr, 31-32; Franklin, 32-33; instr. Eng. & jour, Nebr. State Teachers Col, Peru, 33-37; eng, Univ. Nebr, Omaha, 45-51, asst. prof, 52-58, assoc. prof, 59-66, prof, 66-68; RETIRED. Semantics and linguistics; great Americans who make inspirational biographies for young people. Publ: Young Nathan, 49, Stuart's Landing, 68 & Marnie, 71, Westminster; Words in context, 61 & rev. ed, 73, Chandler; co-auth, The silent storm, Abingdon, 63 & Willa Cather: the woman and her works, Scribner, 69; auth, The pauper prince, Crescent, 73. Add: 2615 N. 52nd St, Omaha, NE 68105.

BROWN, MAURICE F, JR, b. Geneva, Ill, Feb. 1, 28; m. 57; c. 2. AMERICAN LITERATURE. B.A, Lawrence Col, 49; M.A, Harvard, 50, Ph.D, 58. Instr. ENG, Lawrence Col, 53-55; tutor, Harvard, 55-58; from instr. to asst. prof, Colby Col, 58-61; OAKLAND UNIV, 61-64, assoc. prof, 64-69, PROF, 69- U.S.M.C, 51-53. MLA; Am. Stud. Asn; Emerson Soc. Twentieth century American poetry; the Transcendentalists; literary and rhetorical theory. Publ: Estranging dawn: the life and works of William Vaughn Moody, South. Ill. Univ, 73; Santayana's necessary angel, New Eng. Quart, 12/63; Santayana on Emerson, Emerson Soc. Quart, fourth quart, 64; Mark Twain as Proteus, Papers Mich. Acad, 66. Add: Dept. of English, Oakland University, Rochester, MI 48063.

BROWN, MERLE ELLIOTT, b. Benton Harbor, Mich, Mar. 10, 25; m. 51; c. 4. ENGLISH. A.B, Univ. Mich, 48, M.A, 51, Rackham fels, 52-54, Ph.D, 54. Teaching fel. freshman compos, Univ. Mich, 50-52; instr. ENG, Denison Univ, 54-56, asst. prof, 57-59, assoc. prof, 60-64, PROF, 64-67; UNIV. IOWA, 67- Am. Philos. Soc. grant, 61 & 70; Fulbright res. fel, Italy, 65-66; ed, Iowa Rev, 70-; asst. ed, Jour. Aesthetics & Art Criticism, 70-73; Guggenheim fel, 73-74. MLA; Am. Soc. Aesthet; Midwest Mod. Lang. Asn. Literary criticism; modern English poetry; modern American poetry. Publ: Neo-idealistics aesthetics, 66 & Wallace Stevens: the poem as act, 70, Wayne State Univ; Kenneth Burke, Univ. Minn, 69; A reading of the Inferno X, Italica, autumn 71; A critical performance of Thom Gunn's Misanthropos, Iowa Rev, winter 73; The idea of fiction as fiction or fictitious, Stand, autumn 73. Add: 820 Kirkwood Ave, Iowa City, IA 52240.

BROWN, NANCY POLLARD, b. Newton Abbot, Eng, Mar. 16, 21; m. 52. ENGLISH. B.A, Univ. London, 42, Westfield col. & univ. fels, 46-48, Brit. Fed. Univ. Women jr. fel, 47-48, M.A, 48. Instr. ENG, TRINITY COL.(D.C), 59-60, asst. prof, 60-62, assoc. prof, 62-66, PROF, 66-, CHMN. DEPT, 68- Commonwealth Fund fel, Yale, 50-51; Folger Shakespeare Libr. fels, summer 54, summer-fall 55; E. Harris Harbison Award, Danforth Found, 66; res. grant, Huntington Libr. & Art Gallery, 71; Am. Counc. Learned Soc. grant-in-aid, 71-72. Brit. Army, 42-46, Capt. MLA; Renaissance Soc. Am; Shakespeare Asn. Am. Publ: Co-auth, The poems of Robert Southwell, S.J, Clarendon, 67; ed, Robert Southwell: two letters and Short rules of a good life, vol, In: Folger documents on Tudor and Stuart civilization, Univ. Va, 73; auth, On the imagery of Donne's Love's growth, 7/53 & The structure of Robert Southwell's Saint Peter's complaint, 1/66, Mod. Lang. Rev. Add: Dept. of English, Trinity College, Washington, DC 20017.

BROWN, NATHANIEL HAPGOOD, b. New York, N.Y, Apr. 23, 29; m. 59; c. 3. ENGLISH LITERATURE. A.B, Princeton, 51; M.A, Syracuse, 54; Ph.D. (Eng), Columbia Univ, 62. Instr. ENG, MARY WASHINGTON COL, UNIV. VA, 61-63, asst. prof, 63-65, assoc. prof, 65-72, PROF, 72- U.S.A, 51-53. English Romantic period. Add: Dept. of English, Mary Washington College of University of Virginia, Fredericksburg, VA 22401.

BROWN, PEARL LeBLANC, b. Youngsville, La, June 28, 36; m. 60; c. 1. ENGLISH. B.A, Univ. Southwest. La, 57; M.A, Univ. Ark, 58, Ph.D.(Eng), 65. Instr. ENG, Univ. Southwest. La, 58-60; asst. prof, St. Mary's Col. (Minn), 63-66; QUINNIPIAC COL, 66-72, ASSOC. PROF, 72- Romantic poetry, especially Keats. Add: Dept. of English, Quinnipiac College, Hamden, CT 06518.

BROWN, RICHARD E, b. Kansas City, Mo, Feb. 11, 46. ENGLISH LITERATURE. A.B, Stanford Univ, 68; M.A, Cornell Univ, 71, Ph.D.(Eng), 72. ASST. PROF. ENG, UNIV. NEV, RENO, 72- English romanticism; Shelley; 18th century. Add: Dept. of English, University of Nevada, Reno, NV 89507.

BROWN, ROBERT D, b. Whiting, Ind, July 1, 24; m. 52; c. 1. ENGLISH. A.B, Ind. Univ, 49, Jonathan H. Edwards fel. & M.A, 50, Ph.D.(comp. lit), 52. Instr. English, Ore. State Univ, 52-55, asst. prof, 55-59, assoc. prof, 59-65; prof. & chmn. dept, WEST. WASH. STATE COL, 65-67, assoc. acad. dean, 67-68, ACAD. DEAN, 68- Curriculum guide writer, Portland Curriculum Study, 60-61; lectr. & sch. visitor, grader, Advan. Placement Counc, 60-63; inst. rep, Am. Counc. Teacher Educ, 68. U.S.A, 43-48, Sgt. MLA; Am. Comp. Lit. Asn. Anglo-French literary relations of the 19th century; modern poetry; high school English curriculum. Publ: Co-auth, Exposition and persuasion, Appleton, 55 & Writing better themes, Scott, 71; The Bodley Head Press, Papers Bibliog. Soc. Am, first quarter 67. Add: Western Washington State College, Bellingham, WA 98225.

BROWN, ROBERT EDWARD, b. New York, N.Y, Jan. 11, 45; m. 70. MODERN LITERATURE, LITERARY CRITICISM. B.S, Univ. Pa, 66; Ph.D.(Eng. & Am. lit), Univ. Rochester, 70. Instr. Eng, Univ. Rochester, 68-69; ASST. PROF. ENG. & AM. STUD, CALIF. STATE UNIV, LOS ANGELES, 70- MLA. Modern literature; American literature; literary criticism. Publ: Walking and the imagination, Mod. Poetry Stud, 9/73; The structure and function of myth in Gary Snyder's poetry, Sewanee Rev, 74. Add: 1409 Saltair Ave, Los Angeles, CA 90025.

BROWN, RONALD MARTIN, b. Wichita, Kans, Sept. 4, 20; m. 45; c. 2. SPEECH, DRAMA. B.A, Southwest. Col.(Kans), 42; M.A, Univ. Denver, 49; M.A, Bristol Univ, 60. Dean, U.S. Army Inform. & Educ. Sch, Eng, 45; teacher speech & drama & head dept, high sch, Kans, 46-47; ASSOC. PROF. SPEECH & DRAMA, ALFRED UNIV, 49-, DIR, THEATRE, DEPT. PERFORMING ARTS, 72-, tech. dir. theatre, Univ, 49-69, chmn, Dept. Speech & Dramatic Art, 69-72. Consult. speech disorders, N.Y, 49-; Alfred Univ. Res. Found. grant, 62. U.S.A.A.F, 42-46, 1st Lt; Air Medal & Oak Leaf; Distinguished Flying Cross. Speech Commun. Asn; Am. Theatre Asn; Speech Asn. East. States. Linguistics; speech correction. Add: 30 Sayles St, Alfred, NY 14802.

BROWN, RUTH CHRISTIANI, b. Sidney, Mont, Nov. 18, 17; m. 38; c. 3. ENGLISH LITERATURE. B.A, Univ. Mont, 39; M.A, Univ. Tex, El Paso, 62; Ph.D.(Eng), Ariz. State Univ, 71. Lectr. ENG, Ariz. State Univ, 62-65; ASST. PROF, CALIF. STATE UNIV, SAN DIEGO, 66- AAUP; MLA; NCTE. Nineteenth century British novel; modern British novel. Publ: The role of Densher in The wings of the dove, Moderna Sprak, 71; A precursory vision, Poland, 12/72; Nostromo: women opposing the world, the flesh, and the devil, In: Proc. Int. Conrad Conf, H. Mursia, Milan, 74. Add: Dept. of English, San Diego State University, San Diego, CA 92115.

BROWN, SAMUEL ERNEST, b. Chicago, Ill, Oct. 10, 13; m. 52. ENGLISH. A.B, Ind. Univ, 34, M.A, 46; Jr. Sterling fel, Yale, 48-49, Ph.D.(Eng), 55; Fulbright fel, Oxford, 51-52. Lectr. ENG, Ind. Univ, Bloomington, 52-54, South Bend, 54-55; Europ. div, UNIV. MD, COLLEGE PARK, 55-57, from instr. to ASSOC. PROF, 57- U.S.N, 42-46, Res, 46-55, Lt. Mod. Humanities Res. Asn; MLA; Ruskin Asn. Victorian literature; autobiography as a literary type. Publ: The unpublished passages in the manuscript of Ruskin's autobiography, Victorian Newslett, fall 59. Add: Dept. of English, University of Maryland, College Park, MD 20742.

BROWN, STEPHEN JEFFRY, b. Moline, Ill, Mar. 30, 29; m. 69. ENGLISH LITERATURE. B.A, Yale, 50, Ph.D.(Eng), 59; Clare Col. & Paul Mellon fels. & B.A, Cambridge, 52. Instr. ENG, Yale, 57-60; asst. prof, Swarthmore Col, 60-64; assoc. prof, George Washington Univ, 64-68; PROF, GEORGE MASON UNIV, 68-, assoc. dean, 68-70. Summer res. grant, Folger Shakespeare Libr, 73. U.S.A, 54-56. MLA; Shakespeare Asn. Am.

English Renaissance drama and poetry; history, sociology and literature. Publ: Shakespeare's King and beggar, Yale Rev, (in press). Add: Dept. of English, George Mason University, 4400 University Dr, Fairfax, VA 22030.

BROWN, THERESSA WILSON, b. Sewickley, Pa, Jan. 29, 04; m. 39. ENGLISH. A.B, Oberlin Col, 24; A.M, Univ. Pittsburgh, 29, fel, 32-33, Ph.D, 43. Instr. Eng, Va. State Col, 25-27, assoc. prof, 30-32, 33-34; Livingstone Col, 29-30; instr, Miner Teachers Col, 34-46, assoc. prof, 46-50, prof, 50-55; PROF. ENG. & CHMN. DIV, D.C. TEACHERS COL, 55- Vis. prof. Eng, Howard Univ, 69- & Washington Tech. Inst, D.C, 73- NCTE; MLA; Col. Eng. Asn; Conf. Col. Compos. & Commun; Col. Lang. Asn. Biography as a literary type; Victorian biography; literary criticism. Publ: Froude and Carlyle, Univ. Pittsburgh. Add: 1511 Michigan Ave. N.E, Washington, DC 20017.

BROWN, THOMAS DOWNING, b. Downingtown, Pa, Mar. 28, 14. ENGLISH. A.B, Haverford Col, 36; B.S.L.S, Drexel Inst. Technol, 39; A.M, Univ. Pa, 44. Librn, Pennington Sch, 39-40; asst. in reading room & cataloging, Hist. Soc. Pa, 41-42; asst. instr. Eng, Univ. Pa, 42-43; instr, Drexel Inst. Technol, 43-44; asst. ref. librn. & asst. instr. Eng, Temple Univ, 44-46; instr. ENG, DREXEL UNIV, 46-49, from asst. prof. to ASSOC. PROF, 49-, ACAD. COUNR, EVE. COL, 57- Asst. in libr. technol, eve. div, Community Col, Temple Univ, 50-57. Add: Dept. of Literature & Language, Drexel University, Philadelphia, PA 19104.

BROWN, WILLIAM H, JR, b. Corsicana, Tex, Aug. 3, 36. ENGLISH, LINGUISTICS. B.A, Univ. Mich, 58, M.A, 59, M.A, 61, Ph.D.(ling), 63. Asst. prof. ENG, UNIV. SOUTH. CALIF, 65-71, ASSOC. PROF, 71- Stipendiat des Deutchen Akademischen Austauschdienstes, Univ. Heidelberg, 63-65. MLA; Ling. Soc. Am; Mediaeval Acad. Am. Medieval English language and literature; English linguistics. Publ: A syntax of King Alfred's Pastoral care, Mouton, The Hague, 69; Method and style in the Old English Pastoral care, J. Eng. & Ger. Philol, fall 69. Add: Dept. of English, University of Southern California, Los Angeles, CA 90007.

BROWN, WILLIAM J, b. Durham, N.C, Apr. 3, 29; m. 60; c. 2. RENAISSANCE & MEDIEVAL LITERATURE. A.B, Univ. N.C, Chapel Hill, 51, M.A, 59; Princeton, 57-59; Ph.D.(Eng), Duke Univ, 66. Assoc. prof. ENG, Shorter Col.(Ga), 59-60; instr, Univ. Colo, 62-66; asst. prof, SOUTH. ILL. UNIV, CARBONDALE, 66-73, ASSOC. PROF, 73- U.S.N, 52-57, U.S.N.R.R, Lt. MLA; Midwest Mod. Lang. Asn; S.Atlantic Mod. Lang. Asn; Renaissance Soc. Am; Shakespeare Asn. Am; Cent. Renaissance Asn. Shakespeare; Renaissance drama; Medieval studies. Publ: Chaucer's double apology for the Miller's tale, Univ. Colo. Stud. Lang. & Lit, 2/66; Herbert's The collar and Shakespeare's 1 Henry IV, Am. Notes & Queries, 12/67; Marlowe's debasement of Bajazet: Foxe's Actes and monuments and Tamburlaine, part I, Renaissance Quart, spring 71; plus one other. Add: Dept. of English, Southern Illinois University, Carbondale, IL 62901.

BROWN, WILLIAM RICHARD, b. Murfreesboro, Tenn, May 28, 34. ENGLISH. B.S, Mid. Tenn. State Col, 56; M.A, Univ. Ark, 60, Ph.D.(Eng), 65. From instr. to asst. prof. ENG, St. Mary's Col.(Minn), 63-66; asst. prof, QUINNIPIAC COL, 66-72, ASSOC. PROF, 72- MLA. American literature. Publ: Faulkner's paradox in pathology and salvation, Tex. Stud. Lit. & Lang, autumn 67. Add: Dept. of English, Quinnipiac College, Hamden, CT 06514.

BROWNE, DONALD R, b. Detroit, Mich, Mar. 13, 34; m. 58; c. 3. MASS COMMUNICATIONS. A.B, Univ. Mich, 55; M.A, 58, Ph.D.(speech, polit. sci), 61. Radio & TV off, U.S. Inform. Serv, 60-63; asst. prof. mass commun, Boston Univ, 63-65; speech, Purdue Univ, 65-66; assoc. prof. RADIO & TV, UNIV. MINN, MINNEAPOLIS, 66-70, PROF, 70- Off. Int. Prog. res. grant, Univ. Minn, 67-68, 70-, 72-73, grad. sch. res. grant, summer 67; McMillan Fund travel grant, 70- & 72-; Fulbright-Hays vis. prof, Am. Univ. Beirut, 73-74. Outstanding young teacher award, Cent. States Speech Asn, 68. U.S.A, 55-57. Broadcast Educ. Asn; Int. Commun. Asn.(chmn. mass commun. interest group, 68-70); Asn. Educ. in Jour. International broadcasting; comparative broadcasting systems; broadcasting and national development. Publ: The American image as presented abroad by United States television, summer 68 & The BBC and the pirates, spring 71, Jour. Quart; Citizen involvement in broadcasting, Pub. Telecommun. Rev, 10/73; plus others. Add: Dept. of Speech, 411 Folwell Hall, University of Minnesota, Minneapolis, MN 55455.

BROWNE, MICHAEL, b. Newark, N.J, July 19, 12; m. 57; c. 2. COMMUNICATION & THEATRE ARTS. B.A, Rutgers Univ, 35; M.S, Univ. Calif, Los Angeles, 51; M.A, Columbia Univ, 53, Ed.D.(commun. arts), 58. Consult, commun, Rudy Vallee Enterprises, 40-42; Ava Gardner, Tony Bennett & Eddie Fisher, 44-57; Mutual Benefit Life Ins, 54-60; vis. prof. Eng, speech & commun, Yeshiva Univ. Grad. Sch, 60-65; leader training group soc. psychol, Columbia Univ, 61-62; assoc. prof. COMMUN. ARTS, N.Y. INST. TECHNOL, 66-68, PROF, 68-, DEP. CHMN. DEPT, 66-; DRAMATIC ACTOR, BROADWAY & HOLLYWOOD, 37- Consult. child develop, Lou Costello Youth Found, 46-48; consult, Asn. Advan of Blind, 58-59; leader, League Parent Educ, 61-63; drama critic, Morning Tel, 65-66; mem, Stud. Relat. Comt, Nat. Acad. TV Arts & Sci, 68-69. Intel.C, U.S.A, 42-44, Sgt. The use of propaganda in the United States entertainment film; creative analysis for better oral and gestural self-expression; mental health and child guidance. Publ: Chap, In: Film counselor No. I, Film Counc. Am, 53. Add: 689 Columbus Ave, New York, NY 10025.

BROWNE, RAY B, b. Millport, Ala, Jan. 15, 22; m. 52; c. 3. ENGLISH. A.B, Univ. Ala, 43; M.A, Columbia Univ, 47; Ph.D, Univ. Calif, Los Angeles, 56. Instr. Eng, Univ. Nebr, 47-50; Univ. Md, 56-60; assoc. prof, Purdue Univ, 60-67; PROF. POPULAR CULT. & ENG, BOWLING GREEN STATE UNIV, 67- Exec. secy, Popular Cult. Hall of Fame; ed, J. Popular Cult. MLA; Popular Cult. Asn. (secy-treas); Am. Stud. Asn; Am. Folklore Soc. Publ: Popular culture and curricula, 70, Challenges in American culture, 70, Icons of popular culture, 71, Heroes of popular culture, 73 & Lincoln-lore: Lincoln in the popular mind, 73, Popular Press: Melville's drive to humanism, Purdue Univ, 71; The popular culture explosion, W.C. Brown, 72; Popular culture and the expanding consciousness, Wiley, 73; A popular culture reader, Univ. Ill, 74; plus nine others. Add: Dept. of English, Bowling Green State University, Bowling Green, OH 43402.

BROWNE, RICHARD JOSEPH, Germanic Linguistics, History of the English Language. See Volume III, Foreign Languages, Linguistics & Philology.

BROWNE, ROBERT MICHAEL, b. Bayonne, N.J, May 24, 23; m. 52; c. 3. ENGLISH. A.B, Seton Hall Univ, 43; M.A, Columbia Univ, 47; Fulbright scholar, Univ. Paris, 52-53; Ph.D.(Eng), Cath. Univ. Am, 56. Instr. ENG, Fordham Univ, 47-49; asst, Cath. Univ. Am, 49-52; instr, Univ. Notre Dame, 53-55, asst. prof, 55-61; assoc. prof, UNIV. MONTREAL, 61-62, PROF, 62-, chmn. dept, 61-69. U.S.A, 43-46. MLA; NCTE; Asn. Can. Univ. Teachers Eng. Literary criticism; rhetoric. Publ: Grammar and rhetoric in criticism, Tex. Stud. Lit. & Lang, 61; Rhetorical analysis and poetic structure, In: Rhetoric: theories for application, Nat. Counc. Teachers Eng, 67; The typology of literary signs, Col. Eng, 10/71; plus others. Add: Dept. of English, University of Montreal, Montreal 101, P.Q, Can.

BROWNE, THOMAS A, b. Milwaukee, Wis, Jan. 22, 31; m. 53; c. 2. ENGLISH. B.A, Univ. Minn, 52, M.A, 57, Ph.D, 60. Instr. ENG, East. Ill. Univ, 59-61; from asst. prof. to PROF, UNIV. WIS-EAU CLAIRE, 61- Sig.C, U.S.A, 52-54. MLA. Renaissance literature. Add: Dept. of English, University of Wisconsin-Eau Claire, Eau Claire, WI 54701.

BROWNELL, MORRIS RUGGLES, III, b. Boston, Mass, Nov. 19, 33; m. 62; c. 2. ENGLISH LITERATURE. A.B, Princeton, 55; M.A, Univ. Calif, Berkeley, 62, Ph.D.(Eng), 66. Instr. ENG, Tufts Univ, 65-66; ASST. PROF, CORNELL UNIV, 68- Fulbright res. fels, Univ. Col, Univ. London, 66-67 & Birkbeck Col, 67-68. U.S.A.R, 56-57, 1st Lt. Eighteenth century English literature and fine arts. Publ: Alexander Pope, virtuoso, Clarendon. Add: Dept. of English, Cornell University, Ithaca, NY 14850.

BROWNING, WILLIAM GORDON, b. Little Rock, Ark, Mar. 31, 38. ENGLISH. B.A, La. Polytech. Inst, 60; M.A, La. State Univ, 61, Ph.D.(Eng), 66. Instr. ENG. Okla. State Univ, 63-65, asst. prof, 65-66; assoc. prof, EAST. KY. UNIV, 66-70, PROF, 70- Twentieth century literature; linguistics. Publ: Co-auth, Fiction for composition, 68 & Drama for composition, 73, Scott. Add: Dept. of English, Eastern Kentucky University, Richmond, KY 40475.

BROWNLOW, PAUL C, b. Ft. Worth, Tex, Mar. 18, 44; m. 65; c. 2. COMMUNICATION. B.A, Abilene Christian Col, 66, M.A, 67; Ph.D.(commun), Purdue Univ, 70. ASST. PROF. COMMUN, ANGELO STATE UNIV, 70- Speech Commun. Asn; Am. Stud. Asn. Rhetorical criticism in American public address. Publ: Winston Churchill and fraternal association: the history of a phrase, Cent. States Speech J, 12/70; The pulpit and Black America: 1865-1877, Quart. J. Speech, 12/72; The Northern Protestant pulpit and Andrew Johnson, South. Speech Commun. J, 3/74. Add: Dept. of Speech Communication, Angelo State University, San Angelo, TX 76901.

BROWNSTEIN, OSCAR LEE, b. Huntington, W.Va, Nov. 13, 28; m. 57; c. 3. THEATRE HISTORY, PLAYWRITING. B.A, Univ. Mo, Columbia, 55, M.A, 56; M.F.A, Yale, 60; Ph.D.(theatre), Univ. Iowa, 63. Instr. compos, Univ. Iowa, 61-63; asst. prof. Eng, State Univ. N.Y. Binghamton, 63-66; THEATRE, UNIV. IOWA, 66-69, ASSOC. PROF, 69- Dir, Iowa Playwrights Workshop, 71-; mem. exec. comt, Am. Col. Theatre Festival Region VI, 72-; dir, Iowa H.S. Theatre Inst. Am. Soc. Theatre Res; Am. Theatre Asn; Am. Shakespeare Asn. Elizabethan inn-yard playhouses; play script analysis. Publ: Plato's Phaedrus: dialectic as the genuine art of speaking, Quart. J. Speech, 12/65; The popularity of baiting in England before 1600, Educ. Theatre J, 10/69; A record of London inn-playhouse from c. 1565-1590, Shakespeare Quart, winter 71. Add: Dept. of Speech & Dramatic Art, University Theatre, University of Iowa, Iowa City, IA 52242.

BROWNSTONE, PAUL L, b. New York, N.Y, Jan. 21, 23; m. 55; c. 3. SPEECH, EDUCATION. B.A, Brooklyn,Col, 47; M.A, Univ. Denver, 48; Ph.D.(speech), Pa. State Univ, 60. Instr. radio & TV & res. fel, Pa. State Univ, 51-53; lectr. commun, Brooklyn Col, 53-60, asst. prof. rhetoric, 60-69; SR. PROF. HUMANITIES, CHMN. DEPT. SPEECH & THEATRE & DIV. HUMANITIES, LONG ISLAND UNIV, BROOKLYN CTR, 69- Participant, Educ. Media Inst, Cornell Univ, summer, 67. Adult Educ. Asn, U.S; Am. Acad. Polit. Sci; Nat. Soc. Stud. Commun; Speech Commun. Asn; Speech Asn. East. States.(v.pres, 62-63, pres, 70-71); Int. Soc. Gen. Semantics. Educational technology and its applications to higher education; the mass media; radio-TV. Publ: Adult speech education: client educability, Cent. States Speech J, 5/63; Unity in Diversity, Nat. Newslett. Bus. & Prof. Speaking Group, Speech Asn. Am, 3/65; International understanding through communication: one plan—one plea, J. Commun, 6/70; plus one other. Add: 23 Washington Ave, Lawrence, NY 11559.

BRUBAKER, BILL R, b. Blackburn, Okla, May 7, 33; m. 59; c. 1. ENGLISH. B.S, South. Ill. Univ, 55, M.A, 56; Ph.D.(Eng), Ohio State Univ, 66. Instr. AM. LIT, Ohio State Univ, 64-66; asst. prof, FLA. STATE UNIV, 66-72, ASSOC. PROF, 72- U.S.A, 56-58. MLA. Nineteenth century American literature. Publ: Civil service reform and political appointment of writers, Papers Lang. & Lit, summer 69; It was Christmas (fiction) & Hawthorne's experiment in popular form: Mr. Higginbotham's catastrophe, spring 73. South. Humanities Rev. Add: Dept. of English, Florida State University, Tallahassee, FL 32306.

BRUBAKER, EDWARD, b. Lancaster, Pa, Aug. 22, 24. ENGLISH. A.B, Franklin & Marshall Col, 49; M.A, Univ. Pa, 50. Instr. ENG, Wash. Col, 50-52; PROF. DRAMA & CHMN. DEPT. FRANKLIN & MARSHALL COL, 72- Sig.C, U.S.A, 43-46. Shakespeare Asn. Am; AAUP; Am. Theatre Asn. Dramatic literature and history of the theatre. Add: Dept. of Drama, Franklin & Marshall College, Lancaster, PA 17604.

BRUCCOLI, MATTHEW J, b. New York, N.Y, Aug. 21, 37; m. 57; c. 3. ENGLISH. A.B, Yale, 53; M.A, Univ. Va, 56, Ph.D, 61. Instr. Eng, Sch. Engineering, Univ. Va, 58-59, asst. instr, Univ, 60-61; asst. to ed, Bibliog. Am. Lit, 59-60; asst. prof. Eng, Ohio State Univ, 61-64, assoc. prof, 64, prof, 65-69, assoc. text ed, Centenary Hawthorne, 61, gen. ed, 66; PROF. ENG, UNIV. S.C, 69- Ed, Fitzgerald Newslett, 58-68; textual ed, Cross Currents Ser, South. Ill. Univ. Press, 65; mem. exec. comt, Ctr. Editions Am. Authors, 66, dir, 69-; gen. ed, Pittsburgh Ser. in Bibliog, Univ. Pittsburgh, 67. Bibliog. Soc. Am; Bibliog. Soc. Univ. Va; Grolier Club. F. Scott Fitzgerald; bibliography. Publ: The composition of Tender is the night, 63

& F. Scott Fitzgerald: a descriptive bibliography, 72, Univ. Pittsburgh; ed, Raymond Chandler, 68 & co-ed, F. Scott Fitzgerald in his own time, 71, Kent State Univ; ed, Fitzgerald/Hemingway editions annual, 69- & The great Gatsby: a facsimile, 73, NCR Ed; auth, John O'Hara: a checklist, Random, 72; co-ed, As ever, Scott Fitz—, Lippincott, 72. Add: Dept. of English, University of South of South Carolina, Columbia, SC 29208.

BRUCE, CHARLES THOMAS, b. Mt. Vernon, Tex, Aug. 20, 21. ENGLISH. B.A, Tex. Tech Univ, 42, M.A, 47, Ph.D, 60; Stanford Univ, 47; summers, Univ. Tex, 48-50. Instr. ENG, Mt. Vernon High Sch, Tex, 48-56; Tex. Tech Univ, 56-61; asst. prof, Univ. Tex, Arlington, 61-67; ASSOC. PROF, Del Mar Col, 68-69; TEX. WOMAN'S UNIV, 69- Ford fel, 59-60; dir, NDEA Inst. Advan. Stud. Eng, Univ. Tex, Arlington, summer 67. U.S.N, 42-46, Res, 46-, Lt. NCTE; MLA; S.Cent. Mod. Lang. Asn. American novel; literature of Colonial America; 18th century English literature. Publ: The concept of the soldier on the verge of the Civil War, Tex. Conf. Col. Teachers Eng, 61; Circularity: theme and structure in Ethan Frome, Stud. & Critiques, 66. Add: Dept. of English, Texas Woman's University, Denton, TX 76204.

BRUCE, GEORGE HOWARD, b. Washington, D.C, May 6, 30; m. 56; c. 3. ENGLISH, RUSSIAN. B.A, Univ. N.H, 55, M.A, 58; Ph.D.(Eng), Univ. Rochester, 62. Instr. ENG, NORWICH UNIV, 60-62, asst. prof, 62-66, ASSOC. PROF, 66-, ADMIN. DIR. RUSSIAN SCH, 67-, ASST. DIR. SUMMER SCHS, 68- U.S.A, 51-54. John Donne; Russian language and literature; English Romantics. Add: West Hill, Northfield, VT 05663.

BRUCKER, HERBERT, b. Passaic, N.J, Oct. 4, 98; m. 26, 51; c. 3. JOURNALISM, COMMUNICATION. A.B, Williams Col, 21; B.Litt, Columbia Univ, 24; L.H.D, Colby Col, 60, Columbia Univ, 63; LL.D, Williams Col, 64; D.Litt, Univ. Hartford, 65. Reporter, Springfield Union, Mass, 23; Pulitzer traveling scholar, Europe, 24-25; reporter, The World, N.Y, 25-26; ed. staff, World's Work Mag, 26-28; Review of Reviews Mag, 28-32; from asst. to dean to prof, grad. sch. jour, Columbia Univ, 32-44; assoc. ed, Hartford Courant, Conn, 44-47, ed, 47-66; dir. prof. jour. fels, Stanford Univ, 66-69; SYNDICATED NEWSPAPER COLUMNIST, 68- U.S.N.R, 18. Am. Soc. Newspaper Ed.(pres, 63-64). Journalism. Publ: The changing American newspaper, Columbia Univ, 37; Freedom of information, 49 & Journalist; eyewitness to history, 62, Macmillan; Communication is power: unchanging values in a changing journalism, Oxford Univ, 73. Add: Box 127, R.R. 2, Windsor, VT 05089.

BRUECHER, WERNER, b. Alsleben, Ger, Sept. 19, 27; U.S. citizen; m. 62; c. 2. ENGLISH & GERMAN. B.A, Univ. Ariz, 61, M.A, 62, Ph.D.(Eng. & Ger), 71. Instr. ENG. & GER, EAST. ORE. STATE COL, 62-65, asst. prof, 65-70, ASSOC. PROF. & CHMN. DEPT, 70- U.S.A.F, 51-55. MLA; Pac. Northwest Am. Stud. Asn. Add: Dept. of English, Eastern Oregon State College, LaGrande, OR 97850.

BRUEHL, WILLIAM J, b. Philadelphia, Pa, Dec. 29, 31; m. 56; c. 2. ENGLISH, DRAMATIC ARTS. B.A, West Chester State Col, 56; M.A, Univ. Pa, Ph.D.(Eng), 66. Asst. prof. Eng, West Chester State Col, 60-67; Eng. & drama, Univ. Del, 67-69, fac. res. grant, 67, summer, 68; ASSOC. PROF. THEATRE ARTS, STATE UNIV. N.Y. STONY BROOK, 69-, chmn. dept, 69-72, exec. producer, Univ. Theatre, 74. U.S.A, 51-54, Sgt. MLA; Soc. Theatre Res, Eng; Am. Theatre Asn. Modern British and American theatre and dramatic literature; Kabuki theatre of Japan. Publ: Polus Naufrangia, key symbol in ascent of F6, Mod. Drama, 9/67; co-auth, Unconventional possibilities for a conventional theatre, Theatre Crafts, 11/68; auth, A survey of African and Asian theatre studies, Drama Rev, spring 69. Add: Dept. of Theatre Arts, State University of New York at Stony Brook, Stony Brook, NY 11790.

BRUFFEE, KENNETH ALLEN, b. Torrington, Conn, Sept. 1, 34. ENGLISH. B.A, Wesleyan Univ, 56; M.A, Northwest. Univ, 57, Ph.D.(Eng), 64. Instr. ENG, Univ. Va, 62-65; Columbia Univ, 65-66; from instr. to ASSOC. PROF, BROOKLYN COL, 66-, DIR, FRESHMAN WRITING PROG, 70- U.S.A, 57-58. MLA; Keats-Shelley Asn. Am; NCTE; Col. Eng. Asn. Elegiac romance; Conrad; modern novel. Publ: A short course in writing, Winthrop, 71; Collaborative learning: some practical models, Col. Eng, 73; On graduate education in English, ADE Bull, 73; Form and meaning in Nabokov's The real life of Sebastian Knight: an example of elegiac romance, Mod. Lang. Quart, 73; plus six others. Add: Dept. of English, Brooklyn College, Brooklyn, NY 11210.

BRUNAUER, DALMA H, b. Budapest, Hungary, Feb. 4, 24; m. 61. ENGLISH, HUMANITIES. Teaching dipl. & Ph.D.(Eng), Univ. Budapest, 48. Instr. Eng, DePaul Univ, 49-53; asst. prof, Lewis Col, 53-58, chmn. dept, 55-57; instr. Eng. & humanities, Chicago City Col, 58-62, asst. prof, 62-63, ASSOC. PROF, 63-65; HUMANITIES, CLARKSON COL. TECHNOL, 65- Lectr, Univ. Chicago, 53-57. MLA; Conf. Christianity & Lit; Soc. Arts, Relig. & Contemporary Cult.(mem, publ. comt, 73-). World literature; poetry, drama and fiction; literature and religion. Publ: Ed, Literature and religion: Albee and Beckett, In: The theater of the absurd, Clarkson Col, 71; auth, Black and white: the archetypal myth and its development, Barat Rev, spring-summer 71; Creative faith in Wilder's The eighth day, Renascence, autumn 72; plus others. Add: Dept. of Humanities, Clarkson College of Technology, Potsdam, NY 13676.

BRUNDAGE, GLORIA SWEGMAN, b. Kansas City, Kans, Nov. 28, 24; m. 57; c. 1. SPEECH COMMUNICATION, JOURNALISM. B.S, Columbia Univ, 51, M.S, 52; Ph.D.(commun), N.Y. Univ, 69. Reporter, Washington Post, Assoc. Press, Topeka Daily Capital & N.Y. Herald Tribune, 44-53; instr. jour, Univ. South. Miss, 53-55; ASST. PROF, Eng, State Univ. N.Y, 64-67; pub. rels, Boston Univ, 67-69; commun, Univ. Dayton, 69-71; JOUR, MARQUETTE UNIV, 71- Consult, Tufts Univ. Dent. Hyg. Community Awareness Prog, 67-68; mem, Nat. Educ. Adv. Comt, Pub. Rels. Soc. Am, 72- Asn. Educ. in Jour; Speech Commun. Asn; Int. Commun. Asn; Women in Commun. Broadcast law; international communication; censorship in media. Publ: Jonathan Livingston journalist—a pro, 1/73 & Front page women: from Colonial America to the present, 6/73, Cath. Sch. Ed; Example of a class project in reporting ecology and government, Col. Press Rev, winter 73; plus others. Add: College of Journalism, Marquette University, 1135 W. Kilbourn Ave, Milwaukee, WI 53233.

BRUNE, RANDALL, b. Weehawken, N.J, Oct. 7, 30; m. 51; c. 3. ENGLISH. A.B, Columbia Univ, 53, M.A, 54; Ph.D.(Eng), Syracuse Univ, 63. Asst. prof. ENG, Keuka Col, 61-64; State Univ. N.Y. Col. Geneseo, 64-65; assoc. prof, SYRACUSE UNIV, 65-72, PROF, 72-, DIR. LOWER DIV. STUD, 65- U.S.A, 54-56. MLA; NCTE; AAUP; Col. Conf. Compos. & Commun. Romantic; Canadian. Publ: Ed, Freshman English at Syracuse, Wadsworth, 66, 67 & 68; co-auth, Freshman English student manuel, 73 & Freshman English instructor's manual, 73, Syracuse Univ. Add: Dept. of English, 203 Hall of Languages, Syracuse University, Syracuse, NY 13210.

BRUNER, MARJORIE WILLIAMSON, b. Marion, Ind, Dec. 30, 07; m. 36; c. 5. ENGLISH, COMPARATIVE LITERATURE. A.B, Univ. Chicago, 29, univ. fel, 31-33, Ph.D.(comp. lit), 33; Northwest. Univ, 62; Yale, 63-64; W.B. Yeats Int. Summer Sch, Ireland, 64. Asst. prof. & dean women, Kanawha Jr. Col, 33-34; asst. prof. ENG, N.Mex, State Univ, 34-36; instr, CARTHAGE COL, 62-63, asst. prof, 63-65, assoc. prof, 65-71, PROF, 71- Vis. assoc. prof, Chapman Col, 68-69. MLA; NCTE; Am. Stud. Asn; Mod. Humanities Res. Asn. Medieval Irish; Washington Irving; American literature. Publ: Les yeux arraches, Philol. Quart, 4/32; The dream of Cahus in Perlesvaus, Mod. Philol, 8/32; The legend of Sleepy Hollow: a mythological parody, Col. Eng, 1/64; plus others. Add: 1817 S. Main St, Racine, WI 53403.

BRUNSON, MARTHA LUAN, b. Anna, Ill, Sept. 29, 31; m. 54; c. 4. VICTORIAN & EIGHTEENTH CENTURY BRITISH LITERATURE. B.S.Ed, Northwest. Univ, 52; M.A, Tex. Tech Univ, 58, fels, 58-60, 63-64, Ph.D.(Eng, hist), 67. Teacher Eng. & hist, Plainview Independent Sch. Dist, Tex, 53-56; ENG, Lubbock High Sch, 56-58; instr, Del Mar Col, 61-62, 64-65; asst. prof, SOUTHWEST TEX. STATE UNIV, 67-72, ASSOC. PROF. & CHMN. DEPT, 72- Consult, Del Rio Independent Sch. Dist, Tex, 73- MLA; Col. Eng. Asn. Thomas Hardy; Samuel Johnson. Add: Dept. of English & Philosophy, Southwest Texas State University, San Marcos, TX 78666.

BRUNVAND, JAN HAROLD, b. Cadillac, Mich, Mar. 23, 33; m. 56; c. 4. FOLKLORE. B.A, Mich. State Univ, 55, M.A, 57; Fulbright scholar, Univ. Oslo, 56-57; Ph.D, Ind. Univ, 61. Asst. prof. ENG, Univ. Idaho, 61-65; assoc. prof, South. Ill. Univ, 65-66; UNIV. UTAH, 66-71, PROF, 71- Fulbright grant & Guggenheim Found. fel, Romania, 70-71; Int. Res. & Exchanges Bd. grant, Romania, 73-74. Sig.C, U.S.A, 62-63, 1st Lt. Am. Name Soc; Am. Folklore Soc. The folktale; literature of the West; Romanian folklore. Publ: A dictionary of proverbs and proverbial phrases from books published by Indiana authors before 1890, Ind. Univ, 61; The study of American folklore, Norton, 68; A guide for collectors of folklore in Utah, Univ. Utah, 71; The folktale origin of The taming of the shrew, Shakespeare Quart, autumn 66; The regional fiction of H.L. Davis, West. Am. Lit, summer 67; The study of Romanian folklore, J. Folklore Inst, 72; plus others. Add: Dept. of English, University of Utah, Salt Lake City, UT 84112.

BRUSTEIN, ROBERT, b. Brooklyn, N.Y, Apr. 21, 27. ENGLISH. B.A, Amherst Col, 48, Hitchcock fel, 48-49, hon. D.Litt, 72; M.A, Columbia Univ, 50, Ph.D, 57; Fulbright fel, Univ. Nottingham, 53-55; hon. D.Litt, Lawrence Univ, 68. Instr. Eng. Cornell Univ, 55-56; drama, Vassar Col, 56-57; lectr, Drama Sch, Columbia Univ, 57-58, asst. prof. Eng, 58-63, assoc. prof, 63-65, prof, 65-66; PROF. ENG. & DEAN SCH. DRAMA, YALE, 66-, ARTISTIC DIR, YALE REPERTORY THEATRE, 66- Drama critic, New Repub, 59-; Guggenheim fel, 61-62; Ford Found. grant, 64-65; mem. panel, Theatre Div, Nat. Endowment for Arts, 70-72; drama critic, The Observer, London, 72-73; monthly contrib, New York Times, 72- George Jean Nathan Award, 62-63; George Polk Award in Theatre Criticism, 64; Jersey City J. Award in Criticism, 65. U.S. Merchant Marine, 45-47. MLA. Modern and classical drama; Elizabethan and Stuart drama. Publ: Theatre of revolt, Atlantic Monthly, 64; Seasons of discontent, Simon & Schuster, 65; The third theatre, Knopf, 69; Revolution as theatre: notes on the new radical style, Liveright, 71; America's new culture hero, Commentary, 58; Madison Avenue villain, Partisan Rev, 62; Cultural schizophrenia, New York Times Mag, 71. Add: Yale School of Drama, Yale University, New Haven, CT 06520.

BRUTUS, DENNIS (VINCENT), b. Salisbury, South. Rhodesia, Nov. 28, 24; South. African citizen; c. 8. ENGLISH & AFRICAN LITERATURE. Diploma, Ft. Hare Univ, 45, B.A, 47, Univ. Witwatersrand, 62-63. Teacher langs, Paterson High Sch, S.Africa, 61; PROF. ENG. & AFRICAN LIT, NORTHWEST. UNIV, EVANSTON, 71- Vis. prof. Eng. & African lit, Univ. Denver, 70; pres, S.African Non-racial Olympic comt; Int. Defence & Aid Fund rep, UN. Fel. Int. Poetry Soc. African literature. Publ: Sirens, knuckles, boots, Mbari Press, Nigeria & Northwest. Univ, Evanston, 63; Letters to Martha, Heinemanns, London & Humanities, N.Y, 68; Poems from Algiers, Univ. Tex, 70; Thoughts abroad (under name of John Bruin), Troubadour Press, 71; A simple lust, Heinemanns, London & Hill & Wang, N.Y, 73; contrib, Seven South African Poets, Heinemanns, London, 71. Add: Dept. of English, Northwestern University, Evanston, IL 60201.

BRYAN, DANIEL VANCE, b. Dallas Co, Iowa, Oct. 10, 18; m. 40; c. 4. COMMUNICATION, HUMANITIES. B.A, State Univ, Iowa, 40, M.A, 42; Ph.D.(Eng), Univ. Minn, 53. Instr. Eng, Dana Col, 42-43; Drake Univ, 46; COMMUN. & HUMANITIES, UNIV. MINN, MINNEAPOLIS, 46-53, asst. prof, 53-59, assoc. prof, 59-66, PROF, 66-, DIR. COMMUN. PROG, 65- Nat. Inst. Mental Health spec. fel, 67-68; mem. exec. comt, Conf. Col. Compos. & Commun, 65-68. U.S.N.R, 43-46, Lt. MLA; NCTE; Rhetoric Soc. Am. Samuel Butler and G.B. Shaw: creative evolution in literature; bearings of contemporary linguistics and psycholinguistics on rhetoric and communication; implications of linguistics for literary study. Add: Communication Program, 116 Klaeber Ct, University of Minnesota, Minneapolis, MN 55455.

BRYAN, ENID PARKER, b. Chattanooga, Tenn, Sept. 17, 10; m. 44. ENGLISH. A.B, Univ. Chattanooga, 32; M.A, Duke Univ, 33, Ph.D.(class. lang), 42; B.A in L.S, Univ. N.C, 40. Teacher Latin & French, Reinhardt Jr. Col, 36-37; Eng. & French, Greenville High Sch, S.C, 37-39; periodicals & ref. librn, Duke Univ. Woman's Col, 40-45; asst. librn, E.Carolina Col, 48-51; librn, Shorter Col.(Ga), 51-53; prof. Eng, Berry Col, 53-55; Tenn. Wesleyan Col, 55-58; asst. ref. librn, Smithsonian Inst. Libr, 58-60; asst. prof. ENG, UNIV. TENN, CHATTANOOGA, 60-63, assoc. prof, 63-67, PROF, 67- Instr. Eng. & Latin, Univ. Miss, 45-48; vis. instr. libr. sci, George Peabody Col, summers, 52-54. MLA; S.Atlantic Mod. Lang. Asn. Classical backgrounds of English and American literature. Publ: The education of heirs in the Julio-Claudian family, Am. J. Philol, 1/46. Add: Dept. of English, University of Tennessee, Chattanooga, TN 37401.

BRYAN, MARGARET BRYAN, b. Charleston, W.Va. ENGLISH RENAISSANCE LITERATURE. B.A, Marshall Univ, 51; M.A, Univ. N.C, Chapel Hill, 65, Ph.D.(Eng), 70. Instr. ENG, Sacred Heart Col.(N.C), 65-66; UNIV. N.C, CHARLOTTE, 66-70, ASST. PROF, 70- MLA; S.Atlantic Mod. Lang. Asn; Southeast. Renaissance Conf; AAUP. Shakespeare; Renaissance literature; Renaissance women. Publ: Volumnia—Roman matron or Elizabethan huswife, Renaissance Papers, 3/73; Shakespeare in the puppet theatre, CEA Critic, 3/73; Recent studies in Campion, Eng. Lit. Renaissance, winter 74. Add: Dept. of English, University of North Carolina at Charlotte, Charlotte, NC 28202.

BRYAN, MARTIN, b. St. Joseph, Mo, Aug. 10, 08; m. 65; c. 1. SPEECH. Ph.D, Northwest. Univ. Asst. prof. SPEECH, Lake Forest Col, 45-46; assoc. prof, UNIV. CINCINNATI, 46-67, PROF, 67-, assoc. dir. lang. inst, 60, fac. res. grant negative lang. & exec. secy, Counc. Int. Educ. & Prog, 72. Mem, Comt. Coop. For. Univ, 57-68; Fulbright grant, Nat. Univ. Seoul, 62-63, dir, Midwinter Inst. Korean Teachers Eng. as For. Lang; Taft fel. Speech Commun. Asn.(chmn. action caucus negative lang, 73); Commun. Asn. Pac; Cent. States Speech Asn; Teacher Eng. to Speakers of Other Lang; Phonetic Soc. Japan; Japan Speech Soc; Korean Speech Asn. Speech science; speech psychology; computer analysis of negative language intensity. Publ: Dynamic speaking, Macmillan, 62; Rationale for speech as an academic discipline, Cent. State Speech J, 5/65; co-auth, Riders to the sea: reappraised, Tex. Quart, 68 & Lost and not yet found, Intellect, 73; plus others. Add: 2822 Stratford Ave, Cincinnati, OH 45220.

BRYAN, MARY C, b. West Quincy, Mass, Sept. 24, 22. ENGLISH LITERATURE. A.B, Regis Col.(Mass), 44; A.M, Boston Univ, 45, Ph.D.(Eng), 58; Fulbright grant, Univ. Munich, 56-57. PROF. ENG, REGIS COL.(MASS), 58-, CHMN. DEPT, 72- AAUP; MLA. Modern novel; literary criticism; romantic poetry. Publ: Forrest Reid: a critical study, Twayne, 75. Add: Dept. of English, Regis College, Weston, MA 02193.

BRYAN, RALPH TERRY, b. Nashville, Tenn, Oct. 7, 22; m. 45; c. 4. ENGLISH. B.S, Ariz. State Univ, 50, M.A, 58; Ph.D.(Eng), Univ. Colo, 67. Teacher high sch, Ariz, 58-59; asst. prof. ENG, GRAND CANYON COL, 59-64, assoc. prof, 64-67, PROF, 67- U.S.A.A.F, 43-46. MLA. Prose style of the 17th century, particularly Robert Burton; Edmund Spenser's The Faerie Queen; background of Shakespeare's comedies. Add: Dept. of English, Grand Canyon College, 3300 W. Camelback, Phoenix, AZ 85017.

BRYAN, ROBERT A, b. Lebanon, Pa, Apr. 26, 26; m. 53; c. 2. ENGLISH. A.B, Univ. Miami, 50; M.A, Univ. Ky, 51, Ph.D, 56. Part-time instr. ENG, Univ. Ky, 50-54, instr, 56-57; spec. instr, Far East Exten, Univ. Calif, 55-56; asst. prof, UNIV. FLA, 57-63, assoc. prof, 63-68, PROF, 68-, ASST. DEAN GRAD. SCH, 61-, ASSOC. V.PRES, ACAD. AFFAIRS, 71-, dean fac, 70-71. Reader, Educ. Testing Serv, 59-61; consult, South. Asn. Schs. & Cols, 66-73; dean for advan. stud, Fla. Atlantic Univ, 69-70. U.S. Merchant Marine, 44-47; U.S.A, 54-56. MLA; S.Atlantic Mod. Lang. Asn; Southeast. Renaissance Conf. English literature of the 16th and 17th centuries. Publ: Adam's tragic vision in Paradise lost, Stud. Philol, 65; The master and the apprentice, Proc. Counc. Grad. Schs. in U.S, 66; Apostasy and the fourth bead-man in the Fairy queen, Eng. Lang. Notes, 67; plus others. Add: 235 Tigert Hall, University of Florida, Gainesville, FL 32601.

BRYANT, BYRON RALPH, b. Waynesville, N.C, July 2, 23. ENGLISH, HUMANITIES. B.A, Ariz. State Col, Tempe, 45; Steiner fel, Stanford Univ, 45-46, M.A, 47, Rosenberg fel, 48-49, Ph.D.(Eng), 55. Teaching asst. ENG, Stanford Univ, 46, 48-49; instr, Mont. State Univ, 47-48, 49-52; asst. prof, ST. MARY'S COL.(CALIF), 55-62, assoc. prof, 62-70, PROF, 70- MLA; Pan. Am. League; NCTE. Origins of Romanticism; 19th century novel; popular periodical literature of the 19th century. Publ: Ed, New editions, Paperback Ed, Ltd; ed. & contrib, St. Mary's faculty studies, 1965, St. Mary's Col, 66; contrib, The exacting ear, Pantheon, 66. Add: Dept. of English, St. Mary's College, Moraga, CA 94575.

BRYANT, DONALD CROSS, b. New York, N.Y, Sept. 17, 05; m. 32. SPEECH, ENGLISH. A.B, Cornell Univ, 27, A.M, 30, Ph.D, 37. Teacher, high sch, N.Y, 27-29; instr. Eng, N.Y. State Col. Teachers, 29-35; asst. prof, Wash. Univ, 37-43, assoc. prof, 43-48, prof, 48-58, chmn. dept, 56-58; prof. SPEECH, UNIV. IOWA, 58-72, Carver Distinguished Prof, 72-73, CARVER EMER. PROF, 73- Consult. & lectr, Univ. South. Calif, 68; res. leave, Univ. Iowa, spring 62; vis. prof. speech, Univ. Wash, summer 69; vis. scholar, Univ. Ctr, Richmond, Va, 71; distinguished lectr. speech, La. State Univ, 72. MLA; Speech Commun. Asn.(ed, Quart. J. Speech, 57-59, 2nd v.pres, 68, 1st v.pres, 69, pres, 70); AAUP. Edmund Burke; 18th century British parliamentary speaking; rhetorical criticism. Publ: Edmund Burke and his literary friends, Wash. Univ. Stud, 39; co-auth, Fundamentals of public speaking, Appleton, 47, 2nd ed, 53, 3rd ed, 60, 4th ed, 69, 5th ed, 74 & An historical anthology of select British speeches, Ronald, 67; ed, Ancient Greek and Roman rhetoricians: a biographical dictionary, Artcraft Press, 68; auth, Rhetorical dimensions in criticism, La. State Univ, 73; Rhetoric: its function and its scope, 12/53 & Retrospect and prospect: 1970 (presidential address), 2/71, Quart. J. Speech. Add: 903 Highwood St, Iowa City, IA 52240.

BRYANT, HALLMAN B, b. Royston, Ga, Aug. 17, 37; m. 61; c. 2. ENGLISH. B.A, Emory Univ, 59; M.A, Univ. N.C, 62; Ph.D.(Eng), Vanderbilt Univ, 67. ASST. PROF. ENG, CLEMSON UNIV, 67- U.S.A, 60-62. Victorian literature. Add: Dept. of English, Clemson University, Clemson, SC 29631.

BRYANT, JAMES CECIL, JR, b. Lake Wales, Fla, Oct. 21, 31; m. 55; c. 2. ENGLISH. B.A, Stetson Univ, 54; B.D, South. Baptist Theol. Sem, 58; M.A, Univ. Miami, 61; Ph.D.(Eng), Univ. Ky, 67. Asst. prof. Eng, Fla. State Univ, 67-73; ASSOC. PROF. ENG. & CHMN. DIV. HUMANITIES, MERCER UNIV. ATLANTA, 73- Lit. specialist, South. Baptist Writers Conf, 72. U.S.N.R, 48-52. MLA; S.Atlantic Mod. Lang. Asn; Southeast. Renaissance Conf; Col. Eng. Asn; Renaissance Soc. Am; AAUP. English Renaissance drama; American literature and folklore; Baptist pioneer history. Publ: Indian Springs: the story of a pioneer church, Fla. State Univ, 72; Smooth runs the water (novel), Broadman, 73; The Pardoner and the Friar as Reformation polemic, Renaissance Papers, 72; The problematic Friar in Romeo and Juliet, Eng. Stud, 73; The Bible as literature, Event, 73; plus others. Add: Division of Humanities, Mercer University in Atlanta, 3000 Flowers Rd. N.E, Atlanta, GA 30341.

BRYANT, JERRY H, b. Dinuba, Calif, July 5, 28. ENGLISH LITERATURE. B.A, Univ. Calif, Los Angeles, 53, M.A, 55, Ph.D, 59. PROF. ENG. LIT, Ariz. State Univ, 58-63; CALIF. STATE UNIV, HAYWARD, 63- U.S.M.C, 46-48. MLA; Philol. Asn. Pac. Coast. Contemporary American novel. Publ: John Reynolds of Exeter and his canon, Library, 60; The open decision: the contemporary American novel and its intellectual background, Free Press, 70; The hopeful stoicism of William Styron, S.Atlantic Quart, 63; The winter's tale and the pastoral tradition, Shakespeare Quart, autumn 63; From death to life: the fiction of Ernest J. Gaines, Iowa Rev, 71; plus others. Add: Dept. of English, California State University, Hayward, CA 94542.

BRYANT, JOSEPH ALLEN, JR, b. Glasgow, Ky, Nov. 26, 19; m. 46; c. 2. ENGLISH LITERATURE. A.B, West. Ky. State Univ, 40; A.M, Vanderbilt Univ, 41; Ph.D, Yale, 48. Instr, Univ. Ky, 46; Eng. lit, Vanderbilt Univ, 48-50, asst. prof, 50-54, assoc. prof, 54-56; Univ. of the South, 56-59; ENG, Duke Univ, 59-61; prof. & head dept, Univ. N.C. Greensboro, 61-68; prof. & chmn. dept, SYRACUSE UNIV, 68-71; PROF, UNIV. KY, 71-, CHMN. DEPT, 73- Ford Found. fel, 52-53; Sewanee Rev. fel, 58-59; Fulbright lectr, Univ. Nantes, 65-66. U.S.N.R, 42-46. MLA; Renaissance Soc. Am; S.Atlantic Mod. Lang. Asn. Shakespeare; Renaissance drama; modern literature. Publ: Hippolyta's view: some Christian aspects of Shakespeare's plays, Univ. Ky, 61; Eudora Welty, Univ. Minn, 68; The compassionate satirist; Ben Jonson and his imperfect world, Univ. Ga, 73. Add: Dept. of English, University of Kentucky, Lexington, KY 40506.

BRYANT, MARGARET M, English Language, Linguistics. See Volume III, Foreign Languages, Linguistics & Philology.

BRYANT, PAUL THOMPSON, b. Oklahoma City, Okla, Aug. 24, 28; m. 49; ENGLISH. B.S, Univ. Okla, 50, M.S, 52, M.A, 56; Ph.D.(Eng), Univ. Ill, 65. Ed. eng, Wash. State Univ, 54-56; teaching asst. Eng, Univ. Ill, 56-58, asst. ed, Eng. Experiment Sta, 58-61, ed, Col. Eng, 61-64; asst. prof. ENG, COLO. STATE UNIV, 64-67, assoc. prof, 67-71, PROF, 71-, acting chmn. dept, 68-69, chmn, 69-74. Ed, J. Eng. Educ, 58-64; asst. ed, West. Am. Lit, 66-72; co-ed, J. Eng. Teaching Techniques, 67-70. U.S.A, 46-47. MLA; NCTE; Am. Stud. Asn. American studies; literature of the American West; science fiction. Publ: H.L. Davis: viable uses for the past, West. Am. Lit, spring 68; ed. & introd, Geography to geotechnics, selected essays of Benton MacKaye, Univ. Ill, 68. Add: Dept. of English, Colorado State University, Ft. Collins, CO 80521.

BRYANT, WILLIAM ALTON, b. Sanford, Miss, Oct. 24, 07; m. 31; c. 4. ENGLISH. A.B, Univ. Miss, 29, A.M, 39; Ph.D, Vanderbilt Univ, 41. Teaching fel. Eng, Univ. Miss, 29-30; teacher, High Sch, Miss, 30-31; instr, 36-39; instr. & qm, Branham & Hughes Mil. Acad, Spring Hill, Tenn, 31-32; instr, Battle Ground Acad, 32-36; teaching fel. ENG, Vanderbilt Univ, 39-41; asst. prof, UNIV. MISS, 41-45, assoc. prof, 45-46, PROF, 46-, EXEC. V.CHANCELLOR, 72-, dir. summer session, 42-47, acting registr, 44-45, instnl. adv. vet, 45-46, chmn. dept, 47-54, acting dean, univ, 53-54, provost, 54-60, v.chancellor, 60-72. MLA; S.Cent. Mod. Lang. Asn; South. Lit. Festival Asn.(pres, 48). Nineteenth century English literature; conception of America and Americans by the British romantic poets, 1790-1850. Add: Box 128, University, MS 38677.

BRYER, JACKSON ROBERT, b. New York, N.Y, Sept. 11, 37; m. 60; c. 3. ENGLISH. B.A, Amherst Col, 59; M.A, Columbia Univ, 60; Ph.D.(Eng), Univ. Wis, 65. Asst. prof. ENG, UNIV. MD, COLLEGE PARK, 64-68, assoc. prof, 68-72, PROF, 72- Am. Philos. Soc. summer res. grant, 65; head Am. lit. sect, Mod. Lang. Asn. Ann. bibliog, 68-; co-ed, Resources for Am. lit. stud, 71- MLA. Modern American literature; American drama; modern drama. Publ: Co-auth, A checklist of Emerson criticism, 1951-1961, Transcendental, 64; A Wallace Stevens checklist, Swallow, 64; auth, The critical reputation of F. Scott Fitzgerald, Archon Bks, 67; ed, Fifteen modern American authors: a survey of research and criticism, Duke Univ, 69; co-ed, F. Scott Fitzgerald in his own time: a miscellany, Kent State Univ, 71; Dear Scott—Dear Max: the Fitzgerald-Perkins correspondence, 71 & F. Scott Fitzgerald, The Basil and Josephine stories, 73, Scribner; auth, F. Scott Fitzgerald: a review of research and scholarship, Tex. Stud. Lit. & Lang, spring 63; co-auth, The great Gatsby: a study in literary reputation, N.Mex. Quart, winter 63-64; auth, Joyce, Ulysses and the Little review, S.Atlantic Quart, spring 67. Add: Dept. of English, University of Maryland, College Park, MD 20742.

BRYLOWSKI, WALTER MARION, b. Kalamazoo, Mich, May 9, 27; m. 57. ENGLISH. B.A, Kalamazoo Col, 50; M.A, Univ. Conn, 52; Ph.D.(Eng), Mich. State Univ, 64. From assoc. prof. to PROF. ENG, EAST. MICH. UNIV, 55- U.S.A, 45-46. MLA. Modern American literature. Publ: Faulkner's Olympian laugh, Wayne State Univ, 68. Add: Dept. of English, Language & Literature, Eastern Michigan University, Ypsilanti, MI 48197.

BRYSON, KENNETH D, b. Woodbine, Ill, Apr. 3, 24; m. 44; c. 3. SPEECH. B.S, North. Ill. Univ, 47; M.A, Northwest. Univ, 49, Ph.D.(pub. address, psychol. & speech), 52. Instr. SPEECH, MONT. STATE UNIV, 50-52, asst. prof, 52-57, assoc. prof, 57-65, PROF, 65-, CHMN. DEPT, 66- Founder & dir, Treasure State Forum, radio discussion ser, 57-; dir. peace corps training prog, Mont. State Univ, 67-68; dep. dir, Peace Corps, Guyana, 68-70. U.S.A.A.F, 43-46, 1st Lt. Speech Commun. Asn; West. Speech Commun. Asn. Phonetic symbolism; oral communication; audience response. Publ: Co-auth, Effective communication, Prentice-Hall, 2nd ed, 61; Cross-cultural communication: what is it we are studying?, Proc.Speech Commun. Asn, 12/72. Add: Dept. of Speech Communication, Montana State University, Bozeman, MT 59715.

BRYSON, RALPH JOSEPH, b. Cincinnati, Ohio, Sept. 10, 22. ENGLISH, EDUCATION. B.S, Univ. Cincinnati, 47, M.Ed, 50; Ph.D, Ohio State Univ, 53. Instr. ENG, South. Univ, 49; Miles Col, 49-50; assoc. prof, ALA. STATE UNIV, 53-62, PROF. & HEAD DEPT, 62- Lectr. NDEA Insts. & consult, numerous city, state & fed. educ. dist. & prog, 53- U.S.A, 42-45, 1st Sgt. MLA; NCTE; CLA. Teaching of English; American literature; Negro literature. Publ: How much grammar, Bull. Ala. Sec. Sch. Prin, 3/65. Add: Dept. of English, Alabama State University, Montgomery, AL 36202.

BRZENK, EUGENE JOSEPH, b. Milwaukee, Wis. BRITISH LITERATURE. B.S, Milwaukee State Teachers Col, 44; M.A, State Univ. Iowa, 48, Ph.D, 51. Prof. ENG, Bradley Univ, 51-61; ASSOC. PROF, UNIV. NOTRE DAME, 63- U.S.N.R, 44-46. MLA. Walter Pater; the two cultures; the education novel. Publ: Ed, Imaginary portraits by Walter Pater, Harper, 64; auth, The unique fictional world of Walter Pater, Nineteenth Century Fiction, 58; Frances, Lady Shelley, Keats-Shelley Bull, 61; Up-hill and Down- by Christina Rossetti, Victorian Poetry, 72; plus others. Add: Dept. of English, University of Notre Dame, Notre Dame, IN 46556.

BUCCO, MARTIN, b. Newark, N.J, Dec. 3, 29; m. 56; c. 1. ENGLISH. B.A, N.Mex, Highlands Univ, 57; M.A, Columbia Univ, 57; Univ. Calif, Berkeley, 57-58; Ph.D.(Eng, Am. lit), Univ. Mo, 63. Instr. ENG, N.Dak. State Teachers Col, 58-59; Univ. Mo, 59-63; asst. prof, COLO. STATE UNIV, 63-67, assoc. prof, 67-71, PROF, 71-, fac. improv. grants, 65-67. Nat. Humanities Found. grant, summer 68. West. Lit. Asn.(asst. ed, 66-). Theory of the novel; western literature; criticism. Publ: The voluntary tongue, Wurlitzer, 57; Bulfinch's Age of fable, Harper, 66; Frank Waters, Steck, 69; Wilbur Daniel Steele, Twayne, 72; Folk poetry of Robert W. Service, Alaska Rev, fall 65; Sherwood Anderson's Hands, Colo. State Rev, spring 66; The serialized novels of Sinclair Lewis, West. Am. Lit, 69. Add: Dept. of English, Colorado State University, Fort Collins, CO 80521.

BUCHANAN, EDITH, b. Cullowhee, N.C, Oct. 21, 11. ENGLISH. Ph.D.(Eng), Duke Univ, 52. Instr. ENG, Fla. State Univ, 45-46; asst. prof, Ga. State Col. Women, 46-50; instr, Univ. Colo, 51-55; asst. prof, UNIV. N.MEX, 55-64, assoc. prof, 64-70, PROF, 70- Assoc. mem, Am. Counc. Learned Soc, 61-66. MLA; Rocky Mt. Mod. Lang. Asn.(secy-treas, 56); AAUP; Am. Asn. Univ. Women. Italian drama of the renaissance; the epic; seventeenth century literature. Publ: Milton's true knight, S.Atlantic Quart, 72. Add: Dept. of English, Bandelier 119, University of New Mexico, Albuquerque, NM 87106.

BUCHANAN, PEARL LEIGH, b. Vinton, Va. Dec. 21, 93. ENGLISH, SPEECH. B.A, Southwest. Univ.(Tex), 15; M.A, George Peabody Col, 29; Univ. Edinburgh, 57. Head dept. Eng, East. Prep. Sch, Claremore, Okla, 15-17; instr. Univ. Okla, 17; teacher, high sch, Okla, 18-23; assoc. prof. Eng. & speech, East. Ky. Univ, 23-64; RETIRED. Speech Commun. Asn; Nat. Educ. Asn; South. Speech Asn. Play production and dramatics; remedial speech; children's literature. Publ: Co-auth, Harvest of the years, 72 & auth, A late lark singing, 73, Carlton. Add: 240 Summit St, Richmond, KY 40475.

BUCHANAN, RANDALL JOHN, b. Venice, Utah, May 15, 30; m. 68; c. 2. SPEECH, DRAMA. B.A, Brigham Young Univ, 54, M.A, 58; Ph.D.(speech), La. State Univ, 64. Instr. speech & drama & tech. dir, Midwest. Univ, 60-61; asst. prof. speech & drama & dir. theatre, Southeast. La. Univ, 61-64; prof. speech, drama & Eng. & chmn. div. lang. & lit, South. State Teachers Col, 64-66; assoc. prof. SPEECH, TEX. A&I UNIV, 66-72, PROF, 72-, CHMN. DEPT. SPEECH & DRAMA, 66- U.S.A, 54-56. Am. Nat. Theatre Acad; Am. Theatre Asn; Speech Commun. Asn. Add: Dept. of Speech & Drama, Texas A&I University, Kingsville, TX 78363.

BUCHEN, IRVING H, b. New York, N.Y, Sept. 6, 30; m. 55; c. 2. ENGLISH. B.A, N.Y, Univ, 52, fel, 52-53, M.A, 55; fel, Johns Hopkins Univ, 56-60, Ph.D, 60. Instr. ENG, Pa. State Univ, 55-56; jr. instr, Johns Hopkins Univ, 56-60; asst. prof, FAIRLEIGH DICKINSON UNIV, FLORHAM-MADISON CAMPUS, 60-68, assoc. prof, 68-70, PROF, 70- Dir. Eng, Md. Inst, 58-60; Am. Counc. Learned Soc. grant, 67; consult, Univ. South. Calif, 72-73; Bucknell Univ, 73-74. Northeast Mod. Lang. Asn.(pres, 72-73); MLA; Col. Eng. Asn. Romantic, Victorian, and modern periods. Publ: Isaac Bashevis Singer and the eternal past, 68 & The perverse imagination, 70, N.Y. Univ; The modern visionary tradition and romanticism, West. Humanities Rev, winter 67; The aesthetics of the supra-novel, In: The theory of the novel, 73; Humanism and futurism: enemies or allies, In: Learning for tomorrow, 74; plus others. Add: Dept. of English, Fairleigh Dickinson University, Madison, NJ 07940.

BUCHERT, JEAN RUTH, b. Belleville, Ill, June 7, 22. ENGLISH LITERATURE. A.B, Univ. Mo, 47, M.A, 48; Fulbright scholar, Univ. Rome, 53-54; Ph.D, Yale, 57. Instr. ENG, Univ. Mo, 48-51; Univ. Rochester, 55-57; asst. prof, UNIV. N.C, GREENSBORO, 57-60; ASSOC. PROF, 60- Fel, Coop. Prog. Humanities, 67-68. MLA; Renaissance Soc. Am. Elizabethan literature; Italian influence on Elizabethan literature; Elizabethan translations. Publ: Cinthio in the Palace of pleasure: William Painter's translations from Gli Hecatommithi, Renaissance Papers 1969, 70. Add: Dept. of English, University of North Carolina at Greensboro, Greensboro, NC 27412.

BUCKALEW, RONALD EUGENE, b. Wilmington, Del, July 29, 35; m. 58; c. 2. ENGLISH. B.A, Col. Wooster, 57; univ. fel, Univ. Ill, 57-58, M.A, 59, Ph.D.(Eng), 64, study ling, 68; Germanistic Soc. Am. fel, Univ. Münster, 61-62; Univ. Calif, Los Angeles, 66. Teaching asst, Univ. Ill, Urbana, 59-61, 62-63; asst. prof. ENG, PA. STATE UNIV, 63-74, ASSOC. PROF, 74- Consult, Allyn & Bacon, Inc, 65-68; co-ed, Gen. Ling, 70- MLA (bibliogr, Int. Bibliog. Comt, 67-, head sect. Eng. ling, 70-); Ling. Soc. Am; Mediaeval Acad. Am; NCTE; Early Eng. Text Soc; AAUP. English linguistics, especially historical; Old English language and literature, especially Beowulf and Ælfric; Chaucer. Publ: A phonological analysis of present-day standard English, Gen. Ling, fall 72; Night lessons on language, In: Parts of the whole: approaches to Finnegans Wake, Pa. State Univ, 73; Beowulf, lines 1766-1767: 'oðđe' for 'seoððan'?, Neuphilologische Mitteilungen, summer 74; plus others. Add: Dept. of English, 117 Burrowes Bldg, Pennsylvania State University, University Park, PA 16802.

BUCKINGHAM, MINNIE SUSAN, b. Oakley, Ill, Feb. 23, 93. ENGLISH. A.B, Manchester Col, 23, hon. Litt.D, 56; B.D, Bethany Sem. Chicago, 31; M.A, Univ. Chicago, 33; Ph.D, Cornell, 38. Dean women, Bethany Sem. Chicago, 23-31; prof. Eng, Chicago Teachers Col, 38-43; acting head dept. Eng, Shimer Col, 44; prof. ENG. & head dept, SIOUX FALLS COL, 44-62, EMER. PROF, 62- MLA; NCTE. Religious fiction in contemporary American literature; use of religion in fiction of Margaret Oliphant; relation of Charlotte Yonge to the Oxford Movement. Publ: Ed, Church of the Brethren in Southern Illinois, Brethren Publ. House, 50. Add: R.F.D. 1, Oakley, IL 62552.

BUCKLAND, ROSCOE LAWRENCE, b. Blackfoot, Idaho, July 28, 18; m. 41; c. 2. ENGLISH, AMERICAN CIVILIZATION. B.A. & M.A, Univ. Idaho, 48; Ph.D.(Eng, Am. civilization), State Univ. Iowa, 55. Instr. Eng, Wash. State Col, 48-51; asst. prof, Long Beach State Col, 55-58, assoc. prof, 58-63, prof, 63-70, chmn. dept, 60-68; PROF. & CHMN. GEN. STUD, WEST. WASH. STATE COL, 70- Asst, Univ. Iowa, 52-55; summers, consult, tech. writing, U.S. Navy Electronics Lab, San Diego, 61, 62, 63; lectr. Workers Educ. Asn. & Nat. Arts Counc, Sydney, Australia, 68-69. U.S.A.A.F, 42-46, Sgt. Am. Stud. Asn; Philol. Asn. Pac. Coast; MLA; West. Lit. Asn.(ed. adv. bd, 66-). Australian and American frontier literature; American folklore; 19th century pseudo-science. Add: Dept. of General Studies, Western Washington State College, Bellingham, WA 98225.

BUCKLER, WILLIAM E, b. Loretto, Ky, Oct. 10, 28. ENGLISH. A.B, Univ. Ky, 44, fel, 44-45; M.A, 46; fel, Univ. Ill, 48-50, Ph.D.(Eng), 49. Instr. ENG, Univ. Ky, 45-46; Univ. Ill, 50-53; asst. prof, N.Y. UNIV, 53-58, assoc. prof, 58-61, PROF, 61-, v.chancellor acad. planning, 68-69, dean Wash. Square Col. Arts & Sci, 62-68. Fulbright lectr, Univ. London, 49-50; Ford Found. traveling fel, 51-52; ed, The Victorian Newslett. MLA. Victorian literature. Publ: Prose of the Victorian period, 58 & The major Victorian poets: Tennyson, Browning, Arnold, 73, Houghton; Matthew Arnold's books: toward a publishing diary, Droz, Geneva, 58; Passages from the prose writings of Matthew Arnold, N.Y. Univ, 63; co-auth, The literature of England, Scott, 66, 67 & (2 vols) 67; auth, A preface to our times, Am. Bk, 68. Add: Dept. of English, New York University, Washington Square, New York, NY 10003.

BUCKLEY, ANTHONY J, b. Luton, Eng, Aug. 11, 37; m. 61. DRAMA. B.A, Purdue Univ, 62, M.A, 64; Ph.D.(drama), Cornell Univ, 67. ASSOC. PROF. DRAMA, E.TEX. STATE UNIV, 67- Am. Theatre Asn. British theatre; opera. Add: Dept. of Speech & Drama, East Texas State University, Commerce, TX 75428.

BUCKLEY, JEROME HAMILTON, b. Toronto, Ont, Aug. 30, 17; nat; m. 43; c. 3. ENGLISH LITERATURE. B.A, Univ. Toronto, 39; A.M, Harvard, 40, Ph.D, 42. Instr. ENG, Univ. Wis, 42-45, asst. prof, 45-47, assoc. prof, 47-52, prof, 52-54; vis. assoc. prof, Columbia Univ, 52-53, PROF, 54-61; HARVARD, 61- Guggenheim fel, 46-47, 64; vis. prof, Univ. Colo, 60; vis. prof, Eng, Univ. Hawaii, summer 69. Christian Gaus Prize, Phi Beta Kappa, 52. MLA; Tennyson Soc; Int. Asn. Univ. Prof. Eng. Romantic and Victorian literature; poetry; intellectual history. Publ: William Ernest Henley, Princeton, 45; The Victorian temper, 51, Tennyson, the growth of a poet, 60 & The triumph of time, 66, Harvard; ed, Poems of Tennyson, Houghton, 58 & Poetry of the Victorian period, Scott, 65; auth, Victorian poets and prose writers, Appleton, 66; ed, The Pre-Raphaelites, Mod. Libr, Random, 68; auth, Season of youth: Bildungsroman from Dickens to Golding, 74 & chap, In: The Victorian poets, 68, Harvard; contrib, Victorian poetry, Stratford-upon-Avon Stud, London, 72. Add: Dept. of English, Warren House 3, Harvard University, Cambridge, MA 02138.

BUCKNER, CLAUDIA, b. Santa Paula, Calif, May 6, 44. AMERICAN LITERATURE & STUDIES. B.A, Univ. Calif, Berkeley, 67, fel, 67-72, M.A, 69, Ph.D.(Eng), 72. ASST. PROF. ENG, CALIF. STATE COL, DOMINGUEZ HILLS, 72- MLA; Popular Cult. Asn. History of sensation novel in America; American novel. Publ: The rise of the sensation novel in America, Popular Press, 74. Add: Dept. of English, California State College, Dominguez Hills, 1000 East Victoria, Dominguez Hills, CA 90747.

BUCKS, DOROTHY SIMS, b. Aurora, Ill, Oct. 7, 07. ENGLISH. A.B, Univ. Idaho, 29; A.M, Northwest. Univ, 34, Ph.D, 44. Teacher Eng, high sch, Batavia, Ill, 29-32, chmn. dept, 32-36; from instr. to assoc. prof. Eng. & humanities, George Williams Col, 36-47; PROF. ENG, HANOVER COL, 47-, dean, Long Col. for Women, 47-58. MLA; NCTE; Soc. Relig. Higher Educ. American drama; Shakespeare; Renaissance literature. Publ: The torch leads on; co-auth, James A. Herne. Add: P.O. Box 105, Hanover, IN 47243.

BUCKSTEAD, RICHARD C, b. Viborg, S.Dak, Mar. 17, 29; m. 56; c. 2. AMERICAN LITERATURE. B.A, Yankton Col, 50; M.A, Univ. S.Dak, 56; Ph.D.(Eng), State Univ, Iowa, 59. Instr, ENG, Augustana Col.(S.Dak), 57-58; ASST. PROF, Southeast Mo. State Col, 58-61; ST. OLAF COL, 61-, DIR. ASIAN STUD, 71-, asst. dean, 64-67. Assoc. Cols. Midwest grant Asian stud, 67-68; vis. prof, Chulalongkorn Univ, Bangkok, 67-68. Eng.C, U.S.A, 51-54, M/Sgt. MLA; Asn. Asian Stud. The novels of Yukio Mishima; Japanese prose; Chinese poetry. Publ: Kawabata and the divided self, China Printing, Taipei, 72; The meaning of symbol in Kawabata's Thousand cranes, Tamkang Rev, Taipei, 11/72; The search for a symbol in Kawabata's Snow country, Asian Profile, 6/73. Add: Dept. of English, St. Olaf College, Northfield, MN 55057.

BUDD, LOUIS JOHN, b. St. Louis, Mo, Aug. 26, 21; m. 45; c. 2. ENGLISH. A.B, Univ. Mo, 41, A.M, 42; Ph.D.(Eng), Univ. Wis, 49. Instr. ENG, Univ. Mo, 42,-46; from instr. to asst. prof, Univ. Ky, 49-52; from asst. prof. to assoc. prof, DUKE UNIV, 52-66, PROF, 66-, CHMN. DEPT, 73- Vis. assoc. prof, Northwest. Univ, summer 61; Guggenheim fel, 65-66; Fulbright-Hays lectr, Am. Stud. Res. Ctr, Hyderabad, 67 & fall 72. U.S.A.A.F, 42-45. MLA; Am. Stud. Asn; S.Atlantic Mod. Lang. Asn. Mark Twain; realism and naturalism; American literary history, 1865-1920. Publ: Mark Twain: social philosopher, Ind. Univ, 62; Robert Herrick, Twayne, 71. Add: Dept. of English, 325 Allen Bldg, Duke University, Durham, NC 27706.

BUDICK, SANFORD, b. New York, N.Y, July 5, 42; m. 68; c. 1. ENGLISH LITERATURE. A.B, Harvard, 63; M.A, Yale, 64, Ph.D.(Eng), 66. Instr.

ENG, CORNELL UNIV, 66-67, asst. prof, 67-72, ASSOC. PROF, 72- Vis. sr. lectr, Hebrew Univ. Jerusalem, 70-71, assoc. prof, 72-74. MLA. Restoration poetry and theology; Augustan poetics; Milton. Publ: Dryden and the abyss of light: a study of religio laici and The hind and the panther, 70 & Poetry of civilization: mythopoetic displacement in the verse of Milton, Dryden, Pope, and Johnson, 74, Yale Univ. Add: Dept. of English, Cornell University, Ithaca, NY 14850.

BUECHMANN, CLAUS-PETER, b. Schlamin, Ger, Aug. 3, 35. ENGLISH. Kiel Univ, Ger, 58; M.A, Univ. Kans, 65; Univ. N.Mex, 68-69. Instr. ENG, Univ. N.Mex, 67-68; ASST. PROF, GUSTAVUS ADOLPHUS COL, 68- MLA. Renaissance drama; analytical bibliography; 17th century poetry and prose. Add: Dept. of English, Gustavus Adolphus College, St. Peter, MN 56082.

BUELL, ARTHUR L, b. Nelsonville, Ohio, Oct. 7, 31; m. 52; c. 2. SPEECH. B.A, Marietta Col, 58; M.A, Kent State Univ, 59; fel, Ohio Univ, 61-63; Ph.D. (speech), 65. Instr. SPEECH, Marietta Col, 59-61; teaching fel, Ohio Univ, 61-63; asst. prof, MARIETTA COL, 63-66, assoc. prof, 66-73, PROF, 73-, DIR. SUMMER ACTIVITIES, 69- U.S.A.F, 50-54, S/Sgt. Speech Commun. Asn. Early United States settlement research. Add: Dept. of Speech, Marietta College, Marietta, OH 45750.

BUELL, LAWRENCE I, b. Bryn Mawr, Pa, June 11, 39; m. 62; c. 2. ENGLISH. A.B, Princeton, 61; M.A, Cornell Univ, 62, Ph.D.(Eng), 66. Instr. ENG, Tunghai Univ, 63-65; asst. prof, OBERLIN COL, 66-72, ASSOC. PROF, 72- Chmn. bd. trustees, Oberlin Shansi Mem. Asn, 72. MLA; Am. Stud. Asn; Brit. Asn. Am. Stud. American literature; twentieth century literature; comparative study of literatures in English. Publ: The design of literature, Pendulum Bks, 73; Literary transcendentalism: style and belief in the American Renaissance, Cornell Univ, 73; Unitarian aesthetics and Emerson's poet-priest, spring 68 & The Unitarian movement and the art of preaching in 19th century America, 72, Am. Quart; Transcendentalist catalogue rhetoric, vision vs. form, Am. Lit, winter 68. Add: Dept. of English, Oberlin College, Oberlin, OH 44074.

BUELL, STEPHEN DAVID, b. Manhattan, Kans, Sept. 28, 10; m. 46; c. 2. SPEECH. B.S, N.Tex. State Univ, 47, M.S, 48; Ph.D, Ohio State Univ, 62. Teacher, Jr. High Sch, Calif, 48-49; instr. speech, N.Tex. State Univ, 49-53; asst. radio-TV, Ohio State Univ, 53-55; PROF. SPEECH & DIR. EDUC. RADIO-TV, MARSHALL UNIV, 55- U.S.A, 41-45, 46, Sgt. Speech Commun. Asn; Nat. Asn. Educ. Broadcaster; Asn. Higher Educ; NEA. History and development of WSAZ-TV. Add: 1220 Ninth St, Huntington, WV 25701.

BUELL, THOMAS C, b. Newport, R.I, Aug. 14, 27; m. 55; c. 3. ENGLISH. B.A, Princeton, 50; Yale, fall 53; Harvard, summer 60; Ph.D.(Eng), Univ. Wash, 65. Asst. prof. ENG, PORTLAND STATE UNIV, 65-70, ASSOC. PROF, 70-, acting head dept, 67-68. U.S.A, 45-47. MLA; Philol. Asn. Pac. Coast. American 19th century literature. Publ: A fable of critics, Independant Sch. Bull, spring 60. Add: Dept. of English, Portland State University, Portland, OR 97207.

BUFFINGTON, ROBERT RAY, b. Belleville, Ill, Feb. 11, 33; m. 71; c. 3. MODERN AMERICAN LITERATURE. B.A, Rollins Col, 54; M.A, Vanderbilt Univ, 58, fel, 59-60, Ph.D.(Eng), 67; M.F.A, Univ. Iowa, 62. Instr. ENG, Vanderbilt Univ, 60-62; Rollins Col, 62-64; La. State Univ, Baton Rouge, 64-66; asst. prof, West. Ill. Univ, 66-68; Fla. State Univ, 68-72; assoc. prof, La. Tech Univ, 72-73; ASSOC. ED, UNIV. GA. PRESS, 73- Ed. consult, Contemporary Poetry Series, Univ. Ga. Press, 68-73. U.S.A, 54-56. MLA; S.Atlantic Mod. Lang. Asn; S.Cent. Mod. Lang. Asn; Soc. Stud. South. Lit. Modern American poetry; literary theory. Publ: The equilibrist: a study of John Crowe Ransom's poems, 1916-1963, Vanderbilt Univ, 67; Mr. Davidson in the formal garden, Ga. Rev, spring 70; The directing mind: Allen Tate and the profession of letters, South. Lit. J, spring 73; Ransom's poetics: Only God, my dear, Mich. Quart. Rev, fall 73; plus others. Add: University of Georgia Press, Athens, GA 30602.

BUFKIN, ERNEST CLAUDE, JR, b. Monticello, Miss, Apr. 27, 29. ENGLISH. B.A, Tulane Univ, 50, M.A, 52; Harvard, 58-59; Ph.D.(Eng), Vanderbilt Univ, 64. Instr. ENG, UNIV. GA, 63-65, asst. prof, 65-69, ASSOC. PROF, 69- MLA. Publ: Twentieth-century novel in English, Univ. Ga, 67; Quest in the novels of P.H. Newby, Critique, fall 65; The ironic art of William Golding's The inheritors, Tex. Stud. Lit. & Lang, winter 68; A pattern of parallel and double: the function of Myrtle in The great Gatsby, Mod. Fiction Stud, winter 69-70. Add: Dept. of English, University of Georgia, Athens, GA 30601.

BUGGE, JOHN MICHAEL, b. Milwaukee, Wis, June 3, 41; m. 66. MEDIEVAL ENGLISH LITERATURE. B.A, Marquette Univ, 63; Fulbright scholarship, Univ. Tübingen, 63-64; Danforth fel. & M.A, Harvard, 66, Ph.D.(Eng), 70. ASST. PROF. ENG, EMORY UNIV, 68- Mem. screening comt, Harbison Award for Distinguished Teaching, Danforth Found, 71-72, Grad. Fels. for Women, 72-74; Nat. Endowment for Humanities Young Humanist fel, 73-74. MLA; Mediaeval Acad. Am. Concepts of virginity and female sexuality in Medieval literature; the Medieval English alliterative tradition; Chaucer. Publ: Damyan's wanton Clyket and an ironic new twiste to the Merchant's tale, Annuale Mediaevale, 74; Rhyme as onomatopoeia in The dry salvages, Papers Lang. & Lit, 74. Add: Dept. of English, Emory University, Atlanta, GA 30322.

BUHL, PAULINA ESTELLA, English. See NOBLE, PAULINA BUHL.

BUHLER, CURT FERDINAND, Medieval Literature & History. See Volume I, History.

BUITENHUIS, PETER MARTINUS, b. Eng, Dec. 8, 25; ENGLISH, AMERICAN STUDIES. B.A, Oxford, 48, M.A, 53; Coe fel. & Ph.D.(Am. stud), Yale, 55. Instr. Eng, Univ. Okla, 49-51; Eng. & Am. stud, Yale, 55-59; asst. prof. ENG, Victoria Col, Univ. Toronto, 59-63, assoc. prof, 63-66; vis. prof, Univ. Calif, Berkeley, 66-67; PROF. & DIR. GRAD. STUD, McGILL UNIV, 67- Lectr. Am. stud, summer sch, Yale, 59, 61; Macalester Col, 62, 64, 67; Can. Counc.'fel, 63-64; Am. Counc. Learned Soc. grant, 72-73. R.N, 43-46, Sub. Lt. Am. Stud. Asn; Brit. Asn. Am. Stud; Can. Asn. Am. Stud.(treas, 67-). First World War and the British and American novel; modern British, American and Canadian novel. Publ: Ed, Henry James' French writers and American women, Compass Publ, 60; auth, The grasping imagination: the American writings of Henry James, Univ. Toronto, 70; ed, The selected poems of E.J. Pratt, Macmillan, 68; Twentieth century interpretations of the portrait of a lady, Prentice-Hall, 68; auth, Crane's The open boat as existentialist fiction, Mod. Fiction Stud, 60; Edith Wharton and the First World War, Am. Quart, fall 66; Hugh Maclennan, Forum, 69; plus other articles and reviews on American, British and Canadian fiction in several journals and quarterlies. Add: Dept. of English, McGill University, Montreal, P.Q, Can.

BULLEN, JOHN SAMUEL, b. Logan, Utah, Apr. 14, 29; m. 59; c. 4. ENGLISH. B.S, Utah State Univ, 50; M.A, Stanford Univ, 55, Ph.D.(Eng), 64. Instr. ENG, Utah State Univ, 54-56, asst. prof, 59-64, assoc. prof, 64-66; CALIF. STATE COL, SONOMA, 66-70, PROF. & CHMN. DEPT, 70- Qm-C, U.S.A, 62-64, Res, 64-66, 1st Lt. MLA; West. Lit. Asn.(bibliog. ed, 66-, v.pres, 72-73, pres. elect, 73-74); Dickens fel. English novel; western American literature. Publ: Time and space in the novels of Samuel Richardson, Utah State Univ, 65; ed, Annual bibliography of studies in western literature, West. Am. Lit, 67, 68, 71 & 72. Add: Dept. of English, California State College, Sonoma, 1801 E. Cotati Ave, Rohnert Park, CA 94928.

BULLIS, JERALD LEROY, b. Sioux City, Iowa, May 5, 44; m. 68. ENGLISH & AMERICAN LITERATURE. B.A, Wash. Univ, 66; M.A. & Woodrow Wilson fel, Cornell Univ, 69, Ph.D.(Eng), & Lane Cooper fel, 70. ASST. PROF. AM. & ENG. LIT, LAWRENCE UNIV, 70- Nat. Endowment for Arts grant, 73. Modern English literature; poetry. Publ: Taking up the serpent (poetry), Ithaca House, 73. Add: Dept. of English, Lawrence University, Appleton, WI 54911.

BULLITT, JOHN MARSHALL, b. Seattle, Wash, July 9, 21; div; c. 4. ENGLISH. A.B, Harvard, 43, Ph.D, 50. Teaching fel, HARVARD, 47-50, instr. ENG, 50-53, asst. prof, 53-56, assoc. prof, 56-62, PROF, 62-, master, Quincy House, 57-66. Regional dir. Peace Corps, Cochabamba, Bolivia, 66-68. U.S.A, 43-46, Capt. Eighteenth century English literature. Publ: Jonathan Swift and the anatomy of satire; co-ed, Samuel Johnson, idler and adventurer, Yale, 62 & 18th Century poetry and prose, Ronald, 73. Add: Dept. of English, Harvard University, Cambridge, MA 02138.

BULTMANN, PHYLLIS WETHERELL, English, History. See Volume I, History.

BUMP, JEROME FRANCIS ANTHONY, b. Pine River, Minn, June 13, 43; m. 64; c. 1. ENGLISH LITERATURE, CULTURAL GEOGRAPHY. B.A, Univ. Minn, Minneapolis, 65; Woodrow Wilson fel, Univ. Calif, Berkeley, 65-66, NDEA fel, 67-70, M.A, 66, Ph.D.(Eng), 72. ASST. PROF. ENG, UNIV. TEX, AUSTIN, 70- Hopkins Soc. English literature, 1780-1940; comparative studies. Publ: The wreck of the Deutschland and the dynamic sublime, ELH, 3/74; Hopkins, the humanities, and the environment, Ga. Rev, 6/74; Hopkins and Keats, Victorian Poetry, 9/74; plus others. Add: Dept. of English, University of Texas, Austin, TX 78712.

BUNCOMBE, MARIE HELEN, b. Washington, D.C, July 4, 29. ENGLISH. B.A, Howard Univ, 50, M.A, 52; Ph.D.(Eng. & humanities), Stanford Univ, 66. Instr. Eng, South. Univ, 52-55; A&T State, 55-56; Howard Univ, 56-59; asst. prof, Calif. State Col, Los Angeles, 63-66; assoc. prof, Wilmington Col. (Ohio), 66-72, prof. lit. & lang, 72-74; ASSOC. PROF. LIT, NEW SCH. LIB. ARTS, BROOKLYN COL, 74- Univ. Calif, Los Angeles-NDEA nat. for. lang. grant to African stud. sem, summers 68 & 69. MLA; NCTE. English Renaissance. Add: New School of Liberal Arts, Brooklyn College, Brooklyn, NY 11201.

BUNDTZEN, LYNDA KATHRYN, b. Morris, Minn. ENGLISH LITERATURE. B.A, Univ. Minn, Minneapolis, 68; A.M, Univ. Chicago, 69, Ph.D.(Eng), 72. ASST. PROF. ENG, WILLIAMS COL, 72- MLA; AAUP. Sylvia Plath; criticism; Renaissance drama. Add: Dept. of English, Williams College, Williamstown, MA 01267.

BUNGE, ELDO FREDERICK, b. Linton, N.Dak, Feb. 10, 08. ENGLISH. A.B, Luther Col, 31; A.M, State Univ. Iowa, 32, Ph.D, 40. Teacher, High Sch, Iowa Falls, Iowa, 32-34; instr, Ellsworth Jr. Col, 34-38; assoc. prof, Augustana Col. & Theol. Sem, 38-43; PROF. ENG. & HEAD DEPT, WASHBURN UNIV, 46- U.S.N.R, 43-46, Lt. Comdr. MLA; NCTE. Hero legends concerning Siegfried; Siegfried in English and German literature; Shakespeare festivals in England and North America. Add: 2405 W. 19th St, Topeka, KS 66604.

BURBANK, REX JAMES, b. Flint, Mich, Sept. 6, 25; m. 55; c. 3. ENGLISH LANGUAGE & LITERATURE. B.A, Univ. Mich, 50, M.A, 52, fel, 57, Ed.D, 60. Instr. ENG, Mankato State Col, 57-59; asst. prof, SAN JOSE STATE UNIV, 59-63, assoc. prof, 63-68, PROF, 68-, dean fac, 69-72. Res. grants, San Jose State Found, 61, Am. Philos. Soc, 63; Fulbright lectr, Thailand, 68-69. U.S.A.A.F, 43-45, 2nd Lt. Am. Stud. Asn; Melville Soc. Am. Literary criticism. Publ: Thornton Wilder, 61 & Sherwood Anderson, 64, Twayne; Idea and form, Holt, 66; co-auth, The literature of early America, 67, Literature of the American renaissance, 68 & American literature of the realistic period, 68, C.E. Merrill. Add: Dept. of English, San Jose State University, San Jose, CA 95114.

BURBICK, WILLIAM GEORGE, b. Geneva, Ohio, Apr. 27, 18; m. 41; c. 1. SPEECH & DRAMA. B.A, Bluffton Col, 41; M.A, Ohio State Univ, 47, Ph.D. (speech), 63. Instr. Eng. & speech, High Sch, Ohio, 41-42; SPEECH & DRAMA, Bluffton Col, 48-50; asst. prof, WESTMINSTER COL, 51-63, assoc. prof, 63-66, PROF, 66-, CHMN: DEPT, 63- U.S.A, 42-46, 2nd Lt. Speech Commun. Asn. Add: Dept. of Speech & Drama, Westminster College, New Wilmington, PA 16142.

BURCAW, ROBERT THEODORE, b. Bethlehem, Pa, July 3, 29; m. 57; c. 4. LITERATURE. B.A, Moravian Col, 51; M.A, Univ. Pa, 56, Ph.D, 63. Instr. ENG, overseas br, Univ. Md, 54-55; Albright Col, 55-56; assoc. prof, MORAVIAN COL, 56-69, PROF. & CHMN. DEPT, 69- Chmn. & lectr. humanities, Gen. Educ. Prog. Teachers, Temple Univ, 64- U.S.A, 53-55. NCTE; MLA. Shakespeare; the art of poetry; communication theory and mass media. Publ: The sound stratum of poetry, J. Reading Specialist,

12/65; The sound stratum of poetry, In: The initial teaching alphabet and the world of English, Initial Teaching Alphabet Found, 66. Add: Dept. of English, Moravian College, Bethlehem, PA 18018.

BURCH, FRANCIS FLOYD, S.J, b. Baltimore, Md, May 15, 32. COMPARATIVE LITERATURE, THEOLOGY. A.B, Fordham Univ, 56, M.A, 58; Ph.L, Woodstock Col, 57, S.T.L, 64; Dr, Univ. Paris, 67. Teacher Eng. & French, Gonzaga High Sch, Wash, D.C, 57-60; asst. prof. ENG, ST. JOSEPH'S COL. (PA), 67-71, ASSOC. PROF. & TRUSTEE, 71-, ASST. ACAD. DEAN, 72- AAUP; MLA; Renaissance English Text Soc. Ironic, conversational poetry 1850 to the present, French and Anglo-American; the neoplatonic tradition in literature and religion; Tristan Corbière. Publ: Tristan Corbière: l'originalité des Amours jaunes et leur influence sur T.S. Eliot, Nizet, Paris, 70; co-ed, Tristan Corbière: oeuvres complètes, Gallimard, Paris, 70; auth, Corbière and Verlaine's Romances sans paroles, Mod. Lang. Rev, 58; Clement Mansfield Ingleby on Poe's Raven, Am. Lit, 63; Soirées bretonnes: the first published verse of Alexis and Edouard Corbière, Romance Notes, 70. Add: Dept. of English, St. Joseph's College, 54th & City Line, Philadelphia, PA 19131.

BURCH, JAMES CHARLIE HORTON, b. Durham, N.C, May 4, 07; m. 45; c. 3. ENGLISH. A.B, Duke Univ, 28, A.M, 29, Ph.D.(Eng), 33. Instr. ENG, Duke Univ, 35-36; asst. prof, Ga. Inst. Technol, 45-50; assoc. prof, GA. STATE UNIV, 50-55, PROF, 55-, dean sch. arts & sci, 51-67. U.S.A, 42-45, Sgt. S.Atlantic Mod. Lang. Asn. Language of John Gower. Publ: Notes on the language of John Gower, Eng. Stud, 12/34. Add: Dept. of English, Georgia State University, 33 Gilmer St. S.E, Atlanta, GA 30303.

BURD, VAN AKIN, b. Apr. 19, 14; m. 42; c. 1. ENGLISH. A.B, Univ. Chicago, 36; M.A, Stanford Univ, 41; Ph.D, Univ. Mich, 51. Teacher, Pub. Schs, Mich, 36-40; teaching fel. & jr. instr. ENG, Univ. Mich, 46-51; prof, STATE UNIV. N.Y. COL. CORTLAND, 51-74, DISTINGUISHED PROF, 73-, chmn. dept, 59-60, 61-63 & 65-68, res. found. fels, 55, 65, 68 & 73. Am. Counc. Learned Soc. fel, 60-61, grant-in-aid, 68-69; Am. Philos. Soc. grants-in-aid, 60, 68 & 73. U.S.N, 42-46, Lt. Comdr. MLA; NCTE; Thoreau Soc; Victorian Soc. Romantic and Victorian periods of English literature, especially John Ruskin. Publ: Ed, The Winnington letters: the correspondence of John Ruskin and M.A. Bell, Harvard, 69 & The Ruskin family letters, Cornell Univ, 73; auth, A new light on the writing of modern painters & Background to modern painters: the tradition and the Turner controversy, PMLA; Ruskin's quest for a theory of imagination, Mod. Lang. Quart. Add: Dept. of English, State University of New York College at Cortland, Cortland, NY 13045.

BURDA, HELEN ELIZABETH, D.H.S, b. Jewett City, Conn, Dec. 9, 17. ENGLISH & AMERICAN LITERATURE. A.B, Annhurst Col, 60; M.A, Fordham Univ, 63; Boston Col, 63. Prin, Putnam Cath. Acad, 62-65; instr. ENG, ANNHURST COL, 65-71, ASST. PROF, 73- Milton; drama; modern poetry. Add: Annhurst College, Rte. 2, Woodstock, CT 06281.

BURDA, ROBERT WARREN, b. Chicago, Ill, Jan. 16, 32; m. 63; c. 1. MODERN LETTERS. B.S, Northwest. Univ, Evanston, 52; M.Div, Union Theol. Sem, 55; M.A, San Francisco State Col, 65. Asst. prof. ENG, ILL. WESLEYAN UNIV, 65-71, ASSOC. PROF, 71- Yeats; African literature. Publ: The varieties of hemlock, Ill. Wesleyan Univ, 73. Add: Dept. of English, Illinois Wesleyan University, Bloomington, IL 61701.

BURELBACH, FREDERICK MICHAEL, JR, b. Yonkers, N.Y, Mar. 28, 34; m. 62; c. 2. ENGLISH. B.A, Haverford Col, 56; M.A, Univ. Mich, 57; Ph.D. (Eng), Harvard, 65. Instr. ENG, Georgetown Univ, 61-63; asst. prof, Calif. State Polytech. Col, 63-65; Vanderbilt Univ, 65-67; STATE UNIV. N.Y. COL. BROCKPORT, 67-68, assoc. prof, 68-73, PROF, 73- Southeast. Inst. Medieval & Renaissance Stud. fel, summer 66; Vanderbilt Univ. res. grants, 66-67; State Univ. N.Y. res. counc. grant-in-aid, 67-68; dir. Conversation in the disciplines, State Univ. N.Y. trustees, 4/69; State Univ. N.Y. Res. Found. res. grants, 69-71; v.pres. for acad, Senate Prof. Asn, Inc, 73- MLA; Malone Soc; Renaissance Soc. Am; Southeast Renaissance Conf; Northeast Mod. Lang. Asn.(ed, journ. & mem. exec. bd, 68-). English Renaissance drama (including Shakespeare); English literature 1540-1660; bibliography. Publ: Ed, Proceedings: computer applications to problems in the humanities, State Univ. N.Y. Col. Brockport, 70; War and Peace in The shoemakers' holiday, Tenn. Stud. Lit, 68; Theme and structure in The Spanish gypsy, Humanities Asn. Bull, 68; plus one other. Add: Dept. of English, State University of New York College at Brockport, Brockport, NY 14420.

BURGAN, MARY A, b. Charleston, W.Va, Nov. 10, 35; m. 65; c. 1. ENGLISH. B.A, Seton Hill Col, 58; M.A, Univ. Ill, 60, Ph.D.(Eng), 64. Asst. prof. ENG, IND. UNIV, BLOOMINGTON, 64-69, ASSOC. PROF, 69- MLA. Nineteenth century and modern fiction. Publ: Teaching the short story in high school, Eng. Curriculum Stud. Ctr, Ind. Univ, 66; Feeling and control: a study of the proposal scenes in Jane Austen's major novels, In: The English novel in the 19th century, Univ. Ill, 72; Sister Carrie and the pathos of naturalism, Criticism, 9/73; plus one other. Add: Dept. of English, Indiana University, Bloomington, IN 47401.

BURGESS, CHARLES OWEN, b. New York, N.Y, Jan. 30, 29. ENGLISH. A.B, Johns Hopkins Univ, 48; M.A, Univ. Chicago, 49; Ph.D.(Eng), Columbia Univ, 63. Instr. ENG, Ohio State Univ, 53-55; OLD DOM. UNIV, 55-56, asst. prof, 56-63, assoc. prof, 63-66, PROF, 66-, PROVOST, 72-, dir. grad. prog, 65-72. MLA; Renaissance Soc. Am; Shakespeare Asn. Am. Shakespeare; 16th century English literature; English and continental drama. Add: Dept. of English, Old Dominion University, Norfolk, VA 23508.

BURGESS, CHESTER FRANCIS, b. Brockton, Mass, Oct. 30, 22; m. 45; c. 2. ENGLISH. B.A, Yale, 45; M.A, Univ. Notre Dame, 61, Ph.D.(Eng), 62. Instr. Eng, Yale, 46-48; private bus, 48-60; instr. ENG, Univ. Notre Dame, 60-62; asst. prof, VA. MIL. INST, 62-63, assoc. prof, 63-67, PROF, 67- Am. Philos. Soc. res. grants, 63-65; Ford Found. fel, 65-66; Folger Libr. fel, summer 68; Am. Counc. Learned Soc. sr. fel, 71. U.S.M.C, 43-46, 51-52, Capt. MLA; S.Atlantic Mod. Lang. Asn; Shakespeare Asn. Am. Joseph Conrad; Restoration period; eighteenth century drama. Publ: The letters of John Gay, Clarendon, 66; Gay's Beggar's opera and companion pieces, Appleton, 66; Conrad's The nigger of the Narcissus, Eng. Lit. in Transition, fall 72; contrib, America spreads her sails, U.S. Naval Inst, 73; auth, Othello's occupation, Shakespeare Quart, fall 73; plus numerous others. Add: Dept. of English, Virginia Military Institute, Lexington, VA 24450.

BURGHARDT, LORRAINE HALL, b. Fall River, Mass, July 9, 42; m. 66; c. 1. MODERN BRITISH & AMERICAN DRAMA. B.A, Univ. Chicago, 64, M.A, 65, Ph.D.(Eng), 68. ASST. PROF. ENG, UNIV. TENN, KNOXVILLE, 68-, ASST. DEAN LIB. ARTS, 72- S.Atlantic Mod. Lang. Asn; MLA; Am. Dialect Soc; AAUP. Theater of the absurd; William Butler Yeats; regional dialect studies, especially Tennessee. Publ: Ed, Dialectology: problems and perspectives, Univ. Tenn, 72; auth, Paul Claudel's Le Soulrer de Satin as Baroque drama, 71 & Game playing in three by Pinter, 74, Mod. Drama; The anti-hero in contemporary American and British drama, Notes Contemporary Lit, 74. Add: Dept. of English, University of Tennessee, Knoxville, TN 37916.

BURHANS, CLINTON SEARLES, JR, b. Rochester, N.Y, Mar. 26, 24; m. 49; c. 4. ENGLISH. B.A, Syracuse Univ, 48; M.A, Univ. Wis, 51, Ph.D.(Eng), 62. Instr. ENG, Univ. Md, 52-53; Univ. B.C, 55-59; MICH. STATE UNIV, 59-63, asst. prof, 63-67, assoc. prof, 67-71, PROF, 71- U.S.A, 43-46. MLA. Late 19th century American literature, particularly Mark Twain; 20th century American literature, particularly F. Scott Fitzgerald and Hemingway; contemporary American literature, particularly John Cheever and John Updike. Publ: Co-auth, 31 stories, Prentice-Hall, 60; auth, The would-be writer, Ginn & Blaisdell, 66; A critical guide to Ernest Hemingway, Am. R.D.M, 69; The old man and the sea: Hemingway's tragic vision of man, 1/60 & The sober affirmation of Mark Twain's Hadleyburg, 11/62, Am. Lit; The complex unity of In our time, Mod. Fiction Stud, fall 68. Add: Dept. of English, Michigan State University, East Lansing, MI 48823.

BURIAN, JARKA MARSANO, b. Passaic, N.J, Mar. 10, 27; m. 51. DRAMATIC ART. B.A, Rutgers Univ, 49; M.A, Columbia Univ, 50; Martin Sampson fel, Cornell Univ, 53-54; Ph.D, 55. Instr. Eng. Cornell Univ, 54-55; asst. prof. STATE UNIV. N.Y. ALBANY, 55-59, assoc. prof, 59-63, PROF. SPEECH & DRAMATIC ART, 63-, CHMN. DEPT. THEATRE, 71- Vis. assoc. prof. dramatic art, Univ. Calif, Berkeley, 61-62; U.S. State Dept. specialist's lect. grant, Czechoslovakia, fall 65; Inter-Univ. Comt. Travel Grants res. grant, Czechoslovakia, 68-69; producer & artistic dir, Arena Summer Theatre, Albany, 59 & 63-64, 66-68 & 72-73. U.S.A, 46-47, 50-51, S/Sgt. Am. Theatre Asn; U.S. Inst. Theatre Technol; Am. Soc. Theatre Res. Comparative literature; play production. Publ: American drama and theatre art, Univ. Brno, 66; The scenography of Josef Svoboda, Wesleyan Univ, 71; Theatre in Czechoslovakia; reflections of a participating observer, Drama Surv, summer 67; Arena theatre: theatre of today, Interscena, summer 67; Post-war drama in Czechoslovakia, Educ. Theater J, 73. Add: Dept. of Theatre, State University of New York at Albany, 1400 Washington Ave, Albany, NY 12222.

BURKE, ALAN RUCKER, b. West Point, Nebr, Mar. 25, 36; m. 67. VICTORIAN LITERATURE. B.A, Princeton, 58; M.A, Ind. Univ, 62, Ph.D.(Eng), 66. Teaching assoc. ENG, Ind. Univ, 60-64; instr, UNIV. ARIZ, 64-66, asst. prof, 66-72, ASSOC. PROF, 72- MLA; Dickens Soc. Victorian novel, especially Dickens; Victorian urban affairs; Victorian literature of travel and exploration. Publ: Strategy and theme of urban observation in Bleak House, Stud. Eng. Lit, autumn 69; The house of Chuzzlewit and the architectural city, Dickens Stud. Annual, summer 73. Add: Dept. of English, University of Arizona, Tucson, AZ 85721.

BURKE, ARMAND F, b. Wilkes-Barre, Pa, Dec. 24, 13; m. 42; c. 2. ENGLISH. B.A, Univ. Ala, 36, M.A, 37; Ed.D.(Eng), Columbia Univ, 50. Instr. ENG, Fairleigh Dickinson Univ, 46-47; asst. prof, STATE UNIV. N.Y. COL. BROCKPORT, 47-48, assoc. prof, 48-52, PROF, 52-, PROVOST, ALTERNATE COL, 72-, assoc. dean acad. affairs, 68-69, dean, 69-70, v.pres. for instr. & curriculum, 70-72. Vis. lectr, Univ. Md. Europ. Div, 62-63; consult, N.Y. State Eng. Counc, State Univ, N.Y. community cols, private cols. & pub. sec. schs; adv, Univ. of the Air, State Univ. N.Y. U.S.C.G, 42-46, Lt. MLA; NCTE; Conf. Col. Compos. & Commun. American literature; communication; rhetoric. Publ: Co-auth, The standardized test and ability to write: an experiment, Col. Compos. & Commun, 5/58; auth, Using the teacher-constructed diagnostic test effectively, Eng. Rec, 5/62; The changing family in American fiction, Contemporary Rev, 3/66. Add: Dept. of English, State University of New York College at Brockport, Brockport, NY 14420.

BURKE, DANIEL, F.S.C, b. Pittsburgh, Pa, Oct. 25, 26. LITERARY THEORY, ENGLISH. B.A, Cath. Univ. Am, 49, M.A, 52, fel, 54-57, Ph.D.(Eng), 57; Univ. Pa, 50-51. Lectr. ENG, DeLaSalle Col, 52-57; asst. prof, LA SALLE COL, 57-62, assoc. prof, 63-69, PROF, 69-, PRES, 69-, acad. v.pres, 60-69. Mem, Woodrow Wilson Nat. fel. comt, 65-68, chmn. region IV, 68; secy, Cath. Comn. Cult. & Intellectual Affairs, 72. Nat. Cath. Educ. Asn.(mem. exec. comt, higher educ. sect, 72); MLA; Am. Soc. Aesthetics. Literary structure; prosody. Publ: Metrical Roughness, Cath. Univ, 57; Versification, In: Encyclopedia Americana, Grolier, 61; Christian schools, secular subjects, Commonweal, 1/65; Salinger's Esmé, Mod. Fiction Stud, autumn 66. Add: Office of the President, La Salle College, Philadelphia, PA 19141.

BURKE, EDWARD J, C.M, b. Niagara Falls, N.Y, Jan. 5, 12. ENGLISH. B.A, St. Joseph's Col.(N.J), 36; M.A, St. John's Univ.(N.Y), 49, Ph.D.(Eng), 55. Chmn. dept. Eng, Niagara Univ, 55-59; dean col. lib. arts, St. John's Univ. (N.Y), 59-61, pres, 61-65; PROF. ENG, NIAGARA UNIV, 65- Col. Eng. Asn. Victorian literature; Shakespeare; contemporary theatre. Publ: Ed, That all may know thee, Niagara Univ, 56; auth, Relating to the liberal arts, Occasional Papers, 63; Chinese humanism and America, Chinese Cult, 10/65; What's a university for?, Niagara Univ. Alumni Quart, winter 69. Add: Dept. of English, Niagara University, Niagara, NY 14109.

BURKE, HERBERT CARYL, b. Vancouver, B.C, Can, Mar. 25, 17; nat; m. 42; c. 8. ENGLISH. B.A, Univ. B.C, 39; M.A, Claremont Cols, 49; univ. scholar, Stanford Univ, 49-50, Steiner fel, 50-51, Ph.D.(Eng), 54. Instr. Eng, Univ. Detroit, 54-55; asst. prof, Univ. Santa Clara, 55-57; asst. librn, Marquette Univ, 57-59; assoc. prof. ENG, St. John's Univ.(Minn), 59-66,

PROF, 66-67; MT. ALLISON UNIV, 67- Participant & scholar, York Writer's Workshop, 8/71. U.S.A, 42-46, Capt. MLA; Can. Counc. Teachers Eng; Asn. Can. Univ. Teachers. Contemporary writing: novel, lyric poetry & short story; 17th century culture and literature; interactions of fine arts, literature & pop culture. Publ: Thomas Merton: man of letters, Contiuum, summer 69; Austin C. Clarke: critical resume, 1/73 & Jack Ludwig: critical resume, 6/73, Contemporary Novelists; plus others. Add: Dept. of English, Mt. Allison University, Sackville, N.B, Can.

BURKE, JOHN EDWARD, b. Huntington, W.Va, Aug. 10, 42; c. 2. BIOMEDICAL & MASS COMMUNICATIONS. B.A, Marshall Univ, 65; M.F.A, Ohio Univ, 66; Ph.D.(commun), Ohio State Univ, 71. Instr. telecommun, Kent State Univ, 66-69; ASST. PROF. COMMUN. & MED. COMMUN, OHIO STATE UNIV, 71-, DIR. DIV. MED. COMMUN, SCH. ALLIED MED. PROF, COL. MED, 71-, asst. dir, Telecommun. Ctr, 69-71. Consult, Cleveland Bd. Educ, 68; int. proj. dir, Ohio Valley Med. Microwave Proj, 70-71; assoc. ed, J. Allied Health, 72- Nat. Asn. Educ. Broadcasters; Health Sci. Commun. Asn; Asn. Schs. Allied Health Prof; Nat. Acad. TV Arts & Sci; Speech Commun. Asn; Asn. Dirs. Biomed. Commun. Biomedical communication; telecommunications in public service; public broadcasting. Publ: Medical adaptation of microwave to health delivery, Ohio Valley Health Serv. Found, 71; The Public Broadcasting Act of 1967. Historical origins and the Carnegie Commission, 4/72, Development of the legislation, 6/72 & Congressional action and final passage, 8/72, Educ. Broadcasting Rev; plus others. Add: Medical Communications Div, Ohio State University, 1583 Perry St, Columbus, OH 43210.

BURKE, JOHN EMMETT, b. Chicago, Ill, Aug. 22, 08; m. 50; c. 4. ENGLISH & LIBRARY SCIENCE. A.B, DePaul Univ, 30, B.S, 31, M.A, 36; B.L.S, Univ. Chicago, 47; Ed.D.(admin), Univ. Denver, 57. Teacher & asst. prin, Evanston High Sch, Ill, 30-36; dean of men & asst. librn, St. Mary's Col. (Minn), 36-40; head librn, Christian Bros. Col, 43-49; George Peabody Col, 49-53; PROF. LIT. & LANG. & DIR. LIBR. & LIBR. SCI, E.TEX. STATE UNIV, 53- Consult, Univ. Dallas, 54-55; Sam Houston State Univ, 56-58. MLA; Am. Libr. Asn; NEA; NCTE. Research libraries; education research; dissertation research, growth of doctoral programs. Publ: The school librarian at work, 54, Guideposts to improved library service, 58, Planning the modern functional library, 61 & The rising tide—the research library, 65, Univ. Press. Add: Dept. of Literature, East Texas State University, Commerce, TX 75428.

BURKE, KENNETH, b. Pittsburgh, Pa, May 5, 97; m. 19, 33; c. 5. ENGLISH. Ohio State Univ, 16-17; Columbia Univ, 17-18. WRITER, 31- Lectr. lit. criticism, New Sch. Soc. Res, 37; Bennington Col, 43-62; summers, Kenyon Col, 50 & Ind. Univ, 52, 58; vis. prof, Univ. Chicago, summer 38, 49-50; Drew Univ, 62; Pa. State Univ, 63. Guggenheim fel, 35; Am. Acad. Arts & Let. & Natl. Inst. Arts & Let. grant, 46; mem, Inst. Advan. Stud, 49; fel, Ctr. Advan. Stud. Behavioral Sci, 57-58. Dial Award, 28. Natl. Inst. Arts & Let. Literature; criticism; philosophy. Publ: Counter statement, Harcourt, 31; Grammar of motives, Prentice-Hall, 45; Rhetoric of religion, Beacon, 61. Add: R.D. 2, Andover, NJ 07821.

BURKE, (LAWRENCE) MORRILL, JR, b. Portland, Maine, Sept. 13, 25; m. 50, 71; c. 5. AMERICAN LITERATURE. Ph.D.(Eng. lit), Columbia Univ, 70. Instr. ENG, Univ. N.H, 51-55; asst. prof, Univ. Maine, Portland, 58-72; ASSOC. PROF, UNIV. MAINE, PORTLAND-GORHAM, 72- U.S.A, 43-46. MLA. Robert Penn Warren; Chaucer, John Neal. Add: 96 Falmouth St, Portland, ME 04105.

BURKE, RICHARD C, b. Buffalo, N.Y, Aug. 3, 32; m. 59; c. 3. RADIO-TELEVISION, SPEECH. B.A, Univ. Buffalo, 54; M.A, Cath. Univ. Am, 59; fel, Univ. Mich, 60-62, Ph.D.(speech), 63. Instr. commun.arts, Seton Hall Univ, 59-60; ASST. PROF. speech, Cent. Mich. Univ, 62-64; RADIO & TV, IND. UNIV, BLOOMINGTON, 64- Adv. instruct. TV, U.S. Agency Int. Develop, Ministry Educ, San Salvador, 68-69; UNESCO educ. TV adv, Fac. Sci, Univ. Buenos Aires, summer 70; Fulbright prof. educ. TV, Inst. Mod. Lang, Ministry Educ, Buenos Aires, 71. U.S.A, 53-56. Latin Am. Stud. Asn; Soc. Int. Develop. Communications in education; mass media and national development. Publ: Ed, Instructional television; bold new venture, Ind. Univ, 71; Some unresolved problems in broadcast history, In: Mass media and the national experience, Harper, 71. Add: Dept. of Radio-Television, Indiana University, Bloomington, IN 47401.

BURKE, VIRGINIA M, b. Hopedale, Mass, May 19, 16. ENGLISH, ENGLISH EDUCATION. B.S. in Ed, Worcester State Teachers Col, 38; M.A, Boston Univ, 42; Grace Dodge fel, Columbia Univ, 51-52, Ed.D, 56. Teacher, High Schs, Mass, 38-46; instr. ENG, UNIV. WIS-MILWAUKEE, 46-55, asst. & assoc. prof, 55, assoc. prof, 56-60, PROF, 60-, dir, NDEA Insts. Eng, summers 66, 67. Consult, U.S. Off. Educ, 66. NCTE; Conf. Col. Compos. & Commun.(secy, 67-69); MLA; Col. Lang. Asn. Rhetoric composition; Black American literature; American dialectology. Publ: Newsletter writing and publishing, Bur. Publ, Teachers Col, 58; The lay reader program: backgrounds and procedures, Wis. Counc. Teachers Eng, 61; ed, The paragraph in context, 69 & co-ed, Black Americans: images in conflict, 70, Bobbs, A various language: perspectives on American dialects, Holt, 71 & The new century composition-rhetoric, Appleton, 71; auth, The composition-rhetoric pyramid, Col. Compos. & Commun, 2/65; The paragraph: dancer in chains, In: Rhetoric: theories for application, NCTE, 67. Add: Dept. of English, University of Wisconsin-Milwaukee, Milwaukee, WI 53201.

BURKETT, EVA MAE, b. Culleoka, Tenn, Apr. 9, 03. AMERICAN LITERATURE. B.S, Mid. Tenn. State Col, 27; M.A, George Peabody Col, 30, Ph.D, 36. Assoc. prof. Eng, Mid. Tenn. State Col, 35-47; asst. prof, Drake Univ, 47-51. teacher, McKendree Col, 51-52; educ. adv, U.S. Army Educ. Prog, Otsu, Japan, 52-54; asst. prof. Eng, Tenn. Polytech. Inst, 54-56; teacher, Anatolia Col, Greece, 56-57; assoc. prof, South. State Coll, 57-60, prof, 60-63, chmn. humanities div, 57-63; prof. Eng, State Col, Ark, 63-71. MLA; Col. Eng. Asn; NCTE; Am. Dialect Soc. American literature; teaching of composition; American dialects. Publ: Co-auth, Introductory readings in literary criticism, Addison-Wesley, 68; auth, Prose, a systematic approach to writing, Cummings Publ, 70. Add: 206 Experiment Lane, Columbia, TN 38401.

BURKHART, CHARLES, b. Macon, Mo, Sept. 13, 24. ENGLISH. A.B, Cornell Univ, 48, A.M, 49; Fulbright scholar, Oxford, 49-51; Ph.D.(Eng), Univ. Md, 58. Instr. ENG, Europ. div. & home campus, Univ. Md, 52-56; asst. prof, TEMPLE UNIV, 56-63, assoc. prof, 63-67, PROF, 67- U.S. Naval Intel, 43-46, Ens. MLA; AAUP; Victorian Soc. Am. Victorian and modern British novel; European drama. Publ: Compton-Burnett, 65 & Charlotte Bronte, 73, Gollancz; Ada Leverson, Twayne, 73. Add: Dept. of English, Temple University, Philadelphia, PA 19122.

BURKHART, LLOYD L, b. Oregon, Pa, July 30, 18; m. 42; c. 3. ENGLISH. A.B, Franklin & Marshall Col, 41; M.A, Harvard, 48, Ph.D.(Eng), 41. Asst. prof. ENG, MORAVIAN COL, 50-54, assoc. prof, 54-56, PROF, 56-, chmn. dept, 62-72. U.S.A.A.F, 42-45. MLA; NCTE. English Renaissance; contemporary prose; Chaucer. Add: Dept. of English, Moravian College, Bethlehem, PA 18018.

BURKHART, ROBERT EDWARD, b. Pittsburgh, Pa, Jan. 11, 37; m. 66; c. 1. ENGLISH. B.B.A, Univ. Pittsburgh, 58, M.A, 63; Ph.D.(Shakespeare), Univ. Cincinnati, 67. Instr. ENG, Univ. Ky, 65-67; asst. prof, EAST. KY. UNIV, 67-69, assoc. prof, 69-71, PROF, 71- U.S.A, 59-61, Res, 61-67, Capt. MLA; Shakespeare Asn. Am; S.Atlantic Mod. Lang. Asn; AAUP. Shakespeare; Renaissance literature. Publ: Co-ed, Perspectives on our time, Houghton, 70; auth, Chaucer's Absolon: a sinful parody of the miller, Cithara, 68-69; The evidence for a provincial performance of Q1 Romeo and Juliet, Eng. Lang. Notes, 70-71. Add: Dept. of English, Eastern Kentucky University, Richmond, KY 40475.

BURKMAN, KATHERINE H, b. Chicago, Ill, June 13, 34; m. 65; c. 2. COMPARATIVE LITERATURE, THEATRE. A.B, Radcliffe Col, 55; M.A. & cert. educ, Univ. Chicago, 56; Ph.D.(theatre), Ohio State Univ, 68. Teacher Eng, Columbia High Sch, 57-59; Fieldston High Sch, Riverdale, N.Y, 59-63; promotion writer textbooks, Harcourt, Brace & World, 63-64; teaching asst. rhet, Univ. Iowa, 64-65; instr. Eng, Butler Univ, 65-66; ASST. PROF. COMP. LIT, OHIO STATE UNIV, 68- Dir, Nat. Endowment for Humanities grant, 69-70, 71-72; dir, The Collection, 69-73. AAUP; Am. Theatre Asn. Modern drama; uses of theatre in teaching literature. Publ: The dramatic world of Harold Pinter: it's basis in ritual, Ohio State Univ, 71; Pinter's A slight ache as ritual, Mod. Drama, winter 68. Add: Div. of Comparative Literature, 309 Administration Bldg, Ohio State University, N. Oval Dr, Columbus, OH 43210.

BURKS, DON MARVIN, b. Huntington, W.Va, Sept. 2, 30. RHETORIC & COMMUNICATION. B.A, Marshall Univ, 52; M.A, Ohio Univ, 54; Ph.D, Univ. Wis, 62. Instr. speech, North. Ill. Univ, 56-59; asst. prof, Ill. State Univ, 62-63, assoc. prof, 63-64; asst. prof, Univ. Wash, 65-70, ASSOC. PROF. COMMUN, PURDUE UNIV, WEST LAFAYETTE, 70- Assoc. ed, Quart. J. Speech, 75-78. Sig.C, U.S.A, 54-56. Speech Commun. Asn; Cent. States Speech Asn.(award, 63). Rhetoric and philosophy. Publ: John Dewey and rhetorical theory, West. Speech, spring 68; co-auth, Rhetorical sensitivity and social interaction, Speech Monogr, 6/72; auth, Persuasion, self-persuasion and rhetorical discourse, Philos. & Rhet, spring 70; plus others. Add: Dept. of Communication, Purdue University, West Lafayette, IN 47907.

BURLIN, ROBERT B, b. Cleveland, Ohio, Oct. 7, 28. ENGLISH. B.A, Yale, 50, Ph.D.(Eng), 56; Fulbright grant, France, 50-51. Instr. Eng, Yale Col, 55-59, Morse fel, Yale Univ, 59-60; asst. prof. ENG, BRYN MAWR COL, 60-67, assoc. prof, 67-69, PROF, 69-, CHMN. DEPT, 68- MLA; Mediaeval Acad. Am. Old and Middle English literature. Publ: The Old English advent, Yale, 68; ed, Old English studies in honour of John C. Pope, Toronto, 74. Add: Dept. of English, Bryn Mawr College, Bryn Mawr, PA 19010.

BURLINGAME, ROBERT NORTHCUTT, b. Pratt, Kans, Nov. 15, 22; m. 72; c. 6. ENGLISH & AMERICAN LITERATURE. A.B, Univ. N.Mex, 46, A.M, 47; Fulbright scholar, Univ. London, 53-54; Ph.D.(Eng), Brown Univ, 54. Instr. ENG, Univ. Wyo, 49-51; Kans. State Univ, 52-53; PROF, UNIV. TEX, EL PASO, 54- Borestone Mt. Poetry Award, 61. Nat. Inst. Arts & Lett. Comparative literature; the life and writings of Hermann Hesse; the prose, fictional and non-fictional, of Leo Tolstoy. Publ: This way we walk (poems), Este Es Press, 64; Nine poems, Cibola, 66; Marsden Hartley's Androscoggin; Return to place, New Eng. Quart, 12/58; More than we had thought: Cabeza de Vaca, Haniel Long, and Our day, Southwest Rev, autumn 68; contrib, The new breed; plus numerous poems in magazines and journals, including Southwest Rev, Saturday Rev, Poetry Northwest, West. Rev. and others. Add: 409 Robinson, El Paso, TX 79902.

BURNAM, TOM, b. Swan Lake, Mont, Oct. 2, 13; m. 40. AMERICAN LITERATURE, CREATIVE WRITING. A.B, Univ. Idaho, 36, fel, 36-37, A.M, 37; Ph.D, Univ. Wash, 49. Instr. Eng, North. Idaho Col, 38-42, 45-46; advan. writing & lit, Univ. Wash, 48-50, secy. advan. writing staff, 49-50; asst. prof. ENG, Colo. State Col, 50-53, assoc. prof, 53-56, PROF, 56-63; PORTLAND STATE UNIV, 63- U.S. State Dept, lectr, Am. Stud. Sem, Helsinki & Fulbright vis. prof. Am. lit, Univ. Helsinki, Finland, 61; lectr, Am-Scand. Seminar, Leangkollen, Norway, 61; spec. lectr. Am. short story, Univ. Caen, France, May 61. MLA; Philol. Asn. Pac. Coast. Mark Twain; modern American novelists; writing of fiction and poetry. Publ: Short stories, poems, and essays in various magazines, scholarly journals and anthologies. Add: 2765 S.W. Park Rd, Lake Oswego, OR 97034.

BURNE, GLENN S, b. Los Angeles, Calif, Apr. 2, 21; m. 57; c. 4. ENGLISH, COMPARATIVE LITERATURE. B.A, Univ. Calif, Berkeley, 47; dipl. of studies, Univ. Paris, 50; M.A, Univ. Wash, 52, Ph.D.(comp. lit), 56. Assoc. Eng, Univ. Wash, 52-54, 55-56; asst. prof, Idaho State Col, 56-59; Eng. & comp. lit, Kent State Univ, 59-62, assoc. prof, 62-63; Eng. Harpur Col, 63-68; prof. Eng. & comp. lit, Kent State Univ, 68-71, acting chmn. dept. Eng, 69-71; PROF. ENG. & CHMN. DEPT, UNIV. N.C, CHARLOTTE, 71- Summers, Kent State Univ. Res. Counc. res. grant, 62 & State Univ. N.Y. Res. Found. res. fels, 64 & 65. U.S.N.R, 42-46, Lt.(jg). MLA; Am. Comp. Lit. Asn; Am. Comt. Irish Stud. Modern Romance literature; literary relations of France, England and America in last 100 years; contemporary literature. Publ: Remy de Gourmont: his ideas and influence in England and America, South. Ill. Univ, 63; ed. & transl, Remy de Gourmont; selected writings, Univ. Mich, 66; auth, Julian Green, Twayne, 72; T.S. Eliot and Remy de Gourmont, Bucknell Rev, 59; An approach to Valery's Leonardo, French

Rev, 60; Remy de Gourmont and the aesthetics of symbolism, Comp. Lit. Stud, spring 67. Add: Dept. of English, University of North Carolina at Charlotte, Charlotte, NC 28223.

BURNE, KEVIN GEORGE, b. Los Angeles, Calif, May 22, 25; m. 56; c. 4. ENGLISH, LINGUISTICS. A.B, Univ. Calif, Los Angeles, 50; M.S, Univ. South. Calif, 55, M.A, 59, Ph.D.(ling), 73. From instr. to PROF. ENG, LONG BEACH CITY COL, 56-, CHMN. LANG. ARTS DIV, 70-; RES. & WRITING, 59- Consult. ed. Eng. & ser. ed, Macmillan Publ. Co, 65-70, advising ed. & ser. ed, Dickenson Publ. Co, 65-70. U.S.N, 43-46. NCTE. Grammar and rhetoric for freshman and remedial students, especially junior college, analysis of written syntax of some fourth, fifth and sixth grade Caucasian children. Publ: Co-auth, Functional English for writers, Scott, 64; Rx: remedies for writers, 64 & Limits and latitudes, 65, Lippincott, Add: 15402 Maryknoll St, Westminster, CA 92683.

BURNET, MacCURDY, English, Linguistics. See Volume III, Foreign Language, Linguistics & Philology.

BURNEY, WILLIAM A, b. Iowa City, Iowa, Aug. 11, 27; m. 64; c. 1. ENGLISH. B.A, Univ. Iowa, 49, M.A, 54, Ph.D.(Eng), 62; Yale, 49-51. Master, Mt. Hermon Sch. Boys, 51-52; instr. ENG, Univ. Iowa, 54-55; Wayne State Univ, 56-57; Windham Col, 57-58; Mich. State Univ, 58-63; assoc. prof, CENT. CONN. STATE COL, 63-67, PROF, 67- U.S.N.R, 45-46. MLA. American and British fiction and poetry, 1900-1950. Publ: Wallace Stevens, Twayne, 68. Add: Dept. of English, Central Connecticut State College, 1615 Stanley St, New Britain, CT 06050.

BURNIM, KALMAN A, b. Malden, Mass, Mar. 7, 28; m. 48; c. 3. DRAMA & THEATER, ENGLISH. B.A, Tufts Col, 50; univ. fel. & M.A, Ind. Univ, 51; Sterling jr. fel, Yale, 57-58, Ph.D.(theater hist), 58. Lectr. speech, Northeast. Univ, 53-54; Folger Shakespeare Libr. res. fel, 57-58; asst. prof. drama, Valparaiso Univ, 58-59; Univ. Pittsburgh, 59-60; TUFTS UNIV, 60-61, assoc. prof. & dir. univ. theatre, 61-65, prof. drama, 65-69, FLETCHER PROF. DRAMA & ORATORY, 69-, CHMN. DEPT. DRAMA & SPEECH, 66- Lectr. speech, Gary Exten, Ind. Univ, 58-59; Guggenheim fel, 64-65; Am. Counc. Learned Soc. grant-in-aid, summer 66 & summer 73; Nat. Endowment for Humanities proj. grant, 67-68; Folger Shakespeare Libr. fel, summers 71 & 73. U.S.A, 46-47. Univ. Resident Theatre Asn; Am. Soc. Theatre Res; Soc. Theatre Res, Gt. Brit; MLA; Speech Commun. Asn; Am. Theatre Asn; Shakespeare Asn. Am. Renaissance and baroque scene design; Renaissance drama and theater; 18th century English theater. Publ: David Garrick: director, Univ. Pittsburgh, 60; co-auth, Aaron Hill's The prompter, Blom, 66 & Biographical dictionary of actors, actresses, musicians, dancers, managers, and other stage personnel in London, 1660-1800, South. Ill. Univ, 73; auth, Eighteenth-century theatrical illustrations in the light of contemporary documents, Theater Notebook, winter 59/60; La scena per Angolo—magic by the Bibienas?, Theater Surv, 61; David Garrick's early will, Theater Res, 5/65. Add: Dept. of Drama & Speech, Tufts University, Medford, MA 02155.

BURNS, LANDON CRAWFORD, b. Baltimore, Md, July 2, 29. ENGLISH. B.A, Yale, 51, M.A, 56, Ph.D.(Eng), 59. Instr. ENG, Univ. Pa, 58-61, asst. prof, 61-67; assoc. prof. & dean, Washington Col, 67-69; PROF, PA. STATE UNIV, DELAWARE COUNTY CAMPUS, 69- U.S.N, 51-54, Lt. MLA. Modern fiction and poetry; the short story. Publ: Ed, Nicholas Rowe's Tamerlane, Univ. Pa, 66; auth, Henry James' mysterious fount, Tex. Stud. Lit. & Lang, 63; The novels of Mary Renault, Critique, 65; ed, A cross-referenced index of short fiction anthologies and author-title listing, Stud. Short Fiction, 70 & 71. Add: Dept. of English, Pennsylvania State University, Delaware County Campus, 25 Yearsley Mill Rd, Media, PA 19063.

BURNS, NORMAN T, b. Brooklyn, N.Y, July 25, 30; m. 58; c. 3. ENGLISH LITERATURE, INTELLECTUAL HISTORY. A.B, Queens Col.(N.Y), 52; A.M, Univ. Mich, 53, Ph.D.(Eng. lit), 67. Asst. ed, Publ. Serv, Inst. Sci. & Technol, Univ. Mich, 58-62, head, Publ. Serv, 62-68; asst. prof. ENG, STATE UNIV. N.Y. BINGHAMTON, 68-73, ASSOC. PROF, 73- Fel, Henry E. Huntington Libr. & Art Gallery, summer 73. Milton Soc. Am; AAUP. Milton; 17th century English poetry; literature of religious controversy. Publ: Christian mortalism from Tyndale to Milton, Harvard Univ, 72. Add: Dept. of English, State University of New York at Binghamton, Binghamton, NY 13901.

BURNS, REX SEHLER, b. San Diego, Calif, June 13, 35; m. 59; c. 3. AMERICAN STUDIES, ENGLISH. B.A, Stanford Univ, 58; M.A, Univ. Minn, 63, Ph.D.(Am. stud), 65. Asst. prof. Eng. & dir. freshman Eng, Cent. Mo. State Col, 65-68; asst. prof. ENG, UNIV. COLO, DENVER, 68-70, ASSOC. PROF, 70-, chmn. fac. assembly, 73-74. Fulbright lectr, Univ. Thessaloniki, 69-70; consult, Dist. Attorney's Off, Denver, 71-; chmn, Nat. Am. Stud. Fac: Proj. Globeville, 73. U.S.M.C, 58-61, Res, 61-71, Capt. MLA; Am. Stud. Asn; Mod. Humanities Res. Asn. American culture 1800-1850; contemporary fiction and poetry. Publ: Co-ed, English 10:20 readings, Wadsworth, 69; Yeoman mechanic, Venturous conservative, Rocky Mountain Soc. Sci. J, 67; co-auth, A new approach to freshman English, Sch. & Community, 68; auth, Hawthorne's romance of traditional success, Tex. Stud. Lang. & Lit, 70. Add: Dept. of English, University of Colorado, 1100 14th St, Denver, CO 80202.

BURNS, STUART LeROY, b. Webster City, Iowa, Oct. 17, 32; m. 60; c. 3. AMERICAN LITERATURE. B.A, Parsons Col, 54; M.A, Drake Univ, 60; Ph.D.(Eng), Univ. Wis, 64. Asst. prof. ENG, DRAKE UNIV, 63-68, assoc. prof, 68-72, PROF, 72- Vis. prof, Eng, Ga. Col. Milledgeville, summer 73. U.S.A, 54-56. Sci. Fiction Res. Asn. Flannery O'Connor; narrative point of view as metaphor; duality in American fiction. Publ: St. Petersburg re-visited: Helen Eustis and Mark Twain, West. Am. Lit, summer 70; The rapist in Norris's The octopus, Am. Lit, 1/71; Freaks in a circus tent: Flannery O'Connor's Christ-haunted characters, Flannery O'Connor Bull, 72; plus six others. Add: Dept. of English, Drake University, Des Moines, IA 50311.

BURNS, WAYNE, b. Fincastle, Ohio, Aug. 26, 16. ENGLISH LITERATURE. A.B, Miami Univ, 38; A.M, Harvard, 40; Duke Univ, 39-40; Ph.D, Cornell Univ, 46. Instr. ENG, Miami Univ, 41-44; Cornell Univ, 44-46; Harvard, 46-47; Univ. Calif, 47-48; asst. prof, UNIV. WASH, 48-54, assoc. prof, 54-63, PROF, 63- Res. fel, Henry E. Huntington Libr, 55- MLA; Mod. Humanities Res. Asn, Gt. Brit; Am. Soc. Aesthet; Col. Eng. Asn. Victorian and modern fiction; theories of criticism; literature and psychoanalysis. Publ: Charles Reade: a study in Victorian authorship, Twayne; Towards a contextualist aesthetic of the novel, Genitron, 68; The panzaic principle, Pendejo Press, Vancouver, 72; contrib, Charles Reade and his contemporaries, In: From Jane Austen to Conrad, Univ. Minn, 67. Add: Dept. of English, University of Washington, Seattle, WA 98105.

BURRELL, EDWARD WILLIAM, b. Providence, R.I, Apr. 28, 27; m. 53. ENGLISH, EDUCATION. A.B, Fordham Univ, 49; A.M, Boston Univ, 59; Ed.D. (Eng, educ), Harvard, 64. Teacher, Providence Sch. Syst, 57-65; asst. prof. ENG. & EDUC, SALVE REGINA COL, 65-68, assoc. prof, 68-71, PROF, 71-, CHMN. COMT. GRAD. PROG, 73-, DEAN COL. & DIR. GRAD. STUD, 74- Mem, Gov. Comn. Educ. TV, R.I, 67-69. NCTE; MLA; Nat. Soc. Study Educ. Nineteenth century textbooks on all levels of instruction in fields related to teaching English, especially English grammar. Publ: Our country, In: Your reading, Am. Bk. Co, 65. Add: 48 S. Angell St, Providence, RI 02906.

BURRESS, LEE ALLAN, b. Wichita, Kans, Jan. 20, 18; m. 40; c. 3. ENGLISH. B.A, Univ. Wichita, 42; B.D, Garrett Bibl. Inst, 49; Ph.D.(Eng), Boston Univ, 55. Instr. Eng, Univ. Wichita, 46-48, asst. prof. philos, 49-51; ENG, Southwest. Col.(Kans), 53-54; prof. & head dept, Col. of Emporia, 54-58; prof. & chmn. dept, Wis. State Univ-Stevens Point, 58-68, prof, 69-71; Fed. City Col, 68-69; DEAN MAXWELL BECTON COL. LIB. ARTS, FAIRLEIGH DICKINSON UNIV, RUTHERFORD, 71- MLA; NCTE. American literature; censorship; folklore. Add: Fairleigh Dickinson University, 1000 River Rd, Teaneck, NJ 07666.

BURRIS-MEYER, HAROLD, Acoustics. See 12th Edition, American Men & Women of Science, Physical & Biological Section.

BURROUGHS, BALDWIN WESLEY, b. Houston, Tex, Feb. 22, 15. DRAMA. B.A, Wiley Col, 36; M.A, Northwest. Univ, 38; M.F.A, Yale, 50; Ph.D. (drama), West. Reserve Univ, 60. Mem. fac. DRAMA, SPELMAN COL, 42-43, 50-57, PROF, 58-, chmn. dept, 50-73. U.S.N, 43-45. Am. Theatre Asn; Nat. Asn. Dramatic & Speech Arts. African theatre. Add: Dept. of Drama, Spelman College, Atlanta, GA 30314.

BURROWAY, JANET GAY, b. Tucson, Ariz, Sept. 21, 36; div; c. 2. ENGLISH LITERATURE, CREATIVE WRITING. B.A, Barnard Col, 58; A.B, Cambridge, 60, M.A, 65; Yale Sch. Drama, 60-61. Instr. Eng. lit, Harpur Col, 61-62; lectr, Univ. Sussex, 65-70; adv, Writing Lab, Univ. Ill, 72; ASSOC. PROF. ENG. LIT, FLA. STATE UNIV, 72- Publ: Descend again, Faber, London, 60; The dancer from the dance, Faber, 65, Little, 67; Eyes, Faber & Little, 66; The buzzards, Little, 69, Faber, 70; The truck on the track, Jonathan Cape, London, 70, Bobbs, 71; The giant jam sandwich, Jonathan Cape, 72, Houghton, 73. Add: Dept. of English, 330 William Bldg, Florida State University, Tallahassee, FL 32306.

BURROWS, DAVID JAMES, b. Paterson, N.J, Aug. 30, 36; m. 58; c. 4. AMERICAN LITERATURE. B.A, Univ. N.C, 56, M.A, 57; Ph.D.(Eng), N.Y. Univ, 64, Instr. humanities, Hobart & William Smith Cols, 58-60; Eng, DOUGLASS COL, RUTGERS UNIV, 60-64, asst. prof, 64-70, ASSOC. PROF. AM. LIT, 70- Fulbright-Hayes lectr. Am. Lit, Univ. Lund, 65-66; ed, J. Rutgers Univ. Libr, 67-70. MLA (Editing Award, 67). Nineteenth and 20th century American literature. Publ: Co-auth, Private dealings: eight American writers, Almqvist & Wiksell, 69; ed, W.D. Howells' The son of Royal Langbrith, Ind. Univ, 69; co-ed, Alienation, 69 & Racism, 71, Crowell; Afro-American literature, Harcourt, 71 & Myths and motifs in literature, Free Press, 73; auth, Manuscript & typescript materials relating to Howells' Son of Royal Langbrith, J. Rutgers Univ. Libr, 6/66. Add: Dept. of English, Douglass College, Rutgers University, New Brunswick, NJ 08903.

BURROWS, DOROTHY M, b. Afton, Iowa, Sept. 19, 06. ENGLISH. A.B, Univ. Ill, 27, univ. scholar. & A.M, 28, fels, 31-33, Ph.D.(Eng), 33. Instr. Eng, Thornburn Jr. High Sch, Urbana, Ill, 29-31; prof. & head dept, Danville Jr. Col, 33-35; instr, MacMurray Col, 35-38, prof. & head dept, 38-53; instr. Eng. & humanities, UNIV. MINN, MINNEAPOLIS, 53-55, LIT. & WRITING, 55-56, asst. prof, 56-60, assoc. prof, 60-69, PROF, 69- NCTE. Conf. Col. Compos. & Commun. Comparative literature, especially English and French; effectiveness of composition instruction. Publ: Composition study in progress, Col. Conf. Compos. & Commun, 60; ed. & co-auth, Notes for the general college writing laboratory, Univ. Minn, 56, 57, 59, 61, 63; co-auth, The search for awareness, Prof. Develop. Rev, winter 68. Add: 3814 Edmund Blvd, Minneapolis, MN 55406.

BURROWS, ROBERT NELSON, b. North Reading, Mass, Dec. 21, 23; m. 51; c. 3. AMERICAN LITERATURE. B.A, Colo. Col, 47; dipl, Univ. Edinburgh, Scotland, 49; dipl, Univ. Poitiers, France, 49; dipl, Univ. Innsbruck, Austria, 50; M.A, Univ. Pa, 56, Ph.D, 59. Instr. Eng, Hardin-Simmons Univ, 51-52; asst. prof, 52-53, assoc. prof, 53-54; asst. prof, East. Baptist Col, 54-59, lectr. Coe Found. Am. Civilization Prog, 59; prof. Eng. & chmn. div. humanities & grad. counc, Ouachita Baptist Col, 59-61; prof. ENG, E.Cent. State Col, 61-65; PROF. & CHMN. DEPT, UNIV. WIS-WHITEWATER, 65- Danforth assoc, 58- U.S.M.C, 42-46, Capt. S.Cent. Col. Eng. Asn.(pres, 62-63); MLA; NCTE; Am. Stud. Asn; Am. Civil Liberties Union. The New York City novel; Theodore Dreiser; American topographical literature. Publ: Faulkner's view of Christianity, Miss. Quart, 61; Theme as controlling device in Howells' A hazard of new fortunes, Wis. Eng. J, 67. Add: Dept. of English, University of Wisconsin-Whitewater, Whitewater, WI 53190.

BURT, ARTHUR K, b. Pocatello, Idaho, Jan. 26, 03. DRAMA. B.A, Oxford, 26, M.A, 31. Instr. ENG, Univ. Wis, 26-29; assoc. prof, CITY COL. NEW YORK, 31-71, EMER. PROF, 71- U.S.N.R, 42-46, Lt. Comdr. MLA; Shakespeare Asn. Am. Elizabethan literature. Add: 220 MacFarlane Dr, Delray Beach, FL 33444.

BURT, FORREST DEAN, b. Flora, Ill, Nov. 8, 39; m. 61; c. 3. ENGLISH. B.A, Wayland Baptist Col, 62; M.A, Tex. Tech Univ, 65, Ph.D.(Eng), 67.

Teacher, Union High Sch, 63-64; instr. ENG, Tex. Tech Univ, 66; from asst. prof. to ASSOC. PROF. TEX. A&M UNIV, 67- Nat. Endowment for Humanities grant, 71; dir, Tex. Conf. Placement, Exemption & Credit in Eng, 72. Conf. Col. Compos. & Commun; MLA; NCTE. Freshman English and the training of teachers of English; psychological criticism of literature; Victorian and modern British prose and poetry. Publ: Co-auth, The Forand writer, Brady Publ, 73; auth, William Somerset Maugham: an Adlerian Interpretation, J. Individual Psychol, 70; Equivalency testing: a major issue for college English, NCTE/ERIC, 74. Add: Dept. of English, Texas A&M University, College Station, TX 77843.

BURT, NATHANIEL, b. Moose, Wyo, Nov. 21, 13; m. 41; c. 2. ENGLISH, MUSIC. B.S, Mus. Ed, N.Y. Univ, 39; M.F.A, Princeton, 49. Asst. MUSIC, Princeton, 39-41; RES. & WRITING, 41- U.S.N, 42-45, Lt. Soc. Am. Hist; Century Asn; Auth. League Am; PEN Club. Publ: Rooms in a house, 47 & Question on a kite, 50, Scribner; Scotland's burning, 54, Make my bed, 57, The perenniel Philadelphians, 63, Leopards in the garden, 68 & First families, 70, Little; War cry of the west, Holt, 64; Opera in Arcadia, Musical Quart, 55; Student life in Nassau Hall, Princeton, 56; The garden poets, N.J. Lit, 64. Add: 20 Hibben Rd, Princeton, NJ 08540.

BURTNESS, PAUL SIDNEY, b. Chicago, Ill, June 30, 23; m. 45; c. 2. OLD & MIDDLE ENGLISH. A.M, Univ. Chicago, 47, Ph.D, 53. Instr. ENG, Univ. Kans. City, 49-53; asst. prof, NORTH. ILL. UNIV, 53-57, assoc. prof, 57-62, PROF, 62-, DEAN COL. LIB. ARTS & SCI, 69- Ellis L. Phillips intern acad. admin, Stanford Univ, 65; Univ. Mich, 66; consult, Coronet Films, 71-; mem, Counc. Cols. Arts & Sci. U.S.N.R, 43-46, Lt.(jg). MLA; NCTE; Conf. Col. Compos. & Commun; Am. Asn. Higher Educ; Am. Conf. Acad. Deans. The language and art of Chaucer and Milton; English composition—grammar and rhetoric; the governance and development of American institutions of higher learning. Publ: Co-auth, The puzzle of Pearl Harbor, 62 & The close reading of factual prose, 62, Harper; co-ed, The new university reader, Am. Bk. Co, 66; co-auth, Practical English for colleges, 68 & Effective English for business communication, 70, South-West; co-ed, The strategy of prose, Van Nostrand, 70; co-auth, Research methodology: The problem of Pearl Harbor intelligence reports, Mil. Affairs, fall 61, The strange assignment of USS Lanikai, U.S. Naval Inst. Proc, 10/63 & Secretary Stimson and the first Pearl Harbor investigation, Australian J. Polit. Sci. & Hist, spring 68; plus others. Add: College of Liberal Arts & Sciences, 214 Reavis East, Northern Illinois University, DeKalb, IL 60115.

BURTON, DOLORES MARIE, b. Boston, Mass, Aug. 21, 32. ENGLISH, LINGUISTICS. A.B, Emmanuel Col.(Mass), 53; M.A, Boston Col, 61; Am. Asn. Univ. Women fel, Univ. London, 65-66; Ph.D.(Eng), Harvard, 68. Teacher, Notre Dame Acad, 56-62; asst. prof. Eng, Emmanuel Col.(Mass), 64-69; RHET, BOSTON UNIV, 69-72, ASSOC. PROF, 73- Dir, Educ. Prof. Develop. Act Prog. in Standard Eng. as Second Dialect, Emmanuel Col, 69-70; deleg, Comt. Shakespeare & Comput. Stud, World Shakespeare Congr, 8/71; Fulbright-Hays sr. lectr, Univ. Lodz, 73-74. MLA; Ling. Soc. Am; Shakespeare Asn. Am; Asn. Comput. Mach. Computer-assisted analysis of the grammatical style of Shakespeare; Shakespeare's stylistic development; theory and method of stylistic analysis. Publ: Co-auth, English stylistics: a bibliography, Mass. Inst. Technol, 68; ed, Language and learning: investigations and interpretations, Harvard Educ. Rev, 72; auth, Shakespeare's grammatical style, Univ. Tex, 73; Some uses of a grammatical concordance, Comput. & Humanities, 3/68; Intonation patterns of sermons in seven novels, Lang. & Style, 70; co-auth, The style function, Poetics, 73. Add; Div. of Rhetoric, Boston University, 871 Commonwealth Ave, Boston, MA 02215.

BURTON, DWIGHT L, b. Stuntz, Minn, Aug. 9, 22; m. 68; c. 2. ENGLISH EDUCATION. B.A, Univ. Minn, 43, M.A, 47, Ph.D.(Eng. educ), 51. Instr, High Sch, Wis, 46-47; Univ. Minn. High Sch, 47-49, head dept. Eng, 49-52; asst. prof. Eng. educ, FLA. STATE UNIV, 52-54, assoc. prof, 54-57, PROF. Eng. educ, 57-62, ENG, 65-, ASSOC. DEAN, COL. EDUC, 73-, head dept. Eng. educ, 62-73. Ed. Eng. J, 55-64; field reader, Bur. Res, U.S. Off. Educ, 65-; mem. adv. bd, NCTE-ERIC, 66-, distinguished lectr, NCTE, 68, chmn, Res. Found, 69-72. U.S.A, 43-46, Capt. NCTE (award, 64, v.pres, 65; distinguished serv. award, 70); Nat. Conf. Res. Eng; Conf. Eng. Educ.(chmn, 64-66). Teaching of English in the high schools; teaching of literature; teacher education in English. Publ: Co-auth, Patterns of literature (4 vols), Singer, 67; auth, Literature study in the high schools, 70 & co-auth, Teaching English in today's high schools, 70, Holt; English in no man's land: some suggestions for the middle years, Eng, J, 1/71; The content of literature in the high school, In: Reaching children and young people through literature, Int. Reading Asn, 71; The elitist ideal in the teaching of English, Educ. Forum, 3/73; plus three others. Add: College of Education, Florida State University, Tallahassee, FL 32306.

BURTON, HOWARD A, b. Houston, Tex, Aug. 15, 16; m. 52; c. 3. ENGLISH LITERATURE. A.B, Howard Col, 36; Jr. Dupont fel, Univ. Va, 36-37, M.A, 47; Ph.D, Univ. Calif, Berkeley, 52. Assoc. prof. educ, Ala. Col, 46; instr. ENG, Bradley Univ, 46-48; Apprentice Sch, U.S. Naval Yard, Vallejo, Calif, 52; Purdue Univ, 52-56; from instr. to ASSOC. PROF, RIVERSIDE CITY COL, 56-, FAC. LECTR, 64- U.S.A.A.F, 43-46, S/Sgt. NCTE. Eighteenth century English literature; art and aesthetics of the motion picture; teaching techniques in literature. Publ: Everyman rides again, Film Quart, fall 53; Ends shaped, not rough hewed, Prairie Schooner, fall 55; Development of taste in movies, Col. Eng, 1/56, reprinted 63. Add: Dept. of English, Riverside City College, Riverside, CA 92506.

BURTON, KATHERINE, b. Trumbull, Conn, June 5, 06. ENGLISH LITERATURE. A.B, Mt. Holyoke Col, 27, Bardwell Mem. fel, Radcliffe Col, 27-28, A.M, 28. Instr, Carnegie Inst. Technol, 28-29; from instr. to assoc. prof, ENG, WHEATON COL.(MASS), 29-51, prof, 51-72, EMER. PROF, 72- MLA. Social backgrounds of American literature; 18th century English literature. Add: Box 367, Norton, MA 02766.

BURTON, MARY ELIZABETH, b. St. Louis, Mo, Oct. 11, 00. LITERARY HISTORY. A.B, Univ. Louisville, 22, A.M, 25; Ph.D, Cornell Univ, 34. Instr. ENG, Ill. Woman's Col, 24-25; Randolph-Macon Woman's Col, 25-29; from instr. to prof, UNIV. LOUISVILLE, 29-70, EMER. PROF, 70- MLA; Mod. Humanities Res. Asn; AAUP; Eng-Speaking Union. Creative writing, prose; Wordsworth research. Publ: The one Wordsworth, Univ. N.C, 42 & Archon Bks, 72; The letters of Mary Wordsworth, Clarendon, 58. Add: 3125 Randolph Ave, Louisville, KY 40206.

BURTON, THOMAS R, b. Ogden, Utah, Oct. 7, 33; m. 59; c. 3. ENGLISH LITERATURE. B.S, Brigham Young Univ, 59, fel, 59-60, M.A, 60; Ph.D. (Eng), Univ. Wash, 67. Instr. ENG, WEBER STATE COL, 63-65, asst. prof, 66-68, assoc. prof, 69-73, PROF. & CHMN. DEPT, 73- U.S.N, 53-55. Restoration and eighteenth century English literature; Renaissance and early seventeenth century English literature. Publ: The animal love and fable traditions in Dryden's The hind and the panther, Univ. Microfilms, 67; Literature and the technological society, Phi Kappa Phi J, fall 71; The word and the sword: rhetoric in Marlowe's Tamberlaine, Rocky Mountain Mod. Lang. Asn, 72. Add: Dept. of English, Weber State College, Ogden, UT 84403.

BURWELL, ROSE MARIE, b. Mar. 12, 34; c. 6. MODERN FICTION, FILM. B.A, Augustana Col.(Ill), 59; M.A, Univ. Iowa, 66, Ph.D.(Eng), 69. ASST. PROF. ENG, NORTH. ILL. UNIV, 70- MLA; AAUP. English novel. Publ: A chronological catalogue of D.H. Lawrence's reading, spec. issue D.H. Lawrence Rev, fall 70; A chronological catalogue of D.H. Lawrence's reading: addenda, D.H. Lawrence Rev, spring 73; Joyce Carol Oates and an old master, Critique, summer 73; Schopenhauer, Hardy and Lawrence: toward a new understanding of Sons and lovers, Twentieth Century Literature, winter 74. Add: Dept. of English, Northern Illinois University, DeKalb, IL 60115.

BUSACCA, BASIL, b. Racine, Wis, Nov. 24, 17; m. 40, 62; c. 2. ENGLISH. B.A, Univ. Wis, 39, M.A, 41, univ. fels, 44-45, 46, Ph.D, 50. Instr. Eng, Exten. Div, Univ. Wis, 46-48, lib. stud. & comp. lit, Univ, 48-49, comp. lit, 50-52; Eng. Carroll Col, 49-50; asst. prof, Ripon Col, 52-55; assoc. prof. ENG. & COMP. LIT, OCCIDENTAL COL, 55-63, PROF, 63-, CHMN. DEPT, 70- Summers, guest prof. comp. lit, Univ. South. Calif, 57, 60 & Queens Col.(N;Y), 62; consult. interdisciplinary progs, Calif. State Col, Long Beach, 62, lectr, 68; consult. adv. placement teaching, State Calif. Dept. Educ, 67. U.S.A, 45-46. Col. Eng. Asn.(regional v.pres, 62-63; pres, 63-64); MLA; Conf. Col. Compos. & Commun; NCTE; Philol. Asn. Pac. Coast; Am. Comp. Lit. Asn; Int. Comp. Lit. Asn. Analytical scholarship; analysis of novel, drama, and critical theory. Publ: Common premises in the new drama, In: Proceedings of the fourth international congress of the International Comparative Literature Association, Mouton, The Hague, 66; Brecht and the destruction of theatre, In: Medieval epic to the epic theatre of Brecht, Univ. South. Calif, 68; This earth my brother, In: Africa report, 71; plus others. Add: Dept. of English, Occidental College, Los Angeles, CA 90041.

BUSCH, FREDERICK MATTHEW, b. Brooklyn, N.Y, Aug. 1, 41; m. 63; c. 2. AMERICAN & MODERN LITERATURE. A.B, Muhlenberg Col, 62; Woodrow Wilson fel, Columbia Univ, 62-63, M.A, 67. Writer, N.Am. Precis Syndicate, Inc, 64-65; assoc. ed, Sch. Mgt. Mag, 65-66; ASSOC. PROF. ENG, COLGATE UNIV, 66-, Ford Found grant, 70. AAUP. Fiction writing; modern American fiction; 19th century British fiction. Publ: I wanted a year without fall (novel), 71 & Breathing trouble (short fiction), 73, Clader & Boyars, London; Hawkes: a guide to his fictions, Syracuse Univ, 73; But this is what it is to live in hell: William Gass's In the heart of the heart of the country, spring 73 & The whale as shaggy dog: Melville and the man who studied Yoga, summer 73, Mod. Fiction Stud; contrib, O'Henry prize stories 1974, Doubleday, 74. Add: Dept. of English, Colgate University, Hamilton, NY 13346.

BUSFIELD, ROGER M, JR, b. Ft. Worth, Tex, Feb. 4, 26; m. 48; c. 3; m. 62; c. 1. SPEECH. A.B, Southwest. Univ, 47, M.A, 48; Ph.D, Fla. State Univ, 54. Asst. prof. drama, Southwest. Univ, 47-49; instr. speech, Univ. Ala, 49-50; Fla. State Univ, 50-54; asst. prof, Mich. State Univ, 54-59; consult, Gen. Motors Corp, 60; Consumers Power Co, 60-61; dir. educ. & pub. relat, Mich. Hosp. Asn, 61-66, assoc. dir, 66-71, Dir, 71-73; EXEC. DIR, ARK. HOSP. ASN, 73- Vis. lectr, Ohio Univ, 62; trustee, Cent. Mich. Univ, 67-78; mem, Gov. Comn. Higher Educ, Mich, 72- U.S.M.C, 43-46. Speech Commun. Asn; Am. Theatre Asn. Speech writing; playwriting; dramatic criticism. Publ: The playwright's art, 58 & co-auth, The children's theatre, 60, Harper; Theatre art bibliography, 1953-57, Am. Educ. Theatre Asn, 63. Add: P.O. Box 1489, Conway, AR 72032.

BUSH, DOUGLAS, b. Morrisburg, Ont, Mar. 21, 96; nat; m. 27; c. 1. ENGLISH LITERATURE. B.A, Univ. Toronto, 20, M.A, 21, hon. Litt.D, 58; Ph.D.(Eng), Harvard, 23; hon. Litt.D, Tufts Univ, 52, Princeton, 58, Oberlin Col, 59, Harvard, 59, Swarthmore Col, 60, Boston Col, 65, Mich. State Univ, 68 & Merrimack Col, 69; hon. L.H.D, South. Ill. Univ, 62 & Marlboro Col, 66. Sheldon traveling fel. from Harvard, Eng, 23-24; instr. ENG, Harvard, 24-27; asst. prof, Univ. Minn, 27-28, assoc. prof, 28-31, prof, 31-36, chmn. dept, 35-36; assoc. prof. HARVARD, 36-37, prof, 37-57, Gurney prof, 57-66, EMER. PROF, 66- Guggenheim fel, Eng, 34-35; Am. Philos. Soc. Jayne lect, 67; lect, Piedmont Univ. Ctr, Winston-Salem, N.C, 68; mem, Comt. Scholars for Friends of Am. Counc. Learned Soc, 68-; lectr, Va. Univ. Ctr, spring 69. Am. Counc. Learned Soc. Award, 57. Mod. Humanities Res. Asn, Gt. Brit.(pres, 55); cor. fel. Brit. Acad; MLA; Am. Philos. Soc. Classical tradition in English literature; Renaissance and 17th century; English poetry of the 19th century. Publ: Mythology and the Renaissance tradition in English poetry, Univ. Minn, 32, rev. ed, Norton, 63; Mythology and the romantic tradition in English poetry, Harvard, 37, Norton 63 & Harvard, 67; The Renaissance and English humanism, Univ. Toronto, 39, 62; Paradise lost in our time, Cornell Univ, 45; English literature in the earlier seventeenth century, Clarendon, 45, rev. ed, 62; Portable Milton, Viking, 49; Science and English poetry, Oxford, 50, 67; English poetry: the main currents from Chaucer to the present, Methuen, Oxford, 50, rev. ed, 61, 63, 68; Tennyson selections, 51; John Keats: selected poems and letters, 59 & Complete poetical works of J. Milton, 65, Houghton; co-auth, Shakespeare's sonnets, 61; auth, John Milton, 64, John Keats, 66, Matthew Arnold, 71 & Jane Austen, 75, Macmillan; Prefaces to Renaissance literature, Harvard & Norton, 65; Engaged and disengaged, Harvard, 66; Pagan myth and Christian tradition in English poetry, Am. Philos. Soc, 68; Latin and Greek poems, Vol. I, 70 & co-auth, Minor English poems, Vol. II, 72,

In: Variorum commentary on the poems of John Milton, Routledge & Columbia Univ; auth, Milton, In: English poetry: select bibliographical guides, Oxford, 71. Add: 3 Clement Circle, Cambridge, MA 02138.

BUSH, GEORGE EDWARD, b. Brooklyn, N.Y, Dec. 8, 38. ENGLISH. B.A, St. John's Univ.(N.Y), 60, asst. & M.A, 62, fel. & Ph.D.(Eng), 65. Asst. Eng, St. John's Univ.(N.Y), 61-62, teaching fel, 64-65; asst. prof. ST. FRANCIS COL.(N.Y), 65-71, ASSOC. PROF. ENG, 71-, PROF. BALLET, 73- Am. Philos. Soc. res. grant, 67-68; abstractor, Abstr. Eng. Stud; ballet soloist, N.J. Class. Ballet Co, 72 & Igor Youskevitch Concert Dance Group, 72. MLA; NCTE. Medieval and eighteenth century English literature. Publ: The fable in the English literary periodical; Univ. Microfilms, 65; Gulliverania, I, II & III, Scholar's Facsimilies, 70, 71 & 72; A bibliography of modern mythic plays, Bull. New York Pub. Libr, fall 69; James Purdy: a checklist, Bull. Bibliog, 1-3/71. Add: 71-40 112th St, Forest Hills, NY 11375.

BUSH, JARVIS E, b. Bay City, Mich, July 5, 11; m. 34; c. 2. ENGLISH. A.B, West. Reserve Univ, 34, M.A, 41. Instr. Eng, Adelbert Col, West. Reserve Univ, 38-42, asst. dean, 41-42; teacher Eng, Wauwatosa Sr. High Sch, Wis, 52-60; dir. sec. sch. Eng, Wauwatosa Pub. Schs, 60-62; asst. prof. ENG, UNIV. WIS-OSHKOSH, 62-72, ASSOC. PROF, 72-, DIR. DIV. COMPOS. & SURV, DEPT. ENG, 68- Chmn. comt. affiliate policy, NCTE, 60-61, secy. sect, 62- Meritorious serv. award, Wis. Counc. Teachers Eng, 59. NEA; NCTE; Col. Eng. Asn; Conf. Col. Compos. & Commun; MLA. Secondary school English curriculum; nature of composition; structural linguistics. Publ: Writing is for readers, Britannica Press, 61; Non-fiction 1, 61 & Currents in nonfiction, 68, Macmillan. Add: Dept. of English, University of Wisconsin-Oshkosh, Oshkosh, WI 54901.

BUSH, OAKLEIGH ROSS, Geography of Europe & Soviet Union, Political Geography. See 12th Edition, American Men & Women of Science, Social & Behavioral Sciences Section.

BUSH, ROBERT B, b. Roseland, N.J, Feb. 19, 17. ENGLISH, AMERICAN LITERATURE. A.B, Princeton, 38; A.M, Columbia Univ, 49; Ph.D.(Eng), Univ. Iowa, 57. Instr. ENG, Univ. Va, 49-52; La. State Univ, 54-55; asst. prof, The Citadel, 56-59; instr, Hunter Col, 59-66, asst. prof, LEHMAN COL, 66-72, ASSOC. PROF, 72- Newberry Libr. fel, Chicago, spring 62. U.S.A, 41-45, 1st Lt; Bronze Star Medal; Fr. Croix de Guerre; Belg. Croix de Guerre; Belg. Chevalier, Ordre de Couronne. Nineteenth century Southern fiction. Publ: Co-ed, Paddy McGann and As good as a comedy, Vol. III, In: Centennial edition writings William Gilmore Simms, Univ. S.C, 72; ed. & contrib, Grace King of New Orleans, La. State Univ, 73; Will N. Harben's Northern Georgia fiction, Miss. Quart, spring 67; Grace King and Mark Twain, Am. Lit, 3/72. Add: Dept. of English, Herbert H. Lehman College, Bedford Park Blvd. W, Bronx, NY 10468.

BUSH, SARGENT, JR, b. Flemington, N.J, Sept. 22; 37; m. 60; c. 2. ENGLISH, AMERICAN LITERATURE. A.B, Princeton, 59; M.A, Univ. Iowa, 64, Ph.D.(Eng), 67. Asst. prof. ENG, Washington & Lee Univ, 67-71; UNIV. WIS-MADISON, 71-73, ASSOC. PROF, 73- Summer stipend, Nat. Endowment for Humanities, 69; Coop. Prog. Humanities fel, 69-70; Am. Counc. Learned Soc. fel, 74; mem, Am. Lit. Sect, MLA. U.S.A, 59-60, 61-62. Midwest Mod. Lang. Asn. Thomas Hooker; Nathaniel Hawthorne; colonial, early national and 19th century American literature. Publ: Bosom serpents before Hawthorne: the origins of a symbol, Am. Lit, 5/71; Thomas Hooker and the Westminster Assembly, William & Mary Quart, 4/72; The growth of Thomas Hooker's The poor doubting christian, Early Am. Lit, spring 73; plus others. Add: Dept. of English, University of Wisconsin-Madison, Helen White Hall, Madison, WI 53706.

BUSHING, ARTHUR STORY, b. Oroville, Wash, Mar. 24, 22; m. 44; c. 4. ENGLISH LITERATURE. A.B, Maryville Col, 43; Stanford Univ, 44; Sorbonne, 45; A.M, Univ. Tenn, 48; State Univ. Iowa, summers, 48, 49; scholar, Duke Univ, summer, 56. Instr. physics, MARYVILLE COL, 43, from asst. prof. to ASSOC. PROF. ENG. LIT, 47-, DIR. SUMMER SCH, 69-, DIR. CONTINUING EDUC, 73-, dean men, 57-65. Ford Found. fel. Asian stud, Univ. Chattanooga, 65-66. U.S.A, 43-45. Am. Asn. Higher Educ. William Shakespeare; Henry Fielding. Publ: Manual of outlining and research, Maryville Col, 72. Add: Dept. of English Literature, Maryville College, Maryville, TN 37801.

BUSHMAN, JOHN CONRAD, b. Chicago, Ill, Mar. 28, 14; m. 38; c. 2. ENGLISH. A.B, Univ. Ill, 36, A.M, 37, Ph.D, 43. Asst, Univ. Ill, 37-43, instr, 43-46; asst. prof. ENG, St. Louis Univ, 46-53; asst. prof, CALIF. STATE UNIV, LOS ANGELES, 53-56, assoc. prof, 56-62, PROF, 62- NCTE. American literature; teacher training; textbooks for high school and junior high school English classes. Publ: Co-auth, American college English & Readings for college English, 61 & 66, co-auth, Read and write, 61, 66 & 72, co-ed, Scope reading series (6 vols), 65 & 67; co-auth, Language in your life (4 vols), 70 & co-ed, Read and write, 72, Harper, co-ed, Channel one, Dickenson, 70. Add: 207 N. Pasqual Ave, San Gabriel, CA 91775.

BUTCHER, PHILIP, b. Washington, D.C, Sept. 28, 18; m. 48; c. 2. ENGLISH. A.B, Howard Univ, 42, A.M, 47; Gen. Educ. Bd. fel, 48-49; Whitney opportunity fel, 51-52; Ph.D.(Eng. & comp. lit), Columbia Univ, 56. From instr. to assoc. prof. ENG, MORGAN STATE COL, 47-59, PROF, 59-, DEAN, GRAD. SCH, 72- Lit. ed, Opportunity Mag, 47-49; Am. Philos. Soc. res. grants, 68-69 & 73. U.S.A, 43-46, T/Sgt. MLA; Col. Lang. Asn.(creative scholar. award, 64). American literature; American studies. Publ: George W. Cable: the Northampton years, Columbia Univ, 59; George W. Cable, Twayne, 62; ed, The William Stanley Braithwaite reader, Univ. Mich, 72; auth, Mark Twain's installment on the national debt, spring 69 & W.S. Braithwaite's Southern exposure: rescue and revelation, spring 71, South. Lit. J; Two early Southern realists in revival, CLA Jour, 9/70. Add: Graduate School, Morgan State College, Baltimore, MD 21239.

BUTLER, A. Z, b. Loris, S.C, Nov. 16, 13. ENGLISH. A.B, Univ. S.C, 35; A.M, Vanderbilt Univ, 42. Teacher, High Sch, S.C, 35-37; prin, Travelers Rest, 37-41; teaching fel, Vanderbilt Univ, 41-42; instr. Eng, Booles Sch, 42-44; Ala. Polytech. Inst, 44-45; teaching asst, Univ. Wis, 46-48; from asst. prof. to assoc. prof. ENG, LA TECH UNIV, 48-70, PROF, 70- Browning's Paracelsus. Add: 610 N. Vienna St, Ruston, LA 71270.

BUTLER, FRANCELIA M, b. Cleveland, Ohio, Apr. 25, 13; m. 39; c. 1. ENGLISH, HISTORY OF MEDICINE. B.A, Oberlin Col, 34; Rockefeller res. grant, 51-52; M.A, Georgetown Univ, 59; Virginia Mason Davidge fel, Univ. Va, 59-62, Elizabeth Garrett fel, 62-63, Ph.D.(Eng), 63. ASST. PROF. ENG, Univ. Tenn, 63-65; UNIV. CONN, 65-, fac. res. grant, 67-68. Fac. res. grant, Univ. Tenn, 64; Ford Found grant, Southeast. Renaissance Conf, 65; Fulbright-Hays lectr, Jagiellonian Univ, 67-68; mem, Eng. Inst. MLA; South. Mod. Lang. Asn. Medical-scientific undercurrents of literature; children's literature. Publ: The skip rope book, Dial, 63; The strange critical fortunes of Shakespeare's Timon of Athens, Iowa State Univ, 66; ed, The doctor on the stage, medical undercurrents of seventeenth century drama, Univ. Tenn, 67; ed, Children's literature, Vols. I, II & III, 72, 73 & 74; co-auth, James Marion Sims: pioneer cancer protagonist, Cancer, 3/50; auth, John Penkethman's pseudonymous plague works, 1625-1636, Stud. Philol, 10/60; The Ruskin Commonwealth: an American experiment in Marxian socialism, Tenn. Hist. Quart, 12/64. Add: Dept. of English, University of Connecticut, Storrs, CT 06268.

BUTLER, GLENN ALLEN, b. Braman, Okla, Aug. 8, 28; m. 52; c. 2. COMMUNICATIONS, HIGHER EDUCATION. B.A, Univ. Okla, 50, M.Ed, 53; Kellogg Found. res. fel, Okla. State Univ, 56-57, M.S, 62, Ed.D, 65. Asst. prof. JOUR, Cent. State Col.(Okla), 53-60; assoc. prof, Findlay Col, 62-63; ASST. PROF, Okla. State Univ, 63-66; UNIV. FLA, 66-, CHMN. DEPT. PUB. RELAT, 72- Bk. consult, Jour. Educ. Asn, 63- Outstanding Adv. Award, Southwest. Region, Nat. Counc. Col. Publ. Adv, 65. Nat. Guard, 48-52; A.U.S, 50-52, M/Sgt. Am. Col. Pub. Relat. Asn. Cost comparison analysis and management procedures for college publications; communications problems of business, industry, education and organizations; typographic design and layout of publications. Publ: Co-auth, Modern journalism, Pitman, 62 & Sports publicity, Col. Pub. Relat. Quart, 56. Add: Dept. of Public Relations, College of Journalism, University of Florida, Gainesville, FL 32611.

BUTLER, JAMES ALBERT, b. Pittsburgh, Pa, May 18, 45; m. 67; c. 2. ENGLISH & AMERICAN LITERATURE. B.A, LaSalle Col, 67; Woodrow Wilson fel, Cornell Univ, 67-68, Danforth fel, 67-71, M.A, 70, Ph.D.(Eng), 71. Features ed, Philadelphia Cath. Standard & Times, 67; ASST. PROF. ENG, LA SALLE COL, 71- Assoc. ed, Four Quarters, 72- MLA; AAUP. Wordsworth; English Romantic period; contemporary poetry. Publ: Ferlinghetti: dirty old man? Renascence, spring 66; Samuel Johnson: defender of Admiral Byng, Cornell Libr. J, winter 69; Wordsworth in Philadelphia area libraries, Wordsworth Circle, winter 73. Add: Dept. of English, La Salle College, Philadelphia, PA 19141.

BUTLER, JAMES HARMON, b. Cathlamet, Wash, Dec. 16, 08; m. 37. DRAMA. A.B, West. Wash. Col. Educ, 37; A.M, Univ. South. Calif, 39, Ph.D, 48. Teacher, Pub. Schs, Wash, 34-38; High Sch, Calif, 39-40; asst. prof. speech, W.Tex. State Col, 40-42, 43-44; San Jose State Col, 45-46; DRAMA, UNIV. SOUTH. CALIF, 46-48, from assoc. prof. to DeMILLE PROF, 48-, chmn. dept, 53-70. U.S.A, 42-43. Am. Theatre Asn.(pres, 68); Am. Soc. Theatre Res. History of the theatre; staging of period dramas; filmstrips. Publ: History of the physical theatre; English playhouses; The theatre and drama of Greece and Rome, Chandler, 72. Add: 5030 W. Slauson Ave, Los Angeles, CA 90056.

BUTLER, MARIA HOGAN, b. Yazoo City, Miss, Sept. 23, 17. ENGLISH. B.A, Miss. State Col. Women, 38; M.A, Univ. N.C, 43, Rockefeller Found. Gen. Educ. Bd. fel, 49-50, Ph.D.(Eng), 52. Teacher, Pub. Schs, Miss, 38-44; assoc. prof. ENG, Limestone Col, 44-52; Miss. State Col. Women, 52-55, PROF, 55-61; DELTA STATE COL, 61- Instr, Univ. N.C, 51; fel, Fac. Summer Sch, Cambridge, Mass, 60 & 62; chmn, Miss. Eng. Comn, 64-66; mem. ed. bd, Miss. Folkore Register, 68- MLA; NCTE; S.Cent. Mod. Lang. Asn.(secy, 19th century sect, 62-63, chmn, 63-64); Renaissance Soc. Am; S.Cent. Renaissance Conf; Shakespeare Asn. Am. Robert Southey's interest in ballads and romances; Lord Byron's treatment of fatalism and original sin. Publ: Byron's revision of act III of Manfred, Stud. Philol, 63. Add: 702 Ninth Ave, Cleveland, MS 38732.

BUTLER, MARY MARGUERITE, R.S.M, b. June 21, 02; U.S. citizen. SPEECH, DRAMA. A.B, Univ. Notre Dame, 30; M.A, Cath. Univ. Am, 43; Fordham Univ, 49; fel, Univ. Mich, 55, Ph.D.(theatre), 59. Asst. prof. SPEECH & THEATRE, MERCY COL.(MICH), 47-49, PROF, 49-, CHMN. DEPT. SPEECH & DRAMA, 51- Researcher medieval drama & theatre, Univ. Mich, 72-73. Brooks Van Horn Award, 65. Nat. Cath. Theatre Conf. (award, 50; mem. bd. & v.pres, 59); Am. Theatre Asn; Am. Nat. Theatre & Acad. Medieval theatre; modern theatre; theatre history. Publ: Hrotsvitha: the theatricality of her plays, Philos. Libr, 60; transl, 2 plays, In: Medieval and Tudor drama, Bantam, 63 & Hrotsvitha play from Latin, In: Treasury of the theatre, Holt, 67; Hrotsvitha, In: The readers encyclopedia of world drama, Crowell, 69. Add: Dept. of Speech & Drama, Mercy College, 8200 W. Outer Dr, Detroit, MI 48219.

BUTMAN, ROBERT H, b. Washington, D.C, May 14, 24; m. 61; c. 1. DRAMA, ENGLISH. A.B, Univ, N.C, 45, M.A, 48; Univ. London, 50-51. Instr. Eng, George Washington Univ, 46-47; Univ. N.C, 47-49; instr. gen. stud, St. John's Col.(Md), 53-55; DRAMA, BRYN MAWR COL. & HAVERFORD COL, 56-58, asst. prof, 58-62, assoc. prof, 62-70, PROF, 70- Private secy. to Christopher Fry, 50-53; Ford Found. fel, St. John's Col.(Md), 53-55; dir, Am. Shakespeare Theatre Acad, 56; Old Dom. fel, Haverford Col, 67; deleg, World Shakespeare Congr, Vancouver, 71; Ford Found. fel, 71. U.S.N.R, 42-46, Lt.(jg). Publ: Co-auth, Shakespeare: soul of an age, NBC-TV, 63; auth, New Jersey: 300th harvest, CBS-TV, 65. Add: 4 College Circle, Haverford, PA 19041.

BUTRYM, ALEXANDER JOHN, b. Trenton, N.J, Apr. 20, 35; m. 62; c. 3. ENGLISH LITERATURE. B.A, LaSalle Col, 56; M.A, Duquesne Univ, 58; Duke Univ, 58-59; Ph.D.(Eng), Rutgers Univ, 71. Instr. Eng, Trenton Jr. Col, 59-60; Seton Hall Univ, 61-64; sr. med. ed, Smith Kline & French Labs, 64-66; instr. ENG, SETON HALL UNIV, 66-68, asst. prof, 68-73, ASSOC.

PROF, 73-, DIR. FRESHMAN ENG, 72- Consult-teacher, Port Authority of N.Y. & N.J, 68-72. MLA; NCTE; Conf. Col. Compos. & Commun; Am. Med. Writers Asn; Early Eng. Text Soc. Medieval prose; technical and scientific communication. Publ: Marlowe's echo in Kyd, Notes & Queries, 58; C.S. Lewis' four loves, Marriage Mag, 62. Add: Dept. of English, Seton Hall University, S. Orange Ave, South Orange, NJ 07079.

BUTT, WILLIAM GIBSON, b. Waterville, Minn, May 11, 16; m. 42; c. 1. COMMUNICATION SKILLS. B.A, Mich. State Univ, 40, M.A, 47; univ. fel, Univ. Miss, 51-53, Ed.D.(educ. admin), 53. From instr. to asst. prof. commun. skills, Mich. State Univ, 47-58, assoc. prof. Eng, 58-67; ACAD. DEAN, BAY DE NOC COMMUNITY COL, 67- A.U.S, 41-45, Res, 45-, Lt. Col. Creative and research writing; critical analysis of current educational writing. Add: Bay de Noc Community College, Escanaba, MI 49829.

BUTTEL, ROBERT WILLIAM, b. Brooklyn, N.Y, June 10, 23; m. 47; c. 2. ENGLISH. A.B, Williams Col.(Mass), 47; A.M, Columbia Univ, 49, Ph.D, 62. Instr. ENG, Sch. Commerce, N.Y. Univ, 49; Williams Col.(Mass), 49-51; lectr, Columbia Col, 51-58, instr, Columbia Univ, 58-59; Univ. Cincinnati, 59-62; asst. prof, TEMPLE UNIV, 62-65, assoc. prof, 65-67, PROF, 67-, CHMN. DEPT, 68- U.S.A.A.F, 42-45. MLA; NCTE. Wallace Stevens. Publ: Wallace Stevens: the making of harmonium, Princeton, 67. Add: Dept. of English, Temple University, Philadelphia, PA 19122.

BUTTERFIELD, STEPHEN THOMAS, b. Boston, Mass, Mar. 17, 42; m. 60; c. 3. LITERATURE. B.S, Boston Univ, 63; M.A, Tufts Univ, 65; Ph.D. (Eng), Univ. Mass, Amherst, 72. Teaching asst, ENG, Tufts Univ, 64-65; instr, Univ. Cincinnati, 65-67; teaching asst, Univ. Mass, Amherst, 67-69; instr, R.I. Col, 69-70; ASST. PROF, CASTLETON STATE COL, 70- Black American autobiography; contemporary poetry; theories of criticism. Publ: Black autobiography in America, Univ. Mass, 74; The charades of Vanity fair, Mass. Stud. Eng, fall 68; The use of language in the slave narrative, Negro Am. Lit. Forum, fall 72. Add: Dept. of English, Castleton State College Castleton, VT 05735.

BUTTERICK, GEORGE F, b. Yonkers, N.Y, Oct. 7, 42; m. 65; c. 2. AMERICAN LITERATURE, MODERN POETRY. B.A, Manhattan Col, 64; Ph.D. (Am. lit), State Univ. N.Y. Buffalo, 70. From instr. to asst. prof. ENG, Wilson Col, 68-70; UNIV. CONN, 70-72, LECTR. & CUR. CHARLES OLSON ARCH, 72- Ed, Olson: Jour. of Charles Olson Arch, 73- Post-modern American writing; the history of ideas; myth. Publ: Co-auth, A bibliography of works by Charles Olson, Phoenix Bk. Shop, 67; ed, Charles Olson's Poetry and truth, Four Seasons Found, 71; auth, The Norse, Inst. Further Stud. 73. Add: Charles Olson Archives, University of Connecticut Library, Storrs, CT 06268.

BUTTERS, RONALD RICHARD, Dialectology, Linguistic Theory. See Volume III, Foreign Languages, Linguistics & Philology.

BUTTS, JOHN RUSSELL, b. Apr. 27, 22; U.S. citizen; m. 44; c. 3. SPEECH COMMUNICATION, RELIGION. B.A, David Lipscomb Col, 53; M.A, Cent. Mich. Univ, 63; Ph.D.(speech), Mich. State Univ, 70. Lectr. speech, Cent. Mich. Univ, 63-65, instr, 65-66, asst. prof, 66-67; COMMUN, STEPHEN F. AUSTIN UNIV, 67-70, ASSOC. PROF, 70- Ord.C, U.S.A, 42-45. Speech Commun. Asn. Interpersonal relations; conflict resolution. Add: Dept. of Communication, Box 3048, Stephen F. Austin State University, Nacogdoches, TX 75961.

BUXTON, EARL W, b. Toronto, Ont, Nov. 17, 10; m. 36; c. 3. ENGLISH, EDUCATION. B.A, Univ. Alta, 40, B.Ed, 48; M.A, Univ. Wash, 54; Ph.D. (Eng, educ), Stanford Univ, 58. Teacher pub. schs, Alta, 29-36 & Edmonton, 44-48; prin. high schs, Sask, 38-41; PROF. ENG. & EDUC, Univ. Calgary, 48-54; UNIV. ALTA, 55- Mem. pub. relat. comt, NCTE, 63-66 & comt. res. teaching Eng, 66-70. NCTE; Can. Counc. Teachers Eng. Teaching composition and rhetoric; teaching literature; especially in the secondary schools. Publ: Creative living, bk. V, 53, Teachers' guidebook for creative living, bk. V, 54, co-auth, Guide to modern English, 59 & Prose for discussion, 68, W.G. Gage; auth, Teaching writing in Canada, In: A common purpose, NCTE, 66; preface, Looking at language, W.G. Gage, 66; The professor as teacher, In: Teaching in the universities, McGill-Queens Univ, 74; plus one other. Add: Dept. of Secondary Education, University of Alberta, Edmonton, Alta, Can.

BUYS, WILLIAM E, b. Muskegon, Mich, Oct. 22, 19; m. 43; c. 2. SPEECH. B.A, Albion Col, 41; Ph.M, Univ. Wis, 47, Ph.D, 52. Teacher high sch, Mich, 41-43; supv. teacher, Univ. Sch, Univ. Wis, 47-52; asst. prof. speech, Wayne Univ, 52-55; assoc. prof. speech educ, South. Ill. Univ, 55-64; PROF. COMMUN, WEST. MICH. UNIV, 64- Weather Serv, U.S.A.A.F, 43-46. NEA; Speech Commun. Asn. Methods of speech education; psychology of speech. Publ: Co-auth, Discussion and debate, 64, auth, Speaking by doing, 67, co-auth, Speech activities in the high school, 68 & Play production in the high school, 68, Nat. Textbk; auth, Extracurricular discussion in the secondary school, Bull. Nat. Asn. Sec. Sch. Prin. Add: Dept. of Communication Arts & Sciences, Western Michigan University, Kalamazoo, MI 49001.

BUZZARD, CHARLES EUGENE, b. Normal, Ill, Oct. 11, 27; m. 54; c. 1. SPEECH. B.A, State Univ, Iowa, 50; M.A, Univ. South. Calif, 54, M.Ed, 65, M.S, 66. Asst. prof. speech, Muskingum Col, 60-61; Tex. Technol. Col, 61-65; PROF. SPEECH & RADIO, PHOENIX COL, 65- Educ. TV consult, Sheppard Air Force Base, Tex, summer 62; gen. mgr, Radio Sta. KMCR-FM, Maricopa County Community Col. Dist, 70- Air Intel, U.S.N.R, Comdr. Soc. Motion Picture & TV Engineers; Speech Commun. Asn; Asn. Prof. Broadcasting Educ; Nat. Asn. Educ. Broadcasters. Educational television; job opportunities in the radio and television profession; free material for educational broadcast use. Add: Dept. of Speech, Phoenix College, Phoenix, AZ 85013.

BYARD, MARGARET MATHER, b. Glasgow, Scotland, July 6, 10; U.S. citizen; m. 35; c. 2. ENGLISH. B.A, Smith Col, 33; M.A, Columbia Univ, 54; Lizette A. Fisher scholar, 59-60, Margaret Pickel scholar, 60-61, M.A, Williams scholar, 61-62, Ph.D, 62. Lectr, Hunter Col, 60-64; Eng. & Am. Lit, Sch. Gen. Stud, Columbia Univ, 64-72; RETIRED. Prof. Milton-Renaissance course, Douglass Col, Rutgers Univ, 67-69. MLA; Renaissance Soc. Am; Milton Soc. Am. Sixteenth and 17th century English literature: Countess of Bedford and her circle; musical background of some of Milton's poems. Add: 140 E. 92nd St, New York, NY 10028.

BYARS, JOHN A, b. Marion, S.C, June 24, 30; m. 51; c. 5. ENGLISH. A.B, Furman Univ, 51; M.A, Univ. N.C, 56, Ph.D.(Eng), 62. Instr. ENG, Greensboro Col, 57-59; asst. prof, Centre Col, 63-65; ASSOC. PROF, CONVERSE COL, 65- Guest lectr, Trinity Col.(Dublin), 61. S.Atlantic Mod. Lang. Asn; MLA. Contemporary drama. Publ: Yeat's introduction to the heroic type, Mod. Drama, winter 65. Add: Dept. of English, Converse College, Spartanburg, SC 29301.

BYERS, BURTON H, b. Cedar Falls, Iowa, June 29, 13; m. 38. SPEECH. B.A, State Col. Iowa, 34; M.A, State Univ. Iowa, 40; Ed.D, Columbia Univ, 57. Teacher Eng. & speech, High Schs, Iowa, 34-43; assoc. prof. speech, Henderson State Teachers Col, 46-57; asst. prof, George Peabody Col, 47-53; educ. consult, Provost Marshal Gen. Sch, U.S. Army, Ft. Gordon, Ga, 53-56; asst. prof. speech educ, Queens Col.(N.Y), 56-67; ASSOC. PROF. COMMUN, UNIV. HAWAII, MANOA, 67- U.S.A, 43-46; Sgt. Int. Commun. Asn.(first v.pres. & pres, 54-56); Speech Asn. East. States (exec. secy, 62-65); Speech Commun. Asn; West. Common Asn. Development of materials for testing-training in interpersonal communication; cross cultural communication; satellite communication. Publ: Classroom interaction, satellite-interposed, Eric Ed, 4/72; Testing-teaching communication, Eng. in New Guinea, 72-73; Testing proficiency in interpersonal communication, Speech & Drama, 6/73; plus others. Add: Program in Communication, University of Hawaii at Manoa, Honolulu, HI 96822.

BYINGTON, ROBERT HAROLD, b. East Orange, N.J, Sept. 10, 27; m. 53; c. 3. ENGLISH. B.A, Pa. State Univ, 50; M.A, Lehigh Univ, 52; Ph.D.(Eng. & folklore); Univ. Pa, 59. Asst. instr. Eng, Lehigh Univ, 50-52; Univ. Pa, 52-53, asst. instr, 55-58; instr, Univ. Cincinnati, 53-55; asst. prof, Univ. Tenn, 58-60; asst. prof, Lycoming Col, 60-62, assoc. prof, 62-67, prof, 67-70, chmn. dept, 62-70; Eng. & folklore, Point Park Col, 70-74; SR. FOLKLORIST, SMITHSONIAN INSTN, 74- U.S.A, 44-47. Am. Folklore Soc.(v.pres, 73-). Popular beliefs and superstitions, especially in Pennsylvania; literature of Anglo-American expatriates; biography of Mary Butts, British writer (1890-1937). Publ: The frontier hero; refinement and definition, Tex. Folklore Soc, 62; co-auth, Two penny ballads & four dollar whiskey, Folklore Assoc, 65; auth, The journal of Mary Butts, Art & Lit, winter 65. Add: Div. of Performing Arts, Smithsonian Institution, Washington, DC 20560.

BYRD, LEMUEL BRIAN, b. Hamlet, N.C, Mar. 30, 28. AMERICAN & BRITISH LITERATURE. A.B, Univ. Miami, 48; M.A, George Peabody Col. Teachers, 51; Harvard, summer 58; Univ. Minn, Minneapolis, summer 62; fels, Univ. Colo, Boulder, 67-68, 68-69, Ph.D.(Eng), 69. Teacher Eng, Dade County Pub. Schs, Miami, Fla, 48-50, 53-65; asst. prof. social stud, Trenton State Col, 65; teaching assoc. Eng, Univ. Colo, Boulder, 65-68; asst. prof, Kans. State Teachers Col. Emporia, 69-70; asst. prof. Eng. & acting chmn. div. humanities, Ind. Univ, Kokomo, 70-71; ASST. PROF. ENG, UNIV. ALASKA, ANCHORAGE, 71- Judge, Alaska Speech & Drama Festival, 72, 73; coord. Alaska achievement awards prog, NCTE, 72-75; ed, Alaskan Eng. J, 73-74. U.S.A, 51-53, Res, 53-58. NCTE; MLA. The novel as it relates to the time in which it was written; characterization in Ernest Hemingway's fiction, 1925-1952. Publ: Staff organization, Scholastic Ed, 65; Incentives for joining a yearbook staff, Photolith, 65; Using the resources of Alaska in the teaching of English, Alaskan Eng. J, 3/74; plus others. Add: Division of Humanities, University of Alaska, 3211 Providence Dr, Anchorage, AK 99504.

BYRD, MILTON BRUCE, b. Boston, Mass, Jan. 29, 22; m. 53; c. 3. ENGLISH. A.B, Boston Univ, 48, M.A, 49; Ph.D.(Am. stud), Univ. Wis, 53. Instr. Eng, Univ. Wis, 49-53; from instr. to asst. prof, Ind. Univ, 53-58; head div. humanities, South. Ill. Univ, 58-60, assoc. dean, 60-62; prof, humanities & v.pres. acad. affairs, North. Mich. Univ, 62-66; PRES, CHICAGO STATE UNIV, 66- Ind. Univ. summer res. grant, 55; Carnegie Corp. fel. admin. higher educ, Univ. Mich, 61-62. U.S.A.A.F, 43-46. NCTE; NEA; Asn. Higher Educ; MLA. Publ: Co-auth, Publication guide for literary and linguistic scholars, Wayne State Univ, 58; auth, Nathaniel Ames and his minister, William & Mary Quart, 10/57; New faculty orientation, N.Cent. News Bull, 3/65; plus others. Add: Office of the President, Chicago State University, Chicago, IL 60621.

BYRD, THOMAS L, JR, b. Atlanta, Ga, June 28, 36; m. 73. ENGLISH, RELIGION. A.B, Emory Univ, 58; M.A, Brown Univ, 60; Ph.D(Eng), Univ. Fla, 68. Instr. ENG, Univ. Fla, 61-67; assoc. prof, Austin Peay State Univ, 67-69; ASST. PROF, LOYOLA UNIV. CHICAGO, 7 69- MLA; AAUP; Am. Acad. Relig. Add: Dept. of English, Loyola University of Chicago, 820 N. Michigan Ave, Chicago, IL 60611.

BYRNE, MARY ENDA EILEEN, M.S.C, b. New York, N.Y, Mar. 27, 25. ENGLISH. Ph.B, Loyola Univ.(La), 52; M.A, Univ. Notre Dame, 57; Ph.D. (Eng), Univ. South. Miss, 68. Teacher, elem. schs, 42-54; sec. schs, 54-63; instr. ENG, OUR LADY OF HOLY CROSS COL, 57-65, asst. prof, 65-67, assoc. prof, 67-69, PROF, 69-, PRES, 70-, dean stud, 69-70. Secy, La. Found, Private Cols, 73- MLA; NCTE; Speech Commun. Asn. William Faulkner; James Joyce; Louisiana and Mississippi writers. Add: 4123 Woodland Dr, New Orleans, LA 70114.

BYRNES, EDWARD T, b. Elizabeth, N.J, Dec. 4, 29; m. 62. DRAMATIC LITERATURE, LINGUISTICS. A.B, Seton Hall Univ, 55; M.A, N.Y. Univ, 57, Ph.D, 67. Lectr. ENG, SETON HALL UNIV, 56-57, instr, 57-60, asst. prof, 60-68, assoc. prof, 68-74, PROF, 74-, CHMN. DEPT, 68- U.S.A, 51-53, Sgt. MLA; Mediaeval Acad. Am; Col. Eng. Asn; Early Eng. Text Soc; NCTE. Mediaeval Celtic studies; 18th century drama and theatre. Publ: Co-auth, Middle English literature, Harcourt, 73. Add: Dept. of English, Seton Hall University, South Orange, NJ 07079.

BYRNES, JOSEPH ALFRED, b. Elizabeth, N.J, June 2, 28. ENGLISH. A.B, Seton Hall Univ, 54; A.M, N.Y. Univ, 55, Univ-Woodrow Wilson fel, 61-62, Ph.D, 63. Instr. ENG, Univ. Col, N.Y. Univ. 56-61; City Col. New York, 63-64; N.Y. UNIV, 64-66, asst. prof, 66-73, ASSOC. PROF, 73-, ASST. SECY.

UNIV. 69-, asst. dean, Grad. Sch. Arts & Sci, 67-69. U.S.A, 51-53. Soc. Theatre Res, Eng; Am. Soc. 18th Century Stud; Theatre Libr. Asn; Am. Soc. Theatre Res; Int. Fed. Theatre Res. British dramatic and theatrical history; Restoration and 18th century. Add: Dept. of English, New York University, 19 University Pl, New York, NY 10003.

BYRNS, LOIS ELIZABETH ANN, b. Lodi, Wis. ENGLISH. B.A, Univ. Wis, 29, M.A, 31, Ph.D, 43; Columbia Univ, 44-45. Asst. Bur. Guid. & Rec, Univ. Wis, 29-43; asst. prof. ENG, Col. New Rochelle, 43-46; Grad. Sch, Loyola Univ, 46-48; assoc. prof, Trinity Col, 48-52; Manhattanville Col. Sacred Heart, 52-60; UNIV. WIS-STOUT, 60-62, PROF, 62-, head dept, 62-68. Lectr, Fordham Univ, 44-46; assoc. prof, Cath. Univ. Am, summers 50-61, prof, 68. MLA. Comparative and recusant literature. Publ: Recusant books in America 1559-1640, 59, Recusant books in America, 1640-1700, 61 & Recusant books in America 1700-1829, 64, Peter Kavanagh. Add: Dept. of English, University of Wisconsin-Stout, Menomonie, WI 54751.

BYRNS, RICHARD HOWARD, b. Willits, Calif, Aug. 11, 15; m. 39; c. 2. ENGLISH, COMPARATIVE LITERATURE; B.A, Univ. North. Colo, 38; M.A, Univ. Calif, Berkeley, 45; Ph.D.(Eng. lit), Univ. Edinburgh, 55. Instr. ENG, N.Idaho Col. Educ, 46-47; Univ. Alaska, 47-48, assoc. prof, 48-51, prof, 53-57; from assoc. prof. to prof, South. Ore. Col, 57-66, head dept, 65-66; PROF, UNIV. NEV, LAS VEGAS, 66-, chmn. dept. Eng, 66-67, dean, Col. Humanities, 67-71. Dir. mil. br, Univ. Alaska, 50-51; Fund for Advan. Educ. fel, 51-52. Fac. man of year, South. Ore. Col, 64; Mosser Award, Ore, 66. Philol. Asn. Pac. Coast; MLA; Am. Comp. Lit.Asn. English; comparative literature. Publ: Current research in Alaska, Univ. Alaska, 54; Some unpublished works of De Quincey, 12/56 & De Quincey's revisions in the Dream fugue, 3/62, PMLA; Nationalism and cosmopolitanism in the English Romantic essay, Proc. Int.Comp. Lit. Asn, 66; plus others. Add: College of Arts & Letters, University of Nevada, Las Vegas, NV 89154.

BYRON, KENNETH HUGH, b. Buffalo, N.Y, July 16, 25; m. 52; c. 1. ENGLISH. B.A, Univ. Richmond, 56, M.A, 57; Ph.D.(Eng), Univ. Fla, 62. Instr. ENG, Univ. Richmond, 57-60; asst. prof, UNIV. FLA, 62-70, ASSOC. PROF, 70-, ADV, UNIV. COL, 69- U.S.A.F, 43-46, 49-53, Capt. MLA. Victorian literature; Arthurian legend. Publ: The pessimism of James Thomson (B.V.) in relation to his times, Mouton, The Hague, 65. Add: Dept. of English, University of Florida, Gainesville, FL 32601.

C

CABLE, CHESTER HUBBARD, b. Monmouth, Ill, July 19, 06; m. 39. ENGLISH. A.B, Monmouth Col, 27; A.M, Univ. Wis, 32; Ph.D, Univ. Chicago, 48. Asst, Univ. Wis, 30-32; instr, Univ. Chicago, 43-46; Eng, Wayne State Univ, 46-48, asst. prof, 48-53, assoc. prof, 53-74; RETIRED. Seventeenth century English verse satire; modern poetry; criticism. Add: 4744 Second Ave, Detroit, MI 48201.

CABLE, THOMAS MONROE, b. Conroe, Tex, June 17, 42; m. 66; c. 1. ENGLISH LANGUAGE & LINGUISTICS. B.A, Yale, 64; Sorbonne, 64-65; Am. Counc. Learned Soc. fel, Univ. Ill, summer 68; Ph.D.(Eng), Univ. Tex, 69. Asst. prof. ENG, Univ. Ill, Urbana-Champaign, 69-72; ASSOC. PROF, UNIV. TEX, AUSTIN, 72- MLA; Mediaeval Acad. Am; Ling. Soc. Am; NCTE. History of English prosody; English stylistics; Indo-European meter and song. Publ: The meter and melody of Beowulf, Univ. Ill, 74; Rules for syntax and metrics in Beowulf, J. Eng. & Ger. Philol, 1/70; Constraints on Anacrusis in Old English meter, Mod. Philol, 11/71; Timers, stressers, and linguists: contention and compromise, Mod. Lang. Quart, 9/72. Add: Dept. of English, University of Texas, Austin, TX 78712.

CABOTAJE, ARSENIA ABELLERA, b. La Union, Philippines, Feb. 9, 07; m. 32; c. 4. ENGLISH, EDUCATION. A.B, Union Theol. Sem.(Philippines), 28; scholar, Bibl. Sem. New York, 29-32, B.R.E, 31, M.R.E, 32; B.S.E, Union Col. Manila, 40; Crusade scholar, 46-47; M.A, Northwest. Univ, 47; Ed.D, Am. Univ.(D.C), 62. Teacher Eng, Union High Sch, Manila, Philippines, 34-41; prin, Bethel Girl's High Sch, 45-57; prof. Eng. & educ, Univ. of the East, 50-57; asst. educ, Am. Univ.(D.C), 57-59; teacher ENG, Otego Cent. Sch. N.Y, 59-62; PROF, Claflin Col, 62-64; BETHUNE-COOKMAN COL, 64- NCTE. Religious education; guidance; school administration. Add: Bethune-Cookman College, Daytona Beach, FL 32015.

CADE, DOZIER COPELAND, b. Eufaula, Ala, Sept. 8, 17; m. 49; c. 2. JOURNALISM. A.B, Univ. Ala, 39; Bastian scholar, Northwest. Univ, 39-40, M.S.J, 40; Ph.D.(mass communs), State Univ. Iowa, 54. Telegraph ed, Tuscaloosa News, Ala, 40; from reporter to asst. city ed, Atlanta Jour, Ga, 46-50; asst. prof. jour. & head news-ed. sequence, div. jour, Emory Univ, 50-52; asst. prof. JOUR, Northwest. Univ, 52-56; prof. & head dept, Ga. State Col, 56-72, PROF, UNIV. TENN, KNOXVILLE, 72- Copyreader, Chicago Daily News, Ill, 55; asst. ed, Jour. Quart. Harrington Award, Northwest. Univ, 40; Distinguished Jour. Alumnus Award, Univ. Ala, 63. U.S.A, 40-46, Res, 46-, Col. Am. Soc. Jour. Sch. Adminr.(pres, 67-68); Asn. Educ. in Jour.(exec. comt, 67-68); Am. Col. Pub. Relat. Asn. Press performance; public opinion and propaganda. Publ: Co-auth, Modern journalism, Pitman, 62; auth, Witch-hunting, 1952: role of the press, Jour. Quart, autumn 52; The challenges of journalism, Quill, 6/63; On evaluating teachers, Jour. Educ, spring 68. Add: Dept. of Journalism, University of Tennessee, Knoxville, TN 37916.

CADY, EDWIN HARRISON, b. Old Tappan, N.J, Nov. 9, 17; m. 39; c. 2. ENGLISH & AMERICAN LITERATURE. A.B, Ohio Wesleyan Univ, 39, Litt.D, 64; M.A, Univ. Cincinnati, 40; Ph.D, Univ. Wis, 43; Litt.D, Okla. City Univ, 67. Instr. ENG, Univ. Wis, 45; Ohio State Univ, 46; asst. prof, Syracuse Univ, 46-47; assoc. prof, 47-53, prof, 53-59; Rudy prof, Ind. Univ, 59-73; PROF, DUKE UNIV, 73- Vis. prof, Royal Univ. Uppsala & Univ. Stockholm, Sweden, 51-52; Guggenheim fel, 54-55; mem. exec. comt, Ctr. Editions Am. Authors, 63-69; gen. ed, A Selected Edition of W.D. Howells, 64-68; assoc. ed, Am. Lit. Mag, 73- Am. Field Serv, 43-44; U.S.N, 45. MLA; NCTE (adv, Col. Eng, 59-61); Am. Stud. Asn. American literature, especially in relation to American cultural history. Publ: The gentleman in American, 49 & William Dean Howells: dean of American letters, 1837-1920, 58, Univ. Syracuse; Stephen Crane, Twayne, 62; John Woolman, Washington Square, 65; ed, The American poets, 1800-1900, Scott, 66; auth, The light of common day: realism in American fiction, Ind. Univ, 71; ed, W.D. Howells as critic, Routledge & Kegan Paul, 73. Add: Dept. of English, Duke University, Durham, NC 27706.

CADY, JOSEPH L, JR, b. Mt. Pleasant, N.Y, Oct. 31, 38. AMERICAN LITERATURE. B.A, Amherst Col, 60; Woodrow Wilson fel, Univ. Calif, Berkeley, 60-61, M.A, 62, Ph.D.(Eng, 19th century Am. lit), 68. Instr. ENG, Columbia Univ, 66-68, ASST. PROF, 68-69; RUTGERS UNIV, NEW BRUNSWICK, 69- Andrew Mellon postdoctoral fel, Univ. Pittsburgh, 70-71. MLA; Am. Stud. Asn. Literature and society in late 19th century America; 19th and 20th century American fiction; American poetry. Add: Dept. of English, Rutgers University, New Brunswick, NJ 08903.

CAHILL, DANIEL JOSEPH, b. Chicago, Ill, Mar. 3, 29; m. 63; c. 1. ENGLISH & AMERICAN LITERATURE. B.A, Loyola Univ. Chicago, 51, M.A, 54; Ph.D.(Eng), Univ. Iowa, 66. Asst. prof. ENG, St. Ambrose Col, 55-62; St. Olaf Col, 65-68; assoc. prof, UNIV. NORTH. IOWA, 68-71, PROF. & HEAD DEPT, 71- V.pres, Conf. Christianity & Relig, 69-71. Eng.C, U.S.A, 53-55. MLA; NCTE; Am. Acad. Relig. Nineteenth and 20th century British literature; contemporary novel. Publ: Harriet Monroe, Twayne, 73; Jerzy Kosinski: retreat from violence, Twentieth Century Lit, 70. Add: 2618 Willow Lane, Cedar Falls, IA 50613.

CAIN, EARL RICHARD, b. Terry, S.Dak, Aug. 11, 19; m. 53; c. 2. SPEECH. B.A, Univ. S.Dak, 42; M.A, Northwest. Univ, 47; Ph.D, 50. Instr. SPEECH, Ore. State Univ, 47-48; St. Louis Univ, 50-51, asst. prof, 51-53; instr, Univ. Calif, Los Angeles, 53-55, asst. prof, 55-59; CALIF. STATE UNIV, LONG BEACH, 59-62, from assoc. prof. & chmn. dept. to PROF, 62- U.S.A.A.F, 42-46, Staff Sgt. West. Speech Asn.(exec. secy, 61-63, v.pres, 65-66, pres, 66); Speech Commun. Asn. History of criticism of public address; rhetorical theory and criticism; congressional debate. Publ: A method for rhetorical analysis of congressional debate, West. Speech J, 3/54; Hiram Johnson: orator of isolationism, winter 58 & Obstacles to early congressional reporting, spring 62, South. Speech J. Add: Dept. of Speech Communication, California State University, Long Beach, 6101 E. Seventh St, Long Beach, CA 90801.

CAIN, ROY EDWARD, b. Red Rock, Tex, June 11, 28; m. 53; c. 1. ENGLISH, LINGUISTICS. B.A, N.Tex. State Univ, 52, M.A, 54; Ph.D.(Eng), Univ. Tex, 63. Instr. ENG, Tex. A&M Univ, 56-58, asst. prof, 60-64; South. Ill. Univ, 64-65 & 66-67; assoc. prof, Angelo State Univ, 65-66; STEPHEN F. AUSTIN STATE UNIV, 67-69, PROF. & HEAD DEPT, 69- Vis. prof, George Peabody Col, summer 66; Stephen F. Austin State Univ. fac. res. grant, summer 68 & 69. U.S.A.F, 46-49, S/Sgt. MLA; AAUP; S.Cent. Mod. Lang. Asn; Asn. Dept. Eng. Eighteenth century British literature; transformational grammar. Publ: Co-auth, Richardson's role in an attack on Hume and Bolingbroke, Papers Lang. & Lit, summer 68; Holgrave: Hawthorne's antithesis to Carlyle's Teufelsdrockh, Res. Stud, 3/70 & A new D.A. in English at Stephen F. Austin State University, Bull. Asn. Dept. Eng, 11/71. Add: Dept. of English & Philosophy, Stephen F. Austin State University, Nacogdoches, TX 75961.

CAIN, THOMAS HENRY, b. Toronto, Can, Feb. 23, 31; m. 63. ENGLISH. B.A, Univ. Toronto, 53, M.A, 56; Kohler & Knapp fels, Univ. Wis, 57-59, Ph.D, 59. Instr. ENG, YALE, 59-63, asst. prof, 63-66; ASSOC. PROF, McMASTER UNIV, 66- Morse fel, Yale, 65-66. MLA; Renaissance Soc. Am. Panegyric in the Renaissance; Spenser; Shakespeare. Publ: Common sense about writing, Prentice-Hall, 67; The Caselli collection: Italian Renaissance books at McMaster University, Renaissance & Reformation, 4/68; The strategy of praise in Spenser's Aprill, Stud. Eng. Lit, winter 68; Spenser and the Renaissance Orpheus, Univ. Toronto Quart, autumn,71. Add: Dept. of English, McMaster University, Hamilton, Ont. L8S 4L9, Can.

CALARCO, N. JOSEPH, b. New York, N.Y, Mar. 19, 38; m. 64. DRAMA. A.B, Columbia Univ, 59, M.A, 62; Ph.D.(theatre), Univ. Minn, 66. Asst. prof. dramatic art, Univ. Calif, Berkeley, 66-68; speech, WAYNE STATE UNIV, 68-71, ASSOC. PROF. THEATRE, 71- Mem. humanities inst, Univ. Calif, summer 68; mem. bd. dirs, fine arts sect, Mich. Acad. Sci, Arts & Lett, 70-73. Am. Theatre Asn. Directing; actor training; dramatic theory. Publ: Tragic being: Apollo and Dionysus in western drama, Univ. Minn, 68; Vision without compromise: Genet's The screens, Drama Surv, spring 65; Tragedy as demonstration, Educ. Theatre J, 10/66. Add: University Theatre, Wayne State University, Detroit, MI 48202.

CALDER, DANIEL GILLMORE, b. Lubec, Maine, Feb. 10, 39. ENGLISH & MEDIEVAL LITERATURE. A.B, Bowdoin Col, 60; M.A, Univ. Iowa, 62; M.A, Ind. Univ, Bloomington, 67, Ph.D.(Eng), 69. Instr. Eng. & drama, Bowdoin Col, 62-64; ASST. PROF. ENG, Univ. Wash, 69-71; UNIV. CALIF, LOS ANGELES, 71- MLA; Mediaeval Acad. Am. Old English literature. Publ: Setting and mode in The seafarer and The wanderer, Neuphilol. Mitt, 71; Setting and ethos: the pattern of measure and limit in Beowulf, Stud. Philol, 72; The vision of paradise: a symbolic reading of the Old English Phoenix, Anglo-Saxon Eng, 1/72. Add: Dept. of English, University of California, Los Angeles, 405 Hilgard Ave, Los Angeles, CA 90024.

CALDER, GRACE J, b. Chippewa Falls, Wis, Feb. 18, 00. ENGLISH. A.B, Macalester Col, 21, Litt.D, 55; A.M, Univ. Wis, 25; Ph.D, Yale, 33. Teacher, high schs, Wis, 21-23; Okla, 25-28; asst. prof, Milwaukee-Downer Col, 31-41; from instr. to prof. ENG, HUNTER COL, 41-70, EMER. PROF, 70- MLA; Asn. Scottish Lit. Stud; Res. Soc. Victorian Periodicals; Browning Inst; William Morris Soc. Nineteenth century English literature; Carlyle; Morris. Publ: The writing of Past and present, Yale, 49; George Petrie and The ancient music of Ireland, Dolmen, 68; ed, William Morris, The story of Kormak, William Morris Soc, 70. Add: 6 E. 37th St, New York, NY 10016.

CALDER, ROBERT LORIN, b. Moose Jaw, Sask, Apr. 3, 41; m. 65; c. 2. ENGLISH LITERATURE. B.A, Univ. Sask, 63, M.A, 65; Can. Counc. fel, Univ. Leeds, 67-70, Ph.D.(Eng), 70. Instr. ENG. UNIV. SASK, 65-67, lectr, 70-71, ASST. PROF, 71- Can. Asn. Univ. Teachers; Asn. Can. Teachers Eng. Twentieth century English literature; the novel. Publ: W. Somerset Maugham and the quest for freedom, Heinemann, 72, Doubleday, 73. Add: Dept. of English, University of Saskatchewan, Saskatoon, Sask, S7N 0W0, Can.

CALDERWOOD, JAMES LEE, b. Corvallis, Ore, Apr. 7, 30; m. 55; c. 2. ENGLISH. B.S, Univ. Ore, 53; Ph.D.(Eng), Univ. Wash, 63. Instr. ENG, Mich, State Univ, 61-63; asst. prof, UNIV. CALIF, Los Angeles, 63-66, assoc. prof, IRVINE, 66-71, PROF, 71- Summers, fac. fel, 64 & Humanities Inst. award, 66, Univ. Calif. U.S.A, 52-54, 1st Lt. Shakespeare; English and continental drama; Renaissance literature. Publ: Co-ed, Forms of poetry, 68, Forms of drama, 69, Essays in Shakespearean criticism, 69, Forms of prose fiction, 72 & Forms of tragedy, 72, Prentice-Hall; Perspectives on drama, Perspectives on poetry & Perspectives on fiction, Oxford, 68; ed, Love's labour lost, W.C. Brown, 70; auth, Shakespearean metadrama, Univ. Minn, 71; Love's labor lost: a wantoning with words, 65 & Coriolanus: meaningless words and wordless meanings, 66, Stud. Eng. Lit; I Henry IV; art's gilded lie, Eng. Lit, Renaissance, 73. Add: Dept. of English, University of California, Irvine, CA 92664.

CALDWELL, DAVID KELLER, Vertebrate Marine Biology. See 12th Edition, American Men & Women of Science, Physical & Biological Section.

CALDWELL, MARY ELLEN, b. El Paso, Ark, Aug. 6, 08; m. 36; c. 1. ENGLISH & AMERICAN LITERATURE. Ph.B, Univ. Chicago, 31, M.A, 33. Instr. ENG, Univ. Ark, 40-42; Univ. Toledo, 46-48; UNIV. N.DAK, 66-67, asst. prof, 67-72, ASSOC. PROF, 72- MLA; NCTE; Conf. Col. Compos. & Commun; Am. Asn. Univ. Women. Nineteenth century American literature; mid-western literature. Publ: The North Dakota division of the American Association of University Women, 1930-1963: a history, Univ. N.Dak, 64; Review of Edward Kern and American expansion by Robert V. Hine, N.Dak. Quart, winter 62; A new consideration of the intercalary chapters in The grapes of wrath, Markham Rev, 5/73. Add: 514 Oxford, Grand Forks, ND 58201.

CALDWELL, ROBERT ATCHISON, b. Oklahoma City, Okla, Nov. 14, 07; m. 36; c. 1. ENGLISH PHILOLOGY. A.B, Colo. Col, 30; A.M, Univ. Colo, 32; Ph.D, Univ. Chicago, 38. Instr. Eng, Univ. Ark, 36-39, asst. prof, 39-42; res. analyst, U.S. Dept. War, 42-46; assoc. prof. ENG, Univ. Toledo, 46-49; UNIV. N.Dak, 49-54, PROF, 54- MLA; Mediaeval Acad. Am; Int. Arthurian Soc; Mod. Humanities Res. Asn. Geoffrey of Monmouth; Middle English chronicles; literary relations between Ireland and England. Add: 514 Oxford St, Grand Forks, ND 58201.

CALDWELL, S. ANTHONY, b. Cincinnati, Ohio, June 14, 30; m. 53; c. 3. ENGLISH. B.A, Columbia Col, 52, M.A, Columbia Univ, 53; Ph.D.(Eng. lit), Harvard, 68. Instr. ENG, UNIV. N.H, 57-68, ASST. PROF, 68- U.S.A, 53-56. Elizabethan and Jacobean drama; 16th and 17th century British literature. Add: Box 222, RFD. 2, Dover, NH 03820.

CALHOUN, RICHARD JAMES, b. Jackson, Tenn, Sept. 5, 26; m. 54; c. 3. ENGLISH. B.A, George Peabody Col, 48; scholar, Johns Hopkins Univ, 48-50, M.A, 50; South. fel, Univ. N.C, 57-58, Ph.D, 59. Jr. instr, Johns Hopkins Univ, 48-50; instr. Eng, Jacksonville State Col, 50-51; asst, Univ. N.C, 53-57; asst. prof. ENG, Davidson Col, 58-61; CLEMSON UNIV, 61-63; assoc. prof, 63-66, prof, 66-69, ALUMNI PROF, 69- Duke Univ-Univ. N.C. Coop. Prog. Humanities fel, 64-65; Fulbright-Hays lectr, Univ. Ljubljana & Univ. Sarajevo, 69-70. MLA; S.Atlantic Mod. Lang. Asn; Soc. Stud. South. Lit. Contemporary poetry; southern American literature; American literature. Publ: Co-ed, A tricentennial anthology of South Carolina literature, Univ. S.C, 71; ed, James Dickey: the expansive imagination, Everett Edwards, 73; contrib, A bibliographical guide to the study of Southern literature, La. State Univ, 69; auth, The ante-bellum literary twilight: Russell's Magazine, South. Lit. J, fall 70; contrib, Modern American poetry, Everett Edwards, 72; plus three others. Add: Dept. of English, Clemson University, Clemson, SC 29631.

CALHOUN, THOMAS O, b. Pittsburgh, Pa, Mar. 1, 40; m; c. 1. ENGLISH. A.B, Princeton, 62; M.A, Univ. Pittsburgh, 63; fel. & Ph.D.(Eng), Univ. Mich, 67. Instr. Eng. & class. lit, Univ. Mich, 63-67; ASST. PROF. ENG. & COMP. LIT, UNIV. DEL, 67-, res. grant, summer 68. MLA; Renaissance Soc. Am. Literature of the English Renaissance, 16th and 17th centuries. Publ: Co-auth, Andrew Marvell: The garden, C.E. Merrill, 70; auth, Hawthorne's gothic, Genre, 70; On John Milton's A masque at Ludlow, Milton Stud, 74; George Wither. . .loose poetics, Tex. Stud. Lit. & Lang, 74. Add: Dept. of English, University of Delaware, Newark, DE 19711.

CALKINS, ROGER WILLARD, b. Greenfield, Mass, June 21, 34; m. 61; c. 1. ENGLISH. B.A, Bard Col, 56; M.A, Yale, 57, Ph.D.(Eng), 65. Instr. humanities, Clarkson Col. Technol, 59-61; asst. prof. ENG, MT. ALLISON UNIV, 64-68, ASSOC. PROF, 68- U.S.A, 57-59. MLA; Humanities Asn. Can. Shakespeare—the comedies. Publ: The Renaissance idea of imitation and Shakespeare's Twelfth night, In: Twenty-seven to one, Clarkson Col. Technol, 74. Add: Dept. of English, Mt. Allison University, Sackville, N.B, Can.

CALL, REGINALD, b. Antrim, N.H, Jan. 28, 08; m. 36; c. 2. ENGLISH. A.B, Columbia Univ, 33, M.A, 41, Gottsberger fel, 49-50. Instr. ENG, N.Y. Univ, 41-51; asst. prof, Univ. N.H, 51-58; ASSOC. PROF, WITTENBERG UNIV, 59- Am. Counc. Learned Soc. grant-in-aid, 58. MLA; Mediaeval Acad. Am; AAUP. Chaucer and the Middle Ages; English Romantic period. Publ: Coauth, New highways in college composition, Prentice-Hall; Whan he his papir soghte, Mod. Lang. Quart; The plimpton Chaucer and other problems of Chaucerian portraiture, Speculum. Add: 1009 Woodlawn Ave, Springfield, OH 45504.

CALLAGHAN, JOSEPH CALVIN, b. Battle Creek, Mich, Aug. 7, 10; m. 38; c. 3. SPEECH. A.B, Univ. Mich, 31, M.A, 32; Ph.D.(speech), Univ. Wis, 49. Asst. Eng, Univ. Mich, 31-32; instr. Eng. & speech, Lawrence Inst. Technol, 34-36; Lehigh Univ, 36-39, asst. prof, 39-44; tech. ed, Columbia Univ. Div. War Res, 44-45; asst. prof. speech, Syracuse Univ, 45-49, assoc. prof, 49-67, chmn. dept. pub. address, Sch. Speech & Dramatic Art, 49-61; PROF. SPEECH, UNIV. N.C, CHAPEL HILL, 67- Found. Econ. Educ. fel, summer 57; consult, Light Mil. Electronics Dept, Gen. Electric Co, Utica, N.Y, 58-63, Defense Syst. Dept, Syracuse, summer 59; Portable Compressor Div, Ingersoll-Rand Co, 69-73. AAUP; Am. Inst. Parliamentarians; Speech Commun. Asn; East. Commun. Asn.(1st v.pres, 56-57, pres, 57-58). American public address; persuasion and discussion leadership; industrial communications. Publ: Annual meeting of the Pennsylvania Anti-Slavery Society, 1860, In: Anti-slavery and disunion, 1858-1860, 63; co-auth, Industry and the professor, Advan. Mgt, 11/60; auth, On teaching parliamentary procedure, In: Essays on teaching speech in the high school, Ind. Univ, 71; plus many others. Add: 127 Glendale Dr, Chapel Hill, NC 27514.

CALLAHAN, EDWARD F, b. Brockton, Mass, Apr. 13, 25; m; c. 3. ENGLISH. A.B, Boston Col, 50, M.A, 52; Ph.D, Univ. Wis, 56. Instr. ENG, Univ. N.Dak, 56-57; asst. prof, COL. HOLY CROSS, 57-61, assoc. prof, 61-68, PROF, 68-, dir. spec. stud, 61-65, chmn. dept. Eng, 65-71. Vis. prof, Assumption Col, summer 62, 64, spring 66 & Univ. Calif, Los Angeles, summer 74. U.S.A.A.F, 43-45. MLA; New Eng. Col. Eng. Asn.(dir, 62-). Shakespeare; 20th century British literature; modern Irish literature. Add: Dept. of English, College of the Holy Cross, Worcester, MA 01610.

CALLAHAN, JENNIE WAUGH, b. Tarkio, Mo; m. 39; c. 2. COMMUNICATIONS. B.A, Tarkio Col, 28; M.A, Northwest. Univ, 29; fel. & Ph.D, Univ. Berlin, 36. Dir. dramatics, Hastings Col, 29-34; prof. Eng, Tarkio Col, 36-37; res. fel, Yale, 37-38; asst. prof. Eng, Sweet Briar Col, 38-39; instr. COMMUN, HUNTER COL, 39-50, asst. prof, 50-55, assoc. prof, 55-60, PROF, 60- Nat. Asn. Educ. Broadcasters; Asn. Childhood Educ. Int. Children's literature; educational television. Publ: The theatre as a mirror of American democracy, Junker & Duenhaupt, Ger, 36; Radio workshop for children, 48 & Television in school, college, and community, 53, McGraw-Hill. Add: Dept. of Communications, Hunter College, 695 Park Ave, New York, NY 10021.

CALLAHAN, JOHN FRANCIS, b. Meriden, Conn, Dec. 31, 40; m. 70; c. 1. AMERICAN LITERATURE. B.A, Univ. Conn, 63; M.A, Univ. Ill, 64, Ph.D.(Am. lit), 70. Instr. ENG, LEWIS & CLARK COL, 67-68, asst. prof, 68-73, ASSOC. PROF, 73- Vis. asst. prof. Eng, Calif. State Univ, Hayward, summer 70; Nat. Endowment for Humanities younger humanist fel, 73-74. MLA; Am. Lit. Group, Mod. Lang. Asn; Northwest Am. Stud. Asn. The American novel; black literature and history; 20th century Irish literature and history. Publ: The illusions of a nation: myth and history in the novels of F. Scott Fitzgerald, Univ. Ill, 72. Add: Dept. of English, Lewis & Clark College, 0615 S.W. Palatine Hill Rd, Portland, OR 97219.

CALLAHAN, MARY GENEROSA, C.D.P, b. Coyle, Okla, Aug. 10, 01. ENGLISH, RELIGION. B.A, Our Lady of the Lake Col, 27; M.A, Cath. Univ. Am, 34; Ph.D, Univ. Tex, 45. Teacher pvt. schs, La. & Tex, 23-33; instr. ENG, OUR LADY OF THE LAKE COL, 34-56, prof, 56-71, EMER. PROF. & ARCHIVIST, 71- Mem. integration high sch. & col. Eng. workshops, Agr. & Mech. Col. Tex, 46-; South. Fel. Fund grant, 57; Piper prof, Minnie Piper Stevens Found, 62. NCTE; Am. Counc. Learned Soc. John Martin Moye; Lorraine and Alsace history in the 18th century; Shakespeare and Elizabethan drama history with Latin background. Publ: History of the Sisters of Divine Providence of San Antonio, Texas, 55 & John Martin Moye, founder, educator, 64, Bruce; contrib. & transl, Une spiritualité missionaire, 70 & co-ed, Le bienheureux J. Martin Moye, 73, Apostolat des editions, Paris; auth, Apuleius and A midsummer-night's dream, Stud. Philol, 4/45; plus others. Add: Archives, Our Lady of the Lake College, 411 S.W. 24th St, San Antonio, TX 78285.

CALLAN, EDWARD T, b. Ireland, Dec. 3, 17; U.S. citizen; m. 55; c. 2. ENGLISH LITERATURE, AFRICAN STUDIES. B.A, Univ. Witwatersrand, S.Africa, 47; M.A, Fordham Univ, 54; D.Lit. & Philos, Univ. S.Africa, 59. Teacher ENG, Transvaal Educ. Dept, 47-49; instr, Fordham Univ, 52-54; Loyola Univ.(Ill), 54-57; asst. prof, WEST. MICH. UNIV, 57-61, assoc. prof, 61-63, PROF, 63- Lectr, Brit. Ministry Inform, 50-52; Carnegie grant, St. Antony's Col, Oxford, 60-61; consult, Choice: Bks. for Col. Libr, Am. Libr. Asn, 64-; external examr. doctoral theses, Rhodes Univ, S.Africa, 66-70; vis. prof, Univ. Mich, spring 68. S.African Army, 42-46. MLA; Eng. Acad. South. Africa; fel, African Stud. Asn. Modern poetry and drama; African history. Publ: Annotated checklist . . . , W.H. Auden, A. Swallow, 58; Albert John Luthuli, West. Mich. Univ, 62, rev. ed, 65; Alan Paton, Twayne, 68; ed, The long view, Praeger & Pall Mall, London, 68; auth, Hamburger bibliographien: Alan Paton, Hans Christians Verlag, Hamburg, 70; W.H. Auden: the farming of a verse, South. Rev, spring 67; Song of sorrow and thanksgiving, Saturday Rev, 11/69; W.B. Yeats on the coming age, Dublin Mag, summer 72; plus others. Add: Dept. of English, Western Michigan University, Kalamazoo, MI 49001.

CALLANDER, LOWANNE JONES, Comparative Literature, Medieval Romance Languages. See Volume III, Foreign Languages, Linguistics & Philology.

CALLAWAY, JAMES E, b. Springfield, Mo, Dec. 1, 21; m. 42; c. 3. JOURNALISM. B.S. Jour, Northwest. Univ, 48; M.A, Univ. Mo, 62; Ind. Univ, 62-66. News ed. radio news, 46-47; TV & radio news, WBAP & WBAP-TV, 48-51; regional mgr, Brown Bros. Advert, Inc, 51-53; dir, Lindsey-Robinson & Co, Inc, 53-59; sales rep, King Merritt & Co, 59-61; asst. instr. JOUR, Univ. Mo, 61-62; lectr, IND. UNIV, BLOOMINGTON, 62-68, ASSOC. PROF, 68- U.S.N.R, 42-45, Res, 45-66, Lt. Am. Acad. Advert.(pres, 68-69). General semantics in journalism and advertising; halo image attitude studies. Add: Dept. of Journalism, Indiana University, Bloomington, IN 47401.

CALLOW, JAMES T, b. Toledo, Ohio, June 17, 28; m. 54; c. 1. ENGLISH. B.S.S, John Carroll Univ, 50; M.A, Univ. Toledo, 52; Ph.D.(Am. cult), West. Reserve Univ, 64. Instr. ENG, UNIV. DETROIT, 54-59, asst. prof, 60-65, assoc. prof, 66-68, PROF, 69-, DIR. FOLKLORE ARCH, 68- Lectr. grad. sch, Mary Manse Exten, Cath. Univ. Am, summer 61; mem. Bibliog. comt, Am. Lit. Group, MLA, 63-; Nat. Endowment for Humanities res. grant, 73-75. Am. Stud. Asn; Am. Folklore Soc; Soc. Archit. Hist; Arch. Am. Art.

Knickerbocker writers; American folklore and painting; The Sketch Club 1829-1869. Publ: Kindred spirits: Knickerbocker writers and American artists, 1807-1855, Univ. N.C, 67; Edward Taylor obeys St. Paul, Early Am. Lit, 70. Add: Dept. of English, University of Detroit, College Park Station, Detroit, MI 48221.

CALVER, EDWARD THOMAS, b. Pontiac, Mich, Oct. 13, 10. ENGLISH. A.B, Univ. Mich, 32, A.M, 33, Ph.D, 46. Teaching fel, Univ. Mich, 37-44, instr, 44-47; asst. prof, Cent. Wash. State Col, 47-48; vis. asst. prof, Columbia Univ, 48-49; asst. prof. ENG, Wayne Univ, 50-53; Mich. Col. Mining & Technol, 55-56; assoc. prof, FLINT COL, UNIV. MICH-FLINT, 56-60, prof, 60-73, EMER. PROF, 73- Add: Jacksonville Stage, Charlemont, MA 01339.

CALVERT, WILLIAM JONATHAN, JR, b. Pittsboro, N.C, July 3, 01; m. 38; c. 1. ENGLISH. A.B, Va. Mil. Inst, 20; A.M, Harvard, 22, Ph.D, 29. Instr. Wash. & Lee Univ, 22-23; asst, Univ. Calif, Los Angeles, 24-26; instr, Williams Col, 28-30; asst. prof. Eng, Ala. State Teachers Col, 33-37, assoc. prof, 37-47, prof, 47-72; dean, Col. Arts & Sci, Jacksonville State Univ, 72-73; RETIRED. S.Atlantic Mod. Lang. Asn. Byron, romantic paradox; freshman forum; the class writes a play. Publ: Saul, Blue & Grey Press, 73. Add: 615 N. Pelham Rd, Jacksonville, AL 36265.

CAMDEN, CARROLL, b. Parkersburg, W.Va, Mar. 24, 03; m. 25; c. 2. ENGLISH. A.B, Centre Col, 25; Harvard, 26-27; fel, State Univ. Iowa, 27-28, Ph.D, 30. Instr, State Univ, Iowa, 28-30; from instr. to assoc. prof. ENG, RICE UNIV, 30-50, PROF, 50-, chmn. dept, 57-63. Vis. lectr, Univ. Tex, 46-47; Eng-Speaking Union, res. fel, 55-56; deleg, Int. Shakespeare Conf, Stratford, 55, 64; vis. prof, South. Methodist Univ, summer 59; res. fel, Folger Libr, 54, 62; founding ed, Stud. Eng. Lit, 61-73; lectr. Shakespeare, Univ. P.R, 64; vis. prof, Univ. Wis, 66; mem. ed. bd, Eng. Lit. Renaissance; consult, PMLA; consult-reader, Univ. Wis. Press. Eng-Speaking Union; MLA; S-Cent. Mod. Lang. Asn; Shakespeare Asn. Am; Malone Soc; Renaissance Soc. Am; S.Cent. Reanissance Conf.(pres, 59-60); Renaissance Eng. Text Soc. Literature of English Renaissance; Elizabethan and Jacobean drama; Elizabethan science and pseudo-science. Publ: Auth, The Elizabethan woman, Elsevier, New York & Amsterdam & Cleaver-Hume, London, 52; co-auth, Studies in English drama presented to Baldwin Maxwell, Univ. Iowa, 62; ed, Restoration and eighteenth century literature: essays in honor of A.D. McKillop, 63 & Literary views: critical and historical essays, 64, Univ. Chicago; co-auth, Shakespeare 400, Holt, 64 & Studies in honor of DeWitt T. Starnes. Univ. Tex, 67; auth, Elizabethan almanacs and prognostications, In: The library, Oxford, 41; Memory, the warder of the brain, Philol. Quart, 39; Iago on women, J. Eng. & Ger. Philol, 49. Add: Dept. of English, Rice University, P.O. Box 1892, Houston, TX 77001.

CAMERON, ANGUS FRASER, Old English Language & Literature. See Volume III, Foreign Languages, Linguistics & Philology.

CAMERON, DONALD J, b. Miles City, Mont, Sept. 2, 31; m. 63. SPEECH. B.A, Univ. Mont, 53, M.A, 57; Ph.D.(speech), Northwest. Univ, 60. Asst. prof. SPEECH, CALIF. STATE UNIV, NORTHRIDGE, 60-64, assoc. prof, 64-68, PROF, 68- U.S.A, 54-55. Speech Commun. Asn; Am. Forensic Asn. Argumentation; rhetoric and public address. Add: Dept. of Speech Communication, California State University, Northridge, 18111 Nordhoff St, Northridge, CA 91324.

CAMERON, JOHN, b. Chicago, Ill, June 24, 30; m. 59. ENGLISH. B.A, Yale, 52, M.A, 57, Ph.D, 63; dipl, Edinburgh Univ, 55; hon. M.A, Amherst Col, 70. Instr. ENG, AMHERST COL, 58-61, asst. prof, 61-65, assoc. prof, 65-70, PROF, 70- Am. Philos. Soc. grant, 73. U.S.A, 52-54, Sgt. MLA; AAUP. Novel; Scottish literature; Sir Walter Scott. Add: Dept. of English, Amherst College, Amherst, MA 01002.

CAMERON, KENNETH NEILL, b. Barrow-in-Furness, Eng, Sept. 15, 08; nat; m. 46; c. 1. ENGLISH LITERATURE. A.B, McGill Univ, 31, hon. D.Litt; Rhodes scholar, Oxford, 31, B.A, 33, B.Litt, 34, M.A, 36; Ph.D, Univ. Wis, 39. Ed, News, McGill Grad. Soc, 34-35; asst, Univ. Wis, 36-39; instr. Eng, Ind. Univ, 39-43, asst. prof, 43-47, assoc. prof, 47-52; ed, Shelley and his circle, Carl H. Pforzheimer Libr, 52-66; PROF. ENG, N.Y. UNIV, 63- Vis. assoc. prof, Univ. Chicago, 50; Guggenheim fel, 67-68. MLA (Macmillans award, 49). Romantic period. Publ: The young Shelley, Macmillan, 50: Shelley: selected poetry and prose, Holt, 51; Shelley and his circle, (4 vols), Harvard & Oxford, 61; The Esdaile notebook, Knopf, 64; Humanity and society: a world history, Ind. Univ, 73; ed. & contribr, Romantic rebels: essays on Shelley and his circle, 73 & Shelley: the golden years, 74, Harvard. Add: 19 University Pl, New York University, New York, NY 10003.

CAMERON, KENNETH WALTER, b. Martins Ferry, Ohio, Oct. 12, 08. AMERICAN LITERATURE. A.B, Univ. W.Va, 30, A.M, 31; fel, Berkeley Divinity Sch, 34-38; S.T.B, Gen. Theol. Sem, 35; Ph.D, Yale, 40. Instr. ENG, N.C. State Coll, 38-44; asst. prof, Temple Univ, 45-46; TRINITY COL.(CONN), 46-57, ASSOC. PROF, 57- Archivist, Episcopal Diocese of Conn, 51- MLA; Col. Eng. Asn; Mod. Humanities Res. Asn; Melville Soc; Thoreau Soc; Milton Soc. Am; S.Atlantic Mod. Lang. Asn; Anglican Soc; Emerson Soc.(ed, Quart. & exec. secy, 55-). Tudor drama; Anglican church history; mediaeval world. Publ: Emerson the essayist (2 vols), Thistle, 45; Transcendentalists and Minerva (3 vols), 58, Transcendental climate (3 vols), 63, Emerson among his contemporaries, 67, Transcendental epilogue, (3 vols), 67 & ed, Thoreau's Fact book (3 vols), 67, Transcendental. Add: Dept. of English, Trinity College, Hartford, CT 06106.

CAMERON, RUTH ALLEN, b. Lisbon Falls, Maine, Jan. 15, 29; m. 50; c. 2. ENGLISH LANGUAGE & LITERATURE. B.A, East. Nazarene Col, 50; M.A, Boston Univ, 64, Ph.D, 72. Instr, East. Nazarene Col, 50-52, asst. prof, 64-68; teacher, Abington High Sch, 59-60; vis. prof, Northwest Nazarene Col, 68-69; ASSOC. PROF. ENG. EAST. NAZARENE COL, 71- Danforth Assoc, 64. MLA; NCTE; Conf. Christianity & Lit. English literature; stylistics. Add: Dept. of English, Eastern Nazarene College, 23 E. Elm Ave, Wollaston, MA 02170.

CAMP, DENNIS DAVID, b. Grand Rapids, Mich, Dec. 14, 37; div; c. 2. LITERATURE. B.A, Hope Col, 59; M.A, Rutgers Univ, New Brunswick, 61; Ph.D.(Eng), Univ. Wis-Madison, 69. Teaching asst. Eng, Rutgers Univ, 59-61; instr, Hope Col, 61-63; teaching asst, Univ. Wis, 63-66; asst. prof & assoc. chmn. dept, Univ. Wis-Rock County Campus, 66-69; asst. prof, Wis. State Univ-Whitewater, 69-70; ASSOC. PROF. LIT, SANGAMON STATE UNIV, 70- MLA. Vachel Lindsay; romanticism. Publ: Browning's Pompilia and the truth, Personalist, 66; Wordsworth's Lines composed a few miles above Tintern Abbey, 22-24, Explicator, 71. Add: Dept. of Literature, Sangamon State University, Springfield, IL 62707.

CAMP, GEORGE CARR, b. Nov. 19, 02; m. 28; c. 3. ENGLISH. A.B, Ohio Wesleyan Univ, 25; M.A, Ohio State Univ, 30; Ph.D.(Eng), Univ. Ill, 52. Teaching fel, Ohio Wesleyan Univ, 27-28; instr, Ohio State Univ, 28-30; dir. ENG, Williamsport Dickinson Jr. Col, 30-34; asst, Univ. Ill, 35-47; asst. prof, SOUTH. ILL. UNIV, CARBONDALE, 47-70, EMER. ASST. PROF, 70- MLA. English Romanticism; S.T. Coleridge. Add: Dept. of English, Southern Illinois University, Carbondale, IL 62903.

CAMP, JAMES E, b. Alexandria, La, Apr. 29, 23. ENGLISH. B.A, La. State Univ, 49; M.A, Columbia Univ, 50; Ph.D.(Eng), Univ. Mich, 65. Instr. ENG, Olivet Col, 50-54; ASSOC. PROF, NEWARK COL. ENGINEERING, 62- MLA; Univ. Film Asn. Modern poetry; American literature, especially Melville; cinema. Publ: Co-auth, Mark Twain's Frontier, Holt, 63; auth, An edict from the emperor (poetry), Burning Deck, 69; co-ed, Pegasus descending, MacMillan, 71. Add: Dept. of Humanities, Newark College of Engineering, Newark, NJ 07102.

CAMP, LEON RAYMOND, b. Kearney, Nebr, Sept. 25, 35; m. 59; c. 2. SPEECH, POLITICAL SCIENCE. B.A, Sioux Falls Col, 58; M.A, Ind. Univ, Bloomington, 61; Ph.D.(speech), Ps. State Univ, 69. Instr. speech & Eng, Torrington High Sch, Wyo, 58-60; speech, Millsaps Col, 61-63; Pa. State Univ, 63-66; asst. prof, Univ. Conn, 66-69; ASSOC. PROF. ENG, N.C. STATE UNIV, 69- Consult, U.S. Dept. Health, Educ. & Welfare, 65; grants, Univ. Conn, 68-69; N.C. State Univ, 71-72, 73-74. Speech Commun. Asn; Am. Forensic Asn. American public address; argumentation; rhetorical theory. Publ: Co-auth, Preaching in America, Abingdon, 69; auth, The Rhode Island debates of 1672, Quaker Hist, fall 63; co-auth, A study of stock issues, judging criteria, and decisions in debate, South. Speech J, spring 64. Add: Dept. of English, North Carolina State University, Box 5110, Raleigh, NC 27607.

CAMP, PAUL ALFRED, b. Willits, Calif, June 25, 11. DRAMA. A.B, Whittier Col, 39, A.M, 46. Art dir, Pasadena Playhouse Lab. Theatre, Calif, 35-36; art & tech. dir, Memphis Little Theatre, Tenn, 36-38; teaching fel, Whittier Col, 38-40; head dept. drama, high sch, Long Beach, Calif, 40-43; staff instr, Pasadena Playhouse, 46-47; assoc. prof. DRAMA, UNIV. GA, 47-68, PROF, 68- U.S.A, 43-45, Sgt. Am. Theatre Asn; U.S. Inst. Theatre Technol.(mem, Performing Arts Training & Educ. Comn, 71-). Play production. Publ: Co-auth, Designing the play, Appleton, 42. Add: Dept. of Drama, University of Georgia, Athens, GA 30602.

CAMP, TRUMAN WILDES, b. Newington, Conn, Dec. 6, 04; m. 40; c. 1. ENGLISH LITERATURE. A.B, Yale, 26, Ph.D, 35. Instr. Eng, Univ. Tex, 28-31, 33-34; mem. fac, Conn. Jr. Col. Commerce, 34-35; instr. ENG, TEX. TECH UNIV, 35-40, asst. prof, 40-42, assoc. prof. & chmn. dept, 46-49, prof, 49-73, EMER. PROF, 73-, head dept, 49-62. U.S.A.F, 42-46, Capt. MLA; Col. Eng. Asn; S.Cent. Mod. Lang. Asn; NCTE. Shakespeare; Swift; Johnson. Publ: Journal of Joseph Camp, 1859, Nebr. Hist, 65; Henry IV, Part 1 & Ballad of Chevychace, Notes & Queries, 66; Boswell and Johnson's theory of biography, CEA Critic, 66. Add: 2611-25th, Lubbock, TX 79410.

CAMPBELL, ALPHONSUS PATRICK, b. Souris, P.E.I, Can, June 4, 12; m. 54; c. 5. ENGLISH LITERATURE. B.A, Laval Univ, 37; M.A, Fordham Univ, 47, Can. Humanities Asn. grant, 54, Ph.D.(Eng), 59. Prof. ENG, St. Dunstan's Univ, 46-48; St. Thomas Col.(N.B), 49-59; from asst. prof. to PROF, UNIV. OTTAWA, 59- Can. Counc. grant-in-aid, St. Louis Univ. Libr, summer 60; Nuffield Found. grant, Brit. mus, summer 66; Can. Counc. sr. fel, 67-68. MLA; Mediaeval Acad. Am; Can. Ling. Soc. Medieval English literature; Anglo-Saxon and Middle English. Publ: The first time I saw the sea (poems), Charlottetown, P.E.I, 69; Kaki-Wahoo (children's book), Borealis, 73; Red clay soil (poems), Square Deal, (in press); The Tiberius psalter, Univ. Ottawa, (in press); ed, Guido Faba's Rota Nova, Bibliotheca di Quadrivium, Italy, (in press); auth, The time element of interlace structure in Beowulf, Neuphilologische Mitteilungen, 69; Ars dictaminis: order, beauty and our daily bread, Humanities Asn. Bull, 71; The Seafarer: wanderlust and our heavenly home, Rev. Univ. Ottawa, 73; plus others. Add: Dept. of English, University of Ottawa, Ottawa, Ont. K1N 6N5, Can.

CAMPBELL, ANNE LUCILLE, b. Peoria, Ill, Oct. 12, 10. ENGLISH. B.A, Bradley Univ, 30; M.A, Northwest. Univ, 35; fel, N.Y. Univ, 46-48, Ph.D. (Eng), 56. Instr. ENG, PRAIRIE VIEW AGR. & MECH. COL, 30-35, asst. prof, 35-45, assoc. prof, 49-56, PROF. & HEAD DEPT, 56- Lectr, human relat. workshop, Kansas City Univ, summers 57, 59; mem, Am. Counc. Human Rights, 61; chmn, revision comt, NCTE, 63-64; lectr, NDEA Inst, Wiley Col, 65. Minnie Stevens Piper Award, 64. NCTE; MLA; Col. Eng. Asn. Modern trends in English teaching; language and the culturally disadvantaged; social implications in dialect usage of the disadvantaged. Publ: Perspectives of the Negro college teachers's world, Col. Lang. Asn. J, 59; Composition for these times: some objectives and techniques, Tex. State Teachers Asn. Bull, 60. Add: Dept. of English, Prairie View Agricultural & Mechanical College, Prairie View, TX 77445.

CAMPBELL, CHARLES ALEXANDER, b. Springfield, Mass, Feb. 12, 25; m. 52; c. 3. ENGLISH. B.A, Univ. Mass, 47; M.A, Univ. Chicago, 48; Ph.D.(Eng), Univ. Minn, 51. Instr. ENG, Phillips Acad, Andover, Mass, 51-52; Mary Inst, St. Louis, Mo, 52-54; high sch, Mass. 54-66; asst. prof, UNIV. MASS, BOSTON, 66-70, ASSOC. PROF, 70- acting coord, teacher certification prog, 67-68 & 69-71. Exchange teacher, Burnham Grammer Sch, Bucks, Eng, 61-62; dir, NDEA Inst. Eng, summer 68; Title I evaluator, U.S. Off. Educ, 70-72. U.S.N, 43-46, Lt.(jg). NCTE; Conf. Eng. Educ. Preparation of teachers of English; American literature. Publ: The new English—a Luddite view, Eng. J, 5/67; Think-talk-write: a behavioristic pedagogy for scribal fluency, Col. Eng, 11/69. Add: 42 Woodland St, Natick, MA 01760.

CAMPBELL, DAVID EUGENE, Romance Languages. See Volume III, Foreign Languages, Linguistics & Philology.

CAMPBELL, ELIZABETH McCLURE, b. Jefferson City, Mo, Nov. 29, 91; wid; c. 2. ENGLISH. A.B, Univ. Mo, 14; A.M, Univ. Colo, 28; Univ. Chicago, 33-35. Mem. fac, Cottey Col, 26-33; asst. prof. Eng, Park Col, 35-56, assoc. prof, 56-57; Nat. Col, 57-59; RETIRED. NCTE. Evolution of a writing laboratory; orientation English; Missouri history. Publ: Co-auth, Orientation English, 39, 46 & Communications handbook, 53, 55, Burgess; auth, The Cottey sisters of Missouri, Park Col, 70. Add: 831 Main St, Parkville, MO 64152.

CAMPBELL, GLADYS, b. Terre Haute, Ind, Feb. 17, 92. ENGLISH, PHILOSOPHY. M.A, Univ. Chicago. From teacher univ. high sch. to assoc. prof. HUMANITIES, UNIV. CHICAGO, 46-57, PROF, 57- Vis. instr, East. Ill. State Teachers Col; Wis. Teachers Col, La Crosse; Whitney prof, Va. Union Univ, 57-59. Literature and philosophy. Publ: Co-auth, Magazines and newspapers of today, Reading English literature & Reading American literature; auth, The momentary beach (poetry), privately publ, 72. Add: 1157 E. 56th St, Chicago, IL 60637.

CAMPBELL, HARRY MODEAN, b. Terrell, Tex, Nov. 18, 08; m. 40; c. 1. ENGLISH. A.B, South. Methodist Univ, 29, A.M, 35; Ph.D, Vanderbilt Univ, 42. Instr, Univ. Ala, 41-42; Va. Polytech. Inst, 42-44, asst. prof, 44-45; instr, Univ. Tex, 45-46, asst. prof, 46-47; assoc. prof. Eng, Univ. Miss, 47-49, prof, 49-60; prof, Okla. State Univ, 60-71, head dept, 60-68; RETIRED. Ford fel, Harvard, 52-53; Fulbright lectr, Italy, 55-57; Okla. State Univ. Res. Found. grant, 68- MLA; Am. Stud. Asn; S.Cent. Mod. Lang. Asn. English and American literature; Russian literature; modern philosophy. Publ: Collab, William Faulkner: a critical appraisal, 51 & Elizabeth Madox Roberts: American novelist, 56, Univ. Okla. Add: 126 S. Duck, Stillwater, OK 74074.

CAMPBELL, HILBERT HAYNES, b. Lookout, W.Va, Nov. 8, 34; m. 59; c. 2. ENGLISH LITERATURE. B.A, Marshall Univ, 58, M.A, 60; Danforth fel, Univ. Ky, 63, 64, 65, 66, Ph.D.(Eng), 66. Instr. ENG, Marshall Univ, 59-60, 61-63, asst. prof, 66-67; VA. POLYTECH. INST. & STATE UNIV, 67-70, ASSOC. PROF, 70- U.S.N, 52-55; Res, 55-60. MLA. Intellectual background of eighteenth century literature; Joseph Addison; James Thomson. Publ: Addison's Cartesian passage and Nicolas Malebranche, Philol. Quart, 7/67; Thomson and the Countess of Hertford, Mod. Philol, 5/70; Shiels and Johnson: biographers of Thomson, Stud. Eng. Lit, summer 72; plus other articles, rev. & bibliog. Add: Dept. of English, Virginia Polytechnic Institute & State University, Blacksburg, VA 24060.

CAMPBELL, JACKSON JUSTICE, b. Nowata, Okla, Jan. 9, 20. ENGLISH. A.B, Yale, 41, Ph.D, 50; A.M, Univ. Pa, 46. Asst. instr, Univ. Pa, 45-46; Yale, 46-48, instr, 48-51; asst. prof. ENG, Univ. Ill, 51-54; Princeton, 54-58, assoc. prof, 58-64, Annan preceptor, 56-57; PROF, UNIV. ILL, URBANA, 64- MLA; Ling. Soc. Am; Mediaeval Acad. Am; Early Eng. Text Soc. Old English literature and language. Publ: Ed, William Shakespeare Troilus and Cressida, Yale, 55; auth, Advent lyrics, Princeton, 58; co-auth, Poems in Old English, Harper, 62; auth, Learned rhetoric in Old English poetry, Mod. Philol, 66; Cynewulf's multiple revelations, Medievalia et Humanistica, 72; Polonius among the pilgrims, Chaucer Rev, 73. Add: Dept. of English, University of Illinois, Urbana, IL 61801.

CAMPBELL, JANE LUND, b. Parry Sound, Ont, June 4, 34; m. 65. ENGLISH. B.A, Queen's Univ.(Ont), 56; Can. Fed. Univ. Women Margaret McWilliams fel, 58-59; B.Litt, Oxford, 59; Can. Counc. fel, 59-61; Ph.D.(Eng), Univ. Toronto, 65. Lectr. ENG, WILFRED LAURIER UNIV, 61-64, asst. prof, 64-68, ASSOC. PROF, 69- Can. Counc. postdoctoral res. grant, 70-71. Asn. Can. Univ. Teachers Eng. Early 19th century poetry and critical theory. Publ: The retrospective review (1820-28) and the revival of seventeenth-century poetry, Wilfred Laurier Univ, 72. Add: Dept. of English, Wilfred Laurier University, University Ave, Waterloo, Ont. N2L 3C5, Can.

CAMPBELL, JEFFERSON HOLLAND, b. Beaumont, Tex, Jan. 19, 31; m. 52; c. 3. ENGLISH. B.A, South. Methodist Univ, 52, B.D, 55; Ph.D.(Am. lit), Duke Univ, 63. Asst. prof. ENG, Southwest. Univ, 62-65, assoc. prof, 65-66, PROF. & CHMN. DEPT, 66-74; MIDWEST. UNIV, 74- Vis. prof, Perkins Sch. Theol, South. Methodist Univ, summer 68. Am. Stud. Asn; MLA; Asn. Dept. Eng; AAUP. American literature; contemporary literature; theological implications of contemporary literature. Publ: John Howard Griffin, Steck, 70; An American tragedy revisited, Relig. in Life, summer 69; Bellow's intimations of immortality: Henderson the rain king, Stud. Novel, fall 69; Polarity and paradox: Faulkner's Light in August, CEA Critic, 1/72; plus others. Add: Dept. of English, Midwestern University, Wichita Falls, TX 76308.

CAMPBELL, JOAN PATRICK, b. Chicago, Ill, July 1, 29. MODERN LITERATURE. B.A, Loretto Heights Col, 50; May Bonfils Mem. scholar. & M.A, Cath. Univ. Am, 63; Ph.D.(Eng), Univ. Iowa, 70. Teacher ENG, Bishop Toolen High Sch, Mobile, Ala, 54-57; chmn. dept, St. Agnes Regional High Sch, Springfield, Mo, 57-62; instr, Loretto Heights Col, 62-64; Webster Col, 64-65; ASSOC. PROF, JACKSON STATE COL, 70- Am. Counc. Learned Soc. fel, Univ. Kans, summer 72; co-ed, Jackson State Col. Rev. S.Cent. Mod. Lang. Asn; NCTE; AAUP. The novel; communications pedagogy. Publ: Matthew Arnold and the novel, Jackson State Col. Rev, summer 73. Add: Dept. of English, Jackson State College, 1325 Lynch St, Jackson, MS 39217.

CAMPBELL, MARIE ALICE, b. Tamms, Ill. FOLKLORE, ENGLISH LITERATURE. B.A, South. Ill. Univ, Carbondale, 32; M.A, George Peabody Col, 37; Ph.D.(folklore, Eng. lit), Ind. Univ. Bloomington, 56. Assoc. prof. Eng, W.Ga. Col, 40-53; Ind. Univ, Bloomington, 53-56; ENG. & FOLKLORE, Glassboro State Col, 57-58, prof, 58-60; assoc. prof, Ohio State Univ, 60-63; UNIV. MASS, AMHERST, 63-64, prof, 64-73, EMER. PROF, 73- Guggenheim fel, 44-45 & 56-57; Univ. Ky. Press fel, 55-56; pt. time prof. creative writing, Univ, Pa, 57-60. Am. Folklore Soc; PEN Club; MLA. Collecting folk tales and black folklore. Publ: Cloud-walking, Rinehart, 42, Ind. Univ, 71; Folks do get born, 46 & A house with stairs, 50, Rinehart; Tales from the cloud-walking country, Ind. Univ, 58; plus numerous others. Add: 111 Sunset Ave, Amherst, MA 01002.

CAMPBELL, MARY ELIZABETH, b. Cambridge, Ohio, Feb. 11, 03. ENGLISH LITERATURE. A.B, Radcliffe Col, 25, A.M, 26; Ph.D.(Eng. lit), Yale, 37. Instr. ENG, IND. UNIV, BLOOMINGTON, 27-39, asst. prof, 39-53, assoc. prof, 53-71, prof, 71-73, EMER. PROF, 73- Instr, Harvard, 45. MLA; NCTE. Modern drama; modern comparative literature; the 17th century. Publ: Defoe's first poem; What makes an educated woman?; The statement of Edward Albee's Tiny Alice, Papers Lang. & Lit, winter 68. Add: 520 S. Jordan Ave, Bloomington, IN 47401.

CAMPBELL, MICHAEL LEE, b. Roanoke, Va, Oct. 10, 42. ENGLISH & AMERICAN LITERATURE. B.S, Va. Polytech. Inst, 64; Woodrow Wilson fel, Univ. N.C, Chapel Hill, 64-66, M.A, 65, Ph.D.(Eng), 69. Instr. ENG, VA. POLYTECH. INST. & STATE UNIV, 68-69, ASST. PROF, 69- Nineteenth and 20th century English and American literature; cinema. Publ: Fellini: modern Roman satirist, Maelstrom, 66; Rosebud in Citizen Kane, Am. Notes & Queries, 5/73; Thomas Hardy's attitude toward animals, Victorians Inst. J, 7/73. Add: Dept. of English, Virginia Polytechnic Institute & State University, Blacksburg, VA 24061.

CAMPBELL, PAUL NEWELL, b. Washington, D.C, Feb. 27, 23. COMMUNICATION. Ph.D.(commun), Univ. South. Calif, 59. Asst. prof. speech & drama, Calif. State Univ, Los Angeles, 59-65, assoc. prof, 65-71; PROF. COMMUN. ARTS & SCI, QUEENS COL.(N.Y), 71- Speech Commun. Asn; East.Commun. Asn. Language theory; rhetoric; communication aesthetics. Publ: Oral interpretation, Macmillan, 66; The speaking and the speakers of literature, 67 & Rhetoric-ritual: a study of the communicative and aesthetic dimensions of language, 72, Dickenson; Language as intrapersonal and poetic process, fall 69 & Poetic-rhetorical, philosophical, and scientific discourse, winter 73, Philos. & Rhet; A rhetorical view of locutionary, illocutionary and perlocutionary acts, Quart. J. Speech, 10/73; plus others. Add: Dept. of Communication Arts & Sciences, Queens College, Flushing, NY 11367.

CAMPBELL, STEPHEN COADY, b. New Waterford, N.S, Feb. 4, 39; m. 63; c. 4. ENGLISH LITERATURE. B.A, St. Francis Xavier Univ, 60, B.Ed, 61; M.A, Univ. N.B, 66. Lectr. Eng. & hist, St. Joseph's Univ, 61-63; ENG, UNIV. MONCTON, 63-66, asst. prof, 66-69, ASSOC. PROF, 69-, CHMN. DEPT, 73-, acting chmn, 62-66. Counr, Moncton City Counc, 70-; v.pres, Cities of N.B, 73-74. Humanities Asn. Can; Maritime Soc. 18th Century Stud; Asn. Can. Univ. Teachers Eng. John Hunter Duvar, minor writer of early Canadian period; Macbeth. Publ: Poems, X-Writes, 60. Add: Dept. of English, University of Moncton, Moncton, N.B. E1A 3E9, Can.

CAMPBELL, THOMAS PATTERSON, III, b. Denver, Colo, May 2, 42; m. 67; c. 1. ENGLISH LITERATURE, LINGUISTICS. B.A, Stanford Univ, 64; Ph.D.(Eng. lang), Ind. Univ, Bloomington, 72. ASST. PROF. ENG, UNIV. CALIF, DAVIS, 70- Old English language and literature; medieval drama; linguistics. Publ: The treasure motif in four Old English elegies, Laurentian Univ. Rev, 69. Add: Dept. of English, University of California, Davis, CA 95616.

CAMPBELL, WILLIAM ROYCE, b. Elmira, N.Y, June 7, 38; m. 61; c. 3. ENGLISH. B.A, San Jose State Col, 61; M.A, Univ. Ore, 63, Ph.D.(Shelley, Blake), 67. Asst. prof. ENG, UNIV. KY, 67-72, ASSOC. PROF, 72- Romantic period. Publ: Ed, Parts and patterns: readings for writers, Dickenson Co, 67; Shelley's concept of conscience, 70 & Shelley's view of history, 73, Keats-Shelley J. Add: Dept. of English, University of Kentucky, Lexington, KY 40506.

CANADAY, NICHOLAS, JR, b. New York, N.Y, Dec. 22, 28; m. 52; c. 3. ENGLISH. A.B, Princeton, 50; M.A, Univ. Fla, 55, Ph.D, 57. Instr. ENG, LA. STATE UNIV, BATON ROUGE, 57-59, asst. prof, 59-65, assoc. prof, 65-73, PROF, 73- Fulbright lectr, Japan, 63-64; Danforth Black Stud. fel, Yale, 70-71. U.S.A, 50-52. NCTE; MLA; Melville Soc. Am; Am. Stud. Asn; Col. Eng. Asn; Conf. Christianity & Lit. American literature. Publ: Melville and authority, Univ. Fla, 68; Hawthorne's minister and the veiling deceptions of self, Stud. Short Fiction, 67; Melville's Pierre: at war with social convention, Papers Lang. & Lit, 69; Community and identity at Blithedale, S.Atlantic Quart, 72. Add: Dept. of English, Louisiana State University, Baton Rouge, LA 70803.

CANANT, RAY MOSCHEL, b. Abilene, Tex. ENGLISH. B.A, Univ. Ky, 61, M.A, 63; M.A, Univ. Tex, Austin, 70, Ph.D.(Eng), 72. Instr. Eng, Bryan Sta. Sr. High Sch, Lexington, Ky, 61-62; Eng. & music, Southeast. Christian Col, 62-65; from teaching asst. to asst. instr. ENG, Univ. Tex, Austin, 65-71; from asst. prof. to ASSOC. PROF, HARDIN-SIMMONS UNIV, 71- MLA; AAUP; NEA; NCTE; S.Cent. Mod. Lang. Asn; Conf. Col. Teachers Eng. Twentieth century American literature. Publ: A catalogue of the Carl Sandburg collection at University of Texas at Austin, Univ. Microfilms, 73. Add: Dept. of English, Hardin-Simmons University, Abilene, TX 79601.

CANARIO, JOHN WIST, b. Hilo, Hawaii, June 27, 20; m. 48; c. 1. AMERICAN LITERATURE. A.B, Univ. Calif, Berkeley, 49, B.L.S, 50, M.A, 50; Ph.D, Univ. Wash, 63. Asst. librn, Sacramento County Schs. Libr, 50-51; librn, Riverside City Col, 51-54; assoc, Univ. Wash, 55-56, librn, SAN JOSE STATE UNIV, 56-57, instr. ENG, 57-62, asst. prof, 62-65, assoc. prof, 65-69, PROF, 69- U.S.N, 40-45. American literature; American and European contemporary literature. Publ: The Harlequin in Heart of darkness, Stud. Short Fiction, spring 67; The dream in The tell-tale heart, Eng. Lang. Notes, 3/70. Add: Dept. of English, San Jose State University, 125 S. Seventh St, San Jose, CA 95114.

CANARY, ROBERT HUGHES, b. Providence, R.I, Feb. 1, 39; m. 61; c. 2. ENGLISH. B.A, Denison Univ, 60; M.A, Univ. Chicago, 62, Ph.D.(hist. of cult), 63. Asst. prof. ENG, San Diego State Col, 63-66; Grinnell Col, 66-68; vis. asst. prof, Univ. Mich, summer 68; ASSOC. PROF, Univ. Hawaii, 68-70; UNIV. WIS-PARKSIDE, 70- Vis. asst. prof, Hofstra Univ, summer 67; co-ed, CLIO: An interdisciplinary Jour. of Lit, Hist. & Philos. of Hist, 71- MLA; James Branch Cabell Soc; Catch Soc. Am.(assoc. ed, 69-71); AHA; Orgn. Am. Hist; Soc. Stud. South. Lit; AAUP. American literature and popular culture; critical theory as applied to historiography. Publ: William Dunlap, 70 & George Bancroft, 74, Twayne; William Dunlap and the search for an American audience, Midcontinent Am. Stud, spring 63; Cabell's dark comedies, Miss. Quart, spring 68; Playing the game of Life, J. Popular Cult, spring 68. Add: Dept. of English, University of Wisconsin-Parkside, Kenosha, WI 53140.

CANAVAN, P. JOSEPH, b. Cambridge, Mass, June 22, 15; m. 53; c. 2. ENGLISH, WORLD LITERATURE. B.A, Bates Col, 39; M.A, Univ. South. Calif, 48, Ph.D.(Eng), 50. Teacher ENG, Danforth High Sch, Maine, 39-41; Whitman High Sch, Mass, 41-42; CHMN. DEPT, MT. SAN ANTONIO COL, 48- Fulbright lectr, Denmark, 52-53; mem, Col. Comn. Commun. & Compos. U.S.C.G, 42-45, Lt. NEA. Publ: Co-auth, The library research paper, Kendall-Hunt, 62; co-auth, The way to reading improvement, 66 & co-auth, Developing reading skills, 68, Allyn & Bacon; auth, Paragraphs and the short theme, Heath, 69; co-auth, Workbook for writers, Van Nostrand, 70; auth, Effective English, Dickenson, 70; Elements of college reading and writing, McGraw, 71. Add: Dept. of English, Mt. San Antonio College, 11 N. Grand Ave, Walnut, CA 91789.

CANDELARIA, FREDERICK HENRY, b. El Paso, Tex, Dec. 2, 29; m. 53; c. 2. ENGLISH. B.A, Univ. Tex, 54; Yale, 54-55; Ph.D, Univ. Mo, 59. Instr. Eng, Univ. Mo, 55-59; Univ. Ore, 59-61, asst. prof, & dir. compos, 61-65; ASSOC. PROF. ENG. & ED, W.COAST REV, SIMON FRASER UNIV, 65- Off. sci. & scholarly res. awards, Univ. Ore, summers 62, 63; Simon Fraser Univ. Pres. res. grants, 65-68; Koerner Found. grant, 66-67; Can. Counc. sr. fel, 67-68. Mil. Intel, U.S.A, 51-53. MLA. Seventeenth century English and Spanish poetry. Publ: Perspectives on epic, 65 & Perspectives on style, 68, Allyn & Bacon; co-auth, The voices of prose, McGraw, 66; auth, Dimensions, Morriss, Victoria, 67; Science and grammar: a compromise, Col. Eng, 4/60; Ovid and the indifferent lovers, Renaissance News, 60; The necklace of Wyatt's Diere, Eng. Lang. Notes, 63. Add: Dept. of English, Simon Fraser University, Burnaby 2, B.C, Can.

CANEDO, ANTHONY, b New York, N.Y, July 26, 24; m. 44; c. 1. ENGLISH. B.A, Univ. Wash, 54, Ph.D.(Eng), 65. Instr. Eng. & Span, Olympic Col, 61-62; asst. prof, ENG, CENT. WASH. STATE COL, 62-66, assoc. prof, 66-70, PROF, 70-, assoc. dean arts & sci, 69-70, asst. v.pres. acad. affairs, 70-71, acting dean, 72-73. U.S.N, 42-49. MLA; NCTE; Col. Eng. Asn. American literature; the novel; literature and culture of Spain. Add: Dept. of English, Central Washington State College, Ellensburg, WA 98926.

CANFIELD, FAYETTE CURTIS, b. Bridgeport, Conn, July 29, 03; m. 27; c. 1. DRAMA. A.B, Amherst Col, 25, L.H.D, 55; M.A, Yale, 54; LL.D, Emerson Col, 56. From instr. to prof. dramatics, Amherst Col, 27-54, Stanley King prof. dramatic arts, 52-54, dir, Kirby Mem. Theatre, 38-54; prof. drama, Yale, 54-68, chmn. dept, 54-55, dir. univ. theatre, 54-65, dean drama sch, 55-65, fel. Saybrook Col; Univ. prof. THEATRE ARTS, UNIV. PITTSBURGH, 68-73, EMER. PROF, 73- Trustee, Nat. Theatre Conf, 58-62; Am. Shakespeare Festival Theatre & Acad, 63-; mem. exec. comt, Shakespeare Anniversary. U.S.N.R, Lt. Comdr. Nat. Theatre Conf.(pres, 64). Publ: Plays of the Irish Renaissance, 29; Plays of changing Ireland, 36; The seed and the sowers, 55; The craft of play directing, 63. Add: 36 Dana St, Amherst, MA 01002.

CANFIELD, FRANCIS X, b. Detroit, Mich, Dec. 3, 20. ENGLISH. B.A, Sacred Heart Sem, 41; M.A, Catholic Univ, 45; A.M.L.S, Univ. Mich, 50; Ph.D.(Eng), Univ. Ottawa, 51. Prof. Eng, SACRED HEART SEM, 46-63, RECTOR & PRES, 63- MLA; NCTE; Am. Libr. Asn; Cath. Libr. Asn.(pres, 61-63). Catholic Church history in Michigan; Melville; Catholic fiction. Publ: Literature and the modern mind, Sacred Heart Sem, 63; Moby Dick and the Book of Job, Cath. World; A diocese so vast, Mich. Hist, fall 67; plus others. Add: 157 Lake Shore, Grosse Pointe, MI 48236.

CANFIELD, JOHN DOUGLAS, b. Washington, D.C, Feb. 4, 41; m. 63; c. 1. ENGLISH & AMERICAN LITERATURE. A.B, Univ. Notre Dame, 63; M.A.T, Yale, 64; M.A, Johns Hopkins Univ, 66; U.S. Steel Found. fel, Univ. Fla, 66-68; Ph.D (Eng), 69. ASST. PROF. ENG, UNIV. CALIF, LOS ANGELES, 69- MLA; Am. Soc. 18th Century Stud. Restoration drama and its English and continental backgrounds. Publ: Nicholas Rowe and Christian tragedy, Univ. Fla, 74; Blessed are the merciful: the understanding of the promise in Paradise lost, Milton Quart, 5/73; The unity of Boileau's Le Lutrin: the counter-effect of the mock-heroic, Philol. Quart, 74; The jewel of great price: mutability and constancy in Dryden's All for love and its Renaissance predecessors, ELH, 74. Add: Dept. of English, University of California, Los Angeles, CA 90024.

CANNING, GEORGE R, JR, b. Lexington, Mo, Sept. 14, 20; m. 50. VICTORIAN LITERATURE. A.B, Mo. Valey Col, 42; cert, Yale, 44; M.A, Univ. Chicago, 49; Ph.D, Univ. Wis, 58. Instr. ENG, Wentworth Mil. Acad, 46-48, prof, 49-54; teaching asst, Univ. Wis, 54-58; asst. prof, ILL. STATE UNIV, 58-60, from assoc. prof. to PROF, 60- U.S.A, 42-46, Sgt. MLA; William Morris Soc. & Kelmscott Fel. William Morris. Add: Dept. of English, Illinois State University, Normal, IL 61761.

CANNON, CHARLES DALE, b. Bruce, Miss, May 27, 28; m. 52; c. 2. ENGLISH. B.A, Univ. Miss, 51, fel, 51-52, M.A, 52; Ph.D.(eng), Univ. Mo, 64. Instr. Eng, Copiah-Lincoln Jr. Col, 53-55; Univ. Mo, 55-56; investigator, U.S. Civil Serv. Comn, 56-57; asst. prof. ENG, Miss. Col, 57-59; Univ. Miss, 64-65; Southeast Mo. State Col, 65-66; UNIV. MISS, 66-68, assoc. prof, 68-71, PROF, 71- Finance C, 46-49. MLA; Malone Soc; Renaissance Soc. Am; Shakespeare Asn. Am. Domestic tragedy: the Puritan controversy over the stage. Publ: A warning for fair women: a critical edition, Mouton, The Hague, 74; The religion of the Anglo-Saxons, Univ. Miss. Stud. Eng, 64; A warning for fair women and the Puritan controversy, Stud. Eng, 68; contrib, Literature & society, 1966-1970: a selective bibliography, Univ. Miami, 74; plus others. Add: Dept. of English, University of Mississippi, University, MS 38677.

CANNON, CHARLES KENDRICK, b. Michigan City, Ind, Feb. 26, 25; m. 56; c. 2. ENGLISH. B.A, Yale, 50, M.A, 53, Ph.D.(Eng), 58. Instr. ENG, Coe Col, 55-57, asst. prof, 57-62, assoc. prof, 62-66; Drake Univ, 66-69, PROF, 69-71; COE COL, 71- Folger Shakespeare Libr. fel, 68. U.S.A.A.F, 43-46, 2nd Lt. MLA. Biblical exegesis in 16th century; Renaissance religious drama. Publ: The relation of the additions of The Spanish tragedy to the original play, Stud. Eng. Lit, spring 62; Chapman on the unity of style and meaning, J. Eng. & Ger. Philol, 4/69; As in a theatre: Hamlet in the light of Calvin's doctrine of predestination, Stud. Eng. Lit, spring 71; plus one other. Add: Dept. of English, Coe College, Cedar Rapids, IA 52402.

CANNON, GARLAND H, Linguistics, British Literature. See Volume III, Foreign Languages, Linguistics & Philology.

CANTRALL, WILLIAM RANDOLPH, Linguistics, English Education. See Volume III, Foreign Languages, Linguistics & Philology.

CANTRELL, DOROTHY DEAN, b. Milan, Tenn, May 26, 34. ENGLISH. B.A, Lambuth Col, 56; M.A, George Peabody Col, 61; Ph.D.(Eng), Univ. Tenn, Knoxville, 70. Teacher, Milan Schs, Tenn, 55-56, 56-58; Nurnberg Sch, Ger, 58-59; ENG, John F. Polytechnic High Sch, Los Angeles, Calif, 59-60; Regan High Sch, Houston, Tex, 60-62; instr, BERRY COL, 62-65, asst. prof, 65-70, ASSOC. PROF, 70-, CHMN. DEPT. ENG. & SPEECH, 71- MLA; NCTE; Soc. South. Lit; S.Atlantic Mod. Lang. Asn. Womens studies; the novel, Jane Austen. Publ: Tous les hommes et toute les femmes sont-ils egaux?, Delta Kappa Gamma Int. Bull, summer 72. Add: Dept. of English & Speech, Berry College, Mount Berry, GA 30149.

CANZLER, DAVID GEORGE, b. Multnomah Co, Ore, Feb. 27, 28; m. 55; 68; c. 4. ENGLISH RENAISSANCE DRAMA. B.A, Linfield Col, 51; M.A, Univ. Ore, 58, Ph.D.(Eng), 61. Instr. ENG, Univ. Ore, 60-61, asst. prof, Concord Col, 61-66; CENT. WASH. STATE COL, 66-70, ASSOC. PROF, 70- U.S.A, 46-47. MLA. Publ: Quarto editions of Play of the Wether, Papers Bibliog. Soc. Am, fall 68. Add: Dept. of English, Central Washington State College, Ellensburg, WA 98926.

CANZONERI, ROBERT WILBURN, b. San Marcos, Tex, Nov. 21, 25. CREATIVE WRITING, MODERN AMERICAN LITERATURE. B.A, Miss. Col, 48; fel, Univ, Miss, 50-51, M.A, 51; Ph.D.(Eng, Am. lit), Stanford Univ, 65. Instr. ENG, Univ. Miss, 53-55; assoc. prof, Livingston State Teachers Col, 55; Georgetown Col, 55-57; Miss. Col, 57-60; La. Col, 61-63; asst. prof, OHIO STATE UNIV, 65-66, assoc. prof, 66-68, PROF, 68- Henry H. Bellamann Award, 65. U.S.N, 43-46; Distinguished Flying Cross; Air Medal & 5 Oak Leaf Clusters. Writing fiction, poetry and non-fiction. Publ: I do so politely: a voice from the South, Houghton, 65; Watch us pass, Ohio State Univ, 68; Men with little hammers, 69 & Barbed wire and other stories, 70, Dial; co-ed, Fiction and analysis: seven major themes, Scott, 70; Charles Evers: Mississippi's representative man?, Harper's Mag, 7/68; Wallace Stegner, South. Rev, autumn 73; The boot, Iowa Rev, autumn 73. Add: Dept. of English, Ohio State University, 164 W. 17th Ave, Columbus, OH 43210.

CAPEL, ROBERT BENNETT, b. Oskaloosa, Iowa, Jan. 26, 06; m. 35; c. 2. SPEECH. B.A, William Penn Col, 28; M.A, Univ. Wis, 29, Ph.D.(speech), 41; Columbia Univ, 30-31; N.Y. Univ, 31-32. Instr. SPEECH, N.Y. Univ, 29-32; prof, Upper Iowa Univ, 32-34; prof. & head dept, Hendrix Col, 35-44; prof, Northwest. State Col. La, 44-49; PROF. & HEAD DEPT, STEPHEN F. AUSTIN STATE UNIV, 49- South. Speech Commun. Asn.(ed, Jour, 39-42, 3rd v.pres, 42-44, 62-63, pres, 44-46); Speech Commun. Asn. Effect of debate on debaters and audiences; accuracy of judging contest speakers; the speech to entertain. Publ: Co-auth, Oral argument, Harper, 34. Add: Dept. of Speech, Stephen F. Austin State University, Nacogdoches, TX 75962.

CAPP, GLENN RICHARD, b. Westminster, Tex, Sept. 21, 10. SPEECH. A.B, Okla. Baptist Univ, 33, hon. Litt.D, 65; J.D, Baylor Univ, 38; A.M, Northwest Univ, 48. Instr. SPEECH, Okla. Baptist Univ, 33-34; PROF, BAYLOR UNIV, 34- Consult, Brooks Army Med. Hosp. Admin. Prog, 52- U.S.A.A.F, 42-46, Capt. Speech Commun. Asn; South. Speech Asn.(pres, 49). Rhetoric and argumentation; manuals for high school debaters. Publ: Co-auth, Practical debating, Lippincott, 49; auth, How to communicate orally, 61 & co-auth, Principles of argumentation and debate, 65, auth, Basic oral communication, 71 & Student guide to basic oral communication, 71, Prentice-Hall; Famous speeches in American history, Bobbs, 63; The Great Society: a source book of speeches, Dickenson, 67. Add: Dept. of Oral Communication, Baylor University, Waco, TX 76703.

CAPPON, ALEXANDER P, b. Milwaukee, Wis, May 11, 00; m. 22; c. 1. ENGLISH LITERATURE. Ph.B, Univ. Chicago, 25, A.M, 26, Ph.D, 35. Instr. Eng, Univ. Tulsa, 26-27; assoc. Eng. lit, Univ. Wash, 27-29; instr, Mont. State Col, 32-33, asst. prof, 34-37; instr, West. Ill. State Teachers Col, 34; from assoc. prof. to prof. Eng. lang. & lit, UNIV. MO-KANSAS CITY, 37-70, ed, Univ. Rev, 37-42, 53-70, chmn. dept. Eng, 41-44, 48-51, EMER. PROF. ENG, 70- MLA; Col. Eng. Asn; NEA; Royal Inst. Philos. Nineteenth century English literature and criticism; philosophy. Publ: Shelley's philosophy and religion, Christian Register; The democratically administered university, J. Higher Educ; Irving Babbit and his thinking, The Humanist. Add: Dept. of English Language & Literature, University of Missouri-Kansas City, 5100 Rockhill Rd, Kansas City, MO 64112.

CAPPS, JACK L, b. Liberty, Mo, July 16, 26; m. 53; c. 2. ENGLISH. B.S, U.S. Mil. Acad, 48; M.A, Univ. Pa, 60, Ph.D, 63. U.S. ARMY, 48-, instr. ENG, U.S. MIL. ACAD, 59-61, assoc. prof, 61-67, PROF. & DEP. HEAD DEPT, 67- Vis. prof, Univ. Mass, summer 67; chmn. adv. bd, Concordance of Works of William Faulkner, 70-; vis. prof. Am. lit, Am. Univ. Beirut, 71-72. U.S.A, 48-, Col. AAUP; NCTE; MLA; Col. Conf. Compos. & Commun. Nineteenth and 20th century American literature. Publ: Emily Dickinson's reading 1836-1886, Harvard, 66; co-ed, Benet's John Brown's body, Holt, 68; Advanced freshman English at West Point, Col. Compos. & Commun, J, 5/63; West Point's William Faulkner room, Ga. Rev, spring 66; Modern education and the military academy, J. Haile Selassie I Mil. Acad, Harar, Ethiopia, 72. Add: Dept. of English, U.S. Military Academy, West Point, NY 10966.

CAPPS, RANDALL, b. Peytonsburg, Ky, Oct. 23, 36; m. 61; c. 1. SPEECH. B.A, Ky. Wesleyan Col, 57; M.A. West. Ky. Univ, 61; Univ. of the Pac, 62; Ed.D.(speech-educ), Univ. Va, 70; Vanderbilt Univ, summer 72. Instr. Eng. & speech, WEST. KY. UNIV, 62-64, asst. prof, 64-68, ASSOC. PROF, SPEECH, 68-, HEAD DEPT. SPEECH & THEATRE, 70-, acting head dept, 68-70. Speech Commun. Asn; Am. Forensic Asn; Am. Theatre Asn; Comn. Am. Parliamentary Procedure. Public address; history of speech education; forensics. Add: 1512 Barnard Way, Bowling Green, KY 42101.

CAPPUCCILLI, RALPH MICHAEL, b. Monroe, Mich, Aug. 10, 23; m. 54; c. 5. SPEECH & DRAMA. B.A, St. Joseph's Col, 47; M.A, Univ. Mich, 51; Ph.D.(speech), Purdue Univ, 67. Instr. Eng, St. Joseph's Col.(Ind), 49-52; teacher pub. schs, Mich, 52-54; asst. prof. SPEECH, ST. JOSEPH'S COL. (IND), 54-56, ASSOC. PROF, 56-, CHMN. DEPT, 60- Guedelhoffer Oratory Award, 47. Speech Commun. Asn; Nat. Soc. Stud. Commun; Nat. Cath. Theatre Conf. Rhetoric; communication; theatre and interpretation. Add: Dept. of Communications & Theatre Arts, St. Joseph's College, Rensselaer, IN 47978.

CAPUTI, ANTHONY FRANCIS, b. Buffalo, N.Y, Dec. 22, 24; m. 48; c. 4. ENGLISH. B.A, Univ. Buffalo, 49, M.A, 51; Fulbright fel, 54-55; Ph.D. (Eng), Cornell Univ, 56. Asst. ENG, Univ. Buffalo, 50-51; Sampson teaching fel, CORNELL UNIV, 52-53, instr, 53-58, asst. prof, 58-62, assoc. prof, 62-67, PROF, 67- Houpt Prize, Univ. Buffalo, 49; Fulbright res. fel, 64-65; Guggenheim fel, 64-65; fel, Villa I Tatti, 64-65; Nat. Endowment for Humanities fel, 71-72. U.S.A, 43-46. English Renaissance literature; British and American drama; modern British and American literature. Publ: John Marston, Satirist, Cornell, 61; Norton anthology of modern drama, Norton, 66; Masterworks of world drama (6 vols), Heath, 68; Loving Evie, Harper, 74; The shallows of modern serious drama, Mod. Drama, 61; Scenic design in Measure for measure, J.Eng. & Ger. Philol, 61; Antony and Cleopatra; tragedy without terror, Shakespeare Quart, 65; plus others. Add: Dept. of English, Cornell University, Ithaca, NY 14850.

CAPWELL, RICHARD LEONARD, b. East Greenwich, R.I, May 6, 20; m. 59; c. 2. ENGLISH. A.B, Brown Univ, 42; M.A, Yale, 46; South. Humanities fel, Duke Univ, 56-57, Ph.D.(Eng), 64. Instr. ENG, Admiral Billard Acad, 42-44; Milton Acad, 44-45; Univ. Mo, 46-49; Ohio Wesleyan Univ, 52-54; asst. prof, E.CAROLINA UNIV, 57-64, assoc. prof, 64-66, PROF, 66-, DEAN, COL. ARTS & SCI, 69- Contributing ed, Abstr. of Eng. stud, 60- MLA; AAUP; Renaissance Soc. Am. Restoration drama; seventeenth century poetry; Robert Herrick. Publ: John Crowne: a biographical and critical study, Univ. Microfilms, 64; What to read, N.C. Eng. Teacher, 62; Herrick and the aesthetic principle of variety and contrast, S.Atlantic Quart, autumn 72. Add: College of Arts & Sciences, East Carolina University, P.O. Box 2713, Greenville, NC 27834.

CARAWAY, (SARAH) HERMINE, b. Wadesboro, N.C, Sept. 26, 16. ENGLISH, EDUCATION. A.B, Univ. N.C, Greensboro, 37, M.Ed, Chapel Hill, 55; Delta Kappa Gamma state scholar, 57-58, univ. fel, 57-59, Ph.D.(Eng. educ), 59. Teacher, jr. high sch, N.C, 37-41, high sch, 41-54; dir. guidance, jr. high sch, N.C, 55-57; asst. prof. Eng, E.CAROLINA UNIV, 59-61, assoc. prof, 61-65, PROF. ENG. & DIR. PROG. ENG. EDUC, 65- Workshop consult, revising & upgrading Eng. curriculum, grades 9-12, Claremont High Sch, Hickory, N.C, 63; mem. team evaluate high sch. Eng. dept. for accreditation by South. Asn. Schs. & Cols, 65-68. Col. Eng. Asn.(secy-treas, 60-63); NCTE; MLA; Conf. Eng. Educ; Am. Asn. Cols. Teacher Educ.(instnl. rep, 71-). Collecting and compiling folk tales of Anson County, N.C; English for gifted students; strengthening the college curriculum for prospective teachers of English. Publ: English as a foundation for guidance, 56 & CEA-NCETA liaison, fall 71, N.C. Eng. Teacher; Anson anecdotes, N.C. Folklore, 55. Add: 110 Rose Terr, Wadesboro, NC 28170.

CARB, NATHAN R. E, JR, b. Brooklyn, N.Y, Apr. 22, 33; m. 56; c. 2. ENGLISH. B.A, Col. William & Mary, 54; M.A, Univ. Pa, 56, Ph.D, 59. Instr. ENG, W.Va, Univ, 56-59; GLASSBORO STATE COL, 59-60, asst. prof, 60-63, assoc. prof, 63-65, PROF, 65- English Romantic poets, especially Byron; Late Victorian drama, especially Sir Arthur Wing Pinero. Publ: Byron as critic—not a neo-classicist, W.Va, Univ. Philol. Papers, 5/58; The Leon-Noel anagram, Notes & Queries, 1/64. Add: Dept. of English, Glassboro State College, Glassboro, NJ 08028.

CARD, JAMES VAN DYCK, b. Montclair, N.J, Apr. 14, 31. ENGLISH. B.A, Rutgers Univ, 53; M.A, Columbia Univ, 57, Ph.D.(James Joyce), 64. Lectr. basic courses, Hunter Col, 61-62; instr, Wash. & Jefferson Col, 63-64; vis. asst. prof. 20th CENTURY BRIT. LIT, Franklin & Marshall Col, 64-66; asst. prof, OLD DOMINION COL, 66-71, ASSOC. PROF, 71- U.S.A, 53-56. MLA; South. Mod. Lang. Asn; James Joyce Soc. Twentieth century British Literature. Publ: In just proportion: notes on final scene of Measure for measure, Topic, spring 64. Add: Dept. of English, Old Dominion College, Norfolk, VA 23508.

CARDACI, PAUL FRANCIS, JR, b. Haverstraw, N.Y, Sept. 22, 36; m. 65; c. 2. COMPARATIVE LITERATURE. B.A, Univ. Md, College Park, 59, M.A, 63, Md. fel, 67-69, Ph.D.(comp. lit), 72. Lectr. ENG, Univ. Md, Munich Campus, W.Ger, 63-67; instr, GEORGETOWN UNIV, 69-72, ASST. PROF, 72-, res. grant, summer 73. Lectr, Am. Stud. Conf, Koenigswinter, W.Ger, summer 67. MLA; Am. Comp. Lit. Asn. Comparative study of Goethe and Dostoevsky; evolution of novel, especially in the 19th century. Publ: Dostoevsky's Underground as allusion and symbol, Symposium, 74. Add: Dept. of English, Georgetown University, Washington, DC 20007.

CARDEN, GUY, Linguistics. See Volume III, Foreign Languages, Linguistics & Philology.

CARDWELL, GUY ADAMS, b. Savannah, Ga, Nov. 14, 05; m. 35; c. 4. ENGLISH. A.B, Univ. N.C, 26, Ph.D, 36; A.M, Harvard, 32; Gen. Educ. Bd. traveling fel, 34-35. Instr, Wake Forest Col, 36-37, asst. prof, 37-38; ENG, Tulane Univ, 38-41, assoc. prof, 41-42, prof, 42-45; prof. & chmn. dept, Univ. Md, 45-49; WASH. UNIV, 49-68, EMER. PROF, 68- Am. Counc. Learned Soc. fel, 50-51; Fulbright vis. prof, Univ. Vienna, 51-52; res. fel, Henry Huntington Libr, 54-55; vis. prof, Univ. Buenos Aires, 57; Nat. Univ. Mex, 60-61; prof, State Univ. N.Y. Albany, 68-70. MLA. American literature; cultural history. Publ: Uncollected poems of Henry Timrod, Univ. Ga; Readings from the Americas, Ronald; Twins of genius, Mich. State Univ, 53; ed, Discussions of Mark Twain, Heath, 63; ed. & introd, Life on the Mississippi, Dodd, 68; contrib. poems, short stories and arts. in var. periodicals. Add: Box 163, Moose, WY 83012.

CARENS, JAMES F, b. Newburyport, Mass, Nov. 13, 27; m. LITERATURE. B.A, Harvard Col, 49; M.A, Yale, 51; Ph.D, Columbia Univ, 59. Instr. ENG, BUCKNELL UNIV, 55-59, asst. prof, 59-65, assoc. prof, 65-70, PROF, 70- Am. Philos. Soc. grant, summer 67; gen. ed, Irish Writers Ser, Bucknell Univ. Press, 69- MLA; James Joyce Soc; James Joyce Found; Int. Asn. Study Anglo-Irish Lit. Twentieth century literature in English; Irish literary Renaissance, especially Yeats, Joyce, Gogarty. Publ: The satiric art of Evelyn Waugh, Univ. Wash, 66; ed. & contrib, Many lines to thee: letters of Oliver St. John Gogarty to G.K.A. Bell, Dolmen, 71; ed, The plays of Oliver St. John Gogarty, Proscenium, 71; contrib, Gogarty and Yeats, In: Modern Irish literature, Iona-Twayne, 72 & Joyce and Gogarty, In: New light on James Joyce, Ind. Univ, 72. Add: Dept. of English, Bucknell University, Lewisburg, PA 17837.

CAREY, GEORGE GIBSON, b. Orange, N.J, July 21, 34; m. 58. FOLKLORE, ENGLISH. B.A, Middlebury Col, 58; NDEA fel. & M.A, Ind. Univ, 62, univ. fel. & Ph.D.(folklore), 66. Instr. Eng, Middlebury Col, 64-65; asst. prof, Univ. Md, 66-71, res. fel, summer 68; ASSOC. PROF. ENG. & FOLKLORE, UNIV. MASS, AMHERST, 71- Am. Counc. Learned Soc. & Am. Philos. Soc. grants-in-aid, summer 68; Am. Counc. Learned Soc. grant-in-aid, Eng, summer 73. U.S.A, 54-56. Am. Folklore Soc; Northeast Folklore Soc; Eng. Folklore Soc. Revolutionary War prison songs; New England regional maritime communities. Publ: Maryland folklore and folklife, 71 & Maryland folk legends and folksongs, 72, Cornell Maritime; A faraway time and place: lore of the Eastern shore, R.B. Luce, 72; The tradition of the St. Elmo's Fire, Am. Neptune, 1/63; A collection of airborne cadence chants, J. Am. Folklore, 1/65; John G. Whittier roots in a folk culture, Essex Inst. Hist. Publ, 1/68. Add: Juggler Meadow Rd, Amherst, MA 01002.

CAREY, GLENN OWAROFF, b. Jeannette, Pa, May 8, 19; m. 48; c. 3. ENGLISH. B.A, Pa. State Univ, 48, M.A, 49; Ph.D.(Eng), Univ. Ill, 62. Asst. Eng. compos. & asst. ed, Accent, Univ. Ill, 49-51, asst. Eng. compos. & Am. lit, 53-58, dir. univ. writing clin, 55-56; asst. prof. Am. & Eng. lit, State Univ. N.Y. Col. Cortland, 58-62; prof. Eng, State Univ. N.Y. Col. Potsdam, 62-67; PROF. ENG. & ASSOC. DEAN COL. ARTS & SCI, EAST. KY. UNIV, 67- Ed. consult, Scribner, 59 & Bobbs-Merrill, 73; State Univ. N.Y. Res. Found. summer fac. res. fels, 65, 67; vis. Fulbright Am. lit. lectr, under sponsorship of U.S. Educ. Found. in Cyprus, Nicosia, 65; Fulbright prof. Eng. & Am. lit, Univ. Jordan, 65-66. U.S.A, 42-46, 51-53, Res, 53-72, Lt. Col. MLA; Col. Eng. Asn.(nat. dir, 70-72, chmn. nat. publ. comt, 70-72, 2nd v.pres, 72-73, 1st v.pres, 73-74, pres, 74-75); AAUP; Am. Stud. Asn; Am. Conf. Acad. Deans; Soc. Stud. South. Lit; Conf. Col. Compos. & Commun. William Faulkner; American literature; modern fiction—American and continental. Publ: Ed, Quest for meaning—modern short stories, McKay, 75; Samuel Butler's theory of evolution: a summary, Eng. Lit. in Transition, winter 64; William Faulkner: a critical evaluation, Ariz. Quart, spring, 65; An interpretation of Keats' Ode on a Grecian Urn, Cyprus Literary Chronicle, 5/66; plus over 20 articles in scholarly journals. Add: College of Arts & Sciences, Eastern Kentucky University, Richmond, KY 40475.

CAREY, MARY CECILIA, O.P, b. Casselton, N.Dak, Aug. 17, 21. LITERATURE. B.S, Edgewood Col, 46; M.A, Univ. Wis, 52, Ph.D, 59. Chmn. dept. Eng, Edgewood Col, 55-63, chmn. div. lang. & lit, 60-63; chmn. dept. lang, Escuela Normal, Bolivia, 63-67; PRES, EDGEWOOD COL, 68- Mem. staff, Inst. Santo Domingo, Bolivia, 63-64; secy, Wis. Found. Independent Cols, 71- MLA; Relig. Educ. Asn; Nat. Cath. Educ. Asn. Contemporary American and Renaissance English literature. Publ: Written communication and total growth, Cath. Educ. Rev, 9/61; Baudelaire's influence on The waste land, Renascence, 62; Poetry of Marianne Moore, Thought, 64. Add: Edgewood College, 855 Woodrow St, Madison, WI 53711.

CAREY, RUTH MIRIAM, S.S.N.D, b. Baltimore, Md, Apr. 29, 27. ENGLISH. B.A, Col. Notre Dame (Md), 48; M.A, Cath. Univ. Am, 63. Teacher Eng. & French, Inst. Notre Dame, 50-59; instr. ENG, COL. NOTRE DAME (MD), 59-66, asst. prof, 66-71, ASSOC. PROF, 71- Grant, Georgetown Writers Conf, 67. NCTE; Col. Eng. Asn. English literature; Romantic period 1798-1832. Add: Dept. of English, College of Notre Dame of Maryland, 4701 N. Charles St, Baltimore, MD 21210.

CARGAS, HARRY JAMES, b. Hamtramck, Mich, June 18, 32; m. 57; c. 6. WORLD & AMERICAN LITERATURE. B.A, Univ. Mich, Ann Arbor, 57, M.A, 58; Ph.D.(Eng), St. Louis Univ, 68. Teacher Eng, St. David's Sch, N.Y, 58-60; Montclair Acad, N.J, 60-61; ed-in-chief, Cath. Bk. Reporter, N.Y.C, 61-62; Queen's Work Mag, St. Louis Mo, 63-64; dir. orientation, Eng. for For. Stud, St. Louis Univ, 64-69; CHMN. DEPT. ENG, WEBSTER COL, 69-, COORD. HUMANITIES DIV. IV, 73- MLA; AAUP. Contemporary world literature; process theology. Publ: I lay down my life, Daughters, 65; ed, Graham Greene, 69 & The continuous flame: Teilhard in the great traditions, 70, Herder; co-auth, English as a second language, W.C. Brown, 70; co-ed, Death and hope, Corpus, 71; contrib. numerous arts, America, Commonweal, James Joyce Quart, Renascence, Laurel Rev, and others. Add: Dept. of English, Webster College, Webster Groves, MO 63119.

CARLILE, CLARK STITES, b. Jetmore, Kans, Mar. 28, 12. SPEECH. A.B, Ft. Hays Kans. State Col, 39; A.M, Colo. State Col. Educ, 42; summers, State Univ. Iowa, 43, 46. Teacher rural grade sch, Kans, 32-35; high schs, 39-43; mem. staff, educ. & personal depts, Beech Aircraft Corp, Wichita, 43-46; assoc. prof. speech & acting head dept, Tex. Col. Arts & Industs, 46-47; from asst. prof. to prof. SPEECH & DIR. REQUIRED FRESHMAN SPEECH, IDAHO STATE UNIV, 47-73, EMER. PROF, 73- Speech Commun. Asn. Public address. Publ: Brief project text for public speaking, 57 & Project text for public speaking, rev. ed, 62 & 72, Harper; 38 basic speech experiences, Clark Publ, 4th ed, 66, 6th ed, 72. Add: Rte. 3, Box 353A, Pocatello, ID 83201.

CARLILE, SENE R, b. Jetmore, Kans, Nov. 4, 17; m. 42. SPEECH. A.B, Ft. Hays Kans. State Col, 40, B.S, 40; M.A, Colo. State Col, 43; Ph.D, Univ. Wis, 51; Univ. London, 61-62. Teacher elem. schs, Kans, 40-41, high sch, 41-44; pers. technician, Beech Aircraft, Wichita, 44-45; mem. fac. SPEECH, WEST. WASH. STATE COL, 47-48, asst. prof, 48-51, assoc. prof, 51-56, PROF, 56-, chmn. dept, 51-68. Speech Commun. Asn; West Speech Commun. Asn. Phonetics; public address; speech pathology. Add: Dept. of Speech, Western Washington State College, Bellingham, WA 98225.

CARLIN, CLAIRE MADELEINE, S.N.J.M, b. San Francisco, Calif, July 28, 04. ENGLISH. A.B, Col. Holy Names, 35; M.A, Cath. Univ. Am, 45, Ph.D, 50. Instr. ENG, Cath. Univ. Am, 46-47; asst. prof, HOLY NAMES COL. (CALIF), 38-40, assoc. prof, 40-45, PROF, 50-, chmn. dept. Eng, speech & drama, 50-70, grad. dean, 60-65. Mem, region XV, Woodrow Wilson Screening Comt, 60-61; mem. & secy, Calif. Fulbright Comt, 67- MLA; Cath. Renascence Soc; NCTE; Nat. Cath. Educ. Asn. Nineteenth century literature, English and French literary criticism. Publ: John Keats' knowledge of Greek art; a study of some early sources. Add: Holy Names College, 3500 Mountain Blvd, Oakland, CA 94619.

CARLISLE, CAROL WHITT JONES, b. May 11, 19; U.S. citizen; m. 42; c. 2. SHAKESPEARE, 19TH CENTURY THEATRE. B.A, Wesleyan Col.(Ga), 40; M.A, Univ. N.C, Chapel Hill, 41, Ph.D.(Eng), 51. Instr. ENG, Pearl River Jr. Col, Miss, 42-43; acting asst. prof, Wesleyan Col.(Ga), 43; instr, UNIV. S.C, 46-50, asst. prof, 50-58, assoc. prof, 58-69, PROF, 69- Fel, Folger Shakespeare Libr, summer 54; mem. ed. bd, The Explicator, 54-66; Coop. Prog. Humanities fel, Univ. N.C-Duke Univ-Ford Found, 67-68. Shakespeare Asn. Am; Renaissance Soc. Am; Am. Soc. Theatre Res; MLA; Southeast. Renaissance Conf.(v.pres, 73-74). Shakespearean criticism; Shakespeare in the theatre; 19th century theatrical history. Publ: Shakespeare from the greenroom: actors' criticisms of four major tragedies, Univ. N.C, 69; The nineteenth century actors versus the closet critics of Shakespeare, Stud. Philol, 54; The Macbeths and the actors, Renaissance Papers, 58; Hamlet's cruelty in the nunnery scene: the actors' views, Shakespeare Quart, 67. Add: Dept. of English, University of South Carolina, Columbia, SC 29208.

CARLISLE, ERVIN FREDERICK, b. Delaware, Ohio, Mar. 20, 35; m. 55, 73; c. 4. ENGLISH. B.A, Ohio Wesleyan Univ, 56; M.A, Ohio State Univ, 57; Ph.D. (Eng), Ind. Univ, 63. Instr. ENG, Ohio Univ, 62-63; asst. prof. DePauw Univ, 63-66; MICH. STATE UNIV, 66-68, assoc. prof, 68-72, PROF, 72-, DIR. UNDERGRAD. PROG, 68-, assoc. chmn. dept. Eng, 68-72. Nat. Endowment for Humanities fel, 72-73. U.S.A.F, 57-60, Res, 60-, Capt. MLA. American literature; literature; language and science. Publ: The uncertain self: Whitman's drama of identity, Mich. State Univ, 72; Captain Amasa Delano: Melville's American fool, 65 & Walt Whitman: the drama of identity, 68, Criticism; The Puritan structure of Edward Taylor's poetry, Am. Quart, 68; plus others. Add: Dept. of English, Michigan State University, East Lansing, MI 48824.

CARLISLE, JOHN CHARLES, b. West Frankfort, Ill, Feb. 27, 30; m. 67; c. 1. AMERICAN STUDIES, AMERICAN LITERATURE. B.S.Educ, South. Ill. Univ, Carbondale, 60, M.S.Educ, 62; Univ. Nebr, Lincoln, 63-64; M.A, Wayne State Univ, 69; Ph.D.(Am. cult), Univ. Mich, Ann Arbor, 72. Dir. stud. activities, Univ. Nebr, 63-65; asst. dean, Oakland Community Col, 65-68; ASST. PROF. ENG, PURDUE UNIV, CALUMET CAMPUS, 72- Am. Stud. Asn; Popular Cult. Asn; Col. Art Asn. Am. American culture during 1930's; American film. Add: Dept. of English, Purdue University, Calumet Campus, Hammond, IN 46323.

CARLISLE, LILYBELLE MOUTRIE LEWIN, b. Lindsborg, Kans, July 5, 00. CLASSICAL LITERATURE. A.B, Bethany Col.(Kans), 20, B.E, 21; A.M, Univ. Colo, 26; Columbia Univ, 33-34, 50; Univ. London, Eng, 35; State Univ. Iowa, 37; Univ. Colo, 40; Wash. Univ, 41; Middlebury Col, 45, 49; Danforth summer scholar, Northwest. Univ, 53. PROF. speech & dramatics, Marymount Col, 29-37; ENGLISH LIT, KANS. WESLEYAN UNIV, 38-72, chmn. fine arts div, 58-72, EMER. PROF, 72- Speech Asn. Am; NCTE. Shakespeare. Add: 1919 Simmons St, Kraft Manor, Salina, KS 67401.

CARLOCK, MARY SUE, b. Honey Grove, Tex, Sept. 5, 08. AMERICAN LITERATURE. B.A, South. Methodist Univ, 30; M.A, Univ. Tex, 35; Ph.D, Columbia Univ, 58. Teacher, pub. schs, Tex, 30-36; head dept. ENG, Murray State Col, 36-43; instr, U.S. Army Col. Training Prog, 43-44; Univ. Tex, 45-48, 49-52; TEX. TECH UNIV, 52-58, asst. prof, 58-62, assoc. prof, 62-71, PROF, 71- MLA; NCTE; Am. Stud. Asn. Contemporary American novel; American autobiography; American studies. Publ: American autobiographies, 1840-1870: a bibliography, Bull. Bibliog, 61; Humpty Dumpty and the autobiography, Genre, 70; contrib, Hunters and healers: folklore types and topics, Tex. Folklore Soc, 71. Add: Dept. of English, Texas Tech University, Lubbock, TX 79409.

CARLSEN, GEORGE ROBERT, b. Bozeman, Mont, Apr. 15, 17; m. 41; c. 4. ENGLISH. B.A, Univ. Minn, 38, B.S, 40, M.A, 43, Ph.D, 48. Instr. Eng, pub. schs, Minn, 40-42; instr. Eng. & educ, Univ. Minn, 42-47; assoc. prof, Univ. Colo, 47-52; curriculum & instr, Univ. Tex, 52-58; PROF. ENG. & EDUC, UNIV. IOWA, 58- Summers, mem. fac, Univ. Colo, 53, 55, 58; Univ. Hawaii, 57, 71; consult, Los Angeles Co. Sch. system, 70-73; dir. Iowa Young Adults Bk. Prog, Univ. Iowa, 72- Conf. Eng. Educ; NCTE (2nd v.pres, 58, 1st v.pres, 61, pres, 62, Distinguished Serv, Award, 71). Reading interests and habits of adolescents; discovery versus expository methods of teaching. Publ: Co-auth, Brown-Carlsen test of listening comprehension, World Publ, 50; auth, Books and the teenage reader, Bantam, 67 & 72 & Harper, 67 & 72; sr. ed, Themes and writers series, McGraw, 67, rev. ed, 73; auth, The interest rate is rising, 5/70 & Some random observations about the English curriculum, 10/72, Eng. J; chap, In: Children & Literature, Int. Reading Asn; plus two others. Add: College of Education, University of Iowa, Iowa City, IA 52240.

CARLSON, BERNADINE P, b. Cissna Park, Ill, Aug. 25, 18; m. 37; c. 2. ENGLISH LANGUAGE & LITERATURE. B.A, West. Mich. Univ, 52, M.A, 57; Ed.D.(Eng), Univ. Mich, 72. ASST. PROF. ENG, WEST. MICH. UNIV, 53- Commun. & writing consult, Paper Indust. & Mgt. Asn, 67-72; commun. consult, Engelhard Minerals & Chemicals N.J, 68-72. NCTE; Col. Eng. Asn; Conf. Col. Compos. & Commun. English language; usage; teaching of writing skills. Publ: English usage tests for graduate students, 72 & Course of study for technical communication, 72, West. Mich. Univ. Add: Dept. of English, 720 Sprau Tower, Western Michigan University, Kalamazoo, MI 49001.

CARLSON, CHARLES VERNON, b. Jamestown, N.Y, Oct. 25, 31; m. 55; c. 3. INTERPERSONAL COMMUNICATION. B.A, Ohio Wesleyan Univ, 55; M.Ed. (speech), Kent State Univ, 64. Teacher hist. & speech, Minerva Pub. Schs, 55-63; chmn. dept. speech & drama, Massillon Pub. Schs, 63-65, dir. pub. relat, 65-66; asst. prof. speech, OHIO UNIV, 66-70, ASSOC. PROF. INTERPERSONAL COMMUN, 70- Dir. grant, speech prospective teacher fel. prog, NDEA-Ohio Univ, 67-70; consult, Ohio Dept. Educ, 67-73; Ohio Div. Correction, 70-73. Speech Commun. Asn. Speech education; criminal justice. Publ: Co-auth, Speech communication in the high school curriculum, Speech Teacher, 11/68; auth, Certification changes for the prospective speech teacher in Ohio, Ohio Speech J, 71; Proposed educational programming for Southern Ohio Correctional Facility: interpersonal communication, Off. Continuing Educ, Ohio Univ, 71. Add: Dept. of Interpersonal Communication, College of Communication, Ohio University, Athens, OH 45701.

CARLSON, ERIC WALTER, b. Sweden, Aug. 20, 10; U.S. citizen; m. 38; c. 3. ENGLISH. B.S, Boston Univ, 32, A.M, 36, Ph.D.(Eng), 47. Instr. ENG, Portland Jr. Col, 34-36; Boston Univ, 38-41; Babson Inst, 41-42; from instr. to PROF, UNIV. CONN, 42- MLA; AAUP; Poe Stud. Asn. (pres, 73-75). American literature, especially from 1800 to present; symbolic and cultural values in literary criticism; Poe, Emerson and Dickinson. Publ: The recognition of Edgar Allan Poe, Univ. Mich, 66; Introduction to Poe, Scott, 67; ed, Edgar Allan Poe: The fall of the house of Usher, Merrill, 71; co-ed, Emerson's relevance today: a symposium, Transcendental, 71; Symbolism in The grapes of wrath, Col. Eng, 1/58; Symbolism and sense in Poe's Ulalume, Am. Lit, 3/63. Add: Dept. of English, University of Connecticut, Storrs, CT 06268.

CARLSON, HARRY GILBERT, b. New York, N.Y, Sept. 27, 30; m. 57. DRAMA & SPEECH. B.A, Brooklyn Col, 52; M.A, Ohio State Univ, 55, scholar, 55-56, Ph.D.(theatre hist), 58; N.Y. Chap. fel, Am-Scand. Found, Stockholm, Sweden, 56-57. Instr. drama & speech, Southwest Mo. State Col, 57-59; asst. prof, Valparaiso Univ, 59-61; North. Ill. Univ, 61-64; assoc. prof. THEATRE & DRAMA, Univ. Ga, 64-66; QUEENS COL.(N.Y), 67-72, PROF, 72- Guggenheim Found. fel, 66-67; U.S. deleg, 5th Int. Symp. Prof. Training of the Actor, summer 67; City Univ. New York Res. Found. grant, 70-71; mem. theatre arts screening comt, Comt. Int. Exchange Persons, 68-71, chmn, 71-72. U.S.A, 52-54, Sgt. Am. Theatre Asn; Soc. Advan. Scand. Stud; Am-Scand. Found.(publ. consult, 68-; Strindberg Soc. Scandinavian drama and theatre; theatre history; translation. Publ: Ed. & transl, Martin Lamm's August Strindberg, Blom, 71; co-ed. & contrib, Handbook of contemporary drama, Crowell, 71 & Encyclopedia of world drama, McGraw, 72; auth, Lars Forssell—poet in the theatre, Scand. Stud, 2/65; Dialogue at the Berliner Ensemble, Drama Rev, 1/67; The Odin Theater in Holstebro, Am-Scand. Rev, 4/71; plus others. Add: Dept. of Drama & Theatre, Queens College, Flushing, NY 11367.

CARLSON, JAMES RICHARD, b. Staples, Minn, Dec. 16, 17. THEATER ARTS. B.A, Hamline Univ, 40; M.A, Univ. Minn, 47. Teacher, High Sch, Minn, 40-41; educ. dir, Civilian Pub. Serv. camps, Mich. & N.J, 42-46; asst. prof. speech & theater & dir. theater, Hamline Univ, 47-64; PROF. HUMANITIES & THEATRE, ECKERD COL, 64-, THEATRE ARTS, CREATIVE ARTS COLLEGIUM, 73- Am. deleg, Int. Conf. Relig. Drama, Oxford, 55 & Paris, 60; Danforth fel, 58-59; co-ed, Religious Theatre, 64- Am. Theatre Asn. Theatre of religious and social relevance; motion picture aesthetics; theatre direction. Add: Creative Arts Collegium, Eckerd College, St. Petersburg, FL 33733.

CARLSON, MARVIN A, b. Wichita, Kans, Sept. 15, 35; m. 60; c. 2. SPEECH, DRAMA. B.S.Ed, Univ. Kans, 57, M.A, 58; fel, Cornell Univ, 58-60, Ph.D, 60. Instr. speech & drama, CORNELL UNIV, 60-61, asst. prof, 61-66, assoc. prof, THEATRE ARTS, 66-73, PROF, 73-, CHMN. DEPT, 66-68 & 73- Guggenheim fel, 69. Am. Educ. Theatre Asn; Am. Soc. Theatre Res. Theatre history; dramatic literature. Publ: André Antoine's memories of the Théâtre-Libre, Univ. Miami, 64; The theatre of the French Revolution, Cornell Univ, 66; The French stage in the nineteenth century, 72 & The German stage in the nineteenth century, 72, Scarecrow. Add: Dept. of Theatre Arts, Cornell University, Ithaca, NY 14850.

CARLSON, NORMAN EUGENE, b. Chicago, Ill, July 21, 34; m. 55; c. 4. ENGLISH. B.A, Carleton Col, 55; M.A, Rutgers Univ, 58, Ph.D.(Eng), 62. Instr. ENG, DePauw Univ, 58-63; asst. prof, WEST. MICH. UNIV, 63-67, ASSOC. PROF, 67- MLA. Seventeenth century literature; Milton; Renaissance drama. Publ: Wither and the stationers, Stud. Bibliog, 66; George Wither and the statute office, Notes & Queries, 69; George Wither—dead at last!, Mich. Academician, 69; plus one other. Add: Dept. of English, Western Michigan University, Kalamazoo, MI 49001.

CARLSON, THOMAS CLARK, b. Elizabeth, N.J, May 13, 44; m. 70; c. 1. AMERICAN LITERATURE. A.B, Bucknell Univ, 66; M.A, Rutgers Univ, New Brunswick, 70, Ph.D.(Eng), 71. ASST. PROF. ENG, MEMPHIS STATE UNIV, 70- Asst. bibliog. ed, Poe Stud. Asn, 72- MLA; Poe Stud; Asn; Melville Soc; AAUP. Colonial American literature; Melville; 19th century American theatre. Publ: Who's afraid of Moby-Dick? an approach to teaching Ishmael's autobiography, Interpretations: Studies in Language & Literature, 11/73. Add: Dept. of English, Memphis State University, Memphis, TN 38152.

CARLTON, CHARLES ROGERS, b. Paris, Tex, June 18, 19. ENGLISH, LINGUISTICS. B.M, Univ. Tex, 48, B.A, 49; M.A, Univ. Mich, 50, Ph.D, 58. Instr. ENG, Butler Univ, 51-53; N.Mex. State Univ, 55-57; asst. prof, CALIF. STATE UNIV, NORTHRIDGE, 58-63, assoc. prof, 63-69, PROF, 69- Ling. consult, Nat. Asn. Standard Med. Vocab, 63- U.S.A, 42-45, T/Sgt. Ling. Soc. Am; Philol. Asn. Pac. Coast. Old English syntax; structure of modern English; teaching of English. Publ: Descriptive syntax of the Old English charters, Mouton, The Hague, 70; The word order of noun modifiers in Old English prose, J. Eng. & Ger. Philol, 10/63; Sentence classification, Calif. Eng. J, 1/67; contrib, Readings for the history of the English language, Allyn & Bacon, 68. Add: Dept. of English, California State University, Northridge, 18111 Nordoff St, Northridge, CA 91324.

CARMICHAEL, KATHERINE KENNEDY, b. Birmingham, Ala, Oct. 1, 12. ENGLISH. A.B, Birmingham-South. Col, 32; M.A, Vanderbilt Univ, 39, fel, 41-42, Ph.D.(Eng), 43. Teacher, pub. schs, Ala, 32-38; instr. Eng, Tex. State Col. Women, 39-40; asst. prof. Eng. & dean women, West. Md. Col, 42-44; instr. & chmn. Eng, Hockaday Sch, 44-46; INSTR. ENG, UNIV. N.C,

CHAPEL HILL, 46-, ASSOC. DEAN SUPPORTIVE SERV, 73-, dean women, 46-72. Fulbright lectr, Philippine Norm. Col, 51-52; Delta Kappa Gamma Soc. scholar, 55-56; Smith-Mundt prof, Univ. Saigon, 61-62. MLA; Nat. Asn. Women Deans & Counsel. John Keats. Publ: A critical edition of the early poems of John Keats, with a philosophical supplement. Add: Steele Bldg, University of North Carolina at Chapel Hill, Chapel Hill, NC 27514.

CARMODY, ROBERT JOSEPH, S.J, b. Seattle, Wash, Oct. 3, 07. ENGLISH. A.B, Gonzaga Univ, 31, A.M, 32; S.T.L, Alma Col.(Calif), 39; Ph.D, Univ. Wash, 49. Instr. ENG, SEATTLE UNIV, 40-45, asst. prof, 45-46, PROF, 46- MLA; NCTE; Am. Arbit. Asn. Shakespeare's knowledge and the use of theology. Add: Dept. of English, Seattle University, Seattle, WA 98122.

CARNELL, CORBIN SCOTT, b. Ormond Beach, Fla, July 7, 29; m. 51; c. 4. ENGLISH. B.A, Wheaton Col, 52; M.A, Columbia Univ, 53; Rockefeller Found. South. fel, Univ. Fla, 56-58, Ph.D.(Eng), 60. Instr. ENG, Bethany Col.(W.Va), 53-56; teaching assoc, UNIV. FLA, 58-60, asst. prof, 60-68, ASSOC. PROF, 68- Episcopal Church Soc. Col. Work Award for summer study, Harvard,60; instr, Georgetown Univ, summer 61; Danforth Found. regional selection chmn. for Danforth Assoc. Prog, 65-69, mem. nat. adv. counc, 67-70; instr, Fla. Presby. Col, summer 68; assoc. prof, Young Life Grad. Ecumenical Inst, Colorado Springs, summers 72 & 73. MLA; Conf. Christianity & Lit.(v.pres, 64-65). Contemporary American and British literature; history of ideas, especially interrelationships of literature, philosophy and theology; film studies. Publ: Two short novels by Henry James, Prentice-Hall, 63; ed. & introd, A slow, soft river: 7 stories by Lawrence Dorr, 73 & Bright shadow of reality: C.S. Lewis and the feeling intellect, 74, Eerdmans; auth, Why sentimentality is wrong, Eternity, 11/67; C.S. Lewis on Eros as a means of grace, In: Imagination and the spirit, Eerdmans, 71; plus others. Add: Dept. of English, University of Florida, Gainesville, FL 32611.

CARNEY, JOHN JOSEPH, JR, b. Yonkers, N.Y, Sept. 8, 32; m. 59; c. 4. SPEECH. B.S, State Univ. N.Y. Col. Geneseo, 60; M.A, Pa. State Univ, 61. Speech corrector, Bd. Coop. Educ. Serv, Avon-Livonia, N.Y, 60; asst. prof. SPEECH, State Univ. N.Y. Col. Potsdam, 61-65; assoc. prof, STATE UNIV. N.Y. COL. ONEONTA, 65-70, PROF, 70- Dir, summer inst. pub. sch. teachers, N.Y. State Educ. Dept, 67, 70, consult, In-Serv. Educ, summer 70; consult. & lectr, Speech Commn. Asn. Inst, summer 73; manuscript reviewer commun, Int. Textbook Co. Speech Commun. Asn; East. States Speech Commun. Asn; Irish-Am. Cult. Inst; Am. Comt. Irish Stud. Oral persuasion and the mass media; propaganda; Irish oratory. Publ: Ed. & contrib, Communication for education, Int. Textbook Co, 71; compiler, Crises in communications—three speeches, N.Y. State Speech Asn, 71; auth Anyone who writes well can speak well?, Improv. Col. & Univ. Teaching, 11/64; A dash of negligence, 9/64 & The unperceived audience, 9/65, Today's Speech. Add: Dept. of Speech & Theater, State University of New York College at Oneonta, Oneonta, NY 13820.

CARNICELLI, DOMENICK D, b. Brooklyn, N.Y, Oct. 28, 31; m. 64; c. 2. ENGLISH & AMERICAN LITERATURE. B.A, Brooklyn Col, 52; M.A, Columbia Univ, 59, Ph.D.(Eng. & comp. lit), 66. Teacher ENG, New Utrecht High Sch, 52-59; lectr, Brooklyn Col, 60-66; instr, Hunter Col, 66-69; asst. prof, LEHMAN COL, 69-72, assoc. prof, 72-74, PROF, 74- City Univ. N.Y. res. award, 69-70, 70-71; vis. prof. Eng, Univ. Kent, Canterbury, 70-71. U.S.A, 53-56. English Renaissance; comparative literature of Renaissance; Anglo-Italian literary relations in the Renaissance. Publ: Auth. & ed, Lord Morley's Tryumphes of Fraunces Petrarcke: the first English translation of the Trionfi, Harvard, 71; auth, Bernardo Illicino and the Renaissance commentaries on Petrarch's Trionfi, Romance Philol, 69; Beauty's rose: love and marriage in Shakespeare and Adler, In: Alfred Adler: his influence on psychology, Noyes, 73. Add: Dept. of English, Herbert H. Lehman College, Bedford Park Blvd. W, Bronx, NY 10468.

CARNICELLI, THOMAS ANTHONY, b. Boston, Mass, July 23, 37; m. 58; c. 2. ENGLISH. B.A, Princeton, 58; Woodrow Wilson fel, Harvard, 58, M.A, 60, Ph.D.(Eng), 65. Instr. ENG, Dartmouth Col, 63-66, asst. prof, 66-67; UNIV. N.H, 67-68, ASSOC. PROF, 68- Mediaeval Acad. Am. Old English; medieval drama; linguistics and literature. Publ: King Alfred's version of St. Augustine's soliloquies, Harvard, 69. Add: Dept. of English, University of New Hampshire, Durham, NH 03824.

CARNOCHAN, WALTER BLISS, b. New York, N.Y, Dec. 20, 30; m. 55; c. 4. ENGLISH LITERATURE. A.B, Harvard, 53, A.M, 57, Ph.D, 60. Instr. ENG, STANFORD UNIV, 60-62, asst. prof, 62-68, assoc. prof, 68-73, PROF, 73-, chmn. dept, 71-73. Publ: Ed, The man of mode, Univ. Nebr, 66; auth, Lemuel Gulliver's Mirror for man, Univ. Calif, 68. Add: Dept. of English, Stanford University, Stanford, CA 94305.

CAROTHERS, FRANCIS BARTON, JR, b. St. Louis, Mo, Apr. 18, 19; m. 45; c. 7. ENGLISH. B.A, San Francisco State Col, 38; M.A, Univ. Ore, 41; Ph.D.(Eng), Univ. South. Calif, 54. Instr. ENG, LOYOLA MARYMOUNT UNIV, 47-50, asst. prof, 50-54, assoc. prof, 54-62, PROF, 62-, CHMN. DEPT, 59-63 & 69-, asst. chmn, 53-57, acting chmn, 57-59. U.S.A, 42-44. MLA. Romantic poets; English novel. Add: Dept. of English, Loyola Marymount University, Los Angeles, CA 90045.

CAROTHERS, ROBERT LEE, b. Sewickley, Pa, Sept. 3, 42; c. 2. ENGLISH. B.S.Ed, Edinboro State Col, 65; fel, Kent State Univ, 65-68, M.A, 66, Ph.D. (Eng), 69; Gannon Col, 71-72. Asst. ENG, Kent State Univ, 65-68; instr, EDINBORO STATE COL, 68-70, asst. prof, 70-71, assoc. prof, 71-73, PROF, 73- U.S.A, Sgt. American studies; Afro-American studies; counseling. Publ: Freedom and other times, Poet's Press, 72. Add: Dept. of English, Edinboro State College, Edinboro, PA 16412.

CAROZZA, DAVY ANGELO, Comparative Literature, Romance Languages. See Volume III, Foreign Languages, Linguistics & Philology.

CARPENTER, CHARLES ALBERT, JR, b. Hazleton, Pa, June 8, 29; m. 50; c. 4. ENGLISH, MODERN DRAMA. B.A, Allegheny Col, 51; M.A. in L.S, Kent State Univ, 52; M.A, Cornell Univ, 59, Samuel S. Fels Fund grant, 61-62, Ph.D.(Eng), 63. Instr. ENG, Univ. Del, 62-64, asst. prof, 64-67; STATE UNIV. N.Y. BINGHAMTON, 67-70, ASSOC. PROF, 70- Univ. Del, summer fac. fel, 65. MLA. Drama since World War II; literary bibliography; drama in English since 1890. Publ: Bernard Shaw and the art of destroying ideals: the early plays, Univ. Wis, 69; Shaw's cross section of anti-Shavian opinion, Shaw Rev, 9/64; Modern American drama, Bernard Shaw: Candida, and Harold Pinter: The birthday party, The dumb waiter, The caretaker, In: Insight 4: analyses of modern British and American plays, Hirschgraben, 74; Modern drama: an annual bibliography, Mod. Drama, 74. Add: Dept. of English, State University of New York at Binghamton, Binghamton, NY 13901.

CARPENTER, EDWIN CECIL, b. Peoria, Ill, Apr. 27, 33; m. 55; c. 2. PUBLIC ADDRESS. B.S, Ill. State Univ, 55, M.S, 56; Ph.D.(pub. address), South. Ill. Univ, 66. Asst, Ill. State Univ, 56; teaching fels, South. Ill. Univ, 59 & summers 59-63; instr. speech, Ill. Wesleyan Univ, 56-60, asst. prof. & dir. debate, 60-64, assoc. prof, 64-66; dean col, Lincoln Col, 66-69, admin. v.pres, 69-73; HEAD DIV. LANG. & LIT, NORTHEAST MO. STATE UNIV, 73- Vis. scholar educ. admin, Harvard, summer 68. U.S.A.R, 58. Am. Counc. Educ; Speech Asn. Am; Am. Asn. Higher Educ. The Chautauqua movement in America; history and criticism of public address and communication theory; political movement in Indiana in the 1860's to 1870's. Add: 1410 E. Normal, Kirksville, MO 63501.

CARPENTER, FREDERIC IVES, b. Chicago, Ill, Feb. 1, 03; m. 26; c. 4. ENGLISH. A.B, Harvard, 24, A.M, 27; Ph.D, Univ. Chicago, 29. Instr, Univ. Chicago, 25-29; Harvard, 29-34; lectr, Univ. Calif, 46-50; ed. adviser, Col. Eng, 50-54; RES. ASSOC. ENG, UNIV. CALIF, BERKELEY, 54- Ed, New Eng. Quart, 29-38. MLA. American literature and philosophy. Publ: Emerson handbook, Hendricks, 53; American literature and the dream, Philos. Libr, 55; Robinson Jeffers, 62, Eugene O'Neill, 64 & Laurens van der Post, 69, Twayne; The American myth..., PMLA, 10/59. Add: 2589 Pine Knoll Dr, Number 5, Walnut Creek, CA 94595.

CARPENTER, MARGARET ANN, b. Snyder, Tex, May 17, 43; m. 70; c. 1. ENGLISH. B.A, Southwest Tex. State Univ, 65, M.A, 67; Ph.D.(Eng), Univ. Tex, Austin, 70. ASST. PROF, ENG, ANGELO STATE UNIV, 70- MLA; Am. Stud. Asn; Browning Inst. American folklore; Victorian poets; women and literature. Publ: A bibliography of the Brownings: 1965-1968, Browning Newslett, 69; The railroad in American folk song, In: Diamond Bessie and the shepherds, Tex. Folklore Soc, 72; The salvation motif in Browning's poetry, Proc. Conf. Col. Teachers Eng, 73. Add: 3101 Cumberland Dr, San Angelo, TX 76901.

CARPENTER, MARGARET HALEY, b. Frederick Hall, Va. ENGLISH. B.A, Univ. Richmond. RES. & WRITING. Ed. Va. Auth. Yearbk, 56-58; guest ed, The Lyric, 55, Adv. ed, 74; poetry reviewer, Chicago Tribune, 62-63; book reviewer, Athens Daily News, Ga, 73; v.pres, Va. Humanities Found. Keats Mem. Award, 61; James & Helen Rushfeldt Duff Mem. Prize, 73; Nancy Byrd Turner Mem. Prize, 73. Poetry Soc. Am.(co-winner, Arthur Davison Ficke Award, 56); Poetry Soc, Eng.(Greenwood Prize, 57); Vachel Lindsay Asn.(adv. bd). Twentieth century American poetry. Publ: Ed, Poems by Marion Cummings, 57 & David Morton's Journey into time, 58, Pentelic Press; co-ed, Anthology of magazine verse for 1958, 59, auth, Sara Teasdale: a biography, 60 & illustrator, A gift for the princess of springtime, 64, Schulte. Song of Sara, based on Teasdale biog.(bk. & music by Daniel Jahn), produced Cape Cod, 72 & N.Y.C, 73. Add: 1032 Cambridge Crescent, Norfolk, VA 23508.

CARPENTER, NAN COOKE, b. Louisa Co, Va, July 29, 12. ENGLISH, MUSIC. Mus.B, Hollins Col, 34; A.M, Univ. N.C, 41; fels, Yale, 43-45, A.M, 45, Ph.D, 48. Teacher, Jr. High Sch, Va, 35-40, 41-42; instr. Eng, Univ. Conn, 48; asst. prof, Univ. Mont, 48-53, assoc. prof, 53-57, prof, 57-65, chmn. dept, 56-57; PROF. fine arts, Syracuse Univ, 65-66; ENG. & COMP. LIT, UNIV. GA, 67-, DIR. GRAD. STUD. COMP. LIT, 72- Ford fel, Cambridge, 54-55; ed. univ. press, Univ. Mont, 57-58; Am. Counc. Learned Soc. fel, 58-59, mem. fel. selection comt, 61; Am. Philos. Soc. fel, summer 60; vis. prof. Eng, South. Ill. Univ, 64-65. MLA; Renaissance Soc. Am; Int. Comp. Lit. Asn; Am. Musicol. Soc. Music history; Renaissance and comparative literature; English literature. Publ: Rabelais and music, Univ. N.C, 54; Music in the mediaeval and Renaissance universities, Univ. Okla, 58; John Skelton, Twayne, 68; Skelton & music, Eng. Lang. Notes, 12/70; Milton & music, In: Milton Encycl, (in press); Music education to 1600, In: Grove's dictionary of music, (in press); plus others. Add: Dept. of Comparative Literature, Park Hall, University of Georgia, Athens, GA 30602.

CARPENTER, RICHARD COLES, b. Melrose, Mass, Aug. 30, 16; m. 45; c. 2. ENGLISH. B.A, Tufts Col, 38; M.A, Boston Univ, 39, Ph.D.(Eng), 51. Instr. ENG, Boston Univ, 47-53; from asst. prof. to PROF, BOWLING GREEN STATE UNIV, 53- U.S.A, 42-46. MLA; Col. Eng. Asn. Victorian novel, literary criticism; aesthetics. Publ: Thomas Hardy, Twayne, 64; co-auth, Examined life, World, 67; auth, The mirror and the sword, 64 & Hawthorne's polar explorations, 69, Nineteenth Century Fiction; contrib, Thomas Hardy: an annotated bibliography, North. Ill. Univ, 73; plus others. Add: Dept. of English, Bowling Green State University, Bowling Green, OH 43402.

CARPENTER, WILLIAM E, b. Winnsboro, La, Jan. 26, 38; m. 60; c. 2. LITERATURE, DRAMA. B.A, Centenary Col, 60; Ph.D.(Eng), Univ. Kans, 67. Asst. prof. ENG, Univ. Del, 67-69; State Univ. N.Y. Stony Brook, 69-73; ASSOC. PROF, KANS. STATE UNIV, 73- Ed, Freshman Eng. Shop Talk, Kans. State Univ, 73- U.S.A, 60-61, Res, 61-68, Capt. NCTE; Conf. Col. Compos. & Commun; Col. Eng. Asn. Restoration drama; composition; Southern American literature. Publ: Co-ed, The art of drama, 69 & The art of modern drama, 69 & co-auth, Instructor's manual for The art of modern drama, 69, Holt; ed, Destination tomorrow, & auth, Instructor's manual, 72 & co-ed, Elements of fiction, 74, W.C. Brown; auth, Department of English TA program, Grad. Sch. Newslett, 9-10/70; Training TA's: involving the entire department, Freshman Eng. News, spring 73. Add: 1806 Laramie, Manhattan, KS 66506.

CARPENTER, WILLIAM MORTON, b. Cambridge, Mass, Oct. 31, 40; m. 62; c. 1. ENGLISH & HUMANITIES. B.A, Dartmouth Col, 62; Ph.D.(Eng. & art hist), Univ. Minn, 67. Instr. Eng, Nazareth Col, summer 66; asst. prof. Eng. & humanities, Univ. Chicago, 67-73; MEM. FAC. HUMANITIES, COL.

OF THE ATLANTIC, 73- MLA. W.B. Yeats; modern poetry; Renaissance poetry. Publ: The Green helmet poems and Yeats' myth of the Renaissance, Mod. Philol, 8/69. Add: Dept. of Humanities, College of the Atlantic, Bar Harbor, ME 04609.

CARPER, THOMAS ROBSON, b. Morristown, N.J, Nov. 3, 36; m. 64. ENGLISH & AMERICAN LITERATURE. B.A, Harvard, 58; M.A, N.Y. Univ, 67; Ph.D.(Eng), Boston Univ, 73. Recordings ed. for. lang, Holt, Rinehart & Winston, Inc, 58-64; Eng. ed, Odyssey Press, Inc, 64-67; instr. ENG, UNIV. MAINE, PORTLAND-GORHAM, 67-71, ASST. PROF, 71- Poetry Publ: The one writing of Thomas Gray: a reading of all the poetry, Univ. Microfilms, 73; The whole history of Thoreau's My prisons, Emerson Soc. Quart, 68; Congreve's popular tragedy, Thoth, fall 71; Gray's Orders of insects, a mnemonic device, Notes & Queries, 6/73. Add: Dept. of English, University of Maine at Portland-Gorham, Gorham, ME 04038.

CARPINELLI, FRANCIS PAUL, b. Philadelphia, Pa, July 2, 35; m. 69; c. 2. ENGLISH. B.A, LaSalle Col, 57; M.A, Univ. Notre Dame, 59, Ph.D.(Eng), 72. Ed. & commun. specialist, Bendix Corp, Bendix Mishawaka Div, 59-62; asst. prof. ENG, BENEDICTINE COL, 64-70, ASSOC. PROF, 72-, chmn. dept, 66-70, dir. pub. relat, 70-71. Commun. consult, Miles Labs, Elkhart, Ind, 62-63; ed, The Raven Rev, Benedictine Col, 70-71; Kansas City Regional Counc. Higher Educ. summer res. grant, 71. NCTE; Conf. Col. Compos. & Commun; Milton Soc. Am. Late 16th century English poetry; English renaissance literature. Publ: Sir Orfeo, Explicator, 60; Charles Peguy's Basic verities, Masterpieces Cath. Lit, 65. Add: Dept. of English, Benedictine College, Atchison, KS 66002.

CARR, ARTHUR JAPHETH, b. Bad Axe, Mich, Apr. 21, 14; m. 41; c. 4. ENGLISH. A.B, Univ. Mich, 35; A.M, Syracuse Univ, 37; Ph.D.(Eng), Univ. Ill, 47. Instr. Eng, Syracuse Univ, 37-40; Univ. Ill, 47-49; asst. prof, Univ. Mich, 49-54, from assoc. prof. to prof, 55-67; EDWARD DORR GRIFFIN PROF. LIT, WILLIAMS COL, 71-, chmn. dept. Eng, 67-74. Adv. Victorian Stud, 62-66. U.S.N.R, 43-45, Lt. Nineteenth century English poetry and history of ideas. Publ: Masterpieces of drama, Macmillan; ed, Victorian poetry; Clough to Kipling, Holt, 59, rev. ed, 72; plus others. Add: Dept. of English, Williams College, Williamstown, MA 01267.

CARR, ELIZABETH BALL, b. Okla. City, Okla, Feb. 11, 01; m. 25; c. 1. SPEECH. A.B, Univ. Okla, 24, A.M, 40; Univ. Wis; Columbia Univ; Univ. Calif; Univ. Hawaii; Yale; Ph.D.(speech), La. State Univ, 53. Teacher, State Dept. Pub. Instr, Okla, 31-35; instr. SPEECH, UNIV. HAWAII, 43-47, asst. prof, 47-54, assoc. prof, 54-61, chmn. dept, 54-57, from prof. & chmn. dept. to EMER. PROF, 61- Exchange prof, Univ. Calif, 50; vis. lectr. Eng, Chulalonkgorn Univ, Bangkok, 68-70. U.S.N, 47-52. Speech Commun. Asn, Ling. Soc. Am. Phonetics; linguistics; teaching of foreign students. Publ: Da Kine Talk: from pidgin to standard English in Hawaii, Univ. Hawaii, 72; plus three others. Add: 1832 Wilhelmina Rise, Honolulu, HI 96816.

CARR, JOAN CHRISTINE, b. St. Paul, Minn, Apr. 5, 47. ENGLISH LITERATURE. B.A, Univ. Md, College Park, 68; M.A, Univ. Va, 69, Ph.D.(Eng), 73. ASST. PROF. ENG, UNIV. CALIF, DAVIS, 73- MLA. Renaissance literature. Add: Apt. 420, 2950 Portage Bay Ave, Davis, CA 95616.

CARR, MARIE BERNICE, b. Aberdeen, S.Dak, Oct. 13, 17. SPEECH COMMUNICATION. B.A, San Jose State Col, 39; M.A, Stanford Univ, 42, Ph.D. (rhetoric, pub. address), 57. Asst. speech, San Jose State Col, 39-43; field rep, 12th Region, U.S. Civil Serv. Comn, 43-46; from instr. to assoc. prof, SPEECH, SAN JOSE STATE UNIV, 46-57, PROF, 57- Speech Commun. Asn. Scottish rhetoric of the 18th century; realism in the plays of James A. Herne; rhetoric and public address. Add: Dept. of Speech-Communication, San Jose State University, San Jose, CA 95114.

CARR, VIRGINIA MASON, b. Washington, D.C, Jan. 12, 47; m. 67. ENGLISH LITERATURE. B.A, Univ. Mich, 68, M.A, 70, Rackham Prize fel, 71-72, Ph.D.(Eng), 72. Teacher ENG, Plymouth Jr. High Sch, 68-69; instr, Calif. State Univ, Los Angeles, 72-73; ASST. PROF, ALLEGHENY COL, 73- MLA. Renaissance drama; Shakespeare. Publ: Animal imagery in 2 Henry VI, Eng. Stud, 10/72. Add: Dept. of English, Allegheny College, Meadville, PA 16335.

CARRA, LAWRENCE, b. Salina, Italy, Jan. 20, 09; U.S. citizen; m. 35; c. 3. DRAMA, THEATRE. B.A, Harvard, 31; M.F.A, Yale, 37. Instr. DRAMA, Northwest. Univ, 38-39; head dept, Shimer Col, 39-40; asst. prof, Univ. Tex, 40-42, acting head dept, 42-46; assoc. prof, CARNEGIE-MELLON UNIV, 46-48, acting head dept, 48-50, PROF, 56- Guest lectr, Stanford Univ, 45; producer, Pulitzer Prize Playhouse, ABC-TV, New York, 50-52; guest dir, Ind. Univ, 51; dir, Mill Playhouse, N.J, 52-; guest lectr, Columbia Univ, 56; producer & dir, Great Lakes Shakespeare Festival, Cleveland, Ohio, 66-; dir, Leave it to Jane, off-Broadway play; producer, KDKA Westinghouse Broadcasting Co; producer & dir, WQED Educ. TV; dir, Shaw's Candida, Broadway, 70. Producing and directing. Publ: Co-auth, Fundamentals of play directing, Holt, 3rd. ed, 74; auth, The great magician, a commedia dell' arte play, NBC-TV, 38; contrib, The American theatre, French, 71. Add: Dept. of Drama, Carnegie-Mellon University, 5000 Forbes Ave, Pittsburgh, PA 15213.

CARRIAR, SHIRLEY MAY, b. Superior, Wis, May 19, 17. ENGLISH EDUCATION. B.Ed, Superior State Col, 37; M.A, Univ. Wis, 44; summers, Univ. Colo, 49, Univ. Minn, 50; Ed.D.(sec. educ), Colo. State Col, 58. Teacher high sch, Mich, 37-38, jr. high sch, Wis, 39-41, high sch, 41-46; Eng. & libr. sci, Superior State Col, 46-56; asst. prof. ENG, UNIV. NORTH. COLO, 58-62, assoc. prof, 62-66, PROF, 66- Ford Found. grant stud. teaching Eng. in sec. schs, 65; dir. placement serv, Conf. Eng. Educ, 66-; Kettering consult, 67. NCTE; Conf. Eng. Educ. Problems of beginning English teachers. Publ: Christmas story project—a junior high unit, 11/55 & One use of theme files in junior high school English, 3/61, Eng. J. Add: Dept. of English, University of Northern Colorado, Greeley, CO 80631.

CARRIER, WARREN PENDLETON, b. Cheviot, Ohio, July 3, 18; m. 47, 73; c. 1. ENGLISH. A.B, Miami Univ, 42; summers, Nat. Univ. Mex, 41, Duke Univ, 42, Univ. Havana, 46; Univ. N.C, 42-44; A.M, Harvard, 48; Ph.D, Occidental Col, 62. Instr. Romance langs, Univ. N.C, 42-44; Boston Univ, 45-49; asst. prof. Eng, State Univ. Iowa, 49-52; from asst. prof. to assoc. prof. lit, Bard Col, 53-57; vis. prof. Eng, Sweet Briar Col, 58-60; prof. lang, lit, & philos, Deep Springs Col, 60-62; Eng, Portland State Col, 62-64, prof. Eng. & chmn. dept, Univ. Mont, 64-68; prof. Eng. & compt. lit. & assoc. dean, Livingston Col, Rutgers Univ, 68-69; dean Col. Arts & Lett, Calif. State Univ, San Diego, 69-72; V.PRES. ACAD. AFFAIRS, UNIV. BRIDGEPORT, 72- Founder Quart Rev. Lit, 43, ed, 43-44; assoc. ed, West. Rev, 49-50; mem. lit. fac, Bennington Col, 55-58. MLA; NCTE; Am. Comp. Lit. Asn; fel, Royal Soc. Arts. Comparative literature; modern American and European literature; creative writing. Publ: The hunt; Bay of the damned, Day, 57; ed, Reading modern poetry; Toward Montebello, Harper, 66. Add: Office of Vice President for Academic Affairs, University of Bridgeport, Bridgeport, CT 06602.

CARRINGER, ROBERT L, b. Knoxville, Tenn, May 12, 41; m. 68. AMERICAN LITERATURE, FILM STUDIES. A.B, Univ. Tenn, 62; M.A, Johns Hopkins Univ, 64; Ph.D.(Eng), Ind. Univ, 70. ASST. PROF. ENG, UNIV. ILL, URBANA, 70-, fac. fel, summers 70 & 72. Mem. ed. bd, Am. Stud, 72- Midwest Mod. Lang. Asn; Mid-Continent Am. Stud. Asn. American studies; film and literature; American literature. Publ: Circumscription of space and the form of Poe's Arthur Gordon Pym, PMLA, 5/74. Add: Dept. of English, University of Illinois, Urbana, IL 61801.

CARRINGTON, GEORGE CABELL, JR, b. Wash, D.C, Nov. 27, 28; m. 54; c. 1. ENGLISH. A.B, Haverford Col, 50; A.M, Harvard, 53; Ph.D.(Eng), Ohio State Univ, 59. Instr. ENG, Ohio State Univ, 59-60; Rutgers Univ, 60-62; asst. prof, Case Inst. Technol, 62-66; ASSOC. PROF, NORTH. ILL. UNIV, 67- Fulbright lectr, Univ. Tehran, 66-67. MLA; Am. Stud. Asn. Publ: The immense complex drama: the world and art of the Howells novel, Ohio State Univ, 66. Add: Dept. of English, Northern Illinois University, De Kalb, IL 60115.

CARRINGTON, RICHARD H, b. Fort Wayne, Ind, Oct. 8, 25; m. 60; c. 1. SPEECH, THEATRE. B.A, Kalamazoo Col, 49; M.A, Univ. Wis, 52, Ph.D. (speech), 65. Admis. counsel, Ripon Col, 54-55, instr. speech, 55-56; teaching asst, Univ. Wis, 56-59, instr, Ctr. Syst, Racine & Kenosha, 59-65, asst. prof, UNIV. WIS-PARKSIDE, 65-71, ASSOC. PROF. COMMUN, 71- U.S.N, 43-46. Speech Commun. Asn; Cent. States Speech Asn. Oral interpretation; mass communication through radio, TV and film. Add: Div. of Humanistic Studies-Communication, University of Wisconsin-Parkside, Wood Rd, Kenosha, WI 53140.

CARRITHERS, GALE H, JR, b. Chadron, Nebr, Apr. 24, 32; m. 56; c. 2. ENGLISH. B.A, Col. William & Mary, 53; M.A, Yale, 57, Ph.D, 60; M.Arch, State Univ. N.Y. Buffalo, 73. Instr. ENG, Duke Univ, 57-62; asst. prof, STATE UNIV. N.Y. BUFFALO, 62-66, assoc. prof, 66-71, PROF. & DIR. TEACHING FELS, 71- Res. assoc. urban planning, Buffalo Orgn. Social & Technol. Innovation, 70-71; representative curriculum counc, Hamburg Cent. Sch. Dist, 71-73. U.S.A.R, 53-55, Capt. Literature and theology; literature of education; urban planning. Publ: Donne at sermons, State Univ. N.Y, 72; Fitzgerald's triumph, In: The great Gatsby, a study, Scribner, 62; Milton's Ludlow mask: from chaos to community, ELH, 66; Demythologizing genre, Col. Eng, 67. Add: Dept. of English, State University of New York at Buffalo, Buffalo, NY 14214.

CARROLL, BENJAMIN HAWKINS, JR, b. Merryville, La, Dec. 16, 12; m. 39; c. 1. ENGLISH. A.B, La. State Univ, 35, M.A, 39; Ph.D.(Eng), 48. Instr. ENG, FLA. STATE UNIV, 46-48, asst. prof, 48-51, ASSOC. PROF, 51- U.S.A, 43-46, Sgt. MLA; Mediaeval Acad. Am. Old English. Publ: An essay on the Walther legend, Fla. State Univ. Stud, 52, The genealogy of the Walther legend, Ger. Rev, 2/53. Add: Dept. of English, Florida State University, Tallahassee, FL 32306.

CARROLL, DAVID BARRY, b. Rossland, B.C, June 14, 42. ENGLISH & AMERICAN LITERATURE. B.A, Univ. B.C, 64; M.A, Univ. Calif, Riverside, 67; Ph.D.(Eng), Rice Univ, 71. ASST. PROF. ENG, CALIF. STATE UNIV, LOS ANGELES, 69- Romantic literature; critical theory. Add: Dept. of English, California State University, Los Angeles, 5151 State University Dr, Los Angeles, CA 90032.

CARROLL, HAZEL HORN, b. Dallas, Tex, Mar. 9, 09; m. 44. SPEECH, EDUCATION. B.A, South. Methodist Univ, 30, 31, 34, 39, 44 & 50; Rice Sch. Dramatics & Theatre, 31; M.Ed, Tex. Wesleyan Col, 52; Cornell Univ, 55. Teacher, pub. schs, Tex, 34-44; Wash, D.C, 44-45; Tex, 48-50; ASST. DIR. READING CLIN. & ASST. PROF. EDUC, SOUTH. METHODIST UNIV, 50- Consult, Independent Sch. Dist, Midland, Tex, Aug. 62; mem. affiliation comt, Int. Reading Asn, 64-65, chmn. TV comt, 64-72, mem. citations & awards comt, 65-67; participant, summer workshop for teachers, Marquette Univ, 65; mem. eve. sch. stud. counc, Lamar Inst. Technol, fall 65; participant, teacher workshop, Univ. Tex, Port Arthur, June 65; auth, Charlie McCarthy's reading problem, produced by Wm. Brown Studio, Hollywood, 66; consult, beginning prog. for disadvantaged, Port Arthur Independent Sch. Dist, 66-67; secy. & mem. bd./dir, Nat. Reading Conference, 66-; consult. for many cols, univs, sch. dists. & other insts. in U.S. Int. Reading Asn; Nat. Reading Conf. Oral interpretation of literature; accuracy in oral interpretation and reading; usefulness of phonic generalizations. Publ, Play like series (dramatizations for young children), Taylor Publ, 69; Developing flexibility, In: Recent Developments in Reading, Univ. Chicago, 65; Magic of presenting materials through television, In: Vistas in reading, (Vol. II), Int. Reading Asn, 67; The language experience approach, In: The fourth international reading symposium, London, Cassell, London, 67. Add: Box 162, Southern Methodist University, Dallas, TX 75275.

CARROLL, JOHN J, b. Peoria, Ill, Aug. 11, 29; m. 62; c. 3. ENGLISH. B.A, Univ. Ill, 50, M.A, 51; B.A, Oxford, 53; Ph.D.(Eng), Harvard, 60. Lectr. ENG, UNIV. TORONTO, 58-61, asst. prof, 61-65, assoc. prof, 65-67, PROF, 67-, CHMN. DEPT, 68- Can. Counc. fel, 65-66 & 71-72. U.S.A, 53-55, Sgt. Modern English and American novel, 18th century English novel. Publ: Ed, Selected letters of Samuel Richardson, Oxford, 64 & Samuel Richardson: a collection of critical essays, Prentice-Hall, 69; contrib, Samuel Richardson, Vol. II, In: New Cambridge bibliography of English literature, Cambridge, 71; auth, Lovelace as tragic hero, Univ. Toronto Quart, 72; contrib, Richardson at work, In: Studies in the eighteenth century II, Australian Nat. Univ, 73; plus others. Add: Dept. of English, University College, University of Toronto, Toronto, Ont, Can.

CARROLL, JOSEPH P, b. New York, N.Y, Nov. 26, 22; m. 53; c. 2. ENGLISH. B.A, L.I. Univ, 51; M.S, Ft. Hays Kans. State Col, 57; M.A, Univ. Kans, 67. Teacher, St. Catherine's Sch, 54-56; jr. high sch, 56-61; asst. instr, ENG, Univ. Kans, 61-63; instr, KEARNEY STATE COL, 63-69, ASST. PROF, 69- U.S.A, 43-45. NEA; NCTE; MLA. Jack London; relevance of American authors in American public school curriculum. Add: 4004 Ave. F, Kearney, NE 68847.

CARROLL, WILLIAM DENNIS, b. Sydney, Australia, Aug. 25, 40; m. 68; c. 2. DRAMA. B.A, Univ. Sydney, 62, M.A, 66; M.F.A, Univ Hawaii, 65; Ph.D. (drama), Northwest. Univ, 69. ASST. PROF. DRAMA, UNIV. HAWAII, MANOA, 69- Am. Theatre Asn. Australian theatre and drama; film theory and criticism. Publ: The United States in recent Australian drama, Educ. Theatre J, 10/73. Add: Dept. of Drama & Theatre, University of Hawaii at Manoa, 1770 East West Rd, Honolulu, HI 96822.

CARROLL, WILLIAM MEREDITH, b. Jonesboro, Ark, Nov. 8, 10; m. 43. ENGLISH. A.B, Ark. State Col, 33; A.M, Ind. Univ, 38, Ph.D.(Eng. & comp. philol), 50. Instr. ENG, Ark. State Col, 34-36; teacher, Ind. Univ, 36-40, 46-48; instr, Ala. Polytech. Inst, 41-44; PROF, Univ. Corpus Christi, 48-73; TEX. A&I UNIV, CORPUS CHRISTI, 73- Transl, Off. Censorship, U.S. Govt, 43-45. MLA. English Renaissance; Chaucer. Publ: Animal conventions in English Renaissance non-religious prose, 1550-1600; co-auth, A note on Shakespeare and The celestina, Rev. Estudios Hisp, 1/71 & The falcon as a symbol of destiny: de Rojas and Shakespeare, Romanische Forschungen, 71. Add: 5902 Idylwood Dr, Corpus Christi, TX 78412.

CARRUTH, HAYDEN KENNA, SR, b. Auburn, Miss, Sept. 14, 11; m. 38; c. 4. SPEECH. B.A, Asbury Col, 37; M.A, Univ. Mich, Ann Arbor, 39, Ph.D. (speech), 55. Instr. SPEECH, UNIV. MICH, ANN ARBOR, 48-52, asst. prof, 52-58, assoc. prof, 58-69, PROF, 69-, ASSOC. DEAN FAC. AFFAIRS, 68-, asst. dean acad. coun, Col. Lit, Sci. & Arts, 61-68. Assoc. ed, Speech Teacher, 60-63. U.S.N.R, 43-46, Lt. Comdr. Communication; mass media; educational administration. Publ: Curricular speech in Michigan high schools 1948-49, 49, Curricular speech in Michigan high schools 1956-57, 57 & Curricular speech in Michigan high schools 1960-61, 61, Univ. Mich; ed, Mass Media and persuasion, 60. Add: College of Literature, Science & the Arts, University of Michigan, Ann Arbor, MI 48104.

CARRUTH, HAZEL E, b. Cavour, S.Dak, Nov. 11, 13; m. 67. ENGLISH. B.S. in Ed, Taylor Univ, 38; M.A, Ind. Univ, 46, Ph.D.(Eng), 54. Teacher, rural sch, S.Dak, 32-35, high sch, 38-40; ENG, Ft. Wayne Bible Inst, 41-45; mem. fac, TAYLOR UNIV, 46-50, 53-55, PROF. & HEAD DEPT, 55-, chmn. div. lang. & lit, 55-68. MLA; NCTE. T.S. Eliot; romanticism; American literature. Add: Taylor University, Upland, IN 46989.

CARRUTHERS, MARY, b. Jan. 15, 41; U.S. citizen. ENGLISH LITERATURE & LANGUAGE. B.A, Wellesley Col, 61, Alice Freeman Palmer fel, 62-63; univ. fels, Yale, 61-62, 63-64, Ph.D.(Eng), 65. Instr. ENG. LANG. & LIT, Smith Col, 64-66, ASST. PROF, 66-73; CASE WEST. RESERVE UNIV, 73- MLA; Mediaeval Acad. Am. Old and Middle English literature; history of the English language. Publ: The search for St. Truth: a study of meaning in Piers Plowman, Northwest. Univ, 73; Letter and gloss in the Friar's and Summoner's tales, J. Narrative Tech, 72; Fantasy in The merchant's tale, Criticism, 70; Piers Plowman: the tearing of the pardon, Philol. Quart, 70; plus one other. Add: Dept. of English, Case Western Reserve University, Cleveland, OH 44106.

CARSON, HERBERT LEE, b. Philadelphia, Pa, Oct. 3, 29; m. 53; c. 3. DRAMA. B.A, Univ. Pittsburgh, 53; M.A, Columbia Univ, 55; Ph.D, Univ. Minn, 59. Teacher, Orange High Sch, 53-55; instr. Eng. Univ. Minn, 56-59; speech & theater, Univ. Nebr, 59-60; asst. prof. HUMANITIES, FERRIS STATE COL, 60-64, assoc. prof, 64-68, PROF, 68- Mem. staff dramatic lit. & playwriting, correspondence stud. div, Univ. Minn, 57; vis. prof, Youngstown Univ, summer 66; Nat. Endowment for Humanities & Ford Found. grant & dir, Inst. on Blacks in Film, summer 69. U.S.A, 46-48. The existential tragic challenge; mythology; modern fiction. Publ: Steps in successful speaking, Van Nostrand, 67; co-ed, The impact of fiction, Cummings, 70; auth, Royall Tyler: a critical biography, Twayne, 76; The philanthropist (fiction), Kans. Quart, 72; A smile for the professor (fiction), West. Rev, 73; A sound in the night (fiction), Amaranthus, 73; plus others. Add: Dept. of Humanities, Ferris State College, Big Rapids, MI 49307.

CARSON, J. ANGELA, b. Danbury, Conn. ENGLISH. A.B, Col. New Rochelle, 43; M.A, Fordham Univ, 51, Ph.D.(Eng), 68. PROF. ENG, Col. New Rochelle, 48-51; Ursuline Acad, Dela, 51-56; COL. NEW ROCHELLE, 57- Mem, C.G. Jung Found. Anal. Psychol. MLA; Mediaeval Acad. Am; Int. Arthurian Soc; Milton Soc. Am. Arthurian literature; Middle English literature; Jungian psychology. Publ: Morgan la Fée as the principle of unity in Gawain and the Green Knight, Mod. Lang. Quart, 3/62; Aspects of elegy in the Middle English Pearl, Stud. Philol, 1/65; Rhetorical structure in The owl and the nightingale, Speculum, 1/67; plus one other. Add: Dept. of English, College of New Rochelle, New Rochelle, NY 10801.

CARSON, NORMAN MATTHEWS, b. Denver, Colo, Apr. 20, 25; m. 53; c. 4. ENGLISH LITERATURE. B.A, Geneva Col, 47; M.A, State Univ. Iowa, 49; Reformed Presby. Theol. Sem, 49-52; Univ. Chicago, 53-54; teaching fels, Boston Univ, 55-57, Ph.D, 62. Instr, ENG, GENEVA COL, 57-59, asst. prof, 59-63, assoc. prof, 63-66, PROF, 66-, CHMN. DEPT, 69- Mem. bd. ed, Christian Scholar's Rev, 70- U.S.A, 44-46. Conf. Christianity & Lit, (pres, 72-74); MLA. Renaissance; modern drama; the novel. Add: Dept. of English, Geneva College, Beaver Falls, PA 15010.

CARSON, ROBERT ROSE, b. Geneva, N.Y, Jan. 5, 12. PUBLIC SPEAKING. B.S, Hamilton Col, 35; A.M, Hobart Col, 36; Cornell Univ, 44-48. Instr, Am. Univ. Cairo, 36-39; Eng. & pub. speaking, Iowa State Col, 39-42; PUB. SPEAKING, Cornell Univ, 43-49; asst. prof, HAMILTON COL, 49-69, assoc. prof, 69-73, EMER. ASSOC. PROF, 73- Speech Commun. Asn. Rhetoric and public address; public discussion. Add: 13 Fountain St, Clinton, NY 13323.

CARSON, WILLIAM GLASGOW BRUCE, b. St. Louis, Mo, Sept. 1, 91. ENGLISH, DRAMA. A.B, Wash. Univ, 13, A.M, 16; Columbia Univ. Instr. Eng, Iowa State Col, 16-19; WASH. UNIV, 19-23, asst. prof, 23-35, assoc. prof, 35-50, prof. ENG. & DRAMA, 50-57, EMER. PROF, 57- Am. Educ. Theatre Asn; Am. Nat. Theatre & Acad; Theatre Libr. Asn; Nat. Col. Players. The theatre on the frontier; letters of Mr. and Mrs. Charles Kean relating to their American tours; one act plays. Publ: Managers in distress, St. Louis Hist. Doc. Found, 49; Dear Josephine, Univ. Okla, 63; Peter and Brownie follow the trace, Eden, 65. Add: 7006 Maryland Ave, St. Louis, MO 63130.

CARTER, ALBERT HOWARD, III, b. Washington, D.C, Mar. 14, 43; m. 67; c. 1. COMPARATIVE LITERATURE, HUMANITIES. A.B, Univ. Chicago, 65; NDEA fel, Univ. Iowa, 66-69, M.A, 67 & 71, Ph.D.(comp. lit), 71; Presby. Grad. fel, Florence, Italy, 69-70. Asst. prof. lit. & drama, Tarkio Col, 70-71; vis. asst. prof. lit, ECKERD COL, 71-72, ASST. PROF. COMP. LIT. & HUMANITIES, 72- MLA; S.Atlantic Mod. Lang. Asn; Conf. Christianity & Lit; Soc. Relig. Higher Educ; Am. Comp. Lit. Asn. Twentieth century European fiction; American fiction since 1950; the arts, meaning and consciousness. Publ: Poems in: Churchman, 12/71, Christian Century, 12/72, Konglomerati, spring 72 & For the time being, fall 73. Add: Comparative Literature, Eckerd College, St. Petersburg, FL 33733.

CARTER, BERNICE ALLEEN, b. Maury City, Tenn, Oct. 1, 03. ENGLISH. A.B, Union Univ.(Tenn), 28; A.M, George Peabody Col, 40. Teacher, high schs, Tenn, 28-45; asst. prof, Eng, Carson Newman Col, 45-55, dean women, 45-73; RETIRED. Add: Capri Apts, Lambuth Blvd, Jackson, TN 38301.

CARTER, BETTY, b. Collierville, Tenn, July 6, 07; m. 30; c. 1. ENGLISH, FRENCH. B.A, Lambuth Col, 28; M.A, La. State Univ, 35; E.Tex. State Univ, 66-67. Mem. fac. French, Sch, Medina, Tenn, 28-29; sch, Pope, Miss, 29-30; Eng, St. Mary's of Memphis, 42-43; French, Belhaven Col. & Eng, Southwest. at Memphis, 43-44; prof. French, Texarkana Col, 53-65, Eng, 65-69; RETIRED. Mem. bd. trustees, Texarkana Col, 69- Am. Asn. Teachers Fr; MLA; NCTE; Col. Eng. Asn. Add: P.O. Box 5249, Texarkana, TX 75501.

CARTER, EVERETT, b. New York, N.Y, Apr. 28, 19; m. 40; c. 2. ENGLISH. A.B, Univ. Calif, Los Angeles, 39, A.M, 43, Ph.D, 47. Asst. prof. ENG, Claremont Col, 47-49; Univ. Calif, Berkeley, 49-57; assoc. prof, UNIV. CALIF, DAVIS, 57-62, PROF, 62-, v.chancellor, 59-62, spec. asst. to pres, 62-63, univ. dean res, 63-66; dir. ctr. stud, Univ. Calif. at Univ. Bordeaux, 70-72. Guggenheim fels, 52-53, 61-62; lectr, Salzburg Sem, Austria, 53; Fulbright fel, Univ. Copenhagen, 54-55, Fulbright lectr, 61-62; vis. lectr, Harvard, 57-58; Fulbright lectr, Nice Sem. Am. Stud, France, summers 58, 62 & 68; lectr, Asian Ctr. Am. Stud. Hyderabad, 65; Fulbright lectr, Univ. Strasbourg, 67-68. Nonfiction Gold Medal, Commonwealth Club, Calif, 54. MLA; Am. Soc. Composers, Authors & Publ; Am. Stud. Asn. American literature, especially fiction. Publ: Howells and the age of realism, Lippincott, 54; ed, The rise of Silas Lapham, Harper's, 58, 65; The damnation of Theron Ware, Harvard, 60; The meaning in and of realism, Antioch Rev, 50. Add: 734 Hawthorn Lane, Davis, CA 95616.

CARTER, JOHN ARCHER, JR, b. Marion, Va, Dec. 3, 31; m. 62. ENGLISH LITERATURE. B.A, Univ. Va, 53; M.A, Princeton, 55, Ph.D, 56. Instr. ENG, Univ. Va, 58-61; asst. prof, WAKE FOREST UNIV, 61-65, assoc. prof, 65-72, PROF, 72-, chmn. dept, 68-71. U.S.A, 56-58. AAUP; Res. Soc. Victorian Periodicals; MLA. Victorian literature. Add: Dept. of English, Wake Forest University, Winston-Salem, NC 27109.

CARTER, JOSEPH CLEVELAND, b. Corinth, Vt, Oct. 22, 09. JOURNALISM. Ph.B, Univ. Vt, 32; A.M, Syracuse Univ, 45. Teacher & pub. adv, Black River Acad, Ludlow, Vt, 32-34; dir. jour, Spaulding High Sch, Barre, Vt, 34-44; instr, Syracuse Univ, 44-46; from asst. prof. to PROF. JOUR, TEMPLE UNIV, 46-, ed. in chief, Fac. Rec, 48-60, dir. univ. press tournament, 49-69, chmn, Sch. Press Improv. Serv, 50-57. Correspondent, Burlington Free Press, Rutland Herald & Barre Times, Vt, 31-37; columnist, Hanover Gazette, N.H. & White River Junction Landmark, Vt, 31-37; travel counr, State Publicity Dept, Vt, 36-41; correspondent, Burlington News, 37-39; copy-ed, Syracuse Post-Standard, 45-46; judge, Quill & Scroll, 46-54, contrib. ed, 48-, copy-ed, Camden Courier-Post, N.J, 47; adv. ed, Scholastic Ed, 48-69; pub. relat. writer, Curtis Pub. Co, 51; copy-writer, Ecoff & James Advert. Agency, 52; instr, Int. Bus. Mach. Sch, 53; reporter & ed, Weekly-Rev. Newspapers, 54, 55; instr. & tech. writer, Burroughs Corp. Res. Ctr, 56, 57; instr. tech. writing, Int. Resistance Co, Pa, 57; C. Schmidt & Son, Phila, Pa, 57, 58; bus. writing, Am. Viscose Corp, 59; dir, Blitman Libr, 70- Lord Baden-Powell Award, 53; Gold Key Award, Columbia Scholastic Press Asn, 60. Asn. Educ. Jour. Magazine and newspaper journalism; industrial and business articles. Add: Dept. of Journalism, Temple University, Philadelphia, PA 19122.

CARTER, KATHERINE DAVIS, b. Berkeley, Calif; m. 66. RENAISSANCE LITERATURE, RHETORIC. B.A, Stanford Univ, 64; M.A, Univ. South. Calif, 66, Ph.D.(Eng), 71. ASST. PROF. ENG, CALIF. STATE UNIV, LOS ANGELES, 70- Consult, Adult Basic Educ. Inst, Pepperdine Univ, summer 71. MLA. Renaissance rhetoric; Michael Drayton. Publ: Diction & Milton's use of Renaissance dictionaries and encyclopedias, In: A Milton encyclopedia, Univ. Wis, (in press); Drayton's craftsmanship: the Encomium and the Blason in Englands Heroicall Epistles, Huntington Libr. Quart, (in press). Add: Dept. of English, California State University, Los Angeles, 5151 State University Dr, Los Angeles, CA 90032.

CARTER, PAUL JEFFERSON, b. Los Angeles, Calif, Dec. 9, 12; m. 37; c. 3. ENGLISH. A.B, Centre Col, 34; A.M, Univ. Ky, 35; Taft fel, Univ. Cincinnati, 37-39, Ph.D, 39. Instr. DePauw Univ, 39-41, asst. prof, 41-42; instr, U.S. Naval Acad, 42-46; asst. prof, West. Reserve Univ, 46-47; assoc. prof. ENG, UNIV. COLO, BOULDER, 47-56, PROF, 56- Ed, The Colo. Quart, 53-; Ford fac. fel, 55-56. U.S.N.R, 42-46, Comdr. MLA. American literature; American studies. Publ: Co-ed, Literature and society, 1961-1965; a selective bibliography, Univ. Miami, 67; auth, Waldo Frank, Twayne, 67; Olivia Clemens edits Following the equator, Am. Lit; Mark Twain describes a San Francisco earthquake, PMLA; Influence of the Nevada frontier on Mark Twain, West. Humanities Rev. Add: Dept. of English, Hellems 118, University of Colorado, Boulder, CO 80302.

CARTER, ROLAND DeBUSKE, b. Gate City, Va, Sept. 19, 02; m. 30; c. 2. ENGLISH. A.B, Lincoln Mem. Univ, 29, L.H.D, 68; George Peabody Col, 30; A.M, Duke Univ, 35. Instr. ENG, Ala. State Teachers Col, Jacksonville, 36-37; head dept, Hiwassee Col, 37-42; asst. prof, Univ. Tenn, Chattanooga, 42-64, assoc. prof, 64-72; RETIRED. Election exam, Nat. Labor Relat. Bd, 44-, Alaska, 45; Carnegie univ. grant-in-aid, 47. Charles Brockden Brown and the Gothic novel; grammatical functions in English; creative fiction. Publ: English grammar with a halo, Col. Eng, 12/45; Some coincidences in Oresteia and the Christian tradition, 6/58 & Desertion of truth in humor, 11/68, CEA Critic. Add: 2509 E. Fourth St, Chattanooga, TN 37404.

CARTER, WILLIAM HOYT, JR, b. Ferrisburg, Vt, Aug. 14, 14; m. 41, 69; c. 5. ENGLISH. A.B, Middlebury Col, 36; A.M, Harvard, 38, Ph.D, 51. Instr. ENG, Conn. Col. Women, 40-42; Mass. Inst. Technol, 42-43; CLARK UNIV, 49-51, asst. prof, 51-55, assoc. prof, 55-67, PROF, 67-, CHMN. DEPT, 66- English literature of the 17th and 18th century. Add: Dept. of English, Clark University, Worcester, MA 01610.

CARTIER, FRANCIS ARTHUR, Speech Science, Communication. See Volume III, Foreign Languages, Linguistics & Philology.

CARVER, ANN CATHEY, b. Hendersonville, N.C, May 13, 40; wid. ENGLISH. B.A, Limestone Col, 62; M.A, Univ. Ark, 64; fel, Emory Univ, 66-67, Ph.D, 68. Instr. Eng. & humanities, Parsons Col, 63-65; asst. prof. ENG, Morehouse Col, 68-69; UNIV. N.C, 69-73, ASSOC. PROF, 73- MLA. The plays of John Ford: a critical analysis; 17th century drama. Add: Dept. of English, University of North Carolina, Charlotte, NC 28205.

CARVER, JAMES EDWARD, b. Louisville, Ky, Apr. 30, 02; m. 28; c. 3. ENGLISH. A.B, Univ. Richmond, 26; A.M, Univ. N.C, 30; Ph.D, N.Y. Univ, 38. Instr, Clemson Col, 26-27; assoc. prof. Eng. & acting head dept, Shorter Col, 28-29; instr, Mt. Holyoke Col, 30-33; from instr. to asst. prof, City Col. New York, 33-50; prof. Eng. & head dept, William Jewell Col, 50-57; Univ. Dubuque, 57-62; prof. Eng, ST. ANDREWS PRESBY. COL, 62-69, chmn. div. lang. & lit, 62-65, acting chmn, 67-68, EMER. PROF. ENG, 69- Am. Philos. Soc. fel, Eng, 39-40; vis. prof. Eng, Pembroke State Univ, 69-71; vis. prof. humanities, Voorhees Col, 72. MLA; Mediaeval Acad. Am. Old and Middle English language and literature. Publ: The north English homily cycle, 40; Date of the northern homily cycle and missionaries to the Saracens, Mod. Lang. Notes, 4/37; Medieval English sermon literature, In: New Cath. Encycl. McGraw, 67. Add: Lakewood Hills, Rte. 1, Laurinburg, NC 28352.

CARY, RICHARD, b. New York, N.Y, Nov, 18, 09; m. 54. ENGLISH. A.B, N.Y. Univ, 48, M.A, 49; Ph.D, Cornell Univ, 52; hon. M.A, Colby Col, 63. Instr. ENG, Cornell Univ, 49-52; COLBY COL, 52-54, asst. prof, 54-57, assoc. prof, 57-62, PROF, 62- Cur. rare bks. & manuscripts, ed. Colby Libr. Quart. & dir. Colby Col. Press; mem. adv. bd, Am. Lit. Abstr, 68- MLA. Nineteenth century New England authors: Edwin Arlington Robinson; Sarah Orne Jewett. Publ: The genteel circle, Cornell, 52; Sarah Orne Jewett letters, 56, 67, ed, Appreciation of Edwin Arlington Robinson: 28 interpretive essays, 69, The uncollected short stories of Sarah Orne Jewett, 71, Appreciation of Sarah Orne Jewett: 29 interpretive essays, 73 & Early reception of Edwin Arlington Robinson: the first twenty years, 74, Colby Col; Sarah Orne Jewett, 62 & Mary N. Murfree, 67, Twayne; Deephaven and other stories by Sarah Orne Jewett, Col. & Univ. Press, 66; Edwin Arlington Robinson's letters to Edith Brower, Harvard, 68; ed, Thomas Hardy, The return of the native, 68 & Thomas Hardy, The mayor of Casterbridge, 69, Cambridge Bk. Co; plus many articles in scholarly jour. on lit. subjects, 54-74. Add: Dept. of English, Colby College, Waterville, ME 04901.

CASAGRANDE, DIANE OAKS, b. Detroit, Mich, Dec. 20, 38; m. 59; c. 3. SPEECH. A.B, Wayne State Univ, 59; M.A, Temple Univ, 69. Teacher Eng. & speech, Madison High Sch, Mich, 59-61; ASSOC. PROF. SPEECH, WEST CHESTER STATE COL, 69-, COORD. SPEECH FUNDAMENTALS, 73- Fel, Temple Univ, 69- Int. Soc. Gen. Semantics; Speech Commun. Asn. Argumentation; competency based education in oral communication; general semantics. Publ: Ed, Packet of student materials for speech 101, 72 & Speech 101 packet, 73, Sharing Way Press. Add: Dept. of Speech, West Chester State College, West Chester, PA 19380.

CASAGRANDE, PETER JOSEPH, b. Pen Argyl, Pa, Dec. 19, 38; m. 61; c. 4. ENGLISH. B.A, Gettysburg Col, 60; M.A, Ind. Univ, 63, fel, 66-67, Ph.D. (Eng), 67. From asst. prof. to ASSOC. PROF. ENG, UNIV. KANS, 67-, ASSOC. DEAN, COL. ARTS & SCI, 72-, assoc. chmn. dept. & chmn. humanities, 71-72, dir, N.Col, 72-73. Elizabeth M. Watkins summer fac. fel, 68; contrib. 215 abstr, Sec. Bibliog. Thomas Hardy, spring 73; Nat. Endowment for Humanities fel, 73-74. U.S.A, 64-66, Capt. MLA. Novels and poems of Thomas Hardy; novels of George Eliot. Publ: The shifted centre of altruism in Thomas Hardy's The woodlanders, Eng. Lit. Hist, 3/71. Add: Dept. of English, University of Kansas, Lawrence, KS 66044.

CASALE, OTTAVIO MARK, b. Cleveland, Ohio, Jan. 23, 34; m. 62; c. 2. ENGLISH. B.A, Kent State Univ, 55; M.A, Univ. Mich, 59, Ph.D.(Eng), 65. Teaching fel. Eng, Univ. Mich, 60-62, ed, Inst. Sci. & Technol, 62-65; asst. prof. ENG, KENT STATE UNIV, 65-69, ASSOC. PROF, 69- Fulbright-Hays lectr. Am. lit, Univ. Pisa, 71-72. U.S.A, 55-57. MLA; Poe Stud. Asn. Nineteenth century American literature and comparative literature. Publ: Co-ed, The Kent affair: documents and interpretations, Houghton, 71; auth, Poe on transcendentalism, Emerson Soc. Quart, 1/68; The battle of Boston: a revaluation of Poe's Lyceum appearance, Am. Lit, 11/73; plus two others. Add: Dept. of English, Kent State University, Kent, OH 44242.

CASE, KEITH EDMOND, b. Creston, Iowa, May 11, 11; m. 34; c. 4. SPEECH, COMMUNICATION. A.B, Augustana Col, 34; A.M, Colo. State Col. Educ, 35; Ph.D, Univ. Denver, 48. Chmn. dept. Eng. & speech, Garden City Jr. Col, 35-41; chmn. dept. speech & dean men, Augustana Col, 41-43; assoc. prof. speech, UNIV. DENVER, 48-61, dir. clinics, 48-49, chmn. dept. basic commun, 49-63, div. commun, 51-63, asst. to dean col. arts & sci, 50-53, PROF. SPEECH, 61- Consult. commun. U.S.N.R, 43-46, Lt. Speech Commun. Asn; Social Stud. Commun. Personality bases of speech and communication; basic process of communication. Publ: Co-auth, Mastering speech skills, 56, Mature reading and thinking, 59, Developing reading competence, 61, Mastering vocabulary skills, 57 & Communicating effectively through speech, 64, Commun. Found. Ltd. Add: Dept. of Speech Communications, College of Arts & Sciences, University of Denver, Denver, CO 80210.

CASEY, DANIEL JOSEPH, b. Brooklyn, N.Y, Feb. 11, 37; m. 58; c. 3. IRISH LITERATURE, ENGLISH EDUCATION. B.A, St. John's Univ.(N.Y), 58, M.S, 60, M.A, 63; Ph.D.(philol), Univ. Helsinki, 68. Teacher Eng, High Sch, N.Y, 58-63; Fulbright lectr, Univ. Cagliari, 63-64; instr. Eng. educ, Univ. Del, 64-66; Fulbright lectr. ENG, Univ. Helsinki & Univ. Oulu, 66-68; from assoc. to asst. prof, STATE UNIV. N.Y. COL. ONEONTA, 68-72, PROF, 72- Ed, Del. Eng. J, 69-70; Eng. Record, 70-; State Univ. N.Y. Res. Found. fels, 70-72; co-ed, Carleton Newslett, 71-73; N.Y. State Eng. Counc. fel, 73-; dir, Conversations in the Disciplines, 73- MLA; Int. Asn. Study Anglo-Irish Lit; Am. Comt. Irish Stud. Publ: Benedict Kiely, Bucknell Univ, 73; Benedict Kiely and Irish writing in America, Aquarius, V: 84-88; Writing and imaginative writing, Eng. Record, summer 72; An Aran requiem: setting in Riders to the sea, Antigonish Rev, spring 72. Add: Dept. of English, State University of New York College at Oneonta, Oneonta, NY 13820.

CASEY, ELLEN MILLER, b. Evanston, Ill, Dec. 7, 41; m. 65; c. 3. ENGLISH LITERATURE. B.S, Loyola Univ. Chicago, 62; M.A, Univ. Iowa, 63; Ph.D.(Eng), Univ. Wis-Madison, 69. Instr. ENG, Mt. Mary Col, 65-66; asst. prof, UNIV. SCRANTON, 69-74 ASSOC. PROF, 74- Nat. Endowment for Humanities younger humanist fel, 74-75. MLA; NCTE; AAUP; Dickens Soc; Res. Soc. Victorian Periodicals. The English novel; Victorian literature; literature and society. Add: Dept. of English, University of Scranton, Scranton, PA 18510.

CASEY, FLOYD W, b. Scobey, Miss, Nov. 2, 23. VICTORIAN & MODERN BRITISH & AMERICAN LITERATURE. B.A, Harding Col, 44; M.A, Univ. Mo, 45; Ph.D.(Eng), Univ. Wis, 51. Instr. ENG, Knox Col, 52-54; asst. prof, Univ. Md, 54-56; assoc. prof, Memphis State Univ, 56-59; instr, LEHMAN COL, 61-65, asst. prof, 65-71, ASSOC. PROF, 71- MLA; NCTE. Victorian fiction. Publ: A guide to George Eliot's The mill on the floss, 65, A guide to Conrad's Victory and other novels, 65 & A guide to Dana's Two years before the mast, 66, Thor; George Eliot's practice as a novelist considered in relation to her critical theory, Wis. Abstr. Dissertations, 51; George Eliot's theory of fiction, W.Va. Univ. Bull, 53; A visit with Alan Sellitoe, Shantih, spring 73. Add: Dept. of English, Herbert H. Lehman College, Bedford Park Blvd. W, Bronx, NY 10468.

CASEY, MARY ELIZABETH, b. Rockland, Mass, Dec. 20, 20. ENGLISH. B.S, Mass. State Col. Bridgewater, 42; M.A, Boston Univ, 45. Instr. ENG, Mass. State Col. Salem, 52-57, asst. prof, 57-59, ASSOC. PROF, 59-66; BOSTON STATE COL, 66- MLA. Add: Dept. of English, Boston State College, 625 Huntington Ave, Boston, MA 02115.

CASH, ARTHUR HILL, b. Gary, Ind, Feb. 4, 22; m. 46; c. 2. ENGLISH LITERATURE. A.B, Univ. Chicago, 48; M.S, Univ. Wis, 50; Ph.D, Columbia Univ, 61. Instr. ENG, Univ. Colo, 52-57; Univ. N.Mex, 57-58; asst. prof, Colo. State Univ, 58-65, assoc. prof, 65-67; PROF, STATE UNIV. N.Y. COL. NEW PALTZ, 67- Prog. chmn, Laurence Sterne Bicentenary Conf, York, 68. U.S.A, 42-46. AAUP; Augustan Reprint Soc; MLA; Mod. Humanities Res. Asn.(int. monogr. competition winner, 64). Laurence Sterne; 18th century literature; history of the novel. Publ: Sterne's comedy of moral sentiments: the ethical dimension of the Journey, Duquesne Univ, 66; co-ed, The winged skull: papers from the Laurence Sterne Bicentenary Conference, Kent State Univ, 71; auth, Laurence Sterne: the early and middle years, Methuen, 75; The Lockean psychology of Tristram Shandy, 6/55 & The sermon in Tristram Shandy, 12/64, ELH; Some new Sterne letters, Times Lit. Suppl, 4/65; plus others. Add: Dept. of English, State University of New York College at New Paltz, New Paltz, NY 12561.

CASH, EARL A, b. Nassau, Bahamas, Sept. 27, 45. TWENTIETH CENTURY AMERICAN LITERATURE. B.A, Xavier Univ. La, 68; M.A, Marquette Univ, 70; Ph.D.(Eng), Univ. N.Mex, 72. Asst. prof. Eng. & dir. black prog, N.Mex. State Univ, 72-73; ASST. PROF. ENG. & DIR. SEEK PROG, JOHN JAY COL. CRIMINAL JUSTICE, 73- Ford Found. fel, 72-73. MLA. Black American novel; 20th century American fiction; Medieval literature. Publ: The evolution of a black writer: John A. Williams, Third Press, 74; Narrators of Invisible man & Notes from underground: brother in the spirit, CLA J, 6/73; Interview with John A. Williams, Black World, 6/73; The new black novel, Cross Currents, spring 74; plus others. Add: SEEK Dept, John Jay College of Criminal Justice, 445 W. 59th St, New York, NY 10019.

CASH, JOE LYNN, b. Knox City, Tex, Dec. 14, 39; m. 63; c. 2. ENGLISH & COMPARATIVE LITERATURE. B.A, Abilene Christian Col, 62; M.A, Tex. Tech Univ, 67, Ph.D.(Eng), 72. Instr. ENG, Abilene Christian Col, 62-67; teacher, Lubbock Pub. Schs, 67-68; instr, Tex. Tech Univ, 69-70; ASST. PROF, Lubbock Christian Col, 72; McNEESE STATE UNIV, 72- NCTE; S.Cent. Mod. Lang. Asn; MLA; Col. Eng. Asn. Modern British literature; British Victorian literature. Add: Dept. of Languages, McNeese State University, Lake Charles, LA 70601.

CASHMAN, DANIEL EDWARD, b. Minneapolis, Minn, Feb. 22; 38; m. 70; c. 2. THEATRE, INTERDISCIPLINARY STUDIES. B.A, Univ. Minn, 60, M.A, 62; Andrew Mellon fel. & Ph.D.(drama), Carnegie-Mellon Univ, 67. Instr. theatre, Ely Jr. Col, 61-62; drama, Miami Univ, 62-65; lectr. THEATRE, Ind. Univ, Ft. Wayne, 66-67; ASSOC. PROF, PURDUE UNIV, FT. WAYNE, 67- Consult, Freedom Readers, Pa, 65-66; co-founder-dir, Wawasee Arts Found, Ind, 68-69; co-founder-adv, Ctr. Stud. of the Person, 72- Am. Theatre Asn; AAUP; Am. Film Inst. Actor training; modern serious comedy. Add: Div. of Theatre, Purdue University, 2101 Coliseum Blvd. E, Ft. Wayne, IN 46805.

CASHMAN, PAUL H, b. Des Moines, Iowa, June 30, 24; m. 51; c. 4. SPEECH COMMUNICATION. B.S, Univ. Minn, 48, M.A, 50, Ph.D.(speech), 57. Instr. speech, Univ. Minn, 49-50; dir. forensics, Hamline Univ, 50-53; instr. speech, UNIV. MINN, MINNEAPOLIS, 53-57, asst. prof. rhetoric, 57-59, assoc. prof, 59-61, prof, 61-65, asst. v.pres. educ. relat. & develop, 65-68, V.PRES. STUD. AFFAIRS, 68- U.S.A.F, 43-45, 1st Lt. Speech Commun. Asn; Nat. Soc. Stud. Commun. Communication theory; discussion; persuasion. Publ: Co-auth, Report of the Minnesota inter-institutional television feasibility study, Univ. Minn, 65 & A handbook for beginning debaters, Burgess, 3rd ed, 66; auth, Break the barrier to communications, Nat. Asn. Suggestion Syst. Quart, autumn 63; The role of agriculture in a changing Minnesota, Proc. Staff Seminar Inst. Agr, 64; Orientation—reality or illusion, Proc. Orientation Dir. Conf, 65; plus others. Add: Office of the Vice President of Student Affairs, University of Minnesota, Minneapolis, MN 55455.

CASKEY, EDNA PAYNE, b. St. Jo, Tex, June 26, 99; m. 25; c. 3. ENGLISH. A.B, Baylor Univ, 21, A.M, 49. Instr, Ohio Univ, 46-48; from instr. to prof. ENG, BAYLOR UNIV, 48-71, EMER. PROF, 71- Conf. Col. Teachers Eng; S.Cent. Mod. Lang. Asn. Eighteenth century; Jonathan Swift; James Boswell and his times. Publ: Aurora Leigh, a study in Victorian taste, Tex. Conf. Col. Teachers Eng. J, 50; Dr. Johnson's island, S.Cent. Bull, 3/61. Add: Dept. of English, Baylor University, Waco, TX 76710.

CASMIR, FRED L, b. Berlin, Ger, Dec. 30, 28; U.S. citizen; m. 52; c. 2. SPEECH COMMUNICATION. B.A, David Lipscomb Col, 50; M.A, Ohio State Univ, 55, Ph.D.(speech, educ. psychol), 61. Instr. speech & Ger, PEPPERDINE UNIV, MALIBU, 56-57, asst. prof, 57-62, assoc. prof. speech, 62-70, PROF. SPEECH COMMUN, 71- Assoc. prof. speech, San Fernando Valley State Col, 61-; lectr. Pepperdine Year-In-Europe prog, Ger, 65-66; participant, Proj. Talkback, pilot study speech, improvment culturally handicapped, 67; Fed. Drug. Admin. study grant attitudes within health professions & pilot stud. attitudes toward drug usage, 67-68; mem. Gov. State Scholar. & Loan Comn, Calif, 67-74; dir. First Int. Colloquium on Speech Commun. Arts & Sci, Heidelberg, Ger, 68; consult. oral commun, Mgt. Training Corp, 68-70; participant, Conf. on Television & Minorities; Police-Community Sem, 69-70; Speech Commun. Asn. coord, Third Int. Colloquium, Hattingen, Ger, 71. Speech Commun. Asn; AAUP; West. Speech Commun. Asn; Ger. Speech Asn. Mass communication and communication theory; political speech of the 1930's with emphasis on the speech of dictators, especially Hitler; social impact of television. Publ: In the public interest, Pepperdine Col, 62; co-auth, Sprache and Sprechen, Vol. II, Ger. Speech Asn, 65; co-ed. International studies of national speech education systems, Vol. I, Burgess, 70; auth, Tell it again, Today's Speech, 9/64; Two unusual East German radio stations, J. Broadcasting, fall 68; co-auth, A study of attitudes towards drug control, Med. Opinion & Rev, 8/69; plus others. Add: Div. of Communication, Pepperdine University, Malibu, 24255 Pacific Coast Hwy, Malibu, CA 90265.

CASPER, LEONARD RALPH, b. Fond du Lac, Wis, July 6, 23; m. 56; c. 2. AMERICAN LITERATURE, ASIAN STUDIES. B.A, Univ. Wis, 48, M.A, 49, Ph.D.(Am. lit), 53; fel, Stanford Univ, 51-52. Asst. ENG, Univ. Wis, 49-51; instr, Cornell Univ, 52-53; asst. prof, Univ. Philippines, 53-56; instr, BOSTON COL, 56-57, asst. prof, 57-60, assoc. prof, 60-63, PROF, 63- Summers, dir. creative writing, Univ. R.I, 58, Bread Loaf creative writing scholar, 61; Fulbright lectr, Univ. Philippines, 62-63; Am. Counc. Learned Soc-Soc. Sci. Res. Counc. grant-in-aid, 65; Asia Soc. grant-in-aid, 65; Boston Col. creative writing grant, summer 67. Nat. Arts Award, 71. A.U.S, 43-46. Asia Soc. Contemporary American literature; Philippine studies. Publ: Six Filipino poets, Benipayo, Manila, 55, Robert Penn Warren, Univ. Wash, 60 & The wayward horizon, Community, Manila, 61; co-auth, The world of short fiction, Harper, 62; auth, Modern Philippine short stories, Univ. N.Mex, 62, The wounded diamond, Bookmark, Manila, 64 & New writing from the Philippines, Syracuse Univ, 66; A lion unannounced: twelve stories and a fable, South. Methodist Univ, 71; Apprenticed in Provence, Poetry, 12/52; Journey to the interior: The cave, Mod. Fiction Stud, spring 60; Cultural resurgence in Philippine literature, Lit. E. & W, 3/65. Add: Dept. of English, Boston College, Chestnut Hill, MA 02167.

CASS, CARL BARTHOLOMEW, b. Dakota, Minn, Dec. 9, 01; m. 42. DRAMA, SPEECH. B.A, Univ. Minn, 27; Ph.M, Univ. Wis, 30, Ph.D, 46. Master forensics & drama, Mercersburg Acad, Pa, 27-28; asst. prof. speech & drama, Univ. Pittsburgh, 30-38; assoc. dir. theatre, Univ. Wis, 38-42; civilian instr. radio mechanics, Army Air Force Tech. Command, 42-43; asst. prof. speech & drama, Purdue Univ, 43-45; from assoc. prof. to PROF. DRAMA, UNIV. OKLA, 45- Am. Theatre Asn; Speeech Commun. Asn; Southwest. Theatre Conf. Theatre direction; voice and articulation; stage make-up. Publ: A manner of speaking, Putnam, 61. Add: Dept. of Drama, University of Oklahoma, Norman, OK 73069.

CASS, MICHAEL McCONNELL, b. Macon, Ga, July 1, 41; m. 65; c. 1. AMERICAN LITERATURE & HISTORY. B.A, Univ. of the South, 63; univ. fel, Emory Univ, 65, NDEA fel, 67-68, Ph.D.(Am. stud), 71. Instr. ENG. & INTERDISCIPLINARY STUD, MERCER UNIV, 69-71, ASST. PROF, 71- S.Atlantic Mod. Lang. Asn; South. Hist. Asn; Southeast. Am. Stud. Asn. Southern literature, including black literature; southern culture. Publ: Charles C. Jones, Jr. and the Lost cause, Ga. Hist. Quart, summer 71. Add: Dept. of English, Mercer University, Macon, GA 31207.

CASS, WALTER J, b. Salem, Mass, June 12, 21; m. 46; c. 4. ENGLISH, EDUCATION. A.B, Northeast. Univ, 43; M.A, Boston Univ, 47, Ed.D. (philos. & hist. of educ), 67. Instr. Eng. & German, Suffolk Univ, 46-48; Bradford Durfee Col. Technol, 48-52, asst. prof, 52-58, assoc. prof, 58-66; PROF. ENG. & EDUC, SOUTHEAST. MASS. UNIV, 66- U.S.A, 43-45, Sgt. Am. Stud. Asn. Col. Eng. Asn; Adult Educ. Asn. U.S. Publ: A primer in philosophy of education, Kendall-Hunt, 74; Report on Bradford Durfee College, Textile Reporter, summer 56; The importance of socially meaningful work, Boston Univ, J. Educ, fall 66; Five poems, Southeast. Mass. Technol. Inst. Talker Rev, spring 68. Add: Dept. of English, Southeastern Massachusetts University, North Dartmouth, MA 02747.

CASSADY, MARSHALL GARY, b. Johnstown, Pa, June 12, 36; m. 58; c. 5. THEATRE. B.A, Otterbein Col, 58; M.A, Kent State Univ, 67, fels, summers 68 & 70, Ph.D.(theatre), 72. Teacher, Stone-Creek-Jefferson Schs, Ohio, 59-60; staff writer, Daily Reporter, Dover, 60-63; teacher, Garaway Sch, Sugarcreek, 63-64; Cent. High Sch, New Philadelphia, 64-66; instr. SPEECH & THEATRE, Kent State Univ, 67-72; ASST. PROF, MONTCLAIR STATE COL, 72- Actor & property master, Ohio Outdoor Hist. Drama Asn, 70; adj. ast. prof, Long Island Univ, summer 73; adj. assoc. prof, Seton Hall Univ, 73-; dir. children's theatre, Westfield Community Cult. Asn, N.J, 73- Speech Commun. Asn. American theatre history; dramturgy. Add: Dept. of Speech & Theatre, Montclair State College, Upper Montclair, NJ 07043.

CASSELL, RICHARD ALLAN, b. Chicago, Ill, Oct. 20, 21; m. 50; ENGLISH. B.A, Univ. Chicago, 46, M.A, 47, Von der Marwitz fel, 58, Ph.D, 59. Instr. langs, lit. & philos, Ill. Inst. Technol, 47-51; assoc. prof. ENG. & head dept. Dakota Wesleyan Univ, 51-58; PROF, BUTLER UNIV, 59- U.S.A, 43-46. NCTE; MLA; AAUP. English novel; short story; literary criticism. Publ: Ford Madox Ford: a study of his novels, Johns Hopkins, 61; auth, What is the play?, Scott, 67; ed, Ford Madox Ford: modern judgments, Macmillan, London, 72. Add: 502 W. Hampton Dr, Indianapolis, IN 46208.

CASSIDY, FREDERIC GOMES, b. Jamaica, B.W.I, Oct. 10, 07; m. 31; c. 4. ENGLISH & AMERICAN LANGUAGE. A.B, Oberlin Col, 30, A.M, 32; Ph.D, Univ. Mich, 38. Teaching fel, Eng, Univ. Mich, 34-35, 36-38, instr, 38-39; lectr. Eng. lang, Univ. Strasbourg, France, 35-36; instr. ENG, UNIV. WISMADISON, 39-42, asst. prof, 42-46, assoc. prof, 46-49, PROF, 49-, DIR. ENG. LANG. SURV, 48- Res. asst. & ed, Early Mod. Eng. Dict, 31-35, 36-37, Mid. Eng. Dict, 51; field worker, Ling. Atlas of U.S. & Can, Ohio & Wis, 39-41; Fulbright res. scholar, 51-52, 58-59; consult, Dialect Surv. Brit. Caribbean, 54-; vis. prof. Eng. lang, Columbia Univ, summer 56; first hon. fel, Univ. Col. West Indies, 58-59; vis. prof. Eng. lit, Stanford Univ, 63-64; consult, Funk & Wagnalls, 64-70; dir. & ed, Dict. Am. Regional Eng, 65- Silver Musgrave Medal, Inst. Jamaica, 62. Ling. Soc. Am; Am. Dialect Soc. (pres, 55-57); MLA; Mediaeval Acad. Am; Soc. Caribbean Ling.(pres, 72-74). Pidgin and Creole languages; English lexicography. Publ: Place names of Dane County, Wisconsin, PADS, 47 & Univ. Wis, 68; Jamaica talk, Macmillan, 61; co-auth, Dictionary of Jamaican English, Cambridge, 67; Toward the recovery of early English-African Pidgin, CAS-CCTA Pub. No. 87, 62; How free was the Anglo-Saxon scop?, In: Franciplegius, N.Y. Univ, 65; The dictionary of American regional English, J. Lancashire Dialect Soc, 68. Add: 6123 Helen White Hall, Madison, WI 53706.

CASSIDY, JOHN ALBERT, b. Apr. 5, 08; U.S. citizen; m. 44; c. 1. ENGLISH. A.B, Westminster Col, 30; M.A, West. Reserve Univ, 47, Ph.D.(Eng), 50. Instr. ENG, West. Reserve Univ, 48-50; asst. prof, Univ. Notre Dame, 50-54; IND. UNIV, SOUTH BEND, 57-64, assoc. prof, 64-68, PROF, 68-, ASST. CHMN. DEPT, 65- Am. Counc. Learned Soc, 48-; Ind. Univ. summer res. grant, 63- U.S.A.A.F, 42-46, Capt. MLA; Midwest Mod. Lang. Asn. Victorian English literature—Swinburne, Robert Buchanan and D.G. Rossetti; musical backgrounds of English literature. Publ: A.C. Swinburne, 64 & R.W. Buchanan, 73, Twayne; Robert Buchanan and the Fleshly controversy, 3/52 & The original source of Hardy's Dynasts, 12/54, PMLA; Robert Buchanan, Sydney Dobell, In: Encycl. Americana, Groliers, 54 & 60. Add: Dept. of English, Indiana University at South Bend, 1825 Northside Blvd, South Bend, IN 46615.

CASTEEN, JOHN, b. Portsmouth, Va, Dec. 11, 43; div; c. 1. OLD ENGLISH LITERATURE, HISTORY OF THE ENGLISH LANGUAGE. B.A, Univ. Va, 65, M.A, 66, Ph.D.(Eng), 70. Asst. to dean, col. arts & sci, Univ. Va, 69-70; ASST. PROF. ENG, UNIV. CALIF, BERKELEY, 70- Regional assoc, MLA proj. to republ. Am. Lit. Manuscripts, 72- Patristics; early American literature. Publ: Co-auth, The Jefferson papers of the University of Virginia, Univ. Va, 73. Add: Dept. of English, University of California, Berkeley, CA 94720.

CASTLES, WILLIAM HENRY, JR, b. Lancaster, S.C, Jan. 11, 29. ENGLISH. A.B, Univ. S.C, 49, univ. fel, 49-50, M.A, 50; Ph.D, Univ. Tenn, 62. Asst, Univ. Tenn, 50-51; instr. ENG, Carnegie Inst. Technol, 54-57, ASST. PROF, 57-61; Memphis State Univ, 62-63; UNIV. S.C, 63- MLA. Eighteenth century American literature; American novel, 1800-1850. Add: Dept. of English, University of South Carolina, Columbia, SC 29208.

CATALANO, COSMO A, b. Cleveland, Ohio, Feb. 10, 27; m. 48; c. 3. DRAMATIC ART. B.A, Allegheny Col, 50; M.F.A, Yale, 53. Instr. DRAMATIC ART, Ohio Univ, 53-56, asst. prof, 56-62; Univ. Mass, 62-66; ASSOC. PROF, UNIV. IOWA, 66- U.S.N, 48. Am. Educ. Theatre Asn. Directing; acting. Add: Dept. of Speech & Dramatic Art, University of Iowa, Iowa City, IA 52240.

CATE, GEORGE ALLAN, b. Philadelphia, Pa, Apr. 16, 35; m. 58; c. 2. ENGLISH LITERATURE. B.A, Rutgers Univ, 60; NDEA fel, Duke Univ, 61-64, M.A, 62, Ph.D.(Eng), 68. Grad. tutor ENG, Duke Univ, 63-64; instr, UNIV. MD, COLLEGE PARK, 64-67, ASST. PROF, 67-, fac. res. award, 72. MLA; Ruskin Asn. English literature of the Victorian period; late Victorian and Edwardian literature; comparative literature. Add: Dept. of English, University of Maryland, College Park, MD 20742.

CATE, HOLLIS LANIER, b. Brunswick, Ga, Aug. 13, 28; m. 50; c. 5. AMERICAN LITERATURE. A.B, Presby. Col, 51; M.Ed, Univ. Ga, 57, Ph.D, 62. Instr. ENG, Univ. Ga, 57-61; asst. prof, Northeast La. State Col, 61-63; assoc. prof. & chmn. dept, Presby. Col.(S.C), 63-64; prof. & chmn. dept, N.Ga. Col, 64-67; PROF, GA. SOUTH. COL, 67- U.S.A, 51-53, 1st Lt. MLA; Col. Eng. Asn. Nineteenth century Anglo-American literary relations; 19th century American criticism; Victorian literature. Publ: George Eliot's Middlemarch: its initial American publication and reception, 1871-1874, Xavier Univ. Stud, 12/65; Emily Dickinson and The prisoner of Chillon, Am. Notes & Queries, 9/67. Add: Dept. of English, Georgia Southern College, Statesboro, GA 30458.

CATER, A. CATHERINE, b. New Orleans, La, Mar. 18, 17. ENGLISH & THE HUMANITIES. A.B, Talladega Col, 38; A.M, Univ. Mich, Ann Arbor, 39, A.B.L.S, 40, Rosenwald fel, 43, Ph.D.(Eng), 45. Circulation librn. & instr. Eng, Fisk Univ, 40-43; mem. fac, Olivet Col, 45-49; from instr. to prof. Eng. & gen. educ, Moorhead State Col, 49-62; PROF. HUMANITIES & ENG, N.DAK. STATE UNIV, 62- Vis. prof. Eng, Jackson State Col, summer 47; prof, Tri-Col. Univ. Humanities Forum, 72-73. Nat. Col. Honors Counc; MLA; NCTE. Literature of the South; myth and symbol in literature; philosphical anthropology. Publ: Four voices out of the South, Mich. Alumnus

Quart, winter 44; Myth and the contemporary southern novelist: a note, Midwest J, winter 49. Add: Dept. of English, North Dakota State University, Fargo, ND 58102.

CATHCART, ROBERT S, b. Los Angeles, Calif, Jan. 30, 23; m. 44; c. 2. RHETORIC & PUBLIC ADDRESS. A.B, Univ. Redlands, 44, fel, 46-47, M.A, 47; fel, Univ. South. Calif, 47; Ph.D.(rhet. & pub. address), Northwest. Univ, 53. Instr. pub. address, Purdue Univ, 47-49; Univ. Md, 53-55; prof. speech, Calif. State Univ. Los Angeles, 55-68, dir. commun. res. ctr, 58-68; PROF. COMMUN, QUEEN'S COL.(N.Y), 68-, chmn. communicative arts & sci, 68-71. Consult, instr. prep. prog, Reserve Off. Training Corp, U.S. Navy, 53; conf. leadership training prog, U.S. Army Ord. Ctr, Aberdeen, Md, 55; consult, Calif. Casualty & Surety Underwriters Asn, 62-63; lectr, Pa. State Univ, 63; lectr, Univ. Tex, summer 64; sr. vis, Oxford, spring 66; consult, Carnation Corp, 66-68; sr. ed, Bicentennial Monogr, Speech Commun. Asn, 73- U.S.N.R, 42-46, 51-53, Lt. Speech Commun. Asn; West. Speech Commun. Asn. Rhetoric and criticism; group communication; business and industrial communication. Publ: Co-auth, Ideas and issues, Ronald, 63 & Student, school and society, Chandler, 63; auth, Post-communication, Bobbs, 66; co-auth, Small group communication, W.C. Brown, 70, rev. ed, 74. Add: Dept. of Communicative Arts & Sciences, Queens College, Flushing, NY 11367.

CATMULL, JOSEPH F, b. Idaho Falls, Idaho, Feb. 27, 04; m. 27; c. 5. SPEECH. M.S, Univ. Utah, 39, Ph.D, 60; Univ. Minn, 44-45. Prof. speech, Ricks Col, 33-44; instr, Univ. Minn, 44-46; assoc. prof, UNIV. UTAH, 47-64, prof. SPEECH & head interpretation area, 64-71, EMER. PROF, 71- Biblical literature, especially the Book of Job. Add: Dept. of Speech & Theatre, University of Utah, Salt Lake City, UT 84112.

CATRON, LOUIS E, b. Springfield, Ill, Apr. 1, 32. THEATRE, PLAYWRITING. A.B, Millikin Univ, 58; M.A, South. Ill. Univ, 59, Woodrow Wilson fel, 63-64, Ph.D.(theatre), 66. Instr. theatre & speech, Lincoln Col, 59-63; asst prof. THEATRE, Ill. State Univ, 64-65; ASSOC. PROF, COL. WILLIAM & MARY, 66- Auth, A baby is crying, produced by Tex, Christian Univ, 65, The actions of tigers 66 & Lincoln at Springfield: January, 1859, 66, produced by South. Ill. Univ, Centaur, Centaur!, 67 & The rainbow sign, 71, produced by Col. William & Mary; plus other plays. John Golden travel fel, 66; vis. artist, Youngstown State Univ. & Millikin Univ, 68. U.S.N, 52-56. Am. Theatre Asn; Speech Commun. Asn. Playwriting; theatre direction; history of the American theatre. Publ: Where have all the lightning bugs gone, Touch the bluebird's song & At a beetle's pace (plays in bk. form), Samuel French, 72; The actions of tigers, One Act Publ. Co. 73; At a beetle's pace (play), 5/71, Where have all the lightning bugs gone (play), 11/71 & Touch the bluebird's song (play), 12/71, Dramatics; plus others. Add: Dept. of Theatre & Speech, College of William & Mary, Williamsburg, VA 23185.

CAUTHEN, IRBY BRUCE, JR, b. Rock Hill, S.C, Aug. 24, 19; m. 54; c. 2. ENGLISH LITERATURE. B.A, Furman Univ, 40; M.A, Univ. Va, 42, Dupont fel. & Bradshaw fel, Ph.D.(Eng), 51; summers, Breadloaf Sch, Eng, 47, Shakespeare Inst, 51. Instr. ENG, Univ. Va, 49-50; asst. prof, Hollins Col, 51-54; UNIV. VA, 54-58, assoc. prof, 58-64, PROF, 64-, DEAN COL. ARTS & SCI, 62-, asst. dean, 56-58. Regional chmn, Woodrow Wilson Fel. Found, 61-72. Adj. Gen. Dept, 42-46, Lt. MLA; Shakespeare Asn. Am; S.Atlantic Mod. Lang. Asn; Southeast Renaissance Conf. Shakespeare and 17th century English literature. Publ: Ed, The Coxcomb in dramatic works of Beaumont and Fletcher, Cambridge, 66, Sackville and Norton, Gorboduc, Univ. Nebr, 70 & Two mementoes from the Poe-Ingram collection, Univ. Va, 71. Add: 126 Wilson Hall, University of Virginia, Charlottesville, VA 22903.

CAVANAUGH, JEAN C, b. Clare, Iowa. ENGLISH. B.A, Webster Col, 30; M.A, St. Louis Univ, 32; Pace scholar, Cath. Univ, 38-41, Ph.D.(Eng), 42; summers, Fribourg Univ, 49, Northwest. Univ, 52, Columbia Univ, 55. Instr. ENG, Webster Col, 41-46; prof. & chmn. dept, Loretto Heights Col, 46-58; prof, Webster Col, 58-67, chmn. dept, 58-65; PROF, FAIRMONT STATE COL, 67- Scholar, Breadloaf Sch. Eng, summer 62; Folger Shakespeare Libr. res. grant, summer 63; Danforth Found. stud. grant, summer 63; Am. Counc. Learned Soc. grants-in-aid, summers 65 & 66. MLA. English literature; Renaissance. Publ: Technogomia by Barten Holyday: a critical edition, Cath. Univ. Am, 42; New light on Robert Johnson, The king's musician, Shakespeare Quart, spring 65; The library of Lady Southwell and Captain Sibthorpe, Stud. Bibliog, 67. Add: Dept. of English, Fairmont State College, Fairmont, WV 26554.

CAVANAUGH, M. ANNE FRANCIS, R.S.M, b. Emporium, Pa, June 21, 24. ENGLISH, ANGLO-IRISH LITERATURE. B.A, Mercyhurst Col, 46; M.A, Cath. Univ. Am, 58; Ph.D.(Anglo-Irish), Univ. Col, Dublin, 68. Lectr. ENG. LIT, MERCYHURST COL, 58-61, asst. prof, 62-67, PROF. & CHMN. DEPT, 67- MLA; NCTE. Modern Irish fiction; Mary Lavin. Publ: The two voices of Seumas O'Kelly, Gill-MacMillan, Dublin, (in press). Add: Dept. of English Literature, Mercyhurst College, Erie, PA 16501.

CAVANAUGH, WILLIAM CHARLES, b. Johnstown, Pa, Dec. 18, 32; m. 59; c. 3. ENGLISH. A.B, Univ. Pittsburgh, 54, M.A, 59; Ph.D.(Eng), Univ. Wis, 66. Instr. ENG, Loyola Univ.(Ill), 61-65; asst. prof, DePAUW UNIV, 65-71, ASSOC. PROF, 71- U.S.A.F, 54-57, Capt. MLA. Victorian and modern British literature; writing poetry. Publ: Coriolanus and the ascent of F-6, Drama Critique, 61; Kite string youth (poem), Va. Quart, fall 68. Add: Dept. of English, DePauw University, Greencastle, IN 46135.

CAVELL, ANTHONY JOSEPH, Linguistics, Comparative Philology. See Volume III, Foreign Languages, Linguistics & Philology.

CAVITCH, DAVID, b. Traverse City, Mich, June 13, 33; m. 60; c. 2. ENGLISH & AMERICAN LITERATURE. A.B, Univ. Mich, 55; M.A, Univ. N.Mex, 60; Ph.D.(Eng), Univ. Calif, Berkeley, 66. Instr. ENG, Idaho State Col, 59-60; Smith Col, 64-66, asst. prof, 66-70, ASSOC. PROF, 70-72; TUFTS UNIV, 72-, fac. summer fel, 73. Vis. asst. prof, Univ. Calif, Riverside, 66-67; Am. Philos. Soc. grant, summers 67, 70. Fac. Scholar. Award, Smith Col, 70. U.S.A, 55-57. MLA. Modern British and American literature. Publ: D.H. Lawrence and the New World, Oxford, 69, 71; Solipsism and death in Lawrence's late works, Mass. Rev, summer 66. Add: Dept. of English, Tufts University, Medford, MA 02155.

CAWELTI, JOHN GEORGE, b. Evanston, Ill, Dec. 31, 29; m. 55; c. 3. AMERICAN CIVILIZATION. B.A, Oberlin Col, 51; M.A, State Univ. Iowa, 56, Ph.D.(Am. civilization), 60. Instr. humanities, UNIV. CHICAGO, 57-59, asst. prof, 59-64, assoc. prof. ENG. & HUMANITIES, 64-68, PROF, 68-, CHMN. COMT. GEN. STUD. IN HUMANITIES, 70- Consult, Nat. Humanities Fac, 71- U.S.A, 51-54, 1st Lt. Am. Stud. Asn; Popular Cult. Asn. History of popular culture; literature and culture; American literature. Publ: Co-auth, Sources of The American Republic, Scott, 61; auth, Apostles of the self-made man, Univ. Chicago, 65; The six-gun mystique, Bowling Green Popular Press, 70; A focus on Bonnie and Clyde, Prentice-Hall, 73; Prolegomena to the Western, Stud. Pub. Commun, 62; Form as cultural criticism in the work of Henry James, In; Literature and society, Univ. Nebr, 64; America on display: the World's Fairs of 1876, 1893, and 1933, In: America and the age of industrialism, Free Press, 68. Add: 5817 Blackstone, Chicago, IL 60637.

CAWLEY, ELIZABETH HOON, Modern History. See Volume I, History.

CAYER, ROGER L, b. Southampton, Mass, Feb. 20, 26; m. 60. ENGLISH, ENGLISH EDUCATION. A.B, N.Y. Univ, 53, A.M, 54, A.M, 59, Ph.D.(Eng. educ), 64. Instr. ENG. EDUC, SCH. EDUC, N.Y. UNIV, 57-64, asst. prof, 64-66, assoc. prof, 66-72, PROF. & HEAD DIV. ENG. SPEECH & EDUC, THEATRE, 72-, dep. head, 67-72. Consult. res. Eng. educ. & chmn. res. comt, N.Y. State Eng. Counc, 67-; mem. nat. comt. recruitment & retention of Eng. Teachers, NCTE, 67-; mem. comt. on prep. & cert. teachers of Eng, NCTE-Conf. Eng. Educ, 68- U.S.A.A.F, 43-46. MLA; NCTE; Col. Eng. Asn; Conf. Eng. Educ; Am. Res. Asn. Teacher preparation in English; communications-oral English. Publ: Co-auth, Listening and speaking in the English classroom, Macmillan, 71; The NCTE-CEE guidelines and the urban school situation, N.Y. State Eng. Counc. Newslett, 11/68. Add: 829 Shimkin Hall, Div. of English Education, Speech & Educational Theatre, School of Education, New York University, New York, NY 10003.

CECIL, CURTIS DRAKE, b. Washington, D.C, Jan. 23, 21; Can. citizen; m. 50; c. 2. ENGLISH. B.A, Dartmouth Col, 43; B.A, Oxford, 51, B.Litt, 56, M.A, 53. Assoc. prof. ENG, McGILL UNIV, 57-72, PROF, 72- U.S.A, 42-46. Drama; 18th and 19th century literature. Publ: Co-ed, The journals and letters of Fanny Burney (Madame D'Arblay), Clarendon, Vol. I, 72; auth, An audience for Wallace Stevens, Essays in Criticism, 4/65; Raillery in Restoration comedy, Huntington Libr. Quart, 2/66; Puns in Restoration comedy, Mod. Lang. Rev, 10/66. Add: Dept. of English, McGill University, Montreal 2, P.Q, Can.

CECIL, LEVI MOFFITT, b. Anderson, S.C, May 6, 14; m. 41; c. 3. ENGLISH. B.A, Wofford Col, 35; M.A, Duke Univ, 38; Ph.D.(Eng), Vanderbilt Univ, 47. Instr. ENG, Tex. Technol. Col, 40-41; Vanderbilt Univ, 46-47; from asst. prof. to PROF, TEX. CHRISTIAN UNIV, 47- Transportation C, U.S.A, 41-46, Ret. Res, Lt. Col. MLA; Am. Stud. Asn. American fiction; American literary criticism; southern literature. Publ: The two narratives of Arthur Gordon Pym, Tex. Stud. Lit. & Lang, summer 63; Simm's Porgy as national hero, Am. Lit, 1/65; Virtuous attachment in James' The ambassadors, Am. Quart, winter 67; plus others. Add: Dept. of English, Texas Christian University, Ft. Worth, TX 76129.

CEDERSTROM, MOYLE F, b. Elbow Lake, Minn, Nov. 17, 02; m. 27; c. 3. ENGLISH. B.A, Univ. Minn, 23, M.A, 27; Ph.D, Univ. Wash, 32. Assoc. ENG, Univ. Wash, 27-35; prof, WEST. WASH. STATE COL, 35-70, EMER. PROF, 70- Add: Dept. of English, Western Washington State College, Bellingham, WA 98225.

CEGALA, DONALD JOSEPH, b. Buffalo, N.Y, Aug. 3, 46; m. 67. SPEECH COMMUNICATION. B.A, Univ. Wis-Madison, 68; M.A, Purdue Univ, Lafayette, 69; Ph.D, Fla. State Univ, 72. Instr. COMMUN, Fla. State Univ, 71-72; ASST. PROF, OHIO STATE UNIV, 73- Chairperson consensus comt, Nat. Proj. on Speech Commun. Competencies Pre-kindergarten-12th Grade, 73-74. U.S.A, 69-75. Speech Commun. Asn; Int. Commun. Asn; Am. Psychol. Asn; Am. Educ. Res. Asn. Attitude change; tolerance for cognitive inconsistency; instructional objectives. Publ: Measuring communication effects, In: Speech communication behavior, Prentice-Hall, 71; co-auth, Hypnosis and the reduction of speech anxiety, Cent. States Speech J, 72 & Writing behavioral objectives, a programmed article, Speech Teacher, 73; plus others. Add: Dept. of Communication, Ohio State University, 154 N. Oval Dr, Columbus, OH 43210.

CELLA, CHARLES RONALD, b. Frankfort, Ky, June 16, 39; m. 62; c. 2. AMERICAN LITERATURE. B.A, Transylvania Col, 61; M.A, Univ. Ky, 62, Ph.D.(Eng), 68. Instr. ENG, East. Ky. Univ, 63-64; asst. prof, MURRAY STATE UNIV, 68-71, ASSOC. PROF, 71- MLA; Am. Stud. Asn. American novel; theories of realism in fiction. Add: Dept. of English, Murray State University, Murray, KY 42071.

CERMELE, DOMINICK JOSEPH, b. Newark, N.J, Sept. 8, 28; m. 58; c. 2. THEATRE. B.A, Antioch Col, 57; M.F.A, Boston Univ, 59. Instr. speech, Urbana Col, 60-61; theatre, Cent. State Univ, 61-63; artistic dir, Toledo Repertoire Theatre, 63-65; ASSOC. PROF, drama, Univ, Tampa, 65-68; THEATRE, ST. CLOUD STATE COL, 68- U.S.M.C, 46-48, 50-51. Am. Nat. Theatre & Acad; Am. Theatre Asn; Speech Commun. Asn; Asn. Col. & Univ. Concert Mgr. Educational theatre; educational television; educational radio. Add: Dept. of Theatre, St. Cloud State College, St. Cloud, MN 56301.

CEROVSKI, JOHN, b. Omaha, Nebr, Dec. 26, 25. ENGLISH. B.A, Univ. Nebr, 50; M.A, Northwest. Univ, 52, Ph.D.(Eng), 60. Asst, Northwest. Univ, 56-57; instr. Eng, Knox Col, 57-62; asst. prof. N.CENT. COL.(ILL), 62-66, assoc. prof, 66-70, PROF. ENG. & CHMN. LANG. & LIT. DIV, 70- U.S.A, 43-46. Add: 214 N. Ellsworth, Naperville, IL 60540.

CERVO, NATHAN ANTHONY, b. New Haven, Conn, June 19, 30; m. 64; c. 1. ENGLISH LANGUAGE & LITERATURE. B.A. & M.A, Univ. Conn, 54; Northrop Frye fel, Victoria Col.(Ont), 57; Ph.D.(Eng, philos), Univ. Toronto, 59. Reader Eng, Univ. Toronto, 56-57; instr, Boston Col, 58-59; asst. prof, La. State Univ, Baton Rouge, 60-61; from asst. prof. to assoc. prof. Eng. & Dante, St. Joseph Col.(Conn), 61-66; asst. prof. Eng. & Latin, Hartwick Col, 66-69; independent study, Italy, 69-70; from assoc. prof. to PROF.

ENG. & LATIN, FRANKLIN PIERCE COL, 70- Fulbright res. fel, Univ. Florence, 59-60; fel, Yale, 63-65. MLA. The pre-Raphaelites; the aesthetes; Tennyson and Browning. Publ: Our lady of the gulls: a case of polite revenge, Barat Rev, fall/winter 71; Melville's Bartleby: imago dei, Am. Transcendental Rev, spring 72; The botanical sublime in Mann's The infant prodigy, North. New Eng. Rev, summer 73; plus others. Add: Humanities Division, Dept. of English, Franklin Pierce College, Rindge, NH 03461.

CEVASCO, GEORGE ANTHONY, b. Brooklyn, N.Y, Sept. 22, 24; m. 54; c. 2. ENGLISH. A.B, St. John's Univ.(N.Y), 48; M.A, Columbia Univ, 49; hon. D.Litt, Univ. London. Instr. ENG, Gannon Col, 51-52; asst. prof, Notre Dame Col, Staten Island, 52-54, assoc. prof, 54-55; asst. prof, ST. JOHN'S UNIV.(N.Y), 55-71, ASSOC. PROF, 71-, asst. dean, St. John's Col, 65-69. Lectr, Fordham Univ, 54-67; consult, Choice, 65-; abstractor, Abstr. Eng. Stud. U.S.A.A.F, 43-46. MLA; Am. Soc. Aesthet; Soc. Huysmans. Life and works of J-K. Huysmans; American grammar; aestheticism and decadence in British literature, 1870-1890. Publ: J-K. Huysmans in England and America; a bibliographic study, Univ. Va, 62; co-auth, Wordcraft, Benitas Press, 61 & Functional English, Republic, 63; auth, Salvador Dali: master of surrealism and modern art, 71 & Oscar Wilde, British author, poet and wit, 72, Samhar Press. Add: Dept. of English, St. John's University, Jamaica, NY 11432.

CHACE, WILLIAM MURDOUGH, b. Newport News, Va, Sept. 3, 38; m. 64; c. 2. ENGLISH & AMERICAN LITERATURE. B.A, Haverford Col, 61; M.A, Univ. Calif, Berkeley, 63, Ph.D.(Eng), 68. Instr. ENG, Stillman Col, 63-64; acting instr, Univ. Calif, Berkeley, 66-68; ASST. PROF, STANFORD UNIV, 68- Politics and literature; problems of modernism; Pound, Eliot and Joyce. Publ: Co-ed, Justice denied: the Black man in white America, Harcourt, 70; Making it new, Canfield, 72; ed, James Joyce: a collection of critical essays, Prentice-Hall, 73; auth, The political identities of Ezra Pound and T.S. Eliot, Stanford Univ, 73; Ezra Pound and the Marxist temptation, Am. Quart, fall 70; T.S. Eliot: the plea against consciousness, Mosaic, fall 71. Add: Dept. of English, Stanford, University, Stanford, CA 94305.

CHAFFEE, ALAN JEWELL, b. Detroit, Mich, June 5, 44; m. 67. ENGLISH LITERATURE, LINGUISTICS. B.A, Wayne State Univ, 66; Ph.D.(Eng), Pa. State Univ, 70. ASST. PROF. ENG, MUSKINGUM COL, 70- MLA; AAUP. English romantic poetry; Shakespeare; theoretical linguistics. Publ: The rendezvous of mind, Wordsworth Circle, 72. Add: Dept. of English, Muskingum College, New Concord, OH 43762.

CHAIKA, ELAINE OSTRACH, Linguistics. See Volume III, Foreign Languages, Linguistics & Philology.

CHAIKIN, MILTON, b. New York, N.Y, Sept. 23, 15; m. 39; c. 1. ENGLISH. B.S.S, City Col. New York, 36; M.A, Columbia Univ, 48; Ph.D.(Eng), N.Y. Univ, 54. Assoc. prof. ENG, GA. INST. TECHNOL, 52-72, PROF, 72- U.S.A.A.F, 42-45. MLA; NCTE. George Moore; modern drama. George Moore's A mummer's wife and Zola, Rev. Lit. Comp, 1-3/57; The workbook in freshman composition, Col. Compos. & Commun, 5/60; Maupassant's Bel-Ami and Balzac, Romance Notes, spring 60; plus others. Add: Dept. of English, Georgia Institute of Technology, Atlanta, GA 30332.

CHALDECOTT, DENNIS, b. Los Angeles, Calif, Dec. 20, 29. ENGLISH. A.B, Univ. Calif, Los Angeles, 52, M.A, 55, Ph.D.(Eng), 65. Instr. ENG, Univ. Hawaii, 59-62; asst. prof, San Francisco State Col, 64-66; SAN JOSE STATE UNIV, 66-71, ASSOC. PROF, 71- Victorian literature; romantic literature; literary criticism. Add: Dept. of English, San Jose State University, 125 S. Seventh St, San Jose, CA 95114.

CHALFANT, EDWARD ALLAN, b. Cleveland, Ohio, Aug. 15, 21; m. 47. ENGLISH. A.B, Dartmouth Col, 42; M.A, Columbia Univ, 47; Harrison fel, Univ. Pa, 50-51, Ph.D.(Am. civilization), 54. Instr. ENG, Dartmouth Col, 47-49; HOFSTRA UNIV, 53-56, asst. prof, 56-63, assoc. prof, 63-72, PROF, 72- Acting chmn. dept, 59-60. Res. grant, William Volker Fund, 56-58. U.S.A.A.F, Off. Historian, 42-45, S/Sgt. MLA. Add: Dept. of English, Hofstra University, Hempstead, NY 11550.

CHALFANT, FRAN CERNOCKY, b. Chicago, Ill; m. 70. ENGLISH LITERATURE, LONDON HISTORY. B.A, Drake Univ, 65; NDEA fel, Univ. N.C, Chapel Hill, 65-68, Woodrow Wilson fel, 68-69, Ph.D.(Eng), 71. Instr. ENG, Univ. N.C, Chapel Hill, 69-70; ASST. PROF, W.GA. COL, 70- AAUP; Shakespeare Asn. Am. Sixteenth-seventeenth century English literature; Welsh studies. Add: Dept. of English, West Georgia College, Carrollton, GA 30117.

CHALIFOUR, CLARK LESTER, b. Salem, Mass, June 11, 39; m. 60; c. 1. ENGLISH LITERATURE. B.A, Tufts Univ, 60; M.A, Brown Univ, 67, Ph.D. (Eng), 70. ASST. PROF. ENG, STATE UNIV. N.Y. COL. OSWEGO, 69- U.S.N, 60-64, Res, 64-66, Lt. MLA; Renaissance Soc. Am; Milton Soc. Am; Col. Eng. Asn; AAUP. Sixteenth and 17th century nondramatic British literature; Milton. Add: Dept. of English, State University of New York College at Oswego, Oswego, NY 13126.

CHAMBERLAIN, DAVID S, b. Boston, Mass, Feb. 10, 31; m. 54; c. 6. ENGLISH, COMPARATIVE LITERATURE. B.A, Dartmouth Col, 52, Reynolds fel; M.A, Oxford, 58; Ph.D.(Eng), Princeton, 66. Instr. ENG, UNIV. IOWA, 61-66, asst. prof, 66-69, ASSOC. PROF, 69- U.S.N, 54-58, Lt. MLA; Mediaeval Acad. Am. Chaucer; music in medieval thought and literature; medieval literature, romance and lyric. Publ: Philosophy of music in the Consolatio of Boethius, Speculum, 69; The music of the spheres and the Parlement of Foules, Chaucer Rev, 71; Wolbero of Cologne: a zenith of musical imagery, Mediaeval Stud, 71. Add: 505 River St, Iowa City, IA 52240.

CHAMBERLAIN, WILLIAM FREDERICK, b. Columbus, Ohio, Dec. 22, 36. AMERICAN LITERATURE. B.A, Ohio State Univ, Columbus, 59; Woodrow Wilson fel, Ind. Univ, Bloomington, 59-60, univ. fel, 60-61, Ph.D.(Eng), 69. Asst. prof. Eng, Fresno State Col, 64-65; ASSOC. PROF. AM. THOUGHT & LANG, MICH. STATE UNIV, 65- Twentieth century literature; radical American literature; the counter culture. Publ: Contrib, The minor and later transcendentalists, Transcendental, 70. Add: 2323 Haslett Rd, East Lansing, MI 48823.

CHAMBERS, ALEXANDER B, b. Bristow, Okla, Jan. 19, 33; m. 59; c. 2. ENGLISH LITERATURE. B.A, Vanderbilt Univ, 54, M.A, 55; Ph.D, Johns Hopkins Univ, 60. Asst. prof. ENG, Univ. Calif, Davis, 60-64; assoc. prof, Tulane Univ, 64-65; UNIV. WIS-MADISON, 65-71, PROF, 71- MLA; Renaissance Soc. Am. Seventeenth century English literature; Milton. Add: Dept. of English, University of Wisconsin-Madison, Madison, WI 53706.

CHAMBERS, LELAND HUGH, b. Los Angeles, Calif, Mar. 11, 28; m. 55; c. 3. COMPARATIVE LITERATURE. B.A, Univ. South. Calif, 53; M.A, Ind. Univ, 57; Ph.D.(comp. lit), Univ. Mich, 62. Instr. Eng, Cent. Mich. Univ, 58-62, asst. prof, 62-63; ENG. & COMP. LIT, UNIV. DENVER, 63-68, ASSOC. PROF, 68- Shell Found. grant, 67; Am. Philos. Soc. grant, 70. Am. Comp. Lit. Asn; MLA. Literature of the Baroque, especially English, Spanish and French; Latin American literary relations; translation. Publ: Comparative literature programs in the U.S. and Canada, Yearbk. Comp. & Gen. Lit, 71; In defense of The weeper, Papers Lang. & Lit, spring 67; Form and the search for truth in the Quijote, Hisp. Rev, 10/67. Add: Dept. of English, University of Denver, Denver, CO 80210.

CHAMBERS, ROBERT DOUGLAS, b. Montreal, Que, Oct. 17, 32; m. 59; c. 3. ENGLISH LITERATURE. B.A, McGill Univ, 53; B.Litt, Oxford, 56. Instr. ENG, Univ. Sask, 55-58, asst. prof, 58-65; TRENT UNIV, 65-66, assoc. prof, 66-70, PROF. ENG. LIT, 71-, chmn. dept, 67-70. Ed. bd, J. Can. Stud, 66- Johnson Soc. Cent. Region. Canadian literature; 18th century English literature. Publ: Co-ed, A book of essays, Macmillan, Toronto & St. Martin's, 63; auth, Addison at work on the Spectator, Mod. Philol, 2/59; Hugh MacLennan's novels, J. Can. Stud, 8/67. Add: Dept. of English Literature, Trent University, Peterborough, Ont, Can.

CHAMETZKY, JULES, b. Brooklyn, N.Y, May 24, 28; m. 53; c. 3. ENGLISH. B.A, Brooklyn Col, 50; M.A, Univ. Minn, 52, Ph.D.(Eng. lit), 58. Instr. Eng, Univ. Minn, 54-56; humanities, Boston Univ, 56-58; vis. lectr. ENG, UNIV. MASS, AMHERST, 58-59, asst. prof, 59-64, assoc. prof, 64-69, PROF, 69- Ed, Faulkner Stud, 53-54; Mass. Rev, 59-; Fulbright prof, Univ. Tübingen, 62-63; Univ. Zagreb, 66-67; mem. bd, dir, Coord. Counc. Lit. Mag, 67-; guest prof. Am. stud, Free Univ. Berlin, 70-71. MLA; Am. Stud. Asn; Asn. Lit. Mag. Am.(pres, 65-67). Modern British and American fiction; literature of immigration and ethnicity; literature of the 1930's. Publ: Co-ed, Black and white in American culture, 69; auth, Abraham Cahan's Rise of David Levinsky, In: American dreams, American nightmares, South. Ill. Univ, 70; Regional literature and ethnic realities, Antioch Rev, fall 71; plus three others. Add: Dept. of English, University of Massachussetts, Amherst, MA 01002.

CHAMPION, LARRY STEPHEN, b. Shelby, N.C, Apr. 27, 32; m. 56; c. 2. LITERATURE. A.B, Davidson Col, 54; Philip Francis DuPont fel. & M.A, Univ. Va, 55; Ph.D, Univ. N.C, 61. Instr. Eng, Davidson Col, 55-56; teaching fel, Univ. N.C, 58, instr, 59-60; ENG, N.C. STATE UNIV, 60-61, asst. prof, 61-65, assoc. prof, 65-68, PROF, 68-, HEAD DEPT, 71-, asst. head dept, 67-68, assoc. head, 68-71. Ed. consult, Papers on Lang. & Lit, 67-; Can. Counc, 68-; consult, MLA, 70- U.S.A, 56-58. MLA; NCTE; Renaissance Soc. Am; Southeast. Renaissance Conf; S.Atlantic Mod. Lang. Asn; S.Atlantic Asn. Dept. Eng.(v.pres, 73-74). Elizabethan and Jacobean drama, especially Shakespeare and Jonson; seventeenth century poetry, especially Herbert and Milton. Publ: Ben Jonson's Dotages: a reconsideration of the last plays, Univ. Ky, 67; The evolution of Shakespeare's comedy, Harvard, 70; ed, Quick springs of sense: studies in the eighteenth century, Univ. Ga, 73; Laertes' return to Elsinore, Shakespeare Quart, 12/66; From melodrama to comedy: a study of the comic perspective in Dekker's The honest whore, Stud. Philol, 72; The tragic perspective in Othello, Eng. Stud, 73; plus others. Add: Dept. of English, North Carolina University, Raleigh, NC 27607.

CHAN, JACHIN YIN-MAN, b. Canton, China, July 27, 32; U.S. citizen; m. 63; c. 2. ENGLISH. Th.B, Hong Kong Baptist Theol. Sem, 55; B.A, Chung Chi Col, Hong Kong, 57; B.D, New Orleans Baptist Theol. Sem, 58, Th.M, 60; fel, Univ. South. Miss, 60-61; Ph.D.(ling, Eng), La. State Univ, 67. Asst. prof. gen. lit, Mobile Col, 64-66; prof. Eng, Ouachita Baptist Univ, 66-69; SR. LECTR. ENG. LANG. & LIT. & HEAD DEPT. ENG, HONG KONG BAPTIST COL, 69-, V.PRES, COL, 71- MLA; NCTE. Application of linguistic knowledge to the teaching of English to native speakers of English and to foreigners. Publ: Distribution of Cantonese phonemes, Univ. Microfilms, 67. Add: Dept. of English, Hong Kong Baptist College, 224 Waterloo Rd, Kowloon, Hong Kong.

CHANDLER, ALICE, b. May 29, 31; U.S. citizen; m. 54; c. 2. ENGLISH. A.B, Barnard Col, Columbia Univ, 51; M.A, Columbia Univ, 53, Lizette Fisher fel, 55-56, Ph.D.(Eng), 60. Instr. ENG, Skidmore Col, 53-54; lectr, Barnard Col, Columbia Univ, 54-55; Hunter Col, 56-57; instr, CITY COL. NEW YORK, 61-64, asst. prof, 64-70, assoc. prof, 70-73, PROF, 73- MLA. Victorian literature; 19th century American literature; woman novelists of the 19th century. Publ: The prose spectrum, Allyn & Bacon, 68; ed, The theme of war, W.C. Brown, 69; auth, The rationale of rhetoric, 70 & co-auth, The rationale of the essay, 71, Holt; auth, A dream of order: the medieval ideal in nineteenth-century literature, Univ. Nebr, 70 & Routledge & Kegan Paul, 71; The quarrel of the ancients and the moderns: Thomas Love Peacock and the medieval revival, Bucknell Rev, 12/65; Tennyson's Maud and The song of songs, Victorian Poetry, 6/69; The visionary race: Poe's attitude toward his dreamers, In: New approaches to Poe: a Symposium, 70; plus others. Add: Dept. of English, City College of New York, Convent Ave. & 138th St, New York, NY 10031.

CHANDLER, ARNOLD, b. Auburn, Mass, Jan. 31, 25; m. 51; c. 4. ENGLISH, COMPARATIVE LITERATURE. A.B, Clark Univ, 48; Univ. Paris, 49-50; A.M, Brown Univ, 52; Ph.D.(Eng), Univ. Tex, 67. Instr. Eng. & French, Columbus Acad, 51-53; ENG, Ohio State Univ, 53-58; chmn. dept, Tex. Southmost Col, 58-64; asst. prof, Southwest Tex. State Col, 64-67; assoc. prof, WEST. ILL. UNIV, 67-72, PROF, 72- U.S.N, 42-46. MLA. Joseph

Conrad: the hero in modern British literature; attitudes toward colonialism in modern British literature. Add: Dept. of English, Western Illinois University, Macomb, IL 61455.

CHANDLER, DANIEL ROSS, b. Wellston, Okla, July 22, 37. SPEECH COMMUNICATION, RELIGION. B.S, Univ. Okla, 59; M.A, Purdue Univ, 65; B.D, Garrett Theol. Sem, 68; Ph.D.(commun), Ohio Univ, 69; Harvard, 72. ASST. PROF. SPEECH, Cent. Mich. Univ, 69-70; State Univ. N.Y. New Paltz, 70-71; BARUCH COL, 71- Ordained minister, United Methodist Church, 57-60; asst. pastor, Peoples Church of Chicago, 65-66; chmn. denominational affairs comt, Community Church of New York, 72-, secy. John Haynes scholarship comt, 72- Speech Commun. Asn; Int. Commun. Asn; Speech Commun. Asn. East. States. The liberal religious movement in America; the communication of mass movements. Publ: The blacksmith and the professor: spokesmen for religious liberalism, Ohio Speech J, 71; Protestant preaching and the liberal tradition, Today's Speech, winter 73. Add: Box 511, F. D. R. Sta, New York, NY 10022.

CHANDLER, PATRICIA RICHARDSON, b. Biloxi, Miss, Apr. 23, 44; m. 72; c. 1. ENGLISH LITERATURE. B.A, Univ. South. Miss, 66, M.A, 67; Ph.D. (Eng), Auburn Univ, 71. ASST. PROF. ENG, FLORENCE STATE UNIV, 71- Medieval English literature; 18th century English literature. Add: Dept. of English, Box 577, Florence State University, Florence, AL 35630.

CHANG, JOSEPH S, M.J, b. Honolulu, Hawaii, Sept. 1, 35; m. 61; c. 5. ENGLISH. B.A, St. Mary's Col.(Calif), 56; M.A, Univ. Wis, 60, Ph.D.(Eng), 65. Asst. prof. ENG, Tulane Univ, 64-66; UNIV. WIS-MILWAUKEE, 66-71, ASSOC. PROF, 71- Southeast. Inst. Medieval & Renaissance Stud. fel, 65. MLA; Renaissance Soc. Am. Shakespeare; Elizabethan drama; history of ideas in the Renaissance. Publ: Machiavellianism in Daniel's The civil wars, Tulane Stud. Eng, 65; Of mighty opposites: stoicism and Machiavellianism, Renaissance Drama, 66; The language of paradox in Romeo and Juliet, Shakespeare Stud, 67. Add: Dept. of English, University of Wisconsin-Milwaukee, Milwaukee, WI 53211.

CHAPIN, CHESTER FISHER, b. Greensboro, N.C, Dec. 13, 22. ENGLISH. A.B, Harvard Col, 48; Ph.D.(Eng), Columbia Univ, 54. Instr. Eng, Miss. State Col, 54-56; Marshall Col, 56-57; asst. prof, UNIV. MICH, ANN ARBOR, 57-64, assoc. prof, 64-71, PROF. HUMANITIES & ENG, 71- MLA; NCTE. English literature of the 18th century; Johnson. Publ: Personification in eighteenth century English poetry, Octagon, 68; The religious thought of Samuel Johnson, Univ. Mich, 68. Add: Dept. of English, College of Engineering, University of Michigan, Ann Arbor, MI 48104.

CHAPIN, PAUL GIPSON, Linguistics. See Volume III, Foreign Languages, Linguistics & Philology.

CHAPIN, RICHARD EARL, b. Danville, Ill, Apr. 29, 25; m. 49; c. 3. COMMUNICATIONS, LIBRARY SCIENCE. B.A, Wabash Col, 48; M.S, Univ. Ill, 49, Ph.D.(commun), 55. Instr. libr, Fla. State Univ, 49-50; asst, Univ. Ill, 50-53; asst. prof. libr. sci, Univ. Okla, 53-55; assoc. prof. jour. & assoc. librn, MICH. STATE UNIV, 55-59, PROF. JOUR. & DIR. LIBR, 59- Consult, Mich. State Univ. adv. group, Vietnam, 58; U.S. Dept. Agr, 62; U.S. Dept. Commerce, 63; Kellogg Found, 66-67; E.D.U.C.O.M, 68. U.S.N, 43-46, Lt.(jg). Am. Libr. Asn; Asn. Col. & Res. Libr; Asn. Res. Libr. Library administration; information retrieval. Publ: Mass communications, Mich. State Univ, 57; co-auth, Libraries, In: Colliers encyclopedia, Collier-Macmillan, 60 & Comparative costs of converting records, J. Libr. Automation, 68; auth, Administrative and economic considerations for library automation, Proc. 1967 Clinic Data Processing Libr, 68. Add: Library, Michigan State University, East Lansing, MI 48824.

CHAPMAN, ABRAHAM, b. Chicago, Ill, Apr. 27, 15; m. 34; c. 2. ENGLISH, AMERICAN STUDIES. Univ. Chicago, 35-37; C.Sc, Ph.D, Inst. Mod. Philol, Acad. Sci, Prague, 63. Res. fel. Philippines, Inst. Pac. Relat, 48-50; res. assoc. AM. LIT, Inst. Mod. Philol, 55-63; lectr, Charles Univ, 60-63; assoc. prof, UNIV. WIS-STEVENS POINT, 64-66, PROF, 66-, res. grant, 64-65. Wis. State Res. Comt. grant, 66-67; vis. prof, NDEA Inst, Univ. Wis-Milwaukee, 67; Tex. South. Univ, 68-69; host consult, Ethnic & Minority Writers Workshop, Nat. Ctr. Audio Exp. & Univ. Wis-Stevens Point, summer 73; contrib. ed, Negro American Lit. Forum, Ind. State Univ, Terre Haute, 73- Inform. & Educ. Detachment, U.S.A, 45-46. MLA; Melville Soc. Am; NCTE; Col. Lang. Asn.(creative scholar. award, 68); Am. Stud. Asn; Asn. Stud. Negro Life & Hist. American and world literature; ethnic literatures of the United States; theory and history of literature. Publ: The Negro in American literature, Wis. Counc. Teachers Eng, 66; ed, Black voices: an anthology of fiction, poetry, autobiography and literary criticism by Afro-American writers, 68 & New black voices: an anthology of contemporary Afro-American literature, 72, New Am. Libr; Steal away: stories of the runaway slaves, Praeger 71 & rev. ed, Benn, Eng, 73; auth, Democracy as a poetic principle in Leaves of grass, Wis. Stud. Lit, 66; The image of man as portrayed by Saul Bellow, 6/67 & The Harlem renaissance in literary history, 9/67, CLA J. Add: Dept. of English, University of Wisconsin-Stevens Point, Stevens Point, WI 54481.

CHAPMAN, ALFRED KING, b. Portland, Maine, Apr. 29, 04. ENGLISH. A.B, Colby Col, 25, L.H.D, 68; A.M, Harvard, 28; Columbia Univ, 40-41. Instr. ENG, COLBY COL, 28-32, asst. prof, 33-40, 41-42, assoc. prof, 45-52, prof, 52-72, chmn. dept, 52-65, EMER. PROF, 72- U.S.A.A.F, 42-45. MLA; NCTE; Keats-Shelley Asn. Am. English literature. Add: Dept. of English, Colby College, Waterville, ME 04901.

CHAPMAN, FREDERICK LAMAR, b. Sussex, N.J, Apr. 8, 29; m. 65; c. 6. THEATRE, DRAMA IN EDUCATION. B.A, Berea Col, 49; M.F.A, Tulane Univ, 64, Ph.D.(theatre), 71. Asst. prof. THEATRE, UNIV. TOLEDO, 64-70, ASSOC. PROF, 70- Del, Int. Asn. Theatre for Children & Youth Convention, 72-73; dir, The Princess & the Ogre, 7/72 & The Magic Carpet, 7/73, Univ. Toledo & Ohio Arts Counc; Durrenmatt's The Visit, Univ. Toledo, 9/72; mem, Bi-Centennial Children's Theatre Festival, 73-76. U.S.N, 51-61, Res, 61-73, Comdr. Am. Theatre Asn. Make-up, theatrical, film and television; children's theatre. Add: Dept. of Theatre, University of Toledo, 2801 W. Bancroft, Toledo, OH 43606.

CHAPMAN, GERALD W, b. Rusk, Tex, July 20, 27; div; c. 2. ENGLISH. B.A, South. Methodist Univ, 49, M.A, 51; Willard fel, Harvard, 51-53, Ph.D, 57. Teaching fel, South. Methodist Univ, 49-51; Harvard, 53-54; instr. Eng, Northwest. Univ, 54-57; Eng. & gen. educ, Harvard, 57-60, lectr. ENG, 60-61; asst. prof, Univ. Tex, 61-62; assoc. prof, UNIV. DENVER, 62-66, PROF, 66-, PHIPPS PROF. HUMANITIES, 68-, chmn. dept. Eng, 62-68. Assoc. ed. & co-founder, Denver Quart, 66-; summer vis. prof, Harvard, 68 & 70, mem. bd. overseers vis. exam. Eng, 68- U.S.N, 45-46. MLA; NCTE. Shakespeare; Renaissance and 18th century English literature. Publ: Co-auth, Essays on Shakespeare, Princeton, 65; auth, Literary criticism in England, 1660-1800, Knopf, 66; Edmund Burke: the practical imagination, Harvard, 67. Add: Dept. of English, University of Denver, Denver, CO 80210.

CHAPMAN, PAUL HIRAM, b. Marietta, Ohio, Feb. 13, 17; m. 41; c. 3. ENGLISH. B.A, Marietta Col, 39; M.A, Ohio State Univ, 46, Ph.D.(Eng), 51. Assoc. prof. ENG, Geneva Col, 51-55; asst. prof, Wittenberg Col, 55-57; PROF. & CHMN. DEPT, MT. UNION COL, 57- U.S.A, 42-45, Capt. MLA. Victorian period; folklore; the novel. Add: Dept. of English, Mt. Union College, Alliance, OH 44601.

CHAPMAN, ROBERT HARRIS, b. Highland Park, Ill, Apr. 14, 19. DRAMA. A.B, Princeton, 41; hon. M.A, Harvard, 56. Instr. Eng. & Am. lit, Princeton, 46-48; instr. dramatic art, Univ. Calif, Berkeley, 48-50; instr. ENG, HARVARD, 50-52, asst. prof, 52-56, assoc. prof, 56-67, PROF, 67-, DIR. LOEB DRAMA CTR, 60- Consult, Rockefeller Found, 54-56; Nat. Arts Found, 66-68; Juilliard Sch. Drama, Lincoln Ctr, 66-68; mem, Univ. Pa. Adv. Counc. for Performing Arts, 68- U.S.N, 42-45, Lt. Shaw Soc. Publ: Co-auth, Billy Budd (play), Princeton, 51. Add: Loeb Drama Center, Harvard University, 64 Brattle St, Cambridge, MA 02138.

CHAPPELL, BEN ARLEN, b. Dallas, Tex, May 22, 30; m. 60. PUBLIC ADDRESS. B.A, N.Tex. State Univ, 55, teaching fel, 55, M.A, 56; teaching fel, Cornell Univ, 56-57; teaching fel, Univ. Okla, 60, Ph.D, 63. Asst. prof. pub. address, N.Tex. State Univ, 57-60; Univ. South. Miss, 61-62, assoc. prof, 62-63, prof. commun, 63-67; ASSOC. PROF. speech, Tex. Christian Univ, 67-71; SPEECH & DRAMA, N.TEX. STATE UNIV, 71- U.S.A.F, 50-54. Speech Commun. Asn; South. Speech Commun. Asn; Am. Forensic Asn. Rhetoric and public address; American history. Publ: The League of Nations debate: a lesson in public education, South. Quart, 63. Add: Dept. of Speech & Drama, North Texas State University, Denton, TX 76203.

CHAPPELL, FRED DAVIS, b. Canton, N.C, May 28, 36; m. 59; c. 1. ENGLISH. B.A, Duke Univ, 61, NDEA & Woodrow Wilson fels, 61-63, M.A, 64. Instr. ENG, UNIV. N.C, GREENSBORO, 64-65, asst. prof, 65-68, assoc. prof, 68-70, PROF, 70- Rockefeller Found. grant, 67-68; Nat. Inst. Arts & Letts. grant, 68. Creative writing; 18th century and contemporary literature. Publ: It is time, Lord, Atheneum, 63; The inkling, 65, Dagon, 68 & The gaudy place, 72, Harcourt; L'Hamecon d'or, Gallimard, 65; The world between the eyes, La. State Univ, 71; Prodigious words, South. Writing in 60's, 66; Gothic perplexities, Red Clay Reader, 66; The crawling eye, Malahat Rev, 68. Add: Dept. of English, University of North Carolina at Greensboro, Greensboro, NC 27412.

CHAPPELL, WINN OWNBEY, b. Norman, Okla, June 21, 14. ENGLISH. A.B, Vanderbilt Univ, 35, A.M, 36. Instr, Va. Intermont Col, 36-39; ASST. PROF. ENG, HUNTINGDON COL, 45-46, 49- S.Atlantic Mod. Lang. Asn. Modern French literature. Add: Dept. of English, Huntingdon College, Montgomery, AL 36106.

CHARD, LESLIE FRANK, II, b. Dunkirk, N.Y, Sept. 2, 34; m. 61; c. 3. ENGLISH. B.A, Trinity Col.(Conn), 56, M.A, 58; James B. Duke fel, Duke Univ, 58-59, Ph.D.(Eng), 62. Instr. ENG, Duke Univ, part-time, 57-58, 59-61; Emory Univ, 61-64, asst. prof, 64-66; ASSOC. PROF, UNIV. CINCINNATI, 66-, asst. to head dept, 68-70. Frank L. Weil fel. stud. relig. & humanities, Hebrew Union Col, 67; Inst. Human Values & Med. fel, 73-74. MLA; Midwest Mod. Lang. Asn; AAUP. Romanticism; intellectual history; human values and the city. Publ: Dissenting Republican: Wordsworth's early life and thought in their political context, Mouton, 72; Outward forms and the inner light: Coleridge and Gatsby, Fitzgerald/Hemingway Annual, 73; Two new Blake engravings: Blake, James Earle, & the surgeon's art, Blake Stud, 73; Jane Austen and the obituaries: the names of Northanger Abbey, Stud. in Novel, 74; plus two others. Add: Dept. of English, University of Cincinnati, Cincinnati, OH 45221.

CHARI, V. K, b. India, Nov, 28, 24; m. 45; c. 2. ENGLISH & AMERICAN LITERATURE. B.A, Banaras Hindu Univ, 44, M.A, 46, Ph.D.(Eng), 50, dipl. French, 65. Asst. prof, ENG, Govt. Educ. Serv, Madhya Pradesh, India, 50-62; reader, Banaras Hindu Univ, 62-66; ASSOC. PROF, CARLETON UNIV, 66- Fulbright fel, N.Y. Univ, 59-60; vis. prof, State Univ. N.Y. Col. New Paltz, 60-61. American Romantic poetry, especially Whitman; modern and contemporary American and English poetry; Western and Indian literary aesthetics and criticism. Publ: Whitman in the light of Vedantic mysticism, Univ. Nebr, 64; Decorum as a critical concept in Indian and Western poetics, J. Aesthet. & Art Criticism, fall 67; The limits of Whitman's symbolism, J. Am. Stud. 8/71; The structure of Whitman's Catalogue poems, Walt Whitman Rev, 3/72; plus others. Add: Dept. of English, Carleton University, Ottawa, Ont, Can.

CHARLES, AMY MARIE, b. Pittsburgh, Pa, Dec. 12, 22. ENGLISH. A.B, Westminster Col.(Pa), 43; A.M, Univ. Pa, 44, Moore fel, 49-50, Ph.D.(Eng), 51. Teacher, high schs, Pa, 44-46; instr. ENG, Westminster Col.(Pa), 46-51, asst. prof, 51-55, assoc. prof, 55-56; asst. prof, UNIV. N.C. GREENSBORO, 56-60, assoc. prof, 60-68, PROF, 68- MLA; Mediaeval Acad. Am; Renaissance Soc. Am; Malone Soc; AAUP. English Renaissance; 17th century poetry; English drama, 1580-1800. Publ: The poetry of Ralph Knevet; co-auth, Freshman writing; The shorter poems of Ralph Knevet, Ohio State Univ, 66; The Williams Manuscript of George Herbert's poems, Univ. S.C. for Renaissance Eng. Text Soc, 75; George Herbert: priest, poet, musician, J. Viola da Gamba Soc, Am, 67; The Williams Manuscript and The temple, Renaissance Papers, 71. Add: 515 Kenilworth St, Greensboro, NC 27403.

CHARLES, ISABEL, O.P, b. Brooklyn, N.Y, Mar. 10, 26. ENGLISH, AMERICAN LITERATURE. B.A, Manhattan Col, 54; M.A, Univ. Notre Dame, 60,

Schmitt fel, 64-65, Ph.D.(Eng), 65. Chmn. dept. ENG, high sch, Ohio, 54-59; St. Mary of the Springs Acad, 59-62; asst. prof, Ohio Dominican Col, 65-67, prof, 67-73, chmn. dept, 67-68; v.pres. & acad. dean, 69-73; ASST. DEAN COL. ARTS & LETTS, UNIV. NOTRE DAME, 73- Vis. scholar higher educ, Univ. Mich, 68-69. MLA; NCTE. American literature; the works of Willa Cather. Publ: Death comes for the archbishop: a novel of love and death, N.Mex. Quart, spring 67; My Antonia: a dark dimension, West. Am. Lit, winter 67; The professor's house: an abode of love and death, Colby Libr. Quart, spring 68. Add: College of Arts & Letters, University of Notre Dame, Notre Dame, IN 46556.

CHARLES, ROBERT ALAN, b. Harrisburg, Pa, Apr. 5, 24; div; c. 5. ENGLISH, COMPARATIVE LITERATURE. B.A, Gettysburg Col, 48; M.A, Univ. Wis, 49; dipl, Univ. Toulouse, France, 50; Ph.D.(comp. lit), Pa. State Univ, 52. Instr. Romance langs, Pa. State Univ, 52-53; asst. prof. Eng, Col. William & Mary, 53-56; Mont. State Univ, 56-62; assoc. prof. Eng. & comp. lit. & chmn. humanities div, Alaska Methodist Univ, 62-66, prof. comp. lit, 66-67; Parsons Col, 66-71, PROF. ENG. & CHMN. DEPT. LANG. & LIT, MOREHEAD STATE UNIV, 71- Dir, Brit. Isles stud. tour, NCTE, summer 67; pres, Alaska Eng. Counc. U.S.A.A.F, 43-46, Sgt. Maj. MLA; Col. Eng. Asn; NCTE. Eighteenth to 19th century English German-French relations; 14th century romances; modern novel. Publ: The English reception of German literature: a survey of French mediation, Univ. N.C, 54; Alaska literary directory, Alaska Methodist Univ, 65; contrib, Yearbook of comparative & general literature, Indiana, annually, 53- Add: 933 N. Wilson Ave, Morehead, KY 40351.

CHARNEY, MAURICE MYRON, b. Brooklyn, N.Y, Jan. 18, 29; m. 54. ENGLISH. A.B, Harvard, 49; M.A, Princeton, 51, Ph.D.(Eng), 52. Instr. ENG, Hunter Col, 53-54; RUTGERS UNIV, NEW BRUNSWICK, 56-59, asst. prof, 59-62, assoc. prof, 62-67, PROF, 67- Fulbright prof, Univs. Bordeaux & Nancy, 60-61; summer vis. prof, Hunter Col, 63, Harvard, 65, Shakespeare Inst. Can, 69, Shakespeare Inst. Am, 70 & 71. U.S.A, 54-56. MLA (chmn. sect. five, Shakespeare, 72-73); Malone Soc; Shakespeare Asn. Am. Shakespeare and Elizabethan drama; American literature and civilization; history and theory of the drama. Publ: Shakespeare's Roman plays, Harvard, 61; Discussions of Shakespeare's Roman plays, Heath, 64; Shakespeare's Timon of Athens, New Am. Libr, 65; Shakespeare's Julius Caesar, Bobbs, 68; Style in Hamlet, Princeton, 69; How to read Shakespeare, McGraw, 71; Hawthorne and the Gothic style, New Eng. Quart, 61; The persuasiveness of violence in Elizabethan plays, Renaissance Drama, 69; This mist, my friend, is mystical: place and time in Elizabethan plays, In: The rarer action: essays in honor of Francis Fergusson, Rutgers Univ, 70. Add: Dept. of English, Rutgers University, New Brunswick, NJ 08903.

CHARTIER, MYRON RAYMOND, b. Ft. Morgan, Colo, Jan. 13, 38; m. 59; c. 2. SPEECH COMMUNICATION, HISTORY. B.A, Univ. Colo, Boulder, 60; B.D, Calif. Baptist Theol. Sem, 63; M.A, Ft. Hays Kans. State Col, 69; Ph.D.(speech commun), Univ. Denver, 71. Teaching asst. SPEECH, Univ. Denver, 68-71; ASST. PROF, AM. BAPTIST SEM. OF THE WEST, 71- Mem, Assoc. in Human Commun, 72-; consult, Franciscan Commun. Ctr, 72-73. Int. Commun. Asn; Speech Commun. Asn; Acad. Mgt. Simulation games related to learning effects; interpersonal communication ethics; relationship of theology to the behavioral sciences. Publ: The social views of Dwight L. Moody in relation to the workingman of 1860-1900, Ft. Hays Kans. State Col, 69; co-auth, Communication for laity: a report to the Lilly Foundation, Univ. Denver, 70; auth, Eve meets atom, Sunday Dig, 71; Learning effect: an experimental study of a simulation game and instrumented discussion, Simulation & Games, 72; Group decision making Baptist style, Church Adminr, 74. Add: American Baptist Seminary of the West, 1300 E. Covina Hills Rd, Covina, CA 91724.

CHARYN, JEROME, b. New York, N.Y, May 13, 37; m. 65; div. ENGLISH. B.A, Columbia Col, 59. Lectr. ENG, City Col. New York, 65; asst. prof, Stanford Univ, 65-68; LEHMAN COL, 68-71, ASSOC. PROF, 71- Exec. ed, Fiction, 72- PEN Club. Contemporary American fiction. Publ: Once upon a Droshky, 64 & On the darkening green, 65 (novels), McGraw; The man who grew younger (stories), Harper, 67; Going to Jerusalem, 67 & American scrapbook, 69 (novels), Viking; The single voice, anthology of contemporary fiction, 69 & The troubled vision, 70, Macmillan; Eisenhower, my Eisenhower, 71 & The tar baby, 73 (novels), Holt; The angels of Adonai, Simon, 74. Add: Dept. of English, Lehman College, Bedford Park Blvd. W, Bronx, NY 10468.

CHASE, ROWLAND KIMBALL, b. New York, N.Y, Dec. 30, 18; m. 41; c. 3. SPEECH, THEATRE. A.B, Antioch Col, 43; Am. Acad. Dramatic Arts, 46-47; A.M, Columbia Univ, 49; Univ. Iowa, summer 50; Ford Found. fel, Northwest. Univ, 53-54, univ. fel, 55-56, Ph.D, 58. Instr. speech, Grinnell Col, 49-53, asst. prof, 54-55; assoc. prof, Knox Col, 56-65, Prof, 65-66, chmn. dept. & dir. theatre, 56-66; DIR. COMMUNITY SERV, FOOTHILL JR. COL. DIST, 66- Regional auditioner, Am. Acad. Dramatic Arts, 58- U.S.N.R, 42-46, Lt. Nat. Counc. Community Serv. Add: 785 Wildwood Lane, Palo Alto, CA 94303.

CHATFIELD, EUGENE HALE, b. Passaic, N.J, Mar. 26, 36; m. 57; c. 4. ENGLISH & AMERICAN LITERATURE. B.A, Wesleyan Univ, 57; NDEA fel, Rutgers Univ, New Brunswick, 60-63, A.M, 63. Instr. ENG, HIRAM COL, 64-66, asst. prof, 66-73, ASSOC. PROF, 73-, DEAN STUDENTS, 71- Consult, Experiment in Higher Educ, South. Ill. Univ, 68-70; co-chmn. lit. adv. panel, Ohio Arts Counc, 68-72. U.S.N.R, 57-60, Res, 54-57, 60-66, Lt. Poetry and poetics; literature and psychology. Publ: The young country and other poems, Privately publ, 58; Teeth, Crossing, 67; At home, Ashland Poetry Press, 71; co-ed, Ark of bones and other stories by Henry Dumas, 70 & co-ed, Poetry for my people by Henry Dumas, 70, South. Ill. Univ; co-ed, Growing up: understanding late childhood and adolescent development through literature, Allyn & Bacon, 75. Add: Dept. of English, Hiram College, Hiram, OH 44234.

CHATFIELD, MINOTTE McINTOSH, b. New Haven, Conn, Apr. 11, 15; m. 44; c. 1. ENGLISH. A.B, Yale, 36; M.A, Lehigh Univ, 55, James Ward Packard fel, 59-60, Ph.D.(Eng), 61. Teacher ENG, New London Jr. Col, 50; asst, Lehigh Univ, 51-52, instr, 52-53; MUHLENBERG COL, 53-61, asst. prof, 61-66, assoc. prof, 66-74, PROF, 74- Ford Found. prepubl. grant, summer 73. U.S.A, 41-46. Col. Eng. Asn; AAUP; MLA. Romantic era, especially Wordsworth; Chaucer, especially in the eighteenth century; Victorian era. Add: 3081 South Dr, Allentown, PA 18103.

CHATMAN, SEYMOUR B, b. Detroit, Mich, Aug. 30, 28; m. 51. ENGLISH. Ph.D.(Eng), Univ. Mich, 56. Res. assoc, Cornell Univ, 51-52; instr. Eng, Wayne Univ, 54-56; asst. prof, Univ. Pa, 56-60; asst. prof, RHETORIC, UNIV. CALIF, BERKELEY, 60-64, assoc. prof, 64-68, PROF, 68- Fulbright res. grant, Denmark, 63-64; Guggenheim fel, 69-70. Ling. Soc. Am; MLA. Linguistics, poetics and literary theory; stylistics; narrative structure. Publ: A theory of meter, Mouton, 65; co-ed, Essays on the language of literature, 67; ed, Literary style: a symposium, Oxford, 71; auth, The later style of Henry James, Blackwells, 72; ed, Approaches to poetics, Eng. Inst. Papers, Columbia Univ, 73; New ways of narrative analysis, Lang. & Style; On the formalist-structuralist definition of character, J. Lit. Semantics; On defining form, New Lit. Hist; plus others. Add: Dept. of Rhetoric, University of California, Berkeley, CA 94720.

CHATTERTON, ROYLANCE WAYNE, b. Franklin, Idaho, July 14, 21; m. 45. ENGLISH LITERATURE. Dipl. & cert. educ, Albion State Normal Sch, 42; B.S, Brigham Young Univ, 45, M.A, 46; Ph.D.(Eng), Univ. Utah, 63. Chmn. dept. Eng. & drama, Carbon Jr. Col, 46-47; instr. Eng. & dir. drama, South. Idaho Col. Educ, 47-48; assoc. prof. ENG, Col. Idaho, 49-62, PROF, 62-68; BOISE STATE UNIV, 68- Lectr, Sun Valley summer sessions, Col. Idaho, 56-57; Danforth fel, grad. sem, Pac. Sch. Relig, summer 60; lectr, insts. Am. stud, Col. Idaho, 61-62; ed. consult, Meeting censorship in the schs, NCTE, 67-; co-ed, Western Writers Ser, Boise State Univ, 72. U.S.M.C, 42-44. NCTE (dir, 66-68); Conf. Col. Compos. & Commun; Conf. Eng. Stud. Lord Byron's dramas; modern American novel; literature of the American West. Publ: Vardis Fisher: the frontier and regional works, In: Western writers series, Boise State Univ, 72; Current sourcebooks: 4, 5/67 & Textbook uses of Hemingway and Faulkner, 10/72, Col. Compos. & Commun. Add: Dept. of English, Boise State University, Boise, ID 83701.

CHAUVIN, CLARICE B, S.S.A, b. Webster, Mass, Nov. 13, 13. ENGLISH. Ph.D, Cath. Univ. Am, 51. PROF. ENG, ANNA MARIA COL. WOMEN, 51-, HEAD. DEPT, 51-, REGISTR, 73- Lectr, Assumption Col.(Mass), 59-61; instr. compos, NDEA summer Eng. inst, Miles Col, 67. MLA; Am. Nat. Theatre & Acad; Am. Soc. Aesthet; NCTE; Col. Eng. Asn; AAUP; New Eng. Asn. Col. Registr. & Admis. Off. Modern novel and poetry; modern drama. Publ: Elizabeth Leseur: model of the lay apostle, Cath. World, 1/57. Add: Dept. of English, Anna Maria College for Women, Paxton, MA 01612.

CHAVEZ, EDMUND MANUEL, b. San Antonio, Tex, Nov. 20, 26; m. 53; c. 1. DRAMATICS. B.A, Southwest Tex. State Col, 49; M.F.A, Univ. Tex, 51. Teaching fel, Stanford Univ, 51; PROF. DRAMATICS, UNIV. IDAHO, 51-, CHMN. DEPT, 67- Vis. lectr. drama, Univ. Manchester, 73. U.S.N, 44-46, Ens. Am. Educ. Theatre Asn; Speech Commun Asn; Am. Nat. Theatre & Acad. Physical development of the theatre; heraldry; technical aspects of theatre production. Add: 1416 Chinook, Moscow, ID 83843.

CHEN, MATTHEW YUAN-CHUAN, Linguistics, Chinese Linguistics. See Volume III, Foreign Languages, Linguistics & Philology.

CHENEY, ANNE, b. Birmingham, Ala, Nov. 1, 44. ENGLISH. B.A, Birmingham-South. Col, 66; M.A, Fla. State Univ, 68, fel, 70-71, Ph.D.(Eng), 71. Instr. ENG, VA. POLYTECH. INST. & STATE UNIV, 68-71, ASST. PROF, 71- S.Atlantic Mod. Lang. Asn; Soc. Stud. South. Lit. Modern American literature; women's studies; southern literature. Publ: Millay in the village, Univ. Ala, 74; Changing status of women (film), Va. Polytech. Inst. & State Univ, 74; Lorraine Hansberry, Twayne, 76; Creativity on campus, Contexts, 74. Add: Dept. of English, Virginia Polytechnic Institute & State University, Blacksburg, VA 24061.

CHENEY, DAVID RAYMOND, b. Castle Dale, Utah, Jan. 23, 22; m. 48; c. 1. ENGLISH. B.A, Univ. Utah, 48, M.A, 49; M.A, Harvard, 51; Ph.D.(Eng), Univ. Iowa, 55; Univ. Alta, summer 58. Asst. ENG, Univ. Iowa, 53-55; instr, Lewis & Clark Col, 56-58; assoc. prof, Southwest Mo. State Col, 58-63, prof, 63-65; assoc. prof, UNIV. TOLEDO, 65-67, PROF, 67- U.S.A, 41-46. MLA; Midwest Mod. Lang. Asn; Mod. Humanities Res. Asn; Shakespeare Asn. Am; Renaissance Soc. Am; Milton Soc. Am. Shakespeare; Leigh Hunt; English Renaissance animal symbolism. Publ: Ed, Leigh Hunt: musical evenings or selections vocal and instrumental, Univ. Mo, 64; auth, The meaning of the cloud in Hamlet, Shakespeare Quart, summer 59; Hamlet and the killing of Polonius, Shakespeare Newsletter, 12/67; Leigh Hunt's efforts to encourage an appreciation of classical music, Keats-Shelley J, 68. Add: Dept. of English, University of Toledo, Toledo, OH 43606.

CHENEY, DONALD SHEPLEY, JR, b. Lowell, Mass, July 14, 32; m. 56; c. 2. ENGLISH. B.A, Yale, 54, M.A, 57, Sterling fel. & Ph.D, 61; Fulbright grant, Univ. Rome, 54-56. Instr. ENG, Yale, 60-64, asst. prof, 64-67; ASSOC. PROF, UNIV. MASS, AMHERST, 67- Morse fel, Yale, 64-65; mem. ed. bd, Eng. Lit. Renaissance, 70-; cor. ed, Spenser Newslett, 70-74, ed, 74- MLA (chmn. Eng. 4 group, 69, lit. & other arts group, 71 & Comp. Lit. 4 group, 74); Renaissance Soc. Am. Renaissance poetry and drama. Publ: Spenser's Image of nature: wild man and shepherd in The faerie queene, Yale, 66; introd. to Goldoni, The comic theatre, Nebr, 69; Spenser's Hermaphrodite, PMLA, 72. Add: Dept. of English, University of Massachusetts, Amherst, MA 01002.

CHENEY, LOIS A, b. Cleveland, Ohio, May 2, 31. SPEECH & DRAMA. B.A, Muskingum Col, 54; M.A, Kent State Univ, 57; Mich. State Univ, Ph.D.(speech), 61. Teacher, high sch, Ohio, 54-56, chmn. dept. 56-59; prof. speech & drama, Tarkio Col, 61-64; assoc. prof, ORAL INTERPRETATION, BOWLING GREEN STATE UNIV, 64-72, PROF, 72- Speech Commun. Asn; Cent. States Speech Asn. Oral interpretation; readers theatre. Publ: God is no fool, Abingdon, 70; Working relationships between oral interpretation and speech communication, Ohio Speech J, 68; chap. on oral interpretation, In: Introduction to speech communication, W.C. Brown, 68. Add: Dept. of Speech Bowling Green State University, Bowling Green, OH 43402.

CHENEY, MERLIN GENE, b. Rexburg, Idaho, May 18, 39; m. 59; c. 4. NINETEENTH CENTURY BRITISH LITERATURE, LINGUISTICS. B.S, Brigham Young Univ, 61, M.A, 66; fel, Bowling Green State Univ, 69-71, Ph.D.(19th century fiction), 71. Instr. Eng. & speech, Weber County Schs, Utah, 63-65; hist. & Eng, Weber State Col, 65-68; instr. ENG, Bowling Green State Univ, 70-71; ASST. PROF, WEBER STATE COL, 71- Rocky Mountain Mod. Lang. Asn. Nineteenth century; Hardy, Swinburne, Rossetti; writers laboratory for composition. Publ: Vanity fair and Gone with the wind, Brigham Young Univ, 66; ed, Thomas Hardy abroad (a continental view), Bowling Green State Univ, 71; The damning grace, 73 & From hoarded joy to barren spring, 73, Midwest Mod. Lang. Asn. Add: Dept. of English, Weber State College, Harrison St, Ogden, UT 84401.

CHENEY, THOMAS E, b. Victor, Idaho, Nov. 2, 02; m. 27; c. 2. FOLKLORE. B.S, Utah State Univ, 30; M.A, Univ. Idaho, 36; Univ. South. Calif, 45-48. Supt. pub. schs, Victor, Idaho, 30-34; Moreland, Idaho, 34-36; prin, Latter-Day Saint Sem, Blackfoot, Idaho, 36-44; prof. ENG. & LIT, BRIGHAM YOUNG UNIV, 44-72, researcher West. folklore, 60, EMER. PROF, 72- NCTE; Am. Folklore Soc. Utah and Western folklore. Publ: Songs of the Wasatch and Tetons, Ind. Univ, 64; Scandinavian immigrant stories, 59 & Facts and folklore in the story of John Wilkes Booth, 63, West. Folklore. Add: Dept. of English & Literature, Brigham Young University, Provo, UT 84601.

CHENOWETH, EUGENE CLAY, b. Marshall, Ill, Aug. 9, 00. SPEECH. B.S, Univ. Ill, 26; summer, Univ. Colo, 37; A.M, State Univ. Iowa, 38, Ph.D, 42. Prin. high sch, Ill, 26-28; asst. speech, State Univ. Iowa, 37-40, 41; Univ. Ill, 40-41; assoc. prof, Cent. Mich. State Col, 42-46; asst. prof. speech & dir. forensics, IND. UNIV, BLOOMINGTON, 46-71, EMER. ASSOC. PROF. SPEECH, 71- Speech Commun. Asn; Am. Forensic Asn; Cent. States Speech Commun. Asn. Instrumentality of argumentation, discussion and debate in the evolution of democratic processes in Great Britain; ancient and modern forums in Europe. Publ: Historical importance of debate; Discussion and debate; Discussion and debate project book. Add: Dept. of Speech & Theatre, College of Arts & Sciences, Indiana University, Bloomington, IN 47401.

CHERNISS, MICHAEL DAVID, b. Los Angeles, Calif, Apr. 7, 40; m. 67; c. 1. ENGLISH. A.B, Univ. Calif, Berkeley, 62, M.A, 63, fel, 63-64, Ph.D.(Eng), 66. Asst. prof. ENG, UNIV. KANS, 66-70, ASSOC. PROF, 70- Elizabeth M. Watkins summer fac. fel, 67; Univ. Kans. fac. res. grants, summers 68-73. MLA; Mediaeval Acad. Am; Midwest Mod. Lang. Asn. Old and Middle English literature; continental medieval literature. Publ: Ingeld and Christ, Mouton, The Hague, 72. Add: Dept. of English, University of Kansas, Lawrence, KS 66045.

CHERRY, CHARLES LESTER, b. Baltimore, Md, July 30, 42; m. 68. ENGLISH & AMERICAN LITERATURE. B.A, Loyola Col.(Md), 64; M.A, Univ. N.C, Chapel Hill, 66, Ph.D.(Eng), 68. Asst. ENG, Univ. N.C, 65-68; ASST. PROF, VILLANOVA UNIV, 68-, DIR. HONORS PROG, 72- Commun. consult, fed. govt. & ins. indust, 71- MLA; NCTE; Nat. Col. Honors Counc. Nineteenth century British literature; written communication; 20th century American literature. Publ: Co-auth, Contemporary composition, Prentice-Hall, 70; auth, The apotheosis of desire: dialectic and image in The French Revolution, Visions of the daughters of Albion, and the Preludium to America, Xavier Univ. Stud, 7/69; William Blake and Mrs. Grundy: suppression of Visions of the daughters of Albion, Blake Newslett, 8/70; One approach to a course in the methods of teaching composition, Eng. Educ, 73. Add: Dept. of English, Villanova University, Villanova, PA 19085.

CHERRY, DOUGLAS RAYMOND, b. Saskatoon, Sask, Feb. 25, 20; m. 42; c. 2. ENGLISH. B.A, Univ. Sask, 40, M.A, 47; Imp. Order Daughters Empire fel, Univ. London, Eng, 48-49; Ph.D, Univ. Toronto, 52. Instr. ENG, UNIV. SASK, 46-47, 49-50, asst. prof, 50-56, assoc. prof, 57-66, PROF, 66-, head dept, 66-72. R.C.A.F, 42-46. Victorian prose and poetry; Romantic poetry. Publ: The Fabianism of Shaw, Queen's Quart, winter, 62; Shaw's novels, Dalhousie Rev, winter, 63; The two cultures of Matthew Arnold and T.H. Huxley, Wascana Rev, 6/66. Add: Dept. of English, University of Saskatchewan, Saskatoon, Sask, Can.

CHERRY, KENNETH HOLLAND, b. Pennington Gap, Va, May 1, 35; m. 72; c. 1. AMERICAN LITERATURE. B.A, E.Tenn. State Univ, 61; Woodrow Wilson fel, Univ. Wash, 61; M.A, Univ. Tenn, Knoxville, 65. Asst. ed, Duke Univ. Press, 66-70; managing ed, UNIV. GA. PRESS, 71-73, ED, 73- Poetry explication. Publ: Poems in, Above Ground Rev, fall 70, Tenn. Poetry J, fall 70 & Scholarly Publ, 10/72; plus others. Add: University of Georgia Press, Athens, GA 30602.

CHERUBINI, WILLIAM, b. Philadelphia, Pa, Oct. 24, 11. ENGLISH LITERATURE. A.B, West. Reserve Univ, 33, A.M, 40, Ph.D, 44; Harvard, 33-34. From instr. to assoc. prof. ENG, CLEVELAND STATE UNIV, 42-60, PROF, 60-, univ. grant, 68. MLA; NCTE. Publ: Shelley's own symposium, Stud. Philol, 7/42; A basic quantitative-stylistics routine for poetry, Lang. & Style, (in press). Add: Dept. of English, Cleveland State University, Cleveland, OH 44115.

CHESEBRO, JAMES WILLIAM, U.S. citizen. SPEECH COMMUNICATION. B.A, Univ. Minn, Minneapolis, 66, Ph.D.(speech commun), 72; M.S, Ill. State Univ, 67. Instr. SPEECH COMMUN, Concordia Col.(Moorhead, Minn), 67-69; teaching assoc, Univ. Minn, Minneapolis, 69-72; ASST. PROF, TEMPLE UNIV, 72- Ed, Moments in Contemporary Rhet. & Commun, 71-73; mem. bd. evaluators, Speech Commun. Module, Educ. Resources Inform. Ctr, Speech Commun. Asn, 73-75. Speech Commun. Asn; Rhet. Soc. Am; Cent. States Speech Commun. Asn; East. Commun. Asn; Am. Inst. Polit. Commun. Contemporary rhetorical theory and criticism; political communication; popular culture. Publ: Co-auth, Public policy decision-making: systems analysis and comparative advantages debate, 73 & The evolution of the counter culture—a rhetorical analysis, 74, Harper; co-auth, The small group technique of the radical revolution: a synthetic study of consciousness raising, Speech Monogr, 6/73; auth, Cultures in conflict—a generic and axiological view, Today's Speech, spring 73; co-auth, A movement perspective on the 1972 Presidential campaign, Quart. J. Speech, 4/73; plus others. Add: Dept. of Speech, Temple University, Philadelphia, PA 19122.

CHESTER, ALLAN GRIFFITH, b. Philadelphia, Pa, Jan. 13, 00; m. 33, 46. ENGLISH LITERATURE. A.B, Univ. Pa, 22, A.M, 24, Ph.D, 30. Instr. Eng. UNIV. PA, 23-36, asst. prof, 36-40, assoc. prof, 40-53, prof, 53-67, Felix Schelling prof. ENG. LIT, 67-70, grad. chmn. Eng. dept, 46-48, 54-56, 60-62, chmn. dept, 62-65, EMER. PROF, 70- MLA; Mod. Humanities Res. Asn, Gt. Brit; Mediaeval Acad. Am; Renaissance Soc. Am. English Renaissance; English Bible. Publ: Thomas May, man of letters, 32, Hugh Latimer, apostle to the English, 54 & co-auth, George Joye: a chapter in the history of the English Bible, 62, Univ. Pa; auth. & ed, Selected sermons of Hugh Latimer, Univ. Va, 68. Add: 975 Mayberry Rd, Gulph Mills, Conshohocken, PA 19428.

CHESTER, GIRAUD, b. New York, N.Y, Apr. 4, 22. SPEECH. A.B, Brooklyn Col, 42; A.M, Univ. Wis, 43, Ph.D, 47. Asst, Univ. Wis, 47; asst. prof. speech, Cornell Univ, 47-49; Queens Col, 49-55; prog. exec, NBC, 54-57; exec, Ted Bates Advert. Agency, 58; v.pres, ABC-TV, 58-62, NBC-TV, 62-64; EXEC. V.PRES, GOODSON TODMAN PROD, 64- Assoc. ed, Quart. J. Speech, 48-56; Ford Fund Advan. Educ. fel, 53-54. U.S.N.R, 43-46, Lt.(jg). Speech Commun. Asn. Television; American public address. Publ: Embattled maiden: life of Anna Dickinson, Putnam, 51; co-auth, Television and radio, Appleton, 50, 56, 63, 71; The ninth juror, Random, 70. Add: 1010 Fifth Ave, New York, NY 10028.

CHEWNING, LAWRENCE HARRIS, JR, b. Greenville, S.C, Oct. 26, 15; m. 43, c. 2. ENGLISH. B.A, Furman Univ, 37; M.A, Univ. Va, 41, Ph.D.(Eng), 51. Teacher, high sch, S.C, 38-42; instr. ENG, Emory Univ, 46-48; PROF. & CHMN. DEPT, Queens Col. (N.C), 51-57; WOFFORD COL, 57- U.S.N.R, 42-45, Lt. MLA; Southeast Renaissance Conf. Milton; Shakespeare; Victorian literature. Publ: Text of the envoy to Alison, Stud. Bibliog; William Michael Rossetti and the Shelley Renaissance, Keats-Shelley J. Add: 104 Beth Court, Spartanburg, SC 29302.

CHIARENZA, FRANK JOHN, b. New Britain, Conn, Dec. 10, 26. ENGLISH LITERATURE. A.B, Yale, 49, Sterling fel, 51-52, univ. fel, 52-53, Ph.D. (Eng), 56; M.A, Rutgers Univ, 50; Fulbright fel, Univ. Rome, 53-54; cert, Inst. Educ. Mgt, Harvard, 70. Instr. Eng, Hillyer Col, 55-57, asst. prof, 57-58; UNIV. HARTFORD, 58-61, assoc. prof, 61-66, prof, 66-67, ACAD. DEAN COL. ARTS & SCI, 67-, Prof. of the year, 61. Lectr, Univ. Conn, 54-55; mem, Am. Counc. Educ; mem. conf, Proj. Improve Col. Teaching, AAUP-Asn. Am. Cols, 70; mem. adv. counc, Career Opportunities Prog, 70-; mem. Conn. State Master Plan, Comn. Higher Educ, 72-73. U.S.N, 44-46. MLA; NEA; Asn. Higher Educ; Nat. Col. Honors Counc; Am. Conf. Acad. Deans. Chaucer; Elizabethan drama; history of the English language. Publ: Browning's Bishop of St. Praxed's Explicator, 61; Aldous Huxley: the satirist's last word, Univ. Hartford Newslett, 64; College teaching: private challenge, Hartford Times, 66. Add: Office of the Dean, College of Arts & Sciences, University of Hartford, West Hartford, CT 06117.

CHIASSON, ELIAS JOSEPH, b. Margaree, Can, May 29, 18; m. 44; c. 7. ENGLISH. A.B, St. Francis Xavier Univ, 42; A.M, Univ. Toronto, 48, Ph.D. (Eng), 60. Instr. ENG, Rockhurst Col, 50-53; ST. LOUIS UNIV, 53-59, asst. prof, 59-61, assoc. prof, 61-65, PROF, 65- R.C.N, 43-45. Restoration and 18th century British literature. Publ: Tennyson's Ulysses—a re-interpretation, Univ. Toronto Quart, 7/54; Dryden's apparent scepticism in Religio Laici, Harvard Theol. Rev, 7/61; Swift's clothes philosophy in the Tale and Hooker's Concept of law, Stud. Philol, 1/62. Add: Dept. of English St. Louis University, St. Louis, MO 63103.

CHICHESTER, WILLIAM TAYLOR, b. New York, N.Y, Oct. 29, 13; m. 45; c. 1. SPEECH, DRAMA. A.B, Univ. N.C, 41, Rockefeller fel. & A.M, 46. Designer & tech. dir, Woman's Col, Univ. N.C, 46-47; assoc. prof. drama & designer, Baylor Univ, 47-49; sr. adv, spec. serv. div, U.S. Dept. Army, Wash, D.C, 49-55; exec. producer, indust. theatre, Dramaturgy, Inc, 55-56; assoc. Andrews, Bartlett & Assocs, Inc, 56-58; assoc. prof. speech & drama & assoc. dir. theatre, N.Dak. State Univ, 58-62; PROF. DRAMA & DIR. THEATRE, UNIV. MONTEVALLO, 62- Co-auth, Trail West, produced Mandan Hist. Develop. Asn, N.Dak, 59, 60, 61. U.S.A, 42-45, Sgt. Am. Theatre Asn; Speech Commun. Asn. Technical theatre; directing; playwriting. Add: Dept. of Speech & Theatre, University of Montevallo, Montevallo, AL 35115.

CHICKERING, HOWELL D, JR, b. Wilmington, Del, Feb. 23, 38; m. 58; c. 3. MEDIEVAL & MODERN LITERATURE. B.A, Dartmouth Col, 59; Fulbright scholar, Cambridge, 59-60; Ph.D.(Eng), Ind. Univ, 65. Asst. prof. ENG, AMHERST COL, 65-71, ASSOC. PROF, 71- MLA; Mediaeval Acad. Am. Publ: Robert Frost, romantic humorist, Lit. & Psychol, winter 66. Add: Dept. of English, Amherst College, Amherst, MA 01002.

CHILD, RUTH CARPENTER, b. Putnam, Conn, Dec. 23, 99. ENGLISH. A.B, Mt. Holyoke Col, 22; fel. from Mt. Holyoke Col, univ. fel. & A.M, Univ. Mich, 24, Ph.D, 35. Asst. dept. Eng, Mt. Holyoke Col, 22-23; assoc. prof. Eng, Defiance Col, 24-25; instr, Goucher Col, 26-31, 33-34; head dept, Williamsport Dickinson Jr. Col, 34-37; instr, Wellesley Col, 37-41, asst. prof, 41-51; head dept, Columbia Sch, Rochester, 51-55; teacher Eng, MacDuffie Sch. for Girls, 55-65, dramatics dir, 55-68, head librn, 67-73; RETIRED. Modern literary criticism. Publ: The aesthetic of Walter Pater, Macmillan, 40 & Octagon, 69; Swinburne's mature standards of criticism, PMLA; The early critical work of T.S. Eliot, Col. Eng. Add: 169 Maple St, Springfield, MA 01105.

CHILDS, BARNEY, b. Spokane, Wash, Feb. 13, 26; div; c. 2. MUSIC. B.A, Univ. Nev, 49; Rhodes scholar, Oxford, 49-51, B.A, 51, M.A, 55; fel, Stanford Univ, 53-54, Ph.D, 59. Acting instr. Eng, Stanford Univ, 51-54; instr, Univ. Ariz, 56-60, asst. prof, 60-65; dean, Deep Springs Col, 65-69; composer-in-residence, Conserv, Wis. Col, 69-71; fac. fel. Eng. & music, Johnston Col, UNIV. REDLANDS, 71-73, PROF. MUSIC & COMPOSER-IN-RESIDENCE, 73- Koussevitsky Mem. Award, 54; Woolley Mem. Chamber Music Comn, Bennington Col, 58; mem, MacDowell Colony, 63, 68 & 70; assoc. ed, Genesis West, 62-65; regents lectr, Univ. Calif, San Diego, 67. Am. Composers Alliance; Am. Soc. Univ. Composers (ed, Proceedings); Am. Music Soc. Eng. Musical composition; contemporary music theory; interrelation of poetry and music. Publ: Co-ed, Contemporary composers on contemporary music, Holt, 67; auth, Ben Johnston's Quintet for groups,

Perspectives New Music, 69; Indeterminacy and theory: some notes, Composer, 69; Musical continuity, Proc. Am. Soc. Univ. Composers, 73; plus others. Add: School of Music, University of Redlands, Redlands, CA 92373.

CHILDS, HERBERT ELLSWORTH, b. Mayville, N.Dak, Sept. 21, 05; m. 29; c. 4. LITERATURE. A.B, Oberlin Col, 26; Ph.D, Univ. Wash, 32. Instr. ENG, Jr. Col. Boise, 33-35; ORE. STATE UNIV, 35-38, asst. prof, 38-43, assoc. prof, 43-47, prof, 47-73, EMER. PROF, 73- Prof. Eng, Willamette Univ, 73-74. Chaucer Soc; MLA; Philol. Asn. Pac. Coast; Shakespeare Asn. Am. Shakespeare; Old and Middle English. Publ: Co-auth, The range of literature, Am. Bk. Co, 60, 67, 73; auth, Emily Dickinson, spinster, West. Humanities Rev, 10/49; Emily Dickinson and Sir Thomas Browne, Am. Lit, 1/51; On the Elizabethan staging of Hamlet, Shakespeare Quart, autumn, 62. Add: 1515 S.W. Brooklane Dr, Corvallis, OR 97330.

CHILDS, MARYANNA, O. P, b. New York, N.Y, Jan. 16, 10. ENGLISH. B.A, Col. St. Mary of the Springs, 42; M.A, Cath. Univ. Am, 48; Univs. Columbia, Marquette, Notre Dame & Wash, 39-50. Teacher parochial schs, 30-45; MEM. FAC. ENG, OHIO DOMINICAN COL, 45-, chmn. dept, 47-67. Summers, Knights of Columbus travel grant & conductor creative writing workshop, Dominican Col, Dublin, 61, mem. staff writers conf, Georgetown Univ, 62, Am. Irish Found. Author's travel grant, Ireland, 65; lectr. creative writing, Capital Univ, 68-69. MLA; Cath. Poetry Soc. Am. Ireland; creative writing. Publ: With love and laughter, 60 & With joy and gladness, 64, Doubleday; My little book of manners, Bruce, 63; The sounds of Ireland, Our Sunday Visitor Press, 69; plus others. Add: Dept. of English, Ohio Dominican College, Columbus, OH 43219.

CHING, JAMES CHRISTOPHER, b. Honolulu, Hawaii, Oct. 12, 26; m. 50; c. 1. SPEECH, DRAMA. B.A, Wabash Col, 51; M.A, Univ. Hawaii, 53; Ph.D. (speech), Univ. Mo, 62. Instr. speech, Univ. Mo, 53-56; Univ. Hawaii, 56-58; asst. prof, Wabash Col, 60; Tulane Univ, 60-63, assoc. prof. speech & drama, 63-67; prof. speech, Ill. State Univ, 67-68; prof. speech & dramatic arts & chmn. dept, Univ. Bridgeport, 68-69; vis. prof. speech, Univ. Mo, 69-70; PROF. SPEECH & THEATRE & CHMN. DEPT. SPEECH & THEATRE ARTS, HAMLINE UNIV, 70- U.S.A, 44-46. Speech Commun. Asn; Am. Theatre Asn; South. Speech Commun. Asn. Rhetorical theory; history of the theatre; African studies. Publ: Co-auth, Advanced public speaking, Holt, 66; auth, Mass communications in the Republic of the Congo, Jour. Quart, spring 64; Public address in the formation of the democratic Republic of the Congo, Quart. J. Speech, 2/65; Public education trends in the democratic Republic of the Congo: 1960-1967, Comp. Educ. Rev, fall 68. Add: Dept. of Speech & Theatre Arts, Hamline University, St. Paul, MN 55104.

CHINN, HAROLD BRUCE, b. Norwich, Conn, Nov. 24, 05; m. 29; c. 2. ENGLISH LANGUAGE & LITERATURE. A.B, Howard Univ, 29, fel. & A.M, 32. Head dept. Eng, Del. State Col, 29-30; teacher, pub. schs, Wash, D.C, 43-45; instr, Howard Univ, 47-53; instr, Morgan State Col, 53-54, Eng. & speech, 54-63, asst. prof, 63-71, assoc. prof. speech commun, 71-73, chmn, Humanities Div, 67-71; RETIRED. Speech Asn. East. States; Am. Forensic Asn; East. Forensic Asn. Speech. Add: 4115 Meade St. N.E, Washington, DC 20019.

CHINOY, HELEN KRICH, b. Newark, N.J, Sept. 25, 22; m. 48; c. 2. ENGLISH, THEATRE. B.A, N.Y. Univ, 43, fel, 43-44, M.A, 45; cert, Univ. Birmingham, 47; Ph.D, Columbia Univ, 63. Instr. Eng, N.Y. Univ, 44-45; Queens Col.(N.Y), 45, 50; Newark Col, Rutgers Univ, 46-48; Smith Col, 52-55, theatre, 56-60; lectr. Eng, Univ. Leicester, 63-64; THEATRE, SMITH COL, 65-68, ASSOC. PROF. & CHMN. DEPT. THEATRE & SPEECH, 68- Nat. Theatre Conf; Am. Theatre Asn; Am. Soc. Theatre Res. History, theories and techniques of acting and directing; modern European and American drama and theater; Shakespearean staging, especially by modern directors. Publ: Co-ed, Actors on acting, Crown, 49, rev. ed, 70; co-auth, Directors on directing, Bobbs, 63; auth, The profession and the art; directing 1860-1920, In: The American theatre: a sum of its parts, French, 71; Production and direction, In: Encycl. Britannica. Add: 230 Crescent St, Northampton, MA 01060.

CHISHOLM, WILLIAM SHERMAN, b. Detroit, Mich, Feb. 2, 31; m. 53; c. 3. ENGLISH LINGUISTICS. A.B, Baldwin Wallace Col, 53; M.A, West. Reserve Univ, 55; Ph.D.(Eng. lang. & lit), Univ. Mich, 64. Instr. Eng, Univ. Toledo, 56-58, asst. prof, 59-61; instr, Wayne State Univ, 61-63; pronunciation ed, World Publ. Co, 63-65; assoc. prof. ENG, West. Ill. Univ, 65-69; PROF, CLEVELAND STATE UNIV, 69- Ling. Soc. Am. Grammar; stylistics; teacher training. Publ: The new English, Funk, 69; co-ed, Webster's new world dictionary, World Publ, 70; co-auth, The English language: form and use, McKay, 74; The phonemicization of intervocalic T,D, Am. Speech, 5/66; Testimony on the teaching of English in the schools, Ill. J. Educ, 10/66; An exercise in syntactic stylistics, Linguistics, 7/67. Add: Dept. of English, Cleveland State University, Cleveland, OH 44114.

CHORNY, MERRON, b. Ranfurly, Alta, Aug. 31, 22; m. 45; c. 3. ENGLISH EDUCATION. B.Ed, Univ. Alta, 47, M.Ed, 49, Ed.D, 66. Teacher & prin, pub. sch, Alta, 49-58; asst. prof. ENG. EDUC, UNIV. CALGARY, 60-67, assoc. prof, 67-71, PROF, 71- Ed, Eng. Teacher, 61-67; participant, int. conf. teaching Eng, Boston, 65; Anglo-American sem. teaching Eng, Dartmouth Col, 66; prog. chmn, Int. Conf. Teaching Eng, Vancouver, 67, mem, int. steering comt, 67-, chmn, 69-71 & 73-74; Can. sr. fel, Imp. Relat. Trust, Inst. Educ, Univ. London, 69-70; participant & assessor, Int. Conf. Learning & Teaching Eng, York, Eng, 71. R.C.A.F, 43-45, Flying Off. NCTE (dir-at-large, 67-70); hon. life mem. Can. Counc. Teachers Eng.(pres, 67-68, dir. spec. proj, 69-). Language. Publ: Just English 1, 2, 3, lang. text ser, J.M. Dent, Ont, 66-68; Professional English associations in Canada, In: A common purpose, NCTE, 66; Teaching English in England, Alta. Eng, spring 71. Add: 3831 Brooklyn Crescent, Calgary, Alta, Can.

CHRIST, CAROL TECLA, b. New York, N.Y, May 21, 44. ENGLISH. B.A, Douglas Col, 66; M.Phil, Yale, 69, Ph.D.(Eng), 70. ASST. PROF. ENG, UNIV. CALIF, BERKELEY, 70- Victorian studies; women's studies. Add: Dept. of English, University of California, Berkeley, CA 94720.

CHRIST, JACK MORELL, b. Oceanport, N.J, July 12, 44; m. 73. AMERICAN & BRITISH LITERATURE. B.A, Dartmouth Col, 66; M.A, Univ. Pa, 67, Ph.D.(Eng), 70. ASST. PROF. ENG, RIPON COL, 70- MLA. Black American literature; autobiography. Add: Dept. of English, Ripon College, Ripon, WI 54971.

CHRISTENSEN, ALLAN CONRAD, b. New York, N.Y, Dec. 16, 40. ENGLISH LITERATURE. A.B, Harvard, 62; Fulbright fel, Univ. Oslo, 62-63; Ph.D.(Eng. lit), Princeton, 67. ASST. PROF. ENG, UNIV. CALIF, LOS ANGELES, 67- Asst. ed, Nineteenth Century Fiction, 71-73. Nineteenth century English novel; Victorian prose non-fiction. Publ: A Dickensian hero retailored, Stud. Novel, 71; On the naming of Hardy's Egdon Heath, Victorian Newsletter, 71; Edward Bulwer: 1st Baron Lytton of Knebworth, Nineteenth Century Fiction, 73. Add: Dept. of English, University of California, Los Angeles, CA 90024.

CHRISTENSEN, BONNIEJEAN McGUIRE, b. Los Angeles, Calif, July 19, 31. RHETORIC & MEDIEVAL STUDIES. B.A. & M.A, Univ. South. Calif, 53, NDEA fel, 66-69, Ph.D.(Eng), 69. Asst. prof. ENG, North. Ill. Univ, 69-74; ASSOC. PROF, UNIV. N.DAK, 74- Reader, Col. Entrance Exam. Bd, 69-71. MLA; NCTE (judge awards prog, 70-); Conf. Col. Compos. & Commun; Col. Eng. Asn; AAUP; NEA. Rhetoric; Middle English literature; medieval tradition in modern literature. Publ: Issac Bashevis Singer: a bibliography, Bull. Bibliog, 69; J.R.R. Tolkien's creative technique: Beowulf and The hobbit, Orcrist, 72; ed, The course in advance composition for teachers, Col. Compos. & Commun, 73. Add: Dept. of English, University of North Dakota, Grand Forks, ND 58201.

CHRISTENSEN, MERTON AUBREY, b. Minneapolis, Minn, May 16, 24; m. 44; c. 2. ENGLISH. A.B, Columbia Union Col, 49; A.M, Univ. Md, 50, Ph.D, 54. Instr. Eng, Columbia Union Col, 49-51, asst. prof, 53-56; instr, Univ. Md, 52-53; Univ. Southwest. La, 56-57; assoc. prof, Rockford Col, 57-58; Ill. State Univ, 58-62; UNIV. DEL, 62-69, PROF. ENG. & COMP. LIT, 69- Bollingen Found. grant, 68; Bollingen Ser. grant from Princeton Univ, 70- MLA; Col. Eng. Asn. Anglo-German relationships, 1780-1840; Romantic period. Publ: Co-ed, Coleridge notebooks, Vols. IV & V, (in prep); ed, Coleridge marginalia to the German theologians and to Swedenborg, Vol. XII, In: The collected works of S.T. Coleridge, (in press); auth, Deism in Barlow's early work, Am. Lit; Thomas Arnold's debt to German theologians, Mod. Philol; Taylor of Norwich and the higher criticism, J. Hist. Ideas; plus others. Add: Dept. of English, University of Delaware, Newark, DE 19711.

CHRISTENSEN, NORMAN F, b. Cass Lake, Minn, Nov. 4, 21; m. 46; c. 3. ENGLISH. B.A, St. Olaf Col, 43; M.A, Univ. Minn, 46; Ph.D.(Am. lit), Univ. Wis, 60. Instr, high sch, Minn, 43-45; ENG, Bemidji State Col, 46-54, asst. prof, 54-58, assoc. prof, 58-61, PROF, 61-64; UNIV. WIS-SUPERIOR, 64-, CHMN. DEPT. ENG, 68-, chmn. dept. lang. & lit, 64-68. MLA; NCTE. American literature; literary criticism; Wordsworth. Publ: A terminal course in literature for sophomores, Col. Eng; A Virgilian line in The prelude, Notes & Queries, 5/62; Doing our thing, Wis. Eng. J, 4/70. Add: Dept. of English, University of Wisconsin-Superior, Superior, WI 54880.

CHRISTIAN, HENRY ARTHUR, b. Jersey City, N.J, Aug. 22, 31; m. 52; c. 3. AMERICAN LITERATURE & CIVILIZATION. B.A, Yale, 53, M.A, 54; univ. fel, Brown Univ, 59-60, Beneficial Found. fel, 60-61, Ph.D.(Am. civilization), 67. Inst. Eng, Hopkins Grammar Sch, 54-58; Fulbright teacher Am. civilization, Denmark, 58-59; teaching assoc, Brown Univ, 61-62; instr. Eng, RUTGERS UNIV, NEWARK, 62-67, asst. prof. ENG, 67-72, ASSOC. PROF, 72-, DIR. GRAD. PROG, 73-, chmn. freshman Eng. prog, 67-69. Asst. dir. Am. stud, Yale Univ. for For. Stud, 55; mem, Fulbright Regional Interviewing Comt, 59-; Rutgers Univ. Res. Counc. grant, summer 68, Res. Fund grant, 68-69, fac. fel. for res, 69-70. MLA; Am. Stud. Asn; Immigration Hist. Soc. Twentieth century American literature; the 1930's; World War II. Publ: Louis Adamic: a checklist, Kent State Univ, 71; Thematic development in T.S. Eliot's Hysteria, Twentieth Century Lit, 7/60; Fitzgerald and Superman: an unpublished letter to Louis Adamic, Fitzgerald Newslett, fall 65; Ten letters to Louis Adamic, Princeton Libr. Chronicle, winter 67. Add: Dept. of English, Rutgers University, Newark, NJ 07102.

CHRISTIAN, MILDRED GAYLER, b. New Orleans, La. ENGLISH LITERATURE. A.B, Tulane Univ, 22, fel, 22-24, A.M, 24; fel, Univ. Chicago, 29-30, Ph.D, 32. From instr. to prof. ENG, NEWCOMB COL, TULANE UNIV, 22-65, Pierce Butler prof, 65-67, EMER. PROF, 67- Carnegie grants, 47, 48, 50 & 52; Am. Asn. Univ. Women fel, 57-58. MLA; S.Cent. Mod. Lang. Asn; Renaissance Soc. Am; Milton Soc. Am; Brontë Soc. English Renaissance drama; 19th century novel. Publ: Carlyle and Dickens: their social and literary relationship & A census of Brontë manuscripts in the United States, The Trollopian; co-auth, Reading for ideas, Farrar & Rinehart, 42; auth, The Brontës' in Victorian fiction: a guide to research, Harvard, 64; plus others. Add: 721 Lowerline St, New Orleans, LA 70118.

CHRISTIANI, DOUNIA BUNIS, b. Dubno, Russia, Aug. 15, 13; U.S. citizen; m. 36; c. 3. ENGLISH, DRAMA. B.A, Hunter Col, 34; M.A, Columbia Univ, 56, Ph.D.(Eng), 63. Asst. prof. ENG, UNIV. WIS-EAU CLAIRE, 64-67, assoc. prof, 67-69, PROF, 69- MLA. Playwriting; psychoanalysis; philology. Publ: Scandinavian elements of Finnegans wake, Northwest. Univ, 65; transl. & ed, The wild duck, Norton, 68; auth, H.C. Earwicker the Ostman, James Joyce Quart, spring 65; The polyglot poetry of Finnegans wake, Tex. Tech Comp. Lit. Symp, 69. Add: Dept. of English, University of Wisconsin-Eau Claire, Eau Clair, WI 54701.

CHRISTIANSEN, KENNETH A, b. Sansarc, S.Dak, July 20, 13; m. 43; c. 2. SPEECH. B.E, Moorhead State Teachers Col, 38; M.A, Univ. Denver, 39; Ed.D, Univ. Mo, 49. Instr. speech, Hutchinson Jr. Col, 39-40; asst. prof. Univ. S.Dak, 40-42, asst. dir. radio sta, 44-45; asst. prof, Ind. State Teachers Col, 45-46; dir. radio-TV prod, Stephens Col, 46-53; proj. dir, Educ. TV, South. Regional Educ. Bd, 53-56; prog. mgr. & asst. to pres, Educ. TV & Radio Ctr, 56-59; PROF. JOUR. & COMMUN, CHMN. DEPT. BROADCASTING & DIR. TV, UNIV. FLA, 59- Educ. adv. & consult. ed. comt, South. States Work Conf, 58; consult, Fla. Educ. Task Force Comn, 59-61; mem. adv. bd, Tex. Educ. TV Proj, 60-62; dir. TV proj, Ministry of Broadcasting & Inform. & Ministry of Educ, New Delhi, India, 60-65; mem. educ. TV counc, South. Regional Educ. Bd, 60-66; chmn. nation network affliates comn, Nat. Educ. TV, 62-64, mem. counc, 65-70; Fulbright lect, Univ. Leeds, 64; mem. nat. adv. comt, Nat. Instruct. TV, 64-70, chmn, 70-72.

Nat. Asn. Educ. Broadcasters (dir-at-large, 59-63); Broadcast Educ. Asn. (mem. int. training & liaison comt, 66-67). Publ: Radio announcing: a preliminary view, Debaters, 3/47; Florida's Educational Television Network, NAEB J, 5-6/60. Add: 11129 N.W. 12th Pl, Gainesville, FL 32601.

CHRISTIE, JOHN ALDRICH, b. Northampton, Mass, Apr. 12, 20; c. 3. ENGLISH & AMERICAN LITERATURE. B.A, Oberlin Col, 42; M.A, Wesleyan Univ, 43; M.A, Yale, 46; Ph.D, Duke Univ, 55. Asst. oral Eng, Wesleyan Univ, 42-43; instr. ENG, Univ. Ill, 43-44; VASSAR COL, 46-55, asst. prof, 55-58, assoc. prof, 58-65, PROF, 65-, DIR. MULTIDISCIPLINARY PROG, 73-, fac. fels, 62, 67-78. Consult. dept. Eng, Nyack High Sch, 58-65; Fulbright vis. prof, Univ. Delhi, summer 66; Univ. Delhi & Am. Stud. Res. Ctr, Hyderabad, India, 68; mem. adv. comt, Int. Exchange of Persons Fulbright Comn, 66- AAUP; Thoreau Soc; Am. Stud. Asn; NCTE; MLA; Eng. Inst. Publ: Thoreau as world traveler, Columbia Univ. & Am. Geog. Soc, 65; A new chapter in American literature, Vassar Alumnae Mag; Some remarks upon enrichment of high school English, Eng. Rec, 2/63; Thoreau and civil resistance, Emerson Soc. Quart, summer 70; plus others. Add: Dept. of English, Vassar College, Poughkeepsie, NY 12601.

CHRISTIN, ROBERT E, JR, b. Detroit, Mich, June 25, 21; m. 46; c. 10. AMERICAN LITERATURE. B.A, Ohio State Univ, 47, M.A, 49, Ph.D, 58. Instr. ENG, Ohio State Univ, 50-52; St. Ambrose Col, 52-53; asst. prof, Univ. Notre Dame, 53-58, assoc. prof, 58-65, dir. freshman Eng, 53-65; dir. Wash. off, Inst. Serv. Educ, 65-66; Educ. Proj. Inc, 66-67; pres, Educ. Assoc. Inc, 67-69; pres, St. Norbert Col, 69-73; EDUC. CONSULT, 73- Consult, Educ. Serv, Inc, Newton, Mass, 64-65; mem, White House Task Force on Higher Educ, 67. Thomas Madden Award for Teaching Excellence, Univ. Notre Dame, 64. U.S.N, 42-46. MLA; NCTE; Col. Eng. Asn. Nineteenth and 20th century American literature and culture; teaching and curriculum development in high school or college; administration of colleges and universities. Add: 1031 Grand Ave, Keokuk, IA 52632.

CHRISTMAS, ROBERT A, b. Pasadena, Calif, July 12, 39; m. 60, 71; c. 3. ENGLISH. A.B, Stanford Univ, 61; A.M, Univ. Calif, Berkeley, 63; Ph.D. (Eng), Univ. South. Calif, 68. Instr. ENG, Idaho State Univ, 63-64; Univ. South. Calif, 66-67; asst. prof, San Jose State Col, 67-68; Col. South. Utah, 68-72; RES. & WRITING, 72- Salesman, United Van Lines, 73- Fiction and verse writing. Publ: Rodney the raper (poem), West. Humanities Rev, spring 72; Massage parlor (poem), Screw, 5/72; I want a prayer, Dad, In: Stories Southwest, Prescott Col, 73; plus others. Add: Box 739, Rosemead, CA 91770.

CHRISTOPHER, GEORGIA B, b. Barnesville, Ga. RENAISSANCE ENGLISH LITERATURE. B.A, Anges Scott Col, 55; Univ. Southampton, 55-56; M.A.T, Yale, 57, Ph.D.(Eng), 66. Teacher ENG, Needham Broughton High Sch, Raleigh, N.C, 57-59; instr, Mercer Univ, 59-62; asst. prof, Univ. N.C, Chapel Hill, 66-71; ASSOC. PROF, WESTHAMPTON COL, 71-, acting chmn. dept, 73. MLA; South. Mod. Lang. Asn; Milton Soc. Am; Renaissance Soc. Am. Milton; Renaissance prose narrative. Publ: Homeopathic physic and natural renovation in Samson Agonistes, ELH, 9/70; A note on the blind mouths of Lycidas, Notes & Queries, 10/73; Et in Arcadia, Calvin . . . a study of nature in Henry Vaughan, Stud. Philol, 10/73. Add: Dept. of English, Westhampton College, Richmond, VA 23173.

CHRISTY, (FREDERICK) LYNN, b. Pittsburgh, Pa, Nov. 11, 10; m. 38; c. 2. ENGLISH COMPOSITION. B.A, Pa. State Univ, 35, M.Ed, 36. Instr. ENG. COMPOS, PA. STATE UNIV, 38-43, asst. prof, 43-46, ASSOC. PROF, 46-, DIR, WRITING CLIN, 72-, coord. Eng, Commonwealth Campuses, 60-66. Assoc. prof, U.S. Naval Postgrad. Sch, 66-67; consult, Intel. Syst. Lab, H.R.B-Singer, Inc, 68- NCTE; Conf. Col. Compos. & Commun. Publ: Suggestions for teaching, a monthly manual issued for teachers, Harper's Mag, 44-54. Add: 242 Nimitz Ave, State College, PA 16801.

CHUPACK, HENRY, b. New York, N.Y, Mar. 10, 15; m. 48. ENGLISH, AMERICAN LITERATURE. B.A, Brooklyn Col, 36; Ph.D.(Eng), N.Y. Univ, 52. Asst. prof. ENG, Santa Ana Col, 56-59; assoc. prof, C.W. Post Col, L.I. Univ, 59-66; PROF. & CHMN. DEPT, N.Y. Inst. Technol, 66-68; KINGSBOROUGH COMMUNITY COL, 68- U.S.A.F, 41-45. Col. Eng. Asn; AAUP; MLA. Colonial literature; 19th century American novel; 20th century American novel and poetry. Publ: Roger Williams, In: United States authors series, Twayne, 69; Walt Whitman and the Camden Circle, Proc. N.J. Hist. Soc, fall 55; A new look at freshman writing, CEA Critic, 5/63. Add: 5 Colgate Rd, Great Neck, NY 11023.

CHURCH, DAN McNEIL, Twentieth-Century French Drama. See Volume III, Foreign Languages, Linguistics & Philology.

CHURCH, HARRISON LEON, b. St. Louis, Mo, June 16, 41. JOURNALISM, LAW. B.S, Univ. Ill, Urbana, 63, M.S, 65, J.D, 71. Instr. jour, Dickinson State Col, 66-68, asst. prof, 68-69 & 71-72, assoc. prof, 72-73; RES. & WRITING, 73- Asst. ed, Caveat, 70-71. Publ: Handset newspaper stays alive, Quill, 11/69; Doc Hubbard, Minneapolis Tribune Sunday Mag, 12/69; They hiss and puff like the big ones, Dakota Farmer, 2/72; plus others. Add: 1320 W. Second St, Dickinson, ND 58601.

CHURCH, MARGARET, b. Boston, Mass, Apr. 8, 20. ENGLISH. A.B, Radcliffe Col, 41, Ph.D, 44; A.M, Columbia Univ, 42. Instr, Temple Univ, 44-46; mod. Eng. & Am. lit, Duke Univ, 46-53; ENG, PURDUE UNIV, WEST LAFAYETTE, 53-55, asst. prof, 55-61, assoc. prof, 61-65, PROF, 65- MLA; Am. Comp. Lit. Asn. Modern English, Continental and American literature; time theories in modern English, Continental and American literature. Publ: Time and reality: studies in contemporary fiction, Univ. N.C. & Oxford, 63; Don Quixote: the knight of La Mancha, N.Y. Univ, 71; Thomas Wolfe, dark time, PMLA; Death in Venice: a study of creativity, Col. Eng, 62; A triad of images: nature in Madame Bovary, Mosaic, 72. Add: Dept. of English, Purdue University, West Lafayette, IN 47906.

CHURCH, RALPH BRUCE, b. N.C, July 9, 27; m. 45; c. 6. AMERICAN LITERATURE. A.B, Wake Forest Col, 49; M.A, Columbia Univ, 51; George Washington Univ, 59-61; South. Univs. fel, 59-61. Teacher, high schs, N.C. & Ala, 49-50, 51-52, 52-54; chmn. dept. Eng, Mitchell Col, 54-56, acting dean & asst. to pres, 55-56; asst. prof. Eng. & jour, Shepherd Col, 56-61, assoc. prof, 61-62; asst. prof. ENG, Muskingum Col, 62-66; JUNIATA COL, 66-67, ASSOC. PROF, 67-, CHMN. DEPT, 70- U.S.N.R, 45-46. MLA; S.Atlantic Mod. Lang. Asn. American fiction; creative writing; contemporary literature. Publ: Ed, The red badge of courage, 69 & A Connecticut yankee in King Arthur's court, 69, Cambridge Bk; auth, Two loves: Abelard and Heloise, Juniata Col, 70. Add: Juniata College, Huntingdon, PA 16652.

CHURCHILL, IRVING LESTER, b. Madison, Wis, Apr. 9, 01; m. 35; c. 2. ENGLISH & AMERICAN LITERATURE. B.S, Univ. R.I, 22; A.M, Yale, 27, Ph.D, 32. Instr. ENG, Univ. N.H, 23-25; Univ. Rochester, 27-30; asst. prof, Univ. R.I, 32-34; Bucknell Univ, 34-37; prof, COE COL, 37-69, head dept, 37-55, 59-66, chmn. div. lang. & lit, 46-54, dir. summer session, 47, acad. dean, 51-53, EMER. PROF, 69- Fulbright vis. prof, Silliman Univ, Philippines, 55-56; pres, Iowa Col. Eng. Conf, 40-44; vis. prof, Tunghai Univ, 64-65; Warren Wilson Col, 69- MLA; Col. Eng. Asn. English literature of the age of Johnson. Publ: Thomas Percy, scholar, In: Age of Johnson: essays presented to Chauncey Brewster Tinker, Yale, 49; Percy-Warton letters, 33 & Shenstone, 36 & 37, PMLA. Add: Warren Wilson College, Swannanoa, NC 28778.

CIANCIO, RALPH ARMANDO, b. Pittsburgh, Pa, Dec. 1, 29; m. 59; c. 3. AMERICAN & ENGLISH LITERATURE. A.B, Duquesne Univ, 57; M.A, Pa. State Univ, 58; Ph.D.(Eng), Univ. Pittsburgh, 64. Instr. ENG, Carnegie-Mellon Univ, 59-62, asst. prof, 62-65; SKIDMORE COL, 65-68, ASSOC. PROF, 68- U.S.A, 51-53. MLA; Melville Soc. Am. American fiction; 20th century European novel; the grotesque. Publ: Faulkner's existential affinities, Carnegie Series in Eng, 61; The achievement of Saul Bellow's Seize the day, In: Vol. 7, Literature and theology, Eng. Monogr. Series Tulsa, 69; The sweetness of the twisted apples: unity of vision in Winesburg, Ohio, PMLA, 72. Add: Dept. of English, Skidmore College, Saratoga Springs, NY 12866.

CIANCIOLO, PATRICIA JEAN, b. Chicago, Ill, Oct. 24, 29. ENGLISH, LITERATURE. Ph.B, Cardinal Stritch Col, 49; M.E, Univ. Wis, Milwaukee, 54; Ph.D.(children's lit, educ), Ohio State Univ, 63. Teacher pub. schs, Wis, 49-58; instr. children's lit. & curriculum, Marquette Univ, 58-60, asst. prof. children's lit, 62-64; instr. children's lit. & curriculum, Ohio State Univ, 60-62; assoc. prof. CHILDREN'S LIT, MICH. STATE UNIV, 64-70, PROF, 70- Delta Kappa Gamma spec. scholar, 60-61; vis. prof, Univ. Hawaii, summer 67; field reader, lang. arts & reading & libr. serv, U.S. Off. Educ, 67; consult. critical reading lit. proj, Mott Found. & Garfield Sch, Flint, Mich, 68; vis. prof, Univ. Nev, Las Vegas, 71; specialist Eng. lang. arts, Systems Develop. Corp, 72. NCTE (mem. elem. booklist comt, 65-69, chmn, 69-; mem, auth. & illustrators comt); Int. Reading Asn.(mem, libr. & lit. comt); Am. Libr. Asn.(chmn, Melcher Scholarship Comt, 69-; mem, Newberry Caldecott comt, 72-); Nat. Soc. Stud. Educ; Asn. Childhood Educ, Int. Establishment of criteria for use of trade books in elementary school; teaching critical reading of literature to elementary school children. Publ: Co-auth, Study guide for educational psychology, Wadsworth, 67 & Literary time-line in American history, Doubleday, 69; auth, Illustrations in children's books, W.C. Brown, 70; co-auth, A forum for focus: the language arts in the elementary school, NCTE, 73; Picture books for children, NCTE & Am. Libr. Asn, 73; auth, The example is vitally important!, Eng. Educ, winter 71; Use wordless picture books to teach reading, visual literacy and to study literature, Top of News, 4/73; The role of children's books in the open school, Elem. Eng, 3/73. Sharing time, Let's make up a story & Rhythm, rhythm everywhere (films), Coronet; Children's literature series (36 filmstrips), McGraw, 73. Add: College of Education, Michigan State University, 360 Erickson, East Lansing, MI 48823.

CIARDI, JOHN (ANTHONY), b. Boston, Mass, June 24, 16; m. 46; c. 3. POETRY. B.A, Tufts Univ, 38, Litt.D, 60; M.A, Univ. Mich, 39; D.Hum, Wayne State Univ, 63; L.H.D, Kalamazoo Col, 64; LL.D, Ursinus Col, 64. Instr. Eng, Univ. Kansas City, 40-42, 46; Harvard, 46-48, asst. prof, 48-53; lectr, Rutgers Univ, 53-54, assoc. prof, 54-56, prof, 56-61; DIR, BREAD LOAF WRITERS CONF, 55-; POETRY ED, SATURDAY REV, 56- Lectr. poetry, Salzburg Sem. Am. Stud, Austria, 51; Ford Found. Fund. Advan. Educ. fel, 52-53; Prix de Rome fel, Am. Acad. Arts & Lett, 56. Avery Hopwood Award in Poetry, 39; Blumenthal Prize, Poetry Mag, 44; Eunice Tietjens Award, 45; Levinson Prize, 47; Harriet Monroe Mem. Award, 55. U.S.A.A.F, 42-45, T/Sgt. Col. Eng. Asn.(pres, 55-56); fel. Am. Acad. Arts & Sci; Nat. Inst. Arts & Letts. The form of poetry; Dante. Publ: Homeward to America, 40; Other skies, 47; Live another day, 49; Mid-Century American poets (anthology), 50; From time to time, 51; transl, Dante's inferno, Rutgers Univ. & Mentor, 54 & Dante's Purgatorio, Mentor, 61; auth, As if: poems new and selected, 55, I marry you, 58, 39 poems, 59, In the stoneworks, 61, In fact, 62, Person to person, 64 & This strangest everything, 66, Rutgers Univ; The Reason for the pelican, 59, Scrappy the pup, 60, Man who sang the sillies, 61, You read to me, I'll read to you, 62, Dialogue with an audience, 63, John J. Plenty and Fiddler Dan, 63, You know who, 64, King who saved himself from being saved, 65, Monster den, 66 & Alphabestiary, 67, Lippencott; I met a man, Houghton, 61; auth, Mid-century American poets, Twayne; How does a poem mean?, In: Introduction to literature, part III, Houghton, 60. Add: 359 Middlesex Ave, Metuchen, NJ 08840.

CIRILLO, ALBERT RICHARD, b. Brooklyn, N.Y, May 2, 33. ENGLISH. B.A, Fordham Univ, 55, M.A, 59; Ph.D.(Eng), Johns Hopkins Univ, 64. Asst. prof. ENG, NORTHWEST. UNIV, 64-68, ASSOC. PROF, 69- Folger Shakespeare Libr. fel, summer 65; Huntington Libr. fel, summer 66. U.S.A, 56-58. MLA; Milton Soc. Am; Renaissance Soc. Am. Sixteenth and seventeenth century literature, especially Spenser and Milton; Italian literature of the Renaissance. Publ: Crashaw's Epiphany hymn: the dawn of Christian time, Stud. Philol, 70; Tasso's Il mondo creato: providence and the created universe, Milton Stud, 71; As you like it: pastoralism gone awry, ELH, 71; plus others. Add: Dept. of English, Northwestern University, Evanston, IL 60201.

CIRILLO, NANCY ROCKMORE, b. Amityville, N.Y, Feb. 22, 32; m. 59; c. 2. COMPARATIVE LITERATURE, MODERN POLITICAL HISTORY. M.A, Univ. Chicago, 54; Ph.D.(comp. lit), N.Y. Univ, 69. Instr. ENG, Univ. Nebr, 54-56; tutor, Brooklyn Col, 58-60; instr, Rutgers Univ, Newark, 60-64; UNIV. ILL, CHICAGO CIRCLE, 64-69, ASST. PROF, 69- Literature and politics, the intellectual and aesthetic roots of fascism; French, Italian, German, English literature and thought. Publ: Transl, The child in the family, Regnery, 71. Add: Dept. of English, University of Illinois at Chicago Circle, Chicago, IL 60680.

CLAEYSSENS, ASTERE EVARIST, b. Waukegan, Ill, Apr. 25, 24. CREATIVE WRITING. B.A, Univ. Ill, 48; M.A, Columbia Univ, 52. Asst. prof. Eng, Carnegie Inst. Technol, 49-56; Monmouth Col, 56-59; ed. & lit. critic, 56-65; ASSOC. PROF. CREATIVE WRITING, GEORGE WASHINGTON UNIV, 65- Mem. fac, Hunter Col, 59-; auth. & performer, One to One (educ. TV ser), 68-; artistic consult, APA-Phoenix Theatre Co, N.Y, 68- U.S.A, 43-45. American literature; Shakespeare; fiction, poetry and playwriting. Publ: Andre Maurois, 10/66 & Contemporary world drama, 10/67, Quart. J. Speech; Three American novelists, Dialogue, Vol. 2, No. 2. Add: Dept. of English, George Washington University, Washington, DC 20006.

CLAGETT, JOHN HENRY, b. Bowling Green, Ky, Apr. 6, 16; m. 43; c. 2. AMERICAN STUDIES. B.S, U.S. Naval Acad, 40; Ph.D.(Am. stud), Yale, 54. Third secy. & v.consul, U.S. Dept. State, 46-49; instr. ENG, MIDDLEBURY COL, 55-57, asst. prof, 57-63, assoc. prof, 63-73, PROF, 73- U.S.N, 36-46, Lt. Comdr. Novels; research and writing in American studies, especially James Fenimore Cooper; American Naval history. Publ: Cradle of the sun, 52 & The slot, 58-63, Crown; U.S. Navy in action, Calman-Levy, Suede-Nederlandse & Monarch Pubs, 63. Add: Dept. of English, Middlebury College, Middlebury, VT 05753.

CLAIBORNE, JAY WOOD, b. Lubbock, Tex, Nov. 28, 39; m. 66; c. 1. VICTORIAN STUDIES. B.A, South. Methodist Univ, 62; M.A, Univ. Tex, Austin, 65, Ph.D.(Eng. & hist), 69. Teaching asst. Eng. compos, Univ. Tex, Austin, 65-66; asst. prof. Eng. lit, George Washington Univ, 68-73; summer res. grant, 70. MLA; Res. Soc. Victorian Periodicals (chmn. grants & fels, 70-73). John Ruskin and the history of aestheticism; autobiography and narrative theory. Publ: John Ruskin and Charles Augustus Howell, some new letters, Tex. Stud. Lit. & Lang, 73. Add: Beach Plum, Madaket Rd, Nantucket, MA 02554.

CLAIR, JOHN A, b. Pittsburgh, Pa, May 21, 27; m. 55; c. 6. ENGLISH, AMERICAN LITERATURE. A.B, Duquesne Univ, 51, M.A, 55; Ph.D.(Eng), West. Reserve Univ, 63. Instr. ENG, DUQUESNE UNIV, 57-60, asst. prof, 60-63, assoc. prof, 63-67, PROF, 67-, chmn. dept, 64-73. U.S.N.R, 45-46. MLA; Mod. Humanities Res. Asn; Asn. Depts. Eng. Victorian novel; 17th century English literature. Publ: The ironic dimension in the fiction of Henry James, 64. Add: Dept. of English, Duquesne University, Pittsburgh, PA 15219.

CLANCEY, RICHARD W, b. Cleveland, Ohio, Nov. 10, 28. ENGLISH, THEOLOGY. A.B, John Carroll Univ, 54; M.A, Univ. Notre Dame, 59; M.A, Holy Cross Col.(D.C), 59; Ph.D.(Eng), Univ. Md, 66. From instr. to ASST. PROF. ENG, Dunbarton Col, 59-65; JOHN CARROLL UNIV, 65- MLA; NCTE. Publ: The priest in the university, Cath. Educ. Rev, 5/67; Death of God in the American Catholic college, Thought, spring 68; The rhetorical method in the textual revisions of Newman's Dublin discourses, Renascence, winter 68. Add: Dept. of English, John Carroll University, Cleveland, OH 44118.

CLANCY, JOSEPH P, b. New York, N.Y, Mar. 8, 28; m. 48; c. 5. ENGLISH. B.A, M.A. & Ph.D, Fordham Univ. Instr, Fordham Col, 49-50; from asst. prof. to PROF. ENG, & CHMN. DEPT, MARYMOUNT MANHATTAN COL, 50- Am. Philos. Soc. grant, 63, 67; Nat. Transl. Ctr. fel, 67. MLA. Seventeenth century English literature; English drama to 1700; mediaeval Welsh poetry. Publ: The odes and epodes of Horace, Univ. Chicago, 60; Medieval Welsh lyrics, St. Martins, 65; The literary genres in theory and practice, Col. Eng, 4/67. Add: Dept. of English, Marymount Manhattan College, 221 E. 71st St, New York, NY 10021.

CLAPP, EDWIN ROOSA, b. Albany, N.Y, Apr. 18, 02; m. 29; c. 2. ENGLISH LITERATURE. A.B, Stanford Univ, 23; A.M, Harvard, 25, Ph.D, 31. Instr, Washington & Lee Univ, 24-26; univ. col, N.Y. Univ, 26-29; ENG, Univ. Utah, 31-32, asst. prof, 32-35, assoc. prof, 35-42, prof, 42-60, head dept, 52-60; prof, WEST. WASH. STATE COL, 60-69, chmn. dept, 63-66, EMER. PROF, 69- Assoc. prof, Univ. Hawaii, 37-38; lectr, Univ. Wash, 45-46. Bowdoin Prize, Harvard, 30. Philol. Asn. Pac. Coast; MLA. Literary criticism; 19th century literature; humanities. Publ: A freeman's forum, the college quad; Why the devil don't you teach freshmen to write?, Saturday Rev, 2/65. Add: Dept. of English, Western Washington State College, Bellingham, WA 98225.

CLAPPER, RONALD (EARL), b. Long Beach, Calif, July 5, 38. ENGLISH, AMERICAN LITERATURE. B.A, Univ. Calif, Los Angeles, 61, M.A, 62, fel, 65-66, Ph.D.(Eng), 67. ASST. PROF. ENG, UNIV. VA, 67- MLA. Thoreau, American Renaissance. Add: Dept. of English, University of Virginia, Charlottesville, VA 22903.

CLARESON, THOMAS DEAN, b. Austin, Minn, Aug. 26, 26; m. 54; c. 1. ENGLISH. B.A, Univ. Minn, 46; M.A, Ind. Univ, 49; Ph.D.(Eng), Univ. Pa, 56. From assoc. prof. to PROF. ENG, COL. WOOSTER, 55- Danforth grant, summer 59; Am. Philos. Soc. grant, summers 60 & 64, 66-67; ed, Extrapolation, 59-; mem. ed. bd, Victorian Poetry, 64-; chmn, Sci. Fiction Res. Asn, Inc, 70- MLA; Am. Stud. Asn. Publ: Science and society; midcentury readings, Harper, 61; co-ed, Victorian essays: a symposium, 67 & ed, Science fiction criticism: an annotated checklist, 72, Kent State Univ; ed, Science fiction: the other side of realism, Bowling Green Univ, 71 & A spectrum of worlds, Doubleday, 72; Science fiction: a dream of other worlds, Tex. A&M Univ, 73. Add: 545 Kieffer St, Wooster, OH 44691.

CLARK, BRUCE BUDGE, b. Georgetown, Idaho, Apr. 9, 18; m. 46; c. 6. ENGLISH. A.B, Univ. Utah, 43, Ph.D, 51; A.M, Brigham Young Univ, 48. Teaching asst, Brigham Young Univ, 46-47; Univ. Utah 47-50; asst. prof. ENG, BRIGHAM YOUNG UNIV, 50-55, assoc. prof, 56-59, PROF, 59-, DEAN COL. HUMANITIES, 65-, dir. dept. humanities, 58-60, chmn. dept. Eng, 60-65. U.S.A, 43-46. MLA; NCTE. English literature of the 19th and 20th century, particularly poetry and fiction. Publ: Narrative poems of Robinson Jeffers, 47, Romanticism through modern eyes, 70 & Brigham Young on education, 70, Brigham Young Univ; English sonnet sequence: 1850-1900, Univ. Utah, 51; Out of the best books, Vol. I, 64 & co-auth, Vols. II, III, IV & V, 66-68, Deseret Bk; Oscar Wilde: a study in genius and tragedy, 70 & ed, Richard Evans quotebook, 72, Publ. Press; Spectrum of faith in Victorian literature, 62 & The challenge of teaching, 65, Brigham Young Univ. Stud. Add: Office of Dean, 129 J.K.B.A, College of Humanities, Brigham Young University, Provo, UT 84602.

CLARK, CHARLES MARSTON, b. Geneva, N.Y, Sept. 25, 14. ENGLISH. A.B, Cornell Univ, 37, M.A, 38, Ph.D.(Eng), 42. Instr. ENG, Cornell Univ, 38-40; AM. UNIV, 41-42, asst. prof, 46-48, assoc. prof, 48-53, PROF, 53- U.S.N.R, 42-46, Lt. Col. Eng. Asn.(pres, 63-64); NCTE; MLA. Eighteenth and 19th century English literature. Add: 3033 New Mexico Ave, Washington, DC 20016.

CLARK, DAVID GILLIS, b. Lubbock, Tex, May 14, 33. JOURNALISM, MASS COMMUNICATION. B.A, Tex. Technol. Col, 55; M.A, State Univ. Iowa, 56; Ph.D.(mass commun), Univ. Wis, 65. News ed, KCBD-AM-TV, 52-54; Instr. jour, Univ. Nebr, 58-59; Eng, Univ. Cincinnati, 59-61; asst. prof. commun, Stanford Univ, 65-67; jour, Univ. Wis, 67-70, assoc. prof, 70-73; PROF. TECH. JOUR. & CHMN. DEPT, COLO. STATE UNIV, 73- Writer-photographer, Lincoln Star, Nebr, 58-59; vis. assoc. prof, Univ. Wash, 70-71; consult, U.S. Surgeon General's Comt. TV & Social Behavior, 70-71. Sig.C, U.S.A, 56-58. Asn. Educ. in Jour; AAUP. Mass communications history; legal aspects of mass media. Publ: Co-ed, The American newspaper, Iowa State Univ, 69 & Mass media and the law, Wiley Intersci, 70; co-auth, You and media, Canfield, 73; co-auth, Trends in violent content in selected mass media, Vol. I, In: Media content and control, Television and social behavior, Nat. Inst. Ment. Health, 72. Add: Dept. of Technical Journalism, Colorado State University, Ft. Collins, CO 80521.

CLARK, DAVID MERRIETT, b. Sterling, Ill, Jan. 5, 36; m. 59; c. 2. THEATRE HISTORY. B.S.Ed, North. Ill. Univ, 58, M.A, 62; Woods Found. grant, Univ. Nebr, 66-67. Instr. Eng. & speech, Fenton High Sch, 58-59; assoc. dir, Wesley Found, North. Ill. Univ, 59-61; instr. SPEECH & THEATRE, NEBR. WESLEYAN UNIV, 62-65, asst. prof, 65-70, ASSOC. PROF, 70- Am. Theatre Asn; Children's Theatre Conf. American theatre history; theatre criticism; play direction. Publ: Something there is (one-act play), Gen. Bd. Educ, Methodist Church, 63; co-auth, Experimental theatre: innovational by intent?, Cue, spring 67. Add: Dept. of Speech & Theatre Arts, Nebraska Wesleyan University, 50th & St. Paul, Lincoln, NE 68504.

CLARK, DAVID RIDGLEY, b. Seymour, Conn, Sept. 17, 20; m. 48; c. 4. ENGLISH. B.A,Wesleyan Univ, 47; M.A, Yale, 50, Ph.D, 55. Instr. ENG, Mohawk Col, 47; teaching fel, Ind. Univ, 48-50; instr, Univ. Mass, 51-56; lectr, Smith Col, 56-57; asst. prof, UNIV. MASS, AMHERST, 58, assoc. prof, 58-65, PROF, 65- Saxton fel, 57; Bollingen Found. grant-in-aid, 57 & fels, summers 61, 62, 63; Am. Philos. Soc. grant, 57; Am. Counc. Learned Soc. grant-in-aid, summers 58, 65; lectr, Yeats Int. Summer Sch, Ireland, 60; Fulbright lectr, Univ. Iceland, 60-61 & Univ. Col, Dublin, 65-66; vis. assoc. prof, Univ. Mich, summer 66; vis. prof, Syracuse Univ. spring 68; Nat. Endowment for Humanities proj. grant, 69; vis. prof. Eng, Univ. Victoria (B.C), 71-72; Sir George Williams Univ, summer 72. MLA; Am. Com. Irish Stud; AAUP; Can. Asn. Irish Stud. W.B. Yeats and the modern literature of Ireland; the poetry of Hart Crane; modern poetry. Publ: Co-auth, A curious quire, 62 & auth, Lyric resonance: Yeats, Frost, Crane, Cummings, and others, 72, Univ. Mass; auth, W.B. Yeats and the theatre of desolate reality, Dolmen, Dublin & DuFour, Pa, 65; co-auth, Irish Renaissance, 65, auth, Dry tree, 66 & co-ed, A tower of polished black stones: early versions of The shadowy waters, 71, Dolmen, Dublin; co-auth, Reading poetry, Harper, 68; ed, Riders to the sea, 70 & Studies in The bridge, 70, C.E. Merrill & Twentieth century interpretations of Murder in the Cathedral, Prentice-Hall, 71; co-ed, Druid craft: the writing of The shadowy waters, Univ. Mass, 71 & Dolmen, Dublin, 72; auth, Ecclesiasticus and Prospero's epilogue, Shakespeare Quart, winter 66; Landscape painting effects in Pope's Homer, In: Essential articles for the study of Alexander Pope, Archon Bks, 68; Asmodeus and the Fishy fume: Paradise lost, IV, 153-171, Stud. Eng. Lit, winter 72; plus others. Add: Dept. of English, University of Massachusetts, Amherst, MA 01002.

CLARK, EARL JOHN, b. Omaha, Nebr, Apr. 17, 27; m. 52. ENGLISH LITERATURE. A.B, Loyola Univ.(Ill), 49, A.M, 52, Ph.D.(Eng), 56; Harvard, 49-50. Instr. ENG, Loyola Univ.(Ill), 50-56, asst. prof, 56-65; assoc. prof, NORTHEAST. ILL. UNIV, 65-69, PROF, 69- U.S.A, 45-46. MLA; Renaissance Soc. Am. Works of Edmund Spenser; critical theories of the English Renaissance poetry; lyric poetry of English Renaissance. Add: 115 Le-Moyne Pkwy, Oak Park, IL 60302.

CLARK, EDWARD, b. Elyria, Ohio, Oct. 25, 23. ENGLISH. A.B, Miami Univ, 49; Rotary Found. fel, Cambridge, 49-50; Univ. Paris; Univ. Heidelberg; Strauss fel, Ind. Univ, 54-55, Ph.D.(Eng), 55. Asst. prof, ENG, St. Lawrence Univ, 55-61; assoc. prof, SUFFOLK UNIV, 61-65, PROF, 65- Fulbright lectr, Kiel Univ, 58-59. U.S.A, 43-46. MLA; Col. Lang. Asn; AAUP. Leatherstocking tales of Fenimore Cooper; American and British novel; racial literature. Publ: Winesburg, Ohio: an interpretation, Die Neueren Sprachen, 59; Images of the Negro in the American novel, Jahrbuch für Amerikastudien, 60; Studying and teaching Afro-American literature, CLA, 72. Add: Dept. of English, Suffolk University, 41 Temple St, Boston, MA 02114.

CLARK, EDWARD DEPRIEST, b. Wilmington, N.C, May 24, 30; m. 52; c. 1. ENGLISH. B.S, Agr. & Tech. Col, N.C, 48; M.A, N.Y. Univ, 55, summers 56-58; Ph.D.(Eng), Syracuse Univ, 71. Asst. prof. ENG, Albany State Col, 57-59; South. Univ, 60-61; FAYETTEVILLE STATE UNIV, 61-62, assoc. prof, 62-71, PROF, 71-, CHMN. DEPT, 62-, lectr, NDEA Eng. Inst, summer 66. Rep, Phelps Stokes Fund Advan. Educ, 57-59; state consult, Teachers Eng, Ga, 57-59. U.S.A, 61-63, Sgt. MCTE; CLA; Conf. Col. Compos. & Commun; MLA. The American novel; transcendentalism in American literature; comparative literature. Add: Box 923, Fayetteville State University, Fayetteville, NC 28301.

CLARK, EDWARD WILLIAM, b. Warren, Ohio, Aug. 31, 43; m. 65; c. 1. ENGLISH, AMERICAN LITERATURE. B.A, Otterbein Col, 65; M.A, Purdue Univ, Lafayette, 67; Ph.D.(Eng), Univ. Wis-Madison, 72. Instr. ENG, Purdue Univ, Calumet Campus, 67-69; ASST. PROF, WINTHROP COL, 72- MLA; Southeast Mod. Lang. Asn. Colonial American literature; the frontier and American literature; the Indian captivity narrative. Add: Dept. of English, College of Arts & Sciences, Winthrop College, Rock Hill, SC 29730.

CLARK, F. DONALD, b. Wellington, Kans, July 15, 13; m. 39; c. 1. FINE ARTS. B.S, Kans. State Teachers Col, Emporia, 36; M.A, Univ. Iowa, 38. Instr, Kans. State Teachers Col, Emporia, 36-37, 38; Parsons Jr. Col, 38-40; Amarillo Col, 40-45; radio news ed, KFDA, Tex, 44-46; from asst. prof. radio to assoc. prof. DRAMA, UNIV. OKLA, 46-61, PROF, 61-, DEAN COL. FINE ARTS, 61-, acting dean, 59-61. Mem. bd, Nat. Counc. Arts in Educ. Southwest Theatre Conf.(pres, 62); Nat. Counc. Fine Arts Deans (chmn, 64). Art; dance; drama; music. Add: College of Fine Arts, University of Oklahoma, Norman, OK 73069.

CLARK, FRANK M, b. Punxsutawney, Pa, Nov. 1, 30; m. 66. THEATRE HISTORY, CRITICISM. B.S, Ind. Univ. Pa, 52; M.F.A, Ohio Univ, 67; Pa. State Univ, Wroxton Col, Eng, Univ. Sask, Royal Holloway Col, Eng. & Univ. Pittsburgh, 67-74. Teacher Eng. & Speech, Cranberry Area High Sch, Seneca, Pa, 52-64; chmn. lang. arts, 64-67; asst. prof. SPEECH & THEATRE, CLARION STATE COL, VENANGO CAMPUS, 67-73, ASSOC. PROF, 73- Speech Commun. Asn; Am. Theatre Asn. Publ: The theatre of Pithole, Pennsylvania, oil boom town, West. Pa. Hist. Mag, 1/73. Add: Dept. of Speech Communication & Theatre, Clarion State College, Venango Campus, 1801 W. First St, Oil City, PA 16301.

CLARK, GEORGE E, b. Benton, Ky, June 1, 26; m. 53; c. 2. ENGLISH. A.B, Union Univ, 49; B.D, South. Baptist Theol. Sem, 52, Th.M, 53; M.A, George Peabody Col, 52, Ford fel, 59-60, Ph.D.(Eng), 62; summer, Vanderbilt Univ. & Univ. Bridgeport, 67. Teacher, Brewers High Sch, 53-54; asst. educ, George Peabody Col, 54-55; asst. prof. Eng, Belmont Col, 55-57, assoc. prof. Eng. & dir. pub. relat, 57-59; asst. ENG, George Peabody Col, 59-60; PROF. & HEAD DEPT, UNION UNIV, 61- NCTE; S.Cent. Mod. Lang. Asn. Elizabethan drama; contemporary drama; Southern life and literature. Publ: English programs in Southern Baptist colleges, South. Baptist Educator, 2/63. Add: Dept. of English, Union University, Jackson, TN 38301.

CLARK, GEORGE PEIRCE, b. Indianapolis, Ind, Sept. 8, 15; m. 46; c. 4. ENGLISH & AMERICAN LITERATURE. A.B, Col. Wooster, 38; Ph.D.(Eng), Yale, 48. Asst. prof. Eng, Coe Col, 48-50; North. Ill. Univ, 50-53, assoc. prof, 53-56, prof, 56-57; vis. lectr, Univ. Ill, 57-58; assoc. prof, Mich. State Univ, 59-60; cult. affairs off, U.S. Inform. Agency, 60-67; PROF. ENG. & CHMN. DEPT, HANOVER COL, 67- Ford fac. fel, Harvard, 53-54; Fulbright prof, Univ. Mainz, 56-57; vis. prof. Eng, Grad. Sch, Ind. Univ, Bloomington, summer 73. U.S.A.A.F, 42-45, Staff Sgt. MLA; AAUP. Nineteenth-century American literature; Edgar Allan Poe. Publ: Co-auth, Student and society, Harper, 59, Journals and miscellaneous notebooks of Ralph Waldo Emerson, Vol. I, Harvard, 60, Winds of change in Haitian education, Negro Hist. Bull, 10/69 & The tangled web of Haitian education, Int. Educ. & Cult. Exchange, summer 70; auth, Two unnoticed recollections of Poe's funeral, Poe Stud, 6/70; plus others. Add: P.O. Box 62, Hanover College, Hanover, IN 47243.

CLARK, GEORGE RICHARD, b. Paducah, Ky, Feb. 13, 32; m. 58; c. 1. ENGLISH. B.A, Humboldt State Col, 54; M.A, Univ. Calif, Berkeley, 57; fel, Harvard, 59, Ph.D.(Eng), 61. Instr. Eng, Univ. Wis, 61-63, grant, univ. res. comt, summer, 62; asst. prof. ENG, Univ. Tex, 63-65; ASSOC. PROF, QUEEN'S UNIV.(ONT), 65- Fulbright lectr, Univ. Helsinki, 66-67; Am. Counc. Learned Soc. fel, 72-73. Mod. Lang. Soc. Finland; Viking Soc. North. Res; MLA; Mediaeval Acad. Am. Old Norse; Anglo-Saxon poetry; Chaucer. Publ: The traveler recognizes his goal..., J. Eng. & Ger. Philol, 65; Beowulf's armor, ELH, 65; The battle of Maldon: a heroic poem, Speculum, 68. Add: Dept. of English, Queen's University, Kingston, Ont, Can.

CLARK, IRA GRANVILLE, III, b. Berkeley, Calif, Sept. 28, 40; m. 62; c. 2. ENGLISH. B.A, N.Mex. State Univ, 62; univ. fel. & M.A, Northwest. Univ, 63, univ. fel, Inland Steel-Ryerson Found. fel. & Ph.D.(Eng), 66. Asst. prof. ENG, Johns Hopkins Univ, 68-72; ASSOC. PROF, UNIV. FLA, 72- Lectr, Univ. Col, Univ. Md, summer 67. U.S.A, 66-68, Capt. MLA; Milton Soc. Am; Renaissance Soc. Am; S.Atlantic Mod. Lang. Asn. Milton and seventeenth-century English literature; sixteenth-century English literature; Tudor-Stuart drama. Publ: Samuel Daniel's Complaint of Rosamond, Renaissance Quart, 70; Lord, in thee the beauty lies in the discovery: Love unknown and reading Herbert, ELH, 72; Paradise regained and the Gospel according to John, Mod. Philol, 73. Add: Dept. of English, University of Florida, Gainesville, FL 32617.

CLARK, JAMES DRUMMOND, b. Lake Forest, Ill, Mar. 1, 40; m. 66. ENGLISH. B.A, Colo. Col, 63; NDEA fel, Univ. Ariz, 63-66, Ph.D.(Eng), 67. ASST. PROF. ENG, MIAMI UNIV, 67- Malone Soc. Italian-English connections in early Elizabethan drama. Add: Dept. of English, Miami University, Oxford, OH 45056.

CLARK, JAMES JEFFERSON, b. High Point, N.C, Nov. 19, 19; m. 56; c. 2. ENGLISH. B.A, Univ. N.C, 40; M.A, Columbia Univ, 46; M.F.A, West. Reserve Univ, 49; Ph.D, N.Y. Univ, 56. From assoc. prof. to PROF. ENG, SAN JOSE STATE UNIV, 58-, CHMN. DEPT, 70- Eng.C, 40-45, 1st Lt. American literature, 1920-1940. Publ: Ed, Success in America, Wadsworth, 66 & Social rebel in American literature, Odyssey, 68. Add: Dept. of English, San Jose State University, San Jose, CA 95192.

CLARK, JOHN L, b. Mason, Nev, Mar. 30, 19; m. 44; c. 1. ENGLISH, DRAMA. B.A. & M.A, Univ. Wis, 46; Ph.D.(theater), Stanford Univ, 55. Instr. speech, Univ. Buffalo, 46-47; asst. prof. drama, Beloit Col, 47-49; Eng, San Francisco State Col, 51-55, assoc. prof, 55-60, prof, 60-65, prof. drama & chmn. dept, 65-68; dean of fac, Sonoma State Col, 68-70; DEAN, ILL. WESLEYAN UNIV, 70- Fulbright lectr, Damascus Univ, 62-63. U.S.A.A.F, 41-45, Maj. Am. Theatre Asn. Theater and drama; English dramatic literature. Publ: Educational dramatics in 19th century colleges, In: History of speech education in America, Appleton, 54. Add: Office of the Dean, Illinois Wesleyan University, Bloomington, IL 61701.

CLARK, JOHN R, b. Phila, Pa, Oct. 2, 30; m; c. 2. ENGLISH LITERATURE. B.A, Pa. State Univ, 52; M.A, Columbia Univ, 56; Ph.D.(Eng), Univ. Mich, 65. Instr. ENG, Bloomfield Col, 56-57; Alfred Univ, 58-61, asst. prof, 63-65; Muhlenberg Col, 65-66; City Col. New York, 66-68; Fordham Univ, 68-69; assoc. prof, N.Y. Univ, 69-73, asst. chmn. dept, Univ. Col, 69-72, acting chmn. dept, 72-73, grad. adv. & asst. to head dept, Washington Sq, 72-73; PROF. ENG. & CHMN. DEPT, UNIV. S.FLA, 73- Asst. prof. Eng, Univ. Mich, summer 68, vis. assoc. prof, summer 69. U.S.N.R, 52-54. MLA; NCTE; Am. Philol. Asn; Am. Soc. 18th Century Stud; Col. Eng. Asn. Jonathan Swift and 18th century; satire. Publ: Form and frenzy in Swift's Tale of a tub, Cornell Univ, 70; ed, Satire—that blasted art, Putnam, 73; auth, Ise Dais: the honor of Achilles, Arethusa, fall 69; Formal straining: recent criticism of satire, Col. Eng, 71; Further Iliads in Swift's Nutshell, Philol. Quart, 10/72; plus others. Add: Dept. of English, University of South Florida, Tampa, FL 33620.

CLARK, JOHN WILLIAMS, b. Excelsior, Minn, Dec. 23, 07; m. 30. ENGLISH. A.B, Univ. Minn, 28, Ph.D, 41; A.M, Harvard, 29. Instr. ENG, Rensselaer Polytech. Inst, 29-30; UNIV. MINN, 30-42, asst. prof, 42-49, assoc. prof, 49-53, chmn. dept, 58-69, prof, 53-73, EMER. PROF. ENG, 73- Old and Middle English; English language. Publ: British and American English since 1950, Andrew Dakers, 51; Early English: a study of Old and Middle English, Andre Deutsch, 57, rev. ed, 67. Add: 403 Oak Grove, Minneapolis, MN 55403.

CLARK, JOSEPH DEADRICK, b. Jonesboro, Tenn, June 14, 93; m. 23; c. 1. ENGLISH. A.B, Columbia Univ, 14; Oxford Univ, 19; A.M, Harvard, 21; Univ. Chicago, 26, 28. Head dept. Eng, high sch, Tenn, 14-16, prin, Va, 19-22; instr. ENG, Va. Polytech. Inst, 22-23; from asst. prof. to prof, N.C. STATE UNIV, 23-62, EMER. PROF, 62- U.S.A, 17-19, Sgt. Brown-Hudson Folklore Award, N.C. Folklore Soc, 72. Folklore. Publ: Beastly folklore, Scarecrow, 68; North Carolina popular beliefs and superstitions, N.C. Folklore J, 7/68 & 1/70. Add: 15 Furches St, Raleigh, NC 27607.

CLARK, JUSTUS KENT, b. Blue Creek, Utah, Sept. 29, 17; m. 39; c. 3. ENGLISH. A.B, Brigham Young Univ, 39; Ph.D, Stanford Univ, 50. Instr, Stanford Univ, 42-43, 46-47; ENG, CALIF. INST. TECHNOL, 47-50, asst. prof, 50-54, assoc. prof, 54-60, PROF, 60- U.S.A, 43-46, Lt. Eighteenth century English literature; Jonathan Swift; modern poetry. Publ: King's agent, 58 & co-auth, Dimensions in drama, 64, Scribner, Add: Dept. of English, California Institute of Technology, Pasadena, CA 91109.

CLARK, L. D, b. Gainesville, Tex, Oct. 22, 22; m. 51. ENGLISH. B.A, Columbia Univ, 53, M.A, 54, W. Bayard Cutting traveling fel, 60-61, Ph.D.(Eng), 63. Instr. ENG, Agr. & Mech. Col. Tex, 54-55; UNIV. ARIZ, 55-62, lectr, 62-63, asst. prof, 63-65, assoc. prof, 65-70, PROF, 70- Assoc. prof, Univ. Nice, 73-74. U.S.A.A.F, 41-45, M/Sgt. Philol. Asn. Pac. Coast; MLA. British literature of the 20th century, chiefly D.H. Lawrence. Publ: The dove tree, Doubleday, 61; Dark night of the body: D.H. Lawrence's The plumed serpent, Univ. Tex, 64; co-auth, Approaches to the twentieth-century novel, Crowell, 65 & The habitat of the plumed serpent, Tex. Quart, 62; auth, The apocalypse of Lorenzo, D.H. Lawrence Rev, summer 70. Add: Dept. of English, University of Arizona, Tucson, AZ 85721.

CLARK, LARRY DALE, b. Gainesville, Mo, Sept. 18, 32; m. 54. DRAMATIC ART. B.S.Ed, Southwest. Mo. State Col, 56; M.A, Univ. Mo, 61; Ph.D.(speech), Univ. Ill, 63. Teacher high sch, Mo, 50-52 & 56-61; asst. speech, Univ. Ill, 62-63; asst. prof. DRAMATIC ART, Univ. Iowa, 63-66; UNIV. MO-COLUMBIA, 66-68, assoc. prof, 68-71, PROF, 71-, ASST. PROVOST ACAD. AFFAIRS, 73-, chmn. dept. speech & dramatic art, 70-73. Mem, Speech Asn. Am-NCTE Joint Comt. Teacher Training, 64-66. Gold Medallion Award, Am. Col. Theatre Festival, 73. U.S.A.F, 62-66, S/Sgt. Am. Theatre Asn; Speech Commun. Asn; Cent. States Speech Asn.(exec. secy, 66-69, pres, 72-73); Popular theatre; American theatre history; theatre aesthetics. Publ: Maude Adams at Stephens College..., Speech Teacher, 65; The Toby show, American rural harlequinade, Cent. States Speech J, 68; Directing: from analysis to action, Players Mag, 6-7/71. Add: 820 Bourn Ave, Columbia, MO 65201.

CLARK, MARDEN J, b. Morgan, Utah, July 13, 16; m. 41; c. 6. ENGLISH. A.B, Brigham Young Univ, 48, M.A, 49; fel, Univ. Wash, 55-57, Ph.D, 57. Instr. ENG, BRIGHAM YOUNG UNIV, 49-56, asst. prof, 56-59, assoc. prof, 59-64, PROF, 64- Brigham Young Univ. res. grants, summers 62 & 65-68, spring 65; sr. lectr, Fulbright Comt. Int. Exchange of Persons, Finland, 70-71. MLA; AAUP; Rocky Mt. Mod. Lang. Asn. Creative writing; modern American literature; 20th century English and Continental literature. Publ: Co-ed, About language: contexts for college writing, Scribner, 70; auth, Modern and classic: the wooing both ways, C.E. Merrill & Brigham Young Univ, 72; Tragic effect in The hairy ape, Mod. Drama, 2/68; Some implications of human freedom, summer 70 & On the Mormon commitment to education, spring 73, Dialogue; plus others. Add: Dept. of English, Brigham Young University, Provo, UT 84601.

CLARK, RICHARD, b. Phila, Pa, Mar. 3, 41; m. 66; c. 1. ENGLISH. A.B, Temple Univ, 63, M.A, 67. Asst. ENG, Temple Univ, 63-66; ASST. PROF, COMMUNITY COL. PHILA, 66- Instr. Eng, Tougaloo South. Christian Col, 65. MLA; NCTE. Shakespeare; Renaissance studies; rhetoric. Publ: Co-auth, Writing by patterns, Knopf, 68. Add: Dept. of English, Community College of Philadelphia, Philadelphia, PA 19107.

CLARK, ROBERT DONALD, b. Maywood, Nebr, Mar. 30, 10; m. 32; c. 3. RHETORIC. A.B, Pasadena Col, 31; A.M, Univ. South. Calif, 35, Ph.D, 46; hon. LL.D, Univ. Santa Clara, 68, Gonzaga Univ, 70 & Willamette Univ, 73. From asst. to instr, Pasadena Col, 31-39; asst. prof, Stockton Jr. Col, 39-43; Col. Pac, 43; speech, Univ. Ore, 43-46, assoc. prof, 46-50, prof, 50-64; asst. to dean, Col. Lib. Arts, 49-51, asst. dean, 51-55, acting dean, 55-56, dean, 56-61, dean faculties, 61-64; PRES, San Jose State Col, 64-69; UNIV. ORE, 69- Guggenheim fel, 50-51; mem. steering comt, Nat. Urban Coalition, 71. 1970 Speaker of the Year, Delta Sigma Rho-Tau Kappa Alpha. Speech Commun. Asn; AAUP; Am. Soc. Church Hist; West. Speech Asn,(ed, West. Speech, 39-43, pres, 47); Orgn. Am. Hist. History of public address. Publ: Handbook for fundamentals of speaking, Pac. Bks, 47; Life of Mathew Simpson, Macmillan, 56; plus others. Add: Office of the President, University of Oregon, Eugene, OR 97403.

CLARK, ROBERT KING, b. Springfield, Mass, Apr. 12, 34; m. 66; c. 2. SPEECH. B.A, Univ. Wyo, 56; M.A, Univ. Tenn, Knoxville, 60; Ph.D. (speech), Ohio State Univ, 71. Radio announcer, WSYB, Rutland, Vt, 56-57; radio-TV film writer & producer, Univ. Tenn, Knoxville, 57-59; instr. SPEECH, Westminster Col, 59-61; BOWLING GREEN STATE UNIV, 63-66, asst. prof, 66-71, ASSOC. PROF, 71- Production mgr, WBGU-TV, 64-66, prog. dir, 66-68; asst. prof. speech, Univ. Maine, Orono, 68-69. Broadcast Educ. Asn. Filmmaking; children's television; sociology of mass communications. Publ: Contrib, Introduction to speech communication, Brown, 68; co-auth, Small market media managers, J. Broadcasting, spring 72. Add: Dept. of Speech, Bowling Green State University, Bowling Green, OH 43403.

CLARK, ROGER G, b. St. Louis, Mo, Nov. 1, 37; m. 68. ENGLISH. A.B, Univ. Mo, 59, M.A, 61; Ph.D.(Eng), Univ. Colo, Boulder, 69. Instr. Eng, Univ. Mo, 61-62; proj. mgr, NCTE-Educ. Resources Inform. Ctr. Clearinghouse Teaching Eng, 67-69; ASST. PROF. ENG. & ASST. DEAN GRAD. COL, UNIV. ILL, URBANA-CHAMPAIGN, 69- Tech. consult, Abstracts Eng. Stud, 65-67; user-consult, Colo. Concordances, 66-67. Nat. Guard & U.S.A.R, 55-63. MLA. Seventeenth century prose; information retrieval. Publ: Co-auth, The integration, storage, and retrieval of bibliographic data in English studies, Univ. Colo, 65 & Information retrieval through bibliographic integration, Quart. Bull. Computer Soc. Can, summer 67; Henry King and the rise of modern prose style, J. Eng. & Ger. Philol, 74; plus others. Add: Graduate College, 314 Administration Bldg, University of Illinois at Urbana, Urbana, IL 61801.

CLARK, THOMAS LLOYD, b. Havre, Mont, July 10, 39; m. 60; c. 3. LINGUISTICS, DIALECTOLOGY. B.A, Univ. Utah, 64, M.A, 66; NDEA fel, Ohio Univ, 66-67, Ph.D.(Eng. ling), 70. Teaching asst. Eng, Univ. Utah, 64-66; Dict. Am. Regional Eng. res. assoc, Univ. Wis, 67-68; teaching assoc. ENG, Ohio Univ, 68-69, instr, 69-70; asst. prof, UNIV. NEV, LAS VEGAS, 70-73, ASSOC. PROF, 73- Consult, Barnhart Publ. Co, 73-74. U.S.N, 57-59. Am. Dialect Soc; MLA; NCTE; Am. Name Soc.(dir, Nev. surv, 73-); Int. Reading Asn. Descriptive linguistics; general and structural linguistics. Publ: Workshops in regional and social dialects, NCTE, 74; Erosion of a speech island, Am. Dialect Soc, 74; Principles of elicitation in linguistic fieldwork, Am. Speech, spring/summer 71; The environment of names in the classroom, Elem. Eng, 11/72; Pedagogical aspects of onomastics, In: Current trends in onomastics. Current trends in linguistics, Humanities Press. Add: Dept. of English, University of Nevada, Las Vegas, NV 89154.

CLARK, WALTER HOUSTON, JR, b. Pittsfield, Mass, Oct. 6, 31; m. 67. ENGLISH, PHILOSOPHY OF EDUCATION. B.A, Swarthmore Col, 54; A.M.T, Harvard, 58, Ph.D.(philos. educ), 65. From asst. prof. to ASSOC. PROF. ENG, UNIV. MICH, ANN ARBOR, 65- Fulbright lectr, Graz Univ, 71-72. Ord.C, U.S.A, 54-56. MLA; NCTE (mem. comn. lit, 73-75); Am. Soc. Aesthet. Theory and language of criticism. Publ: On the role of choice in aesthetic education, 7/68 & Skill and art in teaching literature, 1/73, J. Aesthet. Educ; Seeing as and knowing that, In: Aesthetic concepts and education, Univ. Ill, 69. Add: Dept. of English, University of Michigan, Ann Arbor, MI 48104.

CLARK, WILLIAM KEITH, b. Columbus, Ind, Apr. 11, 26; m. 51; c. 3. SPEECH. A.B, Wabash Col, 49; M.A, Univ. South. Calif, 50; Univ. Fla, 52-53; Purdue Res. Found. summer grants, Purdue Univ, 59 & 60, Ph.D. (speech), 60. Instr. speech & debate & debate dir, Wabash Col, 50-51, instr. speech & drama & drama dir, 51-52; assoc. prof. speech & debate dir, McMurry Col, 53-54, assoc. prof. speech & chmn. dept, 54-57; chmn. dept. speech, Hiram Col, 58-60, chmn. dept. speech & drama, 60-67; ASSOC. PROF. RHETORIC & PUB. ADDRESS, KEARNEY STATE COL, 67-, fac. res. grants, 71, 72 & 73. Ed. & publ, Digest Res. Relig. Speaking, 61-63; res. ed, Preaching, 66-; U.S. Off. Educ. grants, 67, 68 & 70. Qm.C, U.S.N, 44-46. Speech Commun. Asn. Religious speech, especially seminary speech education; David Lloyd George's speaking, especially on his 1923 United States tour. Publ: Bibliography of research in religious speech, Preaching, 66-; Seminary speech education (1959), 67 & Seminary speech education, 1959-1969, 71, Speech Teacher; plus one other. Add: Dept. of Speech, Kearney State College, Kearney, NE 68847.

CLARK, WILMA HARMON, b. Meadville, Pa, Jan. 25, 38; m. 61; c. 2. ENGLISH LANGUAGE, ENGLISH & AMERICAN LITERATURE. A.B, Allegheny Col, 59; M.A, West. Mich. Univ, 66; Ph.D.(Eng), Mich. State Univ, 72. ASST. PROF. ENG, UNIV. WIS-SUPERIOR, 72- MLA; Midwest Mod. Lang. Asn; NCTE; Col. Eng. Asn; Popular Cult. Asn. Popular and elitist taste in literature; the teaching of English; linguistics and literature. Publ: The teaching of poetry : a case for structure in the student-centered class, Nebr. Eng. Counselor, 5/72 & in, CEA Forum, 12/72; Four popular poets: a century of taste, In: New dimensions in popular culture, Bowling Green State Univ, 72. Add: Dept. of English, University of Wisconsin-Superior, Superior, WI 54880.

CLARKE, DOUGLASS BURNS, b. Montreal, Que, Oct. 13, 07; m. 39; c. 2. ENGLISH, FINE ARTS. B.A, Sir George Williams Univ, 37, hon. LL.D, 73; M.A, McGill Univ, 43. Asst. prof. Eng. & fine arts, Sir George Williams Univ, 38-42, assoc. prof, 43-49, prof, 50-73, registr, 43-56, v.prin. & registr, 56-62, acad. v.prin, 62-69; RETIRED. Can. Psychol. Asn; Am. Soc. Aesthet. Psychology of art. Add: 365 Lansdowne Ave, Westmount, P.Q, H3Z 2L5, Can.

CLARKE, GORDON WILSON, b. Chicago, Ill, May 1, 23; m. 43; c. 3. ENGLISH, LINGUISTICS. A.B, Univ. Ill, 43, A.M, 47, fel, 47-49, Ph.D.(Eng), 49. Assoc. prof. Eng, Ala. State Col, Florence, 49-50; East. Ore. Col, 50-59, prof, 59-68, chmn. dept, 67-68; PROF. HUMANITIES, ORE. COL. EDUC, 68- Ed, East. Ore. Eng. Bull, 53-57; Tektronix fel, Univ. Mich, 55. U.S.A, 43-46, Lt. MLA; NCTE; Am. Dialect Soc. American novel; linguistics. Publ: Handbook for research papers, Florence State Col, 50; asst. ed, Magill's quotations in context, Salem, 65. Add: Dept. of Humanities, Oregon College of Education, Monmouth, OR 97361.

CLARKE, JOHN J, b. Wilkes-Barre, Pa, Apr. 22, 25; m. 56; c. 3. JOURNALISM, ENGLISH LITERATURE. A.B, Univ. Scranton, 48; M.A, Fordham Univ, 50; M.S, Columbia Univ, 50; Ph.D.(Eng), Brown Univ, 57. Reporter, copy ed. & feature writer, The Providence, R.I, Jour-Bull, 50-55; news ed, The Scranton, Pa, Times, 55-67; ASSOC. PROF. JOUR, OHIO STATE UNIV, 67- Lectr, Univ. Scranton, 57-67; Marywood Col, 60-67; mideast dir, Newspaper Fund Copy Editing Intern Prog, 70- U.S.A, 43-46. Asn. Educ. in Jour. Journalism and literature; American literature; newspaper copy editing. Publ: The achievement of Flannery O'Connor, Esprit, 64. Add: 2100 Haviland Rd, Columbus, OH 43221.

CLARKE, KENNETH WENDELL, b. Spokane, Wash, Jan. 6, 17; m. 60; c. 1. FOLKLORE. B.A, Wash. State Univ, 48, M.A, 49; Ph.D, Ind. Univ, 58. Instr. ENG, Wash. State Univ, 50-53; assoc. prof, Chico State Col, 55-60; Univ. Nev, 60-62; Ind. Univ, 62-64; PROF, WEST. KY. UNIV, 64- U.S.N, 42-45. Am. Folklore Soc; Nat. Univ. Exten. Asn; Adult Educ. Asn. U.S. African folklore and Afro-American folklore. Publ: Co-auth, Introducing folklore, Holt, 63, A folklore reader, A.S. Barnes, 65 & A concise dictionary of folklore, Ky. Folklore Soc, 65; auth, Uncle Bud Long, birth of a Kentucky folk legend, Univ. Ky, 73. Add: Dept. of English, Western Kentucky University, Bowling Green, KY 42101.

CLARKE, LORI MARIE, b. Chicago, Ill, Nov. 28, 28. ENGLISH, ENGLISH EDUCATION. B.A, Alverno Col, 50; M.A, Marquette Univ, 66; Ph.D.(Eng, educ), Univ. Iowa, 70. Elem. teacher, 50-57; sec. teacher, 58-67; asst. prof, ENG, UNIV. UTAH, 70-73, ASSOC. PROF, 73- Consult, Fed. Grant for Prev. Juv. Delinq, 72-73; mem, Nat. Comt. Teacher Prep. & Cert, 72- NCTE; AAUP; Rocky Mountain Mod. Lang. Asn.(chmn. teaching sect, 72-73); Conf. Eng. Educ. Publ: Creative teaching, why not creative testing?, Eng. Educ, fall 72; The Pigman—a novel of adolescence, 11/72 & Tunis' novel of global conscience, 5/73: Eng. J; plus others. Add: Dept. of English, University of Utah, Salt Lake City, UT 84112.

CLARKE, MARY WASHINGTON, b. Scarbro, W.Va, Feb. 4, 13; m. 60. ENGLISH, FOLKLORE. A.B, Marshall Univ, 33; M.A, W.Va. Univ, 36; Ph.D.(Eng), Univ. Pa, 60. Teacher, High Sch, 35-44; case worker, Am. Red Cross, 44-45; instr. ENG, Marshall Univ, 46-49, asst. prof, 49-53, assoc. prof, 53-54; Ind. State Univ, 54-58; asst. prof, Chico State Col, 58-60; spec. assignment, Indiana Univ. Pa, Jeffersonville Campus, 62-64; assoc. prof, WEST. KY. UNIV, 64-67, PROF, 67- Co-ed, Ky. Folklore Rec, 64-70. MLA; Am. Folklore Soc. American dialect; American literature; American folklore. Publ: Co-auth, Introducing folklore, Holt, 63, A folklore reader, A.S. Barnes, 65 & A concise folklore dictionary, Ky. Folklore Soc, 65; auth, Jesse Stuart's Kentucky, McGraw, 68; Jesse Stuart preserves passing folk idiom, South. Folklore Quart, fall 64; Bridging the generation gap: the ending of Steinbeck's Grapes of wrath. Add: Dept. of English, Western Kentucky University, Bowling Green, KY 42101.

CLARKE, PETER, b. Evanston, Ill, Sept. 19, 36; m. 62; c. 1. COMMUNICATION RESEARCH, JOURNALISM. B.A, Univ. Wash, 59; M.A, Univ. Minn, 61; Ph.D.(jour. & mass commun), 63. Owner, Peter Clarke & Assoc, 54-59; res. asst. JOUR, Univ. Minn, 59-61, instr, 61-63; acting asst. prof, Univ. Wash, 63-64, asst. prof, 64-67, assoc. prof, 67-72, dir. commun. ctr, 65-68, dir. sch. commun, 71-72; PROF, UNIV. MICH, ANN ARBOR, 72-, CHMN. DEPT, 73- U.S.A.R, 54-62, Sgt. Asn. Educ. Jour.(mem. res. comt, 70-, head theory & methodology div, 72-73); Am. Asn. Pub. Opinion Res; Am. Sociol. Asn. Mass communications research; communication effects on public attitudes about public affairs and government; mass communications, and social change. Publ: Co-ed, Annual reviews of communication research, 72 & ed, New models for communication research, 73, Sage; auth, Factors affecting the reporting of protest, In: Report to Presidential committee on causes & prevention of violence, 11/68; co-ed, Youth and the mass media, 1/71 & auth, Teenager's coorientation and information seeking about pop music, 3/73, Am. Behav. Sci; plus one other. Add: Dept. of Journalism, 2040 LS & A, University of Michigan, Ann Arbor, MI 48104.

CLARKSON, PHILIP B, b. Garden City, N.Y, July 29, 24; m. 59. DRAMATIC LITERATURE & ENGLISH. B.A, Wesleyan Univ, 46; M.A, Columbia Univ, 50; Ph.D.(drama), Stanford Univ, 63. Admin. asst, Wesleyan Univ, 46-47; instr. Eng. & dir. debate, Worcester Polytech. Inst, 47-49; asst. prof. Eng. & dir. drama, Norwich Univ, 50-54; assoc. prof. speech & drama & chmn. dept, Morningside Col, 56-59; prof. speech & drama & chmn. dept, Ripon Col, 63-73, acting v.pres. & dean fac, 68-69; PROF. COMMUN. & THEATRE ARTS & DEAN HUMANITIES, STATE UNIV. N.Y. COL. PLATTSBURGH, 73- Res. consult, Am. Stage proj. for U.S. Inform. Agency, Corcoran Gallery Art, 56. Uhrig Award, Ripon Col, 67, Severy Award, 70. AAUP. Dramatic literature; acting and directing. Add: 18 Champlain Dr, Cliff Haven, Plattsburgh, NY 12901.

CLAUDEL, ALICE MOSER, b. New Orleans, La, Apr. 5, 15; m. 43; c. 1. ENGLISH LITERATURE. B.A, Tulane Univ, 64, M.A, 68. Asst. ed, publicity dir. & bus. mgr, Experiment, 45-54; teacher Eng, St. Bernard Parish, La, 56-64; instr. Eng, W.Va. Wesleyan Col. & poetry ed, Laurel Rev, 66-70; LECTR. AM. LIT, EASTERN SHORE COMMUNITY COL, 71- Conductor poetry workshops, Deep South Writers Conf, Univ. Southwest. La. & Nat. League State Poetry Soc; judge of poetry; lectr. poetry & lit; auth. poems read on Columbia Broadcasting Syst, N.Y, New Orleans Pub. Libr. & KTKA, Tex; ed, New Laurel Rev, 70-; reviewer & consult, Choice, 71-; Nat. Endowment for the Arts & Md. Arts Counc. poet-in-residence grant, 71- NCTE; MLA; S.Atlantic Mod. Lang. Asn; Nat. Fed. State Poetry Soc; Col. Eng. Asn. Edgar Allan Poe, particularly the poetry; Hogarth and his relation to the theatre, eighteenth century; modern poetry. Publ: Southern season (poems), Appalachian Stud. Ctr, Pikeville Col, 72; Poe's journey in To Helen, Emerson Soc. Quart, fall 70; co-auth, Poe's journey in To Helen, In: New approaches to Poe, Transcendental Bks, 70 & Mystic symbols in Poe's The city in the sea, In: Papers on Poe (Festschrift to John Ward Ostrom), Wittenberg Univ, 72; plus others. Add: Eastern Shore Community College, Wallops Island, VA 23337.

CLAUSEN, CHRISTOPHER JOHN, b. Richmond, Va, May 14, 42. ENGLISH LITERATURE. B.A, Earlham Col, 64; Woodrow Wilson fel, Univ. Chicago, 64-65, M.A, 65; Can. Counc. fel, Queen's Univ.(Ont), 70-72, Ph.D.(Eng), 72. Instr. ENG, Univ. Hawaii, 65-66; ASST. PROF, Concord Col, 66-68; VA. POLYTECH. INST. & STATE UNIV, 73- Vis. lectr. Eng, Univ. Guelph, 73. MLA; S.Atlantic Mod. Lang. Asn. Oriental influences in English thought. Publ: The kingdom of ice (poems), Carrefour, London, 74; Tolkien's Lord of the Rings and Chesterton's Ballad of the white horse, S.Atlantic Bull, 74; A source for Thomas Becket's temptation in Murder in the cathedral, Notes & Queries, 74; contrib. poems, Ga. Rev, Quarry, and others. Add: Dept. of English, Virginia Polytechnic Institute & State University, Blacksburg, VA 24061.

CLAUSSEN, ERNEST NEAL, b. Petersburg, Ill, Aug. 15, 33; m. 61; c. 2. SPEECH COMMUNICATION. B.S, Ill. State Univ, 55; M.A, South. Ill. Univ, Carbondale, 59, Ph.D.(speech), 63. Instr. speech & econ, Mendota High Sch, Ill, 55-56; asst. prof. SPEECH, Colo. State Col, 59-61; BRADLEY UNIV, 63-67, assoc. prof, 67-71, PROF, 71-, assoc. dean col. lib. arts & sci, 69-71. Nat. Endowment for Humanities younger scholar stipend, 68. U.S.A, 56-58. Speech Commun. Asn; Rhetoric Soc. Am. Rhetorical theory; rhetorical criticism; public communication. Publ: Co-ed, John Lawson's lectures concerning oratory, South. Ill. Univ, 72; auth, John Sharp Williams: pace-setter for democratic keynoters, South. Speech, 65; Hendrick B. Wright and the nocturnal committee, Pa. Mag. Hist. & Biography, 65; He kept us out of war: Martin H. Glynn's keynote, Quart. J. Speech, 66; plus one other. Add: Dept. of Speech & Theatre Arts, Bradley University, Peoria, IL 61606.

CLAVADETSCHER, CARL JULIUS, b. Seattle, Wash, Sept. 29, 43; m. 65; c. 2. SPEECH COMMUNICATION. B.S, Mont. State Univ, 65; M.S, South. Ill. Univ, Carbondale, 66; NDEA fel, Univ. Ore, 67, Ph.D.(speech), 73. ASST. PROF. SPEECH COMMUN, UNIV. PUGET SOUND, 72-, ADJ. PROF. LAW, 73- Proj. evaluator, Modesto Prog. Speech & Lang. Disabilities, 71- U.S.A, 69-71, Res, 62-73, Capt. West. Speech Commun. Asn; AAUP. Propaganda; public opinion; mass communications. Add: Dept. of Communications, University of Puget Sound, Tacoma, WA 98416.

CLAXTON, EVELYN, b. Murray, Ky, Mar. 29, 24; m. 47; c. 3. LANGUAGE & LITERATURE. B.A, Univ. Mich, 45, M.A, 46; Ph.D.(Eng), Univ. Kans, 70. Instr. Eng, Univ. Mo, 46-47; Stephens Col, 47-49; Henry Ford Community Col, 49-52; exten. div, Univ. Kans, 52-53; creative writing instr, YWCA, Kans. City, Mo, 54-61; assoc. prof, Eng. & chmn. dept, Nat. Col, 62-65; INSTR. ENG. & JOUR, REND LAKE COL, 70- Creative writing instr, Raytown Adult Educ. Prog, 60-62. NCTE; MLA; Nat. Counc. Col. Publ. Adv.(Distinguished Adv. Award, 73). American literature; Thornton Wilder's novels; creative writing. Add: Rt. 2, West Frankfort, IL 62896.

CLAY, EDWARD MILLER, b. Minneapolis, Minn, June 8, 32. ENGLISH. B.A, Univ. Minn, 54, M.A, 58; Ph.D.(Eng), Univ. Mo, 65. Instr. ENG, Univ. Mo, 59-61, 62-65; Valparaiso Univ, 61-62; asst. prof, CALIF. STATE UNIV, HAYWARD, 65-68, ASSOC. PROF, 68-, chmn. Am. stud, 71-72. U.S.N, 55-57, Res, 57-61. MLA; AAUP. American literature before 1900; medieval English literature; linguistics. Publ: The dominating symbol in Hawthorne's Last phase, Am. Lit, 1/68. Add: Dept. of English, California State University, Hayward, Hayward, CA 94542.

CLAYDON, MARGARET, S.N.D, b. New York, N.Y, July 19, 23. ENGLISH LANGUAGE & LITERATURE. A.B, Trinity Col.(D.C), 45; M.A, Cath. Univ. Am, 53, Ph.D, 59; Oxford, 58; L.H.D, Georgetown Univ, 67. Instr. Eng, TRINITY COL.(D.C), 52-54, asst. prof, 56-59, PRES, 59- Vis. lectr, Notre Dame Col, Scotland, 58-59; mem. bd. trustees, Mid. States Asn, 65-72; mem. bd. dir, Nat. Counc. Independent Cols. & Univs, 71-; trustee, Emmanuel Col.(Mass), 72- Nat. Cath. Educ. Asn.(pres, col. & univ. dept, 68-70). Metaphysical poets; 17th century English literature. Publ: Richard Crashaw's paraphrases of the Vexilla Regis, Stabat Mater, Adoro Te, Lauda Sion, Dies Irae, O Gloriosa Domina, Cath. Univ. Am, 59. Add: Office of the President, Trinity College, Washington, DC 20017.

CLAYES, STANLEY ARNOLD, b. Brookline, Mass, July 4, 22. ENGLISH LITERATURE. A.B, Ursinus Col, 47; M.A, Univ. Pa, 50, Ph.D, 51. Asst. prof. mod. lit, Ore. State Col, 51-60; San Francisco State Col, 60-62; SHAKESPEARE, LOYOLA UNIV. CHICAGO, 62-64, assoc. prof, 64-70, PROF, 70- MLA. Modern drama; Shakespeare. Publ: Co-ed, Contemporary drama, 13 plays, Scribner, 61, 70; co-ed, Contexts for composition, 65, 69, 72 & auth, Drama and discussion, 67, Appleton. Add: Dept. of English, Loyola University of Chicago, 820 N. Michigan Ave, Chicago, IL 60611.

CLAYTON, CHARLES CURTIS, b. Cambridge, Nebr, June 3, 02; m. 25; c. 2. JOURNALISM. B.J, Univ. Mo, 25. Prof. JOUR, SOUTH. ILL. UNIV, CARBONDALE, 56-71, EMER. PROF, 71- Distinguished Serv. Medal for jour, Univ. Mo, 52; ed, The Quill, 56-61; Fulbright lectr, grad. sch, Nat. Chengchi Univ, 61-62, vis. prof. jour, 70-71; dir. mass commun. ctr. & chmn. dept. jour, Chinese Univ. Hong Kong, 65-66. Asn. Educ. Jour. Journalism history; mass communications. Publ: Newspaper reporting today, Odyssey, 47; Fifty years for freedom, 59 & Little Mack: Joseph B. McCullagh of the St. Louis Globe-Democrat, 69; South. Ill. Univ; co-auth, The Asian newspapers reluctant revolution, Iowa State Univ, 71. Add: 805 Taylor Dr, Carbondale, IL 62901.

CLAYTON, JOHN J, b. New York, N.Y, Jan. 5, 35; m. 56; c. 2. MODERN LITERATURE, HUMANITIES. B.A, Columbia Univ, 56; M.A, N.Y. Univ, 59; Ph.D.(Eng. & Am. lit), Ind. Univ, 66. Instr. Eng. Univ. Victoria (B.C), 62-63; lectr, Univ. Md. European div, 63-64; asst. prof. humanities, Boston Univ, 64-69; ASSOC. PROF. MOD. LIT. & CREATIVE WRITING, UNIV. MASS, AMHERST, 69- Summer lectr. Eng, Univ. B.C, 63, Univ. Victoria (B.C), 66, 67 & 69, Calif. State Col. Hayward, 68. Modern fiction; creative writing. Publ: Saul Bellow: in defense of man, Ind. Univ, 68; I am staying where I am, Antioch Rev, 70; Cambridge is sinking, Mass. Rev, 72 & Best Am. Short Stories, 73. Add: Dept. of English, University of Massachusetts, Amherst, MA 01002.

CLAYTON, LAURA BLAND, Classics, English. See Volume III, Foreign Languages, Linguistics & Philology.

CLAYTON, THOMAS, b. New Ulm, Minn, Dec. 15, 32; m. 55; c. 4. ENGLISH. B.A, Univ. Minn, 54; Rhodes scholar & D.Phil.(Eng), Oxford, 60. Instr. ENG, Yale, 60-62; asst. prof, Univ. Calif, Los Angeles, 62-67; assoc. prof, 67-68; UNIV. MINN, MINNEAPOLIS, 68-70, PROF, 70- Am. Counc. Learned Soc. grant, 62-63; fel, Inst. for Humanities, Univ. Calif, 66-67; fel, Grad. Sch, Univ. Minn, summer 71, res. leave, fall 72; assoc, Danforth Assoc. Prog, 72. Distinguished Teaching Award, Col. Lib. Arts, Univ. Minn, 70. U.S.A, 55-57. MLA; NCTE; Renaissance Soc. Am; Renaissance Eng. Text Soc; Int. Shakespeare Asn; Shakespeare Asn. Am. Earlier 17th century English poetry; Shakespeare; literary criticism. Publ: The Shakespearean addition in the Booke of Sir Thomas Moore, Ctr. Shakespeare Stud, 69; ed, The non-dramatic works of Sir John Suckling, Clarendon, Oxford, 71; auth, The quibbling Polonii and the pious bonds: the rhetoric of Hamlet I.iii, 67 & Internal evidence and Elizabethan dramatic authorship: an essay in literary history and method, 69, Shakespeare Stud; Morning glew and other sweat leaves in the folio text of Andrew Marvell's major pre-Restoration poems, Eng. Lit. Renaissance, 72; plus others. Highlights of five Shakespearean plays (scripts and video-tapes), KTCA-TV, 71. Add: Dept. of English, University of Minnesota, Minneapolis, MN 55455.

CLEARY, JAMES WILLIAM, b. Milwaukee, Wis, Apr. 16, 27; m. 50; c. 3. COMMUNICATION, COMPARATIVE LITERATURE. Ph.B, Marquette Univ, 50, A.M, 51; fel, Univ. Wis, 54-55, Ph.D, 56. From instr. to prof. speech, Univ. Wis, 56-69, v.chancellor acad. affairs, 66-69; PRES, CALIF. STATE UNIV, NORTHRIDGE, 69- Lectr, Credit Union Nat. Asn; Law Enforcement Off. & Parole Off. Insts; Univ. Wis. Exten; Wis. Bell Tel. Co, 57-65; Ellis L. Phillips Found. fel, 63-64. U.S.A, 45-47, 2nd Lt. Cent. States Speech Asn; Speech Commun. Asn. Communication theory; public address; parliamentary procedure. Publ: Co-ed, Rhetoric and public address: a bibliography, Univ. Wis, 64; co-auth, Robert's rules of order newly revised, Scott, 70; ed, John Bulwer's Chirologia ... Chironomia 1644: a critical edition, South. Ill. Univ, 74; plus numerous articles & monogr. Add: Office of the President, California State University, Northridge, 18111 Nordhoff, Northridge, CA 91324.

CLEARY, THOMAS RAYMOND, b. New York, N.Y, May 23, 40; m. 65; c. 2. ENGLISH. B.A, Queens Col.(N.Y), 65; Woodrow Wilson fels, Princeton, 65-66, 67-69, M.A, 67, Ph.D.(Eng), 70. Instr. ENG, Princeton, 67-68; ASST. PROF, UNIV. VICTORIA,(B.C), 69- U.S.A, 59-62. MLA; Johnson Soc. Northwest (secy, 73-74). Eighteenth century English literature; Fielding. Add: Dept. of English, University of Victoria, Victoria, B.C, Can.

CLEATH, ROBERT LEROY, b. Minneapolis, Minn, Oct. 9, 28; m. 49; c. 4. SPEECH COMMUNICATION. B.A, Northwest. Col, 50; M.A, Univ. Ore, 51; Ph.D.(speech), Univ. Wash, 63; M.Div, San Francisco Theol. Sem, 65. Asst. prof. SPEECH, Westmont Col, 53-55; Whitworth Col, 56-58; Univ. Calif, Santa Barbara, 59-61; ASSOC. PROF, CALIF. POLYTECH STATE UNIV, SAN LUIS OBISPO, 68- Asst. ed, Christianity Today, 66-68. Speech Commun. Asn; West. Speech Commun. Asn. Publ: Contrib, Dictionary of Christian ethics, Baker, 73; auth, articles to Christianity Today & Action-Reaction. Add: 177 Naomi, Shell Beach, CA 93449.

CLEAVER, CHARLES GRINNELL, b. Ft. Wayne, Ind. Dec. 9, 22; m. 48; c. 2. ENGLISH & AMERICAN STUDIES. B.A, Yale, 47; M.A, Univ. Minn, 50, Carnegie fel. & Ph.D.(Am. stud), 56. Instr. Eng. & Am. hist, Hanover Col, 47-49; ENG, Univ. Cincinnati, 54-55; asst. prof, GRINNELL COL, 56-60, assoc. prof. 60-66, PROF, 66- Fulbright lectr. Am. civilization, Tohuku Univ, Japan, 63-64. U.S.A, 42-46, 50-52, Lt. Am. Stud. Asn; Mid-Continent Am. Stud. Asn. American literature; twentieth century American culture; cultural comparison, Japan and United States. Publ: Frank B. Kellogg's view of history and progress, In: 75 prose pieces, Scribner, 61; The contrast in American literature and politics, Tohoku Bunka, Sendai, Japan, autumn 65; Finding a new voice: 20th century American literature, Rising Generation, Tokyo, 3 & 4/66. Add: 1226 Broad St, Grinnell, IA 50112.

CLECAK, PETE E, Social Thought. See Volume I, History.

CLEES, JAMES C, b. Montoursville, Pa, Jan. 2, 21. ENGLISH. B.A, Duke Univ, 41, M.A, 47; Ph.D.(Eng), Columbia Univ, 65. Instr. ENG, Manhattan Col, 47-49; Univ. Md, 49-52; Carnegie Inst. Technol, 55-59; asst, Am. Univ. (D.C), 59-64; ASSOC. PROF, PACE COL, 64- Consult, U.S. Steel Corp, 57-59. Sig.C, U.S.A, 41-45, Sgt. MLA; Col. Eng. Asn. American literature; James Fenimore Cooper. Add: Dept. of English, Pace College, 41 Park Row, New York, NY 10038.

CLEMENTS, ARTHUR LEO, b. Brooklyn, N.Y, Apr. 15, 32; m. 55; c. 4. ENGLISH. B.A, Princeton, 54; M.A, Univ. Conn, 58; Ph.D.(Eng), Syracuse Univ, 64. Lectr. ENG, Syracuse Univ, 62-64; asst. prof, HARPUR COL, STATE UNIV. N.Y. BINGHAMTON, 64-69, ASSOC. PROF, 69- Res. Found. State Univ. N.Y. fel. & grant-in-aid, 65 & 66, fels, summers 68, 69, 73 & 74; Nat. Endowment for Humanities fel, 67-68. U.S.A, 54-56. MLA. Seventeenth century religious poetry; Renaissance English literature; literature and religion. Publ: John Donne's poetry: a critical edition, Norton, 66; The mystical poetry of Thomas Traherne, Harvard Univ, 69; Thomas Traherne: a chronological bibliography, Libr. Chronicle, 69; Theme, tone, and tradition in George Herbert's poetry, Eng. Lit. Renaissance, 73; co-auth, Harmonized voices in Donne's Songs and sonets, Stud. Eng. Lit, 74; plus others. Add: Dept. of English, Harpur College, State University of New York at Binghamton, Binghamton, NY 13901.

CLEMO, RICHARD F, b. Ontario, Ore, Sept, 23, 21. SPEECH & DRAMATIC ART. A.B, Univ. Portland, 41; M.A, Columbia Univ, 48. Instr, pub. schs, Ore, 41-42, 45-46; asst. prof. speech & dramtic art, Univ. Portland, 46-48; lectr. speech educ, Columbia Univ, 48-50; asst. prof. SPEECH & DRAMATIC ART, ADELPHI UNIV, 50-54, assoc. prof, 54-62, PROF, 62-, DEAN COL. ARTS & SCI, 68-, DEAN FAC, 71-, dean univ. col, 56-68. Consult, L.I. Indust. Asn, 60-61. U.S.A, 42-45, M/Sgt. Speech Commun. Asn; Asn. Univ. Eve. Cols; Am. Theatre Asn. Group discussion; continuing education for adults. Publ: Discussion methods, 52; co-auth, Play production: a manual, Adelphi Col, 56; Educational theatre: what and where, L.I. Rev, 3/68. Add: Office of Dean of Faculty, Adelphi University, Garden City, NY 11530.

CLEMONS, WALTER, (JR), b. Houston, Tex, Nov. 14, 29. AMERICAN HISTORY, ENGLISH LITERATURE. B.A, Princeton, 51, Hodder fel, 59-60; Rhodes scholar, Oxford, 51-53, M.A, 53. Prix de Rome fel. & writer-in-residence, Am. Acad. Rome, 60-62; mem, Ford Found. Prog. for Poets & Fiction Writers, Alley Theatre, Houston, Tex, 62-63; ed. Am. hist, McGraw-Hill Bk. Co, 66-67, sr. ed, 68; MEM. STAFF HIST. & POETRY, N.Y. TIMES

BK. REV, 68- American history; English literature. Publ: The poison tree, Houghton, 59. Add: New York Times Book Review, 229 W. 43rd St, New York, NY 10036.

CLENDENNING, JOHN, b. Huntington, W.Va, Oct. 12, 34. AMERICAN LITERATURE & CIVILIZATION. B.A, Calif. State Univ, Los Angeles, 57; M.A, Univ. Iowa, 58, Ph.D, 62. Instr. ENG, CALIF. STATE UNIV, NORTHRIDGE, 60-62, asst. prof, 62-65, assoc. prof, 65-68, PROF, 68-, CHMN. DEPT, 73- Am. Counc. Learned Soc. stud. fel, 64-65 & fel, 68-69; Wesleyan Univ. Ctr. Advan. Stud. jr. fel, 64-65; Guggenheim fel, 71-72. MLA; Am. Stud. Asn. Philosophical themes in literature; American poetry. Publ: Letters of Josiah Royce, Univ. Chicago, 70; Cummings, comedy and criticism, Colo. Quart, summer 63; Time, doubt and vision: Emerson and Eliot, Am. Scholar, winter 66-67; Introd. to Josiah Royce's The feud of Oakfield Creek, 70; plus others. Add: Dept. of English, California State University, Northridge, 18111 Nordhoff St, Northridge, CA 91324.

CLERC, CHARLES, b. Pocatello, Idaho, Mar. 16, 26; m. 46; c. 1. m. 66; c. 3. ENGLISH. B.A, Idaho State Col, 49, B.A, 55; M.A, Univ. Utah, 57; Ph.D.(Eng), Univ. Iowa, 63. Instr. ENG, Univ. Iowa, 62-63; asst. prof, UNIV. OF THE PAC, 63-66, assoc. prof, 66-70, PROF, 70-, acting chmn. dept, 68-69, res. grant, 67, 71 & 74. Dir. first-year Eng, Univ. of the Pac, 66-68, lectr, NDEA Inst. Eng, mod. lit. critical methods, summer 66 & dir, 68; lectr, KOVR-TV, Calif. series on The modern American novel, fall 67; auth, The pillar (play), produced by Delta Col. Theatre, 3/73. U.S. Merchant Marine, 44-46; U.S.A, 51-53, Lt. MLA. Modern literature, especially American novel; writing of fiction and drama; literary criticism. Publ: Co-auth, Seven contemporary short novels, Scott, 69; auth, The rake's progress, Satire Newslett, fall 67; Sunrise on the river: the whole world of Huckleberry Finn, Mod. Fiction Stud, spring 68. Add: Dept. of English, University of the Pacific, Stockton, CA 95204.

CLEVENGER, THEODORE, b. Kansas City, Mo, Dec. 2, 29; m. 51; c. 4. SPEECH. B.A, Baylor Univ, 51, M.A, 52; Ph.D, Fla. State Univ, 58. Instr. SPEECH, Henderson State Col, 53-54, Fla. State Univ, 55-57; Univ. Ill, 57-59; asst. prof, Univ. Wis, 59-62; assoc. prof, Univ. Pittsburgh, 62-65; prof, Univ. Tex, 65-67; PROF. & CHMN. DEPT, FLA. STATE UNIV, 67- Instr. sems, Agency Int. Develop, 58- Nat. Soc. Stud. Commun; Am. Psychol. Asn; Speech Commun. Asn; Ling. Soc. Am. Human communication theory and analysis of communication behavior. Publ: Audience analysis, Bobbs, 66; co-auth, Speech and social action, Prentice-Hall, 67. Add: Dept. of Speech, Florida State University, Tallahassee, FL 32306.

CLEVER, GLENN, b. Champion, Alta, 1918. EIGHTEENTH CENTURY & CANADIAN LITERATURE. B.A, Univ. Ottawa, 64, M.A, 66, Ph.D.(Eng. lit), 69. Lectr. ENG. LIT, UNIV. OTTAWA, 67-69, asst. prof, 70-71, ASSOC. PROF. & CHMN. DEPT, 72- Med.C, Can. Army, 39-66, Res, 66-, Maj. Am. Soc. 18th Century Stud; Can. Soc. 18th Century Stud; Asn. Can. Univ. Teachers Eng. Dryden and Pope; 18th century narrative poetry; Canadian novel. Publ: Ed, Selected stories of D.C. Scott, Univ. Ottawa, 72, Index to Canadian literature, Golden Dog, 73 & Selected poetry of D.C. Scott, Tecumseh, 73; auth, Narrative technique of The rape of the lock, J. Narrative Technique, 70; Callaghan's More joy in heaven as a tragedy, Can. Fiction Mag, 71; Samuel Pepys' world of pleasure, Inscape, 71. Add: Dept. of English, University of Ottawa, 173 Waller St, Ottawa, Ont. K1N 6N5, Can.

CLICK, JOHN WILLIAM, b. Huntington, Ind, Apr. 22, 36; m. 60; c. 2. JOURNALISM. B.A, Ball State Univ, 58; M.S, Ohio Univ, 59; Univ. Mo, 61; Ohio State Univ, 71-72. Instr. Eng. & jour, Findlay Col, 59-60; JOUR, Cent. Mich. Univ, 60-65; asst. prof, OHIO UNIV, 65-71, ASSOC. PROF, 71- Pub. Relations Soc. Am, Found. Educ. & Res. Pub. Relations fel, summer 67. Asn. Educ. Jour.(chmn. indust. & tech. jour. comt, 63-65); Nat. Counc. Col. Publ. Adv.(pres, 71-, chmn. awards comt, 68-71). Perception of graphic presentation of content; journalism and student publications in secondary schools and colleges. Publ: Co-auth, Magazine editing and production, Brown, 74; auth, Corporate identity relationships with public relations, Pub. Relations Quart, winter 73; Appraisal of mass media, In: Journalism: dateline, the world, Rosen, 73. Add: School of Journalism, Ohio University, Athens, OH 45701.

CLIFFORD, FREDERICK BURR, b. Samaria, Mich, June 3, 14; m. 43; c. 3. HUMANITIES. A.B, North. Mich. Col, 35; A.M, Univ. Mich, 37, Ph.D, 43; B.D, Oberlin Grad. Sch. Tehol, 46; summers, Univ. Chicago, 48; Union Theol. Sem.(N.Y), 50. PROF. humanities, Adrian Col, 47-53; Emory-at-Oxford, 53-58; ENG. & CLASSICS, SOUTHWEST. UNIV.(TEX), 58-, DEAN COL. ARTS & SCI, 62- Am. Philol. Asn; NCTE; Class. Asn. Mid.W. & S. Classical comedy; Roman and English satire; Renaissance literature. Add: Office of the Dean, Southwestern University, Georgetown, TX 78626.

CLIFFORD, JAMES LOWRY, b. Evansville, Ind, Feb. 24, 01; m. 40; c. 3. ENGLISH. A.B, Wabash Col, 23, L.H.D, 56; B.S, Mass. Inst. Technol, 25; A.M, Columbia Univ, 32, Cutting traveling fel, 35-36, Ph.D, 41; D.Litt, Evansville Col, 55; L.H.D, Ind. Univ, 63, Lehigh Univ, 72. Gen. mgr, Young Car Co, Evansville, Ind, 26-28; master ENG, Evans Sch, Tucson, Ariz, 28-32; from instr. to assoc. prof, Lehigh Univ, 37-44; from assoc. prof. to William Peterfield Trent prof, COLUMBIA UNIV, 45-69, EMER. PROF, 69- Ed, Johnsonian News Lett, 40-; Eng. Inst, secy, 46; Guggenheim fel, 51-52 & 65-66. MLA; fel. Royal Soc. Lit. U.K; Am. Soc. 18th Century Stud.(pres, 72-73). Eighteenth century English literature; Dr. Samuel Johnson and his circle; the art of biography. Publ: Hester Lynch Piozzi (Mrs. Thrale), Clarendon, 41; Johnsonian studies, 51 & co-ed, Samuel Johnson: a survey and bibliography of critical studies, 70, Univ. Minn; auth, Young Sam Johnson, McGraw, 55; ed, Biography as an art, 62 & Smollett's Peregrine pickle, 64, Oxford; ed, Man vs. society in 18th-century Britain, Cambridge, 68; auth, From puzzles to portraits: problems of a literary biographer, Univ. N.C, 70; plus others. Add: 25 Claremont Ave, New York, NY 10027.

CLIFFORD, JOHN E, b. Cleveland, Ohio, Nov. 21, 35; m. 59; c. 3. THEATRE ARTS. B.S.S, John Carroll Univ, 58; M.A, St. Louis Univ, 59; summer, Univ. Ill, 60; Ph.D.(theatre), Mich. State Univ, 66. Instr. speech, Loras Col, 59-62; asst. prof. THEATRE, BRADLEY UNIV, 64-70, ASSOC. PROF, 70- Am. Nat. Theatre & Acad; Am. Theatre Asn; Speech Commun. Asn. Educational theatre management; theatre styles; directing. Publ: Educational theatre management, Nat. Textbk, 72; An aesthetic obligation, Newman, 8/60; Memo: to teachers of broadcasting, Feedback, 10/64. Add: Dept. of Speech & Drama, Bradley University, Peoria, IL 61606.

CLIFTON, ERNEST SMITH, b. Darlington, S.C, July 31, 14; m. 40; c. 4. ENGLISH. B.A, Univ. Va, 35; M.A, La. State Univ, 37, Ph.D.(Eng), 40; Int. fel, Heidelberg, & Univ. Cologne, 38-39. Instr. ENG. N.TEX. STATE UNIV, 39-40, asst. prof, 40-46, PROF, 46-, DIR. DEPT. 50- MLA; S.Cent. Mod. Lang. Asn. Shakespeare; American dialectology. Publ: Workbook for English composition & Reading and writing, Holt; plus others. Add: Box 13827, North Texas State University, Denton, TX 76203.

CLIFTON, LUCILE, b. Columbus, Ohio, May 4, 14. ENGLISH. B.A, Ohio State Univ, 35, M.A, 36, B.Sc, 38, Ph.D, 48. Teacher, high schs, Ohio, 38-41; instr. ENG, Ohio State Univ, 46-48; asst. prof, BALL STATE UNIV, 48-51, assoc. prof, 51-57, PROF, 57- U.S.C.G, 43-46, Lt.(jg). MLA; NEA; NCTE; Conf. Col. Compos. & Commun.(secy, 63-64). Regional studies in American literature; English in general education program of colleges; South African literature. Publ: Early theatre in Columbus, Ohio: 1820-1840, Ohio State Archaeol. & Hist. Quart. Add: Dept. of English, Ball State University, Muncie, IN 47306.

CLIFTON, YERGER HUNT, b. Jackson, Miss, July 26, 30. ENGLISH. B.A, Duke Univ, 52; M.A, Univ. Va, 58; Ph.D, Trinity Col, Dublin, 62. Instr. ENG, Col. William & Mary, 58-60; Univ. Ky, 62-65; asst. prof, SOUTHWEST. AT MEMPHIS, 65-68, ASSOC. PROF, 68-, DEAN BRIT. STUD. AT OXFORD, 70- Lectr. humanities, Memphis Acad. Arts, 66-69; pres, South. Literary Festival, 67, dir, 68-69. U.S.N.R, 53-56, Res, 56-, Lt. MLA; S.Cent. Mod. Lang. Asn; AAUP; Irish Georgian Soc. British drama, 1600-1800; 18th century; Milton; British novel. Add: Dept. of English, Southwestern at Memphis, Memphis, TN 38112.

CLIMENHAGA, JOEL RAY, b. Bulawayo, Rhodesia, Apr. 9, 22; U.S. citizen; m. 55; c. 4. DRAMATIC LITERATURE, CREATIVE WRITING. B.A, Univ. Calif, Los Angeles, 53, M.A, 58; Stanford Univ, 61-62, 66-67. Asst. prof. Eng, Wilmington Col.(Ohio), 58-61; ASSOC. PROF. dramatic art, Univ. N.C, Chapel Hill, 62-63; speech & drama, Culver-Stockton Col, 63-68; SPEECH, KANS. STATE UNIV, 68- Am. Theatre Asn.(chmn. playwright's prog, Am. Educ. Theatre Asn, 60-65); Am. Poetry League; World Poetry Soc. Intercontinental. Contemporary American drama; 20th century American poetry; the history of American drama. Publ: Heathen pioneer (play), 56 & Marriage wheel (play), French; Hawk and chameleon (poetry), Auth. Press. Am, 72; Belief in chaos (poetry), Lincoln-Shaw, 73. Add: Dept. of Speech, Kansas State University, Manhattan, KS 66506.

CLINARD, TURNER NORMAN, b. Robertson Co, Tenn, Mar. 5, 17; m. 42; c. 2. ENGLISH. B.A, Bethel Col.(Tenn), 39; M.A, George Peabody Col, 41; Ph.D.(Eng), Vanderbilt Univ, 56, theol, 64-66. Teacher, Elem. Schs, Tenn, 39-41; High Sch, Ga, 41-42; Ala, 43-45; chaplain & teacher, Martha Berry Schs, Ga, 45-47; pastor, Brookhaven Cumberland Presby. Church, Tenn, 47-52; asst. prof. ENG, Tusculum Col, 59-64, assoc. prof, 64-65; EMORY & HENRY COL, 65-68, chmn, div. humanities, 68-71, PROF, 68- Pastor, First Cumberland Presby. Church, Ala, 42-45; Greeneville Cumberland Presby. Church, Tenn, 52-65; McConnell scholar, Emory & Henry Col, summer 70. MLA; Southeast. Renaissance Conf; S.Atlantic Mod. Lang. Asn; AAUP. Pre-Elizabethan sonnet; Christianity; birds in American poetry. Publ: The Holy Spirit comes through the worshipping community, Pioneer, 71; In a word, bi-weekly column in Cumberland Presby, 67-; A suggestion for required pre-seminary studies, Relig. in Life, summer 67; An appeal for firm direction and specific guidelines, Theol. Educ, autumn 67; A word in season, Tidings, 74. Add: Dept. of English, Emory & Henry College, Emory, VA 24327.

CLINE, CLARENCE LEE, b. Belton, Tex, Jan. 6, 05; m. 33; c. 2. ENGLISH. A.B, Baylor Univ, 26; A.M, Univ. Tex, 31, Ph.D, 38; Univ. Chicago, summers, 33-34. Teaching fel. ENG, UNIV. TEX, AUSTIN, 28-31, instr, 31-45, asst. prof, 45-49, assoc. prof, 49-52, PROF, 52-, chmn. dept, 49-52, 62-68. MLA; Mod. Humanities Res. Asn, Gt. Brit. Victorian novel; the short story; George Meredith. Publ: Byron, Shelley and their pisan circle, Harvard & John Murray; Rinehart book of short stories, Holt, 52, alternate ed, 64; The letters of George Meredith, Clarendon, 70. Add: Dept. of English, University of Texas at Austin, Austin, TX 78712.

CLIPPER, LAWRENCE JON, b. Clairton, Pa, Dec. 13, 30; m. 55; c. 2. ENGLISH LITERATURE. A.B, Brown Univ, 53; M.A, George Washington Univ, 58; Ph.D.(Eng), Univ. N.C, 63. ASST. PROF. Eng. & Am. Lit, Dickinson Col, 61-64; Eng. ling, Ball State Univ, 64-67; ENG, IND. UNIV, SOUTH BEND, 67- Ball State Univ. res. grant, 66-67; res. fel, Ind. Univ, summer 68. U.S.N, 53-56, Lt.(jg). Midwest Mod. Lang. Asn; Col. Eng. Asn. Charles Dickens; the English novel; G.K. Chesterton. Publ: Bantam ERA guide to Pride and prejudice, 66, Silas Marner, 67 & Return of the native, 67, Bantam ERA. Add: Dept. of English, Indiana University at South Bend, South Bend, IN 46615.

CLOGAN, JULIE SYDNEY, b. Phoenix, Ariz, Sept. 25, 46; m. 72; c. 1. ENGLISH & AMERICAN LITERATURE. A.B, Univ. Ariz, 67, fel, 67-69, M.A, 69; fel, Case West. Reserve Univ, 69-72, Ph.D.(Eng), 72. Ed. asst, Ariz. Quart, Univ. Ariz, Tucson, 67-69; MANAGING ED, MEDIEVALIA HUMANISTICA, Case West. Reserve Univ, 69-72; N.TEX. STATE UNIV, 72- MLA. Medieval literature; 19th century English and American literature. Publ: Creatures like ourselves: the romantic criticism of Chaucer, Diss. Abstr, 73. Add: P.O. Box 13348, North Texas State University, Denton, TX 76203.

CLOGAN, PAUL MAURICE, b. Milton, Mass, July 9, 34; m. 72; c. 1. ENGLISH, COMPARATIVE LITERATURE. A.B, Boston Col, 56, fel, 56-57, M.A, 57; fel, Univ. Ill, 57-61, Ph.D.(Eng), 61; Ph.L, St. Michael's Col, 58. Instr. Eng, Duke Univ, 61-63, asst. prof, 63-65; assoc. prof. Eng & comp. lit, Case West. Reserve Univ, 65-71; adj. prof, Cleveland State Univ, 71-72; PROF. ENG, N.TEX. STATE UNIV, 72- Duke Found. grant, 62-63; Am. Counc. Learned Soc. fel, 62-64, 71-72; Fulbright-Hays res. fel, Italy, 65-66, Scuola Vaticana di Paleografia e Diplomatica, 66-67; vis. lectr, Univ. Pisa, 65; Am. Philos. Soc. grants, 65-67, 69-70; U.S-United Kingdom cult. exchange vis. lectr, Univ. Keele, 66; Bollingen Found. & Prix de Rome fels,

66-67; fel. Am. Acad. Rome, 67; managing ed, Medievalia et Humanistica, 68-; mem. steering comt, Asn. Ctr. Medieval & Renaissance Stud; Nat. Endowment for Humanities fel, 70-71. Am. Philol. Asn; MLA; Mediaeval Acad. Am; Mod. Humanities Res. Asn; Dante Soc. Am; Int. Comp. Lit. Asn; Int. Arthurian Soc.(Am. Comt, 65); Soc. Stud. Mediaeval Lang. & Lit; Early Eng. Text. Soc. Old and Middle English language and literature; comparative literature; Mediaeval Renaissance Latin culture. Publ: Medieval Achilleid, Brill, 68; ed, In Honor of S. Harrison Thomson, 70, Medieval and Renaissance studies in review, 71 & Social dimensions in Medieval and Renaissance studies, 72, Case West. Rev. Univ; Medieval and Renaissance spirituality, 73 & Medieval historiography, 74, N.Tex. State Univ; auth, Chaucer's use of the Thebaid, Eng. Miscellany, 67; The figural style and meaning the The second nun's prologue and tale, 72 & From complaint to satire: the art of the Confessio Amantis, 73, Medievalia et Humanistica; plus others. Add: P.O. Box 13348, North Texas State University, Denton, TX 76203.

CLOSS, FREDERIC THOMAS, b. Orange, N.J, Jan. 31, 29; m. 57; ENGLISH. A.B, Lafayette Col, 51; M.A, Univ. Pa, 52, Ph.D.(Eng), 64. Asst. to dir. admis, Lafayette Col, 55-58; asst. prof. ENG, Paterson State Col, 60-64; LAFAYETTE COL, 64-71, ASSOC. PROF, 71- U.S.A, 52-54. MLA; AAUP. Twentieth century British and American poetry. Publ: Ed, Selected poems of MacKnight Black, Vantage, 70. Add: 619 McCartney St, Easton, PA. 18042.

CLOUGH, GALEN WEARE, b. Boston, Mass, Aug. 17, 35; m. 60; c. 3. ENGLISH. A.B, Dartmouth Col, 58; M.A, Ind. Univ, 63, Ph.D.(Eng), 67. Instr. ENG, UNIV. EVANSVILLE, 63-66, asst. prof, 67-70, ASSOC. PROF, 70- MLA. Eighteenth and 19th century American literature. Add: 527 S. St. James Blvd, Evansville, IN 47714.

CLOUGH, WILSON OBER, b. New Brunswick, N.J, Jan. 7, 94; m. 21; c. 3. ENGLISH & AMERICAN LITERATURE. A.B, Union Col.(N.Y), 17, Litt.D, 57; Univ. Montpellier, France, 19; A.M, Univ. Colo, 25; Univ. Chicago, 29; fel, Univ. Wis, 30-31; LL.D, Univ. Wyo, 61. Teacher, high schs, Ill, Mo, Colo. & Idaho, 17, 19-24; instr. Eng, UNIV. WYO, 24-26, asst. prof, 26-31, assoc. prof, 31-39, secy. fac, 39-46, prof, 39-56, chmn. dept, 46-49, Coe prof. AM. STUD, 56-61, EMER. PROF, 61- MLA. American intellectual history. Publ: History of the University of Wyoming, Univ. Wyo; Brief oasis, Swallow; Intellectual origins of American national thought, Corinth Bks, 61; The necessary earth, Univ. Tex, 64; transl. & ed, Honegger's I am a composer, St. Martin's, N.Y. & Faber, London, 66 & Simonin's Rocky Mountain West in 1867, Univ. Nebr, 66; auth, Academic and otherwise: selected papers, Univ. Wyo, 69; Past's persisting: selected poems, privately publ, 72; Poe's The city in the sea revisited, In: Essays on American literature, Duke Univ, 67; plus others. Add: Dept. of American Studies, University of Wyoming, Laramie, WY 82070.

CLUBB, LOUISE GEORGE, Comparative Literature. See Volume III, Foreign Languages, Linguistics & Philology.

CLUBB, MERREL D, JR, b. New Haven, Conn, June 7, 21; m. 49; c. 4. ENGLISH. B.A, Okla. State Univ, 43; M.A, Yale, 49; Ph.D.(Eng. lang & lit), Univ. Mich, 53. Instr. ENG, Univ. Kans, 46-48; Univ. Ore, 49-51; asst. prof, Univ. Houston, 53-54; assoc. prof, UNIV. MONT, 54-65, PROF, 65-, CHMN. DEPT, 68- Fulbright lectr. ling. & Eng, Italy, 56-58, Colombia, 62-63, ling, Burma, 61-62. U.S.N, 43-46, Lt. MLA; Ling. Soc. Am; NCTE. Literature; linguistics; application of linguistics to teaching foreign languages. Publ: The General form and English as a foreign language, Mod. Lang. J, 60; The second personal pronoun in Moby Dick, Am. Speech, 60; The Heraclitean element in Eliots Four quartets, Philol. Quart, 61. Add: Dept. of English, University of Montana, Missoula, MT 59801.

CLUBBE, JOHN LOUIS EDWIN, b. New York, N.Y, Feb. 21, 38. ENGLISH. A.B, Columbia Col, 59; A.M,Columbia Univ, 60, Ph.D.(Eng), 65; Univ. Sorbonne, 60-61. Lectr. ENG, Univ. Münster, 65-66; asst. prof, DUKE UNIV, 66-70, ASSOC. PROF, 70-, summer fac. res. fel, 69, 73, endowment grant, 71-72. Nat. Endowment for Humanities Younger humanists fel, 71-72; Huntington Libr. fel, 72. MLA; S.Atlantic Mod. Lang. Asn; Keats-Shelley Asn. Am; Byron Soc.(mem. Am. comt, 73-). Nineteenth century English literature; comparative literature. Publ: Victorian forerunner: the later career of Thomas Hood, 68, asst. ed, Collected letters of Thomas and Jane Welsh Carlyle, 1812-1828 (4 vols), 70, ed, Two reminiscences of Thomas Carlyle, 74, co-ed, Nineteenth century literary perspectives: essays in honor of Lionel Stevenson, 74, ed, Carlyle and his circle: essays in honor of Charles Richard Sanders, 75 & assoc. ed, Collected letters of Thomas and Jane Welsh Carlyle, 1828-1834 (3 vols), 75, Duke Univ; ed, Selected poems of Thomas Hood, Harvard Univ, 70; auth, John Carlyle in Germany and the genesis of Sartor resartus, In: Romantic and Victorian: studies in memory of William H. Marshall, Fairleigh Dickinson Univ, 71; Byron and Scott, Tex. Stud. Lang. & Lit, spring 73; The new Prometheus of new men: Byron's 1816 poems and Manfred, In: Nineteenth century literary perspectives, Duke Univ, 74; plus others. Add: Dept. of English, Duke University, Durham, NC 27706.

CLUETT, ROBERT, b. New York, N.Y, Nov. 18, 32; m. 57; c. 3. ENGLISH, STYLISTICS. B.S, Columbia Univ, 54, M.A, 61, Relm Found. res. fel, 63-64, Richter Found. fel, 64-65, Ph.D.(Eng), 69. Master ENG, Kent Sch, Conn, 58-67; ASSOC. PROF, YORK UNIV, 67- Mem. cent. selection comt, Morehead Found, 65-68, trustee, 68-; staff mem, NDEA Inst. Eng, Columbia Univ, 65-66. U.S.C.G, 54-58, Res, 51-54, 58-59, Lt.(jg). MLA; Humanities Asn. Can; Asn. Can. Univ. Teachers Eng. History of prose style; Renaissance and Restoration literature; computerized stylistics. Publ: Effective English prose, Random, 65; co-auth, The Hamden intellectual skills survey, Guidance Ctr, 66; auth, Our linguistic inflation, Teachers Col. Rec, 3/65; Style, precept, personality: a test case, Computers & Humanities, 5/71. Add: Dept. of English, 234 Winters College, York University, Downsview, Ont. M3J 1P3, Can.

CLUGSTON, GEORGE ALAN, b. Boulder, Colo, Apr. 8, 29. ENGLISH LITERATURE. A.B, Harvard, 50; M.A, Univ. Mich, 51, teaching fel, 52-56. Instr, Univ. Mich, 56-58, lectr, 62-63; instr. ENG, Duke Univ, 58-62; asst. prof, WELLS COL, 63-67, ASSOC. PROF, 67- MLA. Elizabethan drama. Add: Dept. of English, Wells College, Aurora, NY 13026.

CLYDE, GLENDA ESTELLE, b. Phillipsburg, Mo, Apr. 18, 38. SPEECH. B.A, Colo. State Col, 58; M.A, Univ. Denver, 62; Ph.D.(speech), South. Ill. Univ, 66. Teacher, Herculaneum High Sch, 59-60; Northwest High Sch, 60-62; instr. SPEECH, Wayne State Col, 62-63; asst, South. Ill. Univ, 64-65; assoc. prof, NORTHEAST MO. STATE UNIV, 65-70, PROF, 70- Mem, Inst. Gen. Semantics. Int. Soc. Gen. Semantics; Speech Commun. Asn; Int. Commun. Asn. General semantics; oral interpretation; rhetoric and public address. Dept. of Speech, Division of Language & Literature, Northeast Missouri State University, Kirksville, MO 63501.

COAD, ORAL SUMNER, b. Mt. Pleasant, Iowa, Dec. 27, 87; m. 15; c. 1. ENGLISH. A.B, Knox Col, 09; A.M, Columbia Univ, 11, Ph.D.(Eng), 17. Instr. ENG, Ohio Wesleyan Univ, 11-14; Columbia Univ, 16-23; asst. prof, DOUGLASS COL, RUTGERS UNIV, 23-26, assoc. prof, 26-27, prof. & chmn. dept, 27-58, EMER. PROF, 58- MLA. American literature and drama; New Jersey in literature. Publ: William Dunlap, a study of his life and works and of his place in contemporary culture, Dunlap Soc, 17, Russell, 62; co-auth, The American stage, Yale, 29; ed, Edgar Poe and his critics, Rutgers Univ, 49; New Jersey in the Revolution: a bibliography of historical fiction, 1784-1963, New Brunswick Hist. Club, 64; auth, New Jersey in travelers' accounts 1524-1971: a descriptive bibliography, Scarecrow, 72; Jersey Gothic, Proc. N.J. Hist. Soc, 4/66; Some traveler's-eye views of the Jerseyman, J. Rutgers Univ. Libr, 72. Add: 13 Sandford St, New Brunswick, NJ 08902.

COAKLEY, JAMES FRANCIS, b. Pittsburgh, Pa, Dec. 12, 33. DRAMA, ENGLISH. B.F.A, Carnegie-Mellon Univ, 55; M.A, Univ. Minn, 59; Ph.D. (drama), Northwest. Univ, 64. ASST. PROF. speech & drama, Loyola Univ. (Ill), 64-66; speech, Univ. Mich, Ann Arbor, 66-71; DRAMATIC PROD, NORTHWEST. UNIV, 71- Vis. lectr, Goodman Theatre & Sch. Drama, 65-66; drama-music desk, Chicago Today, 73- Sig.C, 56-58, Sgt. Am. Educ. Theatre Asn; Speech Commun. Asn. Modern drama; Shakespeare; history of the theatre. Publ: Williams and Camino Real, Drama Critique, spring 68; Thalia in Dublin: O'Casey and Roman comedy, Comp. Drama, winter 70. Add: Dept. of Theatre, Northwestern University, Evanston, IL 60201.

COALE, SAMUEL CHASE, b. Hartford, Conn, July 26, 43; m. 72. ENGLISH, AMERICAN CIVILIZATION. A.B, Trinity Col.(Conn), 65; Mary A. Terry fel, Brown Univ, 65-67, Ford Found. summer res. & travel grants, 69-71, A.M. & Ph.D.(Am. civilization), 70. ASST. PROF. ENG, WHEATON COL. (MASS), 68- Wheaton res. & travel grant, Wordsworth-Coleridge Conf, Eng, 72. MLA. Modern American literature; 19th century American literature; English romantic poets. Publ: The quest for the elusive self: the fiction of Jerzy Kosinski, Critique, 73; Walt Whitman's war: the march of a poet, Walt Whitman Rev, 74; The emblematic encounter of Robert Frost, Frost Centennial Essays, 74. Add: Dept. of English, Wheaton College, Norton, MA 02766.

COARD, ROBERT L, b. Quincy, Ill, June 30, 21. ENGLISH. A.B, Quincy Col, 43; M.A, Univ. Ill, 46, Ph.D.(Eng), 52. Teacher ENG, high schs, Ill, 43-46; instr, Univ. Nebr, 46-48; asst. prof, N.Dak. State Teachers Col, Minot, 52-55, assoc. prof, 55-57; asst. prof, Univ. Ala, 57-60; ST. CLOUD STATE COL, 60-63, assoc. prof, 63-66, PROF, 66- NEA; Col. Eng. Asn; AAUP; MLA; Am. Name Soc; Am. Stud. Asn. American literature and language; Mark Twain; Sinclair Lewis. Publ: Names in the fiction of Sinclair Lewis, Ga. Rev, 62; Mark Twain's The gilded age & Sinclair Lewis's Babbitt, Midwest Quart, spring 72; Vulgar barnyard illustrations in Elmer Gantry, Sinclair Lewis Newslett, 72; plus others. Add: Dept. of English, St. Cloud State College, St. Cloud, MN 56301.

COATES, KENNETH DANIEL, b. Smithfield, N.C, Apr. 4, 04; m. 28; c. 1. ENGLISH. A.B, Univ. N.C, 25, M.A, 32. Teacher & athletic dir, High Sch, N.C, 25-26, teacher, 27-28; from instr. to assoc. prof. ENG, WOFFORD COL, 28-50, prof, 50-72, EMER. PROF, 72- Acting ed, Spartanburg J, 43-45. S.Atlantic Mod. Lang. Asn. American literature; creative writing. Publ: A city looks at itself, Add: Dept. of English, Wofford College, Spartanburg, SC 29301.

COBAU, WILLIAM W, b. New Castle, Pa, Mar. 31, 33; m. 63; c. 2. ENGLISH. B.A, Amherst Col, 55; Yale Divinity Sch, 57-58; M.A, Columbia Univ, 60; Ph.D.(Eng), Pa. State Univ, 64. Asst. ENG, Pa. State Univ, 60-63; from instr. to asst. prof, Carnegie Inst. Technol, 63-66; ASSOC. PROF, WITTENBERG UNIV, 66- Fulbright-Hays exchange prof, St. Katherine's Col. Educ. Liverpool, Eng, 70-71. U.S.A, 55-57. Add: Dept. of English, Wittenberg University, Springfield, OH 45501.

COBB, ROBERT PAUL, b. Ashdown, Ark, Aug. 22, 25; m. 49; c. 2. AMERICAN LITERATURE. B.A, Baylor Univ, 49; M.A, Univ. Mich, 50, fel, 53-54, Ph.D, 55. Instr. ENG, Univ. Mich, 54-55; asst. prof, Baylor Univ, 55-57; UNIV. KANS, 57-62, assoc. prof, 62-67, PROF, 67-, ASSOC. DEAN, COL. LIB. ARTS & SCI, 66-, asst. dean, 62-66, dean Int. Prog, 69-71. Consult-exam, N.Cent. Asn. Cols. & Sec. Schs, 68-; consult-panelist, Nat. Endowment for Humanities, 72- U.S.N, 43-45. MLA; African Stud. Asn; AAUP. African literature; 19th century and colonial American literature. Add: 206 Strong Hall, University of Kansas, Lawrence, KS 66045.

COBERLY, JAMES HAROLD, b. Elkins, W.Va, Aug. 12, 08; m. 49; c. 2. ENGLISH. A.B, George Washington Univ, 33, A.M, 38, fel, 39-42, Ph.D. (Am. lit), 49. Asst. prof. Eng, Wash. Col, 38; instr, GEORGE WASHINGTON UNIV, 45-47, asst. prof, 47-54, assoc. prof. Am. lit, 54-58, PROF. ENG, 58- MLA; Am. Stud. Asn. American fiction. Add: Dept. of English, George Washington University, Washington, DC 20006.

COBES, JON P, b. Ecorse, Mich, Sept. 7, 32. THEATRE, MUSIC. B.Sc, Ohio State Univ, 58, M.A, 61, Ph.D.(theatre design), 67; A.M.L.S, Univ. Mich, 71. Tech. dir. theatre & assoc. dir. summer theatre, Univ. Wyo, 64-66; asst. prof. tech. theatre, Ohio State Univ, 67-69, dir. inform. serv, Mechanized Inform. Ctr, 71-73; HEAD LIBRN, OHIO STATE UNIV, MANSFIELD, 73- Consult. & builder, rehearsal hall for Ohio String Festival, Put-in-Bay, Ohio, 67; consult, Ohio State Univ. theatre plant, 67-68; tech. dir, Stadium Theatre, Columbus, Ohio, 67-69. Med.C, U.S.A, 52-54. Speech Commun. Asn; Am. Theatre Asn; U.S. Inst. Theatre Technol; Univ. & Col. Theatre Asn. Seventeenth century opera, theatres and staging; modern materials and technology adaptable to the theatre; modern theatre architecture and acoustics. Add: Library, Ohio State University, Mansfield Regional Campus, 1640 University Dr, Mansfield, OH 44906.

COBIN, MARTIN THEODORE, b. New York, N.Y, Oct. 20, 20; m. 44; c. 4. SPEECH, DRAMA. B.F.A, Ohio Univ, 42; M.A, Univ. Wis, 47, Ph.D.(speech, theatre), 53. Asst. prof. speech, W.Va, Univ, 47-55; SPEECH & THEATRE, Univ. Ill, 55-59, assoc. prof, 59-61; from assoc. prof. to PROF, UNIV. COLO, BOULDER, 61-, chmn. dept. speech & drama, 68-71. U.S. Dept. Health, Educ. & Welfare grant, 60-61; with Am. Broadcasting Co, 62-63. U.S.A, 42-46, 2nd Lt. Speech Commun. Asn; Nat. Asn. Educ. Broadcasters. Theatre; broadcasting; educational television. Publ: Theory and technique of interpretation, Prentice-Hall, 59; co-auth, Speech and theater, Ctr. Appl. Res. Educ, Inc, 63; Television instruction, course content, and teaching experience level, Speech Monogr, 3/61. Add: Dept. of Communication, University of Colorado, Boulder, CO 80302.

COBURN, KATHLEEN, b. Stayner, Ont, Sept. 7, 05. ENGLISH LITERATURE. B.A, Univ. Toronto, 28, M.A, 30; Imp. Order Daughters of the Empire War Mem. traveling scholar, 30-31; B.Litt, Oxford, 32; Int. Fed. Univ. Women fel; Guggenheim fel, 53-54, 56-57; Commonwealth Res. fel, Univ. London, Eng, 62-63; hon. LL.D, Queen's Univ.(Ont), 64; hon. D.H.L, Haverford Col, 72; hon. D.Litt, Trent Univ, 73. From reader to prof. ENG, VICTORIA COL, UNIV. TORONTO, 28-30, 32-71, EMER. PROF, 71- Hon. fel, St. Hugh's Col, Oxford, 70; hon. fel, Champlain Col, Trent Univ, 72. Off, Order of Can. Fel. Royal Soc. Can; cor. fel. Brit. Acad. Coleridge. Publ: The philosophical lectures of S.T. Coleridge, 1818-1819 & Inquiring spirit, Routledge & Kegan Paul, London; The notebooks of Samuel Taylor Coleridge (5 vols), Vol. I, 57, Vol. II, 62 & Vol. III, 73 & gen. ed, The collected works of Samuel Taylor Coleridge (25 vols), Bollingen Found, N.Y. & Routledge & Kegan Paul, London, 61- Add: Dept. of English, Victoria College, University of Toronto, Toronto 5, Ont, Can.

COBURN, MARK DAVID, b. New York, N.Y, July 7, 41; m. 67. AMERICAN LITERATURE & CIVILIZATION. A.B, Univ. Chicago, 63; Woodrow Wilson fel, Stanford Univ, 63-64, M.A, 66, Ph.D.(Eng. & humanities), 69. ASST. PROF. ENG, Queens Col.(N.Y), 67-71; FT. LEWIS COL, 71-, dir. adult educ.prog, 72-73. American studies. Publ: Training is everything: communal opinion and the individual in Pudd'nhead Wilson, Mod. Lang. Quart, 70. Add: Dept. of English, Ft. Lewis College, Durango, CO 81301.

COCHRAN, BUD T, b. Albuquerque, N.Mex, May 27, 26; m. 55; c. 4. AMERICAN LITERATURE. B.A, Col. Steubenville, 55, M.A, Ohio State Univ, 57, Ph.D.(Am. fiction), 67. Instr. Eng, UNIV. DAYTON, 58-60, asst. prof, 60-68, ASSOC. PROF, 68- U.S.N, 43-46. NCTE; MLA. American fiction of the 19th century; English Renaissance drama. Publ: Lincoln Steffens and the art of autobiography, Col. Compos. & Commun, 5/65. Add: Dept. of English, University of Dayton, 300 College Park Ave, Dayton, OH 45469.

COCHRAN, ROBERT WILLARD, b. Williamsport, Pa, July 2, 26; m. 48; c. 2. ENGLISH. A.B, Ind. Univ, 48; Univ. Notre Dame, 44-45; M.A, Univ. Mich, 49, Ph.D.(Eng), 57. Instr. ENG, UNIV. VT, 54-58, asst. prof, 58-63, assoc. prof, 63-72, PROF, 73- Univ. Vt. summer res. fel, 67. U.S.N, 44-45. MLA. The serious novels of John P. Marquand; first-person narration in modern fiction. Publ: Hawthorne's choice: veil or jaundiced eye, Col. Eng, 2/62; Circularity in The sun also rises, Mod. Fiction Stud, 11/68; Dead fish and cold cash in Petrified man, Explicator, fall 68. Add: 322 Old Mill, University of Vermont, Burlington, VT 05401.

CODER, RALPH VERNON, b. La Belle, Mo, Aug. 19, 04; m. 30, 43. ENGLISH LITERATURE. A.B, William Jewell Col; M.A, State Univ. Iowa, 36, Ph.D, 41. Mem. fac, FT. HAYS KANS. STATE COL, 41-46, PROF. ENG. & CHMN. DIV. LANGS, LIT. & SPEECH, 46-, dean grad. div, 50-70. A.U.S, 42-46, Capt. NCTE; MLA; NEA. Chaucer; modern poetry. Publ: Chaucer's wife of Bath. Add: 526 W. 27th, Hays, KS 67601.

CODY, RICHARD JOHN, b. London, Eng, Jan. 5, 29; m. 56; c. 2. ENGLISH. B.A, London Univ, 52; fel, Univ. Miss, 53-54; M.A, Univ. Minn, 58, Ph.D. (Eng), 61; hon. M.A, Amherst Col, 68. Instr. ENG, Univ. Minn, 60-61, asst. prof, 61-63; assoc. prof, AMHERST COL, 63-68, PROF, 68-, COL. LIBRN, 70-, chmn. dept. Eng, 71-73. Readership, Folger Shakespeare Libr, summer 65. British Army, 47-49; R.A.S.C. MLA. Renaissance; modern literature. Publ: The landscape of the mind: pastoralism and Platonic theory in Tasso's Aminta and Shakespeare's early comedies, Clarendon, 69. Add: Dept. of English, Amherst College, Amherst, MA 01002.

COE, CHARLES NORTON, b. Rahway, N.J, Apr. 29, 15; m. 53; c. 2. ENGLISH LITERATURE. B.A, Amherst Col, 37; M.A, Trinity Col.(Conn), 40; Ph.D, Yale, 50. Instr. Eng, Williston Acad, 37-39; asst. Eng, Trinity Col. (Conn), 39-43, 46-47; headmaster, Williston Jr. Sch, 47-48; asst. prof. Eng, Univ. Idaho, 48-51, assoc. prof, 51-54, prof, 54-59, head dept. humanities, 54-59; prof. Eng. & dean grad. sch, North. Ill. Univ, 59-64; prof. Eng. & v.pres. acad. affairs, MONMOUTH COL, 64-73, DEAN GRAD. STUD. & SPEC. ASST. TO PRES, 73- Mem, Counc. Grad. Schs. U.S. U.S.A, 43-46, Lt. MLA; Col. Eng. Asn; NCTE; NEA; Asn. Higher Educ. Wordsworth and Shakespeare. Publ: Wordsworth and the literature of travel; Shakespeare's villains; Demi-devils: the character of Shakespeare's villains. Add: Monmouth College, West Long Branch, NJ 07764.

COELHO, RICHARD JOSEPH, b. Newark, Ohio, July 26, 13; m; c. 4. SPEECH, COMMUNICATIONS. A.B, Denison Univ, 35; M.A, Univ. Denver, 54, Ph.D.(speech), 55. Chief clerk, freight traffic dept, Pa. R.R, 37-41; gen. off. & credit mgr, Lucien Lelong Inc, 46-48; traffic & credit mgr, Robbins Incubator Co, 50-53; instr, Univ. Denver, 54-55; Am. thought & lang, MICH. STATE UNIV, 55-61, PROF. AM. THOUGHT & LANG, 62-, ASSOC. DEAN, UNIV. COL, 70-, coord. continuing educ. & dir. residence instr, 62-70. Dir, Binational Cult. Ctr, U.S. Inform. Serv, Juiz de Fora, Brazil, 59-61; rep. educ. dept, Mich. Cath. Conf. Bishops, 63- U.S.A, 41-46, 48-50, U.S.A.R, Col.(Ret). Int. Soc. Gen. Semantics; Speech Commun. Asn; Nat. Soc. Stud. Commun; Nat. Asn. Gen. & Lib. Stud. Methodologies and effects; general semantics; American minority groups, cultural contributions. Publ: Content centered teaching of communication skills, Gen. Semantics Bull, 12-60; Discussion leading, Centro Cult. Brasil-Estados Unidos, 1/61; co-auth, A condensed course in creative thinking, J. Am. Soc. Training Dir, 4/50; plus others. Add: 221 N. Hagadorn Rd, East Lansing, MI 48823.

COENS, MARY XAVIER, B.V.M, b. Chicago, Ill, Jan. 16, 18. DRAMA, ENGLISH. B.A, Mundelein Col, 39; M.A, Cath. Univ. Am, 43; Univ. Iowa, 45; Univ. Minn, 50; Univ. Kans, 65. Teacher pub. schs, Ill, 39-40; drama & Eng, Mt. Carmel Acad, Wichita, 43-47; ASSOC. PROF. SPEECH & DRAMA & CHMN. DEPT, CLARKE COL, 47- Toured Europ. Command for Defense Dept, summer 63 & Northeast. Command, summer 67; chmn. fine arts comn, Sisters of Charity, 70-74; dir, NCTE Workshop in Creative Drama, Clarke Col, summer 74. Nat. Cath. Theatre Conf.(chmn. cent. region, 67-); Am. Educ. Theatre Conf; Children's Theatre Conf; Speech Commun. Asn; Am. Nat. Theatre & Acad. Creative drama for children and parents; improvisation as an aid for creative writing and expression. Publ: History of Catholic Theatre Conference, Cath. Univ. Am, 47; G.I. Nun, Kenedy, 67; GIs and the girl from Dubuque, Reader's Digest, 6/65; A star is born, Cath. Theatre, 2/66; The theatre today, Nat. Counc. Cath. Men J, 5/66. Add: Dept. of Speech & Drama, Clarke College, Dubuque, IA 52001.

COFFEE, BERNICE FRENCH, b. Rector, Ark, Dec. 23, 06; m. 33. ENGLISH. B.S, Univ. Kans, 46, M.S, 47; Gregory fel, Univ. Mo, Columbia, 53-54, Ph.D. (Eng), 56. Prin, Clay County Sch, Ark, 26-42; chemist, Atlas & Hercules Powder Co, 42-45; instr. Eng, Univ. Kans, 45-47; head dept, Clay County Sch, 47-48; supvr. teacher training, Ark. State Univ, 48-49; instr. Eng. & dir. writing clinic, Univ. Mo, Columbia, 49-53; prof. ENG. & head dept, Shaw Univ, 58-62; PROF, UNIV. WIS-PLATTEVILLE, 63- Exten. staff, Ark. State Univ, 47-48. NCTE; Shakespeare Asn. Am; MLA. Medieval drama; English Renaissance; 17th century English. Publ: The Chester play of Balaam and Balak, Wis. Stud. Lit, 67. Add: Dept. of English, University of Wisconsin-Platteville, Platteville, WI 53818.

COFFEY, JEROME EDWARD, b. Elmira, N.Y, Aug. 4, 40; m. 64; c. 2. ENGLISH LANGUAGE & LINGUISTICS. A.B, Canisius Col, 62; fel. & M.A, State Univ. N.Y. Buffalo, 65, Ph.D.(Eng. lang), 68. Asst. prof. ENG, West. Ill. Univ, 66-68; State Univ. N.Y. Col. Brockport, 68-72; ASSOC. PROF, MONT. STATE UNIV, 72- Ling. Soc. Am; MLA. Oral poetry in Old and Middle English; the Faeroese language and bardic poetry. Add: Dept. of English, Montana State University, Bozeman, MT 59715.

COFFIN, ARTHUR BONNEAU, b. Berlin, N.H, Apr. 24, 29; m. 56; c. 1. AMERICAN & COMPARATIVE LITERATURE. B.A, Univ. N.H, 51; M.A, Boston Col, 58; Ph.D, Univ. Wis-Madison, 65. Instr. Eng, St. Vincent Col, 58-60; asst, Univ. Wis-Madison, 63-64 & 64-65; asst. prof. Am. lit. & humanities, Wash. State Univ, 65-71, assoc. prof, 71-72; ASSOC. PROF. ENG. & THEATRE ARTS & HEAD DEPT, MONT. STATE UNIV, 72- U.S.N.R, 51-56, Res, 56-73, Lt. Comdr. MLA; Rocky Mt. Mod. Lang. Asn. Twentieth century American literature and comparative fiction; literary criticism; 19th century American and European intellectual history. Publ: Robinson Jeffers: poet of inhumanism, Univ. Wis, 71; Robinson Jeffers, In: Encyclopedia of world literature in the 20th century, Ungar, 68. Add: Dept. of English & Theatre Arts, Montana State University, Bozeman, MT 59715.

COFFIN, TRISTRAM POTTER, b. San Marino, Calif, Feb. 13, 22; m. 44; c. 4. ENGLISH. B.S, Haverford Col, 43; Univ. Va, 43-44; A.M, Univ. Pa, 47, Ph.D, 49. Instr. Eng, Denison Univ, 49-50, asst. prof, 50-55, assoc. prof, 56-58; Eng. & folklore, UNIV. PA, 58-64, PROF. ENG, 64-, v.dean, Grad. Sch. Arts & Sci, 65-68. Guggenheim fel, 53. Sig.C, U.S.A, 43-46. MLA; Am. Folklore Soc.(secy-treas, 60-65, 2nd v.pres, 67-). Anglo-American ballad; folk literature; American Indian and Negro. Publ: The British traditional ballad in North America, Am. Folklore Soc; co-auth, Ancient ballads traditionally sung in New England (4 vols), Univ. Pa, 60 & Critics and the ballad, South. Ill. Univ, 61; co-ed, Folklore in America, 70 & Folklore from the working folk of America, 73, Doubleday; auth, Uncertain glory: folklore and the American revolution, Gale Res, 71; The old ball game: baseball in folklore and fiction, 71 & The book of Christmas Folklore, 73, Seabury. Add: Box-509, Wakefield, RI 02880.

COFFMAN, STANLEY KNIGHT, JR, b. Huntington, W.Va, Dec. 30, 16. ENGLISH. A.B, Haverford Col, 39; A.M, Ohio State Univ, 40, Ph.D, 48. Instr. ENG, Ohio State Univ, 46-48; asst. prof, Univ. Okla, 48-51, assoc. prof, 51-55, prof, 55-62, asst. dean, univ. col, 54-62; prof. Eng. & v.pres. acad. affairs, Bowling Green State Univ, 62-72; PROF. ENG. & PRES, STATE UNIV. N.Y. COL. NEW PALTZ, 72- MLA. Contemporary English and American poetry. Publ: Imagism, Okla; Symbolism in The bridge & Form and meaning in Passage to India, PMLA. Add: State University of New York College at New Paltz, New Paltz, NY 12561.

COGDILL, JOHN L. JACK, b. Lubbock, Tex, Feb. 1, 26; m. 49; c. 4. THEATER, SPEECH. B.A, Tex. Technol. Col, 46; M.A, N.Tex. State Univ, 50; Ph.D.(theater), Univ. Denver, 55. Teacher, high schs, Tex. & Colo, 47-54; prof. speech & radio & head dept, Panhandle Agr. & Mech. Col, 55-59; prof. speech & drama & chmn. dept. Okla. City Univ, 59-64; prof. THEATRE ARTS, Tex. Christian Univ, 64-65, chmn. dept, 65-70; PROF. & CHMN. DEPT, STATE UNIV. N.Y. COL. FREDONIA, 70- Consult, Jarvis Christian Col, 67- Speech Commun. Asn; NEA; Am. Theatre Asn; U.S. Inst. Theatre Technol. Add: Dept. of Theatre Arts, State University of New York College at Fredonia, Fredonia, NY 14063.

COGER, LESLIE IRENE, b. Huntsville, Ark, Jan. 18, 12. SPEECH. B.A, Col. Ozarks, 33; M.A, Univ. Ark, 40; Ph.D.(speech), Northwest. Univ, 52. Asst. instr, Col. Ozarks, 33; teacher Eng. & speech, Ark. State Voc. Sch, Huntsville, 33-38; instr. speech & phys. educ, Cent. Col.(Ark), 38-43; PROF. SPEECH, SOUTHWEST MO. STATE UNIV, 43- Consult. speech textbooks, McGraw-Hill Pub. Co; ed, Ark. Speech J, 42 & Players Mag, 57-59; dir. overseas touring play, Am. Educ. Theatre Asn, 61, dir. overseas shows, 65, 68 & 72, mem. overseas touring comt, 66-; res. profess. acting, Eng, 61-62; consult, oral interpretation workshop, Kans. State Univ, 62; interpreters theatre workshop, Univ. Mich, 63; lectr. oral interpretation, Queens Col.(N.Y), summer 66; courtesy fel, Univ. South. Calif, fall 66; conductor, Readers Theatre Workshop for Nat. Convention of Speech Asn. Am. & Am. Theatre Asn, 66. Sarett Award, Northwest Univ, 46. Speech Commun. Asn. (chmn. interpretation div, 71-72); Am. Theatre Asn. Publ: Oral interpretation, Nat. Thespian Soc, 58; co-auth, Studies in Readers Theatre, S.&F. Press, 63, Readers Theatre handbook, Scott, 67, rev. ed, 73 & Studies in interpretation, Rodopi N.V, Netherlands, 72; auth, Interpreters theatre: theatre of the mind, Quart. J. Speech, 63; Stanislavsky changes his mind, In: Stanislavsky and America, Hill & Wang, 66; plus others. Add: 941 Weller St, Springfield, MO 65802.

COGNARD, ROGER ALLEN, b. Omaha, Nebr, Mar. 15, 46; m. 67; c. 2. ENGLISH. B.A.Ed, Nebr. Wesleyan Univ, 67; M.A, Tex. Christian Univ, 69, Ph.D.(Eng), 71. Instr. ENG, Tex. Christian Univ, 69-71; ASST. PROF, NEBR. WESLEYAN UNIV, 71- MLA; Renaissance Soc. Am. The poetry of John Donne. Publ: C.S. Lewis's English literature in the sixteenth century: the work and its reviews, In: Papers on literature: models and methods, Holt, 70. Add: Dept. of English, Nebraska Wesleyan University, 50th & St. Paul, Lincoln, NE 68504.

COGSWELL, ANDREW COLVILLE, b. Livingston, Mont, Dec. 10, 04; m; c. 1. JOURNALISM. A.B, Univ. Mont, 27; A.M, Univ. Minn, 43. Reporter, Anaconda Standard, Mont, 27-28; ships reporter, Honolulu Star-Bull, Hawaii, 28-29; asst. city ed, Mont. Standard, Butte, 29-30; publicity writer, Portland Cement Asn, Chicago, 30-31; instr. JOUR, UNIV. MONT, 31-36, asst. prof, 36-43, assoc. prof, 43-46, prof, 46-70, secy-treas, alumni asn, 45-55, dir. pub. serv. div, 46-55, dean stud, 55-70, EMER. PROF. JOUR. & EMER. DEAN STUD, 70- Add: 404 Pattee Canyon Dr, Missoula, MT 59801.

COGSWELL, FREDERICK, b. East Centreville, N.B, Nov. 8, 17; m. 44; c. 2. ENGLISH. B.A, Univ. N.B, 49, M.A, 50; Imp. Order Daughters Empire scholar & Ph.D.(Eng), Univ. Edinburgh, 52. Asst. prof. ENG, UNIV. N.B, 52-57, assoc. prof, 57-62, PROF, 62- Can. Counc. sr. fel, 67-68. Can. Army, 40-45. Humanities Asn. Can.(ed. Bull, 67-72); Asn. Can. Univ. Teachers Eng; League Can. Poets; Independent Publ. Asn. Modern French Canadian poetry. Publ: The stunted strong, 54; Descent from Eden, Ryers Press, 59; Lost dimension, Col. Press, Dulwich, 60; co-auth, The arts in New Brunswick, Brunswick, 66 & The enchanted land, W. J. Gage, 67; auth, Star-people, 68, Immortal plowman, 69, ed. & transl, One hundred poems of modern Quebec, 70 & 71 & A second hundred poems of modern Quebec, 71, auth, In praise of chastity, 71, Chains of Liliput, 71, The house without a door, 73 & Face to face, 73, Fiddlehead Poetry Bks; chaps, In: Literary history of Canada, 66 & The poetry of modern Quebec, In: On Canada, 73, Univ. Toronto; Eros or Narcissus: the male Canadian poet, Mosaic, winter 68; plus others. Add: 769 Reid St, Fredericton, N.B, Can.

COGSWELL, THEODORE R, b. Coatesville, Pa, Mar. 10, 18; m. 65; c. 2. ENGLISH. B.A, Univ. Colo, 47; M.A, Univ. Denver, 48; Univ. Minn, 49-53. Asst. commun, Univ. Denver, 48-49, instr. Eng, 56-57; instr. commun, Univ. Minn, 49-53; ENG, Univ. Ky, 54-56, 57-58; asst. prof, Ball State Univ, 58-65; PROF, KEYSTONE JR. COL, 65- Dir, Inst. Twenty-First Century Stud, 62- Span. Republican Army, 38-39; U.S.A.A.F, 42-45, Capt; Order of Cloud & Dragon, Repub. of China, 45. NCTE; Conf. Col. Compos. & Commun; AAAS; Sci. Fiction Writers Am.(ed, Forum, 70-71, 73-). Science fiction. Publ: The wall around the world, Pyramid, 62; The third eye, Belmont, 68; The specter general, In: The science fiction hall of fame, Doubleday, Vol. II, 73. Add: Dept. of English, Keystone Junior College, La Plume, PA 18440.

COHEN, BENJAMIN BERNARD, b. Baltimore, Md, May 30, 22; m. 52. ENGLISH. A.B, Univ. Md, 43, univ. fel, 43-44, M.A, 44; univ. fel, Ind. Univ, 46-47, Strauss fel, 47-48, Ph.D.(Eng), 50. Teaching fel. Eng, Ind, Univ, 45-46; instr, Wayne Univ, 48-52; Am. Counc. Learned Soc. res. scholar, Yale, 52-53; asst. prof. ENG, Ga. Inst. Tech, 53-55; Ind. State Teachers Col, Terre Haute, 55-57; assoc. prof, Jacksonville State Col, 57-59; Oglethorpe Univ, 59-60; Wichita State Univ, 60-65, PROF, 65-68; UNIV. MO-ST. LOUIS, 68- Fulbright lectr, Univ. Oslo & Univ. Trondheim, 73. MLA; NCTE; Col. Conf. Compos. & Commun; Midwest Mod. Lang. Asn. American literature of the 19th and 20th centuries; Nathaniel Hawthorne. Publ: Writing about literature, 63, rev. ed, 73, ed, Literature for understanding, 66 & Working for literary understanding, 66, Scott; ed, The recognition of Nathaniel Hawthorne, Univ. Mich, 69 & Whitman in our season: a symposium, Transcendental Press, 71; auth, Emerson's The young American and Hawthorne's The intelligence office, Am. Lit; Hawthorne and Parley's universal history, Papers Bibliog. Soc. Am. Add: Dept. of English, University of Missouri-St. Louis, 8001 Natural Bridge Rd, St. Louis, MO 63121.

COHEN, EDWARD H, b. Washington, D.C, Nov. 6, 41; m. 64; c. 2. ENGLISH. B.A, Univ. Md, 63; M.A, Univ. Iowa, 64; Ph.D.(Eng), Univ. N.Mex, 67. Asst. prof. ENG, ROLLINS COL, 67-71, ASSOC. PROF, 71- H.H. Powers Found. grant, 69; Am. Philos. Soc. grant, 71; Arthur Vining Davis fel, 71-72; Henry E. Huntington Libr. fel, 72. MLA. Victorian poetry and prose; bibliography and methods. Publ: Gerard Manley Hopkins: a comprehensive bibliography, Cath. Univ. Am, 69; Ebenezer Cooke: the sotweed canon, Univ. Ga, 74; The Henley-Stevenson quarrel, Univ. Fla, 74. Add: Dept. of English, Rollins College, Winter Park, FL 32789.

COHEN, EDWIN, b. Sunbury, Pa, Feb. 2, 31; m. 66; c. 2. INTERPRETATION, DRAMA. A.B, Calif. State Col, Long Beach, 56, M.A, 64; Ph.D.(oral interpretation), Univ. South. Calif, 71. Teacher speech, drama & Eng, Orange Unified Sch. Dist, Calif, 57-59; Downey Sr. High Sch, 61-68; teaching asst. & lectr. speech & oral interpretation, Univ. South. Calif, 68-71; ASST. PROF. INTERPRETATION & COORD. THEATRE & INTERPRETATION, CENT. MICH. UNIV, 71- Asst. dir. prog, personnel supv, Camp Saratoga, Calif, summers 58-60, 63 & 64; teacher guitar, Montebello Adult Sch, 65-69; prin, For. Stud. League, Evian & Melun, France, summer 67; lectr. speech, Calif. State Col, Los Angeles, 69-71. U.S.A, 52-54. Speech Commun. Asn; Am. Theatre Asn; AAUP; West. Speech Commun. Asn; Cent. States Speech Asn. Oral interpretation; public address; theatre. Publ: Co-auth, The Wilberforce-Huxley debate, West. Speech, winter 73. Add: 1011 N. Fairfield Dr, Mt. Pleasant, MI 48858.

COHEN, EILEEN Z, b. Baltimore, Md, Dec. 15, 32. ENGLISH LITERATURE. B.S, Univ. Md, 53, M.A, 58, Ph.D.(Eng. lit), 65. Instr. Eng, Temple Univ, 61-65, asst. prof, 65-68; ST. JOSEPH'S COL.(PA), 68-71, ASSOC. PROF. ENG. LIT, 71- Conf. Brit. Stud; AAUP; Northeast Mod. Lang. Asn; MLA; Renaissance Soc. Am; NCTE. Renaissance drama; 17th century poetry and prose. Publ: The visible solemnity: ceremony and order in Shakespeare and Hooker, Tex. Stud. Lit. & Lang, summer 70; Alex in wonderland, or Portnoy's complaint, Twentieth Century Lit, 7/71; The Portnoy connection, Fourth Friday, 12/71. Add: Dept. of English, St. Joseph's College, 54th St. & City Line Ave, Philadelphia, PA 19131.

COHEN, HENNIG, b. Darlington, S.C, Aug. 26, 19; m. 46; c. 3. AMERICAN STUDIES, LITERATURE. A.B, Univ. S.C, 41, M.A, 48; fel, Tulane Univ, 50-51, Ph.D, 51. Radio news ed, Columbia, S.C, 45-46; dir. pub. relat, Univ. S.C, 46-56; asst. prof. ENG, UNIV. PA, 56-61, assoc. prof, 61-65, PROF, 65- Ed, Am. Quart, 57-70, chmn. ed. bd, 71-; Guggenheim fel, 60; Am. Counc. Learned Soc. grant, 60; vis. lectr, Bryn Mawr Col, 62-63; Swarthmore Col, 63-65; vis. prof, Stanford Univ, summer 68; Fulbright chair, Univ. London, 73-74. U.S.A.A.F, 41-45, T/Sgt. MLA; Am. Stud. Asn.(exec. secy, 56-61); Melville Soc. Am.(secy, 69-). American literary history. Publ: South Carolina Gazette, 1732-1775, Univ. S.C, 53; ed, Selected poems of Herman Melville, 62, co-ed, Documents in American civilization, 63, Folklore in America, 66 & Folklore of the working folk of America, 73, Doubleday; ed, Battlepieces of Herman Melville, Yoseloff, 63; ed, The Confidence man by Herman Melville, 64 & White jacket by Herman Melville, 67, Holt; co-ed, Humor of the Old Southwest, 64, ed, The American experience, 68 & The American culture, 68, Houghton; ed, Landmarks of American writing, Basic Bks, 69. Add: 37 Amherst Ave, Swarthmore, PA 19108.

COHEN, HERMAN, b. Superior, Nebr, Dec. 29, 24; m. 47; c. 2. SPEECH. B.A, State Univ, Iowa, 48, M.A, 49, Ph.D.(speech), 54. Instr. SPEECH, Univ. Ore, 49-54, asst. prof, 54-59, assoc. prof, 59-65, prof, 65-67; Univ. Mass, Amherst, 67-70; PROF. & HEAD DEPT, PA. STATE UNIV, 70- Assoc. ed, Quart. J. Speech, 62-64; vis. scholar, Univ. Edinburgh, 64; Off. Sci. & Scholarly Res, Univ. Ore. travel grant, 64; ed, West. Speech, 64-67. U.S.A, 43-46. Speech Commun. Asn.(sec. v.pres, 72-73, first v.pres, 73-74); West. Speech Asn; East. Speech Asn; Nat. Soc. Stud. Commun. Rhetorical theory and criticism; 18th century rhetoric. Publ: Co-auth, Fundamentals of speech, Macmillan, 63; auth, Hugh Blair on speech education, South. Speech J, fall 63; Leechman's anticipation of Campbell, West. Speech, 68; contrib, Language-rhetoric I & II, Holt, 69; plus others. Add: Dept. of Speech, 210 Sparks Bldg, Pennsylvania State University, University Park, PA 16802.

COHEN, JOSEPH, b. Central City, Ky, Apr. 27, 26; m. 52; c. 3. ENGLISH. B.A, Vanderbilt Univ, 49, M.A, 51; Ph.D.(Eng), Univ. Tex, 55. Taft teaching fel, Univ. Cincinnati, 51-52; instr. ENG, Univ. Tex, 53-55; NEWCOMB COL, TULANE UNIV, 55-58, asst. prof, 58-63, ASSOC. PROF, 63-, ASSOC. DEAN, 67-, asst. dean, Col. Arts & Sci, 57-58, resident prof, Tulane-Newcomb jr. year in Gt. Brit, 59-60, dir, 60-61; acad. asst. to dean, Newcomb Col, 61-67. Assoc. dir, scholars & fels. prog, Tulane Univ, 64-65, dir, 65-67, dir. scholars prog, 67-68; participant, Danforth Found. Lib. Arts Workshop, summer, 66; contrib. ed, J. Higher Educ, 68-71; chmn. region XII selection comt, Woodrow Wilson Nat. Fel. Found, 70- U.S.A, 45-46. MLA; Nat. Col. Honors Counc.(pres, 70-71); S.Cent. Mod. Lang. Asn; Bibliog. Soc. Am. Contemporary literature, particularly British literature; 20th century war literature; life-styles of college educated women. Publ: Ed, Proceedings of the Southern Honors Symposium, Tulane Univ, 68; Wouk's Morningstar and Hemingway's Sun, S.Atlantic Quart, 59; In memory of W.B. Yeats—and Wilfred Owen, J. Eng. & Ger. Philol, 10/59; The American edition of Wilfred Owen's poems, In: A tribute to Wilfred Owen, Birkenhead Inst, Liverpool, 64. Add: 7029 Freret St, New Orleans, LA 70118.

COHEN, MARY B, U.S. citizen. MODERN LITERATURE, WOMEN'S STUDIES. B.A, DePauw Univ, 62; M.A, Univ. Ill, Urbana, 63, Ph.D.(Eng), 68. ASST. PROF. ENG, TEMPLE UNIV, 68- MLA; AAUP. Modern English literature; concrete poetry; women in literature and in American culture. Publ: Out of the chaos, a new kind of strength: Doris Lessing's The golden notebook, In: An anthology of critical feminist writings, Anchor, 74; Ford Madox Ford's The good soldier, Stud. Novel, spring 74; Ian Hamilton Finlay, In: Semiotic trends in contemporary poetry, Mouton, The Hague, 74. Add: Dept. of English, Temple University, Philadelphia, PA 19122.

COHEN, MICHAEL MARTIN, b. Akron, Ohio, Apr. 27, 43; m. 67; c. 2. ENGLISH LANGUAGE & LITERATURE. A.B, Univ. Ariz, 65, M.A, 67, Ph.D. (Eng), 71. Instr. ENG, LA. STATE UNIV, NEW ORLEANS, 70-72, ASST. PROF, 72- MLA. Restoration and 18th century poetry and drama; Renaissance drama. Publ: Providence and constraint in two Lillo tragedies, Eng. Stud, 71; Plot unity in Southerne's Oroonoko, Xavier Univ. Stud, 72; Some alternatives to the freshman composition textbook, Eng. Rec, 72. Add: Dept. of English, Louisiana State University in New Orleans, Lakefront, New Orleans, LA 70122.

COHEN, MORTON NORTON, b. Calgary, Alta, Feb. 27, 21; U.S. citizen. ENGLISH LITERATURE. A.B, Tufts Univ, 49; M.A, Columbia Univ, 50, Ph.D, 58; Ford Found. fac. fel, 51-52; Fulbright fel, Eng, 54-55. Instr. ENG, W.Va. Univ, 50-51; tutor, CITY COL. & GRAD. SCH, CITY UNIV. NEW YORK, 52-53, lectr, 53-59, instr, 59-62, asst. prof, 63-65, assoc. prof, 66-70, PROF, 71- Lectr, Rutgers Univ, 52-53; mem. adv. comt, Eng. Lit. in Transition, 61-65; Am. Philos. Soc. Penrose Fund res. grant, 62 & 64; Am. Counc. Learned Soc. grant-in-aid, 63; vis. prof, Syracuse Univ, 65-66, 67-68; Guggenheim fel, 66-67; Nat. Endowment for Humanities sr. fel, 70-71. Sig.C, U.S.A, 43-45, Res, 45-53, 2nd Lt; Bronze Star Medal. MLA; Kipling Soc; PEN Club; Housman Soc; Lewis Carroll Soc; William Morris Soc. & Kelmscott Fel. Victorian literature; the novel; biography. Publ: Rider Haggard: his life and works, Hutchinson, London, 60, Walker, New York, 61 & Macmillan, London, 2nd ed, 68; co-auth, A brief guide to better writing, Oceana, 60; ed, Rudyard Kipling to Rider Haggard: the record of a friendship, Hutchinson, London, 65 & Fairleigh Dickinson Univ, 68; auth, The search for Rudyard Kipling, Syracuse Univ, 66; co-auth, Lewis Carroll's Loss of consciousness, Bull. New York Pub. Libr, 1/69; auth, Love and Lewis Carroll, Times, 11/71; plus others. Add: Apt. 3N, 72 Barrow St, New York, NY 10014.

COHEN, RALPH, b. New York, N.Y, Feb. 23, 17; m. 41; c. 2. ENGLISH. B.A, City Col. New York, 37; scholar, New Sch. Soc. Res, 38-39; dean's fel. & M.A, Columbia Univ, 46, Ph.D, 52. Instr. Eng, City Col. New York, 46-51; from asst. prof. to prof, Univ. Calif, Los Angeles, 51-67; prof. ENG, UNIV. VA, 67-73, WILLIAM R. KENAN, JR. PROF, 73-, MEM, CTR. ADVAN.

STUD, 67- Ford fel, 54-55; Guggenheim fel, 55-56; Am. Counc. Learned Soc. fel, 61-62; supvr. gen. stud, Otis Art Inst. Los Angeles, 62-67; mem. bd. ed, Eighteenth-Century Stud, 67; ed, New Lit. Hist, Jour. Theory & Interpretation, 69- Distinguished Visitor Award, Australia, summer 66. U.S.A, 42-46. Augustan Reprint Soc. Publ: The art of discrimination, Univ. Calif, 64; ed, Essential works of David Hume, 65 & The adventures of Huckleberry Finn, 66, Bantam; auth, The unfolding of the seasons, 70 & ed, New directions in literary history, 74, Routledge & Kegan Paul & Johns Hopkins; auth, A preface to Performances, New Lit. Hist, 71; Evaluative aspects of literary history, 72 & The aesthetic aspects of literary history, 73, Neohelicon; plus ten others. Add: Dept. of English, University of Virgina, Charlottesville, VA 22903.

COHEN, RICHARD, b. Boston, Mass, Jan. 27, 28; m. 59; c. 2. ENGLISH. B.S, Northeast. Univ, 52; M.A, Tex. West. Col, 55; Ph.D.(Eng), Univ. Mass, Amherst, 68. Instr. ENG, Husson Col, 60-62, asst. prof. & chmn. dept, 62-65, assoc. prof, 65-68, prof, 68-72, exec. chmn. div. lib. stud, 65-70, dir. planning res, 70-72; PROF. ENG. & CHMN. DEPT, ILL. BENEDICTINE COL, 72-, ASST. TO DEAN, 74- Ed, Husson Rev. U.S.A, 46-47. MLA; Col. Eng. Asn. Add: Dept. of English, Illinois Benedictine College, Lisle, IL 60532.

COHN, ALAN MARTIN, b. St. Louis, Mo, Aug. 21, 26; m. 53; c. 1. ENGLISH, LIBRARY SCIENCE. A.B, Wash. Univ, 49, A.M, 50, Heermans fel, 50-51, 53-54; M.S.L.S, Univ. Ill, 55. Asst. Eng, Wash. Univ, 51-53; instr. humanities, SOUTH. ILL. UNIV, CARBONDALE, 55-58, asst. prof, 58-66, assoc. prof. ENG, 66-72, PROF, 72-, HUMANITIES LIBRN, 55- Bibliogr, Dickens Stud. Newslett, 70- & James Joyce Quart, 72-; assoc. ed, ICarbS, 73- U.S.N, 44-46. MLA; Mod. Humanities Res. Asn; Bibliog. Soc. Am; Music Libr. Asn; James Joyce Found. James Joyce; bibliography. Publ: Rosenbach, Copinger, and Sylvia Beach in Finnegans wake, PMLA, 6/62; The Spanish translation of A portrait of the artist, Rev. Lit. Comp. 7-9/63; On the basic English translation of Anna Livia Plurabelle, Papers Bibliog. Soc. Am, 71; plus others. Add: Morris Library, Southern Illinois University, Carbondale, IL 62901.

COHN, ALBERT MARCUS, b. Providence, R.I, Nov. 10, 12. DRAMA. B.Ed, R.I. Col, 40; A.M, West. Reserve Univ, 47; Northwest. Univ, 53-54. Instr. drama, Emerson Col, 47-49, asst. prof, 49-55; DIR. DRAMA, R.I. SCH. DESIGN, 55-, ASSOC. PROF. ENG, 64- U.S.A.A.F, 42-45. Am. Theatre Asn; New Eng. Theatre Conf. Theatre history; dramatic production. Publ: Salvation Nell: an overlooked milestone in American theatre, Educ. Theatre J, 3/57; Imitation in drama of the inward life, Quart. J. Speech, 10/57. Add: Dept. of English, Rhode Island School of Design, Providence, RI 02903.

COHN, JAN KADETSKY, b. Cambridge, Mass, Aug. 9, 33; m. 69; c. 2. ENGLISH & AMERICAN LITERATURE, AMERICAN STUDIES. B.A, Wellesley Col, 55; M.A, Univ. Toledo, 61; Ph.D.(Eng. lang. & lit), Univ. Mich, Ann Arbor, 64. From instr. to asst. prof, ENG, Univ. Toledo, 64-68; ASSOC. PROF, Univ. Wis-Whitewater, 68-70; CARNEGIE-MELLON UNIV, 70- Am. Counc. Learned Soc. fel, summer 72; Nat. Endowment for Humanities jr. fel, 72-73. MLA; Mod. Humanities Res. Asn; NCTE; Popular Cult. Asn; AAUP. American literature and culture; 19th century and 20th century American literature; literary criticism. Publ: The negro character in northern Civil War fiction of the 1860's, New Eng. Quart, XLIII: 572-592; The theory of poetic value in Richard's Principles of literary criticism and Shelley's A defence of poetry, Keats-Shelley J, XXI-XXII: 95-111; The houses of fiction: domestic architecture in Howells and Edith Wharton, Tex. Stud. Lang. & Lit, fall 73. Add: Graduate Studies Dept. of English, Carnegie-Mellon University, Schenley Park, Pittsburgh, PA 15213.

COHN, RUBY H, b. Columbus, Ohio, Aug. 13, 22. LITERATURE. B.A, Hunter Col, 42; D. Univ, Univ. Paris, 52; Ph.D, Wash. Univ, 60. Lectr. Eng, Univ. Calif, 60-61; asst. prof. Eng. & world lit, San Francisco State Col, 61-64, assoc. prof, 64-67, prof, 67-70; fel, Calif. Inst. Arts, 70-72; PROF. COMP. DRAMA, UNIV. CALIF, DAVIS, 72- Guggenheim fel, 65-66. MLA; Am. Comp. Lit. Asn. Publ: Samuel Beckett: the comic gamut, Rutgers, 62; ed, Midnight monologues, Macmillan, 63; co-ed, Twentieth century drama, Random, 66; ed, Casebook on Waiting for Godot, Grove, 68; co-ed, Classics for contemporaries, 69 & auth, Dialogue in American drama, 71, Ind. Univ; Back to Beckett, Princeton Univ, 73. Add: Dept. of Comparative Literature, University of California, Davis, CA 95616.

COLACURCIO, MICHAEL JOSEPH, JR, b. Cincinnati, Ohio, July 2, 36; m. 60; c. 3. AMERICAN LITERATURE, INTELLECTUAL HISTORY. A.B, Xavier Univ.(Ohio), 58, M.A, 59; Ph.D.(Eng), Univ. Ill, 63. Asst. prof. ENG, Cornell Univ, 63-68; ASSOC. PROF, Ohio State Univ, 68-69; CORNELL UNIV, 69- MLA. American intellectual history from Puritanism to the major writers of the American Renaissance. Publ: Henry Adams medievalism, 12/65 & Adams flirtation with pragmatism, 3/67, Am. Quart; Occasion and audience in Edward Taylor, Am. Lit, 11/67. Add: Dept. of English, College of Arts & Sciences, Cornell University, Ithaca, NY 14850.

COLBATH, ARNOLD, b. East Millinociet, Maine, Mar. 16, 23; m. 58; c. 1. SPEECH, THEATRE. B.S, Univ. Maine, 48; M.A, West. Reserve Univ, 50, M.F.A, 51, Ph.D.(dramatic arts), 62. Instr. speech & theatre, George Washington Univ, 51-52; theatre, Duquesne Univ, 53-54; asst. prof. speech & theatre, Catawba Col, 54-60; lectr, Kent State Univ, 60-62; assoc. prof. theatre, Elmira Col, 62-68; speech & theatre, UNIV. MAINE, ORONO, 68-69, PROF. SPEECH & DIR. MAINE MASQUE THEATRE, 69-, fac. summer res. grant, 73. Lectr. theatre, Cornell Univ, summer 65; Col. Ctr. of Finger Lakes grant-in-aid for res. on Jacques Copeau, Nat. Libr, Paris, summer 66. U.S.A, 43-45. Am. Theatre Asn. Japanese Noh theatre; avant-garde drama and theatre of 19th and 20th centuries; Elizabethan drama and theatre. Publ: Outdoor historical drama in the United States, Drama, 11/56; The Noh and its relation to Zen Buddhism, Theatre J, 71-72; plus others. Add: Dept. of Speech, Stevens Hall, University of Maine, Orono, ME 04473.

COLBOURN, FRANK E, b. New Haven, Conn, July 5, 26; m. 52; c. 4. DEBATE, COMMUNICATIONS. B.S. Bus. Admin, Boston Univ, 48; LL.B, 50; S.J.D, Brooklyn Law Sch, 56. Asst. to secy, Household Finance Corp, Chicago, 50-52; real estate exec, F.W. Woolworth Co, N.Y, 52-60; from assoc. prof. to PROF. SPEECH & DEBATE COACH, PACE UNIV, 60- Adj. assoc. prof. speech, grad. sch, C.W. Post Col, L.I. Univ, 64-; dir. L.I. Debate Inst, 65-; L.I. Pub. Address Conf, 66; lectr. speech, Mercer Sch. Theol, 66-70; dir, Pace Speech Assocs, 67- U.S.N.R, 44-46. East. Forensic Asn; Speech Commun. Asn; Am. Forensic Asn. Problems in the negotiation of leases for retail location; communication theory; debate theory. Publ: Legal aspects of negotiation of long term leases for chain stores in shopping centers, Brooklyn Law Rev, 4/62 & 12/62. The art of debate (record), Listening Libr, 71. Add: Dept. of Speech & Drama, Pace University, Pace Plaza, New York, NY 10038.

COLBRUNN, ETHEL B, b. Cleveland, Ohio, Feb. 14, 13. ENGLISH. A.B, Col. Wooster, 34; M.A, Ohio State Univ, 41; fel, Univ. Fla, 52-54, Ph.D. (Eng), 54. Teacher, Eustis Pvt. Sch, Fla, 35-37; high sch, Ohio, 37-46; asst. prof. Fr. & Span, Southwest. Col, 47-51; assoc. prof. ENG, Wesleyan Col, 54-55; prof. & head dept, Shorter Col.(Ga), 56-59; asst. prof, STETSON UNIV, 59-62, assoc. prof, 62-66, PROF, 66- English Renaissance literature; Victorian literature. Publ: Co-auth, A short guide to writing research papers, manuscript form and documentation, 63, rev. 65, A short guide to writing a critical review, 64 & The student writer's guide, 70, Everett Edwards. Add: Dept. of English, Stetson University, DeLand, FL 32720.

COLBURN, C. WILLIAM, b. Bloomington, Ill, Mar. 31, 39; m. 60; c. 2. SPEECH. B.A, Ill. Wesleyan Univ, 61; M.A, Bowling Green State Univ, 62; Ph.D.(speech), Ind, Univ, 67. ASST. PROF. SPEECH, UNIV. MICH, ANN ARBOR, 65- Distinguished Serv. Award, Univ. Mich, 68. Speech Commun. Asn; Am. Forensic Asn; Cent. States Speech Asn. Fear arousing appeals: information theory. Publ: Strategies for educational debate, Holbrook, 72; co-auth, Communication and consensus, Harcourt, 72; auth, Fear arousing appeals, In: Speech communication, Allyn & Bacon, 67. Add: Dept. of Speech, University of Michigan, Ann Arbor, MI 48104.

COLBURN, WILLIAM ELLIOT, b. Chicago, Ill, Feb. 16, 23; m. 48; c. 3. ENGLISH. B.A, Univ. Ill, 47, M.A, 49, Ph.D, 52. Asst. ENG, Univ. Ill, 48-52, instr, 52-53; Univ. Ore, 53-55; asst. prof, Cent. Mich. Univ, 55-59, assoc. prof, 59-62; vis. assoc. prof, Emory Univ, 62-63; prof, Mansfield State Col, 63-64; ASSOC. PROF, Wichita State Univ, 64-66; GA. STATE UNIV, 66- Vis. assoc. prof, Emory Univ, summer 64. U.S.A.A.F, 42-45, Lt. NCTE; MLA; AAUP. Victorian literature; fiction. Publ: Ed, Concise bibliography for students of English, Stanford Univ, 72; The Vizetelly Extracts, Princeton Libr. Chronicle, winter 62; Dr. Maugham's prescription for success, Emory Univ. Quart, spring 63; Ruskin and Browning: the poet's responsibility, Stud. Lit. Imagination, 4/68; plus others. Add: Dept. of English, Georgia State University, Atlanta, GA 30303.

COLBY, ARTHUR LEROY, b. New York, N.Y, May 28, 33; m. 60; c. 3. ENGLISH. B.A, Univ. Mass, 61; M.A, Univ. N.C, 62, Ph.D.(Eng), 69. ASST. PROF. ENG, ARIZ. STATE UNIV, 65- U.S.A.F, 52-56. Sixteenth century non-dramatic literature; Shakespeare; Renaissance drama exclusive of Shakespeare. Add: Dept. of English, Arizona State University, Tempe, AZ 85281.

COLBY, FRANCES L, b. Oakland, Calif, June 17, 18. ENGLISH. B.A, Mills Col, 40; M.A, Johns Hopkins Univ, 43, Ph.D.(Eng), 48. Instr. ENG, Ohio State Univ, 46-48; STATE UNIV. N.Y. ALBANY, 48-51, assoc. prof, 51-63, PROF, 63- MLA; Soc. Relig. Higher Educ. Add: Dept. of English, State University of New York at Albany, Albany, NY 12203.

COLBY, ROBERT ALAN, b. Chicago, Ill, Apr. 15, 20; m. 47. ENGLISH, LIBRARY SCIENCE. B.A, Univ. Chicago, 41, M.A, 42, Ph.D.(Eng), 49; Penfield fel, N.Y. Univ, 42-43; M.S, Columbia Univ, 53. Instr. Eng, DePaul Univ, 46-47; Eng. & speech, Ill. Inst. Technol, 47-49; asst. prof. Eng, Lake Forest Col, 49-51; lectr, Hunter Col, 51-53; head lang. lit. & arts div, Libr, Queens Col.(N.Y), 53-64; assoc. prof. LIBR. SCI, South. Conn. State Col, 64-66; QUEENS COL.(N.Y), 66-69, PROF, 69- Vis. fac, Sch. Librarianship, Univ. Wash. summer 61. Med.C, U.S.A, 43-46. MLA (prog. chmn, Victorian Group, 72); Bibliog. Soc. Am; AAUP; Am. Libr. Asn; Asn. Am. Libr. Schs. History of reading taste; history of books and printing; library history. Publ: Co-auth, The singular anomaly: Mrs. Oliphant and the Victorian literary marketplace, Archon, 66; auth, Fiction with a purpose: major and minor nineteenth century novels, Ind. Univ, 67; contrib, European authors, Wilson, 67 & Newman's Apologia pro vita sua, Norton, 68. Add: Dept. of Library Science, Queens College, Kissena Blvd, Flushing, NY 11367.

COLBY, VINETA, b. New York, N.Y, May 12, 22; m. 47. ENGLISH. B.A, N.Y. Univ, 42, M.A, 43; Ph.D.(Eng), Yale, 46. Instr. ENG, Roosevelt Univ, 47-49, asst. prof, 49-51; instr, QUEENS COL.(N.Y), 57-65, asst. prof, 65-70, assoc. prof, 70-74, PROF, 74- MLA. Nineteenth century English novel. Publ: Co-auth. & ed, Twentieth century authors, 55, auth. & ed, American culture in the sixties, 64 & co-auth, European authors, 67, Wilson; co-auth, The equivocal virtue: Mrs. Oliphant and the Victorian literary marketplace, Archon Bks, 66; auth, The singular anomaly: women novelists of the nineteenth century, N.Y. Univ, 70; Yesterday's woman: domestic realism in the English novel, Princeton, 74; plus others. Add: Dept. of English, Queens College, Flushing, NY 11367.

COLDWELL, JOAN, b. Huddersfield, Eng, Nov. 3, 36. ENGLISH. B.A, Bedford Col, London, 58, M.A, 60; fel, Harvard, 64, Can. Counc. scholar, 65, Ph.D.(Eng), 67. Instr. ENG, Univ. Victoria (B.C), 60-65, asst. prof, 65-72; ASSOC. PROF, McMASTER UNIV, 72- Bk. ed, Victoria Daily Times, 66-69. Asn. Can. Univ. Teachers Eng; Humanities Asn. Can; Northeast Mod. Lang. Asn. Shakespeare; Charles Lamb; Canadian literature. Publ: Yeats and the little magazine 65 & A note on bookcovers, 65, In: The world of W.B. Yeats, Univ. Wash; Mad shadows as psychological fiction, J. Can. Fiction, 73. Add: Dept. of English, McMaster University, Hamilton, Ont. L8S 4M4, Can.

COLE, AILENE, b. Fort Benton, Mont, Aug. 26, 15. SPEECH, DRAMA. B.A, Gustavus Adolphus Col, 36; M.A, Univ. Minn, 49, Ph.D, 74. TEACHER, High Schs, Minn, 36-56; SPEECH & DRAMA, AUGSBURG COL, 56- Consult, Minn. State High Sch. League, 66- Am. Theatre Asn; Speech Commun. Asn; Children's Theatre Conf. Add: Dept. of Speech & Drama, Augsburg College, Minneapolis, MN 55404.

COLE, CHARLES ORR, b. Olney, Tex, May 8, 24; m. 52; c. 4. JOURNALISM. B.A, Tex. Christian Univ, 50; M.A, Los Angeles State Col, 53. Instr. jour. & dir. pub, Southwest Col, Kans, 53-55; from instr. to ASSOC. PROF. JOUR, WASH. STATE UNIV, 56- U.S.N, 42-46. Asn. Educ. Jour. Publ: Co-auth, Modern journalism, Pitman, 63. Add: Dept. of Communications, Washington State University, Pullman, WA 99163.

COLE, CHARLES WILLIAM, b. Washington, D.C, Feb. 11, 09; m. 42; c. 1. ENGLISH. A.B, George Washington Univ, 30, M.A, 31, Sanders res. fel, 31-32; Ph.D, 39; Univ. Calif, Berkeley, 32-33. Instr. ENG, GEORGE WASHINGTON UNIV, 39-41, asst. prof, 41-45, assoc. prof, 45-52, PROF, 52-, dean summer sessions, 60-74, chmn. dept. Eng, 50-63. Am. Stud. Asn; MLA. American literary and cultural nationalism; American drama. Add: Dept. of English, George Washington University, Washington, DC 20006.

COLE, DAVID WILLIAM, b. Worcester, Mass, Feb. 16, 39; m. 65; c. 2. ENGLISH LITERATURE, COMPOSITION. B.A, Oberlin Col, 61; M.A, Syracuse Univ, 63; Ford fel, Univ. Wis-Madison, 67-68, Ph.D.(Eng), 70. Instr. ENG, Univ. Wis-Fox Valley, 65-66; UNIV. WIS. CTR-BARABOO, 68-70, ASST. PROF, 70- Wis. Higher Educ. Aids Bd. grant, 71. AAUP; MLA; NCTE; NEA. Victorian and Edwardian literature and culture; modern drama; modern rhetoric. Publ: Contrib, Gilbert and Sullivan Papers, Univ. Kans, 71; A new chapter in the book of snobs: the Ph.D. and the two year college, CEA Forum, 10/72; Fugal structure in the sirens episode of Ulysses, Mod. Fiction Stud, summer 73. Add: Dept. of English, University of Wisconsin Center-Baraboo-Sauk County, Box 320, Baraboo, WI 53913.

COLE, DOUGLAS, b. New York, N.Y, July 25, 34; m. 57; c. 4. ENGLISH. A.B, Univ. Notre Dame, 57; M.A, Univ. Chicago, 57; Woodrow Wilson fel, Princeton, 57-58, Danforth Found. fel, 57-60, Ph.D.(Eng), 61. Instr. ENG, Yale, 60-64, asst. prof, 64-67, assoc. prof, 67-69; PROF, NORTHWEST. UNIV, 69-, CHMN. DEPT, 74-, dir. grad. stud, 70-73. Danforth Found. fel, Harvard, 62-63; Morse fel, Yale, 66-67; Am. Philos. Soc. res. grant, 66. MLA; Soc. Relig. Higher Educ; Shakespeare Asn. Am. Mediaeval, Elizabethan and modern drama; dramatic theory. Publ: Suffering and evil in the plays of Christopher Marlowe, Princeton, 62; ed, 20th century interpretations of Romeo and Juliet, Prentice-Hall, 70; Faust and anti-Faust in modern drama, Drama Surv, spring 66; The comic accomplice in Elizabethan revenge tragedy, Renaissance Drama IX, Northwest. Univ, 67. Add: Dept. of English, Northwestern University, Evanston, IL 60201.

COLE, EDWARD CYRUS, b. Pawtucket, R.I, Mar. 26, 04; m. 30; c. 2. DRAMA. A.B, Dartmouth Col, 26; M.F.A, Yale, 42. Instr. tech. prod, YALE, 30-34, asst. tech. dir. univ. theatre, 30-32, tech. dir, 32-46, prod. mgr, 46-71, exec. off, Sch. Drama, 59-64, acting dean, 65-66, asst. prof. DRAMA, 34-46, assoc. prof, 46-71, EMER. ASSOC. PROF, 71- Assoc. fel, Timothy Dwight Col, Yale, 49-59, fel, 59-71, sr. fac. fel, 66-67; mem. bd. gov, Am. Playwrights Theatre, 63-73; cent. comt, Am. Col. Theater Festival, 63-71; dir, U.S. Inst. Theatre Technol, 60-70. Founders Award, U.S. Inst. Theatre Technol, 71; Gold Medal, Am. Col. Theater Festival, 72, Silver Medal, 73. Fel. Am. Theatre Asn.(v.pres, 57, pres, 58, award of merit, 64); Am. Nat. Theatre & Acad.(2nd v.pres, 62, dir, 53-, secy, 67-); New Eng. Theatre Conf.(regional citation, 67); Am. Counc. Arts in Educ. (exec. secy, 62-68, deleg-at-large, 62-). Theatre technical production; architectural planning of theatres; theatre management and administration. Publ: Stage manager's manual, privately pub, 30; co-auth, Scenery for the theatre, Little, 38 & 71 & Theatres and auditoriums, Reinhold, 49 & 64. Add: School of Drama, Yale University, New Haven, CT 06520.

COLE, ELMER JOSEPH, JR, b. New Haven, Conn, Nov. 17, 35; m. 63; c. 2. ENGLISH, B.A, Yale, 60; M.A, Univ. Mont, 64; Ph.D.(Eng), Univ. N.Mex, 70. Instr. ENG, Univ. Mont, 64-67; teaching asst, Univ. N.Mex, 67-69; ASST. PROF, UNIV. NEV, RENO, 70- Restoration and early 18th century English literature; comedy and satire. Add: Dept. of English, University of Nevada, Reno, NV 89507.

COLE, HOWARD CHANDLER, b. Oak Park, Ill, May 9, 34; m. 61; c. 2. ENGLISH LITERATURE. B.A, Wheaton Col.(Ill), 56; Danforth Found. fel, 56-62; M.A, Yale, 61, Ph.D, 63. Instr. ENG, UNIV. ILL, URBANA, 62-63, asst. prof, 63-70, ASSOC. PROF, 70- U.S.A, 58-59, Res, 59-64. MLA; Midwest Mod. Lang. Asn; Renaissance Soc. Am. Elizabethan romantic comedy; Italian and French backgrounds of Shakespearean comedy. Publ: A quest of inquirie: some contexts of Tudor literature, Bobbs, 73; The Christian context of Measure for measure, JEGP, 7/65. Add: 131 English Bldg, University of Illinois, Urbana, IL 61801.

COLE, PETER, Linguistics, Language Teaching. See Volume III, Foreign Languages, Linguistics and Philology.

COLE, RICHARD CARGILL, b. Kansas City, Kans, Apr. 16, 26; m. 56; c. 2. ENGLISH. B.A, Hamilton Col, 50; M.A, Yale, 51, Ph.D.(Eng), 55. Instr. ENG, Manlius Sch, 51-52; Univ. Tex, 54-57; from assoc. prof. to prof, Radford Col, 57-61; PROF, DAVIDSON COL, 61- U.S.A.A.F, 44-46. MLA. Eighteenth century English literature; James Boswell. Publ: James Boswell and the Irish Press, 1767-1795, Bull. New York Pub. Libr, 69; Oliver Goldsmith's reputation in Ireland, Mod. Philol, 70; A new letter by James Boswell, Stud. Scottish Lit, 71. Add: Dept. of English, Davidson College, Davidson, NC 28036.

COLE, ROBERT CARLTON, b. Beaver, W.Va, June 2, 37; m. 58, 73; c. 2. AMERICAN LITERATURE, JOURNALISM. B.A, Marshall Univ, 59; M.A, Wake Forest Univ, 64; Ph.D.(Eng), Lehigh Univ, 71. Reporter, Huntington Herald-Dispatch, W.Va, 57-59; Winston-Salem Journal-Sentinel, 59-64; asst. dir. publ, Lehigh Univ, 64-70, assoc. dir, 70-72, ASST. PROF. ENG, 72-73; TRENTON STATE COL, 73- American Romantic literature; sport and literature. Add: 198 S. Canal St, Yardley, PA 19067.

COLE, ROGER WILLIAM, Linguistics, English. See Volume III, Foreign Languages, Linguistics & Philology.

COLE, WENDELL, b. Chicago, Ill, May 15, 14; m. 48. THEATRE, DRAMA. A.B, Albion Col, 36; A.M, Univ. Mich, 37; Ph.D, Stanford Univ, 51. Acting head dept. speech, Alma Col, 43-45; instr. SPEECH & DRAMA, STANFORD UNIV, 45-51, asst. prof, 51-54, assoc. prof, 54-63, PROF, 63-, ACTING EXEC. HEAD STANFORD REPERTORY THEATRE, 67-, scene designer, Stanford players, 45-65, acting exec. head dept. speech & drama, 56-57, 58-59, 60-61, 63-72, chmn. dept. drama, 72-73. Am. Theatre Asn; Speech Commun. Asn; West. Speech Commun. Asn; Am. Nat. Theatre & Acad; U.S. Inst. Theatre Technol; Soc. Archit. Hist. Publ: Elements of scene design, Comma, 62; ed, Story of the Meininger, Univ. Miami, 63; auth, Kyoto in the Momoyama period, Univ. Okla, 67; Theatre architecture (film), Olesen, 70; Theatre projects of Frank Lloyd Wright, Educ. Theatre J, 60; Early theatre in America west of the Rockies: a bibliographical essay, Rech. Theatrales, Vol. IV, No. 1; Scenografija u doba marina drziča, Forum, autumn, 67. Add: 853 Esplanada Way, Stanford, CA 94305.

COLEMAN, ARTHUR, b. New York, N.Y, June 29, 26; m. 48; c. 2. ENGLISH, AMERICAN CIVILIZATION. B.A, Manhattan Col, 46; M.A, N.Y. Univ, 48, Ph.D.(Am. civilization), 53. Instr. ENG. & AM. CIVILIZATION, Bennett Col, 52-53; Iona Col, 53-54; Hofstra Univ, 54-56; ASST. PROF, C.W. POST COL, LONG ISLAND UNIV, 60- Bibliography. Publ: Co-auth, Drama criticism (2 Vols), Swallow, 66 & 70; auth, Epic and romance criticism (2 Vols), 73 & Petals on a wet black bough, 73, Watermill; Animal imagery in Sherlock Holmes tales, Baker St. J, 12/72. Add: 104 Searingtown Rd, Albertson, NY 11507.

COLEMAN, E. CLAUDE, m. 25; c. 5. ENGLISH. A.B, Univ. Ill, 24, Ph.D, 36; M.A, Univ. Wis, 27. Teacher, High Sch, Ill, 24-27; chmn. dept. ENG, Sul Ross State Col, 36-46; prof, SOUTH. ILL. UNIV, 46-72, EMER. PROF, 72- NCTE; Int. Soc. Gen. Semantics. Dr. Johnson and James Boswell. Publ: Brother, brother, Rev. Gen. Semantics; Wanted: more men, fewer fractions, New York Times Sunday Mag, 9/61; Liberal education for survival, Campus Illustrated, 11/61. Add: 10265 Gulf Blvd, Apt. 206, St. Petersburg, FL 33706.

COLEMAN, LEON DUNCAN, b. Chicago, Ill, July 9, 20; m. 53; c. 2. ENGLISH, AFRO-AMERICAN STUDIES. B.A, Roosevelt Univ, 48; M.A, DePaul Univ, 49; Ph.D.(Am. stud), Univ. Minn, 69. Asst. prof. Eng. & humanities, Ricker Col, 65-69; ASSOC. PROF, Baldwin-Wallace Col, 69-71; ENG. & BLACK STUD, UNIV. MD, COLLEGE PARK, 71- Am. Stud. Asn; Nat. Conf. Artists; Asn. Study Afro-Am. Life & Hist; Popular Cult. Asn. Afro-American literature; Afro-American art. Add: Dept. of English, University of Maryland, College Park, MD 20742.

COLEMAN, MARION MOORE, Polish Literature, American Drama. See Volume III, Foreign Languages, Linguistics & Philology.

COLEMAN, TOM C, III, b. Louisville, Ky, Aug. 25, 20; m. 56. ENGLISH. A.B, Transylvania Col, 48; M.A, Univ. Louisville, 50; Ph.D, Univ. South. Calif, 59. Asst. prof. Eng. & humanities, Ark. Agr. & Mech. Col, 55-59, assoc. prof, 59-60, chmn. dept. humanities, 55-60, prof. Eng. & chmn. div. lang. & lit, 60-67; prof. Eng, East. Ky. Univ, 68-71; PROF, ENG. & CHMN. DEPT. LANG. & LIT, UNIV. ARK, MONTICELLO, 71- U.S.A, 42-45. MLA; Col. Eng. Asn. Nineteenth and twentieth century American novel; Shakespeare and American studies. Add: Dept. of Language & Literature, University of Arkansas, Monticello, AR 71655.

COLEMAN, VIRALENE JOHNSON, b. Waterloo, Ark, Feb. 5, 28; m. 49; c. 2. ENGLISH LITERATURE. B.A, Ark. A&M Col, Pine Bluff, 50; M.A, Univ. Ark, Fayetteville, 59, NDEA fel, 65, Title III grant, 67-69, Ph.D.(Eng), 69. Instr. ENG, UNIV. ARK, PINE BLUFF, 60-63, asst. prof, 63-69, assoc. prof, 69-71, PROF, 71- Bd. mem, Bd. World Missions, 70-73. NCTE; Conf. Col. Compos. & Commun; AAUP. Eighteenth century literature. Add: Dept. of English, University of Arkansas, N. Cedar, Pine Bluff, AR 71601.

COLEMAN, WILLIAM EMMET, b. New York, N.Y, Sept. 8, 42; m. 67; c. 1. ENGLISH LITERATURE, MEDIEVAL LANGUAGES & LITERATURE. B.A, Providence Col, 65; DuPont fel. & M.A, Univ. Va, 66; Ph.D.(Eng), City Univ. New York, 70. Lectr. ENG, Hunter Col, 66-68; Queensborough Community Col, 68-69; Suffolk County Community Col, 69-70; ASST. PROF, JOHN JAY COL. CRIMINAL JUSTICE, 70- Am. Counc. Learned Soc. grant-in-aid, 62-; Nat. Endowment for Humanities res. grant, summer 70; vis. scholar, Inst. Advan. Stud, summer 71; City Univ. Res. Found. res. grants, 71- Mediaeval Acad. Am; MLA. Liturgical drama; Boccaccio and Chaucer. Add: 18 Beechknoll Rd, Forest Hills, NY 11375.

COLEMAN, WILLIAM S. E, b. June 7, 26; m; c. 2. DRAMA, SPEECH. B.S, Slippery Rock State Col, 49; fel. & M.A, Pa. State Univ, 53; Ph.D.(theatre hist), Univ. Pittsburgh, 65. Instr. high sch, Pa, 49-52; asst. prof. theatre, speech & Eng, Slippery Rock State Col, 53-55; assoc. prof. & head dept, Glenville State Col, 55-63; asst. prof. theatre & speech, State Univ. N.Y Buffalo, 65-66; PROF. THEATRE ARTS & SPEECH, HEAD DEPT. & DIR. UNIV. THEATRE, DRAKE UNIV, 66- Chmn, W.Va. State Comt. Re-study Speech Teacher Educ, 61-62; mem. planning comt, W.Va. Centennial Showboat, 62-63, touring dir, summer 63; dir, Loving knife, N.Y. Stage Co, 65; Danforth Teacher study grant, 63 & 64; State Univ. N.Y. Found. res. grant; Drake Univ. study grant, summers 67, 68. Third prize, Arts of the Theatre Found. Playwriting Contest, 55; Third Prize, Naugatuck Footlighters One Act Play Contest, 62; First Prize, W.Va. Centennial Folk Play Contest, 63. Am. Theatre Asn. Publ: Planning for the theatre, Univ. Pittsburgh, 65; Found: an author (play), The Playshop, 2/52; Post-restoration Shylocks prior to Macklin, Theatre Survey, 5/67; Buffalo Bill on stage, Players Mag, 12/71; co-auth, Artand on an American campus, Oblique, 9/73; plus auth, dir. & producer of several plays & articles. Add: 1334 31st St, Des Moines, IA 50311.

COLES, WILLIAM ALLAN, b. Boston, Mass, Oct. 15, 30. ENGLISH. A.B, Harvard, 51, M.A, 52, Ph.D, 57. Teaching fel. Eng, Harvard, 53-54, gen. educ, 54-56; instr. ENG, Univ. Va, 56-58; asst. prof, Univ. N.C, 58-62; UNIV. MICH, ANN ARBOR, 62-67, assoc. prof, 67-72, PROF, 72- Dir, Class. Am, 68-71, ed, 71- MLA; Keats-Shelley Asn. Am; Soc. Archit. Hist, Gt. Brit; Victorian Soc. Am; Irish Georgian Soc. Nineteenth century literature; history of architecture; aesthetic theory. Publ: Co-auth, Architecture in America: a battle of styles, Appleton, 61; auth, Architecture and society: the essays of Henry Van Brunt, Harvard Univ, 68; Proof sheets of Keats' Lamia, Harvard Libr. Bull; Thomas Noon Talfourd on Byron and the imagination, Keats-Shelley J, 60; Richard Morris Hunt and his library, Art Quart, 68. Add: Dept. of English, Haven Hall, University of Michigan, Ann Arbor, MI 48104.

COLES, WILLIAM ELIOT, JR, b. Summit, N.J, Jan. 30, 32; m. 61; c. 2. ENGLISH. B.A, Lehigh Univ, 53; fel, Univ. Conn, 53-55, M.A, 55; fel, Univ. Minn, 55-60, Ph.D.(Eng), 67. Instr. Eng, Amherst Col, 60-63, asst. prof, 63-65; humanities, Case West. Reserve Univ, 65-70; ASSOC. PROF. ENG, DREXEL UNIV, 70- NCTE. Nineteenth century; the teaching of writing. Publ: Composing, Hayden, 74; Freshman composition: the circle of unbelief, Col. Eng, 11/69; The Sense of nonsense as a design for sequential writing assignments, 12/70 & An unpetty pace, 12/73, Col. Compos. & Commun. Add: 305 Michigan Ave, Swarthmore, PA 19081.

COLLET, GEORGES-PAUL, French & Comparative Literature. See Volume III, Foreign Languages, Linguistics & Philology.

COLLETT, JONATHAN H, b. Wilmington, Ohio, Mar. 16, 38; m. 61; c. 2. ENGLISH. B.A, Haverford Col, 60; Woodrow Wilson fel, Columbia Univ, 60-61, Danforth fel, 60-66, M.A, 62, Ph.D;(Eng), 67. Instr. Eng. Wesleyan Univ, 66-67, asst. prof, 67-70; ASSOC. PROF. HUMANITIES, STATE UNIV. N.Y. COL. OLD WESTBURY, 70- MLA; Soc. Relig. Higher Educ. Milton; seventeenth century English literature. Add: Dept. of Humanities, State University of New York College at Old Westbury, Old Westbury, NY 11568.

COLLETTE, CAROLYN PENNEY, b. Boston, Mass, Aug. 2, 45; m. 67. MEDIEVAL ENGLISH LITERATURE. A.B, Mt. Holyoke Col, 67; Woodrow Wilson fel, Univ. Mass, 67-68, NDEA fel, 68-69, M.A, 68, Ph.D.(Eng. lit), 71. Instr. ENG. LIT, MT. HOLYOKE COL, 69-71, ASST. PROF, 71-, fac. fel, 73-74. MLA; William Morris Soc. Old and Middle English literature; Gothic revival in England 1750-1870. Publ: Milton's Psalm translations; petition and praise, Eng. Lit. Renaissance, fall 72. Add: Dept. of English, Mt. Holyoke College, South Hadley, MA 01075.

COLLEY, JOHN SCOTT, b. Charlottesville, Va, June 29, 42; m. 64; c. 1. ENGLISH LITERATURE. B.A, Randolph-Macon Col, 64; M.A, Univ. Chicago, 65, Ph.D.(Eng), 69. Asst. prof. ENG. LIT, VANDERBILT UNIV, 68-74, ASSOC. PROF, 74- Asst. ed, Ctr. Shakespeare Stud. Publ, 68-72. MLA; Shakespeare Asn. Am; Southeast Renaissance Asn. Shakespeare; Renaissance drama; aesthetics. Publ: Ed, The Blackfriars Shakespeare Troilus and Cressida, W.C, Brown, 70; auth, Disguise and new guise in Cymbeline, Shakespeare Stud, 73; Opinion and the reader in John Marston's The metamorphosis of Pigmalions image, Eng. Lit. Renaissance, 73; Music in the Elizabethan private theaters, Yearbk. Eng. Stud, (in press). Add: Dept. of English, Vanderbilt University, Box 79, Sta. B, Nashville, TN 37235.

COLLIE, MICHAEL JOHN, b. Eng, Aug. 8, 29. ENGLISH & FRENCH LITERATURE. B.A, Cambridge, 52, M.A, 56. Asst. prof. ENG, Univ. Man, 57-61; staff tutor, Exeter Univ, Eng, 61-62; asst. prof, Mt. Allison Univ, 62-64, assoc. prof, 64-65; YORK UNIV.(ONT), 65-67, PROF, 67-, DEAN GRAD. STUD, 69-, chmn. dept. Eng, 67-69. MLA; Mod. Humanities Res. Asn, Gt. Brit; Asn. Can. Univ. Teachers Eng; Int. Asn. Univ. Prof. Eng. Twentieth century French poetry; seventeenth century thought; nineteenth century fiction. Publ: Skirmish with fact, Ryerson, 60; Jules Laforgue derniers vers, Univ. Toronto, 65; auth, The house, Macmillan, 67; Kerdrul notebook, Rampant Lions Press, 72. Add: Dept. of English, York University, Downsview, Ont. M3J 1P3, Can.

COLLIER, GAYLAN JANE, b. Fluvanna, Tex, July 23, 24. SPEECH & DRAMA. B.A, Abilene Christian Col, 46; M.A, Univ. Iowa, 49; Ph.D, Univ. Denver, 57. Instr. speech & drama, Woman's Col, Univ. N.C, 47-48; asst. prof, Greensboro Col, 49-50; from asst. prof. to assoc. prof. speech & drama & dir. theatre, Abilene Christian Col, 50-60; assoc. prof. drama, Idaho State Col, 60-63; Sam Houston State Col, 63-65; PROF. speech & drama, 65-67; THEATRE ARTS, TEX. CHRISTIAN UNIV, 67- Guest lectr, Idaho State Col, summers 58, 59; guest dir. theatre, Univ. Denver, 62; chmn, Children's Theatre Dir, Children's Theatre Asn, 64-65, admin. asst. to dir, 65-67; guest lectr. drama, Wis. State Univ, Whitewater, summer 65; dir, The imaginary invalid, Tex. Christian Univ, summer 70 & The rainmaker, Ft. Worth Repertory Theatre, summer 72. Am. Theatre Asn; Rocky Mt. Theatre Conf.(v.pres, 62-63); Children's Theatre Asn. Directing; dialects for the stage; acting, especially period styles of acting. Publ: Assignments in acting, Harper, 66; George Handel Hill: the Yankee of them all, South. Speech, 58; Linguist par excellence, West. Speech, 59, Add: Dept. Theatre Arts, Texas Christian University, Ft. Worth, TX 76129.

COLLIER, LEWIS ARLEN, b. Vernal, Utah, Jan. 30, 33; m. 60; c. 2. ENGLISH & AMERICAN LITERATURE. B.A, Univ. Calif, Santa Barbara, 60, M.A, 61; Ph.D.(Eng), Univ. Wash, 66. Teacher high sch, Calif, 61-62; asst. prof. ENG, Calif. State Univ, Hayward, 64-69; ASSOC. PROF, UNIV. NEV, LAS VEGAS, 69- U.S.A, 52-54. MLA; Rocky Mt. Mod. Lang. Asn; Philol. Asn. Pac. Coast; NCTE; Conf. Col. Compos. & Commun. Shakespeare; Renaissance; drama. Publ: All the world's a mousetrap in Hamlet II, ii, CLA J, 68; Censorship of ideas and I.B.M, or Swift's modern are winning again, West. Rev, 70; Separating the goats from the sheep, Phi Kappa Phi J, 71. Add: Dept. of English, University of Nevada, Las Vegas, NV 89154.

COLLINS, ARTHUR NETHAWAY, b. Howe Cave, N.Y, Nov. 25, 24; m. 48; c. 4. ENGLISH. B.A, State Univ. N.Y. Col. Teachers, Albany, 48; Shevlin fel, Univ. Minn, 49-50, M.A, 51, Ph.D.(Eng), 64. Teaching asst. Eng, Univ. Minn, 50-51; instr, STATE UNIV. N.Y. ALBANY, 51-53, asst. prof, 53-58, assoc. prof, 58-65, PROF, 65-71, ENG. & COMP. LIT, 71-, dir. Dr. Arts planning group, 70-73. Danforth Found. summer res. grant, 61; State Univ. N.Y. Res. Found. summer fac. res. fel, 65, grant-in-aid, 65-66; Fulbright lectr. Am. lit, Univ. of the Congo, 66-67; mem, Eng. Inst. U.S.A.A.F, 43-46. MLA; NCTE; Am. Acad. Polit. & Soc. Sci; Res. Soc. Victorian Periodicals. The novel; George Meredith; literary criticism. Publ: Ed, Readings for introduction to college, State Univ. Bk. Store, Albany, 59; auth, Images of the hero: Meredith and his biographers 1909-1959, Univ. Microfilms, 64; Style sheet for bibliography and footnotes, Faculty-Stud. Asn, State Univ. N.Y. Albany, 65, 68; Publish or perish: the middle way, Eng. Rec, 12/62; Meredith's ataxia: a corrective note, Eng. Lang. Notes, 12/64; The D.A. of State University of New York at Albany, In: Proceedings of the Wingspread Conference on the Doctor of Arts degree, Counc. Grad. Schs. U.S, 71; plus others. Add: 151 S. Allen St, Albany, NY 12208.

COLLINS, CARVEL, b. West Union, Ohio, June 14, 12; m. 39; c. 1. AMERICAN LITERATURE. B.S, Miami Univ, 33; A.M, Univ. Chicago, 37, Ph.D, 44. Instr, Colo. State Col, 38-39; Stephens Col, 39-40; Harvard, 43-46, asst. dean col, 45-46; asst. prof, Swarthmore Col, 46-47; ENG, Harvard, 47-51; PROF, Mass. Inst. Technol, 51-67; UNIV. NOTRE DAME, 67- Libr. Congr. fel, 46; vis. prof, Univ. Tokyo, 61-63; Am. Philos. Soc. grant, 63; Fidelis Found. grant, 63; Bollingen Found. fel, 64-65. U.S.N, 42-43, Lt. (jg). MLA; Mod. Humanities Res. Asn, Gt. Brit; Col. Eng. Asn; Am. Stud. Asn; Bibliog. Soc. Am; NCTE. William Faulkner; 20th century American fiction; 19th century American fiction. Publ: American sporting gallery, Harvard Univ, 49; Samuel Ward in the gold rush, Stanford Univ, 49; co-auth, Literature in the modern world, George Peabody Col, 54; ed, William Faulkner: New Orleans sketches, Evergreen Bks, 61 & Random, 68, Erskine Caldwell's Men and women, Little, 61 & William Faulkner: early prose and poetry, Atlantic Monthly Press, 62; auth, The interior monologues of The sound and the fury, In: Psychoanalysis and American fiction, Dutton, 65; William Faulkner, The sound and the fury, In: The American novel, Basic Bks, 65; Miss Quentin's paternity again, In: Studies in The sound and the fury, C.E. Merrill, 70. Add: Dept. of English, University of Notre Dame, Notre Dame, IN 46556.

COLLINS, CHRISTOPHER, b. Red Bank, N.J, July 8, 36; m. 68; c. 1. MODERN POETRY, AMERICAN LITERATURE. B.A, St. Anselm's Col, 58; Woodrow Wilson fel. & M.A, Univ. Calif, Berkeley, 59; Ph.D.(comp. lit), Columbia Univ, 64. Asst. prof. ENG, Nassau Community Col, 63-65; from asst. prof. to assoc. prof. & chmn. dept, Borough of Manhattan Community Col, 65-68; ASSOC. PROF, N.Y. UNIV, 68- Ed. consult, poetry, Col. Div, Random House, 68-70; vis. scholar, Gonville & Caius Col, Cambridge, 70; ed. consult. poetry, Col. & Univ. Div, McGraw Hill, 72- Contemporary poetry; backgrounds and forms of contemporary cultural expression. Publ: The act of poetry, Random, 70; The uses of observation: correspondential vision in the writings of Emerson, Thoreau, and Whitman, Mouton, The Hague, 71; transl. & auth, introd, The Daphnis and Chloe of Longus, Imprint Soc, 72; Figure, ground, and open field, N.Y. Quart, winter 71; If your drink is bitter, be wine, Nation, 5/72; Notes on prosody, In: The logic of poetry (Monaco & Briggs), 74. Add: Dept. of English, New York University, 19 University Pl, New York, NY 10003.

COLLINS, DAN STEAD, b. Williamsport, Pa, Dec. 5, 19; m. 55. ENGLISH. B.S, Univ. Pa, 41; M.A, Univ. N.C, 51, Ph.D, 60. Instr. ENG, Univ. Tenn, 46-47; part-time instr, Univ. N.C, 49-52; from instr. to asst. prof. UNIV. MASS, AMHERST, 53-73, ASSOC. PROF, 73- Managing ed, Eng. Lit. Renaissance, 72- U.S.A.A.F, 42-45. Col. Eng. Asn; MLA; Renaissance Soc. Am. Milton. Add: Dept. of English, University of Massachusetts, Amherst, MA 01002.

COLLINS, FLETCHER, JR, b. Nov. 19, 06; U.S. citizen; m. 32; c. 4. MEDIEVAL LITERATURE, DRAMATIC ARTS. Ph.B, Yale, 28, Larned fel, 30-31, Ph.D.(Eng), 34. Asst. Eng, Yale, 29-30; instr, Montclair State Teachers Col, 32-34; dir. music & drama, Arthurdale Community Sch, W.Va, 34-36; PROF. Eng. & drama, Elon Col, 36-42; DRAMATIC ARTS, MARY BALDWIN COL, 46- Southeast. Theatre Conf; Mediaeval Acad. Am; Am. Theatre Asn. Medieval church music-drama; traditional British and American folksong; liturgical drama. Publ: The production of Medieval church music-drama, 72 & co-ed, Theater wagon: plays of place and anyplace, 73, Univ. Va; ed, Alamance play-party songs and singing games, Norwood Ed, 73; contrib, Community schools in action, Viking, 39. Add: 437 E. Beverley St, Staunton, VA 24401.

COLLINS, HAROLD, b. S.Seaville, N.J, Sept. 10, 15; m. 40; c. 3. ENGLISH. A.B, Duke Univ, 37; A.M, Columbia Univ, 38, Ph.D, 51. Instr. ENG, Catawba Col, 39; Cent. Methodist Col, 40-42; asst. prof, Wilkes Col, 45-47; instr, Waterbury br, Univ. Conn, 47-55; from asst. prof. to assoc. prof, KENT STATE UNIV, 55-66, PROF, 66- U.S.A, 43-45. MLA; Ling. Soc. Am. West, East and South African fiction in English. Publ: Amos Tutuola, Twayne, 70; Kurtz, the cannibals and the second-rate helmsman, West. Humanities Rev; Roy Campbell: the talking bronco, Boston Univ. Stud. Eng, 60; The novel in Nigeria, In: Writers the other side of the horizon, NCTE, 64. Add: Dept. of English, Kent State University, Kent, OH 44240.

COLLINS, JOHN D, b. Akron, Ohio, Sept. 10, 32; m. 58; c. 3. ENGLISH, SPEECH. B.A, Univ. Akron, 57, M.A, 59; Ph.D.(drama), State Univ. Iowa, 63. ASSOC. PROF, ENG. & SPEECH, Edinboro State Col, 63-67; Am. Univ. Beirut, 67-71; HILLSDALE COL, 71- Regional speech consult, Pa. Dept. Pub. Instr, 66-67. U.S.A.F, 50-53. Speech Commun. Asn; MLA. Publ: Blending liberal arts and professional training, Pa. Sch. J, 11/65; Henry Abbey: image maker of the flash age, Educ. Theatre J, 10/66; Playwright, orator and tragedy, Pa. Speech Annual, 67. Add: Dept. of English, Hillsdale College, Hillsdale, MI 49242.

COLLINS, JOSEPH JOHNSON, b. Memphis, Tenn, Nov. 25, 33; m. 64; c. 3. ENGLISH LITERATURE. B.A, Univ. Richmond, 56, M.A, 61; NDEA fel, Fla. State Univ, 68-70, Ph.D.(Eng), 70. Instr. ENG, Ga. Mil. Col, 59-60; VA. POLYTECH. INST. & STATE UNIV, 61-67, ASST. PROF, 68- MLA; S.Atlantic Mod. Lang. Asn; Victorians Inst. Victorian poetry, especially Tennyson; Victorian philosophy and religion; 19th century philosophy and religion. Publ: Tennyson and Kierkegaard, Victorian Poetry, winter 73; Tennyson and the spasmodics, Victorian Newsletter, fall 73. Add: Dept. of English, Virginia Polytechnic Institute & State University, Blacksburg, VA 24061.

COLLINS, LESLIE MORGAN, b. Alexandria, La, Oct. 4, 17. ENGLISH & AMERICAN DRAMA. A.B, Dillard Univ, 36; A.M, Fisk Univ, 37; Rosenwald fel, West. Reserve Univ, 44-45, Ph.D, 45, M.S.L.S, 52; summers, Univ. Wis, 38, 40, Univ. South. Calif, 41-43, Univ. Havana, 47, Univ. Oslo, 49 & Univ. Florence, 60; Univ. Madrid, 66. Instr, Ft. Valley State Col, 37-39; ENG, South. Univ, 39-40; Bennett Col, 40-41; Lincoln Univ, 41-44; assoc. prof, FISK UNIV, 45-54, PROF, 54- Fund Advan. Educ. fel, West. Reserve Univ, 51-52; sr. bk. reviewer, Nashville Tennessean. Am. Libr. Asn; Col. Lang. Asn; Am-Scand. Found. The Negro author; comparative literature;

Milton. Publ: Notes from a teacher of Negro literature, Eng. Rec, winter 62; Stevedore, In: Beyond the blues, Hand & Flower Press, 62. Add: Dept. of English, Fisk University, Nashville, TN 37203.

COLLINS, PASCHAL JAY, b. Jacksonville, Fla, Oct. 23, 33; m. 61; c. 3. AMERICAN LITERATURE. B.S.Ed, Fla. A&M Univ, 59; M.A, Univ. Denver, 68; univ. fel, Univ. Fla, 72-74. ASST. PROF. ENG, UNIV. S.FLA, TAMPA, 70- U.S.A.F, 51-55. Black American writers; the symbolist movement. Publ: Final reckoning (short story), Manhunt, 63; Black bottom (short story), Negro Dig, 64; Rape is a nasty word (short story), Men's Dig, 64; plus others. Add: Dept. of English, University of South Florida, Fowler Ave, Tampa, FL 33620.

COLLINS, ROBERT GEORGE, b. Danbury, Conn. MODERN ENGLISH & COMPARATIVE LITERATURE. B.A, Miami Univ, 50, M.A, 52; fel, Rutgers Univ, 50-51; Columbia Univ, summer 52; Univ. Calif, Berkeley, 55-56; Ph.D.(Eng, comp. lit), Univ. Denver, 59. Instr, Miami Univ, 51-52; Univ. Ala, 52-53; asst. prof. ENG, Colo. State Univ, 56-57, 58-59; Pa. State Univ, 57-58; Calif, State Univ, Los Angeles, 59-62; vis. assoc. prof, State Univ. N.Y. Buffalo, 62-63; assoc. prof, San Jose State Univ, 63-65; PROF, Univ. N.H, Keene Campus, 65-66; Parsons Col, 66-68; UNIV. MAN, 68- Ed, Colo. Rev, 56-59; vis. prof. Eng, Univ. of the Americas, summer 57; ed, Mosaic: J. Comp. Lit, 70-; Can. Counc. advan. res. fel, 71-73. U.S.N, 42-47, Res, 47-51. MLA; Asn. Can. Univ. Teachers Eng. Literary critical theory; the novel aesthetics. Publ: Virginia Woolf's Black arrows of sensation, Arthur Stockwell, 62; ed, New views of the English and American novel, 71, Ulyssess and The waste land fifty years after, 72, auth, The novel and its changing form, 72, From an ancient to a modern theatre, 72 & ed, The novels of William Faulkner, 73, Univ. Man; plus others. Add: Dept. of English, University of Manitoba, Winnipeg, Man. R3T 2N2, Can.

COLLINS, ROWLAND LEE, b. Bristow, Okla, Sept. 17, 34; m. 65; c. 3. ENGLISH. A.B, Princeton, 56; Nat. Woodrow Wilson fel, Stanford Univ, 56-57, Woodrow Wilson teaching fel. & M.A, 59, Ph.D, 61. Lectr, ENG, Ind. Univ, 59-61, instr, 61-62, asst. prof, 62-65, assoc. prof, 65-67; PROF, UNIV. ROCHESTER, 67-, CHMN. DEPT, 72-, acting chmn. dept, 70-71. Acad. adv. Montfort & Allie Brown Jones Found, 61-; ed. consult, Victorian Stud, 63-66; campus rep, Nat. Woodrow Wilson Found, 63-67; mem. ed. bd, Your Musical Cue, 64-69; fel. Counc. Humanities, Princeton, 65-66; fel. Guggenheim Found, 65-66; founding ed, Year's Work in Old Eng. Stud, 68- MLA; Mediaeval Acad. Am; Tennyson Soc.(Am. secy. publ. bd, 63-69, Am. rep, 67-); Bibliog. Soc, Eng; Grolier Club; Early Eng. Text Soc; Am. Name Soc; Cambridge Bibliog. Soc. Old English literature and language; the Tennysons; George Eliot. Publ: Fourteen British and American poets, Macmillan, 63; co-auth, The devil and the lady and unpublished early poems by Alfred Lord Tennyson, 64 & Beowulf, 65, Ind. Univ; auth, The Frederick Tennyson collection, Victorian Stud, 63; A reexamination of the Old English glosses in The Blickling Psalter, Anglia, 63; Six words in the Blickling homilies, In: Philological essays: studies in Old and Middle English literature in honour of Herbert Dean Meritt, Mouton, The Hague, 70. Add: Dept. of English, University of Rochester, Rochester, NY 14627.

COLLINS, SARAH HUFF, b. Harlan, Ky, May 22, 35; m. 65; c. 3. ENGLISH LITERATURE. B.A, Ctr. Col. Ky, 57; M.A, Ind. Univ, 66, Ph.D.(Eng), 70. Teacher music, Lynch Publ Schs, Ky, 58-59; instr. Eng, Ctr. Col. Ky, 61-63; asst. prof. LANG. & LIT, ROCHESTER INST. TECHNOL, 67-71, ASSOC. PROF, 71- MLA; AAUP; Asn. Gen. & Lib. Stud. English literary scholarship; 18th century English language and literature; English biography. Publ: Co-auth, Milton's History of Britain, In: Milton Encycl, Univ. Wis, 74. Add: College of General Studies, Rochester Institute of Technology, One Lomb Memorial Dr, Rochester, NY 14623.

COLLINS, SHERWOOD CLARK, b. Dwight, Kans, July 7, 24; m. 58; c. 2. DRAMA. B.S, Kans. State Univ, 48; M.F.A, State Univ. Iowa, 53, Ph.D. (drama), 55. Asst. prof. theater, Univ. Wis, 55-61; asst. prof. DRAMA, TUFTS UNIV, 61-66, ASSOC. PROF, 66- U.S.A.F, 43-45, Res, Maj. Am. Theatre Asn. Playwriting; contemporary British theater. Publ: House of Bernara Alba: director's notes, spring 66 & The intermission, spring 67, Drama Critique; Boston's eighteenth century street theatre, Educ. Theatre J, 12/73. Add: Dept. of Drama, Tufts University, Medford, MA 02155.

COLLINS, THOMAS JOSEPH, b. London, Ont, Aug. 23, 36; m. 60; c. 3. ENGLISH. B.A, Univ. Ont, 59, M.A, 61; Ph.D.(Eng), Ind. Univ, 65. Asst. prof. ENG, King's Col, 64-66; UNIV. WEST. ONT, 66-68, ASSOC. PROF, 68- Summers, Can. Counc. grants, 65 & 68; Am. Counc. Learned Soc. grant, 66. MLA; Asn. Can. Univ. Teachers Eng. Publ: Robert Browning's Moral-aesthetic theory, 1833-1855, Univ. Nebr, 67; Browning's Essay on Shelley: in context, spring 64 & Shelley and God in Browning's Pauline, summer 65, Victorian Poetry; Toronto conference on editing 19th century materials, Victorian Stud, 12/66. Add: Dept. of English, University of Western Ontario, London, Ont, Can.

COLLMER, ROBERT GEORGE, b. Guatemala City, Guatemala, Nov. 28, 26; U.S. citizen; m. 48; c. 2. ENGLISH. B.A, Baylor Univ, 48, M.A, 49; Ph.D. (Eng), Univ. Pa, 53. Asst. instr. Eng, Univ. Pa, 49-52; assoc. prof, Hardin-Simmons Univ, 54-57, prof, 57-61; prof. & dean col, Wayland Baptist Col, 61-66; Fulbright prof. Eng. & Am. lit, Nat. Univ. Paraguay, 66-67; prof. Eng, Tex. Tech Univ, 67-73, dir. grad. stud, 69-70, acting chmn. dept. Eng, 70; PROF. ENG. & CHMN. DEPT, BAYLOR UNIV, 73- Smith-Mundt prof. Eng. & Am. lit, Inst. Technol, Mex, 58-60; South. Fel. grant, 58; State Tex. Res. Fund grant, summer 70; Tex. Tech Univ. fac. develop. grant, spring 71; res. prof. Eng, Sir Thomas Browne Inst, Univ. Leiden, spring 71. U.S.A, 45-46. MLA; Renaissance Soc. Am; S.Cent. Mod. Lang. Asn; S.Cent. Renaissance Conf.(pres, 70-71); Am. Asn. Teachers Span. & Port. English literature of late Renaissance; Anglo-Dutch literary relations: Anglo-Hispanic literary relations. Publ: Donne and Borges, Rev. Litt. Comp, 69; The displaced person in the novels of Gabriel Casaccia, Re: Arts & Lett, 70; Latin-American education: an outsider's inside view outside, Arlington Quart, 70; plus others. Add: Dept. of English, Baylor University, Waco, TX 76703.

COLQUITT, BETSY FEAGAN, b. Fort Worth, Tex, Mar. 5, 26; m. 54; c. 2. ENGLISH & AMERICAN LITERATURE. B.A, Tex. Christian Univ, 47; scholarship & M.A, Vanderbilt Univ, 48. Instr. Eng, Ala. State Col. Women, 48-49; Univ. Kans, 49-53; TEX. CHRISTIAN UNIV, 54-60, asst. prof, 60-70, ASSOC. PROF, 70- AAUP; Col. Conf. Teachers Eng. Modern literature. Publ: Ed, A part of space: ten Texas writers, 69, Studies in medieval, Renaissance, and American literature, 71, Space against time in modern poetry, 71, A hope of wisdom, 73 & Texas Christian University: a hundred years of history, 74, Tex. Christian Univ; auth, Symbolism: writer, worth, reader, Eng. Tex, 65; George Orwell: a traditionalist in wonderland, Discourse, 65; Thoreau's poetics, Am. Transcendental Quart, 71 & In: Artist & citizen Thoreau; plus several poems in var. jours. Add: Dept. of English, Texas Christian University, TCU Sta, Fort Worth, TX 76129.

COLSON, LILYAN, b. Mooresville, N.C. Jan. 19, 08. AMERICAN LITERATURE. A.B, E.Carolina State Teachers Col, 29; A.M, Peabody Col, 37; Univ. N.C, 50. Mem. fac, Delta State Teachers Col, Miss, 38-40; Lenoir Rhyne Col, 40-48; Winthrop Col, 48-49; from asst. prof. to assoc. prof. AM. LIT, CATAWBA COL, 49-71, EMER. ASSOC. PROF, 71- American literary clubs. Add: Dept. of American Literature, Catawba College, Salisbury, NC 28144.

COLSON, THEODORE, b. Hancock, N.Y, July 12, 35; m. 57; c. 1. ENGLISH. A.B, Wesleyan Col.(N.Y), 57; M.A, Syracuse Univ, 62; Ph.D.(Eng), Univ. Mich, 67. Asst. prof. ENG, UNIV. N.B, FREDERICTON, 67-74, ASSOC. PROF, 74- U.S.A, 57-59. MLA. American fiction. Add: Dept. of English, University of New Brunswick, Fredericton, N.B, Can.

COLTHARP, LURLINE HUGHES, b. Bridgeport, Tex, May 9, 13; m. 35, 63; c. 2. ENGLISH, LINGUISTICS. B.A, Univ. Tex, Austin, 35, M.A, 51, Ph.D. (Eng. ling), 64. Teacher, Ysleta Grade Sch, 32-34, 45-47, 49-50, 52-53; instr. Eng, UNIV. TEX, EL PASO, 54-61, asst. prof, 61-65, assoc. prof, 65-70, PROF. LING. & ENG, 70- Training asst, Peace Corps Colombia IV Proj, 62-63; conductor, sem. prof. Eng, Univ. Durango, 64 & Univ. Sinaloa, 64 & 66; Ling. Sem. Teachers Eng, State N.Mex, Apr. 65; vis. lectr, Inst. Mex. Am. Relac. Cult, Hermosillo, Mex, 66; assoc. dir, NDEA Inst. Eng. Second Lang, summer 66; vis. lectr, NDEA inst. bilingualism, Univ. Tex, Austin, June 68; guest lectr, Univ. Philippines, summer 72; guest lectr. sem. teaching Eng. lang, Inst. Politecnico Nac, Mexico City, fall 72. S.Cent. Mod. Lang. Asn.(chmn. Eng. VI, 70-71); Am. Name Soc; Ling. Soc. Am; MLA; Teachers Eng. Speakers Other Lang; Am. Dialect Soc; Int. Phonetic Asn. Dialect study; teaching English as a foreign language. Publ: The tongue of the Tirilones: a linguistic study of a criminal argot, Univ. Ala, 65; Invitation to the dance, In: Texas studies in bilingualism, Walter Gruyter & Co, Berlin, 68; A digital classification of place names: a note, Names, 9/72. Add: Dept. of English, University of Texas at El Paso, El Paso, TX 79968.

COLTON, AGNES LOUISE, b. Colton, S.Dak, Nov. 25, 05. ENGLISH LITERATURE. B.A, Whitman Col, 25; M.A, Univ. Ore, 28; Ph.D, Univ. Wash, 39. Teacher Eng. & Latin, Dixon High Sch, Mont, 25-26; asst, Univ. Ore, 26-27; teacher Eng, hist. & Latin, Franklin High Sch, Portland, Ore, 27-39; teaching fel, Univ. Wash, 39-42, from assoc. to asst. prof. & lectr. Eng, 42-54; from asst. prof. to prof. hist. & eng, East. Wash. State Col, 54-72; RETIRED. Fulbright grant, Italy, 59-60. NCTE; Conf. Col. Compos. & Commun; Renaissance Soc. Am. Seventeenth century, especially English poets and the Civil War. Publ: Co-auth, Introductory exposition, Pacific Bks, 59. Add: Dept. of English, Eastern Washington State College, Cheney, WA 99004.

COLVERT, JAMES B, b. Paris, Tex, June 8, 21; m. 44; c. 2. ENGLISH. B.A, Henderson State Col, 47; M.A, E.Tex. State Univ, 49; Ph.D.(Eng), La. State Univ, 53. Instr. Eng, Univ. Tex, 53-55, asst. prof, 55-57; Univ. Conn, 57-58; assoc. prof, Univ. Va, 59-68; PROF. ENG, UNIV. GA, 68-, HEAD DEPT, 72- Ed, Ga. Rev, 68-72. U.S.A.A.F, 43-46, Capt. American literature. Publ: Views of Southern character in some Northern novels, Miss. Quart, 65; introd, Great short works of Stephen Crane, Harper, 68; contrib, The works of Stephen Crane, Vol. I, 69, Vol. VI, 70 & Vol. IX, 71, Univ. Va; plus others. Add: Dept. of English, University of Georgia, Athens, GA 30601.

COLVILLE, DEREK, b. Scarborough, Eng, Feb. 23, 23. ENGLISH. Fulbright scholar. & B.A, Univ. Durham, 50; A.M, Wash. Univ, 52, Ph.D, 53. Lectr. Eng. lit, Univ. Toronto, 53-54; instr. ENG, Yale, 54-58; asst. prof, Univ. Calif, Riverside, 58-63; assoc. prof, STATE UNIV. N.Y. BINGHAMTON, 63-69, PROF, 69- Jubilee-prize, Univ. Durham, 49; Cornelison prize, 52-53. R.A.F, 40-46. Counc. Basic Educ. Nineteenth century English literature; American literature; comparative education. Publ: Craft of writing, Harper, 61; Victorian poetry and the romantic religion, State Univ. N.Y, 70; Comprehensives and university: notes from America, Critical Survey, winter 70. Add: Dept. of English, State University of New York at Binghamton, Binghamton, NY 13901.

COLWELL, CHARLES CARTER, b. Chicago, Ill, Aug. 19, 32; m. 52; c. 3. ENGLISH. B.A, Univ. Chicago, 49; B.A, Cambridge, 52, M.A, 57; Danforth Found. fel, 55-58; Ph.D.(lib. arts), Emory Univ, 58. Instr. ENG, Oxford Col, Emory Univ, 52, 55; asst. prof, STETSON UNIV, 58-64, assoc. prof, 64-70, PROF, 70- U.S.A, 53-55, Sgt. S.Atlantic Mod. Lang. Asn. Literary criticism. Publ: A student's guide to literature, Washington Sq, 68; The tradition of British literature, Putnam, 71; co-auth, What's the usage? the writer's guide to English grammar and rhetoric, Reston, 73; auth, Literary criticism and process thought: Blackmur, Brooks, Sartre, and Whitehead, Process Stud, winter 72; plus others. Add: Dept. of English, Stetson University, Box 1293, De Land, FL 32720.

COLWELL, JAMES LEE, b. Brush, Colo, Aug. 31, 26; m. 57; c. 2. AMERICAN STUDIES. B.A, Univ. Denver, 49; M.A, Colo. State Col, 51; Ph.D. (Am. stud), Yale, 61. Teacher, high schs, Colo, 48-52; civilian educ. adv, U.S. Air Force, Japan, 52-55; asst. command educ. dir, hq, Far East Air Force, Tokyo, 55-56; lectr, overseas progr, Univ. Md, 56-57; assoc. dir. for. stud. inst, Yale, 60-61; asst. dir. & lectr. hist. & Eng, Univ. Md. Europ. Div, Heidelberg, Ger, 61-65; assoc. prof. Eng. & dir. int. educ, Univ. Colo, Boulder, 65-72; PROF. AM. STUD. & DEAN, COL. ARTS & EDUC, UNIV. TEX. OF THE PERMIAN BASIN, 72- Exchange prof, Teachers Col, Goettingen, Ger, 70; dir, Ger-Am. Workshop on Educ. Exchange, Bonn, 72. U.S.A.F, 45, Res, 46-, Lt. Col. Am. Stud. Asn; NEA; Orgn. Am. Hist; Am. Asn. Univ. Adminr; MLA; Rocky Mt. Soc. Sci. Asn.(pres. elect, 73-74, pres,

74-75); Nat. Asn. For. Stud. Affairs. American intellectual and cultural history; American-German relations; American literary history. Publ: From stone to steel: American contributions to the revolution in flour milling, Rocky Mt. Soc. Sci. J, 69; Huckleberries and humans: on the naming of Huckleberry Finn, PMLA, 71; German students view the American character: freedom, tolerance and a certain generosity, Exchange, 71; plus others. Add: College of Arts & Education, University of Texas of the Permian Basin, Odessa, TX 79762.

COLYER, RICHARD HALL, b. Detroit, Mich, May 6, 31; m. 66; c. 2. MODERN LITERATURE, FILM. Ph.D.(Eng), Univ. Iowa, 72. Instr. ENG, Drake Univ, 63-64; asst, Univ. Iowa, 64-68; ASST. PROF, UNIV. KANS, 68- U.S.N, 56-64. MLA; Midwest Mod. Lang. Asn; AAUP. Post-realistic fiction; modern poetry; film esthetics. Publ: Thoreau's color symbols, PMLA, 10/71. Add: Dept. of English, University of Kansas, Lawrence, KS 66045.

COMBS, JOHN R, b. Stafford, Okla, Dec. 9, 29; m. 50; c. 3. ENGLISH. B.A, Southwest. State Col, 51; B.D, South. Methodist Univ, 54; M.A, Tex. A&M Univ, 64; Ph.D.(Eng), Univ. Tex, 68. Pastor, First Methodist Church, Coalgate, Okla, 54-56 & Newkirk, Okla, 56; campus pastor & instr. relig, Okla. State Univ, 56-60; Tex. A&M Univ, 60-64; asst. prof. ENG, McMurry Col, 67-69; ASSOC. PROF, KY. WESLEYAN COL, 69-, chmn. dept, 69-72. U.S.N.R, 47-51. MLA; Col. Eng. Asn. Nineteenth century English literature; English novel; Jewish American fiction. Publ: George Eliot's mind and the clerical characters in her fiction, Microfilms, Inc, 68; The trinity in Hopkins' God's grandeur, CEA Critic, 5/73; Cleaving in Hardy's convergence at the twain, CEA Forum, (in press). Add: Dept. of English, Kentucky Wesleyan College, Owensboro, KY 42301.

COMERY, ROBERT WHITFIELD, b. Pawtucket, R.I, Dec. 23, 18; m. 46; c. 2. ENGLISH. B.A, Yale, 40; M.A, Brown Univ, 49, Ph.D, 57. Instr. ENG, Kiski Sch, Saltsberg, Pa, 46; Brown Univ, 47-56; asst. prof, R.I. COL, 57-60, assoc. prof, 60-64, PROF, 64-, chmn. dept, 60-66. Lectr. Eng. for. off, Naval War Col, 56-59. U.S.A, 41-45. NCTE. Shakespeare; English literature of the 19th century; humanities. Add: Dept. of English, Rhode Island College, Providence, RI 02908.

COMITO, TERRY ALLEN, b. Santa Ana, Calif, Dec. 17, 35. ENGLISH. A.B, Stanford Univ, 57, A.M, 58; Ph.D.(Eng), Harvard, 68. Instr. ENG, Rutgers Univ, New Brunswick, 63-67, ASST. PROF, 67-71; HUNTER COL, 71- Renaissance Soc. Am. Shakespeare; English and Italian Renaissance; 17th century English literature. Publ: Touch of evil, Film Comment, summer 71; Renaissance gardens and the discovery of paradise, J. Hist. Ideas, 10-12/71; The Lady in a landscape and the poetics of Renaissance pastoral, Univ. Toronto Quart, spring 72. Add: Dept. of English, Hunter College, 695 Park Ave, New York, NY 10021.

COMPARETTI, ALICE PATTEE, b. South Bend, Ind, Dec. 07; m. 38; c. 2. ENGLISH LITERATURE. A.B, Rockford Col, 30; A.M, Cornell Univ, 34, Ph.D, 36. Teacher, pub. schs, South Bend, 30-33; instr. ENG, COLBY COL, 36-41, asst. prof, 41-53, assoc. prof, 53-59, PROF, 60- A critical edition of Wordsworth's White Doe of Rylstone. Publ: Gregory's angels, Eerdmans, 73; The hammer of Thor, Lyons, Eng, 73. Add: Dept. of English, Colby College, Waterville, ME 04901.

COMPRONE, JOSEPH JOHN, b. Lanesdowne, Pa, Mar. 11, 43; m. 65; c. 1. ENGLISH. B.A, Springfield Col, 65; M.A, Univ. Mass, 67, Ph.D.(Eng), 70. Teaching asst. Eng, Univ. Mass, 66-69, asst. dir. freshman Eng, 68-69; asst. prof. Eng. & coord. compos, Univ. Minn, Morris, 69-72; ASSOC. PROF. ENG. & DIR. FRESHMAN ENG, UNIV. CINCINNATI, 72- Freshman Eng. consult, Holt, Rinehart & Winston, N.Y, 73-74. NCTE; Conf. Col. Compos. & Commun; AAUP. Modern literature; rhetoric and composition; narrative technique in fiction. Publ: From experience to expression, W.C. Brown, 74; Goodbye to all that, Freshman Eng. News, fall 73; Using film, photography and painting to teach narration, Col. Eng, 11/73; Training the new teaching assistant, Col. Compos. & Commun, 2/74. Add: Dept. of English, McMicken Hall, University of Cincinnati, Cincinnati, OH 45221.

COMTOIS, MARY ELIZABETH, b. Pittsburgh, Pa; m. 61; c. 2. THEATER ARTS. B.A, Wellesley Col, 48; Royal Acad. Dramatic Art, 50; M.A, San Francisco State Col, 61; Ph.D.(theater, commun), Univ. Colo, Boulder, 70. Actress & dir, summer theater, Avon & Unionville, Conn, 49-50; studio asst. TV drama & casting dir. commercials, Young & Rubicam, Inc, 50-52; asst. to Martyn Green, Gilbert & Sullivan Co, Broadway, N.Y, 52-53; managing dir, Group 20 Players, Inc, Boston, Mass, 53-55; play & story ed, Kermit Bloomgarden, 55-60; instr. Eng, San Francisco State Col, 61-62, 63-64, lectr, spring 70; ASST. PROF. PLAYWRITING, CRITICISM & THEATER ARTS, DOUGLASS COL, RUTGERS UNIV, 70- Dramatic theory; theater aesthetics; text and performance criticism. Prod: The accident (play), 68 & Wall dogs (play), 69, Boulder, Colo. Add: Dept. of Theater Arts, Douglass College of Rutgers University, New Brunswick, NJ 08903.

CONARROE, JOEL OSBORNE, b. West Orange, N.J, Oct. 23, 34. ENGLISH. B.S, Davidson Col, 56; M.A, Cornell Univ, 57; Woodrow Wilson fel, Danforth fel, Cornell jr. fel. & Ph.D.(Eng), N.Y. Univ, 66. Instr. Eng, Davidson Col, 57-58; Univ. Pa, 64-66; asst. prof. Eng. & dir. freshman Eng, UNIV. PA, 66-69, ASSOC. PROF. ENG, 71-, CHMN. DEPT, 73-, undergrad. chmn, 69-71, univ. ombudsman, 71-73. Univ. Pa. res. grant, 66-67; Yaddo fel, 70-71. Lindback Distinguished Teaching Award, Univ. Pa, 68. U.S.A, 58-59. MLA; Am. Stud. Asn. American literature; modern poetry; John Berryman. Publ: William Carlos Williams' Paterson: language and landscape, Univ. Pa, 70; Melville's Bartleby and Charles Lamb, Stud. Short Fiction, winter 68; The measured dance: Williams' Pictures from Brueghel, J. Mod. Lit, winter 71; plus others. Add: Dept. of English, University of Pennsylvania, Philadelphia, PA 19104.

CONDEE, RALPH WATERBURY, b. Chicago, Ill, Jan. 11, 16; m. 42; c. 3. ENGLISH LITERATURE. B.A, Univ. Ill, 37, Ph.D.(Eng), 49; A.M, Univ. Chicago, 39. Asst. instr, Univ. Ill, 45-48; instr. Eng. lit, PA. STATE UNIV, 49-51, asst. prof, 51-56, assoc. prof, 56-58, PROF. ENG. LIT. & HUMANITIES, 58-, assoc. dir, Ctr. Continuing Lib. Educ, 58-62. Sr. res. fel, Glasgow Univ, 69-70. U.S.N, 42-46. MLA; NCTE; Milton Soc. Am. The Renaissance; Milton. Publ: The case for poetry, Prentice-Hall, 2nd ed, 65; Ovid's exile and Milton's rustication, Philol. Quart, 10/58; Bedlam at Edinburgh, Reporter, 10/62; The structure of Milton's Epitaphium Damonis, Stud. Philol, 7/65. Add: Burrowes Bldg, Pennsylvania State University, University Park, PA 16802.

CONDREN, EDWARD IGNATIUS, b. New York, N.Y, Oct. 25, 34; m. 57; c. 4. MEDIEVAL LITERATURE. B.A, Fordham Univ, 56; M.A, Cornell Univ, 64; Ph.D.(Medieval lit), Univ. Toronto, 69. Instr. ENG, Univ. Col, Univ. Toronto, 65-67; asst. prof, UNIV. CALIF, LOS ANGELES, 67-73, ASSOC. PROF, 73- U.S.N, 56-62, Lt. Mediaeval Acad. Am; MLA; Medieval Asn. Pac. Old and Middle English literature; Medieval French literature; Old Norse literature. Publ: The troubadour and his labour of love, Mediaeval Stud, 72; The pardoner's bid for existence, Viator, 73; On civilizing Hrafnkell, Mod. Lang. Notes, 73. Add: Dept. of English, University of California, Los Angeles, CA 90024.

CONE, MARY, b. Doddsville, Miss, Mar. 13, 23. ENGLISH & MODERN DRAMA. B.A, Miss. State Col. Women, 45; M.A, Univ. Miss, 53, Ph.D. (Eng), 70. Teacher Eng. & Span, Glen Allen High Sch, Miss, 45-48; Bay St. Louis, 48-49; Eng, Minter City High Sch, 49-51; Span. & Eng, Morgan City High Sch, 51-53; instr. ENG, Northwest Miss. Jr. Col, 53-58; Univ. Miss, 58-65; asst. prof, MISS. STATE COL. WOMEN, 65-70, ASSOC. PROF, 70- S.Cent. Mod. Lang. Asn; Am. Asn. Univ. Women. English drama of the Renaissance; 20th century American literature. Add: Apt. M, 900 S. Fifth Ave, Columbus, MS 39701.

CONGLETON, JAMES EDMUND, b. Slade, Ky, Nov. 16, 01. ENGLISH. A.B, Berea Col, 26; A.M, George Peabody Col, 28; Univ. Chicago, 30; Ph.D, Univ. N.C, 36. Instr. high sch, Ky, 25-28, prin, Miss, 28-31; instr, Tulane Univ, 36-37; ENG, Univ. Fla, 37-41, asst. prof, 41-44, assoc. prof, 44-46, PROF, 46-59; FINDLAY COL, 60-, head dept, 60-73, dean sch. humanities & sci, 62-64. Managing ed, South. Folklore Quart, 43-45. MLA; Johnson Socs. Cent. Region, U.S, London & Lichfield, Eng; NCTE. Literary criticism; communications courses for freshmen; theory of pastoral poetry in England. Publ: College English: the first year, Harcourt; Theories of pastoral poetry in England, 1684-1798, Univ. Fla; James Thomson Callander, Johnson and Jefferson, In: Johnsonian studies, Cairo; Sir Herbert Croft on revising Johnson's Dictionary, Tenn. Stud. Lit, XIII: 49-62; plus others. Add: Dept. of English, Findlay College, Findlay, OH 45840.

CONKLE, ELLSWORTH PROUTY, b. Peru, Nebr, July 10, 99. DRAMA. A.B, Univ. Nebr, 21, A.M, 23, hon. D.Litt, 70; Yale, 26-28; Guggenheim fel, 30; Rockefeller fel, State Univ. Iowa, 35-36, Ph.D, 36. Instr. Eng, Univ. N.Dak, 24-26; asst. prof, Univ. Del, 28-30; speech, State Univ. Iowa, 36-38; assoc. prof. DRAMA, UNIV. TEX, AUSTIN, 39-45, prof, 45-73, grad. sch. res. grant, 67, EMER. PROF, 73- Rockefeller fel, 45. Playwriting. Add: 510 Cater Dr, Austin, TX 78704.

CONKLIN, ROYAL FORREST, b. Washington, D.C, Aug. 5, 27; m. 58. SPEECH. B.A, Howard Payne Col, 49; M.A, Baylor Univ, 50; Ph.D.(speech), Ohio Univ, 67. Instr. speech, Clarke Mem. Col, 50-54, assoc. prof, Carson-Newman Col, 54-68; ASSOC. PROF. SPEECH & DIR. FORENSICS, UNIV. NORTH. IOWA, 68- U.S.N.A.F, 45-47. Speech Commun. Asn; Am. Forensic Asn. Forensics; rhetorical theory; communication theory. Add: Dept. of Speech, University of Northern Iowa, Cedar Falls, IA 50613.

CONLAN, MARY SAMUEL, O.P, b. San Francisco, Calif, Mar. 10, 27. ENGLISH. B.A, Dominican Col.(Calif), 48; M.A, Cath. Univ. Am, 57; Ph.D. (Eng), Stanford Univ, 63. Instr. ENG. & HUMANITIES, DOMINICAN COL, SAN RAFAEL, 57-60, asst. prof, 63-66, ASSOC. PROF, 66-, PRES, 68-, dean stud, 63-67, acad. dean, 67-68. English metaphysical poets of the seventeenth century. Publ: Contrib, New Catholic encyclopedia, McGraw, 68; articles on Crashaw, Donne & Herbert, In: Corpus instrumentorum dictionary, 68. Add: Dominican College of San Rafael, San Rafael, CA 94901.

CONLEY, JOHN ALLAN, b. Hamilton, Mont, Jan. 2, 12; m. 40. ENGLISH. A.B, Univ. Calif, 34; Ph.D.(Eng), Stanford Univ, 56. Acting instr, Stanford Univ, 43-45; instr, Ohio State Univ, 45-47, asst. prof, 47-49; ENG, John Carroll Univ, 50-56, assoc. prof, 57-61; Queen's Col.(N.Y), 61-68; PROF. UNIV. ILL, CHICAGO CIRCLE, 68- Vis. assoc. prof, Brandeis Univ, 59-60; Univ. Calif, Riverside, 64-65; Am. Philos. Soc. grant, summer 71. MLA; Mediaeval Acad. Am; Mod. Humanities Res. Asn, Gt. Brit; Early Eng. Text Soc; Scottish Text Soc. Mediaeval English and Scottish literature; Medieval rhetoric and poetic. Publ: Ed. & contrib, The Middle English Pearl: critical essays, Univ. Notre Dame, 70; auth, The doctrine of friendship in Everyman, Speculum, 69; plus others. Add: Dept. of English, University of Illinois at Chicago Circle, Box 4348, Chicago, IL 60680.

CONLIN, MATTHEW THOMAS, O.F.M, b. Barker, N.Y, Dec. 8, 19. ENGLISH. B.A, St. Bonaventure Univ, 41; Ph.D.(Eng), Univ. Dublin, 53. Instr. ENG, SIENA COL.(N.Y), 45-50, asst. prof, 53-56, assoc. prof, 56-60, PROF, 60-, PRES, 70-, acad. dean, 64-67, exec. v.pres, 69-70. Shakespeare Asn. Am. Anglo-Irish literature. Publ: The tragic effect in autumn fire and desire under the elms, Mod. Drama, 59; T.C. Murray: Ireland on the stage, Renascence, 62; Bears and the bard: an Adirondack reverie, Folklore Quart, 66; plus one other. Add: Siena College, Loudonville, NY 12211.

CONN, EARL LEWIS, b. Marion, Ind, Aug. 12, 27; m. 53; c. 6. JOURNALISM. B.A, Univ. Ky, 50; Marion Col, 53-54; M.S, Ball State Univ, 57; D.Ed. (mass commun, higher educ), Ind. Univ, Bloomington, 70. Staff writer, United Press, 50-51; wire ed, Chronicle-Tribune, Marion, Ind, 52-54; teacher jour. & publ. adv, Somerset High Sch, Ind, 54-57; Richmond High Sch, 57-58; instr. jour, Ball State Univ, 58-62; ed, Quaker Life, Friends United Meeting, 62-64; asst. dir, Pub. Inform. Serv, BALL STATE UNIV, 64-65, from asst. prof. to PROF. JOUR, 65- U.S.N, 45-46; U.S.A.F, 51-52. Asn. Educ. in Jour; Oral Hist. Asn; Nat. Counc. Col. Publ. Adv; Jour. Educ. Asn. Journalism history; reporting and newswriting; mass communications. Publ: Editing and headlines, Ball State Univ, 59; Tentative conceptualization of the newswriting process, Jour. Quart, summer 68; Communication: where the church stands, Quaker Life, 4/71; What freedom of the press means, Ind. Publ, 4/73. Add: Dept. of Journalism, Ball State University, Muncie, IN 47306.

CONN, PETER JAMES, b. Rockville Centre, N.Y, Sept. 27, 42; m. 64; c. 3. ENGLISH & AMERICAN LITERATURE. A.B, Providence Col, 64; M.A, Yale, 66, M.Phil, 67, Ph.D.(Eng), 69. Instr. ENG, UNIV. PA, 67-69, asst. prof, 69-73, ASSOC. PROF, 73-, ASSOC. DEAN, COL. ARTS & SCI, 71-, v.dean, 70-71. The modern novel; American puritanism. Publ: Co-ed, Afro-American literature (4 vols), Houghton, 70 & critical ed, The power and the glory, Viking, 70; auth, Seeing and blindness in The beast in the jungle, Stud. Short Fiction, 70; Roderick Hudson: the role of the observer, Nineteenth-Century Fiction, 71; plus others. Add: Dept. of English, 119 Bennett Hall, University of Pennsylvania, Philadelphia, PA 19174.

CONNELLY, KENNETH AMOR, JR, b. Billings, Mont, June 28, 20. ENGLISH. B.A, Univ. Wash, 42; Morse fel, Yale, 55-56, Ph.D.(Eng. lang. & lit), 56. Instr. Eng, Col. William & Mary, 49-50; Yale, 50-55, asst. prof. Eng, 56-58; assoc. prof, SMITH COL, 58-65, PROF. ENG. LANG. & LIT, 65-Mem. fac, Bread Loaf Sch. Eng, 62-67; vis. prof, Yale, 68; Aegean Inst, 68-71. U.S.A, 42-45. Epic, contemporary and 17th century literature; Shakespeare; Greek literature. Add: Dept. of English, Smith College, Northampton, MA 01060.

CONNER, FREDERICK WILLIAM, b. Rochester, N.Y, May 16, 09; m. 35; c. 1. ENGLISH. A.B, Univ. Rochester, 30; A.M, Univ. Pa, 34; Ph.D, 44. Instr. Eng, Univ. Fla, 35-39, asst. prof, 39-44, assoc. prof, 44-48, prof, 48-71, asst. dean grad. sch, 57-61, exec. v.pres, 66-68, v.pres, acad. affairs, 68-71; PROF. ENG. & HUMANITIES, UNIV. ALA, BIRMINGHAM, 71-, DEAN SCH. HUMANITIES, 73- Dean col. arts & sci, Univ. Ala, 61-66. Am. Stud. Asn; MLA; NCTE; Col. Eng. Asn. American literature; Emerson and Whitman; philosophical themes in the literature of the twentieth century. Publ: Cosmic optimism—interpretation of evolution by American poets from Emerson to Robinson, Univ. Fla, 49, Octagon, 73; Lucifer and the last puritan, Am. Lit, 3/61; Poe and John Nichol—notes on a source of Eureka, In: All these to teach: essays in honor of C.A. Robertson, Univ. Fla, 65; Aldous Huxley's epistemological route to salvation, Sewanee Rev, spring 73. Add: School of Humanities, University of Alabama in Birmingham, Birmingham, AL 35294.

CONNER, JACK EDWARD, b. Marfa, Tex, Jan. 16, 21; m. 47; c. 2. ENGLISH. B.A, Tex. Col. Arts & Indust, 39, B.S, 42; Ph.D.(Eng. philol), Stanford Univ, 52. Teacher schs, Tex, 40-43; v. consul & third secy. of embassy, U.S. For. Serv, 46-49; from instr. to assoc. prof. ENG, Rice Univ, 52-62; from assoc. prof. to PROF, CALIF. STATE UNIV, HAYWARD, 62- U.S.N.R, 43-46. Philol. Asn. Pac. Coast. History of the English language; modern English grammar. Publ: Co-auth, Your Texas and mine, 60 & Flags of Texas, 64, Harlow; co-auth, Speaking of rhetoric, 65 & auth, Grammar of standard English, 68, Houghton; auth, English prosody from Chaucer to Wyatt, Mouton (in press); Phonemic discrimination of M.E. dialects, Rice Inst, 55; Old French dissyllables and the great vowel shift, Eng. Stud, 63. Add: Dept. of English, California State University, 25800 Hillary St, Hayward, CA 94542.

CONNOLLY, THOMAS EDMUND, b. New York, N.Y, Nov. 15, 18; m. 48; c. 5. ENGLISH LANGUAGE & LITERATURE. S.B, Fordham Univ, 39; A.M, Univ. Chicago, 47, Ph.D, 51. Instr. ENG, Univ. Idaho, 50-51; asst. prof, Creighton Univ, 51-53; STATE UNIV. N.Y. BUFFALO, 53-64, PROF, 64-, SUMMER CHMN. DEPT, 63-, acting provost fac. arts & lett, 70-71, res. grant, 70-72. Fulbright sr. prof. Eng. & Am. lit, Univ. Col, Dublin, 66-67. U.S.A, 42-46. MLA; AAUP. Nineteenth century British literature; modern British and American literature; literary theory and criticism. Publ: Personal library of James Joyce: a descriptive bibliography, Univ. Buffalo, 55, 2nd ed, 57, 3rd ed, 67; co-auth, From Ararat to suburbia: the history of the Jewish community of Buffalo, Jewish Publ. Soc. Am, 60; auth, James Joyce's scribbledehobble: the ur-workbook for Finnegans wake, Northwest. Univ. & Oxford, 61; Joyce's portrait: criticisms and critiques, Appleton, 62, Owen, London, 64; Swinburne's theory of poetry, State Univ. N.Y, 64; Nathaniel Hawthorne: Young Goodman Brown, Merrill, 68; ed, Nathaniel Hawthorne: the Scarlet letter and selected tales, Penguin, 70; Fate and the agony of will: determinism in some novels of William Faulkner, Kent State Stud. Eng, 64; Joyce's A painful case, In: Dubliners, Faber, 69. Add: 28 Beard Ave, Buffalo, NY 14214.

CONNOR, GEORGE C, b. Chattanooga, Tenn, Sept. 1, 20. ENGLISH. A.B, Univ. Chattanooga, 47; M.A, Middlebury Col, 55. Teacher Eng, Chattanooga Pub. Schs, 48-52; exec. dir, Adult Educ. Coun. Chattanooga, 52-58; asst. prof. ENG, UNIV. TENN, CHATTANOOGA, 59-64, assoc. prof, 64-69, PROF, 69-, chmn. dept, 63-69, exec. asst. to chancellor, 67-70. Dir, NCTE, 71- U.S.A, 42-45, S/Sgt. MLA; S.Atlantic Mod. Lang. Asn; AAUP. American literature; modern poetry; biblical literature. Publ: Co-auth, Discovering modern poetry, Holt, 61. Add: Dept. of English, University of Tennessee, Chattanooga, TN 37401.

CONNORS, JAMES VICTOR, b. South Bend, Wash, Nov. 18, 18. SPEECH, DRAMA. B.A, Gonzaga Univ, 52; S.T.B, Santa Clara Univ, 59; M.A, San Francisco State Col, 60. Instr. Latin, speech, Eng, Seattle Prep. Sch, 53-54; ASST. PROF. DRAMA, SEATTLE UNIV, 61- U.S.A.A.F, 42-46, S/Sgt. Am. Theatre Asn; Speech Commun. Asn; Nat. Cath. Theatre Conf. Educational theatre. Add: Dept. of Fine Arts, Seattle University, Seattle, WA 98122.

CONNORS, THOMAS EDWARD, b. Waltham, Mass, Jan. 21, 29; m. 56; c. 2. ENGLISH. A.B, Brandeis Univ, 56; A.M, Boston Univ, 57. Asst, Boston Univ, 56-57; instr. ENG, SUFFOLK UNIV, 57-60, asst. prof, 60-64, assoc. prof, 64-70, PROF, 70- U.S.M.C, 46-48. MLA. Writing of fiction; Hawthorne; Chaucer. Publ: Inamorata, Perspective, 6/56; My kinsman, Major Molineux, Mod. Lang. Notes, 4/59; God, the devil..., Quart. Rev. Lit, 9/63. Add: Dept. of English, Suffolk University, Boston, MA 02114.

CONOLLY, LEONARD WILLIAM, b. Birmingham, Eng, Sept. 13, 41; m. 64; c. 2. ENGLISH LITERATURE. B.A, Univ. Wales, 63, Can. Counc. fel, 67-70, Ph.D.(Eng. lit), 70; M.A, McMaster Univ, 64. Instr. ENG, Univ. Sask, 65-67; asst. prof, UNIV. ALTA, 70-74, ASSOC. PROF, 74- Co-ed. & co-founder, Nineteenth Century Theatre Res, 73- Soc. Theatre Res. Theatre history; drama and society; literary censorship. Publ: The abolition of theatre censorship in Great Britain, Queen's Quart, 68; The censor's wife at the theater: the diary of A.M. Larpent, 1790-1800, Huntington Libr. Quart, 71; A case of political censorship at the Little Theatre in the Haymarket in 1794, Restoration & 18th Century Theatre Res, 10/71. Add: Dept. of English, University of Alberta, Edmonton, Alta. T6G 2E1, Can.

CONOVER, JAMES HARRINGTON, b. Chicago, Ill, Apr. 1, 30; m. 56; c. 2. THEATER, ORAL INTERPRETATION. B.A, St. Ambrose Col, 51; M.A, Northwest. Univ, 55, Ph.D.(interpretation), 62. Instr. theater, Grinnell Col, 55-56; Beloit Col, 56-58; MacMurray Col, 60-61; asst. prof, OHIO UNIV, 62-65, assoc. prof, 65-70, COMP. ARTS, 70-71, PROF, 71- Lectr, Univ. Sask-Theatre Stud. Tour in Eng, summers 68-72. U.S.A, 51-53, Sgt. Am. Nat. Theatre Acad; Speech Commun. Asn; Am. Theater Asn; Royal Soc. Arts. Renaissance theater and drama; oral interpretation. Publ: Thomas Dekker: an anlysis of dramatic structure, Mouton, 68; Four Elizabethan intermissions!, Educ. Theatre J, 5/63. Add: Dept. of Comparative Arts, Ohio University, Athens, OH 45701.

CONOVER, THEODORE E, b. Philadelphia, Pa, Aug. 10, 21; m. 44; c. 3. JOURNALISM. B.S.J, Ohio Univ. 59; M.A, Ohio State Univ, 60. Publ: Twin City News, 46-48; Miami Gazette, 48-49; managing ed, Daily Standard, 50-52; publ, Centerburg Gazette, 53-60; asst. prof. JOUR, UNIV. NEV, 60-65, assoc. prof, 65-70, PROF, 70-, CHMN. DEPT, 66- Publ. W.Liberty Banner, 49-59; founder & publ, Reynoldsburg Rec, 56-60; Pub. Relat. Soc. Am. fel, 63; Am. Bus. Press fel, 64; secy-mgr, Nev. State Press Asn, 67- U.S.A, 42-46. Am. Soc. Jour. Sch. Adminr.(pres, 73-74); Asn. Educ. in Jour. Publ: What about the weeklies?, Quill, 8/49; How goes news freedom in Ohio?, 12/59 & A good little paper, but..., 4/66, Nat. Publ. Add: Dept. of Journalism, University of Nevada, Reno, NV 89507.

CONRAD, EUNICE J, b. La Porte, Ind, Feb. 25, 30. ENGLISH. A.B, Wheaton Col, 52; M.A, Ind. Univ, 58. ASSOC. PROF. ENG. & CHMN. DEPT. COMMUN, FT. WAYNE BIBLE COL, 57- NCTE; Conf. Christianity & Lit. Add: Dept. of English, Ft. Wayne Bible College, Ft. Wayne, IN 46807.

CONRAD, LAWRENCE H, JR, b. Royal Oak, Mich, Oct. 27, 20; m. 49; c. 3. ENGLISH LANGUAGE & LITERATURE. B.A, Kalamazoo Col, 42; M.A, N.Y. Univ, 47, M.A, 54; Ph.D, Univ. Pa, 62. Instr. high sch, N.J, 47-48, 54-57; ENG, Bloomfield Col, 48-54; asst. prof, GLASSBORO STATE COL, 57-70, ASSOC. PROF, 70- U.S.A.A.F, 42-46. Early 18th century British popular literature; H.D. Thoreau; current oral literature. Add: Dept. of English, Glassboro State College, Glassboro, NJ 08028.

CONRON, ALFRED BRANDON, b. St. John, N.B, Nov. 29, 19; m. 49; c. 3. ENGLISH. B.A, Univ. West. Ont, 41, M.A, 47; A.M, Harvard, 48, Ph.D, 51. Lectr. ENG, UNIV. WEST. ONT, 49-51, asst. prof, 51-53, assoc. prof, 53-56, PROF, 56-58, 61-, prin, Middlesex Col, 58-61. Can. Counc. sr. fel, 67-68. Can. Army, 41-46, Lt. Col. MLA; Humanities Asn. Can; Asn. Can. Univ. Teachers Eng; Asn. Commonwealth Lang. & Lit. Stud. Restoration and 18th century literature; American-Canadian and commonwealth literature. Publ: Co-auth, Canadian writers: ecrivains Canadiens, Ryerson Press, 64, rev, 66; Morley Callaghan, Twayne, 66; contrib, Literary history of Canada, Univ. Toronto, 65. Add: 605 Windermere Rd, London, Ont, Can.

CONROY, KENNETH C, b. Judith Gap, Mont, May 28, 27; m. 58; c. 5. ENGLISH. A.B, Carroll Col.(Mont), 50; M.A, Colo. State Col, 56; Ph.D.(Eng), Univ. Wash, 64. Teacher. high schs, Mont, 53-57; instr. ENG, Univ. Mont, 57-58; asst. & acting instr, Univ. Wash, 58-63; asst. prof, Univ. Ariz, 63-67; from assoc. prof. to PROF, UNIV. W.FLA, 67-, PROVOST ALPHA COL, 69-, chmn. dept, 67-69. U.S.A, 51-53. NCTE; MLA. Medieval literature, especially textual studies. Add: Dept. of English, University of West Florida, Pensacola, FL 32504.

CONSACRO, DOMINIC PETER, b. New York, N.Y, Jan. 29, 33; m. 73. MEDIEVAL ENGLISH LITERATURE & LANGUAGE. B.A, Don Bosco Col, 56; Ecole Superieure de Theologie, Lyon, France, 58-62; M.A, Fordham Univ, 66, Ph.D.(Eng), 71. Teaching fel, Salesian Prep, N.Y, 56-58; asst. prof. ENG, Sacred Heart Univ, 69-70; ASST. PROF, UNIV. TENN, CHATTANOOGA, 70-, DIR. INTERDISCIPLINARY STUD, 73- Univ. Chattanooga Found. res. grant, summer 72; fel, Southeast. Inst. Medieval & Renaissance Stud. Mediaeval Acad. Am; MLA; Nat. Col. Honors Counc; NCTE. Medieval language and letters, medieval church; history of ideas. Add: Interdisciplinary Honors Program, University of Tennessee, Chattanooga, TN 37401.

CONSOLO, DOMINICK PETER, b. Ridgway, Pa, Feb. 5, 23; m. 48; c. 2. ENGLISH. B.A, Miami Univ, 48, M.A, 50; Writers' Conf. scholar, Univ. Colo, 51; Ph.D, State Univ. Iowa, 58. Teaching asst, Miami Univ, 48-50; State Univ. Iowa, 52-57; instr. ENG, 57-58; asst. prof, DENISON UNIV, 58-67, PROF, 67-, CHMN. FRESHMEN-SOPHOMORE SEM, 72- Reader, Nat. Counc. Teachers Eng, 62, 63 & 68; Fulbright-Hays lectr, Israel, 64-65. U.S.A, 43-45, S/Sgt. Johnson Soc. Great Lakes Region (recording secy, 60); MLA. Nineteenth century American literature; Renaissance; Chaucer. Publ: Critical casebook on D.H. Lawrence, C.E. Merrill, 69; The unity of Brighton Rock, Renascence, fall, 62; Art and stylistics in five novels, In: Critical symposium, Univ. Ky, 63. Add: Dept. of English, Denison University, Granville, OH 43023.

CONSTANTINE, ANIKO VINCZE, b. Manhattan, N.Y, June 11, 43; m. 64; c. 1. ENGLISH NOVEL. A.B, Hartwick Col, 65; M.A, Univ. Ill, Urbana, 66, Clark Found. fel. & Ph.D.(Eng), 72. Teaching asst, Univ. Ill, 67-68, 68-72; ASST. PROF. ENG, ALLEGHENY COL, 72- NCTE. Women novelists; basic writing techniques. Add: Dept. of English, Allegheny College, Meadville, PA 16335.

CONWAY, JOHN ASHBY, b. Wilkinsburg, Pa, Jan. 15, 05. DRAMA. A.B, Carnegie Inst. Technol, 27; private study & res, Europe, the Orient, Yucatan & Alaska. PROF. DRAMA & ART DIR. CAMPUS THEATRES, UNIV. WASH, 27- V.chmn, Munic. Art Comn, Seattle, Wash; Chmn, Wash. State Arts Comn, Am. Theatre Asn; Soc. Theatre Res, Gt. Brit; Soc. Hist. Theatre, Paris. Technical and historical drama; Robert Burns, a play. Publ: History of the theatre. Add: School of Drama, University of Washington, Seattle, WA 98105.

CONWAY, MARGARET MARY, F.S.P.A, b. Livingston, Mont, Dec. 29, 23. SPEECH & THEATRE ARTS, ENGLISH. B.A, Ambrose Col, 43; M.A, Cath. Univ. Am, 51; summers, Marquette Univ, Univ. Detroit & Loyola Univ, 52, 53, 60 & 61; Univ. Wash, 65; Univ. Ill, 67. Head dept. theatre arts & speech, Aquinas High Sch, Wis, 43-48; Eng. & speech, Cathedral High Sch, Wis, 48-54; prin, DePadua High Sch, Wis, 54-58; head dept. Eng. & speech, Kuemper High Sch, Iowa, 58-64; Marycliff High Sch, Wash, 64-68; dir. forensics, GONZAGA UNIV, 68-72, ASST. PROF. SPEECH, 72- Auth, sec. sch. editorials, Players Mag, 48-52; NDEA summer stud. arts & humanities, 65-67. Walter Peck Nat. Sec. Sch. Theatre Award, 66. Am. Theatre Asn.(chmn. sec. sch. proj, 50-54, chmn. awards comt, 69); Sec. Sch. Theatre Conf. Aesthetic education; relevance of debate to political science; comparative analysis of theatre forms. Publ: St. Francis in drama, Franciscan Educ, 51; Miracle not mayhem, Cath. Theatre, 3/62. Add: Dept. of Speech, Gonzaga University, Spokane, WA 99202.

COOGAN, MARY PHILIPPA, B.V.M, b. Lincoln, Ill, Aug. 15, 08. ENGLISH LANGUAGE & LITERATURE. A.B, Marquette Univ, 33; A.M, Cath. Univ. Am, 39, Ph.D, 47. Instr. Eng, Mundelein Col, 39-41, Clarke Col, 41-43, chmn. dept, 46-57; Mundelein Col, 57-63; supvr. sec. sch. teachers Eng, B.V.M. Schs, 63-67; PROF. ENG, St. Mary of the Lake Sem, 67-69; NILES COL, LOYOLA UNIV. CHICAGO, 69- Summers, vis. prof, Cath. Univ. Am. & Pac. Coast Br, Cath. Univ. Am; dir. nat. comn. compos. & lectr. Eng. compos, NCTE, 68-71. NCTE; Conf. Eng. Educ; Conf. Col. Compos. & Commun. Medieval and Renaissance English literature; preparation of teachers of English in secondary schools; problems in the teaching of composition. Publ: An interpretation of the moral play, Mankind, Cath. Univ. Am, 47; If I had my way, 64 & The well-prepared student teacher, 68, Conf. Eng. Educ; ed, Student's right to write, NCTE, 71; co-auth, Round-table on National Assessment of Education Program, Res. in Teaching Eng, spring 72. Add: Dept. of English, Niles College, Loyola University of Chicago, 7135 N. Harlem, Chicago, IL 60631.

COOGAN, ROBERT M, b. New York, N.Y, Sept. 21, 29. ENGLISH. B.A, Iona Col, 54; M.A, De Paul Univ, 58; Ph.D.(Eng), Loyola Univ.(Ill), 67. Teacher, & chmn. depts. Latin & Eng, Leo High Sch, 60-65; instr. ENG, Lewis Col, 67-69; ASSOC. PROF, Iona Col, 69-73; UNIV. MD, COLLEGE PARK, 73-, DIR. FRESHMAN ENG, 74- Fac. res. grant, Lewis Col, summer 68; Nat. Endowment for Humanities fel, summer 69; dir. honors prog, Iona Col, 69-73; Newberry Libr. fel, summer 72; Folger Shakespeare Libr. fel, fall 72. NCTE; MLA; Renaissance Soc. Am; Rhetoric Soc. Am; Amici Thomae Mori. Petrarch and the English Renaissance; Thomas More. Publ: Petrarch's Latin prose and the English Renaissance, Stud. Philol, 71; Nunc vivo ut volo, Meliora, festschrift in Moreana, 71; Surrey's Petrarchism and Tudor concepts of translation, Eng. Miscellany, 74; plus others. Add: Dept. of English, University of Maryland, College Park, MD 20740.

COOK, ALBERT BALDWIN, III, English, Linguistics. See Volume III, Foreign Languages, Linguistics & Philology.

COOK, ALBERT SPAULDING, JR, b. Exeter, N.H, Oct. 28, 25; m. 48; c. 3. COMPARATIVE LITERATURE. M.A, Harvard, 47, jr. fel, 48-51; Univ. Paris, 52-53. Asst. prof. Eng, Univ. Calif, 53-56; Fulbright res. prof. comp. lit, Univ. Munich, 56-57; assoc. prof. Eng, West. Reserve Univ, 57-62, prof. comp. lit. 62-63; prof. Eng. & chmn. dept, STATE UNIV. N.Y. BUFFALO, 63-66; PROF. COMP. LIT, 63-, dir. comp. lit. prog, 66-71. Fel, YADDO, N.Y, 58; Fulbright sr. prof. Am. lit, Univ. Vienna, 60-61; fel, Ctr, Adv. Stud. Behav. Sci, Calif, 66-67; Hardt Found. fel, Geneva, summer 68; Guggenheim Found. fel, 69-70; Soviet Ministry of Educ. Exchange Treaty sr. fel, Moscow State Univ, 72. U.S.A, 43-44. MLA; Am. Philos. Asn. Theory of literary genres; modern poetry; Greek, French and Shakespearian drama. Publ: The dark voyage and the golden mean, 49 & 69; The meaning of fiction, 60; Progressions, (poems), Univ. Ariz, 63; The classic line, 66, Prisms, 67 & The root of things, 68, Ind. Univ; The charges (poems), 70 & 72, Enactment—Greek tragedy, 71, French tragedy—the power of enactment, 74 & Adapt the living (poems), 74, Swallow; The death of Trotsky (play), Drama & Theatre, 71; co-auth, Anthology of Greek tragedy, Bobbs, 72; ed, Homer's Odyssey, Norton, 73. Add: Dept. of English, State University of New York at Buffalo, Buffalo, NY 14214.

COOK, CHARLES HENRY, JR, b. Saugus, Mass, July 3, 19; m. 45; c. 2. ENGLISH. A.B, Northeast. Univ, 44; A.M, Boston Univ, 45; Ph.D, 57; summer scholar, Harvard, 49. Instr. ENG, Sampson Col, 46-49; Colby Col, 49-51; asst. prof, WESTMINSTER COL. (PA), 53-57, assoc. prof, 57-63, PROF, 63-, CHMN. DEPT, 69- NCTE; MLA. Recent American literature, especially Robert Frost; 19th century American literature, especially Herman Melville; early English literature, Chaucer to Milton. Publ: Ahab's intolerable allegory, In: Discussions of Moby-Dick, Heath, 60; Memorization revisited, Col. Eng; Short-wave radio in language teaching, Mod. Lang. J. Add: 310 New Castle St, New Wilmington, PA 16142.

COOK, DANIEL, b. Bismarck, N.Dak, Aug. 21, 14; m. 41, 66; c. 3. LINGUISTICS, ENGLISH. B.A, Univ. Wis, 40, M.A, 41, Mary Adams fel, 41-42; Ph.D.(Eng), Univ. Calif, Berkeley, 54. Instr. Eng, Duke Univ, 50-52; assoc. ed, G. & C. Merriam Co, Springfield, Mass, 52-57; assoc. prof. Eng, South. Ill. Univ, 57-65; PROF. ENG. & LING, AM. UNIV. BEIRUT, 65- Consult. lang. textbks, McGraw-Hill Publ. Co, 59-60; Harcourt, Brace & World Publ. Co, 63; sch. dictionaries, Follett Publ. Co, 61-62;lexicography, Grolier Soc, Inc, 61-62; Fulbright lectr. ling, Damascus Univ, 61-62; vis. prof, Am. Univ. Beirut, 63-64. U.S.N.R, 42-46, Lt. Mediaeval Acad. Am; MLA; Ling. Soc. Am; Am. Dialect Soc. Mediaeval English literature; teaching of English as a second language; general linguistics. Publ: The Canterbury tales of Geoffrey Chaucer, 61 & ed. with introd. & notes, Geoffrey Chaucer's Troilus and Criseyde, 66, Doubleday; assoc. ed, Webster's new international dictionary, 3rd ed, 61; co-auth, American English, Part 8, In: English grammar and composition, Harcourt, 65; auth, Lexicographic method, Am. Speech, 2/59. Add: Dept. of English, American University of Beirut, Beirut, Lebanon.

COOK, DAVID M, b. Martinsburg, Pa, Jan. 29, 30. ENGLISH. B.A, Ohio State Univ, 52, B.S, 54, M.A, 59, Ph.D.(Eng. educ), 64. Teacher, high sch, 56-58; asst. prof. Eng, Ind. Univ. Pa, 59-61; instr. Eng. educ, Ohio State Univ, 61-64; asst. prof, Rutgers Univ, 64-65; PROF. ENG, INDIANA UNIV. PA, 65- Prof, NDEA Eng. Inst, Ohio State Univ, summers 65-68. U.S.A, 54-56. NCTE; MLA. Colonial American literature; modern American fiction; English education. Publ: Co-auth, Small town in American literature, Dodd, 68. Add: Dept. of English, Indiana University of Pennsylvania, Indiana, PA 15701.

COOK, DON L, b. Craig, Colo, Jan. 28, 28; m. 52; c. 2. AMERICAN LITERATURE. B.A, Univ. Calif, Los Angeles, 49, univ. fel, 58-59, Ph.D, 60. Instr. ENG, IND. UNIV, BLOOMINGTON, 59-62, asst. prof, 62-66, assoc. prof, 66-71, PROF, 71- Fulbright lectr, Japan, 68-69; gen. ed, Selected Ed. of W.D. Howells, 69- U.S.N.R, 51-54, Res, 54-, Comdr. MLA; NCTE; Am. Stud. Asn. Nineteenth century fiction and textual editing; 20th century American fiction. Publ: Ed, Royall Tyler's Algerine Captive, Univ. & Col, 70; co-ed, The current voice, Prentice, 68 & 71; auth, Practical editions: the writings of W.D. Howells, In: Proof, Vol 2, Univ. S.Carolina, 72. Add: Dept. of English, Indiana University, Bloomington, IN 47401.

COOK, DOUGLAS NEILSON, b. Phoenix, Ariz, Sept. 22, 29; m. 56; c. 3. DRAMA. B.F.A, Univ. Ariz, 53; M.A, Stanford Univ, 56. Scenic artist, Stanford Univ, 54-56; instr. DRAMA, San Mateo Jr. Col, 55-57; Univ. Calif, Riverside, 57-59, asst. prof, 59-56, assoc. prof, 66-70; PROF. THEATRE & HEAD DEPT, PA. STATE UNIV, UNIVERSITY PARK, 70- Dir, Millbrae Community Players, 55-57; assoc. producer & artistic dir, Utah Shakespearean Festival, 66-; mem, Univ. Calif. Humanities Inst, 66-67; fel. scenic design, Polakov Studio of Scenic Design, New York, N.Y, 68; producer, Pa. Festival of Am. Theatre, 70-; designer, Adams Mem. Shakespearean Festival Theatre, Cedar City, Utah, 72. Am. Theatre Asn; Am. Nat. Theatre & Acad; Theatre Libr. Asn; Am. Soc. Theatre Res; U.S. Inst. Theatre Technol; Univ. Resident Theatre Asn. American scenic design; design theory and criticism; theatre production. Add: Dept. of Theatre Arts, College of Arts & Architecture, 103 Arts Bldg, Pennsylvania State University, University Park, PA 16802.

COOK, GEORGE ALLAN, b. Unionville, Mo. ENGLISH. A.B. & B.S, Univ. Mo, 38, M.A, 39; Ph.D.(Am. lit), Columbia Univ, 51. Instr. Eng, Wentworth Mil. Acad, Lexington, Mo, 39-41; lectr, Polytech. Inst, Brooklyn, 47; Columbia Univ, 47-48; asst. prof, Wagner Lutheran Col, 50-56; from asst. prof. to assoc. prof, E.Carolina Col, 56-61, prof, 61-64; assoc. prof. Am. lit. & Shakespeare, Am. Univ. Cairo, 64-66; PROF. AM. LIT, TEX. A&I UNIV, 66- Fulbright lectr. & assoc. prof. Am. lit, Univ. Saarland, Ger, 58-60; ed, Tex. A&I Univ. Stud. 69- U.S.A, 41-46, Capt. MLA; Am. Stud. Asn. American colonial history and literature; romantic period in American literature; the American novel. Publ: John Wise, early American democrat, Octagon, 66; The beginnings of Porgy, S.Cent. MLA Bull, winter 68; The rocking chair in Dreiser's Sister Carrie, 68 & Porgy reexamined, 72, Tex. A&I Univ; plus one other. Add: Box 2228, Texas A&I University, Kingsville, TX 78363.

COOK, JAMES WYATT, b. Hickman, Ky, Sept. 8, 32; m. 54; c. 3. ENGLISH. B.A, Wayne State Univ, 54, Ph.D.(mid. Eng), 64; M.A, Univ. Mich, 55. Instr. ENG, ALBION COL, 62-64, asst. prof, 64-68, ASSOC. PROF, 68-, CHMN. DEPT, 71- Great Lakes Cols. Asn. programming grant, 64-66; Shell grant, 66; consult, Educ. Methods, Inc, 65-67; Univ. Mich. Ctr. Prog. Instr. Bus, 66-68; Carnegie Found. & Great Lakes Cols. humanities grant, 67; pres, Validated Instr. Assoc, 73. U.S.A, 56-58. MLA; Mediaeval Soc. Am; Nat. Soc. Prog. Instr. Medieval language and literature; Chaucer; educational technology. Publ: Poetry: method and meaning, Educ. Methods, 68; Augustinian neurosis and therapy of orthodoxy, Universitas, Wayne State Univ, spring 64; Questions net training decisions; In: Design and development, Univ. Mich, 72. Add: Dept. of English, Albion College, Albion, MI 49224.

COOK, LARRY WAYNE, b. Cushing, Okla, Sept. 28, 34; m. 55. AMERICAN LITERATURE. B.A, Tex. Tech Univ, 56, M.A, 58; Ph.D.(Eng), Duke Univ, 68. Instr. ENG, WEST. TEX. STATE UNIV, 58-61, asst. prof, 64-67, ASSOC. PROF, 67- MLA. American fiction and poetry of the 19th century; modern American drama. Add: Dept. of English, West Texas State University, Canyon, TX 79015.

COOK, MARJORIE ELIZABETH, b. Warsaw, Ind, Apr. 25, 40. LITERATURE, COMPOSITION. A.B, Taylor Univ, 61; Austin Col, summers 59, 60; Ind. Univ, summer 61; NDEA fel, South. Ill. Univ, 63-67, M.A, 65, Ph.D.(Eng), 72. Instr. ENG, MIAMI UNIV, 67-71, ASST. PROF, 72-, ASST. DEAN, COL. ARTS & SCI, 74- MLA. Robert Frost; modern poetry; American literature. Add: Dept. of English, Miami University, Oxford, OH 45056.

COOK, MARY ANN, S.N.D, b. Baltimore, Md, Jan. 13, 37. ENGLISH. B.A, Trinity Col.(D.C), 60; M.A, Cath. Univ. Am, 61; D.Phil.(old Eng. lit), Oxford, 67. Instr. ENG, TRINITY COL.(D.C), 64-67, ASST. PROF, 67-, ACAD. DEAN, 74- Intern, Acad. Admin. Internship Prog, Am. Counc. Educ, 73-74. MLA; Mediaeval Acad. Am. Arts of discourse in the Middle Ages; Chaucer; Old English homiletic literature and its Latin backgrounds. Add: Dept. of English, Trinity College, Washington, DC 20017.

COOK, RAYMOND ALLEN, b. Thomson, Ga, July 19, 19; m. 45; c. 1. AMERICAN LITERATURE. A.B, Univ. Ga, 47, M.A, 48; Ph.D, Emory Univ, 53. Prin, Stellaville Jr. High, 40-41; teaching fel. Eng, Emory Univ, 50-52; asst. prof, Univ. Fla, 53-54; prof, Ga. State Col, 54-64, univ. found. grant, 61; pres, Young Harris Col, 64-66; head Eng. dept. & chmn. humanities div, VALDOSTA STATE COL, 66-71, PROF. ENG, 71- Fulbright lectr. Am. lit, Univ. Shiraz, Iran, 61-62. U.S.N.A.F, 42-45, Lt.(jg). Relationship between literature and science. Publ: This the while, Towle, 44; Fire from the flint, Blair, 68; The man behind the Birth of a nation, N.C. Hist. Rev, autumn 62; Is John Donne's metaphysical poetry really metaphysical?, Ga. State Col. Res. Papers, 9/67; Byron Herbert Reece: ten years after, Ga. Rev, spring 68. Add: Dept. of English, Valdosta State College, Valdosta, GA 31601.

COOK, REGINALD LANSING, b. Mendon, Mass, Nov. 5, 03. AMERICAN LITERATURE. B.S, Middlebury Col, 24, A.M, 26, D.Litt, 60, hon. D.H.L, 72; B.A, Oxford, 29. Teacher Eng, Wyoming Sem, Pa, 24-25; prof. Am. lit, Middlebury Col, 29-67, Charles A. Dana prof, 67-69; RETIRED. Dir, Bread Loaf Sch. Eng, 46-64. Publ: The Concord saunterer; Passage to Walden, Russell, 49; Dimensions of Robert Frost, Holt, 58; Selected prose and poetry of Ralph Waldo Emerson, 69; Robert Frost: the living voice, Univ. Mass, 74. Add: Pulp Mill Bridge Rd, Middlebury, VT 05753.

COOK, RICHARD IRVING, b. St. Louis, Mo, Aug. 3, 27; m. 55; c. 1. ENGLISH. B.A, Wash. Univ, 50, M.A, 53; Univ. Paris, 54-55; Ph.D.(Eng), Univ. Calif, Berkeley, 60. Instr. ENG, Rutgers Univ, 60-62; asst. prof, Univ. Wash, 62-65, assoc. prof, 65-67; PROF, KENT STATE UNIV, 67- U.S.N, 45-46. Eighteenth century English literature. Publ: Jonathan Swift as a Tory pamphleteer, Univ. Wash, 67; Bernard Mandeville, Twayne, 74; The uses of Saeva indignatio: Swift's political tracts (1710-1714) and his sense of audience, Stud. Eng. Lit. 1500-1900, summer 62; The audience of Swift's Tory tracts, 1710-1714, Mod. Lang. Quart, 3/63; Mr. Examiner and Mr. Review: the Tory apologetics of Swift and Defoe, Huntington Libr. Quart, 2/66; plus others. Add: Dept. of English, Kent State University, Kent, OH 44240.

COOK, ROBERT GEIGER, English, Medieval Literature. See Volume III, Foreign Languages, Linguistics & Philology.

COOK, THOMAS EDWIN, b. Ft. Smith, Ark, Jan. 11, 35; m. 56; c. 1. ENGLISH.LITERATURE. B.A, Hendrix Col, 56; fels, Tulane Univ, 57-61, M.A, 58, Ph.D.(Eng), 61. Instr. ENG, Douglass Col, Rutgers Univ, 61-63, asst. prof, 63-69; ASSOC. PROF, RUSSELL SAGE COL, 69-, CHMN. DEPT, 72- MLA. Romantic literature in England; modern drama; 19th century American literature. Publ: Keats' sonnet To Homer, Keats-Shelley J, XI: 8-12. Add: Dept. of English, Russell Sage College, Troy, NY 12180.

COOKE, PAUL P, b. New York, N.Y, June 29, 17; m. 40; c. 4. ENGLISH. B.S, Miner Teachers Col, 37; M.A, N.Y. Univ, 41; M.A, Cath. Univ. Am, 43; Ed.D.(teaching Eng), Columbia Univ, 47; Am. Univ, 50-51. Instr. Eng, Miner Teachers Col, 44-50, asst. prof, 50-51, assoc. prof, 51-54, prof, 54-55; D.C. Teachers Col, 55-62, acting dean, 62-64; dir, Model Sch. Div, D.C, Publ. Sch, 64-65; PROF. ENG, D.C. TEACHERS COL, 65-, PRES, 66- Vis. lectr, Howard Univ, summers 54-65; lectr, U.S. State Dept, U.S. Labor Dept, U.S. Inform. Agency, Wash. Int. Ctr, 61-68; consult, experienced teacher fel. prog, U.S. Off. Educ, 65; NDEA Inst. for Personnel for Disadvantaged, 65; Nat. Teacher Corps, U.S. Off. Educ, 65-68, Title III, Elem Sec. Educ, 65-68; vis. lectr, Trinity Col.(D.C), 66. U.S.A.A.F, 45-46. Am. Acad. Polit. & Soc. Sci; Am. Asn. Cols. Teacher Educ. Equal educational opportunity and the United States economy and culture; teaching English language and literature with respect to cultural differences; Piers Plowman, fourteenth century English workers. Publ: Six workers in Piers Plowman, 43, Aims of English in vocational high schools, 47 & Civil rights in the United States, 66, Meridian House Found; Delinquency prevention through educational intervention, J. Negro Educ, spring 66; The art of Africa for the whole world, Negro Hist. Bull, fall 66; Equal educational opportunity: some findings and conclusions, J. Negro Educ. Yearbk, summer 68; plus others. Add: 11th & Harvard St. N.W, Washington, DC 20009.

COOLEY, E. MASON, b. Johnson City, Tenn, Dec. 5, 27. ENGLISH & COMPARATIVE LITERATURE. B.A, San Diego State Col, 51; M.A, Univ. Calif, Berkeley, 53, Ph.D.(Eng), 62. Lectr. ENG, Univ. Calif, Berkeley, 58-59; instr, Columbia Univ, 59-63; asst. prof, 63-68; RICHMOND COL, CITY UNIV. NEW YORK, 67-69, ASSOC. PROF, 69- The novel; Victorian literature; modern British literature. Add: 438 W. 116th St, New York, NY 10027.

COOLEY, FRANKLIN DELANY, b. Harford Co, Md, Dec. 28, 06; m. 30. ENGLISH. A.B, Johns Hopkins Univ, 27, Ph.D, 40; A.M, Univ. Md, 33. Teacher, high schs, Md, 27-31; asst, UNIV. MD, COLLEGE PARK, 31-33, instr, 33-36, asst. prof. ENG, 39-43, assoc. prof, 45-61, prof, 61-71, EMER. PROF, 71- U.S.N.R, 43-45. MLA; Mediaeval Acad. Am; Am. Folklore Soc; Medieval literature; Victorian literature; folklore. Publ: Early Danish criticism of Beowulf, J. Eng. Lit. Hist; Two notes on the chess terms in the book of the Duchess, Mod. Lang. Notes; Contemporary reaction to the identification of Hygelac, Philologica. Add: 105 Longridge Ct, Timonium, MD 21093.

COOLEY, JOHN RYDER, b. Oneonta, N.Y, Oct. 26, 37; m. 60; c. 2. AMERICAN LITERATURE. B.A, Syracuse Univ, 59, M.A, 60; Oxford Univ, 66; Ph.D.(Eng), Univ. Mass, 69. From instr. to asst. prof. ENG, State Univ. N.Y. Utica, 63-65; lectr, Univ. Mass, 66-68; from asst. prof. to ASSOC. PROF, WEST. MICH. UNIV, 68- Consult. lit, Choice, 64-; Danforth Found. fac. assoc, 72- U.S.A, 61-63, 1st Lt. MLA. Contemporary poetry and fiction; environmental literature. Publ: Blacks as primitives in Eudora Welty's fiction, Ball State Forum, summer 73; Poetic ripeness, the poetry of John Woods, Mod. Poetry Stud, autumn 73; George Economou, Leonard Nathan & Thomas Parkinson, In: Contemporary poets, St. James Press, London, 74; plus numerous others. Add: Dept. of English, Western Michigan University, Kalamazoo, MI 49001.

COOLEY, MARIANNE, English Language & Linguistics. See Volume III, Foreign Languages, Linguistics & Philology.

COOLEY, THOMAS WINFIELD, b. Gaffney, S.C, June 24, 42; m. 64; c. 1. AMERICAN LITERATURE, AMERICAN STUDIES. B.A, Duke Univ, 64; M.A, Ind. Univ, Bloomington, 68, Ph.D.(Eng), 70. ASST. PROF. ENG, OHIO STATE UNIV, 70- Nat. Endowment Humanities summer stipend, 72. U.S.N, 64-66, Res, 66-70, Lt. MLA. American literary realism; autobiography. Publ: Lincoln Steffens: American innocent abroad, Am. Lit, 1/72. Add: Dept. of English, Ohio State University, 164 W. 17th Ave, Columbus, OH 43210.

COOLIDGE, ARCHIBALD CARY, JR, b. Oxford, Eng, June 9, 28; U.S. citizen; m. 51; c. 7. ENGLISH. B.A, Harvard, 51; M.A, Brown Univ, 54, Morgan-Edwards fel, 55-56, Ph.D.(Eng), 56. Teacher, sch, N.Y, 46-47; instr. ENG, UNIV, IOWA, 56-59, asst. prof, 59-65, ASSOC. PROF, 65- U.S.M.C, 45-46. MLA; Midwest Mod. Lang. Asn; Mod. Humanities Res. Asn. Dickens; the relationship of story form to philosophy and social situation; English history. Publ: Charles Dickens as serial novelist, Iowa State Univ, 67; Dickens and the philosophic basis of melodrama, Victorian Newslett, 12/61; Charles Dickens and Mrs. Radcliffe: a farewell to Wilkie Collins, The Dickensian, 5/62; Dickens's use of Hazlitt's principle of the sympathetic imagination, Miss. Quart, 4/62; plus others. Add: 304 Brown St, Iowa City, IA 52240.

COOLIDGE, JOHN STANHOPE, b. Laramie, Wyo, July 26, 26; m. 64; c. 2. ENGLISH & COMPARATIVE LITERATURE. B.A, Harvard, 49, M.A, 51, Ph.D.(Eng), 57. Instr. ENG, Swarthmore Col, 56-60; asst. prof, UNIV. CALIF, BERKELEY, 60-67, ASSOC. PROF, 67- Huntington Libr. grant-in-aid, 64-65. U.S.N.R, 44-47. MLA; Renaissance Soc. Am; NCTE. Puritanism and the Bible; influence of classical on later literature. Publ: Fielding and conservation of character, 5/60 & Marvell and Horace, 11/65, Mod. Philol; Great things and small: the Virgilian progression, Comp. Lit, winter 65. Add: Dept. of English, University of California, Berkeley, CA 94720.

COOLIDGE, LOWELL WILLIAM, b. Sherborn, Mass, Sept. 18, 06; m. 31; c. 1. ENGLISH. A.B, Boston Univ, 27, A.M, 28; Ph.D, West. Reserve Univ, 37. From instr. to PROF. ENG, COL. WOOSTER, 28-, dir. summer session, 48, 49, 51, chmn. dept, 59-71. Vis. lectr, West. Reserve Univ, 40-41, vis. prof, summer, 57, 64; res, Huntington Libr, Calif, 49-50; vis. prof, Bowling Green State Univ, summer 60. Instr. Navy V-5, 43-45. MLA; NCTE; Milton Soc. Am; Shakespeare Soc. Am; Renaissance Soc. Am. Milton; literature of English Renaissance; American literature. Publ: Co-ed, Complete prose works of John Milton, Vol. II, Yale, 59. Add: 404 Bloomington Ave, Wooster, OH 44691.

COON, ARTHUR MUNSON, b. Buffalo, N.Y, Nov. 4, 03; m. 34; c. 4. ENGLISH. B.A, Cornell Univ, 25; fel, Univ. Mich, 30-31, M.A, 31; Ph.D, Cornell Univ, 38. Reporter, Buffalo Evening News, 25-26; asst. advert. mgr, Dunlop Tire & Rubber Co, 26-28; asst. prof. Eng, Miss. State Col. Women, 28-30; Miami Univ, 32-33; Univ. Wyo, 34-35; instr, Univ. Minn, 38-40; asst. prof, Beloit Col, 40-43, assoc. prof, 43-45; prof. & head dept. Eng, Univ. Akron, 45-46; prof. & head Eng, Assoc. Cols, Upper N.Y. & dean lib. arts, Sampson Col, 46-49; owner, Arthur M. Coon & Co, Wholesale Stationery, Penn Yan, N.Y, 49-56; assoc. dir, Creative Educ. Found, Buffalo, N.Y, 56-57; asst. prof. commun. skills, Mich. State Univ, 57-59, Am. thought & lang, 59-60; prof. Eng, Calif. State Col.(Pa), 60-66, head dept. Eng. & speech, 61-66; prof. Eng, Salem State Col, 66-74; RETIRED. Univ. Minn. res. grants, 38-40; ed, Seventeeth-Century News, 48-51; Mich. State Univ. grant-in-aid, 59-60. MLA; NCTE. Milton Soc. Am; Conf. Col. Compos. & Commun. Izaak Walton; Shakespeare; comparative literature. Publ: The life of Izaak Walton, Cornell Univ. Abstracts of Theses, 38; Izaak Walton, Colliers encyclopedia, Collier-Macmillan, 49; Dr. William Warde, author of The arte of angling, 1577?, J. Eng. & Ger. Philol, 62. Add: 18 Beach Ave, Salem, MA 01970.

COON, GILBERT DENNIS, b. Orange, N.J, Oct. 29, 42; m. 65; c. 2. AMERICAN STUDIES & LITERATURE. B.A, Wilmington Col, 64; Ph.D.(Am. stud), Wash. State Univ, 71. Teaching asst. ENG, Wash. State Univ, 67-69; ASST. PROF, CENT. MO. STATE UNIV, 69- Am. Studies Asn; West. Am. Lit. Asn. Western American literature; American folklore; American history. Add: Dept. of English, Central Missouri State University, Warrensburg, MO 64093.

COON, ROGER WOOLDRIDGE, Religion, Communications. See Volume IV, Philosophy, Religion and Law.

COONEY, JAMES FRANCIS, b. Lancaster, Ohio, Sept. 22, 28; m. 68. ENGLISH. B.A, Col. St. Charles Borromeo, 50; Lic. Sacred Theol, Gregorian Univ, 54; M.A, Ohio State Univ, 61, Ph.D.(Eng), 66. Instr. Eng. & speech, Col. St. Charles Borromeo, 57-66; Eng, Col. St. Mary of Springs, 66-68, dean men, 64-68; ASST. PROF. ENG, KENT STATE UNIV, 68- ASST. DIR. SALEM CAMPUS, 74-, asst. chmn. dept. Eng, 70-73. MLA; Renaissance Soc. Am; St. Thomas More Soc. Rhetoric in the English Renaissance; the preaching tradition and 17th century English poetry; sacred liturgy. Publ: Co-auth, Together at Mass, Gregorian Inst, Am, 59; auth, Bible devotions of Christian penance, Liturgical Conf, 64; The cask of Amontillado: some further ironies, Stud. in Short Fiction, 74. Add: Dept. of English, Kent State University, Kent, OH 44242.

COONRADT, FREDERIC CHAPIN, b. Portland, Ore, Apr. 17, 13; m. 40; c. 1. JOURNALISM. A.B, Stanford Univ, 34; M.A, Univ. South. Calif, 50. Reporter, San Francisco Exam, 35; night city ed, Los Angeles Daily News, 36-38, picture ed, 45-47; mgr. Los Angeles bur, Time Mag, 38-40; pub. mgr, Douglas Aircraft Co, Inc, 40-45; lectr. JOUR, UNIV. SOUTH. CALIF, 48-50, asst. prof, 50-55, ASSOC. PROF, 55- Add: Dept. of Journalism, University of Southern California, Los Angeles, CA 90007.

COOPER, BERNARR, b. New York, N.Y. Oct. 6, 12; m. 45; c. 2. MASS COMMUNICATIONS, SPEECH. A.B, Wabash Col, 32; Northwest. Univ, 32-34; Univ. Mich, 44-45; Ph.D, Stanford Univ, 56. Dir. & producer, radio, prof. & little theatres, 34-41; audio-visual educ. adv, UN Command, Far East. 46-54; teacher high sch, 55; asst. prof. speech & dir. univ. TV & radio, Univ. New Mex, 56-59; assoc. prof. speech, Fla. State Univ, 59-62; CHIEF, BUR. MASS COMMUN, STATE EDUC. DEPT. N.Y, 62-; DIR, EDUC. USES OF SATELLITES, 72-, PROJ. ADMINR. RACIAL ISOLATION, 73- Adv, Broadcast Corp. Japan, 46-54; guest consult. radio prod, Australian Broadcasting Comn, 47; consult, Dept. Instr, Nova Scotia, 62-; Hofstra Univ, 64-66; northeast regional chmn, Nat. Comt. Full Develop. Instruct. TV Fixed Serv. Fed. Commun. Comn, 65-; consult, Syracuse Univ, 65-; Univ. Miss, 67-; Stephens Col, 67-68; expert commun. consult. to UN, 68. Sig.C, & Mil. Intel, A.U.S, 43-46. Nat. Asn. Educ. Broadcasters; Speech Commun. Asn. Foreign language development; higher educational administration; public address. Publ: Introduction to radio production-directing, Nippon Hoso Shuppan; co-auth, Instructional television fixed service, what it is, how to plan, Fed. Commun. Comn, 67; auth, The microphone is yours & Criticism is not enough, NAEB Jour; co-auth, Understanding television, Commun. Arts, 64. Add: Van Leuven Dr. S, Rensselaer, NY 12144.

COOPER, CHARLES WILLIAM, b. Edgewood, Pa, Jan. 12, 04; m. 28; c. 1. DRAMA. A.B, Univ. Calif, 25, A.M, 26, Ph.D, 31. Instr. & chmn. dept, San Bernardino Jr. Col, Calif, 27-29, 30-33; assoc. prof. Eng, Whittier Col, 33-36; Fresno State Col, 36-38; prof. ENG, WHITTIER COL, 38-55, prof-at-large, 55-68, dir. poet theatre, 38-46, asst. to pres, 61-67, EMER. PROF, 68- Esthetics; dramaturgy; English literature. Publ: Preface to poetry, Harcourt; Arts and humanity, Philos. Libr; Preface to drama, Ronald, 55; Whittier, independent college in California, Ritchie, 67; co-auth, The term paper, a manual and model, Stanford Univ, 4th ed, 67; ed, Break the new ground, Friends World Comt, Birmingham, Eng, 69. Add: 251 Cloydon Circle, Santa Barbara, CA 93108.

COOPER, JOHN REX, b. Edmonton, Alta, May 14, 32; m. 65; c. 2. ENGLISH LITERATURE. A.B, State Univ. N.Y. Albany, 54; M.A, Yale, 57, Ph.D.(Eng), 62. Instr. Eng. & humanities, Univ. Chicago, 61-63, asst. prof. 63-67; lit. & humanities, Reed Col, 67-68, assoc. prof, 68-70; PORTLAND STATE UNIV, 70-73, PROF, 73- U.S.A, 54-56. MLA. Seventeenth century prose; Shakespeare; aesthetics. Publ: The art of The compleat angler, Duke Univ, 68; Shylock's humanity, Shakespeare Quart, 69. Add: Dept. of English, Portland State University, Portland, OR 97207.

COOPER, JUNE MARGARET, b. New York, N.Y, Apr. 3, 33; m. 66; c. 2. SPEECH PATHOLOGY. B.A, Queens Col, 54; M.A, Brooklyn Col, 56; Ph.D. (speech), N.Y. Univ, 64. Speech therapist, Queens Col, 53; instr. speech & theater, Brooklyn Col, 59-61; asst. prof. speech, Hofstra Univ, 61-66; CALIF. STATE UNIV, LONG BEACH, 66-71, ASSOC. PROF. COMMUNICATIVE DISORDERS, 71- Consult, admin. training prog, Long Beach Community Improvement League, summer 67, Proj. Head Start, 68- Am. Asn. Mental Deficiency; Am. Speech & Hearing Asn. Speech and language of the culturally different child; neurological language problems of children. Add: Dept. of Speech, California State University, Long Beach, 6101 E. Seventh St, Long Beach, CA 90801.

COOPER, PHILIP, JR, b. Jackson, Miss, Jan. 5. 26; m. 56; c. 5. ENGLISH, COMPARATIVE LITERATURE. B.A, Tulane Univ, 47; M.A, Columbia Univ, 56; Ph.D.(Eng), Univ. Rochester, 67. Instr. Eng, Dartmouth Col, 56-57; humanities, Eastman Sch. Music, Univ. Rochester, 57-63, assoc, ENG, univ. 63-65; asst. prof, Hollins Col, 65-68; UNIV. MD. BALTIMORE COUNTY, 68-71, ASSOC. PROF, 71- U.S.N.R, 43-46, Lt. Eng. Inst; MLA. Poetry; twentieth century English and American literature; theory of literature. Publ: The autobiographical myth of Robert Lowell, Univ. N.C, Chapel Hill, 70; Gifts of form, Kenyon Rev, XXXII, Issue 1: 143-151. Add: 429 Drury Lane, Baltimore, MD 21229.

COOPER, ROBERT M, b. Manchester, Eng, Feb. 4, 17; U.S. citizen; m. 44; c. 2. ENGLISH. B.A, Trinity Col, 40; Theodore Whitfield Hunt fels, Princeton, 41 & 46, M.A, 46, Ph.D.(Eng), 47. Asst. prof. Eng, Roanoke Col, 47-49, assoc. prof, 49-52; account exec. & exec. v.pres, advertising agency, 52-65; assoc. prof. ENG, SOUTHWEST. AT MEMPHIS, 65-72, PROF, 72- Southwest. at Memphis summer res. grants, 67 & 68. U.S.A.A.F, 42-45, T/Sgt. Poetry and criticism of Dante Gabriel Rossetti. Add: 5249 Sycamore Grove, Memphis, TN 38117.

COOPER, SHEROD MONROE, JR, b. Norristown, Pa, Jan. 28, 27; m. 53; c. 4. ENGLISH. B.S, Temple Univ, 51, M.A, 53; Univ. Pittsburgh, 54-55; Ph.D. (Eng), Univ. Pa, 63. Teacher high sch, N.J, 52-54; instr. Eng, Westminster Col.(Pa), 54-56; UNIV. MD, COLLEGE PARK, 57-63, asst. prof, 63-67, ASSOC. PROF. ENG, 67- U.S. Merchant Marine, 45-46; U.S.A, 46-47. MLA; Renaissance Soc; AAUP. English poetry of the 16th century; Shakespeare. Publ: The sonnets of Astrophel and Stella: a stylistic study, Mouton, 68; contrib, annual bibliog, PMLA, 61-67. Add: Dept. of English, University of Maryland, College Park, MD 20742.

COOPERMAN, HASYE (MRS. N.B. MINKOFF), b. New York, N.Y. Feb. 2, 07; m. 31; c. 2. AMERICAN & COMPARATIVE LITERATURE. B.A, Hunter Col, 27; M.A, Columbia Univ, 28, Ph.D.(Romance lang. & lit), 31. LECTR. & WRITER, 29-; LECTR. COMP. LIT, AM. LIT. & AESTHET, NEW SCH. SOCIAL RES, 51-, head dept. lit, 61-67. Mem. ed. staff. World Syndicate Publ. Co, 36-42. Poetry Soc. Am; Am. Lit. Asn.(Nat. Poetry Award, 57). Publ: The aesthetics of Stephane Mallarme, Koffern Press, 33 & Russell, 71; Men walk the earth, William-Frederick; The bube-maiseh, & The three classical Yiddish writers: Mendele, Sholom Aleikem and Peretz, In: Jewish heritage reader, B'nai B'rith, 65; Night within us, day without, In: The diamond anthology, Poetry Soc. Am, 71 & International who's who in poetry anthology, London, 72; plus others. Add: Dept. of Literature, The New School for Social Research, 66 W. 12th St, New York, NY 10011.

COOPERMAN, STANLEY R, b. New York, N.Y, Oct. 22, 29. ENGLISH & AMERICAN LITERATURE. A.B, N.Y. Univ, 51; fel, Ind. Univ, 55-59, Lilly fel, 58, univ. fel, 60-61, Ph.D, 62. Instr. ENG, Univ. Ore, 61-62, asst. prof, 62-63; Hofstra Univ, 63-65; from assoc. prof. to PROF, SIMON FRASER UNIV, 65- Fulbright lectr, Univ. Teheran, 59-60; Can. Counc. sr. fel, 67-68. MLA; NCTE; Overseas Educ. Asn; League Can. Poets. Nineteenth and twentieth century literature, English and American. Publ: World War I and the American novel, Johns Hopkins Univ, 68; The day of the parrot, Univ. Nebr, 68; The owl behind the door, McClelland & Stewart, 68; Cappelbaum's dance, Univ. Nebr, 70; Cannibals, Oberon, 72; Shakespeare's anti-hero: Hamlet and the underground man, Shakespeare Stud, 65; American war novels, Yale Rev, 70; Philip Roth, Twentieth Century Lit, (in press), plus others. Add: Dept. of English, Simon Fraser University, Burnaby, B.C, Can.

COPE, JACKSON IRVING, b. Muncie, Ind, Sept. 1, 25; m. 48, 69; c. 2. ENGLISH. B.A, Univ. Ill; Ph.D.(Eng), Johns Hopkins, 52. Instr. ENG, Ohio State Univ, 52-54; asst. prof, Wash. Univ, 54-58; assoc. prof, Rice Univ, 58-60, prof, 60-61; assoc. prof, Johns Hopkins Univ, 62-63, prof, 63-72; LEO S. BING PROF, UNIV. SOUTH. CALIF, 72- Guggenheim fel, 58-59; Am. Counc. Learned Soc. fel, 63-64. U.S.A.A.F, 43-45, 2nd Lt. MLA; Renaissance Soc. Am; James Joyce Soc; Int. Asn. Univ. Prof. & Lectr. Renaissance drama; modern British literature. Publ: Joseph Glanvill, Anglican apologist, 56 & co-auth, Thomas Sprat's History of the Royal Society, 58, Wash. Univ; auth, Metaphoric structure of Paradise lost, 62 & The theater and the dream: from metaphor to form in Renaissance drama, Johns Hopkins, 73. Add: Dept. of English, University of Southern California, Los Angeles, CA 90007.

COPELAND, THOMAS ARTHUR, b. Houston, Tex, Oct. 27, 44; m. 66; c. 1. ENGLISH. B.A, Oberlin Col, 66; M.A, Northwest. Univ, 67, Ph.D.(Eng), 71. Teaching asst. ENG, Northwest. Univ, 67, instr, 69-70; ASST. PROF, YOUNGSTOWN STATE UNIV, 71- MLA; Renaissance Soc. Am. Seventeenth century English literature; prosody; oral literature. Add: Dept. of English, Youngstown State University, 410 Wick Ave, Youngstown, OH 44503.

COPELAND, THOMAS WELLSTED, b. East Cleveland, Ohio, July 10, 07. ENGLISH LITERATURE. A.B, Yale, 28, Ph.D, 33; Harvard, 28-29; hon. D.Litt, Univ. Sheffield, 72; Univ. Dublin, 73. Instr, Yale, 29-30, Eng, 34-39, Sterling fel, 39-40, asst. prof. Eng, 40-49; instr, Cornell Univ, 33-34; assoc. prof. ENG, Univ. Chicago, 49-57; from prof. to COMMONWEALTH PROF, UNIV. MASS, AMHERST, 57- Gen. ed, Correspondence of Edmund Burke, 53- U.S.N.R, 42-45, Lt. Comdr. MLA. Edmund Burke. Publ: Our eminent friend Edmund Burke; A checklist of the correspondence of Edmund Burke; ed, Correspondence of Edmund Burke, Vol. I, Univ. Chicago & Cambridge, 58. Add: Dept. of English, University of Massachusetts, Amherst, MA 01002.

COPPEDGE, WALTER RALEIGH, b. Morelia, Mex, Jan. 18, 30; U.S. citizen; m. 58; c. 1. ENGLISH. B.A, Univ. Miss, 52; B.Litt, Oxford, 58; M.A, Memphis State Univ, 63; Ph.D.(Eng), Ind. Univ, 67. Asst. prof. Eng, Ala. Col, 57-60; headmaster, Lausanne Sch. Girls, Tenn, 60-66; pres, Col. Charleston, 66-68; asst. v.pres. acad. affairs, VA. COMMONWEALTH UNIV, 68-71, PROF. ENG, 71- U.S.A.R, 60, Lt. Asn. Am. Rhodes Scholars; MLA; English-Speaking Union. Add: 2602 Monument Ave, Richmond, VA 23220.

COPPERUD, ROY HERMAN, b. Crystal Falls, Mich, June 28, 15; m. 46; c. 3. JOURNALISM. B.A, Univ. Minn, 42. Ed. editorial pages, Pasadena Star-News & Independent, 59-64; asst. prof. JOUR, UNIV. SOUTH. CALIF, 64-66, assoc. prof, 66-70, PROF, 70- Dir. ed. workshop dept, Ed. & Publ. Mag, 52-; mem. usage panel, Am. Heritage Dictionary, 64-; consult, Washington Post, 64-65; Eng. Lang. Inst. Am, 66-; Webster Living Encycl. Dictionary, 70-71. Asn. Educ. in Jour; AAUP. English usage. Publ: Words on paper, 60 & A dictionary of usage and style, 64, Hawthorn; American usage: the consensus, Van Nostrand, 70; Foreword, A dictionary of contemporary and colloquial usage, Eng. Lang. Inst. Am, 71. Add: School of Journalism, University of Southern California, University Park, Los Angeles, CA 90007.

COPPLE, ROBERT NEALE, b. Albuquerque, N.Mex, Apr. 19, 23; m. 47; c. 2. JOURNALISM. B.A, Univ. Nebr, 47; B.S, Northwest. Univ, 48. Instr. jour, sch. jour, Univ. Nebr. & reporter Nebr. State J, Lincoln, 48-49; copyreader, Milwaukee J, 49-51; asst. Sunday ed, Sunday J. & Star, Lincoln, 51-52; city ed, Lincoln J, Nebr, 52-59; asst. prof. JOUR, SCH. JOUR, UNIV. NEBR, LINCOLN, 59-62, assoc. prof, 62-70, PROF, 70-, DIR. SCH. JOUR, 66- Lectr, Am. Polit. Sci. Asn. newspaper sem, Univ. Tex, 60; grants, Reader's Digest Found, 60- & Newspaper Fund, Inc, Wall St. J, 61- U.S.A.A.F, 43-45, 1st Lt. Asn. Educ. Jour. Reporting in depth—teaching and professional practice; journalism history. Publ: Tower on the plains, Lincoln Centennial Comn, 49; Depth reporting, Prentice-Hall, 63. Add: School of Journalism, University of Nebraska, Lincoln, NE 68508.

CORBETT, EDWARD PATRICK JOSEPH, b. Jamestown, N.Dak, Oct. 29, 19; m. 44; c. 7. ENGLISH. M.A, Univ. Chicago, 48; Ph.D.(Eng), Loyola Univ. (Ill), 56. Instr. ENG, Creighton Univ, 48-50; Loyola Univ.(Ill), 50-53; asst. prof, Creighton Univ, 53-56, assoc. prof, 56-61, prof, 61-66; PROF. & V.CHMN. ENG. & DIR. FRESHMAN ENG, OHIO STATE UNIV, COLUMBUS, 66- Assoc. ed, Quart. Jour. Speech, 72-; mem. ed. bd, Philos. & Rhet. 72-; ed, Col. Compos. & Commun, 74- U.S.M.C, 43-46. MLA; NCTE; Conf. Col. Compos. & Commun; Speech Commun. Asn. Classical and Renaissance rhetoric; 18th century literature. Publ: Classical rhetoric for the modern student, 65 & 71, co-auth, Teaching freshman composition, 67 & auth, Rhetorical analyses of literary works, 68, co-ed, Teaching high school composition, 70, Oxford: co-auth, The rhetoric of Blair, Campbell and Whately, Holt, 68; auth, The little English handbook, Wiley, 73; America's Sainte-Beuve, Commonwealth, 5/60; What is being revived?, Col. Compos. & Commun, 10/67; A new look at old rhetoric, In: Rhetoric: theories for application, NCTE, 67; plus others. Add: Dept. of English, Ohio State University, Columbus, OH 43210.

CORBIN, GERMAINE, C.C.V.I, b. Oak Park, Ill, Oct. 15, 35. THEATRE HISTORY. B.A, Incarnate Word Col, 62; M.A, Cath. Univ. Am, 64; univ. fel, Univ. Ill, Champaign, 68-69, Ph.D.(theatre hist), 71. Jr. high teacher, St. Mary Magdalen Sch, San Antonio, Tex, 57-60; instr. Eng, Incarnate Word Col, 60-62, Eng. & speech, 64-68, asst. acad. dean, 64-67; instr. drama, Univ. Ill, Champaign, 69-70; INCARNATE WORD COL, 70-71, asst. prof, 71-72, PROF. DRAMA & ACAD. DEAN, 72- Critic judge, Univ. Interscholastic League, 68-73; col. rep, San Antonio Arts Counc, 71-72; Am. Counc. on Educ. fel, Inst. Acad. Deans, summer 73. Am. Theatre Asn; Am. Theatre Res. Soc; AAUP; Am. Asn. Higher Educ; Am. Conf. Acad. Deans. American theatre history; liberal arts and interdisciplinary studies. Publ: The acting of Otis Skinner, Univ. Ill, 71; Shakespeare on tour, Playbill, 66. Add: Office of Academic Dean, Incarnate Word College, 4301 Broadway, San Antonio, TX 78209.

CORBIN, RICHARD, b. Schenectady, N.Y, Nov. 4, 11; m. 38; c. 3. ENGLISH. B.A, Colgate Univ, 33; M.A, Columbia Univ, 39. Teacher Eng, Bay Shore High Sch, N.Y, 33-37; head dept, Peekskill High Sch, N.Y, 37-60; chmn. high sch. Eng. dept. & lectr. Eng. & educ, Hunter Col, 60-73, RETIRED. Co-dir. Eng. workshop, Colgate Univ, summer 49; lectr, Eng. workshop, Cornell Univ, summer 54; dir. Eng. workshop, Appalachian State Col, summer 56; Univ. Colo, summer 59; teachers col, Columbia Univ, summer 61, vis. lectr, summer 62; Hay fel, Bennington Col, summer 60; dir. compos. workshop, Los Angeles Bd. Educ, summer 61; consult, Eng. workshop, Univ. Mo, summer 61; proj. Eng. ctr, Hunter Col, 62; lit. heritage prog, Macmillan Co, 65-; mem. int. sem. on teaching Eng, Dartmouth Col, summer 66; mem. ed. bd, NCTE, 72-74. Conf. Col. Compos. & Commun; NCTE (pres, 64-65). Teaching of composition; poetry; education of the gifted and disadvantaged. Publ: Research paper project, N.Y. State Eng. Counc. Rev. 61; Poetry 1, 62, The teaching of writing in our schools, 66 & co-auth, Stories in song and verse, 68, Macmillan; Guide to modern English, Scott, 5 vols, 55, 60, 63; co-ed, Twelve modern American plays, Scribner, 69, 73; Language Programs for the disadvantaged, NCTE, 64. Add: 50 Oakridge, Peekskill, NY 10566.

CORBIN, WILLIAM N, b. Vanderlip, W.Va, July 28, 15; m. 42. PUBLIC ADDRESS. B.B.A. & B.A, St. Marys' Univ, San Antonio, 52; M.A, Univ. Denver, 53; summers, 54-59. Personnel dir, U.S. Air Force civilian personnel, 45-50; debate coach, Classen High Sch, Okla. City, Okla, 53-55; DIR. FORENSICS, IDAHO STATE UNIV, 55- Univ. parliamentarian, Idaho State Univ, 60- U.S.A.F, 40-45, Sgt. Am. Arbit. Asn; Speech Commun. Asn; West. Speech

Commun. Asn; AAUP; Am. Inst. Parliamentarians; Am. Forensic Asn; West. Forensic Asn. Study of ancient rhetoric; general semantics; debate propositions. Add: Dept. of Speech, Idaho State University, Pocatello, ID 83201.

CORCORAN, MARY IRMA, B.V.M, b. Anamosa, Iowa, Nov. 10, 05. ENGLISH. B.A, Clarke Col, 27; M.A, Columbia Univ, 31; Ph.D.(Eng), Cath. Univ. Am, 45. Instr. ENG, MUNDELEIN COL, 30-37, asst. prof, 37-39, assoc. prof, 45-46, prof, 46-73, EMER. PROF, 73- Atlantic Monthly scholar, Breadloaf Sch, Eng, 48; Am. Asn. Univ. Women Marion Talbot fel, 62-63; Am. Philos. Soc. grant for res. on life of Thomas Holme, 66. Best lyric of the year award, Shards, 35. MLA. English literature of the 16th and 17th centuries, especially Milton; American colonial history, especially 17th century; English civil wars. Publ: Milton's paradise with reference to the hexameral background, Cath. Univ, 45 & 67; plus other articles and poems. Add: Dept. of English, Mundelein College, 6363 Sheridan Rd, Chicago, IL 60626.

CORDER, JIMMIE WAYNE, b. Jayton, Tex, Sept. 25, 29; m. 51; c. 3. ENGLISH. B.A. & M.A, Tex. Christian Univ, 54; Ph.D.(Eng), Univ. Okla, 58. Instr. ENG, Univ. Okla, 57-58; asst. prof, TEX. CHRISTIAN UNIV, 58-61, assoc. prof, 61-66, PROF. & CHMN. DEPT, 66- U.S.A, 50-52, Sgt. NCTE; MLA. English literature of the 18th century; rhetoric. Publ: Co-auth, A college rhetoric, 62 & auth, Rhetoric: a text-reader, 65, Random; co-auth, Handbook of current English, 68 & ed, Finding a voice, 73, Scott; auth, Uses of rhetoric, Lippincott, 71; Gulliver in England, Col. Eng, 11/61; The study of rhetoric, Col. Compos. & Commun, 5/61; Rhetoric and meaning in Religion Laici, PMLA 5/67. Add: Dept. of English, Texas Christian University, Ft. Worth, TX 76129.

CORDONNIER, MAX EDWARD, b. Carthage, Mo, Sept. 19, 34; m. 56; c. 1. ENGLISH. B.A, Park Col, 56; M.A, Univ. Kans, 58, Ph.D.(Eng), 65. Asst. instr. ENG, Univ. Kans, 56-60; instr, Southeast Mo. State Col, 60-63, asst. prof, 63-66; Univ. Tenn, 66-67; assoc. prof, SOUTHEAST MO. STATE UNIV, 67-72, PROF, 72- Ed, Cape Rock J. MLA; Midwest Mod. Lang. Asn. English Romantic Age; Victorian age. Publ: Poem and critique, Poet & Critic, winter 66; Siegfried in Ireland: a study of Moore's The lake, Dublin Mag, spring 67. Add: Dept. of English, Southeast Missouri State University, Cape Girardeau, MO 63701.

CORE, GEORGE, b. Kansas City, Mo, Jan. 12, 39; m. 60; c. 4. BRITISH & AMERICAN LITERATURE. B.A, Vanderbilt Univ, 59, M.A, 60; fel, Univ. N C, Chapel Hill, 64-65, Ph.D.(Eng), 71. Teaching asst, Univ. N.C, Chapel Hill, 65-66; instr. Eng, Davidson Col, 66-68; asst. prof. Eng. & sr. ed, Univ. Press, Univ. Ga, 68-73; ED, SEWANEE REV. & ASSOC. PROF. ENG, UNIV. OF THE SOUTH, 73- Nat. Endowment for Humanities younger humanist fel, 72-73. U.S.M.C, 60-64, Res, 64-, Maj. MLA; S.Atlantic Mod. Lang. Asn; Soc. Stud. South. Lit.(secy-treas, 73-). Modern British and American fiction, especially Henry James; contemporary literary criticism; southern literary renaissance. Publ: Ed, Regionalism and beyond: essays of Randall Stewart, Vanderbilt Univ, 68; co-ed, The southern tradition at bay, Arlington House, 68; ed, Southern fiction today, 69 & co-ed, K.A. Porter: a critical symposium, 69, Univ. Ga; auth, The literalists of the imagination: southern new critics and the profession of letters, La. State Univ, 74; The confessions of Nat Turner and the burden of the past, South. Lit. J, spring 70; Ordered life and the abysses of chaos: Parade's end, South. Rev, summer 72; Henry James and the comedy of the New England conscience, In: The comic imagination in American literature, Rutgers Univ, 73. Add: Sewanee Review, Sewanee, TN 37375.

COREY, KATHARINE TUBBS, Classical Philology. See Volume III, Foreign Languages, Linguistics & Philology.

COREY, ORLIN RUSSELL, b. Nowata, Okla, May 4, 26; m. 49. SPEECH & DRAMA. B.A, Baylor Univ, 50, M.A, 52; cert, Cent. Sch. Speech & Drama, London, 56; Univ. London, 55-56. Asst. prof. drama, Georgetown Col, 52-55, ASSOC. PROF, 56-59; DRAMA & SPEECH, CENTENARY COL, 60- Adv. relig. drama, South. Baptist Sunday Sch. Bd, 55-; dir, Ky. Mountain Theater, Inc, 59-; producer, The Everyman players, 59-; U.S. deleg, Int. Children's Theatre Asn, Hauge Conf, 68; guest artist, Univ. N.H, 68 & Univ. Fla, 71; guest lectr. drama, Univ. Cape Town & Bristol Univ, 69; chmn, U.S. Ctr. Int. Asn. Theatre for Children and Youth, 72- U.S.N, 44-46. Am. Educ. Theatre Asn; Speech Commun. Asn; Children's Theatre Asn.(pres, 71-73). Theatre for youth; religious drama in the contemporary theater; adaptation of religious literature to stage and production today. Publ: The Book of Job, arranged for stage, 60 & Theatre for children: kid-stuff or art?, 73, Anchorage. Add: The Everyman Players, Box 4154, Shreveport, LA 71104.

CORMIER, RAYMOND JOSEPH, Medieval French Literature. See Volume III, Foreign Languages, Linguistics & Philology.

CORNELIUS, DAVID K, b. Butler, Pa, Feb. 24, 24; m. 49; c. 2. ENGLISH. B.A, Westminster Col.(Pa), 48; M.A, Columbia Univ, 50, Ph.D.(Eng), 56. Instr. ENG, Colby Col, 50-52; RANDOLPH-MACON WOMAN'S COL, 54-56, asst. prof, 57-60, assoc. prof, 61-64, PROF, 65- U.S.A.A.F, 43-46, S/Sgt. MLA; Milton Soc. Am. English literature of the 17th century; Renaissance literature. Publ: Co-auth, Cultures in conflict, Scott, 64; auth, Keats' Ode on a Grecian urn, 3/62 & Donne's Holy sonnet XIV, 11/65, Explicator; co-auth, A somewhat formal conversation, Lib. Educ, 12/64. Add: Dept. of English, Randolph-Macon Woman's College, Lynchburg, VA 24504.

CORNELIUS, SAMUEL ROBERT, b. New Bethlehem, Pa, Aug. 14, 19; m. 51; c. 4. ENGLISH. B.A, Maryville Col, 41; scholar, Vanderbilt Univ, 42-43, M.A, 43; Ph.D.(Eng), Univ. Pittsburgh, 49. Instr. Eng, Univ. Pittsburgh, 46-49; assoc. prof, Memphis State Col, 49-56, PROF, 56-57; ALMA COL, 57-, chmn. dept. Eng, speech & theater, 59-65, head div. humanities & fine arts, 61-65, dean fac, 65-67, dean humanities, 67-69. Am. Asn. Higher Educ. English Renaissance; Shakespeare; 20th century fiction and criticism. Publ: Ed. & co-auth, Foundations of Western civilization (4 vols), Alma Col, 61; ed, Alma College American assembly on the population dilemma, Alma Col. Perspective, spring 67. Add: Dept. of English, Alma College, Alma, MI 48801.

CORNELL, LOUIS LONGACRE, b. New York, N.Y, Aug. 5, 34; m. 56; c. 3. ENGLISH. B.A, Columbia Univ, 56, M.A, 57, Ph.D.(Eng), 63. Instr. Eng, Dartmouth Col, 61-63; asst. prof, Columbia Univ, 63-69, lectr, 69-73, Lawrence H. Chamberlain fel, 66-67. MLA; Ling. Soc. Am. Victorian literature; English philology. Publ: Kipling in India, Macmillan, London, 66; The American venture, In: Rudyard Kipling, Weidenfeld & Nicolson, 72. Add: 35 E. Wheelock St, Hanover, NH 03755.

CORNWELL, CLIFTON, b. Wheeling, Mo, Sept. 11, 20; m. 43; c. 4. SPEECH. B.S, Northeast Mo. State Col, 41; A.M, Univ. Mo, 42, Ph.D.(speech), 65. Asst. prof. speech, Univ. Hawaii, 47-49; dir. forensics, Univ. Mo, 49-50; overseas contract coordinator, A.S. Aloe Co, Mo, 52-58; asst. prof. SPEECH, South. Ill, Univ, Edwardsville, 58-64, asst. dean, 64-65; assoc. prof, UNIV. MO, COLUMBIA, 65-67, chmn. dept. & asst. dean faculties, 67-68, PROF, 68-, assoc. dean faculties, 68-71, dean faculties, 71-72, provost acad. affairs, 72-74. U.S.A, 42-46 & 50-52, 1st Lt. Speech Commun. Asn; Am. Asn. Higher Educ; Cent. States Speech Asn. Rhetorical theory; communication behavior. Add: 1024 Westwinds Ct, Columbia, MO 65201.

CORNWELL, ETHEL FRAZIER, b. Chattanooga, Tenn, June 12, 24; m. 53; c. 2. ENGLISH. A.B, Univ. Chattanooga, 47; M.A, Middlebury Col, 49; Ph.D.(Eng), Tulane Univ, 55. Instr. ENG, Waynesburg Col, 47-49; Univ. South. Miss, 50-51; asst. prof, Univ. Toledo, 66-69; ASSOC. PROF, SHEPHERD COL, 69- Nat. Endowment for Humanities fel, 72-73. MLA; S.Atlantic Mod. Lang. Asn. Modern literature. Publ: The still point, Rutgers Univ, 63; The green wind, Pageant, 70; Nunc Dimittis The Fiddlehead, winter 68; Samuel Beckett: the flight from self, PMLA, 1/73; Decreasing aesthetic distance: the problem of universality, Philol. Papers, 73, Add: 537 Carrollton Dr, Frederick, MD 21701.

CORREALE, ROBERT M, b. Troy, N.Y, Mar. 26, 32; m. 59; c. 3. ENGLISH LITERATURE. A.B, St. Bonaventure Univ, 55; M.A, Siena Col, 60; Ph.D. (Eng), Univ. Cincinnati, 71. Instr. ENG, LaSalle Col, 61-64, asst. prof, 64-67; WRIGHT STATE UNIV, 71-73, ASSOC. PROF, 73- MLA; Mediaeval Acad. Am; NCTE; Col. Eng. Asn. Chaucer; backgrounds of Chaucer's poetry; middle English literature. Publ: St. Jerome and the conclusion of The Friar's tale, Eng. Lang. Notes, 65; Chaucer's parody of compline in The Reeve's tale, Chaucer Rev, 66. Add: Dept. of English, Wright State University, Col. Glenn Highway, Dayton, OH 45431.

CORRIGAN, FRANCIS XAVIER, b. Long Island City, N.Y, May 7, 14; m. 42; c. 8. ENGLISH. B.S, St. John's Univ.(N.Y), 38, M.A, 47; Columbia Univ. Teacher, High Sch, 40-43, 46-47; instr. Eng, Fordham Univ, 47-48; asst. prof. Good Counsel Col, 48-49; asst. prof, St. John's Univ.(N.Y), 59- 63; ASST. PROF. ENG, PACE COL, 64- Lectr, Marymount Col, 47-48; Fordham Univ, 48-52. U.S.A, 43-46. MLA; Col. Eng. Asn. English philology and modern grammar; British-American contemporary literature. Publ: An etymological treatment of significant words selected from the Knight's tale of Chaucer's Canterbury tales; Middle English readings in translation, Christopher, 65. Add: 157 Clay Pitts Rd, Greenlawn, NY 11740.

CORRIGAN, MATTHEW ANTHONY, b. Dublin, Ireland; Can. citizen. ENGLISH & AMERICAN LITERATURE. B.A, Univ. Toronto, 62; Ph.D.(Eng), State Univ. N.Y. Buffalo, 69. Asst. prof. ENG, STATE UNIV. N.Y. BINGHAMTON, 68-72, ASSOC. PROF, 72- Can. Counc. grant, 72-; assoc. ed, Boundary 2, 73- Modern literature; modern philosophy and literary theory. Publ: Ed, Charles Olson: essays, reminiscences, reviews, State Univ. N.Y. Binghamton, 74; auth, Malcolm Lowry, New York publishing, and the new illiteracy, Encounter, 7/70; The writer as consciousness, Can. Lit, spring 71; plus others. Add: Dept. of English, State University of New York at Binghamton, Binghamton, NY 13901.

CORRIGAN, RALPH L, JR, b. New Rochelle, N.Y, June 24, 37; m. 61; c. 3. ENGLISH. B.A, Iona Col, 59; M.A, Fordham Univ, 62, N.Y. State Regents fel, 60-63, Ph.D.(Eng), 73. Instr. ENG, Siena Col, 62-66, ASST. PROF, 66-67; SACRED HEART UNIV, 67, CHMN. DEPT, 72- Ed, Conn. Eng. Jour, Conn. Counc. Teachers Eng. Conf. Col. Compos. & Commun; NCTE; Asn. Depts. Eng. Rhetoric; history of the English language; developmental writing. Publ: Themes for study, Holt, 66; Teaching language awareness, Leaflet, 9/70; Language studies, Elem. Eng, 1/74. Add: Dept. of English, Sacred Heart University, Park Ave, Bridgeport, CT 06604.

CORRIGAN, ROBERT ANTHONY, b. New London, Conn, Apr. 21, 35; m. 56; c. 3. AMERICAN CIVILIZATION. A.B, Brown Univ, 57; univ. fel. & M.A, Univ. Pa, 59, Harrison fel, 62-63, Ph.D.(Am. civilization), 67; Smith-Mundt grant, Sweden, 59-60. Res. asst, Phila. Hist. Comn, 57-59; lectr. Am. civilization & lit, Gothenburg Univ, 59-62; Eng. & Am. lit, Bryn Mawr Col, 62-63; instr. Am. civilization, Univ. Pa, 63-64; Eng. & Am. civilization, UNIV. IOWA, 64-66, asst. prof, Am. civilization, 66-69, ASSOC. PROF. ENG. & AM. CIVILIZATION, 69-, EXEC. SECY. AM. CIVILIZATION PROG, 66-, COMT. AFRO-AM. CULT, 68- Fulbright lectr, Sweden, 60-62; lectr, Phila. Mus. Col. Art, 63-64; Old Gold Found. res. fel, 68; Nat. Endowment for Humanities grant, 69-73; vis. prof. Am. stud, Grinnell Col, 70-71; Rockefeller Found. grant, 72-75. Standard Oil Award, 68. Am. Stud. Asn; AHA; MLA; Nordic Asn. Am. Stud; Midwest Mod. Lang. Asn; Am. Civil Liberties Union; Mid-Continent Am. Stud. Asn.(exec. secy, 71-); Popular Cult. Asn; AAUP. American popular culture; contemporary American literature; minority groups in American civilization. Publ: Co-auth, American fiction and verse: an anthology, Gleerups, Lind, 62, 70; ed, Uncle Tom's Cabin, Airmont, 67; auth, The artist as censor: J.P. Donleavy and The ginger man, spring 67 & Ezra Pound and the Bollinger Prize controversy, fall 67, Mid-Continent Am. Stud. Asn. J; What's my line?: Ezra Pound, Bennet Cerf and the American poet, Am. Quart, 72. Add: 1040 E. Court St, Iowa City, IA 52240.

CORRIGAN, ROBERT WILLOUGHBY, b. Portage, Wis, Sept. 23, 27; m. 63. DRAMA. A.B, Cornell Univ, 50; M.A, Johns Hopkins Univ, 52; Ph.D.(comp. lit), Univ. Minn, 55. Instr. drama & theatre, Johns Hopkins Univ, 50-52; speech & theatre arts, Univ. Minn, 52-53, class. langs. & lit, 53-54; asst. prof. speech & drama, Carleton Col, 54-57; assoc. prof. theatre, Tulane Univ, 57-61; Andrew Mellon prof. drama & head dept, Carnegie Inst. Technol, 61-64; prof. dramatic lit, N.Y. Univ, 64-68, dean. sch. arts, 65-68; pres, Calif. Inst. Arts, 68-72; PROF. ENG. & THEATRE, UNIV. MICH, ANN

ARBOR, 73- Dir. critics prog, Nat. Endowment Humanities, 67-68; adv. ed. drama and theatre to Dell Publ. Co, Inc, Houghton Mifflin Co. & Chandler Publ. Co; chmn, Int. Counc. Fine Arts Deans, 70-71; Avery Hopwood Mem. Lectr, Univ. Mich, spring 73; consult, Samuel Rubin Found, 73-; chmn. bd, SPACE for Innovative develop, New York, N.Y, 73- Presidential citation of merit, Niagara Univ, 67. Am. Theatre Asn; Nat. Theatre Conf; Nat. Counc. Fine Arts Deans. Modern theatre; arts education. Publ: Ed. & transl, Chekhov: six plays, Holt, 62; ed, Theatre in the twentieth century, Grove, 63, The new theatre of Europe II, 64 & The new theatre of Europe III, 68, Delta; auth, The modern theatre, Macmillan, 64; co-auth, The art of the theatre, 64 & The context and craft of drama, 64, ed, Comedy: meaning and form, 65 & Tragedy: vision and form, 65, Chandler; ed, Laurel classical drama series, 64-65 & Laurel British drama series, 65, Dell; auth, Masterpieces of the modern theatre, Collier Bks, 66; Arthur Miller: 20th century views, Prentice-Hall, 68; Theatre in search of a fix, Delacorte, 73; The transformation of the avant garde, Univ. Mich. Quart, winter 74. Add: Dept. of English, University of Michigan, Ann Arbor, MI 48104.

CORRINGTON, JOHN WILLIAM, b. Memphis, Tenn, Oct. 28, 32; m. 59; c. 4. MODERN ENGLISH, AMERICAN LITERATURE. A.B, Centenary Col, 56; fel, Rice Univ, 56-60, M.A, 60; D.Phil.(lit), Univ. Sussex, 64; Tulane Univ, law, 73- Instr. Eng, La. State Univ, 60-65, asst. prof, 65-66; assoc. prof, Loyola Univ.(La), 66-73, chmn. dept, 68-69. La. State Univ. grad. counc. grants, 63-65; vis. prof, Univ. Calif, Berkeley, 68. Charioteer Poetry Prize, 62; Nat. Endowment Arts Award, 67. MLA. James Joyce; contemporary American literature; literary theory. Publ: Where we are, Charioteer, 62; And wait for the night, 64, The upper hand, 67 & The lonesome traveler, 68, Putnam; The anatomy of love, Roman Bks, 64; Mr. Clean and other poems, Amber House, 64; Lines to the South, 65, co-ed, Southern writing in the sixties: fiction, 66 & Southern writing in the sixties: poetry, 67, La. State Univ; auth, The bombardier, Putnam, 70; The sisters, In: Essays on Dubliners, Faber, 69; contrib, Best American short stories, 1973, Houghton, 73; Contemporary American poetry, Random, 73; plus others. Co-auth.(screenplays), Von Richtofen and Brown, United Artists, 69, The omega man, Warner Bros, 70, Boxcar Bertha, Am. Int. Prod, 71, Battle for the planet of the apes, 20th Century-Fox, 72, The arena, New World Pictures, 73 & Killer bees, Am. Broadcasting Corp, 74. Add: 1724 Valence, New Orleans, LA 70115.

CORSA, HELEN STORM, b. Amherst, Mass, Sept. 27, 15. ENGLISH. B.A, Mt. Holyoke Col, 38; M.A. & Ph.D.(Medieval Eng), Bryn Mawr Col, 42. Asst. prof. ENG, Hartwick Col, 42-43; from instr. to asst. prof, Russell Sage Col, 43-48; from asst. prof. to prof, WELLESLEY COL, 48-71, MARTHA HALE SHACKFORD PROF, 71-, CHMN. DEPT, 72- MLA. Chaucer; the English novel; psychoanalytic criticism. Publ: Chaucer: poet of mirth and morality, Univ. Notre Dame, 64; A fair but frozen maiden: a study of Jane Austen's Emma, Vol. XIX, No. 2 & To the lighthouse: death, mourning and transfiguration, Vol. XXI, Nov. 3, Lit. & Psychol; Dreams in Troilus and Criseyde, Am. Imago, spring 70; plus others. Add: Dept. of English, Wellesley College, Wellesley, MA 02181.

CORTISSOZ, PAUL, b. New York, N.Y, Nov. 9, 24; m. 49; c. 3. ENGLISH. B.A, Manhattan Col, 47; M.A, Columbia Univ, 49; Ph.D, N.Y. Univ, 55. Instr. ENG, MANHATTAN COL, 47-53, asst. prof, 53-59, assoc. prof, 59-65, PROF, 65-, HEAD DEPT, 63-67 & 70- U.S.A.A.F, 42-45, Sgt. MLA; NCTE. American literature; 19th century English literature; Elizabethan and Restoration dramatic literature. Publ: Co-auth, Perspectives, W.C. Brown, 63. Add: Dept. of English, Manhattan College, Bronx, NY 10471.

CORTRIGHT, RUPERT L, b. Jackson Co, Mich, Apr. 2, 05; m. 34; c. 2. SPEECH. A.B, Albion Col, 26; A.M, Univ. Mich, 29, Ph.D, 35. Teacher high sch, Mich, 26-28; instr. SPEECH, Syracuse Univ, 28-30; WAYNE STATE UNIV, 30-36; asst. prof, 36-41, assoc. prof, 41-46, prof, 46-70, chmn. dept, 47-55; chmn. grad. comt, 60-69, EMER. PROF, 70- Summers, vis. instr. speech, Northwestern Univ, 30 & 31, vis. prof, Univ. Denver, 47, Univ. Mich, 48, Univ. Hawaii, 50, Univ. Wyo, 50; trustee, Albion Col, 46-52; mem. staff, NDEA Inst. Advan. Stud. Speech, Calif. State Col, Fullerton, summer 68; lectr. var. states. Speech Commun. Asn.(exec. secy, 39-45, pres, 48, chmn. educ. policies bd, 68). Radio speech and American oratory; debate and discussion; graduate studies in speech. Publ: Co-auth, Creative discussion, Macmillan, 59 & Effective speech, Holt, 5th ed, 70; The uses and abuses of discussion, In: Language behavior, Mouton, Hague, 70. Add: Apt. 211, 2630 Pearce Dr, Clearwater, FL 33516.

CORTS, PAUL RICHARD, b. Terre Haute, Ind, Sept. 15, 43; m. 65; c. 2. SPEECH, THEATRE. B.A, Georgetown Col, 65; M.A, Ind. Univ, Bloomington, 67, Ph.D, 71; Ind. Univ. res. grant, London, 69. Assoc. pastor educ, First Baptist Church, Suffolk, Va, 65-66; asst. dir, Stud. Speakers Bur, Ind. Univ, Bloomington, 66-68; ASST. PROF. SPEECH, WEST. KY. UNIV, 68-, ASST. DEAN INSTRUCT, 73-, DIR, OFF. ACAD. AFFAIRS & COORD, INT. EDUC. PROGS, 72-, staff asst. to dean, Potter Col. Arts & Humanities, 71-72, coord, Eagle Univ. Consortium Proj. & Eagle PREP Prog, 72-73. Prog. chmn, Int-Cross Cult. Commun. Strengthening Int. Educ. at Undergrad. level planning grant, 72-74; mem, Comn. Am. Parliamentary Procedure humanities planning grant. Nat. Col. Honors Counc; Speech Commun. Asn. Publ: Randolph vs. Clay: a duel of words and bullets, Filson Club Hist. Quart, 69; The formal strain: studies in Augustan imitation and satire, Quart. J. Speech, 69; I.A. Richards on rhetoric and criticism, South. Speech J, 70; plus others. Add: Office of Academic Affairs, Western Kentucky University, Bowling Green, KY 42101.

COSBEY, ROBERT CULBERTSON, b. Philadelphia, Pa, Nov. 30, 14; m. 40; c. 4. ENGLISH. A.B, Columbia Univ, 40, A.M, 41; Ph.D, Ohio State Univ, 49. Asst, Ohio State Univ, 41-44; teacher, Monticello Col, 44-47; asst. prof. ENG, Roosevelt Univ, 47-55, assoc. prof, 55-61, PROF, 61-66; UNIV. SASK, 66-, assoc. dean arts & sci, 69-73. Can. Counc. leave fel, 73-74. MLA; Am. Folklore Soc; NCTE; Thoreau Soc. Saskatchewan oral history; skipping songs of Saskatchewan school children; Twain. Publ: Co-auth, Vocabulary development program, 65 & auth, The writer's job, 66, Scott; Thoreau at work: the writing of Katahdin, Bull. N.Y. Pub. Libr, 1/61; Thoreau on Katahdin, Appalachia, 6/61; Folksong: U.S, In: Encycl. Britannica, 64. Add: Dept. of English, University of Saskatchewan, Regina, Sask, S4S 0A2, Can.

COSGRAVE, PEARL-JOAN, b. Lincoln, Nebr, May 2, 06. ENGLISH, LANGUAGES. B.Sc.Ed, Univ. Nebr, Lincoln, 26, M.A, 28. Teacher French & Spanish & dramatics coach, St. Ursula's Col, 26-27; instr. econ, psychol. & French & head dept. secretarial sci, Villa Maria Col, 30-31; teacher French & secy. to dean exten. div, Univ. Denver, 31-32; librn. archit, dept. archit, col. engineering, Univ. Nebr, Lincoln, 33-37; asst. librn, Univ. Chicago High Sch, 37-38; asst. librn. & instr. libr. sci, St. Mary's Col.(Ind), 38-39; head librn. high sch, Ill, 39-40; secy, Nebr. Unicameral Legis. Session, 61; counsel. psychol. testing & voc. counseling, Nebr. State Employment Serv, 61-63; teacher creative writing & French, dept. adult educ. & head librn, Scottsbluff Col, 63-65; head librn. & instr. Eng. Hiram Scott Col, 65-66; from asst. prof. Eng. to prof, Chadron State Col, 66-71; WRITER-LECTR, 71- Assoc. ed, Prairie Schooner, 33-38; panelist, Omaha Writers Conf, 48. Am. Name Soc; Int. Platform Asn; AAUP; fel. Int. Poetry Soc. Color blindness; onomatology; etymology. Publ: Love and wrestling, Cent. Names Inst, E.Tex. State Univ, 72; Jottings, Vol. XXIII, No. 3-4 & Verbal novelties, Vol. XXIV, No. 3, Am. Speech; Rondeau, In: International who's who in poetry anthology, Kay, London, 72. Add: 1201 J St, Apt. 309, Lincoln, NE 68508.

COSGROVE, MARK FRANCIS, O.S.B, b. Detroit, Mich, Sept. 15, 30. ENGLISH LITERATURE, THEOLOGY. B.A, St. Benedict's Col.(Kans), 53; prof. degree, St. Leo Sch. Theol, 56; M.A, Univ. Detroit, 61; Univ. Mich, Ann Arbor, 64-65; Ph.D.(Eng), Univ. Fla, 70. Teacher Eng. & music, St. Leo Col. Prep. Sch, 53-64, instr, St. Leo Col, 62-66, asst. prof, Eng, 69-70, chaplain, 59-64, chmn. dept. ENG, 60-64; asst. prof, Univ. Ala, Huntsville, 70-73; ASSOC. PROF. & CHMN. DEPT, LENOIR RHYNE COL, 73- Subprior, St. Leo Abbey, Fla, 61-64; mem, Am. Benedictine Acad. MLA; S.Atlantic Mod. Lang. Asn; Renaissance Soc. Am. English Renaissance; modern media and education. Add: Dept. of English, Lenoir Rhyne College, Hickory, NC 28601.

COSGROVE, WILLIAM EMMETT, b. South St. Paul, Minn, Jan. 29, 39; m. 66; c. 2. AMERICAN & BLACK LITERATURE. B.A, St. Thomas Col.(Minn), 62; M.A, Marquette Univ, 66; fel, Univ. Iowa, 68-70, Ph.D.(Eng), 72. Teacher ENG, Cretin High Sch, Minn, 62-64; teaching asst, Marquette Univ, 64-66; Univ. Iowa, 66-68; ASST. PROF, N.DAK. STATE UNIV, 70- Am. Lit. Group, MLA. American novel; contemporary American poetry. Publ: Modern black writers: the divided self, Negro Am. Lit, 3/74; Family lineage and narrative technique in Cooper's Littlepage trilogy, Univ. Houston Forum, (in press). Add: Dept. of English, North Dakota State University, Fargo, ND 58102.

COSMAN, MADELEINE PELNER, b. New York, N.Y, Dec. 4, 37; m. 58; c. 2. COMPARATIVE MEDIEVAL LITERATURE, MEDIEVAL MEDICINE. B.A, Barnard Col, Columbia Univ, 59; fel, Hunter Col, 59-60, M.A, 60; fac. of philos. fel, Columbia Univ, 60-61, N.Y. State fel, 61-63, Ph.D.(comp. medieval lit), 64. Lectr. Eng, Hunter Col, 59-61; instr, medieval Eng, Lehman Col, 61-64; asst. prof. MEDIEVAL ENG. & COMP. LIT, CITY COL. NEW YORK, 64-71, ASSOC. PROF, 71-, DIR. INST. MEDIEVAL & RENAISSANCE STUD, 70- Nat. Endowment for Humanities grants, 72, 73. Mediaeval Acad. Am; Int. Arthurian Soc; MLA; Hist. Sci. Soc; Soc. Hist. Med. Medieval medical malpractice; medieval and Renaissance music, especially songs of the troubadours and minnesingers; Arthurian literature. Publ: The education of the hero in Arthurian romance, Univ. N.C, 66, Oxford, 67; Dr. Elias Sabot and King Henry IV, 68 & Medieval medical malpractice and Chaucer's physician, 72, N.Y. State J. Med; Medieval medical malpractice: the dicta and the dockets, Bull. N.Y. Acad. Med, 73. Add: Institute of Medieval & Renaissance Studies, The City College of New York, Convent Ave. at 138th St, New York, NY 10031.

COSPER, RUSSELL, b. Lansing, Mich, May 30, 10; m. 36; c. 3. ENGLISH. A.B, West. Mich. Col. Educ, 33; A.M, Univ. Mich, 36, Ph.D, 48. Teacher high sch, Mich, 34-36; supvr. lang, Mich. State Norm. Col, 36-46; asst. prof. ENG, PURDUE UNIV, WEST LAFAYETTE, 46-56, PROF, 56- head dept, 61-69. U.S.N.R, 43-46, Lt. Ling. Soc. Am; NCTE; MLA; Am. Dialect Soc. English language. Add: Dept. of English, Purdue University, West Lafayette, IN 47907.

COSTA, RICHARD HAUER, b. Philadelphia, Pa, July 5, 21; m. 50; c. 1. ENGLISH. B.S, West Chester State Col, 43; Univ. Mo, Columbia, 43-44; M.A, Syracuse Univ, 50; David Ross fel, Purdue Univ, 65-67, Ph.D.(Eng), 69. Asst. prof. Eng. & Jour, Utica Coll, 61-68, assoc. prof, ENG, 68-70; TEX. A&M UNIV, 70-73, PROF, 73- Ed. & publ, Quartet Mag, 68-; Tex. A&M Univ. res. grant, summer 71, Col. Lib. Arts fac. grant, summer 73; Tex. Comn. Arts & Humanities grant, 73. A.U.S, 42-46, Res, 46-65, Capt. MLA. British and Continental modern fiction; Edmund Wilson; metamorphosis of the American short story. Publ: H.G. Wells, 67 & Malcolm Lowry, 72, Twayne; Ulysses, Lowry's Volcano and the Voyage between: study of an unacknowledged kinship, Univ. Toronto Quart, 7/67; The epistolary monitor in Pamela, Mod. Lang. Quart, 3/70; Pietá, Pelado and the ratification of death: ten-year evolvement of Lowry's Volcano, J. Mod. Lit, 71; plus others. Add: 1119 Neal Pickett Dr, College Station, TX 77840.

COSTAIN, KEITH MICHAEL, b. Ramsey, Isle-of-Man, Nov. 9, 34; Brit. citizen; m. 58; c. 3. ENGLISH LITERATURE. B.A. & dipl. educ, Univ. Keele, 57; M.A. & Fulbright scholarship, Univ. Nottingham, 61; Ph.D.(Eng), Wash. Univ, 69. Schoolmaster hist, Milner Girls Sch, Leek, Eng, 57-61; teaching asst. Eng, Wash. Univ, 61-64, lectr, 64-65, asst. dean arts & sci, 65-68; lectr. ENG, UNIV. SASK, REGINA, 68-69, asst. prof, 69-72, ASSOC. PROF, 72-, chmn. dept, 70-72. Can. Asn. Univ. Teachers; Victorian Stud. Asn. West. Can. The relationship of historiography to the novel; Victorian non-fictional prose; Victorian poetry. Publ: The prince and the provost, Stud. Scottish Lit, 7/68; Theoretical history and the novel: the Scottish fiction of John Galt, Eng. Lit. Hist, (in press); plus others. Add: Dept. of English, University of Saskatchewan, Regina, Sask. S4S 0A2, Can.

COSTELLO, DONALD PAUL, b. Chicago, Ill, Aug. 4, 31; m. 52; c. 6. ENGLISH. A.B, De Paul Univ, 55; Wilson Found. fel, 55; Danforth fel, Univ. Chicago, 55-60, M.A, 56, Ph.D, 62. Instr, Roosevelt Univ, 57-60; Chicago, City Jr. Col, 58-59; ENG, UNIV. NOTRE DAME, 60-61, asst. prof, 61-66, assoc. prof, 66-71, PROF, 71- Soc. Relig. Higher Educ. fel, 64-65; mem. fac, Sumer Inst. Teachers Eng. at Predominantly Negro Cols, Ind. Univ, summer 65; NDEA Inst. Advan. Stud. Eng, Loretto Heights Cols, summer 66; Carnegie-Mellon Univ, summer 68; consult, Educ. Assoc, Inc. for Proj. Upward Bound, Wash, D.C, 66- U.S.N, 51-53. Soc. Relig. Higher Educ. American literature; modern drama; cinema. Publ: The serpent's eye: Shaw and the cinema, Univ. Notre Dame, 65; The language of The catcher in the rye, Am. Speech, 10/59; The structure of The turn of the screw, Mod. Lang. Notes, 4/60; Tennessee Williams' Fugitive kind, Mod. Drama, 5/72; plus one other. Add: Dept. of English, University of Notre Dame, Notre Dame, IN 46566.

COSTELLO, MARY ANGELICA, R.S.M, b. Grand Island, Nebr, Nov. 5, 12. ENGLISH. Ph.B, Creighton Univ, 46; M.A, Marquette Univ, 54; Ph.D.(Eng), Fordham Univ, 62. Prin, Blessed Sacrament Sch, Nebr, 41-44; instr. Eng, Assumption Acad, 46-50, prin, 47-50; instr. ENG, St. Joseph High Sch, Colo, 50-54; St. John's High Sch, Nebr, 54-55; from instr. to PROF, COL. ST. MARY (NEBR), 57-59, 62-, PRES, 70- NDEA grantee, Eng. Inst, Univ. Nebr, Lincoln, summer 68; mem, Omaha Chamber of Commerce Higher Educ. Comt, 72-; exec. secy, Nebr. Independent Col. Found, 72-73, v.chmn, 73-74; post-doctoral summer stud, Exeter Col, Oxford. NCTE; MLA; Am. Asn. Univ. Adminr. Chaucer. Add: 1901 S. 72nd, Omaha, NE 68124.

COSTELLO, MARY CLEOPHAS, R.S.M, b. Baltimore, Md, Feb. 10, 05. LITERARY THEORY. A.B, St. Mary's Col.(Ind), 37; M.A, Cath. Univ. Am, 39, Ph.D, 47. Chmn. div. humanities, LOYOLA COL.(MD), 46-53, pres, 53-67, prof. ENG, 68-70, EMER. PROF. & CHMN. DEPT. COMMUN. ARTS, 70- Lectr. Eng. lit. & lit. theory, Cath. Univ. Am; dir, lit. theory work shops; NDEA Inst. Ling, 68-69. Andrew White medal, Loyola Col, 68. MLA. Theory of poetry; works of T.S. Eliot. Publ: Between fixity and flux, Add: Dept. of Communication Arts, Loyola College, Baltimore, MD 21209.

COSTY, JAMES OTTO, b. Cleveland, Ohio, Mar. 21, 19; m. 42, 66; c. 2. SPEECH. B.A, Santa Barbara Col, 45; M.A, Univ. Wash, 46; Ph.D.(theatre), Univ. Denver, 54. Asst. prof. drama, Univ. Miami, 46-49; teacher Eng, drama, speech & radio, Palos Verde Jr. Col, 51-52; asst. prof. speech, theatre & radio & dir. radio & TV, Tex. Christian Univ, 54-59; teacher DRAMA, Skyline High Sch, Oakland, Calif, 59-64; ASSOC. PROF, CALIF. STATE UNIV, HAYWARD, 64-, DRAMA COORD, 72- Play dir, Ohlone Summer Drama Festival, summer 72 & 73. Speech Commun. Asn; Am. Nat. Theatre & Acad; Am. Educ. Theatre Asn. Theatre and television. Add: Dept. of Drama, California State University, Hayward, 25800 Hillary St, Hayward, CA 94542.

COTE, ANDRE, b. Biddeford, Maine, Oct. 25, 34. ENGLISH. B.A, LaMennais Col, 59; M.A, Cath. Univ. Am, 62; Ph.D.(Eng), St. Louis Univ, 67. Teacher, high sch, Mass, 56-60; Mt. Assumption Sch, N.Y, 60-61; instr. ENG, WALSH COL, 62-65, from asst. prof. to ASSOC. PROF, 67-, ACAD. DEAN, 70-, head dept. & chmn. humanities div, 68-70. Am. Conf. Acad. Deans. Poetry of Andrew Marvell; irony in the poetry of Ovid. Add: Office of the Academic Dean, Walsh College, 2020 Easton, Canton, OH 44720.

COTHRAN, ANDREW NEILSON, b. Kreole, Miss, Oct. 6, 29; m. 55; c. 3. AMERICAN LITERATURE & INTELLECTUAL HISTORY. B.A, Baylor Univ, 51; M.A, Columbia Univ, 54; Univ. Am. Stud. fel, Univ. Md, 65-66, Ph.D. (Am. stud), 66. Teacher pub. schs, Ala, 51-53; dir. pub. relat, Judson Col, 54-55; asst. dir. pupil personnel pub. schs, Ky, 55-57; instr. Eng, Univ. Louisville, 57-60, asst. prof, 60-63, assoc. prof, 66-67; prof. Eng. & chmn. div. humanities, Prince George's Community Col.(Md), 63-66; cult. attache & chmn. U.S. educ. found, U.S. Dept. State, Norway, 66-71; PRES, TUSCULUM COL, 71- Med.C, U.S.A, 47-48. Am. Stud. Asn. American popular culture in the twentieth century; determinism, literary naturalism, in American literature. Add: Tusculum College, Greeneville, TN 37743.

COTHRAN, KAY LORRAINE, b. Atlanta, Ga, Mar. 16, 47. FOLKLORE & SOCIOLINGUISTICS. A.B, Ga. State Col, 68; Woodrow Wilson fel, Nat. Sci. Found. traineeship & A.M, Univ. Pa, 69, univ. fel, & Ph.D.(folklore, folklife), 72. ASST. PROF. ENG, UNIV. MD, COLLEGE PARK, 72- Am. Folklore Soc; Am. Anthrop. Asn. Folklore as social communication; folklore and women; history of folklore studies. Publ: Talking with your mouth full: a communications approach to food rules, Tenn. Folklore Soc. Bull, 72; Women's tall tales: a problem of the social structure of fantasy, St. Andrews Rev, 72; Participation in tradition, Keystone Folklore, 73. Add: Dept. of English, University of Maryland, College Park, MD 20742.

COTTEN, LYMAN ATKINSON, b. Newport, R.I, Apr. 25, 09. ENGLISH. A.B, Univ. N.C, Chapel Hill, 36; Ph.D, Yale, 41. PROF. ENG, UNIV. N.C, CHAPEL HILL, 41- MLA. Victorian and modern literature. Add: Dept. of English, University of North Carolina at Chapel Hill, Chapel Hill, NC 27515.

COTTER, JAMES FINN, b. Boston, Mass, July 5, 29; m. 60; c. 3. ENGLISH LITERATURE, PHILOSOPHY. A.B, Boston Col, 54, M.A, 55; M.A, Fordham Univ, 58, Ph.D.(Eng), 63; St. Albert de Louvain, 58-60. From instr. to asst. prof. ENG, Fordham Univ, 60-63; assoc. prof. MT. ST. MARY COL. (N.Y), 63-68, PROF, 68- Nat. Endowment for Humanities grant, summer 68; Fulbright-Hays lectr, Univ. Oran, 70-71. MLA; Conf. Christianity & Lit. Renaissance poetry; Sir Philip Sidney; Gerard Manley Hopkins. Publ: Inscape: the Christology and poetry of Gerard Manley Hopkins, Univ. Pittsburgh, 72; The songs in Astrophil and Stella, Stud. Philol, 4/70; The baiser group in Sidney's Astrophil and Stella, Tex. Stud. Lit. & Lang, fall 70; The Wife of Bath's lenten observance, Papers on Lang. & Lit, summer 71. Add: 372 Grand St, Newburgh, NY 12550.

COTTRELL, BEEKMAN WALDRON, b. Toledo, Ohio, July 26, 22. ENGLISH. A.B, Univ. Fla, 46; M.A, Columbia Univ, 47, Ph.D.(Eng. novel), 56. Statist. asst, Econ. Coop. Admin, Paris, France, 48-49; instr. Eng. & speech, Univ. Ky, 51-52; asst. ed, Richards Topical Encycl, 52-53; from instr. to asst. prof. ENG, CARNEGIE-MELLON UNIV, 53-62, assoc. prof, 62-71, PROF. & DIR. UNDERGRAD. STUD, 71-, head humanities, 67-68. Dir, Am. Inst. Lang, Baghdad, 60-61. U.S.A, 43-46. MLA; NCTE. The American novel, especially the southern novelists; contemporary European fiction; modern drama. Publ: Insight: the experience of literature, 68, Insight: the search for wisdon, 68 & Insight: human weakness; reality and illusion, 68, Noble; co-auth, Love in the tenth grade, 63 & A genuine accumulation, 65, Eng. J; auth, The winter's tale, In: Lovers meeting, Carnegie Ser. Eng, 64; plus others. Add: Dept. of English, Carnegie-Mellon University, Pittsburgh, PA 15213.

COUCHMAN, GORDON WARD, b. Earlville, Iowa, May 1, 12; m. 47; c. 2. ENGLISH. A.B, State Univ. Iowa, 38; B.S, Columbia Univ, 44, A.M, 45; Ph.D, Univ. Pa, 52. Asst. to chief of stack, Pub. Libr, New York, N.Y, 43-45; instr. Eng, Syracuse Univ, 45-47; asst. instr, Univ. Pa, 47-48; instr, Pa. State Col, 48-49; prof. Eng. & acting chmn. dept, Moravian Col. Women, 49-54; head libr, Nebr. Wesleyan Univ, 54-55; asst. prof. ENG, Rider Col, 56-58; PROF. & CHMN. DEPT, ELMHURST COL, 58- MLA; NCTE; Shakespeare Asn. Am. Shakespeare and Shaw; linguistic theories of literature; drama. Publ: This our Caesar: a study of Bernard Shaw's Caesar and Cleopatra, Mouton, Hague, 73; Arthur Miller's tragedy of Babbitt, Educ. Theatre J, 10/55 & In: The Merrill studies in Death of a salesman, 72; The first playbill of Caesar: Shaw's list of authorities, 5/70 & Bernard Shaw and the gospel of efficiency, 1/73, Shaw Rev; plus three others. Add: 195 Schiller St, Elmhurst, IL 60126.

COULLING, SIDNEY MATHIAS B, b. Bluefield, W.Va, Feb. 13, 24; m. 58; c. 3. ENGLISH LITERATURE. B.A, Washington & Lee Univ, 48; M.A, Univ. N.C, 49, Ph.D, 57. Instr. ENG, Fla. State Univ, 49-52; Univ. Md, 55-56; from instr. to assoc. prof, WASHINGTON & LEE UNIV, 56-65, PROF, 65- U.S.A, 43-46. MLA. Nineteenth century British literature; Matthew Arnold. Publ: Contrib. to Rev. Eng. Stud; Philol. Quart; Stud. Philol. Add: Dept. of English, Washington & Lee University, Lexington, VA 24450.

COULSON, JAMES PETER, b. Greenville, S.C, Apr. 17, 33. THEATRE, DRAMA. B.F.A, Univ. Ariz, 55, M.A, 58; Ph.D.(theatre, drama), Univ. Kans, 65. Dir. theatre, McPherson Col, 58-62; Ariz. West. Col, 64-67; assoc. prof. theatre & drama & dir. theatre, Wis. State Univ, Eau Claire, 67-70; DIR. GRAD. STUD. & PROF. THEATRE, SOUTHWEST TEX. STATE UNIV, 70- Sig.C, U.S.A, 55-57. Am. Theatre Asn. Directing; American theatre history. Add: Dept. of Speech & Drama, Southwest Texas State University, San Marcos, TX 78666.

COULTER, JOHN KNOX, JR, b. Collins, Miss, Mar. 27, 26; m. 50; c. 3. ENGLISH. A.B, Transylvania Col, 52; Ph.D.(Eng), Ind. Univ, 65. Instr. ENG, OTTERBEIN COL, 56-59, asst. prof, 59-65, assoc. prof, 65-70, PROF, 70- U.S.N, 44-46. MLA; AAUP. Eighteenth century English literature; Shakespeare. Add: Dept. of English, Otterbein College, Westerville, OH 43081.

COUNCIL, NORMAN BRIGGS, b. Pensacola, Fla, Nov. 13, 36; m. 63; c. 1. ENGLISH LITERATURE. B.A, Univ. of the South, 58; M.A, Stanford Univ, 64, Ph.D.(Eng), 67. Instr. ENG. LIT, Univ. Vt, 64-67; ASST. PROF, UNIV. CALIF, SANTA BARBARA, 67- Mem. fac, Inst. Elizabethan Arts & Lit, Nat. Humanities Inst, 67-68; fel, Regents Humanities Inst, Univ. Calif, 70; vis. fac, Claremont Grad. Sch, summer 72. Shakespeare; Tudor politics and the arts; Renaissance allegory. Publ: When honour's at the stake: ideas of honour in Shakespeare's plays, Allen & Unwin, London, 73; Prince Hal: mirror of success, Shakespeare Stud, 72. Add: Dept. of English, University of California, Santa Barbara, CA 93106.

COURSEN, HERBERT R, JR, b. Newark, N.J, Mar. 28, 32; m. 58; c. 3. ENGLISH. B.A, Amherst Col, 54; M.A, Wesleyan Univ, 62; Ph.D. Univ. Conn, 65. Teacher, The Choate Sch, 58-62; asst. ENG, Univ. Conn, 62-64; instr, BOWDOIN COL, 64-65, asst. prof, 65-69, ASSOC. PROF, 69- Dir. compos. prog, Upward Bound, Bowdoin Col, 67-68; Folger Shakespeare Libr. fel, 70. U.S.A.F, 54-58, 1st Lt. Shakespeare; Elizabethan drama; teaching of writing. Publ: The rarer action: Hamlet and revenge, Univ. Wis. 69; ed, As up they grew, Scott, 70; auth, Storm in April (poetry), Arco, 73; Style and technique in the narrative, Harper, 73; Christian ritual and the world of Shakespeare's tragedies, Bucknell Univ, 74; Prospero and the drama of the soul, Shakespeare Stud, 69; Survivor (poetry) Ktaadn, 74; Lookout point (poetry), Samisdat, 74; plus others. Add: Dept. of English, Bowdoin College, Brunswick, ME 04011.

COURT, FRANKLIN EDWARD, b. Youngstown, Ohio, Nov. 26, 39; m. 63; c. 2. ENGLISH LITERATURE. B.A, Youngstown State Univ, 62; M.A, Univ. Md, 64; Satterfield fel, Kent State Univ, 68-69, Ph.D.(Eng), 69. Teaching asst. ENG, Univ. Md, 62-64; teacher, Chardon High Sch, Ohio, 64-65; instr, Kent State Univ, 65-69; ASST. PROF, NORTH. ILL. UNIV, 69- Victorian Inst; MLA; Midwest Mod. Lang. Asn; Steinbeck Soc. Am. Victorian literature; age of transition, 1880-1920. Publ: The theme and structure of Spenser's Muiopotmos, Stud. Eng. Lit, 70; Pater and the subject of duality, Eng. Lit. Transition, 72; co-auth, Salomé, the moon, and Oscar Wilde's aesthetics: a reading of the play, Papers Lang. & Lit, 72. Add: Dept. of English, Northern Illinois University, DeKalb, IL 60115.

COURTER, ELOISE NORMA, b. Baltimore, Md, June 18, 16. EDUCATION, ENGLISH. B.A, Douglass Col, Rutgers Univ, 37; M.A, Teachers Col, Columbia Univ, 46; Ph.D, Univ. Minn, 63. Teacher ENG, Whittier Sch, Plainfield, N.J, 37-41; Bound Brook High Sch, N.J, 41-46; assoc. prof, State Univ. N.Y. Agr. & Tech. Inst, Canton, 46-58; asst. prof, St. Cloud State Col, 58-63, assoc. prof, 63-66; PROF, STATE UNIV. N.Y. COL. BUFFALO, 66- Nat. Educ. Asn; NCTE; Conf. Col. Compos. & Commun; Conf. Eng. Educ. Teaching of English language arts; the English language. Add: Dept. of English, New York State University College at Buffalo, Buffalo, NY 14222.

COURTNEY, RICHARD, b. Newmarket, Suffolk, June 4, 27; Brit. & Can. citizen; m. 52; c. 2. DRAMA. B.A, Univ. Leeds, 51, dipl. educ, 52. Sr. lectr. DRAMA, Trent Park Col, Inst. Educ, Univ. London, 58-67; assoc. prof, Univ. Victoria (B.C), 68-71; PROF, UNIV. CALGARY, 71- Ed, Discussions in Develop. Drama, Univ. Calgary, 72-; mem, Creative Educ. Found. R.A.F, 44-47. Fel. Royal Soc. Arts; Can. Conf. Arts (nat. pres, 73-); Can. Child & Youth Drama Asn.(pres, 70-72); Brit. Soc. Phenomenology; Brit. Soc. Aesthetics; Am. Soc. Aesthetics; Soc. Theatre Res, Eng; Brit. Theatre Technicians; Folklore Soc, London; Brit. Children's Theatre Asn; Educ. Drama Asn; Soc. Teachers Speech & Drama. Developmental drama, the relationship of enactment to philosophy, ethnology, education, psychology and sociology. Publ: Drama for youth, 64 & The drama studio, 67, Pitman; ed, College drama space, Univ. London, 64; auth, Teaching drama, 65, The school play, 66 & Play, drama and thought, 68, Cassell; On Langer's dramatic illusion, 70, Imagination and the dramatic act, 71 & Theatre and spontaneity, 73, J. Aesthetics & Art Criticism; plus others. Add: Div. of Developmental Drama, Dept. of Drama, University of Calgary, Calgary, Alta. T2N 1N4, Can.

COURTS, PATRICK LAWRENCE, b. Chicago, Ill, Apr. 28, 44; m. 69; c. 1. ENGLISH EDUCATION, AMERICAN LITERATURE. B.S, Chicago State Col, 66; M.A, Mich. State Univ, 68, Ph.D.(Eng), 71. Teacher ENG, Chicago Bd. Educ, 66-68; instr, Mich. State Univ, 68-71; ASST. PROF, STATE UNIV. N.Y. COL. FREDONIA, 71- MLA; NCTE. Preparation of English Teachers for high school and college; teaching of composition and literature; theories of language acquisition. Publ: Co-auth, Creative word VI, Random, 73; auth, A student-centered composition course, In: Lecture alternatives, Mich. Coun. Teachers Eng, 71; New English: from theory to practice, Eng. Rec, 73; Pre-service and in-service preparation of college English teachers, ADE Bull, 73. Add: Dept. of English, State University of New York College at Fredonia, Fredonia, NY 14063.

COUSINS, PAUL MERCER, b. Luthersville, Ga, Dec. 1, 89. AMERICAN LITERATURE. A.B, Mercer Univ, 10, LL.D, 36; A.M, Columbia Univ, 19, Ph.D. (Am. lit), 66. Instr. Greek, Mercer Univ, 09-10; v.pres. & instr. Eng, Locust Grove Inst, 10-15; prof, Shorter Col, 15-17; Georgetown Col, 19-20; Shorter Col, 20-48, pres, 33-48; PROF. ENG, MERCER UNIV, 48-69, EMER. PROF, 69- Paul M. Cousins Chair of Eng, estab. Shorter Col, 72. S.Atlantic Mod. Lang. Asn. Publ: Joel Chandler Harris: a biography. Add: Dept. of English, Mercer University, Macon, GA 31207.

COUTS, GILBERT DURHAM, Linguistics, English. See Volume III, Foreign Languages, Linguistics & Philology.

COVICI, PASCAL, JR, b. New York, N.Y, Sept. 2, 30; m. 52; c. 2. ENGLISH. A.B, Harvard, 52, M.A, 55, Ph.D.(Eng), 57. Asst. prof. ENG, SOUTH. METHODIST UNIV, 57-62, assoc. prof. 62-68, PROF, 68- South. Methodist Univ. grad. counc. humanities fel, 61-72, summer 67; Bollinger Found. fel, summers 63-66; prog. assoc. in humanitites, Inst. Serv. Educ. 68-70. Tex. Writers Round-up Award, 62. MLA; S.Cent. Med. Lang. Asn. American literature, execpially 19th century humor and novel. Publ: Mark Twain's humor; the image of a world, South. Methodist Univ, 62; ed, The Viking portable Steinbeck, Viking, 71; auth, Dear Master Wattie: correspondence between Mark Twain and David Watt Bowser, Southwest Rev, 60; Toward a reading of Poe's Narrative of A. Gordon Pym, Miss. Quart, summer 68. Add: Dept. of English, Southern Methodist University, Dallas, TX 75222.

COVINGTON, PHILIP STANHOPE, b. Moultrie, Ga, Nov. 28, 12; m. 39; c. 3. ENGLISH. A.B, Emory Univ, 34; M.A, Duke Univ, 40; Litt.D, Wofford Col, 59. Teacher, pub. schs, Ga, 34-36; practicing lawyer, Covington & Covington, 36-39; teacher, pub. schs, Fla, 40-42, high sch, S.C, 42-47; assoc. prof. ENG, WOFFORD COL, 47-50, PROF, 50-, dean stud, 50-53, dean col, 53-72. Add: Wofford College, Spartanburg, SC 29301.

COVO, JACQUELINE, b. Salonika, Greece, Dec. 1, 31; U.S. citizen; m. 56. ENGLISH. A.B, Am. Int. Col, 60; M.A, Mt. Holyoke Col, 61, fel, 62; fel, Brandeis Univ, 63, Ph.D.(Eng), 67. Instr. ENG, REGIS COL, 66-67, asst. prof, 67-72, ASSOC. PROF, 72- Danforth Found. Post-doctoral Black Stud. fel, 70-71. MLA; Col. Lang. Asn. Afro-American literature. Publ: Ralph Waldo Ellison: bibliographic essays and finding list of American criticism, 1952-1964; Ralph Ellison in France: bibliographic essays and checklist of French criticism, 1954-1971. Add: Dept. of English, Regis College, Weston, MA 02193.

COWAN, GREGORY M, b. Seattle, Wash, Aug. 17, 35; m. 56; c. 2. ENGLISH. B.A, Whitman Col, 57; M. A, Univ. Wash, 59. Teacher ENG, Clark Col. (Wash), 60-67; from asst. prof. to ASSOC. PROF, FOREST PARK COMMUNITY COL, 67- NCTE (comt. col. Eng. teaching load, 66-67); Conf. Col. Compos. & Commun; MLA. Junior college composition; non-transfer English programs for junior colleges; preparation of junior college English teachers. Publ: Co-auth, Plain English please, 66 & Background for writing, 67, Random; co-auth, Will the real terminal student please stand up?, Jr. Col. J, 9/64. Add: Dept. of English, Forest Park Community College, 5600 Oakland Ave, St. Louis, MO 63110.

COWAN, JAMES COSTELLO, b. Albany, Ga, Sept. 16, 27; m. 60; c. 4. ENGLISH. A.B, Mercer Univ, 50; M.A, Okla. State Univ, 56; Ph.D.(Eng), Univ. Okla, 64. Instr. ENG, Tulane Univ, 63-64, asst. prof, 64-66; UNIV. ARK, FAYETTEVILLE, 66-67, assoc. prof, 67-72, PROF, 72- Founder, The D.H. Lawrence Rev, 68, ed, 68- U.S.A, 52-54. MLA; S.Cent. Mod. Lang. Asn.(chmn. Am. Lit. II, 67, 73). Modern English and American fiction; American literature; D.H. Lawrence secondary annotated bibliography. Publ: D.H. Lawrence's American journey, Case West. Res. Univ, 70; The theory of relativity and The bridge, Hartford Stud. Eng, Vol. III, No. 2; The image of water in William Carlos Williams' Paterson, J. Mod. Literature, 5/71; Lawrence's Phoenix: an introduction, D.H. Lawrence Rev, fall 72; plus four others. Add: Dept. of English, University of Arkansas, Fayetteville, AR 72701.

COWAN, LOUISE SHILLINGBURG, b. Ft. Worth, Tex, Dec. 22, 16; m. 39; c. 1. ENGLISH & AMERICAN LITERATURE. A.B, Tex. Christian Univ, 46, M.A, 47; fel, Vanderbilt Univ, 52-53, Ph.D.(Eng), 53. Lectr. Eng, Vanderbilt Univ, 50-53; asst. prof. Eng. & creative writing, Tex. Christian Univ, 53-56, assoc. prof, 56-59; PROF. ENG, UNIV. DALLAS, 59-, GRAD. DEAN, 71-, chmn. dept, 59-71. MLA; S.Cent. Mod. Lang. Asn; Am. Stud. Asn. Modern poetry and criticism; Southern literature; Russian literature. Publ: The fugitive group, La. State; Nature and grace in Caroline Gordon, Critique, The pietas of southern poetry, Doubleday; plus others. Add: Dept. of English, University of Dallas, P.O. Box 1330, Irving, TX 75060.

COWAN, MICHAEL HEATH, b. Kansas City, Mo, July 26, 37; m. 63; c. 2. ENGLISH, AMERICAN STUDIES. B.A, Yale, 59, Danforth fel, 59-62, Woodrow Wilson fel, 63-64, Ph.D.(Am. stud), 64; Rotary Found. fel, Cambridge, 62-63. Instr. Eng. & Am. stud, Yale, 63-66, asst. prof, 66-69; assoc. prof. lit. & community stud, UNIV. CALIF, SANTA CRUZ, 69-73, PROF. LIT, 73- Adv, Old Dom. Found. Fel. Prog, 66-69; Morse fel, 67-68; mem. selection comt, Danforth Found. Fel Prog, 67-68. MLA; Am. Stud. Asn. American literary and intellectual history; nineteenth-century English literature; urban studies. Publ: City of the West: Emerson, America, and urban metaphor, Yale, 67; ed, Twentieth century interpretations of The sound and the fury, Prentice-Hall, 68; auth, The Americanness of Norman Mailer, In: Twentieth century views of Norman Mailer, Prentice-Hall, 72. Add: Merrill College, University of California, Santa Cruz, CA 95060.

COWASJEE, SAROS D, b. Secundrabad, India, July 12, 31; Can. citizen. ENGLISH. M.A, Agra Univ, 55; Ph.D.(Eng), Univ. Leeds, 60. Asst. ed, Times of India Press, Bombay, 61-63; PROF. ENG, UNIV. SASK, REGINA, 63- Can. Counc. leave fels, 68-69, 74-75, res. grants, 70-71, 74-75. Humanities Asn. Can; Can. Asn. Irish Stud; Asn. Can. Univ. Teachers Eng. Irish drama; Indian fiction; fiction. Publ: Sean O'Casey: the man behind the plays, 63 & Sean O'Casey, 66, Oliver & Boyd, Edinburgh & London; Stories and sketches, 70 & ed, Author to critic: the letters of Mulk Raj Anand, 73, Writers Workshop, Calcutta; ed. & auth, Introds, Mulk Raj Anand's Untouchable, 70, Private life of an Indian prince, 70 & Coolie, 72 & auth, Goodbye to Elsa (novel), 74, Bodley Head, London & New Press, Toronto; ed. & auth, Introd, Mulk Raj Anand's Seven summers, Cedric Civers, U.K, 70; contrib, The sting and the twinkle, Macmillan, London, 74. Add: Dept. of English, University of Saskatchewan, Regina, Sask. S4S 0A2, Can.

COWDEN, DAVID, b. Dayton, Ohio, July 26, 20. ENGLISH. B.A, Swarthmore Col, 42; M.A, Harvard, 47, Ph.D.(Eng), 50. Instr. ENG, SWARTHMORE COL, 50-53, asst. prof, 53-59, assoc. prof, 59-68, PROF, 68- MLA. Victorian and modern English novel. Add: Dept. of English, Swarthmore College, Swarthmore, PA 19081.

COWELL, CATHERINE ROSE, b. Davis, Okla, Oct. 9, 22. SPEECH COMMUNICATION. B.A, Univ. Denver, 66, M.A, 67, Ph.D.(speech), 71. ASST. PROF. SPEECH, ANGELO STATE UNIV, 69- AAUP; Speech Commun. Asn. Communication theory; group process; oral interpretation. Publ: Content analysis of group process, Ky. J. Commun. Arts, 11/71; Group process as metaphor, J. Commun, 6/72; Group process as metaphor, In: Small group communication: a reader, W.C. Brown, 74. Add: Dept. of Fine Arts, Angelo State University, San Angelo, TX 76901.

COWIE, ALEXANDER, b. St. Paul, Minn, Mar. 8, 96; m. 26; c. 2. AMERICAN LITERATURE. A.B, Univ. Minn, 19, A.M, 20; Ph.D, Yale, 30; M.A, Wesleyan Univ, 49. Instr. ENG, Univ. Ill, 20-22; Univ. Minn, 22-23; WESLEYAN UNIV, 24-27, asst. prof, 27-45, assoc. prof, 45-49, prof, 49-64, EMER. PROF, 64- Summers, vis. lectr, Ohio State Univ, 41; Univ. Minn, 45, Univ. Pa, 49 & Boston Col, 61; vis. lectr, Trinity Col.(Conn), 41; guest lectr. U.S. Dept. State, Univ. Lund & Gothenburg Univ, Sweden, 51-52; vis. prof, Salzburg Sem. Am. Stud, Austria, 60; Fulbright lectr, Univ. Coimbra, 64-65; distinguished vis. scholar, Kent State Univ, 67-68. U.S.A, 18. MLA; Col. Eng. Asn; New Eng. Col. Eng. Asn.(pres, 66). The American novel; contemporary American literature. Publ: Rise of American novel, Am. Bk. Co; John Trumbull, Connecticut wit, Univ. N.C; American writers today, Radiotjänst; Still a good light to guide by, New York Times, 9/63; The bridge of Thornton Wilder, In: Essays on American literature, Duke Univ, 67; introd. to Karl P. Harrington's Richard Alsop: a Hartford wit, Wesleyan Univ, 69. Add: 118 Pine St, Middletown, CT 06457.

COWLER, ROSEMARY ELIZABETH, b. Ft. Wayne, Ind, May 10, 25. ENGLISH LITERATURE. B.A, N.J. Col. Women, Rutgers Univ, 46; fel, Ind. Univ, 46-49, M.A, 49; Ph.D.(Eng), Yale, 56. Instr. ENG, LAKE FOREST COL, 55-57; asst. prof, 57-62, assoc. prof, 62-68, PROF, 68-, dir, Prog. II, 67-68. Am. Counc. Learned Soc. grant-in-aid, 61. MLA; Am. Soc. 18th Century Stud. Eighteenth century literature, especially Pope. Publ: Shadow and substance: a discussion of Pope's correspondence, In: The familiar letter in the eighteenth century, Univ. Kans, 66; ed, Twentieth century interpretations of Pamela, Spectrum Bks, Prentice-Hall, 69. Add: Dept. of English, Lake Forest College, Lake Forest, IL 60045.

COWLEY, JOHN, b. Cleveland, Ohio, Nov. 29, 04; m. 32; c. 2. ENGLISH. B.A, Heidelberg Col, 28; M.A, Munic. Univ. Wichita, 30; Ph.D, Yale, 43. Asst. prof. Eng. & speech, Colo. State Col. Agr. & Mech. Arts, 30-36; instr, Jr. Col. Commerce, 37-43; dean, 42-43; instr. commun, Ind. Univ, 43-45; asst. prof. Eng, UNIV. NORTH. IOWA, 45-48, assoc. prof, 48-51, prof, 51-73, acting head dept. langs, speech & lit, 61-62, EMER. PROF. ENG, 73- NCTE; Col. Eng. Asn. Romantic literature in England, especially Walter Scott. Publ: Sir Walter Scott's the lawyer and the bishop, Juridical Rev; Lockhart and the publication of Marmion, Philol. Quart. Add: 2617 Tremont, Cedar Falls, IA 50613.

COWPERTHWAITE, LOWERY LeROY, b. Princeton, Kans, Mar. 22, 17; m. 49; c. 2. SPEECH. B.A, Ottawa Univ, 39; M.A, State Univ. Iowa, 46, Ph.D. (speech), 50. Teacher speech & social stud, high sch, Kans, 39-41, Am. govt. & speech, 41-42; instr. speech, State Univ. Iowa, 48-49; assoc. prof, Richmond Area Univ. Ctr, Va, 49-54; PROF. SPEECH & DIR. SCH. SPEECH, KENT STATE UNIV, 54- U.S.A.A.F, 42-46, Capt. Cent. States Speech Asn; Speech Commun. Asn; Asn. Dept. & Adminr. Speech Commun. (v.pres, 72-73). American public address; history of speech education in America. Publ: Forensics at the state university, 1860-1924, Iowa J. Hist. & Polit, 48; co-auth, Intercollegiate debating, In: A history of speech education in America, Appleton, 54; Franklin D. Roosevelt, a study in leadership through persuasion, In: American public address: studies in honor of Albert Craig Baird, Univ. Mo, 61. Add: School of Speech, Kent State University, Kent, OH 44242.

COX, CARROL BYRON, JR, b. Benton Harbor, Mich, July 22, 30; m. 52; c. 2. ENGLISH. A.B, West. Mich. Univ, 51; fel, Univ. Mich, 56-59, M.A, 57, Ph.D.(Eng), 65. Instr. ENG, North. Mich. Col, 59-61; ASST. PROF, ILL. STATE UNIV, 61- U.S.A.F, 51-55, S/Sgt. MLA; New Univ. Conf. Alexander Pope; Ezra Pound; scholarship and revolutionary activism. Add: Dept. of English, Illinois State University, Normal, IL 61761.

COX, BETTY SMITH, b. Richmond, Va, Nov. 11, 25; m. 50; c. 2. MEDIEVAL ENGLISH, RENAISSANCE ENGLISH. Ph.B, Northwest. Univ, 53; M.A, Univ. Pittsburgh, 61, Ph.D.(Eng), 64. Asst. prof. Eng, Pa. State Univ, Mt. Alto Campus, 63-66; assoc. prof, Mars Hills Col, 66-68; PROF. ENG. & CHMN.

DEPT. ENG. LANG. & LIT, GARDNER-WEBB COL, 68- Piedmont Univ. Ctr. of N.C. lectr, spring 68; consult, Washington Elem. Sch, Shelby, N.C, 70, 71; assoc, Ctr. Medieval & Renaissance Stud, Univ. Calif, Los Angeles, summer 72. Mediaeval Acad. Am; Col. Eng. Asn. Medieval, especially literary, and historical; Renaissance, especially Shakespeare; Milton. Publ: Cruces of Beowulf, Mouton, The Hague & Paris, 71; A creative critical essay: Malcolm Cowley's Five acts of the Scarlet Letter, Pa. Speech J, spring 61; The diaphany, Averett J, spring 68. Add: Dept. of English Language & Literature, Humanities Div, Gardner-Webb College, Boiling Springs, NC 28017.

COX, CARROL BYRON, JR, b. Benton Harbor, Mich, July 22, 30; m. 52; c. 2. ENGLISH. A.B, West. Mich. Univ, 51; fel, Univ. Mich, 56-59, M.A, 57, Ph.D.(Eng), 65. Instr. ENG, North. Mich. Col, 59-61; ASST. PROF, ILL. STATE UNIV, 61- U.S.A.F, 51-55, S/Sgt. MLA; New Univ. Conf. Alexander Pope; Exra Pound; scholarship and revolutionary activism. Add: Dept. of English, Illinois State University, Normal, IL 61761.

COX, ERNEST HAYNES, b. Ashland City, Tenn, Aug. 17, 07; m. 36; c. 2. RENAISSANCE LITERATURE. A.B, Carson-Newman Col, 27; A.M, Univ. Tenn, 30; Ph.D, Univ. N.C, 36. Assoc. prof. Eng, Mary Hardin-Baylor Col, 36-38; prof. Eng. & dean, Blue Mt. Col, 38-47; prof. Eng, Univ. Fla, 47-72, asst. dean, Univ. Col, 62-65, asst. dean Arts & Sci, 65-72; RETIRED. Am. Dialect Soc; Shakespeare Asn. Am; S.Atlantic Mod. Lang. Asn. Add: 2159 N W Ninth Ave, Gainesville, FL 32603.

COX, HEADLEY MORRIS, JR, b. Mt. Olive, N.C, July 25, 16; m. 40; c. 3. ENGLISH. A.B, Duke Univ, 37, A.M, 39; Univ. Colo, 44-45; Ph.D.(Eng), Univ. Pa, 58. From instr. to PROF. ENG, CLEMSON UNIV, 39-, DEAN COL. LIB. ARTS, 69-, head dept. Eng. & Mod. Lang, 50-69. Fulbright sr. lectr, Graz Univ, 58-59. U.S.N.R, 44-46, Lt. MLA; S.Atlantic Mod. Lang. Asn; Am. Dialect Soc. History of the English language; dialectology. Add: College of Liberal Arts, Clemson University, Clemson, SC 29631.

COX, JAMES MELVILLE, b. Independence, Va, Aug. 4, 25; m. 48; c. 6. AMERICAN LITERATURE. B.A, Univ. Mich, 48, M.A, 49; John H. Edwards fel, Ind. Univ, 54-55, Ph.D, 55. Asst. prof. ENG, Emory & Henry Col, 50-52; instr, Dartmouth Col, 55-57; Ind. Univ, 57-58, asst. prof, 58-61, assoc. prof, 61-63; DARTMOUTH COL, 63-65, PROF, 65-, fac. fel, 66-67. Fel, Ind. Univ. Sch. Let, 60-; Am. Counc. Learned Soc. fel, 60-61; Guggenheim fel, 72-73. E. Harris Harbison distinguished teaching award, Danforth Found, 68. U.S.N, 43-46. MLA; Dante Soc. Am. Publ: Twentieth century views: Robert Frost, Prentice-Hall, 62; Mark Twain: the fate of humor, Princeton, 66; The muse of Samuel Clemens, Mass. Rev, autumn 63; Edgar Poe: style as pose, winter 68 & Autobiography and America, spring 70, Va. Quart. Rev; plus others. Add: Dept. of English, Dartmouth College, Hanover, NH 03755.

COX, JAMES WILLIAM, Religion. See Volume IV, Philosophy, Religion & Law.

COX, JOHN FRANCIS, b. Hartford, Conn, Feb. 9, 36; m. 71. ENGLISH LITERATURE. B.A, North. Ariz. Univ, 64, M.A, 65; Ph.D.(Eng), Ariz. State Univ, 73. Instr. ENG, Black Hawk Col, 65-66; South. Utah State Col, 66-68; Ariz. State Univ, 68-73; CHMN. DEPT, MOHAVE COMMUNITY COL, 73- NCTE; Conf. Col. Compos. & Commun; MLA; Col. Eng. Asn. Pre-Raphaelite brotherhood; Victorian historical background; Jack Kerouac and the beat movement. Publ: On the naming of Huck Finn, PMLA, 10/71; Uncle Tom's cabin: a pre-Raphaelite's reaction, Notes & Queries, 3/75. Add: Dept. of English, Mohave Community College, 1971 Jagerson Ave, Kingman, AZ 86401.

COX, KENNETH DALE (JR), b. Harrisonville, Mo, Aug. 28, 38; m. 66; c. 1. THEATRE HISTORY. B.A, Lindenwood Col, 61; Univ. Iowa, 61-62; M.A, Univ. Nebr, Lincoln, 68, Ph.D(theatre), 73. ASST. PROF. THEATRE & HUMANISTIC STUD, OKLA. STATE UNIV, 70- Consult, Speech Dept, Bacone Col, 72-73. Am. Theatre Asn; Southwest Theatre Asn. Black theatre; 18th century German theatre. Add: Theatre Div, Humanistic Studies, 100B Seretean Center for Performing Arts, Oklahoma State University, Stillwater, OK 74074.

COX, LEE SHERIDAN, b. Darlington, Ind, Oct. 19, 16. ENGLISH LITERATURE. A.B, DePauw Univ, 38; Ph.D.(Eng), Ind. Univ, 62. Instr. ENG, OHIO STATE UNIV, COLUMBUS, 62-63, asst. prof, 63-68, assoc. prof, 68-73, PROF, 73- Vis. prof, Mich. State Univ, summer 67. Ind. Univ. Writers' Conf. Fiction Award, 67. English Renaissance literature; Milton; Shakespeare. Publ: Andy and Willie, Scribner, 67; Figurative design in Hamlet: the significance of the dumb show, Ohio State Univ, 73; Food-word imagery in Paradise regained, 9/61 & Natural science and figurative design in Samson Agonistes, 3/68, ELH; A question of order in the Canterbury tales, Chaucer Rev, fall 67. Add: Dept. of English, Ohio State University, 164 W. 17th Ave, Columbus, OH 43210.

COX, LUTHER BIGBY, b. Belton, S.C, May 30, 01. ENGLISH. A.B, Univ. S.C, 22; cert, Oxford, 37; M.A, Columbia Univ, 38; Duke Univ, summers 40, 41. Teacher, pub. schs, S.C, 22-27; math, Mid-Pac. Inst, Honolulu, 27-30; mem. fac. Eng, Doshisha Univ, Japan, 30-34; Lingnam Univ, 34-35; Am. Univ, Beirut, 35-37; Okla. Baptist Univ, 37-41; Marion Mil. Inst, Ala, 41-42; res. analyst, U.S. Dept. Army, 42-51; mem. fac. Eng, Inter-Am. Univ. P.R, 51-67; Warren Wilson Col, 67-71; RETIRED. MLA. English literature of the 18th and 19th century. Add: 205 Brown Ave, Belton, SC 29627.

COX, MARTHA HEASLEY, b. Calico Rock, Ark, Feb. 26, 19; m. 49. ENGLISH. A.B, Ark. Col, 35; M.A, Univ. Ark, 43, Ph.D, 55; Univ. Wis, 48; Univ. Tex, 53. Instr. speech, Univ. Ark, 53-54; PROF. ENG, SAN JOSE STATE UNIV, 55-, DIR. STEINBECK RES. CTR, 73- Vis. prof, San Fernando Valley State Col, 68-69; mem. bd. dir, Conf. Visual Learning, 69- MLA; NCTE; Conf. Col. Commun. & Compos. American literature; especially Maxwell Anderson and Nelson Algren; films and other media for the teaching of English; John Steinbeck. Publ: Maxwell Anderson bibliography, Univ. Va, 58; Writing: form, process, purpose, 62, A reading approach to college writing, (13 editions), 59-73, Better writing with student papers for analysis, 64 & ed, Classic short American novels, 70, Chandler; auth, Image and value: an invitation to literature, Harcourt, 66; English institutes, In: Special media institute impact study, Dept. Audio-Visual Instr, Nat. Ed. Asn, 66; Maxwell Anderson & Nelson Algren, In: The encyclopedia of world literature in the twentieth century, Ungar, 67. Add: Dept. of English, San Jose State University, San Jose, CA 95114.

COX, MARY ELIZABETH, b. Marietta, Ohio, July 12, 12. ENGLISH. A.B, W. Liberty State Col, 50; M.A, Marquette Univ, 52; Ph.D, Ohio State Univ, 60. Instr. ENG, W.LIBERTY STATE COL, 52-55, asst. prof, 57-60, assoc. prof, 60-64, PROF, 64- Contrib, Ann. Bibliog. of Eng. Lang. & Lit, Mod. Humanities Res. Assoc, 67- W.A.V.E.S, 44-46. NCTE; Conf. Col. Compos. & Commun; MLA; Mod. Humanities Res. Asn, Gt. Brit; Asn. Higher Educ. William Dean Howells and naturalism; early 18th century English literature; contemporary German literature. Publ: With Bernard De Mandeville, Philol. Papers, 12/61. Add: Dept. of English, West Liberty State College, West Liberty, WV 26074.

COX, ROBERT STURGEON, JR, b. Amarillo, Tex, May 19, 37; m. 63; c. 4. ENGLISH, LINGUISTICS. B.A, Ariz. State Col, 59; Woodrow Wilson fel, Ind. Univ, 59-60, Ph.D.(Eng), 65; Fulbright fel, Univ. Col, London, 63-64. Instr. ENG, Rice Univ, 64-65, asst. prof, 65-71; ASSOC. PROF, UNIV. OF THE PAC, 72- Summers, asst. prof, Tex. South. Univ, 65, Ind. Univ, 67, South. Ore. Col, 71. Mediaeval Acad. Am; MLA; Ling.Soc. Am; Medieval Asn. Pac. Publ: Flecknoe and The man of mode, Mod. Lang. Quart, 68; The Old English dicts of Cato, Anglia, 72. Add: Dept. of English, University of the Pacific, Stockton, CA 95204.

COX, ROGER LINDSAY, b. Manson, Iowa, Mar. 23, 31; m. 51; c. 4. ENGLISH & COMPARATIVE LITERATURE. B.A, Morningside Col, 51; M.A, Univ. Calif, Los Angeles, 52; Sorbonne, 54-55; Fulbright scholar, Univ. Florence, 55-56; Lydia Roberts fel. & Ph.D.(Eng), Columbia Univ, 61. Instr. ENG, Bates Col, 58-61; asst. prof, DePauw Univ, 61-65, ASSOC. PROF, 65-71; UNIV. DEL, 71- Great Lakes Cols. Asn. humanities award, 67-68; Am. Counc. Learned Soc. stud. fel, 67-68; Andrew Mellon fel, Univ. Pittsburgh, 69-70. Transp.C, U.S.A, 52-54. MLA. Tragedy; Shakespeare; the novel. Publ: Between earth and heaven: Shakespeare, Dostoevsky, and the meaning of Christian tragedy, Holt, 69; Johnny the horse in Joyce's The dead, James Joyce Quart, 67; Tragedy and the gospel narratives, Yale Rev, 68; plus others. Add: 404 Vassar Dr, Newark, DE 19711.

COX, SOREN FRANKLIN, Linguistics, English. See Volume III, Foreign Languages, Linguistics & Philology.

COYLE, LEO PERRY, b. Union City, N.J, Mar. 27, 25; m. 51; c. 2. ENGLISH. B.S, St. Peter's Col, 49; M.A, West. Reserve Univ, 50, Ph.D, 59; Rutgers Univ, 50-53. Instr. ENG, Rutgers Prep. Sch, 51-53; lectr, JOHN CARROLL UNIV, 53-54, instr, 54-57, RES. FEL, 57- Div. info. mgr, Ohio Bell Tel. Co, 57- U.S.A, 43-46. Indust. Audio-Visual Asn.(past pres). American literature; American history; visual arts. Publ: George Ade, U.S. Auth. Ser, Twayne, 63; Mark Twain and William Dean Howells, Ga. Rev; Howell's campaign biography of R.B. Hayes, Ohio Hist. Quart, 10/57; Kenneth Roberts and the American historical novel, In: Popular Literature in America, Bowling Green Univ; plus one other. Add: 3405 Hollister Rd, Cleveland Heights, OH 44118.

COYLE, WILLIAM, b. Edinboro, Pa, Nov. 8, 17; m. 40; c. 3. AMERICAN LITERATURE. B.S, Edinboro State Col, 38; M.Litt, Univ. Pittsburgh, 40, M.A, 42; Ph.D, West. Reserve Univ, 48. Instr. ENG, Univ. Pittsburg, 39-42, 45-46; West. Reserve Univ, 46-48; prof, Wittenberg Univ, 48-68; assoc. prof, FLA. ATLANTIC UNIV, 68-69, PROF, 69- Fulbright lectr, Univ. Sao Paulo, Brazil, 62-63. U.S.M.C.R, 42-45, Lt. MLA; Am. Stud. Asn; NCTE; Col. Eng. Asn. American fiction; regionalism; 19th century humor. Publ: Ohio authors and their books, World Publ, 62; The poet and the president, 62 & The young man in American literature, 68, Odyssey; Paragraphs for practice, Holt, 62; co-auth, Six early American plays, C.E, Merrill, 68. Add: Dept. of English, Florida Atlantic University, Boca Raton, FL 33432.

COZART, WILLIAM REED, b. San Antonio, Tex, Oct. 13, 36; m. 61; c. 1. ENGLISH. A.B, Univ. Tex, 58; Danforth Found. fel, Harvard, 58-63, A.M, 60, Ph.D.(Eng), 63. Instr. Eng, Mundelein Col, 62-64; lectr. medieval lit, Free Univ. Berlin, 64-65; asst. prof. ENG, CALIF. INST. TECHNOL, 65-73, ASSOC. PROF, 73- Mediaeval Acad. Am. Chaucer; fourteenth century English literature; literature and science. Publ: Ed, Dialogue on science, Bobbs, 67; auth, Chaucer's Knight's tale: a philosophical re-appraisal of a medieval romance, In: Medieval epic to the epic theatre of Brecht, Univ. South. Calif, 68. Add: Dept. of English, California Institute of Technology, 1201 E. California Blvd, Pasadena, CA 91109.

CRABB, ALFRED LELAND, JR, b. Bowling Green, Ky, Mar. 4, 19; m. 45; c. 5. ENGLISH. A.B, Peabody Col, 40, M.A, 41; Univ. N.C, 46-50. Instr. Eng, UNIV. KY, 50-56, asst. prof, 56-73, ASSOC. PROF. ENG. EDUC, 73- Ed, Ky. Eng. Bull, 66-69; exec. secy, Ky. Counc. Teachers of Eng, 69- A.U.S, 42-46. NCTE; Conf. Col. Compos. & Commun. Conf. Eng. Educ. (exec. comt, 67-73). English education; composition. Publ: Structural grammar, winter 60 & Ambiguity, fall 67, Ky. Eng. Bull; Keep your eye on the mark, Peabody J. Educ, 5/68. Add: Dept. of English, University of Kentucky, Lexington, KY 40506.

CRABTREE, JOHN HENRY, JR, b. Raleigh, N.C, Nov. 11, 25; m. 48; c. 4. ENGLISH. B.A, Univ. N.C, 50, M.A, 51, fel, 54, Ph.D, 59. Assoc. prof. ENG, Presby. Jr. Col, 51-54; FURMAN UNIV, 57-64, PROF, 64-, CHMN. DEPT, 73-, asst. dean acad. affairs, 65-67, assoc. dean, 67-68, dean stud, 68-73. South. fel, summer 59. U.S.N, 44-46. S.Atlantic Mod. Lang. Asn; Nat. Asn. Stud. Personnel Adminr, Nat. Asn. For. Stud. Affairs; Shakespeare Asn. Am. Jacobean drama; drama of Restoration and 18th century England, Shakespeare and English Renaissance drama. Publ: Philip Massinger's use of rhetoric in The Roman actor, 5/60 & The comedy in Marlowe's Dr. Faustus, 11/61, Furman Stud. Add: Rte. 3, Hathaway Circle, Greenville, SC 29609.

CRACROFT, RICHARD HOLTON, b. Salt Lake City, Utah, June 28, 36; m. 59; c. 3. AMERICAN LITERATURE. B.A, Univ. Utah, 61, M.A, 63; Ford fel, Univ. Wis, 68, Ph.D.(Am. lit), 69. PROF. ENG, BRIGHAM YOUNG UNIV, 63- Assoc. ed, Dialogue: a Jour. of Mormon Thought, 69-73; res. ed, West.

Am. Lit, 73- Nat. Guard, 53-62. West. Am. Lit. Asn; Rocky Mountain Mod. Lang. Asn; NCTE. Western American literature; Mark Twain; Mormon literature. Publ: Co-ed, A believing people: literature of the Latter-day Saints, Brigham Young Univ, 74; auth, The big sky: A.B. Guthrie's use of historical sources, West. Am. Lit, fall 71; The gentle blasphemer: Mark Twain, holy scripture and the Book of Mormon, Brigham Young Univ. Stud, winter 71; A pebble in the pool: organic unity in Thomas Wolfe's You Can't go home again, Mod. Fiction Stud, winter 72; plus others. Add: Dept. of English, Brigham Young University, Provo, UT 84602.

CRADDOCK, PATRICIA BLAND, b. New Orleans, La, Oct. 28, 38. ENGLISH. B.A, Ind. Univ, 59; Woodrow Wilson fel, Stanford Univ, 59-60, M.A, 60; fel, Yale, 61-62, Lewis-Farmington fel, 62-63, M.A, 63, Ph.D, 64. Instr. ENG, Ala. Col, 60-61; Connecticut Col, 63-66; asst. prof, Goucher Col, 66-72; ASSOC. PROF, BOSTON UNIV, 72- Guggenheim fel, 71-72. MLA; AAUP; Col. Eng. Asn; Eng. Inst. English literature of the 18th century; the English novel; history and structure of the English language. Publ: Ed, The English essays of Edward Gibbon, Clarendon, 73; Gibbon's revisions of the Decline and fall, Stud. Bibliog, 68; An approach to the discrimination of similar styles: two English historians, Style, 69; plus others. Add: 106 Hillside Dr, Sylacauga, AL 35150.

CRAFT, HARVEY MILTON, b. Hattiesburg, Miss, Nov, 22, 25; m. 46; c. 4. ENGLISH. B.A, Univ. South. Miss, 45, M.A, 56; M.A, Univ. Ala, 48; Ph.D. (Eng), Tulane Univ, 64. Asst. prof, ENG, Delta State Col, 57-58; Univ. South. Miss, 59-61; instr, Tulane Univ, 61-63, asst. prof, 63-69, dir. freshman-sophomore Eng, 63-67, acting asst. dean col. Arts & Sci, 66-67, acting head dept, 67, head dept, 68-69; PROF. ENG. & DEAN INSTR, MISS. STATE COL. WOMEN, 69- U.S.A, 51-53, Res, 53-61, Capt. MLA. American literature; composition. Publ: Ed, Logic, style and arrangement: literature for the composition course, Macmillan, 71. Add: Mississippi State College for Women, Columbus, MS 39701.

CRAIG, GEORGE ARMOUR, b. Cleveland, Ohio, Nov. 15, 14; m. 39; c. 2. ENGLISH LITERATURE. A.B, Amherst Col, 37; A.M, Harvard, 38, Ph.D, 47. Instr. ENG, Harvard, 38-40; AMHERST COL, 40-43, asst. prof, 43-49, assoc. prof, 49-55, PROF, 55- Vis. lectr, Harvard, 55-56. MLA. Seventeenth century English philosophy and literature; 19th century prose fiction. Add: Dept. of English, Amherst College, Amherst, MA 01002.

CRAIG, HARRY E, b. New Brighton, Mar. 15, 23; m. 51; c. 2. AMERICAN LITERATURE, LINGUISTICS. A.B, Geneva Col, 49; M.Litt, Univ. Pittsburgh, 55, Ph.D.(Eng), 67. Teacher high schs, Pa, 49-61; assoc. prof. ENG, IND. UNIV. PA, 61-67, PROF, 67- Consult, Penn Trafford Schs, 65-67; Armstrong County Schs, 67. U.S.N, 42-43. NCTE; MLA; AAUP. Modern American novel; criticism. Add: Dept. of English, Indiana University of Pennsylvania, Indiana, PA 15701.

CRAIG, HERBERT RUSH, b. New Albany, Miss, Oct. 10, 23; m. 47; c. 2. SPEECH, ENGLISH. B.A, Univ. Ala, 48; M.A, Univ. Iowa, 54, Ph.D. (speech), 56. Asst. prof. speech, SAN JOSE STATE UNIV, 56-63, assoc. prof, 63-68, SPEECH & HUMANITIES, 68-70, PROF, 70- U.S.A.A.F, 43-46; Intel.C, 51-52, Capt. Speech Commun. Asn. Radio-television and the presidential campaign; speech criticism; the idea and practice of conciliation. Add: Dept. of Speech Communications, San Jose State University, 125 S. Seventh St, San Jose, CA 95114.

CRAIG, OPAL FRAZIER, b. Tecumseh, Okla, Oct. 12, 05; m. 56; c. 1. SPEECH, ENGLISH. A.B, Okla. Baptist Univ, 26; M.A, Univ. Okla, 53. Instr. SPEECH, OKLA. BAPTIST UNIV, 47-53, asst. prof, 53-59, ASSOC. PROF, 59- Speech Commun. Asn. Public address: speech criticism; oral interpretation. Add: Dept. of Speech, Oklahoma Baptist University, Shawnee, OK 74801.

CRAIN, HAROLD, b. Iowa, Jan. 9, 11. SPEECH, DRAMATIC ARTS. A.B, Morningside Col, 35; A.M, Syracuse Univ, 37; Ph.D, State Univ. Iowa, 47. Instr. Eng, Syracuse Univ, 37-40; N.Y. State Teachers Col, Buffalo, 40-45; speech, State Univ. Iowa, 45-47, assoc. prof. speech & dramatic arts, 47-55; PROF. DRAMA, SAN JOSE STATE UNIV, 55-, ASSOC. DEAN SCH. HUMANITIES & ARTS, 73-, head dept. speech & drama & chmn. fine arts area, 55-63. Fund Advan. Educ. fel, 53-54; vis. prof, Univ. Kans, 65-66. Speech Commun. Asn; Children's Theatre Conf; Northwest Drama Conf; Am. Theatre Asn.(regional chmn. playwriting awards). Dramaturgy. Publ: Co-auth, Projects in oral interpretation, Holt-Dryden, 59. Add: Dept. of Drama, San Jose State University, San Jose, CA 95114.

CRAMER, MAURICE BROWNING, b. Camden, N.J, Apr. 24, 10; m. 35; c. 2. ENGLISH LITERATURE. A.B, Princeton, 31, A.M, 34, Ph.D, 37. Instr. Eng. Mt. Holyoke Col, 34-40; asst. prof, 40, assoc. prof, Univ. Tampa, 40-41, prof, 41-42, chmn. dept, 40-42; lectr, Princeton, 42-43; asst. prof. humanities Col, Univ. Chicago, 45-48, assoc. prof, 48-53, prof, 53-59, chmn. humanities staff, 51-57; prof. ENG, PA. STATE UNIV, 59-72, EMER. PROF, 72- Reader, Col. Entrance Exam. Bd, 37, 38; Fulbright prof. Am. life & civilization, Nat. Univ. Athens, 57-58; Thomas Shipley lectr, Haverford Col, 64; humanities consult. & external exam, New Sch. Soc. Res, 67-68. Quantrell Award, 57. MLA; Am. Civil Liberties Union; AAUP. Nineteenth century English literature; Browning; Wordsworth. Publ: Phoenix at East Hadley, Houghton; Browning's friendships and fame before marriage, PMLA; Maisie Ward and Browning biography: a new era; Mod. Philol, 71; The ring and the book: underthought, In: Directions in literary criticism, Pa. State Univ, 73; plus one other. Add: 413 Longleaf Dr, Chapel Hill, NC 27514.

CRANE, CHARLES LACOSTE, JR, b. Hickory, N.C, July 23, 15; m. 60; c. 2. ENGLISH. A.B, Davidson Col, 37; M.A, Univ. N.C, 39; Columbia Univ, 47-50; Univ. Col, Univ. London, 64-65. Teacher ENG, high sch, High Point, N.C, 37-38; instr, Ga. Inst. Technol, 39-42; U.S. NAVAL ACAD, 45-48, asst. prof, 48-51, ASSOC. PROF, 51- Assoc. prof, Univ. Md, 60-61; Anne Arundel Community Col, 61- U.S.N.R, 42-47, Lt. Comdr. Col. Eng. Asn. American literature; contemporary British literature. Publ: Co-auth, Cruise ports, U.S. Naval Inst, 56. Add: Dept. of English, U.S. Naval Academy, Annapolis, MD 21402.

CRANE, GEORGE FRANCIS, II, b. Pasadena, Calif, Oct. 9, 21; m. 66; c. 5. ENGLISH. A.B, Stanford Univ, 45; M.A, Univ. Calif, Los Angeles, 48; Ph.D. (Eng), Univ. Calif, Berkeley, 60. Instr. ENG, Purdue Univ, 55-57; Calif. State Col. San Diego, 57-58; asst. prof, CALIF. STATE UNIV, LONG BEACH, 58-63, assoc. prof, 63-68, PROF, 68- English Renaissance, especially Elizabethan, Publ: The effete (sonnet), Poetry Mag, Chicago, 45. Add: Dept. of English, California State University, Long Beach, 6101 E. Seventh St, Long Beach, CA 90804.

CRANE, JOHN KENNY, b. New York, N.Y, Mar. 14, 42; m. 66; c. 2. ENGLISH, LINGUISTICS. A.B, St. Louis Univ, 63, fel. & M.A, 64; Ph.D.(Eng), Pa. State Univ, 66. Asst. prof. ENG, U.S. Air Force Acad, 66-68, ASSOC. PROF, 68-70; Univ. South. Calif, 70-71; PA. STATE UNIV, UNIVERSITY PARK, 71- Lectr, Univ. Colo, 68-69; vis. prof, Univ. Wash, 70. U.S.A.F, 66-70, Capt. MLA (bibliogr. bibliog. comt, 67-71); Mod. Humanities Res. Asn; Rocky Mountain Mod. Lang. Asn. Modern British literature; literature and science; literature and philosophy. Publ: T.H. White, Twayne, 74; Bushwhacked on the road to Valhalla: British authors in the age of determinism, 1880-1930, Ind. Univ, (in press); Crossing the bar twice; postmortem consciousness in Bierce, Hemingway, and Golding, Stud. Short Fiction, fall 68; The four levels of time in Sir Gawain and the Green Knight, Annuale Mediaevale, 69; To thwack or be thwacked: an evaluation of available translations and editions of Beowulf, Col. Eng, 70. Add: Dept. of English, Pennsylvania State University, 233 S. Burrowes Bldg, University Park, PA 16802.

CRANE, LOREN DANFORD, b. Las Vegas, Nev, Oct. 3, 33; m. 63; c. 4. INTERPERSONAL COMMUNICATION, PUBLIC ADDRESS. B.A, Brigham Young Univ, 58; M.A, Ohio State Univ, 60, Ph.D.(commun), 63. Asst. prof. SPEECH, Ohio State Univ, 62-63; Wis. State Univ-Whitewater, 63-65, assoc. prof, 65; asst. prof, WEST. MICH. UNIV, 65-70, ASSOC. PROF, 70- U.S.A, 57. Physiological measures of cognition and emotion. Publ: Co-auth, Physiological responses to communication, Vol. 2, Listening: readings, 71; auth, Toward a theory of arrangement, Ohio Speech J, 62; co-auth, The physiological response to the communication modes: reading, listening, writing, speaking, and evaluating, J. Commun, 9/70. Add: Dept. of Communication Arts & Sciences, Western Michigan University, Kalamazoo, MI 49001.

CRANE, MAURICE AARON, b. Atlantic City, N.J, June 6, 26; m. 50; c. 4. ENGLISH. Princeton; Villanova Univ, M.A, Univ. Chicago, Ph.D, Univ. Ill, 53. From instr. commun. skills & humanities to PROF. HUMANITIES & DIR. NAT. VOICE LIBR, MICH. STATE UNIV, 53- U.S.N, 44-46. Publ: Academic overture, 71. Add: Voice Library, Michigan State University, East Lansing, MI 48823.

CRANE, MILTON, b. Hartford, Conn, May 24, 17; m. 40; c. 2. ENGLISH & AMERICAN LITERATURE. A.B, Columbia Univ, 37, A.M, 38; Lehman & univ. fels, Harvard, 38-40, A.M, 41, Ph.D, 42. Instr. Eng, Col. William & Mary 42-43; Hunter Col, 44-47; asst. prof, Univ. Chicago, 47-52; res. dir, U.S.Dept. State, 52-61, chief div. res. Brit. Commonwealth, North. & Cent. Europe, 61-64; PROF. ENG. LIT, GEORGE WASHINGTON UNIV, 64- Educ. & res. analyst, Off. Strategic Serv, 43-45; assoc. ed, Bantam Bk, Inc, 45-46; prof. lectr, George Washington Univ, 55, 61, 63. MLA; Shakespeare Asn. Am. Shakespeare; George Bernard Shaw. Publ: Shakespeare's prose, Univ. Chicago & Cambridge, 52, 63; Fifty great short stories, 52, Fifty great poets, 62 & Fifty great American short stories, 65, Bantam; ed, Shakespeare's Henry VI, part III, New Am. Libr, 68 & Shakespeare's art, Univ. Chicago, 73. Add: Dept. of English, George Washington University, 2023 G St. N.W, Washington, DC 20006.

CRANFILL, THOMAS MABRY, b. Dallas, Tex, July 20, 13. ENGLISH LITERATURE. A.B, Univ. Tex, 34; A.M, Harvard, 37, Ph.D, 44. Instr. ENG, Ga. Inst. Technol, 37-39; teaching fel. & resid. tutor, Harvard, 42-43; instr, Northwest. Univ, 44-45; asst. prof, UNIV. TEX, AUSTIN, 45-49, assoc. prof, 49-61, PROF, 61- Fel, Folger Shakespeare Libr, 47-48; Huntington Libr, 49-50. MLA. Elizabethan literature. Publ: Rich's farewell to military profession, The muse in Mexico, 59 & Image of Britain (2 vols), 61, Univ. Tex. Add: Dept. of English, University of Texas at Austin, Austin, TX 78712.

CRANNELL, KENNETH C, b. Lynn, Mass, Apr. 5, 34; m. 60; c. 2. ORAL INTERPRETATION. B.A, Emerson Col, 55, M.A, 57; Univ. Mich, 59; Ph.D. (oral interpretation), Northwest. Univ, 70. Instr. SPEECH, EMERSON COL, 57-60, asst. prof, 60-61, assoc. prof, 61-69, PROF. & CHMN. DIV. ORAL INTERPRETATION, 69- Asst, Northwest. Univ, 61-62, instr. interpretation, 64-65; speech consult, St. John's Sem, 67-68; vis. instr. homiletics, Pope John XXIII Sem, 70-73; consult, Harvard Divinity Sch, 73. Speech Commun. Asn.(v.chmn. interpretation div, 73, chmn, 74); East. States Commun. Asn.(mem. ed. bd, 72-74); New Eng. Speech Asn. Prosody; oral performance; modern poetry. Publ: Co-auth, Oral interpretation; graduate programs, Speech Teacher, 72; contrib, Oral interpretation bibliography, N.C. Speech J, 73. Add: 9 Orient Ave, Melrose, MA 02176.

CRAUN, EDWIN DAVID, b. Riverside, Calif, Mar. 17, 45; m. 67; c. 1. ENGLISH POETRY & PROSE. B.A, Wheaton Col.(Ill), 67; Ph.D.(Eng), Princeton, 71. ASST. PROF. ENG, WASHINGTON & LEE UNIV, 71- MLA; Renaissance Soc. Am; Southeast. Renaissance Conf. Medieval and Renaissance narrative poetry. Add: Dept. of English, Washington & Lee University, Lexington, VA 24450.

CRAVEN, ALAN ELLIOTT, b. Kansas City, Mo, Nov. 12, 35; div; c. 3. ENGLISH. A.B, Univ. Kans, 58, M.A, 63, Ph.D.(Eng), 65. Asst. prof. ENG, Univ. Ariz, 65-71; Brandeis Univ, 72-73; PROF. & DIR. DIV, UNIV. TEX, SAN ANTONIO, 73- MLA. Shakespeare textual criticism; Renaissance literature. Publ: The compositors of the Shakespeare quartos printed by Peter Short, 71 & Two Valentine Simmes compositors, 73, Papers Bibliog. Soc. Am; Simmes' compositor A and five Shakespeare quartos, Stud. Bibliog, 73. Add: Div. of English, University of Texas at San Antonio, 4242 Piedras Dr. E, San Antonio, TX 78284.

CRAVEN, DOROTHY HADLEY, b. Coldwater, Kans, Nov. 12, 14; wid. ENGLISH LITERATURE. A.B, William Penn Col, 38; A.M, Univ. Kans, 41; Ph.D, Univ. Colo, 53. Teacher, high sch, Burrton, Kans, 41-43, Larned, 43-

46; instr, Ill. Wesleyan Univ, 46-47; asst. prof, FRIENDS UNIV, 47-49, PROF. ENG. & HEAD DEPT, 49-, ACTING DEAN, 72-, dean, 60-65. Mem. comt. lib. arts educ, N.Cent. Asn. Cols. & Sec. Schs, 61-64. NCTE; MLA. Lafcadio Hearn as an interpreter and critic of the British poets; Cowper's use of slight connection in the task: a study in structure and style. Add: Div. of Language & Literature, Friends University, Wichita, KS 67213.

CRAWFORD, JERRY L, b. Whittemore, Iowa, Aug. 20, 34; m. 56; c. 3. DRAMA. B.F.A, Drake Univ, 56; M.A, Stanford Univ, 57; Ph.D.(drama), Univ. Iowa, 64. Instr. drama, UNIV. NEV, LAS VEGAS, 62-64, asst. prof, 64-65, assoc. prof, 65, PROF, 65-70, THEATRE ARTS, 70-, acting dean fac, 65-66, dean fac, 66-68, chmn. dept. speech & drama, 68-70. U.S.A, 57-59. Am. Theatre Asn. Best New Play Award, Southeast. Theatre Conf, 74. Theory, technique and practice of playwriting; contemporary dramatic literature; acting and directing in the contemporary theatre. Publ: The dark roots, 61 & Half a pound of tea, 63, Univ. Iowa; The look of eagles, Univ. Vt, 65; co-auth, The actor: in person and in style, 75; auth, The auction tomorrow, Southeast. Theatre Conf. J, fall 74. Add: Dept. of Theatre Arts, University of Nevada, Las Vegas, Las Vegas, NV 89154.

CRAWFORD, JOHN CHAPMAN, b. Iron Mountain, Mich, July 5, 26; m. 46; c. 5. LINGUISTICS. B.S, Univ. Mich, Ann Arbor, 47, M.A, 48, Ph.D.(ling), 60. Field worker appl. ling, Summer Inst. Ling, Mex, 51-69, assoc. dir, 62-63, 66-67, dir. lang. surv, 64-66, coord. literacy, 68-69; ASSOC. PROF. ENG, Cent. Mich. Univ, 67-68; UNIV. N.DAK, 69-, summer res. prof, 73. Am. Counc. Learned Soc. summer grant ling, 71. U.S.N.R, 45-46, Ens. Linguistic theory; American Indian languages; English language. Publ: Totontepec Mixe phonotagmemics, Summer Inst. Ling, 63; co-auth, Frequency studies of English consonants, Lang. & Speech, 60; auth, Transculturacion linguistica y la traduccion de la Biblia, Proc. Cong. Int. Am, 64. Add: Dept. of English, University of North Dakota, Grand Forks, ND 58201.

CRAWFORD, JOHN W, b. Ashdown, Ark, Sept. 2, 36; m. 62; c. 2. ENGLISH. B.S.E Ouachita Baptist Univ, 59; M.S.E, Drake Univ, 62; Ed.D, Okla. State Univ, 68. Instr, high sch, Iowa, 59-60; Jefferson Sch. Syst, 60-62; ENG, Clinton Community Col, 62-66; asst. prof, HENDERSON STATE COL, 67-68, assoc. prof, 68-73, PROF, 73- NEA; Col. Eng. Asn; S.Cent. Mod. Lang. Asn; S.Cent. Col. Eng. Asn; Int. Poetry Soc. Shakespearian and Victorian research. Publ: A unifying element in Tennyson's Maud, Victorian poetry, winter 69; The garden imagery in Great expectations, Res. Stud, 3/71; Shakespeare: a lesson in communications, Clearing House, 4/73; plus several others. Add: Dept. of English, Box H-2652, Henderson State College, Arkadelphia, AR 71923.

CRAWFORD, PAUL K, b. Cameron, Mo, Nov. 15, 06; m. 30; c. 1. SPEECH. A.B, Baker Univ, 28; Ph.M, Univ. Wis, 36; fel, Northwest. Univ, 38, 44-45, Ph.D.(speech), 49. Instr. high sch, Mo, 28-29; head dept. SPEECH, sr. high sch, Ill, 29-40; instr, NORTH. ILL. UNIV, 40-43, asst. prof, 43-48, assoc. prof, 48-50, PROF, 50- Ed, Ill. Speech News, 34-39; discussion dept, Speech Mag, 40-43; assoc. ed, Masque & Gavel Mag, 40-42; mem. ed. bd, Am. Poetry Mag, 44-49. Cardinal Newman Award, 60. Speech Commun. Asn; Nat. Asn. Standard Med. Vocab; NEA; Asn. Higher Educ; Am. Acad. Polit. & Soc. Sci; Acad. Polit. Sci; Am. Forensic Asn; Rhetoric Soc. Am; AAUP; Int. Inst. Arts & Lett; Am. Arbit. Asn.(mem, nat. panel of arbitrators, 67); Am. Inst. Parliamentarians. Parlimentary law; speech as a social force; American social and intellectual history. Publ: An outline of parliamentary law, Col. Publ. Co, Wis, 35; The Lincoln-Douglas debate at Freeport, North. Ill. Univ. & Lincoln-Douglas Soc, 58; co-auth, Communication in the high school curriculum: speaking and listening, Off. Supt. Pub. Instr, State Ill, 61; auth, Significance of debates to modern campaigning, In: The Freeport debate and its centennial commemoration, Lincoln-Douglas Soc, 59; Parliamentary procedure in the Dail Eireann, Parliamentary J, 1/68; John Redmond: Ireland's voice of moderation, Cent. States Speech J, summer 68; plus one other. Add: Dept. of Speech Communication, Northern Illinois University, DeKalb, IL 60115.

CRAWFORD, WALTER BYRON, b. Chamberlain, S.Dak, Apr. 26, 19; m. 40; c. 2. ENGLISH. B.A, Univ. Col.(Nebr), 41; Univ. Nebr, Lincoln, 41-42; M.A, Columbia Univ, 47; Univ. Calif, Berkeley, 47-48; Ph.D.(Eng), Univ. Calif, Los Angeles, 61. Assoc. prof. ENG, La Sierra Col, 48-53; asst. prof, CALIF. STATE UNIV, LONG BEACH, 63-67, assoc. prof, 67-72, PROF, 72- Calif. State Univ, Long Beach Found. summer res. fel, 67, grants-in-aid res, 68-69, 71-72, 72-73; mem. bd. trustees, Monterey Park Pub. Libr, Calif, 66-69, pres, 68-69. U.S.A.A.F, 42-45, S/Sgt. MLA; NCTE. Samuel Taylor Coleridge, 1772-1834; English prosody and stylistics. Publ: Research activity and writing, Dickenson, 67; ed, A portfolio of twenty drawings commemorating the bicentenary of the birth of Coleridge, Long Beach Calif. State Univ. Found, 72; auth, A three-decker novel in Wordsworth's library, 1802, Notes and Queries, 1/64; co-auth, Recent Coleridge scholarship, winter & fall 72 & Coleridge in narrative and drama, Parts I & II, 72 & 73, Wordsworth Circle. Add: Dept. of English, California State University, Long Beach, 6101 E. Seventh St, Long Beach, CA 90840.

CRAWLEY, DEREK FRENCH, b. Broadview, Sask, Jan. 24, 24; m. 52; c. 3. ENGLISH. B.A, Univ. Man, 47; B.A, Oxford, 54, M.A, 58; Ph.D.(Eng), Northwest. Univ, 63. Instr. ENG, Northwest. Univ, 55-56; Univ. Ill, Chicago, 56-59; lectr, QUEEN'S UNIV.(ONT), 59-62, asst. prof, 62-65, assoc. prof, 65-70, PROF, 70- Can. Counc. summer grant, 67. Can. Army, 43. Malone Soc; Asn. Can. Univ. Teachers Eng. Elizabethan drama; Spenser. Publ: Ed, William Kirby's The golden dog, McClelland & Stewart, Toronto, 69; The effect of Shirley's hand on Chapman's The tragedy of Chabot, Stud. Philol, 10/66; Decision and character in Chapman's The tragedy of Caesar and Pompey, Stud. Eng. Lit, spring 67. Add: Dept. of English, Queen's University, Kingston, Ont, Can.

CREED, HOWARD HALL, b. Macon, Mo, May 21, 08; m. 37; c. 1. ENGLISH. B.A, Cent. Methodist Col, 30; M.A, Vanderbilt Univ, 32, Ph.D, 42. Instr. ENG, Moberly Jr. Col, 33-37; Cent. Methodist Col, 37-42, asst. prof, 42-43; assoc. prof, BIRMINGHAM-SOUTH. COL, 46-50, PROF, 50-, CHMN. DEPT, 63- Teaching fel, Vanderbilt Univ, 40-42; Ford Found. fel, 54-55; U.S.N.R, 43-46, Lt. MLA; S.Atlantic Mod. Lang. Asn; NCTE. Romanticism; literary criticism; present-day English. Publ: Ed, Essays in honor of Richebourg Gaillard McWilliams, Birmingham-Southern Col, 70; Coleridge on Taste, Eng. Lit. Hist, 6/46; Coleridge's matacriticism, PMLA, 12/54; The ancient mariner: a rereading, Eng. J, 4/60. Add: Dept. of English, Birmingham-Southern College, Birmingham, AL 35204.

CREED, ROBERT PAYSON, b. Philadelphia, Pa, Apr. 22, 25; div; c. 2. ENGLISH. B.A, Swarthmore Col, 48; M.A, Harvard, 49, Ph.D.(Eng), 56. Teaching fel. gen. educ, 51-52; instr. ENG, Smith Col, 52-56; asst. prof, Brown Univ, 56-61, assoc. prof, 61-65; State Univ. N.Y. Stony Brook, 65-67, PROF, 67-69; UNIV. MASS, AMHERST, 69- Guggenheim fel, 62-63. U.S.N.R, 43-46, Lt.(jg). MLA; Mediaeval Acad. Am. Old English literature; linguistics; traditional poetry and saga. Publ: Afterword to Beowulf, New Am. Libr, 63; co-ed, Franciplegius: medieval and linguistic studies in honor of Francis Peabody Magoun, Jr, N.Y. Univ, 65; ed, Old English poetry: fifteen essays, Brown Univ, 67; auth, On the possiblity of criticizing Old English Poetry, Tex. Stud. Lit. & Lang, spring 61; The singer looks at his sources, In: Studies in Old English literature in honor of Arthur G. Brodeur, 63; A new approach to the Rhythm of Beowulf, PMLA, 66. Add: Dept. of English, University of Massachusetts, Amherst, MA 01002.

CREED, WALTER GENTRY, b. Philadelphia, Pa, Dec. 30, 31; m. 63; c. 2. ENGLISH LITERATURE. B.A, Univ. Pa, 60, M.A, 61, Ph.D.(Eng. lit), 68. Instr, ENG, Lafayette Col, 65-66, ASST. PROF, 69; UNIV. HAWAII, MANOA, 69- Ord.C, U.S.A, 55-56. MLA. Twentieth century British literature; the novel; literature and science. Publ: Pieces of the puzzle: the multiple-narrative structure of The Alexandria quartet, Mosaic, winter 73. Add: Dept. of English, University of Hawaii at Manoa, Honolulu, HI 96822.

CREEGER, GEORGE RAYMOND, b. Attleboro, Mass, Sept. 1, 25; m. 51; c. 3. ENGLISH. B.A, DePauw Univ, 45; M.A, Yale, 48, Ph.D.(Eng), 53. Instr. Eng. & German, DePauw Univ, 46-47; ENG, WESLEYAN UNIV, 51-53, asst. prof, 57, assoc. prof, 57-63, PROF, 63-, dean col, 70-73. Fulbright guest prof, Wurzburg Univ, Ger, 59-60, John F. Kennedy Inst. Am. Stud, Free Univ, Berlin, 68-69. U.S.A.A.F, 46-47, Sgt. MLA; Melville Soc. Nineteenth century American and English literature. Publ: Selected prose and poetry of the Romantic period, Holt, 64; ed, George Eliot: twentieth century views, Prentice-Hall, 70; An interpretation of Adam Bede, ELH, 56; Symbolism of whiteness in Melville's prose fiction, 60 & Animals in exile: imagery and theme in Capote's In cold blood, 69, Jahrbuch Amerika-Studien. Add: Box F, Wesleyan Station, Middletown, CT 06457.

CREEL, GEORGE W, b. Guyandotte, W.Va, Oct. 27, 15; m. 37; c. 6. ENGLISH LITERATURE. A.B, Univ. Denver, 38, A.M, 39; Ph.D, Univ. Calif, 48. Teaching fel, Univ. Denver, 38-39; instr. Eng, Ore. State Col, 45-46; teaching fel, Univ. Calif, 46-47; asst. prof, ENG, CALIF. STATE UNIV. SACRAMENTO, 48-51, assoc. prof, 51-56, PROF, 56- Fulbright lectr, Univ. Salamanca, 61-62; resident dir, Calif. State Cols. Int. Prog, Spain, 66-67, mem. acad. counc, Calif. State Univs. & Cols. Int. Prog, 70- Col. Eng. Asn. English poetry of 19th century; critical theory. Add: Dept. of English, California State University, Sacramento, Sacramento, CA 95819.

CREETH, EDMUND HOMER, b. Oakland, Calif, Apr. 11, 28; m. 52; c. 3. ENGLISH. A.B, Univ. Calif, 51, M.A, 53, Ph.D, 56. Assoc. ENG, Univ. Calif, 52-55, lectr, 55-56; instr, Pomona Col, 56-58; UNIV. MICH, ANN ARBOR, 58-61, asst. prof, 61-64, ASSOC. PROF, 64- Vis. lectr, Univ. Essex, fall 68. MLA; Malone Soc; Renaissance Soc. Am. Medieval and Elizabethan drama; Milton. Publ: Ed, Tudor plays, 66 & Tudor prose, 69, Doubleday; auth, Moral and tragic recognition: the uniqueness of Othello, Macbeth, and King Lear, Papers, Mich. Acad. Sci. Arts & Lett, 60; The begetting and the exaltation of the son, Mod. Lang. Notes, 61. Add: Dept. of English, University of Michigan, Ann Arbor, MI 48104.

CREIGHTON, AILEEN SWAFFORD, b. Gainesville, Tex, Aug. 27, 11; m. 38; c. 1. ENGLISH, RENAISSANCE. B.A, Univ. Tex, 30, M.A, 32, Ph.D. (Eng), 60. Instr. high schs, 31-38; librn, Corpus Christi Pub. Libr, Tex, 38-39; instr. ENG, DEL MAR COL, 39-59, PROF. & CHMN. DEPT, 59- Mem, Nat. Conf. Teaching Eng. in Jr. Col, Ariz, Feb, 65; mem. comt. to form nat. orgn. on Eng. in two-year col, NCTE & Conf. Col. Comp. & Commun, Oct, 66; chmn. southwest regional conf, Eng. Two-Year Col, 67, mem. steering comt, 68-69. MLA; Renaissance Soc. Am. Sixteenth century; links between science and the Reformation; teaching of disadvantaged students in junior college English. Publ: William Turner as reformer, Univ. Microfilms, 60; English courses for adults and community service, In: Research and the development of English programs in the Junior college, NCTE, 65. Add: Dept. of English, Del Mar College, Corpus Christi, TX 78404.

CREPEAU, GEORGE PAUL, b. Ironwood, Mich, Mar. 22, 22; m. 46; c. 2. DRAMA. B.A, Univ. Mich, 49, M.A, 50; Ph.D, Cornell Univ, 62. Teaching fel, Univ. Mich, 49-50; tech. dir, Kalamazoo Civic Theatre, 50-51; instr. speech & drama, Cornell Univ, 51-57; asst. prof. dramatic production, Northwest. Univ, 57-59; asst. prof. SPEECH, OHIO STATE UNIV, COLUMBUS, 59-65, assoc. prof, 65-71, PROF, 71-, ASSOC. PROVOST, 72-, asst. v.pres for acad. affairs, 71-72. U.S.A, 43-46. Speech Commun. Asn.; Am. Theatre Asn; Am. Nat. Theatre & Acad; Am. Asn. Advan. Slavic Stud. International theatre studies; East European theatre education and studies; non-traditional modes of higher education. Publ: The heritage of theatre, In: The communicative arts and sciences of speech, C.E. Merrill, 67. Add: Office of Academic Affairs, Ohio State University, 190 N. Oval Dr, Columbus, OH 43210.

CRESWELL, THOMAS JAMES, b. Chicago, Ill, July 22, 20; m. 53; c. 2. ENGLISH. B.Ed, Chicago Teachers Col, 43; M.A, Univ. Chicago, 52. Teacher, Pub. Schs, Ill, 46-58; instr. ENG, CHICAGO STATE UNIV, 58-62, asst. prof, 62-71, ASSOC. PROF, 71-, dir. publs, 65-66, dean instr, 68-71, dir. educ. exp, 68-69. Asst. ed, Chicago Schs. Jour, 58-63, managing ed, 63-65; Am. Counc. Learned Soc. fel, 64-65; consult. ling, Sci. Res. Assoc, 65-66, dir. dept. lang. arts & lit, 66-68; chmn. ed. bd, Ill. Schs Jour, 71- U.S.A, 43-45. NCTE; Conf. Col. Compos. & Commun; MLA; Ling. Soc. Am. The teaching of English; modern American language; social dialectology. Publ: Co-auth, Linguistics and the teaching of reading, Elem. Eng, 1/63; auth, The twenty billion dollar misunderstanding, In: Social dialects and language learning, NCTE, 65; Literary dialect in Nelson Algren's Never come morning, In: Studies in linguistics in honor of Raven I. McDavid, Jr, Univ. Ala, 72; plus one other. Add: Dept. of English, Chicago State University, 95th & King Dr, Chicago, IL 60628.

CREW, LOUIE, b. Anniston, Ala, Dec. 9, 36; m. 74. ENGLISH LITERATURE, RHETORIC. B.A, Baylor Univ, 58; fel, Auburn Univ, 58-59, M.A, 59; Wurlitzer Found. fel, summer 63; Ph.D.(Eng), Univ. Ala, 71. Master Eng, Darlington Sch, Rome, Ga, 59-62; St. Andrew's Sch, Middletown, Del, 62-65; Penge Sch, London, Eng, 65-66; asst, Univ. Ala, 66-68, instr, 68-70; dir, Acad. Prog. Exp. Int. Living, Eng, 70-71; prof. ENG, Claflin Col, 71-73; ASSOC. PROF, FT. VALLEY STATE COL, 73- Nat. Endowment for Humanities summer res. fel, Univ. Calif, Berkeley, 74; guest lectr, Lavender Univ, summer 74. NCTE; Col. Eng. Asn; Am. Asn. Higher Educ; Dickens Soc; Dickens Fel. Black studies; gay studies. Publ: Wrenched black tongues: democratizing English, Col. Comp. & Commun, 2/74; Charles Dickens as a critic of the U.S, Mid-West Quart, 10/74; co-ed, Spec. issue, The homosexual imagination, Col. Eng, 11/74; plus others. Add: Dept. of English, Box 1203, Ft. Valley State College, Ft. Valley, GA 31030.

CREWS, FREDERICK C, b. Philadelphia, Pa, Feb. 20, 33; m. 59; c. 1. ENGLISH & AMERICAN LITERATURE. A.B, Yale, 55; Ph.D, Princeton, 58. Instr. ENG, UNIV. CALIF, BERKELEY, 58-60, asst. prof, 60-63, assoc. prof, 63-66, PROF, 66- Fulbright lectr. Am. lit, Univ. Turin, 61-62; Am. Counc. Learned Soc. & Ctr. Advan. Stud. Behav. Sci. fels, Stanford Univ, 65-66; Guggenheim fel, 70-71. MLA. Nineteenth and 20th century fiction; British and American; psychoanalytic literary criticism. Publ: Tragedy of manners; moral drama in the later novels of Henry James, Yale, 57; E.M. Forster: the perils of humanism, Princeton, 62; The pooh perplex: a freshman casebook, 63 & The Patch Commission, 68, Dutton; The sins of the fathers: Hawthorne's psychological themes, Oxford, 66; The Random House handbook, Random, 74. Add: 636 Vincente Ave, Berkeley, CA 94707.

CRICKARD, ANNETTE PEEK, b. Indianapolis, Ind, May 15, 04; wid; c. 1. ENGLISH, HUMANITIES. A.B, Baldwin-Wallace Col, 33; A.M, West. Reserve Univ, 38; Ph.D, Univ. N.C, 53. Head dept. ENG, E.Miss. Jr. Col, 54-60; ASSOC. PROF, Miss. State Univ, 60-68; E.MISS. JR. COL, 68- Fulbright lectr, Damascus, Syria, 61-62. MLA. Victorian studies; education of women; Dante research. Add: Dept. of English, East Mississippi Junior College, Scooba, MS 39358.

CRIDER, ALLEN BILLY, b. Mexia, Tex, July 28, 41; m. 65; c. 2. CONTEMPORARY AMERICAN FICTION. B.A, Univ. Tex, Austin, 63, Ph.D.(Eng), 72; M.A, N.Tex. State Univ, 67. Teacher ENG, Corsicana High Sch, 63-65; ASSOC. PROF, HOWARD PAYNE COL, 71- MLA; Col. Eng. Asn. Detective fiction; science fiction. Publ: Race Williams, private investigator, J. Popular Cult, 73. Add: Dept. of English, Howard Payne College, Brownwood, TX 76801.

CRIDER, JOHN RICHARD, b. Gainesville, Tex, Dec. 16, 31; m. 59; c. 2. ENGLISH. B.A, Baylor Univ, 53, M.A, 54; Ph.D.(Eng), Rice Univ, 60. Instr. ENG, Emory Univ, 60-62; asst. prof, Austin Col, 62-65, ASSOC. PROF, 65-66; TEX. TECH UNIV, 66- U.S.A.F. 54-57, 1st Lt. MLA; NCTE. Restoration and 18th century English literature. Publ: Structure and effect in Collins' Progress poems, Stud. Philol, 63; The anti-poet in Dryden's Mac Flecknoe, Brno Stud. Eng, 70. Add: Dept. of English, Texas Tech University, Lubbock, TX 79409.

CRIEGH, GEOFFREY CREIGH, b. Bristol, Eng, Dec. 20, 35; m. 62; c. 2. ENGLISH LITERATURE. B.A, Univ. Reading, 59; Shakespeare Inst. scholar, Univ. Birmingham, 60-62, Ph.D.(Eng), 63. Vis. asst. prof. ENG, Univ. Ala, 62-64; asst. prof, UNIV. B.C, 64-67, ASSOC. PROF, 67- Fulbright exchange lectr, 62-64. R.A.F, 54-56. Renaissance literature; late nineteenth century novel. Publ: Zelauto and Italian comedy, Mod. Lang. Quart, 6/68. Add: Dept. of English, University of British Columbia, Vancouver, B.C, V6T 1W5, Can.

CRIPE, NICHOLAS M, b. Goshen, Ind, Jan. 25, 13; m. 45. SPEECH. A.B, Goshen Col, 49; M.A, Northwest. Univ, 49, Ph.D, 53. Instr. SPEECH, Univ. Vt, 49-50; asst. prof, Grinnell Col, 52-53; PROF. & HEAD DEPT, BUTLER UNIV, 53- Baxter Award, Butler Univ, 54, Outstanding Prof. Award, 62, 63. U.S.A, 42-46. Speech Commun. Asn.(chmn. comt. int. discussion & debate, 72-73); Am. Forensic Asn.(pres, 61-63); Cent. States Speech Asn; Midwest. Forensic Asn. Public address; debate; conference participation and leadership. Publ: Co-auth, Argumentation and debate, Holt, 63. Add: Dept. of Speech, Butler University, Indianapolis, IN 46208.

CRIPPS, THOMAS ROBERT, American History. See Volume I, History.

CRIST, LYLE MARTIN, b. Alliance, Ohio, May 1, 24; m. 46; c. 2. ENGLISH, JOURNALISM. B.S, Purdue Univ, 46; M.A, Ind. Univ, 47. Asst. instr. sci, Purdue Univ, 45-46; instr. math, Ind. Univ, 46-47; Eng, Iowa State Univ, 47-48; teacher Eng. & sci, Alliance High Sch, Ohio, 48-52; asst. prof. ENG. & JOUR, MT. UNION COL, 52-57, assoc. prof, 57-67, PROF, 67- NCTE. Publ: Man expressed: the realm of writing, Macmillan-Glencoe, 71; Through the rain and rainbow, Abingdon, 74; chap, In: Improving college teaching, Ore. State Univ, 65. Add: Dept. of English, Mt. Union College, W. State St, Alliance, OH 44601.

CRISWELL, CLOYD M, b. Columbia, Pa, Dec. 8, 08; m. 42; c. 1. ENGLISH. B.S, Pa. State Teachers Col, Millersville, 33; A.M, N.Y. Univ, 37. Head dept. ENG, high sch, Pa, 33-38; teacher, high sch, N.Y, 38-42; asst. prof, LEHIGH UNIV, 48-72, ASSOC. PROF, 72- U.S.N, 42-47, Lt. Comdr. Publ: Asiatic station, Decker, 48; High twelve, Kaleidograph, 49; Three stones, Golden Quill, 55; Arrow by day, Marshall-Jones, 62. Add: Dept. of English, Lehigh University, Bethlehem, PA 18015.

CROCKER, LIONEL, b. Ann Arbor, Mich, Jan. 17, 97; m; c. 2. SPEECH. A.B, Univ. Mich, 18, A.M, 20, Ph.D, 33; hon. Dr. Pedagogy, Otterbein Col, 67; hon. Dr. Humanities, Drury Col, 67. Instr, Univ. Minn, 19; Univ. Mich, 19-20, 22-26, 27-28; prof, Waseda Univ.(Japan), 20-21; Am. Floating Univ, 26-27; SPEECH, DENISON UNIV, 28-67, EMER. PROF, 67- Res. fel, Ministers Res. Found, Inc; prof. pub. utilities exec. prog, Grad. Sch. Bus, Univ. Mich, 61-63; assoc. ed, J. Commun, 62; mem, comt. advan. tests speech, Educ. Testing Serv, 63; vis. prof, Ind. State Univ, 67-68; prof, Univ. Redlands, summer 69, 70, 71. Med. C, U.S.A, 18-19. Speech Commun. Asn. (2nd v.pres, 33, 1st v.pres, 51, pres, 52): Cent. States Speech Asn.(ed, jour, 49-). Stephen A. Douglas speaking tour of the South; Carlos P. Romulo, orator; Matthew Arnold's tour of the United States of America. Publ: Effective speaking 58 & Argumentation and debate, 62, Am. Inst. Banking; Public speaking for college students, Am. Bk. Co, 4th ed, 64; Readings in rhetoric, 66, An analysis of Lincoln and Douglas as speakers and debators, 68 & ed, Harry Emerson Fosdick's art of preaching, 71, C.C, Thomas; Rhetorical analysis of speeches, Allyn & Bacon, 67. Add: 423 E. College ST, Granville, OH 43023.

CROFT, BLANTON, b. Salem, Ky, Oct. 27, 33; m. 57; c. 3. SPEECH, DRAMA. B.S, Murray State Univ, 56; M.A, Univ. Mich, Ann Arbor, 62; fel, Purdue Univ, West Lafayette, 69-71, Ph.D.(speech educ), 71. Forensic dir. speech, Godwin Heights High Sch, Grand Rapids, Mich, 56-67; dir. forensics, W.Ga. Col, 66, 67-68; asst. debate coach, Purdue Univ, West Lafayette, 68-69; ASST. PROF. SPEECH & DRAMA & DIR. SPEECH & DRAMATIC EDUC, UNIV. MD, COLLEGE PARK, 71- U.S.A, 57-59, Res, 59-61. Speech Commun. Asn; Am. Forensic Asn. Speech and drama education; public address; communication. Publ: Senator Birch Bayh and the case for direct election, 11/69 & co-auth, An experimental study to determine the best instructional strategy for teaching discussion, 2/71, Ind. Speech J; co-auth, Handbook for high school speech, an aid to: Basic rhetoric of speech-communication, Addison-Wesley, 73. Add: Dept. of Secondary Education, University of Maryland College of Education, College Park, MD 20740.

CROFT, KENNETH, Linguistics, English as a Second Language. See Volume III, Foreign Languages, Linguistics & Philology.

CROMAN, CHARLOTTE, b. Boston, Mass. DRAMA, SPEECH. B.S, N.Y. Univ, 55, Ph.D.(drama), 63; M.S, South. Conn. State Univ, 59. Assoc. prof. Eng. & speech, MANHATTAN COMMUNITY COL, 64-71, PROF. SPEECH & THEATRE ARTS, 71-, chmn. dept, 64-69. Am. Fed. Teachers res. grant, 70-71; City Univ. New York res. grant, 71. Status of women in higher education. Publ: Co-ed, Social history of poverty, Garrett, 71. Add: Dept. of Speech Communication & Theatre Arts, Manhattan Community College, 1633 Broadway, New York, NY 10020.

CROMPTON, LOUIS, b. Port Colborne, Ont, Apr. 5, 25. ENGLISH. B.A, Univ. Toronto, 47, M.A, 48; A.M, Univ. Chicago, 50, Ph.D.(Eng), 54. Lectr. math, Univ. B.C, 48-49; ENG, Univ. Toronto, 53-55; asst. prof, UNIV. NEBR, 55-60, assoc. prof, 60-64, PROF, 64- Vis. asst. prof, Univ. Chicago, summer 60, Univ. Calif, Berkeley, spring 61. Christian Gauss Book Award, Nat. Phi Beta Kappa, 69. MLA; AAUP. Bernard Shaw; Victorian literature. Publ: Shaw the dramatist, Univ. Nebr, 69; ed, Shaw, the road to equality, Beacon, 71; plus others. Add: Dept. of English, University of Nebraska, Lincoln, NE 68508.

CROMWELL, HARVEY, b. Wanette, Okla, Aug. 16, 07; m. 31; c. 2. SPEECH. B.S, Okla. E.Cent. Col, 30; State Univ. Iowa, 37; M.A, Univ. Okla, 40; Ph.D. (pub. address & speech correction), Purdue Univ, 49. Instr, high schs, Okla, 29-33; agent, Metropolitan Life Insurance Co, Okla. City, Okla, 33-37; head dept. speech, El Reno Jr. Col. & high sch, Okla, 38-40; McMurry Col, 40-42; coordinator instr. training, U.S. Army Air Force Tech. Command, 42-44; instr. speech & coach debate, Purdue Univ, 44-49; PROF. SPEECH, MISS. STATE COL. WOMEN, 49-, DEAN GRAD SCH, & DIR. RES, 65-, head dept. speech, 49-67, dir. prog. superior stud, 62-64, dean instr, 67-69. Summer vis. prof, North. Mich. Univ, 50, 53; Univ. Miss, 51-54; Univ. Southwest. La, 56-59; N.Mex Highlands Univ. 60; mem, Nat. Intercol. Questions Comt, 60-62; mem, Pres. Comt. Employment of Handicapped, 66-; mem, Gov. Comt. Employment of Handicapped, Miss, 72. Speech Commun. Asn; South. Speech Commun. Asn; Conf. Deans South. Grad. Schs. Shifts of opinion resulting from oral propaganda; business and professional interviewing; motivation in public speaking. Publ: Working for more effective speech, 55, 64, 68 & Study guide for speech, 56, 64, 67, Scott; co-auth, Oral approach to phonetics, Merrill, 69; auth, The compact guide to parliamentary procedure, Crowell, 72; plus others. Add: Graduate School, Mississippi State College for Women, Columbus, MS 39701.

CRONEBERG, CARL GUSTAF, b. Sågmyra, Sweden, Apr. 26, 30; m. 61; c. 3. ENGLISH, LINGUISTICS. B.A, Gallaudet Col, 55; M.A, Cath. Univ. Am. 59. Instr. ENG, GALLAUDET COL, 57-60, asst. prof, 60-67, ASSOC. PROF, 67- English literature; anthropology. Publ: Co-auth, A dictionary of American sign language on linguistic principles, Gallaudet Col, 65. Add: Dept. of English, Gallaudet College, Washington, DC 20002.

CRONIN, GROVER JEREMIAH, JR, b. Waltham, Mass, June 23, 14; m. 46; c. 5. ENGLISH LITERATURE. A.B, Boston Col, 35; B.A, Oxford, 37, M.A, 41; Ph.D, Univ. Wis, 41. Asst, Univ. Wis, 37-39; instr. ENG, FORDHAM UNIV, 39-42, asst. prof, 46-52, from assoc. prof. to PROF, 52-, chmn. dept, 52-65. Mem. staff, Yale ed, Horace Walpole's Correspondence, 46-53. U.S.C.G, 43-46, Lt. Mediaeval Acad. Am; MLA; Mod. Humanities Res. Asn; Liturgical Arts Soc. Chaucer; taste and sensibility 1650-1800; English novel. Add: Dept. of English, Fordham University, Bronx, NY 10458.

CRONIN, JAMES EMMET, b. New York, N.Y, Nov. 10, 08. ENGLISH. A.B, Wesleyan Univ, 30, A.M, 34; Ph.D, Yale, 46. Instr, St. Joseph Col.(Conn), 35-38; Col. New Rochelle, 38-42; asst. circulation promotion mgr, Time Mag, 45-47; assoc. prof. Eng, St. Louis Univ, 48-62; adj. prof, Wesleyan Univ, 62-74; dir. grad. summer sch, 63-74; RETIRED. Lectr, Hunter Col, 47-48. U.S.N.R, 42-45, Lt. Comdr. Eighteenth century American literature. Publ: Hermann von Schrenk: a biography, Kuehn, Chicago, 59; co-auth, Literary types and themes, Holt, 60; ed, The diary of Elihu Hubbard Smith, Am. Philos. Soc. 73. Producer, Songs of the people (ballad album), Radio Corp. Am. Custom, 60. Add: Box 16, Townshend, VT 05353.

CRONIN, MORTON JOHN, b. Ann Arbor, Mich, Nov. 13, 17. ENGLISH, ANTHROPOLOGY. B.A, Wayne State Univ, 44, M.A, 45; fel, Am. Counc. Learned Socs, 51; Ph.D.(Am. stud), Univ. Minn, 53. Instr. Eng, Wayne State Univ, 44-46; Ore. State Col, 47-49; Eng. & anthrop, Univ. Minn, 52-55; from asst. prof. to PROF. ENG, CALIF. STATE UNIV, LOS ANGELES, 55- American studies. Publ: Currier & Ives, a content analysis, Am. Quart; Hawthorne on romantic love and the status of women, PMLA; Some notes on Emerson's prose diction, Am. Speech. Add: Dept. of English, California State University, Los Angeles, 5151 State College Dr, Los Angeles, CA 90032.

CRONKHITE, GEORGE FERRIS, b. Glens Falls, N.Y, July 25, 16. ENGLISH AND AMERICAN LITERATURE. A.B, Harvard, 38, A.M, 39, Ph.D.(Eng), 49. Teaching fel. & tutor, Harvard, 40-42, 46; instr. Eng. & Am. lit, Cornell Univ, 47-52, asst. prof. Eng, 52-59, dir. freshman Eng, 53-56, asst. dean, 59-63, lectr. Eng, 59-67, assoc. dean & secy. col. arts & sci, 63-67; assoc. prof. ENG, ITHACA COL, 67-69, PROF, 69-, chmn. dept, 72-73. Mem. exam. comt. in Eng. compos, Col. Bd. Advan. Placement Prog, 54-55. U.S.A, 42-45. MLA; Am. Stud. Asn. Nineteenth century American literature. Publ: The transcendental railroad; Howells turns to the inner life, New Eng. Quart, 57; Some varieties of inspiration, In: Aspects of American poetry, Ohio State Univ, 62. Add: Dept. of English, Ithaca College, Ithaca, NY 14850.

CROOK, EUGENE JOSEPH, b. Red Bud, Ill, Dec. 25, 41; m. 66; c. 4. ENGLISH. A.B, Univ. Ill, 66, M.A, 67, Ph.D.(Eng), 70. Teaching asst. ENG, Univ. Ill, 67-68; ASST. PROF, East. Ill. Univ, 69; FLA. STATE UNIV, 70- S.Atlantic Mod. Lang. Asn.(Old Eng. secy, 73-74); MLA; Early Eng. Text Soc; Mediaeval Acad. Am. Middle English language; medieval English literature; medieval religion. Publ: Ed, Handbook of Middle English grammar: phonology, Mouton, The Hague, 74; co-auth, The manciple: typology of the traitor, Lang. Quart, 73; auth, The place of medieval literature, Mo. Eng. Bull, 73; Pagan gold in Beowulf, Am. Benedictine Rev, 74. Add: Dept. of English, Florida State University, Tallahassee, FL 32306.

CROSBY, HARRY HERBERT, b. New England, N.Dak, Apr. 18, 19; m. 43; c. 4. AMERICAN LITERATURE, RHETORIC. B.A, Univ. Iowa, 41, M.A, 47; Ph.D, Stanford Univ, 53. Instr. rhetoric, Univ. Iowa, 46-47; San Jose State Col, 49-50; Univ. Iowa, 50-51, asst. prof, 51-58, writing supvr, 56-58; assoc. prof. COMMUN, BOSTON UNIV, 58-59, PROF. & CHMN. DEPT, 59- Consult, U.S. Air Force Acad, 53-60; dir. stud, Pakistan Air Force Acad. & educ. adv. to comdr-in-chief, Pakistan Air Force, 60-62. U.S.A.F, 42-46, Lt. Col. NCTE; Conf. Col. Compos. & Commun; MLA. Modern rhetoric; teaching methods and evaluation; American literature. Publ: Co-auth, Language, form, and idea, McGraw, 63; College writing, the rhetorical imperative, 68 & Just rhetoric, 72, Harper; The McLuhan explosion, Am. Bk. Co, 68; auth, The great diamond fraud, Am. Heritage, 57; plus others. Add: Dept. of Rhetoric, College of Basic Studies, Boston University, 871 Commonwealth Ave, Boston, MA 02215.

CROSBY, MURIEL, b. Wash, D.C, Mar. 1, 08. ENGLISH. B.S, Wilson Teachers Col, 36; M.A, Univ. Md, 42, D.Ed, 51. Teacher, Elem. Pub. Schs, Wash, D.C, 28-37, supvr, 37-47; assoc. dir. res, Curriculum Div, Silver-Burdett Publ. Co, 47-49; asst. supt. in charge elem. educ, PUB. SCHS, WILMINGTON, DEL, 51-65, asst. supt. DIV. EDUC. PROG, 65-67, acting supt, 67-68, ASSOC. SUPT, 68. Consult. urban educ, various sch. syst. & univs, 68- NEA Pacemaker Award, 64; Am. Asn. Univ. Women Award, 65; Nat. Conf. Christians & Jews Ann. Brotherhood Award, 65. NCTE (pres, 65, Distinguished Serv. Award, 69, Distinguished Lectr, 70); Asn. Supv. & Curriculum Develop.(pres, 66). English; human relations; supervision. Publ: Supervision as cooperative action, Appleton, 57; ed, Reading ladders for human relations, Am. Counc. Educ, 63; auth, Curriculum development for elementary schools in a changing society, Heath, 64; co-ed, Language programs for the disadvantaged, NCTE, 65; auth, An adventure in human relations, 65 & gen. ed, The world of language, Follett Elem. Eng. ser, 74, Follett; Elementary-school programs for the education of the disadvantaged, In: The educationally retarded and disadvantaged, Nat. Soc. Stud. Educ, 67; Meeting the needs of other divergent learners, In: The administrator and reading, Int. Reading Asn, 72; Who changes the curriculum and how?, In: Curriculum: quest for relevance, Houghton, 71. Add: 1627 N. Franklin St, Wilmington, DE 19806.

CROSLAND, GEORGE NATHANIEL, b. San Francisco, Calif, Oct. 22, 26; m. 58; c. 3. ENGLISH. B.A, Univ. Calif, Los Angeles, 53, M.A, 56, Ph.D. (Eng), 61. Instr. ENG, Ariz. State Univ, 59-61, asst. prof, 61-62; Univ. Puget Sound, 62-66, ASSOC. PROF, 66-68; CALIF. STATE UNIV, CHICO, 68- U.S. Merchant Marine, 45-48. English literature of the 17th and 18th centuries; contemporary English and American poetry. Publ: Dostoevski's The peasant Marey, Explicator, XXIV: item 64; Note on an unpublished manuscript by Robert Heath (fl 1650), Notes & Queries, 1/72. Add: Dept. of English, California State University, Chico, CA 95926.

CROSMAN, ROBERT TRUE, b. Feb. 18, 40; U.S. citizen; m. 67; c. 1. ENGLISH & AMERICAN LITERATURE. B.A, Univ. Calif, Berkeley, 63; pres. fel, Columbia Univ, 64, M.A, 65, N.Y. Regents fel, 68, Ph.D.(Eng), 71. Preceptor ENG, Columbia Col, 65-68; ASST. PROF, WILLIAMS COL, 69- Milton Soc. Am; MLA. John Milton; Norman Mailer; 17th and 20th English and American literature. Publ: Who was M'Intosh?, James Joyce Quart, winter 68; Review of four Mailer books, Kritikon Litterarum, 72. Add: 28 Cushing St, Providence, RI 02906.

CROSS, DONALD LEROY, b. Augusta, Maine, Sept. 7, 21; m. 46; c. 2. ENGLISH. B.A, Bowdoin Col, 43; M.A, Harvard, 47; Univ. Pa, 55. Instr. ENG, Mass. Inst. Technol, 47-48; Dartmouth Col, 48-51; ASST. PROF, UPSALA COL, 54-, DIR. FRESHMAN ENG, 60- U.S.A, 43-46. MLA; Col. Eng. Asn; Am. Stud. Asn. American civilization; 19th century American literature. Add: Dept. of English, Upsala College, East Orange, NJ 07017.

CROSS, GILBERT B, b. Manchester, Eng, May 2, 39; m. 65; c. 1. ENGLISH LITERATURE. B.A, Manchester Univ, 61; cert. educ, Univ. London, 62; M.A, Univ. Louisville, 65; Ph.D.(Eng), Univ. Mich, 71. Lectr. ENG, East. Ky. Univ, 65-66; instr, EAST. MICH, UNIV, 66-70, ASST. PROF, 70- AAUP; Brontë Soc; Soc. Theatre Res; Soc. Educ. in Film & TV. Drama; Brontes; theatre. Publ: Co-auth, Drury Lane Journal: selections from the diaries of James Winston 1819-1827, Soc. Theatre Res, 74; auth, Farewell to Hoffman?, Brontë Soc. Trans, 70; co-auth, The Drury Lane Portico, 1820, Nineteenth Century Theatre, 9/73 & E.J. Longley and the editorship of the Theatric Tourist, Theatre Notebook, 74. Add: Dept. of English, Eastern Michigan University, Ypsilanti, MI 48197.

CROSS, OLIVE HARDWICK, b. Conyers, Ga, July 13, 99; m. 24; c. 1. ENGLISH. A.B, Agnes Scott Col, 18; M.A, Columbia Univ, 20. Instr. ENG, FLA. STATE UNIV, 39-49, ASST. PROF, 49- Vis. prof. Eng. & Am. lit, Univ. Damascus, Syria, 59-61, Smith-Mundt grant, 59-60, Fulbright grant, 60-61; Smith-Mundt vis. prof. practical Eng. stud, Univ. Free Vietnam, 62-63. NCTE; MLA; Soc. Am. Archaeol. American fiction and newspapers; foreign students in the United States. Publ: Social and anti-social effects of the American newspaper, Columbia Univ, 20; Broken leg of a journey, Viewpoints, 62; Does current American fiction truly reflect American life?, Vietnamese-Am. Quart. J, 63. Add: 2302 Ellicott Dr, Tallahassee, FL 32303.

CROSS, RICHARD KEITH, b. Hackensack, N.J, May 19, 40; m. 70. ENGLISH, COMPARATIVE LITERATURE. A.B, Princeton, 62; univ. fels, Stanford Univ, 62-63 & 64, Woodrow Wilson fel, 65-66, M.A, 66, Ph.D.(Eng, comp. lit), 67. Instr. ENG, Dartmouth Col, 66-68; asst. prof, UNIV. CALIF, LOS ANGELES, 68-74, ASSOC. PROF, 74- Univ. Calif, Los Angeles summer fac. fel, 69; Univ. Calif. Humanities Inst. fel, fall 70; Fulbright Hays sr. lectr, Univ. Wuerzburg, Ger, 71-72; Am. Counc. Learned Soc. grant-in-aid, 73-74; Univ. Calif. Regents' fac. fel, spring 74. Philol. Asn. Pac. Coast. Modern British, French and American literature. Publ: Flaubert and Joyce: The rite of fiction, Princeton, 71; The humor of The Hamlet, 20th Century Lit, 1/67; Malcolm Lowry and the Columbian Eden, Contemporary Lit, winter 73. Add: Dept. of English, University of California, Los Angeles, CA 90024.

CROSSMAN, LESTER GERALD, b. Rosetown, Sask, May 24, 13; m. 44; c. 2. ENGLISH. B.A, Univ. Sask, 38, B.Ed, 41, M.A, 46; Ph.D.(Eng), Univ. Wash, 57. Asst. prof. ENG, UNIV. SASK, REGINA, 48-58, assoc. prof, 58-65, PROF, 65- R.C.A.F, 42-45. Asn. Can. Univ. Teachers Eng. Mark Twain; Shakespeare; Shaw. Add: Dept. of English, University of Saskatchewan, Regina, Sask, S4S 0A2, Can.

CROUCH, JACK HERBERT, b. Montpelier, Idaho, Aug. 13, 18; m. 39; c. 3. ENGLISH. A.B, Univ. Calif, Los Angeles, 39; M.A, Cornell Univ, 41, Ph.D. (drama, theatre), 51. Instr. drama, Mills Col, 41-42; instr. ENG, UNIV. COLO, BOULDER, 46-48, asst. prof, 48-54, assoc. prof, 54-60, PROF, 60- Lectr, Carleton Drama Festival, Carleton Col, 53; founder & dir, Colo. Shakespeare Festival, Boulder, 58-; vis. prof, Univ. Sask, 59-60; guest dir, Ore. Shakespeare Festival, 62; mem, Pres. Nat. Comt. to commemorate Shakespeare Quadricentennial, summer 64. U.S.N, 44-46. MLA; Nat. Theatre Conf. Elizabethan staging; contemporary drama; dramatic structure, tragedy and comedy. Publ: The theatre as literary experience, Carleton Drama Rev, 53. Add: Dept. of English, University of Colorado, Boulder, CO 80302.

CROUSHORE, JAMES HENRY, b. Freeburg, Pa, June 10, 14. AMERICAN LITERATURE. A.B, Lehigh Univ, 36, A.M, 40; Ph.D, Yale, 44. Instr, Mt. Union Col, 40-41; Carnegie Inst. Technol, 43; Lehigh Univ, 46-47; PROF. ENG, MARY WASHINGTON COL, 47-, DEAN, 72-, assoc. dean, 67-72. U.S.A, 44-46. MLA. The American novel; John W. De Forest. Add: Office of the Dean, Mary Washington College, Fredericksburg, VA 22402.

CROW, CHARLES ROHRER, JR, b. Braddock, Pa, June 27, 08. ENGLISH. A.B, Univ. Pittsburgh, 30, Ph.D, 48. Asst. ENG, UNIV. PITTSBURGH, 31-33, instr, 33-42, asst. prof, 46-51, assoc. prof, 51-55, prof, 55-70; distinguished serv. prof, 70-73, EMER. PROF, 73- A.U.S, 42-45, Staff Sgt. MLA. Publ: Co-auth, Style in prose fiction, Columbia Univ, 59; auth, Chiding the plays: then till now, Shakespeare Surv. 18, 65. Add: 210 Earlham St, Pittsburgh, PA 15205.

CROW, MARTIN MICHAEL, b. Crow's Mills, Pa, Oct. 30, 01. MIDDLE ENGLISH. A.B, Washington & Jefferson Col, 24; univ. scholar, Harvard, 24-25, A.M, 25; fel, Univ. Chicago, 32-33, Ph.D, 34. Instr. ENG, Univ. Ark, 25-28; Washington & Jefferson Col, 28-30; asst. prof, 30-31; UNIV. TEX, 34-45, assoc. prof, 45-50, prof, 50-72, EMER. PROF, 72-, chmn. dept, 46-49. Vis. prof, Univ. Chicago, 55-56; Univ. Tex. Res. Inst. res. grants, 52-53, 54-55, 58, 66-67; Am. Counc. Learned Soc. grants-in-aid, 58-59, 67-68; mem, Chaucer Libr. Comt, MLA, 67- U.S.A.AF, 42-44, Res, 44-53, Capt. MLA; Mod. Humanities Res. Asn, Gt. Brit; Mediaeval Acad. Am; S.Cent. Mod. Lang. Asn; Int. Arthurian Soc. Middle English dialects; 14th century England; Chaucer life-records. Publ: Co-ed, Chaucer's world, Columbia Univ. & Oxford, 48 & Chaucer life-records, Clarendon & Univ. Tex, 66; auth, Corrections in the Paris manuscript of Chaucer's Canterbury tales, XV: 5-18 & Materials for a new edition of the Chaucer life-records, XXXI: 1-12, Tex. Stud. Eng; John of Angoulême and his Chaucer manuscript, Speculum, XVII: 86-99; plus others. Add: Dept. of English, University of Texas, Austin, TX 78712.

CROWDER, ASHBY BLAND, JR, b. Richmond, Va, June 29, 41; m. 73. ENGLISH & AMERICAN LITERATURE. B.A, Randolph-Macon Col, 63; M.A, Univ. Tenn, Knoxville, 65; Ph.D.(Eng), Univ. London, 72. Instr. ENG, Centre Col, Ky, 65-67; ASST. PROF, East. Ky. Univ, 69-74; HENDRIX COL, 74- Ed, The complete works of Robert Browning (14 vols), Ohio Univ, 74- MLA; S.Atlantic Mod. Lang. Asn; Browning Inst; AAUP; South. Humanities Conf.(del-at-large, 74). Victorian literature; 20th century American fiction. Publ: A note on section VIII of Browning's Inn album, Stud. Browning, 73; Browning's intention in Christmas Eve, Aevum, 73. Add: Dept. of English, Hendrix College, Conway, AR 72032.

CROWDER, RICHARD H, b. Remington, Ind, Oct. 7, 09; m. 51. AMERICAN LITERATURE. A.B, DePauw Univ, 31, A.M, 33; Yale, 36-37; Ph.D, State Univ. Iowa, 44. Teacher, High Sch, Ind, 34-35; instr. ENG, Valparaiso Univ, 35-36; PURDUE UNIV, WEST LAFAYETTE, 37-45, asst. prof, 45-50, assoc. prof, 50-57, PROF, 57-, Res. Found. grant, 55, 63. Am. Philos. Soc. grant, 55; Church Soc. Col. Work fel, 58; Fulbright lectr, Univ. Bordeaux, 63-65. MLA; Midwest Mod. Lang. Asn. History of American poetry; American studies. Publ: Those innocent years: James Whitcomb Riley, Bobbs, 57; No featherbed to heaven: Michael Wigglesworth, Mich. State Univ, 62; Carl Sandburg, Twayne, 64; E.A. Robinson and the meaning of life, Chicago Rev, summer 61; Robinson's reputation: six observations, Colby Libr, Quart, 69; Poetry: 1900 to the 1930's, In: American literary scholarship, an annual, Duke Univ, 73; plus others. Add: Dept. of English, Purdue University, West Lafayette, IN 47907.

CROWELL, MICHAEL GARDNER, b. Philadelphia, Pa, June 17, 31; m. 56; c. 4. ENGLISH LITERATURE & LANGUAGE. B.A, Amherst Col, 53; M.A,

Northwest. Univ, 59, Ph.D.(Eng), 66. From asst. prof. to ASSOC. PROF. ENG, KNOX COL.(ILL), 61- U.S.N.R, 53-57, Lt.(jg). Ling. Soc. Am; NCTE. Application of linguistic theory; history of reactions to American English. Publ: Co-auth, Modern English grammar for teachers, Ronald, 70; auth, Richard Grant White and Americanisms, Am. Speech, 67; John Russell Bartlett's dictionary of Americanisms, Am. Quart, 72; Hunters of fishers? what kind of teacher do we train?, Eng. Educ, 72. Add: Dept. of English, Knox College, Galesburg, IL 61401.

CROWELL, NORTON B, b. Sioux City, Iowa, Jan. 10, 14. ENGLISH. B.S, South. Methodist Univ, 35, A.M, 37; A.M, Harvard, 39, Ph.D, 46. Instr. ENG, Carnegie Inst. Tech, 40-46, asst. prof, 46-47; Univ. N.Mex, 47-52, assoc. prof, 52-60, PROF, 60-69; ILL. STATE UNIV, 69- MLA. Romantic and Victorian periods, especially Browning. Publ: Alfred Austin: Victorian, 53, Triple soul: Browning's theory of knowledge, 63, The convex glass: the mind of Robert Browning, 68 & A reader's guide to Robert Browning, 73, Univ. N.Mex. Add: Dept. of English, Illinois State University, Normal, IL 61761.

CROWLEY, CORNELIUS PATRICK JOSEPH, b. Toronto, Ont, Sept. 14, 14. ENGLISH. B.A, Univ. Toronto, 36; M.A, Univ. Mich, 46, Ph.D.(Eng), 50. Head dept. Eng, UNIV. WINDSOR, 50-67, PROF. ENG. & DEAN GRAD. STUD, 67- Mem, Am. Counc. Learned Soc. Can. Asn. Univ. Res. Adminr; Can. Asn. Grad. Deans; Asn. Can. Univ. Teachers Eng; Mod. Humanities Res. Asn. Contemporary British fiction and literary criticism; cultural communications. Publ: Co-auth, Modern Catholic poetry, 38 & auth, A first book of modern Catholic prose & poetry, 47, Dent; The human image, Assumption Univ, 60; The human image in contemporary British fiction, C.S.M, Toronto, 62; The grail poetry of Charles Williams, Univ. Toronto Quart, 7/56; A view of executive obsolescence, Bus. Quart, 68; Stress and structure, In: Explorations in the psychology of stress and anxiety, Longmans, 69. Add: Graduate Studies, University of Windsor, Windsor, Ont. N9B 3P4, Can.

CROWLEY, JOSEPH DONALD, b. Middletown, Ohio, Oct. 31, 32; m. 54; c. 2. ENGLISH, AMERICAN LITERATURE. A.B, Univ. Notre Dame, 55; M.A, Ohio State Univ, 58, Ph.D.(Eng), 64. Instr. ENG, Ohio State Univ, 55-63; Univ. Del, 63-65, asst. prof, 65-67; assoc. prof, UNIV. MO-COLUMBIA, 67-72, PROF, 72- Hist. ed, Hawthorne's Short Fiction, Centenary Ed, 70-; Nat. Endowment Humanities fel, 71-72; Am. Philos. Soc. grant-in-aid, 72; ed. consult, Nineteenth Century Fiction, 72- MLA; Midwest Mod. Lang. Asn. Nineteenth century American literature; eighteenth century English fiction; Hawthorne, Defoe, Austen. Publ: Ed, Hawthorne: the critical heritage, 70 & Hawthorne: profiles in literature, 71 Routledge & Kegan Paul; ed, Robinson Crusoe Vol I, Oxford, 72; co-ed, Twice-told tales, Vol VIII, Centenary Ed, 74; Mosses from an old manse, Vol IX, Centenary Ed, 74 & The Snow image and other Twice-told tales, Vol X, Centenary Ed, 74; Ohio State Univ; The artist as mediator, In: Melville and Hawthorne in the Berkshires, Kent State Univ, 68; The unity of Hawthorne's Twice-told tales, Stud. Am. Fiction, spring 73; Hawthorne and Frost: the making of a poem, In: Frost centennial essays, Univ. Miss, 74. Add: Dept. of English, University of Missouri-Columbia, Columbia, MO 65201.

CROWNE, DAVID K, Comparative Literature, English. See Volume III, Foreign Languages, Linguistics & Philology.

CROWTHER, J. D. W, b. Folkestone, Eng, May 23, 19; Can. citizen. MIDDLE ENGLISH. B.A, Univ. B.C, 61; M.A, Bryn Mawr Col, 62, Ph.D.(Eng), 67. Asst. prof. ENG, UNIV. ALTA, 67-73, ASSOC. PROF, 73- Add: Dept. of English, University of Alberta, Edmonton, Alta. T6G 2E1, Can.

CROZIER, ALICE COOPER, b. New York, N.Y, June 29, 34; m. 68. AMERICAN LITERATURE. B.A, Radcliffe Col, 56; Ph.D.(hist. Am. civilization), Harvard, 64. Instr. ENG, Smith Col, 61-66; asst. prof, DOUGLASS COL, RUTGERS UNIV, 66-72, ASSOC. PROF, 72- Am. Asn. Univ. Women fel, 64-65; Nat. Endowment for Humanities fel, 71-72. American literature. Add: Dept. of English, Douglass College, Rutgers University, New Brunswick, NJ 08903.

CRUM, MABEL T, b. Symsonia, Ky, Sept. 26, 03; m. 50. ENGLISH LANGUAGE & LITERATURE. A.B, Univ. Ky, 33, fels, 37-38, 49-50, M.A, 38, Ph.D, 56. Teacher, pub. schs, Marshall County, Ky, 22-35, high schs, Trimble County, 35-37; from instr. to assoc. prof. ENG, WEST. CAROLINA UNIV, 38-56, prof, 56-70, head dept, 54-70, EMER. PROF, 70- NCTE; S.Atlantic Mod. Lang. Asn; Col. Eng. Asn; MLA. Lexington Theatre. Add: Dept. of English, Western Carolina University, Cullowhee, NC 28723.

CRUMP, GAIL BRUCE, b. Kirksville, Mo, Apr, 5, 42. MODERN BRITISH & AMERICAN LITERATURE. B.A. & B.S.Ed, Northeast Mo. State Col, 64; M.A, Univ. Ark, Fayetteville, 65, Ph.D.(Eng), 69. ASST. PROF. ENG, CENT. MO. STATE UNIV, 69- MLA; AAUP. Modern British and American fiction; modern drama; literature and film. Publ: Ed, Doctoral dissertations on D.H. Lawrence, 1931-1968: a bibliography, 70, auth, Gopher prairie or papplewick?, The virgin and the gipsy, as film, 71 & Women in love: novel and film, 71, D.H. Lawrence Rev. Add: Dept. of English, Central Missouri State University, Warrensburg, MO 64093.

CRUMP, GALBRAITH M, b. Elizabeth, N.J, Nov. 2, 29; m. 52; c. 5. ENGLISH. B.A, Hamilton Col, 51; M.A, Univ. Reading, Eng, 55; D.Phil, Oxford, 59. Asst, Univ. Wis, 55-56; instr. ENG, Yale, 58-62, asst. prof, 62-65; PROF, KENYON COL, 65-, CHMN. DEPT, 73- Morse res. fel, 61-62. Mil. Intell, U.S.A, 51-53. MLA. Renaissance and 18th century literature. Publ: Poems and translations of Thomas Stanley, Clarendon, 62; ed, Poems on affairs of state, 1685-1688, Yale, 68 & Twentieth century interpretations: Samson Agonistes, Prentice-Hall, 68. Add: Dept. of English, Kenyon College, Gambier, OH 43022.

CRUMP, REBECCA W, b. Elgin, Ill, Nov. 29, 44; m. 72. ENGLISH LITERATURE. B.A, State Col. Boston, 67; Ph.D.(Eng), Univ. Tex, Austin, 70. ASST. PROF. ENG, LA. STATE UNIV, BATON ROUGE, 70- Victorian literature, particularly the poetry of Christina Rossetti. Publ: Eighteen

moments' monuments: Christina Rossetti's Bouts-Rimes, sonnets in the Troxell collection, Princeton Univ. Libr. Chronicle, spring 72. Add: Dept. of English, Louisiana State University, Baton Rouge, LA 70803.

CRUPI, CHARLES WILLIAM, b. Wadsworth, Ohio, Apr. 6, 39; m. 60; c. 3. ENGLISH. A.B, Harvard, 61; M.A, Univ. Calif. Berkeley, 63; Ph.D.(Eng), Princeton, 67. Instr. ENG, Princeton, 66-68, asst. prof, 68-74; ASSOC. PROF, ALBION COL, 74- Vis. prof, Drew Univ, 73. MLA. Shakespeare; morality drama; modern drama. Add: Dept. of English, Albion College, Albion, MI 49224.

CRYMES, RUTH HELEN, b. Chattanooga, Tenn, Apr. 21, 24. ENGLISH, LINGUISTICS. B.A, Univ. Ore, 45, M.A, 48; dipl, Columbia Univ, 63, Ph.D. (Eng. ling), 65. Teacher Eng, high sch, Ore, 45-46, 48-50; asst, Univ. Ore, 46-48; teacher, Mid-Pac. Inst, Hawaii, 50-53; 54-56; Fulbright teacher, Thailand, 53-54; Kyoto, Japan, 56-58; instr. Eng. as for. lang, UNIV. HAWAII, 58-63, asst. prof, ENG. AS SECOND LANG, 63-67, assoc. prof, 67-72, PROF. & CHMN. DEPT, 72- Preceptor. prog. in Am. lang. instr. for. stud. ctr, Columbia Univ, 62-63; vis. lectr. Eng. & educ, Univ. N.Mex, summers 63 & 65; vis. asst. prof. ling, Teachers Col, Columbia Univ, 65-66. NCTE; Nat. Asn. For. Stud. Affairs; Ling. Soc. Am. Teachers of Eng. to Speakers of other Lang.(mem. ed. adv. bd, Quart, 72-75); Am. Counc. Teaching For. Lang. English as a second language; modern English grammar. Publ: Co-auth, Teaching English as a second language: a classified bibliography, East-West, 65; auth, Some systems of substitution correlations in modern American English, Mouton, 68; co-auth, Developing fluency in English, Prentice-Hall, 74. Add: Dept. of English as a Second Language, University of Hawaii, 1890 East-West Rd, Honolulu, HI 96822.

CUBBAGE, MOYNE L, b. Ohio, Sept. 14, 30; m. 60; c. 2. SPEECH COMMUNICATION. B.A, East. Mich. Univ, 52; M.A, Univ. Mich, 53, Ph.D. (speech), 61. Debate coach, Univ. Mich, 55-57, lectr. pub. address, 57-61; asst. prof. speech, Int. Christian Univ, Tokyo, 61-64; vis. asst. prof. speech & forensics, Cent. Mich. Univ, 64-65; assoc. prof. SPEECH, East. Mich. Univ, 65-67; PROF, R.I. COL, 67-, COORD. SPEECH COMMUN. AREA, 72-, chmn. dept. speech & theatre, 67-69. Mgr, Mich. High Sch. Forensic Asn, 57-61; deleg. adv. counc, Comt. on Discussion & Debate, Nat. Univ. Exten. Asn, 57-61, mem, Nat. Discussion & Debate Wording Comt, 58-61; vis. asst. prof. speech, Univ. Colo, summer 65; mem. comt. cooperation with for. univs, Speech Asn. Am, 66-69. Int. Commun. Asn; Speech Commun. Asn. (mem. comn. int. & intercult. commun, 69-); Int. Soc. Gen. Semantics; AAAS. Intercultural communication; decision making; conflict resolution. Publ: Speech education in Japan, Hist. Speech Educ. Newslett, 9/64; Labor management relations: analysis and interpretation, Forensic Quart, 4/65; Add: Dept. of Speech Communication and Theatre, Mt. Pleasant Ave, Providence, RI 02908.

CUBETA, PAUL MARSDEN, b. Middletown, Conn, Mar. 12, 25; m. 48; c. 3. ENGLISH. B.A, Williams Col.(Mass), 47; Ph.D.(Eng), Yale, 54. Instr. ENG, Williams Col.(Mass), 47-49; MIDDLEBURY COL, 52-55, asst. prof, 55-60, assoc. prof, 60-64, PROF, 64-, ACAD. V.PRES, 70-, chmn. div. humanities, 63-67, dean fac, 67-70. Asst. dir, Bread Loaf Writers' Conf, 55-64, dir. Sch. Eng, 64-; vis. fel, Harvard, 56-57; Carnegie Found. grant, U.S.N.R, 42-46, Lt.(jg). MLA. Shakespeare; modern drama. Publ: Modern drama for analysis, Holt, 50, 55, 62; ed, Twentieth Century interpretations of Richard II, Prentice-Hall, 71; Celebration of Charis: an evaluation of Jonsonian poetic strategy, Eng. Lit. Hist, 58; Jonsonian ideal: to Penshurst, Philol. Quart, 63; Marlowe's poet in Hero and Leander, Col. Eng, 4/65. Add: Old Chapel, Middlebury College, Middlebury, VT 05753.

CULBERT, TAYLOR, b. Brooklyn, N.Y, Sept. 15, 17; m. 49; c. 3. ENGLISH LITERATURE. B.A, Yale, 39; M.A, Univ. Mich, 47, Ph.D. 57. Instr. ENG, OHIO UNIV, 53-57, asst. prof, 57-61, assoc. prof, 61-65, PROF, 65-, EXEC. V.PRES. & DEAN FAC, 70-, PRES. UNIV. PRESS, 63-, dean grad. col, 65-70. U.S.A, 40-46, 46-65, Lt. Col. MLA. Medieval literature. Add: Office of Executive Vice President & Dean of Faculties, Ohio University, Athens, OH 45701.

CULBERTSON, HUGH McCLELLAN, b. Ferndale, Mich, Oct. 21, 35; m. 59; c. 2. COMMUNICATION THEORY. B.S, Mich. State Univ, 57, Ph.D.(commun), 66; M.S, Univ. Wis, 58. Asst. exten. ed, Coop. Exten. Serv, Mich. State Univ, 59-63; from asst. prof. to assoc. prof. JOUR, OHIO UNIV, 66-74, PROF, 74- Ohio Univ. Res. Inst. fac. res. award, 69-70. U.S.M.C, 58-59, Res, 59-63. Asn. Educ. Jour; Int. Commun. Asn. Interpretation of verbal and non-verbal symbols as a unit; factors affecting news judgement. Publ: Co-auth, Fundamentals of news reporting, Kendall-Hunt, 2nd ed, 73; co-auth, A study of graph comprehension difficulties, Audio-Visual Commun. Rev, 59; auth, The effect of art work on perceived writer stand, Jour. Quart, 69; The interpretation of a message in light of contextual magnitude & relevance, J. Commun, 70. Add: School of Journalism, Ohio University, Athens, OH 45701.

CULBERTSON, JAMES EDWIN, b. Kiowa, Okla, July 9, 12. SPEECH. B.S, Okla. State Univ, 34, A.M, 35, D.Ed, 46; Univ. South. Calif; N.Y. Univ; Univ. London; cert, Citizen House Sch. Theatre, Eng. Chmn. speech dept, Southeast. State Col, 37-43; Univ. Wyo, 43-46; lecture tour, 46-47; asst. prof. speech, IND. UNIV, BLOOMINGTON, 47-72, EMER. PROF. SPEECH & THEATRE, 72- Fulbright lectr, Univ. Manila, 53-54. Am. Theatre Asn; Speech Commun. Asn. Voice science; speech arts; history and phonetics of the theatre. Add: Dept. of Speech, Indiana University, Bloomington, IN 47401.

CULLEN, JACK B, b. Columbus, Ohio, Feb. 11, 20; m. 45; c. 1. SPEECH, B.Sc, Ohio State Univ, 41, M.A, 50, Ph.D.(speech), 55. Teacher, high sch, Ohio, 45-50; instr. speech educ, Ohio State Univ, 51-55; PROF. SPEECH, CALIF. STATE UNIV, LOS ANGELES, 55- U.S.A, 44-46, Sgt. Speech Commun. Asn. History and surveys of speech education; historical and experimental public speaking; recent American history. Add: Dept. of Speech, California State University, Los Angeles, CA 90032.

CULLEN, MAURICE RAYMOND, JR, b. Cambridge, Mass, May 18, 27; m. 57; c. 4. JOURNALISM, MASS COMMUNICATIONS. B.S, Boston Univ, 54, M.S, 55; Ph.D.(higher educ), Mich. State Univ, 66. Instr. JOUR, St.

Bonaventure Univ, 55-58; asst. prof, Univ. S.C, 58-64; Rutgers Univ, 66-68; ASSOC. PROF, BOSTON UNIV, 68- U.S.N, 44-46. Asn. Educ. in Jour. History of journalism and mass communications; American biography; mass communications and society. Publ: The Boston Gazette: a community newspaper, spring 59 & William Gilmore Simms, Southern journalist, summer 61, Jour. Quart; The school newspaper as an instrument in school-community relations, High Sch. J, 5/68. Add: School of Public Communication, Boston University, Boston, MA 02215.

CULLEN, PATRICK COLBORN, b. Crisfield, Md, Oct. 7, 40. ENGLISH. B.A, Wash. Col, 62; M.A, Brown Univ, 64, Ph.D.(Eng), 67. Asst. prof. ENG, RICHMOND COL.(N.Y), 67-71, ASSOC. PROF, 71-, MEM. FAC. GRAD. CTR, 73- City Univ. New York res. grant, 68-69; Am. Counc. Learned Soc. grant-in-aid, 70. MLA; Renaissance Soc. Am; Milton Soc. Am. English and comparative Renaissance literature; English and comparative medieval literature; Victorian literature. Publ: Spenser, Marvel, and Renaissance pastoral, Harvard, 70; Infernal triad: the flesh, the world, and the devil in Spenser and Milton, Princeton, 74; Imitation and metamorphosis: the golden-age eclogue in Spenser, Milton and Marvell, 69 & Marvell's Little T.C, 70, PMLA; Guyon Microchristus: the cave of Mammon re-examined, ELH, 70. Add: 300 W. 108th St, 8D, New York, NY 10025.

CULLEN, WILLIAM H, b. Brosher Falls, N.Y, Feb. 11, 19; m. 43; c. 1. ENGLISH, EDUCATION. B.S, State Univ. N.Y. Col. Potsdam, 47; M.Ed, St. Lawrence Univ, 52. Instr. Eng, Chateaugay Cent. Sch, 47-64; asst. prof. ENG. & ENG. EDUC, STATE UNIV. N.Y. COL. POTSDAM, 64-66, ASSOC. PROF, 66- U.S.A.A.F, 42-45, 1st Lt. NEA; NCTE; Conf. Eng. Educ. English education, especially secondary; group speech and informal classroom dramatics. Publ: The first thirty minutes of choral speaking, Eng. J, 3/68. Add: Dept. of English, State University of New York College at Potsdam, Potsdam, NY 13676.

CULLER, ARTHUR DWIGHT, b. McPherson, Kans, July 25, 17; m. 41; c. 2. ENGLISH. A.B, Oberlin Col, 38; Mitchell & univ. fels, Yale, 39-41, Ph.D.(Eng), 41; hon. D.Litt, Merrimack Col, 72. Instr. ENG, Cornell Univ, 41-42; Yale, 46-49, asst. prof, 49-55, assoc. prof, Univ. Ill, 55-58; PROF, YALE, 58- Fulbright res. fel, Eng, 50-51; Gugenheim fel, 61-62; mem, PMLA Adv. Comt, 71-74. Civilian Pub. Serv, 43-46. MLA. Victorian literature. Publ: Imperial intellect, 55 & Imaginative reason: the poetry of Matthew Arnold, 66, Yale; ed, Apologia Pro Vait Sua, 56 & Poetry and criticism of Matthew Arnold, 61, Houghton. Add: 852 Yale Station, New Haven, CT 06520.

CULLER, HELEN SIMPSON, b. Dallas, Tex, Mar. 21, 15; m. 41; c. 2. ENGLISH. B.A, South. Methodist Univ, 35, M.A, 36; Ph.D.(Eng), Yale, 43. Instr. ENG, Morris Col.(Tex), 36-38; South. Methodist Univ, 38-40; lectr, Univ. Ill, Urbana, 56-58; asst. prof, SOUTH. CONN. STATE COL, 58-66, assoc. prof, 67-72, PROF, 72- Victorian literature; Dante Gabriel Rossetti; drama. Publ: Co-auth, Sources of Rosetti's The king's tragedy, Stud. Philol, 7/44. Add: Dept. of English, Southern Connecticut State College, New Haven, CT 06515.

CULMSEE, CARLTON FORDIS, b. St. Ansgar, Iowa, Sept. 18, 04; m. 32; c. 1. JOURNALISM. B.S, Brigham Young Univ, 32, A.M, 37; Univ. South. Calif, 33; Ph.D, State Univ, Iowa, 40. Secy. exten. div, Brigham Young Univ, 32-39, dir, 39-45, instr, jour, 34-37, asst. prof, 37-39, assoc. prof, 39-40, prof, 40-45; prof. AM. CIVILIZATION & dean col. humanities & arts, UTAH STATE UNIV, 45-71, EMER. PROF, 71- Vis. prof, Nat. Chengchi Univ, 55-56. U.S.N, 42-45, Lt. Comdr. Am. Soc. Jour. Sch. Admin. American civilization; concept of hostile nature in frontier literature; responsible exercise of creative power; isolation and unity. Add: College of Humanities & Arts, Utah State University, Logan, UT 84321.

CULP, JAMES WILLIAM, b. Benton, Ky, Sept. 2, 18; m. 46. ENGLISH. B.A, Abilene Christian Col, 49; M.A, Vanderbilt Univ, 50, South. Fel. Fund fel, 55-56, Ph.D.(Eng), 56. Instr. ENG, David Lipscomb Col, 50-52; asst. prof, Abilene Christian Col, 52-56, assoc. prof, 56-59, prof. & head dept, 59-67; PROF, TEX. TECH UNIV, 67-, ASSOC. DEAN ARTS & SCI, 74- U.S.A, 42-45. Col. Eng. Asn; MLA; NCTE; Renaissance Soc. Am; Shakespeare Asn. Am. English Renaissance drama; 20th century British poetry. Add: 3315 20th St, Lubbock, TX 79409.

CULP, RALPH BORDEN, b. Monroe, La, Nov. 13, 29; m. 56; c. 4. SPEECH & DRAMA. B.A. & M.A, South. Methodist Univ, 57; Ph.D.(speech & drama), Cornell Univ, 62. Asst. speech, Cornell Univ, 58-59; instr, Rutgers Univ, 59-62, asst. prof, 62-65; assoc. prof. drama & speech, Univ. Tex, El Paso, 65-67, prof, 67-71, dir. theatre, 65-68, chmn. dept, 68-71; PROF. SPEECH & DRAMA, N.TEX. STATE UNIV, 71-, dir. div. drama, 71-73. Lectr. theatre hist, Adult Educ. Counc. Raritan Valley, 62-65; consult. speech, N.J. 4-H Club Pub. Speaking Proj, 64-65; drama ed, South. Speech Commun. J, 71-; consult, Dallas Independent Sch. Dist, 73- U.S.A.F, 50-55, Res, 55-58, 1st Lt. Speech Commun. Asn; Am. Theatre Asn; AAUP. Theatre history and criticism; speech communication; playwriting. Publ: Basic types of speech, 68 & The theatre and its drama: principles and practice, 71, W.C. Brown; Charles Sears Baldwin, Speech Teacher, 9/61; Drama and theatre in the American Revolution, Speech Monogr, 3/65; A study of Falstaff as a tragic character, Shakespeare Newslett, 3/65. Add: Dept. of Speech & Drama, North Texas State University, Denton, TX 76203.

CULROSS, JACK LEWIS, b. Rochester, N.Y, June 4, 41; m. 66; c. 2. ENGLISH. B.S, Spring Hill Col, 63; M.A, La. State Univ, Baton Rouge, 66, Ph.D.(Eng), 70. Instr. ENG, La. State Univ, 68-70; ASST. PROF, EAST. KY. UNIV, 70- Victorian literature; literary criticism. Add: Dept. of English, Eastern Kentucky University, Richmond, KY 40475.

CULVER, MONTGOMERY MORTON, b. Pittsburgh, Pa, Feb. 22, 29; m. 51, 57; c. 2. ENGLISH. B.A, Univ. Pittsburgh, 49, M.A, 50; Ph.D.(Eng), Univ. Ill, 59. Instr. ENG, UNIV. PITTSBURGH, 53-56, asst. prof, 56-62, assoc. prof, 62-69, PROF, 69- MLA. Study and teaching of imaginative writing; short story and novel structure. Publ: Black water blues, Atlantic, 5/50; Lousy luck, Esquire, 7/62; Chance of a lifetime, Saturday Evening Post, 1/66. Add: 14 Forest Hills Rd, Pittsburgh, PA 15221.

CUMINGS, MELINDA FELDT, b. San Francisco, Calif, Oct. 10, 43; m. 68. MODERN LITERATURE. B.A, Lone Mountain Col, 65; M.A, Purdue Univ, Lafayette, 66; Ph.D.(Eng), Univ. Wis-Madison, 72. Asst. prof. Eng, Purdue Univ, 72-73. MLA. Publ: Night and day: Virginia Woolf's visionary synthesis of reality, Mod. Fiction Stud, fall 72. Add: 721 W. Wrightwood, Chicago, IL 60614.

CUMMING, ELIZABETH CHANDLER, b. Danvers, Mass, Jan. 27, 06; m; c. 2. ENGLISH. B.A, Smith Col, 26; B.A, Oxford, 28, M.A, 32. Mem. fac. Eng, Smith Col, 28-31; assoc. prof, Queens Col.(N.C), 53-63; Fulbright travel grant, prof. Am. lit. & dir. inst. spoken Eng, Annamalai Univ, Madras, 63-64. Vis. prof, Shikoku Col, Japan, summer 64; assoc. prof, Davidson Col, summer 66. S.Atlantic Mod. Lang. Asn. American literature, especially Hawthorne. Publ: Tales and romances of Nathaniel Hawthorne, Smith Col. Stud. Mod. Lang; Hawthorne's spectator, New Eng. Quart; co-auth, The treasure of Alnwick Castle, Am. Heritage, 69. Add: 313 Woodland St, Davidson, NC 28036.

CUMMING, WILLIAM PATTERSON, b. Nagoya, Japan, Oct. 31, 00; U.S. citizen; m. 31; c. 2. ENGLISH. A.B, Davidson Col, 21; A.M, Princeton, 22, Ph.D, 25. Instr, Williams Col, 26-27; asst. prof. ENG, DAVIDSON COL, 27-29, assoc. prof, 29-37, prof, 37-61, Irvin prof, 61-68, chmn. dept, 46-48, 52-54, 61-63, 64-67, EMER. IRVIN PROF, 68- Attaché, U.S. Dept. State, 45-46; Guggenheim fel, 58-59; Fulbright lectr, Annamalai Univ, 63-64; vis. prof, Shikoku Col, Japan, 64; Nebenzahl lectr. hist. cartog, Newberry Libr, spring 70. MLA; S.Atlantic Mod. Lang. Asn. (pres, 56-57). Middle English; early American historical cartography and travel literature. Publ: Revelations of St. Birgitta, Oxford, 29; Discoveries of John Lederer, Univ. Va, 58; Southeast in early maps, Princeton, 58, 2nd ed, Univ. N.C, 62; North Carolina in maps, 66 & Captain James Wimble, his maps and the colonial cartography of the North Carolina coast, 69, N.C. Dept. Arch. & Hist; co-auth, The discovery of North America, Am. Heritage, 71, Albin Michel, Paris & C. Bertelmann, Berlin, 72; co-ed, A map of the British Empire by Henry Popple, H. Margary, 72; auth, Influence of Ovid's Metamorphoses on Spenser's Mutabilitie Cantos, Stud. Philol, 4/31; Geographical misconceptions of the Southeast in the cartography of the seventeenth and eighteenth centuries, J. South. Hist, 38. Add: Box 306, Davidson, NC 28036.

CUMMINGS, DONALD WAYNE, b. Seattle, Wash, May 21, 35; m. 56; c. 3. ENGLISH. B.A, Univ. Wash, 58, M.A, 64, Ph.D.(Eng), 65. Instr. Eng, CENT. WASH. STATE COL, 60-63, asst. prof, 63-66, assoc. prof. ENG, 66-71, PROF, 71-, dir. compos, 66-71. Teacher Eng, Newport High Sch, Bellevue, 71-72. Poetics; semantics; English pedagogy, especially teaching writing. Publ: Co-auth, Writing: plans, drafts, and revisions, Random, 71, Tempo: life, work, and leisure, Houghton, 74; Metrical boundaries and rhythm-phrases, Mod. Lang. Quart, 12/67, Rhetorical syntax, economy and the theme-rheme distinction, 69 & Semantic recurrence and rhetorical form, 71, Lang. & Style. Add: Dept. of English, Central Washington State College, Ellensburg, WA 98926.

CUMMINGS, PETER MARCH, b. Manchester, N.H, Nov. 28, 41; m. 65; c. 1. ENGLISH LITERATURE. B.A, Cornell Univ, 63, Danforth fel, 63-64, M.A, 64; Danforth fel, Univ. N.C, Chapel Hill, 64-68, Ph.D.(Eng), 71. Lect. asst, Cornell Univ, 63-64; instr. ENG. LIT, Copenhagen Univ, 64-65; Washington & Lee Univ, 68-69; ASST. PROF, HOBART & WILLIAM SMITH COLS, 70- AAUP. Renaissance poetry and drama; literary criticism. Publ: Co-auth, 24 American poets, Gad, Copenhagen, 66; auth, Spenser's Amoretti as an allegory of love, Tex. Stud. Lang. & Lit, 70; Northrop Frye and the necessary hybrid: criticism as aesthetic humanism, In: The quest for imagination, Case West. Reserve Univ, 71; Bicycle story: some theory and practice, Boston Phoenix, spring 74; plus others. Add: Dept. of English, Hobart & William Smith College, Pulteney St, Geneva, NY 14456.

CUMMINGS, SHERWOOD, b. Weehawken, N.J, Mar. 5, 16; m. 39; c. 2. ENGLISH. B.S, Univ. Ill, 38; M.A, Univ. Wis, 46, Ph.D.(Eng), 51. Asst. Eng, Univ. Wis, 46-48; instr, Univ. S.Dak, 48-51, asst. prof, 51-53, assoc. prof, 53-56, prof, 56-63, assoc. prof. AM. LIT, CALIF. STATE UNIV. FULLERTON, 63-65, PROF, 65- MLA; Am. Stud. Asn; Am. Lit. Group. Literature and science; 19th century American literature. Add: 1810 Skyline Way, Fullerton, CA 92631.

CUMMINS, JOHN W, b. Bellevue, Pa, Aug. 17, 20; m. 48; c. 1. ENGLISH. B.A, Ohio Wesleyan Univ, 42, M.A, 48; Ph.D.(Eng), Univ. Pa, 64. Teaching fel. ENG, Ohio Wesleyan Univ, 46-47; Univ. N.C, 47-50; asst. instr, Univ. Pa, 50-54; asst. prof, CHATHAM COL, 54-64, assoc. prof, 65-72, PROF, 72-, Buhl assoc. prof, 68-69. U.S.N.R, 42-46, Lt.(sg). MLA; NCTE. Victorian literature; English literature, 1880-1938. Add: Dept. of English, Chatham College, Pittsburgh, PA 15232.

CUMMINS, WALTER M, b. Long Branch, N.J, Feb. 2, 36; m. 57; c. 2. ENGLISH. B.A, Rutgers Univ, 57; M.A. & M.F.A, Univ. Iowa, 62, Ph.D.(Eng), 65. Instr. ENG, Univ. Iowa, 62-65; asst. prof, FAIRLEIGH DICKINSON UNIV, 65-69, ASSOC. PROF, 69- U.S.A.R, 58-64. AAUP; Col. Eng. Asn. Publ: A stranger to the deed, 68 & Into temptation, 68, Caravelle Bks; co-ed, The other sides of reality, Bryd & Fraser, 72. Add: 285 Madison Ave, Madison, NJ 07940.

CUNDIFF, PAUL A, b. Somerset, Ky, Nov. 14, 09. ENGLISH. A.B, Georgetown Col, 33; A.M, Univ. Ky, 35; Ph.D, Cornell Univ, 40. Teacher, high sch, Ky, 33; instr, Univ. Ky, 35-36; Cornell Univ, 36-40; mem. faculty, Wright Jr. Col, 40-42; instr, Northwest. Univ, 45-46; assoc. prof. ENG. & head dept, Sampson Col, 46-47; prof, Butler Univ, 47-61, head dept, 47-53, dean col. lib. arts & sci, 53-59; H. RODNEY SHARP PROF, UNIV. DEL, 62-, chmn. dept. 61-66. U.S.A, 42-45. MLA. Robert Browning. Publ: Browning's ring metaphor and truth, Scarecrow, 72. Add: Dept. of English, University of Delaware, Newark, DE 19711.

CUNNINGHAM, DOLORA GALLAGHER, b. Calif, Sept. 4, 20; div. ENGLISH. A.B, Stanford Univ, 44, M.A, 46, Ph.D.(Eng), 53. Instr. humanities & lit, Reed Col, 52-54; ENG, State Univ. N.Y. Harpur Col, 54-56, asst. prof, 56-59; from asst. prof. to PROF, SAN FRANCISCO STATE UNIV, 59- Summers, Folger Shakespeare Libr. fel, 55; Huntington Libr. fel, 59; exec. dir,

Inst. Renaissance Stud, Ore. Shakespeare Festival, Ashland, 63-68; Am. Philos. Soc. grant, summer 66. MLA; Renaissance Soc. Am. Shakespeare and Elizabethan drama; literary criticism; Renaissance intellectual history. Publ: The Jonsonian masque as a literary form, E.L.H, 6/55 & In: Ben Jonson: a collection of critical essays, Prentice-Hall, 63; The characterization of Shakespeare's Cleopatra, Winter 55 & Macbeth: tragedy of the hardened heart, Winter 63, Shakespeare Quart. Add: Dept. of English, San Francisco State University, San Francisco, CA 94132.

CUNNINGHAM, DONALD HAYWARD, b. Columbia, Mo, May 21, 35; m. 57; c. 1. ENGLISH LITERATURE. A.B, Univ. Mo-Columbia, 61, M.A, 62, Ph.D.(Eng), 72. Instr. ENG, Univ. Mo-Columbia, 62-66; South. Ill. Univ, Carbondale, 66-71, asst. prof, 71-72; ASSOC. PROF, MOREHEAD STATE UNIV, 72- Ed, Tech. Writing Teacher, 73- U.S.N, 53-57, Nat. Guard, 52-53. NCTE; Asn. Teachers Tech. Writing. Technical writing; bibliography. Publ: Ed, A reading approach to professional police writing, C.C. Thomas, 72; co-auth, An annotated bibliography on the teaching of technical writing, 5/70 & auth, Books on police writing, 5/72, Col. Compos. & Commun; Toward a comprehensive bibliography on technical writing, J. Tech. Writing & Commun, winter 73. Add: Div. of Languages & Literature, Morehead State University, Morehead, KY 40351.

CUNNINGHAM, FRANK ROBERT, b. Philadelphia, Pa, Aug. 15, 37. ENGLISH, DRAMA. A.B, Villanova Univ, 59, M.A, 62; Parkhurst res. fel, Lehigh Univ, 69-70, Ph.D.(Eng), 70. Instr. ENG, Lehigh Univ, 66-68; ASST. PROF, Franklin & Marshall Col, 68-69; Fordham Univ, 70-71; KANS. STATE UNIV, 71- Vis. asst. prof, Calif. State Univ, San Jose, 73-74. MLA; Midwest Mod. Lang. Asn; Midwest Am. Stud. Asn. Modern drama; 20th century American literature. Publ: The O. Henry prize story awards, 1919-1966, Sewanee Rev, summer 69; Joyce's Exiles: a problem of dramatic stasis, Mod. Drama, 2/70; The great god Brown, and Eugene O'Neill's Romantic vision, Ball State Univ. Forum, summer 73. Add: Dept. of English, Kansas State University, Manhattan, KS 66506.

CUNNINGHAM, IRMA EWING, American Dialectology, Modern Grammar. See Volume III, Foreign Languages, Linguistics & Philology.

CUNNINGHAM, JAMES VINCENT, b. Cumberland, Md, Aug. 23, 11; m; c. 1. RENAISSANCE LITERATURE. A.B, Stanford Univ, 34, Ph.D, 45. Instr. ENG, Stanford Univ, 37-45; asst. prof, Univ. Hawaii, 45-46; Univ. Chicago, 46-52; Univ. Va, 52-53; from assoc. prof. to PROF, BRANDEIS UNIV, 53- Guggenheim fels, 59-60, 67-68; Nat. Endowment on Arts grant-in-aid, 66-67. Shakespeare; epigram; poetry. Publ: Woe or wonder, 51, The exclusions of a rhyme, 60, Tradition and poetic structure, 60, To what strangers, what welcome, 64 & The collected poems and epigrams, 71, Swallow; plus others. Add: Dept. of English, Brandeis University, Waltham, MA 02154.

CUNNINGHAM, JOHN M, b. Wichita Falls, Tex. ENGLISH LITERATURE. B.A, South. Methodist Univ, 57; M.A, Duke Univ, 59, Ph.D.(Eng), 69. Grad. tutor ENG, Duke Univ, 60-61 & 62-63; instr, Trinity Univ, 64-65; Univ. N.C, Greensboro, 65-66; Duke Univ, 67-69; asst. prof, HOLLINS COL, 69-73, ASSOC. PROF, 73-, CHMN. DEPT, 74- MLA; S.Atlantic Mod. Lang. Asn. English Romantic poets; 18th century literature; 17th century poetry. Publ: Review essay on Flannery O'Connor, South. Humanities Rev, (in press). Add: Dept. of English, Hollins College, Hollins College, VA 24020.

CUNNINGHAM, RICHARD EARLE, b. Utica, N.Y, Nov. 7, 28; m. 56; c. 6. ENGLISH. A.B, Univ. Notre Dame, 50, M.A, 58; Ph.D.(Eng), Univ. Ill, 65. Asst. prof. ENG, Marquette Univ, 64-67; assoc. prof, KEENE STATE COL, 67-71, PROF, 71- Danforth Found. Assoc, 68-, chmn, New Eng. nominating comt, 73-76. Intel.C, U.S.A, 54-56, Spec. agent. MLA; Thoreau Soc. American literature of the 17th, 18th and 19th centuries; English literature of the 19th century. Add: Dept. of English, Keene State College, Keene, NH 03431.

CUNNINGHAM, VELMA TERESA, b. Woodbine, Iowa, Nov. 27, 08; m. 38; c. 2. ENGLISH. B.A, Univ. Iowa, 30, M.A, 35. Teacher, pub. schs, Iowa, 30-35, supvr. auditorium activities & drama, high sch, 35-37; ASSOC. PROF. ENG, JUDSON COL, 37-39, 46- NCTE; S.Atlantic Mod. Lang. Asn. English drama; romantic English poetry; English novel. Add: 113 Murfee Ave, Marion, AL 36756.

CUNNINGHAM, WILLIAM F, JR, b. Holyoke, Mass, Feb. 9, 31; m. 56. ENGLISH LITERATURE. A.B, Col. Holy Cross, 54; M.A, Boston Col, 56; Ph.D, Univ. Pittsburgh, 61. Asst, Boston Col, 54-55; instr. ENG, Duquesne Univ, 55-60; asst. prof, 60-63; LeMOYNE COL.(N.Y), 63-65, assoc. prof, 65-71, PROF, 71-, chmn. dept, 65-71. MLA; NCTE; Am. Soc. 18th Century Stud; AAUP. English literature and art, 1660-1800; satire. Publ: Charles Churchill and the satiric portrait, In: Essays and studies in language and literature, Duquesne Univ, 64; contrib, Symposium: the concept of the persona in satire, Satire Newletter, spring 66; The Rosciad of 1750, Restoration & 18th-Century Theatre Res, 5/71. Add: Dept. of English, LeMoyne College, Syracuse, NY 13214.

CURRAN, EILEEN MARY, b. Ann Arbor, Mich, May 11, 27. ENGLISH LITERATURE. B.A, Cornell Univ, 48, Ph.D.(19th century Eng. lit), 57; B.A, Cambridge, 50, M.A, 53. Instr. ENG, Univ. N.H, 51-54; Ohio Univ, 56-58; COLBY COL, 58-60, asst. prof, 60-66, assoc. prof, 66-73, PROF, 73- MLA. Victorian literature. Publ: Assoc. ed, The Wellesley index to Victorian periodicals, Vol. I, 66 & co-ed, Vol. II, 72, Univ. Toronto; auth, The Foreign quarterly review on Russian and Polish literature, Slavonic & E.Europ. Rev, 12/61; Carlyle's first contribution to the Foreign quarterly review, Victorian Periodicals Newslett, 6/68; George Darley and the London English professorship, Mod. Philol, 73. Add: Dept. of English, Colby College, Waterville, ME 04901.

CURRAN, MARY DOYLE, b. Holyoke, Mass, May 10, 17. ENGLISH. A.B, Univ. Mass, 40; A.M, State Univ. Iowa, 41, Ph.D, 46. Instr, State Univ. Iowa, 46; Wellesley Col, 46-49, asst. prof. ENG, 49-55; lectr, Queens Col. (N.Y), 55-56, asst. prof, 56-61, assoc. prof, 61-67; PROF, UNIV. MASS, BOSTON, 67- Fulbright lectr, Am. & Eng. lit, Finland, 62-63. Gerard Manley Hopkins; Irish literature, particularly Yeats and Joyce; creative writing. Publ: The devil's advocate (a story), autumn-winter 64-65; Mrs. Reardon's gamble, winter 66 & My mother and politics, winter-spring 72, Mass. Rev, plus others. Add: Dept. of English, University of Massachusetts, 100 Arlington St, Boston, MA 02116.

CURRAN, RONALD THOMAS, b. Pittsburgh, Pa, Oct. 6, 38; m. 69; c. 1. AMERICAN LITERATURE & STUDIES. A.B, Grove City Col, 60; M.A, Univ. Pittsburgh, 62; Goethe Inst, Munich, 64; Am. Quart. fel, Univ. Pa, 67-68, Ph.D.(Eng), 69. Instr, Turkish War Col, 62-64; ENG. & AM. LIT, Univ. Pa, 68-69; ASST. PROF, UNIV. PITTSBURGH, 69-, fac. arts & sci. res. fel, 70 & 74. Instr, Univ. Md. Near E. Div, 63; ed. asst, Am. Quart, 67-69; lectr, Univ. Pittsburgh Community Lect. Ser, 70, 71 & 74. Melville Soc; MLA (Am. Lit. Group); Asn. Dept. Eng. American Renaissance; Modern American literature; American studies. Publ: Ed, Witches, wraiths & warlocks: supernatural tales of the American Renaissance, Fawcett, 71; auth, The individual & the military institution in Hemingway's novels and Collier's dispatches, Rev. Langues Vivantes, 68; Fallen King as scapegoat in Fiedler's Nude croquet, Notes Contemporary Lit, 74; The reluctant Yankee in Hawthorne's abortive Gothic romances, Nathaniel Hawthorne J, 74. Add: Dept. of English, University of Pittsburgh, Pittsburgh, PA 15260.

CURRAN, SONIA TERRIE, b. New York, N.Y, Dec. 12, 42; m. 66. MEDIEVAL ENGLISH LITERATURE. B.A, City Col. New York, 64; M.A, Ind. Univ. Bloomington, 66; Ph.D.(Eng), Univ. Wis-Madison, 73. Instr. ENG, Youngstown State Univ, 66-69; teaching asst, Univ. Wis-Madison, 71-73; ASST. PROF, PROVIDENCE COL, 73- Add: Dept. of English, Providence College, Providence, RI 02918.

CURRAN, THOMAS M, b. Cambridge, Mass, Jan. 5, 22. ENGLISH. A.B, Spring Hill Col, 47; M.A, Boston Col, 55; Ph.D, Fordham Univ, 60. Asst. prof. ENG, Lenox Div, Boston Col, 59-66; Fairfield Univ, 66-71; from assoc. prof. to PROF, TUSKEGEE INST, 71- MLA. Literary theory and criticism; Chaucer. Add: Dept. of English, Tuskegee Institute, Tuskegee, AL 36088.

CURRENT-GARCIA, EUGENE, b. New Orleans, La, July 8, 08; m. 35; c. 3. AMERICAN LITERATURE. B.A, Tulane Univ, 30, fel, 30-32, M.A, 32; A.M, Harvard, 42, Ph.D.(Am. civilization), 47. Instr. Eng, Univ. Nebr, 36-39; tutor Am. lit, Harvard, 42-43; dir. lang. teaching prog, Nicaragua, 43-44; instr. Eng, La. State Univ, 44-47; asst. prof. AM. LIT, AUBURN UNIV, 47-50, assoc. prof, 50-53, prof, 53-64, HARGIS PROF, 64- Ford Found. fel, Princeton, 53-54; Fulbright lectr. Am. lit, Univ. Salonika, Greece, 56-58; U.S. State Dept. specialist, lecturing in S.Am, 61; co-ed, South. Humanities Rev. S.Atlantic Mod. Lang. Asn.(exec. comn, 66-68); South. Humanities Conf.(secy-treas, 60-63, v.chmn, 67-68); MLA; Int. Inst. Arts & Lett; Soc. Stud. South. Lit. Southwest frontier humor writers; development of the short story in America; 19th century American literature. Publ: Co-auth, American short stories, 52, 64, What is the short story?, 61 & 74, Realism and romanticism in fiction, 62 & co-ed, Short stories of the western world, 69, Scott; auth, O. Henry: William Sydney Porter, Twayne, 65; co-ed, Shem, Ham, & Japheth: the papers of William O. Tuggle, Univ. Ga, 73; auth, Mr. Spirit and the big bear of Arkansas, Am. Lit, 55; O. Henry's Southern heritage, 64 & Sut Lovingood's rare ripe Southern garden, spring 72, Stud. Short Fiction; plus one other. Add: Dept. of English, Auburn University, 9086 Haley Ctr, Auburn, AL 36830.

CURRIE, EVA GARCIA, b. Coahuila, Mex, Aug. 28, 12; nat; m. 35; c. 1. SPEECH A.B, Univ. Tex, 33, A.M, 44, 47-49; summers, ling. insts, Georgetown Univ, 55; Univ. Tex, Austin, 60 & 61. Tutor Romance langs, UNIV. TEX, AUSTIN, 45-46, instr, 46-47, speech, 47-, spec. instr, 50-72, acad. supvr, SPEECH COMMUN. LAB, 60-69, DIR, 69-, ASST. PROF. SPEECH COMMUN, 72-, dir. oral Eng. lab. sec. lang. learners. Ling. Soc. Am; Accoust. Soc. Am; Speech Commun. Asn; Int. Sociol. Asn.(mem. res. comt. sociolinguistics). Speech communication; phonetics and phonology; sociolinguistics. Publ: Linguistic and sociological considerations of some populations of Texas, South. Speech J, 50; Proposal for programs in speech communication using the medium of Spanish, Dept. Speech Commun, Univ. Tex, Austin, 72; co-auth, Sociolinguistics and the two American linguistic orthodoxies, Regional Res. Assoc, 73. Add: 1811 Alameda Dr, Austin, TX 78704.

CURRIE, HAROLD WILLIAM, United States History. See Volume I, History.

CURRIE, SHELDON, b. Reserve, N.S, Feb. 25, 34; m. 60; c. 3. ENGLISH. B.A, St. Francis Xavier Univ, 57, B.Ed, 58; M.A, Univ. N.B, 60; Ph.D. (Eng), Univ. Ala, 67. Lectr, ENG, St. Thomas Univ.(N.B), 60-63; asst. prof, ST. FRANCIS XAVIER UNIV, 65-71, ASSOC. PROF, 71- Add: Dept. of English, St. Francis Xavier University, Antigonish, N.S, Can.

CURRY, ELIZABETH REICHENBACH, b. Evanston, Ill, Jan. 31, 34; m. 58; c. 1. ENGLISH. B.A, Northwest. Univ, 56; Univ. Ill, 56-58; Knapp advan. fel, Univ. Wis, 60, Ph.D.(Eng), 63. Instr. ENG, Univ. Wis-Milwaukee, 63-65; asst. prof, Alfred Univ, 65-69; SLIPPERY ROCK STATE COL, 69-71, ASSOC. PROF, 71- Res. found. grant, Alfred Univ, 67-68. MLA. Female studies in literature; minority literature; British literature of the World War II period. Publ: Rex Warner, In: Twayne's English authors series, Twayne (in press); Warner on tragedy: a study in conflict & conformity, In: The achievement of Rex Warner, Wentworth, 65; Rex Warner on the allegorical novel, power politics, and the contemporary scene: a personal interview, Genre, Vol. V, No. 4. Add: 206 N. Main St, Slippery Rock, PA 16057.

CURRY, JOHN VINCENT, S.J, b. New York, N.Y, May 4, 10. ENGLISH. A.B, Woodstock Col, 34, Ph.L, 35; S.T.L, 43; M.A, St. Louis Univ, 38, fel, Columbia Univ, 45-46, Ph.D, 51. Instr, high sch, Wash, D.C; Eng, St. Ignatius Col; from asst. prof. to prof. Eng. & chmn. dept, Le Moyne Col, 47-63, dir. honors prog, 60-63; prof. eng. & chmn. dept, Bellarmine Col.(N.Y), 63-64; prof. Eng, Sch. Lib. Arts, Boston Col, 64-65; chmn. dept. Eng, Sch. Philos. & Lett, Fordham Univ, 66-69; PROF. ENG, LE MOYNE COL, 69- Dir, NCTE, 62-63, mem. Nat. Adv. Bd. Achievement Awards Prog, 63-66; consult, N.Y. State Educ. Dept, lang. arts curriculum revision, 63; mem. N.Y. State Eng. Counc. MLA; Eng. Inst. Elizabethan drama; Shakespeare; teaching of English in high schools and colleges. Publ: Deception in Elizabethan comedy; Language arts program in secondary schools as a preparation for college, Eng. Rec, 57. Add: St. Andrew Hall, 420 Demong Dr, Syracuse, NY 13214.

CURRY, KENNETH, b. Orlando, Fla, Oct. 24, 10. ENGLISH. A.B, Rollins Col, 32; Ph.D, Yale, 35. Instr. & asst. prof. ENG, UNIV. TENN, 35-46, assoc. prof, 46-60, PROF, 60- MLA; S.Atlantic Mod. Lang. Asn; Bibliog. Soc. Am; Mod. Humanities Res. Asn; Int. Asn. Prof. Eng. Nineteenth century English literature; Coleridge, Scott, Southey and Wordsworth. Publ: New letters of Robert Southey, Columbia Univ, 65; Southey, In: English romantic poets and essayists: a review of research, N.Y. Univ, 66; The Knoxville of James Agee's A death in the family, Tenn. Stud. Lit, 69. Add: Dept. of English, University of Tennessee, Knoxville, TN 37916.

CURRY, RALPH LEIGHTON, b. Bowling Green, Ky, Feb. 19, 25; m. 49; c. 2. ENGLISH. A.B, West. Ky. State Col, 48; M.A, Univ. Pa, 51, Ph.D.(Eng), 56. Assoc. prof. ENG, GEORGETOWN COL, 51-56, PROF, 56- Dir, Stephen Leacock Home, 57-; Fulbright prof, Univ. Iceland, 65-66. U.S.A, 43-46. MLA; S.Atlantic Mod. Lang. Asn; Am. Stud. Asn; AAUP. American literature and humor; Canadian-American literature. Publ: Stephen Leacock; humorist and humanist, Doubleday, 59; Stephen Leacock and Robert Benchley: an acknowledged literary debt, Am. Bk. Collector. Add: Dept. of English, Georgetown College, Georgetown, KY 40324.

CURRY, STEPHEN JEFFERIS, b. New York, N.Y, Oct. 21, 33; m. 58; c. 1. ENGLISH. B.A, Columbia Univ, 55; M.A, Univ. Ill, 57; spec. summer fel, Univ. Wis, 62, Ph.D.(Eng), 62. Asst. prof. ENG, Duquesne Univ, 62-63; Univ. Wis, Milwaukee, 63-65; Alfred Univ, 65-69; ASSOC. PROF, SLIPPERY ROCK STATE COL, 69- Res. grant, Univ. Wis, 61-62; consult, Choice, 66-; Res. Found. grant, Alfred Univ, 67-68; asst. ed, Stud. Burke & His Time, 68-69. U.S.A.R, 55-62, S/Sgt. MLA. Eighteenth century literary criticism; medieval language and literature. Publ: The use of history in Bishop Hurd's literary criticism, Trans. Wis. Acad, 65; Richard Hurd's genre criticism, Tex. Stud. Lit. & Lang, summer 66; The literary criticism of William Warburton, Eng. Stud, 10/67. Add: 206 N. Main St, Slippery Rock, PA 16057.

CURRY, WADE C, b. Bessemer, Pa, Jan. 18, 32; m. 58; c. 2. SPEECH, DRAMA. B.A. & M.A, Univ. Pittsburgh, 53; Ph.D.(speech, drama), Univ. Ill, 57. Asst, Univ. Pittsburgh, 53; Univ. Ill, 55-57; teacher speech & drama, Chicago Teachers Col, 57-58; instr, Queens Col, 58-61; PROF. SPEECH & DRAMA, TRENTON STATE COL, 61-, DEAN ARTS & SCI, 70-, assoc. dean, 61-70. Speech Commun. Asn; Speech Asn. East. States; Am. Theatre Asn. American theatre history; play writing. Publ: Scared, Today's Speech, 11/61; Play direction, I, II & III, Clearing House, 2, 3 & 4/66; The real MacKaye, Am. Educ. Theatre J, 11/66. Add: Trenton State College, Trenton, NJ 08625.

CURTIN, FRANK DANIEL, b. Crafton, Pa, Nov. 10, 05; m. 41; c. 4. ENGLISH LITERATURE. A.B, Univ. Pittsburgh, 27, A.M, 29; Ph.D, Univ. Chicago, 39. Instr. ENG, Univ. Pittsburgh, 29-37; Cornell Univ, 38-42; from asst. prof. to assoc. prof, St. Lawrence Univ, 42-47; assoc. prof, Wash. & Jefferson Col, 47-48; prof. & head dept, ST. LAWRENCE UNIV, 48-71, EMER. PROF, 71- Ford Fel, Yale, 53-54. MLA; AAUP. Ruskin and his followers; Victorian novel; style in the novel. Publ: Aesthetics in English social reform: Ruskin, In: Nineteenth century studies, Cornell, 40; Arnold Bennett and after, In: If by your art, Univ. Pittsburgh, 48; Ruskin in French criticism, PMLA, 62. Add: 419 Meadow Rd, Glenshaw, PA 15116.

CURTIN, WILLIAM MARTIN, b. Brooklyn, N.Y, Mar. 19, 27; m. 55; c. 2. ENGLISH. A.B, St. John's Univ.(N.Y), 50; A.M, Columbia Univ, 52; Ph.D, Univ. Wis, 59. Instr. ENG, Georgetown Univ, 52-53; asst, Univ. Wis, 53-58; instr, Univ. Ill, 58-61, asst. prof, 61-68, ASSOC. PROF, 68-69; UNIV. CONN, 69- Instr. hist, Edgewood Col, 54-55; Am. Philos. Soc. grant, 63; consult, Nat. Study High Sch. Eng. Prog, 63-64; consult, Study Teaching Eng. Brit. Sec. Schs, 67-68; Fulbright-Hays lectr, Univ. Dijon, 68-69. U.S.M.C, 45-46. MLA; NCTE. American literature; modern American fiction. Publ: The world and the parish: Willa Cather's essays and reviews, 1893-1903, Univ. Nebr, 69; Willa Cather, In: Lexikon der Weltliteratur in 20. Jahrhundert, Herder, Freiburg, 60; Willa Cather; Individualism and style, Colby Libr. Quart, 6/68. Add: Dept. of English, University of Connecticut, Storrs, CT 06268.

CURTIS, JARED RALPH, b. Oneonta, N.Y, Mar. 25, 36; m. 56; c. 2. ENGLISH. B.A, Yale, 57; M.A, Univ. Mich, 61; Ph.D.(Eng), Cornell Univ, 66. Instr. ENG, Susquehanna Univ, 61-64; asst. prof. Ind. Univ, 66-70; vis. assoc. prof, Univ. Ariz, 70-71; ASSOC. PROF, SIMON FRASER UNIV, 71- Res. awards, Ind. Univ, 67 & Simon Fraser Univ, 72; summer res. grant-in-aids, Nat. Endowment for Humanities, 68, Am. Counc. Learned Soc, 70 & Am. Philos. Soc, 71. Asn. Can. Univ. Teachers Eng; MLA. Wordsworth and poetry of the early 19th century; Shakespeare's plays; Renaissance lyric poetry. Publ; Wordsworth's experiments with tradition, Cornell Univ, 71; William Wordsworth and English poetry of the sixteenth and seventeenth centuries, winter 66 & From the language of men to the language of vision: 2 versions of Wordsworth's Resolution and independence, spring 70, Cornell Libr. J; My speculative and offic'd instrument; reason and love in Othello, Shakespeare Quart, spring 73. Add: Dept. of English, Simon Fraser University, Burnaby, B.C. V5A 1S6, Can.

CURTIS, RICHARD K, b. Worcester, Mass, Jan. 22, 24; m. 45; c. 3. SPEECH. Th.B, North. Baptist Theol. Sem, 50; M.S, Purdue Univ, 51, Ph.D. (speech), 54. Chmn. dept. Eng. & speech, Barrington Col, 52-56; chmn. dept. speech, Bethel Col.(Minn), 56-62; pastor, Immanual Baptist Church, Kansas City, Kans, 62-67, chmn. dept. speech, Muskingum Col, 67-69; PROF. COMMUN, IND. UNIV-PURDUE UNIV, INDIANAPOLIS, 69- Lectr. speech, Univ. Mo, Kansas City, 63-67. U.S.A.A.F, 43-46, 1st Lt; Air Medal with five Oak Leaf Clusters; Distinguished Flying Cross. Speech Commun. Asn.(chmn. res. comt, Relig. Speech Sect, 58-62. Religious speech and language; language and freedom; language and communication. Publ: They called him Mister Moody, Doubleday, 62 & Eerdmans, 67 & 68; Language and theology: basic considerations (ser. of 3), Gordon Rev, 55-56. Add: Dept. of Communications, Indiana University-Purdue University at Indianapolis, Indianapolis, IN 46205.

CURVIN, JONATHAN WADHAMS, b. Brockport, N.Y, July 14, 11; m. 35; c. 2. SPEECH, DRAMA. B.A, Cornell Univ, 32, M.A, 34, Ph.D.(dramatic prod), 41. Chmn. dept. drama & theatre, Hobart & William Smith Cols, 34-41; Vanderbilt Univ, 41-43; assoc. prof. SPEECH, UNIV. WIS-MADISON, 48-56; PROF, 56- Fulbright res. grant theatre arts, Helsinki, Finland, 57-58; U.S. deleg, Int. Theatre Congr, Helsinki, 59. U.S.N, 43-46, Lt. Am. Theatre Asn.(ed, Educ. Theatre J, 62-65); Speech Commun Asn. American drama and theatre; dramatic theory. Publ: Regional drama in one world, 12/47 & The Army-McCarthy hearings as theatre, 2/55, Quart. J. Speech; The theatre in Finland, World Theatre, spring 59. Add: Dept. of Theatre & Drama, Vilas Hall, University of Wisconsin-Madison, University Ave, Madison, WI 53706.

CURZON, GORDON ANTHONY, b. Sutton, Eng, Mar. 14, 19; U.S. citizen; div; c. 4. ENGLISH. B.S, DePaul Univ, 41; B.A, St. Mary's Sem.(Mo), 45; M.A, West. Wash. State Col, 65; Ph.D.(Eng), Univ. Calif, Riverside, 69. Asst. ENG, Univ. Calif, Riverside, 65-67; instr, Col. of the Desert, 67-70; ASSOC. PROF, CALIF. POLYTECH. STATE UNIV, SAN LUIS OBISPO, 70- Ed, Calif. State Poetry Quart, 73- Utopian literature; contemporary poetry. Add: Dept. of English, California Polytechnic State University, San Luis Obispo, CA 93407.

CUSAC, MARIAN HOLLINGSWORTH, b. Georgetown, Ky, Feb. 22, 32; m. 65; c. 2. ENGLISH & AMERICAN LITERATURE. A.B, Mary Baldwin Col, 54; M.A, Univ. N.C, Chapel Hill, 57, Ph.D.(Eng), 64. Instr. Eng, Mercer Univ, 57-61; asst. prof, Wright State Univ, 64-65; Erskine Col, 65-66, assoc. prof, 66-67; res. & writing, 67-73; LECTR, FRANCIS MARION COL, 73- Publ: Narrative structure in the novels of Sir Walter Scott, Mouton, 69; Americanism in Franklin Evans, Walt Whitman Rev, 12/62; Keats as enchanter: an organizing principle of The Eve of St. Agnes, Keats-Shelley J, 68. Add: Lipscomb St, Marion, SC 29571.

CUSHMAN, BIGELOW PAINE, b. Bronxville, N.Y, Aug. 14, 28; m. 54; c. 2. ENGLISH, AMERICAN LITERATURE. B.A, Cornell Univ, 51; M.A, Univ. Conn, 58; Ph.D, Univ. Wis, 65. Instr, Univ. Del, 63-65; H.F. Du Pont asst. prof. ENG, 65-70; ASSOC. PROF, WEST. CONN. STATE COL, 70- Am. Philos. Soc. Penrose Fund grant, 66. Qm.C, U.S.A, 51-53, 1st Lt. MLA; Am. Stud. Asn; NCTE. Nathaniel Hawthorne; Mark Twain; Albert Bigelow Paine. Add: Dept. of English, Western Connecticut State College, Danbury, CT 06810.

CUSHMAN, KEITH MAXWELL, b. Jefferson City, Mo, Dec. 23, 42; m. 69; c. 1. ENGLISH LITERATURE. B.A, Harvard, 64; Ph.D.(Eng), Princeton, 69. Fulbright tutor ENG, Patna Univ, 64-65; lectr, Chulalongkorn Univ, Bangkok, 65-66; ASST. PROF, UNIV. CHICAGO, 69- Nat. Endowment for Humanities summer grant, 72. D.H. Lawrence; Victorian and modern English novel. Publ: The making of The Prussian officer: a correction, D.H. Lawrence Rev, fall 71; Some varieties of D.H. Lawrence criticism, Mod. Philol, 11/71; D.H. Lawrence at work: the making of Odour of chrysanthemums, J. Mod. Lit, 71-72. Add: Dept. of English, University of Chicago, Chicago, IL 60637.

CUTLER, BRUCE, b. Evanston, Ill, Oct. 8, 30; m. 54; c. 3. POETRY. B.A, Univ. Iowa, 51; M.S, Kans. State Univ, 57; Fulbright scholar, Univ. Naples, Italy, 57-58. Instr. Eng, Kans. State Univ, 58-60; WICHITA STATE UNIV, 60-61, asst. prof, 61-63, assoc. prof, 63-66, prof, 67-73, DISTINGUISHED PROF. HUMANITIES, 73- Fulbright lectr, Univ. Paraguay, 65; Ecuador, 67; Univ. Zaragoza, 68-69; adv. ed, Kans. Quart, 68-; mem. adv. bd, Nimrod, 72- Fel. Soc. Relig. Higher Educ; MLA; NCTE. Publ: The year of the green wave, 60, A west wind rises, 62, Sun city, 64, A voyage to America, 67 & The arts at the grass roots, 68, Univ. Kans; co-auth, Developing awareness through poetry, Ctr. 20th Cent. Stud, Univ. Wis-Milwaukee, 72; auth, The swallow and the hawk, Soundings, fall 72; The familiar and the other, Prairie Schooner, summer 72; plus one other. Add: Dept. of English, Wichita State University, Wichita, KS 67208.

CUTLER, JEAN VAL JEAN, b. Hampton, Va, Feb. 8, 27; m. 73; c. 4. THEATRE AESTHETICS & PRODUCTION. B.A, Lynchburg Col, 55; Univ. N.C, Chapel Hill, 55; M.A, Univ. Ill, Urbana, 59, Ph.D.(speech & theatre), 62; Univ. Calif Los Angeles, summer 67. Instr. THEATRE, UNIV. ORE, 62-63, asst. prof, 63-67, assoc. prof, 67-73, PROF, 73- Producer & dir, Out of chaos, Jean Erdman, Amor (film), 67, Web (film), 68; res. grants, 68, 69, 70, 73. U.S.N.R, 45-46. Am. Theatre Asn; Speech Commun. Asn; Univ. Film Producers Asn. Avant-garde and experimental film and theatre production; Chinese classical poetry and theater. Add: Theatre, Dept. of Speech, University of Oregon, Eugene, OR 97403.

CUTLER, JOHN LEVI, b. Bangor, Maine, Dec. 26, 09. ENGLISH. A.B, Univ. Maine, 31, A.M, 33; Ph.D, Ohio State Univ, 49. Asst, Ohio State Univ, 35-38; instr. ENG, UNIV. KY, 38-47, from asst. prof. to ASSOC. PROF, 47- MLA; Ling. Soc. Am; S.Atlantic Mod. Lang. Asn. Middle English literature and versification; linguistics. Publ: Co-auth, Gilbert Patten and his Frank Merriwell saga, Univ. Maine, 34; Supplement to the Index of Middle English verse, Univ. Ky, 65. Add: Dept. of English, University of Kentucky, Lexington, KY 40506.

CUTLER, RONALD JOHN, b. Llangollen, Wales, Dec. 28, 06; U.S. citizen; m. 40; c. 2. ENGLISH. A.B.E, Univ, Fla, 32, M.A, 37; Ed.D.(Eng), Columbia Univ, 57. Mem. fac. ENG, UNIV. FLA, 46-59, ASSOC. PROF, 59-, fac. develop. grant, 68. U.S.A, 43-45. NCTE. English composition and rhetoric; literary regionalism. Publ: The autobiography as creative writing, Col. Compos. & Commun, 2/58. Add: Dept. of English, University of Florida, Gainesville, FL 32601.

CUTNAW, MARY FRANCES, b. Dickinson, N.Dak. SPEECH, ENGLISH. B.S, Univ. Wis-Madison, 53, M.S, 57. Teacher speech & Eng, Pulaski High Sch, Milwaukee, Wis, 53-55; asst. speech, Univ. Wis-Madison, 56-57; instr. speech & Eng, UNIV. WIS-STOUT, 57-58, asst. prof. SPEECH, 58-64, ASSOC. PROF, 64- Hon. scholar, Univ. Wis-Madison, 59-60, 67-68; mem, Ctr. Stud. Democratic Insts. NEA; Speech Commun. Asn; NCTE; Am. Civil Liberties Union; Nat. Asn. Educ. Broadcasters. Speech proficiency and teaching success; curricular speech for special occupational groups; speech as a tool in guidance. Publ: More curricular speech please, 5/53 & Speech spells opportunity, 10/58, Wis. J. Educ. Add: Red Cedar Farm, Box 282, Menomonie, WI 54751.

CUTTING, ROSE MARIE. b. St. Paul, Minn. AMERICAN LITERATURE, WOMEN'S STUDIES. B.A, Col. St. Catherine, 62; Woodrow Wilson fel, Univ. Mich, Ann Arbor, 62-63, M.A, 63; NDEA fel, Univ. Minn, Minneapolis, 69-70, Ph.D.(Eng. & Am. lit), 72. Instr. ENG, Aquinas Col, 63-65; ASST. PROF, UNIV. TEX, AUSTIN, 71- MLA. Bibliography. Publ: America discovers its literary past, Early Am. Lit, (in press); A wreath for Fanny Burney's last novel: The wanderer's contribution to women's studies, Ill. Quart, (in press); Defiant women: the growth of feminism in Fanny Burney's novels, Stud. Eng. Lit, (in press). Add: Dept. of English, University of Texas at Austin, Austin, TX 78712.

CUTTS, JOHN P, b. Goldthorpe, Eng, Sept. 20, 27; m. 59; c. 3. LITERA-TURE & DRAMA. A.B, Univ. Reading, Eng, 51, res. scholars, 51-53, M.A, 53; Morley Bursary grant res, 51-52; dipl. & A.B, Cambridge, 54; res. scholars, Univ. Birmingham, Eng, 54-56, Ph.D, 56. Instr. ENG, State Univ, Iowa, 56-57; vis. asst. prof, Univ. Mo, 57-58; asst. prof, Univ. Alta, 58-60; assoc. prof, Univ. Okla, 60-63; Wayne State Univ, 63-66, PROF, 66-70, OAKLAND UNIV, 70-, chmn. dept, 70-73. Summers, Can. Counc. res. grant, 59, 60, Am. Philos. Soc. res. grant, 62, 64. R.A.F, 45-48, Res, 48-. Sgt. Renaissance Soc. Am; MLA. Mod. Humanities Res. Asn. Renaissance; Shakespeare; 17th century literature. Publ: Seventeenth-century songs, Univ. Mo, 59; Musique de scène de la troupe de Shakespeare, 59; The shattered glass: a dramatic pattern in Shakespeare's early plays, Wayne State Univ, 68; Rich and strange: a study of Shakespeare's last plays, Wash. State Univ, 68; The left hand of God: a critical interpretation of the plays of Christopher Marlowe, Haddarfield House, 73; plus others. Add: Dept. of English, Oakland University, Rochester, MI 48063.

CUTTS, RICHARD, b. Kittery Point, Maine, Nov. 24, 23; m. 48; c. 4. EN-GLISH. B.A, Univ. Maine, 48, M.A, 49; Ph.D, Pa. State Univ, 58. Instr. Eng. compos. & lit, DuBois Ctr, Pa. State Univ, 52-60; asst. prof. ENG, NORWICH UNIV, 60-61, assoc. prof, 61-70, PROF, 70-, HEAD DEPT, 68- U.S.A, 43-46. MLA; NCTE; Conf. Col. Compos & Commun. American literature; C.A. Stephens; Chaucer. Publ: Index to The youth's companion, Scarecrow, 72. Add: Dept. of English, Norwich University, Northfield, VT 05663.

CYPESS, SANDRA MESSINGER, Spanish, Portuguese. See Volume III, Foreign Languages, Linguistics & Philology.

D

DACE, LETITIA SKINNER, b. Washington, D.C, Sept. 13, 41. DRAMATIC LITERATURE. A.B, Sweet Briar Col, 63; M.A, Kans. State Univ, 67, Ph.D. (Eng. lit), 71. Instr. speech & drama, Kans. State Univ, 67-71; ASST. PROF. SPEECH, DRAMA & ENG. & BUS. MGR. DEPT, JOHN JAY COL. CRIMINAL JUSTICE, 71- Kans. State Univ. fac. res. award, 69-70; City Univ. New York fac. res. awards, 72 & 73; asst. ed, Shakespearean Res. & Opportunities, 71- MLA; Am. Soc. Theatre Res; Theatre Libr. Asn; Bibliog. Soc. Am. Modern drama; contemporary British drama; contemporary American drama. Publ: LeRoi Jones (Imamu Amiri Baraka): a checklist of works by and about him, Nether Press, London, 71; co-auth, The theatre student: modern theatre and drama, Richards Rosen, 73; auth, LeRoi Jones: a Negerek Mozgalmanak Dramairoja, Nagyvilag, 12/70; On Jean Genet and Martin Esslin or here absurdist, there absurdist, everywhere..., Kans. Quart, spring 71; contribr, Black American writers: eleven bibliographical essays, Resources for Am. Lit. Stud, 74. Add: Dept. of Speech, Drama and English, South Hall, John Jay College of Criminal Justice, 444 W. 56th St, New York, NY 10019.

DACE, WALLACE, b. Rome, N.Y, Aug. 11, 20; m; c. 3. DRAMA. A.B, Ill. Wesleyan Univ, 43; M.F.A, Yale, 48; Ph.D.(drama), Univ. Denver, 52. PROF. SPEECH, KANS. STATE UNIV, 63- Am. Theatre Asn. Publ: Co-auth, The theatre student: modern theatre and drama, Richards Rosen, 72; auth, Subsidies for the theater: a study of the European system of financing drama, opera and ballet, AG Press, 73. Add: Dept. of Speech, Kansas State University, Manhattan, KS 66502.

DAEGER, GILES ALOYSIUS, b. Shorewood, Wis, June 4, 25; m. 48, 71; c. 2. ENGLISH. Ph.B, Marquette Univ, 49, M.A, 51; Univ. Wis, 55-56. Instr. ENG, Milwaukee Sch. Engineering, 51-52; MARQUETTE UNIV, 52-55, lectr, 55-56, instr, 56-63, ASST. PROF, 63-, ASST. CHMN. DEPT, 68-, dir. col. lib. arts eve. div, 58-64. Dir, Where the action is (documentary film), U.S. Off. Educ, 67. U.S.A, 44-46. NCTE; Conf. Col. Compos & Commun; Conf. Eng. Educ; MLA. History of English language; literature of Kwakiutl Indians; preparation of teachers of English. Publ: Co-auth, You and your job (5 booklets & manual), U.S. Off. Educ, 67, J.G. Ferguson, 68 & The youthful deeds of the Cid, Exposition, 69. Add: Dept. of English, Marquette University, Milwaukee, WI 53233.

DAGHLIAN, PHILIP BEWER, b. Aintab, Turkey, Apr. 25, 15; m. 42; c. 3. ENGLISH LITERATURE. A.B, Yale, 36, Ph.D, 41. Instr. ENG, Yale, 41-43; Univ. Rochester, 43-46; IND. UNIV, BLOOMINGTON, 46-48, asst. prof, 48-54, assoc. prof, 54-62, PROF, 62-; asst. chmn. dept, 54-61, 62-64, acting chmn. dept, 61-62, assoc. chmn. regional campuses, 67-69. MLA. Eighteenth century English literature; bibliography and textual criticism. Publ: Co-ed, Walpole's Anecdotes of painting, Yale Univ, 37; auth, The familiar letter in the 18th century, Univ. Kans, 66; Teaching literature in grades nine through twelve, 68, Books for teachers of English, 68 & ed, Essays on 18th century biography, 68, Ind. Univ. Add: Dept. of English, Indiana University, Bloomington, IN 47401.

DAHL, CURTIS, b. New Haven, Conn, July 6, 20; m. 52. ENGLISH LITERA-TURE. A.B, Yale Col, 41, A.M, Yale, 42, Ph.D, 45. Asst. to dean, Yale Col, 44; dir. fels, Dodd, Mead & Co, Pubs, 45-47; instr. Eng, Univ. Tenn, 47-48; asst. prof, WHEATON COL.(MASS), 48-53, assoc. prof, 53-58, prof, 58-66, SAMUEL VALENTINE COLE PROF. ENG. LIT, 66-, acting head dept. classics, 50-51. Carnegie vis. fel, Harvard, 54-55; Guggenheim fel, 57-58; vis. prof, South. Ill. Univ, summers 64, 66; Fulbright prof, Univ. Oslo, 64-66; vis. prof, Univ. Wash, summer 67; Brown Univ, 70; mem, Eng. Inst. MLA; Melville Soc; Am. Stud. Asn; Col. Eng. Asn. Victorian; Bulwer-Lytton; archaeology and English literature. Publ: Robert Montgomery Bird, Twayne, 63; ed, Ben Ezra Stiles Ely, There she blows: a narrative of a whaling voyage, Wesleyan Univ, 71; Bulwer-Lytton and the school of catastrophe, Philol. Quart; Morris Chapel in Lyonesse, Stud. Philol; The Victorian wasteland, Col. Eng, 55. Add: 189 N. Washington St, Norton, MA 02766.

DAHLBERG, CHARLES, b. Wagner, S.Dak, Jan. 7, 19. ENGLISH. B.A, Yankton Col, 40; B.A, Univ. London, 48; Fulbright scholar, Univ. Paris, 50-51; Ph.D.(Eng), Princeton, 53. Instr, Princeton, 51-52; Univ. Chicago, 52-54; ENG, QUEENS COL.(N.Y), 54-60, asst. prof, 61-64, assoc. prof, 65-70, PROF, 70-, chmn. dept, 64-66. City Univ. N.Y. Res. Found. grant 71-72 & 73-74; Am. Counc. Learned Soc. grant-in-aid, 72-73. U.S.A.A.F, 42-46. MLA; Mediaeval Acad. Am. Chaucer; medieval literature. Publ: Transl, Guillaume De Lorris and Jean De Meun, The romance of the rose, Princeton, 71; auth, Macrobius and the unity of the Roman de la rose, Stud. Philol, 10/61; co-auth, Wolfram's Lapsit exillis (parzival), Mediaeval Stud, 68; auth, Love and the Roman de la rose, Speculum, 69. Add: Dept. of English, Queens College, Flushing, NY 11367.

DAHLE, THOMAS L, b. Mt. Horeb, Wis, Sept. 7, 16; m. 41; c. 2. ADULT EDUCATION, COMMUNICATION. B.S, Univ. Wis, Madison, 38, M.S, 49; Ph.D.(speech), Purdue Univ, 54. From instr. speech to asst. prof. commun, Purdue, 49-54; asst. prof. commun, skills & continuing educ, Mich. State Univ, 54-59; dir. & assoc. prof. adult educ, Univ. Idaho, 59-61; assoc. dir. commun. & assoc. prof. continuing educ, Univ. Wis, Milwaukee, 61-63; PROF. SPEECH & DIR. ADULT EDUC, UNIV. ORE, 63- Consult, Ford Motor Co, DuPont Corp, & others, 54-59; consult. ed, Speech Teacher, 54-56; mem, exec. bd, Mt. Plains Adult Educ. Asn, 61-63. U.S.A. & U.S.A.F, 41-45, Capt. Adult Educ. Asn. U.S; Nat. Soc. Stud. Commun. Communication problems; adult education; gerontology. Publ: An objective study of 5 methods of communicating information, Speech Monogr, 54; auth, Empirical research, In: An introduction to graduate research, Mich. State Univ, 61; auth, How to tell an administrator from a teacher, Phi Delta Kappan, 62. Add: Dept. of Speech, University of Oregon, Eugene, OR 97403.

DAIGLE, RICHARD JOSEPH, Linguistics, Russian Literature. See Volume III, Foreign Languages, Linguistics & Philology.

DAIKER, DONALD ARTHUR, b. Passaic, N.J, Jan. 20, 38; m. 62; c. 4. AMERICAN & ENGLISH LITERATURE. A.B, Rutgers Univ, 59; Woodrow Wilson fel, Univ. Calif, Berkeley, 60-61; univ. fel, Ind. Univ, 61-63, Ph.D. (Eng), 69. Instr. ENG, MIAMI UNIV, 64-69, asst. prof, 69-74, ASSOC. PROF, 74- U.S.A, 60, Res, 61-64, Capt. MLA; Melville Soc. The American Renaissance; American short story; Melville. Publ: Hugh Nissenson's In the reign of peace, Stud. Short Fiction, summer 73; The pied piper in The sun also rises, Fitzgerald-Hemingway Annual, 75. Add: Dept. of English, Miami University, Oxford, OH 45056.

DAILEY, VIRGINIA FLOOD, Linguistics, English. See Volume III, Foreign Languages, Linguistics & Philology.

DALE, THOMAS RANDALL, b. Toronto, Ont, July 27, 16; m. 42; c. 3. EN-GLISH. B.A, Univ. Toronto, 38, M.A, 39; univ. fel, Univ. Chicago, 49-50, Ph.D.(Eng), 51. Lectr. Eng. & hist, St. John's Col, Can, 40-41; instr. ENG, Univ. West. Ontario, 46-49; asst. prof, Monmouth Col, 50-53; North. Ill. State Teachers Col, 53-55; assoc. prof, LAWRENCE UNIV, 55-58, PROF, 58- R.C.N, 42-46, Lt. Comdr. NCTE. Add: 518 N. Mary St, Appleton, WI 54911.

DALEY, ARTHUR STUART, b. Osceola, N.Y, Sept. 16, 08. ENGLISH RE-NAISSANCE LITERATURE. A.B, Syracuse Univ, 32; Harvard, 32-33; Ph.D, Yale, 42. Instr, Syracuse Univ, 35-37; Ind. Univ, 46-47; Univ. Calif, Los Angeles, 47-49; asst. prof. ENG, Univ. Nev, 49-54; prof. & chmn. dept, Coe Col, 54-59; PROF, DRAKE UNIV, 59-, COORD. HUMANITIES DIV, 67-, chmn. dept, Eng, 59-67. Asst. ed, Guide to Comp. Lit. U.S.A, 41-46, 51-53; Res, 53-68, Lt. Col.(Ret). MLA; Brontë Soc; Medieval Acad. Am; Renaissance Soc. Am; Shakespeare Asn. Am. Shakespeare imagery and iconography; Wuthering Heights problems of chronology in the novel. Publ: Chaucer's Droghte of March in medieval farm lore, Chaucer Rev, 70; The moons and almanacs of Wuthering heights, Huntington Libr. Quart, 8/74. Add: Div. of Humanities, Drake University, 202 Medbury, Des Moines, IA 50311.

DALGARNO, EMILY K, b. New York, N.Y, Feb. 17, 31; m. 62, 72; c. 1. EN-GLISH, AMERICAN LITERATURE. B.A, William Smith Col, 53; Ph.D.(Eng), Brown Univ, 62. Instr. ENG, Conn. Col, 56-59; BOSTON UNIV, CHARLES RIVER CAMPUS, 59-63, asst. prof, 63-69, ASSOC. PROF, 69- Travel grants, Am. Philos. Soc, 64; Boston Univ, 67; Am. Counc. Learned Soc. 67 & 72; Am. Asn. Univ. Women, Alice Freeman Palmer fel, 67-68. MLA. Contemporary English and American literature. Publ: The composition of The spoils of Poyton, Tex. Stud. Lit. & Lang, winter 65; Revisions in the Ms. of the first section of The sound and the fury, Stud. Bibliog, 67; Under Western eyes and the problems of serial publication, Rev. Eng. Stud, 11/72. Add: Dept. of English, Boston University, Charles River Campus, 236 Bay State Rd, Boston, MA 02215.

DALLAS, MEREDITH, b. Detroit, Mich, Dec. 3, 16; m. 40; c. 4. DRAMA. B.A, Albion Col, 39; M.A, West. Reserve Univ, 48. Res. asst, Fels Res. Inst, ANTIOCH COL, 45-46, asst. to dean, 46-47, instr. DRAMA, 48-49, asst. prof, 50-53, assoc. prof, 54-61, PROF, 62- Actor & dir, Shaw Festival, Martha's Vineyard, Mass, 51; co-founder, actor & dir, Antioch Shakespeare Festival, 52, 53, 55; actor, Group 20, Wellesley, Mass, 56; dir, Trotwood Circle Theatre, Ohio, 57, 58, 60; consult, Phoenix Theatre, N.Y,

58-59; artistic dir, Antioch Amphitheatre, 61-64; Great Lakes Col. Asn. fel, Japan & Greece, 66-67. Publ: As large a charter as the wind, J. Human Relat, spring 58. Add: 110 E. Whiteman St, Yellow Springs, OH 45387.

DALLINGER, CARL ARTHUR, b. Atlantic, Iowa, Nov. 24, 12; m. 49; c. 1. SPEECH, RHETORIC. B.A, Park Col, 34; M.A, State Univ. Iowa, 38, Ph.D, 52. Instr. speech, Park Col, 34-38, asst. prof, 38-42, prof, 42-46; Univ. Dubuque, 46-47, dean col. lib. arts, 47-50; instr, State Univ. Iowa, 50-52, asst. prof. speech & commun. skills, 52-55, assoc. prof, 55-62, supvr. speech, commun. skills prog, 50-55, coord. rhetoric prog, 56-62; PROF. SPEECH, Ill. State Univ, 62-65; NORTH. ILL. UNIV, 65- Assoc. ed, commun. skills, Quart. J. Speech, 57-59; rhet. & pub. address ed, Speech Teacher, 65-66; consult. ed. speech educ, Cent. States Speech J, 66-69. Speech Commun. Asn; Int. Commun. Asn; Cent. States Speech Asn. Fundamentals of speech and communication; public address; speech education. Publ: Co-auth, Communication skills: an experiment in instructional methods, State Univ. Iowa, 58 & Charles Sumner, In: History and criticism of American public address; McGraw, 43; auth, Theodore Roosevelt, the preacher militant, In: American public address: studies in honor of Albert Craig Baird, Univ. Mo, 61. Add: 4 Evergreen Circle, De Kalb, IL 60115.

DALTON, WILLIAM THEO, b. Pike Co, Ala, Aug. 21, 10; m. 41. ENGLISH, TEACHER EDUCATION. B.S, Univ. Ala, 32; M.Ed, Duke Univ, 36; Univ. South. Calif, 38; Ph.D.(teacher educ. & Eng); George Peabody Col, 43. Teacher, Pike Co. Schs, Ala, 29-36, prin, 36-43; prin. & dir. stud. teaching, Elon Col, 44-45; dir. instr, Alamance Co. Schs, N.C, 45-47; dir. demonstration sch, Univ. N.C, Greensboro, 47-48; prof. elem. & Eng. educ, Univ. Ga, 48-51; Auburn Univ, 51-63; Eng, Troy State Univ, 63-72; RETIRED. NEA; NCTE. Language arts at elementary, secondary and college levels; school supervision and the instructional program; freshman and sophomore English programs. Publ: Individualized instruction, 48 & Language arts and the child, 54, Childhood Educ; Classroom atmosphere, Educ. Leadership, 51. Add: Rte. 1, Goshen, AL 36035.

DALVEN, RAE, b. Preveza, Greece, Mar. 25, 04; U.S. citizen. ENGLISH, FOREIGN LANGUAGE. B.A, Hunter Col, 25; M.A, N.Y. Univ, 28, Ph.D. (Eng), 61; M.F.A, Yale, 41. Asst. prof. drama, Fisk Univ, 52-53; prof. ENG. & chmn. dept, LADYCLIFF COL, 62-73, EMER. PROF, 73- Instr. Eng, Fairleigh Dickinson Univ, Teaneck, 57-60; adj. prof. Eng, Pace Col, 61-68. Authors' League Am; Poetry Soc. Am; MLA; Am. Theatre Asn. Modern Greek literature; theatre; the Jews in Greece. Publ: Modern Greek poetry, Gaer Asn, 49 & Russell, 71; The complete poems of Cavafy, Hogarth, London & Harcourt, N.Y, 61; Anna Comnena, Twayne, 72; Modern Greek theatre In: The reader's encyclopedia of world drama, Crowell, 69; Greek authors, In: European authors 1000-1900, Wilson, 67; Jews in Greece, In: Encyclopedia Judaica, 70. Add: 11 Fifth Ave, New York, NY 10003.

DALY, SARALYN RUTH, b. Huntington, W.Va, May 11, 24. ENGLISH. A.B, Ohio State Univ, 44, A.M, 45, univ. fel, 46-47, Ph.D, 50; univ. scholar, Yale, 45-46. Instr. ENG, Ohio State Univ, 47-49; prof. & head dept, Col. Emporia, 49-50; prof, Midwest. Univ, 50-61; assoc. prof, Tex. Christian Univ, 61-62; asst. prof, CALIF. STATE UNIV, LOS ANGELES, 62-66, assoc. prof, 66-72, PROF, 72- Consult. teaching Eng. as for. lang, Exp. Int. Living, 62; Fulbright-Hays prof, Am. Univ. Beirut, 64-65; Tokyo Univ. Lib. Arts & Tsuda Col, 67-68; Fulbright-Hays prof, Univ. Bujumbura, Burundi, 70-71. MLA; Mediaeval Acad. Am; Early Eng. Text Soc. Structural linguistics; Juan Ruiz' Libro de buen amor; Chaucer. Publ: Katherine Mansfield, Twayne, 65; Genesis, Epos; Peter Comestor, master of histories, Speculum; Eudora Welty's A worn path retrod, Stud. Short Fiction; plus others. Add: Dept. of English, California State University, Los Angeles, 5151 State University Dr, Los Angeles, CA 90032.

DAM, HARI NARAYAN, b. Sylhet, India, Oct. 1, 21. HISTORY, MASS COMMUNICATION. B.A, Univ. Calcutta, 44, M.A, 47, dipl. jour, 52; M.A, Univ. Minn, 61, Ph.D.(mass commun), 68. Asst. prof. commun, Mont. State Univ, 64-68, ASSOC. PROF, 68-70; JOUR, TEX. A&I UNIV, 70- Asn. Educ. in Jour. History of journalism; mass media and society and the international press. Publ: The intellectual odyssey of Walter Lippmann: a study of his protean thought, Gordon, 73. Add: Dept. of Journalism, Box 171, Texas A&I University, Kingsville, TX 78363.

DAMASER, HARVEY G, b. Brooklyn, N.Y, Sept. 27, 36; m. 61; c. 3. ENGLISH, AMERICAN DRAMA. A.B, Univ. Pa, 56, M.A, 63; Univ. Neuchâtel, 56-57; M.A, N.Y. Univ, 59; Harvard, 59-60. Lectr. ENG, Univ. Calif, Los Angeles, 64-66; ASST. PROF, WITTENBERG UNIV, 66- Am. Stud. Asn; MLA. American literature; Afro-American literature; American Indian literature and culture. Publ: Co-auth, Six early American plays: 1798-1890, C.E. Merrill, 68. Add: Dept. of English, Wittenberg University, Springfield, OH 45501.

DAMERON, JOHN LASLEY, b. Burlington, N.C, July 29, 25; m. 49; c. 2. ENGLISH. B.S, Univ. N.C, 50, M.A, 52; Ph.D.(Eng), Univ. Tenn, 62. Instr. ENG, Emory & Henry Col, 53-55; Univ. Tenn, 58-59, 61-62; asst. prof, MEMPHIS STATE UNIV, 62-66, assoc. prof, 66-72, PROF, 72- Nat. Endowment Humanities grant, 67-68. U.S.N, 43-46. MLA; Bibliog. Soc. Am; Am. Stud. Asn; S.Atlantic Mod. Lang. Asn; Cambridge Bibliog. Soc. Nineteenth century American and English literature; American authors, mid-19th century; bibliography of the criticism of Edgar Allan Poe. Publ: Edgar Allan Poe in the mid-20th century, Univ. Microfilms, 63; Edgar Allan Poe: a checklist of criticism, 1942-1960, Bibliog. Soc. Va, 66; co-auth, An index to Poe's critical vocabulary, 66 & co-ed, Emerson's relevance today, 71, Transcendental; Poe at mid-century: Anglo-American criticism, 1928-1960, Ball State Univ. Forum, 67; Schiller's Das lied von de glocke as a source of Poe's The bells, Notes & Queries, 67; Symbolism in the poetry of Poe and Stephen Crane, In: New approaches to Poe: a symposium, Transcendental, 70; plus others. Add: Dept. of English, Memphis State University, Memphis, TN 38152.

DAMERST, WILLIAM A, b. Pelham, Mass, Aug. 21, 23; m. 46; c. 3. ENGLISH. B.S, Univ. Ill, Urbana, 46; M.A, Univ. Mass, Amherst, 55. Instr. ENG, PA. STATE UNIV, UNIVERSITY PARK, 55-60, asst. prof, 60-65, assoc. prof, 65-72, PROF, 72- Consult. tech. writing, Gulf Oil Corp aid-to-educ. grant, 59, 60. U.S.A.A.F, 43-45, 1st Lt; Air Medal & 5 Oak Leaf Clusters. Sr. mem. Am. Bus. Commun. Asn.(v.pres. E, 67-70, 1st v.pres, 71, pres, 72); sr. mem. Soc. Tech. Commun. Technical writing; business writing; creativity. Publ: Good Gulf letters and reports, Gulf Oil Corp, 59; Resourceful business communication, 66 & Clear technical reports, 72, Harcourt; Creativity in the business-writing course, Am. Bus. Commun. Asn. Bull, 5/67; Forms for technical writing—massage or irritation?, Proc. Tech. Commun. Conf, 5/69. Add: Dept. of English, S-228 Burrowes Bldg, Pennsylvania State University, University Park, PA 16802.

DAMMERS, RICHARD HERMAN, b. Passaic, N.J, May 27, 43; m. 68; c. 1. ENGLISH LITERATURE. A.B, Holy Cross Col.(Mass), 65; M.A, Univ. Va, 66; Arthur J. Schmitt fel, Univ. Notre Dame, 70, Ph.D.(Eng), 71. Instr. ENG, Holy Cross Col.(Mass), 66-67; ASST. PROF, ILL. STATE UNIV, 71- Vis. prof. Eng, Mem. Univ. Nfld, summer 72. Am. Soc. 18th Century Stud; MLA. Restoration drama; 18th century literature. Publ: The Duke of guise: Dryden's vision of kingship, Notre Dame Eng. J, 71; Nicholas Rowe and the miscellany of 1701, Library, 73. Add: Dept. of English, Illinois State University, Normal, IL 61761.

DAMROSCH, LEOPOLD, JR, b. Manila, Philippines, Sept. 14, 41; U.S. citizen; m. 64; c. 2. ENGLISH LITERATURE. B.A, Yale, 63; Marshall scholar, Cambridge, 64-66, M A, 66; Ph.D, Princeton, 68. Asst. prof. ENG, UNIV. VA, 68-73, ASSOC. PROF, 73- Nat. Endowment for Humanities Younger Humanist fel, 72-73. MLA. Eighteenth century English literature. Publ: Samuel Johnson and the tragic sense, Princeton Univ, 72; The Life of Johnson: an anti-theory, Eighteenth-Century Stud, fall 73; Johnson's manner of proceeding in the Rambler, ELH, spring 73. Add: Dept. of English, University of Virginia, Charlottesville, VA 22901.

DANA, MARGARET ELIZABETH, b. Lexington, Ky, Feb. 1, 32; m. 52; c. 3. ENGLISH LITERATURE. B.A, Univ. Calif, Riverside, 64, M.A, 66, Ph.D. (Eng), 71. Teaching asst, Univ. Calif, Riverside, 66-70; ASSOC. PROF. ENG, CALIF. BAPTIST COL, 71- MLA. English Renaissance non-dramatic literature; literature and psychology; women and literature. Publ: Pastoral and heroic: Sidney's Arcadia as masquerade, Comp. Lit, fall 73. Add: Dept. of English, California Baptist College, 8432 Magnolia Ave, Riverside, CA 92504.

DANA, ROBERT PATRICK, b. Allston, Mass, June 2, 29; m. 51; c. 3. ENGLISH. B.A, Drake Univ, 51; M.A, State Univ. Iowa, 54. Instr. Eng. & jour, CORNELL COL, 54-58, asst. prof. ENG, 58-62, assoc. prof, 62-68, PROF, 68- Danforth stud. grant, 58-59; Rinehart fel, 60-61; ed, N.Am. Rev, 64-; Ford-Assoc. Col. Midwest stud. grant, 66-67. U.S.N, 46-48. MLA. Publ: My glass brother and other poems, Constance, 57; The dark flags of waking, Qara Press, 64; Journeys from the skin, Hundred Pound, 66; Some versions of silence, Norton, 67; The power of the visible, Swallow Press, 71; Picking it up, The stone garden, The drunkard & The joy tree (poems), Quart. Rev. Lit, 72; Vision and transformation (poem), New Yorker, 72; At North Cheyenne Canyon (poem), Christian Sci. Monitor, 73; plus others. Add: Dept. of English, Cornell College, Mt. Vernon, IA 52314.

DANCE, FRANK ESBURN XAVIER, b. Brooklyn, N.Y, Nov. 9, 29; m. 54; c. 5. SPEECH COMMUNICATION. B.S, Fordham Univ, 51; M.A, Northwest. Univ, 53, Ph.D.(speech), 59. Instr. speech, Chicago City Jr, Col, 57-58; asst. prof, St. Joseph's Col.(Ind), 58-60; Univ. Kans, 60-63, assoc. prof, summer, 63; assoc. prof. speech, Univ. Wis-Milwaukee, 63-66, prof. commun, 66-71, dir. speech commun. ctr, 63-71; PROF. SPEECH COMMUN, UNIV. DENVER, 71- Ed, Jour. Commun, 54-57; Knapp Univ. scholar, 68. Standard Oil Found. outstanding teacher award, Univ. Wis-Milwaukee, 67. U.S.A.R, 54-62, 1st Lt. Speech Commun. Asn; Adult Educ. Asn; Nat. Soc. Stud. Commun.(pres, 67); West. Speech Asn; Speech Asn. East. States. Speech communication psychology; adult speech communication; public address. Publ: The citizen speaks, Wadsworth, 62; co-auth, Business & professional speech communication, 65, auth, Human communication theory; original essays, 67 & co-auth, Speech communication: concepts and behavior, 72, Holt; co-auth, Perspectives on communication, Helix, 69; Brainwashing: a distortion of the communication cycle, Adult Leadership, 1/62; Speech communication theory and Pavlov's second signal system, J. Commun, 3/67; The functions of speech communication as an integrative concept in the field of communication, Int, Congr. Commun, Genoa, 10/67; plus others. Add: Dept. of Speech Communication, University of Denver, Denver, CO 80210.

DANDO, JOHN, b. Stafford, Eng, July 9, 17. ENGLISH. B.A, McGill Univ, 38, M.A, 45; fel, Columbia Univ. Lectr. Eng. lit, McGill Univ, 39-48, French lit, 40-41; instr. Eng. lit, TRINITY COL.(CONN), 50-55, from asst. prof. Eng. lit. to assoc. prof. ENG, 55-67, PROF, 67- Lectr, Hartford Col, 54, 55, 57; Voice of Am. Add: Dept. of English, Trinity College, Hartford, CT 06106.

D'ANDREA, PAUL, b. Boston, Mass, Feb. 2, 39. ENGLISH. B.A, Harvard, 60, M.A, 62, Ph.D.(Eng), 66; Oxford, 60-61. Asst. prof. Eng, Univ. Chicago, 66-72; ASSOC. PROF. HUMANITIES & CHMN. DEPT, UNIV. MINN, MINNEAPOLIS, 72- MLA; Renaissance Soc. Am; Shakespeare Asn. Am. Literary criticism; Shakespeare; modern drama. Add: Humanities Program, Ford Hall 314, University of Minnesota, Minneapolis, MN 55455.

DANDRIDGE, EDMUND PENDLETON, JR, b. Pittsburgh, Pa, Feb. 4, 15; m. 42; c. 2. ENGLISH. A.B, Kenyon Col, 37; summers, Univ. Pittsburgh, 37, McGill Univ, 38; A.M, Univ. Mich, 46; Ph.D, Univ. Va, 59. Instr. Eng. & French, Woodberry Forest Sch, Va, 37-41; teaching fel. engineering Eng, Univ. Mich, 46-47; instr, 51-63, assoc. ed, Engineering Res. Inst, 56-63; asst. prof. lang. & lit, Lynchburg Col, 50-51; ASSOC. PROF. ENG, N.C. STATE UNIV, 63- Proprietor, Dandridge Assoc, 64-; ed. consult. to indust, govt. & publ. orgns. U.S.N.R, 41-46, Lt. Comdr. Col. Eng. Asn; NCTE; Soc. Tech. Commun. Eighteenth century British periodical criticism; stylistic analysis of expository prose. Publ: Proposals of nine printers for a new edition of the Journals of the Continental Congress, 1785, In: Studies in Bibliography, II, 45-50; collab, Subject index to eighteenth century periodicals; plus other articles related to non-fiction. Add: Dept. of English, North Carolina State University, Raleigh, NC 27607.

DANDRIDGE, RITA BERNICE, b. Richmond, Va. ENGLISH & AMERICAN LITERATURE. B.A, Va. Union Univ, 61; M.A, Howard Univ, 63, Ford Found. grant, 68, Ph.D.(Eng), 70. ASST. PROF. ENG. LIT, Morgan State Col, 64-71; UNIV. TOLEDO, 71- MLA; NCTE; Col. Eng. Asn. Seventeenth century English satire; 20th century Black literature; the novel. Publ: Co-auth, Relevant expository techniques and programmed grammar, Kendall Hunt, 71; auth, The Prioress's disobedience of the Benedictine rule, Col. Lang. Asn, 68. Add: Dept. of English, University of Toledo, 2800 W. Bancroft, Toledo, OH 43607.

D'ANGELO, FRANK JOSEPH, b. New Orleans, La, Nov. 29, 28; m. 61; c. 5. RHETORIC, STYLISTICS. B.S, Loyola Univ.(La), 60; M.A, Tulane Univ, 63; advan. cert, Univ. Ill, Urbana, 67; Ph.D.(Eng), Univ. Nebr, Lincoln, 70. Instr. ENG, Univ. Nebr, Lincoln, 67-70; ASST. PROF. & DIR. FRESHMAN ENG, ARIZ. STATE UNIV, 70- NCTE; Rhetoric Soc. Am. Rhetorical theory; discourse theory; style. Publ: Co-ed, The growing edges of secondary English, Nat. Counc. Teachers Eng, 68; auth, Imitation and style, 10/73, The rhetoric of Graffiti, 5/74, Col. Compos. & Commun; New and renewed rhetorics, Ariz. Eng. Bull, 2/74. Add: Dept. of English, Arizona State University, Tempe, AZ 85281.

DANIEL, CARTER ANDERSON, b. Charlottesville, Va, Aug. 23, 38. ENGLISH. A.B, Davidson Col, 59; A.M, Duke Univ, 60; Ph.D.(Eng), Univ. Va, 65; M.B.A, Rutgers Univ, 74. Instr. ENG, Kent State Univ, 60-62; ASST. PROF, UPSALA COL, 65-; EXEC. ASST. TO PRES, 72- Vis. lectr. Eng, Kuwait Univ, 70-71. MLA; AAUP. Elizabethan court drama; John Donne; university administration. Publ: West's revisions of Miss Lonelyhearts, Stud. Bibliog, 63. Add: Office of the President, Upsala College, East Orange, NJ 07019.

DANIEL, MAGGIE BROWNE, b. LaGrange, Tex, Oct. 31, 08; m. 24. ENGLISH & AMERICAN LITERATURE. B.A, Wiley Col, 26; M.A, Univ. Wis, 30, fel, 46-47, Ph.D, 53. From instr. to prof. Eng, Wiley Col, 28-36; instr, Tex. South. Univ. 36-37; Bennett Col, 39-43; prof, Huston-Tillotson Col, 43-48; from asst. prof. to prof, Ala. State Col, 48-62; PROF. ENG. & AM. LIT. WILEY COL, 62- Gen. Educ. Bd, fel, 38-39. MLA; Col. Lang. Asn; NCTE; Conf. Col. Compos. & Commun; Howells Soc. William Dean Howell's attitude toward criticism of the English and their literature. Add: Dept. of English, Wiley College, Marshall, TX 75670.

DANIEL, ROBERT WOODHAM, b. Memphis, Tenn, Apr. 13, 15; m. 40; c. 2. ENGLISH LITERATURE. A.B, Univ. South, 35; Ph.D, Yale, 39. Instr. ENG, Yale, 39-44; asst. prof, Univ. Okla, 44-47; Univ. Tenn, 47-52, assoc. prof, 52-60; PROF, KENYON COL, 60-, chmn. dept, 64-73. Instr, Harvard, 44; Fulbright prof, Univ. Athens, 54-55. MLA; Col. Eng. Asn; AAUP. Wordsworth; contemporary literature; rhetoric. Publ: Co-ed, Theme and form, 56, rev. ed, 62, 69 & The written word, 60, Prentice-Hall; auth, A contemporary rhetoric, Little, 67. Add: Box 247, Gambier, OH 43022.

DANIEL, WALTER CLARENCE, b. Macon, Ga, May 12, 22. ENGLISH. B.A, J.C. Smith Univ, 44; M.S, S.Dak. State Univ, 59; Ph.D.(Eng), Bowling Green State Univ, 62; hon. D.H, Lincoln Univ.(Mo), 72. Teacher, Los Angeles City Schs, 46-56; Jr. High Sch, Los Angeles, 56-68; asst. prof. Eng, N.C. Col. Durham, 62-63; instr, Bowling Green State Univ, 60-62; chmn. dept. St. Augustine's Col, 62-63; chmn. dept. Eng, & dir. div. humanities, A&T State Univ, 63-69, dir. 13-col. curriculum prog, 67-68; pres, Lincoln Univ.(Mo), 69-73; V.CHANCELLOR, UNIV. MO-COLUMBIA, 73- Piedmont Univ. res. grant, summer 58; mem, N.C. State Dept. Pub. Instr. accreditation teams, 66, 67, 68; chmn, N.C. Comt. Articulation Between Community Cols. & Univs. in Eng. U.S.A.A.F, 2nd Lt. NCTE; MLA; Col. Lang. Asn. Afro-American literature; 20th century British literature; higher education. Publ: Absurdity in the death of Bessie Smith, 9/64 & Countee Cullen as literary critic, 3/71, Col. Lang. Asn. J; Black Janus, J. Am. Alumni Counc, 4/70; plus others. Add: 1 Alhambra Dr, Columbia, MO 65201.

DANIELLS, ROY, b. London, Eng, Apr. 6, 02; Can. citizen; m. 48; c. 2. ENGLISH. B.A, Univ. B.C, 30; M.A, Univ. Toronto, 31, Ph.D.(Eng), 36, LL.D, 64; LL.D, Queen's Univ.(Ont), 64; hon. D.Litt, McMaster Univ, 70, Windsor Univ, 71. Instr. ENG, Univ. Toronto, 34-37; PROF, Univ. Man, 37-46; UNIV. B.C, 46- Mem, Humanities Res. Counc. Can, various times; Governor-General's Awards Comt, 51-56. Lorne Pierce Medal, 70; Companion, Order Can, 72. Asn. Can. Univ. Teachers. Eng; Royal Soc. Can. Milton; Canadian literature. Publ: Deeper into the forest (poems), 48 & The chequered shade (poems), 63, McClelland & Stewart; Milton, mannerism and baroque, 63 & co-ed. & contrib, Literary history of Canada, 65, Univ. Toronto; auth, Alexander Mackenzie and the northwest, Faber, 69. Add: Dept. of English, University of British Columbia, Vancouver 8, B.C, Can.

DANIELS, EDGAR F, b. Dayton, Ohio, Apr. 21, 21; m. 51; c. 1. ENGLISH. A.B, Otterbein Col, 47; M.A, Stanford Univ, 48, Ph.D.(Eng), 52. Instr. ENG, West. Wash. State Col, 51-53; from instr. to assoc. prof, BOWLING GREEN STATE UNIV, 53-70, PROF, 70-, CHMN. DEPT, 71- Contrib. ed, Filmmakers Newsletter, 70-; assoc. ed, Seventeenth Century News, 72- U.S.N, 43-45. Milton Soc. Am; MLA. Seventeenth-century literature. Publ: Contrib. to Eng. Lang. Notes, Col. Eng, Seventeenth-Century News, Am. Notes & Queries, Notes & Queries, Explicator & Stud. Short Fiction. Add: 3525 Beechway Blvd, Toledo, OH 43614.

DANIELS, ELIZABETH ADAMS, b. Westport, Conn, May 8, 20; m. 42; c. 4. ENGLISH. B.A, Vassar Col, 41, col. fel, 42, col. fac. fel, 52; M.A, Univ. Mich, 42; Ph.D.(Eng), N.Y. Univ, 54. From asst. prof. to assoc. prof. Eng, VASSAR COL, 48-66, PROF. ENG, 66-, asst. dean, 55-58, dean stud, 66-73. MLA; Mid. Atlantic States Eng. Asn; Am. Asn. Col. Deans. Victorian literature; risorgimento and Victorian writers; interconnections. Publ: George Meredith's women: a study of changing attitudes in Victorian England; Jessie White Mario, risorgimento revolutionary, Ohio Univ, 73; Mazzini e Meredith, In: Rassegua storica del risorgimento, 62; Jessie White Mario, Nation, 1/66; plus one other. Add: 129 College Ave, Poughkeepsie, NY 12603.

DANIELS, ROBERTSON BALFOUR, b. Princeton, N.J, Aug. 6, 00; m. 36; c. 2. ENGLISH. A.B, Princeton, 22; J.D, Yale, 25, A.M, 32, Ph.D, 34. Instr. Eng, Univ. Tenn, 35; head dept, Edinburg Col, 35-37; assoc. prof, Kans. State Teachers Col, Pittsburg, 37-39; asst. prof, UNIV. HOUSTON, 39-45, assoc. prof, 46-47, prof, 47-70, acting dean col. arts & sci, 50-51, dean, 51-58, dean GRAD. SCH, 58-69, EMER. DEAN, 69-, EMER. PROF. ENG, 70- U.S.A.F, 42-46, Res, 47-59, Lt. Col. MLA; Am. Name Soc. English literature. Publ: Some seventeenth century worthies, Univ. N.C, 40, Russell, 71; To the dark covert, Falmouth; Figures of rhetoric in John Gower's English works; The wit and humor of Samuel Butler, N.Dak. Quart, 8/66; God and Samuel Butler, Proc. Conf. Col. Teachers Eng. Tex, 9/67; Names in the fiction of Samuel Butler, S.Cent. Bull, XXIX: 129-132; plus others. Add: 20 N. Wynden Dr, Houston, TX 77027.

DANIELSON, LARRY WILLIAM, b. Lindsborg, Kans, Aug. 8, 40; m. 62; c. 2. FOLKLORE, AMERICAN CIVILIZATION. B.A, Bethany Col.(Kans), 62; Ford Found. fel, Ind. Univ, Bloomington, 65-66, M.A, 68, univ. fel, 69-70, Ph.D.(folklore, Am. stud), 72. Instr. hist. & folklore, Univ. Ill, Chicago Circle, 70-72, ASST. PROF, 72-73; FOLKLORE & LIT, UNIV. ILL, URBANA-CHAMPAIGN, 73- Am. Folklore Soc. American folklore and popular culture; American immigrant culture; film art. Publ: Kaarle Krohn's Die folkloristische Arbeitsmethode: a critical abstract, Folklore Forum, 69; Public Swedish-American ethnicity in central Kansas: a festival and its functions, Swed. Pioneer Hist. Quart, 1/74. Add: Dept. of English, University of Illinois at Urbana-Champaign, Urbana, IL 61801.

DANIELSON, ROBERT WALTER, b. Mason City, Iowa, Nov. 28, 22; m. 52; c. 2. ENGLISH. B.A, Univ. Minn, 50; San Diego State Col, 55-56, 58. Teacher high schs, 56-61; MEM. FAC. ENG, GROSSMONT COL, 61-, chmn. dept, 61-72. Chmn, Pac. Coast regional conf. Eng. two-year col, NCTE-Conf. Col. Compos. & Commun, 66-68, mem. nat. jr. col. comt, 67- U.S.N, 42-46, 52-54, Lt. NCTE; Col. Conf. Compos. & Commun.(exec. comt, 67-). Junior college curriculum development and English instruction; teacher education. Add: Dept. of English, Grossmont College, 8800 Grossmont College Dr, El Cajon, CA 92020.

DANNA, SAMMY RICHARD, b. Monroe, La, Mar. 26, 34. SPEECH. B.A, Northeast La. Univ, 56, M.Ed, 62; M.A, La. State Univ, Baton Rouge, 60; Univ. Ill, Urbana, 62-63; Ph.D.(radio-TV, speech), Univ. Mo-Columbia, 67; M.Div, Cath. Theol. Union, 72. Instr. jour. & speech, Neville High Sch, La, 56-57, 59-61; Southside High Sch, 57-59; grad. asst. speech, Univ. Ill, Urbana, 62-63; instr, Ill. State Univ, 63-64; grad. res, Radio-TV & speech, Univ. Mo-Columbia, 64-67; instr, Quincy Col, 67-68; dir. relig. radio, Franciscan Friars, Ill, 68-69; lectr, LOYOLA UNIV. CHICAGO, 69-71, ASST. PROF. RADIO-TV, 71- Minister, Franciscan Friars, 67- Broadcast. Educ. Asn; Nat. Asn. Educ. Broadcasters; Speech Commun. Asn. Broadcasting history; film history; radio-TV fundamentals. Publ: Broadcast editorializing, 65, Death of broadcasting option time, 65, TV's fight for courtroom access, 68, The rise of radio news, 68 & The press-radio war, 68, Univ. Mo. Add: Dept. of Communication Arts, Loyola University of Chicago, 820 N. Michigan Ave, Chicago, IL 60611.

DANSON, LAWRENCE NEIL, b. New York, N.Y, Nov. 10, 42; m. 67; c. 2. ENGLISH. B.A, Dartmouth Col, 64; M.A, Oxford, 66; Ph.D.(Eng), Yale, 69. Instr. ENG, PRINCETON, 68-70, ASST. PROF, 70- MLA; Shakespeare Asn. Am. Shakespeare; Renaissance and modern drama. Publ: Tragic alphabet: Shakespeare's drama of language, Yale, 74; Metonymy and Coriolanus, Philol. Quart, 1/73; Device of wonder: Titus Andronicus and revenge tragedies, Tex. Stud. Lit. & Lang, spring 74. Add: Dept. of English, Princeton University, Princeton, NJ 08540.

DANZIG, ALLAN (PETER), b. New York, N.Y, Apr. 21, 31; m. 58; c. 1. ENGLISH.LITERATURE. B.A, Cornell Univ, 52; M.A, Yale, 56, Ph.D, 61. Instr. ENG, Northwest. Univ, 58-59; Univ. Mich, 60-61; asst. prof, Lafayette Col, 61-64; CITY COL. NEW YORK, 64-71, ASSOC. PROF, 71- U.S.A.F, 52-54, Res, 54-, Maj. MLA; NCTE. Tennyson; Victorian, late 18th century and 19th century poetry. Publ: The contraries: a central concept in Tennyson's poetry, PMLA, 12/62; Lolita and the lechers, Satire Newslett, fall 64; Tennyson's The princess: a definition of love, Victorian Poetry, spring 66. Add: Dept. of English, City College of New York, New York, NY 10031.

DANZIGER, MARLIES KALLMANN, b. Feb. 16, 26. ENGLISH. B.A, Queens Col.(N.Y), 46; M.A, Stanford Univ, 49; Sterling fel, 50-51; Ph.D.(Eng), Yale, 56. Instr. ENG, Smith Col, 51-57, asst. prof, 57-58; instr, HUNTER COL, 58-62, asst. prof, 63-67, assoc. prof, 67-73, PROF. & CHMN. COMP. LIT. PROG, 73- V.chmn, Sch. & Col. Conf. Eng, 66-69, chmn, 70-71. MLA. Eighteenth century novel and drama; 18th and 19th century comparative literature. Publ: Co-auth, Introduction to literary criticism, 62 & An introduction to the study of literature, 65, Heath; co-auth, A poetry anthology, Random, 68; Heroic villains in eighteenth century criticism, Comp. Lit, 59. Add: 25 Chesterfield Rd, Scarsdale, NY 10583.

DARDEN, FRANCES K, b. Waco, Tex. ENGLISH. B.A, Univ. Tex, 34; M.A, Columbia Univ, 37; Ph.D.(Eng), Univ. Birmingham, 51. Instr. ENG, Tex. Woman's Univ, 36-46, asst. prof, 46-58, assoc. prof, 58-61; PROF, Sam Houston State Col, 61-66; MIDWEST. UNIV, 66- S.Cent. Mod. Lang. Asn; S.Cent. Renaissance Conf. Comparative literature, especially British, 19th century and Renaissance. Add: Dept. of English, Midwestern University, Wichita Falls, TX 76308.

DARLINGTON, BETH MARY, b. Wis, Mar. 17, 41. ENGLISH LITERATURE. B.A, Univ. Wis-Madison, 63; M.A, Cornell Univ, 65, Ph.D.(Eng), 70. Instr. ENG, VASSAR COL, 67-70, ASST. PROF, 70- MLA; AAUP. Wordsworth; 19th century English literature. Publ: Co-ed. & contrib, Bicentenary Wordsworth studies, Cornell Univ, 70. Add: Dept. of English, Vassar College, Poughkeepsie, NY 12601.

DARNELL, DONALD GENE, b. Galveston, Tex, Mar. 10, 32; m. 53; c. 1. AMERICAN LITERATURE. B.S, Tex. Technol. Col, 53; M.A, Univ. Okla, 62; Ph.D.(Eng), Univ. Tex, 64. Instr. ENG, Univ. Wichita, 57-60; teaching asst, Univ. Tex, 62-64; instr. UNIV. N.C, GREENSBORO, 64-65, asst. prof, 65-72, ASSOC. PROF, 72- MLA; S.Atlantic Mod. Lang. Asn. Nineteenth century American literature: Cooper, Hawthorne, and William Hickling Prescott. Publ: Uncas as hero: the Ubi sunt formula in The last of the Mohicans, Am. Lit, 11/65; Cooper and Faulkner: land, legacy, and the tragic vision, S.Atlantic Bull, 5/69; Doctrine by Ensample: the emblem and The marble faun, Tex. Stud. Lit. & Lang, summer, 73. Add: Dept. of English, University of North Carolina, Greensboro, NC 27412.

DARRETTA, JOHN LAWRENCE, b. Yonkers, N.Y, Oct. 4, 38. AMERICAN LITERATURE, COMMUNICATION ARTS. B.A, Iona Col, 63; M.A, Fordham Univ, 66, Ph.D.(Am. lit), 72. Instr. Eng. & Am. lit, Marian Col.(Ind), 65-67; IONA COL, 69-71; ASST. PROF. AM. LIT. & FILM, 71- AAUP; MLA; NCTE. The violent and the grotesque in American fictions; Flannery O'Connor; architectonic approach to modern fictions and films. Publ: Vittorio de Sica's Vision of cycles, In: The classic cinema, Harcourt, 73. Add: Dept. of English, Iona College, North Ave, New Rochelle, NY 10801.

DATHORNE, OSCAR RONALD, b. Georgetown, Guyana, Nov. 19, 34; Brit. citizen; m. 59; c. 2. MODERN BRITISH & WORLD BLACK LITERATURE. B.A, Univ. Sheffield, 58, M.A, 60, Ph.D.(black lit), 66; cert. educ, Univ. London, 59, dipl. educ, 67. Asst. prof. Eng. educ, Ahmadu Bello Univ, Nigeria, 59-63; assoc. prof. Eng, Univ. Ibadan, 63-66; UNESCO expert, Univ. Sierra Leone, 67-68, prof. Eng. & chmn. dept, 68-69; PROF. Afro-Am. stud, Univ. Wis-Madison, 70-71; ENG. & BLACK STUD, OHIO STATE UNIV, 71- Lectr, Northwest. Univ, 69, Yale, 70, Fed. City Col, 70, Howard Univ, Univ. P.R, 71, Col. Virgin Islands, 71, Univ. Nev. & Mich. State Univ. MLA; Am. Counc. Teaching For. Lang; Royal Soc. Arts; Royal Econ. Soc. D.H. Lawrence's poetry; African literature; Afro-American and Caribbean literature. Publ: Dumplings in the soup (novel), 63 & The scholar man (novel), 64, Cassell, London; ed, Caribbean prose, 65 & Caribbean verse, 67, Heinemann, London; ed, African poetry, Macmillan, London, 69; co-ed, Africa in prose, Penguin, London, 69; auth, The black mind, Univ. Minn, 74; plus numerous articles. Add: Dept. of Black Studies, Ohio State University, Columbus, OH 43210.

DAUBER, KENNETH MARC, b. Brooklyn, N.Y, Apr. 3, 45; m. 68. AMERICAN LITERATURE. A.B, Columbia Col, 66; Woodrow Wilson fel, Princeton, 66-67, M.A, 68, Ph.D.(Eng), 73. ASST. PROF. ENG, STATE UNIV. N.Y. BUFFALO, 70- MLA. American literature; theory of the novel. Add: Dept. of English, State University of New York at Buffalo, Buffalo, NY 14214.

DAUGHERTY, WILSON, b. Detroit, Mich, Mar. 3, 20; m. 44; c. 2. ENGLISH, COMPARATIVE LITERATURE. B.A, East. Mich. Univ, 42, M.A, Univ. Mich, 49, summer, 66, 67. Asst. prof. ENG, Alma Col, 47-54; teacher, jr. high sch, Mich, 55-58; asst. prof, LAWRENCE INST. TECHNOL, 58-66, ASSOC. PROF, 66- MLA; NCTE. Homeric Age; modern poetry; the Faustian tradition; the Victorian mind. Publ: Co-auth, Principles of advertising, Pitman, 63; auth, The Iliad, the Odyssey, Barnes & Noble, 66. Add: 1119 Lincoln Ave, Ann Arbor, MI 48104.

DAUNER, LOUISE, b. Indianapolis, Ind, May 22, 07. ENGLISH, AMERICAN LITERATURE. A.B, Butler Univ, 36, M.A, 41; Ph.D.(Am. lit), State Univ. Iowa, 44. Teacher high sch, Ind, 36-39, 41; instr, Univ. Wis, 45-46; asst. prof. Eng, Butler Univ, 46-47, assoc. prof, 47-48; Am. & world lit, Drake Univ, 48-63, prof, 63; assoc. prof, IND. UNIV-PURDUE UNIV, INDIANAPOLIS, 63-71, PROF, 71-, asst. chmn. dept. Eng, 65-71. Am. Asn. Univ. Women Morrison fel, 44-45; lectr, adult educ. ctr, Ind. Univ, 51-52, 53-54, vis. lectr, 61-62. MLA. American literature; world literature. Publ: What happened in the cave? further reflections on A passage to India, Reprinted in: Perspectives on A passage to India, Barnes & Noble, 68; Two Robinson revisions: Mr. Flood's party and The dark hills, Colby Libr. Quart, 6/69; The pernicious rib: E.A. Robinson's concept of feminine character, Reprinted in: Appreciation of Edwin Arlington Robinson, Colby Col, 69; plus others. Add: Indiana University-Purdue University at Indianapolis, 925 W. Michigan St, Indianapolis, IN 46202.

D'AVANZO, MARIO L, b. New Britain, Conn, Nov. 11, 31; div; c. 2. ENGLISH. A.B, Dartmouth Col, 53; M.A, Trinity Col.(Conn), 54; Ph.D.(Eng), Brown Univ, 63. Instr. ENG, Providence Col, 60-63, asst. prof, 63-65, ASSOC. PROF, 65-68; QUEENS COL.(N.Y), 68- U.S.N, 54-57, Lt.(jg). MLA. English Romantic poetry; American literature. Publ: Keats's metaphors for the poetic imagination, Duke Univ, 67; auth, Keats's and Vergil's underworlds: source and meaning in Book II of Endymion, Keats-Shelley J, winter 67; King Francis, Lucrezia, and the figurative language of Andrea del Sarto, Tex. Stud. Lang. & Lit, winter 68; The literary sources of My kinsman, Major Molineux': Shakespeare, Coleridge, Milton, Stud. Short Fiction, spring 73. Add: Dept. of English, Queens College, Flushing, NY 11367.

DAVEE, PAUL WILSON, b. Helena, Mont, June 18, 15; m. 39; c. 2. DRAMATIC ARTS. B.E, Wis. State Col. River Falls, 35; M.A, Univ. Iowa, 39, Ph.D.(dramatic art), 50. Teacher, Pub. Schs, Mont, 35-37; instr. drama & speech, Mont. State Col, 39-40; head dept. drama, Christian Col, 40-43; instr. DRAMATIC ART, Univ. Iowa, 46-50, asst. prof, 50-53; assoc. prof. Fla. State Univ, 53-57; PROF, SAN JOSE STATE UNIV, 57- U.S.N.R, 43-46, Lt. Am. Theatre Asn; Speech Commun. Asn. Acting and directing; dramatic art education. Publ: Co-auth, A college program in communications skills, W.C. Brown, 47 & Directory of American college theatre Am. Educ. Theatre Asn, 60. Add: 1963 Kobara Lane, San Jose, CA 95124.

DAVENPORT, GUY MATTISON, b. Anderson, S.C, Nov. 23, 27. ENGLISH. A.B, Duke Univ, 48; B.Litt, Oxford, 50; Ph.D.(Eng), Harvard, 61. Instr, ENG, Wash. Univ, 52-55; tutor, Harvard, 57-60; asst. prof, Haverford Col, 60-63; PROF, UNIV. KY, 63- Adv. Jonathan Williams Found, 67- U.S.A, 50-52. Post-1910 American and European literature; Greek, archaic period; 19th century American and English intellectual history. Publ: Co-auth, Motive and method in the cantos of Ezra Pound, Columbia Univ, 53; auth, The intelligence of Louis Agassiz, Beacon, 63; Carmina Archilochi, Univ. Calif, 64; Sappho: Poems and fragments, Univ. Mich, 65; The Iliad: a handbook, 66 & The Odyssey: a handbook, 67, Educ. Res. Assoc; Tatlin!, Scribner's, 74; Pound and Frobenius, In: Method and motive in the Cantos of Ezra Pound, Columbia Univ, 54; Ezra Pound's effulgent gists, Wis. Stud. Contemporary Lit, 62; Persephone's Ezra, In: New Approaches to Ezra Pound, Univ. Calif, 68. Add: 621 Sayre Ave, Lexington, KY 40508.

DAVENPORT, JOHN STEWART, b. Buffalo, N.Y, May 12, 07. ENGLISH. A.B, Cornell Univ, 28; A.M, Harvard, 29; Ph.D.(Eng), Univ. N.C, 34. Instr. ENG, Carnegie Inst. Technol, 29-31; Univ. Tenn, 34-44; from asst. prof. to prof, KNOX COL.(ILL), 45-72, EMER. PROF, 72- Col. Eng. Asn. Publ: European crowns since 1800, 47, German talers since 1800, 49, Multiple talers of the Brunswick Duchies, 56, German talers, 1700-1800, 58, European crowns 1700-1800, 61, German church and city talers 1600-1700, 67, Triskelion: three plays, 70 & Large size silver coins of the world, 72, privately publ: The silver dollars of Africa, Whitman Publ. Co, 59; The talers of the Austrian noble houses, Orgn. Int. Numismatists, 72. Add:Dept. of English, Knox College, Galesburg, IL 61401.

DAVENPORT, WILLIAM HENRY, b. Bridgeport, Conn, Mar. 26, 08; c. 2. ENGLISH LITERATURE. A.B, Dartmouth Col, 29; summers, Harvard, 30, Univ. Munich, Ger, 36; A.M, Tufts Col, 31; Ph.D, Yale, 38. Teaching fel, Tufts Col, 29-31; instr. Eng, Carnegie Inst. Tech, 31-35; Smith Col, 38; asst. prof. Eng. Lang. & lit, Univ. South. Calif, 38-42, assoc. prof, 42-49, prof, 49-57, acting head dept, 48-49, head dept, 55-57; prof. Eng. & chmn. dept. humanities, HARVEY MUDD COL, 57-68, prof. LIT, 69-73, EMER. PROF, 73- Vis. lectr, Calif. Inst. Technol, 44-47; ed, U.S. Rocket, 44-45; Ford Found. consult. in humanities, Univ. Calif, Los Angeles, 61-65; res. assoc. prog. technol. & soc, Harvard Univ, 68-69. Philol. Asn. Pac. Coast; Soc. Hist. Technol. Technology, literature and art interplay. Publ: Ed, Nine modern American plays, Appleton, 57; Voices in court, 59 & The good physician, 62, Macmillan; co-auth, Biography past and present, Scribner, 65; co-auth, Engineering: its role and function in human society, 67 & auth, The one culture, 70, Pergamon; co-ed, Technology and culture, Schocken, 72; auth, Resource letter on technology, literature and art, Am. J. Physics, 4/70; Antitechnological attitudes in modern literature, Technol. & Soc, 1/73. Add: 616 Purdue Dr, Claremont, CA 91711.

DAVEY, FRANK, b. Vancouver, B.C, Apr. 19, 40; m. 69; c. 2. CANADIAN & AMERICAN LITERATURE. B.A, Univ. B.C, 61, M.A, 63; Ph.D.(Eng), Univ. South. Calif, 68. Lectr. ENG, Royal Roads Mil. Col, 63-66, asst. prof, 67-70; YORK UNIV, 70-72, ASSOC. PROF, 72- Writer-in-residence, Sir George Williams Univ, 69-70. Asn. Can. Univ. Teachers Eng; Can. Asn. Univ. Teachers. Canadian literature; post-modern American poetry. Publ: Five readings of Olson's Maximus, Bowering, Montreal, 70; Earle Birney, Copp Clark, Toronto, 71; Our nature/our voices: a guide to English-Canadian literature since 1960, Press Porcepic, Vol. 2, 74; E.J. Pratt: apostle of corporate man, Can. Lit, winter 70; Gwendolyn MacEwen: the secret of alchemy, spring 73 & Atwood walking backwards, summer 73, Open Letter. Add: 133 Calumet College, York University, Downsview, Ont. M3J 1P3, Can.

DAVID, ALFRED, b. Hamburg, Ger, Mar. 31, 29; U.S. citizen; m. 68. ENGLISH. A.B, Harvard, 51, A.M, 54, Ph.D, 57. Instr. ENG, IND. UNIV, BLOOMINGTON, 58-61, asst. prof, 61-65, assoc. prof, 65-68, PROF, 68- Sheldon traveling fel, 57-58; Guggenheim & Fulbright fels, 67-68. U.S.A, 51-53. MLA; Mediaeval Acad. Am. Chaucer. Publ: Literary satire in the House of fame, 60 & The man of law vs. Chaucer, 67, PMLA; The hero of the Troilus, Speculum, 62. Add: Dept. of English, Indiana University, Bloomington, IN 47401.

DAVID, MARY ELIZABETH MEEK, b. New York, N.Y, July 14, 24; div. OLD & MIDDLE ENGLISH LITERATURE. A.B, Wells Col, 46; M.A, Ohio State Univ, 47; Ph.D.(Eng), Radcliffe Col, 56. Instr. ENG, N.Y. State Teachers Col, 48-51; Bryn Mawr Col, 56-57; lectr, Ind. Univ, Bloomington, 58-68; ASSOC. PROF, UNIV. PITTSBURGH, 70- MLA; Mediaeval Acad. Am. Publ: Co-ed. & contrib, The frog king and other tales of the Brothers Grimm, New Am. Libr-Signet, 64 & The twelve dancing princesses and other fairy tales, New Am. Libr-Signet, 64 & Ind. Univ, 74; transl, Emile Benveniste's Problems in general linguistics, Univ. Miami, 72 & Guido delle Colonne's Historia destructionis Troiae, Ind. Univ, (in press). Add: Dept. of English, University of Pittsburgh, Pittsburgh, PA 15213.

DAVIDOW, MARY C, b. Pawtucket, R.I, Dec. 14, 17. ENGLISH. Ed.B, R.I. Col, 39; A.M, Brown Univ, 54, Ph.D.(Eng), 60; Fulbright scholar, Univs. Innsbruck & Vienna, 55-56. Teacher, Pub. Schs, R.I, 40-53; instr. ENG, Brown Univ, 57-60; assoc. prof, WILLIAM PATERSON COL. N.J, 60-65, PROF, 65- MLA; Col. Eng. Asn. Late Victorian period; editing the letters of Charlotte M. Mew (1869-1928), English poet. Publ: Co-auth, The internship program at the William Paterson College of New Jersey, Improving Col. & Univ. Teaching, (in press); auth, Queen Mab to Prometheus out of bounds (poem), winter 73 & The Christminister mystique and the immanent will in Hardy's Jude the obscure, spring 74, Christianity and Lit; plus others. Add: Dept. of English, William Paterson College of New Jersey, 300 Pompton Rd, Wayne, NJ 07470.

DAVIDSON, C. MELVIN, JR, b. Meridian, Idaho, Dec. 13, 27; m. 51; c. 3. THEATRE, ENGLISH. B.A, Hamline Univ, 48; M.A, Univ. Nebr, Lincoln, 56; Ph.D.(dramatic arts), Univ. Iowa, 62. Teacher, Great Falls, Mont, 48-49; teacher & asst. prin, Pueblo, Colo, 49-56; asst. prof. speech, Nebr. Wesleyan Univ, 56-60; chmn. div. arts, Stephens Col, 61-72, coord. performing arts, 72-74, acting head dept. fashion, 73-74, prof. humanities, 61-74; DEAN COL. FINE & COMMUN. ARTS, LOYOLA MARYMOUNT UNIV, 74- Mem. comn. teacher cert, NEA, 53-54; Danforth teacher, 58-59; examr, N.Cent. Asn. Cols. & Sec. Schs, 72- Asn. Gen. & Lib. Stud; AAUP; Am. Theatre Asn. Dramatic theory; literary criticism. Add: 7440 W. 89th St, Los Angeles, CA 90045.

DAVIDSON, CHARLES EDWARD, b. Walton, N.Y, Mar. 21, 22; m. 54; c. 3. ENGLISH. A.B, Princeton, 46; M.A, Yale, 49, Ph.D.(Eng), 53. Instr. ENG, COL. WILLIAM & MARY, 49-53, asst. prof, 53-58, assoc. prof, 58-64, PROF, 64- MLA; Mediaeval Acad. Am; AAUP. Old English; Middle English literature. Add: 215 Kingswood Dr, Williamsburg, VA 23185.

DAVIDSON, CLIFFORD OSCAR, b. Faribault, Minn, Oct. 29, 32; m. 54. ENGLISH. B.S, St. Cloud State Col, 54; Univ. Minn, 54-59; fel, Wayne State Univ, 59-61, M.A, 61, Ph.D.(Eng), 66. Instr. ENG, Wayne State Univ, 61-65; asst. prof, WEST. MICH. UNIV, 65-72, ASSOC. PROF, 72-, fac. res. grant, 67, res. fel, 71 & 74. Co-ed, Comp. Drama, West. Mich. Univ, 67-; bd. mem, Medieval Inst, 69-74. U.S.A, 56-58. Renaissance Soc. Am; Mediaeval Acad. Am. Religion and literature; English literature of the late Middle Ages and

Renaissance. Publ: The primrose way: a study of Shakespeare's Macbeth, 70 & ed, Torquato Tasso's Aminta English: the Henry Reynolds translation, 72, Westburg & Studies in medieval drama in honor of William L. Smoldon on his 82nd birthday, 74; auth, Doctor Faustus of Wittenberg, 62 & The idol of Isis Church, 69, Stud. Philol; The Saint play of Mary Magdalene in Digby manuscript, 33, Annuale Mediaevale, 72; plus others. Add: Dept. of English, Western Michigan University, Kalamazoo, MI 49001.

DAVIDSON, EDITH T. ANEY, b. New York, N.Y, Nov. 21, 23; m. 57; c. 5. ENGLISH, WORLD LITERATURE. A.B, State Univ. N.Y. Albany, 44; M.A, Univ. Pa, 49, Ph.D.(Eng), 54. Asst. ENG, Univ. Pa, 47-52, 53-54; instr. Ohio Univ, 54-55, asst. prof, 56-59; lectr, Am. Col. for Girls, Istanbul, 59-62; PROF, STATE UNIV. N.Y. COL. ONEONTA, 62-, dir. prog, Univ. Wurzburg, 69-70, Univ. Tel Aviv & Hebrew Univ. Jerusalem, 71-72. Mil. Intel, W.A.A.C, 44-46. MLA; Soc. Advan. Scand. Stud. Modern British poetry, Auden and the Left of the 1930's; Scandinavian literature; existentialism and the modern novel. Add: Dept. of English, State University of New York College at Oneonta, Oneonta, NY 13820.

DAVIDSON, EDWARD HUTCHINS, b. Mason, Nev, July 23, 12. AMERICAN LITERATURE. A.B, Am. Univ.(D.C), 34; Ph.D, Yale, 40. From instr. to assoc. prof, Ohio Univ, 38-42, 46-50; assoc. prof. ENG, Hunter Col, 50-51; UNIV. ILL, 51-55, PROF, 55- Vis. prof, Harvard, 62-63; Guggenheim fel, 65-66. MLA. Colonial American writing; Poe and Hawthorne; 19th century American novel. Publ: Hawthorne's last phase, Yale Univ, 49; Poe: a critical study, 57 & Jonathan Edwards: the narrative of a Puritan mind, 68, Harvard Univ. Add: Dept. of English, University of Illinois, Urbana, IL 61801.

DAVIDSON, KEITH CARLYLE, b. White Hall, Ill, Sept. 10, 19; m. 45; c. 2. SPEECH. B.Ed, Ill. State Normal Univ, 42; M.S, Columbia Univ, 50; Univ. Mo, 54-57. Teacher U.S. hist. & speech, Lombard Sch, Galesburg, Ill, 45-50; ASST. PROF. SPEECH, Ithaca Col, 50-53; Fla. State Univ, 57-59; ILL. STATE UNIV, 59- U.S.C.G, 42-45. Cent. St. Speech Asn; Speech Commun. Asn.(chmn. dialect stud. proj, 61-); Am. Speech & Hearing Asn. Longitudinal study of dialect and linguistic areas of United States. Add: Dept. of Speech Pathology & Audiology, Illinois State University, Normal, IL 61761.

DAVIDSON, LLOYD JOHNSTON, b. Louisville, Ky, May 26, 11; m. 37. ENGLISH LITERATURE. Ph.B, Univ. Chicago, 32, univ. fel, 33-34, A.M, 34, Am. Counc. Learned Soc. fel, 46-47, Ph.D, 47. Instr. ENG, State Col. Wash, 34-35; Univ. Nebr, 35-36; Univ. Chicago, 36-42; asst. prof, Johns Hopkins Univ, 48-51; vis. lectr, Univ. Wash, 51-52; prof. & chmn. dept, Wells Col, 52-55; PROF, VA. MIL. INST, 55-, dean fac, 55-65. Mem, Eng. Inst. U.S.A.F, 42-46, Maj. MLA. Victorian literature; 20th century literature and literary criticism; college curricula. Add: Dept. of English, Virginia Military Institute, Lexington, VA 24450.

DAVIES, PHILLIPS GEORGE, b. El Paso, Tex, Oct. 12, 25; m. 49. ENGLISH LITERATURE. B.A, Marquette Univ, 46; M.A, Northwest. Univ, 47, Ph.D, 60. Asst. instr. ENG. LIT, Northwest. Univ, 47-49; instr, City Col. San Francisco, 49-51; Univ. San Francisco, summer 51; IOWA STATE UNIV, 54-59, asst. prof, 59-64, assoc. prof, 64-73, PROF, 73- Instr, Drake Univ, summers, 62, 63; ed, Iowa Eng. Yearbook, 64-68. MLA. Romantic and Victorian literature. Publ: Preparing the research paper, Educr. Publ. Serv, 67; The miscegenation theme in the works of Thackeray, Mod. Lang. Notes 4/61; Hemingway's Fifty grand and the Jack Britton—Mickey Walker prize fight, Am. Lit, 11/65; The attack on Shelley at Tanyrallt: a suggestion, Keats-Shelley Mem. Asn. Bull, 72. Add: Dept. of English, Ross Hall, Iowa State University, Ames, IA 50010.

DAVIES, ROBERT MORTON, b. Carmi, Ill, Sept. 22, 20; m. 55; c. 3. ENGLISH. B.A, Wheaton Col.(Ill), 41; B.D, Faith Theol. Sem, 44; M.A, Univ. Pa, 45, Ph.D.(Eng), 54. Instr. Eng, King's Col, 43-45, asst. prof, 45-47, assoc. prof. & dean men, 47-50; dean men, Perkiomen Sch, 51-52; mem. fac. Eng, Valley Forge Mil. Jr. Col, 52-55, admin. asst, 53-55; instr, State Univ. N.Y. Maritime Col, 55-58; asst. prof, Thiel Col, 58-59, assoc. prof, 59-62, prof, 62-64; dean, Col. Arts & Sci, Ithaca Col, 64-66, Provost, 66-72, consult. educ. admin, 72-73; V.PRES. ADMIN, STATE UNIV. N.Y. COL. PURCHASE, 73- Lectr, Univ. Pa, 46; Rutgers Univ, 55-58. MLA; Asn. Instnl. Res; Am. Asn. Univ. Adminr; Asn. Higher Educ; Am. Mgt. Asn. Literary criticism; short story; educational theory. Publ: The humanism of Paul Elmer More, Bookman Assoc, 58; The effective teacher, J. Higher Educ, 5/57; American education: the age of responsibility, Mod. Age, fall 59; The process of liberal education, Improving Col. & Univ. Teaching, winter 64. Add: State University of New York College at Purchase, Purchase, NY 10577.

DAVIES, ROBERTSON, b. Thamesville, Ont, Aug. 28, 13; m. 40; c. 3. ENGLISH. B.Litt, Oxford, 38; hon. LL.D, Univ. Alta, 57, Queen's Univ.(Ont), 62, Univ. Man, 72; hon. D.Litt, McMaster Univ, 59, Univ. Windsor, 71, York Univ, 73; D.C.L, Bishop's Univ.(Can), 67. Actor & teacher, Old Vic Repertory Co, Eng, 38-40; lit. ed, Saturday Night, Ont, 40-42; ed, Examiner, Ont, 42-58, publ, 58-68; PROF. ENG, UNIV. TORONTO, 60-, MASTER MASSEY COL, 62- Sen, Stratford Shakespearean Festival, Stratford, Ont, 53-; Royal Soc. Can. fel, 67. Lorne Pierce Medal, Royal Soc. Can, 61; Companion, Order of Can, 72; Gov. Gen. Lit. Award, 72. Dramatists Guild. Drama: 1650 to the present; history of the theatre; Bernard Shaw and his contemporaries. Publ: Shakespeare's boy actors, Dent, 39 & Russell, 64; co-auth, Renown at Stratford, 53, Twice have the trumpets sounded, 54 & Thrice the brinded cat hath mew'd, 55, Clarke Irwin; auth, A voice from the attic, Knopf, 60 & McClelland & Stewart, 60; The personal art, Secker & Warburg, 61; Shakespeare over the port, 61 & Changing fashions in Shakespearean production, 63, In: Papers on Shakespeare, Gage; Ben Jonson and alchemy, In: Stratford Papers 1968-1969, McMaster Univ, 72. Add: Massey College, 4 Devonshire Pl, Toronto, Ont. M5S 2E1, Can.

DAVIES, ROSEMARY REEVES, b. Sibley, Iowa, Dec. 17, 25; m. 49. ENGLISH & AMERICAN LITERATURE. B.S, Northwest. Univ, Evanston, 47, M.A, 48. ASST. PROF. ENG, IOWA STATE UNIV, 54- MLA. British literature, Romantic and Victorian. Publ: The Rosenbluth case: federal justice on trial, Iowa State Univ, 70; Charles Brockden Brown's Ormond, Philol. Quart, 1/64; co-auth, Hemingway's Fifty grand, Am. Lit, 11/65; auth, The Rosenbluth case, Forest Hist, 10/70. Add: Dept. of English, Ross Hall, Iowa State University, Ames, IA 50010.

DAVIS, ABRAHAM, JR, b. Beaufort, S.C, May 14, 23; m. 58; c. 2. RHETORIC & PUBLIC ADDRESS, SPEECH PATHOLOGY & THERAPY. B.A, Houghton Col, 55; M.A, Temple Univ, 56; Univ. Iowa, Pa. State Univ. & West. Reserve Univ, 57-60; Ph.D.(rhetoric & pub. address), Ind. Univ, Bloomington, 71. Instr. speech & speech therapist, S.C. State Col, 56-58; county speech therapist, Pub. Schs, Greenville, S.C, 58-61; instr. speech & Eng, Houghton Col, 61-64, assoc. prof. SPEECH, 64-65; teaching assoc, Ind. Univ, Bloomington, 65-67; assoc. prof, HOUGHTON COL, 67-70, PROF, 71- Sabbatical lectr, 72-73; vis. lectr, Asbury Col, 73; vis. lectr. & adminr, Messiah Col, Philadelphia, 74. Eng.C, U.S.A, 43-46. Speech Commun. Asn; Speech Asn. East. States. Education of the academically disadvantaged Afro-American; oral interpretation of Afro-American rhetoric and literature; serious rhetoric in the Negro spirituals. Publ: An accelerated speech curriculum for selected educationally disadvantaged Negroes, Dissertation Abstr, Int, 71. Add: Dept. of Speech, Houghton College, Houghton, NY 14744.

DAVIS, ARTHUR PAUL, b. Hampton, Va, Nov. 21, 04. ENGLISH LITERATURE. A.B, Columbia Univ, 27, A.M, 29, Ph.D, 42. PROF. ENG, N.C. Col, 27-28; Va. Union Univ, 29-44; HOWARD UNIV, 44- MLA. Life and works of Isaac Watts; the Negro caravan. Add: Dept. of English, Howard University, Washington, DC 20001.

DAVIS, BARBARA HILLYER, b. Creston, Iowa, Mar. 1, 34; m. 58; c. 3. ENGLISH LITERATURE, HUMAN RELATIONS. B.A, Rockford Col, 56; M.A, Claremont Grad. Sch, 57; Ph.D.(Eng), Univ. Wis, 62. Instr. Eng, Mundelein Col, 62-64; acting instr, Loyola Univ, Chicago, 64; Univ. Calif, Santa Barbara, 67; VIS. ASST. PROF. ENG. & ADJ. ASST. PROF, HUMAN RELAT, UNIV. OKLA, 73- Am. Asn. Univ. Women fel, 62. MLA. Women in literature; women's studies. Add: 736 Nancy Lynn Terr, Norman, OK 73069.

DAVIS, BERTRAM HYLTON, b. Ozone Park, L.I, N.Y, Nov. 30, 18; m. 46; c. 3. ENGLISH. A.B, Columbia Univ, 41, M.A, 48, Ph.D.(Eng), 56. Lectr, ENG, Hunter Col, 47-48; instr, Dickinson Col, 48-51, asst. prof, 51-57; staff assoc, AM. ASN. UNIV. PROF, 57-62, dep. gen. secy, 63-67, GEN. SECY, 67-, ed, Bull, 60-65. Am. Philos. Soc. grants, 62, 66. U.S.A, 41-46, Capt. MLA; Am. Soc. 18th Century Stud. Eighteenth century English literature. Publ: Johnson before Boswell, Yale Univ, 60; ed, The life of Samuel Johnson, LL.D, Macmillan, 61; auth, A proof of eminence, the life of Sir John Hawkins, Ind. Univ, 73. Add: 3009 Daniel Lane N.W, Washington, DC 20015.

DAVIS, CHARLES ROGER, b. Peoria, Ill, Aug. 9, 43. ENGLISH. B.A, Yale, 65; M.A, Princeton, 69, Ph.D.(Eng. lang. & lit), 73; M.S, Columbia Univ, 72. N.AM. BIBLIOGR, UNIV. VA. LIBR, 72- U.S.A, 63-65, 65-66. MLA; Am. Libr. Asn; Renaissance Soc. Am; Bibliogr. Soc. Eng; Bibliogr. Soc. Am. Renaissance poetry and prose; 18th century booktrade. Add: Acquisitions Dept, University of Virginia Library, Charlottesville, VA 22901.

DAVIS, CHARLES TWITCHELL, b. Hampton, Va, Apr. 29, 18; m. 43; c. 2. ENGLISH. A.B, Dartmouth Col, 39; Barker fel, Univ. Chicago, 39-40, Rosenwald fels, 40-42, A.M, 42; Ph.D.(Am. civilization), N.Y. Univ, 51. Instr. ENG, N.Y. Univ, 48-53, asst. prof, 53-55; Princeton, 55-61; assoc. prof, Pa. State Univ, 61-63, PROF, 63-70; UNIV. IOWA, 70- Mem. supv. comt, Eng. Inst, 62-65; assoc. ed, J. Gen. Educ, 63-; consult. ed, Sch. Arts, 63-65; Fulbright prof, Univ. Turin, 66-67. Adj.Gen.C, U.S.A, 42-46, Capt. MLA. American romanticism; American poetry; British romanticism. Publ: Co-auth, Walt Whitman's poems, N.Y. Univ, 55; auth, Edwin Arlington Robinson: selected early poems and letters, Holt, 60; A New England girlhood by Lucy Larcom, Corinth Bks, 61; Image patterns in the poetry of Edwin Arlington Robinson, Col. Eng, 3/61; Impressionism as a cultural impulse, Sch. Arts, LXIII, No. 6; Poetry: 1910-1930, In: American literary scholarship: an annual: 1963, Duke Univ, 65. Add: Dept. of English, University of Iowa, Iowa City, IA 52240.

DAVIS, CYNTHIA ANN, b. Ft. Worth, Tex, June 9, 47. BRITISH & AMERICAN LITERATURE. B.A, Univ. Tex, Austin, 68; M.A, Univ. Wis-Madison, 69, Ph.D.(Eng), 72. ASST. PROF. ENG, TEX. A&I UNIV, 72- MLA. Twentieth century American and British literature; women's studies. Publ: Interview with Stanley Kunitz, Contemporary Lit, 1/74. Add: Dept. of English, Texas A&I University, Kingsville, TX 78363.

DAVIS, DALE W, b. Moorewood, Okla, Dec. 13, 39; m. 65; c. 2. ENGLISH LITERATURE. B.A, Cent. State Univ, 61; M.A, Univ. Okla, 64, Ph.D.(Eng. lit), 68. Instr. Eng, Ft. Hays Kans. State Col, 64-66; spec. instr, Univ. Okla, 67-68; asst. prof, TEX. TECH UNIV, 68-73, ASSOC. PROF. ENG, 73- Col. Eng. Asn; MLA; NCTE; AAUP. Victorian literature; religious dimensions of literature; undergraduate literary pedagogy. Publ: Euphemistic cussin', Word Stud, 2/68; Teaching critical discipline, CCTE Proc, 9/71; The Victorian syndrome—then and now, In: Studies in relevance: Victorian writers, Univ. Salzburg, 73. Add: Dept. of English, Texas Tech University, Lubbock, TX 79409.

DAVIS, DARYL RICHARD, b. Aurora, Ill, Apr. 3, 41; m. 65; c. 2. ENGLISH & AMERICAN LITERATURE, MEDIEVAL STUDIES. B.A, Carleton Col, 62; Woodrow Wilson fel, Ind. Univ. Bloomington, 62-63, M.A, 65, Ph.D.(Eng), 70. Instr. ENG, Ohio Wesleyan Univ, 65-69; asst. prof, NORTH. MICH. UNIV, 69-73, ASSOC. PROF. & HEAD DEPT, 73- MLA; Mediaeval Acad. Am; Int. Reading Asn; AAUP; Midwest Mod. Lang. Asn. Chaucer; Medieval literature; reading development. Add: Dept. of English, Northern Michigan University, Marquette, MI 49855.

DAVIS, DELMER IVAN, b. St. Helena, Calif, Nov. 6, 39; m. 65; c. 2. ENGLISH. B.A, Pac. Union Col, 62, M.A, 64; Ph.D.(Eng), Univ. Colo, 68. Asst. prof. ENG, Loma Linda Univ, 67-69; assoc. prof, Walla Walla Col, 69-71; ASSOC. PROF. & CHMN. DEPT, LOMA LINDA UNIV, 71- American literature: Willa Cather, Puritanism, Samuel Sewall. Add: Dept. of English, Loma Linda University, Riverside, CA 92505.

DAVIS, EARLE ROSCO, b. Coin, Iowa, Jan. 3, 05; m. 38; c. 5. ENGLISH. A.B. & B.Mus, Monmouth Col, 27; M.A, Univ. Ill, 28; Ph.D.(Eng), Princeton, 35. Instr. ENG, Monmouth Col, 28-33; prof. & head dept, Univ. Wichita, 35-49; PROF, KANS. STATE UNIV, 49-, head dept, 50-69. Fulbright lectr, Univ. Adelaide, Australia, 62, Univ. Col, Cork, 69-70. MLA; NCTE. Nineteenth century English fiction, especially Dickens; modern American poetry, especially E. Pound. Publ: An American in Sicily; Flint and the flame, the artistry of Charles Dickens, Univ. Mo, 63; Vision fugitive: Ezra Pound and economics, Univ. Kans, 68; plus others. Add: 1711 Fairchild St, Manhattan, KS 66502.

DAVIS, F. MARK, b. Edgarton, W.Va, June 4, 32; m. 64; c. 1. ENGLISH. B.A, Bryan Col, 56; M.A, Univ. Tenn, 58; Ph.D.(Eng), Duke Univ, 66. Instr. Eng, Northwest. Col, 58-65, dean stud, 65-66; asst. prof. ENG, Maryville Col, 66-68; ASSOC. PROF, AUGSBURG COL, 68-, ASSOC. DEAN FAC, 73-, chmn. dept. Eng, 68-72, Am. Counc. on Educ. acad. admin. intern, 72-73. NCTE; Melville Soc; MLA. American literature, especially Herman Melville. Add: Dept. of English, Augsburg College, Minneapolis, MN 55404.

DAVIS, FRANK BELL, b. Alba, Mo, Jan. 3, 13; m. 41; c. 3. SPEECH. A.B, Hendrix Col, 35; A.M, State Univ. Iowa, 36; Ph.D, La. State Univ, 49. Instr, Colo. State Univ, 37-39; debate coach, 39-42, assoc. prof, 47-48; PROF. SPEECH & CHMN. DEPT, AUBURN UNIV, 48- Speech Commun. Asn; South. Speech Commun. Asn.(pres, 55). Speech education; history of speech. Add: Dept. of Speech Communication, Auburn University, Auburn, AL 36830.

DAVIS, GWENN, b. Camden, N.J, Mar. 31, 39. ENGLISH LITERATURE. B.A, Wellesley Col, 60; M.A, Oxford, 62; Ph.D.(Eng), Univ. Mich, 66. Instr. ENG, Bryn Mawr Col, 66-68, ASST. PROF, 68-71; UNIV. OKLA, 71- Nat. Endowment for Humanities summer stipend, 64. MLA; Renaissance Soc. Am; AAUP. Renaissance satire; pastoral; Spenser. Publ: The satiric technique of Thomas Nashe, Diss. Abstr, 67. Add: Dept. of English, University of Oklahoma, Norman, OK 73069.

DAVIS, HAROLD EDMUND, b. Pueblo, Colo, Jan. 29, 24; m. 56; c. 2. ENGLISH. B.A, Univ. Denver, 49, M.A, 50; Ph.D.(Eng), La. State Univ, 56. Instr. ENG, Iowa State Univ, 50-53; asst, La. State Univ, 53-56; asst. prof, East. N.Mex. Univ, 56-58; assoc. prof, Univ. Albuquerque, 58-64; PROF, 64-69; ANGELO STATE UNIV, 71-, head dept, 69-71. Honorarium, Iowa State Univ, summer 56; Danforth assoc, 70- U.S.A, 41-46, Sgt. MLA; Popular Cult. Asn; Am. Stud. Asn. Contemporary fiction—existential trends; impressionism in the novel—Conrad, Ford, James; American popular culture. Publ: Symbolism in Nigger of the Narcissus, Twentieth Century Lit, 4/56; Conrad's revisions of the secret agent, Mod. Lang. Quart, 9/58; Shifting rens in a thick fog: point of view in the novels of Joseph Conrad, Conradiana, winter 69-70; plus one other. Add: Dept. of English, Angelo State University, San Angelo, TX 76901.

DAVIS, HARRY BARRETT, b. Putnam, Conn, Dec. 2, 05; m. 42. SPEECH. B.L.I, Emerson Col, 29, hon. M.A, 59; cert, Am. Acad. Dramatic Arts, 32, Royal Acad. Dramatic Arts, 39. Teacher & master, speech & theatre, Hotchkiss Sch, 29-39; assoc. prof. & head div, Southwest. Univ, 40-42; prof. speech & head div. speech & theatre, LEHIGH UNIV, 46-72, EMER. PROF. SPEECH, 72- U.S.A, 42-46. Speech Commun. Asn; Speech Asn. East. States (2nd v.pres, 53-54, 1st v.pres, 54-55, pres, 55-56). Debate; dramatics; parliamentary language. Add: 55 Bridle Path Rd, Bethlehem, PA 18017.

DAVIS, JACK LAVERNE, b. Portland, Ore, Mar. 22, 35; m. 61; c. 2. AMERICAN LITERATURE. B.A, Wash. State Univ, 57, M.A, 59; Ph.D.(Am. stud), Univ. of N.Mex, 67. Asst. prof. Eng, UNIV. IDAHO, 67-74, ASSOC. PROF, 74- Nat. Endowment for Humanities fel, 73-74. Rocky Mountain Mod. Lang. Asn; Nat. Am. Stud. Asn; AAUP. American studies; Satire in American literature; 20th century, native and western American literature. Publ: Roger Williams among the Narragansett Indians, New Eng. Quart, 12/70; Transcendental vision in The dry salvages, Emerson Soc. Quart, 12/70; Mark Schorer's Sinclair Lewis, Sinclair Lewis Newslett, 71. Add: Dept. of English, University of Idaho, Moscow, ID 83843.

DAVIS, JACK M, b. Newark, N.J, Sept. 4, 24; m. 46; c. 2. ENGLISH. B.A, N.Y. Univ, 49; M.A, Columbia Univ, 54, Ph.D.(Eng), 62. Instr. ENG, UNIV. CONN, 56-62, asst. prof, 62-64, assoc. prof, 64-69, PROF, 69- Nat. Found. for Humanities fel, 67-68. U.S.A, 43-45, Staff Sgt. MLA. English Romantic writers; contemporary European fiction; literary criticism. Publ: Ed, Discussions of Wordsworth, Heath, 64; co-auth, Shakespeare's 71st sonnett, Tex. Stud. Lang. & Lit, 63. Add: Dept. of English, University of Connecticut, Storrs, CT 06268.

DAVIS, JAMES PAXTON, b. Winston-Salem, N.C, May 7, 25; m. 51, 73; c. 3. JOURNALISM, WRITING. B.A, Johns Hopkins Univ, 49. Reporter, Winston-Salem, 49-51; Richmond Times-Dispatch, Va, 51-52; Twin City Sentinel, Winston-Salem, 52-53; asst. prof. JOUR, WASHINGTON & LEE UNIV, 53-58, assoc. prof, 58-63, PROF, 63-, HEAD DEPT, 68- Fel, Bread Loaf Writers Conf, summer 56; ed. writer, Winston-Salem J. & Sentinel, summer 60 & bus. ed, summer 61; book ed, Roanoke Times, Va, 61-; vis. scholar, Scott Polar Res. Inst, Cambridge, summer 73. U.S.A, 43-46, Sgt; Two Bronze Stars. S.Atlantic Mod. Lang. Asn. Antarctic exploration; American Civil War. Publ: Two soldiers: two short novels, Simon & Schuster, 56; The battle of new market, Little, 63; One of the dark places, 65 & The seasons of heroes, 67, William Morrow; The world we live in: the novels of Eric Ambler, Hollins Critic, 71; Breadth, depth & elevation; George Garrett's Death of the fox, Mill Mt. Rev, 71. Add: 402 E. Main St, Fincastle, VA 24090.

DAVIS, JED HORACE, JR, b. Stillwater, Minn, July 31, 21; m. 45; c. 3. SPEECH, THEATRE. B.A, Univ. Minn, 47, M.A, 49, Ph.D, 58. Instr. speech & theatre, Macalester Col, 47-50, asst. prof, 50-53, tech. dir, 47-53, dir. children's theatre, 50-53; asst. prof. speech & theatre & dir. children's theatre, Mich. State Univ, 53-60; asst. prof. SPEECH & DRAMA, UNIV. KANS, 60-62, assoc. prof, 62-65, PROF, 65-, DIR. CHILDREN'S THEATRE, 60-, HEAD THEATRE DIV, 67- Vis. prof, Univ. Minn, summers 66, 68. Sig.C, U.S.A, 42-45. Fel. Am. Theatre Asn.(2nd v.pres, 70, 1st v.pres, 71, pres, 72); Children's Theatre Conf. (asst. dir, 61-63, dir, 63-65, Edwin Strawbridge Award, 67); Nat. Theatre Conf. Children's theatre; creative dramatics; interpretative reading. Publ: Co-auth, Children's theatre: play production for the child audience, Harper, 60; ed. & compiler, A directory of children's theatres in the United States, Am. Educ. Theatre Asn, 68; auth, Producing theatre for child audiences, In: Children's theatre and creative dramatics, Univ. Wash, 61; Prospectus for research in children's theatre, Educ. Theatre J, 12/61; Theatre for children, In: Encyclopedia Americana, Grolier, 71. Add: 2602 Louisiana, Lawrence, KS 66044.

DAVIS, JIMMIE D, b. Magazine, Ark, Jan. 12, 40; m. 65; c. 1. JOURNALISM. B.A, Ark. Polytech. Col, 62; M.A, Univ. Iowa, 66. Copy-ed, Des Moines Register, 63-66; PROF. JOUR, Kans. State Univ, 66-67; Univ. Nebr-Lincoln, 67-69; CALIF. STATE UNIV, LONG BEACH, 69- Nat. Inst. for Humanities fel, Stanford Univ, summer 69; founder & ed, Rev. South. Calif. Jour, 71- Media criticism; law of mass communications; graphic design. Publ: Twenty years of experience and still enthusiastic, Ed. & Publ, 6/69; The credibility gap in the business press, IABC Notebk, 6/71; co-auth, LA Times: retrenching in Washington?, Columbia Jour. Rev, 9-10/73. Add: Dept. of Journalism, California State University, Long Beach, 6101 E. Seventh St, Long Beach, CA 90804.

DAVIS, JOE LEE, b. Lexington, Ky, Feb. 22, 06; m. 29; c. 1. ENGLISH & AMERICAN LITERATURE. A.B, Univ. Ky, 26, A.M, 27; Ph.D, Univ. Mich, 34; hon. D.Litt, North. Mich. Univ, 71. Instr. ENG, Univ. Ky, 27-30; UNIV. MICH, ANN ARBOR, 30-37, asst. prof, 37-44, assoc. prof, 44-48, PROF, 48-, chmn. Am. cult. prog, 52-69. MLA; James Branch Cabell Soc.(pres, 68-69). Renaissance drama; American literature; novel. Publ: Co-ed, American literature: an anthology and critical survey (2 vols), Scribner, 49; ed, Charlotte Bronte's Jane Eyre, Holt, 50; auth, James Branch Cabell, Twayne, 62; The sons of Ben: Jonsonian comedy in Caroline England, Wayne State Univ, 67. Add: Dept. of English, University of Michigan, Ann Arbor, MI 48104.

DAVIS, JOHN LOWELL, b. Morehead, Ky, Sept. 4, 04; m. 27; c. 2. ENGLISH LITERATURE. A.B, Eureka Col, 28, hon. LL.D, 57; Chicago Theol. Sem, 27-28; Univ. Chicago, 29-30; A.M, Univ. Cincinnati, 31, Taft fel, 31-32, Ph.D, 33; hon. D.D, Pac. Sch. Relig, 65. Minister, Christian Church, Deland, Ill, 25-27; asst. pastor, First Congregational Church, Maywood, 27-28; minister, Christian Church, Silver Grove, Ky, 28-29; asst. & recreation, St. Chrysostom's Community Centre, Chicago, Ill, 29-30; prof. Eng. & chmn. div. langs. & lit, Lynchburg Col, 33-42, dean, 36-42; exec. secy. bd. higher educ, Disciples of Christ, 42-46; prof. Eng, Hiram Col, 46-57, dean, 47-50, 55-57; pres. CHAPMAN COL, 57-71, EMER. PRES, 71- Coord, North Cent. Study Lib. Arts Educ, 50-; co-dir, workshop higher educ, Univ. Chicago, 50-; secy, Asn. Independent Calif. Cols. & Univs, 62-; staff, Develop. Prog, Chapman Col, 71- MLA. William Blake; influence of Jacob Boehme on Blake. Add: Chapman College, 333 N. Glassell St, Orange, CA 92666.

DAVIS, JOSEPH KIMBRELL, b. New Orleans, La, Jan. 8, 31; m. 57, 69; c. 3. AMERICAN LITERATURE, ENGLISH. B.S, Univ. South. Miss, 53; fel, Univ. Miss, 53-54, M.A, 55; fels, Emory Univ, 55-57, 58-59, Ph.D, 60. Instr. Eng, Emory Univ, 59-60; asst. prof, Univ. Ala, 60-63; ASSOC. PROF, The Citadel, 63-65; AM. LIT, GA. STATE UNIV, 65- Res. grant, Univ. Ala, summer 62; Fulbright lectr. Am. lit, Univ. Lodz, 64-65; Univ. Bonn, 71-72; Ger. Res. Asn. res. lectr, Univ. Stuttgart, 72-73; lectr. & consult, Univ. Md, Europ. Div, Heidelberg, W.Ger, 73-74. U.S.A, 50-52. MLA (sect. chmn. south. lit. sem, 71-72); S.Atlantic Mod. Lang. Asn.(sect. chmn. Am. lit. progs, 69-70); AAUP; Soc. Stud. South. Lit. Modern fiction; literature and urban life; literature and myth. Publ: Ed, Man in crisis, Scott, 70; auth, The city as radical order: James Joyce's Dubliners, Stud. Lit. Imagination, 70; The South as history and metahistory: the mind of W.J. Cash, Spectrum, 72; The American South as mediating image in the plays of Tennessee Williams, In: Amerikanisches Drama in Literatur und Film, Vandenhoeck & Ruprecht, Göttingen, 74; plus others. Add: Apt. H 1-203, 6355 Memorial Dr, Stone Mountain, GA 30083.

DAVIS, KEITH EDWIN, b. Winchester, Tenn, Jan. 28, 25; m. 65; c. 3. EDUCATION, COMMUNICATIONS. B.S, E.Tenn. State Univ, 59, M.A, 56; Univ. Tenn, 50; Ed.D, Univ. Ky, 65. Prin, Washington County Sch. Syst, Tenn, 51-56; teacher Eng, Lafayette High Sch, Lexington, Ky, 56-59; asst. prof. COMMUN, East. Ky. State Univ, 59-61; W.Va. Inst. Technol, 61-62; instr, Pensacola Jr. Col, 62-63; Ocala Jr. Col, 63-65; ASSOC. PROF, GA. SOUTHWEST. COL, 65-, ed, Inst. Self-study, 71-72, chmn. self-study comt. Eng. & humanities, 71-72. Consult, Learning Resources Ctrs, 65-66; guest lectr, Univ. Del, 72. U.S.M.C, 41-45. AAUP. Applied language skills. Publ: Pariterra (poetry), 50 & The inconstant moon (short stories), 60, Exposition; How grows the willow (novel), Markham, 64; Researching and reporting for term paper writers, 70 & The novel: introduction, model, example, student analysis, 72, Kendall Hunt. Add: 223 Sun Valley Dr, Americus, GA 31709.

DAVIS, KENNETH WALDRON, b. Holland, Tex, June 15, 32. ENGLISH. B.A, Tex. Tech. Col, 54; Woodrow Wilson fel, Vanderbilt Univ, 54-55, M.A, 55, univ. fel, 58-60, Ph.D, 63. Instr. Eng, TEX. TECH. UNIV, 55-63, instr. Eng. & admin. asst. to dept. head, 63, asst. prof. Eng. & chmn. sophomore Eng, 63-65, assoc. prof. ENG. 65-68, PROF, 68-, chmn. grad. stud. Eng, 65-69. MLA; NCTE; S.Cent. Mod. Lang. Asn. English novel; 19th century English literature; literature of the English Renaissance. Publ: A bibliography of William Henry Smith, The Libr, 63; The Ruskin-Blackwood controversy, Victorian Newsletter, fall 66; Themes of initiation in the works of Larry McMurtry and Tom Mayer, Arlington Quart, winter 69-70; plus others. Add: Dept. of English, Texas Tech. University, Lubbock, TX 79409.

DAVIS, LEONARD M, b. Duffy, W.Va, July 14, 19; m. 48; c. 3. SPEECH. A.B, W.Va. Univ, 48, M.A, 50; Ph.D.(speech), Northwest. Univ, 58. Asst. prof. SPEECH, Ala. Col, 50-53; teaching asst, Northwest. Univ, 53-54; instr, W.VA. UNIV, 54-57, asst. prof, 57-60, assoc. prof, 60-66, PROF, 66-, chmn. dept, 66-72. Lectr. commun, W.Va. schs. banking, 59-72; vis. lectr, Pa. State Univ, 60-72; lectr, Va-Md. banking schs, 61-72; vis. prof. speech, Univ. Calif, Santa Barbara, 65-66 & 67-68; Univ. Ariz, summer consult. commun, Grad. Sch. Bus. Admin, Univ. Calif, Los Angeles, 67-68; Vandenberg AFB, Calif, 68; lectr, exten, Univ. Calif, Berkeley, 68. U.S.A, 41-45. Speech Commun. Asn; Int. Commun. Asn. Nineteenth century British public address; management communication problems; communications in high risk occupations, especially deep mine coal operations. Publ: Co-auth, Nathan Goff: statesman and orator, W.Va. Hist, 51. Add: Dept. of Speech Communication, West Virginia University, Morgantown, WV 26506.

DAVIS, MADGE, b. Anson, Tex, July 1, 95. AMERICAN LITERATURE. A.B, Univ. Tex, 17, A.M, 34, summers, 42-44, Blanton fel, 45-46, Ph.D, 48; fel, Univ. Colo, 24-25. Teacher Spanish, High Sch, Ft. Worth, Tex, 17-19; instr, Univ. Tex, 19-20; Tex. Wesleyan Col, 20-22; prof. ENG, MIDWEST. UNIV, 26-63, EMER. PROF. & HISTORIOGRAPHER, 63-, chmn. dept. Eng. & jour, 46-63. Gen. Educ. Bd. grant, 42-46; vis. prof, Hardin-Simmons Univ, 63-64; Eng. & educ, Univ. Ariz, 66-67; chmn. int. comt. on scholarships, Delta Kappa Gamma Soc, Int, 68-72; mem. Willa Cather Pioneer Found. Willa Cather; evolution of Willa Cather's art. Add: 2505 Fain St, Wichita Falls, TX 76308.

DAVIS, MARGARET, b. Wichita, Kans, May 31, 16. ENGLISH. A.B, George Washington Univ, 37, A.M, 41, 44-68; summer, Harvard, 36; Am. Univ.(D.C), 46-47; summer, Middlebury Col, 49; Georgetown Univ, 53. Libr. asst, Wash. Post, 38-41, ed. asst, 41-42, reporter, 42-46; spec. writer, George Washington Univ, 46-52, asst. dir. pub. relat, 52-60, assoc. dir, 60-68; pub. inform. specialist, Econ. Develop. Admin, U.S. Dept. Commerce, 68-69, WRITER-ED, 69-73; VET. ADMIN, 73- Treas, Wash. Press Club, 49-50; pres, Am. Newspaper Women's Club, 62-63. Soc. Women Geog; Educ. Press Asn. Am. Daniel Defoe's middle class ideals; the presidents and federal taxes; development of the new kind of university magazine. Publ: A university in the nation's capital, George Washington Univ, 47; From aspirin to Elizabethan ethics, Alma Mater, Am. Alumni Counc, 1/65; Magazine happenings, Col. & Univ. J, fall 67; Magazine mailings, Techniques, 11-12/67. Add: 1657 31st St. N.W, Washington, DC 20007.

DAVIS, MARIANNA W, b. Philadelphia, Pa, Jan. 8, 29; m. 53; c. 1. ENGLISH, EDUCATION. B.A, S.C. State Col, 49; M.A, N.Y. Univ, 53; summer, Univ. Ore, 59; Crusade scholar, Boston Univ, 64-66, D.Ed, 66. Teacher, Pub. Schs, S.C, 49-51, 55-56; asst. prof. Eng, S.C. State Col, 56-64; prof. Eng. & educ, Voorhees Col, 66-68; Claflin Col, 66-69; PROF. ENG. & CHMN. DIV. LANG. & LIT, BENEDICT COL, 69- Consult. lang. arts, St. Marks Sch, S.C, 62; ling, Lincoln-Sudbury High Sch, Mass, 66; lectr, upward bound prog, Tufts Univ, summer 66; vis. prof, NDEA inst. ling, Boston Univ, summer 67; consult, Ford Found. Eng. Inst, Benedict Col, 68; mem. adv. bd, Nat. Task Force on Racism & Bias in Teaching of Eng, 70-; IBM-United Negro Col. Fund fel, summer 71; Nat. Endowment for Humanities scholar, 71; examr. Eng. tests, Educ. Testing Serv, 71-73; comnr, S.C. Comn. on Higher Educ, 73-; consult, FEDCO, Inc, Columbia, 73- NCTE (dir, 60-64); Conf. Eng. Educ; Col. Lang. Asn; Nat. Soc. Stud. Educ; AAUP; Conf. Col. Compos. & Commun. Transformational-generative grammar; linguistics; Gullah dialect; teaching English. Publ: Sentences and transformational grammar, Mouton, 73; Verb structures in sentences written by a group of pre-college students, CLA J, 12/70; Black scholars and white professional organizations, Negro Am. Lit. Forum, fall 71; Comments on reading for black college students, Freshman Eng. News, fall 73; plus others. Add: P.O. Box 3097, Columbia, SC 29203.

DAVIS, MARY ANN KELSO, b. Washington, D.C, Mar. 12, 42; m. 64; c. 1. ENGLISH LITERATURE. A.B, Ind. Univ, Bloomington, 64; M.A, Univ. Rochester, 68, Ph.D.(Eng), 72. Instr. ENG, ST. JOHN FISHER COL, 68-72, ASST. PROF, 72- MLA; NCTE; AAUP. Nineteenth century English literature; the drama. Add: Dept. of English, St. John Fisher College, 3690 East Ave, Rochester, NY 14618.

DAVIS, NELSON V, b. Pittsburgh, Pa, June 12, 21; m. 47; c. 2. ENGLISH ROMANTICS, CHAUCER. A.B, Franklin & Marshall Col, 43; M.A, Princeton, 46, Ph.D.(Eng), 57. Instr. ENG, Princeton, 46; asst. prof, Marietta Col, 47-56; from asst. prof. to PROF, RIPON COL, 56-, chmn. dept, 61-68. Fulbright fel, Italy, 50-51. U.S.A.A.F, 46-47. MLA; AAUP. The British Romantics and Napoleon Bonaparte. Add: Dept. of English, Ripon College, Ripon, WI 54971.

DAVIS, NUEL PHARR, b. Ft. Worth, Tex, Oct. 21, 15; m. 41. ENGLISH. Ph.D, Univ. Ill, 55. Asst. prof. ENG, UNIV. ILL, URBANA, 57-69, ASSOC. PROF, 69- MLA. Publ: Life of Wilkie Collins, Univ. Ill, 56; Lawrence and Oppenheimer, Simon & Schuster, Herder, Fawcett, Jonathan Cape, London & Garzanti Ed, Milan, 68-71. Add: Dept. of English, University of Illinois, Urbana, IL 61801.

DAVIS, PAUL B, b. Calais, Maine, Apr. 30, 34; m. 58; c. 3. ENGLISH LITERATURE. A.B, Oberlin Col, 56; Woodrow Wilson fel, Univ. Wis, 56-57, M.A, 57, Ph.D, 61; Fulbright res. fel, Univ. London, Eng, 60-61. Instr. ENG, UNIV. N.MEX, 61-62, asst. prof, 62-68, ASSOC. PROF, 68-, dir. freshman Eng, 69-72. Consult, Albuquerque Pub. Schs. future schs. stud. prog, 67-68. Univ. N.Mex. Outstanding Teaching Award, 67. MLA. Victorian literature; the novel; Dickens. Publ: Co-auth, Contemporary controversy, 66 & Controversy in literature, 68, Scribner; Dickens and the American press, 1842, Dickens Stud, 3/68. Add: Dept. of English, University of New Mexico, Albuquerque, NM 87131.

DAVIS, PHILIP HARVEY, b. Coshocton, Ohio, Feb. 22, 08. ENGLISH. A.B, Miami Univ, 30, A.M, 35; Harvard, 31-32; Univ. N.C, 37-39, 40. Instr, Miami Univ, 30-31, 34-37; Univ. N.C, 37-39; Eng, N.C. State Univ, 39-43, asst. prof, 43-45, assoc. prof, 45-73; RETIRED. U.S.N, 43-45. Byron in the periodicals of the early 19th century; handbook of English; reading, writing and speaking. Add: 814 Woodburn Rd, Raleigh, NC 27605.

DAVIS, RICHARD BEALE, b. Accomac, Va, June 3, 07; m. 36. ENGLISH. A.B, Randolph-Macon Col, 27, Litt.D, 55; A.M, Univ. Va, 33, Ph.D, 36. Instr. Eng, McGuire's Univ. Sch, 27-30; Randolph-Macon Acad, 30-32; Univ, Va, 33-36, assoc. prof, Mary Washington Col, 36-40; Univ. S.C, 40-46, prof, 46-47; UNIV. TENN, 47-62, ALUMNI DISTINGUISHED SERV. PROF. AM. LIT, 62- Guggenheim fels, 47-48, 60-61; Huntington Libr. fels, 47, 50; Am. Philos. Soc. grants, 51, 58, 62; Fulbright vis. prof, Univ. Oslo, 53-54; Folger Libr. fel, 55; spec. lectr, U.S. Dept. State, India, 57; mem. exec. comt, Ctr. Ed, Am. Auth, MLA, 63-69; vis. prof, Duke Univ, summer 65; Am. Counc. Learned Soc. grant, 66; mem. ed. bd, Am. Lit, 65-68; Nat. Endowment for Humanities sr. fel, 74. MLA; Bibliog. Soc. Am; Am. Stud. Asn; S.Atlantic Mod. Lang. Asn.(pres, 65); Int. Asn. Univ. Prof. Eng; South. Humanities Conf.(chmn, 61); Soc. Stud. South. Lit.(pres, 69-71); Am. Antiq. Soc. Intellectual life in the Colonial South, 1585-1800; early national American literature; Edgar Allan Poe. Publ: George Sandys, poet adventurer, Columbia Univ, 55; ed, American cultural history, 1607-1829, 61 & Collected poems of Samuel Davies, 68, Scholars Facsimiles; auth, William Fitzhugh and his Chesapeake world, 1676-1701, 63 & Intellectual life in Jefferson's Virginia, 1790-1830, 64, Univ. N.C; The colonial Virginia satirist, Am. Philos. Soc, 67; American literature through Bryant, Goldentree Bibliog, Appleton, 69; ed, Tennessee studies in literature, Univ. Tenn, Vols. I-XVII, 56-72; auth, Literature and society in early Virginia, La. State Univ, 73; Mrs. Stowe's characters-in-situations and a Southern library tradition, In: Essays on American literature in honor of Jay B. Hubbell, Duke Univ, 67; William Byrd: taste and tolerance, In: Major writers of early American literature, Univ. Wis, 72; plus others. Add: Dept. of English, McClung Tower 304, University of Tennessee, Knoxville, TN 37916.

DAVIS, ROBERT BERNARD, b. Chicago, Ill, Jan. 20, 17; m. 42; c. 2. ENGLISH. A.B, Univ. Chicago, 40, A.M, 47, Ph.D.(Eng), 56. Instr. Eng. & philos, Washington & Jefferson Col, 48-50; asst. prof. Eng, Heidelberg Col, 50-53, assoc. prof, 53-57, prof, 57-62; prof. & head dept, Parsons Col, 62-65; Midwest. Col, 65-68; PROF. LIT. & DRAMA, TARKIO COL, 68-, chmn. div. lang, 68-73. Vis. assoc. prof, Occidental Col, 60-61. U.S.A.F, 41-45, Res, 45-70, Lt. Col. NCTE; Conf. Col. Compos. & Commun; Am. Comt. Irish Stud.(archivist, 72-). Modern British and Irish literature; George William Russell; applied linguistics-teaching of foreign languages. Add: Div. of Language & Literature, Tarkio College, Tarkio, MO 64491.

DAVIS, ROBERT EDWARD, b. Washington, Iowa, Dec. 25, 23; m. 50. RHETORIC & PUBLIC ADDRESS. B.A, Univ. Ill, 47, M.A, 51, Ph.D, 59. Teacher speech & Eng, Sparta High Sch, Ill, 47-49; Taylorville High Sch, 50-56; asst, Univ. Ill, 57-59; from asst. prof. to assoc. prof. SPEECH, ARIZ. STATE UNIV, 59-72, PROF, 72- Speech Commun. Asn. British public address. Publ: Parliamentary practices of the Fourth Party, Quart. J. Speech, 10/61. Add: Dept. of Speech, Arizona State University, Tempe, AZ 85281.

DAVIS, ROBERT GORHAM, b. Cambridge, Mass, June 8, 08; m. 39; c. 3. ENGLISH. A.B, Harvard, 29, A.M, 30. Instr. Eng, Rensselaer Polytech. Inst, 30-33; instr, Harvard, 34-40, Briggs-Copeland fac. instr. Eng. compos, 40-43; lectr, ENG, Smith Col, 43-45, assoc. prof, 45-52, prof, 52-58, chmn. dept, 54-58; PROF, COLUMBIA UNIV, 58- Fulbright vis. prof, Univs, Graz & Innsbruck, Austria, 54-55 & Univ. La Plata, 65; lectr. Salzburg Sem. Am. Stud, 55, 58; summer vis. prof, Univ. Guanabara, Brazil, 62; Guggenheim Found. fel, 72-73; mem, YADDO. MLA; PEN Club. Contemporary literature; history of prose fiction; higher education. Publ: Meet the U.S.A, Inst. Int. Educ, 58; ed, Ten modern masters, 2nd ed, 58 & 3rd ed, 72 & Ten masters of the modern essay, 66, Harcourt; auth, John Dos Passos, Univ. Minn, 62; C.P. Snow, Columbia Univ, 65. Add: Dept. of English, Lewisohn 701, Columbia University, New York, NY 10027.

DAVIS, ROBERT MURRAY, b. Lyons, Kans, Sept. 4, 34; m. 58; c. 3. ENGLISH. B.S, Rockhurst Col, 55; M.A, Univ. Kans, 58; Ph.D.(Eng), Univ. Wis, 64. Instr. ENG, Loyola Univ.(Ill), 62-64, asst. prof, 64-65; Univ. Calif, Santa Barbara, 65-67, UNIV. OKLA, 67-70, ASSOC. PROF, 70-, DIR. GRAD. PROG, 73- Mem. ed. bd, Evelyn Waugh Newslett, 67-; regional assoc, Comt. on Am. Lit. Manuscripts, 69-; mem. adv. bd, Genre, 69- MLA. The novel as a genre; satire in the novel; the modern British and American novel. Publ: Ed, The novel: modern essays in criticism, 69 & Steinbeck: modern essays in criticism, 72, Prentice-Hall; ed, Evelyn Waugh, Herder, 69 & Modern British short novels, Scott, 72; co-auth, Evelyn Waugh: a checklist, Whitston, 72; auth, From artifice to art: the technique of Firbank's novels, Style, winter 68; Shrinking gardens and new exits: the comic-satiric novel in the 20th century, Kans. Quart, summer 69; ed, Symposium: allegory in the modern novel, Genre, winter 72; plus others. Add: Dept. of English, University of Oklahoma, Norman, OK 73069.

DAVIS, RUTH BRANT, b. Clinton, Iowa, Oct. 25, 14; m; c. 4. ENGLISH. B.A, Univ. Ariz, 54, M.A, 57; Ph.D.(Eng), Brandeis Univ, 70. Instr. Eng, Univ. Ariz, 56-62, lectr, humanities, 71; ASSOC. PROF. ENG, SHELBY STATE COL, 73- MLA. Medieval staging. Publ: The scheduling of the Chester cycle plays, Theatre Notebk, winter 72/73. Add: P.O. Box 4262, Tucson, AZ 85717.

DAVIS, THOMAS M, b. Ashland, Kans, July 20, 30; m. 59; c. 3. ENGLISH. B.S, Kans. State Univ, 57, M.S, 59; Ph.D.(Eng), Univ. Mo, 68. Teaching asst. Eng, Kans. State Univ, 57-59; instr, Univ. Mo, 59-65; asst. prof. & dir. gen. stud. in Eng, South. Ill. Univ, 65-69; ASSOC. PROF. ENG, KENT STATE UNIV, 69- Mem. ed. bd, Early Am. Lit, 73- U.S.N, 48-50, 51-53. NCTE. An edition of the works of Edward Taylor. Publ: 14 by Emily Dickinson, Scott, 64; co-auth, Anthology of American literature, Bobbs, 66 & The traditions of Puritan typology, In: Typology and early American literature, Univ. Mass, 72; auth, Edward Taylor on the Day of Judgment, Am. Lit, 72; ed, Edward Taylor's Valedictory poems, Early Am. Lit, 72; plus others. Add: Dept. of English, Kent State University, Kent, OH 44242.

DAVIS, WALTER RICHARDSON, b. Middletown, Conn, Aug. 17, 28; m. 51; c. 5. ENGLISH. B.A, Trinity Col.(Conn), 50; Ph.D.(Eng), Yale, 57. Instr. ENG, Univ. Rochester, 54-55; Dickenson Col, 56; Williams Col, 56-59; asst. prof, Mass. Inst. Technol, 59-60; UNIV. NOTRE DAME, 60-64; assoc. prof, 64-68, PROF, 68- Vis. prof, Harvard, summer 72. MLA. Non-dramatic literature of the English Renaissance, especially prose; theory of fiction. Publ: A map of Arcadia: Sidney's romance in its tradition, Yale Univ, 65; ed, The works of Thomas Campion, Doubleday, 67 & Twentieth-century views of Much ado about nothing, Prentice-Hall, 69; auth, Idea and act in Elizabethan fiction, Princeton Univ, 69; Actaeon in Arcadia, Stud. Eng. Lit, 62; The imagery of Bacon's late work, Mod. Lang. Quart, 66; Fantastickly I sing: Drayton's Idea of 1619, Stud. Philol, 69; plus others. Add: Dept. of English, University of Notre Dame, Notre Dame, IN 46556.

DAVIS, WENDELL EUGENE, b. Toledo, Ohio, Sept. 30, 34; m. 62. ENGLISH LITERATURE. B.A, Bowling Green State Univ, 56, fel, 57-68, M.A, 58; fel, West. Reserve Univ, 58-61, Ph.D, 62. ASST. PROF. ENG, Thiel Col, 61-63; PURDUE UNIV, WEST LAFAYETTE, 63- Mem. res. & bibliog. comt, conf. Eng. lit. in transition, MLA, 66-; Fulbright prof, Humboldt Univ, Freiburg, Ger, 69-70. Midwest Mod. Lang. Asn; MLA. The English novel; English literature 1880-1920; Victorian literature. Publ: Co-auth, Thomas Hardy: an annotated bibliography of writings about him, North. Ill. Univ, 73 & The transitional age: British literature 1880-1920, Whitston, 73; auth, The poetry of Mary Webb: an invitation, Eng. Lit. Transition, Vol. XI, No. 2; Mr. Golding's optical delusion, Eng. Lang. Notes, 12/65; Some ambiguities concerning a pure woman, Nineteenth Century Fiction, 3/68. Add: Dept. of English, Purdue University, West Lafayette, IN 47906.

DAVIS, WESLEY FORD, b. Orange Co, Fla, Mar. 13, 21; c. 3. MODERN BRITISH & AMERICAN LITERATURE. B.A, Rollins Col, 47; M.A, Univ. Ark, 50; Ph.D.(Eng), Stanford Univ, 70. Asst. prof. ENG, Univ, Ark, 56-60; assoc. prof, UNIV. S.FLA, 64-70, PROF, 70- U.S.A, 40-45, Capt. History of the novel; recent fiction. Publ: The time of the panther, Harper, 58; The undertow, In: Best American short stories, Houghton, 56; The oldest enemy, Colliers Mag, 57; J.P. Donleavy, In: Cross currents, Twayne, 72. Add: 303 Bannockburn, Temple Terrace, FL 33617.

DAVIS, WILLIAM F, JR, b. Phoenixville, Pa, Apr. 19, 26. ENGLISH. A.B, Princeton, 50; M.A, Yale, 54, Ph.D.(Eng), 64. Instr. ENG, Univ. N.Mex, 57-59; COL. WILLIAM & MARY, 60-64, asst. prof, 64-68, ASSOC. PROF, 68- U.S.A, 44-46. MLA. American literature; Romantic period. Add: Dept. of English, College of William & Mary, Williamsburg, VA 23185.

DAVIS, WILLIAM VIRGIL, b. Canton, Ohio, May 26, 40. ENGLISH, RELIGION. A.B, Ohio Univ, 62, M.A, 65, Ph.D.(Eng), 67; B.D, Pittsburgh Theol. Sem, 65; M.Div, 71. ASST. PROF. ENG, Ohio Univ, 67-68; Cent. Conn. State Col, 68-71; Tunxis Community Col, 71-72; UNIV. ILL, CHICAGO CIRCLE, 72- Scholar in poetry, Breadloaf Writers' Conf, summer 70. MLA. English and American literature; creative writing; religion and theology. Publ: Ed, George Whitefield's journals, 1737-1741, Scholars' Facsimilies, 69; The renewal of dialogic immediacy in Edward Lewis Wallant, Renascence, winter 72; The sound and the fury: a note on Benjy's name, Stud. Novel, spring 72; The loss of time in Counterparts, James Joyce Quart, spring 73; plus numerous articles and poems. Add: Dept. of English, University of Illinois at Chicago Circle, Chicago, IL 60680.

DAVISON, RICHARD ALLAN, b. Montreal, P.Q, Sept. 11, 34; U.S. citizen; m. 66; c. 2. AMERICAN LITERATURE. B.A, Middlebury Col, 56; M.A, Univ. Rochester, 58; Ph.D.(Eng. & Am. lit), Univ. Wis, 64. Instr. Eng, Gettysburg Col, 58-60; Teaching asst. Am. lit, Univ. Wis, 60-63; asst. prof. Eng. & Am. lit, Seattle Univ, 63-66, assoc. prof, 66-68; dir. Eng. grad. prog. & vis. assoc. prof. AM. LIT, UNIV. DEL, 68-71, PROF. & ASSOC. CHMN. DEPT. ENG, 71- Seattle Univ. res. grants, 64-68. MLA; West. Lit. Asn. Nineteenth and twentieth century American literature. Publ: Edward Albee's Tiny Alice: a re-examination, Mod. Drama, 5/68; Ambivalent imagery in Whitman's Lilacs, Walt Whitman Rev, 6/68; The remaining seven of Norris' weekly letters, Am. Lit. Realism, summer 68. Add: Dept. of English, University of Delaware, Newark, DE 19711.

DAVLIN, MARY CLEMENTE, O.P, b. Chicago, Ill, Mar. 6, 29. ENGLISH. B.A, Rosary Col, 50; M.A, Univ. Wis, 51; Pius XII Inst, Italy, 51-52; Sophia Univ, Japan, 61; Ph.D.(Eng), Univ. Calif, 64. Teacher, high sch, Ill, 52-54; from instr. to asst. prof. Eng, Edgewood Col, 56-59, assoc. prof, 63-66, prof, 66-70, chmn. dept, 66-69, mem. coord. comt. stud. curriculum, 69-70; PROF. ENG, ROSARY COL, 70-, CHMN. DEPT, 73- MLA; Mediaeval Acad. Am; Women's Caucus Mod. Lang. Piers Plowman; Chaucer; Dante. Publ: Treuthe in Piers Plowman, Univ. Microfilms, 64; Kynde Knowyng as a major theme in Piers Plowman B, Rev. Eng. Stud. 2/71; Petrus, id est, Christus: Piers Plowman as the whole Christ, Chaucer Rev, Vol. 4. Add: Dept. of English, Rosary College, 7900 W. Division, River Forest, IL 60305.

DAVY, FRANCIS XAVIER, b. Los Angeles, Calif, Jan. 24, 16; m. 47; c. 5. ENGLISH, COMPARATIVE LITERATURE. A.B, St. Mary's Col.(Calif), 41; M.A, Univ. Calif, Berkeley, 44; Ph.D, Columbia Univ, 58. Instr. Latin, St. Mary's Col, 42-46; Eng, Manhattan Col, 46-51, asst. prof, 51-59, assoc. prof, 59-63; Nassau Community Col, 63-66; prof. Eng. & humanities & chmn. dept, Sullivan County Community Col, 66-67; PROF. ENG, EAST. KY. UNIV, 67-, chmn. dept. humanities, 67-68. S.Atlantic Mod. Lang. Asn; Am. Soc. 18th Century Stud; NCTE. American colonial literature; 18th century English literature (Jonathan Swift); Epicureanism among the Romans. Publ: Benjamin Franklin, satirist, Univ. Microfilms, 58; co-auth, Perspectives in college, W.C. Brown, 63; auth, Swift's Gulliver's travels, Barrister Publ, 67; co-auth, Perspectives on our time, Houghton, 70. Add: Lancaster Woods, Richmond, KY 40475.

DAWIRS, HARVEL NICK, Communications, Engineering. See 12th Edition, American Men & Women of Science, Physical & Biological Sciences Section.

DAWSON, CARL, b. Leeds, Eng, May 2, 38; m. 63; c. 2. ENGLISH. A.B, Occidental Col, 59; M.A, Columbia Univ, 60; Ph.D.(Eng), 66. Instr. ENG, Dartmouth Col, 64-66; asst. prof, Univ. Calif, Berkeley, 66-70; ASSOC. PROF, UNIV. N.H, 70- Fulbright grant, Berlin, 67-68; Univ. Calif. fac. fel, summer 67; Am.Counc. Learned Soc. fel, 72-73. MLA. Romantic literature; Matthew Arnold. Publ: Thomas Love Peacock, 68 & Matthew Arnold: the critical heritage, 73, Routledge; His fine wit: a study of Thomas Love Peacock, Univ. Calif, 70. Add: Dept. of English, University of New Hampshire, Durham, NH 03824.

DAWSON, EDWARD BARKER, b. Birmingham, Ala, July 2, 12; m. 39; c. 2. AMERICAN LITERATURE. A.B, Vanderbilt Univ, 34, A.M, 35, Ph.D.(Eng), 37; summers, Univ. Chicago, 41, Columbia Univ, 48. Instr. ENG, Vanderbilt Univ, 35-37; from asst. prof. to prof, GA. COL, 37-73, EMER. PROF, 73- U.S.N, 43-46. Georgia place names. Add: Rte. 4, Box 160, Lake Sinclair, Milledgeville, GA 31061.

DAWSON, GILES EDWIN, b. Columbus, Ohio, Mar. 4, 03; m. 26, 59; c. 4. ELIZABETHAN LITERATURE. A.B, Oberlin Col, 25; A.M, Cornell Univ, 26, fel, 30-31, Ph.D, 31; fel, West. Reserve Univ, 29-30. Instr, Univ.N.Dak, 26-27; West. Reserve Univ, 27-32; ref. libn, FOLGER SHAKESPEARE LIBR, 32-46, cur. books & manuscripts, 46-68, CONSULT, 68- Lectr. Elizabethan lit, Cath. Univ. Am, 35-67, prof. Eng, 67-71; lectr, Hopkins Univ, 50-52; assoc. ed, Shakespeare Quart, 50-72; lectr, Howard Univ, 71-; Univ. Md, College Park, 73- U.S.N.R, 42-45, Lt. Comdr. Shakespeare; bibliography; paleography. Publ: Ed, July and Julian; auth, Plays and players in Kent, 1450-1642, Malone Soc, 65; co-auth, Elizabethan handwriting, 1500-1650, Norton, 66; auth, Robert Walker's editions of Shakespeare, Eng. Renaissance Drama, 59; Four centuries of Shakespeare publication, Univ. Kans. Publ. Libr, Ser. 22, 64; John Payne Collier's great forgery, Stud. Bibliog. Add: 3025 Macomb St. N.W, Washington, DC 20008.

DAWSON, HUGH JOSEPH, b Portland, Maine, June 14, 33. AMERICAN STUDIES & LITERATURE. A.B, Georgetown Univ, 59; M.A, Univ. Ill, Urbana, 60, Ph.D.(Eng), 71. ASST. PROF. ENG, UNIV. SAN FRANCISCO, 69- Nat. Endowment for Humanities younger humanist fel, 73-74. U.S.A, 54-56. Am. Stud. Asn; Can. Asn. Am. Stud. Thorstein Veblen; technology and culture; rhetoric of social criticism. Add: Dept. of English, University of San Francisco, San Francisco, CA 94117.

DAWSON, LAWRENCE R, JR, b. Kalamazoo, Mich, Apr. 6, 21; m. 42; c. 1. LITERATURE. B.A, West. Mich. Univ, 43; teaching fel, Univ. Mich, 47-51, M.A, 48, Ph.D, 60. Instr. ENG, high schs, Davison & Warren, Mich, 46-47; Colo. State Univ, 51-56, asst. prof, 56-62, assoc. prof, 62-68; PROF, CENT. MICH. UNIV, 68-, chmn. dept, 68-72, admin. res. leave, Univ. Denver, 72-73. Colo. State Univ. res. found. grant, summer 60; Episcopal Church fel, Kenyon Col, summer 60. U.S.A.A.F, 43-46, Sgt. MLA; Counc. Basic Educ. Oxford Movement; 17th and 20th century English literature; Charles Williams and William Laud. Publ: A checklist of reviews by Charles Williams, Papers, Bibliog. Soc. Am, 61; contrib, Abstracts Eng. Stud, 58-; articles in Bull. Asn. Dept. Eng & Mich. Hist. Add: Dept. of English, Central Michigan University, Mt. Pleasant, MI 48858.

DAWSON, MILDRED AGNES, b. Sumner, Iowa, June 4, 97. ENGLISH COMPOSITION. B.A, Iowa State Teachers Col, 22; M.A, Univ. Chicago, 28; Ed.D, N.Y. Univ, 36. Teacher, Pub. Sch, Iowa, 16-19; supvry. teacher, Ind. State Teachers Col.(Pa), 22-24; teacher educ, Iowa State Teachers Col, 25-27; res. asst. educ. psychol, Univ. Chicago, 28-29; asst. prof. educ. & head dept, Univ. Wyo, 29-35; assoc. prof. & head dept, Univ. Ga, 36-37; Univ. Tenn, 37-45; dir. elem. educ, Pub. Schs, Kingston, N.Y, 47-49; prof. educ. State Univ. N.Y. Col. Fredonia, 49-52; Appalachian State Teachers Col, 52-54; prof. EDUC. & CHILDREN'S LIT, CALIF. STATE UNIV, SACRAMENTO, 54-65, EMER. PROF, 65- Conf. Res. Eng.(past pres. & secy-treas); NCTE; Nat. Educ. Asn; Int. Reading Asn.(pres, 66-67); Asn. Childhood Educ. Int; Asn. Supv. & Curriculum Develop. Publ: Co-auth, Language for daily use, grades 2-8, 48, 52, 55, 59 & Guiding language learning, 57, 63, Harcourt; co-auth, Fundamentals of basic reading instruction, McKay, 59, 63; co-auth, Adventures in reading, 67 & Oral reading and linguistics, 69, Benefic; co-auth, The cornerstone readers, 70, The kaleidoscope readers, 70 & Target yellow, 72, Field. Add: 5232 Piner Ct, Kelseyville, CA 95451.

DAWSON, ROBERT MacGREGOR, b. Pittsburgh, Pa, Mar. 29, 27; Can. citizen; m. 55; c. 2. ENGLISH LANGUAGE & LITERATURE. B.A, Univ. Toronto, 49, M.A, 50; B.Litt, Oxford, 53, Can. Counc. fel, 66-67. Lectr. ENG, Univ. Man, 55-59, asst. prof, 59-60; KING'S COL, DALHOUSIE UNIV, 60-65, ASSOC. PROF, 65- Cor. mem, Humanities Res. Counc. Can, 62- MLA. Blickling homilies; Nova Scotia place names. Publ: The structure of the Old English gnomic poems, J. Eng. & Ger. Philol, 62; Two new sources for Blickling homilies, 4/67 & Damaged pages in Blickling Homily XV, 1/68, Notes & Queries. Add: Dept. of English, Dalhousie University, Halifax, N.S, Can.

DAY, ARTHUR GROVE, b. Philadelphia, Pa, Apr. 29, 04; m. 28. ENGLISH. A.B, Stanford Univ, 26, Loomis fel, 41-43, A.M, 42, Ph.D, 44. Res. asst, inst. educ. res, Columbia Univ, 26-27; free-lance writer, 27-30; res. asst, sch. engineering, Stanford Univ, 31-41, off. mgr. & asst. dir. engineering, Sci. & Mgt. War Training, 41-44, acting instr. ENG, 43-44; asst. prof, UNIV. HAWAII, 44-46, assoc. prof, 46-50, prof, 50-61, sr. prof, 61-69, chmn. dept, 48-53, EMER. SR. PROF, 69- Proprietor, White Knight Press, Hawaii, 48-; sr. Fulbright res. fel, Australia, 55; Smith-Mundt vis. prof. Am. stud, Univ. Barcelona, 57-58; Fulbright vis. prof. Am. stud, Univ. Madrid, 61-62. MLA. American literature; history of Western America; history and literature of Pacific area. Publ: Coronado's quest, Univ. Calif, 40; co-auth, Rascals in paradise, Random, 57; auth, Hawaii and its people, Duell, 2nd ed, 60, 3rd ed, 68; American Indian poetry: North America, In: Encyclopedia of poetry and poetics, Princeton, 65; Hawaii, In: Encyclopaedia Britannica, 68; Literary adventures in paradise, Holiday, 7/67. Add: Apt. 1223, 1434 Punahou St, Honolulu, HI 96822.

DAY, DENNIS G, b. Gary, Ind, Oct. 14, 36; m. 58; c. 2. SPEECH. B.A, Col. Pac, 58; fel, Univ. Ill, 58-60, M.A, 60, Ph.D, 61. Asst. prof. speech, San Diego State Col, 61-63; Univ. Wis, Madison, 63-66; assoc. prof. SAN FRANCISCO STATE UNIV, 66-72, PROF. SPEECH COMMUN, 72- Speech Commun. Asn; West. Speech Commun. Asn; Cent. States Speech Asn. Rhetoric and public address; psycholinguistics; semantics. Publ: Persuasion and the concept of identification, Quart. J. Speech, 60; Learning and communication theory, 64 & The ethics of democratic debate, 66, Cent. States Speech J. Add: Dept. of Speech Communication, San Francisco State University, 1600 Holloway Ave, San Francisco, CA 94132.

DAY, DOUGLAS TURNER, III, b. Colon, Panama, May 1, 32; U.S. citizen; m. 54, 67, c. 4. ENGLISH LITERATURE. B.A, Univ. Va, 54, M.A, 59, Ph.D. (Eng), 62. Asst. ENG, Univ. Va, 59-60; instr, Washington & Lee Univ, 60-62; asst. prof, UNIV. VA, 62-64, assoc. prof, 64-68, PROF, 68- Fel, Folger Shakespeare Libr, summer 62; Am. Philos. Soc. grant-in-aid, summer 63; Am. Coun. Learned Soc. fel, summer 64; Fulbright vis. prof, Univ. Zaragoza, Spain, 65-66; Ctr. Advan. Res. fel, Univ. Va, 69-70. U.S.M.C, 54-58, 1st Lt. MLA. Modern British and American literature; literary critisim; modern comparative literature. Publ: Poetry and criticism of Robert Graves, Oxford, 63; The stranger: a critical commentary, RDM Corp, 65; Malcolm Lowry: a biography, New Am. Libr, 68 & Oxford, 73; ed, Dark as the grave wherein my friend is laid, New Am. Libr, 68 & Flags in the dust, Random, 73; The origin of the new criticism, J. Aesthet. & Art Criticism, spring 66; Robert Graves: el viejo poeta en su mundo autoconstruido, Papeles de Son Armadans, winter 66; The death of Malcolm Lowry, Atlantic Monthly, 10/73; plus others. Add: Dept. of English, University of Virginia, Charlottesville, VA 22901.

DAY, GEORGE FREDERICK, b. Superior, Nebr, July 1, 26; m. 48; c. 3. AMERICAN LITERATURE. B.A, Dartmouth Col, 58; M.A.T, Harvard, 59; George F. Reynolds fel, Univ. Colo, Boulder, 66-67, Ph.D.(Am. lit), 68. Instr. ENG, Punahou Sch, Honolulu, Hawaii, 59-62; Univ. Colo, Boulder, 62-66; asst. prof, UNIV. NORTH. IOWA, 67-70, ASSOC. PROF, 70- U.S.N, 44-45. MLA; West. Lit. Asn. Western and Midwestern American literature; 19th century American literature; life and works of Vardis Fisher. Add: Dept. of English Language & Literature, University of Northern Iowa, 24th & College Sts, Cedar Falls, IA 50613.

DAY, MALCOLM MacEWAN, b. Minneapolis, Minn, Apr. 5, 28; m. 54; c. 4. ENGLISH. B.A, Univ. Fla, 53, M.A, 58; fel, West. Reserve Univ, 55-58, Ph.D.(Eng), 64. Instr. ENG, Hanover Col, 58-61; lectr, Ind. Univ, South Bend, 61-64, asst. prof, 64-70; ASSOC. PROF, INDIANA UNIV. PA, 70- Ind. Univ. summer grant, 67; Newberry Libr. summer grant, 67. U.S.N, 50-52. MLA; Renaissance Soc. Am; Int. Soc. Stud. Symbols. Seventeenth century non-dramatic poetry and history of ideas, especially Neoplatonism and mysticism; linguistics; Renaissance. Publ: Study of Traherne, Twayne, (in prep); Thomas Traherne and the doctrine of pre-existence, 1/68 & Naked truth and the language of Thomas Traherne, 71, Stud. Philol. Add: Dept. of English, Indiana University of Pennsylvania, Indiana, PA 15701.

DAY, MARTIN STEELE, b. Baltimore, Md, Jan. 25, 17; m. 54; c. 3. ENGLISH. A.B, Univ. Pa, 38; Ph.D, Johns Hopkins Univ, 47. Asst. prof. ENG, George Washington Univ, 41-54; UNIV. HOUSTON, 54-62, PROF, 62- Fulbright vis. prof, Univ. New Eng, Australia, 69-70; lectr, Univs. in New Guinea, Philippines, Hong Kong, Thailand & India, 70. U.S.A, 43-46. MLA; NCTE; Col. Eng. Asn. Eighteenth century and romantic English literature; English novel. Publ: History of English literature to 1660, 63, History of English literature, 1660-1837, 63, History of English literature, 1837-1963, 64, History of American literature from the beginning to 1910, 70 & History of American literature from 1910 to the present, 71, Doubleday. Add: Dept. of English, University of Houston, Houston, TX 77004.

DAY, RICHARD C, b. Covington, Ky, July 19, 27. ENGLISH. B.S, Univ. Mich, 50, M.A, 52; Ph.D.(Eng), State Univ. Iowa, 60. Asst. prof. ENG, HUMBOLDT STATE UNIV, 59-64, assoc. prof, 64-69, PROF, 69- MLA. Modern American literature; the novel and the short story as genres; seventeenth century British literature. Publ: A time to pluck up (story), Stories for the Sixties, spring 63; The hospital (story), Mass. Rev, summer 63; No hard feelings (story), Kenyon Rev, spring 65. Add: Dept. of English, Humboldt State University, Arcata, CA 95521.

DAY, ROBERT ADAMS, b. Providence, R.I, Oct. 3, 24. ENGLISH. A.B, Brown Univ, 48; M.A, Harvard, 49, Dexter traveling fel. & Ph.D, 52. Instr. ENG, Dartmouth Col, 52-54; QUEENS COL. (N.Y), 54-62, asst. prof, 63-65, assoc. prof, 66-70, PROF, 70-, GRAD. CTR, CITY UNIV. NEW YORK, 70-, COMP. LIT, 73- Vis. fel, Newberry Libr, summer 65. Med. Dept, U.S.A, 43-45. MLA; Eng. Asn, Gt. Brit; Eng. Inst; Mod. Humanities Res. Asn; Am. Soc. 18th Century Stud. History of fiction; 18th and 20th century literature. Publ: Told in letters: epistolary fiction before Richardson, Univ. Mich, 66; The city man in The waste land, PMLA, 6/65; Joyce's Waste land and Eliot's Unknown god, In: Vol. IV, 71, Literary monographs, Univ. Wis; Minor fiction, In: Vol. II, 71, New Cambridge bibliography of English literature, Cambridge Univ; plus others. Add: Dept. of English, Queens College, Flushing, NY 11367.

DAYANANDA, JAMES YESUPRIYA, b. Bangalore, India, Oct. 27, 34; m. 69; c. 1. AMERICAN & ENGLISH LITERATURE. B.A, Univ. Mysore, 56; cert, Cent. Inst. Eng, India, 58; fel, Temple Univ, 66-69, Ph.D.(Eng. lit), 69. Lectr. Eng, N.G.M. Col.(Madras Univ), 56-64; assoc. prof, LOCK HAVEN STATE COL, 69-71, PROF. ENG. & CHMN. DEPT. ENG. & PHILOS, 72- External mem, doctoral comt, Queens Univ.(Ont), 72-73. AAUP; MLA; Asn. Commonwealth Lit. & Lang. Stud; African Stud. Asn; Am. Transl. Asn. Literary criticism, theory and practice; Indian literature in English; 20th century American and English literature. Publ: Marxist contribution to Edmund Wilson's literary criticism, Univ. Microfilms, 70; M. Malgonkar, Twayne, 74; Rhythm in M. Malgonkar's The princes, Lit. East & West, 3/71; The death of Ivan Ilych: a psychoanalytic study on death and dying, Lit. & Psychol, 11/72; Edmund Wilson's Marxist criticism, Indian J. Am. Stud, 6/73. Add: Dept. of English & Philosophy, Lock Haven State College, Lock Haven, PA 17745.

DEAKIN, MOTLEY F, b. Ephraim, Utah, Mar. 5, 20; m. 50; c. 1. ENGLISH. B.A, Brigham Young Univ, 47; Univ. Md. For. Study Ctr, Paris, 48-49; M.A, Univ. Calif, Berkeley, 55, Ph.D, 60. Teacher Eng. & hist, Duchesne High Sch, 47-48; instr. ENG, Col. Holy Names, 55-58; lectr, Univ. Calif, 59-60; asst. prof, Tex. West. Col, 60-62; UNIV. FLA, 62-67, ASSOC. PROF, 67- Ed. Interchange, Fla. AAUP Conf, 71- U.S.A, 42-45. MLA; NCTE; AAUP; Comp. Lit. Asn. American literature; aesthetics. Publ: Co-ed, From Irving to Steinbeck: essays in honor of Harry Warfel, Univ. Fla, 72; Introd. to The home book of the picturesque, Scholars' Facsimiles, 67; The real and fictive quest of Henry James, Bucknell Rev, 5/66; Daisy Miller, tradition and the European heroine, Comp. Lit. Stud, 3/69. Add: Dept. of English, University of Florida, Gainesville, FL 32601.

DEAKINS, ROGER LEE, b. Decatur, Ill, Dec. 4, 33; m. 67; c. 1. ENGLISH LITERATURE. B.A, Univ. Ill, 56; M.A, Harvard, 58, Ph.D.(Eng), 65. Instr. ENG, Beloit Col, 61-65; City Col. New York, 65-68; asst. prof, N.Y. UNIV, 68-72, ASSOC. PROF, 72- Am. Counc. Learned Soc. fel, 72-73. Renaissance literature; philosophy; history. Publ: Ed, Il Moro: Ellis Heywood's dialogue in memory of Thomas More, Harvard, 72. Add: Dept. of English, New York University, Washington Square, New York, NY 10003.

DEAM, WILLIAM LUTHER, b. Cleveland, Ohio, Dec. 1, 13; m. 42; c. 1. SPEECH, GENERAL LINGUISTICS. A.B, Denison Univ, 36; Purdue Univ; M.A, Univ. Mich, 38, Ph.D.(philos), 53; West. Reserve Univ. Instr. speech & dir. drama, Purdue Univ, 39-42; Univ. Md, 44-45; instr. speech & tech. dir, Miami Univ, 45-47; PROF. SPEECH, UNIV. MIAMI, 50- Teaching fel, Univ. Mich, 47-50; state dir. educ. for labor, Am. Fed. Labor, 51-54; speech consult, Dade County Bd. Pub. Instr, 54- U.S.N.R, 42-44, Lt. Speech Commun. Asn; South. Speech Commun. Asn. Rhetoric and discussion; political speech writing; communications. Publ: Biographical study of Jessie Bonstelle; History of the Howell Opera House. Add: 3622 Le Jeune Rd, Coral Gables, FL 33134.

DEAN, CHRISTOPHER, b. Middlesbrough, Eng, Mar. 13, 30; m. 53; c. 3. ENGLISH. B.A, Univ. Leeds, 51, Ph.D.(Eng), 53. Lectr. ENG, Univ. Malaya, 57-59; asst. prof, Queen's Univ.(Ont), 59-62, assoc. prof, 62-63; Univ. West. Ontario, 63-66; PROF, UNIV. SASK, 66- R.A.F, 54-57, Flying Off. MLA; Asn. Can. Univ. Teachers Eng. Medieval English literature; the imagery of Chaucer's poetry. Publ: The dialect of George Meriton's A Yorkshire dialogue (1683), Yorkshire Dialect Soc. Reprint III, Eng, 62; Is there a distinctive literary Canadian English?, Am. Speech, 63; Chaucer's use of function words with substantives, Can. J. Ling, 64; Weal wundrum heah, wyrmlicum fah and the narrative background of The wanderer, Mod. Philol, 65. Add: Dept. of English, University of Saskatchewan, Saskatoon, Sask, Can.

DEAN, DENNIS RICHARD, b. Belvidere, Ill, May 29, 38; m. 68. ENGLISH, HISTORY OF SCIENCE. A.B, Stanford Univ, 60, A.M, 62; Ph.D.(Eng), Univ. Wis-Madison, 68. Instr. ENG, Kenosha Ctr, Univ. Wis, 67-68; asst. prof, UNIV. WIS-PARKSIDE, 68-73, ASSOC. PROF, 73- Assoc. ed, Clio, 73. U.S.A, 62-64. AAUP; MLA (bibliog. comt, 66-). Literature and science; British romantics; history of science, especially geology. Publ: Scott and Mackenzie: new poems, Philol. Quart, 73; James Hutton and his public, 1785-1802, Ann. Sci, 73. Add: Division of Humanistic Studies, University of Wisconsin-Parkside, Wood Rd, Kenosha, WI 53140.

DEAN, HAROLD LESTER, b. Springfield, Vt, June 5, 08; m. 38; c. 1. ENGLISH. Ph.B, Brown Univ, 34, A.M, 36, Ph.D, 43. Instr, Brown Univ, 42-46; ENG, MARIETTA COL, 46-47, asst. prof, 47-49, assoc. prof, 49-58, PROF, 58- MLA; Am. Stud. Asn. American literature; Colonial period; 19th century. Add: Dept. of English, Marietta College, Marietta, OH 45750.

DEAN, JAMES L, b. Pullman, Wash, Feb. 9, 36; m. 65; c. 2. ENGLISH. B.S, Utah State Univ, 58, M.S, 60; Ph.D.(Eng), Univ. N.Mex, 68. Instr. ENG, Univ. N.Mex, 65-66; asst. prof, SOUTH. ORE. COL, 66-71, ASSOC. PROF, 71- U.S.A, 59-61, 1st Lt. Late 19th century American literature; western American literature. Publ: Howells' travels toward art, Univ. N.M, 70. Add: Dept. of English, Southern Oregon College, Ashland, OR 97520.

DEAN, JAMES SEAY, b. Philadelphia, Pa, Dec. 2, 38; m. 64; c. 2. ENGLISH LITERATURE. B.A, Col. William & Mary, 60; Ph.D.(Eng), Univ. Birmingham, 62. Asst. prof. ENG, Wright State Univ, 65-70; ASSOC. PROF, UNIV. WIS-PARKSIDE, 70- Co-ed, Clio: Interdisciplinary J. Lit, Hist. & Philos. of Hist, 71-73. U.S.A, 63-64, Capt. MLA; Midwest Mod. Lang. Asn. English Renaissance; music; Brazilian literature. Publ: Co-auth, The art of double bass playing, Summy, 73; auth, Robert Greene: an addendum and supplementary bibliography of editions, biography and criticism, 1945-1969, Res. Opportunities in Renaissance Drama, 70-71; Crossing the line from Portuguese to English, Luso-Brazilian Rev, summer 73; Robert Greene's heroines: caught up in knowledge and power?, Ball State Univ. Forum, fall 73; plus others. Add: Div. of Humanities, University of Wisconsin-Parkside, Kenosha, WI 53140.

DEAN, LEONARD FELLOWS, b. Three Rivers, Mich, Dec. 24, 09. ENGLISH. A.B, Harvard, 31; A.M, Univ. Mich, 33, Ph.D, 40. Teaching fel, Univ. Mich, 37-39; from instr. to prof. ENG, Tulane Univ, 39-48, chmn. dept, 48; prof. & head dept, Univ. Conn, 48-65; Univ. Ill, 65-67; PROF, N.Y. UNIV, 67- MLA; NCTE. Renaissance historiography; Elizabethan literature; Shakespeare. Add: Dept. of English, New York University, New York, NY 10003.

DEAN, NANCY, b. New York, N.Y, July 19, 30. ENGLISH, MEDIEVAL LITERATURE. B.A, Vassar Col, 52; Ford fel, Radcliffe Col. & Harvard, 53, M.A.T, Radcliffe Col, 53; Louise Hart Van Leon fel. from Vassar Col, N.Y. Univ, 59-60, Penfield scholar, 61-62, Woodrow Wilson & Jay F. Krakauer scholars, 62-63, Ph.D.(Eng), 63. Teacher, Madeira Sch, 53-55; Wakefield High Sch, 55-56; instr. Eng, Am. Col. Girls, Istanbul, 56-59; Vassar Col, 62; lectr. Eng, HUNTER COL, 63, instr, 63-68, asst. prof, 68-72, ASSOC. PROF. ENG. & MEDIEVAL STUD, 72-, adv. for. stud, 64-65, asst. dean instr, 67-68. MLA; Mediaeval Acad. Am; AAUP. Chaucer and Ovid. Publ: In the mind of the writer, Canfield, 73; Ovid's Elegies from exile and Chaucer's House of fame, Hunter Col. Stud, 66; Chaucer's Complaint, a genre descended from the Heroides, Comp. Lit, winter 67. Add: Dept. of English, Hunter College, 695 Park Ave, New York, NY 10021.

DEANE, PAUL C, b. Boston, Mass, Aug. 20, 28; m. 70; c. 2. AMERICAN STUDIES. B.S, Boston Univ, 51, A.M, 53; Ph.D.(hist. Am. civilization), Harvard, 66. Instr. ENG, Boston Univ, 53-57; Suffolk Univ, 57-60, asst. prof, 60-64; assoc. prof, BENTLEY COL, 64-70, PROF, 70- Lect, Worcester Art Mus, 70- American literature; American fine arts; Irish civilization and arts. Publ: Herman Melville, The quality of balance, Serif, 70; Motion picture techniques in James Joyce's The dead, James Joyce Quart, 69; American elements in Walter Van Tilburg Clark's The track of the cat, Rev. Langues Vivantes, 73; plus others. Add: Dept. of English, Bentley College, 500 Beaver St, Waltham, MA 02154.

DEARIN, RAY DEAN, b. Paragould, Ark, Dec. 17, 41; m. 64; c. 2. SPEECH. B.A, Harding Col, 63; M.A, Univ. Ill, Champaign, 65, Ph.D.(speech), 70. Instr. SPEECH, IOWA STATE UNIV, 65-67, asst. prof, 68-71, ASSOC. PROF, 71- Cent. States Speech Asn.(consult. ed, jour, 73-); Speech Commun. Asn. Rhetoric; public address. Publ: Aristotle on psychology and rhetoric, Cent. States Speech J, 11/66; The philosophical basis of Chaim Perelman's theory of rhetoric, Quart. J. Speech, 10/69; Justice in ethics, politics and rhetoric, Iowa J. Speech, fall 69. Add: Dept. of Speech, Iowa State University, Ames, IA 50010.

DEARING, BRUCE, b. Erie Co, Pa, Jan. 11, 18; m. 40; c. 2. ENGLISH. A.B, Allegheny Col, 39; M.A, State Univ. Iowa, 40, Ph.D.(Eng), 42; M.A, Swarthmore Col, 54; LL.D, Allegheny Col, 65. Instr. Eng, Univ. Minn, 42-43; Cornell Univ, 46-47; asst. prof, Swarthmore Col, 47-55, assoc. prof, 55-57; prof. Eng. & dean sch. arts & sci, Univ. Del, 57-65; pres, State Univ. N.Y. Binghamton, 65-71; V.CHANCELLOR ACAD. PROG, STATE UNIV. N.Y, 71-

Am. Counc. Learned Soc. fac. stud. fel, 52-53; dir, Am. Humanities Ctr, 55-; consult, Asn. Higher Educ, 61-; mem, West. Interstate Comn. Higher Educ; Nat. Comn. Accrediting; chmn, Mid. States Eval. Team. U.S.N.R, 43-46, 50-52, Capt. Col. Eng. Asn.(pres, 54); MLA; NCTE; Nat. Asn. State Univs. & Land Grant Cols; Soc. Advan. Educ; Inst. Col. & Univ. Adminr. (chmn. adv. comt, 69-70); Am. Counc. Educ; Am. Asn. State Cols. & Univs. (chmn. adv. bd, Four-Year Servicemen's Opportunity Col, 73-). Modern poetry; social psychology; English, medieval and Renaissance literature. Publ: Coordination—a view from the campus, In: Higher education: from autonomy to systems, 72; General education and radical social change, J. Gen. Educ, 10/72; A double handful of suggestions, Intellect, 73; plus others. Add: Office of Academic Programs, State University of New York, 99 Washington Ave, Albany, NY 12210.

DEARING, VINTON ADAMS, b. San Francisco, Calif, July 30, 20; m. 46; c. 2. ENGLISH LITERATURE. A.B, Harvard, 40, A.M, 42, Ph.D, 49. Instr. Eng. lit, UNIV. CALIF, LOS ANGELES, 49-51, asst. prof, 51-57, assoc. prof, 57-63, PROF. ENG. & COMPUT. APPLNS. IN LIT, 63- U.S.A, 42-46. Bibliog. Soc, London; AAAS; Soc. Biblical Lit. Restoration and 18th century English literature; bibliography and textual studies; computer applications in literature. Publ: Co-ed, Works of John Dryden, 54-, auth, Manual of textual analysis, 59 & Principles and practice of textual analysis, 74, Univ. Calif; ed, Poems and prose of John Gay, Clarendon, 74. Add: Dept. of English, University of California, Los Angeles, CA 90024.

DeARMOND, ANNA JANNEY, b. Philadelphia, Pa, Feb. 10, 10. ENGLISH & AMERICAN LITERATURE. A.B, Swarthmore Col, 32; Bryn Mawr Col, 32-33, 34-35; A.M, Columbia Univ, 34; Ph.D, Univ. Pa, 47. Instr. ENG, UNIV. DEL, 35-39, 41-47, asst. prof, 47-50, assoc. prof, 50-68, PROF, 68- Fulbright lectr, Univ. Munich, 56-57; mem. summer sch. fac, Univ. Pa, 60-63; Goucher Col, 64; dir, NDEA Eng. Inst, 66; vis. lectr. Eng. Lit, Univ. Sheffield, 67; vis. prof, Univ. New Eng, Australia, 74. MLA; Col. Eng. Asn; NCTE. American colonial journalism; English neo-classical literature; American 19th century fiction. Publ: Andrew Bradford, colonial journalist, Univ. Del, 49, Greenwood, 69; Some aspects of character-writing in the period of the Restoration, Del. Notes, 43; Cornelia Smith Bradford, In: Notable American Women, Harvard Univ, 71; plus others. Add: Dept. of English, University of Delaware, Newark, DE 19711.

DEASY, PHILIP C, b. New York, N.Y, Oct. 25, 09; m. 60. ENGLISH. A.B, Manhattan Col, 33; M.A, Cath. Univ. Am, 35, Ph.D, 37. Instr. ENG, De La-Salle Col, 34-37; from instr. to prof, Manhattan Col, 37-56; instr, Inst. Filippin, Treviso, Italy, 56-57; from assoc. prof. to PROF, ST. PETER'S COL.(N.J), 58- Col. Eng. Asn. Modern English novel, chiefly D.H. Lawrence and James Joyce. Add: Dept. of English, St. Peter's College, Jersey City, NJ 07306.

DEAUX, GEORGE RICHARD, b. Springfield, Mass, Feb. 23, 31; m. 65; c. 2. MODERN AMERICAN LITERATURE. B.A, Univ. Minn, Duluth, 57; Woodrow Wilson fel, Ind. Univ, Bloomington, 57-58, M.A, 61. Instr, ENG, Univ. Southwest. La, 61-63; from instr. to ASSOC. PROF, TEMPLE UNIV, 63-, dir, Eng. Lang. Enrichment Ctr, 71-73. U.S.M.C, 50-54, Res, 54-61, Capt. AAUP. Modern fiction; medieval history and literature. Publ: The humanization of Eddie Cement, Simon & Schuster, N.Y. & Arthur Barker, London, 64; Exit, 66 & Superworm, 68, Simon & Schuster; The black death, 1347, Hamish Hamilton, London & Weybright & Talley, N.Y, 69. Add: Dept. of English, Temple University, Broad & Montgomery Sts, Philadelphia, PA 19122.

DEAVER, FRANK, b. Shawnee, Okla, Dec. 18, 32; m. 57; c. 2. JOURNALISM, AMERICAN ECONOMIC HISTORY. B.S, Sam Houston State Univ, 58, M.A, 59; Newspaper Fund fel, Univ. Ore, 65; Newspaper Fund fel, Univ. Tex, Austin, 68, Ph.D.(jour. hist), 69. Instr. hist. & econ, Sam Houston State Univ, 58-62; jour. & hist, Victoria Col.(Tex), 62-69; asst. prof. JOUR, UNIV. ALA, 69-73, ASSOC. PROF, 73- U.S.A.F, 53-55. Asn. Educ. in Jour; Jr. Col. Jour. Asn.(chmn. jr-sr. insts. liaison comt, 71-72, res. comt, 72-73); Nat. Counc. Col. Publ. Adv. Student publications; media and society; media history, local and regional. Publ: Junior college journalism in Alabama, Ala. State Dept. Educ, 71; Journalism and student publications in American junior colleges, Taylor Publ, 72; Freedoms and responsibilities of junior college newspapers, Jour. Quart, fall 68; The state of journalism education today, Community & Jr. Col. J, 11/72. Add: School of Communication, University of Alabama, P.O. Box 4135, University, AL 35486.

DeBELLIS, JACK ANGELO, b. Philadelphia, Pa, Aug. 19, 35; m. 64. ENGLISH. B.A, Univ. Fla, 57; M.A, Univ. Calif, Los Angeles, 60, Ph.D.(Eng), 64. Teaching asst. Eng, Univ. Calif, Los Angeles, 59-61, teaching fel, 62-64, instr, 64; asst. prof, San Fernando Valley State Col, 64; AM. LIT, LEHIGH UNIV, 64-69, ASSOC. PROF, 69- Inst. of Res. grant, 66; Fulbright-Hays lectr, Univ. Toulouse, 67-68; U.S. Educ. Comn. lectr, Conf. Danish Teachers Eng, Middlefart, Denmark, 68; grant, Humanities Perspectives on Technol, fall 73. MLA; Soc. Stud. South. Lit; Monumental Brass Soc. Southern literature; modern literature; contemporary fiction. Publ: Sidney Lanier, Twayne, 73; John Updike and the group, Sewanee Rev, summer 64; Andrew Lytle's A name for evil: transformation of The turn of the screw, Critique, spring-summer 66; The maternal father in McCullers's Heart is a lonely hunter, In: Carson McCullers and the critics, Edward/Everett, 74; plus others. Add: 1137 Lehigh Pkwy. E, Allentown, PA 18103.

DEBOO, K.E, Nineteenth & Twentieth Century Literature. See MARRE, K.E. DEBOO.

DeCAMP, DAVID, English, Linguistics. See Volume III, Foreign Languages, Linguistics & Philology.

DeCAMP, JACQUELINE L, b. Carthage, Mo, Mar. 20, 16. SPEECH. B.S.E, Northeast. State Col, 41; teaching fel, Northwest. Univ, 47-48, M.A, 49; Ph.D.(theatre), Univ. Mich, 67. Spec. teacher speech arts, pub. schs, Little Rock, Ark, 41-47; asst. prof. speech, Ark. State Teachers Col, 49-57; instr, Univ. Mich, 59-62; asst. prof. SPEECH, South. Conn. State Col, 62-67; PROF, MIDWEST. UNIV, 67- Summers, asst. develop. reading prog, Univ. Denver, 53, dir. drama, high sch. inst, Univ. Wis, 61. Speech Commun. Asn. Punctuation in Shakespeare. Add: Dept. of Speech & Drama, Midwestern University, Wichita Falls, TX 76308.

DeCATUR, LOUIS AUBREY, b. Washington, D.C, Apr. 27, 31; m. 65; c. 2. RENAISSANCE LITERATURE. B.A, Univ. Md, College Park, 54, M.A, 63, Ph.D.(Eng), 70; Univ. Minn, Minneapolis, 58-59. Lectr. ENG, Univ. Md, Europ. Div, 63-65, instr, Univ. Md, College Park, 65-68; ASST. PROF, U.S. Naval Academy, 68-70; URSINUS COL, 70- U.S. Naval Acad. Res. Counc. grant, summer 69. U.S.A.F, 54-56, 1st Lt. MLA; AAUP; Renaissance Soc. Am. Renaissance prose fiction; folklore, prose; Renaissance drama. Add: Dept. of English, Ursinus College, Collegeville, PA 19426.

DECAVALLES, ANDONIS GEORGE (MANGANARIS), b. Siphnos, Greece, Jan. 25, 20; U.S. citizen; m. 61; c. 3. ENGLISH, COMPARATIVE LITERATURE. LL.M, Nat. Univ. Athens, 47; M.A, Northwest. Univ, 57, Ph.D.(Eng, comp. lit), 60. Vis. lectr. Eng, Univ. Mass, 58-59; lectr, City Col. New York, 60; classics, Brooklyn Col. & N.Y. Univ, 60-61; asst. prof. ENG. & COMP. LIT, FAIRLEIGH DICKINSON UNIV, 61-64, assoc. prof, 64-69, PROF, 69- Consult, Libr. Congr, 60; exec. ed. & contrib, Charioteer, 60-; lectr. series mod. Am. poetry, Voice of Am, fall 61; consult. ed, Ctr. Neo-hellenic Stud, 66-; consult. mod. Greek theatre & cinema, Am. Counc. Learned Socs, summer 67. Hellenic Royal Navy, 41-44, Ensign. MLA; Col. Eng. Asn; Mod. Greek Stud. Asn. Modern English, American and European poetry; the work of Pandelis Prevelakis; some labyrinths in literature. Publ: Nimoule-Gondokoro (poems in Greek), 49, Akis (poems in Greek), 50 & Ta Tessera Kouartetta (transl, Eliot, Four quartets), 53, Mavrides, Athens; co-ed, The voice of Cyprus, October, 65; auth, Okeanidhes (Greek poems), Ikaros, Athens, 70; More of Cavafy, Works, winter-spring 72; Elysium in fragments: the Pisan cantos, Indian J. Am. Stud, 12/72; plus others. Add: Dept. of English, Fairleigh Dickinson University, 285 Madison Ave, Madison, NJ 07940.

DeCHAINE, FABER, b. Kent, Wash, Oct. 1, 28; m. 51; c. 2. THEATRE ARTS. B.S, Univ. Ore, 52; M.A, Mich. State Univ, 53; Ph.D, Univ. Minn, 63. Instr. Eng, Whitman Col, 53-55; assoc. prof. SPEECH, West. Mich. Univ, 55-64; UNIV. ORE, 64-70, PROF. & DIR. UNIV. THEATRE, 70- Dir. workshop, Cent. City Opera House Asn, Univ. Denver, 59, 60; archit. consult, Trend Assoc, Kalamazoo, Mich, 63-64. U.S.A, 46-48. Am. Theatre Asn; Speech Commun. Asn. Add: Dept. of Speech & Theatre Arts, University of Oregon, Eugene, OR 97403.

DECKER, PHILIP H, b. Lakewood, Ohio, Apr. 19, 32; m. 55; c. 2. SPEECH & DRAMA. B.A, Knox Col, 54; fel, Northwest. Univ, 54-55, M.A, 55, summers, 57, 58, Danforth grant, 59, univ. fel, 60-61, Ph.D.(theatre), 66. Asst. prof. SPEECH & THEATRE ARTS, MacMURRAY COL, 57-66, assoc. prof, 66-71, PROF, 71-, chmn. dept, 66-73. Danforth assoc, 62-66. U.S.A, 55-57, 1st Lt. Speech Commun. Asn; Am. Educ. Theatre Asn; Cent. States Speech Asn. Dramatic literature, especially 20th century English, American and Elizabethan; theatre history. Publ: Co-auth, an annotated bibliography of sources for period patterns, Educ. Theatre J, 3/62. Add: Dept. of Speech & Theatre Arts, MacMurray College, Jacksonville, IL 62650.

DEDMON, DONALD NEWTON, b. Wright Co, Aug. 13, 31; m; c. 2. SPEECH. B.S. in Ed, Southwest Mo. State Col, 53; M.A, State Univ. Iowa, 56, Ph.D, 61. Instr. speech, State Univ. Iowa, 56-59; asst. prof, St. Cloud State Col, 59-60, assoc. prof, 60-62; South Ill. Univ, 62-64; chmn. dept. speech, Colo. State Univ, 64-66; commun. consult, Smith, Kline & French Lab, Phila, 67-68; dean, Col. Arts & Sci. exec. v.pres, v.pres. acad. affairs & acting pres, Marshall Univ, 69-72; PRES, RADFORD COL, 72- U.S.A, 53-55. Speech Commun. Asn. Contemporary public address; undergraduate speech instruction. Publ: Translating Le Cid, Quart. J. Speech, 2/64; The functions of discourse in the Hawaiian Statehood Debates, Speech Monogr, 3/66; A comparison of university and business communication practices, J. Commun, 9/70. Add: Radford College, Box 359, Radford, VA 24141.

DEDMOND, FRANCIS BERNEIL, b. Salisbury, N.C, Aug. 19, 18; m. 65. ENGLISH. A.B, Catawba Col, 40; Th.M, South. Baptist Sem, 45; A.M, Duke Univ, 50; Univ. N.C, 49-52; Ph.D, Fla. State Univ, 69. Instr. ENG, Oak Ridge Mil. Inst, 45-47, prof. & head dept, 47-49; Gardner-Webb Col, 52-65; assoc. prof, CATAWBA COL, 65-69, PROF, 69-, CHMN. DEPT, 66- MLA; Am. Lit. Group, MLA; S.Atlantic Mod. Lang. Asn. Poe; contemporary American drama; contemporary American fiction. Publ: Lengthened shadows: a history of Gardner-Webb College, 1907-56, Gardner-Webb Col, 57; Economic protest in Thoreau's Journal, Studia Neophilologia, 53-54; The cask of Amontillado and the war of the literati, Mod. Lang. Quart, 6/54; Thoreau and the ethical concept of government, Personalist, winter 55. Add: Dept. of English, Catawba College, Innis St, Salisbury, NC 28144.

DEEGAN, WILLIAM JOHN, b. Wheeling, W.Va, Aug. 29, 22; m. 56; c. 4. ENGLISH, PHILOLOGY. A.B, W.Va. Univ, 48, M.A, 49; Univ. N.C, 51-53; Ph.D. (Eng), Univ. Pittsburgh, 61. Instr. ENG, W.Va. Univ, 49-51; ROANOKE COL, 53-56, asst. prof, 56-61, assoc. prof, 61-66, PROF, 66- U.S.A.A.F, 42-46, 1st Lt. English prosody and philology; structural linguistics. Add: 714 Beech Rd, Salem, VA 24153.

DEER, IRVING, b. Chicago, Ill, Aug. 15, 24; m. 54; c. 4. ENGLISH LITERATURE. B.S, Univ. Mich, 47; M.A, Univ. Minn, 51; Ford Found. internship, 53-54, Ph.D, 56. Asst, Univ. Minn, 51-52, instr. Eng, speech & humanities, 52-56; asst. prof. interpretation of lit, Univ. Calif, Santa Barbara, 56-58; prof. Eng. & drama, N.Dak. State Teachers Col, Ellendale, 58-59; assoc. prof. Eng, Lock Haven State Col, 59-61, prof, 61-64; prof. & chmn. dept, Dickinson State Col, 64-66; prof. lang. & lit. & assoc. dean div, UNIV. S.FLA, 66-71, PROF. ENG, 71- Consult, Am. Libr. Asn, 63-; participant, Col. Eng. Exam. Bd. Inst, Harvard, 65; dir, summer NDEA Eng. Insts, 65, 66. Pres. writing Award, Univ. Calif, 58. U.S.A.A.F, 42-46, 1st Lt. MLA; NCTE; Popular Cult. Asn.(mem. nat. adv. bd, 72-). Dramatic literature; modern European and American literature; contemporary literary criticism. Publ: Co-auth, The popular arts, Scribner, 67; co-ed, Person to person: rhetoric, reality and change, Holt, 73; auth, Ibsen's Brand: paradox and the symbolic hero, In: Twentieth century views: Ibsen, Prentice-Hall, 65;

Strindberg's dream vision: prelude to the film, Criticism, 72; Science, literature and the new consciousness, Bull. Asn. Depts. Eng, 72; plus others. Add: Dept. of English, University of South Florida, Tampa, FL 33620.

DEETHARDT, JOHN F, JR, b. Mishawaka, Ind, June 3, 27; m. 58; c. 2. SPEECH EDUCATION. B.A, Ind. Univ, 51, M.A, Northwest. Univ, 64, Ph.D. (speech), 67. Teacher, high schs, Ind. & Ill, 55-64; ASST. PROF. speech, South. Colo. State Col, 66-68; SPEECH & EDUC, TEX. TECH UNIV, 68- U.S.A, 45-47, T/Sgt. Speech Commun. Asn; Int. Commun. Asn; South. Speech Commun. Asn; Ger. Soc. History and psychology of speech education; responsive environment for speech communication; system analysis applied to speech communication training. Publ: Speech education in Germany, In: International studies of national speech education systems, Burgess, 70; Searching for a relevant rhetoric in Germany, 11/71 & Classroom questioning behavior of teachers, (in press), Speech Teacher. Add: Dept. of Speech, Texas Tech University, Lubbock, TX 79409.

DE FALCO, JOSEPH MICHAEL, b. Wash, Pa, Aug. 17, 31; m. 52. ENGLISH. B.A, Washington & Jefferson Col, 56; M.A, Univ. Fla, 58, fel, summer 60, Ph.D, 61. Instr. ENG, Univ. Fla, 60-61; asst. prof, Washington & Jefferson Col, 61-64, ASSOC. PROF, 64-66; Univ. R.I, 66-67; MARQUETTE UNIV, 67- Am. Counc. Learned Soc. grant-in-aid, summer 63; Am. Lit. consult, Choice, 68- Sig.C, U.S.A, 48-51, Res, 53-, Capt. MLA. American literature. Publ: The hero in Hemingway's short stories, Univ. Pittsburgh, 63; ed, Collected poems of Christopher Pearse Cranch, Scholar's Facsimiles, 71; auth, Frost's Paul's wife: the death of an ideal, South. Folklore Quart, 12/65; Thoreau's social ethic, Topic, fall 66; Hemingway's islands and streams, In: Hemingway in our time, Ore. State Univ, 74; plus others. Add: Dept. of English, Marquette University, Milwaukee, WI 53233.

DEFORD, SARA W, b. Youngstown, Ohio, Nov. 9, 16. ENGLISH. A.B, Mt. Holyoke Col, 36, M.A, 38; Univ. Mich, 36-37; Ph.D, Yale, 42. Instr. ENG, Barnard Col, Columbia, 42-46; asst. prof, GOUCHER COL, 46-51, assoc. prof, 51-57, PROF, 57- Eugene F. Saxton Mem. fel, 48; Fulbright lectr, Japan, 54-55, 61-62; vis. prof. Eng, Tsuda Col, Tokyo, 69-70. Mediaeval Acad. Am; Col. Eng. Asn. Versification; medieval and 17th century English; prosody; Milton and Chaucer. Publ: The city of love, Exposition, 58; Lectures in modern American poetry, 56 & The shorter love poems of John Donne, 71, Hokuseido, Tokyo; co-ed. & co-transl, The pearl, Croft, 67; auth, Paradise lost, Books I and II, an exposition, Shinozaki, Tokyo, 67; co-auth, Forms of verse, British and American, Appleton, 71. Add: 921 Dulaney Valley Ct, Towson, MD 21204.

DE GROOT, ELIZABETH MARIE, b. Passaic, N.J, Nov. 6, 27. ENGLISH. B.A, N.Y. Univ, 49, M.A, 57, Ph.D.(Eng), 67. Teacher Eng. & Latin, Clifton Pub. Schs, N.J, 51-61; ASSOC. PROF. ENG, WILLIAM PATERSON COL, 61- MLA. Victorian literature; 19th century American literature. Publ: Middlemarch and Dorothea Brooke: the saints go marching out, Christianity & Lit, fall 72. Add: Dept. of English, William Paterson College of New Jersey, 300 Pompton Rd, Wayne, NJ 07470.

de GROOT, HANS BART, b. Voorburg, Netherlands, Apr. 20, 39; Can. citizen; m. 64; c. 1. ENGLISH LITERATURE. Lit. kand, State Univ. Groningen, 59; B.A, Univ. Durham, 61, M.A, 64; Ph.D.(Eng. lit), London, 69. Lectr. ENG. LIT, UNIV. TORONTO, 65-70, ASST. PROF, 70- Can. Coun. fel, 71-72; co-ed, Victorian Periodicals Newsletter, 73. Asn. Can. Univ. Teachers Eng; Res. Soc. Victorian Periodicals; Can. Asn. Univ. Teachers. Nineteenth century English poetry; Victorian periodicals; Anglo-Dutch literary relationships. Publ: Albert Verwey, Keats en Matthew Arnold, Nieuwe Taalgids, 68; The ouroboros and the romantic poets: a Renaissance emblem in Blake, Coleridge and Shelley, Eng. Stud, 69; Lord Brougham and the founding of the British and foreign review, Victorian Periodicals Newsletter, 70. Add: Dept. of English, University College, University of Toronto, Toronto, Ont. M5S 1A1, Can.

DeGRUSON, EUGENE HENRY, b. Girard, Kans, Oct. 10, 32. AMERICAN LITERATURE & BIBLIOGRAPHY. B.S, Kans. State Col. Pittsburg, 54, M.A, 58; fel, Univ. Iowa, 58-59. Instr. Eng, KANS. STATE COL. PITTSBURG, 60-63, asst. prof, 63-68, BIBLIOGRAPHER HUMANITIES, 68- Ed, Libr. Bull, Kans. State Col. Pittsburg, 68- Bibliog. Soc. Am; Am. Libr. Asn; NCTE. Bibliography; modern poetry. Publ: Kansas authors of best sellers: a bibliography, Kans. State Col. Pittsburg, 70. Add: Library, Kansas State College of Pittsburg, Pittsburg, KS 66762.

De HOFF, BERNARD C, b. York, Pa, Feb. 4, 25; m. 43; c. 4. ENGLISH, JOURNALISM. B.A, Franklin & Marshall Col, 51; M.A, Ind. Univ, 52. Teacher, Eng. & drama, Jackson High Sch, Sardinia, Ind, 52-54; instr. Eng. compos, UNIV. NORTH. IOWA, 55-58, asst. prof, 59, Ger, 62-64, jour, 64-67, admin. asst. & asst. prof. compos, 67-73, ASSOC. PROF. JOUR. & COMPOS, 73- Grad. asst. Ger, Ind. Univ, 51-52, Eng, 54-55. U.S.M.C, 43-46. NCTE; Nat. Counc. Col. Publ. Adv.(mem. standards comt, 68-); Asn. Educ. in Jour; Conf. Col. Compos. & Commun. German and English composition; journalism. Add: 716 W. 12th St, Cedar Falls, IA 50613.

DEIMAN, WERNER JOHN, b. Mineola, N.Y, Sept. 15, 37. ENGLISH & COMPARATIVE LITERATURE. Catherine Campbell Scholar, Robert Alexander Scholar, Charles James Andrews Scholar & B.A, Washington & Lee Univ, 59; Woodrow Wilson fel, Yale, 59-60, M.A, 64, Ph.D.(Eng), 66; Dankstipendium, Univ. Munich, 62-63. Instr. ENG, BATES COL, 64-67, asst. prof, 67-74, ASSOC. PROF, 74- Nat. Endowment for Humanities Younger Scholar, summer 68. MLA. Virginia Woolf; twentieth century and comparative literature; romanticism and the 19th century. Publ: History, pattern, and continuity in Virginia Woolf, Contemporary Lit, winter 74. Add: 169 College St, Lewiston, ME 04240.

DEITZ, JONATHAN ERIC, b. Washington, D.C, Mar. 18, 46; m. 68; c. 1. ENGLISH LITERATURE. B.A, Johns Hopkins Univ, 67; M.A, Univ. Pa, 68, Ph.D.(Eng), 72. Instr. ENG, Combs Col. Mus, 68-70; adj. instr, Franklin & Marshall Col, 72; ASST. PROF, UNIV. ARIZ, 72- MLA. Restoration and eighteenth century drama; modern drama; eighteenth century novel. Add: Dept. of English, University of Arizona, Tucson, AZ 85721.

DEKKER, GEORGE GILBERT, b. Long Beach, Calif, Sept. 8, 34. ENGLISH & AMERICAN LITERATURE. B.A, Univ. Calif, Santa Barbara, 55, M.A, 58; M.Litt, Cambridge, 61; Ph.D.(Eng), Univ. Essex, 66. Lectr. ENG, Univ. Wales, 62-64; Univ. Essex, 64-66, sr. lectr, 66-70, reader, 70-72; ASSOC. PROF, STANFORD UNIV, 72- American historical literature; English and American Romanticism; Coleridge. Publ: Sailing after knowledge: the cantos of Ezra Pound, 63, James Fenimore Cooper the novelist, 67 & co-ed, James Fenimore Cooper: the critical heritage, 73, Routledge & Kegan Paul; co-ed, The American democrat by James Fenimore Cooper, Penguin, 69. Add: Dept. of English, Stanford University, Stanford, CA 94305.

DeKOSTER, LESTER RONALD, b. Zeeland, Mich, Apr. 21, 15; m. 41; c. 4. SPEECH. A.B, Calvin Col, 37; A.M, Univ. Mich, 42, A.M.L.S, 55, Ph.D. (libr. sci), 64; Mich. State Univ, 50. Teacher, high sch, Mich, 37-43, 45-46; instr. speech, Calvin Col, 47-48, from asst. prof. to prof, 49-69, dir. libr, 51-69; ED, THE BANNER, CHRISTIAN REFORMED CHURCH, 69- Lectr, Univ. Mich. Exten, 63; adj. prof. libr. sci, West. Mich. Univ, 69- U.S.N, 43-45. Evangel. Press Asn. Publ: All ye that labor, Communism and Christian faith, 62, Vocabulary of communism, 63, Christian and John Birch Society, 66 & Citizen and John Birch Society, 68, Eerdmans. Add: Christian Reformed Publishing House, 2850 Kalamazoo Ave. S.E, Grand Rapids, MI 49508.

DELAHAYE, ALFRED NEWTON, b. Brusly, La, June 4, 29. JOURNALISM, ENGLISH. B.A, La. State Univ, Baton Rouge, 49, M.A, 51; Ph.D.(jour), Univ. Mo-Columbia, 70; Inst. Sci. of Press, Holland, 73. Dir. publ, Nicholls State Col, 57-67; instr. JOUR, Univ. Mo-Columbia, 67-69; ASSOC. PROF, NICHOLLS STATE UNIV, 69- Bibliogr, Jour. Quart, 70-; ed, Temple, Phi Kappa Theta Int. Fraternity, 71- U.S.M.C, 51-53. Asn. Educ. Jour. International communications. Add: 138A Elder St, Thibodaux, LA 70301.

DELANY, PAUL, b. Purley, Eng, July 18, 37; Can. citizen; m. 62; c. 2. ENGLISH LITERATURE. B. Comm, McGill Univ, 57; A.M, Stanford Univ, 58; M.A, Univ. Calif, 61, Ph.D.(Eng), 65. Instr. ENG, Columbia Univ, 64-66, asst. prof, 66-70; ASSOC. PROF, SIMON FRASER UNIV, 70- Can. Coun. res. fel, 73-74. MLA; Asn. Can. Univ. Teachers Eng. Seventeenth century literature; modern British literature; literature and psychology. Publ: British autobiography in the seventeenth century, Routledge & Kegan Paul & Columbia Univ, 69; Marvell's mourning, Mod. Lang. Quart, 3/72; Joyce's political development and the aesthetic of Dubliners, Col. Eng, 11/72. Add: Dept. of English, Simon Fraser University, Burnaby 2, B.C, Can.

DELASANTA, RODNEY, b. Winchendon, Mass, Nov. 6, 32; m. 53; c. 4. ENGLISH LITERATURE. A.B, Providence Col, 53; A.M, Brown Univ, 55, Ph.D, 62. Teaching asst, Brown Univ, 55-57, instr. Eng, 57-61; asst. prof, PROVIDENCE COL, 61-65, assoc. prof, 65-70, PROF. ENG. LIT, 70-, CHMN. DEPT. ENG, 72- Vis. prof. Eng. lit, Univ. Fribourg, 68-70; Univ. Neuchatel, 69-70. MLA; Medieval Acad. Am. English medieval and Renaissance literature. Publ: The epic voice, Mouton, 67; Christian affirmation in the Book of the Duchess, PMLA, 1/69; The theme of judgment in the Canterbury tales, Mod. Lang. Quart, 9/70; And of great reverence: Chaucer's Man of law, Chaucer Rev, spring 71; plus others. Add: Dept. of English, Providence College, Providence, RI 02918.

DeLAURA, DAVID JOSEPH, b. Worcester, Mass, Nov. 19, 30; m. 61; c. 3. ENGLISH LITERATURE. A.B, Boston Col, 55, A.M, 58; Ph.D, Univ. Wis, 60. Instr. Eng, Univ. Tex, Austin, 60-62, asst. prof, 62-64, assoc. prof, 64-68, prof, 68-74; AVALON FOUND. PROF. HUMANITIES & PROF. ENG, UNIV. PA, 74- Guggenheim Found. Mem. fel, 67-68. MLA (award, 64). Nineteenth and 20th century English literature. Publ: Ed, John Henry Newman's Apologia pro vita sua, Norton, 68; auth, Hebrew and Hellene in Victorian England: Newman, Arnold, and Pater, Univ. Tex, 69; ed, Matthew Arnold: a collection of critical essays, Prentice-Hall, 73 & Victorian prose: a guide to research, Mod. Lang. Asn, 73; The place of the classics in T.S. Eliot's Christian humanism, In: Hereditas: seven essays on the modern experience of the classical, Univ. Tex, 64; Arnold and Carlyle, PMLA, 3/64; The ache of modernism in Hardy's later novels, ELH, 9/67. Add: Dept. of English, University of Pennsylvania, Philadelphia, PA 19104.

DeLEEUW, WILLIAM LEWIS, b. Rome, Ga, Oct. 19, 45. MEDIEVAL LITERATURE & LINGUISTICS. B.A, Berry Col, 66; M.A, Auburn Univ, 69, Ph.D.(Eng), 72. Instr. ENG, Auburn Univ, 69-72; ASST. PROF, HIGH POINT COL, 72- MLA; Col. Eng. Asn; Mediaeval Acad. Am. Creative writing. Add: Dept. of English, High Point College, High Point, NC 27262.

DELIGIORGIS, STAVROS GEORGE, b. Romania, Sept. 14, 33; m. 60; c. 2. ENGLISH & COMPARATIVE LITERATURE. B.A, Nat. Univ. Athens, 60; Fulbright-Smith Mundt fel. & M.A, Yale, 58; Brown fel, Univ. Calif, Berkeley, 63-64, Rosenberg fel, 64-65, Ph.D.(comp. lit), 66. Asst. prof. ENG. & COMP. LIT, UNIV. IOWA, 65-68, assoc. prof, 68-73, PROF, 73- Assoc, Ctr. Neohellenic Stud, Austin, Tex, 67; fel, ctr. advan. stud, Univ. Ill, Urbana, 68-70, vis. assoc. prof. Eng, 69-70. Mediaeval Acad. Am; Am. Comp. Lit. Asn; MLA. Classical Mediaeval and Renaissance literature; esthetics and critical theory; mythology, anthropology and folklore. Publ: Transl. into Greek, Theory of literature, Diphros, Athens, 65; co-ed, Publication No. 2, Univ. Iowa, 73; Boccaccio and the Greek romances, Comp. Lit, 5/67; Levi-Strauss and the science of the self: an essay in theoretical anthropology, J. Europ. Stud, 1: 32-36; Systematics of communication: comparative literature and the social sciences, Actes Int. Comp. Lit. Conf, 73. Add: Dept. of English, University of Iowa, Iowa City, IA 52240.

DELL, GEORGE W, b. St. Paul, Minn, July 9, 26; m; c. 2. RHETORIC. B.S, Univ. South. Calif, 51, M.A, 55, Ph.D, 60. Speech correctionist, Los Angeles city schs, 51-55; instr. speech, Los Angeles City Col, 55-59; Univ. Calif, Los Angeles, 59-61; asst. prof, SAN FRANCISCO STATE UNIV, 61-64, assoc. prof, 64-72, PROF. SPEECH COMMUN, 72- Am. Sch. Class. Stud, Athens, 67-68; consult, Calif. Sens, 72- U.S.A.A.F, 46-47. Speech Commun. Asn; Am. Fed. Teachers. Public speaking; Dr. Robert Maynard Hutchins; rhetorical criticism and political persuasion. Publ: The Republican nominee: Barry M. Goldwater, Quart J. Speech, 12/64; Philosophic judgments in contemporary rhetorical criticism, West. Speech, spring 66. Add: 2250 Rosewood Dr, San Bruno, CA 94066.

DELL, ROBERT MERRITT, b. New York, N.Y, Oct. 5, 20; m. 46; c. 2. ENGLISH, AMERICAN DRAMA. A.B, Franklin & Marshall Col, 42; M.A, Columbia Univ, 47, dipl. teaching Eng, 48; Ph.D.(drama), N.Y. Univ, 60. Instr. Eng, Manhattan Col, 46-49; Eng. & speech, PACE UNIV, 48-49, asst. prof. ENG. & DRAMA, 49-53, assoc. prof, 53-60, PROF, 60-, head div. arts & sci, Westchester Br, 67-69, chmn. depts. Eng, speech & for. lang, 68-73, chmn. dept. Eng, Main Br, 63-68. Vis. teacher, Poole Grammar Sch, Eng, 61-62; adj. prof, Col. Pharmaceutical Sci, Columbia Univ, 65-71; mem. Liaison Comt. Pub. Relat, NCTE, 66-; adj. prof, Proj. Respect for Drugs, 67. U.S.N.R, 42-46, Lt. NCTE; Bronte Soc, Eng. American drama 1880-1910; speech; Byron and Hardy. Add: Dept. of Literature and Communication, Pace University, Westchester Campus, 861 Bedford Rd, Pleasantville, NY 10570.

DELMAGE, RUTHERFORD EARLE, b. Hermon, N.Y, Dec. 5, 10. ENGLISH & AMERICAN LITERATURE. A.B, St. Lawrence Univ, 32; A.M, Cornell Univ, 33, Ph.D, 37. Instr. ENG, Univ. Tenn, 35-37; asst. prof, ST. LAWRENCE UNIV, 37-45, assoc. prof, 46-48, CRAIG PROF, 48- Shreve fel, Princeton, 47-48. Am. Philos. Asn. res. grant, 47. NCTE. Idea of progress in America; Shakespeare; history of ideas. Add: Dept. of English, St. Lawrence University, Canton, NY 13617.

DeLOCHE, JOHN BRUCE, JR, b. Pittsburgh, Pa, Nov. 16, 35; m. 64; c. 2. ENGLISH. B.S, Ind. Univ. Pa, 61; M.A, Univ. Pittsburgh, 62, Ph.D.(Eng), 67. Instr. ENG, State Univ, N.Y. Col. Oswego, 63-64; asst. prof, Monmouth Col. N.J, 65-69; Ind. Univ, South Bend, 69-70, ASSOC. PROF, MONMOUTH COL, 70- U.S.A.F, 53-57. MLA; Shakespeare Asn. Am. Renaissance drama; English novel. Add: Dept. of English, Monmouth College, West Long Branch, NJ 07764.

DEL PORTO, JOSEPH ANTONY, b. Erie, Pa, Feb. 13, 13; m. 39; c. 2. JOURNALISM. A.B, Univ. Pa, 35; A.M, Univ. Chicago, 36; Ph.D, Mich. State Univ, 53. Mem. advert. sales staff, New York Am, 38; advert. res, Chicago Daily News, 41-42; mem. ed. staff, Chicago Daily Tribune, 42-43; reporter, Chicago City News Bur, 43-44; teacher Eng, New Caldonia, S.Pac, 45; mem. ed. staff, Erie Dispatch-Herald, Pa, 46-47; asst. prof. jour, Mich. State Univ, 47-54, assoc. prof, 54; prof, Sch. Pub. Commun, Boston Univ, 54-68, chmn. div, 54-64; PROF. JOUR, BOWLING GREEN STATE UNIV, 68-, dir. sch. jour, 68-73. Advert. intern, Detroit Times, 48; TV newscaster, Cambridge, Mass, 55. U.S.A.A.F, 44-46. Asn. Educ. in Jour; Pub. Relat. Soc. Am. History of journalism; journalism law and ethics. Add: School of Journalism, Bowling Green State University, Bowling Green, OH 43403.

DELSON, ABE, b. Lebanon, Pa, Aug. 3, 30; m. 60; c. 2. ENGLISH & AMERICAN LITERATURE. B.A, City Col. New York, 51; M.A, N.Y. Univ, 57, Ph.D.(Eng), 68. Instr. ENG, WESTFIELD STATE COL, 58-65, asst. prof, 65-69, ASSOC. PROF, 69-, CHMN. DEPT, 73- Abstractor, Abstr. Eng. Stud, 72-; Nat. Endowment for Humanities summer stipend, Univ. Fla, 73. Ord.C, U.S.A, 53-54. MLA; Col. Eng. Asn; Asn Dept. Eng. Romantic literature; short story. Publ: The symbolism of sun and moon in The rime of the ancient mariner, Tex. Stud. Lit. & Lang, winter 73. Add: Dept. of English, Westfield State College, Westfield, MA 01085.

DEL TUFO, JOSEPH P, b. West Orange, N.J, Apr. 21, 24; m. 66; c. 2. ENGLISH. M.A, Berchmans Col, 49; M.A, Woodstock Col, 56; M.A, Fordham Univ, 59, Ph.D.(Eng), 61. Chmn. dept. ENG, Xavier Univ, 61-62; Ateneo de Manila Univ, 62-66; assoc. prof, DEL. STATE COL, 66-68, PROF, 68-, dir. honors prog, 67-73. Mem, Del. Humanities Counc, Nat. Endowment for Humanities, 73- Educational television—script writing and teaching; theory of poetry. Publ: Speech course, 62 & Introduction to poetry, 65, Ateneo de Manila Univ; Can art be immoral?, Philippine Stud, 63; William Shakespeare and Richard III, Fac. J, 72-73. Add: 118 Beech Dr, Dover, DE 19901.

DE LUCA, VINCENT ARTHUR, b. New York, N.Y, Jan. 9, 40. ENGLISH. A.B, Hamilton Col, 61; M.A, Yale, 62, Ph.D.(Eng), 67. Instr. ENG, Cornell Univ, 64-67, ASST. PROF, 67-70; ERINDALE COL, UNIV. TORONTO, 70- MLA Romantic poetry and prose. Publ: An interpretation of DeQuincey's Revolt of the Tartars, Stud. Romanticism, 69; Icon and allegory in Blake's Prophecies, Criticism, 70; Mutual influence in Wordsworth and DeQuincey, Tex. Stud. Lit. & Lang, 71. Add: Dept. of English, Erindale College, University of Toronto, Clarkson, Ont, Can.

DE MARIA, ROBERT, b. New York, N.Y, Sept. 28, 28; m. 47; c. 4. ENGLISH. B.A, Columbia Univ, 48, M.A, 49, Ph.D.(Eng), 59. Instr. Eng, Univ. Ore, 49-52; asst. prof, Hofstra Univ, 52-61; assoc. dean, New Sch. Soc. Res, 61-64; PROF. ENG, DOWLING COL, 65-, dir, Mediter. Inst, Spain, 69-70. Ed/Publ, Mediter. Rev, 69- Auth. League Am; PEN Club. The English novel; Utopian literature; creative writing. Publ: A theme-correction guide, Holt, 57; co-auth, Subject and sources, first series, 61 & second series, 63, Norton; auth, Carnival of angels, 61 & The language of grammar, 64, Macmillan; Clodia, 65 & Don Juan in Lourdes, 66, St. Martin's; The satyr (novel), Bobbs, 72; The decline and fall of America (novel), 73 & The atheist (novel), 74, Saturday Rev. Press. Add: Brown Hills, Orient, NY 11957.

DeMARR, MARY JEAN, b. Urbana, Ill, Sept. 20, 32. ENGLISH. B.A, Lawrence Col, 54; Fulbright fel, Univ. Tübingen, 54-55; A.M, Univ. Ill, Urbana, 57, Univ. fel, 56-58, Ph.D.(Eng), 63; Univ. Moscow, 61-62. Asst. prof, ENG, Willamette Univ, 64-65; asst. prof, IND. STATE UNIV, TERRE HAUTE, 65-70, ASSOC. PROF, 70- MLA; Mod. Humanities Res. Asn; NCTE; AAUP; Col. Eng. Asn. American literature. Publ: Contrib. ed, Annual bibliography of English language and literature, 66-72 & co-ed, 72-, Mod. Humanities Res. Asn; auth, Hemingway's narrative methods, spring 70 & The cook and the shark: a reading of The open boat, fall 71, Ind. Eng. J. Add: Dept. of English, Indiana State University, Terre Haute, IN 47809.

DEMBO, LAWRENCE SANFORD, b. Troy, N.Y, Dec. 3, 29; m. 53. ENGLISH. B.A, Syracuse Univ, 51; M.A, Columbia Univ, 52; Ph.D, Cornell Univ, 55. Instr. ENG, Cornell Univ, 59-60; asst. prof, Univ. Calif, Los Angeles, 60-65; PROF, UNIV. WIS-MADISON, 65- Fulbright lectr, Univ. Montpellier, France, 63-64; ed, Contemporary Lit, 66-; Guggenheim fel, 68-69; mem. ed. bd, Am. Lit, 73- U.S.N, 56-59, Lt.(jg). MLA. Modern American literature. Publ: Hart Crane's Sanskrit charge: a study of the bridge, Cornell Univ, 60; The Confucian odes of Ezra Pound; a critical appraisal, Univ. Calif, & Faber & Faber, 63, 64; Conceptions of reality in modern American poetry, Univ. Calif, 66; ed, Nabokov: the man and his work, 67 & Criticism: speculative and analytical essays, 68 & co-ed, The contemporary writer: interviews with sixteen novelists and poets, 72, Univ. Wis; Louis Zukofsky: objectivist poetics and the quest for form, Am. Lit, 3/72; The existential world of George Oppen, Iowa Rev, winter 72; Charles Olson and the moral history of Cape Ann, Criticism, winter 72. Add: Dept. of English, University of Wisconsin-Madison, Madison, WI 53706.

DeMENT, JOSEPH WILLIS, b. Reno, Nev, July 24, 25; m. 50; c. 3. ENGLISH. A.B, Univ. Redlands, 54; Ph.D.(Eng), Ind. Univ, 65. Instr. ENG, Bucknell Univ, 58-64; asst. prof, Hiram Col, 64-66; asst. prof, OAKLAND UNIV. 66-71, PROF, 71-, CHMN. DEPT, 73- Vis. lectr, Univ. Mich, summer 66. U.S.A, 44-46, 47-50, 1st Sgt. MLA; Shakespeare Asn. Am. Shakespeare; Restoration drama; literary criticism. Publ: A possible reference to Hamlet, Shakespeare Quart, autumn 64. Add: Dept. of English, Oakland University, Rochester, MI 48063.

DEMETZ, PETER, German, Comparative Literature. See Volume III, Foreign Languages, Linguistics & Philology.

DEMING, ROBERT HOWARD, b. Hartford, Conn, Oct. 12, 37; m. 62; c. 3. ENGLISH. B.A, Union Col, 59; M.A, Univ. Kans, 61; Ph.D.(Eng), Univ. Wis, 65. Asst. prof. ENG, Miami Univ, 65-70; assoc. prof, STATE UNIV. N.Y. COL. FREDONIA, 70-72, PROF, 72- Renaissance Soc. Am. Seventeenth century English literature; James Joyce; literary criticism. Publ: A bibliography of James Joyce studies, Univ. Kans. Libr, 64, 65, rev. ed, 74; ed, Joyce: the critical heritage, Routledge & Kegan Paul, 70; auth, Ceremony and art: Robert Herrick's poetry, Mouton, Hague, 74; Love and knowledge in the Renaissance lyric, Tex. Stud. Lang. & Lit, 74. Add: Dept. of English, State University of New York College at Fredonia, Fredonia, NY 14063.

DeMORDAUNT, WALTER JULIUS, b. Pueblo, Colo, Aug. 31, 25; m. 54; c. 3. LITERARY CRITICISM. B.A, Univ. Colo, 49, M.A, 50; Ph.D, Univ. Denver, 53. Instr. ENG, Mesa County Jr. Col, 53-55; asst. prof, N.Mex. State Univ, 55-64; assoc. prof, Calif. State Col. Los Angeles, 64-67; SOUTH. ORE. COL, 67-72, PROF, 72-, DIR. COMPOS, 68- Publ: Assignments in rhetoric, Macmillan, 63; A writer's guide to literature, McGraw, 65; Teaching literature in translation, Improving Col. & Univ. Teaching, summer 67; Accent on communication (column), Libr-Col. J, winter 69-spring 71. Add: Dept. of English, Southern Oregon College, Ashland, OR 97520.

DeMOTT, BENJAMIN (HAILE), b. L.I, N.Y, June 2, 24; m. 46; c. 3. ENGLISH. John Harvard scholar, Harvard, 49-50, univ. fel, 50-51, Ph.D.(Eng), 53. Teaching fel. ENG, Harvard, 50-51; instr, AMHERST COL, 51-54, asst. prof, 54-57, assoc. prof, 57-60, PROF, 60- Vis. prof, Mass. Inst. Technol, 62; Guggenheim fel, 63, 67; Fulbright lectr, 65; mem. bd. ed, Col. Eng, 65-; vis. prof, Univ. Birmingham, 65; Utah, 66; mem. exec. comt, Teachers & Writers Collaborative, 66-; prog. adv. comt, MLA, 68-; comn. lit, NCTE, 68-; vis. prof, Yale, 69. American literature; history of drama. Publ: The body's cage, Little, 59; Hells & benefits, Basic Bks, 62; You don't say, Harcourt, 66; A married man, 68; Supergrow, 69; Surviving the seventies, 71; Scholarship for society, 74. Add: Dept. of English, Amherst College, Amherst, MA 01002.

DeMOUGEOT, WILLIAM ROBERT, b. New York, N.Y, Apr. 1, 21; m. 44; c. 2. SPEECH, DRAMA. B.A, N.Y. Univ, 47; fel, Cornell Univ, 47-51, M.A, 50, Ph.D, 59. Instr. SPEECH, Princeton, 51-54; asst. prof, N.TEX. STATE UNIV, 54-58, assoc. prof, 58-61, PROF, 61- Part-time instr, Rutgers Univ, 51-54; mem. speakers bur, Am. Med. Asn, 61-; Outstanding Prof. on Campus Award, 62. U.S.A.A.F, 42-46. Speech Commun. Asn; Am. Forensic Asn. Public address; communication; undergraduate instruction. Publ: High school debate kit, Blue Cross-Blue Shield Tex, 63. Add: Dept. of Speech Communication and Drama, North Texas State University, Denton, TX 76203.

DENDINGER, LLOYD N, b. New Orleans, La, July 28, 29; m. 51; c. 3. ENGLISH. B.A, Tulane Univ, 53; M.A, Vanderbilt Univ, 61; Ph.D.(Eng), La. State Univ, 66. Instr. ENG, Nicholls State Col, 61-64; La. State Univ, 64-66; asst. prof, UNIV. S.ALA, 66-70, ASSOC. PROF, 70- U.S.A.F, 46-49, Sgt. S.Atlantic Mod. Lang. Asn. Publ: The irrational appeal of Frost's Dark deep woods, South. Rev, fall 66; Crane's inverted use of images of The rime of the ancient mariner, Stud. Short Fiction, winter 68; Robert Frost: the popular and central poetic images, Am. Quart, winter 69. Add: Dept. of English, University of South Alabama, Mobile, AL 36688.

DENEAU, DANIEL PIERRE, b. Kankakee, Ill, Feb. 2, 32. ENGLISH. B.A, St. Joseph's Col.(Ind), 53; fel, Univ. Notre Dame, 54-55, M.A, 55, Ph.D.(Eng), 59. Lectr, South Bend Ctr, Ind. Univ, 57-58; instr. ENG, Spring Hill Col, 58-60; asst. prof, 60-62; Seton Hall Univ, 62-63; Spring Hill Col, 63-64, assoc. prof, 64-67, prof, 67-72, chmn. dept, 68-71; assoc. prof, Univ. Saskatchewan, 72-73; res. & writing, 73-74. MLA; S.Atlantic Mod. Lang. Asn. Nineteenth-century British literature; modern European fiction. Publ: The river and the web in the works of George Eliot, Res. Stud, 6/67; Joyce's Minute Maria, J. Narrative Tech, 1/72; Coleridge's Limbo: a riddling tale?, Wordsworth Circle, spring 72; plus others. Add: 115 S. Conception St, Mobile, AL 36602.

DeNEEF, ARTHUR LEIGH, b. Newton, N.J, Apr. 16, 42; m. 64; c. 2. ENGLISH LITERATURE. B.A, Iowa Wesleyan Col, 64; M.A, Pa. State Univ, 65, Ph.D.(Eng), 69. Instr. ENG, Pa. State Univ, 68-69; ASST. PROF, DUKE UNIV, 69- MLA (bibliogr, 65-); Renaissance Soc. Am; Southeast. Renaissance Conf. Renaissance poetry; Renaissance rhetorical theory; literary criticism. Publ: Co-ed, Renaissance papers, 70-72, Southeast. Renaissance Conf, 71, 72, 73; auth, This poetick liturgie: Robert Herrick's ceremonial mode, Duke Univ, 74; Robertson and the critics, Chaucer Rev, 68; Herrick's Corinna and the ceremonial mode, S.Atlantic Quart, 71; Epideictic rhetoric and the Renaissance lyric, J. Medieval & Renaissance Stud, 73. Add: Dept. of English, Allen Bldg, Duke University, Durham, NC 22706.

DENENFELD, PHILIP S, b. Detroit, Mich, Mar. 30, 24; m. 48; c. 3. ENGLISH. B.A, Wayne State Univ, 50; M.A, Northwest. Univ, 51, Ph.D.(Eng), 57. Teaching asst. ENG, Northwest. Univ, 51-53; instr, Chicago City Cols, Wilson Campus, 53-55; asst. prof, WEST. MICH. UNIV, 56-60, assoc. prof, 60-63, PROF, 63-, ASSOC. V.PRES. ACAD. AFFAIRS, 72-, assoc. dean col. lib. arts & sci, 68-72. Assoc. & managing ed, AAUP Bull, 65-67; assoc. ed, Academe, 65-67. U.S.A.A.F, 42-45. Col. Eng. Asn; NCTE. Eighteenth century English literature; communication theory; constitutional rights. Add: Dept. of English, Western Michigan University, Kalamazoo, MI 49001.

DENHAM, ROBERT DAYTON, b. Mooresville, N.C, Oct. 20, 38; m. 61; c. 2. ENGLISH & AMERICAN LITERATURE. A.B, Davidson Col, 61; M.A, Univ. Chicago, 64, Ph.D.(Eng), 72. Instr. ENG, EMORY & HENRY COL, 66-69, ASST. PROF, 69- Lectr, Univ. Ill, Chicago Circle, 71-72; Nat. Endowment for Humanities younger humanist fel, summer 73. U.S.A, 64-66, Capt. MLA; Northeast Mod. Lang. Asn; S.Cent. Mod. Lang. Asn; NCTE; AAUP. History and theory of criticism; poetics and aesthetics; modern fiction. Publ: Northrop Frye: an enumerative bibliography, Scarecrow, 74; R.S. Crane's critical method and theory of poetic form, Conn. Rev, 4/72; Northrop Frye's theory of rhetoric, Xavier Univ. Stud, spring 72; Frye's theory of symbols, Can. Lit, 74. Add: Dept. of English, Emory & Henry College, Emory, VA 24327.

DENMAN, DAWSON FORMAN, English. See GAILLARD, DAWSON FORMAN.

DENNISTON, ELLIOTT AVERETT, b. Philadelphia, Pa, June 8, 40; m. 66; c. 2. ENGLISH. B.A, Princeton, 62; M.A, Univ. Mich, Ann Arbor, 67, fel, 69-70, Ph.D.(Eng), 70. ASST. PROF. ENG, KY. WESLEYAN COL, 70- Ed, Green River Rev, 73- U.S.N, 62-66, Lt. MLA. Ben Jonson; English Renaissance drama; British drama. Add: Dept. of English, Kentucky Wesleyan College, Owensboro, KY 42301.

DENT, ROBERT WILLIAM, b. Portland, Ore, Sept. 8, 17. ENGLISH. B.A, Univ. Ore, 40, M.A, 42; Ph.D.(Eng), Univ. Chicago, 51. Instr. humanities, col, Univ. Chicago, 47-51; ENG, UNIV. CALIF, LOS ANGELES, 52-54, asst. prof, 54-59, assoc. prof, 60-65, PROF, 66-, ASSOC. DEAN, COL. LETT. & SCI, 70- Bibliographer, Shakespeare Soc. Am, 59-65. U.S.N.R, 42-45, Lt. MLA; Renaissance Soc. Am; Malone Soc. Elizabethan-Jacobean literature, especially drama. Publ: John Webster's borrowing, Univ. Calif, 60. Add: Dept. of English, University of California, Los Angeles, CA 90024.

DePORTE, MICHAEL VITAL, b. Albany, N.Y, Apr. 24, 39; m. 58; c. 2. ENGLISH LITERATURE. B.A, Univ. Minn, 60; M.A, Stanford Univ, 65, Ph.D. (Eng), 66. Instr. Eng. & humanities, Univ. Chicago, 65-66, asst. prof, 66-72; ENG, UNIV. N.H, 72-73, ASSOC. PROF, 73- Inland Steel fac. fel, fall 68; vis. asst. prof. Eng, Stanford, summer 72. MLA. English literature of the Restoration and eighteenth century. Publ: Ed, Henry More's Enthusiasmus triumphatus, 66 & Thomas Tryon's A discourse on madness, 73, Augustan Reprint Soc; auth, Nightmares and hobbyhorses: Swift, Sterne, and Augustan ideas of madness, Huntington Libr, (in press); Digressions and madness in A tale of a tub and Tristram Shandy, Huntington Libr. Quart, 70; Byron's strange perversity of thought, Mod. Lang. Quart, 72. Add: Dept. of English, University of New Hampshire, Durham, NH 03824.

DeROCCO, JOSEPH, b. Secaucus, N.J, July 3, 23; m. 51; c. 2. ENGLISH. Ph.D.(Eng), Columbia Univ, 68. Instr. ENG, Wayne State Univ, 53-57; assoc. prof, BRIDGEWATER STATE COL, 58-70, PROF, 70- U.S.M.C, 43-46, T/Sgt. English romantic poets. Add: Dept. of English, Bridgewater State College, Bridgewater, MA 02324.

DERRICK, CLARENCE, b. New Britain, Conn, Apr. 8, 12; m. 45; c. 2. ENGLISH, HUMANITIES. A.B, Trinity Col.(Conn), 35; Harvard; M.A, West. Reserve Univ; Walgreen fel, Univ. Chicago, 45, 47, Ph.D.(educ), 53. Teacher, Avon Sch, Conn, 35-41; Univ. Sch, Shaker Heights, Ohio, 41-47; asst. dir. dept. exam, Bd. of Educ, Chicago, Ill, 48-49; supvr. humanities sect, test develop, Educ. Testing Serv, Princeton, N.J, 49-53; assoc. prof. ENG. & HUMANITIES, UNIV. FLA, 53-59, PROF, 59-, CHMN. DEPT. HUMANITIES, 62- Evaluation; general education. Publ: Three aspects of reading comprehension as measured by tests of different lengths, 53 & co-auth, Cooperative reading tests, rev. ed, 60, Educ. Testing Serv; auth, What do you expect?, 2/60 & Tests of writing, 10/64, Eng. J; Humanities and/vs English, Col. Eng, 6/63. Add: Dept. of Humanities, 419 W.W. Little Hall, University of Florida, Gainesville, FL 32601.

DERRIG, PATRICK AUSTIN, C.M, b. Dublin, Ireland, July 27, 25; U.S. citizen. ENGLISH & AMERICAN LITERATURE. B.A, Mary Immaculate Sem, 52; M.A, St. John's Univ.(N.Y), 57, Ph.D, 63. Instr. Eng, Niagara Univ, 52-53; St. Joseph's Col.(N.J), 53-56; St. John's Univ.(N.Y), 56-57, asst. prof. Eng. & assoc. dean col. arts & sci, 57-61; dean & acad. v.pres, Niagara Univ, 65-67; ASST. PROF. ENG, ST. JOHN'S UNIV.(N.Y), 67. NCTE; MLA. Add: 8150 Utopia Pkwy, Jamaica, NY 11432.

DERRYBERRY, WILLIAM EVERETT, b. Columbia, Tenn, Oct. 11, 06; m. 33; c. 2. ENGLISH LANGUAGE & LITERATURE. A.B, Univ. Tenn, 28; Rhodes scholar, Oxford, 28-32, B.A. & M.A, 32; hon. D. Litt, Univ. Chattanooga; hon. LL.D, Pepperdine Univ. Head dept. Eng, Burritt Col, 32-33; univ. jr. col, Univ. Tenn, 33-38; dept. lang. & lit, Murray State Col, 38-40; PRES, TENN. TECHNOL. UNIV, 40- Nat. Educ. Asn. Add: Tennessee Technological University, Cookeville, TN 38501.

DERUS, DAVID LEE, b. Kaukauna, Wis, Mar. 10, 31; m. 60. ENGLISH LITERATURE. A.B, Cath. Univ. Am, 52; M.A, Univ. Chicago, 56; Ph.D.(Eng), Yale, 61. Instr. ENG, Univ. Notre Dame, fall 56 & spring 67; asst. prof, Univ. Ill, 60-66; UNIV. SAN FRANCISCO, 66-73, ASSOC. PROF, 73- MLA; AAUP. Literary criticism; Victorian literature; modern British and Commonwealth literature. Publ: Chesterton as literary critic, Renascence, winter 73. Add: Dept. of English, University of San Francisco, San Francisco, CA 94117.

de SCHWEINITZ, GEORGE W, b. Portland, Ore, Dec. 3, 13; m. 41; c. 2. ENGLISH. B.A, Univ. Colo, 35; Oxford, 36-38; M.A, State Univ. Iowa, 44, Ph.D.(Eng. lit), 49. Instr. ENG, State Univ. Iowa, 43-45, 46-49; asst. prof, Univ. Ala, 49-56; assoc. prof, W.Tex. State Univ, 56-59, PROF, 59-66, res. counc. grant, 63; LAMAR UNIV, 66- Writer & co-dir. NDEA Inst, W.Tex. State Univ, 65. S.Cent. Mod. Lang. Asn; Am. Stud. Asn; NCTE. Contemporary American literature; creative writing. Publ: Death of a salesman: a note on epic and tragedy, West. Humanities Rev, winter 60; Huck and Holden, Eng. in Tex, 65; Two poems, Tex. Observer, 68. Add: Dept. of English, Lamar University, Beaumont, TX 77704.

DESMOND, ROBERT WILLIAM, b. Milwaukee, Wis, July 31, 00; m. 27; c. 1; m. 49; c. 2. JOURNALISM. A.B, Univ. Wis, 22; A.M, Univ. Minn, 30; Ph.D, Univ. London, 36. Mem. ed. staff, Milwaukee Jour, 22-25; New York Herald, Paris, 26-27; instr. jour, Univ. Mich, 27-28; instr. & asst. prof, Univ. Minn, 28-32; mem. ed. staff, Christian Sci. Monitor, Boston & London, 33-38; prof. JOUR, Medill Sch. Jour, Northwest. Univ, 38-39; prof, UNIV. CALIF, BERKELEY, 39-68, chmn. dept, 39-54, 62-63, 67, EMER. PROF, 68- Mem. press staff, Williamstown Inst. Polit, 32; acting assoc. prof, Stanford Univ, 38; radio news commentator, KSFO, San Francisco, 41-42; Fulbright lectr, Univ. Amsterdam, 55-56; Univ. Baghdad, 65-66; Univ. Teheran, 68-69; mem. staff, New York Times, Louisville Courier-J, San Francisco Examr. & San Francisco Chronicle; UNESCO Comt. Tech. Needs, Paris, 47; lectr, ctr. advan. stud. jour, Univ. Strasbourg, 58; consult. & writer, Encyclopedia Americana; consult, Int. Press Inst, Zurich, 60-61; sect. ed, Jour. Quart; consult, Hartford Times, 64; fac, San Diego Union, 69-73; columnist, Copley News Serv, 71- U.S.A, 18, 43-45, Maj. Asn. Educ. in Jour; Am. Asn. Schs. & Dept. Jour.(pres, 47). Public opinion. foreign affairs; international news and world press. Publ: Newspaper reference methods; Press and world affairs; Professional training of journalists, UNESCO; co-auth, Contemporary world politics, Wiley, 39, rev. 40; auth, Professional secrecy and the journalist, Int. Press Inst, Zurich, 62; Les tendances de l'enseigement du journalisme aux Etats-Unis, Etudes de Press, 59. Add: 314 Ricardo Pl, La Jolla, CA 92037.

DESSEL, MARY FRANCIS JOSEPH, O.S.F, b. Ossian, Iowa, Dec. 22, 18. SPEECH, DRAMA. B.A, Briar Cliff Col, 48; M.A, Cath. Univ. Am, 52. Teacher, Sacred Heart Sch, Sioux City, Iowa, 37-40; St. John High Sch, Bancroft, 40-47, Eng, 49-51; Immaculate Conception Acad, Dubuque, 48-49; ASSOC. PROF. SPEECH & DRAMA, BRIAR CLIFF COL, 52-, chmn. dept, 52-73. Am. Theatre Asn; Am. Speech & Hearing Asn; Shakespeare Asn. Am; Am. Nat. Theatre & Acad. Dramatic works of Dion Boucicault. Add: Dept. of Speech & Drama, Briar Cliff College, Sioux City, IA 51104.

DESSEN, ALAN CHARLES, b. Baltimore, Md, Nov. 16, 35; m. 63; c. 2. ENGLISH. B.A, Harvard, 57; M.A, Johns Hopkins Univ, 61, Ph.D.(Eng), 63. Instr. ENG, Univ. Wis-Madison, 63-65, asst. prof, 65-68, assoc. prof, 68-69; Northwest. Univ, 69-73; PROF, UNIV. N.C, CHAPEL HILL, 73- U.S.A, 57-58, Res, 57-63. MLA; AAUP. Elizabethan-Jacobean drama and dramatic history; Shakespeare; Ben Jonson. Publ: Jonson's Moral comedy, 71 & co-ed, Renaissance drama, Vol. V, 72, Northwest. Univ; auth, Hamlet's poisoned sword: a study in dramatic imagery, 69 & The intemperate knight and the politic prince: late morality structure in 1 Henry IV, 71, Shakespeare Stud; The morall as an Elizabethan dramatic kind, Comp. Drama, 71; plus others. Add: Dept. of English, University of North Carolina, Chapel Hill, NC 27514.

DESSNER, LAWRENCE JAY, b. New York, N.Y, Mar. 29, 34; m. 61; c. 2. ENGLISH LITERATURE. B.A, Yale, 55; M.A, N.Y. Univ, 67; Ph.D.(Eng), 69. Asst. prof. ENG, UNIV. TOLEDO, 69-74, ASSOC. PROF, 74- MLA; Midwest Mod. Lang. Asn; Popular Cult. Asn. British Victorian literature; popular culture. Publ: Woodstock, a nation at war, J. Popular Cult, 71; Thomas Wolfe's Mr. Katamoto, Mod. Fiction Stud, 72; H.G. Wells, Mr. Polly, and the uses of art, Eng. Lit. in Transition, 73. Add: Dept. of English, University of Toledo, Toledo, OH 43606.

DeSUA, WILLIAM JOSEPH, Italian & Comparative Literature. See Volume III, Foreign Languages, Linguistics & Philology.

DETTERING, RICHARD WHITSON, b. Seattle, Wash, July 19, 14. SEMANTICS, EDUCATION, PHILOSOPHY. A.B, Univ. Calif, 37; M.A, San Francisco State Col, 53; Ed.D.(educ. philos), Stanford Univ, 56. Teaching asst. Eng. & philos, Univ. Calif, 38-40; asst. rural rehabilitation supvr, Farm Security Admin, 41; training off, Veterans Admin, 46-48; exec. dir, Calif. Fed. Civic Unity, 49-52; instr. lang. arts, SAN FRANCISCO STATE UNIV, 53-56, asst. prof, 56-59, assoc. prof. ENG. & EDUC, 59-64, PROF, 64- U.S.A, 42-45. Far West. Philos. Educ. Soc; Int. Soc. Gen. Semantics (asst. ed, Etc, Rev. Gen. Semantics, 56-59, ed, 59-60, assoc. ed, 60-; pres, 61, 63-64). Publ: Linguistic superfluity in science, Philos. Sci, 10/59; The prospect for semiotic unity, 3/64 & The language of moral responsibility, 12/67, Etc, Rev. Gen. Semantics; plus others. Add: School of Humanities & Education, San Francisco State University, 1600 Holloway, San Francisco, CA 94132.

DEUBACH, VILA APRILL, b. Greeley, Colo, Apr. 5, 09. AMERICAN LITERATURE. A.B, Univ. North. Colo, 33, M.A, 35; Ph.D.(Eng), Univ. Colo, Boulder, 49; B.L.S, Univ. Calif, Berkeley, 52. Teacher music, Sargent Consolidated Sch, Colo, 34-35; dean women, ANDERSON COL, 35-45, PROF. ENG, 45-, HEAD LIBRN, 58-, dir. student personnel, 45-58, chmn. dept. Eng, 45-72. Publ: Abstract of The social conscience in the short story of American magazines, 1890-1930, Univ. Colo, Boulder Publ, 49. Add: 705 High St, Anderson, IN 46012.

DEUTSCH, ALFRED HENRY, O.S.B, b. St. Paul, Minn, Jan. 9, 14. ENGLISH. B.A, St. John's Univ, 36; M.A, Univ. Ill, 42, Ph.D.(Eng), 45. PROF. ENG, ST. JOHN'S UNIV. (MINN), 56-, ACAD. DEAN, SCH. DIVINITY, 71-, chmn. dept. Eng, 53-71. MLA; Midwest Mod. Lang. Asn; NCTE. Milton; contemporary drama. Publ: Bruised reeds and other stories, St. John's Univ, 70. Add: Dept. of English, St. John's University, Collegeville, MN 56321.

DEUTSCH, BABETTE (MRS. AVRAHM YARMOLINSKY), b. New York, N.Y, Sept. 22, 95. POETRY. B.A, Barnard Col, 17; hon. Litt.D, Columbia Univ, 46. Lectr. Eng, Columbia Univ, 44-71; RETIRED. Nat. Inst. Arts. & Lett; PEN Club. Publ: Banners, Doran, 19; Honey out of the rock, Appleton, 25; Fire for the night, 30 & Epistle to Prometheus, 30, Cope & Smith; This modern poetry, Norton, 35; One part love, Oxford, 39; ed, Poems from The book of hours, 41; auth, Walt Whitman, builder for America, 41 & The reader's Shakespeare, 46, Messner; Take them stranger, Holt, 44; transl, Pushkin, Eugene Onegin, Penguin, 51; auth, Poetry in our time, Holt, 52, Columbia Univ, 56 & 58, Doubleday, 63; Animal, vegetable, mineral, Dutton, 54; Poetry handbook: a dictionary of terms, Funk 57, rev. ed, 62, 3rd rev ed, 69, 4th, (in press); Coming of age, 59 & 63 & Collected poems, 1919-1962, 63, Ind. Univ; ed, Poems of Samuel Taylor Coleridge, Crowell, 67; auth, The collected poems of Babette Deutsch, Doubleday, 69; plus others. Add: 300 W. 108th St, New York, NY 10025.

DEVEREUX, JAMES ASHTON, S.J, b. Philadelphia, Pa, Mar. 31, 28. ENGLISH. A.B, Woodstock Col.(Md), 51, M.A, 54; licence, Facultés de la Companie de Jésus à Louvain, 59; Ph.D.(Eng), Univ. N.C, 64. Asst. prof. ENG, Univ. Scranton, 64-66; UNIV. N.C, CHAPEL HILL, 66-69, ASSOC. PROF, 69- Consult, Int. Comn. Eng. in Liturgy, 65-68; Folger Shakespeare Libr. fel, summer 69; mem. bd. dirs, Georgetown Univ, 73- MLA; Renaissance Soc. Am. Renaissance literature; early English liturgy. Publ: The primers and the prayer book collects, Huntington Libr. Quart, 68; The collects of the first Book of common prayer as works of translation, Stud. Philol, 69; The object of love in Ficino's Philosophy, J. Hist. Ideas, 69; plus others. Add: Dept. of English, University of North Carolina, Chapel Hill, NC 27514.

DEVIN, PHILIP LEE, b. Glendale, Calif, Apr. 28, 38; m. 58; c. 2. DRAMA. A.B, San Jose State Col, 58; M.A, Ind. Univ, 61, Ph.D.(speech & drama), 67. Lectr. speech & drama, Ind. Univ. Exten, 60-62; instr. & tech. dir, Univ. Va, 62-66; instr. drama, Vassar Col, 66-67, asst. prof, 67-71; ASSOC. PROF. ENG. & DIR. THEATRE, SWARTHMORE COL, 71- Vis. artist, Ball State Univ, 64; guest dir, High Tor Opera Co, fall 67; vis. dir, The Arena, Pa, summers 67, 68; NEA fel-grant, 74. Am. Theatre Asn. Acting; playwriting. Publ: Ballad for a wanton boy, 72 & Elegy for Irish Jack, 73, Earplay; Vox populous, St. Paul Chamber Orchestra, 73. Add: Dept. of English Literature, Swarthmore College, Swarthmore, PA 19081.

DEVINE, MARY ELIZABETH, b. Evanston, Ill, Aug. 12, 38. ENGLISH LITERATURE. A.B. & NDEA fel, Loyola Univ. Chicago, 60, Ph.D.(Eng), 64. Instr. ENG, Mich. State Univ, 63-64, asst. prof, 64-69; ASSOC. PROF, SALEM STATE COL, 69- Res. professorship, Mich. State Univ, 64. AAUP; Am. Soc. Theatre Res. Dramatic literature; 18th-century literature. Publ: Co-ed, Restoration and 18th-century theatre research: a bibliographical guide, 1900-1968, South. Ill. Univ, 71. Add: Dept. of English, Salem State College, Salem, MA 01970.

DEVINE, THOMAS G, b. Somerville, Mass, Jan. 18, 28; m. 56; c. 1. ENGLISH, EDUCATION. A.B, Boston Univ, 50, A.M, 52, Ed.D.(educ), 61. Teacher Pub. Schs, Mass, 50-61; ASSOC. PROF. Eng, R.I. Col, 61-65; EDUC, BOSTON UNIV, 66- Consult. schs, Mass, 64-; consult. to publ, Addison-Wesley, Ginn & Co, Blaisdell & World Publ, 64-; ed. adv, J. Reading, 72-; mem. comt. res, NCTE, 72- NCTE (dir, 62-63); Int. Reading Asn.(pres. Boston Counc, 65). Teaching of English and reading in the secondary schools. Publ: Achievement through reading, 65 & Exploration through reading, 67, Ginn; co-auth, Reading in the secondary schools, Kendall-Hunt, 71; auth, Reading and linguistics, J. Reading, 4/66; Listening, Rev. Educ. Res, 4/67; Reading and listening, Elem. Eng, 4/68. Add: Dept. of English Education, Boston University School of Education, 576 Commonwealth Ave, Boston, MA 02215.

DeVINNEY, RUSSELL N, b. Elizabeth, N.J, Sept. 7, 18; m. 47. ENGLISH, SPEECH. A.B, Muhlenberg Col, 48; M.A, Lehigh Univ, 50; summers, Columbia Univ. Asst. prof. Eng. & speech, PA. STATE UNIV, 55-69, ASSOC. PROF. ENG. & HUMANITIES, 69- Am. Soc. Engineering Educ-Eng-Speaking Union grant, Eng, 68; vis. lect, Further Educ. Staff Col, Coombe Lodge, Bristol, Eng, 70; Bolton Tech. Col. & Bolton Inst. Technol, 70-71. U.S.A.A.F, 41-45, Maj, Res, 45-70, Lt. Col. NCTE. Rhetoric; the humanities; British literature. Publ: The Pennsylvania survey, Col. Eng, 1/60. Add: Box 727, R.R, Coopersburg, PA 18036.

DE VITIS, ANGELO A, b. Akron, Ohio, Nov. 6, 25. ENGLISH. B.A, West. Reserve Univ, 48, M.A, 49; Ph.D.(Eng), Univ. Wis, 54. Assoc. prof. ENG, PURDUE UNIV, 53-70, PROF, 70- U.S.A, 43-46. MLA. Contemporary literature; Victorian studies. Publ: Graham Greene, 64 & Anthony Burgess, 72, Twayne; co-auth, Words in context, Appleton, 61 & 66; auth, For remembrance, Col, Eng, 5/60; Rex Warner and the cult of power, Twentieth Century Lit, 10/60; The Catholic as novelist, In: Graham Greene, Univ. Ky, 63. Add: Dept. of English, Purdue University, Lafayette, IN 47907.

DeVITO, JOSEPH A, b. New York, N.Y, Aug. 1, 38. SPEECH. B.A, Hunter Col, 60; M.A, Temple Univ, 62; Ph.D.(speech), Univ. Ill, 64. Instr. SPEECH, Lehman Col, 64-66, asst. prof, 66-68, assoc. prof, 68-70; PROF, QUEENS COL.(N.Y), 71- Consult. ed, Random House, 73- Speech Commun. Asn; Int. Soc. Gen. Semantics. Psycholinguistics; interpersonal communication; sexology. Publ: The spychology of speech and language: an introduction to psycholinguistics, Random, 70; General semantics: guide and workbook, 71 & General semantics—nine lectures, 71, Everett/Edwards; Communication: concepts and processes, 71 & Language: concepts and processes, 73, Prentice-Hall; Psycholinguistics, Bobbs, 72; plus others. Add: Communication Arts & Sciences, Queens College, Flushing, NY 11367.

DEVLIN, FRANCIS PATRICK, b. Phila, Pa, Mar. 31, 39. ENGLISH. B.S, Mt. St. Mary's Col.(Md), 60; M.A, Niagara Univ, 61; Ph.D.(Eng), Ind. Univ, 68. Instr. ENG, Col. Holy Cross, 65-68, asst. prof, 68-72; DIR. WRITING WORKSHOP, ROGER WILLIAMS COL, 72- MLA. Victorian literature. Publ: Dramatic irony in early sections of Tennyson's In memoriam, Papers Lang. & Lit, 72. Add: 21 Creighton St, Providence, RI 02906.

DEVLIN, VIANNEY MARTIN, O.F.M, b. New Haven, Conn, Dec. 26, 29. ENGLISH. B.A, St. Bonaventure Univ, 54; M.A, Univ. Notre Dame, 59; Ph.D. (Eng), Univ. London, 66. Asst. prof. ENG, SIENA COL.(N.Y), 66-73, ASSOC. PROF, 73-, chmn. dept, 67-71. Shakespeare Asn. Am; Dante Soc. Am; MLA; Cath. Renascence Soc. Medieval drama; Shakespearean theatre. Publ: In memoriam: E.P, Greyfriar, 72. Add: Dept. of English, Siena College, Loudonville, NY 12211.

DEVOL, KENNETH STOWE, b. Los Angeles, Calif, Apr. 3, 29; m. 51; c. 2. JOURNALISM, MASS COMMUNICATION. A.B, Univ. South. Calif, 51, M.S, 54, Ph.D.(higher educ), 65. Publicity asst, Hollywood Bowl, 46-50; instr. JOUR, Los Angeles Valley Col, 55-61; asst. prof, Calif. State Univ. Northridge, 61-65, assoc. prof, 65-69; PROF. & CHMN. DEPT, 69- Reporter-editor, Valley Times, Hollywood, 57-60; researcher-writers, Andrews-Yagemann Prod, 65; Nat. Endowment Humanities grant jour. law & ethics, Stanford Univ, summer 69; judge, News & Doc. Competition, Nat. Acad. TV Arts & Sci, 70-73; vis. prof, Calif. State Univ, Fullerton, summer 73. Asn. Educ. Jour; Am. Asn. Schs. & Dept. Jour; AAUP; Am. Civil Liberties Union. Freedom of the press; mass media and society; student publications. Publ: Ed, Mass media and the supreme court; the legacy of the Warren years, Hastings, 71; co-auth, Writing style for journalists, Brewster, 62; plus others. Add: Dept. of Journalism, California State University, Northridge, Northridge, CA 91324.

DEW, ARTEOLA BILBREY, b. Altus, Okla, Aug. 17, 08; m. SPEECH, HUMANITIES. B.F.A, Univ. Okla, 29, M.F.A, 44; Columbia Univ; Univs. Colo; N.Mex. Mem. staff, pub. schs, N.Mex, 39-46; head dept. speech & drama, CENT. STATE COL.(OKLA), 46-54, asst. prof. speech & humanities, 54-72, ASSOC. PROF. HUMANITIES, 72- Mem. fac, Santa Fe Secretarial Col, 39-40; speaker, Int. Conf. Gen. Semantics; Mex. City, Mex, 58, Honolulu, Hawaii, 60. Nat. Soc. Stud. Commun; Int. Soc. Gen. Semantics; Renaissance Soc. Am; Metaphys. Soc. Am. General semantics; psychology; philosophy. Add: Dept. of Language Arts & Humanities, Central State College, Edmond, OK 73034.

DEW, DONALD, b. Baltimore, Md, Mar. 26, 28; m. 68; c. 4. SPEECH COMMUNICATION. B.A, Univ. Md, 50; M.A, Univ. Iowa, 56, Ph.D.(speech path), 58. Speech therapist, Wicomico County Pub. Sch, Md, 50-53; Baltimore County Pub. Sch, 53-54; asst. prof. SPEECH, Univ. Md, 58-61; Univ. Ala, 61-63; Univ. Fla, 63-69; vis. assoc. prof, Univ. Wash, 69-70; ASSOC. PROF, UNIV. FLA, 70- Assoc. ed, Speech Monogr, 66-68; Quart. J. Speech, 68-71. U.S.N, 45-46. Acoust. Soc. Am; AAAS; fel. Am. Speech & Hearing Asn; Int. Soc. Phonetic Sci; Speech Commun. Asn. Phonetics; speech acoustics; speech physiology. Publ: Audio-tutorial program in phonetic transcription, C.E. Merrill, 74; co-auth, Phonational frequency ranges of adults, J. Speech & Hearing Res, 71 & Wing movements of calling katydids: fiddling finesse, Science, 72; auth, The phonetic transcription proficiency test: description and preliminary evaluation, Speech Monogr, 73; plus others. Add: Dept. of Speech, Communication Sciences, ASB 68, University of Florida, Gainesville, FL 32611.

DEWEES, CHARLES WILLIAM, JR, b. Philadelphia, Pa, July 17, 33. ENGLISH LITERATURE. B.A, Univ. Pa, 55, A.M, 57, Ph.D.(Eng), 73. PROF. ENG, PHILA. COL. TEXTILES & SCI, 58- Instr. Eng, Spring Garden Inst, summers 59, 60; mem, Walt Whitman Birthplace Asn. Mil.Intel, U.S.A, 52-63. Am. Soc. 18th Century Stud; MLA; NCTE; AAUP. Eighteenth century; British fiction. Add: Dept. of Humanities, Philadelphia College of Textiles & Science, School House Lane & Henry Ave, Philadelphia, PA 19144.

DEWEY, THOMAS BLANCHARD, b. Elkhart, Ind, Mar. 6, 15. ENGLISH LITERATURE. B.S, Kans. State Teachers Col, 36; M.A, Univ. Calif, Los Angeles, 66, Ph.D.(Eng), 73. Instr, Univ. Calif, Los Angeles, 69-70, commun, 70-71; ASST. PROF. ENG, ARIZ. STATE UNIV; 71- Mediaeval Acad. Am. Medieval English literature; Middle Scots literature; medieval stylistics. Publ: Some careless seventeenth century rhymes, Bull. N.Y. Pub. Libr, 3/65; plus numerous novels. Add: Dept. of English, Arizona State University, Tempe, AZ 85281.

DEWSNAP, TERENCE F, b. Revere, Mass, Sept. 24, 33; m. 57; c. 4. ENGLISH. B.A, Boston Col, 55, M.A, 57; Ph.D, Univ. Wis, 61. Asst, Boston Col, 55-56; Univ. Wis, 56-60; from instr. to asst. prof. ENG, LeMoyne Col. (N.Y), 60-63; from asst. prof. to PROF, BARD COL, 63-, CHMN. DIV. LANG. & LIT, 72- MLA. T. Sturge Moore; contemporary; Victorian. Add: Div. of Languages & Literature, Bard College, Annandale-on-Hudson, NY 12504.

DEXTER, ERWIN BROWNELL, b. South Wareham, Mass, June 5, 20; m. 59; c. 1. ENGLISH LANGUAGE, LITERATURE. A.B, Boston Univ, 45, M.Ed, 51, Ed.D, 61; New Sch. Social Res, 73-74. Housemaster & dir. guid, Wayside Inn Sch. for Boys, Mass, 42-43; teacher Eng. & social stud, Dallas Tex. Country Day Sch, 45-46; head dept. lang, Aroostock Cent. Inst, Maine, 46-47; head speech & drama, Chapman Tech. High Sch, Conn, 47-48; teacher Eng. & speech, Dartmouth High Sch, Mass, 48-53; speech therapist, New Bedford Pub. Schs, 53-55; chmn. hist. & Eng, Tantasqua Regional High Sch, 55-57; speech therapist, Hempstead Pub. Schs, N.Y, 57-62; PROF. ENG, JERSEY CITY STATE COL, 62- Grants, West. Reserve Univ, 63 & Columbia Univ, 65; educ. consult, St. Paul's Roman Cath. Sch, N.J, 71-72. NEA; Am. Speech & Hearing Asn; Int. Reading Asn; Counc. Exceptional Children; NCTE. Speech pathology; literature; linguistics. Publ: Co-auth, Guidelines for better speech in the schools, Kendall-Hunt, 65. Add: 376 Fairmount Ave, Jersey City, NJ 07306.

DE YOUNG, JAMES LEE, b. Milwaukee, Wis, Feb. 13, 38; m. 59; c. 2. THEATRE ARTS. B.A, Beloit Col, 59; M.A, Bowling Green State Univ, 60; Ph.D, Univ. Minn, 74. Tech. dir. & instr. speech, Hope Col, 60-63; instr. speech, MONMOUTH COL.(ILL), 63-73, ASST. PROF. SPEECH & DRAMA, 73-, dir. theatre, 63-73. Dir. Arts of London Prog, Assoc. Cols. Midwest, 72-73. Am. Theatre Asn. Dramatic literature; dramatic theory and criticism; directing. Publ: A directory of plays published in Theatre Arts, Asn. Educ. Theatre Asn, 67; Sound in the theatre & The Guthrie Theatre: an interview, Players Mag, 68. Add: Dept. of Speech Communication Arts, Monmouth College, Monmouth, IL 61462.

D'HARNONCOURT, EVERARD, b. Velke Losiny, Czech, June 20, 20; U.S. citizen. DRAMATIC ART. Dipl, Univ. Fribourg, Switz, 48; Ph.D.(dramatic art), Univ. Vienna, Austria, 51; scholar, Univ. Calif, Los Angeles, 52-53, Lectr. dramatic art, Univ. Vienna, Austria, 49-51; Dramaturg, profess. theatre, United States Graz, Austria, 53-57; from asst. prof. to PROF. DRAMATIC ART, UNIV. CALIF, DAVIS, 62- Am. Theatre Asn; Speech Commun. Asn. Seventeenth century French theatre history; motion picture aesthetics. Add: Dept. of Dramatic Art, University of California, Davis, CA 95616.

DHESI, NIRMAL SINGH, b. Lyallpur, Pakistan, Nov. 24, 29; U.S. citizen; m. 65; c. 3. ENGLISH LITERATURE. B.A, Panjab Univ, 50, M.A, 54; Ph.D.(Eng), Mich. State Univ, 68. Lectr. ENG, Sikh Nat. Col, India, 54; Govt. Col, Narnaul, 54-56; Govt. Col, Maler Korla, 56-59; instr, West. Wash. State Col, 62-64; asst. prof, CALIF. STATE COL, SONOMA, 64-68, assoc. prof, 68-73, PROF, 73- Eng. Asn. Gt. Brit; Renaissance Soc. Am; AAUP. Add: Dept. of English, California State College, Sonoma, 1801 E. Corati Ave, Rohnart Park, CA 94928.

DIAL, ROBERT, b. Marshall, Mo, Sept. 17, 29; m. 51; c. 2. ENGLISH LANGUAGE & LITERATURE. B.S, Cent. Mo. State Col, 51; M.A, Univ. Kans. City, 56, Ph.D, 63. Teacher ENG. & chmn. dept, Ctr. High Sch, Kans. City, Mo, 51-56; asst. prof. & chmn. dept, Nat. Col, 59-62; asst. prof, Cent. Mo. State Col, 62-64, assoc. prof, 64-65; asst. prof, UNIV. AKRON, 66-70, ASSOC. PROF, 70- Late 19th century literature; English and American comparative literature. Add: Dept. of English, University of Akron, Akron, OH 44304.

DIAMOND, ARLYN, b. San Francisco, Calif, Jan. 15, 41. MEDIEVAL LITERATURE. B.A, Univ. Calif, Berkeley, 61, Ph.D.(Eng), 70; M.A, Columbia Univ, 62. Teaching asst. ENG, Univ. Calif, Berkeley, 63-66; ASST. PROF, UNIV. MASS, AMHERST, 68- Lectr, Miles Col, summer 65; Stillman Col, summer 66. Mediaeval Acad. Am; MLA. Alliterative poetry; Medieval romance; women writers. Publ: Co-ed, American voices, American women, Avon, 73; auth, Germaine Greer and Elizabeth Janeway, Mass. Rev, 72. Add: Dept. of English, University of Massachusetts, Amherst, MA 01002.

DIAMOND, ROBERT E. ENGLISH. B.A, State Univ. Iowa, 41, M.A, 48; Ph.D, Harvard, 54. Instr. ENG, Univ. Wis, 53-56; asst. prof, Wayne State Univ, 56-63, ASSOC. PROF, 63-68; UNIV. NEV, RENO, 68- U.S.N.R, 42-46, Lt. MLA; Mediaeval Acad. Am. Middle and old English; Chaucer; philology and linguistics. Publ: Diction of the Anglo-Saxon metrical psalms, Mouton, 63; Old English grammar and reader, Wayne State Univ, 70; Diction of signed poems of Cynewulf, Philol. Quart, 59; Theme as ornament in Anglo-Saxon poetry, PMLA, 61. Add: Dept. of English, University of Nevada, Reno, NV 89507.

DIAS, EARL JOSEPH, b. New Bedford, Mass, Mar. 23, 16; m. 51. ENGLISH, DRAMA. A.B, Bates Col, 37; M.A, Boston Univ, 38; summers, Shakespeare Inst, Stratford, Eng, 57, 60 & Univ. London, 60. Teacher, Fairhaven High Sch, Mass, 39-57; asst. prof. ENG, New Bedford Inst. Technol, 57-60; assoc. prof, SOUTHEAST. MASS. UNIV, 60-64, PROF, 64-, CHMN. DEPT, 72- Drama & music critic, New Bedford Standard-Times, 48-; ed. consult, D.C. Heath & Co, 58-59 & Wadsworth Publ. Co, 65-66; Wilkes Fund lectrs, New Bedford Pub. Libr, 60-61. Col. Eng. Asn; NCTE; Shakespeare Asn. Am. Shakespeare; modern drama; nineteenth and twentieth century American literature. Publ: Melodramas and farces for young actors, 56, One-act plays for teen-agers, 61 & New comedies for teen-agers, 67, Plays; Mark Twain's letters to the Rogers family, 71 & Henry Huttleston Rogers: portrait of a capitalist, 74, Millicent Libr; Daniel Ricketson and Henry Thoreau, New Eng. Quart, fall 53; Full-scale Albee, Drama Critique, fall 65; E.E. Cummings and Buffalo Bill, CEA Critic, 12/66. Add: 52 Walnut St, Fairhaven, MA 02719.

DIBBLE, JERRY ALLEN, b. Washington, D.C, Mar. 31, 42; m. 65; c. 1. ENGLISH & COMPARATIVE LITERATURE. B.S, Purdue Univ, Lafayette, 63; M.A, Stanford Univ, 66, Ph.D.(Eng, comp. lit), 71; Ger. Acad. Exchange Serv. fel, 67-68. Instr. ENG, STATE UNIV. N.Y. STONY BROOK, 68-71, ASST. PROF, 71- Consult, Nat. Endowment for Humanities, 73-; mem. rev. bd, Romantic Movement: A Selective & Critical Bibliog, 73- MLA. Nineteenth century non-fiction prose; Anglo-German literary relations; novel. Publ: Carlyle's British reader and the structure of Sartor Resartus, Tex. Stud. Lang. & Lit, (in press); Thomas Carlyle and the rhetoric of idealism, Bull. N.Y. Pub. Libr, (in press); Review of The English historical novel by Avrom Fleishman, Novel: a forum on fiction, spring 74. Add: Dept. of English, State University of New York at Stony Brook, Stony Brook, NY 11790.

DI BONA, HELENE, b. New York, N.Y; c. 2. ENGLISH LITERATURE. B.A, Univ. Wis-Madison, 52; M.A, Univ. Calif, Berkeley, 55, Ph.D.(Eng), 70. Assoc. subject A, Univ. Calif, Berkeley, 52-61; supvr, 61-64, instr. comp. lit, 62-64; ENG, Boston Univ, 64-65; asst. prof, N.C. CENT. UNIV, 68-70, ASSOC. PROF, 70- Harvard summer grant, 69. Modern British and American fiction; comparative literature; teacher training. Add: Dept. of English, North Carolina Central University, Durham, NC 27707.

DiCESARE, MARIO ANTHONY, b. New York, N.Y, Aug. 21, 28; m. 69; c. 6. ENGLISH & COMPARATIVE LITERATURE. B.A, St. Mary's Sem.(Ill), 52; M.A, Columbia Univ, 54, Samuel S. Fels fel, 58-59, Ph.D.(Eng. & Comp. Lit), 60. Assoc. ENG, Ind. Univ, 53-54; instr, Duquesne Univ, 54-55; Pratt Inst, 55-59; HARPUR COL, STATE UNIV. N.Y. BINGHAMTON, 59-61, asst. prof, 61-64, assoc. prof, 64-68, chmn. dept, 68-73, PROF, 68-, res. found. fels, summers 62, 63, 65 & 66, master, Newing Col, 67-68. Lectr, Rutgers Univ, 57-58 & summer 61; Brooklyn Col, summers 59-61; Guggenheim Mem. fel, 63-64; vis. assoc. prof, N.Y. Univ, summers 65, 67; vis. prof, Univ. Pittsburgh, summer 69. MLA; Renaissance Soc. Am; Am. Comp. Lit. Asn; Am. Philol. Asn. The epic tradition, Greek, Roman, European and English; the Renaissance, English and Italian; modern English literature. Publ: Vida's Christiad and Vergilian epic, 64 & The alter and the city: a reading of Vergil's Aeneid, 74, Columbia Univ; co-auth, transl, Juan Ruiz, The book of good love, State Univ. N.Y, 70; auth, Bibliotheca vidiana, Sansoni, Florence, 73; Advent'rous song: the texture of Milton's epic, In: Language and style in Milton, Ungar, 67; Paradise lost and epic tradition, Milton Stud. I, 69. Add: Dept. of English, Harpur College, State University of New York at Binghamton, Binghamton, NY 13901.

DICHMANN, MARY ETHEL, b. New Orleans, La, Nov. 22, 13. ENGLISH LITERATURE, A.B, Tulane Univ, 35, Ph.D, 53; A.M, Univ. N.C, 38. Teacher ENG, high sch, Canton, Miss, 35-37; instr, UNIV. SOUTHWEST. LA, 38-42, asst. prof, 42-46, assoc. prof, 46-54, PROF, 54-, HEAD DEPT, 56- Enochs fel, Am. Asn. Univ. Women, 52-53, mem. int. fel. awards comt, 64-70; Guggenheim fel, 54-55; mem. comn. cols, South. Asn, Cols. & Schs, 68-74; Fulbright selection comt, Inst. Int. Educ, 72- U.S.N.R, 43-46, Lt. MLA. Nineteenth century English literature; Wordsworth's relationship with Matthew Arnold and T.S. Eliot. Add: Dept. of English, Box 21, University of Southwestern Louisiana, Lafayette, LA 70501.

DICK, BERNARD FRANCIS, b. Scranton, Pa, Nov. 25, 35. CLASSICAL PHILOLOGY. B.A, Univ. Scranton, 57; M.A, Fordham Univ, 60, Ph.D.(classics), 62. Asst, Fordham Univ, 57-60; instr. classics, Iona Col, 60-64, asst. prof, 64-67, assoc. prof. & chmn. dept, 67-70; assoc. prof. ENG, FAIRLEIGH DICKINSON UNIV, TEANECK, 70-73, PROF. & CHMN. DEPT, 73- Lectr. Latin, St. Peter's Col.(N.J), 60; Col. New Rochelle, 62-63; class. lit, Hunter Col, summer 63; columnist, Class. World, 61-68; adj. asst. prof, Manhattan Col, 65-67. Am. Philol. Asn; Class. Asn. Atlantic States; MLA; Am. Comp. Lit. Asn. Myth; literary and film criticism; comparative literature, especially Renaissance and modern. Publ: William Golding, Twayne, 67; The Hellenism of Mary Renault, South. Ill. Univ, 72; The apostate angel: a critical study of Gore Vidal, Random, 74; The technique of prophecy in Lucan, Trans. Am. Philol. Asn, 63; Ancient pastoral and the pathetic fallacy, Comp. Lit, winter 68; Myth and popular culture, Colo. Quart, summer 72; plus others. Add: 989 Wilson Ave, Teaneck, NJ 07666.

DICK, DONALD, b. Lincoln, Nebr, June 21, 32; m. 55; c. 3. SPEECH. B.A, Union Col.(Nebr), 55; M.A, Univ. Nebr, 57; Ph.D.(speech), Mich. State Univ, 65. Instr. speech, La Sierra Col, 57-61, asst. prof, 61-65, assoc. prof, 65-67; Loma Linda Univ, 67-68; PROF. SPEECH & HEAD DEPT. COMMUN, SOUTH. MISSIONARY COL, 68- Pres, Adventist Radio Network, 65-; secy-treas. adv. bd, Faith for Today. Speech Commun. Asn; Broadcast Educ. Asn. Broadcasting audience research; religious radio broadcasting. Add: Box 556, Collegedale, TN 37315.

DICK, ROBERT CHRISTOPHER, b. Hutchinson, Kans, May 25, 38; m. 57; c. 3. SPEECH COMMUNICATION. B.S.Ed, Kans. State Teachers Col, 60; M.A, Univ. N.Mex, 61; Ph.D.(rhetoric & pub. address), Stanford Univ, 69. Instr. SPEECH, Tex. Technol. Col, 61-62; Stanford Univ, 62-65; asst. prof, Univ. N.Mex, 65-66; lectr, San Francisco State Col, 66-67; asst. prof, UNIV. N.MEX, 67-71, ASSOC. PROF, 71- N.Mex. dir, Nat. Univ. Exten. Asn, 67-69; N.Mex. coord, ERIC Clearinghouse Reading & Commun. Skills, 72; consult. ed, West. Speech: J. West. Speech Commun. Asn, 73- Am. For. Asn; Speech Commun. Asn. Argumentation; black rhetoric; criticism of rhetorical movements and campaigns. Publ: Argumentation and rational debating, Brown, 72; Black protest: issues and tactics, Greenwood, (in press); Topoi: an approach to inventing arguments, Speech Teacher, 11/64; Rhetoric of ante-bellum black separatism, Negro Hist. Bull, 10/71; Negro oratory in the anti-slavery societies: 1830-1860, In: Language communication and rhetoric in black America, Harper & Row, 72. Add: Dept. of Speech Communication, University of New Mexico, 1801 Roma N.E, Albuquerque, NM 87131.

DICKASON, DAVID HOWARD, b. Wooster, Ohio, Aug. 21, 07. AMERICAN LITERATURE. A.B, Col. Wooster, 29; A.M, Univ. Calif, 31; Ph.D, Ohio State Univ, 40. Instr. Eng, Col. Americano, Barranquilla, Colombia, 29-30; Prince Royal's Col, Siam, 31-35; Rangoon, 35-36; from instr. to PROF. ENG, IND. UNIV, BLOOMINGTON, 39- Res. analyst & liaison off, Off. Strategic Serv, Wash, D.C, 44-46; Guggenheim fel, 54-55; adv, Thai Ministry Educ, Bangkok, 56-58; lectr, Univ. San Marcos, Peru, 61; Fulbright sr. res. fel, U.K, 63-64. Pre-Raphaelite movements in America; English for foreign students; early American fiction. Publ: Daring young men: the story of the American pre-Raphaelites, Ind. Univ, 53, N.Y, 70; Introduction to literature in English, Bangkok, 58; ed, Mr. Penrose: journal of Penrose Seaman, Ind. Univ. & London, 69; William Williams, novelist and painter of Colonial America, Ind. Univ, 70. Add: Dept. of English, Indiana University, Bloomington, IN 47401.

DICKENS, MILTON (CLIFFORD), b. St. Louis, Mo, July 25, 08. SPEECH. A.B, Univ. South. Calif, 30; A.M, Syracuse Univ, 31, Ph.D, 39. From fel. to asst. prof. & dir. debate activities, Syracuse Univ, 29-43; statist. analyst, Douglas Aircraft Co, Inc, 43-45; from assoc. prof. to PROF. SPEECH, HEAD DEPT. & CHMN. DIV. COMMUN, UNIV. SOUTH, CALIF, 46- Speech Commun. Asn; West. Speech Commun. Asn.(v.pres, 50, pres, 56). Group discussion; psychology in relation to social and political problems; measurements of stage fright. Publ: Co-auth, Guidebook for speech practice, 61 & auth, Speech: dynamic communication, 2nd ed, 63, Harcourt. Add: Dept. of Speech, University of Southern California, Los Angeles, CA 90007.

DICKERSON, DAVID, b. Oklahoma City, Okla, Apr. 26, 33; m. 53; c. 3. ENGLISH. A.B, Greenville Col, 55; M.A, Univ. South. Calif, 58, Ph.D.(Eng), 64. Instr. ENG, Los Angeles Pac. High Sch. & Col, 55-59; asst, Univ. South. Calif, 59-61; assoc. prof, Los Angeles Pac. Col, 62-63; GREENVILLE COL, 63-68, PROF, 68-, CHMN. DEPT, 65-, ASST. TO V.PRES. ACAD. AFFAIRS, 73- MLA; Conf. Col. Compos. & Commun; Conf. Christianity & Lit. (treas, 68-). Add: Dept. of English, Greenville College, Greenville, IL 62246.

DICKEY, FRANKLIN MILLER, b. Milwaukee, Wis, Apr. 19, 21; m. 47; c. 1. ENGLISH. B.A, Univ. Wis, 42; fel, Univ. Calif, Los Angeles, 48-50, Ph.D. (Eng), 54. Instr. ENG, Univ. Mich, 50-55; asst. prof, Univ. Ore, 56-61; from assoc. prof. to PROF, UNIV. N.MEX, 61-, chmn. dept, 61-65. Folger fel, summers 57, 59; Guggenheim fel, 57-58; summer grants, Huntington Libr, 60 & Newberry Libr, 63. U.S.A, 42-43. MLA; Malone Soc; Bibliog. Soc, London. English Renaissance; contemporary drama and film. Publ: Not wisely but too well, Huntington Libr, 57; co-ed, Amyntas and the lamentations, Newberry Libr, 67; The old man at work: forgeries in the stationers' registers, Shakespeare Quart, 60; plus others. Add: Dept. of English, University of New Mexico, Albuquerque, NM 87131.

DICKEY, IMOGENE BENTLEY, b. Nashville, Tenn, Sept. 30, 08; m. 60. ENGLISH. M.A, George Peabody Col, 32, Ph.D.(Eng), 41. Teacher pub. sch, Tex, 27-30, high sch, 30-34; teacher, Eng. & Spanish, Paris Jr. Col, 34-42, teacher Eng. & dean col, 42-44; PROF. ENG, N.TEX. STATE UNIV, 44-, dean women, 44-68. Teaching fel, George Peabody Col, 39-40. Nat. Asn. Women Deans & Counsel. Publ: Texas literary and educational magazines; Are you teaching a classic; The unassigned duties of a dean of women. Add: Dept. of English, North Texas State University, Denton, TX 76203.

DICKEY, JAMES, b. Atlanta, Ga, Feb. 2, 23; c. 2. ENGLISH. B.A, Vanderbilt Univ, 49, M.A, 50. Instr. Eng. & creative writing, Rice Univ, 50, 52-54; Univ. Fla, 55-56; copywriter to creative dir. var. advert. agencies, N.Y. & Atlanta, Ga, 56-62; writer-in-residence, Reed Col, 63-64; San Fernando Valley State Col, 64-66; Univ. Wis-Madison, 66; consult. poetry, Libr. Congr, Wash, D.C, 66-68; writer-in-residence, Wash. Univ, 68; Franklin distinguished prof. Eng, Ga. Inst. Technol, 68; POET-IN-RESIDENCE & PROF. ENG, UNIV. S.C, 69- Guggenheim fel, 62-63; Nat. Inst. Arts & Lett. grant, 67. Nat. Bk. Award for poetry, 66. U.S.A.F, W.W. II & Korea. Am. Acad. Arts & Sci; Nat. Inst. Arts & Lett. Publ: Into the stone, Scribner, 60; Drowning with others, 62, Helmets, 64, Buckdancer's choice, 65 & Poems 1957-1967, 67, Wesleyan Univ; Babel to Byzantium, Farrar, Straus, 68; The eyebeaters, 70, Self-interviews, 70 & Sorties, 71, Doubleday; Deliverance (novel), Houghton, 70; Screenplay for Deliverance, Warner Bros, 71. Add: 4620 Lelia's Court, Columbia, SC 29206.

DICKEY, WILLIAM, b. Bellingham, Wash, Dec. 15, 28; m. 59. ENGLISH. B.A, Reed Col, 51; Woodrow Wilson fel, 51-52; M.A, Harvard, 55; M.F.A, State Univ. Iowa, 56; Fulbright scholar, Oxford, 59-60. Instr. Eng, Cornell Univ, 56-59; asst. prof, Denison Univ, 60-62; SAN FRANCISCO STATE UNIV, 62-65, assoc. prof, 65-69, PROF, ENG. & CREATIVE WRITING, 69- Vis. prof. Eng, Univ. Hawaii, spring 73. Union League Found. prize, Poetry Mag, 62. MLA. English and American poetry; 18th century English literature. Publ: Of the festivity, Yale Univ, 59; Interpreter's house, Ohio State Univ, 64; Rivers of the Pacific Northwest, Two windows, 69; More under Saturn, Wesleyan Univ, 71. Add: Dept. of English, San Francisco State University, San Francisco, CA 94132.

DICKINSON, HUGH, b. Ridgway, Pa, July 9, 15; m. 42; c. 1. SPEECH, DRAMA, THEATRE. A.B, Pa. State Univ, 37; M.F.A, Yale, 49; Ph.D, Northwest. Univ, 61. Instr. speech, Lehigh Univ, 49-50; speech, drama & theatre, Loyola Univ.(Ill), 50-53, asst. prof, 53-58, assoc. prof, 58-65; assoc. prof. SPEECH & THEATRE, UNIV. ILL, CHICAGO CIRCLE, 65-70, PROF, 70- Lectr. theatre hist. & dramatic lit, Goodman Theatre & Sch. Drama, Chicago, Ill, 59-65; assoc. ed, Drama Critique, 59-63, ed, 63-64; drama critic, The New World, 62- U.S.A, 42-45, M/Sgt. Dramatic literature and dramaturgy; history of theatre; oral interpretation of literature. Publ: Myth on the modern stage, Univ. Ill, 69; Time and interpretation, Cent. States Speech J, autumn 58; Readers or rhapsodes?, Quart J. Speech, fall 59; The reformation of Prince Hal, Shakespeare Quart, winter 61. Add: 2812 Payne St, Evanston, IL 60201.

DICKINSON, LEON TOWNSEND, b. Chicago, Ill, Jan. 24, 12; m. 70; c. 3. ENGLISH. A.B, Williams Col, 33; A.M, Univ. Chicago, 34, Ph.D, 45. Instr, Whitman Col, 34-35; Morgan Park Jr. Col, 37-40; North Park Col, 40-41; Chicago City Jr. Col, 41-43; Univ. Chicago, 43-46; asst. prof. ENG, UNIV. MO-COLUMBIA, 46-50, assoc. prof, 50-60, PROF, 60- Fulbright lectr, Netherlands, 52-53, Belgium, 63-64, France, 71-72. MLA; Am. Stud. Asn. American literature; Mark Twain. Publ: A guide to literary study, Holt, & co-auth, English literature: a college anthology, Macmillan, 60. Add: Dept. of English, University of Missouri-Columbia, Columbia, MO 65201.

DICKINSON, LOREN, b. Bemidji, Minn, Sept. 1, 32; m. 57; c. 2. SPEECH. B.A, Union Col, 57; M.A, Univ. Nebr, 60; Ph.D.(speech), Univ. Denver, 68. Instr. speech & dir. pub. relat, Columbia Union Col, 58-62; PROF. SPEECH, WALLA WALLA COL, 62- Med.C, U.S.A, 53-55. Speech Commun. Asn. Add: Dept. of Speech, Walla Walla College, College Place, WA 99324.

DICKISON, ROLAND BISHOP, b. Colorado Springs, Colo, Apr. 10, 21; m. 52; c. 6. AMERICAN FOLKLORE, ENGLISH LITERATURE. B.A, Colorado Col, 43; B.S, U.S. Merchant Marine Acad, 45; M.A, Univ. Fla, 48, Ph.D. (Eng), 50. Prof. Eng, Brenau Col, Gainesville, Ga, 50-53; Florence State Univ, 53-58; prof. & dean, Ark. Col, 58-61; Fulbright lectr, Univ. Damascus, 61-62; dir. acad. planning, Sacramento State Univ, 62-66; prof. Eng. & dean, Col. Virgin Islands, 66-68; PROF. ENG, CALIF. STATE UNIV, SACRAMENTO, 68- South. Fel. Fund. award educ. TV, summer 55; partic, Pakistan Study Comn, Calif. State Cols, 65-66; assoc. ed, West. Folklore, 73- U.S. Merchant Marine, 43-46. Am. Name Soc; Am. Folklore Soc. Onomastics; Chaucer. Publ: Superstitions and commonsense refutations in 15th century England, South. Folklore Quart, 6/60. Add: Dept. of English, California State University, Sacramento, 6000 J St, Sacramento, CA 95819.

DICKSON, DAVID WATSON DALY, b. Portland, Maine, Feb. 16, 19; m. 51; c. 3. ENGLISH LITERARY HISTORY. A.B, Bowdoin Col, 41; Shattuck fel. & A.M, Harvard, 42, Rosenwald fel. & Ph.D, 49. Instr. Eng, Mich. State Univ, 48-49, asst. prof, 49-58, assoc. prof, 58-63; prof. & chmn. dept, North. Mich. Univ, 63-66, dean arts & sci, 66-67, v.pres. acad. affairs, 67-68; provost & v.pres. acad. affairs, Federal City Col, 68-69; prof. Eng, State Univ. N.Y. Stony Brook, 69-73, asst. to pres, 69-72, dean continuing educ, 72-73; PRES, MONTCLAIR STATE COL, 73- Rosenwald fel, 42-43; Ford Found. fac. fel, 55-56; Smith-Mundt fel, Damascus Univ, 58-59; mem. comt. policies & purposes, Am. Asn. State Cols. & Univs, 72; mem. policy bd, Asn. Am. Cols, 73. Mich. State Univ. Distinguished Teacher Award, 52. U.S.A, 43-46, 1st Lt. MLA; Milton Soc. Am. Milton; early 17th century prose and poetry; Biblical literature. Publ: Education for the world we want, Sci. Teacher, 5/70. Add: Montclair State College, Upper Montclair, NJ 07043.

DICKSTEIN, MORRIS, b. New York, N.Y, Feb. 23, 40; m. 65; c. 2. ENGLISH & COMPARATIVE LITERATURE. A.B, Columbia Univ, 61; Woodrow Wilson fel. & M.A, Yale, 63; Danforth fel. & Ph.D.(Eng), 67; Cambridge, 63-64. Instr. Eng. & comp. lit, Columbia Univ, 66-67, asst. prof, 67-71; ASSOC. PROF. ENG, QUEENS COL.(N.Y), 71- Soc. Relig. Higher Educ. fel, 69-70; Chamberlain fel, Columbia Univ, 69-70; Guggenheim fel, 73-74. MLA; Soc. Relig. Higher Educ. English and European romanticism; modern literature and criticism; Victorian social thought. Publ: Keats and his poetry: a study in development, Univ. Chicago, 71; Allen Ginsberg and the 60's, Commentary, 1/70; The black aesthetic in white America, Partisan Rev, winter 71-72; Coleridge, Wordsworth, and the conversation poems, Centennial Rev, fall 72. Add: Dept. of English, Queens College, Flushing, NY 11367.

DIEDERICH, PAUL BERNARD, b. Muskogee, Okla, Sept. 29,06; m. 37; c. 2 ENGLISH. A.B, Harvard, 28, Ed.M, 30; Ph.D, Columbia Univ, 39. Teacher Latin, Ohio State Univ. Sch, 32-35; researcher Eng. & art, Progressive Educ. Asn, 35-41; exam. in Eng, Univ. Chicago, 41-49; SR. RES. ASSOC, EDUC. TESTING SERV, 49- NCTE; Conf. Res. Eng; Nat. Counc. Measurement Educ. Use of lay readers to assist English teachers; factors in judgments of writing ability; programmed instruction in English. Publ: Co-auth, Critical thinking in reading and writing, Holt, 55; auth, Factors in judgments of writing ability, Educ. Testing Serv, 61; co-auth, Vocabulary for college books A, B, C, D, Harcourt, 67. Add: Educational Testing Service, Princeton, NJ 08540.

DIEDRICH, DUANE NORMAN, b. Anderson, Ind, Jan. 3, 35. PUBLIC ADDRESS, RHETORIC. A.B, Univ. Mich, 56, M.A, 57, fel, 57-59, Ph.D, 61. Instr. speech, Univ. Mich, 59-61; from asst. prof. Eng. to ASSOC. PROF. SPEECH & ASST. TO DEAN COL. SCI. & HUMANITIES, BALL STATE UNIV, 61- AHA; Am. Polit. Sci. Asn; Orgn. Am. Hist; Newcomen Soc; Nat. Counc. Soc. Stud; Speech Commun. Asn; Am. Mgt. Asn; Manuscript Soc; Am. Numismat. Asn. Philanthropic foundations; the American presidency; retailing and college administration. Publ: Stanley Sebastian Kresge: a rhetorical ideational study of the Kresge Foundation's principal public spokesman. Add: Office of the Dean, College of Sciences & Humanities, Ball State University, Muncie, IN 47306.

DIEHL, JOHN DORNFIELD, b. New York, N.Y, Aug. 22, 27; m. 58; c. 3. ENGLISH. B.A, Yale, 47; M.A, Columbia Univ, 56, Ph.D.(Eng), 66. Lectr. ENG, Columbia Univ, 57-58, instr, 60-61; Skidmore Col, 61-65; ASST. PROF, SYRACUSE UNIV, 65- U.S.A, 51-53. MLA. Victorian literature; great books; Milton. Publ: What's wrong with Freshman writing?, Col. Bd. Rev, 59. Add: Dept. of English, Syracuse University, Syracuse, NY 13210.

DIEKER, RICHARD J, b. Olpe, Kans, June 29, 37; m. 62; c. 1. COMMUNICATION. B.S, Kans. State Teachers Col, 59, M.S, 62; Ph.D.(commun), Mich. State Univ, 67. Coord. commun. sem, Mich. State Univ, 64-65; instr. COMMUN, Univ. Ill, Urbana, 65-66; asst. prof, WEST. MICH. UNIV, 66-70, ASSOC. PROF, 70- Vis. lectr, Univ. Kans, summer 66. Speech Commun. Asn; Int. Commun. Asn; Cent. States Speech Asn. Attitude change; self-confrontation and changes in the self-concept; intercultural communication. Add: Dept. of Communication, Western Michigan University, Kalamazoo, MI 49001.

DIEKHOFF, JOHN SIEMON, b. Ann Arbor, Mich, Oct. 23, 05; m. 29. ENGLISH LITERATURE. A.B, Univ. Mich, 26, A.M, 27; Oxford, 27-28; Ph.D, West. Reserve Univ, 37; hon. L.H.D, Rutgers Univ, 59. Instr. rhet, Univ. Mich, 28-29, prof. higher educ, 63-65; Eng, Oberlin Col, 29-40; asst. prof, Queens Col.(N.Y), 40-47, assoc. prof, 48-50; dir, Ctr. Stud. Lib. Educ. Adults, Chicago, Ill, 50-52; prof. educ. & dir. inst. res, Hunter Col, 52-56; dean Cleveland Col, CASE WEST. RESERVE UNIV, 56-63, prof. eng, 65-70, assoc. dean, 65-67, v.provost, 67-70, EMER. PROF. ENG, 70- Res. consult, Bd. Higher Educ, New York, N.Y, 47; Rockefeller fel, 48. U.S.A, 43-46, Capt. MLA; Milton Soc. Am. Milton; higher education. Publ: Milton on himself, Oxford; Milton's Paradise lost, a commentary, Columbia Univ; The domain of the faculty, Harper; NDEA and modern foreign languages, Mod. Lang. Asn, 65; A maske at Ludlow, Case West. Reserve Univ, 68. Add: Dept. of English, Case Western University, Cleveland, OH 44106.

DIERLAM, ROBERT JACKSON, b. San Francisco, Calif, Feb. 1, 17; m. 45; c. 1. SPEECH. A.B, State Univ. Iowa, 38; A.M, Univ. Colo, 39; Ph.D. (drama & the theatre), Cornell Univ, 48. Instr. speech, Ill. Wesleyan Univ, 43-44; Eng, Univ. Colo, 44-46; fel, Nat. Theatre Conf, 46-47; asst. prof. speech, Univ. Fla, 48-50; vis. asst. prof, Stanford Univ, 51; Fulbright res. scholar, Vienna, Austria, 51-52; instr. commun. arts & sci, QUEENS COL. (N.Y), 52-57, asst. prof, 57-61, assoc. prof, 61-70, PROF. DRAMA & THEATRE, 70- Vis. assoc. prof, Stanford Univ, 57-59. Am. Educ. Theatre Asn; MLA; Speech Asn. Am; Am.Soc. Theatre Res.(secy, 73-76). History of the theatre; audience organizations; the Volksbühne movement. Publ: Trans, Goethe's Gotz von Berlichingen, In: Ten major tragedies, Bantam, 69. Add: Dept. of Drama and Theatre, Queens College, Flushing, NY 11367.

DIERS, HERMAN H, b. Dubuque, Iowa, Sept. 23, 31; m. 53; c. 3. DRAMA. B.A, Wartburg Col, 53; M.A, Univ. Ill, Urbana, 57, Ph.D, 65. Asst. theatre Univ. Ill, 56, theatre & Eng, 57-60; asst. prof. DRAMA, UNIV. MIAMI, 60-65, ASSOC. PROF, 65-, CHMN. DEPT, 67-, arts & humanities grant, summer 68. Managing dir, South. Shakespeare Repertory Theatre, 61-66, exec. dir, 67-; dir, Fiddler on the roof, Coconut Grove Playhouse, 72, The Boy Friend, 4/72 & Jacques Brel, 4/73, Kennedy Ctr; dir, London Theatre Inst, summers 72-73; Ring Theatre, 73- Angel award for best play, Miami Herald, 66, for best dir, 67. Speech Commun. Asn; Am. Theatre Asn; Southeast. Theatre Conf.(exec. secy-treas, 62-64); Am. Nat. Theatre & Acad. Fritz Leiber, actor and producer of Shakespeare in America; the American theatre during the Civil War; the contemporary theatre. Add: Dept. of Drama, University of Miami, Coral Gables, FL 33124.

DIETRICH, JOHN E, b. Spokane, Wash, Nov. 13, 13; m. 49; c. 2. SPEECH & DRAMA. B.A, Univ. Wis, 37, M.A, 41, Ph.D, 45. Instr. pub. speaking, Purdue Univ, 37-41; lectr. speech, Univ. Wis, 42-45, asst. prof, 45-47, assoc. prof, 47-52, prof, 52-55; prof. speech & dir. theatre, Ohio State Univ, 55-59; prof. speech & chmn. dept, MICH. STATE UNIV, 59-64, ASST. PROVOST ACAD. ANAL. & PLANNING, 64- Deleg, White House Conf. Children & Youth, 60. Speech Commun. Asn.(2nd v.pres, 57, 1st v.pres, 58, pres, 59); Am. Counc. Educ; Am. Theatre Asn; Cent. States Speech Asn. (pres, 53); Am. Nat. Theatre & Acad. Objective analyses of theatrical art form. Publ: Play direction, 53 & Practical speaking for the technical man, 58, Prentice-Hall. Add: Office of the Provost, Michigan State University, East Lansing, MI 48823.

DIETRICH, RICHARD FARR, b. Sandusky, Ohio, Jan. 16, 36. ENGLISH. A.B, Miami Univ, 58; M.A, Bowling Green State Univ, 60; Ph.D.(Eng), Fla. State Univ, 65. Asst. prof. ENG, Univ. Del, 63-68; UNIV. S.FLA, 68-70, ASSOC. PROF, 70-, grants, 69 & 73. Univ. Del. summer fac. fel, 66. MLA; Shaw Soc. Am. Bernard Shaw and his times; the Bible and other world literature; modern literature. Publ: Co-auth, The art of fiction, 67, The art of drama, 69 & The art of modern drama, 69, Holt; auth, Portrait of the artist as a young superman: a study of Shaw's novels, Univ. Fla, 69; ed, The realities of literature, Xerox, 70; Shaw and the passionate mind, Shaw Rev, 5/61; Conotations . . . in The use of force, Stud. Short Fiction, summer 66; The training of graduate assistants, Del. Eng, J. spring 68. Add: Dept. of English, University of South Florida, Tampa, FL 33620.

DIGGES, M. LAURENTIA, C.S.J, b. Roswell, N.Mex, Aug. 16, 10. ENGLISH. B.A, Mt. St. Mary's Col.(Calif), 45; M.A, Cath. Univ. Am, 49, Ph.D, 51. PROF. ENG, MT. ST. MARY'S COL.(CALIF), 51- MLA; NCTE; Col. Eng. Asn. Contemporary literature, especially poetry. Publ: Transfigured world; design, theme, and symbol in the liturgy; Adam's haunted sons, Macmillan, 67; Structure and symbol in T.S. Eliot's Portrait of a lady, Am. Lit; plus others. Add: Dept. of English, Mt. St. Mary's College, 12001 Chalon Rd, Los Angeles, CA 90049.

DIJKSTRA, ABRAHAM J, b. Tandjung Pandan, Indonesia, July 5, 38; m. 64. AMERICAN & COMPARATIVE LITERATURE. B.A, Ohio State Univ, 61, M.A, 62; Ph.D.(Eng), Univ. Calif, Berkeley, 67. Acting instr. AM. & COMP. LIT, UNIV. CALIF, SAN DIEGO, 66-67, asst. prof, 67-73, ASSOC. PROF, 73- MLA. The visual arts and literature; sociology of literature; literature and psychoanalysis. Publ: Faces in skin, Oyez, 65; The hieroglyphics of a new speech; cubism, Stieglitz and the early poetry of William Carlos Williams, Princeton, 69; contrib, Encounters: essays in literature and the visual arts, Studio Vista, London, 71; Un Rêve Américain: Norman Mailer et l'esthétique de la domination, Temps Mod, Paris, 4/72. Add: Dept. of Literature, University of California, San Diego, La Jolla, CA 92037.

DIKE, DONALD ALBYN, b. New York, N.Y, Dec. 6, 20; m. 42; c. 2. ENGLISH. A.B, Columbia Col, 41; Mitchell fel, Columbia Univ, 41-42, A.M, 42; Ph.D.(Eng), Syracuse Univ, 53. Instr. ENG, SYRACUSE UNIV, 46-54, asst. prof, 54-59, assoc. prof, 59-63, PROF, 63- Med.C, U.S.A, 43-45. MLA. Modern British literature; literary criticism; structure of the novel. Publ: Co-ed, Selected essays of Delmore Schwartz, Univ. Chicago, 70; A modern Oedipus: The mayor of Casterbridge, Essays in Criticism, 52; The difficult innocence: Blake's Songs and pastoral, ELH, 61; The tempest of Axel Heyst, Nineteenth-Century Fiction, 62. Add: Dept. of English, Syracuse University, Syracuse, NY 13210.

DILGARD, CYNTHIA CORLEW, b. Cheatham Co, Tenn, Apr. 10, 38; m. 57; c. 2. EIGHTEENTH CENTURY ENGLISH & MODERN LITERATURE. B.A, David Lipscomb Col, 59; M.A, George Peabody Col, 64; Ph.D.(Eng), Vanderbilt Univ, 72. Instr. sci. & math, Goodlettsville High Sch, 59-60; Kingston Springs Jr. High Sch, 62-63; ASST. PROF. ENG, DAVID LIPSCOMB COL, 64- MLA; AAUP; Hopkins Soc. William Blake; Jame Joyce. Add: Dept. of English, David Lipscomb College, Belmont Blvd, Nashville, TN 37203.

DILL, STEPHEN HORTON, b. Armour, S.Dak, Aug. 4, 31; m. 53; c. 4. ENGLISH. B.S.E, Univ. Ark, 55, Ph.D.(Eng), 65; W.R. Coe fel. & M.A, Univ. Wyo, 55. Instr. ENG, Sheridan Col, 55-58, 59-60; Washburn Univ, 63-65; UNIV. S.DAK, 65-68, ASSOC. PROF, 68- U.S.A.F, 51-53, Staff Sgt. Eighteenth century prose style; the criticism of Joseph Addison; contemporary British fiction. Publ: Co-auth, Current slang—1969-1971, Univ. S.Dak, 71. Add: Dept. of English, University of South Dakota, Vermillion, SD 57069.

DILLARD, HERBERT NASH, JR, b. Rocky Mt, Va, Sept. 22, 13; m. 61; c. 3. ENGLISH. B.A, Va. Mil. Inst, 34; A.M, Harvard, 36, Ph.D.(Eng), 41. PROF. ENG, VA. MIL. INST, 52-, HEAD DEPT, 55- Ford fel, 51-52. U.S.N.R, 42-46, Lt. Comdr; Bronze Star Medal. MLA; Keats-Shelley Asn. Am; Col. Eng. Asn.(v.pres, 55-56). English romantic poets; John Keats; Shakespeare. Publ: Rules for written work, Stone, 69. Add: Dept. of English, Virginia Military Institute, Lexington, VA 24450.

DILLARD, RICHARD HENRY WILDE, b. Roanoke,Va, Oct. 11, 37; m. 65. ENGLISH. B.A, Roanoke Col. 58; Woodrow Wilson fel, Univ. Va, 58-59; M.A, 59, DuPont fel, 59-61, Ph.D.(Eng), 65. Asst. prof. ENG, HOLLINS COL, 64-68, ASSOC. PROF, 68- Mem. novel award comt, William Faulkner Found, 63-66. Acad. Am. Poets Prize, 61. Auth. Guild; James Branch Cabell Soc; Emerson Soc; Melville Soc; Count Dracula Soc; Acad. Horror Films & Sci. Fiction Films. American literature; contemporary British and American literature; film. Publ: The day I stopped dreaming about Barbara Steele and other poems, 66 & News of the Nile, 71, Univ. N.C; co-auth, The Hollins poets, Univ. Va, 67; co-ed, The experience of America, Macmillan, 69 & The sounder few, Univ. Ga, 71; auth, After Borges, La. State Univ, 72 & The book of changes, Doubleday, 74; Not text but texture: the novels of Vladimir Nabokov, 6/66 & Toward an existential realism: the novels of Colin Wilson, 10/67, Hollins Critic; Drawing the circle: a devolution of value in three horror films, Film J, 1-3/73; plus others. Add: Dept. of English, Hollins College, VA 24020.

DILLAVOU, GEORGE JACKSON, b. Billings, Mont, May 18, 22. SPEECH, PUBLIC ADDRESS. A.B, Univ. Ill, 46; A.M, Columbia Univ, 51; Pa. State Univ, 51-53; Ph.D.(adult ed), Univ. Chicago, 70. Instr. Eng. & speech, Tex. A&M Col, 46-50; asst. prof, Univ. Md, 52-55; dir. overseas div, 56-60; dir. field serv, Univ. Chicago, 60-62; coord. field serv, Univ. Ariz, 62-64; fel, Carnegie Univ. Exten. Admin, 64-66; dean, Col. Continuing Educ, Roosevelt Univ, 66-71; PROF. SPEECH & EDUC. & DEAN UNIV. EXTEN, UNIV. R.I, 71- U.S.A, 42-45. Am. Asn. Higher Educ; Speech Commun. Asn; Nat. Univ. Exten. Asn; Asn. Univ. Eve. Cols; Adult Educ. Asn. U.S. Chautauqua movement in the United States and Canada; special degree programs for adults. Add: University Extension, University of Rhode Island, Promenade & Gaspee Sts, Providence, RI 02908.

DILLE, RALPH GUY, b. Ridgeway, Ohio, Oct. 20, 26; m. 50; c. 6. ENGLISH, EDUCATION. B.A. & B.S, Bowling Green State Univ, 50, M.A, 52; fel, Ball State Univ, 70-72. Instr, high sch, Ohio, 50-54, head dept. Eng, 54-60; chmn. dept. Eng. & dir. summer sch. admin, Univ. of the South, 60-63; chmn. dept. Eng, Interlochen Arts Acad. & Col. Creative Arts, 63-66; asst. pres, STATE UNIV. N.Y. AGR. & TECH. COL. ALFRED, 66-67, ASSOC. PROF. ENG, 67-70, 72- Panelist, NCTE, 54-64; consult, Nat. Asn. For. Stud. Affairs, 66-68; NDEA Inst. multimedia instr, Stephens Col, 67; State Univ. N.Y. personnel orientation, 68. C.Eng, U.S.A, 46-48, Sgt. Nat. Asn. For. Stud. Affairs; NCTE; MLA; Am. Asn. Jr. Col. American literary realism, Harold Frederic; English education; comparative education, socialist. Publ: The instructor: who is he?, In: Professional development for two-year college faculty, State Univ. N.Y. at Buffalo, 69; What is our future?, In: Thinkable limits, Ball State Univ, 71. Add: Dept. of English, State University of New York Agricultural & Technical College at Alfred, Alfred, NY 14802.

DILLE, ROLAND, b. Dassel, Minn, Sept. 16, 24; m. 48; c. 4. ENGLISH. B.A, Univ. Minn, 49, Ph.D.(Eng), 62. Instr, high sch, Minn, 49-50; ENG, Univ. Minn, 53-56; St. Olaf Col, 56-61; asst. prof, Calif. Lutheran Col, 61-63; MOORHEAD STATE COL, 63-64, assoc. prof, 64-66, PROF, 66-, PRES, 68-, assoc. acad. dean, 66-67, acad. dean, 67-68. U.S.A, 43-46. NCTE; MLA. Publ: Ed, Four romantic poets, Holt, 69. Add: 516 Ninth St. S, Moorhead, MN 56560.

DILLER, KARL CONRAD, Linguistics, Teaching English As A Second Language. See Volume III, Foreign Languages, Linguistics & Philology.

DILLER, WILLIAM FRANKLIN, b. Lancaster, Pa, Nov. 7, 02; m. 35. ENGLISH. A.B, Franklin & Marshall Col, 25; A.M, Univ. Pa, 31; Temple Univ, 55-57. Teacher, sec. schs, Pa, 25-29, 34-55; asst. prof. ENG, MILLERSVILLE STATE COL, 55-57, assoc. prof, 57-71, EMER. ASSOC. PROF, 71- AAUP. Local history. Publ: St. James's Church at mid-century, Lancaster Press, 71. Add: 1455 Hollywood Dr, Lancaster, PA 17601.

DILLIGAN, ROBERT JAMES, b. New York, N.Y, Oct. 4, 40; m. 64; c. 3. ENGLISH LITERATURE. B.S, Fordham Univ, 62; M.A, Columbia Univ, 64; Ph.D.(Eng), Univ. Wis, 70. ASST. PROF. ENG, UNIV. SOUTH. CALIF, 70- MLA; AAUP. Computer analysis of literary style; nineteenth century British poetry; computational linguistics. Publ: Co-auth, Concordance to the English poetry of Gerard Manley Hopkins, Univ. Wis, 70, Concordance to Joseph Conrad's Heart of darkness, South. Ill. Univ, 73, The lapses of time, Univ. Edinburgh, 73 & Concordance to the poetry of Alexander Pope, Gale Res. Co, 74; auth, Robert Bridges Experiment in English quantitative verse, Style, 72; co-auth, Computers and the history of prosody, Col. Eng, 73. Add: Dept. of English, University of Southern California, Los Angeles, CA 90007.

DILLINGHAM, FAYE ELIZABETH, b. Kemp, Okla, June 26, 15. ENGLISH. B.A, Southeast. State Col, 36; M.E, Univ. Okla, 45; Columbia Univ, 56; W.Tex. State Univ, 57; Univ. Colo, 59; Tex. Womans Univ, 60; Ed.D.(Eng. educ), N.Tex. State Univ, 66. From instr. Eng. to head dept. high schs, Okla. & Tex, 36-64; asst. prof. educ, N.Tex. State Univ, 64-66; Eng, Cent. Mo. State Col, 66-69; assoc. prof, Okla. Christian Col, 69-71; RETIRED. Judge, NCTE Achievement Awards, 60-66. NEA. Teaching vocabulary; supervision of English. Add: 3425 Baird Dr, Edmond, OK 73034.

DILLINGHAM, WILLIAM B, b. Atlanta, Ga, Mar. 7, 30; m. 52; c. 3. AMERICAN LITERATURE. A.B, Emory Univ, 55, A.M, 56; Beck Found grant & univ. fel, Univ. Pa, 58-59, Ph.D, 61. Asst. EMORY UNIV, 55-56, instr. ENG, 56-58, 59-62, asst. prof, 62-66, assoc. prof, 66-68, PROF, 68- Fulbright lectr, Univ. Oslo, 64-65. U.S.A, 50-52. MLA; S.Atlantic Mod. Lang. Asn; Melville Soc. Nineteenth century American literature. Publ: Co-auth, Humor of the old Southwest, 64 & Practical English handbook, 65, 4th ed, 74 & auth, Frank Norris, 68, Houghton; An artist in the rigging: the early work of Herman Melville, Univ. Ga, 72; Structure and theme in The house of the seven gables, Nineteenth Century Fiction, 59; Insensibility in The red badge of courage, Col. Eng, 63; The narrator of Moby Dick, Eng. Stud, 68. Add: Dept. of English, Emory University, Atlanta, GA 30322.

DILLON, BERT, b. Cherokee, Okla, June 23, 37; m. 66. ENGLISH. B.A, Univ. Colo, 60; M.A, Columbia Univ, 63; Ph.D.(Eng), Duke Univ, 72. Instr. ENG, UNIV. S.C, 65-72, ASST. PROF, 72- MLA; Mediaeval Acad. Am. Chaucer; Middle English literature; Malory. Publ: Formal and informal pronouns of address in Malory's Morte D'Arthur, Annuale Mediaevale, 69. Add: Dept. of English, University of South Carolina, Columbia, SC 29205.

DILLON, GEORGE LEWIS, b. Pittsburgh, Pa, Sept. 26, 44; c. 2. ENGLISH, LINGUISTICS. B.A, Yale, 65; M.A, Univ. Calif, Berkeley, 66, Ph.D.(Eng), 69. ASST. PROF. Eng, South. Methodist Univ, 69-71; ENG. & LING, IND. UNIV, FT. WAYNE, 71- Ling. Soc. Am. English language; stylistics; semantics. Publ: Perfect and other aspects in a case grammar of English, 9/73 & Some postulated characterizing volitive NP's, 74, J. Ling; Complexity and change of character in neo-classical criticism, J. Hist. Ideas, 1-3/74. Add: Dept. of English & Linguistics, Indiana University at Ft. Wayne, 2101 Coliseum Blvd. E, Ft. Wayne, IN 46805.

DILLON, JOHN JOSEPH, JR, b. Pittsburgh, Pa, Oct. 22, 15; m. 41; c. 1. ENGLISH. A.B, Duquesne Univ, 35; A.M, St. Vincent Col, 37; Ph.D, Univ. Pittsburgh, 39; hon. L.H.D, St. Joseph Col.(Maine), 72. Lectr. class. antiq, Carnegie Mus, 37-39; philos, Univ. Pittsburgh, 39-40; PROF. ENG, MT. ST. MARY'S COL.(MD), 40-, PRES, 71-, dir. athletics, 50-69, exec. v.pres, 69-71. Lectr, contemporary Am. lit, Col. Notre Dame (Md), 63; Ford Found. grant, 63-64. MLA; Col. Eng. Asn; NCTE; Nat. Educ. Asn; Asian Soc. Cicero; contemporary literature; classical literature. Add: President's Office, Mount St. Mary's College, Emmitsburg, MD 21727.

DILLON, RICHARD TAYLOR, b. Waterbury, Conn, Aug. 19, 33; m. 60; c. 2. ENGLISH & AMERICAN LITERATURE. B.A, Yale, 55; M.A, Univ. Calif, Berkeley, 62, Ph.D.(Eng), 70. Instr. ENG, UNIV. COLO, DENVER, 69-70, ASST. PROF, 70- U.S.N.R, 55-59, Lt.(jg). Technology and literature; Faulkner. Publ: Some sources for Faulkner's version of the first air war, Am. Lit, 1/73. Add: Division of Arts & Humanities, University of Colorado, 1100 14th St, Denver, CO 80202.

DILLOW, HARRY C, b. New York, N.Y, Aug. 17, 22; m. 68; c. 1. ENGLISH LITERATURE. B.A, City Col. New York, 47; M.A, Columbia Univ, 51; Ph.D.(Eng), Univ. London, 70. Instr. ENG, Adelphi Col, 60-61; UNIV. SASK, REGINA, 61-64, lectr, 64-66, asst. prof, 66-71, ASSOC. PROF, 71- U.S.A, 42-46; Bronze Star Medal. Asn. Can. Univ. Teachers Eng; Can. Asn. Univ. Teachers. English metrics in the 16th and 17th centuries; development of the 17th century lyric. Add: Dept. of English, University of Saskatchewan, Regina, Sask. S4S 0A2, Can.

DiLORENZO, RONALD EUGENE, b. New York, N.Y, Nov. 16, 31; m. 53; c. 9. ENGLISH. B.A, Oberlin Col, 53; M.A, Univ. Iowa, 58, Ph.D.(Eng), 68. Instr. ENG, Univ. Idaho, 62-65; from instr. to asst. prof, Sacred Heart Univ, 65-69; ASST. PROF, ST. LOUIS UNIV, 69- U.S.A, 55-57, Res, 57-61. MLA. English burlesque literature of the 17th and 18th century; 18th century drama and fiction. Publ: Ed, Three burlesque plays of Thomas Duffett, Univ. Iowa, 72. Add: Dept. of English, St. Louis University, St. Louis, MO 63103.

DILWORTH, ERNEST NEVIN, b. Pittsburgh, Pa, Sept. 9, 12. ENGLISH LITERATURE. Ph.B, Kenyon Col, 33; A.M, Univ. Pittsburgh, 37; Eng. Grad. Union fel, Columbia Univ, 46, Ph.D, 48. Instr. ENG, Carnegie Inst. Tech, 38-41; Princeton, 46-48; assoc. prof. & acting head dept, Hartwick Col, 48-49; asst. prof, LEHIGH UNIV, 49-61, assoc. prof, 61-67, PROF, 67- AAUP. Eighteenth century literature. Publ: Co-auth, Smith unbound: a conversation piece, Macmillan, 47; auth, The unsentimental journey of Laurence Sterne, King's Crown, 48; transl, Voltaire Philosophical letters, 61 & Boileau Selected criticism, 65, Bobbs; auth, Walter Savage Landor, Twayne, 71; Add: Dept. of English, Lehigh University, Bethlehem, PA 18015.

DINGS, JOHN GARETSON, b. Covina, Calif, Jan. 13, 39; m. 61; c. 3. ENGLISH. B.A, Carleton Col, 61; M.A, Cornell Univ, 62, Ph.D.(Eng), 68. Instr. ENG, Wash. Univ, 65-67, ASST. PROF, 67-68; STATE UNIV. N.Y. Buffalo, 68- U.S.A.R, 56-64. Nineteenth century English literature. Publ: The mind in its place: Wordsworth, Michael, and the poetry of 1800, Univ. Salzburg, 73. Add: Dept. of English, State University of New York at Buffalo, Buffalo, NY 14214.

DINN, AGNES LUCY, b. Jessup, Pa, Oct. 24, 32; m. 71. SIXTEENTH AND SEVENTEENTH CENTURY ENGLISH POETRY & PROSE. B.A, Carlow Col, 60; M.A, Univ. Notre Dame, 65, Ph.D.(Eng), 70. Instr. ENG, Marywood Col, 68-71; ASST. PROF, BEHREND COL, PA. STATE UNIV, 71- Lectr, Kilroe Sem, Honesdale, Pa, 68-69. Northeast Mod. Lang. Asn; MLA; NCTE; Col. Eng. Asn. English Renaissance drama, especially comedies of Ben Jonson; Renaissance art. Add: 5336 Station Rd, Erie, PA 16510.

DI PASQUALE, PASQUALE, JR, b. Boston, Mass, Oct. 6, 28; m. 61; c. 3. ENGLISH. B.A, Univ. Notre Dame, 55; M.A, Oxford, 61; Ph.D.(Eng), Univ. Pittsburgh, 65. Head dept. Eng, St. Mary's Sem, Tanganyika, 57-61; instr, Seton Hill Col, 61-63, asst. prof, 63-65; Univ. Ore, 65-68, assoc. prof, 68-69; prof. & dir. grad. stud, Ill. State Univ, 69-72; PRES, ASSUMPTION COL.(MASS), 72- Mem. comt. for book of year award, Conf. Christianity & Lit, 67-68; mem, Benedictine Acad. Am. U.S.M.C.R, 47-52. MLA; NCTE; Mediaeval Acad. Am; Col. Eng. Asn. Medieval English literature; literary theory and criticism; medieval culture. Publ: Coleridge's framework of objectivity and Eliot's objective correlative, J. Aesthet. & Art Criticism, summer 68; Sikernesse and fortune in Troilus and Criseyde, Philol. Quart, 4/70; The imagery and structure of Middlemarch, Eng. Stud, 10/71; plus others. Add: Assumption College, 500 Salisbury St, Worcester, MA 01609.

DIPPLE, ELIZABETH DOROTHEA, b. Brodhagen, Ont, May 8, 37. ENGLISH, COMPARATIVE LITERATURE. B.A, Univ. West. Ont, 59; M.A, Johns Hopkins Univ, 61, Ph.D.(Eng), 63. Instr. Eng, Univ. Wash, 63-64, asst. prof, 64-68, Eng. & comp. lit, 68-69, ASSOC. PROF, 69-71; ENG, NORTHWEST. UNIV, 71- Folger Shakespeare fel, summer 67; lectr, NDEA summer inst, Univ. Mass, 67. MLA; Renaissance Soc. Am. Renaissance literature. Publ: Plot, Methuen, 70; The fore conceit of Sidney's Eclogues, Lit. Monogr, 67; Harmony and pastoral in the Old Arcadia, ELH, 68; plus others. Add: Dept. of English, Northwestern University, Evanston, IL 60201.

DIRCKS, PHYLLIS, b. Long Island City, N.Y, Jan. 8, 35; m. 63; c. 2. ENGLISH. B.A, St. John's Univ.(N.Y), 57; Woodrow Wilson fel. & M.A, Brown Univ, 60; Danforth teacher grants, 65-67 & Ph.D.(Eng), N.Y. Univ, 67. Instr. ENG, Col. New Rochelle, 58-61; St. John's Univ.(N.Y), 61-63; C.W. POST COL, L.I. UNIV, 63-64, 67-68, asst. prof, 68-71, ASSOC. PROF, 71- Am. Counc. Learned Soc. stud. fel, 72-73. MLA; Am. Soc. 18th Century Stud; Am. Soc. Theatre Res; Am. Comt. Irish Stud. Eighteenth century drama; Colonial American literature; English musical drama. Publ: The poet and the astronomer: Neoclassic aspects of Holmes' Satiric technique, Res. Stud, 12/69; The catch on the eighteenth century stage: a consideration of two Burlettas, Theatre Notebook, spring 71; Shakespeare's use of the catch as dramatic metaphor, Shakespeare Quart, winter 73. Add: Dept. of English, C.W. Post College, Long Island University, Greenvale, NY 11548.

DIRCKS, RICHARD J, b. New York, N.Y, May 22, 26; m. 63; c. 4. ENGLISH. A.B, Fordham Col, 49, M.A, Fordham Univ, 50, Ph.D, 61. From instr. to asst. prof. Eng, Seton Hall Univ, 50-56; from asst. prof. to assoc. prof. ENG, ST. JOHN'S UNIV.(N.Y), 56-65, PROF, 65-, ASSOC. DEAN GRAD. SCH. ARTS & SCI, 73-, dept. rep, 62-64, chmn. dept, 64-67. U.S.A, 44-45. MLA; Conf. Brit. Stud; Am. Soc. 18th Century Stud; AAUP; Int. Asn. Stud. Anglo-Irish Lit. Criticism and aesthetics; 18th century literature. Publ: Co-auth, Functional English, Republic, 59; co-ed, Dodsley's An essay on fable, Augustan Reprint Soc, 65; auth, Richard Cumberland's political associations, Stud. Burke & His Times, 70; Cumberland, Richardson and Fielding: changing patterns in the eighteenth century novel, Res. Stud, 70; Les fetes champetres 1774: literary and theatrical perspectives, Philol. Quart, 71; plus others. Add: Graduate School of Arts & Sciences, St. John's University, Jamaica, NY 11439.

DIRKS, MARVIN J, b. Halstead, Kans, Dec. 21, 11; m. 36; c. 4. SPEECH, HOMILETICS, RELIGION. A.B, Bethel Col.(Kans), 36; M.Mus, Northwest. Univ, 47; B.D, Bethany Bibl. Sem, 50; Th.D, Boston Univ, 68. Instr. voice, church music, Bethany Bibl. Sem, 47, asst. prof, voice, church music & Bible, 52; prof. voice & speech, Mennonite Bibl. Sem, 58-62; asst. prof. SPEECH, EAST. NAZARENE COL, 63-64, assoc. prof, 65-71, PROF, 71- Hymn Soc. Am; Speech Commun. Asn; Nat. Asn. Teachers Singing. Preaching of Helmut Thielicke; humnology. Publ: Laymen look at preaching, Christopher, 72. Add: 11 Florence St, Wollaston, MA 02170.

DISBROW, JIMMIE LYNN, b. Blackwell, Okla, Apr. 17, 38; m. 66; c. 2. AMERICAN LITERATURE. B.S, Okla. Baptist Univ, 60; M.Ed, Northwest. State Col, 65; Dr.Ed.(Eng), Okla. State Univ, 71. Instr. ENG, Dodge City Community Jr. Col, 65-67; ASST. PROF, E.CENT. STATE COL, 69- S.Cent. Mod. Lang. Asn. Theological reflections in 20th century American literature. Add: Dept. of English, East Central State College, Ada, OK 74820.

DISTLER, PAUL ANTONIE, b. Easton, Pa, May 5, 37. THEATRE THEORY & PRACTICE. B.A, Williams Col, 59; M.A, Tulane Univ, 61, Ph.D, 63. Asst. prof, theatre, Tulane Univ, 63-67; assoc. prof, VA. POLYTECH. INST. & STATE UNIV, 67-72, PROF. THEATRE & CHMN. DEPT. PERFORMING ARTS & COMMUN, 72- Nat. Endowment for Humanities planning grant, summer 72. Speech Commun. Asn; Univ. & Col. Theatre Asn.(pres, 71-73); Am. Theatre Asn; Southeast. Theatre Conf; South. Speech Asn. American vaudeville; Elizabethan drama; cinema history and theory. Publ: Exit the racial comics, Educ. Theatre J, 10/66; Nobody writes good theatre criticism, Columbia Scholastic Press Assoc. Bull, 1/67. Add: Dept. of Performing Arts & Communications, Virginia Polytechnic Institute & State University, Blacksburg, VA 24061.

DITSKY, JOHN MICHAEL, b. Detorit, Mich, Mar. 9, 38; m. 62; c. 1. ENGLISH. Ph.B, Univ. Detroit, 58, fel, 59-61, M.A, 61; Ph.D.(Eng), N.Y. Univ, 67. Asst. ENG, N.Y. Univ, 61-64; instr, Univ. Detroit, 64-66; Wayne State Univ, 66-67; asst. prof, UNIV. WINDSOR, 67-71, ASSOC. PROF, 71- Poetry ed, Univ. Windsor Rev. John Steinbeck Soc. Am.(mem. ed. bd, Steinbeck Quart, 72-); Can. Asn. Am. Stud; MLA. Modern drama; American literature, especially 20th century and fiction. Publ: Carried away by numbers: the rhapsodic mode in modern fiction, Queen's Quart, 72; The man on the Quaker Oats box: characteristics of recent experimental fiction, Georgia Rev, 72; contrib, Steinbeck's literary dimension, Scarecrow, 73. Add: Dept. of English, University of Windsor, Windsor, Ont, Can.

DIX, WILLIAM SHEPHERD, b. Winchester, Va, Nov. 19, 10; m. 35; c. 3. ENGLISH. A.B, Univ. Va, 31, A.M, 32; Ph.D, Univ. Chicago, 46; LL.D, Univ. Fla, 67; hon. L.H.D, Washington Col, 71. Master, Darlington Sch. Boys, 32-39; dir. comt. private res, West. Reserve Univ, 41-42; instr. Eng, Williams Col, 42-44; res. assoc, radio res. lab, Harvard, 44-46, instr. Eng, 46-47; assoc. prof. Eng. & librn, Rice Inst, 47-53; LIBRN, PRINCETON, 53-, LECTR. ENG, 56- Chmn. U.S. Nat. Comn, UNESCO, 59-61; bd. dir, Franklin Bk. Progs, 65-68; Counc. Libr. Resources, 66- Melville Dewey Medal, 69; Lippincott Medal, 71. Asn. Res. Libr.(chmn, 62); Am. Libr. Asn.(pres, 69-70). American literature; the American novel; amateur spirit in scholarship. Add: Library, Princeton University, Princeton, NJ 08540.

DIXON, ARTHUR WILSON, b. Jacksonville, Fla, Mar. 9, 21. ENGLISH. B.A, Univ. N.C, 42; Ph.D.(Eng), Yale, 53. Instr. ENG, Univ. Mich, 50-51; Northwest. Univ, 53-57; asst. prof, UNIV. N.C, GREENSBORO, 57-65, ASSOC. PROF, 65- U.S.A.A.F, 42-46, S/Sgt. MLA. James Boswell; Romanticism. Add: Dept. of English, University of North Carolina at Greensboro, Greensboro, NC 27412.

DIXON, MAURICE EDWARD, b. Belding, Mich, Mar, 28, 36; m. 58; c. 3. THEATRE, EDUCATION. B.A, Ball State Teachers Col, 59; M.A, Purdue Univ, Lafayette, 64. Teacher speech & theatre & head dept, Chesterton High Sch, Ind, 59-62; ASSOC. PROF. COMMUN. & CREATIVE ARTS, PURDUE UNIV, CALUMET CAMPUS, 64-, ASST. CHMN. DEPT, 70- Announcer, WIMS Radio, Ind, 60-62; consult, U.S. Steel Corp, 70-; Am. Oil Co, 72. Speech Commun. Asn; Cent. States Speech Asn. Theatre direction; arts in community; creative dramatics. Add: Dept. of Communication & Creative Arts, Purdue University, Calumet Campus, 2233 171st St, Hammond, IN 46323.

DIXON, TERRELL FRANCIS, b. Dallas, Tex, June 8, 40; m. 63. ENGLISH. A.B, Univ. Okla, 62; Woodrow Wilson fel, Ind. Univ, 62-63, Ph.D.(Eng), 70. Instr. Eng. & humanities, South. Methodist Univ, 67-70; ASST. PROF. ENG, UNIV. HOUSTON, 71- MLA; AAUP. Contemporary English novel; Victorian novel; Southwestern American fiction. Publ: The art of autobiography in Bound for glory, Southwest. Am. Lit, 6/72; The use of literary history in Hurry on down, Notes Contemporary Lit, 3/72; Puppetry and the art of Vanity fair, Forum, 6/73. Add: Dept. of English, University of Houston, Houston, TX 77004.

DOANE, ALGER NICOLAUS, b. Fairfield, Calif, Aug. 16, 38; m. 61; c. 3. ENGLISH & MEDIEVAL EUROPEAN LITERATURE. B.A, Univ. Calif, Berkeley, 61, M.A, 63; Province Ont. fel, Univ. Toronto, 63-65, Ph.D.(Eng), 71. Lectr. ENG, Victoria Univ. Wellington, 65-71; ASST. PROF, UNIV. WIS-MADISON, 71- Am. Counc. Learned Soc. fel, 73-74. Mediaeval Acad. Am; Australasian Univ. Lang. & Lit. Asn. Old English scriptural poetry; Chaucer; Dante. Publ: Heathen form and Christian function in The wife's lament, Mediaeval Stud, 66; Lexis and meaning in Old English poetry, Neuphilologische Mitteilungen, 74. Add: Dept. of English, University of Wisconsin-Madison, 600 N. Park St, Madison, WI 53706.

DOBBINS, AUSTIN CHARLES, b. Nashville, Tenn, Oct. 14, 19; m. 47; c. 2. ENGLISH. B.A, Miss. Col, 41; Univ. Tulsa, 43; Univ. Louisville, 45; M.A, Univ. N.C, 48, Ph.D.(Eng), 50. U.S. govt. inspector, Jeffersonville Ordnance Works, 41-42; chem. operator, B.F. Goodrich Co, 42-43; asst. prof. ENG, SAMFORD UNIV, 50-51, assoc. prof, 51-52, PROF, 52-, HEAD DEPT, 57-, MEM. GRAD. COUNC. & CHMN. ENG. GRAD. COUNC, 64-, chmn. div. humanities, 62-65. Eng. consult, State Farm Mutual Insurance Co, Birmingham, Ala, 55-60; fel, Folger Shakespeare Libr, 57; summer fel, Found. Econ. Educ, 58; Duke Univ. Libr, 63; vis. scholar, Univ. Calif, Los Angeles, 63-64. U.S.A, 43-45. NCTE; S.Atlantic Mod. Lang. Asn; MLA; Renaissance Soc. Am; Am. Bus. Writing Asn. Eighteenth century English literature; Milton; Chaucer. Publ: Co-auth, A research paper manual, privately publ, 67; auth, Foxe, Wicliff and the Church of England, Rev. & Expositor; Dryden's character of a good parson, Stud. in Philol; The language of the cultivated, Col. Eng, 56. Add: 1113 S. Shadesview Terr, Birmingham, AL 35209.

DOBLER, GEORGE RONALD, b. Poughkeepsie, N.Y, Dec. 10, 35; m. 57; c. 4. ENGLISH, EDUCATION. B.A, West. Reserve Univ, 57, M.A, 59; Ph.D.(Eng, educ), Univ. Iowa, 73. Teacher ENG. & head dept, Mentor Pub. Schs, Ohio, 57-63; Maple Heights Pub. Schs, 63-66; from instr. to ASSOC. PROF, Parsons Col, 66-72; MOREHEAD STATE UNIV, 72- Lectr. Eng, Cleveland State Univ,

63-66; instr, Keokuk Community Col, 67-68. NCTE; Col. Eng. Asn; Int. Reading Asn. Reading interests of adolescents; the nature of development of students' attitudes toward learning; poetry. Publ: Team teaching at Maple Heights High School, Ohio Eng. Teacher, 65; contrib, MHRA annual bibliography of the English language and literature, Mod. Humanities Res. Asn, 73. Add: Dept. of English, Morehead State University, P.O. Box 871, Morehead, KY 40351.

DOBSON, EUGENE, German, Comparative Literature. See Volume III, Foreign Languages, Linguistics & Philology.

DOBSON, WILLIS BORING, b. Shreveport, La, June 29, 06; m. 33; c. 1. ELIZABETHAN DRAMA. A.B, Centenary Col, 28; A.M, Univ. Tex, 29, fel, 40, Ph.D.(Eng), 56. Instr. Eng, Agr. & Mech. Col. Tex, 29-31; prof, Bethany-Nazarene Col, 32-72, chmn. div. humanities, 49-70, registr, 32-45; prof. ENG, OLIVET NAZARENE COL, 72, EMER. PROF, 72- Vis. prof, Pasadena Col, 60-61, summers 61, 62, fall 67. MLA; S.Cent. Mod. Lang. Asn; Renaissance Soc. Am; NCTE; Southwest. Am. Lit. Asn. Publ: Edward III: a study of the composition of the play in relation to its sources. Add: 4611 N. Donald St, Bethany, OK 73008.

DODD, MARY CAROLINE, b. Winchester Springs, Ont. ENGLISH LITERATURE. A.B, Marion Col.(Ind), 21; A.M, Univ. Wis, 24; Harvard, 27; Ph.D, Univ. Chicago, 48. Prof. Eng, John Fletcher Col, 21-23; instr. acad, MARION COL.(IND), 23-26, prof. Eng. lang. & lit, 26-65, distinguished serv. prof, 65-69, EMER. DISTINGUISHED SERV. PROF, 69- Researcher, Chatsworth House, Eng, summer 57; lectr, Wesleyan Bible Col, Glenroy, Australia, summer 65; part-time teacher, Marion Col.(Ind), 69-70. NCTE; Col. Eng. Asn; MLA; Milton Soc. Am. Add: Dept. of English, Marion College, Marion, IN 46952.

DODD, WAYNE DONALD, b. Clarita, Okla, Sept. 23, 30; m. 58; c. 2. ENGLISH. B.A, Univ. Okla, 55, M.A, 57, South. Fel. Fund fel, 59-60, Ph.D.(Eng), 63. Teaching asst. ENG, Univ. Okla, 55-59; instr, Univ. Colo, 60-64, asst. prof, 64-68; assoc. prof, OHIO UNIV, 68-73, PROF, 73- Ed, Abstr. Eng. Stud, 62-65; Am. Counc. Learned Soc. study fel, 64-65; Univ. Colo. summer fac. fel, 66; mem. ed. bd, Eng. Lang. Notes, 66-68; ed, Ohio Rev, 71- U.S.N, 48-52. Renaissance intellectual history and English studies; 17th-century English literature; contemporary poetry. Publ: A new look at cultural history, Bucknell Rev, 5/67; But I'll set down the pegs that make this music, Neuphilol. Mitteilungen, summer 67; Tragedy and the mortal condition, Centennial Rev, summer 68. Add: Dept. of English, Ohio University, Athens, OH 45701.

DODDS, JOHN WENDELL, b. Grove City, Pa, July 20, 02; m. 28; c. 2. ENGLISH. A.B, Col. Wooster, 24, D.Litt, 45; A.M, Yale, 27, Ph.D, 32; L.H.D, Ohio Wesleyan Univ, 64. Mem. dept, Eng, Univ. Pittsburgh, 27-37; assoc. prof, STANFORD UNIV, 37-39, prof, 39-67, dean sch. humanities, 42-48, dir. spec. prog. humanities, 48-67, EMER. JACKSON REYNOLDS PROF. HUMANITIES, 67- Trustee, Mills Col, 43-53; Guggenheim fel, 47-48; Viking Fund fel, 48; vis. lectr. consult, Emory Univ, 52; vis. prof, Univ. Hawaii, 52; trustee, Pomona Col, 55-68; mem. bd. dir, Wenner-Gren Found. Anthrop. Res, 54-, pres, 65-; Col. Wooster, 66-; mem. comn. teaching humanities; Nat. Humanities Endowment, 67-68. MLA. English prose fiction; Victorian and American social history. Publ: Thackeray: a critical portrait; The age of paradox: England, 1841-1851; American memoir, Holt, 61; Everyday life in 20th century America, Putnam, 65. Add: 729 Frenchman's Rd, Stanford, CA 94305.

DODEZ, M. LEON, b. Cuyahoga Falls, Ohio, May 4, 34; m. 54. SPEECH, PHILOLOGY. Ph.D.(speech), Ohio State Univ, 63. Instr. SPEECH, Ohio State Univ, 61-63; lectr, Univ. Md, 63-64; PROF, MIAMI-DADE COMMUNITY COL, 64-, CHMN. COMMUN. ARTS & PHILOS, 72- Vis. prof, Fla. Atlantic Univ, 67-68. U.S.A, 58-59. Speech Commun. Asn; South. Speech Commun. Asn. Oral interpretation; children's theatre; readers' theatre. Add: Dept. of Speech, Miami-Dade Community College, 11011 S.W. 102nd St, Miami, FL 33156.

DODGE, EVELYN C, b. Boston, Mass, Apr. 20, 15. ENGLISH. B.S, Mass. State Col. Salem, 42; A.M. Boston Univ, 48, Ph.D.(Eng), 63. Asst. prof. ENG, Emerson Col, 58-60; inst, FRAMINGHAM STATE COL, 60-63, assoc. prof, 66-68, PROF, 68- Col. Eng. Asn; MLA. American literature; creative writing. Add: Dept. of English, Framingham State College, Framingham, MA 01701.

DODGE, ROBERT KENDALL, b. Cortland, N.Y, Mar. 29, 41; m. 63; c. 2. ENGLISH. B.A, Rice Univ, 63; M.A, Univ. Tex, Austin, 64, Ph.D.(Eng), 67. ASST. PROF. ENG, Wis. State Univ, Stevens Point, 67-70; UNIV. NEV, LAS VEGAS, 70- Nat. Endowment for Humanities summer sem. stipend, 73. James Fenimore Cooper's Leatherstocking tales; literature of the American Indian; Herman Melville. Publ: Co-ed, Voices from Wah' Koh-tah, an anthology of native American poetry, Int. Publ, 74; auth, Didactic humor in the almanacs of early America, J. Popular Cult, winter 71. Add: Dept. of English, University of Nevada, Las Vegas, Maryland Pkwy, Las Vegas, NV 89154.

DODRILL, CHARLES WARD, b. Tioga, W.Va, Aug. 12, 33; m. 54; c. 3. THEATRE. B.A, Glenville State Col, 54; asst. & M.A, Univ. Kans, 56; asst, Northwest. Univ, 56-58; Ph.D.(theatre), Ohio State Univ, 65. Instr. SPEECH & THEATRE, Univ. Kans, 55-56; asst. prof. & dir. theatre, OTTERBEIN COL, 58-65, assoc. prof, 65-69, PROF, 69-, DIR. THEATRE & SPEC. EVENTS, 65-, foreign travel grant, 66. Chmn. theatre mgt. proj, Am. Educ. Theatre Asn, 60-65. Speech Commun. Asn; Am. Theatre Asn; Asn. Col. & Univ. Concert Mgr; resident observer, Lincoln Ctr. Repertory Theatre, spring 68 & Royal Shakespeare Co, London, fall 71. Arena theatre; theatre management; liberal arts college theatre history. Publ: Guest artists in American educational institutions, Players Mag, 5/65; Theatre management: selective bibliography, Am. Educ. Theatre Publ, 66; A London theatre tour, The Cue, winter 70; plus one other. Add: Director of Theatre, Otterbein College, Westerville, OH 43081.

DODSON, CHARLES BROOKS, b. Gary, Ind, Aug. 30, 37. ENGLISH. B.A, De Pauw Univ, 59; M.A, Ind. Univ, 61; F.E. & O.M. Johnson fel, Univ. Nebr, 65-66, Ph.D.(Eng), 67. Instr. ENG, Maryville Col.(Tenn), 61-63; asst. prof, Wis. State Univ, Eau Claire, 66-68; UNIV. WIS-OSHKOSH, 69-72, ASSOC. PROF, 72- Acad. planner, bd. regents Wis. state univs, 68- MLA; NCTE. Victorian literature; English novel; English romantic literature. Publ: Ed, Three novels by Thomas Love Peacock, Holt, 71; contrib, Directory of Victorian journalists, Res. Soc. Victorian Periodicals. Add: Dept. of English, University of Wisconsin-Oshkosh, Oshkosh, WI 54501.

DODSON, DANIEL B, b. Portland, Ore, Mar. 21, 18; m. 43; c. 2. COMPARATIVE LITERATURE. A.B, Reed Col, 41; A.M, Columbia Univ, 47, Ph.D, 54. Instr. ENG, COLUMBIA UNIV, 48-54, asst. prof, 54-59, assoc. prof, 59-68, PROF, 68-, fac. grant, 60. U.S.A.A.F, 42-46, 1st Lt. MLA. Elizabethan drama; modern comparative drama and novel. Publ: The man who ran away, Dutton, 61; ed. with introds, Twelve modern plays, Hawthorne, 69; auth, Malcolm Lowry, Columbia Univ, 70; co-ed, Generations: an approach to the drama, Harcourt, 72; The dance of love, Mason, 74. Add: Dept. of English, 602 Lewisohn, Columbia University, New York, NY 10027.

DOEBLER, BETTIE ANNE, b. Atlantic City, N.J, Aug. 26, 31; m. 54; c. 2. ENGLISH. B.A, Duke Univ, 53, fel, 53-54, M.A, 55; Ph.D, Univ. Wis, 61. Teaching asst. integrated lib. stud, Univ. Wis, 54-59; lectr. Eng, Mundelein Col, 60-61; instr, Dickinson Col, 61-62, asst. prof, 62-68, assoc. prof, 68-70; lectr, ARIZ. STATE UNIV, 71, ASSOC. PROF. HUMANITIES, 71- MLA; AAUP; Nat. Asn. Humanities Educ. Renaissance art and literature: the iconography of Venus; Ars moriendi in the Renaissance, especially in Shakespeare and Donne; poetry and prose of John Donne. Publ: Othello's Angels: the ars moriendi, ELH, 67; Donne's Incarnate Venus, S.Atlantic Quart, fall 72; Despaire and dye: the ultimate temptation of Richard III, Shakespeare Stud, fall 73; plus others. Add: Center for Humanities, Arizona State University, Tempe, AZ 85281.

DOEBLER, JOHN WILLARD, b. Flushing, N.Y, Feb. 9, 32; m. 54; c. 2. ENGLISH. B.A, Duke Univ, 54; M.A, Univ. Wis, 55, Ph.D, 60. Instr. ENG, Northwest. Univ, 59-61; asst. prof, Dickinson Col, 61-66, assoc. prof, 66-70; ARIZ. STATE UNIV, 70-72, PROF, 72- Folger Libr. fel, summer 66. MLA; Renaissance Soc. Am. Renaissance literature; stage iconography; neoplatonism. Publ: The knight of the burning pestle, Univ. Nebr, 67; Shakespeare's speaking pictures, Univ. N.Mex, 75; The tone of George Peele's The old wives' tale, Eng. Stud, 72; The play within the play: the Muscipula Diaboli in Hamlet, Shakespeare Quart, 72; Orlando: athlete of virtue, Shakespeare Surv, 73; plus others. Add: Dept. of English, Arizona State University, Tempe, AZ 85281.

DOGGETT, JOHN RENTZ, b. Houston, Tex, Jan. 28, 38; m. 69. ENGLISH LITERATURE, COMPOSITION. B.B.A, Univ. Tex, Austin, 60, Ph.D.(Eng), 74. Instr. ENG, Univ. Tex, Austin, 67-71; ASST. PROF, FT. HAYS KANS. STATE COL, 72-, dir. compos, 72-74. Supply C, U.S.N, 60-63, Res, 63-70, Lt.(j.g). MLA; NCTE; Soc. Tech. Commun. Technical writing; freshman English; works of William Blake, 1752-1827. Publ: A reading of the Book of Urizen: Diss. Abstr, 71; contrib, A proposal for bilingual composition, Ft. Hays Kans. State Col. Newslett, 72. Add: Dept. of English, Fort Hays Kansas State College, Hays, KS 67601.

DOGGETT, JOSEPH McSWAIN, b. Piedmont, S.C, June 21, 08; m. 42; c. 1. ENGLISH. A.B, Wofford Col, 30; M.A, George Peabody Col, 37, fel, 39-41, Ph.D, 50. Instr. Eng. & educ, Erskine Col, 37-39; from lectr. to asst. prof. Eng, Fla. State Univ, 46-54; vis. prof, UNIV. HOUSTON, 54-55, PROF. ENG, 55-, CHMN. DEPT, 59-, freshman Eng, 55-59. Exchange prof, Univ. Hawaii, 57-58. MLA; NCTE; S.Cent. Col. Eng. Asn.(v.pres, 62-63, pres, 63-64); Conf. Col. Teachers Eng. Periodical essay of the Queen Anne period; social reflections of the early 18th century literary essay; facsimile texts of original first copies of the Tatler and Spectator papers of Addison and Steele. Publ: A college forum, Odyssey, 63; Abstracts of dissertations; An historical account of the English essayperiodical prior to Defoe's Review, Fla. State Univ. Stud; This piebald English opera, Opera News; plus others. Add: Dept. of English, University of Houston, Houston, TX 77004.

DOHENY, JOHN RODNEY, b. Sedro-Woolley, Wash, Oct. 18, 27; m. 51; c. 2. ENGLISH. B.A, Univ. Wash, 54, M.A, 58, Ph.D.(Eng), 72. Lectr, ENG, UNIV. B.C, 60-63, instr, 63-66, ASST. PROF, 66- Asn. Can. Univ. Teachers Eng; Can. Asn. Univ. Teachers. D.H. Lawrence; theory of novel; 19th and 20th century novel. Publ: Alex Comfort as novelist, Limbo, 10/64; The novel is the book of life: D.H. Lawrence and a version of polymorphous perversity, Paunch, 10/66; Lady Chatterley and her lover, W.Coast Rev, 1/74. Add: Dept. of English, University of British Columbia, Vancouver 8, B.C, Can.

DOHN, NORMAN HARDING, b. Clarence, N.Y, Nov. 5, 20; m. 43; c. 2. JOURNALISM. A.B, Otterbein Col, 43; M.A, Ohio State Univ, 47, Ph.D.(hist), 59. Instr. Eng. & jour, Otterbein Col, 46-48; reporter, Sunday ed. & ed. writer, Columbus Dispatch, Ohio, 48-62; int. broadcast specialist, Voice of Am, 63-65; press attache, Am. Embassy, Manila, Philippines, 65-68; PROF. JOUR, OHIO UNIV, 68- Ed, Ohio Vet. For. Wars News, 52-62, 69-; TV newscaster, WBNS TV, Ohio, 52-62. Med.Admin.C, U.S.A.F, 43-46, 1st Lt. Asn. Educ. in Jour; Radio-TV News Dir. Asn. History of American journalism; international communications. Add: School of Journalism, Ohio University, Athens, OH 45701.

DOLAN, PAUL J, b. Brooklyn, N.Y, Apr. 17, 37; m. 59; c. 3. ENGLISH. A.B, St. Francis Col.(N.Y), 58; A.M. & Woodrow Wilson fel, N.Y. Univ, 59, Ph.D.(Eng), 66. From instr. Eng. to asst. prof. & dir. admis, St. Francis Col.(N.Y), 59-66; asst. prof. ENG, STATE UNIV. N.Y. STONY BROOK, 67-70, ASSOC. PROF. & CHMN. DEPT, 70-, asst. to pres, 67-68, asst. dean grad. sch, 68-70. Am. Counc. Educ. Acad. Admin. Intern, Univ. Md, 66-67. MLA. Contemporary and 17th century literature. Publ: Co-auth, The sense of the sixties, 68 & auth, Modes of fiction, 69, Free Press; co-ed, Race awareness, Oxford Univ, 70; Milton & Eliot: a common source, Notes & Queries, 66; Ash Wednesday: a catechumenical poem, 67 & The Quaker graveyard in Nantucket, 68, Renascence. Add: Dept. of English, State University of New York at Stony Brook, Stony Brook, NY 11790.

DOLLAHAN, JUNE RICHEY, b. Crawford Co, Ill, June 18, 12; m. 58; c. 2. ENGLISH. B.Ed, East. Ill. State Teachers Col, 37; M.A, Univ. Ill, 46;

Ph.D, Northwest. Univ, 62. Teacher, Pinkstaff Elem. Sch, 31-33; Moan Sch, 33-36; Latin, math, Eng, Alvin Twp. High Sch, 37-41; Latin & math, Blue Island Community High Sch, 41-46; instr. ENG, undergrad. div, Univ. Ill, 46-58; PROF, VINCENNES UNIV, 58- Fulbright teaching scholar. Eng. & Am. hist, Rotterdam, The Netherlands, 53-54; dir. inst. problems of sch. desegregation, Vincennes Univ, summer 66, dir. inst. teacher aides, 69-70, 70-71; proj. dir. planning consortium, State Plan Involvement Higher Educ. Insts. in Comprehensive Improv. Day Care, Ind, 72-73 & 73-74; mem, Comn. Insts. Higher Educ. N.Cent. Asn, 73-77. NCTE. Teacher training; curriculum; educational psychology. Publ: A study of the preparation of teachers of college English in selected public junior and four-year colleges, Diss. Abstr, 62. Add: 1806 State St, Lawrenceville, IL 62439.

DOLLARD, FRANK DREW, b. San Francisco, Calif, Jan. 3, 24; m. 47; 66; c. 2. ENGLISH. A.B, Univ. Calif, 49, M.A, 50, Ph.D.(Eng), 53; Univ. Paris, Lectr. ENG, Univ. Calif, 52, instr, 53-55; assoc. prof, SAN FRANCISCO STATE UNIV, 55-65, PROF, 65-, EXEC. V.PRES, 71- Supvr, Drew Sch, Calif, 62- U.S.M.C, 41-45; Shakespeare; English drama; Dickens. Add: Dept. of English, San Francisco State University, San Francisco, CA 94132.

DOLLARD, WILLIAM ANTHONY STANISLAUS, b. New York, N.Y, June 26, 01. ENGLISH. A.B, Columbia Univ, 24, A.M, 26, Proudfit fel, 29, Cutting traveling fel, 30; B.A, Cambridge, 32, M.A, 37; D.Litt, Univ. Louisville, 48. Master, Riverdale Sch, N.Y, 24-25; instr. Eng, Wash. Sq. Col, N.Y. Univ, 26-30; prof. Eng. & head dept, St. Francis Xavier Col, Can, 32-33; resid. master, Milton Acad, Mass, 34-35; assoc. prof. ENG, Col. New Rochelle, 35-37; from instr. to asst. prof, Hunter Col, 37-67; asst. prof, Lehman Col, 67-69, assoc. prof, 69-71; RETIRED. Reviewer, N.Y. Times Bk. Rev. & N.Y. Herald Tribune Bks, 38-41, 48, 49 & America, 52-72. Lateran Cross Vatican State; Knight of Malta; Commendatore della Coronna d' Italia. U.S.A, 42-50, suprv. reed prog. Mil. Govt, 43-48, ed. res, Gen. Staff, 48-50; Bronze Star Medal. Experience and expression. Add: 4320 Van Cortlandt Park E, Bronx, NY 10470.

DOLLARHIDE, LOUIS E, b. Okla, Apr. 23, 18; m. 48; c. 5. ENGLISH. B.A, Miss. Col, 42; M.A, Harvard, 47; Ph.D, Univ. N.C, 54. Instr. ENG, Miss. Col, 43-45, assoc. prof, 46-49; instr, Univ. N.C, 49-52; prof, Miss. Col, 52-67, chmn. div. humanities, 61-67; PROF, UNIV. MISS, 67- Summers, instr. Eng. & hist, Mass. Inst. Technol, 45, Folger Shakespeare Libr. fel, 60. U.S.A.A.F, 42-43. S.Atlantic Mod. Lang. Asn; S.Cent. Mod. Lang. Asn. Shakespeare and the English Renaissance. Add: Box 647, University, MS 38677.

DOLMAN, GEOFFREY, b. Swarthmore, Pa, Mar. 1, 19; m. 42; c. 2. ENGLISH. A.B, Univ. Pa, 41, A.M, 49. Chmn. dept. Eng, St. Helena exten, Col. William & Mary, 46-48; asst. to dean admis, Univ. Pa, 48-49; asst. prof. ENG, URSINUS COL, 49-54, ASSOC. PROF, 54-, DEAN ADMIS, 66-, registr, 54-56, dir. admis, 56-66. U.S.A, 41-46, Capt. Publ: Ed, The art of reading aloud. Add: Office of Admissions, Ursinus College, Collegeville, PA 19426.

DOLMETSCH, CARL RICHARD, (JR), b. Kingston, Pa, July 5, 24; m. 48; c. 2. ENGLISH. A.B, Drake Univ, 48, A.M, 49; Hay fel, Columbia Univ, 54-55; Ph.D, Univ. Chicago, 57. Instr. ENG, Drury Col, 49-51; asst. prof, Drake Univ, 56-59; COL. WILLIAM & MARY, 59-63, assoc. prof, 63-67, PROF, 67-, CHMN. DEPT, 70- Am. Philos. Soc. res. grants, 63, 64, 67 & 68; Fulbright-Hays lectr, Free Univ. Berlin, 64-66; vis. prof. Eng, Univ. Ga, 68; lectr, Falkenstein sem. Am. stud, W.Ger, 69, 71. U.S.A.A.F, 43-45. MLA; Am. Stud. Asn; S.Atlantic Mod. Lang. Asn; Ger. Soc. Am. Stud. Colonial American literature; American fiction, 1865 to present; American intellectual history. Publ: Co-auth, The poems of Charles Hansford, Univ. N.C, 61; auth, The smart set: a history and anthology, Dial, 66; contrib, Literatur und Sprache der Vereinigten Staaten, Carl Winter Verlag, Heidelberg, 69 & Amerikanische Literatur im 20. Jahrhundert, Vandenhoeck & Ruprecht, Goettingen, 71; auth, William Byrd II: comic dramatist?, Early Am. Lit, spring 71; plus others. Add: Dept. of English, College of William & Mary, Williamsburg, VA 23185.

DOMVILLE, ERIC WILLIAM, b. Liverpool, Eng, Apr. 27, 29; m. 59; c. 1. ENGLISH. B.A, Univ. London, 61, Ph.D.(Eng), 65. Lectr. ENG, UNIV. TORONTO, 64-66, asst. prof, 66-69, ASSOC. PROF, 69- MLA; Can. Asn. Irish Stud. The collected letters of W.B. Yeats; British and American literature 1880 to the present; the city in literature. Publ: Ed, A concordance to the plays of W.B. Yeats (2 vols), Cornell Univ, 72; contrib, The new Cambridge bibliography of English literature, Vol. 4, Cambridge, 72. Add: Dept. of English, New College, University of Toronto, Toronto, Ont, M5S 1A1, Can.

DONAGHY, HENRY J, b. New York, N.Y, Apr. 11, 30; m. 68; c. 2. ENGLISH. A.B, Stonehill Col, 54; M.A, Fordham Univ, 60; Ph.D.(Eng), N.Y. Univ, 66. Instr. Notre Dame High Sch, 58-59, chmn. dept. Eng, 60-62; asst. prof. ENG, King's Col, 65-66; Ga. State Col, 66-69; ASSOC. PROF, State Univ. N.Y. Col. Oswego, 69-71; Calif. State Univ, Fresno, 71-73; IDAHO STATE UNIV, 73- MLA; Shaw Soc. Am; Rocky Mountain Mod. Lang. Asn; Am. Comt. Irish. Stud. Romantics; Victorians; Irish literature. Publ: James Clarence Mangan, Twayne, 74; The ring and the book: its conception, current reputation and meaning, 4/68 & Love and Mr. Wells: a Shelleyan search for the epipsyche, 10/68, Stud. Lit. Imagination; The apple cart: a Chestertonian play, Shaw Rev, 9/68; plus others. Add: Dept. of English, Idaho State University, Pocatello, ID 83201.

DONAHO, MELVIN WILLARD, b. Canton, Ill, Oct. 2, 30; m. 55; c. 1. RHETORIC & PUBLIC ADDRESS. B.S, Univ. Ill, Urbana, 57, Ed.M, 59; Thomas C. Trueblood fel, Univ. Mich, 61, univ. fels, 61-64, Ph.D.(rhetoric & pub. address), 66. Instr. high schs, Ill, 57-61; instr. speech & forensics, West. Mich. Univ. & speech & debate, univ. high sch, 64-66; asst. prof. speech & debate, Cent. Mich. Univ, 66-68, assoc. prof. speech & dir. debate, 67-69; PROF. COMMUN. & COORD. GEN. STUD, STATE UNIV. N.Y. COL. PLATTSBURGH, 69- Consult, Plattsburgh Air Force Base, 71-; contract grant, U.S.A.F, 73-74. U.S.N, 50-53. Cent. States Speech Asn; Speech Commun. Asn; Am. Inst. Parliamentarians; NEA; Lutheran Acad. Scholar; Am. Forensic Asn; East. Forensic Asn; East. States Commun. Asn. Leadership and communication; personal and organizational advancement; concepts of interviewing. Publ: Leadership and communication, State Univ. N.Y. Col. Plattsburgh, 73; A doctrine of equal time for Christian educators, Lutheran Scholar, 10/65; Leadership and communication for the top three, U.S.A.F, 73. Add: 2 Addoms Pl. South, Plattsburgh, NY 12901.

DONAHUE, CHARLES JAMES, b. New Haven, Conn, Dec. 26, 08. ENGLISH, CELTIC PHILOLOGY. A.B, Yale, 30, Ph.D, 33; LL.D, Iona Col, 63. Sterling fel. from Yale, Copenhagen, 33-34; instr. ENG, Yale, 34-35; GRAD. SCH, FORDHAM UNIV, 35-38, asst. prof, 38-42, assoc. prof, 46-54, PROF, 54- Mil.Intel, U.S.A, 42-46, Maj. MLA; Mediaeval Acad. Am. Early Celtic and Old English literatures; early Medieval thought. Publ: Beowulf and Christian tradition, Traditio, 65; Medieval Celtic literature, In: The Medieval literature of Western Europe, MLA, 66; Patristic exegesis summation, In: Critical approaches to Medieval literature, Columbia Univ, 60. Add: Dept. of English, Fordham University Graduate School, New York, NY 10458.

DONALDSON, CHRISTINE HUNTER, b. Haddonfield, N.J, Nov. 3, 17; div; c. 1. ENGLISH, WORLD LITERATURE. B.A, Wellesley Col, 39; M.A, Yale, 41, Ph.D.(Am. hist, arts, letters), 48. ASSOC. PROF, ENG, SOUTH. CONN. STATE COL, 66- MLA; AAUP. Shakespeare; American drama; oriental literature. Add: 11 Clark Rd, Woodbridge, CT 06525.

DONALDSON, ETHELBERT TALBOT, b. Bethlehem, Pa, Mar. 18, 10; m. 41, 67, 71; c. 1. ENGLISH LITERATURE. A.B, Harvard, 32; Ph.D, Yale, 43. Instr, Kent Sch, 32-38, 39-40; Yale, 42, instr, 46-47, asst. prof, ENG, 47-51, assoc. prof, 51-56, prof, 56-67, fel, Saybrook Col; PROF, Columbia Univ, 67-70; YALE, 70- Vis. prof. & Guggenheim fel, Univ. London, 51-52, vis. prof, King's Col, 71-72; Am. Counc. Learned Soc. grant-in-aid, 61-62; vis. prof. Eng, Univ. Mich, 73-74. U.S.A.F, 43-46, Capt. MLA; Acad. Lit. Stud; fel. Mediaeval Acad. Am. Middle English language and literature. Publ: Piers plowman; the C-text and its poet, Yale Univ, 49; Chaucer's poetry: an anthology for the modern reader, Ronald, 58; co-ed, Norton anthology of English literature, 62, 68 & auth, Beowulf: a translation, 66, Norton; auth, Speaking of Chaucer, Athlene, London & Norton, 70. Add: Dept. of English, Yale University, New Haven, CT 06520.

DONALDSON, SCOTT, b. Minneapolis, Minn, Nov. 11, 28; m. 57; c. 3. AMERICAN LITERATURE & STUDIES. B.A, Yale, 51; M.A, Univ. Minn, 52, Ph.D.(Am. stud), 66. Reporter, Minneapolis Star, 55-57; ed. & publ, Bloomington Sun, 58-63; asst. prof. ENG, COL. WILLIAM & MARY, 66-69, ASSOC. PROF, 69-, summer res. grants, 70, 72. Fulbright lectr, Turku Univ, 70-71; Am. Philos. Soc. grant, summer 72; vis. prof, Univ. Leeds, 72-73. MLA; Am. Stud. Asn; Orgn. Am. Hist. Fitzgerald and Hemingway; American poetry; American realism. Publ: The suburban myth, Columbia Univ, 69; Poet in America: Winfield Townley Scott, Univ. Tex, 72; Minding Emily Dickinson's business, New Eng. Quart, 12/68; The dark truth of The Piazza tales, PMLA, 10/70; Hemingway's morality of compensation, Am. Lit, 11/71. Add: Dept. of English, College of William & Mary, Williamsburg, VA 23185.

DONELSON, KENNETH L, b. Holdrege, Nebr, June 16, 27; m. 70; c. 2. ENGLISH EDUCATION. B.A, State Univ, Iowa, 50, M.A, 51, Ph.D.(Eng. educ), 63. Teacher, High Schs, Iowa, 51-63; asst. prof. Eng. & educ, Kans. State Univ, 63-65; ENG, ARIZ. STATE UNIV, 65-67, assoc. prof, 67-70, PROF, 70- Mem. exec. bd, Southwest Inst. Film Teachers, 70-; mem. exec. comt, Conf. Eng. Educ, 72-76; columnist, Eng. J, 73-74. NCTE (prog. chmn, West. Interstate Conf. Teachers of Eng, 70, mem. comt. Affiliate Relat. & Censorship & Bias in Elem. Sch, 73-76). Censorship; adolescent literature; film. Publ: Ed, The students' right to read, NCTE, 72; auth, The Southwest in literature: a new horizon for the English class, 2/72 & White walls and high windows: some contemporary censorship problems, 11/72, Eng. J; co-auth, Adolescent literature: you mean that garbage written for kids who can't read?, Clearing House, 3/73. Add: Dept. of English, Arizona State University, Tempe, AZ 85281.

DONER, DEAN BENTON, b. Brookings, S.Dak, May 1, 23; m. 44; c. 3. ENGLISH. B.S, S.Dak. State Col, 47; M.F.A, State Univ, Iowa, 48, fel. & Ph.D, 53. Instr. Eng, Univ. Idaho, 50-53; Purdue Univ, 53-56, asst. prof, 56-60, assoc. prof, 60-66, prof, 66-67, assoc. dean sch. humanities, 63-67; prof. Eng. & dean col. lib. arts & sci, Univ. Ill. Chicago Circle, 67-73; V. PRES, BOSTON UNIV, 73- Assoc. ed, Mod. Fiction Stud; vis. prof, Univ. Hamburg, 66; mem. fac, Salzburg sem. in Am. Stud, Salzburg, 66. U.S.A.A.F, 43-46. MLA. Modern fiction; the novel; creative writing. Publ: Co-auth, The writing laboratory, Scott, 64; auth, Spinoza's ethics and Maugham, Univ. Kans. City Rev; Virginia Woolf: the service of style, Mod. Fiction Stud; Rabbit Angstrom's unseen world, New World Writing, 62. Add: Boston University, 147 Bay State Rd, Boston, MA 02215.

DONNA, ROSE BERNARD, C.S.J, b. Dalton, Mass, 09. ENGLISH. A.B, Col. St. Rose, 38; A.M, Cath. Univ. Am, 44, Ph.D, 49. Instr. Eng, Latin & French, high schs, N.Y, 31-44; asst. prof. ENG, COL. ST. ROSE, 47-54, PROF, 54-, chmn. dept. grad. Eng, 49-67, head dept. undergrad. Eng, 54-62. Mem, Eng. Inst. MLA; Mediaeval Acad. Am; Cath. Renascence Soc. Medieval and Renaissance English; patristic and medieval Latin. Publ: Despair and hope: a study in Langland and Augustine, 48 & transl, Saint Cyprian: letters (1-81), Vol. LI, In: The fathers of the church series, 64, Cath. Univ. Am; Notes on Cyprian's De habitu virginum, its source and influence, Traditio, 10/46. Add: Dept. of English, College of St. Rose, Albany, NY 12203.

DONNELL, RICHARD STOVER, b. Winthrop, Mass, Dec. 10, 26; m. 52; c. 5. ENGLISH. A.B, Princeton, 47; M.A, Harvard, 48, Ph.D.(Eng), 60. Instr. ENG, Tufts Univ, 51-55; MIAMI UNIV, 55-60, asst. prof, 60-65, assoc. prof, 65-71, PROF, 71-, DIR. FRESHMAN ENG, 69- U.S.N, 45-46. MLA; NCTE; Conf. Col. Compos. & Commun. American literature; naturalism; modern fiction. Publ: William Faulkner: a study, Thought, Delhi, 4/52; Williams' The yachts, Explicator, 5/59. Add: Dept. of English, Miami University, Oxford, OH 45056.

DONNELLY, JEROME JAMES, b. Ann Arbor, Mich, Feb. 18, 36; m. 59; c. 3. ENGLISH LITERATURE. A.B, Univ. Mich, Ann Arbor, 58, M.A, 60, Ph.D. (Eng), 66. Asst. prof. ENG, Univ. Wis, 65-70; ASSOC. PROF, FLA. TECHNOL. UNIV, 70- Eng-Speaking Union grant, summer 71. S.Atlantic Mod.

Lang. Asn; MLA; Col. Eng. Asn. Eighteenth century British literature; literary theory; comparative literature. Publ: Stendhal and Thackeray: the source of Henry Esmond, Rev. Lit. Comparée, 65; Movement and meaning in Dryden's MacFlecknoe, Tex. Stud. Lit. & Lang, 71. Add: 621 Osceola Ave, Winter Park, FL 32789.

DONNER, STANLEY T, b. Norfolk, Nebr, Dec. 1, 10; m. 43; c. 5. COMMUNICATIONS. A.B, Univ. Mich, 32; M.A, Northwest. Univ, 40, Ph.D. (rhetoric), 46. Prin, Plymouth High Sch, Nebr, 32-34; teacher, Maumee Valley Country Day Sch, Ohio, 34-37; instr, Univ. Toledo, 37-38; asst, sch. speech, Northwest. Univ, 38-42, asst. prof, 46-48; speech & drama, Stanford Univ, 48-51, assoc. prof, 51-58, prof, 58-62, communication, 62-65, dir. radio & TV, Stanford Radio-TV Film Inst, 48-65, acting exec. head dept. speech & drama, 61-62, assoc. exec. head dept. commun, 62-65; PROF. COMMUN, UNIV. TEX, AUSTIN, 65-, chmn. dept. radio-TV-film, 65-71, res. grant, Eng. & France, 70. Sr. Fulbright res. grant, Paris, 55-56; U.S. rep, UNESCO Meeting Cult. Exchange Radio, Paris, 56; educ. consult, Westinghouse Broadcasting Corp. Conf. Pub. Affairs, 59; Fulbright lectr, Univ. London, 63-64. TV prog. awards for People, Places & Politics, 52-53, The Fine Line, 55 & Careers, 62. U.S.N.R, 42-46, Lt. Comdr. Speech Commun. Asn; West. Speech Commun. Asn; Nat. Asn. Educ. Broadcasters; Asn. Prof. Broadcasting Educ. Educational Television; responsibility of commercial television; mass media and culture. Publ: Co-auth, Educational television: the next ten years, Stanford Univ, 62; ed, The future of commercial television, 65 & The meaning of commercial television, 67, Univ. Tex; co-auth, The farther vision: educational television today, Univ. Wis, 68; auth, The curriculum dilemma, J. Nat. Asn. Educ. Broadcasters, 1-2/60; Ralph Dennis, a great teacher, Speech Teacher, 9/62; Education by television and correspondence: the American experience, In: Report of a conference held at Ditchley Park, Oxford, 64. Add: Dept. of Radio-TV-Film, University of Texas at Austin, Austin, TX 78712.

DONNO, DANIEL J, b. Manhasset, N.Y, Nov. 12, 20; m. 50. ENGLISH & COMPARATIVE LITERATURE. A.B, Miami Univ, 45, M.A, 47; Rutgers Univ, 43-44; Fulbright fel, Univ. Padua, Italy, 50-51; Ph.D, Columbia Univ, 59. Asst. ENG, Miami Univ, 46-47; instr, Rutgers Univ, 47-49; QUEENS COL.(N.Y), 59-61, asst. prof, 62-65, assoc. prof, 66-67, PROF, 68-, chmn. dept, 66-69. U.S.A, 42-46, Staff Sgt. MLA; Renaissance Soc. Am; Mod. Humanities Res. Asn, Gt. Brit; Mediaeval Acad. Am; Dante Soc. Am. Dante; comparative Renaissance; 16th century English. Publ: Transl, Introd. & notes, Boccaccio's The nymph of Fiesole, Columbia Univ, 60 & Machiavelli, The Prince and selected discourses, Bantam, 66; auth, Dante's Argenti: episode and function, Speculum, 10/65; Recent scholarship on Dante, Renaissance Quart, summer 67. Add: Dept. of English, Queens College, Flushing, NY 11367.

DONNO, ELIZABETH STORY, b. Kennewick, Wash, June 12, 21; m. 50. ENGLISH. A.B, Whitman Col, 44; univ. fel, Columbia Univ, 44-45, A.M, 46, Ph.D, 59; Fulbright fel, Univ. London, 49-50. Instr. Eng. & comp. lit, COLUMBIA UNIV, 59-62, asst. prof, 62-64, assoc. prof. ENG, 65-70, PROF, 70- Fisher fel, 56-57; Folger fel, summer 57; Guggenheim fel, 63-64; Huntington Libr. fels, summer 65 & 70-71; summer fels, Newberry Libr, 66 & John Carter Brown Libr, 67; Columbia Univ. Counc. res. fel. humanities, summer 68, 69. Renaissance Soc. Am.(ed, Renaissance Quart, 61-); Shakespeare Asn. Am; MLA; Mod. Humanities Res. Asn, Gt. Brit. Sixteenth century literature. Publ: Sir John Harington's Metamorphosis of Ajax, 62 & Elizabethan minor epics, 63, Routledge & Kegan Paul; ed, Complete poetry of Andrew Marvell, Penguin, 72. Add: Dept. of English, Columbia University, New York, NY 10027.

DONOGHUE, JOHN D, b. Springfield, Mass, May 12, 09; m. 36; c. 4. ENGLISH. A.B, St. Michael's Col.(Vt), 32, M.A, 61. Announcer & producer, WMAS, 32-34; reporter, ed. & critic, Springfield Daily News, 34-44, 46; instr. jour, St. Michael's Col.(Vt), 47-61, asst. prof. jour. & ed, St. Michael's Rev, 61-66, dir. pub. relat, 47-66, lectr. humanities, 52-61; asst. to provost, Vt. State Cols, 66-69; exec. ed, VT. CATH. TRIBUNE, 69-73, ED, 73- Music critic, Burlington Free Press, 52-; comnr, Educ. Comn. States, 65-69; consult, Nat. Counc. Cath. Men, 68- U.S.A, 44-46, S/Sgt. Am. Col. Pub. Relat. Asn; AAUP. Music criticism; educational public relations; Gaelic folk lore. Publ: Ed, Task force report: parochial schools of Vermont, Burlington Diocese, 68; Teaching is public relations, Col. & Univ. J, winter 68. Add: 40 Hayden Pkwy, South Burlington, VT 05401.

DONOHEW, ROBERT LEWIS, b. Owingsville, Ky, May 9, 29; m. 50; c. 3. COMMUNICATION. A.B, Univ. Ky, 51, M.A, 61; Ph.D.(commun), Univ. Iowa, 65. Ed, Pikeville Daily News, 51-52; city ed, Owensboro Messenger & Inquirer, 54-57; dir. inform. serv, UNIV. KY, 58-62, instr. jour, 64-65, from asst. prof. to PROF. COMMUN, 65-, res. assoc, Ctr. Develop. Change, 66-68. Res. prof, Inst. Mass Commun. Res, Univ. Oslo, 69-70. Int. Commun. Asn; Int. Asn. Mass Commun. Res; Asn. Educ. in Jour.(mem. comt. on res, 71-). Human information seeking; communication and development. Publ: Co-auth, Content analysis of communication, Macmillan, 67, Psychophysiological measurement of information selection: two studies, J. Commun, 72 & chap, In: New models for communication research, Sage, 73; plus 21 others. Add: School of Communication, University of Kentucky, Lexington, KY 40506.

DONOHUE, AGNES McNEILL, b. Sheboygan, Wis, Sept. 17, 17; m. 44. ENGLISH & AMERICAN LITERATURE. B.A, Rosary Col, 39; M.A, Univ. Wis, 40; Ph.D.(Eng), Loyola Univ. (Ill), 54. Instr. ENG, Univ. Minn, 44-45; Univ. Ill, Chicago, 46-54; prof. & chmn. dept, Barat Col, 54-65; assoc. prof, LOYOLA UNIV. CHICAGO, 65-67, PROF, 67- Lectr, Univ. Chicago, 46-48; Grad. Sch, Loyola Univ, 57- MLA; NCTE. Novels of Ronald Firbank; irony and theology of Nathaniel Hawthorne; puritanism in Robert Frost. Publ: A casebook on the Hawthorne question, 63 & A casebook on the Grapes of wrath, 68, Crowell; From whose bourn no traveler returns: a reading of Roger Malvin's burial, Nineteenth Century Fiction 6/63 & In: The short story: an inductive approach, Harcourt, 67. Add: Dept. of English, Loyola University, 6525 N. Sheridan Rd, Chicago, IL 60626.

DONOHUE, JAMES JOHN, b. Cedar Rapids, Iowa, June 28, 06. ENGLISH. A.B, Loras Col, 28; Cath. Univ. Louvain, 28-32; A.M, Cath. Univ. Am, 35; Ph.D, State Univ. Iowa, 41. Prof. Eng, Loras Col, 33-68. Lectr, Clarke Col; Cath. Univ. Am. Cath. Theatre Conf.(pres, 45-47, ed, Bull, 45-49). MLA. Literary theory; history of theory of literary kinds in classical antiquity; Chaucer translation. Publ: Chaucer's prolog and five tales in present-day English, Loras Col, 54-66. Add: Villa Raphael, 1235 Mt. Loretta, Dubuque, IA 52001.

DONOHUE, JOSEPH WALTER, JR, b. Brookline, Mass, Sept. 12, 35; m. 59; c. 3. ENGLISH. A.B, Johns Hopkins Univ, 56; M.A, Georgetown Univ, 62; Frelinghuysen fel, Princeton, 64-65, Ph.D.(Eng), 65; Fulbright jr. fel, Univ. London, 65-66. Instr. ENG, Mt. Vernon Sem, 58-60; Dunbarton Col, 60-61; asst. prof, Princeton, 66-71; ASSOC. PROF, UNIV. MASS, AMHERST, 71- John E. Annan bicentennial preceptor, Princeton, 67-70; Am. Counc. Learned Soc. grant, 67, grant-in-aid, 69, travel grant, 73; Folger Shakespeare Libr. fel, 68; Huntington Libr. grant, 73; vis. assoc. prof, Columbia Univ, 73-74. U.S.A, 57, 61-62, Res, 57-61, 62-63, Lt. MLA; Am. Soc. Theatre Res; Soc. Theatre Res, Eng; Int. Fed. Theatre Res. History and criticism of British drama and theatre; the 19th century stage; historiography and theory of the theatre. Publ: Dramatic character in the English Romantic age, 70 & ed, The theatrical manager in England and America, 71, Princeton Univ; auth, Burletta and the early nineteenth century English theatre, Nineteenth Century Theatre Res, 73; plus others. Add: Dept. of English, Bartlett Hall, University of Massachusetts, Amherst, MA 01002.

DONOVAN, DENNIS GEORGE, b. Springfield, Ill, Mar. 1, 32; m. 55; c. 2. ENGLISH. B.S, Ill. State Univ, 59; M.A, Univ. Ill, 61, Ph.D.(Eng), 65. ASSOC. PROF. ENG, UNIV. N.C, CHAPEL HILL, 65- U.S.A, 51-54, Sgt. MLA; NCTE; Renaissance Soc. Am. Sixteenth and seventeenth century drama; seventeenth century prose; bibliography. Publ: Thomas Dekker, Thomas Heywood, and Cyril Tourneur: a checklist, 67, Thomas Middleton and John Webster: a checklist, 67 & Sir Thomas Browne and Robert Burton: a checklist, 68, Nether, London; gen. ed, Renaissance bibliography, Studies in Philology, Univ. N.C, 67-; auth, Robert Burton, Anglican minister, Papers Southeast Renaissance Conf, 68. Add: Dept. of English, 513 Greenlaw Hall, University of North Carolina at Chapel Hill, Chapel Hill, NC 27514.

DONOVAN, JOSEPHINE CAMPBELL, b. Manila, P.I, Mar. 10, 41. COMPARATIVE LITERATURE, WOMEN'S STUDIES. B.A, Bryn Mawr Col, 62; M.A, Univ. Wis, 67, Ph.D.(comp. lit), 71. Lectr. HONORS PROG, UNIV. KY, 68-70, ASST. PROF, 71- MLA; Comp. Lit. Asn; Women's Caucus Mod. Lang. Literature and history of ideas. Publ: Feminist style criticism, In: Images of women in fiction, Bowling Green Univ, 72 & In: Female studies VI, Feminist Press, 72; Sexual politics in Sylvia Plath's short stories, Minn. Rev, summer 73. Add: Honors Program, 233 Office Tower, University of Kentucky, Lexington, KY 40506.

DONOVAN, MORTIMER JOHN, b. Rochester, N.Y, Mar. 12, 17; m. 50; c. 6. ENGLISH. A.B, Canisius Col, 39; A.M, Harvard, 41, Ph.D, 51. Instr. ENG, Carnegie Inst. Tech, 46-47; UNIV. NOTRE DAME, 50-51, asst. prof, 51-54, ASSOC. PROF, 54-65, MEDIAEVAL INST, 65- U.S.A.A.F, 41-46, Maj. MLA; Mediaeval Acad. Am; Int. Arthurian Soc. Medieval English; French literature. Publ: The Breton lay: a guide to varieties, Univ. Notre Dame, 69; Lai du Lecheor: a reinterpretation, Romanic Rev, 4/52; Breton lays, In: A manual of the writings in Middle English 1050-1500, Connecticut Acad. Arts & Sci, 67. Add: 1225 Blaine Ave, South Bend, IN 46616.

DONOVAN, RICHARD A, b. Rochester, N.Y, May 23, 37. ENGLISH, DRAMA. A.B, Univ. Notre Dame, 59, fel, 59-61, A.M, 61; fel, Univ. Minn, 61-63, Ph.D.(Eng), 68. Instr. ENG, Univ. Minn, 64-67; chmn. dept, Nazareth Col. (N.Y), 67-69; fel, U.S. Off. Educ. & spec. asst. dep. asst. secy. planning res & eval, 69-70; ASSOC. PROF. ENG. & ASSOC. DEAN EDUC. DEVELOP, BRONX COMMUNITY COL, 72- Reader, Folger Shakespeare Libr, 66-67; consult, Off. Econ. Opportunity, 67- MLA. Elizabethan and modern drama; Yeats. Add: Dept. of English, Bronx Community College, 120 E. 184th St, New York, NY 10468.

DONOVAN, ROBERT ALAN, b. Chicago, Ill, Sept. 27, 21; m. 42; c. 3. ENGLISH. Ph.B, Univ. Chicago, 48, M.A, 50; Ph.D.(Eng), Wash. Univ, 53. Instr. ENG, Cornell Univ, 53-57, asst. prof, 57-62; PROF. ENG, STATE UNIV. N.Y. ALBANY, 62- U.S.A, 42-45. MLA. Nineteenth century English literature; prose fiction; literary criticism. Publ: The shaping vision: imagination in the English novel from Defoe to Dickens, Cornell Univ, 66; The method of Arnold's Essays in criticism, PMLA, 56; Carlyle and the climate of hero-worship, Univ. Toronto Quart, 73; plus others. Add: Dept. of English, State University of New York at Albany, Albany, NY 12222.

DONOW, HERBERT S, b. Long Beach, N.Y, June 6, 36; m. 61; c. 2. ENGLISH. B.A, Cornell Univ, 58; Ph.D.(Eng), Univ. Iowa, 66. Instr. ENG, Univ. Iowa, 62-63; Colo. State Univ; asst. prof, SOUTH. ILL. UNIV, CARBONDALE, 66-73, ASSOC. PROF, 73- off. res. & proj. res. grant, 68-69. Am. Counc. Learned Soc. grant, 69-70; Am. Philos. Soc. grant, 70-71. MLA. Computational literary analysis; Shakespeare; 16th century nondramatic English literature. Publ: A concordance to the sonnet sequences of Daniel, Drayton, Shakespeare, Sidney and Spenser, South. Ill. Univ, 69; Herman Melville and the craft of fiction, Mod. Lang. Quart, 6/64; Shakespeare's caskets: unity in The merchant of Venice, Shakespeare Stud, 69; Prosody and the computer: a text processor for stylistic analysis, Proc. Conf. Am. Fed. Inform. Processing Soc, 70; plus others. Add: Dept. of English, Southern Illinois University, Carbondale, IL 62901.

DOODY, AGNES G, (MRS. ARTHUR D. JEFFREY), b. New Haven, Conn, Apr. 12, 30; m. 62. SPEECH. A.B, Emerson Col, 52; M.A, Pa. State Univ, 54, Ph.D, 61. Instr. speech, State Univ. N.Y. Col. Geneseo, 57-58; asst. prof. speech & dir. forensics, UNIV. R.I, 58-67, assoc. prof. SPEECH, 67-70, PROF, 70-, chmn. dept, 67-74. Assoc. ed, Today's Speech, 68-70. New Eng. Speech Asn.(treas, 65-67, 1st v.pres, 67-68, pres, 68-69); Speech Commun. Asn; Int. Commun. Asn; AAUP; Am. Speech & Hearing Asn; Speech Asn. East. States; Am. Forensic Asn. Public speaking; contemporary history; intercultural communication. Add: Dept. of Speech, University of Rhode Island, Kingston, RI 02881.

DOOLEY, DAVID JOSEPH, b. Halifax, N.S, Sept. 8, 21; m. 60; c. 2. ENGLISH. B.A, Univ. West. Ont, 42; M.A, Univ. Toronto, 47; Ph.D.(Eng), State Univ, Iowa, 55. Instr. ENG, Creighton Univ, 47-48; St. Francis Xavier

Univ, 49-52; lectr, Royal Mil. Col, 52-55, asst. prof, 55-58, assoc. prof, 58-60; asst. prof, ST. MICHAEL'S COL, UNIV. TORONTO, 60-62, assoc. prof, 62-66, PROF, 66-, CHMN. DEPT, 72- Can. Army, 42-46, Capt. Satire in the English novel, especially early 20th century. Publ: The art of Sinclair Lewis, Univ. Nebr, 67; Compton Mackenzie, G.K. Hall, 74; The limitations of George Orwell, Univ. Toronto Quart, 4/59; Science as cliché, fable & faith, Bull. Atomic Scientists, 11/59; The hour-glass pattern in The ambassadors, New Eng. Quart, 6/68. Add: Dept. of English, St. Michael's College, University of Toronto, Toronto 5, Ont, Can.

DOOLEY, ROGER BURKE, b. Buffalo, N.Y, May 15, 20; m. 51; c. 1. ENGLISH. A.B, Canisius Col, 40; Knights of Columbus fels, Cath. Univ. Am, 40-42, 53-54, M.A, 42, Ph.D.(Eng), 56. From instr. to asst. prof. ENG, Canisius Col, 46-53; asst. prof, Iona Col, 54-55; Grad. Sch, St. John's Univ. (N.Y), 55-56, assoc. prof, 56-60; prof. & head dept, Queensborough Community Col, 60-64; PROF, MANHATTAN COMMUNITY COL, 64-, CHMN. DEPT, 72- PEN Club; Authors League Am. American films of the 1930's; earlier 20th century society; 18th century novel. Publ: Less than the angels, Bruce, 46, All Saints, 62; Days beyond recall, 49 & Gone tomorrow, 61, Bruce; The house of Shanahan, Doubleday, 52; Flashback, Doubleday, 69 & Pyramid, 71; Broadway in the '20's, In: Studies in language & literature, Harper, 74. Add: 220 Central Park S, New York, NY 10019.

DORAN, EDWINA BEAN, b. Sparta, Tenn; m. 53. ENGLISH. B.S, Tenn. Technol. Univ; Univ. Tenn, 55, 56; M.A, George Peabody Col, 60, Ed.S, 62, Ph.D.(Eng), 69. Teacher, high schs, Tenn, 49-60; Ford teaching fel. Eng, George Peabody Col, 61-62; instr. Eng. & edic, EUREKA COL, 62-64, asst. prof, 64-68, assoc. prof, 68-70, PROF. ENG. & HUMANITIES, 70- Dir. Ill. Title III Ling. Workshop, spring 72. NCTE; Conf. Col. Compos. & Commun; Col. Eng. Asn; Midwest Mod. Lang. Asn; MLA; Am. Folklore Soc; NEA. Humanities; folklore; comparative literature. Add: Dept. of English, Eureka College, Eureka, IL 61530.

DORAN, MADELEINE, b. Salt Lake City, Utah, Aug. 12, 05. ENGLISH. A.B, Stanford Univ, 27, fel, 28-30; Ph.D, 30; A.M, Univ. Iowa, 28; Litt.D, Wheaton Col, 63. Instr. Eng. lit, Wellesley Col, 30-33; Eng, UNIV. WIS-MADISON, 35-39, asst. prof, 39-47, assoc. prof, 47-52, prof, 52-67, RUTH C. WALLERSTEIN PROF. ENG. LIT, 67- Am. Counc. Learned Soc. fel, 33-34; Am. Asn. Univ. Women fel, 46-47; Calkins vis. prof, Wellesley Col, 57; vis. prof, Stanford Univ, 60; Huntington Libr. grant, 60, 64; Folger Shakespeare Libr. fel, 64; Guggenheim fel, 67-68; mem, Inst. Res. in Humanities, Univ. Wis, 70- MLA (mem, exec. counc, 64-67); Renaissance Soc. Am.(mem, counc, 63-64, 67-70); Shakespeare Asn. Am; Am. Acad. Arts & Sci. Shakespeare; Elizabethan drama; Renaissance literature. Publ: Text of King Lear, Stanford Univ; Endeavors of art, 54 & Something about swans: essays, 73, Univ. Wis; ed, A midsummer night's dream, Penguin, 59; The language of hyperbole in Antony and Cleopatra, Queen's Quart, spring 65; Good name in Othello, Stud. Eng. Lit, spring 67; Iago's if: an essay on the syntax of Othello, In: The drama of the renaissance, Brown Univ, 70; plus one other. Add: 4238 Wanda Pl, Madison, WI 53711.

DORAN, PAUL RICHARD, b. Wilkinsburg, Pa, Jan. 10, 20; m. 71. ENGLISH LITERATURE, EDUCATION. B.A, Cath. Univ. Am, 40; M.A, Univ. Pa, 45, Ph.D.(Eng), 71. Teacher ENG, La Salle High Sch, 40-49; asst. prof, LA SALLE COL, 49-63, ASSOC. PROF, 63-, chmn. dept, 51-54, dean arts & sci, 56-69. MLA; Col. Eng. Asn; NCTE. Eighteenth century English literature; Jonathan Swift; Anglo-Irish literature. Publ: Trials of Christ the teacher, La Salle Catechist, 41; The dean looks at the library, Cath. Libr. World, 68. Add: Dept. of English, La Salle College, 20th St. & Olney Ave, Philadelphia, PA 19141.

DORE, WILLIAM JOHN, JR, b. Seattle, Wash, Apr. 19, 32; m. 59; c. 2. THEATRE, FINE ARTS. B.A, Univ. Wash, 54, M.A, 57. Teaching asst. drama, Univ. Wash, 56-57; chmn. dept. drama, Lower Columbia Col, 57-61; producer-dir, Music-Go-Round, Inc, 61-63; ASSOC. PROF. SPEECH & DRAMA, SEATTLE UNIV, 63-, CHMN. DEPT. FINE ARTS, 73- Consult, State Supt. Pub. Instruct, 73- U.S.A, 54-56. Am. Theatre Asn. Drama, art and music. Add: Dept. of Fine Arts, Seattle University, Broadway at Madison, Seattle, WA 98122.

DOREMUS, ROBERT BARNARD, b. Newton, Mass, May 19, 15; wid; c. 2. ENGLISH LITERATURE. A.B, Harvard, 35, A.M, 36, Ph.D, 40. Instr. ENG, UNIV. WIS-MADISON, 40-42, 46, asst. prof, 46-49, assoc. prof, 49-53, PROF, 53-, ASSOC. DEAN, COL. LET. & SCI, 50-, asst. dean, 47-50, asst. dir. freshman Eng, 46-47. U.S.A, 42-46. MLA; NCTE. Victorian literature, British. Publ: Writing college themes, Oxford, 60; co-ed, Patterns in writing, Holt, 63. Add: 201 South Hall, University of Wisconsin-Madison, Madison, WI 53706.

DORENKAMP, JOHN HENRY JR, b. St. Louis, Mo, Jan. 25, 31; m. 56; c. 4. ENGLISH. A.B, St. Louis Univ, 54, M.A, 57; Ph.D.(Eng), Univ. Ill, 62. Instr. ENG, COL. HOLY CROSS, 61-63, asst. prof, 63-66, assoc. prof, 66-73, PROF, 73-, acting chmn. dept, 67-68, chmn, 71-74. Vis. assoc. prof, Univ. Nebr, summer 67; mem. Eng. Inst, 67. U.S.A, 54-56. MLA. Renaissance drama; bibliographical evidence; contemporary fiction. Publ: The compositors of the Cambridge platform, Stud. Bibliog, 70; The unity of Motre D'Urban, Univ. Dayton Rev, fall 71; The Bay psalm book and the Ainsworth Psalter, Early Am. Lit, spring 72; plus others. Add: Dept. of English, College of the Holy Cross, Worcester, MA 01610.

DORFMAN, DEBORAH, b. New York, N.Y. ENGLISH ROMANTIC POETRY. B.A, Queens Col, 55; M.A, Yale Univ, 57, Ph.D.(Eng. lit), 64. Asst. instr. ENG, Univ. Calif, Santa Barbara, 57-58; lectr, Queens Col. Sch. of Gen. Stud, 59-60; Hunter Col, 60-61; instr, Temple Univ, 62-64; City Col. New York, 64-66; asst. prof, Wesleyan Univ, 66-70; ASSOC. PROF, STATE UNIV. N.Y. ALBANY, 70- Keats-Shelley Soc; MLA; AAUP; Am. Asn. Univ. Women. English Romantic poets; Blake. Publ: Blake in the nineteenth century, Yale, 70. Add: Dept. of English, State University of New York at Albany, 1400 Washington Ave, Albany, NY 12222.

DORGAN, (CLAUDE) HOWARD, b. Ruston, La, July 5, 32; m. 61; c. 2. RHETORIC AND PUBLIC ADDRESS, THEATRE. B.A, Univ. Tex, El Paso, 53; M.F.A, Univ. Tex, Austin, 57; Ph.D.(speech), La. State Univ, 71. Asst. prof. SPEECH, Lamar Univ, 66-69; teaching asst, La. State Univ, 69-71; ASSOC. PROF, APPALACHIAN STATE UNIV, 71- Ed, N.C. J. Speech & Drama, 73- South. Speech Commun. Asn; Speech Commun. Asn. Southern rhetoric and public address; theatre history. Publ: The cult of southern womanhood in rhetoric of confederate veterans, spring 72 & Marlowe and history: the Edward II-Piers Gaveston relationship, spring 73, N.C. J. Speech & Drama; General John B. Gordon and The last days of the confederacy, Quart. J. Speech, 2/74; plus others. Add: Dept. of Speech, Appalachian State University, Boone, NC 28607.

DORIUS, RAYMOND JOEL, b. Salt Lake City, Utah, Jan. 4, 19. ENGLISH. B.A, Univ. Utah, 40; M.A, Harvard, 47, Ph.D, 51. Instr. ENG, Yale, 49-54, asst. prof, 54-58; assoc. prof, Smith Col, 58-62; PROF, Univ. Hamburg, Ger, 62-64; assoc. prof, SAN FRANCISCO STATE UNIV, 64-68, PROF, 68- Morse fel, Yale, 53-54. Shakespeare; lyric poetry; the drama. Publ: Ed, Yale Shakespeare: Henry V, Yale Univ; Shakespeare's English histories, Heath, 63; co-auth, Reading for understanding, Macmillan, 68; ed, Twentieth century interpretation of 1 Henry IV, Prentice-Hall, 69; auth, Shakespeare's English histories, Shakespeare Quart, 60. Add: Dept. of English, San Francisco State University, 1600 Holloway, San Francisco, CA 94132.

DORLAG, ARTHUR H, b. St. Louis, Mo, Sept. 6, 22; m. 47; c. 3. SPEECH, THEATRE. B.S.Ed, Southeast Mo. State Col, 47; M.S, Univ. Wis, 47, Ph.D, 53. Asst. prof. speech, Southeast Mo. State Col, 47-50, from assoc. prof. to prof, 53-57, dir. theatre, 47-57; ASSOC. PROF. THEATRE & DIR. THEATRE, FLA. STATE UNIV, 58-; res. counc. grant, summer 63. Vis. lectr, Univ. Wis, 57-58; founder & gen. dir, Asolo Theatre Comedy Festival, Sarasota, Fla, 60-62. U.S.A.A.F, 43-45, Res, 45-, Maj. Soc. Theatre Res, Eng; Am. Soc. Theatre Res; Am. Theatre Asn. Theatre history. Publ: Co-auth, The stage works of Charles MacArthur, Fla. State Univ. Found, 74. Add: School of Theatre, Florida State University, Tallahassee, FL 32306.

DORNBERG, CURTIS LEON, b. Mankato, Minn, Mar. 26, 29; m. 59; c. 2. ENGLISH. B.A, Mankato State Col, 51; M.A, State Univ. Iowa, 59, Ph.D.(Eng), 65. Instr. ENG, MANKATO STATE COL, 59-61, asst. prof, 61-63, assoc. prof, 63-65, PROF, 65- U.S.A, 51-52. NCTE; Midwest Mod. Lang. Asn. Nineteenth century English literature. Add: Dept. of English, Mankato State College, Mankato, MN 56001.

DORNBUSCH, CLYDE HENRY, b. Cincinnati, Ohio, Dec. 25, 30; m. 53; c. 2. AMERICAN LITERATURE. B.A, DePauw Univ, 53; univ. fel, Duke Univ, 53-55, M.A, 55, Ph.D, 57. Instr. Eng, Wake Forest Col, 57-58, asst. prof, 58-61; assoc. prof. & dir. freshman Eng, Parsons Col, 61-62; assoc. prof. ENG, OHIO NORTH. UNIV, 62-68, PROF, 68-, CHMN. DEPT, 64-, HEAD DIV. HUMANITIES, 67- Participant, Asn. Depts. Eng. sem, summers, 70, 71, 72. MLA; NCTE; Midwest Mod. Lang. Asn; Asn. Depts. Eng. American literature, 19th and 20th century fiction; Whitman; Dickinson. Publ: Spelling reform by presidential edict, Am. Speech, 10/61; Joel Chandler Harris visits the White House, Ga. Hist. Quart, 3/62. Add: Dept. of English, Ohio Northern University, Ada, OH 45810.

DOROUGH, CHARLES DWIGHT, b. Gober, Tex, Apr. 14, 12. ENGLISH. B.A. & M.A, Univ. Tex, 36, Ph.D, 46. Instr. Eng, Northwest Mo. State Teachers Col, 37-38; Univ. Ark, 38-41; Eng. & communs, Univ. Tex, 41-44; asst. prof. ENG, Memphis State Col, 44-46; assoc. prof, Birmingham-South. Col, 46-48; UNIV. HOUSTON, 48-51, PROF, 51-, asst. dean arts & sci, 51-55, assoc. dean, 55-58, chmn. Eng. dept, 54-58, assoc. dean, Grad. Sch, 58-59. Sam Rayburn res. grant, 60-62; Dept. Health, Educ. & Welfare grant, 60-63. MLA; S.Cent. Mod. Lang. Asn; Col. Eng. Asn; Am. Stud. Asn. American and Southern literature. Publ: Mr. Sam, Random, 62; co-auth, Automated instruction of remedial English, U.S. Dept. Health, Educ. & Welfare-Univ. Houston, 63; ed, An invitation to philosophy, McCutchan, 70. Add: 5330 Jackwood, Houston, TX 77035.

DORRIS, GEORGE EDWARD, b. Eugene, Ore, Aug. 3, 30. ENGLISH LITERATURE. B.A, Univ. Ore, 52; M.A, Northwest. Univ, Evanston, 53, Ph.D (Eng), 62; Fulbright fel, Univ. Rome, 55-56. Instr. ENG, Duke Univ, 59-60; Rutgers Univ, 60-62; asst. prof, Univ. of the Pacific, 62-64; instr, Queens' Col.(N.Y), 64-67; ASST. PROF, YORK COL.(N.Y), 67- Newberry Libr. fel, 64; assoc. ed, Ballet Rev, 68- MLA; Am. Soc. 18th Century Stud; AAUP. Restoration and 18th century English literature; Baroque opera and drama; history of dance. Publ: Paolo Rolli and the Italian circle in London 1715-1744, Mouton, 67; Scipione Maffei amid the dunces, Rev. Eng. Stud, 8/65; Griffith in retrospect, In: Man and the movies, La. State Univ, 67; The conception of Pavlova, Ballet Rev, Vol. IV, No. 4. Add: Dept. of English, York College, Jamaica, NY 11432.

DORSEY, DAVID FREDERICK, JR, Linguistics. See Volume III, Foreign Languages, Linguistics & Philology.

DORSEY, JOSEPH B, C.S.B, b. Syracuse, N.Y, May 10, 15. ENGLISH. B.A, Univ. Toronto, 38; M.A, Cath. Univ. Am, 46. Instr. ENG, St. Michael's Col, Univ. Toronto, 47-57, asst. prof, 58-61; ASSOC. PROF. & DEAN, ST. JOHN FISHER COL, 61-, v.pres, 67-70, exec. v.pres, 70-72. MLA; NCTE; NEA; East. Asn. Deans. Nineteenth century English literature; American literature; S.T. Coleridge. Add: Dept. of English, St. John Fisher College, 3690 East Ave, Rochester, NY 14618.

DORWEILER, VIRGIL WALTER, b. Guttenberg, Iowa, Feb. 8, 30; m. 63; c. 2. JOURNALISM, ENGLISH LITERATURE. B.A, Univ. Iowa, 56, M.A, 59. Teacher ENG, Granavillo High Sch, Iowa, 58-59; Whitefish Bay High Sch, Wis, 59-62; grad. asst, Univ. Iowa, 62-63; instr, Chapman Col, 63-65; ASSOC. PROF, WESTMAR COL, 65- U.S.A, 51-53; Nat. Guard, 73- NCTE; AAUP; Am. Asn. Higher Educ. Freshman composition; pre-school education; Renaissance literature. Publ: Improving writing skills, Iowa Eng. Yearbk, 61; Voice of turle, column in LeMars Daily Sentinel, 69-; Summer of the swans: review, Elem. Eng, 2/71. Add: Dept. of English, Westmar College, LeMars, IA 51031.

DOSS, ERMA SUE HARRISON, b. Amity, Ark, Apr. 13, 23; m. 46; c. 3. ENGLISH. B.S, Col. Ozarks, 45; M.A, Univ. Ark, 50, Ph.D, 58. Asst. ENG, Univ. Ark, 49-52, 55-56; asst. prof, Ark. Agr. & Mech. Col, 52-55; ARK. POLYTECH. COL, 56-59, assoc. prof, 59-62, PROF, 62-, HEAD DEPT,

67-, dir. freshman Eng, 57-63, chmn. div. lang. & lit, 63-67. MLA; Renaissance Soc. Am; AAUP; Am. Asn. Univ. Women. Shakespeare's imagery and songs. Publ: More sinned against than sinning?, S.Cent. Mod. Lang. Asn. Bull, winter 73. Add: Dept. of English, Arkansas Polytechnic College, Russellville, AR 72801.

DOSTER, WILLIAM CLARK, b. Rochelle, Ga, Feb. 28, 21; m. 42; c. 2. ENGLISH. A.B, Mercer Univ, 42; M.A, Univ. Fla, 48, Ph.D.(Eng), 55. Asst. Eng, Univ. Fla, 46-47; instr, Univ. Ga, 47-51; teaching fel, Univ. Fla, 51-53, instr, 53-55; prof. & chmn. dept, Ouachita Baptist Univ, 55-58; Okla. Baptist Univ, 58-60; chmn. div. commun, Miami-Dade Jr. Col, 60-63, dir. div. humanities, 63-67, prof. ENG, 67-69; INSTR, COL. DuPAGE, 69- Consult, Educ. Testing Serv, 62-67. U.S.A.A.F, 42-45, S/Sgt. NCTE; Conf. Col. Compos. & Commun. American literature. Publ: First perspectives on language, Am. Bk. Co, 63, 69; co-auth, Poetry is for people, Allyn & Bacon, 65 & Toward better writing, W.C. Brown, 67; auth, The differing eye, Glencoe, 70; ed. & co-auth, How to take the CLEP Test, Barron, 73. Add: Dept. of English, College of DuPage, Glen Ellyn, IL 60137.

DOTY, GLADYS, b. Shelbyville, Mo, Nov. 7, 08; m. 32. ENGLISH, SPEECH. A.B, Univ. Colo, 29, M.A, 49; State Univ. Iowa. Instr. speech, Univ. Colo, 48-52; asst, State Univ. Iowa, 53-54; sr. instr. SPEECH, UNIV. COLO, BOULDER, 54-62, asst. prof, 62-73, EMER. ASSOC. PROF, 73- Nat. Asn. For. Stud. Adv; Speech Commun. Asn; Teachers Eng. to Speakers Other Lang. Public address; teaching English as a foreign language. Publ: Co-auth, Language and life in the U.S.A, Row, Peterson, 60, 2nd ed, Harper, 68, 3rd ed, 73 & Writing English, Harper, 65. Add: 2550 University Heights, Boulder, CO 80302.

DOTY, GRESDNA ANN, b. Oelwein, Iowa, Feb. 22, 31. SPEECH, THEATRE. B.A, Iowa State Teachers Col, 53; M.A, Univ. Fla, 57; Ph.D.(theatre), Ind. Univ, 67. Instr. SPEECH & THEATRE, Southwest Tex. State Col, 57-62, asst. prof, 64-65; LA. STATE UNIV, BATON ROUGE, 67-72, ASSOC. PROF, 72- Am. Soc. Theatre Res; Speech Commun. Asn; Am. Theatre Asn. Theatre history; directing. Publ: The career of Anne Brunton Merry in the American theatre, La. State Univ, 71; The shape of American theatre, 1965, South. Speech J, summer 65; Anne Brunton in Bath and London, Theatre Surv, 5/67. Add: Dept. of Speech, Louisiana State University, Baton Rouge, LA 70803.

DOUBLEDAY, NEAL FRANK, b. Lake Mills, Wis, Feb. 19, 05. ENGLISH. A.B, Univ. Wis, 30, A.M, 32, Ph.D, 38; hon. D.Litt, Millikin Univ, 73. Instr, Univ. Wis, 36-39; Mont. State Univ, 39-40; Univ. Conn, 40-45, asst. prof, 45-46; assoc. prof. ENG, MILLIKIN UNIV, 46-51, prof, 51-70, EMER. PROF, 70- MLA. American literature; Hawthorne. Publ: Studies in poetry, Harper & Brothers, 49; Studies in reading, 57, Mark Twain's picture of his America, 60 & Hawthorne: tales of his native land, 62, Heath; Hawthorne's early tales, a critical study, Duke Univ, 72; Channing on the nature of man, J. Relig, 10/43; Hawthorne's use of three Gothic patterns, Col. Eng, 2/46; Hawthorne's estimate of his early work, Am. Lit, 1/66. Add: 1379 W. Macon St, Decatur, IL 62522.

DOUGHERTY, ADELYN (O'CONNELL), b. Highland Park, Ill, Oct. 5, 30. ENGLISH. B.A, Barat Col, 55; M.A, San Francisco Col. Women, 62; Ph.D. (Eng), Cath. Univ. Am, 66; Oxford, 66. ASSOC. PROF. ENG, Barat Col, 66-69; Coe Col, 69-71; IND. STATE UNIV, TERRE HAUTE, 71- MLA; Midwest Mod. Lang. Asn; AAUP. Literary theory and criticism; modern literature; interdisciplinary studies. Publ: Rhythmic structure in the verse of William Butler Yeats, Mouton, The Hague, 73; Intensity as excellence: Keats and The eve of St. Agnes, Barat Rev, 1/68; Literature and theology, In: Theology in revolution, Alba House, 70; The concept of person in D.H. Lawrence's The rainbow, Christianity & Lit, summer 72. Add: Dept. of English, Indiana State University, Terre Haute, IN 47809.

DOUGHERTY, CHARLES THOMAS, b. N.Dak, Jan. 29, 18; m. 42; c. 2. ENGLISH. A.B, Sioux Falls Col, 39; M.A, Univ. Notre Dame, 41; Ph.D.(Eng), Univ. Toronto, 53. Instr. ENG, St. Louis Univ, 46-53, asst. prof, 53-56, assoc. prof, 56-64, PROF, 64-65; UNIV. MO-ST. LOUIS, 65- U.S.A, 41-46. MLA. Victorian literature. Add: Dept. of English, University of Missouri-St. Louis, St. Louis, MO 63121.

DOUGHERTY, JAMES P, b. Wichita, Kans, Mar. 20, 37; m. 62; c. 2. ENGLISH. B.A, St. Louis Univ, 59; NDEA fel. & Ph.D.(Eng), Univ. Pa, 62. Instr. ENG, Univ. Alta, 62-63, asst. prof, 63-66; UNIV. NOTRE DAME, 66-69, ASSOC. PROF, 69-, DIR. GRAD. STUD, 71- Am. Stud. Asn. American literature; religious symbology; American studies. Publ: Robert Frost's directive to the wilderness, Am. Quart, 66; The church and the image of the city, Cross Currents, 66; Language as a reality in E.E. Cummings, Bucknell Rev, 68. Add: Dept. of English, University of Notre Dame, Notre Dame, IN 46556.

DOUGHTIE, EDWARD ORTH, b. Columbus, Ga, Nov. 21, 35; m. 57; c. 2. ENGLISH. A.B, Duke Univ, 58; M.A, Harvard, 60, teaching fels, 60-61, 62-63, Ph.D, 64; Fulbright fel, Univ. London, Eng, 61-62. Asst. prof. ENG, RICE UNIV, 63-69, ASSOC. PROF, 69- Cor. ed,Spenser Newsletter, 69-73; ed, Stud. Eng. Lit, 73- MLA; Renaissance Soc. Am; Lute Soc. Am. English Renaissance. Publ: George Handford's Ayres: unpublished Jacobean song verse, Anglia, 64; ed, Lyrics from English airs, 1596-1622, Harvard Univ, 70; plus others. Add: 3119 Jarrard, Houston, TX 77005.

DOUGLAS, DONALD G, b. Kirksville, Mo, Feb. 8, 30; m. 60; c. 2. ENGLISH, PHILOSOPHY. B.A, Pac. Lutheran Univ, 59; M.A, Univ. Ore, 60; Ph.D. (speech & philos), Univ. Okla, 64. Instr. SPEECH, Univ. Ore, 59-60; Pa. State Univ, 60-61; asst. prof, Wartburg Col, 62-64; assoc. prof, Calif. Lutheran Col, 64-68; ASST. PROF, UNIV. WASH, 68- U.S.A.F, 50-54. Speech Commun. Asn; Am. Forensics Asn; West. Speech Commun. Asn. Publ: A neo-Kantian approach to the ethics of rhetoric, Univ. Mich, 65; co-ed, The vanishing landscape, 70, Justice on trial, 71, ed, Philosophers on rhetoric, 72 & co-ed, Poverty in perspective, 73, Nat. Textbk; co-auth, Traditional and emerging views of rhetoric, 72, auth, Spinoza and reflective knowledge in rhetoric, 72 & Neo-Kantian approach to judgment in criticism, 72, In: Philosophers on Rhetoric; plus others. Add: Dept. of Speech, University of Washington, Seattle, WA 98105.

DOUGLAS, GEORGE HALSEY, b. East Orange, N.J, Jan. 9, 34; m. 61; c. 1. AMERICAN LITERATURE & STUDIES. A.B, Lafayette Col, 56; M.A, Columbia Univ, 66; Ph.D.(philos), Univ. Ill, 68. Instr. ENG, UNIV. ILL, URBANA, 66-69, ASST. PROF, 69- MLA; Am. Soc. Aesthet; Am. Stud. Asn; Pop. Cult. Asn. Literary criticism in America; American culture. Publ: Edmund Wilson and the two worlds of scholarship, J. Aesthet. Educ, 10/72; The new Puritanism of the youth culture, Mod. Age, 3/73; Norman Mailer and the battle of the sexes, Urban style, New Orleans Rev, 3/73. Add: Dept. of English, 317B David Kinley Hall, University of Illinois, Urbana, IL 61801.

DOUGLAS, LOYD, b. Uvalde, Tex, June 15, 06; m. 33; c. 5. ENGLISH LITERATURE. A.B, Tex. Christian Univ, 31, univ. fel, 32-33, M.A, 33; univ. fel, Univ. Tex, 42-43, Ph.D, 45. Asst. prof. ENGLISH, N.Tex. Agr. Col, 33-42; assoc. prof, Tex. Col. Arts & Indust, 45-46; OKLA. STATE UNIV, 46-48, prof, 48-71, EMER. PROF, 71- NCTE (dir, 54, judge, achievement awards, 62-63); MLA. Jonathan Swift; Alexander Pope; 18th century English literature. Publ: Co-auth, Teaching guide for the languages arts, Okla. State Dept. Educ, 57; The worlds of Lemuel Gulliver, Okla. State Univ. Monogr, 68; A severe animadversion on Bossu, PMLA, 9/47; Whose business is articulation?, Okla. Teacher, 2/53. Add: 636 S. Jefferson St, Stillwater, OK 74074.

DOUGLASS, KATHRYN FLOYD, b. Birmingham, Ala, May 18, 28. ENGLISH. B.S, Auburn Univ, 49, fel, 50-52, M.A, 52; Ph.D.(Eng), Univ. Ill, 63. Teaching asst. ENG, Univ. Ill, 54-62; asst. prof, Southeast. La. Col, 62-64; assoc. prof, MERRIMACK COL, 64-67, PROF, 67-, acting chmn. dept, 65-66, chmn, 66-71. MLA; Col. Eng. Asn. Nineteenth century English literature; 20th century Southern literature; William Hazlitt. Add: Dept. of English, Merrimack College, North Andover, MA 01845.

DOVE, GEORGE NAFF, b. Bristol, Tenn, Oct. 28, 13; m. 39; c. 2. ENGLISH. A.B, West. Reserve Univ, 35, M.A, 36; Ed.D.(Eng. educ), Univ. Tenn, 52. Asst. prof. ENG, E.TENN. STATE UNIV, 47-51, assoc. prof, 51-53, CHMN. DEPT, 51-, PROF, 53-, DEAN COL. ARTS & SCI, 56- Am. Asn. Univ. Adminr; Am. Asn. Higher Educ. English education; British and American fiction, especially 19th and 20th centuries; detective fiction. Publ: Appreciation: the need for a working definition, Am. Asn. Univ. Prof. Bull; The haunted personality in Henry James: Tenn. Stud. Lit; The whodunit as introduction to fiction, In: Popular culture methods, 72; plus others. Add: 1801 Seminole Dr, Johnson City, TN 37601.

DOVRE, PAUL J, b. Minnesota, Minn, Jan. 7, 35; m. 58; c. 2. SPEECH, DRAMA. B.A, Concordia Col.(Moorhead, Minn), 58; M.A, Northwest. Univ, 59, Ph.D.(speech), 63; Rockefeller fel, Luther Theol. Sem, 59-60. Instr. speech, Northwest. Univ, 62-63; asst. prof, CONCORDIA COL.(MOORHEAD, MINN), 63-65, assoc. prof, 65-71, PROF. SPEECH COMMUN. & THEATRE ARTS, V.PRES. ACAD. AFFAIRS DEAN COL, 71-, chmn. speech & drama, 64-68, assoc. acad. dean, 67-68, acting dean of Col, 68-69. Mem. bd. trustees, Nat. Debate Tournament Comt, 68-74; bk. rev. ed, J. Am. Forensic Asn, 69-73; asst. to provost, Cent. Mich. Univ, 70-71. U.S.A, 54-56. Speech Commun. Asn; Midwest Forensic Asn.(v.pres, 65-67, pres, 67-68); Cent. States Speech Asn; Am. Forensic Asn. Rhetorical criticism; argumentation theory; rhetorical theory. Publ: Co-auth, Readings in argumentation, Allyn & Bacon, 68; auth, The Non-Partisan League: an expression of agrarian protest, Discourse, autumn 65; The future of speech in the private college, West. Speech, winter 69; The basic course in argumentation: a prospectus, Cent. States Speech J, winter 71. Add: Concordia College, Moorhead, MN 56560.

DOW, MARGUERITE RUTH, b. Ottawa, Ont, June 13, 26. ENGLISH, DRAMA. B.A, Univ. Toronto, 49, M.A, 70, Ed.B, 71; sr. cert, Univ. Alta, 56. Librn. & head dept. Eng, Listowel Dist. High Sch, Ont, 50-52; Renfrew Col. Inst. & Voc. Sch, 52-53; teacher Eng, Brockville Col. Inst. & Voc. Sch, 53-55; Fisher Park High Sch, 55-59; head dept. Eng, Laurentian High Sch, 59-65; assoc. prof. ENG. & THEATRE ARTS, ALTHOUSE COL. EDUC, UNIV. WEST. ONT, 65-72, PROF, 72- Mem. Res. comt, Ont. Dept. Educ, 58-72; lectr, Ont. Sec. Sch. Teachers' Fed, 60-62; critic teacher, Ont. Col. Educ, Univ. Toronto, 63; mem, Stratford Shakespearean Festival Found. Can, 67-; lectr, Can. Counc. Teachers Eng, 69; Althouse Col. Educ. Res. & Develop. Comt. grant, 71-72. Can. Asn. Univ. Teachers; Can. Counc. Teachers Eng; NCTE; fel. Intercontinental Biog. Asn; Eng. Speaking Union Commonwealth; Can. Child & Youth Drama Asn; Can. Col. Teachers. Curriculum design and evaluation techniques in English and theatre arts; secondary school teacher education; culture of China. Publ: Ed, Light from other windows, Macmillan Can, 64; auth, The magic mask, a basic textbook of theatre arts, 66, Macmillan Can; co-auth, Courses of study in the theatre arts, Ont. Inst. Stud. Educ, 69; contrib, Drama activities, Barry Friesen, 71; auth, The influence of the cultural revolution on the teaching of English in the People's Republic of China, Eng. Lang. Teaching, 74. Add: Althouse College of Education, University of Western Ontario, 1137 Western Rd, London, Ont. N6G 1G7, Can.

DOWDEN, WILFRED SELLERS, b. Sebree, Ky, Apr. 5, 17; m. 44; c. 1. ENGLISH. A.B, Vanderbilt Univ, 39, M.A, 40; Ph.D, Univ. N.C, 49. From asst. prof. to assoc. prof. ENG, RICE UNIV, 50-60, PROF, 60-, chmn. dept, 63-68. Fulbright lectr, Univ. Vienna, Austria, 52-53. U.S.N, 42-45. MLA; S.Cent. Mod. Lang. Asn.(pres, 66). Nineteenth century English literature; English and German literary relations of the 19th century; Byron. Publ: Ed, The letters of Thomas Moore, Clarendon, 64; auth, Joseph Conrad: the imaged style, Vanderbilt Univ, 70; Byron and the Austrian censorship, Keats-Shelley J. Add: Dept. of English, Rice University, Houston, TX 77001.

DOWELL, GEORGE BRENDAN, b. New York, N.Y, Dec. 15, 09. SPEECH & DRAMA. Dipl. playwrighting, Yale, 33; B.S, N.Y. Univ, 45; M.A, Columbia Univ, 46, Ed.D.(commun. arts), 55; Oxford, summer 58. Asst. prof. theatre, Smith Col, 48-55; drama, Skidmore Col, 55-57; assoc. prof. & dir. centennial prog, Vassar Col, 57-61; PROF. SPEECH & DRAMA, GOUCHER COL, 62-, stud. grant, Sophia Univ, Tokyo, summer 66. Co-dir, summer theatre, Bryn Mawr Col, 50, 51; spec. lectr. & dir. theatre prog, Manhattanville Col, winter 60-61; dir. theatre sect, Inst. Hist. Performing Arts in Am, Peabody Conserv. Music & Goucher Col, summer 67, 68; Fulbright grant, summer 70. U.S.A.A.F, 42-44. Am. Theatre Asn; Speech Commun. Asn; AAUP. Playwrighting; history of the American theatre; Noh theatre studies. Publ: Co-ed, Heritage—75th anniversary play, 51 & Covenant—75th anniversary play, 52, Smith Col; co-auth, The magnificent enterprize, Vassar Col. Centennial Chronicle, 62; auth, The second American college company tour of Great Britain, Am. Educ. Theatre J, 53; Herodes reconstructed, Players Mag, 57; Sean O'Casey on the twilight of life, Baltimore Sun Papers, 65. Add: Dept. of Speech & Drama, Goucher College, Towson, Baltimore, MD 21204.

DOWELL, PETER WINTHROP, b. New York, N.Y, Jan. 31, 37; m. 61; c. 1. ENGLISH, AMERICAN STUDIES. A.B, Princeton, 58; Woodrow Wilson fel, Univ. Minn, 58-59, M.A, 61, univ. fel, 62-63, Ph.D.(Am. stud), 65. Instr. ENG. EMORY UNIV, 63-65, asst. prof, 65-70, ASSOC. PROF. ENG. & AM. STUD, 70- Am. Stud. Asn. American literary and cultural history, 1890-1930; 20th century American poetry; Afro-American literature. Publ: Counter-images and their function in the poetry of Robert Frost, Tenn. Stud. Lit, 69; Van Wyck Brooks and the progressive frame of mind, Mid-continent Am. Stud. J, spring 70. Add: Dept. of English, Emory University, Atlanta, GA 30322.

DOWELL, RICHARD WALKER, b. Bloomington, Ind, Nov. 26, 31; m. 57; c. 4. ENGLISH, AMERICAN LITERATURE. B.S, Ind. State Univ, 57; M.A, Univ. Colo, 60; fel, Ind. Univ, 61-63, Ph.D.(Eng), 68. Instr. ENG, Univ. Colo, 57-60; IND. STATE UNIV, TERRE HAUTE, 63-66, asst. prof, 67-71, ASSOC. PROF, 71- U.S.N, 49-53. American literature, 1875-1925; Theodore Dreiser. Add: Dept. of English, Indiana State University, Terre Haute, IN 47809.

DOWNES, DAVID ANTHONY, b. Victor, Colo, Aug. 17, 27; m. 49; c. 3. ENGLISH. B.A, Regis Col, 49; M.A, Marquette Univ, 50; Ph.D.(Eng), Univ. Wash, 55. Instr. Eng, Gonzaga Univ, 50-53; asst. prof, Seattle Univ, 53-59, assoc. prof, 59-64, prof. & chmn. dept, 64-67; PROF. ENG, CALIF. STATE UNIV, CHICO, 68-, COORD. HUMANITIES PROG, 73-, dean humanities, 68-72, dean educ. develop, 72-73, res. grant, 70. Seattle Univ. res. grants, 61-63; res. grant, Brit. Mus, summer 67; Am. Counc. Educ dean insts. fel, fall 72. MLA. The genius of John Ruskin; criticism; western novel. Publ: Gerard Manley Hopkins: a study of his ignatian spirit, 60, Victorian portraits: Hopkins and Pater, 65 & The temper of Victorian belief: studies in the religious novels of Pater, Kingsley and Newman, 72, Twayne; The Hopkins enigma, Thought, 60; Hopkins and Aquinas, Victorian Poetry, 65; Studies in structure, Renascence, 66. Add: Dept. of English, California State University, Chico, CA 95926.

DOWNEY, JEAN, b. New York, N.Y, Aug. 19, 23. ENGLISH & AMERICAN LITERATURE. B.S, N.Y. Univ, 46, M.A, 50; Ph.D.(Eng), Univ. Ottawa, 56. Instr. ENG, Hillyer Col, 54-56; PROF, SOUTH. CONN. STATE COL, 56- West. Hist. Asn; Soc. Am. Arch; Eng-Speaking Union. American literature of the west; Chinese in American literature. Publ: Ed, Kavanaugh: a tale, 65 & Franklin Evans, Col. & Univ, 67; auth, Three unpublished letters: Howells-Cooke, Am. Lit, 1/61; Whittier and Cooke: unpublished letters, Quaker Hist, spring 63; Atlantic friends: Howells and Cooke, Am. Notes & Queries, 5/63; plus others. Add: Madison Towers 5-D, 111 Park St, New Haven, CT 06511.

DOWNING, EDNA C, b. Minneapolis, Minn. ENGLISH. B.S, Univ. Minn, 41; M.E, Macalester Col, 53. Teacher high sch, Minn, 42-44, teacher & dir. speech, 44-51; teacher jr. high sch, Minn, 51-52; TEACHER ENG, SANFORD JR. HIGH SCH, MINNEAPOLIS, 52-, chmn. dept, 52-70. State judge, Achievement Awards Prog, NCTE, 57-67, mem. comt. publ. of affiliates, 58-, chmn, 63-67, consult, 67-, mem. sec. sect. comt, 71-74; lectr, Univ. Iowa & Syracuse Univ, 62-69, Univ. Minn, 67-69; acting consult. sec. Eng. & humanities, Minneapolis Pub. Schs, 70-71. Valley Forge Medal & Citation, Freedoms Found, 65. NCTE (liaison officer; dir); NEA. English; speech; Latin. Publ: Units for English grades 7-12 on how to read and use the newspaper, Am. Newspaper Publ. Asn, 61; Latin lives at Maria Sanford Junior High School, Clearing House, 12/59; The newspaper—a dynamic reading textbook, Minn. J. Educ, 9/65; Units on the newspaper—grades XI and XII, In: Using mass media in the schools, Appleton, 62. Add: 3935 Fremont Ave. N, Minneapolis, MN 55412.

DOWNS, CALVIN W, b. El Dorado, Ark, Sept. 21, 36; m. 63; c. 1. COMMUNICATION, SPEECH. B.A, Harding Col, 58; M.A, Mich. State Univ, 59, Ph.D.(speech), 63. Resident-coord. Agency Int. Develop. sems. commun, Mich. State Univ, 61-62; asst. prof. speech, Univ. Md, 62-64; speech & business, Northwest. Univ, 64-67; SPEECH, UNIV. KANS, 67-71, ASSOC. PROF, 71- Asst. prof. speech, Univ. Denver, summer 66; Found. Econ. Educ. fels, Continental Can Co, summer 67 & Santa Fe Railway, summer 68. Speech Commun. Asn; Nat. Soc. Stud. Commun; Int. Soc. Gen. Semantics; Cent. States Speech Commun. Asn. Organizational communication; interviewing. Publ: Speech for the professional, Nat. Textbk, 68; What the selection interview accomplishes, 68 & Perceptions of the interview, 68, Personnel Admin. Add: Dept. of Speech Communication, University of Kansas, Lawrence, KS 66044.

DOWNS, LENTHIEL HOWELL, b. Goshen, N.Y, May 26, 15; m. 52; c. 2. MODERN DRAMA, COMPARATIVE LITERATURE. B.A, Tusculum Col, 36; M.A, State Univ. Iowa, 37; Ph.D.(Am. lit), 40; Univ. Sorbonne, 50-51; Columbia Univ, summer 63. Prof. ENG, Presbyterian Col, 40-42; asst. prof, Univ. Tulsa, 46-47; DENISON UNIV, 47-49, assoc. prof, 49-54, PROF, 54- U.S.A, 42-46; Bronze Star Medal. Modern drama. Publ: Co-auth, A primer for playgoers, Prentice-Hall, 2nd ed, 69 & Contemporary literature of the Western World (4 vols), Barron's Educ. Ser, 73. Add: Dept. of English, Denison University, Granville, OH 43023.

DOXEY, WILLIAM SANFORD, JR, b. Miami, Fla, Jan. 20, 35; m. 59; c. 3. AMERICAN & CONTINENTAL LITERATURE. B.A, Fla. State Univ, 61, M.A, 63; Ph.D.(Eng), Univ. N.C, Chapel Hill, 70. Instr. ENG, Mid. Tenn. State Col, 63-65; asst. prof, W.GA. COL, 68-71, ASSOC. PROF, 71- S.Atlantic Mod. Lang. Asn; MLA. William Blake; contemporary novel; short story. Publ: A dissenting opinion of Flannery O'Connor's A good man is hard to find, Stud. Short Fiction, spring 73; contrib, Prairie Schooner, Mich. Quart. Rev. & Southwest Rev. Add: Dept. of English, West Georgia College, Carrollton, GA 30117.

DOYLE, ANNE THERESE, b. Boston, Mass, Oct. 3, 34. ENGLISH. A.B, Regis Col.(Mass), 56; M.A, Univ. Ill, 57, fel, 56-58, Ph.D.(Eng), 63. Instr. ENG, MT. HOLYOKE COL, 60-63, asst. prof, 63-71, ASSOC. PROF, 71- Fel. Restoration drama, William Andrews Clark Mem. Libr, Los Angeles, summer 65; vis. asst. prof, Univ. Calif, Santa Barbara, 66-67. MLA. Seventeenth century literature and drama. Publ: Dryden's authorship of Notes and observations on the Empress of Morocco, Stud. Eng. Lit, 66. Add: Dept. of English, Mt. Holyoke College, South Hadley, MA 01075.

DOYLE, CHARLES DESMOND, b. Birmingham, Eng, Oct. 18, 28; m. 59; c. 4. ENGLISH, AMERICAN STUDIES. B.A, Victoria Univ, N.Z, 57, M.A, 59; Ph.D, Univ. Auckland, 68. Tutor ENG, Victoria Univ, N.Z, 57-58; lectr, Univ. Auckland, 61-66, sr. lectr, 66-68; ASSOC. PROF, UNIV. VICTORIA (B.C), 68- UNESCO Writer's fel, 58-59; Am. Counc. Learned Soc. fel, 67-68; vis. fel, Am. Stud, Yale, 67-68. Am. Stud. Asn; Can. Asn. Univ. Teachers. William Carlos Williams; W.B. Yeats' A vision; American poetry. Publ: A splinter of glass, Pegasus Press, N.Z, 56; Distances, Pauls, 63; Messages for Herod, 65 & Recent poetry in New Zealand, 65, Collins; R.A.K. Mason, Twayne, 70; Earth meditations, Coach House, Toronto, '71; Earthshot, Exeter Bks, Eng, 72; The moral world of Faulkner, Renascence, fall 66; A reading of Paterson III, Mod. Poetry Stud, 70; The occasions of Irving Layton, Can. Lit, 72; plus others. Add: Dept. of English, University of Victoria, Victoria, B.C, Can.

DOYLE, ESTHER M, b. Boston, Mass, Mar. 21, 10. ENGLISH, SPEECH. B.L.I, Emerson Col, 35; M.A, Boston Univ, 40; Rockefeller Found. scholar, summer 43; Danforth Found. fel, summer 53; Ph.D.(interpretation), Northwest. Univ, 64. Teacher elem. schs, Mass, 29-37; oral Eng. supvr. & teacher, high schs, N.Y, 37-44; hosp. recreation worker, Mil. Welfare Serv, Am. Red Cross, 44-45; from instr. to prof. ENG, JUNIATA COL, 45-64, DANA PROF, 64-, CHMN; DEPT, 67- Lectr, Bethany Bibl. Sem, 60-61; prof, NDEA Inst, Univ. Ariz, summer 67, vis. prof, spring 71; participant, Nat. Humanities Series progs, 69-73; co-ed, Stud. in Interpretation, Amsterdam, 72- Speech Commun. Asn; NCTE; MLA. Verse drama. Add: Dept. of English, Juniata College, Huntingdon, PA 16652.

DOYLE, JOHN ROBERT, JR, b. Dinwiddie Co, Va, Jan. 10, 10; m. 42; c. 1. ENGLISH & AMERICAN LITERATURE. B.A, Randolph-Macon Col, 32; M.A, Univ. Va, 37; M.A, Bread Loaf Sch. Eng, 41; Univ. N.C, 44-45. Head dept. Eng, high sch, Va, 32-40; instr, Clemson Col, 40-41; asst. prof, The Citadel, 41-44; lectr. physics, Univ. N.C, 44-45; mem. fac. lit, Stephens Col, 45-46; asst. prof. ENG, THE CITADEL, 46-57, assoc. prof, 59-63, PROF, 63- Smith-Mundt vis. prof. Am. lit, Univs. Cape Town & Witwatersrand, 58. MLA. English literature, especially Renaissance; American literature, especially modern poetry; South African literature, especially poetry in English, 1820 to present. Publ: The poetry of Robert Frost, Hafner & Univ. Witwatersrand, 63; William Plomer, 68, Francis Carey Slater, 71 & Thomas Pringle, 72, Twayne; Pacing the long street with Donald Davidson, autumn 66 & The poetry of William Plomer, autumn 67, Sewanee Rev; A reading of Robert Frost's Directive, Ga. Rev, winter 68; plus others. Add: Dept. of English, The Citadel, Charleston, SC 29409.

DOYLE, JOSEPH, b. Jersey City, N.J, Dec. 13, 15; m. 42; c. 1. ENGLISH. A.B, Princeton, 37; scholar, Columbia Univ, 39-40, M.A, 41, univ. fel, 47-48; Ph.D.(Eng), 52. Instr. French, Peekskill Mil. Acad, 38-39; asst. Eng, Columbia Univ, 41-43, instr, 46-47; asst. prof, Washington & Jefferson Col, 48-50; prof. lit. & dean, Washington Col, 53-58; acad. dean, Am. Int. Col, 58-60; PROF. ENG, UNIV. HARTFORD, 60-, dean Sch. Arts & Sci, 60-66. U.S.N.R, 43-46, Lt. Col. Eng. Asn; MLA; East. Asn. Deans (pres, 59-62). Nineteenth century American literature; life and works of G.E. Woodberry; the later influence of transcendental idealism on American literature. Add: Dept. of English, University of Hartford, 200 Bloomfield Ave, West Hartford, CT 06117.

DOYLE, PAUL A, b. Carbondale, Pa, Dec. 6, 25; m. 54; c. 3. ENGLISH. A.B, Univ. Scranton, 46; A.M, Fordham Univ, 48, Ph.D.(Eng), 55. Instr. ENG, Fordham Univ, 48-54, asst. prof, 54-60; St. John's Univ, 60-61, assoc. prof, 61-62; NASSAU COMMUNITY COL, 62-65, PROF, 65-, ED-IN-CHIEF, NASSAU REV, 70- Contributing ed, Best sellers, 61-; consult, Nat. Educ. Asn. J. in choosing 100 best educ. bks. of year, 64-; consult, Choice: books for college libr, 65-; ed-in-chief, Evelyn Waugh newslett, 67-; bibliog. adv, Eng. Lit. in Transition, 72- NCTE; Am. Inst. Hist. Pharmacy; Am. Comt. Irish Stud. Contemporary British and American novel; contemporary Continental and American drama; twentieth century Anglo-Irish literature. Publ: Co-auth, Basic college skills, Rinehart, 59 & Alexander Pope's Iliad: An examination by William Melmoth, Cath. Univ. Am, 60; auth, Readings in pharmacy, Wiley, 62; Pearl S. Buck, 65, Sean O'Faolain, 68 & Liam O'Flaherty: a critical introduction, 71, Twayne; A concordance to the collected poems of James Joyce, Scarecrow, 66; Evelyn Waugh, Eerdmanns, 68; Paul Vincent Carroll, Bucknell Univ, 71; co-ed, Henry David Thoreau: studies and commentaries, Fairleigh Dickinson Univ, 72; ed, Liam O'Flaherty: an annotated bibliography, Whitson, 72; co-ed, Evelyn Waugh: a checklist of primary and secondary material, Whitston, 72; auth, O'Flaherty's real view of The informer, Dublin Rev, spring 70; Whitman and Sean O'Faolain, Walt Whitman Rev, 12/70; ed, Sheila Kaye-Smith: an annotated bibliography of writings about her, Eng. Lit. in Transition, 72; plus many others. Add: 161 Park Ave, Williston Park, NY 11596.

DOYLE, TERESA ANN, O.S.B, b. St. Joseph, Mo, July 8, 05. ENGLISH. A.M, Univ. Kans, 38; Ph.D, Fordham Univ, 48; Cambridge, summer 64. Instr. Eng. & Latin, BENEDICTINE COL, 42-44, asst. prof, 48-50, assoc. prof, 50-51, PROF, 52-, head dept, 52-64. Ed, Benedictine Rev, 49-64; ed, Am. Benedictine Rev, 64-69; mem. int. bd. eds, Cistercian Publ, 69-; res, Brit. Mus, 70-71; mem, Am. Benedictine Acad. MLA; Mediaeval Acad. Am, Cath. Renascence Soc. Medieval and Renaissance literature; monastic studies and spirituality. Publ: Assoc. ed, American profile, Sadlier, 44. Add: Benedictine College, South Campus, Atchison, KS 66002.

DOYNO, VICTOR A, b. Chicago, Ill, July 12, 37; m. 59; c. 3. ENGLISH. B.A, Miami Univ, 59; M.A, Harvard, 60; Ph.D.(Eng), Ind. Univ, 66. Instr. ENG, Rutgers Univ, 63-65; Princeton, 65-66; asst. prof, STATE UNIV. N.Y. BUFFALO, 66-74, ASSOC. PROF, 74-, res. fel. & grant. Eng. Inst; MLA; Renaissance Soc. Am. American and Renaissance literature. Publ: Ed, Parthenophil and Parthenophe, South. Ill. Univ, 71; auth, Patterns in The Great Gatsby, winter 66 & Over the author's shoulder: structure and composition of Huck Finn, summer 68, Mod. Fiction Stud; Blake's composition of London, Essays in Criticism, 1/72; plus others. Add: Dept. of English, State University of New York at Buffalo, Buffalo, NY 14214.

DRAKE, ALBERT DEE, b. Portland, Ore, Mar. 26, 35; m. 60; c. 3. CONTEMPORARY AMERICAN LITERATURE, CREATIVE WRITING. B.A, Univ. Ore, 62, M.F.A, 66. Res. asst, Ore. Res. Inst, 63-64; Univ. Ore, 65, teaching asst. ENG, 65-66; asst. prof, MICH. STATE UNIV, 66-70, ASSOC. PROF, 70-, fac. grant, 68. Training Teacher Trainers teaching fel, 71-72; Coord. Counc. Lit. Mag. grant, 72. Experimental fiction; contemporary poetry; small presses and literary magazines. Publ: Co-auth, 3 northwest poets, Quixote, 70; auth, Pomes, Stone, 72; The chicken which became a rat, In: Best American Short Stories, 1971, Houghton, 72. Add: Dept. of English, Michigan State University, East Lansing, MI 48823.

DRAKE, GERTRUDE COYNE, Comparative Study of Literature. See Volume III, Foreign Languages, Linguistics & Philology.

DRAKE, ORMOND JOHN, b. Blissfield, Mich, Apr. 15, 06. SPEECH. A.B, Univ. Mich, 30, A.M, 31; Univ. Wis, 31; Columbia Univ; Litt.D, Hartwick Col, 64. Instr. speech, Mich. State Col, 30-35; instr, N.Y. Univ, 36-37; adv. instr. Eng, Princeton, 37-38; from asst. prof. to prof. speech, col. arts & sci, N.Y. UNIV, 38-71, dir. admis, univ. col. & col. engineering, 42-45, asst. dean univ. col, 45-54, asst. secy, dir. pub. occasions, univ, 54-56, assoc. dean, sch. continuing educ. & dir. Town Hall, 56-71, EMER. PROF. SPEECH, 71- Moderator TV prog, Univ-WATV, WCBS & others, 54-; consult, var. orgns, N.Y, 56-; trustee, Parsons Sch. Design, 65-68; mem. nat. bd. overseers, Dropsie Col, 68-; consult. commun, Cunningham & Walsh Advert. Agency, 73- Distinguished serv. award from Mayor, New York, 65. Publ: Handbook of objective speaking. Add: 225 Canal St, Ft. Plain, NY 13339.

DRAKE, ROBERT (YOUNG, JR), b. Ripley, Tenn, Oct. 20, 30. ENGLISH. B.A, Vanderbilt Univ, 52, M.A, 53; M.A, Yale, 54, Ph.D, 55. Instr. ENG, Univ. Mich, 55-58; Northwest. Univ, 58-61; asst. prof, Univ. Tex, 61-65; assoc. prof, UNIV. TENN, KNOXVILLE, 65-73, PROF, 73- Res. grants, Bollingen Found, Northwest. Univ. & Inst. Philos. & Hist. Stud, 60; lectr. fiction, Annual Writers' Conf, N.C, 66; N.Mex, 67; writer in residence, annual meeting, Ga. Writers' Asn, 66; dir. short fiction conf, Newberry Col, 68. MLA; S.Atlantic Mod. Lang. Asn; Soc. Stud. South. Lit. Practical criticism; creative writing; contemporary literature. Publ: Amazing grace, Chilton, 65; Flannery O'Connor, Eerdmans, 66; ed, The writer and his tradition, proceedings of the 1969 Southern Literary Festival, Univ. Tenn, 69; auth, The single heart, 71 & The burning bush, 74, Aurora; Saki: some problems and a bibliography, Eng. Fiction in Transition, spring 62; plus others. Add: Dept. of English, University of Tennessee, Knoxville, TN 37916.

DRAKE, WILLIAM D, b. Russell, Iowa, Aug. 22, 22. ENGLISH, LINGUISTICS. B.A, Univ. Iowa, 45, M.A, 48; Ph.D.(Am. lit), Univ. Ariz, 67. Instr. Eng, Univ. Iowa, 46-48; Univ. Wyo, 48-49; Univ. Ariz, 61-67; assoc. prof. Am. lit. & ling, STATE UNIV. N.Y. COL. OSWEGO, 67-71, PROF. ENG. & CHMN. DEPT, 71- State Univ. N.Y. fel, summer 68; assoc. ed, Complete writings of Thoreau, Princeton, 71-; dir. summer stud. prog, Univ. London, 73; chmn. Am. lit, State Univ. N.Y. Awards Comt, 73-76. MLA; Thoreau Soc; NCTE. MLA; NCTE. American literature, especially transcendentalism and puritanism. Publ: The way to spell, Chandler Publ, 67; The way to punctuate, Intext Publ, 71; Walden and A week on the Concord and Merrimack Rivers, In: Thoreau, Prentice-Hall, 62; Spiritual ideals and scientific fact; Thoreau's search for reality, In: Thoreau western centenary, Utah State Univ. Monogr. Ser, 63; Progress without pain: what can be done about the undergraduate English curriculum, Asn. Dept. Eng. Bull, fall 71. Add: Dept. of English, State University of New York College at Oswego, Oswego, NY 13126.

DRAPER, JOHN WILLIAM, b. Hastings-on-Hudson, N.Y, July 23, 93; m. 19; c. 3. ENGLISH CULTURE. A.B, N.Y. Univ, 14, A.M, 15; A.M, Harvard, 18, Ph.D, 20. Instr. Eng, N.Y. Univ, 16-17; Univ. Minn, 20-21; lectr. Eng. lit, Bryn Mawr Col, 21-22; assoc. prof. ENG, Univ. Maine, 22-24, prof, 24-29; W.VA. UNIV, 29-63, EMER. PROF, 63- Guggenheim fel, Eng, 28-29; guest prof, Univ. Munich, 49; Univ. Toulouse, 52. MLA; Mod. Humanities Res. Asn, Gt. Brit. Eighteenth century culture; Shakespeare and Spenser; Oriental culture. Publ: The humors and Shakespeare's characters, Duke Univ, 45 & AMS Press, 65; The Twelfth night of Shakespeare's audience, Stanford Univ, 50; The Othello of Shakespeare's audience, Didier, Paris, 52 & Octagon, 66; The tempo-patterns of Shakespeare's plays, Carl Winters, Heidelberg, 57; Stratford to Dogberry, Univ. Pittsburg, 61; Hamlet of Shakespeare's audience, 66, Funeral elegy and the rise of English romanticism, 67 & Eighteenth century English aesthetics: a bibliography, 67; Octagon; Orientalia and Shakespearena, Vantage, 74. Add: 100 McLane Ave, Morgantown, WV 26505.

DREHER, BARBARA BENDER, b. Waterbury, Conn, Dec. 27, 33; m. 56; c. 2. SPEECH. B.A, Univ. Conn, 55; M.A, Univ. Ill, 56; Ph.D.(speech), Ohio State Univ, 66. Asst. prof. SPEECH, WRIGHT STATE UNIV, 66-74, ASSOC. PROF, 74- Speech Commun. Asn; Am. Speech & Hearing Asn. Phonetics; language development. Publ: Phonological development in formal and informal learning environments, Hispanic, 5/73; co-auth, Non-semantic auditory discrimination: foundation for second language learning, Mod. Lang. J, 4/72; auth, Bibliotherapy for the communication disordered: rationale and materials, Asha, 9/73. Add: Dept. of Speech, Wright State University, Dayton, OH 45431.

DRESSER, WILLIAM R, b. Highland Park, Mich, Nov. 3, 29; m. 55; c. 2. SPEECH. B.A, Denison Univ, 51; M.A, Northwest. Univ, 54, Ph.D, 62. Instr. Eng, Univ. N.H, 54-56; speech, Boston Univ, 58-60; asst. prof, DENISON UNIV, 60-66, assoc. prof, 66-72, PROF. SPEECH COMMUN, 72- Speech Commun. Asn; Am. Forensic Asn; Int. Commun. Asn. Persuasion; perception of oral stimuli. Publ: Co-ed, Dimensions of meaning, Bobbs, 70; auth, Studies of the effects of evidence: implications for forensics, Am. Forensic Asn. Register, 62; Effects of satisfactory and unsatisfactory evidence in a speech of advocacy, Speech Monogr, 63; The impact of evidence on decision making, J. Am. Forensic Asn, 5/66. Add: Dept. of Speech, Denison University, Granville, OH 43023.

DREW, FRASER BRAGG, b. Randolph, Vt, June 23, 13. ENGLISH. A.B, Univ. Vt, 33; fel, Duke Univ, 34-35, A.M, 35, scholar, 35-36; Syracuse Univ, 39-41; Ph.D.(Eng), Univ. Buffalo, 52. Instr. Latin & Eng, Green Mt. Jr. Col, 36-39; ENG, STATE UNIV. N.Y. COL. BUFFALO, 45-47, asst. prof, 47-52, PROF, 52-, DISTINGUISHED TEACHING PROF, 73-, chmn. dept, 57-63. State Univ. N.Y. Res. Found. grants-in-aid, 60, 67; St. Patrick Scholar. Fund scholar, Ireland, 67. Irishman of the Year Award, 70. Poetry Soc. Am; Acad. Am. Poets; Irish Am. Cult. Inst; Am. Comt. Irish Stud; Col. Eng. Asn; Housman Soc. Twentieth century poetry and fiction; bibliography and collecting; Irish studies. Publ: John Masefield's England: a study of the national themes in his work, Fairleigh Dickinson Univ, 73; Contributions to a bibliography of John Masefield, Papers Bibliog. Soc. Am, 59; Next parish to Boston: the Blaskets and their literature, spring 68 & The Irish influence on Robinson Jeffers, summer 68, Eire-Ireland; plus others. Add: 119 Thurston Ave, Kenmore, NY 14217.

DREWRY, CECELIA HODGES, b. New York, N.Y, Jan. 10, 26; m. 52. SPEECH & DRAMA, ENGLISH. A.B, Hunter Col, 45; A.M, Columbia Univ, 48; Cert. stud. in Shakespeare, Univ. Birmingham, 49; Ph.D.(speech), Northwest. Univ, 67; cert. African stud, Univ. Ghana at Legon, summer 69. Instr. speech, Talledega Col, 46-47; teacher jr. & sr. high schs, N.Y, 47-59; high sch. N.J, 59-61; instr. speech, Douglass Col, Rutgers Univ, 62-65, asst. prof, 65-70, assoc. prof. speech & dramatic art, 70; ASSOC. PROF. LECTR. ENG. & ASST. DEAN COL, PRINCETON, 70- Dir. speech, Penthouse Dance & Drama Theatre, N.Y, 49-51; mem. acad. counsel, Rutgers Univ, 63-67; vis. instr, Teachers Col, Columbia Univ, spring 68; vis. lectr, Princeton, fall 68; vis. team mem, Mid. States Asn. Col. & Sec. Schs, 68-; Danforth Assoc, 69; mem, Ctr. Am. Woman and Politics, Eagleton Inst. Politics, Rutgers Univ, 70-; mem. bd. trustees, Nat. Educ. TV-Channel 13, 71-; mem. bd. trustees, Carnegie Comn. Higher Educ, 71- MLA; Speech Commun. Asn; Am. Educ. Theatre Asn; AAUP. Samuel Daniel; oral interpretation of literature—works of Dylan Thomas; oral tradition of literature in Ghana. Publ: Co-ed, Afro-American history: past to present, Scribner, 71; contrib, Black life and culture in the U.S, Crowell, 71. Add: Dept. of English, Princeton University, Princeton, NJ 08540.

DREWRY, JOHN ELDRIDGE, b. Griffin, Ga, June 4, 02; m. 25, 50; c. 1. JOURNALISM. A.B, Univ. Ga, 21, B.J, 22, A.M, 25; summers, Columbia Univ, 24, 25. Instr. JOUR, Grady Sch. Jour, UNIV. GA, 22-24, adj. prof, 24-26, assoc. prof, 26-30, prof, 30-69, dir, 32-40, dean sch, 40-69, EMER. PROF. & DEAN, 69- Organizer press bur, Univ. Ga, 21, publicity dir, 21-28, 30-32, assoc. ed, Univ. Alumni Rec, 25-39; lectr, Lucy Cobb Inst, 25-26; organizer & univ. dir, Ga. Scholastic Press Asn; organizer & dir, Ga. Col. Press Asn; univ. adminr, George Foster Peabody Radio & TV Awards; Ga. Radio & TV Inst; Ga. Press Inst; South. Indust. Ed. Inst; reporter & news ed, Athens Banner Herald; capitol reporter & state ed, Assoc. Press; correspondent, Atlanta Constitution, Atlanta J. & Christian Sci. Monitor. Asn. Educ. Journ(v.pres, 28, pres, 30, past chmn & secy, joint comt. on educ. for jour); Am. Asn. Schs. & Dept. Jour.(past v.pres); NEA; Newcomen Soc; Am. Counc. Educ. Jour. Publ: Contemporary journalism; Dimensional journalism; Journalism is communications; Concerning the fourth estate; Book reviewing; Post biographies of famous journalists; New horizons in journalism; The what, why and how of communications; Journalistic escalation; plus others. Add: Grady School of Journalism, University of Georgia, Athens, GA 30601.

DREXLER, MALCOLM BURTON, b. Brooklyn, N.Y, Dec. 27, 25; m. 57; c. 1. SPEECH, DRAMA. B.A, Johns Hopkins Univ, 49; M.A, Univ. Minn, 51; Purdue Univ, 51-52; Ph.D.(theatre), Univ. Ill, 64. Asst. speech & theatre, Purdue Univ, 51-52; instr. speech & drama, IOWA STATE UNIV, 52-56, asst. prof, 56-65, assoc. dir. theatre, 52-65, assoc. prof. SPEECH & DRAMA, 65-72, PROF, 72-, DIR. INTERPRETATION, 66- Iowa State Arts Counc. Drama consultation grant, 68. Hosp.C, U.S.N.R, 44-46. Speech Commun. Asn; Am. Theatre Asn; Am. Interprof. Inst. Dramatic criticism; oral interpretation; theatre history. Publ: Contrib, A digest of 500 plays: plot outlines and contributor production notes, Crowell-Collier Press, 63. Add: Dept. of Speech, Iowa State University, Ames, IA 50010.

DREYFUS, LEE SHERMAN, b. Milwaukee, Wis, June 20, 26; m. 47; c. 2. SPEECH, JOURNALISM. B.A, Univ. Wis, 49, M.A, 52, Ph.D.(rhetoric), 57. Instr. speech, Wayne State Univ, 52-56, asst. prof, 56-60, assoc. prof, 60-62; prof, Univ. Wis, 62-67; PROF. COMMUN, UNIV. WIS-STEVENS POINT, 67-, CHANCELLOR, 72-, pres, 67-72. Dir. Res. Consults, 57-61; consult, Nat. Educ. TV & Radio Ctr, 59-61; Nat. Instr. Libr, 63-66; chief of mission Vietnam contract for higher educ, Univ. Wis-Stevens Point Found, Inc, 67; mem. comt. fed. relat, Am. Asn. State Cols. & Univs, 68; mem. reviewing comt. Comn. Cols. & Univs, N.Cent. Asn. Cols. & Sec. Schs, 69; chmn. adv. panel, Army ROTC affairs, 70. U.S.N, 44-46. Nat. Asn. Educ. Broadcasters (bd. dir, 65-); Speech Commun. Asn. Radio; television; propaganda. Publ: Analysis of persuasion techniques in Congress, Univ. Microfilms, 58; co-auth, Televised instruction, RCA & Wayne Univ, 62 & The farther vision—ETV today, Univ. Wis, 67; auth, Wisconsin's the early bird again, Am. Sch. Bd. J, fall 65; Students visit via satellite, Nat. Asn. Educ. Broadcasters J, 5/66; The development and promise of technology in education, J. Animal Sci, spring 68. Add: University of Wisconsin-Stevens Point, Stevens Point, WI 54481.

DRINNON, RICHARD, American History, American Studies. See Volume I, History.

DRISCOLL, LORETTO MARIE, C.D.P, b. Ludlow, Ky, Nov. 11, 16. ENGLISH. A.B, Villa Madonna Col, 39; B.S. in L.S, Cath. Univ. Am, 46, M.A, 50; Ph.D.(Eng), Fordham Univ, 59. Librn, THOMAS MORE COL.(KY), 50-55, asst. prof. ENG, 60-72, ASSOC. PROF. & CHMN. DEPT, 72- Summer grants, Union for Res. & Experimentation in Higher Educ, 68 & 69; NDEA, Stephens Col, 69; Am. Counc. Learned Soc, Univ. Kans, 72; Nat. Endowment for Humanities, Boston, 73; Nat. Endowment for Humanities grant, Ireland, 74-75. MLA; NCTE; Asn. Depts. Eng. Poetry; criticism; innovative teaching. Add: Dept. of English, Thomas More College, Box 85, Ft. Mitchell, KY 41017.

DRISKELL, LEON VINSON, b. Athens, Ga, Dec. 6, 32; m. 56; c. 5. ENGLISH, HUMANITIES. A.B, Univ. Ga, 55, M.A, 56; Ph.D.(Eng), Univ. Tex, 64. Instr. Eng, Univ. Ga, Athens, 55-56, hist, Augusta, 56-57; hist. & Eng, Univ. Md, Far East Div, 57-58; asst. prof. Eng, Birmingham-South. Col, 60-62; instr. Eng, Univ. Cincinnati, 62-64; asst. prof, UNIV. LOUISVILLE, 64-68, assoc. prof, 68-73, PROF. ENG. & HUMANITIES, 73-, ASSOC. THEATRE ARTS, 69- Evaluator, Health, Educ. & Welfare Region III Dramatics Enrichment Prog, 66-68; Nat. Found. for Humanities & grad. sch. coord, humanities inst, Univ. Louisville, summer 67, prog. coord, 20th Century Lit. Conf, 73; Nat. Found. for Humanities Younger Scholar Award for Henry Fielding Proj, summer 68; guest, Yaddo artist colony, Saratoga Springs, N.Y, summer 70. Sig.C, U.S.A, 56-58. Eighteenth century British literature, chiefly fiction; creative writing; contemporary literature. Publ: Co-auth, The eternal crossroads: the art of Flannery O'Connor, Univ. Ky, 71; auth, The progressive structure of The windhover, Renascence, fall 66; Looking for Dustwich, Tex. Stud, spring 67; Parker's back vs. The partridge festival, Flannery O'Connor's Critical choice, Ga. Rev, winter 67; plus poems and stories. Add: Dept. of English, University of Louisville, S. Third St, Louisville, KY 40208.

DRIVER, TOM FAW, Theology, Literature. See Volume IV, Philosophy, Religion & Law.

DRMOLA, EVZEN, b. Prostejov, Czechoslovakia, May 15, 27; m. 54; c. 1. THEATRE. M.F.A. & Ph.D.(theatre, comp. lit), Charles Univ, Prague, 52. Dir, Carlsbad City Theatre, 50-51; actor, Jihlava, Munic. Theatre, 51-52; chief dramatic producer, Munic. Theatre, Prague, 54-68; dramatic producer, Royal Dramatic Theatre, Sweden, 68; ASST. PROF. SPEECH & DRAMATIC ART, UNIV. IOWA, 70- Adv, Rassegna dei teatri stabili, Florence, Italy, 66-; Ballet Acad. & Opera, Stockholm, 68-; dir, Nat. Theatre, Graz, Austria & Acad. Theatre, Brussels, Belgium, 70-71; prof, Univ. Stockholm, Univ. Vienna, Graz Univ. & Free Univ. Brussels. Award, St. Louis Univ. Theatre Festival, 70. Breath, acting and directing technique; theory of reflexes. Add: University Theatre, University of Iowa, Iowa City, IA 52240.

DRUCKER, DARRELL IRVING, American Studies. See Volume I, History.

DRUHMAN, ALVIN WILLIAM, b. Cincinnati, Ohio, Nov. 24, 17. ENGLISH. B.A, St. Joseph's Col.(Ind), 39; St. Charles Sem, 43; M.A, St. John's Univ, (N.Y), 50, Ph.D.(Eng), 52. Instr. relig. & philos, Viterbo Col, 45-48; Eng. & philos, ST. JOSEPH'S COL. (IND), 48-49, 52-54, asst. prof. ENG. & HUMANITIES, 54-56, assoc. prof, 56-63, PROF, 63-, chmn. honors, 66-69. Shakespeare Asn. Am; Shakespeare; contemporary literature; Chaucer. Add: Dept. of English, St. Joseph's College, Rensselaer, IN 47978.

DRUM, DALE DOUGLAS, b. Portland, Ore, Dec. 16, 26; m. 53; c. 3. SPEECH, PSYCHOLOGY. A.B, Univ. South. Calif, 50, A.B, 54, M.A, 54, Ph.D.(speech), 58; M.A, Long Beach State Col, 60. Instr. SPEECH, Univ. Calif, Santa Barbara, 54-55; Pa. State Univ, 55-56; CALIF. STATE UNIV, LONG BEACH, 56-58, asst. prof, 58-61, from assoc. prof. to PROF, 61- Instr. psychol, Orange Coast Col, 60- U.S.N, 45-46, 50-52, Res, 46-50, 52-54. Speech Commun. Asn; West. Speech Commun. Asn; Int. Commun. Asn; AAAS; Am. Psychol. Asn; Am. Film Inst. Philosophy and methodology of scientific research, especially communications; persuasion and propaganda; history and aesthetics of film. Publ: A study of the Pachuco gang problem in Los Angeles, 5th dist, U.S. Navy, 51; Dreyer's great dream, Calendar, 69; Dreyer's short films, Films in rev, 71; Den Rigtige Sunset Boulevard, Sunset Blvd, 73. Add: Dept. of Speech Communication, California State University, Long Beach, 6101 E. Seventh St, Long Beach, CA 90840.

DRUMMOND, DONALD FRAZIER, b. St. Johns, Ohio, May 31, 14. ENGLISH. A.B, Colo. State Col, 38, A.M, 40; D.Ed, Stanford Univ, 49. Chmn. dept. Eng, Menlo Jr. Col, 45-47; asst. prof, Colo. State Col, 47-48; asst. prof. ENG, UNIV. MO-COLUMBIA, 48-57, from assoc. prof. to PROF, 57-, DIR. PROG. IMPROVEMENT INSTR, 48- Asn. Higher Educ. English education; modern poetry; analysis of theories of criticism for teachers of English. Publ: No moat, no castle, 49, Battlement, 56 & Drawbridge, 62, The grey tower, 66 & The mountain, 71, Swallow. Add: 231 Arts & Sciences, University of Missouri-Columbia, Columbia, MO 65201.

DRUMMOND, EDWARD JOSEPH, S.J, b. East St. Louis, Ill, Apr. 6, 06. ENGLISH. A.B, St. Louis Univ, 28, A.M, 30, fel, 35-37, S.T.L, 38; Ph.D, State Univ. Iowa, 42. Instr. Eng, Latin & Greek, Creighton Prep. Sch, 31-34; ed, Mo. Province News-Lett, 34-36; lectr. relig. & ethics, State Univ. Iowa, 42; instr. Eng, Marquette Univ, 42-44, assoc. prof, 44-62, dean grad. sch, 44-53, acting dir. dept. Eng, 47-48, acting v.pres, 53-54, acad. v.pres, 54-62; assoc. prof. ENG, ST. LOUIS UNIV, 62-72, PROF, 72-, EXEC. V.PRES. MED. CTR, 73-, v.pres, 62-73. Mem. comn. grad. stud, Jesuit Educ. Asn, 45-51, chmn, 48-49; comnr. & mem. exec. bd. comn. cols. & univs, N.Cent. Asn. Cols. & Sec. Schs, 58-64, v.chmn, 61-62, chmn, 62-64, mem. bd. dir, Asn, 62-64, v.pres, 67-68, pres, 68-; v.chmn. counc, Fed. Regional Accrediting Comn. Higher Educ, 64-66, chmn, 66-; participant, White House Conf. Health, 65-; mem. bd. comnr, Nat. Comn. Accrediting, 67-; mem, Nat. Adv. Allied Health Prof. Counc, 68- Nat. Cath. Educ. Asn; Asn. Am. Med. Cols; Am. Hosp. Asn; Nat. League Nursing. Publ: The pursuit of truth to make men free, Marquette Univ, 55; Pursuit of truth to make men free, Cath. Mind, 55; The hospital school as school, Hosp. Progress, 2/69. Add: Dept. of Education, St. Louis University, St. Louis, MO 63103.

DRYDEN, EDGAR A, b. Salisbury, Md, June 28, 37; m. 59; c. 3. AMERICAN LITERATURE. B.A, Wash. Col, 59; M.A, Univ. R.I. 61; Ph.D.(Am. lit), Johns Hopkins Univ, 65. Asst. prof. ENG, Johns Hopkins Univ, 65-67; STATE UNIV. N.Y. BUFFALO, 67-68, ASSOC. PROF, 68-, ASSOC. PROVOST FAC. ARTS & LETT, 72- MLA. American literature; the novel. Publ: Melville's thematics of form, Johns Hopkins Univ, 68; Hawthorne's castle in the air: form and theme in The house of the seven gables, ELH, 6/71; History and progress: some implications of form in Cooper's Littlepage novels, NCF, 6/71. Add: Dept. of English, Annex A, State University of New York at Buffalo, Buffalo, NY 14214.

DUBE, ANTHONY ZENON, b. Mt. Carmel, P.Q, July 9, 26; U.S. citizen; m. 63; c. 1. AMERICAN LITERATURE, MODERN DRAMA. A.B, Univ. South. Calif, 58; M.A, Univ. Tex, El Paso, 64; Ph.D.(Eng), Tex. Tech Univ, 67. Teacher ENG, Hobbs High Sch, N.Mex, 63-64; instr, Tex. Tech Univ, 66; asst. prof, Tex. Wesleyan Col, 66-68, PROF. & CHMN. DEPT, 68-70; ARK. STATE UNIV, 70- Consult, Proj. Change fed. grant, 66-68; South. Accreditation Agency, 68-69; Ed. bd, Houghton Mifflin Co, 71-72. Med.C, U.S.N, 44-46. MLA; Conf. Col. Teachers Eng. William Dean Howells; American drama; composition. Publ: Co-auth, The Forand writer, Brady Publ, 73 & Structure and meaning, Houghton, 74; auth, The pink bicycle, El Burro Mag, 63; Revenge, Harbinger, 65; William Dean Howells' theory and practice of drama, Univ. Mich, 68; plus others. Add: Division of English, Philosophy and Languages, Drawer Q, Arkansas State University, State University, AR 72467.

DUBERMAN, MARTIN, United States History. See Volume I, History.

DUBINSKI, ROMAN RUDOLPH, b. Sudbury, Ont, June 9, 36; m. 59; c. 3. ENGLISH LITERATURE. B.A, Univ. West. Ont, 58, M.A, 63; Ph.D.(Eng), Univ. Toronto, 69. Lectr. ENG, Univ. Waterloo, 64-68, ASST. PROF, 68- MLA; Can. Asn. Univ. Teachers; Can. Counc. Teachers Eng. Seventeenth century literature. Publ: Othello: Iago's mission impossible, Eng. Quart, 71. Add: Dept. of English, University of Waterloo, Waterloo, Ont. N2L 3G1, Can.

DUBLER, WALTER, b. Brooklyn, N.Y, Mar. 22, 34; m. 67; c. 1. AMERICAN LITERATURE. B.A, Yeshiva Univ, 55; M.A, Tulane Univ, 58; Ph.D.(Eng), Harvard, 64. Instr. ENG, Hunter Col, 64-67; asst. prof, LEHMAN COL, 67-70, ASSOC. PROF, 70-, CHMN. DEPT, 74- Modern drama; composition. Publ: Co-auth, Writing college English: an analytic method, Holt, 67; auth, Theme and structure in Melville's The confidence man, Am. Lit, 61; The Princess Casamassima: its place in the James Canon, Mod. Fiction Stud, 66. Add: Dept. of English, Herbert Lehman College, Bedford Park Blvd, Bronx, NY 10468.

DuBOIS, PAUL ZINKHAN, American Studies & Literature. See Volume I, History.

DUCEY, CATHRYN ANNETTE, b. Olean, N.Y, Oct. 7, 35. ENGLISH, AMERICAN LITERATURE. A.B, Goucher Col, 57; M.A, Yale, 58; M.A, Univ. Hawaii, 68. Res. asst. alcohol stud, Yale, 58-60, polit. sci, 60-61; instr. ENG, R.I. COL, 61-63, ASST. PROF, 63-, ASSOC. DEAN ARTS & SCI, 73-, asst. dean stud, 61-62, asst. dean arts & sci, 72-73. Mem. & consult, Nat. Am. Stud. Fac, 72- Am. Stud. Asn; Col. Eng. Asn; NCTE; Am. Cath. Hist. Asn. Eighteenth and 19th century American literature. Publ: Co-auth, Student publications: pride or paranoia, Col. J, fall 67; Response of a single sex college graduate, Goucher Quart, spring 72. Add: 130 Elmgrove Ave, Providence, RI 02906.

DUCHEMIN, LLOYD ALLISON, b. Sydney, N.S, Dec. 6, 08; m. 40; c. 3. ENGLISH. B.A, Dalhousie Univ, 29; M.A, Univ. Toronto, 33, Ph.D.(Eng), 55; Univ. London, 38-39. Asst. prof. ENG, Univ. New Brunswick, 46-47; PROF. & HEAD DEPT, MT. ALLISON UNIV, 47- Humanities Asn. Can; Asn. Can. Univ. Teachers Eng. Add: Dept. of English, Mt. Allison University, Sackville, N.B, Can.

DUCHOVNAY, GERALD CHARLES, b. Philadelphia, Pa, Dec. 6, 44; m. 68; c. 2. ENGLISH & AMERICAN LITERATURE. B.A, Univ. Pa, 66; M.A, Ind. Univ, Bloomington, 68, Ph.D.(Eng), 71. ASST. PROF. ENG, JACKSONVILLE UNIV, 71- MLA; Am. Soc. Eighteenth Century Stud; Counc. for Basic Educ; AAUP. Restoration and 18th century English literature; the novel; literary criticism. Add: Dept. of English, Jacksonville University, Jacksonville, FL 32211.

DUCKETT, MARGARET RUTH, b. Greenwood, S.C, Mar. 11, 06. AMERICAN LITERATURE. A.B, Winthrop Col, 26; Columbia Univ, 31; M.A, Univ. N.C, 41; Bread Loaf Sch. Eng, 42. Instr. ENG, Univ. N.C, summer 46; Univ. Tenn, 46-47; from instr. to asst. prof, Univ. Wash, 47-63, assoc. prof, 63-71, EMER. ASSOC. PROF, 72- Am. Counc. Learned Soc. res. grant, 65-66. Roll of Honor, Am. Auth, 53. Bret Harte and Mark Twain. Publ: Mark Twain and Bret Harte, Univ. Okla, 64; God the Father (short story), Ariz. Quart, winter 53; Bret Harte and the Indians of Northern California, Huntington Libr. Quart, 11/54; The crusade of nineteenth-century liberal, Tenn. Stud. Lit, 59. Add: 2410 Boyer East, Apt. 207, Seattle, WA 98112.

DUCKWORTH, ALISTAIR McKAY, b. Balmullo, Scotland, Aug. 4, 36; m. 64; c. 2. ENGLISH. M.A, Univ. Edinburgh, 58; M.A. Johns Hopkins Univ, 64, Ph.D.(Eng), 67. Instr. ENG, Johns Hopkins Univ, 63-67; asst. prof, Univ. Va, 67-73; ASSOC. PROF, UNIV. FLA, 73- Summer lectr. Eng. lit, Univ. Edinburgh, 71 & 72; sesquicentennial assoc, Ctr. Advan. Stud, Univ. Va, 71-72; lectr, State Univ. N.Y. Buffalo, summer 74. MLA; S.Atlantic Mod. Lang. Asn. English novel. Publ: The improvement of the estate: a study of Jane Austen's novels, Johns Hopkins Univ, 71. Add: Dept. of English, University of Florida, Gainesville, FL 32601.

DUCKWORTH, JAMES E, English. See Volume III, Foreign Languages, Linguistics & Philology.

DUDEK, LOUIS, b. Montreal, P.Q, Feb. 6, 18; m. 44. ENGLISH. B.A, McGill Univ, 39; M.A, Columbia Univ, 46, Ph.D.(Eng), 55. Instr. ENG, City Col. New York, 46-51; lectr, McGILL UNIV, 51-53, asst. prof, 53-62, ASSOC. PROF, 62-, GREENSHIELDS PROF, 72- Mem, Humanities Res. Counc. Can, 71- Can. Counc. Teacher Eng.(dir-at-lg, 70-). European literature, especially Romantic and contemporary periods; modern British and American poetry; Canadian poetry. Publ: East of the city; Literature and the press; The transparent sea; ed, Poetry of our time, Macmillan, Toronto, 65; co-ed, The making of modern poetry in Canada, Ryerson, 67; auth, The first person in literature, CBC Publ, 67; Collected poetry, Delta Can, 67. Add: Dept. of English, McGill University, Montreal, P.Q, Can.

DUDLEY, BARBARA HUDSON, b. St. James, Minn, Feb. 2, 21; m. 71; c. 2. SPEECH, DRAMA. B.A, Univ. Iowa, 42; M.A, Univ. South. Calif, 51. Teacher speech & drama, Southgate High Sch, Calif, 44-45; youth dir,

Hollywood Presby. Church, 45-46; prin, Isabelle Buckley Schs, 48-50; tech. writer, Litton Indust, 59-60; ASSOC. PROF. SPEECH & DRAMA & CHURCH DRAMA DIR, CALIF. LUTHERAN COL, 61- Free lance radio, TV & films script writing, prod. & acting, 46- Am. Theatre Asn. Church drama. Publ: The Henrietta Mears story, Revell, 57; Going with God, World Vision, 57; Where is God?, Augsburg, 73; The teacher as a human being, Resource, 71; Drama for heavens sake, Learning With—Jr. & Sr. Eds, 73. Add: 1851 Village Ct, Thousand Oaks, CA 91360.

DUDLEY, EDWARD J, Spanish, English. See Volume III, Foreign Languages, Linguistics & Philology.

DUDLEY, ELFORD SAMUEL, b. Norfolk, Va, Oct. 17, 23; m. 47; c. 2. COMMUNICATION. B.B.A, Univ. Mich, 50, M.A, 55, Ph.D.(speech), 60; summer, Am. Univ, 53. Teacher jr. high sch, Va, 51-52; instr. SPEECH, Univ. Mich, 57-59; asst. prof, Univ. Ala, 59-62; PROF. & HEAD DEPT, MISS. STATE UNIV, 62- Dir. coop. tele-lect. prog. grant, Miss. State Univ. & Miss. Valley State Col, 67-68; chmn, Miss. TV Counc. Higher Educ, 68- U.S.A, 43-45, T/Sgt. Speech Commun. Asn; South. Speech Commun. Asn.(pres, 71-72); Asn. Dept. & Adminr. Speech Commun. Contemporary public address; interpersonal communication; group discussion and conference. Publ: The speech critic looks at contemporary American pressure groups, South. Speech J, fall 61; Warfare at the Waldorf, Today's Speech, 11/63; Evaluation of department heads, Bull. Asn. Depts. & Adminr. Speech Commun, 4/73. Add: Dept. of Communication, Drawer NJ, Mississippi State University, Mississippi State, MS 39762.

DUDLEY, JUANITA H. WILLIAMS, b. Anna, Ill, Nov. 27, 18; m. 40, 70; c. 2. ENGLISH. B.A, Wash. Univ.(University City), 40; M.A, Univ. Kans, 61; M.F.A, State Univ. Iowa, 64. Ed-in-chief, Extramural Independent Stud. Ctr, Univ. Kans, 63-64; ed. & sci. writer, Menninger Found, 64-65; lectr. Eng. & sci. writing, Ill. Inst. Technol, 65-67; asst. prof. Eng, Iowa State Univ, 67-69; curriculum consult. & instr. Eng, Col. Du Page, 69-70; inform. specialist res. coord, Northwest. Univ, 70-71; ASST. PROF. ENG, PURDUE UNIV, WEST LAFAYETTE, 73- Coord. & auth. proposals, Cook County Hospital, Chicago, 65-66; lectr. med. writing, Am. Med. Asn, Chicago, 65; U.S. Dept. Health, Educ. & Welfare grant, 68; proposal coord, Seton Psychiat. Inst, Baltimore, Md, summer 69; lectr, North. Ill. Gas Co, Naperville, spring 70. NCTE; Conf. Col. Compos. & Commun; Am. Bus. Commun. Asn; AAAS; Nat. Counc. Univ. Res. Adminr. The proper placement of composition courses in an engineering curriculum; follow-up survey of gifted women who entered the St. Louis public school system between 1920 and 1930. Publ: A guide to the principles of writing, Menninger Found, 65; Testing the writing skills of engineering and science students, J. Bus. Commun, fall 70; Writing skills of engineering and science students, Trans. Inst. Electronics & Elec. Eng, 6/71; A serviceable approach to a service course, ABCA Bull, 12/72; plus others. Add: Dept. of English, Heavilon Hall, Purdue University, West Lafayette, IN 47907.

DUER, LESLIE THRASHER, b. Philadelphia, Pa, Aug. 13, 38; m. 66. ENGLISH LITERATURE. B.A, Johns Hopkins Univ, 60; fel, Univ. Conn, 63-65, M.A, 65; Ph.D.(Eng), Univ. Col, Dublin, 71. Teacher ENG, Baltimore Pub. Schs, Md, 60-61; Greenwich County Day Sch, Conn, 61-62; Rosemary Hall Sch, 62-63; lectr, McGILL UNIV, 65-71, ASST. PROF, 71- MLA; Northeast Mod. Lang. Asn. Shakespeare; Elizabethan and Jacobean drama. Add: Dept. of English, McGill University, P.O. Box 6070, Sta. A, Montreal, P.Q. H3C 3G1, Can.

DUERKSEN, ROLAND A, b. Goessel, Kans, Oct. 23, 26; m. 55; c. 3. ENGLISH. A.B, Bethel Col.(Kans), 54; M.A, Ind. Univ, 58, Ph.D.(Eng), 61. Instr. ENG, Purdue Univ, 61-62, asst. prof, 62-66, assoc. prof, 66-68; assoc. prof, MIAMI UNIV, 68-72, PROF, 72- Vis. assoc. prof, Mich. State Univ, 67-68. Keats-Shelley Asn. Am. English and American literature, 19th century. Publ: Shelleyan ideas in Victorian literature, Mouton, 66; ed, Percy Bysshe Shelley's The Cenci, Bobbs, 70 & Shelley: political writings, Appleton, 70; auth, Shelley and Shaw, PMLA, 3/63; plus others. Add: Dept. of English, Miami University, Oxford, OH 45056.

DUERR, EDWIN, b. Las Vegas, N.Mex, Feb. 21, 06. THEATRE. A.B, Univ. Calif, 26; M.A, Cornell Univ, 31. Instr. pub. speaking, Univ. Nev, 26-30; dir. theater, Univ. Calif, 31-40; asst. prof. drama, West. Reserve Univ, 40-43; lectr. theater, Carnegie Inst. Technol, 43; radio-tv dir, N.Y.C, 43-61; assoc. prof. drama, CALIF. STATE UNIV, FULLERTON, 64-71, PROF. THEATRE, 71- Directing. Publ: Radio and television acting, 52 & The length and depth of acting, 62, Holt. Add: Dept. of Theatre, California State University, Fullerton, 800 N. State College Ave, Fullerton, CA 92634.

DUFF, GERALD ALDINE, b. Beaumont, Tex, Sept. 20, 38; m. 72; c. 2. NINETEENTH CENTURY ENGLISH LITERATURE, MODERN POETRY. B.A, Lamar Univ, 61; M.A, Univ. Ark, Fayetteville, 63; Ph.D.(Eng), Univ. Ill, Urbana, 66. ASST. PROF. ENG. LIT, Vanderbilt Univ, 66-72; KENYON COL, 72- Vanderbilt Univ. res. grants, 67, 68 & 69; assoc. dir, Ohio Poetry Circuit, 72-; Ford Found-Kenyon Col. Fac. grants, summer 73; vis. prof, West. N.Mex. Univ, summer 73. S.Atlantic Mod. Lang. Asn. English novel. Publ: William Cobbett and the politics of earth, 72 & ed, Letters of William Cobbett, 73, Univ. Salzburg; Leigh Hunt's criticism of the novel, Col. Lang. Asn. J, 69; William Cobbett and the prose of revelation, Tex. Stud. Lit. & Lang, 70; Speech as theme in The rime of the ancient mariner, Humanities Asn. Bull, 70; plus others. Add: Dept. of English, Kenyon College, Gambier, OH 43022.

DUFF, SAMUEL E, b. Versailles, Mo, Dec. 24, 98; m. 30. ENGLISH. A.B, Univ. Mo, 21, M.A, 23; Univ. Calif, 24-28. Instr. ENG, Univ. Mo, 22-24; teaching fel, Univ. Calif, 24-27; instr, Modesto Jr. Col, 28-46; City Col. San Francisco, 46-64; assoc. prof, Armstrong Col.(Calif), 64-71; RETIRED. Publ: Co-auth, Correctness and precision in writing, Houghton, 38. Add: 2170 Leimert Blvd, Oakland, CA 94602.

DUFFEY, BERNARD, b. Cincinnati, Ohio, Oct. 18, 17. LITERATURE. A.B, Oberlin Col, 39; A.M, Ohio State Univ, 42, fel, 42-43, Ph.D, 47. Asst, Ohio State Univ, 40-44, instr, 44-45; Univ. Minn, 45-47; asst. prof. Eng. lit, Mich. State Univ, 47-55, assoc. prof. ENG, 55-60, PROF, 60-63; DUKE UNIV, 63- Fel, Newberry Libr, 48-49; co-chmn, Conf. 20th Century Lit, 61-63. MLA; S. Atlantic Mod. Lang. Asn; Am. Stud. Asn; AAUP. American and British modern literature; Anglo-American theories of poetry, 1910-1945; Chicago's literary Renaissance 1890-1925. Publ: The Chicago Renaissance in American letters, Mich. State Univ, 54, 56; ed, Modern American literature, Holt, 51; auth, Romantic coherence and romantic incoherence in American poetry, Centennial Rev, spring 63, fall 64; Williams' Paterson and the measure of art, In: Essays in honor of Jay B. Hubbell, 67; Humor Chicago style, In: The comic imagination in America, Rutgers Univ, 73. Add: Dept. of English, Duke University, Durham, NC 27706.

DUFFY, EDWARD THOMAS, b. New York, N.Y, Mar. 30, 42; m. 67; c. 3. ENGLISH & COMPARATIVE LITERATURE. B.A, Manhattan Col, 63; M.A, Columbia Univ, 65, Ph.D, 71. ASST. PROF. ENG. LIT, UNIV. CALIF, SANTA BARBARA, 71- English poetry; French literature; romanticism. Publ: The cunning spontaneities of romanticism, Wordsworth Circle, fall 72. Add: Dept. of English, University of California, Santa Barbara, CA 93106.

DUFFY, JOHN JOSEPH, b. Trenton, N.J, Nov. 17, 34; m. 61; c. 1. ENGLISH. B.S.S, Georgetown Univ, 57; M.A, Univ. Vt, 58; Ph.D.(Eng), Syracuse Univ, 65. Master Eng, Mercersburg Acad, 58-59; instr, Rider Col, 60-61; asst. prof, Univ. Md, 65-68; Rensselaer Polytech. Inst, 68-69; assoc. prof. Am. lit, Univ, N.H, 69-71; adj. prof, Univ. Vt, 71-72; PROF. HUMANITIES & CHMN. DEPT, JOHNSON STATE COL, 72- Univ. Md. gen. res. grant, summer 67; Am. Philos. Soc. res. grant, 68; ed, Vt. Hist, 71- U.S.A, 57. MLA. Nineteenth and early 20th century English and American literature. Publ: Ed, Coleridge's American disciples, Univ. Mass, 73; auth, The stories of Frederick Wedmore, James Joyce Quart, 68; T.S. Eliot's objective correlative, New Eng. Quart, 70; Transcendental letters from George Ripley to James Marsh, Emerson Soc. Quart, 70; plus others. Add: Div. of Humanities, Johnson State College, Johnson, VT 05656.

DUFNER, MARY ANGELINE, b. Buxton, N.Dak, Nov. 30, 35. ENGLISH. B.A, Col. St. Benedict, 57; M.A, Univ. Notre Dame, 66; D.A.(Eng), Idaho State Univ, 73. Teacher ENG, Albany Pub. Sch, Minn, 57-61; ASST. PROF, COL. ST. BENEDICT, 61- NCTE; AAUP. William Faulkner; J.F. Powers; American black in white fiction. Publ: The Negro in the American novel, 3/67 & The sainting of Father Urban, 9/73, Am. Benedictine Rev. Add: Dept. of English, College of St. Benedict, St. Joseph, MN 56374.

DUGAN, EDWARD BARNETT, b. Lester, Iowa, Mar. 29, 11. JOURNALISM. B.J, Univ. Mo, 33, A.M, 40. Reporter, Messenger, Menard, Tex, 33, reporter & ed, Leader, Graham, 33-36, ed, Examiner, Navasota, 36; instr. Hardin-Simmons Univ, 36-37; from instr. to PROF. JOUR, UNIV. MONT, 37- Educ. Jour. Asn. Advertising. Add: School of Journalism, University of Montana, Missoula, MT 59801.

DUGGAN, FRANCIS XAVIER, b. Philadelphia, Pa, Nov. 12, 25; m. 50; c. 4. ENGLISH. A.B, Univ. Notre Dame, 48; Purdue Univ, 43-44; M.A, Univ. Pa, 50, Ph.D, 60. Instr. ENG, Univ. Notre Dame, 48-49; Chestnut Hill Col, 54-58; asst. prof, St. Joseph's Col.(Ind), 58-62; UNIV. SANTA CLARA, 62-64, assoc. prof, 64-68, PROF, 68-, CHMN. DEPT, 73- Mem. bd. trustees, Univ. Santa Clara, 68- U.S.M.C, 43-45, 50-52, Res, 52-66, Maj. American literature; new humanism. Publ: Paul Elmer More, Twayne, 66; Paul Elmer More and the New England tradition, Am. Lit, 1/63; Doctrine and the writers of the American Renaissance, Emerson Soc. Quart. II, 65; P.E. More: The Nation's conservative editor, Nation, 3/65. Add: Dept. of English, University of Santa Clara, Santa Clara, CA 95053.

DUGGAN, MARY KATHLEEN, G.N.S.H, b. North Tonawanda, N.Y, Aug. 15, 26. ENGLISH LITERATURE. A.B, D'Youville Col, 47; A.M, St. Louis Univ, 58, Ph.D.(Eng. lit), 64. Instr. Eng, D'Youville Col, 52-55; teacher Eng. & Latin, Melrose Acad, Phila, Pa, 55-60; instr. ENG, D'YOUVILLE COL, 62-63, asst. prof, 63-68, PROF, 68-, V.PRES. ACAD. AFFAIRS, 64-, dean arts & sci, 63-68. MLA; Milton Soc. Am; NEA. The Renaissance; John Milton; irony in Paradise lost. Add: D'Youville College, 320 Porter Ave, Buffalo, NY 14201.

DUHAMEL, PIERRE ALBERT, b. Putnam, Conn, Feb. 6, 20; m. 43; c. 1. ENGLISH LITERATURE. A.B, Col. Holy Cross, 41; A.M, Boston Col, 42; Ph.D, Univ. Wis, 45. Asst, Univ. Wis, 42-45, instr, 45; Univ. Chicago, 45-47, asst. prof, 47-49; prof. ENG, BOSTON COL, 49-56, PHILOMATHEIA PROF, 56-, LIT. ED, BOSTON HERALD TRAVELER, 65- Lectr, Univ. Wis, 48, 50; mem, Pulitzer Prize jury, 68, 69, 70 & 73. MLA; Cath. Comn. Intellectual & Cult. Affairs. English Renaissance; Thomas More. Publ: Essays in American Catholic tradition, Holt, 62; co-auth, Rhetoric: principles and usage, 63, Persuasive prose, 64, Literature: form & function, 65 & Principles of rhetoric, 67, Prentice-Hall; auth, Novelist as prophet, In: Art & mind of Flannery O'Connor, Fordham Univ, 66. Add: Dept. of English, Boston College, Chestnut Hill, MA 02167.

DUKE, CHARLES RICHARD, b. West Stewartstown, N.H, July 6, 40; m. 73. AMERICAN LITERATURE & WRITING. B.Ed, Plymouth State Col, 62; M.A, Middlebury Col, 68; Ph.D.(Eng. educ), Duke Univ, 72. Chmn. dept. ENG, Sunapee High Sch, N.H, 62-68; instr, PLYMOUTH STATE COL, 68-71, asst. prof, 71-73, ASSOC. PROF, 73- Consult, Durham County Pub. Schs, N.C, 72. NCTE (mem. adv. bd, achievement awards prog, 73-76); AAUP; Popular Cult. Asn; Conf. Eng. Educ. The teaching of writing; drama; American literature 1900-1960. Publ: Ed, Granite State writers, N.H. Asn. Teachers Eng, 72; auth, Is 15% good enough, Eng. Rec, spring 73; Testing for levels of appreciation, Exercise Exchange, spring 73; Drama, In: Creative approaches to the teaching of English: secondary, F.E. Peacock, 74; plus others. Add: Dept. of English, Plymouth State College, Plymouth, NH 03264.

DUKE, JOHN HAMILTON, b. Dallas, Tex, July 3, 13; m; c. 1. JOURNALISM. B.J, Univ. Tex, 35; M.A, Univ. South. Calif, 42, Ph.D, 56. Teacher Eng. & jour, Santa Ana High Sch, Calif, 42-45; instr. JOUR, Santa Ana Jr. Col, 45-46; PROF, CALIF. STATE UNIV, FRESNO, 46-, chmn. dept, 69-72. Publ. adv, San Joaquin Valley Scholastic Press Asn, 60; Fulbright lectr, Korea, 65-66. Asn. Educ. Jour. Scholastic journalism, especially on the secondary level; mass communications. Add: Dept. of Journalism, California State University, Shaw & Cedar Ave, Fresno, CA 93726.

DUKE, MAURICE, b. Richmond, Va, Oct. 4, 34; m. 60. AMERICAN LITERATURE, BIBLIOGRAPHY. A.B, Col. William & Mary, 62; M.A, Univ. Iowa, 65, Ph.D(Eng), 68. Asst. ENG, Univ. Iowa, 63-66; asst. prof. VA. COMMONWEALTH UNIV, 66-71, ASSOC. PROF, 71- Lit. columnist & bk. page ed, Richmond Times-Dispatch, 69-; ed. & publ, Resources Am. Lit. Stud, 71- MLA; Soc. Stud. South. Lit.(mem. bibliog. comt, 69-). Nineteenth century American literature; bibliography; editing. Add: Dept. of English, Virginia Commonwealth University, Richmond, VA 23284.

DUKORE, BERNARD F, b. New York, N.Y, July 11, 31. DRAMA. A.B, Brooklyn Col, 52; M.A, Ohio State Univ, 53; Ph.D, Univ. Ill, 57. Instr. drama, Hunter Col, 57-60; asst. prof, Univ. South. Calif, 60-62; Los Angeles State Col, 62-66; exec. off. Ph.D. prog. in theatre, City Univ. New York, 66-72; PROF. DRAMA & THEATRE & CHMN. DEPT, UNIV. HAWAII, MANOA, 72- Guggenheim fel, 69-70; City Univ. New York Res. Found. award, 70-71; mem. bd. dirs, Theatre Develop. Fund, 71-72. Am. Educ. Theatre Asn; Am. Soc. Theatre Res; Pirandello Soc. Am. Drama and theatre. Publ: Saint Joan: a screenplay by Bernard Shaw, Univ. Wash, 68; co-ed, Twentieth century drama: England, Ireland, the United States, Random, 66; co-ed, Treasury of the theatre, Vol. II, 70, ed, Drama and revolution, 71 & Dramatic theory and criticism: Greeks to Grotowski, 74, Holt; auth, Bernard Shaw, director, Univ. Wash. & Allen & Unwin, 71; Bernard Shaw, playwright, Univ. Mo, 73; The undershaft maxims, Mod. Drama, 5/66; Shaw on Hamlet, Educ. Theatre J, 5/71; A womans place, In: A casebook on Harold Pinter's The homecoming, Grove, 71; plus others. Add: Dept. of Drama & Theatre, University of Hawaii at Manoa, Honolulu, HI 96822.

DULAI, SURJIT SINGH, Comparative Literature, South Asian Studies. See Volume III, Foreign Languages, Linguistics & Philology.

DUMBLETON, WILLIAM A, b. Troy, N.Y, Dec. 31, 27; m. 66; c. 3. ENGLISH. B.A, State Univ. N.Y. Albany, 50, M.A, 52; Ph.D.(Eng), Univ. Pa, 66; M.A, Univ. Col, Dublin, 71. Instr. ENG, STATE UNIV. N.Y. ALBANY; 53-55, asst. prof, 57-63, ASSOC. PROF, 63- Lectr, Am. Univ. Cairo, 64; Union Col.(N.Y), 65-66. MLA; Northeast Mod. Lang. Asn; Int. Asn. Stud. Anglo-Irish Lit; Can. Asn. Irish Stud; Hopkins Soc. Romantic literature; Irish literature. Publ: Auth, intro. & co-ed, James Cousins' The sleep of the king and the sword of Dermot, DePaul Univ, 73; auth, Coleridge and Gerard Manley Hopkins, Ariel, 4/72; Bridges and the Hopkins Mss, Thought, autumn 72. Add: Dept. of English, State University of New York at Albany, Albany, NY 12222.

DUME, THOMAS LESLIE, b. Reading, Pa, July 20, 06. ENGLISH. A.B, Univ. Mich, 28; M.A, Columbia Univ, 36; Ph.D.(Eng), Temple Univ, 50. Teacher high sch, Mich, 30-42; Eng. & speech, Edinboro State Col, 49-50; Detroit Inst. Technol, 50-56; assoc. prof. ENG, EAST. MICH. UNIV, 56-72, prof, 72-74, EMER. PROF, 74- U.S.A, 43-45. MLA; Col. Eng. Asn; Speech Commun. Asn; Conf. Col. Compos. & Commun. Contemporary literature; composition and communication. Add: Dept. of English, Eastern Michigan University, Ypsilanti, MI 48197.

DUMIT, EDWARD S, b. Tulsa, Okla, Aug. 14, 29. BROADCASTING, HISTORY OF FILM. B.A, Univ. Tulsa, 51, M.A, 57; Northwest. Univ, 57-66; Univ. Okla, 67-69. Announcer, KWON, Bartlesville, Okla, 49; KMUS, Muskogee, 51-52; KFMJ, Tulsa, 52-55; from instr. to ASSOC. PROF. BROADCASTING & FILM, UNIV. TULSA, 55-, mgr, KWGS, 55-72. Opera preview lectr, Tulsa Opera, Inc, 70- Broadcast Educ. Asn; Speech Commun. Asn. Broadcast performance and production; history of music. Publ: Co-auth, The announcer's handbook, Holt, 59; auth. & narrator, Say it right! (record & booklet), Grayhill, Inc, 59. Add: 1560 S. Gillette, Tulsa, OK 74104.

DUNBAR, GEORGIA SHERWOOD, b. Baltimore, Md, Mar. 27, 19; m. 41; c. 2. ENGLISH LITERATURE. A.B, Barnard Col, Columbia Univ, 41, A.M, Columbia Univ, 45, Ph.D, 53. Instr. ENG, HOFSTRA UNIV, 46-52, asst. prof, 53-59, assoc. prof, 59-70, PROF, 70-, chmn. dept, 60-64. Lectr, grad. Eng. dept, Columbia Univ, 55-60; mem, Eng. Inst. Keats-Shelley Asn. Am; MLA; AAUP. Nineteenth century British literature; prosody. Publ: Verse rhythms of Antony and Cleopatra, Style, fall 71. Add: Dept. of English, Hofstra University, Hempstead, NY 11550.

DUNBAR, JOHN RAINE, b. Eugene, Ore, May 21, 11. AMERICAN LITERATURE. A.B, Univ. Ore, 32, A.M, 36; Ph.D, Harvard, 47. Head dept. Eng, sr. high sch, Ore, 36-39; instr, Tufts Col, 42-43; Ga. Inst. Technol, 43-46; asst. prof, Miami Univ, 46-47; CLAREMONT MEN'S COL, 47-48, assoc. prof, 48-57, prof, 57-71, J.O. WEEKS PROF. LIT. & CHMN. DEPT. LIT. & LANG, 71- Fulbright lectr, Finland, 56-57, Univ. Vienna, 65-66 & Am. lit, Univ. Delhi, 69-70. Naturalism in American literature; western writers; the American novel. Publ: The Paxton papers, M. Nijhoff, the Hague, 57; The combat at the barrier, Castle, 67. Add: Dept. of English, Claremont Men's College, Claremont, CA 91711.

DUNCAN, CHARLES THOMAS, b. Marietta, Minn, May 20, 14; m. 40; c. 3. JOURNALISM. A.B, Univ. Minn, 36, M.A, 46; Univ. Wash, 41. Instr. jour, Univ. Nev, 40-42; asst. prof, Univ. Nebr, 46-47; Univ. Minn, 47-48, assoc. prof, 48-50; Univ. Ore, 50-52, prof, 52-62, dean sch, 56-62, prof. & dean sch, Univ. Colo, 62-65; asst. dean fac, UNIV. ORE, 65-67, dean fac, 67-70, PROF. JOUR, 70-, assoc. dean fac, 70-72. Consult, Ford Found, 64-65. U.S.N.R, 42-45, Lt. Propaganda and public opinion; international journalism; history. Publ: Ed, Horace Greeley's overland journey to San Francisco, 1859, 63. Add: Allen Hall, University of Oregon, Eugene, OR 97403.

DUNCAN, DOUGLAS J. M, b. St. Andrews, Scotland, June 14, 31; Brit. citizen. ENGLISH LITERATURE. B.A, Oxford, 53; Ph.D, Aberdeen Univ, 61. Asst. ENG, Aberdeen Univ, 56-58; lectr, Univ. Southampton, 58-64; prof, Univ. Ghana, 64-67; vis. prof, Univ. West. Ont, 67-68; assoc. prof, McMASTER UNIV, 68-70, PROF, 71-, CHMN. DEPT, 73- Can. Coun. fel, 72-73. R.N.V.R, 53-55, Sub-Lt. Renaissance literature; Scottish literature; classical tradition. Publ: Thomas Ruddiman, 65, Emily Dickinson, 65 & ed, Ben Jonson, Bartholomew fair, 72, Oliver & Boyd. Add: Dept. of English, McMaster University, Hamilton, Ont, Can.

DUNCAN, EDGAR HILL, b. Front Royal, Va, Sept. 1, 05; m. 47. ENGLISH. A.B, Randolph-Macon Col, 28; A.M, Univ. South. Calif, 36; Ph.D, Vanderbilt Univ, 40. Instr. ENG, VANDERBILT UNIV, 37-40, asst. prof, 40-45, assoc. prof, 45-56, prof, 56-73, acting chmn. dept, 63-66, EMER. PROF, 73- Am. Philos. Soc. grant, Eng; 53-54; Nat. Sci. Found. grant to edit Alchemical texts, 67-69. MLA; Renaissance Soc. Am; Mediaeval Acad. Am. Victorian literature; medieval and Renaissance literature and science. Add: Dept. of English, Vanderbilt University, Box 1538, Station B, Nashville, TN 37235.

DUNCAN, HARRY A, b. Keokuk, Iowa, Apr. 19, 16; m. 61; c. 3. JOURNALISM. A.B, Grinnell Col, 38, L.H.D, 73; Duke Univ, 38-40. Asst. prof. jour, Univ. Iowa, 56-60, assoc. prof, 60-67, prof, 67-72, dir. grad. stud, 70-72; PROF. FINE ARTS & DIR. FINE ARTS PRESS, UNIV. NEBR. AT OMAHA, 72- Pres, Cummington Press, 41-; consult, Nat. Found. Arts & Humanities, 67-68; Nat. Found. Arts grant, 68-70; Roberts lectr, Grinnell Col, 73. Typography; history of books and printing; the private press. Publ: Poems and translations; Scribner, 54; The scarf, Schirmer, 58. Add: Dept. of Fine Arts, Annex 19, University of Nebraska at Omaha, P.O. Box 688, Omaha, NE 68101.

DUNCAN, IVAR LOU MYHR, b. Nashville, Tenn, June 8, 04; m. 47. ENGLISH. B.A, Vanderbilt Univ, 24, Ph.D.(Eng), 40; M.A, Peabody Col, 29; Oxford & Cambridge, 32-33; Yale, 36-37; Univ. South Calif, 48; N.Y. Univ, 50. Prof. Eng, & hist. Belmont Col, 38-40; chmn. Eng. compos. & asst. prof. Eng, Hollins Col, 41-45; PROF. SPEECH, DRAMA, & LANG, BELMONT COL, 51-, chmn. dept. eng, 45-71. S.Atlantic Mod. Lang. Asn; MLA; Renaissance Soc. Am; Eng. Inst; Nat. Eng. Counc; Renaissance Soc. South. Renaissance literary criticism, especially of the Italian Renaissance; American literature. Add: 3627 Valley Vista Rd, Nashville, TN 37205.

DUNCAN, JOSEPH ELLIS, b. Louisville, Ky, June 19, 21. ENGLISH. B.A, Univ. Louisville, 43, M.A, 46; Ph.D.(Eng), Columbia Univ, 51. Instr. ENG, Univ. Wash, 52-54; DULUTH CAMPUS, UNIV. MINN, 54-62, assoc. prof, 62-65; PROF, 65- MLA; Milton Soc. Am. Seventeenth century English literature; Milton; modern revival of metaphysical poetry. Publ: Revival of metaphysical poetry, Univ. Minn, 59; Milton's earthly paradise, Univ. Minn, 72; The modality of the audible in Joyce's Ulysses, PMLA; plus others. Add: 2420 E. Fifth St, Duluth, MN 55812.

DUNCAN, KIRBY LUTHER, b. Deport, Tex, Dec. 2, 36; m. 66. ENGLISH. B.A, Arlington State Col, 63; M.A, Tex. Technol. Col, 64; Ph.D.(Eng), Univ. S.C, 67. Instr. ENG, Univ. S.C, 66-67; asst. prof, STEPHEN F. AUSTIN STATE UNIV, 67-72, ASSOC. PROF, 72- U.S.A, 57-59. MLA; NCTE; Am. Stud. Asn. Novels of Henry James; Pamela Hansford Johnson; teaching college composition. Publ: Vardis Fisher and William Golding, Col. Eng, 12/65. Add: Dept. of English, Stephen F. Austin State University, Nacogdoches, TX 75961.

DUNCAN, ROBERT W, b. McKeesport, Pa, June 23, 17; m. 42; c. 3. ENGLISH. B.A, Univ. Mo, 41; M.A, Univ. Cincinnati, 47, Taft fel, 47, 49, Ph.D, 55. Instr. ENG, Wayne State Univ, 53-55; asst. prof, Univ. Wichita, 55-57; Alton Campus, SOUTH. ILL. UNIV, EDWARDSVILLE, 57-60, assoc. prof, 60-67, PROF, 67- U.S.N, 41-45, Lt. Comdr. MLA. Renaissance; 19th century; poetry. Add: Dept. of English, Southern Illinois University, Edwardsville, IL 62025.

DUNDES, ALAN, b. New York, N.Y, Sept. 8, 34; m. 58; c. 3. FOLKLORE. B.A, Yale, 55, M.A.T, 58; Ph.D.(folklore), Ind. Univ, Bloomington, 62. Instr. Eng, Univ. Kans, 62-63; asst. prof. anthrop, UNIV. CALIF, BERKELEY, 63-65, assoc. prof, 65-68, PROF. ANTHROP. & FOLKLORE, 68- Guggenheim fel, 66-67; Nat. Endowment for Humanities sr. fel, 72-73. U.S.N.R, 55-57, Lt. Comdr. Am. Folklore Soc; Am. Anthrop. Asn. Symbolism; structuralism. Publ: The morphology of North American Indian folktales, Acad. Sci. Fennica, Helsinki, 64; ed, The study of folklore, 65, Every man his way: readings in cultural anthropology, 68, & Mother wit from the laughing barrel: readings in the interpretation of Afro-American folklore, 73, Prentice-Hall; auth, From etic to emic units in the structural study of folktales, J. Am. Folklore, 62; Metafolklore and oral literary criticism, Monist, 66; Thinking ahead: a folkloristic reflection of the future orientation in American worldview, Anthrop. Quart, 69. Add: Dept. of Anthropology, University of California, Berkeley, CA 94720.

DUNHAM, DANA DEAN, JR, b. Omaha, Nebr, Oct. 31, 37; m. 59; c. 2. ENGLISH LITERATURE & COMPOSITION. B.A, Hastings Col, 60; M.A, Univ. Ark, Fayetteville, 62; Ph.D.(Eng), Univ. Nebr-Lincoln, 70. Teacher Eng. & world hist, Doniphan High Sch, Nebr, 59-60; teaching asst, Univ. Ark, Fayetteville, 60-61; from instr. to asst. prof, William Jewell Col, 61-65; teaching asst, Univ. Nebr-Lincoln, 65-69; ASSOC. PROF. & CHMN. DEPT, WILLIAM JEWELL COL, 69- MLA; NCTE; Col. Eng. Asn. Add: Dept. of English, William Jewell College, Liberty, MO 64068.

DUNHAM, ROBERT E, b. Portsmouth, Ohio, Nov. 20, 31; m. 53; c. 3. SPEECH. B.S. in Ed, Otterbein Col, 53; M.A, Ohio State Univ, 57, Ph.D. (speech), 59. Instr. speech, High Sch, Ohio, 53-56; asst, Ohio State Univ, 56-58, instr, 58-59, dir, Ohio High Sch. Speech League, 56-59, res. assoc. psycholing. lab, Res. Found, summer, 59; instr. SPEECH, PA. STATE UNIV, UNIVERSITY PARK, 59-60, asst. prof, 60-65, assoc. prof, 65-72, PROF, 72-, ASST. TO V.PRES. FOR RES. INSTR, 66-, acting head dept, 65-66. Dir, Pa. High Sch. Speech League, 61-67; dir. & consult, ESEA Title III, Pa. Region J, Oral Commun. Prog, 65; consult. speech, Pa. Dept. Pub. Instr, 65. Speech Commun. Asn; Speech Commun. Asn. East. States; Nat. Univ. Exten. Asn. Speech education; curriculum development; communication theory. Publ: An examination of the spoken vocabulary used in air traffic control, Oper. Applications Lab, Air Force Cambridge Res. Ctr, 59; co-auth, Debater's guide, Pa. High Sch. Speech League, 62, Index and table of contents of the Southern Speech Journal, Western Speech Journal, Central States Speech Journal and Today's Speech, 66 & Development of oral communication in the classroom, Bobbs, 68; co-auth, Ethos: a confounding element in communication research, Speech Monogr, 66 & Direct assessment of effectiveness of student speakers, J. Commun, 66; auth, Staying human in a world of technology, In: Penetration for transformation, Bd. Publ, E.U.B. Church, 67. Add: Dept. of Speech, Pennsylvania State University, University Park, PA 16802.

DUNLAP, ARTHUR RAY, b. N.S, Can, June 24, 06; nat; m. 36; c. 1. ENGLISH PHILOLOGY. B.A, Acadia Univ, 26; A.M, Harvard, 28; Ph.D, Yale, 34. From instr. to assoc. prof. ENG, UNIV. DEL, 28-31, 35-51, prof, 51-71, EMER. PROF, 71- MLA; Am. Dialect Soc; Am. Name Soc. Middle English language and literature; English and American speech; American place-names. Publ: Co-auth, Indian place-names in Delaware, Archaeol. Soc. Del, 50; auth, Dutch and Swedish place-names in Delaware, Univ. Del, 56; co-auth, Dutch explorers, traders and settlers in the Delaware Valley: 1609-1664, Univ. Pa, 61. Add: Dept. of English, University of Delaware, Newark, DE 19711.

DUNLAP, BENJAMIN BERNARD, b. Columbia, S.C, Dec. 3, 37; m. 63; c. 3. ENGLISH & AMERICAN LITERATURE, FILM STUDIES. B.A, Univ. South, 59; Rhodes scholar, Oxford, 59-62, B.A. hon, 62, M.A, 66; Ph.D.(Eng), Harvard, 67. Instr. ENG, Harvard, 67-68; asst. prof, UNIV. S.C, 68-73, ASSOC. PROF, 73- Ford Found. fel, Coop. Prog. Humanities, Duke Univ-Univ. N.C, Chapel Hill, 69-70; vis. prof, Harvard, summer 72. Victorians Inst; S.Atlantic Mod. Lang. Asn; William Morris Soc. & Kelmscott Fel. Victorian literature; 19th century American literature; pre-Raphaelitism. Publ: Bear me witness to love: Morris's Love is enough, Victorians Inst. J, 7/73. Add: Dept. of English, University of South Carolina, Columbia, SC 29208.

DUNLAP, GEORGE ARTHUR, b. Philadelphia, Pa, Apr. 30, 93. AMERICAN LITERATURE. A.B, Haverford Col, 16; A.M, Univ. Pa, 28, Ph.D, 34. Instr. Eng, Lincoln Univ, 25-26; teacher, French & hist, St. Luke's Sch, Wayne, Pa, 26-27; jr. & sr. high schs, 28-29; assoc. prof. Eng, Okla. Baptist Univ, 29-30; instr, Friends Univ, 30-31; head dept, Ashland Col, 34-39; Dickinson Jr. Col, 40-44; N.C. State Col, Pembroke, 44-45; Col. of Emporia, 45-46; assoc. prof, Wheaton Col.(Ill), 46-47; instr. Pa. State Teachers Col, East Stroudsburg, 47-51; head dept, Larson Col, 51-52; Curry Col, 53-54; prof, Sterling Col, 54-58; William Penn Col, 58-64; St. Paul's Col.(Va), 64-65; Methodist Col, 66-67; RETIRED. U.S.A, 18-19, Sgt. MLA; NCTE; Col. Eng. Asn. American novel. Publ: The city in the American novel, Russell, 65; A collector of colleges, 1912-1966, 67 & Gleanings from camp and campus, 73, Vantage; Giving it the good old college try, Carlton, 70; A stone, a leaf, a door, 11/54 & Charles Lamb and the Quakers, 11/55, Sterling Col. Fac. Bull. Add: 34 W. Montgomery Ave, Ardmore, PA 19003.

DUNLAP, JAMES FRANCIS, b. Dec. 2, 15; m. 42; c. 1. SPEECH, THEATRE. B.S, Wilmington Col, 38; A.M, Ohio State Univ, 49, Ph.D, 54. Instr, high schs, Ohio & Idaho, 38-48, 54-55; asst. dept. theatre, Ohio State Univ, 48-49, 51-53; asst. prof. speech & dir. dept. speech & theatre, Hanover Col, 49-51; from asst. prof. speech & play dir. to PROF. SPEECH, UNIV. AKRON, 55-, HEAD DEPT. SPEECH & THEATRE ARTS, 69- U.S.A, 42-45. Nat. Col. Players (pres, 71-). Nineteenth century American theatre. Publ: Sophisticates and dupes: Cincinnati audiences. Add: Dept. of Speech & Theatre Arts, University of Akron, Akron, OH 44325.

DUNLAP, MARY MONTGOMERY, b. Woodruff, S.C, Sept. 24, 33; m. 64; c. 2. AMERICAN & ENGLISH LITERATURE. B.A, Converse Col, 55; M.A, Appalachian State Univ, 67; McClintock fel. & Ph.D.(Am. lit), Univ. S.C, 70. Instr. Eng. lit, APPALACHIAN STATE UNIV, 67-68; ASST. PROF. AM. LIT, 70- MLA; S.Atlantic Mod. Lang. Asn. Faulkner; 19th century American humorists, T.E. Lawrence. Publ: Sex and the artist in Mosquitoes, summer 69 & Knight's gambit, summer 70, Miss. Quart. Add: Dept. of English, Appalachian State University, Boone, NC 28607.

DUNLAP, RHODES, b. Bryan, Tex, Mar. 11, 11. ENGLISH. A.B, Rice Inst, 31, A.M, 32; Univ. Iowa, 34-35; Rhodes scholar, Oxford, 35-38, B.Litt, 38, Ph.D, 39. Instr. ENG. UNIV. IOWA, 38-42, assoc. prof, 47-53, PROF, 53- Res. fel, Folger Libr, 51; mem. ed. bd, Philol. Quart, 51- U.S.N, 42-46. MLA; NCTE; Col. Eng. Asn; Renaissance Soc. Am. Literature of the Renaissance and 17th century. Publ: Ed, Poems of Thomas Carew, Clarendon; co-auth, Studies in English Renaissance drama, Columbia Univ, 59. Add: Dept. of English, University of Iowa, Iowa City, IA 52242.

DUNLEAVY, GARETH WINTHROP, b. Willimantic, Conn, Feb. 24, 23; m; c. 3. ENGLISH. A.B, Clark Univ, 47; M.A, Brown Univ, 49; Ph.D, Northwest. Univ, 52. Asst. prof, Bradley Univ, 52-56; UNIV. WIS-MILWAUKEE, 56-59, assoc. prof, Eng, 59-63, prof, 63-67, ASSOC. DEAN GRAD. SCH, 67-68, chmn. dept. Eng, 64-67, coord. grad. stud, 70-72. Summer res. grants, Am. Philos. Soc, 71 & 73 & Am. Counc. Learned Soc, 72; mem, Wis. Comt. Humanities, 73-; co-grantee, Am-Irish Found, 73. U.S.A, 42-45. Am. Comt. Irish Stud; MLA; Mediaeval Acad. Am; Int. Asn. Stud. Anglo-Irish Lit. Old English poetry; Chaucer; Anglo-Irish cultural relations. Publ: Colum's other island: the Irish at Lindisfarne, Univ. Wis, 60; Douglas Hyde, Bucknell Univ, 73; Wound and the comforter: consolations of Geoffrey Chaucer, Papers Lang. Lit, summer 67; co-ed, Moore to playwright Hyde, Irish Univ. Rev, spring 73, co-auth, The catalog of the O'Connor papers, Studies, spring 74; plus others. Add: Dept. of English, University of Wisconsin-Milwaukee, Milwaukee, WI 53201.

DUNLEAVY, JANET EGLESON, b. New York, N.Y, Dec. 16, 28. ENGLISH & IRISH LITERATURE. B.A, Hunter Col, 51; M.A, N.Y. Univ, 62, Ph.D.(Eng), 66. Instr. ENG, Hunter Col, 64-66; asst. prof, State Univ, N.Y. Stony Brook, 66-70; UNIV. WIS-MILWAUKEE, 70-71, ASSOC. PROF, 71- Am. Counc. Learned Socs. grant, 71; Am. Irish Found. grant, 73. MLA; Am. Comt. Irish Stud.(ed, ACIS, Newsletter, 71-, secy, 72-); Int. Asn. Stud. Anglo-Irish Lit. Irish literature in English; narrative techniques in prose fiction; English literature of the Transition period. Publ: Design for writing, Glencoe, 70; George Moore: the artist's vision, the storyteller's art, Bucknell Univ, 73; Christ and Cuchulain: interrelated arche-types of divinity and heroism in Yeat's poetry, Eire-Ireland, spring 69; co-auth, Editor Moore to playwright Hyde: on the making of The tinker and the fairy, Irish Univ. Rev, spring 73; co-auth, The catalog of the O'Connor papers: a summary, Studies, spring 74. Add: Dept. of English, University of Wisconsin-Milwaukee, Milwaukee, WI 53201.

DUNN, ALBERT ANTHONY, b. Boston, Mass, Apr. 17, 44; m. 67. ENGLISH & COMPARATIVE LITERATURE. B.A, Univ. Notre Dame, 66; M.A, Univ. Va, 68, Ph.D.(Eng), 72. ASST. PROF. ENG, STATE UNIV. N.Y. COL, FREDONIA, 72- Dickens Soc. Continental novel; Victorian literature; Dickens. Publ: The articulation of time in The ambassadors, Criticism, 72. Add: Dept. of English, State University of New York College at Fredonia, Fredonia, NY 14063.

DUNN, CATHERINE MARY, b. San Diego, Calif, Mar. 5, 30. ENGLISH. Ph.D.(Eng), Univ. Calif, Los Angeles, 67. ASSOC. PROF. ENG, CALIF. STATE UNIV, NORTHRIDGE, 67- Ed, Renaissance Ed, 68-; Nat. Endowment for Humanities awards, 73-75. MLA; Shakespeare Asn. Am. Shakespeare; Ramus; Scaliger. Publ: Ed, The logike of Peter Ramus, 69 & H.C. Agrippa: of the Vanitie of Arts and Sciences, 74, Renaissance Ed; auth, The function of music in Shakespeare's romances, Shakespeare Quart, autumn 69. Add: Dept. of English, California State University, 18111 Nordhoff St, Northridge, CA 91324.

DUNN, ELLEN CATHERINE, b. Baltimore, Md, July 30, 16. ENGLISH. A.B, Col. Notre Dame (Md), 38; M.A, Cath. Univ. Am, 40, Ph.D, 47. Lectr. ENG, Col. Notre Dame (Md), 45-47; instr, CATH. UNIV. AM, 47-52, asst. prof, 52-63, PROF, 63-, CHMN. DEPT, 69- MLA; Mediaeval Acad. Am; Asn. Depts. Eng; AAUP; S.Atlantic Asn. Depts. Eng.(pres, 72-73). Medieval English and Latin drama; Renaissance English drama. Publ: The literary style of the Towneley plays, Am. Benedictine Rev, 69; Voice structure in the liturgical drama, In: Medieval English drama: essays, critical and contextual, Univ. Chicago, 72; Popular devotion in the vernacular drama of Medieval England, Medievalia et Humanistica, 73; plus others. Add: Dept. of English, Catholic University of America, Washington, DC 20017.

DUNN, ESTHER CLOUDMAN, b. Portland, Maine, May 5, 91. ENGLISH. A.B, Cornell Univ, 13; Ph.D, Univ. London, 22; hon. D.Litt, Smith Col. & Wheaton Col. Instr, Bryn Mawr Col, 13-17, dir. Eng. compos, 17-19; asst. prof. ENG, SMITH COL, 22-24, assoc. prof, 24-26, prof, 26-44, Jordan prof, 44-59, chmn. dept, 42-45, EMER. PROF, 60- Vis. lectr. Eng, Univ. Mass, 63-71. Ben Jonson's art; Shakespeare in America. Publ: Literature of Shakespeare's England; Pursuit of understanding; co-auth, The Trollope reader; plus others. Add: 82 Massasoit St, Northampton, MA 01060.

DUNN, MARGARET MARY, R.S.C.J, b. New York, N.Y, Sept. 15, 22. ENGLISH & NORWEGIAN LANGUAGE & LITERATURE. B.A, Hunter Col, 44; M.A, Columbia Univ, 47; Ph.D.(Eng), Fordham Univ, 66; M.A, Univ. Chicago, 68. From instr. to assoc. prof. Eng, Manhattanville Col, 58-67, acad. dean freshmen, 65-66, dean sophomores, 66-67; ASST. PROF. ENG, BARAT COL. OF THE SACRED HEART, 67-, CHMN. DEPT, 70- Am-Scand. Found. fel; Strong summer fel, Norway, 67; scholar, Int. Summer Sch, Oslo, 67; Ibsen sem, summer 68. MLA. Nineteenth century English literature; nineteenth and twentieth century Scandinavian literature. Publ: The master of Hestviken: a new reading, Scand. Stud, Univ. Wash, Part 1, 11/66 & Part II, 9/64. Add: Dept. of English, Barat College of the Sacred Heart, Lake Forest, IL 60045.

DUNN, MILLARD CHARLES, JR, b. Durham, N.C, Dec. 24, 39; m. 63. ENGLISH. B.A, Duke Univ, 62; Woodrow Wilson fels, Ind. Univ, 62-63, 65-66, univ. fel, 63-64; Ph.D.(Eng), 66. Asst. prof. ENG, Washington & Lee Univ, 66-69; IND. UNIV. SOUTHEAST, 69-72, ASSOC. PROF, 73- MLA; NCTE; Conf. Col. Compos. & Commun. Language and literature; writing fiction and verse. Add: Dept. of English, Indiana University Southeast, 4201 Grand Line Rd, P.O. Box 679, New Albany, IN 47150.

DUNN, N. E, b. Beckley, W.Va, Dec. 23, 24. ENGLISH. A.B, Madison Col. (Va), 46; M.A, Univ. Pa, 53, F.S. Pepper fel, 61-62, Ph.D.(Eng), 68. Teacher high schs, Va, 46-55; instr. Eng, Webster Col, 55-56, dir, dept. lib. arts, 56-58; instr. ENG, UNIV. MD, COLLEGE PARK, 58-68, ASST. PROF, 68-, res. award, summer 73. MLA; AAUP. Moral concepts of Ellen Glasgow; 19th century American literature; 20th century American literature. Publ: Wreck and yesterday: the meaning of failure in Lancelot, 9/71 & Riddling leaves: Robinson's Luke Havergal, 3/73, Colby Libr. Quart, co-auth, The significance of upward mobility in Martin Eden, Jack London Newslett, 1-4/72; plus others. Add: Dept. of English, Div. of Humanities, University of Maryland, College Park, MD 20742.

DUNN, RICHARD JOHN, b. Pittsburgh, Pa, June 8, 38; m. 61; c. 3. NINETEENTH CENTURY ENGLISH. B.A, Allegheny Col, 60; NDEA fels, West. Reserve Univ, 61, 64, M.A, 61, Ph.D.(Eng), 64. Lectr. ENG, Univ. Colo. Colorado Springs, 66-67; instr, U.S. Air Force Acad. Prep. Sch, 64-65; asst. prof, U.S. Air Force Acad, 65-67; UNIV. WASH, 67-71, ASSOC. PROF, 71- U.S.A.F, 64-67, Capt. MLA. English novel; Victorian literature. Publ: Ed, Norton critical edition of Jane Eyre, Norton, 71; auth, David Copperfield: all Dickens is there, Eng. J, 12/65; Inverse sublimity: Carlyle's theory of humor, Univ. Toronto,Quart, 70; plus others. Add: Dept. of English, University of Washington, Seattle, WA 98195.

DUNN, ROBERT FRANCIS, b. Phila, Pa, Mar. 23, 29; m. 60; c. 1. LITERATURE. B.S, St. Joseph's Col.(Pa), 55; fel, Univ. Notre Dame, 55-57, M.A, 57; Univ. Pa, 60-66. Instr. ENG, ST. JOSEPH'S COL.(PA), 57-61, ASST. PROF, 62- Nineteenth and 20th century British literature; Drama; public speaking. Add: Dept. of English, St. Joseph's College, Philadelphia, PA 19131.

DUNN, ROBERT PAUL, b. Rockford, Ill, Nov. 18, 41; m. 63; c. 2. RENAISSANCE ENGLISH LITERATURE. B.A, Pac. Union Col, 63; M.A, Univ. Wis-Madison, 66, Ph.D.(Eng), 70; South. Calif. Sch. Theol, 73- Asst. prof. ENG, LOMA LINDA UNIV, 69-73, ASSOC. PROF, 73- Ed, Adventist Eng. Newslett, 72- MLA; Conf. Christianity & Lit; Cath. Renascence Soc. Shakespeare; religion and literature. Publ: Ed, Religion and literature in the Seventh-day Adventist Church, Loma Linda Univ, 74. Add: Dept. of English, Graduate School, Loma Linda University, Riverside, CA 92505.

DUNN, THOMAS FRANKLIN, b. Nashville, Tenn, Apr. 17, 06; m. 27; c. 2. ENGLISH. A.B, Wash, Univ. 29, A.M, 30; Ph.D, Univ. Chicago, 39. Instr, Wash, Univ, 30-34; N.Dak. State Col, 35-36; prof. ENG, DRAKE UNIV, 36-62, EMER. PROF, 62- Am. Counc. Learned Soc. fel, 49; Fund Advan. Educ. fel, Harvard, 52-53; Fulbright lectr, Univ. Philippines, 60-61; prof. Eng, Canisius Col, 66-71; dean, Lingnan Col. Hong Kong, 71-72; sr. lectr. Eng, Hong Kong Baptist Col, 72-73. MLA; Renaissance Soc. Am. Renaissance; Reformation; Shakespeare. Publ: Facetiae of the Mensa Philosophica, Wash. Univ, 34; co-auth, Learning our language, Ronald, 50. Add: Dept. of English, Drake University, 25th & University, Des Moines, IA 50311.

DUNN, THOMAS PECKHAM, b. Boston, Mass, Oct. 18, 40; m. 64; c. 3. MEDIEVAL STUDIES. B.S, Ohio Wesleyan Univ, 63; M.A, Univ. Cincinnati, 67, Ph.D.(Eng), 72. Teacher ENG, W. Clermont Local Schs, 63-66; lectr, Univ. Cincinnati, summer 68; instr, MIAMI UNIV, HAMILTON CAMPUS, 68-71, ASST. PROF, 72- MLA; Medieval Acad. Am. Middle English literature of the West Midlands; Shakespeare; folklore and popular culture. Add: Dept. of English, Miami University, Hamilton Campus, 208 Peck Blvd, Hamilton, OH 45011.

DUNNE, MICHAEL FRANCIS, b. Philadelphia, Pa, Aug. 10, 41; m. 66; c. 2. AMERICAN LITERATURE. B.A, Fordham Univ, 64; NDEA fels, La. State Univ, Baton Rouge, 64-67, 68-69, M.A, 66, Ph.D.(Eng), 69. Instr. ENG, La. State Univ, 67-68; asst. prof, MID. TENN. STATE UNIV, 69-73, ASSOC. PROF, 73- English Institute. Hawthorne; 20th century American literature; critical theory. Add: Dept. of English, Middle Tennessee State University, Murfreesboro, TN 37130.

DUNNING, ARTHUR STEPHEN, JR, b. Duluth, Minn, Oct. 31, 24; m. 50; c. 4. ENGLISH. B.A, Carleton Col, 49; B.S. & M.A, Univ. Minn, 51; Ph.D.(Eng. & educ), Florida State Univ, 59. Teacher jr. & sr. high schs, 51-59; asst. prof. EDUC, Duke Univ, 59-61, assoc. prof, 61-62; Northwest. Univ, 62-64; UNIV. MICH, ANN ARBOR, 64-67, PROF, 67- Chmn, scholarly appraisals comt, NCTE, 62-65, ad hoc comt, teaching Eng. in jr. high, 65-66, dir. insts, Eng. in the middle grades, 68, mem. exec. comt, Conf. Eng, Educ, 66-70, nat. chmn, 70-72, dir. comn. on lit, 72-; mem. adv. bd, Campus Bk. Club, Scholastic Bks, 64-; mem. adv. bd, Scholastic Int, 72-; supvr. ed, Scholastic Lit. Units. Teaching of poetry; literature for adolescents; methods in the teaching of English. Publ: Co-auth, Reflections on a gift of watermelon pickle. . . and other modern verse, 66, auth, Teaching literature to adolescents: poetry, 66, Teaching literature to adolescents: short stories, 68 & co-ed, Some haystacks don't even have any needle, 69, Scott; Ed, To-day's poets, Folkways/Scholastic, 67; ed, English for the junior high years, NCTE, 69; co-ed, Poetry, 70, ed, Mad, sad, and glad, 70, co-ed, Superboy/ supergirl, 71 & Short story, 73, Scholastic Bk. Serv; auth, What is basic in methods?, In: Method in the teaching of English, NCTE, 67; I really liked it: short stories and taste, Eng. J, 5/68. Add: Dept. of English, University of Michigan, Ann Arbor, MI 48103.

DUNNINGTON, HAZEL BRAIN, b. Thorp, Wash, Oct. 31, 12; m. 49; c. 2. LANGUAGE DEVELOPMENT, CHILDREN'S DRAMA. B.A, Cent. Wash. State Col, 35; fel, Northwest. Univ, 38-40, M.A, 40; Moholy Nagy Sch. Design, 40; Univ. Wash, 46, 62. Teacher. elem. schs, Wash, 32-38; instr. theater arts, Stanford Univ, 40-43; recreation dir, Am. Red. Cross, India & China, 43-46; asst. prof. Eng. & child drama, CENT. WASH. STATE COL, 46-50, CHILD DRAMA, 56-68, ASSOC. PROF, 68- U.S. Off. Educ-NDEA Eng. Inst. grant, summer 66; consult. instruct. materials lab, Cent. Wash. State Col, 66-67. Am. Theatre Asn; Children's Theatre Conf. Creative dramatics; poetry for children; language development in elementary school. Publ: Co-ed, Children's theatre and creative dramatics, Univ. Wash, 61; auth, Creative dramatics with little children, chap. 7, In: Creative dramatics, 58 & Adaptations from Tolstoy and from Ruskin In: Children's literature for dramatization, 64, Harper. Add: Dept. of Theatre & Drama, Central Washington State College, Ellensburg, WA 98926.

DUPEE, FREDERICK WILCOX, b. Chicago, Ill, June 25, 04; m. 46; c. 2. ENGLISH. Ph.B, Yale, 27; Litt.D, Bard Col, 65. Instr. ENG, Bowdoin Col, 27-29; Columbia Univ, 40-44; assoc. prof, Bard Col, 44-48; COLUMBIA UNIV, 48-57, prof, 57-71, EMER. PROF, 71- Guggenheim fel, 52-53; Beckman vis. prof, Univ. Calif, Berkeley, 74. Henry James; modern comparative literature; Shakespeare. Publ: Henry James, Sloan, 51; ed, Great short French novels, Dial, 52 & The question of Henry James, Holt, 45; auth, The king of the cats (essays), Farrar, Straus, 65; co-ed, The selected letters of E.E. Cummings, Harcourt, 69. Add: 25704 Tierra Grande Dr, Carmel, CA 93921.

DUPLER, DOROTHY, b. Pa, Jan. 1, 10. SPEECH. A.B, Bridgewater Col, 31; A.M, Cath. Univ. Am, 43; Columbia Univ, 47; Ph.D, Univ. South. Calif, 61. Asst. prof. SPEECH, LA VERNE COL, 45-61, assoc. prof, 61-71, PROF, 71- Speech Commun. Asn; Am. Theatre Asn; West. Speech Commun. Asn. Rhetorical analysis of selected plays of George Bernard Shaw. Add: Dept. of Speech, La Verne College, La Verne, CA 91750.

DUPREE, JOHN DAVID, b. Detroit, Mich; m. 65; c. 2. COMMUNICATION, FOREIGN LANGUAGES. B.A, Mich. State Univ, 64, M.A, 66; Ph.D.(mass commun), Univ. N.C, Chapel Hill, 69; N.Mex. State Univ, 70-73; Univ. Calif, Berkeley, 73-74. Res. asst, Univ. N.C, Chapel Hill, 66-69; tech. ed. & writer, IBM Corp, 67-69; PROF. JOUR, N. MEX. STATE UNIV, 69- Nat. Sci. Found. fel, summer 70; Reporter, Traverse City Record, Mich, 72; Nat. Endowment for Humanities fel, 73-74. Asn. Educ. in Jour. International and cross-cultural communication. Publ: International communications, view from A window on the world, Gazette, World J. Commun. Stud, winter 72; contrib, International and cross-cultural communication, Holt, spring 74. Add: Dept. of Journalism & Mass Communications, New Mexico State University, Box 3J, Las Cruces, NM 88003.

DUPREE, ROBERT SCOTT, b. Alexandria, La, May 4, 40; m. 73. ENGLISH & COMPARATIVE LITERATURE. B.A, Univ. Dallas, 62; Fulbright award, Univ. Caen, 62-63; M.A, Yale, 64, Ph.D.(Eng), 66. Asst. prof. ENG, UNIV. DALLAS, 66-73, ASSOC. PROF, 73- Nat. Endowment for Humanities fel. grant, summer 71. S.Cent. Renaissance Conf. Menippean satire—relationship between French and English literature; 16th, 17th and 18th century literature, especially medieval lyric poetry. Publ: Boileau and Pope: the Horatian perspective in France and England, Univ. Microfilms, 66; The Southern poets, 74. Add: 1827 Pilgrim Dr, Irving, TX 75061.

DURANT, JACK DAVIS, b. Birmingham, Ala, Sept. 7, 30; m. 58; c. 2. ENGLISH LITERATURE. A.B, Maryville Col, 53; M.A, Univ. Tenn, 55, fel, 61-62, Ph.D.(Eng), 63. Instr. ENG, Maryville Col, 57-58; Presby. Col, 58-60; Univ. Tenn, 62-63; asst. prof, Auburn Univ, 63-67, ASSOC. PROF, 67-71; N.C. STATE UNIV, 71- S.Atlantic Mod. Lang. Asn. Imagery in the prose of Jonathan Swift. Publ: The moral focus of The school for scandal, S.Atlantic Bull, 72; Sheridan's Royal sanctuary: a key to The rivals, Ball State Univ. Forum, 73; Prudence, providence, and the direct road of wrong: The school for scandal and Sheridan's Westminster Hall speech, Stud. Burke & His Time, 73; plus others. Add: Dept. of English, North Carolina State University, Raleigh, NC 27607.

DURER, CHRISTOPHER, b. Warsaw, Poland, Sept. 15, 28; U.S. citizen; m. 67; c. 1. ENGLISH, COMPARATIVE LITERATURE. B.Ed, Chicago Teachers Col, 61; M.A, Univ. Calif, Berkeley, 63, Ph.D.(comp. lit), 69; Univ. Bonn, 67-68. Instr. humanities, Univ. Mo-Rolla, 63-64; comp. lit, San Francisco State Col, 65-67; Univ. Calif, Berkeley, 68-69; asst. prof. Eng, UNIV. WYO, 69-73, ASSOC. PROF. ENG, & MOD. LANG, 73- U.S.A, 56-59. MLA; Am. Comp. Lit. Asn; Int. Comp. Lit. Asn; Am. Soc. 18th Century Stud. Comparative theory and history; English 18th century literature; 20th century drama. Publ: Co-ed, The madman and the nun and other plays by S.I. Witkiewicz, Wash. Univ, 68; ed, Readings in comparative literary criticism, Mouton, (in press); contrib, Molière and the Commonwealth of letters, Univ. South. Miss, 74 & Proceedings of the Seventh Congress of the International Comparative Literature Asn, (in press). Add: Dept. of English, University of Wyoming, Laramie, WY 82070.

DURHAM, JOHN, b. Wichita Falls, Tex, Dec. 10, 25; m. 50, 64; c. 4. EDUCATION, FICTION WRITING. B.A, Grinnell Col, 51; M.A, State Univ. Iowa, 54; Ph.D.(comp. lit), Occidental Col, 68. Asst. prof. ENG, Calif. State Col. Los Angeles, 61-67; assoc. prof, Calif. State Polytech. Univ, 67-70; ASST. PROF, SAN JOSE STATE UNIV, 70- Writer-in-residence, Los Angeles City Schs, 66-68. Edgar Allan Poe Award, 60. U.S.N, 44-46. Fiction writing, especially educational material for culturally deprived. Publ: Queen of diamonds (juvenile novel), Putnam, 60; co-auth, Plain style (text), 67 & auth, Take the short way home (stories), 68, McGraw; plus others. Add: Dept. of English, San Jose State University, San Jose, CA 95114.

DURHAM, PHILIP, b. Portland, Ore, Feb. 7, 12; m. 55; c. 1. ENGLISH. B.S, Linfield Col, 35; M.A, Claremont Grad. Sch, 46; Ph.D.(Eng), Northwest. Univ, 49. Prof. Eng. & chmn. dept, Elmhurst Col, 49-51; personnel mgr, John Plain Co, Chicago, Ill, 51-52; instr. ENG, UNIV. CALIF, LOS ANGELES, 53-55, asst. prof, 55-61, assoc. prof, 61-66, PROF, 66- Am. Counc. Learned Soc. fel, 52-53; Fulbright prof, Univ. Helsinki, 55-56; Guggenheim fel, 60-61; Nat. Endowment for Humanities award, 67-69. U.S.M.C, 42-45, Maj. Am. Stud. Asn; MLA; West. Writers Am; West. Lit. Asn. American frontier literature; popular American literature. Publ: Down these mean streets a man must go: Raymond Chandler's Knight, Univ. N.C, 63; co-auth, Harbrace college reader, Harcourt, 59, 64, 68 & 72; The Negro cowboys, 65 & The adventures of the Negro cowboys, 66, Dodd; ed, Seth Jones and Deadwood Dick & co-ed, The frontier in American literature, 69, Odyssey; ed, The Virginian, Houghton, 68; co-auth, American fiction in Finland, Soc. Neophilologique, 60; auth, The Black Mask School, In: Tough guys of the thirties, South. Ill. Univ, 68. Add: Dept. of English, University of California, Los Angeles, CA 90024.

DURNING, RUSSELL EDWARD, b. Dallas, Tex, June 25, 38; m. COMPARATIVE LITERATURE. B.A. & B.B.A, South. Methodist Univ, 60; Ph.D.(comp. lit), Univ. N.C, 65. Teaching asst. Eng, Univ. N.C, 61-64; instr, Univ. Wis-Milwaukee, 64-65, asst. prof, 65-66, comp. lit, 66-70, chmn. dept, 66-67 & 69; asst. prof. ENG, NORTH. ILL. UNIV, 70-71, ASSOC. PROF, 71- Am. Philos. Soc. grant, summer 65; Fulbright lectr, Univ. Tübingen, 67-68; co-ed, Complit: Can. J. Comp. Lit, 73- Nat. Guard, 55-60. Midwest Mod. Lang. Asn.(chmn. comp. lit. sect, 70-71); MLA; Am. Comp. Lit. Asn. Transcendentalism; German-American literary relations; masterpieces of world literature. Publ: Margaret Fuller, citizen of the world: an intermediary between European and American literature, C. Winter Universitätsverlag, Heidelberg, 69; Margaret Fuller's translation of Goethe's Prometheus, Jahrbuch Am-Stud, 67; The changing political thought of Coleridge and Wordsworth, 1789-1805, Complit, Vol. I, No. 1. Add: Dept. of English, Northern Illinois University, DeKalb, IL 60115.

DUROCHER, AURELE A, b. Marquette, Mich, Dec. 4, 12; m. 47. AMERICAN STUDIES. A.B, North. State Teachers Col, 40; A.M, Univ. Mich, 45; Ph.D, Univ. Minn, 55. Teacher, A.E. Smith Sch, Mich, 40-42, 44-45, Everett Sch, 45-47; PROF. ENG, N.Mich. Univ, 47-66; GRAND VALLEY STATE COL, 66- U.S.A.A.F, 42-43, 2nd Lt. Am. Stud. Asn; Col. Eng. Asn; MLA. Impact of ideas upon literature; intellectual history; effect of technology upon art and thought. Publ: Mark Twain and the Roman Catholic Church, J. Cent. Miss. Valley Am. Stud. Asn, 60; The social ideas of Henry George, Am. J. Econ. & Sociol, 10/61; The story of Fruitlands: transcendental wild oats, Mich. Academician, spring 69. Add: Dept. of English, Grand Valley State College, College Landing, Allendale, MI 49401.

DURRANT, GEOFFREY H, b. Derbyshire, Eng, July 27, 13; Can. citizen; m. 41; c. 3. ENGLISH. B.A, Cambridge, 35; Univ. London, 35-36; Tübingen Univ, 37-39; D.Litt, Univ. S.Africa, 67. Lectr. ENG, Univ. Durham, 36-37; sr. lectr. & acting head dept, Univ. Stellenbosch, 39-41; prof. & head dept, Univ. Natal, 45-60; prof, Univ. Man, 61-66, head dept, 64-66; PROF, UNIV. B.C, 66-, head dept, 66-69. Rep. Univ. Natal, Joint Matriculation Bd, 48-61; Nat. Counc. Soc. & Humanistic Res, Pretoria, 50-61; Carnegie fel, 60. S.African Army, 40-45, Intel, 42-45, Capt. Asn. Can. Univ. Teachers Eng; Asn. Commonwealth Lit. & Lang. Stud; MLA. Wordsworth; Shakespeare. Publ: William Wordsworth, 69 & Wordsworth and the great system, 70, Cambridge Univ; Measure for measure—a comedy, Stratford Shakespeare Stud, 72; plus others. Add: Dept. of English, University of British Columbia, Vancouver 8, B.C, Can.

DURST, MARTIN I, b. New York, N.Y, Sept. 5, 39; m. 63; c. 1. ENGLISH & AMERICAN LITERATURE. B.A, Queens Col.(N.Y), 61; M.A, Univ. Ore, 63, Ph.D.(Eng), 67. Instr. ENG, Univ. Ore, 64-67; ASST. PROF, Lycoming Col, 67-72; LANEY COL, 72- Vis. lectr, Queens Col.(N.Y), summer 65. American and English literature; humanistic psychology. Publ: William Carlos Williams: introduction and bibliography, W.Coast Rev, 67; Flowers, women, and song in the poetry of William Carlos Williams, Inscape, 68. Add: Dept. of English, Laney College, 900 Fallon St, Oakland, CA 94607.

DUSSINGER, JOHN ANDREW, b. Reading, Pa, Nov. 18, 35; m. 59; c. 2. ENGLISH. A.B, Lehigh Univ, 58; Fulbright scholar, Univ. Copenhagen, 58-59; I.I.E, Oxford, 59; Woodrow Wilson fel. & M.A. Princeton, 61, Ph.D.(Eng), 64. Instr. ENG, Douglass Col, 62-65; asst. prof, UNIV. ILL, URBANA-CHAMPAIGN, 65-68, ASSOC. PROF, 68-, fac. summer res. fels, 67-68. Lectr. Eng. lit, Aarhus Univ, 70-72. MLA; Johnson Soc. Midwest (pres, 68-69) Am. Soc. 18th Century Stud. Eighteenth century prose; the novel; history of ideas. Publ: The discourse of the mind in 18th century fiction, Mouton, 74; Conscience and the pattern of Christian perfection in Clarissa, PMLA, 66; What Pamela knew: an interpretation, JEGP, 70; Style and intention in Johnson's Life of savage, ELH, 70; plus others. Add: 1612 Chevy Chase Dr, Champaign, IL 61820.

DUST, ALVIN IRWIN, b. Chicago, Ill, Mar. 20, 22; m. 53; c. 3. ENGLISH. B.A, Univ. Ill, Urbana, 50, M.A, 51, Ph.D.(Eng), 60. Asst. ENG, Univ. Ill, Urbana, 52-60; lectr, UNIV. WATERLOO, 60-61, asst. prof, 61-67, ASSOC. PROF, 67- Can. Counc. for arts grant, 69. Sig.C, U.S.A, 42-45. Conf. Col. Compos. & Commun; NCTE; Can. Counc. Teachers Eng; Renaissance Soc. Am; MLA; Can. Comp. Lit. Asn. Bibliographical study of rare books; the Restoration period; English drama. Publ: The Seventh and last canto of Gondibert and two dedicatory poems, J. Eng. & Ger. Philol, 4/61; An aspect of the Addison-Steele literary relationship, Eng. Lang. Notes, 3/64; co-auth, A defense of innocencio, Publ: Bibliog. Soc. Am, 10/67. Add: 250 Humanities Bldg, University of Waterloo, Waterloo, Ont, N2L 3G1, Can.

DUST, PHILIP CLARENCE, b. Centralia, Ill, Dec. 13, 36; m. 67; c. 1. ENGLISH RENAISSANCE LITERATURE. B.A, St. Mary of the Lake Sem, 59; V.B.S, East. Ill. Univ, 61; M.A, Univ. Ill, 64, Ph.D.(Eng), 68. Teacher Latin, Pekin Community High Sch, 61-63; teaching asst. ENG, Univ. Ill, 64-68; ASST. PROF, NORTH. ILL. UNIV, 68- Col. Eng. Asn; Midwest Mod. Lang. Asn; MLA. Renaissance neo-Latin poetry and prose; Renaissance English poetry and prose. Publ: Alberico Gentili's Commentaries on utopian war, Moreana, 2/73; New light on Milton's Two-handed engine: a possible neo-Latin source, Humanistica Lovaniensia, fall 73; The theme of Kinde in Gorboduc, Salzburg Stud. Eng. Lit, 73; plus others. Add: Dept. of English, Northern Illinois University, DeKalb, IL 60115.

DUSTAN, W. GORDON, b. Moncton, N.B, Can, Sept. 9, 07; m. 49; c. 1. ENGLISH LITERATURE. B.A, Mt. Allison Univ, 27; M.A, Dalhousie Univ, 28; Univ. Toronto, 30; Ph.D, Univ. Edinburgh, Scotland, 33. Chmn. dept. Eng, Monticello Col, 39-41; instr, Col. Wooster, 41-42; prof. & adj, Valley Forge Mil. Jr. Col, 42-46; asst. prof, Bucknell Univ, 46-47; prof. & chmn. dept, Keuka Col, 47-58; prof. Eng. lang. & lit, KUTZTOWN STATE COL, 58-72, EMER. PROF. ENG, 72- Add: Dept. of English, Kutztown State College, Kutztown, PA 19530.

DUUS, LOUISE, b. Wilmington, Del, Feb. 12, 29. ENGLISH, AMERICAN STUDIES. B.A, Oberlin Col, 49; M.A, Univ. Mich, 50; univ. fel, Univ. Minn, 62, Ph.D.(Am. stud), 67. Registr. & part-time instr. Eng, Hanover Col, 53-57; lectr. Eng, State Univ. N.Y. Buffalo, 63-67, asst. prof, 67-69, acting dir, prog. Am. stud, 66-68; vis. scholar humanities, Philander Smith Col, spring 69; ASST. PROF. ENG. & AM. CIVILIZATION, LAFAYETTE COL, 69- MLA; Am. Stud. Asn. American novel; utopian fiction; American communal experience. Add: Dept. of English, Lafayette College, Easton, PA 18042.

DUVALL, SEVERN PARKER COSTIN, b. Norfolk, Va, Mar. 25, 24; m. 50; c. 3. AMERICAN LITERATURE. A.B, Univ. Va, 48; M.A, Princeton, 51, Ph.D, 55. Instr. Eng, Princeton, 50-51; from instr. to assoc. prof, Dartmouth Col, 53-62; PROF. ENG. & HEAD DEPT, WASHINGTON & LEE UNIV, 62- Fulbright lectr, Univ. Mainz, 57-58 & Univ. Warsaw, 71. U.S.M.C, 43-46, 51-52, Capt. MLA. Nineteenth century poetry and prose. Add: Dept. of English, Payne Hall, Washington & Lee University, Lexington, VA 24450.

DWYER, RICHARD ANTHONY, b. Riverside, Calif, Nov. 24, 34; m. 64; c. 1. ENGLISH, MEDIEVALISM. B.A, Univ. Calif, Los Angeles, 56, M.A, 60, Ph.D.(Eng), 65. Instr. ENG, Purdue Univ, 64-65, asst. prof, 65-66; Univ. Fla, 66-70, assoc. prof, 70-71, res. assoc. commun. sci. lab, 68-70; PROF. ENG, FLA. INT. UNIV, 71-, chmn. dept, 71-73. Adj. Gen.C, U.S.A.R, 57-63. MLA; Mediaeval Acad. Am; NCTE. Medieval Anglo-French literary relations; Boethius; general linguistics. Publ: Co-auth, The nonpareil press of T.S. Harris, Dawson, 57, The songs of the Gold Rush, 64 & Songs of the American West, 68, Univ. Calif; auth, Villon's Boethius, Ann. Mediaevale, 70; Asenath of Egypt in Middle English, Medium Aevum, 70; The appreciation of handmade literature, Chaucer Rev, (in press). Add: Dept. of English, Florida International University, Miami, FL 33144.

DWYER, WILLIAM GUENTHER, b. Olean, N.Y, Nov. 26, 37; m. 62; c. 3. ENGLISH & AMERICAN LITERATURE. B.A, Grove City Col, 59; M.A, Syracuse Univ, 68, Ph.D.(Eng. & Am. lit), 71. Instr. ENG, U.S. AIR FORCE ACAD, 68-69, asst. prof, 71-72, ASSOC. PROF, 72- Lectr. Eng, Colo. Springs Ctr, Univ. Colo, 68-69 & 71- U.S.A.F, 59-, Lt. Col. MLA; Renaissance Soc. Am; Shakespeare Asn. Am. Shakespeare; Elizabethan and Jacobean drama. Publ: A study of John Webster's use of Renaissance natural and moral philosophy, Int. Eng. Sprache und Lit, Univ. Salzburg, 73. Add: Dept. of English & Fine Arts, U.S. Air Force Academy, CO 80840.

DYCKE, MARJORIE L, b. New York, N.Y, Mar. 12, 16; m. 54. THEATRE EDUCATION. A.B, Hunter Col, 36; A.M, Columbia Univ, 38; summer, Yale, 42; Ph.D, N.Y. Univ, 48. Teacher-in-training speech, high schs, City Bd. Educ, New York, 37-38, teacher, 39-46; tutor, Hunter Col, 46-48; founding chmn. dept. drama, Sch. Performing Arts, Bd. Educ, N.Y.C, 48-51, chmn, 51-73; ADJ. ASST. PROF. TEACHER PREP, YORK COL.(N.Y), 72. Mem. panel dramatic art, U.S. Nat. Comn, UNESCO, 52-; consult, Gov. Sch, Winston-Salem, N.C, 63; chmn. Comn. Save N.Y. Pub. Libr. for Performing Arts, Lincoln Ctr, 72. Fel. Am. Theatre Asn.(2nd v.pres, 60, 1st v.pres, 61, pres, 62); Am. Nat. Theatre & Acad. Theatre; speech education. Publ: The Negro actor and desegregation, 3/59 & The Presidential address, 1962, 12/62, Educ. Theatre J. Add: 33-37 163rd St, Flushing, NY 11358.

DYER, ARMEL, b. Columbia, Mo, Sept. 13, 09; m. 37; c. 2. SPEECH, AMERICAN STUDIES. B.S.Ed, Univ. Mo, 33, M.A, 38; Infantry Sch, 42; U.S. Army Command & Gen. Staff Col, 43; U.S. Naval War Col, 46; Strategic Intel. Sch, 56; Ph.D.(speech), Univ. Ore, 68. Instr. Eng. & speech, Joplin Jr. Col, 38-40; speech, Univ. Mo, 46, assoc. prof, Wabash Col, 46-47; instr. speech & Eng, N.Mex. Mil. Inst, 62-63; asst. prof. SPEECH, Univ. Hawaii, 65-68; PROF, CALIF. STATE UNIV, CHICO, 69- U.S.A.R, 33-46, U.S.A, 47-62, Col.(Ret). Speech Commun. Asn. Rhetoric; national defense; propaganda. Publ: Great military captains address their armies, spring 69 & Speechmaking in the military, fall 70, Pac. Speech Quart. Add: Dept. of Speech, California State University, Chico, First & Normal St, Chico, CA 95926.

DYER, HENRY HOPPER, b. Fishers Ferry, Pa, May 1, 21. AMERICAN CIVILIZATION, ENGLISH. A.B, Bucknell Univ, 49; A.M, Univ. Pa, 51, Ph.D. Ph.D.(Am. civilization), 65. Off. & instr, Fork Union Mil. Acad, 51-52; assoc. prof. ENG, RADFORD COL, 56-65, PROF, 65-, chmn. dept, 67-68 & 70. C.Engr, U.S.A, 42-45. American literature; American social and cultural history. Add: Dept. of English, Radford College, Radford, VA 24141.

DYGOSKI, LOUISE A, b. New York, N.Y, July 26, 11. SPEECH. B.A, East. Nazarene Col.(Mass), 39; summer, Columbia Univ, 44; M.A, Northwest. Univ, 47; Boston Univ, 52-53; Ph.D.(speech), Univ. Wis, 61. Asst. prof. SPEECH, EAST. NAZARENE COL.(MASS), 44-47, assoc. prof, 47-61, PROF, 61- Asst. prof, Univ. Wis, 59-60; vis. scholar, Univ. Mich, 68-69. Speech Commun. Asn. Oral interpretation; rhetoric; public address. Add: Dept. of Speech, Eastern Nazarene College, Quincy, MA 02170.

DYKSTRA, GERALD, Linguistics, Education. See Volume III, Foreign Languages, Linguistics & Philology.

DYROFF, JAN MICHAEL, b. Fayetteville, N.C, Aug. 7, 42; m. 72; c. 2. RENAISSANCE STUDIES, CREATIVE WRITING. A.B, Vilanova Univ, 64; A.M, Boston Univ, 65, Ph.D.(Eng), 72. Asst. prof. lit, Lakehead Univ, 70-73; LECTR. WRITING, BOSTON UNIV, 73- Ed. consult, LeChronic, Roxbury, Mass, 68; dir. writing prog, St. Anne's Sch, Arlington Heights, 68-70; ed. consult, Allyn & Bacon, Boston, 70; Chancellor's Fund award, Lakehead Univ, 71; commun. specialist, Wm. Underwood Co, 74. Renaissance Soc. Am; Cath. Rec. Soc, Eng; Bibliog. Soc, Eng; Renaissance Eng. Text Soc; MLA. Renaissance studies, classicism and definitions of Renaissance style; creative writing, production and pedagogy; literature of the 18th century, poetry and its backgrounds in society. Publ: The poems of Rufinos, 73 & Journies and shows, 74, Borealis, Ottawa; Verse: Canadian style, Lit. Currents, 70; Sylvia Plath: perceptions in Crossing the water, Art & Lit. Rev, 72; Swift the drapier and Wood's money, Coin, Stamp & Antique News, 73. Add: 179 Newtonville Ave, Newton, MA 02158.

E

EAGAN, M. CLEMENT, C.C.V.I, b. Ennis, Tex, Jan. 30, 93. ENGLISH, LATIN. A.B, Incarnate Word Col, 23; A.M, Univ. Tex, 27; Columbia Univ, 28. Teacher, Notre Dame Acad, Tex, 16-19; ENG, High Sch, INCARNATE WORD COL, 19-28, PROF, 38-69, DEAN INSTR, 28-69, dean & registr, 36-47, EMER. DEAN, 69- Natl. Cath. Educ. Asn; MLA. Publ: Poems of Prudentius; American profile; A concordance to Statius. Add: Dept. of English, Incarnate World College, San Antonio, TX 78209.

EAKER, JAY GORDON, b. Hudson, Iowa, Feb. 6, 04; m. 33; c. 3. ENGLISH LITERATURE. A.B, State Univ. Iowa, 28, fel, 30-32, A.M, 31, Ph.D, 32. Asst, State Univ. Iowa, 29; asst. prof. Eng, Kans. State Col. Pittsburg, 32-33; assoc. prof, 33-37, prof, 37-46, head dept. lang. & lit, 44-46; prof. ENG. & head dept, Jersey City Jr. Col, 46-54; assoc. prof, UNIV. HOUSTON, 54-55, PROF, 55- S.Cent. Mod. Lang. Asn. Victorian English literature; Shakespeare; Greek literature. Publ: Walter Pater, a study in methods and effects; Robert Bridges concept of nature, PMLA, 39; Meredith's human comedy, Nineteenth-Century Fiction, 51. Add: 7910 Locke Lane Apt. 8, Houston, TX 77042.

EAKIN, PAUL JOHN, b. Cleveland, Ohio, Mar. 8, 38; m. 64; c. 3. ENGLISH. A.B, Harvard, 59, A.M, 61, Ph.D.(Eng), 66; Univ. Paris, 59-60. Asst. prof. ENG, IND. UNIV, BLOOMINGTON, 66-72, ASSOC. PROF, 72- Sr. Fulbright-Hays lectr, Univ. Paris XII, Val de Marne, 72-73. MLA; AAUP. Henry James; reflections of the New England mind in nineteenth century fiction; American transcendentalism. Publ: Sarah Orne Jewett and the meaning of country life, 1/67, Hawthorne's imagination and the structure of The custom-house, 11/71 & Poe's sense of an ending, 3/73, Am. Lit. Add: Dept. of English, College of Arts & Sciences, Indiana University, Bloomington, IN 47401.

EAKINS, ROLLIN GENE, b. Springfield, Ohio, June 28, 29; m. 53; c. 6. SPEECH. A.B, Wittenberg Univ, 51, B.S, 53; M.Ed, Kent State Univ, 59; Ph.D.(speech), Ohio State Univ, 66. Instr. SPEECH, Ohio State Univ, 62-64; Bowling Green State Univ, 64-66; asst. prof, Univ. Iowa, 66-69; ASSOC. PROF, WRIGHT STATE UNIV, 69- Consult. commun, U.S. Civil Serv, 68-73. U.S.A, 48-50. Speech Commun. Asn; Am. Forensic Asn. Speech education; rhetoric; metaphorical utilization in small groups. Publ: The ethics of high school debating, Ohio Speech J, 63; Problems in coaching debate, Rostrum, 64; Aristotelian influences in the rhetoric of Kenneth Burke, Conn. Speech J, spring 68. Add: Dept. of Speech Communication, Wright State University, Col. Glenn Highway, Dayton, OH 45431.

EARLY, JAMES, b. Worcester, Mass, Apr. 19, 23; m. 49; c. 3. ENGLISH. A.B, Bowdoin Col, 47; M.A, Harvard, 49, fel, 52-53, Ph.D, 53. Instr. ENG, Yale, 53-57; instr, Vassar Col, 57-59, asst. prof, 59-64; assoc. prof, SOUTH. METHODIST UNIV, 64-68, PROF, 68-, ASSOC. DEAN HUMANITIES & SCI, 71-, grad. counc. humanities, 66-67, chmn. dept. Eng, 68-71. U.S.A, 42-46. MLA; Col. Art Asn. American literature and architecture; Shakespeare. Publ: Romanticism and American architecture, A.S. Barnes,

65; co-auth, Adventures in American literature, Harcourt, 68; The making of Go, down Moses, South. Methodist Univ, 72. Add: 7015 Lakeshore Dr, Dallas, TX 75214.

EARLY, RAYMOND R, b. Detroit, Mich, Oct. 24, 12; m. 39; c. 2. AMERICAN LITERATURE. A.B, West. Mich. Col. Educ, 39; A.M, State Univ. Iowa, 40; Univ. Mich; Univ. Calif. Demonstration teacher, sch. educ, Univ. Mich, 41-43; asst. prof, Mich. State Col, 44-46; from assoc. prof. to lectr. ENG, UNIV. SAN FRANCISCO & CITY COL. SAN FRANCISCO, 47- Asst. ed, Webster's New World Dictionary, 44. Hopwood Award, 42. United States history and literature. Publ: Columbia: gold town, Fearon, 57; Spelling made easy, 66 & Punctuation games and exercises, 66, Acad. Guild. Add: Dept. of English, University of San Francisco, San Francisco, CA 94117.

EARNEST, ERNEST, b. Hummelstown, Pa, Sept. 19, 01; m. 27; c. 3. ENGLISH LITERATURE. B.S, Lafayette Col, 23; Harvard, 23-24; A.M, Princeton, 27, Ph.D, 36. Instr, Ga. Sch. Tech, 24-26; from instr. to prof. ENG, TEMPLE UNIV, 27-29, dir. Havertown unit, 45-50, EMER. PROF, 69- English romantic poetry; American literature. Publ: John and William Bartram, 40 & S. Weir Mitchell, novelist and physician, 50, Univ. Pa; Academic procession, an informal history of the American college, 1636-1953, Bobbs, 53; Expatriates and patriots, Duke Univ, 68; The single vision: the alienation of American intellectuals, 1910-1930, N.Y. Univ, 70; The American eve in fact and fiction, 1775-1914, Univ. Ill, (in press). Add: 428 Righters Mill Rd, Gladwyne, PA 19035.

EASSON, KAY PARKHURST, b. Tulsa, Okla, Oct. 17, 40; m. 70. ENGLISH LANGUAGE & LITERATURE. B.A, Univ. Tulsa, 62, M.A, 68, Ph.D.(Eng), 70. ASST. PROF. ENG, ILL. STATE UNIV, 70- Co-ed. & co-founder, Blake Stud, 68-, co-founder & secy-treas. bd. dirs, Am. Blake Found, Inc, 70-; Nat. Endowment for Humanities Younger Humanist fel, 71. MLA. William Blake: British romantic literature and art; 20th century British literature. Publ: The attitudes of rhetoric: a guide, Prentice-Hall, 70; co-ed, Materials for the study of William Blake: a fascimile series for the general reader, Am. Blake Found, 73-; auth, William Blake and the smiling tyger, In: William Blake: The tyger, C.E. Merrill, 69. Add: Dept. of English, Illinois State University, Normal, IL 61761.

EASSON, ROGER RALPH, b. Carthage, Mo, Nov. 22, 45; m. 70. ENGLISH LANGUAGE & LITERATURE. B.A, Kans. State Col. Pittsburg, 66, M.A, 67; Ph.D.(Eng), Univ. Tulsa, 70. ASST. PROF. ENG, ILL. STATE UNIV, 70- Co-ed, Blake Stud, 68-; chmn. exec. bd. dirs, Am. Blake Found, Inc, 70- MLA. The art and poetry of William Blake; rhetorical criticism. Publ: Co-auth, William Blake: book illustrator, Vol. I, 72 & co-ed, Materials for the study of William Blake: a facsimile series for the general reader, 73, Am. Blake Found; auth, William Blake and the contemporary art market, Blake Newsletter, 71; William Blake and his reader in Jerusalem, In: Blake's sublime allegory, Univ. Wis, 73. Add: Dept. of English, Illinois State University, Normal, IL 61761.

EASTMAN, ARTHUR M, b. Roslyn, L.I, N.Y, Sept. 8, 18; m. 41; c. 4. ENGLISH. B.A, Oberlin Col, 40; M.A, Yale, 42, Ph.D.(Eng), 47. Instr. Univ. N.H, 46-47; Univ. Mich, 47-51, from asst. prof. to prof. ENG, 51-68; PROF. & HEAD DEPT, CARNEGIE-MELLON UNIV, 68- Mem. Anglo-Am. sem. Eng, Dartmouth Col, 66; Nat. Endowment for Humanities sr. fel, 74. U.S.A, 43-46. MLA; Col. Eng. Asn; Shakespeare Asn. Am; NCTE. Shakespeare; 18th century criticism and modern drama; American post-colonial history, 1785-1825. Publ: Franklin to Frost (64 TV tapes), Midwest Prog. Airborne TV Instr, 62; co-ed, Shakespeare's critics, Univ. Mich, 64; gen. ed, The Norton reader, Norton, 65, rev. ed. 69 & 73; co-ed, Masterpieces of the drama, Macmillan, 2nd ed, 66; auth, A short history of Shakespearean criticism, Random, 68; coord. ed, The Norton anthology of poetry, Norton, 70; ed, Proceedings of the Conference on the Doctor of Arts Degree, Counc. Grad. Schs. U.S, 70; auth, Behavioral objectives, Bacon, and relevance, West. Humanities Rev, summer 70; Soliloquy in an academic cloister, Bull. Asn. Depts. Eng, 71; Othello as ironist, In: In honor of Austin Wright, Carnegie-Mellon Univ, 72; plus others. Add: 1400 N. Highland Ave, Pittsburgh, PA 15206.

EASTMAN, RICHARD MORSE, b. Locust Valley, N.Y, Aug. 20, 16; m. 42; c. 3. ENGLISH. B.A, Oberlin Col, 37; M.A, Univ. Chicago, 49, Ph.D.(Eng), 52. Instr. ENG, N.CENT. COL, 46-49, asst. prof, 49-52, assoc. prof, 52-55, PROF, 55-, DEAN FAC. & V.PRES. ACAD. AFFAIRS, 70-, chmn. dept. Eng, 52-70, chmn. div. humanities, 61-70. U.S.A, 41-46, Maj. NCTE; Am. Conf. Acad. Deans. The novel; modern drama. Publ: A guide to the novel, Chandler, 65; Style, Oxford Univ, 70; Murder and imagination: a defense of liberal humanism, Col. Eng, 2/71; plus others. Add: 961 E. Porter Ave, Naperville, IL 60540.

EASTON, EDWARD RAYMOND, b. Chattanooga, Tenn, Feb. 1, 19; m. 43, 70; c. 4. ENGLISH. A.B, Columbia Univ, 40, A.M, 41, Ph.D, 67. Instr, Carnegie Inst. Technol, 42-44; Worcester Polytech. Inst, 44-47; N.Y. Univ, 47-50; lectr, City Col. New York, 50-51; instr, L.I. Univ, 51-54; instr. & adj. assoc. prof. ENG, PACE UNIV, 54-57, asst. prof, 57-68, assoc. prof, 68-73, PROF, 73-, chmn. dept, 70-72. MLA; Mod. Humanities Res. Asn. Gt. Brit; Am. Asn. Advan. Slavic Stud; Hopkins Soc. Nineteenth century Russian novel; French novel; psychological and social themes in 19th and 20th century western literature. Add: 25 Parade Pl, Brooklyn, NY 11226.

EATON, ANTHONY HASKELL, b. Cochrane, Ont, Dec. 26, 20; U.S. citizen; m. 47; c. 2. ENGLISH, HUMANITIES. A.B, Bowdoin Col, 42; M.A, Univ. Chicago, 48. Asst. prof. ENG, FISK UNIV, 50-54, ASSOC. PROF, 55- U.S.A.A.F, 42-46. MLA; NCTE; Ling. Soc. Am. Old English; Chaucer. Add: Dept. of English, Box 20, Fisk University, Nashville, TN 37203.

EATON, CHARLES EDWARD, b. Winston-Salem, N.C, June 25, 16; m. 50. ENGLISH. A.B, Univ. N.C, 36; Princeton, 36-37; M.A, Harvard, 40. Instr. Eng, Univ. Mo, 40-42; v.consul, Am. Embassy, Brazil, 42-46; asst. prof. Eng, Univ. N.C, 46-51; RES. & WRITING, 51- Delivered lects, N.C. Poetry Circuit, 63. Ridgely Torrence Award, 51. American literature. Publ: The bright plain (poems), Univ. N.C, 42; The shadow of the swimmer (poems), Fine Ed, 51; The greenhouse in the garden (poems), Twayne, 56; Write me from Rio (short stories), Blair, 59; Countermoves (poems), 63 & On the edge of the knife (poems), 70, Abelard; The girl from Ipanema (short stories), North Country Publ, 72; Karl Knaths: five decades of painting, Int. Exhibitions Found, 73; contrib. O. Henry Prize stories, Doubleday, 72. Add: Merlin Stone, Woodbury, CT 06798.

EATON, MARY ELEANOR, S.N.D. de N, b. Watsonville, Calif, Oct. 8, 09. ENGLISH. A.B, Stanford Univ, 32, A.M, 33, Ph.D, 54. PROF. ENG, COL. NOTRE DAME, 47- Middle English literature; the English mystics. Add: Notre Dame Villa, Saratoga, CA 95070.

EATON, RICHARD BOZMAN, JR, b. Parksley, Va, May 27, 31; m. 61; c. 3. ENGLISH. B.A, Richmond Col, 53; M.A, Univ. N.C, 55, Ph.D.(Eng), 67. Instr. ENG, Winthrop Col, 55-56; Wake Forest Col, 60-64; asst. prof, Richmond Col, 65-67; W.VA. UNIV, 67-72, ASSOC. PROF, 72-, senate fels, 68, 70. Prosody; Southern literature; heraldy. Publ: Contributions of James Rush to prosodic theory, Philol. Papers, 7/72; Poe's prosody in perspective, Poe Stud, 12/72; Tennyson's descendants, Victorian Poetry, spring 73. Add: Dept. of English, West Virginia University, Morgantown, WV 26506.

EATON, WINIFRED K, b. Merrimack, N.H, Dec. 11, 02; m. 31; c. 3. ENGLISH, ASIAN STUDIES. B.A, Wellesley Col, 25; M.A, Univ. Wis, 27; exchange fel, Hamburg Univ, 29-30; Ph.D.(humanities), Syracuse Univ, 65. Instr. Eng, Univ. Wis, 27-28; teacher, Liggett Sch, 28-29; Solvey High Sch, 53-54; writer phonics, Iroquois Publ. Co, 54-57; ed. spec. reports, Gen. Electric Co, 57-58; instr. Eng, Cazenovia Col.(N.Y), 58-66, asst. prof, 66-68, assoc. prof. Eng. & Asian stud, 68-70; RETIRED. Ctr. Int. Stud. fac. fel, Cornell Univ, 63-65; grants, Col. Ctr. of Finger Lakes for sem. on Japan, 65-66, Cazenova Col. for Syracuse Univ. sem. on China, 66, Six Col. Consortium for sem. on China, 66-67 & on India, 68-69, Colgate Univ. for sem. on Indian Arts, summer 67 & Col. Ctr. grant for independent Asian Stud, summer 68. MLA; Am. Asn. Jr. Cols; NCTE; Asn. Asian Stud. Comparative drama in Greece, England and Sweden; the spread of the hero legends of India into Southeast Asia, especially the Rama legends. Publ: Co-auth, Phonics series, Iroquois, 56; Representation of death on the stage by Sophocles, Webster and Strindberg, Univ. Salzburg, 74. Add: 511 E. Seneca St, Manlius, NY 13104.

EAVES, MORRIS EMERY, b. Monroe, La, May 12, 44; m. 63; c. 1. ART & LITERARY CRITICISM. B.A, L. I. Univ, 66; Ph.D.(Eng), Tulane Univ, 72. Asst. prof. ENG, UNIV. N.MEX, 70-73, ASSOC. PROF, 74- Managing ed, Blake Newsletter: Illus. Quart, 70- MLA. William Blake; English romanticism; narrative literature. Publ: Decision and revision in James Merrill's (Diblos) Notebook, Contemporary Lit, spring 71; A reading of Blake's Marriage of heaven and hell, plates 17-20: on and under the estate of the west, Blake Stud, spring 72; The title-page of The book of Urizen, In: William Blake: essays in honour of Sir Geoffrey Keynes, Oxford Univ, 73. Add: Dept. of English, University of New Mexico, Albuquerque, NM 87131.

EAVES, THOMAS CARY DUNCAN, b. Union, S.C, Oct. 11, 18. ENGLISH. A.B, Univ. N.C, 39; A.M, Univ. Cincinnati, 40; A.M, Harvard, 43, Ph.D, 44. Teaching fel. & tutor, Harvard, 42-43; instr, Rutgers Univ, 44-46; asst. prof, Col. William & Mary, 46-47; ENG, UNIV. ARK, FAYETTEVILLE, 49-52, assoc. prof, 52-57, PROF, 57- Guggenheim fel, 57-58; Fulbright lectr, Univ. Florence, Italy, 60-61. MLA. English and American literature; 18th century novel, especially Samuel Richardson; English book illustration. Publ: Co-auth, The letters of William Gilmore Simms (5 vols) Univ. S.C, 52-56. Add: Dept. of English, University of Arkansas, Fayetteville, AR 72703.

EBAUGH, BESSIE MONROE, b. Houston, Tex, June 29, 05; m; c. 1. ENGLISH, CLASSICAL LANGUAGES. A.B, Newcomb Col, Tulane Univ, 25; A.M, Columbia Univ, 27; summers, Univ. Calif, Los Angeles, Univ. Tex, Harvard, Oxford, Cambridge. Instr. class. langs, Newcomb Col, Tulane Univ, 28; assoc. prof. ENG, UNIV. HOUSTON, 41-48, PROF, 48-, dean women, 55-70. MLA; NCTE; Nat. Asn. Women Deans & Counsel. Add: 400 Emerson Ave, Houston, TX 77006.

EBBITT, WILMA ROBB, b. Can, June 29, 18; nat; m. 42. ENGLISH. B.A, Univ. Sask, 38, M.A, 40; Ph.D.(Eng), Brown Univ, 43. Instr. ENG, Brown Univ, 43-45; Univ. Chicago, 45-48, asst. prof, 48-54, assoc. prof, 54-66, prof, 66-68; lectr, Univ. Colo, 68-69; vis. prof, Univ. Tex, Austin, 73-74; PROF, PA. STATE UNIV, 74- NCTE; MLA. American literature; rhetorical theory; the novel. Publ: Co-auth, Structure in reading and writing, 61, Dictionaries and that dictionary, 62, Writer's guide and index to English, 4th ed, 65, 5th ed, 72 & co-ed, The writer's reader, 68, Scott; Margaret Fuller's ideas on criticism, Boston Pub. Libr. Quart. Add: Dept. of English, Pennsylvania State University, University Park, PA 16802.

EBBS, JOHN DALE, b. Carbondale, Ill, Sept. 26, 25; m. 53; c. 2. ENGLISH LITERATURE. A.B, Univ. N.C, 48, M.A, 49, Ph.D, 58. Teacher, high sch, N.C, 49-50; instr. ENG, Agr. & Mech. Col. Tex, 50-54, asst. prof, 59-60; instr, Univ. N.C, 55-58; assoc. prof, High Point Col, 58-59; E.CAROLINA UNIV, 60-63, PROF, 63- State dir. lang. arts & reading, N.C. State Dept. Pub. Instr, 66-67; vis. prof, Univ. Nebr, 67-68; mem. adv. ed. bd. Literary Heritage Series, Macmillan Co, N.Y, 67-72; dir. Nat-Int. Scholarships, E.Carolina Univ, 68-; Eng. teaching informant, NCTE, 71- U.S.A.A.F, 43-45, S/Sgt; Distinguished Flying Cross; Air Medal with Five Oak Leaf Clusters. NCTE; MLA; Mediaeval Acad. Am. English Renaissance literary style; the background and development of English drama; the influence of medieval English literature. Publ: Stylistic mannerisms of the Gawain-Poet, J. Eng. & Ger. Philol, 58; Milton's treatment of poetic justice in Samson Agonistes, Mod. Lang. Quart, 61; The principle of poetic justice as illustrated in Restoration tragedy, In, Salzburg studies in English literature, 73; plus others. Add: Dept. of English, East Carolina University, E. Fifth St, Greenville, NC 27834.

EBEL, HENRY, b. Berlin, Ger, July 5, 38; U.S. citizen; m. 60; c. 1. ENGLISH, COMPARATIVE LITERATURE. A.B, Columbia Col, 59; B.A, Cambridge, 61, M.A, 65; Ph.D.(Eng), Columbia Univ, 65. Instr. Eng, Wesleyan Univ, 64, asst. prof, 65-68; assoc. prof. humanities, Fordham Univ, 68-70; vis. assoc. prof. ENG, Hebrew Univ. Jerusalem, 70-71; ASSOC. PROF,

RICHMOND COL.(N.Y), 71- Res. assoc, Suburban Action Inst, 73; contrib. ed, Hist. Childhood Quart, 73- MLA. Victorian literature; classics; history of ideas. Publ: After Dionysus: an essay on where we are now, Fairleigh Dickinson Univ, 72; Odyssey through the dead land, Argonaut Bks, 73; Matthew Arnold and classical culture, Arion, summer 65; The primaeval fountain of human nature: Mil, Carlyle and the French Revolution, Victorian Newslett, fall 66; The killing of Lykaon: Homer and literary structure, Col. Eng, 4/68. Add: 6 Horizon Rd, Ft. Lee, NJ 07024.

EBEL, JULIA GRACIA, b. Antwerp, Belgium, Jan. 1, 38; U.S. citizen; c. 1. ENGLISH. B.A, Barnard Col, Columbia Univ, 59; N.Y. State Regents fels, Columbia Univ, 59-60, 61-64, M.A, 60, Ph.D.(Eng), 64; Cambridge, 60-61. Instr, The New Sch, summer 61; lectr. Eng. & freshman adv, Barnard Col, Columbia Univ, 62-64; instr. ENG, BROOKLYN COL, 64-67, asst. prof, 68-73, ASSOC. PROF, 73- Am. Counc. Learned Soc. stud. fel, 67-68; vis. sr. lectr. Eng. lit, Haifa Univ, 70-71; res. grants, City Univ. New York, summers 70 & 73. History of nationalism; translation theory; medieval iconography. Publ: In search of stature: linguistic theory and practise in the sixteenth century, Inc. Linguist, 1/69; Translation and cultural nationalism in the reign of Elizabeth, J. Hist. Ideas, 12/69; Eyeless in Gaza: problems of teaching Renaissance literature in Israel, Col. Eng, 1/73; plus others. Add: Dept. of English, Brooklyn College, Brooklyn, NY 11210.

EBERHART, RICHARD, b. Austin, Minn, Apr. 5, 04; m. 41; c. 2. ENGLISH. A.B, Dartmouth Col, 26, D.Litt, 54; B.A, Cambridge, 29, M.A, 33; Harvard, 32-33; D.Litt, Skidmore Col, 66; hon. L.H.D, Col. Wooster, 69; D.Litt, Colgate Univ, 74. Tutor to son of King of Siam, 31; master Eng, St. Mark's Sch, 33-41; poet in residence, Univ. Wash, 52-53; prof, Univ. Conn, 53-54; vis. prof. & poet in residence, Wheaton Col, 54-55; Gauss lectr. & resid. fel, Princeton, 55-56; prof. ENG, DARTMOUTH COL, 56-68, class of 25 prof, 68-70, EMER. PROF, 70-, POET IN RESIDENCE, 56- Asst. mgr, Butcher Polish Co, 46-52, v.pres, 52-58, dir, 58-; founder & pres, Poet's Theatre, Inc, Cambridge, Mass, 50; dir, YADDO, Saratoga Springs, N.Y, 55-; consult. poetry, Libr. Congr, 59-61, hon. consult. Am. lett, 63-66, 66-69; mem. adv. comt, John F. Kennedy Mem. Ctr, Wash, D.C, 59-; Elliston lectr, Univ. Cincinnati, 61; lectr, Washington & Lee Univ, Trinity Col. (Conn), Swarthmore Col. & Col. William & Mary, 63; Robert Frost mem. lect, San Francisco Pub. Libr, 64; Wallace Stevens Prog, Univ. Conn, 65; contrib. bk. revs, N.Y. Times Bk. Rev; vis. prof. poetry, Univ. Wash, 72. Harriet Monroe Mem. Award, Univ. Chicago, 55; Bollingen prize, Yale, 62; Pulitzer Prize, 66. U.S.N.R, 42-46, Lt. Comdr. Fel. Acad. Am. Poets; Poetry Soc. Am.(Shelley Award, 51; hon. pres, 72); MLA; Nat. Inst. Arts & Lett; Nat. Acad. Arts & Sci. Publ: Undercliff, poems 1946-1953, 53 & Great praises, 57, Oxford; Collected poems, 1930-1960, 60, The quarry, 64, Shifts of being, 68 & Fields of grace, 72, Oxford Univ. & Chatto & Windus, London; Collected verse plays, Univ. N.C, 62; The bride from Mantua, (verse adaption, Lope de Vega, Justice without revenge), Hopkins Ctr, Dartmouth Col, 64; Richard Eberhart: selected poems 1930-1965, New Directions, 65; Thirty one sonnets, Eakins, 67; plus others. Add: Dept. of English, Dartmouth College, Hanover, NH 03755.

EBERLE, GERALD JOSEPH, b. Milwaukee, Wis, Dec. 6, 12; m. 72; c. 3. ENGLISH. A.B, St. Norbert Col, 34; A.M, Univ. Wis, 36, Ph.D, 45. Instr. ENG, Loyola Univ.(La), 36-38, asst. prof, 39-45, assoc. prof, 45-49, prof, 49-66, chmn. dept, 59-66; PROF. & DIR. LIBR, UNIV. NEW ORLEANS, 66- Res. fel, Folger Shakespeare Libr, Wash, D.C, 46-47. MLA; Am. Libr. Asn; Bibliog. Soc. Eng. Analytical bibliography; editing early texts; composition and printing of Middleton's A mad world, my masters. Add: Dept. of English, Louisiana State University in New Orleans, Lake Front, New Orleans, LA 70122.

EBERLY, RALPH DUNBAR, b. Norfolk, Va, Mar. 25, 17; m. 40; c. 3. ENGLISH. B.A, Univ. Va, 39; univ. fel. & Ph.D.(Eng. lit), Univ. Mich, 53. From instr. to asst. prof, Purdue Univ, 46-55; asst. prof. ENG, N.Tex. State Univ, 55-57, assoc. prof, 57-61, prof, 61-67; COOPER PROF, UNIV. ARK, LITTLE ROCK, 67- U.S.N.R, 44-46, Lt.(j.g). MLA; AAUP. English and American novel; William Faulkner; Rogerian teaching. Publ: Col. Jekyll and Mr. Hyde (verse), 10/70, If this be tree, son (verse), 12/70 & Syntax for the birds (verse), 1/71, Eng. J; plus others. Add: Dept. of English, University of Arkansas, Little Rock, AR 72204.

EBERLY, RALPH STEPHENS, b. Asheboro, N.C, May 11, 44; m. 66. MODERN NOVEL. B.A. & Woodrow Wilson fel, Univ. Tex, Austin, 66; M.A, Univ. Mich, Ann Arbor, 67, Ph.D.(Eng), 70. ASST. PROF. ENG, WEST. CAROLINA UNIV, 70- NCTE; MLA; AAUP; Am. Fed. Teachers. British, American and French novel; modern and contemporary drama; experimental teaching techniques. Add: Dept. of English, Western Carolina University, Cullowhee, NC 28723.

EBIN, LOIS A, b. New York, N.Y, Oct. 27, 42; m. 65; c. 1. ENGLISH & MEDIEVAL LITERATURE. B.A, Smith Col, 64; Woodrow Wilson fel, 64-65, Columbia Univ, M.A, 65, Woodrow Wilson dissertation fel, 68-69, Ph.D. (Eng), 69. ASST. PROF. ENG, BARNARD COL, COLUMBIA UNIV, 69- Nat. Endowment for Humanities fel, 73-74. MLA; Medieval Acad. Am. Middle Scots literature; Middle English literature, 14th and 15th century. John Barbour's Bruce: poetry, history and propaganda, Stud. Scottish Lit, 4/72; The theme of poetry in Dunbar's Goldyn targe, Chaucer Rev, 72; Boethius, Chaucer and The Kingis Quair, Philol. Quart, (in press). Add: Dept. of English, Barnard College, Broadway & 117th St, New York, NY 10027.

EBLE, KENNETH EUGENE, b. Shelby, Iowa, Dec. 6, 23; m. 49; c. 3. ENGLISH. B.A, State Univ. Iowa, 48, M.A, 49; Lydia Roberts fel, Columbia Univ, 50-52, Ph.D, 56; hon. L.H.D, St. Francis Col.(Maine), 73. Asst. prof. jour. & Eng, Upper Iowa Univ, 49-50; instr. ENG, sch. gen. stud, Columbia Univ, 53-54; asst. prof, Drake Univ, 54-55; instr, UNIV. UTAH, 55-58, asst. prof, 58-62, assoc. prof, 62-66, PROF, 66-, chmn. dept, 64-69. Andersen vis. prof, Carleton Col, 67; dir, Proj. Improve Col. Teaching, 69-71; chmn. teaching, res. & publ. comt, AAUP, 72- U.S.A, 43-45. NCTE; MLA; AAUP. American literature; humanities; higher education. Publ: The profane comedy: American higher education in the sixties, 62 & A perfect education, 66, Macmillan; ed, Howells: a century of criticism, South. Methodist Univ, 62; auth, F. Scott Fitzerald, Twayne, 63; co-ed, The intellectual tradition of the West, (2 vols), Scott, 67; auth, The recognition and evaluation of teaching, 70 & Career development of effective college teachers, 71, AAUP; Professors as teachers, Jossey-Bass, 72; ed, F. Scott Fitzgerald, McGraw-Hill, 73; contrib, The tenure debate, Jossey-Bass, 72. Add: 1534 Garfield Ave, Salt Lake City, UT 84105.

EBNER, IVAN DEAN, b. Spokane, Wash, May 7, 37; m. 60; c. 2. ENGLISH. A.B, Wheaton Col.(Ill), 59; univ. fel, Stanford Univ, 60, Woodrow Wilson fel, 64, Ph.D.(Eng), 65. Spec. instr. ENG, Wheaton Col.(Ill), 59-60; teaching asst, Stanford Univ, fall 63; asst. prof, WHITWORTH COL.(WASH), 64-67, ASSOC. PROF, 67-, chmn. dept, 67-71. Qm.C, U.S.A, 60, Res, 60-67, Capt. MLA. Renaissance English literature. Publ: Autobiography in 17th century England, Mouton, 70; The tempest: rebellion and the ideal state, Shakespeare Quart, spring 65; Chaucer's precarious knight, In: Imagination & the spirit, Eerdman's, 68. Add: Dept. of English, Whitworth College, Spokane, WA 99218.

EBY, CECIL DeGROTTE, b. Charles Town, W.Va, Aug. 1, 27; m. 56; c. 2. AMERICAN LITERATURE. B.A, Shepherd Col, 50; M.A, Northwest. Univ, 51; Ph.D, Univ. Pa, 58. Instr. ENG, High Point Col, 55-56, asst. prof, 56-57; Madison Col.(Va), 57-59, assoc. prof, 59-60; asst. prof, Wash. & Lee Univ, 60-62, assoc. prof, 62-65; UNIV. MICH, ANN ARBOR, 65-68, PROF, 68- Fulbright lectr. Am. lit, Lit. Univ. Salamanca, 62-63, Am. stud, Univ. Valencia, 67-68. U.S.N, 45-46. Nineteenth Century American travel books: Spanish Civil War in literature; the nineteen-thirties. Publ: The old South illustrated, 59, Porte Crayon: the life of David H. Strother, 60 & A Virginia Yankee in the Civil War, 61, Univ. N.C; The siege of the Alcázar, Random, 65; Between the bullet and the lie: American volunteers in the Spanish Civil War, Holt, 69; That disgraceful affair: the Black Hawk War, Norton, 73. Add: Dept. of English, University of Michigan, Ann Arbor, MI 48104.

EBY, EDWIN HAROLD, b. Los Angeles, Calif, Oct. 21, 00. AMERICAN LITERATURE. Ph.B, Univ. Chicago, 23; Ph.D, Univ. Wash, 27. Instr. ENG, UNIV. WASH, 27-32, asst. prof, 32-42, assoc. prof, 42-48, prof, 48-68, EMER. PROF, 68- MLA; Pac. Coast Philol. Asn. Emerson; Thoreau; Hawthorne. Publ: Concordance to Walt Whitman's Leaves of Grass and selected prose; co-auth, Main currents in American thought, Harcourt, 30. Add: 11511 Exeter Ave, Seattle, WA 98125.

ECCLES, MARK, b. Oxford, Ohio, July 13, 05. ENGLISH LITERATURE. A.B, Oberlin Col, 27; A.M, Harvard, 28, Ph.D, 32, Univ. London, 29-30. Am. Counc. Learned Soc. traveling fel, 33-34; lectr, UNIV. WIS-MADISON, 34-36, asst. prof, 36-39, assoc. prof. ENG, 39-47, prof, 47-69, R.E. NEIL DODGE PROF, 69- Res. fel, Huntington Libr, Calif, 40-41; Guggenheim fel, 55; Fulbright lectr, Stratford-on-Avon, 55-56. MLA; Shakespeare Asn. Am; Renaissance Soc; Malone Soc; Int. Asn. Univ. Prof. Eng. Shakespeare; Elizabethan poetry and drama; medieval drama. Publ: Christopher Marlowe in London, Harvard, 34; Shakespeare in Warwickshire, Univ. Wis, 61; ed, Othello, 46 & Twelfth night, 48, Crofts, Richard III, Signet, 64 & Macro plays, Early Eng. Text Soc, 69; contrib, Encyclopedia Britannica. Add: 2 N. Roby Rd, Madison, WI 53705.

ECKHARDT, CAROLINE DAVIS, b. New York, N.Y, Feb. 27, 42; m. 64; c. 2. ENGLISH & COMPARATIVE LITERATURE. B.A, Drew Univ, 63; M.A, Ind. Univ, Bloomington, 65; Ph.D.(comp. lit), Univ. Mich, Ann Arbor, 71. ASST. PROF. ENG. & COMP. LIT, PA. STATE UNIV, 71- MLA; Medieval Acad. Am; Int. Arthurian Soc; Am. Comp. Lit. Asn. Medieval romance; medieval lyric; Chaucer. Publ: The influences of the church on Medieval culture, In: The urbanization of man, McCutchan, 72; Canterbury tales D 1554, Notes & Queries, 73; co-auth, Facts of scholarly publishing, PMLA, 74. Add: Dept. of English, 117 Burrowes, Pennsylvania State University, University Park, PA 16802.

ECKLEY, GRACE ESTER, b. Alliance, Ohio, Nov. 11, 32; m. 54; c. 3. MODERN LITERATURE, MYTHOLOGY. A.B, Mt. Union Col, 55; M.A, Case West. Reserve Univ, 64; Ph.D.(Eng), Kent State Univ, 70. Teacher ENG, North High Sch, Willoughby, Ohio, 62-63; instr. Simpson Col, 65-68; from instr. to asst. prof, DRAKE UNIV, 68-74, ASSOC. PROF, 74- Am. Comt. Irish Stud; MLA; Am. Asn. Univ. Women; James Joyce Found; Irish Am. Cult. Inst. Modern Irish literature; James Joyce. Publ: Benedict Kiely, Twayne, 72; Edna O'Brien, 74 & co-auth, Narrator and character in Finnegans' wake, 74, Bucknell Univ; auth, Petween peas like ourselves: the folklore of the prankquean in Finnegan's wake, James Joyce Quart, winter 71; Eggoarchicism and the bird lore of Finnegan's wake, Lit. Monogr, 73; Truth at the bottom of the well: J.M. Synge's Well of the saints, Mod. Drama, 9/72. Add: Dept. of English, Drake University, Des Moines, IA 50311.

ECKLEY, WILTON, b. Alliance, Ohio, June 25, 29; m. 54; c. 3. ENGLISH. A.B, Mt. Union Col, 52; M.A, Pa. State Univ, 55; John Hay fel, Yale, 61-62; Ph.D.(Am. stud), Case West. Reserve Univ, 65. Chmn. dept. Eng, high sch, Ohio, 55-61; lectr, Kent State Univ, 62-63; asst. prof. Eng. & dir. teacher training, Hollins Col, 63-65; assoc. prof. ENG, DRAKE UNIV, 65-67, PROF, 68-, CHMN. DEPT, 67- Fulbright lectr. Am. lit, Univ. Ljubljana, 72-73. MLA; Midwest Mod. Lang. Asn. Southern American literature; folklore; 19th century American literature. Publ: Whitman's A noiseless, patient spider, Explicator, 63; T.S. Stribling; pioneer in the Southern renaissance, Iowa Eng. Yearbook, 66; Hear the guns roar: the feud in Southern mountain fiction, In: Popular literature in America, Bowling Green Univ, 72. Add: Dept. of English, Drake University, Des Moines, IA 50311.

ECKMAN, FREDERICK, b. Continental, Ohio, Oct. 27, 24; m. 61. ENGLISH. B.A, Ohio State Univ, 48, M.A, 49, Ph.D, 54. Instr. ENG, Glenville State Col, 49-51; asst. instr, Ohio State Univ, 52-54; instr, Univ. Tex, 54-57, asst. prof, 57-59, assoc. prof, 59-60; asst. prof, BOWLING GREEN STATE UNIV, 61-63, assoc. prof, 63-67, PROF, 67- U.S.A, 43-46. MLA. Contemporary literature; creative writing; American literature. Publ: The exile, Nordic, 56; Cobras and cockleshells: modes in recent poetry, 58 & Epistemology of loss, 63, Sparrow; The noon-day devil, 67, ed, Poems from Bowling Green, 66 & auth, Nightmare township, 74, Winesburg Editions; Sandusky and back, Elizabeth Press, 70. Add: 905 Wallace Ave, Bowling Green, OH 43402.

ECKSTEIN, NEIL T, b. Winchester, Wis, May 16, 23; m. 48; c. 4. ENGLISH, AMERICAN STUDIES. B.A, St. Olaf Col, 48; B.Th, Luther Theol. Sem, 51;

M.A, Univ. Pa, 61, Ph.D.(Am. civilization), 65. Asst. prof, Wartburg Col, 61-65; ASSOC. PROF, UNIV. WIS-OSHKOSH, 65- U.S.N.R, 43-46, Lt.(jg). MLA; Norweg-Am. Hist. Asn. Literature of Scandinavian immigrants; early New England poetry; Benjamin Tompson. Add: Dept. of English, University of Wisconsin-Oshkosh, Oshkosh, WI 54902.

ECONOMOU, GEORGE DEMETRIOS, b. Great Falls, Mont, Sept. 24, 34; m. 62. ENGLISH, COMPARATIVE LITERATURE. A.B, Colgate Univ, 56; M.A, Columbia Univ, 57, Ph.D.(Eng), 67. Instr. ENG, LONG ISLAND UNIV, 61-64, asst. prof, 65-67, assoc. prof, 68-73, PROF, 73- MLA; Mediaeval Acad. Am. Medieval English, Renaissance and contemporary literature; comparative literature. Publ: The goddess Natura in Medieval literature, Harvard Univ, 72; Januarie's sin against nature: The merchant's tale and the Roman de la rose, Comp. Lit, summer 65; The character genius in Alan de Lille, Jean de Meun, and John Gower, Chaucer Rev, 70. Add: 606 W. 116th St, New York, NY 10027.

ECROYD, DONALD HOWARTH, b. Arkansas City, Kans, Jan. 3, 23; m. 45; c. 3. SPEECH. A.B, State Univ. Iowa, 44, A.M, 45, Ph.D, 49; Cornell Univ, 46. Instr. Simpson Col, 45-47; State Univ. Iowa, 47-49; asst. prof. SPEECH, Univ. Ala, 49-51, assoc. prof, 51-56; asst. prof, Mich. State Univ, 56-58, assoc. prof, 58-62; TEMPLE UNIV, 63-66, PROF, 66- Vis. scholar, Princeton Theol. Sem, 62-63; consult, Dept. Pub. Instr, Pa, 65; consult. ESEA Title I proj. in dialectalalia, Temple Univ, 64-65, St. Mary's Dominican Col, La, 65-67, Phila. pub. schs, 66-68 & Chester, Pa. pub. schs, 67-68; proj. dir. ESEA Title III, Charleroi, Pa. pub. schs, 69-71. Speech Commun. Asn; East. Commun. Asn.(pres, 71); NCTE. Speech pedagogy; language acquisition; social dialects. Publ: Speech in the classroom, Prentice-Hall, 60, 69; co-auth, Voice and articulation: a handbook, 66, Voice and articulation: programed instruction, 66 & Voice and articulation: recorded exercises, 66, Scott; The relevance of oral language development to classroom teaching, Today's Speech, winter 73. Add: Dept. of Speech, Temple University, Philadelphia, PA 19122.

EDDINS, DWIGHT, L, b. Decatur, Ala, July 6, 39; c. 2. ENGLISH. B.A, Univ. Ala, 61; B.A, Oxford, 63; Ph.D.(Eng), Vanderbilt Univ, 67. Instr. ENG, UNIV. ALA, 66-67, asst. prof, 67-70, ASSOC. PROF, 70-, CHMN. DEPT, 72- MLA; S.Atlantic Mod. Lang. Asn; Asn. Am. Rhodes Scholars; AAUP. Modern British and American poetry; modern British novel; philosophy and literature. Publ: Yeats: the nineteenth century matrix, Univ. Ala, 71; Wallace Stevens: American the primordial, Mod. Lang. Quart, 3/71; Poet and state in the verse of Robert Lowell, Tex. Stud. Lang. & Lit, summer 73; plus others. Add: Dept. of English, University of Alabama, University, AL 35486.

EDDLEMAN, FLOYD EUGENE, b. Mena, Ark, Dec. 3, 30. WORLD LITERATURE. B.S.E, State Col. Ark, 51; M.A, Univ. Ark, 55, Ph.D, 61. Asst. ENG, Univ. Ark, 53-55, 56-58; instr, Univ. Colo, 55-56; TEX. TECH UNIV, 58-62, asst. prof, 62-65, ASSOC. PROF, 65- C.Eng, U.S.A, 51-53, Sgt. MLA; NCTE; AAUP. Thoreau; Conrad; drama. Publ: The brothers Karamazov in English, Proc. Comp. Lit. Symp, 4/68; Thoreau and Lempriere, Class. Folia, 71; Donne's The computation, Explicator, 4/72; plus others. Add: Dept. of English, Texas Tech University, Lubbock, TX 79409.

EDDY, DARLENE M, b. Elkhart, Ind, Mar. 19, 37; wid. RENAISSANCE & NINETEENTH CENTURY AMERICAN STUDIES. B.A, Goshen Col, 59; Woodrow Wilson Nat. fel, Rutgers Univ, 59-62, M.A, 61, univ. grad. honors fel, 64-65, Ph.D.(Eng), 66. Instr. ENG, Douglass Col, 62-64; Rutgers Univ, 64-65; summer sessions, asst. prof, BALL STATE UNIV, 67-70, ASSOC. PROF, 70-, fac. res. grant, 68-69 & 71, creative teaching grants, 70, 72. Univ. rep, Ind. Comn. for Humanities, 71- MLA; NCTE; Col. Eng. Asn; Shakespeare Asn. Am; Renaissance Soc. Am; Melville Soc; Nat. Asn. Humanities Educ; AAUP. Shakespearean studies; humanities, inter-disciplinary studies; Melville's response to Elizabethan-Jacobean literature. Publ: The worlds of King Lear, Ball State Univ. Monogr, autumn 70; Melville's Sicilian moralist, Eng. Lang. Notes, 3/71; Bloody battles and high tragedies: Melville and the theatre of 1840's, Forum, winter 72; plus others. Add: Dept. of English, English Bldg. 207B, Ball State University, Muncie, IN 47306.

EDDY, DONALD DAVIS, b. Norfolk, Va, Apr. 19, 29; m. 54; c. 2. ENGLISH LITERATURE. B.A, Dartmouth Col, 51; M.A, Univ. Chicago, 56, Ph.D.(Eng. lit), 71. Instr. ENG. LIT, CORNELL UNIV, 61-64, asst. prof, 64-71, ASSOC PROF, 71-, LIBRN. & HEAD DEPT. RARE BKS, UNIV. LIBR, 68-, asst. librn, 64-68. U.S.N, 52-55, Lt.(jg). Bibliog. Soc, Eng; Bibliog. Soc. Am; MLA. Eighteenth-century English literature; descriptive bibliography. Publ: A bibliography of John Brown, Bibliog. Soc. Am, 71. Add: Dept. of English, Cornell University, Ithaca, NY 14850.

EDEL, (JOSEPH) LEON, b. Pittsburgh, Pa, Sept. 9, 07; m. 50. ENGLISH & AMERICAN COMPARATIVE LITERATURE. M.A, McGill Univ, 28, hon. D.Litt, 63; Dr-es-Lettres, Univ. Paris, France, 32; hon. D.Litt, Union Col. (N.Y), 63. Instr, McGill Univ, 27-28; asst. prof, Sir George Williams Col, 32-34; Guggenheim fel, 37-39; vis, prof, N.Y. Univ, 50, 52; Christian Gauss Sem, Princeton, 53; assoc. prof. Eng, N.Y. Univ, 53-54; vis. prof. criticism, Ind. Univ, 54-55; prof. Eng, Wash. Sq. Col, N.Y. Univ, 55-67, Henry James prof. Eng. & Am. lett, 67-72; CITIZENS PROF. ENG, UNIV. HAWAII, MANOA, 72- Alexander lectr, Univ. Toronto, 56; vis. prof, Harvard, 59-60; Bollingen fel, 59-61; chmn. congr, Int. Fed. Mod. Lang. & Lit, 63; mem. ed. bd, PMLA, 63-68, adv. ed, 19th century fiction & Stud. fiction; centenary prof, Univ. Toronto, 67; mem. educ. adv. bd, Guggenheim Found, 67-75. Nat. Bk. Award, 63; Pulitzer Prize, 63. U.S.A, 43-46, Lt. Auth. Guild; PEN Club; Nat. Inst. Arts & Lett.(award, 59; secy, 64-67); fel. Am. Acad. Arts & Sci; Am. Stud. Asn; Mod. Humanities Res. Asn; Am. Acad. Arts. & Lett; fel. Royal Soc. Lit. U.K. Editing the Edmund Wilson papers; the Bloomsbury group; editing the Henry James letters. Publ: Henry James, The untried years: 1843-1870, Vol. I, 53, The conquest of London: 1870-1881, Vol. II, 62, The middle years: 1882-1895, Vol. III, 62, The treacherous years: 1895-1901, Vol. IV, 69 & The master, Vol. V, 72, Lippincott; Literary biography, Doubleday, 59; Modern psychological novel, Grossett, 64. Add: Dept. of English, University of Hawaii at Manoa, 1733 Donaghho Rd, Honolulu, HI 96822.

EDELEN, GEORGES, b. Ill, July 18, 24; m. 57; c. 3. ENGLISH. B.S.S, Georgetown Univ, 49; Ph.D.(Eng), Harvard, 55. Teaching fel. gen. ed, Harvard, 51-55, instr. Eng. & gen. ed, 55-58; asst. prof. ENG, IND. UNIV, BLOOMINGTON, 58-64, assoc. prof, 64-69, PROF, 69- Folger Libr. fel, 62. U.S.A.A.F, 43-46. MLA; Renaissance Soc. Am. English literature of the Renaissance and Restoration. Publ: Ed, William Harrison: the description of England, Folger Libr, Cornell Univ, 68; Hooker's prose style, In: Studies in Richard Hooker, Case West. Reserve Univ, 72. Add: Dept. of English, Indiana University, Bloomington, IN 47401.

EDELMAN, SUSANNE POPPER, b. Vienna, Austria, Nov. 17, 30; U.S. citizen; m. 67; c. 1. ENGLISH, COMPARATIVE LITERATURE. B.A, Hunter Col, 52; M.A, Columbia Univ, 53, Ph.D.(comp. lit), 68. Instr. Eng, Douglass Col, 61-62; LONG ISLAND UNIV, 62-65, ASST. PROF. ENG. & COMP. LIT, 66- Dir, Inwood Chamber Opera Players, 53- Nat. Opera Asn; MLA; Nat. Audubon Soc; Metrop. Opera Guild. Relationship of music and literature; theoretical writings on French theatre; literary and symbolic materials in opera. Publ: Music for Shakespeare, 5/64 & Music by Beaumarchais, 2/71, Opera News. Add: Dept. of English, Long Island University, Flatbush Ave, Brooklyn, NY 11201.

EDELSTEIN, ARNOLD STANLEY, b. Brooklyn, N.Y, July 29, 38; m. 63; c. 2. ENGLISH & AMERICAN LITERATURE. A.B, Columbia Univ, 59, A.M, 62; Ph.D.(Eng), Univ. Calif, 71. Instr. ENG, San Jose State Col, 64-65; ASST. PROF, UNIV. HAWAII, MANOA, 69- MLA. American novel; American literature; the novel. Publ: The tangle of life: levels of meaning in The spoils of Poynton, Hartford. Stud. Lit, 70. Add: Dept. of English, University of Hawaii at Manoa, Honolulu, HI 96822.

EDENBAUM, ROBERT I, b. New York, N.Y, Jan. 8, 30; m. 61; c. 3. ENGLISH & AMERICAN LITERATURE. B.A, Brooklyn Col, 52; M.A, Univ. Minn, 56; Ph.D.(Eng. & Am. lit), Univ. Calif, Berkeley, 61. Instr. ENG, TEMPLE UNIV, 61-63, asst. prof, 63-66, assoc. prof, 66-72, PROF, 72- U.S.A, 53-55. MLA. Modern American fiction. Publ: John Hawkes: The lime twig and other tenous horros, Mass. Rev, summer 66; Delacroix's Hamlet studies, Art J, summer 67; The poetics of the private eye: the novels of Dashiell Hammett, In: Tough guy writers of the thirties, South. Ill. Univ, 68. Add: Dept. of English, Temple University, Philadelphia, PA 19122.

EDER, DORIS LEONORA, b. Teplitz, Bohemia, Czech, May 12, 36; U.S. citizen; m. 61. MODERN & CONTEMPORARY BRITISH & AMERICAN LITERATURE. B.A, Barnard Col, 61; M.A, Hunter Col, 65, Ph.D.(Eng. & comp. lit), 68. From instr. to ASST. PROF, ENG, Ohio State Univ, 66-70; UNIV. ROCHESTER, 70- MLA; AAUP. Modern English and European literature. Publ: Wallace Stevens: the war between mind and eye, South. Rev, summer 71; Wallace Stevens' Landscapes and still lifes, Mosaic, summer 71; Stevens' Never-ending meditation, Stud. Twentieth Century, fall 72; plus three others. Add: Dept. of English, University of Rochester, River Station, Rochester, NY 14627.

EDGERTON, WILLIAM BENBOW, Slavic Languages. See Volume III, Foreign Languages, Linguistics & Philology.

EDGERTON, WILLIAM L, b. Chestertown, N.Y, Dec. 23, 12; m. 48; c. 1. ENGLISH. A.B, Univ. Pa, 34, M.A, 49, Ph.D, 51. Asst. prof. ENG, Norwich Univ, 51-53, assoc. prof, 53-59, res. grant, 57, prof. & chmn. dept, 59-60; prof, Wilkes Col, 60-63, chmn. dept, 61-63, res. grant, 61; assoc. prof, Howard Univ, 63-67; West. Wash. State Col, 67-68; PROF, EDINBORO STATE COL, 68- U.S.A.A.F, 42-45, S/Sgt. Mod. Humanities Res. Asn; Shakespeare Asn. Am; Renaissance Soc. Am. Early Tudor drama; bibliography; Shakespeare. Publ: Nicholas Udall, Twayne, 65; The calendar year in sixteenth-century printing, J. Eng. & Ger. Philol, 60; The date of Roister Doister, Philol. Quart, 11/65; The forum speech of Brutus, Shakespeare Quart, summer 73; plus others. Add: Dept. of English, Edinboro State College, Edinboro, PA 16412.

EDMONDS, DALE HARLAN, II, b. Ft. Worth, Tex, Dec. 27, 34; m. 66. TWENTIETH CENTURY BRITISH & AMERICAN ENGLISH. B.A, Tex. Christian Univ, 57; fel, Univ. Tex, summer 63, Ph.D.(Eng), 65. Spec. instr. ENG, Univ. Tex, 64-65; asst. prof, TULANE UNIV, 65-71, ASSOC. PROF, 71-, Res. Counc. summer grants, 66, 67. Univ. Tex. Grad. Sch. res. & travel grant, summer 64; Fulbright lectr, Romania, 68-69; Int. Res. & Exchanges Bd. grant, 71. Adj. Gen.C, U.S.A, 57-59, Capt. MLA; S.Cent. Mod. Lang. Asn. Malcolm Lowry; Carson McCullers; Earle Birney. Publ: The short fiction of Malcolm Lowry, 67 & Under the volcano: a reading of the immediate level, 68, Tulane Stud. Eng. Add: Dept. of English, Tulane University, New Orleans, LA 70118.

EDMONDSON, ELSIE FANNIE, b. Atlanta, Ga, Dec. 9, 09; c. 1. ENGLISH. A.B, Spelman Col, 30; A.M, Atlanta Univ, 34; Ph.D.(Eng), Univ. Mich, 54. Prof. Eng, Ark. Baptist Col, 39-40; guest lectr, Philander Smith Col, summers 40-41, from asst. prof. to assoc. prof, 41-53, dean women, 48-53; assoc. prof. ENG, South. Univ, 53-59; PROF, Morris Brown Col, 59-73; CLARK COL, 73- Non-Western Stud. Prog, Atlanta Univ. Ctr, 63. MLA. Victorian literature, especially Browning; American literature, especially novel. Publ: Shadwell: a study, South. Univ. Bull, 58. Add: 188 Griffin St, N.W, Atlanta, GA 30314.

EDMONDSON, HAROLD S, b. Claiborne Co, Tenn, June 23, 22; m. 44; c. 3. SPEECH CORRECTION. B.A, Univ. Miami, 46; M.S, Univ. Mich, 49, Ph.D, 53. Speech pathologist, Columbus Hearing Soc, 56-58; asst. prof. SPEECH, CAPITAL UNIV, 58-63, assoc. prof, 63-72, PROF, 72- Vis. lectr. aphasia, Grad. Sch, Univ. Ill, summer, 60. U.S.A, 43-46, 1st Lt. Am. Speech & Hearing Asn.(cert, 60). Aphasia; speech science and pathology. Publ: Co-auth, Cues for vowel discrimination, J. Speech & Hearing Disorders, 9/50. Add: Dept. of Speech, Capital University, Columbus, OH 43209.

EDNEY, CLARENCE WILLIAM, b. Stamford, Nebr, Aug. 15, 09; m. 35. SPEECH. A.B, Univ. Nebr, 34, A.M, 36; Ph.D, State Univ. Iowa, 46. Teacher, high sch, Gering, Nebr, 34-35, Beatrice, 35-38; dir, SPEECH, pub. schs, Sioux City, Iowa, 38-42; instr, State Univ. Iowa, 42-45, asst. prof, 45-48; PROF, FLA. STATE UNIV, 48-, head dept, 48-59. Speech Commun. Asn. Public address; classical and 18th century rhetoric; group deliberation and leadership. Publ: Speech handicapped school children; History of speech education in America; Oral communication in general education. Add: College of Communication, Florida State University, Tallahassee, FL 32306.

EDWARDS, CHRISTINE, b. New York, N.Y, Aug. 13, 09. SPEECH, THEATRE. Ph.D, N.Y. Univ, 60. Asst. prof. SPEECH & THEATRE, L.I. UNIV, 61-64, assoc. prof, 64-70, prof, 70-72, EMER. PROF, 72- Adj. prof. speech & theatre, Wagner Col, 72- Dramatic art. Publ: The Stanislavsky heritage, N.Y. Univ, 65. Add: Dept. of Speech & Theatre, Long Island University, Brooklyn, NY 11201.

EDWARDS, CLIFFORD DUANE, b. Atwood, Kans, Jan. 20, 34; m. 54; c. 3. ENGLISH. A.B, Ft. Hays Kans. State Col, 58; Woodrow Wilson fel. & M.A, Univ. Mich, 59, univ. fel, 59-62, Ed.D.(Eng), 63. Lectr. ENG, Univ. Mich, 63, asst. prof, Ft. Hays Kans. State Col, 63-65, assoc. prof, 65-69; PROF; & HEAD DEPT, UNIV. WIS-PLATTEVILLE, 69- Danforth assoc, 66-73; dir, NDEA Inst. Eng, 68; Eng. Inst. Educ. Prof. Develop. grant, U.S. Off. Educ, 69. U.S.A.F, 51-55, S/Sgt. MLA; NCTE. American literature; literary criticism; teaching English in secondary school. Publ: Conrad Richter's Ohio trilogy, Mouton, 70; Arnold and Pater discuss Dylan Thomas: a conversation in limbo, LIT, 59; Existential absurdity on the campus, Christianity today, 5/67. Add: Dept. of English, University of Wisconsin-Platteville, Platteville, WI 53818.

EDWARDS, CORLISS HINES, JR, b. Macon, Ga, June 11, 34; m. 61; c. 2. AMERICAN & SOUTHERN LITERATURE. A.B, Mercer Univ, 56; M.A, Univ. Ga, 60, Ph.D.(Eng), 70. Instr. ENG, Clemson Univ, 61-64; asst. prof, W.GA. COL, 66-72, ASSOC. PROF, 73- S.Atlantic Mod. Lang. Asn; Soc. Stud. South. Lit. Publ: Richard Malcolm Johnston's view of the Old-field school, Ga. Hist. Quart, 66; Lanier's The symphony, Explicator, 72; A foggy scene in Deliverance, Notes Contemporary Lit, 72. Add: Dept. of English, West Georgia College, Carrollton, GA 30117.

EDWARDS, HERBERT JOSEPH, b. Columbus, Ohio, Dec. 21, 00. AMERICAN LITERATURE. A.B, Ohio State Univ, 23, Ph.D, 30; A.M, Princeton, 27. Asst. ENG, Ohio State Univ, 23-26, instr, 27-46; asst. prof, UNIV. MAINE, ORONO, 46-55, assoc. prof, 55-58, prof, 58-68, EMER. PROF, 68- MLA. Publ: Co-auth, Lincoln the writer, 60 & James A. Herne—the rise of realism in the American drama, 64, Univ. Maine. Add: 3 Grove St, Orono, ME 04473.

EDWARDS, JOHN, b. San Francisco, Calif, Oct. 16, 22; m. 47; c. 3. ENGLISH. A.B, Univ. Calif, 47, Ph.D.(Eng), 52; M.A, Columbia Univ, 48. Lectr. Eng, Univ. Calif, 51-52, instr, 52-54, asst. prof, 54-59, asst. to v.pres, 59-60; assoc. prof. ENG, SAN FRANCISCO STATE UNIV, 60-65, PROF, 65-, exec. v.pres, 70-72. Am. Philos. Soc. res. grants, 54-55; Phelan award, 54. Off. Strategic Servs, U.S.A, 43-46. MLA; Am. Stud. Asn. American literature; Ezra Pound: annotated index to Cantos and biography of Pound; American studies. Publ: Preliminary checklist to the writings of Ezra Pound; Annotated index to the Cantos of Ezra Pound. Add: 1290 Monterey, San Francisco, CA 94127.

EDWARDS, LEE R, b. Brooklyn, N.Y, Apr. 30, 42; m. 64; c. 1. ENGLISH LITERATURE. B.A, Swarthmore Col, 62; Univ. Bristol, 62-63; M.A, Univ. Calif, Berkeley, 65; Ph.D.(Eng), Univ. Calif, San Diego, 69. ASST. PROF. ENG. & AM. LIT, UNIV. MASS, AMHERST, 67- MLA; Women's Caucus Mod. Lang. Asn. Modern fiction; women's studies. Publ: Ed, Charles Brockden Brown's Alcuin, Grossman, 71; co-ed, Woman: an issue, Little, 72; American voices, American women, Avon, 73; contrib, Twentieth century interpretations of Moll Flanders, Prentice-Hall, 70; auth, Women, energy and Middlemarch, Mass. Rev, winter-spring, 72. Add: Dept. of English, University of Massachusetts, Amherst, MA 01002.

EDWARDS, MARY JANE, b. St. Thomas, Ont. CANADIAN LITERATURE. B.A, Univ. Toronto, 60, Ph.D.(Eng), 69; M.A. Queens Univ.(Ont), 63. Lectr. ENG, Acadia Univ, 61-63; instr. II, Univ. B.C, 66-69, asst. prof, 69-70; CARLETON UNIV, 70-73, ASSOC. PROF, 73- Vis. lectr, McMaster Univ, summer 71; vis. prof, Univ. B.C, summer 73. Asn. Can. Univ. Teachers Eng; Asn. Can. Lit; Bibliog. Soc. Can; Can. Asn. Univ. Teachers. English and French Canadian literature. Publ: Ed, The evolution of Canadian literature in English: Vol. I, Beginnings to 1867, 73 & co-ed, Vol. II, 1867-1914, 73, Vol. III, 1914-1945, 73 & Vol. IV, 1945-1970, 73, Holt, Toronto; co-auth, Le theme de la solitude dans les romans de Langevin, Rev. Univ. Ottawa, 7-9/62; auth, Fiction and Montreal, 1769-1885: a bibliography, Papers Bibliog. Soc. Can, 69; Essentially Canadian, Can. Lit, spring 72. Add: Dept. of English, Carleton University, Ottawa, Ont. K1S 5B6, Can.

EDWARDS, RALPH W, b. Brunswick, Maine, July 16, 06. ENGLISH. B.A, Bowdoin Col, 29; M.A, Bread Loaf Sch. Eng, 50; Ph.D.(Eng), Boston Univ, 61. Prof. ENG, New Eng. Col, 47-64; prof. & head dept, Sterling Col, 64-65; PROF, CALIF. STATE COL.(PA), 65- Col. Eng. Asn. Shakespeare; early English drama; Elizabethan literature. Add: Dept. of English, California State College, California, PA 15419.

EDWARDS, THOMAS C, b. Lykens, Pa, Oct. 1, 11; m. 45; c. 1. ENGLISH LITERATURE. A.B, Lebanon Valley Col, 34; A.M, Univ. Mich, 39, fel, 46-49. Teacher Eng, Suffield Acad, Conn, 34-39; headmaster, Suffield Jr. Sch. 39-42; INSTR. ENG, Ind. Univ, 50-51; COL. ENGINEERING, UNIV. MICH, ANN ARBOR, 51- U.S.N.R, 42-46, Lt. MLA. Criticism; Walter Savage Landor; pash to proverbs. Add: Dept. of Humanities, College of Engineering, University of Michigan, Ann Arbor, MI 48104.

EDWARDS, THOMAS ROBERT, JR, b. Findlay, Ohio, Oct. 12, 28; m. 57; c. 2. ENGLISH. B.A, Amherst Col, 50; Am. Counc. Learned Soc. fel, 50-51; M.A, Harvard, 51, Dexter fel. & Ph.D.(Eng), 56. Teaching fel. ENG, Harvard, 52-56; instr. Univ. Calif, Riverside, 56-58; asst. prof, 58-63, assoc. prof, 63-64; RUTGERS UNIV, NEW BRUNSWICK, 64-66, PROF, 66-, CHMN. DEPT, 73- Dir, Rutgers-NDEA Inst. Teaching Eng, 65; Guggenheim fel, 72-73. MLA; Eng. Inst; PEN Club. English neo-classicism; English novel; contemporary culture. Publ: This dark estate: a reading of Pope, Univ. Calif, 63; Imagination and power, Oxford Univ, 71; contrib, Twentieth century literature in retrospect, Harvard Univ, 71; plus others. Add: Dept. of English, Rutgers University, New Brunswick, NJ 08903.

EEK, NATHANIEL S, b. Maryville, Mo, Oct. 16, 27; m. 52; c. 3. DRAMA. B.A, Univ. Chicago, 48; B.S, Northwest. Univ, 50, M.A, 54; Ph.D, Ohio State Univ, 59. Instr. speech & drama, Univ. Kans, 54-57; asst. prof, Mich. State Univ, 59-62; PROF. DRAMA, UNIV. OKLA, 62- Mem. bd, Okla. Theatre Ctr, 72-73; adv. panel, Okla. Arts & Humanities Counc, 72- U.S.N, 46; U.S.A, 51-53, 1st Lt. Am. Theatre Asn; Children's Theatre Asn.(dir, 65-67); Southwest Theatre Conf.(1st v.pres, 66-68); Nat. Theatre Conf.(trustee, 67-69); Int. Asn. Theatres Children & Youth (v.pres, 68-70, pres, 72-74). Theatre administration and management; stage direction. Publ: Children's theatre, In: Encyclopedia of education, 71. Add: Room 209, School of Drama, University of Oklahoma, 563 Elm Ave, Norman, OK 73069.

EFRON, ARTHUR, b. Chicago, Ill, Nov. 2, 31; m. 54; c. 1. ENGLISH. B.A, Univ. Wash, 58, Ph.D.(Eng), 64; Univ. Calif, Los Angeles, 58-60. Instr. ENG, STATE UNIV. N.Y. BUFFALO, 63-64, asst. prof, 64-69, ASSOC. PROF, 69-, fac. res. fels, summers 65, 68 & 71. Founder & ed, Paunch, 63-; Cervantes lectr, Romance langs, Fordham Univ, 73; mem, Coord. Counc. Lit. Mag. U.S.A, 52-54, Res, 54-60, Sgt. MLA; Am. Soc. Aesthet. Critical theory; literature and philosophy; Cervantes. Publ: Don Quixote and the dulcineated world, Univ. Tex, 71; Logic, hermeneutic, and literary context, Genre, 68; Philosophy, criticism, and the body, Paunch, 4/73. Add: Dept. of English, State University of New York at Buffalo, 3435 Main St, Buffalo, NY 14214.

EGAN, JOHN CHESTER, Communication Law, English. See Volume IV, Philosophy, Religion & Law.

EGERER, MARY TERESA, b. Los Angeles, Calif, June 3, 25. ANGLO-IRISH & AMERICAN LITERATURE. B.A, St. Mary's Col.(Ind), 48; M.A, Univ. Notre Dame, 54; Ph.D.(Eng), Radcliffe Col, 62. Lectr. Am. & Eng. lit, St. Mary's Col.(Ind), 54-55, instr, 61-62, asst. prof, 62-65, ASSOC. PROF, 65-69; ENG, CHICAGO STATE UNIV, 69- MLA; NCTE; Col. Eng. Asn. William Butler Yeats: sources and early poetry; modern poetry; rhetoric. Add: Dept. of English, Chicago State University, 95th & King Dr, Chicago, IL 60628.

EGGENSCHWILER, DAVID LEE, b. Canton, Ohio, Oct. 11, 36; m. 62; c. 1. ENGLISH. B.A, Harvard, 58; M.A, Ariz. State Univ, 61; Ph.D.(Eng), Stanford Univ, 65. ASST. PROF. ENG, Univ. Minn, 64-66; UNIV. SOUTH. CALIF, 66- U.S.A.F.R, 58-64, Staff Sgt. Victorian and English romantic literature; modern British and American literature. Publ: The Christian humanism of Flannery O'Connor, Wayne State Univ, 72; Arnold's passive questers, Victorian Poetry, spring 67; Wordsworth's Discordia Discors, Stud. in Romanticism, winter 69; Eustacia Vye: Queen of night and courtly pretender, Nineteenth Century Fiction, 3/71; plus others. Add: 341 Fourth St, Manhattan Beach, CA 90266.

EGGERS, GRAYDON POE, b. N.C, Oct. 13, 03; m. 38; c. 2. ENGLISH. B.A, Carson-Newman Col, 27; A.M, Duke Univ, 32, Ph.D.(Eng), 38; Austin scholar, Harvard, 32-33. Instr. ENG, APPALACHIAN STATE UNIV, 27-32, assoc. prof, 32-38, prof, 38-72, chmn. dept, 46-69, EMER. PROF, 69- MLA. Victorian novel; middle English. Publ: Transl, The owl and the nightingale, Duke & The king's quail, Christopher. Add: 500 Tracy Circle, Boone, NC 28607.

EGGERS, WALTER FREDERICK, JR, b. Mt. Vernon, N.Y, May 31, 43; m. 67; c. 2. ENGLISH LITERATURE. B.A, Duke Univ, 64; Ph.D.(Eng), Univ. N.C, 71. Asst. prof. ENG, St. Andrews Presby. Col, 67-68; instr, Univ. N.C, 68-69; from instr. to ASST. PROF, UNIV. WYO, 69- MLA; Rocky Mountain Mod. Lang. Asn; Shakespeare Asn. Am. Elizabethan literature; Shakespeare; critical theory. Publ: From language to the art of language: Cassirer's aesthetic, In: The quest for imagination, Case West. Reserve Univ, 71; Love and likeness in The merchant of Venice, Shakespeare Quart, 75; Shakespeare's Gower and the role of the authorial presenter, Philol. Quart, 75. Add: Dept. of English, University of Wyoming, Laramie, WY 82071.

EGLOFF, SUSAN JUNE, b. Buffalo, N.Y, June 25, 46. ENGLISH & AMERICAN LITERATURE. B.A, Cornell Univ, 68; Woodrow Wilson fel, 68-69; M.Phil, Yale, 70, Ph.D.(Eng), 72. ASST. PROF. ENG, UNIV. PA, 72- MLA. Sixteenth and 17th century English literature; 19th century American literature. Add: Dept. of English, University of Pennsylvania, Philadelphia, PA 19174.

EHNINGER, DOUGLAS, b. Mich. City, Ind, Oct. 24, 13. SPEECH. B.S, Northwest. Univ, 36, A.M, 38; Ph.D, Ohio State Univ, 49. Instr. SPEECH, Purdue Univ, 37-38; West. Reserve Univ, 38-43; asst. prof, George Washington Univ, 46; Univ. Va, 48-50; Univ. Fla, 50-55, assoc. prof, 55-60, PROF, 60-61; UNIV. IOWA, 61- Ed, South. Speech J, 53-57; Speech Monogr, 60-62. Speech Commun. Asn.(assoc. ed, Jour, 48-50, 58-60; pres, 68). History of rhetorical theory; 18th century rhetoric; history of argument. Publ: Ed, Elements of rhetoric, South. Ill. Univ, 63; co-auth, Principles of speech, 64, Speakers resource book, 66 & Principles and types of speech, 67 & ed, Contemporary rhetoric: a reader's coursebook, 72; & Influence, belief and argument, 74, Scott. Add: Dept. of Speech, University of Iowa, Iowa City, IA 52240.

EHRENPREIS, ANNE HENRY, b. Boston, Mass, Apr. 19, 27; m. 61; c. 1. ENGLISH. B.A, Bryn Mawr Col, 48; Fulbright fel, Oxford, 51-53, B.Litt, 53. Bibliographer, Harvard Col. Libr, 53-61; RES. & WRITING, 61- MLA; Bibliog. Soc. Univ. Va.(mem. counc, 67-). Swinburne; bibliography; Charlotte Smith. Publ: Co-auth, An abridgement of Boswell's Life of Johnson, Washington Square, 65; ed, The literary ballad, Edward Arnold, London, 66; ed, Charlotte Smith's The old manor house, 69 & Charlotte Smith's Emmeline, 71, Oxford Univ; ed, Jane Austen's Northanger Abbey, Penguin, 72; auth, A reconstructed Swinburne ballad, Harvard Libr. Bull, 58; Swinburne's edition of popular ballads, PMLA, 63; Northanger Abbey: Jane Austen and Charlotte Smith, Nineteenth Century Fiction, 70. Add: 1830 Fendall Ave, Charlottesville, VA 22903.

EHRENPREIS, IRVIN, b. New York, N.Y, June 9, 20; m. 61; c. 1. ENGLISH. A.B, City Col. New York, 38; A.M, Columbia Univ, 39; Ph.D.(educ), 44; hon. Dr, Univ. Besançon, 65. Instr. ENG, Ind. Univ, 45-50, asst. prof, 50-55, assoc. prof, 55-61, prof, 61-65; UNIV. VA, 65-67, COMMONWEALTH PROF, 67- Fulbright fel, Eng, 49-50; Guggenheim fel, 55-56, 61-62; Am. Counc. Learned Soc. fel, 58-59; vis. prof, Brandeis Univ, 61; summer, Univ. Minn, 60; Harvard, 62; Univ. Wash, 64; mem, supvry. comt, Eng. Inst, 66-69, chmn, 68-69; Nat. Endowment Humanities sr. fel, 67-68. MLA. English literature, 1660-1800; American poetry since 1945. Publ: Swift, Vols. I & II, Harvard Univ, 62, 67; Fielding: Tom Jones, 64 & assoc. ed, American poetry, 65, Arnold, London; ed, Prose works of Jonathan Swift, Vol. XIV, Blackwell, Oxford, 68 & Wallace Stevens: a critical anthology, Penguin, 72; Literary meaning and Augustan values, Univ. Va, 74; plus others. Add: Dept. of English, University of Virginia, Charlottesville, VA 22903.

EHRENSBERGER, RAY, b. Indianapolis, Ind, Dec. 7, 07; m. 39; c. 2. SPEECH. A.B, Wabash Col, 29, hon. LL.D, 66; A.M, Butler Univ, 30; fel, Syracuse Univ, 34-36, Ph.D, 37; Ind. Univ; Univ. Wis. Instr. speech, Doane Col, 30-32; asst. prof. & head dept, Franklin Col, 32-35; assoc. prof, UNIV. MD, COLLEGE PARK, 36-39, prof. & chmn. dept. speech & dramatic art, 39-52, dean col. spec. & continuation stud, 52-59, dean, UNIV. COL, 59-70, CHANCELLOR, 70-, dir. Europ. prog, Heidelberg, 49-50. Dir. bi-nat. ctr, U.S. Dept. State, Ankara, Turkey, 51-52. Except. serv. medal, U.S. Air Force, 67; distinguished civilian serv. medal, U.S. Army, 72. Speech Commun. Asn. Dramatic art; public speaking. Publ: Co-auth, A notebook for public speaking. Add: University College, University of Maryland, College Park, MD 20742.

EHRENSPERGER, EDWARD CHARLES, b. Indianapolis, Ind, May 23, 95. ENGLISH LANGUAGE & LITERATURE. A.B, Harvard, 16, Sheldon fel, 16-17, A.M, 18, Ph.D, 21. Sheldon Prize fel. from Harvard, Univ. Bonn, 21-22; Am-Scand. Found. fel, Sweden, 22-23; instr. ENG, Northwest. Univ, 23-25; asst. prof, Wellesley Col, 25-32; prof, UNIV. S.DAK, 32-64, dir. honors, 62-64, head dept. Eng, 32-62, acting dir. grad. schs, summers, 39, 46-50, acting dean, 57, EMER. PROF, 72- Head dept. Eng, Yankton Col, 64-72. Ord.C, U.S.A, 18-19. MLA; Col. Eng. Asn; NCTE; Am. Dialect Soc; Shakespeare Asn. Am; Am. Name Soc. Dreams in Middle English literature; Shakespeare; South Dakota place names. Add: 1002 Mulberry St, Yankton, SD 57078.

EHRLICH, HEYWARD BRUCE, b. Mt. Vernon, N.Y, Nov. 24, 29. AMERICAN STUDIES. M.A, Univ. Chicago, 51; Ph.D, N.Y. Univ, 63. Dir. station relat, MCA, 54-55; staff writer, WABD-TV, New York, N.Y, 55-56; pub. dir, WABC-TV-AM-FM, 56-57; press mgr, NBC Films, 57-58; asst. news ed, Sponsor Mag, 58-63; asst. prof. Am. thought & lang, Mich. State Univ, 63-67; ENG, RUTGERS UNIV, NEWARK, 67-73, ASSOC. PROF, 73- Mich. fieldworker, Arch. Am. Art, 63-64. U.S.A, 51-53. Am. Stud. Asn. New York literary history. Publ: C.F. Briggs and Lowell's Fable for critics, Mod. Lang. Quart, 9/67; Lippard's Quaker City and urban gothic, Emerson Soc. Quart, 18: 50-65; The Putnams on copyright, Papers Bibliog. Soc. Am, 63: 15-22; plus others. Add: Dept. of English, Newark College of Arts & Sciences, Rutgers University, Newark, NJ 07102.

EHRSAM, THEODORE GEORGE, b. New York, N.Y, Dec. 7, 09; m. 42; c. 1. ENGLISH. B.A, Lehigh Univ, 31, M.A, 32; Ph.D.(Eng), N.Y. Univ, 48. Instr. Eng. & speech, Lehigh Univ, 34-36; Hofstra Col, 36-38; Lehigh Univ, 43-44; gen. lit, N.Y. UNIV, 44-50, asst. prof, 50-54, assoc. prof, 54-62, PROF, 62-64, ENG, 64- MLA; life fel. Int. Inst. Arts & Lett. Shelley; Byron; bibliography. Publ: Co-auth, Bibliographies of twelve Victorian authors, Wilson, 36 & Octagon, 68; auth, Bibliography of Alfred Edward Housman, Faxon, 41; Major Byron, Charles Boesen, 51; A bibliography of Joseph Conrad, Scarecrow, 69. Add: 2797 Claflin Ave, Bronx, NY 10468.

EHRSTINE, JOHN W, b. Detroit, Mich, Nov, 27, 37. ENGLISH, LINGUISTICS & PHILOLOGY. B.A, Univ. Colo, 60; M.A, Wayne State Univ, 61, Ph.D.(eng (Eng), 64. Instr. ENG, Wayne State Univ, 63-64; asst. prof, WASH. STATE UNIV, 64-68, assoc. prof, 68-73, PROF, 73-, COORD. LIB. ARTS PROG, 70-, asst. dir. honors prog, 68-70. Vis. prof, Emory Univ, summer 65. MLA. British Romantic, Victorian, and modern periods. Publ: William Blake's poetical sketches, 67 & co-ed, On stage and off: eight essays in English literature, 68, Wash. State Univ; auth, The metaphysics of Byron: a reading of the plays, Mouton, 74; A calling of the wits together: recent romantic theory, ESQ, 6/72; Byron and the metaphysic of self-destruction, Stud. Dark Romanticism, 9/73; Edith Sitwell: a critical bibliography, 1950-1973, Bull. Bibliog, 7/74; plus others. Add: Dept. of English, Washington State University, Pullman, WA 99163.

EICHELBERGER, CLAYTON L, b. Strang, Nebr, May 3, 25; m. 56; c. 3. ENGLISH, AMERICAN LITERATURE. B.A, Univ. Colo, 49, M.A, 50; Ph.D. (Eng), Univ. Tex, Austin, 56. Instr. ENG, Univ. Tex, Austin, 55-56; assoc. prof, UNIV. TEX, ARLINGTON, 56-60, PROF, 60-, ED, AM. LIT. REALISM, 1870-1910, 67- U.S.A, 50-52, M/Sgt. MLA; NCTE; Am. Stud. Asn. The American novel, focusing on the realistic novel, 1870-1910. Publ: A guide to critical reviews of United States fiction, 1870-1910, Scarecrow, 71; Thomas Wolfe's No door: the brink of discovery, Ga. Rev, fall 67; Philanthropy in Frederics The market-place, Am. Quart, spring 68; Reynolds Price: A banner in defeat, J. Popular Cult, spring 68. Add: Dept. of English, University of Texas at Arlington, Arlington, TX 76019.

EICHNER, MAURA, S.S.N.D, b. Brooklyn, N.Y, May 5, 15. ENGLISH. A.B, Col. Notre Dame Md, 41; A.M, Cath. Univ. Am, 42. PROF. ENG, COL. NOTRE DAME (MD), 42- MLA; NCTE; Dante Soc. Am. Verse and prose. Publ: Initiate the heart, 46 & The word is love, 58, Macmillan; Walking on water, Paulist Press, 72; Bell sound and vintage, Contemporary Poetry, 66. Add: Dept. of English, College of Notre Dame of Maryland, Baltimore, MD 21210.

EIDSON, DONALD RAY, b. Okmulgee, Okla, Oct. 12, 34; m. 59; c. 2. ENGLISH. B.A, Northeast. State Col, 60; M.A, Okla. State Univ, 62; Ph.D. (Eng), Univ. Mo-Columbia, 69. Instr. ENG, Okla. State Univ, 62-64; Univ. Mo-Columbia, 64-68; PROF. & HEAD DEPT, CENT. METHODIST COL, 69- Lectr, Univ. Ala, Huntsville, summer 68; Danforth Workshop in Higher Educ. fel, summer 72. U.S.A, 52-54, 55-57. MLA. Shakespeare; Milton. Publ: Co-auth, A technical writer's handbook, Holt, 71; The theme of Henry IV, Part I, Shakespeare Quart, winter 68; auth, Poet: 1967, Midlands, spring 68. Add: Dept. of English, Central Methodist College, Classic Hall 306, Fayette, MO 65248.

EIDSON, JOHN OLIN, b. Johnston, S.C, Dec. 10, 08. AMERICAN LITERATURE. A.B, Wofford Col, 29, Litt.D, 54; A.M, Vanderbilt Univ, 30; fel, Duke Univ, 34-36, Ph.D, 41. Teacher, High Sch, N.C, 30-34; instr. ENG, Univ. Ga, 36-38, asst. prof, 38-46, assoc. prof, 46-50, prof, 50-68, dir. coord. col, 47-53, univ. ctr, 53-57, dean Col. Arts & Sci, 57-68; pres, Ga. South. Col, 68-71; V.CHANCELLOR, UNIV. SYST. GA, 71- Ed, Ga. Rev, 50-57, mem. ed. bd, 57-; Fulbright prof, Univ. Freiburg, 56. Michael Award, 50. U.S.A, 42-46, Maj. MLA; S.Atlantic Mod. Lang. Asn; Am. Stud. Asn; Am. Conf. Acad. Deans; Eng. Asn. Gt. Brit. Publ: Tennyson in America, 43 & Charles Stearns Wheeler: friend of Emerson, 51, Univ. Ga; co-auth, Reading for pleasure, Dryden, 48. Add: University System of Georgia, 244 Washington St, S.W, Atlanta, GA 30334.

EIGNER, EDWIN MOSS, b. Boston, Mass, Apr. 3, 31; m. 56; c. 2. ENGLISH & AMERICAN LITERATURE. B.A, Cornell Univ, 53; M.F.A, State Univ. Iowa, 55, Ph.D.(Eng), 63. Instr. ENG, Univ. Md. Overseas Prog, 56-57; Northwest. Univ, 60-63; asst. prof, Univ. Kans, 63-66, assoc. prof, 66-70; PROF, UNIV. CALIF, RIVERSIDE, 70-, CHMN. DEPT, 72- Elizabeth M. Watkins res. scholar, summer 66; Fulbright-Hays grant & Fulbright lectr, Univ. Erlangen, Ger, 67-68; Nat. Endowment Humanities younger scholar fel, 69. MLA. History of prose fiction. Publ: Robert Louis Stevenson and romantic tradition, Princeton, 66; The romantic unity of Melville's Omoo, Philol. Quart, 1/67; Bulwer's Accommodation to the Realists, In: The 19th century reader and his audience, Univ. Kans, 69; Hawthorne: The house of the seven gables, In: Der Amerikanische Roman, Bagel Verlag, 73; plus others. Add: Dept. of English, University of California, Riverside, CA 92502.

EINBOND, BERNARD LIONEL, b. New York, N.Y, May 19, 37. ENGLISH. A.B, Columbia Univ, 58, A.M, 60, Ph.D.(Eng. & comp. lit), 66. Lectr. ENG, Columbia Col, 61-62; preceptor, Columbia Univ, 62-63; lectr, Hunter Col, 64-66, instr, 66-68; asst. prof, LEHMAN COL, CITY UNIV. NEW YORK, 68-72, ASSOC. PROF, 73- MLA; Am. Soc. 18th Century Stud. Lyric poetry and poetic theory; Shakespeare; Samuel Johnson. Publ: Samuel Johnson's allegory, Mouton, 71; co-auth, Frost's Two tramps in mud time, Explicator, 11/70; contrib.(poems), Live poetry, Holt, 71 & Invention, Winthrop, 73; plus others. Add: Dept. of English, Lehman College, City University of New York, Bronx, NY 10468.

EISENBERG, RUTH F, b. New York, N.Y, Jan. 20, 27; div; c. 2. ENGLISH, SPEECH. B.A, N.Y. Univ, 46; M.A, Univ. Wis, 47. Asst. prof. ENG, Westchester Community Col, 59-67; PACE UNIV, 67-73, ASSOC. PROF, 73- NCTE. Adolescent in literature; American literature. Publ: Co-auth, Reading for recognition, 69 & auth, Not quite twenty, 70, Holt. Add: 90 Bryant Ave, White Plains, NY 10605.

EISENBERG, WILLIAM DAVID, b. Philadelphia, Pa, May 24, 30; m. 63; c. 2. ENGLISH & AMERICAN LITERATURE. B.A, Univ. Del, 53; M.A, Lehigh Univ, 55; Duke Univ, 55-58; Bucknell Univ, 60. Asst. ENG, Lehigh Univ, 53-55; grad. reader, Duke Univ, 55-56; asst. prof, West Chester State Col, 59-60; instr, BLOOMSBURG STATE COL, 60-64, asst. prof, 64-68, ASSOC. PROF, 68- Partic, Centro Stud. Scambi Int. MLA; Int. Poetry Soc. History of poetic symbolism; literature for children; 20th century United States history. Publ: Moonshine: or the ballad of sneaky Pete, Wilmington, Del. Poetry Soc, 59; Forever is not long, Centro Stud. Scambi, 72; Morals, morals, everywhere: values in children's fiction, Elem. Sch. J, 71; Children and poetry: help them like it, Instructor, 12/73. Add: 5380 Old Berwick Rd, Bloomsburg, PA 17815.

EISENSTEIN, SAM A, b. Bakersfield, Calif, May 18, 32; m. 59. ENGLISH, COMPARATIVE LITERATURE. B.A, Univ. Calif, Los Angeles, 54, M.A, 59, fel, 60, Ph.D.(Eng), 65. Instr. jr. high sch, 55-57; extended day div, Los Angeles City Col, 59-60, Eng, 60-62, asst. prof, 62-69; assoc. prof. Eng. & creative writing & chmn. dept, Pitzer Col, 69-72; PROF. ENG, LOS ANGELES CITY COL, 72- Fulbright fel, Japan, 65-66; drama ed, Coast Mag. & Los Angeles News Advocate, 69-; Univ. Minn. Off. Advan. Drama Res. Grant, 71; ed, Garuda, 73- Creative writing; comparative mythology; surrealism. Publ: Boarding the ship of death: D.H. Lawrence's Quester heroes, Mouton, Hague, 74; All the monkeys (short story), Trans-Pacific, summer 69 & In: American literary anthology, Vol. 4, Harper, 71; Post coitus tristus (story); Penthouse Int, 1/70; Foxglove (poem), New York Quart, summer 71; plus several others. Add: 3116 Lake Hollywood Dr, Los Angeles, CA 90068.

EISINGER, CHESTER EMANUEL, b. Chicago, Ill, May 11, 15; m. 37; c. 3. ENGLISH. B.A, Univ. Calif, Los Angeles, 37; M.A, Univ. Mich, 38, Ph.D, 45. Asst. ed, Dictionary Proverbs in Eng, Univ. Mich, 40-45; assoc. prof. ENG, PURDUE UNIV, WEST LAFAYETTE, 53-57, PROF, 57- Fulbright grant lectr, Fouad Univ, Egypt, 51-52, Univ. Innsbruck, Austria, 60-61, Aoyama-Gakuin Univ. & Tokyo Metrop. Univ, Japan, spring 71; dean & lectr, Kyoto Summer Sem. Am. Stud, 71; consult. Am. stud. prog, Indonesian Govt, Jodjokarta, summer 71; Nat. Endowment for Humanities sr. fel, 74-75. MLA; Am. Stud. Asn. Nathaniel Hawthorne; contemporary American fiction; 17th and 18th century American agrarian thought. Publ: Fiction of the forties, Univ. Chicago, 63; ed, The 1940's: profile of a nation in crisis, Doubleday, 69; auth, Introd. to Norman Mailer's The naked and the dead, Holt, 68; plus others. Add: 1729 Sheridan Rd, West Lafayette, IN 47906.

EISNER, SIGMUND, b. Red Bank, N.J, Dec. 9, 20; m. 49; c. 6. ENGLISH. B.A, Univ. Calif, Berkeley, 47, M.A, 49; Ph.D, Columbia Univ, 55. Instr. ENG, Ore. State Col, 54-57, asst. prof, 57-58; Fulbright award, Ireland, 58-59; asst. prof, Dominican Col. San Rafael, 60-63, assoc. prof, 63-66; UNIV ARIZ, 66-67, PROF, 67- U.S.A, 42-46, Sgt. MLA; Int. Arthurian Soc; Mediaeval Acad. Am; NCTE. Arthurian period. Publ: A tale of wonder, a source study of the wife of Bath's tale, John English, Ireland, 57; The Tristan legend, Northwest. Univ, 69. Add: Dept. of English, University of Arizona, Tucson, AZ 85721.

EITNER, WALTER HUGO, b. Mt. Holly, N.J, Dec. 7, 19; m. 46; c. 2. AMERICAN LITERATURE. B.A, Univ. Denver, 48, Ph.D.(Am. lit), 59; M.A, Univ. Mich, 49. Instr. Eng. compos. & Eng. as second lang, Univ. Denver, 52-54; Eng. compos, Eng. as second lang. & Am. Lit, KANS. STATE UNIV, 54-60, asst. prof. AM. LIT, 60-68, ASSOC. PROF, 68- U.S.A.A.F, 42-45, S/Sgt. AAUP; MLA; Thoreau Soc. Early American literature and 19th century poetry; American language. Publ: Affirmative Any more in present-day American English, Papers Mich. Acad. Sci, Arts, & Lett, 51; Walt Whitman in the Kansas Magazine, Kans. Mag, 68; Will Rogers: another look at his act, Kans. Quart, spring 70. Add: Dept. of English, Kansas State University, Manhattan, KS 66506.

EKEBERG, GLADYS WINIFRED, b. Rockford, Ill, July 15, 05. ENGLISH LANGUAGE & LITERATURE. B.S, Northwest. Univ, 27, A.M, 30; Univ. South. Calif, summers, 34, 36; Ph.D, Univ. Wis, 42. Teacher Eng, high sch, Menominee, Mich, 27-29, Rockford, Ill, 30-42; head dept. LANG. & LIT, State Teachers Col, Dickinson, 43-45; assoc. prof, EAST. ILL. UNIV, 45-58, prof, 58-73, EMER. PROF, 70- NEA. Publ: Morning in Cambodia (poem), Saturday Evening Post, 2/61; Lincoln's mothers (poem), Christian Century, 2/64; Last days of Alexander (poem), Nation, 11/71; plus others. Add: 1531 Third St, Charleston, IL 61920.

EKFELT, FRED EMIL, b. Burnside, Iowa, Mar. 28, 07; m. 35; c. 2. ENGLISH. A.B, State Univ. Iowa, 31, A.M, 32, Ph.D, 41. Instr, Miss. State Col, 34-38; Agr. & Mech. Col. Tex, 38-41, asst. prof, 41-44, assoc. prof, 44-46; asst. prof, Univ. Tex, 46-49; assoc. prof. ENG, Tex. A&M Univ, 49-51, PROF, 51-67; STEPHEN F. AUSTIN STATE COL, 67- English literature of the 17th century; Shakespeare; British novel. Publ: Co-ed, Readings for thought and expression, Macmillan, 55; auth, The graphic diction of Milton's English prose, 1/46 & Latinate diction in Milton's English prose, 1/49, Philol. Quart. Add: 2926 Dogwood St, Nacogdoches, TX 75961.

EKROTH, LAUREN E, b. Superior, Wis, Jan. 14, 35. SPEECH, COMMUNICATION. B.S, Univ. Minn, 56, M.A, 58, Ph.D.(commun), 67. Instr. high sch, Minn, 57-58; lectr. speech & Eng, Univ. Md, Europ. Div, 60-63; instr. speech, Univ. Minn, 64-65, res. assoc. commun, 65-66; ASST. PROF. SPEECH & COMMUN, UNIV. HAWAII, MANOA, 67- U.S.A, 58-60. Speech Commun. Asn; Nat. Soc. Stud. Commun. Intercultural face-to face communication; persuasion; small group communication. Publ: Assessing a speech to persuade, 12/67 & A selected bibliography for the study of intercultural communication, 5/68, Pac. Speech Quart; Some dimensions of nonverbal communication, In: Speech-Communication: theory in practice, McCutchan, 68. Add: Dept. of Speech, University of Hawaii at Manoa, Honolulu, HI 96822.

EKSTROM, WILLIAM FERDINAND, b. Rockford, Ill, June 14, 12. ENGLISH. A.B, Univ. Ill, 35, M.A, 36, Ph.D, 47; I.A, Harvard, 43. Asst. ENG, Univ. Ill, 36-42, instr, 46-47; asst. prof, UNIV. LOUISVILLE, 47-51, assoc. prof, 51-56, PROF, 56-, EXEC. V.PRES, 73-, head dept. Eng, 55-68, v.pres. acad. affairs, 67-72, acting pres. univ, 72-73. U.S.A.A.F, 43-45. MLA; Col. Eng. Asn; NCTE; Am. Stud. Asn. American literature. Publ: Co-auth, Toward better English, rev. ed, 49 & Guide to composition, 53, Lippincott. Add: Office of the President, University of Louisville, 2301 S. Third St, Louisville, KY 40208.

ELAGIN (MATVEIEV), IVAN, b. Vladivostok, U.S.S.R, Dec. 1, 18; U.S. citizen; m. 58; c. 2. RUSSIAN LITERATURE. Columbia Univ, 51-52; Ph.D, N.Y. Univ, 69. Instr. Russ. lang. & lit, N.Y. Univ, 68-70, asst. prof, 70; ASSOC. PROF. RUSS. LIT, UNIV. PITTSBURGH, 70- Vis. lectr. Russ. lit, Middlebury Col, summers 68, 72, 73 & 74; assoc. in Russ, Barnfard Col, 70. AAUP; Am. Asn. Teachers Slavic & E.Europ. Lang.(chmn. poetry reading sect, 73); Poetry Soc. Am. Publ: Po doroge ottuda (Journey from there), Chekhov, 53; transl, Five ideas that change the world, Praeger, 61; auth, Otsvety nocnye (Gleaming in the night), 63 & Kosoj poljot (The slanted flight), 67, New Rev; Drakon na kryshe (Dragon on the roof), Kamkin, 73; Certain difficulties in translating poetry, World of Transl, 5/70; Poe in Blok's literary heritage, Russ. Rev, 10/73; Telo Dzona Brauna (transl, John Brown's body), Am. Illus, 2/70; plus others. Add: Dept. of Slavic Languages & Literatures, University of Pittsburgh, Pittsburgh, PA 15213.

ELAM, JULIA CORENE, b. Saxe, Va. ENGLISH, AMERICAN LITERATURE. A.B, Va. State Col, 57, M.A, 64; Ford Found advan. stud. grant & D.A, Carnegie-Mellon Univ, 70. Chmn. Eng. & foreign lang. dept, Cent. High Sch, Waverly, Va, 57-62; J. & J. Moore High Sch, 62-64; PROF. ENG. & DIR. EDUC. TECHNOL, BOWIE STATE COL, 64- Instr. Eng, Va. State Col, 61-62; resource person instrnl. commun, Coppin State Col, Md, 70-71; resource person, Teacher Training in Desegregating Sch, Bowie State Col, 70-72; lectr, 70- NCTE; Nat. Asn. Educ. Broadcasters; MLA. American literature, including Afro-American literature; language and communication. Publ: How words derive their specific meanings, Va. State Col. Gazette, 62. Add: 8670 Brae Brooke Dr, Lanham, MD 20801.

ELBOW, PETER HENRY, b. New York, N.Y, Apr. 14, 35; m. 72. ENGLISH. B.A, Williams Col, 57; Oxford, 59, M.A, 63; Harvard Grad. Sch. Arts. & Sci, 59-60; Ph.D.(Eng), Brandeis Univ, 69. Instr. humanities, Mass. Inst. Technol, 60-63; chmn. core curriculum, Franconia Col, 63-65, assoc. dean fac, 64-65; lectr. lit, Mass. Inst. Technol, 68-69, asst. prof, 69-72; FAC. MEM, EVERGREEN STATE COL, 72- English Inst. Prize Essay, 66. NCTE. Chaucer; education. Publ: Writing without teachers, Oxford, 73; Chaucer's dialectic, Wesleyan Univ, 74; Two Boethian speeches in Troilus and Criseyde and Chaucerina irony, In: Literary criticism and the historical understanding, Columbia Univ, 67; Real learning and nondisciplinary courses, J. Gen. Educ, 7/71; Do you teach or give credit: a model for higher education, Soundings, fall 71; plus others. Add: Evergreen State College, Olympia, WA 98505.

ELDER, ANDREW THOMSON, b. Medicine Hat, Alta, Feb. 19, 14; m. 42; c. 3. ENGLISH. B.A, Univ. Alta, 38; M.A, Univ. Toronto, 48, Ph.D.(Eng), 55. Lectr. ENG, Univ. ALTA, 50-53, asst. prof, 53-57, assoc. prof, 57-63, PROF, 63- R.C.A.F, 41-45, Squadron Leader. Asn. Can. Univ. Teachers Eng. Literature of the Canadian prairies; 18th century English literature. Publ: Irony and humour in the Rambler, Univ. Toronto Quart, 10/60; Western panorama: settings and themes in Robert J.C. Stead, Can. Lit, summer 63; Thematic patterning and development in Johnson's essays, Stud. Philol, 7/65. Add: Dept. of English, University of Alberta, Edmonton, Alta. T6G 2E1, Can.

ELDER, ARLENE ADAMS, b. Los Angeles, Calif, May 11, 40; m. 64. BLACK & AMERICAN LITERATURE. A.B, Immaculate Heart Col, 61; M.A, Univ. Denver, 62; Ph.D.(Eng), Univ. Chicago, 70. Instr. ENG, Emmanuel Col, 62-65; lectr. UNIV. CINCINNATI, 70-71, ASST. PROF, 71- MLA. Black literature; 19th century American literature; American novel. Publ: Swamp versus plantation: symbolic structure in W.E.B. DuBois' The quest of the silver fleece, Phylon, 12/73. Add: Dept. of English, University of Cincinnati, Cincinnati, OH 45223.

ELDER, MARJORIE J, b. Salina, Kans, July 3, 21. ENGLISH. B.S. Ed, Marion Col.(Ind), 45, A.B, 47; M.A, Univ. Wis, 50; Inland Steel fel, Univ. Chicago, 62-63, Ph.D.(Eng), 63. Instr. speech & Eng, MARION COL.(IND), 49-51, asst. prof, 52-57, assoc. prof, 58-61, PROF. ENG, 63-, CHMN. DIV. MOD. LANG. & LIT, 67- MLA; Ling. Soc. Am; NCTE. American literature; linguistics; speech. Publ: Nathaniel Hawthorne; transcendal symbolist, Ohio Univ, 69. Add: Dept. of English, Marion College, Marion, IN 46952.

ELDREDGE, FRANCES, b. Malden, Mass, Dec. 31, 09. ENGLISH LITERATURE & ARTS. A.B, Wellesley Col, 32; A.M, Tufts Col, 34; Workman fel. from Wellesley Col, Univ. Chicago, 42, univ. fel, 42-43, Ph.D, 47. Teaching fel. Eng, Tufts Col, 32-34; asst. Eng. compos, Wellesley Col, 35-37; instr. ENG, Conn. Col, 37-41; Univ. Chicago, 43-47; asst. prof. Rockford Col, 47-49, assoc. prof. & chmn. dept, 49-53; assoc. prof, CHATHAM COL, 53-59, PROF, 59-, CHMN. DEPT. ENG, 60-, chmn. dept. arts, 61-66. Mem. comt. humanities, Pa. Dept. Pub. Instr, 61-63; vis. prof, grad. sch, Univ. Pittsburgh, summer 63; consult. humanities, Norfolk div, Va. State Col, 63; mem. team, Mid. States Evaluation Lib. Arts Col, 63-; mem, Eng. Inst; consult. humanities, Bennett Col, winter 66. NCTE. Theory of lyric poetry and history in 17th century England. Publ: Further debts and allusions to John Donne, Eng. Lit. Hist; Herbert's Jordan, Explicator; Why the source theme?, Col. Eng. Add: Dept. of English, Chatham College, Pittsburgh, PA 15232.

ELDREDGE, LAURENCE MILTON, b. Melrose, Mass, May 21, 31; m. 56; c. 2. MIDDLE ENGLISH & MEDIEVAL LATIN LITERATURE. A.B, Colgate Univ, 53; M.A, Columbia Univ, 59, Ph.D.(Eng), 63. Instr. lit, Antioch Col, 62-68, asst. prof, 68-69; assoc. prof. ENG, UNIV. OTTAWA, 69-72, PROF, 72- MLA; Medieval Acad. Am; Asn. Can. Univ. Teachers Eng; Humanities Asn. Can. Fourteenth century poetry; 14th century philosophy, 14th and 15th century English culture. Publ: Chaucer's Hous of fame and the Via moderna, Neuphilologische Mitt, 70; Poetry and philosophy in the Parlement of Foules, Univ. Ottawa Rev, 70; Walter of Chatillon and the decretum of Gratian, Stud. Medieval Cult, 70. Add: Dept. of English, Faculty of Arts, University of Ottawa, Ottawa, Ont. K1N 6N5, Can.

ELDRIDGE, HERBERT G, b. Woodbury, N.J, Nov. 17, 23; m. 46; c. 3. ENGLISH. B.A, Univ. Pa, 49, M.A, 50, Ph.D, 61. Instr. ENG, Tex. A&M Univ, 50-52; from instr. to assoc. prof, N.C. State Univ, 54-67; PROF, UNIV. COLO, DENVER, 67-, DEAN. COL. UNDERGRAD. STUD, 71- A.U.S, 43-46, Sgt. MLA; Am. Stud. Asn; Mod. Humanities Res. Asn; NCTE. Publ: Careful disorder: the structure of Moby-Dick, Am. Lit, 5/67; Anacreon Moore and America, PMLA, 3/68. Add: College of Undergraduate Studies, University of Colorado, 1100 14th St, Denver, CO 80202.

ELIAS, ROBERT HENRY, b. New York, N.Y, Sept. 17, 14. ENGLISH, AMERICAN STUDIES. A.B, Williams Col, 36; A.M, Columbia Univ, 37; Harrison fel, Univ. Pa, 41-42, Ph.D, 48. Instr. Eng. & asst. hist, Univ. Pa, 42-45; instr. Eng, CORNELL UNIV, 45-49, asst. prof, 49-51, assoc. prof, 51-59, Ernest I. White prof. Am. stud. & chmn. comt, 59-64, prof. ENG, 59-68, GOLDWIN SMITH PROF, 68- Ford fel, 52-53; assoc. ed, Epoch, 47-54; Fulbright lectr, Univ. Toulouse, 63-64; Fulbright-Hays lectr, Ctr. for Eng. & N.Am. Stud, Pau, France, summer 68. MLA (mem. adv. counc, Am. Lit. sect, 72-74); Am. Stud. Asn. American literature and studies. Publ: Theodore Dreiser, apostle of nature, Knopf, 49, Cornell Univ, 70; ed, Chapters of Erie, Cornell Univ, 56 & Letters of Theodore Dresier, Univ. Pa, 59; auth, Entangling alliances with none: an essay on the individual in the American twenties, Norton, 73; The first American novel, Am. Lit, 1/41; James Thurber: the primitive, the innocent, and the individual, Am. Scholar, summer 58; contrib, Sixteen Modern American Authors, Duke Univ. & Norton, 73. Add: Dept. of English, Cornell University, Ithaca, NY 14850.

ELIASON, NORMAN ELLSWORTH, b. Glenwood, Minn, Mar. 12, 07; m. 30. ENGLISH LITERATURE & LINGUISTICS. A.B, Luther Col, 27, Litt.D, 67; A.M, State Univ. Iowa, 31; Univ. Nebr, 30-32; Ph.D, Johns Hopkins Univ, 35. Prin, high sch, Iowa, 27-28; instr. ENG, Luther Col, 28-29; Univ. Nebr, 29-32; instr. & asst. prof, Ind. Univ, 32-37; acting prof. & prof, Univ. Fla, 37-46; prof, UNIV. N.C, 46-66, KENAN PROF, 66- Fulbright guest prof, Univ. Innsbruck, 56; vis. prof, King's Col, London, 62-63. U.S.N.R, 42-46, Lt. Comdr. MLA; Ling. Soc. Am; Am. Dialect Soc; S.Atlantic Mod. Lang. Asn. Old and middle English literature; the English language. Publ: Tarheel talk, Univ. N.C, 56; co-auth, Effect of stress upon quantity in dissyllables, Ind. Univ, 39; co-ed, Studies in heroic legend and current speech, 59 & AElfric's first series of Catholic homilies, 66 & auth, The language of Chaucer's poetry, 72, Rosenkilde & Bagger, Copenhagen. Add: Dept. of English, University of North Carolina at Chapel Hill, Chapel Hill, NC 27514.

ELIOSEFF, LEE ANDREW, b. Brooklyn, N.Y, Aug. 28, 33; m. 63. ENGLISH. B.A, Univ. Rochester, 55; Johns Hopkins Univ, 55-56; M.A, N.Y. Univ, 56, Penfield fel, 58-59, Ph.D, 60. Instr. ENG, Univ. Tex, 59-62, asst. prof, 62-66; assoc. prof, Tufts Univ, 66-70; lectr, Univ. Mass, Boston, 70-71; ASSOC. PROF, UNIV. KY, 71- Univ. Tex. res. inst. grant, 61; Am. Counc. Learned Soc. stud. fel. & fel, Ctr. Advan. Stud. Behav. Sci, 63-64. Ling. Soc. Am; MLA; Am. Soc. Aesthet; Am. Soc. 18th Century Stud. Aesthetics of literature, critical theory and history; 18th century English literature. Publ: Cultural milieu of Addison's literary criticism, Univ. Tex, 63. Add: Dept. of English, University of Kentucky, Lexington, KY 40506.

ELKIN, STANLEY LAWRENCE, b. New York, N.Y, May 11, 30; m. 53; c. 3. AMERICAN LITERATURE. B.A, Univ. Ill, 52, M.A, 53, Ph.D, 61. Asst. ENG, Univ. Ill, 57-60; instr, WASH. UNIV, 60-62, asst. prof, 62-66, assoc. prof, 66-69, PROF, 69- Vis. prof, Smith Col, 64-65; Guggenheim fel, 66-67; Rockefeller Found. grant, 68-69; Nat. Endowment for Humanities grant, 72-73; Nat. Inst. Arts & Lett. & AAAS award, 74. Longview Award, 61. U.S.A, 55-57. Faulkner; novel. Publ: Boswell, 64, Criers and kibitzers, kibitzers and criers, 66, A bad man, 67, The Dick Gibson show, 71 & Searches and seizures, 73, Random; ed, Stories from the sixties, Doubleday, 71; auth, The making of Ashenden, Covent Garden Press, London, 72. Add: 225 Westgate, University City, MO 63130.

ELKINS, AUBREY CHRISTIAN, JR, b. Beaumont, Tex, Oct. 7, 39; m. 62. ENGLISH. B.A, Agr. & Mech. Col. Tex, 61; M.A, Univ. Tex, 63; Ph.D. (Eng), Cornell Univ, 68. ASST. PROF. ENG, UNIV. MICH, ANN ARBOR, 68- U.S.A.F, 63-65, 1st Lt. MLA. The Romantic period in England; English poetry. Add: Dept. of English, University of Michigan, Ann Arbor, MI 48104.

ELLEDGE, SCOTT BOWEN, b. Pittsburgh, Pa, Jan. 7, 14; m. 50. ENGLISH LITERATURE. A.B, Oberlin Col, 35; A.M, Cornell Univ, 36, Ph.D, 41. Instr. ENG, Purdue Univ, 36-40; Cornell Univ, 41-45; Harvard, 45-47; assoc. prof, Carleton Col, 47-52, prof, 52-62, chmn. dept, 51-62; PROF, CORNELL UNIV, 62- Lectr, Salzburg Sem. in Am. Stud, Austria, 52; Ford fel, 54-55; chmn. panel exam. Eng, Col. Entrance Exam. Bd, 65-68; vis. prof. Am. lit, Thammasat Univ, 69-70. Milton; 18th century, English literary criticism. Publ: Ed, Eighteenth-century critical essays, Cornell Univ, 61; co-ed, Continental model, Carleton Col. & Univ. Minn, 60, rev. ed, Cornell Univ, 70; ed, Milton's Lycidas, Harper, 65; ed, Hardy's Tess, 67 & Milton's Paradise lost, 74; Theories of generality and particularity, PMLA. Add: Dept. of English, Cornell University, Ithaca, NY 14850.

ELLEDGE, W. PAUL, b. Memphis, Tenn, Oct. 24, 38. ENGLISH. B.A, Univ. Mo, 60; M.A, Tulane Univ, 62, Ph.D.(Eng), 65. Instr. ENG, VANDERBILT UNIV, 65-66, asst. prof, 66-68, assoc. prof, 68-72, PROF, 72- MLA; Keats-Shelley Asn. Am; Byron Soc. Nineteenth century English literature. Publ: Byron and the dynamics of metaphor, Vanderbilt Univ, 68; co-ed, Romantic and Victorian: studies in memory of William H. Marshall, Fairleigh Dickinson Univ, 71; auth, Byron's hungry sinner: the quest motif in Don Juan, J. Eng. & Ger. Philol, 69; Fountains within: motivation in Coleridge's Dejection: an ode, Papers Lang. & Lit, 71. Add: Dept. of English, Vanderbilt University, Nashville, TN 37235.

ELLERY, JOHN BLAISE, b. Brooklyn, N.Y, Feb. 3, 20; m. 46; c. 5. COMMUNICATION. A.B, Hamilton Col, 48; M.A, Univ. Colo, 50; Ph.D, Univ. Wis, 54. Instr. Eng, Univ. Colo, 48-50; asst. prof. rhet, Univ. Iowa, 52-56; assoc. prof, Ala. Col, 56-57; radio & TV, Wayne State Univ, 57-61; prof. Eng. & chmn. dept, East Tenn. State Univ, 61-66; head dept. Eng. & acting dean, Njala Univ. Col, Sierra Leone, 66-68; PROF. COMMUN. & ASST. TO CHANCELLOR, UNIV. WIS-STEVENS POINT, 68-, acting dean col. appl. arts & sci, 69-70, dean col. natural resources, 70-72. Nat. Asn. Educ. Broadcasters res. fel, 57; res. grant, Nat. Educ. TV & Radio Ctr, 58. U.S.N.R, 38-41, Ens; U.S.A, 41-45. Linguistics; African literature. Publ: John Stuart Mill, Twayne, 63; co-auth, Introduction to graduate study in speech and theatre, Mich. State Univ, 61. Add: Office of the Chancellor, University of Wisconsin-Stevens Point, Stevens Point, WI 54481.

ELLINGSON, MARY ROSS, Classical Archaeology & Languages, English. See Volume III, Foreign Languages, Linguistics & Philology.

ELLINGSWORTH, HUBER W, b. Corydon, Iowa, Aug. 13, 28; m. 52; c. 3. SPEECH, COMMUNICATION. B.A, Pac. Univ, 49; M.A, Wash. State Univ, 50; Ph.D.(speech), Fla. State Univ, 55. Instr. Eng, Southeast. La. Col, 50-51; speech, Univ. Conn, 54-56; asst. prof, Mich. State Univ, 56-59, commun, 59-63; PROF. speech, Frostburg State Col, 63-66; SPEECH & COMMUN, UNIV. HAWAII, MANOA, 66-, CHMN. DEPT. COMMUN, 72- Consult, Agency Int. Develop, 59, Nat. Proj. Agr. Commun, 61-62, U.S. Chamber Commerce, 62 & Environmental Sci. Serv. Admin, 66-67. Speech Commun. Asn; Nat. Soc. Stud. Commun. Communication training for foreign aid trainees; communication with underprivileged persons; technological development in emerging nations. Publ: Speech and social action, Prentice-Hall, 67; Weather communication, U.S. Weather Bur, 67; Communication and technological change, Praeger, 68; Magazine readership in Latin America, Int. Asn. Mass Commun. Res. Bull, autumn 63; Teacher preference for newspaper items, Jour. Quart, winter 63; Education in communication, Today's Speech, 11/64. Add: Dept. of Communication, University of Hawaii at Manoa, Honolulu, HI 96822.

ELLIOTT, CRAIG CLIFFORD, b. Camrose, Alta; m. 58; c. 3. ACTING, CREATIVE DRAMA. B.A, Univ. Wash, 58, M.A, 59, Ph.D.(drama), 68. Instr. drama & speech, Northwest. Col, 60-66; acting & speech, Univ. Wash, 66-68; ASSOC. PROF. ACTING & CREATIVE DRAMA, UNIV. CALGARY, 67- Am. Theatre Asn; Speech Asn. Am; Can. Child & Youth Drama Asn; Can. Asn. Univ. Teachers. Dramatic process; perceptual learning; drama with and for native Canadians. Publ: Early Victorian theatre, B.C. Hist. Soc, winter 70; Sensory communication, Early Childhood Counc. J, 11/70; Creative drama in controversy, Fine Arts Counc. J, summer 71; plus two others. Add: Dept. of Drama, University of Calgary, Calgary, Alta. T2N 1N4, Can.

ELLIOTT, DALE EUGENE, Linguistics. See Volume III, Foreign Languages, Linguistics & Philology.

ELLIOTT, GARY DOUGLAS, b. Chickasha, Okla, Oct. 10, 40; m. 63; c. 2. ENGLISH. B.A, Harding Col, 62; M.A, N.Tex. State Univ, 68; Ph.D.(Eng), Kans. State Univ, 73. Teacher Eng. & Bible, Ft. Worth Christian Acad, 62-65, prin, 65-66; head. Eng. dept, Ft. Worth Christian Col, 66-67; instr. ENG, Harding Col, 67-69; asst. Kans. State Univ, 69-71; ASST. PROF, HARDING COL, 71-73, CHMN. DEPT, 73- NCTE; MLA; S.Cent. Mod. Lang. Asn; Conf. Col. Compos; & Commun. Emily Dickinson; Ernest Hemingway. Publ: Code-breakers in Hemingway's Green hills of Africa, Kans. Eng, 2/71; The solitary dissenter: a study of Emily Dickinson's concept of God, Emily Dickinson Bull, 3/72. Add: Dept. of English, Harding College, Box 916, Searcy, AR 72143.

ELLIOTT, GEORGE PAUL, b. Knightstown, Ind, June 16, 18. ENGLISH LITERATURE. A.B, Univ. Calif, 39, A.M, 41; hon. L.H.D, St. Lawrence Univ, 71. Asst. prof. Eng, St. Mary's Col.(Calif), 47-55; asst. prof, Cornell Univ, 55-56; Barnard Col, Columbia Univ, 57-60; lectr, writers workshop, State Univ. Iowa, 60-61; Univ. Calif, Berkeley, 62; St. Mary's Col.(Calif), 62-63; PROF. SYRACUSE UNIV, 63- Hudson Rev. fel, 56-57; Guggenheim fel, 61-62, 70-71; Ford Found. fel, 65-66. Nat. Inst. Arts & Lett. Award, 69. Publ: Parktilden Village, Beacon, 58; Among the Dangs, Holt, 61; David Knudsen, 62 & A piece of lettuce, 64, Random; In the world, Viking, 65; An hour of last things, 68 & From the Berkeley Hills, 69, Harper; Conversions, 71 & Muriel, 72, Dutton. Add: Dept. of English, Syracuse University, Syracuse, NY 13210.

ELLIOTT, GORDON R, b. Vancouver, B.C, Apr. 19, 20. ENGLISH. B.A, Univ. B.C, 51, dipl. educ, 52, M.A, 54; A.M, Harvard, 56. Researcher hist, B.C, Arch, Victoria; res. asst. hist. & lit, Margaret Ormsby's British Columbia: a history & R.E. Watters, ed, British Columbia: a centennial anthology, 56-58; instr. ENG, Univ. B.C, 57-65; from asst. prof. to ASSOC. PROF, SIMON FRASER UNIV, 65- Can. Army, 41-42; R.C.A.F, 42-46, Flight Sgt. British Columbia history and literature; Canadian history and literature; Australian literature. Publ: Quesnel, commercial centre of Cariboo gold rush, Cariboo Hist. Soc, 59; ed, The journals of Norman Lee, Robert R. Reid, 60; Klondike cattle drive, Mitchell, 60; auth, The games bibliographers play, Papers Bibliog. Soc. Can, 71; Henry P. Pellew Crease: confederation or no confederation, B.C, Stud, winter 71-72; James McIntyre: neglected emigre, Dalhousie Rev, winter 72-73; plus others. Add: Dept. of English, Simon Fraser University, Burnaby 2, B.C, Can.

ELLIOTT, JEANNE BATE, b. Kearney, Nebr; m. 68; c. 1. ENGLISH LITERATURE. A.B, Univ. Calif, Berkeley, 45, M.A, 49, Anne Sampson fel, 50-52, Am. Asn. Univ. Women Calif. fel, 55-56, Ph.D.(Eng), 56; Ind. Univ, Bloomington, summer 64. Teaching asst. ENG, Univ. Calif, Berkeley, 52-54, lectr, 56-57; instr, Univ. Nev, Reno, 54-56; asst. prof, SAN JOSE STATE UNIV, 57-61, assoc. prof, 61-68, PROF, 68- Resident linguist, Eng. as second lang, Peace Corps Training Prog, summer 65. MLA; AAUP; Nat. Asn. For. Stud. Affairs. The Victorian novel; women in British literature. Add: Dept. of English, San Jose State University, San Jose, CA 95192.

ELLIOTT, JOHN RICHARD, JR, b. Hartford, Conn, Feb. 27, 37; m. 58; c. 2. ENGLISH. A.B, Harvard, 58; M.A, Univ. Calif, Berkeley, 60, Ph.D.(Eng), 64. Instr. ENG, Univ. N.C, 62-64; vis. asst. prof, Univ. Va, 64-65; ASST. PROF, UNIV. CALIF, SANTA BARBARA, 65- Newberry Libr. fel, summer 64; Univ. Calif. Humanities Inst. fel, 65; Nat. Humanities Found. younger scholar fel, 68-69; Am. Counc. Learned Soc. grant-in-aid, 71. Berlioz Soc. MLA. Medieval and Renaissance English literature. Publ: Ed, The prince of poets: essays on Edmund Spenser, N.Y. Univ, 68; auth, Shakespeare and the double image of King John, Shakespeare Stud, 65; History and tragedy in Richard II, Stud. Eng. Lit, 68; The sacrifice of Isaac as comedy and tragedy, Stud. Philol, 68. Add: Dept. of English, University of California, Santa Barbara, CA 93106.

ELLIOTT, JOHN WESLEY, JR, b. Shelby, N.C, Sept. 13, 33. ENGLISH ROMANTIC LITERATURE. A.B, Univ. N.C, 57; S.T.B, Harvard, 60; M.A, Columbia Univ, 64, Ph.D.(Eng), 71. Instr. ENG, FAIRLEIGH DICKINSON UNIV, 62-66, asst. prof, 66-71, ASSOC. PROF, 71- Am. Fed. Teachers. Religion and imaginative literature. Publ: Reader's guide to Coleridge, Reader's guide to Bacon, Reader's guide to Wordsworth & Reader's guide to More, Simon & Schuster. Add: Dept. of English, Fairleigh Dickinson University, 1000 River Rd, Teaneck, NJ 07666.

ELLIOTT, LEONARD REECE, b. Elk City, Okla, Aug. 31, 41; m. 62; c. 2. COMMUNICATION THEORY, PUBLIC ADDRESS. B.A, Southwest. State Univ, 63; M.S, South. Ill. Univ, Carbondale, 66, Ph.D.(speech), 71. Instr. speech, Enid Pub. Schs, Okla, 63-65; Stephen F. Austin State Univ, 66-68; resident teacher stud. affairs, South. Ill. Univ, Carbondale, 68-71; ASST. PROF. SPEECH, AUSTIN PEAY STATE UNIV, 71- South. Speech Commun. Asn. Rhetorical criticism. Add: Dept. of Speech & Theatre, Austin Peay State University, College St, Clarksville, TN 37040.

ELLIOTT, NATHANIEL Y, b. Jamestown, N.Y, Aug. 30, 28; m. 58; c. 3. ENGLISH. B.S, State Univ. N.Y. Fredonia, 51; M.A, Syracuse Univ, 57; Ph.D.(Scottish lit), Cornell Univ, 67. Instr. ENG, Drexel Inst. Technol, 57-59; asst. prof, COL. WILLIAM & MARY, 63-70, ASSOC. PROF, 70-, alumni grant, 67. U.S.N, 51-53. S.Atlantic Mod. Lang. Asn. Victorian and Scottish literature. Publ: Robert Louis Stevenson and Scottish literature, Eng. Lit. in Transition, 69. Add: Dept. of English, College of William & Mary, Williamsburg, VA 23185.

ELLIOTT, PATRICK FRANK, b. Ft. Worth, Tex, Dec. 23, 26; m. 67. LITERATURE, HUMANITIES. A.B, Ottawa Univ.(Kans), 50; B.D, Univ. Chicago, 53, M.A. & Ph.D.(theol. & lit), 64; Danforth summer scholar, 61. Instr. humanities, Emory Univ, 58-60; Eng, Davidson Col, 60-61; prof. & chmn. dept, Sioux Falls Col, 62-65; assoc. prof, Univ. S.Dak, 65-66; PROF. HUMANITIES, SHAW UNIV, 66-, chmn. dept, 66-72. U.S.A, 45-47. S.Atlantic Mod. Lang. Asn; NCTE. Nineteenth century American studies; Herman Melville; contemporary literature. Publ: Introduction to literature, Sioux Falls Col, 63. Add: Div. of Humanities, Shaw University, Raleigh, NC 27602.

ELLIOTT, ROBERT CARL, b. Indianapolis, Ind, Nov. 23, 14. ENGLISH LITERATURE. A.B, Wabash Col, 36; A.M, Columbia Univ, 37; Ph.D, Brown Univ, 46. Instr, Univ. Hawaii, 37-39, 41; Eng, Ohio State Univ, 46-47, asst. prof, 47-53, assoc. prof, 53-59, PROF, 59-64; ENG. LIT. UNIV. CALIF, SAN DIEGO, 64-, chmn. dept. lit, 68-71. Ford fel, 52-53; Guggenheim fel, 62-63, 72. U.S.N, 42-45. MLA; Int. Asn. Univ. Prof. Eng. English 18th century literature, history and criticism; genre studies. Publ: Power of satire; magic, ritual, art, Princeton Univ, 60; ed, Looking backward by Edward Bellamy, Houghton, 66; auth, The shape of utopia, Univ. Chicago,

70; ed, Twentieth century interpretations of Moll Flanders, Prentice-Hall, 70; Gulliver as literary artist, ELH; Saturnalia, satire, and utopia, 66 & Swift's I, 73, Yale Rev; plus others. Add: Dept. of Literature, University of California, San Diego, La Jolla, CA 92037.

ELLIOTT, THOMAS JOSEPH, b. Boston, Mass, Jan. 25, 41; m. 66. ENGLISH LITERATURE, MEDIEVAL STUDIES. A.B, Boston Col, 63, M.A, 67; fels, Univ. Mich, 68-69, 69-70, Ph.D.(Eng), 70. Teacher Eng. & Latin, St. Dominic Savio High Sch, East Boston, Mass, 63-67; ASST. PROF. ENG, CALIF. STATE POLYTECH. UNIV, POMONA, 70-, fac. sen, 71-74. MLA; Mediaeval Acad. Am; Col. Eng. Asn; Irish Am. Cult. Inst. Medieval English literature; literary history; Irish studies. Publ: A medieval bestiary, David R. Godine, 71; Complaint as a middle English genre, Mouton, 74; Middle English complaints against the times: to contemn the world or to reform it?, Annuale Mediaevale, 73. Add: Dept. of English & Modern Languages, California State Polytechnic University, Pomona, W. Temple Ave, Pomona, CA 91768.

ELLIOTT, VIRGINIA AGNES, b. Pittsburgh, Pa, July 22, 09. ENGLISH. B.A, Wilson Col, 30; M.A, Columbia Univ, 31; Univ. Pittsburgh, 43-46. Teacher Eng, Mt. Lebanon High Sch, 40-65; lectr. Eng. & educ, UNIV. PITTSBURGH, 65-72, ASSOC. PROF. ENG, 72- Instr. compos, summer inst. comn. Eng, Univ. Pittsburgh, 62; John Hay fel, 63-64. NCTE. The exceptionally able student. Publ: Ed, English for superior students, NCTE, 64; auth, Identifying the academically talented in English, In: English for the academically talented student, NCTE & NEA, 60. Add: Dept. of English, University of Pittsburgh, Pittsburgh, PA 15260.

ELLIOTT, WILLIAM DOUGLAS, b. Bemidji, Minn, Jan. 13, 38; m. 60; c. 2. ENGLISH. B.A, Miami Univ, 60; M.A, Univ. Mich, 61, Ed.D.(Eng), 67; M.F.A, Univ. Iowa, 62. Teaching asst. ENG, Univ. Mich, 60-61, fel, 62-63; instr, Muskingum Col, 64-65; Washtenaw Community Col, 66-67; asst. prof, BEMIDJI STATE COL, 67-68, ASSOC. PROF, 68- Am. Philos. Asn. res. grant, 74. MLA (group 12, world lit. written in Eng). British Commonwealth literature, especially Australia; creative writing; the modern British novel. Publ: Henry Handel Richardson, Twayne, 75; Her song (poems), Epoch, fall 71; H.H. Richardson: the education of an Australian realist, Stud. in Novel, summer 72; Moving out (story), New Orleans Rev, spring 73; plus others. Add: Dept. of English, Bemidji State College, Bemidji, MN 56601.

ELLIS, BROBURY PEARCE, b. Oakland, Calif, Apr. 18, 13; m. 42; c. 2. SPEECH, DRAMA. B.A, Stanford Univ, 37, M.A, 46; Ph.D, Cornell Univ, 54. Instr. Eng. & speech, Fairleigh Dickinson Jr. Col, 46-47; asst. prof, CENT. CONN. STATE COL, 47-61, assoc. prof, SPEECH & THEATRE, 61-65, PROF, 65- Danforth Found. grant, 63. New Eng. Forensic Conf.(pres, 64-65). Speech education; history of theatre and drama. Publ: Beaumarchais, the barber of Seville, 66 & Beaumarchais, the marriage of Figaro, 66, Appleton; The true original copies, Tulane Drama Rev, 60. Add: Dept. of Speech & Theatre, Central Connecticut State College, New Britain, CT 06050.

ELLIS, CARROLL BROOKS, b. Booneville, Miss, May 24, 19; m. 46; c. 3. SPEECH, RELIGION. B.S, N.Tex. State Teachers Col, 41; M.A, La. State Univ, 45, Ph.D.(speech), 49. Teacher SPEECH, high sch, Tex, 41-43; instr, La. State Univ, 45-49; PROF, DAVID LIPSCOMB COL, 49-, CHMN. DEPT, 52- Lectr, Freed-Hardeman Col, 54; Pepperdine Christian Col, 57; Abilene Christian Col, 62; mem. ed. staff, Gospel Advocate; minister, Otter Creek Church of Christ, 69-; lectr, Freed-Hardeman Col, 73 & Ala. Christian Col, 73. Speech Commun. Asn; Am. Forensic Asn; South. Speech Asn.(1st v.pres, 64, pres, 65); South. Humanities Conf; Int. Commun. Asn. Rhetorical criticism; preaching theory; undergraduate speech teaching. Publ: The Bible, inspirative, relevancy, authority, Lubbock Christian Col, 68; In the last times, Ft. Worth Christian Col, 68; Religion and the presidency, In: Sermons in American history, Abingdon, 71; contrib, That which is perfect, Freed-Hardeman Col, 73. Add: Dept. of Speech, David Lipscomb College, Granny White Pike, Nashville, TN 37203.

ELLIS, CHARLES MERRILL, b. Bates, Ark, Dec. 15, 13; m. 45; c. 2. ENGLISH. M.A, Univ. Ark, 47; Ed.D.(Eng. & educ), Univ. Fla, 55. Prin. high sch, Ark, 36-38; instr. Eng, Gulf Coast Mil. Acad, 38-42; ed, Farm Bur. Press, Little Rock, Ark, 46-47; instr. Eng. & Latin, Henderson State Col, 47-51; teacher, high sch, 51-53; assoc. prof. ENG, West. Ill. State Col, 55-57; PROF. & CHMN. DEPT, HENDERSON STATE COL, 57- U.S.A, 42-45, Sgt. NCTE; Conf. Col. Compos. & Commun; S.Cent. Mod. Lang. Asn. Journalism. Add: Dept. of English, Henderson State College, Arkadelphia, AR 71923.

ELLIS, DEAN S, b. Odgen, Utah, Oct. 14, 38; m. 60; c. 3. MANAGEMENT COMMUNICATIONS, PSYCHOLOGY. B.S, Univ. Utah, 60, M.S, 63; Ph.D. (organizational commun), Purdue Univ, 65. Res. asst. & instr, Purdue Univ, 63-65; asst. prof. speech, W.Ga. Col, 65-67; UNIV. HAWAII, 67-73, ASSOC. PROF. MGT. & MKT, 73- Acad. Mgt; Am. Psychol. Asn; Speech Commun. Asn; Am. Forensic Asn. Psycho-linguistics; gaming theory; organizational communication. Publ: Speech and social stature in America, Soc. Forces, 67; How good are debate judges, J.Am. Forensic Asn, 67; A union authorization election: the key to winning, Personnel J, 72. Add: Dept. of Management & Marketing, College of Business, University of Hawaii, Honolulu, HI 96822.

ELLIS, F. PATRICK, F.S.C, b. Baltimore, Md, Nov. 17, 28. ENGLISH. A.B, Cath. Univ. Am, 51; univ. scholar, Univ. Pa, 53-54, A.M, 54, Ph.D.(Eng), 60. Teacher Eng. & relig, W.Cath. High Sch. Boys, 51-56, chmn. dept. Eng, 56-58, guidance dir, 59-60; asst. prof. Eng, La Salle Col, 60-62; princ, La Salle High Sch, Miami, 62-64; assoc. prof. ENG, LA SALLE COL, 64-74, PROF, 74-, DIR. HONORS PROG, 64-, DIR. DEVELOP, 69- Northeast Mod. Lang. Asn; Col. Eng. Asn. Poetry of John Dryden; history of literary criticism; structure of undergraduate liberal arts education. Publ: A critical analysis of John Dryden's The hind and the panther, Univ. Microfilms, 60. Add: Dept. of English, La Salle College, Philadelphia, PA 19141.

ELLIS, FRANK HALE, b. Chicago, Ill, Jan. 18, 16; m. 40; c. 1. ENGLISH. B.S, Northwest. Univ, 39; M.A, Yale, 41, Ph.D, 48. Instr. ENG. LIT, Univ. Buffalo, 41-42; from instr. to asst. prof, Yale, 46-51; from asst. prof. to PROF, SMITH COL, 58- Mem, Conn. Acad. Arts & Sci. Morse fel, 50-51. U.S.A, 42-46, M/Sgt; Bronze Star. MLA. Eighteenth century English literature. Publ: Swift's discourse, Oxford, 67; ed, Twentieth century interpretations of Robinson Crusoe, Prentice-Hall, 69, Poems on affairs of state, Vol. VI, 70 & Vol. VII, 74, Yale. Add: Dept. of English, Smith College, Northampton, MA 01060.

ELLIS, HERBERT ALEXANDER, b. Salisbury, N.C, June 1, 11; m. 41. LITERATURE. A.B, Duke Univ, 32; M.A, Univ. N.C, 45, Ph.D, 63. Teacher Eng. & French, Consol. High Schs, N.C, 38-40, 41-42; Eng, French, Ger, Georg Washington High Sch, Danville, Va, 42-49; prin, Forest Hills Sch, Danville, 49-53; prof. Eng. & acting head, King Col, 54-55; instr, Univ. N.C, 55-56; prof. & chmn. dept, Lander Col, 59-65, acad. dean, 62-65; prof. Eng. & chmn. dept, Erskine Col, 65-70; PROF. ENG, LANDER COL, 70- U.S.A.A.F, 33. S.Atlantic Mod. Lang. Asn; NCTE. Chaucer and Middle Ages; Shakespeare and Renaissance. Publ: Shakespeare's lusty punning in Love's labour's lost, Mouton, The Hague, 73. Add: 719 Chinquapin Rd, Greenwood, SC 29646.

ELLIS, JAMES DELMONT, b. Painesville, Ohio, Dec. 7, 35; m. 63. ENGLISH DRAMA. B.A, Oberlin Col, 57; Woodrow Wilson fels, N.Y. Univ, 57-58; M.A, Univ. Iowa, 60, Ph.D.(dramatic arts), 64. Instr. ENG, Univ. Rochester, 61-62 MT. HOLYOKE COL, 62-64, asst. prof, 64-69, assoc. prof, 69-72, PROF, 72- Mem. ed. bd, Mass. Rev, 66-; Nat. Endowment for Humanities summer stipend, 67; co-ed, Victorian Periodicals Newsletter, 70-; co-ed, The London Stage 1800-1900: a Calendar of Performances, 73- Am. Soc. Theatre Res; Soc. Theatre Res, Eng; MLA. Modern drama; Victorian theatre. Publ: Ed, The Bab ballads of W.S. Gilbert, Harvard Univ, 70 & The Shakespeare promptbooks of Samuel Phelps, Folger Shakespeare Libr. Add: Dept. of English, Mt. Holyoke College, South Hadley, MA 01075.

ELLIS, JAMES NELSON, b. Dallas, Tex, Sept. 24, 32; m. 60. ENGLISH. B.A, Univ. Okla, 54, M.A, 58; Ph.D.(Eng), Univ. Tex, 63. Spec. instr. ENG, Univ. Tex, 62-63; asst. prof, UNIV. N.C, GREENSBORO, 63-68, ASSOC. PROF, 68- Fulbright lectr. Am. lit, Univ. Thessaloniki, Greece, 67-68. Univ. N.C. Greensboro alumni excellence in teaching award, 67. U.S.N, 54-57, Res, 57-67, Lt.(jg). MLA; Publ: Fitzgerald's fragmented hero: Dick Diver, Univ. Rev, autumn 65; A new reading of The Sea Wolf, West. Am. Lit, summer 67; The Stoddard lectures in The great Gatsby, Am. Lit, 11/72; plus others. Add: Dept. of English, University of North Carolina at Greensboro, Greensboro, NC 27412.

ELLIS, JOHN C, b. San Francisco, Calif, Oct. 11, 21; m. 50. ENGLISH. B.A, Univ. Ore, 49, M.A, 51, Ph.D, 59; Univ. Calif, Berkeley, 51-52. Instr. Eng, Univ. Ore, 52-54, Greek, 54-55; ENG, ARIZ. STATE UNIV, 57-58, from asst. prof. to ASSOC. PROF, 58- U.S.A.A.F, 41-46, 2nd Lt. Shakespeare. Add: Dept. of English, Arizona State University, Tempe, AZ 85281.

ELLIS, SETH HOWARD, b. Delmar, Del, Oct. 12, 29; div; c. 1. ENGLISH LANGUAGE & LITERATURE. A.B, Univ. Del, 51; A.M, Univ. Mo, 54; Ph.D, Univ. South. Calif, 59. Asst. prof. ENG, Univ. Ala, 60-62; Univ. Redlands, 62-63; UNIV. N.C, CHARLOTTE, 63-67, assoc. prof, 67-71, PROF, 71-, DIR. SUMMER SESSIONS, 67-, EVE. PROG, 70- U.S.A, 51-53, Sgt. MLA; Col. Eng. Asn; NCTE; Nat. Asn. Summer Schs. Modern novel, poetry and drama. Add: Dept. of English, University of North Carolina, Charlotte, NC 28213.

ELLISON, CURTIS WILLIAM, b. Jasper, Ala, Oct. 3, 43; m. 66; c. 2. AMERICAN STUDIES. B.A, Univ. Ala, 65; M.A, Univ. Minn, Minneapolis, 67, Ph.D.(Am. stud), 70. Asst. prof. ENG, MIAMI UNIV, 70-74, ASSOC. PROF, 74-, DIR. PROG. AM. STUD, 70- Am. Stud. Asn; MLA; South. Hist. Asn; Popular Cult. Asn. Methodology of culture studies; American literature; American history. Add: Program in American Studies, Miami University, Oxford, OH 45056.

ELLISON, (EARL) JEROME, b. Maywood, Ill, Oct. 28, 07; m. 34, 50; c. 2. ENGLISH. A.B, Univ. Mich, 30; M.A, South. Conn. State Col, 64. Asst. ed, Life Mag, 32-33; assoc. ed, Reader's Digest, 35-42; ed-in-chief, Liberty Mag, 42-43; managing ed, Collier's Mag, 43-44; ed. dir, bur. overseas pubs, Off. War Inform, 44-45; instr, night sch, N.Y. Univ, 45; founder & pub, Mag. of the Year, 45-47; writer, 47-55; assoc. prof. jour, Ind. Univ, 55-60; writer, 60-64; assoc. prof. ENG. & HUMANITIES, UNIV. NEW HAVEN, 64-69, PROF, 70- Ed. & publ, Best Articles & Stories Mag, 57-61; lectr, Div. Continuing Educ, Univ. Conn, 69-71. Literary criticism; contemporary fiction; literature of social protest. Publ: Report to the creator: John Brown's soul; The dam; A serious call to an American (r)evolution, Bulldog Bks, 67; God on Broadway, John Knox, 71; co-auth, The life beyond death, Putnam, 71; auth, The last-third-of-life club, United Church, 73; Criticism for a new age: a literary manifesto, Southwest Rev, autumn, 66; LSD, Christian Herald, 10/66; How to catch a whale: Melville and evolutionary criticism, Mich. Quart. Rev, 4/67. Add: Durham Rd, Guilford, CT 06437.

ELLISON, RHODA C, b. Centreville, Ala, Feb. 15, 04. ENGLISH. B.A, Randolph-Macon Woman's Col, 25; M.A, Columbia Univ, 29; Rosenwald fel, Univ. N.C, 44-45, Ph.D, 45. Asst. prof. ENG, HUNTINGDON COL, 30-35, assoc. prof, 35-45, prof, 45-72, chmn. dept, 59-72, EMER. PROF, 72- S.Atlantic Mod. Lang. Asn; NCTE; MLA. Southern literature and publishing. Publ: Check list of Alabama imprints, 1807-1870, 46, Early Alabama publications: study in literary interests, 47, History & bibliography of Alabama newspapers, 54 & History of Huntington College, 1854-1954, 54, Univ. Ala. Add: Dept. of English, Huntingdon College, Montgomery, AL 36106.

ELLMANN, RICHARD DAVID, b. Highland Park, Mich, Mar. 15, 18; m. 49; c. 2. ENGLISH & AMERICAN LITERATURE. A.B, Yale, 39, A.M, 41, Rockefeller fel, 46-47, Ph.D, 47; B.Litt. Univ. Dublin, 47; M.A, Oxford, 70. Instr, Harvard, 42-43, 47-48, Briggs-Copeland asst. prof, 48-51; prof. Eng, Northwest. Univ, 51-63, Franklin Bliss Snyder prof, 63-68; prof, Yale, 68-70; GOLDSMITHS PROF. ENG. LIT, OXFORD, 70- Guggenheim fels, 50, 57 & 70; Am. Philos. Soc. grant, 53; Kenyon Rev. fel, 55; fel, Ind. Univ, 56, 60, sr. fel, 67-71; Carpenter vis. prof, Univ. Chicago, 59; chmn, Eng. Inst, 61-62; mem. exec. counc, MLA, 61-64, ed. comt, publs, 68-73; fel,

New Col, Oxford, 70- Nat. Bk. Award, 60. U.S.N. & Off. Strategic Serv, 43-45. Fel. Royal Soc. Lit. U.K; fel. Am. Acad. Arts & Sci; fel. Nat. Inst. Arts & Lett. Modern and Victorian literature. Publ: Yeats: the man and the masks, Dutton, 48; transl, Selected writings of Henri Michaux, New Directions, 51; auth, The identity of Yeats, 54, James Joyce, 59, Eminent domain, 67, co-ed, The modern tradition, 65, auth, Ulysses on the Liffey, 72 & Golden codgers, 73, Oxford Univ; ed, Edwardians and late Victorians, Columbia Univ, 61; My brother's keeper, 58, Letters of James Joyce, Vols. II & III, 66, Giacomo Joyce, 68, co-ed, Critical writings of James Joyce, 59 & ed, Selected letters of James Joyce, 74, Viking; ed, Oscar Wilde: twentieth century views, Prentice-Hall, 69 & The author as critic: critical writings of Oscar Wilde, Random, 69; co-ed, Norton anthology of modern verse, Norton, 73; plus others. Add: New College, Oxford University, Oxford, England.

ELLSWORTH, RICHARD GRANT, b. Salt Lake City, Utah, July 11, 27; m. 49; c. 8. AMERICAN CIVILIZATION, ENGLISH. A.B, Brigham Young Univ, 51, M.A, 52; Ph.D.(Am. civilization), Univ. Md, 59. Asst. prof. ENG, BRIGHAM YOUNG UNIV, 58-64, ASSOC. PROF, 64- U.S.N.R, 45-46. Publ: Dilemma of a pernicious Zion, summer 68 & Notes and comments: pro-Mormon drama, spring 72, Brigham Young Univ. Stud; Ah sweet misery of life—adolescence, literature, and the marketplace, Utah Libr, fall 70. Add: 1267 Apple Ave, Provo, UT 84601.

ELMQUIST, KARL ERIK, b. Evanston, Ill, Jan. 7, 12; m. 43. ENGLISH. A.B, South. Methodist Univ, 32; fel, Univ. Chicago, 34-35; A.M, Univ. Tex, 39. Instr. ENG, TEX. A&M UNIV, 35-41, asst. prof, 41-47, ASSOC. PROF, 47- Instr, North Park Col, 39-40. A.U.S, 42-46, Capt. Ling. Soc. Am. Linguistics; English phonetics and phonemics; English word order. Add: Dept. of English, Texas A&M University, College Station, TX 77843.

ELSBREE, LANGDON, b. Trenton, N.J, June 23, 29; m. 52; c. 1. ENGLISH. B.A, Earlham Col, 52; M.A, Cornell Univ, 54; Ph.D.(Eng), Claremont Grad. Sch, 63. Instr. Eng, Miami Univ, 54-57; Harvey Mudd Col, 58-59; humanities, Scripps Col, 59-60; from instr. to assoc. prof. ENG, CLAREMONT MEN'S COL, 60-71, PROF, 71- Hays-Fulbright lectr. Am. lit, Cairo, 66-67; Claremont Men's Col. summer res. grant, 68 & 72; lectr. grad. Eng. prog, Calif. State Univ, Los Angeles, 68-70. Eng. Folk & Dance Soc; MLA. Use of the dance as theme and symbol in the novel; the fiction and poetry of Thomas Hardy and D.H. Lawrence; theme of time in 19th century English and American fiction. Publ: Co-auth, Heath's college handbook of composition, 8th ed, 72, Brief handbook of usage, 68, rev. ed, 72 & Brief guide to rhetoric, 68, rev. ed, 72, Heath; auth, Huck Finn on the Nile, S.Atlantic Quart, autumn 70; The writer as professional, D.H. Lawrence Rev, summer 71; The purest and most perfect form of play: some novelists and the dance, Criticism, fall 72; plus others. Add: Dept. of English, Bauer Center, Claremont Men's College, Claremont, CA 91711.

ELSER, RALPH DONALD, b. North Lima, Ohio, Jan. 15, 15; m. 41; c. 4. SPEECH, DRAMA. A.B, Youngstown Univ, 35; M.Litt, Univ. Pittsburgh, 39; summers, N.Y. Univ, 50, Am. Conserv. Music, 37. Asst. prof. Eng, speech & dramatics, YOUNGSTOWN STATE UNIV, 46-60, asst. prof. SPEECH & DRAMATICS, 61-68, ASSOC. PROF, 68-, DIR. UNIV. THEATRE, 61- U.S.A.A.F, 43-45. Am. Theatre Asn; Speech Commun. Asn; Cent. States Speech Asn. Publ: Balcony scene, 47, Special guest, 48 & The pink dress, 49, Harper; A ticket to the city (play), French, 67; plus others. Add: Dept. of Speech & Drama, Youngstown State University, Youngstown, OH 44503.

ELSON, CHARLES, b. Chicago, Ill, Sept. 5, 09; m. 38; c. 1. DRAMA. Ph.B, Univ. Chicago, 32; M.F.A, Yale, 35. Instr. drama, State Univ. Iowa, 35-36; dir. art, Fed. Theatre Proj, Los Angeles, 36-37; assoc. prof. drama, Univ. Okla, 37-43; engr. in charge three dimensional training devices, U.S. Navy Training Aids Ctr, 43-45; asst. designer BROADWAY PRODUCTIONS, 45-47, DESIGNER, 47-; EMER. PROF. DRAMA, HUNTER COL, 74- Assoc. prof, Hunter Col, 48-63, prof, 63-74; vis. prof, Yale, 50, 64-70; mem, United Scenic Artists Exam. Comt, 53-; Fulbright lectr. & consult, India, 59; mem, Young Artists Selection Comt, Inst. Int. Educ, 62; prof. theatre, City Univ. New York, 64-; U.S. Off. Educ. Conf. Theatre Res, 67. Life fel. Int. Inst. Arts & Lett. New dramatic forms; lighting projections; traditional Indian rural theatre forms; the aesthetics of color in light. Publ: Plan for theatre development in India, Premier Mondiales, Paris, 61; Am. ed, Stage design throughout the world, 1935-50, 56 & Stage design throughout the world, 1950-60, 63, Elsevier, Brussels. Add: Faraway Farm, 1 Faraway Lane, Armonk Village, NY 10504.

ELSON, JAMES HINSDALE, b. East Cleveland, Ohio, Mar. 21, 04. ENGLISH. A.B, Oberlin Col, 26; M.A, Syracuse Univ, 28; univ. fel, Columbia Univ, 39, Ph.D, 46. Instr. ENG, SYRACUSE UNIV, 26-47, asst. prof, 46-48; assoc. prof, 48-52, prof, 52-69, EMER. PROF, 69-, v.chmn. dept, 49-65, chmn. dept, 65-68. U.S.A.A.F, 42-45, M/Sgt. MLA. English literature of the 17th century; Milton. Publ: John Hales of Eton, Kings Crown Press, 48. Add: Dept. of English, Syracuse University, Syracuse, NY 13210.

ELTON, W.R, b. New York, N.Y, Aug. 15, 21. ENGLISH. A.B, Brooklyn Col, 41; A.M, Univ. Cincinnati, 42; Am. Counc. Learned Soc. scholar, Europe, 51-52; Ph.D, Ohio State Univ, 57. Asst, Ohio State Univ, 42-45, instr, 45-46; Brown Univ, 46-50; N.Y. Univ, 50-51; asst. prof. Eng, Univ. Conn, 52-53; Ohio State Univ, 53-55; Univ. Calif, Riverside, 55-62, assoc. prof, 62-67, PROF, 67-69; ENG. LIT, GRAD. SCH, CITY UNIV. NEW YORK, 69-, fac. res. award, 70-73. Huntington Libr. grants, 59-62, sem, 63; Folger Shakespeare Libr. grants, 59, 70 & 71; Am. Counc. Learned Soc. grants, 60-61; Am. Philos. Soc. grant, 61; Fulbright lectr, India, 61-62; prof, City Col. New York, 63-64; ed, Shakespearean Res. & Opportunities, Univ. Calif, 65-69; adv. ed, Shakespeare Stud, 65-; ed, New Variorum Shakespeare Timon of Athens. PEN Club; Eng. Inst; Renaissance Soc. Am; Shakespeare Asn. Am; MLA (secy, Conf. Opportunities Res. in Shakespearean Stud, 65-); Malone Soc. Shakespeare; Renaissance drama; Renaissance intellectual history, especially philosophy and theology. Publ: Guide to the new criticism, Mod. Poetry Asn, 5th ed, 53; ed, Aesthetics and language, Blackwell, Oxford & Philos. Libr, 54; auth, King Lear and the gods, Huntington Libr, 66, 2nd ed, 68; Shakespeare's Ulysses and the problem of value, Shakespeare Stud, 66; transl, Shakespeare's Ulysses und die Frage des Wertes, Shakespeare Jahrbuch, Weimar, 68; ed, Shakespeare's King Lear, W.C. Brown, 71; contrib, Shakespeare and the thought of his age, In: New companion to Shakespeare studies, Cambridge, 71. Add: P.h.D. Program in English, Graduate School, City University of New York, 33 W. 42nd St, New York, NY 10036.

ELWOOD, WILLIAM ALLEN, b. Evanston, Ill, Jan. 6, 32; m. 54; c. 2. ENGLISH LITERATURE. B.S, Northwest. Univ, 54; M.A, Univ. Miss, 59; Ph.D.(Eng), Univ. Chicago, 66. Instr. ENG, Wis. State Col, Eau Claire, 59-61; Northwest. Univ, 63; asst. prof, UNIV. VA, 64-70, ASSOC. PROF, 70-, ASST. TO PRES. FOR SPEC. PROGS, 69- Am. Counc. Learned Soc. grant, 64; Folger Shakespeare Libr. fel, 66; Danforth assoc, 68-; managing ed, New Lit. Hist, 68-71. U.S.M.C, 54-56, Res, 56-60, 1st Lt. MLA; Bibliog. Soc. Univ. Va. Add: Dept. of English, University of Virginia, Charlottesville, VA 22903.

ELWOOD, WILLIAM ROBERT, b. Smith Center, Kans, July 25, 35; m. 61; c. 4. THEATRE HISTORY, CONTINENTAL DRAMATIC LITERATURE. B.A,(speech & B.A.(educ), West. Wash. State Col, 57; M.A, State Univ. Iowa, 61; Ph.D.(theatre, Univ. Ore, 66. Lectr, THEATRE, West. Wash. State Col, 62-63; Univ. Ore, 63-66; asst. prof, UNIV. WIS-MADISON, 66-72, ASSOC. PROF, 72- Fulbright-Hays fel, Free Univ, Berlin, 66-67; Univ. Wis. res. grants, summer 68 & 72; Am. Philos. Soc. grant, 70. Am. Theatre Asn; Brecht Soc; Am. Soc. Theatre Res; Int. Fed. Theatre Res. Nineteenth and 20th century German theatre history; German expressionism; 19th and 20th century German dramatic literature. Publ: Possibilities for German theatre research, South. Speech J, summer 70; The german dramaturg and the American theatre scene, Mod. Drama, 12/70; Hasenclever and Brecht: a critical comparison of two Antigones, Educ. Theatre J, 3/72; plus one other. Add: Dept. of Theatre, 6178 Vilas Hall, University of Wisconsin-Madison, Madison, WI 53706,

EMANUEL, JAMES A, SR, b. Alliance, Nebr, June 14, 21; m. 50; c. 1. AMERICAN & ENGLISH LITERATURE. B.A, Howard Univ, 50; M.A, Northwest. Univ, 53; Ph.D.(Am. lit), Columbia Univ, 62. Asst, Off. Inspector Gen, War Dept, U.S. Army, D.C, 42-44, chief pre-induction sect, U.S. Army & U.S. Air Force Induction Sta, Ill, 50-52; teacher, Upper Manhattan Br, YWCA, 54-56; instr. AM. & ENG. LIT, CITY COL. NEW YORK, 57-62, asst. prof, 62-69, assoc. prof, 69-73, PROF, 73- Saxton Mem. Trust fel, 64-65; Fulbright prof. Am. lit, Univ. Grenoble, 68-69; gen. ed, Broadside Critics Ser, Broadside Press, Mich, 69-; consult. Black lit, N.Y. State Off. Educ, 70; Bd. Educ, Yonkers, N.Y, 71; Bd. Coop. Educ. Serv, 71; vis. prof. Am. lit, Univ. Toulouse, 71-73. U.S.A, 44-46, S/Sgt. Early American literature; American poetry; Black American literature, especially poetry. Publ: Langston Hughes, Vol. 123, In: Twayne's United States authors series, Twayne, 67; The treehouse and other poems, 68 & Panther man, 70, Broadside; co-auth, Dark symphony: Negro literature in America, Free Press, 68; contrib, Black expression, Weybright Talley, 68; contrib, Langston Hughes, Black genius, William Morrow, 71; contrib, The Black aesthetic, Dodd, 71; co-auth, How I write/2, Harcourt, 72; contrib, Contemporary novelists of the English language, St. James, 72; contrib, Modern Black poets: a collection of critical essays, Prentice-Hall, 73. Add: Dept. of English, City College of New York, Convent Ave. at 138th St, New York, NY 10031.

EMBLER, WELLER BEARDSLEY, b. West Haven, Conn, Aug. 15, 06; m. 30; c. 2. ENGLISH. A.B, Syracuse Univ, 29, M.A, 31; Yale, 29-30. Instr. ENG, Syracuse Univ, 31-37, asst. prof, 37-45; prof, COOPER UNION, 45-69, head dept. humanities, 45-65, EMER. PROF, 69- Dir, Cummington Sch. Arts, 49-50; summer vis. prof, New York Univ, 57-59; Univ. Hawii, 60, 63; Manhattan Sch. Music, 64-67. Emily Clark Balch Essay Award, Va. Quart. Rev, 57; Irving Rossi Publ. Award, Cooper Union, 66. Col. Eng. Asn. Literary criticism; modern drama; American literature. Publ: Metaphor and meaning, Everett Edwards, 66; F. Scott Fitzgerald and the future, In: F. Scott Fitzgerald; the man & his work, Collier, 51; Comedy of manners, 1927-1939, In: Modern American drama, 68. Add: Bidwell Hill Rd, Watertown, CT 06795.

EMERSON, DONALD CONGER, b. Toronto, Ont, Sept. 17, 13; U.S. citizen; m. 43; c. 2. ENGLISH. B.A, Univ. Wis, 38, M.A, 46, Ph.D, 50. Instr. ENG, UNIV. WIS-MILWAUKEE, 48-54, assoc. prof, 55-59, PROF, 60-, asst. dean, col. lett. & sci, 58-62. MLA; NCTE; Midwest Mod. Lang. Asn.(v.pres, 62-63). Henry James; the novel; 20th century American literature. Publ: Span across a river, 67 & Court decision, 68, McKay; American literature, In: Encyclopedia of world literature in the twentieth century, Ungar, 67. Add: Dept. of English, University of Wisconsin-Milwaukee, Milwaukee, WI 53201.

EMERSON, EVERETT HARVEY, b. Malden, Mass, Feb. 16, 25; m. 49; c. 1. ENGLISH. A.B, Harvard Col, 48; M.A, Duke Univ, 49; Ph.D, La. State Univ, 55. Instr. Eng, West. Carolina Col, 49-51; master, Christchurch Sch, Va, 51-52; instr, La. State Univ, 53-55; Lehigh Univ, 55-58, asst. prof, 58-60, assoc. prof. lit, Fla. Presby. Col, 60-63, prof, 63-65; assoc. prof. ENG, UNIV. MASS, AMHERST, 65-67, PROF, 67- Folger Shakespeare Libr. fel, 61 & summer 57, 71-72; secy, Conf. Early Am. Lit, 66-68; ed, Early Am. Lit, 69- U.S.M.C, 43-46, 2nd Lt. MLA (chmn, Early Am. Lit. Group, 69); Milton Soc. Am. Puritanism; American literature. Publ: John Cotton, 65 & Captain John Smith, 71, Twayne; English Puritanism from John Hooper to John Milton, Duke Univ, 68; ed, Major writers of early American literature, Univ. Wis, 72. Add: Dept. of English, Bartlett Hall, University of Massachusetts, Amherst, MA 01002.

EMERSON, LAURA SALOME, b. Clarence, Iowa, Aug. 11, 07. HUMANITIES, SPEECH. B.S. & A.B, Marion Col. Ind, 30; A.M, Univ. Wis, 39. Teacher, high sch, Lake View, Iowa, 28-29; instr, Miltonvale Wesleyan Col, 31-35; assoc. prof. speech, Marion Col.(Ind), 35-72. Vis. prof. speech, Kingsley Col, Melbourne, Australia, 73. Speech Commun. Asn. Publ: Twenty-five inspiring readings, Lillenas, 52; Storytelling, the art and purpose, 59 & Effective readings for special days, 61, Zondervan; Aunt Laura's storyhour, (record), Diadem, 68. Add: 223 E. 42nd St, Marion, IN 46952.

EMERSON, O. B, b. Ripley, Tenn, Mar. 1, 22. AMERICAN LITERATURE. B.A, Lambuth Col, 43; M.A, Vanderbilt Univ, 46, Ph.D, 62. Assoc. prof. LIT, UNIV. ALA, 46-70, PROF, 70- Univ. Ala. Outstanding Prof. Award, 66. MLA; Am. Dialect Soc; NCTE (liaison off. & state dir, 66-68); South.

Lit. Festival Asn.(mem. exec. bd, 67-69). William Faulkner and William March; Alabama writers; utopias in America. Publ: Co-auth, Short fiction criticism: a checklist of interpretations, Swallow, 60; auth, Billy Budd and Typee notes, Cliff's Notes, 67; Prophet next door, In: Reality and myth: essays in American literature in memory of Richard Croon Beatty, Vanderbilt Univ, 64; plus others. Add: Dept. of English, University of Alabama, University, AL 35486.

EMERY, CLARK MIXON, b. Marysville, Calif, July 8, 09; m. 37; c. 1. ENGLISH LITERATURE. A.B, Whitman Col, 32; A.M, Wash. Univ, 33; Ph.D, Univ. Wash, 39. Instr. ENG, Ore. State Univ, 36-40; Ind. Univ, 40-44; assoc. prof, UNIV. MIAMI, 46-49, PROF, 49- Ford Found. fel, 52-53. U.S.N.R, 44-46, Lt. MLA. Relations between science and literature; contemporary poetry. Add: Dept. of English, University of Miami, Coral Gables, FL 33146.

EMERY, EMOGENE, b. Howe, Okla, Feb. 25, 11. SPEECH, DRAMA. B.A, Okla. Baptist Univ, 31; M.A, Univ. Okla, 37; Northwest. Univ, 49. Teacher Eng. & Span, Earlsboro High Sch, 31-33; Eng. & speech, Chattanooga High Sch, 33-34; speech, Shawnee High Sch, Okla, 34-40; head dept. speech, Mary Hardin-Baylor Col, 40-47; teacher speech & debate coach, Univ. Tex, 47-54; PROF. SPEECH & DRAMA, HARDIN-SIMMONS UNIV, 54-, head dept, 55-65. Asst, Northwest. Univ, 54. South. Speech Commun. Asn; Speech Commun. Asn; Am. Inst. Parliamentarians. Debate; fundamentals of speech; parliamentary procedure. Publ: Rehabilitating women's debate, South. Speech J, 3/52. Add: Dept. of Speech & Drama, Hardin-Simmons University, Abilene, TX 79601.

EMERY, JOHN PIKE, b. Albany, N.Y, June 27, 05; m. 30. ENGLISH. B.A, Wesleyan Univ, 28; M.A, Harvard, 29, Ph.D.(Eng), 36. Instr. ENG, Ohio Univ, 36-41; Butler Univ, 41-42; Univ. Kans, 42-44; asst. prof, TEMPLE UNIV, 44-63, ASSOC. PROF, 64- MLA; Col. Eng. Asn. English drama; Shakespeare; 18th century novel. Publ: Arthur Murphy an eminent English dramatist of the eighteenth century, Univ. Pa; The way to keep him and five other plays by Arthur Murphy, N.Y. Univ; Restoration dualism of the court writers, Rev. Langues Vivantes, 66. Add: 420 E. Mt. Pleasant Ave, Mt. Airy, Philadelphia, PA 19119.

EMMA, RONALD DAVID, b. London, Eng, July 21, 20; U.S. citizen; m. 48; c. 1. ENGLISH, PHILOLOGY. B.B.A, City Col. New York, 41; summer, Bread Loaf Sch. Eng, 48; M.A, Duke Univ, 51, Ph.D, 60. Instr. Eng, Col. William & Mary, 54-60; asst. prof, Cent. Mich. Univ, 60-61; South. Conn. State Col, 61-64, assoc. prof, 64-66; PROF. ENG. & CHMN. DIV. HUMANITIES, WINDHAM COL, 66-, chmn. dept. Eng, 66-70. Summer instr. orientation prog. for. stud, Inst. Int. Educ, 50-53; asst, Duke Univ, 52-53; Col. William & Mary res. grants-in-aid, 58 & 59. U.S.A, 43-46, T/Sgt. MLA; Milton Soc. Am; Yeats Soc. Grammar and style in Milton; Milton and 17th century poetry; contemporary Irish poetry. Publ: Milton's grammar, Mouton The Hague, 63; co-ed, Language and style in Milton, Ungar, 67 & Seventeenth-century English poetry, Lippincott, 69; plus others. Add: Dept. of English, Windham College, Putney, VT 05346.

EMMEL, JAMES ROBERT, b. Johnstown, Pa, Mar. 26, 23. SPEECH. A.B, East. Nazarene Col, 45; A.M, Northwest. Univ, 50; Univ. Okla, 50; Ph.D, Pa. State Univ, 59. Teacher, high sch, Pa, 45-46; instr. speech, East. Nazarene Col, 46; assoc. prof, Bethany Nazarene Col, 46-59; speech consult, Am. Dependent Schs, Ger, 59-61; prof. speech & chmn. dept, Pasadena Col, 61-67; HEAD DEPT. SPEECH COMMUN, CALIF. POLYTECH. STATE UNIV, 67- Fulbright prof, Padua Univ, 59-60. Speech Commun. Asn; Europ. Speech Asn.(pres, 59-61). The persuasive techniques of Charles G. Finney as a revivalist and social reform speaker; modern public address; speaking and speeches of Roy Tilman Williams. Add: Dept. of Speech Communication, California Polytechnic State University, San Luis Obispo, CA 93401.

EMMETT, VICTOR JAY, JR, b. Boulder, Colo, Jan. 29, 32; m. 58; c. 2. ENGLISH LITERATURE. A.B, Harvard, 54; Univ. Colo, Boulder, summer 57; M.F.A, Univ. Iowa, 61, Ph.D.(Eng), 67. Instr. Am. lit, Wis. State Col-Oshkosh, 61-63; asst. prof. ENG. LIT, KANS. STATE COL. PITTSBURG, 67-70, ASSOC. PROF, 70- U.S.N.R, 54-56, Res, 58-67, Lt. Comdr. MLA. Victorian literature; modern British literature; fiction. Publ: Marriage in Hardy's later novels, Midwest Quart, 7/69; The aesthetics of anti-imperialism: ironic distortions of the Vergilian epic mode in Conrad's Nostromo, Stud. Novel, 9/72; Verbal truth and truth of mood in E.M. Forster's A passage to India, Eng. Lit. in Transition, 9/72. Add: 602 W. Euclid St, Pittsburg, KS 66762.

EMMONS, WINFRED S, JR, b. Sikes, La, Feb. 9, 20; m. 43; c. 3. ENGLISH. B.A, La. Polytech. Inst, 47; DuPont sr. fel, Univ. Va, 48-49, M.A, 49; Ph.D, La. State Univ, 52. Teaching fel, La. State Univ, 49-51; prof, ENG, Ouachita Baptist Col, 52-55; assoc. prof, LAMAR UNIV, 55-60, PROF, 60- U.S.A, 41-45. MLA; Col. Eng. Asn. Horror fiction; improvement of sub-standard readers. Publ: Katherine Anne Porter: the regional stories, Steck, 67; A reading of E.B.B.'s How do I love thee, In: Poetry: a thematic approach, Wadsworth, 68. Add: Dept. of English, Lamar University, Beaumont, TX 77704.

EMRY, HAZEL THORNBURG, U.S. citizen; m. 30; c. 2. COMPARATIVE & AMERICAN LITERATURE. B.A, Earlham Col, 25, M.A, 41; Ind. Univ, 46-52. Instr. Eng. & Am. lit, Nebr. Cent. Col, 26-30; COMP. LIT. & COMPOS, Ind. Univ, 46-52; asst. prof, CENT. MICH. UNIV, 53-60, ASSOC. PROF, 60- Founder & mem. bd, Richmond Civic Theatre, Ind, 41-; assoc. prof. NCTE summer workshop, Southwest. Mo. State Col, 66. MLA; Melville Soc. Am. Euripides; Hawthorne; Spenser. Publ: Two houses of pride: Spenser's and Hawthorne's, Philol. Quart, 1/54; Who teaches the teacher?, Col. Compos. & Commun, 12/57; The warning, Voices, winter 62; plus others. Add: Dept. of English, Anspach Hall, Central Michigan University, Mt. Pleasant, MI 48858.

ENDE, STUART ALAN, b. New York, N.Y, Nov. 14, 42; m. 66. ENGLISH LITERATURE. A.B, Cornell Univ, 65, Ph.D.(Eng. lit), 70. ASST. PROF. ENG, CALIF. INST. TECHNOL, 70- Graves Award, Am. Counc. Learned Soc, 73. MLA; Keats-Shelley Asn. British romantic poetry; Yeats. Publ: Keat's music of truth, ELH, spring 73; The melancholy of the descent of poets, Boundary 2, fall-winter 73. Add: Div. of the Humanities, California Institute of Technology, 1201 E. California Blvd, Pasadena, CA 91109.

ENDICOTT, NORMAN JAMIESON, b. Kiating, China, July 19, 02; Can. citizen; m. 28; c. 3. ENGLISH. B.A, Univ. Toronto, 24; B.A, Oxford, 26, B.Litt, 28. From lectr. ENG. to assoc. prof, UNIV. TORONTO, 29-50, prof, 50-68, EMER. PROF, 68- English literature of the 17th century; English and American literature, 1890 to the present. Publ: Ed, The prose of Sir Thomas Browne, Doubleday, 67; auth, Sir Thomas Browne as Orphan, 61 & Sir Thomas Browne's Letter to a friend, 66, Univ. Toronto Quart; Some aspects of self-revelation in Religio Medici, In: Essays . . . presented to Professor A.S.P. Woodhouse, Univ. Toronto, 64. Add: Dept. of English, University College, University of Toronto, Toronto, Ont. M5S 1A1, Can.

ENELL, GEORGE O, b. Los Angeles, Calif, July 11, 34; m. 55; c. 2. SPEECH. A.B, Pomona Col, 55; B.D, Fuller Theol. Sem, 58; Ph.D.(speech), Univ. South. Calif, 66. Instr. SPEECH, Fuller Theol. Sem, 60-63; Univ. Wash, 63-65; asst. prof, CALIF. STATE UNIV, FULLERTON, 65-72, ASSOC. PROF, 72- Speech Commun. Asn; Nat. Soc. Stud. Commun. Oral interpretation of literature; collegiate speech education; history of rhetoric and poetics. Add: Dept. of Speech, California State University, Fullerton, Fullerton, CA 92631.

ENGAR, KEITH M, b. Preston, Idaho, Apr. 2, 23; m. 46; c. 4. SPEECH. B.A, Univ. Utah, 47, M.A, 48; Ph.D, Univ. Minn, 51; summers, Univ. Calif, Los Angeles. Instr. speech, Univ. Minn, 50-51; asst. prof. speech & theatre arts, UNIV. UTAH, 51-56, assoc. prof. speech & theatre arts, 56-62, prof. speech, 62-64. CHMN. DEPT. THEATRE & EXEC. DIR. PIONEER MEM. THEATRE, 64-, dir. radio & TV serv, 56-64. Fulbright res. scholar, Paris, France, 56-57; chief, educ. broadcasting br, Fed. Commun. Comn, 62; consult. educ. TV to Peace Corps, 62-63; mem. bd, Utah State Inst. Fine Arts, 64-; pres, Utah Acad. Sci, Arts & Lett, 73-74. U.S.A.A.F, 43-46, 1st Lt. Univ. Resident Theatre Asn.(pres, 69-73); Am. Theatre Asn; West. Speech Asn. American theatre; educational radio and television. Publ: Arthur and the magic sword, Children's Theatre, 52; Montrose crossing, 54 & co-auth, All in favor (bk. & lyrics to musical), 67, Latter-Day Saints Church; auth, Challenging the superior student by making the study of Russian available in the elementary school curriculum via television, U.S. Off. Educ, 63; Humanities and the theatre, Am. Theatre Asn, 73; Instructor-directed television, Nat. Asn. Educ. Broadcasters J, 66; auth, Growth and function of ETV, Am. Rev, 63. Add: Pioneer Memorial Theatre, University of Utah, Salt Lake City, UT 84112.

ENGDAHL, BONNIE THOMAN, b. Berkeley, Calif, Dec. 30, 31; m. 64; c. 2. ENGLISH. B.A, Univ. Calif, Los Angeles, 53, M.A, 59, Ph.D.(Eng), 67. Asst. humanities, UNIV. CALIF, LOS ANGELES, 60-62, assoc, 62-65, instr, 67, LECTR. ENG. & HUMANITIES, 67- MLA; Am. Stud. Asn. American Colonial literature; American and European Romanticism. Add: 1834 Pandora Ave, Los Angeles, CA 90025.

ENGEL, BERNARD B, b. Cleveland, Ohio, June 9, 31; m. 53; c. 2. DRAMA. A.B, Allegheny Col, 57; R.C.A-N.B.C. fel, Yale, 59-60, M.F.A, 60; Ph.D. (drama), Univ. Pittsburgh, 68. Instr. DRAMA, Univ. Pittsburgh, 61-64; asst. prof, Carnegie Inst. Technol, 64-65; UNIV. ALTA, 65-68, assoc. prof, 68-73, PROF, 73- Dir. Beaux' Stratagem, Nat. Theatre Sch. Can, 69; free-lance acting, writing, TV films, Can. Broadcasting Corp, 69-73; actor, Stratford Shakespeare Festival, Nat. Theatre Can, 70-72; assoc. artistic dir, Asolo State Theatre Co, Fla, 73- U.S.N, 51-55. Am. Theatre Asn; Asn Can. TV & Radio Artists; Can. Theatre Ctr. United States 19th century theatre history. Publ: Operation Mewkow, Ellery Queen's Mystery Mag, 11/63; Fun, games, therapy, theatre, Insight, fall 68; Every Night at 8:30, Praline, W.Ger, fall 68. Add: Dept. of Drama, University of Alberta, Edmonton, Alta, Can.

ENGEL, BERNARD F, b. Spokane, Wash, Nov. 25, 21; m. 46. ENGLISH, AMERICAN LITERATURE. B.A, Univ. Ore, 46; M.A, Univ. Chicago, 49; Ph.D.(Eng), Univ. Calif, Berkeley, 56. Instr. Eng, Univ. Idaho, 49-50; Ore. State Col, 52-53; Sacramento State Col, 54-57; from asst. prof. AM. THOUGHT & LANG. to PROF, MICH. STATE UNIV, 57-, CHMN. DEPT, 67- Fulbright lectr. Am. lit, Univ. Argentina, 63; consult. Eng, Univ. Wash. press, 67- U.S.A, 42-45. MLA; NCTE; Col. Conf. Compos. & Commun. Modern American poetry. Publ: History of 413th infantry, Warren Lewis, 46; co-auth, Timberwolf tracks, Infantry Jour. Press, 46; auth, Marianne Moore, 64 & Richard Eberhart, 71, Twayne; The achievement of Richard Eberhart, Scott, 68; Dr. Williams as exhorter, 61 & Marianne Moore: the matrix of poetry, 63, Papers Mich. Acad; A democratic vista of religion, Ga. Rev, spring 66. Add: Dept. of American Thought & Language, Bessey Hall, Michigan State University, East Lansing, MI 48823.

ENGELBERG, EDWARD, b. Ger, Jan. 21, 29; U.S. citizen; m. 50; c. 3. COMPARATIVE LITERATURE & ENGLISH. B.A, Brooklyn Col, 51; teaching fel, Univ. Ore, 51-52, M.A, 52; teaching fel, Univ. Wis, 52-55, Ph.D, 57; Fulbright fel, Cambridge, 55-56. Instr. Eng, Univ. Mich, 57-60, asst. prof, 60-64, assoc. prof, 64-65; COMP. LIT, BRANDEIS UNIV, 65-67, PROF, 67-, CHMN. JOINT PROG. LIT. STUD, 71-, chmn. comp. lit. prog, 65-72, chmn. dept. romance lang. & comp. lit, 71-72. Rackham summer res. fels, Univ. Mich, 59, 63; Am. Counc. Learned Soc. summer travel grant, 70. MLA; Am. Comp. Lit. Asn. Romanticism and literary history; modern poetry. Publ: The vast design; patterns in W.B. Yeats's aesthetic, Univ. Toronto, 64; The symbolist poem: the development of the English tradition, Dutton, 67; The unknown distance: from consciousness to conscience, Goethe to Camus, Harvard Univ, 72; The beast image in Tennyson's Idylls of the king, ELH, 12/55; Escape from the circles of experience: D.H. Lawrence's The rainbow as a modern Bildungsroman, PMLA, 3/63; James and Arnold: conscience and consciousness in a Victorian Kunstlerroman, Criticism, spring 68. Add: Dept. of Romance Languages & Comparative Literature, Brandeis University, Waltham, MA 02154.

ENGELHARDT, GEORGE JOHN, b. Naugatuck, Conn, Apr. 16, 15; m. 50. ENGLISH. A.B, Harvard, 36; Ph.D.(Eng), Yale, 43. Instr. ENG, St. Lawrence Univ, 43-44; Univ. Conn, 44-47, asst. prof, 47-50; LOYOLA UNIV. CHICAGO, 50-54, from assoc. prof. to PROF, 54- C.W.S, U.S.A, 42-43. MLA; Mediaeval Acad. Am. General medieval literature; literary criticism; linguistics. Publ: Beowulf: a study in dilatation & Medieval vestiges in the rhetoric of Erasmus, PMLA; The De contemptu mundi of Bernardus Morvalensis: a study in commonplace, Mediaeval Stud, 60, 64, 67; plus others. Add: Dept. of English, Loyola University of Chicago, 6525 N. Sheridan Rd, Chicago, IL 60626.

ENGELMAN, HERTA, b. Duisburg, Ger, Feb. 25, 11; U.S. citizen. ENGLISH. B.A, Wheaton Col.(Ill), 48; M.A, Northwest. Univ, 50, Ph.D.(Eng. lit), 56. Instr. Eng, Knoxville Col, 49-50; Eng. & Ger, Augsburg Col, 50-51; asst. prof, Whitworth Col.(Wash), 51-53; vis. prof. ENG, Wheaton Col.(Ill), 54-55; PROF, DANA COL, 55- NCTE. Status and function of women in the 19th century; courtesy books and women's rights literature of England. Add: 2535 College Dr, Blair, NE 68008.

ENGELS, NORBERT ANTHONY, b. Green Bay, Wis, Sept. 4, 03; m. 29; c. 3. ENGLISH. Mus.B, Univ. Notre Dame, 26, A.M, 28. Prof. ENG, UNIV. NOTRE DAME, 27-69, EMER. PROF, 69- Cath. Poetry Soc. Am; Int. Mark Twain Soc. Creative writing; poetry; essays and drawing. Publ: Thou art my strength, Benedictine, 48; Man around the house, Prentice-Hall, 49; co-auth, Writing techniques, 62 & Experience and imagination, 65, McKay. Add: Half Moon Lake, Pound, WI 54161.

ENGELSON, HENRIETTE RIEGER, b. New York, N.Y; m. 65. COMMUNICATION DISORDERS. B.F.A, N.Y. Univ, 35; M.A, Columbia Univ, 50; Adelphi Univ, Lehigh Univ. & Temple Univ, 54-71. Instr. speech, Hunter Col, 50-63; asst. prof, C.W. Post Col, 63-65; speech correctionist, Lehigh County Pub. Sch. Syst, 65-66; asst. prof. speech sci, KUTZTOWN STATE COL, 66-71, ASSOC. PROF. SPEECH, 71- Speech & hearing therapist, N.Y. League for Hard of Hearing, 50-65; therapist, pvt. pract, 50-65; mem. bd, Lehigh Valley Asn. Children with Learning Disabilities, 67-71, 73- Am. Speech & Hearing Asn; AAUP; Asn. Children with Learning Disabilities. Publ: Co-auth, The school daze of the learning disability child (cassettes-3 bks), Alpern Commun. Film Strips, 71. Add: Dept. of Speech & Theatre, Kutztown State College, Main St, Kutztown, PA 19530.

ENGLAND, ANTHONY BERTRAM, b. July 29, 39; Brit. citizen; m. 64; c. 2. ENGLISH LITERATURE. B.A, Univ. Manchester, 61, M.A, 63; Ph.D.(Eng), Yale, 69. Asst. lectr. ENG, Univ. Manchester, 63-64; instr, Univ. B.C, 64-66; ASST. PROF, UNIV. VICTORIA (B.C), 69- Swift's poetry; Byron and the 18th century; early 18th century burlesque poetry. Publ: Byron's Don Juan and eighteenth century literature, Bucknell Univ, 74; World without order: some thoughts on the poetry of Swift, 1/66 & Private and public rhetoric in Swift's Journal to Stella, 4/72, Essays in Criticism; Some thematic patterns in Franklin's Autobiography, Eighteenth Century Stud, spring 72. Add: Dept. of English, University of Victoria, Victoria, B.C, Can.

ENGLAND, KENNETH MURCHISON, b. Wadley, Ga, Nov. 25, 17. SOUTHERN LITERATURE. B.S, Ga. Teachers Col, 37; M.A, Univ. Ga, 39; Ph.D, Vanderbilt Univ, 57. Prin, Matthews Pub. Sch, 37-38; head dept. ENG, Fitzgerald Pub. Sch, 39-42; asst. prof, N.Ga. Col, 42-45; Ga. Inst. Technol, 45-46; 47-52; N.C. State Col, 46-47; PROF, GA. STATE UNIV, 52-, DEAN STUDENTS, 62-, dean men, 57-62. Southern literature. Publ: Co-auth, A manual of style, Hewett, 61. Add: Dept. of English, Georgia State University, Atlanta, GA 30303.

ENGLAND, MARTHA WINBURN, b. Clark Co, Ark, Sept. 14, 09; wid. ENGLISH. A.B, Ouachita Col, 30; M.A, Radcliffe Col, 50, Ph.D.(Eng), 53. Instr. ENG, Smith Col, 52-55; QUEENS COL.(N.Y), 55-63, asst. prof, 63-65, assoc. prof, 65-69, PROF, 69- Fel, Folger Libr; Am. Asn. Univ. Women fel. & grant, 63-64; mem, Eng. Inst. Hymnody; William Blake; 18th century theater. Publ: Garrick and Stratford, 62 & co-auth, Hymns unbidden, 66, N.Y. Pub. Libr; auth, Garrick's Jubilee, Ohio Univ, 64; Teaching The sound and the fury, Col. Eng; Apprenticeship at the Haymarket?, In: Blake's visionary forms dramatic, Princeton, 70; Sir Philip Sidney and Francois Perrot de Messieres: their verse versions of the psalms, 1/71; The transactional therapy of Dr. Eric Berne and Dr. Samuel Johnson, 74. Transl, Rossini's Otello, opening at Lake George Summer Festival, 68. Add: Hotel Dover, 14A, 687 Lexington Ave, New York, NY 10022.

ENGLAND, THEORA, b. Lincoln, Kans, Mar. 9, 05; m. 26; c. 2. SPEECH & DRAMA, ENGLISH. B.A, Simpson Col, 25; M.A, Univ. Minn, Minneapolis, 52, Ph.D.(speech & drama), 64; Mich. State Univ, 54; Union Theol. Sem, 60. Instr, high sch, Iowa, 25-26; math & Eng, Northwest. Acad, 42-48; asst. prof. Eng. & speech, NORTHWEST. COL, 48-52, prof. speech & drama, 52-66, PROF. SPEECH & CHMN. DIV. FINE ARTS, 67-, chmn. dept. humanities, 66-67, Lectr, Univ. S.Dak, 3/68 & 7/68. Col. & Community Theatre Distinguished Serv. Award, 57; Concordia Col. Conf. Speech Activities Citation, 65; Teaching Citation, 67. Speech Commun. Asn; Am. Theatre Asn; Cent. States Speech Asn; Children's Theatre Conf. Educational theatre in church-related colleges; religious drama; choral reading. Add: 409 Second N.W, Orange City, IA 51041.

ENGLE, PAUL HAMILTON, b. Cedar Rapids, Iowa, Oct. 12, 08; m. 36; c. 2. CREATIVE WRITING. B.A, Coe Col, 31, Litt.D; M.A, Univ. Iowa, 32; Roberts fel, Columbia Univ, 32-33; B.A, Oxford, 36, M.A, 39; Litt.D, Monmouth Col, Nat. Col. Educ, Buena Vista Col, Iowa Wesleyan Col. PROF. ENG. & CREATIVE WRITING, UNIV. IOWA, 37-, CLARK FISHER ANSLEY PROF. CREATIVE WRITING & DIR, 71- Ford.Found. fel, 53; Guggenheim fel, 54; Rockefeller fel, 63; prof, La. State Univ, 55; summer, Harvard, 56; mem. Nat. Adv. Counc, Nat. Cult. Ctr, 61-; mem. adv. comt, John F. Kennedy Cult. Ctr; mem, Nat. Counc. on Arts. Creative writing in poetry; novel. Publ: American song, Doubleday, 34; American child, Random, 45, rev. ed, 60 & An old-fashioned Christmas, 64, Dial; On creative writing, Dutton, 64; Poems in praise, 61, A woman unashamed (poems), 64 & Embrace (poems), 69, Random; plus others. Add: Dept. of English, University of Iowa, Iowa City, IA 52240.

ENGLE, RONALD G, b. Billings, Mont. THEATRE ARTS. B.A, Univ. Mont, 63; M.A, Univ. Ariz, 65; Univ. Cologne, 66-67; Ph.D, Univ. Ill, Urbana, 68. CHMN. DEPT. THEATRE ARTS, UNIV. N.DAK, 68- John Golden Award, 66. Brecht Soc; Am. Theatre Asn; Am. Soc. Theatre Res; Brit. Soc. Theatre Res; Int. Fed. Theatre Res. German theatre. Publ: Lang's discourse on stage movement, 5/70 & Samule Phelps and his German critics, 10/72, Educ. Theatre J. Jesuit Educational theatre, N.Dak. Quart, summer 73. Add: Dept. of Theatre Arts, Box 8182, University of North Dakota, Grand Forks, ND 58201.

ENGLER, LEO F, Linguistics. See Volume III, Foreign Languages, Linguistics & Philology.

ENGLISH, EARL F, b. Lapeer, Mich, Jan. 29, 05; m. 30; c. 2. JOURNALISM, PSYCHOLOGY. B.A, West. Mich. Col, 28, B.S, 32; M.A, Iowa State Univ, 37, Ph.D.(psychol), 44. Reporter, Kalamazoo Gazette, Mich, 26-28; instr. JOUR, Peoria High Sch, Ill, 28-36; assoc. State Univ. Iowa, 36-45; PROF, UNIV. MO-COLUMBIA, 45-, EMER. DEAN, 70-, dean, 51-70. Ed, Iowa Publ, 40-42; consult, Allen Kander & Co, 57-60; mem. bd, Lee Enterprises, Inc, 69- Am. Med. Writers Asn; Am. Soc. Newspaper Ed; Am. Asn. Schs. & Depts. Jour.(pres, 53-54); Asn. Educ. Jour.(pres, 58-59). Typography; psychology in advertising; general semantics. Publ: Exercises in high school journalism, 35-50 & co-auth, Scholastic journalism 5 eds, 50-, Iowa State Univ; contrib, Journalism research, La. State Univ, 37; auth, Readability of newspaper headline types, 44 & Split-run techniques in advertising typography, 46, Jour. Quart. Add: 115 Walter Williams Hall, University of Missouri-Columbia, Columbia, MO 65201.

ENGLISH, HUBERT MORTON, JR, b. Gary, Ind, July 2, 25; m. 46; c. 3. ENGLISH LANGUAGE & LITERATURE. A.B, Carleton Col, 50; Woodrow Wilson fel, 50; A.M, Yale, 52, Ph.D, 55. Instr. ENG, Univ. Mich, 54-58, asst. prof, 58-59; lectr, Univ. Leeds, Eng, 59-60; asst. prof, UNIV. MICH, ANN ARBOR, 60-63, assoc. prof, 63-68, PROF, 68-, A.U.S, 43-46. English Renaissance. Add: Dept. of English, University of Michigan, Ann Arbor, MI 48104.

ENGLISH, THOMAS HOPKINS, b. Dow, Ill, Dec. 28, 95; m. 24. ENGLISH LITERATURE. B.Litt, Princeton, 18, A.M, 22, Ph.D, 24; Litt.D, Blackburn Col, 58. Instr. Eng, Univ. Wis, 20-21; Yale, 24-25; from asst. prof. to assoc. prof, EMORY UNIV, 25-33, prof, 33-64, chmn. dept, 42-52, ed, Emory Sources & Reprints, 43-58, ed, Univ. Quart, 45-64, univ. historian, 64-66, EMER. PROF. ENG, 64- Consult, res. & publ. proj, Asn. Southeast. Res. Libr, 67-68; exec. secy, Friends of the Emory Univ. Libr, 70-, ed, Ex Libris, 71- U.S.A, 18. S.Atlantic Mod. Lang. Asn.(ed, Bull, 35-50, pres, 46). Seventeenth and 18th century English literature; Milton; bibliography. Publ: Co-auth, What to read, 29 & Essentials of composition, 39; auth, Memory book: occasional verse, 53; Emory University 1915-1965, Emory Univ, 66; Roads to research, Univ. Ga, 68; Memory book, privately publ, 71; On choosing a southern hundred, Princeton Univ. Libr. Chronicle, autumn 65; The other Uncle Remus, Ga. Rev, summer 67; Emory University Library, In Encycl. Libr. Info. Sci, Vol. 8, 72; plus others. Add: 1982 N. Decatur Rd. N.E, Atlanta, GA 30307.

ENNIS, DARDANELLA VIRGINIA, b. Crossett, Ark, Jan. 18, 30; m. 51; c. 1. ENGLISH, SPEECH. B.A, Philander Smith Col, 52; M.A, Univ. Mich, 55; Ph.D.(speech, Eng), Ind. Univ, 70. Teacher, Daniel High Sch, 43-58; asst. prof. Eng. & speech, Grambling Lab. High Sch, 58-69; PROF. ENG, GRAMBLING COL, 70-, HEAD DEPT, 73- NCTE; Nat. Asn. Humanities Educ; AAUP; Am. Asn. Cols. Teacher Educ; Speech Commun. Asn. American literature; freshman composition. Add: P.O. Box 91, Grambling, LA 71245.

ENROTH, CLYDE ADOLPH, b. Minneapolis, Minn, Apr. 26, 26; m. 47; c. 3. ENGLISH. Ph.D.(Eng), Univ. Minn, 56. Instr. Eng. Univ. Minn, 50-56; asst. prof. humanities, CALIF. STATE UNIV, SACRAMENTO, 56-61, assoc. prof. ENG, 61-66, PROF, 66- Fulbright prof. Am. lit, Cairo Univ, 64-65 & Univ. Sao Paulo, 71-72; gen. ed, Major Brit. Auth. Ser, Aspects of English, Holt, Rinehart & Winston, Inc; dir, Calif. State Univ. Prog, Ireland, 70-71; vis. prof. Am. lit, Univ. Nottingham, 73-74. U.S.N, 43-46, 51-53, Lt. Comdr. MLA. Twentieth century British and American literature. Publ: Ed, Early modern poets, 69, Joyce and Lawrence, 69 & Major British authors, 70, Holt; auth, Mysticism in two of Aldous Huxley's early novels, Twentieth Century Lit, 10/60. Add: 4440 Clytie Way, Sacramento, CA 95825.

ENSCOE, GERALD E, b. Orofino, Idaho, July 17, 26; m. 50; c. 2. ENGLISH. B.A, Univ. Wash, 52, fel, 53-56, Ph.D.(Eng), 62. Instr. ENG, Clark Jr. Col, 56-57; instr, Wayne State Univ, 57-60; from instr. to asst. prof, Franklin & Marshall Col, 60-65, assoc. prof, 65-71; PROF. LIT. & ENVIRON. STUD, STOCKTON STATE COL, 71- Vis. lectr, Swarthmore Col, spring 65; vis. prof, Univ. Mass, 69; mem. acad. policies comt, Thomas Edison Col, 73- U.S. Merchant Marine, 43-49. MLA; NCTE; Northeast Mod. Lang. Asn.(pres, 70-71). English romantic movement; contemporary poetry and fiction; literature and psychology. Publ: Co-auth, Romanticism: points of view, Prentice-Hall, 62; auth, Eros and the romantics, Mouton, 67; co-auth, The disciplined imagination, Addison-Wesley, 69; auth, The cavern and the dome; ambivalence in Coleridge's Kubla Khan, Bucknell Rev, 64; The content of vision: Blake's Mental traveller, Papers on Lang. & Lit, 68-69. Add: Div. of Arts & Humanities, Stockton State College, Pomona, NJ 08240.

ENSLEY, ROBERT WILLIAM, b. Collins, Ohio, Sept. 2, 10; m. 33; c. 3. SPEECH, DRAMA. A.B, Ohio Wesleyan Univ, 32; M.A, Columbia Univ, 34; La. State Univ, Baton Rouge, 35; Univ. Pittsburgh, 55-56; Ohio State Univ, 40. Teacher speech, Kiser High Sch, Ohio, 36-46; instr, Sinclair Col, 35-46; ASSOC. PROF. SPEECH, DRAMA & ENG, IND. UNIV. PA, 46- Am. Theatre Asn; Southeast. Theatre Conf. Publ: High school theatre (series of 8 articles), 54-55, The musical director of stage plays (series of 8 articles), 63-64 & A Finnish first, 11/67, Dramatics Mag. Add: 73 Shady Dr, Indiana, PA 15701.

ENSOR, ALLISON RASH, b. Cookeville, Tenn, Oct. 3, 35; m. 58; c. 2. ENGLISH. B.A, Tenn. Technol. Univ, 57; M.A, Univ. Tenn, 59; Rockefeller fel, Union Theol. Sem.(N.Y), 59-60; fel, Ind. Univ. Grad. Sch, 64-65, Ph.D. (Eng), Ind. Univ, 65. Asst. prof. ENG, UNIV. TENN, KNOXVILLE, 65-71, ASSOC. PROF, 71-, fac. res. grants, 68, 70 & 71. MLA; Am. Lit. Group, MLA; S.Atlantic Mod. Lang. Asn; NCTE; Conf. Col. Comp. & Commun. Mark Twain. Publ: Mark Twain and the Bible, Univ. Ky, 69; The contributions of Charles Webster and Albert Bigelow Paine to Huckleberry Finn, Am. Lit, 5/68; Whispers of the bad angel: a Scarlet letter passage as a commentary on Young Goodman Brown, Stud. Short Fiction, summer 70;

Mark Twain's The war prayer: its ties to Howells and hymnology, Mod. Fiction Stud, winter 70-71; plus others. Add: Dept. of English, University of Tennessee, Knoxville, TN 37916.

ENZOR, EDWIN HAROLD, JR, b. Washington, D.C, Oct. 10, 35; m. 56; c. 1. COMMUNICATION. B.A, David Lipscomb Col, 57; M.A, Abilene Christian Col, 59; Ph.D.(speech), La. State Univ, 64. ASSOC. PROF. COMMUN, ABILENE CHRISTIAN COL, 65-, ASST. ACAD. DEAN, 72- Speech Commun. Asn; Cent. States Speech Asn. Public address: homiletics. Add: Office of Assistant Academic Dean, Abilene Christian College, Abilene, TX 79601.

EOYANG, EUGENE CHEN, Comparative Literature, East Asian Studies. See Volume III, Foreign Languages, Linguistics & Philology.

EPPERSON, JAMES ALLEN, III, b. Salt Lake City, Utah, Sept. 17, 31; m. 56; c. 2. ENGLISH. A.B, San Francisco State Col, 60; M.A, Univ. Calif, Berkeley, 61, Ph.D.(Eng), 66. Asst. prof. ENG, DARTMOUTH COL, 64-72, ASSOC. PROF, 72-, fac. fel, 68-69. MLA; Renaissance Soc. Am; New Eng. Renaissance Soc. Renaissance historiography; Elizabethan narrative poetry. Add: Dept. of English, Dartmouth College, Hanover, NH 03755.

EPSTEIN, EDMUND LLOYD, b. New York, N.Y, Oct. 15, 31; m. 65; c. 3. ENGLISH, LINGUISTICS. B.A, Queens Col.(N.Y), 51; M.A, Yale, 53; Ph.D.(Eng), Columbia Univ, 67. Ed. dictionaries, various publ, 53-55; instr. Eng, Univ. Buffalo, 55-57; ed. trade-and-text-bks, G.P. Putnam's Sons, 57-63; Farrar, Straus & Giroux, 63-65; assoc. prof. ENG, SOUTH. ILL. UNIV, CARBONDALE, 65-71, PROF, 71- Ed-in-chief, James Joyce Rev, 57-61; consult, James Joyce Quart, 63-; ed-in-chief, Lang. & Style, 68-; vis. scholar, Univ. Col, Univ. London, 71-72. Excellence in Teaching Award, Standard Oil Found, Ind, 71. MLA; Ling. Soc. Am; Mediaeval Acad. Am. Modern British literature; linguistics, the analysis of style, structural semantics, the analysis of meaning. Publ: The ordeal of Stephen Dedalus: conflict of the generations in James Joyce's A portrait of the artist as a young man, South. Ill. Univ, 71; co-auth, Linguistics and English prosody, Stud. Ling, 58; Interpretation of Finnegans wake, James Joyce Quart, summer 66; plus others. Add: Dept. of English, Southern Illinois University, Carbondale, IL 62901.

EPSTEIN, HARRY SOL, b. Beaver Falls, Pa, May 30, 42; m. 64; c. 1. ENGLISH. B.A, Univ. Calif, Berkeley, 65; M.A, Univ. Chicago, 67, Ph.D.(Eng), 72. Instr. ENG, Univ. Ill, Chicago Circle, 69-70; ASST. PROF, UNIV. KY, 70- MLA. Theory of genre; theory of the novel; 19th century intellectual history. Publ: Auth, Lord Jim as tragic action, Stud. Novel, fall 73; The divine comedy of The Tempest, Shakespeare Stud, summer 74. Add: Dept. of English, University of Kentucky College of Arts & Sciences, Lexington, KY 40506.

EPSTEIN, WILLIAM HENRY, b. Easton, Pa, Oct. 31, 44; m. 68. ENGLISH LITERATURE. B.A, Dartmouth Col, 66; M.A, Columbia Univ, 67, Ph.D.(Eng, comp. lit), 72. ASST. PROF. ENG. LIT, PURDUE UNIV, WEST LAFAYETTE, 70- MLA; Am. Soc. 18th Cent. Studies. Eighteenth century British literature; biography; the novel. Add: Dept. of English, Purdue University, West Lafayette, IN 47907.

ERAZMUS, EDWARD T, Linguistics. See Volume III, Foreign Languages, Linguistics & Philology.

ERDMAN, DAVID VORSE, b. Omaha, Nebr, Nov. 4, 11; m. 37; c. 2. ENGLISH LITERATURE. A.B, Carleton Col, 33; A.M, Princeton, 35, Ph.D, 36. Prof. & chmn. dept, Agr. & Mech. Col. Ark, Monticello, 36-37; instr, Univ. Wis, 37-41; mem. dept. Eng, Olivet Col, 41-42; asst. prof, The Citadel, 42-43; managing ed. publ, educ. dept, United Automobile Workers-Congr. Indust. Orgn, Detroit, Mich, 43-46; spec. instr. Eng, Wayne Univ, 46; asst. prof, Univ. Minn, 48-54; ED. PUBL, N.Y. PUB. LIBR, 56-68, PART-TIME, 68-; PROF. ENG, STATE UNIV. N.Y. STONY BROOK, 68- Guggenheim fel, 47, 54; vis. prof, Duke Univ, 52-53; Mich. State Univ, 53; chmn, Eng. Inst, 60, archivist, 63-; res. grants, Am. Counc. Learned Soc, 61 & 62-63; Pforzheimer Found, 62-; Bollingen Found, 66; adj. prof, Temple Univ, fall 63-64; guest ed, Keats-Shelley J, 66, mem. ed. bd, 66-; vis. prof, Univ. Mass, Bologna, 66; John Cranford Adams prof, Hofstra Univ, fall 66-67; vis. prof, Albert Schweitzer Prog, N.Y. Univ, 67-68. Poetry Soc. Am. Hamblen Award, 54. MLA (chmn. joint bibliog. comt. & ed. annual bibliog. Romantic movement, 63-); Keats-Shelley Asn. Am; N.Y. Shavians; Conf. Brit. Stud; William Morris Soc; Byron Soc; Wordsworth Stud. Asn. Blake, Coleridge and their contemporaries. Publ: Blake: prophet against empire, 54 & co-ed. & contrib, Blake's visionary forms dramatic, 70 & auth, Coleridge essays on his times, Bollingen series, 75, Princeton; co-ed, Poetry & prose of William Blake, 65 & ed, The illuminated Blake, 74, Doubleday; co-ed, Evidence for authorship, 66 & Concordance to the poetry & prose of Blake, 68, Cornell Univ; Browning's industrial nightmare, Philol. Quart, 57; Suppressed and altered passages in Blake's Jerusalem, Stud. Bibliog, 64; Bryron: life and works, In: Shelley and his circle, Harvard, 70; plus others. Add: Crane Neck Point, Setauket, NY 11733.

ERDMAN, LOULA GRACE, b. Alma, Mo. ENGLISH. B.S. Cent. Mo. State Teachers Col, 31; Univ. South. Calif, 37; A.M, Columbia Univ, 41. Asst. prof. Eng. W.TEX. STATE UNIV, 45-63, WRITER IN RESIDENCE, 63- Fiction; creative writing. Publ: The years of the locust, 47, Many a voyage, 60, Life was simpler then, 63, Another spring, 66, A time to write, 69 & A bluebird will do, 73, Dodd. Add: 2010 S. Austin, Apt. 12, Amarillo, TX 79109.

ERDMANN, LOUIS O, b. Rushford, Wis, July 19, 35; m. 56; c. 3. SPEECH, THEATER. B.A, N.Cent. Col.(Ill), 57; M.A, Kent State Univ, 58; Ph.D.(theater), Ohio State Univ, 66. Instr. speech, Kent State Univ, 58-62; teaching asst. theater, Ohio State Univ, 62-63; asst. prof. SPEECH & THEATER, KENT STATE UNIV, 64-66, assoc. prof, 67-71, PROF, 71- Theater consult, Janson Industs. Ohio, 64-67; Southeast. Mo. State Col, 65-66; Canton Cult. Ctr, Ohio, 66-68; lectr, great contemporary issues, Kent State Univ, 67. Am. Theatre Asn; Speech Commun. Asn; U.S. Inst. Theatre Technol. Medieval dramatic production; scenic lighting design; stage direction. Publ: Broadway's white mask, Spectrum, 4/67; Theatrical performances within sixteenth century festivals, Ohio State Univ. Theatre Collection Bull, 14: 12-23. Add: Dept. of Speech, Kent State University, Kent, OH 44240.

ERHARD, THOMAS A, b. West Hoboken, N.J, June 11, 23; m. 45, 72; c. 5. ENGLISH, DRAMA. B.A, Hofstra Univ, 47; M.A, Univ. N.Mex, 50, sr. fel, 58-60, Ph.D.(Eng), 60. Asst. prof. ENG, N.MEX. STATE UNIV, 60-64, assoc. prof, 64-68, PROF, 68- Ed, Am. Asn. Higher Educ, Wash, D.C, 57- U.S.A, 43-46, Sgt. Asn. Higher Educ; NCTE; NEA; MLA. Playwriting. Publ: Co-ed, Current issues in higher education, Am. Asn. Higher Educ, 63-71; auth, 20 plays & many articles. Add: Dept. of English, New Mexico State University, Las Cruces, NM 88003.

ERICKSEN, DONALD HOWARD, b. Chicago, Ill, Sept. 4, 28; m. 55; c. 3. NINETEENTH CENTURY ENGLISH LITERATURE. B.A, Valparaiso Univ, 50; M.A, Northwest. Univ, 56; M.A, Univ. Ill, Urbana, 65, Ph.D.(Eng), 67. Teacher ENG, York Community High Sch, Elmhurst, Ill, 56-64; asst. prof, Univ. Ariz, 67-69; ASSOC. PROF, ILL. STATE UNIV, 69- U.S.A, 50-52. MLA; Midwest Mod. Lang. Asn; Dickens Soc. Charles Dickens; Oscar Wilde; literature and related arts. Publ: Imagery as structure in Jane Eyre, Victorian Newsletter, fall 66; Demonic imagery and the quest for identity in Dicken's Great Expectations, Ill. Quart, 9/70; Harold Skimpole: Dickens' anticipation of the early art for art's sake movement, J. Eng. & Ger. Philol, 1/73. Add: Dept. of English, Illinois State University, Normal, IL 61761.

ERICKSEN, KENNETH JERROLD, b. Everett, Wash, June 7, 39. ENGLISH. B.A, Pacific Lutheran Univ, 61; M.A, Rice Univ, 63, Ph.D, 67. Asst. prof. ENG, LINFIELD COL, 65-70, ASSOC. PROF, 70-, CHMN. DEPT, 73-, acting chmn. dept. 67-69. MLA. Publ: Co-auth, Multimmediate: multi media and the art of writing, Random, 72. Add: Dept. of English, Linfield College, McMinnville, OR 97128.

ERICKSON, JAMES PAUL, b. Minneapolis, Minn, Dec. 14, 31. ENGLISH. B.A, Univ. Minn, Minneapolis, 55, Payne scholar. & M.A, 57, Greater Univ. fel, 60-61, Ph.D.(Eng), 61. Instr. ENG, Univ. Tex, Austin, 61-64; asst. prof, WICHITA STATE UNIV, 64-68, ASSOC. PROF, 68- U.S.M.C.R, 50-52. MLA. Eighteenth century English literature; Shakespeare; film appreciation. Publ: Evelina & Betsy thoughtless, Univ. Tex. Stud. Lit. & Lang, spring 64; Teaching literature and film: some useful examples, Kans. Quart, spring 72. Add: Dept. of English, Wichita State University, Wichita, KS 67208.

ERICKSON, JOHN DAVID, Romance Languages, Comparative Literature. See Volume III, Foreign Languages, Linguistics & Philology.

ERICKSON, JOYCE QUIRING, b. Sutton, Nebr, June 7, 39; m. 58; c. 2. ENGLISH & AMERICAN LITERATURE. B.A, N.Cent. Col, 65; M.A, Univ. Wash, 66, Ph.D.(Eng), 70. ASST. PROF. ENG, SEATTLE PAC. COL, 70-, DIR, SCH. HUMANITIES, 73-, acting chmn. dept. Eng, 72-73. Graves Found. award humanities, 74-75. MLA; NCTE; AAUP. Eighteenth and 19th century British novel; contemporary fiction; literature and Christianity. Add: Office of Director, School of Humanities, Seattle Pacific College, Seattle, WA 98119.

ERICKSON, MARCELINE LOUISE, b. Galesburg, Ill, May 28, 07. SPEECH. B.A, Lombard Col, 29; M.A, State Univ. Iowa, 32; Ph.D, Univ. Wis, 48. Teacher speech & Eng, Community High Sch, Chadwick, Ill, 29-32; teacher & head dept. speech, William Penn Col, 32-35; Duchesne Col, 35-36; teacher, Cherokee Jr. Col, 36-37; teacher & head dept, Upper Iowa Univ, 38-39; assoc. prof, Stout State Col, 39-49; Mankato State Col, 49-60, prof, 60-67; prof. speech & drama & chmn. dept, Voorhees Col, 67-69, chmn. div. humanities, 68-69; prof. speech & Eng, Savannah State Col, 69-73. NEA; Speech Commun. Asn; South. Speech Commun. Asn. Publ: Importance of the required speech course for the speech profession, 1/62 & Undergraduate course preparation in colleges and universities of the central states for prospective teachers of speech in secondary schools, 11/63, Speech Teacher. Add: 2214 N. Parkwood Dr, Savannah, GA 31404.

ERICKSON, MILDRED BRINKMEIER, b. Hannibal, Mo, Sept. 8, 13; m. 37; c. 2. LITERATURE, HIGHER EDUCATION. B.S, Northwest. Univ, Evanston, 34, M.A, 37; Ph.D.(higher educ, Am. lit), Mich. State Univ, 68. Teacher math, sci, Cent. Jr. High Sch, Mo, 34-35; Eng, French & phys. educ, Sycamore Community High Sch, 35-37; asst. instr. Am. thought & lang, MICH. STATE UNIV, 60-65; instr. & counr, 66-68, asst. prof, 68-71, ASSOC. PROF, 71-72, AM. THOUGHT, 72-, ASST. DEAN CONTINUING EDUC, 72-, counr. & coord, 68-72. Speaker & consult, 72-74. Nat. Univ. Exten. Asn. (mem. resolutions comt, 72-74); Am. Personnel & Guid. Asn; Am. Col. Personnel Asn; Am. Asn. Higher Educ; Asn. Gen. & Lib. Stud. General studies; adult education; Mark Twain. Publ: Co-auth, General studies: a trend in higher education in the seventies, Univ. Col, Mich. State Univ, 72; auth, Our paths have crossed, 67 & Women: potentials and perspectives, 73, Univ. & Col. Quart; The counseling of adults, Res. Educ, 69. Add: Student Affairs Office, 181 Bessey Hall, Michigan State University, East Lansing, MI 48823.

ERICKSON, ROBERT ALLEN, b. Fargo, N.Dak, Apr. 1, 40; m. 66; c. 2. ENGLISH. A.B, Boston Univ, 62; Woodrow Wilson fel, 62; M.A, Yale, 64, Ph.D.(Eng), 66; Fulbright fel, London, 65. ASST. PROF. ENG, UNIV. CALIF, SANTA BARBARA, 66- Univ. Calif. res-travel grant in Eng, summer 67, summer fac. fel, 68. MLA; AAUP. Seventeenth and 18th century literature, especially satire and fiction; Milton; Chaucer. Publ: Co-ed, The history of John Bull, Clarendon, Oxford, 75; Situations of identity in The memoirs of Martinus Scriblerus, Mod. Lang. Quart, 9/65. Add: 2517 Medcliff Rd, Santa Barbara, CA 93109.

ERICSON, EDWARD EINAR, JR, b. Chicago, Ill, Oct. 19, 39; m. 60; c. 2. ENGLISH. A.B, Hope Col, 61; M.A, Univ. Ark, Fayetteville, 63, Ph.D.(Eng), 67. Instr. Eng, Hope Col, 63-65; asst. prof, Westmont Col, 65-69, assoc. prof, 69-72, chmn. dept. Eng. & mod. lang, 70-72, DEAN ACAD. AFFAIRS, NORTHWEST. COL. (IOWA), 73- Nat. fel, Hoover Institution on War, Revolution & Peace, Stanford Univ, 72-73. MLA; NCTE; Milton Soc. Am; Conf. Christianity & Lit.(assoc. bibliographer, 66-). Contemporary culture;

Soviet literature; English literature. Publ: Co-auth, The Jesus people: old-time religion in the age of aquarius, 72 & co-ed, Religion and modern literature: a collection of essays, 74, Eerdmans; auth, The divided mind of the new radicalism, Hoover Inst, (in prep); A structural approach to imagery, Style, fall 69; The Christian humanism of Aleksandr Solzhenitsyn (2 parts), Reformed J, 10/72 & 11/72; The literature of dissent in the Soviet Union, Mod. Age, winter 73. Add: Office of the Dean of Academic Affairs, Northwestern College, Orange City, IA 51041.

ERICSON, ELMER HODSON, b. Ogden, Utah, Sept. 6, 26. RENAISSANCE ENGLISH LITERATURE. B.S, Utah State Univ, 60, M.A, 63; Ph.D.(Eng), Univ. Utah, 71. Instr. ENG, WEBER STATE COL, 63-66, asst. prof, 66-71, ASSOC. PROF, 71-, CHMN. FRESHMAN ENG. COMT. & DIR. COL. COMPOS, 70- NEA; Conf. Col. Compos. & Commun; Rocky Mountain Mod. Lang. Asn. Christopher Marlowe; college composition. Add: Dept. of English, Weber State College, 3750 Harrison Blvd, Ogden, UT 84403.

ERICSON, JON LOUIS, b. Laurel, Nebr, July 16, 36; m. 65. SPEECH. B.A, Univ. Nebr, 60, M.A, 62; Ph.D.(speech), Univ. Wis, 66. Instr. SPEECH, Univ. Conn, 64-65; ASST. PROF, Ind. State Univ, 66-67; DRAKE UNIV, 67- U.S.A, 54-56. Add: 215 Foster Dr, Des Moines, IA 50312.

ERICSON, JON MEYER, b. Three Forks, Mont, Aug. 1, 28; m. 51; c. 4. RHETORIC & PUBLIC ADDRESS. B.A, Pac. Lutheran Univ, 52; univ. & Newhouse scholars, Stanford Univ, 52-53, M.A, 53, Danforth grant, 57-58, Ph.D, 61. Instr. speech & drama, Tex. Lutheran Col, 53-54; asst. prof. speech, Pac. Lutheran Col, 54-57; asst. prof. & dir. forensics, Stanford Univ, 59-64, acting chmn. rhetoric & pub. address, 62-64; from assoc. prof. to prof. speech & drama & chmn. dept, Cent. Wash. State Col, 64-70; DEAN SCH. COMMUNICATIVE ARTS & HUMANITIES, CALIF. POLYTECH. STATE UNIV, 70- U.S.A, 46-48. Speech Commun. Asn. Colonial American rhetoric and public address; argumentation and debate; rhetorical theory and criticism. Publ: Co-auth, The debater's guide, Bobbs, 61 & Demosthenes on the crown: a case study, Random, 68; plus various articles in professional journals. Add: School of Communicative Arts & Humanities, California Polytechnic State University, San Luis Obispo, CA 93401.

ERICSON, ROBERT EDWARD, b. Poplar, Mont, July 19, 26; m. 52; c. 3. THEATRE HISTORY & THEORY. B.S, Pac. Univ, 51; M.A, Ind. Univ, 54; Ph.D, Univ. Ore, 70. Grad. asst. theatre, Ind. Univ, 53-54; asst. prof, Radford Col, 54-55; instr, Columbia Basin Jr. Col, 55-56; asst. prof, Pac. Univ, 56-60; grad. asst, Univ. Ore, 60-63; asst. prof, Ore. Col. Educ, 63-64; dir. univ. theatre, Univ. Nev, 64-70; ASSOC. PROF. THEATRE ARTS, BOISE STATE COL, 70-, CHMN. DEPT, 71- U.S.N.R, 44-46. Am. Theatre Asn; Rocky Mountain Theatre Conf. American theatre history; cinema theory and history; classical theatre. Add: 2505 Sunrise Rim, Boise, ID 83705.

ERISMAN, FRED RAYMOND, b. Longview, Tex, Aug. 30, 37; m. 61; c. 1. AMERICAN STUDIES & LITERATURE. B.A, Rice Inst, 58; M.A, Duke Univ, 60; Ph.D.(Am. stud), Univ. Minn, Minneapolis, 66. Instr. ENG, TEX. CHRISTIAN UNIV, 65-67, asst. prof, 67-71, ASSOC. PROF, 71-, DIR. HONORS PROG, 72-, acting dean col. arts & sci, 70-71, 72-73. Am. Stud. Asn; MLA; Orgn. Am. Hist. American thought and culture; utopian literature; American juvenile literature. Publ: The Southwest in utopian fiction, Southwest. Am. Lit, 71; The environmental crisis and present-day romanticism, Rocky Mountain Soc. Sci. J, 73; The romantic regionalism of Harper Lee, Ala. Rev, 73; plus others. Add: Dept. of English, Texas Christian University, Fort Worth, TX 76129.

ERLANDSON, THEODORE R, b. Detroit, Mich, Feb. 3, 18. ENGLISH LITERATURE. A.B, Loyola Univ.(Calif), 40; Univ. Detroit, 40-41; A.M, Harvard, 47; Ph.D.(Eng), Univ. South. Calif, 64. Instr. ENG, LOYOLA MARYMOUNT UNIV, 46-49, from asst. prof. to assoc. prof, 49-68, PROF, 68-, DEAN COL. LIB. ARTS, 69-, acting head dept. Eng, 49, secy. dept, 50-69, chmn. dept, 63-69. MLA; Col. Eng. Asn; Philol. Asn. Pac. Coast. English literature of the Victorian period; Browning; modern British fiction. Add: Dept. of English, Loyola Marymount University, 7101 W. 80th St, Los Angeles, CA 90045.

ERLER, H. RAPHAEL, F.S.C, b. Rosemount, Minn, Apr. 11, 16. ENGLISH, AMERICAN LITERATURE. B.A, St. Mary's Col.(Minn), 38; M.A, Loyola Univ.(Ill), 42; De Paul Univ, 42-43; Ph.D, Univ. Minn, 59. Teacher, St. George High Sch, Evanston, Ill, 38-41; St. Patrick High Sch, Chicago, 41-43; high sch, Christian Bros. Col, 43-46, 47-49; Cretin High Sch, St. Paul, Minn, 49-54; instr. ENG, ST. MARY'S COL.(MINN), 46-47, 54-56, PROF, 58- Dir, NDEA Inst. in Eng, summers 65 & 67; fel, NDEA Inst. Teacher Preparers of Teachers Eng, summer 66; fel, Training Teacher Trainers Proj. in Multi-Cult. Educ, Univ. Miami, 71-72; lectr, Minn. Humanities Comn, 73; participant, Nat. Endowment for Humanities Summer Sem. Col. Teachers, Univ. Ill, Urbana, 73; lectr, Nat. Humanities Ser, Midwest. Ctr, 73-74. NCTE; MLA; Am. Stud. Asn; Conf. Eng. Educ. Hamlin Garland as regional interpreter; composition in high school and college; linguistics for teachers of English. Publ: A book of stories, 60 & co-auth, English arts and skills, 61, Macmillan; co-auth, Linguistic bibliography for the teacher of English, Minn. Counc. Teachers Eng, 66, 68; auth, A personal philosophy for teaching English, J. Sec. Educ, 5/64. Add: Dept. of English, St. Mary's College, Winona, MN 55987.

ERLICH, BRUCE SEWELL, b. St. Louis, Mo, Oct. 13, 41. COMPARATIVE LITERATURE, HISTORY OF IDEAS. B.A, Wash. Univ, 62, M.A, 64, Ph.D. (comp. lit), 72; Columbia Univ, 62-63. ASST. PROF. ENG. & MOD. LANG, UNIV. NEBR-LINCOLN, 73- MLA. Comparative European literature, 17th-19th century; history of ideas; sociology of literature. Add: Dept. of English, University of Nebraska-Lincoln, Lincoln, NE 68508.

ERLICH, RICHARD DEE, b. Terre Haute, Ind, Feb. 7, 43. ENGLISH LANGUAGE & LITERATURE. A.B, Univ. Ill, Urbana, 65; M.A, Cornell Univ, 66; Ph.D.(Eng), Univ. Ill, Urbana, 71. Instr. ENG, Univ. Ill, Urbana, 68-70; ASST. PROF, MIAMI UNIV, 71- AAUP; MLA; Shakespeare Asn. Am; Pop. Cult. Asn. Shakespeare's plays; science fiction; film criticism. Publ: Catastrophism and coition: universal and individual development in Women in love, Tex. Stud. Lit. & Lang, 67; co-auth, Pope's annotations in his copy of Dryden's Comedies, tragedies and operas, Restoration & 18th Century

Theatre Res, 71; auth, On the necessary uncertainty of historical criticism, J. Phi Kappa Phi, 73. Add: Dept. of English, 244 Upham Hall, Miami University, Oxford, OH 45056.

ERNEST, JOSEPH McDONALD, JR, b. Chattanooga, Tenn, Aug. 27, 15; m. 46; c. 2. ENGLISH. B.A, Maryville Col, 37; M.A, Univ. Tenn, 42, Ph.D.(Eng), 52. Instr. high sch, Tenn, 37-42; Eng, Ga. Sch. Technol, 46; instr. & teaching fel, Univ. Tenn, 46-52; from asst. prof. to assoc. prof, Miss. South. Col, 52-56; prof. Eng. & dean instr, William Carey Col, 56-62; acad. dean, Carson-Newman Col, 62-67; PROF. ENG. & ACAD. V.PRES, WILLIAM CAREY COL, 67- U.S.N.R, 42-67, Lt. Comdr. MLA; Am. Stud. Asn; Asn. Higher Educ; NEA; S-Cent. Mod. Lang. Asn. New England poets of the 19th century; English Renaissance drama. Publ: Whittier and Bayard Taylor, Friends' Intelligencer; Whittier and Whitman, Bull. Friends' Hist. Asn; Whittier and the Feminine Fifties, Am. Lit. Add: 816 Velma St, Hattiesburg, MS 39401.

ERNO, RICHARD B, b. Boyne City, Mich, May 11, 23; m. 49; c. 6. ENGLISH. B.A, Mich. State Univ, 50; M.A, Univ. Denver, 51; Ph.D, Univ. Minn, 61. Instr. ENG, McCook Jr. Col, 53-55; George Washington Univ, 55-57; Ariz. State Univ, 57-58, asst. prof, 58-62; chmn. dept, North. Mont. Col, 62-63; assoc. prof, ARIZ. STATE UNIV, 63-66, PROF, 66- Sig.C, U.S.A, 44-46. The Negro in the ante bellum South; the contemporary novel. Publ: My old man, 55, The hunt, 59, The catwalk, 65, Johnny come jingle-o, 67, Billy Lightfoot, 69 & An ultimate retreat, 71, Crown. Add: Dept. of English, Arizona State University, Tempe, AZ 85281.

ERNST, EARLE, b. Mifflintown, Pa, Dec. 15, 11. DRAMA, THEATRE. A.B, Gettysburg Col, 33; Rockefeller fel, 37-38; M.A, Cornell Univ, 38, Ph.D. (drama & theatre), 40. Mem. fac. DRAMA & THEATRE, UNIV. HAWAII, 40-53, prof, 53-60, sr. prof. & chmn. dept, 60-72, EMER. SR. PROF, 72- Rockefeller grant-in-aid, 51-52; lectr, Waseda Univ, 52 & Ind. Univ, summer 62; consult, U.S. Dept. Health, Educ. & Welfare, 67- Mil. Intel, U.S.A, 44-47, Lt. Am. Theatre Asn; Am. Nat. Theatre & Acad. Aesthetics; Oriental theatre; dramatic literature. Publ: Kabuki Theatre, Oxford, 56 & Grove, 59; Three Japanese plays from the traditional theatre, Oxford, 59 & Grove, 60; No drama, In: Encyclopaedia Britannica, 57; A theatre of beauty without tears, Hudson Rev, 58; The case for Oriental-Western theatre study, In: Yearbook of comparative and general literature, Univ. N.C, 62. Add: 3368 Huelani Dr, Honolulu, HI 96822.

ESAU, HELMUT, Linguistics, Philology. See Volume III, Foreign Languages, Linguistics & Philology.

ESCHHOLZ, PAUL ANDERSON, b. Hartford, Conn, Oct. 15, 42; m. 66; c. 3. AMERICAN LITERATURE, LINGUISTICS. B.A, Wesleyan Univ, 64; M.A, Univ. Vt, 66; Ph.D.(Am. stud), Univ. Minn, Minneapolis, 71. Instr. ENG, UNIV. VT, 69-71, ASST. PROF, 71- Am. Dialect Soc; MLA; NCTE; Col. Eng. Asn; Popular Cult. Asn. Nineteenth century American novel; modern American novel; American English dialects. Publ: Co-ed, Language: introductory readings, 72 & Language awareness, 74, St. Martin's; co-ed, The literature of Vermont: a sampler, Univ. New Eng, 73 & Bibliography of contemporary British and American fiction, 1950-1970, Gale, 75; ed, Critics on William Dean Howells, Univ. Miami, 74; auth, Howells' A modern instance: a realist's moralistic vision of America, S.Dak. Rev, 72; The moral world of Silas Lapham: W.D. Howells' romantic vision of America in the 1800's, Res. Stud, 72; W.D. Howells' use of recurrent character types: the realism of A hazard of new fortunes, Eng. Rec, 73. Add: Dept. of English, 315 Old Mill, University of Vermont, Burlington, VT 05401.

ESKEY, DAVID ELLSWORTH, b. Pittsburgh, Pa, May 22, 33; m. 60; c. 3. ENGLISH, LINGUISTICS. B.A, Pa. State Univ, 55; M.A, Columbia Univ, 58; M.A, Univ. Pittsburgh, 67, Ph.D.(Eng), 69. Instr. Eng, Carnegie-Mellon Univ, 57-60; Am. Inst. Lang, Baghdad, Iraq, 60-61; Am. Univ. Beirut, 61-64, asst. prof, 64-65; lectr. ling, Bangkok Eng. Proj, UNIV. PITTSBURGH, 67-71, ASST. PROF. ENG. & LING, 71- Eng. adv, Univ. Thammasat, 67-71; mem. comt. examr, TOEFL Exam, Educ. Testing Serv, 73- AAUP; MLA; NCTE; Teachers Eng. to Speakers Other Lang. English linguistics; reading; linguistics and literary criticism. Publ: Teaching advanced reading: the structural problem, Eng. Teaching Forum, 9-10/71; A model program for teaching advanced reading, Lang. Learning, 1/74; The case for the standard language, Col. Eng, 4/74. Add: Dept. of Linguistics, University of Pittsburgh, Pittsburgh, PA 15260.

ESKIN, STANLEY GEORGES, Comparative Literature. See Volume III, Foreign Language, Linguistics & Philology.

ESPEY, JOHN JENKINS, b. Shanghai, China, Jan. 15, 13; m. 38; c. 2. ENGLISH. A.B, Occidental Col, 35; Rhodes scholar from Calif. to Oxford, 35, B.A, 37, B.Litt, 38, M.A, 41. Instr. ENG, Occidental Col, 38-41, asst. prof, 41-46, assoc. prof, 46-48; asst. prof, UNIV. CALIF, LOS ANGELES, 48-50, assoc. prof, 50-56, prof, 56-73, EMER. PROF, 73- MLA; Philol. Asn. Pac. Coast. Anglo-American literary relations in the 19th century; 20th century literature. Publ: Ezra Pound's Mauberley: a study in composition, Univ. Calif. & Faber & Faber. Add: Dept. of English, University of California, Los Angeles, CA 90024.

ESSA, AHMED, b. Jodiya, India, Jan. 19, 29; U.S. citizen; m. 62; c. 2. TWENTIETH CENTURY WORLD FICTION, THIRD WORLD LITERATURE. B.S, Ohio Univ, 56; M.A, Univ. South. Calif, 62, Ph.D.(Eng), 69; Shakespeare Inst, Stratford-on-Avon, Eng, 64. Teacher, Crescent Indian Sch, Durban, S.Africa, 57-60; asst. ENG, Univ. South. Calif, 60-62, instr, 62-67; UNIV. NEV, RENO, 67-69, ASST. PROF, 69- NCTE. More effective use of photography in the classroom; teaching literature to non-majors; literature and humanities. Publ: Images and eloquence, Holt, 72; Where do the monkeys come in? (short story), Scrutiny, spring 63; the prisoner (short story), Lit. Rev, fall 71; Paperbacks in world literature, In: The paperback goes to school, 72; plus one other. Add: Dept. of English, University of Nevada, Reno, NV 89507.

ESSICK, ROBERT NEWMAN, b. Los Angeles, Calif, Oct. 19, 42. ENGLISH LITERATURE & ART. B.A, Univ. Calif, Los Angeles, 65, Ph.D.(Eng), Univ. Calif, San Diego, 69. Lectr. ENG, Univ. Calif, Santa Barbara, 69-70; asst.

prof, CALIF. STATE UNIV, NORTHRIDGE, 70-73, ASSOC. PROF, 73- Treas, Essick Found. Inc, 70-; assoc. ed, Blake Stud, 71-; adv. dir, Am. Blake Found, 71-; v.pres, Essick Investment Co, Inc, 72-; Nat. Endowment for Humanities grant, 72-73. AAUP; Renaissance Soc. Am; Am. Soc. 18th Century Stud; MLA. William Blake, the illustrated book. Publ: Co-auth, William Blake; book illustrator, Am. Blake Found, 72; ed, The visionary hand, Hennessey & Ingalls, 73; co-ed, Blake's Night thoughts, Dover, 74; auth, A finding list of reproductions of Blake's art, Blake Newslett, 71; Blake and the traditions of reproductive engraving, Blake Stud, 72; contrib, The altering eye in William Blake: Essays in honour of Sir Geoffry Keynes, Clarendon, 73. Add: Dept. of English, California State University, Northridge, CA 91324.

ESSIG, ERHARDT HERBERT, b. Sawyer, Mich, May 24, 13; m. 46; c. 2. ENGLISH. Dipl, Concordia Theol. Sem, 36; A.M, Univ. Tex, 39; Univ. Mich, 43, 45, 46; Northwest. Univ, 47-49, scholar, 49-50, Ph.D, 51. Instr, Concordia Col.(Tex), 36-40; Concordia High Sch, Ft. Wayne, Ind, 40-46; asst. prof. ENG, Valparaiso Univ, 46-51, assoc. prof, 51-56; CHMN. DEPT, CONCORDIA SR. COL, 56- Vis. prof, St. Francis Col.(Ind), 64- MLA. Thomas De Quincey and R.P. Gillies as champions of German literature; English literature of the Victorian period; Twentieth century British and American literature. Publ: Thomas' Sonnet I, 6/58 & Dickinson's One dignity delays for all, 10/64, Explicator. Add: Dept. of English, Concordia Senior College, 6600 N. Clinton St, Ft. Wayne, IN 46825.

ESTES, EMORY DOLPHOUS, b. Marshall, Tex, July 1, 25; m. 47; c. 2. ENGLISH & AMERICAN LITERATURE. B.A, E.Tex. Baptist Col, 49; M.A, N.Tex. State Univ, 56; Ph.D.(Eng), Tex. Christian Univ, 70. PROF. ENG. & CHMN. DEPT, UNIV. TEX, ARLINGTON, 56- U.S.A, 43-46. MLA; Col. Eng. Asn; Conf. Col. Compos. & Commun; Am. Stud. Asn; S.Cent. Mod. Lang. Asn. American literary realism and naturalism; modern American novel; American Romantic poetry. Publ: Henry Cuyler Bunner: gilded age editor, Am. Stud. Asn. Quart, fall 71. Add: Dept. of English, University of Texas at Arlington, Arlington, TX 76019.

ESTEY, GEORGE FISHER, b. Codys, Can, Jan. 21, 24; U.S. citizen; m. 51; c. 2. ENGLISH. B.A, Tufts Univ, 52; M.A, Univ. Conn, 54; Ph.D, Univ. Ill, 60. Instr. COMMUN, BOSTON UNIV, 59-60, asst. prof, 60-64, assoc. prof, 64-68, PROF, 68-, acting chmn. div, 60-62. U.S.A.F, 42-48, Sgt. MLA; NCTE; Conf. Col. Compos. & Commun; AAUP. English novel; teaching and testing of college writing; rhetoric. Publ: Co-auth, College writing: the rhetorical imperative, Harper, 68; co-ed, Non violence: a reader in the ethics of action, 71 & Violence: a reader in the ethics of action, 71, Xerox; co-auth, Just rhetoric, Harper, 72. Add: Div. of Rhetoric, Boston University, 871 Commonwealth Ave, Boston, MA 02215.

ESTRICH, ROBERT MARK, b. Mt. Pleasant, Mich, Apr. 10, 06; m. 32, 47. ENGLISH PHILOLOGY. A.B, Ohio Univ, 28; A.M, Ohio State Univ, 29, Ph.D, 35. Asst. ENG, OHIO STATE UNIV, 28-29, instr, 29-37, asst. prof, 37-45, assoc. prof, 45-47, prof, 47-72, chmn. dept, 52-64, EMER. PROF, 72- MLA; Mediaeval Acad. Am; Ling. Soc. Am. Anglo-Saxon; Middle English; Chaucer. Publ: Three Keys to Language. Add: Dept. of English, Ohio State University, Columbus, OH 43210.

ESTRIN, HERMAN A, b. North Plainfield, N.J, June 2, 15; m. 49; c. 2. ENGLISH. A.B, Drew Univ, 37; A.M, Columbia Univ, 42, dipl, 50, Ed.D. (guidance), 54. Instr. social stud, Grant Sch, South Plainfield, N.J, 38-42; Eng, NEWARK COL. ENGINEERING, 46-48, from asst. prof. ENG. & asst. exec. assoc. dept. to PROF, 48-, course supvr, div. technol, 49-73. Vis. prof, Calif. West. Univ, 65- Drew Univ. Outstanding Alumnus in the Arts Award, 57; Columbia Scholastic Press Asn. Gold Key Award, 62; Pi Delta Epsilon Medal of Merit; Robert W. Van Houten Award, 70; Distinguished Newspaper Adv. Award, Nat. Counc. Col. Publ. Adv, 70; West. Elect. Fund Award, 71. Exec. off, Army Personnel Affairs Off, U.S. War Dept, 42-46, Capt. NCTE; Am. Soc. Engineering Educ; Conf. Col. Compos. & Commun; Nat. Counc. Col. Pub. Adv.(pres, 63-65; Col. Press citation for leadership, 62). Improvement of the teaching of English; effective teaching in college; improvement of standards of collegiate journalism. Publ: Co-auth, The new scientist, Doubleday, Anchor, 62; auth, Higher education in engineering and science, McGraw, 63; Technical and professional writing, Harcourt, 63; co-auth, College and university teaching, 64 & Freedom and censorship of the college press, 65, W.C. Brown; auth, The teaching of college English to scientific and technical students, Nat. Counc. Teachers Eng, 63; co-auth, The American student and his college, Houghton, 67; co-ed, How many roads? the 70's, Glencoe, 71 & The American language in the 1970's, Boyd & Fraser, 74; co-auth, New Jersey literary history map, 74; auth, An engineering report writing course that works, Improving Col. & Univ. Teaching, winter 68; Motivating engineering students to publish, 4/72 & Engineering alumni speak out about speech, spring 73, J. Tech. Writing & Commun. Add: 315 Henry St, Scotch Plains, NJ 07076.

ETHERIDGE, EUGENE WESLEY, b. Fresno, Calif, June 13, 25; m. 60; c. 3. ENGLISH, COMPARATIVE LITERATURE. A.B, Marshall Univ, 53; B.D, North. Baptist Theol. Sem, 56, Th.M, 57; Ph.D.(humanities), Edinburgh Univ, 59. Asst. practical theol, North Baptist Theol. Sem, 56-57; asst. prof. religion & English, Ottawa, Univ, 60-61; asst. prof. ENG, & dir. dept, Delta Col, 61-63; assoc. prof. & chmn. dept, Northwood Inst, 63-64; ASSOC. PROF, IND. STATE UNIV, TERRE HAUTE, 65- Guest lectr, Coe Found, summer 65. Chaplains C, U.S.A, 53-56, 1st Lt. Midwest Eng. Conf; Col. Eng. Asn; MLA; AAUP. Literature of the English Bible; comparative literature. Publ: Words at work, Hawkins, 63; The man from Uz, Golden Quill, 72; Student rights and the campus riots, Col. & Univ, fall 69; The forms of Biblical poetry, Contemporary Educ, 11/71; The mechanics of writing, Writer's Voice, 74; plus others. Add: Dept. of English, Indiana State University, Terre Haute, IN 47809.

ETTLICH, ERNEST EARL, b. Spokane, Wash, Nov. 9, 37; m. 58; c. 2. SPEECH. B.A, Los Angeles State Col, 59; John Franklin Genung's fel, Univ. Ore, 60, M.S, 61, Ph.D.(speech), 64. Instr. humanities, Univ. Idaho, 61-64, asst. prof, 64-65; SPEECH, WASH. STATE UNIV, 65-68, ASSOC. PROF. & CHMN. DEPT, 68- Assoc. dir, NDEA Inst. speech, Wash. State Univ, 66, 68, dir, 67. Speech Commun. Asn; West. Speech Commun. Asn; Rhetoric Soc. Am; Asn. Dept. & Adminr. Speech Commun. Rhetorical theory; rhetorical criticism. Publ: Auth. & ed, Strategies for change in speech communication, Wash. State Dept. Pub. Instr, 72-; co-auth, NDEA institutes: a challenge to speech educators, Speech Teacher, 9/66; auth, Theories of invention in late nineteenth century American rhetorics, West. Speech, fall 66; John Franklin Genung and the nineteenth century definition of rhetoric, Cent. States Speech J, 11/66. Add: Dept. of Speech, Washington State University, Pullman, WA 99163.

ETULAIN, RICHARD W, American Western & Intellectual History. See Volume I, History.

EUBANK, WAYNE C, b. Claude, Tex, May 23, 09; m. 49. SPEECH. B.S, W.Tex. State Col, 31; A.M, Northwest. Univ, 35; fel, La. State Univ, 39-42, Ph.D, 43. Princ, High Sch, Univ. Tex, 31-35, head speech dept, 35-39; assoc. prof. speech, Univ. Fla, 46-49; PROF. SPEECH & HEAD DEPT, UNIV. N.MEX, 49- A.U.S, 42-46, Capt. West. Speech Commun. Asn.(pres, 55). Classical rhetoric; public address; debate and discussion. Publ: Benjamin Morgan Palmer, southern divine, Quart. J. Speech; Benjamin Morgan Palmer's Thanksgiving sermon, 1860, In: Antislavery and disunion, 1858-1861, Harper, 63; contrib, Rhetoric of the common man, Ed. Rodopi, Amsterdam, 73; plus others. Add: 1113 Florida N.E, Albuquerque, NM 87110.

EUBANKS, RALPH TRAVIS, b. Cecil, Ark, Oct. 22, 20; m. 43; c. 2. RHETORIC, PUBLIC ADDRESS. B.S.Ed, Univ. Ark, 49; M.A, Univ. Fla, 50, Ph.D, 57. Instr. rhetoric & pub. address, Univ. Ark, 50-54, asst. prof, 54-58, assoc. prof, 58-64, prof, 64-67; PROF. & CHMN. FAC. COMMUN. ARTS, UNIV. W.FLA, 67- South. Regional Fel. Fund grant-in-aid, 56-57; Am. Heritage lectr, Abilene Christian Col, July 58; assoc. ed, South. Speech Commun. J, 72-75. U.S.M.C.R, 42-46, Capt. Speech Commun. Asn; South. Speech Asn; Rhetoric Soc. Am. Contemporary rhetorical theory. Publ: Co-auth, Speech in personal and public affairs, McKay, 65; co-ed, Language is sermonic, La. State Univ, 70; auth, The basic derivation of O.K, Am. Speech, 10/60; co-auth, Toward an axiology of rhetoric, Quart. J. Speech 4/62; auth, Nihilism and the problem of a worthy rhetoric, South. Speech J, spring 68; plus others. Add: Dept. of Communication Arts, University of West Florida, Pensacola, FL 32504.

EULERT, DONALD DEAN, b. Russell, Kans, Sept. 12, 35; m. 57, 68; c. 2. ENGLISH. B.A, Ft. Hays Kans. State Col, 57, M.A, 60; Ph.D.(Am. lit), Univ. N.Mex, 69. Instr. Eng, high sch, Kans, 57-61; asst. prof, Wis. State Col. & Inst. Technol, 61-64; sci. writer, Sandia Lab, 64-68; ASSOC. PROF. ENG, U.S. INT. UNIV, 68- Teaching fel, Univ. Kans, 60-61; ed, West. Poet, 61; Am. Haiku, 62-63; workshop leader, Nat. Convention State Poetry Socs, 63; lectr, Col. Conf. Compos. & Commun. Nat. Convention, Mo, 65; sr. programmer, Educ. Res. Assoc, 65-66; consult, Gen. Resources Corp, 68-; Fulbright sr. fel, Am. lit. lectr, Romania, 71-72 & 72-73. William Herbert Carruth Mem. Poetry Award, 61. NCTE; Conf. Col. Compos. & Commun. Haiku in modern English idiom; poetry as ritual activity; modular versus traditional presentation of written information. Publ: Haiku and Senryu, 73 & transl, Blaga, selected poems, 74, Minerva, Bucharest; ed. & transl, Romanian modern poetry, an anthology, Junimea, Iasi, 73; auth, Matter and method: Emerson and the way of Zen, East-West Rev, winter 67; Robert Lowell and W.C. Williams, Eng. Lang. Notes, 12/67; plus others. Add: Dept. of English, United States International University, 10455 Pomerado Rd, San Diego, CA 92131.

EURICH, NELL P, b. Norwood, Ohio, July 28, 19; c. 2. ENGLISH. A.B, Stanford Univ, 41, M.A, 43; Ph.D, Columbia Univ, 59. Dir. stud. union, Univ. Tex, 42-43; counsel, Barnard Col, 44-46; asst. to pres, Woman's Found, 47-49; mem. staff pub. relat, State Univ, N.Y, 49-51, off-in-charge, 51-52; acting pres, Stephens Col, 52; asst. prof. Eng, Wash. Sq. Col, N.Y. Univ, 59-64; acting dean, New Col. Fla, 65; prof. Eng. & dean fac, Vassar Col, 67-71; PROF. ENG. & PROVOST & DEAN FAC, MANHATTANVILLE COL, 71- Trustee, Bank State Col. Educ, 53-55; New Col. Fla, 62-, chmn. educ. policies comt, bd. trustees, 65-; mem. fel. selection comt, Nat. Endowment for Humanities, 66-67; mem, Marshall Scholar. Comt, 67-71; participant, World Soc. Ekistics, Delos Symposium, 68-72; mem. comn. educ. technol, U.S. Dept. Health, Educ. & Welfare, 68-69; mem, Nat. Counc. Women, 69; judge, Fed. Woman's Award, 69; mem. Career Minister Rev. Bd, Dept. State, 72. MLA. Seventeenth century English literature;Renaissance. Publ: Science in Utopia, Harvard, 67; Britain's open university, Acad. Educ. Develop, 71; Learning for tomorrow—the humanities and the future, 72; Querelle des fenmes, Sat. Rev. Lit, 5/63; View from the year 2001, Chronicle Higher Educ, 72. Add: Manhattanville College, Purchase St, Purchase, NY 10577.

EUSTACE, FRANCES REGIS, C.S.J, b. Paterson, N.J, Oct. 30, 21. ENGLISH LITERATURE. B.A, Col. St. Rose, 55; M.A, Cath. Univ. Am, 58, scholar, 60-63, Ph.D.(Eng. & educ), 63. Instr. Eng, COL. ST. ROSE, 56-58, asst. prof, 58-60, 63-66, assoc. prof. ENG. LIT, 66-72, PROF, 72-, CHMN. DEPT. ENG, 67- Ling. Soc. Am. fel, Univ. Calif, Los Angeles, summer 66. NCTE; Conf. Col. Compos. & Commun; Col. Eng. Asn. Freshman English in women's colleges; William Faulkners; language and linguistics. Add: Dept. of English, College of St. Rose, Albany, NY 12203.

EUWEMA, BEN, b. Chicago, Ill, May 3, 04. ENGLISH. A.B, Calvin Col, 25; fel, Univ. Mich, 25-26, A.M, 26; Ph.D, Univ. Chicago, 34. Instr, Westminster Col, 28-29, asst. prof, 29-31, prof. & head dept, 31-36; assoc. prof, Kent State Univ, 36-37; asst. prof. Eng, Mich. State Col, 37-40, assoc. prof, 40-42, prof. & head dept, 42-46, head dept. lit. & fine arts, 44-46, dir. div. lang. & lit, 44-46; dean col. lib. arts, PA. STATE UNIV, 46-64, prof. ENG, 64-69, EMER. PROF, 69- Ed, J. Gen. Educ, 63-67, bk. rev. ed, 67- MLA. Nineteenth century English literature; composition; ethical and social theories of George Eliot. Add: Dept. of English, Pennsylvania State University, University Park, PA 16802.

EVANS, BERGEN BALDWIN, b. Franklin, Ohio, Sept. 19, 04. ENGLISH LITERATURE. A.B, Miami Univ, 24, L.H.D, 59; A.M, Harvard, 25, Ph.D, 32; Rhodes scholar, Oxford, 28-31, B.Litt, 30; D.Litt, Franklin & Marshall Col, 59. Instr. & asst. prof, Miami Univ, 25-28; instr. ENG, NORTHWEST. UNIV, EVANSTON, 32-36, asst. prof, 36-39, assoc. prof, 39-42, PROF, 42- Samuel Johnson; 18th century English literature; popular fallacies; linguistics. Publ: The natural history of nonsense, 47 & The spoor of spooks, 54,

Knopf; co-auth, A dictionary of contemporary American usage, 57 & auth, Comfortable words, 59, Random; Dictionary of quotations, Delacorte, 68; But what's a dictionary for?, Atlantic Monthly, 62. Add: Dept. of English, Northwestern University, Evanston, IL 60201.

EVANS, BETTY DOUGLAS, b. Muskogee, Okla, July 6, 12. ENGLISH. B.A, Univ. Okla, 33, M.A, 44, Ph.D, 57. Instr. ENG, UNIV. OKLA, 46-58, asst. prof, 58-67, ASSOC. PROF, 67- MLA; S.Cent. Mod. Lang. Asn; NCTE. Seventeenth century English literature, especially the age of Dryden; remedial composition and grammar; modern English usage, especially American idioms. Add: 720 W. Boyd, Norman, OK 73069.

EVANS, FALLON, b. Denver, Colo, Nov. 20, 25; m. 51; c. 5. ENGLISH. A.B, Univ. Notre Dame, 50; M.A, Univ. Chicago, 51; Ph.D, Univ. Denver, 53. Instr. ENG, Duquesne Univ, 51-53; assoc. prof, IMMACULATE HEART COL, 54-64, PROF, 64- Co-publ. & managing ed, Twentieth Century Lit. U.S.A, 43-46. Publ: The trouble with Turlow, Doubleday, 61; Pistols and pedagogues, Sheed, 62; co-auth, The Catholic bookman's guide, Hawthorn, 62; Skandal in Stratford (Ger. transl. of Pistols and pedagogues), Mathias-Grunewald, Mainz, 64. Add: Dept. of English, Immaculate Heart College, Los Angeles, CA 90041.

EVANS, FRANK BROOKE, III, b. Philadelphia, Pa, Sept. 6, 13; m. 47; c. 2. ENGLISH LITERATURE. A.B, Amherst Col, 35; A.M, Princeton, 37, Ph.D, 38. Instr. ENG, Tulane Univ, 38-42, asst. prof, 46-47; COL. WILLIAM & MARY, 47-48, assoc. prof, 49-60, PROF, 61- Carnegie intern gen. educ, Yale, 54-55. U.S.N.R, 42-46, Lt. Comdr. MLA; Renaissance Soc. Am. Renaissance literature; literary criticism. Publ: Thomas Taylor, PMLA, 40; Platonic scholarship in 18th century England, Mod. Philol, 43; The printing of Spenser's Faerie queene in 1596, Stud. Bibliog, 65. Add: Dept. of English, College of William & Mary, Williamsburg, VA 23815.

EVANS, GLORIA BUCHANAN, b. Otsego, Mich, Dec. 25, 18. SPEECH. B.S, Univ. Wis, 40; Rosenwald fel, Northwest. Univ, 46, M.A, 48, Ph.D.(mass commun), 63. Instr. lang. arts, JACKSON STATE UNIV, 42-48, assoc. prof. lang. arts, speech dept, 48-63, PROF. SPEECH & ENG, 63- Instr. Eng, LeMoyne Col.(Tenn), 41-42. Speech Commun. Asn; NEA; Nat. Asn. Dramatic & Speech Arts. Mass communications, especially commercial and educational television; drama; literature, particularly poetry. Add: Box 17039, Jackson State College, Jackson, MS 39217.

EVANS, GWYNNE BLAKEMORE, b. Columbus, Ohio, Mar. 31, 12; m. 43; c. 2. ENGLISH. A.B, Ohio State Univ, 34; A.M, Univ. Cincinnati, 36; Dexter traveling fel. & Ph.D, Harvard, 40. Asst. & tutor, Brooklyn Col, 40-41; instr, Univ. Wis, 41-42, 45-46, asst. prof, 46-47; ENG, Univ. Ill, Urbana, 47-51, assoc. prof, 51-56, PROF, 56-67; HARVARD, 67- Guggenheim Mem. Found. fel, 48-49; ed, J. Eng. & Ger. Philol, 55-63; mem, Acad. Lit. Stud. Elizabethan drama; Shakespeare; 17th century prompt materials. Publ: Plays and poems of William Cartwright, Univ. Wis; Shakespearean promptbooks of the 17th century, Vols. I-V, Univ. Va; ed, Supplement, In: Variorum I Henry IV, Shakespeare Asn. Am; textual ed, Complete Works of Shakespeare, Houghton, 74. Add: Warren House, Harvard University, Cambridge, MA 02138.

EVANS, HELEN WARD, b. Battle Ground, Wash, Jan. 22, 27. ENGLISH LITERATURE. B.A, Walla Walla Col, 49; M.A, Stanford Univ, 55, Ph.D.(Eng. lit), 65. Asst, Stanford Univ, 54-55, 60-61; from asst. prof. to PROF. ENG. & DEAN WOMEN, WALLA WALLA COL, 55-, CHMN. DEPT. ENG, 66- Nat. Asn. Women Deans & Counsel; MLA; Renaissance Soc. Am. Milton and learning; Milton and liberty of conscience. Add: Dept. of English, Walla Walla College, College Place, WA 99324.

EVANS, JACK, b. Chicago, Ill, Sept. 12, 32; m. 72; c. 1. ENGLISH. B.A, Hunter Col, 56; M.A, N.Y. Univ, 60, Ph.D, 64, univ. scholar, 65, M.A, 67. Instr. ENG, N.Y. Univ, 59-61; L.I. Univ, 62-63; lectr, Queens Col, 63-64; mem. fac, Mills Col. Educ, 64-67; ASSOC. PROF, QUEENSBOROUGH COMMUNITY COL, 67- Lectr, Brooklyn Col. & Pratt Inst, 62; State Univ. N.Y. fac. res. fels, 70 & 71. U.S.M.C, 50-52. Mediaeval Acad. Am; MLA. Medieval English literature; military history. Publ: Sir John Mandeville, Sir Thomas Malory & Matthew Paris, In: Encycl. World Biog, McGraw, 73; plus others. Add: 9 Prospect St, Great Neck, NY 11021.

EVANS, JAMES EDWARD, b. Savannah, Ga, Sept. 25, 46; m. 69. ENGLISH LITERATURE. B.A, Univ. N.C, Chapel Hill, 67; M.A, Univ. Pa, 68, Ph.D. (Eng), 71. ASST. PROF. ENG, UNIV. N.C, GREENSBORO, 71- MLA; AAUP; Am. Soc. 18th Century Stud. Eighteenth century English prose. Publ: Tristram as critic: Momus' glass versus hobby-horse, Philol. Quart, 10/71; Smollett's verbal performances in Peregrine Pickle, Notre Dame Eng. J, spring 73. Add: Dept. of English, University of North Carolina, 1000 Spring Garden St, Greensboro, NC 27412.

EVANS, JAMES LEROY, b. Paris, Mo, Aug. 21, 27. AMERICAN LITERATURE, FOLKLORE. B.A. & B.S, Cent. Mo. State Col, 50; M.A, Univ. Colo, 55; M.A, Univ. Tex, Austin, 64, Ph.D.(Eng), 67. Teacher Eng. & soc. sci, Pub. schs, 48-60; instr. Am. hist. & sociol, Laredo Jr. Col, 61-64; asst. ENG, Univ. Tex, Austin, 65-67; ASSOC. PROF, PAN AM. UNIV, 67- Med.C, U.S.A, 51-53. Am. Folklore Soc; Am. Name Soc; S.Cent. Mod. Lang. Asn. History and literature of American West; ethnic and geographical names; literature of frontier regions. Publ: The socio-cultural life of the lower Rio Grande Valley to 1859, In: Forms on the frontier, Utah State Univ, 4/69; Why American Indians were named savages, 71 & Why the Chinese were called heathens in nineteenth century California, 73, S.Cent. Names Inst. Publ. Add: Dept. of English, Pan American University, Edinburg, TX 78539.

EVANS, JOHN MARTIN, b. Cardiff, Gt. Brit, Feb. 2, 35; m. 63; c. 2. ENGLISH LITERATURE. B.A, Oxford, 58, state stud, 58-61, Harmsworth scholar, 61-63, M.A. & D.Phil.(Eng), 63. Asst. prof. ENG, STANFORD UNIV, 63-68, ASSOC. PROF, 68- R.A.F, 53-55, Pilot Off. Renaissance Soc. Am. Renaissance English, Old English and medieval English literature; Milton. Publ: Paradise lost and the genesis tradition, Oxford, 68; ed, Paradise lost, Books IX-X, Cambridge Univ, 73; auth, Genesis B and its background, Part I, 2/63 & Part II, 5/63, Rev. Eng. Stud. Add: Dept. of English, Stanford University, Stanford, CA 94305.

EVANS, JOHN X, b. Bennington, Vt, Sept. 22, 33; m. 60; c. 2. ENGLISH. A.B, Holy Cross Col, 55; M.A, Yale, 56, Ph.D.(Eng), 66. Instr. ENG, Middlebury Col, 62-64; asst. prof, ARIZ. STATE UNIV, 64-68, assoc. prof, 68-73, PROF, 73- Nat. Endowment for Humanities fel, 69-70; Am. Philos. Soc. fel, summer 70. Amici Thomae Mori; Renaissance Soc. Am; Cath. Rec. Soc, Eng. English Renaissance literature and history; Tudor literature and theology. Publ: Ed, The Works of Sir Roger Williams, Clarendon, 72; auth, Shakespeare's villainous saltpeter: the dimensions of an allusion, Shakespeare Quart, 64; Imagery as argument in Milton's Areopagitica, Tex. Stud. Lit. & Lang, 66; The art of rhetoric and the art of dying in Tudor recusant prose, Recusant Hist, 70. Add: Dept. of English, Arizona State University, Tempe, AZ 85281.

EVANS, JOSEPHINE, b. Bristol, Va, Dec. 7, 37; m. 70; c. 1. ENGLISH LITERATURE. B.A, Tex. Woman's Univ, 59; Ph.D.(Eng), Rice Univ, 69. Asst. prof. ENG, WESTHAMPTON COL, UNIV. RICHMOND, 69-74, ASSOC. PROF, 74- MLA. Sixteenth century narrative poetry; 19th century British fiction. Add: Dept. of English, Westhampton College, University of Richmond, Richmond, VA 23173.

EVANS, LAWRENCE GOVE, b. Waterbury, Conn, June 29, 35. ENGLISH. A.B, Bates Col, 56; M.A, Harvard, 57, Frank M. Knox fel, 60-61, Ph.D.(Eng), 61. Instr. ENG, Harvard, 61-62; NORTHWEST. UNIV, EVANSTON, 62-63, asst. prof, 63-71, ASSOC. PROF, 71- Vis. assoc. prof, Univ. Pa. summer 68. MLA; Midwest Mod. Lang. Asn. Victorian studies; Walter Pater. Publ: Ed, Letters of Walter Pater, Clarendon, 70; auth Walter Pater, In: Victorian Prose: a guide to research, MLA, 73. Add: Dept. of English, Northwestern University, 633 Clark, Evanston, IL 60201.

EVANS, MARVIN RUSSELL, b. Moreland, Ga, Oct. 26, 15; m. 44; c. 2. ENGLISH. A.B, Berry Col, 36; M.A, Emory Univ, 41; Ph.D, Fla. State Univ, 68. Instr. French, Berry Col, 36-37; teacher high schs, Ga, 37-42; instr. French, Berry Col, 42-47; asst. prof. ENG, Emory Jr. Col, 47-53; VALDOSTA STATE COL, 57-59, assoc. prof, 59-68, PROF, 68- English Renaissance drama, especially Thomas Heywood and his Ages plays. Add: Dept. of English, Valdosta State College, Valdosta, GA 31601.

EVANS, MATTHEW, b. Seattle, Wash, May 14, 13; m. 48; c. 4. HUMANITIES, ENGLISH. A.B, Stanford Univ, 34, Ph.D.(hist), 43; M.A, Univ. Calif, 37. Instr. hist, Stanford Univ, 38-47; asst. prof, Univ. Denver, 47-49; hist. & philos, Canterburg Col.(Ind), 49-51; humanities, SAN FRANCISCO STATE UNIV, 51-55, assoc. prof, 55-59, PROF. HUMANITIES & ENG, 59-, CHMN. DEPT. HUMANITIES, 70- Res. assoc, soc. educ. investigation, Stanford Univ, 39, 40. American art and architecture; 17th and 18th century England. Add: Dept. of Humanities, San Francisco State University, San Francisco, CA 94132.

EVANS, NORMA CAROL, b. Waco, Tex, Sept. 1, 42; m. 67. BIBLIOGRAPHY. B.A, E.Tex. Baptist Col, 63; Ph.D.(Eng. lit. & bibliog), Univ. Tex, Austin, 68; M.A, Cambridge, 73. Asst. prof. Eng, State Univ. N.Y. Albany, 67-73; SR. RES. FEL. BIBLIOG, KING'S COL, CAMBRIDGE, 73- Summer grants, State Univ. N.Y. Res. Found, 69 & 70; Am. Counc. Learned Soc, 71. MLA; Bibliog. Soc. Am; Oxford Bibliog. Soc. Stationers' Company; book production in England, 17th century. Publ: The Stationers' Registers: an indexing challenge, Papers, Bibliog. Soc. Am, 72. Add: King's College, Cambridge, England CB2 1ST.

EVANS, OLIVER W, b. New Orleans, La, Mar. 19, 15. ENGLISH. B.A, La. State Univ, 35; exchange fel, Univ. Milan, Italy, 35-36; M.A, Univ. Tenn, 41. Instr. ENG, Athens Col, 36-37; teaching fel, Ohio State Univ, 41-42; Vanderbilt Univ, 42-43; instr, Univ. Nebr, 47-50; lectr, City Col. New York, 50-51; instr, Univ. Ill, 57-59, asst. prof, 59-62; CALIF. STATE UNIV, NORTHRIDGE, 62-65, assoc. prof, 65-68, PROF, 68- Instr, Tulane Univ, summer 47; Authors League Am. grants, 49; mem. YADDO, Saratoga Springs, N.Y, summer 52; fac. fel, Univ. Ill, summer 60; Fulbright lectr, Chulalongkorn Univ, Bangkok, 66-67. Co-winner, Poetry Soc. Am. Reynolds Lyric Award, 61. U.S.A.A.R, 43-45. Contemporary American literature; 19th century American literature; comparative literature. Publ: Young man with a screwdriver, Univ. Nebr, 50; New Orleans, Macmillan, 60; transl; Clizia, Barron's 62; auth, Carson McCullers: her life and work, Peter Owen, 65; The ballad of Carson McCullers, Coward, 66; Passage to India: a critical commentary, Study Master, 67; Anais Nin, South. Ill. Univ, 68; Hemingway's Snows of Kilimanjaro: a revaluation, PMLA, 12/61; Allegory and incest in Rappaccini's daughter, Nineteenth Century Fiction, 9/64; A pleasant evening with Yukio Mishima, Esquire, 5/72; plus one other. Add: Dept. of English, California State University, Northridge, 18111 Nordhoff St, Northridge, CA 91324.

EVANS, ROBERT EDWARD, b. Romeo, Mich, Oct. 27, 26. MEDIAEVAL ENGLISH & LINGUISTICS. A.B, Univ. Mich, 49, M.A, 50; Ph.D, State Univ. Iowa, 60. Instr. ENG, Ripon Col, 50-51; Brandeis Univ, 55-59, asst. prof, 59-65; BALL STATE UNIV, 65-72, ASSOC. PROF, 72- U.S.A, 45-46. MLA; Mediaeval Acad. Am; Ling. Circle N.Y; NCTE; Ling. Soc. Am. Medieval English; creative writing. Publ: Hemingway and the pale cast of thought, Am. Lit, 5/66; The other Eustacia, Novel, spring 68. Add: Dept. of English, Ball State University, Muncie, IN 47306.

EVANS, ROBERT OWEN, b. Chicago, Ill, Sept. 19, 19; m. 41; c. 3. ENGLISH, COMPARATIVE LITERATURE. A.B, Univ. Chicago, 41; Harvard, 50-51; M.A, Univ. Fla, 50, Ph.D.(Eng, philos, ling), 54. Instr. ENG, Univ. Fla, 48-54; asst. prof, UNIV. KY, 54-58, assoc. prof, 58-66, PROF, 66-, asst. to pres, 66, dir. honors prog, 66-73. Fulbright prof, Univ. Helsinki, 58-59; Univ. Saarlandes, 63-64; vis. lectr, Lincoln Col, Oxford, summer 63; vis. prof. comp. lit, Univ. Wis, 67; vis. prof. Eng, Am. Col. Paris, 70-71. MLA; Milton Soc. Am; Shaw Soc; Renaissance Soc. Am; Int. Asn. Univ. Prof. Eng; Int. Comp. Lit. Asn. Renaissance, especially Milton, Shakespeare and Spenser; the modern British novel. Publ: Ed, Grahm Green: certain critical considerations, 63, auth, The osier cage, 66 & co-transl, Borges, Introduction to American literature, 71 & Borges, Introduction to English literature, 73, Univ. Ky; ed, Style, rhetoric and rhythm, the papers of Morris Croll, Princeton, 66 & the English secretorie, Scholars Facsimiles, 67; Milton's Elision, Univ. Fla, 66; Remarks on Sappho's Phainetai moi, Studium Gen, 22: 1016-1025. Add: 233 Patterson Office Tower, University of Kentucky, Lexington, KY 40506.

EVANS, ROBERT REES, b. Emsworth, Pa, May 25, 29; m. 54; c. 3. HISTORY OF IDEAS. B.A, Harvard Col, 59; NDEA & M.A, Brandeis Univ, 52, Ph.D.(hist. of ideas), 65. Instr. hist, Univ. Mass, Amherst, 63-65, asst. prof, 65-67; asst. prof. ENG, UNIV. MASS, BOSTON, 67-73, ASSOC. PROF, 73-, DIR. PROF. THEATRE PROG, 67- Producer, Am. Theater Co, McCarter Theatre, Princeton, 64. U.S.A, 51-53. AHA; Conf. Brit. Stud. English history, 1688-1714; Greek philosophy and literature; American drama and theatre. Add: Professional Theatre Program, University of Massachusetts, 100 Arlington St, Boston, MA 02116.

EVANS, ROBLEY JO, b. Portland, Ore, Nov. 28, 33; div; c. 1. ENGLISH. B.A, Reed Col, 56; Fulbright scholar, France, 56-57; M.A, Univ. Wash, 61, Ph.D.(Eng), 68. Instr. ENG, CONN. COL, 64-67, asst. prof, 67-74, ASSOC. PROF, 74-, DIR. THEATER STUD, INTERDEPT. PROG, 71- U.S.A, 57-59. Romantic poets; Victorian poets and critics; late 18th century poetry and novels. Publ: J.R.R. Tolkien, Warne Paperback Libr, 72. Add: Dept. of English, Connecticut College, New London, CT 06320.

EVANS, RONALD VERNON, b. Westwood, N.J, Jan. 3, 36; m. 58; c. 3. ENGLISH EDUCATION. B.S, Seton Hall Univ, 61, M.A, 65; NDEA fel, Fla. State Univ, 68, univ. fel, 69-70, Ph.D.(Eng. educ), 71. Chmn. dept. ENG, Antilles Consol. Sch, P.R, 61-67; ASST. PROF, UNIV. W.FLA, 67- Lectr. Eng. & Acting dir, Fla. State Bootstrap Prog, P.R, 65-67; mem, Nat. Comt. Teaching Nonprint Media, 72-73. U.S.A, 54-57, Sgt. NCTE; Southeast Conf. Ling; Conf. Eng. Educ; NEA. Publ: Co-auth, A linguistic handbook for teachers, Univ. W.Fla, 70; auth, How to measure and interpret sentence combining skills, Fla. Educ. Res. & Develop. Counc, 73; Sentence closure in black and white children, Fla. Eng. J, spring 73; The effect of transformational simplification on reading comprehension and selected students, J. Reading Behavior, fall 73; A new look at sentence factors in readability, Fla. Reading Quart, winter 74; plus others. Add: 8011 Stark Ave, Pensacola, FL 32504.

EVANS, VERDA, b. Navarre, Ohio, Mar. 24, 05. LITERATURE. A.B, Otterbein Col, 28, hon. L.H.D, 47; M.A, Radcliffe Col, 40; Columbia Univ, 54-55. Teacher Eng, Cent. High Sch, Euclid, Ohio, 31-34; Eng. & jour, John Adams High Sch, Cleveland, Ohio, 34-46; chmn. dept. Eng, East High Sch, 46-54; asst. supvr. Eng, jr. & sr. high pub. schs, 55-57, supvr, 57-63, dir. supv, 63-72; RETIRED. Fund. Advan. Educ. fel, 54-55; mem. comn. Eng, Col. Entrance Exam. Bd, 59-; lectr, grad. sch, West. Reserve Univ, 59-; trustee, Otterbein Col, 60-; Great Lakes Shakespeare Asn, 65-; consult, E & R Develop. Co, 66; mem. bd. trustees, Schauffler Col. Relig. & Social Work, 73. NCTE; Women's Nat. Bk. Asn.(dir, 58-60). Journalism; language. Publ: Types of literature, 10th grade anthology, Ginn, 66; co-auth, Using your language, Bks. 1,2,3,4 in Sr. high ser, McGraw, 55; A study of Dido and Aeneas, Class. J, 11/37; The mystery as mind-stretcher, Eng. J, 4/72; plus others. Add: 2646 N. Moteland Blvd, Cleveland, OH 44120.

EVANS, WALTER EVERETT, III, b. St. Joseph, Mo, Sept. 23, 46; m. 68; c. 1. ENGLISH & AMERICAN LITERATURE. A.B, Univ. Mo-Columbia, 68, A.M, 69; Ph.D.(Eng. & Am. lit), Univ. Chicago, 72. Instr. ENG, Carthage Col, 71; ASST. PROF, AUGUSTA COL, 72- MLA; S.Atlantic Mod. Lang. Asn; Popular Cult. Asn. American short story; fiction; popular culture. Publ: Poe's revisions in his reviews of Hawthorne's Twice-told tales, Papers Bibliog. Soc. Am, 12/72; The all-American boys: a study of boys' sports fiction, J. Popular Cult, 7/72; Monster movies: a sexual theory, J. Popular Film, 11/73. Add: Dept. of English, Augusta College, Augusta, GA 30904.

EVANS, WILLA McCLUNG, b. Estherville, Iowa, Oct. 16, 99. ENGLISH LITERATURE. A.B, Coe Col, 21; A.M, Columbia Univ, 23, Ph.D, 29. Instr. ENG, Wilson Col, 25-26; HUNTER COL, 28-31, asst. prof, 31-41, assoc. prof, 41-56, prof, 56-64, EMER. PROF, 64- Res. fel, Huntington Libr, 49. MLA; Am. Musicol. Soc; NCTE; Renaissance Soc. Am; Am. Soc. Aesthet. The relation between music and poetry; Ben Jonson and Elizabethan music; Henry Lawes; Cartwright's debt to Lawes, In: Music and English Renaissance drama, Univ. Ky, 68; plus 25 articles. Add: 134 Pennsylvania Ave, Chambersburg, PA 17201.

EVANS, WILLIAM ALFRED, b. Lamar, Mo, Mar. 5, 23; c. 3. ENGLISH. A.B, South. Miss. Univ, 55, M.S, 59; Ph.D.(Eng), Univ. N.Mex, 62. Historian, U.S.A.F, 41-62; asst. prof. ENG, GA. STATE UNIV, 62-67, ASSOC. PROF, 67- U.S.A.F, 41-62, M/Sgt. MLA. American literature; creative writing; linguistics. Publ: History of the Caribbean Air Command, (21 vols), 49, History of the USAF in nuclear testing, 56-58 & co-auth, History of the USAF in the Korean War, 50, U.S. Air Force; auth, Dos Passos' collectivist technique, Univ. Microfilms, 66; Can sing a certain song, winter 66 & At a reading of Lou's letters, spring 67, De Kalb Lit. Arts J. Add: Dept. of English, Georgia State University, Atlanta, GA 30303.

EVANS, WILLIAM HOWARD, b. Spring Lake, N.J, Apr. 28, 24; m. 49; c. 2. ENGLISH, ENGLISH EDUCATION. B.A, Univ. Colo, 50; M.A, Syracuse Univ, 52; Univ. Fla, 52-53; Ed.D.(Eng. educ), Fla. State Univ, 61. Teacher high sch, 53-56; instr. Eng, St. Petersburg Jr. Col, 54-56; Eng. educ, Fla. State Univ, 58-61; assoc. prof, Univ. Ill, 61-66; PROF. ENG, SOUTH. ILL. UNIV, CARBONDALE, 66- Assoc. dir, Ill. State-Wide Curriculum Stud. Ctr. Prep. Sec. Sch. Eng. Teachers, 64-66. U.S.N, 42-46. NCTE (assoc. chmn, methods courses, 61-64, mem. exec. comt, 68-); Conf. Eng. Educ. (chmn, 68-70). Reading; tests and measurements; teacher education in English. Publ: Co-auth, Specialized courses in methods of teaching English, Nat. Counc. Teachers Eng, 64, Individualized English, Follett, 64, Values in literature, Houghton, 65, rev. ed, 68 & New trends in the teaching of English in secondary schools, Rand McNally, 66; auth, Does English have a chance?, 1/63 & The teacher of secondary English as researcher, 2/64, Eng. J; Cooperative research in the preparation of secondary school teachers of English, In: Frontiers in teacher education, Yearbook Am. Asn. Cols. Teacher Educ, 66. Add: Dept. of English, Southern Illinois University, Carbondale, IL 62901.

EVANS, WILLIAM W, b. Cleveland, Ohio, Nov. 30, 30; m. 60; c. 1. ENGLISH, PHILOLOGY. B.A, West. Reserve Univ, 53, M.A, 54; Univ. Grenoble, summer 53; Ph.D.(Eng), Univ. Fla, 59. Instr. ENG, LA. STATE UNIV, BATON ROUGE, 59-62, ASST. PROF, 62- MLA; NCTE; Am. Dialect Soc; AAUP; S.Cent. Mod. Lang. Asn. English and American dialects; language in literature; grammar and usage. Publ: Dramatic use of the second-person singular pronoun in Sir Gawain and the green knight, Stud. Neophilol, 67; You and thou in northern England, S.Atlantic Bull, 69; The survival of the second-person singular in the southern counties of England, S.Cent. Bull, 70. Add: Dept. of English, Louisiana State University, Baton Rouge, LA 70803.

EVANS, WINNIE D, b. Sewell, W.Va, Oct. 3, 94; m. 22; c. 1. ENGLISH. A.B, La. Polytech. Inst, 25; A.M, Peabody Col, 33, Columbia Univ, 46. Teacher & asst. prin, High Schs, La, 15-23; supvr. Eng, La. Tech. Univ, 27-40, assoc. prof, 40-63; RETIRED. S.Cent. Mod. Lang. Asn; Am. Asn. Univ. Women. English in high schools; remedial work in English; American literature. Publ: Historical articles of Lincoln Parish, La. Tech Univ; Folklore, La. Folklore Soc, 58; Educational survey on freshmen, Educ. Admin. & Supv, 43; Doctors of the past-Lincoln Parish, 60. Add: 1307 E. Georgia Ave, Ruston, LA 71270.

EVARTS, PETER G, b. Long Beach, Calif, July 23, 31; m. 55; c. 2. ENGLISH, LINGUISTICS. A.B, East. Mich. Univ, 53; M.A, Univ. Mich, 57; Wayne State Univ, 62, Ph.D.(Eng), 69. Teacher, Waterford Twp. High Sch, 53-56; Pontiac Cent. High Sch, 56-58; head dept. Eng, Pontiac North. High Sch, 58-62; asst. dir. educ, OAKLAND UNIV, 62-65, asst. prof. ENG, 65-68, assoc. prof, 68-72, PROF. & CHMN. DEPT. LEARNING SKILLS, 72- Mediaeval Acad. Am; MLA; NCTE (dir, 58-60). Medieval metrical romance; teaching of English language and composition in secondary schools; Anglo-Saxon poetry. Publ: Creativity in teaching the novel, Education, 10/59; Suburbia: the target area, Wilson Libr. Bull, 10/66; Medieval tradition in the Sicilian Contostoria, Stud. Mediaeval Cult, 12/73. Add: Dept. of Learning Skills, Oakland University, Rochester, MI 48063.

EVERSOLE, RICHARD LANGLEY, b. Hollywood, Calif, Feb. 28, 38; m. 60; c. 2. ENGLISH LITERATURE. B.A, Univ. Ore, 61, M.A, 63; Ph.D.(Eng), Univ. Wis-Madison, 70. ASST. PROF. ENG, UNIV. KANS, 68- MLA; Am. Soc. 18th Century Stud. Eighteenth century literature; Renaissance drama; aesthetics. Publ: Oratorical design of deserted village, Eng. Lang. Notes, 66; Source of Fair maid of Bristow, Rev. Eng. Stud, 73. Add: Dept. of English, University of Kansas, Lawrence, KS 66045.

EVERSON, IDA GERTRUDE, b. New Brighton, N.Y, Mar. 1, 98. ENGLISH. A.B, Columbia Univ, 20, A.M, 29, Ph.D, 43. Ed. asst, Am. Book Co, 20-22; mem. staff, libr, Columbia Univ, 27-37, teacher, eve. & summer session, 38-43; mem. fac, WAGNER COL, 39, 43-49, prof. Eng, 49-68, acting head dept, 50, EMER. PROF, 73- Mem. fac, Hunter Col, 38; vis. prof. Eng, Ill. Col, 68-69. MLA; Mod. Humanities Res. Asn, Gt. Brit. American literature; George Henry Calvert; Irish literary Renaissance. Publ: Goethe's American visitors; W.J. Stillman: Emerson's gallant artist, 3/58 & Lennox Robinson and Synge's Playboy (1911-1930): two decades of American cultural growth, 3/71, New Eng. Quart; Young Lennox Robinson and the Abbey Theatre's first American tour (1911-1912), Mod. Drama, 5/66. Add: 4607 NASA Rd. 1, Seabrook, TX 77586.

EVERT, WALTER H, b. New York, N.Y, Apr. 21, 23; m. 51; c. 3. ENGLISH. B.A, Rutgers Univ, 50; Wilson fel, 50-51; M.A, Princeton, 53, Ph.D.(Eng), 60. Instr. Eng, Princeton, 52-53, asst. to secy. of univ, 53-55; instr. ENG, Williams Col, 55-58; Univ. Calif, Los Angeles, 58-60, asst. prof, 60-63; assoc. prof, UNIV. PITTSBURGH, 63-66, PROF, 66-, assoc. dean humanities, 63-68. U.S.N, 43-46. MLA; Keats-Shelley Asn. Romantic period. Publ: Aesthetic and myth in the poetry of Keats, Princeton, 65. Add: Dept. of English, University of Pittsburgh, Pittsburgh, PA 15260.

EVERTTS, ELDONNA L, b. South Bend, Ind, May 19, 17; wid; c. 2. LANGUAGE ARTS. B.S, Manchester Col, 53; M.S, Ind. Univ, 58, Ed.D, 61. Teacher, pub. schs, Ind, 37-41, 48-58; vis. lectr. & asst. dir. res. oral lang, Ind. Univ, 59-62; asst. prof. elem. educ. & elem. Eng, Univ. Wis, Milwaukee, 62-63; assoc. prof. elem. educ. & elem. Eng, & co-dir, Nebr. Curriculum Develop. Ctr, Univ. Nebr, 63-65; ASSOC. PROF. ELEM. ENG. & ELEM. EDUC, UNIV. ILL, URBANA-CHAMPAIGN, 65- Assoc. dir, Eng. Teacher Prep. Stud, 65-67; dir, Inst. State Supvr. & Eng. & Reading, 68-70. NCTE (asst. exec. secy, 65-69); Conf. Res. Eng; Am. Educ. Res. Asn; Asn. Childhood Educ. Int; Int. Reading Asn; Asn. Supv. & Curriculum Develop. Oral language and relationship to listening and silent and oral reading; composition and syntactical structures; reading and linguistics. Publ: Co-auth, Trade winds, 66, Cross roads, 66 & Seven seas, 66, Harper; ed, Dimensions of dialect, Nat. Counc. Teachers Eng, 67; auth, The influence of linguistics, Educ. Leadership, 3/65; Literature and composition in the elementary grades, In: New directions in elementary English, Nat. Counc. Teachers Eng, 67; An instrument for the syntactical analysis of children's composition, In: Psycholinguistic nature of the reading process, Wayne State Univ, 68; co-auth, Holt basic reading program, Holt, 73. Add: Dept. of Elementary Education, University of Illinois, Urbana-Champaign, Urbana, IL 61801.

EVERWINE, PETER PAUL, b. Detroit, Mich, Feb. 14, 30; div; c. 2. POETRY. B.S, Northwest. Univ, Evanston, 52; Jones fel, Stanford Univ, 58-59; Ph.D.(Eng), Univ. Iowa, 59. Instr. ENG, Univ. Iowa, 59-62; PROF, CALIF. STATE UNIV, FRESNO, 62- Lamont Award, Acad. Am. Poets, 72. U.S.A, 52-54. Philol. Asn. Pac. Coast. Poetry; folklore; ethnopoetics. Publ: In the house of light: (Nahuatl translations), Stone Wall, 70; Collecting the animals (poetry), Atheneum, 73; contrib, Down at the Santa Fe depot (poetry), Giligia, 69. Add: Dept. of English, California State University, Fresno, Maple & Shaw, Fresno, CA 93710.

EVETT, DAVID HAL, b. Denver, Colo, June 17, 36; m. 60; c. 3. ENGLISH. B.A, Univ. South, 58; Univ. Dijon, 58-59; A.M, Harvard, 62, Ph.D.(Eng), 65. Asst. prof. ENG, Univ. Wis-Madison, 65-70; ASSOC. PROF, CLEVELAND STATE UNIV, 70- Univ. Wis. summer support grant, 66; Am. Philos. Soc. grant-in-aid, 68-69. MLA. Spenser and his contemporaries; visual imagery; Shakespeare. Publ: Paradice's other map: Marvell's Upon Appleton House and the Topos of the Locus Amoenus, PMLA, 5/70; Travail of a department, In: Academic supermarkets, Jossey-Bass, 71. Add: Dept. of English, Cleveland State University, Cleveland, OH 44115.

EWBANK, FRANCES WHITE, b. Detroit, Mich, May 20, 16; m. 64; c. 2. ENGLISH. B.A, Wayne State Univ, 36, M.A, 37; Ph.D.(Eng), Univ. Colo, 50. Instr. ENG, Detroit pub. high schs, 37-43; Wheaton Col.(Ill), 43-48, asst. prof, 48; assoc. prof, Asbury Col, 50-52, prof, 52-59; prof. & chmn. dept, Geneva Col, 59-64; PROF, TAYLOR UNIV, 64- Asbury Col. res. grant, Brit. Mus, summer 56. MLA; Conf. Christianity & Lit; NCTE (comt. bibliog. col. teaching Eng, 61-); Renaissance Soc. Am; Shakespeare Asn. Am. William Tyndale; Alfred Tennyson. Publ: Unorthodox tendencies in Tennyson, Rev. Relig, 11/50; William Tyndale, reformer: a study of personal influence, Gordon Rev, spring 58. Add: Dept. of English, Box 307, Taylor University, Upland, IN 46989.

EWBANK, HENRY LEE, JR, b. Albion, Mich, Mar. 26, 24; m. 48; c. 3. SPEECH. B.A, Univ. Wis, 47, M.A, 48, Ph.D.(speech, U.S. hist), 52. Instr. speech & dir. debate, Univ. Hawaii, 49-51; asst. prof. & dir. debate, East. Ill. State Col, 51-53; PURDUE UNIV, WEST LAFAYETTE, 53-56, assoc. prof. SPEECH, 56-72, PROF, 72- Secy-treas, Asn. Col. Hon. Socs, 59-64; vis. assoc. prof, Univ. Hawaii, 63-64; asst. to dir. training & res, Ind. Cooperative Exten. Serv, 66- U.S.A, 42, U.S.M.C.R, 42-44; U.S.N.R, 44-50, Ens. Cent. States Speech Commun. Asn.(exec. secy, 57-60, pres, 61-62); Speech Commun. Asn. Criticism of contemporary public address: group discussion; American social and intellectual history. Publ: Meeting management, W.C. Brown, 68; contrib, New Standard Encyclopedia, 58; Quart. J. Speech; Today's Speech. Add: Dept. of Communication, Purdue University, West Lafayette, IN 47907.

EWEN, DOUGLAS RICHARD, b. Aberdeen, Scotland, Dec. 12, 25. ENGLISH LITERATURE. M.A, Aberdeen Univ, 49; Merton Col, Oxford, 49-51. Sr. lectr. ENG, Univ. Khartoum, 51-64; assoc. prof, Laurentian Univ, 65-66; spec. lectr, York Univ, 66-68; sr. lectr, Univ. W.Indies, 68-70; ASSOC. PROF, YORK UNIV, 70-, CHMN. DEPT, 73- R.N, 44-47, Sub-Lt. Tobias Smollett; Arabic literature in English; West. Indian literature. Add: Dept. of English, York University, Toronto, Ont, Can.

EWERT, LEONORE HELEN, b. Winnipeg, Can, Aug. 6, 35; U.S. citizen. ENGLISH. B.A, Upland Col, 58; M.A, Claremont Grad. Sch, 62, Ph.D.(Eng), 68. Asst. prof. Eng, Upland Col, 63-64; Fulbright exchange teacher, Munich sec. schs, Germany, 64-65; ASST. PROF. ENG, Calif, State Polytech. Col, 66-69; UNIV. VICTORIA (B.C), 69- Head Eng. dept, Neuchatel Jr. Col, Switzerland, 72-73. MLA; Johnson Soc. Northwest. Eighteenth century English literature; 19th century American literature. Add: 1442 Rockland Ave, Victoria, B.C, Can.

EWING, GEORGE WILMETH, b. Robstown, Tex, Jan. 12, 23; m. 46; c. 5. ENGLISH. B.A, Abilene Christian Col, 48; M.A, Univ. Tex, 52, Ph.D.(Eng), 62. Asst. prof. ENG, ABILENE CHRISTIAN COL, 55-63, assoc. prof, 63-68, PROF, 68-, HEAD DEPT, 70-, acting head dept, 67-69. U.S.A.F, 43-46, Sgt. Ling. Soc. Am; MLA; NCTE; Conf. Christianity & Lit; West. Lit. Asn. American literature and social history; religion. Publ: Ed. & annotater, John Lockes Reasonableness of Christianity, Regnery, 65; auth, The well-tempered lyre, South. Methodist Univ, (in prep); The well-tempered lyre: songs of the temperance movement, Southwest Rev, spring 71. Add: Dept. of English, Abilene Christian College, Station ACC, Abilene, TX 79601.

EWING, WALLACE KELLEY, b. Grand Rapids, Mich, Sept. 11, 32; m. 55; c. 4. ENGLISH. B.A, Mich. State Univ, 62, M.A, 64; Ph.D.(Eng), Univ. Ill, Urbana, 71. Instr. Eng, Iowa State Univ, 64-67; Fulbright lectr, Univ. Tehran, 67-68; instr, Univ. Ill, 68-69, asst. prof, 71-72, field dir. in P.R, 70-71; ADJ. ASSOC. PROF. ENG. & DEAN, COLBY COL.(N.H), 72- Specialist consult, Nat. Asn. For. Stud. Affairs, 65-67; spec. consult. Eng. as second lang, Educ. Systs. Corp, 69-71; co-chmn, Nat. Conf. Asn. Teachers Eng. as Second Lang, 73. Am. Asn. Higher Educ; Am. Counc. Educ; Asn. Teachers Eng. to Speakers Other Lang; Am. Counc. Teaching For. Lang. Publ: The mentalist theory of language learning, For. Lang. Annals, 5/72; An internship program for beginning teachers: teaching ESL in Puerto Rico, TESOL Quart, 6/73. Add: Office of Dean, Colby College, New London, NH 03257.

EWING, WILLIAM HOLLIS, b. Gallipolis, Ohio, Nov. 12, 02; m. 24. SPEECH, COMMUNICATIONS. A.B, Rio Grande Col, 22, hon. L.H.D, 65; M.A, Northwest. Univ, 29; Ph.D.(speech educ), Ohio State Univ, 42. Prin, Vinton Pub. Schs, 22-23, supt, 23-24; New Albany Sch, 24-27; instr. speech & theatre, Muskingum Col, 28-31, asst. prof, 31-36, assoc. prof, 36-42; asst. prof, OHIO STATE UNIV, 42-56, assoc. prof. SPEECH & RADIO, 56-73, EMER. ASSOC. PROF, 73- Vis. assoc. prof, Univ. Ore, 49-50; fel, Educ. TV Mgt. Sem, summer 57; mem. teacher screening panel, Mid-west Prog. Airborne TV Instr, 59-60; Ford Found. res. fel. & coord, Greater Columbus Area Res. Proj, 59-61; regional consult, Nat. Stud. on Use of Instruct. TV, 60-61; planning comt, Nat. Conf. Instruct. TV, 63; Fulbright lectr, Glasgow Univ, 65-66; prog. supvr. univ. radio & TV sta & assoc. dir. telecommun. ctr, Ohio State Univ. Nat. Asn. Educ. Broadcasters. Publ: Finding a speaking listing index, Quart. J. Speech, 45; Glasgow educational television, NAEB J, 66; Relevance and Robert Burns, Ohio Eng. Teachers Bull, 12/72. Add: 103 Chatham Rd, Columbus, OH 43214.

EYSSEN, DONALD C, b. Marietta, Ohio, July 5, 02; m. 27; c. 1. SPEECH. A.B, Ohio Wesleyan Univ, 25, A.M, 35; State Univ. Iowa, 40. Prof. SPEECH, Upper Iowa Univ, 34-38; Univ. Dubuque, 38-45; asst. prof, OHIO WESLEYAN UNIV, 45-51, from assoc. prof. to prof, 51-67, EMER. PROF, 67- Speech and dramatics. Add: Dept. of Speech, Ohio Wesleyan University, Delaware, OH 43015.

EZEKIEL, MARGARET ULMER, b. Cleveland Heights, Ohio; m. 47; c. 1. DRAMA, SPEECH. B.S, Northwest. Univ, 44; M.F.A, Yale, 44; Ph.D.(theatre arts), Case West. Reserve Univ, 69. Instr. SPEECH & THEATRE ARTS, Kent State Univ, 62-66; CLEVELAND STATE UNIV, 66-69, ASST. PROF, 69- AAUP; Asn. Int. Theatre Enfance & Jeunesse; Am. Theatre Asn; U.S. Inst. Theatre Technol.(comnr, 74-). Nineteenth century American theatre; the teaching of voice and diction. Publ: All the lighting of the house is done by electricity, 12/71 & A way in, 10/73, Theatre Design & Technol. Add: Dept. of Communications, Div. of Dramatic Arts, Cleveland State University, Cleveland, OH 44115.

F

FABER, ANNA DUNKLE, b. Steelton, Pa, Feb. 16, 15; m. 55. ENGLISH. B.A, Lebanon Valley Col, 48; M.A, Univ. Wis, 50, fel, 51-52, Ph.D.(Eng), 54; Shakespeare Inst, Eng, 62; Univ. London, 66. Asst. librn, LEBANON VALLEY COL, 48-49, 50-51, asst. prof. ENG, 54-59, assoc. prof, 59-70, PROF, 70- Instr. Univ. Wis, 52-54. MLA; Shakespeare Asn. Am; NCTE; Brit. Theatre Asn; Am. Theatre Asn; Renaissance Soc. Am. Elizabethan drama; Victorian literature; theatre. Publ: Concordance to three plays of John Webster. Add: 1404 Executive House, 101 S. Second St, Harrisburg, PA 17101.

FABER, MELVYN D, b. Chicago, Ill, July 24, 36; m. 64; c. 2. SHAKESPEARE, DRAMA. B.A, Univ. Chicago, 59; M.A, Univ. Calif, Los Angeles, 60, Ph.D.(Eng), 64. Instr. ENG, Univ. Calif, Los Angeles, 63-64; asst. prof, Fla. State Univ, 64-66; UNIV. VICTORIA (B.C), 66-72, ASSOC. PROF, 72- Consult, Suicide Prevention Ctr, Los Angeles, 64-; contrib. ed, Shakespeare Newslett, 67-72; Nat. Inst. Ment. Health spec. fel, Ctr. Stud. in Suicide Prevention, Washington, D.C, 70-71; vis. assoc. prof, State Univ. N.Y. Buffalo, 70-71. MLA (chmn. div. lit. & psychol, 73-74). Literature and psychology; Western drama; Shakespeare. Publ: Suicide and Greek tragedy, Sphinx Press, Int. Univs, 70; ed, The design within: psychoanalytic approaches to Shakespeare, Sci. House, 70; plus four others. Add: Dept. of English, University of Victoria, Victoria, B.C, Can.

FABRY, FRANK JOSEPH, b. Somerville, Mass, May 20, 31; m. 64; c. 1. ENGLISH. B.A, Univ. Miami, 58, M.A, 60; Ph.D.(Eng), Univ. Tex, Austin, 64. Instr. ENG, Univ. Tex, Austin, 63-64; asst. prof, UNIV. S.FLA, 64-68, ASSOC. PROF, 68- Assoc. prof, Fla. State Overseas Stud. Ctr, Florence, Italy, 72. MLA; Renaissance Soc. Am. English Renaissance literature; comparative arts in Renaissance; Shakespeare. Publ: Sidney's verse adaptations to two sixteenth century Italian art-songs, Renaissance Quart, fall 70; Sidney's poetry and Italian song-form, Eng. Lit. Renaissance, spring 73. Add: Dept. of English, University of South Florida, Tampa, FL 33620.

FACKLER, HERBERT VERN, b. Monroe, La, Jan. 23, 42; m. 64; c. 2. ANGLO-IRISH & MODERN LITERATURE. B.A, Centenary Col. La, 64; M.A, N.Mex. Highlands Univ, 65; NDEA fel. & Ph.D.(Eng), Univ. N.C, Chapel Hill, 72. Teaching asst. Eng, N.Mex. Highlands Univ, 65; instr, Centenary Col. La, 65-68; asst. prof, Northwest. State Univ. La, 69-70; Univ. Tulsa, 70-71; ASST. PROF. ENG. & DIR. CREATIVE WRITING, UNIV. SOUTHWEST. LA, 71- Col. Eng. Asn.(treas, 72-); S.Cent. Mod. Lang. Asn.(chmn, Anglo-Irish sect, 71); Am. Comt. Irish Stud; Int. Asn. Stud. Anglo-Irish Lit; Irish Am. Cult. Inst. Nineteenth century British literature. Publ: Shakespeare's irregular and wild Glendower, Discourse, 71; Sir Samuel Ferguson's Deirdre works, Eire-Ireland, spring 72; Proust and Celine, Stud. by Mem. S.Cent. Mod. Lang. Asn, winter 73; plus others. Add: Dept. of English, University of Southwestern Louisiana, Lafayette, LA 70501.

FACKLER, MIRIAM ERNESTINE, b. Cedarville, Ill, Oct. 16, 00. ENGLISH LITERATURE & LANGUAGE. B.A, Beloit Col, 22; M.A, Univ. Ill, 24; fel, Univ. Colo, 52-53, Ph.D.(Eng. lit), 55. Instr. Eng, Mt. Morris Col, 24-28; Juniata Col, 28-33, asst. prof, 33-39; Wheaton Col.(Ill), 45-50, assoc. prof, 53-57; prof, Calvary Bible Col, 62-66; Ft. Wayne Bible Col, 67-70; RETIRED. Victorian period and romantic movement of English literature; 19th century hymn writing. Add: 3938 S. Wayne Ave, Ft. Wayne, IN 46807.

FACOS, JAMES FRANCIS, b. Lawrence, Mass, July 28, 24; m. 56; c. 3. ENGLISH. A.B, Bates Col, 49; M.A, Fla. State Univ, 58. Instr. ENG, Vt. Col, 59-68, chmn. dept, 68-72, ASSOC. PROF, VT. COL. DIV, NORWICH UNIV, 72- U.S.A.A.F, 43-45, S/Sgt; Distinguished Flying Cross; Air Medal & 3 Oak Leaf Clusters. NCTE; AAUP; Am. Soc. Group Psychother. & Psychodrama; Acad. Am. Poets. Elizabethan Renaissance; American and English poetics, with comparative literature reference; the modern novel. Publ: The piper o' the may (play), Pioneer Publishers, 62; Morning's come singing (poems), Dorrance, 67; The legacy (play), 67 & A day of genesis (play), 69, Eldridge; The silver lady (novel), Atheneum, 72; Group psychotherapy and psychodrama in a college classroom, Group Psychother, 63 & In: Practical psychotherapy in nonpsychiatric specialities, C.C. Thomas, 69; The application of the Moreno techniques to the nursery school trainee, Group Psychother, 65. Add: 333 Elm St, Montpelier, VT 05602.

FACOS, PETER CHRISTOPHER, b. Lawrence, Mass, Jan. 28, 23; m. 50; c. 2. ENGLISH, EDUCATIONAL ADMINISTRATION. B.S, Yale, 49; M.A, Canisius Col, 55; Ed,D.(educ. admin), State Univ. N.Y. Buffalo, 68. Teacher ENG, KENMORE PUB. SCHS, N.Y, 55-59, chmn. dept, 59-64, AREA CONSULT, 64- NEA; NCTE; Am. Asn. Sch. Adminr. Communication theory; school-community relations. Publ: Education: a national resource & Know your schools, scripts for educ. & commercial TV. Add: Union Free School District 1, 1500 Colvin Blvd, Kenmore, NY 14223.

FADER, DANIEL NELSON, b. Baltimore, Md, Jan. 4, 30; m. 55; c. 2. ENGLISH. B.A, Cornell Univ, 52, M.A, 54; res. scholar, Cambridge, 55-57; Ph.D.(Eng), Stanford Univ, 63. Instr. ENG, UNIV. MICH, ANN ARBOR, 61-63, asst. prof, 63-68, assoc. prof, 68-73, PROF, 73- Proj. dir. grant, U.S. Off. Educ. consult, Divs. Res. elem, sec. & higher educ, 65-67; mem. nat. planning comt, Nat. Conf. Innovation for Large Cols. & Univs, 66; mem. nat. stud. group, Dept. Health, Educ. & Welfare, 66-67; consult, White House Prog. Bks. for Children, 67; participant, Anglo-Am. sem. lang. of failure, Nat. Asn. Teaching Eng. grant, 68; consult, Nat. Endowment for Humanities, 68-70; Select Comt. on Teacher Prep, House of Commons, Eng, 69-70; mem. adv. bd, Educ. Resources Information Ctr. for junior cols, Univ. Calif, Los Angeles, 70-73; consult, Corp. Pub. Broadcasting, 71-72; consult. & witness, Comt. Labor and Publ. Welfare, U.S. Senate, 73. Intel.C, U.S.A, 54-55. MLA; NCTE. Literacy of impoverished children; British periodicals of the 18th and 19th centuries; Shakespeare. Publ: Hooked on books, Berkley Bks, 66; co-auth, Hooked on books: program and proof, Berkley Bks. & Putnam, 68; auth, The periodical context of English literature, 1708-1907, 70; co-auth, British periodicals of the 18th and 19th centuries, I, 72 & British periodicals of the 18th and 19th centuries, II, 73, Xerox; auth, The naked children, Macmillan, 71; Literacy as necessity and pleasure,

Trull Found. Lect, Warton Col, 70; Chilblains and strong tea on dark afternoons, Libr. J, 4/71; plus two others. Add: Dept. of English, Haven Hall, University of Michigan, Ann Arbor, MI 48104.

FADERMAN, LILLIAN, b. Bronx, N.Y, July 18, 40. ENGLISH. B.A, Univ. Calif, Berkeley, 62, M.A, Univ. Calif, Los Angeles, 64, Ph.D.(Eng), 67. PROF. ENG, CALIF. STATE UNIV, FRESNO, 67-, ASST. V.PRES. ACAD. AFFAIRS, 73-, chmn. dept. Eng, 71-72, dean Sch. humanities, 72-73. MLA. American ethnic writing. Publ: Co-ed, Speaking for ourselves: American ethnic writing, Scott, 69 & From the Barrio: a Chicano anthology, Harper, 73. Add: Dept. of English, California State University, Fresno, Fresno, CA 93740.

FAGLES, ROBERT, b. Phila, Pa, Sept. 11, 33; m. 56; c. 2. COMPARATIVE LITERATURE, ENGLISH. A.B, Amherst Col, 55; M.A, Yale, 56, Ph.D. (Eng), 59. Instr. Eng. Yale, 59-60; PRINCETON, 60-62, asst. prof, 62-65, assoc. prof. ENG. & COMP. LIT, 65-70, PROF, 70-, DIR. PROG. COMP. LIT, 65- The epic tradition; Greek tragedy; Greek, Latin & English lyric poetry. Publ: Transl, Bacchylides, complete poems, Yale, 61; co-ed, Homer: A collection of critical essays, Prentice-Hall, 62 & Pope's Iliad and Odyssey, Methuen, Eng. & Yale, 67. Add: Program in Comparative Literature, 333 E. Pyne, Princeton University, Princeton, NJ 08540.

FAIN, JOHN TYREE, b. Nashville, Tenn, Dec. 6, 04; m. 31; c. 1. ENGLISH LITERATURE. A.B, Vanderbilt Univ, 26, A.M, 30, Ph.D.(Eng. & philos), 41; Univ. Ill, 30-32; Univ. Chicago, 36. From instr. to asst. prof, Miss. State Univ, 27-29; teacher, Univ. Ill, 30-32; from instr. to assoc. prof, Auburn Univ, 35-43; assoc. prof. ENG, UNIV. FLA, 47-51, PROF, 51- Economist, War Labor Bd, Atlanta, Ga, 43-46; Am. Philos. Soc. grant, London, summer 60. MLA; S.Atlantic Mod. Lang. Asn. Victorian and American literature. Publ: Ruskin and the economists, 56 & ed, The spyglass, 63, Vanderbilt. Add: 3025 S.W. First Ave, Gainesville, FL 32601.

FAIRBANKS, HENRY GEORGE, b. Maynard, Mass, May 26, 14; m. 46. HUMANITIES. A.B, Boston Col, 38; M.A, Boston Univ, 46; Ph.D, Univ. Notre Dame, 54. Head dept. Eng, High Schs, 38-42; speech, ST. MICHAEL'S COL. (VT), 46-48, asst. prof. Eng, 47-50, from assoc. prof. Eng. & chmn. div. humanities to PROF. HUMANITIES, 51- Assoc. ed, Vt. Cath. Tribune; Smith-Mundt fel, Univ. Saigon, 59-60. U.S.A, 43-46. MLA; Col. Eng. Asn; Am. Cath. Hist. Asn. American literature; living theater; journalism. Publ: The lasting loneliness of Nathaniel Hawthorne, 65 & Laureate of the lost, 73, Magi; Louise Imogen Guiney, Tusas, 74. Sin, free will and pessimism in Hawthorne, PMLA; Hawthorne and the machine age, Am. Lit; Religion in a revolutionary world, Cath. World. Add: Dept. of Humanities, St. Michael's College, Winooski, VT 05404.

FAIRBANKS, ROLLIN JONATHAN, JR, b. St. John's, Mich, July 7, 39; m. 62; c. 2. AMERICAN & COMMONWEALTH LITERATURE. B.A, Cornell Univ, 61; Harvard, 61-62; Univ. Chicago, 62-63; M.A, Northwest. Univ, 65; Ph.D. (Am. lit), Univ. Otago, N.Z, 68. Asst. lectr. ENG, Univ. Otago, N.Z, 65-69; fel, Univ. N.B, 69-70; asst. prof, STATE UNIV. N.Y. COL. POTSDAM, 70-73, ASSOC. PROF, 73-, res. grants, summers 71, 73. MLA; Northeast Mod. Lang. Asn; Can. Asn. Am. Stud. Publ: The deeper roar in poetry, Tex. Quart, 66; Thoreau: speaker for wildness, S.Atlantic Quart, 71. Add: Dept. of English, State University of New York College at Potsdam, Potsdam, NY 13676.

FAIRCLOUGH, GEORGE THOMAS, English. See Volume III, Foreign Languages, Linguistics & Philology.

FAIRES, DENA M. M, b. Marble Rock, Iowa, Oct. 27, 10; m. 42; c. 2. SPEECH. B.A, Iowa State Teachers Col, 31; M.A, Northwest. Univ, 36, Ph.D.(speech), 51; cert. libr, Univ. Wis, 37. Teacher, High Sch, Ill, 32-34, 37-38; Wis, 35-37; speech & Eng, Chicago Bd. Educ, 38-45; asst. speech, Northwest. Univ, 49-50; instr, Chicago Jr. Col, 45-54; Prof, Chicago Teachers Col, Sabin Br, 54-61, Crane Br, 61-62, chmn. dept, North Br, 62-66; PROF, Northeast. Ill. State Col, 67-71; RHETORIC, EDUC. OF THE PACIFIC, 72-; SEMANTICS, UNIV. HAWAII, HILO, 73- Lectr, Human Relat. Inst, summers 62, 63; Shakespeare Inst, Northeast. Ill. State Col, summer 67; inter-col. rep, S.Pac. & S.E. Asia, 67; mem, honor bd, U.S. rep. Interdrama 68, Berlin, 5/68; ed, Northwest. Alumni Asn. of Hawaii Newslett, 72- Chicago City Jr. Col. Outstanding Teacher Award, 50-52. Am. Theatre Asn; Speech Commun. Asn. Speech education; interpreters theatre; creative dramatics. Publ: Co-auth, Fundamentals of speech, 62 & auth, Oral interpretation, 64, Chicago Bd. Educ; Narration in public speaking, Speech Monogr, 51. Add: 1720 Ala Moana, Apt. 704 B, Honolulu, HI 96815.

FAIRWEATHER, CLEMENT WILSON, JR, b. Grantwood, N.J, Feb. 22, 13. ENGLISH LITERATURE. A.B, Rutgers Univ, 35; A.M, Princeton, 37, Ph.D, 42. Asst. prof. ENG, Univ. Toledo, 46-47; UNIV. COL, RUTGERS UNIV, NEW BRUNSWICK, 47-53, assoc. prof, 53-66, PROF, 66- U.S.A, 42-46. MLA. English Renaissance prose; poetry of Pope. Add: Dept. of English, University College, Rutgers University, New Brunswick, NJ 08903.

FALK, ARMAND E, b. Yankton, S.Dak, May 16, 33; m. 56; c. 2. ENGLISH. B.A, Concordia Col.(Moorhead, Minn), 55; B.S, Univ. Minn, Minneapolis, 60; M.A, Univ. Mont, 65; Ph.D.(Eng), Mich. State Univ, 68. Asst. prof. ENG, ST. CLOUD STATE COL, 68-72, ASSOC. PROF, 72- U.S.A, 56-58. MLA; AAUP. American fiction and poetry. Publ: Summer's trance, West. Humanities Rev, winter 70; A problem of limitation, Sinclair Lewis Newslett, spring 70; Fall morning II, Quartet, 73. Add: Dept. of English, St. Cloud State College, St. Cloud, MN 56301.

FALK, DORIS VIRGINIA, b. Savannah, Ga, July 21, 19. ENGLISH. B.A, Univ. Ga, 41, M.A, 42; Ph.D.(Eng), Cornell Univ, 51; cert, Shakespeare Inst, Stratford-on-Avon, 58. Social worker, Settlement houses, New York, 42-47; instr. ENG, DOUGLASS COL, RUTGERS UNIV, 51-54, asst. prof, 55-59, assoc. prof, 59-65, PROF, 66-, res. counc. grant, 61-62, fac. fel, 64-65, chmn. dept, 68-71. Fulbright lectr, Japan, 55-56. MLA; Col. Eng. Asn. American literature and drama; Shakespeare. Publ: Eugene O'Neill and the tragic tension, Rutgers Univ, 58; Proverbs and the Polonius distiny, Shakespeare Quart, winter 67; Poe and the power of animal magnetism, PMLA, 5/69; plus others. Add: Dept. of English, Douglass College, New Brunswick, NJ 08903.

FALK, HEINRICH RICHARD, b. Frankfurt am Main, Ger, May 3, 39; U.S. citizen; m. 65. THEATRE HISTORY, DRAMATIC LITERATURE & CRITICISM. B.A, Wittenberg Univ, 60; Ph.D.(theatre hist), Univ. South. Calif, 70. Lectr. THEATRE, Univ. South. Calif, 64-67; instr, Chapman Col, 66-67; ASSOC. PROF, CALIF. STATE UNIV, NORTHRIDGE, 67- Scholar, Univ. Calif, Los Angeles, 70-72; Nat. Endowment for Humanities, Younger Humanist fel, 72-73. MLA; Am. Theatre Asn; Nat. Asn. Humanities Educ; AAUP. Popular theatre and entertainment; Spanish theatre and dramatic literature; theatre history. Add: Dept. of Drama, California State University, Northridge, 18111 Nordhoff St, Northridge, CA 91324.

FALK, ROBERT PAUL, b. Milwaukee, Wis, Feb. 28, 14; m. 36; c. 2. AMERICAN LITERATURE. A.B, Williams Col.(Mass), 35; A.M, Univ. Wis, 37, Ph.D, 40. Instr. ENG, Mich. State Col, 41-42; asst. prof, Rutgers Univ, 46-49; UNIV. CALIF, LOS ANGELES, 49-55, assoc. prof, 55-63, PROF, 63- Fulbright exchange prof, Univ. Westphalia, 56 & Univ. Copenhagen, 61; vis. prof, Jagiellonian Univ, 61; Fulbright lectr, Kyoto Univ, 65-66. Orient. lang. interpreter, U.S.N.R, 43-45, Lt. MLA. American literary and intellectual history; published work on Emerson, Walt Whitman, Thomas Paine, Thomas Wolfe, Henry James, W.D. Howells and Mark Twain. Publ: Ed, American literature in parody, Twayne, 55; American poetry and prose, 57 & co-ed, American poetry and prose, 5th ed, 71, Houghton; auth, Eight American writers, Norton, 62; The Victorian mode in American fiction, Mich. State Univ, 65; co-auth, The gilded age: a reappraisal, Syracuse Univ, 63. Add: 11209 Cashmere St, Los Angeles, CA 90049.

FALK, SIGNI, b. Chicago, Ill, Sept. 15, 06. ENGLISH. A.B, Cornell Col, 29; M.A, Univ. Hawaii, 33; Yale, 34-35; Ph.D, Univ. Chicago, 48. Mem. fac, Mid-Pac. Inst, Hawaii, 31-34; Colby Jr. Col, 35-47; from asst. prof. to prof. ENG, COE COL, 47-71, EMER. PROF, 71- MLA; Renaissance Soc. Am. Elizabethan drama; the vogue of the courtesan play, 1602-1610. Publ: Tennessee Williams, 62 & Archibald MacLeish, 64, Twayne, Add: 1846 C Ave. N.E, Cedar Rapids, IA 52402.

FALL, CHRISTINE, b. Chireno, Tex, Oct. 15, 03. ENGLISH. A.B, Baylor Univ, 24, A.M, 34; Ph.D, Univ. Tex, 40. From instr. to PROF. ENG, BAYLOR UNIV, 40- South. Mod. Lang. Asn; Tennyson Soc. Literature, especially English, and science; Alfred Lord Tennyson; Frederick Tennyson. Publ: Co-ed, Alfred Tennyson: an annotated bibliography, Univ. Ga, 67. Add: Dept. of English, Baylor University, Waco, TX 76706.

FALLE, GEORGE GRAY, b. Montreal, Que, May 12, 15. ENGLISH. B.A, McGill Univ, 35, M.A, 37; Ph.D.(Eng), Univ. Wis, 52. Lectr. ENG, McGill Univ, 45-48; instr, Univ. N.H, 51-53, asst. prof, 53-54; TRINITY COL, UNIV. TORONTO, 54-62, assoc, 62-68, PROF, 68- Can. Counc. grant, 62 & 70-71; Nuffield Found. grant, summer 66; summer resident grant, King's Col, Cambridge, 66. R.C.A.F, 42-45, Flying Off. Asn. Can Univ. Teachers Eng; Am. Soc. 18th Century Stud; Johnson Soc. Cent. Region(pres, 71-72). English literature of the Restoration, especially Dryden; 18th century dramatic literature; Swift. Publ: Ed, Three Restoration comedies, Macmillan, Toronto, 64; co-ed, Journals and letters of Fanny Burney, Mme d' Arblay, 74; Dryden: professional man of letters, 7/57, Swift's writings and a variety of commentators, 4/65 & Sir Walter Scott as editor of Dryden and Swift, 1/67, Univ. Toronto Quart. Add: Dept. of English, Trinity College, Hoskin Ave, Toronto, ONT, M5S 1H8, Can.

FALLON, RICHARD GORDON, b. New York, N.Y, Sept. 17, 23; m. 46; c. 2. SPEECH & DRAMA. B.A, Columbia Univ, 48, M.A, 51. Asst. prof. speech & theater & dir. theater, Hartwick Col, 48-51; assoc. prof. speech & theater & dir. theater, Md. State Teachers Col, 51-54; gen. dir, Little Theater, Jacksonville, Fla, 54-56; asst. prof. speech & theater, FLA. STATE UNIV, 57-60, assoc. prof. theater, 60-65, PROF. SPEECH & THEATER & DIR. THEATER, 65-, DEAN SCH. THEATRE, 73- Gen. dir, Asolo Theater Festival, 62; mem, Princeton Conf. Theater Res, 66; chmn. Theater Res. Counc. Am, 66-68; theater consult, New Eng. Cols, 67; dir. grant, Cult. Enrichment Through Live Theatre, 67-69; Nat. Conf. Christians & Jews Gold Medal Award, 62; E. Harris Harbison Award for Gifted Teaching, 71. Sig.C, U.S.A, 41-46. Am. Nat. Theatre & Acad; Am. Theatre Asn; Speech Commun. Asn; Nat. Theatre Conf; Univ. Resident Theatre Asn. Development of cultural enrichment through live theatre in high schools of Florida; development of Eddie Dowling University Theatre Foundation for new playwrights; quantitative research in theater audiences in Miami, Florida. Publ: Assoc. ed, Works in progress, Theatre Documentation, 67- Add: Office of the Dean, School of Theatre, Florida State University, Tallahassee, FL 32306.

FALLS, GREGORY ALEXANDER, b. Russellville, Ark, Apr. 4, 22; m. 54; c. 3. DRAMA. B.A, Park Col, 43; M.A, Northwest. Univ, 49, Ph.D.(drama), 53; Fulbright scholar, Cent. Sch. Drama, Eng, 50. Teacher & prin, high sch, Ark, 47; instr. speech, Monmouth Col, 48; speech & drama, Wesleyan Univ, 52; asst. prof. speech, & dir. drama, Univ. Vt, 53-55, assoc. prof, 55; PROF. DRAMA, UNIV. WASH, 62-, CHMN. DRAMA ARTS GROUP, 65-, dir. sch. drama, 62-71. Founding dir, Champlain Shakespeare Festival, 59-62; founder & artistic dir, A Contemporary Theatre, Seattle, 64-; dir, Echoes, Act Theatre, Seattle, 72; mem. bd. trustees, Am. Counc. Arts in Educ, 72- U.S.A, 42-46, Staff Sgt. Am. Col. Theatre Festival Award, 73. Am. Theatre Asn; Northwest Drama Conf; Am. Nat. Theatre & Acad; Nat. Theatre Conf.(v.pres, 70-72, pres, 72-). Theatre and drama. Publ: Co-ed, Guidelines: teaching drama, State Supt. Pub. Instr, Wash, 72; New leadership roles etc, 65 & Comment, summer 66, Arts in Soc; Intellect and the theatre, E.T.J, 3/66. Add: The Highlands, Seattle, WA 98177.

FALLS, MARY ROBERT, English Literature. See FALLS, THERESA C, O.S.U.

FALLS, THERESA C, O.S.U, b. New York, N.Y, Oct. 16, 11. ENGLISH LITERATURE. A.B, Col. New Rochelle, 38; A.M, Cath. Univ. Am, 44, Ph.D, 50. Mem. fac. Eng. & Latin, Ursuline Sch, 38-39; COL. NEW ROCHELLE, 39-43, 44-46, 50-53, assoc. prof. Eng, 62-63, prioress, Ursuline House Stud, 53-56, Ursuline House Grad. Stud, 56-62, pres, 63-70, ON SPEC. ASSIGNMENT IN AFRICA, 70- Renaissance Soc. Am; MLA; NCTE; Relig. Educ. Asn. Literature of English renaissance; studies in Thomas More. Add: Dept. of English, College of New Rochelle, New Rochelle, NY 10801.

FARAG, FAHMY FAWZY, b. Giza, Egypt, June 26, 25; m. 56; c. 1. ENGLISH LITERATURE. B.A, Cairo Univ, 47; Dipl. educ. & psychol, Univ. Exeter, 49; M.A, Univ. Edinburgh, 57, Ph.D.(Eng), 59. Lectr. ENG, Cairo Univ, 53-56; ASST. PROF, Ain Shams Univ, 56-59; UNIV. WINNIPEG, 67- Egyptian govt. res. grant to Eng, 63-67. W.B. Yeats; James Joyce; Anglo-Irish literature. Publ: An anthology of modern poetry, Anglo, 63; co-auth, W.B. Yeats, centenary essays, Ibadan Univ, 65; auth, George Russell and the transcendentalism of Emerson, Annals, 5/63; The theatre of W.B. Yeats, Hiwar, 3/64; Hemingway: the end of a long exile, Am. Culture, spring 64. Add: Dept. of English, University of Winnipeg, 515 Portage Ave, Winnipeg, Man, R3B 2E9, Can.

FARBER, GERALD HOWARD, b. El. Paso, Tex, Mar. 21, 35; m. 67; c. 2. COMPARATIVE LITERATURE, ENGLISH & AMERICAN LITERATURE. B.A, Univ. Calif, Los Angeles, 58; M.A, Calif. State Univ, Los Angeles, 62; Title Ins. & Trust Co. fel, Occidental Col, 64-65, Ph.D.(comp. lit), 70. Lectr. Eng, Calif. State Univ, Los Angeles, 62-65, asst. prof, 66-68; lectr. COMP. LIT, SAN DIEGO STATE UNIV, 68-71, ASST. PROF, 71- Early 20th century European literature; medieval literature; contemporary American literature. Publ: The student as nigger, 70 & The university of tomorrowland, 72, Simon & Schuster. Add: Dept. of Comparative Literature, San Diego State University, San Diego, CA 92115.

FARIES, CLYDE J, b. Rombaur, Mo, July 8, 28; m. 48; c. 3. RHETORIC & PUBLIC ADDRESS. B.S.E.D, Southeast Mo. State Col, 50; M.A, Univ. Mich, 54; Ph.D.(speech), Univ. Mo, 64. Teacher Eng. & speech, high sch, Mo, 50-52; Mich, 52-55; instr. speech, Lincoln Col, 55-57; asst. prof, Ga. South. Col, 57-63; Murray State Col, 63-66; ASSOC. PROF. SPEECH & DIR. FORENSICS, WEST. ILL. UNIV, 66- U.S.A, 46-47. Speech Asn. Am; Cent. States Speech Asn. Rhetoric and public address; forensics—argumentation and debate; speech education. Publ: Co-auth, Introduction to public speaking, Brown, 67; auth, The debater has no case, Forensic, 69; Redneck rhetoric and the last of the redeemers, J. Miss. Hist, 71; contrib, America in controversy: public speaking in American history, W.C. Brown, 73; plus three others. Add: 227 Jana Rd, Macomb, IL 61455.

FARMER, DAVID ROBB, b. Austin, Tex, Dec. 16, 38; m. 60; c. 1. TWENTIETH CENTURY ENGLISH LITERATURE. B.A, Trinity Univ, 61, M.A, 65; Ph.D,(Eng), Univ. Tex, Austin, 70. Teacher Eng, Emerson Jr. High Sch, San Antonio, Tex, 61-63; instr. Tex. Mil Inst, 63-65; res. assoc. Humanities, Res. Ctr, Univ. Tex, 66-70; asst. prof. Eng & bibliog, North. Ill. Univ, 70-72; ASST. PROF. ENG. & ASST. DIR. HUMANITIES RES. CTR, UNIV. TEX, AUSTIN, 72-, ED. LIBR. CHRONICLE, 73- Regional asst, Am. Lit. Manuscripts, 70-; mem. ed. bd, Cambridge Univ. Press Complete Lett. of D.H. Lawrence, 73- Bibliog. Soc, Eng; MLA; Midwest Mod. Lang. Asn; Printing Hist. Soc; Bibliog. Soc. Am. Textual studies, especially D.H. Lawrence and Aldous Huxley; descriptive bibliography; contemporary English and American drama. Publ: Ezra Pound: an exhibition, 67 & Siegfried Sassoon: a memorial exhibition, 69, Humanities Res. Ctr; The bibliographical potential of a twentieth century literary agent's archive: the Pinker papers, Libr. Chronicle, 70; An unpublished version of D.H. Lawrence's introduction to Pansies, Rev. Eng. Stud, 70; D.H. Lawrence's The turning back—the text and its genesis in correspondence, D.H. Lawrence Rev, 72. Add: Dept. of English, University of Texas at Austin, Austin, TX 78712.

FARMER, NORMAN KITTRELL, JR, b. San Antonio, Tex, Aug. 24, 34; m. 59; c. 3. ENGLISH. B.A, Principia Col, 55; M.A, Trinity Univ.(Tex), 60; fel, Univ. Pa, 61-64, Ph.D.(Eng), 66. Teacher, Keystone Sch, 59-60 & Tex. Mil. Inst, 60-61, Tex; instr. ENG, Trinity Univ.(Tex), 60-61; UNIV. TEX, AUSTIN, 64-66, asst. prof, 66-70, ASSOC. PROF, 70-, DIR. FRESHMAN ENG, 68- Am. Philos. Soc. grant, 66; Univ. Tex. Res. Inst. grant, 66, 69. Folger Shakespeare Libr. fel, 67. U.S.A.F, 56-59. MLA; Renaissance Soc. Am. Tudor and Stuart literature; iconography and Renaissance art. Publ: Some poems from a 17th century manuscript with the hand of Robert Herrick, Univ. Tex, 73; A theory of genre for 17th century poetry, Genre, 12/70; Robert Herrick and King Oberon's clothing: new evidence for attribution, Yearbook Eng. Stud, 71; Robert Herrick's commonplace book? some observations and questions, Papers of Bibliog. Soc. Am, 72; plus others. Add: Dept. of English, University of Texas at Austin, Austin, TX 78712.

FARNHAM, ANTHONY EDWARD, b. Oakland, Calif, July 2, 30; m. 57; c. 2. ENGLISH, PHILOLOGY. A.B, Univ. Calif, Berkeley, 51; M.A, Harvard, 57, fel, 58-61, Ph.D.(Eng), 64. Instr. ENG, MT. HOLYOKE COL, 61-64, asst. prof, 64-69, assoc. prof, 69-72, PROF, 72- Vis. asst. prof, Amherst Col, 64-65; lectr, Smith Col, 65-66; vis. asst. prof, Univ. Calif, Berkeley, 66-67. U.S.A, 53-56. Mediaeval Acad. Am; Mod. Humanities Res. Asn. Old and Middle English language and literature; history of the English language. Add: Dept. of English, Mt. Holyoke College, South Hadley, MA 01075.

FARNHAM, WILLARD, b. Wichita, Kans, Sept. 29, 91; m. 21; c. 1; m. 29; c. 2. ENGLISH LITERATURE. A.B, Univ. Wis, 12, A.M, 14; Ph.D, Harvard, 17; LL.D, Univ. Calif, Berkeley, 61. Instr. Eng, Univ. Wis, 17-18; Sheldon traveling fel, Harvard, to Eng, France & Italy, 19-20; assoc. prof. ENG, Wash. & Lee Univ, 20-23; UNIV. CALIF, BERKELEY, 23-35, prof, 35-59, EMER. PROF, 59- Huntington Libr. res. fel, U.S. & Eng, 38-39; vis. lectr, Harvard, 47, 50-51; nat. rep, Woodrow Wilson Natl. Fel. Found, 60-61; vis. prof, Univ. Chicago, 61; Univ. Iowa, 62; Univ. Wis, 63-64. U.S.N, 18-19. MLA; Philol. Asn. Pac. Coast; Shakespeare Asn. Am. Shakespeare; Elizabethan drama; the English Renaissance. Publ: Medieval heritage of Elizabethan tragedy, Univ. Calif, 36 & Basil Blackwell, Eng, 56; Shakespeare's tragic frontier: the world of his final tragedies, Univ. Calif, 50, 63 & Basil Blackwell, 73; co-ed, Shakespeare's Hamlet, Penguin, 57, Shakespeare's Troilus and Cressida, Crofts Classics, Appleton, 66 & Twentieth century interpretations of Doctor Faustus, Prentice-Hall, 69; auth, The Shakespearean grotesque: its genesis and transformations, Clarendon, Eng, 71. Add: 3 Greenwood Common, Berkeley, CA 94708.

FARNSWORTH, DEAN BURTON, b. Montpelier, Idaho, July 2, 19; m. 41; c. 6. ENGLISH LITERATURE; B.A, Univ. Utah, 46, M.A, 47; Ph.D, Univ. Calif, Berkeley, 50. Mem. fac. English, Weber Col, 50-53; PROF, Brigham Young Univ, 53-59; libr. sci. & English, Nat. Teachers Col, Tehran, Iran, 59-61; ENGLISH, BRIGHAM YOUNG UNIV, 61- Rosenberg grad. fel, Univ. Calif, Berkeley, 49-50. Sig.C, U.S.A, 42-46, 1st Lt. NCTE; Conf. Col. Compos. & Commun. Victorian satire and fiction, especially Dickens, Thackeray and W.S. Gilbert; United States western folklore; Renaissance English drama. Add: 295 N. Fourth West, Orem, UT 84057.

FARNSWORTH, ROBERT M, b. Detroit, Mich, May 5, 29; m. 50; c. 5. ENGLISH. B.A, Univ. Mich, 50; M.A, Univ. Conn, 52; Ph.D.(Eng), Tulane Univ, 57. Instr. ENG, Univ. Ky, 55-56; Wayne State Univ, 57-60; asst. prof, UNIV. MO, KANSAS CITY, 60-64, assoc. prof, 64-69, PROF, 69-, CHMN. DEPT, 70- Fulbright-Hays lectr, Univs. Nagpur & Raipur, India, 66-67, Haceteppe Univ, Turkey, 73-74. MLA. Publ: Co-ed, Richard Wright: impressions and perspectives, 73 & auth, introd. to C. Chesnutt's The conjure woman, 70, Univ. Mich; Israel Potter: pathetic comedy, In: Critics on Melville, Univ. Miami, 72; plus six others. Add: Dept. of English, University of Missouri-Kansas City, 5315 Holmes, Kansas City, MO 64110.

FARR, CLEBURNE L, Cleburne, Tex, Nov. 1, 18; m. 39; c. 2. SPEECH. B.S. & M.A, Southwest Tex. State Col, 53; Ph.D.(speech), State Univ, Iowa, 59. Instr. SPEECH, W.Tex. State Col, 56-57, asst. prof, 57-61; E.TEX. STATE UNIV, 61-65, assoc. prof, 65-68, PROF, 68- Am. Forensic Asn. Forensics; public address; rhetoric. Add: Dept. of Speech & Drama, East Texas State University, Commerce, TX 75428.

FARR, JUDITH BANZER, b. New York, N.Y, Mar. 13, 37; m. 62; c. 1. ENGLISH & AMERICAN LITERATURE. B.A, Marymount Manhattan Col, 57; M.A, Yale, 59, Ph.D.(Eng. & Am. lit), 66. Instr. ENG, Vassar Col, 61-63; asst. prof, St. Mary's Col.(Calif), 64-68; STATE UNIV. N.Y. COL. NEW PALTZ, 68-71, ASSOC. PROF, 71- State Univ. N.Y. res. award fel, 72. Modern English and American poetry; the novel; modern British fiction. Publ: Ed, Twentieth century interpretations of Sons and lovers, Prentice-Hall, 69; auth, Compound manner: Emily Dickinson and the metaphysical poets, Am. Lt, 1/61; The butterfly, winter 65 & The dead woman, spring 66, Minn. Rev. Add: Moores Mills R.D. 1, Pleasant Valley, NY 12569.

FARRAGHER, BERNARD PATRICK, b. Boston, Mass, Aug. 11, 20; m. 44; c. 2. ENGLISH. A.B, Boston Col, 42, A.M, 47; Ohio State Univ, 43; Ph.D. (Eng. lit), Boston Univ, 56. Teaching fel. ENG, Boston Col, 42-43, instr, 46-48, asst. prof, 48-56, assoc. prof, 56-60, PROF, ASSUMPTION COL, 60-, chmn. dept, 61-69. Vis. prof, Clark Univ, 67-68. Instr. & off-in-charge, U.S. Naval Schs, 43-46; mem, U.S. Naval Educ. Specialists. MLA; NCTE; Nat. Cath. Educ. Asn; Cath. Renascence Soc; Col. Eng. Asn. English mediaeval literature; modern British literature; contemporary literature. Publ: Humanistic poetry, Boston Col, 48. Add: 44 Navasota Ave, Worcester, MA 01602.

FARRELL, JOHN PHILIP, b. New York City, N.Y, Nov. 19, 39; m. 64; c. 2. ENGLISH. B.A, Fordham Univ, 61; Ph.D.(Eng), Ind. Univ, 67. Asst. prof. ENG, UNIV. KANS, 66-71, ASSOC. PROF, 71- Watkins fac. fel, summer 68; Nat. Endowment for Humanities younger humanist fel, 72-73. MLA. Victorian literature; modern American poetry. Publ: Hamlet's final role, Bucknell Rev, 5/66; Matthew Arnold's tragic vision, PMLA, 70; The beautiful changes in Richard Wilbur's poetry, Contemporary Lit, 71. Add: Dept. of English, University of Kansas, Lawrence, KS 66044.

FARRELL, ROBERT THOMAS, b. New York, N.Y, Nov. 16, 38. ENGLISH. B.A, Fordham Univ, 60, M.A, 61, Ph.D.(Old Eng), 68; B.Phil, Oxford, 67. Instr. Eng, Fordham Univ, 61-65; asst. prof, CORNELL UNIV, 67-73, ASSOC. PROF. ENG. MEDIEVAL STUD. & ARCHAEOL, 73- Archaeol. Inst. Am; Mediaeval Acad. Am. Old English language and literature; Middle English; American literature. Publ: Beowulf: Swedes and Geats, Viking Soc, 72; Daniel and Azarias, Methuen's Old Eng. Libr, 74; Eight notes on Old English exodus, 66 & The structure of Old English Daniel, 68, Neuphilol, Mitt; The unity of Old English Daniel, Rev. Eng. Stud, 67. Add: Dept. of English, Cornell University, Ithaca, NY 14850.

FARRELL, WILLIAM JOSEPH, b. Milwaukee, Wis, Aug. 17, 36; m. 59; c. 3. ENGLISH, RHETORIC. B.S, Marquette Univ, 58; M.A, Univ. Wis, 59, Ph.D. (Eng), 61. Instr. Eng. & humanities, Univ. Chicago, 61-63, asst. prof, 63-68; ASSOC. PROF. ENG, MARQUETTE UNIV, 68- Inland Steel fel, summer 65; vis. prof, Univ. Calif, Berkeley, 67-68. MLA. Eighteenth century English literature; the novel; rhetoric. Publ: Art vs. nature as a comic pattern in Tristram Shandy, EHL, 3/63; The style and the action in Clarissa, Stud. Eng. Lit, summer 63; The mock-heroic form of Jonathan Wild, Mod. Philol, 2/66. Add: Dept. of English, Marquette University, Milwaukee, WI 53233.

FARRIS, JACK D, b. Forest, Tex, Feb. 27, 21; m. 48; c. 2. ENGLISH. B.A, Ouachita Col, 49; M.A, Univ. Mich, 50. Asst. prof. ENG, Ark. State Col, 52-55; N.Mex. Mil. Inst, 55-56; assoc. prof. Union Univ, 56-60; Windham Col, 60-61; SOUTHWEST. AT MEMPHIS, 61-67, PROF, 67- U.S.N, 39-45. S.Cent. Mod. Lang. Asn. Fiction; 19th century romantic poetry; existentialism and modern literature. Publ: Ramey, 53 & A man to ride with, 56, Lippincott. Add: Dept. of English, Southwestern at Memphis, Memphis, TN 38112.

FARRISON, WILLIAM EDWARD, b. Orangeburg, S.C, Aug. 19, 02; m. 32. ENGLISH PHILOLOGY. A.B, Lincoln Univ.(Pa), 26; A.M, Univ. Pa, 28; Univ. Mich, 29; Ph.D, Ohio State Univ, 36. Instr. ENG, Lincoln Univ. (Pa), 26-28; W.Va. State Col, 28-31; chmn. dept, Bennett Col, 32-39; prof. & chmn. dept, N.C. CENT. UNIV, 39-70, EMER. PROF, 70- Consult, Triangle Asn. Cols. S.C. & Ga, 71-72. Asn. Study Afro-Am. Life & History; Col. Lang. Asn.(pres. 38-39); MLA; NCTE. William Wells Brown; American English; American Negro literature. Publ: William Wells Brown: author and reformer, Univ. Chicago, 69; ed, William Wells Brown's Clotel: or, The president's daughter, 69 & William Wells Brown's The Negro in the American Rebellion, 71, Citadel; auth, George Moses Horton: poet for freedom, 3/71, Langston Hughes: poet of the Negro renaissance, 6/72 & Lorraine Hansbury's last dramas, 12/72; CLA J, plus one other. Add: 905 Dupree St, Durham, NC 27701.

FARROW, ANTHONY, b. Bolton, Eng, May 28, 44; m. 66; c. 1. MODERN BRITISH & CONTEMPORARY LITERATURE. B.A, Univ. Toronto, 68; M.A, Cornell Univ, 71, Ph.D.(Eng), 72. Instr. ENG, Cornell Univ, 69-70; ASST. PROF, ST. BONAVENTURE UNIV, 72- MLA; Northeast Mod. Lang.

Asn. Irish literature. Publ: Ed, Diarmuid and Grania, DePaul Univ, 74; auth, The cosmic point of view in Bleak house, Cithara, spring 74. Add: Dept. of English, St. Bonaventure University, St. Bonaventure, NY 14778.

FASEL, IDA DRAPKIN, b. Portland, Maine, May 9, 09; m. 46. ENGLISH. B.A, Boston Univ, 31, M.A, 45, fel, 45-46; Tex. Woman's Univ, 58-59; Ph.D.(Eng), Univ. Denver, 63. Instr. Eng, Univ. Conn, New London, 46-50; asst. librn. & registr, Okla. Mil. Acad, 52-57; reference librn, Midwest. Univ, 58-59; instr. ENG, Colo. Woman's Col, 59-62; UNIV. COLO, DENVER CTR, 62-64, asst. prof, 64-72, ASSOC. PROF, 72-, univ. counc. res. & creative work res. grant-in-aid, summer 65, fac. fel. & res. grant-in-aid, 67-68. MLA; Milton Soc. Am; Poetry Soc. Am. Faulkner; Whitman; Milton. Publ: Whitman and Milton, fall 67 & Song of myself as prayer, 3/71, Walt Whitman Rev; A conversation between Faulkner and Eliot, Miss. Quart, fall 67; plus poetry and other articles. Add: 165 Ivy St, Denver, CO 80220.

FATOUT, PAUL, b. Indianapolis, Ind, Mar. 4, 97; m. 33. ENGLISH. B.S, Purdue Univ, 20; M.S, Pa. State Col, 23; M.A, Columbia Univ, 26. From instr. to asst. prof. agr, Pa. State Col, 20-25; instr. ENG, Wash. State Col, 26-27; from instr. to prof, PURDUE UNIV, 27-65, EMER. PROF, 65-U.S.N, 18, Ens. American literature, especially Mark Twain and Ambrose Bierce; Civil War. Publ: Ambrose Bierce, the devil's lexicographer, 51 & Ambrose Bierce and the Black Hills, 56, Univ. Okla; Letters of a Civil War surgeon, 61 & Indiana canals, 73, Purdue Univ. Stud, Mark Twain on the lecture circuit, 61, Mark Twain in Virginia City, 64 & Meadow Lake: gold town, 69, Ind. Univ; Mark Twain, litigant, 3/59 & Mark Twain's nom de plume, 3/62, Am. Lit; Ambrose Bierce, Am. Lit. Realism, fall 67. Add: 808 Rose St, West Lafayette, IN 47906.

FATTIC, GROSVENOR RUSSELL, b. Kalispell, Mont, July 2, 40; m. 67; c. 1. MEDIEVAL ENGLISH LITERATURE, DRAMA. B.A, Andrews Univ, 62, M.A, 63; Ph.D.(Eng), Mich. State Univ, 72. ASST. PROF. ENG, ANDREWS UNIV, 67- Medieval drama. Add: Dept. of English, Andrews University, Berrien Springs, MI 49104.

FAULES, DON F, b. Haxtun, Colo, Mar. 25, 34; m. 55; c. 1. BEHAVIORAL COMMUNICATION. B.A, McPherson Col, 56; M.A, South. Ill. Univ, 57; Ph.D.(commun), Ohio State Univ, 63. Asst. prof. speech, Colo. State Col, 57-59, 61-62; instr, Ohio Univ, 62-63, asst. prof, 63-66, ASSOC. PROF. commun, 66-68; SPEECH, UNIV. UTAH, 68- Commun. consult, Ohio sanitarians, 63; consult, peace corps trainees, Ohio Univ, 65; lectr. speech commun, Am. Fed. Labor-Congr. Indust. Orgn. summer sch, 67; Title V lectr. persuasion, sec. sch. teachers, 67. Speech Commun. Asn; Nat. Soc. Stud. Commun. Interpreting feedback; campaign communication. Publ: Co-auth, Directing forensics: debate & contest speaking, Int. Textbook, 68; auth, Quantitative analysis of peer group evaluating, Ohio Speech J, 66; Measuring refutation skill: an exploratory study, J. Am. Forensic Asn, 67; Communicator ability and the ability to elicit & interpret feedback under four conditions, J. Commun, 67. Add: Dept. of Speech, University of Utah, Salt Lake City, UT 84112.

FAULKNER, CLAUDE WINSTON, b. Barbourville, Ky, Apr. 24, 16; m. 44; c. 4. ENGLISH. A.B, Union Col.(Ky), 36, Litt.D, 61; A.M, Univ. Ky, 38; Ph.D, Univ. Ill, 47. Asst. ENG, Univ. Ill, 39-42, 46-47, instr, 47; asst. prof, UNIV. ARK, FAYETTEVILLE, 47-48, assoc. prof, 48-53, PROF. & CHMN. DEPT, 53- U.S.A.F, 42-46, Res, 46-, Lt. Col. MLA; NCTE; Conf. Col. Compos. & Commun. Modern world literature; linguistics; rhetoric. Publ: Writing good sentences, 57 & co-auth, Writing good prose, 71, Scribner. Add: Dept. of English, University of Arkansas, Fayetteville, AR 72701.

FAULKNER, ROSE MAUREEN, b. Barbourville, Ky, Dec. 11, 03. ENGLISH. A.B, Berea Col, 26; A.M, Univ. N.C, 32; Univ. Cincinnati; Bread Loaf Sch. Eng; Columbia Univ. Teacher, High Sch, Ala. & Ga, 26-42; from instr. to prof. ENG, BEREA COL, 42-72, EMER. PROF, 72- Art songs of the 17th century. Add: Dept. of English, Berea College, Berea, KY 40403.

FAULKNER, SELDON, b. St. Louis, Mo, Mar. 23, 29; m. 52; c. 2. DRAMA. B.A, Shurtleff Col, 53; M.A, St. Louis Univ, 54; Ph.D, State Univ. Iowa, 57. Managing dir. univ. theater, St. Louis Univ, 57-59; asst. prof. speech & drama, Univ. Colo, 59-65, dir. univ. theater, 63-65; PROF. DRAMA. & CHMN. DEPT, UNIV. WIS-STEVENS POINT, 65- Dir. Far East Theatre Tour, Am. Educ. Theatre Asn, U.S. Defense & State Depts. & United Serv. Orgn, 61. U.S.A, 46-49, 50-51. Am. Theatre Asn; Am. Nat. Theatre & Acad. Music theatre; theatre management; audience analysis. Publ: The Octoroon War, Educ. Theatre J, 3/63; Set—for a thousand plays, Dramatics, 63; co-auth, Pirandello confesses, Chorus, 2/60. Add: Dept. of Drama, University of Wisconsin-Stevens Point, Stevens Point, WI 54481.

FAUROT, RUTH MARIE, b. Amsterdam, Mo, Mar. 28, 16. ENGLISH, LINGUISTICS. A.B, Park Col, 38; M.A, Univ. Kans, 40; Ph.D.(Eng), Univ. N.C, 53. Teacher high sch, Kans, 41-43; instr. Eng, Scottsbluff Jr. Col, 43-46; prof, Inter-Am. Univ. P.R, 46-62; PROF. ENG, UNIV. OF THE PAC, 62-, PROF. ENG. AS SECOND LANG, ELBERT COVELL COL, 62- MLA; Teachers Eng. to Speakers Other Lang. Nineteenth century novel and Victorian literature; teaching of English as a second language; new humorists of the 1890's. Publ: Jerome K. Jerome, Twayne, 74; W.W. Jacobs, 75, In: Twayne English authors series; Stevenson's The black arrow and the Paston letters, Stud. Eng. Lit, fall 65; Hardy's Lucetta Templeman in The mayor of Casterbridge, Eng. Lit. in Transition, 5/68; Mrs. Shandy observed, Stud. Eng. Lit, fall 70. Add: Dept. of English, Elbert Covell College, University of the Pacific, Stockton, CA 95204.

FAUST, ALICE L.P, b. Richwood, Ohio, Aug. 27, 23; m. 71. SPEECH, DRAMA. B.S, Univ. Wis, 44, M.A, 52, Ph.D, 61; Garret Bibl. Inst, 47. Teacher Eng, speech & music, Santiago Col, Chile, 48-50; speech & Eng, West High Sch, Madison, Wis, 52-55; instr. speech, theatre & drama, Temple Univ, 55-56; asst. instr, Univ. Md, 56-59; asst. prof, Mt. Union Col, 60-61; PROF. DRAMA, UNIV. WIS-STEVENS POINT, 61- Vis. lectr, Univ. Wis, summer 61. U.S.N, 44-46. Speech Commun. Asn. Am; Am. Theatre Asn; Am. Nat. Theatre & Acad; U.S. Inst. Theatre Technol. Simultaneous scenery; medieval theatre. Add: Dept. of Drama, University of Wisconsin-Stevens Point, Stevens Point, WI 54481.

FAUSTI, REMO P, b. Walla Walla, Wash, Apr. 11, 17; m. 41; c. 3. SPEECH. B.A, Wash. State Univ, 39, B.Ed, 40, M.A, 47; Univ. Wash, 50; Ed.D.(educ. psychol), Univ. North. Colo, 56. Asst. speech, Wash. State Univ, 39-40; teacher speech & Eng, Clarkston High Sch, Wash, 40-42; Toppenish High Sch, 42-43; instr. SPEECH, WASH. STATE UNIV, 46-51, asst. prof, 51-56, assoc. prof, 56-61, PROF, 61- U.S.N, 43-46. West. Speech Commun. Asn; Speech Commun. Asn; Am. Inst. Parliamentarians. Discussion; public speaking and speech pedagogy. Publ: Elements of deliberative debating, Wadsworth, 68; Understanding oral communication, 72 & Introductory readings in oral communication, 72, Cummings; The use of discussion as a teaching technique, The Gavel, 62; A phenomenological approach to discussion, 65 & A survey of the affiliative relationship between the student and the teacher, 66, The Speech Teacher. Add: Dept. of Speech, Washington State University, Pullman, WA 99163.

FAVERTY, FREDERIC EVERETT, b. Sparta, Ill, Sept. 29, 02; m. 34; c. 2. ENGLISH LITERATURE. A.B, Wash. Univ, 24; A.M, Harvard, 29, Ph.D, 30. Instr, West. Reserve Univ, 25-28; ENG, NORTHWEST. UNIV, 30-33, asst. prof, 33-39, assoc. prof, 39-45; prof. & chmn. dept, 45-58, Morrison prof, 58-71, EMER. MORRISON PROF, 71- Overseer's vis. comt. for Eng. dept. to Harvard, 50-55; panelist & consult, Nat. Found. Arts & Humanities, 66-68. MLA. Literature of the Middle Ages; 19th century English. Publ: Matthew Arnold the ethnologist, Northwest. Univ, 51; Your literary heritage, Lippincott, 59; ed. & contrib, Victorian poets: a guide to research, Harvard Univ, 56, 68; Legends of Joseph in Old and Middle English, PMLA, 3/28; The story of Joseph and Potiphar's wife in medieval literature, In: Harvard studies and notes in philology and literature, 3/31. Add: 1423 Judson Ave, Evanston, IL 60201.

FAVORINI, ATTILIO ANTHONY, b. New York, N.Y, Aug. 30, 43; c. 2. HISTORY OF THEATRE, THEATRE CRITICISM. B.A, Fordham Univ, 65; Richard Lanpher fel, Yale, 66-67, Ph.D.(hist. of theatre), 69. ASST. PROF. THEATRE, UNIV. PITTSBURGH, 69-, HEAD DIV, 72- Co-ed, Theatre Survey, 69-71, ed, 71- Am. Theatre Asn.(mem. bd. res, 73-); Am. Soc. Theatre Res. American theatre, 1880-1920; history of scenography, Renaissance-Baroque; contemporary theatre. Publ: The old school of acting and the English provinces, Quart. J. Speech, 4/72; Richard's himself again!, R. Mantell's Shakespearean debut, Educ. Theatre J, 12/72. Add: Dept. of Speech & Theatre Arts, 1117 CL, University of Pittsburgh, Pittsburgh, PA 15260.

FAYEN, GEORGE S, JR, b. Sept. 19, 31; U.S. citizen. ENGLISH. B.A, Yale, 53, Sterling fel. & Ph.D, 60; Henry fel. & M.A, Oxford, 60. Instr. ENG, Yale, 60-63, asst. prof, 63-68; ASSOC. PROF, SMITH COL, 68- Morse fel, 63-64; Guggenheim fel, 66-67; mem, Eng. Inst. MLA. Victorian literature; prose fiction. Publ: Hardy's The woodlanders: inwardness and memory, Stud. Eng. Lit, 61; Thomas Hardy, In: Victorian fiction, Harvard, 64; Alienation again: before and after, Yale Rev, 65. Add: 143 Cottage St, New Haven, CT 06511.

FEDDER, NORMAN JOSEPH, b. New York, N.Y, Jan. 26, 34; m. 55; c. 2. PLAYWRITING, DRAMATIC LITERATURE. B.A, Brooklyn Col, 55; M.A, Columbia Univ, 56; Ph.D, N.Y. Univ, 62. Asst. prof. Eng, Trenton State Col, 60-61; ASSOC. PROF. Eng. & speech, Indiana State Col.(Pa), 61-64; Eng, Fla. Atlantic Univ, 64-67; drama, Univ. Ariz, 67-70; SPEECH & THEATRE, KANS. STATE UNIV, 70- Judge, Am. Col. Theatre Festival playwriting competition, 72-; consult, Prairie Playwriting Proj, 73- Winner, Sacramento State Col. Nat. Playwriting Competition, summer 70. Am. Theatre Asn; AAUP; Speech Commun. Asn. Playwriting; dramatic literature; directing. Publ: The influence of D.H. Lawrence on Tennessee Williams, Mouton, 66 & Humanities, 66. Prod: Auth, The eternal kick, produced by Ind. State Col, 63; My old room, 67 & A thousand at the branches, 68, produced by Univ. Ariz; We can make our lives sublime, produced by Univ. Ariz, 68 & CBS TV, 70; The planter may weep, produced by Univ. Ariz, 69 & Univ. Judaism, 70; Some events connected with the early history of Arizona, produced by Ariz. Pioneers Hist. Soc, Kans. State Univ. & Sacramento State Col, 70; Earp!, produced by Kans. State Hist. Theatre, 71; co-auth, Monks, produced by Kans. State Univ, 72; PUBA, produced by Univ. N.C, 73. Add: Dept. of Speech, Kansas State University, Manhattan, KS 66506.

FEDDERSEN, DONLEY F, b. Clinton, Iowa, Jan. 27, 15; m. 41; c. 4. RADIO-TELEVISION, SPEECH. A.B, Wayne State Col, 37; M.A, Northwest. Univ, 42, 42-44. Teacher sr. high sch, Nebr, 37-42; instr. radio & TV, Northwest. Univ, 44-47, asst. prof, 47-50, assoc. prof, 50-54, prof, 54-60, chmn. dept, 47-56; dir. programming, Nat. Educ. TV, 60-64; acting dir. broadcasting, Univ. Fla, 64, prof. radio & TV, 64-65; PROF. TELECOMMUN. & DIR. RADIO-TV SERV, IND. UNIV, BLOOMINGTON, 65- Dir, Northwest. Univ. Reviewing Stand, 45-47; dir, NBC-Northwest. Univ. Broadcasting Inst, 47-56; mem. broadcast adv. comt, U.S. Inform. Agency, 50-63, mem. acad. liaison comt, 67-; dir. & moderator, Forum of the Air, WIND, Chicago, Ill, 52-56; prog. assoc, Nat. Educ. TV & prog. consult, Nat. Educ. TV, 56-58; prog. mgr. & dir. spec. proj, WTTW, Chicago, Ill, 58-60. Asn. Prof. Broadcasting Educ.(pres, 53); Nat. Asn. Educ. Broadcasters. Educational and public broadcasting; instructional television. Publ: The egghead and the others, Coachhouse, 55; Can ETV afford to be rich?, Nat. Asn. Educ. Broadcasters J, 67. Add: Dept. of Radio & Television, Indiana University, Bloomington, IN 47401.

FEDER, LILLIAN, b. New York, N.Y, July 10, 23. ENGLISH, CLASSICS. B.A, Brooklyn Col, 45; M.A, Columbia Univ, 47; Ph.D.(Eng. & Latin), Univ. Minn, 51. Teaching asst. ENG, Univ. Minn, 47-48, instr, 48-51; QUEENS COL.(N.Y), 51-59, asst. prof, 60-63, assoc. prof, 64-66, PROF, 67- Am. Asn. Univ. Women grant, 62-63; prof. Eng, Grad. Ctr, City Univ. New York, 63-, prof. comp. lit, 72-; Nat. Endowment for Humanities sr. fel, 74-75. MLA; Class. Asn. Atlantic States. Relationship between classical Greek and Latin literature and English literature. Publ: Crowell's handbook of classical literature, Crowell, 64; Ancient myth in Modern poetry, Princeton, 71; The symbol of the desert island in Sophocles' Philocletes, Drama Surv, spring-summer 63; Sermo or satire: Pope's definition of his art, Stud. Criticism & Aesthet. 1660-1800, 67; The voice from Hades in the poetry of Ezra Pound, Mich. Quart. Rev, summer 71; plus others. Add: Dept. of English, Queens College, Flushing, NY 11367.

FEENEY, JOSEPH JOHN, S.J, b. Philadelphia, Pa, Oct. 8, 34. AMERICAN & MODERN BRITISH LITERATURE. A.B, Fordham Univ, 58, M.A, 61; S.T.B, Woodstock Col, 64, S.T.L, 66; St. Beuno's Col, Wales, 66-67; fel, Univ. Pa, 67-69, Ph.D.(Eng), 71. Teacher Eng, St. Joseph's Prep. Sch, 59-60; Eng. & Latin, Loyola High Sch, Md, 60-62; lectr. ENG, ST. JOSEPH'S COL.(PA), 69-71, instr, 71-72, ASST. PROF, 72- MLA; Northeast Mod. Lang. Asn; AAUP; NCTE. American literature 1910-1930; war and modern American literature; modern American and British novel. Publ: Teaching students to write poetry, Eng. J, 5/65; The laughter of Christ, Univ. Ottawa Rev, 10/65. Add: Dept. of English, St. Joseph's College, Philadelphia, PA 19131.

FEENEY, WILLIAM JACKSON, b. Gary, Ind, Nov. 28, 20; m. 61; c. 2. ENGLISH. B.A, Univ. Kans, 46, M.A, 48; Ph.D.(Eng), Univ. Ore, 55. Instr. ENG, Univ. Kans, 46-48; Purdue Univ, 48-49; Univ. Ore, 49-54; DE PAUL UNIV, 54-55, asst. prof, 55-57, assoc. prof, 57-68, PROF, 68- Eng.C, 43-45. Am. Comt. Irish Stud. Irish drama; 18th century English literature. Publ: Gen. ed, Irish Drama Ser. Vol. I-X, DePaul Univ, 66-; auth, Ulysses and the Phoenix Park murders, James Joyce Quart, summer 64; Henry Mackenzie's man of feeling: the sentimental hero, Delta Epsilon Sigma Bull, 10/64; The rugged path: modern view of informers, Eire-Ireland, spring 67. Add: Dept. of English, DePaul University, 2323 N. Seminary Ave, Chicago, IL 60614.

FEIDELSON, CHARLES, JR, b. Savannah, Ga, Feb. 27, 18; m. 47; c. 3. ENGLISH & AMERICAN LITERATURE. A.B, Yale, 38, Ph.D, 48; Henry fel, Cambridge, 38-39. Instr. Eng. & Am. lit, YALE, 47-52, asst. prof. ENG, 52-58, assoc. prof, 58-59, PROF, 59- Guggenheim fel, 55-56; Fulbright lectr, Italy, 60-61. MLA. Contemporary literature; literary theory. Publ: Symbolism and American literature, Univ. Chicago, 53; The modern tradition, Oxford Univ, 65. Add: Dept. of English, Yale University, New Haven, CT 06520.

FEIGENBAUM, LAWRENCE H, b. New York, N.Y, Oct. 21, 18; m. 47; c. 2. ENGLISH, EDUCATION. B.A, Brooklyn Coll, 39; George Washington Univ, 40-42; M.A, N.Y. Univ, 47, Ph.D.(contemporary Am. lit), 50. Teacher Eng, New York City pub. schs, 45-55; asst. princ, John D. Wells Jr. High Sch, 55-58; chmn. acad. dept, McKee High Sch, 58-63; PRIN, Dreyfus Jr. High Sch, 63-71; SOUTH SHORE HIGH SCH, 71- Lectr, City Col.New York, 47-68; ed. consult, Globe Bk. Co, 50-; Joint Counc. Econ. Educ. fel, 51; lectr, grad. pediatrics div, Maimonides Hospital, 63; co-inventor & patent holder, Programmed Instr. Device, 65; vis. prof, Richmond Col, summer 68-; specialist in remedial reading & reading disabilities. U.S.A, 42-45. NCTE (regional dir, 59-). Remedial reading and reading disabilities; programmed instruction; teaching films. Publ: Effective reading, 53 & Successful reading, 58, Globe Bk; co-auth, This is a newspaper, Follett, 65 & Israel: crossroads of conflict, Rand-McNally, 68; auth, From a city rooftop, Eng. J, 6/50; America's reading problem, 5/53 & Rally round the apostrophe, boys!, 1/66 High Points. Auth. & actor, Teaching modern literature (film), 63. Add: South Shore High School, 6565 Flatlands Ave, Brooklyn, NY 11236.

FEIN, RICHARD J, Brooklyn, N.Y, Dec. 5, 29; m. 55; c. 2. ENGLISH. B.A, Brooklyn Col, 53, M.A, 55; Ph.D, N.Y. Univ, 60. Teaching fel, N.Y. Univ, 56-57; lectr. ENG, Hunter Col, 58-60; instr, Fairleigh Dickinson Univ, 60-61; asst. prof, Univ. P.R, 61-63; STATE UNIV. N.Y. COL. NEW PALTZ, 63-67, ASSOC. PROF, 67- State Univ. N.Y. summer res. grant, 67 & 74; Fulbright lectr. Am. lit, Univ. Madras, India, 71-72. Founders' Day Distinguished Scholar Award, N.Y. Univ, 61. U.S.A, 48-49. MLA. American literature; modern Jewish literature. Publ: Robert Lowell, Twayne, 71; Modern war poetry, Southwest Rev, autumn 62; The Jewish story, Midstream, 3/68; Lord Weary's castle revisited, PMLA, 1/74; plus one other. Add: Dept. of English, State University of New York College at New Paltz, New Paltz, NY 12561.

FEINBERG, LEONARD, b. Vitebsk, Russia, Aug. 26, 14; U.S. citizen; m. 38; c. 1. ENGLISH. Ph.D.(Eng), Univ. Ill, 46. Instr. ENG, Univ. Ill, 38-43; asst. prof, IOWA STATE UNIV, 46-50, assoc. prof, 50-57, PROF, 57-, DISTINGUISHED PROF, 73- Lectr. Am. lit, Univ. Ceylon, 57-58. U.S.N, 43-45. Satire. Publ: Co-auth, Handbook of English: unified exercises, Oxford, 59; auth, The Satirist, 63 & Introduction to satire, 67, Iowa State Univ; Asian laughter, John Weatherhill, Tokyo, 71; Satire: in the Orient and in the West, Costerus, Amsterdam, 72; Satire: recent definitions, Genre, 1/68. Add: Dept. of English, Iowa State University, Ames, IA 50010.

FEINSTEIN, BLOSSOM, b. Brooklyn, N.Y, Sept. 8, 23; m. 46; c. 2. ENGLISH. B.A, Brooklyn Col, 44; M.A, Queens Col.(N.Y), 64; Ph.D.(Eng. & comp. lit), Hunter Col, 67. Instr. ENG, C.W. POST COL, L.I. UNIV, 67-68, asst. prof, 68-72, ASSOC. PROF, 72- MLA. Mythology; Bible as literature; interdisciplinary offerings. Publ: The hymns of John Milton and Gianfrancesco Pico, Comp. Lit, 68; The Faerie Queene and cosmogonies of the Near East, J. Hist. Ideas, 68; Hermeticism, In: Dictionary of the history of ideas, Scribner, 73; plus one other. Add: Dept. of English, C.W. Post College, Greenvale, NY 11548.

FEINSTEIN, HERBERT CHARLES VERSCHLEISSER, b. New York, N.Y, May 28, 27. ENGLISH, MASS MEDIA OF COMMUNICATIONS. A.B, Columbia, Univ, 48; J.D, Harvard, 51: Lilly fel, Ind. Univ, Bloomington, 58; M.A, Univ. Calif, Berkeley, 59, Am. Acad. Arts & Sci. grant, 59, Danforth teacher grant, 63-64, 66, comt. on res. grant-in-aid, 64, dean grad. div. grant-in-aid, 67, Ph.D.(Eng), 68. Lawyer, Admiralty law off, Harry Kisloff, Boston, 51-53; mem. res. counsel, Fund for Repub, Harvard Law Sch, 53-54; corp. lawyer & adminr, Music Corp. Am, Universal Studios, Calif, 55-56; lectr. speech, Univ. Calif, Berkeley, 57-59; asst. prof. Eng. & jour, SAN FRANCISCO STATE UNIV, 59-66, assoc. prof. ENG, 66-72, PROF, 72- Admitted to law practice, Bar of Mass, 51 & Calif, 55; mem, Fed. Int. Presse Cinematographique, 67-; Am. Counc. Learned Soc. fel, 69-70, grant-in-aid, 72; Huntington Libr. & Art Gallery fel, 73, film consult, 73-; lectr. & tutor, Nat. Film Sch, Eng, 74. U.S.N.R, 44-45, 50, Ens. MLA (copyright comt, 70-72); Am. Judicature Soc; Am. Bar Asn.(int. copyright treaties & laws comt, 72); Am. Stud. Asn. Clemens scholarship; mass media communications, especially films; relationship between literature and the law. Publ: Two pair of gloves: Mark Twain and Henry James, Am. Imago, winter 60; Mark Twain and the pirates, Harvard Law Sch. Bull, 4/62; 3 in search of cinema, Columbia Univ. Forum, summer 65. Add: Dept. of English, San Francisco State University, San Francisco, CA 94132.

FELDMAN, IRVING, b. Brooklyn, N.Y, Sept. 22, 28; m. 55; c. 1. ENGLISH LITERATURE. B.S.S, City Col. New York, 50; M.A, Columbia Univ, 53. Instr. Eng. & humanities, Univ. P.R, 54-56; asst. prof. ENG, Kenyon Col, 58-64; assoc. prof, STATE UNIV. N.Y. BUFFALO, 64-68, PROF, 68- Fulbright scholar, 56; Ingram Merrill Found. grant, 63; Guggenheim fel, 73-74. Kovner Mem. Award, Jewish Bk. Counc. Am, 62; Nat. Inst. Arts & Lett. Award, 73. Publ: Works and days, and other poems, Atlantic Monthly Press, 61; The Pripet marshes, and other poems, Viking, 65; Magic papers, and other poems, Harper, 70; Lost Originals (poems), Holt, 72. Add: Dept. of English, State University of New York at Buffalo, Buffalo, NY 14214.

FELDMAN, REYNOLD, b. New York, N.Y, Nov. 6, 39; m. 63; c. 1. ENGLISH & INDONESIAN STUDIES. B.A, Yale, 60, Yale Col. fel, 61-62, M.A, 62, Wilson-Univ. fels, 62-63 & 64-65, McCormick fel, 63-64, Ph.D.(Eng), 66. Lectr. ENG, Queens Col.(N.Y), 65-67; asst. prof, Univ. Hawaii, 67-71, coord. exp. non-major B.A. Prog, 68, intercult. activities officer, Ctr. Cult & Tech. Interchange, East-West Ctr, 69-70, asst. dir, New Col, 70-72; lectr. Eng, Univ. Md, Europ. Div, 72-73; DIR, CTR. PROG. DEVELOP, NORTHEAST. ILL. UNIV, 73- Univ. Hawaii res. grant, 68-69. MLA. Mysticism and literature; 19th century American fiction; Indonesian area studies. Add: Center for Program Development, Northeastern Illinois University, 5500 N. St. Louis, Chicago, IL 60625.

FELHEIM, MARVIN, b. Cincinnati, Ohio, Oct. 9, 14. ENGLISH. A.B, Univ. Cincinnati, 36, A.M, 37; Ph.D, Harvard, 48; hon. Litt.D, Alma Col, 72. Instr. Univ. Mo, 45-47; ENG, UNIV. MICH, ANN ARBOR, 48-50, asst. prof, 50-56, assoc. prof, 56-61, PROF, 61-, DIR. PROG. AM. CULT, 70-, collegiate prof, 73-75. Smith-Mundt vis. prof, Nat. Taiwan Univ, 54-55; lectr, Nagano Sem, Japan, summer 55; hon. fel, Shakespeare Inst, Eng, 57-58; Fulbright lectr, France, summer 58 & vis. prof, Univ. Athens, 62-63; vis. prof, Univ. Hawaii, summer 64; lectr, Cockefair chair continuing educ, Univ. Mo, Kansas City, 65 & 67; film panel mem, Comt. Inst. Coop, 71- U.S.A.A.F, 42-45, Capt. MLA; NCTE. Shakespeare; world drama; American literature. Publ: Co-auth, Modern short stories, Oxford, 52; auth, Theater of Augustin Daly, Harvard, 56; Comedy: plays, criticism, theory, Harcourt, 63; co-auth, The living Aristophanes, Univ. Mich, 73; The problem of structure in some poems by Whitman, In: Aspects of American poetry, Ohio State Univ, 62; Eudora Welty and Carson McCullers, In: Contemporary American novelists, South. Ill. Univ, 64. Add: Office of the Directer, Program in American Culture, 1054 Literature, Science and Arts Bldg, University of Michigan, Ann Arbor, MI 48104.

FELLOWS, HUGH PRICE, b. Cottondale, Fla, Apr. 25, 15; m. 41; c. 1. SPEECH, ENGLISH. B.A, Bob Jones Univ, 35; M.A, Northwest. Univ, 37; Fulbright scholar, Univ. London, 51-52, Ph.D.(speech), N.Y. Univ, 55. Acting head dept. SPEECH, Bob Jones Univ, 36-37; head dept. McMurry Col, 37-41; head unit, City Col. N.Y, 46-51; assoc. prof. & coord, N.Y. Univ, 55-62; PROF. UNIV. TAMPA, 64-68, CHMN. DEPT. SPEECH & DRAMA, 68- Dir, prof. summer stock, 46, 48, 51, 52, 59; speech consult, West. Electric Co, Johns-Manville Corp, Gen. Foods, N.Y. State Labor Bd. and other, 52-62; tour dir, Tauck Tours, summers, 54-65. Founders' Day Award, N.Y. Univ, 56; Citation, Libr. Congr, 57; Alumni Asn. Award, Univ. Tampa, 65. U.S.N.R, 41-45, Lt. Speech Commun. Asn. Publ: Dark needs no candles, Kaleidograph, 42; The art and skill of talking with people, Prentice-Hall, 64, Heron Bks, 67. Add: Dept. of Speech, University of Tampa, Tampa, FL 33606.

FELPERIN, HOWARD MICHAEL, b. New York, N.Y, Aug. 1, 41; m. 65. ENGLISH LITERATURE. B.A, Columbia Col, 62; Woodrow Wilson fel, Harvard, 62-63, Danforth fel, 62-66, M.A, 63, Ph.D.(Eng), 66. Teaching fel. ENG, Harvard, 63-66; instr, YALE, 66-67, asst. prof, 67-72, ASSOC. PROF, 72- Shakespeare Asn. Am. Shakespeare and Renaissance literature. Publ: Shakespearean romance, Princeton Univ, 72; Shakespeare's Henry VIII, Stud. Eng. Lit, 66; Shakespeare's miracle play, Shakespeare Quart, 67. Add: Dept. of English, Yale University, New Haven, CT 06520.

FELSTINER, JOHN, b. Mt. Vernon, N.Y, July 5, 36; m. 66. ENGLISH. B.A, Harvard, 58, Ph.D.(Eng), 65. Asst. prof. ENG, STANFORD UNIV, 65-72, ASSOC. PROF, 72- Fulbright lectr. Am. Lit, Univ. Chile, 67-68; Nat. Endowment for Humanities jr. fel, 71-72. Kenyon Rev. Prize in Criticism, 67. U.S.N, 58-61, Lt.(jg). Max Beerbohm and the nineties; poetry of Pablo Neruda and T.S. Eliot; modern British and American poetry. Publ: The lies of art: Max Beerbohm's parody and caricature, Knopf, 72; Neruda in translation, Yale Rev, winter 72; Pablo Neruda and T.S. Eliot, Anales, Univ. Chile, 73; plus two others. Add: Dept. of English, Stanford University, Stanford, CA 94305.

FELTES, NORMAN NICHOLAS, b. Chicago, Ill, Mar. 20, 32; m. 59; c. 3. ENGLISH. A.B, Univ. Notre Dame, 53; M.A, Univ. Col, Dublin, 57; B.Litt, Oxford, 59. Lectr. ENG, Univ. Col, Dublin, 60; asst. prof, Loyola Col.(Que), 60-63; Kenyon Col, 63-65; Emory Univ, 65-69; ASSOC PROF, YORK UNIV, 69- MLA; Can. Asn. Univ. Teachers; Asn. Can. Univ. Teachers Eng. Victorian prose; Victorian fiction and social history. Publ: George Eliot and the unified sensibility, PMLA, 3/64; Bentham and Coleridge: Mill's completing counterparts, Mill Newslett, spring 67; George Eliot's pier-glass: the development of a metaphor, Mod. Philol, 69; plus others. Add: Dept. of English, York University, 4700 Keele St, Downsview, Ont. M3J 1P3, Can.

FELTHAM, FREDRIK GEORGE, b. London, Eng, Apr. 5, 10; nat; m. 43; c. 2. ENGLISH. Ph.D.(Eng), Univ. Chicago, 50. Instr. Eng, Woodrow Wilson Jr. Col.(Ill), 46-50; assoc. prof. LANG. ARTS, CALIF. STATE UNIV, SAN FRANCISCO, 50-60, PROF, 60- Fulbright lectr, Univ. Andes, Colombia, 59-60; participant, White House Conf. Educ, July 65; Fulbright lectr, Univ. Valladolid, Spain, 66-67. U.S.A, 42-43; U.S.A.A.F, 43-45. Literary criticism; 17th century English drama; linguistics. Add: Dept. of English, California State University, San Francisco, 1600 Holloway Ave, San Francisco, CA 94132.

FELTSKOG, ELMER NATHANIEL, b. Chicago, Ill, July 7, 35; m. 59; c. 3. ENGLISH. B.A, Augustana Col.(Ill), 57; M.A, Wash. State Univ, 59; Ph.D, Univ. Ill, 65. Asst. ENG, Wash. State Univ, 57-59; Univ. Ill, 60-64, instr, 64-65; asst. prof, UNIV. WIS-MADISON, 65-69, ASSOC. PROF, 69- MLA. The frontier and the South; colonial period; American literary naturalism.

Publ: Ed, Oregon Trail, 68 & Irving's Mahomet, 69, Univ. Wis; Lambert's Travels, DaCapo, 69. Add: Dept. of English, University of Wisconson-Madison, Madison, WI 53706.

FELVER, CHARLES STANLEY, b. Easton, Pa, Oct. 13, 16; m. 41; c. 3. ENGLISH. B.A, Lafayette Col, 48; Currier fel. & M.A, Yale, 49; Ph.D.(Eng), Univ. Mich, 56. Instr. Eng, Univ. Kans, 49-50; teaching fel, Univ. Mich, 50-52, lectr. Eng, Grad. Sch, 52-55, supvr. grad. residence ctr, Saginaw, 52-55; asst. prof. ENG, Kent State Univ, 55-57, assoc. prof, 57-61; PROF, CALIF. STATE UNIV, CHICO, 61-, chmn. dept. Eng. & div. lang. arts, 61-67. Folger Shakespeare Lib. fel, summer 61; consult. on NDEA insts. & experienced teacher fel. prog, U.S. Off. Educ, 66-67; asst. ed, Shakespeare Newsletter. U.S.A, 56-59. NCTE. Shakespeare; fools and folly in the Middle Ages and Renaissance; 19th century English book illustrators. Publ: Robert Armin, Shakespeare's fool, Kent State Univ, 61; co-auth, Poetry, an introduction and anthology, C.E. Merrill, 67; auth, Joseph Crawhall: the Newcastle wood engraver, 1821-1896, Frank Graham, Newcastle upon Tyne, Eng, 72; Robert Armin, Shakespeare's source for touchstone, Shakespeare Quart; The Commedia Dell'Arte and English drama in the 16th and early 17th centuries, Renaissance Drama VI, 63. Add: Dept. of English, California State University, Chico, First & Normal St, Chico, CA 95926.

FENAUGHTY, THOMAS J, b. Danbury, Conn, Sept. 28, 30. ENGLISH. Ed.D, Columbia Univ, 63. Teacher spec. educ, Lotte Kaliski Sch, New York, 61-62; instr. Eng, Columbia Univ, 62-65; ASST. PROF. SPEECH & THEATRE, ST. JOHN'S UNIV. (N.Y), 65- Dir, Green Room, an acting sch, 64-65; consult, Clark Ctr. Performing Arts, N.Y, 65-67; actor & dir, summer stock, off Broadway, & TV. U.S.A.F, 52-54, Res, 54-, Capt. Am. Theatre Asn; Speech Commun. Asn. Theatre; speech for the actor. Add: 392 Central Park W, 14F, New York, NY 10025.

FENDELMAN, EARL BARRY, b. St. Louis, Mo, Apr. 26, 38; m. 69. BRITISH & AMERICAN MODERN LITERATURE. A.B, Univ. Chicago, 60; Woodrow Wilson fel, Harvard, 60-61; M.A, Yale, 69, Ph.D.(Am. stud), 71. Instr. ENG, Lafayette Col, 70-71; ASST. PROF, LEHMAN COL, 71- Fulbright lectr. Am. lit, Univ. Rome, 71-73. American autobiography; English and American novel; contemporary writing. Publ: Co-auth, A role for American studies?, New Eng. Social Stud. Bull, spring 65; auth, Gertrude Stein and the Cubists, J. Mod. Lit, 11/72; A new realism in American fiction, Theory & Criticism, spring 74. Add: Dept. of English, Herbert H. Lehman College, Bedford Park Blvd. W, Bronx, NY 10468.

FENDERSON, LEWIS H, b. Baltimore, Md, July 24, 07; m. 65. ENGLISH. B.A, Univ. Pittsburgh, 41, M.Litt, 42, Ph.D, 48; cert, Am. Stud. Prog, Oxford, 50. Educ. voc. counsel, Soho Community House, Pittsburgh, 40-41; Urban League Pittsburgh, 41-42; assoc. prof. ENG, W.Va. State Col, 48-49; from asst. prof. to assoc. prof, HOWARD UNIV, 49-66, PROF, 67- Correspondent, Pittsburgh Courier, 35-45; vis. prof, Tex. South. Univ, summers 56-67; consult, Conf. Problems Anal. Eng, Univ. Tex, Austin, June 59; reading conf, Tex. Asn. Improvement Reading, Tex. South. Univ, Aug, 59 & 60; ed. adv, Howard Univ. Lib. Arts Bull, 60-65; vis. prof, D.C. Teachers Col, 62-; consult. curriculum evaluation, Educ. Serv, Inc, Mass. Inst. Teachers Eng. in Predominantly Negro Col, Ind. Univ, 64; mem. curriculum design comt. Tex. South. Univ. at Univ. Mex, summer 65; Wash. Evening Star grant to develop book-length epic poem on American Negro, 65; mem. evaluation team, Mid. States Asn. Cols. & Sec. Schs, 66- U.S.A.A.F, 42-45, 2nd Lt. MLA; CLA. American literature and journalism. Publ: The development of the Negro press: 1827-1948, Univ. Pittsburgh, 48; co-auth, Modern journalism, Pitman, 62, Effective expression, Merrill, 65, The black man in the United States: our nation's unfinished business, Scott, 69 & Many shades of black, William Morrow, 69; auth, Thurgood Marshall, tiger in the courtroom, Rutledge, 69; In his hands a sword: eight poems, Howard Univ. Mag, 1/64; Howard University centennial ode, Howard Univ, 67. Add: Box 914, College of Liberal Arts, Howard University, Washington, DC 20001.

FENNELL, FRANCIS LEROY, JR, b. Pawtucket, R.I, May 8, 42; m. 63; c. 3. ENGLISH LITERATURE, WRITING. A.B, Univ. Rochester, 64; univ. fel, Northwest. Univ, 64-65, M.A, 65, NDEA fel, 65-68, Ph.D.(Eng), 68. ASST. PROF. ENG, LOYOLA UNIV. CHICAGO, 68- MLA; NCTE; Conf. Col. Compos. & Commun. English Victorian poetry; teaching of writing. Publ: The verdict in Whistler v. Ruskin, Victorian Newslett, 12/71; The Rossetti collection at the Library of Congress: a checklist, Bull. Bibliog, 9/73. Add: Dept. of English, Loyola University of Chicago, Chicago, IL 60626.

FENNER, ARTHUR FRANCIS, JR, b. Albany, N.Y, Nov. 12, 18; m. 46; c. 4. ENGLISH. A.B, Loyola Univ.(Ill), 40; M.A, Univ. Chicago, 46; Ph.D, Yale, 54. Instr. ENG, Northwest. Univ, summer, 46; Cornell Univ, 46-47; Univ. Notre Dame, 52-54, asst. prof, 54-61; assoc. prof, Cath. Univ. Am, 61-71; PROF, UNIV. DETROIT, 71- U.S.N.R, 41-46, Lt. MLA; Col. Eng. Asn. History of criticism; 18th century English literature. Publ: The Wartons romanticize their verse, Stud. in Philol, 56; The unity of Pope's Essay on criticism, Philol. Quart, 60. Add: Dept. of English, University of Detroit, 4001 W. McNichols Rd, Detroit, MI 48221.

FENNER, THEODORE LINCOLN, b. Hornell, N.Y, Feb. 13, 19; m. 46. ENGLISH ROMANTIC WRITERS. B.S, Columbia Univ, 51, A.M, 53, Ph.D.(Eng), 67. Lectr. Eng, Flint Col, Univ. Mich, 65-67, asst. prof, 67-68; humanities, Clarkson Col. Technol, 68-72. U.S.A.A.F, 43-44, S/Sgt. MLA. Publ: Leigh Hunt and opera criticism: the Examiner years, 1808-1821, Univ. Kans, 72; The making of an opera critic: Leigh Hunt, Musical Quart, 10/69. Add: 21 Bay St, Potsdam, NY 13676.

FENNIMORE, KEITH JOHN, b. Parma, Mich, Nov. 20, 17; m. 41; c. 2. ENGLISH. A.B, Albion Col, 39; M.A, Univ. Mich, 40; Ph.D, Mich. State Univ, 55. Dir. educ, Starr Commonwealth Boys, 41-42; instr. ENG, Kemper Jr. Col, 43-45; asst, Univ. Ill, 45-46; from asst. prof. to PROF, ALBION COL, 46- Dean & registr, Bay View Summer Col. Lib. Arts, 64-69. MLA; NCTE; AAUP. Anglo-American novel; American literature. Publ: Booth Tarkington; man and novelist, Tusas, 74. Add: Dept. of English, Albion College, Albion, MI 49224.

FENTON, MARY ARTHUR, O.P, b. New York, N.Y, Mar. 27, 19. ENGLISH. B.A, Col. St. Mary of the Springs, 47; M.A, Marquette Univ, 57. Teacher, Elem. Schs, Ohio, Pa. & N.Y, 38-45; instr. Eng, St. Mary of the Springs Acad, 46-48; Ohio Dominican Col, 48-54, asst. prof, 54-66, assoc. prof, 66-68; Albertus Magus Col, 68-72: DIR. COMMUN, ST. MARY OF THE SPRINGS, 72- NCTE; MLA. Arthurian romance; Milton; higher education. Publ: Knowledge versus love, Cath. Educator, 1/51; An experimental program for superior students, Dominican Educ. Bull, spring 59. Add: St. Mary of the Springs, Columbus, OH 43219.

FENYO, JANE K, b. Jamaica, N.Y, Aug. 9, 15; m. 36; c. 3. ENGLISH, LINGUISTICS. B.A, Hofstra Univ, 62; M.A, Queens Col.(N.Y), 64; Ph.D.(Eng), Hunter Col, 68. Instr. ENG, C.W. POST COL, LONG ISLAND UNIV, 67-70, asst. prof, 70-73, ASSOC. PROF, 73- MLA. Renaissance; art; music. Add: 146 W. Lena Ave, Freeport, NY 11520.

FERGUSON, FRANCES COTTRELL, b. New Orleans, La, Aug. 23, 47. ENGLISH LITERATURE. B.A, Wellesley Col, 69; Woodrow Wilson designate, Yale, 69-70, Danforth fel, 69-73, M.Phil, 71, Ph.D.(Eng), 73. Instr. ENG, Yale, 71-72; ASST. PROF, JOHNS HOPKINS UNIV, 73- MLA. Wordsworth; English romanticism; theories of language. Publ: Robert Lowell's poetry through the Notebooks, Partisan Rev, (in press); The Lucy poems: Wordsworth's quest for a poetical object, ELH, 73. Add: Dept. of English, Johns Hopkins University, Baltimore, MD 21218.

FERGUSON, GEORGE BURNHAM, b. Chicago, Ill, Mar. 23, 25; m. 48; c. 3. ENGLISH LITERATURE. B.A, Univ. Minn, 48; B.S, St. Cloud State Col, 52, M.S, 55; Ph.D, Univ. Ill, 62. Asst. ENG, Univ. Ill, 55-60; asst. prof, St. Cloud State Col, 60-62, assoc. prof, 62-66; prof. Carthage Col, 66-69, chmn. dept, 68-69; PROF, BRADLEY UNIV, 69-, V.PRES. ACAD. AFFAIRS, 71-, chmn. dept, 69-71. Hill Found. grant, 62; Danforth fel, 63. U.S.N, 42-46. Malone Soc; MLA; NCTE; Conf. Col. Compos. & Commun. Renaissance drama in England; Beaumont and Fletcher Stud; literature from Old English to 18th century. Publ: The woman's prize, Mouton, 66. Add: Office of the Vice-President for Academic Affairs, Bradley University, Peoria, IL 61606.

FERGUSON, JAMES LEE, b. Iberia, Mo, Apr. 26, 28; m. 58; c. 2. ENGLISH, COMPARATIVE LITERATURE. A.B, Occidental Col, 50, M.A, 54, Ph.D. (comp. lit), 63. Teaching asst. Eng. & hist. civilization, Occidental Col, 57-60, instr, 60-63; asst. prof. ENG, HANOVER COL, 63-67, ASSOC. PROF, 67- U.S.A, 51-53. AAUP. Twentieth century literature; the novel; Proust. Publ: Classical rhetoric: composition and literature, Col. Compos. & Commun, 10/65; Symbolic patterns in Call it sleep, Twentieth Century Lit, 1/69. Add: Dept. of English, Hanover College, Hanover, IN 47243.

FERGUSON, MARY ANNE HEYWARD, b. Charleston, S.C, July 25, 18; m. 48; c. 3. OLD ENGLISH. A.B, Duke Univ, 38, fel, 39-40, M.A, 40; Ph.D, Ohio State Univ, 65. Instr. Eng, Univ. N.C, 45-46; Queens Col.(N.Y), 47; Univ. Conn, 48; Ohio Wesleyan Univ, 49-60; Ohio State Univ, 63-64; vis. prof, Ohio Univ, 65-66; asst. prof, UNIV. MASS, BOSTON, 66-69, ASSOC. PROF. ENG, 70- E. Howald fel, Ohio State Univ, 69-70. MLA (mem. comn. on women, 70-73, assembly del, 73-76). History of language; women in literature. Publ: Ed, Images of women in literature, Houghton, 73 & Bibliography of English translations from medieval sources, Columbia Univ, 74; plus articles in Romanic Rev. & J. Eng. & Germanic Philol. Add: Dept. of English, College I, University of Massachusetts, Boston, MA 02125.

FERGUSON, OLIVER WATKINS, b. Nashville, Tenn, June 7, 24; m. 49; c. 2. ENGLISH. B.A, Vanderbilt Univ, 47, M.A, 48; Rotary Int. Found. fel, Univ. London, 52-53; Ph.D.(Eng), Univ. Ill, 54. Instr. ENG, Univ. Ark, 48-50; asst. prof. Ohio State Univ, 54-57; DUKE UNIV, 57-62, assoc. prof, 62-67, PROF, 67-, chmn. dept, 67-73. Guggenheim fel, 63-64. U.S.A, 41-43. MLA; S.Atlantic Mod. Lang. Asn.(ed, S.Atlantic Quart, 72-). Eighteenth century English literature. Publ: Jonathan Swift and Ireland, Univ. Ill, 62; The materials of history: Goldsmith's Life of Nash, PMLA, 9/65; Jonathan Swift, In: The New Cambridge Bibliography of English Literature, Vol. 2, 71. Add: 1212 Arnette Ave, Durham, NC 27707.

FERGUSON, SUZANNE C, b. Stroudsburg, Pa, Aug. 13, 39; m. 60; c. 1. MODERN ENGLISH & AMERICAN LITERATURE. B.A, Converse Col, 60; Woodrow Wilson fel, Vanderbilt Univ, 60-61, M.A, 61; Stanford-Wilson dissertation fel, Stanford Univ, 65-66, Ph.D.(Eng), 66. Asst. prof. ENG, Univ. Calif, Santa Barbara, 66-71; ASSOC. PROF, OHIO STATE UNIV, COLUMBUS, 71- Univ. Calif, Santa Barbara summer fac. fel, 70. MLA; Midwest Mod. Lang. Asn; Soc. Stud. South. Lit. Historical study of the English short story. Publ: The poetry of Randall Jarrell, La. State Univ, 71; Mme. Laure and operative irony in Middlemarch, Stud. Eng. Lit, 63; The estranged heart: the short stories of Djuna Barnes, South. Rev, 69; A spectral beauty; the writings of Richard Middleton, In: English literature in transition, 74. Add: Dept. of English, Ohio State University 164 W. 17th Ave, Columbus, OH 43210.

FERGUSON, WILLIAM CRAIG, b. Minnedosa, Man, July 28, 29. ENGLISH. B.A, Univ. Man, 50, M.A, 52, B.Ped, 53; Ph.D, Univ. Birmingham, Eng, 60. Librn, Brandon Col, 52-53; teacher, Earl Oxford Jr. High Sch, Man, 53-56; ENG, Queen Elizabeth Col. Sch, 58-62; asst. prof, QUEEN'S UNIV. (ONT), 62-69, ASSOC. PROF, 69- Bibliog. Soc. Univ. Va; Bibliog. Soc, Eng; Bibliog. Soc, Can. Elizabethan typography; Stationers' Company records. Publ: Valentine Simmes, Bibliog. Soc. Univ. Va, 68; Thomas Creede's pica roman, Stud. Bibliog, 70. Add: Dept. of English, Queen's University, Kingston, Ont. Can.

FERGUSSON, FRANCIS, b. Albuquerque, N.Mex, Feb. 21, 04; m. 31; c. 2. COMPARATIVE LITERATURE, DRAMA. B.A, Oxford, 26; fel, Ind. Univ, 50; hon. D.Litt, Univ. New Mex, 55. Asst. dir, Lab. Theatre, New York, 27-30; dramatic critic, The Bookman, 30-32; exec. secy. & lectr, New Sch. Social Res, 32-34; mem. fac. humanities & drama, Bennington Col, 34-47; mem, Inst. Advan. Stud, 47-49, dir. sem. literary criticism, Princeton, 49-52; vis. prof, Ind. Univ, 52-53; Univ. prof. COMP. LIT, Rutgers Univ, 52-69; PROF, PRINCETON, 73- Nat. Inst. Arts & Lett; Dante Soc. Am. Greek plays in modern translation; critical essays; poetry. Publ: The idea of a theatre, 50 & Dante's drama of the mind, 52, Princeton; The human image in dramatic literature, Anchor Bks, 57; Dante, Macmillan, 65. Add: P.O. Box 143, Kingston, NJ 08528.

FERNANDEZ, THOMAS L, b. Gary, Ind, Jan. 24, 30; m. 51; c. 4. SPEECH AND DRAMA. B.A, Marietta Col, 52; M.A, Univ. Ala, 53; Ph.D.(speech), Univ. Mo, 60. Instr. speech, Univ. Mo, 53-54, 57-59; asst. prof. speech & Eng, Westminster Col.(Mo), 59-61; speech Marietta Col, 61-63; assoc. prof, Monmouth Col.(Ill), 63-69; V.PRES. STUD. & ACAD. SERV, EMORY UNIV, 69- Am. Counc. Educ. fel, 67-68. U.S.A, 54-56. Speech Commun. Asn. Rhetoric; public address; oral interpretation of literature. Publ: Ed, Oral interpretation & the teaching of English, NCTE, 69; auth, Oral interpretation and secondary teachers of English, Speech Teacher, 1/68; Jonathan Baldwin Turner at Illinois College: era of protest, Today's Speech, 9/68; plus others. Add: 402 Administration Bldg, Emory University, Atlanta, GA 30322.

FERNS, HENRY JOHN, b. Ottawa, Ont, Apr. 26, 41; m. 64; c. 2. ENGLISH & CANADIAN LITERATURE. B.A, Oxford, 64, Commonwealth scholar, 64-67, M.A, 67; dipl. educ, Univ. Nottingham, 64; M.A, Univ. West. Ont, 66, Can. Counc. fel, 68-70, Queen Elizabeth II Ont. fel, 69-70, Ph.D.(Eng), 71. Instr. ENG, Univ. West. Ont, 67-68; lectr, McMASTER UNIV, 70-71, ASST. PROF, 71- Asn. Can. Univ. Teachers Eng; Hopkins Soc; Tennyson Soc. Victorian and Canadian poetry. Publ: Co-auth, The antlered boy (poems), Fiddlehead, 70; auth, The wreck of the Deutschland: voice and structure, Victorian Poetry, 71; Oliver Twist: the destruction of love, Queen's Quart, 72; Kravitz in context: sympathy and judgement in Mordecai Richler's Duddy Kravitz, J. Can. Fiction, 74; plus others. Add: Dept. of English, McMaster University, Hamilton, Ont, Can.

FERRANTE, JOAN M, b. Jersey City, N.J, Nov. 11, 36. COMPARATIVE MEDIEVAL LITERATURE. B.A, Barnard Col, Columbia Univ, 58; Woodrow Wilson fel, Columbia Univ, 58-59, M.A, 59, Fels fel, 61-62, Ph.D.(comp. medieval lit), 63. Lectr. Eng, Hunter Col, spring 61; Italian & Eng, Barnard Col, COLUMBIA UNIV, 62-63; instr. Eng. & comp. lit, GEN. STUD. & GRAD. FAC, 63-66, asst. prof. COMP. LIT, 66-70, ASSOC. PROF, 70- Lectr. Dante, Swarthmore Col, spring 68; Am. Counc. Learned Soc. fel, 69-70. Mediaeval Acad. Am; Renaissance Soc. Am; Dante Soc. Am; Int. Arthurian Soc. Medieval romance and allegory; Dante; Provençal poetry. Publ: The conflict of love and honor: a study of the Medieval Tristan legend, Mouton, 73; The frame characters of the Decameron: a progression of virtues, 65 & The Malebolge as the key to the structure of Dante's Inferno, 67, Romance Philol; The relation of speech to sin in the Inferno, Dante Stud, 69. Add: Dept. of English & Comparative Literature, 601D Philosophy Hall, Columbia University, New York, NY 10027.

FERRAR, HAROLD, b. Brooklyn, N.Y, July 17, 35; m. 59; c. 2. ENGLISH, COMPARATIVE LITERATURE. S.B, Mass. Inst. Technol, 56; A.M, Boston Univ, 58; Ph.D.(Eng. & comp. lit), Columbia Univ, 68. Instr. Eng, Hunter Col, 66-67; lectr. ENG. & COMP. LIT, COLUMBIA UNIV, 67-68, ASST. PROF, 68-, Counc. Res. in Humanities grants, 69-72. Instr. Irish lit, New Sch. Social Res, 66-74. U.S.A, 59; Nat. Guard, 59-63. Drama; Irish literature; literature and sociology. Publ: John Osborne, Columbia Univ, 73; Denis Johnston's Irish theater, 73 & co-auth, The Dublin Drama League, 74, Dolmen; auth, The theater season, In: Encycl. Americana Yearbk, 69-74; Gaelic literature, In: Funk & Wagnall's Encycl, 71; Irish Renaissance and contemporary Irish literature, In: Collier's Encycl, 74. Add: 210 Riverside Dr, New York, NY 10025.

FERRELL, WILFRED A, b. Houston, Tex, Jan. 25, 23; m. 49; c. 4. AMERICAN LITERATURE. B.A, Univ. Tex, 50, M.A, 52, Ph.D, 59. Instr. ENG, Agr. & Mech. Col, Tex, 52-56, asst. prof, 56-59; ARIZ. STATE UNIV, 59-61, assoc. prof, 61-65, PROF, 65-, CHMN. DEPT, 71-, asst. dean grad. col, 67-71. U.S.N.R, 42-46, Lt.(jg). Conf. Col. Compos. & Commun. American prose fiction; college composition. Publ: Co-auth, Strategies in prose, Holt, 68. Add: Dept. of English, Arizona State University, Tempe, AZ 85281.

FERRES, JOHN HOWARD, b. Perth, Australia, Oct. 17, 32; U.S. citizen; m. 58; c. 3. AMERICAN & BRITISH COMMONWEALTH LITERATURE. B.A, Univ. W. Australia, Perth, 54; Fulbright Exchange stud, 55-59, La. State Univ, M.A, 56, Ph.D.(Am. lit), 59. Asst. prof. Eng, Carlow Col, 60-64; PROF. AM. THOUGHT & LANG, MICH. STATE UNIV, 64- Vis. prof, Hofstra, 68-69; vis. lectr. U.S. Inform. Serv, Europe, 72. Am. Stud. Asn; Can. Am. Stud. Asn; Asn. Commonwealth Lit. & Lang. Stud; MLA. Commonwealth literature; Canadian literature; modern American literature. Publ: Ed, Sherwood Anderson's Winesburg, Ohio, Viking, 65; Twentieth century interpretations of The crucible, Prentice-Hall, 72; co-ed, Modern Commonwealth literature, Ungar, 74; auth, Still in the present tense: The crucible today, Univ. Col. Quart, 5/72; New perspectives in Canadian literary criticism, Am. Rev. Can. Stud, spring 73. Add: Dept. of American Thought & Language, Michigan State University, East Lansing, MI 48824.

FERRIER, STEPHEN WILFRED, b. Geelong City, Australia. LITERARY THEORY, PSYCHOMETRICS. B.S, Wayne State Col, 66; M.A, Ohio Univ, 67; fel, Harvard, 68-70, M.A.T, 69, Ed.D.(lang. & lit), 72; M.Ed, Boston State Col, 73. Instr. French, Wayne State Col, 66; teaching asst. Eng, Ohio Univ, 66-67; asst. prof, State Univ. N.Y. Col. Buffalo, 68-70; lectr. speech, Northeast. Univ, 70; instr. rhet, Boston Univ, 70-73, asst. prof, 73-74; ASSOC. PROF. TESTS & MEASUREMENT, BOSTON STATE COL, 74- Res. aid, Ocean Recovery Corp, 67-68; consult, Resident Interns Counc, Mass. State Hosp, Medfield, 71-74. Royal Australian Navy, 53-63, Lt; Med.C, U.S.A, 73- MLA; NCTE; Conf. Col. Compos. & Commun; Brit. Film Inst. Semantic measurements in language and literature; quantitative evaluation of student writing and faculty grading practices; psycholinguistics. Publ: Use of the computer for examining grading practices of composition instructors, In: On common ground, NCTE-Conf. Col. Compos. & Commun, 72; Report on the workshop on the open classroom, Col. Compos. & Commun, 10/72. Add: Dept. of Secondary Education, Boston State College, Boston, MA 02115.

FERRY, ANNE D, b. New York, N.Y, Nov. 17, 30; m. 58; c. 2. ENGLISH. A.B, Vassar Col, 51; A.M, Columbia Univ, 52, Ph.D.(Eng), 56; Fulbright fel, Cambridge, 55-56. ASSOC. PROF. ENG, BOSTON COL, 67- Lectr. Hunter Col, 53-55; instr. Wellesley Col, 56-58; lectr, Harvard, 58-66; Am. Asn. Univ. Women Sabin fel, 66-67. Milton; 17th century prose and lyric poetry. Publ: Milton's epic voice, 63 & Milton and the Miltonic Dryden, 68, Harvard;

ed, 17th century minor English poetry, Dell, 64; co-ed, Beginning with poems, Norton, 66; ed, Religious prose of 17th century England, Knopf, 67. Add: Dept. of English, Boston College, Chestnut Hill, MA 02167.

FERRY, DAVID RUSSELL, b. Orange, N.J, Mar. 5, 24; m. 58; c. 1. ENGLISH LITERATURE. A.B, Amherst Col, 48; M.A, Harvard, 49, Ph.D, 55. Instr. ENG, WELLESLEY COL, 52-55, asst. prof, 55-61, from assoc. prof. to prof, 61-73, HART PROF, 73-, CHMN. DEPT, 61- U.S.A.A.F, 43-46, Sgt. Romantic poetry; 20th century poetry. Publ: The limits of mortality, an essay on Wordsworth's major poems, 59 & On the way to the island, 60, Wesleyan Univ. Add: Dept. of English, Wellesley College, Wellesley, MA 02181.

FERTIG, WALTER L, b. Noblesville, Ind, June 27, 17; m; c. 4. AMERICAN LITERATURE. A.B, Wabash Col, 38; A.M, Harvard, 41; Univ. Zurich, 47-48; Ph.D, Univ. Maryland, 52. Instr, Wabash Col, 40-42, 46-47; grad. asst, Univ. Md, 48-49; from asst. prof. to assoc. prof. ENG, WABASH COL, 49-57, PROF, 57-, chmn. dept, 57-71. Ford fel, 54-55. John Sullivan Dwight. Add: Dept. of English, Wabash College, Crawfordsville, IN 47933.

FESSENDEN, SETH A, b. Onawa, Iowa, Sept. 29, 03; m. 37; c. 3. SPEECH. B.S, Univ. Ill, 33, M.S, 34; fel, N.Y. Univ, 39-40, Ph.D, 41; summers, Univ. Mont, 37, Cornell Univ, 38, State Univ. Iowa, 46. Teacher, High Sch, Ill, 35-37; asst. prof, East. Ill. State Col, 38-42; prof. speech & head dept, W.Tex. State Col, 42-43; dir. speech area, Kutztown State Col, 43-45; prof. speech & head dept, Cornell Col, 45-48; assoc. prof. speech, coord. res. & dir. grad. prog, Sch. Speech, Univ. Denver, 48-54; dir. res. speech & commun, Mont. State Univ, 54-57; dir. educ. res, Toastmasters, Int, 57-59; prof. SPEECH COMMUN. & chmn. dept, CALIF. STATE UNIV, FULLERTON, 59-73, EMER. PROF, 73- Danforth scholar, Univ. South. Calif, 54; Thomas A. Rousse Mem. Lect, Univ. Tex, 65. Certificate of Distinguished Teaching, Calif. State Univ, Fullerton, 69. Speech Commun. Asn; Nat. Col. Players; West. Speech Commun. Asn; Nat. Soc. Stud. Commun. Speech and communication; listening: a form of social behavior; listening: basic medium for learning and communication. Publ: Speech and the teacher, 46 & co-auth, Understanding and being understood, 57, Longmans; auth, Designed for listening, 51 & co-auth, Speech for the creative teachers, 68, W.C. Brown; Bonney-Fessenden sociograph, 55, Straight talk, 63 & Speech for today, 65, McGraw; Basic experience in speech, Prentice-Hall, 2nd ed, 58; Helping the Bible speak, Asn. Press, 63; How to read the bible aloud, Reflection, 65; Manual for effective listening, Toastmasters Int, 67; auth, Listening: message perception and analysis, Found. Press, 70; A program for listening development, Pac. Speech, 8/67; plus articles in J. Commun. and others. Add: Dept. of Speech Communication, California State University, Fullerton, 800 N. State College Blvd, Fullerton, CA 92634.

FEST, THORREL BROOKS, b. Audubon, Iowa, Aug. 23, 10; m. 34; c. 2. SPEECH. A.B, North. Iowa Univ, 32; M.Ph, Univ. Wis, 38, fel, 50-51, Ph.D, 53. Teacher sec. schs, Iowa, 32-34, 34-39, asst. prof. speech, Univ. N.Dak, 39-40; Albion Col, 40-44; mem. fac. sci, Exten. Div, Univ. Tenn, 44-45; asst. prof. SPEECH, UNIV. COLO, BOULDER, 45-54, assoc. prof, 54-58, PROF, 58-, chmn. dept. speech & drama, 60-68. Mem. staff, Manhattan Proj, Clinton Engineer Works, Oak Ridge, 44-45; summer vis. prof, West. State Col, 56; Syracuse Univ, 61; consult. hdqrs. staff, N.Am. Air Defense command, 56-71; mem. adv. comt, Alexander Hamilton Bicentennial Comn, 56-59; Nat. Univ. Exten. Asn. Comt. on discussion & debate, 57-; consult, U.S. Chamber Commerce, 59-; vis. prof, Univ. Hawaii, 63, summer 59; v.pres. & prog. dir, Nat. Ctr. Commun. Arts & Sci, 65- N.Am. Defense Command spec. citation, 66. Int. Commun. Asn.(pres, 61); West. Speech Commun. Asn.(v.pres, 63); Int. Soc. Gen. Semantics; life fel. Int. Inst. Arts & Lett; Am. Forensic Asn; Cent. States Speech Commun. Asn. Group methods; intercultural and organizational communication. Publ: Co-auth, Speech and theatre, Libr. Educ, 63 & Group discussion: theory and technique, Appleton, 64; auth, Personal and structural factors in communication of scientific information, Inst. Radio Engineers Trans. Engineering Writing & Speech, 62. Add: Dept. of Communication, University of Colorado, Boulder, CO 80302.

FESTA, CONRAD, b. LaSalle, Ill, Sept. 4, 30; m. 54; c. 4. VICTORIAN & ROMANTIC POETRY. B.A, Wheaton Col, 52; B.A, Westminster Col.(Pa), 58; M.A, Cornell Univ, 60; Ph.D.(Eng), Univ. S.C, 69. ASSOC. PROF. ENG, OLD DOM. UNIV, 61-, res. found. grant, summer 71. Ed, Victorians Inst. J, 71-73; lectr, Int. Summer Stud. Inst, Oxford, 72. Teaching Excellence Award, Am. Depts. Eng-MLA, 72. MLA; S.Atlantic Mod. Lang. Asn. Victorian, Romantic and contemporary poets. Publ: Artists, chartists, and relevance, Old Dom. Univ. Mag, winter 72; Symbolism in Christina Rossetti's A birthday, Eng. Lang. Notes, fall 73. Add: Dept. of English, Old Dominion University, Hampton Blvd, Norfolk, VA 23508.

FETLER, ANDREW, b. Riga, Latvia, July 24, 25; U.S. citizen; m. 60; c. 2. ENGLISH. B.S, Loyola Univ.(Ill), 59; M.F.A, Univ. Iowa, 64. Instr. ENG, UNIV. MASS, AMHERST, 64-65, asst. prof, 65-68, ASSOC. PROF, 68-, fac. growth grant, 65. Iowa Industs. fel, 62-63. Coolbrith Poetry Award, 52; Atlantic Monthly First Award, first prize, 62. U.S.A, 44-46. Creative writing. Publ: The travelers, Houghton, 65; plus others. Add: Dept. of English, University of Massachusetts, Amherst, MA 01002.

FETTING, HANS FREDERICK, Historical Linguistics, Medieval Literature. See Volume III, Foreign Languages, Linguistics & Philology.

FETZ, HOWARD WILLIAM, b. Spokane, Wash, July 30, 40; m. 63; c. 2. ENGLISH & AMERICAN LITERATURE. B.A, Portland State Univ, 63; NDEA fel, Univ. Ore, 63, D.A.(Eng), 70, Ph.D.(Eng), 74. Instr. ENG, Univ. Ore, 66-67; asst. prof, EAST. ORE. STATE COL, 67-70, ASSOC. PROF, 70- MLA. Contemporary British and American literature; Ring Lardner; literature of sport. Publ: Of time and the novel, Xavier Univ. Stud, 7/69. Add: Dept. of English, Eastern Oregon State College, La Grande, OR 97850.

FICCA, JOHN, b. Follansbee, W.Va, Aug. 2, 29; m. 53; c. 4. DRAMA. B.A, W. Liberty State Col, 54; M.A, State Univ. Iowa, 55, Ph.D, 62. Assoc. prof. DRAMA, ILL. WESLEYAN UNIV, 65-, PROF. & DIR. SCH, 68- U.S.A, 48-51. Dramatic theory; history and literature; Eugene O'Neill. Add: School of Drama, Illinois Wesleyan University, Bloomington, IL 61701.

FICK, LEONARD J, b. Rich Fountain, Mo, Sept. 6, 15. ENGLISH & AMERICAN LITERATURE. A.B, Pontifical Col. Josephinum, 37; M.Ed, St. Louis Univ, 46; Univ. Calif, Berkeley, 46; Ph.D, Ohio State Univ, 51. Ed, Josephinum Rev, PONTIFICAL COL. JOSEPHINUM, 47-67, PROF. AM. LIT, 51-, CHMN. DEPT. ENG, 52- Lectr. mod. lit, Ohio Dominican Col, 48-69. MLA; NCTE. Nineteenth century American fiction. Publ: The light beyond: a study of Hawthorne's theology, 55 & What about Theresa Neumann?, 51, Newman. Add: Dept. of English, Pontifical College Josephinum, Worthington, OH 43085.

FIEDLER, LESLIE AARON, b. Newark, N.J, Mar. 8, 17; m. 73; c. 8. ENGLISH LITERATURE. A.B, N.Y. Univ, 38; A.M, Univ. Wis, 39, Ph.D, 41. Asst. Eng, Univ. Wis, 40-41; instr, Univ. Mont, 41-43; Rockefeller fel. humanities, Harvard, 46-47; asst. prof. ENG, Univ. Mont, 47-48, assoc. prof, 48-52, PROF, 54-65, chmn. dept, 54-56; STATE UNIV. N.Y. BUFFALO, 64- Fulbright fel. & lectr, Univs. Rome & Bologna, Italy, 52-54; jr. fel, sch. let, Ind. Univ, 53-; resident fel. creative writing & Gauss lectr, Princeton, 56-57; Kenyon Rev. fel. criticism, 56-57; Am. Counc. Learned Soc. grants-in-aid, 60-61; Fulbright fel, Univ. Athens, Greece, 61-62; assoc. ed, Ramparts; Eng. adv, St. Martin's Press; lit. ed, The Running Man; vis. prof. Am. stud, Univ. Sussex, Eng, 68; assoc. fel, Calhoun Col, Yale, 70-; vis. prof, Univ. Vincennes, Paris, 71-72. U.S.N.R. 42-46, Lt.(jg). The novel; 19th and 20th century American and British literature; humanities. Publ: An end to innocence; Love and death in the American novel; The second stone; plus others. Add: 154 Morris Ave, Buffalo, NY 14214.

FIEHLER, RUDOLPH, b. Ashland Co, Wis, Apr. 21, 07; m. 38; c. 3. ENGLISH. A.B, Valparaiso Univ, 31; M.A, Marquette Univ, 38; Ph.D, Univ. Tex, 50; dipl, Univ. Tubingen, Ger, summer, 61. Teacher, Lutheran parish schs, 27-34; pub. schs, Mo, 36-44; news writer, St. Louis Post-Dispatch, 44-46; instr. Tex. Lutheran Col, 46-50; head dept. Eng, South. State Col, 50-56; assoc. prof, La. Tech Univ, 56-72; ED, ED. PROD. SERV, 72- MLA; South. Humanities Conf. (ed, Humanities in the South, 62-70). Historical origins in Shakespeare; Russian language study. Publ: How Oldcastle became Falstaff, Mod. Lang. Quart, 3/55; Sir John Oldcastle, privately publ, 67. Add: Ruston Daily Leader, P.O. Box 520, Ruston, LA 71270.

FIELD, BRADFORD S, JR, b. Buffalo, N.Y, Apr. 19, 29; m. 66. ENGLISH. B.A, Hiram Col, 52; M.A, Kent State Univ, 55; Ph.D.(Eng), Univ. Md, 63. Instr. ENG, Marshall Col, 55-56; asst, Univ. Md, 56-59; instr. Pa. State Univ, 59-61; Univ. Va, 61-63; asst. prof, Wis. State Univ, 64-66, assoc. prof, 66-68; ASST. PROF, WAYNE STATE UNIV, 68- MLA. Renaissance drama; modern drama; Shakespeare. Publ: Hamartia in Death of a salesman, 20th Century Lit, 1/72; Ibsen's Ghosts: repetitions and repetitions, Papers Lang. & Lit, fall 72. Add: 16725 Fenmore Ave, Detroit, MI 48235.

FIELD, JOHN PAUL, b. Newton, Mass, Sept. 21, 36; m. 62. ENGLISH & AMERICAN LITERATURE. A.B, Bowdoin Col, 58; M.B.A, Harvard, 60; Woodrow Wilson fel, Univ. Mich, Ann Arbor, 61; A.M, Univ. Cincinnati, 67, Ph.D.(Eng), 70. ASSOC. PROF. ENG, WEST CHESTER STATE COL, 70- U.S.A, 60-61, Res, 61-67, Capt. MLA; AAUP. Modern poetry; English novel. Publ: Richard Wilbur: a bibliographical checklist, Kent State Univ, 71. Add: Dept. of English, West Chester State College, West Chester, PA 19380.

FIELD, LESLIE A, b. Montreal, Can, Sept. 19, 26; U.S. citizen; m. 53; c. 2. AMERICAN & ENGLISH LITERATURE. B.A, Wayne State Univ, 53, M.A, 55; Ind. Univ, 56, Sch. Lett, summers 57 & 62. Instr. Eng, PURDUE UNIV, WEST LAFAYETTE, 56-57, 58-65, res. ed, Agr. Exp. Sta, 57-58, asst. prof. ENG. & AM. LIT, 65-71, ASSOC. PROF, 71- Purdue Univ. res. found. travel grant to France, 60; sr. fel. & lectr, Bar-Ilan Univ, Israel, 69-70. R.C.N, 45. MLA; NCTE; Acad. Comt. Soviet Jewry. Jewish-American fiction; American fiction; Hebrew and Yiddish fiction. Publ: Co-ed, Thomas Wolfe's Purdue speech: Writing and living, Purdue Univ, 64, Writing and living by Thomas Wolfe, Kobunsha, Japan, 66 & All the king's men: a critical handbook, Wadsworth, 66; ed, Thomas Wolfe: three decades of criticism, 68 & co-ed, Bernard Malamud and the critics, 70, N.Y. Univ; auth, The Virgil-Lewis Aeneid as literature . . . , Bucknell Rev, 12/62; Thomas Wolfe and the kicking season again, S. Atlantic Quart, 70; Ethnic studies: benefit or boondoggle?, Bull. Rocky Mountain Mod. Lang. Asn, 73; plus two others. Add: Dept. of English, Purdue University, West Lafayette, IN 47907.

FIELD, MICHAEL JAY, b. New York, N.Y, May 1 43; m. 64; c. 2. ENGLISH LITERATURE. B.A, State Univ. N.Y. Stony Brook, 64; M.A, Cornell Univ, 65, Ph.D.(Eng), 70. Instr. ENG, Temple Univ, 68-70, ASST. PROF, 70-72; BEMIDJI STATE COL, 72- Nat. Endowment for Humanities summer fel, 73. MLA. Sixteenth and 17th century English literature; poetry. Add: Dept. of English, Bemidji State College, Bemidji, MN 56601.

FIELDING, RAYMOND, b. Brockton, Mass, Jan. 3, 31. CINEMA. A.B, Univ. Calif, Los Angeles, 53, M.A, 56; Ph.D.(commun), Univ. South. Calif, 61. Lectr. film, Univ. Calif, Los Angeles, 57-61, asst. prof, 61-65, assoc. prof. 65-66, curator Nazi-Ger. film arch, 59-66; assoc. prof, Univ. Iowa, 66-69. PROF. COMMUN, TEMPLE UNIV, 69- Univ. Calif, Los Angeles res. grants, 58-63; vis. prof, Univ. South. Calif, summers 60, 61; Univ. Calif, Los Angeles fac. fel, summer 62; vis. prof, N.Y. Univ, summer 65; consult, NASA, 66-67; v.pres, Int. Congr. Schs. Cinema & TV, 67-68; trustee, Univ. Film Found, 71-74; consult, MCA, Inc, 73; trustee, Am. Film Inst, 73-79. First Prize, Thirteenth Int. Exposition Bks & periodicals on Cinema, Venice Int. Film Festival, 68. U.S.A.F.R, 55-63. Indust. Film Producers Asn.(pres, 61-62); Univ. Film Asn.(pres, 67-68); Soc. Motion Picture & TV Engineers(chmn. hist. comt, 52-); Soc. Cinema Stud.(pres, 72-); Univ. Information Film Producers Am.(pres, 61-62). Motion picture history; technology and economics; the documentary, news and progaganda film. Publ: The technique of special effects cinematography, Hastings, 65; A technological history of motion pictures and television, Univ. Calif, 67; The American newsreel, 1911-1967, Univ. Okla, 72; Time flickers out—notes on the passing of The march of time, Quart. Film, Radio & TV, 57; Mirror of discontent—the march of time and its politically controversial film issues, West. Polit. Quart, 59; plus others. Add: Dept. of Radio, Television & Film, Temple University, Philadelphia, PA 19122.

FIELDS, ALBERT WHITEHEAD, b. Stanford, Ky, Oct. 11, 27; m. 64; c. 1. ENGLISH. A.B, Centre Col. Ky, 51; M.A, Univ. Ky, 52, NDEA fel, 65-67, Ph.D. (Eng. & philos), 67; John Hay fel, Yale, 58-59. Instr. & head dept. Eng, High Sch, Ga, 52-60; instr. Eng. & humanities, Chipola Jr. Col, 60-63; ENG, Univ. Ala, Dothan, 63; teaching fel, Univ. Ky, 63-65; assoc. prof, UNIV. SOUTHWEST. LA, 67-72, PROF, 72- Distinguished Prof. Award, Univ. Southwest. La. Found, 72. U.S.A, 45-46. MLA; S.Cent. Mod. Lang. Asn; Renaissance Soc. Am; Milton Soc. Am; S.Cent. Renaissance Soc; AAUP. Literature of the English Renaissance, Milton and Shakespeare. Publ: Milton and self-knowledge, PMLA, 5/68; The Nosce Teipsum commonplace in English literature, 1500-1900, Diss. Abstr, 69; Milton's ethics, In: Milton encyclopedia, Univ. Wis, 74. Add: Dept. of English, University of Southwestern Louisiana, Lafayette, LA 70501.

FIELDS, BEVERLY, b. Chicago, Ill, Dec. 7, 17; m. 40; c. 2. ENGLISH. B.A, Northwest. Univ, 39, M.A, 58, Ph.D.(Eng. romantic lit), 65. Instr. ENG, Lake Forest Col, 61-62; Northwest. Univ, 62-65; asst. prof. UNIV. ILL, CHICAGO, 65-69, ASSOC. PROF, 69- MLA. English romantic literature; English and American contemporary literature; literary criticism. Publ: Reality's dark dream: dejection in Coleridge, Kent State Univ, 68; The poetry of Anne Sexton, Northwest. Univ. Tri-Quart, fall 63; The poetry of Anne Sexton, In: Poets in progress, 2nd ed, Northwest, Univ. 67. Add: Dept. of English, University of Illinois at Chicago Circle, Chicago, IL 60680.

FIELDS, KENNETH WAYNE, b. Colorado City, Tex, Aug. 1, 39; m. 61; c. 1. ENGLISH. B.A, Univ. Calif, Santa Barbara, 61; Wallace E. Stegner creative writing fel, 62; George Loomis fel, Stanford Univ, 66, Ph.D.(Eng. & Am. lit), 67. Asst. prof. ENG. & AM. LIT, STANFORD UNIV, 67-72, ASSOC. PROF, 72- Adj.Gen.C, U.S.A, 61-63, 1st Lt. American poetry, 1910-1930; literary theories of the 19th century decadence in England and France; the poetry and criticism of Yvor Winters. Publ: Co-auth, The quest for reality, an anthology of short poems in English, Swallow, 68; auth, Strategies of criticism, autumn 66, The poetry of Mina Loy, summer 67 & Free verse of Yvor Winters & W.C. Williams, summer 67, South. Rev. Add: Dept. of English, Stanford University, Stanford, CA 94305.

FIELER, FRANK BERNARD, b. Dayton, Ky, Jan. 8, 33; m. 56; c. 3. ENGLISH. B.S, Morehead State Col, 55; M.A, Univ. Fla, 58, Ph.D.(Eng), 60. Instr. ENG, OHIO UNIV, 60-62, asst. prof, 62-66, assoc. prof, 66-71, PROF. & CHMN. DEPT, 71- MLA; Renaissance Soc. Am; Southeast. Renaissance Conf; Bibliog. Soc, Eng. Medieval and Renaissance English drama; Elizabethan fiction; bibliography. Publ: Tamburlaine, part I and its audience, Univ. Fla, 62; co-auth, Geoffrey Whitney's A choice of emblems, Blom, 67; ed, Eglogs, epytaphes and sonettes by Barnabe Googe, Scholars' Facsimiles, 68; auth, the David McCandless McKell collection, G.K. Hall, 73; The impact of Bacon and the new science upon Ben Jonson's critical thought in Timber, Renaissance Papers, 60; Gascoigne's use of courtley love conventions in The adventures passed by Master F.J, Stud. Short Fiction, fall 63; The eight madmen in the Duchess of Malfi, Stud. Eng. Lit, spring 67. Add: Dept. of English Language & Literature, Ohio University, Athens, OH 45701.

FIESS, EDWARD, b. New York, N.Y, Aug. 26, 14. ENGLISH. A.B, Antioch Col, 40; A.M, Wesleyan Univ, 41; Ph.D, Yale, 51. Instr. ENG, Carnegie Inst. Tech, 41-42; Oberlin Col, 43-48; asst. prof, Bard Col, 50-53; Brooklyn Col, 53-56; lectr, Queens Col.(N.Y), 56-57; ASSOC. PROF, STATE UNIV. N.Y. STONY BROOK, 57- Fulbright lectr. Am. lit, Univ. Strasbourg, 64-65. MLA; NCTE; Melville Soc. Am.(exec. v.pres, 72-); Am. Stud. Asn. American and English literature; Mark Twain; the novel. Publ: Toynbee as poet. Add: Dept. of English, State University of New York at Stony Brook, Stony Brook, NY 11790.

FIESTER, BENJAMIN F, JR, b. Hazleton, Pa, July 9, 32; m. 54; c. 2. ENGLISH. A.B, Wilkes Col, 55; M.A, Bucknell Univ, 60; Ph.D.(Eng), Pa. State Univ, 66. Instr. ENG, WILKES COL, 56-60, asst. prof, 64-66, assoc. prof, 66-68, PROF. & CHMN. DEPT, 68- MLA.(ed. comt, Annual Bibliog). Medieval romance; modern novel. Add: Dept. of English, Wilkes College, Wilkes-Barre, PA 18703.

FIFE, HILDA MARY, b. Greenland, N.H, Aug. 13, 03. ENGLISH. A.B, Colby Col, 26; summers, Boston Univ, 27-28; Chicago, 29; A.M, Cornell Univ, 33, Ph.D, 41. From instr. to assoc. prof, Hampton Inst, 26-37; asst, Cornell Univ, 38-41; asst. prof, Alfred Univ, 41-45; teacher, Concord Acad, 45-46; asst. prof. ENG, UNIV. MAINE, 46-54, assoc. prof, 54-63, prof, 63-69, EMER. PROF, 69- MLA; Milton Soc. Am. Seventeenth century English literature; Maine history and literature; European literature. Publ: Madam Wood's Recollections, Colby Libr. Quart, 9/65; An unpublished manscript by Madam Wood, In: A handful of spice, Univ. Maine, 68. Add: 6 Sherwood Dr, Eliot, ME 03903.

FIFER, CHARLES N, b. Evanston, Ill, Aug. 29, 22; m. 55. ENGLISH. B.A, Northwest. Univ, 47, M.A, 49; Sterling fel, Yale, 53-54, Ph.D, 54. Instr. ENG, Iowa State Col, 49; Lawrence Col, 49-51; Univ. Ill, 54-56; asst. prof, STANFORD UNIV, 56-61, assoc. prof, 61-69, PROF, 69- Grants-in-aid, Am. Counc. Learned Soc. 57-58, 62-63 & Am. Philos. Soc, 57-58, 62-63. U.S.A, 43-46, S/Sgt. MLA; Philol. Asn. Pac. Coast; Am. Soc. 18th Century Stud. Dr. Samuel Johnson's literary club; 18th century literature; the English novel. Publ: Co-auth, English literature 1660-1800: a bibliography of modern studies, Vols. V & VI, Princeton, 72; ed, The correspondence of James Boswell with certain members of the club, McGraw, N.Y. & Heinemann, Eng, 74; Dr. Johnson and Bennet Langton, 55 & Boswell and the decorous Bishop, 62, J. Eng. & Ger. Philol; co-auth, English literature, 1660-1800: a current bibliography, Philol. Quart, 64-70. Add: Dept. of English, Stanford University, Stanford, CA 94305.

FIFIELD, MERLE, b. Berlin, N.Y, Apr. 19, 34. ENGLISH, LINGUISTICS. B.A, N.Y. State Col. Teachers, Albany, 54, M.A, 55; Ph.D, Univ. Ill, 60. Asst. ENG, Univ. Ill, 55-60; instr, Bowling Green State Univ, 60-61, asst. prof, 61-62; BALL STATE UNIV, 62-67, ASSOC. PROF, 67- Vis. lectr, Univ. Detroit, summer 62. MLA; Midwest Mod. Lang. Asn; Am. Name Soc. Structure and production of medieval drama; Chaucer's imagery; Beowulf structure. Publ: The five-action structure of the English morality, Univ. Leeds; The castle in the circle 67 & Theoretical approaches to Chaucer's metrical variety, 73, Ball State Monogr, Ser; Chaucer the theatre-goer, Papers Lang. & Lit, summer 67; plus one other. Add: Dept. of English, Ball State University, Muncie, IN 47303.

FIGH, MARGARET GILLIS, b. Brewton, Ala, July 12, 96. SOUTHERN LITERATURE & FOLKLORE. A.B, Judson Col, 16; A.M, Univ. Ala, 17, Columbia Univ, 25. Head dept. ENG, High Sch, Ala, 17-23; from asst. prof. to assoc. prof, HUNTINGDON COL, 24-73, EMER. ASSOC. PROF, 73- Instr, Montogomery Ctr, Univ. Ala, 37-42; Carnegie Found. res. grants, 47, 48 & 49. S.Atlantic Mod. Lang. Asn; Am. Folklore Soc; Southeast. Folklore Soc. Folklore; Southern literature. Publ: Co-auth, Thirteen Alabama Ghosts, Strode, 69; Bartow Lloyd, humorist and philosopher, Ala. Hist. Rev; Folklore and tall talk in Rufus Saunders' work & Nineteenth century outlaws in Alabama folklore, 61, South. Folklore Quart. Add: 2442 Agnew St, Montgomery, AL 36106.

FIKE, FRANCIS GEORGE, JR, b. Meridale, N.Y, June 11, 33; m. 56; c. 2. ENGLISH. B.A, Duke Univ, 54; M.Div, Union Theol. Sem, 57; M.A, Stanford Univ, 58, Ph.D.(Eng. lit), 64. Teaching asst. Eng, Stanford, 58-61, acting instr. Eng, 61-63; instr. Eng. lit, Cornell Univ, 63-65, asst. prof. Eng. poetry & Victorian lit, 65-68; ASSOC. PROF. 19th CENTURY ENG. LIT, HOPE COL, 68- MLA. English literature of the Victorian period; American literature; English lyric. Publ: Bitter herbs and wholesome medicines: love as theological affirmation in Wuthering heights, Nineteenth Century Fiction, 68; Ben Jonson's On my first sonne, Gordon Rev, 69; Gerard Manley Hopkins' interest in painting after 1868, Victorian Poetry, 70; plus others. Add: Dept. of English, Hope College, Holland, MI 49423.

FILER, CHARLOTTE COLLEEN, b. McMinnville, Ore, Mar. 7, 32. JOURNALISM. B.A, Linfield Col; M.A, State Univ. Iowa. Social ed, Daily News-Register, McMinnville, Ore, 54-55; DIR. NEWS BUR, LINFIELD COL, 55-, ASSOC. PROF. JOUR, 68-, acct. prof, 60-68. Asn. Educ. Jour; Nat. Counc. Col. Publ. Adv.(State Citation of Commendation, 67). The community press; humanistic news reporting; student publications. Publ: Humanistic reporting in the weekly, Publ. Auxiliary, 9/71; Can the humanistic style work for weeklies?, Mil. Jour, winter 72. Add: Dept. of Communications, Linfield College, McMinnville, OR 97128.

FILLION, BRYANT PAUL, b. Kingston, N.Y, Oct. 18, 38; m. 61; c. 2. RHETORICAL THEORY, ENGLISH EDUCATION. B.A, Univ. Mich, Ann Arbor, 60; M.S, C.W. Post Col, 65; NDEA fel, Univ. Ill, Urbana, 66-67, advan. cert. educ, 67; Ph.D.(Eng. educ), Fla. State Univ, 69. Teacher Eng, South Huntington Pub. Schs, N.Y, 62-66; ASSOC. PROF. ENG. EDUC, UNIV. ILL, URBANA, 69-, undergrad. instruct. award, 73. NCTE (promising researcher award, 70); Conf. Eng. Educ; Nat. Conf. Res. Eng. Contemporary rhetorical theory; humanistic education; performance-based teacher education. Publ: Co-auth, Teaching skills in secondary English, Ind. Univ, 73 & Teaching English today, Houghton, (in press); auth, Turning on: selling of the present, 1970, Eng. J, 3/71; Communication experiences needed by new teachers, Eng. Educ, 2/72; Visual literarcy, Clearing House, 1/73. Add: College of Education, University of Illinois at Urbana, Urbana, IL 61801.

FINCH, HARDY RUNDELL, b. Salamanca, N.Y, Apr. 5, 05; m. 33; c. 2. ENGLISH & AMERICAN LITERATURE. B.A, Antioch Col, 27; M.A, St. Bonaventure's Univ, 30; dipl, Columbia Univ, 33; Rutgers Univ, summer, 61. Res. asst, pub. schs, Winnetka, Ill, 26-27; teacher Eng. & hist. & asst. prin, Ten Broeck Acad, Franklinville, N.Y, 27-31, head Eng. dept, high sch, Briarcliff Manor, N.Y, 31-32; high sch, Greenwich, Conn, 33-62, supvr. Eng, PUB. SCHS, 62-72; EDUC. CONSULT. & WRITER, 72- Lectr, Univs. Conn, Mo, W.Va, Syracuse & Columbia, 48-; mem, Comn. Basic Issues Teaching Eng, 59-60; World Heritage Film & Bk. Comt, 62-63; lectr, Clarion State Col, 70-73. Scholastic Nat. Film & Filmstrip awards, 50, 55, 57, 59. Dept. Sec. Sch. Teachers (pres, 49); NCTE (citation for outstanding contributions to teaching of sec. Eng, 59, v.pres, 60); Int. Reading Asn. The drama; the novel; motion pictures, television and mass media. Publ: Introduction to Stevenson's Kidnapped, Washington Square, 58; co-auth, Spelling for you, Prentice-Hall, 59, Study guide to A comedy of errors and King Lear, Am. Shakespeare Festival Theater, 63 & Shaw's Pygmalion, Dell, 66; auth, High adventure, 65 & co-auth, Adventure and suspense, 73, Scholastic Bk. Serv; auth, Shaw's Pygmalion (filmstrip), Popular Sci, 68. Add: 236 Milbank Ave, Greenwich, CT 06830.

FINCH, JEREMIAH STANTON, b. Albany, N.Y, Apr. 27, 10; m. 37; c. 2. ENGLISH LITERATURE. A.B, Cornell Univ, 31, A.M, 33, Ph.D, 36; hon. L.H.D, St. Lawrence Univ, 72. Instr. Eng, Cornell Univ, 34-36; PRINCETON, 36-40, asst. prof. pub. speaking, 40-46, lectr. ENG, 46-52, assoc. prof, 52-55, PROF, 55-, asst. dean col, 46-55, dean, 55-61, secy. of univ, 66-74. Mem. comn. insts. higher educ, Mid. States Asn. Cols. & Sec. Schs, 58-64, pres, 70-; staff mem, with J.B. Conant, Stud. Educ. Am. Teachers, 61-62; trustee, Danforth Found, 64-; Ripon Col, 71- Charles Lamb Soc; Century Asn. Seventeenth century literature and thought; 19th century literature. Publ: Sir Thomas Browne: a doctor's life of science and faith, Abelard. Add: 99 McCosh Circle, Princeton, NJ 08540.

FINCH, JOHN, b. Newburgh, N.Y, Dec. 22, 11; m 52; c. 3. ENGLISH. B.A, Wesleyan Univ, 33; M.A, Harvard, 40; hon. M.A, Dartmouth Col, 55. Instr. & tutor ENG, Harvard, 34-39; instr, DARTMOUTH COL, 39-42, asst. prof. 42-52, prof, 52-68, WILLIAM R. KENAN PROF, 68-, CHMN. DEPT. DRAMA, 67- Dir, Salzburg Sem. Am. Stud, 49-50; lectr, Charles Univ, Prague, 50. U.S.N.R, 42-45, Lt. MLA. Shakespeare and Elizabethans; American literature. Publ: Wanhope building, Am. Nat. Theatre & Acad, 47; Downstairs dragon, Dartmouth Col. & Yale, 54; The winner, Dartmouth Col, Hopkins Ctr, 63. Add: 1 Buell St, Hanover, NH 03755.

FINDLAY, ROBERT R, b. Joliet, Ill, Aug. 16, 32. THEATRE & DRAMA. B.S, Ill. State Univ, 57; M.F.A, Ohio Univ, 59; Ph.D.(theatre), Univ. Iowa, 64. Instr. speech & drama, Allegheny Col, 59-60; Bowling Green State Univ, 63-64, asst. prof, 64-67; THEATRE & DRAMA, UNIV. KANS, 67-69, assoc. prof, 69-73, PROF, 73- Am. Soc. Theatre Res; Am. Theatre Asn. Modern and contemporary theatre and drama. Publ: Co-auth, Century of innovation: a history of European and American theatre and drama since 1870, Prentice-Hall, 73; auth, A confrontation in waiting: Godot and the Wakefield play, Renascence, 69; The Emperor Jones: O'Neill as scene designer, Players, 69; plus others. Add: Dept. of Speech & Drama, University of Kansas, Lawrence, KS 66045.

FINEGAN, EDWARD J, English Language & Linguistics. See Volume III, Foreign Languages, Linguistics & Philology.

FINESTONE, HARRY, b. Atlanta, Ga, July 19, 20; m. 55; c. 3. AMERICAN LITERATURE. A.B, Emory Univ, 41; M.A, Univ. Chicago, 42, Ph.D, 53. Instr. Eng, Univ. Va, 53-56; asst. prof, Woman's Col, Univ. N.C, 56-62; CALIF. STATE UNIV, NORTHRIDGE, 62-67, prof. & chmn. dept, 67-70, DEAN ACAD. PLANNING, 70- South. Fel. Found. res. grant, summer 57; Fulbright lectr. Am. lit, Univ. Oslo, 59-60; Woman's Col, Univ. N.C, res. grant, 60-62; pres, Calif. State Col. Eng. Counc, 67-69. U.S.A.A.F, 42-45, Sgt. MLA; NCTE. Literary criticism; 19th century American literature; contemporary American literature. Publ: Bacon's rebellion: contemporary news sheets, Univ. Va, 56; co-ed, The world of the short story: archetypes in action, Knopf, 71, Prospects for the 70's: English departments and multi-disciplinary study, MLA Materials Ctr, 73 & The conscious reader, Macmillan, 74; contrib, American literary scholarship, Duke Univ, 64, 65, 67, 68. Add: Dean of Academic Planning, California State University, Northridge, 18111 Nordhoff St, Northridge, CA 91324.

FINIZIO, VICTOR LEE, b. Westerly, R.I, Jan. 18, 35; m. 58; c. 2. THEATRE RESEARCH. B.A, Univ. R.I, 56; M.A, Ohio State Univ, 59; Ph.D.(theatre), Univ. Iowa, 65. Instr. speech & drama, Marymount Col.(Kans), 63-65; asst. prof. SPEECH & THEATRE, CENT. CONN. STATE COL, 65-73, ASSOC. PROF, 73- Am. Theatre Asn; Speech Commun. Asn. American theatre; dramatic theory. Publ: Clare Kummer—who's she?, Players Mag, 12-1/68. Add: 37 Wardwell Rd, West Hartford, CT 06107.

FINK, JACK E, b. Baltimore, Md, Mar. 25, 17. ENGLISH. A.B, Wash. Univ, 39, A.M, 40; Fulbright award, Sorbonne, 52; Ph.D, Stanford Univ, 54. Instr. ENG, Wash. Univ, 42-46; acting instr, Stanford Univ, 46-50, 51-52; instr. Univ. Ore, 52-53; asst. prof, SAN JOSE STATE UNIV, 53-56, assoc. prof, 56-59, PROF, 59- MLA; NCTE; Philol. Asn. Pac. Coast. Anglo-French literary relations; 17th century literary criticism; music. Publ: The string shortage, Music J, 5-6, 56; A humanities program for superior students, Calif. Teachers Asn. J, 1/60; Humanities program at San Jose State Superior Stud, 3/60. Add: 950 Colby Ave, Menlo Park, CA 94025.

FINK, MARY JOANNA, English. See LIVIX, MARY JOANNA (FINK).

FINK, ZERA S, b. Holdrege, Nebr, Aug. 8, 02; m. 27; c. 1. ENGLISH LITERATURE. A.B, Grinnell Col, 24; A.M, Northwest. Univ, 28, Ph.D, 31. Instr. ENG, Grinnell Col, 25-27; NORTHWEST. UNIV, 27-30, 31-34, asst. prof, 34-40, assoc. prof, 40-44, prof, 44-70, acting chmn, 54, 57 & 58, EMER. PROF, 70- Am. Counc. Learned Soc. grant, 59-60. MLA; Mod. Humanities Res. Asn, Gt. Brit; Int. Asn. Univ. Prof. Eng. Milton; romantic literature; relations of literature and political theory. Publ: The classical republicans, Northwest. Univ, 45, 2nd ed, 62; Early Wordsworthian milieu, Clarendon, 58; Wordsworth and the English republican tradition, J. Eng. & Ger. Philol, 48; plus others. Add: 6880 Hawthorne Ln, Tucson, AZ 85710.

FINKELPEARL, PHILIP J, b. Pittsburgh, Pa, June 9, 25; m. 48; c. 2. ENGLISH. A.B, Princeton, 48; A.M, Harvard, 49, Ph.D.(Eng), 54. From instr. to asst. prof. ENG, Brandeis Univ, 52-57; from asst. prof. to assoc. prof, Vassar Col, 62-70; Lehman Col, 70-71; UNIV. MASS, BOSTON, 71-72, PROF, 72- Guggenheim fel, 71-72. U.S.N, 44-46. MLA. Elizabethan drama and poetry. Publ: John Marston of the middle temple, Harvard Univ, 69; From Petrarch to Ovid, ELH, 9/65; Wit in Francis Beaumont's poetry, Mod. Lang. Quart, 3/67; Beaumont, Fletcher and Beaumont & Fletcher, Eng. Lit. Renaissance, spring 71; plus others. Add: Shaker Village, Harvard, MA 01451.

FINKENTHAL, STANLEY MELVIN, Spanish Drama, Comparative Literature. See Volume III, Foreign Languages, Linguistics & Philology.

FINNBERG, F. FAITH, b. Minneapolis, Minn, May 10, 13. FRENCH, ENGLISH. B.A, Univ. Minn, 35, B.S, 36, M.A, 37, Ph.D, 55. Chmn. mod. lang. dept, Black Hills Teachers Col, 40-44; instr. Eng, MacMurray Col, 44-46, asst. prof, 46-53; counselor, UNIV. MINN, MINNEAPOLIS, 54-55, instr. LIT. & WRITING, 55-57, asst. prof, 57-60, assoc. prof, 60-69, PROF, 69- NCTE; Conf. Col. Compos. & Commun. French literature; English grammar and composition; student transfers between colleges and subsequent performance. Publ: Co-auth, Notes for the general college writing laboratory, Univ. Minn, 59, 61 & 63; co-auth, The search for awareness, Prof. Develop. Rev, winter 68. Add: General College, University of Minnesota, Minneapolis, MN 55455.

FINNEGAN, MARY JEREMY, O.P, b. Chicago, Ill. MEDIEVAL LITERATURE. Ph.B, Univ. Chicago, 29, A.M, 31; Ph.D, Yale, 42. Teacher, St. Clara Acad, Sinsinawa, Wis, 31-39; assoc. prof. ENG, ROSARY COL, 42-56, PROF, 56-, chmn. dept, 56-66. Fiske Prize. MLA. Publ: Scholars and mystics, Regnery, 62; transl, Memoirs of Father Samuel Mazzachelli, O.P, Priory, 67; Legenda Aurea, Caxton. Add: Dept. of English, Rosary College, River Forest, IL 60305.

FINNERAN, RICHARD JOHN, b. New York, N.Y, Dec. 19, 43. ENGLISH & AMERICAN LITERATURE. B.A, N.Y. Univ, 64; Ph.D, Univ. N.C, Chapel Hill, 68. Instr. ENG, Univ. Fla, 67-68; N.Y. Univ, 68-70; ASST. PROF, NEWCOMB COL, TULANE UNIV, 70- Lectr, Yeats Int. Summer Sch, Sligo, Ireland, 72. MLA (chmn. Celtic group, 72); S.Cent. Mod. Lang. Asn.(chmn. Anglo-Irish sect, 72); Int. Asn. Stud. Anglo-Irish Lit; S.Atlantic Mod. Lang. Asn; Am. Comt. Irish Stud. Anglo-Irish literature, especially W.B. Yeats. Publ: Ed, W.B, Yeats' John Sherman and Dhoya, Wayne State Univ, 69; William Butler Yeats: the Byzantium poems, Merrill, 70; auth, The prose fiction of W.B. Yeats: the search for those simple forms, Dolmen, 73; ed, Letters of James Stephens, Macmillan, 74; auth, Old lecher with a love on every wind: a study of Yeats' Stories of Red Hanrahan, Tex. Stud. Lit. & Lang, 72; Yeats' revisions in The Celtic twilight, 1912-1925, Tulane Stud. Eng, 72. Add: Dept. of English, Newcomb College, Tulane University, New Orleans, LA 70118.

FINNEY, FRANK, b. Bartlesville, Okla, Nov. 26, 17; m. 50; c. 1. ENGLISH. B.A, Univ. Okla, 39, Ph.D.(Eng), 61; M.A, Univ. Tex, 41. Instr. ENG, Univ. Okla, 47-48, 57-59; Univ. Richmond, 53-57; asst. prof, CENT. STATE UNIV, 59-61, assoc. prof, 61-62, PROF, 63-, DEAN, SCH. LIB. ARTS, 71-, chmn. dept. Eng, 62-65, chmn. div. lang. arts & humanities, 65-71. U.S.C.G, 41-46. NCTE. Twentieth century American fiction. Add: Dept. of English, Central State University, Edmond, OK 73034.

FINNEY, GRETCHEN LUDKE, b. Browns Valley, Minn, Dec. 12, 01; m. 30; c. 2. ENGLISH, MUSIC. B.A, Carleton Col, 23; Radcliffe Col, 23-24; M.A, Univ. Calif, Berkeley, 25. Instr. Eng, Carleton Col, 25-29; Smith Col, 44-48; RES. & WRITING. Huntington Libr. res. grant, 52. English literature; music; medicine. Publ: Musical backgrounds for English literature 1580-1650, Rutgers Univ, 62; Medical theories of vocal exercise and health, 66, Vocal exercise in the sixteenth century related to theories of physiology and disease, 68 & Fear of exercising the lungs related to iatro-mechanics, 71, Bull. Hist. Med; plus others. Add: 2015 Geddes Ave, Ann Arbor, MI 48104.

FINNEY, ROBERT GEORGE, b. Newark, N.J, Mar. 31, 35; m. 60; c. 6. COMMUNICATION. A.B, Marietta Col, 56; M.A, Ohio State Univ, 57, Ph.D. (commun), 71. Personnel adminr, Radio Corp. Am, 61-64; instr. speech, Univ. Cincinnati, 64-66; teaching assoc, Ohio State Univ, 66-68; assoc. prof. commun. & acting dean sch, Shaw Univ, 68-71; assoc. prof. speech & dir. broadcasting, Memphis State Univ, 71-73; PROF. COMMUN. & DIR. BROADCASTING, MADISON COL, 73- Dir. curriculum develop. in commun. proj, Dept. Health, Educ. & Welfare Title III, 68-71; consult, Parents Without Partners, Ohio Bell Tel, Inner City Learning Workshops, Sch. Desegregation Workshops & Dept. Health, Educ. & Welfare Migrant Worker Proj, 68-; field reader, Dept. Health, Educ. & Welfare, 70-73. U.S.N, 57-61, Res, 61-, Lt. Comdr. Am. Asn. Higher Educ; AAUP; Int. Commun. Asn; Broadcast Educ. Asn. Mass communication; political communication; organizational communication. Publ: Co-ed, Curriculum development in communications (3 vols), Dept. Health, Educ. & Welfare, 67-70; transl, Delreuelle VossWinkel's Television et famille en urbain environ, 67 & auth, Another TV rating study?, 68, Educ. Broadcasting Rev, 68. Add: Dept. of Communication Arts, Madison College, Harrisonburg, VA 22801.

FINNIE, W. BRUCE, b. Batesville, Miss, Mar. 6, 34; m. 55; c. 3. ENGLISH. B.A, Univ. Akron, 55; M.A, Columbia Univ, 60; Ph.D.(Eng), Ohio State Univ, 65. Instr. ENG, Ohio State Univ, 64-65; UNIV. DEL, 65-66, asst. prof, 66-70, ASSOC. PROF, 70- Fac. fel. grant, Univ. Del, summer 66, instr. NDEA Ling. Inst, summer 67, excellence in teaching award, 68, instructional improvement grant, summer 68; vis. prof. Eng, Univ. Essen, fall 71. U.S.A.F, 55-58, 1st Lt. Mediaeval Acad. Am; Am. Dialect Soc; Am. Name Soc; MLA; Int. Arthurian Soc. Middle and Old English; history of English language; Arthurian literature. Publ: Topographic terms in the Ohio Valley, 1748-1800, Am. Dialect Soc, 70; co-ed, Words on words: a language reader, Random, 71; auth, The stages of English: texts, transcriptions, exercises, Houghton, 72; Ohio Valley localisms, topographical terms, 1750-1800, Am. Speech, 10/63; American English: a critical bibliographical essay, Del. Eng. J, spring 69; The structural function of names in the works of Chretien de Troyes, Names, 6/72. Add: Dept. of English, University of Delaware, Newark, DE 19711.

FINNIGAN, DAVID FRANCIS, b. Omaha, Nebr, Oct. 30, 33; m. 55; c. 2. ENGLISH LITERATURE. A.B, Univ. Colo, 56, M.A, 57; Univ. N.Mex, 59; Ph.D.(Eng. lit), Univ. Ore, 70. Instr. ENG, ORE. STATE UNIV, 57-60, asst. prof, 60-71, ASSOC. PROF, 71- English literature of the Renaissance; Milton studies. Publ: The man himself: Emerson's prose style, Emerson Soc. Quart, 65. Add: Dept. of English, Oregon State University, Corvallis, OR 97331.

FIORE, PETER AMADEUS, O.F.M, b. Glens Falls, N.Y, Sept. 8, 27. ENGLISH. B.A, Siena Col, 49; M.A, Cath. Univ. Am, 55; Ph.D.(Eng), London Univ, 61. Instr. ENG, SIENA COL, 56-58, asst. prof, 61-64, assoc. prof, 64-71, PROF, 71-, chmn. dept, 62-67, chmn. div. arts, 67-71. U.S.A, 46-47. MLA; Milton Soc. Am; NCTE. Milton. Publ: Th'upright heart and pure, Duquesne Univ, 67; Just so much honor, Pa. State Univ, 72; Freedom, liability, and the state of perfection in Paradise lost, Milton Quart, 71; Milton and Kubrick: Eden's apple or A clockwork orange, CEA Critic, 73; Eight arts. on Milton & the Church fathers, In: Milton encyclopedia, Univ. Wis, 74; plus others. Add: Dept. of English, Siena College, Loudonville, NY 12211.

FIRCHOW, PETER EDGERLY, b. Needham, Mass, Dec. 16, 37. ENGLISH & COMPARATIVE LITERATURE. B.A, Harvard, 59, M.A, 61; Univ. Vienna, 59-60; Knapp Trust fel, Univ. Wis, 64-65, Ph.D.(Eng), 65. Asst. prof. Eng, Univ. Mich, 65-67; ENG. & COMP. LIT, UNIV. MINN, MINNEAPOLIS, 67-69, assoc. prof, 69-73, PROF, 73-, CHMN. COMP. LIT. PROG, 72- Univ. Mich. Horace H. Rackham grant, 66-67. MLA; Am. Comp. Lit. Asn. Modern literature, English, European and American. Publ: Ed, Friedrich Schlegel's Lucinde and the fragments, 71 & auth, Aldous Huxley, satirist and novelist, 72, Univ. Minn; Nadja and Le Paysan de Paris: two surrealist novels, Wis. Stud. Contemporary Lit, autumn 65; The satire of Huxley's Brave new world, Mod. Fiction Stud, winter 67; In search of A handful of dust, J. Mod. Lit, winter 72. Add: Dept. of English & Comparative Literature, University of Minnesota, Minneapolis, MN 55455.

FIREBAUGH, JOSEPH JESSE, b. Denver, Colo, May 15, 12; m. 60; c. 1. ENGLISH. B.A, Univ. Colo, 36; A.M, Duke Univ, 38; Am. Counc. Learned Soc. grant, 41-42; Ph.D, Univ. Wash, 52. Instr. Eng, Univ. Ark, 38-41; N.Mex. Agr. & Mech. Col, 42-43; Univ. Mo, 43-44; State Col, Wash, 44-46; Univ. Denver, 46-47; asst. prof. humanities, Univ. Fla, 47-49; ENG, Univ. Mich, 52-53; Queens Col. (N.Y), 53-56; assoc. prof, UNIV. MICH-FLINT, 56-60, PROF, 60-, chmn. dept, 65-70. Vis. prof, Univ. Cape Town, 56; Fulbright prof, Univ. Col. Wales, 62. MLA. The fiction of Henry James; modern fiction; literary criticism. Publ: Pragmatism of Henry James, Va. Quart. Rev; Relativism of Henry James, J. Aesthet. & Art Criticism; The Ververs, Essays in criticism. Add: Dept. of English, University of Michigan-Flint; Flint, MI 48503.

FISCHER, JEROME J, b. New York, N.Y, Dec. 11, 18; m. 60; c. 3. ENGLISH LITERATURE. A.B, Brooklyn Col, 41; M.A, Columbia Univ, 47. Instr. ENG, VILLANOVA UNIV, 47-49, asst. prof, 49-56, ASSOC. PROF, 56- NCTE. British literature of the 19th century; American naturalists as literary figures; English prosody. Publ: Co-auth, Handbook of logic, 56 & Workbook of logic, 56, W.C. Brown. Add: Dept. of English, Villanova University, Villanova, PA 19085.

FISCHER, JOHN IRWIN, b. Chicago, Ill, May 26, 40; m. 62. ENGLISH. A.B, Ohio State Univ, 62; Ph.D.(Eng), Univ. Fla, 68. Instr. ENG, Univ. Fla, 56-58; ASST. PROF, LA. STATE UNIV, BATON ROUGE, 68- MLA; S.Cent. Mod. Lang. Asn. Early 18th century English poetry, especially the poetry of Jonathan Swift. Publ: The uses of virture: Swift's last poem to Stella, In: Essays in honor of Esmond Linsworth Manilla, La. State Univ, 70; How to die: Verses on the death of Dr. Swift, Rev. Eng. Stud, 11/70. Add: Dept. of English, Louisiana State University, Baton Rouge, LA 70803.

FISCHER, RAYMOND LOUIS, b. Detroit, Mich, Feb. 12, 28; m. 56; c. 2. RHETORIC & PUBLIC ADDRESS. B.S, East. Ill. Univ, 54, M.S, 56; Ph.D. (speech), Univ. Ill, Urbana, 68. Instr. SPEECH, Mattoon High Sch, Ill, 54-58; asst. prof, Ill. State Univ, Normal, 58-68; ASSOC. PROF, Univ. Wis-Oshkosh, 68-71; UNIV. N.DAK, 71- Intel.C, U.S.A, 46-47, 52-53, Sgt. Speech Commun. Asn; Cent. States Speech Commun. Asn. History. Publ: Speaking to communicate, Dickenson, 72; Illinois' Ingersoll, Ill..Speech J, fall 68; Ingersoll on the lecture platform, Cent. States Speech J, summer 71. Add: Dept. of Speech, University of North Dakota, University Station, Grand Forks, ND 58201.

FISH, CHARLES KELLEWAY, JR, b. Rutland, Vt, July 27, 36; m. 60; c. 1. ENGLISH, AMERICAN STUDIES. B.A, Northwest. Univ, 58; B.A, Oxford, 60; M.A, Princeton, 62, Ph.D.(Eng), 64. Instr. ENG, Princeton, 63-66, asst. prof, 66-68; ASSOC. PROF, WINDHAM COL, 68-, ACAD. DEAN, 69- Am. Stud. Asn. American literature; American studies. Publ: Henry IV: Shakespeare and Holinshead, Stud. Philol, 4/64; Beginnings: O'Neill's The web, Princeton Libr. Chronicle, fall 65; Form and revision: the example of Watch and ward, Nineteenth-Century Fiction, fall 67. Add: Dept. of English, Windham College, Putney, VT 05346.

FISH, ROBERT STEVENS, b. New York, N.Y, Feb. 26, 41. SPEECH, ORAL INTERPRETATION. B.A, State Univ. N.Y, Albany, 63; M.A, Univ. Okla, 65, Ph.D.(Speech), 70. Instr. SPEECH, State Univ. N.Y. Albany, 66-69; ASST. PROF, SOUTH. ILL. UNIV, CARBONDALE, 70- Speech Commun. Asn. Twentieth century American literature; rhetoric. Publ: The tempering of faith in E. A. Robinson's The man against the sky, Colby Libr, Quart, 3/72. Add: Dept. of Speech, Southern Illinois University, Carbondale, IL 62901.

FISH, STANLEY E, b. Providence, R.I, Apr. 19, 38; m. 59; c. 1. MEDIEVAL & RENAISSANCE ENGLISH. A.B, Univ. Pa, 59; M.A, Yale, 60, Ph.D.(Eng), 62. Instr. ENG, Univ. Calif, Berkeley, 62-63, asst. prof, 63-67, assoc. prof, 67-70, PROF, 70-74; JOHNS HOPKINS UNIV, 74- Am. Counc. Learned Soc. grant-in-aid, 65; humanities res. professorship, Univ. Calif, Berkeley, 66 & 70; Guggenheim fel, 69; vis. prof, Johns Hopkins Univ, 71; Leo S. Bing vis. prof, Univ. South. Calif, 73-74. MLA; Milton Soc. Am. Medieval and Renaissance English literature; contemporary literary theory; the reader in literature. Publ: John Skelton's poetry, Yale Univ, 65; Surprised by sin: the reader in Paradise lost, Macmillan, 67; ed, Seventeenth century prose: modern essays in criticism, Oxford Univ, 71; auth, Self-consuming artifacts: the experience of seventeenth century literature, Univ. Calif, 72; What is stylistics and why are they saying such terrible things about it, In: Approaches to poetics, Columbia Univ, 73. Add: Dept. of English, Johns Hopkins University, Baltimore, MD 21218.

FISHER, BENJAMIN FRANKLIN IV, b. Orwigsburg, Pa, July 21, 40. NINETEENTH & TWENTIETH CENTURY LITERATURE. B.A, Ursinus Col, 62; M.A, Duke Univ, 63, Ph.D.(Eng), 69. Instr. ENG, Univ. Pa, 67-69, asst. prof, 69-73; ADJ. PROF, HAHNEMANN MED. COL, 73- MLA; AAUP; NCTE, Poe Stud. Asn; Dickens Soc. Nineteenth century English and American literature; novel. Publ: Poe's Metzengerstein: not a hoax, Am. Lit, 1/71; Swinburne's Tristram of Lyonesse in process, Tex. Stud. Lit. & Lang, fall 72; Rossetti and Swinburne in tandem: The laird of Waristoun, Victorian Poetry, fall 73. Add: 302 E. Market St, Orwigsburg, PA 17961.

FISHER, JAMES A, b. Philadelphia, Pa, Dec. 26, 19; m. 51. ENGLISH LITERATURE. A.B, Boston Univ, 43, M.A, 49. Instr. HUMANITIES, COL. BASIC STUD, BOSTON UNIV, 51-54, asst. prof, 54-57, assoc. prof, 57-60, PROF, 60-, CHMN. DIV, 54- Mil.Intel, U.S.A, 43-46. Utopian speculation; philosophy. Publ: The humanities in general education, W.C. Brown, 60; co-auth, Critical thinking in the humanities, Boston Univ, 56. Add; Div. of Humanities, College of Basic Studies, Boston University, Boston, MA 02215.

FISHER, JAMES RANDOLPH, b. Norfolk, Va, Nov. 5, 06. ENGLISH LANGUAGE & LITERATURE. A.B, Howard Univ, 31, A.M, 33; Ohio State Univ, 38-39; Univ. Oslo, Norway, 54. Chmn. dept. lang. & lit, Rust Col, 35-38; Allen Univ, 40-43; sophomore Eng, Tenn. State Col, 45-47; prof. ENG, SAVANNAH STATE COL, 47-72, chmn. sophomore Eng, 48-74, chmn. dept. lang. & lit, prof, 72-74, EMER. PROF, 74- MLA; Mod. Humanities Res. Asn; Int. Asn. Univ. Prof. Eng; Col. Eng. Asn; CLA; Milton Soc. Am. Publ: What American credo means to me, 55, What is American way of life?, 62 & The American credo, 63, Freedoms Found. Add: Dept. of English, Box 20434, Savannah State College, Savannah, GA 31404.

FISHER, JOHN HURT, b. Lexington, Ky, Oct. 26, 19; m. 42; c. 3. ENGLISH. A.B, Maryville Col, 40; A.M, Univ. Pa, 42, Ph.D, 45; hon. Litt.D, Middlebury Col, 70; hon. L.H.D, Loyola Univ. Chicago, 70. From asst. to instr, Univ. Pa, 42-45; instr, Wash. Sq. Col, N.Y. Univ, 45-48, asst. prof. ENG, 48-55; assoc. prof, Duke Univ, 55-58, prof, 58-60; Ind. Univ, 60-62; N.Y. Univ, 62-72; JOHN C. HODGES PROF, UNIV. TENN, KNOXVILLE, 72- Vis. lectr, Univ. South. Calif, summer 55; Univ. Mich, summer 56; consult, U.S. Off. Educ, 62-65; mem, U.S. Comn, UNESCO, 63-69; chmn, Am. Counc. Learned Soc. Conf. Secys, 65-68; mem. exec. comt, Int. Fed. Mod. Lang. & Lit, 67-71, Am. v.pres, 72-; trustee, Woodrow Wilson Nat. Fel. Found, 72-; dir, Maryville col, 72- MLA (asst. secy, 49-51, treas, 52-55, exec. secy. & ed, PMLA, 63-71, pres, 74); Mediaeval Acad. Am; Ling. Soc. Am; NCTE (distinguished lectr, 71-72); Mod. Humanities Res. Asn, Gt. Brit. Medieval literature and the English language. Publ: Ed, Tretyse of love, Early Eng. Text Soc, 51; auth, John Gower: moral philosopher and friend of Chaucer, N.Y. Univ, 64; co-auth, The college teaching of English, Appleton, 65; ed, The Medieval literature of Western Europe: a review of research, N.Y. Univ, 66; co-auth, In forme of speche is chaunge, Prentice-Hall, 74. Add: Dept. of English, University of Tennessee, Knoxville, TN 37916.

FISHER, MARVIN, b. Detroit, Mich, Nov. 19, 27; m. 56; c. 3. AMERICAN STUDIES. A.B, Wayne Univ, 50, A.M, 52; Ph.D, Univ. Minn, 58. Instr. ENG, Gen. Motors Inst, 52-53; Univ. Minn, 53-58; asst. prof, ARIZ. STATE UNIV, 58-60, assoc. prof, 60-66, PROF, 66- Huntington Libr. res. fel, 60; Fulbright lectr, Greece, 61-63, Norway, 66-67; vis. prof, Univ. Calif, Davis, 69-70. U.S.A, 46-47. MLA; Am. Stud. Asn; NCTE; Melville Soc. Am. American Reniassance; 19th century technology and its impact on the American imagination; Herman Melville. Publ: Workshops in the wilderness, Oxford, 67; Pattern of conservatism in Johnson's Rasselas and Hawthorne's Tales, J. Hist. Ideas, 58; The garden and the workshop, New Eng. Quart, 61; Melville's Tartarus: the deflowering of New England, Am. Quart, 71; plus many others. Add: Dept. of English, Arizona State University, Tempe, AZ 85281.

FISHER, STEPHANIE ANNE, b. Portland, Ore, Jan. 18, 37; div; c. 2. RENAISSANCE LITERATURE. B.A, Portland State Univ, 64; Reed Col, 64-66; M.A, Univ. Minn, 68, Sam Holt Monk fel. & Ph.D.(Eng), 71. Teacher Eng. & biol, Grant High Sch, Ore, 64-66; Instr. ENG, Univ. Minn, 66-70; ASST. PROF, WEST. MICH. UNIV, 71- Nat. Endowment for Humanities stipend, 72. NCTE; MLA. Renaissance literature; images of women in literature; relationship between visual arts and literature. Publ: Milton's Raphael as a lover, Explicator, 75. Add: Dept. of English, Western Michigan University, Kalamazoo, MI 49001.

FISHER, WALTER RAY, b. Honolulu, Hawaii, Jan. 4, 31; m. 52; c. 2. SPEECH, DRAMA. B.A, San Diego State Col, 56, M.A, 57; Ph.D, Univ. Iowa, 60. Asst. prof. SPEECH, Los Angeles State Coll, 60-65, assoc. prof, 65; asst. prof, UNIV. SOUTH. CALIF, 65-67, assoc. prof, 67-71, PROF, 71- U.S.M.C, 48-52; U.S.A.F.R, 56-61, 1st Lt. Speech Commun. Asn; Rhetoric Soc. Am. Theories of rhetoric and communication; rhetorical criticism. Publ: Co-auth, Armament and disarmament: the continuing dispute, Wadsworth, 64; co-ed, British public addresses, 1828-1960, Houghton, 71; co-auth, The nature and functions of argument, In: Perspectives on argumentation, Scott, 66; auth, A motive view of communication, 4/70 & Reaffirmation and subversion of the American dream, 4/73, Quart. J. Speech. Add: Dept. of Speech Communication, University of Southern California, Los Angeles, CA 90007.

FISHER, WILLIAM ANDREW, b. Noblesville, Ind, July 10, 23; m. 48; c. 2. JOURNALISM. A.B, Franklin Col, 45; M.S.J, Northwest. Univ, 49. Newspaperman, 45-50; from asst. prof. to assoc. prof. JOUR, KENT STATE UNIV, 50-66, PROF. & ASSOC. CHMN. SCH. JOUR, 66- Journalism and mass communications. Add: School of Journalism, Kent State University, Kent, OH 44240.

FISHER, WILLIAM J, b. Brooklyn, N.Y, Dec. 10, 19; m. 48; c. 3. ENGLISH. A.B, Col. William & Mary, 41; M.A, Univ. Ariz, 45; Ford Found. fel, 51-52; Ph.D.(Eng), N.Y. Univ, 52. Teaching fel. ENG, Univ. Ariz, 44-45, instr, 45-47; N.Y. Univ, 47-52; lectr. & instr, UNIV. COL, RUTGERS UNIV, 52-57, asst. prof, 57-62, assoc. prof, 62-69, PROF, 69-, fac. res. fel, 66-67. Lectr, Eng, fac. philos, Columbia Univ, 55-57; Fulbright lectr, India, 61-63. NCTE; MLA. Eugene O'Neill; modern tragedy; literature of madness. Publ: Co-ed, O'Neill and his plays, N.Y. Univ, 61; ed-in-chief, American literature of the 19th century, Eurasia, New Delhi, 65; auth, What ever happened to Saroyan?, Col. Eng; Poetry of D.H. Lawrence S.Atlantic Quart; Pirandello's Enrico IV, Setting the stage, 67. Add: 1 W. 85th St, New York, NY 10024.

FISHMAN, JOSHUA AARON, Sociolinguistics. See Volume III, Foreign Languages, Linguistics & Philology.

FISK, NORMA JEAN, b. Baton Rouge, La, Sept. 11, 43. ENGLISH LITERATURE, RENAISSANCE DRAMA. B.A, Rice Univ, 65; M.A, Univ. Tex, Austin, 69, Ph.D.(Eng), 73. Teaching asst. ENG, Univ. Tex, Austin, 65-68, 69-70, instr, 70-71; ASST. PROF, UNIV. MO-COLUMBIA, 73- MLA; AAUP. Modern drama. Add: Dept. of English, University of Missouri-Columbia, Columbia, MO 65201.

FISKIN, ABRAM M. I, b. Winnipeg, Man, Apr. 3, 16; U.S. citizen; m. 49. ENGLISH. B.A, Univ. Man, 36; M.A, Univ. Minn, 41, Ph.D, 64. Instr. ENG, Northwest. Univ, 43-47; asst. prof, Denver Univ, 48-51; assoc. prof, Drake Univ, 64-66; vis. assoc. prof, Chapman Col, World Campus Afloat, 66-67; ASSOC. PROF, PA. STATE UNIV, UNIVERSITY PARK, 67- MLA; AAAS; AAUP; Soc. Tech. Commun. English drama; 20th century literature; technical and business writing. Publ: Ed, Writers of our years, Univ. Denver, 50; auth, Way of the world, 66, The rivals and The school for scandal & The alchemist, 67, Cliffs; Luigi Pirandello: the tragedy of the man who thinks, Italica, 3/49; Basic unity of Eugene O'Neill, In: Writers of our years, Univ. Denver, 50. Add: Dept. of English, Pennsylvania State University, University Park, PA 16802.

FITCH, JOSEPH CLAY, b. Springville, Tenn, June 16, 21; m. 48; c. 3. THEATRE ARTS. B.S, Murray State Col, 42, M.A, 46; M.F.A, Yale, 49. Assoc. prof. THEATRE ARTS, MONT. STATE UNIV, 49-65, PROF. & CHMN. DEPT, 65-; PRES, LOFT THEATRE, INC, 67- Consult, theatre archit, 58-; res. assoc, Frontier Theatre Res. Ctr, 62-; Fulbright-Hays lectr, Univ. San Carlos, Philippines, 64-65; chmn. liaison comt, Am. Theatre Asn-Philippines Educ. Asn, 68-; consult, Douglass House Found, 69-; exec. comt, Bicentennial Adv. Coun, 73- U.S.M.C, 42-63, Maj. Am. Theatre Asn; Am. Nat Theatre & Acad; Asia Soc.(mem. Philippines Counc); Asn. Asian Stud; Rocky Mountain Theatre Conf.(pres, 66-67); fel. Am. Playwrights Theatre. Theatre architecture; current status of Peking opera in Peoples Republic of China; the political usage of literature and the arts in Asia. Publ: Peking opera: its nature as a tool for the Chinese Communist Party, Solidarity, Manila, 5/72; The Filipinos' search for cultural identity through theatre, Proc. 28th Int. Cong. Orientalists, 73. Add: Dept. of Theatre Arts, Montana State University, Bozeman, MT 59715.

FITCH, RAYMOND E, b. Boston, Mass, Jan. 23, 30; m. 52. NINETEENTH CENTURY LITERATURE, CRITICISM. A.B, Harvard, 52; A.M, Univ. Mich, 55; Ph.D.(Eng), Univ. Pa, 65. Asst. prof. ENG, Pa. Mil. Col, 57-60; S.Conn. State Col, 61-66; ASSOC. PROF, OHIO UNIV, 66- MLA. Literature and myth; works of Ruskin; critical theory. Publ: Ed, Dramatic romances and lyrics, Vol. IV, In: Complete Works of Robert Browning, Ohio Univ, 73. Add: Dept. of English, Ohio University, Athens, OH 45701.

FITE, OLIVE, b. Berryville, Ill, Nov. 21, 11. ENGLISH. Ph.D.(Eng), Northwest. Univ, 56. Teacher, elem. schs, Ill, 37-46; asst. prof. ENG, Ind. Cent. Col, 46-47; WEST. ILL. UNIV, 47-56, assoc. prof, 56-61, prof, 61-72, EM EMER. PROF, 72- Melville Soc. Am. Melville. Publ: Billy Budd, Claggart, and Schopenhauer, Nineteenth Century Fiction, 12/68. Add: 907 Stadium Dr, Macomb, IL 61455.

FITTERER, HAROLD JOSEPH, b. Mapleton, Minn, July 9, 26; m. 56; c. 3. ENGLISH, ENGLISH EDUCATION. B.S, Mankato State Col, 50; M.A, Univ. Wis-Madison, 55; alumni fel, Columbia Univ, 61-62; Ph.D.(Eng, educ), Univ. Minn, Minneapolis, 70. Instr. Eng, debate & drama, Mankato Pub. Schs, Minn, 50-61, 62-64; Eng. & educ, Columbia Univ, 61-62; PROF. ENG, MANKATO STATE COL, 64- Dir. reading inst, Queens Col.(N.Y), summer 63. U.S.N, 44-46. NCTE. Teaching of English in secondary school. Publ: Co-auth, The college and the future, Mankato State Col, 72; auth, Minnesota English project, Minn. Eng. J, fall 68. Add: 2047 Roecrest Dr, North Mankato, MN 56001.

FITZ GERALD, A. GREGORY, b. New York, N.Y, Apr. 23, 23; div; c. 1. ENGLISH. A.B, Boston Univ, 46; M.A, Breadloaf Sch. Eng, Middlebury Col, 53; Ph.D.(Eng), Univ. Iowa, 67. Chmn. Eng, High Sch, 50-52; instr, Briscoe Sch, 52-54; Univ. Iowa, 55-61, 64; Jackson Jr. Col, 61-62; asst. prof, Ind. State Univ, 62-65; dir. compos, Ithaca Col, 65-67; dir. creative writing, STATE UNIV. N.Y. COL. BROCKPORT, 67-70, PROF. ENG, 73- Smith-Mundt grant, Damascus, Syria, 55-56; State Univ. N.Y. Res. Found. grant-in-aid, 68-70, summer fels, 69, 70 & 74; chmn. fine arts sub-comt, State Univ. N.Y. Albany Univ. Awards Comt, 73-74. MLA; NCTE. Satire; contemporary poetry and short fiction; creative writing. Publ: Modern satiric stories: the impropriety principle, Scott, 71; co-auth, Past, present, and future perfect, Fawcett, 73; auth, Hunting the yahoos, Balthus, Wales, 74; The satiric short story: a definition, Stud. Short Fiction, summer 69; A touch of nature, Fiction Int, fall 73; Player as for an old flamenco, Poetry Newslett, spring 74; plus others. Add: Dept. of English, State University of New York College at Brockport, Brockport, NY 14420.

FITZGERALD, GERALD PIERCE, b. Boston, Mass, Apr. 29, 30; m. 53; c. 2. ENGLISH & COMPARATIVE LITERATURE. A.B, Harvard, 52, Nat. scholar. & M.A, 57, jr. fel. & Ph.D.(comp. lit), 63. Instr. hist, lit. & Romance lang, Harvard, 62-63; asst. prof. ENG, BOSTON UNIV, 63-66, assoc. prof, 67-73, PROF, 73-, univ. prof, 73-74. Med.C, U.S.A, 52-55. MLA; Renaissance Soc. Am. Comparative literature of Renaissance, Neo-Latin, Italian literature. Publ: The wordless flesh and other poems, 60 & Daughters of earth, sons of heaven (poems), 69, Identity; transl, The theory of the avant-garde, Harvard, 68; Virgil's sixth ecologue, 67, auth, The heart of Earth: Quasimodo's poetry, 67 & On Shakespeare's Sonnet 104, 68, Boston Univ. Grad. J; transl, Mallarmé's L'Après, Midi d'un Faune, Boston Univ. J, autumn, 73 Add: Dept. of English, Boston University, Boston, MA 02215.

FITZGERALD, HUGH D, b. Riverside, Ill, July 8, 26. SPEECH, THEATRE, ENGLISH. Ph.B, Loyola Univ.(Ill), 51; M.A, Cath. Univ. Am, 54; Univ. Wis, summers, 57-61, 63. Instr. speech, Loras Col, 54-55, asst. prof, 55-56; instr. speech, theatre & Eng, QUINCY COL, 56-59, asst. prof, 59-63, ASSOC. PROF. ENG. & DRAMA, 63- Artistic dir, Progressive Playhouse, Quincy, 58-; mem. bd, Jr. Theatre, 62- U.S.N.R, 44-46. Nat. Cath. Theatre Conf. Theatre production. Add: Dept. of Fine Arts, Quincy College, Quincy, IL 62301.

FITZGERALD, ROBERT PAUL, b. Elmira, N.Y, Nov. 5, 32; wid; c. 1. ENGLISH. A.B, Cornell Univ, 53; M.A, Univ. Iowa, 59, Ph.D.(Eng), 64. Instr. ENG, Univ. Iowa, 59-62; Univ. N.C, 62-65, asst. prof, 65-67; ASSOC. PROF, PA. STATE UNIV, 67- U.S.A, 53-55, Sgt. MLA. Anglo-Saxon poetry; pre-romantic poetry; Jonathan Swift. Publ: The wife's lament and The search for the lost husband, J. Eng. & Ger. Philol, 10/63; The style of Ossian, Stud. Romanticism, 10/66; The allegory of Luggnagg and the Struldbruggs in Gulliver's travels, Stud. Philol, 7/68. Add: Dept. of English, Pennsylvania State University, University Park, PA 16802.

FITZGERALD, ROBERT STUART, b. Geneva, N.Y, Oct. 12, 10; m. 47; c. 6. ENGLISH. A.B, Harvard, 33; hon. D.Litt, Col. Holy Cross, 67. Reporter, N.Y. Herald Tribune, 33-35; writer, Time Mag, 36-49; instr. ENG, Sarah Lawrence Col, 46-53; Princeton, 50-52; vis. prof, Notre Dame Univ, 57; Univ. Wash, 61; Mt. Holyoke Col, 64; PROF, HARVARD, 64- Fel, Univ. Ind. Sch. Lett, 51-; Guggenheim fel, 52-53 & 71-72; Ford Found. grant, 59. Poetry Soc. Am. Shelley Mem. Award, 55; Bollingen Award, 61. U.S.N.R, 43-46, Lt. Fel, Nat. Inst. Arts & Lett.(award, 57); fel, Am. Acad. Arts & Sci; Cath. Comn. Intellectual & Cult. Affairs. Poetry; translation. Publ: Poems, Arrow Eds, 35; co-transl, Antigone of Sophocles, 39 & Oedipus Rex of Sophocles, 49 & transl, Oedipus at Colonus by Sophocles, 41, Harcourt; auth, A wreath for the sea, 43, In the rose of time, 56 & Spring shade, 71, New Directions; transl, The Odyssey of Homer, 61 & The Iliad of Homer, 74, Doubleday; ed, The collected short prose of James Agee, Houghton, 69. Add: Dept. of English, Harvard University, Cambridge, MA 02138.

FITZGIBBONS, ELEANOR, I.H.M, b. Detroit, Mich, Sept. 20, 09. ENGLISH. Ph.D, Cath. Univ. Am, 43. Instr, ENG, MARYGROVE COL, 36-42, asst. prof, 43-50, assoc. prof, 51-58, PROF, 58- MLA; NCTE. Elizabethan drama. Publ: Ed, The odd couple, Cath. Univ. Am, 43. Add: Dept. of English, Marygrove College, 8425 W. McNichols, Detroit, MI 48221.

FITZHUGH, ROBERT TYSON, b. Baltimore, Md, Aug. 15, 06; m. 29; c. 3. LITERATURE. B.S, Wesleyan Univ, 27; A.M, Harvard, 29; Ph.D, Cornell Univ, 35. Teacher, Germantown Friends Sch, Pa, 28; instr. ENG, Univ. Md, 29-34, asst. prof, 35-40, assoc. prof, 41-46; Lehigh Univ, 46-47; BROOKLYN COL, 47-56, prof, 56-70, EMER. PROF, 70- U.S.N.R, 43-44, Lt. MLA; Col. Eng. Asn.(exec. secy. & ed, Critic, 45-49, pres, 50). Robert Burns; 18th century literature; comedy and satire. Publ: Handbook of writing; Robert Burns, his associates and contemporaries; Robert Burns: the man and the poet, Houghton, 70. Add: No Ruz Farm, Craryville, NY 12521.

FITZMAURICE, JAMES BARRY, b. Ventura, Calif, July 23, 43; m. 65; c. 3. ENGLISH RENAISSANCE LITERATURE. B.A, Occidental Col, 65; M.A, Calif. State Univ, Long Beach, 67; Ph.D.(Eng), Univ. Iowa, 71. Teaching asst. rhet, Univ. Iowa, 69-70, core lit, 70-71; ASST. PROF. ENG, NORTH. ARIZ. UNIV, 71- Fel, Newberry Libr, summer 73. MLA; Renaissance Soc. Am; NCTE. Edmund Spenser's Faerie Queene; iconography; mythography. Publ: A gathering of emblem books, Bks. at Iowa, spring 71. Add: Box 15700, Center for Integrated Studies, Northern Arizona University, Flagstaff, AZ 86001.

FITZPATRICK, EDWARD CLEMENT, JR, b. Elkader, Iowa, Nov. 3, 14; m. 41; c. 2. SPEECH, DRAMA. B.A, State Univ. Iowa, 36; Yale, 36-39; M.A, Univ. N.C, 51. Instr. speech & drama, Univ. Del, 47; speech & radio, Womans Col, Univ. N.C, 47-50, asst. stage lighting, Univ, 50-51; instr. SPEECH & DRAMA, Univ. Colo, 51-54; asst. prof, Univ. Santa Clara, 54-56; Los Angeles State Col, 56-61; ASSOC. PROF, SOUTH. ORE. COL, 61- U.S.N.R, 41-42. Theatre design; art history; technical theatre. Add: Dept. of Speech & Drama, Southern Oregon College, Ashland, OR 97520.

FITZPATRICK, EDWARD TIMOTHY, b. New York, N.Y, July 27, 21; m. 53; c. 7. ENGLISH. B.S, Fordham Univ, 45, Ph.D.(Eng), 67; M.A, St. John's Univ.(N.Y), 47. Teacher Eng, All Hallows High Sch, 41-49; librn, New York Pub. Libr, 50-52; teacher ENG. & chmn. dept, Sacred Heart High Sch, Yonkers, 52-62; asst. prof, ST. FRANCIS COL.(PA), 62-70, assoc. prof, 70-73, PROF, 73- NCTE. Add: Dept. of English, St. Francis College, Loretto, PA 15940.

FITZSIMMONS, THOMAS, b. Lowell, Mass, Oct. 21, 26; m. 52; c. 2. ENGLISH. B.A, Stanford Univ, 51; cert. Fr. lit, philos. & int. affairs, Sorbonne & Inst. Sci. Polit, 49 & 50; M.A, Columbia Univ, 52. Staff writer, New Repub. Mag, 52-54, assoc. ed, 54-55; dir. res. anthrop, Human Relat. Area Files, 55-59; asst. prof. ENG, OAKLAND UNIV, 59-61, assoc. prof, 62-65, PROF, 65- Spec. consult, Hist. Div. Dept. of Defense, 52; res. assoc, Yale, 56-59; Fulbright prof, Tokyo Univ. Educ. & Tsuda-Juku Women's Col, Japan, 62-64; vis. prof, Am. stud. sem, Pakistan, summer 64, Univ. Bucharest, 67-68, Univ. Nice, summer 68; Nat. Found. for Arts poetry grant, 67; prof, Tokyo Univ. Educ. & vis. poet, Japan Women's Univ. & Keio Univ, Japan, 73-75. U.S. Merchant Marine, 42-45, Lt.(jg); U.S.A.A.F, 45. PEN Club. Poetry; cultural anthropology; philosophy of symbolism. Publ: Co-auth, RSFSR (2vols), 57 & USSR, 60, Human Relat. Area Files, Yale Univ; auth, Blues for tomorrow (poems), Tribe Gentle Press, 66; co-auth. & transl, Japanese poetry now, Rapp & Whiting, London, 69, Schocken, New York & Whiting/Deutsch, London, 72; co-auth, Ghazals of Ghalib, Columbia Univ, 71; auth, With the water (poems), New Voices Press, 72; Playseeds (poems), Pilot Press, 73; plus others. Add: Dept. of English, Oakland University, Rochester, MI 48063.

FIXLER, MICHAEL, b. Kisvarda, Hungary, Aug. 14, 27; U.S. citizen; m. 49; c. 3. ENGLISH LITERATURE. B.A, Univ. Wis, 48; Sorbonne, 48-51; B.A, Oxford, 54, M.A, 59; M.F.S, Univ. Md, 55; Alvia K. Brown fel, Univ. Chicago, 54-55, Univ. fels, 55-56, Ph.D, 61. Instr. ENG, Northwest. Univ, 57-61; asst. prof, TUFTS UNIV, 61-64, assoc. prof, 64-68, GOLDSMITH PROF, 68- Danforth Found. stud. grant, 59-60; Soc. Relig. Higher Educ. fel, 67-; vis. scholar, Harvard Divinity Sch, 67-68; mem. ed. bd, Milton Stud, 68- MLA; Renaissance Soc. Am; Milton Soc. Am. John Milton and the 17th century; aesthetic movement in English literature. Publ: Milton and the kingdoms of God, Faber & Faber & Northwest. Univ, 64; ed, The Mentor Bible, New American Libr, 73; auth, Milton's passionate epic, In: Milton Studies I, Univ. Pittsburgh, 69; The apocalypse in Paradise lost, In: Gravity and ease, Univ. Calif, 69; The Orphic technique of L'Allegro and Il Penseroso Eng. Lit. Renaissance, spring 71; plus three others. Add: Dept. of English, Tufts University, Medford, MA 02155.

FJELDE, ROLF GERHARD, b. Brooklyn, N.Y, Mar. 15, 26; m. 64; c. 3. MODERN DRAMA. B.A, Yale, 46; M.A, Columbia Univ, 47; Am-Scand. Found. fel, Univ. Copenhagen, 52-53; Univ. Heidelberg, 53; Univ. Oslo, 65. Instr. Eng, PRATT INST, 54-58, asst. prof, 58-64, assoc. prof, 64-69, PROF. ENG. & DRAMA, 69- Fel, YADDO Found, 52, 54; playwright-in-residence, Eugene O'Neill Mem. Theater Ctr, 66, 67, 70; fel, Nat. Transl. Ctr, Ford Found, 67-68; lectr. drama, Juilliard Sch, 73- Dramatists Guild; Auth. League Am; Am. Theater Asn; Soc. Advan. Scand. Stud; Am-Scand. Found.(mem. publ. comt, 67). Henrik Ibsen; modern drama; Scandinavian literature. Publ: Washington (poems), Caliban Press, 55; The imaged word (poems), Adlib Press, 62; transl. & ed, Peer Gynt, 64, Four major plays, Vol. I, 65 & Four major plays, Vol. II, 70, New Am. Libr; ed, Ibsen: a collection of critical essays, Prentice-Hall, 65; auth, Peer Gynt, naturalism and the dissolving self, Drama Rev, 69; The dimensions of Ibsen's dramatic world, Universitetsforlaget, 71; Plotting Pinter's progress, In: A casebook on Harold Pinter's The homecoming, Grove Press, 71. Add: Dept. of English, Pratt Institute, Brooklyn, NY 11205.

FLAMM, DUDLEY, b. Brooklyn, N.Y, Mar, 25, 31; m. 59; c. 2. ENGLISH, COMPARATIVE LITERATURE. A.B, Columbia Univ, 52, M.A, 58, Ph.D. (Eng. & comp. lit), 64. Teacher Eng. lang. & lit, N.Y.C. sch. syst. & Eng. as second lang, N.Y.C. adult educ, 57-58; lectr. ENG. LANG. & LIT, Fairleigh Dickinson Univ, 58-60; Brooklyn Col, 63-65; asst. prof, ST. OLAF COL, 65-69, ASSOC. PROF, 69- U.S.N, 52-56, Lt.(jg). Nat. Indian Educ. Asn; MLA. Publ: Thackeray's critics, Univ. N.C, 67; The ambiguous Nazarene in Lord Jim, Eng. Lit. in Transition, 68; Herzog—victim & hero, Zeitschrift für Anglistikund Amerikanistik, 69; The prosecutor within: Dickens' final explanation, Dickensian, 69. Add: Rte. 1, Northfield, MN 55057.

FLANAGAN, JOHN T, b. Jan. 15, 06; m. 29; c. 3. AMERICAN LITERATURE. A.B, Univ. Minn, 27, A.M, 28, Ph.D, 35. Instr. ENG, Univ. N.Dak, 28-29; Univ. Minn, 29-38, asst. prof, 38-45; prof, South. Methodist Univ, 45-46; assoc. prof. UNIV. ILL, URBANA, 46-49, PROF, 49- Guggenheim fel, 43-44; Newberry fel, 44; vis. lectr, Kyoto Univ, Japan, summer, 52; Fulbright lectr, Univ. Bordeaux, 52-53; Univs. Brussels, Liège & Ghent, Belgium, 60-61; vis. lectr, Univs. Moscow & Leningrad, 63; mem. ed. bd, Am. Lit, 68-71. MLA; Am. Folklore Soc; Orgn. Am. Hist; Am. Stud. Asn. Literature of the Middle West; 19th century American literature; American folklore. Publ: James Hall, literary pioneer of the Ohio Valley, 41 & America is west, 45, Univ. Minn; co-auth, Folklore in American literature, Row, Peterson & Co, 58; ed, Profile of Vachel Lindsay, C.E. Merrill, 70; auth, Folklore, In: American literary scholarship, 1966-1972: an annual, Duke Univ, 68-74; The fiction of Jessamyn West, Ind. Mag. Hist, 12/71; Three Illinois poets, Centennial Rev, fall 72; plus others. Add: 705 W. Michigan, Urbana, IL 61801.

FLANAGAN, THOMAS JAMES BONNER, b. Greenwich, Conn, Nov. 5, 23; m. 49; c. 2. ENGLISH. A.B, Amherst Col, 46; A.M, Columbia Univ, 48, Ph.D, 58. Instr. ENG, Columbia Univ, 52-58, asst. prof, 58-60; UNIV. CALIF. BERKELEY, 60-61, from assoc. prof. to PROF, 61-, CHMN. DEPT, 73- Am. Counc. Learned Soc. grant-in-aid, 62; Guggenheim fel, 62-63. U.S.N.R, 43-46. MLA; Am. Comt. Irish Stud; Int. Asn. Stud. Irish Lit. Modern British literature; Irish literature; Irish cultural history. Publ: The Irish novelist, Columbia Univ, 60; plus articles in Kenyon Rev, Irish Univ. Rev, Victorian Stud. & Hibernia. Add: Dept. of English, University of California, Berkeley, CA 94720.

FLANDERS, BERTRAM HOLLAND, b. Statesboro, Ga, Aug. 25, 92; m. 30. ENGLISH. A.B, Emory Univ, 29, fel, 29-30, M.A, 30; Ph.D.(Eng), Duke Univ, 42. Asst. prof. ENG, Emory Univ, 30-37; prof. & head dept, N.Ga. Col, 38-49; prof. & head dept, GA. STATE COL, 49-60, EMER. PROF, 60- Walker Award, 56. Southern periodicals; Joseph Addison Turner, patron of Joel Chandler Harris. Publ: Early Georgia magazines, Univ. Ga; A new frontier in education, Ga. State Col; ed, Gems of the Atlanta Authors Guild, Franklin Press; The Confederate Navy Yard at Safgold, Georgia, In: Collections of Early County Historical Society, Early Co. Hist. Soc, 71. Add: 304 River St, Blakely, GA 31723.

FLANNAGAN, ROY C, b. Richmond, Va, Dec. 2, 38; div; c. 2. ENGLISH. B.A, Washington & Lee Univ, 60; M.A, Univ. Va, 61, Ph.D.(Eng), 66. Asst. prof. ENG, Va. Mil. Inst, 65-66; ASSOC. PROF, OHIO UNIV, 66- Folger Shakespeare Libr. fel, summer 67; ed, Milton Newsletter, 67-69, Milton Quart, 70-; lectr, Ohio Univ, Italy, summer 68, head summer 70. Ohio Univ Baker Award, 67. MLA. Milton; Renaissance Italian and English literature. Publ: Introd, The life of Adam, Scholar's Facsimiles, 67. Add: Dept. of English, College of Arts & Sciences, Ohio University, Athens, OH 45701.

FLANNERY, MARY CATHERINE, b. St. Cloud, Minn, June 27, 43; c. 1. LITERATURE IN ENGLISH, HISTORY. B.S, Moorhead State Col, 64; M.A, Ind. Univ. Bloomington, 67, Am. Asn. Univ. Women fel, 69-70, Ph.D.(Eng), 73. Teacher ENG, Larkin High Sch, Elgin, Ill, 64-65; teaching assoc, Ind. Univ, Bloomington, 65-69; ASST. PROF, UNIV. TEX, AUSTIN, 70- Ford Found. fel, 73-74. MLA; S.Cent. Mod. Lang. Asn.(secy. Anglo-Irish sect, 73-74). Anglo-Irish literature and history; American literature and history; British literature and history. Add: Dept. of English, University of Texas at Austin, Austin, TX 78712.

FLASCH, NEVA JOY, b. Denison, Tex, Mar. 23, 32; m. 56; c. 3. ENGLISH. B.A.Ed, Southeast. State Col, 51; M.A, Okla. State Univ, 54, Langston Univ. grant, 67-68, Ed.D.(Eng), 69. Instr. High Sch, Okla, 51-53; ENG, Okla. State Univ, 54-62; LANGSTON UNIV, 64-66, asst. prof, 66-67, assoc. prof, 68-69, PROF, 69-, CHMN. DEPT. COMMUN, 73- NCTE. English; Negro Poet Melvin B. Tolson. Publ: Melvin B. Tolson, Twayne, 72; Games people play in Who's afraid of Virginia Woolf, Mod. Drama, 12/67; M.B. Tolson: a great American poet, Okla. Librn, 10/68; Humor and satire in the poetry of M.B. Tolson, Satire Newsletter, fall 69. Add: Rte. 1, Coyle, OK 73027.

FLAUTZ, JOHN THOMAS, b. Columbus, Ohio, Oct. 13, 30; m. 51; c. 2. ENGLISH. B.S, Ohio State Univ, 51; M.A, West. Reserve Univ, 53, Ph.D.(Eng), 63. Instr. ENG, Kent State Univ, 57-61; CEDAR CREST COL, 61-64, asst. prof, 64-69, assoc. prof, 69-73, PROF, 73- AAUP. History of American journalism; American humor, primarily 19th century. Publ: Life: the gentle satirist, Bowling Green Univ, 72; The complete works in English of W—. G—, In: The college experience, Chandler Publ, 62; The dialect sermon in American literature, In: Popular literature in America, Bowling Green Univ, 72. Add: Dept. of English, Cedar Crest College, Allentown, PA 18104.

FLECK, PAUL DUNCAN, b. Montreal, Que, Apr. 17, 34; m. 56; c. 2. ENGLISH. B.A, Univ. West. Ont, 55, M.A, 58; dipl. Eng, Univ. Edinburgh, 59; Ph.D.(Eng), Queen's Univ.(Belfast), 61. Instr. ENG, UNIV. WEST. ONT, 56-58, lectr, 61-62, asst. prof, 62-65, assoc. prof, 65-70, PROF, 70-, CHMN. DEPT, 67- Mem. nat. comt, World Univ. Serv, Can, 63-65; Can. Counc. grant, 64; mem, Eng. comt, Ont. Inst. Stud. Educ, 66-68. MLA; Eng. Inst; Asn. Can. Univ. Teachers Eng. Poetry, 1798-1832; the gothic novel. Publ: Mary Shelley's notes to Shelley's poems and Frankenstein, Stud. Romanticism, summer 67. Add: Dept. of English, University of Western Ontario, London, Ont. N6A 3K7, Can.

FLECK, RICHARD FRANCIS, b. Philadelphia, Pa, Aug. 24, 37; m. 63; c. 3. AMERICAN LITERATURE, NATURAL HISTORY. B.A, Rutgers Univ, New Brunswick, 59; M.A, Colo. State Univ, 62; Ph.D.(Eng), Univ. N.Mex, 70. Bibliog. asst, Princeton Univ. Libr, 62-63; instr. French & Eng, N.Adams State Col, 63-65; ENG, UNIV. WYO, 65-70, ASST. PROF, 70- Contrib. writer, Thoreau Fel, 69-; contrib. writer & lectr, Thoreau Found, 70- U.S.N.R, 61-63. Rocky Mt. Mod. Lang. Asn.(chmn. Am. lit. sect, 70-71); Thoreau Soc; Am. Nature Stud. Soc. Publ: Symbolic landscapes in Edgar Huntly, 71 & Thoreau as mythologist, 72, Res. Stud; Thoreau's New England mythology, Thoreau J. Quart, 72; plus others. Add: Dept. of English, University of Wyoming, Laramie, WY 82070.

FLEISCHAUER, WARREN L, b. Lincoln, Nebr, May 26, 16; m. 42. ENGLISH. A.B, Mich. State Univ, 37; M.A, Columbia Univ, 39; Ph.D.(Eng), West. Reserve Univ, 52. Instr. ENG, Mich. State Univ, 39-42; U.S. Army Univ.(France), 45-46; Mich. State Univ, 46-52, asst. prof, 52-55; John Carroll Univ, 55-60; assoc. prof, C.W. Post Col, Long Island Univ, 60-62; PROF, FROSTBURG STATE COL, 63-, head dept, 67-72. A.U.S, 42-46,

Sgt. MLA; NCTE; Asn. Depts. Eng. English 18th century literature; Shakespeare. Publ: Ed, Johnson's lives of English poets: selections, 55 & Addison and Steele, 57, Gateway Ed; ed, Rasselas, Barron's, 61; auth, Johnson, Lycidas, and the norms of criticism, Johnsonian Stud, Cairo, 62. Add: Dept. of English, Frostburg State College, Frostburg, MD 21532.

FLEISCHER, MARTHA HESTER, b. Portland, Maine, Jan. 25, 37; m. 68; c. 2. SHAKESPEARE, RENAISSANCE ICONOGRAPHY. B.A, Duke Univ, 58; M.A, Columbia Univ, 59, Ph.D.(Eng), 64. ASST. PROF. ENG, Seton Hall Univ, 63-65; Univ. Calif, Riverside, 65-68; STATE UNIV. N.Y. BUFFALO, 68- Woodrow Wilson Found. teaching intern, Seton Hall Univ, spring 65; Univ. Calif, Riverside intercampus res. grant, 65-68; Univ. Calif, Los Angeles fac. fel, summer 66. MLA; AAUP; Renaissance Soc. Am; Shakespeare Asn. Am. Shakespeare; women in literature. Publ: The iconography of the English history play, Salzburg Univ. Inst. Eng. Lang. & Lit, 74; Stage imagery in Shakespearean studies (under name of Martha Hester Golden), SRO, 1: 10-20; Stage imagery (under name of Golden), In: Reader's Encycl. of Shakespeare, Crowell, 66; Review of H.A. Kelly's Divine providence in the England of Shakespeare's histories, (under name of Fleischer), Renaissance Quart, summer 72. Add: Dept. of English, State University of New York at Buffalo, Main St, Buffalo, NY 14214.

FLEISCHER, STEFAN, b. Vienna, Austria, June 4, 37; U.S. citizen; m. 68. ENGLISH & COMPARATIVE LITERATURE. B.A, Univ. Rochester, 58; M.A, Cornell Univ, 60, Ph.D.(comp. lit), 66. Lectr. ENG, Univ. Calif, Riverside, 64-65, asst. prof, 65-67; STATE UNIV. N.Y. BUFFALO, 67-70, ASSOC. PROF, 70- MLA; Am. Soc. Cinema Stud. English and German Romanticism; film. Publ: Bekenntnisse einer schönen seele: figural representation in Wilhelm Meister's Lehnjahre, Mod. Lang. Notes, 12/68; Teaching of film with slides: example of My darling Clementine, J. Mod. Lit, Fall 73. Add: Dept. of English, State University of New York at Buffalo, Buffalo, NY 14214.

FLEISHER, DAVID, b. New York, N.Y, Feb. 8, 11; m. 55; c. 2. ENGLISH LITERATURE. Cert. d'Etudes Francaises, Univ. Grenoble, France, 28; Carnegie traveling fel, Univ. London, Eng, 28-29, dipl. lit, 29; B.S, N.Y. Univ. 30; univ. scholar, Harvard, 30-31, A.M, 31, univ. fel, 31-32, Townsend scholar, 32-33, Shattuck scholar, 33-34, Ph.D, 41. Instr, City Col. New York, 39-44; from asst. prof. to prof. Eng. & CHMN. DIV. LANG. & LIT, YESHIVA UNIV, 44-, ABRAHAM WOUK FAMILY PROF. ENG, 72- Vis. asst. prof, N.Y. Univ, 47-48, colloquium fel. comp. lit, 67- Bowdoin Prize, Harvard, 32. MLA. The romantic movement in English literature. Publ: William Godwin, a study in liberalism, 51; Rabbi Ben Ezra: a new key to an old crux, Victorian poetry, 1/63. Add: 790 Dearborn St, Teaneck, NJ 07666.

FLEISHER, SIEGEL H, b. Marion, Iowa. ENGLISH, COMPARATIVE LITERATURE. B.A, Univ. Iowa, 38; M.A, Harvard, 50. Asst. prof. ENG, State Univ. N.Y. Col. New Paltz, 57-60; ASSOC. PROF, GLASSBORO STATE COL, 60- Houghton Mifflin Lit. fel, 50. First Prize, Emily Clark Balch Short Story Contest, 56. Philosophy; political science. Publ: The lion and the honeycomb, Houghton, 53; The man who lost his wife's body, 55 & The old man's up and around, 56, Va. Quart. Add: Dept. of English, Glassboro State College, Glassboro, NJ 08028.

FLEISHMAN, AVROM, b. New York, N.Y, July 27, 33; m. 60; c. 2. ENGLISH. B.A, Columbia Univ, 54; M.A, Johns Hopkins Univ, 56, Ph.D.(Eng), 63. Instr. ENG, Columbia Univ, 58-59; Hofstra Univ, 60-63; asst. prof, Univ. Minn, 63-66; Mich. State Univ, 66-67; assoc. prof, JOHNS HOPKINS UNIV, 68-70, PROF, 70- Belgian-Am. Educ. Found. fel, 59-60; John Simon Guggenheim fel, 67-68. Modern and Victorian literature. Publ: A reading of Mansfield Park, Univ. Minn, 67; Conrad's politics, 67, The English historical novel, 71 & Virginia Woolf's fictions, 74, Johns Hopkins Univ. Add: Dept. of English, Johns Hopkins University, Baltimore, MD 21218.

FLEISSNER, ROBERT FERDINAND, b. Auburn, N.Y, Oct. 17, 32; div. ENGLISH. B.A, Cath. Univ. Am, 57, M.A, 58; Univ. N.C, 59-60; Bread Loaf Sch. Eng, summers 59, 60; Ohio State Univ, 60-61; Ph.D, N.Y. Univ, 64. Instr. Eng, speech & drama, Spring Hill Col, 58-59; Eng, Ohio State Univ, 60-61; lectr. Eng. & world lit, Bernard Baruch Sch, City Col. New York, 62-64; asst. prof. ENG. & chmn. dept, Dominican Col.(N.Y), 64-66; vis. instr, Univ. N.Mex, 66-67; ASST. PROF, CENT. STATE UNIV, 67- Coord. instr. media, Mary Holmes Col, summer 68. MLA; Dickens Soc. Victorian and Renaissance periods. Publ: Dickens and Shakespeare: a study in histrionic contrasts, Haskell, 65 & 69; Something out of Dickens in Sinclair Lewis, Bull. N.Y. Pub. Libr, 11/70; That Cheek of night: toward the Dark Lady, CLA J, 3/73; Love's labour's won and the occasion of Much ado, Shakespeare Survey, 74; plus others. Add: Dept. of English, Central State University, Wilberforce, OH 45384.

FLEMING, DAVID ARNOLD, S.M, b. Topeka, Kans, Apr. 14, 39. ENGLISH. B.A, St. Mary's Univ.(Tex), 59; Woodrow Wilson fels, Univ. Chicago, 62-63 & 64-65, M.A, 63, univ. fel, 63-64, Ph.D.(Eng), 65; S.T.B, Univ. Fribourg, 67, S.T.L, 69. Instr. ENG, ST. MARY'S UNIV.(TEX), 65-67, ASST. PROF, 67- Bavarian Govt. fel. theol, Univ. Munich, 67-68; dir, Marianist House Stud, San Antonio, Tex, 71-; Am. Counc. Learned Soc. travel grant, 71. Theodore Christian Hoepfner Prize, South. Humanities Rev, 72. Renaissance Soc. Am; MLA; Milton Soc. Am. Renaissance Latin literature; literary hermeneutics; contemporary religious life. Publ: Ed, John Barclay, Euphormio's Satyricon, DeGraaf, 73; auth, Formation and the discovery of identity, Rev. Relig, 5/72; Literary interpretation today: an assessment and a reorientation, South. Humanities Rev, fall 72. Add: Dept. of English, St. Mary's University, San Antonio, TX 78228.

FLEMING, DELMONT FORRIE, b. Taylorsville, Pa, June 20, 34. ENGLISH. B.A, East. Baptist Col, 59; Dept. Health, Educ. & Welfare Nat. Defense fel, Univ. Pa, 59-62, M.A, 60, Ph.D.(Eng), 66. Instr. ENG, Alfred Univ, 62-65; asst. prof, MARY WASHINGTON COL, UNIV. VA, 66-69, ASSOC. PROF, 69- MLA. Twentieth century American literature, particularly modern Southern literature. Add: Dept. of English, Mary Washington College, Box 3047, College Station, Fredericksburg, VA 22401.

FLEMING, JAMES T, b. New Haven, Conn, Aug. 16, 34; m. 64. ENGLISH, LINGUISTICS. S.B, South. Conn. State Col, 57; M.S, Harvard, 61, fel, 61-65, Ed.D, 66. Asst. prof. EDUC, Univ. Calif, Los Angeles, 65-68; City Col. New York, 68-69; PROF, STATE UNIV. N.Y. ALBANY, 69- Mem. proj. develop. staff, Southwest Regional Lab. Res. & Develop, Calif, spring 66; consult. proj. literacy, Cornell Univ, summer 66; Eng, NDEA, Calif, fall 67, Nat. Manpower Training Act, Calif, 67-68; Ctr. Urban Educ, N.Y, 68-69. Int. Reading Asn; NCTE; MLA; Am. Educ. Res. Asn. Children's perception of socially significant speech variants. Publ: Co-auth, Language and learning, Harcourt, 66; auth, Psycholinguistics and the teaching of reading, 69 & Promoting language skills in preschool programs, In: Some persistent questions on beginning reading, 72, Int. Reading Asn; co-auth; Cloze and closure, a second analysis, 21st Yearbk. Nat. Reading Conf, 72 & Perceptual closure and cloze performance: a replication with older subjects, J. Gen. Psychol, winter 72; plus others. Add: Education 226, State University of New York at Albany, 1400 Washington Ave, Albany, NY 12222.

FLEMING, JOHN VINCENT, b. Mountain Home, Ark, May 20, 36; m. 62; c. 2. ENGLISH, FRENCH. B.A, Univ. of the South, 58; Rhodes scholar & B.A. & M.A, Oxford, 61; Ph.D.(Eng), Princeton, 63. Instr. ENG, Univ. Wis, 63-65; asst. prof, PRINCETON, 65-68, assoc. prof, 68-71, PROF, 71-, DIR. GRAD. STUD, 73-, master, Woodrow Wilson Col, 68-72. Medieval literature; intellectual history of the Middle Ages. Publ: The Roman de la rose, Princeton, 69; The moral reputation of the Roman de la rose before 1400, Romance Philol, 5/65; The dream of the rood and Anglo-Saxon monasticism, Traditio, 66; The antifraternalism of the Summoner's tale, J. Eng. & Ger. Philol, 10/66. Add: Dept. of English, Princeton University, Princeton, NJ 08540.

FLEMING, ROBERT EDWARD, b. Shullsburg, Wis, Dec. 18, 36; m. 59; c. 1. AMERICAN LITERATURE, OLD ENGLISH. B.A, North. Ill. Univ, 59, M.A, 64; Ph.D.(Eng), Univ. Ill, 67. Teacher, Jr. High Sch, Ill, 59-60, High Sch, 60-64; teaching asst. ENG, Univ. Ill, 64-67; asst. prof, UNIV. N.MEX, 67-71, ASSOC. PROF, 71- Nat. Endowment for Humanities younger humanist fel, 72. U.S.M.C.R, 57-63. MLA. Black American novelists, Hemingway; American literature since 1860. Publ: Irony as a key to Johnson's Autobiography of an ex-coloured man, Am. Lit, 3/71; The nightmare level of The man who cried I am, Contemporary Lit, spring 73, Sutton E. Griggs: militant black novelist, Phylon, 3/73. Add: Dept. of English, University of New Mexico, Albuquerque, NM 87131.

FLEMINGS, CORINNE KRANZ, b. Oak Park, Ill, May 8, 27; wid; c. 1. SPEECH COMMUNICATION. B.A, Univ. Md, College Park, 48; M.A, Northwest. Univ, Evanston, 51; Univ. Redlands, 57-59; Ph.D.(speech), Univ. Calif, Los Angeles, 70. Instr. speech & Eng, San Bernardino Valley Jr. Col, 56-60; Eng, Univ. Redlands, 57-60; teaching assoc. speech, Univ. Calif, Los Angeles, 60 & 69; instr, State Univ. N.Y. Col, New Paltz, 61-64; asst. prof. & acting head dept, West. Col, 64-68; PROF. SPEECH, CALIF. STATE COL. (PA), 69- Vis. lectr. Eng, Osmania Univ. Women's Col, Hyderabad, India, 67-68. Speech Commun. Asn. Publ: Gettysburg revisited, Today's Speech, 4/66. Add: Dept. of Speech Communication, California State College, California, PA 15419.

FLESER, ARTHUR F, b. Mar. 14, 23; U.S. citizen; m. 47; c. 3. ENGLISH. A.B, John Fletcher Col, 45; M.A, State Univ. Iowa, 50; Univ. Ky, 53-54; Ph.D, Ind. Univ, 62. Instr. Eng. & speech, Pasadena Col, 46-47; speech, Asbury Col, 47-56; teacher Eng. & speech, Columbus Sr. High Sch, Ind, 56-59; teaching assoc. speech, exten. div, Ind. Univ, 59-61; assoc. prof, Geneva Col, 61-64, prof, 64-71, chmn. dept, 61-71; PROF. SPEECH & ENG. & CHMN. DIV, ASBURY COL, 71- Instr, Exten. Div, Purdue Univ, 59; Ind. Univ. Res. Comt. grant, 66; study grant, Geneva Col, summer 68. Speech Commun. Asn. Public address; speech pathology; Calvin Coolidge's rhetoric. Publ: Jam Tempus Agi Res: oratory in history, Quart. J. Speech, 2/63; Coolidge's delivery: everybody like it, South. Speech J, winter 66; A New England education: the early career and rhetorical training of Calvin Coolidge, Vt. Hist, 7/67. Add: Div. of English and & Speech, Asbury College, Wilmore, KY 40390.

FLETCHER, ANGUS S, b. New York, N.Y, June 23, 30. ENGLISH LITERATURE. B.A, Yale, 50, M.A, 52; dipl, Univ. Grenoble, France, 51; Ph.D, Harvard, 58. Instr. ENG. LIT, Cornell Univ, 58-62; asst. prof, Columbia Col, Columbia Univ, 62-67, assoc. prof, 67-68; PROF. STATE UNIV. N.Y. BUFFALO, 68- Vis. prof. Eng. & comp. lit, Univ. Calif, Los Angeles, 73-74. Renaissance Soc. Am. History of opera and mixed media; Renaissance studies; theory of literature. Publ: Allegory: theory of a symbolic mode, 64 & The transcendental masque: an essay on Milton's Comus, 71, Cornell Univ; The prophetic moment: an essay on Spenser, Univ. Chicago, 71; Positive negation: threshold, sequence and personification in Coleridge, Eng. Inst, 72; I. Richards and the art of critical balance, Oxford, 73; Allegory, dictionary of the history of ideas, Scribner, 73; plus one other. Add: Dept. of English, State University of New York at Buffalo, Buffalo, NY 14214.

FLETCHER, JOSEPH GRANT, b. Winchester, Va, Apr. 26, 08; m. 52; c. 1. ENGLISH LITERATURE. B.S, Hampton Inst, 29; A.M, Cornell Univ, 33; Columbia Univ, 35-36. Asst. prof, Hampton Inst, 29-38; prin, High Sch, Richmond, Ky, 38-45; ASSOC. PROF. ENG. LIT, KY. STATE UNIV, 45- NCTE. Vachel Lindsay. Add: 317 Cold Harbor Dr, Frankfort, KY 40601.

FLETCHER, MARIE, b. New Verda, La, Oct. 11, 13. ENGLISH. A.B, La. State Norm. Col, 38; M.A, La. State Univ, 44, Ph.D, 63; Miss. State Col. Instr, High Schs, La, 32-48; ENG, Nicholls State Col, 48-51, asst. prof, 52-55, assoc. prof, 56-63; Northwest. State Col.(La), 63-65, PROF, 65-67; NICHOLLS STATE UNIV, 67-, CHMN. DEPT, 73- Dir. NDEA Inst. Advan. Stud. Eng, Northwest. State Col.(La), summer, 66. S.Cent. Mod. Lang. Asn. American literature. Publ: The southern heroine in the fiction of southern women writers, 1860-1960, Univ. Microfilms, 63; Franklin's General magazine: an image of the Colonial mind, McNeese Rev, 66; The southern woman in the fiction of Kate Chopin, La. Hist, spring 66; The fate of women in a changing South: a persistent theme in the fiction of Caroline Gordon, Miss. Quart, winter 68; plus others. Add: Dept. of English, Nicholls State University, Thibodaux, LA 70301.

FLETCHER, MARY FRANCES, b. Ruston, La, Apr. 11, 07. ENGLISH. A.B, La. Polytech Inst; A.M, Univ. Va; Ph.D, La. State Univ, 55. Asst. ENG, La.

State Univ; teacher, High Sch, La; from assoc. prof. to PROF, LA. TECH UNIV, 40- S.Cent. Mod. Lang. Asn. English literature of the 18th century; literature of north Louisiana. Publ: When Spring has come; The Old Spanish Trail; Lullaby for Guy; plus others. Add: 1102 N. Vienna, Ruston, LA 71270.

FLETCHER, WINONA LEE, b. Hamlet, N.C, Nov. 25, 26; m. 52; c. 1. SPEECH & DRAMA. A.B, J.C. Smith Univ, 47; M.A, State Univ, Iowa, 51; Univ. Ky, summers 58-62; univ. fel, Ind. Univ, 62-68, Ph.D.(speech & theatre), 68. Instr. Eng, Delwatt's Radio & Electronics Inst, 47-50; ENG, SPEECH & THEATRE, KY. STATE UNIV, 51-63, asst. prof, 63-66, assoc. prof, 66-68, PROF, 68-, DIR. THEATRE, 66-, instr. speech & theatre, Black Stud. Inst, summer 70. Costumer & assoc. dir, summer stock theatre, Lincoln Univ, summers 52-60, costumer, Inst. Dramatic Arts, summer 60; costumer, Michiana Summer Theatre, Ind, summer 56; coord. fine arts workshops, Ky. State Col. Proj. Upward Bound, summers 66, 67; consult, Ind. Univ. Bloomington, 70-71, vis. assoc. prof. Afro-Am. stud. & theatre, 71-73; consult-lectr. Black theatre, La. State Univ, fall 72; mem, Nat. Counc. Negro Women. Am. Theatre Asn.(bd. dir, 59-60); Nat. Asn. Dramatic & Speech Arts (exec. secy, 58-62); Speech Commun. Asn; South. Speech Commun. Asn; AAUP; Southeast. Theatre Conf.(Brit. liaison off, 60). American theatre; Black drama and theatre. Publ: Compiler & ed, Directory of American college theatre, Am. Educ. Theatre Asn, 60; auth, Knight errant or screaming eagle?: E.L. Godkin's criticism of Wendell Phillips, South. Speech J, spring 64; A war of words: speechmaking of the N.Y draft riot of 1863, Quart J. Speech, 4/68; contrib, Black theatre in midwestern colleges and universities, Bull. Black Theatre, winter 73; plus others. Add: 317 Cold Harbor Dr, Frankfort, KY 40601.

FLETT, ALEX S, b. Oak Park, Ill, June 6, 22. DRAMA. B.S, Northwest. Univ, 53, M.A, 54; summers, Univ. Denver, Northwest. Univ, Univ. Hawaii. Asst. drama, Northwest. Univ, 54; instr. drama & speech, Valparaiso Univ, 54-56; DRAMA, SAN FRANCISCO STATE UNIV, 56-59, asst. prof, 59-63, ASSOC. PROF, 63- U.S.N, 42-53. Speech Commun. Asn; Am. Theatre Asn. Drama; oral interpretation; dramatic literature and history. Add: School of Creative Arts, San Francisco State University, San Francisco, CA 94132.

FLIBBERT, JOSEPH THOMAS, b. Worcester, Mass, July 24, 38; m. 63; c. 3. AMERICAN LITERATURE. A.B, Assumption Col, 60; M.A, Boston Col, 63; Ph.D.(Eng), Univ. Ill, Urbana, 70. Instr. Eng, Al-Hikma Univ, Bagdad, 61-62; instr. French, Worcester Acad, Mass, 62-63; asst. prof. ENG, Merrimack Col, 63-67; teaching asst, Univ. Ill, Urbana, 67-69; ASSOC. PROF, SALEM STATE COL, 70-, CHAIRPERSON DEPT, 74- U.S.A, 56-62. MLA; NEA; Melville Soc. Am; Popular Cult. Asn. American literature, 1820-1860; popular culture of America; Herman Melville. Publ: Melville and the art of burlesque, Rodopi, Amsterdam, 74; Bleak House and the Brothers Grimm, Victorian Newslett, fall 69; Dickens and the French debate over realism: 1838-1856, Comp. Lit, winter 71. Add: Dept. of English, Salem State College, Loring Ave, Salem, MA 01970.

FLICK, CLARENCE E, b. Arapahoe, Nebr, Mar. 6, 20; m. 48; c. 6. SPEECH, DRAMA. B.Sc, Univ. Nebr, 42, M.A, 48; Ph.D.(speech), Northwest. Univ, 54. Instr. speech & drama, Univ. Nebr, 46-48; teaching fel, Northwest. Univ, 48-51; Ford Found. Adult Educ. fel, Univ. Calif, Los Angeles, 57-58; PROF. TV & FILM, SAN JOSE STATE UNIV, 58- U.S.A, 42-46 & 51-54, Res, 54-, Col; Bronze Star. Nat. Asn. Educ. Broadcasters (res. comt, 56-58); Broadcast Educ. Asn.(curriculum mat. comt, 68-). Television production; children and television; California history. Publ: Torso del Toro, 41 & Return to Surigao, 46, produced at Univ. Nebr; The gondola 57 & The bell tower, 57, produced on TV; plus others. Add: Dept. of Drama, San Jose State University, Seventh & San Fernando St, San Jose, CA 95193.

FLICK, ROBERT GENE, b. Oblong, Ill, Oct. 18, 30; m. 51; c. 4. ENGLISH, HUMANITIES. B.S.Ed, East. Ill. State Col, 52; M.A, Univ. Fla, 54, Ph.D. (Eng), 67. Teacher, High Sch, Ill, 54-56; instr. Eng, Jacksonville Univ, 56-60, asst. prof, 60-67, assoc. prof, 67-68; assoc. prof. & acting chmn, humanities, FLA. TECHNOL. UNIV, 68-69, PROF. & CHMN. DEPT. HUMANITIES, PHILOS. & RELIG, 69- Mem. Fla. Citizens Comt. for Humanities, Nat. Endowment for Humanities. S.Atlantic Mod. Lang. Asn; AAUP; Col. Eng. Asn. Creative writing; Emily Dickinson and 19th century American literature. Add: Dept. of Humanities, Philosophy & Religion, Florida Technological University, Orlando, FL 32816.

FLINT, ALLEN DENIS, b. Park River, N.Dak, Nov. 15, 29; m. 53, 66; c. 5. ENGLISH, AMERICAN STUDIES. Tozer Found. award, Class of 1890 fel, Grad. Sch. award & B.A, Univ. Minn, 55, M.A, 56, Ph.D.(Am. stud), 65; University of Edinburgh, 53-54. Col. Counsel. & freshman adv, Col. Lib. Arts, Univ. Minn, 56-58, scholastic comt. rep, 58-59, sr. scholastic comt. rep, 59-62, instr. & counsel, 62-64, asst. dir, cor. stud. dept, 64-65, acting dir, 65-66; asst. prof. ENG, West. Ill. Univ, 66-69, assoc. prof, 69-70; PROF, UNIV. MAINE, FARMINGTON, 70-, CHMN. DEPT, 71- U.S.A, 50-51, Sgt. MLA; Am. Stud. Asn. American renaissance; Black literature; contemporary literature. Publ: Hawthorne and the slavery crisis, New Eng. Quart, 68; Essentially a day-dream: Hawthorne's Blithedale, Hawthorne J, 72; The saving grace of marriage in Hawthorne's fiction, Emerson Soc. Quart, 73. Add: Dept. of English, University of Maine at Farmington, Farmington, ME 04938.

FLINT, PAUL HARRY, b. Methuen, Mass, Apr. 3, 08; m. 35; c. 1. ENGLISH. A.B, Harvard, 30, A.M, 37, Ph.D, 47; A.M, Tufts Col, 32. Instr. Eng, Tufts Col, 35-45; Mass. Inst. Tech, 45-46; asst. prof, TUFTS UNIV, 46-48, assoc. prof, 48-59, prof, 59-70, asst. dean grad. sch. arts & sci, 52-59, dean, 59-70, EMER. PROF. ENG, 70- U.S.N.R, Capt. MLA; Mediaeval Acad. Am; Soc. Tech. Writers & Pubs.(pres, Soc. Tech. Writers, 54); Am. Soc. Engineering Educ. Germanic philology; history of the English language; Chaucer. Add: 26 Edison Ave, Medford, MA 02155.

FLOAN, HOWARD RUSSELL, b. Spokane, Wash, Nov. 22, 18; m. 41. ENGLISH & COMPARATIVE LITERATURE. Ph.B, Gonzaga Univ, 40; M.A, Univ. Wash, 41; Ph.D, Columbia Univ, 54. From instr. to asst. prof. humanities, MANHATTAN COL, 48-53, assoc. prof. world lit, 54-62, PROF. ENG. & WORLD LIT, 62-, head dept. world lit, 54-63. Vis. prof. Am. lit, Univ. Zaragoza, Spain, 58-59; Fulbright prof, Univs. Zaragoza & Valencia, 66-67. U.S.A.A.F, 42-46, Maj. MLA; Am. Stud. Asn. American literature. Publ: The South in northern eyes, 1831-1861, Univ. Tex, 58 & McGraw, 63; William Saroyan, Twayne, 66; Bryant's Evening post and the ante-bellum South, Am. Quart, fall 56; Saroyan and Cervantes' knight, Thought, 58; Tradicion e invencion en las novelas de Willa Cather, Arbor, 61. Add: 2 Louisiana Ave, Bronxville, NY 10708.

FLOOD, VERLE DENNIS, b. Greenfield, Iowa, Mar. 16, 24; m. 49; c. 1. ENGLISH, HISTORY. B.A, Univ. Iowa, 49, M.A, 50, Ph.D.(Eng), 59; Harvard, 51-53. Instr. ENG, Univ. Iowa, 53-59; assoc. prof, North. State Col, 59-62; MOORHEAD STATE COL, 62-65, PROF, 65- Med.C, U.S.A, 43-46. History of ideas; Mark Twain; national period of American culture; aesthetics of taste. Add: Dept. of English, Moorhead State College, Moorhead, MN 56560.

FLORA, JOSEPH MARTIN, b. Toledo, Ohio, Feb. 9, 34; m. 59; c. 3. ENGLISH. B.A, Univ. Mich, 56, M.A, 57, Ph.D.(Eng), 62. Instr. ENG, Univ. Mich, 61-62; UNIV. N.C, CHAPEL HILL, 62-64, asst. prof, 64-66, ASSOC. PROF, 66-, fac. res. grant, summer 63, asst. dean grad. sch, 67-72. Coop. Prog. Humanities res. grant, summer 66. MLA. American literature; 20th century drama; British literature 1880-1920. Publ: Vardis Fisher, 65 & William Ernest Henley, 70, Twayne; Vardis Fisher and James Branch Cabell, Cabellian, fall 69; Vardis Fisher and the Mormons, Dialogue, fall 69; Biblical allusion in The old man and the sea, Stud. Short Fiction, spring 73; plus others. Add: Dept. of English, University of North Carolina, Chapel Hill, NC 27514.

FLORES, ANGEL, Comparative Literature. See Volume III, Foreign Languages, Linguistics & Philology.

FLORES, RALPH, b. Washington, D.C, Feb. 13, 41. COMPARATIVE LITERATURE. B.A, Queens Col.(N.Y), 62; M.A, Univ. Chicago, 63; Ph.D. (comp. lit), Princeton, 70. ASST. PROF. COMP. LIT, UNIV. CALIF, IRVINE, 70- Theory of the novel; Romanticism; Renaissance literature. Add: Dept. of English, University of California, Irvine, CA 92664.

FLORES, VETAL, b. Brandon, Tex, Sept. 8, 12; m. 45. ENGLISH, SPEECH. B.A, Tex. Technol. Col, 38; N.Tex. State Univ, 40; Univ. Tex, 49, 64, 65; M.A, Hardin-Simmons Univ, 53; Am. fel, Univ. Miami, summer 61 & Abilene Christian Col, summer 63; Univ. Col, Dublin, 68; Oxford, summer 71; Cambridge, summer 73. Teacher, Flower Grove High Sch, 38-40; Bronte High Sch, 40-58; instr. AM. LIT, ANGELO STATE COL, 58-65, ASST. PROF, 65- Teacher, Lake View High Sch, 52-53. U.S.A, 42-45, Sgt. NEA; Int. Reading Asn; NCTE; Nat. Counc. Stud. Educ; MLA; S.Cent. Mod. Lang. Asn; Col. Eng. Asn; Conf. Col. Teachers Eng; Emerson Soc. Publ: Co-auth, The reading program, Tex. Educ. Agency, 56; Literature for frontier children, Southwest. Am. Lit, fall 72. Add: Dept. of English, Angelo State College, San Angelo, TX 76901.

FLOREY, KENNETH, b. Yonkers, N.Y, June 10, 42; m. 67; c. 1. ANGLO-SAXON & MEDIEVAL STUDIES. A.B, Lafayette Col, 64; assistantship, Syracuse Univ, 67 & 70, M.A, 67, Ph.D.(Eng), 70. ASST. PROF. ENG, SOUTH. CONN. STATE COL, 70- MLA; Mediaeval Acad. Am. Anglo-Saxon; Chaucer; history of the English language. Publ: Co-ed, Freshman English at Syracuse, Wadsworth, 67. Add: Dept. of English, Southern Connecticut State College, New Haven, CT 06515.

FLORY, CLAUDE R, b. Nokesville, Va, July 14, 07; m. 73. AMERICAN LITERATURE. B.S, Juniata Col, 29; A.M, Univ. Pa, 33, Ph.D, 35; Oxford, 37-38. Instr. Eng, Juniata Col, 29-32; PROF, McPherson Col, 35-37; ENG. LIT, Washington & Jefferson Col, 39-45; FLA. STATE UNIV, 45- MLA; NCTE. American fiction; Florida short story writers; American drama. Publ: Economic criticism in American fiction 1792-1900; Annie Oakley in the South, N.C. Hist. Rev, summer 66; Antecedents of Anna Christie, PMLA, 1/71; Sean, S.Atlantic Quart, winter 73; plus others. Add: 1551 Crestview Ave, Tallahassee, FL 32303.

FLOSDORF, JAMES WILLIAM, b. Philadelphia, Pa, May 11, 34; m. 68; c. 3. ENGLISH LITERATURE. B.A, Wesleyan Univ, 56; scholar. & fel, Univ. Rochester, 56-58, scholar, 58-59; Ph.D, 60. Asst, Univ. Rochester, 58-59, asst. lectr, ENG, 59-60; instr. Wilson Col, 60-63, asst. prof, 63-68; RUSSELL SAGE COL, 68-69, ASSOC. PROF, 69-, CHMN. FAC. SENATE, 73- Col. Eng. Asn; MLA; AAUP; Milton Soc. Am. Milton; 16th and 17th century English literature. Publ: The Odi et Amo theme in The Jew of Malta, Notes & Queries, 1/60; Gums of glutinous heat: a query, Milton Quart, 3/73; Natural history, Milton Encycl, (in press). Add: Dept. of English, Russell Sage College, Troy, NY 12180.

FLOWER, ANNETTE CHAPPELL, b. Washington, D.C, Oct. 31, 39; m. 60. ENGLISH LITERATURE. B.A, Univ. Md, College Park, 62, M.A, 64, Ph.D. (Eng. lit), 70. Readers' adv, D.C. Pub. Libr, Wash, D.C, 62-63; teaching asst. ENG, Univ. Md, College Park, 63-65, lectr, Overseas Div, 65-66, instr, Univ, 66-69; asst. prof, TOWSON STATE COL, 69-72, ASSOC. PROF, 72- MLA; Shakespeare Asn. Am. Renaissance drama; Shakespeare. Publ: Don't be the Duchess, Md. Eng. J, spring 68; The critical context of the preface to Samson Agonistes, Stud. Eng. Lit, spring 70; Disguise and identity in Pericles, Prince of Tyre, Shakespeare Quart, (in press). Add: Dept. of English, Towson State College, Baltimore, MD 21204.

FLOWER, DEAN SCOTT, b. Milwaukee, Wis, Aug. 17, 38; m. 59; c. 4. ENGLISH. A.B, Univ. Mich, 60; Edward John Noble Found. fel, 60-63; Stanford-Wilson fel, Stanford Univ, 63-64, Ph.D.(Eng), 66. Asst. prof. ENG, Univ. South. Calif, 64-69; ASSOC. PROF, SMITH COL, 69- Consult, Orff-Schulwerk Prof. creativity & participation music educ, 65-67; Res. & Publ. Fund grant, Univ. South. Calif, 68-69. MLA. American literature; contemporary prose fiction. Publ: Ed, The great short works of Henry James, Harper, 66; ed, Eight short novels, 67 & Counterparts: classic and contemporary American stories, 71, Fawcett; auth, Henry James in Northampton: visions and revisions, Neilson Libr, 71. Add: Dept. of English, Smith College, Northampton, MA 01060.

FLUHARTY, GEORGE WATSON, b. Preston, Md, Oct. 5, 17. SPEECH. B.S, Boston Univ, 43; M.A, Columbia Univ, 47, 47-50; Ph.D, N.Y. Univ, 58. Dir.

drama & speech, Elizabeth Peabody House, Boston, Mass, 40-43; instr. speech, New Sch. Soc. Res, 46-47; Princeton Theol. Sem, 47-49; Wash. Sq. Col, N.Y. Univ, 49-54; dir. speech & drama, Kent Sch, Conn, 54-55; instr. bus. speaking, Sch. Commerce, N.Y. UNIV, 55-59, asst. prof. bus. commun, 59-63, assoc. prof, 63-70, ASSOC. PROF. SPEECH EDUC. & DIR. SPEECH ARTS-EDUC. PROG, SCH. EDUC, 70- U.S.N, 43-46. Speech Commun. Asn; Int. Commun. Asn; East. Speech Asn. Public speaking; speech and voice improvement; business communication. Publ: Co-auth, Public speaking, Barnes & Noble, 66. Add: 40 E. Ninth St, New York, NY 10003.

FLYNN, LAWRENCE JEROME, S.J, b. Bellevue, Ky, Sept. 5, 14. SPEECH. A.B, Xavier Univ.(Ohio), 36; Ph.L, Loyola Univ.(Ill), 43, M.A, 47, S.T.L, 51; Ph.D, Univ. Fla, 55. From teacher speech to PROF. COMMUN. ARTS, XAVIER UNIV. (OHIO), 56-, CHMN. DEPT. COMMUN. ARTS, 66-, GEN. MGR. & DIR. RADIO WVXU-FM, 73- Speech Commun. Asn. Rhetoric, especially medieval. Publ: Aristotle: art and faculty of rhetoric, South. Speech J, summer 56; The De arte rhetorica of Cyprian Soarez, S.J, Quart. J, 12/56; Aristotelian basis for the ethics of speaking, Speech Teacher, 9/57 & In: Ethics and persuasion, selected readings by Richard L. Johannesen, Random, 67. Add: Dept. of Communication Arts, Xavier University, Cincinnati, OH 45207.

FODASKI-BLACK, MARTHA HALLER, b. Milford, Mich, May 3, 29; m. 70; c. 3. ENGLISH, COMPARATIVE LITERATURE. B.A, Wayne State Univ, 51; Mary Adams fel. & M.A, Univ. Wis, 52, fels, 52-57, Ford Found. South. fels, 58, 59, Ph.D.(Eng), 60. Asst. prof. ENG, Madison Col, 57-60, assoc. prof, 60-62; instr, BROOKLYN COL, 62-66, asst. prof, 66-70, ASSOC. PROF, 70-, participant televised humanities sem, spring 74. Lectr, Scarsdale Adult Sch, 67-68 & 70-73; lectr. Eng. lit, Westchester Community Col, N.Y, summer 72; women in lit, Edgemont Sch, 73; assoc. dir. humanities, Inst. Irish Stud, 73-74. MLA; NCTE; Int. Asn. Stud. Anglo-Irish Lit. Irish studies; contemporary literature, women's studies. Publ: George Barker, Twayne, 68; Dylan Thomas: the elemental poet, Wis. Acad. Arts, Sci. & Lett, 55; Emily Dickinson's Twas like a maelstrom, Explicator, 60; contrib, George Barker, In: Encyclopedia of world literature in 20th century, Ungar; contrib, Masterpoems of the English language, Trident, 66; George Barker, In: Encycl. of world literature in 20th century, Ungar, 68. Add: Dept. of English, Brooklyn College, Bedford Ave. & Ave. H, Brooklyn, NY 11210.

FOFF, ARTHUR (RAYMOND), b. San Francisco, Calif, Nov. 12, 22; m. 44; c. 2. ENGLISH, EDUCATION. Scholar, Univ. Calif, 44-45; Ed.D, Stanford Univ, 53; D.Litt, Univ. Hiroshima, 60. From instr. to asst. prof. lang. arts, SAN FRANCISCO STATE UNIV, 49-57, from assoc. prof. lang. arts to PROF. ENG, 57- Fulbright prof, Hiroshima, Japan, 59-60; Damascus, S.A.R, 61-; chair in Eng. & Am. lit, Univ. Damascus, 61-64; Columbia Univ. prof. U.S. lit, Mid.E, 66-67. Creative writing; modern American and English literature; teacher education. Publ: Glorious in another day; co-ed, Readings in education & co-auth, History of education, 59, Harpers; auth, North of market, Harcourt, 60; Beautiful golden-haired Mamie, Atlantic Monthly. Add: Dept. of English, San Francisco State University, San Francisco, CA 94132.

FOGARTY, ROBERT STEPHEN, History. See Volume I, History.

FOGEL, EPHIM (GREGORY), b. Odessa, Russia, Nov. 15, 20; nat; m. 41; c. 4. ENGLISH. B.A, City Col. New York, 41; M.A, N.Y. Univ, 47; univ. fel, Ohio State Univ, 47-48, Ph.D.(Eng), 58. Asst. instr. ENG, Ohio State Univ, 46-47; instr, CORNELL UNIV, 49-55, asst. prof, 55-61, assoc. prof, 61-66, PROF, 66-, dir. grad. stud. Eng, 63-65, chmn. bd. ed, Cornell Stud. Eng, 66-70, chmn. dept. Eng, 66-70, Soc. for Humanities fac. fel, 74-75. Mem. supvry. comt, Cornell Concordances, Cornell Univ, 61-; chmn. selection comt, George Jean Nathan Drama Criticism Award, 66 & 69; Nat. Endowment Humanities grant, 67; hon. adv, Joint Comt. Summer Schs, U.K, 69- U.S.A, 42-46. MLA; Renaissance Soc. Am; Shakespeare Asn. Am; AAUP. Elizabethan literature, especially Sir Philip Sidney and Shakespeare; dramatic literature; modern American and Russian poetry. Publ: Co-auth, Evidence for authorship, Cornell Univ, 66; auth, The mythical sorrows of Astrophil, In: Studies in language and literature in honour of Margaret Schlauch, Polish Sci. Publ, Warsaw, 66; The tragedy of Othello, In: Teaching Shakespeare, New Am. Libr, 69; Seven St. Petersburg poems by Osip Mandelshtam, Granite, spring 73; plus others. Add: Dept. of English, Cornell University, Ithaca, NY 14850.

FOGLE, FRENCH R, b. Marietta, Ohio, Feb. 28, 12; m. 55. ENGLISH LITERATURE. A.B, Marietta Col, 33, hon. D.Litt, 58; Drew Univ, 33-34, 36; M.A, Columbia Univ, 38; Cutting traveling fel, 40-41, Rockefeller fel, 45-46, Ph.D, 49. Instr. Eng, City Col. New York, 41-42; Barnard Col, 46-49, asst. prof, 49-51; fel, Huntington Libr, 51-52, res. fel. Eng. Renaissance & ed, Huntington Libr. Quart, 52-57; PROF. ENG. LIT, CLAREMONT GRAD. SCH, 57- Lectr, Columbia Univ, summer, 52; Scripps Col, 53-56; Am. Philos. Soc. fel, 63-64; vis. prof. Eng. lit, N.Y. Univ, 66-67. U.S.M.C, 42-45, Res, 45-66, Col; Silver Star Medal, 44. MLA; Milton Soc. Am.(pres, 56-57); Philol. Asn. Pac. Coast (pres, 70-71); Int. Soc. Hist. Ideas; Renaissance Eng. Text Soc; Malone Soc. English literature and history of the 16th and 17th centuries; historiography of the 17th century. Publ: Co-auth, An index to the complete works of John Milton (2 vols), Columbia Univ, 40; auth, A critical study of William Drummond of Hawthornden, King's Crown Press, 52; ed, The complete poetry of Henry Vaughan, Doubleday, 64, Norton, rev. ed, 69; ed, Pacific Coast philology, Vol. V, Philol. Asn. Pac. Coast, 70 & Milton's History of Britain, Vol. V, In: Complete prose works of John Milton, Yale Univ, 71; auth, Milton lost and regained, Huntington Libr. Quart, 52; Milton as Historian, In: Milton and Clarendon, W.A. Clark Libr, Univ. Calif, 65; The action of Samson Agonistes, In: Essays in American and English literature, Ohio Univ, 67; Recent studies in the English Renaissance, Stud. Eng. Lit, spring 71. Add: Dept. of English, Claremont Graduate School, Claremont, CA 91711.

FOGLE, RICHARD HARTER, b. Canton, Ohio, Mar. 8, 11. ENGLISH. A.B, Hamilton Col, 33, Litt.D, 67; A.M, Columbia Univ, 36; Ph.D, Univ. Mich, 44. Eng. master, Brent Sch, Baguio, P.I, 36-38; Somerset Hills Sch, 39; instr. ENG, Univ. Rochester, 39-40; Univ. Mich, 43-46; asst. prof, Tulane Univ, 46-48, assoc. prof, 48-51, prof, 51-66, chmn. dept, 57-60, 63-66, head dept. Eng, arts & sci, 54-63; prof, UNIV. N.C, CHAPEL HILL, 66-67, UNIV. DISTINGUISHED PROF, 67- Guggenheim fel, 50-; mem. ed. bd, Keats-Shelley J, 54-; Am. Lit, 64-70; ed. consult, Northwest-Newberry Libr. ed, Herman Melville, 65-; mem. selection comt, Christian Gauss Award, 67-69. MLA (chmn, J.R. Lowell Prize Comt, 73-74); Melville Soc; Keats-Shelley Asn. Am; S.Atlantic Mod. Lang. Asn; Mod. Humanities Res. Asn. Keats, Shelley, Hawthorne and Coleridge; English and American literature of the early 19th century; romanticism, contemporary and modern criticism. Publ: Imagery of Keats and Shelley, Univ. N.C, 49; Hawthorne's fiction, 52, rev. ed, 60 & 64, Melville's Shorter tales, 60 & Hawthorne's imagery, 69, Univ. Okla; Idea of Coleridge's criticism, Univ. Calif, 62; co-ed, Eight American writers, Norton, 63; ed, The romantic movement in American writing, Odyssey, 66; Romantic poets and prose-writers, Golden-tree Bibliog, Appleton-Century; auth, Organic form in American criticism, In: The development of American criticism, Univ. N.C, 55; John Taaffe's annotated copy of Adonais, Keats-Shelley J, 68. Add: Dept. of English, University of North Carolina, Chapel Hill, NC 27514.

FOLADARE, JOSEPH, b. Los Angeles, Calif, July 9, 09; m. 35; c. 1. ENGLISH. B.S, Calif. Inst. Technol, 30; A.M, Claremont Cols, 31; Ph.D, Yale, 36. Instr. ENG, Iowa State Col, 35-37, asst. prof, 37-40; UNIV. CALIF, SANTA BARBARA, 40-41, assoc. prof, 41-49, PROF, 49-, chmn. dept, 47-51. Dir. pub, Off. Sci. Res. & Develop. contract, Calif. Inst. Technol, 41-46. Presidential Cert. Merit, 48. MLA. Publ: Co-auth, Index to private papers of James Boswell, Oxford Univ, 37; auth, Ballistics of artillery rockets, Calif. Inst. Technol, 47; Gray's Frail memorial to West, PMLA, 3/60. Add: Dept. of English, University of California, Santa Barbara, CA 93106.

FOLEY, JOSEPH JEREMIAH, b. Lowell, Mass; m. 67; c. 3. ENGLISH. A.B, Holy Cross Col, 51; M.A.T, Boston Col, 57, ESEA fel, 68-71, Ph.D.(educ. res), 71. Asst. prof. ENG, Worcester State Col, 59-65; ASSOC. PROF, BOSTON STATE COL, 65- Res. assoc, Comput. Ctr, Mass. Inst. Technol, 63-64; vis. lectr, Grad. Sch. Educ, Univ. Chicago, summer 67. U.S.N, 52-55, Lt. Am. Educ. Res. Asn; Nat. Counc. Measurement in Educ; Col. Eng. Asn; Conf. Col. Compos. & Commun; NCTE. Computational stylistics; computer content analysis. Publ: Co-auth, Orwell in English and newspeak: a machine translation, Col. Compos. & Commun, 66; auth. chap, In: Handbook of formative and summative evaluation of student learning, McGraw-Hill, 71. Add: Dept. of English, Boston State College, Huntington Ave, Boston, MA 02115.

FOLEY, MICHAEL MYLES, b. Gaspe, P.Q, Apr. 27, 40; m. 64; c. 2. MIDDLE ENGLISH. B.A, St. Thomas Univ, 60; Can. Counc. scholar, Ottawa Univ, 61-62, M.A, 63, Ph.D, 68. Instr, Gaspe Sem, 60-61, 63-64; St. Joseph Teacher's Col, 64-65; St. Dunstan's Univ, 66-67, ASST. PROF, 68-69; UNIV. P.E.I, 69- Can. Asn. Univ. Teachers; Asn. Can. Univ. Teachers Eng. The Gawain-poet; teaching Middle English literature. Publ: Middle English literature for undergraduates: coping with the dialect problem, In: Improving college and university teaching, 73; The God of Patience; pattern for princes, Ottawa Univ. Rev, 74; A bibliography of Purity (cleanness), 1864-1972, Chaucer Rev, 74. Add: Dept. of English, University of Prince Edward Island, Charlottetown, P.E.I, Can.

FOLEY, MILTON J, b. Birmingham, Ala, Nov. 11, 32; m. 53; c. 3. ENGLISH. A.B, Birmingham-South. Col, 57; M.A, Univ. Ala, Tuscaloosa, 65, Ph.D.(Eng), 70. Discount clerk, Gen. Motors Acceptance Corp, 57-58; salesman, Rockwool Mfg. Co, 58-59; Ala. Gas Corp, 59-62; Celotex Corp, 62-63; PROF. ENG, UNIV. MONTEVALLO, 65- Eng.C, U.S.A, 53-55. S.Atlantic Mod. Lang. Asn. Thomas Middleton and 17th century English comedy. Add: Dept. of English, University of Montevallo, Montevallo, AL 35115.

FOLEY, WILLIAM JAY, b. Rockland, Mass, Nov. 28, 20; c. 2. SPEECH. B.S, Univ. Mass, 42; M.A, Columbia, 47; Ph.D.(speech), Univ. Wis, 52. Asst. prof. SPEECH, Berea Col, 46-49, 50-51; assoc. prof, Lawrence Col, 52-54; PROF. & CHMN. DEPT, SOUTH. CONN. STATE COL, 55- AAUP; Speech Commun. Asn; Eng-Speaking Union. Publ: Public speaking in the political career of James M. Curley (record album), Linguaphone Co, 52. Add: Dept. of Speech, Southern Connecticut State College, New Haven, CT 06515.

FOLKENFLIK, ROBERT, b. Newark, N.J, May 23, 39; m. 65; c. 2. ENGLISH. B.A, Rutgers Univ, 61; M.A, Univ. Minn, 66; Class of 1916 fel, Cornell Univ, 66-67, Ph.D.(Eng), 68. Instr. ENG, UNIV. ROCHESTER, 67-68, ASST. PROF, 68-, DIR. FRESHMAN ENG, 71- Asst. ed, Stud. in Burke & his time, 72-, Nat. Endowment for Humanities younger humanist fel. Eng. Inst; MLA; Am. Soc. 18th Century Stud. Eighteenth-century literature; the novel; biography. Publ: A room of Pamela's own, ELH, 12/72; Johnson's art of anecdote, Stud. Eighteenth Century Cult, 73; Child and adult: historical perspective in Gibbon's Memoirs, Stud. in Burke & His time, fall 73. Add: Dept. of English, University of Rochester, Rochester, NY 14627.

FOLLAND, HAROLD FREEZE, b. Salt Lake City, Utah, Oct. 1, 06; m. 46; c. 1. ENGLISH & AMERICAN LITERATURE. A.B, Harvard, 29, Sheldon traveling fel, 29-30, A.M, 34, Ph.D, 40. Instr. & tutor, Harvard, 30-38; instr. Eng, UNIV. UTAH, 38-39; asst. prof, 39-44, assoc. prof, 44-48, PROF, 48-65, ENG. & THEATRE, 65-, head dept. Eng, 61-64. Ed, Utah Humanities Rev, 47-48. U.S.A, 42-46. English and American theatrical history; Dickens. Publ: Co-auth, The shepherd of the ocean, Gambit, Boston & Bodley Head, London, 69; co-auth, Sir Harry Vane: his life and times (1613-1662), Gambit, 73. Add: 1571 Harvard Ave, Salt Lake City, UT 84105.

FOLSOM, GORDON RAYMOND, b. South Berwick, Maine, Sept. 12, 24; m. 48; c. 2. ENGLISH. B.A, Univ. N.H, 49, M.A, 51; Ph.D, Univ. Wis, 60. Instr. ENG, CARROLL COL. (WIS), 53-56, asst. prof, 56-58, assoc. prof, 58-60; PROF, 60-, CHMN. DEPT, 58- Consult, Am. Appraisal Co, 66- U.S.A.A.F, 43-46, Sgt. MLA; Col. Eng. Asn; NCTE (dir, 66-67); Shakespeare Asn. Am. Shakespeare; English language. Publ: Banish all the world: education as ritual and education as experience in Shakespeare's second tetralogy, Wis. Stud. Lit, No. 2, 65; Structure as integrator in the teaching of English, Wis. Eng. J, 1 & 4/67. Add: Dept. of English, Carroll College, Waukesha, WI 53186.

FOLSOM, JAMES K, b. Cleveland, Ohio, Aug. 9, 33. ENGLISH, AMERICAN STUDIES. B.A, Northwest. Univ, 55; Fulbright fel, Univ. Graz, Austria; Ph.D, Princeton, 59. Instr. Eng. & Am. stud, Yale, 59-64, asst. prof. & dean,Saybrook Col, 64-68; assoc. prof. ENG, UNIV. COLO, 68-69, PROF, 69-, DIR. GRAD. STUD, 73- Samuel F.B. Morse fel, 63-64; Bruern fel. Am. lit, Univ. Leeds, Eng, 66-67. MLA; West. Lit. Asn. American and western American literature. Publ: Co-auth, The American literary record, Lippincott, 61; auth, Man's accidents and God's purposes: multiplicity in Hawthorne's fiction, 63, The American western novel, 66 & ed, Biographical memoir of Daniel Boone, 67, Col. & Univ; auth, Timothy Flint, Twayne, 65; Harvey Fergusson, Steck, 69; English westerns, spring 67 & Western themes and western films, fall 67, West. Am. Lit; Shane and Hud: two stories in search of a medium, West. Humanities Rev, autumn 70; plus others. Add: Dept. of English, University of Colorado, Boulder, CO 80302.

FOLSOM, JOHN B, b. New Haven, Conn, Dec. 26, 31; m. 53; c. 2. ENGLISH. B.A, Yale, 53; M.A, Univ. Calif, Berkeley, 56, Ph.D.(Eng), 61; Shakespeare Inst, Eng, 58-59. Instr. ENG, Boston Univ, 59-61; prof. & head dept, Anatolia Col, Greece, 61-63; asst. prof, Boston Univ, Charles River Campus, 63-70; ASSOC. PROF, MONTANA STATE UNIV, 70- Lectr, Boston Area Sem. Int. Stud, 63, 64, 68; NDEA Inst. Advan. Stud. Eng, Boston Univ, 65, 67. MLA; NCTE; Conf. Col. Compos. & Commun; Pac. Northwest Renaissance Conf; AAUP. Elizabethan poetry; modern rhetoric; communications theory. Publ: Co-auth, Guide to freshman English, Boston Univ, 64; auth, The endless mirror, Crowell, 74; co-auth, Guidelines for teaching advanced compostion, Col. Compos. & Commun, 67. Add: Dept. of English, Montana State University, Bozeman, MT 59715.

FONE, BYRNE REGINALD SPENCER, b. Elmira, N.Y, Dec. 28, 36. ENGLISH. A.B, Harpur Col, 58; M.A, Univ. Va, 59; Ph.D.(Eng), N.Y. Univ, 66. Asst. ENG, N.Y. Univ, 60-63; lectr, Queens Col.(N.Y), 63-64; instr, N.Y. Univ, 64-65; CITY COL. NEW YORK, 65-68, ASST. PROF, 68- City Col. New York Res. Comt. grant, 67-68. MLA; Am. Soc. Theatre Res; Grolier Club. American literature of 18th and 19th century; English literature and drama, 1660-1800. Publ: Ed, Colley Cibber's Apology, Univ. Mich, 68; The Augustan translators, AMS Press, 74; auth, History of English literature, Cliffs, 74; Colley Cibber's Love's last shift, 68 & Love's last shift and sentimental comedy, 69, Restoration & 18th Century Theatre Res. Add: Dept. of English, City College of New York, Convent Ave. at 138th St, New York, NY 10031.

FONER, PHILIP SHELDON, History, Literature. See Volume I, History.

FONG, DAVID DOUGLAS, b. Shanghai, China, Dec. 7, 37; Brazilian citizen; m. 73; c. 1. ENGLISH LITERATURE. A.B, Stanford Univ, 60, Ph.D.(Eng), 67; M.A, Columbia Univ, 62. Lectr. humanities, Resselaer Polytech. Inst, 62; ENG, Colby Col, 62-63; ASST. PROF, Univ. Hawaii, Manoa, 66-71; CALIF. STATE UNIV, LOS ANGELES, 71- MLA. English literature 1750-1850; criticism; the novel. Publ: Macaulay and Johnson, Univ. Toronto Quart, fall 70; Macalay: the essayist as historian, Dalhousie Rev, spring 71; Johnson, Goldsmith and The traveller, New Rambler, fall 71. Add: Dept. of English, California State University, 5151 State University, Los Angeles, CA 90032.

FOOKS, JAQUETTA BETH, b. Wichita, Kans, Nov. 27, 45. THEATRE HISTORY, RUSSIAN THEATRE. B.A, Abilene Christian Col, 66; M.A, Univ. Kans, 68, Ph.D.(theatre), 70. Dir. theatre arts, Pepperdine Univ, Los Angeles, 70-72, Pepperdine Univ, Malibu, 72-74. Am. Theatre Asn; AAUP. Nineteenth century Russian theatre; Soviet theatre; European film-makers. Publ: A woman's captivity: translation and adaptation of a play by Alexander Ostrovsky, 68 & The Serf theatre of Imperial Russia, 70, Univ. Kans. Add: 1018 Alamosa, Carlsbad, NM 88220.

FOOTE, IRVING FLINT, b. Laconia, N.H, Aug. 19, 30; m. 68; c. 5. MODERN LITERATURE, FOLKLORE. A.B, Princeton, 52; Yale, 52; M.A, Univ. Conn, 58. Instr. ENG, Univ. Conn, 53-56; Arnold Sch, Pembroke, Mass, 56-57; from instr. to ASSOC. PROF, GA. INST. TECHNOL, 57- Nat. Endowment for humanities proj. staff, 71-72, 72-73, dir, 73. S.Atlantic Mod. Lang. Asn; MLA; Science Fiction Res. Asn. American humor; science fiction. Publ: Richard Condon, & David Karp, In: Contemporary novelists, St. Martin, 72. Add: Dept. of English, Georgia Institute of Technology, Atlanta, GA 30332.

FORBES, ALLAN EDWARD, b. San Francisco, Calif, July 15, 26. SPEECH. A.B. & A.M, Stanford Univ, 48, Ed.D, 52; Univ. Edinburgh, 57. Asst. prof. speech, CALIF. STATE UNIV, CHICO, 48-49, assoc. prof, 49-60, PROF. SPEECH & DRAMA, 60-, HEAD DEPT. & DIR. SPEECH & HEARING CLINIC, 49-, ASSOC. V.PRES. ACAD. AFFAIRS, 71- Consult, schs, Calif, 49-50; Nat. Asn. Standard Med. Vocab, 63. Med. C, U.S.A, 54. Speech Commun. Asn; West. Speech Commun. Asn; Am. Speech & Hearing Asn; Acad. Polit. Sci. Speech corrections in the classroom: the relationship of effective oral communication to success in student teaching. Publ: Teaching listening, Grade Teacher, 61. Add: 1400 Kentfield Rd, Chico, CA 95926.

FORCE, WILLIAM M, b. Newark, N.J, Aug. 15, 16; m. 20; c. 3. ENGLISH, DRAMA. B.A, Colgate Univ, 40, M.A, 48; Northwest. Univ, 49-50. ASSOC. PROF. Eng. & drama, Mo. Valley Col, 51-58; speech, Clarion State Col, 59-60; ENG, IND.UNIV. PA, 61- U.S.A.A.F, 43-46, 1st Lt. Publ: Orestes and Electra, Houghton, 68; Plays should be heard in the classroom, Eng. J, 3/63. Add: 106 Shady Dr, Indiana, PA 15701.

FORD, GEORGE HARRY, b. Winnipeg, Man, Dec. 21, 14; U.S. citizen; m. 42; c. 2. ENGLISH LITERATURE. B.A, Univ. Man, 36; M.A, Univ. Toronto, 38; Ph.D, Yale, 42. Instr. & lectr, Univ. Man, 38-42, 45-46; assoc. prof. ENG, Univ. Cincinnati, 46-55, prof, 55-58; UNIV. ROCHESTER, 58-67, JOSEPH H. GILMORE PROF, 67-, chmn. dept, 60-72. Porter Prize, Yale, 42; vis. prof, Univ. Chicago, 48; Johns Hopkins Univ, 49; Univ. B.C, 53; Am. Counc. Learned Soc. fel, 59-60; Guggenheim fel, 63-64; mem. adv. bd, Victorian Stud, 61-69; Mosaic: J. Comp. Lit, 69- Can. Army, 42-45, Capt. MLA; Int. Asn. Univ. Profs. Eng; Asn. Chmn. Depts. Eng; Dickens Fel. (v.pres, 72-). Nineteenth and twentieth century English literature, especially the novel. Publ: Keats and the Victorians, Yale Univ, 44; Dickens and his readers, Princeton Univ, 55; co-auth, The Dickens critics, Cornell Univ, 61 & Norton anthology of English literature, Norton, 68; auth, Double measure: D.H. Lawrence's novels, Holt, 65; Dickens and the Voices of time, In: Dickens Centennial essays, Univ. Calif, 71. Add: Dept. of English, University of Rochester, Rochester, NY 14627.

FORD, GORDON BUELL, JR, Linguistics, English. See Volume III, Foreign Languages, Linguistics & Philology.

FORD, HOWARD LEE, b. Anna, Tex, Mar. 22, 38; m. 68. ENGLISH. B.A. & M.A, N.Tex. State Col, 60; Ph.D.(Eng), La. State Univ, 63. Asst. prof. ENG, N.TEX. STATE UNIV, 63-67, ASSOC. PROF, 67- English Renaissance drama. Publ: Some aspects of technical writing, Round Table, 61. Add: Dept. of English, North Texas State University, Denton, TX 76203.

FORD, HUGH D, b. Washington, N.J, Dec. 11, 25; m. 51; c. 2. ENGLISH. B.A, Dickinson Col, 50; M.A, Stanford Univ, 52; Ph.D.(Eng), Univ. Pa, 62. Instr. ENG, W. Nottingham Acad, 52-55; Col. Wooster, 55-57; Univ. Pa, 57-58; PROF, TRENTON STATE COL, 58- Am. Philos. Soc. grants, 63, 67; Fulbright prof, Univ. Chile, 65; Am. Counc. Learned Soc. grant, 70; Nat. Endowment for Humanities sr. fel, 72. U.S.A, 44-46. Spanish Civil War literature; 20th century American and British literature. Publ: A poet's war, Univ. Pa, 65; Nancy Cunard, Chilton, 68; co-auth, These were the hours, South. Ill. Univ, 68; Negro, Ungar, 70; The left bank revisited, Pa. State Univ, 72; Published in Paris, Macmillan, 74. Add: Dept. of English, Trenton State College, Trenton, NJ 08625.

FORD, JAMES LAWRENCE COLLIER, b. Foochow, China, Apr. 7, 07; m. 29; c. 2. JOURNALISM. A.B, Lawrence Col, 28; A.M, Univ. Wis, 39; Stanford Univ, 40-41; Coffman fel, Univ. Minn, 45, Ph.D, 48. Mem. staff, United Press, N.Y.C; Assoc. Press, San Francisco, Calif; Chicago Tribune, N.Y.C; Popular Sci. Monthly; asst. prof. JOUR, Univ. Ore; Univ. Calif; prof. & dean sch. jour, Univ. Mont; PROF, SOUTH. ILL. UNIV, 55- Consult. ed, Focus/Midwest Mag, 66- Asn. Educ. Jour; Am. Counc. Educ. Jour. Journalism education; magazines and specialized publications; foreign affairs. Publ: Co-auth, The new survey of journalism, Harper; auth, Magazines for millions: the story of specialized publications, South. Ill. Univ, 70. Add: 807 Skyline Dr, Carbondale, IL 62901.

FORD, MARGARET PATRICIA, b. Erie, Pa, Mar. 17, 25. ENGLISH. A.B, Lake Erie Col, 45; M.A, West. Reserve Univ, 46, Ph.D, 57. Instr. biol, Lake Erie Col, 46-48; ENG, Valparaiso Univ, 48-51; teaching fel, West. Reserve Univ, 53-55; instr. La. State Univ, 55-57; assoc. prof, Grove City Col, 57-64; HOOD COL, 64-68, PROF, 68- Col. Eng. Asn; MLA. American literature, 1870-1900, especially the Cleveland, Ohio literary scene; fiction of William Faulkner. Publ: Co-auth, Who's who in Faulkner, La. State Univ, 63, rev. ed, 66; contrib, Popular literature in America, Bowling Green Univ, 72. Add: Box 191, Burton, OH 44021.

FORD, NEWELL F, b. Portland, Ore, Mar. 10, 12. ENGLISH. A.B, Reed Col, 36; A.M, Harvard, 38; Ph.D, Univ. Calif, 45. Teaching asst, Univ. Calif, 39-42, 43-45; instr.ENG, STANFORD UNIV, 45-48, asst. prof, 48-55; assoc. prof, 55-63, PROF, 63- MLA; Keats-Shelley Asn. Am. Romantic period of English literature. Publ: The prefigurative imagination of John Keats, Stanford Univ, 51 & 64; plus several arts. on Eng. Romantic poets. Add: Dept. of English, Stanford University, Stanford, CA 94305.

FORD, NICK AARON, b. Ridgeway, S.C, Aug. 4, 04; m. 27, 68; c. 1. ENGLISH. A.B, Benedict Col, 26; A.M, State Univ, Iowa, 34, Gen. Educ. Bd. fel, 44-45, Ph.D, 45. Prin, Schofield Norm. Sch, 26-28; prof. ENG, Fla. Norm. & Indust. Inst, 29-36; Langston Univ, 36-43; PROF. & HEAD DEPT, MORGAN STATE COL, 45- Consult. higher educ, U.S. Off. Educ, 64-66, res. grant, 64-67; mem. bd. dir, Nat. Counc. Teachers Eng, 64-67; mem. admin. comn, Asn. Depts. Eng, 67-70; Nat. Endowment for Humanities res. grant, 70-72. NCTE; Col. Lang. Asn; Col. Eng. Asn; MLA. The Negro in American literature; teaching communication skills to cultural disadvantaged college freshmen; Black studies in American colleges and universities. Publ: The contemporary Negro novel & Best short stories by Afro-American writers, Meador; co-auth, Basic skills for better writing, Putnam, 59 & 62; auth, American culture in literature, Rand McNally, 67; Language in uniform, Odyssey, 67; ed, Black insights: significant literature by Black Americans, 1760-present, Ginn, 71; auth, Black studies: threat or challenge?, Kennikat, 73; Improving reading and writing skills of disadvantaged college freshmen, Compos. & Commun, 5/67; Black literature and problem of evaluation, 2/71 & Teaching Black literature with aid of anthologies, 4/73, Col. Eng; plus others. Add: 919 E. 43rd St, Baltimore, MD 21212.

FORD, OLA M, b. Wetumpka, Ala, Sept. 14, 04; m. 68. ENGLISH. B.S, Ill. Inst. Technol, 33; B.A, Langston Univ, 39; M.S, Kans. State Col. Pittsburg, 44; Loyola Univ.(Ill), 51-52; Inst. Int. Educ. grant, Univ. Oslo, summer 63. Soc. worker, Chicago, Ill, 33-38; teacher, High Sch, Okla, 41-48; ENG, Stowe Teachers Col, 48-49; instr, Agr. Mech. & Norm. Col, Ark, 49-52; Jackson State Col, 52-53; asst. prof, 54-63, assoc. prof, 63-68; instr, MORGAN STATE COL, 68-71, ASST. PROF, 71- Consult. evaluating Eng. prog. high schs, Miss; grant, Shakespeare Inst, Conn, 66. NCTE; Conf. Col. Compos. & Commun; MLA; Col. Lang. Asn; Col. Eng. Asn. Add: 919 E. 43rd St, Baltimore, MD 21212.

FORD, THOMAS WELLBORN, b. Houston, Tex, Dec. 23, 24; m. 53; c. 2. AMERICAN LITERATURE. B.A, Rice Univ, 50; M.A, Univ. Tex, 51, univ. fel, 56-58, Ph.D, 59. Instr, Kinkaid Prep. Sch, Houston, Tex, 53-55; spec. instr. ENG, Univ. Tex, 58-59; Univ. S.C, 59-61; asst. prof, 61-66; assoc. prof, UNIV. HOUSTON, 66-71, PROF, 71- U.S.A.A.F, 43-46, Sgt. MLA. Western American literature; 19th century and contemporary American literature. Publ: Heaven beguiles the tired: death in the poetry of Emily Dickinson, Univ. Ala, 66; A.B. Guthrie, Jr, Steck-Vaughn, 68; Howells and the American Negro, Tex. Stud. Lit. & Lang, 64; Emily Dickinson and the Civil War, Univ. Rev, 65; The American rhythm: Mary Austin's poetic principle, West. Am. Lit, 70; plus others. Add: Dept. of English, University of Houston, Houston, TX 77004.

FORDYCE, RACHEL POOLE, b. Greensburg, Pa, June 5, 42; m. 69; c. 1. ENGLISH, DRAMA. B.A, Univ. Pittsburgh, 63, Mellon fel. & M.A, 64, Ph.D. (Eng), 72; Northwest. Univ, 66-67. Instr. ENG, Lake Erie Col. Women, 64-

66; ASST. PROF, Fairmont State Col, 67-69; VA. POLYTECH. INST. & STATE UNIV, 71- Secy-treas, Resource Systs, Inc, 69- MLA; Am. Theatre Asn; Col. Eng. Asn. Caroline drama; contemporary drama; children's theatre. Publ: Co-ed, Children's literature: the great excluded, Univ. Conn, Vol. II, 73, Vol. III, 74. Add: Dept. of English, Virginia Polytechnic & Institute & State University, Blacksburg, VA 24061.

FOREMAN, WALTER CYRIL, b. Moline, Ill, Sept. 3, 10; m. 36; c. 1. ENGLISH LANGUAGE & LITERATURE. A.B, Union Co.(Nebr), 33; A.M, Univ. Nebr, 37; Columbia Univ, 38; Ph.D, Univ. Calif, 48. Instr, Univ. Nebr, 38-41; asst, Univ. Calif, 44-48; from assoc. prof. to PROF. ENG, ORE. STATE UNIV, 48-, CHMN. DEPT, 65- Marjorie Bailey mem. lectr, Inst. Renaissance Stud, Ore. Shakespearean Festival, summer 66. NCTE; MLA; Conf. Col. Compos. & Commun; Conf. Eng. Educ; Renaissance Soc. Am. Samuel Butler, a study in satiric process and method; Shakespeare; comedy and satire. Publ: Co-auth, English in Oregon secondary schools, Ore. State Dept. Educ, 66. Add: Dept. of English, Oregon State University, Corvallis, OR 97331.

FORKER, CHARLES RUSH, b. Pittsburgh, Pa, Mar. 11, 27. ENGLISH LITERATURE. A.B, Bowdoin Col, 51; B.A, Merton Col, Oxford, 53, M.A, 55; Ph.D, Harvard, 57. Instr. Eng, Univ. Wis, 57-59; asst. prof, IND. UNIV, BLOOMINGTON, 59-64, assoc. prof, 64-68, PROF. ENG. LIT, 68- Fulbright scholar, Eng, 51-53; Folger Shakespeare Libr. fel, 63; Am. Counc. Learned Soc. grant, 65-66; vis. prof, Univ. Mich, Ann Arbor, 68-69; Huntington Libr. fel, 69. MLA; Shakespeare Asn. Am. Shakespeare studies; Elizabethan drama. Publ: Shirley's The cardinal, Ind. Univ, 64; Shakespeare's Henry V, W.C. Brown, 71. Add: Dept. of English, Indiana University, Bloomington, IN 47401.

FORREST, JAMES FRENCH, b. Wishaw, Scotland, Feb. 21, 24; m. 58; c. 2. ENGLISH. M.A, Glasgow Univ, 51, B.Litt, 58; Glasgow Univ - Cornell Univ. exchange fel, Cornell Univ, 56-57, M.A, 57, univ. sr. fel, 58-60, Ph.D. (Milton), 60. Teacher high sch, Scotland, 52-58; asst. prof. ENG, UNIV. ALTA, 60-64, assoc. prof, 64-71, PROF, 71- Sr. mem, Univ. Col, Cambridge, 67-68; Can. Counc. Sr. fel, 67-68. R.N, 42-46. MLA; Milton Soc. Am; Asn. Can. Univ. Teachers Eng. Milton and moral theology; Bunyan and the Puritan Ethos; drama, especially Shakespeare. Publ: An edition of Bunyan's Holy war, N.Y. Univ, 68; Bunyan's ignorance and the flatterer: a study in the literary art of damnation, Stud. Philol, 63; Mercy with her mirror, Philol. Quart, 63; Some spiritual symbols in Puritan literature, Can. J. Theol, 63. Add: Dept. of English, University of Alberta, Edmonton, Alta, Can.

FORREST, WILLIAM CRAIG, b. St. Louis, Mo, Aug. 5, 27; m. 63. ENGLISH. A.B, St. Louis Univ, 52, Ph.D, 60; M.A, Marquette Univ, 55. Instr. ENG, Loras Col, 55-56; LE MOYNE COL, 59-60, asst. prof, 60-64, assoc. prof, 64-69, PROF, 69- Vis. prof. rhetoric, Univ. Calif, Berkeley, 69-70; co-ed, Oral Eng, 72-. MLA; NCTE; Am. Soc. Aesthet; Brit. Soc. Aesthet; Ling. Soc. Am; Speech Commun. Asn. Nineteenth and 20th century poetry; literary theory and criticism; aesthetics. Publ: Inside the poem, Le Moyne Col. Bookstore, 62; The kinesthetic feel of literature, Bucknell Rev, 12/68; Literature as aesthetic object: the kinesthetic stratum, J. Aesthet. & Art Criticism, summer 69; The poem as a summons to performance, Brit. J. Aesthet, 7/69. Add: Dept. of English, Le Moyne College, Le Moyne Heights, Syracuse, NY 13214.

FORSBERG, ROBERTA JEAN, b. Everett, Mass, Apr. 18, 14. COMPARATIVE LITERATURE. A.B, Whittier Col, 36, A.M, 37; Ph.D, Univ. South. Calif, 50. Instr, Bakersfield Jr. Col, Calif, 41-42; from asst. prof. to PROF. ENG, WHITTIER COL, 43- Col. Eng. Asn; Am-Scand. Found; Eng-Speaking Union. Relation of the novel to aviation; cultural history of the Anglo-American tie; symbolism in the modern novel. Publ: Ed, Redman echoes; co-auth, Mme. de Stael and freedom today, 64, auth, Mme. de Stael and the English, 68 & The world of David Beaty: the place of the images, 71, Astra Bks; Chief mountain: story of Canon Middleton, Hist. Soc. Alta, 64; An analysis of the work of David Beaty, In: Contemporary novelists, St. Martin's, 72. Add: Dept. of English, Whittier College, Whittier, CA 90608.

FORSYTH, JOSEPH H, b. Ft. Lewis, Wash, Jan. 16, 24; m. 48; c. 2. ENGLISH. B.A, N.Mex, State Univ, 48; M.A, Columbia Univ, 49, Ed.D, 61. Instr. ENG, N.MEX. STATE UNIV, 50-54, asst. prof, 54-59, assoc. prof, 59-65, PROF, 65-, assoc. producer sci. films, phys. sci. lab, 55-57, chmn. comt. freshman Eng, 57-61, Robert L. Westhafer Teaching Award, 60. Consult, Vimax, West. N.Mex. Univ, 72- U.S.A, 43-46, S/Sgt. NCTE; Conf. Col. Compos. & Commun. American regional novelists; design of the literary utopia. Publ: Composition, the overhead, and the team, J. Conf. Col. Compos. & Commun, 10/65. Add: Box 4401, University Park, NM 88003.

FORTENBERRY, GEORGE E, b. Childress, Tex, Aug. 15, 20; m. 48; c. 2. AMERICAN LITERATURE. B.A, Tex. Christian Univ, 48, M.A, 51; Ph.D. (Eng), Univ. Ark, 67. Instr. ENG, UNIV. TEX, ARLINGTON, 55-57, asst. prof, 57-67, assoc. prof, 67-72, PROF, 73- Assoc. ed, Am. Lit. Realism 1870-1910, 68-71; Arlington Quart, 67-68; Harold Frederic Ed, 73- MLA; Am. Stud. Asn. American literature, 1930's; William Dean Howells. Publ: Ambrose Bierce (1842-1914): a critical bibliography of secondary comment, Am. Lit. Realism 1870-1910, winter 71; William Dean Howells In: Fifteen American authors before 1900, Univ. Wis, 71; A checklist of books and essays about American Negro novelists, Stud. in the Novel, summer 71; plus others. Add: Dept. of English, University of Texas at Arlington, Arlington, TX 76010.

FORTER, ELIZABETH TUSTEN, b. Wichita, Kans, Nov. 19, 22. ENGLISH. B.A, Univ. Wichita, 43; Adams fel, Univ. Wis, 44, M.A, 45, Ph.D, 55. Instr. ENG, Univ. Wichita, 45-47, 52-53; instr. LAWRENCE UNIV, 53-57, asst. prof, 57-60, assoc. prof, 60-63, PROF, 63-, EDWARDS-ALEXANDER CHAIR ENG, 62-, chmn. dept, 59-64. MLA; NCTE; AAUP. George Bernard Shaw; modern British fiction; comedy. Publ: Co-auth, The comic in theory and practice, 60, ed, G.B. Shaw's Caesar and Cleopatra, 65 & G.B. Shaw's Major Barbara, 71, Appleton. Add: Dept. of English, Lawrence University, Appleton, WI 54911.

FORTIN, RENE E, b. Woonsocket, R.I, Feb. 21, 34; m. 55; c. 5. ENGLISH. A.B, Providence Col, 55; M.A, Brown Univ, 60, Ph.D.(Eng), 64. Instr. ENG, PROVIDENCE COL, 58-62, asst. prof. 63-65, ASSOC. PROF, 66-, DIR. DEVELOP. WEST. CIVILIZATION PROG, 72-, chmn. dept, 70-72. Danforth Found. Harbison prize, 69. U.S.A, 56, Res, 56-, Capt. MLA. Shakespearean drama; 17th century poetry. Publ: Allegory and genre in Othello, Genre, 6/71; Twelfth night: Shakespeare's drama of initiation, Papers Lang. & Lit, spring 72; Tongues in trees: symbolic patterns in As you like it, Tex. Stud. Lit. & Lang, winter 73; plus others. Add: Dept. of English, Providence College, Providence, RI 02918.

FORTSON, FRANCES KAY, b. Maud, Okla, Jan. 9, 31; m. 49, 64; c. 3. ENGLISH & AMERICAN LITERATURE. B.A, Univ. Tulsa, 61, Foster Brooks Parriott fel, 61-62, M.A, 62; Okla. State Univ, 69-74. Asst. prof. ENG, PHILLIPS UNIV, 62-72, ASSOC. PROF, 72- Nat. Endowment for Humanities summer sem. participant, Ohio State Univ, 73. NCTE; Col. Eng. Asn. Comedy and tragedy; Saul Bellow. Add: Div. of Humanities, Phillips University, Enid, OK 73701.

FORTUNA, DIANE DE TURO, b. New York, N.Y, Dec. 7, 36; c. 2. ENGLISH. A.B, N.Y. Univ, 58; Gilman fel, Johns Hopkins Univ, 58-62, A.M, 61, Ph.D. (Eng), 67. Instr. ENG, Univ. N.H, 62-64, ASST. PROF, 65-66; Southampton Col, Long Island Univ, 67-68; STATE UNIV. N.Y. STONY BROOK, 68- Univ. N.H. summer fac. fel, 65. MLA. Contemporary novel; James Joyce. Add: Dept. of English, State University of New York at Stony Brook, Stony Brook, NY 11790.

FORTUNE, MICHAEL J, b. New York, N.Y, Aug. 28, 22; m. 44; c. 8. ENGLISH. B.S, Wis. State Col, Stevens Point, 49; M.A, Univ. Minn, 57; teacher grant, Univ. Wis, 64, Ph.D.(Eng), 65. Teacher, Three Lakes High Sch, 49-51; Stevens Point High Sch, 51-56; assoc. prof. Eng, Wis. State Col, Stevens Point, 56-67; prof. & chmn. dept, Mundelein Col, 67-72; PROF. & CHMN. DEPT. FOR. LANG, UNIV. WIS-STEVENS POINT, 72- Johnson Found. excellence in teaching award, 66. U.S.A.F, 43-46. MLA; Renaissance Soc. Am. English drama of the Renaissance; the theme of quest in modern literature, especially English, continental and American. Publ: An unpublished letter of Camus, French Rev, spring 67. Add: Dept. of Foreign Languages & Comparative Literature, University of Wisconsin-Stevens Point, Stevens Point, WI 54481.

FOSCUE, VIRGINIA ODEN, b. Bellamy, Ala, June 23, 33. ENGLISH LINGUISTICS. B.A, Univ. Ala, 55; M.A, 59; Ph.D.(Eng), Univ. Wis, 66. Instr. ENG, UNIV. ALA, 64-66, asst. prof, 66-70, ASSOC. PROF, 70- Ling. Soc. Am; MLA; NCTE. Freshman English; place names; linguistic geography. Publ: Place names of Sumter County, Alabama, Ala. Rev, 1/60; Background and preliminary survey of the linguistic geography of Alabama, Diss. Abstr, Vol. 28, No. 1. Add: Dept. of English, University of Alabama, University, AL 35486.

FOSDICK, JAMES ALBERT, b. Liberty, Ind, Aug. 29, 18; m. 45; c. 3. MASS COMMUNICATIONS, JOURNALISM. A.B, Hillsdale Col, 40; M.S, Northwest. Univ, 41; Ph.D.(mass commun), Univ. Wis, 63. Reporter & photographer, Muncie Evening Press, Ind, 41-42; asst. ed, Ind. Mag, West. Electric Co, Ill, 42; asst. prof. JOUR, Kent State Univ, 46-51, assoc. prof, 51-56, prof, 56-58; teaching asst, UNIV. WIS-MADISON, 58-60, lectr, 60-64, assoc. prof, 64-71, PROF, 71- Critic, Engineering Col. Mag. Assoc, 66-68. Adj. Gen.C, U.S.A, 42-46, Capt. Asn. Educ. in Jour.(head photojour. div, 66-68); Nat. Press Photographers Asn. Pictorial communication; mass communication audiences. Publ: Co-auth, The encoder's intent and use of stylistic elements in photographs, Jour. Quart, spring 64; auth, Research in photojournalism, Jour. Educ, fall 64; co-auth, The effect of lighting angle on the judgment of photographed subjects, Audio-Visual Commun. Rev, Vol. 8, No. 6. Add: School of Journalism, 425 Henry Mall, University of Wisconsin-Madison, Madison, WI 53706.

FOSSO, DOYLE RICHARD, b. Austin, Minn, Aug. 15, 33; m. 58; c. 2. ENGLISH. B.A, Harvard, 55, fac. arts & sci. fel, 57-58, Danforth fel, 57-59, Ph.D.(lit), 65; Fulbright scholar, Univ. Oslo, 55-56; Danforth fel. & M.A, Univ. Mich, 57. Instr. ENG, Univ. Vt, 60-64; WAKE FOREST UNIV, 64-65, asst. prof, 65-71, ASSOC. PROF, 71- Mem, Southeast. Inst. Medieval & Renaissance Stud, summer 66. MLA; Renaissance Soc. Am. Sixteenth and seventeenth century English prose and poetry. Add: Dept. of English, Wake Forest University, Winston-Salem, NC 27106.

FOSSUM, ROBERT H, b. Beloit, Wis, Mar. 19, 23; m. 52; c. 3. ENGLISH & AMERICAN LITERATURE. B.A, Beloit Col, 48; M.A, Univ. South. Calif, 50; fel, Claremont Grad. Sch, 59-61, Lilly Found. fel, 59-60, Shell Oil Co. fel, 60-61, Ph.D, 63. Teaching asst. Eng, Univ. South. Calif, 48-50; instr, Beloit Col, 50-54, asst. prof, 55-57, assoc. prof, 58-62, acting chmn. dept. Eng, 55-56, 58-59, chmn. div. langs. & commun, 61-62; asst. prof. Eng, Los Angeles State Col, 62-63; assoc. prof, CLAREMONT MEN'S COL, 63-68, PROF. ENG. & AM. LIT, 68-, chmn. dept. lit. & lang, 65-71. Lectr, Univ. South. Calif, 53-54; Claremont Men's Col, 59-60; vis. asst. prof, Harvey Mudd Col, 63; mem. fac, Claremont Grad. Sch, 63-; vis. prof. Eng, Calif. State Univ, Los Angeles, summer 69; Fulbright prof. Am. lit, Univ. Vienna & Graz Univ, 69 & 70. U.S.A, 43. MLA. Contemporary British and American literature; 19th century American literature, especially Hawthorne; contemporary continental novel. Publ: William Styron: a critical essay, Eerdmans, 68; Hawthorne's inviolable circle, Everett Edwards, 72; The devil and Saul Bellow, Comparative Lit. Stud, spring 66; Time and the artist in Hawthorne's Legends of the Province House, 3/67 & The summons of the past: Hawthorne's Alice Doane's appeal, 12/68, Nineteenth-century Fiction. Add: Dept. of Literature & Languages, Claremont Men's College, Claremont, CA 91711.

FOSTER, CHARLES HOWELL, b. Elizabeth, N.J, Aug. 3, 13; m. 34; c. 4. ENGLISH. A.B, Amherst Col, 36; A.M, State Univ, Iowa, 37, Ph.D, 39. Breadloaf Writers Conf. fel, 37. Asst, State Univ. Iowa, 37-38, instr, 29-42, asst. prof, 42-44; assoc. prof, Univ. Colo, 44-47; prof. Eng, Grinnell Col, 47-58, chmn. dept, 48-49, 50-51, dir. adv. commun, 52-56, chmn. div. lang. & lit. 54-56; prof. Eng, Univ. Minn, Minneapolis, 58-74, dir. Eng. grad. work, 61-64. Am. Counc. Learned Soc. fel, 51; mem. ed. bd, New Eng. Quart, 58-73; vis. prof, Bowdoin Col, 64-65. MLA; Soc. Am. Hist; Am.

Stud. Asn.(mem. exec. counc). New England intellectual history; abolition movement; American novel. Publ: Emerson's Theory of poetry; The rungless ladder: Harriet Beecher Stowe and New England Puritanism, Duke Univ, 54 & Cooper Square Union, 70; Something in emblems: a reinterpretation of Moby Dick; ed, Beyond Concord: selected writings of David Atwood Wasson, Ind. Univ, 65 & Kennikat, 73; plus others. Add: Rte. 1, Box 220, Luray, VA 22835.

FOSTER, CHARLES WILLIAM, b. Chattanooga, Tenn, Jan. 1, 39; m. 62; c. 2. AMERICAN LITERATURE, DIALECT GEOGRAPHY. B.S, Univ. Chattanooga, 61; M.A, E.Tenn. State Univ, 63; Ph.D.(Eng), Univ. Ala, 68. Teacher Eng. & geog, Hixson High Sch, 61-62; instr. Eng, Univ. Ala, 66-68; asst. prof, FLORENCE STATE UNIV, 68-70, assoc. prof, 70-73, PROF. & HEAD DEPT, 73- NCTE res. grant; assoc. ed, Ling. Atlas Gulf States. U.S.A, 57-68, Sgt. MLA; Am. Dialect Soc; NCTE; Conf. Col. Compos. & Commun. American, specifically Appalachian, folklore. Publ: Co-auth, A manual for dialect research in the southern states, Ga. State Univ, 72; auth, The phonology of negro speech in Charles W. Chesnutt's The conjure woman, Univ. Ala-Am. Dialect Soc, (in press); The butcher's boy in Newmarket, Alabama, Tenn. Folklore Soc. Bull, 69. Add: Dept. of English, Florence State University, Florence, AL 35630.

FOSTER, DAVID EARLE, b. Lexington, Va, Aug. 17, 38; m. 63; c. 2. ENGLISH & AMERICAN LITERATURE. A.B, Bowdoin Col, 60; M.A, Univ. Wis, 61, Ph.D.(Eng), 69. ASST. PROF. ENG, DRAKE UNIV, 69- Intel.C, U.S.A, 63-65, Lt. Victorian novel; 20th century novel; theory of prose composition. Publ: Rhetorical strategy in Richard Feverel, Nineteenth Century Fiction, fall 71; The fall in Baldwin's novels, Critique, winter 71. Add: Dept. of English, Drake University, Des Moines, IA 50311.

FOSTER, EDWARD E, b. West New York, N.J, Nov. 19, 39; m. 66. ENGLISH. A.B, St. Peter's Col.(N.J), 61; Ph.D.(Eng), Univ. Rochester, 65. Instr. Eng, Grinnell Col, 64-65, asst. prof, 65-68, assoc. prof, 68-73; PROF. ENG. & DEAN, COL. ARTS & SCI, UNIV. SAN DIEGO, 73- MLA; Midwest Mod. Lang. Asn; Medieval Acad. Am. Middle English narrative: Restoration and 18th century political and religious poetry; literary taxonomy. Publ: Co-auth, A modern lexicon of literary terms, Scott, 68; Humor in the knight's tale, Chaucer Rev, 68; Allegorical consolation in the book of the Duchess, Ball State Univ. Forum, 70; The text of William of Palerne, Neuphilol. Mitt, 73. Add: Dept. of English, University of San Diego, San Diego, CA 92110.

FOSTER, EDWARD FRANCIS, b. Springfield, Ky, Mar. 18, 23; m. 60; c. 2. ENGLISH. B.A, Univ. Dayton, 48; M.A, Ohio State Univ, 51; Ford Found. fel, Vanderbilt Univ, 54-56; Ph.D, 57. Instr. ENG, Univ. Ky, 57-62; asst. prof, BALL STATE UNIV, 62-67, ASSOC. PROF, 67- U.S.A, 43-46, 51-52, 1st Lt. Am. Folklore Soc; Am. Stud. Asn. Humor, early and modern; 19th century American literature; folklore. Add: Dept. of English, Ball State University, Muncie, IN 47306.

FOSTER, JOHN BURT, b. Faribault, Minn, May 8, 11; m. 45; c. 4. ENGLISH. A.B, Swarthmore Col, 33; summer, Am. Counc. Learned Soc. grant-in-aid, Harvard, 40; M.A, Univ. Ill, 47, Ph.D.(Eng), 52; summer, Am. Counc. Learned Soc. grant-in-aid, Ind. Univ, 52. Lectr. Eng, Cent. China Col, 34-40; ed. asst, Off. War Inform, 42-45; pub. affairs off, for. serv. reserve, U.S. Dept. State, 45-47; asst. prof. ENG, MANKATO STATE COL, 52-58, assoc. prof, 58-61, PROF, 61-, COORD. PEACE STUD. PROG, 73- AAUP; MLA; Ling. Soc. Am; Asn. Asian Stud; Am. Stud. Asn; NCTE. Chinese influences on American literature; linguistics of English; American literature since the Civil War. Add: Dept. of English, Mankato State College, Mankato, MN 56001.

FOSTER, JOHN BURT, JR, b. Chicago, Ill, Dec. 19, 45; m. 70. COMPARATIVE LITERATURE, ENGLISH. A.B, Harvard, 67; M.Phil, Yale, 70, Ph.D. (comp. lit), 74; Ger. Acad. Exchange fel, Univ. Konstanz, 71-72. ASST. PROF. ENG. & COMP. LIT, STANFORD UNIV, 72- MLA; Am. Comp. Lit. Asn. The novel; Nietzsche and modern literature; literary theory. Add: Dept. of English, Stanford University, Stanford, CA 94305.

FOSTER, JOHN LAWRENCE, b. Chicago, Ill, Nov. 11, 30; m. 56; c. 3. ENGLISH. A.B, Kalamazoo Col, 52; Harvard, 52-53; M.A, Univ. Mich, 57, univ. fel, 59-61, Ph.D.(Eng), 61. Instr. ENG, Univ. Conn, 61-64; assoc. prof Wis. State Univ, Whitewater, 64-66; PROF, ROOSEVELT UNIV, 66-, chmn. dept. Eng. & Speech, 66-70. Nat. Endowment Humanities fel, 71; mem, Am. Res. Ctr. Egypt, 71- U.S.A, 53-56. MLA. Ezra Pound; ancient Egyptian literature; American poetry. Publ: Love songs of the new kingdom, Scribner, 74; Pound's revision of Cantos I-III, Mod. Philol, 2/66; Translations of ancient Egyptian love songs, Poetry, 71. Add: Dept. of English, Roosevelt University, 430 S. Michigan Ave, Chicago, IL 60605.

FOSTER, LESLIE DONLEY, b. Chicago, Ill, Oct. 19, 30; m. 68; c. 1. LITERARY THEORY, RENAISSANCE LITERATURE. B.A, Univ. Chicago, 54, M.A, 60; Univ. Toronto, 62-63; Ph.D.(Eng), Univ. Notre Dame, 74. Instr. ENG, Valparaiso Univ, 59-62, 63-64; NORTH. MICH. UNIV, 67-71, ASST. PROF, 71- Consult, Conf. Tenure, Marietta Col, 73; consult. on tenure, Mich. Conf, AAUP, 73; humanist-consult, Nat. Humanities Series, Nat. Endowment for Humanities, 74. MLA; AAUP (mem. spec. comt. on non-tenured fac, 72-); Am. Civil Liberties Union; Mod. Humanities Res. Asn; Eng. Inst. Sir Philip Sidney. Publ: Sidney's praise of man: a reassessment of the nature of the literary theory in the Defence of Poesie, Univ. Microfilms, 74; Dimensions of the critic's concern, Notre Dame Eng. J, fall 65; Walden and its audiences: troubled sleep and religious and other awakenings, Mod. Lang. Rev, 10/72; Heroic strivings in The playboy of the western world, Eire-Ireland, spring 73. Add: Dept. of English, Northern Michigan University, Marquette, MI 49855.

FOSTER, MALCOLM BURTON, b. Montreal, P.Q, Feb. 24, 31; m. 54; c. 4. TWENTIETH CENTURY BRITISH & AMERICAN ENGLISH. B.A, Syracuse Univ, 55, Univ. Minn, 56-59. Instr. ENG, Mich. Col. Mining & Technol, 58-60; Univ. Cincinnati, 60-63; lectr, SIR GEORGE WILLIAMS UNIV, 63-65, asst. prof, 65-68, ASSOC. PROF, 68- Can. Counc. grants, 64, 65, 67-68; Brit. Counc. travel grant, 64; Houghton Mifflin Lit. fel, 67-68. Asn. Can. Univ. Teachers Eng; Can. Asn. Am. Stud. British literature since 1914. Publ: The Prince with a hundred dragons, Doubleday, 63; A casebook on Alan Paton's Cry the beloved country, Cole, Toronto, 65; Joyce Cary: a biography, Houghton, 68; The colour of my true love's hair, Story, fall 63; Fell of the lion, fleece of the sheep, Mod. Fiction Stud, winter, 64. Add: Dept. of English, Sir George Williams University, Montreal 25, P.Q, Can.

FOSTER, MILTON P, b. Pittsburgh, Pa, Apr. 23, 21; m. 46; c. 3. LITERATURE. A.B, Waynesburg Col, 43; A.M, Univ. Pittsburgh, 47; Ph.D.(Eng), Univ. Mich, 54. Instr. ENG, Waynesburg Col, 46-47; EAST. MICH. UNIV, 47-54, asst. prof, 54-57, assoc. prof, 57-61, PROF, 61-, HEAD DEPT, 68-, dir, NDEA inst, 67. U.S.A, 43-46, Sgt. MLA; NCTE; Conf. Eng. Educ. American literature; 18th century literature; literary criticism. Publ: A casebook on Gulliver among the Houyhnhnms, Crowell, 61; Voltaire's Candide and the critics, Wadsworth, 62; Levels of meaning in A separate peace, Eng. Record, 4/68. Add: Dept. of English, Eastern Michigan University, Ypsilanti, MI 48197.

FOSTER, RICHARD JACKSON, b. Rochester, N.Y, Mar. 14, 28; m. 65; c. 1. ENGLISH. B.A, Oberlin Col, 49, M.A, 50; Univ. Mich, 50-53; Ph.D.(Eng), Syracuse Univ, 57. Asst. prof. ENG, Univ. Minn, 58-62; assoc. prof, 62-65, prof, 65-68; Macalester Col, 68-74; PROF. & CHMN. DEPT, UNIV. HAWAII, MANOA, 74- Vis. assoc. prof, Williams Col, 64-65; Fulbright lectr, Univ. Toulouse, France, 65-66. MLA. American literature; 20th century British and American literature; literary criticism. Publ: The new romantics, Ind. Univ, 62; co-ed, Modern criticism, theory and practice, Odyssey, 63; ed, Six American novelists of the nineteenth century, 68 & auth, Norman Mailer, In: American writers series, 68, Univ. Minn; ed, The novels of Elizabeth Stoddard, Johnson Reprint, 72; auth, Criticism as rage: D.H. Lawrence, In: D.H. Lawrence, Prentice-Hall, 63; Mailer and the Fitzerald tradition, Novel, A Forum on Fiction, spring 68; On teaching literary criticism, Twentieth Century Lit, summer 68. Add: Dept. of English, University of Hawaii at Manoa, Honolulu, HI 96822.

FOSTER, RUEL E, b. Springfield, Ky, Nov. 30, 16; m. 47; c. 6. ENGLISH. A.B, Univ. Ky, 38, A.M, 39; Ph.D, Vanderbilt Univ, 41. Instr. ENG, W.VA. UNIV, 41-46, asst. prof, 46-51, assoc. prof, 51-57, PROF, 58-, CHMN. DEPT, 67- U.S.A, 42-45. Contemporary American and English literature. Publ: William Faulkner, 51 & co-auth, Elizabeth Madox Roberts, American novelist, 56, Univ. Okla; auth, Jesse Stuart, Twayne, 66. Add: Dept. of English, West Virginia University, Morgantown, WV 26506.

FOSTER, TEDDY JOE, b. Mt. Vernon, Ill, Sept. 7, 36; m. 55; c. 3. SPEECH COMMUNICATION. B.S, South. Ill. Univ, 58, M.A, 59; Ph.D.(commun), Ohio Univ, 67. From instr. to asst. prof. speech, Univ. Evansville; from asst. prof. to ASSOC. PROF. INTERPERSONAL COMMUN, OHIO UNIV, 65- Reader, J. Am. Forensic Asn, 73- Speech Commun. Asn; AAUP; Am. Forensics Asn.(mem. res. comt); Cent. States Speech Asn. Debate; public address; communication theory and process. Publ: Co-ed, Annual Bibliog. Exp. Stud. Commun, 68-; Annual Bibliog. Stud. in Argumentation & Debate, 69-72. Add: Dept. of Speech, 309 Kantner Hall, Ohio University, Athens, OH 45701.

FOULKE, ROBERT DANA, b. Minneapolis, Minn, Apr. 25, 30; m. 53; c. 2. ENGLISH LITERATURE. A.B, Princeton Univ, 52; M.A, Univ. Minn, 57, Ph.D.(Eng), 61; Fulbright fel, Birkbeck Col, Univ. London, 59-60. Teaching asst. ENG, Univ. Minn, 54-56, instr, 56-58, 60-61; asst. prof. Trinity Col. (Conn), 61-66, assoc. prof, 66-70; PROF. & CHMN. DEPT, SKIDMORE COL, 70- Vis. prof. lit. criticism, NDEA inst, Univ. Minn, 65; stylistics, NDEA inst, Macalester Col, 67. MLA; NCTE; New Eng. Col. Eng. Asn.(dir, 66-68); Col. Eng. Asn.(dir, 69-71 & chmn. comt. undergrad. curriculum, 71-73); Joseph Conrad Soc. Joseph Conrad; 19th and 20th century novel; theory of literary criticism and stylistic analysis. Publ: Co-auth, An anatomy of literature, Harcourt, 72; Criticism and the curriculum, Part II, Col. Eng, 10/64; auth, Postures of belief in The nigger of the Narcissus, Mod. Fiction Stud, summer 71; The undergraduate curriculum: a position paper, Peabody J. Educ, fall 72 & In: The future of college English, Col. Eng. Asn, 72; plus others. Add: Dept. of English, Skidmore College, Saratoga Springs, NY 12866.

FOWKE, EDITH MARGARET, b. Lumsden, Sask; m. 38. ENGLISH, FOLKLORE. B.A, Univ. Sask, 33, M.A, 70. ASSOC. PROF. ENG, YORK UNIV, 71- Asn. Can. Univ. Teachers Eng; Can. Folk Music Soc.(dir, 63-); Am. Folklore Soc. Canadian folklore; Anglo-American folk songs. Publ: Co-auth, Folksongs of Canada, 54, co-auth, Folk songs of Quebec, 57 & co-auth, More folk songs of Canada, 67, Waterloo Music Co; ed, Logging with Paul Bunyan, Ryerson, 57; co-auth, Canada's story in song, Gage, 60 & Songs of work and freedom, Roosevelt Univ, 60; auth, Traditional singers and songs from Ontario, Folklore Assoc, 65; Sally go round the sun, McClelland & Stewart, 69; Lumbering songs from the Northern woods, Univ. Tex, 70; contrib, Literary history of Canada, Univ. Toronto, 67; plus numerous articles. Add: 5 Notley Place, Toronto, Ont. M4B 2M7, Can.

FOWLER, AUSTIN, b. New York, N.Y, Jan. 26, 28; m. 55; c. 4. ENGLISH, SPEECH. B.A, Iona Col, 48; M.A, Fordham Univ, 58; Columbia Univ, 58- Master Eng, St. David's Sch, 55-58; lectr, City Col. New York, 59-65; instr. Eng. & speech, JOHN JAY COL. CRIMINAL JUSTICE, 65-72, LECTR. SPEECH, 72- Adj. assoc. prof. speech, Eng. & drama, Pace Col, 60-; guidance off, Baruch Col, City Univ. New York, 65-68; assoc. ed, J. Commun. Disorders, 67-; lectr. commun, Roosevelt Hospital Nursing Sch, 68-; assoc. ed, Express, Publ. L.I. Speech Asn, 68- Sig.C, U.S.A, 50-52. MLA. Tennyson. Publ: The red badge of courage: a study, 66, The Great Gatsby: a study, 66 & Henry James Turn of the screw: a study, 67, Barrister, Simon & Schuster; Wallace Stevens, Pace Mag, summer 67; Three poems, Express, 1/68. Add: Dept. of Speech, John Jay College of Criminal Justice, 315 Park Ave. S, New York, NY 10010.

FOWLER, CAROLYN, Afro-French & Afro-American Literature. See Volume III, Foreign Languages, Linguistics & Philology.

FOWLER, DAVID COVINGTON, b. Louisville, Ky, Jan. 3, 21; m. 43; c. 2. ENGLISH. A.B, Univ. Fla, 42; A.M, Univ. Chicago, 47, Ph.D, 49. Instr. ENG, Univ. Pa, 49-51; UNIV. WASH, 52-53, asst. prof, 53-59, assoc. prof, 59-63, PROF, 63- Guggenheim fel, 62-63. MLA; Am. Folklore Soc. Old and Middle English language and literature; text of Piers the Plowman. Publ: Co-ed, A critical edition of the Aversion of Piers the plowman, Johns Hopkins Univ, 52; auth, Prowess and charity in the Perceval of Chretien de Troyes, 59 & Piers the plowman: literary relations of the A and B texts, 61, Univ. Wash; A literary history of the popular ballad, Duke Univ, 68; John Trevisa and the English Bible, Mod. Philol, 11/60; The date of the Cornish Ordinalia, Mediaeval Stud, 61; New light on John Trevisa, Traditio, 62. Add: Dept. of English, University of Washington, Seattle, WA 98195.

FOWLER, ELIZABETH THOMAS, b. Birmingham, Ala, June 10, 16; m. 39; c. 4. AMERICAN & ENGLISH LITERATURE. B.S, Birmingham-South. Col, 37; B.Div, Vanderbilt Univ, 40; M.A, Univ. Tenn, Knoxville, 63, Ph.D.(Am. lit), 68. Teacher sci. & math, Lipscomb Jr. High Sch, Birmingham, Ala, 37; Neely's Bend Elem. Sch, Nashville, 47-48; Cent. High Sch, Savannah, Tenn, 51-52; instr. relig. & Eng, Martin Col, 55-61; teaching asst. ENG, Univ. Tenn, 62-65, instr, 65-69; ASST. PROF, MARYVILLE COL.(TENN), 69- AAUP; S.Atlantic Mod. Lang. Asn; Col. Eng. Asn. Vachel Lindsay, American poet and letter writer; King Arthur in American and English literature; medieval English language and literature. Publ: Annotated edition of Vachel Lindsay's letters to Nellie Vieira, Diss. Abstr, 69; Nellie's niche, 1/73 & Search for King Arthur—success or failure, 2/74, Maryville Col. Bull. Add: Dept. of English, Maryville College, Maryville, TN 37801.

FOWLER, KNOX, b. Boulder, Colo, Nov. 8, 28; m. 53; c. 1. THEATRE ARTS. B.A, Univ. Colo, 50; M.A, Univ. Calif, Los Angeles, 54; Fulbright scholar, Great Britain, 54-55. Instr. acting, exten. div, Univ. Calif, Los Angeles, 57-58; assoc. dir, Leontovich Studio, Hollywood, Calif, 57-58; dir. theatre training, Players Ring Theatre, 58-59; founder-dir, Theatre Studio, 60-61; CHMN. DEPT. THEATRE ARTS & DIR. SUMMER THEATRE, ROCKFORD COL, 61- U.S.A, 51-53. Integration of arts. Add: Dept. of Theatre Arts, Rockford College, Rockford, IL 61103.

FOWLER, LOIS JOSEPHS, b. Pittsburgh, Pa, Nov. 4, 25; m. 47; c. 2. ENGLISH. B.S, Carnegie Inst. Technol, 47; M.A, Univ. Pittsburgh, 56, Ph.D. (Eng), 66. Teacher, Taylor Allderdice High Sch, 55-61; asst. prof. ENG, CARNEGIE-MELLON UNIV, 61-66, ASSOC. PROF, 66-, mem. proj. Eng. contract, 62-64, pres. panel on teacher educ, 63. NCTE; Conf. Eng. Educ; MLA; NEA. Women in literature; teaching of English; George Meredith and his heroines. Publ: Anthology of American literature for high school—grade 11, 4 vols, Noble, 68; co-auth, English for the academically talented, NEA/NCTE, 68; auth, Diana of the crossways: a prophecy for feminism, Carnegie Ser, 72; ed, Norton Library edition of Diana of the crossways, Norton, 73; auth, Shakespeare and a colerigean synthesis, Shakespeare Quart, 12/67; plus others. Add: Dept. of English, Carnegie-Mellon University, Pittsburgh, PA 15213.

FOWLER, MARY ELIZABETH, b. Lewiston, Idaho, Dec. 16, 11. ENGLISH. B.A, Univ. Wash, 33, M.A, 39; Ph.D.(Eng. educ), N.Y. Univ, 54. Teacher & dean girls, high sch, Conn, 40-43; teacher, high sch, Mass, 43-44; asst. prof. ENG, CENT. CONN. STATE COL, 46-54, assoc. prof, 54-60, PROF, 60- NCTE; Conf. Col. Compos. & Commun; New Eng. Asn. Teachers Eng. (pres, 60-62); Conf. Eng. Educ. The teaching of literature for international understanding; methods of teaching secondary English. Publ: Teaching language, composition and literature, McGraw, 65; Another road to international understanding, J. Educ; Using semantic concepts in the teaching of composition, Col. Compos. & Commun. Add: 46 Selden Hill Dr, West Hartford, CT 06107.

FOX, ARNOLD BENJAMIN, b. New York, N.Y, Aug. 2, 17; m. 53, 63; c. 2. ENGLISH LITERATURE. B.S.S, City Col, New York, 38; A.M, N.Y. Univ, 39, Ph.D, 48. Instr, high sch, 40-41; Grove Sch, Madison, Conn, 43-45; Rutgers Univ, 45; ENG, State Univ. Iowa, 45-52, asst. prof, 49-52; Bowling Green State Univ, 53-54; Wright Br, Chicago City Jr. Col, 54-55; assoc. prof, NORTH. ILL. UNIV, 55-60, PROF, 60- MLA. English romanticism; aesthetics. Add: Dept. of English, Northern Illinois University, DeKalb, IL 60115.

FOX, CHARLES FRANKLIN. ENGLISH. A.B, Washington & Lee Univ, 48; M.A, Ind. Univ, 54, Ph.D.(speech), 67. Instr. ENG, HANOVER COL, 49-55, asst. prof, 55-59, assoc. prof, 59-68, PROF, 68- Ed, Forum of Phi Eta Sigma, 68- AAUP; MLA. Italian late Middle Ages and early Renaissance with emphasis on Dante; English literature from 1660 to the Romantic Period with emphasis on Jonathan Swift; contemporary fiction. Publ: Defoe's rhetorical damnation of Sacheverell, Hanover Forum, spring 61. Add: Box 437, Hanover, IN 47243.

FOX, CLYDE MAYNARD, b. Larned, Kans, May 22, 13; m. 36; c. 3. ENGLISH. A.B, Ft. Hays Kans. State Col, 37, fel, 38, M.S, 39; Ph.D.(Eng), Univ. Colo, 63. Instr, Bison High Sch, 37-38; asst. instr. Eng, Univ. Kans, 40-42; instr, S.Dak. State Col. Agr. & Mech. Arts, 42-44; asst. prof, Univ. Toledo, 46-47; S.Dak. State Col. Agr. & Mech. Arts, 47-49, assoc. prof, 49-57, prof, 57-64; assoc. prof. LIT, FT. LEWIS COL, 64-67, PROF, 67-, CHMN. DEPT. ENG. & THEATRE, 68- Teaching assoc, Univ. Colo, 62-63. U.S.N.R, 44-46, Lt.(jg). Col. Eng. Asn; West. Lit. Asn. (v.pres, 74, pres, 75). Literature and the environment; Willa Cather. Publ: The bearded face set toward the sun, Forum, 61; Two primitives: Huck Finn and Tom Outland, spring 66 & Proponents of order: Tom Outland and Bishop Latour, summer 70, West. Am. Lit; plus others. Add: Dept. of English, Ft. Lewis College, Durango, CO 81301.

FOX, DENTON, b. Denver, Colo, May 15, 30; m. 55; c. 4. ENGLISH. B.A, Yale, 52, M.A, 54, Ph.D, 56. Instr. ENG, Yale, 56-58; asst. prof, Grinnell Col, 58-60, assoc. prof, 61-62; asst. prof, VICTORIA COL, UNIV. TORONTO, 62-63, assoc. prof, 63-68, PROF, 68- Middle Scots and English literature; Old Norse. Publ: Ed, The testament of Cresseid, Nelsons, 68; auth, Henryson's Fables, ELH, 62; Njals saga and the western literary tradition, Comp. Lit, 63; The Scottish Chaucerians, In: Chaucer and Chaucerians, Univ. Ala, 66. Add: Dept. of English, Victoria College, University of Toronto, Toronto, Ont, M5S 1A1, Can.

FOX, DOROTHY HAYNIE, b. Alexandria, La, Nov. 27, 17; m. 38; c. 2. ENGLISH, EDUCATION. B.S, La. State Univ, Baton Rouge, 55; M.A, 59; Tulane Univ, 62, 66-67; dipl. Eng, Univ. Edinburg, 63; La. State Univ, New Orleans, 66. Teacher Eng, Istrouma Jr. High Sch, Baton Rouge, La, 55-59; instr. Eng. educ, St. Mary's Dom. Col, 59-60; teacher ENG, Isidore Newman Sch, New Orleans, 60-65; asst. prof, Delgado Jr. Col, 65-67; ASSOC. PROF, SOUTHEAST. LA. UNIV, 67- NCTE; Conf. Col. Compos. & Commun; Rhet. Soc. Am. Critical work in British literature. Add: 607 N. General Patton, Hammond, LA 70401.

FOX, HUGH BERNARD, JR, b. Chicago, Ill, Feb. 12, 32; m. 57; c. 3. AMERICAN LITERATURE. B.A, Loyola Univ.(Ill), 54, M.A, 55; Ph.D, Univ. Ill, 58. Asst, Univ. Ill, 56-58; instr. Am. lit, Loyola Univ.(Calif), 58-60, asst. prof, 60-68; asst. prof. AM. STUD, MICH. STATE UNIV, 68-72, ASSOC. PROF, 72- Smith Mundt grant & vis. prof, Univ. Sonora, Mex, 61; vis. prof. Am. stud, Inst. Pedag. & Cath. Univ. Caracas, 64-66; fel. John Carter Brown Libr, Brown Univ, summer 68; ed, Ghost-Dance. Contemporary North American poetry; contemporary poetry and communications theory; 20th century avant-garde aesthetics. Publ: America hoy: un cursillo en estudios Americanos, 65 & Problemas de nuestro tiempo, 66, Garcia, Caracas; Eye into now, 67 & Soul-catcher songs, 67, Ed. Frontera; Henry James: a critical study, Westburg, 68; Countdown on an empty streetcar (novel), Abyss Publ, 68; The omega scriptures (autobiog), Ghost Dance Press, 70; Peeple (short prose), 73 & Charles Potts: a biocritical study, 74, Dustbooks; An aesthetics for the year 10,000, 73 & ed, The living underground: an anthology of contemporary American poetry, 73, Whitston; Some thoughts on Celine from The avant-garde mind, Camels Coming Newsletter, 1/72; U.S. iconography and the Yippie media termites, TriQuarterly, winter/spring 72; Some meditations on the social significance of recent architecture, Arts in Soc, fall-winter 72; plus others. Add: Dept. of American Thought & Language, Michigan State University, East Lansing, MI 48823.

FOX, LESLIE HOWARD, b. Norristown, Pa, June 19, 11; div; c. 3. THEATRE. B.A, Temple Univ, 34; M.A, Northwest. Univ, 41; Columbia Univ, 46-47; Ph.D, N.Y. Univ, 60. Teacher Eng, Woodbury High Sch, N.J, 35-36; Adm. Farragut Acad, N.J, 36-38; pub. speaking, Belleville High Sch, N.J, 38-44; THEATRE & SPEECH, MONTCLAIR STATE COL, 44-, chmn. dept. speech, 54-70, grad. dean, 70-72. Development Fund grant, 59; theatre design consult, Wash. Col; Bergen County Voc. Sch, Hackensack, N.J; Mem. Auditorium, Montclair State Col, convertible studio theater, 67-; Bergen County Community Col, 67; Marymount Col, 67-; U.S. rep, Int. Inst. Theatre Technol, 71; guest dir, Springer Theater Co, Columbus, Ga, 73. Am. Theatre Asn; U.S. Inst. Theatre Technol.(N.Y. area proj. rep); Speech Commun. Asn; Speech Asn. East. States; Nat. Theatre Conf. Educational theatre; speech education; theatre architecture. Add: Dept. of Speech & Theater, Montclair State College, Upper Montclair, NJ 07043.

FOX, ROBERT CHARLES, b. Portland, Ore, Apr. 17, 20. ENGLISH. B.A, Univ. Portland, 42; M.A, Columbia Univ, 47, Ph.D.(Eng), 56. Instr. ENG, Wayne Univ, 47-49; lectr. & instr, Rutgers Univ, 50-55; instr, ST. FRANCIS COL.(N.Y), 55-57, asst. prof, 57-62, assoc. prof, 62-68, PROF, 68-, CHMN. DEPT, 73- U.S.N, 42-46, Lt. MLA; Milton Soc. Am; NCTE; Renaissance Soc. Am. English literature of the 17th century; Milton; Chaucer. Publ: Soc. Am. English literature of the 17th century; Milton; Chaucer. Publ: Allegory of sin and death in Paradise lost, Mod. Lang. Quart, 12/63; contrib, Readers encyclopedia of Shakespeare, Crowell, 66 & Milton Encycl, 74; plus others. Add: 175 Adams St, Apt. 6F, Brooklyn, NY 11201.

FOX, ROBERT PAUL, Linguistics, English As Second Language. See Volume III, Foreign Languages, Linguistics & Philology.

FOX, STEPHEN DOUGLAS, b. Roanoke, Va, Aug. 10, 43. COMPARATIVE LITERATURE. B.A, Duke Univ, 65; M.A, Emory Univ, 66, Ph.D.(comp. lit), 70. Teaching asst. freshman Eng, Emory Univ, 66-68; instr. Eng, W.Ga. Col, 68-69; ASST. PROF. ENG. & COMP. LIT, UNIV. CINCINNATI, 70- Instr. philos, Gov. Sch. N.C, summer 66. MLA; AAUP. Twentieth century novel, especially Virginia Woolf; 20th century drama. Publ: The fish pond as symbolic center in between the acts, Mod. Fiction Stud, fall 72; Hemingway's The doctor and the doctor's wife, Ariz. Quart, spring 73. Add: Dept. of English, University of Cincinnati, Cincinnati, OH 45221.

FOXEN, JOHN ROBERT, b. Cherokee, Iowa, Apr. 18, 26; m. 49; c. 2. SPEECH. B.A, Morningside Col, 50; M.A, State Univ, Iowa, 51, Ph.D. (speech), 57. Instr. speech, Univ. N.H, 51-52; Univ. Conn, 52-54; asst. prof, Coe Col, 55-57; DePauw Univ, 57-59, assoc. prof, 59-67, prof, 67-70; PROF. SPEECH COMMUN. ARTS & CHMN. DEPT, MONMOUTH COL, 70- Ind. Univ. non-west. stud. grant, 64-65; Great Lakes Asn. fel, res. in Japan, 65-66; lectr, int. div, Waseda Univ, Tokyo, 65-66; mem. comn. int. & intercult. commun, Speech Commun. Asn, 71- U.S.N.R, 44-46. AAUP; Speech Commun. Asn; Cent. States Speech Asn; Asn. Am. Univ. Rhetorical theory; public address; non-western rhetoric. Publ: Co-auth, The propaganda play, Civil War Hist. J, 9/55; auth, Fukuzawa Yukichi and the introduction of western rhetoric to Japan, Bull. Japan Cult. Soc, 12-1/67-68. Add: Dept. of Speech-Communication Arts, Monmouth College, Monmouth, IL 61462.

FOY, JOHN VAIL, b. Salamanca, N.Y, Jan. 15, 23; m. 50; c. 2. ENGLISH & AMERICAN LITERATURE. B.A, Cornell Univ, 47, A.M, 48, Ph.D.(Am. lit), 61; Indust. Col. Armed Forces, 71; U.S. Army War Col, 72. Teaching asst. Eng, Cornell Univ, 48-52; instr, Univ. Idaho, 52-59, asst. prof, 59-66, assoc. prof, 66-68; Ed, Comt. on Alaska Earthquake, Nat. Acad. Sci, Wash, D.C, 65-67, 68-70; PROF. ENG, CARTHAGE COL, 70- Mem. consult. fac, U.S. Army Command & Gen. Staff Col, 70- U.S.A, 43-45, Med.C, Res, 49-, Col. MLA; AAUP. Narrative poetry; American romantic movement; American novel. Publ: Robinson's impulse for narrative, Colby Libr. Quart, 3/69. Add: Dept. of English, Carthage College, Alford Dr, Kenosha, WI 53140.

FOY, ROBERT JOHN, b. Concord, N.H, Apr. 12, 29. ENGLISH. B.Ed, Plymouth State Col, 51; M.A, George Peabody Col, 52, Ed.S, 59; M.Ed, Harvard, 60, Ed.D.(Eng), 66. Instr. ENG, Pensacola High Sch, Fla. & Pensacola Jr. Col, 54-55; Bradley Univ, 55-57; asst. prof, LOWELL STATE COL, 57-62, 63-66, assoc. prof, 66-68, PROF, 68-, ACAD. DEAN, 70-, dir. Eng. educ, 63-70. Lectr, NDEA Inst. Anthrop. & Sociol. Ling, Harvard, summer 68. U.S.A, 52-54, Res, 54-55, Sgt. Col. Eng. Asn; NCTE; Conf. Col. Compos. & Commun; Am. Acad. Polit. & Soc. Sci. History of linguistics;

philosophy of language; teaching of English. Publ: Evaluation of English methods courses, Peabody J. Educ, 11/64. Add: 19 Appleton St, Boston, MA 02116.

FRADIN, JOSEPH IRWIN, b. Parksville, N.Y, May 11, 25; m. 57; c. 2. ENGLISH. B.A, Columbia Univ, 47, M.A, 48, Ph.D.(Eng), 56. Instr. ENG, Cornell Univ, 56-60; asst. prof, STATE UNIV. N.Y. BUFFALO, 60-64, assoc. prof, 64-69, PROF, 69-, CHMN. DEPT, 71-, assoc. chmn. dept, 68-71. U.S.N, 44-46, Lt.(jg). MLA. English fiction; Dickens; theory of fiction. Publ: The absorbing tyranny of everyday life: Bulwer-Lytton's A strange story, Nineteenth Century Fiction, 6/61; Will and society in Bleak house, 3/66 & Anarchist, detective, and saint: the possibilities of action in The secret agent, 10/68, PMLA. Add: Dept. of English, State University of New York at Buffalo, Buffalo, NY 14214.

FRAIBERG, LOUIS, b. Detroit, Mich, Sept. 18, 13; m. 45; c. 1. ENGLISH. A.B, Wayne Univ, 37, M.A, 39; M.S.W, Univ. Mich. 46, Ph.D.(Eng), 56. Instr. ENG, Wayne State Univ, 38-39, 51-52, 53-57; teaching fel, Univ. Mich, 52-53; asst. prof, La. State Univ, 58-60, assoc. prof, 60-63; PROF, UNIV. TOLEDO, 63-, chmn. dept, 63-66. Lectr, New Orleans Psychoanalytic Inst, 61-63. MLA; NCTE; Col. Eng. Asn; Am. Stud. Asn. American and Victorian literature; literary criticism. Publ: Psychoanalysis and American literary criticism, Wayne State Univ, 60; Unattainable self: D.H. Lawrence's Sons and lovers, In: Twelve original essays on great British novels, Wayne State Univ, 60; New views on art and the creative process in psychoanalytic ego psychology, Lit. & Psychol, spring 61; Durrell's Dissonant quartet, In: Contemporary British novelists, South. Ill. Univ, 65. Add: Dept. of English, University of Toledo, Toledo, OH 43606.

FRANCHERE, HOYT C, b. Sioux City, Iowa, Oct. 16, 04; m. 28; c. 1. ENGLISH & AMERICAN LITERATURE & LANGUAGE. B.A, Univ. Iowa, 28, M.A, 31; Ph.D.(Eng), Univ. Wash, 50. Instr. Eng, Lincoln Col, 28-29; Ill. Col, 29-32; asst. prof, 32-37; ed, Scott, Foresman, 37-38; lectr. Eng. Univ. Calif, Berkeley, 38-40; asst. prof, Univ. Ore, 40-46; gen. exten. div, Ore. State Syst. Higher Educ, 47-55; from assoc. prof. Eng. to prof. Eng. & Dean div. arts & lett, PORTLAND STATE UNIV, 55-70, EMER. PROF. ENG. & EMER. DEAN ARTS & LETT, 70- Am. Philos. Soc. fel, spring 59; Portland State Col. Fel. Fund. fel, 61-62, 65. NCTE; Philol. Asn. Pac. Coast. American literature; Harold Fredric. Publ: Co-auth, Harold Frederic, Twayne, 61; auth, Adventure at Astoria, Univ. Okla, 67; Edwin Arlington Robinson, Twayne, 68; transl. & ed, The overland diary of Wilson Price Hunt, Ore. Bk. Soc, 73; plus others. Add: Dept. of English, Portland State University, Portland, OR 97207.

FRANCIS, CEDRIC JAMES, b. Bolton, Eng, Dec. 15, 26; m. 66. ENGLISH. B.A, Univ. Manchester, 51; M.A, 52, res. stud, 52-54, Ph.D.(Eng), 55. Asst. lectr. ENG, Univ. Malaya, Singapore, 55-57, lect, 57-62; asst. prof, MEM. UNIV. NFLD, 62-67; assoc. prof, 67-72, PROF, 72-, ASSOC. DEAN GRAD. STUD, 74- Brit. Army, 44-48. Asn. Can. Univ. Teachers Eng. George Gissing and Victorian literature; Lawrence Sterne; 20th century literature, especially drama. Publ: Gissing's characterisation, 3 parts, 67, Veranilda, 71 & The revision of Thyrza 71, Gissing Newslett; plus two others. Add: Dept. of English, Memorial University of Newfoundland, St. John's, Nfld, Can.

FRANCIS, ELEANOR M, b. Ft. Smith, Ark, Jan. 3, 13; m. 42, 63; c. 1. AMERICAN LITERATURE. B.A, Ark. State Teachers Col, 36; M.A, Univ. Tex, 40; Univ. Ark, 52; Univ. Colo, 58. Instr. ENG, Henderson State Teachers Col, 40-42; asst. prof, Arlington State Col, 45-47; ASST. PROF, LITTLE ROCK UNIV, 47- MLA; NCTE; S.Cent. Mod. Lang. Asn; Soc. Stud. South. Lit; Nat. Inst. Arts & Lett; AAUP. Bibliography of Arkansas writers; writers of the South, especially in Arkansas during post Civil War period; women writers of the South, 1950-1960. Add: 5323 Southwood Rd, Little Rock, AR 72205.

FRANCIS, HERBERT EDWARD, JR, b. Bristol, R.I, Jan. 11, 24. LITERATURE. B.A, Univ. Wis, 48; grant, Brown Univ, 49-50, M.A, 50; Fulbright scholar, Oxford, 53-54. Instr. Eng. Pa. State Univ, 50-52; Univ. Tenn, 52-56; North. Ill. Univ, 56-58; asst. prof. Emory Univ, 58-66; assoc. prof. ENG. LIT, UNIV. ALA, HUNTSVILLE, 66-71, PROF, 71- Fulbright lectr. & assoc. prof. Brit. & Am. lit, Nat. Univ. Cuyo, 64-66, 68 & 70; ed, Poem. U.S.A.A.F, 42-45, S/Sgt. MLA; S.Atlantic Mod. Lang. Asn. Twentieth century British poetry and fiction; modern drama; creative writing. Publ: Toda la gente que nunca tuve, Burnichon, Buenos Aires, 66; The itinerary of beggars (stories), Univ. Iowa, 73; One of the boys, In: The best American short stories of 1967, Houghton, 67; contrib, Alabama prize stories, Nineteen Seventy, Strode, 70; plus others. Add: 508 Clinton Ave. N.E, Huntsville, AL 35801.

FRANCIS, NELLE TREW, b. Prague, Okla. ENGLISH. B.A, Hardin-Simmons Univ, 34; M.A, Univ. Tex, 42, Delta Kappa Gamma scholars, 54, 55-57, univ. fel, 55-56, Ph.D.(Eng), 61. Teacher high schs, Tex, 34-46; instr. ENG, Tex. West. Col, 46-54, asst. prof, 65-67; teaching fel, Univ. Tex, Austin, 56-58, spec. instr, 58-59; assoc. prof, McMurry Col, 60-61; asst. prof, Arlington State Col, 61-63; ASSOC. PROF, Howard Payne Col, 63-64; LA. TECH UNIV, 67- Mod. Humanities Res. Asn, Gt. Brit; MLA; NCTE. Nineteenth century English literature. Publ: Co-auth, Patterns for prose writing: from notes to theme, Scott, 69. Add: Dept. of English, Louisiana Tech University, Ruston, LA 71270.

FRANCIS, RICHARD LEE, b. Los Angeles, Calif, May 24, 30. ENGLISH, AMERICAN STUDIES. A.B, Kenyon Col, 52; M.A, Duke Univ, 54; Ph.D, Yale, 61. Instr. ENG, Univ. Del, 54-57; Rutgers Univ, 60-62; asst. prof, Brown Univ, 62-69; ASSOC. PROF, WEST. WASH. STATE COL, 69- Vis. prof, South. Ore. Col, summer 68; vis. assoc. prof, Univ. Toledo, 68-69; consult, Nat. Humanities Fac, 73-74. MLA; Eng. Inst; Am. Stud. Asn. Add: 349 Cove Rd, Bellingham, WA 98225.

FRANCIS, WINTHROP NELSON, Linguistics. See Volume III, Foreign Languages, Linguistics & Philology.

FRANCOIS, WILLIAM EDWARD, b. Chicago, Ill, Mar. 11, 24; m. 44; c. 1. MASS COMMUNICATIONS, JOURNALISM. B.S, Northwest. Univ, Evanston, 49, M.S, 50; Ph.D.(mass commun), Ohio State Univ, 67. From asst. prof. to assoc. prof. JOUR, Marshall Univ, 59-66, prof. & chmn. dept, 67-69; PROF, DRAKE UNIV, 69- Cert. of Merit, Am. Bar Asn, 71 & 73. U.S.A, 42-45, Res. & Nat. Guard, 62-69. Asn. Educ. in Jour; AAUP. Programed instruction; law and the press; ethics of mass communications. Publ: Automation: industrialization comes of age, Collier Bks, 64; Evaluating programed news-writing instruction, Asn. Educ. in Jour, 71; Law and the writer, Writer's Dig. & Writer's Yearbk, 72- Add: School of Journalism, Drake University, Des Moines, IA 50311.

FRANDSEN, KENNETH D, b. Coeur d'Alene, Idaho, Aug. 4, 37; m. 59; c. 2. COMMUNICATION. B.A, Wash. State Univ, 59; NDEA fel, Ohio Univ, 59-62, M.A, 61, Ph.D.(rhetoric & pub. address), 62. Asst. theatre, Ohio Univ, summer 60, instr. speech, 61, res. assoc. mass commun, summer 62; asst. prof. SPEECH, South. Ill. Univ, 62-64; Univ. Wis, Milwaukee, 64-68, assoc. prof, 68-69, res. fel. speech commun, 65-69; ASSOC. PROF, PA. STATE UNIV, UNIVERSITY PARK, 69-, prog. consult. appln. group, Comput. Ctr, 69-71. Instr. debate workshop, summers 60 & 61; res. grant, Univ. Wis. Grad. Sch, summer 65, fel, summer 67; fel, Univ. Fla. Commun. Sci Lab, 67; Am. Counc. Learned Soc. fel, Inst. Humanistic Comput, Univ. Kans, 70. Am. Acad. Polit. & Soc. Sci; Int. Commun. Asn; Asn. Comput. Ling; Asn. Comput. Mach.(spec. interest group on lang. anal. & stud. in humanities, 70-); Speech Commun. Asn. Speech communication; psycholinguistics; research design and measurement. Publ: Ed, Author and key word index, 1951-1968, J. Commun. Suppl. to Vols. 1-18, 69; contrib, Language behavior: a book of readings, Mouton, The Hague, 70; co-auth, Fundamental interpersonal relations orientations in Dyads, Speech Monogr, 6/73. Add: Dept. of Speech, 212 Sparks Bldg, Pennsylvania State University, University Park, PA 16802.

FRANK, CHARLES EDWARD, b. Philadelphia, Pa, May 5, 11; m. 41; c. 5. ENGLISH LITERATURE. Haverford Col, 33; A.M, Princeton, 38, Ph.D, 39. Asst. ENG, Haverford Col, 33-35, instr, 35-37; from asst. prof. to prof, Ill. Col, 39-55; assoc. prof, Univ. Nev, 55-57; PROF, ILL. COL, 57- Ford fac. fel, 53-54; res. consult, Ill. Legislative Counc, 59-61. U.S.N.R, 42-45, Lt. Comdr. Am. Soc. 18th Century Stud. Henry James; Edward Young; community studies. Publ: Six Franks abroad: one man's sabbatical, World, 67; British universities, old and new, Educ. Rec, spring 66; Of sabbaticals in general, Lib. Educ, 5/66; Education in England, Forum, Ball State Univ, spring 67; plus others. Add: 236 Park St, Jacksonville, IL 62650.

FRANK, CHARLES PAUL, b. Kansas City, Mo, Jan. 27, 35; m. 58; c. 2. ENGLISH & AMERICAN LITERATURE. B.S, Univ. Wis, 57; M.A, Univ. Mich, 58, Ph.D.(Eng), 64. Asst. prof. ENG, Ind. Univ, Ft. Wayne, 64-68; ASSOC. PROF, UNIV. PUGET SOUND, 68-, res. grants, summers 71, 72, 73. Ind. Univ. fac. res. grants, summers 66, 68. Philol. Asn. Pac. Coast; Soc. Phenomenol. & Existential Philos. American literature; criticism; phenomenology. Publ: Edmund Wilson, Twayne, 70. Add: Dept. of English, University of Puget Sound, Tacoma, WA 98416.

FRANK, EDWARD JOHN, b. Hamilton, Ont, Feb. 9, 34; U.S. citizen; m. 69; c. 1. THEATRE, DRAMATIC CRITICISM. A.B, San Francisco State Univ, 57; M.A, San Diego State Univ, 66; Ph.D.(theatre), Univ. Ore, 72. Teacher Eng, Helix High Sch, 59-72; teacher & dir. speech & theatre, Univ. Ore, 72; ASST. PROF. SPEECH & DIR. THEATRE, UNIV. ARK, MONTICELLO, 72- AAUP; Speech Commun. Asn; Am. Theatre Asn. Audience behavior; perception; creative process. Publ: Strindberg's Damascus plays: the pilgrimage of an uneasy rider, South. Speech Commun. J, winter 74. Add: Dept. of Speech & Dramatic Art, University of Arkansas, Monticello, AR 71655.

FRANK, FREDERICK STILSON, b. Cobleskill, N.Y, Dec. 23, 35; m. 60; c. 3. ENGLISH & AMERICAN LITERATURE. A.B, Union Col.(N.Y), 57; A.M, Columbia Univ, 59; Danforth fel, Rutgers Univ, New Brunswick, 67, Ph.D. (Eng), 68. Teaching asst. ENG, Rutgers Univ, New Brunswick, 60-64; instr, Boston Univ, 64-68, ASST. PROF, 68-70; ALLEGHENY COL, 70- Ord.C, U.S.A, 58-64. MLA. The English Gothic novel; Byronic romanticism; Gilbert and Sullivan studies. Publ: The demon and the thunderstorm; Bryon and Madame de Staël, Rev. Lit. Comp, 7-8/69; The Gothic novel: a checklist of modern criticism, Bull. Bibliog, 4-6/73; Coleridge in Germany, Rev. Lang, Vivantes, 73. Add: P.O. Box 90, Allegheny College, Meadville, PA 16335.

FRANK, JOSEPH, b. Chicago, Ill, Dec. 20, 16; m. 46, 69; c. 3. ENGLISH. B.A, Harvard, 39, M.A, 47, Ph.D.(Eng), 53. Instr. ENG, Univ. Rochester, 48-53, asst. prof, 53-58, assoc. prof, 58-63, prof, 63-67; prof. & chmn. dept, Univ. N.Mex, 67-69; PROF. & HEAD DEPT, UNIV. MASS, AMHERST, 69- Huntington fel, 55-56; Guggenheim fels, 58-59, 61; Folger Shakespeare Libr. fel, 61-62; assoc. ed, Seventeenth Century News, 61-; consult, Univ. Fla, City Col. New York, & Roger Williams, Ft. Lewis & Mass Community Cols, 68-72. U.S.A, 43-45. MLA; Asn. Depts. Eng.(pres, 69). Pedagogy; modern drama; 17th century literature. Publ: The levellers, 55 & Beginnings of the English newspaper, 61, Harvard Univ; Literature from the Bible, 63 & Modern essays in English, 66, Little; Hobbled Pegasus, Univ. N.Mex, 68; ed, You, Harcourt, 72 & The doomed astronaut, Winthrop, 72. Add: Dept. of English, University of Massachusetts, Amherst, MA 01002.

FRANK, LUANNE THORNTON, German & Comparative Literature. See Volume III, Foreign Languages, Linguistics & Philology.

FRANK, MORTIMER HENRY, b. New York, N.Y, Jan. 14, 33; m. 61; c. 1. ENGLISH, MUSICOLOGY. A.B, N.Y. Univ, 54, M.A, 58; Ph.D.(Eng), 68. Instr. ENG, N.Y. Univ, 62-65; BRONX COMMUNITY COL, 65-68, asst. prof, 68-71, ASSOC. PROF, 71- State Univ. N.Y. res. fels, summer 69 & 70. MLA. American literature; 17th century poetry; relationship between poetry and music. Publ: Ed, Huneker on music, John Colet, 74; auth, Mencken on music, Carnegie Hall Mag, 1/66; In praise of Huneker, Univ. Windsor Rev, fall 73; plus articles in Seventeenth century news & Listen: a music monthly. Add: Dept. of English, Bronx Community College, 181st St. & University Ave, Bronx, NY 10453.

FRANK, ROBERT JOSEPH, b. Dickinson, N.Dak, July 7, 39; m. 64; c. 2. ENGLISH LITERATURE. B.A, St. John's Univ.(Minn), 62; M.A, Univ. Minn,

68, Ph.D.(Eng), 69. ASST. PROF. ENG, Ore. State Univ. 69-70; East. Mich. Univ, 70-71; ORE. STATE UNIV, 71- MLA; Philol. Asn. Pac. Coast. Literature of the Romantic period. Add: Dept. of English, Oregon State University, Corvallis, OR 97331.

FRANK, ROBERT WORTH, JR, b. Logansport, Ind, Apr. 8, 14; m. 40; c. 2. ENGLISH. B.A, Wabash Col, 34; residence scholar & M.A, Columbia Univ, 39; univ. scholar & Ph.D.(Eng), Yale, 48. Instr. ENG, Lafayette Col, 37-39; Univ. Rochester, 40-42; Princeton, 42-44; Northwest. Univ, 44-48; asst. prof, Ill. Inst. Technol, 48-54, assoc. prof, 54-58; PROF, PA. STATE UNIV, UNIVERSITY PARK, 58-, assoc. head dept, 66-72. Am. Counc. Learned Soc. fac. stud. fel, 51-52, 60-61; Fund Advan. Educ. fac. fel, 55-56; co-ed, Chaucer Rev, 66-71, ed, 71-; Guggenheim Mem. Found. fel, 71-72; vis. fel, Clare Hall, Cambridge, 72-73. MLA; Mediaeval Acad. Am; Int. Asn. Univ. Prof. Eng; Mod. Humanities Res. Asn. Chaucer; Piers Plowman; medieval literature and society. Publ: Piers Plowman and the scheme of salvation, Yale; co-auth, The responsible man: the insights of the humanities, Doubleday, 65; auth, Chaucer and the Legend of good women, Harvard Univ, 73; Troilus and Criseyde: the art of amplification, Medieval Lit. & Folklore Stud, 71; The Reeve's tale and the comedy of limitation, Directions in Lit. Criticism, 73; plus others. Add: Dept. of English, 117 Burrowes Bldg, Pennsylvania State University, University Park, PA 16802.

FRANK, ROBERTA, b. New York, N.Y, Nov. 9, 41. MEDIEVAL ENGLISH, OLD NORSE. B.A, N.Y. Univ, 62; M.A, Harvard, 64, Ph.D.(comp. lit), 68. Asst. prof. ENG. & MEDIEVAL STUD, UNIV. TORONTO, 68-73, ASSOC. PROF, 73- Am. Counc. Learned Soc. fel, 73-74. MLA; Mediaeval Acad. Am.(Elliott Prize, 72). Old English; Middle English; Old Norse poetry. Publ: Co-ed, Computers and Old English concordances, 70 & A plan for the dictionary of Old English, 73, Univ. Toronto; auth, Anatomy of a Skaldic double entendre: Rǫgnualdr Kali's Lausavisa 7, In: Studies offered to Einar Haugen, Mouton, 72; Some uses of paronomasia in Old English scriptural verse, Speculum, 72; Marriage in twelfth and thirteenth century Iceland, Viator, 73; plus others. Add: Ctr. for Medieval Studies, University of Toronto, 39 Queen's Park Crescent E, Toronto, Ont. 181, Can.

FRANK, WILLIAM L, b. New York, N.Y, Aug. 16, 29; m. 60; c. 3. ENGLISH, AMERICAN LITERATURE. B.A, Univ. South. Miss, 56, M.A.Ed, 57; M.A, Northwest. Univ, 59, Ph.D.(Eng), 64. Asst. prof. ENG, Delta State Col, 58-63; Southeast Mo. State Col, 63-64, assoc. prof, 64-67, prof, 67-68; PROF. & CHMN. DEPT, LONGWOOD COL, 68- Eng. curriculum consult, Festus, Mo. Pub. Schs, 65-66; team teaching consult, Charleston, Mo. Pub. Sch. Syst, summer 68. U.S.A.F, 48-52, S/Sgt. NCTE; Conf. Col. Compos. & Commun.(co-chmn, compos. sect, 68-); MLA; S.Atlantic Asn. Dept. Eng. American literature, 19th century. Publ: Catherine Sherwood Bonner McDowell: a critical biography, Twayne, 74; Warren's achievement, Col. Eng, 5/58; The diary of Sherwood Bonner (3 part series), Notes on Miss. Writers, Vol. III, No. 3 & Vol. IV, Nos. 1 & 2. Add: Dept. of English, Longwood College, Farmville, VA 23901.

FRANK, YAKIRA H, b. New York, N.Y, Nov. 15, 23; m. 45; c. 2. LINGUISTICS. A.B, Hunter Col, 43; Am. Counc. Learned Soc. fel, Univ. Wis, 43; fel. & M.A, Univ. Pa, 45; Am. Counc. Learned Soc. fel, Univ. Mich, 45-46, 48, univ. fel, 46-48, Ph.D, 49. Instr. ENG, UNIV. CONN, 62-63, asst. prof, 63-67, ASSOC. PROF, 67- Lectr, Hunter Col, 51-55, 58; Univ. Conn, Stamford, 61-62. Ling. Soc. Am; NCTE; MLA; Ling. Circle N.Y. Stylistics; dialect geography; bi-lingualism. Add: 34 Hazelwood Lane, Stamford, CT 06905.

FRANKLIN, BENJAMIN V, b. Gallipolis, Ohio, Sept. 10, 39; m. 62; c. 2. AMERICAN LITERATURE. B.A. & B.S, Ohio State Univ, 65; M.A, Ohio Univ, 66, Ph.D.(Eng), 69. ASST. PROF. ENG, UNIV. MICH, ANN ARBOR, 69- Co-ed, Under the sign of Pisces: Anais Nin and her circle, Ohio State Univ, 70-73; mem. ed. bd, First printings of American authors: a bibliographical guide, 74- MLA. Publ: Ed, The poetry of the minor Connecticut wits, Scholars Facsimiles & Reprints, 70; auth, Anais Nin: a bibliography, Kent State Univ, 73; Anais Nin: a bibliographical essay, In: The Anais Nin casebook, World, 73. Add: Dept. of English, University of Michigan, Ann Arbor, MI 48104.

FRANKLIN, H. BRUCE, b. Brooklyn, N.Y, Feb. 28, 34; m. 56; c. 3. ENGLISH & AMERICAN LITERATURE. B.A, Amherst Col, 55; Ph.D, Stanford Univ, 61. Asst. prof. Eng. & Am. lit, Stanford Univ, 61-64, Sloan lectr, 62-63; asst. prof. ENG, Johns Hopkins Univ, 64-65; assoc. prof, Stanford Univ, 65-72; vis. fel, Ctr. for Humanities, Wesleyan Univ, spring 74. Vis fel, Ctr. for Humanities, Wesleyan Univ, fall 64; Am. Counc. Learned Soc. grant-in-aid, 66-67 & fel, 68-69. MLA. U.S.A.F, 56-59, Res, 59-65, Capt. Literature and society; American literature; science fiction. Publ: The wake of the gods: Melville's mythology, Stanford Univ, 63; Future perfect: American science fiction of the 19th century, Oxford, 66; ed, The confidence-man, Bobbs, 67; auth, From the movement: toward revolution, Van Nostrand, 71; ed, The essential Stalin, Doubleday, 72; auth, The island worlds of Darwin and Melville, Centennial Rev, summer 67; Chic Bleak in fantasy fiction, Saturday Rev, 7/72; The teaching of literature in the highest academies of the empire, In: The politics of literature, Pantheon, 72. Add: Center for the Humanities, Wesleyan University, Middletown, CT 06457.

FRANKLIN, PHYLLIS, b. New York, N.Y. EARLY AMERICAN LITERATURE. A.B, Vassar Col, 54; M.A, Univ. Miami, 65, Danforth fel. & Ph.D.(Eng), 69. Teaching asst. ENG, UNIV. MIAMI, 65, ASST. PROF, 69- Nat. Endowment for Humanities summer stipend, 71. MLA. American literary realism, Robert Herrick; women's studies. Publ: Show thyself a man . . ., Mouton, The Hague, 69; Robert Herrick as novelist and journalist, Am. Lit. Realism, 70; Traditional literary study—in the subjunctive mood, In: Female studies VI, MLA, 72; co-auth, Storytellers and gatekeepers, In: Black image, W.C. Brown, 71; plus four others. Add: 1429 Garcia Ave, Coral Gables, FL 33146.

FRANKLIN, RALPH WILLIAM, b. Ojus, Fla, Aug. 20, 37. ENGLISH, BIBLIOGRAPHY. B.A, Univ. Puget Sound, 59; Danforth fel, 59-64, Northwest. Univ, 59-64, M.A, 60, Ph.D.(Am. lit), 65; univ. fel. & M.A, Univ. Chicago, 68. Asst. prof. Eng, Univ. Wis, 64-66; asst. prof. & cur, Abernethy Libr, Middlebury Col, 68-70; asst. chief tech. serv. & develop, Wash. State Libr, 70-71; ASST. PROF. & DEAN STUD, GRAD. LIBR. SCH, UNIV. CHICAGO, 71- Univ. Wis. res. grant, spring 66; consult, Wash. State Libr, 71- Asn. Col. & Res. Libr; Am. Libr. Asn. Emily Dickinson; bibliography and textual criticism. Publ: The editing of Emily Dickinson, Univ. Wis, 67; Housman's Shropshire, Mod. Lang. Quart, 63; The narrative management of As I lay dying, Mod. Fiction Stud, 67; Editing unfinished writing: Emily Dickinson, CEAA Newsletter, 68. Add: 5401 Hyde Park Blvd, Chicago, IL 60615.

FRANKLIN, ROSEMARY FUTRELLE, b. Birmingham, Ala, Dec. 15, 41. AMERICAN LITERATURE. A.B, Birmingham-South. Col, 63; M.A, Wake Forest Univ, 64; NDEA fel, Emory Univ, Ph.D.(Am. lit), 68. ASST. PROF. ENG, Ga. State Univ, 67-69; UNIV. GA, 69- MLA; S.Atlantic Mod. Lang. Asn. Romantic period of American literature; Faulkner; Henry James. Publ: Index to Henry James's Prefaces to the New York Edition, Univ. Va, Bibliog. Soc, 66; Animal magnetism in As I lay dying, Am. Quart, 66. Add: Dept. of English, University of Georgia, Athens, GA 30601.

FRANKLIN, WILLIAM GLENWOOD, b. Hyde Park, Pa, July 21, 32; m. 58; c. 2. SPEECH SCIENCE, ORAL INTERPRETATION. A.B, Heidelberg Col, 59; M.A, Bowling Green State Univ, 61; Ph.D.(speech sci), Pa. State Univ, University Park, 70. Asst. prof. speech & drama & head dept, Bethany Col, 60-64; asst. prof. SPEECH, Pa. State Univ, University Park, 65-67; ASSOC. PROF, N.C. STATE UNIV, 70- Lectr, Univ. Fribourg, 73; Swiss Nat. Found. Res. grant, Kanton Hosp, St. Gallen, Switz, 73; mem. res. team, Speech & Hearing Div, Ear Nose & Throat Clin, 73- South. Speech Commun. Asn. Language development and acquisition; acoustic phonetics. Publ: Oral interpretation as process, N.C. Speech & Drama J, spring 72; Acoustic characteristics of simulated emotion, South. Speech Commun. J, winter 72; contrib, Proceedings, 1972 German-American Communication Colloquim, East. Ill. Univ, 73. Add: Dept. of English, Speech Div, North Carolina State University, Box 5110, Raleigh, NC 27607.

FRANSON, JOHN KARL, b. Coalville, Utah, Nov. 18, 41; m. 65; c. 5. ENGLISH LITERATURE. B.A, Brigham Young Univ, 66, M.A, 69; Ph.D.(Eng), Univ. Ill, Urbana, 72. Grad. asst. ENG, Brigham Young Univ, 66-68; teaching asst, Univ. Ill, Urbana, 68-72, res. asst, 69-70; ASST. PROF, ARK. STATE UNIV, 72-, fac. res. grant, 73. Milton; Renaissance; literature and the fine arts. Publ: Blake's illustrations of Milton's Paradise regained (Abstr), 7/73 & Dean Donne's cup of blood: mixing self with congregation to achieve salvation (abstr), 7/74, Tenn. Philol. Bull. Add: Division of English, Philosophy and Languages, Arkansas State University, State University, AR 72467.

FRANTZ, DAVID OSWIN, b. Lancaster, Pa, Aug. 16, 42; m. 70; c. 1. RENAISSANCE LITERATURE. B.A, Princeton, 64; M.A, Univ. Mich, 65; fel, Univ. Pa, 66-67; Ph.D.(Eng), 68. ASST. PROF. ENG, OHIO STATE UNIV, 68- Renaissance Soc. Am.(rep, 73, 74); MLA. Renaissance erotica; minor Elizabethan writers; England and Italy in the Renaissance. Publ: Auth, Leud Priapians and Renaissance pornography, Stud. Eng. Lit, 72. Add: Dept. of English, Ohio State University, 164 W. 17th Ave, Columbus, OH 43210.

FRANTZ, DONALD H, JR, b. Youngstown, Ohio, Sept. 25, 20; m. 43; c. 4. HUMANITIES. B.A, Redlands Univ, 46; M.A, Stanford Univ, 47; Ph.D, Univ. South. Calif, 60. Instr. world relig. & humanities, Bakersfield Col, 49-60; assoc. prof. world & Eng. lit, Stanislaus State Col, 60-62; Fulbright lectr. humanities, Chulalongkorn Univ, Thailand, 62-64; prof. Eng, Whitworth Col, 64-66; exec. dir, U.S. Educ. Comn. Korea, 66-67; prof. Eng, Univ. Md. Far East, 67; assoc. prof. humanities, Univ. S.Fla, 67-70; PROF. ENG, APPALACHIAN STATE UNIV, 70-, dir, Watauga Col, 72-73. Acting instr. Eng, Stanford Univ, 47-49; asst. prof, Fresno State Col, summers 50-52; Danforth Found. grant, 54, assoc, 54-58; Knoles fel, 55; feature writer, Calif. Crossroads, 60-64; lectr, Quaker Conf. South. Asia, Bangkok, Thailand, 63; Shell grant, Whitworth Col, 64-65, fac. res, 64-66; prof. Eng, Ft. Wright Col, summer 65; fel, Inst. Southeast Asia, Hamline Univ, 66; consult, Inst. Southeast Asia, Cent. Wash. State Univ, 66; U.S. Dept. Health, Educ. & Welfare grants, NDEA Inst. S.Asia, 69-70, Triple T Prog, Appalachian State Univ, 71-72; exhib. Appalachian lore, scenery & character, Poems & Fibers, Appalachian State Univ, 72-74, Renolda House Art Ctr, Winston-Salem, 73; Carnegie Ctr, Wash, D.C, 74, Poems and Fibers II, Clemson Univ. & Regional Gallery, Boone, 74-; mem, Ctr. Stud. Democratic Insts. Korean Broadcasting Co. Spec. Commendation, 67; Distinguished Prof. & Excellence in Teaching Award, Appalachian State Univ, 70. U.S.A, 42-45. NCTE; Siam Soc; Asn. Asian Stud; Asia Soc; Japan Soc; Korea Br. Royal Asiatic Soc. Literature and arts of Southeast Asia and Korea; comparative religion, especially Theravedan Buddhism; Appalachian studies. Publ: The humanities: a study of cultural archetypes, 2 vols, Bakersfield Col, 59; Poems and fibers, 74; Neither praise nor condemnation, winter 71, Theory X and theory Y, spring 72 & Quest for meaning, summer 72, Triple T News; plus many others. Add: Dept. of English, Appalachian State University, Boone, NC 28608.

FRANTZ, ROBERT O, b. Altoona, Pa, Mar. 29, 19; m. 48; c. 3. ENGLISH. A.B, Franklin & Marshall Col, 40; A.M, Univ. Chicago, 47, 47-50. Lectr. ENG, Roosevelt Univ, 47-50; instr, Univ. S.C, 54-55; asst. prof, Wofford Col, 55-57; ASSOC. PROF, SHIPPENSBURG STATE COL, 57- A.U.S, 43-46, 50-51, M/Sgt. Nineteenth century American literature. Add: 101 Richwalter St, Shippensburg, PA 17257.

FRASER, JOHN, b. London, Eng, July 18, 28; m. 56. ENGLISH. B.A, Oxford, 51, M.A, 55; Columbia Univ, 53; Ph.D.(Eng), Univ. Minn, 61. Instr. ENG, Rollins Col, 54-55; asst. prof, DALHOUSIE UNIV, 61-66, assoc. prof, 66-74, PROF, 74- Mem, Can. Counc. Pre-Doctoral Fel. Selection Comt, 66, leave fel, 69-70. R.A.F, 46-48. English literature and society, 1880-1920; literary theory; crime fiction. Publ: Violence in the arts, Cambridge, 74; Modern poetics: twentieth century American and British, In: Encyclopedia of poetry and poetics, Princeton, 65; Stretches and languages: a contribution to critical theory, Col. Eng, 71; Rereading Traven's The death ship, South. Rev, 73; plus others. Add: Dept. of English, Dalhousie University, Halifax, N.S, Can.

FRASER, RUSSELL ALFRED, b. Elizabeth, N.J, May 31, 27; m. 47; c. 2. ENGLISH. Choate fel, Dartmouth Col, 47, A.B, 47; A.M, Harvard, 49, Ph.D. (Eng), 50. Instr. ENG, Univ. Calif, 50; Duke Univ, 52-55, asst. prof, 55-56; asst. prof, Princeton, 56-61, assoc. prof, 61-65, assoc. dean grad. sch, 62-

65; PROF, Vanderbilt Univ, 65-67; UNIV. MICH, ANN ARBOR, 68-, chmn. dept, 68-73. Reynolds fel, Dartmouth Col; Am. Counc. Learned Soc. scholar, 51-52, grant, 68; Nat. Sci. Found. grant, 64-67; Counc. of Humanities jr. fel, Princeton, 60; consult, Nat. Endowment for Humanities, 66-; Guggenheim fel, 73-74. U.S.N, 44-46. MLA; fel. Am. Philos. Soc; Renaissance Soc. Am; Shakespeare Asn. Am; AAUP. Shakespeare; Renaissance and Medieval periods. Publ: The court of Venus, Duke Univ, 55; The court of virtue, 61 & Shakespeare's poetics, 62, Routledge & Kegan Paul; King Lear, New Am. Libr, 63; ed, Oscar Wilde, Houghton, 69; auth, The war against poetry, 70 & The Dark Ages and the Age of Gold, 73, Princeton Univ; An essential Shakespeare, Macmillan, 72. Add: 2105 Tuomy Rd, Ann Arbor, MI 48104.

FRAYNE, JOHN (PATRICK), b. New York, N.Y, June 13, 31; m. 58; c. 2. ENGLISH. A.B, Fordham Univ, 53; A.M, Columbia Univ, 61, Ph.D, 67. Preceptor ENG, Columbia Col, Columbia Univ, 63-65; instr, UNIV. ILL, URBANA, 65-66, asst. prof, 66-71, ASSOC. PROF, 71-, summer fac. fels, 67, 68. Undergrad. Instruct. Award, Univ. Ill, Urbana, summer 70. U.S.A, 53-55, 1st Lt. MLA; Am. Comt. Irish Stud. Anglo-Irish literature; film and literature studies; fiction of Thomas Mann. Publ: Ed, Uncollected prose by W.B. Yeats, Vol. I, Early articles and reviews, 1886-1896, 70 & co-ed, Uncollected prose of W.B. Yeats, Vol. II, 1897-1939, (in press), Macmillan, Eng. & Columbia Univ; Brian Moore's wandering Irishman—the not-so-wild colonial boy, In: Modern Irish literature: festschrift for W.Y. Tindall, Iona Col, 72. Add: 100 English Bldg, University of Illinois, Urbana, IL 61801.

FRAZER, FRANCES MARILYN, b. Edmonton, Alta, Aug. 13, 32. ENGLISH LITERATURE. B.A, McMaster Univ, 54; M.A, Univ. B.C, 60; Ph.D.(Eng), Univ. London, 69. Teaching asst. ENG, Univ. B.C, 56-60, lectr, 60-61; asst. prof, Univ. Alta, 63-65; Simon Fraser Univ, 65-69; ASSOC. PROF, UNIV. PRINCE EDWARD ISLAND, 69- Asn. Can. Univ. Teachers Eng; NCTE; Can. Counc. Teachers Eng; Humanities Asn. Can. George Bernard Shaw; 19th century poetry and fiction; children's literature. Publ: Agic-may ords-way: magic words, In: Looking at language, W.J. Gage, 66; Saint Joan, In: Studies of major works in English, Oxford Univ, 68. Add: Dept. of English, University of Prince Edward Island, Charlottetown, P.E.I, Can.

FRAZER, WINIFRED LOESCH DUSENBURY, b. Chicago, Ill, Jan. 30, 16; m. 37; c. 3. ENGLISH. B.S, Univ. Wis, 37; M.A, Univ. Maine, 40; Ph.D.(Eng), Univ. Fla. 56. Instr. ENG, UNIV. FLA, 55-59, asst. prof, 59-64, assoc. prof, 64-71, PROF, 72-, fac. develop. grant, 71-72. MLA; NCTE; Col. Eng. Asn; S.Atlantic Mod.Lang. Asn. American literature; modern American drama; modern world drama. Publ: The theme of loneliness in modern American drama, 60, 2nd ed, 67 & Love as death in The iceman cometh, 67, Univ. Fla; King Lear and Hickey: bridegroom and iceman, Mod. Drama, 12/72; Iceman—not ice man, Am. Lit, 1/73; The teachers ego, In: Classroom practices in teaching English, 1972-1973, NCTE, 72; plus others. Add: Dept. of English, University of Florida, Gainesville, FL 32611.

FREASE, CYNTHIA RICE, b. Lawrence, Kans, Aug. 27, 18; m. 46; c. 1. ENGLISH. B.A, Univ. Kans, 39; M.A, Univ. Minn, 40; Col. fel, Univ. Wis, 41-42; Ed.D.(Eng), Colo. State Col, 61. Teacher, high sch, Calif, 43-46; instr. ENG, Temple Univ, 46-49; teacher, high sch, Colo, 53-54; 55-59; instr, Univ. Calif, Los Angeles, fall 54; Univ. Md, Seoul, Korea, 61-62; UNIV. NORTH. COLO, 63-66, asst. prof, 66-70, ASSOC. PROF, 70- Vis. lectr. Eng, Univ. Helsinki, 70. MLA; Am. Soc. 18th Century Stud. Eighteenth century English literature; biography. Add: Dept. of English, Michener Library L41, University of Northern Colorado, Greeley, CO 80639.

FREDEMAN, PAT HINES, b. Nashville, Ark. ENGLISH & AMERICAN LITERATURE. B.A, Univ. Okla, 56, Ph.D.(Eng), 72; M.A, Univ. B.C, 64. Instr. Eng. & humanities, West. Wash. State Col, 63-67; ENG, Univ. Okla, 70-71; ASST. PROF, NORTHWEST. STATE COL, 71- MLA; AAUP. Renaissance drama and poetry; American fiction and poetry. Add: Dept. of English, Northwestern State College, Oklahoma Blvd, Alva, OK 73717.

FREDEMAN, WILLIAM EVAN, b. Pine Bluff, Ark, July 19, 28; m. 64; c. 1. ENGLISH. B.A, Hendrix Col, 48; M.A, Univ. Okla, 50, Ph.D.(Eng), 56. Teacher ENG, high sch, Okla, 48-53; instr, UNIV. B.C, 56-58, asst. prof, 58-63, assoc. prof, 63-67, PROF, 67- Can. Counc. sr. res. fel, 59-60, leave fel, 71-72; Guggenheim fels, 65-66, 72-73; mem. adv. bd, Victorian Stud, 70-; adv. ed, Wellesley Index to Victorian Periodicals, 70-; Killam sr. fel, Univ. B.C, 71-72; mem. adv. bd, Victorian Poetry, 74- U.S.N.R, 45-46, 46-50; U.S.A.R, 50-58, 1st Lt. MLA; Int. Asn. Univ. Prof. Eng; Bibliog. Soc, Eng; Res. Soc. Victorian Periodicals (v.pres, 69-71). Pre-Raphaelitism; Victorian literature; bibliography. Publ: Pre-Raphaelitism: a bibliocritical study, Harvard Univ, 65; A pre-Raphaelite gazette: The Penkill letters of Arthur Hughes to William Bell Scott and Alice Boyd, 1886-1897, 67 & Prelude to the last decade: Dante Gabriel Rossetti in the summer of 1871, 71, John Rylands Libr; ed, The P.R.B. Journal, Clarendon, 74; auth, The pre-Raphaelites, In: The Victorian poets, Harvard Univ, 2nd ed, 68; A sign betwixt the meadow and the cloud: the ironic apotheosis of Tennyson's St. Simeon stylites, Univ. Toronto Quart, 68; The sphere of common duties: the domestic solution in Tennyson's poetry, Bull. John Rylands Libr, 72; plus others. Add: Dept. of English, University of British Columbia, Vancouver, B.C, Can.

FREDERICK, ANTHONY PETER, S.M, b. New Baden, Ill, Jan. 14, 00. ENGLISH LITERATURE. A.B, Univ. Dayton, 25; A.M, St. Louis Univ, 35. Teacher, high sch, Tex, 20-27, Mo, 27-35; from instr. to PROF. ENG, ST. MARY'S UNIV, 35-, chmn. Eng. dept, 39-61, dean, sch. arts & sci, 61-64, gen. chmn. self study for South. Asn. Cols. & Schs. Evaluation Prog, 61-62. Piper Prof, Piper Found, 73. MLA; NCTE (dir, 53-68). Publ: The term paper in theory and example, St. Mary's Univ, 42, rev. ed, 67; co-auth. & ed, Annotated index to the English journal, Nat. Counc. Teachers Eng, 65; A man called brother, In: Why I became a brother, Newman, 54. Add: Dept. of English, St. Mary's University, 2700 Cincinnati Ave, San Antonio, TX 78284.

FREDMAN, ALICE GREEN, b. New York, N.Y, Oct. 24, 24; m. 50; c. 2. ENGLISH & COMPARATIVE LITERATURE. A.B, Swarthmore Col, 45; Martha E. Tyson grant, Smith Col, 45, univ. fel, 45-46, M.A, 46; Ph.D.(comp. lit), Columbia Univ, 53. Instr. Eng, Smith Col, 46-47; Eng. & humanities, Hobart & William Smith Cols, 49-51; lectr. Eng, Queens Col.(N.Y), 52; instr. ENG. & COMP. LIT, COLUMBIA UNIV, 53-55, asst. prof, 55-60, assoc. prof, 61-72, PROF, 72- Am. Counc. Learned Soc. fel, 62-63; Columbia Univ. Counc. Res. Humanities fel, 62-63, 71; Carl & Lily Pforzheimer Found. travel grant, 69. Ansley Award, 53. MLA; Keats-Shelley Asn. Am. Eighteenth century Anglo-French comparative studies in literature; history of the English novel; comparative fiction. Publ: Diderot and Sterne, 55 & Anthony Trollope, 71, Columbia Univ; auth, Diderot's fictional worlds & co-auth, Diderot and the Abbe Dulaurens, In: Diderot Studies I, Syracuse Univ, 50; contrib, English writers of the eighteenth century, Columbia Univ, 71; plus others. Add: 30 Harbour Rd, Kings Point, NY 11024.

FREDMAN, RAYMOND M, b. Evanston, Ill, May 22, 30; m. 57. ENGLISH, DRAMA. B.A, Augustana Col.(Ill), 55; M.A, Wayne State Univ, 58; Ph.D. (Eng), Univ. Wis-Madison, 69. Instr. ENG, Univ. Cincinnati, 57-60; Wis. State Univ, Oshkosh, 60-62; asst. prof, Ill. Wesleyan Univ, 63-67; ASSOC. PROF, CUYAHOGA COMMUNITY COL, 67-, head dept, 67-71. Mem. exec. comt, Midwest Regional Conf. Eng. in the Two-yr. Col, 71-; consult, Oxford Univ. Press, 71- Col. Conf. Compos. & Commun; MLA; NCTE; Shakespeare Asn. Am; Renaissance Soc. Am. Shakespeare; Renaissance and modern drama. Publ: Co-auth, Guidelines for the training of junior college English teachers, NCTE, 72 & A student's book of college English, Glencoe, 74; auth, Community college and graduate education in English, ADE Bull, 2/71 & Midwest Mod. Lang. Asn. Bull, spring 71; contrib. ed, Shakespeare Newsletter. Add: Dept. of English, Cuyahoga College, 2900 Community College Ave, Cleveland, OH 44115.

FREDRICKSON, ROBERT STEWART, b. Minneapolis, Minn, June 16, 40; m. 64; c. 1. ENGLISH & AMERICAN LITERATURE. B.A, DePauw Univ, 61; M.A, Univ. Minn, 64; Ph.D.(Eng), Univ. N.C, Chapel Hill, 70. Instr. ENG, Univ. N.C, Charlotte, 64-66; instr, Univ. N.C, Chapel Hill, 66-69; ASST. PROF, GETTYSBURG COL, 69- MLA. Psychology and literature; 19th century realism. Publ: Hjalmar Hjorth Boyesen: Howells' out realisted, Markham Rev, 3/73; Gulley Jimson's Painterly prose, Bucknell Rev, spring 74. Add: Dept. of English, Gettysburg College, Gettysburg, PA 17325.

FREE, WILLIAM JOSEPH, b. Chattanooga, Tenn, Mar. 18, 33; m. 57. ENGLISH. A.B, Univ. Chattanooga, 57; M.A, Univ. N.C, 59, fel, 61-62, Ph.D. 62. Instr. ENG, UNIV. GA, 62-64, asst. prof, 64-68, ASSOC. PROF, 68- MLA; S.Atlantic Mod. Lang. Asn.(chmn. film group, 72-73). Literary criticism; contemporary drama; literature and film. Publ: History into drama: a source book on symphonic drama, Odyssey, 63; The Columbian magazine and American literary nationalism, Mouton, 68; Aesthetic and moral value in Bonnie and Clyde, Quart. J. Speech, 69; William Cullen Bryant on nationalism, originality and imitation, Stud. Philol, 69; The ironic age of David Storey, Mod. Drama, 74; plus twelve others. Add: Dept. of English, University of Georgia, Athens, GA 30601.

FREE, WILLIAM NORRIS, b. Seaford, Del, Aug. 25, 33; m. 57; c. 3. ENGLISH. B.A, Yale, 55, Robert R. McCormick fel, 57-59, Ph.D, 61; M.A, Ind. Univ, 57. Lectr. ENG, Ind. Univ, 59-61, instr, 61-66; assoc. prof, UNIV. TOLEDO, 66-71, PROF, 71-, CHMN. DEPT, 72- U.S.A.R, 55-68, Capt. MLA. English literature of the 18th century. Publ: Walpole's letters: the art of being graceful, In: The familiar letter in the eighteenth century, Univ. Kans, 66; William Cowper, Twayne, 71. Add: Dept. of English, University of Toledo, Toledo, OH 43606.

FREEBURG, DOROTHY DUMBLE, b. Marion, Ohio, June 21, 10; m. 43. ENGLISH. B.A, Ohio State Univ, 32, M.A, 34; summer, Oxford, 38; Columbia Univ, 40-41. INSTR. Eng, Vermont Col, 35-37; Am. Col. Girls, Istanbul, 37-40; Hunter Col, 41-42; Harcum Jr. Col, 42-43; Eng. & sociol, Child Educ. Found, Adelphi Col, 45-47; ENG, Endicott Jr. Col, 48-58; PHOENIX COL, 59- Lectr-teacher, Istanbul Univ, 39-40; Fulbright teaching award, Netherlands, 58-59; lectr-teacher, Inter-Am. Univ, P.R, summers 65 & 66. Teachers of Eng. to Speakers of Other Lang. English as a second language; 18th century English literature. Add: 521 W. Palm Lane, Phoenix, AZ 85003.

FREEDMAN, MORRIS, b. New York, N.Y, Oct. 6, 20; m. 45; c. 2. ENGLISH & COMPARATIVE LITERATURE. B.A, City Col. New York, 41; M.A, Columbia Univ, 50, Ph.D, 53. Lectr. & instr. Eng, City Col. New York, 46-54; assoc. ed, Commentary, 54-55; asst. prof. Eng, Univ. N.Mex, 55-59, assoc. prof, 59-63, PROF, 63-66; ENG. & COMP. LIT, UNIV. MD, COLLEGE PARK, 66-, head dept, 67-72. MLA; NCTE; Milton Soc. Am. Later 17th century; Milton; creative writing and contemporary drama; American studies. Publ: Ed, Essays in the modern drama, Heath, 64; auth, The compact English handbook, McKay, 65; The moral impulse, 67 & American drama in social context, 71, South. Ill. Univ; co-ed, Controversy in literature, Scribner, 68; auth, Dryden's miniature epic, J. Eng. & Ger. Philol, 58; Milton and Dryden on rhyme, Huntington Libr. Quart, 61; Success and the American dramatist, Am. Theatre, 67; plus others. Add: Dept. of English, University of Maryland, College Park, MD 20742.

FREEDMAN, RALPH (WILLIAM BERNARD), b. Hamburg, Ger, Feb. 24, 20; m. 48; c. 2. ENGLISH. A.B, Univ. Wash, 47; M.A, Brown Univ, 50; Sterling fel. & Ph.D.(comp. lit), Yale, 54. Instr. comp. lit, Univ. Iowa, 53-56, asst. prof. 56-61, assoc. prof. Eng, 61-64, prof, 64-65; vis. prof. & sr. fel. humanities, PRINCETON, 65-66, PROF. comp. lit. & Germanic lang, 66-68, COMP. LIT, 68- Lewis & Clark Northwest Award, 47. U.S.A, 42-45. MLA; Am. Comp. Lit. Asn.(mem. adv. bd, 65-69). History of ideas from the 18th to 20th centuries; history and theories of literary criticism from the 18th to 20th centuries; 18th to 20th century English, French and German literature, especially poetry and prose fiction. Publ: Divided; The lyrical novel: studies in Hermann Hesse, André Gide, and Virginia Woolf, Princeton, 63, 66; Modern poetics: 1750-1900, In: Encyclopedia of poetry and poetics, Princeton, 65; Wallace Stevens and R.M. Rilke: two versions of a poetic, In: The poet as critic, Northwest. Univ, 67; The possibility of a theory of the novel, In: The disciplines of criticism, Yale, 68; plus others. Add: Program in Comparative Literature, 331 East Pyne Bldg, Princeton University, Princeton, NJ 08540.

FREEDMAN, RICHARD, b. New York, N.Y, Feb. 14, 32; m. 58; c. 2. LITERATURE OF EIGHTEENTH & NINETEENTH CENTURIES. A.B, N.Y. Univ,

52, M.A, 53; M.S, Columbia Univ, 54; Ph.D.(Eng), Cornell Univ, 67. Grad. asst. freshman Eng, Cornell Univ, 55-59; instr. ENG, Columbia Univ, 59-64; SIMMONS COL, 64-66, asst. prof, 67-70, ASSOC. PROF, 70- Panelist, Nat. Endowment for Humanities, 70-73. Cornell Univ. Guilford prize, 50. MLA. English prose fiction; 19th century English literature. Publ: Hemingway's Spanish Civil War correspondence, Univ. Tex. Stud. Lang. & Lit, 59. Add: Dept. of English, Simmons College, 300 The Fenway, Boston, MA 02115.

FREEHAFER, JOHN HENRY, b. Philadelphia, Pa, Mar. 1, 20. ENGLISH. B.S, Univ. Pa, 45, M.S, 46, M.A, 47, Ph.D.(Eng), 50. Instr. ENG, TEMPLE UNIV, 49-56, asst. prof, 56-61, assoc. prof, 61-72, PROF, 72-, chmn. dept, 56-58, chmn. div. arts, community col, 58-68, summer res. grants, 64 & 67. Ed, Nat. Philatelic Mus. Mag, 50-57. U.S.A, 43-45. MLA; Soc. Theatre Res, Eng; Shakespeare Asn. Am; AAUP; Bibliog. Soc. Univ. Va. English literature 1500-1800; bibliography; American studies. Publ: Cardenio, by Shakespeare and Fletcher, PMLA, 69; The marble faun and the editing of nineteenth-century texts, Stud. Novel, 70; Perspective scenery and the Caroline playhouses, Theatre Notebook, 73; plus others. Add: Dept. of English, Temple University, Philadelphia, PA 19122.

FREELEY, AUSTIN J, b. Boston Mass, Mar. 14, 22; m. 47. SPEECH. A.B, Boston Univ, 44, M.A, 46; Ph.D.(rhetoric & pub. address), Northwest. Univ, 55. Instr. speech, Boston Univ, 47-50, asst. prof, 51-57, dir. forensics, 47-57; assoc. prof. SPEECH, JOHN CARROLL UNIV, 57-62, PROF, 63-, DIR. FORENSICS, 57- Chmn, Nat. Comt. Intercol. Debate & Discussion, 54-73; Nat. Comt. Speech Profession on Presidential Campaign Debating, 59-; vis. prof, Syracuse Univ, 62; consult, Ohio Bell Telephone Co, 62; vis. prof, Univ. Colo, summer 66; Wash. State Univ, summer 67; consult, Ernst & Ernst, 69-72. Am. Forensic Asn.(pres, 52-54, assoc. ed. Jour, 66-68); East. Forensic Asn.(pres, 50-52); Speech Asn. Am.(exec. counc, legis. assembly, 66-68); Speech Asn. Cent. States (assoc. ed, Jour, 66-68); Nat. Soc. Stud. Commun. Argumentation and debate; presidential campaign debating; contemporary public address. Publ: Argumentation and debate, Wadsworth, 61, 2nd ed, 66, 3rd ed, 71; contrib, Readings in argumentation, Allyn & Bacon, 69, Counterpoint, Scarecrow, 69 & Rhetorical criticism: methods and models, W.C. Brown; 71; plus two others. Auth, Argumentation and debate, Recordings for Blind, Inc, 62. Add: Dept. of Speech, John Carroll University, Cleveland, OH 44118.

FREEMAN, ARTHUR, b. Cambridge, Mass, July 31, 38. ENGLISH. A.B, Harvard, 59, soc. fels, 62-65, Ph.D.(Eng), 65. Asst. prof. ENG, BOSTON UNIV, 65-68, assoc. prof, 68-73, PROF, 73-, grad. sch. summer res. grant, 67. Nat. Endowment Humanities younger scholar fel, 69; Am. Counc. Learned Soc. fel, 71-72. Bibliog. Soc. Eng. English Renaissance literature; Elizabethan and Stuart history; writing poetry. Publ: Apollonian poems, Atheneum, 61; Estrangements, Harcourt, 66; Thomas Kyd: facts and problems, Oxford, Clarendon, 67; ed, Henry VI part II, Signet, 67; auth, Assays of bias, Godine, 70; ed, Eighteenth century Shakespeare (31 vols), Frank Cass, 71-74; ed, The English stage: attack and defense (50 vols), Garland, 73-74; auth, The authorship of The tell-tale, J.Eng. & Ger. Philol, 63; Shakespeare and Solyman and Perseda, Mod. Lang. Rev, 63; The fatal vesper and The doleful evensong, Library, 67. Add: Dept. of English, Boston University, Charles River Campus, Boston, MA 02215.

FREEMAN, BERNICE, b. LaGrange, Ga, Aug. 8, 09. ENGLISH EDUCATION. A.B, Tift Col, 30; Univ. Ga, 30, 51-52; M.A, Univ. N.C, Chapel Hill, 32; summer, Cornell Univ, 38; Ed.D.(Eng. educ), Columbia Univ, 52; Auburn Univ, 61-62, 64-65. Teacher, high schs, Ga, 30-42; instr. & critic, demonstration high sch, Ga. Col. Milledgeville, 42-48, asst. prof. & prin, 48-51; co-dir, Ga. Educ. Ctr, 50-51; instructional supvr, Troup County Schs, Ga, 51-67; assoc. prof. educ, W.GA. COL, 67-69, PROF. EDUC, 69-, CHMN. DEPT. SEC. EDUC, 73-, coord, 69-73. Mem, high sch. sect. comt, NCTE, 52-54, mem, bd. dir. elem. sect, 66-69; mem, publ. & constructive stud. comt, Dept. Rural Educ, NEA, 58-65, mem, exec. bd, 64-69, mem, exec. comt, 65-69; assoc. dir, NDEA Inst. Elem. Eng, W.Ga. Col, summers 65-67. NCTE; NEA; MLA; S.Atlantic Mod. Lang. Asn. The short story as a means of identifying a place; the Georgia short story. Publ: Co-auth, The teaching of English in Georgia, Ga. Counc. Teachers Eng, 52, Readers digest skill builder, grade V, part 3, 60 & grade I, part 1, 63, Reader's Digest; auth, Costumes of Love's labors lost, Twelfth night, and The tempest, Shakespeare Asn. Bull, 4/36; Teaching short stories, Eng. J, 5/55; Georgia, In: The teaching of English in the South, South. Humanities Conf, 61. Add: 305 Park Ave, LaGrange, GA 30240.

FREEMAN, DONALD CARY, b. Boston, Mass, Mar. 19, 38; m. 62; c. 2. ENGLISH, LINGUISTICS. A.B, Middlebury Col, 59; Charlotte Beebe Wilbour fel, Brown Univ, 60-61, A.M, 61; State Conn. scholar, Univ. Conn, 64-65, Ph.D.(Eng), 65. Asst. prof. Eng, Univ. Calif, Santa Barbara, 65-68; from asst. prof. to assoc. prof. Eng. & ling, UNIV. MASS AMHERST, 68-71, PROF. LING, 71-, ASSOC. DEAN FAC. HUMANITIES & FINE ARTS, 72- Nat. Sci. Found-Am. Counc. Learned Soc. stud. grant ling, summer 66; appointee, humanities inst, Univ. Calif, summers 66, 67; Nat. Sci. Found. res. fel. ling, Mass. Inst. Technol, 67-68; dir. ling. inst, Ling. Soc. Am. 70-74; vis. prof. Eng, Univ. Lancaster, 71-72. MLA; Ling. Soc. Am. English stylistics; metrics; the teaching of English. Publ: Ed, Linguistics and literary style, Holt, 70; auth, On the primes of metrical style, Lang. & Style, spring 68; Current trends in metrics, Current Trends in Stylistics, 72; plus others. Add: Dept. of Linguistics, University of Massachusetts, Amherst, MA 01002.

FREEMAN, RONALD EDWARD, b. Cincinnati, Ohio, Mar. 22, 26; div; c. 3. ENGLISH. B.A, Univ. Colo, 49, M.A, 50; non-res. fel, Univ. Ill, 54-55, Ph.D.(Eng. lit), 57. Teaching asst, Univ. Ill, 50-56; asst. prof. Eng, Univ. South. Calif, 56-61, assoc. prof. & chmn. compos, 61-66; ASSOC. PROF. ENG. & HEAD FRESHMAN ENG, UNIV. CALIF, LOS ANGELES, 66- U.S.A, 44-46. MLA (chmn. Eng. sect, 70, mem. del. assembly, 71-74); NCTE; Conf. Col. Compos. & Commun.(chmn, 70). Victorian literature especially the Brownings and William Allingham. Publ: Co-ed, Letters of the Brownings to George Barrett, Univ. Ill, 58; ed, Annual Victorian bibliography, Victorian Stud, spring 66- Add: Dept. of English, University of California, Los Angeles, CA 90024.

FREEMAN, SIDNEY LEE, b. Madison, Wis, Jan. 23, 27; m. 67; c. 3. ENGLISH & SPEECH. B.S, Univ. Wis, 47; M.A, Bowling Green State Univ, 49; Ph.D.(speech & drama), Cornell Univ, 51. Instr. ENG, Sweet Briar Col, 51-55, ASST. PROF, 55-57; J.C. SMITH UNIV, 57- Minister, Unitarian Church of Charlotte, 57-; lectr, Albert Schweitzer Col, Switz, summer 59; Starr King Sch, Ministry, Berkeley, summer 64. AAUP; Unitarian Universalist Ministers Asn. U.S.N.R, 44-51, Lt.(jg). Add: 4500 Rockford Ct, Charlotte, NC 28209.

FREER, COBURN, b. New Orleans, La, Nov. 5, 39; m. 61; c. 2. ENGLISH. B.A, Lewis & Clark Col, 60; Ph.D.(Eng), Univ. Wash, 68. Instr. ENG, Univ. Ariz, 65-67; asst. prof, UNIV. MONT, 67-72, ASSOC. PROF, 72- Fulbright lectr, Univ. Oulu, 71-72; Am. Counc. Learned Soc. fel, 75. MLA; AAUP. Renaissance and 17th century literature; modern poetry. Publ: Music for a king: George Herbert's style and the metrical psalms, Johns Hopkins, 72; Theodore Roethke's love poetry, Northwest Rev, 71. Add: Dept. of English, University of Montana, Missoula, MT 59801.

FREESTONE, NORMAN W, b. Los Angeles, Calif, Jan. 17, 12; m. 35; c. 3. SPEECH. A.B, Brigham Young Univ, 35; M.A, Univ. South. Calif, 37, Ph.D. (speech), 41. PROF. SPEECH, OCCIDENTAL COL, 41- Assoc. prof. Calif. Col. Med, 45-65. Am. Speech & Hearing Asn. Language rehabilitation; speech therapy; electroencephalography. Publ: Phonic manual for reading, John A. McCarthy Found, 73; EEG study on moment of stuttering, Am. Speech Asn, 42; Wish for defective speech, Am. Speech & Hearing Asn, 48. Add: Dept. of Speech, Occidental College, Los Angeles, CA 90041.

FREIBERT, LUCY MARIE, b. Louisville, Ky, Oct. 19, 22. AMERICAN LITERATURE. A.B, Spalding Col, 59; M.A, St. Louis Univ, 62; Ph.D.(Eng), Univ. Wis-Madison, 70. Teacher, St. Cecilia Sch, Louisville, Ky, 47-52; Holy Name Sch, 52-57; Presentation Acad, 57-60; asst. prof. ENG, Spalding Col, 60-65, 69-71; ASST. PROF. & DIR. UNDERGRAD. PROG, UNIV. LOUISVILLE, 71- MLA (Am. lit. sect). Herman Melville; American literature; women's studies. Add: Dept. of English, University of Louisville, Louisville, KY 40208.

FREIERT, WILLIAM KENDALL, b. Baltimore, Md, Apr. 26, 41; m. 70. CLASSICS. B.A, St. Louis Univ, 65, M.A, 66; Ph.D.(classics), Univ. Minn, 72. Chmn. CLASSICS, Gonzaga High Sch, 66-69; ASST. PROF, GUSTAVUS ADOLPHUS COL, 72- Am. Philol. Soc; Am. Counc. Teachers Foreign Lang; Am. Class. League; Class. Asn. Mid-West & South. Epic poetry; mythology; Greek and Roman religion. Publ: The 1969 Northeast Conference, Class. World, 9/69. Add: Dept. of Classics, Gustavus Adolphus College, St. Peter, MN 56082.

FREIMARCK, VINCENT, b. New York, N.Y, June 11, 18. ENGLISH. A.B, N.Y. Univ, 39; A.M, Columbia Univ, 41; Ph.D, Cornell Univ, 50. Asst, N.Y. Univ, 40, instr, 41-42; Carnegie Inst. Tech, 42-43; asst, Cornell Univ, 46-48; instr. ENG, Wesleyan Univ, 48-52; asst. prof, STATE UNIV. N.Y. BINGHAMTON, 52-59, assoc. prof, 59-71, PROF, 71- U.S.N.R, 43-45. MLA. American literature of the 18th and 19th centuries; 18th century English criticism. Publ: Auth, Introd. & ed, Robert Lowth's Lectures on the sacred poetry of the Hebrews (2 vols), Georg Olms Verlag, Hildesheim, 69; co-ed, Race and the American romantics, Schocken, 71; auth, Rhetoric at Yale in 1807, Proc. Am. Philos. Soc, 7/66. Add: Dept. of English, State University of New York at Binghamton, Binghamton, NY 13901.

FRENCH, DAVID PLUNKETT, b. New York, N.Y, Jan. 27, 25; m. 51; c. 2. ENGLISH LITERATURE. A.B, Harvard, 45, A.M, 47, Ph.D, 54; French govt. scholar, Univ. Paris, 45-46; cert, Sorbonne, 46. Instr. Eng, Duke Univ, 47-49; teaching fel, Harvard, 50-51, gen. educ, 51-54; instr. ENG, Queens Col.(N.Y), 54-60; asst. prof, UNIV. OKLA, 60-64, assoc. prof, 64-69, PROF, 69- Mem. adv. bd, Genre, 71- Regents' Award Super. Teaching, 65. Eighteenth century English literature, especially Swift and Johnson. Publ: Swift, Temple and A digression on madness, Tex. Stud. Lit. & Lang, 63; introd, Minor English poets: 1660-1780, (10 vols), Blom, 67-; Pope, Milton and the Essay on man, Bucknell Rev, 5/68. Add: 1600 Holly Circle, Norman, OK 73069.

FRENCH, PAUL DOUGLAS, F.S.C, b. Grafton, N.Dak, July 25, 32. ENGLISH. B.A, St. Mary's Col.(Minn), 55, M.A, 60; Ph.D.(Eng), Loyola Univ, (Ill), 67. Teacher Eng, high schs, Ill, 55-63; instr, LEWIS COL, 63, asst. prof, 66, pres, 67-71, PROF. ENG, 71- MLA. Dramatic literature; humanities. Add: Lewis College, Lockport, IL 60441.

FRENCH, ROBERTS WALKER, b. New York City, N.Y, July 16, 35; m. 61; c. 2. ENGLISH. B.A, Dartmouth Col, 56; M.A, Yale, 59; Ph.D.(Eng. lit), Brown Univ, 64. Asst. prof. ENG, UNIV. MASS, AMHERST, 64-71, ASSOC. PROF, 71- MLA; Milton Soc. Am. Add: Dept. of English, University of Massachusetts, Amherst, MA 01002.

FRENCH, WARREN GRAHAM, b. Philadelphia, Pa, Jan. 26, 22. ENGLISH. B.A, Univ. Pa, 43; M.A, Univ. Tex, 48, fel, 50-51, Ph.D.(Eng), 54. Instr, Univ. Miss, 48-50; Univ. Ky, 54-56; asst. prof, ENG, Stetson Univ, 56-58; Univ. Fla, 58-62; assoc. prof, Kans. State Univ, 62-65; Univ. Mo-Kansas City, 65-66, PROF. & CHMN. DEPT, 66-70; IND. UNIV-PURDUE UNIV, INDIANAPOLIS, 70- Ed. current bibliog, Twentieth Century Lit, 58-67; mem. film adv. comt, Mo. Counc. Arts, 65-; vis. prof. Eng, State Univ. N.Y. Col. New Paltz, 70; vis. lectr, Dalhousie Univ, summer 73. U.S.A, 43-46; U.S.N, 51-53, Lt. NCTE; Conf. Col. Compos. & Commun; Am. Stud. Asn; MLA; Midwest Mod. Lang, Asn; Midwest. Am. Stud. Asn.(adv. ed, 65-); Soc. Cinema Stud; John Steinbeck Soc. Am.(pres, 67-). Contemporary American fiction; history of the novel; film as a literary genre. Publ: John Steinbeck, 61, rev. ed, 74; Frank Norris, 62 & J.D. Salinger, 63, Twayne; Companion to The grapes of wrath, Viking, 63; The social movement at the end of an era, South. Ill. Univ, 66; ed, The Thirties: fiction, poetry, drama, 67, The Forties: fiction, poetry, drama, 69 & The Fifties: fiction, poetry, drama, 71, Everett Edwards; co-auth, American winners of the Nobel Prize in literature, Univ. Okla, 68; auth, Season of promise, Univ. Mo, 68; A filmguide to The grapes of wrath, Ind. Univ, 73. Add: Dept. of English, Indiana University-Purdue University at Indianapolis, Indianapolis, IN 46205.

FRENCH, WILLIAM WIRT, b. Beckley, W.Va, June 26, 32; div; c. 2. ENGLISH LITERATURE. B.A, W.Va. Univ, 54; M.A, Univ. Pittsburgh, 60, Ph.D.(Eng), 67. Asst. to dean, Col. Arts & Sci, Univ. Pittsburgh, 62-64; instr. ENG, W.VA. UNIV, 64-67, asst. prof, 67-71, ASSOC. PROF, 71-, summer grant, 66, asst. chmn. dept, 68-72. MLA; Shakespeare Asn. Am. Shakespeare; English Renaissance drama. Publ: Double view in Dr. Faustus, W.Va. Univ. Philol. Papers, fall 69. Add: Dept. of English, West Virginia University, Morgantown, WV 26506.

FRENZ, HORST, b. Oberlauringen, Bavaria, Ger, June 29, 12; nat; m. 39; c. 2. ENGLISH, COMPARATIVE LITERATURE. Univ. Breslau, 30-31; Univ. Heidelberg, 31-32; Univ. London, 33-34; Ph.D, Univ. Göttingen, 36; A.M, Univ. Ill, 39. Asst, Univ. London, 33-34; res. asst, Univ. Ill, 38-40; instr. Eng, IND. UNIV, BLOOMINGTON, 40-45, asst. prof. Eng. & dir. world lit, 45-49, assoc. prof, Eng, 49-54, prof, 54-69, DISTINGUISHED PROF, 69-, CHMN. COMP. LIT, 49-, instr. in charge Ger. area prog, Army Spec. Training Prog, 43-44. Vis. lectr, Univ. Wis, 47-48; vis. prof. Eng, N.Y. Univ, summers 50, 60; Fund Advan. Educ. fel, 52-53; assoc. ed, Yearbk. Comp. & Gen. Lit, 52-60, ed, 60-; vis. prof. Am. lit, Univ. Hamburg, 54-55; Am. Philos. Soc. grants, 55, 63; Fulbright vis. prof. Am. lit, Univs. Göttingen & Hamburg, 62-63; Guggenheim fel, 68-69; examr-consult, N.Cent. Accreditation Asn, 65-; vis. prof. Am. stud, Univ. Erlangen, summer 69. Int. Comp. Lit. Asn.(v.pres, 61-64, pres, 74-76); Am. Comp. Lit. Asn.(v.pres, 68-71, pres, 71-74); AAUP; Am. Soc. Theatre Res; Mod. Humanities Res. Asn; Ger. Soc. Am. Stud; MLA; Theatre Libr. Asn; NCTE. Comparative and American literature; drama and the theatre; European-American literary and cultural relations. Publ: Whitman and Rolleston, Browne & Nolan, Dublin, 52; ed, Nobel Prize lectures in literature, 1901-1967, Elsevier, 69; auth, Eugene O'Neill, Unger, 71; Eugene O'Neill's Desire under the elms and Henrik Ibsen's Rosmersholm, Jahrbuch Amerikastudien, 64; Nationalism and cosmopolitanism in American letters: a backward glance, Proc. IVth Cong. Int. Comp. Lit. Asn, 66; The art of translation, In: Comparative literature: method and perspective, Univ. South. Ill, rev. ed, 71. Add: 421 Blue Ridge Dr, Bloomington, IN 47401.

FRESHLEY, DWIGHT LOWELL, b. Homeworth, Ohio, June 27, 24; m. 50; c. 4. SPEECH. A.B, N.Cent. Col, 50; A.M, Northwest. Univ, 51; Ph.D. (speech), Ohio State Univ, 55. Instr. speech & coach of debate, Lehigh Univ, 51-53; instr. speech, Ohio State Univ, 53-55; from asst. prof. to assoc. prof. speech & dir. forensics, Vanderbilt Univ, 55-63; from assoc. prof. to PROF. SPEECH & CHMN. DEPT, UNIV. GA, 63- Fulbright prof, Athens Col, 58-59; ed, South. Speech J, 69-72. U.S.A, 43-46. Speech Commun. Asn; South. Speech Commun. Asn.(v.pres, 73-74, pres, 74-75). Public address; psychology of speech. Publ: Co-ed, Readings in interpersonal and organizational communication, Holbrook, 69; co-auth, Speech communication in society, Allyn & Bacon, 72; A study of attitudes of management personnel toward communication, J. Commun; plus others. Add: Dept. of Speech Communication, University of Georgia, Athens, GA 30602.

FREUND, HANS JOACHIM, b. Cologne, Ger, Mar. 10, 19; U.S. citizen; m. 69. COMPARATIVE LITERATURE. B.S, Columbia Univ, 53, M.A, 54, Ph.D. (comp. lit), 71. Asst. prof. Eng. & Ger, Rensselaer Polytech. Inst, 56-64, ASSOC. PROF. ENG, GER. & CLASSICS, UNION COL.(N.Y), 64- U.S.A, 45-48. MLA; AAUP. Hebrew and Greek origins in Western thought; Romanticism. Add: Humanities Ctr, Union College, Schenectady, NY 12308.

FREUND, JOHN RICHARD, b. Chicago, Ill, Nov. 16, 26; m. 48; c. 2. ENGLISH LITERATURE. A.B, Miami Univ, 49, M.A, 50; Ph.D.(Eng), Ind. Univ. Bloomington, 55. Asst. prof. ENG, West. Mich. Univ, 54-58; assoc. prof, 58-64; Grand Valley State Col, 64-68; PROF, King's Col.(Pa), 68-71; IND. UNIV. PA, 71- Dir, Writing Ctr, King's Col,(Pa), 68-71; co-ed, The Dialogist, 70-72; ed, Stud. in Humanities, 72- U.S.N.R, 44-46. MLA. Communication; Shakespeare. Publ: Coming to our senses in media res, Dialogist, spring 69; An environment for environmental studies, Perspectives, 10/69; co-auth, Distortion in communication, In: Readings for communication, West. Mich. Univ, 61 & In: Communication probes, Sci. Res. Assocs, 74; plus others. Add: Dept. of English, Indiana University of Pennsylvania, Indiana, PA 15701.

FRICKE, DONNA GILLESPIE, b. Coatesville, Pa, Mar. 29, 43; m. 66; c. 1. EIGHTEENTH CENTURY LITERATURE. B.A, Gettysburg Col, 65; M.A, Pa. State Univ, University Park, 67, Ph.D.(Eng), 71. Instr. ENG, Pa. State Univ, University Park, 69-70; ASST. PROF, BOWLING GREEN STATE UNIV, 71- Contrib, MLA Bibliog, 67- MLA (mem. bibliog. comt, 69-); Tennyson Soc; Am. Soc. 18th Century Stud. Novel; satire; Swift. Publ: Ed, John William DeForest's Witching times, Bald Eagle, 71; co-auth, George Herbert: a recent bibliography, Seventeenth Century News, 68; auth, Tennyson's Hesperides, Tennyson Soc. Bull, 70. Add: Dept. of English, Bowling Green State University, Bowling Green, OH 43403.

FRIED, HARVEY, b. Brooklyn, N.Y, Mar. 4, 28. ENGLISH. B.A, Brooklyn Col, 49; M.A, Ind. Univ, 51; Ph.D.(Eng), N.Y. Univ. 59. Instr. ENG, Wash. Univ, 55-56; N.Y. Univ, 57-59; QUEENS COL.(N.Y), 59-66, asst. prof, 66-74, ASSOC. PROF, 74- U.S.A, 53-55. MLA. Shakespeare; Elizabethan drama. Add: Dept. of English, Queens College, Flushing, NY 11367.

FRIED, LEWIS FREDRICK, b. New York, N.Y, Jan. 29, 43. AMERICAN LITERATURE. B.A, Queens Col.(N.Y), 64, univ. fel, 65, M.A, 66; univ. fel, Univ. Mass, 67-68, NDEA fel, 68-69, Ph.D.(Am. lit), 69. Asst. ed. fiction, Tower Publ, 66; copy-ed, Mass. Rev, 66; pub. serv. intern, Commonwealth Serv. Corps of Mass, summer 67; instr. Eng, Off. Econ. Opportunity, summer 68; ASST. PROF. AM. LIT, KENT STATE UNIV, 69- Vis. prof, Int. Grad. Ctr. Hebrew & Judaica, World Union Jewish Stud, Israel, 73-74. American literary naturalism; American proletarian fiction; American-Jewish literature. Publ: Document of rage, In: The middle of the country, Avon, 70; James T. Farrell: shadow and act, Jahrbuch Amerikastud, 72; The disinherited: the worker as writer, New Lett, fall 72; plus others. Add: Dept. of English, Kent State University, Kent, OH 44242.

FRIED, MARTIN B, b. New York, N.Y, Mar. 2, 08; m. 42; c. 4. ENGLISH. B.S, State Univ. N.Y. Col. Buffalo; A.M, Harvard, 31; Ph.D, Univ. Chicago, 51. Instr, high schs, N.Y, 31-46; asst. prof. ENG, Mohawk Col, 46-47, assoc. prof, 47-48; asst. prof, STATE UNIV. N.Y. COL. BUFFALO, 48-49, assoc. prof, 49-51, PROF, 51- U.S.A.A.F, 43-45. American literature and novel; Mark Twain. Publ: Mark Twain's Roughing it; sources, composition, success; Mark Twain in Buffalo, Buffalo Hist. Soc, 59; Mark Twain on the art of writing, Salisbury Club, 61; Hy Slocum, Carl Byng, and Mark Twain, winter 70 & Mark Twain as editor: the Courier vs. the Express, summer 72, Niagara Frontier. Add: Dept. of English, State University of New York College at Buffalo, 1300 Elmwood Ave, Buffalo, NY 14222.

FRIEDENBERG, ROBERT VICTOR, b. Washington, D.C, Sept. 9, 43. AMERICAN PUBLIC ADDRESS, RHETORICAL THEORY. B.S, Towson State Col, 65; M.A, Temple Univ, 67, Ph.D.(speech), 70. Asst. prof. SPEECH COMMUN, MIAMI UNIV, 70-74, ASSOC. PROF, 74- Speech Commun. Asn; Am. Forensic Asn; Orgn. Am. Hist; Inst. Early Am. Hist. & Cult; Cent. States Speech Commun. Asn.(outstanding young teacher award, 74). Early American political rhetoric; contemporary political rhetoric; argumentation and debate theory. Publ: John A. J. Creswell of Maryland: reformer in the post office, Md. Hist. Mag, summer 69; America's most widely read speech teachers: the brothers McGuffey, Speech Teacher, 3/72; The constitution in debate, In: America in controversy, W.C. Brown, 73. Add: Dept. of Communication & Theatre, Miami University, Oxford, OH 45056.

FRIEDERICH, WERNER PAUL, German & Comparative Literature. See Volume III, Foreign Languages, Linguistics & Philology.

FRIEDERICH, WILLARD JULIUS, b. Summerfield, Ill, Apr. 6, 16; m. 40; c. 2. DRAMA, SPEECH. A.B, McKendree Col, 38; univ. fel, Univ. Ill, 38-40, A.M, 39; Penfield fel, N.Y. Univ, 40-41; Northwest. Univ, 43. Instr. speech & Eng, Univ. Ill, 41-43; asst. prof. speech & drama, Dakota Wesleyan Univ, 43-45; drama, Carroll Col, 45-46; from assoc. prof. to PROF. DRAMA & SPEECH, MARIETTA COL, 46- Ed, bk rev. sect, Dramatics Mag, 53-62. Speech Commun. Asn; Am. Theatre Asn. Dramatic production and history; stage design; interpretation. Publ: High-school drama course, Nat. Thespian Soc, 58; co-auth, Scenery design for amateur stage, 50 & Teaching speech in high schools, 53, Macmillan; contrib, Oral interpretation and the teaching of English, NCTE, 69. Add: Dept. of Drama & Speech, Marietta College, Marietta, OH 45750.

FRIEDLAENDER, MARC, History, Literature. See Volume I, History.

FRIEDMAN, ALAN, b. New York, N.Y, Jan. 4, 28. ENGLISH. B.A, Harvard, 49; M.A, Columbia Univ, 50; Ph.D.(Eng. lit), Univ. Calif, Berkeley, 64. Instr. ENG, Queens Col, 57-59; lectr, Univs. Cagliari & Rome, Italy, 59-61; acting instr. & assoc, Univ. Calif, Berkeley, 61-65; asst. prof, Columbia Univ, 65-67; assoc. prof, Swarthmore Col, 67-70; VIS. ASSOC. PROF, QUEENS COL. (N.Y), 73- PEN Club. Modern fiction. Publ: The turn of the novel: the transition to modern fiction, Oxford, 66, Galaxy, 70; Hermaphrodeity, Knopf, New York & Jonathan Cape, London, 72. The stream of conscience as a form in fiction, Hudson Rev, winter 64-65; The other Lawrence, Partisan Rev, 70; The novel, In: The twentieth century mind, Vol. 1: 1900-1918, Oxford, 72. Add: 86 W. 12th St, New York, NY 10011.

FRIEDMAN, ALBERT BARRON, b. Kansas City, Mo, Aug. 16, 20. ENGLISH PHILOLOGY. A.B, Univ. Mo, 41; Shattuck & Derby fels, Harvard, 41-42, Ph.D, 52; Oxford, 46; Fulbright fel, Univ. London, 51-52. Instr. ENG, Harvard, 52-55, asst. prof, 55-60; assoc. prof, CLAREMONT GRAD. SCH, 60-62, prof, 62-69, WILLIAM STARKE ROSECRANS III PROF, 69- Guggenheim fel, 58-59, 65-66; lectr. comp. lit, Univ. Paris, 59; medieval lit, Univ. Calif, Los Angeles, 62-63; Am. Counc. Learned Soc. grants, 62, 66; supvr, Eng. Inst, Columbia Univ, 64-67; ed, Western Folklore, 66-; Nat. Endowment for Humanities sr. fel, 71-72. Legionnaire, Legion of Merit, 44; Royal Order of Phoenix; Royal Order of George I, Greece, 45, 47; Kaiser-i-Hind, Govt. India, 46; Int. Folklore Soc. Prize, 61. U.S.A, 42-46, Capt. MLA; Medieval Asn. Pac.(v.pres, 70-72); Int. Arthurian Soc; fel. Am. Folklore Soc.(ed, jour, 59); Mediaeval Acad. Am. Medieval literature; folklore; cultural history of the 18th and 19th centuries. Publ: Folk ballads of the English speaking world, Viking, 56; The ballad revival, Univ. Chicago, 61; Ywain and Gawain, Oxford, 64; co-auth, Creativity in graduate education, Claremont Col, 64; contrib, American folk legend, Univ. Calif, 71. Add: Dept. of English, McManus Hall, Claremont Graduate School, Claremont, CA 91711.

FRIEDMAN, ARTHUR, b. Maroa, Ill, Dec. 13, 06; m. 57; c. 2. ENGLISH LITERATURE. A.B, Univ. Calif, Los Angeles, 28; Ph.D, Univ. Chicago, 38. Res. asst. Eng, UNIV. CHICAGO, 32-35, instr. humanities, 35-39, ENG, 39-42, asst. prof, 42-46, assoc. prof, 46-52, prof, 52-71, DISTINGUISHED SERV. PROF, 71-, chmn. dept. 60-63. Guggenheim fel, 57-58; chmn. Eng. selection comt, Woodrow Wilson Dissertation Fel. Prog, 62-65, 66-67; ed, Mod. Philol, 67-73. MLA. Eighteenth century English literature and bibliography. Publ: Co-auth, English literature, 1660-1800: a bibliography of modern studies, Vols. II & III, Princeton, 50-62; ed, Collected works of Oliver Goldsmith, 5 vols, Oxford, Clarendon, 66, Goldsmith's She stoops to conquer, 68 & Goldsmith's The vicar of Wakefield, 74, Oxford. Add: Dept. of English, University of Chicago, Chicago, IL 60637.

FRIEDMAN, BARTON ROBERT, b. Brooklyn, N.Y, Feb. 5, 35; m. 58; c. 4. ENGLISH. B.A, Cornell Univ, 56, Cornell Univ-Woodrow Wilson fel, 60, Ph.D.(Eng), 64; M.A, Univ. Conn, 58. Instr. ENG, Bowdoin Col, 61-63; UNIV. WIS-MADISON, 63-65, asst. prof, 65-71, ASSOC. PROF, 71- Alumni res. fund summer grants, 63 & 66. MLA; Am. Comt. Irish Stud. The Irish literary revival; modern prose romance; 19th century literature. Publ: To tell the sun from the druid fire: imagery of good and evil in The ring and the book, Stud. Eng. Lit, autumn 66; William Blake to James Stephens: the crooked road, Eire-Ireland, fall 66; Returning to Ireland's fountains: nationalism and James Stephens, Ariz. Quart, autumn, 66. Add: Dept. of English, University of Wisconsin-Madison, Madison, WI 53706.

FRIEDMAN, DONALD M, b. New York, N.Y, Apr. 8, 29; m. 59; c. 2. ENGLISH. B.A, Columbia Univ, 49; Henry fel, Cambridge, 49, Fulbright fel, 50, Leigh fel, 51-53, M.A, 58; Ph.D, Harvard, 60. Teaching fel, Harvard, 56-60, instr. ENG, 60-61; asst. prof, UNIV. CALIF, BERKELEY, 61-67, assoc. prof, 67-73, PROF, 73- U.S.A, 54-56. MLA; Renaissance Soc. Am; Milton Soc. Am. Tudor poetry; 17th century poetry. Publ: Marvell's pastoral art, Routledge & Kegan Paul, 70; Lycidas: the swain's paideia, In:

Milton studies, Univ. Pittsburgh, Vol. III, 71; Memory and the art of salvation in Donne's Good Friday poem, Eng. Lit. Renaissance, 73. Add: Dept. of English, University of California, Berkeley, CA 94720.

FRIEDMAN, JOEL JOSEPH, b. New York, N.Y, Apr. 24, 21; m. 47. THEATRE, PLAYWRIGHTING. B.F.C, Univ. Calif, 44; M.A, Smith Col, 48. Instr. Eng, Mills Col. Educ, 63; asst. prof. THEATRE, TEMPLE UNIV, 67-71, ASSOC. PROF, 71- Dir. var. theatres, 50- Sig.C, U.S.A, 42-46, T/Sgt. Applied psychoanalysis; 19th century English literature and painting. Publ: Co-auth, Chorus in Sophocles' Oedipus Tyrannus, 50, Orestes, 51 & Odysseus: the return of the primal father, 52, Psychoanal. Quart. Producer, The tribe of O, Temple Univ, 72. Add: 80 First Ave, New York, NY 10009.

FRIEDMAN, JOHN BLOCK, b. Troy, N.Y, Dec. 8, 34; m. 62; c. 2. MEDIEVAL ENGLISH LITERATURE. B.A, Reed Col, 60; Woodrow Wilson jr. fel, Johns Hopkins Univ, 60-61, M.A, 61; Ph.D.(Eng), Mich. State Univ, 65. Asst. prof. ENG, Conn. Col, 65-68; Sir George Williams Univ, 68-69, assoc. prof, 69-71; PROF, UNIV. ILL, URBANA, 71- Res, Ctr. Study Medieval Civilization, Poitiers, France, 73. MLA (secy, lit. & arts, 68-69, chmn, 69-70); Mediaeval Acad. Am. Medieval literature and iconography; survival of the classics. Publ: Orpheus in the Middle Ages, Harvard Univ, 70; Antichrist and the iconography of Dante's Geryon, J. Warburg & Courtauld Insts, 72; The Nun's Priest's tale: the preacher and the mermaid's song, Chaucer Rev, 73; plus others. Add: Dept. of English, University of Illinois, Urbana, IL 61801.

FRIEDMAN, JOSEPH RICHARD, Military History. See Volume I, History.

FRIEDMAN, LENEMAJA, b. Nubruck, Ger, Oct. 9, 24; U.S. citizen; m. 49; c. 4. ENGLISH LITERATURE. B.A, Univ. Wash, 46; M.A, State Univ. N.Y. Albany, 66; Ph.D.(Eng. lit), Fla. State Univ, 69; summers, Cornell Univ, 62; State Univ. N.Y. Col. Oneonta, 63; State Univ. N.Y. Col. New Paltz, 68. Teacher Eng, Roxbury High Sch, N.Y, 60-61; Margaretville High Sch, 61-65; New Paltz High Sch, 65-67; asst. freshman Eng, Fla. State Univ, 68-69; ASSOC. PROF. ENG. LIT, COLUMBUS COL, 69- AAUP; S.Atlantic Mod. Lang. Asn; NCTE; Conf. Col. Compos. & Commun. Restoration and 18th century theater; 18th century literature, especially Swift; American literature. Publ: Shirley Jackson, Twayne, (in press); Bibliography of Restoration and 18th century plays containing children's roles, Restoration & 18th Century Theatre Res, 5/72. Add: Dept. of Language & Humanities, Columbus College, Columbus, GA 31907.

FRIEDMAN, MARTIN BORIS, b. New York, N.Y, June 12, 34; m. 60; c. 3. ENGLISH, COMPARATIVE LITERATURE. A.B, Dartmouth Col, 55; dipl, Univ. Sorbonne, 56; Ph.D.(comp. lit), Yale, 62. Instr. ENG, Trinity Col. (Conn), 61-62; lectr, Univ. Paris, 62-63; asst. prof, Tufts Univ, 63-69; ASSOC. PROF, CALIF. STATE UNIV, HAYWARD, 69- MLA; Am. Comp. Lit. Asn. English and French romanticism; 19th century literary criticism. Publ: Ed, Alfred de Vigny, Chatterton, Marcel Didier, Paris, 67 & Aldous Huxley, Brave new world, Librarie Bordas, Paris, 70. Add: Dept. of English, California State University, Hayward, 25800 Hillary St, Hayward, CA 94542.

FRIEDMAN, MELVIN JACK, b. Brooklyn, N.Y, Mar. 7, 28; m. 58; c. 2 ENGLISH, COMPARATIVE LITERATURE. A.B, Bard Col, 49; Fulbright fel, Univ. Lyon, France, 50-51; A.M, Columbia Univ, 52; univ. fel, Yale, 51-52, Jr. Sterling fel, 52-54, Am. Counc. Learned Soc. sr. fel, 52-53, Ph.D.(comp. lit), 54. Assoc. ed, French Stud, Yale, 51-53; assoc. prof. COMP. LIT, Univ. Md, 62-66; PROF, UNIV. WIS-MILWAUKEE, 66- Mem. ed. bd, J. Popular Cult, 71-, Renascence, 72-; vis. sr. fel, Univ. E.Anglia, spring 72. U.S.A, 54-56. MLA. Twentieth century novel; 20th century literary criticism. Publ: Ed, Configuration critique de Samuel Beckett, 64 & co-ed, Configuration critique de William Styron, 67 & co-auth, Calepin de bibliographie Samuel Beckett, 71, Lett. Mod; co-ed, The added dimension, 66 & ed, The vision obscured, 70, Fordham Univ; ed, Samuel Beckett now, Univ. Chicago, 70; co-ed, The shaken realist, La. State Univ, 70; co-ed, William Styron's The confessions of Nat Turner, Wadsworth, 70; auth, Novels of Samuel Beckett: an amalgam of Joyce and Proust, Comp. Lit, 60; Samuel Beckett and the Nouveau Roman, Wis. Stud. Contemporary Lit, 60; William Styron: an interim appraisal, Eng. J, 61. Add: Dept. of Comparative Literature, University of Wisconsin-Milwaukee, Milwaukee, WI 53201.

FRIEDMAN, MURIEL SANDEROW, b. Chicago, Ill; m. 41. ENGLISH EDUCATION, BIBLIOGRAPHY. B.S, Loyola Univ. Chicago, 65, fel, 65-72, M.A, 67, Ph.D.(Eng), 74. Asst. to ed, Restoration & 18th Century Theatre Res, 67-72; INSTR. ENG. & EVE. CHMN. DEPT, KENNEDY-KING COL, 72- MLA; NCTE; Conf. Col. Compos. & Commun; Col. Eng. Asn. The plays of John O'Keeffe; history of drama and bibliography. Publ: Co-ed, Index, Bibliography of medieval drama, Frederick Ungar, Vol. II, 72. Add: 4300 Marine Dr, Chicago, IL 60613.

FRIEDMAN, NORMAN, b. Boston, Mass, Apr. 10, 25; m. 45; c. 2. ENGLISH. A.B, Harvard, 48, A.M, 49, fel, 50-52, Ph.D.(Eng), 52. Instr. ENG, Univ. Conn, 52-57, asst. prof, 57-61, assoc. prof, 61-63; vis. assoc. prof, QUEENS COL.(N.Y), 63-64, assoc. prof, 64-67, PROF, 68- Am. Counc. Learned Soc. grants, 59 & 60; Fulbright lectr, Univs. Nantes & Nice, 66-67; consult, PMLA. Bowdoin Prize, 48; Northwest Rev. annual poetry prize, 63; Borestone Mountain poetry awards, 64, 67. U.S.N.R, 43-46, Lt.(jg). MLA; NCTE; AAUP. Literary criticism and critical theory; Victorian poetry; modern English and American literature. Publ: E.E. Cummings: the art of his poetry, Johns Hopkins Univ, 60; co-auth, Poetry: an introduction to its form and art, Harper, 61 & Logic, rhetoric, and style, Little, 63; auth, E.E. Cummings: the growth of a writer, South. Ill. Univ, 64; ed, E.E. Cummings: a collection of critical essays, Prentice-Hall, 72; auth, Newman, Aristotle, & the new criticism, PMLA, 6/66; The Wesleyan poets, 4 parts, Chicago Rev, 7/66, fall 66, spring 67 & 6/67; From Victorian to modern, Victorian newsletter, fall 67. Add: Dept. of English, Queens College, Flushing, NY 11367.

FRIEDMAN, PHILIP ALLAN, b. Brooklyn, N.Y, July 19, 27. ENGLISH LITERATURE, AMERICAN PHILOSOPHY. B.A, N.Y. Univ, 48; Columbia Univ, 49; Fulbright grant & cert. ling. & philol, Univ. Heidelberg, 54-55. Reporter & bk. reviewer, Jewish Examiner, 48-49; prod. asst, Toby Press, N.Y.C, 50-51; asst. ed, Random House, Inc, N.Y.C, 51-52; instr. Eng. compos. & contemporary lit, Wayne State Univ, 53-54, 55-58; ASSOC. PROF. AM. LIT. & STUD, CALIF. STATE UNIV, LOS ANGELES, 59- Consult, State Dept. Comt. on For. Visitors, Mich, 53-54, 55-58; consult. & mem. bd, Jewish Community Libr, Jewish Fed. Counc. Greater Los Angeles, 72- U.S.N, 45-46, Res, 46-63, Lt.(j.g). AAUP. American literature and culture; philosophy of science. Publ: Co-ed, The man from main street: a Sinclair Lewis reader, selected essays, Random, 53; contrib, Studies in Babbitt, C.E. Merrill, 71; auth, In retrospect: Sinclair Lewis, 71 & The disunited States pursues the exotic, 72, Twentieth Century; plus others. Add: Dept. of English, California State University, Los Angeles, 5151 State University Dr, Los Angeles, CA 90032.

FRIEDMAN, ROBERT PHILLIP, b. Stuttgart, Ark, Feb. 17, 26; m. 64; c. 3. RHETORIC & PUBLIC ADDRESS. B.A, Univ. N.C, 48; M.A, Univ. Mo, 50, Ph.D.(speech), 54. Instr. SPEECH, Dartmouth Col, 54-55; asst. prof, Purdue Univ, 55-58; Univ. Mo, 58-61, assoc. prof, 61-64, prof, 64-65; vis. prof, UNIV. ORE, 65-66, PROF, 66- U.S.N.R, 43-46, Res, 46-59, Lt.(jg). Speech Commun. Asn; Cent. States Speech Asn.(ed. jour, 64-67); Nat. Univ. Exten. Asn.(co-ed, Forensic Quart, 65-70); West. Speech Commun. Asn.(ed, West. Speech, 71-73); History and criticism of American public address debate; freedom of speech; ethics of persuasion. Publ: Co-ed, Foreign aid: discussion and debate manual, 66, Combating Crime: discussion and debate manual, 67, Compulsory service systems: discussion and debate manual, 68 & co-ed, Military commitments: discussion and debate manual, 69, Artcraft; auth, Arthur M. Hyde: articulate antagonist, Mo. Hist. Rev, 61; The products of debate activities: habits of mind, Forensic Quart, 69; Reflections of an incompetent judge, J. Am. Forensic Asn, 72. Add: Dept. of Speech, University of Oregon, Eugene, OR 97403.

FRIEDMAN, SIDNEY JOSEPH, b. Des Moines, Iowa, June 8, 39; m. 62; c. 2. ENGLISH, DRAMA. A.B, Princeton, 61; univ. fel. & M.A, Univ. Iowa, 63, Ph.D.(speech & drama), 66. ASSOC. PROF. ENG. & DRAMA, WASH. UNIV, 66- Am. Theatre Asn. Acting; directing; dramatic criticism. Add: Dept. of English, Washington University, St. Louis, MO 63130.

FRIEDRICH, GERHARD GUNTER, b. Graudenz, Ger, Feb. 4, 16; m. 47; c. 1. ENGLISH & COMPARATIVE LITERATURE. A.B, Guilford Col, 42; Univ. N.C. & Columbia Univ, 45-46; Brown fel. & A.M, Haverford Col, 47; Ph.D, Univ. Minn, 51. Instr. Eng. & Am. lit, Pa. State Univ, 47-49; Univ. Minn, 49-51; asst. prof. Eng, Haverford Col, 51-58; prof. & head dept, Cedar Crest Col, 58-61; prof. & chmn. dept. Eng. & chmn. div. humanities, Calif. State Univ, Fullerton, 61-64; ASSOC. DEAN & DEAN ACAD. PROG. & RESOURCE PLANNING, OFF. CHANCELLOR, CALIF. STATE UNIV. & COLS, 64- Chmn, Col. Entrance Exam. Bd. Advan. Placement Lit. & Eng. Compos. Comt, 58; pres, Eng. Counc, Calif. State Univ. & Cols, 62-64; pres, Calif. Coun. Teachers Eng, 63-64; mem, Nat. Surv. Undergrad. Prog. Eng. Adv. Comt, 64-; mem-at-large, Comn. Higher Educ, 68- NCTE (dir, 62-, chmn. comt. comp & world lit, 71-). Emerson; Melville; Joyce; Japanese literature. Publ: In pursuit of Moby Dick: Melville's image of man, Pendle Hill, 58; co-auth, High school-college articulation of English, NCTE, 63; auth, A course in advanced placement English (2 vols), Univ. Nebr, 64, 65; A major influence on Theodore Dreiser's The bulwark, Am. Lit, 5/57; The perspective of Joyce's Dubliners, Col. Eng, 3/65; The English teacher and the process of communication, Eng. J, 1/66; plus others. Add: Office of the Chancellor, California State University & Colleges, 5670 Wilshire Blvd, Los Angeles, CA 90036.

FRIEDRICH, GUSTAV WILLIAM, b. Hastings, Nebr, Mar. 2, 41; m. 62; c. 1. SPEECH COMMUNICATION. B.A, Univ. Minn, Minneapolis, 64; M.A, Univ. Kans, 67, Ph.D.(speech commun), 68. Teacher, St. John's Lutheran Sch, Minn, 61-62; ASSOC. PROF. COMMUN, PURDUE UNIV, W.LAFAYETTE, 68- Am. Educ. Res. Asn; Cent. States Speech Asn.(Outstanding Young Teacher Award, 70); Int. Commun. Asn; Speech Commun. Asn.(planner & participant, nat. conf. of teacher educ. in speech commun, 71-73, chmn. instrn. develop. interest group, 73-74). Classroom communication; interpersonal communication; experimental research methodology. Publ: Co-auth, Teaching speech communication in the secondary school, Houghton, 73; auth, An empirical explication of a concept of self-reported speech anxiety, 70 & Verbal and non-verbal correlates of human leave-taking behavior, 73, Speech Monogr, Affect and interpersonal attraction: a comparison of trait and state measures, J. Personality & Social Psychol, 73. Add: Dept. of Communication, Purdue University, 307B Heavilon Hall, West Lafayette, IN 47907.

FRIEDRICH, WALTER GEORGE, b. Knoxville, Tenn, Mar. 2, 97; m. 32. ENGLISH. Concordia Col, 16-18; A.B, Ind. Univ, 20; A.M, Columbia Univ, 23; Ph.D, Johns Hopkins Univ, 34. Instr. Eng, Ky. Mil. Inst, 20-22; univ. exten, Columbia Univ, 22-23; mod. langs, Univ. Rochester, 23-24; asst. prof, Univ. Md, 24-29; ENG, Univ. Pittsburgh, 29-33; instr, Johns Hopkins Univ, 34-36; PROF, VALPARAISO UNIV, 36-, dean fac. & col. arts & sci, 38-46, acting pres, 39-40. U.S.A, 17-18, 2nd Lt. MLA. English literary history; Elizabethan non-dramatic literature. Add: 303 Washington St, Valparaiso, IN 46383.

FRIEDSON, ANTHONY M, b. Shoreham, Eng, June 13, 24; div; c. 2. ENGLISH. A.B, Simpson Col, 51; M.A, State Univ. Iowa, 55, Ph.D.(Eng), 59. Asst. ENG, State Univ. Iowa, 52-56; lectr, Ind. Univ, 57-58; instr, Univ. B.C, 58-63; asst. prof, UNIV. HAWAII, MANOA, 63-67, ASSOC. PROF, 67- R.A.F, 43-47, Flight Sgt. MLA. Restoration and 18th century literature, especially Restoration comedy and early fiction; modern British fiction and drama. Publ: Literature through the ages, Sterling, 64; Let's pan a magazine, Can. Lit, winter 60; Wycherley and Molière: satirical point of view in The plain dealer, Mod. Philol, 2/67. Add: Dept. of English, University of Hawaii at Manoa, Honolulu, HI 96822.

FRIEND, ALBERT CHARLES, b. Milwaukee, Wis, July 14, 06. LITERATURE. A.B, Harvard, 27, A.M, 29; Ph.D, Oxford, 36. Teaching fel. Eng, N.Y. Univ, 31-34; from instr. to prof, City Col. New York, 36-73; RETIRED. Fulbright res. grant, 50-51. MLA; Mediaeval Acad. Am. Middle English; Latin literature of the Middle Ages. Publ: The proverbs of Serlo of Wilton, Mediaeval Stud, 54; Medieval Latin literature, In: The medieval literature of Western Europe, N.Y. Univ, 66; The captive bird in Chaucer's Squire's tale, Medievalia Humanistica, 69; plus others. Add: 768 Madison Ave, New York, NY 10021.

FRIEND, JEWELL ANNE, b. New York, N.Y, Feb. 15, 23; wid. ENGLISH, LINGUISTICS. A.B, Univ. Miami, 59; A.M, Tulane Univ, 60; Ph.D.(Eng, educ), South. Ill. Univ, Carbondale, 70. Mem. fac. Eng, Stephens Col, 60-67; ASSOC. PROF. ENG. & ASSOC. DIR. UNDERGRAD. STUD. ENG. & LING, SOUTH. ILL. UNIV, CARBONDALE, 67- Fel. ling. inst, Univ. Mich, Ann Arbor, summer 71. U.S.C.G, 42-45. Ling. Soc. Am; Conf. Eng. Educ; NCTE; Teachers Eng. to Speakers Other Lang; Conf. Col. Compos. & Commun. Teacher training in English education; English as a foreign or second language; applied linguistics. Publ: Writing English as a second language, Scott, 71; contrib, TESOL Quart, Eng. J, Col. Compos. & Commun, Eng. Forum & var. poetry jour. Add: Dept. of English, Southern Illinois University, Carbondale, IL 62901.

FRIERSON, JAMES WRIGHT, b. Gainesville, Tex, Sept. 8, 06; m. 43; c. 2. ENGLISH. A.B, Tulane Univ, 29, LL.B, 33; Ph.D, Stanford Univ, 53. Asst. Stanford Univ, 48-49, acting instr, 49-50; asst. prof, ENG, UNIV. HAWAII, MANOA, 50-60, assoc. prof, 60-72, EMER. ASSOC. PROF, 72- Res. fel, Yale, 56-57. U.S.N, 42-45, Lt. Comdr. MLA; Mod. Humanities Res. Asn; Victorian Soc. Nineteenth century literary criticism; history of the development of Matthew Arnold's criticism; Matthew Arnold and French culture. Publ: Matthew Arnold, philosophe, Stud. Voltaire & 18th Century, 63; The strayed reveller of Fox How, Victorian Poetry, summer 67. Add: Dept. of English, University of Hawaii at Manoa, Honolulu, HI 96822.

FRIES, MAUREEN HOLMBERG, b. Buffalo, N.Y, July 14, 31; m. 53; c. 4. ENGLISH LITERATURE. A.B, D'Youville Col, 52; M.A, Cornell Univ, 53; N.Y. State fel, State Univ. N.Y. Buffalo, 67-68, Ph.D.(Eng), 69. Instr. ENG, State Univ. N.Y. Buffalo, 64-69; asst. prof, STATE UNIV. N.Y. COL. FREDONIA, 69-73, ASSOC. PROF, 73-, summer res. fels, 71, 72. MLA; Am. Class. League; Int. Arthurian Soc. Medieval English literature; the political novel; women's studies. Publ: Co-ed, A bibliography of writings by and about British women authors, 1957-1969, Women's Caucus Mod. Lang, 71; auth, A historical analogue to the Shipman's tale?, Comitatus, 73; Feminism and antifeminism in Under western eyes, Conradiana, 73; 'Slydynge of corage': Chaucer's Criseyde as feminist and victim, In: An anthology of feminist criticism, Avon, 74; plus others. Add: Dept. of English, State University of New York College at Fredonia, Fredonia, NY 14063.

FRIES, PETER H, Linguistics, English Grammar. See Volume III, Foreign Languages, Linguistics & Philology.

FRIESNER, DONALD NEIL, b. West Rushville, Ohio, Dec. 24, 28; m. 67; c. 1. ENGLISH & AMERICAN LITERATURE. LL.B, LaSalle Exten. Univ, 58; A.B, Ohio Univ, 62; M.A, Univ. Calif, Davis, 65; Ph.D.(Eng), Univ. Calif, Los Angeles, 73. Teaching asst. ENG, Univ. Calif, Davis, 63-64; instr, Westmont Col, 65-67; ASST. PROF, GENEVA COL, 70- U.S.A, 51-53. MLA; Renaissance Soc. Am; Shakespeare Asn. Am; Brontë Soc; Conf. Christianity & Lit. Shakespearean drama; English Renaissance poetry; Victorian poetry. Publ: Stranger on this planet, Comet, 59; Ellis Bell and Israfel, Brontë Soc. Trans, 64; William Shakespeare, conservative, Shakespeare Quart, spring 69. Add: 513 Blackhawk Rd, Beaver Falls, PA 15010.

FRIMAN, ANNE ELIZABETH, b. Seneca, S.Dak, June 3, 16. ENGLISH. B.S, North. State Col, 38; fel, Marquette Univ, 57-58, M.A, 58; fel, Univ. Tenn, 59-61, Ph.D.(Eng), 64. Instr. ENG, Univ. Tenn, 61-62, 63-64; asst. prof, Knoxville, Col, 62-63; Marquette Univ, 64-65; Cent. Wash. State Col, 65-67; assoc. prof, SOUTHEAST. LA. UNIV, 67-73, PROF, 73- Medieval English literature; American novel, 1900-1930. Publ: Determinism and point of view in The house of mirth, Papers Eng. Lang. & Lit, spring 66. Add: Dept. of English, Southeastern Louisiana University, Hammond, LA 70401.

FRITH, MAY BEATRICE, Can. citizen. ENGLISH. B.A, Univ. London, 61; M.A, Columbia Univ, 63. Teacher, Launiston Primary Sch, London, Eng, 56-60; res. asst. & teacher lang. develop, Inst. Develop. Stud, N.Y, 62-64; lectr. Eng, Fac. Educ, Univ. West Indies, 64-67; asst. prof. ENG. & EDUC, McGILL UNIV, 67-70, ASSOC. PROF, 70- Can. rep, Int. Conf. Teaching & Learning Eng, York Univ, 71. Can. Counc. Teachers Eng; NCTE (mem. comt. 100+, 72-74); Can. Asn. Univ. Teachers; Asn. Teachers Eng. to Speakers Other Lang. Education; linguistics. Publ: Co-auth, Teaching English to non-native speakers, 70 & Handwriting in the language arts, 72, Dept. Educ. P.Q; auth, Developing a course in the teaching of English as a second language, Elem. Eng, 1/73. Add: Faculty of Education, McGill University, 3700 McTavish St, Montreal, P.Q, Can.

FRITZ, EDWARD McDONEL, b. Baltimore, Md, Apr. 10, 19. ENGLISH, HISTORY OF IDEAS. A.B, Dartmouth Col, 40; Middlebury Col, summer 40; Harvard, 40-41; M.A, Univ. Chicago, 42; scholar, Johns Hopkins Univ, 43-44. Instr. Eng, Amherst Col, 45-46; Wesleyan Univ, 46-48; Overseas Div, Univ. Md, 50-53; asst. prof. Eng. & philos, East. Col, 53-60, dean lib. arts, 60-70, acad. v.pres, 69-70; ASSOC. PROF. ENG, UNIV. BALTIMORE, 70-, V.PRES. STUD. SERV, 72- Nat. Asn. Stud. Personnel Adminr. Add: University of Baltimore, 1420 N. Charles St, Baltimore, MD 21201.

FRITZELL, PETER ALGREN, b. Minneapolis, Minn, Aug. 23, 40; m. 62; c. 2. ENGLISH, HUMANITIES. B.A, Univ. N.Dak, 62; M.A, Stanford Univ, 66, Ph.D.(Eng. & humanities), 66. ASST. PROF. ENG, LAWRENCE UNIV, 66-, CHMN. DEPT, 73- Vis. lectr, NDEA Inst. Conceptual Approach Am. Hist, Lawrence Univ, summer 68; vis. asst. prof. humanities, Stanford Univ, summer 68, 74, Nat. Endowment for Humanities fel, 72-73; vis. scholar environ. stud, Dartmouth Col, 72-73; vis. lectr, Univ. Wis-Green Bay, 74. MLA; Am. Stud. Asn. American literature of the 17th and 18th centuries, especially descriptive prose; nature writing. Publ: The wilderness and the garden, Forest Hist, 4/68; auth, Introd, Henry Wansey's Journal of an excursion, 1794, 69 & H.B. Möllhausen's Diary of a journey (2 vols), 69, Johnson Reprint. Add: Dept. of English, Lawrence University, Appleton, WI 54911.

FROGNER, ELLEN A, b. Sargeant, Minn, May 24, 06. ENGLISH, ENGLISH EDUCATION. B.S, Univ. Minn, 27, M.A, 33, Ph.D.(Eng. educ), 38. Teacher, high schs, Minn. & Mich, 27-32, 35-38; mem. faculty, Eng. & Eng. educ, Chicago Teachers Col, 38-43, 46-49; asst. prof. Eng. educ, Univ. Man, 43-46; Eng. & Eng. educ, Univ. Minn, Duluth, 49-52, assoc. prof, 52-59; prof. Eng. & chmn. dept, Univ. Sch, South. Ill. Univ, Carbondale, 59-67, prof,

ENG. & ENG. EDUC, HUMANITIES DIV, SOUTH ILL. UNIV, EDWARDSVILLE, 67-70, EMER. PROF, 70- Chmn. comt, jr. high sch, reading list, NCTE, 50-56, mem. comt, reading in sec. schs, 68- Conf. Res. Eng; NCTE; Nat. Educ. Asn. Language—sentence structure and attitudes; Indian folklore, especially Chippewa folk tales and cultural background. Publ: Comt. chmn, Your reading, NCTE, 54; co-auth, The adventures of Eagle Wing, Greenwich Bk, 56 & Ojibwa myths and legends, Ross & Haines, 62; auth, The language inquiry, 69, Using the Language inquiry, 69 & A study of responses to the Language inquiry, 69, Univ. Ill; Problems of sentence structure in pupils' themes, 11/33 & Grammar approach versus thought approach in teaching sentence structure, 9/39, Eng. J; co-auth, Indian Cinderella, Child Life, 6-7/63. Add: 128 Robinson Dr, Prescott, AZ 86301.

FROHNEN, RICHARD GENE, b. Omaha, Nebr, Mar. 26, 30; m. 58; c. 2. JOURNALISM. B.A, Calif. State Col, Los Angeles, 54, M.S, 61. Pub. relat. dir, First Congregational Church Los Angeles, 53-54, 58-59; reporter & relig. ed, Los Angeles Times, 59-61; from instr. to asst. prof. jour, East. Mont. Col, 61-65, dean men, 62-65; Sunday mag. ed, Spokesman-Rev, Wash, 65-67; from asst. prof. to ASSOC. PROF. JOUR, UNIV. NEV, RENO, 67- Dir, Great West. Exped, 58-; ed, The Scouter, Nev. Counc, Boy Scouts Am, 68-70; pub. relat. consult, Sch. Med. Sci, Univ. Nev, Reno, 69-; ed, Health News, 69-72, co-ed, 72- U.S.A.F, 50-51; U.S.M.C, 54-58, Res, 58-, Lt. Col. Asn. Educ. in Jour; Int. Commun. Asn; Int. Platform Asn. Journalism and society; public opinion formation and persuasion; reporting and editing. Publ: Ed, Life and health sciences library, 70 & ed, Health sciences program, 71, Univ. Nev, Reno; co-ed, Journalism and society, Seminar, 3/72. Add: Dept. of Journalism, University of Nevada, Reno, NV 89507.

FROKE, MARLOWE D, b. Vienna, S.Dak, Nov. 4, 27; m. 59; c. 2. JOURNALISM. B.S, S.Dak. State Col, 51; M.S, Northwest. Univ, 55. Instr. JOUR, Univ. Ill, 55-59; asst. prof, PA. STATE UNIV, UNIVERSITY PARK, 59-62, ASSOC. PROF, 62-, DIR. MEDIA & LEARNING RESOURCES, 70-, chmn. major in broadcasting, 60-70, dir. broadcasting, 65-70. U.S.A, 45-49. Asn. Prof. Broadcasting Educ. Radio and television journalism. Publ: Co-auth, The mass media, Pa. State Univ. Ctr. for Continuing Lib. Educ, 61; Pronunciation guide to place names in Pennsylvania, Pa. Asn. Broadcasters, 62. Add: Office of Continuing Education, 212 Keller Bldg, Pennsylvania State University, University Park, PA 16802.

FROMM, GLORIA GLIKIN, b. Newark, N.J, Nov. 14, 31. ENGLISH. B.A, N.Y. Univ, 52, M.A, 56, Am. Asn. Univ. Women fel, 59-60, Ph.D.(Eng), 61; Bread Loaf Sch. Eng, summers 52-54. Asst. ENG, sch. commerce, N.Y. Univ, 57-59; instr, Brooklyn Col, 61-65; asst. prof, 65-70; ASSOC. PROF, UNIV. ILL, CHICAGO CIRCLE, 70- Am. Philos. Soc. grant-in-aid, summer 65; Am. Counc. Learned Soc. grant-in-aid, 67; City Univ. New York summer res. grant, 67. MLA. Twentieth century biography and autobiography. Publ: Dorothy M. Richardson: the personal Pilgrimage, PMLA, 12/63; Bibliography of Dorothy Richardson, Eng. Lit. Transition, spring 65; Through the novelist's looking-glass, Kenyon Rev, summer 69; plus one other. Add: Dept. of English, University of Illinois at Chicago Circle, Box 4348, Chicago, IL 60680.

FROMM, HAROLD, b. New York, N.Y, July 19, 33. ENGLISH, HUMANITIES. B.A, Brooklyn Col, 54; M.A, Columbia Univ, 56; Ph.D.(Eng), Univ. Wis, 62. Instr. ENG, Oakland Univ, 60-62; asst. prof, Wayne State Univ, 62-67; Brooklyn Col, 68-70; ASSOC. PROF, IND. UNIV. NORTHWEST, 70- Wayne State Univ. fac. res. grant, 66. Literary criticism; philosophy; music. Publ: Bernard Shaw and the theater in the nineties, Univ. Kans, 67; Spenserian jazz and the aphrodisiac of virtue, 66 & To the lighthouse: music and sympathy, 68, Eng. Miscellany; Emerson and Kierkegaard: the problem of historical Christianity, Mass. Rev, fall 68. Add: Dept. of English, Indiana University Northwest, Gary, IN 48408.

FROST, ORCUTT WILLIAM, JR, b. Cloquet, Minn, June 3, 26; m. 54. ENGLISH. Univ. fel, Univ. Ill, 49-51, 53-54, Ph.D.(Eng), 54; Fulbright scholar, France, 52-53. Instr. Eng, Willamette Univ, 54-56, asst. prof, 56-59, assoc. prof, 59-63; PROF. ENG, ALASKA METHODIST UNIV, 63-, dean. lib. arts, 63-71. U.S.A, 44-46. NCTE; MLA. Lafcadio Hearn; literature of the Northwest; Joaquin Miller. Publ: Young Hearn; Children of the levee, Univ. Ky, 57; Joaquin Miller, Twayne, 67; ed, Contemporary Alaskan literature, 69, Crosscultural arts in Alaska, 70 & Tales of Eskimo Alaska, 71, Alaska Methodist Univ. Add: Dept. of English, Alaska Methodist University, Anchorage, AK 99504.

FROST, WILLIAM, b. New York, N.Y, June 8, 17; m. 42; c. 3. ENGLISH. A.B, Bowdoin Col, 38; A.M, Columbia Univ, 42; Ph.D, Yale, 46; Instr. ENG, Carnegie Inst. Tech, 42-44; Yale, 46-47; asst. prof, Wesleyan Univ, 47-51; UNIV. CALIF, SANTA BARBARA, 51-55, assoc. prof, 55-61, PROF, 61-, acting chmn. dept, 65-66. Vis. assoc. prof, Yale, 58-59; Guggenheim fel, 59-60; Am. Counc. Learned Soc. res. grant, 66-67; Nat. Endowment for Humanities res. grant, 72-73; mem, Int. Fed. Mod. Lang. & Lit. Medieval Acad. Am; MLA. Comparative literature; English literature to 1750; age of Pope. Publ: Dryden and the art of translation, Yale, Univ, 55; assoc. ed, Pope's Homer, Methuen & Yale Univ, 67; co-ed, Dryden's works, Vol. IV, Univ. Calif, 74; auth, Dryden and satire, Stud. Eng. Lit, 71; What is a Canterbury tale?, West. Humanities Rev, 73; plus others. Add: Dept. of English, University of California, Santa Barbara, CA 93106.

FRUMAN, NORMAN, b. New York, N.Y, Dec. 2, 23; m. 58; c. 3. ROMANTICISM, AESTHETIC THEORY. B.A, City Col. N.Y, 46, M.A, Columbia Univ, 48; Univ. Paris, 50-51; Ph.D.(Eng), N.Y. Univ, 60. Instr. Eng, Teachers Col, Columbia Univ, 47-; City Col. N.Y, 47-50; ed. fiction; Best Syndicated Features, 51-55; res. & writing, 55-59; PROF. ENG, CALIF. STATE UNIV, LOS ANGELES, 59- Vis. prof. Eng, Univ. Tel-Aviv, 64-65; Univ. Clermont-Ferrand, 72-73; Univ. Nice, summer 73. U.S.A, 43-45, Lt; two Bronze Star Medals. MLA; Philol. Asn. Pac. Coast; AAUP. Early English Romanticism; aesthetic theory. Publ: Co-ed, J.D. Salinger: reviews, essays, critiques, Odyssey, 63; auth, Coleridge: the damaged archangel, Braziller, 71. Add: Dept. of English, California State University, Los Angeles, 5151 State University, Los Angeles, CA 90032.

FRUMKIN, GENE, b. New York, N.Y, Jan. 29, 28; m. 55; c. 2. ENGLISH. B.A, Univ. Calif, Los Angeles, 51. Asst. prof. ENG, UNIV. N.MEX, 66-71,

ASSOC. PROF, 71- MLA; AAUP. The writing of poetry and fiction; contemporary literature. Publ: The hawk and the lizard, Swallow, 63; The Rainbow-Walker, Grasshopper Press, 68; Dostoyevsky and other nature poems, Solo Press, 72; Locust cry: poems 1958-65, San Marcos Press, 73. Add: Dept. of English, University of New Mexico, Albuquerque, NM 87131.

FRUSHELL, RICHARD CLAYTON, b. Pittsburgh, Pa, Aug. 25, 35; m. 58; c. 5. ENGLISH. B.Ed, Duquesne Univ, 61, NDEA doctoral fel, 66-68, Ph.D.(Eng), 68; NDEA Inst. fel, Univ. Pittsburgh, summer 65. Teacher ENG, Oliver High Sch, Pittsburgh, Pa, 61-66; asst. prof, IND. STATE UNIV, TERRE HAUTE, 68-71, ASSOC. PROF, 71- Contrib, Annual Bibliog. Eng. Lang. & Lit, Mod. Humanities Res. Asn, 71- U.S.A.F, 54-58. Renaissance Soc. Am; Am. Soc. 18th Century Stud; Am. Soc. Theatre Res; MLA; Mod. Humanities Res. Asn; Johnson Soc. Cent. Region; Augustan Reprint Soc. Restoration and 18th century English literature; Renaissance English literature; drama. Publ: Ed, The case of Mrs. Clive submitted to the publick (1744), Augustan Reprint Soc, 73; auth, The textual relationship and biographical significance of two Petite pieces by Mrs. Catherine (Kitty) Clive, Restoration & Eighteenth Century Theatre Res, 70; Kitty Clive as dramatist, Durham Univ. J, 71; An incarnate nightmare: moral grotesquerie in The black cat, Poe Stud, 72. Add: Dept. of English, Indiana State University, Terre Haute, IN 47809.

FRY, CARROL LEE, b. New Hampton, Mo, July 31, 32; m. 57. ENGLISH. B.S, Northwest Mo. State Col, 57; M.A, Univ. Omaha, 62; Univ. Kans, 62-63; Ph.D.(Eng), Univ. Nebr, 70. Teacher hist. & Eng, Maysville High Sch, Mo, 57-58; asst. ENG, Univ. Kans, 62-63; from instr. to assoc. prof, Mankato State Col, 63-72; ASSOC. PROF. & CHMN. DEPT, NORTHWEST MO. STATE UNIV, 72- Ed. consult, Houghton Mifflin Co, 71- U.S.A, 53-55, Res, 55-57, Sgt. AAUP; MLA; Midwest Mod. Lang. Asn. Eighteenth century English fiction; Jane Austen's novels; contemporary fiction. Publ: The concept of the sublime in Gothic fiction, Mankato Stud. Eng, spring 66; Fictional conventions in Dracula, Victorian Newslett, spring 72. Add: Dept. of English, Northwest Missouri State University, Maryville, MO 64469.

FRY, DONALD KLEIN, b. Raleigh, N.C, Mar. 31, 37; m. 65. ENGLISH. A.B, Duke Univ, 59; M.A, Univ. Calif, Berkeley, 64, Ph.D.(Eng), 66. Asst. prof. ENG, Univ. Va, 66-69, fac. fel, summers 67, 68; assoc. prof, STATE UNIV. N.Y. STONY BROOK, 69-73, PROF, 73-, res. fels, 70, 71, res. grant, 72. Nat. Endowment for Humanities summer stipend, 69. U.S.N, 59-62, Lt. MLA; Mediaeval Acad. Am; Early Eng. Text Soc; Soc. Medieval Archaeol. Old and Middle English literature; medieval archaeology, Chaucer. Publ: The Beowulf-poet: a collection of critical essays, Prentice-Hall, 68; Beowulf and the fight at Finnsburh, a bibliography, Univ. Va, 69; Finnsburh episode and fragment, Methuen, 74; plus others. Add: Dept. of English, State University of New York at Stony Brook, Stony Brook, NY 11790.

FRY, KENNETH RICHARD, b. Missouri Valley, Iowa, Nov. 17, 27. HUMANITIES, VICTORIAN LITERATURE. B.S.Ed, Northwest Mo. State Univ, 49; M.A, Univ. Nebr, Lincoln, 51; Ph.D.(Eng), Univ. Mo-Columbia, 66. Instr. ENG, Univ. Mo-Columbia, 60-62; asst. prof, Kans. State Teachers Col, 62-65; Va. Commonwealth Univ, 66-70; ASSOC. PROF, Mid. Ga. Col, 70-72; JACKSON STATE COL, 72- Sig.C, U.S.A, 51-53, Res, 55-56. AAUP; NCTE. Modern literature. Add: Dept. of English, Jackson State College, Jackson, MS 39217.

FRY, TIMOTHY PAUL, O.S.B, b. Paxico, Kans, Feb. 12, 15. ENGLISH. A.B, St. Benedict's Col, 38; Yale, 43-44; Ph.D, Univ. N.C, 48. Prof. Eng, St. Benedict's Col.(Kans), 48-68, dir. priesthood students, 48-56, chmn. dept. Eng, 58-66, student chaplain, 60-62; ED, AM. BENEDICTINE REV, 68- Sylvester Schmitz fac. res. award, Europe, 56-57; master of novices, St. Benedict's Abbey, 62-66. MLA; Mediaeval Acad. Am; Renaissance Soc. Am. Mediaeval literature, especially the drama and English literature of the mediaeval period. Publ: The unity of the Ludus Coventriae, Stud. Philol, 51; The alleged influence of pagan ritual on the formation of the English mystery plays, 58 & The antiquity of the tradition of the triads in the English cycle plays, 12/67, Am. Benedictine Rev; plus others. Add: American Benedictine Review, Second & Division St, Atchison, KS 66002.

FRY, ZELLA JEANNE, b. Moyie, B.C, Oct. 30, 09; U.S. citizen; m. 50. SPEECH, DRAMA. B.A, Univ. Alta, 31, dipl. sec. educ, 32; sr. dipl. theatre, Univ. B.C, 40; Univ. Wash, 41; M.A, Columbia Univ, 44. Teacher Eng, French, speech & hist, Glendale, Lomond, High River & Edmonton Schs, Alta, 31-42; supv. prin, Lomond Consolidated Sch. Dist, 33-35; asst. prin, High River High Sch, 35-38; Univ. Alta. demonstration teacher Eng, dramatics & art, McCauley Jr. High Sch, 38-39 & McDougall Sr. High Sch, 39-42; instr, Calgary & Edmonton Norm. Schs, 42-45; from asst. prof. to assoc. prof. speech, creative drama & lang. arts, Univ. Alta, 45-51; asst, Teachers Col, Columbia Univ, 51-52; asst. prof. philos, hist. of educ. & adolescent psychol, Glassboro State Col, 53; teacher Eng, French, speech & theatre, Selbyville High Sch, Del, 54-57; ASSOC. PROF. ENG, SPEECH & THEATRE, KEAN COL. N.J, 58- Producer of plays broadcast by Univ. Sta. CKUA, Edmonton, 42-51; adj. prof. elem. educ, Univ. Exten, Univ. Del, Dover Ctr, 55-57; consult, Creating clear images, Vols. I & II, Fideler Publ. Co, Mich, 67-69; co-ed, J. Speech Asn. N.J, 68-72, consult, 68 & 73-74; consult. speech textbk. revision, Macmillan Co, 72- AAUP; Am. Theatre Asn; Speech Commun. Asn; NEA; Am. Col. & Univ. Theatre Asn. Movement and mime in the theatre; creative drama; the arts in the USSR. Publ: Co-auth, Alberta school broadcasts, Dept. Educ, Alta, 42-46; contrib, Creating clear images (improving speaking and writing), Vols. I & II, Fideler, 67-69; auth, Construction and use of a shadow box in teaching sensory imagery in poetry and prose, Elem. Eng, 12/68; 140 electrical transcriptions, Wonder Box Prog, Univ. Sta. CKUA, 42-51; over 50 plays for children & 25 for adults, 42-74; plus others. Add: 6 Edgewood Court, North Plainfield, NJ 07060.

FRYE, DEAN CARSON, b. Bridgeport, Conn, Mar. 29, 32; m. 53; c. 1. ENGLISH. B.A. N.Y. Univ, 54, M.A, 56; Ph.D.(Eng), Univ. Wis, 61. Lectr. ENG, McGILL UNIV, 61-64; asst. prof, 64-67, ASSOC. PROF, 67- Renaissance Soc. Am; MLA. Elizabethan drama. Publ: The context of Lear's unbuttoning, Eng. Lit. Hist, 65; The question of Shakespearean parody; Essays in Criticism, 65; Commentary in Shakespeare: the case of Coriolanus, Shakespeare Stud, 66. Add: Dept. of English, McGill University, Montreal 110, P.Q, Can.

FRYE, (HERMAN) NORTHROP, b. Sherbrooke, Que, July 14, 12. ENGLISH LITERATURE. B.A, Univ. Toronto, 33; M.A, Oxford, 40; LL.D, Carleton Univ, 57, Queen's Univ, 62, Univ. Saskatchewan, 68, Franklin & Marshall Col, 68, Univ. Victoria (B.C), 69; D.D, Univ. Winnipeg, 58; Dr.Lett, Univ. New Brunswick, 60, Mt. Allison Univ, 62, Univ. B.C, 63, Univ. Man, 64, St. Lawrence Univ, 66, Dartmouth Col, 67; D.H.L, Princeton, 66, Univ. Chicago, 67; D.Litt, Acadia Univ, 69, Univ. West. Ont, 69, York Univ, 69, Middlebury Col, 69, Univ. Windsor, 70, Univ. Waterloo, 72, Harvard, 72; L.H.D, Univ. Calif, Irvine, 69, Boston Col, 72. Prof. ENG. LIT, Victoria Univ.(Ont), 47-67; UNIV. PROF, UNIV. TORONTO, 67- Guggenheim fel, 50-51; mem, Can. Radio-TV Comn, 68; hon. fel, Merton Col, Oxford, 73. Companion, Order of Can, 72. Hon. fel, Am. Acad. Arts & Sci; Eng. Inst; MLA. Symbolism in English literature; William Blake. Publ: Fearful symmetry: a study of William Blake, 47; Anatomy of criticism, 57; The welltempered critic, 63 & The critical path, 71, Ind. Univ; The educated imagination, Can. Broadcasting Corp, 63; Fools of time, Univ. Toronto, 67; The modern century, Oxford Univ, 67; A study of English romanticism, Random, 68; The stubborn structure, Methuen, London & Cornell Univ, 70; The bush garden, Anansi, 71; contrib, The prison and the pinnacle, Univ. Toronto, 73 & Literary theory and structure: essays in honour of William K. Wimsatt, Yale Univ, 73. Add: Dept. of English, Massey College, University of Toronto, 4 Devonshire Pl, Toronto, Ont. M5S 2E1, Can.

FRYE, ROLAND MUSHAT, b. Birmingham, Ala, July 3, 21; m. 47; c. 1. ENGLISH. A.B, Princeton, 43, Procter fel, 51-52, Ph.D.(Eng), 52; Princeton Theol. Sem, 50-52. Instr. ENG, Howard Col, 47-48; from asst. prof. to prof, Emory Univ, 52-61; res. prof, Folger Shakespeare Libr, 62-65; PROF, UNIV. PA, 65- Guggenheim res. fel, 56-57 & 73-74; Stone lectr. & vis. lectr, Princeton Theol. Sem; Am. Counc. Learned Soc. grant, 66 & 71; Am. Philos. Soc. grant, 68 & 71; Nat. Endowment Humanities res. grant, 73-74; mem, Inst. Advan. Study, Princeton, 73-74; mem. ed. bd, Shakespeare Quart 73- U.S.A, 43-46, Maj. MLA; Renaissance Soc. Am; Milton Soc. Am; Shakespeare Soc. Am. Literature; art; theology. Publ: God, man and Satan, 60, Shakespeare and Christian doctrine, 63 & Shakespeare's life and times, 67, Princeton; Perspective on man: literature and the Christian tradition, Westminster, 61; ed, The Bible: selections for study as literature, 65 & Shakespeare: the art of the dramatist, 70, Houghton. Add: Dept. of English, University of Pennsylvania, Philadelphia, PA 19174.

FRYXELL, BURTON L, b. Moline, Ill, Mar. 21, 10; m. 33; c. 2. LITERATURE. B.A. & M.A, Univ. Wis, 33, Ph.D, 37. Instr. Eng, James Millikin Univ, 37-38, asst. prof, 38-39, assoc. prof, 39-41, prof. & head dept, 41-47; Fairmont State Col, 47-50; prof. Eng. & dir. dramatics, Univ. Alaska, 50-52, univ. res. grant, 52-53; prof. humanities & soc. stud. & head dept, MICH. TECHNOL. UNIV, 53-70, EMER. PROF. HUMANITIES & SOC. STUD, 70- Ed, Blazing Alaska's trails, Univ. Alaska, 53. Add: Dept. of Humanities, Michigan Technological University, Houghton, MI 49931.

FRYXELL, DONALD RAYMOND, b. Moline, Ill, Apr. 13, 15; m. 42; c. 1. ENGLISH. A.B, Augustana Col.(Ill), 38; M.A, Univ. Chicago, 39; Ph.D.(Eng), Univ. Ky, 53. Instr. ENG, N.Mex. State Univ, 39-41; Auburn Univ, 41-46; Wayne Univ, 46-47; asst. prof, Gustavus Adolphus Col, 47-51; PROF. & CHMN. DEPT, AUGUSTANA COL.(S.DAK), 53-, chmn. div. humanities, 65-72. U.S.A.A.F, 42-46, S/Sgt. NCTE; MLA; Asn. Depts. Eng. Shakespeare; contemporary European literature. Publ: A note on Jane Austen's method, Notes & Queries, 53; The significance of Hamlet's delay, Discourse, autumn 63; Toward an understanding of J. Alfred Prufrock, In: Robert Frost's Chicken feathers and other essays, Augustana, 69. Add: 2716 S. Lincoln Ave, Sioux Falls, SD 57105.

FRYXELL, LUCY DICKINSON, b. Opelika, Ala, Feb. 9, 19; m. 42; c. 1. ENGLISH. A.B, Brenau Col, 40; M.S, Auburn Univ, 41; Martha Voorhees Haggin fel, Univ. Ky, 52-53, Ph.D.(Eng), 55. Instr. ENG, Auburn Univ, 41-45, asst. prof, 45-46; instr, Wayne Univ, 46-47; asst. prof, Gustavus Adolphus Col, 47-51; AUGUSTANA COL.(S.DAK), 53-55, assoc. prof, 55-63, PROF, 63- Reviewer, Choice, 66- NCTE; MLA. Contemporary British literature; linguistics. Publ: Grammar, yes! an introduction to comparative modern English grammar, Holt, 75; George Herbert: anti-metaphysical poet?, Discourse, autumn 63; Browning's Soliloquy of the Spanish cloister, Explicator, 12/63; Teaching aids from the new grammars, Eng. Notes, 10/67. Add: 2716 S. Lincoln Ave, Sioux Falls, SD 57105.

FU, SHERWIN S. S. (SHAW-SHIEN FU), b. Hangchow, China, Dec. 14, 34. ENGLISH, COMPARATIVE LITERATURE. B.A, Nat. Taiwan Univ, 56; M.A, Marquette Univ, 61; Ph.D.(Eng), Univ. Wis, 67. Instr. ENG, West. Carolina Col, 64-66; asst. prof, Cent. Mo. State Col, 67-69; ASSOC. PROF, UNIV. WIS-OSHKOSH, 69- MLA. Contemporary British and American literature; 19th century British literature; comparative literature. Add: Dept. of English, University of Wisconsin-Oshkosh, Oshkosh, WI 54901.

FUCHS, DANIEL, b. New York, N.Y, Aug. 12, 34; m. 59; c. 2. ENGLISH & AMERICAN LITERATURE. A.B, Columbia Univ, 55, Ph.D.(Eng), 60; A.M, Brandeis Univ, 56. Instr. ENG, Rensselaer Polytech. Inst, 60-61; Univ. Mich, 61-62; Univ. Chicago, 62-64, asst. prof, 64-67; RICHMOND COL.(N.Y), 68-71, ASSOC. PROF, 71- Fulbright lectr. Am. lit, France, 67-68; City Univ. N.Y. fac. res. grant, 72-73; American literature since 1875; modern European literature; history of the novel. Publ: The comic spirit of Wallace Stevens, Duke Univ, 63; Ernest Hemingway, literary critic, Am. Lit, 1/65; Wallace Stevens and Santayana, In: Patterns of committment in American literature, Univ. Toronto, 67; Saul Bellow and the modern tradition, Contemporary Lit, winter 74. Add: Dept. of English, Richmond College, 130 Stuyvesant Pl, Staten Island, NY 10301.

FUCHS, THEODORE, b. New York, N.Y, Jan. 28, 04; m. 34. DRAMATICS. B.S, Polytech. Inst. Brooklyn, 23; A.M, Northwest. Univ, 37. Instr. DRAMATIC PROD, NORTHWEST. UNIV, 32-38, asst. prof, 38-43, assoc. prof, 43-47, prof, 47-71, chmn. dept. & dir. univ. theater, 39-51, EMER. PROF, 71- Nat. Theatre Conf; Am. Theatre Asn; Speech Commun. Asn; U.S. Inst. Theatre Technol. Dramatic production; theatre planning and equipment; theatre management. Publ: Stage lighting, Little, 29, Blom, 64; Lighting equipment for the small stage, French, 39. Add: 1426 Chicago Ave, Evanston, IL 60201.

FUEGI, JOHN B, Comparative Literature. See Volume III, Foreign Languages, Linguistics & Philology.

FUJIMURA, THOMAS H, b. Brighton, Colo, Nov. 27, 19; m. 53. ENGLISH. B.A, Univ. Calif, 42; M.A, Nebr, 43; Ph.D.(Eng), Columbia Univ, 50. Tutor. ENG, Queens Col(N.Y), 46-47; instr, Univ. Conn, 47-50; asst. prof, UNIV. HAWAII, MANOA, 51-57; assoc. prof, 57-63, PROF, 63- Ford Fund Advan. Educ. fel, 53; Am. Counc. Learned Soc. grant-in-aid, 61. MLA; NCTE; Col. Eng. Asn. Restoration literature; John Dryden. Publ: Restoration comedy of wit, Princeton Univ, 52; Mode and structure in The merchant of Venice, 12/66 & The personal drama of Dryden's The hind and the panther, 5/72; PMLA; plus others. Add: Dept. of English, University of Hawaii at Manoa, Honolulu, HI 96822.

FULBECK, JOHN F, b. New York, N.Y, Dec. 19, 16; m. 60; c. 3. COMPARATIVE LITERATURE. Ph.D, Univ. South. Calif, 60. Assoc. prof. lang. arts, CALIF. STATE POLYTECH. UNIV, POMONA, 58-67, PROF. COMP. LIT, 67- U.S.N, 42-46, Lt. Comdr. English and world literature. Publ: I sleep with strangers, Savage, 51; co-auth, Adventures in English literature, Harcourt, 56; auth, Gilgamesh. . .oldest of the epics, Daporte, 58; A comparative study of poetic elements in selected plays by John Millington Synge and Federico Garcia Lorca, Univ. Mich, 60. Add: Dept. of English & Modern Languages, California State Polytechnic University, Pomona, CA 91768.

FULGHUM, WALTER BENJAMIN, JR, b. Merchantville, N.J, Mar. 24, 07; m. 35; c. 1. ENGLISH. B.A, Univ. Mich, 30; M.A, South. Methodist Univ, 31; Ph.D.(Eng), Northwest. Univ, 43. Instr. ENG, Ill. Inst. Technol, 33-39; Northwest. Univ, 39-45; teacher, Stephens Col, 45-54; PROF, CENT. CONN. STATE COL, 54, chmn. dept, 54-66. Assoc. dean, V-12 prog, Northwest. Univ, 45-49. Walt Whitman; the Bible as literature. Publ: A dictionary of biblical allusions in English literature, Holt, 65. Add: Dept. of English, Central Connecticut State College, New Britain, CT 06050.

FULKERSON, RAYMOND GERALD, b. Owensboro, Ky, Feb. 19, 41; m. 60; c. 3. RHETORICAL CRITICISM, AMERICAN PUBLIC ADDRESS. B.A, David Lipscomb Col, 63; M.A, Univ. Ill, Champaign-Urbana, 66, Ph.D.(speech), 71. CHMN. DEPT, COMMUN, FREED-HARDEMAN COL, 65- Speech Commun. Asn; Asn. Stud. Afro-Am. Life & Hist; South. Speech Commun. Asn. Rhetoric of the abolition movement; theories and methods of rhetorical criticism. Publ: Frederick Douglass and the Kansas-Nebraska Act: a case study in agitational versatility, Cent. State Speech J, winter 72; Exile as emergence: Frederick Douglass in Great Britain, 1845-1847, Quart. J. Speech, 2/74. Add: Dept. of Communication, Freed-Hardeman College, Henderson, TN 38340.

FULKERSON, RICHARD PAUL, b. Carterville, Ill, Feb. 9, 42; m, 63; c. 2. BRITISH LITERATURE. B.S, South. Ill. Univ, Carbondale, 63; Ph.D.(Eng), Ohio State Univ, 70. Teaching assoc. ENG, Ohio State Univ, 65-70; ASST. PROF, E.TEX. STATE UNIV, 70- MLA; Col. Eng. Asn; NCTE; Dickens Soc. The teaching of English in college; Victorian fiction and drama. Publ: Freshman English in Texas, Freshman Eng. Newslett, 3/72; Using full-length books in Freshman English, Col. Compos. & Commun, 5/73; Oliver Twist in the Victorian theatre, Dickensian, (in press). Add: Dept. of Literature and Languages, East Texas State University, Commerce, TX 75428.

FULKS, LEWIS, b. Burkburnett, Tex, Feb. 11, 26; m. 48. DRAMA, SPEECH. B.A, Abilene Christian Col, 48; M.A, Univ. South. Calif, 50, 59-61. Designer drama & assoc. dir, Abilene Christian Col, 49-58; dir. drama, Pepperdine Col, 58-61; DIR. DRAMA & ASSOC. PROF. COMMUN, ABILENE CHRISTIAN COL, 61- Am. Theatre Asn. Directing and designing play productions; designing and executing sets. Add: Dept. of Communication, Abilene Christian College, Abilene, TX 79601.

FULLER, ANNE ELIZABETH HAVENS, b. Pomona, Calif, Jan. 20, 32; m. 61; c. 2. ENGLISH. B.A, Mt. Holyoke Col, 53; Fulbright fels, B.A. & M.A, Oxford, 55; univ. fels, Bardwell Mem. Fel. & Ph.D.(Eng), Yale, 58. Instr. Eng, Mt. Holyoke Col, 57-59; Pomona Col, 59-61; asst. prof. humanities, Univ. Fla, 61-63; ENG, Univ. Denver, 64-68; assoc. prof, Prescott Col, 68-70; adj. prof, Univ. Denver, 71-73; PROF. & DEAN FAC, SCRIPPS COL, 73- MLA; Mod. Humanities Res. Asn; NCTE. Chaucer; Medieval romance; George Eliot. Publ: Scripture in Piers plowman B, Mediaeval Stud, 1/63; Bethump'd with words: a view of two modern dictionaries, winter 71 & Unhumane letters: the Christian allegorist critics of Medieval literature, summer 72, Denver Quart; plus others. Add: Scripps College, Claremont, CA 91711.

FULLER, CLAUDE C, b. Kemp, Tex, Mar. 19, 27; m. 49; c. 3. SPEECH. B.S, W.Tex. State Univ, 53, M.A, 54; fel, Fla. State Univ, 58-59; La. State Univ, summers, 60-62, 66-67. Instr. speech & drama, Frank Phillips Col, 54-58; asst. prof. SPEECH, NORTHEAST LA. UNIV, 59-72, ASSOC. PROF, 72- U.S.A, 45-46; U.S.A.F, 50-51, Sgt. Radio programming; semantic concepts of names, attitudes toward television commercials. Add: Dept. of Speech, Northeast Louisiana University, Monroe, LA 71201.

FULLER, DOROTHY VAN ARSDALE, b. New York, N.Y, July 21, 03. ENGLISH. A.B, Univ. Ariz, 25; A.M, Columbia Univ, 28. From instr. to PROF. ENG, UNIV. ARIZ, 28-, MEM. BD. DIR, UNIV. POETRY CTR, 61-, acting chmn. freshman composition, 39-40. Univ. rep, Ariz. Col. Asn. MLA; AAUP; Philol. Asn. Pac. Coast. English literature and composition, especially contemporary poetry; American literature. Add: Dept. of English, University of Arizona, Tucson, AZ 85721.

FULLER, EDMUND, b. Wilmington, Del, Mar. 3, 14; m. 36; c. 4. ENGLISH. Teacher playwriting, New Sch. Soc. Res, 40-43; mem. fac. Eng, Kent Sch, 52-63; St. Stephen's Sch, Rome, 65-66; RES. & WRITING. Teacher creative writing & comp. lit, sch. gen. stud, Columbia Univ, 52-54; trustee & chmn. acad. comt, Wykeham Rise Sch, Washington, Conn; ed, Invitation to Shakespeare text ser, Dell Publ. Co; gen. ed, Adventures in Good Bks. ser, Harcourt, Brace & World; lectr, univs, cols, schs. & prof. asns. Publ: A star pointed north (novel); Brothers divided (novel); The corridor (novel); ed, The Christian idea of education, 57 & Schools and scholarship, 62, Yale; auth, Man in modern fiction, 58, Books with men behind them, 62 & Successful calamity: a writer's follies on a Vermont farm, 66; Random; George Bernard Shaw; ed, Affirmations of God and man & Journey into the self; co-auth, Four American novels, 59, Four novels for appreciation, 60, co-ed, Four novels for adventure, 60, Four American biographies, 61, Three world classics, 63, Four adventures in courage, 63 & co-auth, Idea of man: an anthology of literature, 67, Harcourt; auth, Pageant of the theatre, Crowell, 65; John Milton & Commentary on All Hallow's Eve, 67, Seabury; plus others. Add: Kent, CT 06757.

FULLER, EDNEIL ELIZABETH, b. Muskogee, Okla, Dec. 14, 24. ENGLISH & AMERICAN LITERATURE. B.A, Fisk Univ, 46, M.A, 48; Univ. Okla, summers, 52, 53, 61; South. Fels. Fund, Syracuse Univ, 60; Columbia Univ, summer 68. Instr. Eng, Va. State Col, 48-51; Lincoln Univ, 51-52; instr, UNIV. ARK, PINE BLUFF, 52-58, asst. prof, 58-63, ASSOC. PROF, 63- NCTE; NEA; Conf. Col. Compos. & Commun; AAUP. Eugene O'Neill; Victorian poetry. Publ: Foreign correspondence, Fisk Herald, 42. Add: Dept. of English, Box 104, University of Arkansas, Pine Bluff, AR 71601.

FULLMAN, CHRISTOPHER EDWARD, b. Bellevue, Pa, Jan. 23, 18. ENGLISH, PHILOSOPHY. A.B, St. Vincent Col, 40, M.A, 42; M.A, Univ. Wis, 49, Adams fel, 49-50, Ph.D.(Eng), 54; Oxford, 51. Teacher Eng. & chmn. dept, St. Vincent Prep. Sch, 43-48; asst. prof. Eng, St. Vincent Col, 55-62; asst. prof. philos. & theol, Seton Hill Col, 62-65; ENG, Rider Col, 65-67; assoc. prof, UPSALA COL, 67-72, PROF, 72-, alumni fel, spring 73. Aquinas lectr, Mt. Mercy Col, 56; mem, Am. Benedictine Acad, chmn, lang. & lit. sect, 61-63; Titmus Fund lectr, Col. William & Mary, 63; mem, Fulbright Sem, Cairo, summer 65. MLA; Col. Eng. Asn; AAUP; Am. Teilhard de Chardin Asn. Contemporary British literature, especially work of Charles Williams, novelist, playwright and poet, 1886-1945; thought of Teilhard de Chardin; imagery in Melville's Billy Budd. Publ: Co-auth, Energetics of love in The world of Teilhard de Chardin, Helicon, 61; auth, Dante and the Felix Culpa, Am. Benedictine Rev, spring 52. Add: Dept. of English, Upsala College, Prospect St, East Orange, NJ 07019.

FULMER, CONSTANCE MARIE, b. Montgomery, Ala, Nov. 21, 38. ENGLISH LITERATURE. B.A, David Lipscomb Col, 58; M.A, Harding Col, 60; M.A, Univ. Ala, 62; M.A, Vanderbilt Univ, 65, Ph.D.(Eng), 70. Teacher math, Cabot High Sch, Ark, 58-60; ASST. PROF. ENG, DAVID LIPSCOMB COL, 60- Nineteenth century novel; George Eliot; contemporary southern American literature. Add: Dept. of English, David Lipscomb College, Nashville, TN 37203.

FULMER, OLIVER BRYAN, b. Vilonia, Ark, July 11, 31. ENGLISH. B.A, Univ. Ark, 57; M.A, Univ. N.C, 58; Ph.D(Eng), Tulane Univ, 65. Instr. ENG, Southeast. La. Col, 59-62; teaching asst, Tulane Univ, 62-64, instr, 64-65; asst. prof, Univ. Ill, Chicago Circle, 65-66; ASSOC. PROF, E.Carolina Univ, 66-68; UNIV. SOUTHWEST. LA, 68- U.S.N, 51-54. Keats-Shelley Asn. Am; MLA. English romantic poetry. Publ: The death of the fox in D.H. Lawrence's The fox, Stud. Short Fiction, spring 68; The ancient mariner and The wandering Jew, Stud. Philol, 10/69. Add: Dept. of English, University of Southwestern Louisiana, Lafayette, LA 70506.

FULTON, ALBERT RONDTHALER, b. Kennebunk, Maine, Oct. 4, 02. ENGLISH. A.B, Hamilton Col, 26; A.M, Harvard, 33; Ph.D, Cornell Univ, 36. Teacher ENG, Mt. Hermon Sch, Mass, 26-28; mem. fac, Hobart Col, 29-33; N.Dak. State Teachers Col, Valley City, 34-35; from instr. to prof, PURDUE UNIV, WEST LAFAYETTE, 36-71, EMER. PROF, 71- Dramatic literature; the theater; motion pictures. Publ: Drama and theater illustrated by seven modern plays, 46; Motion pictures: the development of an art from silent films to the age of television, Univ. Okla, 60. Add: 3009 Geddes Ave, Ann Arbor, MI 48104.

FULTON, HENRY LeVAN, b. Pittsburgh, Pa, Apr. 16, 35; m. 59; c. 2. ENGLISH LITERATURE. B.A, Wesleyan Univ, 57; M.A, Univ. Mich, 60, Ph.D.(Eng), 67. Instr. ENG, Univ. Mich, 65-67; asst. prof, CENT. MICH. UNIV, 67-70, ASSOC. PROF, 70- MLA; Johnson Soc. Midwest. Eighteenth century English literature; Scottish literature; Shakespeare. Add: Dept. of English, Central Michigan University, Mt. Pleasant, MI 48859.

FULTZ, MARY CATHERINE, b. Mt. Solon, Va. ENGLISH, RELIGIOUS EDUCATION. B.A, Bridgewater Col, 36; M.A, Duke Univ, 42; Assemblys Training Sch, summer 46; M.R.E, Biblical Sem. N.Y, 55; Univ. Richmond, 59-60; Virginia Mason Davidge fel, Univ. Va, 67, Emily Clark Balch fel, 67, Ph.D.(Eng), 68. Teacher Eng. & hist, Patrick County Schs, Va, 37-41; relig. educ, Rackingham County Pub. Schs, 42-46; Martinsville Pub. Schs, 46-51; Bd. World Missions Presby. Church in U.S. educ. & evangelistic missionary, Kinjo Gakuin Univ, Japan, 51-68; asst. prof. ENG, Madison Col.(Va), 68-70; VA. UNION UNIV, 70-73, ASSOC. PROF, 73- MLA; South. Mod. Lang. Asn; Am. Asn. Higher Educ. American literature, especially 19th century. Publ: The narrative art of Sarah Orne Jewett, Univ. Microfilms, 69 & Diss. Abstr, 1-3/69. Add: Dept. of English, Virginia Union University, 1500 N. Lombardy, Richmond, VA 23220.

FULWEILER, HOWARD W, b. Media, Pa, Aug. 26, 32; m. 53; c. 4. ENGLISH LITERATURE. B.A, Univ. S.Dak, 54, fel, 56-57, M.A, 57; fels, Univ. N.C, 59-60, Ph.D, 60. Asst. prof. ENG, UNIV. MO-COLUMBIA, 60-64, assoc. prof, 64-70, PROF, 70-, chmn. dept, 67-71. U.S.A, 54-56, Res, 56-64, Capt. MLA. Nineteenth century English literature. Publ: Letters from the Darkling plain: language and the grounds of knowledge in the poetry or Arnold and Hopkins, Univ. Mo, 72; Tennyson and the Summons from the sea, Victorian Poetry, 65; Gerald Manley Hopkins and the Stanching quenching ocean of a motionable mind, Victorian Newsletter, fall 66; plus others. Add: Dept. of English, 231 Arts & Science Bldg, University of Missouri-Columbia, Columbia, MO 65201.

FUNK, ALFRED A, b. Taft, Ore, June 24, 15; m. 56; c. 2. SPEECH, HISTORY. B.S, Univ. Ore, 59, M.S, 53; M.A, Univ. Wash, 61, Ph.D.(speech), 65. ASST. PROF. SPEECH, Tex. Technol. Col, 65-68, UNIV. WYO, 68- Fulbright grant, Iraq, 55-56, Burma, 57-58. Speech Commun. Asn; West. Speech Commun. Asn; AAUP. Rhetoric and public address; rhetorical criticism; interpersonal communication. Publ: Logical and emotional proofs: a counter-view, Speech Teacher, 9/68; Chain of argument in the British free-trade debates, Quart. J. Speech, 4/72; Henry David Thoreau's Slavery in Massachusetts, West. Speech, summer 72. Add: Apt. 8, 1609 Baker, Laramie, WY 82070.

FUNK, FRANK E, b. Jersey City, N.J, Feb. 21, 23; m. 49; c. 2. SPEECH. B.S, Syracuse Univ, 49, M.S, 52; Ph.D.(pub. address), Purdue Univ, 56. Instr. speech & dir. radio workshop, Lehigh Univ, 49-52; asst. speech, Purdue Univ, 52-55, instr, 55-56; ASST. PROF. PUB. ADDRESS, SYRACUSE UNIV, 56-, DEAN UNIV. COL, 71-, asst. dean, 66-71, chmn. dept. pub. address, 62-66. U.S.A.A.F, 42-45. Speech Asn. East. States; Nat. Soc. Stud. Commun. Business and industrial communication; psychology of speech; public speaking. Publ: Co-auth, Business and industrial communication from the viewpoint of the corporation president & What communications means to the corporation president, Advan. Mgt. Add: College of Liberal Arts, Syracuse University, Syracuse, NY 13210.

FUNSTON, JAY LOUIS, b. New York, N.Y, June 12, 28; m. 54; c. 4. ENGLISH LITERATURE & COMPOSITION. B.A, Rutgers Univ, New Brunswick, 49; M.A, Columbia Univ, 55; Ph.D.(Eng), Univ. Ariz, 68. Instr. Eng, Univ. Ariz, 55-66; asst. prof, N.Tex. State Univ, 66-70; ASSOC. PROF. ENG. & COORD. FRESHMAN ENG, MADISON COL, 70- U.S.A, 51-53. NCTE; Conf. Col. Compos. & Commun. Renaissance drama; Shakespeare; composition and rhetoric. Publ: Tests and exercises for Holt guide to English, Holt, 72; ed, A critical edition of Love's Hospital, Salzburg Inst. Eng. Stud, 73; auth, Troilus and Cressida and the absurd, Madison Stud. & Res, 73. Add: Dept. of English, Madison College, Harrisonburg, VA 22801.

FURAY, MICHAEL MORTIMER, b. Detroit, Mich, Jan. 8, 37; m. 58; c. 3. ENGLISH, AFRICAN STUDIES. B.A, East. Mich. Univ, 58; M.A, Univ. Chicago, 60. Instr. ENG, Chabot Col, Calif, 61-65; Fulbright prof, Univ. Sierra Leone, 65-67; INSTR. ENG, LANEY COL, 67- Asst. prof, Calif. State Col, 64-65; lectr. extension div, Univ. Calif, 68. NCTE; MLA; African Stud. Asn. Recent British and American literature; African literature. Publ: Black writing, New Republic, 7/66; Negritude and the Dakar Festival, Bull. Asn. African Lit, fall 66; Africa in Negro American poetry, African Lit. Today II, 68. Add: Dept. of English, Laney College, 300 Fallon St, Oakland, CA 94607.

FURNESS, EDNA LUE, b. Knox Co, Nebr, Jan. 26, 06. ENGLISH & SPANISH. A.B. & B.E, Univ. Colo, 28, M.A, 39, univ. scholar, 39-41, trustee fel, 50-51, Ed.D, 51; Nat. Univ. Mex, summers 30, 31, 37; trustee fel, Smith Col, 41-42. Teacher, high schs, Colo, 28-33; Wyo, 33-39; instr. Span, Pueblo Col, 42-45; Eng. & mod. lang, Casper Col, 45-47; from asst. prof. to prof. Eng. & for. lang. educ, Univ. Wyo, 47-61; prof. Eng. & Span, KEARNEY STATE COL, 61-72, EMER. PROF. LANG. & LIT, 72- Instr, Univ. Colo, 50-51; Delta Kappa Gamma res. grant, 60-61; U.S. Off. Educ. res. grant, 66-67, humanities res. grant, 71-72; mem. adv. bd, Poet Lore. NEA. Comparative literature; translation; children's literature. Publ: Co-auth, Diagnostic and instructional techniques in the language arts; auth, Spelling for the millions, Appleton, 64; co-auth, New dimensions in the teaching of English, Pruett, 67; auth, Trends in literature on teaching the language arts, contrib, Teaching of listening, Scarecrow, 71, Linguistics in the elementary school classroom, Macmillan, 71 & Language arts in the elementary school, Lippincott, 72. Add: 725 S. Alton Way, Denver, Co 80231.

FURNISS, WARREN TODD, b. Pelham, N.Y, June 5, 21; m. 49; c. 2. ENGLISH. B.A, Yale, 42, M.A, 48, Lewis-Porter fel, 48-49, Ph.D.(Eng), 52. Part-time instr, Wesleyan Univ, 46; Yale, 47; instr, Mt. Holyoke Col, 49-51; Eng, Ohio State Univ, 52-55, asst. prof, 55-59, assoc. prof, 59-64, asst. to dean, Col. Arts & Sci, 53-55, asst. dean, 57-60, assoc. dean, 60-64; prof. Eng. & dean, col. arts & sci, Univ. Hawaii, 64-69; DIR. OFF. ACAD. AFFAIRS, AM. COUNC. EDUC, 69- Carnegie Corp. travel grant, 62-63; mem. comn. arts & sci, Nat. Asn. State Univs. & Land Grant Cols, 66-68, chmn, 68; v.pres, Counc. Cols. Arts & Sci, pres, 67, bd. dir, 68; mem, Comn. Non-Traditional Study, 70-72. Med.Serv.C, 42-46, Capt. MLA; Am. Ornithol. Union; Wilson Ornithol. Soc. Renaissance English literature. Publ: Auth, Steady-state staffing in tenure-granting institutions, 73, co-ed, Women in higher education, 74 & ed, American universities and colleges, 73, Am. Counc. Educ. Add: Office of Academic Affairs, American Council on Education, One Dupont Circle, Washington, DC 20036.

FURR, LEANORA REILLY, b. Ferguson, Mo, Feb. 19, 05; m. 29. ENGLISH, LATIN. A.B, Wash. Univ, 26, A.M, 28; fel, Cornell Univ, 28-29, Ph.D. (Latin, Greek, lang. & lit), 30. Instr. ENG. & LATIN, COL. OF THE DESERT, 62-70, EMER. PROF, 70- English; Latin; world literature. Add: 81242 Alberta Ave, Indio, CA 92201.

FUS, DENNIS ANTHONY, b. Indiana Harbor, Ind, June 10, 38; m. 64; c. 3. SPEECH COMMUNICATION. B.A, St. Joseph's Col.(Ind), 60; M.A, Ind. Univ, Bloomington, 62, Ph.D.(speech), 72. Instr. SPEECH, Univ. Omaha, 62-68; ASST. PROF, UNIV. NEBR. AT OMAHA, 68- Cent. States Speech Commun. Asn; Speech Commun Asn. Women in American public address; classical rhetorical theory. Add: Dept. of Speech, University of Nebraska at Omaha, Omaha, NE 68101.

FUSILLO, ROBERT JAMES, b. Brooklyn, N.Y, Nov. 21, 27; m. 67; c. 5. THEATRE HISTORY, ENGLISH LITERATURE. B.A, Ft. Hays Kans. State Univ, 51, M.S, 52; Ph.D.(Eng), Univ. Birmingham, 66. Assoc. prof. Eng, Fla. South. Col, 54-59; Univ. Tampa, 59-61; Stephen F. Austin State Univ, 63-66; CHMN. HUMANITIES DIV, OGLETHORPE UNIV, 66- Assoc. dir. Shakespeare Sem, Lakehead Univ. summers 65 & 66. Malone Soc. Elizabethan stage conventions and terminology. Publ: On the date of Sir Gyles Goosecap, Notes & Queries, 8/54; Tents on Bosworth Field, spring 55, Enter Prince John: quarto or folio?, spring 63, Shakespeare Quart. Add: Humanities Division, Oglethorpe University, Atlanta, GA 30319.

FUSON, BENJAMIN WILLIS, b. Canton, China, Feb. 17, 11; m. 38; c. 2. ENGLISH. A.B, Col. Emporia, 32; A.M, Univ. Kans, 33; Ph.D, State Univ. Iowa, 42. Instr. Eng, First Sun Yatsen Univ, 33-34, 36; educ. & tech. asst, Lingnan, 34-36; instr. ENG, Allahabad Christian Col, 36-37; lower div, Berea Col, 37-40; assoc. prof, Mary Baldwin Col, 42-44; Bridgewater Col, 44-46; Lynchburg Col, 46-48; Park Col, 48-58; Fulbright vis. prof. Am. lit, Univ. Meshed, Iran, 58-60; PROF, KANS. WESLEYAN UNIV, 60- Ed, Sunflower Seeds, 64-68; vis. prof, Kobe Women's Col, 66-67, 73-74. MLA; NCTE. The dramatic monolog; Asian literature; Kansas bibliography. Publ: Browning and his predecessors in the English dramatic monolog, Univ. Iowa, 48; Centennial bibliography of Kansas literature, 61 & Kansas literature since 1960, 70, Kans. Wesleyan Univ; Oriental literature study guide, 70 & Islamic study guide, 74, Univ. Kans; Tennyson's priority over Browning in the dramatic monolog before 1836, Kobe Col. Stud, Japan, 2/67; Asian anti-war poems, New Lett, summer 72; Three Kansas utopian novels, Kans. Quart, fall 73; Literary maps of Missouri and Kansas. Add: Dept. of English, Kansas Wesleyan University, Salina, KS 67401.

FUSON, RICHARD ELWYN, b. Hingham, Mont, Aug. 20, 16. ENGLISH. B.A, State Univ. Iowa, 38, M.A, 40; Columbia Univ, 40. Instr. Eng. & dir. music, radio sta. KOAC, Ore. State Col, 43-46; instr. Eng, Ind. Univ, 46-47; asst. prof, Univ. Tulsa, 47-48; Evansville Col, 48-50; instr, State Univ. Iowa, 52-54; Eng. & speech, Europ. Div, Univ. Md, 54-58; asst. prof. ENG, Idaho State Col, 59-62; PROF, CUMBERLAND COL, 62- Vis. lectr. Am. lit, Mem. Univ. Nfld, 55. History of opera; American fiction and drama; history of language. Add: Dept. of English, Cumberland College, Williamsburg, KY 40769.

FUSSELL, EDWIN, b. Pasadena, Calif, July 4, 22; m. 71. ENGLISH & AMERICAN LITERATURE. A.B, Pomona Col, 43; A.M, Harvard, 47, Ph.D, 49. Instr. Eng, Univ. Calif, Berkeley, 49-51; asst. prof, Pomona Col, 51-55; Claremont Grad. Sch, 55-56, assoc. prof. Eng. & Am. lit, 56-62, PROF, 62-67; AM. LIT, UNIV. CALIF, SAN DIEGO, 67- Fulbright univ. lectr, Univs. Florence & Pisa, 67-68. MLA. Publ: Edwin Arlington Robinson, Univ. Calif, 54; Frontier: American literature and the American west, 65 & Lucifer in harness: American meter, metaphor and diction, 73, Princeton; The purgatory poems, Little Sq. Rev, 67. Add: Dept. of Literature, University of California, San Diego, La Jolla, CA 92073.

FUSSELL, IVA MILDRED, b. Dawson, Tex, Oct. 18, 19. ENGLISH. B.A, N.Tex. State Col, 39, M.A, 41; Ph.D.(Eng), Univ. Tex, 55. Instr. ENG, South. Methodist Univ, 51-53; asst. prof, MARY HARDIN-BAYLOR COL, 54-56, assoc. prof, 56-58, PROF. & CHMN. DEPT, 58- W.A.C, 43-46. MLA; S.Cent. Mod. Lang. Asn; Am. Stud. Asn. Coleridge, especially social and economic views; English romantic poets; American transcendentalism. Add: Dept. of Communications, Box 415, Mary Hardin-Baylor College, Belton, TX 76513.

FUSSELL, PAUL, JR, b. Pasadena, Calif, Mar. 22, 24; m. 49; c. 2. ENGLISH. B.A, Pomona Col, 47; M.A, Harvard, 49, Ph.D.(Eng), 52. Instr. ENG, Conn. Col, 51-55; asst. prof, RUTGERS UNIV, 55-59, assoc. prof, 59-64, PROF, 64- Fulbright lectr, Heidelberg, 57-58; regional chmn, Woodrow Wilson Nat. Fel. Found, 62-64, dissertation fels. selection comt, 71-72; consult, ed, Random House, 63-64; Christian Gauss sem. criticism, Princeton, 67; Nat. Endowment for Humanities sr. fel, 73-74. James D. Phelan Award, 64; Lindback Found. Award, 71. U.S.A, 43-46, Lt. MLA; Acad. Lit. Stud. English versification and poetics; 18th century English literature; modern poetry and criticism. Publ: Theory of prosody in eighteenth-century England; co-auth, The presence of Walt Whitman, Columbia Univ, 62; auth, Poetic meter and poetic form, Random, 65; The rhetorical world of Augustan humanism, Clarendon, 65; co-ed, Eighteenth century English literature, 69 & auth, Samuel Johnson and the life of writing, 71, Harcourt; ed, English Augustan poetry, Doubleday, 72. Add: 26 Lilac Lane, Princeton, NJ 08540.

FYFE, ALBERT JOHN, b. Hespeler, Ont, Jan. 18, 15; m. 45; c. 2. ENGLISH LITERATURE. B.A, Univ. Toronto, 38, M.A, 39; Ph.D, Univ. Chicago, 51. Asst. prof. ENG, Univ. B.C, 46-49; Rocky Mt. Col, 51-53; instr, N.Mex. Agr. & Mech. Col, 53-54; prof, Morningside Col, 54-57; PROF, IND. STATE UNIV, TERRE HAUTE, 57- Can. Army, 40-46. MLA. Nineteenth century British literature; the novel. Publ: Articles on the Victorian Age. Add: Dept. of English, Indiana State University, Terre Haute, IN 47809.

G

GABBARD, EARNEST GLENDON, b. Berea, Ky, Nov. 1, 19; m. 42; c. 2. THEATRE ARTS. A.B, Berea Col, 41; La. State Univ, 41-42; M.A, State Univ. Iowa, 47, Ph.D.(speech, dramatic art), 54; Univ. Ill, summer 50, 51. From instr. to PROF. SPEECH & THEATRE, EAST. ILL. UNIV, 47-, CHMN. DEPT. THEATRE ARTS, 63- Asst. prof, State Univ. Iowa, summer 57. U.S.N.R, 42-45, Lt. Add: Dept. of Theatre Arts, Eastern Illinois University, Charleston, IL 61920.

GABBARD, GREGORY NORMAN, b. Ft. Smith, Ark, Oct. 4, 41. ENGLISH, LINGUISTICS. B.S, Mass. Inst. Technol, 62; M.A, Univ. Tex, Austin, 64, Ph.D.(Eng), 68. Asst. prof. Eng, Old Dom. Col, 67-68; N.Mex. Highlands Univ, 68-69; Univ. Nev, Reno, 69-74. Medieval Acad. Am; NCTE; Ling. Soc. Am; AAUP; Malone Soc; James Branch Cabell Soc; Early Eng. Text Soc; Scottish Text Soc. Middle English literature; English linguistics; science fiction. Publ: Browning's Metamorphoses, Victorian Poetry, winter 66; Deems Taylor's musical version of Jurgen, Cabellian, 70; Count Manuel and Peer Gynt, Kalki, 73. Add: P.O. Box 9154, Reno, NV 89507.

GABEL, BARBARA BENNETT, b. Columbus, Ohio, Jan. 10, 25; m. 59; c. 1. AMERICAN LITERATURE. A.B, Dickinson Col, 45; A.M, Peabody Col, 46; fel, Univ. N.C, 51-52, Ph.D.(Am. lit), 54; cert, Nat. Defense Lang. Inst, 61. Instr. ENG, Ark. State Col, 46; asst. prof, Cent. Mich. Col, 47; instr, Ala. State Col. Women, summer 47; asst. prof, Rollins Col, 47-50; assoc. prof, Stetson Univ, 53-55; Augusta Col, 60-61; Methodist Col, 64-65; asst. prof, N.C. State Univ, 65-67; ASSOC. PROF, NAVAL POSTGRAD. SCH, 67- Instr. Eng, Ala. State Col. Women, summer 47. W.A.C, 55-59, Capt. MLA; Am. Ord. Asn. Henry James; programmed learning. Add: Dept. of English, Naval Postgraduate School, Monterey, CA 93940.

GABEL, JOHN BUTLER, b. Doe Run, Pa, May 25, 31; m. 54; c. 2. ENGLISH. M.A, Ohio State Univ, 54, fel, 56-57, Ph.D, 61; A.M, Wheaton Col.(Ill), 57. Instr. ENG, Univ. Ill, 61-63, asst. prof, 63-65; assoc. prof, OHIO STATE UNIV, 65-69, PROF, 69-, CHMN. DEPT, 71-, acting chmn. dept, 68-69. MLA; Renaissance Eng. Text Soc; NCTE. Tudor translations of Cicero; plays of George Chapman. Publ: Ed. & transl, John Caius' De pronunciatione (1574), Leeds Univ, 68. Add: Dept. of English, Ohio State University, 164 W. 17th Ave, Columbus, OH 43210.

GABLE, MARIELLA, O.S.B, b. St. Croix Falls, Wis, Dec. 15, 99. LITERATURE, RHETORIC. A.B, Col. St. Benedict (Minn), 25; A.M, Univ. Minn, 28; Columbia Univ, 31-32; Ph.D.(lit), Cornell Univ, 34. Asst. prof. ENG, COL. ST. BENEDICT (MINN), 28-34, prof. & head dept, 34-58, EMER. PROF, 62- Prof, Mt. Angel Col, 58-59; Marillac Col, 59-63; Mem. Benedictine Acad, chmn. lang. & lit. sect, 65-67. MLA; NCTE. Teilhard de Chardin; Flannery O'Connor; relationship between Christianity and literature. Publ: They are people, 42, Our Father's house, 45, This is Catholic fiction, 48 & Many-colored fleece, 50, Sheed & Ward; Prose satire and the modern Christian temper, 3-6/60 & Ecumenic core in Flannery O'Connor's fiction, 6/64, Am. Benedictine Rev. Dante and Teilhard de Chardin, In: The continuous flame, Harder Bk, 71. Add: Dept. of English, College of St. Benedict, St. Joseph, MN 56374.

GADO, FRANK, b. Fairview, N.J, Nov. 15, 36; m. 67; c. 3. ENGLISH. A.B, Dartmouth Col, 58; NDEA fel. & M.A, Duke Univ, 61, Ph.D.(Am. lit), 68. Instr. ENG, UNION COL.(N.Y), 63-67, asst. prof, 67-70, ASSOC. PROF, 70- Fulbright-Hays lectr. Am. lit, Univ. Uppsala, 66-67, lectr, 69-70. MLA. Modern American fiction; the films of Ingmar Bergman. Publ: Ed, First person, Union Col, Syracuse Univ, 73. Add: Dept. of English, Union College & University, Schenectady, NY 12308.

GAEBELEIN, FRANK ELY, b. Mt. Vernon, N.Y, Mar. 31, 99; m. 23; c. 3. BIBLE, CHRISTIAN EDUCATION. A.B, N.Y. Univ, 20; A.M, Harvard, 21, hon. Litt.D, Wheaton Col.(Ill), 31; hon. D.D, Reformed Episcopal Theol. Sem, 51; LL.D, Houghton Col, 60. Headmaster, STONY BROOK SCH, 22-63, EMER. HEADMASTER, 63-, chmn. dept. Bible, 24-63. Griffith Thomas Mem. lectr, Dallas Theol. Sem, 44, 52; lectr, Conservative Baptist Theol. Sem, Colo, 53; v.chmn. comt, revision Scofield Ref. Bible, Oxford Univ. Press, 55-; fac. lectr, Houghton Col, 56, 67; Bauman Mem. lectr, Grace Col. & Theol. Sem, 62; co-ed, Christianity Today, 63-66; dir. fac. summer sem, Integration Faith & Learning, Wheaton Col.(Ill), 69-72; Lilly Lectr, East. Baptist Col.(Pa), 70, scholar-in-residence, 71; gen. ed, The expositor's Bible commentary, 71- U.S.A, 18, 2nd Lt. Counc. Relig. Independent Schs.(chmn, 60-63); Headmasters Asn; Soc. Bibl. Lit. & Exegesis; Nat. Asn. Bibl. Instr; Evangel. Theol. Soc. English Bible; philosophy of Christian education; Christianity and aesthetics. Publ: Christian education in democracy, 51 & The pattern of God's truth, 54, Oxford; The practical Epistle of James, Channel Press, 55; A varied harvest, Eerdmans, 67; ed, A Christianity today reader, Meredith, 67; auth, Four minor prophets, Moody, 70; Beethoven: a bicentennial tribute, 12/70 & Crisis in Christian education, 5/71, Christianity Today; Reflections on men and mountains, Explorers J, 6/71; plus four others. Add: 3816 Lorcom Lane, Arlington, VA 22207.

GAFFNEY, FLOYD, b. Cleveland, Ohio, June 11, 30; m. 59; c. 4. DRAMA, DANCE. B.A, Adelphi Univ, 59, M.A, 62; Andrew Mellon fel, Carnegie Inst. Technol, 64-65, Ph.D.(drama), 65. Teaching asst. dance, Adelphi Univ, 59-61, instr, 62; asst. prof. speech, Clark Col, 62-64; theatre, Ohio Univ, 66-69; ASSOC. PROF. DRAMA, Univ. Calif, Santa Barbara, 69-71; UNIV. CALIF, SAN DIEGO, 71- Instr. dance-movement, Jerome Sch. Dancing, 60-61; teacher dance, Waltann Sch. Creative Arts, 62; Coop. Res. Prog. U.S. Off. Educ. res. grant, 66; dir. fine arts, Proj Upward Bound, Fla. A&M Univ, summer 66; fac. senate grant, Univ. Calif, Santa Barbara, 69-70; Ford Found. res. grant, 70; mem, Nat. Humanities Fac, 74-75. U.S.N, 51-55. Am. Theatre Asn.(chmn. Black theatre prog, 73); AAUP; Am. Theatre Res. Soc. Dance-movement; Black studies. Publ: The myth of American university theatre, Players Mag, 10/69; Black theatre: commitment and communication, Negro Dig, 6/70; Dramatic art and the secondary school: changing modes of expression, Sec. Sch. Theatre, winter 72. Add: 12889 Indian Trail, Poway, CA 92064.

GAFFNEY, WILBUR GEOFFREY, b. Burlington, Iowa, Aug. 9, 06. ENGLISH. A.B, Univ. Nebr, 27, fel, 27-28, M.A, 28; N.Y. Univ, 28-30; B.S.L.S, Columbia, 33; Univ. Calif, 49. Asst. instr. Eng, N.Y. Univ, 28-30; instr, N.Dak. Agr. Col, 30-31; ed, Am. Book Co, 33-37; ed-in-chief, Stackpole Sons Col. Bk. Dept, 40-42; Stackpole & Heck, 46-48; lectr, ENG, exten. div, Univ. Calif, 49; asst. prof, UNIV. NEBR, LINCOLN, 49-63, assoc. prof, 63-69, PROF, 69- Consult. & writer, World Scope Encycl, 46-67; Univ. Nebr. res. grant, Eng, 65. U.S.A.A.F, 42-45, Sgt. MLA; Rocky Mountain Mod. Lang. Asn; NCTE; Am. Name Soc. Anglo-American cultural lags; social customs as reflected in popular art; sources for works of Lewis Carroll. Publ: Co-auth. & co-ed, Twelve hundred years: a survey of English literature, Stackpole; co-auth. & ed, The Fillmore County story, a history of Fillmore Co, Nebraska, 1860-1967, Geneva Community Grange, Nebr, summer 68; auth, Christ-Knight in Piers Plowman, PMLA; Bestiary of T.S. Eliot, Prairie Schooner; Lewis Carroll, Thomas Hobbes and Humpty-Dumpty, West. Humanities Rev, spring 68. Add: Dept. of English, University of Nebraska, 132 Andrews Hall, Lincoln, NE 68508.

GAGE, ELINOR, b. Parker, S.Dak, Jan. 20, 06; m. 35; c. 3. ENGLISH. B.A, Huron Col, 27; M.A, State Univ. Iowa, 32; Univ. Chicago, 30. Eng. & debate coach, Huron Col. Acad, 26-27; teacher high schs, S.Dak. & Iowa, 26-35; instr. ENG. & SPEECH, MILLIKIN UNIV, 46-56, asst. prof, 56-72, chmn. fine arts ser, 54-72, dir. forensics, 53-63, mgr, Kirkland Fine Arts Ctr, 70-72, EMER. ASST. PROF, 72- Asn. Col, Univ. & Community Arts Adminr. Add: 1580 W. Wood St, Decatur, IL 62522.

GAGEN, JEAN ELIZABETH, b. Marion, Ohio, Aug. 30, 20. ENGLISH. B.A, Ohio Wesleyan Univ, 41; M.A, Columbia Univ, 42, Ph.D, 50; univ. fel, Northwest. Univ, 42-43. Instr. Eng, Adelphi Col, 47-49, 50-51; Bryn Mawr Col, 51-54; asst. prof, Univ. N.C. Greensboro, 54-58, ASSOC. PROF, 58-66; vis. prof. RESTORATION & 18th CENTURY DRAMA, UNIV. KANS, 66-67, PROF, 67- Fel, Shakespeare Inst, Eng, summer 54; Am. Asn. Univ. Women fel, 57-58; vis. prof, Univ. N.C. Chapel Hill, summer 68. MLA; S.Atlantic Mod. Lang. Asn. Renaissance and 17th century drama; 17th century prose and poetry. Publ: The new woman: her emergence in English drama, Twayne, 54; Love and honor in Dryden's heroic plays, 6/62 & Congreve's Mirabell and the ideal of the gentleman, 9/64, PMLA; Hector's honor, Shakespeare Quart, spring 68. Add: Dept. of English, University of Kansas, Lawrence, KS 66044.

GAILLARD, DAWSON FORMAN, b. Marietta, Ga, Sept. 26, 38; m. 70. ENGLISH. B.S, La. State Univ, 59; Univ. Houston, 63-64; M.A, Tulane Univ, 65, Ph.D.(lit), 70. Instr. Eng, LOYOLA UNIV.(LA), 68-70, ASST. PROF. AM. LIT, 70- Fiction ed, New Orleans Rev. NCTE; MLA; Women's Caucus Mod. Lang. American literature, 19th century; southern literature. Publ: The narrator in The ballad of the sad cafe, Miss. Quart, fall 72; Gone with the wind as Bildungsroman; or, why did Rhett Butler really leave Scarlett O'Hara?, Ga. Rev, 3/74. Add: 616 Royal St, New Orleans, LA 70130.

GAIR, WILLIAM REAVLEY, b. North Shields, Eng, Jan. 3, 39; m. 73. RENAISSANCE LITERATURE, DRAMA. B.A, St. Catharine's Col, Cambridge, 64, M.A, 66, Ph.D.(Eng), 68. Lectr. ENG, Univ. Col. S.Wales, 66-68; ASSOC. PROF, UNIV. N.B, 68- R.N, 57-59, Res, 59-68, Lt. Renaissance studies. Publ: Contrib, Lacompagnie des Enfants de St. Paul, Ed. Nat. Ctr. Sci. Res, 67; auth, The politics of scholarship, Elizabethan Theatre III, 73; Milton and science, New Cambridge Students' Milton, 73. Add: Dept. of English, University of New Brunswick, Fredericton, N.B, Can.

GAISER, GERHARD WALTER, b. Lewiston, Minn, Aug. 24, 09; m. 40; c. 2. THEATRE. A.B, Bowling Green State Univ, 33, B.S, 35; M.A, Ohio State Univ, 37; Ph.D.(dramatic art), State Univ, Iowa, 53. Teacher, high sch, Ind, 33-35; Ohio, 35-40; asst. to dir, Cain Park Munic. Theatre, summer 39, asst. to gen. mgr, summer 42; instr. speech & dramatic art & technician, Univ. Lab. Sch. & theatre, State Univ, Iowa, 41-44; instr. SPEECH & THEATRE, IND. UNIV, BLOOMINGTON, 44-54, asst. prof, 54-65, ASSOC. PROF, 65- Theatre consult, Wabash Col, Ind. Univ. campus ctrs. theatres & Indianapolis Convention & Exposition Ctr, 54-; mem, Comt. Advan Speech Test & Theatre & Drama Test, Educ. Testing Serv, 63-67, 68-71; theatre ed, Computer Stud. Verbal Behavior & Humanities. Am. Theatre Asn. (formed Exp. Res. Proj, 63, ed. newsletter, chmn, Exp. Res Proj, 63-); U.S. Inst. Theatre Technol.(assoc. ed, Theatre Design & Technol, 65-70, guest ed, fall & winter 67, mem, exec. comt, bd. dir, 66-67, deleg, Int. Orgn. Scenography & Theatre Technol, 68 & 69 & 3rd Congr. at Avignon, France, 73); Speech Commun. Asn; AAAS. Evaluation of directing in the theatre from audience standpoint; studies in theatre technology, focussed on increasing exactness of measurement; function of the consultant in the theatre. Publ: Professional sound facilities in the theatre, 10/65, The architect, the owner, and the consultant, 10/66 & co-auth, Spectrophotometric comparison of effects of light on expendable color media, 5/67, Theatre design & Technol; plus others. Add: Dept. of Theatre & Drama, College of Arts & Sciences, Indiana University, Bloomington, IN 47401.

GAITHER, MARY ELIZABETH, b. Alton, Ind, May 1, 17. ENGLISH. B.A, Univ. Louisville, 38, M.A, 49; Ph.D.(comp. lit), Ind. Univ, 53. Teacher, high schs, Ky, 38-43; instr. ENG, Univ. Louisville, 47-49; from instr. to asst. prof, IND. UNIV, BLOOMINGTON, 52-60, assoc. prof, 60-69, PROF, 69- Authenticator for. lit, Standard Encycl, 55-; examiner comn. cols. & univs, N.Cent. Asn, 67- U.S.N.R, 43-46, Lt.(jg). MLA; NCTE. Children's literature; 20th century British literature. Publ: German criticism of American drama, Am. Quart, 55; Children's books, 1956, In: Book knowledge annual; Literature and the arts, In: Comparative literature: method and perspective, South. Ill. Univ, 62. Add: 615 S. Park Ave, Bloomington, IN 47401.

GALE, ROBERT LEE, b. Des Moines, Iowa, Dec. 27, 19; m. 44; c. 3. ENGLISH & AMERICAN LITERATURE. B.A, Dartmouth Col, 42; M.A, Columbia Univ, 47, Ph.D.(Eng), 52. Lectr. Eng, Columbia Univ, 47-48; instr, Univ. Del, 49-52; asst. prof, Univ. Miss, 52-56, assoc. prof, 56-59; asst. prof, UNIV. PITTSBURGH, 59-60; assoc. prof. ENG. & AM. LIT, 60-65, PROF, 65-, dir. grad. stud. Eng, 66-73. Fulbright vis. prof, Oriental Inst, Naples, 56-58; guest lectr, Am. Stud. Ctr, Naples & Nat. Sem. Am. Lit, Rome, 57-58. MLA. American literature. Publ: Thomas Crawford, American sculptor, Univ. Pittsburgh, 64; The caught image: imagery in the fiction of Henry James, Univ. N.C, 64; Plots and characters in Henry James, 65, Plots and characters in Nathaniel Hawthorne, 69 & Plots and characters in Mark Twain, 73, Archon Bks; Study guide to James' The ambassadors, Bantam, 66; Simplified approach to Emerson and transcendentalism, Barron's, 66; Study guide to Dreiser's Sister Carrie, Littlefield, 68; Richard Henry Dana, Jr, 69, Francis Parkman, 73, Twayne; Roderick Hudson and Thomas Crawford, Am. Quart, 61; The abasement of Mrs. Warren Hope, PMLA, 3/63; Henry James, In: Eight American authors, Norton, 71. Add: 131 Techview Terr, Pittsburgh, PA 15213.

GALE, STEVEN H, b. San Diego, Calif, Aug. 18, 40; m. 73. ENGLISH. B.A, Duke Univ, 63; M.A, Univ. Calif, Los Angeles, 65; Ph.D.(Eng), Univ. South. Calif, 70. Assoc, Univ. Calif, Los Angeles, 68-70; vis. lectr, Univ. P.R, 70-71, asst. prof, 71-73; Fulbright prof. Eng. & Am. lit, Univ. Liberia, 73-74; ASSOC. PROF. ENG, UNIV. FLA, 74- Univ. P.R. grants, 71 & 72; consult. & lectr. Am. film hist, U.S. Inform. Serv, Monrovia, 73-74; spec. adv, Liberian Ministry Educ, 73-74. MLA; Col. Eng. Asn; Conf. Col. Compos. & Commun; AAUP. American literature; drama; English literature. Publ: Harold Pinter: butter's going up, Duke Univ, 74; Introducing poetry: the connotation/denotation word association game, Pedagogia, 1-12/73; The West African novel: economic reflections, J. Liberian Econ, (in press); American studies in Liberia, Am. Stud, (in press); plus others. Add: Dept. of English, University of Florida, Gainesville, FL 32611.

GALLAGHER, EDWARD JOSEPH, b. Lansdowne, Pa, Dec. 12, 40; m. 64; c. 5. AMERICAN LITERATURE. B.S, St. Joseph's Col.(Pa), 64; NDEA fel, Univ. Notre Dame, 67-68, Ph.D.(Eng, Am. Lit), 70. Instr. ENG, Univ. Notre Dame, 68-69; ASST. PROF, LEHIGH UNIV, 69- Nat. Endowment for Humanities summer stipend, 72; co-dir, Humanities Perspectives on Technol. Prog, Lehigh Univ, 73- Colonial and 19th century American literature; science fiction. Publ: Edward Loomis's Wounds, Stud. Short Fiction, summer 72; The rhetorical strategy of Franklin's Way to wealth, Eighteenth

Century Stud, summer 73; Hawthorne's Sir William Phips, ESQ: A J. of Am. Renaissance, 73. Add: Dept. of English, Lehigh University, Bethlehem, PA 18015.

GALLAGHER, KENT G, b. Oak Park, Ill, Nov. 9, 33; m. 57; c. 3. DRAMATIC LITERATURE. A.B, Carleton Col, 57; A.M, Ind. Univ, 60, Edwards fel, 61, Ph.D.(theatre), 62. Asst. prof. speech & theatre, Ball State Univ, 62-66; asst. prof. THEATRE & DRAMA, WASH. STATE UNIV, 66-69, ASSOC. PROF, 69-, AM. STUD. PROG, 71-, DIR. THEATRE ARTS & DRAMA PROG, 68- Ball State Univ. Found. grant, 64; Woodrow Wilson travel & study grant, 66; Wash. State Univ. humanities study grant, summer 69; prof, Northwest Interinstnl. Study Abroad Prog, London, 72-; dir, Pac. North Region, Am. Col. Theatre Festival, 72-; proj. off. grants & res, arts & humanities, Wash. State Univ, 73- Am. Nat. Theatre & Acad; Northwest Drama Conf; Am. Theatre Asn; Speech Commun. Asn. Dramatic theory and criticism; American theatre and drama. Publ: The foreigner in early American drama, Mouton, The Hague, 66; Emotion in tragedy and melodrama, Educ. Theatre J, 10/65; Harold Pinter's dramaturgy, Quart. J. Speech, 10/66; contrib. & ed, Individualism in the Drama of Boker, In: Symposium on 19th Century American theatre, ESQ, 6/74; plus others. Add: Dept. of Speech & Theatre, Washington State University, Pullman, WA 99163.

GALLAGHER, MARY BRIGID, b. Pittsburgh, Pa. THEATRE, SPEECH. B.A, Mercyhurst Col, 50; M.A, Cath. Univ. Am, 58; fel, Univ. Pittsburgh, 66, Ph.D.(rhet), 71. Asst. prof. drama, Mercyhurst Col, 58-66; ASSOC. PROF. SPEECH, RADFORD COL, 69-, CHMN. DEPT. SPEECH & THEATRE, 72- Speech Commun. Asn; South. Speech Commun. Asn. Charismatic leaders; revolution and speakers; comedy as an art form. Publ: Poetic play script, Cath. Sch. J, 5/49; John L. Lewis: rhetoric of invective, Today's Speech, 9/61; Public address of Fidel Castro Ruz: charismatic leader of a modern revolution, U.C.L.A. Bibliog. Annual, 71. Add: Dept. of Speech, Radford College, 162 Porterfield Hall, Radford, VA 24141.

GALLAGHER, SEAN FINBARR, b. Dublin, Ireland, Nov. 16, 31; Can. citizen; m. 57; c. 1. ENGLISH LITERATURE. B.A, Univ. Col, Dublin, 54, higher dipl. educ, 55, Ph.D.(Eng), 66; M.A, Univ. West. Ont, 61, Can. Counc. fel, 65. Asst. master, Queen Elizabeth Grammar Sch, 55-57; asst. teacher Eng. & hist, Cath. Cent. High Sch, London, Ont, 57-58; instr. Eng. & Latin, King's Col, Univ. West. Ont, 58-61, lectr. Eng, 61-65, asst. prof, 65-67; St. Thomas More Col, Univ. Sask, 67-68, ASSOC. PROF. ENG. & LIT, 68-69; TRENT UNIV, 69- Can. Counc. fel, 67. Can. Asn. Univ. Teachers.(mem. comt. prof. orientation, 71-73, Ont. rep. to bd. dir, 72-73, mem. exec. comt, 72-73). Restoration and 18th century English literature; modern drama, especially Anglo-Irish; higher education. Add: Dept. of English Literature, Trent University, Peterborough, Ont. K9J 7B8, Can.

GALLAWAY, MARIAN, b. Savannah, Ga, Mar. 1, 03; m. 24. DRAMA. A.B, Univ. Mich, 25, A.M, 29; Ph.D, State Univ. Iowa, 41. Dir, Community Players, Cedar Rapids, Iowa, 35-36; instr, Ariz. State Univ, 42-44; asst. prof, East. Ill. State Col, 44-46; State Univ. Iowa, 46-48; speech, Univ. Ala, 48-73. Am. Theatre Asn; Southeast. Theatre Conf.(pres, 67-68, Susan Davis award, 69, dist. career award, 73). New playwrights; anthropology. Publ: Constructing a play, Prentice-Hall, 50, Director in the theatre, Macmillan, 63. Add: 29 Woodridge, Tuscaloosa, AL 35401.

GALLAWAY, REUBEN JACKSON, b. Aquilla, Tex, July 18, 08; m. 39; c. 2. ENGLISH. B.A, Rice Univ, 31; M.A, Univ. Tex, 43, Ph.D.(Eng. lit), 51. Teacher Eng, pub. schs, Ranger, Tex, 33-35, sci. & Eng, San Angelo, 35-42; assoc. prof. ENG, Schreiner Inst, 42-46, asst. prof, TEX. A&I UNIV, 46-50, assoc. prof, 50-51, PROF, 51-, chmn. dept, 57-71. MLA. Restoration; 18th century English literature. Add: Dept. of English, Box 2047, Texas A&I University, Kingsville, TX 78363.

GALLICK, SUSAN LYDIA, b. San Francisco, Calif, July 15, 45. MEDIEVAL LITERATURE. B.A, Univ. Calif, Berkeley, 66; Ph.D.(Eng), Ind. Univ, 72. ASST. PROF. ENG, UNIV. MD, COLLEGE PARK, 72-, gen. res. bd. summer grant, 73. Chaucer; the Medieval sermon and its influence on Chaucer's poetry; rhetoric manuscripts in the Middle Ages, their popularity and history. Add: Dept. of English, University of Maryland, College Park, MD 20742.

GALLIGAN, EDWARD LAWRENCE, b. Taunton, Mass, Jan. 14, 26; m. 49; c. 2. LITERATURE. B.A, Swarthmore Col, 48; A.M, Columbia Univ, 49; Ph.D, Univ. Pa, 58. Instr. ENG, DePauw Univ, 49-54, asst. prof, 54-58; WEST. MICH. UNIV, 58-63, assoc. prof, 63-67, PROF, 67- U.S.N, 43-46. Col. Eng. Asn; MLA; Eng. Inst. American literature; modern fiction; comedy. Publ: Intuition and concept, Tex. Stud. Lit. & Lang, winter 67; Hemingway's staying power, Mass. Rev, summer 67; Simenon's mosaic of small novels, S.Atlantic Quart, autumn 67. Add: Dept. of English, Western Michigan University, Kalamazoo, MI 49001.

GALLO, ERNEST A, b. New York, N.Y, Nov. 10, 32; m. 54; c. 4. ENGLISH. B.A, St. John's Univ, 54; M.A, N.Y. Univ, 56. ASST. PROF. ENG, St. John's Univ.(N.Y), 59-65, UNIV. MASS, AMHERST, 65- MLA. Medieval literature; rhetorical theory; artes predicandi. Publ: The poetria nova and its sources in early rhetorical doctrine, The Hague, 71; Matthew of Vendôme: introductory treatise on the art of poetry, 74. Add: Dept. of English, University of Massachusetts, Amherst, MA 01002.

GALLO, LOUIS JACOB, b. New Orleans, La, Sept. 6, 45; m. 66; c. 1. ENGLISH. B.A, Tulane Univ, 67; fel, La. State Univ, New Orleans, 67-68, M.A, 69; fel, Univ. Mo-Columbia, 69-70, Ph.D.(Eng), 73. Instr. ENG, Univ. Mo-Columbia, 70-72; asst. prof, Northeast Mo. State Univ, 72-73; INSTR, UNIV. NEW ORLEANS, 73- Co-ed, Books: a New Orleans Rev, 73-; ed, Barataria Rev, 74- MLA. Contemporary poetry and fiction; modern literature. Publ: Walker Percy: struggles with unbelief, Courier, 9/73; Shirley Ann Grau: a profile, New Orleans Mag, 2/74; Kenneth Burke: the word and the world, N.Dak. Quart, 74. Add: Dept. of English, University of New Orleans, Lakeshore Dr, New Orleans, LA 70122.

GALLOWAY, DAVID ROBERTSON, b. Kilmarnock, Scotland, Dec. 13, 19; m. 48; c. 3. ENGLISH LITERATURE. B.A, Cambridge, 43, M.A, 47. Sr. Eng. master, Christ's Col.(N.Z), 48; asst. prof. Eng, Univ. N.B, 48-52, assoc. prof, 52-61, prof, 61-67; Univ. Waterloo, 67-69; PROF. ENG. & HEAD DEPT, UNIV. N.B, FREDERICTON, 69- Humanities Res. Counc. Can. grant, 50, mem, Nat. Comt, 62-; fel, Shakespeare Inst, 54-55; summer lectr, Univ. Waterloo, 61; mem. nat. exec, Dominion Drama Festival of Can, 62-70; Can. Counc. sr. res. fel, U.K, 63-64, leave fel, 71-72 & res. grant, summer 73; Folger Shakespeare Libr. res. fel, summer 65; vis. scholar, Univ. Bridgeport, summer 73. Brit. Army, 41-46, Capt, Mil. Cross, Gt. Brit. Mod. Humanities Res. Asn, Gt. Brit; Humanities Asn. Can; Shakespeare Asn. Am; Renaissance Soc. Am; Asn. Can. Univ. Teachers Eng; Malone Soc; MLA. Dramatic records of the city of Norwich, c. 1450-1642; new world in Elizabethan literature; early Newfoundland literature. Publ: Ed, The tempest, 69 & ed, Elizabethan Theatre (3 vols), 69-73, Macmillan (Can); auth, Shakespeare, Can. Broadcasting Corp, 61; Literature of the voyagers, In: Literary history of Canada, Univ. Toronto, 65; Robert Hayman (1575-1629): some materials for the life of a colonial governor and first Canadian author, William & Mary Quart, 1/67. Add: Dept. of English, University of New Brunswick, Fredericton, N.B, Can.

GALPER, PAMELA A, b. Indianapolis, Ind, Feb. 19, 36; m. 66. ENGLISH & AMERICAN LITERATURE. B.A, DePauw Univ, 58; Davidge & DuPont fels. & M.A, Univ. Va, 60; univ. fel, summer grant & Ph.D.(Eng), Cornell Univ, 63. Asst, Cornell Univ, 63; ASST. PROF. ENG, DePaul Univ, 63-66; ST. JOHN'S UNIV.(N.Y), 66- MLA; Southeast. Renaissance Conf. Novels of William Faulkner; modern novel; American literature. Publ: The one in Donne's poetry, Renaissance Papers, 61; Sonnet to blue, In: National poetry anthology, 69. Add: Dept. of English, St. John's University, Grand Central & Utopia Pkwy, Jamaica, NY 11432.

GALVIN, BRENDAN JAMES, b. Everett, Mass, Oct. 20, 38; m. 68; c. 3. MODERN POETRY. B.A, Boston Col, 60; fel, Northeast. Univ, 63-65, M.A, 64; grad. fel, Univ. Mass, Amherst, 65, M.F.A, 68, Ph.D.(Eng), 70. Instr. ENG, Northeast. Univ, 63-65; ASST. PROF, Slippery Rock State Col, 68-69; CENT. CONN. STATE COL, 69- Nat. Endowment for Arts subsidy, 74. Younger Poet Award, Atlantic Monthly, 65. AAUP; MLA; Assoc. Writing Prog. Modern poetry in English; modern poetry in translation; poetry and physiology. Publ: The narrow land (poetry), Northeast. Univ, 71; The salt farm (poetry), Fiddlehead Bks, 72; No time for good reasons (poetry), Univ. Pittsburgh, 74; T.S. Eliot's New Hampshire, Mass. Stud. Eng, 67; Kenneth Burke and Theodore Roethke's lost son poems, Northwest Rev, 71; Theodore Roethke's proverbs, Concerning Poetry, 72. Add: 7 Webster Hill, New Britain, CT 06051.

GAMBONE, KENNETH F, b. Norristown, Pa, Feb. 16, 26; m. 58; c. 2. ENGLISH, HUMANITIES. B.S.Ed, West Chester State Col, 51; M.A, Pa. State Univ, 53, D.Ed.(Eng), 72; summers, Univ. Pa, Temple Univ, Univ. Pittsburgh, Villanova Univ, Hofstra Univ. & C.W. Post Col, 53-71. Teacher Eng, Saltsburg High Sch, Pa, 52-55; Pottsgrove High Sch, 55-57; West Chester High Sch, 57-64; SUPVR. ENG, OYSTER BAY HIGH SCH, N.Y, 64- Mem, Mid. States Asn. Cols. & Sec. Schs, 65-67; teacher Eng, Grad. Sch, Long Island Univ, 65-68; Nassau Community Col, 72- U.S.A.A.F, 44-46. Asn. Supv. & Curriculum Develop; NCTE; MLA; Nat. Humanities Asn. Eighteenth century English literature; 20th century American literature. Publ: LP recordings for English language arts, Chancellor Press, 63; Common literary terms, Biehn Press, 65; ed, Readings for adults, Educ. Develop. Labs, 65-66; auth, Blueprints for the mother tongue, C.W. Post. Col, 67; Write to your student teacher, J. Teacher Educ, 63; contrib, Dictionary of American regional English, Univ. Wis. & Am. Dialect Soc, 66-69; auth, A preface to foibles: Dryden, Lyrismos, 67; plus others. Add: Dept. of English, Oyster Bay High School, E. Main St, Oyster Bay, NY 11771.

GANGEWERE, ROBERT JAY, b. New York, N.Y, Nov. 9, 36; m. 59; c. 2. ENGLISH. B.S, Kutztown State Col, 58; M.A, Univ. Conn, 61, Ph.D.(Eng), 66. Asst. instr. ENG, Univ. Conn, 58-63; ASST. PROF, Am. Univ. Cairo, 63-65; Kutztown State Col, 65-67; CARNEGIE-MELLON UNIV, 67- Scaife grant, summer 68; Nat. Endowment for Humanities summer grant, 71; ed, Carnegie Mag, 73. MLA. Modern American poetry; aesthetics. Publ: The exploited Eden: literature on the American environment, Harper, 72. Add: Dept. of English, Carnegie-Mellon University, Pittsburgh, PA 15213.

GANZ, ARTHUR FREDERICK, b. Milwaukee, Wis, May 15, 28; m. 62. ENGLISH. B.A, Univ. Wis, 49; M.A, Univ. Tenn, 50; Ph.D, Columbia Univ, 57. Lectr. ENG, Columbia Univ, 55-58; instr, Rutgers Univ, 59-61, asst. prof, 61-65; CITY COL. NEW YORK, 65-71, ASSOC. PROF, 71- U.S.A, 51-52. MLA. History of the drama. Publ: Co-auth, A reader's guide to literary terms, Farrar, Straus, 60; ed. & contrib, Pinter: a collection of critical essays, Prentice-Hall, 72; auth, A clue to the Pinter puzzle: the triple self in The homecoming, Educ. Theatre J, 5/69; The ascent to heaven: a Shavian pattern, Mod. Drama, 12/71; Human and suprahuman: ambiguity in the tragic world of Jean Giraudoux, PMLA, 3/72. Add: Dept. of English, City College of New York, 138th & Convent Ave, New York, NY 10031.

GANZ, MARGARET LEONORE, b. Antwerp, Belgium, Feb. 1, 27; U.S. citizen; m. 62. ENGLISH & COMPARATIVE LITERATURE. B.A, Hunter, 48; univ. scholar, Univ. Wis, 48-49, M.A, 49; Fulbright scholar, Univ. Paris, 49-50; Lizette Andrews Fisher fel, Columbia Univ, 50-51, Ph.D.(Eng. & comp. lit), 60. Instr. ENG, BROOKLYN COL, 60-65, asst. prof, 66-71, ASSOC. PROF, 71- The Victorian novel; comparative literature of the 19th century, France and England; the 18th century novel. Publ: Elizabeth Gaskell: the artist in conflict, Twayne, 68; co-ed, The enduring voice: literary concerns present and past, Macmillan, 72; The decline of Dickens' humor, Dickens Stud, 3/69; Humor's alchemy: the lesson of Sketches by Boz, Genre, 10/68. Add: Dept. of English, Brooklyn College, Brooklyn, NY 11216.

GANZ, ROBERT NORTON, JR, b. Boston, Mass, July 27, 25. ENGLISH. A.B, Harvard, 49, A.M, 51, Ph.D, 58. Teaching fel. & tutor Eng, Harvard, 52-55; instr, Yale, 56-59; asst. prof, Univ. Va, 59-64; assoc. prof, GEORGE WASHINGTON UNIV, 64-71, PROF, 71- Mellon fel, 60-61. U.S.A, 43-46. MLA. Nineteenth and twentieth century English and American literature. Publ: Robert Frost and the play of belief, Ohio Univ, Chatto & Windus, 69. Add: Dept. of English, George Washington University, Washington, DC 20006.

GANZEL, DEWEY ALVIN, JR, b. Albion, Nebr, July 5, 27; m. 55; c. 3. ENGLISH LITERATURE. B.A, Univ. Nebr, 49; M.A, Univ. Chicago, 54, Noyes scholar, 54-55, univ. fel, 56-58, Ph.D, 58; Fulbright fel, U.K, 55-56. Teacher, high sch, Nebr, 49-52; Fulbright vis. instr. ENG, Univ. Punjab, Pakistan, 52-53; instr, OBERLIN COL, 58-60, asst. prof, 60-63, assoc. prof, 63-70, PROF, 70- U.S.N, 45-47. MLA; Early 19th century drama; American literature. Publ: Mark Twain abroad: the cruise of the Quaker City, Univ. Chicago, 68; Patent wrongs and patent theatres, PMLA; Chronology in Robinson Crusoe, Philol. Quart; Cabestro and Vaquilla: the symbolic structure of the Sun also rises, Sewanee Rev, winter 68; plus others. Add: Dept. of English, Oberlin College, Oberlin, OH 44074.

GARAB, ARRA M, b. Woodcliff, N.J, May 24, 30; m. 56; c. 3. ENGLISH. B.A, Swarthmore Col, 51; M.A, Columbia Univ, 52, Ph.D.(Eng), 62; Seabury-West. Theol. Sem, 68-70. Instr. ENG, Colby Col, 57-61, asst. prof, 61-63; Kent State Univ, 63-66; assoc. prof, NORTH. ILL. UNIV, 66-71, PROF, 71- Mem, Col. Work Comn. Episcopal Church, 61-; fac. sem, Regional Counc. Int. Educ, 64-65; Kent State Univ. fac. res. fel, summer 65; consult, Scott, Foresman & Co, 65-; adv. ed, Eng. Lit. in Transition, 1880-1920, 68-; asst, St. Paul's Episcopal Church, DeKalb, Ill, 70-; bk. rev. ed, Armenian Digest, 70-; lectr. theol, Loyola Univ.(Chicago), 72-; chaplain, North. Ill. Univ. Police Dept. & Ill. Police Training Inst, 73- U.S.A, 52-54. MLA; Midwest Mod. Lang. Asn. British literature since 1880; poetry and poetic theory; literature and theology. Publ: Co-auth, Teaching English to non-English speakers, USARCARIB, 53; auth, A new university, 68 & Beyond Byzantium: the last phase of Yeats's career, 69, North. Ill. Univ; co-auth, Modern essays, Scott, 4th ed, 69; ed, Hovhannes Toumayan: a selection of stories, lyrics and epic poems, T&T Publ, 71; auth, Yeats and The forged Casement diaries, Eng. Lang. Notes, 6/65; Fabulous artifice: Yeats's Three bushes sequence, Criticism, summer 65; Times of glory: The municipal gallery revisited, Ariz. Quart, autumn 65. Add: Dept. of English, Northern Illinois University, De Kalb, IL 60115.

GARAVAGLIA, ABDON LEWIS, F.S.C, b. Detroit, Mich, Dec. 16, 15. WORLD LITERATURE. B.A, Cath. Univ. Am, 42; M.A, Manhattan Col, 48; St. John's Univ.(N.Y), 48-50; Columbia Univ, 50-51; Ford fel, Harvard, 51-52; hon. Litt.D, Col. Mt. St. Vincent, 70. Instr. WORLD LIT, MANHATTAN COL, 50-54, asst. prof, 54-58, ASSOC. PROF, 58-, DIR. GRAD. DIV, 70-, dean arts & sci, 62-70. Mem. univ. seminar higher educ, Columbia Univ, 62- Cath. Renascence Soc; Asn. Higher Educ. Publ: Humanities: central to education, Relig. Educ, 58; Traditional Catholic college, Nat. Cath. Educ. Proc, 64. Add: Dept. of English, Manhattan College, Bronx, NY 10471.

GARBATY, THOMAS JAY, b. Berlin, Ger, Jan. 10, 30; m. 60; c. 2. ENGLISH. B.A, Haverford Col, 51; Univ. Geneva, Switz, 52; Yale Law Sch, 52; M.A, Univ. Pa, 54, Ph.D, 57. Res. asst, Univ. Pa, 56; asst. prof. ENG, Clemson Univ, 57-60; instr, UNIV. MICH, ANN ARBOR, 60-62, asst. prof, 62-66, assoc. prof, 66-71, PROF, 71- Asst. ed, Mid. Eng. Dictionary, 60; vis. prof, Univ. Bern, 71-; ed, Sir Thopas, Variorum Chaucer, 71- Early Eng. Text Soc; MLA; Int. Arthurian Asn; Mediaeval Acad. Am. Chaucer; the 1890's; literary folklore. Publ: Poetry and prose of Medieval England, Crowell (in prep); The monk and the Merchant's tale: an aspect of Chaucer's building process in the Canterbury tales, Mod. Philol, 69; plus others. Add: Dept. of English, University of Michigan, Ann Arbor, MI 48104.

GARBER, EUGENE K, b. Birmingham, Ala, Oct. 5, 32; m. 54; c. 2. ENGLISH LITERATURE. B.A, Tulane Univ, 54; M.A, Univ. Iowa, 59, Ph.D, 62. Instr. ENG, Parsons Col, 61-62; Univ. Iowa, 62-68; ASSOC. PROF, WEST. WASH. STATE COL, 68- U.S.N, 54-57, Lt. MLA; NCTE. Creative writing; modern fiction. Publ: Co-auth, Better reading, 66 & Liberal and conservative: issues for college students, 68, Scott. Add: Dept. of English, Western Washington State College, Bellingham, WA 98225.

GARBER, FREDERICK MEYER, b. Boston, Mass, Dec. 18, 29; m. 57; c. 3. COMPARATIVE LITERATURE, ROMANTICISM. B.A, Boston Univ, 57; Ph.D.(comp. lit), Yale, 63. Asst. prof. Eng, Univ. Wash, 61-66; STATE UNIV. N.Y. BINGHAMTON, 66-69, assoc. prof. COMP. LIT, 69-71, PROF, 71- Am. Counc. Learned Soc. fel, 71. Am. Comp. Lit. Asn.(secy-treas, 71-); Int. Comp. Lit. Asn.(secy, 71-); MLA. Contemporary poetry and criticism. Publ: Co-ed, Microcosm, Chandler Publ, 68; ed, Ann Radcliffe's The Italian, Oxford Univ, 68; auth, Wordsworth and the poetry of encounter, Univ. Ill, 71. Add: Dept. of Comparative Literature, State University of New York at Binghamton, Binghamton, NY 13901.

GARCIA-ZAMOR, MARIE ANNE, Linguistics. See Volume III, Foreign Languages, Linguistics & Philology.

GARDNER, BURDETT H, b. Ashland, Maine, Aug. 14, 17; m. 64; c. 2. ENGLISH. B.A, Boston Univ, 40; M.A, Harvard, 47, 48-49, Ph.D.(Eng), 54. Instr. ENG, Univ. Minn, 47-48; Univ. Idaho, 49-50; Fla. State Univ, summer 50; Ga. Inst. Technol, 50-52; asst. prof, Heidelberg Col, 54-55; lectr, Harvard, 55-56; asst. prof, Elmira Col, 56-60; assoc. prof, Bloomsburg State Col, 61-62; assoc. prof. & chmn. dept, Park Col, 62-63; PROF. & CHMN. DEPT, Ky. Wesleyan Col, 63-64; MONMOUTH COL.(N.J), 64- Sig.C. Intel, 42-46, T/Sgt. Victorian literature—Critical study of Vernon Lee (Violet Paget); German literature and philosophy. Add: Dept. of English, Monmouth College, West Long Branch, NJ 07764.

GARDNER, DOROTHEA BREITWIESER, b. Pittsburgh, Pa, Oct. 5, 15; wid. ENGLISH. B.A, Col. Wooster, 37; M.A, Univ. Pittsburgh, 46, Owens fel, 48, Ph.D.(Eng), 59. Teacher ENG, high schs, Pittsburgh, 37-45; instr, Univ. Pittsburgh, 46-59; asst. prof, SHIPPENSBURG STATE COL, 59, assoc. prof, 59-60, PROF, 61- NCTE; Nat. Educ. Asn. History of the Nixon Theater, Pittsburgh; American literature; contemporary drama. Add: Dept. of English, Dauphin Humanities Ctr, Shippensburg State College, Shippensburg, PA 17257.

GARDNER, JOHN B, b. Boston, Mass, May 17, 29; m. 52; c. 4. ENGLISH. A.B, Harvard, 51; M.A, Univ. Pa, 53, Ph.D.(Am. civilization), 61. Instr. ENG, Brown Univ, 56-60, asst. prof, 60-66; ASSOC. PROF. & ASST. TO PRES, NORTH. ILL. UNIV, 68- Spec. asst. to chmn, Nat. Endowment for Humanities, 66-68. MLA; Am. Stud. Asn; Am. Hist. Asn. American images of the Chinese; poetry of Robert Frost; John Brooks Wheelwright. Add: Office of the President, Northern Illinois University, DeKalb, IL 60115.

GARDNER, JOSEPH HOGUE, b. McDonough, Ga, Sept. 15, 38; m. 61; c. 2. ENGLISH & AMERICAN LITERATURE. A.B, Harvard Univ, 60; M.A, Univ. Calif, Berkeley, 63, Ph.D.(Eng), 69. Acting instr. ENG, Univ. Calif, Berkeley, 65-66; instr, UNIV. KY, 66-69, asst. prof, 69-71, ASSOC. PROF, 71- MLA; AAUP; Dickens Fel; Dickens Soc. Coleridge; Victorian literature; Anglo-American literary relationships. Publ: Mark Twain and Dickens, PMLA, 69; Howells: the realist as Dickensian, Mod. Fiction Stud, 71; A Huxley essay as poem, Victorian Stud, 71. Add: Dept. of English, University of Kentucky, Lexington, KY 40506.

GARDNER, MARY A, b. Kingston, Ohio, July 19, 20. JOURNALISM, POLITICAL SCIENCE. B.A, Ohio State Univ, 42, M.A, 53; Evansville Evening Col, 42-43; Mex. City Col, 52; Buenos Aires Convention fel, 55; San Marcos Univ, Peru, 54-55; Minneapolis Woman's Club fel, Univ. Minn, 56, univ. fel, Tozer Found. fel. & Orgn. Am. States fel, 59, Ph.D.(jour), 60. Bacteriologist, Mead Johnson & Co, Ind, 42-43; club dir, Land Upper Austria Command, U.S. Army, Camp McCauley, Austria, 48-51; prog. asst, Minneapolis Star & Minn. World Affairs Ctr, 57-59; teaching asst. jour, sch. jour, Univ. Minn, 59-60, lectr, 60-61; copy ed, Minneapolis Star, 60-61; asst. prof. JOUR, Univ. Tex, 61-66; MICH. STATE UNIV, 66-69, ASSOC. PROF, 69- Summers, Am. specialist, U.S. Dept. State, Honduras & Colombia, 62, lectr, Int. Ctr. Advan. Stud. Jour, Quito, Ecuador, 63, consult, Corpus Christi Caller-Times, Inc, 65, Mich. State Univ. res. grants, 67-72, Mich. State Univ. Latin Am. Stud. Ctr. res. grant, 68, 72, hist. researcher, Marine Corps Mus, Quantico, Va, 67, 69, 71 & consult, El Norte, Monterrey, Mex, 70, 72. Newscaster, weekly newspapers, KLRN Educ. TV, Austin, Tex, 63. Commendation, directive counc, Univ. Antioquia, Colombia, 62; teaching excellence award, Univ. Tex, 66. U.S.M.C.R, 43-46, Res, 46-, Col. Women in Commun; Latin Am. Stud. Asn; Asn. Educ. Jour; Inter-Am. Press Asn; Midwest Counc. Latin Am. Stud. Historical and descriptive studies of the press of Latin America; desacato as a cultural and legal concept; Inter-american organizations of the mass media and their roles. Publ: The Inter American Press Association: its fight for freedom of the press, 1926-1960, 67 & The press of Latin America: a selected and tentative bibliography in Spanish and Portuguese, 73, Univ. Tex: The press of Guatemala, Asn. Educ. in Jour, 71; The press of Honduras: a portrait of five dailies, Jour. Quart, winter 63; The press woman's role in Chile, Matrix, winter 72-73; plus others. Add: School of Journalism, Michigan State University, East Lansing, MI 48824.

GARDNER, SARA JANE, b. Altoona, Pa, Aug. 14, 33; m. 51; c. 3. ENGLISH, AMERICAN STUDIES. B.A, Univ. Ariz, 62; Ph.D.(Am. stud), Wash. State Univ, 66. Asst. prof. ENG, HASTINGS COL, 66-72, ASSOC. PROF, 72- Nebr. rep, Mid-Continent Am. Stud. Asn, 67-68. NCTE; Am. Stud. Asn; MLA. Add: Dept. of English, Hastings College, Hastings, NE 68901.

GARDNER, WOFFORD GORDON, b. Winfield, Kans, Mar. 29, 14; m. 36; c. 3. SPEECH. A.B, Southwest. Col.(Kans), 35; M.A, Northwest. Univ, 41, Ph.D, 52. Teacher high sch, Kans, 35-46; instr. SPEECH, UNIV. MAINE, ORONO, 46-48, asst. prof. & acting head dept, 48-50, assoc. prof, 50-52, PROF, 52-, HEAD DEPT, 50- Asst, Northwest. Univ, 49-50. Sig.C, U.S.A, 44-45. Speech Commun. Asn.(legis. assembly, 57-59, 62-64, 66-68, exec. comt. assembly, 64, 67, 68); New Eng. Speech Asn.(v. pres, 57-58, pres, 58-59); Am. Forensic Asn.(nat. counc, 54-56, 60-62, secy-treas, 60-62); East. Commun. Asn.(v.pres, 63-64, pres, 64-65); East. Forensic Asn.(v.pres, 52-54, pres, 54-56); New Eng. Forensic Conf.(pres, 52-53, 56-57). Rhetoric and public address; speech education. Publ: Relative significance of the length and frequency of college classroom speeches in developing skill in public speaking. Add: Dept. of Speech, University of Maine at Orono, Orono, ME 04473.

GARELICK, JUDITH SPRITZER, b. Brooklyn, N.Y, Sept. 28, 39; m. 60; c. 2. AMERICAN & ENGLISH LITERATURE. A.B, Radcliffe Col, 61; M.A.T, Harvard, 62, Ph.D.(Eng. & Am. lit), 72. Teaching intern Eng, Brookline High Sch, Mass, 61-62; teacher, North Quincy High Sch, 62-63; LECTR. HUMANITIES, LESLEY COL, 72- MLA. Modern American poetry; modern and 19th century American fiction; women writers. Publ: Why children's poetry?, Lesley Current, 2/73. Add: Dept. of English, Lesley College, Cambridge, MA 02138.

GAREY, DORIS BATES, b. Brockton, Mass, Apr. 1, 06. ENGLISH. B.A, Mt. Holyoke Col, 27; Adams fel, Univ. Wis, 29-30, Ph.D.(Eng), 41. Instr. ENG, Univ. Colo, 38-42; from instr. to asst. prof, Hamline Univ, 42-48; prof. & chmn. dept, Fisk Univ, 48-55; mem. fac. Midland Col, 56; prof, MANCHESTER COL, 56-72, EMER. PROF, 72- NCTE. General semantics; 18th century literature. Publ: Putting words in their places, Scott, 57. Add: 705 College Ave, North Manchester, IN 46962.

GARGANO, JAMES WILLIAM, b. Buffalo, N.Y, Dec. 14, 17; m. 44; c. 2. AMERICAN & ENGLISH LITERATURE. B.A, Univ. Buffalo, 39, M.A, 46; Ezra Day fel, Cornell Univ, 54-55, Ph.D.(Am. lit), 55. Instr. ENG, Univ. Buffalo, 46-53; asst. prof, WASHINGTON & JEFFERSON COL, 55-58, assoc. prof, 58-65, PROF, 65-, CHMN. DEPT, 66- Fulbright lectr, Univ. Caen, 64-65. U.S.A.A.F, 42-46, S/Sgt. MLA. American fiction of the nineteenth century; Henry James and Edgar Allan Poe. Publ: What Maisie knew: the evolution of a moral sense, Nineteenth-Century Fiction, 6/61; The spoils of Poynton: action and responsibility, Sewanee Rev, fall 61; The question of Poe's narrators, Col. Eng, 12/63. Add: Dept. of English, Washington & Jefferson College, Washington, PA 15301.

GARIEPY, ROBERT JOSEPH, JR, Classics, Comparative Literature. See Volume III, Foreign Languages, Linguistics & Philology.

GARIS, ROBERT, b. Hawley, Pa, May 17, 25. ENGLISH. B.A, Muhlenberg Col, 45; M.A, Harvard, 46, Ph.D, 56; Fulbright fel, Univ. London, 50-51. Teaching fel. gen. educ, Harvard, 46-50; instr. ENG, WELLESLEY COL, 51-56, asst. prof, 56-62, assoc. prof, 62-68, PROF, 68- Sem. leader, Danforth Workshop Lib. Educ, 66- Film; English novel; English drama. Publ: The Dickens theatre, Clarendon, 65; ed, Writing about oneself, Heath, 65;

auth, The two Lambert Strethers: a new reading of The ambassadors, Mod. Fiction Stud, 62. Add: Dept. of English, Wellesley College, Wellesley, MA 02181.

GARLAND, MARGARET WOLFF, b. Ionia, Iowa; m. 58. ENGLISH, JOURNALISM. B.A, Iowa State Teachers Col, M.A, State Univ. Iowa, 40; summers, Univ. Wis, 47, Univ. Minn, 52, 72, Kans. State Univ, 60, State Col. Iowa, 65, Iowa State Univ, 71. Teacher high sch, Iowa & Wis; instr. ENG. & JOUR, WARTBURG COL, 46-50, asst. prof, 50-65, assoc. prof, 65-73, EMER. ASSOC. PROF, 73- Summers, instr, Green Lake Christian Writers & Ed. Conf, Wis, 56-58, contrib, Bread Loaf Writers Conf, Middlebury Col, 59. Nat. Counc. Col. Publ. Adv.(distinguished yearbook adv. award, 65, state chmn, 68-73). Poetry writing; journalism; speech. Publ: The good wine (poems), 72; Breaking into the letters column, In: Techniques of Christian writing, Judson, 60; Not entirely free, Pen Woman, 63; plus others. Add: 1309 Second Ave. S.W, Waverly, IA 50677.

GARLINGTON, JACK, b. Vaughn, N.Mex, Aug. 30, 17; m. 47; c. 3. ENGLISH. Ph.D.(Eng), Univ. Wis, 53. Instr. ENG, UNIV. UTAH, 53-55, asst. prof, 55-59, assoc. prof, 59-63, PROF, 63- Asst. dir. econ. inst, Univ. Colo, summers 58-66; Fulbright lectr, Univ. Madrid, 60-61; ed, West. Humanities Rev, 62-; consult, Ford Found, Univ. Indonesia, Gadjah Mada Univ, Jogjakarta & Nommensen Univ, Sumatra, spring 69; lectr, Fulbright Comn, Cuttington Col, Liberia, 69-71. U.S.A, 41-45, 47-48. Rocky Mountain Mod. Lang. Asn. Publ: Army types and island days, Tex, Quart, 64; Concerning the little magazines, Carleton Miscellany, 66; Saints and symphonies, Holiday, 66; plus others. Add: Dept. of English, University of Utah, Salt Lake City, UT 84112.

GARLITZ, BARBARA. See STANNARD, UNA.

GARMON, GERALD MEREDITH, b. Washington, D.C, Aug. 2, 32; m. 56; c. 2. ENGLISH. B.A, Univ. Richmond, 56, M.A, 60; Univ. Va, 61-63; Ph.D.(Eng), Auburn Univ, 68. Instr. ENG, N.C. Wesleyan Col, 63-65; asst. prof, W.GA. COL, 67-72, ASSOC. PROF, 72- U.S.A, 57-63, S/Sgt. Col. Eng. Asn; Nat. Educ. Asn; MLA. Eighteenth century English literature; nineteenth century American literature; contemporary novel. Publ: Faulkner's The sound and the fury, Explicator, 9/66; Lord Jim as tragedy, Conradiana; Roderick Usher: portrait of the madman as an artist, Poe Stud, 6/72. Add: Rte. 7, Box 23, Carrollton, GA 30117.

GARNER, DONALD P, b. Kennett, Mo, Nov. 5, 29; m. 66; c. 1. SPEECH, DRAMA. B.A, Harding Col, 51; M.A, Kent State Univ, 53; Ohio State Univ, 53-54; Ph.D.(speech, drama), Wayne State Univ, 65. Dir. theatre, David Lipscomb Col, 53-58; discussion, Wayne State Univ, 58-61; lectr. SPEECH, Univ. Md, 61-63; PROF. & HEAD DEPT, EAST. ILL. UNIV, 63- U.S.A, 56-57. Speech Commun. Asn; Cent. States Speech Asn; Am. Theatre Asn. Publ: Ed, Callboard, 58-, Alpha Psi Omega playbill 67 & Delta Psi Omega playbill, 67, Alpha Psi Omega; auth, One act play, production in American colleges, Player's Mag, 53. Add: Dept. of Speech, Eastern Illinois University, Charleston, IL 61920.

GARNER, DWIGHT L, b. Mingo, Iowa, Jan. 9, 13; m. 40; c. 2. SPEECH, ENGLISH. A.B, Univ. South. Calif, 36, A.M, 37, 49-52; Calif. State Col. Long Beach, 58-62. Chmn. div. COMMUN, LOS ANGELES HARBOR COL, 56-66, PROF, 66- NCTE; West. Speech Commun. Asn. Speech pathology. Publ: Co-auth, Writing college English, Chandler, 63 & Speech dynamics, W.C. Brown, 67; auth, Idea to delivery, 67 & College reading and writing, 69, Dickenson. Add: Div. of Communications, Los Angeles Harbor College, 1111 Figueroa Pl, Wilmington, CA 90744.

GARNER, NAOMI ROXIE, b. Pratt Co, Kans, June 2, 03. ENGLISH LITERATURE. A.B, Southwest. Col, 28; A.M, Univ. Colo, 39; Univ. Wis, 44. Teacher, high sch, Kans, 28-36; Greensburg, 36-39, jr. high sch, 39-47; asst. prof. Eng, Ft. Hays Kans. State Col, 47-73; RETIRED. Joseph Conrad's theory of narrative art. Add: 501 Ash, Hays, KS 67601.

GARNER, (LAFAYETTE) ROSS, b. Norristown, Pa, Mar. 28, 14; m. 53; c. 2. ENGLISH. A.B, Haverford Col, 36; LL.B, Univ. Pa, 39; M.A, Univ. Hawaii, 48; Ph.D.(Eng), Univ. Chicago, 55. Asst. prof. ENG, Univ. Nebr, Lincoln, 55-59, assoc. prof, 59-63, PROF, 63-68; PORTLAND STATE UNIV, 68- Woods Found. res. grant, Wales & Eng, 61-62. U.S.A, 41-46. MLA; Renaissance Soc. Am; Milton Soc. Am. Renaissance philosophy; prose style; 17th century poetry. Publ: Henry Vaughan: experience and the tradition, Univ. Chicago, 59; Unprofitable servant in Henry Vaughan, Univ. Nebr, 63. Add: Portland State University, P.O. Box 751, Portland, OR 97207.

GARNER, STANTON BERRY, b. Corning, N.Y, Sept. 1, 25; m. 69; c. 3. ENGLISH. B.S, U.S. Naval Acad, 48; A.M, Brown Univ, 60, Ph.D.(Eng. & Am. lit), 63. Asst. prof. naval sci, Brown Univ, 56-58, instr. Eng, 63-64, asst. prof, 64-68, assoc. prof, 68-70; PROF. AM. LIT, UNIV. TEX, ARLINGTON, 70- Fulbright lectr, Univ. Sao Paulo, 68-69. U.S.A, 43-44; U.S.N, 44-58, Res, 58-73, Comdr. MLA; S.Cent. Mod. Lang. Asn. Nineteenth century American literature; 18th and 19th century English novel; Harold Frederic. Publ: The captain's best mate, Brown Univ, 66; Harold Frederic, Univ. Minn, 69; Some notes on Harold Frederic in Ireland, 3/67 & Harold Frederic and Swinburne's Locrine, 5/73, Am. Lit; Holmes's deadly Book of life, Huntington Libr. Quart, 74; plus others. Add: Dept. of English, University of Texas at Arlington, Arlington, TX 76019.

GARNER, WAYNE LEE, b. St. Marys, Pa, Nov. 17, 20. ENGLISH. A.B, Oberlin Col, 49; A.M, State Univ. Iowa, 51, Ph.D, 63. Instr. Eng. & commun. skills, State Univ. Iowa, 52-58; tech. writer, Sandia Corp, 58-61, tech-researcher, 61-63; dir. educ. syst, Educ. Res. Assoc, 63-66; writer AV presentations, Sandia Corp, 66-69; v.pres. educ. syst, KDI Corp, 69-70; partner, Devine, Garner & Assocs, 70-73; MGT. STAFF, SYST. STUD, SANDIA LABS, 73- Ed, Targets, 60-63. C.Eng, U.S.A, 42-46. Nat. Soc. Prog. Instr. Audiovisual presentations; American humor; automated word processing. Publ: Co-auth, Factual prose workbook, Scott, 55; auth, Programmed instruction, Ctr. Appl. Res. Educ, 66; ed, The critical requirements for training directors, 72, co-auth, The critical requirements for bank tellers, 72, The day Joanna really started punching, 72 & Will the real problem please stand up?, 72, Devine, Garner & Assocs; auth, The dilemmas of programming, Col. Compos. & Commun, 12/66; co-auth, Multimedia machines, Educ. Screen & AV Guide, 6/67. Add: Organization 100, Sandia Labs, Albuquerque, NM 87115.

GARRETT, GEORGE P, b. Orlando, Fla, June 11, 29; m. 52; c. 3. ENGLISH. B.A, Princeton, 52, Proctor fel, 55, M.A, 56. Asst. prof. ENG, Wesleyan Univ, 57-60; vis. lectr, Rice Univ, 61-62; asst. prof, Univ. Va,62-65, assoc. prof, 65-67; PROF, Hollins Col, 67-71; UNIV. S.C, 71- Sewanee Rev. fel. poetry, 58-59; Prix de Rome fel, Am. Acad. Arts & Lett, 58; fel, Am. Acad. Rome, 59-60; Ford Found. grant drama, 60-61; poetry ed, Univ. N.C. Press, 64-69; co-ed, Hollins Critic, 68-70; Nat. Found. Arts sabbatical grant fiction, 67-68; mem, Acad. Am. Poets; contrib. ed, Contempora, 70-; asst. ed, Film J. 71-; pres, Assoc. Writing Prog, 71- Fiction; modern American and Renaissance poetry. Publ: King of the mountain, Scribner, 58; Which ones are the enemy?, Little, 61; Abraham's knife, Univ. N.C, 61; Cold ground was my bed last night, 64 & For a bitter season, 67, Univ. Mo; Do, Lord, remember me, 65, Death of the fox, 71 & The magic striptease, 73, Doubleday; co-auth, Man and the movies, La. State Univ, 67; auth, A wreath for Garibaldi, Hart-Davis, 69; co-ed, The sounder few, Univ. Ga, 70; Film scripts (4 vols), Appleton, 71 & The writer's voice, William Morrow, 73. Add: Dept. of English, University of South Carolina, Columbia, SC 29208.

GARRETT, PETER KORNHAUSER, b. Cleveland, Ohio, Nov. 16, 40; m. 61; c. 2. ENGLISH LITERATURE. B.A, Haverford Col, 62; M.A, Yale, 63, Ph.D.(Eng), 66. Instr. ENG, PRINCETON, 66-68, ASST. PROF, 68- MLA. Victorian and modern fiction. Publ: Ed, Twentieth century interpretations of Dubliners, Prentice-Hall, 68; auth, Scene and symbol from George Eliot to James Joyce, Yale, 69. Add: Dept. of English, Princeton University, Princeton, NJ 08540.

GARRIOTT, HAROLD MILTON, b. Scottsburg, Ind, Jan. 28, 10; m. 38; c. 3. ENGLISH. A.B, DePauw Univ, 31; Cent. Norm. Col.(Ind), 35-36; M.A, Ind. Univ, 54, Ph.D, 60. Instr. ENG, DePAUW UNIV, 47-53, asst. prof, 53-60, from assoc. prof. to PROF, 60- U.S.N, 43-45. NCTE; MLA; Conf. Eng. Educ; Conf. Col. Compos. & Commun; AAUP. Robert Browning; 19th century English literature; American dialectal linguistics. Characterization through metaphor in the Ring and the book, 60. Add: Dept. of English, DePauw University, Asbury Hall, Greencastle, IN 46135.

GARRISON, CHESTER ARTHUR, b. Jersey City, N.J, Aug. 17, 18; m. 49; c. 3. ENGLISH. B.A, Dartmouth Col, 40; M.A, Columbia, 46, Ph.D.(Eng), 64. Instr. ENG, Ohio State Univ, 46-47; Univ. Louisville, 48-50; Univ. Colo, 50-54; ORE. STATE UNIV, 54-58, asst. prof, 58-64, assoc. prof, 64-68, PROF, 68- Lectr, Am. Heritage Prog, London & Paris, summer 65; vis. prof, Univ. Scotland, Stirling, 67-68. MLA. Clyde Fitch in American drama; Thomas Hardy's The dynasts. Publ: Shakespeare's London, Ore. State Univ, 70; The vast venture: Hardy's epic-drama, The dynasts, Univ. Salzburg, 73; introd, Thomas MacDonagh's When the dawn is come, DePaul Univ, 73. Add: Dept. of English, Oregon State University, Corvallis, OR 97331.

GARRISON, JOSEPH M, JR, b. Columbia, Mo, July 25, 34; m. 58; c. 2. ENGLISH. A.B, Davidson Col, 56; M.A, Duke Univ, 57, Ph.D.(Eng), 62. Instr. ENG, Col. William & Mary, 60-62; assoc. prof, St. Andrews Presby. Col, 62-65; MARY BALDWIN COL, 65-71, PROF, 71- Presby. Church in U.S. fel, 64. MLA. Emily Dickinson; William Faulkner; modern poetry. Publ: Teaching Early American literature: some suggestions, Col. Eng, 2/70; The irony of Ligeia, Emerson Soc. Quart, fall 70; Knowledge and beauty in Wordsworth's Composed upon Westminster Bridge, Res. Stud, 3/72; plus others. Add: 741 Opie St, Staunton, VA 24401.

GARRISON, THEODORE ROOSEVELT, b. Marshall, Ark, Jan. 14, 13; m. 35; c. 3. ENGLISH. B.A, Ouachita Baptist Col, 37; M.A, Univ. Ark, 44; Ph.D, Univ. Wis, 60. Instr. ENG, Univ. Ark, 46-47; assoc. prof, Ark. Polytech. Col, 48-60; WEST. ILL. UNIV, 60-65, PROF, 65- Fulbright Lectr, Nat. Univ. Iran, 66-67; consult, Iranian Ministry of Educ. on develop. of Gondi Shahpoor Univ, 67; lectr, Am. Stud. Prog, Iran-Am. Soc, Tehran, 66-67. U.S.N.R, 44-45. Am. Stud. Asn. American folklore; John Greenleaf Whittier. Publ: Co-auth, Report of the Fulbright study team on Gondi Shahpoor University, U.S. Comn. Cult. Exchange with Iran, 67 & Whittier memorabilia, Emerson Soc. Quart, 68; auth, Gondi Shahpoor University and teacher education, In: Report of the Fulbright study team, U.S. Comn. Cult. Exchange with Iran, 67; The influence of Robert Dinsmore upon Whittier, Emerson Soc. Quart, 1/68; plus others. Add: Dept. of English, Western Illinois University, Macomb, IL 61455.

GARSON, HELEN SYLVIA, b. New York, N.Y, Oct. 22, 25; m. 44; c. 3. ENGLISH & AMERICAN NOVEL. B.A, George Washington Univ, 46; fel. & M.A, Univ. Ga, 47; Ph.D.(Eng), Univ. Md, 67. Instr. ENG, George Washington Univ, 47-48; asst, Univ. Md, 61-64, lectr, 64-66; GEORGE MASON UNIV, 66-67, asst. prof, 67-70, ASSOC. PROF, 70-, ASST. TO DEAN, COL. ARTS & SCI, 73- George Mason Found. grant, Oxford, summer 73. MLA; Am. Soc. 18th Century Stud; S.Atlantic Mod. Lang. Asn; Am. Stud. Asn. American naturalistic fiction; sociological changes revealed in fiction; 19th century influences in contemporary literature. Publ: Transportation and fiction, I.C.C. J, 70. Add: Dept. of English, George Mason University, 4400 University Dr, Fairfax, VA 22030.

GARTLEY, JOHN WILLIAM, b. Morgantown, W.Va, Apr. 24, 38; m. 71; c. 1. RADIO & TELEVISION PRODUCTION, MASS COMMUNICATIONS. B.A, W.Va. Univ, 60, M.A, 66; Ph.D.(radio-TV-film, ling), Univ. Mich, Ann Arbor, 71. Teacher speech & theatre, Madison High Sch, Rochester, N.Y, 61-64; Morgantown High Sch, W.Va, 64-67; educ. TV prod, Peace Corps Mass Media Ctr, Addis Ababa, Ethiopia, 67-69; ASST. PROF. radio-TV-speech, Montclair State Col, 71-73; RADIO-TV, NORTHWEST. UNIV, 73- Lectr, U.S. Dept. of State, Ethiopia, summer 71. Speech Commun. Asn. East. States; Cent. States Speech Commun. Asn; Speech Commun. Asn. Broadcasting history; international broadcasting, especially educational broadcasting in Africa; testing and evaluation in educational broadcasting. Publ: Co-ed, The television program, Hill & Wang, 74; auth, Training for educational television and basic production training, 71 & Evaluation: program material in educational television systems, 72, Educ. Broadcasting Int; contrib, Broadcasting in Africa, Temple Univ, 73; plus others. Add: Dept. of Radio-Television-Film, Northwestern University, Sheridan Rd, Evanston, IL 60201.

GARVEY, DANIEL EDWARD, JR, b. Tucson, Ariz, Apr. 10, 33; m. 65. BROADCAST JOURNALISM, COMMUNICATION RESEARCH. B.A, Harvard, 54; M.A, Stanford Univ, 60, Ph.D.(commun), 71. TV Newsman, Nat. Broadcasting Co, 60-63; mgr, west. elections, Am. Broadcasting Co, 63-64; lectr, broadcasting, Stanford Univ, 64-67, dir. summer radio-TV Inst, 65-67; asst. prof. BROADCAST JOUR, SCH. JOUR, UNIV. MO-COLUMBIA, 69-73, ASSOC. PROF, 73-; COMMUN. SPECIALIST, MO. REGIONAL MED. PROG, 69- U.S.A, 54-56, 1st Lt. Radio TV News Dir. Asn; Asn. Educ. Jour. Influences on broadcast news; effects of mass media on children; dissemination of science information, particularly medical information. Add: School of Journalism, University of Missouri, 27 Walter Williams Hall, Columbia, MO 65201.

GARVEY, JAMES JOSEPH, b. Chicago, Ill, July 21, 44. ENGLISH LANGUAGE. B.A, Loyola Univ. Chicago, 66; NDEA fel, Univ. Mich, Ann Arbor, 66-69, M.A, 67, univ. fel, 69-71, Ph.D.(Eng. lang), 72. ASST. PROF. ENG, COLO. STATE UNIV, 71- MLA; Ling. Soc. Am; Int. Ling. Asn. Linguistics and literature; linguistics and composition. Add: Dept. of English, Colorado State University, Ft. Collins, CO 80521.

GARVICK, JOHN DANIEL, b. Reading, Pa, Nov. 8, 39; m. 60; c. 2. ENGLISH & AMERICAN LITERATURE. A.B, Franklin & Marshall Col, 60; M.A, Univ. Del, 65; Ph.D.(Eng), Univ. Pa, 68. Teaching fel, ENG, Univ. Pa, 65-68; ASST. PROF, UNIV. NOTRE DAME, 68- Med.C, U.S.A.F, 61-62, Nat. Guard 62-68, 1st Lt. Eighteenth century English literature; T.S. Eliot; Ernest Hemingway. Publ: The critic as assassin, Notre Dame Eng. J, fall 71. Add: Dept. of English, University of Notre Dame, Notre Dame, IN 46556.

GASKIN, JAMES REUBEN, b. Summerville, Ga, June 20, 21; m. 49; c. 3. ENGLISH. B.A, Univ. Chattanooga, 42; Ph.D, Univ. N.C, 52. Instr. Eng, Young Harris Col, 46-47; UNIV. N.C, CHAPEL HILL, 50-53, from asst. prof. to assoc. prof. ENG, 53-64, PROF, 64-, CHMN. DEPT, 70-, assoc. dean grad. sch, 57-62, dir, freshman & sophomore Eng, 62-64, chmn. dept. ling, Slavic & Orient. lang, 64-65, 66-67, dir. summer session, 64-70. U.S.N, 42-46, Lt. MLA; Ling. Soc. Am. History of English language; early English literature; English linguistics. Publ: Co-auth, A language reader for writers, Prentice-Hall, 66. Add: Dept. of English, University of North Carolina, Chapel Hill, Chapel Hill, NC 27514.

GASSMAN, BYRON W, b. Ephraim, Utah, June 24, 29; m. 55; c. 7. ENGLISH LITERATURE. B.A, Brigham Young Univ, 55; M.A, Univ. Chicago, 56, Container Corp. fel, 57-58, Ph.D, 60. Instr. ENG, Chicago City Jr. Col, 58-60; asst. prof, BRIGHAM YOUNG UNIV, 60-65, assoc. prof, 65-70, PROF, 70- Fulbright lectr. Am. lit, Univ. Helsinki, 66-67. U.S.A, 52-54. MLA; Rocky Mountain Mod. Lang. Asn. Eighteenth century English literature; history and background of the English novel. Publ: French sources of Goldsmith's The good natur'd man, Philol. Quart, 1/60; The Briton and Humphry Clinker, Stud. Eng. Lit, summer 63; The economy of Humphry Clinker, In: Tobias Smollett, Oxford Univ, 71. Add: Dept. of English, A218 JKB, Brigham Young University, Provo, UT 84602.

GASTON, EDWIN W, JR, b. Nacogdoches, Tex, Feb. 22, 25; m. 46; c. 3. ENGLISH. B.S, Stephen F. Austin State Univ, 47, M.A, 50; Univ. Tex, 47-48; fels, Tex. Tech Univ, 53-55, Ph.D, 59. Asst. dir. col. inform, STEPHEN F. AUSTIN STATE UNIV, 50-53, asst. prof. ENG, 55-59, assoc. prof, 61-63, PROF, 63-, head dept, 65-69. Fulbright lectr, Univ. Helsinki, 64-65; ed, Re: Artes Lib, Stephen F. Austin State Univ, 73. U.S.M.C, 42-46. MLA; Conf. Col. Compos. & Commun; Conf. Col. Teachers Eng; Am. Stud. Asn; S.Cent. Mod. Lang. Asn; West. Lit. Asn. American western literature; colonial and federal American literature. Publ: The early novel of the Southwest, Univ. N.Mex, 61; Manual of style, Stephen F. Austin State Col, 61; Conrad Richter, Twayne, 65; Eugene Manlove Rhodes, Steck, 67. Add: 1305 North St, Nacogdoches, TX 75961.

GASTON, THOMAS ELMER, b. Mt. Zion, Ky, Feb. 3, 31; m. 49; c. 4. ENGLISH EDUCATION. B.A, Univ. Ky, 57, M.A, 61; Ed.D.(Eng. educ), Ind. Univ, 72. Instr. ENG, Lafayette Sr. High Sch, Lexington, Ky, 58-59; Univ. Ky. Southeast Community Col, 60-63; chmn. Eng. prog, Univ. Ky. Ft. Knox Community Col, 63-67; chmn. div. Eng, humanities & fine arts, Univ. Ky. Jefferson Community Col, 67-70; chmn. Eng. prog, Univ. Ky. Ft. Knox, 70-72; ASSOC. PROF. & DIR. OFF. WRITING REV, PURDUE UNIV, W.LAFAYETTE, 72- U.S.A, 49-55, Res, 55-58, Sgt. NCTE; Conf. Col. Compos. & Commun; Conf. Eng. Educ. Composition teaching; linguistics and composition. Publ: Teaching a concept of style for literature and composition, Eng. J, 1/70; Grammarians, grammars and grammar school, Ind. Eng. J, spring-summer 72; contrib, Readings for teaching English in secondary schools, Macmillan, 73. Add: Office of Writing Review, Purdue University, West Lafayette, IN 47907.

GATCH, MILTON McCORMICK, JR, b. Cincinnati, Ohio, Nov. 22, 32; m. 56; c. 3. ENGLISH, RELIGION. A.B, Haverford Col, 53; B.D, Episcopal Theol. Sch, 60; M.A, Yale, 61, Ph.D.(relig), 63. Chaplain & mem. fac. humanities, Shimer Col, 64-66, chmn. humanities fac. 66-67; assoc. prof. ENG, North. Ill. Univ, 67-68; UNIV. MO-COLUMBIA, 68-72, PROF, 72-, chmn. dept, 71-74. Nat. Endowment for Humanities sr. fel, 74-75. U.S.A, 65-67. Midwest Mod. Lang. Asn.(v.pres, 73, pres, 74); MLA; Medieval Acad. Am; Am. Soc. Church Hist. Old English literature; Medieval religious prose; Medieval drama. Publ: Death: meaning and mortality in Christian thought and contemporary culture, Seabury, 69; Two uses of Apocrypha in Old English homilies, Church Hist, 64; Eschatology in the anonymous Old English homilies, Traditio, 65; Loyal ties and traditions: man and his world in Old English literature, Pegasus, 71; M.S. Boulognesur-Mer 63 and Aelfric's first series of Catholic homilies, J. Eng. & Ger. Philol, 66; Years' work in Old English Studies—prose, Old Eng. Newslett, annually, 70- Add: Dept. of English, University of Missouri-Columbia, Columbia, MO 65201.

GATES, BARBARA TIMM, b. Sheboygan, Wis, Aug. 4, 36; m. 57; c. 2. ENGLISH LITERATURE. B.A, Northwest. Univ, 58; M.A, Univ. Del, 61; Ph.D. (Eng), Bryn Mawr Col, 71. Lectr. ENG, Widener Col, 65-67; ASST. PROF, UNIV. DEL, 71- MLA; Dickens Soc; AAUP; Soc. Relig. Higher Educ. Early romanticism; Victorian novel; literature and ecology. Publ: "A temple of false goddis": cupidity and mercantile values in Chaucer's fruit-tree episode, Neuphilol. Mitt, (in press); co-auth, The quest for aesthetic truth: Croce and Coleridge, In: Thought, action and intuition, Olms, (in press); Dylan Thomas: in my craft or sullen art, Explicator, (in press). Add: Dept. of English, University of Delaware, Newark, DE 19711.

GATES, JOHN EDWARD, Lexicography. See Volume III, Foreign Languages, Linguistics & Philology.

GATES, NORMAN TIMMINS, b. New York, N.Y, Oct. 4, 14; m. 33; c. 3. ENGLISH & AMERICAN LITERATURE. B.A, Univ. Pa, 65, M.A, 67, Ph.D. (Eng), 69. ASST. PROF. ENG, RIDER COL, 69- AAUP; Col. Eng. Asn; Browning Inst; MLA. Twentieth century English literature; Richard Aldington. Publ: The poetry of Richard Aldington, Pa. State Univ, 74; Richard Aldington and The clerk's press, Ohio Rev, fall 71; Richard Aldington and F.S. Flint: poets' dialogue, Papers Lang. & Lit, winter 72. Add: 520 Woodland Ave, Haddonfield, NJ 08033.

GATES, WILLIAM BRYAN, b. Johns, Miss, Aug. 29, 97; m. 25. ENGLISH & AMERICAN LITERATURE. B.S, Millsaps Col, 18; M.A, Vanderbilt Univ, 21; M.A, Univ. Mich, Ann Arbor, 27; Ph.D.(Eng), Univ. Pa, 32. Instr. ENG, Southwest. Univ.(Tex), 21-24; Univ. Tex, Austin, 24-25; assoc. prof, Tex. Technol. Col, 25-30, prof, 30-40, head dept, 40-46; Tex. Christian Univ, 46-48; prof, TEX. TECH UNIV, 48-64, dean, GRAD SCH, 50-63, EMER. DEAN, 63- Vis. prof. Eng, Trinity Univ.(Tex), 64-67; trustee, Tex. Wesleyan Col, 71-73. MLA; S.Cent. Mod. Lang. Asn. Shakespeare and American novel. Publ: Cooper's indebtedness to Shakespeare, PMLA, 9/52; William Gilmore Simms and the Kentucky tragedy, 5/60 & A neglected satire on James Fenimore Cooper's Home as found, 3/63, Am. Lit; plus others. Add: 3259 W. Ashby Pl, San Antonio, TX 78228.

GATLIN, HALLIE LEON, III, b. Pinehurst, N.C, Aug. 16, 36; m. 59; c. 1. BRITISH VICTORIAN LITERATURE. B.A, Wake Forest Univ, 58; M.A, Univ. Iowa, 60, Ph.D.(Eng. lit), 68. Asst. prof. ENG, St. Andrews Presby. Col, 62-63; instr, UNIV. N.C, CHARLOTTE, 66-68, asst. prof, 68-73, ASSOC. PROF, 73-, DIR. FRESHMAN ENG, 68- Eng-Speaking Union U.S. fel. Eng. art & lit, Univ. London, summer 72. MLA. Thomas Hardy's poetry; Victorian poetry. Publ: Ed, Ben Dixon MacNeill, Sand roots, Blair, 63; auth, Hardy's poetic technique, Ill. Quart, 2/71. Add: Dept. of English, University of North Carolina at Charlotte, UNCC Station, Charlotte, NC 28223.

GATLIN, JESSE C, JR, b. Creswell, N.C, Sept. 30, 23; m. 45; c. 4. ENGLISH. B.S, U.S. Mil. Acad, 45; M.A, Univ. N.C, 57; Ph.D.(Eng), Univ. Denver, 61. U.S. AIR FORCE, 42-, instr. ENG, U.S. AIR FORCE ACAD, 57-59, asst. prof, 61-62, assoc. prof, 62-65, PROF. & HEAD DEPT, 65- U.S.A.F, 42-, Col; Legion of Merit, 71. NCTE; Rocky Mountain Mod. Lang. Asn.(pres, 67-68); Conf. Col. Compos. & Commun; Asn. Depts. Eng. American literature. Publ: The U.S. Air Force in fiction: 1947-1972, U.S. Air Force Acad. Res. Reports, 73; Becket and honor: a trim reckoning, Mod. Drama, 12/65; Of time and character in Faulkner's fiction, Humanities Asn. Bull, Can, fall 66. Add: Dept. of English & Fine Arts, U.S. Air Force Academy, CO 80840.

GATSCHET, PAUL A, b. Hays, Kans, Oct. 1, 34; m. 59; c. 5. ENGLISH, EDUCATION. A.B, Ft. Hays Kans. State Col, 57, M.S, 60, Ed.S, 67; Ph.D. (Eng, educ), Kans. State Univ, 73. TEACHER Latin, Victoria Rural High Sch, 63-64; ENG, Kennedy Middle Sch, 64-65; Hays High Sch, 65-67; FT. HAYS KANS. STATE COL, 67-, CHMN. DEPT, 74- U.S.A, 57-59. Am. Asn. Higher Educ. Using objectives in teaching composition. Add: P.O. Box 306, Hays, KS 67601.

GATTA, JOHN JOSEPH, JR, b. Schenectady, N.Y, Feb. 15, 46; m. 70. AMERICAN LITERATURE. B.A, Univ. Notre Dame, 68; Woodrow Wilson fel, Cornell Univ, 68, NDEA fel, 69-73, M.A, 72, Ph.D.(Eng), 73. Vis. asst. prof. ENG, Univ. Mo-Columbia, 73-74; ASST. PROF, UNIV. CONN, 74- MLA. Colonial and 19th century American literature. Publ: Transformation symbolism and the liturgy of the mass in Pearl, Mod. Philol, 2/74. Add: Dept. of English, University of Connecticut, Storrs, CT 06268.

GATTIKER, GODFREY LEONARD, b. Loretto, Pa, Mar. 13, 31; m. 58. ENGLISH. B.A, Univ. Wis, 56, M.A, 57, fel, 61-62, Ph.D, 62. Instr. Eng, Luther Col, 58-60; teaching asst, Univ. Wis, 60-61; instr. ENG, WILSON COL, 62-64, asst. prof, 64-66, ASSOC. PROF, 67- U.S.A, 52-54, Res, 54-63, 1st Lt. MLA. Old and middle English literature; linguistics. Add: Dept. of English, Wilson College, Chambersburg, PA 17201.

GATTO, LOUIS CONSTANTINE, b. Chicago, Ill, July 4, 27; m. 51; c. 6. ENGLISH MEDIEVAL & RENAISSANCE LITERATURE. B.A, St. Mary's Col. (Minn), 50; Univ. Minn, 50-51; M.A, De Paul Univ, 56; Ph.D.(Medieval lit), Loyola Univ.(Ill), 65. Asst. speech, St. Mary's Col.(Minn), 49-50; staff artist, T.V. Times, Minneapolis, Minn, 50-51; chmn. dept. Eng, Zion-Benton High Sch, 51-56; instr, New Trier High Sch, 56-57; Am. lit, St. Joseph's Col.(Ind), 57-58, asst. prof. Renaissance lit, 58-63, assoc. prof. Medieval & Renaissance lit, 63-66, prof, 66-71, asst. acad. dean, summer 67, assoc. acad. dean, fall 67, acad. dean, 67-68, v.pres. acad. affairs, 68-71; PROF. ENG. & PRES, MARIAN COL, 71- Adv. to pres, Lawrence Univ, 66-67; Am. Counc. Educ. fel, 66-67; guest participant, 19th Nat. Strategy Sem, U.S. Army War Col, 73. U.S.A, 45-46. Renaissance Soc. Am; NCTE; Mediaeval Acad. Am; Nat. Cath. Educ. Asn; Am. Asn. Higher Educ. Yorkshire Medieval English mystics; Renaissance English literature; impressionistic criticism. Publ: An annotated bibliography of critical thought concerning Dryden's Essay of dramatic poesy, Restoration & 18th Century Theatre Res, 5/66; Suicide and utopian philosophy, Ball State Univ. Forum, winter 68; The Walter Hilton-Cloud of unknowing authorship controversy reconsidered, Stud. Medieval Cult, 73; plus one other. Add: Office of the President, Marian College, 3200 Cold Spring Rd, Indianapolis, IN 46222.

GAUBERT, HELEN A, b. New York, N.Y, Apr. 23, 14. DRAMA, SPEECH. B.A, Bennington Col, 36; M.A, West. Reserve Univ, 37; Rockefeller fel, Yale, 37-38; N.Y. Univ, 39-40; Ph.D, Univ. Montreal, 44, dipl. libr. sci, 49. Instr. drama, Eng. & speech, San Francisco Col. Women, 38-39; instr. drama & radio, Marymount Col, 42-43; researcher, feature dept, Int. News Photos, 43; ed. res. asst, Click Mag, 43-44; researcher & cataloguer, James F. Drake, Inc, 43-44; instr. Eng, Pratt Inst, 46-47; prof. & chmn. Eng. & drama, Mex. City Col, 47-48; instr. Eng. & speech, State Univ. N.Y. Col. Plattsburgh, 49-53, asst. prof, 53-54, assoc. prof, 54-60; prof. Eng. & dir. drama, St. Joseph Col.(Conn), 60-65; mem. fac. speech & theatre, Brooklyn Col, 65-68; RES. & WRITING, 68- Dir, French theatre workshop, West. Reserve Univ, summer 38; dir. drama, Carroll Club, 41; dir. Lighthouse Players, New York Asn. for Blind, 42; consult, play dept, Theatre Guild, New York, 56-57; U.S. rep, theatre sect, Int. Fed. Libr. Assoc, 67. Am. Nat. Theatre & Acad.(ed, 60-); Speech Commun. Asn; Am. Soc. Theatre Res; Soc. Theatre Res, Eng; Int. Fed. Theatre Res; Nat. Cath. Theatre Conf; NCTE. Shakespeare's theory of the drama and its relation to modern stage-craft; Eucharistic literature; theatre history of the Champlain Valley. Publ: La dramaturgie de Shakespeare, Parizeau, Montreal, 46; ed, Four classic French plays, 61 & Three plays by Victor Hugo, 64, Washington Sq; co-auth, Performing arts libraries and museums of the world, Ctr. Nat. Rech. Sci, Paris, 2nd ed, 67; auth, Henri Gheon: a mystic in action, 2/62 & Henry de Moutherlant's religious drama, fall 66, winter 67 & spring 67, Drama Critique; France, 1955-1965, In: A history of the theatre, Crown, 68. Add: 15 W. 67th St, New York, NY 10023.

GAUGER, PAUL WILLIAM, b. Milwaukee, Wis, May 2, 14; m. 42. SPEECH & DRAMA. Ph.D, Univ. Wis, 51. Asst. prof. SPEECH, Univ. Wis, 52-58; assoc. prof, UNIV. WIS-PLATTEVILLE, 58-59, PROF, 59-, HEAD DEPT. SPEECH COMMUN, 69- Am. Theatre Asn. Theatre; speech education; interpretation. Publ: The world of the arts, Child's World, 61; A comparison of high school speech students and speech experts in rating a speech performance, J. Educ. Res, 11/48. Add: Dept. of Speech, University of Wisconsin-Platteville, Platteville, WI 53818.

GAULL, MARILYN, b. Boston, Mass, Feb. 6, 38. ENGLISH. B.A, Univ. Mass, 58; fel, Ind. Univ, 62, Ph.D.(Eng), 64. Teaching assoc. ENG, Ind. Univ, 58-62; instr, Col. William & Mary, 63-64; lectr, Univ. Mass, 64-66; asst. prof, TEMPLE UNIV, 67-72, ASSOC. PROF, 72-, res. grant, summer 67. Univ. Mass. fac. res. grants, summers, 65, 66; dir, Rydal Mt. Summer Conf, 70-72; ed. assoc, J. Mod. Lit, 70-; ed, The Wordsworth Circle, 70- MLA; Keats-Shelley Asn. Am; Eng. Inst. Sociology of literature; romantic poetry; American studies. Publ: The romantic context, Norton, 74; Love and order in King Lear, Educ. Theatre J, 10/67 & In: Masterpieces of Western literature, W.C. Brown, Vol. I, 67; Language and identity in E.E. Cummings' The enormous room, Am. Quart, 67. Add: Dept. of English, Temple University, Philadelphia, PA 19122.

GAUMER, FRANK THOMAS, b. Marysville, Ohio, July 22, 13; m. 40; c. 4. JOURNALISM. B.Sc.J, Ohio State Univ, 35, M.A, 65; Univ. Minn, 65-70. Reporter & ed, Union County Jour, Marysville, Ohio, 35-50; ed, Eve. Jour-Tribune, 50-57, ed. & publ, 57-60; lectr. JOUR, OHIO STATE UNIV, 60-65, asst. prof, 65-72, ASSOC. PROF, 72-, ASST. TO DIR, 70- Asn. Educ. in Jour. Law of mass communications; typography and design; press and society. Publ: Police, jurists, newsmen work as usual, Grassroots Ed, 3-4/72; Pow Wow—story on clandestine newspaper published by World War II prisoners of war in Germany, Air Force Dig, 7/72; History of journalism halls of fame in the U.S, (3 part series), Ed. & Publ, 9-10/72; plus others. Add: Ohio State University School of Journalism, 242 W. 18th Ave, Columbus, OH 43210.

GAUMER, MAHLON CONOVER, III, b. St. Louis, Mo, Jan. 12, 43. MEDIEVAL ENGLISH LITERATURE, ENGLISH LINGUISTICS. B.A, Ariz. State Univ, 65, M.A, 67; Ph.D.(Eng), Univ. Wash, 69. Asst. prof. ENG, CALIF. STATE UNIV, NORTHRIDGE, 69-73, ASSOC. PROF, 73- NCTE; Conf. Col. Compos. & Commun; MLA; Philol. Asn. Pac. Coast; Ling. Soc. Am. Fourteenth century English literature; history of the English language; linguistic theory. Add: Dept. of English, California State University, Northridge, CA 91324.

GAVIN, ROSEMARIE JULIE, S.N.D, b. Tropico, Calif, Jan. 26, 17. EDUCATION, ENGLISH. B.Ed, Univ. Calif, Los Angeles, 39; M.A. Cath. Univ. Am, 52; Ph.D.(Educ), Stanford Univ, 55. Teacher, Notre Dame High Schs, Calif, 42-51; PROF. EDUC. & ENG, COL. NOTRE DAME (CALIF), 51-, DIR. GRAD. STUD, 65-, ACAD. DEAN, 68-, dir. teacher educ, 52-70, evening div, 55-65, summer session, 61-68. Delegate, Int. Chapter of Sisters of Notre Dame de Namur, Rome, 68 & 69; mem. bd. trustees, Col. Notre Dame (Calif), 68-; Asn. Independent Calif. Col. & Univ, 68- AAUP; Am. Asn. Higher Educ; Nat. Soc. Study Educ; Nat. Cath. Educ. Asn. Individualized instruction; single campus plan. Publ: Training teachers of secondary school English in Catholic colleges for women, Cath. Educ. Rev, 2/56; Chief influences shaping the poetic imagery of Thomas Merton, Renascence, 57; Hopkins' The candle indoors, Explicator, 2/62. Add: Office of the Academic Dean, College of Notre Dame, 1500 Ralston Ave, Belmont, CA 94002.

GAY, ALVA ANGELL, b. Cleveland, Ohio, Oct. 23, 07; m. 48; c. 3. ENGLISH. A.B, Adelbert Col, West. Reserve Univ, 30, fel, 32-34, Ph.D.(Eng), 34. Instr, Adelbert Col, West. Reserve Univ, 34-37; instr. ENG, WAYNE STATE UNIV, 37-42, asst. prof, 42-59, ASSOC. PROF, 59- Assoc. ed, Criticism, 64-72, ed, 72- Twentieth century fiction; Shakespeare; the period of the English Renaissance. Publ: H.M. Tomlison, essayist and traveller, In: Studies in Honor of John Wilcox, Wayne State Univ, 58; plus others. Add: Dept. of English, Wayne State University, 430 State Hall, Detroit, MI 48202.

GAY, CAROL JANE, b. Youngstown, Ohio, Oct. 30, 33; m. 56; c. 5. AMERICAN LITERATURE. A.B, Youngstown Univ, 54; M.A, Ohio State Univ, 57; Ph.D.(Am. lit), Kent State Univ, 72. ASST. PROF. ENG, YOUNGSTOWN STATE UNIV, 65- MLA (Am. Lit. Sect); NCTE; Thoreau Soc. Seventeenth and 19th century American literature. Add: Dept. of English, Youngstown State University, Wick Ave, Youngstown, OH 44503.

GAY, WILLIAM TEAGUE, b. Montgomery, Ala, Sept. 29, 99; m. 22; c. 4. ENGLISH, WORLD LITERATURE. B.S, Univ. Ala, 21, LL.B, 23, M.A, 28, hon. J.D, 69; Columbia Univ, summers 29, 30, 32; Univ. N.C, 37-38, summers 39, 40; Univ. Calif, Los Angeles, 46-47. Instr. Eng, Univ. Fla, 27-30; head dept, Ga. State Col. Men, Tifton, 30-33; lit. res. & writing, 33-35, 45-61, 63-64; camp educ. adv, Civilian Conserv. Corps, Greenville, Ala, 35-37; head dept. Eng, Bob Jones Col, 38-41; instr. acad. subj, U.S. Army Air Corps, 41-45; Eng, Campbell Col, 61-62; acting chmn. dept, Bluefield State Col, 62-63; asst. prof, Hampden-Sydney Col, 64-65; assoc. prof, Pembroke State Col, 65-66; RES. & WRITING, 66- Spec. ed, Futurist, 68-; Acad. Am. Poets. U.S.A.A.F, 42-46, Capt. Utopian literature; Edward Bellamy; creative writing. Publ: Poems, privately pub, 34; Montgomery, Alabama: a city in crisis, Exposition, 57; Edward Bellamy: nineteenth century futurist, 6/67, Nineteenth century view of the twenty-first century, 4/68, Discarding the elderly, 2/70, The Futurist. Add: 1513 College Ct, Montgomery, AL 36106.

GAYLORD, ALAN THEODORE, b. Los Angeles, Calif. Oct. 12, 33; m. 52; c. 4. ENGLISH LITERATURE. B.A, Pomona Col, 54; Woodrow Wilson fel, Princeton, 54-55, Danforth fel, 54-58, Procter fel, 56-57, Ph.D, 59; hon. M.A, Dartmouth Col, 69. Instr. ENG, Univ. Mich, 58-61, asst. prof, 61-66, assoc. prof, 66-67; DARTMOUTH COL, 67-69, PROF, 69-, DIR. M.A. LIB. ARTS PROG, 73- Andrew Mellon fel, 62-63; acad. dir, Dartmouth alumni col, 69-72. MLA; Mediaeval Acad. Am. Medieval cultural and intellectual history; film criticism; Chaucer. Publ: Sentence and Solaas in fragment VII of the Canterbury tales, PMLA, 67; Friendship in Chaucer's Troilus, 69 & The role of Saturn in the Knight's tale, 74, Chaucer Rev. Add: Dept. of English, Dartmouth College, Hanover, NH 03755.

GAZDA, JOHN M, b. Kansas City, Kans, Oct. 20, 27. ENGLISH, ENGLISH EDUCATION. B.S, Univ. Kans, 50, M.S, 53, Ph.D.(Eng. educ), 65. Teacher, jr. & sr. high schs, Kans, 50-53; elem. sch, Ger, 53-54; high schs, Mo, 54-56; instr. Eng, Kansas City Jr. Col, 56-65; Dir. admis. & registr, Metrop. Jr. Col, 65-68, chmn. dept. Eng, 68-69; dean instr, MAPLE WOODS COMMUNITY COL, 69-70, PRES, 70- U.S.A, 46-48, Sgt. NCTE; Conf. Col. Compos. & Commun; Conf. Eng. Educ; Am. Asn. Community & Jr. Cols; Am. Asn. Higher Educ. Teaching of English; drama education. Add: Office of the President, Maple Woods Community College, 2601 N.E. Barry Rd, Kansas City, MO 64156.

GEARHART, SALLY MILLER, b. Pearisburg, Va, Apr. 15, 31. SPEECH, DRAMA. B.A, Sweet Briar Col, 52; M.A, Bowling Green State Univ, 53; Ph.D, Univ. Ill, 56; Univ. Tex; Univ. Kans, 69-70. Asst, Bowling Green State Univ, 52-53; Univ. Ill, 53-56; asst. prof. speech, Stephen F. Austin State Col, 56-59; assoc. dir. theatre, MacMurray Col. Women, 60; assoc. prof. speech, Tex. Lutheran Col, 60-70, chairperson, Dept. Speech & Drama, 65-70; LECTR. SPEECH, SAN FRANCISCO STATE UNIV, 72- Consult. lesbianism, sexuality & women's consciousness, Esalen Inst, San Francisco, Calif, 72- Speech Commun. Asn. Lesbian feminism; issues of race and class within feminism; alternatives to patriarchy. Publ: Co-auth. & co-ed, Loving women/loving men, Glide Publ, 74; auth, The neglect of the upper ten, Response, 12/62. Add: Dept. of Speech, San Francisco State University, 1600 Holloway, San Francisco, CA 94132.

GEARY, EDWARD ACORD, b. Price, Utah, Dec. 10, 37; m, 61; c. 4. ENGLISH & AMERICAN LITERATURE. B.A, Brigham Young Univ, 60, M.A, 63; Ph.D.(Eng. lit), Stanford Univ, 71. Instr. humanities, Col. East. Utah, 63-64; ASST. PROF. ENG, BRIGHAM YOUNG UNIV, 68- MLA. Twentieth century critical theory and literature. Add: Dept. of English, Brigham Young University, Provo, UT 84602.

GEBHARDT, RICHARD COATE, b. Dayton, Ohio, Apr. 4, 43; m. 65. MODERN LITERATURE, CONTEMPORARY FICTION. B.A, Heidelberg Col, 65; M.A, Mich. State Univ, 67, Ph.D.(Eng), 69. ASST. PROF. ENG, FINDLAY COL, 69-, CHMN. DIV. HUMANITIES, 72-, CHMN. LIB. STUD. PROG, 73-, dir. freshman writing, 69-72, acting dean col, summer 73. Bk. reviewer, Choice, 71-; field ed, Freshman Eng. News, 73-; co-ed, Writing as a Liberating Activity Newslett, 73-; consult. speaker talent file, NCTE, 73- AAUP; Asn. Depts. Eng; Conf. Col. Compos. & Commun; Midwest. Mod. Lang. Asn; NCTE; MLA. Modern literature; teaching sophisticated literature to unsophisticated students; curriculum development for effective college teaching. Publ: Self-awareness through writing: a report of success, Freshman Eng. News, fall 72; Behavioral objectives for English: a reaction, Col. Eng, 1/73; co-auth, Competency-based teacher education and departments of English, Col. Compos. & Commun, 5/74; plus others. Add: Div. of Humanities, Findlay College, Findlay, OH 45840.

GECKLE, GEORGE LEO, b. Danbury, Conn, Dec. 2, 39; m. 61; c. 2. ENGLISH. A.B, Middlebury Col, 61; NDEA fel, Univ. Va, 61-64, M.A, 62, du Pont fel, 64-65, Ph.D.(Eng), 65. Asst. prof. ENG, Univ. Wis-Madison, 65-68; UNIV. S.C, 68-70, ASSOC. PROF, 70- MLA; S.Atlantic Mod. Lang. Asn; Southeast Renaissance Conf. Renaissance English; James Joyce; drama. Publ: Ed, Twentieth century interpretations of Measure for measure, Prentice-Hall, 70; Stephen Dedalus and W.B. Yeats: the making of the Villanelle, Mod. Fiction Stud, spring 69; Fortune in Marston's The malcontent, PMLA, 3/71; Shakespeare's Isabella, Shakespeare Quart, spring 71. Add: Dept. of English, University of South Carolina, Columbia, SC 29208.

GEDULD, HARRY MAURICE, b. London, Eng, Mar. 3, 31. ENGLISH. A.B, Univ. Sheffield, 53, Linley fel. & state scholar, 53-54, A.M, 54; Fulbright fel, 59-60, Ph.D.(Eng), Univ. London, 61. Teaching assoc. Eng, Ind. Univ, Bloomington, 59-60, instr, 62-64, asst. prof, 64-65, assoc. prof, 66-69, prof. Eng. & comp. lit, 69-72; vis. asst. prof. Eng, Queens Col.(N.Y), 65-66; PROF. Eng. & screen arts, Univ. Md, 72-73; COMP. LIT, IND. UNIV, BLOOMINGTON, 73- Travel award, Ind. Univ, 60, fac. fel, 63, res. grant-in-aid, 67-; life mem, Birkbeck Col, Univ. London, 61-; film reviewer, Humanist, 67-; assoc. ed, Film J, 71- MLA; Shaw Soc, Eng.(gen. secy, 59-61); Soc. Cinema Stud; AAUP; Am. Fed. Teachers; Univ. Film Asn; Am. Film Inst. Film; English and American drama; comparative literature. Publ: Ed, Shaw's Rationalization of Russia, 64, auth, Film-makers on film-making, 67, Prince of publishers, 69 & Filmguide to Olivier's Henry V, 73, Ind. Univ; James Barrie: a study, Twayne, 71; Back to Methuselah and the

Birmingham Repertory Theatre, Mod. Drama, 9/59; Bernard Shaw and Adolf Hitler, 1/61 & The textual problem in Shaw, 5/62, Shaw Rev. Add: Dept. of Comparative Literature, Indiana University, Ballantine Hall, Bloomington, IN 47401.

GEE, RONALD CALLAWAY, b. Barron, Wis, July 6, 20; m. 42; c. 4. SPEECH, DRAMA. B.S.E, Wis. State Univ, Platteville, 42; M.S, Univ. Wis-Madison, 51, Ph.D.(theatre), 58. Teacher, high sch, Wis, 46-48; asst. speech, Univ. Wis-Madison, 48-51, instr. theatre, Wis. Idea Theatre, 51-55; from instr. to asst. prof. theatre, State Univ. Iowa, 55-59; from assoc. prof. to PROF. SPEECH & THEATRE, WEST. ILL. UNIV, 59-, chmn. dept. commun. arts & sci, 69-73. Nat. Theatre Conf. fel, 50-51; ed, Wis. Stage, 51-55; res. dir, Rockefeller Found. grant, Univ. Wis, 52-54. U.S.A.A.F, 42-45. Nat. Col. Players; Speech Commun. Asn; AAUP. Oral interpretation. Add: Dept. of Communication Arts & Sciences, Western Illinois University, Macomb, IL 61455.

GEEHERN, RICHARD J, b. Westfield, Mass, Jan. 27, 21; m. 64; c. 1. ENGLISH & AMERICAN LITERATURE. A.B, Harvard, 42; M.A, Univ. N.C, 49, Ph.D.(Eng. lit), 52. Instr. ENG, LEHMAN COL, 52-59, asst. prof, 59-68, ASSOC. PROF, 68-, chmn. dept, 68-71. U.S.A.A.F, 42-45, 1st Lt. Mediaeval Acad. Am. Mediaeval English literature, especially Chaucer; colonial and 19th century American literature. Add: Dept. of English, Herbert H. Lehman College, Bedford Park Blvd, Bronx, NY 10468.

GEEN, ELIZABETH, b. Dallas, Tex, Jan. 8, 03. ENGLISH. A.B, Univ. Calif, 25, A.M, 27; Ph.D.(Eng), State Univ, Iowa, 40; LL.D, Alfred Univ, 53; D.H.L, Col. Notre Dame (Md), 68; Litt.D, Goucher Col, 69; LL.D, Loyola Col, 71. Teacher, High Sch, Calif, 30-34; instr. Eng, Mills Col, 35-38, asst. prof, 40-42; assoc. prof. Eng. & dean women, Alfred Univ, 46-50; prof. Eng, dean & v.pres, Goucher Col, 50-68; consult. to pres. & dean, Mt. St. Agnes Col, 68-69, pres, 69-70; RETIRED. Staff assoc. Mid. States Asn, 68-70. U.S.N.R, 42-46, Lt. Comdr. MLA. Wordsworth. Publ: Man and the modern city, Univ. Pittsburgh, 63; Student evaluation of teaching, Am. Asn. Univ. Prof. Bull; Some thoughts concerning higher education for women, Pi Lambda Theta J; Concept of grace in Wordsworth's poetry, PMLA. Add: 6303 Pinehurst Rd, Baltimore, MD 21212.

GEFVERT, CONSTANCE JOANNA, b. Cleveland, Ohio, May 13, 41. COLONIAL AMERICAN LITERATURE, AMERICAN SOCIOLINGUISTICS. B.A, Cleveland State Univ, 64; M.A, Univ. Minn, Minneapolis, 66, Ph.D.(Am. lit), 71. Instr. ENG, Ill. State Univ, 66-68; ASST. PROF, WAYNE STATE UNIV, 71- MLA; Conf. Christianity & Lit; Soc. Stud. Midwest. Lit; Col. Eng. Asn; AAUP; NCTE. American urban dialects; linguistics and American religion. Publ: Edward Taylor: an annotated bibliography, Kent State Univ, 71. Add: Dept. of English, Wayne State University, Detroit, MI 48202.

GEGENHEIMER, ALBERT FRANK, b. Cleveland, Ohio, Mar. 2, 10; m. 37; c. 2. ENGLISH & AMERICAN LITERATURE. A.B, Yale, 32; A.M, West. Reserve Univ, 36; Harrison fel, Univ. Pa, 38-40, Ph.D, 40. Instr. ENG, Univ. Ariz, 41-43; Univ. Conn, 43; UNIV. ARIZ, 45-46, asst. prof, 46-50, assoc. prof, 50-57, PROF, 57- Ford fel, 53-54. Ed, Arizona Quart, 51- U.S.A, 44-45. Mod. Humanities Res. Asn, Gt. Brit; MLA. American literature, especially colonial period; American novel; American drama. Publ: William Smith, Univ. Pa; Thomas Godfrey, Pa. Hist; Thomas Spence Duché, Pa. Mag. Hist. & Biog. Add: Dept. of English, University of Arizona, Tucson, AZ 85721.

GEHRES, MARY RUTH, b. Evansville, Ind, Apr. 4, 33. ENGLISH. A.B, Brescia Col.(Ky), 62; Ph.D.(Eng), St. Louis Univ, 68. Teacher, elem. schs, Nebr. & Ky, 54-62; from asst. prof. to PROF. ENG, BRESCIA COL.(KY), 68-, CHMN; DIV. HUMANITIES, 73- NCTE. Romantic literature of England in its relationship to twentieth-century literature; contemporary literature; medieval literature of England, especially Chaucer. Add: Dept. of English, Brescia College, Owensboro, KY 42301.

GEHRING, MARY LOUISE, b. Oakdale, La, Mar. 21, 22. SPEECH. B.A, Baylor Univ, 43; M.A, La. State Univ, 49, Ph.D.(speech), 52; Danforth Found-scholar, Union Theol. Sem, summer 55. Instr. speech, Ala. Polytech. Inst, 49-50; assoc. prof. speech & dir. forensics, Miss. South. Col, 52-56; prof. speech, Stetson Univ, 56-65; DEAN, WESTHAMPTON COL, UNIV. RICHMOND, 65- Vis. lectr. educ. & speech, Univ. Wis, 62-63. U.S.C.G, 44-46, Ens. Speech Commun. Asn; Am. Forensic Asn. Public address; forensics. Publ: Co-auth, Speech practices, Harper, 58, 63. Add: Westhampton College, University of Richmond, Richmond, VA 23173.

GEIER, NORBERT JOSEPH, b. Cashton, Wis, Feb. 26, 25. ENGLISH. B.A, Univ. Notre Dame, 48; M.A, Univ. Wis, 49, Ph.D.(Eng), 64. Instr. ENG, Col. St. Teresa (Minn), 50-54, asst. prof, 57-63, assoc. prof, 63-67, chmn. dept, 65-67; assoc. prof, UNIV. WIS-LA CROSSE, 67-69, PROF, 69-, CHMN. DEPT, 73- U.S.N.R, 43-54, Lt.(jg). MLA; Midwest Mod. Lang. Asn; NCTE. Twentieth-century British literature; literary criticism and theory; 20th century American literature. Publ: Tooling up for the future: thoughts occasioned by labor's view of higher education, Encounters, 9/72. Add: Dept. of English, University of Wisconsin-La Crosse, La Crosse, WI 54601.

GEIGER, DON, b. Wichita, Kans, Mar. 4, 23; m. 49; c. 2. SPEECH. B.S, Northwest. Univ, 47, A.M, 48, Ph.D, 51. Instr. interpretation, Northwest. Univ, 48-50; from instr. to PROF. speech, UNIV. CALIF, BERKELEY, 50-69, RHETORIC, 69- Fulbright lectr. poetry & interpretation, Rikkyo Univ, Japan, 60-61; consult, ed, speech, Random House, Inc, 63-; fel, Creative Arts Inst, Univ. Calif, 66-67; assoc. ed, Quart. J. Speech. U.S.A.A.F, 42-45, T/Sgt. Speech Commun. Asn; West. Speech Commun. Asn.(ed, jour, 55). Oral interpretation; literary criticism; literary theory. Publ: Unexpected truce, Round Table Bks; Age of the splendid machine, Hokuseido Press, Japan; Sound, sense and performance of literature, Scott, 63; The dramatic impulse in modern poetics, La. State Univ, 67; The preservation game, Windfall, 72; Modern literary thought, Speech Monogr, 3/53; Melville's Black god, Am. Lit, 1/54; Tolstoy as defender of pure art, J. Aesthet. & Art Criticism, 9/61. Add: Dept. of Rhetoric, University of California, Berkeley, Berkeley, CA 94707.

GEIGER, WILLIAM ANDREW, JR, b. Los Angeles, Calif, Jan. 25, 41; m. 62; c. 2. ENGLISH LANGUAGE & LITERATURE. A.B, Whittier Col, 62; M.A, Univ. South. Calif, 64, Ph.D.(Eng), 73. Instr. ENG, WHITTIER COL, 65-72, ASST. PROF, 72- Prize, Graves Awards, 73-74. MLA. English Renaissance pulpit oratory; English Renaissance humanism. Publ: Felicity, Milton Encycl, (in press). Add: Dept. of English, Whittier College, Whittier, CA 90608.

GEIMER, ROGER ANTHONY, b. Evanston, Ill, Oct. 6, 32; m. 59; c. 5. ENGLISH. B.A, St. Mary's Col.(Minn), 54, M.A, Marquette Univ, 56, Ph.D. (Eng), Northwest. Univ, 65. Instr. ENG, St. Mary's Col, 58-59; Wis. State Univ-Superior, 59-60; asst. prof, Loyola Univ.(Ill), 62-66; PURDUE UNIV, CALUMET CAMPUS, 66-69, ASSOC. PROF, 69- Qm.C, U.S.A, 56-58. MLA; NCTE; Renaissance Soc. Am. English Renaissance non-dramatic literature; Shakespeare; 17th century poetry. Publ: A note on the birthdate of Thomas Churchyard, Notes & Queries, 12/67; Narrative irony in Gulliver's travels, Delta Epsilon Sigma Bull, 5/68; Spenser's rhyme or Churchyard's reason: evidence of Churchyard's first pension, Rev. Eng. Stud, 8/69. Add: Dept. of English, Purdue University, Calumet Campus, Hammond, IN 46323.

GEISSMAN, ERWIN WILLIAM, b. New York, N.Y, Sept. 21, 20; m. 44; c. 5. ENGLISH. A.B, Col. Holy Cross, 42; fel. & Ph.D.(Eng), Yale, 51. Assoc. prof. ENG, GRAD. SCH, FORDHAM UNIV, 48-71, PROF, 71- U.S.A.A.F, 42-45. MLA; Renaissance Soc. Am. Shakespeare; Renaissance history of ideas; modern literature. Publ: Early Jesuitica in America, Thought. Add: Dept. of English Language & Literature, Fordham University, Rosehill Campus, Bronx, NY 10458.

GEIST, ROBERT JOHN, b. Buffalo, N.Y, Feb. 6, 12; m. 37; c. 2. ENGLISH, LINGUISTICS. B.S, Cornell Univ, 32; A.M, Univ. Mo, 34; Ph.D, Univ. Ill, 40. Instr. ENG, Univ. Mo, 35-37; Univ. Ill, 37-47; asst. prof, MICH. STATE UNIV, 47-56, assoc. prof, 56-61, PROF, 61- Consult. Eng, Univ. Ryukyus, 57-60, 64-66. U.S.A.A.F, 42-45, Capt. MLA; NCTE; Ling. Soc. Am; AAUP. Middle English literature; English language; English as a second language. Publ: Co-auth, Current English composition, Rinehart, 51, English pronunciation for speakers of Japanese, Univ. Ryukyus, 59, An English reader for Okinawan students, Tuttle, Tokyo, 61; co-auth, The Macmillan English ser, Vols. III-VI, 67, 69, 73, auth, An introduction to language, 70, an introduction to modern grammar, 70, A short history of English, 70, An introduction to transformation grammar, 71, Macmillan; Current linguistic change, In: Essays presented to Professor Genshu Asato, LL.D, Eihosha, Tokyo, 72. Add: Dept. of English, Michigan State University, East Lansing, MI 48823.

GEIZER, RONALD STANLEY, b. Bronx, N.Y, Sept. 28, 41; m. 70. SPEECH COMMUNICATION. B.A, City Col. New York, 63; Ph.D.(speech commun), Ohio State Univ, 71. ASST. PROF. commun, Univ. Wyo, 71-73; SPEECH COMMUN, UNIV. MINN, MINNEAPOLIS, 73- Speech Commun. Asn; Int. Commun. Asn. Communication theory; nonverbal behavior. Publ: Psychogrammatical measures, Today's Speech, 67; Advertising in Ebony: 1960 and 1969, Jour. Quart, 71; co-auth, Free association responses and the investigation of meaning: a technique for instrument development, Cent. States Speech J, 71. Add: Dept. of Speech Communication, University of Minnesota, Minneapolis, MN 55455.

GELATT, ROD GERALD, b. Des Moines, Iowa, Sept. 20, 26; m. 61; c. 2. JOURNALISM. B.A, Univ. Iowa, 50, M.A, 63. News ed, WHO-AM-TV, Des Moines, Iowa, 50-57; instr. jour, Washington & Lee Univ, 57-59; Univ. Iowa, 59-63; ASSOC. PROF. JOUR, UNIV. MO-COLUMBIA, 63-, DIR. PUB. AFFAIRS, KOMU-TV, 72-, news dir, 63-72. U.S.A.F, 44-46, S/Sgt. Radio-TV News Dir. Asn. Add: School of Journalism, University of Missouri-Columbia, Columbia, MO 65201.

GELBER, NORMAN, b. New York, N.Y, Nov. 15, 17; m. 53; c. 2. ENGLISH. B.A, Univ, Calif, Berkeley, 49; Univ. Edinburgh, 50-51; M.A, Columbia Univ, 58. Lectr. ENG, Univ. Frankfurt, 50-51; teacher, Seaford High Sch, 53-54; instr, Univ. Ky, 54-58; teacher, River Edge Jr. High Sch, 59-61; ASSOC. PROF, EAST STROUDSBURG STATE COL, 61- NCTE. The dramatic mode of Robert Greene; The misalliance theme in Victorian and Edwardian drama; modern English drama. Publ: Robert Greene's Orlando furioso: a study of thematic ambiguity, Mod. Lang. Rev, 4/69; The misalliance theme in Major Barbara, Shaw Rev, 5/72. Add: Dept. of English, East Stroudsburg State College, East Stroudsburg, PA 18301.

GELDERMAN, CAROL WETTLAUFER, b. Detroit, Mich, Dec. 2, 35; div; c. 3. MODERN DRAMA & LITERATURE. B.A, Manhattanville Col, 56; M.A, Northwest. Univ, Evanston, 68; fel. & Ph.D.(Eng, mod. drama), 72. ASST. PROF. ENG, LA. STATE UNIV, NEW ORLEANS, 72- MLA; S.Cent. Mod. Lang. Asn; AAUP; Am. Asn. Univ. Women. Modern drama; autobiography; alcoholism and literature. Publ: Austin Clarke and William Butler Yeats' alleged jealousy of George Fitzmaurice, Eire-Ireland, summer 73. Add: 2622 Camp St, New Orleans, LA 70130.

GELERNT, JULES, b. Berlin, Ger, July 13, 28; U.S. citizen; m. 58; c. 2. ENGLISH LITERATURE. B.A, City Col. New York, 49; M.A, Columbia Univ, 50, fel, 55-56, Ph.D.(comp. lit), 63; Sorbonne, 53-54. Instr. ENG, Hofstra Univ, 56-63; asst. prof, BROOKLYN COL, 63-72, ASSOC. PROF, 72- Mem, comt. comp. & world lit, NCTE, 67- MLA; Dante Soc. Am; Renaissance Soc. Am. Renaissance and comparative literature. Publ: Review notes on Dante's Divine comedy, Monarch, 63; World of many loves: the Heptameron of Marguerite de Navarre, Univ. N.C, 66. Add: Dept. of English, Brooklyn College, Brooklyn, NY 11210.

GELLER, LILA BELLE, b. Chicago, Ill, Oct. 6, 32; m. 52; c. 3. ENGLISH LITERATURE. B.A, Univ. Calif, Los Angeles, 52, Ph.D.(Eng), 69; M.A, San Fernando Valley State Col, 65. Asst. prof. ENG, CALIF. STATE COL, DOMINGUEZ HILLS, 69-73, ASSOC. PROF, 73- MLA. English Renaissance literature; Spenser; Shakespeare. Publ: The Acidalian vision: Spenser's Graces in Book VI of The Faerie Queene, Rev. Eng. Stud, 8/72; Venus and the Three Graces: a noeplatonic paradigm for Book III of The Faerie Queene, J. Eng. & Ger. Philol, (in press). Add: Dept. of English, California State College, Dominguez Hills, 1000 E. Victoria St, Dominguez Hills, CA 90247.

GELLEY, ALEXANDER, b. Czechoslavakia, May 27, 33; U.S. citizen. COMPARATIVE LITERATURE. B.A, Harvard, 55; Fulbright scholar, Univ. Tübingen, 55-56; Ph.D.(comp. lit), Yale, 65. Instr. comp. lit, Univ. Wis-Madison, 57-59; lectr. Eng, City Col. New York, 61-65; Fulbright lectr. Eng. & comp. lit, Tel Aviv Univ, 65-66; Hebrew Univ. Jerusalem, 66-67; asst. prof. comp. lit, Cornell Univ, 67-68, Soc. for Humanities jr. fel, 68-69, asst. prof. COMP. LIT, 69-71; ASSOC. PROF. & DIR. COMP. LIT. PROG, UNIV. CALIF, IRVINE, 71- MLA; Am. Comp. Lit. Asn. The European novel, 18th-20th centuries; contemporary critical theory; the Enlightenment. Publ: Ed. & transl, Mythology and humanism—the correspondence of Thomas Mann and Karl Kerenyi, Cornell Univ, 74; auth, Staiger, Heidegger, and the task of criticism, Mod. Lang. Quart, 9/62; Setting and a sense of world in the novel, Yale Rev, winter 73; The landscape of happiness in La Chartreuse de Parme, Hebrew Univ. Stud. Lit, spring 73. Add: Dept. of English & Comparative Literature, University of California, Irvine, CA 92664.

GELPI, ALBERT JOSEPH, b. New Orleans, La, July 19, 31; m. 65; c. 1. ENGLISH & AMERICAN LITERATURE. A.B, Loyola Univ.(La), 51; M.A, Tulane Univ, 56; Ph.D.(Eng), Harvard, 62. Instr. ENG, Harvard, 62-64, asst. prof, 64-68; PROF, STANFORD UNIV, 68- Dexter fel, Harvard, summer 62, Canaday Fund grant, summer 67; Am. Counc. Learned Soc. grant-in-aid, spring 68. U.S.A, 51-53, 2nd Lt. American poetic tradition. Publ: The poet in America : 1650 to the present, Heath, 73; Emily Dickinson: the mind of the poet, 65 & Emily Dickinson, In: Notable American women, Harvard; The uses of language, South. Rev, fall 67; Adrienne Rich: the poetics of change, In: American poetry since 1960, 73. Add: Dept. of English, Stanford University, Stanford, CA 94305.

GEMMETT, ROBERT JAMES, b. Schenectady, N.Y, Mar. 11, 36; m. 64; c. 3. ENGLISH. B.A, Siena Col, 59; M.A, Univ. Mass, 62; travel fel, Syracuse Univ, 66, Ph.D, 67. Instr. ENG, Clarkson Technol. Col, 64-65; assoc. prof, STATE UNIV. N.Y. COL. BROCKPORT, 65-70, PROF, 70- Res. grants, State Univ. N.Y, 67, 68 & summer fels, 69, 71; assoc. ed, Eng. Record, 67-69. U.S.A, 59, 2nd Lt. British 18th century studies and romantic period. Publ: Ed, Biographical memoirs of extraordinary painters, 69 & Dreams, waking thoughts and incidents, 71, Fairleigh Dickinson Univ; Poets and men of letters, Mansell, London, 72; Vathek, the English edition of 1786 and the French editions of 1787, Scholars' Facsimiles, 72; The composition of William Beckford's Biographical memoirs of extraordinary painters, Philol. Quart, 1/68; The critical reception of William Beckford's Fonthill, Eng. Miscellany, 68; Beckford's Fonthill: the landscape as art, Gazette Beaux-Arts, 12/72. Add: Dept. of English, State University of New York College at Brockport, Brockport, NY 14420.

GENTHE, CHARLES V, b. Detroit, Mich, May 23, 37; m. 63; c. 2. AMERICAN STUDIES, ENGLISH. A.B, Rutgers Univ, 59; M.A, Univ. Wyo, 60; Ph.D.(Am. stud), Wash. State Univ, 67. Instr. Eng, Miami-Dade Jr. Col, 61-63; teaching asst, Wash. State Univ, 63-65; instr, Calif. State Col. Long Beach, 65-66; asst. prof. Eng, CALIF. STATE UNIV, CHICO, 66-73, PROF. ENG. & AM. STUD, 73-, DIR. INT. PROG, 70-, coord. Am. stud, 66-73. U.S.A.R, 60-, Maj. MLA; Am. Stud. Asn. American literary realism and naturalism. Publ: American war narratives, 1914-1918, D. Lewis, 69; ed, Reflection/perception, Ginn, 71; co-ed, Themes in American literature, Heath, 72; auth, Damnation of Theron Ware and Elmer Gantry, Res. Stud, 12/65; How Annandale went out, Colby Libr. Quart, 3/67; Robert Herrick, Am. Lit. Realism, fall 67. Add: International Programs Office, California State University, Chico, Chico, CA 95926.

GENTRY, THOMAS BLYTHE, b. Danville, Ky, Nov. 26, 22; m. 44; c. 2. ENGLISH LITERATURE. B.A, Centre Col, 47; M.A, Univ. Ky, 53, Ph.D, 62; B.A, Va. Mil. Inst, 62. From instr. to assoc. prof. ENG, VA. MIL. INST, 48-66, PROF, 66- U.S.A, 43-46, Res, 46-, Maj. Col. Eng. Asn. Add: Dept. of English, Virginia Military Institute, Lexington, VA 24450.

GENTRY, WILLIAM LARRY, b. Burns, Tenn, July 17, 39; m. 61; c. 2. ENGLISH & AMERICAN LITERATURE. A.B, David Lipscomb Col, 61; M.A, Vanderbilt Univ, 63, Ph.D, 72. Instr. ENG, Memphis State Univ, 63-66; asst. prof, MID. TENN. STATE UNIV, 68-72, ASSOC. PROF, 73- S.Atlantic Mod. Lang. Asn; MLA. Victorian prose; satire. Add: Dept. of English, Middle Tennessee State University, Murfreesboro, TN 37130.

GEORGAS, MARILYN DAVIS, b. Jacksonville, Tex, Jan. 30, 31; m. 49; c. 2. ENGLISH. B.A, Sam Houston State Univ, 52; M.A, Lamar Univ, 63; Ph.D. (Eng), Univ. Tex, Austin, 69. Instr. ENG, LAMAR UNIV, 63-67, asst. prof, 67-72, ASSOC. PROF, 72- MLA; Renaissance Soc. Am. Victorian and Elizabethan literature, especially relationships between the two, and fiction, criticism and cultural milieu. Publ: A new source for Hogg's Justified sinner, Nineteenth Century Fiction, fall 74. Add: Dept. of English, Lamar University, Port Arthur Hwy, Beaumont, TX 77705.

GEORGES, ROBERT A, b. Sewickley, Pa, May 1, 33; m. 56; c. 1. FOLKLORE, LINGUISTICS. B.S, Ind. State Col, 54; Johns Hopkins Univ, 57-58; M.A, Univ. Pa, 61; NDEA fel, Ind. Univ, 62-63, Ph.D, 64. Teacher English, Bound Brook High Sch, N.J, 54-56; South. Regional High Sch, Manahawkin, 58-60; instr. Eng, Univ. Kans, 63-64, asst. prof, 64-66; ENG. & FOLKLORE, UNIV. CALIF, LOS ANGELES, 66-70, ASSOC. PROF, 70-, CHMN. FOLKLORE & MYTHOLOGY GROUP, 68-, v.chmn, 67-68. Guggenheim fel, 69-70. U.S.A, 56-58, Res, 58-62. MLA; Ling. Soc. Am; Am. Folklore Soc. (work-in-prog. ed, 67-, exec. bd, 69-73). Narrating process; narrative analysis; conceptual foundations of folklore and mythology studies. Publ: Ed, Studies on mythology, Dorsey, 68; co-transl, Stilpon P. Kyriakides, Two studies on modern Greek folklore, Inst. Balkan Stud, Thessaloniki, Greece, 68; auth, Toward an understanding of storytelling events, J. Am. Folklore, 69; Recreations and games, In: Folklore and folklife: an introduction, Univ. Chicago, 72; Process and structure in traditional storytelling in the Balkans, In: Aspects of the Balkans: continuity and change, Mouton, The Hague, 72; plus others. Add: Folklore & Mythology Studies, University of California, 405 Hilgard Ave, Los Angeles, CA 90024.

GERBER, GERALD E, b. Elmhurst, Ill, May 12, 32; m. 63; c. 2. ENGLISH, LITERARY CRITICISM. B.S, Northwest. Univ, 54, M.A, 58, fels, 60-62, Ph.D.(Am. lit, lit. criticism), 64. Instr. ENG, DUKE UNIV, 62-65, asst. prof, 65-70, ASSOC. PROF, 70-, summer res. fel, 67. Summer res. award, Duke Univ-Univ. N.C. Coop. Prog. in Humanities, 70. U.S.A, 54-56. MLA; Soc. Stud. South. Lit. American literature, 19th century; Edgar Allan Poe. Publ: Poe's odd angel, Nineteenth Century Fiction, 6/68; James Kirke Paulding and the image of the machine, Am. Quart, fall 70; The Coleridgean context of Poe's Blackwood satires, In: New approaches to Poe: a symposium, 70. Add: Dept. of English, Duke University, Durham, NC 27706.

GERBER, HELMUT E, b. Ger, July 7, 20; nat. m. 47; c. 2. ENGLISH. B.S, Rutgers Univ, 42; M.A, N.Y. Univ, 46; Ph.D.(Eng), Univ. Pa, 52. Instr. ENG, Lafayette Col, 46-52, asst. prof, 52-57; Purdue Univ, 57-62, assoc. prof, 62-68; prof. & dir. grad. stud, North. Ill. Univ, 68-71; PROF, ARIZ. STATE UNIV, 71- Fund. Advan. Educ. fac. fel, 55-56, ed, Eng. Lit. in Transition, 57-; mem, Eng. Inst, 57-; Purdue Res. Found. grants, 59, 61, 62; vis. prof. Eng. & curriculum consult, Univ. Tex, Arlington, summer 66; Counc. Acad. Deans grant, North. Ill. Univ, 70; fac. res. grants, Ariz. State Univ, 72, 73. U.S.A, 42-45, Capt. MLA; NCTE; Rocky Mountain Mod. Lang. Asn. English literature, 1880-1920; bibliographies of criticism; aesthetics and literary history. Publ: The English short story in transition, Pegasus, 67; George Moore in transition, Wayne State Univ, 68; co-ed, Joseph Conrad: an annotated secondary bibliography, 71 & Thomas Hardy, an annotated secondary bibliography, 73, North. Ill. Univ; The nineties: beginning, end, or transition?, In: Edwardians and late Victorians, Columbia Univ, 60; George Moore: from pure poetry to pure criticism, J. Aesthet. & Art Criticism, spring 67; plus others. Add: Dept. of English, Arizona State University, Tempe, AZ 85281.

GERBER, JOHN CHRISTIAN, b. New Waterford, Ohio, Jan. 31, 08; m. 41; c. 2. ENGLISH. A.B, Univ. Pittsburgh, 29, A.M, 31; Ph.D, Univ. Chicago, 41. Instr. Eng, Univ. Pittsburgh, 30-36; Univ. Chicago, 38-41, premeteorology, 41-44; asst. prof. ENG, UNIV. IOWA, 44-47, assoc. prof, 47-49, PROF, 49-, CHMN. DEPT, 61-, DIR. SCH. LETT, 67- Vis. assoc. prof, Univ. South. Calif, summer, 49; summer vis. prof, Univ. N.Mex, 52, 57; Trinity Col, 60, 63; vis. prof, Univ. Calif, Berkeley, 60-61; ed. adv, Scott-Foresman, 55-; mem. Eng. adv. panel, U.S. Off. Educ, 63-65, Eng. consult, 64-65; humanities consult, World Book Encycl, 65-74; chmn, Am. Lit. Group, Mod. Lang. Asn, 69; vis. prof, Univ. Colo, summer 65; vis. lectr, Am. Univ. Cairo, 70; vis. lectr, various Korean univs, summer 72. Distinguished Serv. Award, Iowa Counc. Teachers Eng, 72. Midwest Mod. Lang. Asn. (pres, 65-66); Midcontinent Am. Stud. Asn; NCTE (pres, 55, Hatfield award, 64); MLA; Am. Stud. Asn; Conf. Col. Compos. & Commun.(chmn, 50); Asn. Depts. Eng.(pres, 64). American literature; 19th century American fiction; Mark Twain. Publ: Chmn. ed. bd, Iowa-Calif. Edition of Mark Twain; Twentieth century interpretations of The scarlet letter, Prentice-Hall, 68; Mark Twain's use of the comic pose, PMLA, 6/62; chap. on Mark Twain, In: American Literary Scholarship, Duke Univ, Annually, 63-68. Add: Dept. of English, University of Iowa, Iowa City, IA 52242.

GERBER, SANFORD EDWIN, b. Chicago, Ill, June 16, 33; m. 53, 65; c. 3. SPEECH, LINGUISTICS. B.A, Lake Forest Col, 54; M.S, Univ. Ill, 56; Whittier Col, 57; Ph.D, Univ. South. Calif, 62. Speech therapist, Pub. Schs, Calif, 56-58; sr. human factors specialist, Syst. Develop Corp, 58-60; head, speech & hearing res, Hughes Aircraft Co, 60-65; asst. prof. speech & dir. audiol, UNIV. CALIF, SANTA BARBARA, 65-73, ASSOC. PROF. AUDIOL, 73- Consult. expert, U.S. Dept. Defense, 67-69; consult. psychoacoustics, CBS Labs, 69- Am. Speech & Hearing Asn; Acoust. Soc. Am; Speech Commun. Asn; AAAS; Am. Asn. Phonetic Sci. Speech perception; psychoacoustics; pediatric audiology. Publ: Interaural phase and the release from masking, Audiology, 72; Extension of interaural time delay for intelligibility, J. Acoust. Soc. Am, 72; Biomedical technology and the detection of birth defects, Rehabil. Lit, 72; plus others. Add: Speech and Hearing Center, University of California, Santa Barbara, Santa Barbara, CA 93106.

GERGELY, EMRO J, b. Hungary, Mar. 9, 99; U.S. citizen; m. 28; c. 1. ENGLISH, EDUCATION. A.B, Allegheny Col, 23; M.A, Univ. Pittsburgh, 29; Ph.D.(Am. drama), Univ. Pa, 38. Teacher & head dept. Eng. high schs, Pa, 23-29; prof, Chestnut Hill Col, 29-47; asst. prof, BROOKLYN COL, 47-58, assoc. prof, 58-61, prof. ENG. & EDUC, 61-67, EMER. PROF, 67- Consult, Sec. Educ. Textbk. Prog, Sadlier, 45-60; Dean, St. Francis Col.(Pa), 67-71, dir. instnl. res, 71- Am. Asn. Higher Educ; Asn. Instnl. Res; Nat. Cath. Educ. Asn. Long range planning for higher education; Hungarian cultural and literary contributions to American life; the direction and goals of liberal arts colleges today and tomorrow. Publ: English composition, Westbrook, 35; Hungarian drama in New York, Univ. Pa. & Oxford, 47; co-auth, American history, 55 & English voices, 58, Sadlier; auth, more visions, Eng. Rec, N.Y. State Eng. Counc, winter 58. Add: Office of Institutional Research, St. Francis College, Loretto, PA 15940.

GERHARD, GEORGE B, b. Ft. Wayne, Ind, Feb. 3, 16; m. 41; c. 2. ENGLISH. A.B, Ind. Univ, 48, M.A, 49, Ph.D, 61. Asst. prof. ENG, Mich. Univ. Technol, 52-61; assoc. prof, Wis. State Univ, Superior, 61-62; PROF, Jersey City State Col, 62-65; Iowa Wesleyan Col, 65-67; W.VA. STATE COL, 67- Res. assoc, Ind. Univ, 55-56, 58. U.S.A, 43-46, T/Sgt. Nat. Educ. Asn; Asn. Higher Educ. Middle English; American literature. Publ: Ed, A dictionary of Middle-English musical terms, Ind. Univ, 61; auth, All the king's men: a study, Monarch, 65; The scarlet letter: a critical analysis in depth, Barrister, 66. Add: Dept. of English, West Virginia State College, Institute, WV 25112.

GERHART, MARY, Theology, Literature. See Volume IV, Philosophy, Religion & Law.

GERING, WILLIAM MARVIN, b. Marion, S.Dak, Jan. 24, 23; m. 56; c. 2. SPEECH, THEATRE. B.A, Bethel Col.(Kans), 51; World Counc. Churches scholar, Mainz Univ, 52-53; B.D, Bethany Bibl. Sem, 55; M.A, Ind. Univ, Bloomington, 61, Ph.D.(pub. address), 63. Asst. prof. speech & drama & chmn. dept, Bethel Col.(Kans), 63-65; asst. prof. pub. address, IND. UNIV, SOUTH BEND, 65-67, asst. prof. SPEECH & THEATRE & ASST. CHMN. DEPT, 67-69, ASSOC. PROF, 69- A.U.S, 45-46, Sgt. Speech Commun. Asn; Am. Theatre Asn; AAUP. David Starr Jordan as a speaker and educator; history and training in college oratory; history and criticism of preaching. Publ: David Starr Jordan on flavorless foolishness, Quart. J. Speech, 2/66; John Wesley on preaching, Preaching J. Homiletics, 5-6/67. Add: Dept. of Speech & Theatre, Indiana University, South Bend, IN 46615.

GERLACH, JOHN CHARLES, b. Baltimore, Md, Aug. 1, 41. NINETEENTH CENTURY AMERICAN LITERATURE. B.A, Kenyon Col, 63; M.F.A, Columbia Univ, 65; Ph.D.(Eng), Ariz. State Univ, 69. ASST. PROF. ENG, CLEVELAND STATE UNIV, 68- Film; 19th century American fiction. Publ: The critical index, Teachers Col, Columbia, 74; Messianic nationalism in the early works of Herman Melville, Ariz. Quart, 4/72; James Fenimore Cooper and the kingdom of God, Ill. Quart, 4/73; The last picture show and one more adaptation, Lit. Film Quart, spring 73. Add: Dept. of English, Cleveland State University, Cleveland, OH 44115.

GERMAIN, EDWARD BARNARD, b. Saginaw, Mich, Dec. 30, 37; m. 62; c. 1. ENGLISH LITERATURE, POETRY. B.A, Univ. Mich, Ann Arbor, 61, fel, 65-69, Ph.D.(Eng. lang. & lit), 69. Instr. ENG, East. Mich. Univ, 63-65; ASST. PROF, POMONA COL, 69-, res. grant, 70-71. U.S.N.R, 61-63, Res, 63-65, Lt. Asn. Stud. Dada & Surrealism. Surrealist poetry and poetics; modern poetry, poetics. Publ: Ed, Flag of ecstacy: sel poems of Charles Henri Ford, Black Sparrow, 72 & The surrealist poem in English, Penguin, 75. Add: Dept. of English, Pomona College, Claremont, CA 91711.

GERN, JESS W, b. Littleton, Colo, May 13, 20; m. 41; c. 2. SPEECH, DRAMA. B.A, West. State Col. Colo, 42; M.A, Univ. Denver, 49; Ph.D, Ohio State Univ, 60. Instr. SPEECH & DRAMA, WEST. STATE COL. COLO, 46-50, asst. prof, 50-57, assoc. prof, 57-58, PROF, 58-, DIR, SCH. ARTS & HUMANITIES, 59- U.S.A.A.F, 42-46, 1st Lt. Colorado theatre history. Add: School of Arts & Humanities, Western State College of Colorado, Gunnison, CO 81230.

GERRIETTS, JOHN, b. Chicago, Ill, May 11, 12. ENGLISH. A.B, Loyola Univ.(Ill), 34, M.A, 37, Ph.D.(Eng), 54. Instr. ENG, LOYOLA UNIV. CHICAGO, 37-52, asst. prof, 52-55, assoc. prof, 55-60, PROF, 60-, dir. honors prog, 49-58, chmn. dept, 58-73. Eng. consult, Chicago Bd. Educ, 60-61; chmn. exec. comt, Ill. Stud. Ctr. Preparation Eng. Teacher, 65-66; mem. fac. adv. comt, Ill. Bd. Higher Educ, 66-68. Asn. Depts. Eng.(mem. exec. comt, 63-65); MLA; NCTE. Poetics; Henry James; preparation of English teachers. Publ: The English teacher: a portrait, In: NDEA institute lectures 1965, Univ. Tulsa, 66; What literature—and why?, In: Method in the teaching of English, NCTE, 67. Add: Dept. of English, Loyola University, Chicago, IL 60626.

GERSTENBERGER, DONNA LORINE, b. Wichita Falls, Tex, Dec. 26, 29. AMERICAN LITERATURE. A.B, Whitman Col, 51; M.A, Univ. Okla, 52, Ph.D, 58. Instr. ENG, Southwest Tex. State Col, 55-56; Univ. Colo, 58-60; UNIV. WASH, 60-61, asst. prof, 61-64, assoc. prof, 64-69, PROF, 69-, ASSOC. DEAN ARTS & SCI, 74-, chmn. undergrad. stud. Eng, 71-74. Ed, Abstracts Eng. Stud, 59-; Am. Counc. Learned Soc. res. grant-in-aid, 61-62; Am. Philos. Soc. res. grant, 62-63. MLA; Am. Stud. Asn; Mod. Humanities Res. Asn; Am. Comt. Irish Stud. Modern novel; modern drama; Irish Renaissance. Publ: Co-auth, Directory of periodicals, 59, 65, 70 & The American novel: a checklist of twentieth-century criticism, Vols. I & II, 61 & 70, Swallow; auth, J.M. Synge, Twayne, 64; The complex configuration: modern verse drama, 73 & Iris Murdock, 74, Salzburg Stud. Poetic Drama; Walden: the house that Henry built, Emerson Soc. Quart, 69; Bonnie and Clyde and Christy Mahon: Playboys all, Modern Drama, 9/71; The open boat: additional perspective, Mod. Fiction Stud, winter 71-72. Add: Dept. of English, University of Washington, Seattle, WA 98195.

GERTNER, WILLIS STANLEY, Religion, Speech. See Volume IV, Philosophy, Religion & Law.

GERVAIS, RONALD JAMES, b. Lansing, Mich, May 16, 41; m. 63. AMERICAN LITERATURE. B.A, Mich. State Univ, 63, M.A, 65; Ph.D.(Eng), Univ. Ore, 69. ASST. PROF. AM. LIT, SAN DIEGO STATE UNIV, 69- MLA; AAUP. American Renaissance, especially Poe; American realism-naturalism, especially Twain and Crane; modern American fiction, especially Fitzgerald. Publ: Twain's The mysterious stranger: the fall as salvation, Pac. Coast Philol, 4/70. Add: School of Literature, San Diego State University, 5402 College Ave, San Diego, CA 92115.

GESNER, CAROL, b. Colon, Panama, July 7, 22; U.S. citizen. ENGLISH. B.S, N.J. State Col, 44; M.A, Univ. N.H, 49; fel, La. State Univ, 49-52, Ph.D.(Eng), 56. Instr. ENG, BEREA COL, 54-56, asst. prof, 56-61, assoc. prof, 61-67, PROF, 67- MLA. Shakespeare; Renaissance. Publ: Shakespeare and the Greek romance, Univ. Ky, 70; Crystal spectrum, a cycle of poems, The Pulpit, 65-66; plus two others. Add: Box 863, Berea College, Berea, KY 40403.

GETTMANN, ROYAL ALFRED, b. Portland, Ore, Apr. 5, 04; m. 27; c. 1. ENGLISH & AMERICAN LITERATURE. A.B, Earlham Col, 25; A.M, Haverford Col, 26; Ph.D.(Eng. lit), Univ. Ill, 37. Instr. ENG, Westminster Col. (Pa), 26-28; prof, Penn Col, 28-29; instr, State Col. Wash, 29-31; asst, Univ. Ill, 31-37; from asst. prof. to assoc. prof, Univ. Nebr, 37-45; prof, UNIV. ILL, URBANA, 45-69, EMER. PROF, 69- English and American novel in the 19th century; history of 19th century British publishing. Publ: Turgenev in England and America, Univ. Ill; A Victorian publisher: a study of the Bentley Papers, Cambridge; George Gissing and H.G. Wells, Rupert Hart-Davis. Add: 100 English Bldg, University of Illinois, Urbana, IL 61801.

GEYER, CHARLES WILLIAM, b. Deadwood, S.Dak, July 2, 34; m. 59; c. 2. AMERICAN LITERATURE. B.A, Augustana Col, 58; M.A, Auburn Univ, 60, Danforth grant, 64-66, Ph.D.(Eng), 67. Instr. ENG, Auburn Univ, 59-60; AUGUSTANA COL, 60-64, asst. prof, 67-69, ASSOC. PROF, 69- Fulbright-Hays lectr, Eng. Inst, Univ. Trondheim, 74. MLA. American poetry; contemporary American literature. Publ: Robert Frost's chicken feathers, Augustana Col. Monogr. Series, 69; American literature and the curriculum, Ind. Eng. J, fall 68; A Poulterer's pleasure: Robert Frost as prose humorist, Stud. Short Fiction, fall 71. Add: Dept. of English, Augustana College, Sioux Falls, SD 57102.

GEYER, RICHARD BENNETT, b. Urbana, Ohio, Oct. 24, 19; m. 44; c. 3. ENGLISH. A.B, Miami Univ, 41, M.A, 47; Univ. Aberdeen, Scotland; Ph.D. (Eng), Northwest. Univ, 51. PROF. ENG. & HEAD DEPT, Univ. Dubuque, 50-54; GETTYSBURG COL, 54- U.S.A, 42-46. MLA. Romantic and Victorian period; modern novel. Add: R.D. 3, Gettysburg, PA 17325.

GEZARI, JANET K, b. Newark, N.J, Jan. 27, 45; m. 66. ENGLISH LITERATURE. B.A, Cornell Univ, 66; M.Phil, Yale, 68, Ph.D.(Eng), 71. Instr. ENG, CONN. COL, 70-71, ASST. PROF, 71- MLA; AAUP. Nabokov; the novel; George Eliot. Publ: Borne to live and die, In: Eterne in mutabilitie, Archon Bks, 72; Roman et problème chez Nabokov, Poetique, 74. Add: Dept. of English, Connecticut College, New London, CT 06320.

GHISELIN, BREWSTER, b. Webster Groves, Mo, June 13, 03; m. 29; c. 2. ENGLISH. A.B, Univ. Calif, Los Angeles, 27, M.A, Univ. Calif, 28; Ford Fel, 52-53. Instr. ENG, Univ. Utah, 29-31; asst, Univ. Calif, 31-33; Instr, UNIV. UTAH, 34-38, lectr, 38-39, asst. prof, 39-46, assoc. prof, 46-50, PROF, 50-71, dir. annual writers' conf, 47-66, distinguished res. prof, 67-68, EMER. PROF, 71- Award in Lit, Nat. Inst. Arts & Lett, 70; Blumenthal-Leviton-Blonder Prize, Poetry, 73. MLA. Contemporary British and American literature; prosody; the creative process. Publ: Against the circle, 46 & The nets, 55, Dutton; The creative process: a symposium, Univ. Calif, 52; Writing, Arts Resource Ctr, Am. Asn. Univ. Women, 59; co-auth, Images and impressions, 69 & auth, Country of the Minotaur, 70, Univ. Utah; contrib, Twentieth century interpretation of Dubliners, Prentice-Hall, 68; Allen Tate and his work, Univ. Minn, 72; The form discovered: essays on the achievement of Andrew Lytle, State Univs. of Miss, 73; plus others. Add: Dept. of English, University of Utah, Salt Lake City, UT 84112.

GIAMATTI, ANGELO BARTLETT, b. Boston, Mass, Apr. 4, 38; m. 60; c. 3. ENGLISH, COMPARATIVE LITERATURE. B.A, Yale, 60, Ph.D.(comp. lit), 64. Instr. Ital. & comp. lit, Princeton, 64-65, asst. prof, 65-66; Eng, YALE, 66-68, assoc. prof, 68-71, PROF. ENG. & COMP. LIT, 71-, master, Ezra Stiles Col, 70-72. Guggenheim fel, 69-70; vis. prof. comp. lit, N.Y. Univ, summer 66; fac, Bread Loaf Sch. Eng, summers 72, 73- MLA (mem, new stud. comn, 69-74); Renaissance Soc. Am; Dante Soc. Am.(v.pres, 73-74); Am. Comp. Lit. Asn.(treas, 67-71); Mediaeval Soc. Am. Medieval and Renaissance literature; Italy and England. Publ: Co-ed, The songs of Bernart de Ventadorn, Univ. N.C, 62, 65; auth, The earthly paradise and the Renaissance epic, Princeton Univ, 66; co-ed, Ariosto's Orlando Furioso, Bobbs, 68 & A variorum commentary on the poems of John Milton, Columbia Univ, Vol. I, 70; gen. ed, Western literature (3 vols), Harcourt, 71. Add: Dept. of English, Yale University, New Haven, CT 06520.

GIANAKARIS, CONSTANTINE JOHN, b. Morenci, Mich, May 2, 34; m. 57. ENGLISH. B.A, Univ. Mich, 56, M.A, 57; outstate Scholar fel, Univ. Wis, 61, Ph.D, 61. Asst. to assoc. dean col. let. & sci, Univ. Wis, 58-60; asst. prof, ENG, Ill. State Univ, 61-63, assoc. prof, 63-66; WEST. MICH. UNIV, 66-72, PROF, 72-, fac. res. grant, 67-68. Ill. State Univ. fac. grant, 63-64; co-ed, Comp. Drama; jury panelist, Nat. Endowment for Humanities, 71- MLA; Midwest Mod. Lang. Asn; Renaissance Soc. Am; N.Cent. Renaissance Conf; AAUP; Mod. Greek Stud. Asn; Shakespeare Soc. Am. Drama of Ben Jonson; modern British and American drama; Shakespeare. Publ: Ed, Antony and Cleopatra, W.C. Brown, 69; auth, Plutarch, Twayne, 70; Identifying ethical values in Volpone, Huntington Libr. Quart, 11/68; Rosencrantz and Guildenstern are dead: alterations in absurdism, Drama Surv, fall 68; The humanism of Ben Jonson, Col. Lang. Asn. J, 70. Add: Dept. of English, Western Michigan University, Kalamazoo, MI 49001.

GIANAKOS, PERRY EDGAR, b. Hendersonville, N.C. AMERICAN CIVILIZATION. B.S, N.Y. Univ, 50, M.A, 52, Ph.D.(Am. civilization), 61. Asst. instr. Eng. & advan. compos, Ohio State Univ, 56-58; instr. compos. surv. & Am. lit, N.Y. Univ, 58-59; PROF. AM. THOUGHT & LANG, MICH. STATE UNIV, 59- U.S.A, 42-45, S/Sgt. AHA; Am. Stud. Asn; MLA; Popular Cult. Asn; Soc. Hist. Am. For. Relat; Orgn. Am. Hist; AAUP. American cultural and intellectual history; American imperialism; American literature. Publ: Co-ed, American diplomacy and the sense of destiny, 66 & American civilization since World War II, 68, Wadsworth; auth, The Spanish-American War and the double paradox of the Negro American, Phylon, 65; Ernest Howard Crosby: a forgotten Tolstoyan antimilitarist and anti-imperialist, In: Peace movements in America, Schocken, 73; New left millennialism and American culture, Thought, winter 74. Add: Dept. of American Thought & Language, Michigan State University, East Lansing, MI 48824.

GIANNONE, RICHARD, b. Newark, N.J, Oct. 9, 34. ENGLISH. A.B, Cath. Univ. Am, 56; M.A, Univ. Mich, 57; fel, Brown Univ, 57-58; Fulbright scholar, Univ. Trieste, 60-61; Ph.D.(Eng), Univ. Notre Dame, 64. Instr. ENG, Univ. Notre Dame, 58-60 & 61-62, asst. prof, 64-67; ASSOC. PROF, FORDHAM UNIV, 67- Am. Philos. Soc. grant, summer 64; Notre Dame Humanities Comt. on Grants, grants, summers 65-67. MLA. American literature. Publ: Music in Willa Cather's fiction, Univ. Nebr, 68; The shapes of fiction, Holt, 71; John Keats: a thematic reader, Scott, 72; Eliot's Portrait of a lady and Pound's Portrait d'une femme, Twentieth Century Lit, 10/59; One of ours: Willa Cather's suppressed, Bitter melody, S.Atlantic Quart, winter 65; The quest motif in Thyrsis, Victorian Poetry, spring 65. Add: Dept. of English, Fordham University, Rose Hill Campus, Bronx, NY 10458.

GIBB, CARSON, b. Philadelphia, Pa, Dec. 26, 26; m. 59, 64; c. 3. ENGLISH. B.A, Wesleyan Univ, 48; A.M, Univ. Pa, 50, Ph.D, 62. Instr. ENG, W.Va. Univ, 54-55; Lafayette Col, 55-61; asst. prof, Longwood Col, 61-63; Newark Col. Engineering, 63-65; U.S. Naval Acad, 65-67; ASSOC. PROF, UNIV. BALTIMORE, 70- U.S.N.R, 45-46. MLA; AAUP. Restoration and 18th century English. Publ: Exposition and literature, Macmillan, 71; Figurative structure in restoration comedy, Dissertation Abstr, 63. Add: 1835 Lindamoor Dr, Annapolis, MD 21401.

GIBBENS, VICTOR ELLISON, b. Clay City, Ind, Aug. 16, 07; m. 29; c. 3. ENGLISH. B.S, Purdue Univ, 30; Ind. State Teachers Col, 31; A.M, Univ. Colo, 36; summers, Univ. Mich, 37-38, 40-42. Teacher, high sch, Ill, 31-36; instr. Eng, Purdue Univ, 36-44; laboratory ed, Owens-Corning Fiberglas Corp, 44-45; assoc. ed, Plastics, 45-46; asst. prof. Eng, PURDUE UNIV, WEST LAFAYETTE, 46-50, assoc. prof, 50-61, prof, 61-73, asst. head dept, 63-69, asst. dean grad. sch, 69-73, EMER. PROF. ENG, 73- Am. Dialect Soc; Am. Bus. Writing Asn. American language & civilization; Hoosier folk speech. Publ: Co-auth, Manual of technical writing, Scott; Notes on Indiana speech, Am. Speech; Progress report on a word geography of Indiana, Midwest Folklore. Add: 1526 Sheridan Rd, West Lafayette, IN 47906.

GIBBONS, ROBERT EBBERT, b. Sharon, Pa, Nov. 15, 40; m. 62; c. 4. AMERICAN LITERATURE, CRITICAL THEORY. B.S, John Carroll Univ, 62; M.A, Bowling Green State Univ, 63, Ph.D.(Eng), 67. Instr. hospital admin. & personnel mgt, U.S. Army Med. Field Serv. Sch, 67-69; ASST. PROF. ENG, OUR LADY OF THE LAKE COLLEGE, 69-, lectr, 67-69. Med.Serv. C, U.S.A, 67-69, Capt. NCTE; AAUP; Conf. Col. Compos. & Commun. Theory of literature; language learning. Add: Dept. of English, Our Lady of the Lake College, 411 S.W. 24th St, San Antonio, TX 78285.

GIBBS, LLOYD GRAHAM, b. Union, S.C, Jan. 31, 26. ENGLISH. A.B, Wofford Col, 47, M.A, 48; M.Ed, Univ. S.C, 53, fel, 54-58, Ph.D, 59. Teacher high sch, S.C, 48-54; prof. ENG, Lander Col, 59-61; ASST. PROF, UNIV. S.C, 61- NCTE; MLA; Renaissance Soc. Am; Am. Soc. Theatre Res. Shakespeare; Renaissance. Add: Dept. of English, University of South Carolina, Columbia, SC 29208.

GIBBS, PAUL THOMAS, b. Moline, Kans, Feb. 16, 97; m. 20; c. 1; m. 55. ENGLISH. A.B, Union Col.(Nebr), 19; A.M, Univ. Nebr, 26; Medill Sch. Jour, 28; Ph.D, Univ. Wash, 37. Instr, Enterprise Acad, Kans, 22-25; asst. prof. ENG, Broadview Jr. Col, 26-28; prof, Walla Walla Col, 28-37; Wash. Missionary Col, 37-46; Emmanuel Missionary Col, 46-59; ANDREWS UNIV, 59-63, EMER. PROF, 66- Guest teacher, Newbold Missionary Col, Eng, 53-54. Citation, Distinguished Serv, Emmanuel Missionary Col, 61. Elizabethan period. Publ: Milton's use of the law of nature; Men such as we, 63, Men come alive, 68, Crossroads of the cross, 69, David and his mighty men, 70 & Paul the conqueror, 72, Rev. & Herald; Job and the mysteries of wisdom, South. Publ. Asn, 67. Add: 200 Grove St, Berrien Springs, MI 49103.

GIBBS, ROBERT JOHN, b. St. John, N.B, Feb. 3, 30. CANADIAN & MODERN LITERATURE. B.A, Univ. N.B, 51, Bickle fel. & M.A, 62, Can. Counc. fel. & Ph.D.(Eng), 70; B.A, Cambridge, 54, M.A, 63. Teacher ENG, N.B. Schs, 54-63; lectr, UNIV. N.B, FREDERICTON, 63-70, asst. prof, 70-72, ASSOC. PROF, 72-, DIR. GRAD. STUD, 73- Ed, Fiddlehead Mag, 70-73. Humanities Asn. Can; Asn. Can. Univ. Teachers Eng; Can. Asn. Univ. Teachers; League Can. Poets. Modern poetry. Publ: The living contour: the whale symbol in Melville and Pratt, spring 69, A knocking in the clay: Pratt's unpublished verse drama, winter 73 & Next time from a different country: the poetry of Elizabeth Brewster, winter 74, Can. Lit. Add: Dept. of English, University of New Brunswick, Fredericton, N.B, Can.

GIBSON, BYRON HALL, b. Cullman, Ala, Mar. 13, 08; m. 34; c. 4. ENGLISH LITERATURE. A.B, Birmingham-South. Col, 28; scholar & fel, Univ. Ill, 28-31, A.M, 29, Ph.D, 31. Instr, Univ. Ill, 31-32; prof. Eng, Union Col.(Ky), 32-46, head dept, 32-46, langs, 36-46; PROF. ENG, STETSON UNIV, 46-, HEAD DEPT, 50-, CHMN. DIV. HUMANITIES, 49- MLA. English criticism of prose fiction; early influences on Byron; Shakespeare. Publ: Word power, Everett Edwards, 66. Add: 811 N. Florida Ave, DeLand, FL 32720.

GIBSON, DONALD BERNARD, b. Kansas City, Mo, July 2, 33; m. 63; c. 2. ENGLISH. B.A, Univ. Kansas City, 55, M.A, 57; fel, Brown Univ, 57-58, Ph.D.(Eng), 62. Instr. ENG, Brown Univ, 60-61; Wayne State Univ, 61-64, asst. prof, 64-66; assoc. prof, UNIV. CONN, 66-70, PROF, 70- Lectr, Am. Stud. Sem, Falkenstein, Ger, summer 65; Fulbright-Hayes award, Krakow, Poland, 64-66; Am. Counc. Learned Soc. fel, summer 70; Nat. Endowment for Humanities younger humanist fel, 70-71; vis. prof. Eng, Univ. Iowa, 71. MLA; Col. Lang. Asn. Nineteenth century realism and naturalism; Black American writers; theory of literary criticism. Publ: The fiction of Stephen Crane, South. Ill. Univ, 68; ed, Five Black writers: essays on Wright, Ellison, Hughes, Baldwin and LeRoi Jones, N.Y. Univ, 70; Black and white: stories of American life, Wash. Square, 71; Modern Black poets: a collection of critical essays, Prentice-Hall, 73; auth, The blue hotel and the ideal of human courage, Tex. Stud. Lit. & Lang, autumn 64; The Negro: an essay on definition, Yale Rev, spring 68; Twain's Jim in the classroom, Eng. J, 2/68. Add: Dept. of English, University of Connecticut, Storrs, CT 06268.

GIBSON, EVAN KEITH, b. July 4, 09; m. 32; c. 4. ENGLISH LITERATURE. A.B, Seattle Pac. Col, 33; A.M, Univ. Wash, 35, Ph.D, 47. Instr, schs, Chimacum, Wash, 34-35; Wash. Tech. Inst, 35-41; head dept. Eng, Seattle Pac. Col, 41-43; assoc, Univ. Wash, 46; from asst. to PROF. ENG, Ore. State Univ, 47-64; SEATTLE PAC. COL, 64-, chmn. dept, 68-72. NCTE. Eighteenth and nineteenth century English literature. Publ: Alastor: a reinterpretation & Conception is a blessing, PMLA. Add: 1216 Ninth W, Seattle, WA 98119.

GIBSON, JAMES W, b. Marysville, Ohio, July 15, 32; m. 60; c. 3. SPEECH & DRAMA. B.A, Otterbein Col, 54; M.A, Ohio State Univ, 60, Ph.D.(speech), 62. Teacher speech, High Sch, Ohio, 56-58; High Sch, Ind, 58-59; asst, Ohio State Univ, 59-62; asst. prof, Butler Univ, 62-66; educ, Univ. Omaha, 66-67; assoc. prof. SPEECH, UNIV. MO-COLUMBIA, 67-70, PROF, 70-, CHMN. DEPT, 73- Counter Intel.C, U.S.A, 54-56. Speech Commun. Asn. (chmn, undergrad. speech instr, 68); Am. Educ. Res. Asn; Nat. Social Stud. Commun; Am. Psychol. Asn. Speech education; psychology; public address. Publ: Co-auth, Teaching speech, Merrill, 69; auth, Speech organization: a programmed approach, Rinehart, 71; A reader in speech communication, McGraw, 71; co-auth, A quantitative examination of differences & similarities in written & spoken messages, Speech Monogr, 11/66; A quantitative analysis of selected characteristics of oral & written vocabularies, J. Commun, 6/67; auth, Using video tape in the training of teachers, Speech Teacher, 3/68. Add: Dept. of Speech, University of Missouri-Columbia, Columbia, MO 65201.

GIBSON, MORGAN, b. Cleveland, Ohio, June 6, 29; m. 50, 72; c. 2. POETRY. B.A, Oberlin Col, 50; M.A, Univ. Iowa, 52, Ph.D.(Eng, creative writing), 59. Teaching asst. Eng, Univ. Iowa, 52-53; instr. Eng. & humanities, Shimer Col, 53-54; instr, Wayne State Univ, 54-58, teaching fel. hist, 58-59; asst. prof. Eng, Am. Int. Col, 59-61; from asst. prof. to assoc. prof, Univ. Wis-Milwaukee, 61-72; MEM. GRAD. CORE FAC, GODDARD COL, 72- Poetry ed, Arts in Soc, Univ. Wis-Madison, 66-72. Modern poetry and fiction. Publ: Co-auth, Our bedroom's underground, Kenwood, 63; auth, Mayors of marble, Great Lakes Bks, 66; The best-Browne cottage, Cronopios, 67; Stones glow like lovers' eyes, Morgan, 71; Kenneth Rexroth, Twayne, 72; plus others. Add: Graduate Program, Goddard College, Plainfield, VT 05667.

GIBSON, RICHARD JOSEPH, b. Barbourville, Ky, Aug. 13, 42. RENAISSANCE ENGLISH LITERATURE. A.B, Stetson Univ, 64; M.A, Univ. N.C, Chapel Hill, 68, Ph.D.(Eng), 71. Asst. compos, lit. & bus. writing, Univ. N.C, Chapel Hill, 65-69, instr, 70; ASST. PROF. COMPOS. & LIT, GA. STATE UNIV, 70- Shakespeare; 16th century English literature. Publ: Comic resolution in Measure for measure, J. Tenn. Philol. Asn, 73. Add: Dept. of English, Georgia State University, 33 Gilmer St, Atlanta, GA 30303.

GIBSON, WALKER, b. Jacksonville, Fla, Jan. 19, 19; m. 42; c. 4. ENGLISH. A.B, Yale, 40; M.A, Univ. Iowa, 46. Instr. Eng, Amherst Col, 46-48, asst. prof, 48-54, assoc. prof, 54-57; assoc. prof. Eng. & dir. freshman Eng, N.Y. Univ, 57-61, PROF. ENG, 61-67; UNIV. MASS, AMHERST, 67- Fund Advan. Educ. fel, 55-56; Guggenheim fel, 63-64; consult, U.S. Off. Educ, 64-67; Nat. Endowment for Humanities grants, 73, 74. U.S.A.A.F, 41-45, 1st Lt. MLA; NCTE (pres, 72-73); Conf. Col. Compos. & Commun. Composition; creative writing; teacher training. Publ: The reckless spenders, 54 & Tough, sweet, and stuffy: an essay on modern American prose styles, 66, Ind. Univ; The limits of language, Hill & Wang, 62; Persona, Random, 69; co-ed, The play of language, Oxford, 71; plus others. Add: Dept. of English, University of Massachusetts, Amherst, MA 01002.

GIBSON, WILLIAM ARTHUR, b. Minneapolis, Minn, June 3, 32; m. 56; c. 2. ENGLISH, RENAISSANCE ARCHITECTURE. B.A, Univ. Minn, 55, M.A, 59, Ph.D.(Eng), 64. Asst. prof. ENG, Ohio State Univ, 64-70, assoc. prof, 70-71; IDAHO STATE UNIV, 71-72, PROF. & CHMN. DEPT, 72- Am. Philos. Soc. travel grant, 66; Develop. Fund Fac. summer fel, Ohio State Univ, 66; head Eng. lit. section, MLA Int. Bibliog, 71-; co-ed, Rendezvous: Idaho State Univ. J. Arts & Lett, 71- U.S.A.R, 57-63. MLA; NCTE. Eighteenth century English literature; Renaissance architectural theory; modern rhetoric. Publ: Ed, The art of architecture: a poem in imitation of Horace's Art of poetry, Augustan Reprint Soc, 70; co-auth, The design of prose: exercises in reading and rhetoric, Scribner, 71; auth, Order and emphasis in chapter XV of Gibbon's Decline and fall . . ., In: Rhetorical analyses of literary works, Oxford, 69; Three principles of Renaissance architectural theory in Pope's Epistle to Burlington, Stud. Eng. Lit, 1500-1900, 71; Literary influences on Robert Morris's First excursion into architectural theory, Rendezvous: Idaho State J. Arts & Lett, 71; plus two others. Add: Dept. of English, Idaho State University, Pocatello, ID 83209.

GIBSON, WILLIAM MERRIAM, b. Wilmette, Ill, Jan. 16, 12; m. 43; c. 2. ENGLISH. A.B, Princeton, 33; A.M, Univ. Chicago, 34, Ph.D, 40. Instr, Purdue Univ, 36-37; Univ. Chicago, 37-41; Williams Col, 41-42, asst. prof, 46-49; assoc. prof. ENG, N.Y. UNIV, 49-52, PROF, 52-73; UNIV. WIS-MADISON, 73- Fund Advan. Educ. fel, 54-55; Fulbright lectr. Am. lit, Univ. Turin, Italy, 60-61; U.S. Educ. Found. lectr, Univ. Delhi, India, 63; co-chmn. Congr. Organizing Comt, Int. Fed. Mod. Lang. & Lit, 63; Guggenheim fel, 63-64; dir, MLA Ctr. Ed. Am. Auth, 63-69; mem, adv. comt. Am. lit, Comt. Int. Exchange Persons, 64-67; Am. Counc. Learned Soc. grant, 64; Nat. Endowment Humanities grant, 68, fel, 73. U.S.A, 42-46, Capt. MLA; Am. Stud. Asn. American literature from the Civil War; Clemens; James. Publ: Co-auth, A bibliography of William Dean Howells, N.Y. Pub. Libr, 48; co-ed, Mark Twain Howells letters, Harvard, 60; auth, William D. Howells, Univ. Minn, 67; ed, Literary history of the United States, Macmillan, 74. Add: Dept. of English, Helen C. White Hall, University of Wisconsin-Madison, Madison, WI 53706.

GIDDINGS, G. ELAINE, b. Fargo, N.Dak, Mar. 23, 08. SPEECH, LINGUISTICS. B.A, Andrews Univ, 31; M.A, Univ. South. Calif, 45; Ph.D.(speech), Univ. Mich, 50. Instr. Eng, Helderberg Col, S.Africa, 38-44; chmn. dept, South. Missionary Col, 45-51; script writer, producer & asst. dir, Faith for Today TV, New York, 51-56; CHMN. DEPT. COMMUN, ANDREWS UNIV, 56- Speech Commun. Asn; Am. Asn. Univ. Women. Interpersonal and small group communication; the beginning communication course in college. Add: Dept. of Communication, Andrews University, Berrien Springs, MI 49104.

GIDDINGS, JOSEPH ADDISON, b. Jefferson, Ohio, May 23, 02; m. 31; c. 3. ENGLISH PHILOLOGY. A.B, West. Reserve Univ, 26; univ. scholar, Cornell Univ, 27-28, A.M, 28, fel, 28-29. Asst. ENG, Univ. Ill, 29-31; instr, Cornell Univ, 31-36; from instr. to prof, S.DAK. STATE UNIV, 36-70, head dept, 46-67, EMER. PROF, 70- MLA; NCTE; Col. Eng. Asn. Shakespeare; 19th century; English language and literature. Add: 728 S. Sixth Ave, Brookings, SD 57006.

GIFFIN, KIM, b. Bellaire, Mich, Aug. 20, 18; m. 54; c. 2. SPEECH. A.B, John Fletcher Col, 40; A.M, State Univ. Iowa, 46; Ph.D.(speech), 50. Instr. speech, radio & dramatic art & dir. forensics, Univ. S.Dak, 46-48; asst. prof. speech & drama & dir. debate, UNIV. KANS, 48-53, assoc. prof. speech, 53-60, PROF. SPEECH COMMUN, 60-, DIR, COMMUN. RES. CTR, 63-, head speech commun. div, 56-65. Ed, Kans. Speech J, 49-52; consult. discussion tech, Gen. Assembly, Presby. Churches Am, 49; salesmanship tech, Kans. Bur. Credit Mgrs, 56; consult, Midwest Mgt. Inst, 64-; Nat. Bd. Christian Sci. Lects, 65-; Tex. East. Transmission Corp, 67-; U.S. Off. Civil Defense, 67-; Mich. State Univ. Video Tape Speech Proj, 67-; Am. Asn. Homes for Aged, 67-; Dept. Nursing Educ, Univ. Kans. Sch. Med, 67- U.S.N.R, 42-46. Speech Commun. Asn; Am. Asn. Humanistic Psychol; Int. Commun. Asn. Group interaction processes; interpersonal relations in communication. Publ: Co-auth, Basic readings in interpersonal communication, 71, Fundamentals of interpersonal communication, 71, Problem-solving group interaction, 73 & Interpersonal communication: fundamentals with basic readings, 74, Harper; co-auth, A study of innovation in selected courses of instruction, U.S. Dept. Defense, 72, An inventory of community service and continuing education programs in Kansas institutions of higher education, Kans. Off. Statewide Acad. Exten, 72 & Personal communication in human relations, Merrill, 74; co-auth, Relationships between speech anxiety and motivation, Speech Monographs, 3/71; auth, The measurement of interpersonal trust, In: Research designs in general semantics, Sci. Publ, 71; Interpersonal trust in small group communication, In: Concepts in communication, Allyn & Bacon, 73. Add: Communication Research Center, University of Kansas, Lawrence, KS 66044.

GIFFIN, MARY ELIZABETH, b. Gradatim, Pa, Jan. 1, 97. ENGLISH. B.A, West. Reserve Univ, 19, M.A, 23; Lady Margaret Hall, Oxford, 22-23, 27-28; Ph.D.(Eng), Univ. Chicago, 39. Chmn. dept. Eng, Cedar Crest Col, 23-27, 28-32; dept. humanities, Monticello Col, 33-38; prof. Eng. & acad. dean, Lake Erie Col, 40-45; assoc. prof. ENG, VASSAR COL, 45-57, prof, 57-62, EMER. PROF, 62- Vassar Col. fac. fel, 50-51; vis. prof, Univ. Tehran, Iran, 62-63; Brandeis Univ, 63-64; Cleveland State Univ, 67-69. MLA; Mediaeval Acad. Am; Int. Arthurian Soc; Int. Asn. Univ. Profs. Eng. Old and Middle English; Chaucer. Publ: Studies on Chaucer and his audience, Editions L'Eclair, 56. Add: Wade Park Manor, 1890 E. 107th St, Cleveland, OH 44106.

GIFFORD, DON CREIGHTON, b. Schenectady, N.Y, Feb. 27, 19; m. 44; c. 2. ENGLISH. B.A, Principia Col, 40; Harvard, 40-42. Instr. ENG, Mills Col. Educ, 47-51; WILLIAMS COL, 51-54, lectr, 54-55, asst. prof, 55-58, assoc. prof, 58-64, PROF, 64- Consult. theory invention, Arthur D. Little Co, 57-58. Am. Field Serv, 42-44; A.U.S, 44-46, 2nd Lt. Aesthetic theory; 19th century America; James Joyce. Publ: Ed, The literature of architecture, 66, auth, Notes for Joyce, 67 & Notes for Joyce: Ulysses, 73, Dutton. Add: Dept. of English, Williams College, Williamstown, MA 01267.

GIFFORD, WILLIAM W, b. Plainfield, N.J, Nov. 15, 28; m. 50; c. 2. ENGLISH. B.A, Swarthmore Col, 50; M.A, Univ. Calif, Berkeley, 52, fel, 53-55, Ph.D.(Eng), 55. Instr. ENG, VASSAR COL, 55-61, asst. prof, 61-67, ASSOC. PROF, 67- Vassar Col. fel, 60-61 & 68-69. The sermons of John Donne; the modern novel. Publ: John Donne's sermons on the Grand days, Huntington Libr. Quart, 66; Time and place in Donne's sermons, PMLA, 67; Ernest Hemingway: the monsters and the critics, Mod. Fiction Stud, 11/68. Add: Dept. of English, Vassar College, Poughkeepsie, NY 12601.

GILBERT, ALLAN H, b. Rushford, N.Y, Mar. 18, 88; m. 13; 53; c. 2. ENGLISH & ITALIAN LITERATURE. A.B, Cornell Univ, 09, Ph.D, 12; A.M, Yale, 10. Instr. ENG, Cornell Univ, 12-19; Rice Inst, 19-20; prof, Univ. Tenn, 20-21; DUKE UNIV, 21-57, EMER. PROF, 57- Fulbright res. fel, Italy, 55-56; vis. prof. Ital. lit, Univ. Pa, 59-60; vis. prof. comp. lit, Rutgers Univ, 61-62; lit, Drew Univ, 63-; adj. prof, Columbia Univ, 62-63. Cavaliere, Order of Merit, Italy. MLA (v.pres, 56); Mod. Humanities Res. Asn; Dante Soc. S.Atlantic Mod. Lang. Asn.(pres, 47); Southeast Renaissance Conf.(pres, 56). Shakespeare; Plato; literary criticism. Publ: On the composition of Paradise lost, Univ. N.C, 47; Machiavelli's chief works translated, 63 & Dante's Inferno, a new translation, 68, Duke Univ; Dante and his comedy, N.Y. Univ, 63; Dante's Rimario, Italica, 12/67; Plato's Ion, comic and serious, In: Studies in honor of DeWitt T. Starnes, Univ. Tex, 67; An iconoclast reads Aristotle's Poetics, Renaissance Papers, 72. Add: 503 Compton Pl, Durham, NC 27707.

GILBERT, EDNA, b. Rockford, Ill, Apr. 8, 05. SPEECH. B.L, Northwest. Univ, 26, M.S, 30; scholar, Univ. Wis, 45-46, Ph.D, 50. Teacher speech & drama, Milwaukee-Downer Sem, 26-27; speech & Eng, High Sch, Wakefield, Mich, 27-29; instr. children's lit, MINOT STATE COL, 30-44, dir. speech & hearing clin, 40-71, prof. SPEECH, 48-71, chmn. div. spec. educ, 62-67, EMER. PROF, 71- Nat. Col. Players Award, 26; vis. prof. speech & educ, Univ. Wis, 54-55; pres, Int. North. Great Plains Conf. Spec. Educ. & Rehabil, 60. Speech Commun. Asn; fel, Am. Speech & Hearing Asn; Cent. States Speech Asn.(assoc. ed, 58-62); Counc. Except. Children (Humanitarian Award, 70). Oral reading; articulation and language problems of children; phonetics. Add: 1425 Eighth St, N.W, Minot, ND 58701.

GILBERT, ELLIOT LEWIS, b. New York, N.Y, Dec. 1, 30; m. 57; c. 3. NINETEENTH CENTURY ENGLISH LITERATURE. B.A, N.Y. Univ, 52, M.A, 53; Ph.D.(Eng), Cornell Univ, 63. Instr. ENG, Columbia Univ, 59-63; asst. prof, Brooklyn Col, 63-66; ASSOC. PROF, UNIV. CALIF, DAVIS, 66- Am. Counc. Learned Soc. grant, summer 70; Univ. Calif. Inst. Humanities fel, 73-74. MLA. Nineteenth century literature; prose fiction. Publ: Kipling and the critics, N.Y. Univ, 65; The good Kipling, Ohio Univ, 71; A wondrous contiguity: anachronism in Carlyle's prophecy and art, PMLA, 5/72. Add: Dept. of English, University of California, Davis, CA 95616.

GILBERT, JACK G, b. Odessa, Tex, Aug. 28, 34; m. 73; c. 2. ENGLISH LITERATURE. B.A, La. State Univ, 56, M.A, 59; Univ. Heidelberg, 56-57; Ph.D.(Eng), Univ. Tex, 62. Asst. prof. ENG, LA. STATE UNIV, New Orleans, 62-64; BATON ROUGE, 64-67, ASSOC. PROF, 67-, asst. dean, 65-68, assoc. dean, col. arts & sci, 68-71. Eighteenth century English literature. Publ: Jonathan Swift: romantic and cynic moralist, Univ. Tex, 66. Add: Dept. of English, Louisiana State University, Baton Rouge, LA 70803.

GILBERT, ROBERT B, b. Rock Mills, Ala, July 20, 12; m. 38; c. 2. ENGLISH. A.B. & M.A, Univ. Ala, 34; Ph.D, Vanderbilt Univ, 53. Assoc. prof. ENG, Jacksonville State Col, 37-48; PROF, LIVINGSTON STATE COL, 48- Teaching fel, Vanderbilt Univ, 51-52. American literature. Add: Dept. of English, Livingston State College, Livingston, AL 35470.

GILBERT, SANDRA MORTOLA, b. New York, N.Y, Dec. 27, 36; m. 57; c. 3. MODERN BRITISH & AMERICAN LITERATURE. B.A, Cornell Univ, 57; M.A, N.Y. Univ, 61; Ph.D.(Eng), Columbia Univ, 68. Lectr. ENG, Queen's Col.(N.Y), 63-64, 65-66; Calif. State Univ, Sacramento, 67-68; asst. prof, Calif. State Univ, Hayward, 68-71; vis. lectr, St. Mary's Col.(Calif), 72; ASSOC. PROF, IND. UNIV, BLOOMINGTON, 73- MLA. Modern British and American poetry; romantic poetry; modern fiction. Publ: The poetry of W.B. Yeats, Thor Publ/Simon & Schuster, 66; Acts of attention: the poems of D.H. Lawrence, Cornell Univ, 72; All the dead voices, a study of Samuel Beckett's Krapp's last tape, Drama Surv, spring 68; Beyond the walls of light, Nation, 1/74; plus poetry & fiction in var. lit. jour. Add: Dept. of English, Indiana University, Bloomington, IN 47401.

GILBERT, VEDDER MORRIS, b. Amsterdam, N.Y, May 12, 14; m. 44; c. 2. ENGLISH LITERATURE. A.B, Union Col.(N.Y), 36; Univ. Montpellier, France, 36-37; A.M, Cornell Univ, 38, Ph.D, 52. Instr, Univ. Mo, 38-44; asst, Cornell Univ, 44-46; asst. prof. ENG, Univ. Toledo, 46-51; UNIV. MONT, 52-55, assoc. prof, 55-58, PROF, 58-, chmn. dept, 57-62, for. stud. adv, 57-66, coord. humanities, 67-68. Mem, Nat. Asn. For. Stud. Affairs sem, France, summer 64. MLA; NCTE; Rocky Mount Mod. Lang. Asn.(v.pres, 54, pres, 55); Buckinghamshire Archaeol. Soc. Eng; Col. Eng. Asn; Nat. Asn. For. Stud. Adv; Johnson Soc. Northwest. Dramatic literature; bibliography. Publ: The stage career of John Howard Payne; The career of Maxwell Anderson, Mod. Drama, 60; Thomas Edwards and the bad edition of Shakespeare, Symposium, 64; The American theatre: Missoula 1910, Mont. Mag. of West. Hist, 68; plus others. Add: Dept. of English, University of Montana, Missoula, MT 59801.

GILBREATH, ALLIE LOU FELTON, b. Old Town, Fla, Dec. 17, 95; m. 43. EDUCATION, ENGLISH. B.S, Fla. State Univ, 21; M.A, State Univ. Iowa, 26; D.Litt, Steed Col, 65. Teacher pub. schs, Fla, 13-22; Fla. State Univ, 22-23, prin. demonstration sch, 23-25, supt. training sch, 26-29; part-time teacher, State Univ, Iowa, 25-26; reading consult. & part-time ed, John C. Winston Co, 29-43; supvr. pub. schs, Tenn, 47-50; prof. educ. & Eng. & dir. reading lab. & clin, E.Tenn. State Univ, 50-66; prof. educ. & Eng, Milligan Col, 66-72; RETIRED. NEA; Int. Reading Asn. Publ: Co-auth, Easy growth in reading series grades 1-6, Holt; ed. & compiler, Research in the language arts of East Tennessee State University, E.Tenn. State Univ, Vol. I, 63. Add: 2704 20th Ave. Dr. W, Bradenton, FL 33505.

GILCHRIST, JAMES A, b. Cleveland, Ohio, Mar. 13, 21; m. 55; c. 3. ENGLISH. B.S, John Carroll Univ, 50, M.A, 55; teaching fel, Univ. Notre Dame, 54-56. Head dept. Eng, Lakeville High Sch, Ind, 56-58, asst. prin, 57-58; instr. Eng. & world lit, ST. JOHN COL.(OHIO), 59-61, from asst. prof. to ASSOC. PROF. ENG, 61- Lectr, John Carroll Univ, summer, 54; South Bend Exten, Ind. Univ, 57-59; Borromeo Col. Sem, 59-60; Telshe Yeshiva, 62-63. U.S.A, 42-45, S/Sgt. MLA; Cath. Renascence Soc; NCTE. English Victorian literature and thought; function of the grotesque in literature; the family saga novel. Add: Dept. of English, St. John College of Cleveland, Cleveland, OH 44114.

GILDART, ROBERT HARR, b. Onondaga, Mich, Oct. 9, 14; m. 41; c. 2. ENGLISH & JOURNALISM. A.B, Albion Col, 37; grant, Northwest. Univ, 44-45, M.S, 45. Ed. employee, Newspapers, Mich. & Pa, 37-41, 43-44, 48-54; instr. jour, Medill Sch. Jour, Northwest. Univ, 45-48; asst. prof. Eng, Shepherd Col, 54-56; from asst. prof. to ASSOC. PROF. ENG. & JOUR, ALBION COL, 56-, alumni fel, summer 63. Med.Dept, U.S.A, 41-42. Asn. Educ. Jour. American pioneers in journalism; history of higher education; creative work in novel, short story. Publ: Albion College, 1835-1960, a history, Albion Col, 61; Milton W. Reynolds, Pub. Auxiliary, 44. Add: Dept. of English, Albion College, Albion, MI 49224.

GILDE, HELEN CHENEY, b. Albuquerque, N.Mex, Sept. 12, 32; div. ENGLISH. B.A, Univ. Colo, 53, M.A, 54; Vis. Comt. fel, Univ. Chicago, 55, Ph.D.(Eng), 65. Instr. ENG, CALIF. STATE UNIV, LONG BEACH, 59-61, assoc. prof, 61-70, PROF, 70-, CHMN DEPT, 74-, chmn. Acad. Senate, 72-73. Nat. Endowment for Humanities summer grant, 67. Renaissance Soc. Am; Renaissance Eng. Text Soc; MLA. Literature of the English Renaissance. Publ: The sweet lodge of love and Deare delight: the problem of amoret, Philol. Quart, 1/71; Spenser's Hellenore and some Ovidian associations, Comp. Lit, 23: 233-239. Add: Dept. of English, California State University, Long Beach, 6101 E. Seventh St, Long Beach, CA 90840.

GILDER, ROSAMOND, b. New York, N.Y. DRAMA. From ast. ed. to drama critic & ed, Theatre Arts Monthly, 24-48; secy, AM. NAT. THEATRE & ACAD, 45-50, V.PRES. & MEM. BD, 46-, HON. PRES. & DIR. U.S. CTR, INT. THEATRE INST, 48-, founder, v.pres. & pres. Ed. secy, Nat. Theatre Conf, 32-36; dir. bur. res, Fed. Theatre Proj, 35-36; secy, New York Drama Critics Circle, 46-50, hon. mem, 50-, chmn. U.S. deleg, Int. Theatre Congr, Paris, 47, Prague, 48, Zurich, 49, Paris, 50, Oslo, 51, The Hague, 53, Dubrovnik, 55, Bombay, 56, Athens, 57, Helsinki, 59, Vienna, 61, Warsaw, 63, Tel Aviv, 65 & New York, 67; chmn. panel on dramatic art, Nat. Comn. UNESCO, 48-54; instr. Eng, Barnard Col, Columbia Univ, 49-55; Guggenheim fel, 50; v.chmn, int. cult. exchange prog, Am. Nat. Theatre & Acad-U.S. State Dept, 54-63; Fulbright fel, 55-56; U.S. Am specialist grants, India, 61, Japan, 63. Antoinette Perry Award, 49; Award of Merit, Am. Educ. Theatre, 61; Kelcey Allen Award, 63; Am. Nat. Theatre & Acad. Award, 65; Officier, Arts et Lettres, 65; U.S. Inst. Theatre Technol. Award, 67. Publ: A theatre library, 32, ed, Theater arts anthology, 50 & auth, Enter the actress, 60, Theatre Arts Bks; co-auth, Theatre collection in libraries and museums, 36; auth, John Gielgud's Hamlet, Oxford, 37; plus others. Add: 24 Gramercy Park, New York, NY 10003.

GILHOOLEY, LEONARD, b. Brooklyn, N.Y, Oct. 9, 21. ENGLISH LANGUAGE & LITERATURE. A.B, Loyola Univ, 45; M.Ed, St. John's Univ.(N.Y), 49; M.A, Boston Col, 55; fel, Fordham Univ, 55-59, Ph.D, 61. Lectr. ENG, Fordham Univ, 55-59; asst. prof, Xaverian Col, 61-66, acad. dean, 63-66; asst. prof. FORDHAM UNIV, 66-70, ASSOC. PROF, 70-, V.CHMN. DEPT, 67- Assoc. ed, New Cath. Encycl, 63-66. MLA; Emerson Soc; AAUP. American literature; United States history; Irish history—1900-1925. Publ: Contradiction and dilemma, Fordham Univ, 72. Add: Dept. of English, Fordham University, Rose Hill Campus, Bronx, NY 10458.

GILKES, LILLIAN BARNARD, b. Jacksonville, Fla, Dec. 18, 02. AMERICAN LITERATURE. Columbia Univ. Exten, 21-23. Instr. short story, Columbia Univ. Home Study, 25-31; Hunter Col. Eve. Session & Maplewood Sch. Adult Educ, 34-35; creative writing, Div. Gen. Educ, N.Y. Univ, 44-52; RES. & WRITING, 52- Consult. & judge, Short Story Contest, U.S. Air Force & Div. Gen. Educ, N.Y. Univ, 50; Eugene F. Saxton Mem. fels, 61, 62. MLA. Am. Stud. Asn; Bibliog. Soc. Am. Stephen Crane; American literature 1825-1865, especially biography of Park Benjamin. Publ: A home study course in the technique of short story writing, Columbia Univ, 28; co-auth, Short story craft, Macmillan, 49; auth, Cora Crane: a biography of Mrs. Stephen Crane, Ind. Univ, 60; co-auth, Stephen Crane: letters, N.Y. Univ, 60; auth, Park Benjamin, H.W. Herbert, and Wm. G. Simms: a case of mistaken identity, S.C. Rev, 6/71; Hawthorne, Park Benjamin, and S.G. Goodrich: a three-cornered imbroglio, Hawthorne J, 71; Park Benjamin, literary agent, et cetera, Proof, Yearbk. Am. Bibliog. & Textual Stud. & Univ. S.C, 71; plus others. Add: 129 Wilderness Rd, Tryon, NC 28782.

GILL, BARBARA, S.N.D, b. Somerville, Mass, May 16, 17. ENGLISH & AMERICAN LITERATURE. A.B, Emmanuel Col.(Mass), 38; M.A, Boston Col, 49; Boston Univ, 54; Ph.D.(Eng. & Am. lit), Cath. Univ. Am, 60; Harvard, 64; Stanford Univ, 66-67; Towson Col, summer 70; C.W. Post Col, summer 72. Instr. ENG, EMMANUEL COL.(MASS), 43-47, asst. prof, 50-52, assoc. prof, 53-55, PROF, 60-, CHMN. DEPT, 60-66, 72-, dir, honors prog, 63-66, Am. stud. fac. inst, summer 67. Vis. prof, Col. Notre Dame (Calif), 67 & Univ. San Francisco, 69. AAUP; NCTE; MLA. Publ: Paradoxical patterns in Chaucer's Troilus, Cath. Univ. Am, 60. Add: Dept. of English, Emmanuel College, 400 The Fenway, Boston, MA 02115.

GILL, JAMES EARL, b. El Paso, Tex, June 14, 35; m. 59; c. 2. ENGLISH. B.A, Univ. Tex, Austin, 57; South fel, Univ. N.C, 57-60, Ph.D.(Eng), 66. ASST. PROF. ENG, UNIV. TENN, KNOXVILLE, 65- MLA; S.Atlantic Mod. Lang. Asn; Southeast. Renaissance Conf. Seventeenth and eighteenth century English literature; history of ideas. Publ: Theriophily in antiquity, J. Hist. Ideas, 30: 401-412; Beast over man: theriophilic topics in Gulliver's Voyage to the country of the Houyhnhnms, Stud. Philol, 67: 533-549. Add: Dept. of English, University of Tennessee, Knoxville, TN 37916.

GILL, RICHARD, b. New York, N.Y, May 5, 22. MODERN BRITISH LITERATURE. B.A, N.Y. Univ, 47; M.A, Columbia Univ, 48, Ph.D.(Eng), 66. Instr. ENG, State Univ. N.Y. Buffalo, 50-51; Clarkson Col. Technol, 51-52; PROF, PACE UNIV, 54- U.S.A, 43-46. MLA. Nineteenth and 20th century fiction; modern poetry; existentialist philosophy. Publ: Happy rural seat: the English country house and the literary imagination, Yale Univ, 72; co-ed, The fabric of existentialism: philosophic and literary sources, Prentice-Hall, 73; auth, The corporal works of mercy as a moral pattern in Joyce's Ulysses, Twentieth Century Lit, 4/63; The imagination of disaster: the literature of the First World War, Saturday Rev, 9/64; The soundtrack of Madame Bovary: Flaubert's aural imagery, Lit/Film Quart, summer 73. Add: Dept. of English, Pace University, Pace Plaza, New York, NY 10038.

GILLELAND, LaRUE WESLEY, b. St. Louis, Mo, Feb. 18, 30; m. 62; c. 4. JOURNALISM. B.J, Univ. Mo-Columbia, 52, M.A, 62. Reporter, Honolulu Advertiser, Hawaii, 52-53; staff advert. & dispatch dept, Los Angeles Times, Calif, 54-55; copy ed, Memphis Commercial Appeal, Tenn, 55-56, reporter, 56-57, relig. ed, 57-59; instr. Eng, Ark. State Univ, 62-63; asst. prof. JOUR, UNIV. NEV, RENO, 63-67, assoc. prof, 67-74, PROF, 74- Ed, Jour. Educr, 69- Am. Soc. Jour. Sch. Adminr.(exec. dir, 73-). Press law and ethics; effective reporting methods. Publ: Schools and departments of journalism, In: Editor and publisher international yearbook, 72, 73; For a good-evil world, In: Journalist's prayerbook, Augsburg, 72; Simple formula proves helpful to interviewers, In: Journalism: dateline the world, Richards Rosen, 73. Add: Dept. of Journalism, Mack Social Science Bldg, University of Nevada, Reno, NV 89507.

GILLEN, FRANCIS XAVIER, b. Buffalo, N.Y, Oct. 26, 34; m. 61; c. 2. LITERATURE, MODERN DRAMA. B.S, Canisius Col, 61; M.A, Fordham Univ, 64, Ph.D.(Eng), 69. Asst. prof. ENG, St. John's Univ.(N.Y), 65-71; ASSOC. PROF, UNIV. TAMPA, 71- MLA; S.Atlantic Mod. Lang. Asn; AAUP. E.M. Forster; modern novel and drama. Publ: Apart from the known and the unknown: the unreconciled worlds of Harold Pinter's characters, Ariz. Quart, spring 70; E.M. Forster's neglected narrator, Novel, winter 70; Donald Barthelme's City: a guide, Twentieth Century Lit, 1/72. Add: Dept. of English, University of Tampa, Tampa, FL 33606.

GILLESPIE, C. RICHARD, b. Baltimore, Md, June 2, 30; m. 51. DRAMA. B.A, Principia Col, 51; M.A, State Univ. Iowa, 52, Ph.D.(drama), 60. Instr. THEATRE, Glassboro State Col, 57-60, asst. prof, 60-61; from assoc. prof. to PROF, TOWSON STATE COL, 61-, V.PRES. & DEAN STUDENTS, 70- Stanley Drama Award for Playwriting, 73. Sig.C, 52-54, Sgt. Am. Theatre Asn; Speech Commun. Asn. Acting; directing; playwriting. Add: Dept. of Theatre, Towson State College, Baltimore, MD 21204.

GILLESPIE, EDGAR BRYAN, b. Arcadia, S.C, Dec. 31, 31; m. 58; c. 3. ENGLISH. B.A, Wake Forest Univ, 53; A.M, Duke Univ, 55, Angier B. Duke fel, 59-60, James B. Duke fel, 60-61, Ph.D.(Eng), 66. Instr. ENG, Marshall Univ, 55; Davidson Col, 55-56, 58-59; asst. prof, Furman Univ, 63-66; ASSOC. PROF, STETSON UNIV, 66- Asst. prof, Appalachian State Teachers Col, summer 62. Sig.C, U.S.A, 56-58. MLA; Milton Soc. Am. Milton; Renaissance drama; 17th century English poetry. Add: Dept. of English, Stetson University, De Land, FL 32720.

GILLESPIE, GERALD ERNEST PAUL, Comparative Literature. See Volume III, Foreign Languages, Linguistics & Philology.

GILLESPIE, HAROLD REESE, JR, b. Palestine, Tex, Sept. 2, 29; m. 57; c. 4. ENGLISH. B.A, Univ. Tex, 51, M.A, 56; Ind. Univ, 57-60. Instr. Eng, Laredo Jr. Col, 56-57; asst. prof, Dickinson Col, 60-67, dean stud, 67-73; ASSOC. PROF. ENG, STATE UNIV. N.Y. AGR. & TECH. COL, CANTON, 73- AAUP; MLA; Am. Film Inst. Composition; English, American and European literature. Add: Dept. of English, State University of New York Agricultural & Technical College at Canton, Canton, NY 13617.

GILLESPIE, PATTI PEETE, b. Bowling Green, Ky, Jan. 26, 38; m. 58. DRAMATIC LITERATURE, THEATRE HISTORY. B.S, Univ. Ky, 58; M.A, West. Ky. Univ, 62; Ph.D.(theatre), Ind. Univ, Bloomington, 70. Teacher chem. & physics, Bowling Green High Sch, 59-60; biol, Frances Hammond High Sch, 60-61; chem, Russellville High Sch, 61-66; ASST. PROF. DRAMA, UNIV. IOWA, 70- Speech Commun Asn.(mem. comn. prof. & social problems, 71-72, chmn. publ. comt, 73-); Am. Theatre Asn; AAUP. The well-made play; 19th century theatre; dramatic form and structure. Publ: Antoine at the Odeon, Educ. Theatre J, 10/71; Plays: well constructed and well made, Quart. J. Speech, 10/72; The bells: a re-appraisal, Cent. States Speech J, 10/73. Add: Dept. of Speech & Dramatic Art, University of Iowa, Iowa City, IA 52242.

GILLETTE, ARNOLD SIMPSON, b. Phoenixville, Pa, June 4, 04; m. 32; c. 2. DRAMA. A.B, Univ. Mont, 27; scholar, Yale, 29-31, M.F.A, 31; Rockefeller fel, 35-36. Scenic designer, Berkshire Playhouse, Stockbridge, Mass, 29-31; art dir, Univ. Iowa, 31-71, asst. prof. dramatic art, 35-41, assoc. prof, 41-49, assoc. dir. univ. theatre, 48-56, prof. dramatic art, 49-71, dir. univ. theatre, 56-71; RETIRED. Distinguished Serv. Award, Univ. Mont, 69; 1973 USITT, U.S. Int. Theatre Technol, 73. Am. Theatre Asn.(2nd v.pres, Am. Educ. Theatre Asn, 61, 1st v.pres, 62, pres, 63, award of merit, 69); Nat. Theatre Conf.(trustee, 60, pres, 66 & 67). Scenic design and stagecraft; planning and equipping the educational theatre; the auditorium for the small high school. Publ: Stage scenery: its construction and rigging, 59, 2nd ed, 72 & An introduction to scenic design, 67, Harper; ed, Handbook of technical practice for the performing arts, Scenographic Media, 72. Add: 4 Rowland St, Iowa City, IA 52240.

GILLIAM, HARRIET S, b. Nashville, Tenn, June 26, 44. ENGLISH & AMERICAN LITERATURE. B.A, Vanderbilt Univ, 66; Woodrow Wilson fel, Yale, 66-67, NDEA fel, 67-70, M.Phil, 69, Kent fel, 70-71, Ph.D.(Eng), 71. ASST. PROF. ENG, NORTHWEST. UNIV, EVANSTON, 71- Am. Counc. Learned Soc. fel, 73-74, Nat. Endowment for Humanities fel, 73-74. MLA; AAUP; Soc. Religion Higher Educ. Theory of the novel; modern novel; Victorian poetry. Add: Dept. of English, Northwestern University, Evanston, IL 60201.

GILLILAND, MARSHALL A, b. Hopkinsville, Ky, Feb. 28, 37; m. 60; c. 1. AMERICAN STUDIES, AMERICAN LITERATURE. B.S, Univ. Wis, 62; Ph.D. (Am. stud), Wash. State Univ, 68. ASST. PROF. ENG, UNIV. SASKATCHEWAN, 68- Vis. Fulbright lectr. Am. lit, Poland, 72-73. U.S.N, 54-57. Am. Stud. Asn; Can. Asn. Univ. Teachers. American literature; 20th century American history. Add: Dept. of English, University of Saskatchewan, Saskatoon, Sask, S7N 0W0, Can.

GILLIS, EVERETT ALDEN, b. Cameron, Mo, Mar. 4, 14; m. 43. ENGLISH, FOLKLORE. B.A, Tex. Christian Univ, 36, M.A, 39; Southwest. Baptist Sem, 36-37; Ph.D.(Eng), Univ. Tex, 48. Asst. prof. ENG, Tex. A&I Univ, 47-49; assoc. prof, TEX. TECH. UNIV, 49-55, PROF, 56-, chmn. dept, 64-69. Ford Found. Fund Advanc. Educ. fac. fel, 55-56. U.S.A, 42-46. MLA; S-Cent. Mod. Lang. Asn.(secy, folklore ling. sect, 54, chmn, 55); Am. Folklore Soc; NCTE. Modern poetry; American literature; folklore. Publ: Angles of the wind, Kaliedograph, 54; co-auth, A college forum, Odyssey, 63; auth, Oliver LaFarge, Steck, 67; The Waste land as grail romance, Tex. Tech Univ, 74; Spiritual status of T.S. Eliot's Hollow men, Tex. Stud. Lit. & Lang, 61; Religion in a Sweeney world, Ariz. Quart, 64; Southwest literature: perspectives and prospects, Southwest. Am. Lit, 72. Add: Dept. of English, Texas Tech University, Broadway & University, Lubbock, TX 79409.

GILLIS, HERBERT RUSSELL, b. New York, N.Y, June 8, 21; m. 47; c. 2. ENGLISH, SPEECH & DRAMA. A.B, Kent State Univ, 47, M.A, 49; summer, Univ. Md, 54, 55; fel, West. Reserve Univ, 50-52, Ph.D.(speech educ), 58. Teacher high sch, 47-48; asst. speech & theater, Kent State Univ, 48-49; instr. speech & drama, Univ. Md, 52-58; prof. Eng. & speech, Calif. State Col.(Pa), 58-60; assoc. prof. speech & drama, St. John's Univ, 60-61; PROF. SPEECH, C.W. POST COL, LONG ISLAND UNIV, 61- Lectr, Queens Col.(N.Y), summers 62-; adj. prof. speech & drama, Pace Col, 64-; consult. ed, J. Commun. Disorders, 67- U.S.N.R, 42-46. Am. Speech & Hearing Asn; Speech Commun. Asn; Am. Theatre Asn. Phonetics of English; semantics and communication; oral interpretation of literature. Publ: The makings of a poet, Exposition, 65; Non-identity and the use of non-auditory methods in voice and speech training, Gen. Semantics Bull, 60; The role of communication in the college speech and hearing center, J. Commun. Disorders, 12/67; A classified bibliography of references and aids for teaching speech and languages arts, Express, 1/68. Add: Dept. of Speech, C.W. Post College, Long Island University, Greenvale, NY 11548.

GILLIS, PATRICIA INGLE, b. Grandview, Tex, Sept. 16, 32; m. 67. ENGLISH. A.B, Baylor Univ, 51, A.M, 52; summer, Univ. Tex, 54; Counc. South. Univs. fels, Univ. Ark, 59-61, Ph.D.(Eng), 65. Teacher, high schs, Tex, 52-55; instr. Eng, Navarro Jr. Col, 55-56 & 57-59; asst, Univ. Ark, 56-57 & 61-62; instr, Midwest. Univ, 62-65, asst. prof, 65-66, assoc. prof, 66-67; chmn. div. commun, Ill. Cent. Col, 67-69; vis. prof. ENG, Tex. Tech. Univ, 70-71; assoc. prof, GA. SOUTH. COL, 71-74, PROF, 74- MLA; NCTE; Conf. Col. Compos. & Commun. The drama; Old and Middle English literature; literature for children. Publ: The theme of justice, W.C. Brown, 69; co-ed, Franz Kafka: his place in world literature, Tex. Tech Univ, 71; auth, Tragedy and an uncommon man: a monologue about Tennessee Williams, Stud. Lang. & Lit, fall 70; introd. & contrib, The ship of fools, Folio Soc, London, 71; auth, The roar in the greasepaint, or the Americanization of dramatic expressionism, J. Am. Stud. Asn. Tex, 72. Add: 7 Woodrow Ave, Statesboro, GA 30458.

GILLMOR, FRANCES, b. Buffalo, N.Y, May 21, 03. ENGLISH. B.A, Univ. Ariz, 28, fel. & M.A, 31; Dr. en Let, Nat. Univ. Mex, 57. Teaching fel. ENG, Univ. Ariz, 29-30, instr, 31-33; Univ. N.Mex, 33-34; asst. prof, UNIV. ARIZ, 34-44, assoc. prof, 45-52, prof, 52-72, EMER. PROF, 73- Guggenheim fel, 59-60. MLA; fel. Am. Folklore Soc.(v.pres, 58 & 64); fel. Am. Anthrop. Asn; Auth. League Am; Mex. Folklore Soc. Aztec history; Navajo backgrounds; folklore of the Southwest and Mexico. Publ: Flute of the smoking mirror, Univ. N.Mex, 49 & Univ. Ariz, 68; The king danced in the market place, Univ. Ariz, 64, transl. into Polish, Król tańczyl na targowisku, Państwowy Instytut Wydawniczy, 65 & transl. into Spanish, Moteczuma ilhuicamina: el flechador del cielo, Ed. Diana, Mex, 73; co-auth, Traders to the Navajos, Houghton, 34, Univ. N.Mex, 52; Mouros e Cristaos nó Mexico, 1-4/69 & Diferentes conceitos de Los tastoanes, um drama tradicional de jalisco, 9-12/70, Rev. Brasileira de Folclore. Add: Box 4605, University Station, Tucson, AZ 85717.

GILLON, ADAM, b. Kovel, Poland, July 17, 21; m. 46; c. 2. ENGLISH & COMPARATIVE LITERATURE. Brit. Counc. scholar, 43-45; M.A, Hebrew Univ, Jerusalem, 48; Ph.D, Columbia Univ, 54. Lectr. Eng, Sch. Higher Stud, Jerusalem, 44-45; lectr. Eng. lang. & lit, Hascalla Col. & prin. & teacher Eng. Montefiore Tech. High Sch, Tel-Aviv, 49-50; instr. Eng, Univ. Kans, 56-57; assoc. prof, Acadia Univ, 58-59, prof. & head dept, 59-61; PROF. ENG. & WORLD LIT, STATE UNIV. N.Y. COL. NEW PALTZ, 61- Can. Res. Counc. grant-in-aid, 61; N.Y. State Univ. res. grant, summer, 62-63; ed. Polish ser, Twayne's World Auth. Ser, 64-, Hebrew ser, 65-; State Univ. N.Y. Res. Found. res. grants-in-aid, 65, 66, 68, 70 & 72-73; Alfred Jurzykowski Found. award, 67; U.S. Govt. res. grant, Israel, 68-69; Joseph Fels Found. res. grant, Israel, 68-69. Israel Army of Defence Air Force, Flight Lt. MLA; Am. Comp. Lit. Asn; NCTE; Int. Comp. Lit. Asn; Am. Asn. Teachers Slavic & E.Europ. Lang. English, American, Polish, Russian & Hebrew literatures; creative writing of fiction, poetry and drama; comparative and world literature. Publ: The eternal solitary: a study of Joseph Conrad, 60, 66, Cup of fury, 62, Selected poems and translations, 62, co-ed. & transl, Introduction to modern Polish literature, 64, ed, The dancing Socrates and other poems by Julian Tuwim, 68 & Poems of the ghetto: a testament of lost men, 68, Twayne; auth, In the manner of haiku: seven aspects of man, Twayne, 67 & Rapp & Whiting, London, 68; Daily new and old: poems in the manner of haiku & Strange mutations: in the manner of haiku, 73, Astra Bks; Cosmopolitanism in Conrad's work, Proc. IVth Congr. Int. Comp. Lit. Asn, Mouton, The Hague, 66; Joseph Conrad and Shakespeare, Conradiana, summer & fall, 68, fall 74; Contemporary Israeli literature: a new stance, Bks. Abroad, spring 72; plus others. Add: Dept. of English & World Literature, State University of New York College at New Paltz, New Paltz, NY 12561.

GILMAN, ALBERT, b. New York, N.Y, May 9, 23. ENGLISH, DRAMA. B.A, Brooklyn Col, 43; M.A, Columbia Univ, 47; Ph.D, Univ. Mich, 54. Instr. ENG, Univ. Mich, 52-53; BOSTON UNIV, 53-56, asst. prof, 56-61, assoc. prof, 61-67, PROF, 67- MLA; NCTE; Shakespeare Asn. Am. Shakespeare; linguistics. Publ: Ed, As you like it, New Am. Libr, 63; co-auth, Pronouns of power and solidarity, In: Style in language, Wiley, 60; co-auth, Personality and style in Concord: Emerson and Thoreau, In: Transcendentalism and its legacy, Univ. Mich, 67. Add: Dept. of English, Boston University, Charles River Campus, 236 Bay State Rd, Boston, MA 02215.

GILMAN, HARVEY, b. Brooklyn, N.Y, Aug. 18, 38. ENGLISH, COLONIAL AMERICAN LITERATURE. A.B, Brooklyn Col, 62, M.A, New York Univ, 63, Ph.D.(Eng), Pa. State Univ, 67. Asst. ENG, Pa. State Univ, 63-65, instr, 65-67; asst. prof, Univ. Chicago, 67-73; ASSOC. PROF, CITY COLS. CHICAGO, 74- Seventeenth century English literature. Publ: Crawshaw's reflexive recoil, Seventeenth Century News, spring 64. Add: Dept. of English, University of Chicago, Chicago, IL 60637.

GILMAN, WILBUR ELWYN, b. Amsterdam, N.Y, Nov. 7, 02. ENGLISH RHETORIC. A.B, Cornell Univ, 23, Ph.D, 37. Instr. Eng, Univ. Mo, 23-25; pub. speaking, Cornell Univ, 25-26; asst. prof. Eng, Univ. Mo, 27-30, assoc. prof, 30-40, speech, 40-42, chmn. dept. speech & dramatic art; asst. prof. speech, QUEENS COL.(N.Y), 44-48, assoc. prof, 48-55, prof, 55-71, chmn. dept, 45-66, EMER. PROF, 71- Bk. rev. ed, Quart. J. Speech, 40-42, assoc. ed, 44-47; consult, Curriculum Ctr. in Eng, Northwest. Univ, 63. Speech Commun. Asn.(v.pres, 50, pres, 51); MLA; Cent. States Speech Asn. (pres, 40); Speech Asn. East. States (pres, 49). History and principles of rhetoric; rhetorical criticism of public address. Publ: The rhetoric of John Milton, Univ. Mo, 39; co-auth, Fundamentals of speaking, 51 & 64 & An introduction to speaking, 2nd ed, 68, Macmillan; auth, Public speaking, argumentation and debate, In: Speech, Barnes & Noble, 54; co-auth, Teaching public address and differentiating activities in communication, In: The communicative arts and sciences of speech, C.E. Merrill, 67; Consultant on rhetoric, In: The Random House dictionary of the English language, 66. Add: 57-53 Parsons Blvd, Flushing, NY 11365.

GILMAN, WILLIAM HENRY, b. Boston, Mass, Aug. 9, 11; m. 38, 43; c. 6. ENGLISH. A.B, Harvard, 33; A.M, George Washington Univ, 43; Ph.D. (Eng), Yale, 48. Lectr. ENG, sch. for. serv, Georgetown Univ, 41-44; asst. prof, UNIV. ROCHESTER, 47-52, assoc. prof, 52-59, PROF, 59- Ford fel, 53-54; vis. prof, Stanford Univ, 59; Guggenheim fel, 60-61 & 64-65. MLA. Hero in American literature. Publ: Melville's early life and Redburn, N.Y. Univ, 51; co-ed, The letters of Herman Melville, Yale, 60; The journals and miscellaneous notebooks of Ralph Waldo Emerson, Vols. I-III, Harvard, 60, 61 & 63; ed, Selected writings of Ralph W. Emerson, New Am. Libr, 65; auth, The hero and the heroic in American literature, In: Patterns of commitment in American literature, Toronto, 67. Add: Dept. of English, University of Rochester, Rochester, NY 14627.

GILMER, FRANK WALKER, b. Chicago, Ill, July 11, 35; m. 62; c. 1. MODERN AMERICAN LITERATURE. A.B, Univ. Va, 57; Harvard Law Sch, 57-58; M.A, Northwest. Univ, 59; Ph.D.(Eng), 63. Asst. prof. ENG, DePAUW UNIV, 63-67, ASSOC. PROF, 67- MLA. Modern American literature and the novel. Publ: Horace Liveright: publisher of the twenties, David Lewis, 70. Add: Dept. of English, DePauw University, Greencastle, IN 46135.

GILMORE, ROBERT K, b. Springfield, Mo, June 6, 27; m. 50; c. 3. SPEECH, THEATRE. B.S, Southwest Mo. State Col, 49, B.S.Ed, 50; A.M, St. Louis Univ, 54; Ph.D.(theatre), Univ. Minn, 61. Teacher, High Sch, Mo, 49-57; instr. THEATRE, Univ. Minn, 57-59; asst. prof, SOUTHWEST MO. STATE UNIV, 59-61, assoc. prof, 61-64, PROF, 64-, DEAN FAC, 71-, head dept. theatre, 65-67, dean arts & humanities, 67-71. U.S.N, 45-46. Am. Theatre Asn; Cent. States Speech Asn; Speech Commun. Asn. Speech education; play direction; early Ozarks theatre. Add: Southwest Missouri State University, Springfield, MO 65802.

GILMORE, THOMAS BARRY, JR, b. Chicago, Ill, Nov. 29, 32; m. 57; c. 3. ENGLISH. A.B, Univ. Mich, 54, A.M, 55; Ph.D.(Eng), Univ. Ill, 64. Lectr. ENG, Queens Col.(N.Y), 62-65; asst. prof, Cornell Col, 65-69; ASSOC. PROF, GA. STATE UNIV, 69- Fac. fel, Newberry Libr. Sem. of Humanities, Assoc. Cols. Midwest, 67-68. Qm.C, U.S.A, 55-57. MLA. Eighteenth-century English literature; satire. Publ: Ed, Walter Harte's An essay on satire (1730), Augustan Reprint Soc, 68 & Early eighteenth-century essays on taste, Scholars' Facsimilies & Reprints, 72; auth, The eighteenth-century controversy over ridicule as a test of truth: a reconsideration, Arts & Sci. Res. Papers, Ga. State Univ, 70; plus others. Add: Dept. of English, Georgia State University, Atlanta, GA 30303.

GILPIN, GEORGE HEYBURN, b. San Antonio, Tex, Feb. 20, 41; m. 63; c. 2. EIGHTEENTH CENTURY & ROMANTIC ENGLISH LITERATURE. A.B, Princeton, 63; Ph.D.(Eng), Rice Univ, 67. ASST. PROF. ENG, Vanderbilt Univ, 67-74; UNIV. MIAMI, 74- MLA; AAUP. Romantic poetry, Blake, Coleridge, Wordsworth; 18th century satire. Publ: Strategy of joy: an essay on the poetry of Samuel Taylor Coleridge, Univ. Salzburg, 72; Coleridge and the spiral of poetic thought, Stud. Eng. Lit, autumn 72. Add: Dept. of English, University of Miami, Coral Gables, FL 33124.

GIMMESTAD, HERMAN, b. Galesville, Wis, Feb. 12, 02; m. 36. ENGLISH. B.A, St. Olaf Col, 23; M.A, Harvard, 26; Univ. Wis; D.Litt, Midland Lutheran Col, 67. Instr. Eng, Univ. N.Dak, 26-27; prof. Eng. & chmn. dept, MIDLAND LUTHERAN COL, 27-70, dean men, 34-43, col, 43-49, chmn. div. humanities, 62-70, EMER. PROF. ENG, 70- NCTE; MLA; Am. Stud. Asn; Asn. Lutheran Col. Fac.(pres, 54); Soc. Advan. Scand. Stud. American literature; Norwegian-Americana. Publ: Contribution of the humanities & New horizons in college enrollment, J. Asn. Lutheran Col. Faculties. Add: Dept. of English, Midland Lutheran College, Fremont, NE 68025.

GIMMESTAD, VICTOR EDWARD, b. Galesville, Wis, Aug. 13, 12; m. 37; c. 3. ENGLISH. B.A, St. Olaf Col, 34; M.A, Univ. Wis, 40, Ph.D, 50; Univ. South, Calif. Teacher, High Schs, Minn, Wis. & C.Z, 34-41; asst. prof. ENG, St. Olaf Col, 47-48; ILL. STATE UNIV, 48-51, assoc. prof, 51-57, PROF, 57-, head dept, 60-67. Vis. chmn. dept. Eng, Calif. Lutheran Col, 68-69. Midwest Mod. Lang. Asn.(pres, 63-64); MLA; NEA; Norweg-Am. Hist. Soc; Melville Soc. Am. John Trumbull, the poet; Connecticut literature before 1800; political propaganda in the Revolutionary War era. Publ: John Trumbull, Twayne, 74; John Trumbull's Epithalamion, Yale Univ. Libr. Gazette, 1/74. Add: 204 W. Summit St, Normal, IL 61761.

GINDIN, JAMES J, b. Newark, N.J, May 23, 26; m. 55; c. 2. ENGLISH LITERATURE. B.A, Yale, 49; M.A, Cornell, 50, Ph.D, 54; Cornell-Glasgow exchange fel, Univ. Glasgow, Scotland, 51-52. Instr. Eng. lit, Cornell Univ, 52-54; checker, New Yorker Mag, 54-55; educ. adv, U.S. Air Force, Eng, 55-56; instr. Eng. lit, UNIV. MICH, ANN ARBOR, 56-59, asst. prof, 59-63, assoc. prof, 63-68, PROF. ENG, 68- Fulbright lectr, Univ. Sheffield, 64-65; Nat. Endowment for humanities sr. fel, 73-74. U.S.A.A.F, 44-46, Sgt. Nineteenth and 20th century British and American fiction. Publ: Postwar British fiction: new accents and attitudes, Univ. Calif, 62; ed, Thomas Hardy's The return of the native, Norton, 69; auth, Harvest of a quiet eye: the novel of compassion since 1875, Ind. Univ, 71; Letter from Sheffield, Mich. Quart, fall 67; The fable begins to break down, Wis. Stud. Contemporary Lit, winter 67; Well beyond laughter; directions from fifties' British fiction, Stud. Novel, winter 71; plus others. Add: 1615 Shadford, Ann Arbor, MI 48104.

GINGERICH, MARTIN ELLSWORTH, b. Reedsville, Pa, May 24, 33; m. 58; c. 4. MODERN ENGLISH & AMERICAN LITERATURE. B.S, Shippensburg State Col, 59; M.A, Univ. Maine, Orono, 61; Ph.D.(lang. & lit), Ohio Univ, 67. Instr. ENG, E.Stroudsburg State Col, 61-62, asst. prof, 62-64; instr, Ohio Univ, 64-65, ASST. PROF, 67-68; WEST. MICH. UNIV, 68- Hosp.C, U.S.N, 51-55. Midwest Mod. Lang. Asn; Col. Eng. Asn. Modern poetry; English and American literature; American history. Publ: Rhetoric and meaning in A refusal to mourn, Notes Contemporary Lit, 1/71; Dylan Thomas and the ark of the convenant, 71 & Dylan Thomas: curse-bless, 73, Anglo-Welsh Rev. Add: Dept. of English, Western Michigan University, Kalamazoo, MI 49001.

GIORDANO, FRANK RALPH, JR, b. Bridgeport, Conn, Aug. 13, 42; m. 65; c. 3. ENGLISH LITERATURE. B.S, Cent. Conn. State Col, 64; M.A, Univ. Fla, 66, Ph.D.(Eng), 68. Asst. prof. ENG, Univ. Del, 68-73; ASSOC. PROF, UNIV. HOUSTON, 73- Am. Philos. Soc. grant, summer 70. MLA; S.Cent. Mod. Lang. Asn. Victorian poetry; 19th century English fiction; the novel. Publ: Contrib, Absalom, Absalom! as a portrait of the artist, In: From Irving to Steinbeck, Univ. Fla, 72; auth, Secularization and ethical authority in Jude the obscure, Thomas Hardy Yearbk, 72-73; Jude the obscure and the Bildungsroman, Stud. in Novel, 72; plus three others. Add: Dept. of English, University of Houston, Houston, TX 77004.

GIORGIO, BENJAMIN DAVID, b. Lancaster, Pa, Aug. 23, 40. ENGLISH. A.B, Dickinson Col, 62; M.S, Univ. Wis, Madison, 64, univ. fel, Ford Found. grant & Ph.D.(Eng), 69. ASST. PROF. ENG, Univ. Mo-Kansas City, 68-69; UNIV. ALTA, 69- Vis. fel, Australian Nat. Univ, 74. Can. Asn. Univ. Teachers; Am. Stud. Asn. Literature of the American and Canadian West. Add: Dept. of English, University of Alberta, Edmonton, Alta, Can.

GIOVANNINI, GIOVANNI, b. Heilwood, Pa, Oct. 26, 06; m. 36; c. 2. ENGLISH LITERATURE. A.B, Univ. Detroit, 29; A.M, Univ. Mich, 33, univ. fel, 35-37, Ph.D, 40. Instr, Univ. Detroit, 29-35; teaching fel, Univ. Mich, 37-40; instr, CATH. UNIV. AM, 40-44, asst. prof, 44-47, assoc. prof. Eng. lit, 47-52, from prof. Eng. lit. to prof. ENG. LANG. & LIT, 52-72, EMER. PROF, 72- MLA. Publ: Method in study of literature in relation to other fine arts, J. Aesthet. & Art Criticism; Historical realism and the tragic emotions, Philol. Quart; Melville and Dante, PMLA; Ezra Pound and Dante, Utrecht: Dekker, 61. Add: 2525 Avalon Pl, Hyattsville, MD 20783.

GIOVANNINI, JOHN DANIEL, b. Midland, Mich, Feb. 19, 31; m. 64; c. 3. MASS COMMUNICATIONS. B.S, North. Mich. Univ, 56; cert. media, Stanford Univ, 57; M.F.A, Ohio Univ, 59; Ind. Univ, Bloomington, 65-67. Instr. speech, North. Mich. Univ, 56-58; prog. dir, WLUC-TV, Marquette, Mich, 59-61; WLUK-TV, Green Bay, Wis, 61-63; KVZK-TV, Pago Pago, Am. Samoa, 63-65; asst. prof. sociol, ST. NORBERT COL, 67-70, ASSOC. PROF. COMMUN. ARTS, 70-, DIR. SUMMER SESSIONS, 72- Consult, S.Pac. Comn, Suva, Fiji, 63-65; vis. prof, Lawrence Univ, 68-70; Nat. Endowment for Humanities grant, 71-72. U.S.A.F, 51-54. Nat. Asn. Summer Sessions; Am. Sociol. Asn. Audience measurement; programming; radio and television. Publ: Co-auth, Communication theory, 68, Oral communication, 68 & Written communication, 68, Welch Sci. Add: Dept. of Communication Arts, St. Norbert College, DePere, WI 54115.

GIOVANNINI, MARGARET (COBB), b. Aledo, Ill, June 17, 09; m. 36; c. 2. ENGLISH. A.B, Univ. Mich, 35, M.A, 36; B.Litt, Oxford, 38. Instr. ENG, Ypsilanti State Norm. Col, 39-40; from assoc. prof. to prof, ENG, TRINITY COL.(D.C), 45-74, chmn. dept, 66-68, EMER. PROF, 74- Mod. Humanities Res. Asn; MLA; Mid. Atlantic Col. Eng. Asn. Modern drama; 17th century verse; 18th century satire. Publ: The caged skylark, Paradise lost, & Blake's introduction to The songs of innocence, Explicator, Add: Dept. of English, Trinity College, Washington, DC 20017.

GIRDLER, LEW, b. La Grande, Ore, Feb. 23, 16; m. 40, 73; c. 2. ENGLISH. B.A, Ill. Col, 36; M.A, Univ. Calif, 41, Ph.D.(Eng), Los Angeles, 50. Assoc. prof. ENG, Ariz. State Univ, 49-53; CALIF. STATE UNIV, SAN JOSE, 54-63, prof, 63-71, EMER. PROF, 71- Ford Found. fel, 53-54. U.S.N.R, 45-46. MLA. English novel; semantics. Publ: Staff reference book: San Jose State

College; co-auth, Folktales for adults, 64; Wuthering Heights and Shakespeare, Huntington Libr. Quart. Add: 970 Wildcat Canyon Rd, Berkeley, CA 94708.

GIRLING, HARRY KNOWLES, b. Horsforth, Eng, Apr. 28, 19; m. 51; c. 4. ENGLISH. B.A. & M.A, Oxford, 47. Lectr. ENG, Univ. Witwatersrand, S.Africa, 48-51, sr. lectr, 51-62; assoc. prof, YORK UNIV, 62-71, PROF, 71- Carnegie traveling fel, 61; Can. Counc. leave fel, 69-70. Brit. Army, 40-45, Lt. Asn. Can. Univ. Teacher Eng; Can. Asn. Univ. Teachers; Can. Asn. Am. Stud.(treas, 67-68). Nineteenth century fiction, especially Henry James; structures of narrative fiction; South African novelists. Publ: The function of slang in the dramatic poetry of The golden bowl, Nineteenth-Century Fiction, 56; Wonder and beauty in The awkward age, Essays in Criticism, 58; The strange case of Dr. James and Mr. Stevenson, Wascana Rev, 68. Add: Dept. of English, York University, 4700 Keele St, Downsview, Ont. M3J 1P3, Can.

GISKIN, HENRY, b. New Haven, Conn, Apr. 14, 24; m. 53; c. 4. SPEECH EDUCATION. B.S, Cent. Conn. State Col, 49; M.A, Columbia Univ, 55, Ed.D, (speech educ), 66. Teacher, High Sch, Conn, 49-51 & 53-55; Jr. High Sch, 55-59; assoc. prof. speech & Eng, Clarion State Col, 59-61; lectr. SPEECH, Hunter Col, 61-62; City Col. New York, 62-66; asst. prof, SOUTH. CONN. STATE COL, 66-71, ASSOC. PROF, 71- Supvr. masters' cand. in stud. teaching of speech, Teachers Col, Columbia Univ, 64-66; mem. comt. on problems in elem. speech, Speech Asn. Am, 66-67; consult. speech improvement, summer high sch, Yale, 67; leader in-serv. workshop speech improvement, RESCUE, Conn, 68; dir, Speech Educ. Workshop, Meriden Conn. Bd. Educ, 70. U.S.A.A.F, 43-45. Speech Commun. Asn; East. Commun. Asn; Am. Fed. Teachers. Speech education; internship in college teaching of speech. Publ: Internship in college teaching of speech, Univ. Microfilms, 66, Diss. Abstr, 66 & Speech Monogr, 8/67. Add: Dept. of Speech, Southern Connecticut State College, Crescent St, New Haven, CT 06515.

GISTER, EARLE ROBERT, b. Racine, Wis, Mar. 30, 34; m. 59; c. 3. DRAMA. B.A, Carleton Col, 56; Ind. Univ, 56-57; Tulane Univ, 59-62. Asst. ed. Tulane Drama Rev, Tulane Univ, 59-60, managing ed, 60-62; asst. prof. DRAMA & asst. to head dept, CARNEGIE-MELLON UNIV, 62-64, acting head dept, 64-65, ASSOC. PROF. & HEAD DEPT, 65- Mem. adv. bd, Am. Conservatory Theatre, 65-; adv. counc, Conservatory Found, 68-; adv. bd, WQED-TV, Pa, 68-; theatre comt, Nat. Counc. Arts, 68-73. U.S.A, 57-59. Am. Theatre Asn; Nat. Theatre Conf. (v.pres, 72, 73, pres, 74, 75). Acting and dramatic literature. Add: Dept. of Drama, Carnegie-Mellon University, 5000 Forbes Ave, Pittsburgh, PA 15213.

GITTLEMAN, EDWIN, b. Brooklyn, N.Y, Jan. 20, 29; m. 52; c. 1. AMERICAN LITERATURE. A.B, Columbia Univ, 50, M.A, 57, fel, 58-59, Ph.D. (Eng. & comp.lit), 65. Instr. humanities, Stevens Inst. Technol, 59-63, asst. prof, 63-65; ENG, Dartmouth Col, 65-68, ASSOC. PROF, 68-72; UNIV. MASS, BOSTON, 72- Columbia Univ. Ansley Award, 65. U.S.N, 53-57, Res, 57-68, Lt. MLA; Col. Eng. Asn; Emerson Soc; Thoreau Soc. American literature especially colonial, 19th & 20th century; transcendentalism; Emerson. Publ: Naval communications procedures in the Fifteenth Naval District, U.S. Navy, 56; Jones Very: the effective years (1833-1840), Columbia Univ, 67; Singer's apocalyptic town: Satan in Goray, In: Isaac Bashevis Singer and the critics, South. Ill. Univ, 69. Add: Dept. of English, University of Massachusetts, Boston, MA 02116.

GLADISH, DAVID, b. Chicago, Ill, Mar. 18, 28; m. 52; c. 3. ENGLISH. B.A, Lake Forest Col, 50; M.A, Univ. Ill, 54, Ph.D.(Eng), 61. Asst. ENG, Univ. Ill, 55-61; asst. prof, Franklin Col, 61-62, assoc. prof, 62-67, PROF, 67-72; RES. & WRITING. U.S.A, 50-52. MLA; Renaissance Soc. Am. Publ: Ed, Gondibert, Oxford, 71. Add: St. James, MI 49782.

GLADISH, ROBERT WILLIS, b. Colchester, Eng, Feb. 19, 31; U.S. citizen; m. 62; c. 4. ENGLISH. M.A, Univ. Chicago, 56, Ph.D.(Eng), 64. Instr. ENG, Tex. A&M Univ, 56-58; Univ. Ill, Chicago Circle, 60-65, asst. prof, 65-70, assoc. prof, 70-71; HEAD DEPT, COL, ACAD. OF THE NEW CHURCH, 71- U.S.A, 53-55. MLA. Nineteenth century English language and literature. Publ: Mrs. Browning's contributions to the New York Independent, Bull. N.Y. Pub. Libr, 1/67; Mrs. Browning's A curse for a nation, Victorian Poetry, autumn 69; Elizabeth Barrett and the Centurion, Baylor Browning Interests, 1/73. Add: Dept. of English, College of the Academy of the New Church, Bryn Athyn, PA 19009.

GLANCY, DONALD RAY, b. Gary, Ind, May 8, 27. DRAMA & THEATRE. A.B, DePauw Univ, 49; M.A, Ind. Univ, Bloomington, 59. Teacher Eng, Vandalia High Sch, Ohio, 53-54; Eng. & dramatics, Battle Creek Cent. High Sch, Mich, 54-61; ASSOC. PROF. THEATRE, OHIO STATE UNIV, 63- Speech Commun. Asn.(chmn. theatre & drama interest group, 69-70, mem. comt. awards & recognition, 72-73); Am. Theatre Asn.(chmn. musical theatre proj, Am. Educ. Theatre Asn, 70-71). Dramatic literature and criticism; theatrical production. Publ: Socialist with a valet: the first, last, and only lecture of Jack London, Quart. J. Speech, 2/63; Jack London and Billy the Kid, Am. Bk. Collector, 12/71; Anything to help anybody: the authorship of Daughters of the rich, Jack London Newslett, 1-4/72. Add: Dept. of Theatre, Ohio State University, 1849 Cannon Dr, Columbus, OH 43210.

GLASHEEN, FRANCIS JAMES, b. Torrington, Conn, Jan. 12, 10. ENGLISH. A.B, Yale, 33, Ph.D, 40. Instr. ENG, Univ. Miss, 37-39; St. Louis Univ, 39-40, summer 40; asst. prof, Wheaton Col.(Mass), 45-47; from assoc. prof. to PROF, CENT. CONN. STATE COL, 47- MLA; Col. Eng. Asn. Add: Dept. of English, Central Connecticut State College, New Britain, CT 06050.

GLASRUD, CLARENCE A, b. Cass Co, N.Dak, Oct. 15, 11; m. 48; c. 1. ENGLISH. B.S, Moorhead State Col, 35; Univ. Minn, summers 36-40; Kenyon Col, 43-44 & 48; M.A, Harvard, 51, Ph.D.(Eng), 53. Teacher pub. schs, Minn, 29-42; asst. prof. Eng. jour, MOORHEAD STATE COL, 47-49, assoc. prof. & acting chmn. dept, 49-53, PROF. ENG, 53-, chmn. dept, 53-72. Adv. ed, Stud. Am. Fiction, 73- U.S.A.A.F, 42-45, T/Sgt. MLA; NCTE; Norweg-Am. Hist. Asn.(bd. publ, 72-); Am-Scand. Found. The genteel tradition, 1865-1914; Western American literature, history and ideas; Scandinavian American literary relations. Publ: Ed, The age of anxiety, Houghton Mifflin Res. Ser, 60; auth, Hjalmar Hjorth Boyesen, Norweg-Am. Hist. Asn, 63; Boyesen and the Norwegian immigration, Stud. & Rec, Norweg-Am. Hist. Asn, 59. Add: 422 Sixth St. S, Moorhead, MN 56560.

GLASSER, WILLIAM ARNOLD, b. Chicago, Ill, July 30, 32; m. 57; c. 2. ENGLISH. B.A, Harpur Col, 57; M.A, Univ. Fla, 59; Ph.D.(Eng), Univ. Iowa, 65. Instr. ENG, Rollins Col, 59-62; Trinity Col.(Conn), 63-64; Williams Col, 64-66, asst. prof, 66-70; SKIDMORE COL, 70-72, ASSOC. PROF, 72- Sr. Fulbright-Hayes lectr, Univ. Salzburg, 72-73; lectr, Intercountry Exchange Prog, Univ. Bari & Univ. Pescara, Italy, spring 73. U.S.A.F, 49-53, Sgt. American novels; creative writing. Publ: A farewell to arms, spring 66 & Moby-Dick, summer 69, Sewanee Rev. Add: Dept. of English, Skidmore College, Saratoga Springs, NY 12866.

GLASSHEIM, ELIOT ALAN, b. New York, N.Y, Feb. 10, 38; m. 64, 69; c. 1. AMERICAN LITERATURE. B.A, Wesleyan Univ, 60; M.A, Univ. N.Mex, 66, Ph.D.(Eng), 73. ASST. PROF. Am. lit, Augusta Col, 68-71; EDUC, UNIV. N.DAK, 73-, fel, New Sch, 72-73. Publ, Poetry London-New York, 61-62; ed. & publ, Polylog, 70-71. American values and ideals; literature and society. Publ: The restless giant (poems), San Marcos Press, 68; A dogged interpretation of Poe's Never bet the devil your head, Poe Newsletter, 2/70; A Paul Goodman checklist: 1930-1970, Bull. Bibliog, 8/71; School daze—comments on experimental schools, New Sch. Exchange Newsletter, 9/72. Add: Ctr. for Teaching & Learning, University of North Dakota, Grand Forks, ND 58201.

GLAZIER, LYLE EDWARD, b. Leverett, Mass, May 8, 11; m. 39; c. 3. ENGLISH. A.B, Middlebury Col, 33; A.M, Bread Loaf Sch. Eng, 37; Ph.D, Harvard, 50. Prin. graded sch, Northfield, Mass, 34-35; instr. & housemaster, Mt. Hermon Sch, 35-37; instr. ENG, Bates Col, 37-42; Tufts Col, 42-44; Teaching fel, Harvard, 45-47; from asst. prof. to assoc. prof. Eng. & dir. Am. stud, STATE UNIV. N.Y. BUFFALO, 47-63, prof. ENG, 63-72, EMER. PROF, 72- Am. Counc. Learned Soc. fac. fel, 51-52; Fulbright prof. & chmn. dept. Am. lit, Univ. Istanbul, 61-63; Fulbright lectr, Hacettepe Univ, Ankara, 68-69; vis. prof. Am. lit, spring 70 & 71; Fulbright sem. Am. lit, India, spring 70 & 71; vol. specialist Am. lit, U.S. Info. Serv, India, summer 71. MLA; Am. Stud. Asn. American fiction; poetry; Black literature. Publ: Orchard Park and Istanbul, Big. Mountain Press, Swallow, 65; You too (poems), 69, The dervishes (poems), 71 & VD (poems), 71, Istanbul Matbaasi; Decadence and rebirth, Hacettepe Univ, 71. Add: R.D. 2, Bennington, VT 05201.

GLEASON, GEORGE DONALD, b. Butte, Mont, July 22, 20; m. 49; c. 4. ENGLISH. B.E, Ariz. State Col, Flagstaff, 42; M.A, Northwest. Univ, 48; Ph.D, Univ. Iowa, 56. Teacher, Jr. High Sch, Cottonwood, Ariz, 42; ENG, High Sch, Yreka, Calif, 46-47; critic teacher, Wis. State Col, Superior, 48-50; assoc. prof, SOUTHWEST MO. STATE COL, 55-58, PROF, 58-, DEPT. CHMN, 63- Chmn. fac. senate, 62-74. Contrib. ed, Annual Bibliog. Eng. Lang. & Lit, 65- U.S.N, 42-46, 50-52, Lt. MLA; NCTE; Mod. Humanities Res. Asn; Midwest Mod. Lang. Asn; Conf. Col. Compos. & Commun. Add: Dept. of English, Southwest Missouri State College, Springfield, MO 65802.

GLEASON, JOHN HABERMAN, b. Edinboro, Pa, Oct. 10, 17, JOURNALISM, ADMINISTRATION. B.S, Northwest. Univ, 38; M.S, Columbia Univ, 40, Ed.D, 62. Night ed, United Press, Cleveland, Ohio, 37-38; reporter, Buffalo Eve. News, N.Y, 40-42; asst. managing ed, San Diego Jour, Calif, 45-46; asst. prof, Pa. State Col, 46-47; prof. jour. & dir. div, Boston Univ, 47-54; prof. jour, Univ. Conn, 54-64, head dept, 62-64, dir. div. commun, 54-62; dean, Augusta Col, 64-69; CHMN. DEPT. COMMUN, WOODBURY COL, 70-; LECTR, UNIV. CALIF, LOS ANGELES, 73- For. Policy Asn; Am. Acad. Polit. & Soc. Sci; Counc. For. Relat. Eidolonics: a philosophy of mass communications. Add: Dept. of Communications, Woodbury College, 1027 Wilshire Blvd, Los Angeles, CA 90017.

GLECKNER, ROBERT FRANCIS, b. Rahway, N.J, Mar. 2, 25; m. 46; c. 2. ENGLISH. B.A, Williams Col.(Mass), 48; Ph.D.(Eng), Johns Hopkins Univ, 54. Jr. instr. ENG, Johns Hopkins Univ, 49-51; instr. Univ. Cincinnati, 52-54; Univ. Wis, 54-57, asst. prof, Wayne State Univ, 57-60, assoc. prof, 60-62; PROF, UNIV. CALIF, RIVERSIDE, 62-, DEAN COL. HUMANITIES, 70-; acting chmn. dept. Eng, 62-63, chmn, 63-66, fac. intra-mural res. grant, 62-73; div. dean humanities, 68-70; fac. res. lectr, 73. Ed, U.S. Air Force Res. Stud. Inst, Air Univ, 51-52; Univ. Wis. Grad. Sch. res. grant, 57; Wayne State Univ. Grad. Sch. fac. fel, 60; mem. adv. bd. & consult. reader, Criticism: a Quart. for Lit. & Arts, 62-; Carl & Lily Pforzheimer Found. grant, 67; adv. ed, Blake Stud; mem. adv. bd. dirs, Am. Blake Found, 70- Consult. reader, Stud. Romanticism, Stud. Eng. Lit, Huntington Libr. Quart, 58-, Wayne State Univ. Press, Univ. Wash. Press, Univ. Mass. Press, Univ. Calif. Press, Harvard Press, Univ. Toronto Press, Huntington Libr. Press, 62-, Blake Stud. & PMLA, 69- Emily S. Hamblen Award, Poetry Soc. Am, 60. U.S.A.A.F, 43-45, 1st Lt. Byron Soc. Late 18th and early 19th century poetry and literary criticism, especially Blake, Coleridge, Keats and Byron; romanticism; language of romantic poetry. Publ: The piper and the bard: a study of William Blake, Wayne State Univ, 59; co-ed, Romanticism: points of view, Prentice-Hall, 62, ed, rev. ed, 69 & Selected writings of William Blake, Appleton, 67, ed. rev. ed, 70; auth, Byron and the ruins of paradise, John Hopkins Univ, 67; Joyce and Blake, In: A James Joyce Miscellany, South. Ill. Univ, 62; contrib, A Blake bibliography, Univ. Minn, 64; Blake's verbal technique, In: William Blake: essays for S. Foster Damon, Brown Univ, 69; plus articles in Va. Quart. Rev, Mod. Lang. Quart & Blake Stud, 69- Add: College of Humanities, University of California, Riverside, CA 92502.

GLEDHILL, PRESTON RAY, b. Richfield, Utah, Mar. 19, 15; m. 39; c. 4. SPEECH, DRAMA. A.B, Brigham Young Univ, 39; A.M, Univ. La, 40; Univ. Idaho; Sorbonne & Inst. Phonetique, Paris; Ph.D, Univ. Wis, 51. Instr, br. agr. col, Utah State Col, 43-45; asst. prof, Univ. Ala, 45-46; assoc. prof. speech & drama, BRIGHAM YOUNG UNIV, 47-59, PROF. DRAMATIC ARTS, 59- Speech Commun. Asn; Am. Theatre Asn; Am. Nat. Theatre & Acad; West. Speech Commun. Asn. Current European theatre. Add: F-527, Harris Fine Arts Center, Brigham Young University, Provo, UT 84601.

GLENN, EDGAR MUNGEN, b. Philadelphia, Pa, Sept. 16, 18; m. 43; c. 3. ENGLISH. A.B, Hamilton Col, 40; Ph.D.(Am. lit), Stanford Univ, 55. Instr.

ENG. & WORLD LIT, Northwest. Univ, 49-53; asst. prof, CHICO STATE COL, 53-58, assoc. prof, 58-63, PROF, 63- U.S.N.R, 41-46, Lt. Comdr. MLA. The cantos of Ezra Pound. Publ: Co-ed, Shakespeare and his rivals, Odyssey, 62; auth, A guide to Canto I of Ezra Pound, 60 & A guide to Canto II of Ezra Pound, 62, Analyst; plus others. Add: 6 Begonia Lane, Chico, CA 95926.

GLENN, ROBERT BRUCE, Linguistics. See Volume III, Foreign Languages, Linguistics & Philology.

GLENN, STANLEY LEONARD, b. Philadelphia, Pa, Feb. 8, 23; m. 42; c. 3. SPEECH, THEATRE ARTS. B.A, Univ. Calif, Los Angeles, 48, M.A, 49; Ph.D.(speech & drama), Stanford Univ, 55. Lectr. theatre arts, Univ. Calif, Los Angeles, 50-51; dir. Millbrae Community Players, San Mateo Jr. Col, 52-55; asst. prof. speech & drama, Humboldt State Col, 55-57; UNIV. CALIF, SANTA BARBARA, 57-61, assoc. prof, 61-66, PROF. DRAMATIC ART, 66- Med.C, U.S.A, 44-46. Am. Theatre Asn; Am. Nat. Theatre & Acad. Early American drama, especially comedy; acting, directing and dramatic literature. Publ: Ludicrous characterization in American comedy from the beginning until the Civil War; A director prepares, Dickenson, 73; Echo to the sense, West. Speech J, spring 60; The characterization of the Negro in American comedy before the Civil War, South. Speech J, winter 60; Style and Stanislavski, Quart. J. Speech, 2/63. Add: Dept. of Dramatic Art, University of California, Santa Barbara, CA 93106.

GLICK, ROBERT ALAN, b. Brooklyn, N.Y, Apr. 30, 45; m. 70. ENGLISH & COMPARATIVE LITERATURE. B.A, Brooklyn Col, 65; M.A, Columbia Univ, 67; NDEA fel. & Ph.D.(comp. lit), Ind. Univ, Bloomington, 73. ASST. PROF. Eng. & comp. lit, Univ. Cincinnati, 70-72; ENG, UNIV. MD, BALTIMORE COUNTY, 72- NCTE (comt. comp. lit, 71-); Int. Comp. Lit. Asn; Am. Comp. Lit. Asn; MLA. English romantic literature; European romantic literature; literature and science. Add: Dept. of English, University of Maryland, 5401 Wilkens Ave, Baltimore, MD 21228.

GLICK, WENDELL, b. Evanston, Ill, Mar. 22, 16; m. 48; c. 5. ENGLISH. Ph.D, Northwest. Univ, 50. Instr. Eng, Northwest. Univ, 47-51; Am. Counc. Learned Soc. scholar, 51-52; asst. prof. ENG, UNIV. MINN, DULUTH, 52-55, assoc. prof, 55-58, PROF, 58-, head dept, 66-69. Textual ed, The Thoreau Ed, Ctr. Am. Ed. of MLA. MLA; Am. Lit. Group. American literature; history of American ideas, 1800-1850. Publ: Ed, The recognition of Henry David Thoreau, Univ. Mich, 69 & The reform papers of Henry Thoreau, Princeton, 73. Add: 2230 E. Second St, Duluth, MN 55812.

GLICKFIELD, CHARLOTTE W, b. Johnson City, Tenn, Jan. 12, 24; m. 44; c. 3. ENGLISH ROMANTIC PERIOD. B.S, E.Tenn. State Univ, 44; M.A, Duke Univ, 53; Ph.D.(Eng), Univ. Tenn, 67. Asst. prof. Eng, Milligan Col, 53-57; instr, Univ. Tenn, 61-66; Univ. N.Mex, 66-67; asst. prof, Cent. Mo. State Col, 67-70; PROF. ENG. & CHMN. HUMANITIES, CUMBERLAND COUNTY COL, 70- MLA; Col. Eng. Asn. Publ: Coleridge's prose contributions to the Morning Post, PMLA, 6/54. Add: Dept. of Humanities, Cumberland County College, Vineland, NJ 08360.

GLICKSBERG, CHARLES IRVING, b. Warsaw, Poland, Dec. 13, 00. ENGLISH. B.S, City Col. N.Y, 23; A.M, Columbia Univ, 24; Ph.D, Univ. Pa, 32. Assoc. prof. ENG, BROOKLYN COL, 46-50, prof, 50-71, EMER. PROF, 71-; ADJ. PROF. COMP. LIT, CITY UNIV. NEW YORK, 71- Mem. fac. New Sch. Social Res, 47-64; ed, Am. Vanguard; Fulbright scholar Am. lit, Israel, 58-59; mem. fac. comp. lit, City Univ. New York, 62-71. MLA; NCTE. Comparative literature; literature and politics. Publ: Literature and religion, 60 & Modern literary perspectivism, 70, South. Methodist Univ; Creative writing, Hendricks, 61; Tragic vision in twentieth-century literature, South. Ill. Univ, 63; The self in modern literature, Pa. State Univ, 63; Modern literature and the death of God, 66, The ironic vision in modern literature, 68, The sexual revolution in modern American literature, 71, Literature and society, 72 & The sexual revolution in modern English literature, 73, Nijhoff; Literature of nihilism, Bucknell Univ, (in press). Add: Dept. of Comparative Literature, Graduate Center, City University of New York, 33 S. 42nd St, New York, NY 10036.

GLIKIN, GLORIA, English. See FROMM, GLORIA GLIKIN.

GLIMM, JAMES YORK, b. Mineola, N.Y, May 20, 42; m. 65; c. 2. ENGLISH. A.B, Col. Holy Cross, 64; Ph.D.(Eng), Univ. Tex, Austin, 68. ASSOC. PROF. ENG, MANSFIELD STATE COL, 68- MLA. Mysticism in secular literature; Romantic movement in England; phenomonology. Add: Dept. of English, Mansfield State College, Mansfield, PA 16933.

GLOBE, ALEXANDER VICTOR, b. Hamilton, Ont, Jan. 26, 43; m. 66. ENGLISH, THE BIBLE. B.A, Univ. Toronto, 65, Govt. Ont. fel. & M.A, 66, Govt. Ont. fel, 68-69, Can. Counc. fel, 69-70, Ph.D.(Eng), 70. Instr. ENG, Univ. Toronto, summer 70; ASST. PROF, UNIV. B.C, 70- Can. Counc. res. grants, 71, 72, 74. Asn. Can. Univ. Teachers Eng; Renaissance Soc. Am. The Bible and its influence; Renaissance civilization; 17th century poetry and engraving. Publ: The text and literary structure of Judges 5, 4-5, Biblica, 74. Add: Dept. of English, University of British Columbia, Vancouver, B.C. V6T 1W5, Can.

GLORFELD, LOUIS EARL, b. Buffalo Center, Iowa, July 2, 16; m. 43; c. 1. SPEECH. B.A, Univ. North. Iowa, 48, M.A, 55; Ph.D.(speech), Univ. Denver, 65. Teacher pub. schs, Iowa, 49-55, 56-59; high sch, Calif, 55-56; asst. prof. Eng. & speech, W.Liberty State Col, 59-60; Eng, North. Ill. Univ, 60-64, dir. freshman Eng, 65-67; PROF. COMMUN. THEORY, UNIV. DENVER, 67- NCTE; Conf. Col. Compos. & Commun; Speech Commun. Asn. English; speech; theater. Publ: Co-auth, A concise guide for writers, 63, rev. ed, 68, 74 & The dictionary and usage, 68, Holt; College prep reader, Harper, 65; Language, rhetoric, and idea, 67, The short story—ideas and background, 67, & Plays by four tragedians, 68, C.E. Merrill; auth, A short unit on general semantics, Glencoe, 69; Pursuit (poem), Midwest, spring 58; co-auth, Current financial assistance in the field of speech, Quart. J. Speech, 10/64. Add: Dept. of Speech, University of Denver, Denver, CO 80210.

GLOSTER, HUGH MORRIS, b. Brownsville, Tenn, May 11, 11; m. 57; c. 3. ENGLISH & AMERICAN LITERATURE. B.A, Morehouse Col, 31; univ. fel, Atlanta Univ, 31-33; Gen. Educ. Bd. fel, N.Y. Univ, 38-39, Ph.D, 43. From instr. to prof. Eng, Le Moyne Col.(Tenn), 33-41; prof, Morehouse Col, 41-43; United Serv. Orgn. prog. dir, Ft. Huachuca, Ariz, 43-44, assoc. regional exec, Atlanta, Ga, 44-46; prof. Eng. & chmn. dept. lang. & lit, Hampton Inst, 46-67, dir. summer session, 52-62, dean fac, 63-67; PRES, MOREHOUSE COL, 67- Prof, Atlanta Univ, summers 42, 43; vis. prof. Am. lit, N.Y. Univ, summers 49, 62; Am. Friends Serv. Comt. lectr. Am. lit, U.S. cols. & univs, 53; Fulbright prof, Hiroshima Univ, Japan, 53-55; lectr, Conn. State Cols, 56, 59; prof. Eng. & dir. summer session, Virgin Islands Exptl. Col, St. Thomas, summer 60; U.S. Dept. State vis. prof. Am. lit, Univ. Warsaw, 61-62, Am. specialists prog, Tanganyika, E.Africa, summer 61, vis. lectr. Am. lit, Poland, Spain, summer 63; mem. bd. trustees, Atlanta Univ, Morehouse Col, 67; Col. Entrance Exam. Bd, 67; United Negro Col. Fund, 68, mem. bd. dir, 68; mem. bd. publ, Negro Univs. Press, 68; mem. bd. dir, Am. Asn. Higher Educ, 68; Counc. Protestant Cols. & Univs, 68. Col. Lang. Asn.(pres, 37-38, 48-50; award, 58); MLA; NCTE; Col. Eng. Asn; Asn. Higher Educ. American Negro literature; contemporary American literature and culture. Publ: Negro voices in American fiction, Univ. N.C, 48; co-auth, The brown thrush: an anthology of verse by Negro college students, Malcolm-Roberts, 35 & My Life—my country—my world: college readings for modern living, Prentice-Hall, 52. Add: Morehouse College, Atlanta, GA 30314.

GLOVER, DONALD ELLSWORTH, b. Rochester, N.Y, Apr. 16, 33; m. 55; c. 4. ENGLISH. B.A, Col. William & Mary, 55; Univ. Adelaide, 55-56; Fulbright fel, 56-57; M.A, Univ. Va, 59, Ph.D.(Eng), 65. Assoc. prof. ENG, MARY WASHINGTON COL, UNIV. VA, 61-73, PROF, 73- U.S.A.R, 53-61. MLA. Fantasy in literature; C.S. Lewis. Add: Dept. of English, Mary Washington College, University of Virginia, Fredericksburg, VA 22401.

GLYER, RICHARD T, b. Brooten, Minn, Nov. 4, 12; m. 50; c. 1. SPEECH, DRAMA. A.B, Univ. South. Calif, 38; M.A, Stanford Univ, 41, Ed.D, 57. Instr. Eng, SAN FRANCISCO STATE UNIV, 47-52, asst. prof. DRAMA, 52-57, from assoc. prof. to PROF, 58- Rituals and ceremonies; directing; higher education. Add: Dept. of Drama, San Francisco State University, San Francisco, CA 94132.

GNAROWSKI, MICHAEL, b. Shanghai, China, Sept. 27, 34; Can. citizen; m. 61; c. 3. ENGLISH & CANADIAN STUDIES. B.A, McGill Univ, 56; Ind. Tuition Found. fel, Ind. Univ, 59; M.A, Univ. Montreal, 60, P.Q. scholar, 62; Ph.D.(Can. lit), Univ. Ottawa, 67. Lectr. Eng. lit, Univ. Sherbrooke, 61-62; asst. prof, Lakehead Univ, 62-65, acting chmn. dept, 63-64; asst. prof. mod. & Can. lit, SIR GEORGE WILLIAMS UNIV, 66-68, assoc. prof. & coord. Can. Stud, 68-72; PROF. ENG. & GEN. ED. CARLETON LIBR, CARLETON UNIV, 72- Lectr. Eng. lit, Univ. Montreal, summer 63; Atkinson Found. Toronto res. grant-in-aid, 63; lectr. Can. lit, Sir George Williams Univ, summers 64, 65; res. off. & assoc. res. div, Royal Comn. Bilingualism & Biculturalism, 64, 65; C.D. Howe Mem. Found. fel, 65-66; lectr. Can. lit, Univ. Ottawa, 66; Can. Counc. res. grant-in-aid, 66; vis. fel, Inst. Can. Stud, Carleton Univ, 67-68; vis. prof. Can. lit, Univ. Ottawa, 69-72; gen. ed, Critical views on Canadian writers ser, McGraw-Hill Ryerson, 69- Can. Intel.C, 59-65, Lt. Asn. Can. Univ. Teachers Eng. Canadian literature; modern poetry; bibliographical studies. Publ: Co-auth, Canadian poetry: a supplementary bibliography, Culture, P.Q, 64; auth, Contact, 1952-1954, 66, The rising village of Oliver Goldsmith: a new edition, 68 & ed, Contact press: a check list of titles, 71, Delta Can; co-auth, The making of modern poetry in Canada, 67 & ed, Archibald Lampan, 70, Ryerson; Three early poems from lower Canada, 69 & Joseph Quesnel: selected poems and songs, 70, Lande Found, McGill Univ; Selected stories of Raymond Knister, Univ. Ottawa, 72; auth, A concise bibliography of English-Canadian literature, 73, McClelland & Stewart, 73; The role of little magazines in the development of poetry in English in Montreal, 9/63, Milton Acorn: a review in retrospect, 6/64 & Raymond Souster: au-dessus de la melee, 3/65, Culture; plus contrib. to several reference books. Add: Dept. of English, Carleton University, Ottawa, Ont. K1S 5B6, Can.

GNERRO, MARK LAWRENCE, b. Washington, D.C, Sept. 28, 26. ENGLISH & COMPARATIVE LITERATURE. B.A, St. Mary's Univ, 48; M.A, George Washington Univ, 57; Ph.D, Cath. Univ. Am, 71. Instr. ENG, Loyola Col. (Md), 56-59; George Mason Univ, 64-65; Georgetown Univ, 65-67; ASST. PROF, Loyola Col, 67-70; TOWSON STATE COL, 72- Renaissance and modern literature. Add: 3633 Greenmount Ave, Baltimore, MD 21218.

GOBER, RUTH BELL, b. Cheyenne, Okla, Nov. 29, 00. ENGLISH, EDUCATION, SPEECH. B.F.A, Univ. Okla, 25, B.A, 28, Ed.D, 56; M.A, Northwest. Univ, 41; Univ. Wis; Harvard, summer 57. Teacher pub. schs, 20-21, 26-27, 28-41; instr. Eng. & drama, Univ. Okla, 42-45; from assoc. prof. to PROF. ENG, UNIV. WIS-PLATTEVILLE, 45-72, chmn. dept, 47-54, EMER. PROF, 72- Speech Commun. Asn; NEA; MLA; NCTE; Cent. States Speech Commun. Asn. Literature; the professional theatre in Oklahoma City, 1889-1941. Publ: The American novelist interprets the student of higher education. Add: Dept. of English, University of Wisconsin-Platteville, Platteville, WI 53818.

GOCHBERG, DONALD S, b. Boston, Mass, Aug. 19, 33; m. 56; c. 5. ENGLISH, HUMANITIES. A.B, Bates Col, 55; Univ. Iowa, 55-56; M.A, Univ. Md, 60, fel, 65, Ph.D.(Eng), 66. Instr. Eng, Univ. Md, 60-65; asst. prof. HUMANITIES, MICH. STATE UNIV, 65-71, ASSOC. PROF, 71- U.S.A, 56-58, Res, 58-64, 1st Lt. AAUP. Seventeenth century English literature; Shakespeare; contemporary literature and thought. Add: 6229 Skyline Dr, East Lansing, MI 48823.

GODDIN, MARGARET ANN PURDUM, b. Elkins, W.Va, Feb. 27, 28; m. 50. ENGLISH. B.A, Davis & Elkins Col, 50, hon Litt.M, 73; M.A, W.Va. Univ, 59, Bd. Christian Educ. Presby. fel, 67-68, Ed.D.(Eng. educ), 68; Ohio State Univ, 67. Teacher, Petersburg High Sch, 50-52; exec. secy, U.S. Army, Hq. Commandant, Aberdeen Proving Ground, Md, 53-54; teacher, Coalton High Sch, 55-59; Elkins High Sch, 59-64; asst. prof. ENG. & EDUC, DAVIS & ELKINS COL, 64-69, ASSOC. PROF, 69-, CHMN. DIV. ARTS, 72- Consult, Monongalia County Schs. Lang. Arts Comt, 67-68; Lang. Arts Div, W.V. State Dept. Educ, 71-; coord, Augusta Heritage Arts Workshop, 72. NCTE;

NEA; Col. Eng. Asn. English; linguistics; education. Publ: Study of the English language, 5/68 & A new era in language arts, 5/72, W.V. Educ. Asn. J; A personal view of teacher education, The Dialogue, 5/73. Add: Rte. 1, Box 9, Elkins, WV 26241.

GODFREY, DENIS ROWLEY, b. Ealing, Eng, Jan. 19, 12; Can. citizen; m. 48; c. 3. ENGLISH LITERATURE. B.A, Univ. Dublin, Ireland, 43, Ph.D, 49. Lectr. ENG, Univ. Amsterdam, Netherlands, 47-50; assoc. prof, UNIV. ALTA, 50-67, PROF, 67- R.A.F, 43-46. Romantics; modern fiction; Shakespeare. Publ: A tale that is told, 48, When kings are arming, 50 & The bridge of fire, 54, Jonathan Cape, London; No Englishman need apply, Macmillan, Toronto, 65; E.M. Forster's other kingdom, Oliver & Boyd, 68; Imagination and truth—some romantic contradictions, Eng. Stud, 8/63; Keats and The Grecian urn, Hermathena, summer 65; Shakespeare and the green-eyed monster, Neophilologus, 72; plus one other. Add: Dept. of English, University of Alberta, Edmonton, Alta. T6G 2G2, Can.

GODSHALK, WILLIAM LEIGH, b. Pen Argyl, Pa, July 12, 37; m. 67; c. 1. ENGLISH LITERATURE. B.A, Ursinus Col, 59; St. Andrews Univ, 57-58; M.A, Harvard, 60, fel, 61-62, Ph.D.(Eng), 64. Instr. ENG, Tufts Univ, 60-61; asst. prof, Col. William & Mary, 64-67; assoc. prof, UNIV. CINCINNATI, 67-73, PROF, 73- Shakespeare consult, Widener Mem. Collection, Harvard Col. Libr, 63; fel. coop. prog. in humanities, Duke Univ. & Univ. N.C, Chapel Hill, 65-66; Taft Mem. Fund grants, 68-71; Folger Shakespeare Libr. fel, summer 70; ed, Kalki, James Branch Cabell Soc, 72- MLA; Mod. Humanities Res. Asn; Renaissance Soc. Am. English Renaissance literature; Shakespeare; modern fiction. Publ: Ed, Beyond life: dizain des démiurges, Johnson Reprint, 70 & Voice of the people, Col. & Univ, 72; auth, Patterning in Shakespearean drama, Mouton, 73; Marvell's garden and the teologians, Stud. Philol, 69; Measure for measure, Shakespeare Stud, 70; Marlowe's Dido, Queen of Carthage, ELH, 71; plus others. Add: Dept. of English, University of Cincinnati, Cincinnati, OH 45221.

GOERDT, ARTHUR L, b. Dyersville, Iowa, Jan. 13, 12. ENGLISH. B.S. in educ, Univ. Dayton, 35; B.S. in L.S, Our Lady of the Lake Col, 42; M.Ed, St. Louis Univ, 50. Teacher Eng. & librn, High Schs, Ill, Tex, Mo, Mich. & Wis, 35-57; from instr. to asst. prof, ENG, ST. MARY'S UNIV. (TEX), 57-71, ASSOC. PROF, 71-, adv. stud. newspaper, 63-70, chmn. dept. Eng, 71-73. Dir. Marianist Scholasticate, San Antonio, 57-63; Kaltenborn Found. grants, summers 68-71. NCTE; Cath. Libr. Asn.(pres, 59-61); Conf. Col. Comp. & Commun; S.Cent. Mod. Lang. Asn. Library science; journalism. Publ: A four-year plan for the Catholic Library Association, Cath. Libr. Asn, 60; ed, Campus unrest, St. Mary's Univ, 70; auth, Message to delegates, Cath. Libr. World, 2/66; Conversations with student editors abroad, Syllabus, winter 70-71; Renewal and rededication, Bull, St. Mary's Univ, 10/71; plus two others. Add: Dept. of English, St. Mary's University, 2700 Cincinnati Ave, San Antonio, TX 78284.

GOETZ, WALTER L, b. Bellingham, Wash, Mar. 25, 30. ENGLISH. B.A, West. Wash. State Col, 51, B.A. in Ed, 52; M.A, Univ. Chicago, 53; M.A, Univ. Wash, 54. Instr. ENG, Univ. Nebr, 57-59; Northwest. Univ, 61-64; instr. & asst. prof, Calif. State Univ, Long Beach & Los Angeles, 65-66; assoc, Univ. Calif, Los Angeles, 66-67; asst. prof, Prairie View Agr. & Mech. Col, Tex. A&M Univ. Syst, 67-69; RES. & WRITING, 69- Rev. ed, Prairie Schooner, 57-58; Woodrow Wilson spec. scholar, 59-60; U.S. Off. Educ. nat. teaching fel, hon, 67-68; extended day instr. Eng. & philos, Calif. Community Cols, 67-; lectr. Eng, Calif. State Univ, Fullerton, spring 70; assoc, Univ. Calif, Irvine, 70-71. Sig.C, U.S.A, 54-56. MLA; Am. Soc. 18th Century Stud. Restoration and 18th century literature and philosophy, especially Milton, Dryden, and Johnson; modern British and American life and letters; history and art of the pastoral. Publ: Rhetorical ideas in the poetic criticism of R.P. Blackmur, privately publ, 74. Add: Dept. of English, University of California, Irvine, CA 92664.

GOETZMAN, ROBERT ALBERT, Muscatine, Iowa, Oct. 15, 37. ENGLISH. B.A, St. Louis Univ, 63; M.A, Univ. Iowa, 64; Ph.D.(Eng), 71; Univ. London, summer 66. Teacher Eng. & supvr. student teachers Eng, Univ. High Sch, Iowa, 64; teaching asst. rhetoric, Univ. Iowa, 67-69; asst. prof. ENG, Loras Col, 69-73; ASSOC. PROF, BARBER-SCOTIA COL, 73- MLA; NCTE; Col. Eng. Asn; Eng. Asn, Gt. Brit; Victorian Soc; S.Atlantic Mod. Lang. Asn. Victorian literature; bibliography, methods of literary research; practical criticism of poetry. Publ: The nemesis of faith, by James Anthony Froude: a critical edition (3 vols), Univ. Iowa, 71. Add: Dept. of English, Barber-Scotia College, Concord, NC 28025.

GOFF, LEWIN ALKIRE, b. Okla. City, Okla, Oct. 21, 19; m. 41; c. 2. DRAMA. A.B, Univ. Okla, 41, fel, 41-42, M.F.A, 46; Ph.D, West. Reserve Univ, 48. Asst, Univ. Okla, 45-46; instr, West. Reserve Univ, 47-48; asst. prof. dramatic art, State Univ. Iowa, 48-54; Mich. State Univ, 54-55; assoc. prof, Univ. Kans, 55-61, prof, 61-67, dir. theatre, 55-67; Cornell Univ, 67-68; prof. drama & chmn. dept, Univ. Tex, Austin, 68-72; DIR. THEATRE, Univ. Wis-Madison, 72-73; UNIV. IOWA, 73- Ford Found. dir-observer grant, 60; Fulbright res. grant, Vienna, 62-63; spec. app. Dept. State, E.Europe & Mid.E, spring 71 & 72; chmn, Am. Col. Theatre Festival, 71-73. U.S.A.A.F, 42-45, Capt. Am. Theatre Asn.(2nd v.pres, 67, 1st v.pres, 68, pres, 69); Nat. Theatre Conf.(bd. trustees, 65-66); U.S. Inst. Theatre Technol; Am. Educ. Res. Asn; Int. Theatre Inst.(deleg, biennial congr, Vienna, 61, Warsaw, 63, Tel Aviv, 65 & New York, 67). International theatre exchange programs; actor and director training for the professional theatre; relationship between professional and educational theatre programs. Publ: Report of the Belgian Symposium, Theatre, Paris, 3/63; Teatrul universitar American, Stiri Cultuale Din SUA, 6/63; Amerykanski theatre uniwersytecki, Pamietnik Teatralny, 4/65. Add: University Theatre, University of Iowa, Iowa City, IA 52242.

GOFFE, LEWIS C, b. Litchfield, N.H, Mar. 29, 14; m. 46. AMERICAN LITERATURE, ENGLISH EDUCATION. B.S, Univ. N.H, 35, M.A, 46; Ph.D, Boston Univ, 61. Teacher Eng. & soc. sci, Springfield High Sch, Vt, 36-42; instr. ENG, UNIV. N.H, 46-50, asst. prof, 50-61, ASSOC. PROF, 61-; follow-up consult, Summer Inst. Teachers Eng, 62-63, asst. dir. & follow-up consult, NDEA Inst. Teachers Eng, 68-69. U.S.A, 42-46. NCTE; Col. Eng. Asn; New Eng. Asn. Teachers Eng; New Eng. Col. Eng. Asn.(dir, 67-70). English; education; teaching of high school English. Add: Dept. of English, University of New Hampshire, Durham, NH 03824.

GOFORTH, LYDIA, b. San Antonio, Tex, Dec. 24, 14; m. 40; c. 2. ENGLISH. B.A, Baylor Univ, 38; M.A, Univ. Tex, 52, 59-67; Trinity Univ.(Tex), 61-64. Teacher, High Schs, Tex, 38-43, 48-61; counsel, High Sch, Tex, 61-63; supvr. Eng, San Antonio Independent Sch. Dist, 63-70; curriculum dir, Fredericksburg Independent Sch. Dist, 70-73; DIR. ADULT EDUC, GUADALUPE, GILLESPIE, COMAL, KENDALL & GONZALES COUNTIES, TEX, 73- Pres, Tex. Counc. Teachers Eng, 67-69; mem, Spec. Comt. for Slow Learners Conf, Honolulu, 67; consult, Nat. Educ. TV, 67; nat. consult, L.W. Singer Publ. Co, summer 69; instr. Eng, Eve. Div, San Antonio Col. NCTE (dir, 66-); NEA. Linguistics. Publ: Co-auth, Approaches to literature, 66, rev. ed, 69, Patterns to literature, 69 & American and English literature, 69, Random & L.W. Singer. Add: Box 65, Comfort, TX 78013.

GOHDES, CLARENCE, b. San Antonio, Tex, July 2, 01; m. 38; c. 2. AMERICAN LITERATURE. A.B, Capital Univ, 21; A.M, Ohio State Univ, 22, Harvard, 28; Ph.D, Columbia Univ. 31. Prin. high sch, Ohio, 22-24; master, Riverdale Sch, New York, N.Y, 25-26; instr. Eng, South. Methodist Univ, 26-27; N.Y. Univ, 29-30; from instr. to prof, AM. LIT, DUKE UNIV, 30-61, James B. Duke prof, 61-71; JAMES B. DUKE EMER. PROF, 71- Vis. lectr, Columbia Univ, 32; managing ed, Am. Lit, 32-54, ed. in chief, 54-69; Guggenheim fel, 62. MLA; Comp. Lit. Asn. History of American literature; history of American thought. Publ: American literature in nineteenth century England, Columbia Univ, 44, 2nd ed, 63; Bibliographical guide to the study of the literature of the U.S.A, 59, rev. ed, 63, Literature and theater of the states and regions of the U.S.A, 67 & ed, Essays on American literature in honor of J.B. Hubbell, 67, Duke Univ; co-auth, Literature of the American people, Appleton, 59; ed, Hunting in the Old South, La. State Univ, 67. Add: Dept. of English, Duke University, Durham, NC 27706.

GOHN, ERNEST SALISBURY, b. Memphis, Tenn, Nov. 26, 22; m. 54; c. 1. ENGLISH. Am. Counc. Learned Soc. fel, 42; President's scholar, Johns Hopkins Univ, 46-48, Ph.D.(Eng), 48. Instr. Eng, Univ. Chicago, 48-51; ed, hist. div, Air Univ, 51-54; instr. ENG, Univ. Mich, 54-58; assoc. prof, EAST. MICH. UNIV, 58-63, PROF, 63- U.S.N, 43. MLA; Mod. Humanities Res. Asn, Gt. Brit; Renaissance Soc. Am. Renaissance lyrics; Shakespeare; Milton. Publ: Christian ethic of Paradise Lost and Samson agonistes, Studia Neophilologica, 62; Dating Donne and scholarly sentimentality, Proc. Mich. Acad, 63; The tempest: theme and structure, Eng. Stud, 4/64; plus others. Add: Dept. of English, Eastern Michigan University, Ypsilanti, MI 48197.

GOING, WILLIAM THORNBURY, b. Birmingham, Ala, June 3, 15; m. 51. ENGLISH. A.B, Univ. Ala, 36; fel, Duke Univ, 36-38, A.M, 38; fel, Univ. Mich, 52-53, Ed.D, 54. Teacher, Pub. Schs,Ala, 38-39; from instr. to assoc. prof, Eng, Univ. Ala, 39-57; PROF. ENG, SOUTH. ILL. UNIV, EDWARDSVILLE, 57-, dean acad. affairs, 58-65. Organist, Second Presby. Church, Birmingham, Ala, 39-44; First Methodist Church, Tuscaloosa, 45-51; vis. lectr. Eng, Howard Col, 39; mem. fac. comt, State of Ill. Bd. Higher Educ, 65-70. MLA; NCTE; Midwest Mod. Lang. Asn; Asn. Higher Educ; S.Atlantic Mod. Lang. Asn. American and Victorian literature; teaching of English. Publ: Wilfrid Scawen Blunt and the tradition of the English sonnet sequence in the 19th century, Univ. Microfilms, 54; John Addington Symonds and the Victorian sonnet sequence, Victorian Poetry, spring 70; contrib, William Faulkner's A rose for Emily, Merrill, 70; auth, Browning and the sonnet, Tenn. Stud. Lit, 72; plus others. Add: Dept. of English, Southern Illinois University, Edwardsville, IL 62025.

GOLD, JOEL JAY, b. Brooklyn, N.Y, Dec. 19, 31; m. 56; c. 3. ENGLISH. A.B, Univ. Mo, 55; Woodrow Wilson fel, Ind. Univ, 58-59, univ. fel, 59-60, 62, Ph.D, 62. Instr. ENG, UNIV. KANS, 62-63, asst. prof, 63-66, assoc. prof, 66-72, PROF, 72-, Elizabeth M. Watkins fac. summer fel, 63 & 66. Vis. asst. prof, Bowling Green State Univ, spring 66; vis. assoc. prof. Eng, Univ. Ill, Urbana-Champaign, 70-71; Am. Counc. Learned Soc. grant, 70; Am. Philos. Soc. grant, 70. MLA; Johnson Soc. Cent. Region (pres, 72-73); Midwest Mod. Lang. Asn; AAUP. Eighteenth century English literature; Samuel Johnson; editing John Wilkes's correspondence. Publ: Ed, A voyage to Abyssinia, In: Yale edition of the works of Samuel Johnson, Yale, (in prep); auth, Johnson's translation of Lobo, PMLA, 3/65; Tristram Shandy at the ambassador's chapel, Philol. Quart, 7/69; In defense of single-speech Hamilton, Stud. in Burke & His Time, winter 68-69. Add: Dept. of English, University of Kansas, Lawrence, KS 66045.

GOLD, JOSEPH, b. London, Eng, June 30, 33; m. 55; c. 2. ENGLISH. B.A, Univ. Birmingham, Eng, 55; Ph.D, Univ. Wis, 59. Asst. prof. ENG, Wis. State Col, Whitewater, 59-60; lectr, Univ. Man, 60-62, asst. prof, 62-66, assoc. prof, 66-68, PROF, 68-72; UNIV. WATERLOO, 72- Can. Counc. grant, 67-68. MLA; Brit. Asn. Am. Stud; Can. Asn. Am. Stud. Charles Dickens; theory of the novel. Publ: William Faulkner: a study in humanism from metaphor to discourse, Univ. Okla, 66; The humanism of William Faulkner, The Humanist, 3-4/60; Delusion and redemption in Faulkner's A fable, Mod. Fiction Stud, summer 61; The normality of snopesism: universal themes in Faulkner's The hamlet, Wis. Stud. Contemporary Lit, winter 62. Add: Dept. of English, University of Waterloo, Waterloo, Ont. N2L 3G1, Can.

GOLD, ROBERT S, b. New York, N.Y, June 19, 24; c. 2. ENGLISH. Ph.D. (Eng), N.Y. Univ, 62. Lectr. ENG, Queens Col.(N.Y), 58-63; PROF. JERSEY CITY STATE COL, 63- Instr. Eng, Hunter Col, 62. U.S.C.G, 43-45. Lexicography of jazz; critical writing; anthologies. Publ: A jazz lexicon, Knopf, 64; ed, Point of departure, 67 & The rebel culture, 71, Dell; co-ed, Controversy, Holt, 69; The vocabulary of the jazz world, Am. Speech, 57; plus 13 articles in McGraw-Hill Encyclopedia of World Biography, 73. Add: Dept. of English, Jersey City State College, Jersey City, NJ 07305.

GOLDBERG, ALVIN, b. Detroit, Mich, Aug. 18, 31; m. 55; c. 3. SPEECH. B.A, Wayne Univ, 53; M.A, Univ. Hawaii, 55; Ph.D, Northwest. Univ, 59. Instr. speech, Univ. Hawaii, Hilo, 55; asst. prof, North. Ill. Univ, 58-61; UNIV. DENVER, 61-64, assoc. prof, 64-67, PROF, 67-69, SPEECH COMMUN, 69-, CHMN. DEPT, 71-, dir. grad. stud, 66-69. Consult, Motorola, Inc, 59-61; res. consult, Ill. Div. Voc. Rehabil, 59-61; mem, Commun. Res. Conf, Univ. Pittsburgh, 61; U.S. Off. Educ. res. grant, 68-69. Speech Commun. Asn; Cent. States Speech Asn; West. Speech Commun. Asn; Int. Commun. Asn; AAUP. Group communications; research methods; interpersonal communication. Publ: Co-auth, Language behavior: a book of readings, Mouton, 70, Group communication: discussion processes and applications, Prentice-Hall, (in press) & Resources and strategies for teaching interpersonal communication, Educ. Resources Info. Ctr, (in press); contrib, Research designs in general semantics, Gordon & Breach, 72 & Speech communication instruction, McKay, 72; co-auth, Sampling discussion group interaction, Speech Monogr, 11/72; plus others. Add: Dept. of Speech Communication, University of Denver, Denver, CO 80210.

GOLDBERG, GERALD JAY, b. New York, N.Y, Dec. 30, 29; m. 54; c. 1. ENGLISH. B.S, Purdue Univ, 52; M.A, N.Y. Univ, 55; Ph.D, Univ. Minn, 58. Instr. ENG, Dartmouth Col, 58-60, asst. prof, 61-64; UNIV. CALIF, LOS ANGELES, 64-67, ASSOC. PROF, 68-, summer fac. fel, 65, creative arts fels, 66-67, 68-69. Dartmouth Col. res. grant, 59; Fulbright lectr, Spain, 62-63. Auth. Guild. Modern fiction; literary criticism; creative writing. Publ: Notes from the Diaspora, Atelier, 21, 62; The fate of innocence, 65 & co-auth, The modern critical spectrum, 62, Prentice-Hall; auth, The national standard, Holt, 68; The lynching of Orin Newfield, 70 & 126 days of continous sunshine, 72, Dial; The search for the artist in some recent British fiction, S.Atlantic Quart, 63; The loving tongue, Harper's Bazaar, 2/66; The education of Martin Fogle, Art & Lit, spring 67. Add: Dept. of English, University of California, Los Angeles, CA 90024.

GOLDBERG, HOMER BERYL, b. Chicago, Ill, Feb. 4, 24; m. 56; c. 2. ENGLISH. A.B, Univ. Chicago, 47, A.M, 48, Ph.D.(Eng), 61. Instr. ENG, Univ. Chicago, 50-54, asst. prof, 54-60; Haverford Col, 60-61; assoc. prof, STATE UNIV. N.Y. STONY BROOK, 61-70, PROF, 70- Fulbright lectr, Italy, 56-57; fac. res. fel, State Univ. N.Y. Stony Brook, 62, 67, 69, dir, NDEA Eng. Inst, 65-66, grad. sch. res. grant, 67-68; Danforth assoc, 72- Chancellor's Award for Excellence in Teaching, State Univ. N.Y, 73. U.S.A, 43-46. MLA. The novel; 18th century English literature; literary theory. Publ: The art of Joseph Andrews, Univ. Chicago, 69; Poetic inference: a lecture to beginning students, J. Gen. Educ, 1/58; Comic prose epic or comic romance: the argument of the preface to Joseph Andrews, Philol. Quart, 4/64; The interpolated stories in Joseph Andrews, Mod. Philol, 5/66. Add: Dept. of English, State University of New York at Stony Brook, Stony Brook, NY 11790.

GOLDBERG, JONATHAN S, b. New York, N.Y, June 11, 43; m. 64; c. 2. RENAISSANCE LITERATURE. B.A, Columbia Univ, 64, M.A, 65, Ph.D. (Eng), 68. ASST. PROF. ENG, TEMPLE UNIV, 68- Renaissance Soc. Am. Interdisciplinary Renaissance studies; Spenser. Publ: Donne's journey East: aspects of a seventeenth century trope, Stud. Philol, 10/71; The typology of Musicks empire, Tex. Stud. Lit. & Lang, 10/71; Virga Iesse: analogy, typology and anagogy in a Miltonic simile, Milton Stud, 11/73. Add: Dept. of English, Temple University, Philadelphia, PA 19122.

GOLDBERG, JOSEPH PHILIP, b. Baltimore, Md, June 21, 30; m. 57; c. 2. ENGLISH. B.S, Univ. Md, 52, M.A, 59, Ph.D.(Eng), 62. Instr. ENG, Univ. Md, 62-63; asst. prof, St. Cloud State Col, 63-65; assoc. prof, GALLAUDET COL, 65-68, PROF, 68-, DIR. TUTORIAL CTR, 72- U.S.A, 52-55, Res, 55-60. MLA. English literature of the 18th century; American literature of the colonial and revolutionary periods; English grammar. Publ: Co-auth, Generating English sentences, Gallaudet Col, 68; auth, Joseph Breintnall and a poem in praise of Jacob Taylor, Pa. Mag. Hist. & Biog, 4/62; The numerical method: how it struck a contemporary, Isis, 63; Some conjecture upon John Shippen's Observations on novel-reading, Early Am. Lit. Newsletter, spring 67. Add: Dept. of English, Gallaudet College, Washington, DC 20002.

GOLDBERG, MAXWELL HENRY, Modern Philology. See Volume III, Foreign Languages, Linguistics & Philology.

GOLDBERG, MICHAEL KENNETH, b. Durban, S.Africa, Oct. 2, 30; Can. citizen; m. 58; c. 3. ENGLISH LITERATURE. B.A, Univ. S.Africa, 60, Hons, 61; M.A, Cambridge, 63; Ph.D.(Eng), Cornell Univ, 66. Teaching asst. ENG, Cornell Univ, 63-66; asst. prof, UNIV. B.C, 66-71, ASSOC. PROF, 71-, Killam fel, 72. Tutor Eng, Pembroke Col, Cambridge, 70. Literature and fine art in the 19th century; 19th century novel; Romantic and Victorian poetry. Publ: Carlyle and Dickens, Ga. Univ, 72; Lawrence's The rocking horse winner: a Dickensian fable, Mod. Fiction Stud, winter 69-70; Shaw's Dickensian quintessence, Shaw Rev, 1/71; From Bentham to Carlyle: Dickens' political development, J. Hist. Ideas, 1-3/72. Add: Dept. of English, University of British Columbia, Vancouver 8, B.C, Can.

GOLDBERG, MOSES HAYM, b. New Orleans, La, May 25, 40; m. 64; c. 2. CHILDREN'S THEATRE. B.S, Tulane Univ, 61; M.A, Stanford Univ, 63; M.A, Univ. Wash, 65; Ph.D.(theatre), Univ. Minn, Minneapolis, 69. Instr. speech, Southwest Tex. State Col, 65-67; ASSOC. PROF. THEATRE, FLA. STATE UNIV, 69- Dir. children's theatre, Asolo State Theatre, 69-, U.S. del, Int. Theatre Asn. Children & Young People, 70- Children's Theatre Asn; Am. Theatre Asn; Int. Asn. Theatres Children & Young People (U.S. del, 70-). Directing; theatre in education. Publ: Hansel and Gretel, New Plays Children, 72; Children's theatre: a philosophy and a method, Prentice-Hall, 74; The pedagogue in the eastern European children's theatre, Educ. Theatre J, 72; contrib, Participation plays: a handbook for directors, New Plays Children, 72. Add: School of Theatre, Florida State University, Tallahassee, FL 32306.

GOLDEN, ARTHUR, b. New York, N.Y, Aug. 22, 24; m. 56; c. 1. ENGLISH, AMERICAN LITERATURE. B.A, N.Y. Univ, 47, Ph.D.(Eng. & Am. lit), 62; M.A, Columbia Univ, 48. Instr. ENG, N.Y. Univ, 59-63; CITY COL. NEW YORK, 63-64, asst. prof, 65-69, assoc. prof, 70-73, PROF, 73-, gen. fac. comt. res. & publ. grant, 67. City Univ. New York summer res. grant, 67 & 69; Nat. Endowment for Humanities grant, 70-71. AAUP; MLA; Bibliog. Soc. Am; Am. Stud. Asn. American literature, especially 19th century and Walt Whitman. Publ: Walt Whitman's Blue book: the 1860-61 Leaves of grass containing his manuscript additions and revisions, Vol. I, facsimile & Vol. II, Textual analysis, New York Pub. Libr, 68; Walt Whitman: a collection of criticism, McGraw, 74-; New light on Leaves of grass: Whitman's annotated copy of the 1860 edition, Bull. New York Pub. Libr, 5/65; Passage to less than India: structure and meaning in Whitman's Passage to India, PMLA, 10/73; William Cullen Bryant, Oliver Wendell Holmes, Henry Wadsworth Longfellow, James Russell Lowell, Frederick Goddard Tuckerman, John Greenleaf Whittier & Walt Whitman, In: The McGraw-Hill encyclopedia of world biography, 74. Add: Dept. of English, The City College of New York, Convent Ave. at 138th St, New York, NY 10031.

GOLDEN, BRUCE, b. Rochester, N.Y, June 18, 33; m. 69. ENGLISH & COMPARATIVE LITERATURE. B.S, Northwest. Univ, 55; A.M, Columbia Univ, 58, Ph.D.(Eng, comp. lit), 66; fel, Hunter Col, 60-61. Mem. acad. fac. humanities, Juilliard Sch. Music, 62-65; instr. ENG, CALIF. STATE COL, SAN BERNARDINO, 65-66, asst. prof, 66-71, ASSOC. PROF, 72- Nat. Endowment for Humanities younger humanist fel, 71-72; fel, Folger Shakespeare Libr, summer 73. MLA; Renaissance Soc. Am; Malone Soc. Renaissance dramatic literature; literature and the other arts; popular culture. Publ: Co-auth, The good soldier: a tragedy of self-deception, Mod. Fiction Stud, 63; auth, Calderon's tragedies of honor: topos, emblem, and action in the popular theater of the Siglo de oro, Renaissance Drama, 70. Add: Dept. of English, California State College, San Bernardino, CA 92407.

GOLDEN, DANIEL, b. Bronx, N.Y, June 5, 45; m. 69. AMERICAN & ENGLISH LITERATURE. A.B, Queens Col, 66; A.M, Ind. Univ, 68, Ph.D.(Am. lit), 72. Asst. instr. ENG, Ind. Univ, 67-70; ASST. PROF, STATE UNIV. N.Y. COL. FREDONIA, 70- Asst. ed, Abstr. Eng. Stud, 72- MLA; Northeast Mod. Lang. Asn. American poetry and fiction; genres of the novel. Add: Dept. of English, State University of New York College at Fredonia, Fredonia, NY 14063.

GOLDEN, JAMES L, b. Indian Head, Md, Dec. 17, 19; m. 44; c. 3. SPEECH. A.B, George Washington Univ, 47; M.A, Ohio State Univ, 48; Ph.D.(speech), Univ. Fla, 53. Instr. SPEECH, Univ. Md, 48-51; asst. prof, Univ. Richmond, 53-55; PROF, Pasadena Col, 55-58; Muskingum Col, 58-65; Ill. State Univ, 65-66; OHIO STATE UNIV, 66- Commun. consult, Shaw Univ, 67- U.S.N, 45. Speech Commun. Asn.(deleg, legis. assembly, 66-68); Cent. States Speech Commun. Asn. Rhetorical theory and public address; political communication; literary criticism. Publ: Co-auth, The rhetoric of Blair, Campbell, and Whately, Holt, 68; auth, Changes in the idiom of political speaking since the 1920's, Vital Speeches, 10/63; John F. Kennedy and the ghosts, Quart. J. Speech, 12/66; The rhetorical theory of Adam Smith, South. Speech J, spring 68. Add: Dept. of Speech Communication, Ohio State University, Columbus, OH 43210.

GOLDEN, JOSEPH, b. Winthrop, Mass, Oct. 13, 28; m. 51; c. 2. DRAMA, ARTS PLANNING & ADMINISTRATION. A.B, Tufts Univ, 51; M.A, Ind. Univ, 52; Ph.D.(drama), Univ. Ill, 54. Assoc. prof. theatre arts, Elmira Col, 54-58; asst. prof. speech & drama, Cornell Univ, 58-62; assoc. prof, Syracuse Univ, 62-66; EXEC. DIR. PERFORMING ARTS FACILITY COMT, CULT. RESOURCES COUNC, 66- Tech. consult, N.Y. State Counc. Arts, 67-8 first place awards in nat. & int. playwrighting competitions, 55-68. Qm.C, U.S.A, 46-47. Am. Theatre Asn; Speech Commun. Asn; Assoc. Counc. Arts. American theatre history; contemporary practices in American theatre; arts planning and management. Publ: The death of Tinker Bell: the American theatres in the 20th century, Syracuse Univ, 68; The dangers of doing things to Shakespeare's text, Theatre Arts, 8/61; The hero in the womenless wasteland, TV Quart, winter 62; The lamentable & deadly sins of the playwright, Today's Speech, 9/63. Add: Cultural Resources Council, 113 E. Onondaga St, Syracuse, NY 13202.

GOLDEN, MORRIS, b. Romania, June 29, 26; nat; m. 54; c. 2. ENGLISH. A.B, City Col. N.Y, 48; M.A, N.Y. Univ, 49, Ph.D.(Eng), 53. Instr. ENG, N.Y. Univ, 51-56; Bowling Green State Univ, 56-59, asst. prof, 59-62; assoc. prof, UNIV. MASS, AMHERST, 62-65, PROF, 65- Guggenheim fel, 68-69. U.S.N, 44-46. MLA. Comparative, modern, and 18th century English literature. Publ: In search of stability: the poetry of William Cowper, Bookman Assoc, 60; Richardson's characters, Univ. Mich, 63, Thomas Gray, Twayne, 64; Fielding's moral psychology, Univ. Mass, 66; The self observed; Swift, Johnson, Wordsworth, Johns Hopkins Univ, 72; The family-wanderer theme in Goldsmith, ELH, 58; The broken dream of The deserted village, Lit. & Psychol, 59; Sterility and eminence in the poetry of C. Churchill, J. Eng. & Ger. Philol, 67. Add: Dept. of English, University of Massachusetts, Amherst, MA 01002.

GOLDEN, ROBERT EDWARD, b. St. Louis, Mo, Mar. 2, 45; m. 67. ENGLISH & AMERICAN LITERATURE. A.B, Univ. Mich, Ann Arbor, 67; M.A, Univ. Rochester, 70, Ph.D.(Eng), 72. ASST. PROF. LANG. & LIT, ROCHESTER INST. TECHNOL, 71- MLA; AAUP. Contemporary American novel; the novel; the cinema. Publ: Mass man and modernism: violence in Pynchon's V, Critique, 72; Violence and the arts, Perspective, 72; contrib, American literary manuscripts: a checklist of holdings in academic, historical and public libraries in the United States, Univ. Tex, 74. Add: Dept. of Language & Literature, Rochester Institute of Technology, One Lomb Memorial Dr, Rochester, NY 14623.

GOLDEN, SAMUEL ADLER, b. Boston, Mass, May 31, 09; m. 35. ENGLISH. B.A, Boston Univ, 31; M.A, Univ. Maine, 49; Ph.D.(Eng), Trinity Col.(Dublin), 54. Instr. ENG, WAYNE STATE UNIV, 52-56, asst. prof, 57-62, assoc. prof, 62-66, PROF, 66- Wayne State Univ. fac. res. fel, 62, 64, 66; guest lectr, Trinity Col.(Dublin), Nov. 65; Folger Shakespeare Libr. grant, summer 68. U.S.A, 43-45, 2nd Lt. AAUP. Anglo-Dutch literary relations in the late 17th and early 18th centuries. Publ: F.G. Tuckerman, an American sonneteer, Univ. Maine, 52; co-ed, Writing from observation, Harcourt, 3rd ed, 59; auth, Frederick Goddard Tuckerman, 66; & Jean LeClerc, 72, Twayne; Longfellow, Potgeiter and Pijnappel, Am. Lit, 65: Dryden's praise of Dr. Charleton, Hermathena, Dublin, 66; plus one other. Add: Dept. of English, Wayne State University, Detroit, MI 48202.

GOLDFARB, CLARE R, b. New York, N.Y, Oct. 12, 34; m. 57; c. 2. ENGLISH & AMERICAN LITERATURE. B.A, Smith Col, 56; M.A, N.Y. Univ, 57; Ph.D. (Eng), Ind. Univ. 64. Instr. ENG, WEST. MICH. UNIV, 61-64, asst. prof, 64-68, ASSOC. PROF, 68- Comparative literature. Publ: The poet's role in Passage to India, Walt Whitman Rev, 62; From complicity to Altruria: the use of Tolstoy in Howells, Univ. Rev, Kansas City, 66; An American reaction to Leo Tolstoy: William Dean Howells' discovery and assessments, Comp. Lit. Stud, 71. Add: Dept. of English, Western Michigan University, Kalamazoo, MI 49001.

GOLDFARB, RUSSELL MARSHAL, b. Yonkers, N.Y, Aug. 13, 34; m. 57; c. 1. ENGLISH LITERATURE. B.A, N.Y. Univ, 54, M.A, 57; Ph.D.(Eng. lit), Ind. Univ, 61. Instr. ENG, WEST. MICH. UNIV, 60-61, asst. prof, 61-64, assoc. prof, 64-71, PROF, 71- U.S.A, 54-56, 1st Lt. MLA. Victorian literature; literature and psychology. Publ: Sexual repression and Victorian literature, Bucknell Univ, 70; Late Victorian decadence, J. Aesthet. & Art Criticism, summer 62; The Dowson legend today, Stud. Eng. Lit, autumn 64; Sexual meaning in The last ride together, Victorian Poetry, autumn 65. Add: Dept. of English, Western Michigan University, Kalamazoo, MI 49001.

GOLDGAR, BERTRAND ALVIN, b. Macon, Ga, Nov. 17, 27; m. 50; c. 2. ENGLISH LITERATURE. B.A, Vanderbilt Univ, 48, M.A, 49; M.A, Princeton, 57, Ph.D, 58. Instr. ENG, Clemson Col, 48-50, asst. prof, 51-52; instr, LAWRENCE UNIV, 57-61, asst. prof, 61-65, assoc. prof, 65-71, PROF, 71- Am. Counc. Learned Soc. fel, 73-74. U.S.A, 52-54. MLA; Am. Soc. 18th Century Stud. Eighteenth century English literature; literature and politics of the 18th century. Publ: The curse of party: Swift's relations with Addison and Steele, 61 & ed, The literary criticism of Alexander Pope, 65, Univ. Nebr; Satires on man and the dignity of human nature, PMLA, 12/65; Gulliver's travels and the opposition to Walpole, In: The Augustan milieu, Clarendon, 70. Add: Dept. of English, Lawrence University, Appleton, WI 54911.

GOLDGAR, HARRY, b. Macon, Ga, Dec. 22, 20. ENGLISH, COMPARATIVE LITERATURE. A.B, Mercer Univ, 41; M.A, Vanderbilt Univ, 42; Harvard Univ, 44; D. Univ.(mod. comp. lit), Univ. Paris, 48. Asst. ENG, Vanderbilt Univ, 43-44; instr, State Univ. Iowa, 49-50; Mich. State Univ, 57-58; asst. prof, E.Carolina Col, 58-59; instr, Queens Col.(N.Y), 60-63; asst. prof, Queensborough Community Col, 64-65; assoc. prof, Colo. State Univ, 66-67; TEACHER, The Gunnery, 67-72; PROVIDENCE COUNTRY DAY SCH, 72- U.S.A, 44-46, Sgt. MLA; Am. Comp. Lit. Asn; Int. Comp. Lit. Asn. Twentieth century novel of adolescence; the French symbolist influence on W.B. Yeats; studies of fiction from the point of view of Jungian psychology. Publ: Axël de Villiers de l'Isle-Adam et The shadowy waters de W.B. Yeats, Rev. Lit. Comp, 10/50; The square root of minus one: Freud and Robert Musil's Törless, Comp. Lit, spring 65; Alain-Fournier and the initiation archetype, French Rev, winter 70. Add: 387 Angell St, Providence, RI 02906.

GOLDHAMER, ALLEN DAVID, b. Cleveland, Ohio, Sept. 25, 38. MEDIEVAL LITERATURE, ENGLISH DRAMA. B.A, Trinity Col, 60; M.A, Univ. Chicago, 63, Ph.D.(Eng), 70. Lectr. Eng, Ind. Univ. Northwest, 61-63; instr, Northwest. Univ, 64; Univ. Ill, Chicago Circle, 67-70, asst. prof, 70-73; SR. STAFF WRITER INS, CNA/FINANCIAL CORP, CHICAGO, 73- Scholar-in-residence, Newberry Libr, 68-72; co-ed, Medieval & Renaissance Newslett, 73- MLA. Medieval drama; early Tudor drama; business writing styles. Publ: Everyman: a dramatization of death, Quart, J. Speech, 2/73; co-auth, Alternatives to teaching, In: A guide for job candidates and department chairmen in English and foreign languages, MLA, 73. Add: Apt. 607, 1401 E. 55th St, Chicago, IL 60615.

GOLDHURST, WILLIAM, b. New York, N.Y, Aug. 8, 29; m. 54; c. 2. ENGLISH. B.A, Kenyon Col, 53; M.A, Columbia Univ, 56; Carnegie scholar, Tulane Univ, 56-57, univ. fel, 56-59, South. fel, 59-60, Ph.D.(Eng), 62. Asst. Eng, Ohio State Univ, 55-56; asst. prof, Univ. P.R, 60-63; ASSOC. PROF. HUMANITIES, UNIV. FLA, 64- Fulbright prof. Am. lit, Univ. Buenos Aires, 69-70; Univ. Fla. Humanities Counc. grant, 70, Grad. Counc. grant, 72; Fac. Develop. grant, 70-71. S.Atlantic Mod. Lang. Asn; Auth. League Am. English and American literature; biography; Edgar Allan Poe—biography and works. Publ: F. Scott Fitzgerald and his contemporaries, World Publ, 63; ed, Contours of experience, Prentice-Hall, 67; The major theme of Gawain and the Green Knight, Col. Eng, 11/58; Of mice and men: Steinbeck's parable of the curse of Cain, West. Am. Lit, summer 71; Poe's multiple King Pest: a source study, Tulane Stud. Eng, 72; plus others. Add: Dept. of Humanities, University of Florida, Gainesville, FL 32601.

GOLDIN, FREDERICK, Medieval & Comparative Literature. See Volume III, Foreign Languages, Linguistics & Philology.

GOLDING, ALFRED SIEMON, b. Brooklyn, N.Y, July 13, 24; m. 61; c. 2. THEATRE PERFORMANCE & HISTORY. B.A, City Col. New York, 46; Am. Counc. Learned Soc. fel, Columbia Univ, 43, Ph.D.(theatre hist), 62; M.F.A, Yale, 49. Tutor & lectr, speech, City Col. New York, 50-58; from asst. prof. to assoc. prof. speech & theatre, Danbury State Col, 58-67; theatre arts, Univ. S.Fla, 67-73; PROF. THEATRE & DIR. THEATRE RES. INST, OHIO STATE UNIV, COLUMBUS, 73- Nat. Endowment for Humanities grant, 70-72. Am. Theatre Asn; Speech Commun. Asn. History of acting method, Renaissance, 18th and 19th centuries; psychology of theatrical performance; acting and rhetoric. Publ: Presentational tradition and the repertory company, Educ. Theatre J, 12/68; Old new theatre of metaphor, South. Theatre, 3/72. Add: Dept. of Theatre, Ohio State University, Columbus, OH 43210.

GOLDING, SANFORD, b. New York, N.Y, Aug. 17, 24; m. 50; c. 2. ENGLISH. A.B, City Col. New York, 48; M.A, N.Y. Univ, 54, Ph.D, 59. Instr. ENG, N.Y. Univ, 54-57; Univ. Ill, 57-60, asst. prof, 60-66; ASSOC. PROF, McMICKEN COL, UNIV. CINCINNATI, 66- Instr, N.Y. Univ, 51-54. U.S.A.A.F, 43-46. MLA; Milton Society Am. Milton; 17th century literature; Shakespeare. Publ: The sources of the Theatrum poetarum, PMLA, 3/61. Add: Dept. of English, McMicken College, University of Cincinnati, Cincinnati, OH 45221.

GOLDMAN, ALBERT, b. Dormont, Pa, Apr. 15, 27. ENGLISH, COMPARATIVE LITERATURE. A.M, Univ. Chicago, 50, Ph.D.(comp. lit), Columbia Univ, 61. Lectr. Eng, Columbia Col, 52-54; City Col. New York, 54-55, 58-59; Brooklyn Col, 55-58; instr. Hunter Col, 59-63; asst. prof. Eng. & comp. lit, Columbia Univ, 63-70, adj. assoc. prof, 70-72; RES. & WRITING, 72- U.S.N, 45-46. MLA. European romantic literature and music; American humor; contemporary popular culture, especially music. Publ: Wagner on music and drama: a compendium, Dutton, 64; The mine and the mint: sources for the writings of Thomas De Quincey, South. Ill. Univ, 65; Freakshow, Atheneum, 71; Ladies and gentlemen, Lenny Bruce! Random, 74; Comedy and Lenny Bruce, Commentary, 10/63; Boy-man Schlemiel, Explorations, 67; The emergence of rock, New Am. Rev, 68. Add: 3 E. 82nd St, New York, NY 10028.

GOLDMAN, HANNAH STERN, b. Russia, Aug. 3, 11; m. 34. ENGLISH. B.A, Brooklyn Col, 33; M.A, Columbia Univ, 35, Ph.D, 55. Teacher, High Schs, N.Y, 36-48; instr. ENG, HOFSTRA UNIV, 55-60, asst. prof, 60-67, ASSOC. PROF, 67- Analyst, writer & ed, U.S. Govt, 44-47. MLA. American and Russian comparative literature; comparative history of the novel; design in the novel: the role of the image. Publ: Co-auth, First men, Collier, 62; The tragic gift, Phylon, 63; Season's end, Reporter, 66; Something to warm the soul (short story), Denver Quart, 67. Add: Dept. of English, Hofstra University, Hempstead, NY 11550.

GOLDMAN, LLOYD N, b. St. Louis, Mo, July 22, 37; m. 61; c. 1. ENGLISH & AMERICAN LITERATURE. B.A, Wash. Univ, 58; M.A, Rice Univ, 60; Ph.D.(Eng), Univ. Ill, Urbana, 64. Asst. ENG, Univ. Ill, Urbana, 63-64; instr, City Col. New York, 64-65; asst. prof, Long Island Univ, 65-68; ASSOC. PROF, JERSEY CITY STATE COL, 68- English Renaissance poetry; the lyric; contemporary literature. Publ: Samuel Daniel's Delia and the emblem tradition, J. Eng. & Ger. Philol, 1/68; John Knoepfle's masks of self-deception, Minn. Rev, 3/68. Add: Dept. of English, Jersey City State College, 2039 Kennedy Memorial Blvd, Jersey City, NJ 07305.

GOLDMAN, MARCUS SELDEN, b. Middletown, Ohio, May 12, 94; m. 25; c. 4. ENGLISH & COMPARATIVE LITERATURE. A.B, Miami Univ, 16; A.M, Univ. Ill, 17, Ph.D, 31; Am. Field Serv. fel, Univ. Paris, 19-21; A.M, Harvard, 26. Dramatic & fine arts critic, Europ. ed, New York Herald, 21-23; class. master, Hoosac Sch, N.Y, 23-24; asst. ENG, UNIV. ILL, URBANA, 26-29, instr, 29-31, assoc, 31-36, asst. prof, 36-46, assoc. prof, 46-58, prof, 58-62, EMER. PROF, 62- Vis. prof, Stephens Col, 36-37; Taft Found. lectr, Univ. Cincinnati, 41; commandant, 5961st U.S.A.R. Sch, Champaign, Ill, 51-53. U.S.A, 17-19; U.S.A.A.F, 42-46, Res, 46-, Col; Legion of Merit, 46. MLA; Mod. Humanities Res. Asn; Am. Mil. Inst; Mediaeval Acad. Am. (counr, 63-67); Renaissance Soc. Am; Hakluyt Soc. Prose fiction of the Renaissance; critical theory in the Renaissance; early literature relating to field sports. Publ: Sir Philip Sidney and the Arcadia, Univ. Ill, 34; co-auth, Progressive study of English composition, Odyssey, 41; co-transl, St. Anne and the gouty rector and other plays, Longmans, 50; auth, Poems of the past, Stinehour, 69; Sidney & Harington as opponents of superstition, J. Eng. & Ger. Philol, 10/55; Izaak Walton & The arte of angling, 1577, In: Studies in honor of T.W. Baldwin, Univ. Ill, 58; Henri Ghéon: yesterday, today & tomorrow, Drama Critique, fall 66. Add: 203 W. Michigan Ave, Urbana, IL 61801.

GOLDSBY, ROBERT W, b. Brooklyn, N.Y, Dec. 11, 26; m. 53; c. 3. DRAMA. A.B, Columbia Univ, 50; M.F.A, Yale, 53. Lectr. Eng, Columbia Univ, 54-56; asst. prof. DRAMATIC ART, UNIV. CALIF, BERKELEY, 57-60, assoc. prof, 60-61, PROF, 62-, CHMN. DEPT, 74- Vis. asst. prof. Eng. & comp. lit, Columbia Col, 60-61, consult, univ. art ctr, 62; conservatory dir, actor & stage dir, Am. Conservatory Theatre, 66-68; field reader div. humanities, Off. Educ, Dept. Health, Educ. & Welfare, 66-68. U.S.A, 45-47. French theatre; play directing. Publ: Co-auth, Let's get a divorce, Hill & Wang, 58. Add: Dept. of Dramatic Arts, University of California, Berkeley, CA 94720.

GOLDSMITH, ADOLPH OLIVER, b. Kennett, Mo, Dec. 20, 08; m; c. 3. JOURNALISM. B.A, La. State Univ, 49, M.A, 51; Ph.D.(mass commun), Univ. Iowa, 67. Prod. & prom. mgr, univ. press, LA. STATE UNIV, 50-56, from asst. prof. to assoc. prof. JOUR, 55-68, PROF. & DIR. SCH. JOUR, 68- Ed, Want Ad Builder, 51-54, consult, 54-; v.chmn, La. Comn. Govt. Ethics, 69-72. U.S.A, 42-45. Asn. Educ. in Jour; Nat. Press Photographers Asn. Mass communications; American history; general semantics. Publ: Let there be parody, Nieman Reports, 10/58; Roaring Lyon of Vermont, Jour. Quart, spring 62; Thinking with language and beyond, Phi Kappa Phi J, summer 68; We rely on communication for survival, Grassroots Ed, 5-6/72; plus others. Add: 2213 Ovid St, Baton Rouge, LA 70808.

GOLDSMITH, ARNOLD LOUIS, b. Boston, Mass, Feb. 7, 28; m. 50; c. 3. ENGLISH. B.A, Boston Univ, 48; M.A, Univ. Wis, 49, Ph.D, 53. Teaching asst. ENG, Univ. Wis, 48-53; instr, WAYNE STATE UNIV, 53-57, asst. prof, 57-63; assoc. prof, 63-70, PROF, 70- Vis. prof, Univ. Tulsa, 67. AAUP. Nineteenth and 20th century American literature. Publ: Co-ed, Publication guide for literary and linguistic scholars, Wayne, 58; Modern American literary criticism, 1905-1965, Twayne, (in press); Henry James' reconciliation of free will and fatalism, Nineteenth-Century Fiction; Discovery scene in Billy Budd, Mod. Drama, 61; Thematic rhythm in The red pony, Col. Eng, 65; contrib, Steinbeck: a collection of critical essays, Prentice-Hall, 72; plus one other. Add: 27369 Everett, Southfield, MI 48075.

GOLDSMITH, ROBERT HILLIS, b. East Lansing, Mich, Sept. 3, 11; m. 42; c. 2. ENGLISH. B.A, Pa. State Univ, 36; M.A, Columbia Univ, 43, Ph.D. (Eng), 52. Instr. ENG, Temple Univ, 46-52; Univ. Md, 52-55; assoc. prof, EMORY & HENRY COL, 55-60, prof, 60-74, HENRY CARTER STUART CHAIR, 74-, CHMN. DEPT, 71- Folger Shakespeare Libr. summer readership, 59; fel, southeast inst. medieval & Renaissance stud, Univ. N.C, summer, 65; humanities fel, coop. prog. humanities, Duke Univ-Univ. N.C, 66-67. U.S.A.A.F, 42-46. MLA; Renaissance Soc. Am; Shakespeare Asn. Am; Southeast. Renaissance Conf.(v.pres, 72-73, pres, 73-74); S.Atlantic Mod. Lang. Asn. Publ: Wise fools in Shakespeare, Mich. State Univ, 55, 63, Liverpool Univ, 58; English literature, Harper, Vol. I, 74; Did Shakespeare use the old Timon comedy, Shakespeare Quart, 58; The wild man on the English stage, Mod. Lang. Rev, 10/58; Triumph and tragedy in Samson agonistes, Renaissance Papers, 1968, 69; My lady tongue: the witty woman of the Renaissance, Ill. Quart, 2/72. Add: P.O. Box 55, Emory, VA 24327.

GOLDSTEIN, HARVEY D, b. Chicago, Ill, Aug. 7, 22; m. 51; c. 3. ENGLISH, AESTHETICS. B.S, Northwest. Univ, 50, M.A, 51, Ph.D.(Eng), 60. Asst. ENG, Northwest. Univ, 51-54; instr, Ill. Inst. Technol, 54-55; Williams Col, 55-58; asst. prof, Brandeis Univ, 58-62; Univ. Rochester, 62-68; ASSOC. PROF, UNIV. SOUTH. CALIF, 68- Newberry Libr. fel, summer 61; vis. prof, Univ. Wis, summer 66. A.U.S, 42-46. MLA; Am. Soc. Aesthet; Dante Soc. Am. History of criticism and aesthetics; 18th century English literature. Publ: Enea e Paolo, Symposium, winter 65; Mimesis and Catharsis reexamined, J. Aesthet, summer 66; Ut poesis pictura, 18th-Century Stud, spring 68. Add: Dept. of English, University of Southern California, Los Angeles, CA 90007.

GOLDSTEIN, LAURENCE ALAN, b. Los Angeles, Calif, Jan. 5, 43; m. 68. ROMANTICISM. B.A, Univ. Calif, Los Angeles, 65; Ph.D.(Eng), Brown Univ, 70. ASST. PROF. ENG, UNIV. MICH, ANN ARBOR, 70- Romantic poetry; film history; contemporary poetry. Publ: Familiarity and contempt: an essay on the star-presence in film, Centennial Rev, summer 73; The Auburn syndrome: change and loss in Goldsmith and Wordsworth, ELH, fall 73; Audubon and R.P. Warren, Contemporary Poetry, winter 73. Add: Dept. of English, University of Michigan, Ann Arbor, MI 48104.

GOLDSTEIN, MALCOLM, b. Huntington, W.Va, Aug. 18, 25. ENGLISH. A.B, Princeton, 49; M.A, Columbia Univ, 51, Ph.D, 56. Instr. ENG, Stanford Univ, 53-57, asst. prof, 57-61; QUEENS COL.(N.Y), 61-66, assoc. prof, 66-72, PROF, 72- Guggenheim fel, 67. U.S.A, 44-46, S/Sgt. MLA; Am. Soc. Theatre Res. Literary and theatrical history. Publ: Pope and the Augustan stage, Stanford Univ, 58; The art of Thornton Wilder, Univ. Nebr, 65; The political stage: American drama and theater of the great Depression, Oxford Univ, 74; Drama, In: American literary scholarship, Duke Univ, 63-65; Body and soul on Broadway, Mod. Drama, spring 65; Clifford Odets and the found generation, In: American drama and its critics, Univ. Chicago, 65. Add: Dept. of English, Queens College, Flushing, NY 11367.

GOLDSTEIN, MELVIN, b. New York, N.Y, May 31, 26; m. 49; c. 2. ENGLISH. B.A, L.I. Univ, 49; M.A, Columbia Univ, 50; Ph.D, Univ. Wis, 58; New Sch. Social Res, 57, 61; Nat. Psychol. Asn. Psychoanal, 59, 60; cert. psychol. examr, State of Conn, 73. Asst. prof. Eng, State Univ. Col. New Paltz, 57-62; chmn. lib. arts, Col. Insurance, 62-64; dean, Kingsborough City Col, 64-66; PROF. ENG. & EXEC. SECY, UNIV. HARTFORD, 66- Teaching fel, Univ. Wis, 50-53; State Univ. N.Y. summer res. fel, 59 & 61; psychotherapist, Community Psychiat. Clin, Middlesex Mem. Hosp, Middletown, Conn, 68-; lectr. Eng, Univ. Conn, summer 73. U.S.N, 44-46. MLA; Int. Reading Asn. Psychological analyses of Shakespeare; contemporary literature; literary criticism. Publ: Ed, Metapsychological literary criticism: essays in honor of Leonard Manheim, Univ. Hartford, 73; auth, Identity crises in a midsummer nightmare: comedy as terror in disguise, Psychoanal. Rev, 73; Antonioni's symbology and a hero's negative environment in Blow-up, J. Aesthetic Educ, fall 73; La verita non e stata ancora inventata ... psychological theories in contemporary American and British literary criticism, Yearbk. Comp. Criticism, spring 74; plus others. Add: Dept. of English, University of Hartford, 200 Bloomfield Ave, West Hartford, CT 06117.

GOLDSTEIN, WALLACE L, b. Fall River, Mass, Jan. 23, 21; m. 51; c. 2. ENGLISH, SPEECH. B.S, Mass. State Col. Bridgewater, 42; M.A, Columbia Univ, 46; summer, Boston Univ, 50; Ph.D.(Eng), N.Y. Univ, 56. Teacher, High Sch. & adult educ, Mass, 46-48; instr. Eng, Paul Smith's Col, 48-49; chmn. dept. ENG. & SPEECH, Wright Tech. Sch, 49-56; PROF, WESTFIELD STATE COL, 56-, chmn. dept, 56-72. Vis. lectr, Holyoke Jr. Col, 60-63; consult. curriculum changes sec. Eng, Galstonbury, Conn, 62; consult. teaching Eng. as second lang, Model Cities Prog, Holyoke, Mass, 71-72; Nat. Endowment for Humanities grant, summer 73. N.Y. Univ. Founders Day Award, 56. U.S.A.A.F, 43-46. NCTE; Speech Commun. Asn; Am. Asn. Teachers Eng. as Second Lang. Modern drama; writing processes; linguistics. Publ: Co-auth, You and your speech, W.C. Brown, 69; auth, Reading characteristics in a vocational-technical school, Indust. Arts & Voc. Educ, 1/55; co-auth, The sine qua non, Peabody J. Educ, 3/64; Fringe benefits of writing, Clearing House, 4/74. Add: 150 Captain Rd, Longmeadow, MA 01106.

GOLDSTONE, HERBERT I, b. Mt. Pleasant, Pa, June 5, 21; div; c. 2. ENGLISH. A.B, Univ. Chicago, 42; M.A, Harvard, 47, fel, 48-49, Ph.D.(Eng), 51. Instr. ENG, Cornell Univ, 51-55; asst. prof, N.Y. State Univ. Col. Cortland, 55-58, assoc. prof, 58-62; asst. prof, UNIV. CONN, 62-65, ASSOC. PROF, 65- Summer fels, State Univ. N.Y, 58, 60, Am. Philos. Soc. 67, 68. U.S.A, 42-46. MLA. Modern drama and fiction; Elizabethan drama. Publ: A casebook on the cherry orchard, Allyn & Bacon, 65; co-auth, Poets and poems, Wordsworth, 67; co-ed, Points of departure: a collection of short fiction, Prentice-Hall, 71; auth, In search of community: the achievement of Sean O'Casey, Mercier, Ireland, 73; Interplay in Peele's The old wives tale, Boston Univ. Stud. Eng, winter 56; The unevenness of O'Casey, Forum Univ. Houston, spring 65; Not so puzzling Pinter: The homecoming, Theatre Annual, 69. Add: Dept. of English, University of Connecticut, Storrs, CT 06268.

GOLDSTONE, RICHARD H, b. New York, N.Y, Aug. 8, 21; m. 46. ENGLISH, DRAMATIC LITERATURE. B.A, Univ. Wis, 41; M.A, Columbia Univ, 47, Ph.D.(Eng), 60. Instr. ENG, Syracuse Univ, 46-48; Univ. Ky, 48-50, 52-53; from asst. prof. to ASSOC. PROF, CITY COL. NEW YORK, 61-, OMBUDSMAN, 72- U.S.A.F, 41-65, Lt. Col. MLA. Modern drama; biography of Thornton Wilder. Publ: Co-auth, Mentor book of short plays, 68 & auth, Mentor masterworks of drama, 68, New Am. Libr; Contexts of the drama, McGraw, 68; The making of Americans, Int. Comp. Lit. Asn. Proc, 64; The Wilder image, Four Quarters, 67; the eighth day, Antioch Rev, 67; plus others. Add: Dept. of English, City College of New York, New York, NY 10031.

GOLDWYN, MERRILL HARVEY, b. Boston, Mass, Feb. 7, 31. ENGLISH. A.B, Harvard, 52, A.M, 53; Ph.D.(Eng. & comp. lit), Columbia Univ, 62. Instr. ENG, Suffolk Univ, 56-57; Staten Island Community Col, 60-63, asst. prof, 63-68; ASSOC. PROF, WORCESTER STATE COL, 68- English literature of the 16th century. Publ: Notes on the biography of Thomas Churchyard, Rev. Eng. Stud, 2/66; Some unpublished manuscripts by Thomas Churchyard, Stud. Philol, 6/67; Thomas Churchyard's Marriages, Notes & Queries, 12/67. Add: 225 Walden St, Cambridge, MA 02140.

GOLEMBA, HENRY LAWRENCE, b. Detroit, Mich, Sept. 13, 43; m. 67. NINETEENTH CENTURY AMERICAN LITERATURE. Ph.B, Wayne State Univ, 65, M.A, 67; Ph.D.(Eng), Univ. Wash, 71. Instr. commun, Macomb County Community Col, Mich, 66-67; Tarrant County Jr. Col, Tex, 67-68; ASST. PROF. ENG, WAYNE STATE UNIV, 71- American trancendentalism; American renaissance; psychological novel. Publ: Margaret Fuller's literary criticism, Univ. Miami, 74; George Ripley, Twayne, 75; Steinbeck and the literary fallacy, Mod. Fiction Stud, summer 69; The shape of Moby Dick, Stud. Novel, fall 73. Add: Dept. of English, Wayne State University, Detroit, MI 48202.

GOLFFING, FRANCIS CHARLES, b. Vienna, Austria, Nov. 20, 10. ENGLISH LITERATURE. Univ. Berlin, 29; Univ. Heidelberg, 30-34; Ph.D, Basel, 35. Tutor, Cambridge, 39-40; instr, Queens Col. & City Col, 45-46; asst. prof, Utah State Univ, 46-48; PROF. ENG. LIT, BENNINGTON COL, 48- Dir. Humanities Div, Franklin Pierce Col, 68- Seventeenth century English poetry; linguistics; syntax and grammar. Add: Division of Humanities, Franklin Pierce College, Rindge, NH 03461.

GOLLADAY, GERTRUDE LaDEAN, b. Giles, Tex, Feb. 14, 26. ENGLISH. B.A, W.Tex. State Univ, 46; M.A, Univ. Denver, 52; Delta Kappa Gamma Soc. M. Margaret Stroh scholar, 64-65; Ph.D.(Eng), Tex. Christian Univ, 67. Teacher, Pub. Schs, N.Mex, 46-47 & Tex, 47-59; instr. ENG, UNIV. TEX, ARLINGTON, 59-63, asst. prof, 63-68, ASSOC. PROF, 68- Guest instr, W.Tex. State Univ, summers 46, 53; mem, Comn. for Curriculum Revision Eng. in Tex. Pub. Schs, 51-52; guest instr, Tex. Wesleyan Col, summers 57, 59; M. Margaret Stroh scholar, Delta Kappa Gamma Soc, 64-65. MLA; NCTE. Literary criticism during English Renaissance; poetry of John Dryden; curriculum for English in secondary school. Publ: Co-auth, Suggestions to teachers of English, 48 & Report on English curriculum revision, 52, Tex. Educ. Agency. Add: 1208 W. Lavender Lane, Arlington, TX 76013.

GOLLIN, RICHARD MYRON, b. Chicago, Ill, Aug. 19, 27; m. 50; c. 3. ENGLISH. B.A, Queens Col, 49; M.A, Univ. Minn, 51; Ph.D, 59; Fulbright scholar, Oxford, 53-54. Asst. Eng. & commun, Univ. Minn, 50-53; instr. ENG, Colgate Univ, 54-55; UNIV. ROCHESTER, 55-60, asst. prof, 60-64, ASSOC. PROF, 64-, univ. res. fel, 62-63. Ford Fund Advan. Educ. intern, 54-55; mem. Eng. Inst; prog. dir, Rochester Int. Film Festival, 72- U.S.A.A.F, 46-47. MLA. Victorian drama; film. Publ: Co-auth, Arthur Hugh Clough: a descriptive catalogue, N.Y. Pub. Libr, 67; The 1951 edition of Clough's Poems, Mod. Philol, 62; Dover Beach: the background of its imagery, Eng. Stud, 12/67; Film as drama, Col. Eng, 69. Add: Dept. of English, University of Rochester, Rochester, NY 14627.

GOLLIN, RITA K, b. New York, N.Y, Jan. 22, 28; m. 50; c. 3. ENGLISH LITERATURE. B.A, Queens Col.(N.Y), 49; M.A, Univ. Minn, 50, Am. Asn. Univ. Women fel, 52, Ph.D, 61. Asst, Univ. Minn, 49-53; lectr. ENG, univ. sch, Univ. Rochester, 55-62, 63-64, part-time instr, 60-62, part-time asst. prof, 63-64, asst. prof, 64-67; STATE UNIV. N.Y. COL. GENESEO, 67-68, ASSOC. PROF, 68-, fac. res. fel, 68, chmn. dept. Am. civilization, 70-73. Res. fel, Univ. Rochester, summer, 65, part-time lectr, 72. AAUP; MLA; Am. Stud. Asn. Nineteenth century American fiction, especially Hawthorne and Melville; 20th century American fiction, especially Fitzgerald and Faulkner; American Jewish fiction. Publ: Ed, Northwood, 69 & A little journey in the world, 70, Johnson Reprint; auth, Modes of travel in Tender is the night, Stud. 20th Century, 71; Dream-work in The Blithedale romance, Emerson Soc. Quart, 73; Little souls who thirst for fight in The red badge of courage, Ariz. Quart, 73; plus others. Add: Dept. of English, State University of New York College at Geneseo, Geneseo, NY 14454.

GONDIN, WILLIAM RICHARD, b. New York, N.Y, Aug. 28, 12; m. 35; c. 2. SPEECH. A.B, Columbia Univ, 34, Mitchel fel, 34-35, univ. scholar, 35-36, univ. fel, 36-37, Ph.D, 41. Dir. stud. activities, Seth Low Jr. Col, Columbia Univ, 34-37; instr. SPEECH, CITY COL. NEW YORK, 37-49, asst. prof, 49-54, assoc. prof, 54-61, PROF, 61- Ford fac. fel, 54-55. U.S.N.R, 42-46, Lt. Comdr. Speech Commun. Asn; Am. Inst. Parliamentarians. Rhetoric; philosophical and scientific foundations of speech. Publ: Advanced algebra and calculus, 59, Parliamentary procedure, 63 & co-auth, Art of speaking, 54, Doubleday. Add: 119 Valley Ave, Locust Valley, NY 11560.

GONZALEZ-DEL-VALLE, LUIS TOMAS, Spanish & Spanish American Literatures. See Volume III, Foreign Languages, Linguistics & Philology.

GOOCH, BRYAN NIEL SHIRLEY, b. Vancouver, B.C, Dec. 31, 37. ENGLISH LITERATURE, MUSIC. Vancouver Festival Soc. scholar, Univ. B.C, 56, 57, 59, B.A, 59, B.C. Electric Co. scholar, 59, Woodrow Wilson scholar, 60, M.A, 62; A.R.C.T, Royal Conservatory of Music, Toronto, 57; L.T.C.L, Trinity Col. of Music, London, 59, F.T.C.L, 61; I.O.D.E. scholar, Univ. London, 62-63, 63-64, Ph.D.(Eng), 68. ASST. PROF. ENG, UNIV. VICTORIA, 68-, ASST. DEAN FAC. ARTS & SCI & ACTING DIR. ADV. CTR, 73- Pianist & teacher of pianoforte, Vancouver, B.C, 55-, conductor, 62-, mem. Piano fac, Victoria Conservatory of Music, 67-70; musical dir. & conductor, Nanaimo Symphony Orchestra, 68-71; Univ. Victoria res. grants, 72-73, 73-74; Can. Counc. res. grant 73-74. Royal Can. Sea Cadet Corps, 57-62, Lt. Am. Musicol. Soc; Humanities Asn, Can; MLA; Renaissance Soc. Am; life fel. Royal Commonwealth Soc. Musical settings of British literature: 1870-1970; poetry and music in England: 1660-1760: the Bulwer family in the 19th century. Publ: Co-ed, Poetry is for people, Macmillan, 73; auth, Henry Cart de Lafontaine's The king's musick: the Purcell family index, Notes & Queries, 8/66; ETV and NET: humanities and mass media, Humanities Asn. Bull, spring 69; What is a real reader?, J. Reading, 10/70; plus others. Add: Office of the Dean, Faculty of Arts & Science, University of Victoria, Victoria, B.C, Can.

GOOD, DONALD WILLIAM, b. Winchester, Va, Aug. 13, 33. ENGLISH LITERATURE, ADMINISTRATION. B.A, Berea Col, 55; M.A, La. State Univ, Baton Rouge, 57; Ph.D.(Eng), Ohio State Univ, 68. Instr. ENG, OHIO STATE UNIV, 63-66, asst. prof, 66-70, ASSOC. PROF, 71-, ASST. V.PROVOST ARTS & SCI, 74- Col. Eng. Asn; Conf. Col. Compos. & Commun. Add: College of Arts & Sciences, Ohio State University, 164 W. 17th Ave, Columbus, OH 43210.

GOOD, GRAHAM, b. Ipswich, Eng, Aug. 20, 43; m. 66. ENGLISH & COMPARATIVE LITERATURE. B.A, Oxford, 64, B.Litt, 69; Kent fel, Princeton, 68-70, Ph.D.(comp. lit), 70. ASST. PROF. ENG, Rutgers Univ, Newark,

70-71, UNIV. B.C, 71- MLA; Int. Comp. Lit. Asn; Can. Comp. Lit. Asn. The English and European novel; modern poetry. Publ: Le colonel Chabert: a masquerade with documents, French Rev, 5/69; The death of language in Death in Venice, Mosaic, spring 72; Lukács' theory of the novel, Novel, winter 73. Add: Dept. of English, University of British Columbia, Vancouver, B.C. Can.

GOOD, STEPHEN HANSCOM, b. Columbus, Nebr, July 19, 42; m. 63; c. 2. ENGLISH & AMERICAN LITERATURE. B.A, Nebr. Wesleyan Univ, 64; M.A, Univ. Pittsburgh, 65, Ph.D.(Eng), 72. Instr. ENG, Univ. Nebr, 66-68; MT. ST. MARY'S (MD), 68-69, asst. prof, 69-73, ASSOC. PROF, 73-, CHMN. DEPT, 69- Lectr. Eng, Gettysburg Col, 69-72; Am. Counc. Learned Soc. fel, Inst. Humanistic Computation, Univ. Kans, 72; co-ed, Interdisciplinary Essays. MLA; Am. Soc. 18th Century Stud; Catch Soc. Am; AAUP. Eighteenth century British literature; history of ideas in the 17th and 18th centuries. Add: Dept. of English, Mt. St. Mary's College, Emmitsburg, MD 21727.

GOODE, STEPHEN H, b. Charlotte, N.C, Dec. 25, 24; m. 53; c. 2. ENGLISH. A.B, Univ. Md, 49; M.A, Univ. Pa, 54, Ph.D, 58. Asst. prof. ENG, Rensselaer Polytech. Inst, 58-59; Fairleigh Dickinson Univ, 60-65; ASSOC. PROF. ENG, RUSSELL SAGE COL, 65-, dir. libr, 65-73. Ed, Stud. 20th Century, 68-; pres, Whitston Publ. Co, 68- & Turpin Bk. Co, 72- U.S.A, 43-46, 49-52, 1st Lt. Bibliog. Soc. Am; Bibliog. Soc. Univ. Va; Bibliog. Soc, Eng; Grolier Club; Soc. Indexers. Twentieth century literature; bibliography. Publ: Index to little magazines, 1943-1947, Swallow, 65; Index to Commonwealth little magazines, 1964-1965, 66 & Index to Commonwealth little magazines, 1966-1967, 68, Johnson; Index to American little magazines, 1920-1939, 70, Index to Commonwealth little magazines, 1968-1969, 70 & Index to American little magazines, 1900-1919 (4 vols), 74, Whitston. Add: Dept. of English, Russell Sage College, Troy, NY 12180.

GOODELL, RALPH JEFFERSON, Linguistics. See Volume III, Foreign Languages, Linguistics & Philology.

GOODHEART, EUGENE, b. New York, N.Y, June 26, 31; m. 60; c. 2. ENGLISH, COMPARATIVE LITERATURE. B.A, Columbia Univ, 53, univ. fel, 57-58, Ph.D.(Eng), 61; Dupont Jr. fel, Univ. Va, 53-54, M.A, 54; Fulbright scholar, Sorbonne, 56-57. Instr. Eng, Bard Col, 58-60, asst. prof, 60-62; Univ. Chicago, 62-66; assoc. prof, Mt. Holyoke Col, 66-67; LIT, MASS. INST. TECHNOL, 67-70, PROF, 70- Willett fac. scholar, Univ. Chicago, spring 65; Am. Counc. Learned Soc. fel, 65-66; Guggenheim fel, 70-71. English and European literature of the 19th and 20th centuries. Publ: The utopian vision of D.H. Lawrence, 63 & The cult of the ego, 68, Univ. Chicago; Culture and the radical conscience, Harvard, 73; Job and the modern world, Judaism, winter 61; Lawrence and Christ, Partisan Rev, winter 64; The new apocalypse, Nation, centennial issue, 9/65 & In: The state of the Nation, Prentice-Hall, 66. Add: Dept. of Humanities, Massachusetts Institute of Technology, Cambridge, MA 02138.

GOODIN, GEORGE, b. Texarkana, Tex, Dec. 7, 30; m. 52; c. 7. ENGLISH. B.S, Marquette Univ, 52; Ph.D.(Eng), Univ. Ill, 62. Asst. ENG, Univ. Ill, 55-61; instr, Univ. Kans, 61-62; asst. prof, Holy Cross Col, 62-66; SOUTH. ILL. UNIV, CARBONDALE, 66-72, ASSOC. PROF, 72- U.S.N.R, 52-55, Lt. MLA; NCTE. English romantic criticism. Publ: The comic as a critique of reason, Col. Eng, 12/67. Add: Dept. of English, Southern Illinois University, Carbondale, IL 62901.

GOODMAN, KENNETH, b. Chicago, Ill, Dec. 23, 27; m. 52; c. 3. ELEMENTARY ENGLISH EDUCATION, APPLIED LINGUISTICS. A.B, Univ. Calif, Los Angeles, 49, Ed.D, 63; M.A, Los Angeles State Col, 53. PROF. ELEM. EDUC, WAYNE STATE UNIV, 62- Lectr. oral lang. develop, State Dept. Educ, Hawaii summer 66, 67 & 69; U.S. Off. Educ. coop. res. grants, 66-; adv. ed, Reading Res. Quart, 70-; Res. in Teaching Eng, 72-; lectr, Summer Ling. Inst, Ling. Soc. Am, 73; Nat. Inst. Educ. res. grant, 73-; adv. ed, Visible Lang, 73- NCTE (comn. reading, 71-); Int. Reading Asn. (chmn. psycholing. & reading comt, 68-72); Nat. Conf. Res. Eng.(pres, 71-72); Am. Educ. Res. Asn. Reading process; language differences; disadvantaged children. Publ: Co-auth, Choosing materials to teach reading, 67 & co-auth. & ed, The psycholinguistic nature of the reading process, 68, Wayne State Univ; co-ed, Psycholinguistics and the teaching of reading, Int. Reading Asn, 69; co-auth, Language and thinking in the elementary school, Holt, 71; co-auth, Reading systems levels, 1-21, Scott, 71-73; auth, Dialect barriers to reading comprehension, Elem. Eng, 12/65; Reading: a psycholinguistic guessing game, J. Reading Specialist, 5/67; Reading: the key is in children's language, Reading Teacher, 3/72; plus others. Add: Reading Miscue Research, Wayne State University, Detroit, MI 48221.

GOODMAN, OSCAR B, b. New York, N.Y, Mar. 13, 21; m. 44; c. 2. COMPARATIVE DRAMA. A.B, Brooklyn Col, 45; A.M, Columbia Univ, 47, Ph.D, 53. Instr. ENG, Brooklyn Col, 52-58; STATE UNIV. N.Y. MARITIME COL, 58-60, asst. prof, 60-61, assoc. prof, 61-64, PROF, 64-, CHMN. DEPT. HUMANITIES, 61- Dir, intern instr. prog, State Univ. N.Y, 61-68; lectr, Queens Col.(N.Y), 61-65; Hunter Col, 66-68; Lehman Col, 68-; Mem, acad. freedom comt, Am. Civil Liberties Union, 67-; assoc, Max Reinhardt Arch, 68- U.S.A, 44-45. Col. Eng. Asn; MLA; NCTE; Asn. Depts. Eng. Restoration drama; Shakespeare; theatre and film. Publ: College teaching internship: report on a pilot project, August 1965, Educ. Resources Inform. Ctr, U.S. Off. Educ, 68; co-auth, Lear's darker purpose, Lit. & Psychol, 9/68 & Regan's profession, Eng. Stud, 70. Add: Dept. of Humanities, State University of New York Maritime College, Bronx, NY 10465.

GOODMAN, RALPH MARVIN, b. Chicago, Ill, July 8, 25; m. 55; c. 3. LINGUISTICS, ENGLISH LITERATURE. B.A, Univ. Calif, Los Angeles, 55, M.A, 60, Ph.D.(ling), 70. Assoc. Eng, Univ. Calif, Los Angeles, 57-64; ASSOC. PROF. LING, UNIV. NORTH. IOWA, 64- U.S.C.G, 50-53. Ling. Soc. Am; AAUP. Publ: A generative propositional grammar, Mouton, The Hague, 75; contrib, An introductory English grammar, Holt, 65 & Meaning and literature: a common ground, Mouton, 74. Add: Dept. of English, University of Northern Iowa, Cedar Falls, IA 50613.

GOODMAN, RANDOLPH, b. New York, N.Y, May 29, 08. ENGLISH, DRAMA. B.S, N.Y. Univ, 31; Baker scholar, Yale, 43-44, Rockefeller grant, 45-46, M.F.A, 46; Ph.D.(comp. lit), Columbia Univ, 53. Instr. Eng. & drama, New Sch. Social Res, 50-55; ENG, BROOKLYN COL, 55-58, asst. prof, 58-62, assoc. prof, 62-68, PROF, 68- Inst. Int. Educ. fel, Univ. London, 50; ed. consult. in drama, Holt, Rinehart & Winston, 62; mem, Inst. Advan. Stud. in Theatre Arts; adj. prof, Sch. Theatre Arts, Grad. Div, Columbia Univ, 67- Am. Soc. Theatre Res; Am. Nat. Theatre & Acad. Classical and modern drama; American literature. Publ: I, Walt Whitman, Libr. Assoc, Brooklyn Col, 55; Drama on stage, 61 & Modern drama on stage, 69, Holt; Playwatching with a third eye, Columbia Univ. Forum, spring 67. Add: Dept. of English, Brooklyn College, Brooklyn, NY 11210.

GOODSTEIN, JACK DAVID, b. New York, N.Y, Mar. 30, 39; m. 61; c. 3. ENGLISH. B.A, Queens Col, 59; N.Y. State Col. fel, N.Y. Univ, 59, M.A, 60, Ph.D.(Eng), 68. Temporary instr. ENG, New York Community Col, 64-65; instr, State Univ. N.Y. Col. Fredonia, 65-66, asst. prof, 66-67; assoc. prof, CALIF. STATE COL.(PA), 67-68, PROF, 68- MLA. Victorian and Romantic literature; the novel. Publ: Pattern and structure in Robbe-Grillet's La maison de rendez-vous, Critique, fall 72. Add: Dept. of English, California State College, California, PA 15419.

GOODWIN, FRED BENTON, b. Cape Girardeau, Mo, Sept. 9, 30; m. 51; c. 3. RHETORIC & PUBLIC ADDRESS. B.S, Southeast Mo. State Col, 51; M.A, State Univ. Iowa, 54; fel, Univ. Ill, 67-68, Ph.D.(rhetoric & pub. add), 69. Speech & hearing consult, state serv. for crippled children, State Univ. Iowa, 54-55; asst. prof. SPEECH, SOUTHEAST MO. STATE UNIV, 55-60, assoc. prof, 60-69, PROF, 69-, CHMN. DIV. LANG. & LIT, 71- Speech Commun. Asn.(chmn. debate question comt, 71-72); Cent. States Speech Asn; Am. Forensic Asn; Am. Dialect Soc. Speech retardation; style in speech composition; communication theory. Publ: Co-auth, Pitch level and nasality, 55 & auth, A consideration of etiology in 454 cases of speech retardation, 56, J. Speech & Hearing Disorders; This business of bestness, Forensic, 60. Add: Dept. of Speech, Southeast Missouri State University, Cape Girardeau, MO 63701.

GOODWIN, HARRY EUGENE, b. Council Bluffs, Iowa, Dec. 19, 22; m. 43; c. 4. JOURNALISM. B.A, State Univ. Iowa, 46, M.A, 47. Copy ed, Baltimore Sun, 47-48; night ed, Assoc. Press, Baltimore, Md, 48-50; reporter & columnist, Wash. Star, 50-57; PROF. JOUR. & DIR. SCH. JOUR, PA. STATE UNIV, UNIVERSITY PARK, 57- V.pres, Am. Asn. Schs. & Depts. Jour, 60-61; mem. bd. dir, Mellett Fund for Free & Responsible Press, 66- U.S.A.A.F, 42-45, 1st Lt. Asn. Educ. Jour; Am. Counc. Educ. Jour. Public affairs reporting; government and mass communications. Add: School of Journalism, Pennsylvania State University, University Park, PA 16802.

GOODWIN, JAMES EDWARD, b. Durham, N.C, Nov. 1, 34; m. 56; c. 2. ENGLISH. A.B, Univ. N.C, 62; M.A, Univ. S.C, 67, Ph.D.(Eng), 69. Instr. ENG, North Bakersfield High Sch, 62-65; asst. prof, Idaho State Univ, 69-72; ASSOC. PROF, PA. STATE UNIV, 72-, ASST. HEAD DEPT, 72- MLA; Northeast Mod. Lang. Asn; NCTE. English literature of the 19th century. Add: Dept. of English, 104 Burrowes Bldg, Pennsylvania State University, University Park, PA 16802.

GORAN, SYLVESTER L, b. Pittsburgh, Pa, May 16, 28; m. 53; c. 3. ENGLISH, CREATIVE WRITING. B.A, Univ. Pittsburgh, 52, M.A, 60; Univ. Ala, 71. Instr. humanities, Pa. State Univ. Exten, 58-59; from instr. to asst. prof. ENG, UNIV. MIAMI, 60-67, ASSOC. PROF, 67- C.Eng, 46-48, Cpl. Eighteenth century English novel; English and continental novel since 1870; fiction and other prose of Henry James. Publ: The paratrooper of Mechanic Avenue, 60 & Maria Light, 62, Houghton; The candy butcher's farewell, McGraw, 64; The stranger in the snow, 66 & The demon in the sun parlor, 68, New Am. Libr; The keeper of secrets, Saturday Rev. Press, 71. Add: Dept. of English, University of Miami, Coral Gables, FL 33134.

GORDEN, WILLIAM I, b. Michigan City, Ind, July 24, 29; m. 53; c. 2. SPEECH. B.A, Manchester Col, 50; fel. & res. grants, Purdue Univ, 54-56, M.S, 55, Ph.D.(speech), 58; Northwest. Univ. & Fla. State Univ, 67. Instr. speech, Purdue Univ, 56-58; assoc. prof, Berry Col, 58-62; asst. prof, Southwest. Tex. State Col, 62-64, assoc. prof, 64-68; PROF. SPEECH COMMUN. & COORD. BASIC COURSE, SCH. SPEECH, KENT STATE UNIV, 68- Fel, Northwest. Univ, 67, Fla. State Univ, 68. Speech Commun. Asn. Public address and discussion; small peer groups and academic games. Publ: Kent Grand Jury report quashed, Free Speech Newslett, spring 71; Antiphonal preaching success in Georgia, Preaching Today, 3/72; The art of prediction, Art & Faith, 73; plus many others. Add: Dept. of Speech Communications, Kent State University, Kent, OH 44240.

GORDENSTEIN, ARNOLD S, b. Springfield, Mass, Dec. 1, 34; m. 65; c. 1. AMERICAN STUDIES, LITERATURE. B.A, Univ. Mass, 57; fels, Harvard, 63-67, Ph.D.(Am. civilization), 67. ASST. PROF. ENG. & DIR. AM. STUD, UNIV. DEL, 67- Fulbright-Hays lectr, Rio, Brazil, 69-70. Excellence-in-teaching Award, Univ. Del, 72-73. U.S.A, 57-59, 61-62. Nineteenth and 20th century American literature and art; Negro culture and literature. Add: Dept. of English, College of Arts & Science, University of Delaware, Newark, DE 19711.

GORDON, ALBERT C, b. Greensboro, N.C, Oct. 12, 33; m. 62; c. 2. THEATRE, HUMANITIES. A.B, Univ. N.C, Chapel Hill, 56, M.A, 58; Ph.D. (theatre), Tulane Univ, 65. Instr. drama, Union Col.(Ky), 58-59; assoc. prof. humanities, Armstrong Col.(Ga), 59-62; grad. asst. theatre, Tulane Univ, 62-65; asst. prof, Univ. Toledo, 65-68, assoc. prof, 68-73, prof, 73-74; PROF. FINE ARTS & CHMN. DEPT, WASHINGTON & LEE UNIV, 74- Univ. & Col. Theatre Asn.(secy-comptroller, 72-). Ibsen's last twelve plays; Euripides and The Bacchae. Add: Dept. of Fine Arts, Washington & Lee University, Lexington, VA 24450.

GORDON, AMBROSE, JR, b. Savannah, Ga, May 23, 20; m; c. 2. ENGLISH LITERATURE. B.A, Yale, 42, Ph.D, 52. Instr. Eng, Yale, 51-54; lit, Sarah Lawrence Col, 54-58; asst. prof. ENG, UNIV. TEX, AUSTIN, 58-63; assoc. prof, 63-71, PROF, 71- Fulbright lectr. Am. lit, La Plata, 66 & 69. U.S.N, 42-46, Lt. MLA. Literature of the 20th century. Publ: The invisible tent: the war novels of Ford Madox Ford, Univ. Tex, 64; The double pnin, In: Nabokov the man and his work, Univ. Wis, 67; Borges with, and without,

Borges, J. Mod. Lit, Vol. I, No. 1; Between soft whimsy and the chill, New Repub, 4/71. Add: Dept. of English, University of Texas at Austin, Austin, TX 78712.

GORDON, DAVID J, b. St. Louis, Mo, Dec. 23, 29. ENGLISH. A.B, Harvard, 51, M.A, 52; Ph.D.(Eng), Yale, 61. Instr. ENG, Boston Univ, 56-60; HUNTER COL, 60-66, asst. prof, 66-72, ASSOC. PROF, 72- Modern literature; criticism; literature and psychology. Publ: D.H. Lawrence as a literary critic, Yale, 66. Add: Dept. of English, Hunter College, 695 Park Ave, New York, NY 10021.

GORDON, GROVER BRECKENRIDGE, Religion, Speech. See Volume IV, Philosophy, Religion & Law.

GORDON, JAMES D, b. Philadelphia, Pa, Nov. 17, 01; m. 33; c. 5. ENGLISH. A.B, LaSalle Col, 26; M.A, Univ. Pa, 29, Ph.D, 40. Head dept. Eng, Northeast High Sch, Phila, Pa, 51-52; Cent. High Sch, 52-59; assoc. prof, UNIV. PA, 59-72, dir. advan. placement, 60-72, EMER. PROF. ENG, 72- MLA; NCTE; Mediaeval Acad. Am; Mod. Humanities Res. Asn; Early Eng. Text. Soc. Middle English language and literature. Publ: The teaching of English composition, In: Partners in education, 58 & Chaucer's retraction, In: Studies in Medieval literature, 61, Univ. Pa; The English language: an historical introduction, Crowell, 72; The articles of the creed and the apostles, Speculum, 65. Add: 22 Poe Ave, Wyncote, PA 19095.

GORDON, KATHRYN I, b. Boston, Mass, May 24, 14; m. 44. ENGLISH. B.A, Am. Int. Col, 56, fel, 56-57, M.A, 58; A.M, Boston Univ, 61, Ph.D.(Eng), 68. Instr. Eng, Am. Int. Col, 57-60, asst. prof, 62-69, assoc. prof, 69-74; RETIRED. MLA; Col. Eng. Asn. Dante Gabriel Rossetti; Chaucer. Add: 225 Crane Rd, Clearwater, FL 33516.

GORDON, LOIS G, b. Englewood, N.J, Nov. 13, 38; m. 61; c. 1. ENGLISH & AMERICAN LITERATURE. A.B, Univ. Mich, 60; M.A, Univ. Wis, 62, Ph.D. (Eng), 66. Lectr, ENG, City Col. New York, 64-66; asst. prof, Univ. Mo-Kansas City, 66-68; FAIRLEIGH DICKINSON UNIV, 68-71, ASSOC. PROF, 71- Asst. ed, Lit. & Psychol, 68-71. MLA. Twentieth century English and American literature; the poem. Publ: Stratagems to uncover nakedness: the dramas of Harold Pinter, Univ. Mo, 69; Harold Pinter—past and present, Kans. Quart, spring 71; Death of a salesman: an appreciation, In: The forties, 69 & Myth and meaning—The sound and the fury and The waste-land, In: The twenties, 74, Everett Edwards. Add: Dept. of English, Fairleigh Dickinson University, 840 River Rd, Teaneck, NJ 07666.

GORDON, MARJORIE NEESON, b. Los Angeles, Calif, Jan. 14, 36; m. 73. MEDIEVAL ENGLISH LITERATURE. B.A, St. Joseph Col.(Calif), 61; M.A, Col. Holy Names, 64; Ph.D.(Eng), Univ. Calif, Los Angeles, 71. ASST. PROF. ENG, Marymount Col, Loyola Univ. Los Angeles, 67-72; CALIF. STATE UNIV, LOS ANGELES, 72- Early Eng. Texts Soc; Mediaeval Acad. Am; Medieval Asn. Pac. Editing of medieval texts; Alexander legend in medieval literature. Add: Dept. of English, California State University, Los Angeles, CA 90035.

GORDON, MORTON, b. New York, N.Y, Feb. 11, 26; m. 56; c. 2. SPEECH. M.A, Columbia Univ, 52; M.A, State Univ. Iowa, 55. Asst. prof. SPEECH, Univ. Hawaii, 55-68, INSTR, KAPIOLANI COMMUNITY COL, 68- Fulbright lectr. grant, Cebu Norm. Sch, Philippines, 52-53; McInerny Found. grants, 57 & 58; NDEA grant, 60-62. U.S.A, 43-46. Am. Speech & Hearing Asn. Use of television in teaching speech improvement. Publ: Co-auth, A manual for speech improvement, 61 & auth, Speech improvement, 74, Prentice-Hall; Television education in elementary school speech improvement, Speech Monogr, 3/66. Add: Dept. of Speech, Kapiolani Community College, University of Hawaii, 620 Pensacola St, Honolulu, HI 96814.

GORDON, NICHOLAS KARL, b. Albany, N.Y, July 24, 40; m. 61; c. 3. ENGLISH & AMERICAN LITERATURE. B.A, Queens Col.(N.Y), 61; M.A, Stanford Univ, 66, Ph.D.(Eng), 68. Instr. ENG, N.Y. Univ, 67-69; ASST. PROF, JERSEY CITY STATE COL, 69- Add: Dept. of English, Jersey City State College, Jersey City, NJ 07305.

GORDON, ROBERT CONINGSBY, b. Melbourne, Australia, Oct. 29, 21; U.S. citizen; m. 43; c. 3. ENGLISH LITERATURE. B.A, Univ. N.C, 42; M.A, Harvard, 47, Ph.D, 52. Instr. Eng, Univ. Ore, 50-54, asst. prof, 54-57; SAN JOSÉ STATE UNIV, 57-60, ASSOC. PROF. ENG. & HUMANITIES, 57- Lectr, advan. placement summer prog, Univ. Ore, 62, John Hay Found. prog, summer 63; mem. accreditation comt, Asn. West. Cols, 63; lectr, John Hay summer inst, Williams Col, summer 64; dir, Ore. Summer Inst. Humanities, summer 66; participant, Danforth workshop lib. arts educ, Colo. Col, summer 67; sr. res. scholar, Fulbright Prog, Edinburgh, 71-72. U.S.N.R, 42-45, Lt. MLA. Humanities; teaching of the arts; political origins of British Romanticism. Publ: The expanded moment, Heath, 63; Under which king?: a study of the Scottish Waverley novels, Oliver & Boyd, 69; The bride of Lammermoor: a novel of Tory pessimism, Nineteenth-century Fiction, 9/57; plus others. Add: Dept. of English, San José State University, 125 S. Seventh St, San José, CA 95192.

GORDON, WALTER KELLY, b. Brooklyn, N.Y, Jan. 25, 30; m. 59; c. 1. ENGLISH LANGUAGE & LITERATURE. A.B, Clark Univ, 50; M.A, Univ. Pa, 57, Ph.D, 60. Teaching fel, Univ. Pa, 57-59; instr. ENG, Cedar Crest Col, 59-60, asst. prof, 60-61; Col. S.Jersey, RUTGERS UNIV, CAMDEN, 61-67, ASSOC. PROF, 67-, ACTING DEAN, 73-, assoc. dean, 72-73. U.S.N, 51-56, Lt.(jg). MLA; NCTE. Nineteenth century English literature; studies in the English language. Publ: Co-auth, Exposition and the English language, 63 & auth, Literature in critical perspectives, 68, Appleton. Add: Dept. of English, Rutgers University, Camden, NJ 08102.

GORDON, WILLIAM A, b. Chicago, Ill, Sept. 30, 21; m. 57; c. 1. ENGLISH. A.B, Tulane Univ, 47, M.A, 58, Ph.D, 63. Instr. ENG, Loyola Univ.(La), 55-58, asst. prof, 58-63, ASSOC. PROF, 63-66; Tulane Univ, 66-67; UNIV. KY, 66- U.S.A, 42-46, 1st Lt. MLA. Literary criticism; romanticism; contemporary literature. Publ: The mind and art of Henry Miller, 67 & Writer and critic: a correspondence with Henry Miller, 68, La. State Univ; Autobiography and identity: William Wordsworth, Tulane Stud. Eng, fall 72. Add: Dept. of English, University of Kentucky, Lexington, KY 40506.

GORDON-CRAIG, CHRISTOPHER, b. Remuera, N.Z. ENGLISH. B.A, Univ. Auckland, 65, M.A, 66; Ph.D.(Eng), Univ. N.B, 69; L.T.C.L, Trinity Col, London. Lectr. ENG, Univ. N.B, 68-69; ASST. PROF, UNIV. ALTA, 69- Can. Asn. Univ. Teachers. Renaissance drama; later Victorian literature; children's literature. Add: Dept. of English, University of Alberta, Edmonton, Alta. T6G 2E1, Can.

GORELIK, MORDECAI, b. Shchedrin, Russia, Aug. 25, 99; m; c. 2. THEATRE. Cert, Pratt Inst, 20. Instr. & designer, Sch. Theatre, N.Y, 21-22; mem. fac, Am. Acad. Dramatic Arts, 26-32; Dramatic Workshop New Sch. Soc. Res, 40-41, Biarritz Am. Univ, France, 45-46, Univ. Toledo, 56, Univ. Hawaii & N.Y. Univ, 58, Bard Col, 59 & Brigham Young Univ, 61; res. prof. THEATRE, SOUTH. ILL. UNIV, 60-72, EMER. PROF, 72- Scene painter & stage technician, Provincetown Playhouse, N.Y, 20-21; dir, designer & scenic supvr. numerous plays & films, 24-; Guggenheim Mem. Found. fel, 36-37; consult. theatre, U.S. Mil. Govt, Ger, 49; Rockefeller Found. grant, 49-51; guest prof, Calif. State Univ, Los Angeles, 64, San Jose State Col, 65 & Univ. Mass, Boston, 71; Fulbright grant, Australia, 67; prof, L.I. Univ, 72. Am. Theatre Asn; Speech Commun. Asn; U.S. Inst. Theatre Technol. Stage history; scene design; playwriting. Publ: New theatres for old, 40; transl, Max Frisch, The firebugs, Hill & Wang, 58 & French, 68; plus contrib. articles to numerous mag, jour. & encycl. Add: 19532 Sandcastle Lane, Huntington Beach, CA 92648.

GORHAM, THELMA T, b. Kansas City, Mo, Feb. 21, 13; m. 41; c. 1. JOURNALISM & MASS COMMUNICATION, SOCIOLOGY. A.B, Univ. Minn, 35, M.A, 51; cert. soc. stud, Cent. State Col.(Okla), 57. Ed, Army publ, Ft. Huachuca, Ariz, 42-44; assoc. prof. jour, Lincoln Univ.(Mo), 47-51; teacher, Moon Jr. High Sch, Okla, 56-59; assoc. prof. jour. & Eng, South. Univ, 60-62; teacher, Cent. High Sch, Mo, 62-63; acting dir. pub. relat, Fla. A&M Univ, 63-66, assoc. prof. jour, 63-68; consult. res. & curriculum develop, Twin Cities Opportunities Industrialization Ctr, Inc, Minneapolis, 68-69, exec. dir. manpower training, 69-71; ASSOC. PROF. JOUR. & MASS COMMUN, FLA. A&M UNIV, 71- Lectr, Univ. Hawaii, Manoa, 60; chmn. publicity, nat. convention, Adult Educ. Asn, Fla, 63; instr. commun, Univ. Minn, Minneapolis, 68-71; human relat. consult, Univ. Miss, 68-69; participant human relat. workshop, Baha'i Summer Sch, Davidson, Mich, 70; mem, Nat. Baha'i Pub. Inform. Comt, 71-73; commun. consult, Nat. Baha'i Youth Conf, 73. Nat. Conf. Christians & Jews Mass Media Citation, 55. Am. Acad. Polit. & Soc. Sci; Nat. Counc. Col. Publ. Adv; Jour. Educ. Asn; Am. Asn. Univ. Women; AAUP. The Negro press as a social institution; black appeal radio; racial self-hatred in the Negro press. Publ: Meeting the challenge of change, Joyce-Grimes, 63; Negro newsmen and practices of pressure groups, J. Negro Educ, fall 52; Negro appeal radio, 61, 62 & The Negro press: past, present and future, 63 & 72-73, U.S. Negro World. Add: Div. of Communication, Florida A&M University, P.O. Box 94, Tallahassee, FL 32307.

GORMAN, THOMAS RICHARD, b. Detroit, Mich, Dec. 31, 25; m. 52; c. 4. AMERICAN STUDIES, LITERATURE. A.B, Univ. Notre Dame, 49, M.A, 50; Ph.D, Univ. Pa, 60. Instr. ENG, Georgetown Univ, 52-58; LOYOLA UNIV. CHICAGO, 58-60, asst. prof, 60-64, ASSOC. PROF, 64- U.S.N, 44-46. Am. Stud. Asn; MLA; NCTE; Col. Eng. Asn; Conf. Col. Compos. & Commun. Nineteenth century American literature; American literature and politics of the 20th century. Publ: Five modern British plays, Macmillan, 67. Add: Dept. of English, Loyola University of Chicago, 820 N. Michigan Ave, Chicago, IL 60611.

GORRELL, ROBERT MARK, b. Bremen, Ind, Aug. 9, 14; m. 39; c. 2. ENGLISH. A.B, Cornell Univ, 36, fel, 38-39, Ph.D, 39. Instr. Eng. & hist, Deep Springs Col, 39-42; ENG, Ind. Univ, 42-45; from asst. prof. to assoc. prof, UNIV. NEV, RENO, 45-57, PROF, 57-, DEAN COL. ARTS & SCI, 72-, dean grad. sch, 67-68. Fulbright vis. prof, Sydney Univ, 54-55; Univ. Helsinki, 61-62; chief consult, Ford. Found. High Sch. Curriculum Stud, 59-60. MLA; Renaissance Soc. Am; Shakespeare Asn. Am; NCTE (dir. comn. on compos, 70-73); Conf. Col. Compos. & Commun.(chmn, 63-). English Renaissance literature; English drama of 16th and 17th centuries; rhetoric. Publ: Co-auth, Education for college, Ronald, 61; English as language, 61, co-auth, Reading about language, 71 & co-auth, Writing and language (2 vols), 72, Harcourt; co-auth, Modern English handbook, 3rd ed, 62, 4th ed, 67, 5th ed, 72, co-auth, Modern English reader, 70 & co-auth, Writing modern English, 73, Prentice-Hall; auth, Not by nature: approaches to rhetoric, Eng. J, 4/66; Rhetoric, the teaching of, In: Encyclopedia of education, 71; Rhetoric: how do you carve an elephant, In: NCTE distinguished lectures, 71; plus others. Add: College of Arts & Science, University of Nevada, Reno, NV 89507.

GORSKY, SUSAN RUBINOW, b. Hartford, Conn, Apr. 18, 44; m. 65. ENGLISH & AMERICAN LITERATURE. A.B, Smith Col, 66; M.A, Case West. Reserve Univ, 67, fel, 67-69, Ph.D.(Eng), 69. Vis. asst. prof. ENG, Case West. Reserve Univ, summer 69; asst. prof, CLEVELAND STATE UNIV, 69-73, ASSOC. PROF, 73- Midwest. Mod. Lang. Asn.(secy. mod. lit, 72-73, chmn, 73-74); AAUP; Am. Asn. Univ. Women. Modern literature, form and meaning; modern fiction; 19th century fiction. Publ: Gentle doubters: images of women in English women's novels, 1840-1920, In: Images of women in fiction, Bowling Green State Univ, 72; Old maids and new women: alternatives to marriage in English women's novels, 1840-1920, J. Popular Cult, 73; A ritual drama: Yeats's plays for dancers, Mod. Drama, 74; plus others. Add: Dept. of English, Cleveland State University, Euclid & E. 22nd, Cleveland, OH 44115.

GOSE, ELLIOTT BICKLEY, JR, b. Nogales, Ariz, May 3, 26; m. 50; c. 2. ENGLISH. B.A, Univ. Colo, 49, M.A, 50; Ph.D.(Eng), Cornell Univ, 54. Instr. ENG, La. State Univ, 54-56; UNIV. B.C, 56-58, asst. prof, 58-63, assoc. prof, 63-67, PROF, 67- V.chmn, Vancouver Sch. Bd, 73. U.S.A, 46-47. MLA; Can. Sch. Trustees Asn; Can. Educ. Asn. English novel; 20th century British and American literature. Publ: Imagination indulged: the irrational in the 19th century English novel, McGill-Queens Univ, 72; Coleridge's symbolical language in The rhyme of the ancient mariner, 6/60 & Archetypal symbolism in Lord Jim, 3/64, PMLA. Add: 3862 W. 37th, Vancouver 13, B.C, Can.

GOSHORN, JAMES WILLIAM, b. Fort Wayne, Ind, May 4, 35; m. 60; c. 2. AMERICAN LITERATURE. B.A, Purdue Univ, Lafayette, 60, M.A, 62; Ph.D.(Eng), Univ. N.Mex, 71. Asst. prof. Eng, Adams State Col, 64-65; tech. ed, Sandia Labs, 65-70; ASST. PROF. ENG, MONT. STATE UNIV, 70- NCTE; Conf. Col. Compos. & Commun; MLA; Rocky Mt. Mod. Lang. Asn; Col. Eng. Asn. Contemporary novel; composition. Add: Dept. of English & Theatre Arts, Montana State University, Bozeman, MT 59715.

GOSMAN, MICHAEL THOMAS, b. Washington, D.C, Aug. 24, 40. ENGLISH & AMERICAN LITERATURE. A.B, George Washington Univ, 62; M.A, Cath. Univ. Am, 64, Ph.D.(Eng), 71. Asst. ENG, CATH. UNIV. AM, 64-71, ASST. PROF, DIR. ARTS D. PROG. & UNDERGRAD. STUD, 71- MLA; Eng. Inst; AAUP. Literary theory; prosody; Ezra Pound. Publ: The concept of literary form: representative modern theories, Mouton, (in press), The doctor of arts: make it new, J. Gen. Educ, 10/72. Add: Dept. of English, Catholic University of America, Washington, DC 20017.

GOSS, JAMES, Religion & Literature, Hermeneutics. See Volume IV, Philosophy, Religion & Law.

GOSSE, ANTHONY CABOT, b. New Orleans, La, Aug. 21, 21; m. 53; c. 4. ENGLISH. A.B, Princeton, 46; A.M, Columbia Univ, 51, Ph.D.(Eng), 62. Lectr. ENG, Columbia Univ, 49-51; instr, Brown Univ, 51-60; BUCKNELL UNIV, 60-63, asst. prof. 63-68, ASSOC. PROF, 68- Med.Admin.C, 43-45, Lt. MLA. Restoration drama; Shakespeare. Publ: The omitted scene in Congreve's Love for love, Mod. Philol, 8/63; Plot and character in Congreve's Double dealer, Mod. Lang. Quart, 9/68. Add: Dept. of English, Bucknell University, Lewisburg, PA 17837.

GOSSELINK, ROBERT NICHOLAS, b. Terre Haute, Ind, Mar. 30, 34; m. 60; c. 3. ENGLISH. A.B, Univ. Kans, 57; M.A, Univ. Colo, 62, Develop. Found. fel, 65, Ph.D.(Eng), 66. ASST. PROF. ENG, UNIV. WATERLOO, 66- Asn. Can. Univ. Teachers Eng; Am. Soc. 18th Century Stud; Can. Counc. Teachers Eng. Eighteenth century poetry; 18th century periodicals; bibliography. Publ: The miller's wife in the Reeve's tale: an interpretation, Eng. Quart, spring 73. Add: Dept. of English, University of Waterloo, Waterloo, Ont. N2L 3G1, Can.

GOSSETT, SUZANNE S, b. New York, N.Y, Dec. 24, 41; m. 63; c. 2. ENGLISH & AMERICAN LITERATURE. B.A, Smith Col, 62; Fulbright scholar, St. Hilda's Col, Oxford, 62-63; M.A, Princeton, 65, Ph.D.(Eng), 68. ASST. PROF. ENG, LOYOLA UNIV. CHICAGO, 68- MLA. Renaissance English drama. Publ: Masque influence on the dramaturgy of Beaumont and Fletcher, Mod. Philol, 72; Drama in the English College, Rome, 1591-1660, Eng. Lit. Renaissance, 73. Add: Dept. of English, Loyola University of Chicago, 820 N. Michigan Ave, Chicago, IL 60611.

GOSSETT, THOMAS FRANK, b. Dallas, Tex, July 13, 16; m. 50. AMERICAN LITERATURE & STUDIES. B.A, South. Methodist Univ, 46, M.A, 48; Ph.D.(Am. stud), Univ. Minn, 53. Instr. ENG, South. Methodist Univ, 46-48; Univ. Minn, 49-52; La. State Univ, 53-54; assoc. prof, Wesleyan Col.(Ga), 54-56, PROF, 56-59; Trinity Univ.(Tex), 59-66; WAKE FOREST UNIV, 67-, summer fel, 66. Am. Counc. Learned Soc. fel, 52-53; vis. scholar fel, Duke Univ, 58; summer fel, Trinity Univ, 62; vis. prof, Univ. Ill, Urbana, 66-67. Ralph Waldo Emerson Award, Phi Beta Kappa, 64. U.S.A.A.F, 43-46. Am. Stud. Asn. History of racial theories; history of American attitudes toward war; study of American pessimists. Publ: Race; the history of an idea in America, South. Methodist Univ, 63, Schoeken, 65. Add: 2091 Royall Dr, Winston-Salem, NC 27106.

GOSSMAN, ANN, b. Houston, Tex, Nov. 15, 30. ENGLISH LITERATURE. B.A, Rice Univ, 52, M.A, 54, Ph.D, 57. Grad. asst, Rice Univ, 54-57; instr. ENG, Univ. Tex, 57-59; asst. prof, TEX. CHRISTIAN UNIV, 59-67, assoc. prof, 67-72, PROF, 72- Fel, Southeast. Inst. Medieval & Renaissance Studies, Univ. N.C, summer 67. MLA; Milton Soc. Am; Renaissance Soc. Am. Publ: Lander and the Higher Fountains, Class. J, 57; The ransom in Samson Agonistes, Renaissance News, 60; Milton's Samson as the tragic hero purified by trial, J. Eng. & Ger. Philol, 62. Add: Dept. of English, Texas Christian University, Ft. Worth, TX 76129.

GOTTESMAN, LILLIAN, b. New York, N.Y, Mar. 12, 29. ENGLISH. B.A, Hunter Col, 50; M.A, N.Y. Univ, 53, Ph.D.(Eng), 63. Chief clerk, N.Y.C. Health Dept, 51-55, jr. methods analyst, 55-60; teacher, high schs, N.Y, 60, 63-64; asst. prof. ENG, BRONX COMMUNITY COL, 64-68, assoc. prof, 68-71, PROF, 71-, CHMN. DEPT, 73- Substitute teacher, N.Y.C. schs, 50-60; lectr, Brooklyn Col, 60-63; res. grant, State Univ. N.Y, summer 73. Kelley Gold Medal, 50; N.Y. Univ. Founders' Day Award, 64. MLA; Col. Eng. Asn. Medieval and Renaissance literature; drama from the Medieval period to 1800. Publ: Introd, Sr. Thomas Elyot: four political treatises, 67 & introd, The description of the Contrey of Aphrique, 72, Scholars' Facsimiles & Reprints; auth, English voyages and accounts: impact on Renaissance dramatic presentation of the African, Stud. in Humanities, summer 71; English Renaissance knowledge of Black Africa, CEA Critic, 1/72; Garrick's Lilliput, Restoration & 18th Century Theatre Res, 11/72; plus others. Add: Dept. of English, Bronx Community College, W. 181st St. & University Ave, Bronx, NY 10453.

GOTTESMAN, RONALD, b. Boston, Mass, Jan. 7, 33; m. 56; c. 2. ENGLISH. A.B, Univ. Mass, 55; A.M, Colgate Univ, 57; Ph.D.(Eng), Ind. Univ, 64. Teaching assoc. Eng, Ind. Univ, 57-60; instr, Northwest. Univ, 60-62; lectr, Ind. Univ, 62-64, asst. prof, 64-68, assoc. prof, 68-69, Sinclair archivist, Lilly Libr, 60-69; assoc. prof, Livingston Col, Rutgers Univ, 69-72; PROF. ENG. & HUMANITIES, UNIV. WIS-PARKSIDE, 72- Mem. panel textual experts, editions of Am. auth, MLA, 66-; textual ed, A selected edition of W.D. Howells, MLA, 65-68, gen. ed, 68-69; Guggenheim fel, 69-70; co-gen. ed, Film Focus Series, Prentice-Hall & Filmguides, Ind. Univ. U.S.A.R, 55-63. Univ. Film Asn; MLA; NCTE; Am. Stud. Asn; Soc. Cinema Stud. American literature; film and textual editing. Publ: Lilly Library catalog of Upton Sinclair archives, Lilly Libr, 63; contrib, Professional standards and American editions, MLA, 69; co-auth, Art and error: modern textual editing, Ind. Univ, 70; co-auth, Sergei Eisenstein and Upton Sinclair: the making and unmaking of Que viva Mexico!, Thames & Hudson, London & Ind. Univ, 70; ed, Focus on Citizen Kane, Prentice-Hall, 71; ed, Studies in invisible man, Merrill, 71; co-auth, Guidebook to film: an eleven-in-one reference work, 72 & An illustrated glossary of film terms, 73, Holt; co-auth, Upton Sinclair: a calendar of his literary manuscripts, Ohio State Univ, 73; auth, Upton Sinclair: an annotated checklist, Kent State Univ, 73; Textual commentary to Their wedding journey, Literary friends and acquaintance and Altrurian romances & Literary criticism, In: Books for teachers of English: an annotated bibliography, Ind. Univ, 68; plus many others. Add: Div. of Humanities, University of Wisconsin-Parkside, Woods Rd, Kenosha, WI 53140.

GOTTFRIED, LEON ALBERT, b. Ames, Iowa, Nov. 6, 25; m. 52. ENGLISH. A.B, Univ. Ill, 48, M.A, 52, fel, 52-53, Ph.D, 58. Instr. ENG, Univ. Conn. 53-54; WASH. UNIV, 54-58, asst. prof, 58-63, assoc. prof, 63-69, PROF, 69-, CHMN. ART & ARCHAEOL, 72- Am. Philos. Soc. res. & travel grant, 66 & 71; Fulbright lectr, Univ. Malaya, 70-71. U.S.N.R, 44-46. MLA. Nineteenth century English literature; literature and art. Publ: Matthew Arnold and the romantics, Routledge & Kegan Paul & Univ. Nebr, 63; Death's other kingdom, PMLA, 1/69; The Odysseyan form, In: Essays on European literature, Wash. Univ, 72; Structure and genre in Daniel Deronda, In: The English novel in the nineteenth century, Univ. Ill, 72. Add: Dept. of English, Washington University, St. Louis, MO 63130.

GOTTFRIED, RUDOLF BRAND, b. Chicago, Ill, July 28, 09; m. 35; c. 1. ENGLISH LITERATURE. A.B, Yale, 31, Ph.D, 35. Instr, Univ. Wis, 34-37; res. assoc, Univ. Cincinnati, 37-39; instr. ENG, IND. UNIV, BLOOMINGTON, 39-45, asst. prof, 45-49, assoc. prof, 49-56, PROF, 56- MLA; Renaissance Soc. Am. Renaissance literature; Elizabethan literature. Publ: Ed, Edmund Spenser, Prose works, Johns Hopkins, 49; transl, Pietro Bembo, Gli Asolani, 54 & ed, Orlando Furioso, 63, Ind. Univ; co-auth, Autobiography and art: an Elizabethan borderland In: Literary criticism and historical understanding, Columbia Univ, 67; Our new poet: archetypal criticism and The faerie queene, PMLA, 68. Add: Dept. of English, Indiana University, Bloomington, IN 47401.

GOTTLIEB, MARVIN RONALD, b. Cincinnati, Ohio, Sept. 1, 39; m. 69; c. 2. SPEECH, THEATRE. B.S.S, Northwest. Univ, 61; M.A, Columbia Univ, 67, prof. dipl, 69; Ph.D.(commun), N.Y. Univ, 72. Lectr. Eng, N.Y.C. Community Col, 67-68; SPEECH & THEATRE, LEHMAN COL, 68-72, ASST. PROF, 72- Consult. Eng. & Speech, Med. Serv. Admin. Prog, 69-72; instr. speech, Bilingual Educ. Staff Training Proj, 70-72. Speech Commun. Asn; NCTE. Philosophy of literature; oral interpretation; self concept. Add: Dept. of Speech, Herbert H. Lehman College, Bedford Park Blvd. W, Bronx, NY 10468.

GOTTSCHALK, HANS W, b. Berlin, Ger, Dec. 31, 14; U.S. citizen; m. 41. ENGLISH. B.A, N.Y. Univ, 41, M.A, 43; Ph.D.(Eng), Univ. Iowa, 49. Instr. Eng, Ohio State Univ, 47-50; asst. prof, Wis. State Col, Eau Claire, 50-53; sr. teacher, New Lincoln Sch, N.Y, 54; asst. prof. ENG, Duquesne Univ, 54-55; assoc. prof, STATE UNIV. N.Y. COL. GENESEO, 55-60, PROF, 60-, chmn. dept, 65-71. Mem. Bd. dir, NCTE, 56-65, 68-69; consult. ling. proj, State Univ. N.Y. Buffalo, U.S. Off. Educ, 63-65; fel, N.Y. State Eng. Counc, 65-; dir, NDEA Inst. Eng, U.S. Off. Educ, 66, 68, evaluator of proposals, 66, 67; consult, Harvard sem, NDEA inst. dir. comn. Eng, Col. Entrance Exam. Bd, 66. MLA; Ling. Soc. Am; Nat. Soc. Stud. Commun; NCTE; Col. Eng. Asn; Conf. Col. Compos. & Commun; Conf. Eng. Educ. American literature; English education; communication and applied linguistics. Publ: Study guide to Moby-Dick, 63 & Study guide to Stephen Crane, 63, Shelley; co-auth, Linguistic approach to English, 65 & USOE linguistic project, Vols. I & II, 65, State Univ. N.Y. Buffalo; auth, English augmented: diversity or depth, N.Y. State Educ, 12/59; The basic issues in English and the junior high school, Eng. Record, fall 60. Add: Dept. of English, State University of New York College at Geneseo, Geneseo, NY 14454.

GOTTSCHALK, JANE, b. Milwaukee, Wis, Apr. 25, 23. ENGLISH. B.S, Marquette Univ, 57, M.A, 59; Ph.D.(Eng), Univ. Wis, 65. Instr. ENG, Marquette Univ, 59-62; asst. prof, UNIV. WIS-OSHKOSH, 65-67, assoc. prof, 67-70, PROF, 70- NCTE; MLA. Publ: The owl and the nightingale: lay preachers to a lay audience, Philol. Quart, 10/66; The rhetorical strategy of Booker T. Washington, Phylon, winter 66; The continuity of American letters in The scarlet letter and The beast in the jungle, Wis. Stud. Lit, 67. Add: Dept. of English, University of Wisconsin-Oshkosh, Oshkosh, WI 54901.

GOTTSCHALK, PAUL A, b. Chicago, Ill, Apr. 12, 39; m. 64. ENGLISH. A.B, Harvard, 60; M.A, Univ. Chicago, 61, Ph.D.(Eng), 65. Instr. ENG, Chicago Teachers Col. South, 63-64; CORNELL UNIV, 65-67, asst. prof, 67-73, ASSOC. PROF, 73- MLA. Shakespeare; English Renaissance drama; comparative literature. Publ: The meanings of Hamlet, Univ. N.Mex, 72; Time in Edwin Drood, Dickens Stud. Ann, 70; The universe of madness in King Lear, Bucknell Rev, 71; Hamlet and the scanning of revenge, Shakespeare Quart, 73. Add: Dept. of English, Cornell University, Ithaca, NY 14850.

GOTTSEGEN, ROBERT D, b. Washington, D.C, June 28, 25; m. 47; c. 2. ENGLISH. B.A, Mich. State Univ, 49; A.M, Univ. Pa, 51. Asst. instr. ENG, Univ. Pa, 53-55; from asst. prof. to ASSOC. PROF, CHEYNEY STATE COL, 60-, DIR. RES. AWARDS & GRANTS, 68- Danforth assoc, 61- U.S.A, 43-45. NCTE. Publ: Auth, Series of public affairs documentaries, produced on WCAU-TV, Phila; Choice or chance (career motivational film), produced by Phila. Human Relat. Comn, 9/66; Facts about tires (educ. film), produced by DuPont Co, 2/67. Add: 237 Kenyon Ave, Swarthmore, PA 19081.

GOTTSHALL, JAMES KERWOOD, b. Bluffton, Ohio, Sept. 27, 22; m. 49; c. 3. ENGLISH. A.B, Oberlin Col, 48; M.A, Univ. Pa, 49; Taft fel, Univ. Cincinnati, 52-54, Ph.D, 58. Instr. ENG, Univ. Cincinnati, 49-52; Hiram Col, 54-57; Kent State Univ, 57-59, asst. prof, 59-61; assoc. prof, Cedar Crest Col, 61-63, prof, 63-71, head dept, 61-71; PROF. & HEAD DEPT, ST. CLOUD STATE COL, 71- MLA. U.S.A, 42-46, Capt. Theory of fiction; Charles Dickens. Publ: Devils abroad: unity & significance of Barnaby Rudge, Nineteenth-Century Fiction, 9/61. Add: Dept. of English, St. Cloud State College, St. Cloud, MN 56301.

GOUDIE, ANDREA KAY, b. Minneapolis, Minn, June 9, 40. AMERICAN LITERATURE. B.A, Univ. Minn, Minneapolis, 62; M.A, Ind. Univ, Bloomington, 63, Ph.D.(Eng. lang. & lit), 69. Instr. ENG, Bethany Col, 63-65; ASST.

PROF, WICHITA STATE UNIV, 68- AAUP; MLA; Col. Eng. Asn. Nineteenth and twentieth century American literature. Publ: Exploring the broad margins: Charles Ive's Interpretation of Thoreau, Midwest Quart, spring 72; What fools these mortals be! A puckish interpretation of Mark Twain's narrative stance, Kans. Quart, fall 73; Another path to reality: Emily Dickinson's birds, Concerning Poetry, spring 74. Add: Dept. of English, Wichita State University, Box 14, Wichita, KS 67208.

GOULD, JAY REID, b. Aylesford, N.S, Mar. 15, 06; m. 41; c. 2. ENGLISH DRAMA, TECHNICAL WRITING. B.A, Acadia Univ, 26; A.M, Harvard, 29; summers, Drama League scholar, Eng, 33, 34. Teacher ENG, E.Greenwich Acad, R.I, 28; from asst. prof. to prof, RENSSELAER POLYTECH. INST, 29-72, dir, Tech. Writers' Inst, 53-72, assoc. dir, Med. Writers' Inst, 60-72, chmn. dept. lang & lit, 68-72, EMER. PROF, 72- Consult, N.Y. State Dept. Health, IBM Corp. & var. other firms; consult. commun, Am. Chem. Soc, 72-; vis. prof. commun, Univ. Mass, fall 73; vis. prof, New S.Wales Inst. Technol, 74. Am. Bus. Writing Asn; fel. Soc. Tech. Writers & Publ; NCTE; Am. Med. Writers Asn; fel. Am. Bus. Commun. Asn. Publ: Steps from beyond (play), Baker, 54; co-auth, Technical reporting, Holt, 57; auth, Death of the hired man, 60, The long silence (play), 62 & The necklace (play), Dramatic Publ; Opportunities in technical writing, Award, 64; Practical technical writing, Am. Chem. Soc, 74. Add: Dept. of English, Rensselaer Polytechnic Institute, Troy, NY 12181.

GOULDING, CHARLES BENJAMIN, b. Bridgeport, Conn, Oct. 5, 98; m 40; c. 3. ENGLISH LANGUAGE & LITERATURE. A.B, Yale, 19, A.M, 25, Ph.D, 33. Teacher schs, Ohio, 19-28; from instr. to PROF. ENG, UNIV. BRIDGEPORT, 28-44, 47-73, EMER. PROF, 73- Minor poems of John Lydgate; Anglo-Latin plays of the 16th century. Add: Dept. of English, University of Bridgeport, Bridgeport, CT 06602.

GOULDING, DANIEL JOSEPH, b. Huntington, W.Va, July 6, 35; m. 58; c. 2. COMMUNICATION STUDIES. B.A, Marshall Univ, 57; M.A, Ohio Univ, 59, Ph.D.(commun, hist), 64. Instr. speech, W.Va. Univ, 58-60; asst. prof. speech commun, Albion Col, 62-66; ASSOC. PROF. COMMUN. STUD. & CHMN. DEPT, OBERLIN COL, 66- Speech Commun. Asn; Univ. Film Asn; AAUP; Am. Film Inst. Mass communication; Eastern European cinema; attitude organization and change. Publ: Co-ed, Articulation and learning: new dimensions in research, diagnostics, and therapy, C.C. Thomas, 73; auth, The restless generation, Vital Speeches, 6/66; Macaulay as a critic of parliamentary speaking, Cent. State Speech J, 11/67; Whither the student feature film?, report from Oberlin College, Univ. Film Asn. J, spring 72; plus others. Add: Dept. of Communication Studies, Oberlin College, Oberlin, OH 44074.

GOUSSEFF, JAMES W, b. Des Moines, Iowa, Apr. 12, 28; m. 63. THEATRE. B.S, Iowa State Col, 50; M.A, Cornell Univ, 52; M.F.A, Yale, 56; Ph.D. (theatre), Northwest. Univ, 62. Instr. theatre, Northwest. Univ, summers 57-60; State Univ. Iowa, 59-62, asst. prof, 62-63; PROF. SPEECH & DRAMATIC ARTS, EAST. MICH. UNIV, 63-, DIR. THEATRE, 71- U.S.A, 51-53. Am. Theatre Asn. Acting and directing; pantomime; English Renaissance theatre history. Add: Dept. of Speech & Dramatic Arts, Eastern Michigan University, Ypsilanti, MI 48197.

GOW, JOHN E, b. Attleboro, Mass, Mar. 5, 31; m. 61. SPEECH. B.A, Allegheny Col, 54; M.A, State Univ. Iowa, 58; Univ. Mo, 57-59; M.S, Ill. Inst. Technol, 70. Instr. pub. speaking, Univ. Md, 55-57; Univ. Mo, 57-59; SPEECH, Wright Jr. Col, 59-61; asst. prof, ELMHURST COL, 61-72, ASSOC. PROF, 72- Int. Soc. Gen. Semantics; Int. Commun. Asn; AAUP. General semantics, interpersonal communication theory; American public address. Publ: Re-examining contest speaking, Forensic, 1/68; Review of reality therapy, ETC, 3/70; Public speaking or communication, comprehensive change in the speech curriculum, Today's Speech, fall 72; plus one other. Add: Dept. of Speech, Elmhurst College, Elmhurst, IL 60126.

GOWEN, JAMES ANTHONY, b. Chuquicamata, Chile, Oct. 24, 28; U.S. citizen; m. 61; c. 3. AMERICAN LITERATURE & LINGUISTICS. B.A, Univ. San Francisco, 56; Ph.D.(Eng. & Am. lit), Stanford Univ, 68. Asst. prof. ENG. UNIV. KANS, 64-70, ASSOC. PROF, 70- Mem, comt. col-level exams, Col. Entrance Exam. Bd, 66-68. MLA; NCTE; Conf. Col. Compos. & Commun. American literature; linguistics. Publ: English review manual, 65 & Progress in writing, 73, McGraw; The new writers: enigma and despair, San Francisco Quart, spring 56; The Jesuit discipline of inquiry, Ramparts, 3/63. Add: Dept. of English, University of Kansas, Lawrence, KS 66045.

GOWER, HERSCHEL, b. Nashville, Tenn, Dec. 11, 19. ENGLISH & AMERICAN LITERATURE. B.A, Cumberland Univ, 42; M.A, Vanderbilt Univ, 52, teaching fel, 52-54, Ph.D, 57; Fulbright grant, Univ. Edinburgh, 54-56. Instr. ENG. LIT, VANDERBILT UNIV, 56-58, asst. prof, 58-64, ASSOC. PROF, 64- Award of Merit, Am. Asn. State & Local Hist, 61. U.S.N.A.F, 42-46. S.Atlantic Mod. Lang. Asn. The short story; Southern literature; the English lyric. Publ: Co-ed, Pen and sword: the life and journals of Randal W. McGavock, Tenn. Hist. Comn, 60; contrib, Reality and myth, 63, ed, The hawk's done gone and other stories, 68, Vanderbilt Univ; co-auth, The sense of fiction, Prentice-Hall, 66. Add: Dept. of English, Vanderbilt, University, Nashville, TN 37235.

GOYNE, GROVER CLEVELAND, b. Vicksburg, Miss, Oct. 25, 39; m. 61; c. 2. ENGLISH. B.A, Harding Col, 61; M.A, Vanderbilt Univ, 63, Ph.D.(Eng), 67. Asst. prof. ENG, PEPPERDINE UNIV, 67-70, chmn. dept, 70-72, CHMN. DEPT. COMMUN. ARTS, 71-, DEAN, COL. ARTS & SCI, 72- U.S.A, 57. MLA; Am. Conf. Acad. Deans. Victorian English literature; 18th century English literature. Add: 1121 W. 79th St, Los Angeles, CA 90044.

GOYNE, MINETTA ALTGELT, Germanic Languages, English. See Volume III, Foreign Languages, Linguistics & Philology.

GOZZI, RAYMOND DANTE, b. Mt. Vernon, N.Y, Aug. 1, 20; m. 43; c. 2. AMERICAN LITERATURE. A.B, Amherst Col, 42; A.M, Columbia Univ, 47; Ph.D, N.Y. Univ, 57. Instr. ENG, Univ. Col, N.Y. Univ, 47-53; UNIV. MASS, AMHERST, 58-61, asst. prof, 61-73, ASSOC. PROF, 73- U.S.C.G.R, 42-46, Lt. Thoreau Soc; Emerson Soc; Col. Eng. Asn; MLA. Nineteenth and 20th century American literature. Publ: Tropes and figures: a psychological study of Henry David Thoreau, Thoreau Soc. Bull, winter 58; The variorum Walden and collected poems of Henry Thoreau, New Eng. Quart, 9/64; Some aspects of Thoreau's personality & Mother nature, In: Henry David Thoreau: a profile, Hill & Wang, 71. Add: Dept. of English, University of Massachusetts, Amherst, MA 01002.

GRABAR, TERRY HARRIS, b. Washington, D.C, Dec. 8, 28; m. 51; c. 2. ENGLISH. B.A, Wellesley Col, 50; Ph.D.(James Morier), Univ. Mich, 63. Instr. ENG, Bir Zeit Col, Jordan, 53-54; East. Mich. Univ, 63-64, asst. prof, 64-67, assoc. prof, 67-69; FITCHBURG STATE COL, 70-73, PROF, 73-, CHMN. DEPT, 71- MLA; AAUP; NCTE; Col. Eng. Asn. Victorian fiction and poetry; romantic fiction; early 19th century fiction. Publ: Hajji Baba: fact and fiction, Tex. Stud. Lit. & Lang, fall 69; Scientific education and Richard Feverel, Victorian Stud, 12/70; The English dialogue of Waverley, J. Narrative Tech, 1/71. Add: Dept. of English, Fitchburg State College, Fitchburg, MA 01420.

GRABER, RALPH SCHULTZ, b. East Greenville, Pa, Apr. 2, 25; m. 48; c. 4. ENGLISH. B.A, Lehigh Univ, 46, M.A, 48; Ph.D.(Eng), Univ, Pa, 59. Instr. ENG, Lehigh Univ, 48-51; MUHLENBERG COL, 53-59, asst. prof, 59-62, assoc. prof, 62-69, PROF, 69- AAUP; Col. Eng. Asn; NCTE. Nineteenth and 20th century American literature; sports in literature. Publ: The baseball reader, Barnes, 51; New light on the dedication of Richard Henry Wilde's Hesperia, Ga. Hist. Quart, 60; Baseball in American fiction, Eng. J, 11/67. Add: Dept. of English, Muhlenberg College, 24th & Chew Sts, Allentown, PA 18104.

GRABILL, VIRGINIA LOWELL, b. Hastings, Minn, Apr. 20, 19; m. 52; c. 1. ENGLISH LITERATURE. B.A, Wheaton Col, 41; scholar, Univ. Ill, 41-42, M.A, 42, Ph.D, 47. Asst. ENG, Univ. Ill, 42-47; asst. prof, West. Ill. State Univ, 47-52; assoc. prof, Bethel Col, 52-53, prof, 54-57, chmn. dept, 53-57; assoc. prof, UNIV. EVANSVILLE, 57-61, PROF, 61-, dir. women's counseling, 58-65. NCTE. Grammar and linguistics; short story; magazine articles. Publ: Co-auth, Youth leaders' handbook, Miracle Bks, 51; auth, Words are fun, Correct Eng. Mag, Summer, 41; Mencken from the grave, Christianity Today, Spring, 58; English literature, In: Christ and the modern mind, 72. Add: Dept. of English, University of Evansville, Evansville, IN 47704.

GRABO, NORMAN S, b. Chicago, Ill, Apr. 21, 30; m. 58; c. 2. ENGLISH. B.A, Elmhurst Col, 52; M.A, Univ. Calif, Los Angeles, 55, Ph.D.(Eng), 58. From instr. to asst. prof. Eng, Mich. State Univ, 58-63, res. prof, 61; assoc. prof, Univ. Calif, Berkeley, 63-67, prof, 67-72, humanities res. prof, 66-67; TUTOR HUMANITIES, ST. JOHN'S COL.(MD), SANTA FE, 72- Folger Shakespeare Libr. fel, summer 61; Guggenheim Mem. Found. fel, 70-71. MLA (mem. exec. counc, Ctr. Editions Am. Auth, 63, exec. bd, 64-; chmn. Am. Lit. Sect, 72-73); Am. Stud. Asn; fel. Soc. Relig. Higher Educ. Colonial American literature; early American intellectual history; American theology. Publ: Edward Taylor, Twayne, 61; ed, Edward Taylor's Christographia, Yale, 62; co-auth, American thought and writing, 65 & co-ed, American poetry and prose, 70, Houghton; ed, Edward Taylor's treatise concerning the Lord's Supper, Mich. State Univ, 66. Add: St. John's College, Santa Fe, NM 87501.

GRACE, JOAN CARROLL, b. Brooklyn, N.Y, Mar. 6, 21. ENGLISH. A.B, Trinity Col.(D.C), 43; M.A, Columbia Univ, 51; Ph.D.(Eng. & comp. lit), Columbia Univ, 69. ASST. PROF. ENG, LIB. ARTS COL, FORDHAM UNIV, 68- Col. Eng. Asn; NCTE; MLA; AAUP. Shakespeare; Milton; modern British writers. Publ: Tragic theory in the critical works of Thomas Rymer, John Dennis and John Dryden, Fairleigh Dickinson Univ, 74. Add: 44 Morningside Dr, New York, NY 10025.

GRACE, MATTHEW, b. New York, N.Y, Dec. 7, 36; m. 63. ENGLISH. B.A, Tufts Univ, 57; M.A, Columbia Univ, 61; Ph.D.(Eng), Univ. Wis, 65. Instr. ENG, Emory Univ, 63-65; City Col. New York, 65-69; ASSOC. PROF, BARUCH COL, 69- Mem. fac, The New Sch, 68; assoc. prof, Univ. Clermont-Ferrand, 69-70. MLA; Eng. Inst. Restoration and 18th century English literature. Publ: Ed, The Gray's Inn journal and other essays by Arthur Murphy, Scholars' Facsimiles, 68; auth, A reader's guide to 50 European plays, Washington Square, 73; Mailer at the end of decade, In: Will the real Norman Mailer stand up, Kennikat, 73; Mailer on Mailer-an interview, New Orleans Rev, 73. Add: Dept. of English, Baruch College, 17 Lexington Ave, New York, NY 10010.

GRACE, WILLIAM JOSEPH, b. New York, N.Y, July 3, 10; m. 52; c. 6. ENGLISH LITERATURE. B.A, Oxford, 33, M.A, 37; N.Y. State Educ. Dept. grant, Columbia Univ, summer 62. Asst. prof. ENG, St. Bonaventure Col, 36-37; FORDHAM UNIV, 37-56, assoc. prof, 56-66, PROF, 66-, fac. fel, 61-62, summer 66. Mem. ed. bd, Complete Works of John Milton, 66. MLA. English Renaissance literature; John Milton. Publ: How to be creative with words, Fordham Univ; Approaching Shakespeare, Basic Bks; co-auth, Art of communicating ideas, Devin; auth, Response to literature, McGraw, 65; ed, Milton's a defence, Vol. IV, In: Complete prose works of John Milton, Yale Univ, 66; auth, Ideas in Milton, Univ. Notre Dame, 68. Add: 254 Prospect Ave, Staten Island, NY 10301.

GRADE, ARNOLD E, b. Newton, Mass, Dec. 12, 28; m. 59; c. 2. ENGLISH. B.A, Univ. Mass, 55; scholar, Bread Loaf Sch. Eng, 59-60, M.A, 60; Univ. Minn, 63; Ph.D, Univ. Iowa, 67. Master Eng, Cardigan Mt. Sch, 55-56; The New Hampton Sch, 56-58; lectr, Col. St. Thomas, 58-62, asst. prof. educ, 62-65; PROF. ENG, STATE UNIV. N.Y. COL. BROCKPORT, 67- U.S.A.F, 50-51. Robert Frost; children's literature; creative writing. Publ: The outset and other poems, St. Thomas, 59; A Robert Frost folio, 60; co-ed, New Hampshire's child: the Derry journals of Lesley Frost, 68 & ed, Family letters of Robert and Elinor Frost, 72; State Univ. N.Y; auth, Guide to early juvenile literature, Merrill, 70. Add: Dept. of English, State University of New York College at Brockport, Brockport, NY 14420.

GRADMAN, HARRY LEE, Linguistics, English as a Foreign Language. See Volume III, Foreign Languages, Linguistics & Philology.

GRADY, RICHARD FRANCIS, S.J, b. Philadelphia, Pa, July 27, 05. PSYCHOLOGY OF LITERATURE. A.B, St. Joseph's Col.(Pa), 24; A.M, Woodstock Col, 29; Ph.D. & S.T.L, Gregorian Univ, Rome, 38; Kol. Sankt Andra, Austria, 36-37; hon. L.H.D, Univ. Scranton, 73. Dean, Canisius Col, 37-39; head dept. Eng, Loyola Col.(Md), 39-42; head dept. commun. arts, Fordham Univ, 46-48; prof. ENG, UNIV. SCRANTON, 48-70, EMER. PROF, 70- Ed, Best Sellers, 55-70. U.S.A, 42-46, Chaplain & Lt. Col. Add: Dept. of English, University of Scranton, Scranton, PA 18510.

GRAFF, GERALD EDWARD, b. Chicago, Ill, June 28, 37. ENGLISH. B.A, Univ. Chicago, 59; Ph.D.(Eng), Stanford Univ, 63, Asst. prof. ENG, Univ. N.Mex, 63-66; NORTHWEST. UNIV, 66-70, ASSOC. PROF, 70- Modern literary criticism; Colonial and modern American literature. Publ: Poetic statement and critical dogma, Northwest. Univ, 70; Mythotherapy and modern poetics, winter 68 & The myth of the postmodernist breakthrough, winter 73, Tri-Quarterly; Lukacs in the American university, New Hungarian Quart, autumn 72; plus others. Add: Dept. of English, Northwestern University, Evanston, IL 60201.

GRAFFIN, WALTER RAY, b. Milwaukee, Wis. June 6, 36; div; c. 2. MODERN LITERATURE, POPULAR CULTURE. B.S, Univ. Wis-Madison, 58, M.A, 60, Ph.D.(Eng), 69; Ind. Univ, 60-61. Instr. ENG, Northwest. Univ, 65-68; ASST. PROF, UNIV. WIS-PARKSIDE, 68- Lectr, Nat. Endowment for Humanities Midwest Ctr, spring 73. Col. Conf. Compos. & Commun. Contemporary literature. Publ: Co-ed, Perspectives for the seventies, Dodd, 71. Add: Div. of Humanities, University of Wisconsin-Parkside, Kenosha, WI 53140.

GRAGG, PERRY EARL, b. San Antonio, Tex, June 22, 29; m. 56; c. 3. ENGLISH. B.A, Davidson Col, 50; M.A, Univ. Tex, 55, South. Found. fel, 57-58, Ph.D, 60. Teacher, San Antonio Acad, 53-54; instr. ENG, San Antonio Col, 55-57, asst. prof, 57-60, assoc. prof, 60-63, prof, 63-68, chmn. dept, 64-68; PROF, ANGELO STATE UNIV, 68-, CHMN. DEPT, 71- Vis. prof, Incarnate Word Col, 62-63; Our Lady of the Lake Col, 66-67. U.S.A, 50-52, 1st Lt. MLA; Am. Stud. Asn; NCTE. American literature, 1870-1900; Victorian literature. Add: Dept. of English, Angelo State University, San Angelo, TX 76901.

GRAGG, WILSON B, b. Centralia, Ill, Nov. 25, 09; m. 38. ENGLISH LITERATURE. B.A, Univ. Ill, 36; M.A, Northwest. Univ, 41, Ph.D, 48. Teacher, rural schs, Marion & Clinton Counties, Ill, 28-34; headmaster, Desert Willow Ranch Sch, Tucson, Ariz, 36-37; Ger. master sub-Latin & Ger, Lake Forest Acad, 37-38; teacher ENG, Highland Pub. High Sch, Ill, 38-40; Pekin Community High Sch, Ill, 41-44; instr, U.S. Mil. Acad. Prep, 44-45; Cornell Univ, 45-49; PROF, STATE UNIV. N.Y. COL. BUFFALO, 49- MLA; Col. Eng. Asn; NCTE. Anthony Trollope; Shakespeare; Victorian period. Add: Dept. of English, State University of New York College at Buffalo, 1300 Elmwood Ave, Buffalo, NY 14222.

GRAHAM, ALBERT EDWIN, b. Sherman, Tex, Aug. 8, 26. ENGLISH LITERATURE. B.A, Austin Col, 49; Ph.D.(Eng. lit), Princeton, 60. Instr. ENG, Univ. Cincinnati, 55-59; asst. prof, SOUTH. ILL. UNIV, 59-68, ASSOC. PROF, 68- Med.C, U.S.A, 45-47. NCTE. MLA; AAUP. Eighteenth century English fables. Publ: John Gay's second series, the Craftsman in fables, Papers Lang. & Lit, Vol. V, no. 1. Add: 179 Hammel Ave, Webster Groves, MO 63119.

GRAHAM, DON BALLEW, b. Lucas, Tex, Jan. 30, 40; m. 62; c. 2. AMERICAN LITERATURE, ENGLISH. B.A, N.Tex. State Univ, 62, M.A, 64; Ph.D. (Am. lit), Univ. Tex, Austin, 71. Instr. ENG, Southwest Tex. State Univ, 64-69; ASST. PROF, UNIV. PA, 71-, DIR. FRESHMAN ENG, 72- MLA; NCTE. Frank Norris; contemporary American literature; realism and naturalism. Publ: Utopian turtletops and brunette angels: some remarks on poetry and advertising, CCTE Proc, 9/70; Studio art in The octopus, Am. Lit, 1/73; Frank Norris's Afternoon of a faun, Papers Lang. & Lit, spring 74. Add: Dept. of English, University of Pennsylvania, 34th & Walnut, Philadelphia, PA 19174.

GRAHAM, GAYLORD OWEN, b. Iowa City, Iowa, Jan. 12, 30; m. 57. THEATRE. A.B, State Univ, Iowa, 53, M.A, 56, summers, State Univ. Iowa, 58, Stanford Univ, 59, Univ. South Calif, 60, 62 & 63. Instr. speech arts, CALIF. STATE UNIV, FRESNO, 57-60, asst. prof, 60-67, assoc. prof, 67-72, PROF. THEATRE ARTS, 72- Infantry, U.S.A, 48-49, Sig.C, 53-55, 1st Lt. AAUP; Am. Theatre Asn; Illumin. Eng. Soc; Nat. Inst. Arts & Lett; U.S. Inst. Theatre Technol. Theatrical lighting. Add: Dept. of Theatre Arts, California State University, Fresno, Cedar Ave. & Shaw, Fresno, CA 93740.

GRAHAM, GENE SWANN, b. Murray, Ky, Aug. 26, 24; m. 45; c. 3. JOURNALISM, COMMUNICATIONS. B.S, Murray State Univ, 48; Nieman fel, Harvard, 62-63. Newspaperman, Nashville Tennessean, 48-64; vis. lectr. JOUR, UNIV. ILL, URBANA, 64-65, assoc. prof, 65-73, PROF, 73- Training consult, Boston Globe, 66-70. Pulitzer Prize, 62. U.S.N, 43-45, Ens. Assoc. Press Managing Ed. Asn; Am. Asn. Ed. Cartoonists. Newspaper content shifts of emphasis; mass media impact on society and culture; ethical problems of news media. Publ: One man, one vote: Baker v. Carr and the American Levelers, 72; Lukewarm porridge of the Mama Bear press, 12/65 & History in the deliberate making, 9/66; Nieman Reports; Responsibilities of the doubly damned, Quill, 2/68. Add: College of Communications, 20 Gregory Hall, University of Illinois, Urbana, IL 61801.

GRAHAM, H. RICHARD, b. July 28, 38; m. 56; c. 2. ENGLISH. B.A, Yankton Col, 56; M.A, Temple Univ, 63, Ph.D.(Eng), 66. Instr. ENG, Ohio State Univ, 63-66; asst. prof, FRANKLIN COL, 66-72, ASSOC. PROF, 72- Add: Dept. of English, Franklin College, Franklin, IN 46131.

GRAHAM, JOHN, b. Washington, D.C, Sept. 1, 26; m. 54; c. 4. SPEECH. A.B, Georgetown Univ, 49; M.A, Harvard Univ, 54; Univ. Göttingen, 57-58; M.A, Johns Hopkins Univ, 58, Ph.D, 60. Instr. Eng, Georgetown Univ, 49-50; Marquette Univ, 53-54; teaching fel, Johns Hopkins Univ, 54-56, instr, 56-57; UNIV. VA, 58-60, asst. prof. SPEECH, 60-67, ASSOC. PROF, 67-, ASST. DEAN COL, 66- Fulbright grant & Charles Merrill res. fel, 57-58; res. grant, Oxford, 72. U.S.A.A.F, 44-45. MLA; Speech Commun. Asn; Am. Soc. Aesthet. Aesthetics of the 18th century; rhetoric; the novel. Publ: Ed, Great American speeches, 1898-1963; texts and studies, Appleton, 70; ed, Studies in Second skin, Merrill, 71; auth, The writer's voice, Morrow, 73; Character description and meaning in the romantic novel, Stud. in Romanticism, 66; Ut pictura poesis, In: The dictionary of the history of ideas, Scribner, 73; The value of common materials in the debate course, South. Speech Commun. J, 72; plus others. Add: Dept. of Speech Communication, 1 Dawson's Row, University of Virginia, Charlottesville, VA 22903.

GRAHAM, JOHN WHICHELLO, b. Montreal, Que, Mar. 6, 25; m. 57; c. 3. ENGLISH. B.A, Univ. Man, 45; M.A, Univ. Toronto, 47, Ph.D.(Eng), 52. Instr. ENG, UNIV. WEST. ONT, 49-52, lectr, 52-53, asst. prof, 53-60, assoc. prof, 60-65, PROF, 65-, chmn. dept, 64-67. Royal Soc. Can. scholar, 56-57. Asn. Can. Univ. Teachers Eng. Publ: A negative note on Bergson and Virginia Woolf, Essays in Criticism, 56; Point of view in The waves: some services of the style, Univ. Toronto Quart, 70; Editing a manuscript: Virginia Woolf's The waves, In: Editing twentieth century texts, Univ. Toronto, 72. Add: Dept. of English, University College, University of Western Ontario, London, Ont, Can.

GRAHAM, KENNETH L, b. Coffeyville, Kans, Apr. 25, 15; m. 45; c. 2. SPEECH. B.A, State Univ. Iowa, 36; M.A, Northwest. Univ, 39; Ph.D, Univ. Utah, 47. Teacher speech, dramatics & Eng, Watertown, S.Dak, 36-37; speech & dramatics, North Kansas City High Sch, Mo, 37-38; asst. speech & theatre, UNIV. MINN, MINNEAPOLIS, 39-41, PROF. SPEECH COMMUN. & THEATRE ARTS, 48-, CHMN. DEPT. THEATRE ARTS & DIR. UNIV. THEATRE, 71-, chmn. dept. speech, commun. & theatre arts, 63-71. Dir. Sch. Theatre, Cain Park Community Theatre, Cleveland Heights, Ohio, summers 41-42, 46-47; mem. bd. trustees, Am. Playwrights Theatre, 63-; consult, arts & humanities br, U.S. Off. Educ, 66-71. Merit Award, Am. Col. Theatre Festival, 72. U.S.N.R, 42-46, Lt. Nat. Theatre Conf; fel. Am. Theatre Asn.(exec. secy, 56-58, v.pres, 63, pres, 64); Am. Nat. Theatre & Acad. Theatre. Publ: Relationships between educational theatre and professional theatre, Educ. Theatre J, 11/66. Add: 110 Rarig Center, University of Minnesota, Minneapolis, MN 55455.

GRAHAM, KENNETH WAYNE, b. Winnipeg, Man, Mar. 26, 38; m. 63; c. 2. ENGLISH LITERATURE & BIBLIOGRAPHY. B.A, Royal Mil. Col. Can, 61; M.Ph, Univ. London, 67, Can. Counc. fel, 69, Ph.D.(Eng), 71. Lectr. ENG, UNIV. GUELPH, 66-70, ASST. PROF, 70- Can. Army, 61-64, Capt. Asn. Can. Univ. Teachers Eng; Samuel Johnson Soc. Northwest. Bibliography; 18th century literature; 19th century novel. Publ: Beckford's Vathek: a study in ironic dissonance, Criticism, 72; Who revised the 1823 Vathek, Papers Bibliog. Soc. Am, 73; Vathek in English and French, Stud. in Bibliog, 74. Add: Dept. of English, University of Guelph, Guelph, Ont, Can.

GRAHAM, ROGER JOHN, b. Philadelphia, Pa; m. 62; c. 2. COMMUNICATION, ADULT EDUCATION. B.A, Calif. State Univ, Fresno, 62, M.A, 67; Calif. State Univ, Northridge, 68-71; Univ. Calif, Los Angeles, 72- Journalist, Turlock Daily J, 62; Fresno Guide, 62-63; teacher elem. educ, Riverdale Elem. Sch, 63-64; Raisin City Sch, 64-65; teacher-counr. adult educ, State Prison Sierra Conservation Ctr, 65-66; teacher basic educ, Kirk Elem. Sch, 67; teacher-trainer adult basic educ, Univ. Calif, 67-68; ASSOC. PROF. JOUR, LOS ANGELES VALLEY COL, 68- U.S.N, 55-57. AAUP; Adult Educ. Asn. U.S; Am. Soc. Jounalists; Jr. Col. Jour. Asn.(West. rep, 73). Adult education; career education; communication. Publ: Breaking into press agentry, Jr. Col. J, 11/71; Journalism articulation, fall 72 & Minority scholarships, summer 73, Jr. Col. Journalist. Add: Dept. of Journalism, Los Angeles Valley College, 5800 Fulton Ave, Van Nuys, CA 91401.

GRAHAM, SUSETTE RYAN, b. Plattsburgh, N.Y. Aug. 31, 29, 50; m. 50; c. 6. ENGLISH & AMERICAN LITERATURE. B.A, Wellesley Col, 50; M.A, Univ. Rochester, 65. Lectr. ENG. NAZARETH COL. ROCHESTER, 62-65, instr, 65-68, asst. prof, 68-72, ASSOC. PROF, 72-, CHMN. DEPT, 73-, asst. dean, 67-73. AAUP; MLA. Nineteenth century American literature, especially Dickinson and Melville; William Faulkner. Add: Dept. of English, Nazareth College, 4245 East Ave, Rochester, NY 14610.

GRANBERRY, EDWIN PHILLIPS, b. Meridian, Miss, Apr. 18, 97. CREATIVE WRITING. A.B, Columbia Univ, 20; Harvard, 22-24; D.Litt, Rollins Col, 43. Asst. prof. Romance lang, Miami Univ, 20-22; master Latin & French, Stevens Sch, Hoboken, N.J, 25-30; IRVING BACHELLER PROF. CREATIVE WRITING, ROLLINS COL, 40- O.Henry Mem. Prize, 32. Auth. League Am. Novels. Publ: The ancient hunger, 27, Strangers and lovers, 28 & The erl king, 30, Macaulay; A trip to Czardis, Trident, 67. Add: Dept. of Creative Writing, Rollins College, Winter Park, FL 32789.

GRANELL, LEE E, b. Minneapolis, Minn, Aug. 29, 33; m. 58; c. 2. SPEECH. A.B, San Diego State Col, 56; M.A, Univ. South. Calif, 59, Ph.D.(speech), 64. Instr. SPEECH COMMUN, CALIF. STATE UNIV, FULLERTON, 60-62, asst. prof, 62-65, ASSOC. PROF, 65-, CHMN. DEPT, 68- Sr. lectr, Univ. South. Calif, 67-68; pres, CommData, 73- Speech Commun. Asn; Am. Forensic Asn. Audience analysis methodology; rhetorical theory and criticism; political communication. Add: Dept. of Speech Communication, California State University, Fullerton, 800 N. State College Blvd, Fullerton, CA 92634.

GRANGER, BRUCE INGHAM, b. Philadelphia, Pa, Feb. 28, 20; m. 44; c. 2. ENGLISH. A.B, Cornell Univ, 42, M.A, 43, Ph.D, 46. Instr. ENG, Univ. Wis, 46-50; asst. prof, Univ. Denver, 50-53; assoc. prof, UNIV. OKLA, 53-61, PROF, 61- Am. Philos. Soc. summer grants-in-aid, 55, 58, 66 & 67. MLA. Publ: Political satire in the American Revolution, 1763-1783, 60 & Benjamin Franklin: an American man of letters, 64, Cornell Univ; Illusion and reality in Eugene O'Neill, Mod. Lang. Notes, 3/58; plus others. Add: 944 Chautauqua Ave, Norman, OK 73069.

GRANGER, BYRD HOWELL, b. New Rochelle, N.Y, Oct. 18, 12. ENGLISH, FOLKLORE. A.B, Goucher Col, 34; M.A, Univ. Ariz, 51; Ph.D.(Eng), Univ. Calif, Los Angeles, 62. Instr. Eng, UNIV. ARIZ, 51-60, lectr, 60-63, asst. prof, 63-65, assoc. prof, 65-70, PROF. FOLKLORE & LIT, 70- Consult. Ariz. maps, U.S. Govt. Serv, 59-; lectr. folklore in music, East. Music Camp, 63; Guilford Col, 64; dir, Nat. Place Name Surv, 69-; Nat. Endowment for Humanities grant, 69-73; ed, Ariz. Dictionary of Customs & Beliefs, 69-; ed, Current Trends in Onomastics in U.S. W.A.F. Serv. Pilots, 42-44; Commanding Off. Am. Name Soc.(v.pres, 72-73, pres, 73-); Int. Soc. Ethnol.

& Folklore; Folklore Soc, London, Am. Folklore Soc; Rocky Mountain Mod. Lang. Asn; Int. Soc. Folk Narrative Res. Onomastics; lore of cultural awareness; folklore in literature. Publ: Arizona place names, 60 & Grand Canyon place names, 61, Univ. Ariz; Folklore in Robert Burns' Tam O'Shanter, Folklore Int, 66; Witchcraft in the Southwest, West. N.Mex. Rev, 10/68; Lore in Edgar Allan Poe's The raven, Poe Newslett, winter 72. Add: Dept. of English, University of Arizona, Tucson, AZ 85721.

GRANT, J. PATRICK, b. Bangor, N.Ireland, May 12, 41; m. 64; c. 1. ENGLISH. B.A, Queen's Univ.(Belfast), 64; D.Phil.(Eng), Univ. Sussex, 66. Vis. asst. prof. ENG, Univ. Ill, Urbana, 66-68; ASST. PROF, UNIV. VICTORIA (B.C), 68- Metaphysical poetry; Renaissance Platonism. Publ: Synge in Riders to the sea, New Ireland, 66; Henry Vaughan and hermetic philosophy, J. Eng. & Ger. Philol, summer 68. Add: Dept. of English, University of Victoria, Victoria, B.C, Can.

GRANT, JASON CLIFTON, JR, b. Fredericksburg, Va, July 6, 93; m; c. 2. ENGLISH. A.B, Virginia Union Univ, 15; A.M, Univ. Chicago, 20. Prof. ENG, Wiley Col, 19-23; assoc. prof, HOWARD UNIV, 23-59, EMER. ASSOC. PROF, 59- MLA; Renaissance Soc. Am. Elizabethan critical conceptions of the poet; Elizabethan literary criticism. Add: 1637 Crittenden St. N.E, Washington, DC 20017.

GRANT, JOHN ERNEST, b. Newburyport, Mass, Aug. 28, 25; m. 74; c. 2. ENGLISH. A.B, Harvard, 51, fel. & A.M, 54, Ph.D.(Eng), 60. Instr. ENG, Univ. Conn, 56-61, asst. prof, 61-64, assoc. prof, 64-65; PROF, UNIV. IOWA, 65-, Old Gold fel, summer 66. Univ. Conn. Res. Found. fels, 63-65; Am. Counc. Learned Soc. fel, 68-69; Am. Philos. Soc. fel, 72; vis. prof. Eng, Univ. Alta, 68, 73. U.S.A, 43-45. MLA; AAUP; Midwest Mod. Lang. Asn. The poetry and painting of William Blake; the imagery of apocalypse; literary archetypes. Publ: Discussions of William Blake, Heath, 61; co-ed, Blake's Visionary forms dramatic, Princeton, 70; The revelation of the grand inquisitor, South. Rev, Australia, 67; Two flowers in the garden of experience, William Blake: Essays S. Foster Damon, 68; contrib, Vision in Vala, In: Blake's Sublime allegory, Univ. Wis, 73; plus others. Add: Dept. of English, University of Iowa, Iowa City, IA 52242.

GRANT, RAYMOND JAMES SHEPHERD, b. Aberdeen, Scotland, May 26, 42; m. 73. ANGLO-SAXON & ENGLISH LANGUAGE & LITERATURE. M.A, Univ. Aberdeen, 64; Ph.D.(Eng), Cambridge, 71. Asst. prof. ENG, UNIV. ALTA, 67-74, ASSOC. PROF, 74- Anglo-Saxon verse, homilies and texts transcribed in the 16th and 17th centuries. Publ: A note on The seasons for fasting, Rev. Eng. Stud, 72. Add: Dept. of English, University of Alberta, Edmonton, Alta. T6G 2E1, Can.

GRANT, THOMAS MARK, b. Los Angeles, Calif, Aug. 25, 39; m. 67; c. 3. RENAISSANCE & MODERN DRAMA. B.A, Gonzaga Univ, 61; NDEA fel, Rutgers Univ, 61-63, M.A, 63, Ph.D.(Eng), 71. Instr. ENG, Seattle Univ, 64-66; ASST. PROF, UNIV. HARTFORD, 69- MLA; AAUP. American theatre. Publ: The comedies of George Chapman: a study in development, Univ. Salzburg, 72. Add: Dept. of English, University of Hartford, West Hartford, CT 06117.

GRANT, WILLIAM A, b. Bisbee, Ariz, Aug. 30, 25. ENGLISH. B.A. & M.A, Long Beach State Col; Univ. York, 66-67. Dir. pub. relat, Univ. San Francisco, 47-48; Compton Col, 49-52, prof. Eng, 52-59; INSTR. LANG. & LIT, CABRILLO COL, 59-, chmn. dept, 59-69. Vis. lectr, St. John's Col, York, Eng, 66-67; Fulbright lectr, Sweden, 72-73. Ernest Hemingway; modern short story; Homer. Add: Dept. of English, Cabrillo College, Aptos, CA 95003.

GRANT, WILLIAM EARL, b. Hendersonville, N.C, Aug. 27, 33. AMERICAN LITERATURE & STUDIES. B.A, San Fernando Valley State Col, 61, M.A, 65; Ph.D.(Eng), Claremont Grad. Sch, 71. Instr. ENG, San Fernando Valley State Col, 66-68; ASST. PROF, Immaculate Heart Col, 68-71; UNIV. LOUISVILLE, 71- Ed, Twentieth Century Lit, 68-71, ed. consult, 71-; vis. lectr, Calif. State Univ, Los Angeles, 72. U.S.A.F, 51-55. S.Atlantic Mod. Lang. Asn; MLA; AAUP. American prose fiction; Afro-American literature, contemporary literature. Publ: Benjy's branch: symbolic method in part I of The sound and the fury, Tex. Stud. Lit. & Lang, winter 72; Daisy Miller: a study of a study, Stud. Short Fiction, winter 74. Add: Dept. of English, University of Louisville, Louisville, KY 40208.

GRANTZ, CARL L, b. Long Beach, Calif, Mar. 31, 25; m. 47; c. 4. ENGLISH LITERATURE. B.A, Centenary Col, 49; M.A, Columbia Univ, 52; Ph.D.(Eng), Univ. Tex, Austin, 68. Teacher, high sch, Ark, 49-50; La, 50-55; from instr. to assoc. prof. Eng, Northeast La. Univ, 55-69; PROF. ENG. & JOUR. & HEAD DEPT, PAN AM. UNIV, 69- U.S.A, 43-46. MLA; Col. Eng. Asn; NCTE. Early 19th century English literature. Add: Dept. of English & Journalism, Pan American University, Edinburg, TX 78539.

GRATZ, ROBERT DAVID, b. Bainbridge, Ga, Aug. 6, 44; m. 69; c. 1. SPEECH COMMUNICATION. B.S. Lamar Univ, 65; M.A, Bowling Green State Univ, 66, Ph.D.(speech), 69. Instr. SPEECH, Univ. Toledo, 67-69, asst. prof, SOUTHWEST TEX. STATE UNIV, 69-73, ASSOC. PROF. & CHMN. DEPT, 73- Speech Commun. Asn; Int. Commun. Asn; AAUP. Small group communication; speech education; attitude change. Publ: Problem-solving discussion training and T-group training: an experimental comparison, Speech Teacher, 1/70. Add: Dept. of Speech & Drama, Southwest Texas State University, San Marcos, TX 78666.

GRAUMAN, LAWRENCE, JR, b. Louisville, Ky, Nov. 8, 35; m. 62; c. 2. AMERICAN STUDIES, ENGLISH LITERATURE. Dipl. French lit, Univ. Montpellier, 56; M.A, Univ. Chicago, 63; N.Y. Univ, 64-66. Instr. Eng, Ill. Inst. Technol, 59-63; asst. prof. lit, Antioch Col, 66-67; Eng, Vassar Col, 67-69; ED-IN-CHIEF, ANTIOCH REV, 69- Danforth teaching fel, Antioch Col, 66-67; acting dean, Bard Col, 67-68; assoc. mem, Ctr. Stud. Democratic Insts, 68-, vis. fel. lit, Univ. Calif, Santa Cruz, 70; dir. lit. mag. proj, Twentieth Century Fund, 71-; chmn. lit. adv. bd, Ohio Arts Counc, 73- U.S.A, 54-55. American civilization; contemporary press; American literature. Publ: Ed, George Horace Lorimer's Letters of a self-made merchant to his son, Dutton, 70; Suggestions on the future of The confidence-man, Papers Lang. & Lit, summer 65; An unauthorized introduction to big steel, Antioch Rev, summer 72; plus others. Add: Office of the Editor, The Antioch Press, Yellow Springs, OH 45387.

GRAVELY, WILLIAM HENRY, JR, b. Martinsville, Va, Aug. 22, 03; m. 39; c. 3. ENGLISH. A.B, Col. William & Mary, 25; A.M, Univ. Va, 34, Ph.D, 53. Master Eng. & Greek, Norfolk Acad, Va, 26-30; instr. ENG, Univ. Va, 30-37; UNIV. MD, COLLEGE PARK, 37-44, asst. prof, 44-56, assoc. prof, 56-73, PROF, 73- MLA; Col. Eng. Asn. Nineteenth century American literature; Edgar Allan Poe and his contemporaries; Christopher North and the genesis of The Raven. Publ: Poe and Thomas Dunn English, In: Papers on Poe, Chantry Music Press, 72; New sources for Poe's Hans Pfaall, Tenn. Stud. Lit, 72. Add: Dept. of English, University of Maryland, College Park, MD 20740.

GRAVER, LAWRENCE, b. New York, N.Y, Dec. 6, 31; M. 60; c. 2. ENGLISH LITERATURE. B.A, City Col. New York, 54; M.A, Univ. Calif, Berkeley, 59; Ph.D, 61. Asst. prof. ENG, Univ. Calif, Los Angeles, 61-64; WILLIAMS COL, 64-67, assoc. prof, 67-71, PROF, 72- Bk. reviewer, N.Y. Times Bk. Rev, The New Republic & Saturday Rev. U.S.A, 54-56. MLA. The novel; 19th and 20th century English literature. Publ: Conrad's short fiction, Univ. Calif, 68; Carson McCullers, Univ. Minn, 69. Add: Dept. of English, Williams College, Williamstown, MA 01267.

GRAVES, A. WALLACE, b. Seattle, Wash, Sept. 21, 22; m. 44; c. 1. RHETORIC. B.A, Univ. Wash, 44, M.A, 52, Ph.D, 54. Instr. ENG, Lower Columbia Jr. Col, 55-57; Venetokleion Gymnasium, Rhodes, Greece, 57-59; assoc. prof, CALIF. STATE UNIV, NORTHRIDGE, 59-67, PROF, 67- Fulbright teaching grant, Greece, 57, 58; vis. lectr. Am. lit, Univ. Sri Lanka, 72-73. U.S.N.R, 43-45, Lt.(jg). Abstruse contemporary short fiction; creative writing. Publ: Trixie, Knopf, 69, Andre Deutsch, London, 70, Droste Verlag, Dusseldorf, 71, Dell, N.Y, 71 & Penguin, London, 73; co-auth, From word to story, Harcourt, 72; auth, An interview with Harrison Byrd, Kenyon Rev, 11/66; Mark Twain's Burning shame, 19th Century Fiction, summer 68; Plutarch's Cato utican as a major source for Othello, Shakespeare Quart, spring 74. Add: Dept. of English, California State University, Northridge, Northridge, CA 91324.

GRAVES, R. DORSET, b. Houston, Tex, Oct. 22, 24; m. 51; c. 2. ENGLISH. A.B, Grinnell Col, 50; A.M, Duke Univ, 54, Ph.D.(Melville), 66. Instr. Eng, Idaho State Univ, 53-55; assoc. prof, CHADRON STATE COL, 58-61, PROF. ENG. & CHMN. DIV. LANG. & LIT, 61- U.S.N.R, 43-46. MLA; Col. Eng. Asn; NCTE. Herman Melville, William Blake; Wallace Stevens. Add: Box 977, Chadron, NE 69337.

GRAY, ALFRED ORREN, b. Sun Prairie, Wis, Sept. 8, 14; m. 47; c. 2. JOURNALISM. B.A, Univ. Wis, 39, M.A, 41. Asst. prof. JOUR, WHITWORTH COL, 46-48, assoc. prof, 48-56, PROF, 56-, CHMN. DEPT. & PUBL. ADV, 46-, chmn. div. bus. & commun. arts, 58-66. Ed, The Synod story, Wash. Synod, Presbyterian Church, 51-52; dir, Inland Empire Publ, Clinic, 59- Spec. Recognition Award excellence in teaching jour, Whitworth Col. Alumni Asn, 72. Ord.C, U.S.A, 42-46; Bronze Star Medal. AAUP; Asn. Asn. Educ. in Jour; Nat. Counc. Col. Publ. Adv.(Citation of Commendation, 67, mem. nat. comt. freedom of student press, 67-68); World Future Soc. Communications history, 1765-1783; religious communications; educational history. Publ: Auth. & ed, History of ordnance service in the European Theater of Operations, U.S. Ord. Dept, 46; auth, Not by might, Whitworth Col, 65; It matters how you say it, Christian Educ, 4-6/59; contrib, Public understanding of education as a field of study, Proj. Pub. Inform, 68; Microform complex, Whitworth Col. Today, 5/71; plus others. Add: Dept. of Journalism, Whitworth College, Spokane, WA 99251.

GRAY, CHARLES FARRELL, b. Rome, Ga, Jan. 27, 31; m. 63; c. 3. ENGLISH. B.A, Emory Univ, 51, M.L.S, 52; M.A, Univ. Fla, 58, Ph.D.(Eng), 66. Instr. & asst. librn, Univ. Ga, 54-56; asst. prof. libr, Univ. Fla, 58-62, instr. ENG, 62-63; asst. prof, Jacksonville Univ, 63-66; West. Carolina Univ, 66-68; ASSOC. PROF, Pfeiffer Col, 68-69; WINSTON-SALEM STATE UNIV, 69- U.S.A, 53-54. MLA; S.Atlantic Mod. Lang. Asn. American literature; contemporary literature; modern poetry. Add: 2831 Lansdowne Dr, Winston-Salem, NC 27103.

GRAY, DONALD, b. Waukegan, Ill, Sept. 21, 27; m. 54; c. 2. ENGLISH LITERATURE. Ph.B, Loyola Univ.(Ill), 50; M.A, Univ. Minn, 51; Ph.D, Ohio State Univ, 56. Instr. ENG, IND. UNIV, BLOOMINGTON, 56-59, asst. prof, 59-63, assoc. prof, 63-68, PROF, 68-, chmn. dept, 68-73. U.S.A.A.F, 46-47. MLA; NCTE. Nineteenth century British literature; literary theory. Publ: Ed, Alice in wonderland, Norton, 72; auth, Humor as poetry in 19th century British criticism, J. Eng. & Ger. Philol, 62; The uses of Victorian laughter, Victorian Stud, 67. Add: Dept. of English, Elisha Ballantine Hall, Indiana University, Bloomington, IN 47401.

GRAY, ERNEST WESTON, b. Scituate, Mass, Dec. 19, 02; m. 26; c. 1. ENGLISH. Ph.B, Brown Univ, 24, A.M, 26, Ph.D, Harvard, 31. Instr. ENG, Brown Univ, 25-28; from asst. prof. to prof, Norfolk Div, Col. William & Mary, 31-47; PROF, UNIV. TOLEDO, 47-70; chmn. dept, 49-60, dir. honors prog, 65-70, EMER. PROF, 70- Current English language; 18th century novel; Victorian literature. Publ: A brief grammar of modern written English, World Publ, 67. Add: 111 Maple St, Attleboro, MA 02703.

GRAY, JACK COOPER, b. Salt Lake City, Utah, Apr. 19, 28; m. 53; c. 2. ENGLISH LITERATURE. B.A, Wash. State Univ, 51; M.A, Univ. Conn, 53; Ph.D.(Eng), Syracuse Univ, 64. Instr, Univ. Conn, 51-53; lectr, Syracuse Univ, 53-57; instr. ENG, Flint Community Jr. Col, 57-60; asst. prof, North. Ill. Univ, 60-66; PROF, UNIV. WATERLOO, 66- MLA; Can. Counc. Teachers Eng; Milton Soc. Am; Asn. Can. Univ. Teachers Eng. Poetry of English Renaissance, especially Edmund Spenser. Publ: Words, words and words about dictionaries, Chandler, 63; co-ed, A book of the sonnet, Twayne, 73; auth, Romeo and Juliet and some Renaissance notions of time, love and death, spring 68 & Emptiness and fulfillment as structural pattern in Paradise lost, spring 73, Dalhousie Rev; Paradox in Paradise lost, Milton Quart, 10/73. Add: Dept. of English, University of Waterloo, Waterloo, Ont. N2L 3G1, Can.

GRAY, JAMES, b. Montrose, Scotland, May 11, 23; m. 47; c. 1. ENGLISH LANGUAGE & LITERATURE. M.A, Univ. Aberdeen, Scotland, 43; B.A, Oxford, 48, M.A, 51; Ph.D.(Eng), Univ. Montreal, 70. Prof. Eng. Bishop's Univ.(Can), 48-72, chmn. grad. stud. & mem. senate, 66-72, mem. corp, 67-72, chmn. humanities div, 71-72; PROF. ENG. & CHMN. DEPT, DALHOUSIE UNIV, 72- Mem, Humanities Res. Counc. Can, 62-, rep, Int. Acad. Union's Gen. Assembly, Bucharest, 68; Can. Counc. leave fel, 70-71; mem. senate & fac. counc, Dalhousie Univ. Brit. Army, 43-46, Maj. Humanities Asn. Can.(secy-treas, 54-56, v.pres, 56-58, pres, 58-60); fel. Royal Soc. Arts; Int. Asn. Univ. Prof. Eng; Can. Asn. Chmn. Depts. Eng.(secy-treas, 71-). Eighteenth century literature and theatre; literary criticism. Publ: Johnson's sermons: a study, Clarendon, 72; Dr. Johnson and the King of Ashbourne, Univ. Toronto Quart: Boswell's brother confessor; William Johnston Temple, Tenn. Stud. 61. Add: Dept. of English, Dalhousie University, Halifax, N.S, Can.

GRAY, JAMES L, b. Llano, Tex, Jan. 1, 40; m. 60; c. 2. ENGLISH. B.A, Abilene Christian Col, 61; M.A, Univ. Tex, 64; Ph.D, Duke Univ, 71. Scholar, Duke Univ, 64-66; assoc. prof. ENG, Slippery Rock State Col, 66-68; IND. UNIV. PA, 68-72, PROF, 72- Am. Stud. Asn; MLA; NCTE. American literature; Commonwealth literature; Western Americana. Add: Dept. of English, Indiana University of Pennsylvania, Indiana, PA 15701.

GRAY, JAMES MARTIN, b. Harrow, Middlesex, Eng, Nov. 30, 30; Can. citizen; m. 61; c. 2. ENGLISH. M.A, Univ. Edinburgh, 52, Ph.D.(Eng), 61. Lectr. Eng, McMaster Univ, 62-64, asst. prof, 64-67; VIS. ASST. PROF, Eng, Univ. Sask, 73-74. Can. Counc. res. grants, 67, 68-70. Int. Arthurian Soc; Victorian Soc; Tennyson Soc. The Arthurian Legend; poetic mythopoeia; romantic and Victorian poetry, especially Tennyson. Publ: Tennyson's Doppelgänger: Balin and Balan, Tennyson Soc, Eng, 71; A study in idyl: Tennyson's The coming of Arthur, Renaissance & Mod. Stud, 10/70. Add: 36 St. Mary's Rd, Bingham, Nottingham NG13 8DW, England.

GRAY, JOHN H, S.J, b. Calif, Jan. 27, 24. ENGLISH LITERATURE. B.A, Gonzaga Univ, 48; M.A, Loyola Univ. Los Angeles, 52; S.T.L, St. Albert's Col, Louvian, Belgium, 56; Ph.D, Univ. London, 61. Instr. ENG, UNIV. SANTA CLARA, 49-51, asst. prof, 61-67, ASSOC. PROF, 67-, DEAN, COL. HUMANITIES, 68- MLA; Renaissance Soc. Am; Shakespeare Asn. Am. Shakespeare; Renaissance drama; modern poetry. Add: College of Humanities, University of Santa Clara, Santa Clara, CA 95053.

GRAY, PAUL H, b. Castine, Maine, Mar. 29, 37; m. 60; c. 1. SPEECH. A.B, Marietta Col, 59; M.A, Univ. Ill, 60, Ph.D.(speech), La. State Univ, 66. Instr. SPEECH, Monmouth Col, 60-63; asst. prof, Marietta Col, 66-68, assoc. prof, 68-71; asst. prof, UNIV. TEX, AUSTIN, 71-74, ASSOC. PROF, 74- Speech Commun. Asn; South. Speech Commun. Asn. Add: Dept. of Speech Communication, CMA 7-114, University of Texas at Austin, Austin, TX 78712.

GRAY, PHILIP ALAN, b. Defiance, Ohio, May 10, 36; m. 59; c. 4. SPEECH COMMUNICATION. B.A, Ohio North. Univ, 58; M.A, Ohio State Univ, 62, Ph.D.(speech commun), 66. Teacher speech & Eng, Ohio Pub. Schs, 58-62; instr. SPEECH, Ohio State Univ, 64-66; ASST. PROF, NORTH. ILL. UNIV, 67- Consult, Ill. Div. Voc. Rehab, 66-68; Oak Electro/netics Corp, 69-70; Ill. Off. Pub. Instr. 69-71; Price Waterhouse Corp, 70-72. Speech Commun. Asn; Cent. States Speech Commun. Asn; AAUP. Small group communications; undergraduate education. Publ: The effects of assigned role versus non-assigned role on group consensus, Speech J, 72. Add: Dept. of Speech Communication, Northern Illinois University, DeKalb, IL 60115.

GRAY, PHILIP HAYWARD, b. Detroit, Mich, Apr. 6, 06; m. 30; c. 6. ENGLISH, HUMANITIES. B.A, Yale, 28, Ph.D.(Eng), 36. Instr. Eng. lit, Yale, 29-30; from instr. to asst. prof, Univ. Wis, 36-44; humanities, Univ. Chicago 48-51; from asst. prof. to prof. ENG, SCRIPPS COL, 52-70, Frederick Hard Prof, 70-71, EMER. PROF, 71- MLA; Philol. Asn. Pac. Coast; NCTE. Literary criticism; Shakespeare; modern British and American fiction and drama. Publ: Collab, Shakespeare and modern drama; auth, Four American novels and a myth, winter 57 & Christian tragedy and Shakespeare, summer 62, Claremont Quart. Add: Woodbourne Orchards, Dimock, PA 18816.

GRAY, VIRGINIA POMROY, b. Nitro, W.Va, Oct. 3, 28; m. 63. THEATRE. B.A, W.Va, Univ, 52, fel, 53, M.A, 55; Ph.D.(speech, theatre), Bowling Green State Univ, 73. Teacher, Blackhill Sch, Elizabeth, W.Va, 47-48; Wirt County High Sch, Eliza, W.Va, 52-53; Ocala High Sch, Fla, 54-55; North Miami Sr. High Sch, Fla, 55-59; asst. prof. SPEECH & DRAMA, Morris Harvey Col, 59-71, head dept, 62-71; CHMN. DEPT, W.VA. STATE COL, 71- Auth, dir. & producer, From the Fires of the Diamond, Morris Harvey Col. Add: Dept. of Speech & Drama, West Virginia State College, Institute, WV 25112.

GRAY, WILLIAM SHELTON, b. Shreveport, La, Sept. 11, 26. ENGLISH. B.A, Centenary Col, 50; M.A, La. State Univ, 60; Ph.D.(Eng), Univ. Exeter, 64. Asst. prof. ENG, Olivet Col, 64-66; chmn. dept, Augsburg Col, 66-68; PROF. & CHMN. DEPT, RANDOLPH-MACON COL, 68- MLA; Eng-Speaking Union; Mediaeval Acad. Am. T.S. Eliot; Tennessee Williams. Add: Dept. of English, Randolph-Macon College, Ashland, VA 23005.

GRAY, YOHMA, b. Jamestown, N.Y, July 15, 35. ENGLISH, AMERICAN LITERATURE. Univ. N.Y. State Regents & Maude Grant Kent scholars, Syracuse Univ, 53-57, A.B, 57; univ, Coe, Coe-Kilborn, Boies & Arnold Hazzard fels, Yale, 57-67, A.M, 58, Ph.D.(Am. stud), 67. Instr. ENG, Northwest. Univ, 60-63; Nat. Col. Educ, 63-64; asst. prof, MUNDELEIN COL, 64-69, assoc. prof, 69-74, PROF, 74- Nat. Endowment for Humanities summer sem. participant, 73. MLA; Am. Stud. Asn; NCTE; Col. Eng. Asn. Negro American literature; modern American and British literature. Publ: An American metaphor: the novels of Richard Wright, Univ. Microfilms, 68; The poetry of Louis Simpson, Northwest. Tri-Quart, spring 63 & In: Poets in progress, Northwest. Univ, 67. Add: 1020 Grove St, Evanston, IL 60201.

GRAYSON, JANET, b. Boston, Mass, June 4, 34; m. 58; c. 3. ENGLISH. B.A, Brooklyn Col, 58, M.A, 62; Ph.D.(Eng), Columbia Univ, 68. Lectr. ENG, Brooklyn Col, 63-66; asst. prof, KEENE STATE COL, 66-72, ASSOC. PROF, 72- Mediaeval Acad. Am; Int. Arthurian Soc. English and European medi-

eval literature; Elizabethan literature; classical civilization. Publ: Structure and imagery in Ancrene Wisse, Univ. New Eng, 74. Add: Jackson Hill Rd, Chesterfield, NH 03443.

GRAYSON, NANCY JANE, b. Abilene, Tex, Feb. 10, 34. COMPARATIVE LITERATURE. B.A, Tex. Christian Univ, 56; M.A, Univ. Tex, Austin, 58, Ph.D.(Eng), 68. Instr. Eng, Tex. Christian Univ, 60-61; teaching asst, Univ. Tex. Austin, 61-66, teaching assoc, 66-68; asst. prof, SOUTHWEST. TEX. STATE UNIV, 68-72, ASSOC. PROF. ENG, 72-, DIR. FRESHMAN ENG, 73- AAUP; Col. Conf. Teachers Eng; S.Cent. Mod. Lang. Asn; NCTE; Col. Conf. Compos. & Commun. European novel; structuralism; comparative religion. Add: Dept. of English & Philosophy, Southwest Texas State University, San Marcos, TX 78666.

GRAZIANI, RENÉ, b. Ger, 31; m. 58; c. 3. ENGLISH. B.A, Univ. Leeds, 51, M.A, 52; Ph.D.(Eng), Univ. Manchester, 62. Lectr. ENG, UNIV. TORONTO, 60-64, asst. prof, 64-68, ASSOC. PROF, 68- Huntington Libr. summer fel, 66; Can. Counc. grant, 66-67. Spenser and English 16th century poetry; renaissance iconography. Publ: Elizabeth at Isis Church, PMLA, 64; The rainbow portrait of Queen Elizabeth and its religious symbolism, J. Warb. & Court Inst, 72; Brueghel's Dulle Griet and Dante, Burlington Mag, 73; plus others. Add: Dept. of English, University College, University of Toronto, Toronto, Ont. M5S 1A1, Can.

GREANEY, KATHERINE B, b. Waterville, Maine. ENGLISH. A.B, Colby Col, 28; M.A, George Washington Univ, 37; Temple Univ, Breadloaf Sch. Eng, Univ. Md, Am. Univ. & Cath. Univ. Am, 39-64. Teacher pub. schs, Maine, 29-36; high sch, Md, 37-55; gen. supvr, Montgomery County Sec. Schs, 55-62; supvr. Eng. K-12, Montgomery County, Md, 63-74; RETIRED. U.S.A-Brit. exchange teacher, Eng, 46-47; producer, Montgomery County, Md. Eng. curriculum bull. lit. & compos, 55-68; adv, Md. Counc. Teachers Eng. & Md. Eng. J, 62-; teacher-lectr, NDEA Inst, Univ. Md, summer 65, guest lectr, summer 67. NCTE. Publ: Reducing the English teachers burden. Md. Eng. J, 64; Discussion of book and film excerpts on Scott O'Dell's Island of the blue dolphins, Elem. Eng, 5/67. Add: 4720 Chevy Chase Dr, Chevy Chase, MD 20015.

GREASON, ARTHUR LeROY, JR, b. Newport, R.I, Sept. 13, 22; m. 45; c. 3. ENGLISH. B.A, Wesleyan Univ, 45; M.A, Harvard, 47, Ph.D.(Eng), 54. Asst. to dean, Wesleyan Univ, 45-46; teaching fel, Harvard, 48-52; instr. Eng, BOWDOIN COL, 52-54, asst. prof, 54-62, assoc. prof, Eng. & dean stud, 62-66, PROF. ENG. & DEAN COL, 66- Eighteenth century English literature. Add: 256 Maine St, Brunswick, ME 04011.

GREATHOUSE, GLADYS M, b. Salyersville, Ky, May 22, 00; m. 20; c. 2. DRAMA, SPEECH. A.B, Asbury Col, 32; Haggin fel, Univ. Ky, 42-43, M.Ed, 43; summers, Univ. Wis, 50, 54-56, 58, 60, 65. Teacher, High Sch, Ky, 32-42; critic teacher, Univ. Ky, 44-46; instr. SPEECH & DRAMA, Asbury Col, 46-47, prof. & chmn. dept, 47-60; prof, TAYLOR UNIV, 60-70, chmn. dept, 64-70, EMER. PROF, 70- Prof, exten, Ind. Univ, 60; summer vis. prof, Univ. Mass, 68; vis. prof. drama & speech, Wheaton Col, 73. Am. Theatre Asn; Speech Commun. Asn; AAUP; Am. Asn. Univ. Women. Drama; interpretation; speech education. Add: Dept. of Speech & Drama, Taylor University, Upland, IN 46989.

GREAVES, HALBERT SPENCER, b. Ephraim, Utah, Oct. 19, 07; m. 38; c. 2. SPEECH. A.B, Univ. Utah, 29; M.S, Northwest, Univ, 32; Univ. Berlin, 36; Ph.D, Univ. Wis, 41. Instr. SPEECH, Purdue Univ, 36; asst. prof, Utah State Agr. Col, 36-46; from assoc. prof. to PROF, UNIV. UTAH, 46-, head dept, 61-69. Mountain States Tel. Co. summer fel, 61; chmn. nat. finals, Am. Legion Oratorical Contest, 62; instr. U.S. Naval Postgrad. Sch, summers, 62-64. U.S.N.R, 43-45, Lt. Comdr. Speech Commun. Asn; West. Speech Commun. Asn.(2nd v.pres, 61, 1st v.pres, 64, pres, 65); South. Speech Commun. Asn. Public address; speech education; American history. Publ: Credo for mid-century—toward a course in fundamentals of speech, Quart. J. Speech, 4/50; co-auth, National speech organizations, In: History of speech education in America, Appleton, 54; auth, Persuasion in a theocracy, In: Landmarks in western oratory, Univ. Wyo, 68; plus others. Add: Dept. of Communication, Speech Communication Bldg, University of Utah, Salt Lake City, UT 84112.

GREB, GORDON BARRY, b. Irvington, Calif, Aug. 7, 21; m. 50; c. 2. COMMUNICATION, HISTORY. A.B, Univ. Calif, Berkeley, 47; M.A, Univ, Minn, Minneapolis, 51; Stanford Univ. 51-64; Univ. South. Calif, summer 51. Instr. Eng, San Bernardino Valley Col, 49-50; Jour, Univ. Ore, 50-51; dir. news dept, Radio Station KSJO, San Jose, Calif, 54-57; PROF. MASS COMMUN, SAN JOSE STATE UNIV, 56- Ed. CBS news, Radio Station KNX, Hollywood, Calif, summer 51; consult, NBC, 64, 66; mem. bd. dir, Perham Found, 64-68; vis. prof. mass commun, Univ. Wis-Madison, summers 68-70. U.S.A, 43-46, Sgt. Asn. Educ. in Jour.(res. chmn. Radio-TV Div. 48-); Radio-TV News Dir. Asn; Asn. Prof. Broadcasting Educ. International communication; history of mass communications and public opinion measurement. Publ: Ed, Contemporary issues in American society, Spartan, 67 & KCBS: broadcasting's first station, San Jose State Found, 73; auth, The place of journalism in junior college, Jour. Quart, 54; The golden anniversary of broadcasting, 59 & co-auth, Directory of scholarships for students of broadcasting, 62, J. Broadcasting. Add: Dept. of Journalism, San Jose State University, San Jose, CA 95192.

GREBANIER, BERNARD, b. New York, N.Y, Mar. 8, 03. ENGLISH. A.B, City Col. New York, 26; A.M, N.Y. Univ, 30, Ph.D, 35. Tutor ENG, City Col. New York, 26-30; instr, BROOKLYN COL, 30-35, asst. prof, 36-47, assoc. prof, 48-54, prof, 54-64, EMER. PROF, 64- Lectr. Shakespeare & Greek tragedies in Eng, Sch. Continuing Educ, Hofstra Univ, 71- Composers, Auth. & Artists Am.(nat. v.pres, 73-); Poetry Soc. Am; PEN Club; Auth. League Am. English and continental comparative literature; English literature and its backgrounds. Publ: Heart of Hamlet, 60 & Playwriting, 61, Crowell; Truth about Shylock, Random, 62; Thornton Wilder, Univ. Minn, 63; The great Shakespeare forgery, Norton, 65, Heinemann, 66; Armenian miniatures, Mechitarist, Venice, 67; Life begins tomorrow, Story, 52; The uninhibited Byron: an account of his sexual confusion, Crown, 70, Owen, 71; Edward Arlington Robinson, Poetry Soc. Am, 71; ed, Pegasus in the sixties, McClure, 73; auth, The cloak and I, Gentleman's Quart, 63; Shakespeare, Tex. Quart, 65. Add: 215 W. 88th St, New York, NY 10024.

GREBSTEIN, SHELDON NORMAN, b. Providence, R.I, Feb. 1, 28; m. 53; c. 2. MODERN & AMERICAN LITERATURE. B.A, Univ. South.Calif, 49; M.A, Columbia Univ, 50; fel, Mich. State Univ, 52-53, Ph.D.(Eng), 54. From instr. to asst. prof. ENG, Univ, Ky, 53-62; asst. prof, Univ. S.Fla, 62-63; assoc. prof, STATE UNIV. N.Y. BINGHAMTON, 63-68, PROF, 68-, dir. grad. Eng. stud, 66-72. Fulbright-Hays lectr, Univ. Rouen, France, 68-69. MLA; Northeast Mod. Lang. Asn; AAUP; Col. Eng. Asn. American and contemporary literature; literary criticism; modern American fiction. Publ: Ed, Monkey trial, Houghton, 60; auth, Sinclair Lewis, 62 & John O'Hara, 66, Twayne; ed, Perspectives in contemporary criticism, Harper, 68; ed, Studies in For whom the bell tolls, Merrill, 71; auth, Hemingway's craft, South. Ill. Univ, 73. Add: Dept. of English, State University of New York at Binghamton, Binghamton, NY 13901.

GREEN, BOB REX, b. Nebr, Apr. 4, 19; m. 49; c. 2. ENGLISH LITERATURE. A.B, Seattle Pac. Col, 51; Phillips Univ, 56-57; M.A, Kans. State Teachers Col, 60. Instr. Eng, Caldwell Pub. Schs, Kans, 57-60; prof, Cent. Col. (Kans), 60-63, dean, 63-67; from asst. prof. to ASSOC. PROF. ENG, McPHERSON COL, 67- Add: 803 Cottonwood, McPherson, KS 67460.

GREEN, CHARLES PRICE, b. Mutual, Okla, May 7, 97. SPEECH. A.B, Univ. Okla, 25; A.M, Univ. Mich, 28; Ph.D, Northwest. Univ. Actor & reader, Travers-Newton Chatauqua, 23-24; teacher, High Sch, Okla, 25-27; instr, West. Reserve Univ, 28-34; mem. fac, UNIV. OKLA, 34-39; chmn. dept, 34-44, 45-56, prof. SPEECH, 39-64, regents prof, 64-67, EMER. REGENTS PROF, 67- Actor, Cleveland Play House, 30-34; vis. scholar, Cameron State Col, 68-69. Speech Commun. Asn; Cent. St. Speech Asn.(past pres), Interpretative speech; concepts of rhetorical delivery; speech education. Publ: Lariat laughter (poems), Mitre, London, 70. Add: 809 College, Norman, OK 73069.

GREEN, CLAUD BETHUNE, b. Clayton, Ga, Oct. 23, 14. ENGLISH. A.B, Univ. Ga, 35, A.M, 38; Gen. Educ. Bd. fel, Yale, 46-47; Ph.D, Duke Univ, 53. Teaching fel, Univ. Ga, 37-40; instr. ENG, CLEMSON UNIV, 40-43, asst. prof, 43-48, assoc. prof, 48-53, PROF, 53-, DEAN UNDERGRAD. STUD, 70-, dir. summer sessions, 62-68, asst. dean univ, 68-70. Fulbright lectr, Univs. Sydney & Adelaide, Australia, 56. MLA; Southeast. Am. Stud. Asn.(pres, 68-70); S.Atlantic Mod. Lang. Asn. American literature of the 19th century; Southern American literature. Publ: John Trotwood Moore: a Tennessee man of letters, Univ. Ga, 57. Add: Clemson University, Clemson, SC 29631.

GREEN, DONALD CHARLES, b. Fargo, N.Dak, Jan. 4, 37. ENGLISH, LINGUISTICS. B.A, Carleton Col, 58; M.A, Miami Univ, 60; Ph.D.(Eng), Univ. Wis, Madison, 67. Instr. ENG, Univ. Chicago, 64-66, asst. prof, 66-71; ASSOC. PROF, CALIF. STATE COL, BAKERSFIELD, 71- MLA; Ling. Soc. Am. English literature—Old English, Chaucer. Publ: Formulas and syntax in Old English poetry, Comput. & Humanities, 11/71. Add: Dept. of English, California State College, Bakersfield, 9001 Stockdale Highway, Bakersfield, CA 93309.

GREEN, ELIZABETH ALDEN, b. Morgantown, W.Va, Dec. 11, 08. JOURNALISM, CONTEMPORARY LITERATURE. A.B, Mt. Holyoke Col, 31; A.M, Bryn Mawr Col, 32; Harvard, 34; Rutgers Univ; Oxford, 47. Teacher, High Sch, N.J, 32-37; Emma Willard Sch, Troy, N.Y, 37-41; instr. ENG, Packer Col. Inst, 41-42; from instr. to asst. prof, MT. HOLYOKE COL, 42-70, assoc. prof, 70-73, PROF, 73-, dir. news bur, 42-67. Contemporary journalism; modern poetry; Wallace Stevens. Publ: What to read before college, Case West. Reserve Univ, 70; The urbanity of Stevens, Saturday Rev. Add: Dept. of English, Mt. Holyoke College, South Hadley, MA 01075.

GREEN, ELVENA MARION, b. Los Angeles, Calif, Aug. 28, 30. DRAMATIC ART. B.A, Mills Col, 53; M.A, Cornell Univ, 53; Univ. Calif, Los Angeles, 56-57; Ph.D.(dramatic art), Univ. Iowa, 71. Instr. speech & Eng, Monterey Peninsula Col, 57-59; asst. prof. SPEECH & DRAMA, AGNES SCOTT COL, 59-72, ASSOC. PROF, 73- Am. Theatre Asn; South. Speech Asn. American theatre history; dramatic theory and criticism. Publ: John Rich's art of pantomime as seen in his The necromancer, Restoration & Eighteenth Century Res, 5/65; Three aspects of Richard Steele's theory of comedy, Educ. Theatre J, 5/68; Plato's use of three dramatic elements in Gorgias as means to demonstrate his thought, South. Speech J, summer 68. Add: Dept. of Speech & Drama, Agnes Scott College, Decatur, GA 30030.

GREEN, EUGENE. ENGLISH LINGUISTICS. B.A, Ohio State Univ, 53, M.A, 57; Ph.D.(Eng. lang), Univ. Mich, 62. Asst. prof. Eng, San Diego State Col, 61-64; res. asst. ling, Columbia Univ, 64-66; asst. prof. ENG, BOSTON UNIV, 66-71, ASSOC. PROF, 71- Consult, Multilingual Aphasia Exam. Proj, 67- U.S.A, 63-65. Ling. Circle N.Y; NCTE; Am. Name Soc. Place-names aphasia; dialectology. Publ: Accentual variations in the Slavic component of Yiddish Field of Yiddish III, 68; Phonological and grammatical aspects of aphasic jargon: a case study, Lang. & Speech, 6/69; Psycholinguistic approaches to aphasia, Linguistics. Add: Dept. of English, Boston University, Charles River Campus, Boston, MA 02215.

GREEN, HOWARD LEWIS, b. London, Eng, Dec. 16, 20; nat; m. 46; c. 1. ENGLISH. A.B, Stanford Univ, 41, A.M, 42, Ph.D.(Eng), 52. Acting instr. ENG, Stanford Univ, 46-47, 50-51; instr, VASSAR COL, 51-54, asst. prof, 54-58, ASSOC. PROF, 58- U.S.A.A.F, 42-45. Modern literature. Publ: Isak Dinesen, Hudson Rev, winter 66. Add: Dept. of English, Vassar College, Poughkeepsie, NY 12601.

GREEN, JAMES LEE, b. Baldwin, Kans, Oct. 16, 37; m. 58; c. 3. ENGLISH. A.B, Univ. Kans, 59, M.A, 61; Ph.D, Univ. Nev, Reno, 71. Instr. ENG, ARIZ. STATE UNIV, 67-68, ASST. PROF, 68- Res. ed, Am. Lit. Abstr. Conf. Col. Compos. & Commun; MLA; NCTE. Contemporary English literature; American literature; rhetoric. Publ: Articles in Mod. Fiction, Critique & Eng. J. Add: Dept. of English, Arizona State University, Tempe, AZ 85281.

GREEN, JOHN HURLBUT, b. Meeker, Okla, May 20, 15; m. 39; c. 2. DRAMA. B.A, Okla. Cent. State Col, 37; M.A, Northwest. Univ, 41; Ph.D, Univ. Denver, 54. Instr. speech & drama, Okla. Cent. State Col, 37-40; asst. stage lighting, Northwest. Univ, 40-41; instr. speech & drama, Wilson City Col, 41-43; asst. prof, Okla. State Univ, 46-51, assoc. prof, 51-55; CALIF. STATE UNIV, LONG BEACH, 55-57, chmn. dept, 57-60, PROF. THEATRE ARTS, 60-, chmn. dept. drama, 61-65. Auditorium bldg. consult, for Land-Grant Cols, Okla, 49-55. U.S.N.R, 43-46, Lt. Am. Theatre Asn; U.S. Inst. Theatre Technol. Development of stage rigging in the United States; criteria for theatre building specifications. Add: Dept. of Theatre Arts, California State University, Long Beach, Long Beach, CA 90801.

GREEN, JOHN M, b. Youngstown, Ohio, Sept. 22, 28; m. 53; c. 5. ENGLISH. A.B, Univ. Notre Dame, 52, M.A, 54; Univ. Pa, 56-60. Instr. ENG, VILLANOVA UNIV, 55-59, ASST. PROF, 60- U.S.M.C, 46-47. Victorian literature. Add: Dept. of English, Villanova University, Villanova, PA 19085.

GREEN, JOSEPH G, b. Philadelphia, Pa, June 24, 34; m. 56; c. 2. THEATRE. B.A, Temple Univ, 56; M.A, Ind. Univ, Bloomington, 59, Ph.D, 64. Mgr, Louisville Little Theatre, 59-60; asst. prof. & dir. theatre, Ind. Univ, South Bend, 61-65; asst. prof. theatre & theatre coord, Hunter Col, 65-68; asst. dean fine arts & dir. theatre, YORK UNIV, 68-71, assoc. dean fine arts, 71-73, PROF. THEATRE & DEAN FINE ARTS, 73- Vis. asst. prof. theatre, Teachers Col, Columbia Univ, 67; radio critic, CBC, summer 70; lectr, Stratford Shakespeare Sem, summer 71. Int. Counc. Fine Arts Deans; Can. Theatre Ctr; Can. Asn. Univ. Teachers; Am. Theatre Asn. Publ: Co-auth. & gen. ed, About theatre, Scott, 74; contrib, Quart. J. Speech, South. Speech J, Educ. Theatre J. & Performing Arts in Can. Mag. Add: Dean's Office, Dept. of Fine Arts, York University, 4700 Keele St, Downsview, Ont. M3J 1P3, Can.

GREEN, LOLA BETH, b. Brownwood, Tex, Nov. 8, 09. ENGLISH. B.A, Tex. Tech. Col, 35, M.A, 42; State Delta Kappa Gamma fels, Univ. Tex, 51-52, 52-53, Ph.D, 55. Teacher, Elem. Schs, Tex, 35-37; Jr. High Sch, 37-38; Pub. Schs, 38-43; v.prin. & prin, High Sch, 43-46; instr. ENG, TEX. TECH UNIV, 46-55, asst. prof, 55-59; ASSOC. PROF, 59-, ADV. TEACHER CERTIFICATION, 62-, col. res. grant advan. grammar, summer 63. Consult. & mem. vis. team, Tex. Educ. Agency, 62; curriculum adv, N.J. Dept. Educ, 68-74; consult. high sch. curriculum, South. Am. Schs. & Cols. NCTE; Am. Name Soc; Int. Soc. Gen. Semantics. Southwestern literature; linguistics; American poetry, especially Emily Dickinson. Publ: Co-auth, A manual of technical writing, Rogers Lytho, 57 & Technical writing, Houghton, 61; co-auth, Annotated bibliography. Bold land, Tex. Tech Univ, 70; co-auth, Sunny land in the Southwest: a look at place names, 71 & auth, Names in the Bible Belt: a study from Faulkner's Go down Moses, 72, Tex. Name Soc. Yearbk; Two years: so little time so much to read, Proc. Col. Conf. Eng. Teachers; 62; Graduate scholarship and the teacher (8 articles), Lone Star News, 64-66. Add: 3816 38th St, Lubbock, TX 79413.

GREEN, RICHARD HAMILTON, b. Phoenix, Ariz, Dec. 30, 16; m. 47; c. 6. ENGLISH, MEDIEVAL LATIN LITERATURE. A.B, St. Louis Univ, 39, Ph.Lic, 41, A.M, 42; Ph.D.(Eng), Univ. Calif, 50. Instr. ENG, Univ. Santa Clara, 42-43; asst, Univ. Calif, 46-49; instr, Princeton, 50-53, asst. prof, 53-56; Johns Hopkins Univ, 56-61, assoc. prof, 61-66; prof, Univ. Ill, Urbana, 66-71, acting dir, Ctr. Advan. Stud, 70-71; PROF. ENG. & CHMN. DEPT, UNIV. FLA, 71- Assoc. ed, Mod. Lang. Notes, 56-62; ELH, 57-67; Guggenheim fel. & Fulbright res. grant, 62-63; mem. ed. bd, J. Eng. & Ger. Philol, 68-71. Mediaeval Acad. Am; MLA; S.Atlantic Mod. Lang. Asn; NCTE. Publ: Boethius: consolation of philosophy, Bobbs, 62; Alan of Lille's De planctu naturae, Speculum; Dante's allegory of poets, Comp. Lit; Gawain's shield and the quest for perfection, ELH, 62. Add: Dept. of English, University of Florida, Gainesville, FL 32601.

GREEN, ROSE BASILE, b. New Rochelle, N.Y, Dec. 19, 14; m. 42; c. 2. ENGLISH, AMERICAN LITERATURE. B.A, Col. New Rochelle, 35; M.A, Columbia Univ, 41; Ph.D.(Am. civilization), Univ. Pa, 63. Writer, Am. Guide Series, Conn, 35-36; teacher, High Sch, Conn, 36-42; free lance script writer, radio documentaries, Nat. Broadcasting Co, 40-42; assoc. prof. Eng. & registr, Univ. Tampa, 42-43; instr. Eng, Temple Univ, 53-57; assoc. prof, CABRINI COL, 57-63, prof. & chmn. dept, 63-70, ed, A-Zimuth, 63-70, COL. ADV. BD, 73- Am. Ital. Hist. Asn; Am. Acad. Polit. & Soc. Sci; NCTE; MLA; Am. Stud. Asn. Ethnic studies in higher education; Italian American poetry and drama; biography of St. Francis Cabrini. Publ: The evolution of Italian-American fiction, Univ. Pa, 63; The Cabrinian philosophy of education, Cabrini Col, 67; Toward a more representative American fiction, A-Zimuth, 65; To reason why (poetry), 71 & Primo vino (poems), 73, A.S. Barnes; The Italian American novel (lit. criticism), Fairleigh Dickinson Univ, 73. Add: Manor Rd, Rte. 2824, Philadelphia, PA 19128.

GREEN, RUSSELL EARL, b. Greenville, S.C, Nov. 6, 23; m. 45; c. 4. DRAMA. LL.B, Univ. S.C, 49, fel, 49-50, M.A, 50; Univ. Tenn, 50-52, 57-59; M.F.A, Yale, 56. Teaching asst, Univ. Tenn, 50-51, instr. speech & drama, 51-54, asst. prof, 56-60, assoc. prof, 60-61, tech. dir. univ. & Carousel theaters, 51-53, assoc. dir, 52-54, 56-60; assoc. prof. speech & drama, Whittier Col, 61-65, chmn. dept. 62-65, dir. theatre, 61-65; PROF. & DIR. THEATRE, UNIV. S.C, 65- Asst, Yale, 55-56. U.S.M,C, 42-46, Capt. Speech Commun. Asn; Am. Theatre Asn; Southeast. Theater Asn. Legal and moral restrictions on the colonial American theater; censorship of the contemporary American theater; British and American stage biographies. Add: University Theatre, University of South Carolina, Columbia, SC 29208.

GREEN, WILLIAM, b. New York, N.Y, July 10, 26; m. 60; c. 2. ENGLISH & DRAMA. A.B, Queens Col, 49; M.A, Columbia Univ, 50, Ph.D.(Eng), 59; scholar, Univ. Birmingham, summer 50; fel, Univ. Manchester, 56-57. Lectr. ENG, Upsala Col, 53-56; tutor, QUEENS COL.(N.Y), 57-59, instr, 59-63, asst. prof, 63-67, assoc. prof, 67-72, PROF, 72- Consult, col. proficiency exam. prog, N.Y. State Educ. Dept, 64- U.S.N, 44-46. Col. Eng. Asn; Malone Soc; MLA; Renaissance Soc. Am; Theatre Libr. Asn; Am. Soc. Theatre Res.(secy-treas, 67-73), Int. Fed. Theatre Res.(cor. secy. for U.S, 70-). Shakespeare; Elizabethan drama; modern European and American drama. Publ: Shakespeare's Merry wives of Windsor, Princeton, 62; ed, The Merry wives of Windsor, New Am. Libr, 65; co-ed, Elizabethan drama, Bantam, 67; contrib, The American theatre: a sum of its parts, Samuel French, 71; auth, Puerto Rican portrait, Theatre Arts, 3/56; Humours characters and attributive names in Shakespeare's plays, Names, 9/72. Add: Dept. of English, Queens College, City University of New York, Flushing, NY 11367.

GREENBAUM, LEONARD, English, Research Administration. See Volume I, History.

GREENBAUM, SIDNEY, b. London, Eng, Dec. 31, 29. ENGLISH LINGUISTICS. B.A, Univ. London, 51, M.A, 53, minister's dipl. Hebrew, 53, cert. educ, 54, B.A, 57, Ph.D.(Eng), 67. Instr. ENG, Univ. Col, Univ. London, 67-68; vis. asst. prof, Univ. Ore, 68-69; assoc. prof, UNIV. WIS-MILWAUKEE, 69-72, PROF, 72- Vis. prof, Hebrew Univ. Jerusalem, 72-73. Ling. Asn. Gt. Brit; Ling. Soc. Am; MLA. Modern English grammar; language acceptability. Publ: Studies in English adverbial usage, 69 & 70 & co-auth, Elicitation experiments in English: linguistic studies in use and attitude, 70, Longman-Univ. Miami; auth, Verb-intensifier collocations in English: an experimental approach, Mouton, 70; co-auth, A grammar of contemporary English, Longman-Seminar Press, 72, A concise grammar of contemporary English, Harcourt, 73 & A university grammar of English, Longman, 73; The question of but, Folia linguistica, 69; Adverbial -ing participle constructions in English, Anglia, 73; Informant elicitation of data on syntactic variation, Lingua, 73. Add: Dept. of English, University of Wisconsin-Milwaukee, Milwaukee, WI 53201.

GREENBERG, ALVIN D, b. Cincinnati, Ohio, May 10, 32; m. 55; c. 3. ENGLISH. B.A, Univ. Cincinnati, 54, M.A, 60; Ph.D.(Eng), Univ. Wash, 64. Instr. ENG, Univ. Ky, 63-65; asst. prof, MACALESTER COL, 65-68, assoc. prof, 68-72, PROF, 72- Fulbright lectr. Am. lit, Univ. Kerala, 66-67; ed, Minn. Rev, 67-72. MLA. Literary criticism; 20th century literature; literature and psychology. Publ: The small waves (novel), El Corno, 65; The metaphysical giraffe, 68 & The house of the would-be gardener, 72, (poems), New Rivers; Going nowhere (novel), Simon & Schuster, 71; Dark lands (poems), Ithaca, 73; The death of the psyche: a way to the self in the contemporary novel, Criticism, 66; Openendedness in the novel: toward a structure of values, Paunch, 67; A sense of place in modern fiction, Genre, 73. Add: Dept. of English, Macalester College, St. Paul, MN 55105.

GREENBERG, BERNARD L, b. Bronx, N.Y, May 31, 17; m. 47; c. 3. ENGLISH. B.A, Oberlin Col, 41; M. A, George Washington Univ, 49; Johns Hopkins Univ, 50-54; res. scholar, Queens' Col, Cambridge, 52. Instr. ENG, George Washington Univ, 48-49; Johns Hopkins Univ, 49-54; asst. prof, GALLAUDET COL, 54-57, ASSOC. PROF, 59-, DIR. ADMIS, 64- U.S.A.F, 42-46, Res, 46-, Lt. Col. MLA; Col. Eng. Asn. Eighteenth century literature; English composition; the English novel. Publ: Co-auth, A short guide to English writing, Gallaudet Col, 61; co-auth, Better English usage, Bobbs, 64; co-ed, An annotated edition of Laurence Sterne's Tristram Shandy, Univ. Fla, 74; auth, Laurence Sterne and Chambers cyclopedia, Mod. Lang. Notes, 12/54; Laurence Sterne and Plutarch, Notes & Queries; Measuring the college potential of language handicapped persons, Col. & Univ, summer 71. Add: Dept. of English, Gallaudet College, Washington, DC 20002.

GREENBERG, HERBERT, b. Brooklyn, N.Y, Nov. 13, 35; m. 59; c. 2. ENGLISH. B.A, Brooklyn Col, 56; M.A, Univ. Wis, 57, Ph.D.(Eng), 64. Instr. ENG, Northwest. Univ, 61-64; asst. prof, MICH. STATE UNIV, 64-68, ASSOC. PROF, 68- Publ: Quest for the necessary: W.H. Auden and the dilemma of divided consciousness, Harvard, 68. Add: Dept. of English, Michigan State University, East Lansing, MI 48824.

GREENBERG, MARTIN, b. Norfolk, Va, Feb. 3, 18; m. 62; c. 1. ENGLISH LITERATURE. B.A, Univ. Mich, 38. Ed, Commentary Mag, 53-60; asst. prof. ENG, C.W. POST COL, 63-67, assoc. prof, 67-73, PROF, 73- Guggenheim fel, 62-63. U.S.A, 41-45, S/Sgt; Bronze Star Medal. Nineteenth and 20th century English literature; European literature. Publ: Transl, Franz Kafka: Diaries 1914-1923, Schocken, 48 & Heinrich von Klust: Marquise of O- and other stories, Criterion, 60; auth, Terror of art: Kafka & modern literature, Basic Bks, 68. Add: Dept. of English, C.W. Post College, Greenvale, NY 11548.

GREENBERG, ROBERT ARTHUR, b. Bronx, N.Y, May 16, 30; m. 53; c. 3. LITERATURE. A.B, Brooklyn Col, 50; M.A, N.Y. Univ, 52, Ph.D. (Victorian lit), 57. Instr. ENG, Cornell Univ, 57-61, asst. prof, 61-66; assoc. prof, QUEENS COL.(N.Y), 66-71, PROF, 71- Lectr, Brooklyn Col, 53-55; Am. Counc. Learned Soc. grant, 64-65; co-ed, Victorian Newsletter. MLA. Eighteenth century literature; Victorian literature; Swinburne. Publ: Ed, Gulliver's travels: critical edition, 61 & The writings of Jonathan Swift, 73, Norton; co-auth, Robert Frost: an introduction, Holt, 61 & Modern essays: a rhetorical approach, Macmillan, 62. Add: Dept. of English, Queens College, Flushing, NY 11367.

GREENBERG, S. ROBERT, English Language & Linguistics. See Volume III, Foreign Languages, Linguistics & Philology.

GREENBLATT, STEPHEN JAY, b. Cambridge, Mass, Nov. 7, 43; m. 69. ENGLISH. B.A, Yale, 64, M.Phil, 68, Ph.D.(Eng), 69; Fulbright scholar & B.A, Pembroke Col, 66, M.A, 69. ASSOC. PROF. ENG, UNIV. CALIF, BERKELEY, 69- Nat. Endowment Humanities Younger Humanist fel, 71-72. MLA; Renaissance Soc. Am. Renaissance literature; modern literature; sociology of knowledge. Publ: Three modern satirists: Waugh, Orwell, and Huxley, 65 & Sir Walter Raleigh: the Renaissance man and his roles, 73, Yale. Add: Dept. of English, University of California, Berkeley, CA 94720.

GREENE, DAVID H, b. Boston, Mass, Nov. 4, 13. ENGLISH LITERATURE. A.B, Harvard, 36, A.M, 38, Dexter traveling fel, 39, Ph.D, 42. Instr. ENG, Boston, 39; Col. New Rochelle, 39-41; PROF, U.S. Naval Acad, 41-46; N.Y. UNIV, 46-, HEAD ALL-UNIV. DEPT. ENG, 64- Rockefeller fel, 55-56; Fulbright res. appointment, Nat. Univ. Ireland, 62-63. U.S.N.R, 43-45, Lt. (jg). MLA; Royal Soc. Antiq. Ireland; Int. Asn. Univ. Prof. Eng. Publ: Ed, An anthology of Irish literature; co-ed, One thousand years of Irish prose; co-auth, J.M. Synge, 1871-1909, Macmillan, 59; co-ed, G.B. Shaw: the matter with Ireland, Hill & Wang, 62. Add: Dept. of English, New York University, New York, NY 10003.

GREENE, DAVID MASON, b. Washington, D.C, Mar. 16, 20; m. 44; c. 1. ENGLISH LITERATURE. B.A, San Diego State Col, 51; M.A, Univ. Calif, Berkeley, 52, Ph.D, 58. Lectr. ENG, Univ. Calif, Berkeley, 55-57; instr, Pa. State Univ, 57-58; asst. prof, LEHIGH UNIV, 58-64, assoc. prof, 64-69, PROF, 69- MLA. Emblemata; Joseph Conrad; Thoreau. Publ: The frail duration: a key to symbolic structure in Walden, San Diego State Col, 66; The lady and the dragoon: a broadside ballad in oral tradition, J. Am. Folklore, summer 57; The Welsh characters in Patient Grissil, Boston Univ. Stud. Eng, winter 60; The identity of the emblematic nemesis, Stud. Renaissance, 63. Add: Dept. of English, Lehigh University, Bethlehem, PA 18015.

GREENE, DONALD JOHNSON, b. Moose Jaw, Can, Nov. 21, 16; m. 55; c. 1. ENGLISH. B.A, Univ. Sask, 41, B.A, 46; M.A, Univ. London, 48, Litt.D, 73; Ph.D, Columbia Univ, 54. Lectr. ENG, Univ. Sask, 48-52; asst. prof, Univ. Calif, Riverside, 54-57, prof, 66-67; asst. prof, Brandeis Univ, 58-60; assoc. prof, Univ. N.Mex, 60-63; prof, Victoria Col. Univ. Toronto, 63-66; Vilas prof, Univ. Wis, 67-68; BING PROF, UNIV. SOUTH. CALIF, 68- Guggenheim fel, 57; Can. Counc. sr. fel, 65-66; co-ed, 18th Century Stud, 70-; vis. prof. Eng, Claremont Grad. Sch, 70. Can. Army, 41-45. MLA (ed. comt, 68-73); Johnson Soc. London; Johnsonians; Conf. Brit. Stud.(recording secy, 63); Am. Soc. 18th Century Stud.(secy, 69-73); Int. Soc. 18th Century Stud; Int. Asn. Univ. Prof. Eng. Samuel Johnson; 18th century English literature; intellectual history. Publ: The politics of Samuel Johnson, Yale, 60; ed, Samuel Johnson: twentieth-century views, Prentice-Hall, 65; co-auth, Samuel Johnson: a survey and bibliography of critical studies, Univ. Minn, 70; auth, Samuel Johnson, Twayne, 70; The age of exuberance: backgrounds to eighteenth-century English literature, Random, 70. Add: Dept. of English, University of Southern California, Los Angeles, CA 90007.

GREENE, ELIZABETH, b. New York, N.Y, Sept. 20, 43. MEDIEVAL & MODERN ENGLISH LITERATURE. A.B, Bryn Mawr Col, 65; M.A, Univ. Toronto, 66, Woodrow Wilson fel, 65-66, Prov. Ont. fel, 66-69, Ph.D.(Eng), 69. Lectr. ENG, QUEEN'S UNIV.(ONT), 69-71, ASST. PROF, 71- Mediaeval Acad. Am; MLA; Asn. Can. Univ. Teachers Eng. Anglo-Saxon poetry; Middle English; the Pound era. Add: Dept. of English, Queen's University, Kingston, Ont. K7L 3N6, Can.

GREENE, JAMES J, b. New York, N.Y, Dec. 12, 27; m. 50; c. 6. ENGLISH, DRAMA. B.A, Manhattan Col, 51; M.A, Columbia Univ, 55, Danforth scholars, 60-63, Woodbridge hon. fel, 63-64, Ph.D.(Eng), 64. Lectr. ENG, Manhattan Col, 52-58; assoc. prof, Col. New Rochelle, 54-67; ASST. PROF, CITY COL. N.Y, 67- State Univ. N.Y. sem. Russian stud. grant, Columbia Univ, summers 63-64; lectr. drama & Eng, Manhattanville Col, 63-66. U.S.A, 45-47. Renaissance Soc. Am. Thomas More studies; modern drama. Publ: The essential More, New Am. Libr, 67. Add: Dept. of English, City College of New York, Convent Ave. at 138th St, New York, NY 10031.

GREENE, MAXINE, b. New York, N.Y, Dec. 23, 17; m. 47; c. 2. ENGLISH, PHILOSOPHY. B.A, Barnard Col, Columbia Univ, 38; M.A, N.Y. Univ, 49, Ph.D.(philos. educ), 55. Instr. hist. & philos. educ, N.Y. Univ, 49-56, asst. prof. Eng. & educ, 57-59, assoc. prof, 59-62; asst. prof. Eng, Montclair State Col, 56-57; assoc. prof. educ, Brooklyn Col, City Univ. New York, 62-65; Eng, TEACHERS COL, COLUMBIA UNIV, 65-67, PROF, 67-69, PHILOS. & EDUC, 69- Vis. prof, Univ. Hawaii, summers 60, 62; writer & consult, philos. educ. proj, U.S. Off. Educ. & Univ. Ill, 65-67. Philos. Educ. Soc. (pres, 66-67); NCTE; MLA; Am. Educ. Stud. Asn.(pres, 71-72); Am. Educ. Res. Asn.(v.pres, 71-73); John Dewey Soc. Philosophy of education; literary history; aesthetics. Publ: The public school and the private vision, 65 & Existential encounters for teachers, 67, Random; Teacher as stranger, Wadsworth, 73; The whale's whiteness: the meaning of meaninglessness, J. Aesthet. Educ, 1/68; The aesthetic component, In: Foundations of education, Wiley, 71; Imagination, In: Aesthetic concepts and education, Univ. Ill, 71; plus two others. Add: Dept. of Philosophy and the Social Sciences, Teachers College, Columbia University, New York, NY 10027.

GREENE, MILDRED SARAH, b. Springfield, Mass, May 5, 29; wid; c. 1. ENGLISH, COMPARATIVE LITERATURE. Durant scholar & B.A, Wellesley Col, 51; scholar. & M.A.T, Radcliffe Col, 56; M.A, Univ. Mass, 60; univ. fel, Univ. N.Mex, 62-63, Ph.D.(Eng), 65. ASST. PROF. ENG, ARIZ. STATE UNIV, 66-, stud. grant, summer 67. MLA; Rocky Mountain Mod. Lang. Asn. The heroine of integrity in French, English and American literature from the 18th century to present; perspectives in art and literature, 18th and 19th centuries. Publ: Isolation and integrity: Mme de Lafayette's Princesse de Cleves and George Eliot's Dorothea Brooke, Rev. Lit. Comp, 6/70; Les liaisons dangereuses & The golden bowl, Mod. Fiction Stud, summer 73. Add: Dept. of English, Arizona State University, Tempe, AZ 85281.

GREENE, PHILIP L, b. Brooklyn, N.Y, Dec. 2, 24; m. 55; c. 2. AMERICAN LITERATURE. B.S, Lowell Textile Inst, 49; M.A, N.Y. Univ, 56, Ph.D.(Eng), 62. Instr. ENG, LONG ISLAND Univ, 56-58; N.Y. Univ, 58-59; ASSOC. PROF, ADELPHI UNIV, 59- U.S.A.F, 43-45, Flight Off. MLA; NCTE. Stylistics of fiction; writing fiction. Publ: One of you must be Wendell Corey, Partisan Rev, spring 65; Point of view in The spoils of Poynton, Nineteenth Century Fiction, 3/67; Establish your credentials, Transatlantic Rev, fall 67. Add: Dept. of English, Adelphi University, Garden City, NY 11530.

GREENE, RICHARD LEIGHTON, b. Rochester, N.Y, Jan. 18, 04; wid; c. 2. ENGLISH. A.B, Univ. Rochester, 26; A.M, Princeton, 27, Procter fel. & Ph.D.(Eng), 29; hon. A.M, Wesleyan Univ, 56. From instr. to prof. Eng, Univ. Rochester, 29-42, Gilmore prof. Eng. & chmn. dept, 42-46; pres, Wells Col, 46-50; vis. prof. ENG, Purdue Univ, 51-52, Univ. Calif, 52-53; Calif. Inst. Technol, 53-54; WESLEYAN UNIV, 54-56, prof, 56-69, Wilbur Fisk Osborne Prof, 69-72, EMER. PROF, 72- Am. Counc. Learned Soc. fel, 31-32; Lyric Found. lectr, Union Col.(N.Y) & Wells Col, 54; lectr, Bucknell Univ, 58; Oxford, 59; vis. fels, Princeton, 63 & 68; assoc. fel, Silliman Col, Yale, 73. Alpha Delta Phi Samuel Eells Award, 62. MLA; Mediaeval Acad. Am; Johnsonians; Am. Musicol. Soc; Mod. Humanities Res. Asn, Gt. Brit; Renaissance Soc. Am; NCTE; Col. Eng. Asn; Shakespeare Asn. Am. Middle English lyric; 18th century literature. Publ: Ed, The early English carols, 35 & A selection of English carols, 62, Clarendon; auth, Digressions and indiscretions, Col. Eng. Asn, 68. Add: Graduates Club, 155 Elm St, New Haven, CT 06508.

GREENE, ROBERT ALLAN, b. Boston, Mass, Nov. 6, 31; m. 57; c. 4. ENGLISH. B.A, Boston Col, 53, M.A, 54; Stoughton fel, Harvard, 54-57, univ. fel, 55-58, Ph.D.(Eng), 61; Dexter traveling fel, summer 56, 58. Lectr. ENG, UNIV. TORONTO, 58-61, asst. prof, 62-65, assoc. prof, 66-69, PROF, 69-, DEAN FAC. ARTS & SCI, 72- Leverhulme vis. lectr, Durham Univ, Eng, 62-63. Seventeenth century intellectual history; history of critical theory. Publ: Co-ed, Nath. Culverwell's Discourse of the light of nature 1652, Univ. Toronto, 71; auth, Boyle and More on the spirit of nature, J. Hist. Ideas, 62. Add: Faculty of Arts & Science, University of Toronto, Toronto, Ont. M5S 1A1, Can.

GREENE, THOMAS McLERNON, English. See Volume III, Foreign Languages, Linguistics & Philology.

GREENFIELD, ROBERT MORSE, b. Chicago, Ill, Aug. 11, 38; m. 67. ENGLISH. B.A, Occidental Col, 60; Woodrow Wilson fel, Columbia Univ, 60, M.A, 61, fac. fel, 62-63, pres. fel, 65-66, Ph.D.(20th century Brit. lit), 67. Lectr. ENG, Queens Col.(N.Y), 66-67; asst. prof, LAKE FOREST COL, 67-72, ASSOC. PROF, 72- MLA; Midwest Mod. Lang. Asn; AAUP. Twentieth century British and American literature. Add: Dept. of English, Lake Forest College, Lake Forest, IL 60045.

GREENFIELD, STANLEY BRIAN, b. Brooklyn, N.Y, Mar. 19, 22; m. 51; c. 2. ENGLISH. Ph.D.(Eng), Univ. Calif, 50. Instr. ENG, Univ. Wis, 50-54; Queens Col.(N.Y), 54-59; asst. prof, UNIV. ORE, 59-61, assoc. prof, 61-64, PROF, 64- Am. Counc. Learned Soc. rep, Teachers Ethics & Prof. Standards Conf, 58-60; consult, Portland Pub. Schs, 60-61; Guggenheim fel, 65-66; mem. grad. rec. exam. advan. lit, Eng. Test Comt, Educ. Testing Serv, 67-; Nat. Endowment for Humanities sr. fel, 70-71; ed. comt, Publ. Mod. Lang. Asn, 71-75; ed. bd, Anglo-Saxon Eng, 72- Ersted Award for Distinguished Teaching, 63. U.S.A, 43-45. MLA; Mediaeval Acad. Am. Old English; Middle English. Publ: Co-auth, Guide to English literature from Beowulf through Chaucer and medieval drama, Barnes & Noble, 61; ed, Studies in Old English literature in honor of Arthur G. Brodeur, Univ. Ore, 63; auth, A critical history of Old English literature, N.Y. Univ, 65; co-ed, The poem: an anthology, Appleton, 69 & 72; auth, The interpretation of Old English poems, Routledge & Kegan Paul, 72; The Old English elegies, In: Continuations & beginnings: studies in Old English literature, Nelson, 66; Grammar and meaning in poetry, PMLA, 10/67: The canons of Old English criticism, ELH, 6/67; plus others. Add: Dept. of English, University of Oregon, Eugene, OR 97403.

GREENFIELD, THELMA NELSON, b. Portland, Ore, Sept. 11, 22; m. 51; c. 2. ENGLISH. Ph.D, Univ. Wis, 52. Instr. ENG, UNIV. ORE, 46-47, asst. prof, 63-67, assoc. prof, 67-73, PROF, 73- Arthur Pratt grad. scholar, 44-45. Inst. Int. Educ. scholar, 50. Renaissance Soc. Am; Shakespeare Asn. Am; MLA. Dramatic and non-dramatic literature of the English Renaissance. Publ: Co-ed, Pacific Coast studies in Shakespeare, Univ. Ore, 66; auth, The induction in Elizabethan drama, Univ. Ore, 70; The clothing motif in King Lear, Shakespeare Quart, 54; A re-examination of the patient Pericles, Shakespeare Stud, 68; The language of process in Ford's The broken heart, PMLA, 72. Add: Dept. of English, University of Oregon, Eugene, OR 97403.

GREENHUT, MORRIS, b. Alt Sandetz, Austria, Aug. 22, 08; nat; m. 50. ENGLISH LITERATURE. A.B, Wayne State Univ, 31; A.M, Univ. Mich, 32, univ. fel, 35, Ph.D, 42. Teaching fel. ENG, UNIV. MICH, ANN ARBOR, 36-42, instr, 42-47, asst. prof, 47-53, assoc. prof, 53-64, PROF, 64- Ford Found. Fund Advan. Educ. fel, 52-53; ed, Explicator Check-List. MLA; NCTE. Literary criticism; George Henry Lewes and English classical criticism; modern novel. Add: Dept. of English, University of Michigan, Ann Arbor, MI 48104.

GREENWOOD, JOAN VOSS, b. Montreal, P.Q, Aug. 15, 32; m. 53; c. 2. ENGLISH. B.A, Wellesley Col, 53, univ. fel, Stanford Univ, 54-55, Loomis fels, 54-56, M.A, 56, Ph.D.(Eng), 62. Acting instr. Eng, Stanford Univ, 56-57, teaching asst, 61; lectr, Kobe Col, Japan, 57-58, asst. prof. Eng. & Am. lit, 58-60; asst. prof. Eng. & chmn. dept. humanities, Rosary Col, 61-63; from asst. prof. to assoc. prof. ENG, CALIF. STATE UNIV, FULLERTON, 63-72, PROF, 72-, chair, Fac. Counc, 69-70, chair, dept. Eng, 70-73. MLA; Edith Wharton; modern Japanese fiction; modern Indian fiction. Publ: The nature and results of conflict in Edith Wharton's short stories and nouvelles, 6/59 & Style: the final medium in Edith Wharton's short stories and nouvelles, 2/60, Kobe Col. Stud; After Mishima (poems), Lit. E. & W, 6/71. Add: Dept. of English, California State University, Fullerton, Fullerton, CA 92634.

GREER, ALLEN WILKINSON, b. Indianapolis, Ind, July 25, 24; m. 49; c. 3. ENGLISH. B.A, Harvard, 49; M.A, Columbia Univ, 52; Ph.D.(Eng), Univ. Fla, 65. Instr. ENG, Univ. Fla, 52-54, 55-57, 58-64; lectr, Columbia Univ, 54-55, 57-58; asst. prof, FLA. ATLANTIC UNIV, 64-66, assoc. prof, 66-70, PROF, 70-, ASST. DEAN, COL. HUMANITIES, 67- U.S.A, 43-46, Capt. MLA; S.Atlantic Mod. Lang. Asn; AAUP. Chaucer; medieval literature. Add: College of Humanities, Florida Atlantic University, Boca Raton, FL 33432.

GREGG, ALVIN LANER, English Language & Linguistics. See Volume III, Foreign Languages, Linguistics & Philology.

GREGG, RICHARD BEVVE, b. El Dorado, Kans, Oct. 16, 36; m. 57; c. 3. SPEECH. B.A, Univ. Wichita, 59; M.A, Univ. Pittsburgh, 61, Ph.D.(speech), 63. Assoc. prof. speech, PA. STATE UNIV, UNIVERSITY PARK, 63-70, PROF. SPEECH COMMUN, 70- Speech Commun. Asn; Nat. Social Stud. Commun; Speech Asn. East. States. Rhetorical criticism; political and interpersonal communication. Publ: Co-auth, The rhetoric of Black power: a street level interpretation, Quart. J. Speech, 4/69; auth, The ego-function of the rhetoric of protest, Philos. & Rhetoric, spring 71; contrib, The 1966 Senate Foreign Relations Committee Hearings on Vietnam policy: a phenomenological analysis, In: Explorations of rhetorical criticism, 73; plus others. Add: Dept. of Speech, Pennsylvania State University, University Park, PA 16802.

GREGORY, DONALD, b. Newark, Ohio, Jan. 20, 38; m. 60; c. 2. ENGLISH. B.A, Bucknell Univ, 60; M.A, Ohio State Univ, 62, Ph.D.(Eng), 67. ASST. PROF. ENG, UNIV. NEBR-LINCOLN, 67- MLA. Add: 221 Andrews Hall, University of Nebraska-Lincoln, Lincoln, NE 68508.

GREGORY, ELMER RICHARD, b. Baytown, Tex, Sept. 25, 38; m. 67; c. 1. ENGLISH, COMPARATIVE LITERATURE. B.A, Univ. Tex, Austin, 60; M.A, Rice Univ, 61; Ph.D.(comp. lit), Univ. Ore, 65. Asst. prof. ENG, Univ. Ga, 65-67; UNIV. TOLEDO, 67-72, ASSOC. PROF, 72- Renaissance Soc. Am; Milton Soc. Am; MLA. John Milton; 17th century British literature; Anglo-French literary relations. Publ: Du Bartas, Sidney, and Spenser, Comp. Lit. Studies, 70; Marvell's Horatian ode: a reconsideration, Forum, 72; contrib, Milton Encyclopedia, Univ. Wis, (in press); plus one other. Add: Dept. of English, University of Toledo, Toledo, OH 43606.

GREGORY, HOOSAG, b. Bridgewater, Mass, Sept. 1, 18; m. 52. ENGLISH. A.B, Bates Col, 39; M.A, Univ. Ill, 40; M.A, Harvard, 47, Ph.D, 51. Instr. ENG, Case Inst. Technol, 51-55, asst. prof, 55-58; vis. lectr, Bates Col, 58-60; instr, Northwest. Univ, 60-62; from asst. prof. to ASSOC. PROF, SAN FRANCISCO STATE UNIV, 62- U.S.A, 43-46. MLA. William Cowper; D.H. Lawrence; Victorian England. Publ: The prisoner and his crimes: a summary of a longer study of William Cowper, Lit. & Psychol, 5/56; Cowper's love of subhuman nature: a psychoanalytic approach, Philol. Quart, 1/67. Add: Dept. of English, San Francisco State University, San Francisco, CA 94132.

GREGORY, JOHN ROBERT, b. Chicago, Ill, Dec. 28, 18; m. 41; c. 4. COMMUNICATIONS, MASS MEDIA. B.A, Mont. State Univ, 47, M.A, 48; Ph.D.(commun), Univ. Ill, 61. Instr. & head dept. physics, Wartburg Col, 51-52; asst. prof. speech & mass media, Cent. Mo. State Col, 63-67, ASSOC. PROF, 67-68; pub. address & mass media, Univ. South. Miss, 68-72; MASS MEDIA, JACKSON STATE COL, 73- Commun. consult, 72- Sig.C, A.U.S, 44-45. Soc. Motion Picture & TV Engrs; Nat. Asn. Educ. Broadcasters; Asn. Educ. Commun. & Technol; Speech Commun. Asn. Motion picture communication; radio and television. Publ: The least of these, my brethren (film), privately produced, 72. Add: 260 Carmel Ave, Jackson, MS 39204.

GREGORY, JOHN W, b. Eatonton, Ga, May 26, 15; m. 46; c. 2. HUMANITIES, AMERICAN & ENGLISH LITERATURE. A.B, Mercer Univ, 38; M.A, Univ. Ga, 47; Duke Univ, summers 49, 51; Ed.S, George Peabody Col. Teachers, 55. Prin, Bethel Sch, Rockdale County, 38-40; Muscogee County Sch, 40-41; Columbus Jr. High Sch, 41-42; instr, Ga. Sch. Technol, 46-47; from asst. to ASSOC. PROF, HUMANITIES, OXFORD COL, EMORY UNIV, 47- U.S.A.A.F, 42-46, S/Sgt. NEA; Nat. Social Stud. Commun. Minor Southern authors; Harry Stillwell Edwards. Publ: An approach to functional English in a four-year junior college, Jr. Col. J, 12/58; The basic issues report: a possible renaissance in English teaching, Peabody J. Educ, 7/60; Miscegenation (poem), Nat. Poetry Anthology, 64. Add: Dept. of Humanities, Oxford College of Emory University, Oxford, GA 30267.

GREGORY, THOMAS WEST, b. Norfolk, Va, Sept. 30, 38; m. 66. ENGLISH EDUCATION, LINGUISTICS. B.A, Univ. Va, 61, M.Ed, 66; M.A, Univ. Iowa, 69, Ph.D.(Eng. educ), 72. ASST. PROF. ENG, MORAVIAN COL, 72- Reader, Educ. Resources Inform. Ctr-Reading & Commun. Skills Conf. Eng. Educ, NCTE, 73- NCTE; MLA. Communications. Publ: Experimental reading diagnostic test, Univ. Iowa, 71. Add: Dept. of English, Moravian College, Main St. & Elizabeth Ave, Bethlehem, PA 18018.

GREGORY-PANOPOULOS, JOHN FRED, b. Everett, Mass, July 27, 24; m. 58. COMMUNICATIONS, TELECOMMUNICATIONS. B.A, Occidental Col, 49; M.A, Calif. State Col. Los Angeles, 55; Univ. Calif, Los Angeles, 61-62; Ph.D.(speech), Univ. South. Calif, 66. Prod-dir, actor & publ. radio, TV & films, Venezuela, 58-59; instr. pub. speaking & speech, Los Angeles City Col, 59-61; asst. prof. speech, Calif. State Col. Los Angeles, 61-62, 63-64; assoc. prof. COMMUN, PASADENA CITY COL, 63-73, PROF, 73-, HEAD DEPT. RADIO, 63- Former play reviewer, Player Mag; acad. consult, U.S.A. & Greek Govt. Dept. Defense, 55-57; Venezuelan Ministry Defense, 57-58; prod-dir. radio, TV & films S.Am, U.S.A. & Europe, 59-; instr, eve, Los Angeles City Col, 60-68; TV prod, KABC-TV, 64-68 & 72-73; KHJ-TV, 65-; vis. prof. jour, Calif. State Col. Los Angeles, spring 68; mass commun, Univ. South. Calif, summer 68; consult, Soviet Report; Ctr. For. Technol; ITV comt, KCET, Hollywood; mem. nat. bd, Nat. Educ. Radio, 73- Exec. Shield Award, Int. Broadcasters Soc, Holland, 66; Hollywood area Emmy as producer History of Art ser, 67-68; Abe Lincoln Merit Award, 72; Golden Mike Award, 72. Nat. Acad. TV Arts & Sci; Nat. Asn. Educ. Broadcasters; Speech Commun. Asn; Am. Nat. Theatre Asn; Am. Theatre Asn. Mass communications; international relations; social and behavioral sciences. Publ: Educational TV and Southern California, New Calif, 11/64; Prix Jeunesse 1968, Telefilm Int, fall 68; Assignment: Hollywood, Today's World, 6/73; plus others. Add: Dept. of Telecommunication, Pasadena City College, 1570 E. Colorado Blvd, Pasadena, CA 91106.

GREICUS, MICHAEL S, b. Muncie, Ind, Nov. 1, 32; m. 54; c. 2. MODERN BRITISH LITERATURE. B.A, Tulane Univ, 56, dipl. Eng. stud, Univ. Edinburgh, 57, Ph.D.(Eng), 59. Instr. Eng, Univ, Colo, 59-60, asst. prof, La. State Univ, New Orleans, 60-63, assoc. prof. & asst. dean col. lib. arts, 64-66; assoc. prof. ENG, Univ. Toledo, 66-72; sr. lectr, UNIV. PAPUA, NEW GUINEA, 72-73, ASSOC. PROF. & HEAD DEPT, 74-, acting head dept, 72-73. Vis. prof. Ford Found. Prog, econ. inst, Univ. Colo, summer 62; Fulbright prof, Univ. Jyväskylä, Finland, 63-64. U.S.A, 53-55, Res, 55-63. MLA; Australasian Univs. Lang. & Lit. Asn. Modern British and American fiction. Publ: Contrib. ed, Mod. Humanities Res. Asn. Annual Bibliog. Eng. Lang. & Lit, Cambridge Univ, 56-63; co-auth, Honors programs in Louisiana high schools: a survey, La. State Univ, 67; co-ed, Teaching literature in Papua, New Guinea, 72 & Niugini stories, 73, Dept. Educ, Papua, New Guinea; auth, Prose writers of the First World War, In: British Council writers and their work ser, Longmans, 73. Add: P.O. Box 4820, University Post Office, Papua, New Guinea.

GREINER, DONALD JAMES, b. Baltimore, Md, June 10, 40; m. 64; c. 2. AMERICAN LITERATURE. B.A, Wofford Col, 62; M.A, Univ. Va, 63, Ph.D.(Am. lit), 67. Teaching asst. Eng, Univ. Va, 65-66; asst. prof. AM. LIT, UNIV. S.C, 67-70, ASSOC. PROF, 70- MLA; S.Atlantic Mod. Lang. Asn. American literature; Robert Frost; contemporary American fiction. Publ: Guide to Robert Frost, 69 & Checklist of Robert Frost, 69, Merrill; co-ed,

The notebook of Stephen Crane, Univ. Va, 69; auth, Comic terror: the novels of John Hawkes, Memphis State Univ, 73; Robert Frost: a critical bibliography, Am. Libr. Asn, 74; Education of Robert Jordan: death with dignity, Hemingway Notes, 10/71; Bestiality in James Dickey's Deliverance, S.C. Rev, 10/72; Slaughterhouse-Five and fiction of atrocity, Critique, 6/73; plus five others. Add: Dept. of English, University of South Carolina, Columbia, SC 29208.

GRELLA, GEORGE J, b. Hempstead, N.Y, Dec. 27, 38; m. 63; c. 3. ENGLISH. A.B, Kenyon Col, 60; M.A, Univ. Kans, 65, Ph.D.(Eng), 67. Asst. instr. ENG, Univ. Kans, 62-67; asst. prof. UNIV. ROCHESTER, 67-72, ASSOC. PROF, 72- Mem, Nat. Humanities Fac, 71-; Nat. Endowment for Humanities younger humanist award, 72. MLA; Popular Cult. Asn. Modern American and English literature; the novel; popular literature. Publ: Confrontation (film), Peace Corps, 67; James Bond: culture hero, New Repub, 5/64; The gangster novel: the urban pastoral, In: Tough guy writers of the thirties, Carbondale, Ill, 68; Murder and manners: the formal detective novel, Novel, 70. Add: Dept. of English, University of Rochester, River Station, Rochester, NY 14627.

GRENANDER, MARY ELIZABETH (MRS. JAMES W. CORBETT), b. Rewey, Wis, Nov. 21, 18; m. 62, 72. ENGLISH. A.B, Univ. Chicago, 40, A.M, 41, Ph.D, 48; summer, Sorbonne, 49. Instr. ENG, STATE UNIV. N.Y. ALBANY, 48-53, asst. prof, 53-54, assoc. prof, 54-60, PROF, 61-, State Univ. N.Y. Res. Found. grants-in-aid, 56, 59, 66-67 & 73-74, summer fel, 59 & 73. Huntington Libr. summer fel, 57; Pforzheimer Found. res. fel, 58; Fulbright vis. prof. Am. lit. & Eng, Univs. Lille & Toulouse, France, 60-61; Am. Lit. Group, MLA. U.S.N.R, 42-46, Lt. MLA; Am. Stud. Asn. Ambrose Bierce; literary criticism; aesthetics. Publ: Ambrose Bierce, Twayne, 71; Ambrose Bierce, John Camden Hotten, The fiend's delight, and Nuggets and dust, Huntington Libr. Quart, 8/65; Committeemanship and committeeappointmentmanship, J. Gen. Educ, 7/73. Add: Dept. of English, State University of New York at Albany, Albany, NY 12222.

GRENBERG, BRUCE L, b. Rockford, Ill, Apr. 14, 35; m. 57; c. 1. ENGLISH. B.A, Beloit Col, 57; M.A, Univ. N.C. Chapel Hill, 58, Ph.D.(Eng), 63. Instr. ENG, UNIV. B.C, 63-64, asst. prof, 64-69, ASSOC. PROF, 69- Can. Counc. res. fel, 68-69. U.S.A, 58-60, Res, 60-64. MLA. American and English literature. Publ: The Canon's yeoman's tale: Boethian wisdom and the alchemists, Chaucer Rev, summer 66; Metaphysic of despair: Stephen Crane's The blue hotel, Mod. Fiction Stud, summer 68; The design of heroism in The sun also rises, Fitzgerald Hemingway Annual, 71. Add: Dept. of English, University of British Columbia, Vancouver 8, B.C, Can.

GRENNAN, EAMON, b. Dublin, Ireland, Nov. 13, 41; m. 73; c. 1. ENGLISH LITERATURE. B.A, Univ. Col, Dublin, 63, M.A, 64; A.M, Harvard, 66; Ph.D.(Eng), 73. Lectr. ENG, Univ. Col, Dublin, 66-67; instr, LEHMAN COL, 71-72, ASST. PROF, 73- Shakespeare; Renaissance & Anglo-Irish literature. Publ: Ed, A land of loneliness and other stories by Seumas O'Kelly, Gill & Macmillan, Dublin, 69; auth, Figures in a landscape: the short stories of Seumas O'Kelly, Studies, Dublin, 67. Add: Dept. of English, Herbert H. Lehman College, Bedford Park Blvd, Bronx, NY 10468.

GRENNEN, JOSEPH EDWARD, b. New York, N.Y, Sept. 3, 26; m. 50; c. 6. ENGLISH LITERATURE. B.S, Col. Holy Cross, 47; M.A, Fordham Univ, 54, fel, 55, Ph.D, 60. Instr high sch, N.Y, 47-50; educ. adv, Troop Inform. & Educ. Div, U.S. Army, Ger, 50-55; asst. prof. ENG, FORDHAM UNIV, 56-64, ASSOC. PROF, 64-, CHMN. DEPT, 65- U.S.N.R, 44-47, Lt. Mediaeval Acad. Am; MLA. AAUP. Middle English literature; modern criticism; history of science. Publ: Co-auth, The major Shakespearean tragedies: a critical bibliography, Macmillan, 73; auth, Chaucer's characterization of the canon and his yeoman, J. Hist. Ideas, 63; Science and sensibility in Chaucer's clerk, Chaucer Rev, 72; plus others. Add: Dept. of English, Fordham University, New York, NY 10458.

GRESHAM, FOSTER BAGWELL, B. Chesterfield Co, Va, Apr. 3, 05; m. 44; c. 2. ENGLISH. B.A, Randolph-Macon Col, 27; M.A, Univ. Va, 33, summer 58; Princeton; Ford Fund Advan. Educ. fel, 53-54; Univ. N.C, summer 59. Instr. Eng, Randolph-Macon Acad, Front Royal, Va, 27-31; teacher, high schs, Va, 34-49, chmn. dept, 49-53; asst. prof. eng, Longwood Col, 54-60, assoc. prof. 60-69, prof. 69-73, acting chmn. dept, 65-68; RETIRED. Consult, high schs, Va; ed, Va. Eng. Bull, 50-59. U.S.A, 42-46, Capt. NCTE. Traditional ballad; teaching of English in the secondary school; children's literature. Publ: Co-auth, Better English, Allyn & Bacon; Teaching of English in Virginia high schools, Va. Asn. Teachers Eng. Add: 1004 Fourth Ave. Ext, Farmville, VA 23901.

GREWE, EUGENE FRANCIS, b. Detroit, Mich, Oct. 18, 18; m. 46; c. 5. ENGLISH. B.A, Univ. Detroit, 39, M.A, 47; Ph.D, Univ. Mich, 63. Teaching fel, ENG, UNIV. DETROIT, 46, instr, 46-52, asst. prof, 52-62, assoc. prof, 62-65, PROF, 65-, chmn. freshman Eng, 48-64, chmn. grad. Eng. comt, 64-69. Exec. dir, Detroit Area Consortium Cath. Cols, 71- A.U.S, 41-46, Maj. MLA; NCTE; Conf. Col. Compos. & Commun. Milton, especially the criticism of his Comus, 1637-1941. Publ: Co-auth, The college research paper. Add: 2607 Woodland Ave, Royal Oak, MI 48073.

GRIBBEN, JOHN L, b. New York, N.Y, June 7, 16; m. 56; c. 3. ENGLISH. B.A, Regis Col, 61; M.A, Univ. Colo, 62, Ph.D.(Eng), 64. Instr. ENG, Regis Col, 61-62, asst. prof, 62-65; KENT STATE UNIV, 65-69, ASSOC. PROF, 69- MLA; Milton Soc. Am; Asn. Scottish Scholars. Poets of the Scottish Renaissance; John Milton; metaphysical poets. Publ: Shaw's Saint Joan, Thought, winter 65; Henry Adams: educator, The Serif, 6/67; Steinbeck's East of Eden & Milton's Paradise lost: a discussion of timshel, Steinbeck Quart, spring 72. Add: 725 Park Ave, Kent, OH 44240.

GRIDLEY, ROY E, b. Ellsworth, Kans, Mar. 24, 35; m. 56; c. 2. ENGLISH. B.A, Univ. Kans, 57; Fulbright fel, Reading Univ, Eng, 57-58; M.A, Brown Univ, 59; Ph.D.(Eng), Univ. Ill, 64. Asst. prof. ENG, UNIV. KANS, 64-68: assoc. prof, 68-73, PROF, 73- Outstanding Teacher Award, Standard Oil Co, 69. U.S.A.F.R, 59-65. MLA. Nineteenth century British literature. Publ: Browning, Routledge, London, 72; Browning's Pompilia, J. Eng. & Ger. Philol, 1/68; Browning and his reader, In: Nineteenth century writer and his audience, Univ. Kans, 69. Add: Dept. of English, University of Kansas, Lawrence, KS 66044.

GRIER, EDWARD FRANCIS, b. Elizabeth, N.J, Apr. 23, 17. AMERICAN LITERATURE & CIVILIZATION. B.A, Univ. Pa, 38, Ph.D, 49; M.A, Columbia Univ, 39. Instr, Seton Hall Univ, 39-42; Dartmouth Col, 45-51; asst. prof, UNIV. KANS, 51-57, assoc. prof, 57-62, PROF. AM. LIT, 62-, chmn. Am. stud, 52-64. Vis. asst. prof, Ind. Univ, summer, 55; Fund Advan. Educ. fel, 52-53; Fulbright lectr, Univs. Lyon & Clermont-Ferrand, France, 56-57; Univ. Catania, Ctr. Am. Stud, Rome, 64; vis. assoc. prof, Univ. Pa, summer, 61. U.S.A, 42-45, S/Sgt. MLA; Am. Stud. Asn; Mid-Continent Am. Stud. Asn; Am. Civil Liberties Union. Walt Whitman; 19th and 20th century American literature; American civilization. Publ: Walt Whitman: the eighteenth presidency, Univ. Kans, 57; Programs in American civilization, J. Higher Educ, 4/54; Walt Whitman, In: American literary scholarship, Duke Univ, 64-68; Walt Whitman's earliest known notebook, PMLA, 8/68; plus others. Add: Dept. of English, University of Kansas, Lawrence, KS 66045.

GRIEST, GUINEVERE LINDLEY, b. Chicago, Ill, Jan. 14, 24. ENGLISH. A.B, Cornell Univ, 44; M.A, Univ. Chicago, 47, Ph.D.(Eng), 61; Fulbright fel, Cambridge, 53-55. Instr. Eng, Univ. Ill, Chicago Circle, 47-53, 55-61, asst. prof, 61-66, assoc. prof, 66-73, fac. fel, 62; DEP. DIR. DIV. FEL, NAT. ENDOWMENT FOR HUMANITIES, 73-, prog. off, 69-73. MLA; NCTE. Nineteenth century English literature, especially fiction and poetry; nineteenth century American literature; contemporary literature. Publ: Mudie's circulating library and the Victorian novel, Ind. Univ, 70; A Victorian leviathan, Nineteenth-Century Fiction, 9/65; plus others. Add: Div. of Fellowships, National Endowment for the Humanities, 806 15th St. N.W, Washington, DC 20506.

GRIFFIN, ALICE, b. Washington, D.C, Jan. 10, 24; m. 52; c. 2. LITERATURE. A.B, George Washington Univ, 44; univ. fel, Columbia Univ, 44-45, A.M, 45, Fisher fel, 45-46, Ph.D, 49. Asst. prof. ENG, LEHMAN COL, 47-63, assoc. prof, 63-68, PROF, 69-, COORD. GRAD. STUD, 68- Am. Theatre Asn; MLA; Shakespeare Asn. Am; AAUP. Elizabethan literature; Shakespeare; history of the drama. Publ: Pageantry on the Shakespearean stage, 51, 62 & Living theatre, 52, Twayne; The sources of ten Shakespeare plays, Crowell, 66. Add: Dept. of English, Herbert H. Lehman College, Bedford Park Blvd, Bronx, NY 10468.

GRIFFIN, DUSTIN HADLEY, b. New York, N.Y, July 26, 43; m. 66; c. 2. ENGLISH LITERATURE. B.A, Williams Col, 65; B.A, Oxford, 67; Ph.D. (Eng), Yale, 69. ASST. PROF. ENG, UNIV. CALIF, BERKELEY, 69- MLA. Milton; restoration; 18th century English literature. Publ: Satires against man: the poems of Rochester, Univ. Calif, 73. Add: Dept. of English, University of California, Berkeley, CA 94720.

GRIFFIN, EDWARD M. b. Pittsburgh, Pa, Sept. 25, 37; m. 60; c. 3. ENGLISH & AMERICAN LITERATURE. B.S, Univ. San Francisco, 59; M.A. & Ph.D. (Am. Lit), Stanford Univ, 66. Asst. prof. ENG, UNIV. MINN, MINNEAPOLIS, 66-69, ASSOC. PROF, 69-, DIR. GRAD. STUD. ENG, 72- Nat. Endowment for Humanities younger scholar summer stipend, 68; vis. assoc. prof. Eng, Stanford Univ, 71-72; asst. ed. bibliog, Philol. Quart, 71- U.S.A, 59-62, 1st Lt. MLA; Soc. Relig. Higher Educ; AAUP. American poetry; early American literature. Publ: Jonathan Edwards, Univ. Minn, 71; Notes from a clean, well-lighted place: Ralph Ellison's Invisible Man, 20th Century Lit, 10/69; The structure and language of Taylor's Meditation 2-112, Early Am. Lit, 69; Chauncy and Seasonable thoughts: a new letter, Am. Notes & Queries, 72. Add: Dept. of English, Main Engineering 207, University of Minnesota, Minneapolis, MN 55455.

GRIFFIN, ERNEST GEORGE, b. London, Eng, Nov. 24, 16; m. 47. ENGLISH. B.S, Columbia Univ, 50, A.M, 51, Ph.D.(Eng), 59. Lectr. eng, Columbia Univ, 53-56, instr, 56-61; assoc. prof, Am. Univ. Cairo, 61-62; asst. prof, Univ. Alta, 63-65, assoc. prof. 65-70; YORK UNIV, 70-72, PROF. ENG. & DIR. GRAD. PROG. ENG, 72- Can. Counc. Humanities & Soc. Sci. res. grants, summer 64 & 67, 68-69. MLA; Asn. Can. Univ. Teachers Eng; Can. Asn. Am. Stud; Conf. Christianity & Lit. History of literary criticism; literature and religion; literature in English, 1920-1940, especially American literature. Publ: Co-auth, Manual of English prose composition, Rinehart, 58; auth, John Middleton Murry, Twayne, 68; Pity, alienation and reconciliation in the work of O'Neill, Mosaic, fall 68; The circular and the linear: the Middleton Murry-D.H. Lawrence affair, D.H. Lawrence Rev, spring 69; Sympathetic materialism: a re-reading of Theodore Dreiser, Bull. Humanities Asn. Can, winter 69. Add: Dept. of English, York University, 4700 Keele St, Downsview, Ont. M3J 1P3, Can.

GRIFFIN, ERVILLE GLENN, b. Taylorville, Ill, July 26, 08; m. 38; c. 4. COMMUNICATION. B.A, Univ. Ill, 33, M.A, 43; Univ. Chicago, 35, 42-45. Field worker, Nat. Am. Red Cross, 34-38; teacher ENG, pub. schs, Ill, 38-46; instr, PURDUE UNIV, WEST LAFAYETTE, 46-54, asst. prof, 54-60, assoc. prof, 60-72, PROF, 72- Consult, bus, indust. & schs, 54- Am. Bus. Writing Asn.(v.pres, 53-59, pres, 59, fel, 61-); N.Cent. Reading Asn; NCTE; Nat. Soc. Stud. Commun.(assoc. ed, J. Commun, 59-). Developmental reading; business and technical communication. Publ: Co-auth, Executive development and reading skill, Psycho-tech, Inc, 55, Effective business communication, 3rd ed, Ronald, 66 & Toward better reading skill, 3rd ed, Appleton, 67. Add: 324 Heavilon Hall, Purdue University, West Lafayette, IN 47907.

GRIFFIN, JOHN R, b. Mar. 31, 38; U.S. citizen. ENGLISH, HISTORY. B.S, Xavier Univ, 59, A.M, 61; cert, Univ. Paris, 60; Ph.D.(Eng), Univ. Ottawa, 63; Ph.D.(hist), Trinity Col.(Dublin), 72. Vis. prof. Am. lit, Univ. Torino, 59-60; asst. prof. ENG. LIT, SOUTH. COLO. STATE COL, 63-67, assoc. prof, 67-73, PROF, 73- Summer fels, Harvard, 65-67; Ital. Govt. fel, Ciriolo Italiano, Italy, 68; consult, Choice Mag, 73-74. MLA; Rocky Mountain Mod. Lang. Asn. Medieval, Renaissance and Victorian periods. Publ: The intellectual milieu of Lord Macauley, Ottawa Univ, 65; The Anglican politics of Cardinal Newman, Anglican Theol. Rev, 73; Dr. Pusey and the Oxford movement, 73 & The social implications of the Oxford movement, 74, Hist. Mag. Protestant Episcopal Church. Add: Dept. of English, Southern Colorado State College, 900 W. Orman Ave, Pueblo, CO 81005.

GRIFFIN, LELAND MILBURN, b. Kansas City, Kans, Apr. 9, 20; m. 43; c. 3. SPEECH. A.B, Univ. Mo, 41, A.M, 42; Ph.D, Cornell Univ, 50. Instr, Univ.

Mo, 46-47; teaching fel, Cornell Univ, 47-50; asst. prof. SPEECH, Wash. Univ, 50-54; assoc. prof. & chmn. dept, Boston Univ, 54-56; assoc. prof, NORTHWEST. UNIV, EVANSTON, 56-64, PROF, 64- U.S.N.R, 42-46. Speech Commun. Asn; Cent. States Speech Asn. Rhetorical theory; public address: the anti-Masonic movement. Publ: Rhetorical structure of the anti-Masonic movement, Rhetorical Idiom; Rhetorical structure of the new left movement, Quart. J. Speech, 4/64; A dramatistic theory of the rhetoric of movements, In: Critical responses to Kenneth Burke, Univ. Minn, 69; plus one other. Add: Dept. of Speech, Northwestern University, 633 Clark, Evanston, IL 60201.

GRIFFIN, MARY, b. Chicago, Ill, Dec. 25, 16. ENGLISH. B.Mus.Ed, Mundelein Col, 39, A.B, 43; M.A, Cath. Univ. Am, 50; scholarship, Univ. London, summer, 60; Ph.D.(Eng), Fordham Univ, 62. Instr. Eng, St. Joseph Academy, 42-44; instr. Eng. & music, Clarke Col, 44-49, asst. prof. ENG, 49-54; Mundelein Col, 54-57, asst, Fordham Univ, 59-61; PROF. ENG. & ACAD. DEAN, MUNDELEIN COL, 61- Mem. comn. acad. affairs, Am. Counc. Educ, 65-68; res. fel, Yale, 68-69; vis. prof, Alcorn A&M Col, 71-73; proj. dir, Nat. Endowment Humanities grant, 73- MLA; AAUP; Am. Asn. Higher Educ. American nuns since Vatican II; audio-visual techniques in the teaching of writing. Publ: The trial of Midas II by Chas. Burney, 1677, Univ. Microfilms, 62; Where late the sweet birds sang, Little, 74; Church-related and uneasily secular, New City, 8/65; The operative goals of Catholic higher education, In: Toward new dimensions of Catholic higher education, Educ. Res. Assoc, 67. Add: Mundelein College, 6363 Sheridan Rd, Chicago, IL 60626.

GRIFFIN, ROBERT ARTHUR, b. Cleveland, Ohio, Feb. 6, 26; m. 52; c. 2. SPEECH & HISTORY OF THEATRE. Th.B, Malone Col, 48; B.A, Geneva Col, 51; M.Div, Pittsburgh Theol. Sem, 54; Univ. Gottingen, 55-58; M.A, Ohio State Univ, Columbus, 65, Ph.D.(speech ed), 67. Instr. Eng. & speech, Ohio sec. schs, 59-65; teaching assoc. hist. of ed, Ohio State Univ, Columbus, 65-66, supvr. practice teaching creative drama & speech ed, 66-67; ASSOC. PROF. SPEECH COMMUN, SOUTH. CONN. STATE COL, 73-, acad. planner, 73-74. Speech Commun. Asn; Am. Fed. Teachers. History of Baroque culture and theatre; the practice of pragmatism as modern American culture; classical themes of logic, language and art. Publ: High Baroque culture and theatre in Vienna, Humanities Press, 72; Aristophanes: the social function of Old Greek comedy, Conn. Rev, 4/70; contrib, From Plato to Nietzsche: a philosophical anthology, Kendall Hunt, 71; auth, Logic and the arts, Conn. Rev, 10/72 & West. Humanities Rev, 4/73; plus two others. Add: Dept. of Speech, Southern Connecticut State College, 501 Crescent St, New Haven, CT 06515.

GRIFFIN, ROBERT JULIAN, b. Tallahassee, Fla, Oct. 12, 32. ENGLISH. AMERICAN LITERATURE. B.A, George Washington Univ, 59; fel, Univ. Fla, 59-60, M.A, 61; fel, Univ. Calif, Berkeley, 61-63, Ph.D.(Eng), 65. Instr. Eng, Yale, 64-67, asst. prof, 67-70; assoc. prof, Calif. State Univ. Hayward, 70-72; EXEC. SECY, BERKELEY FAC. ASN, 73- Morse fel, Yale, 69-70; consult. ed. Eng. & Am. lit, Dickenson Publ, 70- U.S.A, 51-53, Sgt. Am. Stud. Asn; Mind Asn; MLA. American literature; 18th century English literature; contemporary arts. Publ: Ed, Twentieth century interpretations of Arrowsmith, Prentice-Hall, 68; auth, Tristram Shandy and language, Col. Eng, 61; These contraries such unity do hold: patterned imagery in Shakespeare's . . . poems, Stud. Eng. Lit, 64; Carrie and music: a note on Dreiser's technique, In: From Irving to Steinbeck, Univ. Fla, 72; plus others. Add: 255 Stanford Ave, Berkeley, CA 94708.

GRIFFIN, ROBERT P, b. Waterbury, Conn, July 7, 28; m. 53; c. 1. ENGLISH. M.A, Univ. Conn, 57, Ph.D.(Eng), 65; fel, Univ. N.C, 59-60. Instr. ENG, Univ. Conn, 55-59 & 60-65; asst. prof, SOUTH. ILL. UNIV, CARBONDALE, 65- MLA. Shakespeare; Jacobean drama; Renaissance literature. Add: Dept. of English, Southern Illinois University, Carbondale, IL 62901.

GRIFFIN, ROBERT STUART, b. Brinson, Ga, Dec. 8, 04. SPEECH, PSYCHOLOGY. B.S, Ore. State Col, 28; A.M, Univ. South. Calif, 35, fel, 40-41, Ph.D, 41. From instr. to prof. Eng, UNIV. NEV, RENO, 28-54, prof. speech & drama & chmn. dept, 54-72, coord, army specialized training prog, 43-44; asst. admin, 44-46, acting dean men, 45-46, dean men, 46-53, EMER. PROF. SPEECH & DRAMA, 72- Speech Commun. Asn. Reasoning and emotion; historical and psychological study of the conviction-persuasion concept in public speaking. Add: 1390 Mallory Lane, Reno, NV 89502.

GRIFFIN, WILLIAM JAMES, b. College Springs, Iowa, Sept. 26, 07; m. 34; c. 3. ENGLISH. A.B, Park Col, 29; M.A, State Univ. Iowa, 30, fel, 30-31, Ph.D.(Eng), 39; summers, Univ. Wis, 33; Univ. Minn, 42. Instr. Eng. & speech, Independence Jr. Col.(Kans), 31-35; Minn. Teachers Col, St. Cloud, 35-39, head div. lang. & lit, 39-43; vis. prof. Am. lit, Brazil, 46-48; assoc. prof. ENG, Ill. State Norm. Univ, 48; GEORGE PEABODY COL, 48-49, prof, 49-73, chmn. dept, 71-73, dir. res, Eng. educ, Inst. Sch. Learning, 64-73, EMER. PROF, 73- Lectr, Inst. Rio Branco, Brazilian Ministry For. Relat, Rio de Janeiro, 47; Carnegie Found. Res. Fund grant, 52; vis. prof, Univ. Lisbon, 57. U.S.N.R, 43-46, Lt. Comdr. MLA; Renaissance Soc. Am; NCTE; Col. Eng. Asn.(pres, 71-73). Elizabethan drama; folklore; psycholinguistics. Publ: Co-auth, Syntax of kindergarten and elementary school children, NCTE, 67; auth, Notes on early tudor control of stage and press, Mod. Lang. Notes; How to misread Faulkner: a powerful plea for ignorance, Tenn. Stud. Lit; Children's development of syntactic control, In: Developments in applied psycholinguistics research, Macmillan, 68; plus others. Add: 3601 Wilbur Foster Dr, Nashville, TN 37204.

GRIFFITH, ALBERT JOSEPH, JR, b. Ft. Worth, Tex, June 5, 32; m. 57; c. 4. ENGLISH. A.B, St. Edward's Univ, 53; M.A, Univ. Tex, Austin, 54, Ph.D, 59. Instr. ENG, OUR LADY OF THE LAKE COL, 58-61, asst. prof, 61-63, assoc. prof, 63-66, PROF, 66-, CHMN. HUMANITIES DIV, 74-, chmn. dept. Eng, 66-69, v.pres. Develop. & Pub. Relat, 69-72. Coord, coop. grad. prog. Eng, United Cols. San Antonio, 73-; Moody prof. Eng, coop. prog, Incarnate Word Col-Our Lady of the Lake Col, 73- U.S.A, 54-56. MLA; NCTE; Soc. Stud. South. Lit; Southwest. Am. Lit. Asn. Contemporary southern fiction; literature of mixed media; 19th century American romanticism. Publ: Peter Taylor, Twayne, 71; Flannery O'Connor, America, 11/65; Linguistics: a revolution in retrospect, Elem. Eng, 5/66; Carson McCullers' myth of the sad cafe, Ga. Rev, spring 67; plus others. Add: Div. of Humanities, Our Lady of the Lake College, 411 S.W. 24th St, San Antonio, TX 78285.

GRIFFITH, BARTON L, b. Topeka, Kans, May 8, 26; m. 49; c. 3. SPEECH. B.A, Washburn Univ, 50; M.A, State Univ. Iowa, 51; Ph.D, Univ. Mich, 59. Prom. dir, WREN, Topeka, Kans, 48-50; instr, teaching fel. & prod. asst, Univ. Mich, 53-55; dir. distribution, Nat. Educ. TV & Radio Ctr, 55-57; PROF. SPEECH & COORD. OFF. INSTRUCT. DESIGN, UNIV. MO-COLUMBIA, 57- Vis. prof, Univ. Hawaii, 66; consult, insts, fed. govt. orgn, state orgn, corp. & univs; dir, three-year Ford Found. proj. for recording on videotape eleven univ. courses; consult. & mem. bd. dir. & oper. comt, Great Plains Nat. Instructional TV Libr. Publ: Co-ed, Improvement of teaching by television, Univ. Mo, 64; co-auth, The social importance of television and radio, In: Academic areas of speech, Merrill, 65; auth, Basic and total teaching by television, Bull. Nat. Asn. Sec. Sch. Prin, 10/66; The Malawi Broadcasting Corporation; a case study of a broadcasting system in a new and developing African country, NAEB Jour, 9-10/67. Add: 404 Jesse Hall, University of Missouri-Columbia, Columbia, MO 65201.

GRIFFITH, BENJAMIN WOODWARD, JR, b. Lanett, Ala, Mar. 30, 22; m. 48; c. 2. ENGLISH. A.B, Mercer Univ, 44; M.A, Northwest. Univ, 48, Ph.D. (Eng), 52. Prof. ENG, Tift Col, 50-55; assoc. prof, Mercer UNIV, 55-59, prof, 59-70, chmn. dept, 61-70, dir. freshman Eng, 55-61; PROF, W.GA. COL, 70-, DEAN GRAD. SCH, 73-, head dept. Eng, 70-73. Vis. scholar, Duke Univ, 55; South. Found. fel, 59; co-ed, Notes Contemporary Lit, 71- U.S.N, 43-46, Lt.(jg). MLA; S.Atlantic Mod. Lang. Asn; Keats-Shelley Asn. Am. Shelley and the romantic poets; English drama of the Restoration and 18th century. Publ: John Dryden's All for love, 61 & John Gay's The beggar's opera, 62, Barron's; ed, The knight of the burning pestle, 63, auth, A simplified approach to Wuthering Heights, 66, co-auth, A simplified approach to Silas Marner, 67, auth, A simplified approach to Mark Twain's Huckleberry Finn, 69, & How to prepare for the graduate record examination in literature, 69, Barron's; A note on Robinson's use of turannos, Concerning Poetry, 71; Faulkner's archaic titles and the second shepherds' play, Notes Miss. Writers, 71; Csardas at Salt Springs: southern culture in 1888, Ga. Rev, 72; plus three others. Add: Graduate School, West Georgia College, Sanford Hall, Carrollton, GA 30117.

GRIFFITH, CLARK, b. Excelsior Springs, Mo, Mar. 27, 25; m. 61. ENGLISH. A.B, Cent. Methodist Col, 47; M.A, South. Methodist Univ. 48; Ph.D, Univ. Iowa, 52. Instr. ENG, South. Methodist Univ, 48-49; Harvard, 52-55; asst. prof, Univ. Iowa, 55-60, assoc. prof, 61-64, PROF, 64-70; UNIV. ORE, 70- Vis. prof. Eng. & consult, grad. prog. Eng, North. Ill. Univ, 61-63; vis. prof, Am. Univ. Cairo, 66-67. U.S.A, 43-45. Nineteenth and twentieth century American literature. Publ: The long shadow: Emily Dickinson's tragic poetry, Princeton, 64; Poe's Ligeia and the English Romantics, Unov. Toronto Quart, fall 54; Sex and death: the significance of Whitman's Calamus themes, Philol. Quart, winter 60; Frost and the American view of nature, Am. Quart, spring 68. Add: Dept. of English, University of Oregon, Eugene, OR 97403.

GRIFFITH, EDWARD E, b. West Winfield, N.Y, Feb. 4, 11; m. 36; c. 3. ENGLISH & DRAMA. B.E, Ithaca Col, 30; Syracuse Univ. Instr. Eng, Le Roy Pub. Schs, N.Y, 30-33; actor, Casford Players, 33-35; instr. ENG. & DRAMA, Ft. Edward, N.Y, 36-43; Manlius Mil. Acad, 43-45; HOBART & WILLIAM SMITH COLS, 46-49, asst. prof, 50-56, assoc. prof, 57-60, PROF, 61- Professional and community theatre production and direction. Add: Dept. of English, Hobart & William Smith Colleges, Geneva, NY 14456.

GRIFFITH, JOHN LINCOLN, b. Chicago, Ill, Aug. 11, 31; m. 55; c. 2. JOURNALISM, MASS COMMUNICATIONS. B.A, Southeast. State Col, 56; M.S, Okla. State Univ, 57, Ed.D.(jour. & higher educ), 67. Reporter, Stillwater News-Press, Okla, 56-57; state ed, Daily Ardmoreite, Ardmore, 59-62; instr. & dir. pub. relat, Northeast. A&M Col, 57-58; North. Okla. Col, 62-65; asst. prof. jour. & commun, Okla. State Univ, 65-67; JOUR, North. Ill. Univ, 67-69; ASSOC. PROF. & CHMN. DEPT, UNIV. FLA, 69- Nat. Guard, 48-50; U.S.A.F, 50-53. Asn. Educ. in Jour. Instructional systems; programmed and computer assisted instruction. Publ: Co-auth, Basic news writing, Prentice-Hall, 74; auth, An evaluation of programmed instruction in journalism, Jour. Quart, 46: 613-617; Item analysis improves testing, Jour. Educr, 27: 42-44; Journalism schools expand use of automation, Ed. & Publ, 7/73. Add: College of Journalism & Communication, University of Florida, Gainesville, FL 32601.

GRIFFITH, KELLEY EDWARD, JR, b. Washington, D.C, Mar. 2, 40; m. 63; c. 2. AMERICAN & 18TH CENTURY LITERATURE. B.A, Wake Forest Univ, 62; M.A, Univ. Pa, 63, Ph.D.(Eng), 68. Instr. ENG, Drexel Inst. Technol, 66-68; ASST. PROF, UNIV. N.C, GREENSBORO, 68- MLA; S.Atlantic Mod. Lang. Asn; Col. Eng. Asn. Turn of the century United States literary history; Hawthorne. Publ: Form in The Blithedale romance, 3/68 & Weir Mitchell and the genteel romance, 5/72, Am. Lit. Add: 501 N. Mendenhall St, Greensboro, NC 27401.

GRIFFITH, MALCOLM A, b. Lima, Ohio, Aug. 27, 37. ENGLISH & AMERICAN LITERATURE. B.A, Oberlin Col, 58; M.A, Ohio State Univ, 62, NDEA fel, 65-66, Ph.D.(Eng), 66. ASST. PROF. ENG, UNIV. WASH, 66- MLA. American literature; fiction; aesthetics. Publ: Theories of the grotesque, In: Ramon del Valle-Inclán: a critical approach to his life and works, 68. Add: Dept. of English, University of Washington, Seattle, WA 98105.

GRIFFITH, PHILIP MAHONE, b. Monroe, N.C, Oct. 1, 22. ENGLISH. A.B, Univ. N.C, 44, M.A, 45; M.A, Johns Hopkins Univ, 50; South. fel, Univ. N.C, 56-57, teaching fel, 57-58, Ph.D, 61. Instr. Eng, Tulane Univ, 45-47; jr. instr, Johns Hopkins Univ, 48-50; instr. ENG, Univ. N.C, 50-53, 58-59; Tulane Univ, 53-56, asst. prof, 59-64, assoc. prof. 64-66; vis. prof. UNIV. TULSA, 66-67, PROF, 67- U.S.A, 43. MLA; NCTE; S.Cent. Mod. Lang. Asn; Augustan Reprint Soc. Eighteenth century English literature; English novel; Dr. Samuel Johnson and his circle. Publ: A study of The adventurer, 1752-1754, Mouton, 69; Fire-scenes in Richardson's Clarissa and Smollett's Humphry Clinker, 61 & Joseph Warton's criticism of Shakespeare, 65, Tulane Stud. Eng; Dr. Johnson's Diction of common life and Swift's Directions to servants, Eng. Monogr. Ser, Univ. Tulsa, 67; plus others. Add: Dept. of English, University of Tulsa, Tulsa, OK 74104.

GRIFFITH, RICHARD RANDOLPH, b. Muncie, Ind, Sept. 25, 26; m. 46, 62; c. 9. ENGLISH. B.A, Univ. Ky, 47, M.A, 49; Ph.D, Ohio State Univ, 56. Instr. ENG, Univ. Ky, 48-51; Univ. R.I, 56-59; asst. prof. 59-62, Ball State Teachers Col, 62-64; assoc. prof, C.W. POST COL, L.I. UNIV, 64-68, PROF, 68- U.S.N.R, 44-46. MLA; Mediaeval Acad. Am. Chaucer; Middle English literature; history of the English language. Publ: A critical guide to Chaucer's Canterbury tales, Littlefield, 68; Westron Wynde, Explicator, 5/63; co-auth, The gifts of the shepherds in the Wakefield Secunda pastorem: an iconographical interpretation, Mediaeval Stud, 10/66; The political bias of Malory's Morte D'Arthur, Viator, 74; plus others. Add: Dept. of English, C.W. Post College, Long Island University, Greenvale, NY 11548.

GRIFFITH, WILLIAM WAYNE, b. Johnstown, Pa, Feb. 11, 08. AMERICAN LITERATURE. A.B, Univ. Pa, 29; A.M, Harvard, 34; B.S, Drexel Inst. Technol, 37; Ph.D, Univ. Pittsburgh, 41. Lectr. Eng, Univ. Pittsburgh, 42-43; from asst. prof. to prof, Mary Washington Col, Univ. Va, 43-73; RETIRED. MLA; Col. Eng. Asn. Add: 1205 Dandridge St, Fredericksburg, VA 22401.

GRIGG, QUAY, JR, b. Charlotte, N.C, Mar. 4, 28. ENGLISH. B.A, Duke Univ, 49, M.A, 50; Ph.D, Univ. Pa, 61. Instr. Eng, Tusculum Col, 50-51; dir. pub. relat, Coker Col, 53-55; instr. ENG, Univ. Del, 58-60; asst. prof, Alfred Univ, 60-63; HAMLINE UNIV, 63-66, ASSOC. PROF, 66- U.S.A, 51-53, Sgt. MLA. American literature; modern drama; fiction. Add: Dept. of English, Hamline University, St. Paul, MN 55104.

GRIGGS, CHARLES IRWIN, b. Blandinsville, Ill, Jan. 6, 02; m. 29; c. 1. ENGLISH. A.B, Univ. Wis, 25, A.M, 27, Ph.D, 37; Adams fel, Univ. London, 30-31. Instr, Univ. Wis, 25-37; ENG. TEMPLE UNIV, 37-42, asst. prof, 42-45, assoc. prof, 45-46, prof, 48-69, acting chmn. dept, 58, EMER. PROF, 69- MLA; Conf. Col. Compos. Commun.(pres, 56). Periodical authorship; William Godwin's novels. Add: Star Route, New Harbor, ME 04554.

GRIGGS, HARRY HUBERT, b. Rockville, Ind, Aug. 20, 27; m. 52; c. 2. JOURNALISM, MASS COMMUNICATION. A.B, Ind. Univ, 47, M.A, 49; Ph.D. (mass commun), Univ. Iowa, 62. Tel. ed, Lafayette Jour. & Courier, 49-50; asst. tel. ed, Ft. Wayne News-Sentinel, 50-53; dir. pub. relat, Wis. State Col. River Falls, 53-54; instr. JOUR, Butler Univ, 54-56; Univ. Iowa, 56-57; asst. prof, UNIV. FLA, 58-62, assoc. prof, 62-67, PROF, 67-, DIR. GRAD. DIV, COL. JOUR. & COMMUN, 62-, dir. res. div, 62-70. Copy ed, Louisville Courier-Jour, summer 64. U.S.A, 46-47. Asn. Educ. Jour. News media performance and personnel; news media and society. Publ: Newspaper public service is defined as many things, Publ. Auxiliary, 9/59; Newspaper performance in recession coverage, Jour. Quart, autumn 63; Women in journalism: threat or promise?, Ed & Publ, 10/66. Add: College of Journalism & Communications, University of Florida, Gainesville, FL 32611.

GRIGGS, SILAS, Linguistics, English Language. See Volume III, Foreign Languages, Linguistics & Philology.

GRIGSBY, LUCY C, b. Louisville, Ky, Dec. 27, 17; m. 46; c. 1. ENGLISH LITERATURE. B.A, Univ. Louisville, 39; M.A, Atlanta Univ, 41; Gen. Educ. Bd. fel, Univ. Wis, 44-45, Rosenwald fel, 48-49. Assoc. prof. ENG, ATLANTA UNIV, 41-72, PROF, 72-, CHMN. DEPT, 70- Consult. lang. arts, Phelps-Stokes Proj. Improv. Sec. Sch. Teaching; assoc. ed, Phylon. NCTE; Col. Lang. Asn.(secy, 65-); S.Atlantic Mod. Lang. Asn. Modern English and American literature; 18th century English literature; teaching of reading and teaching of English as a second language. Add: Dept. of English, Atlanta University, Atlanta, GA 30314.

GRILLO, VIRGIL, b. Brooklyn, N.Y, Jan. 2, 38; m. 59; c. 2. LITERATURE, FILM. B.A, Univ. South. Calif, 60; M.A, Univ. Calif, Berkeley, 62, Ph.D. (Eng), 70. Assoc. speech, Univ. Calif, Berkeley, 63-65, acting instr. ENG, 66-68; asst. prof, UNIV. COLO, BOULDER, 68-73, ASSOC. PROF, 73- Dir, Rocky Mountain Film Ctr, 72- MLA; Am. Fed. Teachers; Nat. Asn. Media Educr. Victorian studies; Charles Dickens; film history and criticism. Publ: Browning's Cuckold of St. Praxed's, Victorian Poetry, spring 73; Charles Dickens' Sketches by Boz: End in the beginning, Colo. Assoc. Univ. Press, spring 74. Add: 101 Hellems, University of Colorado, Boulder, CO 80302.

GRIMES, TERRENCE LAYNE, b. Altus, Okla, July 30, 44. ENGLISH. A.B, Yale, 66; M.A, Duke Univ, 68, Ph.D.(Eng), 72. ASST. PROF. ENG, ATLANTIC CHRISTIAN COL, 71- MLA; S.Atlantic Mod. Lang. Asn. Transitional period 1880-1920, poetry and prose; novels of George Meredith. Add: Dept. of English, Atlantic Christian College, Wilson, NC 27893.

GRIMSHAW, JAMES ALBERT, JR, b. Kingsville, Tex, Dec. 10, 40; m. 61; c. 2. BIBLIOGRAPHY & AMERICAN LITERATURE. B.A, Tex. Technol. Col, 62, M.A, 68; Ph.D.(Eng), La. State Univ, Baton Rouge, 72. U.S. AIR FORCE, 63-, instr. ENG, U.S. AIR FORCE ACAD, 68-69, asst. prof, 72-73, ASSOC. PROF, 74- Lectr, Univ. Colo, Colorado Springs, 73. U.S.A.F, 63-, Capt; Bronze Star Medal, 66. MLA; Rocky Mountain Mod. Lang. Asn; Soc. Stud. South. Lit; Bibliog. Soc. Univ. Va; Rocky Mountain Am. Stud. Asn; Armed Forces Writers League. The short story; 20th century American literature; modern novel. Publ: Robinson's Lost anchors, Explicator, 12/71; Some thoughts on naturalism, Moderne Sprachen, 12/73; Amphibology in Shakespeare's Sonnet LXIV, Shakespeare Quart, 74. Add: Dept. of English & Fine Arts, P.O. Box 156, United States Air Force Academy, CO 80840.

GRINDELL, ROBERT MACLEAN, English Language & Literature. See Volume III, Foreign Languages, Linguistics & Philology.

GRINSTEAD, FRANCES D, b. Nocona, Tex, Apr. 24, 99. JOURNALISM. B.J, Univ. Mo, 21, A.M, 28; Atlantic Monthly scholar, Bread Loaf Sch. Eng, 35. Instr. JOUR, Univ. Mo, 27-31, asst. prof, 31-45; UNIV. KANS, 48-51, assoc. prof, 51-66, dir. writers' conf, 53-66, EMER. ASSOC. PROF, 67-; RES. & WRITING, 66- Delta Kappa Gamma Educ. Found. grant, summer 65; Univ. Kans. res. grants, summers 64-66. Best adult bk. award, Nat. Fed. Press Women, 45. Asn. Educ. Jour. Development of women's magazines in the United States; social history. Publ: The high road, Doubleday, 45. Add: 2318 McClellan Pkwy, Sarasota, FL 33579.

GRISSINGER, JAMES ADAMS, b. Brooklyn, N.Y, Oct. 5, 23; m. 50; c. 2. SPEECH. B.A, Ohio State Univ, 47, M.A, 49, Ph.D, 57. Instr. SPEECH, Col. Wooster, 49-50; PROF. & CHMN. DEPT, OTTERBEIN COL, 50- U.S.A.F, 43-46, Res, 46-, Maj. Speech Commun. Asn; Cent. States Speech Commun. Asn. Public speaking; discussion; debate. Publ: A comparison of the relative effectiveness of discussion and debate, Speech Monogr, 3/59. Add: Dept. of Speech, Otterbein College, Westerville, OH 43081.

GRISSOM, (PATSY) COLEEN, b. Mt. Pleasant, Tex, Jan. 9, 34. ENGLISH. B.A, E.Tex. Univ, 55; M.A, Syracuse Univ, 57; Ph.D.(Eng), Univ. Tex, 66. Instr. Eng. & head resident, Hanover Col, 57-58; TRINITY UNIV, 58-63, ASSOC. PROF. ENG, 63-, DEAN STUD, 72-, assoc. dean stud. life, 63-72. Nat. Assn. Women Deans & Counsel. Student personnel; administration; 20th century British literature. Add: Student Affairs Office, Trinity University, 715 Stadium Dr, San Antonio, TX 78284.

GRISVARD, LARRY EUGENE, b. Hillsdale, Mich, Oct. 12, 34; m. 56; c. 3. THEATRE. B.A, Univ. Toledo, 56; M.A, Bowling Green State Univ, 57; Ph.D.(speech & theatre), Ohio State Univ, 65. Assoc. prof. SPEECH & THEATER, SOUTHEAST MO. STATE UNIV, 59-72, PROF, 72-, DIR. THEATRE, 59- Speech Commun. Asn. The Ludlow & Smith theatrical company in St. Louis; the career of Julia Dean, actress of mid 19th century. Add: Dept. of Speech, Southeast Missouri State University, Cape Girardeau, MO 63701.

GROB, ALAN, b. New York, N.Y, Mar. 12, 32; m. 58; c. 2. ENGLISH LITERATURE. B.A, Utica Col, 52; M.A, Univ. Wis, 57, Ph.D, 61. From asst. prof. to assoc. prof. ENG, RICE UNIV, 61-73, PROF, 73- U.S.N.R, 53-56, Lt.(jg). MLA. Romantic and Victorian poetry. Publ: The philosophic mind, Ohio State Univ, 73; Wordsworth Immortality ode, the quest for identity, ELH; Wordsworth & Godwin: a reassessment, Stud. Romanticism, 67; plus four others. Add: Dept. of English, Rice University, Houston, TX 77001.

GROFF, PATRICK J, b. Crescent City, Calif, Jan. 30, 24; wid; c. 1. ENGLISH EDUCATION. B.S, Univ. Ore, 48, M.S, 50; Ed.D, Univ. Calif, 55. Teacher, Coos Bay Sch. Dist, Ore, 50-53; PROF. EDUC, SAN DIEGO STATE UNIV, 55- Mem, Nat. Conf. Res. Eng, 63-; consult. Eng. educ, San Diego City Schs, 65-66; participant, tri-univ. proj. Univ. Nebr, 67-68. U.S.N, 43-45, Res, Lt. NCTE; Int. Reading Asn. Elementary English. Publ: Co-auth, First grade reading programs, 65 & Individualized reading program, 67, Int. Reading Asn; New frontiers in education, Grune, 66; Resource materials for teachers of spelling, Burgess, 68; auth, Children's attitudes toward reading and their critical reading abilities, J. Educ. Res, 4/62; The culturally deprived child: views of teachers and of Riessman, Except. Children, 10/64; Where are we going with poetry for children, Horn Bk, 8/66. Add: Dept. of Education, San Diego State University, San Diego, CA 92115.

GROH, ALFRED STUART, b. Wilkes-Barre, Pa, Mar. 10, 21. ENGLISH, DRAMA. B.A, Syracuse Univ, 43; M.A, Columbia Univ, 50. Instr. ENG, WILKES COL, 46-50, asst. prof, 50-58, ASSOC. PROF, 58-, DIR. THEATER, 49- Dept. Pub. Instr. & U.S. Dept. Health, Educ. & Welfare grant, summer 67-68. U.S.A.A.F, 43-45, T/Sgt. Am. Nat. Theatre & Acad; Am. Theatre Asn. Add: Dept. of Theatre Arts, Wilkes College, Wilkes-Barre, PA 18703.

GROMAN, GEORGE L, b. New York, N.Y, Sept. 8, 28; m. 61; c. 1. AMERICAN LITERATURE & HISTORY. B.A, N.Y. Univ, 49, Woodrow Wilson fel, 62-63, Ph.D.(Am. civilization), 63; M.A, Columbia Univ, 51. Ed. asst, Columbia Univ. Press, 51-53; prod. ed, Macmillan Co, 54-57; fel. Eng, N.Y. Univ, 57-58, instr, 58-62; Rutgers Univ, Newark, 63-65, asst. prof, 65-70, assoc. prof, LaGUARDIA COMMUNITY COL, 70-73, PROF, 73-, CHMN. DIV. LANG. & CULT, 70- Consult, Nat. Endowment for Humanities, 74. Nat. Guard, 47-53, S/Sgt. MLA; Col. Eng. Asn. Am. Stud. Asn. American political fiction; American social problem fiction; literature of immigration. Publ: Ed. & introd, Political literature of the Progressive Era, Mich. State Univ, 67; The political fiction of William Allen White, Midwest Quart, autumn 66; A sociological classification of literary types, Peabody J. Educ, 10/72; Work internships for the English major: a new look at career possibilities, ADE Bull, 3/73; plus others. Add: Div. of Language & Culture, LaGuardia Community College, 31-10 Thomson Ave, Long Island City, NY 11101.

GRONBECK, BRUCE ELLIOTT, b. Bertha, Minn, Mar. 9, 41; m. 68; c. 2. RHETORIC, SPEECH COMMUNICATION. B.A, Concordia Col.(Moorhead, Minn), 63; M.A, Univ. Iowa, 66, Ph.D.(speech), 70. Lectr. SPEECH, Univ. Mich, 67-70, asst. prof, 70-73; ASSOC. PROF, UNIV. IOWA, 73- Proj. dir, Ctr. Res. & Teaching Grant, Univ. Mich, 67-68; Horace H. Rackham Sch. Grad. Stud. grant, summer 71, fel, summer 73; proj. adminr, Carnegie Corp. grant, 71-73 co-dir. bicentennial film proj, Nat. Endowment for Humanities, 72-73. Speech Commun. Asn; Eng-Speaking Union; Burke Soc. Eighteenth century British political rhetoric; speech communication pedagogy; contemporary culture and communication. Publ: An inventory of attitudes toward the doctor of arts in speech, Speech Teacher, 11/72; contrib, Explorations in rhetorical criticism, Pa. State Univ, 73; contrib, Rhetoric: a tradition in transition, In: Studies in honor of D.C. Bryant, Mich. State Univ, 74. Add: Dept. of Speech & Dramatic Art, University of Iowa, Iowa City, IA 52242.

GROOM, LEMUEL DOWNING, b. Davenport, Okla, Nov. 4, 11; m. 36; c. 2. JOURNALISM, COMMUNICATIONS. B.A, Univ. Okla, 48; M.A, Okla. A&M Col, 52. Co-publ, Davenport, Dispatch, Okla, 32-34; managing ed, Hominy News & J, 37; adv. mgr, Bristow Shopper, 37-40; managing ed, Springdale News, Ark, 40-44; from instr. to ASSOC. PROF. JOUR, OKLA. STATE UNIV, 46- Pub. Relations Soc. Am. fel. & Okla. Publ. Co. fel, summer 61; Found. Econ. Educ. fel, summer 62; Found. Pub. Relations Res. & Educ. fel, summer 63; fel, Rochester Inst. Technol, 68; Int. Commun. Sem. fel, Switz, summer 71. U.S.A, 43-46. AAUP; Am. Acad. Advertising; Asn. Educ. in Jour. Publ: Co-auth, Principles of advertising, Pittman, 63. Add: School of Journalism & Broadcasting, Communications Bldg, Oklahoma State University, Stillwater, OK 74074.

GROPPE, JOHN DANIEL, b. New York, N.Y, Apr. 23, 33; m. 62; c. 3. ENGLISH. B.S. in Ed, City Col. New York, 54; M.A, Columbia Univ, 60. Instr.

ENG, Villanova Univ, 57-58; teaching asst, Notre Dame Univ, 58-60; asst. prof, ST. JOSEPH'S COL.(IND), 62-66, ASSOC. PROF, 66- Fel, Inst. Ecumenical & Cult. Res, St. John's Univ.(Minn), 69-70; Nat. Endowment for Humanities summer sem. participant, 73. U.S.A, 54-56, 1st Lt. NCTE; Conf. Col. Compos. & Commun; AAUP; Rhetoric Soc. Am. Creative writing; stylistics; rhetorical theory. Publ: A shred of decency, West. Humanities Rev, spring 68; Ritualistic language, S.Atlantic Quart, winter 70; You can't always look it up, Thought, 12/71. Add: Dept. of English, St. Joseph's College, Rensselaer, IN 47978.

GROSCOP, HARRIETTE GRAYSON, English. See Klinker, Harriette Grayson.

GROSE, CHRISTOPHER WALDO, b. St. Louis, Mo, Apr. 17, 39; m. 62; c. 2. ENGLISH. A.B, Amherst Col, 61; M.A, Wash. Univ, 63, Ph.D.(Eng), 66. Asst. prof. ENG, UNIV. CALIF, LOS ANGELES, 65-73, ASSOC. PROF, 73- Folger Shakespeare Libr. fel, summer 67; Clark Libr. fel, summer 68. MLA. Seventeenth century literature. Publ: Milton's epic process, Yale, 73; Milton on ramist similitude, In: Seventeenth century imagery, Univ. Calif, 71; Lucky words: process of speech in Lycidas, J. Eng. & Ger. Philol, 71; plus others. Add: Dept. of English, University of California, Los Angeles, CA 90024.

GROSE, LOIS MARGARET, b. Roseby's Rock, W.Va, July 30, 03. ENGLISH. A.B, W.Va. Wesleyan Col, 23; M.A, Columbia Univ, 31. Teacher, high schs, W.Va, 23-35; Pa, 36-53; assoc. dir. instr. Eng, Pittsburgh Pub. Sec. Schs, 54-69; RETIRED. NCTE; Int. Reading Asn. Elizabethan drama; teaching writing in secondary schools. Publ: Co-auth, They found adventure: ninth grade anthology of literature, Prentice-Hall, 60; co-ed, Suggestions for evaluating junior high school writing, Nat. Counc. Teachers Eng; Suggestions for reading and discussion of Riverside edition of Hamlet, Houghton, 65; Teachers manual for Major British writers, Harcourt, 67; Teaching writing in the junior high school, 2/60, Essential conditions for teaching composition, 4/61 & The able student in a city school system, 10/66, Eng. J. Add: 144 N. Dithridge St, Pittsburgh, PA 15213.

GROS LOUIS, KENNETH RICHARD RUSSELL, b. Nashua, N.H, Dec. 18, 36; m. 65; c. 1. ENGLISH & COMPARATIVE LITERATURE. B.A, Columbia Univ, 59, M.A, 60; Ph.D.(Eng), Univ. Wis, 64. Asst. prof. ENG. & COMP. LIT, IND. UNIV, BLOOMINGTON, 64-67, assoc, prof, 67-73, PROF, 73-, CHMN. DEPT. ENG, 73-, asst. chmn. dept. comp. lit, 65-70, assoc. dean, Col. Arts & Sci, 70-73. Chmn. world lit. exam, Educ. Testing Serv, 70- MLA. Medieval literature; 17th century English poetry; mythology. Publ: Robert Henryson's Orpheus and Euridice and the Orpheus traditions of the Middle Ages, Speculum, 10/66; The significance of Sir Orfeo's self-exile, Rev. Eng. Stud, 8/67; The Orpheus tradition in English Renaissance literature, Stud. Eng. Lit, fall 70. Add: Dept. of English & Comparative Literature, Indiana University, Bloomington, IN 47401.

GROSS, ALAN GERALD, b. Brooklyn, N.Y, June 2, 36; m. 70; c. 2. ENGLISH, EDUCATION. B.A, N.Y. Univ, 56; M.A, Princeton, 60, Ph.D.(Eng), 62. Instr. Eng, Wayne State Univ, 62-65, asst. prof, 65-66; prof. commun, MACOMB COUNTY COMMUNITY COL, 66-74, COORD. INSTRUCT. RES, 74- Wayne State Univ. fac. fel, 65; Macomb County Community Col. res. grant, 68. U.S.A, 59-60. Elizabethan drama; pedagogical design; community college. Publ: Contemporary politics in Massinger, Stud. Eng. Lit, 66; The justification of Prince Hal, Tex. Stud, 68; The community college and the working class, Phi Delta Kappan, 74. Add: Dept. of Research & Development, Macomb County Community College, Warren, MI 48093.

GROSS, BARRY EDWARD, b. New York, N.Y, Dec. 22, 38; m. 61; c. 3. AMERICAN LITERATURE, DRAMA. B.A, City Col. New York, 59; M.A, Cornell Univ, 62; Ph.D.(Eng), Ohio State Univ, 66. Asst. prof. ENG, MICH. STATE UNIV, 66-69, ASSOC. PROF, 69- Vis. lectr, Univ. Lancaster, 69-70; Fulbright lectr, Univ. Coimbra, 72-73; Am. Philos. Soc. res. grant, 72-73. Midwest. Mod. Lang. Asn; AAUP; Am. Stud. Asn. American fiction; drama; American studies. Publ: Ed, In our time: contemporary essays, Dodd, 69; auth, Fitzgerald in the fifties, Stud. in the Novel, 73; Back west: time and place in the Great Gatsby, West. Am. Lit, 74; The uninhabitable darkness of Another country, Negro-Am. Lit. Forum, 74; plus others. Add: Dept. of English, Michigan State University, East Lansing, MI 48823.

GROSS, BEVERLY A, b. New York, N.Y, May 5, 38. ENGLISH. B.A, Univ. Mich, 59; M.A, Univ. Chicago, 60, Ph.D.(Eng), 66. Instr. ENG, Northwest. Univ, 63-66; ASST. PROF, Vassar Col, 66-67; QUEENS COL.(N.Y), 67-, DIR. HONORS PROG, 70- Lit. ed, The Nation, 69-70. MLA. History of the novel. Publ: The shapes of fiction, Holt, 70; The poetic narrative: a reading of Flowering Judas, Style, 68; The anti-novels of John Barth, Chicago Rev, 68. Add: Dept. of English, Queens College, Flushing, NY 11367.

GROSS, DAVID STUART, b. Mineola, N.Y, Feb. 22, 42; m. 71; c. 1. ENGLISH, COMPARATIVE LITERATURE. B.A, Wesleyan Univ, 65; M.A, Univ. Iowa, 69, Ph.D.(comp. lit), 73; Am. Counc. Learned Soc. fel, libr, Rouen & Paris, France, 69-70. ASST. PROF. ENG, Winona State Col, 71-73; UNIV. OKLA, 73- MLA; Soc. Amis Flaubert. The novel; literature and society; Marxist theory. Add: Dept. of English, University of Oklahoma, Norman, OK 73069.

GROSS, GEORGE CLAYBURN, b. Wilmington, Calif, May 14, 22; m. 41; c. 2. ENGLISH LITERATURE. A.B, San Diego State Col, 48; M.A, 50; fel, Univ. South. Calif, 58-59, Ph.D.(Eng), 63. Teacher ENG, Grossmont High Sch, Calif, 48-49, teacher & head dept, 51-61; instr, San Diego State Col, 49-51; asst, Univ. South. Calif, 58-59; asst. prof, SAN DIEGO STATE UNIV, 61-64, assoc. prof, 64-68, PROF, 68-, DEAN ACAD. ADMIN, 72-, assoc. dean fac. personnel, 70-72. Elizabeth K. Pleasants teaching & scholarship award & Bing award, Eng. Dept, Univ. South. Calif, 59. A.U.S, 43-45, 2nd Lt. Keats-Shelley Asn; MLA. English romantic poets, especially Keats; Shakespeare; Mary Cowden Clarke. Publ: Mary Cowden Clarke, The girlhood of Shakespeare's heroines, and the Sex education of Victorian women, Victorian Stud, 9/72. Add: Office of Vice President for Academic Affairs, San Diego State University, 5402 College Ave, San Diego, CA 92115.

GROSS, HARVEY, b. Cleveland, Ohio, Mar. 6, 22; m. 49; c. 2. ENGLISH, COMPARATIVE LITERATURE. B.A, Univ. Calif, 47, M.A, 49; Fulbright fel, Austria, 51-52; univ. fel, Univ. Mich, 53-54, Ph.D.(Eng), 55. Teaching fel. ENG, Univ. Mich, 50-54; instr. Hofstra Col, 54-57; asst. prof, Univ. Denver, 57-61, assoc. prof, 61-64, PROF, 64-65; UNIV. CALIF, IRVINE, 65- Am. Counc. Learned Soc. fel, 66; Rockefeller Found. grant, 67. Hopwood award, 53. U.S.A.A.F, 42-45. MLA. Modernism; poetics; cultural history. Publ: Sound and form in modern poetry, 64, Plans for an orderly apocalypse, 68 & The contrived corridor, 71, Univ. Mich; The structure of verse, Fawcett, 66; Reopening the case of Wagner, winter 68-69 & Hegel, Beethoven, Wordsworth, winter 70, Am. Scholar; Metoikos in London, Mosaic, fall 72; plus others. Add: 1106 Essex Lane, Newport Beach, CA 92660.

GROSS, LAILA, b. Riga, Latvia, May 4, 37; U.S. citizen; m. 60. MEDIEVAL LITERATURE. B.A, Hunter Col, 59; M.A, Univ. Colo, 62; Ph.D.(Eng), Univ. Toronto, 67. Instr. ENG, Univ. Ill, Chicago Circle, 65-67, asst. prof, 68-69; FAIRLEIGH DICKINSON UNIV, 69-72, ASSOC. PROF, 72-, grant, 71-72. MLA; Mediaeval Acad. Am. Medieval art; Old English literature. Publ: Ed, An introduction to literary criticism, Putnam, 71; auth, The meaning and oral formulaic use of riot in the alliterative Morte Arthure, Annuale Mediaevale, 68; Telescoping in time in Sir Gawain and the Green Knight, Orbis Litterarum, 69; The two wooings of Criseyde, Neuphilol. Mitt, 73. Add: Dept. of English, Fairleigh Dickinson University, Teaneck, NJ 07666.

GROSS, RAPHAEL H, b. Padua, Ohio, Apr. 5, 12. ENGLISH LITERATURE. A.B, St. Joseph's Col.(Ind), 32, LL.D, 67; A.M, Univ. Mich, 41; Ph.D, Univ. Montreal, 50. PROF. ENG, ST. JOSEPH'S COL.(IND), 41-, DIR. FEL. PROG, 65-, pres, 51-65. Mem. fac, Univ. Montreal, 49-50. Mediaeval Acad. Am; NCTE. Catholic English literature. Publ: Ed, Century of the Catholic essay, Lippencott, 46. Add: Dept. of English, St. Joseph's College, Rensselaer, IN 47978.

GROSS, ROBERT EUGENE, b. Brooklyn, N.Y, May 13, 31; m. 60; c. 2. ENGLISH, AMERICAN LITERATURE. B.A, N.Y. Univ, 52, M.A, 53, Penfield fel, 53-54, 56-57, Ph.D.(Am. lit), 60. Lectr. ENG, IND. UNIV, BLOOMINGTON, 57-60, instr, 60-62, asst. prof, 62-65, assoc. prof, 65-68, PROF, 68- Vis. prof. Eng. & Am. lit, Univ. Zagreb, 63-64; consult, NDEA title IV grad. fel. prog, Off. Educ, 67-69. U.S.A, 54-56, Sgt. MLA; Mod. Humanities Res. Asn. American literature; 20th century poetry; history and theory of criticism. Add: Dept. of English, Indiana University, Bloomington, IN 47401.

GROSS, ROGER DENNIS, b. Spokane, Wash, Jan. 25, 31; m. 51, 73; c. 1. DRAMA. B.A, Univ. Ore, 57, Ph.D, 71; M.A, Univ. Minn, 58. Instr. speech & drama, Univ. Minn, 57-59; Univ. Ore, 59-61; asst. prof, Univ. Santa Clara, 61-71; ASSOC. PROF. SPEECH, BOWLING GREEN STATE UNIV, 71- Producing dir, Calif. Shakespeare Festival, 63-70. U.S.A.F, 51-52. Dramatic theory and interpretation; playwriting; Shakespearean production. Publ: Understanding playscripts, 74; The big thing, 57 & The voice and utterance, 58, Ivory Tower; The aesthetician as a featherbedder, 62 & The living Shakespeare, 5/64, The Owl; On apathy, Voice, 6/66: Musical comedies: The lamentable legend of t. Elmer Buzz, 59; The trouble with college men, 60. Add: Dept. of Speech, Bowling Green State University, Bowling Green, OH 43402.

GROSS, SEYMOUR LEE, b. New York, N.Y, Jan. 28, 26; m. 51; c. 3. ENGLISH. A.B, Univ. Denver, 49, A.M, 50; Ph.D.(Eng), Univ. Ill, 54. Instr. Eng, Univ. Ill, 54-55; Ind. Univ, 55-57, asst. prof, Univ. Notre Dame, 57-60, assoc. prof, 60-66, prof, 66-69; BURKE O'NEILL PROF. AM. LIT, UNIV. DETROIT, 69- Prof. extraordinary, Univ. Skopje, Yugoslavia, 62-63. Med.C, U.S.A, 44-46. MLA. Am. Stud. Asn. American literature; 20th century fiction. Publ: A Scarlet letter handbook, 60 & A Benito Cereno handbook, 65, Wadsworth; Eudora Welty: a bibliography, Univ. Va, 60; American literature survey, 4 vols, Viking, 62, rev. ed, 68; co-auth, Images of the Negro in American literature, Univ. Chicago, 66; auth, The house of the seven gables: text, sources, criticism, Norton, 67; The myth of Nat Turner, Am. Quart, 71. Add: 19519 Shrewsbury, Detroit, MI 48221.

GROSS, THEODORE L, b. Brooklyn, N.Y, Dec. 4, 30; m. 55; c. 2. ENGLISH, AMERICAN CIVILIZATION. B.A, Univ. Maine, 52; M.A, Columbia Univ, 57, Ph.D.(Eng), 60. Asst. ENG, Barnard Col, Columbia Univ, 57; from instr. to assoc. prof, CITY COL. NEW YORK, 58-69, PROF, 69-, ASSOC. DEAN HUMANITIES, 72- Fulbright award, Univ. Nancy, 64-65, vis. prof. 68-69; prof. Am. lit, Pau, France, summer 65; Am. Philos. grant, 66. U.S.A, 52-54. MLA; Am. Stud. Asn; Asn. Depts. Eng; NCTE (comm. lit, 72-). American literature. Publ: Albion W. Tourgee, 63 & Thomas Nelson Page, 67, Twayne; co-auth, An introduction to fiction, Random, 67; co-auth, Dark symphony: Negro literature in America, 68, auth, The heroic ideal in American literature, 72, ed, Representative men, 72, ed, A nation of nations, 72 & ed, The literature of American Jews, 73, Free Press; auth, Our mutual estate: the study of Negro literature, Antioch Rev, fall 68; F. Scott Fitzgerald: the hero in retrospect, S.Atlantic Quart, winter 68; Nathaniel Hawthorne: the absurdity of heroism, Yale Rev, winter 68. Add: Humanities Division, City College of New York, 138th St. & Convent Ave, New York, NY 10031.

GROSSKURTH, PHYLLIS, b. Toronto, Ont, Mar. 16, 24; m. 68; c. 3. ENGLISH. M.A, Univ. Ottawa, 60; Ph.D.(Eng), Univ. London, 62. Lectr. ENG, Carleton Univ, 64-65; asst. prof, UNIV. TORONTO, 65-68, assoc. prof, 68-72, PROF, 72- Comnr, Nat. Film Bd, 66. MLA. English, modern Canadian and modern European literature. Publ: John Addington Symonds, Longmans, 64; The woeful Victorian, Holt, 64; Gabrielle Roy, Forum Press, 68; Leslie Stephen, Brit. Counc, 68. Add: Dept. of English, University College, University of Toronto, Toronto, Ont, Can.

GROSSMAN, ABRAHAM, b. Warsaw, Poland, Jan. 16, 09; U.S. citizen; m. 64; c. 1. DRAMA, ENGLISH. B.A, City Col. New York, 31; N.A, N.Y. Univ, 61; Ph.D.(theater), Univ. Denver, 62. DIR. GRAD. STUD. THEATER, UNIV. DENVER, 63- U.S.A.A.F, 41-45, Capt. MLA; Am. Theatre Asn; Am. Soc. Theatre Res. American theater history; modern theater history, 1870 to present. Add: Dept. of Theater, University of Denver, Denver, CO 80210.

GROSSMAN, ALLEN R, b. Minneapolis, Minn, Jan. 7, 32. ENGLISH. Ph.D. (Eng), Brandeis Univ, 61. ASSOC. PROF. ENG, BRANDEIS UNIV, 67- Publ: Poetic knowledge, Univ. Va, 69; And the dew lay all night upon my branch, Aleph Press, 73. Add: Dept. of English, Brandeis University, Waltham, MA 02154.

GROSSMAN, MANUEL LESTER, b. Brockton, Mass, Sept. 8, 39; m. 63. SPEECH & THEATER. B.A, Univ. Mich, 61; M.A, Brooklyn Col, 64; Ph.D. (drama), N.Y. Univ, 66. Lectr. drama & speech, State Univ. N.Y. Buffalo, 66-67; asst. prof. speech, Boston Col, 67-69; ASSOC. PROF, QUEENS COL. (N.Y), 69- N.Y. Univ. honors scholar, 66-67; Boston Col. summer res. grant, 69 & 70; Boston Col. Title V1-A grant, 69-70; ed, Dada/Surrealism, 72-73; Queens Col.(N.Y) res. award, 72-74. Cinema; mass media and communications; modern theater. Publ: Dada, Pegasus, 71; Alfred Jarry and the theater of his time, Mod. Drama, 5/70; Surrealism in Dog star man, Dada/Surrealism, 11/72; Jean Vigo and the development of surrealist cinema, Symposium, 6/73; plus others. Add: Dept. of Communication Arts & Sciences, Queens College, Flushing, NY 11367.

GROSSMAN, RODNEY C, b. Olean, N.Y, Dec. 27, 38; m. 60; c. 2. ENGLISH. A.B, Allegheny Col, 60; M.A, Kans. State Univ, 62; Ph.D.(Eng), Tulane Univ, 67. Instr. ENG, Univ. Southwest. La, 62-64; asst. prof, Lycoming Col, 66-69; ASSOC. PROF, UNIV. SOUTHWEST. LA, 69- William Wordsworth; media; film making. Add: Dept. of English, University of Southwestern Louisiana, Lafayette, LA 70501.

GROSSVOGEL, DAVID I, French, Romance Studies. See Volume III, Foreign Languages, Linguistics & Philology.

GROTELUESCHEN, PAUL G, b. Carlinville, Ill, Dec. 8, 27; m. 56; c. 5. SPEECH. B.S, Concordia Teachers Col.(Ill), 50; M.A, Northwest. Univ. 54. Instr. SPEECH, CONCORDIA TEACHERS COL.(ILL), 53-57, asst. prof, 57-61, ASSOC. PROF, 61- U.S.A, 45-48, 51-53, Capt. Speech Commun. Asn; Luther Educ. Asn. Speech education; oral interpretation of literature; mass communication. Add: 7400 Augusta St, River Forest, IL 60305.

GROUND, YVONNE, b. Modesto, Calif, Sept. 24, 19; m. 45; c. 2. ENGLISH. A.B, Stanford Univ, 40, M.A, 42. Teacher Eng, Weed High Sch, Calif, 41-42; Eng. & Spanish, Gridley High Sch, 42-44; ENG, Modesto High Sch, 48-52, head dept, 52-57; asst. prof, MERRIMACK COL, 57-69, ASSOC. PROF, 69-, CHMN. DEPT, 71- MLA. American literature, especially the 20th century. Add: Dept. of English, Merrimack College, North Andover, MA 01845.

GROVER, DORYS CROW, b. Pendleton, Ore, Sept. 23, 21; div. AMERICAN STUDIES, BRITISH LITERATURE. B.S, Ore. State Univ, 51; Asian Inst. fel, Univ. Hawaii, summer 62; Univ. Ore, 68; Ph.D.(Am. stud), Wash. State Univ, 69. Instr. ENG, Wash. State Univ, 64-69; prof, Drake Univ, 71-72; ASST. PROF, E.TEX. STATE UNIV, 72-, fac. res. grant, 72-74. MLA; Soc. Stud. Midwest. Lit; Rocky Mt. Mod. Lang. Asn; S.Cent. Mod. Lang. Asn; Am. Stud. Asn; AAUP. American novel and novelists; Colonial American literature. Publ: Vardis Fisher: the novelist as poet, 73 & A solitary voice: critical essays on Vardis Fisher, 73, Revisionist Press; The antelope sonnets, Tex. Quart, 74; Garland's Emily Dickinson—a case of mistaken identity, Am. Lit, 5/74; Emerson Hough, Soc. Stud. Midwest. Lit. Newslett, 6/74; plus others. Add: Dept. of Literature & Languages, East Texas State University, Commerce, TX 75428.

GROVES, FLORENCE, b. Kansas City, Kans, Aug. 10, 12. ENGLISH. B.S. in Ed, Cent. Mo State Col, 32; M.A, Northwest. Univ. 42. TEACHER, high sch, Mo, 32-43; jr. high sch, 43-46; ENG, HANNIBAL-LA GRANGE COL, 46- NCTE. Publ: Martha's eyes were opened (play), Mo. Baptist Convention, 53; Monography, In: Southern Baptist Encyclopedia, Broadman Press, 58. Add: Dept. of English, Hannibal-La Grange College, Hannibal, MO 63401.

GROW, LYNN MERLE, b. Norfolk, Va. Feb. 20, 45. ENGLISH LITERATURE. B.A, Univ. South. Calif, 67, M.A, 68 & 72, NDEA fel, 67-70, Ph.D.(Eng), 71. Teaching asst. ENG, Univ. South. Calif, 70-71, instr, 71-72; ASST. PROF, WICHITA STATE UNIV, 72- MLA; AAUP. Samuel Taylor Coleridge; Ralph Ellison; scholarship in modern American philosophy. Publ: Additional Heinrich Gomperz manuscripts in the Hoose library, fall 71 & Sarah Scott: a reconsideration, spring 73, Coranto; The consistency of the Biographia literaria, Wichita State Univ. Bull: Univ. Stud, 5/73. Add: Dept. of English, Wichita State University, Wichita, KS 67208.

GRUBB, DANIEL STUDD, b. London, Eng, Apr. 1, 28; U.S. citizen; m. 60; c. 1. ENGLISH LANGUAGE & LITERATURE. B.A, Wheaton Col, 53; M.A.T, Duke Univ, 57; M.A, Univ. Mich, 63, fel, 63-67, Ph.D.(Eng. lang), 67. Teacher, high sch, Mich, 57-62, assoc. prof. ENG, INDIANA UNIV. PA, 67-70, PROF, 70- U.S.A, 53-55. MLA; NEA. Charles Kingsley and the 19th century socio-economic novelists. Publ: Another Gulliver?, Stud. in Humanities, 1/74. Add: R.D. 1, 3002 Warren Rd, Indiana, PA 15701.

GRUBE, FRANK WILLIAM, b. Newark, N.J, Aug. 11, 02; m. 30; c. 2. ENGLISH. Ph.B, Shurtleff Col, 28; M.A, Columbia Univ, 29; Ph.D.(Eng. lang), State Univ. Iowa, 33. Asst. prof. Eng, Simpson Col, 29-31; chmn. lang. & lit, Iowa Wesleyan Col, 33-43; assoc. prof. Eng, Univ. Toledo, 43-44; dir. jour, N.E. Okla. State Col, 46-47; chmn. div. LANG. & LIT, NORTHWEST MO. STATE UNIV, 47-73, EMER. PROF, 73- NCTE; Asn. Depts. Eng. Old English; English drama; local legends. Publ: Ed, Grammarian's confusion, (3 vols), Northwest Mo. State Univ, 70-71; auth, Cereal foods of the Anglo-Saxons, Philol. Quart; Meat foods of the Anglo-Saxons, J. Eng. & Ger. Philol. Add: 548 Prather Ave, Maryville, MO 64468.

GRUBER, LOREN CHARLES, b. Carroll, Iowa, Sept. 17, 41; m. 67; c. 1. MEDIEVAL STUDIES, ENGLISH LITERATURE. B.A, Simpson Col, 63; M.A, West. Reserve Univ, 64; Ph.D.(Eng), Univ. Denver, 72. Instr. ENG, Grove City Col, 64-66; SIMPSON COL, 66-69, ASST. PROF, 70- Am. Soc. Aesthet; Mediaeval Acad. Am; MLA; Soc. New Lang. Stud.(exec. secy, 72-). Old English; Chaucer; Old Norse. Publ: Co-ed, New views on Chaucer: essays in generative criticism, 73 & In gear dagum: new views on Old English, 74, Soc. New Lang. Stud; auth, The wanderer and Arcite: isolation and the continuity of the English elegiac mode, In: Four papers for Michio Masui, 72; The manciple's tale: one key to Chaucer's language, In: New views on Chaucer: essays in generative criticism, 73 & The Oððaet phrase in Beowulf: motion, perception, and states of being, In: In gear dagum: new views on Old English, 74, Soc. New Lang. Stud. Add: 1105 N. C St, Indianola, IA 50125.

GRUMBACH, DORIS, b. New York, N.Y, July 12, 18; m. 41; c. 4. LITERATURE, CRITICISM. B.A, N.Y. Univ, 39; M.A, Cornell Univ, 40. Asst. prof. ENG, COL. ST. ROSE, 58-64, assoc. prof, 64-69, PROF, 69- Columnist, The Critic, 60-64; Nat. Cath. Reporter, 68-; vis. univ. fel, Empire State Col, 72-73; lit. ed, New Repub, 73- W.A.V.E.S, 41-43, Ens. MLA; Dante Soc. Contemporary literary criticism; modern American novel. Publ: The spoil of the flowers, 62 & The short throat, the tender mouth, 64, Doubleday; The company she kept, Coward, 67; The silent singers, Commonweal, 5/67; On Mary McCarthy, New York Times, 5/67; co-auth, The postconcilar parish, Kenedy, 67. Add: New Republic, 1244 19th St. N.W, Washington, DC 20036.

GRUNER, CHARLES RALPH, b. Pinckneyville, Ill, Nov. 6, 31; m. 58; c. 2. COMMUNICATION, SPEECH. B.S, South. Ill. Univ, 55, M.S, 56; Ph.D, Ohio State Univ, 63. Teacher speech, Webster Grove High Sch, Mo, 56-57; instr, St. Lawrence Univ, 57-60, asst. prof, 60-64; Univ. Nebr, 64-66, assoc. prof, 66-69; SPEECH COMMUN, UNIV. GA, 69-74, PROF, 74- U.S.A.F, 52-54. Speech Commun. Asn; Nat. Soc. Stud. Commun; Int. Soc. Gen. Semantics. The psychology of humor; psychology of stage fright; behavioral and attitudinal changes resulting from speech training. Publ: Speech communication in society, Allyn & Bacon, 72; A further experimental study of satire as persuasion, Speech Monogr, 8/66; The effect of humor on speaker ethos and information gain, J. Commun, 9/67; Editorial satire as persuasion: an experiment, Jour. Quart, winter 67. Add: GGS 16, University of Georgia, Athens, GA 30602.

GRUSHOW, IRA, b. New York, N.Y, Apr. 11, 33; m. 65; c. 2. ENGLISH. B.A, City Col. New York, 54; M.A, Yale, 57, Ph.D, 63. Instr. ENG, Carnegie Inst. Technol, 60-62; FRANKLIN & MARSHALL COL, 62-63, asst. prof, 63-68, ASSOC. PROF, 68- Nat. Endowment for the Humanities summer stipend, 67. U.S.A, 54-55. MLA; Am. Soc. 18th Century Stud. Satire; 18th century English literature; Sir Max Beerbohm. Publ: The chastened dandy: Beerbohm's Hilary Maltby and Stephen Braxton, Papers Lang. & Lit, fall 72. Add: Dept. of English, Franklin & Marshall College, Lancaster, PA 17604.

GRYBAS, ALGIRD A, b. Detroit, Mich, Sept. 14, 26; m. 53; c. 1. COMMUNICATION. B.A, Univ. Mich, 51, M.A, 53; Ph.D.(speech), Ohio State Univ, 65. From asst. prof to PROF. COMMUN. STUD, CALIF. STATE UNIV, SACRAMENTO, 63- U.S.N, 44-46. Speech Commun. Asn; Int. Commun. Asn; West Speech Commun. Asn. Persuasion; attitude change; commitment. Add: Dept. of Communication Studies, California State University, Sacramento, 6000 J St, Sacramento, CA 95819.

GUBERLET, MURIEL LEWIN, b. Wakefield, Kans, June 5, 89; m; c. 2. ENGLISH. A.B, Bethany Col; M.A, Univ. Wash, 28. Asst. prof. ENG, UNIV. WASH, 43-59, EMER. ASST. PROF, 59- English composition; marine biology. Publ: Animals of the seashore; Seaweeds at Ebb Tide; Famous oceanographic expeditions, Ronald; plus others. Add: Dept. of English, University of Washington, Seattle, WA 98105.

GUDAS, FABIAN JOHN, b. Boston, Mass, June 26, 17; m. 51; c. 3. ENGLISH. A.B, Univ. Chicago, 38, Ph.D.(Eng), 52. Instr. ENG, Univ. Minn, 45-53; LA. STATE UNIV, BATON ROUGE, 53-56, asst. prof, 56-61, assoc. prof. 61-66, PROF, 66- MLA; NCTE; Col. Eng. Asn; Conf. Col. Compos. & Commun; Speech Commun. Asn; Brit. Soc. Aesthet; Am. Soc. Aesthet. Literary criticism; semantics; rhetoric. Publ: Ananda K. Coomaraswamy: the perennial philosophy of art, 62 & I.A. Richards and the principle of complementarity, In: Essays in honor of Esmond Linsworth Marilla, 70, La. State Univ; Concrete universal, Organism, Taste & Tone, In: Encyclopedia of poetry and poetics, Princeton, 65; plus others. Add: Dept. of English, Louisiana State University, Baton Rouge, LA 70803.

GUERARD, ALBERT JOSEPH, b. Houston, Tex, Nov. 2, 14; m. 41; c. 3. ENGLISH & COMPARATIVE LITERATURE. A.B, Stanford Univ, 34, Ph.D, 38; A.M, Harvard, 35; Univ. London, 36-37. Instr. ENG, Amherst Col, 35-36; instr, Harvard, 38-41, fac. instr, 41-43, asst. prof, 46-48, assoc. prof, 48-54, PROF, 54-61; STANFORD UNIV, 61-, CHMN. DEPT. MOD. THOUGHT & LIT, 69- Rockefeller fel, 46-47; Fulbright res. scholar, France, 50-51; Guggenheim fel, 56-57, Ford fel, 59-60; Nat. Found. Arts grant, 67-68. U.S.A, 43-45. MLA; fel. Am. Acad. Arts & Sci. English and comparative literature of the 19th and 20th centuries; techniques of the novel. Publ: Night journey, 50; André Gide, 51 & Conrad the novelist, 58, Harvard; The bystander, Atlantic, Little, 58; The exiles, Macmillan, 63; plus others. Add: Dept. of English, Stanford University, Stanford, CA 94305.

GUERESCHI, EDWARD FRED, b. Fulton, N.Y, Feb. 27, 35. AMERICAN & ENGLISH LITERATURE. A.B, Syracuse Univ, 56, M.A, 62, Ph.D.(Eng), 69. Instr. ENG, ST. JOHN'S UNIV.(N.Y), 67-70, ASST. PROF, 70-, CHMN. AM. STUD, 73- MLA; NCTE. Modern poetry; 19th and 20th century American fiction; Afro-American literature. Publ: Wallace Steven's anti-mythological poem, The comedian as the letter C, Centennial Rev, fall 64; Wallace Stevens and the poetics of secular grace, Erasmus Rev, fall 71; Ralph Ellison's King of the bingo game: anticipations of Invisible man, Negro Am. Lit. Forum, winter 72. Add: Dept. of English, St. John's University, Jamaica, NY 11439.

GUERIN, WILFRED LOUIS, b. New Orleans, July 10, 29; m. 51; c. 6. ENGLISH LITERATURE. B.A, Tulane Univ, 51, Gen. Educ. Bd. fel, 51-52, M.A, 53, South. Fel. Fund. grant, 56-58, Ph.D.(Eng), 58. Instr, Holy Cross High Sch, New Orleans, La, 52-53; ENG, Centenary Col, 53-56, asst. prof, 58-62; assoc. prof, Univ. Southwest. La, 62-63; PROF, Centenary Col. La, 63-74; LA. STATE UNIV, SHREVEPORT, 74- Fel, Southeast. Inst. Medieval & Renaissance Stud, Duke Univ. & Univ. N.C. Chapel Hill, summers 66 & 67; vis. fac. audit prog, Harvard, 70. MLA; NCTE; S.Cent. Mod. Lang. Asn; Col. Eng. Asn; AAUP; S.Cent. Renaissance Conf; Conf. Col. Compos. & Commun. Teilhard de Chardin; Thomas Malory; medieval English literature. Publ: Co-auth, A handbook of critical approaches to literature, 66 & co-auth, Mandala: literature for critical analysis, 70, Harper; auth, The great Gatsby: Christian myth and naturalistic deity, Renascence, 61; Irony and tension in Browning's Karshish, Victorian Poetry, 63; The tale of Gareth: the chivalric flowering, In: Malory's originality, Johns Hopkins Univ, 64; plus others. Add: Dept. of English, Louisiana State University in Shreveport, Shreveport, LA 71105.

GUERINOT, JOSEPH VINCENT, b. Rochester, N.Y, Feb. 18, 28. ENGLISH LITERATURE. B.A, St. Bernard's Sem, 49; M.A, Fordham Univ, 53; univ. fel, Yale, 53-54, Ph.D, 62. Asst, Fordham Univ, 51-52; asst. ENG, Lycee Jules Ferry, France, 54-55; instr, Bucknell Univ, 55-61, asst. prof, 61-65; Hunter Col, 65-67; assoc. prof, UNIV. WIS-MILWAUKEE, 67-71, PROF, 71- Pope; mediaeval Latin literature; Henry James. Publ: Pamphlet attacks on Alexander Pope, 1711-1744: a descriptive bibliography, Methuen, London, 69; ed, Twentieth century views: Pope, Prentice-Hall, 72. Add: Dept. of English, University of Wisconsin-Milwaukee, Milwaukee, WI 53211.

GUETTI, JAMES LAWRENCE, JR, b. Medford, Mass, Nov. 5, 37; m. 62; c. 1. ENGLISH & AMERICAN LITERATURE. A.B, Amherst Col, 59; M.A, Cornell Univ, 61, Ph.D.(Eng), 64. Instr. ENG, RUTGERS UNIV, NEW BRUNSWICK, 64-65, asst. prof, 65-67, ASSOC. PROF, 67- English and American prose fiction; 20th century literature. Publ: The limits of metaphor, Cornell Univ, 67; Action (novel), Dial, 72; Claude (short story), Epoch, spring 61; Heart of darkness and the failure of imagination, Sewanee Rev, summer 64. Add: Dept. of English, Rutgers University, New Brunswick, NJ 08903.

GUFFEY, GEORGE ROBERT, b. Albany, Ky, July 17, 32; m. 58; c. 1. ENGLISH. B.S, Bowling Green State Univ, 58; M.A, Univ. Ill, 60, fel, 60-62, Ph.D.(Eng), 64. Teaching asst. rhetoric, Univ. Ill, 63-64; asst. prof. ENG, UNIV. CALIF, LOS ANGELES, 64-69, ASSOC. PROF, 69- Univ. Calif. fac. fel, summer 66, Inst. Humanities grant, 68-69. MLA; Philol. Asn. Pac. Coast. Metaphysical poetry; 17th century fiction; John Dryden. Publ: Ed, Meditations on the six days of the creation, Augustan Reprint Soc, 66; auth, Elizabethan bibliographies supplements, Vol. VII: Daniel, Drayton, Sidney, 67, Elizabethan bibliographies supplements, Vol. III: Robert Herrick, Ben Jonson, Thomas Randolph, 68 & Elizabethan bibliographies supplements, Vol. XI: Traherne and the seventeenth-century platonists, 70, Nether Press; co-ed, Traherne's Christian ethicks, Cornell Univ, 68; co-ed, The works of John Dryden, Vol. X, Univ. Calif, 70; auth, Standardization of photographic reproductions for mechanical collation, PBSA, 2nd Quarter, 68. Add: Dept. of English, 2225 Rolfe, University of California, 405 Hilgard Ave, Los Angeles, CA 90024.

GUILDS, JOHN CALDWELL, JR, b. Columbia, S.C, Feb. 27, 24; m. 47; c. 3. ENGLISH. A.B, Wofford Coll, 47; A.M, Duke Univ, 49, Ph.D.(Eng), 54. Instr. ENG, Duke Univ, 48-52; asst. prof, Clemson Univ, 52-54; assoc. prof, E.Cent. State Col, 54-56; Tex. Tech Univ, 56-59, prof, 59-62, head dept, 62-64; PROF. & HEAD DEPT, UNIV. S.C, 64-, V.PROVOST LIB. & CULT. DISCIPLINES, 70- Smith-Mundt lectr. Am. lit, Damascus Univ, 59-60; gen. ed, Centennial ed. of writings of William Gilmore Simms, Univ. S.C, 66- U.S.A, 43-46. MLA; Am. Stud. Asn; Int. Asn. Univ. Prof. Eng; S.Atlantic Mod. Lang. Asn. American fiction; Southern literature; life and writings of William Gilmore Simms. Publ: Co-ed, A tricentennial anthology of South Carolina literature, 1670-1970, Univ. S.C, 71; ed, Nineteenth-century Southern fiction, Merrill, 70; auth, The lost number of the Southern Literary Gazette, Stud. Bibliog, 69; The literary criticism of William Gilmore Simms, S.C. Rev, 69; The achievement of William Gilmore Simms: his short fiction, In: The poetry of community: essays on the Southern sensibility of history and literature, 72; plus others. Add: 1321 Milford Rd, Columbia, SC 29206.

GUILHAMET, LEON MAURICE, b. New York, N.Y, Nov. 11, 37. ENGLISH. A.B, Syracuse Univ, 59; A.M, Rutgers Univ, 62; Ph.D.(Eng), Harvard, 67. Instr. ENG, Yale, 67-68; ASST. PROF, 68-71; CITY COL. NEW YORK, 71- U.S.A, 61-62, Res, 62-68, 1st Lt. Am. Soc. 18th Century Stud; MLA. Restoration and 18th century English literature; Romantic period; Shakespeare. Publ: The sincere ideal, McGill-Queen's, 74; Keats's Negative capability and disinterestedness, Univ. Toronto Quart, 70; From Pamela to Grandison, Scolar, 72; A midsummer night's dream as the imitation of an action, Stud. Eng. Lit, (in press). Add: Dept. of English, City College of New York, 138th St. & Convent Ave, New York, NY 10031.

GUILLEBEAU, JOSEPH EDWIN, JR, b. Barnesville, Ga, Dec. 11, 25; m. 48. ENGLISH, HUMANITIES. A.B, Univ. N.C, 47; M.A, State Univ. Iowa, 50, Ph.D.(music), 51. Chmn. dept. music, Ouachita Baptist Col, 52-54; asst. prof. HUMANITIES, OXFORD COL, EMORY UNIV, 55-59, assoc. prof, 60-74, PROF, 74-, CHMN. DEPT, 63- U.S.A, 44-45. NCTE; MLA. Add: Dept. of Humanities, Oxford College, Emory University, Oxford, GA 30267.

GUIMOND, JAMES K, b. Muskegon, Mich, May 19, 36; m. 64; c. 1. ENGLISH & AMERICAN LITERATURE. B.A, Kalamazoo Col, 58; M.A, Ohio Wesleyan Univ, 61; Ph.D.(Eng), Univ. Ill, 65. Asst. prof. ENG, RIDER COL, 63-70, ASSOC. PROF, 70- Fulbright lectr, Univ. Sao Paulo, 73-74. MLA. Modern American poetry; American communitarian societies; mythology. Publ: The art of William Carlos Williams, Univ. Ill, 68; William Carlos Williams and the past: some clarifications, J. Mod. Lit, 71; The leadership of three communitarian societies, Shaker Quart, 71. Add: Dept. of English, Rider College, Trenton, NJ 08602.

GULICK, SIDNEY LEWIS, JR, b. Kobe, Japan, Aug. 17, 02; m. 31; c. 2. ENGLISH LITERATURE. A.B, Oberlin Col, 23, A.M, 25; Ph.D, Yale, 31. Teacher Eng. & piano, Doshisha Univ, Japan, 23-24; assoc. pub. speaking, Univ. Calif, 27-30; instr. Eng, Univ. Rochester, 31-35; asst. prof, Mills Col, 35-42, assoc. prof, 42-45, dir. exten. educ, 35-41, exec. secy, summer session, 36, 37; assoc. prof. Eng, SAN DIEGO STATE UNIV, 45-49, prof, 49-69, dean arts & sci, 59-69, EMER. DEAN ARTS & SCI, EMER. PROF. ENG. & ADMIN. ADV, 69- MLA; Philol. Asn. Pac. Coast. Age of Johnson; 18th century English literature; Elizabethan literature. Publ: A Chesterfield bibliography to 1800, 35, Some unpublished letters of Lord Chesterfield, 37, Gulick vocabulary survey, 1957, 61. Add: 10301 Sierra Vista, La Mesa, CA 92041.

GULLANS, CHARLES BENNETT, b. Minneapolis, Minn, May 5, 29. ENGLISH, POETRY. B.A, Univ. Minn, 48, M.A, 51; fel, Stanford Univ, 52-53, Ph.D.(Eng), 56; Fulbright fel, Durham Univ, 53-55. Mem. staff ENG, Univ. Wash, 55-61; asst. prof, UNIV. CALIF, LOS ANGELES, 61-65, assoc. prof, 65-72, PROF, 72- Fel, Inst. Creative Arts, Univ. Calif, 65-66. Scottish Text Soc.(v.pres, 58-); MLA; Bibliog. Soc, Eng. Seventeenth century English and modern American poetry; book design, 1890 to present. Publ: Moral poems, John Hunter Thomas, 57; Arrivals and departures, Univ. Minn, 62; co-transl, Last letters from Stalingrad, William Morrow, 62; auth, The English and Latin poems of Sir Robert Ayton, Scottish Text Soc, 63; A checklist of trade bindings designed by Margaret Armstrong, Univ. Res. Libr, Univ. Calif, Los Angeles, 68; co-auth, The decorative designers, 1895-1932, an essay, 70 & auth, a bibliography of the published writings of J.V. Cunningham, 73, Univ. Calif. Los Angeles Libr. Add: University of California, 405 Hilgard, Los Angeles, CA 90024.

GULLASON, THOMAS ARTHUR, b. Watertown, Mass, July 1, 24; m. 55. ENGLISH. B.A, Suffolk Univ, 48; M.A, Univ. Wis, 49, Ph.D, 53. Asst. prof. ENG, Heidelberg Col, 52-53; instr, Wis. State Col, 53-54; UNIV. R.I, 54-60, assoc. prof, 60-64, PROF, 64- Mem. ed. comt, Stud. Short Fiction, 65- Sig.C, U.S.A, 43-46. MLA. Modern American literature; realism and naturalism; the short story. Publ: Co-auth, World of short fiction: an international collection, Harper, 62 & 71; ed, Complete short stories and sketches of Stephen Crane, 63 & ed, Complete novels of Stephen Crane, 67, Doubleday; ed, Stephen Crane's career: perspectives & evaluations, N.Y. Univ, 72. Add: Dept. of English, University of Rhode Island, Kingston, RI 02881.

GULLETTE, DAVID G, b. Toledo, Ohio, Jan. 29, 40; m. 64; c. 1. ENGLISH. B.A, Harvard, 62, Ph.D.(Eng), Univ. N.C, Chapel Hill, 68. ASST. PROF. ENG, SIMMONS COL, 67- Ed, Ploughshares, 72- James Joyce; Italian baroque literary theory; Irish literary Renaissance. Publ: Co-transl, Ugo Betti: three plays, Hill & Wang, 66; auth, The Aristotelian telescope of Emanuele Tesauro, Lang. Press, 74. Add: 68 Pembroke St, Newton, MA 02158.

GULLEY, HALBERT EDISON, b. Sesser, Ill, Nov. 21, 19. SPEECH. B.Ed, South. Ill, State Norm. Univ, 40; A.M, State Univ. Iowa, 41, Ph.D, 48. Head speech br, U.S. Army Univ, Eng, 45; from asst. prof. to prof. speech, Univ. Ill, 48-67, supvr. forensics, 48-53, dir. citizen comt, 56-58, head div. gen. stud, 63-67; prof, Colo. State Univ, 67-68; PROF. & CHMN. DEPT, Univ. Ky, 68-70; SPEECH COMMUN, NORTH. ILL. UNIV, 70- Speech Commun. Asn. Small group and family communication; speeches of Winston Churchill; Albert Beveridge. Publ: Essentials of discussion and debate; Discussion, conference and group process, 60, 68, co-auth, Essentials of discussion, 69 & co-auth, Essentials of debate, 71, Holt; co-auth, Antislavery and disunion, Harper, 63. Add: Dept. of Speech Communication, Northern Illinois University, DeKalb, IL 60115.

GUM, COBURN, b. Hazard, Ky, Dec. 27, 14; m. 41. ENGLISH. A.B, Duke Univ, 54, Ph.D, 62. Instr. ENG, Wake Forest Col, 56-57; St. Petersburg Jr. Col, 58-61; from asst. prof. to ASSOC. PROF, CLEMSON UNIV, 62- MLA. Greek language and literature, especially Greek comedy; Russian language and literature; comparative literature. Add: Dept. of English, Clemson University, Clemson, SC 29631.

GUNBERG, EDWIN W, b. Minneapolis, Minn, May 15, 14; m. 40; c. 3. ENGLISH, CLASSICAL STUDIES. A.B, St. Olaf Col, 36; M.A, State Univ. Iowa, 37, Ph.D.(humanities), 41; dipl. philos, Univ. Heidelberg, 37-38. Prof. Eng. & philos, Northland Col, 39-40; Eng. & Greek lang. & lit, Augustana Col. (S.Dak), 40-46, head dept. Eng, 46-53, chmn. div. humanities, 51-53; adj. prof. Eng, Am. Univ. D.C, 55-62; PROF. LECTR. HUMANITIES, GEORGE WASHINGTON UNIV, 58- Dir. publ, Strategic Stud. Ctr, Stanford Res. Inst, 73- Classical and American literature; comparative literature. Add: 7701 Winterberry Pl, Bethesda, MD 20034.

GUNDERSON, ROBERT GRAY, b. Madison, Wis, Oct. 3, 15; m. 42; c. 2. SPEECH. B.S, Univ. Wis, 37, Ph.D, 49; A.M, Oberlin Col, 41. Instr. SPEECH, Oberlin Col, 38-41, 47-48, asst. prof, 49-51, assoc. prof, 51-55, PROF, 55-58, chmn. dept, 52-58; IND. UNIV, BLOOMINGTON, 58-, DIR. AM. STUD. PROG, 69- Huntington Libr. fel, 71-72. Speech Commun. Asn. (exec. v.pres, 61-64, ed, Quart. J. Speech, 66-69); Orgn. Am. Hist; South. Hist. Asn; Am. Stud. Asn. History of American public address: William Henry Harrison; Jacksonian period. Publ: The log-cabin campaign, Univ. Ky, 57; Old gentlemen's convention, Univ. Wis, 61; The Southern Whigs, In: Southern oratory, La. State Univ, 70. Add: 2420 Barbara St, Bloomington, IN 47401.

GUNKLE, GEORGE, b. Chicago, Ill, Nov. 1, 32. SPEECH & DRAMA. B.A, Univ. Ill, 55, M.A, 60; Ph.D.(speech & dramatic art), Univ. Iowa, 63. Instr. speech & theatre, Hunter Col, 63-64; assoc. prof. speech & drama, head dept. & dir. theatre, Drake Univ, 64-66; asst. prof. speech & theatre, Univ. Iowa, 66-70; PROF. DRAMA & CHMN. DEPT, CALIF. STATE UNIV, NORTHRIDGE, 70- Mem. Princeton Conf. Theatre Res, U.S. Dept. Health, Educ. & Welfare, 66-67; vis. lectr. speech, Univ. Hawaii, 69. Am. Theatre Asn.(chmn. exp. res. prog, 69-73, mem. nat. res. bd, 72-73); Speech Commun. Asn; Int. Commun. Asn. Experimental research in theatre. Publ: Co-ed, Empirical research in theatre (2 vols), Bowling Green State Univ, 71 & 72; auth, Aesthetic distance: some meanings for theatre, Theatre Design & Technol, 71; Empirical research in theatre, Educ. Theatre J, 71; Believability in acting: concept into construct, Empirical Res. Theatre, 72; plus others. Add: Dept. of Drama, California State University, 18111 Nordhoff St, Northridge, CA 91324.

GUNN, ALAN MURRAY, b. Alpena, S.Dak, Nov. 3, 06. MEDIEVAL LITERATURE. A.B, Huron Col, 27; A.M, Univ. Denver, 28; Ph.D, Princeton, 38. Prof. ENG, Univ. Pac, 28-35; instr, Princeton, 37-39; assoc. prof, TEX. TECH UNIV, 39-42, 46-49, prof, 49-71, EMER. PROF, 71-; PROF, TEX. CHRISTIAN UNIV, 71- Vis. prof, Tex. Christian Univ, 59-60, 67-68. U.S.A, 42-45. MLA; Mediaeval Acad. Am; Am. Dialect Soc. Medieval literature; rhetoric; history of ideas. Publ: The mirror of love: a reinterpretation of the romance of the Rose, Tex. Technol. Univ. Add: Dept. of English, Texas Christian University, Ft. Worth, TX 76129.

GUNN, DREWEY WAYNE, b. Reidsville, N.C, Aug. 9, 39. AMERICAN LITERATURE. B.A, Wake Forest Col, 61; M.A, Univ. N.C, 62; Ph.D.(Eng), 68; Univ. Tex, 64; Ctr. Intercult. Doc, 70; Alliance Francaise, 73. Instr. Eng, Presby. Col.(S.C), 62-64; Univ. Tex, Austin, 64; Univ. N.C, Chapel Hill, 65-68; asst. prof, Tex. A&I Univ, 68-72; Fulbright lectr. Am. cult, Haslev Sem, Haslev Gym, Hjørring Sem, Hjørring Gym, Copenhagen Dag & Aften Sem, N. Zahles Sem, Denmark, 72-73; PROF. ENG. LANG, INST. REINE, VER-

SAILLES, 73- Upward Bound instr. Eng. & drama, Tex. South. Univ, 66. MLA; AAUP. American and British writers living abroad. Publ: Gunn: a genealogy, privately publ, 72; Mexico in American and British letters: a bibliography, Scarecrow, 74; American and British writers in Mexico, 1556-1969, Univ. Tex, (in press); Three radicals and a revolution, Southwest Rev, fall 70. Add: 55 rue de Provence, 75009 Paris, France.

GUNN, MAUREEN MARY, b. Carlisle, Cumberland, Eng, Sept. 4, 33; Can. citizen; m. 68; c. 2. ENGLISH LITERATURE. B.A, St. Anne's Col, Oxford, 56, B.Litt, 58; Ph.L, Univ. Montreal, 68. Lectr. ENG, CARLETON UNIV, 62-66, asst. prof, 66-69, ASSOC. PROF, 69- Mediaeval Acad. Am. Fourteenth century English literature; 14th century preachers' manuals. Add: Dept. of English, Carleton University, Colonel By Dr, Ottawa, Ont. K1S 5B6, Can.

GUNN, THOMSON WILLIAM, b. Gravesend, Eng, Aug. 29, 29. ENGLISH. B.A, Cambridge, 53, M.A, 58; Stanford Univ, 54-55, 56-58. Lectr. Eng, Univ. Calif, Berkeley, 58-62, asst. prof, 62-65, assoc. prof, 65-66; RES. & WRITING, 66- Levinson Poetry Prize, 55; Somerset Maugham Poetry Award & Arts Counc. Gt. Brit. Poetry Prize, 58. Brit. Army, 48-50, Sgt. Writing poetry; criticism of 20th century poetry. Publ: Fighting terms, Fantasy, Oxford, 54, Hawks Well, 57, Faber & Faber, London, 61; The sense of movement, Faber & Faber, 57, Univ. Chicago, 59; My sad captains, 61 & co-auth, Positives, 66, Faber & Faber & Univ. Chicago; auth, Touch, 67 & Selected poems of Fulke Greville, 68, Faber & Faber & Univ. Chicago, Moly, 71; To be air, Godine, 74; Mandrakes, Rainbow, 74. Add: 1216 Cole St, San Francisco, CA 94117.

GURKO, LEO, b. Warsaw, Poland, Jan. 4, 14; nat; m. 34; c. 2. ENGLISH LITERATURE. A.B, Col. City Detroit, 31; A.M, Univ. Wis, 32, fel, 32-34, Ph.D, 34. Ed, G.P. Putnam's Sons, 35-38; instr. ENG, HUNTER COL, 39-48, asst. prof, 48-52, assoc. prof, 52-57, prof, 57-72, chmn. dept, 54-60, EMER. PROF, 72-; JOHN CRAWFORD ADAMS PROF. ENG. LIT, HOFSTRA UNIV, 72- Dodd, Mead & Co. fac. fel, 46; Ford fel, 53-54. MLA. Novel; contemporary literature; D.H. Lawrence. Publ: Angry decade, Dodd; Heroes, highbrows and the popular mind, Bobbs; Joseph Conrad: giant in exile, Macmillan, 62; Tom Paine, freedom's apostle, 57, The two lives of Joseph Conrad, 65 & Ernest Hemingway and the pursuit of heroism, 68, Crowell; The lost girl: D.H. Lawrence as a Dickens of the midlands, PMLA, 12/63; U.S.A: a 1930's spectacular, In: The proletarian writers of the 30's, South. Ill. Univ, 68; The dehumanizing mind in Washington Square, In: A critical edition of Henry James's Washington Square, Crowell, 68. Add: Dept. of English, Hofstra University, Hempstead, L.I, NY 11550.

GURNEY, ALBERT RAMSDELL, JR, b. Buffalo, N.Y, Nov. 1, 30; m. 57; c. 4. ENGLISH LITERATURE, DRAMA. B.A, Williams Col, 52, M.F.A, Yale, 58. Instr. humanities, MASS. INST TECHNOL, 60-64, asst. prof, 64-66, assoc. prof, LIT, 66-72, PROF, 72- Drama Desk Award, N.Y.C, 71. Publ: Contrib, The best short plays, 1955-56 & 57-58, Beacon, 56 & 58; contrib, Best short plays, 1969 & 70, Chilton, 69 & 70; auth, Scenes from American life (play), 72 & The golden fleece (play), 72, French; The gospel according to Joseph (novel), Harper, 74; plus others. Add: 20 Sylvan Ave, West Newton, MA 02165.

GUS, DONALD LEROY, b. New York, N.Y, July 21, 29; m. 60; c. 3. ENGLISH LITERATURE. B.A, City Col. New York, 50; M.A, Columbia Univ, 52; Fulbright fel, Univ. Rome, Italy; Mary M. Adams fel, Univ. Wis, 55-56, Ph.D, 61. Lectr, City Col. New York, 50-52; instr, Boston Col, 59-60; Rutgers Univ, 60-63, res. grant, 62-63; asst. prof, Wayne State Univ, 63-68; PROF. & CHMN. DEPT, UNIV. CALIF, SANTA BARBARA, 68- Huntington Libr. grant, 63. Sig.C, U.S.A, 52-54. MLA; Renaissance Soc. Am; Am. Asn. Teachers Ital. Seventeenth century English: Renaissance Italian literature. Publ: John Donne, Petrarchist, Wayne State Univ, 67; Donne's conceit and Petrarchan wit, PMLA, 9/63; Wyatt's Petrarchism, Huntington Libr. Quart, 65; A brief epic: Paradise regained, Stud. Philol, 71; plus others. Add: Dept. of English, University of California, Santa Barbara, CA 93106.

GUSTAFSON, DANNY DAVIS, b. New Brunswick, N.J, Sept. 9, 29; m. 57; c. 4. ENGLISH, AMERICAN LITERATURE. B.A, Amherst Col, 51; M.A, Univ. Calif, Berkeley, 57; regents fel, Univ. Nebr, 61-62, Ph.D.(Am. lit), 68. Instr. ENG, Univ. Nebr, 57-60, asst, 60-61, instr, 62-64; asst. prof, Univ. B.C, 64-69; Utica Col, 69-71; ASSOC. PROF. & CHMN. DEPT, LYCOMING COL, 71- U.S.M.C, 51-59, S/Sgt. MLA; American literature and drama; 19th century fiction. Add: Dept. of English, Lycoming College, Williamsport, PA 17701.

GUSTAFSON, RALPH, b. Lime Ridge, P.Q, Aug. 16, 09; m. 58. ENGLISH. B.A, Bishop's Univ, 29, M.A, 30; Overseas scholar, 30-32; B.A, Oxford, 33, M.A, 63; hon. Litt.D, Mt. Allison Univ, 73. Master music, Bishop's Col. Sch, P.Q, 29-30; ENG, St. Alban's Sch, Ont, 33-34; lectr, BISHOP'S UNIV, 63-64, asst. prof, 65-66, assoc. prof, 67-71, PROF, 71-, POET-IN-RESIDENCE, 65- Can. Counc. sr. fel, 59-60, grant, 68, sr. arts award, 71-72; music critic, Can. Broadcasting Corp, 60- Bishop's Univ. Governor Gen. medal, 30; P.Q. Prix David, 32. Brit. Inform. Serv, 42-46. Asn. Can. Univ. Teachers Eng; Humanities Soc; League Can. Poets. Canadian literature; music criticism. Publ: The golden chalice, Nicholson & Watson, London, 35; Alfred the great, Michael Joseph, London, 37; ed, Anthology of Canadian poetry, 42, Canadian accent, 44 & Penguin book of Canadian verse, 58, rev. ed, 67, Penguin; ed, A little anthology of Canadian poetry, New Directions, 43; auth, Flight into darkness, Pantheon, 44; Rivers among rocks, 60, Sift in an hourglass, 66, Ixion's wheel, 69, Selected poems, 72 & Fire on stone, 74, McClelland & Stewart, Toronto; Rocky Mountain poems, Klanak, Vancouver, 60; Theme and variations for sounding brass, Progressive Publ, P.Q, 72; plus others. Add: Dept. of English, Bishop's University, Lennoxville, P.Q. Z0B 1Z0, Can.

GUSTAFSON, RICHARD, b. Missoula, Mont, Aug. 10, 33. LITERATURE. A.B, Gonzaga Univ, 55; M.A, Univ. Kans, 57, Ph.D, 60. Asst. prof. Eng. Lit. IOWA STATE UNIV, 60-65, ASSOC. PROF, ENG, 65- Ed, Poet & Critic, 64- MLA; Am. Civil Liberties Union. Add: Dept. of English, Iowa State University, Ames, IA 50010.

GUTH, HANS PAUL, b. Kolberg, Ger, Apr. 8, 26; nat; m. 51. ENGLISH. M.A, Univ. Mich, 51, Ph.D.(Eng) 55. Asst. prof. ENG, SAN JOSE STATE UNIV, 55-62, PROF, 62- MLA; NCTE; Conf. Col. Compos. & Commun. Composition; criticism. Publ: Words and ideas, Wadsworth, 59 & 69; English today and tomorrow, Prentice-Hall, 64; American English today, 70 & English for a new generation, 73, McGraw. Add: Dept. of English, San Jose State University, 125 S. Seventh St, San Jose, CA 95114.

GUTHRIE, SHIRLEY LAW, b. Des Moines, Iowa, Apr. 4, 40. ENGLISH & COMPARATIVE LITERATURE. B.A, Swarthmore Col, 62; M.A, Ind. Univ, Bloomington, 67, Ph.D.(comp. lit), 73. ASST. PROF. ENG, UNIV. N.MEX, 71- MLA; Mediaeval Acad. Am; AAUP. Classical influence on medieval literature; Medieval English literature; Medieval Latin literature. Add: Dept. of English, University of New Mexico, Albuquerque, NM 87131.

GUTHRIE, WARREN, b. Syracuse, Nebr, June 30, 11. SPEECH. A.B, Nebr. Wesleyan Col, 31; A.M, Univ. Mich, 35; Ph.D, Northwest. Univ, 40. Teacher, high sch, Nebr, 32-34; instr, Adelbert Col, West. Reserve Univ, 34-38; teaching fel, Northwest. Univ, 38-39; asst. prof. speech, Adelbert Col, West. Reserve Univ, 39-45, dir. pub. relat, 41-45, prof. & chmn. dept, 45-64; DIR. PUB. RELAT, STANDARD OIL CO, OHIO, 64- Trustee, Cleveland Hearing & Speech Ctr. U.S.N.R, 42-46, Lt. Comdr. Speech Commun. Asn. Rhetorical theory in colonial America; public address; techniques in radio and television discussion and debate. Add: 2243 Chestnut Hills Dr, Cleveland, OH 44106.

GUTIERREZ, DONALD, b. Alameda, Calif, Mar. 10, 32; m. 53; c. 2. MODERN BRITISH LITERATURE, NOVEL. B.A, Univ. Calif, Berkeley, 56, M.L.S, 58; M.A, Univ. Calif, Los Angeles, 66, Ph.D.(Eng) 68. Ref. librn, Metrop. Mus. Art Libr, N.Y.C, 58-60; res. & asst. head librn, Tamiment Inst. Libr, N.Y.C, 60-61; res. librn, Grosset & Dunlap Bk. Publ, 61-64; ASST. PROF. ENG, UNIV. NOTRE DAME, 68- MLA; Ctr. Stud. Democratic Insts; AAUP. D.H. Lawrence; Anthony Powell. Publ: Circles and arcs: the rhythm of circularity and centrifugality in D.H. Lawrence's Last poems, D.H. Lawrence Rev, fall 71; Ghosts benefic and malign: the influence of the Noh Theatre on three dance plays of Yeats, Univ. Houston Forum, summer 71; Power in A dance to the music of time, Conn. Rev, 4/73. Add: Dept. of English, University of Notre Dame, Notre Dame, IN 46556.

GUTTMAN, SELMA, b. New York, N.Y, Sept. 14. ENGLISH. B.A, Hunter Col, 35; M.A, Columbia Univ, 37, Ph.D.(Eng) 45. Acting instr. ENG, Univ. Wis, 43-44; instr, Univ. Kans, 44-45; State Col. Wash, 45-46; Wayne Univ, 46-50; asst. prof, West. Mont. Col. Educ, 50-51; from assoc. prof. to PROF, JOHNSON STATE COL, 51- AAUP; Col. Eng. Asn. English Renaissance. Publ: Foreign sources of Shakespeare's works; Fencing bout in Hamlet, Shakespeare Asn. Bull; Alexander Barclay, a product of his age, Mich. Acad. Sci, Arts & Lett. Papers. Add: Dept. of English, Johnson State College, Johnson, VT 05656.

GUTTMANN, ALLEN, b. Chicago, Ill, Oct. 13, 32; m. 55; c. 2. ENGLISH, AMERICAN CIVILIZATION. B.A, Univ. Fla, 53; M.A, Columbia Univ, 56; Carnegie fel, Univ. Minn, 56-57, Ph.D.(Am. stud) 61. Instr. ENG. & AM. STUD, AMHERST COL, 59-63, asst. prof, 63-66, assoc. prof, 66-71, PROF, 71- Fulbright Comn. lectr. Am. lit, Ruhr Univ, 68-69; mem. ed. bd, Am. Lit, 70-73 & supv. comt, Eng. Inst, 70-73; Robert Merton prof, Ger. Res. Asn, Tübingen, 73-74. U.S.A, 53-55. Am. Stud. Asn.(treas, 65-68); MLA; Am. Hist. Asn; Orgn. Am. Hist. Publ: Wound in the heart: America and the Spanish Civil War, Free Press, Macmillan, 62; co-ed, Removal of the Cherokee nation, 62, ed, American neutrality and the Spanish Civil War, 63, Communism, the courts and the constitution, 64 & Korea and the theory of limited war, 67, 2nd ed, 72, Heath; auth, The conservative tradition in America, 67 & The Jewish writer in America, 71, Oxford Univ; Jewish writers, Jewish radicals, 63 & Political ideals and the military ethic, 65, Am. Scholar; Washington Irving and the conservative imagination, Am. Lit, 64. Add: 22 Orchard St, Amherst, MA 01002.

GUYER, BYRON, b. Brownwood, Tex, Oct. 16, 15; m. 38; c. 2. ENGLISH. B.A, San Diego State Col, 38; M.A, Univ. Calif, Berkeley, 41; Ph.D, Stanford Univ, 47. Teacher ENG, Exeter Union High Sch, 42; acting instr, Stanford Univ, 44-46; asst. prof, Humboldt State Col, 46-47; lectr, Univ. Calif, Davis, 47-48, asst. prof, 48-50; chmn. dept, Diablo Valley Col, 50-55; PROF. & CHMN. DEPT, CALIF. STATE UNIV, LOS ANGELES, 55- Fel, Int. Inst. Arts & Lett, Geneva, 60. Civilian instr, U.S. Army Air Corps Tech. Training Command, 42-43. Literary criticism and composition; English translations of Aristotle's Poetics. Publ: Co-auth, Patterns of thinking and writing, Wadsworth, 59 & Language in your life, Vol. 3, Harper, 68. Add: Dept. of English, California State University, Los Angeles, 5151 State University Dr, Los Angeles, CA 90032.

H

HAAKER, ANN, b. Chicago, Ill, Nov. 22, 19. ENGLISH, DRAMA. B.A, Univ. Tex, Austin, 41; Northwest. Univ, 48; M.A, Claremont Grad. Sch, 52; Ph.D. (Eng), Univ. Birmingham, 60. Clerk for. serv, Am. Embassy, Mexico City, 44; asst. prof. speech, Univ. Md, Overseas, 54-55; asst. prof. Eng, Pasadena City Col, 60-65; assoc. prof. SHAKESPEARE, CALIF. STATE UNIV, FULLERTON, 65-69, PROF, 69-, grad. coord. Eng, 69-72. MLA; Renaissance Soc. Am; Shakespeare Asn. Am. Shakespeare; 17th century drama; 16th century drama. Publ: Ed, The antipodes, 67 & A jovial crew, 68, Univ. Nebr; The plague, the theatre, and the poet, Renaissance Drama, 68; auth, Non sine causa: emblematic method in Titus Andronicus, In: Research Opportunities in Renaissance Drama, 70-71; contrib, The predecessors of Shakespeare: a survey and bibliography of recent studies in English Renaissance Drama, Univ. Nebr, 74. Add: 31551 Crystal Sands Dr, Laguna Niguel, CA 92677.

HAARBAUER, DON WARD, b. Charleroi, Pa, Sept. 17, 40; m. 64; c. 1. THEATRE HISTORY, DIRECTING. B.S, Univ. Ala, Tuscaloosa, 62, M.A, 65; Ph.D.(theatre), Univ. Wis-Madison, 73. Asst. prof. speech & theatre, UNIV. ALA, BIRMINGHAM, 68-73, ASST. PROF. THEATRE, CHMN. PERFORMING ARTS & ASST. DEAN SCH. HUMANITIES, 73- Dir, Horn in the West, Boone, N.C, 67-71. Southeast. Theatre Conf. Pre-twentieth century English theatre. Add: Dept. of Performing Arts, University of Alabama in Birmingham, University Sta, Birmingham, AL 35294.

HAAS, CHARLES E, b. Withee, Wis, Sept. 26, 25; m. 59; c. 1. SPEECH. B.S, Univ. Wis-Superior, 48; M.A, State Univ. Iowa, 56; Ph.D, Denver Univ, 64. Assoc. prof. INTERPRETATION, UNIV. WIS-LA CROSSE, 64-66, PROF, 66- U.S.A, 51-54. Speech Commun. Asn; Cent. States Speech Asn. Oral interpretation; linguistics; speech in elementary school. Add: Dept. of Speech, University Wisconsin-La Crosse, La Crosse, WI 54601.

HAAS, GAYLORD RAYMOND, b. Chicago, Ill, May 2, 31; m. 59; c. 2. ENGLISH LITERATURE. B.S, Northwest. Univ, 55, M.A, 56, Ph.D.(Eng), 66. Instr. Eng. & humanities, Wright Jr. Col, 56-58, ENG, Univ. Ariz, 59-64; asst. prof, Univ. Cincinnati, 64-67, UNIV. BRIDGEPORT, 67-73, ASSOC. PROF, 73- MLA; NCTE; Col. Eng. Asn. Development of the English novel; 18th century English literature. Add: Dept. of English, University of Bridgeport, Bridgeport, CT 06602.

HABEGGER, ALFRED CARL, b. Chicago, Ill, Feb. 6, 41; m. 64. ENGLISH. B.A, Bethel Col.(Kans), 62; Woodrow Wilson fel. & Danforth fel, Stanford Univ, 62, Ph.D.(Eng), 67. Acting asst. prof. ENG, UNIV. KANS, 66-67, asst. prof, 67-71, ASSOC. PROF, 71- Fulbright lectr, Univ. Bucharest, 72-73. MLA. Nineteenth century American literature, especially realistic fiction. Publ: Ed, Henry James' The Bostonians, Bobbs, 74; auth, Preparing the soul for Christ: the contrasting sermon forms of John Cotton and Thomas Hooker, Am. Lit, 69; The disunity of The Bostonians, 69 & Reciprocity and the market-place in The wings of the dove and What Maisie knew, 71, Nineteenth Century Fiction. Add: Dept. of English, University of Kansas, Lawrence, KS 66045.

HABENICHT, RUDOLPH EVERETT, b. Boston, Mass, May 17, 25. ENGLISH LITERATURE. B.A, Univ. South. Calif, 50; M.A, Columbia Univ, 51; Fulbright scholar, Oxford, 54-56, D.Phil, Merton Col, Oxford, 59. Instr. Eng. lit, Univ. Calif, Los Angeles, 58-60, asst. prof, 60-66; ASSOC. PROF. ENG, SIMON FRASER UNIV, 66- Dir, World Shakespeare Congr, 71. U.S.N.R, 42-45. Malone Soc; Renaissance Soc. Am; Shakespeare Asn. Am.(bibliog, 65-). Early Tudor literature; Shakespeare. Publ: Ed, John Heywood, Dialogue of proverbs, Univ. Calif, 63; ed, Julius Caesar, W.C. Brown, 70; auth, Shakespeare: an annotated world bibliography, Shakespeare Quart, Vols. XVII-XXII, No. iii. Add: Dept. of English, Simon Fraser University, Burnaby, 2, B.C, Can.

HABER, TOM BURNS, b. Rossburg, Ohio, May 5, 00; m. 29. ENGLISH. A.B, Ohio North. Univ, 21, B.S, 22; A.M, Ohio State Univ, 25, Ph.D, 29; summers. Univs. Munich & Paris, 26, Oxford & Univ. London, 28; Oxford & Univ. Berne, 30. Teacher Eng, High Sch, Ohio, 21-24; asst, OHIO STATE UNIV, 24-27, instr, 27-49, asst. prof, 49-66, assoc. prof. comp. lit, 66-67, PROF. COL. HUMANITIES, 68- Lectr, Ohio Col, 25, 26; trustee, Ohioana Libr. NCTE; MLA; Eng-Speaking Union; Eugene Field Soc; Bibliog. Soc. Am; Housman Soc. Anglo-Saxon; manuscript poems of A.E. Housman. Publ: Thirty Housman letters to Witter Bynner, Knopf; Annotated bibliographies 19th century British poetry & co-auth, A grammar of living English, Am. Bk. Co; auth, Comparative study of the Beowulf and the Aeneid, Princeton, 31; Two centuries of anecdotes, Christopher, 32; ed, The realm of reading, (6 vols), Am. Bk. Co, 40-41; auth, Writer's handbook of American usage, Longmans, 42; Handbook of basic English, Appleton, 45; ed, Poems of A.E. Housman, Holt, 59; auth, Making of a Shropshire Lad, Univ. Wash, 66; A.E. Housman, a critical biography, Twayne, 67; Translations and paraphrases in A.E. Housman's poetry, Z. Anglistik u. Amerikanistik, 57; Linguistics: polysemy of dog and other canine names, In: Collections for American speech, 61-66, Ohio State Univ, 66; Forty-nine letters from A.E. Housman, Etudes Anglaises, 68; plus others. Add: 220 Canyon Dr, Columbus, OH 43214.

HABERMAN, DONALD C, b. Passaic, N.J, July 12, 33; m. 57; c. 1. ENGLISH LITERATURE. A.B, Rutgers Univ, 55; Ph.D.(Eng), Yale, 62. Instr. ENG, Lafayette Col, 59-62, asst. prof, 62-65; Univ. Mont, 65-67; ASSOC. PROF, ARIZ. STATE UNIV, 67- MLA. Augustan Age; modern literature. Publ: Thornton Wilder, Wesleyan Univ, 67. Add: Dept. of English, Arizona State University, Tempe, AZ 85281.

HABERMAN, FREDERICK WILLIAM, b. Duquesne, Pa, May 11, 08; m. 34; c. 2. SPEECH. A.B, Allegheny Col, 30; A.M, Univ. Wis; 36; Ph.D, Cornell Univ, 47. Instr, High Sch, Harborcreek, Pa, 30-32; Allegheny Col, 32-36, asst. prof, 42-43; instr, Cornell Univ, 36-38; Princeton, 38-42; asst. prof, SPEECH, UNIV. WIS-MADISON, 47-49, assoc. prof, 49-52, PROF, 52-, chmn. dept, 54-70. Fel, Inst. Res. Humanities, Univ. Wis, 66-67. U.S.N.R, 43-46, Lt. Speech Commun. Asn. Rhetorical theory; history of oratory; British public address. Publ: Co-auth, Bibliography of rhetoric and public address, Univ. Wis, 64 & An historical anthology of select British speeches, Ronald, 67; ed, Nobel lectures—Peace, 1901-1970 (3 vols), Am. Elsevier, 72; auth, The Bell family, a dynasty in speech; John Thelwall; Elocutionary movement. Add: Dept. of Communication Arts, University of Wisconsin-Madison, Madison, WI 53706.

HACH, CLARENCE, b. Clutier, Iowa, Feb. 5, 17. ENGLISH. A.B, Iowa North. Univ. 37; A.M, State Univ, Iowa, 39; Ford Found. fel, 53. Teacher Eng, High Schs, Iowa, 37-38, Eng. & jour, 39-44; Stephens Col, 44-45; EVANSTON TWP, HIGH SCH, ILL, 45-53, chmn. Eng. & publ, 54-67, SUPVR. ENG. & CHMN. PUBL, 67- Mem. comt. exam, in Eng, Col. Entrance Exam. Bd, 59-63; table leader compos. tests, Nat. Assessment in Educ, 69-, consult, lit, 72-; lectr. jour. & Eng. educ, Univ. Mo, Univ. Minn. & Northwest. Univ. Pioneer Award, Nat. Scholastic Press Asn, Newspaper Fund & Reader's Digest Found, 71. NCTE (dir, 63-66); Nat. Educ. Asn; Jour. Educ. Asn.(pres, Asn. Jour. Dir, 51-53). Journalism and English education. Publ: Co-auth, Scholastic journalism, Iowa State, 50, 55, 62, 68, 72; English for today, Lippincott, 50-55 & Modern composition, Holt, 64, 2nd ed, 69; Needed: sequences in composition, Eng. J, 1/68. Add: Dept. of English, Evanston Township High School, 1600 Dodge Ave, Evanston, IL 60204.

HACHTEN, WILLIAM ANDREWS, b. Wichita, Kans, Nov. 30, 24; m. 52; c. 2. JOURNALISM, MASS COMMUNICATION. B.A, Stanford Univ, 47; M.S, Univ. Calif, Los Angeles, 52; Ph.D.(jour), Univ. Minn, Minneapolis, 61. Reporter, Santa Paula Chronicle, Calif, 48-49; Long Beach Press-Telegram, 52-54; news ed, Santa Monica Outlook, 54; copy ed, Los Angeles Examiner, 55-56; admin. asst. JOUR, Univ. Minn, Minneapolis, 56-58; asst. prof, UNIV. WIS-MADISON, 59-63, assoc. prof, 63-67, PROF, 67-, ASST. DIR. DEPT, 73- Fulbright-Hays res. award, Africa, 68; Fulbright-Hays sr. lectr, Univ. Ghana, 72-73; assoc. ed, Jour. Quart, 72- Res. Award Jour, Sigma Delta Chi, 68. U.S.M.C, 43-46, 2nd Lt. Asn. Educ. in Jour; Int. Asn. Mass Commun. Res; Int. Press Inst. Mass communication in Africa; law of mass communication; international communications. Publ: The Supreme Court on freedom of the press, 68 & Muffled drums: the news media in Africa, 71, Iowa State Univ; Mass communication in Africa: an annotated bibliography, Univ. Wis-Madison, 71; Newspapers in Africa: change or decay, Africa Report, 12/70; co-auth, Communication and development: African and Afro-American parallels, Jour. Monogr, 5/73. Add: School of Journalism & Mass Communication, Vilas Hall, University of Wisconsin-Madison, Madison, WI 53706.

HACIKYAN, AGOP JACK, b. Istanbul, Turkey, Nov. 25, 31; Can. citizen; m. 56; c. 1. ENGLISH, PHILOLOGY. B.A, Robert Col, Istanbul, 54; M.A, Univ. Montreal, 60, Ph.D.(Eng), 64. Teacher, Prep Sch, 57-60; Protestant Sch. Bd. Greater Montreal, Can, 60-62; asst. prof. & chmn. dept. Eng. & methodology, Univ. Sherbrooke, 62-65; PROF. ENG, ROYAL MIL. COL. (QUE), 65- Can. Counc. grants, 63 & 67, 69; Dept. Nat. Defense humanities grants, 66-67, 68-69; Can. scholar, Univ. Paris & Univ. Besançon, 71-72. Atherton Lit. Prize, 62. Joint Am. Mission Aid to Turkey, 54-56, 2nd Lt. Teachers of Eng. to Speakers of Other Lang; Prof. Inst. Pub. Serv. Can; MLA; Can. Asn. Univ. Teachers. Anglo-Saxon philology, especially Middle English; contemporary novel; second language teaching. Publ: A linguistic and literary analysis of Old English riddles, Casalini, Montreal, 66; Methodology of teaching English as a second language, 67, co-auth, English pronunciation, 68, auth, Teaching English pronunciation (3 vols), 69-71 & Tomas, 70, Bauchemin, Montreal; The exeter manuscript: riddle 19, Mod. Lang. Notes, 12/65; The literary and the social aspects of the Old English riddles, 66 & Emendations for codex exoniensis part I and part II, 67, Univ. Ottawa Rev. Add: 555 Samford Ave, St. Lambert, P.Q, Can.

HACKE, ROBERT E. LEE, English, Linguistics. See Volume III, Foreign Languages, Linguistics & Philology.

HACKETT, LAURA L, b. Oberlin, Ohio, Apr. 19, 16; m. 36, 59; c. 3. ENGLISH. B.A, Smith Col, 36; M.A, Occidental Col, 55. Instr. Eng, Santa Barbara Jr. Col, 50-59; teacher, High Sch, N.Y, 59-60; PROF. ENG, SUFFOLK COUNTY COMMUNITY COL, 60-, DEAN INSTR, WEST. CAMPUS, 74- NCTE; Col. Conf. Compos. & Commun. Publ: Co-auth, Anatomy of reading, McGraw, 65 & Design for a composition, Harcourt, 66. Add: 19 Hawkins Rd, Stony Brook, NY 11790.

HADDIN, THEODORE, U.S. citizen; m. 61; c. 2. AMERICAN LITERATURE. A.B, Univ. Mich, 55, A.M, 56, Ph.D.(Eng), 68. Teacher ENG, Jackson High Sch, 58-61; Ann Arbor High Sch, Mich, 61-63; instr, Univ. Mich, 65-68; ASST. PROF, St. Louis Univ, 68-73; UNIV. ALA, BIRMINGHAM, 73- MLA; Midwest Mod. Lang. Asn; S.Atlantic Mod. Lang. Asn. American literature 19th century transcendalism; early American literature, poetry and prose; 20th century American poetry. Publ: The child in American literature, St. Louis Univ. Mag, 4/71; Thoreau's reputation once more, Thoreau J. Quart, 1/72. Add: Dept. of English, Humanities Div, University of Alabama in Birmingham, Birmingham, AL 35294.

HADGOPOULOS, SARALYN POOLE, b. Atlanta, Ga, Aug. 31, 31; m. 63; c. 1. ENGLISH, COMPARATIVE LITERATURE. B.S, Columbia Univ, 55; M.A, N.Y. Univ, 61; Ph.D.(comp. lit), Emory Univ, 65. Teacher, Miami Edison Sr. High Sch, 58-60; assoc. prof. Eng, Slippery Rock State Col, 67-69; PROF. ENG. & EUROP. LIT, GEORGE WASHINGTON UNIV, TIDEWATER CTR, 72- MLA; NCTE; Archeol. Inst. Am; Mod. Greek Stud. Asn; Oceanic Soc. English of the 18th, 19th and 20th centuries and selected figures of the 20th century; comparative modern European literature, especially modern Greek and French; contemporary world literature and poetry. Publ: Poems of North Africa, Windy Row, 73; Twilight (poem), In: Columbia University anthology of poetry, Columbia Univ, 53; Kazantzakis: a revolt in salvation, Archon, spring 64. Add: P.O. Box 5582, Bayside Sta, Virginia Beach, VA 23455.

HADLEY, DOROTHY S, b. Elizabeth, Ill, Mar. 24, 05; m. 36; c. 1. ORAL INTERPRETATION. B.S, Ohio State Univ, 28; Pasadena Playhouse Col. Theatre Arts, summer, 30; Univ. Ill, 34-35; M.A, Northwest. Univ, 37; Ph.D, 56; Univ. Mich, 40-41. Teacher speech & drama, Charleston Sr. High Sch, W.Va, 28-34; instr. speech, Univ. Ill, 34-36; speech & oral interpretation, Univ. Miss, 51-54; oral interpretation, Northwest. Univ, 54-55, asst, 55-56; asst. prof. speech & oral interpretation, SAN JOSE STATE UNIV, 56-60, assoc. prof. ORAL INTERPRETATION, 60-69, prof, 69-72, EMER. PROF, 72- Part-time mem. fac, Sweet Briar Col, 37-43, 45-51; Randolph-Macon Woman's Col, 36-43, 45-51; Ohio State Univ, 43-45; assoc. prof. speech, Univ. Hawaii, 64-65; prof. storytelling, Univ. Calif, Santa Cruz Ext. Div, 72- West. Speech Asn; Speech Commun. Asn. Group reading; activities at Chautauqua, New York, 1874-1900; teaching oral interpretation in English schools, colleges and universities. Publ: Tell that story, San Jose State Univ. Bk. Store, 69; Henry Woodfin Grady as a student speaker, Quart. J. Speech, 4/38; A readers theatre performance, Dramatics Mag, fall 63; Chautauqua, In: Studies in Interpretation, Rodopi, Amsterdam, 72. Add: Dept. of Drama, San Jose State University, San Jose, CA 95114.

HADLEY, KLARA SHANNON, b. Tampa, Fla; m. 69. ENGLISH LITERATURE. B.A, Fla. A&M Univ, 63; M.A, Fla. State Univ, 64, Carnegie fel. & Ph.D. (Eng), 69. ASST. PROF. ENG, FLA. A&M UNIV, 64- MLA; AAUP; Am. Asn. Univ. Women; Col. Lang. Asn; Col. Eng. Asn; NCTE. Restoration drama; John Milton; Alexander Pope. Publ: There is no common man, Alpha Kappa Mu J, spring 66; contrib, Abstr. Eng. Stud, 69-70. Add: Dept. of English, Florida A&M University, P.O. Box 363, Tallahassee, FL 32307.

HADWIGER, KEN E, b. Alva, Okla, July 18, 36; m. 57; c. 2. MASS COMMUNICATIONS, COMMUNICATIONS RESEARCH. B.A, Okla. State Univ, 58; M.A,State Univ. Iowa, 59; Ph.D.(commun. theory), Univ. Okla, 64. Dir. & announcer, KCRG-AM & TV, Cedar Rapids, Iowa, 58-60; dir. radio-TV broadcasting, Wichita State Univ, 60-62; radio announcer, KNOR, Norman, Okla, 62-64; asst. prof, EAST. ILL, UNIV, 64-69, ASSOC. PROF. COMMUN, 69-, DEAN COL. ARTS & SCI, 70-, dir. commun, 64-70. Res. asst. broadcasting, State Univ. Iowa, 59; commun. theory, Univ. Okla, 64; commun. consult, Boeing Aircraft Co, Kans, 60-62; Peace Corps, summer 64; Okla. Dent. Asn, summer 65. Asn. Prof. Broadcasting Educ; Cent. States Speech Asn; Speech Commun. Asn.(chmn. Int. Stud, 72-, chmn. Ger-Am. commun. colloquium, 72-); Int. Commun. Asn. Attitude change in communications; broadcasting station ownership in United States; international communications. Publ: Several articles in commun. jour. & other scholarly publ. Add: Office of the Dean, College of Arts & Sciences, 218 Old Main, Eastern Illinois University, Charleston, IL 61920.

HAFER, CAROL BRAXTON, b. Greenville, N.C, Mar. 13, 42; m. 68; c. 1. ENGLISH. B.S, Va. Commonwealth Univ, 65; Pa. State Univ, University Park, 65-66; M.A, Univ. Richmond, 67; A.B.D, North. Ill. Univ, 71, Ph.D. (Eng), 73. Instr. ENG, Va. State Col, 67-68; North. Ill. Univ, 68-72; ASST. PROF, BLUEFIELD COL, 72- MLA; NCTE. English Renaissance; 18th century English; American fiction. Publ: The red badge of absurdity: irony in The red badge of courage, Col. Lang. Asn. J, summer 71. Add: Humanities Div, Bluefield College, Bluefield, VA 24605.

HAFLEY, JAMES ROBERT, b. San Francisco, Calif, June 2, 28. ENGLISH LANGUAGE & LITERATURE; B.A, Univ. Calif, 48, M.A, 49, Ph.D.(Eng), 52. Teaching asst. Eng, Univ. Calif, 49-52; instr, Cath. Univ. Am, 52-55, asst. prof. Eng. lang. & lit, 55-58, assoc. prof, 58-65; PROF. ENG. LIT, ST. JOHN'S UNIV. (N.Y), 65- Lectr. Am. lit, Trinity Col, 59; vis. prof, Columbia Univ, 69 & 71. MLA. Prose fiction; American literature; English literature from 1800 to the present. Publ: The glass roof: Virginia Woolf as novelist, Univ. Calif, 54, Russell, 63; Villain in Wuthering Heights, Nineteenth Century Fiction, 58, Odyssey, 61; A tour of the House of Usher, Emerson Soc. Quart, 63. Add: Dept. of English, St. John's University, Jamaica, NY 11432.

HAFNER, JOHN HENRY, b. Mobile, Ala, July 26, 38; m. 60; c. 2. AMERICAN & ENGLISH LITERATURE. B.S, Spring Hill Col, 60; M.A, Marquette Univ, 62; Ph.D.(Eng), Univ. Wis-Madison, 69. Instr. ENG, U.S. Mil. Acad, 66-68; lectr, Ind. Univ, Bloomington, 68-69, asst. prof, 69-71; ASSOC. PROF. & CHMN. DEPT, SPRING HILL COL, 71- Nat. Endowment for Humanities Summer Sem. Lit. & Cult. in Am, 73. Adj.Gen.C, U.S.A, 65-68, Capt. MLA; S.Atlantic Mod. Lang. Asn. Twentieth century American literature; American studies; fiction. Publ: William Faulkner's narrators, Dissertation Abstracts Int, 69; One way of looking at Thirteen ways of looking at a blackbird, Concerning Poetry, 70. Add: Dept. of English, Spring Hill College, Mobile, AL 36608.

HAFNER, MAMIE, b. Selma, Ala, Aug. 23, 23. ENGLISH. A.B, Univ. Ala, 45; M.A, Univ. N.C, 53; South. Fels. Fund fels, Univ. Wis, 61-62, Ph.D. (Eng), 65. Instr. Eng, Meredith Col, 53-55; asst. Univ. Wis, 55-59; instr. ENG, La. State Univ, 59-61; asst. prof, Meredith Col, 62-66; E.TEX. STATE UNIV, 66-73, PROF, 73- MLA; Conf. Col. Comp. & Commun; NCTE. Mediaeval English and French literature; modern British literature. Add: Dept. of Literature & Languages, East Texas University, Commerce, TX 75428.

HAFNER, YATES, b. Hannibal, Mo, Sept. 19, 33; m. 57; c. 2. ENGLISH LITERATURE. A.B, Univ. Notre Dame, 54; Ph.D.(Eng. & humanities), Stanford, 67. Instr. lit, Antioch Col, 62-65, asst. prof, 65-71, assoc. dean fac, 67-71; DEAN MONTIETH COL, WAYNE STATE UNIV, 71- U.S.A, 56-58. MLA; NCTE; Civil Liberties Union. Humanism and poetry in the English Renaissance. Add: Montieth College, Wayne State University, Detroit, MI 48202.

HAFTER, RONALD, b. U.S, July 28, 32; m. 59. ENGLISH. B.A, Univ. Vt, 54; M.A, Brandeis Univ, 57, teaching fel, 57-59. Part-time instr, Boston Univ, 57-59; Rutgers Univ, 60-61; ASST. PROF. ENG, DALHOUSIE UNIV, 62- U.S.A, 54-56. MLA; Asn. Can. Univ. Teacher Eng. History and theory of literary criticism; 18th century novel. Add: Dept. of English, Dalhousie University, Halifax, N.S, Can.

HAGAN, JOHN H, JR. b. Port Chester, N.Y, Apr. 2, 28; m. 57; c. 2. ENGLISH LITERATURE. B.A, Harvard, 49; M.A, Univ. Chicago, 50, Ph.D, 57. Instr. Eng, W.Va. Univ, 54-55; Wayne State Univ, 56-57; Fulbright fel, Univ. London, 57-58; instr. ENG, Univ. Chicago, 58-59; Wellesley Col, 59-61, asst. prof, 61-64; STATE UNIV. N.Y. BINGHAMTON, 64-66, assoc. prof, 66-71, PROF, 71-, res. found. grant-in-aid, 65-67. Guggenheim Found. fel, 69-70. Nineteenth century English literature; the novel. Publ: On the craftsmanship of War and peace, Essays in Criticism, 1/63; Chekhov's fiction and the ideal of Objectivity, PMLA, 10/66; Control of sympathy in Wuthering Heights, Nineteenth Century Fiction; plus others. Add: Dept. of English, State University of New York, Binghamton, NY 13901.

HAGAN, MICHAEL ROBERT, b. Centralia, Wash, Jan. 21, 38; m. 60; c. 4. SPEECH, RHETORIC. B.A, St. Martin's Col, 60; M.A, Univ. Wash, 62, Ph.D.(speech), 67. ASST. PROF. SPEECH, Kutztown State Col, 64-66; Univ. Wash, 67-69; HAMLINE UNIV, 69- Speech Commun. Asn.(v.chmn. pub. address div, 73-74). Argumentation; rhetorical criticism. Publ: Kenneth Burke and the generative criticism of speeches, Cent. States Speech. J, winter 71-72; A missing chapter in argumentation texts, J. Am. Forensic Asn, summer 72. Add: Dept. of Speech & Theatre, Hamline University, 1536 Hewitt Ave, St. Paul, MN 55104.

HAGAN, ROBERT LYLE, b. Kewanee, Ill, Mar. 17, 13; m; c. 5. DRAMA, SPEECH. B.F.A, Goodman Theatre Art Inst, Chicago, 46, M.F.A, 47; Eureka Col, 45-46; Ph.D.(drama), West. Reserve Univ, 49; Univ. Mex, 58-59. Asst. prof. speech & theatre, Ind. Univ, 49-54; assoc. prof. div. lang, lit. & fine arts, EAST. N.MEX. UNIV, 54-57, PROF. SPEECH & DRAMA, 57-, DEAN SCH. COMMUN, 67-, CHMN. DEPT. THEATRE, 71-, dir. dept. speech & drama, 61-67. Commun. Intel, U.S.N, 42-45. Speech Commun. Asn; Am. Theatre Asn; Southwest Theatre Conf.(ed, The Topics, 67-); Am. Nat. Theatre & Acad; Nat. Theatre Conf. History of the theatre in the state of New Mexico from the Spanish conquest and in the state of Indiana. Publ: National report of summer theatre production list and activities, Am. Educ. Theatre Asn. J, 56-57. Add: School of Communicative Arts & Sciences, Eastern New Mexico University, Portales, NM 88130.

HAGELMAN, CHARLES WILLIAM, JR, b. Houston, Tex, Nov. 9, 20; m. 46; c. 3. ENGLISH. B.A, Univ. Tex, 42, Ph.D.(Eng), 56; Wash. Univ, 42; Va. Mil. Inst, 43-44; M.A, Columbia Univ, 47. Instr. Eng, Muhlenberg Col, 47-51; Univ. Tex, 53-55; Univ. Houston, 55, asst. prof, 56-58, dir. freshman Eng, 57-58, assoc. prof. Eng, 58-59; prof. & head dept, Lamar State Col, 59-66; prof. Eng. & assoc. dean, div. humanities, Univ. Toledo, 66-68; PROF. ENG. & HEAD DEPT, ENG, NORTH. ILL. UNIV, 68- Part-time instr, Columbia Univ, 46-47; teaching fel, Univ. Tex, 52, univ. fel, 52-53; ed. consult, Survival Planning Proj. for Houston-Harris County Area, 56-57; Bus. Rev, Univ. Houston, 57-59; U.S. Steel Award Outstanding Achievement Teaching, 58; Lamar State Col. res. grant, 60-63; consult, N.Cent. Asn. Cols. & Sec. Schs, 70- U.S.A, 42-46. MLA; S.Cent. Mod. Lang. Asn; Keats-Shelley Asn. Am; Am. Stud. Asn; NCTE; Conf. Col. Compos. & Commun; Midwest Mod. Lang. Asn. Computer research in language and literature; 19th century British and American literature. Publ: Co-auth, A concordance to Byron's Don Juan, Cornell Univ, 67; ed, Mary Wollstonecraft's A vindication of the rights of women, Norton, 67; Keat's medical training and the last stanza of the Ode to Psyche, Keats-Shelley J, 62. Add: Dept. of English, Northern Illinois University, DeKalb, IL 60115.

HAGEN, LYMAN B, b. Austin, Minn, Oct. 4, 21; m. 50; c. 1. ENGLISH. M.A, Univ. Wash, 51; Ph.D.(educ), Univ. Portland, 67. Assoc. prof. Eng, St. Ambrose Col, 56-62; asst. prof, Univ. Portland, 62-66; humanities, Ore. Col. Educ, 66-67; ENG, Cent. Wash. State Col, 67-69; ASSOC. PROF, ARK. STATE UNIV, 69- Mem, Col. Eng. Educ. Comt, Educ. Resources Inform. Ctr, 68- U.S.A, 40-45, Res, 45-, Lt. Col. Col. Eng. Asn; NCTE. English education; modern English grammar. Publ: An analysis of transitional devices in student writing, Res. Teaching Eng, fall 71; A college supervisor talks to a student teacher, Improv. Col. & Univ. Teaching, spring 72; Creating confidence with classroom drama, J. Eng. Teaching Tech, spring 72. Add: Dept. of English, Philosophy & Languages, Box 1721, Arkansas State University, State University, AR 72467.

HAGESTAD, WILLIAM THOMSON, b. River Falls, Wis, Apr. 16, 37; m. 59; c. 2. ENGLISH. B.A, Wis. State Univ, River Falls, 59; M.A, Univ. Wis, Madison, 61, Ph.D.(Eng), 66. Instr. ENG, Univ. North. Iowa, 64-66; asst. prof, St. Louis Univ, 66-69; ASSOC. PROF, UNIV. WIS-RIVER FALLS, 69- Fulbright lectr, Univ. Tehran, 70-73. MLA. Text of Daniel Defoe's Moll Flanders; structure of English narrative prose. Add: 358 W. Church St, River Falls, WI 54022.

HAGLER, MARGARET G, b. Denver, Colo, Nov. 29, 19. COMPARATIVE LITERATURE, FOLKLORE. B.A, Univ. Colo, 43; Columbia Univ, 48; M.A, Ind. Univ, 56, Writers Conf. scholar, 60, Wis. State Bd. Regents grant, 62, Ph.D, 71. Journalist, U.S. Merchant Marine, 45; N.Y. Times, 45-48; travel press, 49-51; free-lance ed. & consult, 51-54; assoc, Ind. Univ, Bloomington, 54-57; instr. Eng, North. Ariz. Univ, 57-58; Denver Ctr, Univ. Colo, 58-61; asst. prof, Wis. State Univ. Oshkosh, 61-64; asst. prof, Chicago State Univ, 64-68; MEM. FAC. HUMANITIES, LINCOLN LAND COMMUNITY COL, 70- Participant hon. prog, Univ. Colo; honorarium, Folklore Inst, Ind. Univ, 54. First prize juvenile field, Colo. Auth. League, 50. MLA; Am. Folklore Soc; NCTE; Midwest Mod. Lang. Asn; Am. Comp. Lit. Asn; Int. Comp. Lit. Asn. Interlinguistics, history and analysis of constructed languages; trends in modern novel, drama, poetry and short story; translation theory. Publ: Larry and the freedom man, Lothrop, 59; Larrys grosser ritte, Claudius, Munich, 61; The Esperanto language as a literary medium, Diss. Abstr. Int. Vol. XXXIII: 2; Here it comes—there it goes, In: Best college writing, Random, 61; plus others. Add: Lincoln Land Community College, Springfield, IL 62703.

HAGOOD, ANNABEL DUNHAM, b. Hattiesburg, Miss, Feb. 7, 24; m. 50. SPEECH. A.B, Southwest. La. Inst, 44; A.M, Univ. Wis, 46. Instr. speech, Southwest. La. Inst, 44-45; PROF. SPEECH & DIR. FORENSICS, UNIV. ALA, 46- Chmn, Comt. Int. Discussion & Debate, 53-55; mem. adv. comt. contest & awards, Alexander Hamilton Bicentennial Comn, 56-57; ed, The Register, 56-57; mem, Speaker of Year Bd. of Award, 63-, chmn, 64-66; chmn, Nat. Debate Tournament Comt, 67-68, mem. bd. trustees, 68-, chmn, 68-69, treas, 72-74; consult. ed, Speech Teacher, 56-60. Outstanding Prof. Award, Univ. Ala, 64-65. Speech Commun. Asn; South. Speech Commun. Asn.(3rd v.pres, 56); Am. Forensic Asn.(secy-treas, 52-53, v.pres, 54-55, pres, 56-57, chmn. comt. col. & high sch. relationships, 66-67, chmn. prof. relat. comt, 69-70, ed. comt, Essays in Forensics, 69-70). Discussion, debate; persuasion. Publ: Debating proposition of policy, Houghton, (in press); Prove your contentions, In: NUEA discussion and debate manual, 52; The structural level of the fraternity, Tau Kappa Alpha Manual, 60; plus others. Add: Box 1367, University of Alabama, University, AL 35486.

HAGOPIAN, JOHN V, b. Ambridge, Pa, Mar. 11, 23; div; c. 2. LITERARY CRITICISM. A.B, Wayne Univ, 45, M.A, 50; fel, West. Reserve Univ, 51-53, Ph.D, 55. Spec. instr. Eng, Wayne Univ, 46-49; psychologist (P-3), Veterans Admin, 46-47; teaching fel. Eng, West. Reserve Univ, 50-53; lectr, Ind. Univ, 53-55; instr, Univ. Mich, 55-59, asst. prof, 59-60; prof. & chmn. Am. lit, Univ. Saarland, 60-63; PROF. Eng, STATE UNIV. N.Y. BINGHAMTON, 63-71, ENG. & COMP. LIT, 71- Fulbright prof, Univ. Kiel, 57-58; lectr, U.S. Inform. Serv, 60-63; summer vis. prof, Falkenstein Sem. Am. Stud, 61-63, 68; assoc. ed, Stud. in Short Fiction, 65-; mem, Int. Fed. Mod. Lang. & Lit; vis. prof, Jackson State Col, spring 67; vis. lectr. psychiat, Sch. Med, Univ. Miss, 67-69; vis. prof. Eng, Sir George Williams Univ, summer 71. Sig.C, U.S.A, 43-46. MLA; NCTE; Col. Eng. Asn; Int. Asn. Univ. Prof. Eng; Conf. Col. Compos. & Commun. Psychology of perception in literary studies; psychology and techniques of the I Narrative;

metaphor. Publ: Co-auth, Insight I: analyses of American literature, 62, Insight II: analyses of modern British literature, 64 & Insight III: analyses of British and American poetry, 68, Hirschgraben; auth, J.F. Powers, Twayne, 68; Nihilism in Faulkner's The sound and the fury, Mod. Fiction Stud, 67; Symbolism and metaphor in the transformation of reality into art, Comp. Lit, 68; plus others. Add: Dept. of English, State University of New York at Binghamton, Binghamton, NY 13901.

HAGOPIAN, RICHARD, b. Revere, Mass, Apr. 21, 14. ENGLISH. A.B, Pomona Col, 41; M.F.A, State Univ. Iowa, 47; Huntington Hartford Found. fel, 52, 54. Prof. SPEECH, UNIV. CALIF, BERKELEY, 56-72, EMER. PROF, 72- Bender Award, 45. Sig.C, U.S.A.A.F, 41-42. Int. Mark Twain Soc. Creative writing; methods of teaching the interpretation of literature in speech. Publ: The dove brings peace; Faraway the spring; Wine for the living. Add: Dept. of Rhetoric, University of California, Berkeley, CA 94720.

HAGSTRUM, JEAN HOWARD, b. St. Paul, Minn, Mar. 26, 13; m. 41; c. 2. ENGLISH LITERATURE. A.B, Univ. Minn, 33; A.M, Northwest. Univ, 38; Ph.D, Yale; 41, hon. D.H.L, N.Park Col, 66. Instr. Eng, NORTHWEST. UNIV, 40-42, asst. prof, 46-52, assoc. prof, 52-57, prof, 57-70, JOHN C. SHAFFER PROF. ENG. & HUMANITIES, 70-, chmn. dept, 58-64, co-dir, Curriculum Ctr, 62-64. Chief allocation sect, U.S. Off. Censorship, 42-44; Fulbright res. fel, Italy, 53-54, lectr, Univ. Delhi, 72; trustee, Newberry Libr, 65-; sr. fel, Clark Libr, Univ. Calif, Los Angeles, 70. MLA; NCTE; Am-Swed. Hist. Asn. Literature and psychology; 18th century English literature; Romantic literature. Publ: Sister arts, 58, William Blake poet and painter, 63 & Samuel Johnson's literary criticism, 67, Univ. Chicago; co-auth, A community of scholars (2 vols), Northwest. Univ, 68, 69; plus others. Add: Dept. of English, Northwestern University, Evanston, IL 60201.

HAHN, ELISE STEARNS, b. Los Angles, Calif, June 26, 11. SPEECH. A.B, Univ. Calif, Los Angeles, 32; A.M, Wayne Univ, 42; Ph.D, Northwest. Univ, 47. Instr, Wayne Univ, 42; asst, Northwest. Univ, 45-47; asst. prof. SPEECH, Univ. Calif, Los Angeles, 47-55, assoc. prof, 55-65; PROF. CALIF. STATE UNIV, LOS ANGELES, 65- Consult. cleft palate serv, St. John's Hospital, Santa Monica, Calif. Am. Speech & Hearing Asn.(v.pres, 62); Speech Commun. Asn.(2nd v.pres, 56, v.pres, 57, pres, 58); Am. Cleft Palate Asn.(v.pres, 66, pres, 71). Speech defects of children; voice defects; language development. Publ: Basic voice training for speech, McGraw; Stuttering, Stanford Univ. Add: Dept. of Speech, California State University, Los Angeles, 5151 State University, Los Angeles, CA 90032.

HAICH, GEORGE DONALD, b. Evanston, Ill, Feb. 27, 28; m. 50; c. 3. ENGLISH & AMERICAN LITERATURE. A.B, Univ. Rochester, 52; dipl, Concordia Theol. Sem, 61; M.A, Univ. Nebr, 66; Ph.D.(Eng), Univ. Fla, 70. Asst. prof. Eng, Concordia Col, 61-67; interim instr, Univ. Fla, 67-68; ASST. PROF. ENG. & MEM. URBAN LIFE FAC, GA. STATE UNIV, 70- Ed. consult, Prentice-Hall, Inc, 72-73; Macmillan & Co, 73- U.S.A, 48. NCTE; Conf. Col. Compos. & Commun; MLA; S.Atlantic Mod. Lang. Asn. Victorian literature; freshman composition; literary criticism. Publ: A classroom exercise in literary imagination, Reading Improv, spring 74. Add: Dept. of English, Georgia State University, 33 Gilmer St. S.E, Atlanta, GA 30303.

HAIG, ROBERT LOUIS, b. Terre Haute, Ind, Nov. 3, 25; m. 47; c. 2. ENGLISH. B.A, Kent State Univ, 48; M.A, Ind. Univ, 49, fel. & Ph.D.(Eng), 53; Univ. London, 51-52. Instr. ENG, Univ. Ill, Urbana, 53-56, asst. prof, 56-60, assoc. prof, 60-65, PROF, 65-67; UNIV. N.C, CHAPEL HILL, 67- Guggenheim fel, 60-61. U.S.N, 43-46. MLA; Am. Soc. 18th Century Stud. Eighteenth century English periodicals; bibliography and printing history. Publ: The gazetteer, 1735-1797, South. Ill. Univ, 60. Add: Dept. of English, University of North Carolina, Chapel Hill, NC 27514.

HAIGHT, GORDON SHERMAN, b. Muskegon, Mich, Feb. 6, 01; m. 37. ENGLISH & AMERICAN LITERATURE. A.B, Yale, 23, Ph.D, 33. Master ENG, Kent Sch, Conn, 24-25; Hotchkiss Sch, 25-30; instr, YALE, 33-38, asst. prof, 38-45, assoc. prof, 45-50, EMILY SANFORD PROF, 50-, master, Pierson Col, 49-53. Vis. prof, Grad. Sch, Columbia Univ, 45-46; Univ. Ore, 49; Guggenheim fel, 46-47, 52-53, 60-61; mem. adv. bd, Nineteenth Century Fiction, 49-56, 68-; Victorian Stud, 57-59; Stud. in Eng. Lit, 61-; Wellesley Index to Victorian Periodicals; mem. ed. bd. PMLA, 59-70. Fel. Royal Soc. Lit; cor. fel. Brit. Acad. English novel, 19th century. Publ: Mrs. Sigourney, 30; George Eliot and John Chapman, 40; The George Eliot letters, 7 vols, 54-55; A century of George Eliot criticism, Houghton, 65; George Eliot, a biography, Clarendon, 68; ed, The portable Victorian reader, Viking, 72; co-auth, Realism defined, In: Literary history of the United States, 48; George Eliot's originals, In: From Jane Austen to Joseph Conrad, 58; auth, George Meredith and the Westminster Review, Mod. Lang. Rev, 58; plus three others. Add: 145 Peck Hill Road, Woodbridge, CT 06525.

HAILEY, ROBERT CARTER, b. Donna, Tex, Aug. 22, 26; m. 47; c. 5. DRAMATIC ARTS. B.Mus, DePauw Univ, 47; M.A, Miami Univ, 49; M.F.A, Case West. Reserve Univ, 58; Ph.D.(dramatic arts), 68. Asst. prof. DRAMATIC ARTS, LYNCHBURG COL, 49-58, assoc. prof, 58-68, PROF. & CHMN. DEPT, 68- Am. Theatre Asn; Am. Nat. Theatre & Acad; Southeast. Theatre Conf.(Va. State rep, 68). Add: Dept. of Dramatic Arts, Lynchburg College, Lynchburg, VA 24504.

HAINES, CHARLES MURRAY ROBERT, b. New York, N.Y, Mar. 22, 28. ENGLISH. B.A, Trinity Col.(Dublin), 49; M.A, 54. Asst. ENG, Univ. Bari, 54-55; lettore-reader, Univ. Turin, 55-57; secy. Eng. Inst, Bocconi Univ, Italy, 59-64, lettore, 55-64; acting chmn, Univ. Lecce, Italy, 61-62; asst. prof, CARLETON UNIV. (CAN), 65-66, ASSOC. PROF, 66- Theatre, dance & opera critic, CBO-Ottawa, 70- Asn. Can. Univ. Teachers Eng; MLA. Publ: Co-auth, English, 61 & English is chaos, 61, Vallardi; auth, William Shakespeare and his plays, 68 & Charles Dickins, 70, Watts; introd, Tales and poems by Poe, 61, Gulliver's travels, 64, Robinson Crusoe, 66, Farther adventures of Robinson Crusoe, 68 & Four Shakespeare plays, 69, Club Del Libro; auth, Florence: city of the Renaissance, Watts, 72. Add: Dept. of English, Carleton University, Rideau River Campus, Ottawa, Ont, Can.

HAINES, LEWIS FRANCIS, b. Endicott, N.Y, Oct. 28, 07; m. 30; c. 1. ENGLISH LITERATURE. A.B, Univ. Mich, 30, A.M, 32, Ph.D, 41. Instr. high sch, Wis, 30-34; teaching fel, Univ. Mich, 35-41; acting instr. Eng, UNIV. FLA, 41-42, asst. prof, 42-46, PROF. HUMANITIES, 46-, ed. Univ. Press, 45-67, dir, 49-67. MLA; NCTE; S.Atlantic Mod. Lang. Asn. Charles Reade; realism and naturalism in English fiction. Publ: Social criticism in the novels of Charles Reade. Add: 411 Little Hall, University of Florida, Gainesville, FL 32601.

HAINES, RAYMOND MICHAEL, b. Wilmington, Ohio, July 16, 41; m. 63; c. 3. ENGLISH LITERATURE & COMPOSITION. B.A, Hiram Col, 63; M.A, Ohio State Univ, 66, Ph.D.(Eng), 71. ASST. PROF. ENG, PA. STATE UNIV, UNIVERSITY PARK, 71- Asst. to ed, Chaucer Rev, 73- MLA. Medieval English literature; Chaucer; folklore. Add: Dept. of English, Pennsylvania State University, Burrowes Bldg, University Park, PA 16802.

HAINES, ROBERT EUGENE NED, b. Middletown, Ohio, July 21, 27; m. 49. ENGLISH & AMERICAN LITERATURE. B.A, Ohio State, 54, M.A, 56, Ph.D. (Eng. & Am. lit), Stanford Univ, 68. Instr. Eng. & Spanish, Univ. Md, Bermuda, 60-62; asst. prof. Eng, Univ. Alaska, 67-73; RES. & WRITING, 73- Nat. Endowment for Humanities summer stipend, 72. U.S.N, 45-53, Lt. MLA; Philol. Asn. Pac. Coast; NCTE; Melville Soc. Am; AAUP (secy-treas, 71-73). Literary relationships of Alfred Stieglitz; literature and the graphic arts; photography as a fine art. Publ: Alfred Stieglitz and the new order of consciousness in American literature, Pac. Coast Philol, 4/71. Add: c/o Harold Hard, 5377 Park Lane Ct, Columbus, OH 43229.

HAIR, DONALD SHERMAN, b. Strathroy, Ont, Nov. 24, 37; m. 66. ENGLISH. B.A, Univ. West. Ont, 60; M.A, Univ. Toronto, 61, Queen Elizabeth II fel, univ. fel, Can. Counc. fel, Ph.D.(Eng), 64. Lectr. ENG, UNIV. WEST. ONT, 64-65, asst. prof, 65-69, assoc. prof, 69-73, PROF, 73-, assoc. chmn. dept, 67-73. Can. Counc. leave fel, 73-74. Asn. Can. Univ. Teachers Eng; Humanities Asn. Can. Victorian literature. Publ: Browning's experiments with genre, Univ. Toronto, 72. Add: Dept. of English, University of Western Ontario, London, Ont. N6A 3K7, Can.

HAIRSTON, JOE BECK, b. Taylor, Tex, Sept. 30, 37; m. 68; c. 1. AMERICAN STUDIES & LITERATURE. B.A, Harvard, 60; M.A, Univ. Tex, Austin, 66; Ph.D.(Am. stud), Univ. Minn, Minneapolis, 71. Instr. ENG, West. Mich. Univ, 67-68; ASST. PROF, MIDWEST. UNIV, 71- U.S.N.R, 61-64, Lt.(jg). AAUP; Am. Stud. Asn; MLA. Western American literature. Publ: Community in the West, S.Dak. Rev, spring 73. Add: Rte. 1, Box 93, Taylor, TX 76574.

HAISLIP, JOHN ALPHEUS, b. Lancaster, Pa, Aug. 25, 25; m; c. 4. ENGLISH, CREATIVE WRITING. B.A, Univ. Wash, 50, Ph.D, 65. Instr. ENG, Univ. Idaho, 52-54; Ore. State Univ, 58-62, asst. prof, 62-66, ASSOC. PROF, 66-68; UNIV. ORE, 68- U.S.C.G, 43-46. MLA. Twentieth century literature; 20th century poetry. Publ: Not every year, Univ. Wash, 71; The risk of rediscovery, Northwest Rev, summer 67; plus numerous poems in various lit. journals. Add: Dept. of English, University of Oregon, Eugene, OR 97403.

HAIST, GORDON KEITH, b. Olney, Ill, Mar. 30, 10; m. 39; c. 2. ENGLISH. A.B, N.Cent. Col, 32; A.M, Northwest. Univ, 35. Instr. Eng, ROSE-HULMAN POLYTECH. INST, 46-48, asst. prof, 48-54, assoc. prof, 54-60, PROF, 60-71, HUMANITIES, 71-, head dept. humanities & soc. sci, 61-71. Mem, Inst. Gen. Semantics. Int. Soc. Gen. Semantics; Am. Soc. Engineering Educ.(chmn. div. lib. stud, 66-67). General semantics. Add: Dept. of English, Rose-Hulman Polytechnic Institute, 5500 Wabash Ave, Terre Haute, IN 47803.

HAKUTANI, YOSHINOBU, b. Osaka, Japan, Mar. 27, 35; m. 67; c. 2. AMERICAN LITERATURE, LINGUISTICS. B.A, Hiroshima Univ, Hiroshima, Japan, 57; Int. fel, Univ. Minn, Minneapolis, 57-59, M.A, 59; univ. fel, Pa. State Univ, 61-65, Ph.D.(Eng), 65. Instr. ENG, S.Dak. State Univ, 59-61; asst. prof, Calif. State Univ, Northridge, 65-68; KENT STATE UNIV, 68-71, ASSOC. PROF, 71-, res. fel, 71-72. Instr. Japanese, Yale, summer 60. MLA; Ling. Soc. Am; Conf. Col. Compos. & Commun; Eng. Lit. Asn. Japan. Japanese literature. Publ: Co-ed, The world of Japanese fiction, E.P. Dutton, 73; auth, Dreiser and French realism, Tex. Stud. Lit. & Lang, 7/64; Sister Carrie and the problem of literary naturalism, Twentieth Century Lit, 4/67; co-auth, The syntax of modal constructions in English, Lingua, 12/72. Add: Dept. of English, Kent State University, Kent, OH 44242.

HALE, DAVID GEORGE, b. Worcester, Mass. Mar. 25, 38; m. 64; c. 2. ENGLISH. B.A, Wesleyan Univ, 60; M.A, Duke Univ, 61, Ph.D.(Eng), 65. Tutor ENG, Duke Univ, 61-64; asst. prof, Univ. Cincinnati, 64-67; STATE UNIV. N.Y. COL. BROCKPORT, 67-71, ASSOC. PROF, 71- State Univ. N.Y. Fac. summer fel, 68, 69, 74; Folger Shakespeare Libr. fel, 70. MLA; Mod. Humanities Res. Asn; Renaissance Soc. Am. Renaissance. Publ: The body politic: a political metaphor in Renaissance Engligh literature, Mouton, 71; Shakespeare and James Gordon (1700), Notes & Queries, 71; The source and date of Golding's Fabletalke, Mod. Philol, 72; Aesop in Renaissance England, Libr, 72; plus five others. Add: 26 Meadowview Dr, Brockport, NY 14420.

HALE, FRANK WILBUR, JR, b. Kansas City, Mo, Mar. 24, 27; m. 47; c. 3. SPEECH, POLITICAL SCIENCE. A.B, Univ. Nebr, 50, M.A, 51; Ph.D. (speech, polit. sci), Ohio State Univ, 55; Univ. London, summer 60. Instr. Eng. & speech, Oakwood Col, 51-53, assoc. prof, 55-59; asst. instr. speech, Ohio State Univ, 54-55; prof. Eng. & speech, Cent. State Col, 59-66; pres, Oakwood Col, 66-71; ASSOC. DEAN, GRAD. SCH, OHIO STATE UNIV, 71- Vis. prof, Andrews Univ, summer 57; educ. consult, Xenia, Ohio Bd. Educ, 64-; bk. consult, Choice, 64; commun. consult, career develop. br, U.S.A.F, Wright-Patterson AFB, Ohio, 65-66. Adminr. of Yr. Award, Black Grad. & Prof. Stud. Caucus, Ohio State Univ, 72 & 73. Am. Asn. Sch. Adminr; NCTE; Speech Commun. Asn; MLA; Asn. Stud. Negro Life & Hist. Civil rights movement. Publ: A manual of public speaking, Brown Publ, 64; Sunlight and shadows, South. Publ. Asn, 67; The cry for freedom, A.S. Barnes, 68; Salmon Portland Chase: rhetorician of abolition, J. Human Rights, 62; A speech teacher as a director of a senior lecture series, Speech Teacher,

64; Disadvantaged youth: a challenge to higher education, Educ. Horizons, 65. Add: Graduate School, Ohio State University, 164 W. 19th Ave, Columbus, OH 43210.

HALE, GEORGE HARDIN, b. Kalamazoo, Mich, Sept. 24, 20. SPEECH, DRAMA. A.B, Kalamazoo Col, 42; Trueblood hon. fel, Univ. Mich, 45-46, A.M, 46. Teacher Eng, Pub. Schs, Belding, Mich, 42-43, Dundee, 43-45; teaching fel, speech, Univ. Mich, 45-46; asst. prof. DRAMA & SPEECH, HILLSDALE COL, 46-49, ASSOC. PROF, 49- English; Meyerhold's theories of dramatic production. Add: Dept. of Speech & Drama, Hillsdale College, Hillsdale, MI 49242.

HALE, LESTER LEONARD, b. Rice Lake, Wis, July 6, 13; m. 34; c. 3. SPEECH. B.A, Univ. Wis, 34; M.A, La. State Univ, 35, Ph.D.(speech), 42. Instr. SPEECH, UNIV. FLA, 35-37, asst. prof, 37-39, assoc. prof, 41-45, prof, 45-73, dean men, 56-60, dean stud. affairs, 60-67; v.pres. stud. affairs, 67-73, EMER. PROF. & V.PRES, 73- Vis. prof, Colo. State Teachers Col, summer 46; Univ. Wis, summer 47; Univ. Ala, summer 48; Wayne Univ, summer 50; Univ. Tenn, summer 55; Ohio Univ, summers 56, 57; organizing pastor, Silver Springs Shores Presby. Church, Ocala, Fla, 73- Nat. Asn. Stud. Personnel Adminr; Am. Personnel & Guidance Asn; fel. Am. Speech & Hearing Asn; Speech Commun. Asn; South. Speech Asn.(pres); Am. Col. Personnel Asn. Add: 2245 N.W. Sixth Pl, Gainesville, FL 32601.

HALE, MARGARET RANDOLPH, b. New Orleans, La, Oct. 2, 41; m. 65. COMPARATIVE LITERATURE, ENGLISH. B.A, Bryn Mawr Col, 63; Ger. Acad. Exchange fel, Univ. Tübingen, 63-64; Fulbright fel, Univ. London, 66-67; Ph.D.(comp. lit), Yale, 70. Instr. ENG, George Washington Univ, 67-68; ASST. PROF, UNIV. CONN, 70- MLA; Eng. Inst; Am. Comp. Lit. Asn. Jean Paul Richter; literary theory; romanticism. Publ: Transl. & auth, Introd, Horn of Oberon: Jean Paul Richter's School for aesthetics, Wayne State Univ, 73. Add: Dept. of English, University of Connecticut, Storrs, CT 06268.

HALE, RICHARD OSBORNE, b. Chicago, Ill, Dec. 7, 03. ENGLISH, LANGUAGES. A.B, Northwest. Univ, 27, A.M, 28; fel, Univ. Chicago, 28-29; fel. Univ. Ariz, 35-36; Harvard, 39. Instr. high sch, Ill, 28-29; classics, Univ. N.Dak, 29-30; asst. prof. & head dept, Mo. Valley Col, 30-35; interim instr, Univ. Ariz, 35-36; teaching asst. ENG, Univ. Wis, 36-37; asst. prof. UNIV. N.DAK, 37-67, ASSOC. PROF, 67- NEA. Government spending to combat the depression; debating; vocabulary and the engineer. Add: Dept. of English, University of North Dakota, Grand Forks, ND 58201.

HALEWOOD, WILLIAM H, b. Providence, R.I, Dec. 15, 29; m. 52; c. 3. LITERATURE. B.A, Univ. Wichita, 53; M.A. & Ph.D, Univ. Minn, 59. Asst. prof. lit, Reed Col, 59-64, assoc. prof, 64-67, chmn. div. lett. & arts, 65-67; assoc. prof. ENG, UNIV. COL, UNIV. TORONTO, 67-72, PROF, 72- Am. Counc. Learned Soc. fel, 63-64. MLA. Neoclassical aesthetics; early Protestant theology; 17th and 18th century English literature. Publ: The poetry of Grace: reformation themes and structures in English poetry, Yale, 70; Plutarch in Houyhnhnmland, Philol. Quart, 65; Houyhnhnm est animal rationale, J. Hist. Ideas, 65; Gullivers travels, I, 4, ELH, 67; plus others. Add: Dept. of English, University College, University of Toronto, Toronto, Ont, Can.

HALEY, BRUCE EVERTS, b. St. Paul, Minn, July 19, 33. ENGLISH LITERATURE. B.A, Univ. Wash, 54, M.A, 55; Ph.D.(Eng), Univ. Ill, Urbana, 65. Asst. prof. ENG, UNIV. UTAH, 65-70, ASSOC. PROF, 70- Victorian studies; 19th century novel; romantic poetry. Publ: Sports and the Victorian world, West. Humanities Rev, spring 68; Richard Feverel and Willoughby Patterne: the athlete as egoist, Bucknell Rev, 12/68; The infinite will: Shakespeare's Troilus and the Ode to a nightingale, Keats-Shelley J, 73. Add: Dept. of English, 330 Orson Spencer Hall, University of Utah, Salt Lake City, UT 84112.

HALEY, DAVID BRUCE, b. Oakland, Calif, Aug. 22, 36; m. 65; c. 2. RENAISSANCE ENGLISH LITERATURE. A.B, Harvard, 58, Ph.D, 64. Asst. prof. ENG, UNIV. MINN, MINNEAPOLIS, 64-68, ASSOC. PROF, 68- Add: 324 Prospect Ave. S, Minneapolis, MN 55419.

HALEY, HAROLD LEROY, b. Tidioute, Pa, Feb. 29, 04; m. 28; c. 1. ELIZABETHAN LITERATURE. B.S, Hobart Col, 25; A.M, Harvard, 26; Ph.D, Cornell Univ, 34. Instr. ENG, Ohio Wesleyan Univ, 26-29; asst. prof, MIAMI UNIV, 29-40, assoc. prof, 40-49, prof, 49-71, EMER. PROF, 71- London life in the Elizabethan drama; Shakespeare. Publ: Co-auth, The practice of English fundamentals & The practice of exposition; collab, Designs for writing. Add: 159 Shadowy Hills, Oxford, OH 45056.

HALFOND, MURRAY MICHAEL, b. New York, N.Y, May 14, 25; m. 48; c. 1. SPEECH PATHOLOGY. B.A, Brooklyn Col, 48; M.A, Northwest. Univ, 49, Ph.D.(speech pathology), 52. Medical speech pathologist, Duke Univ. Med. Ctr, 51-53; dir. speech & hearing ctr, TEMPLE UNIV, 53-66, PROF. SPEECH & CHMN. DEPT, 65- Consult, Soc. Crippled Children & Adults, Del. Valley, 53-; fel, Devereux Found, Devon, Pa, 62. U.S.A, 43-46. Am. Speech & Hearing Asn; Am. Cleft Palate Asn; Am. Psychol. Asn. Speech pathology; psychotherapy. Publ: Co-auth, Voice and articulation, Scott, 66, An audiologic and otorhinologic study of cleft-lip and cleft-palate cases, Arch. Otolaryngology, 7/56 & The relationship of pediatrics to nonmedical professions, J. Pediatrics, 1/63; auth, Clinical supervision—stepchild in training, ASHA, 11/64; plus others. Add: Dept. of Speech, Temple University, Philadelphia, PA 19122.

HALIO, JAY LEON, b. New York, N.Y, July 24, 28. ENGLISH. B.A, Syracuse Univ, 50; M.A, Yale, 51, univ. fels, 52, 54-55, Ph.D.(Eng), 56. Instr. ENG, Univ. Calif, Davis, 55-57, asst. prof, 57-63, assoc. prof, 63-68; PROF, UNIV. DEL, 68-, H. Fletcher Brown Prof. lib. stud, 72. Fulbright-Hays lectr, Univ. Malaya, 66-67. MLA; Renaissance Soc. Am; World Ctr. Shakespeare Stud. Elizabethan literature; contemporary English and American literature. Publ: Angus Wilson, 64, ed, Volpone, 68, Macbeth, 73 & King Lear, 73, Oliver & Boyd, Ltd; Approaches to Macbeth, Wadsworth, 66 & Twentieth century interpretations: As you like it, Prentice-Hall, 68; auth, Life of dialogue in education, J. Gen. Educ, 1/63; Fantasy and fiction, South. Rev, 71; Coriolanus: Shakespeare's drama of reconciliation, Shakespeare Stud, 72. Add: Dept. of English, University of Delaware, Newark, DE 19711.

HALKETT, JOHN GEORGE, b. Chicago, Ill, May 3, 33. ENGLISH. B.A, Loyola Univ.(Ill), 55; M.A, Northwest. Univ, 57, Ph.D.(Eng), 64. Instr. ENG, Marycrest Col, 57-59; acting instr, Yale, 62-64, instr, 64-65, asst. prof, 65-69; ASSOC. PROF, SYRACUSE UNIV, 69- MLA; Renaissance Soc. Am. Milton; early seventeenth century. Publ: Milton and the idea of matrimony: a study of the divorce tracts and paradise lost, Yale, 70; co-auth, This powerful rime, Prentice-Hall, 70. Add: 303 Hall of Language, Syracuse University, Syracuse, NY 13210.

HALL, EDWIN MALBURN, b. Freeport, Ill, Apr. 18, 09; m. 35. WORLD LITERATURE, NAVAL HISTORY. B.A, Williams Col, 30; M.A, Univ. Chicago, 31; Ph.D.(Am. lit), Pa. State Univ, 59. Teacher, Prep Schs, 30-38; instr. Eng. compos, Pa. State Univ, 38-42; off-instr. Eng, U.S. Naval Acad, 42-46, asst. prof. Eng. & hist, 46-48, assoc. prof, 48-59, prof, 59-74; RETIRED. U.S.N.R, 42-46, Lt. Comdr. Col. Eng. Asn; MLA. American literature. Publ: Co-auth, Sea power, Prentice-Hall, 60. Add: R.D. 2, Box 282, Arnold, MD 21012.

HALL, ERNEST EUGENE, b. Mansfield, La, June 19, 32; m. 55; c. 3. SPEECH. B.A, La. Col, 53; B.D, South. Baptist Theol. Sem, 56; M.A, La. State Univ, 59, Ph.D.(speech), 63. Asst. prof. speech, Georgetown Col, 62-65; assoc. prof. & chmn. dept, La. Col, 65-67, dean chapel, 67-68; assoc. prof. & chmn. dept, Georgetown Col, 68-71; assoc. prof, West. Ky. Univ. 71-73; ACAD. DEAN, LA. COL, 73- U.S.N, 56-58, Res, 58-67, Lt. Speech Commun. Asn; Int. Commun. Asn. Development of rhetorical theory; history of speech education in America. Publ: Extra-sectional influences in the development of speech education in the South, South. Speech J, winter 61. Add: Office of the Dean, Louisiana College, Pineville, LA 71360.

HALL, HAROLD ERNEST, b. Linden, Iowa, Jan. 26, 24; m. 47; c. 2. ENGLISH. B.A, Simpson Col, 48; M.A, Univ. Pa, 50, Ph.D, 53. Instr. lib. stud, Clarkson Col, 52-53; assoc. prof, ENG, NEBR. WESLEYAN UNIV, 53-59, PROF, 59-, CHMN. DEPT, 56- U.S.N.R, 44-46. MLA; Am. Stud. Asn; NCTE. American literature; prose fiction. Add: 5235 Huntington Ave, Lincoln, NE 68504.

HALL, JAMES B, b. Midland, Ohio, July 21, 18; m. 46; c. 5. ENGLISH. B.A, State Univ. Iowa, 47, M.A, 48. Ph.D, 52; Kenyon Col, 48-49. Instr. Eng. & creative writing, Cornell Univ, 51-53; asst. prof. creative writing & lit, Univ. Ore, 53-57, assoc. prof, 57-60, prof. creative writing, 63-65; prof. Eng. & dir. writing ctr, Univ. Calif, Irvine, 65-68; PROVOST, COL. V, UNIV. CALIF, SANTA CRUZ, 68- Rockefeller grant, 55; writer-in-residence, Writer's Conf. Rocky Mt, Boulder, Colo, 63; fel, Inst. Creative Arts, 67-68; adv, Contemporary Novelists Proj, Eng, 70-72; mem. Western Accreditation Asn, 70-; mem. bd. gov, Assoc. Writing Prog, 72-; consult, Simon Fraser Univ, 72- Ohio Writer of the Year, 54; Ore. State Poetry Prize, 58; Chapelbrook Found. Award, 67-68. U.S.A, 41-46. Philol. Asn. Pac. Coast; Am. Civil Liberties Union; PEN Club. The short story; literary theory. Publ: Co-auth, The short story, 54, Macmillan; auth, 15 x 3, New Directions, 60; Racers to the sun, Obolensky, 61; Realm of fiction: 61 short stories, 65 & co-auth, Modern culture and the arts, 67, McGraw; auth, Mayo sergeant, New American Libr, 67; The hunt within (poetry), La. State Univ, 73. Add: Cardiff House, 1100 High St, Santa Cruz, CA 95060.

HALL, JEANNE LUCILLE, b. Kansas City, Kans, June 29, 15; m. 38; c. 5. SPEECH, DRAMA. B.S, Northwest. Univ, 36; M.A, Univ. South. Calif, 39; Ph.D.(speech), Univ. Mich, 66. Instr. drama, Baker Univ, 36-37; teacher, Glendale City Schs, 54-58; assoc. prof. speech & drama, CALIF. STATE UNIV, HAYWARD, 60-73, PROF, 73- Co-dir, NDEA Inst. Children's Theatre & Creative Dramatics, Humboldt State Col, summer 68. Am. Theatre Asn; Children's Theatre Conf. Values in children's theatre and creative dramatics. Publ: Building the future adult theatre audience, Speech Teacher, 9/65; Opportunity in children's theatre, Educ. Theatre J, 10/66. Add: Dept. of Speech & Drama, California State University, Hayward, 25800 Hillary St, Hayward, CA 94542.

HALL, LAWRENCE SARGENT, b. Haverhill, Mass, Apr. 23, 15; m. 38; c. 2. ENGLISH. A.B, Bowdoin Col, 36; Ph.D.(Eng), Yale, 41. Master Eng, Deerfield Acad, 36-38; instr. Eng. & Am. lit, Ohio Univ, 41-42; Eng. & hist, U.S. Naval Acad, 42-43; ENG, Yale, 46; asst. prof, BOWDOIN COL, 46-59, prof, 59-67, CHAPMAN PROF, 67-, chmn. dept, 64-67. Carnegie vis. assoc. prof, Columbia Univ, 55-56; NDEA lectr. & consult, 66-69. O.Henry Mem. First Prize, 60; Faulkner Found. Award, 61. U.S.N, 42-46, Lt. Comdr. MLA. Criticism; 18th, 19th and 20th century English and American literature. Publ: Stowaway, Little, 61; How thinking is written, Heath, 63; A grammar of literary criticism, Macmillan, 65; Hoist negative: oil and the Maine coast, fall 72 & The experiment, fall 73, N.Am. Rev; A sailor's argument against oil on the Maine coast, Down East, 4/73. Add: Orr's Island, ME 04066.

HALL, LOUIS BREWER, b. Camden, N.J, Aug. 1, 20; m. 50. ENGLISH LITERATURE, LINGUISTICS. B.A, Pa. State Univ, 40; M.A, Univ. Nev, 48; fel, Stanford Univ; Ph.D.(medieval lit. & ling), Univ. Ore, 58. Instr. ENG, Gonzaga Univ, 55-58, asst. prof, 58-61; Univ. Idaho, 61-63; assoc. prof, Alfred Univ, 63-67; UNIV. COLO, 67-69, PROF, 69- Drake-Hopkins res. fel, Oxford, 59-60; asst. dir, Univ. Colo writers conf, 73. U.S.A, 42-46, 1st Lt. MLA; Mediaeval Acad. Am; Renaissance Soc. Am; Rocky Mt. Mod. Lang. Asn; NCTE. Medieval and comparative literature; linguistics. Publ: Boccaccio's De casibus virorum Illustrium, Scholars Facs, 61; transl, Boccaccio, The fates of illustrious men, Ungar, 65; auth, Caxton's Eneydos, 60 & Chaucer's redactions of Vergil, 63, Mediaeval Stud; Gavin Douglas' concept of the Renaissance, Stud. in Renaissance, 61. Add: 4530 Sioux Dr, Boulder, CO 80302.

HALL, MAXCY REDDICK, Social History, History of Journalism. See Volume I, History.

HALL, N. JOHN, b. Orange, N.J, Jan. 1, 33; m. 68; c. 1. ENGLISH LITERATURE. A.B, Seton Hall Univ, 55, M.A, 67; S.T.B, Cath. Univ. Am, 59; Ph.D.(Eng), New York Univ, 70. Lectr. ENG, Sch. Continuing Educ, New York Univ, 67-70; ASST. PROF, BRONX COMMUNITY COL, 70- Lectr, New Sch. Social Res, 70-74; fel, State Univ. N.Y, summers 71 & 72; res. award, City Univ. New York, 71, 72; Am. Counc. Learned Soc. grant-in-aid, 73; Nat. Endowment for Humanities fel, 74. MLA. Nineteenth century English literature; Anthony Trollope; the novel. Publ: Ed, Anthony Trollope's The New Zealander, Clarendon, 72; auth, A Trollope family salmagundi, Beta Phi Mu, 74; ed, The letters of Anthony Trollope, Stanford Univ, (in prep); auth, Trollope and Carlyle, 19th Century Fiction, 9/72; Anthony Trollope: honest and true, Notes & Queries, 11/72. Add: Dept. of English, Bronx Community College, University Ave. & 181st St, Bronx, NY 10453.

HALL, ROBERT NOEL, b. Kevin, Mont, May 18, 32. SPEECH COMMUNICATION. B.A, Univ. Wyo, 54, M.A, 55; Ph.D.(rhetoric), Univ. Mich, 63; Trueblood fel, summer 59; Rackham grant, 60-61. Instr. speech & theatre, Westminster Col, 57-58; Eng. & German, Mich. Technol. Univ, 58-59; speech & debate, Univ. Mich, 59-61; speech, Univ. Ill, 61-64; asst. prof, Univ. Wyo, 65-66; ASSOC. EXEC. SECY, SPEECH COMMUN. ASN, 66- Lectr, State Univ. N.Y. Col. New Paltz, 64; res, Univ. Madrid, 65; Ford Found. res. grant, Univ. Wyo, 66; adj. assoc. prof. propaganda sem, Queens Col. (N.Y), 70- Speech Commun. Asn.(assoc. exec. secy, 66-); South. Speech Commun. Asn; West. Speech Commun. Asn; Am. Civil Liberties Union; Asn. Dept. & Adminr. Speech Commun.(ed. Bull, 72-). Classical and contemporary rhetorical theory and criticism. Publ: Fifty years of international debate: 1922-1972, Speech Commun. Asn, 72; L.B.J.'s speech preparation, Quart. J. Speech, 4/65; plus two others. Add: Apt. 8C, 1 Christopher St, New York, NY 10014.

HALL, VERNON, JR, b. Atlanta, Ga, Nov. 30, 13; m. 38; c. 1. COMPARATIVE LITERATURE. A.B, N.Y. Univ, 36, A.M, 37; Ph.D, Univ. Wis, 40; A.M, Dartmouth Col, 50. Asst. Eng, Univ. Wis, 37-40; instr, Pueblo Jr. Col, 40-41; Dartmouth Col, 41-46, asst. prof. COMP. LIT, 46-50, prof, 50-64, chmn. dept, 49-64; PROF, UNIV. WIS-MADISON, 64- Vis. prof, Univ. Aix-en-Provence, France, 65-66. MLA; Mod. Humanities Res. Asn; Soc. Acad. d'Agen, France. Renaissance and modern literature. Publ: Renaissance literary criticism, Columbia Univ, 45; Life of J.C. Scaliger, Am. Philos. Soc, 50; A short history of literary criticism, N.Y. Univ, 63; Literary criticism: Plato through Johnson, Appleton, 70. Add: Dept. of Comparative Literature, University of Wisconsin, 9th Floor, Van Hise, 1220 Linden Dr, Madison, WI 53706.

HALL, WADE H, b. Union Springs, Ala, Feb. 2, 34. ENGLISH. B.S, Troy State Univ, 53; M.A, Univ. Ala, 57; Ph.D.(Eng), Univ. Ill, 61. Instr. ENG, Univ. Ill, 57-61; asst. prof, Univ. Fla, 61-63; assoc. prof, Ky. South. Col, 63-66, PROF, 66-71; BELLARMINE COL, 71- Ala. Libr. Asn. Lit. Award, 67. U.S.A, 54-56. MLA; Conf. Christianity & Lit; S.Atlantic Mod. Lang. Asn. Literature of the South; American humor; theology and literature. Publ: Reflections of the Civil War in Southern humor, 62 & The smiling phoenix: Southern humor, 1865-1914, 65, Univ. Fla; The high limb, Ky. Poetry Press, 73; Humor and folklore in Vinnie Williams' Walk Egypt, South. Folklore Quart, 9/62; The mirror of humor, Ala. Librn, 1/68; The lonely world of Carson McCullers, Twigs, summer 68. Add: Dept. of English, Bellarmine College, 2000 Norris Place, Louisville, KY 40205.

HALL, WESLEY, b. Konawa, Okla, Sept. 18, 25; m. 48; c. 4. READING. B.A, E.Cent. State Col, 51; M.A, Okla. State Univ, 53; Harvard, 57; Ed.D.(reading), Univ. Tulsa, 63. Instr. Eng. & speech, Pawnee High Sch, 51-53; prof. Eng. & reading, Northeast. State Col, 54-64; Modesto Jr. Col, 64-66; assoc. prof. ENG, SOUTHWEST MO. STATE UNIV, 66-69, PROF, 69- U.S.N, 43-46; U.S.C.G, 47-49. NCTE; NEA. War poetry; developmental reading on the college level. Publ: The reading practicum, Sch. & Community, 10/72. Add: Dept. of English, Southwest Missouri State University, Springfield, MO 65802.

HALL, WILLIAM EDWARD, b. Weston, W.Va, Mar. 21, 23; m. 46, 66; c. 4. COMMUNICATIONS. B.A, Univ. N.Mex, 44; M.S, Columbia Univ, 50; Ph.D, State Univ. Iowa, 54. Reporter & sports ed, Albuquerque, N.Mex. Tribune, 39-43, 46; alumni dir, Univ. N.Mex, 47-53, asst. to pres, 53-54, head dept. jour. & dir. pub. inform. dept, Tex. Tech. Col, 54-56; DIR. SCH. JOUR, Univ. Nebr, 56-66; OHIO STATE UNIV, 66- Pub. relat. consult, Am. Red Cross, 60-66; mem. steering comt, competition accredited schs. jour, W.R. Hearst Found, 62-70; Distinguished Alumni, Columbia Sch. Jour, 63; regional consult, Pulitzer Prize Selection Comt, 63; v.pres, Am. Asn. Schs. & Depts. Jour, 67-68, pres, 68-69. Spec. agent, Counter Intel. Corps, A.U.S, 43-45. Asn. Educ. in Jour.(ed, Jour. Abstracts, 72-); Am. Counc. Educ. Jour. History of journalism; international journalism; journalism law. Publ: Both, not which: undergraduate and graduate journalism, Jour. Educator, spring 67. Add: School of Journalism, Ohio State University, 242 W. 18th Ave, Columbus, OH 43210.

HALLADAY, JEAN RUTH, b. Utica, N.Y, Sept. 4, 32. ENGLISH. A.B, Utica Col, 53; M.A, State Univ. Iowa, 55; Ph.D.(Eng), Univ. Ky, 63. Instr. ENG, Valparaiso Univ, 57-59; asst. prof, High Point Col, 63-64, assoc. prof, 64-65; asst. prof, OLD DOM. COL, 65-68, ASSOC. PROF, 68- MLA; S.Atlantic Mod. Lang. Asn. Victorian literature. Publ: Every gentle maid..., a discussion of some 19th century heroines, High Point Col. Stud, 64; Some errors in the bibliography of the library edition of John Ruskin's works, Papers Bibliog. Soc. Am, 68. Add: Dept. of English, Old Dominion College, Norfolk, VA 23508.

HALLAM, VIRGINIA ANN, b. Fairmont, W.Va, Feb. 19, 34. ENGLISH. B.A, State Univ. Iowa, 55; Ph.D.(Eng), Univ. Pa, 66. Instr. ENG, Wayne State Univ, 61-64; Purdue Univ, 64-66; ASST. PROF, ST. JOHN'S UNIV. (N.Y), 66- MLA. Modern American novel. Add: Dept. of English, St. John's University, Grand Central & Utopia Pkwy, Jamaica, NY 11432.

HALLER, ROBERT S, b. Washington, D.C, July 29, 33; m. 61; c. 2. ENGLISH LITERATURE. B.A, Amherst Col, 55; Ph.D, Princeton, 60. Acting instr. ENG, Univ. Calif, Santa Barbara, 58-59; instr, Univ. Md, 59-60, Emory Univ, 60-61; asst. prof, Univ. Calif, Berkeley, 61-67; UNIV. NEBR-LINCOLN, 67-68, assoc. prof, 68-72, PROF, 72-, prof. univ. stud, 73-75. MLA; Medieval Acad. Am; NCTE. Medieval poetry; rhetoric; semantic theory. Publ: Co-ed, Achievement of Wallace Stevens, Lippincott, 62; auth, The Wife of Bath and the three estates, Annuale Mediavale, 65; The Squire's tale and the uses of rhetoric, Mod. Philol, 65; ed, Philippe de Mezieres, figurative representation of the Virgin Mary in the temple, Univ. Nebr, 71; auth, The knight's tale and the epic tradition, Chaucer Rev, 66; Semantic constituents of constructions taking THAT-clauses, 71 & Presuppositions of name-calling in English, 73, Proc. Mid-Am. Ling. Conf. Add: Dept. of English, University of Nebraska-Lincoln, Lincoln, NE 68508.

HALLETT, CHARLES ARTHUR, (JR), b. New Haven, Conn, July 19, 35; m. 58. SHAKESPEARE, DRAMA. B.A, New Sch. Social Res, 61; M.A, Columbia Univ, 63; D.F.A.(drama), Yale, 67. ASSOC. PROF. ENG. LIT, FORDHAM UNIV, 67- MLA. Elizabethan and Jacobean drama; literary criticism. Publ: Jonson's Celia, Stud. Philol, 1/71; A Shakespeare workshop, Col. Eng, 4/71; The Hobbesian substructure of The country wife, Papers Lang. & Lit, 9/73. Add: 116 E. 91st St, New York, NY 10028.

HALLI, ROBERT WILLIAM, JR, b. Baltimore, Md, Feb. 17, 46; m. 69. ENGLISH LITERATURE. A.B, Boston Col, 68; S.E. Bradshaw fel, Univ. Va, 68-69, M.A, 69, duPont fel, 69-70, Ph.D.(Eng), 72. Grad. instr. ENG, Univ. Va, 69-72; ASST. PROF, UNIV. ALA, 72- MLA. Seventeenth century English nondramatic literature; John Milton; popular ballads. Publ: A study of Herrick's Hesperides, Diss. Abstr. Int, 1/73. Add: Dept. of English, University of Alabama, University, AL 35486.

HALLIBURTON, DAVID GARLAND, b. San Bernardino, Calif, Sept. 24, 33; m. 60; c. 3. ENGLISH, COMPARATIVE LITERATURE. Reed scholar. & B.A, Univ. Calif, Riverside, 55, NDEA fel. & M.A, 63, NDEA fel. & Ph.D.(Eng), 66. Assoc. Eng. & comp. lit, Univ. Calif, Riverside, 63-64; asst. prof. Eng, STANFORD UNIV, 66-72, ASSOC. PROF. ENG, COMP. LIT. & MOD. THOUGHT & LIT, 72- Am. Philos. Soc. grant, 70; Am. Counc. Learned Soc. fel, 71-72. U.S.A, 56-58. MLA. Literary theory and aesthetics; comparative drama and literature; humanities in relation to other disciplines. Publ: Edgar Allan Poe: a phenomenological view, Princeton, 73; Self and secularization in The Princess Casamassima, Mod. Fiction Stud, summer 65; Blake's French Revolution: the Figura and yesterday's news, Stud. Romanticism, spring 66; The Myden Makeles, Papers Lang. & Lit, spring 68. Add: Dept. of English, Stanford University, Stanford, CA 94305.

HALLMUNDSSON, MAY NEWMAN, b. Brooklyn, N.Y, May 19, 31; m. 60. ENGLISH & COMPARATIVE LITERATURE. A.B, Brooklyn Col, 54, univ. fel, 54-56, M.A, 56; Icelandic-Am. Soc. fel, Univ. Iceland, 59-60; Ph.D.(Eng), N.Y. Univ, 70. Lectr. ENG, Brooklyn Col, 56-59; instr. Malaskolinn Mimir, Reykjavik, Iceland, 59-60; L.I. Univ, 61; asst. prof, Notre Dame Col.(N.Y), 70; instr, BROOKLYN COL, 71-72, ASST. PROF, 72- Univ. honors scholar, N.Y. Univ, 70-71; Nat. Endowment for Humanities summer grant, Princeton, 74. Am. Asn. Univ. Women; Am-Scand. Found; Mediaeval Acad. Am; MLA; Renaissance Soc. Am. Medieval literature; Chaucer; Icelandic literature. Publ: Co-ed, An anthology of Scandinavian literature, Collier Bks, 66; co-transl, Volcano: ordeal by fire in Iceland's Westmann Islands, 73 & Reykjavik: a panorama in four seasons, 74, Iceland Rev, Reykjavik; co-auth, Reykjavik: portrait of a city, Broadcasting Found. Am, 9/60; auth, Jon Johannesson, Vid tjarnirnar (By the ponds), Bks. Abroad, 10/71; Agnar Thordarson, The sword, Atlantica & Iceland Rev, 4/72. Add: Dept. of English, Brooklyn College, Bedford Ave, Brooklyn, NY 11210.

HALLORAN, WILLIAM F, b. Spearfish, S.Dak, Sept. 12, 34; m. 61; c. 2. ENGLISH. B.A, Princeton, 56; M.A, Duke Univ, 59, Ph.D.(Eng), 65. Instr. ENG, Univ. N.C, 63-64; N.Y. Univ, 64-66; asst. prof, UNIV. WIS-MILWAUKEE, 66-68, assoc. prof, 68-72, PROF, 72-, DEAN COL. LETT. & SCI, 72-, coord. grad. stud. Eng, 68-69, assoc. dean humanities & commun, 69-72. Consult, N.Cent. Asn, 73- Urhig Award, Univ. Wis-Milwaukee, 68. U.S.A, 57-58. MLA; Midwest Mod. Lang. Asn; AAUP; NCTE. English literature of the Romantic and Victorian periods; English literature of the transition, 1880-1914. Publ: William Blake's The French Revolution, Bull. N.Y. Pub. Libr, 1/68 & In: Blake's visionary forms dramatic, Princeton Univ, 71; Blake's Tiriel, S.Atlantic Quart, spring 71; William Sharp as bard and craftsman, Victorial Poetry, spring 72. Add: College of Letters & Science, University of Wisconsin-Milwaukee, Milwaukee, WI 53201.

HALLWACHS, ROBERT GORDON, b. Cleveland, Ohio, Aug. 3, 14; m. 52; c. 2. ENGLISH LITERATURE. A.B, N.Cent. Col, 36; A.M, Univ. Ill, 37; A.M, Princeton, 41, Ph.D, 42; M.S, Calif. Inst. Technol, 44. Asst. Eng, Univ. Ill, 37-40; instr, Princeton, 46-50, asst. prof, 50-55, bicentennial preceptor, 52-55; prof. & chmn. dept, Wells Col, 55-67, provost, 57-58, dean fac, 58-65; PROF. ENG. & DEAN COL. HUMANITIES & SOC. SCI, DREXEL UNIV, 67- U.S.A.A.F, 42-46, Lt. MLA; Am. Soc. Engineering Educ. Seventeenth century prose style. Add: College of Humanities & Social Sciences, Drexel University, Philadelphia, PA 19104.

HALPEREN, MAX, b. New York, N.Y, Nov. 22, 25; m. 52; c. 2. CONTEMPORARY LITERATURE. B.S, City Col. New York, 50; M.A, Fla. State Univ, 52, Ph.D, 59. Asst, Fla. State Univ, 51-54, 55-57; instr. ENG, Univ. Ky, 54-55; N.C. STATE UNIV, 57-60, assoc. prof, 60-72, PROF, 72-, fac. res. fund grant, 61. Managing ed, South. Poetry Rev, 64-71. S.Atlantic Mod. Lang. Asn; MLA. Modern poetry, fiction and drama, especially Ezra Pound, Edward Albee and James Joyce. Publ: Ezra Pound: poet priest, In: The thirties, 67 & What happens in Who's afraid...?, In: Modern American drama, 68, Everett/Edwards; How to read a canto, In: Merrill studies in the cantos, 71; plus others. Add: Dept. of English, North Carolina State University, Raleigh, NC 27607.

HALPERIN, IRVING, b. New York, N.Y, Jan. 17, 22; m. 56; c. 3. ENGLISH. B.A, Roosevelt Univ, 48; M.A, State Univ. Iowa, 50; Ph.D, Wash. Univ, 57. Teaching asst, Wash. Univ, 51-53, 54; instr. Eng, Univ. Ill, 55-56; Northwest. Univ, 56-57; from assoc. prof. to PROF. ENG. & CREATIVE WRITING, SAN FRANCISCO STATE UNIV, 57- Fulbright teacher, India, 53-54; Fulbright lectr. Am. lit, Univ. Erlangen, 63-64; Nat. Curriculum Res. Inst. grant, 65-66; Nat. Found. Jewish Cult. grant, 66-67. U.S.A.A.F, 43-45. Holocaust literature; American literature. Publ: Messengers from the dead: literature of the holocaust, 70 & Here I am: a Jew in today's Germany, 71, Westminster; co-auth, The story of the Jewish catastrophe in Europe, Am. Asn. Jewish Educ, 68; auth, Torrential production: Thomas Wolfe's writing practices, Ariz. Quart, spring 58; The pulse master, Univ. Kansas City Rev, spring 61; Victim, fighter, martyr: literature of the concentration camps, Christian Century, 7/62; plus others. Add: Dept. of English, San Francisco State University, 1600 Holloway Ave, San Francisco, CA 94132.

HALPERIN, JOHN WILLIAM, b. Chicago, Ill, Sept. 15, 41. ENGLISH LITERATURE. A.B, Bowdoin Col, 63; M.A, Univ. N.H, 66; NDEA fel, Johns Hopkins Univ, 66-69, M.A, 68, Ph.D.(Eng), 69. Reporter, Oxnard Press-Courier, Calif, 62; Wall St. J, 63; ed, Assoc. Press, 63-64; teaching asst, Univ. N.H, 64-66, lectr, 66; asst. prof. Eng. & dean summer sch, State Univ. N.Y. Stony Brook, 69-72, asst. to acad. v.pres, 71-72; ASSOC. PROF. ENG, UNIV. SOUTH. CALIF, 72-, DIR. GRAD. STUD, 73- U.S.A.R, 63-69, S/Sgt. MLA; Am. Philos. Soc. Nineteenth century English literature; English novel; Henry James. Publ: Ed, Henry James's The golden bowl, World Publ/Popular Libr, 72; auth, The language of meditation: four studies in nineteenth-century fiction, Arthur Stockwell Ltd, 73; Egoism and self-discovery in the Victorian novel, Lenox Hill, 74; ed, The theory of the novel: new essays, Oxford, 74; ed, Jane Austen: bicentennary essays, Cambridge, 75. Add: Dept. of English, University of Southern California, Los Angeles, CA 90007.

HALPERN, MARTIN, b. New York, N.Y, Oct. 3, 29; m. 59; c. 2. ENGLISH, DRAMA. B.A, Univ. Rochester, 50, M.A, 53; Fulbright scholar, Italy, 56-57; Ph.D, Harvard, 59. Teaching fels. gen. educ. & Eng, Harvard, 54-56, 57-59; instr. Eng, Univ. Calif, Berkeley, 59-60, asst. prof, 60-64; Univ. Mass, 64-65; THEATER ARTS, BRANDEIS UNIV, 65-66, ASSOC. PROF, 66-, CHMN. DEPT, 73- Howard Found. fel. & Fulbright travel grant, 62-63; consult. drama, WGBH Educ. TV, 67-68. Sig.C, U.S.A, 51-53. Dramatic literature, chiefly 19th and 20th century; playwriting; theory of poetry, chiefly metrics. Publ: Two sides of an island and other poems, Univ. N.C, 63; William Vaughn Moody, Twayne, 64; Keats and the Spirit that laughest, Keats-Shelley J, winter 66; Verse in the theater, Mass. Rev, winter 67; Aeschylus, Atlantic Brief Lives; plus others. Add: Dept. of Theater Arts, Brandeis University, Waltham, MA 02154.

HALPERN, SHELDON, b. New York, N.Y, July 16, 32; m. 57; c. 2. ENGLISH. B.A, City Col. New York, 53; M.A, Columbia Univ, 57, Ph.D.(Eng), 63. Resident lectr. ENG, Ind. Univ, South Bend, 59-63; asst. prof, BOWLING GREEN STATE UNIV, 63-67, assoc. prof, 67-73, PROF, 73- Vis. assoc. prof, Tel-Aviv Univ, 68-69. U.S.A, 53-55. MLA. English romantic literature. Publ: Sydney Smith, Twayne, 66; The imagery of perception in two poems by Wordsworth, J. Popular Cult, fall 70; Michael: Wordsworth's pastoral of common man, Notra Dame Eng. J, fall 72; Evaluating graduate program effectiveness: a suggestion, Bull. Asn. Depts. Eng, 12/72; plus one other. Add: Dept. of English, Bowling Green State University, Bowling Green, OH 43403.

HALSALL, MAUREEN PATRICIA, b. Hamilton, Ont, Jan. 19, 34. ENGLISH. B.A, McMaster Univ, 57; Woodrow Wilson fel, Radcliffe Col, 57-58, M.A, 58, col. fel, 58-59; Can. Counc. fel, Harvard, 59-61, Can. Fed. Univ. Women's traveling fel, 61-62, Ph.D.(Eng), 63. Instr. ENG, Wellesley Col, 62-65; asst. prof, McMASTER UNIV, 65-68, ASSOC. PROF, 68- Can. Counc. sr. leave fel, 70-71. Int. Arthurian Soc; MLA; Mediaeval Acad. Am; Asn. Can. Univ. Teachers Eng. Old and Middle English; Runes. Publ: Vercelli and the Vercelli book, PMLA, 69; Benjamin Thorpe, 69 & More about C. Maier's transcript, 70, Eng. Lang. Notes. Add: Dept. of English, McMaster University, Hamilton Ont. L8S 4M4, Can.

HALSBAND, ROBERT, b. New York, N.Y, Mar. 22, 14; wid. ENGLISH. B.S, N.Y. Univ, 34; A.M, Columbia Univ, 36; univ. fel, Northwest. Univ, 47-48, Ph.D, 48. Instr. ENG, Northwest. Univ, 44-47; asst. prof, Hunter Col, 49-57, assoc. prof, 58-60; adj. prof, Columbia Univ, 63-67, sr. res. assoc, 67-71; PROF, Univ. Calif, Riverside, 71-73; UNIV. ILL, URBANA-CHAMPAIGN, 73- Guggenheim fel, 68-69; judge nonfiction, Nat. Bk. Awards, 60, judge biog, 72. MLA; PEN Club (pres, 67-69); Int. Asn. Univ. Prof. Eng; Am. Soc. 18th Century Stud. Eighteenth century literature; Samuel Johnson; literary patronage. Publ: Ed, The nonsense of common-sense 1737-38, 47; auth, Life of Lady Mary Wortley Montagu, 56 & ed, The complete letters of Lady Mary Wortley Montagu (3 vols), 65-67, Oxford; ed, The selected letters of Lady Mary Wortley Montagu, Longman, London, 70 & St. Martin's, N.Y, 71; auth, Lord Hervey: 18th century courtier, Clarendon, London, 73 & Oxford, N.Y, 74; Lady Mary Wortley Montagu as letter-writer, In: The familiar letter in the eighteenth century, Univ. Kans, 66; contrib, Art and error: essays on textual editing, Ind. Univ. & Methuen, 70; The lady's dressing room explicated by a contemporary, In: The Augustan milieu, Clarendon, 70. Add: Dept. of English, University of Illinois, Urbana, IL 61801.

HALSTEAD, WILLIAM LEWIS, b. Parker City, Ind, May 28, 05. ENGLISH. A.B, DePauw Univ, 27, A.M, 28; Ph.D, Univ. South. Calif, 37. Grad. asst, DePauw Univ, 27-28; instr. Eng, Rose Polytech. Inst, 28-29; Albion Col, 29-31; literary critic, Univ. South. Calif, 31-35; asst. prof. ENG, Northwest. State Col, 35-38; assoc. prof, Florence State Col, 39-41; asst. prof, UNIV. MIAMI, 38-39, prof, 41-72, chmn. dept, 46-51, EMER. PROF, 72- U.S.N.R, Lt. Comdr. MLA; NCTE; S.Atlantic Mod. Lang. Asn. Elizabethan and Jacobean drama. Publ: Collab, Readers companion to world literature, Holt & Mentor Bks, 56; Artifice in Sir Gawain, Univ. Miami, 61; An explanation for the two editions of Marston's Fawne, Stud. in Philol, 1/43; plus others. Add: 4275 Lennox Dr, Coconut Grove, FL 33133.

HALSTEAD, WILLIAM PERDUE, b. Terre Haute, Ind, Feb. 10, 06. SPEECH. A.B, Ind. Univ, 27; Ph.D, Univ. Mich, 35. Instr, Univ. Ariz, 28-29; Sacramento Jr. Col, Calif, 29-33; SPEECH, UNIV. MICH, ANN ARBOR, 35-37, asst. prof, 37-42, assoc. prof, 42-52, PROF, 52- Qm.C, 42-46, Capt. Am. Theatre Asn.(exec. secy, Am. Educ. Theatre Asn, 47-49, v.pres, 51, pres, 52); Am. Nat. Theatre & Acad. Speech; dramatics; collation of all printed acting editions of Shakespeare and all promptbooks of professional productions. Publ: Principles of theatre art; stage management for the amateur theatre. Add: 2409 Vinewood, Ann Arbor, MI 48104.

HALTRESHT, MICHAEL, b. Nahariya, Israel, Oct. 10, 40; U.S. citizen; m. 73. ENGLISH, PSYCHOLOGY. B.A, Hebrew Univ, 63; M.A.(Eng), Stanford Univ, 65; M.A.(Am. stud), Roosevelt Univ, 69; Ph.D.(Eng), Emory Univ, 70; M.A, (theatre, drama), Ind. Univ, 73. Teaching asst. ENG, Emory Univ, 66-67; ASST. PROF, W.GA. COL, 67- MLA; Col. Eng. Asn. Literature. Publ: Space phobias in Conrad's Secret agent, Psychol. & Lit, 71; The Gods of Conrad's Nostromo, Renaissance, 71; The interpretation of visions in literature, J. Eng. Teaching Tech, 73. Add: Dept. of English, West Georgia College, Carrollton, GA 30117.

HALTY-DUBE, ADOLFO, b. San Carlos, Uruguay, Dec. 26, 15; m. 43; c. 5. ART, LATIN AMERICAN DRAMA. B.S, Acad. Poitiers, 35; Ph.D.(fine arts), Sch. Archit, Uruguay, 40; univ. fel, Univ. Ill, 41-42, Coord. of Latin Am. Affairs fel, 42-44. Architect & dir. mural decorations, Nat. Counc. Grammar Schs, Uruguay, 45-48, prof. aesthet, 48-50; instr. Spanish, Ohio State Univ, 50-53; lay-out artist, Lazarus Stores, Ohio, 54-55; transl. Romance langs, Ministry For. Affairs, Uruguay, 55-62; asst. prof. DRAMA, CALIF. STATE UNIV, NORTHRIDGE, 62-66, ASSOC. PROF, 66- Mem. bd, Nat. Sch. Fine Arts, Montevideo, 45; mem. bd. & judge, Nat. Comn. Fine Arts, Montevideo, 48-50; set & costume designer, Nat. Comedy Theatre, Nat. Opera, Montevideo, 49-; prof. art, Columbus Gallery Fine Arts, 51-54; pres, Comn. for UNESCO, Uruguay, 60; Andrew Mellon fel. & vis. prof, Carnegie Inst. Technol, 62; mem, Mayor's Comn. Twin Cities Prog, 66-; San Fernando Valley State Col. Found summer grants, 67-69; adv, Latin Am. Theatre Group, Calif, 68-; Calif. State Cols. grant, 70-71; set design, Todo es Segun el Color & Tola de Zulueta, Madrid, Spain, 70. Speech Commun. Asn; Am. Nat. Theatre & Acad. All media in painting, sculpture and set-design; new media in all these milieus; Latin American theatre—both present and past. Publ: The best of contemporary Uruguay theatre, Arca, Montevideo, 69; ser. 30 articles treating various aspects of visual arts, Nuestra Epoca, 43-48. Add: Dept. of Drama, California State University, Northridge, 18111 Nordhoff St, Northridge, CA 91324.

HALVERSON, JOHN, b. Cedar Rapids, Iowa, Jan. 16, 28. ENGLISH. B.A, Univ. Denver, 51; M.A, Columbia Univ, 52; Ph.D, Univ. Calif, Berkeley, 61. Supvr. Eng. compos, Univ. Calif, Berkeley, 59-61; instr. Eng, Princeton, 61-65; asst. prof. LIT, UNIV. CALIF, SANTA CRUZ, 66-71, ASSOC. PROF, 71- Fulbright lectr, Vidyalankara Univ, Ceylon, 65-66; Univ. Ceylon, 68-69. U.S.A.F, 46-49, S/Sgt. Medieval studies. Add: Dept. of Literature, Stevenson College, University of California, Santa Cruz, CA 95064.

HALWAS, KENNETH ARNOLD, b. Milwaukee, Wis, Dec. 14, 20; m. 48; c. 2. ENGLISH, HUMANITIES. A.B, Univ. Denver, 49, M.A, 50, Ph.D.(Eng), 53. Head dept. Eng, South. State Teachers Col, 53-54; asst. prof. Eng. & humanities, Ohio Wesleyan Univ, 54-58; asst. prof, EAST. WASH. STATE COL, 58-61, coord. humanities, 58, assoc. prof. Eng. & humanities, 61-64, PROF. ENG, 64-, CHMN. DEPT, 70-, interim-dir. div. lang. & lit, 68. U.S.A.A.F, 42-46. MLA; AAUP. German literature; German influences on English and American literature; teaching of English in the two-year college. Publ: Transl, Martin Salander, John Calder, London, 63. Add: Dept. of English, Eastern Washington State College, Cheney, WA 99004.

HAMALIAN, LEO, b. New York, N.Y, Jan. 13, 20; m. 43; c. 3. ENGLISH, COMPARATIVE LITERATURE. B.S, Cornell Univ, 42; M.A, Columbia Univ, 47, Ph.D.(Eng), 54. Instr. Eng, N.Y. Univ, 47-54; from instr. to PROF. ENG. LIT, CITY COL. NEW YORK, 54-, DIR. GRAD. CREATIVE WRITING, 72- Smith-Mundt grant, Syria, 62-64; Am. Stud. Sem. fel, Columbia Univ, 68-; dean, Calif. Inst. of Arts, 70-72; mem. bd. dir, Tuum Est drug rehabil. ctr, Venice, 71- U.S.A, 42, U.S.A.A.F, 43-46. MLA; NCTE; Am. Stud. Asn; Eng. Union. T.S. Eliot; D.H. Lawrence; comparative continental literature. Publ: Grammar in context, 58 & Ten modern short novels, 58, Putnam; The existential imagination, 63 & ed, The naked I, 72, Fawcett; The shape of fiction, 67 & D.H. Lawrence, 73, McGraw; In the modern idion, 73 & An invitation to semantics, 73, Crowell; auth, The gift of guilt in Ulysses, Renasance, winter 66; The secret career of Samuel Roth, J. Popular Cult, summer 68; Hemingway as hunger artist, Lit. Rev, winter 73; plus one other. Add: Dept. of English, City College of New York, New York, NY 10031.

HAMAN, JAMES BLANDING, b. Vaiden, Miss, July 19, 16; m. 48; c. 3. ENGLISH. A.B, DePauw Univ, 38; M.A, Duke Univ, 39; Cornell Univ, summer 41; Ford fac. fel, Univ. Mich, 51-52. Master, Rugby Univ. Sch. Boys, 39-41; instr. ENG, Univ. Nebr, 41-42; GA. INST. TECHNOL, 46-48, asst. prof, 48-54, assoc. prof, 54-61, PROF, 61- U.S.A.A.F, 42-45, T/Sgt. NCTE. American literature; teaching of English; curriculum building. Publ: Co-auth, The rhetoric-reader, Scott, 62. Add: 147 Mobile Ave, N.E, Atlanta, GA 30305.

HAMAR, CLIFFORD E, b. Portland, Ore, Jan. 17, 14; m. 41; c. 3. DRAMA & THEATRE. B.A, Whitman Col, 37; M.A, Stanford Univ, 43, Ph.D.(drama & theatre), 51; Yale, 46-47. Acting instr. speech, Stanford Univ, 48-49; asst. prof. speech & drama, Kenyon Col, 49-51; East. N.Mex. Univ, 51-53; ASSOC. PROF. DRAMA & DIR. DRAMATICS, LEWIS & CLARK COL, 53-, ASST. DEAN FAC. & DIR. OVERSEAS STUD. PROG, 63- DIR. INT. PROGS, 66-, co-chmn. speech arts dept, 53-63, dir. Latin Am. prog, 62-63. Consult. advertising design, Hyster Corp, 55; pres. & mem. bd. trustees, Portland Civic Theatre; pres. Ore. Partners of Alliance for Progress & deleg. Int. Conf, Rio de Janeiro, 67-68. U.S.A, 42-46, Capt. Theatre history; history of educational theatre; international theatre. Publ: Contrib, College and university theatre instruction in the early twentieth century, In: A history of speech education in America; auth, American theatre history; a geographical index, Educ. Theatre J. Add: 0236 S.W. Palatine Hill Rd, Portland, OR 97219.

HAMBLIN, JUNIUS N, b. Salt Lake City, Utah, Apr. 29, 30; m. 57; c. 2. THEATRE. B.S, Utah State Univ, 52; M.S, Brigham Young Univ, 53; Ph.D.(theatre), Ohio State Univ, 66. Teacher, Preston High Sch, 53-54; instr. speech & theatre, La. State Univ, 57-58; theatre, Cornell Univ, 58-61; from asst. prof. to assoc. prof. SPEECH & THEATRE, STATE UNIV. N.Y. COL. ONEONTA, 61-69, PROF, 69- Speech Commun. Asn; Am. Theatre Asn; U.S. Inst. Theatre Technol. Nineteenth century English scenery design and production; uses of new materials in technical theatre. Add: Dept. of Speech & Theatre, State University of New York College at Oneonta, Oneonta, NY 13820.

HAMBRICK, THOMAS GREGORY, b. Princeton, W.Va, Sept. 7, 23; m. 48; c. 4. ENGLISH LITERATURE. A.B, Concord Col, 49; A.M, Miami Univ, 51; Ph.D, Univ. Ill, 61. Instr. commun, Univ. Ill, 52-58; asst. prof. ENG, Wittenberg Univ, 58-61; Univ. Cincinnati, 61-62; assoc. prof, CONCORD COL, 62-65, PROF, 65-, CHMN. DIV. LANG. & LIT, 68- Curriculum consult, W.Va. State Dept. Educ, 69-; sr. consult, Oakey Logan Alexander Found, 70-71. C.Eng, U.S.A, 43-46. MLA; Asn. Chmn. Depts. Eng. Literary and rhetorical critical theory and history; 18th century English literature. Publ: Pure comedy and the classic mode: the example of She stoops to conquer, Proc. 13th Annual Marshall Univ. Eng. Inst, 4/73. Add: Dept. of English, Concord College, Athens, WV 24712.

HAMELIN, MARIE, R.J.M, b. Whitman, Mass, Oct. 4, 07. MEDIAEVAL DEVOTIONAL PROSE. A.B, Trinity Col.(D.C), 28; M.Ed, Cath. Teachers Col, 42; M.A, Fordham Univ, 49, Ph.D, 62; cert, Providence Col, 55-57. Head dept. Eng, Jesus Mary Acad, Fall River, Mass, 36-48; St. Charles High Sch, Providence, R.I, 49-51; Villa Augustina, Goffstown, N.H, 52-53; St. Clare High Sch, Woonsocket, R.I, 54-59; pres, Thevenet Jr. Col, 61-67; asst. prof. Eng, Trinity Col.(D.C), 67-71: RETIRED. MLA; NCTE. Middle English devotional prose; literature of Catholic emancipation in 18th century England; yoga. Publ: Co-ed, Reaching for more, New City Press, 72. Add: 8908 Riggs Rd, Hyattsville, MD 20783.

HAMILTON, ALBERT CHARLES, b. Can, July 20, 21; m. 50; c. 4. LITERATURE. B.A, Univ. Man, 45; M.A, Univ. Toronto, 49; Ph.D, Cambridge, 53. Teaching fel. Eng. lit, Univ. Col, Univ. Toronto, 46-49; supvr. ENG, Cambridge, 50-52; asst. prof, Univ. Wash, 52-58, assoc. prof, 58-63, PROF, 63-68; QUEEN'S UNIV. (ONT), 68- Huntington Libr. fel, 59-60. Can. Navy, 44-45, Lt. MLA; Renaissance Soc. Am. Spenser; Shakespeare; Sidney. Publ: The structure of allegory in The Faerie Queene, Clarendon, 61; ed, Edmund Spenser: selected poetry, New Am. Libr, 65; auth, Early Shakespeare, Huntington Libr, 67; ed, Essential articles for the study of Edmund Spenser, Shoe String, 72; Modern Spenser criticism, In: Six modern authors, 68. Add: Dept. of English, Queen's University, Kingston, Ont, Can.

HAMILTON, ALICE B, b. Bedford, N.S, Oct. 8, 13; m. 43; c. 3. ENGLISH. B.A, Dalhousie Univ, 35, M.A, 36; Eddy travelling fel, Can. Fedn. Univ. Women fel. & Ph.D.(Eng), Univ. London, 39. Asst. curator & lectr, Castle Mus, Eng, 39-43; lectr. ENG, Dalhousie Univ, 46-47; Univ. Manitoba, 59-63, asst. prof, 63-66; assoc. prof, UNIV. WINNIPEG, 66-73, PROF, 73-, grants, 68-73. Can. Counc. res. grant, 68, 73, leave grant, 69-70; Man. Centennial Corp. res. grant, 70; Skillington Trust Fund publ. grant, 72; Leicester City Mus. & Leicester Hist. & Archaeol. Soc. publ. grants, 72; Cert. of Merit, Can. Hist. Soc. Asn. Can. Univ. Teachers Eng; Can. Asn. Univ. Teachers; Mediaeval Acad. Am. Medieval English literature; modern Anglo-Irish and American literature; stained glass, medieval (English) and modern (Canadian). Publ: History of fire fighting, 40 & The parish of York Castle, 42, York Castle Mus; co-auth, John Updike: a critical essay, 68, The elements of John Updike, 69 & co-auth, Samuel Beckett: a critical essay, 74, Eerdmans; auth, Manitoban stained glass, Univ. Winnipeg, 70; co-auth, To be a man—to be a woman, United Methodist, 72 & The chapel of William Wyggestion's Hospital, Leicester Hist. Soc, 74; auth, Helowys and the burning of Jankyn's book, Medieval Stud, 72; co-auth, John Updike's prescription for survival, Christian Century, 72 & Dimensions of the mythic imagination, N.Dak. Quart, 73. Add: Dept. of English, University of Winnipeg, 515 Portage Ave, Winnipeg, Man. R3B 2E9, Can.

HAMILTON, CARSON CRANDALL, b. Glens Falls, N.Y, Sept. 26, 00; m. 31; c. 6. ENGLISH. A.B, Cornell Univ, 24; A.M, Univ. Pittsburgh, 27, Ph.D, 35. From asst. to asst. prof, Univ. Pittsburgh, 26-33; prof, Findlay Col, 34-35; from instr. to assoc. prof. ENG, MICH. STATE UNIV, 35-69, EMER. ASSOC. PROF, 69- Asst. prof, Univ. Ariz, 44-45. English romantic literature; modern American literature; Wordsworth. Publ: The disciplines of writing, Edwards, 61; Wordsworth's decline in poetic power, 63 & Jeff Utter, 64, Exposition. Add: 756 Hartley Ave, Deltona, FL 32763.

HAMILTON, FRANKLIN W, b.Benton, Ill, Nov. 22, 23; m. 56; c. 3. ENGLISH. B.A. & M.A, South. Ill. Univ, 49; M.S, Kans. State Teachers Col, 55; Ed.D. (Eng. & educ), Univ. Kans, 61. Teacher high sch, Ill, 49-50; prof. Eng, Hiwassee Col, 51-52; teacher high sch, Ill, 52-53; asst. prof. ENG, Col. Emporia, 53-55; Ill. State Normal Univ, 55-56; INSTR, FLINT JR. COL, 56- NCTE. American literature; creative writing; poetry. Publ: Leaf scar (poetry), 65 & Love cry (poetry), 70, Brookside, London; Thoreau on the art of writing, 67 & Catch me only with love, 73, Walden. Add: 423 S. Franklin Ave, Flint, MI 48503.

HAMILTON, HARLAN WARE, b. Rantoul, Ill, Oct. 12, 02. ENGLISH LITERATURE. A.B, Oberlin Col, 24; A.M, Columbia Univ, 27; Ph.D, Cornell Univ, 34. Instr. Eng, Univ. Tulsa, 27-31, asst. prof, 31-36, prof. & head dept, 36-37, dir. downtown col, 33-36; asst. prof. Eng, Univ. Akron, 37-40, assoc. prof, 40-43, prof. & head dept, 43-45; prof, CASE WEST. RESERVE UNIV, 45-70, dean sch. arts & scis, 47-52, EMER. PROF. ENG, 70- Winant lectr, England, 57-58; Fulbright prof, Univ. Nancy, 67-68, vis. prof, 70-71. MLA; Mod. Humanities Res. Asn; Int. Asn. Univ. Prof. Eng. Eighteenth century English literature; Samuel Johnson and the profession of letters; Laurence Sterne. Publ: New preface to writing, Odyssey, 60; Doctor Syntax: a silhouette of William Combe, Esq, Kent State Univ, 69; The relevance of Johnson's Lives of the poets, In: English studies today, Ed. Storia e Lett, Rome, 66; William Combe and the original letters of the late Reverend Mr. Laurence Sterne (1788), PMLA, 10/67; Samuel Johnson's appeal to nature, West. Humanities Rev, fall 67. Add: 1 Dover Close, Branksome Park, Poole, Dorset, England BH13 6DZ.

HAMILTON, HORACE ERNST, b. Madison, Ind, Nov. 20, 11; m. 41; c. 3. ENGLISH LITERATURE. A.B, Col. of Wooster, 33; Ph.D, Yale, 41. Master, Columbian Prep. Sch, Wash, D.C, 34-35; instr. Hofstra Col, 37-40; Rensselaer Polytech. Inst, 40-42; from asst. prof. to PROF. ENG, RUTGERS UNIV, 46- Ford Found. vis. scholar, Columbia Univ, 50-51; Carnegie vis. prof, 56-57. U.S.N, 42-45. AAUP. Homer's Iliad and Odyssey; 20th century American literature; theory and techniques of poetry. Publ: Through the moongate; The dry scratch of laurel; Before dark, Rutgers Univ, 66; The cage of form: likeness and difference in poetry, Dickenson, 72; plus others. Add: Dept. of English, Rutgers College, Rutgers University, New Brunswick, NJ 08903.

HAMILTON, JOHN ALLEN, b. Marietta, Ohio, Jan. 15, 07. ENGLISH. B.A, Marietta Col, 27; M.A, Univ. Ill, 29. Asst. ENG, UNIV. ILL, URBANA, 29-40, from instr. to ASSOC. PROF, 41-42, 45- U.S.A.A.F, 42-45. MLA. American fiction, especially 1870-1930; American Puritan history. Add: Dept. of English, 109 English Bldg, University of Illinois, Urbana, IL 61801.

HAMILTON, JOHN BOWEN, b. Oct. 19, 13; m. 48; c. 1. ENGLISH. A.B, Birmingham South. Col, 36; M.A, Univ. N.C, 48, Ph.D.(Eng), 50. Prof. Latin & ancient hist, Birmingham Univ. Sch, 36-37; instr. ENG, Univ. N.C, 48-50; asst. prof, Ga. Inst. Technol, 50-52; prof, Appalachian State Teachers Col, 53-57; assoc. prof, ROLLINS COL, 57-63, PROF, 63-, HEAD DEPT, 72- U.S.A, 40-46. MLA; Col. Eng. Asn. Shakespeare; American literature; science and medicine in American literature. Publ: Diary of Thomas Miles Garrett at the University of North Carolina, 1849-52, N.C. Hist. Rev, 1-10/61; Robert Montgomery Bird, physician and novelist, Bull. Hist. Med, 7-8/70; Hemingway and the Christian paradox, Renascence, spring 72. Add: Dept. of English, Rollins College, Winter Park, FL 32789.

HAMILTON, LOCKARD MITCHELL, b. Magoffin Co, Ky, Mar. 13, 18; m. 38; c. 4. ENGLISH, CLASSICAL LANGUAGES. B.A, Georgetown Col, 40, M.A, 59. Elem. teacher, Magoffin County Bd. Educ, Ky, 38-39; Grant Co. Bd. Educ, 39-44, teacher ENG, 53-55; ASSOC. PROF, CAMPBELLSVILLE COL, 59- Pastor, Sherman Baptist Church, Ky, 38-44, Sand Run Baptist Church, Burlington, 44-48, Mt. Vernon Baptist Church, Waddy, 48-51, Macedonia Baptist Church, Jonesville, 51-55, Gano Ave. Baptist Church, Georgetown, 55-59, Friendship Baptist Church, Campbellsville, 59-67 & Trammell Creek Baptist Church, Greensburg, 72- Teaching of freshman English in church-related colleges; life and work of Edgar Allan Poe. Publ: The princeliest preacher, West. Recorder, 55. Add: Dept. of Literature & Languages, Campbellsville College, Campbellsville, KY 42718.

HAMILTON, MARIE PADGETT, b. Edgefield, S.C, Feb. 25, 95; wid. ENGLISH LANGUAGE & LITERATURE. A.B, Greenville Womans Col, 16; A.M, Univ. Ariz, 26; Ph.D, Cornell Univ, 32; Litt.D, Furman Univ, 57. Instr, High Sch, S.C, 17-18; teacher high sch. subjs, U.S. Veterans' Bur, 20-24; instr. ENG, UNIV. ARIZ, 27-30, asst. prof, 30-37, assoc. prof, 37-47, prof, 47-67, EMER. PROF, 67- Am. Counc. Learned Soc. grant-in-aid, 41; Pac. Coast Comt. Humanities grant, 50; vis. prof, Grad. Sch. Arts & Sci, N.Y. Univ, 50-51; gen. ed. adv. comt, Chaucer Variorum Edition, 68- MLA; Mediaeval Acad. Am; Philol. Asn. Pac. Coast. Old and Middle English; Chaucer; the Pearl-poet. Publ: Notes on Pearl, J. Eng. & Ger. Philol, 58; The dramatic suitability of The man of law's tale, In: Studies in language and literature in honor of Margaret Schlauch, Warsaw, 66; The Pearl poet, In: Manual of the writings in Middle English, Vol. II, Severs, 70. Add: 2202 E. Towner St, Tucson, AZ 85719.

HAMILTON, WILLIAM THORNLEY, b. Ft. Dodge, Iowa, Sept. 6, 39; m. 59; c. 3. ENGLISH & AMERICAN LITERATURE. B.A, Univ. Wash, 61; M.A, Univ. Md, College Park, 63; Ph.D.(Eng), Univ. Minn, Minneapolis, 70. Instr. Eng, Otterbein Col, 63-65; Col. St. Thomas, 67-68; ASST. PROF, OTTERBEIN COL, 68-, CHMN. DEPT. COMMON COURSES, 73-, chmn. dept. Eng, 70-73. Fiction ed, Snowy Egret, 70- Early American and 20th century literature. Add: Dept. of Common Courses, Otterbein College, Westerville, OH 43081.

HAMLETT, MAYME LUCILLE, b. Cooter, Mo, Sept. 8, 06. ENGLISH. A.B, Univ. Mo, 29, B.S.Ed, 30, M.A, 38; Univ. Chicago, 51; Baylor Univ, summers 53-54. Teacher, elem. schs, Mo, 25-28, 33-34; high schs, Mo, 29-33, 34-43; Iowa, 43-44; instr. Eng. & Latin, Southwest Baptist Col, 44-60; Eng, Jr. Col. Broward County, 60-61, instr. lang. & lit. & chmn. dept, 61-64; assoc. prof. Eng, Union Univ.(Tenn), 64-69; La. Col, 69-73; RETIRED. NCTE; Col. Eng. Asn. Missouri place names; language, especially words, etymology of, connotations, comparative; poetry. Publ: This Scepter'd Isle (poetry), Pageant, 60; co-auth, Southwest Baptist Col, In: Encyclopedia of Southern Baptists, Vols. I & II, 58. Add: P.O. Box 3, Cooter, MO 63839.

HAMLIN, CYRUS, Comparative Literature. See Volume III, Foreign Languages, Linguistics & Philology.

HAMLIN, WILLIAM C, b. Little Rock, Ark, Nov. 13, 26; m. 49, 67; c. 2. AMERICAN LITERATURE, MODERN LITERATURE. A.B, Univ. Mo, Columbia, 51, M.A, 53, Ph.D.(Eng), 62. Instr. Eng, Univ. Mo, Columbia, 53-62; asst. prof, UNIV. MO-ST. LOUIS, 63-64, assoc. prof, 64-66, PROF, 66-, chmn. div. humanities, 63-67. Curriculum consult, St. Louis Jr. Col. Dist, 65. U.S.A, 45-46. MLA. American literature; modern American and British literature. Publ: Co-auth, The short story, Am. Bk, 66 & Telelecture, Adult Leadership, 3/68. Add: Dept. of English, University of Missouri-St. Louis, St. Louis, MO 63121.

HAMM, AGNES CURREN, b. New Orleans, La, Jan. 21, 05; m. 34; c. 2. SPEECH. A.B, Maryville Col, 26; certs, Univ. London, 29 & 30; cert, Am. Acad. Dramatic Art, 32. Head dept. SPEECH, Maryville Col, 30-34; asst. prof, MT. MARY COL, 37-55, assoc. prof, 55-73, EMER. ASSOC. PROF, 73- Instr, Marquette Univ, 37-41. Gold medal, London Acad. Music, 30. Speech Commun. Asn. Choral speaking selections and techniques; choral dramas for children; dramatic reading for colleges and clubs. Publ: Co-auth, The speech arts, Lyons & Carnahan, 66; auth, Choral reading and bodily action, In: The speech arts, Lyons & Carnahan, 66. Add: 3948 N. Stowell Ave, Milwaukee, WI 53211.

HAMM, VICTOR MICHAEL, b. Milwaukee, Wis, Feb. 21, 04; m. 34; c. 2. ENGLISH LITERATURE. A.B, Marquette Univ, 26, A.M, 28; A.M, Harvard, 29, Harris scholar, Townsend scholar & Kirkland scholar, Harvard, 29-32, Ph.D, 32. Teaching fel, Marquette Univ, 26-28; Sheldon traveling fel, Harvard, 32-33; instr, St. Louis Univ, 33-34; asst. prof, Col. Mt. St. Joseph-on-the-Ohio, 34-37; assoc. prof. ENG, MARQUETTE UNIV, 37-44, PROF, 45-, fac. summer fel, 67. Vis. prof, Univ. Freiburg, 52; Univ. Wis, 57. MLA. Eighteenth century literary criticism and philosophy; English neoclassicism. Publ: The pattern of criticism, Bruce, 60; The ontology of the literary work of art, In: The critical matrix, Georgetown Univ, 61; Dryden's The Religio Laici and Roman Catholic apologetics, 6/65 & Dryden's The hind and the panther and Roman Catholic apologetics, 5/68, PMLA; plus others. Add: 3948 N. Stowell Ave, Milwaukee, WI 53211.

HAMMACK, HENRY EDGAR, b. Kansas City, Kans, Nov. 20, 28; m. 55; c. 2. THEATRE ARTS. B.A, Univ. Wash, 56, M.A, 62; Ph.D.(theatre), Tulane Univ, 67. Instr. acting, Univ. Wash, summer 57; from instr. to PROF. THEATRE ARTS, TEX. CHRISTIAN UNIV, 57- U.S.M.C, 50-53, Sgt. Am. Theatre Asn. Costuming and acting. Publ: Theatre arts, In: Texas college and career guide, D. Armstrong, 69. Add: Dept. of Theatre Arts, Texas Christian University, Fort Worth, TX 76129.

HAMMACK, JAMES ALAN, b. Lima, Ohio, July 19, 23; m. 52; c. 3. SPEECH, DRAMA. B.S, Kent State Univ, 47 & 48; M.A, Northwest. Univ, 50; Ph.D. (theater), State Univ. Iowa, 54. Teacher, High Sch, Ohio, 48-50; instr. speech & drama, Bowling Green State Univ, 50-51; asst. commun. skills, State Univ. Iowa, 52-53, instr, 53-54; Mich. State Univ, 54-55; asst. prof. speech & drama, Cent. Mich. Univ, 55-59; assoc. prof, 59-61; assoc. prof. & head dept. speech, DePauw Univ, 61-63; assoc. prof. SPEECH & DRAMA, CENT. MICH. UNIV, 63-65, PROF, 65- U.S.N.R, 43-46, Lt. Speech Commun. Asn; Am. Theatre Asn; Cent. States Speech Asn. American theater history; scene design; directing. Publ: Minimum scenery for high school productions, Speech Teacher, 9/58; Settings for Shakespearean productions, Players Mag, 1/65; An index to photographs of scene designs in Theatre Arts, 1916-1964, Theatre Documentation, Vol. III, No. 1 & 2; plus one other. Add: Dept. of Speech & Dramatic Arts, Central Michigan University, Mt. Pleasant, MI 48858.

HAMMERBACHER, GEORGE HENRY, b. Brooklyn, N.Y, Oct. 3, 35; m. 59; c. 4. BRITISH LITERATURE, LINGUISTICS. B.A, St. John's Univ.(N.Y), 57; M.A, Cath. Univ. Am, 59; M.A, N.Y. Univ, 62. Instr. ENG, King's Col. (Pa), 58-59; teacher, Lindenhurst High Sch, N.Y, 59-65, chmn. dept, 61-65; asst. prof, KING'S COL.(PA), 65-70, ASSOC. PROF, 70-, DIR. WRITING CTR, 71- Lectr, Mitchel Col, Long Island Univ, 62-64; teaching asst, Temple Univ, 69-70; educ. lab. dir, Concentrated Employ. Prog, Wilkes-Barre, Pa, 71-72; ling. consult, Tunkhannock Area Schs, Pa, 72-73. MLA; AAUP; NEA. Restoration and the 18th century; John Dryden; pedagogy. Add: Dept. of English, King's College, 133 N. River St, Wilkes-Barre, PA 18702.

HAMMERBACK, JOHN CLARK, b. San Francisco, Calif, Oct. 6, 38; m. 65; c. 2. SPEECH. B.A, San Francisco State Univ, 62; M.A, Univ. Okla, 65; Ph.D.(speech), Ind. Univ, Bloomington, 70. ASSOC. PROF. SPEECH & CHMN. DEPT, CALIF. STATE UNIV, HAYWARD, 68- U.S.N.A.F.R, 62-68. Speech Commun. Asn; Cent. States Speech Asn; West. Speech Commun. Asn. Public address; rhetorical theory. Publ: The rhetoric of a righteous reform: George Washington Julian's 1852 campaign against slavery, Cent. States Speech J, summer 71; Barry Goldwater's rhetoric of rugged individualism, Quart. J. Speech, 4/72; George W. Julian's antislavery crusade, West. Speech, summer 73. Add: Dept. of Speech & Drama, California State University, Hayward, Hayward, CA 94542.

HAMMOND, ANTONY DEREK, b. Auckland, N.Z, June 21, 38. DRAMA, ENGLISH LITERATURE. B.A, Auckland Univ, 61, M.A, 63, Can. Counc. fel, Ph.D.(Eng), 70. Lectr. ENG, York Univ, 66-69; ASST. PROF, McMASTER UNIV, 69- Can. Asn. Univ. Teachers; Am. Soc. 18th Century Stud. Bibliography and textual study; Restoration drama; Shakespeare. Publ: John Wilson and the Andronicus plays, Yearbk. Eng. Stud, 73. Add: Dept. of English, McMaster University, Hamilton, Ont. L8S 4L9, Can.

HAMMOND, BRUCE RAY, b. Buffalo, N.Y, Oct. 26, 38; m. 67; c. 1. COMMUNICATION THEORY, MASS MEDIA. B.S, State Univ. N.Y. Col. Fredonia, 63; M.S, Canisius Col, 67; M.A, State Univ. N.Y. Col. Buffalo, 69, Ph.D. (commun. theory), 72. ASSOC. PROF. COMMUN, CANISIUS COL, 66- Pres, Buffalo Commun, Consult, 72- Ord.C, U.S.A, 56-57, Res, 57-61, Sgt. Speech Commun. Asn; AAUP; Soc. Educ. Film & TV; Am. Film Inst. Cinea Cinema. Add: Dept. of Communication, Canisius College, 2001 Main St, Buffalo, NY 14208.

HAMMOND, CHARLES MONTGOMERY, b. Auburn, N.Y, Apr. 18, 22; m. 47; c. 2. JOURNALISM, ENGLISH. B.A, Syracuse Univ, 47, M.A, 65. Announcer, regional radio & TV sta, 47-57; pub. relat. dir, Barlow Advert. Agency, 57-60; agency prin, Chas. Hammond & Assocs, 60-65; instr. Am. lit, Cazenovia Col, 62-68; asst. majority leader, N.Y. STATE ASSEMBLY, 69-70, PRESS SECY, 70-; ASSOC. PROF. JOUR, STATE UNIV. N.Y. AGR. & TECH. COL. MORRISVILLE, 70- U.S.A.A.F, 43-46. Pub. Relat. Soc. Am. Mass communications; advertising; public relations. Add: Dept. of Journalism, State University of New York Agricultural & Technical College at Morrisville, Morrisville, NY 13408.

HAMMOND, GERALDINE, b. Clinton, Mo, Mar. 14, 09. ENGLISH. A.B, Univ. Wichita, 31; M.A, Univ. Kans, 32; Northwest. Univ, 35; Univ. Chicago, 36; Ph.D.(Eng), Univ. Colo, 44. PROF. ENG, WICHITA STATE UNIV, 32-, COORD. UNDERGRAD. STUD. ENG, 69- Lectr, Ore. State Col, summer 49; East. Ore. State Col, 49-50. William A. Swett Prize for efficiency, Univ. Wichita, 31, Regents Award for excellence in teaching, 66. MLA; NCTE. Modern drama; 17th century English literature; thematic approach to literature. Publ: Wheatland (poem for music), privately publ, 59; co-auth, Kansas varieties—a mosaic of picture-poems, Kans. State Teachers Col, 63; auth, Evidences of the dramatist's technique in Henry Fielding's novels, Univ. Wichita Bull, 10/41; Poetry, Kans. Quart, fall 73. Add: Dept. of English, Wichita State University, Wichita, KS 67208.

HAMMOND, MAC SAWYER, b. Des Moines, Iowa, Feb. 8, 26; m. 60; c. 2. ENGLISH LITERATURE. B.A, Univ. of the South, 48; M.A, Harvard, 50; Ph.D.(Eng), 62. Instr. ENG, Univ. Va, 56-58; West. Reserve Univ, 60-62, asst. prof, 62-63; STATE UNIV. N.Y. BUFFALO, 63-65, assoc. prof, 65-68, PROF, 68- Sewanee Rev. fel. poetry, 55-56; res. assoc. Ctr. Commun. Sci, Mass. Inst. Technol, 60. U.S.N.R, 49-, Lt.(jg). The poetics of Wallace Stevens; poetry and linguistics; structuralism. Publ: The horse opera and other poems, Ohio State Univ, 66; Cold turkey (poems), Swallow, 70; Poetic syntax, Poetics, Proc. First Int. Congr. Poetics, Warsaw, 60. Add: Dept. of English, State University of New York at Buffalo, Buffalo, NY 14214.

HAMMOND, ROBERT MORRIS, Language & Literature. See Volume III, Foreign Languages, Linguistics & Philology.

HAMNER, EUGENIE LAMBERT, b. Darlington, Ala; m. 66; c. 2. AMERICAN LITERATURE. B.A, Huntingdon Col, 58; M.A, Univ. N.C, Chapel Hill, 59, Ph.D.(Eng), 65. Instr. ENG, Winthrop Col, 59-60; Univ. N.C, Chapel Hill, 63-64; ASST. PROF, Huntingdon Col, 64-65; Univ. Ga, 65-66; UNIV. S.ALA, 69- MLA; S.Atlantic Mod. Lang. Asn; NCTE. Twentieth century American literature and criticism; the novel. Add: Dept. of English, University of South Alabama, Mobile, AL 36688.

HAMNER, ROBERT DANIEL, b. Tuscaloosa, Ala, Jan. 16, 41; m. 63; c. 1. ENGLISH & AMERICAN LITERATURE. B.A, Wayland Baptist Col, 64; M.A, Univ. Tex, Austin, 66, Ph.D.(Eng), 71. Instr. ENG, Wayland Baptist Col, 68-70; asst. prof, HARDIN-SIMMONS UNIV, 71-74, ASSOC. PROF, 74- MLA; S.Cent. Mod. Lang. Asn; Conf. Col. Teachers Eng. Twentieth century American and English novel and poetry; British Commonwealth literature; British West Indian literature. Publ: V.S. Naipaul, Twayne, 73; Literary periodicals in world English: a selective checklist, World Lit. Written in Eng. Newslett, 68; contrib, Contemporary novelists, St. Martin, 72. Add: Dept. of English, Hardin-Simmons University, Abilene, TX 79601.

HAMPSTEN, RICHARD FRANKLIN, b. Yale, Ill, Dec. 14, 29; m. 57; c. 5. ENGLISH & COMPARATIVE LITERATURE. A.B, West. Reserve Univ, 51, M.A, 53; French Govt. scholar, Univ. Paris, 52-53; Ph.D.(comp. lit), Univ. Wash, 63. Acting instr. ENG, Univ. Wash, 59-60; instr, Ohio State Univ, 60-64; asst. prof, Univ. Victoria (B.C), 64-66; from asst. prof. to ASSOC. PROF, UNIV. N.DAK, 66-, COORD. HONORS PROG, 73-, fel, New Sch, 71-72. Nat. Endowment for Humanities summer stipend, 67. AAUP; NCTE; Archaeol. Inst. Am. Prosody; English and French literature of the Renaissance; modern lyric. Add: Honors Program, University of North Dakota, Grand Forks, ND 58201.

HAMPTON, CHARLES CHRISTY, JR, b. Amarillo, Tex, Oct. 25, 35; m. 57; c. 2. DRAMA. A.B, South. Methodist Univ, 56; M.F.A, Yale, 59; Ph.D. (hist, criticism), Stanford Univ, 66. Instr. DRAMA, Allegheny Col, 59-63; vis. asst. prof, Mills Col, 65-66; asst. prof, Univ. Calgary, 66-68; ASSOC. PROF, SAN FRANCISCO STATE UNIV, 68- Samuel Beckett; contemporary drama; mix-media theatre. Publ: Polarity and stasis: drama as reflection of a revolution, Yale Theatre, winter 69; Movies that play for keeps, Film Comment, fall 70; Verfremcluhanseffekt, Mod. Drama, 12/71. Add: Dept. of Drama, San Francisco State University, San Francisco, CA 94132.

HAMPTON, CHARLES FRANCIS, b. Kalamazoo, Mich, Apr. 16, 06. ENGLISH. A.B, West. Mich. Col, 30; A.M, Univ. Mich, 40; Northwest. Univ; Mich. State Col; Univ. Colo. Investigator, Fed. Housing Admin, 33-35; chmn. dept. soc. sci, pub. schs, Marshall, Mich, 38-41; dir. speech educ, high sch, Mich, 41-42; spec. rep, Laidlaw Bros, 42-44; instr. soc. sci, N.Y. State Teachers Col, Oswego, 44-45; asst. prof. written & spoken Eng, Mich. State Univ, 45-55; SPEECH, Albion Col, 55-62; assoc. prof, SCH. GEN. EDUC, FERRIS STATE COL, 62-70, EMER. ASSOC. PROF, 70- Rockefeller grant scholar, 48-50; consult. pub. relat, Mich. Dept. Econ. Develop, 52-53. Political persuasion; Michigan's first Presidential campaign, 1840; study of classroom teaching. Publ: Where is that?, Univ. Bkman, fall 65 & Jr. Prof. Geographer, 7/66; Blast away! Minn. Motorist, 4/66. Add: 703 N. Linden St, Marshall, MI 49068.

HAMRICK, WILLIAM, b. Tuttle, Okla, Sept. 23, 30; m. 57. ENGLISH & LINGUISTICS. B.S.B.A, Univ. Denver, 52, M.A, 59; Ph.D.(Eng), Brown Univ, 65. Asst. prof. ENG, UNIV. CINCINNATI, 64-68, ASSOC. PROF, 68- U.S.A, 53-56. Contemporary literature; integrated media—words, music, images; film. Add: Dept. of English, College of Arts & Sciences, University of Cincinnati, Cincinnati, OH 45221.

HAN, PIERRE, b. Milwaukee, Wis, July 12, 29. ENGLISH, COMPARATIVE LITERATURE. B.A, Cath. Univ. Am, 51; M.A, Columbia Univ, 52, fel, 54-55, Ph.D.(comp. lit), 60; Fulbright fel, Univ. Paris, 57-58. Instr. Eng, Univ. Md, 58-64; asst. prof, AM. UNIV, 64-67, assoc. prof. ENG. & COMP. LIT, 67-71, PROF, 71-, chmn. honors bd, 67-69. Sem. dir, Stud. in the Baroque, Folger Inst. Renaissance & 18th century Stud, 73. MLA; Renaissance Soc. Am; S.Atlantic Mod. Lang. Asn. Racine; the Baroque; interdisciplinary studies. Publ: Ed, Jacques de La Taille's La Maniere: a critical edition, Studies in the romance languages and literatures, Univ. N.C, Chapel Hill, 71 & Readings in the Baroque, Mouton, The Hague, (in prep); auth, The labyrinthe: a metaphor of dramatic action in Racine's Phaedre, S.Atlantic Bull, 69; Baroque foreground and background in Samson Agonistes, Rev. Belge de Philologie et d'Hist, 73. Add: Dept. of Literature, American University, Washington, DC 20016.

HANAWALT, LESLIE LYLE, b. Delaware, Ohio, Jan. 18, 98; m. 22; c. 2. ENGLISH. A.B, Oberlin Col, 22, A.M, 25; Ph.D, Univ. Mich, 29. Instr. Eng, Syracuse Univ, 22-23; Oberlin Col, 23-26; Univ. Mich, 26-29; from instr. to assoc. prof, WAYNE STATE UNIV, 29-44, prof. ENG. LANG. & LIT, 44-68, admis. off, 40-45, chmn. dept, Eng, 45-55, historian, 56-68, EMER. PROF, 68- Romantic period. Publ: A place of light: the history of Wayne State University, Wayne State Univ, 68; co-ed, Writing from observation; co-auth, Body snatching in the Midwest, Mich. Hist, spring 71; auth, Henry Fitzbutler: Detroit's first black medical student, Detroit in Perspective, 73. Add: 201 E. Kirby, Detroit, MI 48202.

HANCE, KENNETH GORDON, b. Pasadena, Calif, July 6, 03; m. 28; c. 1. SPEECH. A.B, Olivet Col, 24, A.M, 26, hon. L.H.D, 61; summers, Northwest. Univ, 24, 38; Harvard, 28-30; Columbia Univ, 32; Ph.D, Univ. Mich, 37. Instr. Eng. & speech, Olivet Col, 24-26, asst. prof, 26-30; speech, Albion Col, 30-37, prof, 37-40; asst. prof, Univ. Mich, 40-43, assoc. prof, 43-45; Northwest. Univ, 45-48, prof. speech & asst. dean sch. speech, 48-56; prof. SPEECH, MICH. STATE UNIV, 56-71, EMER. PROF, 71- Consult-panelist, Nat. Endowment Humanities, 70-; asst. to the pres, Olivet Col, 71- Speech Commun. Asn.(v.pres, Speech Asn. Am, 55-57, pres, 60); Cent. State Speech Asn. Rhetorical theory; public address; discussion. Publ: Co-auth, Discussion in human affairs, Harper, 50 & Public speaking and discussion for religious leaders, Prentice-Hall, 61; auth, Principles of speaking, Wadsworth, 62, 68, 74. Add: Olivet College, Olivet, MI 49076.

HANCHER, CHARLES MICHAEL, b. Newark, N.J, May 20, 41. ENGLISH. A.B, Harvard, 63; M.A, Yale, 64, Woodrow Wilson fel, 66-67, Ph.D.(Eng), 67; Fulbright scholar, Birkbeck Col, London Univ, 65-66. Asst. prof. ENG, Johns Hopkins Univ, 67-72; UNIV. MINN, MINNEAPOLIS, 72-73, ASSOC. PROF, 73- Am. Philos. Soc. grant, summer 72. MLA; Am. Soc. Aesthet; Mod. Humanities Res. Asn. Browning; literary theory. Publ: The dramatic situation in Browning's Pauline, Yearbk. Eng. Stud, 71; Poems versus trees: the aesthetics of Monroe Beardsley, J. Aesthetics & Art Criticism, 72; Three kinds of intention, Mod. Lang. Notes, 72. Add: Dept. of English, University of Minnesota, Minneapolis, MN 55455.

HANCOCK, EDWARD ALEXANDER, b. Bluefield, W.Va, Aug. 12, 11. ENGLISH LITERATURE. A.B, Davidson Col, 33; A.M, Univ. Va, 48; Univ. Wis, 37; Univ. Colo, 50. Teacher jr. high sch, W.Va, 33-37; high sch, Tenn, 37-42; from instr. to ASSOC. PROF. ENG, VA. POLYTECH. INST. & STATE UNIV, 46- Teaching fel, Univ. Va, 47-48. U.S.A, 42-45. Add: Dept. of English, Virginia Polytechnic Institute & State University, Blacksburg, VA 24060.

HANDS, CHARLES BERNARD, b. Wilkes-Barre, Pa, Sept. 30, 25; m. 55; c. 2. ENGLISH. A.B, Univ. Notre Dame, 52, Ph.D.(Eng), 59; M.A, Univ. Pa, 53. Teaching asst. ENG, Univ. Notre Dame, 53-54, instr, 54-57; asst. prof, LOYOLA COL.(MD), 57-64, assoc. prof, 64-68, PROF, 68- U.S.A.F, 43-46. MLA; NCTE. Harold Frederic; Robert Frost; Walt Whitman. Publ: The hidden terror of Robert Frost, Eng. J, (in press). Add: Dept. of English, Loyola College, Baltimore, MD 21210.

HANDSCOMBE, RICHARD JAMES, b. Enfield, Eng, Feb. 19, 35; m. 66. ENGLISH. B.A, Cambridge, 59, cert, 60, M.A, 63; dipl, Univ. Leeds, 64. Lectr. Eng, Istanbul Univ, 61-63; assoc. organiser res, Nuffield For. Lang. Teaching Materials Proj, 64-67; asst. prof. ENG, GLENDON COL, YORK UNIV.(ONT), 67-68, ASSOC. PROF, 68-, CHMN. DEPT, 71- R.A.F, 54-56, Pilot Off. Ling. Soc. Am; Brit. Asn. Applied Ling; Ling. Asn. Gt. Brit; Philol. Soc, Eng; Can. Ling. Asn; Nat. Asn. Teaching Eng; Can. Counc. Teachers Eng.(pres, 72-73). Children's language; literary stylistics; English studies, first, second and foreign language. Publ: Co-auth, Castle Zaremba, Queen's Printer, 70; auth, Castle Zaremba: a multi-media approach to teaching Canadian English, fall 71 & Reading literature, spring & summer 72, Eng. Quart. Add: Dept. of English, Glendon College, York University, 2275 Bayview Ave, Toronto, Ont. M4N 3M6, Can.

HANDY, WILLIAM J, b. New Haven, Conn, Feb. 1, 18; m. 52; c. 1. ENGLISH & AMERICAN LITERATURE. Ph.D, Univ. Okla, 54. Instr. ENG, Univ. Tex, 54-57, asst. prof, 57-59, assoc. prof, 59-65; UNIV. ORE, 65-68, PROF, 68-, assoc. dean lib. arts col, 67-69. Vis. lectr. Am. lit, Univ. Belgrade, 61-62; vis. prof, Univ. Rouen, France, 72-73. MLA. Contemporary literary criticism, fiction and poetry. Publ: Kant and the Southern new critics, 63 & ed, Symposium on formalist criticism, 65, Univ. Tex; auth, Modern fiction: a formalist approach, South. Ill. Univ, 71; co-ed, Twentieth century criticism, McMillan, 74; auth, As I lay dying: Faulkner's inner reporter, Kenyon Rev, 59; Ontological theory of the Ransom critics, Univ. Tex. Stud. Eng; Towards a formalist criticism of fiction, In: The novel: modern essays in criticism, Prentice-Hall, 69. Add: Dept. of English, University of Oregon, Eugene, OR 97403.

HANENKRAT, FRANK THOMAS, b. Appomattox, Va, May 24, 39; m. 66; c. 1. ENGLISH, AMERICAN LITERATURE. B.A, Univ. Richmond, 61, M.A, 67; Ph.D.(Eng), Emory Univ, 71. Instr. ENG, Va. Commonwealth Univ, 65-67; teaching asst, Emory Univ, 69-70; instr, Univ. Ga, 70-71; asst. prof, LYNCHBURG COL, 71-73, ASSOC. PROF, 73- U.S.A, 63-65, 1st Lt. Nineteenth and 20th century American literature; American dialects. Publ: Co-auth, Position rifle shooting, 73 & ed, Education of a turkey hunter, 74, Winchester. Add: Dept. of English, Lynchburg College, Lynchburg, VA 24504.

HANEY, JOHN B, b. Milwaukee, Wis, May 2, 31; m. 59; c. 2. COMMUNICATIONS, INSTRUCTIONAL TECHNOLOGY. B.S, Miami Univ, 52; M.A, Univ. Mich, 54, Ph.D.(speech), 60; Mich. State Univ, 53-54. Instr. commun. tech, Air Univ, 54-57; Eng, U.S. Air Force Acad, 59-61, asst. prof, 61-64, assoc. prof, 64; speech, Univ. Ill, Chicago, 64-68, prof, 68-71, dir, Off. Instructional Resources, 64-71; PROF. COMMUN. ARTS & SCI, QUEENS COL.(N.Y), 71- Consult, Mich. State Univ, 65-67; Nat. Asn. Educ. Broadcasters, 66-67; Ford Found. Educ. Facilities Lab, 68-; U.S. Off. Educ, 68-71; bk. rev. ed, AV Commun. Rev, 73- U.S.A.F, 54-64, Capt. Nat. Soc. Stud. Commun.(pres, 62); Soc. Prog. & Automated Learning (pres, 66-68); Speech Commun. Asn. New York on film; design and application of instructional systems. Publ: Co-auth, Planning for instructional resources, Univ. Ill, 67; co-auth, Educational media and the teacher, 70 & Educational communications and technology, 74, W.C. Brown; co-auth, Heuristic dimension of instructional development, Audio-Visual Commun. Rev, 68; plus others. Add: 39 Hawthorne Pl, Manhasset, NY 11030.

HANEY, ROGER DANIEL, b. East Chicago, Ind, May 17, 42; m. 65. COMMUNICATION. B.A, Kans. Wesleyan Univ, 65; M.A, Mich. State Univ, 67, Ph.D.(commun), 71. ASST. PROF. SPEECH, UNIV. KY, 70- Fel, Sem. Int. Commun, Sali, Yugoslavia, summer 71. Int. Commun. Asn; Speech Commun. Asn. Voting behavior; violence in mass media; language and communication. Add: School of Communication, University of Kentucky, Lexington, KY 40506.

HANKEY, CLYDE THOMAS, Linguistics. See Volume III, Foreign Languages, Linguistics & Philology.

HANKINS, JOHN DAVID, b. Lawrence, Kans, Oct. 1, 35; m. 58; c. 4. ENGLISH. A.B, Tufts Univ, 58; Ph.D.(Eng), Ind. Univ, 64. Instr. ENG, UNIV. CONN, STORRS, 62-64, asst. prof, 64-68, ASSOC. PROF. & ASST. DEAN COL. ARTS & SCI, 68- MLA. James Boswell and 18th century letters. Add: Dept. of English, University of Connecticut, Storrs, CT 06268.

HANKINS, JOHN ERSKINE, b. Lake View, S.C, Jan. 2, 05; m. 30; c. 3. ENGLISH LITERATURE. A.B, Univ. S.C, 24, A.M, 25; Ph.D, Yale, 29. Instr. ENG, Univ. S.C, 24-25, adj. prof, 25-26; asst. prof, Ind. State Teachers Col, 29-30; from asst. prof. to prof, Univ. Kans, 30-56; prof, UNIV. MAINE, ORONO, 56-70, head dept, 56-66, EMER. PROF, 70- Guggenheim fel, 49; Fulbright lectr, Univ. Leyden, 53. MLA. The Elizabethan age; 19th century essays; life and works of George Turberville. Publ: Turberville, 40 & Shakespeare's derived imagery, 53, Univ. Kans; Character of Hamlet, Univ. N.C, 41; Source and meaning in Spenser's Allegory, Oxford Univ, 71. Add: Oxford, ME 04270.

HANKINS, (JOHN) RICHARD, b. Charleston, W.Va, Oct. 10, 33; m. 57; c. 2. ENGLISH LITERATURE & LINGUISTICS. A.B, Oberlin Col, 55; M.A, W.Va. Univ, 57; fel, Syracuse Univ, 59-60; Ph.D.(Eng), Case West. Reserve Univ, 69. Instr. ENG, W.Va. Univ, 60-62; asst. prof, Edinboro State Col, 62-66; ASSOC. PROF, BALDWIN-WALLACE COL, 66- U.S.A, 57-59. AAUP; Am. Asn. 18th Century Stud. Eighteenth century British literature; biography as a literary genre; history of the English language. Publ: What ever happened to biography?, Round Table, 1/72. Add: Dept. of English, Baldwin-Wallace College, Berea, OH 44017.

HANLEY, EVELYN ALICE, b. Atlanta, Ga, Dec. 14, 16. ENGLISH. A.B, Brooklyn Col, 35; A.M, N.Y. Univ, 37, Ph.D.(Eng), 44; fel, Hunter Col, 38-40. Temporary instr. ENG, Brooklyn Col, 44-46; instr, Adelphi Col, 46-49; asst. prof, Paterson State Col, 50-51; lectr, HUNTER COL, 63-65, instr, 65-67, asst. prof, 67-73, ASSOC. PROF, 73- Parker Lloyd-Smith poetry prize, 34; Charles Dickens Commemorative Medal, 71; Cert. of Merit for Distinguished Serv. in Poetry & Criticism, Dictionary Int. Biog, London, 73; Bronze Medal for Poetry, Int. Who's Who in Poetry, 74. AAUP; MLA. Victorian literature, especially women poets; Italian literature; English, French and Italian romantic poetry. Publ: Poetic profiles, 62 & Antiphony, 63, Arcade; Stoicism in major English poets of the nineteenth century, Haskell, 64; Nature in theme and symbol: Wordsworth to Eliot, Heathcote, 72; Dora Sigerson Shorter: late Victorian romantic, Victorian Poetry, autumn 65; Dante: after seven centuries, Ital. Times, 4/65; Jan Vermeer, Univ. Rev, winter 66. Add: 82-64 170th St, Jamaica, NY 11432.

HANLEY, KATHERINE, C.S.J, b. Syracuse, N.Y, May 28, 39. ENGLISH. B.A, Col. St. Rose, 61; M.A, Univ. Notre Dame, 63, Ph.D.(Eng), 66. Instr. ENG, COL. ST. ROSE, 63-68, ASSOC. PROF, 68-, COORD. GRAD. STUD. ENG, 67-, DEAN GRAD. SCH, 74-, chmn. dept. Eng, 70-74. Univ. Toronto postdoctoral fel, summer 70. MLA; AAUP; Conf. Christianity & Lit; NCTE. English Renaissance poetry; Milton; fiction. Publ: Temples in the temple: George Herbert's study of the church, Stud. Eng. Lit, 68; Morning or evening? the conclusion of Paradise lost, Eng. Rec, winter 72; Andrew Marvell's A definition of love, Concerning Poetry, fall 69; plus twelve others. Add: Dept. of English, College of St. Rose, Albany, NY 12203.

HANNA, ALLAN JOSEPH, b. St. Paul, Minn, Sept. 4, 29; m. 55; c. 3. ENGLISH. B.A, Univ. Mich, 51, M.A, 53; Univ. Minn, 55-60. Asst. prof. ENG, MOORHEAD STATE COL, 60-71, ASSOC. PROF, 71- Hopwood poetry prize, Univ. Mich, 52; ed, Critique: Stud. in Mod. Fiction, 58- U.S.A, 53-54; U.S.A.F.R. NCTE. Modern British and American literature. Publ: An Allan Seager bibliography, winter 62-63 & The muse of history: Allan Seager and the criticism of culture, winter 62-63, Critique: Stud. Mod. Fiction. Add: Dept. of English, Moorhead State College, Moorhead, MN 56560.

HANNA, BLAKE THOMPSON, Linguistics, Modern Languages. See Volume III, Foreign Languages, Linguistics & Philology.

HANNA, JOHN GREIST, b. Kaiserslautern, Ger, Aug. 31, 14; U.S. citizen; m. 49; c. 2. ENGLISH LITERATURE. B.S, Trinity Col.(Conn), 36; M.A, Harvard, 46; Ph.D, Boston Univ, 61. Instr. ENG, Simmons Col, 46-47; asst. prof, 47-49; 51-52; lectr, Boston Univ, 54-58; asst. prof, Univ. Miami, 58-60; South. Conn. State Col, 60-61; assoc. prof, Lowell Tech. Inst, 62-63; UNIV. MAINE, PORTLAND-GORHAM, 63-65, PROF, 64-, chmn. dept, 66-71. Fulbright lectr. Am. lit, Univ. Helsinki, 62-63. Col. Eng. Asn; NCTE; MLA; AAUP. James Joyce's Ulysses, Greek tragedy; Victorian prose and poetry. Publ: Elizabeth Bowen, Encyclopaedia of world literature, 70. Add: Dept. of English, 411 Bonney Hall, University of Maine at Portland-Gorham, Portland, ME 04102.

HANNA, RALPH, III, b. Los Angeles, Calif, Mar. 6, 42; m. 63; c. 2. ENGLISH. B.A, Amherst Col, 63; Woodrow Wilson fel, Yale, 63-64, M.A, 64, Currier fel, 64-65, Danforth fel, 64-66, univ. fel, 65-66, Ph.D.(Eng), 66. ASST. PROF. ENG, UNIV. CALIF, RIVERSIDE, 66- MLA; Medieval Acad. Am; Medieval Asn. Pac. Middle English alliterative poetry; Piers Plowman; Chaucer. Publ: Co-ed, John Trevisa's translation of Bartholomaeus Anglicus' De proprietatibus rerum, Clarendon, (in press); ed, The awntyrs off Arthure: an edition, Univ. Manchester, (in prep); auth, The awntyrs off Arthure: an interpretation, Mod. Lang. Quart, 70. Add: Dept. of English, University of California, Riverside, CA 92507.

HANNAH, MARY EMILY, b. Denver, Colo, Mar. 14, 36. SPEECH, HISTORY. B.A, Grinnell Col, 58; M.A, Univ. Iowa, 62; Ph.D.(speech), Univ. Ill, 67. Teacher, High Sch, Colo, 58-61; instr. SPEECH, St. Cloud State Col, 62-64; asst. Univ. Ill, 64-65, teaching fel, 65-66; asst. prof, Sacramento State Col, 66-67; assoc. prof. & chmn. dept, ST. CLOUD STATE COL, 68-71, PROF, 71- Speech Commun. Asn; AAUP; Am. Asn. Higher Educ; Int. Commun. Asn. Rhetorical theory and criticism; American history. Add: Dept. of Speech, St. Cloud State College, St. Cloud, MN 56301.

HANNING, ROBERT WILLIAM, b. New York, N.Y, Apr. 21, 38; m. 63; c. 2. MEDIEVAL & RENAISSANCE LITERATURE. B.A. & Woodrow Wilson fel, Columbia Col, 58; B.A. & Kellett fel. from Columbia Univ, Oxford, 60, M.A, 64; Scudder-Johnston fel, Columbia Univ, 60-61, Ph.D.(Eng), 64. Instr. ENG, COLUMBIA UNIV, 63-65, asst. prof, 65-69, assoc. prof, 69-71, PROF, 71- Am. Counc. Learned Soc. fel, 66-67; Guggenheim Found. fel, 72-73. MLA; Medieval Acad. Am; Renaissance Soc. Am; Soc. Stud. Mediaeval Lang. & Lit. Medieval romance; Chaucer; Ovid in Middle Ages and Renaissance. Publ: The vision of history in early Britain, Columbia Univ, 66; Sources of illusion: plot elements and their function in Ariosto's Ginevra episode, Forum Italicum, 71; The social significance of twelfth-century chivalric romance, Medievalia et Humanistica, 72; Thou hast begun a parlous pleye: dramatic mimesis in four Middle English Fall of Lucifer plays, Comp. Drama, 73. Add: 410 Hamilton Hall, Columbia University, New York, NY 10027.

HANSELL, DONALD WADE, b. Chicago, Ill, Apr. 11, 27; m. 60; c. 2. SPEECH & DRAMA. B.S, Purdue Univ, 49, M.S, 54; Ph.D.(pub. address), Denver Univ, 63. Teacher, High Sch, Ind, 49-54, 55-66, chmn. dept, 64-66, teacher, High Sch, Calif, 54-55; ASSOC. PROF. SPEECH, IND. STATE UNIV, TERRE HAUTE, 66- NDEA fel. educ. TV, summer 66. U.S.N.R, 45-46. Speech Commun. Asn; Am. Theatre Asn; Cent. States Speech Asn. Classical rhetoric; speech education; business and professional speaking. Publ: Speech in Indiana high schools 1969-70: a survey, Ind. Speech Notes, 11/70. Add: Dept. of Speech, Indiana State University, Terre Haute, IN 47809.

HANSELL, WILLIAM HAROLD, b. Philadelphia, Pa, Mar. 24, 34; m. 60; c. 2. AMERICAN LITERATURE. B.A, La Salle Col, 60; M.A, Univ. Fla, 62; Ph.D.(Eng), Univ. Wis, 72. Instr. lib. stud, Clarkson Col. Technol, 63-65; ASST. PROF. ENG, UNIV. WIS. CTR-SHEBOYGAN, 65- U.S.M.C, 53-56, Sgt. AAUP. Afro-American literature; 20th century American literature. Publ: Aestheticism vs. political militancy in Gwendolyn Brooks's The Chicago Picasso and The wall, Col. Lang. Asn. J, 9/73; The role of violence in recent poems of Gwendolyn Brooks, Stud. Black Lit, 10/73. Add: Dept. of English, University of Wisconsin Center-Sheboygan, Sheboygan, WI 53081.

HANSEN, ARLEN JAY, b. Rolfe, Iowa, Oct. 24, 36; m. 59; c. 3. ENGLISH & AMERICAN LITERATURE. B.A, Iowa State Univ, 58; M.A, Univ. Iowa, 62, fel, 66-69, Ph.D.(Eng), 69. Instr. ENG, Bradley Univ, 62-66; asst. prof, UNIV. OF THE PAC, 69-71, ASSOC. PROF, 71- MLA; Philol. Asn. Pac. Coast; Rocky Mountain Mod. Lang. Asn; Midwest Mod. Lang. Asn. Nineteenth century American literature; 20th century literature; narrative theory. Publ: Plotinus—an early source of Emerson's view of otherworldliness, Emerson Soc. Quart, 7/72; Celebration of solipsism: a new trend in American fiction, Mod. Fiction Stud, spring 73; Short story, In: Encycl. Britannica, 73. Add: Dept. of English, University of the Pacific, Stockton, CA 95204.

HANSEN, BRIAN KANNE, b. Pasadena, Calif, Feb. 5, 36; m. 58; c. 2. DRAMA, SPEECH. B.A, Univ. Calif, Los Angeles, 60; M.A, Cornell Univ, 61; McPherson fel. & Ph.D.(speech, commun. & theatre arts), Univ. Minn, 66. Instr. speech, Wash. State Univ, 62-64; vis. prof. dramatic arts, Univ. Calif, Santa Barbara, 67; asst. prof. speech arts, San Diego State Col, 67-68; dir. theatre stud, Cent. Midwest. Regional Educ. Lab, 68-70; chmn. theatre arts, Oberlin Col, 70-73; CHMN. DEPT. THEATRE, UNIV. DEL, 73- Staff assoc, Aesthet. Educ. Prog, CEMREL, Inc, Sig.C, U.S.A, 56-58. Am. Theatre Asn; Speech Commun. Asn. Behavioral studies in theatre; theoretical study of theatre; acting and directing. Publ: Curriculum model for theatre in aesthetic education, 70 & co-auth, Theatre game file, 70, CEMREL, Inc; co-auth, A preliminary experiment in measuring attitude shifts as a result of viewing a dramatic production, 6/65 & Measuring the message delivered by a dramatic production, 11/65, Speech Monogr. Add: Dept. of Theatre, University of Delaware, Newark, DE 19711.

HANSEN, BURRELL FENTON, b. Idaho Falls, Idaho, Oct. 7, 18; m. 49; c. 5. SPEECH. B.S, Utah State Agr. Col, 40; Univ, Iowa, 40; M.S, Purdue Univ, 42; Univ. Minn, 43-45, Ph.D, 53; cert, Stanford TV Inst, 53. Instr. speech, Purdue Univ, 42-43; Univ. Denver, 46-47; Univ. Minn, 47-48; asst. prof, UTAH STATE UNIV, 48-55, PROF. SPEECH, 55-, DIR. RADIO & TV, 68-, chmn, 55-68. Chmn. scholar. comt, Nat. Asn. Educ. Broadcasters, 65-67; dir. dept. audio-visual serv, Univ. Strathclyde, 67-68; consult. audio-visual serv, Edinburgh Univ, 68. Speech Commun. Asn; Nat. Asn. Educ. Broadcasters (radio grant, 56); Broadcast Educ. Asn; West. Radio-TV Asn. Radio-television audience analysis; communications theory; informational broadcasting. Publ: Sources of scholarships for students of broadcasting, J. Broadcasting, summer 67; Do not enter box unless . . . , Univ. TV, Nat. Exten. Col, Cambridge, 6/68; plus others. Add: Dept. of Communication, Utah State University, Logan, UT 84322.

HANSEN, CHADWICK (CLARKE), b. Benton Harbor, Mich, Feb. 15, 26; m. 47; c. 4. AMERICAN LITERATURE & STUDIES. B.A, Yale, 48; M.A, Univ. Minn, Minneapolis, 51, Ford teaching internship, 54-55, Ph.D.(Am. stud), 56. Instr. Eng, Pa. State Univ, 55-60, asst. prof, 60-65, assoc. prof, 65-70, PROF. Eng. & Am. stud, 70-71; Univ. Minn, Minneapolis, 71-74; ENG, UNIV. ILL, CHICAGO CIRCLE, 74- Fulbright vis. prof, Univ. Graz, 60-61; curriculum consult, humanities prog. young criminal offenders, Nat. Endowment for Humanities, 68-69. U.S.N.R, 43-46. MLA; Am. Stud. Asn; AHA. Folk and popular culture. Publ: Co-auth, Modern fiction: form and idea in the contemporary novel and short story, Ctr. Continuing Lib. Educ, 59 & The American Renaissance: the history and literature of an era; Diesterweg, 61; auth, Witchcraft at Salem, Braziller, 69; Social influences on jazz style: Chicago, 1920-30, Am. Quart, winter 60; The character of Jim and the ending of Huckleberry Finn, Mass. Rev, autumn 63; The once and future boss: Mark Twain's Yankee, 19th Century Fiction, June 73. Add: Dept. of English, University of Illinois at Chicago Circle, Box 4348, Chicago, IL 60680.

HANSEN, DELMAR J, b. Manilla, Iowa, Dec. 1, 26; m. 58. SPEECH, DRAMA. B.A, Omaha Univ, 52; M.A, Fla. State Univ, 53; Ph.D.(drama), State Univ. Iowa, 60. PROF. SPEECH & THEATRE & CHMN. DEPT, MOORHEAD STATE COL, 58- U.S.A, 42-45, Sgt. Speech Commun. Asn; Am. Theatre Asn. Directing. Add: Dept. of Speech & Theatre, Moorhead State College, Moorhead, MN 56560.

HANSEN, HAROLD R, b. Marshfield, Wis, Mar. 19, 07; m. 33; c. 1. SPEECH, THEATRE. B.A, Carroll Col.(Wis), 28; M.A, Univ. Wis, 41; N.Y. Univ, 63-64. Teacher, High Sch, Wis, 28-40, 42-53; Ill, 41-42; instr. speech & theatre, UNIV. WIS-PLATTEVILLE, 53-58, ASSOC. PROF. SPEECH & THEATRE, 58-, chmn. dept. speech, 58-68. Speech Commun. Asn; NEA. Shakespeare in the high school theatre. Add: Dept. of Speech, University of Wisconsin-Platteville, Platteville, WI 53818.

HANSEN, JANIS T, b. Jerome, Idaho, Apr. 2, 34; m. 56; c. 2. ENGLISH. B.A, Whitman Col, 56; M.A, Univ. Wash, 60; Ph.D.(Eng), Univ. Ore, 65. Asst. prof. Eng, Mankato State Col, 65-68; ASSOC. PROF. ENG. & URBAN STUD, UNIV. PUGET SOUND, 68- Philol. Asn. Pac. Coast; MLA. Picaresque novel; modern Irish literature; contemporary poetry. Publ: The novels of Joyce Cary and the picaresque tradition, Mouton, 69; The English picaresque novel, Mankato Stud. Eng, 66. Add: Depts. of English & Urban Studies, University of Puget Sound, Tacoma, WA 98416.

HANSEN, REGINA, b. Pueblo, Colo, Dec. 13, 19. ENGLISH & AMERICAN LITERATURE. A.B, Mt. St. Scholastica Col, 41; M.Music, Kans. City Conserv. Music, 48; M.A, Marquette Univ, 68, Kans. City Regional Counc. Higher Educ. grant, 71, Ph.D.(Am. lit), 72. Instr, Mt. St. Scholastica Col, 46-51; teacher, St. Peter Paul High Sch, Seneca, Kans, 51-53, 60-62; St. Mary High Sch, Walsenburg, Colo, 53-60; instr, Donnelly Col, 62-71; ASST. PROF. ENG, BENEDICTINE COL, 73- U.S. Off. Educ-Ind. State Univ. Consortium int. stud. grant, India, 72. MLA. Publ: For the Feast of the Seven Dolors (poem), In: Dove flights, Grail Press, 45; Song against mediocrity (poem), 7/49 & A singer of the silver age, 1/51, Benedictine Rev; plus others. Add: Dept. of English, Benedictine College, Atchison, KS 66002.

HANSON, FRANK BURTON, b. Rumford, Maine, Feb. 10, 13; m. 42; c. 2. ENGLISH, DRAMA. B.S, Univ. Maine, 42; M.A, Univ. N.C, 46; Ph.D.(theatre hist. & Eng), Yale, 53. Instr. speech, Univ. Maine Annex, Brunswick, 46-48; asst. prof. speech & drama, Fla. State Univ, 51-53; vis. lectr. Eng, Youngstown State Univ, 53-54; asst. prof, Rensselaer Polytech. Inst, 54-55; teacher speech, Am. Acad. Dramatic Arts, 55-57; asst. prof. drama, Tufts Univ, 57-59; speech, City Col. New York, 60-66; assoc. prof. ENG, MONTCLAIR STATE COL, 66-73, PROF, 73- U.S.A.A.F, 42-45, T/Sgt; Distinguished Flying Cross; Air Medal with four Oak Leaf Clusters. MLA; charter mem. Am. Soc. Theatre Res; Am. Theatre Asn. Theatre history; literary criticism; dramatic literature. Publ: Abstract of speech on training the actor's speaking voice, Folia Phoniatrica, Basle, fall 60; Theatre history of Yale University and New Haven, Connecticut, Enciclopedia della Spettacolo, Rome. Add: 266 N. Mountain Ave, Upper Montclair, NJ 07043.

HANZO, THOMAS A, b. Cleveland, Ohio, Mar. 10, 21; m. 45; c. 3. ENGLISH LITERATURE. B.A, Univ. Colo, 46, M.A, 47; Ph.D, Stanford Univ, 51. Instr. ENGLISH, Univ. Colo, 47-48; UNIV. CALIF, DAVIS, 50-53, asst. prof, 53-59, assoc. prof, 59-65, PROF, 65- U.S.A.A.F, 42-45, 1st Lt. MLA; Philol. Asn. Pac. Coast. Seventeenth century English literature; contemporary literature. Publ: Latitude and restoration criticism, Anglistica, 59; Theme and the narrator of the Great Gatsby, Mod. Fiction, 56; Eliot and Kierkegaard, Mod. Drama, 60; Downward to darkness, Sewanee Rev, autumn 66. Add: 2407 Loyola Dr, Davis, CA 95616.

HAPGOOD, ROBERT (DERRY), b. Lompoc, Calif, Dec. 11, 28; m. 50; c. 2. ENGLISH. A.B, Univ. Calif, 50, A.M, 51; Kofoid fel, 51-52, Johnson fel, 52-53, Ph.D.(Eng), 55. Instr. ENG, Ind. Univ, 55-57; Univ. Calif, Berkeley, 58-59; asst. prof, Univ. Calif, Riverside, 59-65; assoc. prof, UNIV. N.H, 65-71, PROF, 71-; CHMN. DEPT, 72- Fulbright travel grant & vis. prof. Am. lit. & civilization, Univ. Dijon, 57-58; summer fel, Inst. Renaissance Stud, Ashland, Ore, 61; Mellon fel, Univ. Pittsburgh, 64-65; dir. Shakespeare workshop, Bowdoin Col, summers 72- Eng. Inst. prize, 68. U.S.A, 53-55. MLA. Theater criticism; Shakespeare; drama. Publ: Hamlet nearly absurd, Tulane Drama Rev, summer 65; Shakespeare's maimed rites, Centennial Rev, fall 65; Shakespeare's thematic modes of speech, Shakespeare Surv, 67. Add: Dept. of English, University of New Hampshire, Durham, NH 03824.

HAPONSKI, WILLIAM CHARLES, b. Ilion, N.Y, Sept. 12, 32; m. 56; c. 1. ENGLISH. B.S, U.S. Mil. Acad, 56; M.A, Cornell Univ, 63, Ph.D.(Eng), 67. U.S. ARMY, 56-, asst. prof. Eng, U.S. Mil. Acad, 64-67, assoc. prof, 69-71; PROF. MIL. STUD, UNIV. VT, 71- U.S.A, 56-, Lt. Col; Silver Star. Shakespeare Asn. Am. Renaissance literature; Shakespeare; western civilization (philosophy, religion, science, history) in art. Publ: Reply to a Vietnam veteran, Saturday Rev, 10/69; 1971 Champlain Shakespeare festival, fall 71 & Shakespeare in Vermont, 1972, fall 72, Shakespeare Quart. Add: Hurley Ave, Lake Placid, NY 12946.

HAQUE, ABU SAEED ZAHURUL, b. Faridpur, Bangladesh, Jan. 1, 34; m. 61; c. 2. FOLKLORE, COMPARATIVE LITERATURE. B.A, Univ. Dacca, 56; M.A, Univ. Karachi, 59; univ. fel, Ind. Univ, Bloomington, 62-63, Ford Found. fel, 63-64, A.M, 65, Ph.D.(folklore), 68. Instr. Bengali, Sind Muslim Col, Karachi, Pakistan, 59-60; in-charge folklore, Bangla Acad, Dacca, Bangladesh, 61-62; res. asst. folklore, Ind. Univ, Bloomington, 64-66; assoc. prof. soc. sci, ALCORN STATE UNIV, 66-68, PROF, 68-70, ENG, 70- Chmn, Miss. Folklore Bibliog. Comt, 67-; adv, Miss. Arts Comn, 71- Am. Folklore Soc; Asn. Asian Stud; Asian Folklore Soc; AAUP. Literature. Publ: Abishkarer Gorar Katha, Franklin Publ, Dacca, 61; Tepantarer Daityapuri, 62 & Patalpurir Rajkanya, 62, Ideal Publ, Dacca; Kishor Mela, Bangla Acad, Dacca, 62; ed, Annual bibliography of Mississippi folklore, 67, 70 & 72 & auth, On the Panchatantra, 69, Miss. Folklore Register. Add: D Dept. of English & Foreign Languages, Alcorn State University, Lorman, MS 39096.

HARAP, LOUIS, b. New York, N.Y, Sept. 16, 04; m. 57. LIBRARY SCIENCE. A.B, Harvard, 28, A.M, 30, Ph.D.(philos), 32. Librarian, Harvard, 34-39; ed, Jewish Surv, 41-42; Jewish Life, 47-57; librarian, Elizabeth Irwin High Sch, 59-60; New Lincoln Sch, 60-69; RETIRED. Mem. ed. bd, Jewish Currents, 58- U.S.A, 43-45, Tech. Sgt. Philosophy of art; literary criticism and American literary history; Jewish affairs. Publ: Social roots of the arts, Int. Publ, 49; The image of the Jew in American literature, Jewish Publ. Soc, (in press); Karl Marx and the Jewish question, Jewish Currents, 7-8/59; Edgar Allan Poe and journalism, Zweitschrift fur Anglistik und Americanistik, Leipzig, 71; Image of the Jew in American drama: 1794 to 1823, Am. Jewish Hist. Quart, 8/71; plus two others. Add: Belmont, VT 05730.

HARBAGE, ALFRED B, b. Philadelphia, Pa, July 18, 01; m. 26; c. 4. ENGLISH LITERATURE. A.B, Univ. Pa, 24, A.M, 26, Ph.D, 29, hon. Litt.D, 54; hon. Litt.D, Bowdoin Col, 72. Instr. Eng. Univ. Pa, 24-36, asst. prof, 36-38, assoc. prof, 38-42, prof, 42-46, grad. chmn. dept. Eng, 45-46; prof. Eng. lit, Columbia Univ, 47-52; ENG, HARVARD, 52-60, Cabot prof, 60-70, EMER. CABOT PROF, 70- Guggenheim fel, 53-54, 65-67; Alexander lectr, Univ. Toronto, 55. MLA. English drama and theatre from 1500 to 1700. Publ: As they liked it, Harper, 61; Shakespeare and the rival traditions; William Shakespeare: a reader's guide, Farrar, Straus, 63; ed, The Pelican Shakespeare, Penguin, 56-67; auth, Conceptions of Shakespeare, 66 & Shakespeare without words, 72, Harvard; Shakespeare's songs, Macrae Smith, 70. Add: 52 Grant Ave, Cherry Hill, NJ 08034.

HARBERT, EARL NORMAN, b. Cleveland, Ohio, Apr. 1, 34. ENGLISH, AMERICAN LITERATURE. A.B, Hamilton Col, 56; M.A, Johns Hopkins Univ, 61; Ph.D.(Eng), Univ. Wis, 66. Instr. ENG, George Washington Univ, 61-62; asst. prof, TULANE UNIV, 65-69, ASSOC. PROF, 69- Fulbright lectr. Am. lit, Univ. Deusto, Spain, 67-68. U.S.N.R, 57-60, Lt. MLA. American literature. Publ: Co-ed, Fifteen American Authors before 1900

& auth. chap, Henry Adams, Univ. Wis, 71; auth, Washington Irving's Granada, In: Washington Irving Reconsidered, 69; John Quincy Adams and his diary, Tulane Stud. Eng, 70; Charles Francis Adams: a forgotten family man of letters, J. Am. Stud, 72; plus others. Add: Dept. of English, Tulane University, New Orleans, LA 70118.

HARBOUR, CHARLES CLAYTON, b. Neshoba Co, Miss, May 14, 34; m. 58; c. 3. THEATRE HISTORY, DRAMATIC CRITICISM. B.A, Univ. Miss, 56, M.A, 59; Ph.D.(drama), Univ. Tex, Austin, 70. Grad. teaching asst. speech, Univ. Miss, 56-59; head dept, Panola Col, 59-63; from asst. prof. to ASSOC. PROF. & CHMN. DEPT. SPEECH & THEATRE, UNIV. MONTEVALLO, 63- Lectr, drama, Univ. Tex, Austin, 66-68; bk. rev. ed, South. Theatre, 5 years. Southeast. Theatre Conf.(exec. secy-treas, 72-74, v.pres, 74-75); AAUP; Am. Theatre Asn. Dramatic theory. Publ: Auth, numerous articles & bk. rev. for prof. jour; auth. & dir. numerous plays. Add: Dept. of Speech & Theatre, College of Fine Arts, University of Montevallo, Montevallo, AL 35115.

HARCOURT, JOHN BERTRAM, b. Providence, R.I, Oct. 20, 22; m. 50; c. 2. ENGLISH. A.B, Brown Univ, 43, M.A, 47, Ph.D.(Eng), 52. Instr. ENG, Brown Univ, 46-51; Cornell Univ, 51-53; asst. prof, ITHACA COL, 53-55, assoc. prof, 55-61, PROF, 61- Grant-in-aid, Finger Lakes Col. Ctr, 63. U.S.A, 43-46. MLA; Shakespeare Soc. Am. Shakespeare; English Renaissance literature. Publ: I pray you, remember the porter, Shakespeare Quart, 61. Add: Dept. of English, Ithaca College, Ithaca, NY 14850.

HARD, FREDERICK, b. Bessemer, Ala, Aug. 24, 98; m. 31; c. 2. ENGLISH LITERATURE. B.A, Univ. of the South, 22, D.C.L, 41; M.A, Univ. N.C, 24; Ph.D, Johns Hopkins Univ, 28; D.Litt, Occidental Col, 49; LL.D, Tulane Univ, 55. Instr. Eng, Univ. of the South, 22-23; music, Univ. N.C, 23-25; asst. Eng, Johns Hopkins Univ, 24-27; asst. prof, Tulane Univ, 27-31, assoc. prof, 31-38, prof. Eng. & Dean, Newcomb Col, 38-44; pres, SCRIPPS COL, 44-64, EMER. PROF. ENG. & EMER. PRES, 64- Provost, Claremont Col, 47-48, 53-55, 58-59, 63-64; fel, Huntington Libr, Calif, 36-37; mem. bd. of visitors, Tulane Univ, 54-; bd. of dir, Counc. Libr. Resources, Inc, 56-; mem. Am. Counc. Educ; Am. Counc. Learned Soc; Am. Sch. Class. Stud, Greece; West. Col. Asn; vis. prof, Eng, Univ. Pittsburgh, 64-65; fel, Folger Shakespeare Libr, 64-; prof. Univ. Calif, 64-, acting dean div. humanities, 66-67. U.S.A, 18, 2nd Lt. Asn. Am. Col; MLA; Eng-Speaking Union. Writing and reading English prose; English literature of the Renaissance. Publ: The sculptured scenes from Shakespeare, Cornell Univ, 59; ed, The elements of architecture, Univ. Va, 68. Add: 325 14th Ave, Santa Cruz, CA 95060.

HARDEN, EDGAR FREDERICK, b. Scranton, Pa, Feb. 10, 32. ENGLISH. A.B, Princeton, 53; A.M, Harvard, 58, fel, 59-60, Ph.D, 60. Instr. ENG, Oberlin Col, 60-62, asst. prof, 62-66, SIMON FRASER UNIV, 66-68, ASSOC. PROF, 68- Can. Counc. grant, 67-68, 69-70. Mil. Intel, U.S.A, 54-56. MLA. Victorian literature, especially novel; Henry James; William M. Thackeray. Publ: The fields of Mars in Vanity fair, Tenn. Stud. Lit, X: 123-132; The discipline and significance of form in Vanity fair, PMLA, LXXXII: 530-541; Esmond and the search for self, Yearbook Eng. Stud, III: 181-195; plus others. Add: Dept. of English, Simon Fraser University, Burnaby 2, B.C, Can.

HARDEN, ELIZABETH McWHORTER, b. Jamestown, Ky, Nov. 22, 35; m. 66. ENGLISH. B.A, West. Ky. State Univ, 56; M.A, Univ. Ark, 58, Ph.D.(Eng), 65. Asst, Univ. Ark, 56-57, 58-59, 61-63; instr. ENG, Southwest Mo. State Col, 57-58; Murray State Univ, 59-61; asst. prof, Northeast. State Col, 63-65; Wichita State Univ, 65-66; from asst. prof. to assoc. prof, WRIGHT STATE UNIV, 66-72, PROF, 72-, EXEC. DIR. GEN. UNIV. SERV, 74-, assoc. dean, Col. Lib. Arts, 73-74, asst. dean, 71-73. MLA; Midwest Mod. Lang. Asn; Col. Eng. Asn. English Romanticism; English novel; 17th century English literature to 1660. Publ: Maria Edgeworth's art of prose fiction, Mouton, The Hague, 71. Add: Dept. of English, Wright State University, Dayton, OH 45431.

HARDER, HENRY LOUIS, b. Van Buren, Ark, Oct. 8, 36; m. 60; c. 5. ENGLISH & AMERICAN LITERATURE. B.A, Subiaco Col, 58; M.A, Univ. Ark, 61; Ph.D.(Eng), Univ. Md, 70. Instr. ENG, U.S. Naval Acad, 65-69; asst. prof, Anne Arundel Community Col, 69-70; MO. SOUTH. STATE COL, 70-73, ASSOC. PROF, 73-, CHMN. DEPT. LANG. & LIT, 71- U.S.N, 60-69, Res, 69-71, Lt. Comdr. MLA; AAUP; Mod. Humanities Res. Asn; Medieval Acad. Am. Middle English literature; Gower; Chaucer. Add: Dept. of Language & Literature, Missouri Southern State College, Joplin, MO 64801.

HARDER, JAYNE CRANE, Applied Linguistics, English as a Second Language. See Volume III, Foreign Languages, Linguistics & Philology.

HARDER, KELSIE BROWN, b. Pope, Tenn, Aug. 23, 22; m. 60. ENGLISH. B.A, Vanderbilt Univ, 50, scholar, 50-51, M.A, 51; Ph.D.(Eng. ling), Univ. Fla, 54. Instr. ENG, Univ. Fla, 51-53; instr. 53-54; asst. prof, Youngstown Univ, 54-60, prof, 60-64; PROF. & CHMN. DEPT, STATE UNIV. N.Y. COL. POTSDAM, 64- Fulbright lectr. Am. lit, India, 62-63, Am. lit. & ling, Univ. Lodz, Poland, 71-72; consult, Random House Dictionary, 64; ed, Names, 65-; consult, NDEA Progs, Off. Educ, 66-67. C.Eng, U.S.A, 44-46. Am. Dialect Soc; Renaissance Soc. Am; Am. Name Soc. Literature; dialect; folklore. Publ: Studies in honor of Walter Clyde Curry, names, notes and queries, Publ. Am. Dialect Soc. Add: Dept. of English, State University of New York College at Potsdam, Potsdam, NY 13676.

HARDESTY, WILLIAM HOWARD, III, b. Chester, Pa, Sept. 8, 38; m. 63; c. 2. ENGLISH & AMERICAN LITERATURE. A.B, Univ. Pa, 59, A.M, 60, Ph.D. (Eng), 70. Instr. ENG, U.S. Naval Acad, 64-67; MIAMI UNIV, 69-70, ASST. PROF, 70- U.S.N, 61-67, Res, 68-, Lt. Comdr. MLA; NCTE; Midwest Mod. Lang. Asn; Conf. Col. Compos. & Commun. English fiction in transition, 1880-1922; Victorian poetry; 20th century fantasy and science fiction. Add: Dept. of English, 245 Upham Hall, Miami University, Oxford, OH 45056.

HARDIN, RICHARD F, b. Los Angeles, Calif, Nov. 9, 37; m. 59; c. 5. ENGLISH. B.A, St. Mary's Univ.(Tex), 59; M.A, Univ. Tex, 64, Ph.D.(Eng), 66. Teaching asst. ENG, Univ. Tex, 63-65; asst. prof, UNIV. KANS, 66-70, ASSOC. PROF, 70- U.S.A, 59-63, 1st Lt. MLA; Renaissance Soc. Am. English Renaissance literature. Publ: Michael Drayton and the passing of

Elizabethan England, Univ. Kans, 73; Convention and design in Drayton's Heroical epistles, PMLA, 3/68; Ovid in seventeenth century England, Comp. Lit, 1/72; Bunyan, Mr. Ignorance, and the Quakers Stud. Philol, 10/72. Add: Dept. of English, University of Kansas, Lawrence, KS 66044.

HARDING, CLYDE ALBERT, b. Pen Argyl, Pa, Mar. 30, 09; m. 38; c. 1. ENGLISH LITERATURE. A.B, Lehigh Univ, 31, A.M, 32; Columbia Univ, 33-37. Asst. instr, Lehigh Univ, 32-34, instr, 34-35; asst. prof. Eng, Albright Col, 37-48, assoc. prof, 48-63, prof, 63-74; RETIRED. Col. Eng. Asn; NCTE. American literature; 19th century English literature. Add: 1311 College Ave, Reading, PA 19604.

HARDING, HAROLD FRIEND, b. Niagara Falls, N.Y, July 30, 03; m. 35; c. 3. ENGLISH RHETORICAL THEORY. A.B, Hamilton Col, 25, hon. L.H.D, 62; A.M, Cornell Univ, 29, Ph.D, 37; Univ. London, 33. Instr. pub. speaking, Iowa State Col, 25-27; asst. Eng, Harvard, 28; instr. pub. speaking, Cornell Univ, 28-31; asst. prof, George Washington Univ, 31-38, assoc. prof, 38-44, prof, 44-46; Depew prof. speech & exec. off. dept, 46; prof. speech, Ohio State Univ, 46-66; Benedict prof, Univ. Tex, El Paso, 66-73; RETIRED. Rockefeller post-war fel, 46; ed, Quart. J. Speech, 48-51; consult, Battelle Mem. Inst, 60-; vis. prof, Univ. Calif, Santa Barbara, 65-66. U.S.A, 41-45, Res, 46-64, Maj. Gen; Bronze Star Medal, Legion of Merit & Oak Leaf Cluster. Speech Commun. Asn; Inst. Strategic Stud, Eng. English rhetorical theory in the 18th century; contemporary public address; rhetoric and politics. Publ: The age of danger, Random; co-ed, Source book for creative thinking, Scribner, 62; ed, Lectures on rhetoric and belles lettres, South. Ill. Univ, 65; The speeches of Thucydides, Coronado, 73; plus others. Add: 60 Sutton Pl, El Paso, TX 79912.

HARDING, WALTER, b. Bridgewater, Mass, Apr. 20, 17; m. 47; c. 4. ENGLISH. B.S, Bridgewater Teachers Col, 39; M.A, Univ. N.C, 47; Ph.D. (Eng), Rutgers Univ, 50. Instr. ENG, Rutgers Univ, 47-51, asst. prof, 51; Univ. Va, 51-56; assoc. prof, STATE UNIV. N.Y. COL. GENESEO, 56-59, prof, 59-65, univ. prof, 66-73, DISTINGUISHED PROF, 73-, chmn. dept. Eng, 59-65, chmn. div. humanities, 65-66. Am. Counc. Learned Soc. fel, 62-63; mem, Am. Lit. Group, MLA; Am. Specialists Prog. lectr, U.S. Dept. State, Japan, 64, Europe, 67; ed-in-chief, The Thoreau Edition, MLA, 66-72. Civilian pub. serv, 42-46. MLA; Thoreau Soc.(secy, 41-, pres, 63); AAUP. Transcendentalism; Thoreau. Publ: Thoreau: a century of criticism, South. Methodist Univ, 54; Ellis's essay on transcendentalism, 54, Alcott's essays in education, 60 & The collected poems of W. Ellery Channing, 67, Scholars' Facsimiles; co-auth, Correspondence of Henry David Thoreau, 58 & auth, A Thoreau handbook, 59, N.Y. Univ; Thoreau profile, Crowell, 62; The variorum Walden, 63 & The variorum civil disobedience, 67, Twayne; The days of Henry Thoreau, Knopf, 65; Emerson's library, Univ. Va, 67; Henry David Thoreau: a profile, Hill & Wang, 71; co-auth, A bibliography of Thorean Society Bulletin bibliographies, Whitston, 71. Add: Box 115, Groveland, NY 14462.

HARDISON, OSBORNE BENNETT, JR, b. San Diego, Calif, Oct. 22, 28; m. 50; c. 6. ENGLISH. B.A. & M.A, Univ. N.C, 50; Fulbright fel, Univ. Rome, 53-54; Ph.D, Univ. Wis, 56. Asst. ENG, Univ. Wis, 50-53; instr, Univ. Tenn, 54-56; Princeton, 56-57; asst. prof, Univ. N.C, 57-61, assoc. prof, 61-63, prof, 63-69; DIR. FOLGER SHAKESPEARE LIBR, 69- Folger Libr. fel, summer 58; Guggenheim fel, 63-64; chmn, Southeast. Inst. Medieval & Renaissance Stud, 65-66, co-chmn, 69-70; ser. ed, Goldentree Bibliographies, Appleton-Century-Crofts, 66- & Crofts Classics, 67-; ed, Stud. Philol, 67-69; mem, exec. counc, MLA, 68-71. Charles Homer Haskins Gold medal, Mediaeval Acad. Am, 67. MLA; S.Atlantic Mod. Lang. Asn; Renaissance Soc. Am. Renaissance literature; literary criticism; history of criticism. Publ: The enduring monument: the idea of praise in Renaissance literary theory and practice, Univ. N.C, 62; ed, Modern continental literary criticism, 62, ed, Literary criticism: the Renaissance, 63 & auth, Practical rhetoric, 66, Appleton; co-ed, The encyclopedia of poetry and poetics, Princeton Univ, 65; auth, Christian rite and Christian drama in the Middle Ages, 65 & Toward freedom and dignity, 73, John Hopkins; co-auth, Aristotle's poetics: translation and commentary, Prentice-Hall, 68; auth, The quest for imagination, Case West. Reserve Univ, 71. Add: Office of the Director, Folger Shakespeare Library, 201 E. Capitol St, Washington, DC 20003.

HARDMAN, BENEDICT EDWARD, b. Lake Andes, S.Dak, June 29, 09; m. 42. SPEECH, ENGLISH. A.B, Dartmouth Col, 31; M.A, Univ. Minn, 35, Ph.D. (commun, ling), 68. News dir, Iowa Network, Des Moines, 35-37; newscaster, KOMO-KJR, Seattle, Wash, 37-39; news dir, KOB, Albuquerque, N.Mex, 39-43; news writer, Blue Network, Hollywood, Calif, 43-44; newscaster-analyst, CBS-Network, Hollywood, 44-46; ASSOC. PROF. SPEECH, COL. ST. CATHERINE, 62- Fel, Univ. Minn, 71-72. Int. Commun. Asn. Communication, interpersonal and mass. Publ: Everybody called him Cedric, Serendipity, 70; Oral reading and speaking techniques for mass lectors and commentators, Liturgical, 66. Add: Dept. of Speech & Theatre, College of St. Catherine, 2004 Randolph Ave, St. Paul, MN 55105.

HARDMAN, MARION PAYZANT, b. Chemainus, B.C, Nov. 15, 08; U.S. citizen; m. 37; c. 1. ENGLISH. B.A, Univ. Wash, 29; fel, Univ. Mont, 29-30, M.A, 31; Ph.D.(Eng), Univ. Minn, Minneapolis, 39. Asst. prof. Eng, N.Mex. State Univ, 36-37; prof. & head dept, Colo. Woman's Col, 39-40; asst. prof, N.MEX. STATE UNIV, 41-45, assoc. prof. & dean women, 42-50, PROF. ENG, 50- Add: Box 3115, University Park Branch, Las Cruces, NM 88003.

HARDT, HANNO, b. Stettin, Ger, Dec. 4, 34; m. 60; c. 3. COMMUNICATION. M.A, South. Ill. Univ, Carbondale, 63, Ph.D.(mass commun), 67. Instr. MASS COMMUN, South. Ill. Univ, 63-65; asst. prof, Univ. N.Dak, 65-68; UNIV. IOWA, 68-69, ASSOC. PROF, 69- Prof, Inst. Jour, Univ. Münster, 73; lectr, Grinnell Col, 73- Int. Commun. Asn; Deut. Ges. Publizistik & Kommunikationswiss. Legal and ethical problems of communication; problems of cross-cultural communication. Publ: Contrib, Approaches to human communication, Spartan Bks, 72 & Communication and the human condition, Romargraf, Barcelona, 72; auth, The dilemma of mass communication: an existential point of view, Philos. & Rhet, 72. Add: School of Journalism, University of Iowa, Iowa City, IA 52240.

HARDWICK, MARY RUTH, b. Cherokee, Iowa, Apr. 8, 29. THEATRE, SPEECH COMMUNICATION. B.A, Okla. State Univ, 51; M.F.A, Ohio Univ, 56; Union Theol. Sem, 60-62; Ph.D.(theatre), Mich. State Univ, 68. Instr. speech & theatre, All Saints' Episcopal Col, 51-54; asst, Ohio Univ, 54-56; chmn. speech, Colby Jr. Col, 56-57; teacher & dir, Pittsburgh Playhouse, 57-60; creator & dir. fine arts prog, First Presby. Church, 60-64; asst. speech & theatre, Mich. State Univ, 64-67; ASSOC. PROF. SPEECH COMMUN. & THEATRE, CLARION STATE COL, 67- Speech Commun. Asn; Am. Theatre Asn. Oral interpretation of literature; ensemble acting techniques. Add: Dept. of Speech Communication & Theatre, 163 Marwick-Boyd Fine Arts Center, Clarion State College, Clarion, PA 16214.

HARDY, GENE BENNETT, b. Oklahoma City, Okla, Aug. 10, 26; m. 45; c. 2. ENGLISH LITERATURE. B.A, Univ. Okla, 47, M.A, 49; Ph.D, Univ. Ill, 55. Instr. ENG, UNIV. NEBR, LINCOLN, 52-55, asst. prof, 55-63, assoc. prof, 63-68, PROF, 68-, asst. dean arts & sci, 63-67. Consult. & mem. bd. dir, Nebr. Curriculum Ctr. in Eng, Dept. Health, Educ. & Welfare; coord, tri-univ. proj. elem. educ, U.S. Off. Educ. proj. at Univ. Nebr, Univ. Wash. & N.Y. Univ, 68-70, dir, training teacher trainers proj. elem. educ, 70-72. NCTE. Criticism of children's literature. Add: 212 Andrews Hall, University of Nebraska, Lincoln, NE 68508.

HARDY, JOHN EDWARD, b. Baton Rouge, La, Apr. 3, 22; m. 42, 69; c. 6. ENGLISH & AMERICAN LITERATURE. B.A, La. State Univ, 44; M.A, State Univ. Iowa, 46; Ph.D, Johns Hopkins Univ, 56. Instr. English, Univ. Detroit, 45-46; Yale, 46-48; Univ. Okla, 48-52; instr. writing, Johns Hopkins Univ, 52-54; asst. prof. ENG, Univ. Notre Dame, 54-57, assoc. prof, 57-64, prof, 64-66, dir. grad. stud, 65-66; prof. & head dept, Univ. S.Ala, 66-69; prof. & chmn. dept, Univ. Mo-St. Louis, 70-72; PROF. & COORD. GRAD. STUD, UNIV. ILL, CHICAGO CIRCLE, 72- Ford Found. Fund Advan. Educ. fac. stud. fel, 52-53; Sewanee Rev. fel. poetry, 54; Fulbright prof. Am. lit, Am. Inst, Univ. Munich, 59-61; vis. prof. Eng, Univ. Colo, 69-70. MLA. Poetry; literary criticism; modern fiction. Publ: Co-auth, Poems of Mr. John Milton, Harcourt, 51; auth, Certain poems, Macmillan, 58; The curious frame, Univ. Notre Dame, 62; Man in the modern novel, Univ. Wash, 64; ed, The modern talent—an anthology of short stories, Holt, 64 & Images of the Negro in American literature, Univ. Chicago, 66; auth, Katherine Anne Porter, Ungar, 73. Add: Dept. of English, University of Illinois at Chicago Circle, Chicago, IL 60680.

HARGIS, DONALD ERWIN, b. St. Paul, Minn, Aug. 25, 13. SPEECH. A.B, Univ. Calif, 34; A.M, Univ. Minn, 36; Ph.D, Univ. Mich, 43. Instr. SPEECH, Univ. Ore, 36-41; asst. prof, Univ. Mich, 43-47; assoc. prof, UNIV. CALIF, LOS ANGELES, 47-73, PROF, 73- Ed, West. Speech, 56-60. Speech Commun. Asn; West. Speech Asn.(v.pres, 39). Phonetics and interpretation; early California public address; theory of interpretation. Add: Dept. of Speech, University of California, Los Angeles, CA 90024.

HARGRAVE, HARRY A, b. Nashville, Tenn, June 11, 30. ENGLISH. B.A, Vanderbilt Univ, 54, M.A.T, 55, Ph.D.(Eng), 66. Asst. prof. ENG, N.C. STATE UNIV, 60-72, ASSOC. PROF, 72- U.S.M.C, 50-51, Sgt. S.Atlantic Mod. Lang. Asn; Southeast Renaissance Asn; MLA; Victorians Inst.(secy, 71-74). Victorian and Romantic period; film criticism. Publ: Kind hearts and coronets: Dickens and Tennyson, Victorians Inst. J, 7/71; A man: a story, fall 71 & Brief December day, winter 74, South. Humanities Rev. Add: Dept. of English, North Carolina State University, Raleigh, NC 27607.

HARGREAVES, H.A, b. Mt. Vernon, N.Y, Sept. 8, 28; m. 61; c. 3. ENGLISH. B.A, Mt. Allison Univ, 53, M.A, 56; univ. fel, Duke Univ, 57-58, fel, 58-59, Ph.D.(Eng), 60. Lectr. ENG, Mt. Allison Univ, 55-56; instr, Univ. Saskatchewan, 60-63; asst. prof, UNIV. ALTA, 63-68, ASSOC. PROF, 68- U.S.N, 46-49, Res, 49-53. Fel. Royal Commonwealth Soc; Humanities Asn. Can; Asn. Can. Univ. Teachers Eng. Restoration literature; Shakespeare; British drama. Publ: Swinburne's Greek plays and God The supreme evil, Mod. Lang. Notes, 61; New evidence of the realism of Mrs. Behn's Oroonoko, Bull. N.Y. Pub. Libr, 70; Visual contradiction in King Lear, Shakespeare Quart, 70; plus five others. Add: Dept. of English, University of Alberta, Edmonton, Alta, T6G 2G2, Can.

HARGREAVES-MAWDSLEY, WILLIAM NORMAN, History. See Volume I, History.

HARING, LEE, b. New York, N.Y, June 30, 30. FOLKLORE. A.B, Haverford Col, 51; A.M, Columbia Univ, 52, Ph.D, 61. Asst. prof. ENG, Guilford Col, 53-56; lectr, BROOKLYN COL, 57-61, instr, 61-66, asst. prof, 66-72, ASSOC. PROF, 72- Lectr. speech, Greensboro Col, 55-56; Eng, City Col. New York, 56; admin. secy, African Prog, Friends World Inst, 67-69. Am. Folklore Soc; Soc. Ethnomusicol; Int. Folk Music Counc. African folk narrative; American folklore and folk narrative. Publ: Ed, Treasure chest of American folk song, 61 & Folk banjo styles, 62, Elektra Records; auth, The gypsy laddie, Hargail Music Press, 62; ed, Folk songs for guitar, Novello, 64; A college course in the ballad, N.Y. Folklore Quart, 67; Performing for the interviewer, South. Folklore Quart, 72; East African oral narrative, Res. African Lit, fall 72. Add: Dept. of English, Brooklyn College, Brooklyn, NY 11210.

HARKEY, JOSEPH HARRY, b. Wadesboro, N.C, June 21, 32; m. 60; c. 2. ENGLISH & AMERICAN LITERATURE. B.A, Univ. S.C, 57; M.A, Univ. Tenn, 59, Ph.D.(Eng), 67. Instr. & asst. prin. high sch, S.C, 58-59; asst. prof. ENG, N.Ga. Col, 61-62; Adirondack Community Col, 62-64; assoc. prof. & dean men, Frederick Col, 64-66; assoc. prof, VA. WESLEYAN COL, 66-69, PROF, 69-, CHMN. DIV. HUMANITIES, 70- Asst, Univ. Tenn, 57-58, teaching asst, 59-61. U.S.A, 51-54, Sgt; U.S.C.G.R, 59-, Lt. Comdr. NCTE; MLA; S.Atlantic Mod. Lang. Asn; AAUP; Poe Asn. Relationships of literatures in English and Spanish languages; American fiction; creative writing. Publ: Foreshadowing in The monkey's paw, Stud. Short Fiction, 69; On Fortunato's coughing in Poe's The cask of Amontillado, Poe Newslett, 70; Modern chivalry: the Don Quixote of the American Frontier, Early Am. Lit, 73. Add: 4404 Chelsea St, Virginia Beach, VA 23455.

HARKNESS, BRUCE, b. Beaver Dam, Wis, Apr. 16, 23; m. 43, 67; c. 6. ENGLISH LITERATURE. M.A, Univ. Chicago, 48, Carnegie fel, 49-50, Ph.D.(Eng), 50. Instr. Eng, Univ. Ill, 50-54, asst. prof, 54-58, assoc. prof, 58-61, prof, 61-63, exec. secy. dept, 58-63, dir. grad. students, 59-63; prof. ENG. & chmn. dept, South. Ill. Univ. Carbondale, 63-64; prof. & assoc. dean lib. arts, Univ. Ill, 64-66; PROF. & DEAN ARTS & SCI, KENT STATE UNIV, 66- Guggenheim fel, 57-58. U.S.A.A.F, 43-45. MLA; NCTE; Midwest Mod. Lang. Asn. Modern fiction, especially Joseph Conrad's novels; publishing practices of recent periods; critical theory. Publ: Ed, Conrad's heart of darkness, 60 & Conrad's the secret sharer, 62, Wadsworth; Secret of Secret sharer bared, Col. Eng, 65. Add: College of Arts & Sciences, Kent State University, Kent, OH 44242.

HARMAN, ROLAND NELSON, b. Washington, D.C, Sept. 8, 11. ENGLISH. A.B, Georgetown Univ, 33, M.A, 34; Ph.D.(Eng), Yale, 38. Asst. ENG, Yale, 37-38; instr, Brown Univ, 38-42, 47, asst. prof, 47-50; asst. prof. & acting chmn. dept, 50-52, ASSOC. PROF, GEORGETOWN UNIV, 52-, chmn. dept, 52-59. Lectr. jour, Cath. Univ. Am, summer 38. U.S.N.R, 42-46, Lt. Comdr. English Romantic movement; Byron; 20th century American novel. Add: 4474 Reservoir Rd, N.W, Washington, DC 20007.

HARMER, RUTH MULVEY, b. New York, N.Y, June 18, 19; m. 50; c. 1. ENGLISH. A.B, Barnard Col, 41; M.A, Columbia Univ, 42; Ph.D, Univ. South. Calif, 72. Instr. ENG, Univ. South. Calif, 53-60, lectr, 61, 63; from asst. to PROF, CALIF. STATE POLYTECH. UNIV, POMONA, 60- Lectr. Eng. & jour, Univ. Calif, Los Angeles, 52-59; summers, Mex. City Col, 58, 59, 60. NCTE. Nineteenth century English literature; modern novel; Mexican-English literary relationships and influences. Publ: Co-auth, Good food from Mexico, Barrows, 50, Crowell-Collier, 63; auth, The high cost of dying, Crowell-Collier, 63; Unfit for human consumption, Prentice-Hall, 71. Add: Dept. of English, California State Polytechnic University, Pomona, 3801 W. Temple Ave, Pomona, CA 91766.

HARMS, PAUL WILLIAM FREDERICK, b. Ambur, India, Dec. 24, 23; U.S. citizen; m. 50; c. 6. SPEECH, DRAMA. B.A, Concordia Sem, 45, B.D, 48, S.T.M, 54; Wash. Univ, summers 45; Univ. Minn, summers 46, 47; Portland State Univ, 53; Univ. Portland, 54; M.A, Northwest. Univ, 57, Ph.D.(rhetoric), 73. Instr. Eng, Concordia Col.(Minn), 45-47; minister, Grace Lutheran Church, Ashland, Ore, 49-52; asst. prof. ENG. & SPEECH, Concordia Col.(Ore), 52-56; ASSOC. PROF, CONCORDIA SR. COL, 56-, resident counsel, 56-65. Ashland, Ore. Jr. Chamber Commerce Man of Year Award, 51. Am. Personnel & Guidance Asn; Speech Commun. Asn; Lutheran Soc. Worship, Music & Arts. Theology; the arts. Publ: Spirit of power, 64 & co-auth, Portals of prayer, 73 Concordia; auth, The Gospel as preaching, In: The lively function of the Gospel, 66 & contrib, Concordia pulpit, 69, 70 & 72, Concordia; auth, The Gospel in Christian education, Lutheran Educ, 5/70; plus others. Add: 2 Coverdale Pl, Ft. Wayne, IN 46825.

HARNACK, ROBERT VICTOR, b. Milan, Italy, July 29, 27; U.S. citizen; m. 48. SPEECH. B.A, Iowa State Teachers Col, 50; M.A, Univ. Okla, 51; scholar, Northwest. Univ, 52-54, Ph.D.(speech), 54. Instr. speech, Univ. Okla, 51-52; asst. prof, Univ. Colo, 54-60, assoc. prof, 60-64; PROF. SPEECH & HEAD DEPT. SPEECH & THEATRE, UNIV. ILL, CHICAGO CIRCLE, 64- U.S.N, 45-46. Speech Commun. Asn; Nat. Soc. Stud. Commun. Group discussion; psychology of leadership; rhetoric. Publ: Co-auth, Group discussion: theory and technique, Appleton, 64; An experimental study of the effects of training in the recognition and formulation of goals upon intragroup cooperation, Speech Monogr; A study of the effect of an organized minority upon discussion group, J. Commun, 63. Add: Dept. of Speech & Theatre, University of Illinois at Chicago Circle, Chicago, IL 60680.

HARNER, JAMES LOWELL, b. Washington, Ind, Mar. 24, 46; m. 67. ENGLISH LITERATURE. B.S, Ind. State Univ, Terre Haute, 68; M.A, Univ. Ill, Urbana, 70, Ph.D.(Eng), 72. ASST. PROF. ENG, BOWLING GREEN STATE UNIV, 71- Asst. ed, 17th Century News, 73- MLA; Bibliog. Soc, Eng; Renaissance Eng. Text Soc; Oxford Bibliog. Soc. Nondramatic Renaissance literature; bibliography; textual criticism. Publ: Ed, Nicholas Rowe, The tragedy of Jane Shore, Scolar, 73; auth, Addendum to Wing: A letter to a freeholder, Library, 70; co-auth, Pope's annotations in his copy of Dryden's Comedies, histories, and operas, Restoration & 18th Century Theatre Res, 71; auth, Ex libris F.S. Ferguson: a checklist of the F.S. Ferguson collection of Scottish imprints and Scotica at the University of Illinois, Vol. I, In: Robert B. Downs Publication Fund series, Univ. Ill, 72. Add: Dept. of English, Bowling Green State University, Bowling Green, OH 43403.

HARNISH, FRANK JAMES, b. Lake Preston, S.Dak, Oct. 5, 21; m. 46; c. 3. DRAMA, SPEECH. B.A, Wayne State Univ, 47, M.A, Univ. S.Dak, 49; Univ. Minn, summers 51-55; Ind. Univ, 59-60. Instr. speech & drama, Eagle Grove Jr. Col, 47-48; tech. dir. theatre, Univ. S.Dak, 49-50; instr. speech & drama, Sheldon Jr. Col, 50-52; dir. speech activities, Elsworth Col, 52-54; asst. prof. speech & drama, West. Ill. Univ, 59-60; drama, North. Ill. Univ, 60-67; assoc. prof. & chmn. dept, East. N.Mex. Univ, 67-69; DIR. THEATRE, COL. LAKE COUNTY, 69- Tech. dir, Black Hills Playhouse, summer 49; archit. consult, Belfry Theatre, 65-66; consult, Woodstock Fine Arts Asn, 65-67. Nat. Freedoms Found. script award, 52; Region Eight Children's Theatre Conf. first place award, 63. U.S.A, 42-45, Qm.C, 45-46, Lt. Am. Theatre Asn; Speech Commun. Asn; Am. Fed. Teachers; AAUP. Speech and theatre education; community theatre organization; theatre plant design. Publ: History of Black Hills Playhouse, Speech Monogr, 8/50. Add: College of Lake County, 19351 Washington, Grayslake, IL 60030.

HARPER, GEORGE GRAHAM, JR, b. Grand Rapids, Mich, Jan. 11, 24; m. 48; c. 3. ENGLISH. B.A, Calvin Col, 49; Univ. Calif, Los Angeles, 43-44; M.A, Northwest. Univ, 51, Ph.D.(Eng), 59. Instr. ENG, CALVIN COL, 52-58, asst. prof, 58-59, assoc. prof, 59-63, PROF, 63-, CHMN. DEPT, 67- Calvin Col. Fac. Acad. Enrichment Fund Award, summers 63, 66. U.S.A, 43-46, 51, Sgt. MLA; Milton Soc. Am; Midwest Mod. Lang. Asn; Conf. Christianity & Lit. Life and work of Sir Edmund Gosse; Victorian criticism. Publ: An unpublished Thomas Hardy letter, Eng. Lang. Notes, 3/66. Add: Dept. of English, Calvin College, Grand Rapids, MI 49506.

HARPER, GEORGE MILLS, b. Linn Creek, Mo, Nov. 5, 14; m. 44; c. 2. ENGLISH. A.B, Culver-Stockton Col, 40; M.A, Univ. Fla, 47; Univ. Calif, 47-48; Ph.D.(Eng), Univ. N.C, 51. From instr. to assoc. prof. Eng, Univ. N.C, 50-59, prof, 59-66, chmn. dept, 62-66; chmn. dept. Eng, Univ. Fla, 66-69; univ. prof. & dean arts & sci, Va. Polytech. Inst, 69-70; PROF. ENG, FLA. STATE UNIV, 70-, chmn. dept, 70-73. Consult, U.S. Off. Educ, 67, 68 & 69. U.S.N, 42-46, Comdr. MLA; Int. Asn. Stud. Anglo-Irish Lit.(mem. adv. comt, 70-); Col. Eng. Asn.(2nd v.pres, 73-74, 1st v.pres, 74-75, pres, 75-76). William Butler Yeats and the Irish Renaissance; Platonism in the Romantic period. Publ: Neoplatonism of William Blake, Univ. N.C. & Oxford, 61; Yeats' quest for Eden, 65 & Yeats' return from exile, 74, Dolmen; co-auth, Selected writing of Thomas Taylor the platonist, Princeton, 69; Yeats' golden dawn, Macmillan, 74; plus many articles. Add: 407 Plantation Rd, Tallahassee, FL 32303.

HARPER, HOWARD M, JR, b. Wilkinsburg, Pa, Oct. 2, 30; m. 51; c. 3. ENGLISH. B.S, Slippery Rock State Teachers Col, 52; M.A, Pa. State Univ, 57, Ph.D.(Eng), 64. Asst. ENG, Pa. State Univ, 55-58, instr, 58-59; asst. prof, UNIV. N.C, CHAPEL HILL, 64-68, ASSOC. PROF, 68- U.S.N, 52-55, Res, 55-, Comdr. British and American fiction of the 20th century; film. Publ: Desperate Faith, Univ. N.C, Chapel Hill, 67; co-ed, The classic British novel, Univ. Ga, 72; auth, Trends in recent American fiction, Contemporary Lit, XII: 204-229. Add: Dept. of English, University of North Carolina at Chapel Hill, Chapel Hill, NC 27514.

HARPER, HUBERT HILL, JR, b. Mobile, Ala, Apr. 27, 28. CLASSICAL LANGUAGES, ENGLISH. B.A, Birmingham South. Col, 48; fel. & Ph.D.(Latin & Greek), Univ. N.C, Chapel Hill, 52. Instr. classics, Univ. Tenn, Knoxville, 52-53; asst. prof, Xavier Univ.(Ohio), 53-59; lectr, Exten. Ctr, UNIV. ALA, BIRMINGHAM, 61-63, asst. prof. CLASSICS.& ENG, 63-67, ASSOC. PROF, 67-, ASSOC. DEAN GRAD. SCH, 71- Latin consult, Int. Anat. Nomenclature Comt, 71-73; consult, Delphi Proj. Undergrad. Educ, Univ. Tex, Dallas, 73. Am. Philol. Asn; AAUP; MLA; Counc. Grad. Schs. U.S. Homeric studies; Greek tragedy. Publ: Translations of Horatian odes, Carolina Quart, 50; contrib, Catalogue of the Reynolds Historical Library, Univ. Ala, 69 & Nomina anatomica, Am. Asn. Anat, 72. Add: Graduate School, University of Alabama in Birmingham, University Station, Birmingham, AL 35294.

HARPER, KATHLEEN, b. Parkstone, Eng, July 2, 13; Can. citizen. ENGLISH LITERATURE. Dipl. Ger, Univ. Hamburg, 34; B.A, Univ. London, 49; M.A, Bishop's Univ, 51; Ph.D.(Eng), Univ. Montreal, 55. Prin, Sutton High Sch, P.Q, 50-59; Sunnyside High Sch, Rock Island, 59-63; Asst. prof. ENG, BISHOP'S UNIV, 63-67, assoc. prof, 67-70, PROF, 70-, CHMN. DIV. HUMANITIES, 72-, chmn. dept. Eng, 70-72. Fel. Can. Col. Teachers. Old and Middle English literature. Add: Dept. of English, Bishop's University, Lennoxville, P.Q. Z0B 1Z0, Can.

HARPER, PRESTON FRANK, b. Austin, Tex, May 22, 36; m. 58; c. 2. AMERICAN LITERATURE. B.A, Abilene Christian Col, 59; M.A, Univ. Tex, 62; Ph.D.(Eng), Tex. Christian Univ, 72. ASSOC. PROF. ENG, ABILENE CHRISTIAN COL, 65- U.S.A, 54-57. MLA. American novel. Add: Dept. of English, Abilene Christian College, Abilene, TX 79601.

HARPER, ROBERT DONALD, b. Grand Junction, Colo, July 6, 13; m. 42. ENGLISH. A.B, Univ. Denver, 35; A.M, Univ. Chicago, 39, Ph.D, 49. Instr. ENG, Mich. Col. Mining & Tech, 40-42; Univ. Chicago, 46-48; asst. prof, UNIV. NEBR. AT OMAHA, 48-51, assoc. prof, 51-57, PROF, 57-, dean col. lib. arts, 60-72. U.S.N.R, 42-46, Lt. MLA; NCTE; Am. Stud. Asn; West. Hist. Asn; West. Lit. Asn. American literature; drama and theatrical history; Western literary history. Add: Dept. of English, University of Nebraska at Omaha, Omaha, NE 68101.

HARRELL, ROBERT BRUCE, b. Eastland, Tex, Mar. 12, 30; m. 55; c. 2. VICTORIAN & ROMANTIC LITERATURE. B.A, N.Tex. State Univ, 52, M.A, 56; Ph.D.(Eng), Univ. Tex, 66. ASST. PROF. VICTORIAN LIT, SOUTH. ILL. UNIV, CARBONDALE, 64- U.S.A.F, 51-53. MLA; Midwest Mod. Lang. Asn. Victorian novel; modern British novel; novel of the Romantic period. Add: Dept. of English, Southern Illinois University, Carbondale, IL 62901.

HARRIER, RICHARD CHARLES, b. Allentown, Pa, July 31, 23; m. 47. ENGLISH. A.B, Muhlenberg Col, 47; M.A, Harvard, 48, Ph.D.(Eng), 52. Instr. ENG, Colby Col, 52-55, asst. prof, 55-56; vis. lectr, Wellesley Col, 56-57; asst. prof, N.Y. UNIV, 57-62, assoc. prof, 62-74, PROF, 74-, CHMN. DEPT, WASH. SQ. COL, 63- Dexter traveling fel. from Harvard, Eng, 52; Am. Philos. Soc. grant, 54; Folger Libr. reader, 56; ed, Stud. Renaissance, 67-; Furness lectr. Shakespeare, 74. U.S.A, 43-46. MLA; Shakespeare Asn. Am; Renaissance Soc. Am; Malone Soc; Early Eng. Text Soc. Tudor lyric poetry; English literary manuscripts, 1500-1600; Shakespeare and Tudor and Jacobean drama. Publ: Ed, The anchor anthology of Jacobean drama, 2 vols, Doubleday, 63, Norton, 68. Add: Dept. of English, New York University, New York, NY 10003.

HARRIGAN, WILLIAM PATRICK, III, b. New Orleans, La, Aug. 2, 34; m. 58; c. 3. THEATRE. B.S, Loyola Univ.(La), 57; M.F.A, Tulane Univ, 60; Ph.D.(speech-theatre), La. State Univ, 72. Instr. theatre & speech, Lamar State Col. Technol, 60-62; La. State Univ, New Orleans, 62-66, Loyola Univ.(La), 67-68; speech, St. Bernard Jr. Col, 68-69; ASST. PROF. THEATRE & SPEECH, LAMAR UNIV, 69- Am. Theatre Asn; Children's Theatre Asn; Am. Commun. Theatre Asn. History of theatre in southwest; theatre for and of handicapped; oral interpretation of literature. Add: Dept. of Speech, Lamar University, Box 10050, Beaumont, TX 77710.

HARRIMAN, RICHARD, b. Independence, Mo, Sept. 10, 32. ENGLISH. A.B, William Jewell Col, 53; Woodrow Wilson fel, Stanford Univ, 57-58, M.A, 59; Oxford, 63. Instr. ENG, Univ. Dubuque, 60-61, asst. prof, 61-62, WILLIAM JEWELL COL, 62-65, ASSOC. PROF, 65-, acting chmn. dept, 65-69, dir. fine arts prog, 65-; coordinator humanities prog, 65-70. U.S.A, 53-55. MLA; NCTE; Am. Shakespeare Asn; Asn. Col. & Univ. Concert Mgr. Modern American drama; Shakespeare. Add: Dept. of English, William Jewell College, Liberty, MO 64068.

HARRINGTON, DAVID VAN, b. Plainview, Minn, Oct. 29, 29; m. 57; c. 3. ENGLISH. B.A, East. Wash. State Col, 51; M.A, Wash. State Univ, 56; Ph.D, Univ. Wis, 60. Asst. prof. ENG, GUSTAVUS ADOLPHUS COL, 60-65, assoc. prof, 65-68, PROF, 68-, CHMN. DEPT, 70- U.S.A, 51-54. MLA; Dante Soc. Am. Theory of composition; medieval and Renaissance literature; aesthetics. Publ: Benedetto Croce's Dante criticism, West. Humanities Rev, winter 65; Teaching students the art of discovery, Col. Compos. & Commun, 2/68; Narrative speed in the Pardoner's tale, Chaucer Rev, 68; plus others. Add: Dept. of English, Gustavus Adolphus College, St. Peter, MN 56082.

HARRINGTON, DONAL FRANCIS, b. Butte, Mont, Dec. 29, 05. DRAMA. A.B, Univ. Mont, 28; A.M, Columbia Univ, 33. Instr. Univ. Mont, 36-38; from assoc. prof. to prof. drama, UNIV. WASH, 38-73, EMER. PROF, 73- Shakespearean productions in San Francisco stage 1850 through 1855. Add: 4141 Brooklyn N.E, Apt. 307, Seattle, WA 98105.

HARRINGTON, ELBERT WELLINGTON, b. DeMotte, Ind, Jan. 27, 01; m. 29; c. 2. SPEECH. A.B, Iowa State Teachers Col, 26; A.M, State Univ. Iowa, 30, Ph.D, 38. Teacher, Cedar Falls High Sch, Iowa, 26-28; instr, Wis. State Teachers Col, River Falls, 30-31; prof. & dean men, N.Dak. State Teachers Col, Mayville, 31-36; asst. prof. SPEECH, Univ. Col, 37-45; prof, UNIV. S.DAK, VERMILLION, 45-72, head dept, 45-55, dean col. arts & sci, 48-67, EMER. PROF. & EMER. DEAN, 72- Vis. prof. rhetoric & public address, Univ. Nebr, Lincoln, 73. NEA; Speech Commun. Asn; Cent. States Speech Asn. Rhetoric and public address. Publ: Albert Baird Cummins: an analysis of a logical speaker, Univ. Mo, 61; Janus on the campus: status of the liberal arts, Dakota Press, 72; Rhetoric and the scientific method of inquiry; Procrustes on the campus. Add: Dept. of Communication, University of South Dakota, Vermillion, SD 57069.

HARRINGTON, EVANS BURNHAM, b. Birmingham, Ala, Oct. 5, 25; m. 46; c. 1. ENGLISH. B.A, Miss. Col, 48; M.A, Univ. Miss, 51, Ph.D.(Eng), 68. Instr. ENG, UNIV. MISS, 55-60, asst. prof, 62-68, assoc. prof, 68-70, PROF, 70- U.S.N.R, 43-45. MLA. Modern literature, especially creative writing; the works of Thomas Beer and William Faulkner. Publ: The prisoners, Harper, 56; Technical aspects of That evening sun, Faulkner Stud, winter 51; Cooper's Prairie as wasteland, 63 & Sensuousness in the poetry of W.C. Bryant, 66, Univ. Miss. Stud. Eng. Add: Dept. of English, University of Mississippi, University, MS 38677.

HARRINGTON, HENRY R, b. Evanston, Ill, Dec. 23, 43; m. 68; c. 1. ENGLISH LITERATURE & THEOLOGY. A.B, Williams Col, 66; M.A, Stanford Univ, 68, Leverhulme fel, 69-70, Ph.D, 71. ASST. PROF. ENG, UNIV. MONT, 71- MLA; AAUP; Am. Acad. Relig. Victorian literature; contemporary theology and literature; novel. Publ: Childhood and the Victorian ideal of manliness, MLA Victorian Newslett, 10/73. Add: Dept. of English, University of Montana, Missoula, MT 59801.

HARRINGTON, JOHN FREDERICK, JR, b. Missoula, Mont, Sept. 21, 42; m. 65; c. 2. FILM, ENGLISH LITERATURE. B.A, Wash. State Univ, 64, M.A, 66; Ph.D.(Eng), Univ. Ill, Urbana, 70. ASST. PROF. ENG. & FILM, UNIV. MASS, AMHERST, 70-, DIR. FILM STUD, 74-, co-dir, 70-74. Consult, Mass Media Assocs, 72- MLA; NCTE. Film rhetoric; film and literature; 17th century English poetry. Publ: Ed, Male and female: identity, Wiley & Sons, 71; co-ed, Frames of reference, Kendall/Hunt, 72; auth, The rhetoric of film, Holt, 73. Add: Dept. of English, University of Massachusetts, Amherst, MA 01002.

HARRINGTON, NORMAN T, b. Denver, Colo, May 6, 26; m. 60; c. 1. ENGLISH. A.B, Hobart Col, 48; A.M, Harvard, 52, Ph.D.(Eng), 60. Instr. Eng, Hobart Col, 50-52, teaching fel. gen. educ, Harvard, 54-56; instr. ENG, Miami Univ, 57-58; Northwest. Univ, 58-60; asst. prof, BROOKLYN COL, 60-72, ASSOC. PROF, 72- U.S.N.R, 44-46. MLA; Renaissance Soc. Am. Medieval and Renaissance literature. Publ: Co-auth, Ywain and Gawain: a critical edition, Oxford & Early Eng. Text Soc, 64. Add: Dept. of English, Brooklyn College, Brooklyn, NY 11210.

HARRIS, ARTHUR JOHN, b. Chicago, Ill, Mar. 6, 29. ENGLISH. B.S, Cent. Mich. Univ, 51; Ford Found. fel, Shakespeare Inst, 54-55; M.A, Univ. Birmingham, 59, Ph.D.(Eng), 66. Instr. ENG, Cent. Mich. Univ, 59-61; Univ. Mich, 63-66, asst. prof, 66-67; EAST. MICH. UNIV, 67-71, ASSOC. PROF, 71- MLA; Renaissance Soc. Am; Shakespeare Asn. Am. Shakespeare; theatre history; Renaissance literature. Publ: William Poel's Elizabethan stage: the first experiment, Theatre Notebk, summer 63. Add: Dept. of English, Eastern Michigan University, Ypsilanti, MI 48197.

HARRIS, BENNETT, b. Ft. Worth, Tex, Apr. 26, 21; m. 42; c. 1. ENGLISH. A.B, Univ. Cincinnati, 49, M.A, 50, Ph.D.(Eng), 62; Johns Hopkins Univ, 51-53. Instr. ENG, Episcopal Acad, Pa, 53-55; Wayne State Univ, 55-57; asst. prof. Berea Col, 60-64; PROF, KUTZTOWN STATE COL, 64-, dean arts & sci, 68-72. U.S.A.A.F, 42-44, 1st Lt. MLA; NCTE. Works of Herman Melville; works of D.H. Lawrence; John P. Marquand and New England culture. Add: Dept. of English, Kutztown State College, Kutztown, PA 19530.

HARRIS, BRICE, b. Troy, Tenn, Aug. 20, 00; m. 26; c. 1. ENGLISH. A.B, Erskine Col, 21; A.M, Vanderbilt Univ, 25; Ph.D, Harvard, 32. Instr. Eng, Clemson Univ, 23-24; asst. prof, The Citadel, 26-27; asst, Univ. Wis, 27-28; instr, Cornell Univ, 30-37; from instr. to assoc. prof, Univ. Ill, 37-47; prof. Eng. lit, Pa. State Univ, 47-62, head dept, 47-57; prof. ENG, ARIZ. STATE UNIV, 62-71, EMER. PROF, 71- Am. Counc. Learned Soc. grant-in-aid, 34; res. fel, Huntington Libr, Calif, 36-37; vis. prof, N.Mex. Highlands Univ, summer 41; Ohio State Univ, summer 47; Smith-Mundt vis. prof. Am. Stud, Univ. Zaragoza, Spain, 57; vis. prof, Alaska Methodist Univ, summer 65; NDEA Inst, Anchorage, summer 66. NCTE (v.pres, 57, pres, 58); MLA; Col. Eng. Asn. The profession of letters, publishing and printing; 17th century English literature, particularly patronage; Aesopian literature in 17th century England. Publ: Charles Sackville, Earl of Dorset; ed, Eight famous plays of the Restoration; Beggars ape. Add: 1020 E. Laguna Dr, Tempe, AZ 85282.

HARRIS, CHARLES BURT, b. LaGrange, Tex, Nov. 2, 40; m. 68; c. 2. AMERICAN LITERATURE. A.B, Tex. Lutheran Col, 63; M.A, South. Ill. Univ, 65, Ph.D.(Eng), 70. Instr. ENG, South. Ill. Univ, 66-68; asst. prof, ILL. STATE UNIV, 68-72, ASSOC. PROF, 72- MLA; Midwest Mod. Lang. Asn; Col. Eng. Asn. Twentieth century American literature; the novel; recent American fiction. Publ: Contrib, Seize the day, 69 & Phineas: six stories, 70, Creative Approaches to Reading Lit; auth, Contemporary American novelists of the absurd, Col. & Univ. Press, 71; The recent American novel, CEA Critic, 5/73. Add: Dept. of English, Illinois State University, Normal, IL 61761.

HARRIS, CHARLES NEWTON, b. Cabool, Mo, Jan. 15, 02. SPEECH. B.S, Univ. Idaho, 40; Univ. Wash, 35; A.M, Colo. State Col, 45, Ed.D, 60; Univ. Ore. Med. Sch, 61. Teacher high sch. & jr. high sch, Idaho, 37-45; jr. high sch, Ore, 45-46; high sch, Wash, 46; asst. prof. SPEECH, ORE. STATE UNIV, 46-63, prof, 63-72, co-dir. speech therapy, 56-72, EMER. PROF, 72- Lectureship, Exec. Secy. Asn. Ore, 62-63. Am. Speech & Hearing Asn. Comparing methods of therapy in speech correction. Publ: God paints the dawn, Belwin, 51; A rendezvous of love, Review & Herald, 54; Reminiscence of a hard climb, In: Improving college and university teaching, Ore. State Univ, 63. Add: Dept. of Speech, Oregon State University, Corvallis, OR 97331.

HARRIS, DUNCAN SEELY, b. Worland, Wyo, Feb. 22, 44; m. 66; c. 2. ENGLISH & AMERICAN LITERATURE. B.A, Stanford Univ, 65; M.A, Boston Univ, 66; Ph.D.(Eng. lit), Brandeis Univ, 73. Instr. ENG, Tougaloo Col, 69; UNIV. WYO, 70-72, ASST. PROF, 72- MLA. Nineteenth century American literature; Shakespeare; allegory. Add: Dept. of English, University of Wyoming, Box 3353, University Station, Laramie, WY 82071.

HARRIS, HAROLD JOEL, b. Paterson, N.J, Dec. 15, 24; m. 49; c. 3. ENGLISH. A.B, Rutgers Univ, 49, M.A, 50; Ph.D.(Eng), Ohio State Univ, 54. Asst. instr. ENG, Ohio State Univ, 53-54; instr, KALAMAZOO COL, 54-56, asst. prof, 56-61, assoc. prof, 61-65, PROF, 65- Consult, Kellogg Found. Latin Am. Orientation Prog, 67-69; vis. prof, Victorian novel, Mich. State Univ, 68-69; mod. Europ. lit, Inst. Am. Univ, Aix-en-Provence, 69; contrib. reviewer, Choice, 67- U.S.A, 43-46. MLA. English and European novel; literature of the English neo-classical period; Victorian literature. Publ: Lolita and the sly foreword, Mad River Rev, spring-summer 65; Literature the sociology of literature today, Art in Soc, fall-winter, 65; Reviews of books on Orwell, Koestler and Kipling, Mod. Fiction Stud, summer 70 & 73. Add: Dept. of English, Kalamazoo College, 1200 Academy St, Kalamazoo, MI 49007.

HARRIS, JESSE W, b. Saline Co, Ill, Sept. 25, 00; m. 28. ENGLISH. B.S, Univ. Ill, 27, M.A, 28, Ph.D, 35. Instr. ENG, Univ. Ill, 28-37; assoc. prof, Sul Ross State Col, 37-39; asst. prof, SOUTH. ILL. UNIV, 39-44, assoc. prof, 44-52, prof, 52-68, EMER. PROF, 68- Regional ed, Midwest Folklore, 53-57. MLA; Renaissance Soc. Am; Am. Folklore Soc. Publ: John Bale, a study in the minor writings of the reformation, Univ. Ill, 40; co-auth, A handbook in English, Oxford, 44; Dialect of Appalachia in Southern Illinois, Am. Speech, 4/46. Add: 402 S. Forest, Carbondale, IL 62901.

HARRIS, JOSEPH CLARENCE, English & Icelandic Medieval Literature. See Volume III, Foreign Languages, Linguistics & Philology.

HARRIS, KATHRYN MONTGOMERY, English. See HUNTER, KATHRYN MONTGOMERY.

HARRIS, MARK, b. Mt. Vernon, N.Y, Nov. 19, 22; m. 46; c. 3. LANGUAGE ARTS. B.A, Univ. Denver, 50, M.A, 51; Ph.D.(Am. stud), Univ. Minn, 56. Mem. fac, Univ. Minn, 51-54; assoc. prof. ENG, San Francisco State Col, 54-68; PROF, Purdue Univ, 68-70; Calif. Inst. Arts, 70-73; IMMACULATE HEART COL, 73- Fulbright prof, Univ. Hiroshima 57-58; Ford Found. grant, 60; mem. San Francisco Art Comn, 61; vis. prof, Brandeis Univ, 63; U.S. deleg, Dartmouth Conf, Japan, 64; Guggenheim Mem. Found. grant, 65; Nat. Endowment for Arts grant, 66. Nat. Inst. Arts & Lett. Prize, 61. U.S.A, 43-44. Publ: Trumpet to the world, Reynal & Hitchcock, 46; City of discontent, Bobbs & Charter Bks, 52; The southpaw, Bobbs, 53 & Charter Bks, 63; Bang the drum slowly, Knopf & Anchor Bks, 56; A ticket for a seamstitch, Knopf, 57; Something about a soldier, Macmillian, U.S. & Deutsch, Eng, 57; Wake up, stupid, Knopf, U.S. & Deutsch, Eng, 59; Friedman & son (play), 63 & Mark the glove boy, 64, Macmillan; Twentyone twice: a journal, Little, 66; The Goy, 70 & Killing everybody, 73, Dial; Blau & Irving come out of the West, New York Times Mag, 11/21/65; Alan Swallow, 1915-1966, New York Times Bk. Rev, 12/18/66; The flowering of the hippies, Atlantic Monthly, 9/67; plus many others. Screenplay, Bang the drum slowly, Paramount, 73. Add: Immaculate Heart College, Los Angeles, CA 90027.

HARRIS, MARKHAM, b. New York, N.Y, Jan. 2, 07; m. 59; c. 4. CREATIVE WRITING, MEDIEVAL DRAMA. A.B, Williams Col, 29, M.A, 31; Columbia Univ, 34-35. Instr. Eng, Williams Col, 31-34; ed. & mgr, Grolier, Inc, 36-43; from instr. to PROF. ENG, UNIV. WASH, 46- U.S.N.R, 44-46, Lt. AAUP. Imaginative writing; medieval drama, Cornish. Publ: The case for tragedy, Putnam, 32, Russell, 73; High morning fog (novel), Lippincott, 52; transl, The Cornish Ordinalia, a medieval dramatic trilogy, 69 & The life of Meriasek, a medieval Cornish miracle play, (in press), Cath. Univ. Am; auth, Double-solitaire (novella), Story Mag, 39; A memory of Ford Madox Ford, Prairie Schooner, 55. Add: Dept. of English, University of Washington, Seattle, WA 98195.

HARRIS, PATRICIA HARN, b. Galesburg, Ill, May 20, 32; m. 55; c. 1. ENGLISH, ENGLISH LINGUISTICS. B.A, Pomona Col, 54; Bracher fel, Claremont Grad. Sch, 54-55; M.A, Univ. Mo-Columbia, 62, Ph.D.(Eng, ling), 69. LECTR. ENG. LING, UNIV. MO-COLUMBIA, 69- MLA; Am. Dialect Soc; AAUP. History of the study of grammars; changes occurring in present-day American English. Publ: Tag-questions, Trans. Mo. Acad. Sci, 73. Add: 202 W. Broadway, Columbia, MO 65201.

HARRIS, RICHARD M, Linguistics, Modern Indic Languages. See Volume III, Foreign Languages, Linguistics & Philology.

HARRIS, STEPHEN LeROY, b. Aberdeen, Wash, Feb. 5, 37; m. 65. ENGLISH, HUMANITIES. B.A, Univ. Puget Sound, 59; Woodrow Wilson fel, Cornell Univ, 60-61, M.A, 61, Ph.D.(Eng), 64. Acting cur-libr, Wash. State Hist. Soc, 63; asst. prof. Eng, Wash. State Univ, 64-65, CALIF. STATE UNIV, SACRAMENTO, 65-69, ASSOC. PROF, 69-72, HUMANITIES,

72-, CHMN. DEPT, 72- Classical Greek civilization; the English novel; relation between the Hellenic and the Judaeo-Christian traditions in later Western literature. Publ: The humanist tradition in world literature, Merrill, 70. Add: Dept. of Humanities, California State University, Sacramento, 6000 Jay St, Sacramento, CA 95819.

HARRIS, VICTOR, b. Newport News, Va, July 11, 10; m. 38; c. 2. ENGLISH LITERATURE. B.S, Univ. Va, 30, M.S, 32; Ph.D, Univ. Chicago, 45. Instr. Univ. Chicago, 39-45; asst. prof. Eng. State Univ. Iowa, 45-49, assoc. prof, 49-60, PROF, 60-61; ENG. & AM. LIT, BRANDEIS UNIV, 61-, CHMN. DEPT, 63- Fund Advan. Learning fel, 51-52; Huntington Libr. fel, 61. MLA. Publ: All coherence gone, Univ. Chicago, 49; co-auth, English prose, 1600-1660, Holt, 64. Add: Dept. of English, Brandeis University, Waltham, MA 02154.

HARRIS, WENDELL V, b. Oklahoma City, Okla, Jan. 8, 32; m. 54. ENGLISH. B.A, Univ. Okla, 54, M.A, 57; Ph.D.(Eng), Univ. Wis, 61. Instr. Eng, Univ. Colo, 61-62, asst. prof, 62-65, assoc. prof, 65-69, prof, 69-70; PROF. ENG. & ASSOC. PROVOST, NORTH. ILL. UNIV, 70- Fac. fel, Univ. Colo, 65. U.S.A, 55-57, 1st Lt. Short story; novel; Victorian thought. Publ: Arthur Hugh Clough, Twayne, 70; Pater as prophet, Criticism, fall 64; English short fiction in the 19th century, Stud. Short Fiction, fall 68; The shape of Coleridge's public system, Mod. Philol, 8/70. Add: Lowden 307, Northern Illinois University, DeKalb, IL 60115.

HARRIS, WILLIAM OLIVER, b. Ahoskie, N.C, Nov. 22, 23; m. 49; c. 2. ENGLISH. B.A, Wake Forest Col, 50; M.A, Univ. N.C, 52, Ph.D.(Eng), 57. Instr. ENG, Univ. Md, 55-57; Wake Forest Col, 57-58, asst. prof, 58-63; ASSOC. PROF, Univ. Ala, 63-65; UNIV. CALIF, RIVERSIDE, 65- Folger summer fels, 60-61; Huntington Libr. grant-in-aid, 67. U.S.M.C, 43-45, Master Tech. Sgt. MLA. English Renaissance drama; Elizabethan literature; bibliography. Publ: Skelton's Magnyfycence and the cardinal virtue tradition, Univ. N.C, 65; Despair and patience as the truest fortitude in Samson Agonistes, ELH, 63; Love that doth raine: Surrey's creative imagination, Mod. Philol, 69; Early Elizabethan sonnets in sequence, Stud. Philol, 71; plus two others. Add: Dept. of English, University of California, Riverside, CA 92502.

HARRIS, WILLIAM STYRON, JR, b. Elizabeth City, N.C, June 9, 36; m. 65. ENGLISH LITERATURE. B.A, Wake Forest Univ, 58; M.A, Duke Univ, 63; Ph.D.(Eng), 71. Teacher, ENG, N.C. Pub. Schs, 58-63; grad. tutor, Duke Univ, 64-68; instr, Univ. Va, 68-69; grad. tutor, Duke Univ, 70-71; ASST. PROF, E.TENN. STATE UNIV, 71- Coop. Prog. in Humanities scholar, 69-70. MLA; S.Atlantic Mod. Lang. Asn; Col. Eng. Asn; NCTE. Charles Kingsley; English literature of the 19th century; history of the English novel. Add: Dept. of English, East Tennessee State University, Johnson City, TN 37601.

HARRISON, A. CLEVELAND, b. McRae, Ark, Aug. 17, 24; m. 46; c. 2. THEATRE, SPEECH & DRAMA. B.S, Ohio State Univ, 49, M.A, 51; M.A, Univ. Ark, 58; Ph.D.(theatre, drama), Univ. Kans, 67. Instr. Speech & Eng, Little Rock Jr. Col, 49-50, speech & theatre, 51-57; asst. prof, Little Rock Univ, 58-59; Univ. Ark, 59-65, assoc. prof, 65-69, prof. theatre & oral interpretation & head dept, 69-70, coord. basic speech, 60-63, chmn. basic fine arts, 64-65, 68-69; PROF. THEATRE & HEAD DEPT, AUBURN UNIV, 70- Assoc. ed. drama, South. Speech Commun. J, 69- U.S.A, 43-46. Speech Commun. Asn; South. Speech Commun. Asn; Am. Theatre Asn; AAUP. Southeast. Theatre Conf. American drama and criticism of the 19th century; acting and directing. Publ: Co-auth, Principles of effective speaking, Braun-Brumfield, 63; auth, Basic lore of the lecture recital, Speech Teacher, 1/71; Experimental theatre labs in general education, J. Aesthetic Educ, 1/71; Of thee I sing, baby, Players, 9/72; plus others. Add: Dept. of Theatre, School of Architecture & Fine Arts, Auburn University, Samford Ave. at Duncan, Auburn, AL 36830.

HARRISON, CHARLES TRAWICK, b. Union Springs, Ala, July 23, 03. ENGLISH LITERATURE. A.B, Univ. Ala, 23; A.M, Harvard, 25, Ph.D, 32. Instr, Hobart Col, 25-27; asst. prof, Univ. Ala, 27-28; Boston Univ, 29-34; assoc. prof. Eng, Col. William & Mary, 34-38; prof, 38-47; UNIV. OF THE SOUTH, 47-52, from prof. & dean, Col. Arts & Sci. to JESSE SPALDING PROF. ENG. LIT, 52- Dexter traveling fel, Harvard, 32. Seventeenth century English thought. Add: Dept. of English, University of the South, Sewanee, TN 37375.

HARRISON, FRED C, b. Detroit, Mich, Oct. 30, 28; m. 51; c. 4. ENGLISH. B.A, Whittier Col, 52; M.A, Univ. Wash, 57, Ph.D.(Eng), 66. Instr. ENG, Whittier Col, 57-61; asst. prof, PORTLAND STATE UNIV, 62-72, ASSOC. PROF, 72-, dir. compos, 67-69. U.S.A, 46-48. MLA. Early American fiction. Publ: G.W. Greene and Dante, Italica, 3/66; Dante in America: a delayed arrival, Proc. Pac. Northwest Conf. For. Lang, XVI: 9-17. Add: P.O. Box 751, Portland State University, Portland, OR 97207.

HARRISON, HOWARD, b. New York, N.Y, Sept. 27, 30; div; c. 2. ENGLISH. B.S, City Col. New York, 51, M.A, 52. Instr. high schs, N.Y, 51-64; ASSOC. PROF. ENG, STATE UNIV. N.Y. COL. ONEONTA, 64-, dir. NDEA Inst. Eng, summer 65 & 67, resident dir. prog. in Israel, 70-71. Dir, Developmental Reading Inst. L.I, 56-; guest poet, WEVD Radio Prog, Nov, 59; dist. lang. arts consult, Long Beach City Sch. Dist, 61-62; consult, Catskill Area Sch. Stud. Counc, 65; gen. ed. for Premier Bks, Fawcett, 66-68, manuscript consult, 67-68; consult, Bainbridge, Davenport & New York Sch. Dist, 66. MLA; NCTE (dir, 68-, chmn. comt. on workload-70-s in sec. schs, 72-75); Asn. Jewish Stud. The writing of poetry and fiction. Publ: Basic facts of English grammar, 63, 65, Basic facts of English literature, 64, 66 & World literature, 67, Collier Bks; A solution to the power struggle: the teacher-centered school, Educ. Synopsis, winter 67-68; The turn to today in poetry: William Butler Yeats and Among school children, In: Costerus, Ed. Rodopi, Netherlands, 74. Add: 11 East St, Oneonta, NY 13820.

HARRISON, JAMES ERNEST, b. Trincomalee, Shri Lanka, Jan. 15, 27; Brit. citizen; m. 58; c. 4. ENGLISH LITERATURE, HISTORY OF SCIENCE. B.A, Univ. Durham, 51, M.Litt, 68. Lectr. ENG, Bournmouth Municipal Col, 56-59; prin. lectr, Shenstone Col. Educ, 59-69; asst. prof, UNIV. GUELPH, 69-72, ASSOC. PROF, 72- Nineteenth century English literature; evolutionary theory in relation to literature. Publ: Catchment area (poems), O.U.P, 59; ed, Scientists as writers, Methuen & MIT, 65; auth, Erasmus Darwin's view of evolution, J. Hist. of Ideas, 71; Tennyson and evolution, Durham Univ. J, 71; Tennyson and embryology, Humanities Asn. Bull, 72; plus others. Add: Dept. of English, University of Guelph, Guleph, Ont. N1G 2W1, Can.

HARRISON, JOHN FRANCIS, b. Liverpool, Eng, July 30, 18; U.S. citizen; m. 59; c. 2. ENGLISH AND COMPARATIVE LITERATURE. A.B, Columbia, 38; M.A, 40, Ph.D.(comp. lit), 52. Asst. Eng, Columbia Univ, 39-41, instr, Bethany Col,(W.Va), 41-42, Univ. Newark, 46; lectr, sch. gen. stud, Columbia Univ, 46-47, 48-50; copy editor, Current Digest Soviet Press, 50-52, consult, Asst. Secy. Defense, Manpower & Personnel, 52-54; PROF. ENG, TRANSYLVANIA UNIV, 54-, DEAN INSTR, 71-, chmn. dept, 54-71. Consult, Fund Advan. Educ, 52-54. U.S.A, 42-46, Res, 48-68, Maj. MLA; Col. Eng. Asn; NCTE. Comparative literature of the late 18th and early 19th centuries; English literature, 19th century; general humanities. Add: Office of the Dean of Instruction, Transylvania University, Lexington, KY 40508.

HARRISON, JOHN M, b. Oakland, Iowa, Feb. 20, 14; m. 41. JOURNALISM, AMERICAN HUMOR. B.A, Univ. Iowa, 34, M.A, 61; Nieman fel, Harvard, 51-52. Instr. JOUR, Univ. Iowa, 58-61; asst. prof, PA. STATE UNIV, 61-63, assoc. prof, 63-67, PROF, 67- Asn. Educ. in Jour; Am. Stud. Asn. American humor and satire, specifically, David Ross Locke, Finley Peter Dunne and Don Marquis; British Press Council. Publ: Co-auth, The articulates, Bobbs, 57; auth, The man who made Nasby, David Ross Locke, N.C. Univ, 69; co-auth, Mass media and the national experience, Harper, 71; co-ed, Muckraking: past, present and future, Pa. State Univ, 73; ed, American newspapermen, 1790-1933 (reprint ser), Beekman, 73. Add: 628 Fairway Rd, State College, PA 16801.

HARRISON, ROBERT LIGON, b. Wichita Falls, Tex, July 12, 32; m. 57. COMPARATIVE LITERATURE. A.B, Univ. Tex, 53, M.A, 60, Ph.D.(Eng), 64. Instr. Eng, Va. Polytech. Inst, 63-64; asst. prof, UNIV. GA, 64-68, ASSOC. PROF. COMP. LIT, 68- U.S.N.R, 53-57, Res, 57-67, Lt.(jg). Twentieth century comparative literature. Publ: Samuel Beckett's Murphy: a critical excursion, Univ. Ga, 68; co-ed, Masterworks of world literature (2 vols), 3rd ed, Holt, 70; auth, The song of Roland, New Am. Libr, 70; Gallic salt: eighteen fabliaux translated from the Old French, Univ. Calif, 74; Faulkner's The bear: some notes on form, Ga. Rev, fall 66; Donne's To the Countesse of Huntingdon, Explicator, 12/66; Erotic imagery in Crashaw's Mucicks duell, Seventeenth Century News, autumn 67. Add: Dept. of Comparative Literature, Park Hall, University of Georgia, Athens, GA 30601.

HARRISON, STANLEY R, b. Brooklyn, N.Y, Oct. 5, 27; m. 59; c. 4. ENGLISH B.A, Brooklyn Col, 49, M.A, 57; Ph.D.(Eng), Mich. State Univ, 64. Instr. ENG, Univ. R.I, 61-64; asst. prof, Tulane Univ, 64-67; assoc. prof, Va. Polytech. Inst, 67-69; writer-in-residence, Transylvania Col, 69-70; PROF, MANSFIELD STATE COL, 70- MLA; N.East Mod. Lang. Asn. American literature; drama; film. Publ: Machiavelli and the mandrake (play), Tulane Univ, 67; Edgar Fawcett, Twayne, 72; Mark Twain's requiem for the past, Mark Twain J, 71; Stephen Crane and death: a moment between two Romanticisms, Markham Rev, 71; Come with me to Nerja (short story), Cimarron Rev, 73; plus four others. Add: Dept. of English, Mansfield State College, Mansfield, PA 16933.

HARRISON, WILLIAM NEAL, b. Dallas, Tex, Oct. 29, 33; m. 58; c. 3. CREATIVE WRITING, CONTEMPORARY LITERATURE. B.A, Tex. Christian Univ, 55; B.D, Vanderbilt Univ, 58, M.A, 60; Univ. Iowa, 61-62; Guggenheim Found. fel, 72-73. Asst. prof. ENG, Atlantic Christian Univ, 60-61; Tex. A&I Univ, 62-64; UNIV. ARK, FAYETTEVILLE, 64-69, assoc. prof, 69-72, PROF, 72- Dir, Assoc. Writing Prog, 69- AAUP. Fiction. Publ: The theologian, Harper, 65; In a wild sanctuary, William Morrow, 69, Bantam, 70; Lessons in paradise, William Morrow, 71, Popular Libr, 72; Roller ball murder and other stories, William Morrow, 74; plus short stories in Esquire, Playboy, Paris Review, Cosmopolitan, Redbook, Saturday Evening Post & others. Add: Dept. of English, University of Arkansas, Fayetteville, AR 72701.

HARROD, ANN JENNALIE COOK, b. Wewoka, Okla, Oct. 19, 34; m. 56; c. 2. ENGLISH LITERATURE. B.A, Univ. Okla, 56, M.A, 59; Univ. Iowa, 67-68, Danforth fel, 67-72; Ph.D.(Eng), Vanderbilt Univ, 72. ASST. PROF. ENG, UNIV. S.C, 72- Fel, Folger Shakespeare Libr, summer 73; assoc. ed, Shakespeare Stud, 73- MLA; Shakespeare Asn. Am; Southeast. Renaissance Conf; Soc. Relig. Higher Educ. Shakespeare; Renaissance drama. Publ: The audience of Shakespeare's plays: a revaluation, Shakespeare Stud, 74. Add: Dept. of English, University of South Carolina, Columbia, SC 29208.

HARROLD, WILLIAM EUGENE, b. Winston-Salem, N.C, June 24, 36. ENGLISH LITERATURE. B.A, Wake Forest Univ, 59; M.A, Univ. N.C, Chapel Hill, 61, Ph.D.(Eng), 67. Part-time instr. ENG, Univ. N.C, Chapel Hill, 62-65; instr, UNIV. WIS-MILWAUKEE, 65-67, asst. prof, 67-72, ASSOC. PROF, 72- MLA; Mod. Humanities Res. Asn; Avalon Poetry Soc; Midwest Mod. Lang. Asn; Browning Soc; Tennyson Soc. Romantic and Victorian literature; creative writing; mysticism. Publ: Beyond the dream, Branden, 72; The variance and the unity; a study of the complementary poems of Robert Browning, Ohio Univ, 73; Keats' Lamia and Peacock's Rhododaphne, Mod. Lang. Rev, 10/66; Blake's Tyger and Vaughn's Cockcrowing, Notes & Queries, 1/67; Shakespeare's use of Mostellaria in The taming of the shrew, Shakespeare Jahrbuch, West, 70; plus one other. Add: Dept. of English, University of Wisconsin-Milwaukee, Milwaukee, WI 53211.

HARROP, JOHN DOUGLAS, b. Thornaby, Eng, Feb. 13, 32. DRAMA, THEATRE AESTHETICS. B.A, Oxford, 60, M.A, 64; Eng. Speaking Union fel, Stanford Univ, 60-61; M.A, Tulane Univ, 67; Ph.D.(dramatic art), Univ. Calif, 69. Secy, Brit. Diplomatic Serv, 61-66; ASST. PROF. theatre, Univ. Calif, Irvine, 69-70, DRAMATIC ART, UNIV. CALIF, SANTA BARBARA, 71- Fel, Flinders Univ, 70. Brit. Army, 50-52, Res, 52-56, Capt; Mil. Cross, Gt. Brit. Am. Theatre Asn. Contemporary British theatre; history and practice of theatrical direction. Publ: Creative play direction, Prentice-Hall, 74; A constructive promise: Jacques Copeau in New York, Theatre Surv, 11/71; University theatre U.S.A: success and failure, Theatre Quart, 6/73. Add: Dept. of Drama, University of California, Santa Barbara, CA 93106.

HARSH, WAYNE C, b. WaKeeney, Kans, Nov. 13, 24; div. ENGLISH, LINGUISTICS. B.A, Colo. State Col, 50; M.A, Denver Univ, 53; Univ. Groningen, Netherlands, 59-60; Ph.D.(Eng), Univ. Calif, Berkeley, 63. Teacher high sch, Calif, 53-57; asst. prof. ENG, Ohio Univ, 62-64; UNIV. CALIF, DAVIS, 64-67, assoc. prof, 67-73, PROF. ENG. & LING, 73-, CHMN. LING. COMT, 70- NDEA consult, Calif. districts & counties, 66-68; consult, state depts. educ, Calif. & Nev, 66-68; Linguistic Transparency Ser, Doubleday & Co, 67-68; acting chmn. dept. Eng, Univ, Athens, 68-69. U.S.A, 43-46. NCTE; MLA. Historical grammar; applied linguistics; stylistics. Publ: The subjunctive in English, Univ. Ala, 68; Introduction to linguistics: a guidebook for teachers, grades K-12, McCutchan, 68; co-auth, Laidlaw linguistics program, grade 7-8, 69 & Laidlaw language experiences program, grades 3-9, 72, Laidlaw Brothers; auth, introd, Teacher's edition, Elementary school English, Addison-Wesley, 67; Grammar instruction today, 2nd ed, Davis Publ. Eng, 68; Linguistics and the teaching of literature, ERIC Ctr. Applied Ling, 68. Add: Dept. of English & Linguistics, University of California, 109 Sproul Hall, Davis, CA 95616.

HARSHBARGER, HENRY CLAY, b. Quimby, Iowa, July 23, 00. SPEECH. A.B, Grinnell Col, 22; A.M, Columbia Univ, 25; Ph.D, Cornell Univ, 29. Instr, Grinnell Col, 22-24; Iowa State Col, 25-26; Cornell Univ, 26-29; asst. prof. SPEECH, UNIV. IOWA, 29-41, assoc. prof, 41-48, prof, 48-68, asst. dean, 48-63; chmn. dept. speech & dramatic art, 56-68, assoc. dean col. lib. arts, 63-68, EMER. PROF, 68- Rockefeller fel, 37-38; Ford fel, 52; dean, Gottey Col, 68-70. Add: Rte. 6, 6 Longview Knoll, Iowa City, IA 52240.

HART, ALDEN WADSWORTH, b. Torrington, Conn, Jan. 24, 40; div; c. 2. AMERICAN LITERATURE. B.A, Yale, 65; NDEA fel, Univ. Ore, 69-72, Ph.D.(Eng), 72. ASST. PROF. ENG, SLIPPERY ROCK STATE COL, 72- NEA. Early American novel; colonial and federal American literature. Add: Dept. of English, Slippery Rock State College, Slippery Rock, PA 16057.

HART, ANDREW W, b. Midland, Mich, Aug. 9, 21; m. 50; c. 5. ENGLISH, CHEMISTRY. B.S, Mich. State Univ, 49, M.A, 50, Ph.D.(Eng), 55. Tech. writer, Dow Chem. Co, 54-66; ASSOC. PROF. ENG, FERRIS STATE COL, 66- Med.C, U.S.A, 43-45. Publ: Co-ed, Synthetic lubricants, Reinhold, 62; auth, Alkanolamines, In: Vol. 1, 63, Diamines and higher amines, aliphatic, In: Vol. 7, 65 & co-auth, Imines, cyclic, In: Vol. 11, 66, Encyclopedia of chemical technology, Interscience. Add: Dept. of English, Ferris State College, Big Rapids, MI 49307.

HART, DOMINICK JOSEPH, b. Jersey City, N.J, Apr. 22, 42; m. 66; c. 2. ENGLISH LITERATURE. B.S, St. Peter's Col.(N.J), 65; Ph.D.(Eng), Univ. S.C, 71. Teaching asst. ENG, Univ. S.C, 65-70; ASST. PROF, EAST. KY. UNIV, 70- MLA; S.Atlantic Mod. Lang. Asn; Col. Eng. Asn; Southeast. Renaissance Conf. Shakespeare; modern drama and poetry. Add: Dept. of English, Box 932, Eastern Kentucky University, Richmond, KY 40475.

HART, EDWARD, LeROY, b. Bloomington, Idaho, Dec. 28, 16; m. 44; c. 4. ENGLISH LITERATURE. B.S, Univ. Utah, 39; Rhodes scholar, Oxford, 39, D.Phil, 50; A.M, Univ. Mich, 41. Asst. prof. ENG, Univ. Wash, 49-52; BRIGHAM YOUNG UNIV, 52-55, assoc. prof, 55-59, PROF, 59- Am. Counc. Learned Soc. fel, 42; vis. prof, Univ. Calif, Berkeley, 59-60; Am. Philos. Soc. summer grant, 64; Fulbright-Hays lectr, 73-74. U.S.N.R, 42-46, Lt. MLA; Rocky Mt. Mod. Lang. Asn.(pres, 57-58). Am. Soc. 18th Century Stud. Some new sources of Johnson's Lives; contributions of John Nichols to Boswell's Life of Johnson; 18th century biographical works of John Nichols. Publ: Ed, Minor lives, Harvard, 71; auth, John Nichols and the Gentleman's magazine, Bucknell Rev, 62. Add: Dept. of English, Brigham Young University, Provo, UT 84602.

HART, HYMEN H, b. Chicago, Ill, May 25, 18; m. 44; c. 2. ENGLISH LITERATURE. B.A, Univ. Puget Sound, 50; M.A, Univ. Ill, Urbana, 58, Ph.D.(Eng), 67. Instr. accounting, Univ. Puget Sound, 53-57; ENG, Univ. Ill, Chicago, 65-67, asst. prof, 67-71; ASSOC. PROF, MARSHALL UNIV, 71- U.S.A, 41-46 & 50-52, Capt. MLA; Am. Inst. Cert. Pub. Accountants. Shakespeare; Renaissance drama and poetry. Add: 1501 Fifth Ave, Huntington, WV 25701.

HART, JAMES A, b. Pontefract, Eng, Jan. 22, 27; m. 62. AMERICAN LITERATURE. B.A, Univ. London, 47; M.A, Univ. S.C, 58; James B. Duke fel, Duke Univ, 59-60, Wilson fel, 60-61, Ph.D.(Am. lit), 64. Asst. master Eng. & Latin, Withernsea High Sch, Yorkshire, Eng, 50-53; Eng. Speaking Union exchange instr. Eng. & hist, Ga. Teachers Col, 53-54; asst. master Eng, Roundhay Sch, Leeds, Eng, 54-55; instr. ENG. & AM. LIT, Univ. N.C, 61-64; asst. prof, UNIV. B.C, 64-67, ASSOC. PROF, 67- Newberry Libr. grant, 63; Can. Counc. leave fel, 68-69. R.A.F, 48-50, Flying Off. Philol. Asn. Pac. Coast; S.Atlantic Mod. Lang. Asn; Asn. Can. Univ. Teachers Eng; exec. mem. Can. Asn. Am. Stud; Brit. Asn. Am. Stud. Imagism; poetry of World War I; Pope. Publ: The droghte of March: a common misunderstanding, Tex. Stud. Lit. & Lang, winter 63; American poetry of the First World War and the book trade, Papers Bibliog. Soc. Am, 67; Protesting voices: war poetry in left-wing and pro-German periodicals; 1914-1920, In: War and society in North America, Nelson, Toronto, 71. Add: Dept. of English, University of British Columbia, Vancouver 8, B.C, Can.

HART, JAMES DAVID, b. San Francisco, Calif, Apr. 18, 11; m. 38; c. 2. AMERICAN LITERATURE. A.B, Stanford Univ, 32; A.M, Harvard, 33, Ph.D, 36. Instr. ENG, UNIV. CALIF, BERKELEY, 35-41, asst. prof, 41-47, assoc. prof, 47-51, PROF, 51-, DIR. BANCROFT LIBR, 69-, v.chmn. dept, 49-55, chmn, 55-57 & 65-69, v.chancellor, 57-60, acting dir. Bancroft Libr, 61-62. Trustee, Mills Col, 69-, pres. bd, 73- Comdr. Order Brit. Empire, 63. Off. Strategic Serv, 42-45. MLA; Bibliog. Soc. Am; Philol. Asn. Pac. Coast; Am. Acad. Arts & Sci; Am. Antiq. Soc. American literature; literature and history of the western United States. Publ: Oxford companion to American literature, Oxford, 41, rev. ed, 48-56 & 65; Popular book, Oxford, 50 & Univ. Calif, 61; American's literature, Holt, 55; American images of

Spanish California, Bancroft Libr, Univ. Calif, 60; ed, Stevenson: from Scotland to Silverado, 66 & Norris: a novelist in the making, 70, Harvard. Add: 740 San Luis Rd, Berkeley, CA 94707.

HART, JIM ALLEE, History of Journalism. See Volume I, History.

HART, JOHN AUGUSTINE, b. New Haven, Conn, Dec. 6, 17. ENGLISH LITERATURE. A.B, Yale, 40, A.M, 42, Ph.D, 43. Instr. Eng, Rensselaer Polytech. Inst, 43-44; historian, Off. Price Admin, Wash, D.C, 44-46; instr. ENG, CARNEGIE-MELLON UNIV, 46-47, asst. prof, 47-54, ASSOC. PROF, 54- MLA. Shakespeare; 18th century English literature; advanced placement program. Add: Dept. of English, Carnegie-Mellon University, Pittsburgh, PA 15213.

HART, JOHN EDWARD, b. Kans, Feb. 16, 17; m. 42. ENGLISH. A.B, Kans. Wesleyan Univ, 38; A.M, Syracuse Univ, 40, fels, 52-53, 53-54, Ph.D.(Eng), 54. Teaching fel, Syracuse Univ, 40-42; instr, Univ. Cincinnati, 46-49; guest teacher, Odenwald Sch. & lectr, Pedagog, Inst. Darmstadt, Germany, 50-51; asst. prof. ENG, ALBION COL, 54-60, assoc. prof, 60-65, PROF, 65-, summer fac. fel, 64, 70 & 71. U.S.A, 42-45. MLA; AAUP. American literature; British novel; 19th century British literature. Publ: Floyd Dell, Twayne, 71; The scarlet letter—one hundred years after, New Eng. Quart, 9/50; The red badge of courage as myth and symbol, Univ. Kans. City Rev, summer 53; Heroes and houses: the progress of Huck Finn, Mod. Fiction Stud, spring 68; plus others. Add: 412 Fitch St, Albion, MI 49224.

HART, LORING EDWARD, b. Bath, Maine, Sept. 22, 24; m. 50; c. 2. ENGLISH. B.A, Bowdoin Col, 48; M.A, Univ. Miami, 51; fels, Harvard, 54-56, Danforth grant, 60-61, Ph.D.(Eng), 61. Instr. ENG, Univ. Ky, 56-57; asst. prof, NORWICH UNIV, 57-61, assoc. prof, 61-64, PROF, 64-, PRES, 72-, head dept. Eng, 61-68, dean fac, 68-72. U.S.A, 44-46. American literature. Publ: Co-auth, The Norwich guide to writing, Norwich Univ, 66; auth, The beginnings of Longfellow's fame, New Eng. Quart, 3/63. Add: Office of the President, Norwich University, Northfield, VT 05663.

HART, MARY ADORITA, B.V.M, b. Chicago, Ill, Mar. 28, 07. LITERATURE. A.B, Mundelein Col, 33; M.A, Cath. Univ. Am, 41, Ph.D, 52; cert, Univ. London, 60. From instr. to prof. ENG, CLARKE COL, 41-74, chmn. dept, 57-67, EMER. PROF, 74- MLA; NCTE. Nineteenth century English and American literature. Publ: Soul ordained to fail; Louise Imogen Guiney, Pageant, 62; The word spell in Hopkins' The wreck of the Deutschland, Mod. Lang. Notes, 55. Add: Dept. of English, Clarke College, Dubuque, IA 52001.

HART, MILTON BLAIR, b. Delavan, Minn, Sept. 27, 07; m. 46. SPEECH, DRAMATIC ART. B.A, Macalester Col, 32; M.A, State Univ. Iowa, 36; Ed.D.(speech ed), Univ. Denver, 51. Teaching asst, Macalester Col, 33-35; mem. fac. speech & dramatic art, Univ. Ark, 36-40; speech, Henderson State Teachers Col, 46; PROF. SPEECH & DRAMATIC ART, UNIV. ARK, 46-, chmn. dept, 53-68. U.S.A.A.F, 42-45. Speech Commun. Asn; Am. Theatre Asn; Nat. Col. Players.(pres, 64-); Nat. Asn. Study Commun; Southwest. Theatre Conf.(secy, 53-55); South. Speech Asn. Speech education; theatre; interpretation. Publ: The writer: poet's thoughts on oral interpretation, In: Perspectives on oral interpretation, Burgess, 68. Add: 1647 W. Maple St, Fayetteville, AR 72701.

HART, NATHANIEL IRWIN, b. New York, N.Y, Mar. 4, 30; m. 57; c. 8. ENGLISH. B.A, Tulane Univ, 52, M.A, Univ. Conn, 54; Ph.D.(Eng), Univ. Minn, 68. Asst. prof. ENG, UNIV. MINN, MORRIS, 61-70, assoc. prof, 70-73, PROF, 73- Univ. Minn. Grad. Sch. grants-in-aid, 69-70, 70-71, 71-72 & 72-73, Counc. Lib. Educ. grant, 71-72. Browning Inst; Midwest Mod. Lang. Asn; Conf. Col. Compos. & Commun; MLA; NCTE. Nineteenth century English literature; novel. Publ: Browning's The bishop orders his tomb at Saint Praxed's Church, Explicator, 1/71; Pen's Portrait of the Abbé, Browning Newslett, spring 72; Using the personal journal in literature teaching, Reading Improvement, winter 72. Add: Div. of Humanities, University of Minnesota, Morris, MN 56267.

HART, RICHARD, O.F.M, Cap, b. Allenton, Wis, Sept. 12, 29. SPEECH, ENGLISH. M.A.(pub. address), Marquette Univ, 60, M.A.(theol), 72. Mem. fac. speech & Eng, St. Felix Sem, 56-59, dir. brothers, 57-59; mem. fac. speech & Eng, Capuchin Sem. St. Mary, 61-72, rector sem, 67-72; dir. Capuchin Preachers, Midwest Prov, 72- Area chmn, Christian Preaching Conf, 66-72, v.pres, 72-; cert. chmn, Intercom, 72- Speech Commun. Asn. Publ: The priest and interpretative reading, Pastoral Life, 66; Bishop Sheen's television techniques, Preaching, 66; New emphasis on commandments, Relig. Teachers J, 67. Add: 1000 Ballard Rd, Appleton, WI 54911.

HART, ROBERT CHARLES, b. Blairsville, Pa. ENGLISH & AMERICAN LITERATURE. B.A, West. Reserve Univ, 42, M.A, 46; Ph.D.(Eng), Northwest. Univ, 54. Instr. ENG, West. Reserve Univ, 46-48; Northwest. Univ, 48-49; Wayne Univ, 52-54; asst. prof, UNIV. MINN, DULUTH, 55-60, assoc. prof, 60-69; PROF, 69- U.S.A, 42-45. AAUP. Twentieth century American literature; Black literature. Publ: Hemingway on writing, Col. Eng, 57; Black-White literary relations in the Harlem Renaissance, Am. Lit, 73. Add: Dept. of English, University of Minnesota at Duluth, Duluth, MN 55812.

HART, WILLIAM ROBERT, Linguistics, English. See Volume III, Foreign Languages, Linguistics & Philology.

HARTBAUER, ROY ELDEN, Audiology, Speech Pathology. See 12th Edition, American Men & Women of Science, Social & Behavioral Sciences Section.

HARTER, BETSY WELLER, b. Rochester, N.Y, Jan. 25, 37; m. 63. ENGLISH. B.A, St. Lawrence Univ, 58; Woodrow Wilson fel. & M.A, Cornell Univ, 60; Ph.D.(Eng), Univ. Rochester, 66. Instr. ENG, Worcester Jr. Col, 65-66, assoc. prof, 66-68, dir. compos, 67-68; asst. prof, FRAMINGHAM STATE COL, 68-72, PROF, 72- MLA. Early fiction; Renaissance. Add: Dept. of English, Framingham State College, Framingham, MA 01701.

HARTER, CAROL CLANCEY, b. Brooklyn, N.Y, June 1, 41; m. 61; c. 2. ENGLISH & AMERICAN LITERATURE. A.B, Harpur Col, 64; M.A, State Univ. N.Y. Binghamton, 67, Ph.D.(Eng), 70. Grad. asst. ENG, State Univ. N.Y. Binghamton, 64-67, asst. instr, 67-68, res. asst, 68-69, instr, 69-70; ASST. PROF, OHIO UNIV, 70- MLA. Faulkner; contemporary fiction. Publ: Emerson's rhetorical failures in Love, Emerson Soc. Quart, 72; Strange bedfellows: The waste land and An American tragedy, In: Literature of the 20's, Edward/Everett, 73; Recent Faulkner scholarship: five more turns of the screw, J. Mod. Lit, winter 74. Add: Dept. of English, Ellis Hall, Ohio University, Athens, OH 45701.

HARTH, PHILLIP, b. Sioux City, Iowa, Feb. 1, 26; m. 53; c. 3. ENGLISH LITERATURE. A.B, Trinity Col.(Iowa), 46; A.M, Univ. Chicago, 49, Ph.D, 58; Fulbright fel, Univ. London, 54-56. Instr. ENG, Marquette Univ, 49-50, Northwest. Univ, 53-54, 56-58, asst. prof, 58-62, assoc. prof, 62-65; PROF, UNIV. WIS-MADISON, 65- Guggenheim fel, 62-63; sr. fel, Humanities Res. Ctr, Reed Col, 66-67; vis. prof, Univ. Va, 73. U.S.A, 46-48. MLA; Bibliog. Soc; Am. Soc. 18th Century Stud; Int. Asn. Univ. Prof. Eng. Jonathan Swift; John Dryden; 17th and 18th century literature and ideas. Publ: Swift and Anglican rationalism, 61 & Contexts of Dryden's thought, 68, Univ. Chicago; ed, Bernard Mandeville's The fable of the bees, Penguin, 70. Add: Dept. of English, University of Wisconsin-Madison, Madison, WI 53706.

HARTIG, HUGO, b. Minneapolis, Minn, May 7, 21; m. 46; c. 2. ENGLISH, EDUCATION. B.A, St. Olaf Col, 46; M.A, Univ. Minn, 50; Ph.D.(educ, Am. stud), Wash. State Univ, 66. Asst. prof. Eng, Wis. State Univ, River Falls, 55-58; Eng. & educ, East. Ore. Col, 59-63; assoc. prof. ENG, UNIV. WIS-OSHKOSH, 65-72, PROF, 72- Ed. & publ, Academia Press, Reading Improvement & Col. Stud. Surv. NCTE; Int. Reading Asn; Col. Eng. Asn. Publ: Co-auth, The reading improvement handbook, Reading Improvement, 65; co-auth, The reading materials handbook, 68 & Teaching students to read faster, 68, Academia Press; auth, College student attitudes toward high school English activities, Col. Stud. Surv, fall 67. Add: Dept. of English, University of Wisconsin-Oshkosh, Oshkosh, WI 54902.

HARTLEY, ALLAN JOHN, b. Tilbury, Ont, July 24, 13. ENGLISH LITERATURE. B.A, Univ. West. Ont, 49; M.A, Univ. Toronto, 52; Ph.D.(Eng), Univ. London, 63. Asst. prof. ENG, McGill Univ, 57-67; ASSOC. PROF, DALHOUSIE UNIV, 67- Can. Counc. leave fel, 71-72; mem. selection comt, Can. Counc, 73- Can. Asn. Univ. Teachers; Keats-Shelley Asn. Publ: Ed, Frederick Denison Maurice's Sketches of contemporary authors, 1828, Archon, 70; auth, Christian socialism and conversion, Theology, 12/67; The way to unity: Maurice's Exegesis for society, Can. J. Theol, 1/70; F.D. Maurice: disciple and interpreter of Coleridge, Ariel, 4/72. Add: Dept. of English, Dalhousie University, Halifax, N.S, Can.

HARTLEY, JESS (DYSON), JR, b. Greensburg, Pa, Dec. 1, 20; m. 55. ENGLISH. B.S, Ind. State Teachers Col.(Pa), 42; M.A, Univ. Houston, 48; Ph.D.(Eng. & Eng. hist), Univ. Minn, 63. Teacher Eng. & biology, Brockway-Snyder Twp. High Sch, 42-43; Ligionier High Sch, Pa, 46-47; teaching fel, Univ. Houston, 47-48; instr. ENG, Univ. Minn, 53-56; UNIV. HOUSTON, 56-60, asst. prof, 63-72, ASSOC. PROF, 72- U.S.A.A.F, 43-46, Capt. S.Cent. Mod. Lang. Asn. Edmund Spenser's poetry; Tudor history; Michael Drayton's poetry. Add: Dept. of English, University of Houston, Houston, TX 77004.

HARTLEY, LODWICK, b. Batesburg, S.C, June 12, 06. ENGLISH LITERATURE. A.B, Furman Univ, 27, hon. Litt.D, 54; A.M, Columbia Univ, 28; Ph.D, Princeton, 37. Instr. ENG, N.C. STATE UNIV, 27-30, asst. prof, 30-37, assoc. prof, 37-40, PROF, 40-, head dept, 40-71. Vis. prof, Univ. N.C, 40, 50; Univ. Va, 54; Duke Univ, 71, 73; vis. scholar, Univ. Ga, 69. U.S.N.R, 42-45, Lt. Comdr. MLA; Col. Eng. Asn; S.Atlantic Mod. Lang. Asn; NCTE; Int. Asn. Univ. Prof. Eng. English literature of the 18th century; contemporary literature. Publ: William Cowper: humanitarian, 38, William Cowper: the continuing revaluation, 60 & Laurence Sterne in the twentieth century, 66, Univ. N.C; co-auth, Katherine Anne Porter: a critical symposium, Univ. Ga, 70; This is Lorence: a narrative of Rev. Laurence Sterne; Patterns in modern drama. Add: Dept. of English, Box 5308, North Carolina State University, Raleigh, NC 27607.

HARTLEY, ROBERT ARNOLD, b. Chicago, Ill, Aug. 21, 40; m. 66. ENGLISH LITERATURE. B.A, Yale, 62; M.A, Columbia Univ, 64, Ph.D.(Eng), 71. INSTR. ENG, HUNTER COL, 71- MLA; Keats-Shelley Asn. Am.(bibliogr, 73-). Shelley; political symbolism in literature. Publ: Phosphorescence in The revolt Islam, Notes & Queries, 8/73; The Uroboros in Shelley's poetry, J. Eng. & Ger. Philol, 74; ed. & contrib, Annual bibliography: Keats, Shelley, Byron, Hunt, and their circles, Keats-Shelley J, 74 & 75. Add: 545 West End Ave, New York, NY 10024.

HARTMAN, CARL FREDERICK, b. Austin, Tex, July 31, 23; m. 45; c. 1. ENGLISH. B.A, Univ. Ill, 48; M.F.A, State Univ. Iowa, 50. Instr. Eng. compos. & gen. lit, Agr. & Mech. Col, Tex, 51-53; creative writing, Cornell Univ, 53-56; asst. prof. creative writing & contemporary lit, Wash. Univ, 56-58, asst. dean lib. arts, 58-62; assoc. prof. ENG, Mich. State Univ, 62-69; ASST. V.CHANCELLOR ACAD. AFFAIRS, UNIV. CALIF, IRVINE, 69- U.S.A, 43-46, Lt. Creative writing, especially fiction and poetry, for purposes of teaching; editing and publishing. Publ: Co-auth, Short fiction criticism, A. Swallow, 60, 63, Fiction as process, Dodd, 68 & Season of mists, In: Midlands, Random, 60. Add: Office of the Assistant Vice-Chancellor for Academic Affairs, University of California, Irvine, CA 92650.

HARTMAN, GEOFFREY H, b. Ger, Aug. 11, 29; nat; m. 56. ENGLISH & COMPARATIVE LITERATURE. B.A, Queens Col.(N.Y), 49; Fulbright fel, Univ. Dijon, France, 51-52; Sterling fel, Yale, 52-53, Ph.D.(comp. lit), 53. Instr. Eng, Yale, 55-60, asst. prof, 60-62, Morse faculty fel, 58; vis. asst. prof. Eng, Univ. Chicago, 60-61; assoc. prof. ENG. & COMP. LIT, Univ. Iowa, 62-64, PROF, 64-65; Cornell Univ, 65-67; YALE, 67- Vis. lectr, Hebrew Univ, Jerusalem, 58; Am. Counc. Learned Soc. stud. fel, 63; vis. fel, Princeton, 63; vis. prof. Univ. Zürich, 66-67 & summer 73; lectr, Christian Gauss Seminar, Princeton, 67; vis. prof, Princeton, 71; vis. Mellon prof, Univ. Pittsburgh, summer 72; mem. poetry jury, Nat. Book Award, 72; vis. fel, Wesleyan Ctr. Humanities, fall 72. Phi Beta Kappa Christian Gauss Prize, 65; Distinguished Alumnus Award, Queens Col, 71. U.S.A, 53-55. MLA(mem. ed. bd, 74); Keats-Shelley Asn. Am; Am. Comp. Lit. Asn;

Am. Acad. Arts & Sci. European and American poetry, especially romantic and modern; history of criticism. Publ: André Malraux, Hillary, 60; Wordsworth's poetry, 64 & Beyond formalism, Yale, 70; The unmediated vision, Harcourt. Add: 260 Everett St, New Haven, CT 06511.

HARTMAN, JOAN EDNA, b. Brooklyn, N.Y, Oct. 5, 30; ENGLISH LITERATURE. A.B, Mt. Holyoke Col, 51; A.M, Duke Univ, 52; Oxford, 58-59; Ph.D, Radcliffe Col, 60. Instr. ENG, Wash. Col, 52-54; Wellesley Col, 59-62, asst. prof, 62-63; Conn. Col, 63-66; Queens Col.(N.Y), 67-70; STATEN ISLAND COMMUNITY COL, 70-72, ASSOC. PROF, 72- N.Y. State fel, Am. Asn. Univ. Women, 58-59; scholar, Radcliffe Inst, 66-67. MLA (comn. status women in prof, 73-); Col. Eng. Asn.(comt. undergrad. curriculum, 71-); NCTE. English literature of the Renaissance and 17th century; Clarendon; women's studies. Add: 201 E. 21st St, New York, NY 10010.

HARTMAN, MARYANN DORIS, b. Pittsburgh, Pa, Jan. 31, 27; m. 50; c. 4. SPEECH. B.A, Westminster Col, 49; M.A, Kent State Univ, 65; fel, Bowling Green State Univ, 68-69, Ph.D.(speech), 69. Teacher speech & sci, Highland Ave. Elem. Sch, New Castle, Pa, 49-50; instr. SPEECH, Youngstown State Univ, 65-67; ASSOC. PROF, UNIV. MAINE, ORONO, 69- Speech Commun. Asn; Speech Asn. East. States. Women's studies in communication; chautauqua speaking of Robert Lafollette; innovative teaching methodology. Publ: Good speech for all, Ohio Schs, fall 66; The communication gap in high school contests in declamation, Ohio Speech J, spring 69. Add: Dept. Speech, 325 Stevens Hall, University of Maine, Orono, ME 04473.

HARTMAN, MURRAY, b. New York, N.Y, June 8, 19; m. 54; c. 2. ENGLISH, DRAMA. B.A, City Col. New York, 39, M.A, 41; George Washington Univ, 47-48; Ph.D.(Eng), N.Y. Univ, 60. Instr. ENG, George Washington Univ, 47-51; lectr, City Col. New York, 52-57; Hunter Col, 57-58; instr, LONG ISLAND UNIV, 58-60, asst. prof, 60-64, assoc. prof, 64-67, PROF, 67- Founder, L.I.U. Series, Lincoln Ctr, N.Y, 66-68. U.S.A, 43-46, Sgt. MLA. Drama and theatre, especially Shakespeare and modern; Eugene O'Neill and August Strindberg. Publ: Desire under the elms in the light of Strindberg's influence, Am. Lit, 11/61; Lyly, O'Neill, Plautus, Seneca, Strindberg, and Terence in The readers encyclopedia of Shakespeare, Crowell, 66; Strindberg and O'Neill, Educ. Theatre J, 10/66. Add: Dept. of English, Long Island University, Brooklyn, NY 11201.

HARTMANN, THOMAS RAE, b. Chicago, Ill, Nov. 9, 33. ENGLISH. B.A, St. Thomas Univ, 56, M.A, 57; Ph.D.(Eng), N.Y. Univ, 62. Instr. ENG, City Col. New York, 62-63; BROOKLYN COL, 63-66, asst. prof, 67-72, ASSOC. PROF, 72- MLA; Milton Soc. Am. John Milton's poetry and prose; seventeenth century literature. Publ: Ed. & transl, Milton's Prolusions & ed, Milton's of education, In: The prose of John Milton, Doubleday, 67 & N.Y. Univ, 68; contrib, Milton Encyclopedia, Univ. Wis.(in press). Add: Dept. of English, Brooklyn College, Bedford Ave. & Ave. H, Brooklyn, NY 11210.

HARTOG, CURT HARDIN, b. Chicago, Ill, Dec. 3, 41; m. 63; c. 2. ENGLISH LITERATURE. A.B, Univ. Mich, Ann Arbor, 64; M.A, Univ. Calif, Berkeley, 66; Ph.D.(Eng), Univ. Ill, Urbana, 71. Instr. ENG, Univ. N.C, Charlotte, 66-68; ASST. PROF, UNIV. MO-ST. LOUIS, 71- Defoe; 18th century; literature and psychology. Publ: The George Sherburn collection at the University of Illinois, Scriblerian, spring 70; Aggression, femininity, and irony in Moll Flanders, Lit. & Psychol, 22: 121-138. Add: Dept. of English, University of Missouri-St. Louis, St. Louis, MO 63121.

HARTON, MARGARET ELIZABETH, b. Jackson, Tenn, Oct. 12, 07. SPEECH. B.A, La. State Univ, 30; M.A, Univ. Ala, 41; summers, Tex. Col. Arts & Indust, 44, Fla. State Univ, 52, E.Tex. State Col, 58. Teacher, high sch, Okla, 42-44; PROF. SPEECH, SOUTH. STATE COL, 45- Speech Commun. Asn; South. Speech Commun. Asn; Southwest Theatre Conf; Southwest Childrens Theatre Asn. Drama. Publ: Old lady fate; And so they laugh & Sincere hypocrites, Blackfriars. Add: Dept. of Speech, Southern State College, Box 1214 Magnolia, AR 71753.

HARTSOCK, MILDRED EDITH, b. Waynesville, Ohio, Aug. 14, 09. ENGLISH. Ph.D.(Eng), Univ. Cincinnati, 35. Prof. ENG, Ky. Wesleyan Col, 36-37; Lynchburg Col, 37-40; prof. & chmn. dept, ATLANTIC CHRISTIAN COL, 40-73, EMER. PROF, 73- MLA; NCTE; Col. Eng. Asn. Shakespeare; contemporary literature; Henry James. Publ: Biography: the treacherous art, J. Mod. Lit, 70; Major scenes in minor key, Shakespeare Quart, 70; The conceivable child: James and the poet, Stud. Short Fiction, 71. Add: 503 Mt. Vernon Dr, Wilson, NC 27893.

HARTUNG, ALBERT EDWARD, b. Woodcrest, N.J, Oct. 8, 23; m. 46; c. 2. ENGLISH LITERATURE. B.A, Lehigh Univ, 47, M.A, 49, Ph.D, 57. Instr. ENG, LEHIGH UNIV, 49-57, asst. prof, 57-61, assoc. prof, 61-68, PROF, 68- U.S.A, 43-46. MLA; Mediaeval Acad. Am. Chaucer; 15th century literature; medieval romance. Publ: Ed, A manual of the writings in Middle English, 1050-1500, Vol. III, 72 & Vol. IV, 73, Conn. Acad. Arts & Sci; auth, Two notes on the summoner's tale, Eng. Lang. Notes, 67; The non-comic merchant's tale, maximianus, and the sources, Mediaeval Stud, 67; Narrative technique, characterization and the sources in Mabry's Tale of Sir Lancelot, Stud. in Philol, 73. Add: Dept. of English, Lehigh University, Bethlehem, PA 18015.

HARTUNG, CHARLES VINCENT, b. Chicago, Ill, Nov. 26, 13; m. ENGLISH. A.B, Univ. Calif, 38, M.A, 47; Ph.D.(Eng), Stanford Univ, 53. Instr. ENG, Visalia Jr. Col, 41-43; Napa Jr. Col, 47-48; State Col. Wash, 48-50; from instr. to prof, UNIV. CALIF, LOS ANGELES, 54-69, EMER. PROF, 69- U.S.A, 43-46. MLA; NCTE (comn. Eng. lang, 68-70). Modern criticism; Browning; general study of language. Publ: Doctrines of English usage, Eng. J, 12/56; Persistence of tradition in grammar, Quart. J. Speech, 4/62; The scope of linguistic study, Quart J. Speech, 2/64. Add: Division of Humanities, California State College, San Bernardino, 5500 State College Pkwy, San Bernardino, CA 92407.

HARTWIG, HELEN JOAN, b. Lake Wales, Fla, Dec. 22, 36. ENGLISH. B.S, Northwest. Univ, 57; M.A, Univ. Fla, 61; fel, Wash. Univ, 65-66, Ph.D.(Eng), 67. Instr. ENG, Miss. South. Col, 60-61; Univ. N.C, Greensboro, 62-64; asst. prof, Fla. State Univ, 67-72, ASSOC. PROF, UNIV. KY, 72- MLA; S.Atlantic Mod. Lang. Asn; Shakespeare Asn. Am; Southeast. Renaissance Conf. Sixteenth to eighteenth century English literature; Shakespeare. Publ: Shakespeare's tragicomic vision, La. State Univ, 72; The principle of measure in To his coy mistress, Col. Eng, 5/64; Parodic Polonius, Tex. Stud. Lit. & Lang, summer 71; Macbeth, the murderers, and the diminishing parallel, Yearbook Eng. Stud, 73. Add: Dept. of English, University of Kentucky, Lexington, KY 40506.

HARTZLER, SARA KREIDER, b. Newton, Kans, May 1, 43; m. 67; c. 1. NINETEENTH CENTURY BRITISH LITERATURE. A.B, Bluffton Col, 65; M.A, Ind. Univ, Bloomington, 67, Ph.D.(19th century Victorian stud), 71. Asst. prof. ENG, GOSHEN COL, 69-72, ASSOC. PROF, 72- MLA. Position of women in society and literature, 1700-1900; Jane Austen; popular fiction in 18th and 19th century England. Add: 302 Kansas Dr, Goshen, IN 46526.

HARVEY, ELISABETH RUTH, b. Blackpool, Eng, Mar. 6, 44. ENGLISH LITERATURE. B.A, Univ. London, 65, M.Phil, 67, jr. fel, 67-69, Ph.D. (Eng), 70. Spec. lectr. ENG, St. Michael's Col, UNIV. TORONTO, 70-71, ASST. PROF, VICTORIA COL, 71- Res. assoc, Pontif. Inst. Mediaeval Stud, Toronto, 70-71. MLA; Mediaeval Acad. Am; Renaissance Soc. Am; Soc. Renaissance Stud. Mediaeval and Renaissance English literature; history of ideas. Add: Dept. of English, Victoria College, University of Toronto, Toronto, Ont. M5S 1K7, Can.

HARVEY, GINA PAULA, Foreign Languages, English as a Second Language. See Volume III, Foreign Languages, Linguistics & Philology.

HARVEY, J. BAILEY, b. Philadelphia, Pa, Dec. 29, 05; m. 33; c. 2. SPEECH. B.A, City Col. New York, 25. Tutor speech, CITY COL. NEW YORK, 33-38, instr, 38-48, asst. prof, 48-59, assoc. prof, 59-72, prof, 72-74, asst. prof. music, 51-52, EMER. PROF. SPEECH, 74- Dir. glee club, Columbia Univ, 52-69. Speech Commun. Asn. Voice science; Gregorian chant; male chorus repertoire. Add: Dept. of Speech, City College of New York, Convent Ave. at 138th St, New York, NY 10031.

HARVEY, ROBERT D, b. Evanston, Ill, Oct. 5, 26; m. 60; c. 4. AMERICAN LITERATURE & HISTORY. A.B, Northwest. Univ, 48; A.M, Univ. Chicago, 49, Ph.D.(Eng), 65. Instr. ENG, Valparaiso Univ, 52-53; lectr, Univ. Chicago, 53-55; instr, Northwest. Univ, 55-60; lectr, Univ. Calif, Berkeley, 60-62; instr, UNIV. NEV, RENO, 62-65, asst. prof, 65-70, ASSOC. PROF. & CHMN. DEPT, 70- Fulbright lectr. Am. lit, Univ. Caen, 67-68. Sig.C, U.S.A, 44-46. Nineteenth and 20th century American literature; 19th century American historians. Add: Dept. of English, University of Nevada, Reno, Reno, NV 89507.

HARVEY, ROBERT SIDNEY, b. Marion, Ind, Nov. 7, 02; m. 30; c. 3. ENGLISH. B.A, Wabash Col, 28. Reporter, Marion Leader-Tribune, Ind, 22-24; city ed, Marion Chronicle, 28-29; state ed, Indianapolis Star, 29-41; dir. libr, WABASH COL, 41-42, acting dean, 42-46, assoc. prof. Eng, & registr, 46-71, COL. ARCHIVIST, 71- Am. Asn. Col. Registrars & Admis. Off; Soc. Am. Archivists. Add: 1007 S. Grant Ave, Crawfordsville, IN 47933.

HARVEY, WILLIAM RONALD, b. Sioux Falls, S.Dak; div. BRITISH LITERATURE. B.A, Augustana Col.(S.Dak), 57; M.A, Fla. State Univ, 59, Ph.D. (Eng), 66. Instr. ENG, Ohio Univ, 63-65; ASST. PROF, UNIV. S.ALA, 66- Vis. instr. for. langs, N.C. State Univ, summers 65, 66. MLA. British romantic and Victorian literature; English as a second language. Publ: Charles Dickens and the Byronic hero, Nineteenth Century Fiction, 12/69. Add: Dept. of English, University of South Alabama, Mobile, AL 36688.

HARVILL, OLGA DeHART, b. Earlehurst, Va, Mar. 15, 18. ENGLISH. B.A, Lamar State Col. Technol, 59, M.A, 62; Ph.D.(Eng), Univ. Houston, 71. Instr. ENG, LAMAR UNIV, 62-66, ASST. PROF, 66- AAUP. Publ: Thomas' O make me a mask, Explicator, 10/67. Add: Dept. of English, Lamar University, Lamar Station, Beaumont, TX 77705.

HARWARD, VERNON JUDSON, JR, b. Durham, N.C, Dec. 1, 22; m. 45; c. 2. ENGLISH. A.B, Univ. N.C, 43; A.M, Columbia Univ, 48, Ph.D.(Eng), 53. From tutor to asst. prof. ENG, City Col. New York, 48-62; assoc. prof, SMITH COL, 62-66, PROF, 66- Sr. Fulbright Res. fel, U.K, 60-61; Guggenheim fel, 60-61. U.S.N, 43-46, Lt.(jg). MLA. Medieval English and Scottish literature. Publ: The dwarfs of Arthurian romance and Celtic tradition, E.J. Brill, Leiden, 58. Add: Dept. of English, Smith College, Northampton, MA 01060.

HARWELL, GEORGE CORBIN, b. Danville, Va, Jan. 25, 10; m. 50. ENGLISH LITERATURE. A.B, Duke Univ, 32, A.M, 34, Ph.D, 39. Instr. ENG, DUKE UNIV, 35-45, asst. prof, 47-54, ASSOC. PROF, 54- Victorian literature; Matthew Arnold; technical writing. Publ: Workbook for college composition; Technical communication, Macmillan, 60. Add: Dept. of English, Duke University, Durham, NC 27706.

HARWELL, THOMAS MEADE, JR, b. Scottsville, Ky, Sept. 21, 13; m. 43; c. 2. ENGLISH. A.B, South. Methodist Univ, 40, fel, 40-41; A.M, Univ. Chicago, 47; Ph.D.(Eng. & comp. lit), Columbia Univ, 65. Instr. ENG, Univ. Md, 48-50; asst. prof, Pan Am. Col, 54-57, assoc. prof, 57-65; Trinity Univ, 65-68; ARK. STATE UNIV, 68-74, PROF, 74-, res. grants 71 & 73. South. Fels. Fund fel, summer, 57; prog. chmn. Col. Counc. Teachers Eng, 64. U.S.N.R, 42-46, Lt. Col. Eng. Asn; MLA; NCTE; S.Cent. Mod. Lang. Asn.(chmn. 19th century sect, 72); S.Cent. Col. Eng. Asn.(pres, 72, mem. exec. comt, 73-78). Romantic movement; 19th century ideas; John Keats. Publ: Poems from several wildernesses, 46 & Second poems, 49, Swallow; A report on the English issues, Trinity Univ, 67; Keats and the critics, 1848-1900, 72 & ed, Studies in relevance: Romantic and Victorian writers in 1972, 73, Univ. Salzburg; auth, Aristotle again, summer 53 & Power of Plato, winter 56, Southwest Rev; Great books for whom?, Round Table, 3/62; American folklore in 1970; In: Communication for composition, Allyn & Bacon, 73. Add: Dept. of English, Arkansas State University, State University, AR 72467.

HARWICK, ROBERT (DUANE), b. Quinter, Kans, June 28, 26; m. 51; c. 5. ENGLISH. B.A, Univ. Omaha, 52; M.A, Univ. Nebr, 54, Ph.D.(Am. lit), 65. Instr. Eng, Univ. Omaha, 52-53; Univ. Nebr, 54-55; from instr. to asst. prof, Doane Col, 55-58; instr, Univ. Nebr, 58-63, acting dir. freshman Eng, 62-63; assoc. prof. ENG, HASTINGS COL, 63-68, PROF, 68-, DIR. FRESH-

MAN ENG, 63-, CHMN. DEPT. ENG, 66- Dir, NDEA Summer Inst. Eng, 68; ed, Nebr. Eng. Counselor, 67-72. U.S.A.A.F, 44-45. MLA; NCTE. Religious satire in the novels of Sinclair Lewis; humor in the stories and novels of William Faulkner. Add: 714 E. Seventh, Hastings, NE 68901.

HARWOOD, BRITTON JAMES, b. East Rutherford, N.J, July 12, 36; m. 58; c. 5. MEDIEVAL LANGUAGE & LITERATURE. B.A, Hamilton Col, 59; M.S, Canisius Col, 61; NDEA fel. & Ph.D.(Eng), State Univ. N.Y, Buffalo, 70. Instr. Eng. & French, Lyndonville, Cent. High Sch, N.Y, 59-61; ENG, MIAMI UNIV, 64-70, asst. prof, 70-74, ASSOC. PROF, 74- Mediaeval Acad. Am; Eng. Inst; Am. Acad. Relig; Early Eng. Text Soc. Fourteenth century English literature; theories of interpretation; theory of genre. Publ: The Wife of Bath and the dream of innocence, Mod. Lang. Quart, 10/72; Liberum-Arbitrium in the C-text of Piers Plowman, Philol. Quart, 10/73; Clergye and the action of the third vision in Piers Plowman, Mod. Philol, 5/73. Add: Dept. of English, Upham Hall, Miami University, Oxford, OH 45056.

HARWOOD, CHARLES EDWIN, b. Sanilac, Mich, Apr. 3, 13; m. 37; c. 2. ENGLISH. A.B, Olivet Nazarene Col, 35; A.M, Univ. Mich, 40; Ph.D, Univ. Colo, 58. Teacher, High Sch, Mich, 37-42; accountant, Gen. Motors Corp, Flint, Mich, 42-47; tech. instr, Gen. Motors Inst. Tech, 47-49; instr. Eng, Univ. Colo, 49-52; prof, Pasadena Col, 52-58; asst. prof, Calif. State Polytech. Col, 58-60; assoc. prof, N.C. Wesleyan Col, 60-62, prof, 62-66, chmn. div. humanities, 60-66; prof. Eng. & head lang. arts dept, CALIF. STATE POLYTECH. UNIV, 66-70, exec. asst. to pres, 70-71, assoc. v.pres. acad. affairs, 71-74, FIELD COORD. K.A.T.E. PROJ, MINISTRY EDUC, GREECE, 74- MLA. Literary criticism, American selected magazines around 1900; Mark Twain; modern fiction. Add: 20312 Shadow Mountain Rd, Walnut, CA 91789.

HASCALL, DUDLEY L, Linguistics, English Literature. See Volume III, Foreign Languages, Linguistics & Philology.

HASCH, JACK J, b. Spokane, Wash, June 9, 22. SPEECH. B.A, Univ. Ill, 47, M.A, 49; Columbia Univ. N.Y. Univ. Instr. speech, Cortland State Teachers Col, 47; asst, Univ. Ill, 47-49; instr, Dartmouth Col, 49; Col. Arts & Sci, N.Y. UNIV, 49-59, asst. prof. bus. writing & speaking, Sch. Commerce, 59-64, ASSOC. PROF. SPEECH, UNIV. COL, 64- U.S.N.R, 42-45. Speech Commun. Asn; Orgn. Am. Hist; Am. Stud. Asn; Speech Asn. East. States. Communication—written and spoken. Add: Dept. of English & Speech Education, School of Education, New York University, New York, NY 10003.

HASELMAYER, LOUIS A, b. Newark, N.J, June 4, 11. ENGLISH, IOWA HISTORY. B.A, Williams Col, 33; Ph.D, Yale, 37; M.Div, Gen. Theol. Sem, 41; Oxford, 52; summers, Univ. Paris, 55; Goethe Inst, Munich, 56; Univ. Florence, 60. Instr. Eng, Univ. Minn, 36-38; Greek, Gen. Theol. Sem, 38-41; dean, Cathedral Sch, Dallas, 49-50; PROF. ENG, Daniel Baker Col, 50-52; IOWA WESLEYAN COL, 52-, PRES, 70-, head dept. eng, 52-70, chmn. div. humanities, 54-70. Assoc. ed, Anglican Theol. Rev, 48-; lit. critic, Burlington Hawkeye, 52-; founder & ed, Design Mag, 54-; assoc. ed, Iowa Eng. Yearbook, 57-; ed, Iowa Wesleyan fac. lect. ser, 57-; assoc. ed, Lyrical Iowa, 59- MLA; NCTE; Col. Eng. Asn; Church Hist. Soc. World literature; Iowa and Methodist history. Publ: Medieval English Episcopal registers, S.P.C.K, London, 38; Structure of English poetry, Marclay, 50; The 125th anniversary history of Iowa Wesleyan College, Iowa Wesleyan Col, 67; Sestina revival, Iowa Eng. Yearbook, fall 63; Amos Bronson Alcott and southeast Iowa, fall 65 & The Mount Pleasant Collegiate Institute 1842-1855, winter 68, Annals of Iowa; plus others. Add: Iowa Wesleyan College, Mt. Pleasant, IA 52641.

HASHIMOTO, YOKO, b. Tokyo, Japan, Aug. 20, 39. OCCIDENTAL & ORIENTAL THEATRE. B.A, Aoyama-Gakuin Univ, Japan, 64, M.A, 66; M.A, Univ. Mich, Ann Arbor, 67, Ph.D.(theatre arts), 72. Asst. prof. THEATRE ARTS, WEST CHESTER STATE COL, 69-70, ASSOC. PROF, 70- Tech. dir, Theatre Playshop, Beaver Col, 70- Asn. Asian Stud; Am. Theatre Asn. History of Shakespearean performances: 20th century theatre; oriental theatre. Publ: Co-auth, Stage makeup, Roppongi Shuppan, 74. Add: Dept. of Speech & Theatre, West Chester State College, West Chester, PA 19380.

HASKELL, ANN SULLIVAN, b. Washington, D.C; m; c. 4. MEDIEVAL ENGLISH LITERATURE, HISTORY OF THE ENGLISH LANGUAGE. B.S, Clemson Univ, 61; Woodrow Wilson fels, 62-64, univ. fel, 62, M.A, 62, Ph.D. (Eng. philol), 64. Instr. Eng. as second lang, Univ. Pa, 64; from asst. prof. to ASSOC. PROF. MEDIEVAL ENG. LIT, STATE UNIV. N.Y. BUFFALO, 64-, fac. fels, summers 66, 67, 71, 72. Mediaeval Acad. Am.(secy, Ctrs. & Regional Asns. comt, 73-76); MLA; Northeast Mod. Lang. Asn; Mod. Lang. Soc. Helsinki. Chaucer; Medieval drama; medieval marriage. Publ: Ed, A Middle English anthology, Doubleday, 69; auth, Essays on Chaucer's saints, Mouton, The Hague, 74; The host's precious corpus Madrian, J. Eng. & Ger. Philol, LXVII: 430-440; The Doppelgängers in Chaucer's Troilus, Neuphilol. Mitt, LXXII: 723-734; The Paston women on marriage in fifteenth century England, Viator, IV: 531-545. Add: 14 S. Swarthmore Ave, Swarthmore, PA 19081.

HASKELL, GEORGE D, b. Boston, Mass, Oct. 15, 12. ENGLISH LITERATURE. A.B, Harvard, 36, A.M, 37; Ph.D, Fordham Univ, 60. Asst, ENG, Fordham Univ, 53-54, instr, 55-56; LeMOYNE COL. (N.Y), 57-59, ASST. PROF, 59- Sig.C, U.S.A, 42-46, 1st Lt. MLA; Johnson Soc. Great Lakes Region; Shakespeare Asn. Am; Renaissance Soc. Am; Soc. Theatre Res, Gt. Brit; Am. Soc. Theatre Res. Restoration and 18th century theatre and drama; the 18th century; Shakespeare. Add: Dept. of English, LeMoyne College, Syracuse, NY 13214.

HASLAM, GERALD WILLIAM, b. Bakersfield, Calif, Mar. 18, 37; m. 61; c. 5. AMERICAN LITERATURE, LINGUISTICS. A.B, San Francisco State Col, 63, M.A, 65; Wash. State Univ, 65-66. Teaching asst. ENG, Wash. State Univ, 65-66; instr, San Francisco State Col, 66-67; from asst. prof. to ASSOC. PROF, CALIF. STATE COL, SONOMA, 67- Gen. Semantics Found. res. grant, 66; invitational scholar, Polish Acad. Sci, Warsaw, 66; mem. nat. acad. adv. bd, Multi-Cult. Inst, 67- U.S.A, 58-60. Col. Lang. Asn; West. Am. Lit. Asn.(dir, 71-75). The West in American literature; non-

white American writers; American dialects. Publ: William Eastlake, Steck, 70; ed, Forgotten pages of American literature, Houghton, 70; auth, The language of the oil fields: examination of an industrial argot, Old Adobe, 72; Okies, New West Publ, 73; The literature of the people: native American voices, CLA J; American oral literature: our forgotten heritage, Eng. J; Por la causa! Mexican-American literature, Col. Eng. Add: Dept. of English, California State College, Sonoma, 1801 E. Cotati Ave, Rohnert Park, CA 94928.

HASLETT, BETTY JEANNE, b. Hutchinson, Minn, Oct. 8, 45; m. 68; c. 1. COMMUNICATIONS, SOCIOLINGUISTICS. B.A, Univ. Minn, Minneapolis, 67, Ph.D.(speech commun), 71; M.A, Univ. Wis-Madison, 68. ASST. PROF. SPEECH COMMUN, UNIV. DEL, 71- Speech Commun. Asn; Int. Commun. Asn. Communication and language development; communication theory. Publ: Effects of syntactic complexity on processing and retrieval of sentential constituents, J. Exp. Psychol, 10/73. Add: Dept. of Speech Communication, 205 Eliot Hall, University of Delaware, Newark, DE 19711.

HASLEY, LOUIS, b. Amana, Iowa, Nov. 3, 06; m. 35; c. 3. AMERICAN LITERATURE. A.B, Univ. Notre Dame, 30, A.M, 31; summers, Columbia Univ, 32, Univ. Chicago, 33, Univ. Wis, 36. Instr. ENG, UNIV. NOTRE DAME, 31-34; asst. prof, 34-37; assoc. prof, 37-43, prof, 43-72, asst. dean, 42-49, EMER. PROF, 72- Col. Eng. Asn. Critical prose, fiction and poetry: the literature of American humor; creative writing. Publ: The best of Bill Nye's humor, Col. & Univ, 72; Humorists are human, Tomorrow, 7/46; The determination of beliefs in literature, CLA J, 12/61; American literature of the westward movement, Col. Eng, 11/64. Add: 3128 Wilder Dr, South Bend, IN 46615.

HASSAN, IHAB HABIB, b. Cairo, Egypt, Oct. 17, 25; nat; m. 49, 66. ENGLISH. B.Sc, Cairo Univ, 46; Egyptian Educ. Mission fel, 46-48; M.S, Univ. Pa, 48. Harrison scholar, 48-49, Harrison fel, 49-50, M.A, 50, univ. scholar, 50-51, Ph.D.(Eng), 53. Asst. instr. Eng, Univ. Pa, 51-52; instr, Rensselaer Polytech. Inst, 52-54; from instr. to asst. prof, Wesleyan Univ, 54-58, assoc. prof, 58-62, prof, 62-63, Benjamin L. Waite prof, 63-70, chmn, 63-64 & 68-69, dir, Col. Lett, 64-66, dir, Ctr. for Humanities, 69-70; VILAS RES. PROF. ENG. & COMP. LIT, UNIV. WIS-MILWAUKEE, 70- Guggenheim fels, 58-59, 62-63; mem. Eng. Inst; mem. ed. bd, Wesleyan Univ. Press, 63-66 & Am. Quart, 64-66; fel, Sch. Lett, Ind. Univ, 64; tutor, Salzburg Sem. Am. Stud, 65; Fulbright lectr, France, 66-67, 74-75; lectr, U.S. Inform. Agency, France, Belgium, Holland & Ger, 66-74; fel, Camargo Found, 74. MLA; NCTE; Am. Comp. Lit. Asn; Int. Asn. Univ. Prof. Eng; Syndicat Int Critique Litteraires. Modern British and American literature; criticism and poetics; comparative literature. Publ: Radical innocence, Princeton, 61; Crise du Heros Americain, Lettres Modernes, 63; The literature of silence; Miller and Beckett, Knopf, 67; The dismemberment of Orpheus: toward a post modern literature, Oxford, 71; ed, Liberations: new essays on the humanities in revolution, Wesleyan Univ, 71; auth, Contemporary American literature: 1945-1972, Ungar, 73; Paracriticism: seven speculations of the times, Univ. Ill, 74; Post modern ISM, New Lit. Hist, 71-72; Since 1945; the new consciousness & Since 1945: fiction, In: Literary history of the U.S, Macmillan, 74; plus others. Add: 2137 N. Terrace Ave, Milwaukee, WI 53202.

HASSEL, RUDOLPH CHRISTOPHER, JR, b. Richmond, Va, Nov. 16, 39; m. 62; c. 2. ENGLISH, RENAISSANCE. B.A, Univ. Richmond, 61; Woodrow Wilson fel. & M.A, Univ. N.C, 62; univ. fel. & Ph.D, Emory Univ, 68. Instr. ENG, Mercer Univ, 62-65; asst. prof, VANDERBILT UNIV, 68-74, ASSOC. PROF, 74- Researcher, Vanderbilt summer res. grants, 69, 70 & 73. MLA; Shakespeare Asn. Am; Int. Shakespeare Asn. Renaissance, seventeenth century; Shakespeare. Publ: Co-ed, The comedy of errors, Univ. S.C, 74; auth, Shakespeare's comic epilogues: invitations to festive communion, Shakespeare Jahrbuchwest, 70; Donne's Ignatius his conclave and the new astronomy, Mod. Philol, 71; St. Paul and Shakespeare's romantic comedies, Thought, 71. Add: Dept. of English, Box 129-B, Vanderbilt University, Nashville, TN 37235.

HASSENCAHL, FRANCES JANET, b. Hell, Mich, June 22, 42; m. 68. SPEECH COMMUNICATION, U.S. HISTORY. B.A, Goshen Col, 64; M.A, Case West. Reserve Univ, 66, fel, 64-68, Ph.D.(speech), 70. ASST. PROF. SPEECH & DIR. FORENSICS, ALFRED UNIV, 70-, res. found. summer res. grant, 72-73. Speech Commun. Asn; AAUP; Am. Forensic Asn; East. Commun. Asn.(chair person equal opportunity task force, 73-). Political interest groups; forensic speaking; rhetoric of the progressive era. Add: Dept. of Performing Arts, Alfred University, Alfred, NY 14802.

HASSLER, DONALD MACKEY II, b. Akron, Ohio, Jan. 3, 37; m. 60; c. 2. ENGLISH. B.A, Williams Col, 59; M.A, Columbia Univ, 60, Ph.D.(Eng), 67. Instr. ENG, Univ. Montreal, 61-65; KENT STATE UNIV, 65-67, asst. prof, 67-71, ASSOC. PROF, 71-, DIR. EXP. COL, 73- MLA; Am. Soc. 18th Century Stud; Hist. Sci. Soc. Eighteenth and early 19th century English literature; Erasmus Darwin and the early romantics. Publ: The comedian as the letter D: Erasmus Darwin's comic bathos, Serif, 6/69; Erasmus Darwin and enlightenment belief, Enlightenment Essays, 7/70; David Hume and Erasmus Darwin's Zoonomia, Stud. Scottish Lit, 1/71; plus others. Add: 770 Marilyn Dr, Kent, OH 44240.

HASSOLD, ERNEST CHRISTOPHER, b. Corunna, Ind, Jan. 21, 96; m. 28; c. 2. HUMANITIES. Concordia Sem, 18; Ph.D, Univ. Chicago, 34. Instr, Concordia Col.(Ind), 19-21; instr. in charge, Concordia Collegiate Inst, N.Y, 21-25; asst, Univ. Chicago, 25-27; asst. prof. Eng, UNIV. LOUISVILLE, 27-35, assoc. prof, 35-37, prof, 37-60, distinguished prof. HUMANITIES, 60-66, chmn. div, 37-39, 42-63, acting head dept. Eng, 35-37, head dept, 37-55, EMER. DISTINGUISHED PROF, 66- Ed. specialist, Off. Mil. Govt, Hesse, Ger, 48-49. MLA; NCTE; Am. Soc. Aesthet. American studies; literature and art; contemporary literature and thought. Publ: American literature before Civil War; Baroque concept, Coll. Art J; contrib, Louisville program, In: Humanities in general education. Add: Apt. 6, 2030 Bedford St, Durham, NC 27707.

HASTINGS, ARTHUR C, b. Neosho, Mo, May 23, 35. SPEECH. B.A, Tulane Univ, 57; M.A, Northwest. Univ, 58, Ph.D, 62. Asst. prof. SPEECH, Univ. Nev, 60-63; instr, Stanford Univ, 63-64, asst. prof, 64-71; lectr. speech commun, Calif. State Univ, San Jose, 71-72; PRES, HASTINGS ASSOCS. CONSULT. SERV, 72- Mem. fac, Nat. High Sch. Inst, Northwest. Univ, 59-62; asst. prof, Univ. Calif, Santa Barbara, summer 63. Speech Commun. Asn; Am. Soc. Psychical Res; Int. Soc. Gen. Semantics; Parapsychol. Asn; Am. Forensic Asn. Communication; parapsychology; semantics. Publ: Co-auth, Argumentation and advocacy, Random, 65; ed, Macmillan series in speech and communication, Macmillan, 66-; contrib, Changing images of man, 73 & auth, Psychical research, 73, Stanford Res. Inst. Add: 2451 Benjamin Dr, Mountain View, CA 94043.

HASTINGS, ELIZABETH THOMSON, b. Providence, R.I, Sept. 27, 13. ENGLISH. A.B, Brown Univ, 34, A.M, 35; Ph.D, Yale, 39. Instr. ENG, Ill. Col, 39-42, asst. prof, 42-44, PROF, 44-51, CASE WEST. RESERVE UNIV, 51-, DEAN SPEC. ASSIGNMENTS, 72-, dean, Mather Col, 51-72. MLA. English Renaissance literature; Bishop Hugh Latimer; 16th century manuscript translation of Latimer's First sermon before Edward. Add: Dept. of English, Case Western Reserve University, Cleveland, OH 44106.

HASTINGS, GEORGE S, JR, b. Peekskill, N.Y, Mar. 15, 31; m. 53; c. 4. ENGLISH LANGUAGE & LITERATURE. B.A, Swarthmore Col, 53; M.A, Univ. Calif, Berkeley, 55; Ph.D.(Eng), Univ. Pa, 65. Teacher ENG, Tatnall Sch, Inc, 59-60, chmn. dept, 60-65; ASST. PROF, STATE UNIV. N.Y. ALBANY, 65- MLA. Middle English language; English stylistics. Add: Dept. of English, State University of New York at Albany, Albany, NY 12203.

HASWELL, RICHARD ELLIS, b. Joliet, Ill, May 16, 05; m. 33; c. 3. ENGLISH LITERATURE. A.B, Univ. Ill, 26, A.M, 28, Ph.D, 31. Asst. ENG, Univ. Ill, 26-31; assoc. prof, Univ. Louisville, 31-36; assoc, Univ. Ill, 36-38; prof, SOUTHWEST MO. STATE UNIV, 38-70, head dept. Eng. & speech, 50-63, EMER. PROF, 73- English grammar; 17th century; intellectual and cultural history. Add: Box 98, R.F.D. 9, Springfield, MO 65804.

HASWELL, RICHARD H, b. Springfield, Mo. Jan. 30, 40; m. 68. ENGLISH. B.A, Univ. Mo, 61, Gregory fel, 63-64, Ph.D.(Eng), 67; Woodrow Wilson fel, Univ. Wash, 61-62, M.A, 62. ASSOC. PROF. ENG, WASH. STATE UNIV, 67- MLA. English romanticism; French symbolism. Publ: Bavdelaire's self-portrait of Poe, Romance Notes, 69; A narrative point of view in Wordsworth's Lyrical ballads, Papers Lang. & Lit, 70. Add: Dept. of English, Washington State University, Pullman, WA 99163.

HATCH, JAMES V, b. Oelwein, Iowa, Oct. 25, 28. ENGLISH, THEATRE ARTS. B.A, North. Iowa State Univ, 49; M.A, State Univ. Iowa, 55, Ph.D. (theatre arts), 58. Teacher Eng, High Sch, Montecello, Iowa, 49-52; Speech & theatre, Grinnell, 52-55; Eng, North Chicago, Ill, 55-56; asst. prof. theatre, Univ. Calif, Los Angeles, 58-62; Fulbright lectr. cinema, High Cinema Inst, Cairo, Egypt, 62-65; asst. prof. ENG, CITY COL. NEW YORK, 65-70, ASSOC. PROF, 71-, res. grant, 72-74. U.S. Dept. State, lectr. theatre, India & Ceylon, 67-68; consult, Asian Theatre, J.D.R. III Found, 69-70; consult, Drama Bk. Specialist, N.Y.C, 70-73; Nat. Endowment for Humanities grant, 73-74. George Washington Honor Medal, Freedom Found, 58; Obie Award, 62. Am. Theatre Asn. Black theatre history; East Indian theatre; Asian and Middle East cinema. Publ: Black image on the American stage, Drama Bk. Specialists, 70; co-auth, Fly blackbird (musical play), Negro Univs, 70; co-ed, By and about women, Random, 73; ed, Black theatre USA 1847-1974, Free Press, 74; auth, A white folks guide to 200 years of black drama, 72 & co-auth, The popular black entertainer, 73, Drama Rev; auth, Theatre in a time of violence, Nation Mag, 72; plus others. Add: Dept. of English, City College of New York, 138th St. & Convent Ave, New York, NY 10031.

HATCH, MAURICE ADDISON, b. Melrose, Mass, Mar. 5, 10; m. 40; c. 4. ENGLISH. A.B, Univ. Kans, 36, A.M, 40; Ph.D, Cornell Univ, 48. Instr. ENG, Univ. Kans, 35-40; Cornell Univ, 46-48; UNIV. KY, 48-49, asst. prof, 49-61, ASSOC. PROF, 61- Ed, Ky. Eng. Bull, 69- C.Eng, U.S.A, 43-45. NCTE. Freshman English; Humanities. Publ: Roger Ascham, Italianate Englishman, SAMLA Bull; Phasellus Ille, Class. Outlook; The Ascham letters: annotated translation of the Latin correspondence, Ky. Microcards, SAMLA. Add: Dept. of English, 1239 Patterson Office Tower, University of Kentucky, Lexington, KY 40506.

HATCHER, ELIZABETH ROBERTA, b. Bethesda, Md, June 9, 45; m. 71. MEDIEVAL LITERATURE, FOLKLORE. B.A, Dominican Col. San Rafael, 66; Woodrow Wilson fel, 66; univ. fels, Johns Hopkins Univ, 67-69, M.A, 68, Ph.D.(Eng), 70. ASST. PROF. ENG, TOWSON STATE COL, 69- MLA; Mediaeval Acad. Am.(mem. sem. palaeography & textual criticism, summer 70); Dante Soc. Am. Chaucer; palaeography and textual criticism; folktale. Publ: The moon and parchment: Paradiso II, 73-78, Dante Stud, 71; Chaucer and the psychology of fear: Troilus in Book V, ELH, 73; Life without death: the old man in Chaucer's Pardoner's tale, Chaucer Rev, (in press). Add: Dept. of English, Towson State College, Baltimore, MD 21204.

HATCHER, HARLAN HENTHORNE, b. Ironton, Ohio, Sept. 9, 98; m. 42; c. 2. LITERATURE. A.B, Ohio State Univ, 22, A.M, 23, Ph.D, 27; Univ. Chicago, 25; hon. degrees from 28 U.S. Insts. Instr. Eng, Ohio State Univ, 22-28, asst. prof, 28-32, prof, 32-44, dean col. arts & sci, 44-48, v.pres, 48-51; pres, Univ. Mich, 51-67, RETIRED. State dir, Fed. Writers' Proj, Ohio, 37-38; pres, Develop. Great Lakes Megalopolis Res. Proj, 69-; chmn, Univ. Residential Theatre Asn, 70- U.S.A, 18; U.S.N, 42-44. MLA; NCTE; Am. Hist. Soc; Great Lakes Hist. Soc. Modern drama; cultural history of Ohio and the Great Lakes area; urbanization of the Great Lakes region. Publ: Versification of Robert Browning; The Great Lakes; A century of iron and men. Add: 841 Greenhills Dr, Ann Arbor, MI 48105.

HATCHER, JOE BRANCH, b. Ft. Worth, Tex, July 28, 36; m. 57; c. 3. ENGLISH. A.B, Univ. Wichita, 60; M.A, Univ. Kans, 67, Ph.D.(Eng), 68. ASSOC. PROF. ENG, BAKER UNIV, 66- MLA. George Bernard Shaw; English Renaissance. Publ: Shaw the reviewer and James's Guy Domville, Mod. Drama, 12/71. Add: Dept. of English, Baker University, Baldwin, KS 66006.

HATCHER, MILDRED, b. Murray, Ky. ENGLISH, FOLKLORE. B.S, Murray State Univ, 27; M.A, George Peabody Col, 30; Vanderbilt Univ, 30; Univ. Wis, summer 47; Ind. Univ, summer 64; hon. Dr, Protestant Episcopal Univ, 66. Asst. prin. & head dept. Eng, Hardin High Sch, Ky, 27-29; teacher math, Paducah City Schs, 30-34; Eng, Paducah Tilghman High Sch, 34-48; from asst. prof. to assoc. prof, Austin Peay State Univ, 48-60; asst. prof, MURRAY STATE UNIV, 60-61; ASSOC. PROF, 61- Critic teacher, Murray State Univ, summer 46. NCTE (judge, annual achievement awards, 61-64). Folklore and methodology. Publ: Contrib. poems, National Poetry Anthology, annually, 53-60; numerous arts. & poems in prof. jour. Add: Box 3281, Murray State University, Murray, KY 42071.

HATFIELD, GLENN WILSON, JR, b. Georgetown, Ohio, Apr. 14, 29; m. 54. ENGLISH. B.A, Ohio State, 52, M.A, 56, Ph.D.(Eng), 64; Univ. London, 60-61. Instr. ENG, UNIV. WASH, 61-64, asst. prof, 65-68, ASSOC. PROF, 68- U.S.A, 52-54. MLA; Johnson Soc. Eighteenth century English literature. Publ: Henry Fielding and the language of irony, Univ. Chicago, 68; Quacks, pettifoggers and parsons: Fielding's case against the learned professions, Tex. Stud. Lang. & Lit, 67; Puff and politricks: Jonathan Wild and the political corruption of language, Philol. Quart, 67; The serpent and the dove: Fieldings irony and the prudence theme of Tom Jones, Mod. Philol, 67. Add: Dept. of English, University of Washington, Seattle, WA 98105.

HATHAWAY, BAXTER, b. Cincinnati, Ohio, Dec. 11, 09; m. 36; c. 3. ENGLISH. A.B, Kalamazoo Col, 35; A.M, Univ. Mich, 36, Ph.D, 40. From instr. to asst. prof, Univ. Mont, 40-44, from asst. prof. to assoc. prof, 45-46; lectr, Univ. Wis, 44-45; asst. prof. ENG, CORNELL UNIV, 46-50, assoc. prof, 50-62, PROF, 62- Ford fel, 51; ed, Epoch; dir, Assoc. Writing Progs, 68-; sr. ed, Ithaca House, 69- Hopwood Award, 36. MLA. Creative writing; literary criticism. Publ: The stubborn way, Macmillan, 37; Writing mature prose, 51 & A transformational syntax, 67, Ronald; Age of criticism, Cornell Univ, 62; Marvels and commonplaces, Random, 68. Add: Dept. of English, Cornell University, Ithaca, NY 14850.

HATHAWAY, RICHARD DEAN, b. Chillicothe, Ohio, Aug. 8, 27; m. 49; c. 2. AMERICAN LITERATURE. A.B, Oberlin Col, 49; A.M, Harvard, 52, fel, 56; Ph.D.(Am. stud), Case West. Reserve Univ, 64. Instr. ENG, Maritime Col, State Univ. N.Y, 55; Rensselaer Polytech. Inst, 57-62; asst. prof, STATE UNIV. N.Y. COL. NEW PALTZ, 62-65, assoc. prof, 65-70, PROF, 70- Danforth assoc, 60-; assoc. prof, Millsaps Col, 65-66. U.S.N.R, 45-47. MLA; Am. Stud. Asn. New England literature and culture; Sylvester Judd. Publ: Hawthorne and the paradise of children, West. Humanities Rev, 61; Laulu Itsestani (Song of myself), Ita Suomi, 6-7/67; plus poems in Col. Eng, Mass. Rev. and other mag, 69-70. Add: Dept. of English & World Literature, State University of New York,College at New Paltz, New Paltz, NY 12561.

HATHAWAY, STEPHEN CONGER, b. Plymouth, Mich, Dec. 28, 21; m. 45; c. 2. COMMUNICATIONS, SPEECH. A.B, East. Mich. Univ, 48; M.A, Univ. Mich, 49, Ph.D.(speech), 58. Teaching fel. SPEECH, Univ. Mich, 48-50; instr, MIAMI UNIV, 51-53, asst. prof, 53-58, assoc. prof, 58-64, PROF, 64-, DIR. TELECOMMUNICATIONS, 58- U.S.A.A.F, 42-45, S/Sgt. Nat. Asn. Educ. Broadcasters; Asn. Prof. Broadcasting Educ; Speech Asn. Am. Broadcasting; journalism; film. Add: Dept. of Communication & Theatre, Miami University, Oxford, OH 45056.

HATLEN, BURTON NORVAL, b. Santa Barbara, Calif, Apr. 9, 36; m. 61; c. 2. ENGLISH. B.A, Univ. Calif, Berkeley, 58; M.A, Columbia Univ, 59; M.A, Harvard, 61; Ph.D.(Eng), Univ. Calif, Davis, 71. Acting asst. prof. ENG, King Col, 61-62; instr, Univ. Cincinnati, 62-65; asst. prof, UNIV. MAINE, ORONO, 67-73, ASSOC. PROF, 73- MLA. Renaissance and modern British literature; mythic and archetypal patterns in literature. Add: Dept. of English, University of Maine, Orono, ME 04473.

HATTON, THOMAS J, b. Ft. Dodge, Iowa, Dec. 19, 35; m. 60; c. 3. ENGLISH. B.A, Buena Vista Col, 59; M.A, Univ. Nebr, 61, Ph.D.(Eng), 66. Instr. ENG, Univ. Nebr, 63-65; asst. prof, SOUTH. ILL. UNIV, 65-72, ASSOC. PROF, 72- Air Nat. Guard, 58-64. Medieval and Renaissance English literature. Publ: Chaucer's crusading knight, a slanted ideal, Chaucer Rev, fall 68; Absolon, taste and odor in The Miller's tale, Papers Lang. & Lit, fall 71; Nature as poet: Alanus de Insulis' Complaint of nature, Lang. & Style, winter 71; plus others. Add: Dept. of English, Southern Illinois University, Carbondale, IL 62901.

HATVARY, GEORGE EGON, b. Budapest, Hungary, Apr. 2, 21; nat; m. 61; c. 1. ENGLISH. A.B, New Sch. Social Res, 47; A.M, N.Y. Univ, 48; Ph.D. (Eng), 57. Instr. Eng, Boston Univ, 48-49; gen. lit, N.Y. Univ, 54-59; instr. ENG, Queens Col.(N.Y), 59-63; asst. prof, ST. JOHN'S UNIV.(N.Y), 63-65, ASSOC. PROF, 65-, chmn. dept, 68-70. Asst. to ed, complete works of Poe. U.S.A, 43-46. American literature. Publ: Co-ed, Poe's Prose romances, St. John's Univ, 68; auth, Horace Binney Wallace, Twayne, (in prep); Horace Binney Wallace: a study in self-destruction, Princeton Libr. Chronicle, winter 64; Poe's borrowings from H.B. Wallace, Am. Lit, 11/66; plus others. Add: Dept. of English, St. John's University, Jamaica, NY 11432.

HAUCK, RICHARD BOYD, b. Cincinnati, Ohio, Sept. 12, 36; m. 60; c. 2. ENGLISH, AMERICAN LITERATURE. B.A, West. Mich. Univ, 59; M.A, Ohio Univ, 60; fel, Univ. Ill, 64-65, Ph.D.(Eng), 65. Asst. prof. ENG, Univ. Wash, 65-70, ASSOC. PROF, 70-71; UNIV. W.FLA, 71-, res. grant, 73. Univ. Wash. res. grants, summer 68 & 70. U.S.A.R, 59-67, Capt. MLA; Col. Eng. Asn; NCTE; Am. Stud. Asn. Humor in American literature; colonial American literature; American fiction. Publ: A cheerful nihilism: confidence and the absurd in American humorous fiction, Ind. Univ, 71; The comic Christ and the modern reader, Col. Eng, 2/70; The Dickens controversy in The Spirit of the times, PMLA, 2-3/70. Add: Faculty of English, University of West Florida, Pensacola, FL 32504.

HAUG, FREDERICK ERNEST, JR, b. Eau Claire, Wis, Aug. 21, 31; m. 65; c. 2. SPEECH. B.S, Univ. Wis-Eau Claire, 53; M.S, Univ. Wis, Madison, 54, Ph.D.(speech), 65, Teacher, High Sch, Wis, 54-57; instr. SPEECH, Univ. Wis, Ext. Div, 57-65, asst. prof, 65; assoc. prof, UNIV. WIS-EAU CLAIRE, 65-67, PROF. & DEAN SCH. ARTS & SCI, 67- Mem, Nat. Univ. Ext. Asn. Comt. Discussion & Debate, 58-65; guest prof, Univ. Colo, 65-; lectr. & consult, Univ. Wis, 65- Speech Commun. Asn; Am. Asn. Higher Educ; Am. Asn. Univ. Adminr. Add: Dept. of Speech, University of Wisconsin-Eau Claire, Eau Claire, WI 54701.

HAUGEN, CLAIR O, b. Folden Township, Minn, Apr. 11, 35; m. 59. DRAMATIC ART, THEATRE HISTORY. B.A, Concordia Col.(Moorhead, Minn), 57; M.A, Univ. Wis, 58, Vilas travel fel. & Ph.D.(speech & drama), 68; Univ. Iowa, 61-62. Instr. SPEECH & DRAMA, CONCORDIA COL.(MOORHEAD, MINN), 58-63, asst. prof, 63-68, ASSOC. PROF, 68-, CHMN. DEPT. SPEECH-COMMUN. & THEATRE ART, 69- U.S.A.R, 53-61, Sgt. Res. Soc. Victorian Periodicals; Soc. Theatre Res; Am. Theatre Asn. Victorian theatre history; historical foundations of Brecht-Artaud theory. Add: Dept. of Speech-Communication & Theatre Art, Concordia College, Moorhead, MN 56560.

HAUGH, OSCAR M, b. Hallock, Minn, Apr. 30, 09; m. 47; c. 2. ENGLISH, EDUCATION. B.S, Univ. Minn, Minneapolis, 31, M.A, 40, Ph.D.(Eng. & educ), 50. Teacher, Jr. High Sch, Minn, 28-35, chmn. dept. Eng, Jr-Sr. High Sch, 35-40, High Sch, 40-42 & 45-46; asst. prof. Eng. & educ. Wis. State Col, Superior, 46-50; UNIV. KANS, 50-52, assoc. prof. EDUC, 52-55, PROF, 55- Consult. curriculum stud, Kans. & Mo. Pub. Schs, 54-73; vis. prof. Eng. & educ, Univ. Costa Rica, 60-61; trustee Res. Found, NCTE, 61-66; lectr, Tex. Asn. Improvement of Reading, 64-66; insts. in Eng. & reading, NDEA, 66-68; consult. ed, Res. Teaching Eng, 67-73; ed, Eng. Educ, 69-73. Hope Award, 63. U.S.A.A.F, 42-45, Lt; Two Battle Stars & Presidential Citation. NCTE (dir, 54-73); Conf. Eng. Educ.(ed. publ, 67-73); fel. Nat. Conf. Res. Eng; Int. Reading Asn. Measurement of writing ability and English language skills; teaching of literature and literary appreciation; teaching of reading. Publ: Co-auth, Thesis handbook, Interstate, 59 & Effective English, Bks. 1, 2, 3 & 4, Allyn & Bacon, 61; auth, Tests in composition and literature, 64, co-auth, College English placement test, 69, auth, Test 2: composition, TAP, Form S, 71, Test 6: literature, TAP, Form S, 71 & co-auth, A testing program, lit. ser, bks. 7-12, 72, Houghton; co-auth, Teaching composition skills, U.S. Off. Educ, 68, High School English, quality or quantity?, Nat. Asn. Sec. Sch. Prin. Bull, 62; chap, In: Education of teachers of English, Appleton, 63 & Studies in language arts in grades 7-13, Kans. Stud. Educ, 66. Add: 1512 University Dr, Lawrence, KS 66044.

HAUGH, ROBERT FULTON, b. Independence, Kans, Jan. 9, 10; m. 41. ENGLISH. A.B, Univ. Kans, 35; Ph.D.(Eng), Univ. Mich. Asst, Univ. Okla, 39-40; teaching fel, UNIV. MICH, 40-43, instr. ENG, 47-48, asst. prof, 49-56, assoc. prof, 56-63, PROF, 63-, dir. creative writing prog, 66-74. Rackham fel, 46-47; Fulbright lectr, S.Africa, 59-60; mem. bd. gov, Assoc. Writing Progs, 70-74. Hopwood Award, 63. U.S.N, 43-46, Lt. MLA. American literature; modern fiction; creative writing. Joseph Conrad: discovery in design, Univ. Okla, 57; Nadine Gordimer: the meticulous vision, Twayne, 74; Conrad's chance: a progression d'effet, Mod. Fiction Stud; The second secret in the Scarlet letter, Col. Eng; Faulkner's corrupt temple, African Stud. in Eng, 61. Add: Dept. of English, University of Michigan, Ann Arbor, MI 48104.

HAUGHT, EVELYN HUNT, b. Anoka, Minn. ENGLISH, ENGLISH EDUCATION. B.S.Ed, North. Ill. Univ, 61, M.A, 64; Ph.D.(Eng. educ), Univ. Ill, Urbana, 70. Instr. Eng. & speech, Kaneland High Sch, 61-64; asst. prof. ENG, North. Ill. Univ, 61-70; ASSOC. PROF. ENG. & ENG. EDUC, EAST. ILL. UNIV, 70- NCTE (dir, 72-); Counc. Eng. Educ. Thought patterns of students during large and small group discussions of literature. Publ: Themes therapeutic, Clearing House, 12/68. Add: Dept. of English, Eastern Illinois University, Charleston, IL 61920.

HAUSER, DAVID ROSWELL, b. Detroit, Mich, June 2, 31; m. 51; c. 3. ENGLISH. A.B, Grinnell Col, 52; univ. scholar, Johns Hopkins Univ, M.A, 54, Ph.D, 56; Yale, 59-60. Instr. Eng, Miami Univ, 56-58, asst. prof, 58-60; Middlesex Col, Univ. West. Ont, 60-62, assoc. prof, 62-65; exec. dir, Soc. Relig. Higher Educ, 65-69; PROF. ENG. & LIB. STUD, ELMIRA COL, 69- Danforth grad. fel, 52-56; jr. instr, Johns Hopkins Univ, 53-56; res. fel, Yale Divinity Sch, 59-60; chmn. exec. comn, Danforth Teaching fels, 59-60; Can. Counc. fel, 61; mem. ed. bd, Soundings: An Interdisciplinary J, Soc. Relig. Higher Educ. Religion and literature; Romantic poets; higher education. Publ: Pope's Lodona and the uses of mythology, Stud. in Eng. Lit, summer 66; Higher education, Sounding, summer 69; contrib, Institutions in transition, Jossey-Bass, 70; plus others. Add: Dept. of English, Elmira College, Elmira, NY 14901.

HAUSER, GERARD ALAN, b. Buffalo, N.Y, May 20, 43; m. 65; c. 2. RHETORIC. A.B, Canisius Col, 65; M.A, Univ. Wis, Madison, 66, NDEA fel, 66-69, Ph.D.(speech), 70. Teaching asst. SPEECH, Univ. Wis, 66-69; asst. prof, PA. STATE UNIV, UNIVERSITY PARK, 69-73, ASSOC. PROF, 73- Speech Commun. Asn; East. Commun. Asn. History of rhetorical theory; philosophy and rhetoric. Publ: Co-auth, Richard Nixon's April 30th, 1970 address on Cambodia: the ceremony of confrontation, Speech Monogr, 8/73, Weaver's rhetorical theory: axiology and the adjustment of belief, invention, and judgment, Quart. J. Speech, 10/73 & McKeon's philosophy of communication: architectonic and interdisciplinary arts, Philos. & Rhetoric, fall 73; plus four others. Add: Dept. of Speech Communication, 223 Sparks Bldg, Pennsylvania State University, University Park, PA 16802.

HAUTH, LUSTER E, b. Pueblo, Colo, May 17, 29; m. 54; c. 2. RHETORIC, PUBLIC ADDRESS. B.A, Univ. Redlands, 53, M.A, 58; Ph.D.(speech), Univ. Iowa, 62. Instr. SPEECH, Univ. Iowa, 57-60; Phoenix Col, 60-64; ASSOC. PROF, CALIF. STATE UNIV, LONG BEACH, 64-, Found. res. grant, 68. Lectr. & speech consult, Charm Unlimited, Calif, 65- U.S.N.R, Lt.(jg) (Ret). Speech Commun. Asn. Rhetorical criticism; communication; history. Publ: Public speaking; communication in action, Bruno, 70; Voice improvement: the speech teacher's responsiblity, Speech Teacher, 1/61; Uncompromising spirit: George Whitefield, preaching, J. Homiletics, 1/69. Add: Dept. of Speech, California State University, Long Beach, 6101 E. Seventh St, Long Beach, CA 90840.

HAVEN, RICHARD, b. Bennington, Vt, Aug. 22, 24; m. 50; c. 1. ENGLISH LITERATURE. A.B, Harvard, 50; Fulbright fel. & B.Litt, Oxford, 53; Ph.D. (Eng. lit), Princeton, 58. Instr. ENG, UNIV. MASS, AMHERST, 52-58, asst. prof, 58-63, assoc. prof, 63-69, PROF, 69- Danforth Found. teachers grant, 56-57; Fulbright lectr, Lahore, Pakistan, 60-61; Nat. Endowment for Humanities res. grant, 67-68; co-ed, Victorian Periodicals Newsletter, 70; adv. ed, Wordsworth Circle, 70- U.S.A, 43-46. MLA; AAUP; Eng. Inst. Romanticism; S.T. Coleridge; nineteenth-century periodicals. Publ: Patterns of consciousness, Univ. Mass, 69; The romantic art of Charles Lamb, Eng. Lit. Hist, 63; Wordsworth and the language of poetry, Masterpieces of Lit, 66; Ancient mariner in the nineteenth century, Stud. Romanticism, 72; plus others. Add: Dept. of English, University of Massachusetts, Amherst, MA 01002.

HAVENS, DANIEL F, b. Shanghai, China, Jan. 23, 31; U.S. citizen; m. 57; c. 3. ENGLISH, CREATIVE WRITING. B.A, Univ. Mich, 56, M.A, 57, Ph.D. (Eng), 65. Teaching fel. Eng, Univ. Mich, 57-61; instr, Univ. Cincinnati, 61-65; ASSOC. PROF. AM. LIT, SOUTH. ILL. UNIV, EDWARDSVILLE, 65- U.S.N, 51-54. MLA; Midwest Mod. Lang. Asn. Colonial American literature; Early American drama. Publ: The Columbia muse of comedy: the development of a native tradition in early American social comedy, 1787-1845, South. Ill. Univ, 73. Add: Dept. of English, Language & Literature, Southern Illinois University, Edwardsville, IL 62025.

HAVENS, PAUL SWAIN, b. Lawrenceville, N.J, Sept. 19, 03; m. 30; c. 3. ENGLISH. A.B, Princeton, 25; Rhodes scholar, Oxford, 25-28, B.Litt, 28, M.A, 32; LL.D, Washington & Jefferson Univ, 36, Dickinson Col, 46; Lafayette Col, 63; L.H.D, Moore Col. Art, 62; Litt.D, Wilson Col, 70. Instr. Eng, Princeton, 28-30; asst. prof. Eng, Scripps Col, 30-36; pres, WILSON COL, 36-70, EMER. PRES, 70-, trustee. Mem. grad. fac, Claremont Cols, 30-36, secy, Eng. grad. fac, 33-34; ed. The Am Oxonian, 49-55; Frihedsmedaille of King Christian X, Denmark. MLA; Am. Asn. Rhodes Scholars. Add: 124 Norland Ave, Chambersburg, PA 17201.

HAVERFIELD, ROBERT WALTER, b. Kansas City, Mo, June 28, 19; m. 44; c. 2. JOURNALISM, ADVERTISING. B.J, Univ. Mo, 41, A.M, 57. Advertising dir, Mo. Power & Light Co, 45-48; asst. prof. JOUR, SCH. JOUR, UNIV. MO-COLUMBIA, 48-59, assoc. prof, 59-71, PROF, 71-, PLACEMENT DIR, 63- Summer fels, Int. Harvester, 54, Am. Asn. Advertising Agencies, 61, Publ. Relat. Soc. Am, 63; consult, Leo Burnett Ltd, London, 73. Intel.C, U.S.N.R, 41-45, Lt. Asn. Educ. in Jour; Am. Libr. Trustees Asn.(dir, 63-67); Am. Acad. Advertising; Col. Placement Counc. Publ: 100 books on advertising, Univ. Mo, 61, 65, 69 & 73; Newspapers need help, Kans. Publisher, 5/68; Interns earn credits, get training and pay, Ed. & Publ, 7/68; Journalism teachers are in demand, Iowa Journalist, 10/68; plus others. Add: 507 Medavista Dr, Columbia, MO 65201.

HAVHOLM, PETER LEO, b. Portland, Ore, Apr. 15, 42; m. 66; c. 2. ENGLISH, SPEECH. A.B, Shimer Col, 62; A.M, Univ. Conn, 70, Ph.D.(Eng), 72. ASST. PROF. ENG. & SPEECH, COL. WOOSTER, 71- U.S.N, 64-68, Lt.(jg). MLA. Rudyard Kipling's prose and poetry; literary criticism. Add: Dept. of English, College of Wooster, Wooster, OH 44691.

HAVIGHURST, WALTER, b. Appleton, Wis, Nov, 28, 01; m. 30. ENGLISH. A.B, Univ. Denver, 24; Univ. London, 26-27; A.M, Columbia Univ, 28; D.Litt, Lawrence Col, 47, Ohio Wesleyan Univ, 47; L.H.D, Miami Univ, 60, Marietta, Col, 61. Asst. prof. ENG, MIAMI UNIV, 28-35, assoc. prof, 35-42, prof, 42-49, res. prof, 49-68, Regents prof, 68-69, EMER. RES. PROF, 69- Friends of Am. Writers Prize, 46; Ohioana Libr. Asn. Medals, 46-50; Am. Asn. State & Local Hist. Award of Merit, 57. Authors Guild; Soc. Am. Hist. American literature; Great Lakes history and transportation; midwest history and literature. Publ: The long ships passing, 42, Signature of time, 49 & Voices on the river, 64, Macmillan; The Miami years 1809-1959, River to the west, 70 & Men of old Miami, 74, Putnam; The heartland, Harper, 62; Three flags at the straits, Prentice-Hall, 66; Alexander Spotswood: portrait of a governor, Colonial Williamsburg, 67. Add: Shadowy Hills, Oxford, OH 45056.

HAVILAND, J. BERNARD, b. Gloversville, N.Y, Oct. 22, 15; m. 47; c. 2. ENGLISH LITERATURE, DRAMA. B.A, Princeton, 38; M.A, Harvard, 43; Ph.D.(Eng), Univ. Dublin, 60. Teacher. ENG, Westtown Sch, Pa, 38-68; assoc. prof, WEST CHESTER STATE COL, 68-71, PROF, 71- Renaissance Soc. Am; Shakespeare Asn. Am; MLA. Shakespeare. Publ: Reading more effectively: reading shows you what to look for, In: The wonderful world of books, Houghton, 53. Add: Dept. of English, West Chester State College, West Chester, PA 19380.

HAWEELI, EDWARD M, b. Berlin, N.H, Nov. 10, 08; m. 52. ENGLISH. B.A, Univ. N.H, 33; M.A, Cornell Univ, 38; Harvard, summer, 47. Instr. hist. & Eng, Sanborn Sem, 33-35; head dept. Eng, Northwood Sch, Lake Placid, 42-44; Coburn Class. Inst, 44-45; instr, Tilton Sch, 45-47; WORCESTER JR. COL, 47-48, assoc. prof. ENG. & head dept. lib. arts, 48-70, prof, 70-73, EMER. PROF, 73- Col. Eng. Asn; NCTE; MLA. Elizabethan literature; Romantic period in English literature. Add: 24 Saxon Rd, Worcester, MA 01602.

HAWES, DAVID STEWART, b. Showhegan, Maine, June 17, 10; m. 51; c. 4. THEATRE, DRAMA. B.A, Dartmouth Col, 34, M.A, Cornell Univ, 40; Ph.D. (speech, drama), Stanford Univ, 54. Head dept. Eng, High Sch, Maine, 34-40; instr. Eng, Mont. State Col, 40-42; exec. off, U.S. Army Univ, France, 45-46, lectr. acting, 46-49; asst. prof, Eng, East. Mich. Univ, 49-50; speech & drama, Stanford Univ, 50-52; instr. dramatic art, Univ. Calif, Berkeley, 52-54; speech, Univ. ILL, 54-55; ASSOC. PROF. THEATRE & DRAMA, IND. UNIV, BLOOMINGTON, 55- U.S.A.F, 42-46, Capt. Am. Theatre Asn.(news ed, Educ. Theatre J, 57-60); AAUP. American theatre and drama; American humor; acting. Publ: John Brougham as playwright, Educ. Theatre J, 10/57; Artemus Ward will speak a piece, Quart J. Speech, 12/64; Much ado about John Broughham and Jim Fisk, Midcontinent Am. Stud. J, spring 67. Add: Dept. of Theatre & Drama, Indiana University, Bloomington, IN 47401.

HAWES, WILLIAM, b. Grand Rapids, Mich, Mar. 6, 31; m. 61; c. 2. COMMUNICATIONS. A.B, East. Mich. Univ, 55; M.A, Univ. Mich, 56, Ph.D. (speech, broadcasting), 60; Univ. St. Thomas (Tex), 69; Mus. Fine Arts, Houston, 70. Teaching asst, Univ. Mich, 56-58; instr. Eng. & speech, East. Mich. Univ, 58-60; dir. div. radio-TV-film, Tex. Christian Univ, 60-64; vis. asst. prof. & dir. radio, Univ. N.C, Chapel Hill, 64-65; ASSOC. PROF. COMMUN. & TV/FILM PRODUCER, UNIV. HOUSTON, 65- TV instr. drama, East. & Cent. Mich. Univs, WJRT, summer 59; instr. theater, Nat. Music Camp, Interlochen, Mich, summer 59; exec. producer films, Les Preludes, HMS Pinafore, Mathias der Maler, TCU: Century of Challenge, 61-63;

TV staff, WTOP-TV, Wash, D.C, summer 64; exec. producer TV, The Future We Face, KTVT, 61-64; Col. News Conf, KHTV, 67-68, exec. producer & host, Campus Workshop, 72-; producer & anchorman, News on Campus, KHTV & KUHT, 67-72; producer-dir, Holden's Heroes, Variable Annuity Life Ins. Co, 71; owner & assoc. dir, Children's Playhouse, 72-; fac. adv, Pub. Serv. Announcements, KHOU-TV, 72-; fel, Nat. Conf. Broadcasting's Critical Challenges, Int. Radio & TV Soc, N.Y, 73 & 74. Hopwood Award for Drama, Univ. Mich, 57. Air Nat. Guard, 50-54; U.S.A.F, 51-53. Speech Commun. Asn; Broadcast Educ. Asn; Am. Film Inst; Am. Fed. Film Soc; Int. Radio TV Soc. Television performance; history and drama; cinema history and criticism. Publ: Producing and directing, In: Radio broadcasting, Hastings, 67, rev. ed, 73; co-auth, ETV's first station—fifteen years later, EBU Rev, 11/68; auth, Toward professionalism in broadcasting education, Feedback, 2/72; plus others. Add: Dept. of Communications, University of Houston, Houston, TX 77004.

HAWKES, CAROL, b. New York, N.Y, Dec. 28, 21. ENGLISH. A.B, Barnard Col, Columbia Univ, 43; M.A, Columbia Univ, 44, Ph.D.(Eng), 49. Temporary instr. ENG, Hunter Col, 49-50; Lib. Arts Div, Katharine Gibbs Sch, 50-57; PROF, FINCH COL, 57-, DIR. RES. ON GRAD. STUD, 65-, SECY. OF FAC, 66-, CHMN. DEPT. ENG. & COMP. LIT. & FAC. TRUSTEE, 72- MLA; Mod. Humanities Res. Asn; Col. Eng. Asn; NCTE; AAUP. John Galsworthy; T.S. Eliot; master's degree programs, especially in relation to the liberal arts. Publ: Master's degree programs and the liberal arts college, Educ. Resources Inform. Ctr, U.S. Off. Educ, 68; The paradox of realism, Acta Tenth Triennial Congr, Fed. Int. Langues et Lit. Modernes, Librairie Klincksieck, Paris, 68; Galsworthy the realist, Eng. Lit. Transition, 12/70; Interdisciplinary study and the small college curriculum, ADE Bull, 9/72; plus others. Add: Dept. of English, Finch College, 52 E. 78th St, New York, NY 10021.

HAWKES, JOHN C.B, JR, b. Stamford, Conn, Aug. 17, 25; m. 47; c. 4. ENGLISH. A.B, Harvard, 49. Vis. lectr. ENG, Harvard, 55-56, instr, 56-58; asst. prof, BROWN UNIV, 58-62, assoc. prof, 62-67, PROF, 67-, UNIV. PROF, 73- Nat. Inst. Arts & Lett. grant, 62; Guggenheim fel, 62-63; Ford Found. grant, 64-65; mem. Panel Educ. Innovation, Wash, D.C, 66-67; Rockefeller Found. fel, 67-68. U.S.A, 44-45. Am. Acad. Arts & Sci. Creative writing; contemporary fiction and drama. Publ: The cannibal, 49, The beetle leg, 51, The lime twig, 61, Second skin, 64, The innocent party, 66, The blood oranges, 71 & Death, sleep and the traveler, 74, New Directions; co-auth, The personal voice, Lippincott, 64. Add: Dept. of English, Brown University, Providence, RI 02912.

HAWKINS, GARY J, b. Youngstown, Ohio, Sept. 4, 37; m. 64. SPEECH. B.S, Ohio Univ, 59, NDEA fel, 59-62, M.A, 60, Ph.D.(speech), 64. Instr. SPEECH, Univ. Wash, 62-65; asst. prof, SAN FRANCISCO STATE UNIV, 65-68, ASSOC. PROF, 68- Speech Commun. Asn. History of Public address; experimental research in public address. Publ: Co-auth, The effects of variations in speakers' non-fluency upon audience ratings of attitude toward the speech topic and speakers' credibility, Speech Monogr, 3/67; auth, Peter Wentworth's unfinished address on freedom of speech, West. Speech, fall 67. Add: Dept. of Speech, San Francisco State University, San Francisco, CA 94132.

HAWKINS, HARRIETT B, b. Memphis, Tenn. ENGLISH. B.A, Newcomb Col, 60; M.A, Wash. Univ, 62, Ph.D.(Eng), 64; Oxford, 63-64. Instr. ENG, Swarthmore Col, 64-66; asst. prof, VASSAR COL, 66-69, ASSOC. PROF, 69- Folger fel, Folger Shakespeare Libr, summer 67; Nat. Found. Humanities summer grant, 68; Huntington Libr. fel, summer 69; Am. Counc. Learned Soc. fel, 73-74. MLA. Renaissance and Restoration drama. Publ: Likenesses of truth in Elizabethan and Restoration drama, Clarendon, 72; Jonson's use of traditional dream theory in The vision of delight, Mod. Philol, 67; Folly, incurable disease and Volpone, Stud. Eng. Lit, 68; plus one other. Add: Dept. of English, Vassar College, Poughkeepsie, NY 12601.

HAWKINS, MARION ELIZABETH, b. Kinnickinnic, Wis, Dec. 27, 16. ENGLISH. B.S, Wis. State Univ, River Falls, 38; M.S, Univ. Wis, Madison, 49, Ph.D.(Eng), 65; Univ. Minn, 50; Univ. Colo, 57. Teacher & debate coach, New Richmond High Sch, 38-41; chmn. dept. Eng. & dir. drama, Monroe Sr. High Sch, Wis, 41-44; teacher & adv. jour, Milwaukee—Pulaski High Sch, 44-46; assoc. prof. ENG, UNIV. WIS-RIVER FALLS, 64-65, PROF, 65-, dir. forensics, 46-56, dir. for. stud. Eng. & acad. adv. for. stud, 57-65, bd. dir, Univ. Wis. Found. AAUP; NCTE. Periodical essayists of the 18th century with emphasis on Oliver Goldsmith; American public address and discussion techniques; teaching of English as a second language. Add: Dept. of English, University of Wisconsin-River Falls, River Falls, WI 54022.

HAWKINS, ROBERT BENTLEY, b. Grand Rapids, Mich, Oct. 10, 24; m. 67; c. 5. SPEECH. A.B, Univ. Mich, 49, M.A, 52; Ph.D.(speech), Northwest. Univ, 61. Instr. high schs, Mich, 49-50 & 53; Iowa, 53-54; asst. gen. speech, Northwest. Univ, 54-56; instr. gen. speech & forensics, Wright Jr. Col, Ill, 56-59; asst. prof. speech & argument, SOUTH. ILL. UNIV, EDWARDSVILLE, 59-64, assoc. prof. debate, persuasion, radio-TV, 64-72, PROF. SPEECH, 72- C.Eng, U.S.A, 43-46, 50-52, Capt. Speech Commun. Asn. Self-concept studies in speech instruction; instructional development studies for basic course; dyadic non-verbal communication. Publ: Human approach to inter-personal communication in the hospital, Am. Asn. Nurse Anesthetists, 10/68; Reading a manuscript speech & Using audio-visual aids, U.S. Navy Speakers' Guide for 1968. Add: Dept. of Speech, Southern Illinois University, Edwardsville, IL 62025.

HAWKINS, SHERMAN HENRY, b. Akron, Ohio, Oct. 4, 29. ENGLISH. A.B, Harvard, 51; Fulbright fel, Oxford, 53-55, B.A, 55; Ph.D, Princeton, 60; hon. M.A, Wesleyan Univ, 72. Instr. Eng, Princeton, 57-61, asst. prof, Univ. Rochester, 65-71; KENAN PROF. HUMANITIES, WESLEYAN UNIV, 71- Lectr, Bryn Mawr Col, 63-64; Princeton bicentennial preceptorship, 63-65; Folger Libr. fel, 67-68; Am. Counc. Learned Soc. res. grant, 68. U.S.A, 53-55. Shakespeare; Renaissance. Publ: Mutabilitie and the cycle of the months, In: Form and convention in the poetry of Edmund Spenser, Columbia Univ, 61; The two worlds of Shakespearean comedy, Shakespeare Stud, III: 62-80; Samson's catharsis, Milton Stud, II: 211-230; plus others. Add: Dept. of English, Wesleyan University, Middletown, CT 06457.

HAWKS, PAUL NEWTON, JR, b. National City, Calif, Jan. 18, 43; m. 66. COMMUNICATIONS. B.A, Pac. Union Col, 64; M.A, Univ. Calif, Los Angeles, 66, Ph.D.(speech), 72. Asst. prof. SPEECH, Loma Linda Univ, 68-72; ASSOC. PROF, PAC. UNION COL, 72- Speech Commun. Asn. Rhetoric and public address. Add: Dept. of Speech, Pacific Union College, Angwin, CA 94508.

HAWORTH, HELEN ELLIS, b. Kenton, Tenn, July 25, 27; m. 49; c. 2. ENGLISH. B.A, Rollins Col, 49; A.M, Univ. Ill, 52, Ph.D.(Eng), 64. Instr. Eng, Purdue Univ, 56-57, indust. mgt, 57-60, vis. asst. prof, ENG, 64-65; asst. prof, UNIV. WATERLOO, 65-68, ASSOC. PROF, 68-, fac. summer res. fel, 67; Can. Counc. leave fel, 71-72. MLA; Keats-Shelley Asn; Asn. Can. Univ. Teachers Eng; Byron Soc; Wordsworth Soc. English Romantic poets, primarily Keats. Publ: The redemption of Cynthia, Humanities Asn. Bull, fall 67; Keats and the metaphor of vision, J. Eng. & Ger. Philol, summer 68; A thing of beauty is a joy forever?—early illustrated editions of Keats' poetry, Harvard Libr. Bull, 73. Add: Dept. of English, University of Waterloo, Waterloo, Ont, Can.

HAWTHORNE, LUCIA SHELIA, b. Baltimore, Md. SPEECH COMMUNICATION, THEATRE ARTS. B.S, Morgan State Col, 64; M.A, Wash. State Univ, 65; Ph.D.(speech commun), Pa. State Univ, University Park, 71. Teaching asst. speech, Wash. State Univ, 64-65; instr, Morgan State Col, 65-67; teaching asst, Pa. State Univ, 67-69; ASSOC. PROF. SPEECH & THEATRE ARTS & CHMN. DEPT, MORGAN STATE COL, 69- Speech Commun. Asn. (comn. on freedom of speech, 71-, chmn. comn. on prof. & social probs, 71-); East. Commun. Asn. Communication and human interaction; speech education; Black rhetoric. Add: Dept. of Speech Communication & Theatre Arts, Morgan State College, Cold Spring Lane & Hillen Rd, Baltimore, MD 21239.

HAWTHORNE, MARK D, b. Berea, Ohio, Dec. 9, 38; m. 60; c. 1. ENGLISH. B.A, Wake Forest Col, 60; M.A, Univ. Fla, 62, Ph.D.(Eng), 64. Asst. prof. ENG, N.C. State Univ, 64-67; JACKSONVILLE UNIV, 68-73, ASSOC. PROF. & CHMN. DIV. HUMANITIES, 73- MLA; S.Atlantic Mod. Lang. Asn.(chmn. Irish stud. circle, 72-73). Anglo-Irish literature; British Romantic and Victorian poetry and prose fiction. Publ: Doubt and dogma in Maria Edgeworth, Univ. Fla, 67; Tennyson's relation to the drama, South. Speech J, winter 64; Thomas Wolfe's use of the poetic fragment, Mod. Fiction Stud, autumn 65. Add: Dept. of English, Jacksonville University, Jacksonville, FL 32211.

HAY, ELOISE KNAPP, b. Chicago, Ill, Nov. 19, 26; m. 54; c. 2. ENGLISH. B.A, Elmira Col, 48; M.A, Radcliffe Col, 51, traveling fel, 56, Ph.D, 61; fel, Harvard, 51-54. Lectr, Tsuda-Juku Col, Japan, 54-55; asst. prof, Univ. Ill, Chicago, 61-64; assoc. scholar, Inst. Independent Stud, Radcliffe Col, 64-66; lectr. Eng, Univ. Calif, Santa Barbara, 67-70; LECTR. ENG. & AM. LIT, CONTINUING EDUC. DIV, SANTA BARBARA CITY COL, 71- Vis. prof. Am. lit, Univ. Delhi, 70-71; fac. adv, Alpha Lambda Delta, Univ. Calif, Santa Barbara, 71-; U.S.A. chmn, Int. Conf. on Conrad, 74; Nat. Endowment for Humanities sr. fel, 74-75. MLA. Modern British fiction, especially Joseph Conrad; politics in the English novel; modern English and American literature, especially Dickens and Conrad, Hawthorne and James. Publ: The political novels of Joseph Conrad, Univ. Chicago, 63; Lord Jim: from sketch to novel, Comp. Lit, 60 & In: Norton Critical edition of Lord Jim, 68; Conrad, between fact and fiction, Encounter, 72; Conrad, between Sartre and Socrates, Mod. Lang. Quart, 73 & 74. Add: 3310 Los Pinos Dr, Santa Barbara, CA 93105.

HAYASHI, TETSUMARO, b. Sakaido, Japan, Mar. 22, 29; U.S. citizen; m; c. 1 RENAISSANCE ENGLISH LITERATURE. B.A, Okayama Univ, 53; M.A, Univ. Fla, 57; M.A, Kent State Univ, 59, fel, 63-65, Ph.D.(Eng), 68. Asst. prof. Eng. & Japanese & assoc. dir. col. libr, Culver-Stockton Col, 59-63; instr. ENG, Kent State Univ, 65-68; asst. prof, BALL STATE UNIV, 68-72, ASSOC. PROF, 72- Ed-in-chief, Steinbeck Quart, 68-; ed. & proj. dir, Steinbeck Monogr. Ser, 70-; Folger Shakespeare Libr. sr. fel, Wash, D.C, summer 72; liaison off, Albert Schweitzer Awards Int. Counc, 73-75. John Steinbeck Soc. Am.(dir, 66-); Commun. Guild, Eng. Shakespeare and Robert Greene; Steinbeck and Hemingway. Publ: Sketches of American culture, Tarumi Shobo, Japan, 60; John Steinbeck: a concise bibliography, 67, Arthur Miller criticism, 69, ed, A looking glass for London and England, an Elizabethan text, 70 & auth, Robert Green criticism, Scarecrow; co-ed, Steinbeck: the man and his work, Ore. State Univ, 71; ed, Steinbeck's literary dimension, 73; auth, A new Steinbeck bibliography, 73; plus others. Add: Dept. of English, Ball State University, University Ave, Muncie, IN 47306.

HAYDEN, DONALD EUGENE, b. Blairstown, Mo, Aug. 28, 15. ENGLISH. A.B, Univ. Mo, 36, A.M, 37; Ph.D, Syracuse Univ, 46. Instr. Eng, Syracuse Univ, 37-42; head Eng. dept, Westbrook Jr. Col, Maine, 42-47; from assoc. prof. to PROF. ENG, UNIV. TULSA, 47-, asst. dean, 56-57, dean lib. arts, 57-70. Col. Eng. Asn; Int. Soc. Gen. Semantics. 19th century English literature; college English. Publ: A semantics workbook, Fearon Publ; Wordsworth's borderers, Mod. Lang. Notes; After conflict, quiet, Exposition: co-auth, Classics in sematics, 65, Classics in linguistics, 67 & ed, Classics in composition, 71, Philos. Libr; ed. & contrib, Introspection, Univ. Tulsa, 71. Add: Dept. of English, University of Tulsa, Tulsa, OK 74104.

HAYDEN, JOHN OLIN, b. Los Angeles, Calif, Dec. 18, 32; m. 65; c. 2. ENGLISH. B.A, Univ. Calif, Santa Barbara, 58; M.A, Columbia Univ, 59, Noble grant, 59-63; Ph.D.(Eng), 65; Cambridge, 62-63. Asst. prof. ENG, Univ. Colo, 64-66, UNIV. CALIF, DAVIS, 66-70, ASSOC. PROF, 70-, summer grant, 67. Humanities Inst. Award grant, 68 & 69; Nat. Endowment for Humanities fel, 71-72. U.S.A.F, 51-55. MLA. English Romantic literature; the history of literary criticism; Wordsworth. Publ: The romantic reviewers, 1802-24, Univ. Chicago & Routledge & Kegan Paul, 68; ed, Scott: the critical heritage, Barnes & Noble & Routledge and Kegan Paul, 70; Romantic bards and British reviewers, Univ. Nebr. & Routledge & Kegan Paul, 71; The political works of William Wordsworth, Penguin, 74. plus one article. Add: Dept. of English, University of California, Davis, CA 95616.

HAYES, ALBERT McHARG, b. Milwaukee, Wis, Dec. 14, 09; m. 35; c. 2. ENGLISH, HUMANITIES. A.B, Dartmouth Col, 30; Ph.D, Princeton, 33.

Mem. fac. Eng, Williston Acad, 33-34; Duquesne Univ, 34-38; Bowling Green State Univ, 38-43; PROF. ENG. & HUMANITIES, UNIV. CHICAGO, 43-, REGISTRAR, 69-, asst. dean col, 59-65, col. exam, 63-67. Fulbright lectr, Univ. Philippines, 55-56. MLA. General education in humanities. Add: 5515 Woodlawn Ave, Chicago, IL 60637.

HAYES, ANN LOUISE, b. Los Angeles, Calif, May 13, 24; wid. ENGLISH. B.A, Stanford Univ, 48, M.A, 50. Instr. ENG, CARNEGIE-MELLON UNIV, 58-60, asst. prof, 60-65, assoc. prof, 65-74, PROF, 74- Advanced placement English programs; 17th and 20th century poetry. Publ: Co-auth, Model for an advanced placement English course, ERIC, 68; auth, The dancer's step, Three Rivers, 73; Essay on the sonnets in Starre of poets: discussions of Shakespeare, 66 & On reading Marianne Moore, 70, Carnegie Ser. Eng; plus poems in South. Rev, Am. Scholar & Va. Quart. Rev. Add: Dept. of English, Carnegie-Mellon University, Pittsburgh, PA 15213.

HAYES, ELIZABETH GENTRY, b. Sapulpa, Okla, Oct. 22, 09; m. 31; c. 2. ENGLISH, LINGUISTICS. A.B, San Jose State Col, 49; A.M, Stanford Univ, 52, Ph.D.(Eng), 64. Instr. ENG, San Jose State Col, 54-57; asst. prof, Southwest. Univ.(Tex), 58-63; Univ. Hawaii, 64; assoc. prof, SOUTHWEST TEX. STATE UNIV, 64-67, PROF, 67-, dir. freshman Eng, 67-70. Consult, NDEA area stud. prog. Tex. plan for strengthening instr. in sci, math, Eng. & mod. for. lang, 65-66. MLA; AAUP. English literature, especially Restoration and 18th century drama; linguistics, especially grammar for teachers of English. Publ: Charlotte Ramsay Lennox: the female Quixote; or, the adventures of Arabella, Univ. Microfilms & Diss. Abstr, 64. Add: Dept. of English, Southwest Texas State University, San Marcos, TX 78666.

HAYES, JAMES THOMAS, b. Franklin, Ky, Dec. 3, 23; m. 47; c. 2. COMPOSITION & LITERATURE. B.S, Austin Peay State Col, 50; M.A, West. Ky. State Col, 53; Mich. State Univ, 60, 62; L.H.D, Geneva Col, 67. Teacher, High Schs, Ky, 46-54; Mich, 53-62; asst. prof. ENG, MURRAY STATE UNIV, 62-65, ASSOC. PROF. & DIR. FRESHMAN ENG, 65- Spec. lectr. Eng. grammar, Cent. Mich. Univ, 62; consult, Title III proj. in improving instr. in Eng. lang. & lit, 66-67. U.S.A, 43-46, 50-51. NCTE; Conf. Col. Compos. & Commun; Counc. Basic Educ; fel. Royal Soc. Arts. Pedagogy of teaching language command and writing techniques; teacher education and certification; foreign societies for advancement of the arts. Publ: Rhetoric: then and now, Holbrook, 70; Introduction to natal astrology, Univ. Bks, 73; Prescriptive grammar begets decency, Mich. Sec. Sch. J, 62; Instant theme writing, Classroom Practices in Teaching Eng, 66-67; Response to the use of Mr, Col. Compos. & Commun, 10/67. Add: 1605 Belmonte Dr, Murray, KY 42071.

HAYES, MERWYN ALFRED, b. Stambaugh, Mich, Aug. 21, 38; m. 58; c. 2. SPEECH, HISTORY. B.A, Macalester Col, 60; M.A, Univ. Ore, 62; Ph.D. (speech), Univ. Ill, 66. Asst. prof. speech, Univ. Ga, 62-67; WAKE FOREST UNIV, 67-72, ASSOC. PROF. SPEECH COMMUN, 72- Speech Commun. Asn; South. Speech Commun. Asn; Int. Commun. Asn; Am. Soc. Training & Develop. Management; Johnson impeachment trial; Luther Martin. Publ: Co-auth, Interpersonal communication, Holbrook, 74; Georgia symposium series, Speech Teacher, 11/67; Nonverbal communication: expression without words, In: Readings in interpersonal and organizational communication, 2nd ed, Holbrook, 73. Add: Dept. of Speech Communication, Wake Forest University, Box 7347, Winston-Salem, NC 27109.

HAYFORD, HARRISON (MOSHER), b. Belfast, Maine, Nov. 1, 16; m. 38; c. 4. ENGLISH. B.A, Tufts Col, 38, M.A, 40; Selden fel, Yale, 41-42, Ph.D, 45. From instr. to PROF. ENG, NORTHWEST. UNIV, EVANSTON, 42- Ford grant, 51-52; Fulbright prof, Italy, 56; Guggenheim fel, 63. MLA. American literature. Publ: Co-auth, Reader and writer; co-ed, Melville's Billy Budd, sailor. Add: Dept. of English, Northwestern University, Evanston, IL 60201.

HAYMAN, ALLEN, b. Albany, N.Y, Jan. 29, 26; m. 51; c. 3. AMERICAN LITERATURE. A.B, Syracuse Univ, 48; M.A, Univ. Ill, 51, univ. fel, summer 53, Ph.D.(Eng), 61. Asst. ENG, Univ. Ill, 48-58; instr, PURDUE UNIV, WEST LAFAYETTE, 58-61, asst. prof, 61-67, ASSOC. PROF, 67- Ed, Accent, 48-58; adv. ed, Mod. Fiction Stud, 58-; J. Popular Cult, 67-; Purdue Res. Found. grants, summers 61 & 63; Fulbright prof, Univ. Ljubljana, 66-67. U.S.N, 43-46. MLA; Am. Stud. Asn; NCTE; Melville Soc. Nineteenth century periodical criticism of prose fiction; 19th and 20th century American fiction. Publ: Co-ed, New voices in American studies, Purdue Univ, 66; auth, The real and the original: Herman Melville's theory of prose fiction, Mod. Fiction Stud, 62; John Updike, Problemi, 5/67. Add: Dept. of English, Heavilon Hall, Purdue University, Lafayette, IN 47907.

HAYMAN, DAVID, b. New York, N.Y, Jan. 7, 27; m. 51; c. 2. ENGLISH. B.A, N.Y. Univ, 48; D.Univ, Univ. Paris, 55. Instr. Eng, Univ. Tex, 55-57, asst. prof, 57-59, assoc. prof, 59-65; PROF. comp. lit, Univ. Iowa, 65-72, chmn. dept, 66-68; Am. lit, Univ. Paris VIII, 72-73; PROF. COMP. LIT. & CHMN. DEPT, UNIV. WIS-MADISON, 73- Guggenheim fel, 58-59. U.S.N, 45-46. MLA; Mod. Humanities Res. Asn, Gt. Brit; Am. Comp. Lit. Asn. Comparative literature; British modern literature; critical theory. Publ: A first-draft version of Finnegans wake, Univ. Tex, 63; Louis-Ferdinand Céline, Columbia Univ, 65; Ulysses: the mechanics of meaning, Prentice-Hall, 70; The Tristan and Isolde theme in Finnegans wake: a study of the sources and evolution of a theme, Comp. Lit. Stud, 64; Forms of folly in Joyce: a study of clowning in Ulysses, ELH, 68; Au-delà de Bakhtine, Poetique, 73. Add: Dept. of Comparative literature, 924 Van Hise Hall, University of Wisconsin-Madison, 1220 Linden Dr, Madison, WI 53706.

HAYNE, BARRIE STEWART, b. Brisbane, Australia, Jan. 12, 34; m. 73. ENGLISH, AMERICAN LITERATURE. B.A, Univ. Queensland, 56; Frank Knox fel, Harvard, 59, 60, A.M, 60, Ph.D.(Eng), 64. Lectr. ENG, Univ. New Eng, Australia, 57-59; UNIV. TORONTO, 64-65, asst. prof, 65-69, ASSOC. PROF, 69-, chmn. combined depts. Eng, 70-72. Intel. Corps, Citizen Mil. Forces, Australia, 53-58, Lt. MLA; Can. Asn. Am. Stud; Am. Stud. Asn. Nineteenth century America. Publ: Yankee in the patriarchy: T.B. Thorpe's reply to Uncle Tom's cabin, Am. Quart, summer 68; Ossian, Scott and Cooper's Indians, J. Am. Stud, 7/69; Standing on neutral ground: Charles Jacobs Peterson of Peterson's, Pa. Mag. Hist. Biog, 10/69. Add: Dept. of English, New College, University of Toronto, Toronto, Ont. M5S 1A1, Can.

HAYS, JOHN Q, b. Van Buren, Ark, July 27, 06. ENGLISH & AMERICAN LITERATURE. A.B, Univ. Mo, 29, A.M, 32; Univ. Chicago, summers, 34, 36; Ph.D, Univ. Calif, 42. Instr. ENG, Tex. A&M Univ, 29-35, asst. prof, 35-41, assoc. prof, 41-45, PROF, 45-68; STEPHEN F. AUSTIN STATE UNIV, 68- Fulbright vis. prof, Univ. Cape Town, 65. NCTE; MLA; Am. Stud. Asn; S.Cent. Mod. Lang. Asn. Publ: Co-ed, Readings for thought and expression, MacMillan, 55. Add: Dept. of English, Stephen F. Austin State University, Nacogdoches, TX 75961.

HAYS, PETER L, b. Bremerhaven, Ger, Apr. 18, 38; U.S. citizen; m. 63; c. 3. ENGLISH. A.B, Univ. Rochester, 59; M.A, N.Y. Univ, 61; Ph.D.(Eng), Ohio State Univ, 65. Instr. Eng, Ohio State Univ, 65-66; asst. prof, UNIV. CALIF, DAVIS, 66-72, ASSOC. PROF. ENG. & COMP. LIT, 72-, CHMN. DEPT. ENG, 74- summer fac. fel, 67. U.S.A, 59-60. MLA. American literature; myth criticism; drama. Publ: The limping hero, N.Y. Univ, 71. Add: Dept. of English, University of California, Davis, CA 95616.

HAYWARD, RALPH MALCOLM, III, b. Newark, N.J, June 21, 44; m. 67; c. 1. ENGLISH LITERATURE. B.A, Drew University, 67; M.A, Tulane Univ, 68, Ph.D.(Eng. lit), 71. ASST. PROF. ENG, IND. UNIV. PA, 71- MLA; Mediaeval Acad. Am. Nineteenth century British poetry; Renaissance Italian poetry. Add: Armstrong Center, Indiana University of Pennsylvania, Kittanning, PA 16201.

HAYWOOD, CHARLES, Musicology. See Volume I, History.

HAYWORTH, DONALD, b. Toledo, Iowa, Jan. 13, 98; m. 34; c. 3. SPEECH. A.B, Grinnell Col, 18; M.A, Univ. Chicago, 21; Ph.D, Univ. Wis, 29. Prof. speech, Penn Col, 23-27; Univ. Akron, 27-37; Mich. State Univ, 37-65; CONSULT, SOCIAL SECURITY ADMIN, WASH, D.C, 65- Consult, Fed. Exten. Serv, Dept. Agr, Wash, D.C, 63-65. Methods of teaching beginning public speaking; presidential elections. Publ: Introduction to public speaking, 36 & Public speaking, 40, Ronald; co-auth, Oral argument, Harper, 34. Add: 1311 Delaware Ave. S.W, Washington, DC 20024.

HAZARD, PATRICK DAVID, b. Battle Creek, Mich, Feb. 8, 27; div; c. 3. AMERICAN LITERATURE & CULTURE. Ph.B, Univ. Detroit, 49; M.A, West. Reserve Univ, 52, Fund Advan. Educ. fel, 55, Ph.D, 57. Asst. prof. Eng, Trenton State Col, 56-57; fel. Am. civilization, Univ. Pa, 57-59, asst. prof. commun, 59-61; assoc. prof. Eng. & dir. Inst. Am. Stud. E. W. Ctr, Univ. Hawaii, 61-62; PROF, BEAVER COL, 62-, chmn. dept. Eng, 62-69. Dir. films & stud. tours, Ctr. Internationalising Eng, 72- U.S.N.R, 44-46. Am. Stud. Asn; NCTE; MLA. Mass communication history; impact of industrialization on art; English as a world language and literature. Publ: Documentary history of broadcasting, Folkways, 63; Hawaii, Doubleday, 64; co-auth, Language and literacy today, Sci. Res. Assoc, 65 & TV as art: some essays in criticism, Nat. Counc. Teachers Eng, 66; A plea for media pluralism, PCTE J, 72; Skin flix and kultur, FLI Quart, 73. Add: 8 Longford St, Philadelphia, PA 19136.

HAZEL, HARRY CHARLES, JR, b. Seattle, Wash, May 28, 36; m. 65; c. 3. SPEECH COMMUNICATION. A.B, Gonzaga Univ, 60; M.A, Univ. Wash, 66; Ph.D.(speech), Wash. State Univ, 72. Instr. SPEECH, Yakima Valley Col, 66-70; ASST. PROF, GONZAGA UNIV, 71-, DIR. SUMMER SESSIONS & CONTINUING EDUC, 73- Speech Commun. Asn. Medieval communication theory and public address; American political campaigns; homiletics. Publ: The Bonaventuran Ars concionandi, Western Speech, fall 72 & In: S. Bonaventura 1274-1974, Vol. II, Col. St. Bonaventure, Rome, 73; Harry Truman: practical persuader, Today's Speech, spring 74. Add: Dept. of Communication Arts, Gonzaga University, Spokane, WA 99202.

HAZELRIG, MATTHEW S, JR, b. Decatur, Ga, Dec. 10, 21; m. 57. ENGLISH. B.A, Emory Univ, 43; M.A, Univ. Chicago, 48; Columbia Univ, 51-53; South. Fel. Fund, 56-57. Instr. ENG, Auburn Univ, 48-50; Univ. Ky, 53-56; asst. prof, CLEVELAND STATE UNIV, 57-70, ASSOC. PROF, 70- U.S.A.A.F, 43-45, 2nd Lt. MLA. Nineteenth century British literature. Add: Dept. of English, Cleveland State University, Cleveland, OH 44115.

HAZELRIGG, CHARLES T, b. Mt. Sterling, Ky, Aug. 18, 15; m. 42; c. 2. ENGLISH & AMERICAN LITERATURE. A.B, Centre Col, 37; M.A, Yale, 42, Ph.D, 47. Asst. prof. ENG, CENTRE COL, 47-49, assoc. prof, 49-51, prof, 51-72, MATTON PROF, 72-, CHMN. DEPT, 49-, CHMN. DIV. HUMANITIES, 72- Chmn, Danville Counc. Human Relat, 65-67. U.S.N.R, 42-45, Lt. MLA; NCTE. Nineteenth century American literature. Publ: American literary pioneer, Bookman Associates, 53; Want to be a college teacher? Deke Quart, 62; co-auth, Principles and standards in composition, Ky. Counc. Teachers Eng, 56. Add: Dept. of English, Centre College, Danville, KY 40422.

HAZELTON, RICHARD MARQUARD, b. Camden, N.J, Oct. 13, 18; m. 49; c. 3. MEDIAEVAL ENGLISH PHILOLOGY. B.A, Univ. Calif, Los Angeles, 51, M.A, Berkeley, 52; Louis Bevier fel, Rutgers, 53-54, Ph.D.(Eng), 56; Fulbright fel, Oxford, 55. Instr. ENG, Ohio State Univ, 55-58; asst. prof, WASH. UNIV, 58-61, from assoc. prof. to PROF, 61- Vis. prof, Waseda Univ, Japan, 63-64; Guggenheim Found. fel, 64-65. U.S.A.F, 42-49, Capt. Mediaeval Acad. Am; MLA. Chaucer's comic art; Middle English poetry; Mediaeval schoolbook commentaries. Publ: Chaucer and Cato, Speculum, 7/60; Chaucer's Parson's tale and the Moralium Dogma Philosophorum, Traditio, 60; The Manciple's tale: parody and critique, J. Eng. & Germanic Philol, 1/63. Add: Dept. of English, Washington University, Skinker & Forsyth, St. Louis, MO 63130.

HAZEN, ALLEN TRACY, b. Portland, Conn, Nov. 4, 04; m. 45; c. 1. ENGLISH LITERATURE. A.B, Yale, 27, Ph.D, 35; A.M, Harvard, 32. Instr. Eng, Yale, 35-40, res. asst. bibliog, 40-42; fel, Branford Col, 38-42; instr. Eng, Hunter Col, 42-45; assoc. prof, Univ. Chicago, 45-47, prof, 47-48, dir. univ. libr, 47-48; prof. ENG, COLUMBIA UNIV, 48-71, EMER. PROF, 71- Guggenheim fel, 52-53; ed, Yale Ed. Johnson, 55-66. MLA; Bibliog. Soc. Am; Bibliog. Soc, London. Bibliography. Publ: Johnson's prefaces and dedications; Bibliography of Strawberry Hill Press & Bibliography of Horace Walpole, Yale; Catalogue of Horace Walpole's library, 3 vols, Yale, 69. Add: 460 Riverside Dr, New York, NY 10027.

HAZEN, JAMES, b. Boston, Mass, Mar. 9, 35; m. 61; c. 2. ENGLISH. B.A, Princeton Univ, 57; Ph.D.(Eng), Univ. Wis, 63. Res. asst, Univ. Wis, 62-63; instr. ENG, Yale, 63-66; asst. prof, Univ. Mo-St. Louis, 66-71; ASSOC. PROF, UNIV. NEV, LAS VEGAS, 71-, acting dean grad. col, 72. U.S.A.R, 57-65, 1st Lt. MLA. English poetry and fiction, 19th and 20th centuries. Publ: The tragedy of Tess Durbeyfield, Tex. Stud. Lit. & Lang, 69; Blake's Tyger and Milton's Beasts, Blake Stud, summer 71; Love in Neutral tones, Victorian Poetry, autumn 71. Add: Dept. of English, University of Nevada, Las Vegas, NV 89109.

HAZO, SAMUEL J, b. Pittsburgh, Pa, July 19, 28; m. 55; c. 1. ENGLISH & AMERICAN LITERATURE. B.A, Univ. Notre Dame, 48, M.A, Duquesne Univ, 55; Ph.D, Univ. Pittsburgh, 57; D.Litt, Seton Hill Col, 65. From instr. to PROF. ENG, DUQUESNE UNIV, 55-, assoc. dean col, 62-66. Vis. lectr, Univ. Pittsburgh, Mt. Mercy Col, Carnegie-Mellon Univ, 55-; Am. specialist, U.S. Inform. Agency, Mid.East, 65, Jamaica, 66; dir. Int. Poetry Forum, 66- U.S.M.C, 50-57, Capt. Modern American poetry; literary theory. Publ: Discovery and other poems, 59 & Quiet wars, 63, Sheed; Anthology of contemporary religious poetry, Paulist Press, 66; Hart Crane: introduction and interpretation, Barnes & Noble, 63; My sons in God, 66, Blood rights (poems), 68 & Once for the last bandit, 72, Univ. Pittsburgh; Seascript: a Mediterranean logbook, Byblos, 72; The poetry of contact, Commonweal, 63; four articles, In: Encyclopedia of poetry and poetics, Princeton Univ, 65; The poet in America, Barat Rev, 67. Add: International Poetry Forum, 4400 Forbes Ave, Pittsburgh, PA 15213.

HEAD, FAYE EDWARDS, b. Viola, Ky, Nov. 18, 29; m. 53; c. 2. SPEECH & DRAMA. B.A, Murray State Univ, 50; M.A. La. State Univ, 52, Ph.D. (speech, drama), 63. Children's librn, Evansville Pub. Libr, Ind, 50-51; instr. speech & drama, Ga. South. Col, 52-53; teacher, High Sch, Ga, 53-54; instr. speech, Univ. Ariz, 54-56; instr. Eng. for For. Students, La. State Univ, 57-63; ASSOC. PROF. DRAMA, UNIV. GA, 63- Traffic mgr, Station KOPO, Ariz, 55-56. Southeast. Theatre Conf; Am. Theatre Asn. Children's theatre; television acting; Readens theatre. Publ: Evolution and Dear editor, South. Theatre, winter 70-71; Writing for children's theatre, Children's Theatre Rev, 11/70; Fable Frolic, Plays, winter 73. Add: 150 Robin Rd, Athens, GA 30601.

HEADINGS, PHILIP R, b. Bellefontaine, Ohio, Oct. 15, 22; m. 43, 49; c. 1. COMPARATIVE LITERATURE. B.S, Ind. Univ, 50, Ph.D.(comp. lit), 58. Teacher, Pub. Schs, Ind, 50; training supvr, U.S. Naval Ordnance Plant, Indianapolis, Ind, 50-52; teaching assoc. ENG, Ft. Wayne Ctr, Ind. Univ, 54-56; asst. prof, Chico State Col, 58-60; instr, Univ. Ill, 60-61, asst. prof, 61-64; ASSOC. PROF, IND. UNIV, FT. WAYNE, 64- Consult, div. res. & publ, Nat. Endowment Humanities, 66-67; vis. assoc. prof, Univ. Wis, Milwaukee, summer 67. U.S.N.R, 43-46. MLA (mem. bibliog. comt, 63-); NCTE; Am. Comp. Lit. Asn; Int. Comp. Lit. Asn. Writings of T.S. Eliot; theory of drama; literature and psychology. Publ: The Tiresias tradition in Western literature, Univ. Microfilms, 58; T.S. Eliot, Twayne, 64; contrib, MLA International Bibliography, 63-; Tolstoy's What is art? and T.S. Eliot's The wasteland, Rev. Langues Vivantes, 1/66; T.S. Eliot, Contemporary Lit, IX: 265-274. Add: Dept. of English & Linguistics, Indiana University at Ft. Wayne, 2101 Coliseum Blvd. E, Ft. Wayne, IN 46805.

HEADLEE, CLEETIS JUANITA, b. Stockton, Mo, Mar. 25, 11. ENGLISH. B.S.Ed, Univ. Mo, Columbia, 35, M.A, 43; Univ. Calif, Berkeley, 50; Univ. Minn, Minneapolis, 53; Ariz. State Univ, 56. Teacher high schs, 35-46; instr. Eng. & jour, MISSOURI SOUTH. STATE COL, 46-65, asst. prof. & Eng. coord, 64-66, ASSOC. PROF. ENG, 66-, chmn. div. humanities & fine arts, 67-69. Participant, NCTE-Col. Comp. & Commun. Conf. Eng. in Two-Year Col, Ariz, 65. NCTE (dir, 61-66, liaison off, 66-68, judge, achievement awards in writing, 72-74); MLA; Shakespeare Asn. Am; Renaissance Soc. Am; Am. Asn. Univ. Women. Dramatic literature; poetry; writing of non-fiction. Publ: Co-auth, School and community, Mo. State Teachers Asn, 4/51-56 & National poetry anthology, Nat. Poetry Asn, 56; auth, What college English is really like, Mo. Eng. Bull, 10/66. Add: Dept. of Language & Literature, Missouri Southern State College, Joplin, MO 64801.

HEALEY, E. CLAIRE, b. Providence, R.I, Mar. 9, 24; m. 47; c. 5. ENGLISH, AMERICAN LITERATURE. B.S, Boston Univ, 50; M.A, Columbia Univ, 54, Ph.D.(Eng. & comp. lit), 68. Instr. Eng, Hunter Col, 65-68; asst. prof. ENG. & AM. LIT, MONTCLAIR STATE COL, 68-71, ASSOC. PROF, 71-, DIR. GRAD. STUD. IN ENG, 73- Mem. ed. bd, Montclair J. Soc. Sci. & Humanities, Montclair State Col, 72- MLA; AAUP; Col. Eng. Asn; Northeast Hist. & Geneal. Soc. Modern American literature; American poetry. Publ: Amy Lowell: an American abroad, fall 72 & Ezra Pound: a poet in rebellion, fall 73, Montclair J. Soc. Sci. & Humanities; Amy Lowell: a London visit, New Eng. Quart, fall 73; plus two others. Add: Dept. of English, Montclair State College, Upper Montclair, NJ 07043.

HEALY, TIMOTHY S, S.J, b. New York, N.Y, Apr. 25, 23. ENGLISH LITERATURE. A.B, Woodstock Col, 46, Ph.L, 47, M.A, 48; S.T.L, Univ. Louvain, Belgium, 54; M.A, Fordham Univ, 58, fac. fel, 62-63; Kent-Danforth fel, Oxford, 63-66, D.Phil.(Eng), 65. Instr. Eng. & Latin, Fordham Prep. Sch, 47-50; Eng, Fordham Univ, 56-58, asst. prof, 58-62, dir. alumni relat, 57-62, assoc. prof. Eng, 66-68, prof, 68-69, exec. v.pres, 65-69; PROF. ENG. & V.CHANCELLOR ACAD. AFFAIRS, CITY UNIV, NEW YORK, 69- Chmn. bd, N.Y. Col. Bound Corp, 66-69; consult, President's Comn. Campus Unrest, 70; trustee, Marymount Col.(N.Y), 70-; mem. adv. counc, N.Y. State Educ. Dept, 70-; Am. Counc. Learned Soc. grant-in-aid, 71. Chaplain, Nat. Guard, Capt. Col. Eng. Asn; MLA; Recusant Hist. Soc. Publ: Co-auth, John Donne, selected prose, 67 & auth, John Donne's Ignatius his conclave, 68, Clarendon; auth, The debate over school desegregation, New Republic, 4/70; Will Everyman destroy the university, Saturday Rev, 12/71; City University of New York today, In: World yearbook of education, Harcourt, 72. Add: City University of New York, 535 E. 80th St, New York, NY 10021.

HEAP, NORMAN A, b. Baton Rouge, La, June 25, 35; m. 57; c. 2. SPEECH. B.S, La. State Univ, 57, M.A, 59, fel, 67-68, Ph.D.(speech), 68; Pa. State Univ, summer 63. Tech. asst. theatre, La. State Univ, 57-58; asst. prof. SPEECH, Transylvania Col, 58-59; TRENTON STATE COL, 59-73, ASSOC. PROF, 73- Theta Alpha Phi Spec. Acting Award, La. State Univ, 54. Ling. Soc. Am; Am. Dialect Soc; Speech Commun. Asn. Phonetics; grammar; dialects. Publ: A Burley tobacco word list from Lexington, Kentucky, 4/66 & A word list from Olney, Illinois, 11/69, Publ. Am. Dialect Soc. Add: Dept. of Speech, Trenton State College, P.O. Box 940, Trenton, NJ 08625.

HEATH, JEFFREY MORTON, b. London, Ont, Mar. 29, 43. ENGLISH LITERATURE. B.A, Univ. Toronto, 65, M.A, 67, Ph.D.(Eng), 71. Lectr. ENG, VICTORIA COL, UNIV. TORONTO, 69-71, ASST. PROF, 71- Can. Counc. res. fel, summers 71, 72. Can. Asn. Univ. Teachers; Asn. Can. Univ. Teachers Eng. Twentieth century fiction and poetry, British and American; Evelyn Waugh. Publ: Waugh notes, spring 73 & Waugh and Rossetti, winter 73, Evelyn Waugh Newslett; Apthorpe placatus? , Ariel, 1/74. Add: Dept. of English, Victoria College, University of Toronto, Queen's Park Crescent, Toronto, Ont. M5S 1K7, Can.

HEATH, WILLIAM GEORGE, JR, b. Mineola, N.Y, Mar. 3, 44. AMERICAN LITERATURE & INTELLECTUAL HISTORY. B.A, Bowdoin Col, 66; M.A, Univ. Minn, Minneapolis, 68, Ph.D.(Eng), 70. ASST. PROF. ENG, Marietta Col, 70-73; LAKEHEAD UNIV, 73- Mem. staff, Lakehead Univ. Rev, 73- MLA; Asn. Can. Univ. Teachers Eng. The transcendentalists; literature and primitive myth. Publ: Ed, Selected essays of C.A. Bartol, John Colet, 75; auth, Review of The style of innocence, Lakehead Rev, 1/74. Add: Dept. of English, Lakehead University, Oliver Rd, Thunder Bay, Ont. P7B 5E4, Can.

HEATH, WILLIAM WEBSTER, b. Buffalo, N.Y, July 1, 29; m. 52; c. 2. ENGLISH. B.A, Amherst Col, 51; M.A, Columbia Univ, 52; Ph.D.(Eng), Univ. Wis, 56. Teaching asst. ENG, Univ. Wis, 52-56; instr, AMHERST COL, 56-59, asst. prof, 59-63, assoc. prof, 63-69, PROF, 69- Am. Philos. Soc. grant, 67-68, 72; Am. Counc. Learned Soc. grant, 72. MLA; AAUP. Nineteenth century poetry; contemporary British literature; autobiography. Publ: Elizabeth Bowen: an introduction to her novels, Univ. Wis, 61; ed, Discussions of Jane Austen, Heath, 61; auth, Wordsworth and Coleridge, Clarendon, 71; Major British poets of the Romantic period, Macmillan, 72; The literary criticism of John Middleton Murry, PMLA. Add: Dept. of English, Amherst College, Amherst, MA 01002.

HEATON, CHERRILL PAUL, b. Jacksonville, Fla, Apr. 6, 33; m. 64. ENGLISH. B.A, Princeton, 54; M.A, Fla. State Univ, 61, Ph.D.(Eng), 66. Asst. prof. ENG, N.C. STATE UNIV, 66-72; ASSOC. PROF, CAMPBELL COL.(N.C), 72- MLA. American literature; fiction; creative writing. Publ: Style in The old man and the sea, Style, winter 70; The 5-string banjo in North Carolina, South. Folklore Quart, 3/71; Instant innovation: the classroom as a goldfish bowl, S.C. Educ. J, spring 71. Add: 902 Creech Rd, Garner, NC 27529.

HEBERT, CATHERINE ACKERMAN, b. Jackson, Mich, Nov 20, 22; m. 66; c. 1. ENGLISH. A.B, East. Mich. Univ, 45; M.A, Univ. Mich, 46, fel, 52-53, Ph.D.(Eng. lang. & lit), 55. Instr. ENG, EAST. MICH. UNIV, 47-50, 53-55, asst. prof, 55-60, assoc. prof, 60-63, PROF, 63- MLA; NCTE; Renaissance Soc. Am. Literature of the English Renaissance; American literature. Publ: Fashionable Platonism in Caroline poetry, Univ. of Mich, 55; plus various articles and children's verse. Add: 1306 Kingwood Ave, Ypsilanti, MI 48197.

HECHT, ANTHONY EVAN, b. New York, N.Y, Jan. 16, 23; m. 71; c. 3. POETRY. B.A, Bard Col, 44, hon. D.Litt, 70; M.A, Columbia Univ, 50. Instr. ENG, Kenyon Col, 47; N.Y. Univ, 48; Bard Col, 52-54, prof, 61-67; asst. prof, Smith Col, 56-59; PROF, UNIV. ROCHESTER, 67- Prix de Rome, 51; Pulitzer Prize, 68. U.S.A, 43-46. Acad. Am. Poets; Nat. Inst. Arts & Lett. Publ: A summoning of stones, Macmillan, 54; The seven deadly sins, 58 & Aesopic, 68, Gehenna; A bestiary, Kanthos, 60; co-ed, Jiggery pokery, 66 & auth, The hard hours, 67, Atheneum. Add: Dept. of English, University of Rochester, Rochester, NY 14627.

HEDGES, ELAINE RYAN, b. Yonkers, N.Y, Aug. 18, 27; m. 56; c. 2. AMERICAN LITERATURE, WOMEN'S STUDIES. B.A, Barnard Col, 48; M.A, Radcliffe Col, 50; Am. Asn. Univ. Women fel, 53; Ph.D.(Am. civilization), Harvard, 70. Instr, Wellesley Col, 54-56; asst. prof. ENG, TOWSON STATE COL, 67-71, assoc. prof, 71-73, PROF, 73- Mem, Comn. on Status of Women, 70-74. MLA (chairperson, comn. status of women in the prof, 72-73). Nineteenth century American literature; 20th century American poetry. Publ: Ed. Democracy: a man-search, Wayne State Univ, 61 & The yellow wallpaper, Feminist Press, 73; auth, Howells on a Hawthornesque theme, Tex. Stud. Lit. & Lang, spring 61; The Rise of Silas Lapham and Cesar Birotteau: a study in parallels, Nineteenth Century Fiction, 9/62. Add: Dept. of English, Towson State College, Baltimore, MD 21204.

HEDGES, NED S, b. Lincoln, Nebr, Jan. 25, 33; m. 55; c. 2. ENGLISH. B.A, Nebr. Wesleyan Univ, 56; M.A, Univ. Nebr, Lincoln, 61, Ph.D.(Eng), 68. Teacher high schs, Nebr, 56-59; asst. ENG, UNIV. NEBR-LINCOLN, 59-61, instr, 61-68, asst. prof, 68-70, ASSOC. PROF, 70-, ASST. V.CHANCELLOR ACAD. AFFAIRS, 72-, dir. freshman Eng, 65-72. Consult, NDEA Eng. Insts, Univ. Nebr, 63-65 & 68, dir, 67; consult, NDEA Eng. Insts, Midwest. Univ, 66 & Southeast. State Col, 68. Finance C, U.S.A, 53-55, Sgt. MLA; NCTE. Children's literature; John Steinbeck. Add: Dept. of English, Andrews Hall, University of Nebraska-Lincoln, Lincoln, NE 68508.

HEDGES, WILLIAM LEONARD, b. Arlington, Mass, Feb. 16, 23; m. 56. AMERICAN LITERATURE. B.A, Haverford Col, 46; Fulbright fel, Univ. Paris, 49-50; Ph.D, Harvard, 54. Teaching fel, Harvard, 50-53; instr. ENG, Univ. Wis, 53-56; asst. prof, GOUCHER COL, 56-62, assoc. prof, 62-67, PROF, 67-, CHMN. AM. STUD, 72-, chmn. dept, 68-71. Am. Counc. Learned Soc. fel, 63-64; mem. ed. bd, Early Am. Lit, 71-74. U.S.A, 43-45. MLA. American literature and intellectual history. Publ: Co-auth, Major writers of America, Harcourt, 62; auth, Washington Irving: an American study, Johns Hopkins, 65; Towards a theory of American literature, 1765-1800, 69 & Benjamin Rush, Charles Brockden Brown and the American plague year, 73, Early Am. Lit; contrib, Landmarks of American literature, Basic Bks, 69 & The chief glory, South. Ill. Univ, 73; plus two others. Add: 6309 Pinehurst Rd, Baltimore, MD 21212.

HEERMANCE, J. NOEL, b. New York, N.Y, Dec. 30, 39; m. 62; c. 1. ENGLISH. A.B, Amherst Col, 61; A.M.T, Harvard, 62; Ph.D.(Eng), Howard Univ, 70. Instr. ENG, Univ. N.C, 63-64; Howard Univ, 64-70; from asst. prof. to ASSOC. PROF, LINCOLN UNIV, 70-, CHMN. DEPT, 70- Training & staff supvr. cult. enrichment prog, Off. Econ. Opportunity, summer 65, prog. dir. recreation-educ. prog, summer 66; bldg. coord, D.C. Model Sch. Prog, 66; instr, Eng, Upward Bound Prog, Wash, D.C, summers 68, 69; consult-speaker var. insts. & fed. progs, Mo, 72-; proj. coord, Nat. Endowment for Humanities grant, 72-74; proj. dir, Dept. Health, Educ. & Welfare grant, 72-73; instr. black lit, Mo. State Penitentiary & Algoa Reformatory, Jefferson City, 73-74. NCTE; Col. Lang. Asn. Black American literature. Publ: William Wells Brown and Clotelle, 69 & Charles W. Chesnutt: America's first great black novelist, 74, Shoe String; The modern negro novel, Negro Dig, 5/64. Add: Dept. of English, Lincoln University, Jefferson City, MO 65101.

HEFFERNAN, JAMES ANTHONY WALSH, b. Boston, Mass, Apr. 22, 39; m. 64. ENGLISH. A.B, Georgetown Univ, 60; Ph.D.(Eng), Princeton, 64. Instr. ENG, Univ. Va, 63-65; asst. prof, DARTMOUTH COL, 65-70, ASSOC. PROF, 70-, fac. fel, 68-69. Lectr, Wordsworth Summer Sch, Rydal Mount, Eng, 71. MLA. English romantic poetry; English romantic landscape painting. Publ: Wordsworth's theory of poetry: the transforming imagination, Cornell Univ, 69; Wordsworth on the picturesque, Eng. Stud, 12/68; Wordsworth on imagination: a reply to Arthur Pfeffer, PMLA, 1/69; Centripetal vision in Pater's Marius, Victorian Newsletter, spring 69; plus others. Add: Dept. of English, Dartmouth College, Hanover, NH 03755.

HEFFERNAN, MIRIAM MARGARET. AMERICAN LITERATURE. B.A, Brooklyn Col, 33; M.A, Columbia Univ, 38; Ph.D, N.Y. Univ, 49. Instr. ENG, BROOKLYN COL, 49-56, asst. prof, 56-60, assoc. prof, 60-72, PROF, 72- Fel, Am. Stud. Asn. of Metropolitan New York, 54; regional assoc, Am. Counc. Learned Soc, 58-60; First Distinguished Teacher Award, Brooklyn Col, 59; res. grants, City Univ. N.Y, 62, 63; mem. Metropolitan New York Teacher Educ. & Prof. Standards Comn, 63. MLA. Modern poetry; the novel. Publ: Co-auth, The education of teachers: certification, Nat. Educ. Asn, 60. Add: Dept. of English, Brooklyn College, Brooklyn, NY 11210.

HEFFNER, HUBERT CROUSE, b. Maiden, N.C, Feb. 22, 01; m. 22; c. 1. DRAMATIC LITERATURE. A.B, Univ. N.C, 21, M.A, 22, hon. Litt.D, 69; Univ. Chicago, 30-34, 42; Rockefeller Found. grant, France & Eng, 50-51; L.H.D, Ill. Wesleyan Univ, 64. Instr. Eng. & dir. dramatics, Univ. Wyo, 22-23; Univ. Ariz, 23-26; asst. prof. Eng. & assoc. dir. Carolina Playmakers, Univ. N.C, 26-30; prof. drama, Northwest. Univ, 30-39; dramatic lit. & exec. head dept. speech & drama, Stanford Univ, 39-54; chief fine arts div. & head theatre & radio arts, U.S. Army Univ, Biarritz, France, 45-46; Fulbright lectr. & vis. prof. drama, Bristol Univ, 54-55; prof. DRAMATIC LIT, IND. UNIV, BLOOMINGTON, 55-61, distinguished serv. prof, 61-71, EMER. DISTINGUISHED PROF, 71- Summer vis. prof, Northwest. Univ, 30, Stanford Univ, 37, Univ. Calif, Berkeley, 39, Cornell Univ, 48, Univ. Colo, 50, 65, Univ. Denver, 62, Univ. Minn, 63; Int. res. fel, Huntington Libr, 34-35; ed, Quart. J. Speech, 47-50; Folger Libr. res. grant, 53; ed, Educ. Theatre J, 54-56; Carnegie vis. prof. dramatic lit, Univ. Hawaii, 58; mem. humanities comt, Field Educ. Enterprises Corp, 65-68; Berg prof. Eng, N.Y. Univ, 68-69; vis. prof. drama, Tufts Univ, 73-74. Theta Alpha Phi Award, 61. U.S.A, 43-46, Capt. Fel. Am. Theatre Asn.(v.pres, 48, pres, 49, distinguished serv. award, 59); Am. Nat. Theatre & Acad; Nat. Theatre Conf; Am. Soc. Theatre Res; MLA; Am. Stud. Asn; Soc. Theatre Res, Eng. Dramatic theory and criticism; history of American civilization. Publ: Co-auth, Modern theatre practice, Croft, 35; co-ed, Davy Crockett and other plays, Princeton Univ, 40; auth, The nature of drama, Houghton, 59. Add: 1310 Hunter Ave, Bloomington, IN 47401.

HEFFNER, RAY LORENZO, JR, b. Durham, N.C, Mar. 7, 25; m. 51. ENGLISH. B.A, Yale, 48, M.A, 50, Sterling fel. & Ph.D.(Eng), 53; Litt.D, Franklin Col, 66; LL.D, Univ. R.I, 67; D.B.A, Bryant Col, 67. Instr. Eng. Univ. Ky, 50-51; Ind. Univ, 53-56, asst. prof, 56-60, assoc. prof, 60-63, asst. dean fac, 59-62, assoc. dean fac, 62-63; prof. Eng. & v.pres. instr, Univ. Iowa, 63-64; v.pres. & dean fac, Ind. Univ, 64-66; pres, Brown Univ, 66-69; PROF. ENG. & PROVOST, UNIV. IOWA, 69- Guggenheim fel, 60. U.S.N, 43-46, Lt.(jg). MLA; Renaissance Soc. Am; Shakespeare Asn. Am. English poetry and drama of the late 16th and early 17th centuries. Publ: Unifying symbols in the comedy of Ben Jonson, In: English stage comedy, Columbia Univ, 55. Add: Office of the Provost, University of Iowa, Iowa City, IA 52240.

HEFFNER, RICHARD D, b. New York, N.Y, Aug. 5, 25; m. 50; c. 2. COMMUNICATIONS, HISTORY. A.B, Columbia Univ, 46, M.A, 47. Teaching asst. hist, Univ. Calif, Berkeley, 47-48; instr. hist. & govt, Rutgers Univ, 48-50; lectr. contemporary civilization, Columbia Univ, 50-52; prof. hist, Sarah Lawrence Col, 52-53; dir. pub. affairs prog, WNBC-TV, New York, 55-57; prog. dir, Metrop. Educ. TV Asn, 57-59; dir. spec. proj, CBS-TV Network & ed. consult, CBS Inc. Ed. Bd, 59-61; v.pres. & gen. mgr, Educ. Channel 13, New York, 61-63; UNIV. PROF. COMMUN. & PUB. POLICY, RUTGERS UNIV, NEW BRUNSWICK, 64-; PRES, RICHARD HEFFNER ASSOCS, INC, 64- Chmn. ed. bd, Bantam Bks, 66-70; dir, Twentieth Century Fund Comn. Campaign Costs, 68-69; dir, Ford Found. Stud. of TV Environ. Values, 71-72. AAAS; AHA. Communications and public policy; the development of relevant and necessary public attitudes and policy toward the role and responsibilities of mass communications. Publ: Documentary history of the United States; ed, Democracy in America; auth, Television: the subtle persuader, TV Guide, 9/73. Producer & moderator, The open mind, WPIX-TV & PBS, 73- Add: 90 Riverside Dr, New York, NY 10024.

HEFLIN, WILSON L, b. Tuscaloosa, Ala, Sept. 19, 13; m. 39; c. 2. ENGLISH, AMERICAN LITERATURE. A.B, Birmingham-South. Col, 34; M.A, Vanderbilt Univ, 36, Ph.D.(Eng), 52. Instr. ENG, Univ. Ala, 37-41, 42-43; U.S. NAVAL ACAD, 46-48, asst. prof, 48-51, assoc. prof, 51-59, PROF, 59- Lectr, Johns Hopkins Univ, 53-54; Munson Inst. Am. Maritime Hist, 55-56; univ. col, Univ. Md, 59-73. U.S.N.R, 43-47, Lt. Comdr. Melville Soc. Am. (pres, 58). Herman Melville; Stephen Crane. Publ: Co-auth, Moby Dick centennial essays, South. Methodist Univ, 53. Add: Dept. of English, U.S. Naval Academy, Annapolis, MD 21402.

HEGARTY, MARY LOYOLA, C.C.V.I, b. Ireland, Feb. 5, 18; U.S. citizen. ENGLISH LITERATURE. B.S, Loyola Univ.(La), 48; B.A, Sacred Heart Dominican Col, 51; M.A, Cath. Univ. Am, 54. Instr. ENG, Sacred Heart Dominican Col, 54-56, assoc. prof, 56-70, dir. stud. Villa de Matel, 54-70; TEACHER ENG. LIT, ST. ANTHONY HIGH SCH, LONG BEACH, CALIF, 70- MLA; NCTE. Chaucer; history of the Catholic church in Texas. Publ: Serving with gladness: the origin and history of the Sisters of Charity of the Incarnate Word, Houston, Texas, Bruce, 67. Add: St. Mary's Hospital, Long Beach, CA 90801.

HEIDTMANN, PETER, b. Glen Cove, N.Y, Aug. 3, 37; m. 60; c. 1. ENGLISH, B.A, Univ. Rochester, 59; M.A, Univ. N.C, 60; Ph.D.(Eng), Univ. Wis, 65. Instr. ENG, Auburn Univ, 60-61; asst. prof, OHIO UNIV, 64-69, ASSOC. PROF, 69- MLA. Medieval literature; early Renaissance literature. Publ: Wycliffe and the Lollards, Hist. Today, 70; A bibliography of Henryson, Dunbar and Douglas: 1912-1968, Chaucer Rev, 71; The Reverdie Convention and Lenten is come with love to towne, Annuale Mediaevale, 72. Add: Dept. of English, Ohio University College of Arts & Sciences, Athens, OH 45701.

HEILBRUN, CAROLYN G, b. East Orange, N.J; c. 3. ENGLISH LITERATURE. B.A, Wellesley Col, 47; M.A, Columbia Univ, 51, Ph.D.(Eng), 59. Instr. ENG, Brooklyn Col, 59-60; COLUMBIA UNIV, 60-62, asst. prof, 62-67, assoc. prof, 67-72, PROF, 72- Vis. lectr, Union Theol. Sem, 68-70; Swarthmore Col, 70-71; Guggenheim fel, 70-71. MLA; Auth, Guild; Auth. League Am. Modern British literature, 1880-1950; English novel; biography. Publ: The Garnett family, Macmillan, 61; Christopher Isherwood, Columbia Univ, 70; Toward a recognition of androgyny, Knopf, 73; The woman as hero, Tex. Quart, 65; Sayers, Lord Peter and God, Am. Scholar, 67; The masculine wilderness of the American novel, Saturday Rev, 72. Add: Dept. of English, Philosophy Hall, Columbia University, New York, NY 10027.

HEILMAN, ROBERT BECHTOLD, b. Philadelphia, Pa, July 18, 06; m. 35; c. 1. ENGLISH LITERATURE. A.B, Lafayette Col, 27, D. Litt, 67; Tufts Col, 27-28; A.M, Ohio State Univ, 30; A.M, Harvard, 31, Ph.D, 35; hon. LL.D, Grinnell Col, 71; hon. L.H.D, Kenyon Col, 73. Teaching fel, Tufts Col, 27-28; instr. ENG, Ohio Univ, 28-30; Univ. Maine, 31-33, 34-35; La. State Univ, 35-36, asst. prof, 36-42, assoc. prof, 42-46, prof, 46-48; PROF, UNIV. WASH, 48-, chmn. dept, 48-71. Bk. reviewer, Key Reporter, 59-; Guggenheim fel, 64-65; NCTE distinguished lectr, 68; S.Atlantic Grad. Educ. lectr, 71; Nat. Endowment for Humanities sr. fel, 71-72. Ariz. Quart. best essay prize, 56; Explicator bk. prize, 57; Longview essay award, 60. MLA (mem. exec. counc, 66-69); S.Cent. Mod. Lang. Asn; Philol. Asn. Pac. Coast (pres, 59); Int. Asn. Univ. Prof. Eng; Shakespeare Soc. Am. Criticism of drama; criticism of novel; history of English novel. Publ: America in English fiction, 1760-1800, La. State Univ, 37, Octagon Bks, 68; This great stage: image and structure in King Lear, La. State Univ, 48, Magic in the web: action and language in Othello, Univ. Ky, 56; Tragedy and melodrama: versions of experience, Univ. Wash, 68: The iceman, the arsonist, and the troubled agent: tragedy and melodrama on the modern stage, Univ. Wash. & Allen & Unwin, London, 73; The Ghost on the ramparts and other essays in the humanities, Univ. Ga, 73; The criminal as tragic hero: dramatic methods, In: Shakespeare survey 19, Cambridge Univ, 66; The dream metaphor: some ramifications, In: American dreams, American nightmares, South. Ill. Univ, 70; Humanistic education as comedy, South. Rev, summer 72; plus others. Add: Dept. of English, University of Washington, Seattle, WA 98195.

HEIMAN, HAZEL LUCILE, b. Ethan, S.Dak, Jan. 2, 24. SPEECH COMMUNICATION. B.S, South. State Col.(S.Dak), 47; Nat. Life Ins. Inst. scholar, Univ. Pa, summer 52; M.A, Univ. S.Dak, 59; Ph.D.(speech commun), Univ. Minn, 69. Elem. teacher, Delmont Pub. Sch, S.Dak, 43-45; Parkston Pub. Schs, 45-46; teacher Eng. & speech, Mitchell Jr. High Sch, 47-49; speech & theatre, Mitchell Sr. High Sch, 48-54; teacher speech & dir. forensics, Rapid City Sr. High Sch, 54-63; ASSOC. PROF. SPEECH, MORNINGSIDE COL, 63-67; UNIV. N.DAK, 68-, CHMN. DEPT, 71- Speech Commun. Asn; Int. Commun. Asn; Cent. States Speech Commun. Asn; Asn. Dept. & Adminr. Speech Commun. American public address and rhetoric; speech education; small groups. Add: 2303 Tenth Ave. N, Grand Forks, ND 58201.

HEIMER, JACKSON W, b. Florence, Ala, July 21, 25; m. 46; c. 3. ENGLISH. A.B, Univ, Ky, 49, M.A, 52; Ph.D, Univ. Cincinnati, 63. Teacher ENG, Deer Park High Sch, Ohio, 52-55; instr, Univ. Ky, 55-59; asst. prof, Ball State Univ, 59-64, assoc. prof, 64-67; PROF, IND, UNIV. PA, 67- U.S.N, 43-46. MLA. Nineteenth and twentieth century British literature. Publ: The lesson of New England: Henry James and his native region, Ball State Monogr. Series, 67; Patterns of betrayal in the novels of Joseph Conrad, Ball State Univ. Forum, summer 67; The betrayer as intellectual: Conrad's Under western eyes, Polish Rev, autumn 67; Betrayal, confession, attempted redemption and punishment in Nostromo, Tex. Stud. Lit. & Lang, winter 67. Add: Dept. of English, Indiana University of Pennsylvania, Indiana, PA 15701.

HEIMERT, ALAN, b. Oak Park, Ill, Nov. 10, 28; m. 62. AMERICAN CIVILIZATION. A.B, Harvard, 49, Ph.D, 60; M.A, Columbia Univ, 50. Instr. hist, lit. & Eng, HARVARD, 59-60, asst. prof. Eng, 61-65, assoc. prof, 65-70, POWELL M. CABOT PROF. AM. LIT, 70-, MASTER ELIOT HOUSE, 68- Mem. Inst. Advan. Stud, Princeton, 60-61; vis. assoc. prof, Univ. Calif, Berkeley, summer 67. U.S.A, 52-55, Sgt. Am. Stud. Asn. Colonial literature and history; 19th century intellectual history. Publ: Co-auth, A nation so conceived, Scribner, 63; auth, Religion and the American mind: from the great awakening to the Revolution, Harvard, 66; co-ed, The great awakening, Bobbs, 67; auth, Puritanism, the wilderness, and the frontier, New Eng, Quart, 53; Moby Dick and American political symbolism, Am. Quart, 63; Perry Miller: an appreciation, Harvard Rev, 64; plus others. Add: Eliot Master's Lodgings, Harvard University, Cambridge, MA 02138.

HEINES, DONALD SCOTT, b. Jamaica, N.Y, Oct. 7, 24; m. 54; c. 3. ENGLISH. B.A, Wesleyan Univ, 47; M.A, Columbia Univ, 50, Ph.D.(Eng), 64. Instr. Eng, Upsala Col, 47-50; asst. prof, 50-58, assoc. prof, 58-67, prof, 67-71, fac. fel, 65-66; MEM. STAFF LANG. & LIT, CAPE COD COMMUNITY COL, 71- Danforth teacher, 57-58. U.S.N, 43-46, Lt.(jg). MLA; Col.

Eng. Asn. American short story; literary criticism and contemporary theology. Publ: Times four: the short story in depth, Prentice-Hall, 68. Add: Div. of Languages & Literature, Cape Cod Community College, West Barnstable, MA 02668.

HEINEY, DONALD WILLIAM, b. South Pasadena, Calif, Sept. 7, 21; m. 48; c. 1. COMPARATIVE LITERATURE. B.S, U.S. Merchant Marine Acad, 43; B.A, Univ. Redlands, 48; A.M, Univ. South, Calif, 49, Ph.D.(comp. lit), 52. Asst. Eng. & gen. stud, Univ. South. Calif, 48, lectr. comp. lit. & gen. stud, 49-53; instr. Eng, Univ. Utah, 53-54, asst. prof, 54-59, assoc. prof, 59-65; PROF. COMP. LIT, UNIV. CALIF, IRVINE, 65-, dir. prog. comp. lit, 65-70. Fulbright lectr. Am. lit, Univ. Bologna & Univ. Inst. Venice, 59-60; Am. Counc. Learned Soc. & Am. Philos. Soc. comp. lit. res. grants, Italy, 62-63; Am. Counc. Learned Soc. res. grant, Italy, summer 66; vis. prof. Am. lit, Univ. Paris III, 72-73. U.S.N.R, 43-46, Lt. MLA; Am. Comp. Lit. Asn. Contemporary continental literature; contemporary novel, especially English and American; translation theory and practice. Publ: America in modern Italian literature, Rutgers Univ, 64; Three Italian novelist, Univ. Mich, 68; Natalie Ginzburg: the fabric of voices, fall 70 & Calvinismo, fall 71, Iowa Rev; Melville, Bellow, and the innocence of man, Annali de Ca' Foscari, summer-fall, 71. Add: Program in Comparative Literature, University of California, Irvine, CA 92664.

HEINITZ, KENNETH, b. Upland, Nebr, Nov. 13, 26; m. 52; c. 4. AMERICAN LITERATURE. B.A, Concordia Theol. Sem, 47, B.D, 52; M.A, Univ. Kans. City, 51; Aid Asn. Lutherans scholar, Loyola Univ.(Ill), 61, Ph.D, 63; S.T.M, Lutheran Sch. Theol. Chicago, 71. Asst. instr, Lutheran Concordia Acad, Austin, Tex, 49-50; instr. Eng, Concordia Teachers Col.(Ill), 50-51; Concordia Teachers Col.(Nebr), 52-53; pastor, Immanuel Lutheran Church, Twin Falls, Idaho, 53-54; Redeemer Lutheran Church, Salt Lake City, Utah, 54-57; ASST. PROF. ENG. & RELIG, CONCORDIA TEACHERS COL.(ILL), 57- MLA; Am. Soc. Church Hist. Theology. Publ: The linguisticality of God and faith in Gerhard Ebeling, Lutheran Quart, 8/71; Echatological and political in Moltmann's theology, Concordia Theol. Monthly, 6/72; Freedom and authority, Lutheran Educ, 9/72. Add: Dept. of Humanities & Theology, Concordia Teachers College, 7400 Augusta St, River Forest, IL 60305.

HEISER, MERRILL FRANCIS, b. Hamilton, Ohio, May 23, 13; m. 40; c. 2. AMERICAN & COMPARATIVE LITERATURE, AMERINDIAN CULTURE. A.B, Oberlin Col, 34, A.M, 35; Ph.D, Univ. Wis, 47. Asst, Univ. Wis, 41-42, res. asst. 46-47; instr. Eng, State Univ, Iowa, 47-48; asst. prof, 48-53, assoc. prof, 53-57, res. prof. grad. col, 55; vis. prof. Eng, Univ. Hawaii, 57-59, prof, 59-61, 62-65, chmn. dept, 59-61, dean int. col, E-W. Ctr, 61-62; prof. Eng, Colo. State Univ, 65-73, chmn. dept, 65-68; ADMIN. DIR. CTR-IN-SERV. EDUC. SEARCH, 73-, admin. dean, Ctr, 70-72, chmn. bd, 72-73. Vis. prof, N.Mex. Highlands Univ, 56-57; consult, E-W. Ctr, 62-63; Fulbright lectr. Am. lit. & civilization, France, 63-64; vis. prof, Colo. State Univ, 73-; dir, Prospective Teacher Fel. Prog. Eng, 66-70; NDEA Inst. Teachers, summer 68; investigator in anthrop, Nat. Inst. Educ, 73-. U.S.N.R, 43-45, Lt. NCTE; Int. Comp. Lit. Asn; Am. Anthrop. Asn; West. Lit. Asn. Foreign American literary relations; conceptual development among native American children; multicultural education. Publ: Co-auth, Transitions in American literary history, Duke Univ, 54. Add: Center for Inservice Education, Search, Box 181, Flagstaff, AZ 86001.

HEISERMAN, ARTHUR R, b. Evansville, Ind, Jan. 10, 29; m. 49; c. 5. ENGLISH LITERATURE. A.B, Univ. Chicago, 48, A.M, 51, Ph.D, 59. Asst. prof. Eng. & dir. summer quarter, UNIV. CHICAGO, 59-63, assoc. dir. univ. exten, 61-63, assoc. prof. Eng, & dir. Univ. exten, 63-67, PROF. ENG, 67-, master, Humanities Col, 65-66. Guggenheim fel, 63-64. MLA. Medieval and Renaissance literature. Publ: Skelton & satire, Univ. Chicago, 61. Add: Dept. of English, University of Chicago, Chicago, IL 60637.

HEISEY, DAVID RAY, b. Gladwin, Mich, Jan. 9, 32; m. 59; c. 3. SPEECH COMMUNICATION. A.B, Greenville Col, 54; Th.B, Messiah Col, 57; M.A, Ohio State Univ, 55; Univ. Edinburgh, 59-60; Ph.D.(speech), Northwest. Univ, 64. Instr. speech, Messiah Col, 55-59, assoc. prof, 62-66; RHETORIC & COMMUN, KENT STATE UNIV, 66-70, PROF, 70- Yale Univ. res. fel, summer 68; res. grants, Regional Counc. Int. Educ, 68-69; Kent State Univ. Res. Counc, summer 69; vis. prof. int. commun, Univ. Louvain, 72-73. Int. Commun. Asn; Speech Commun. Asn; Int. Asn. Symbolic Anal; Cent. States Speech Commun. Asn. American public address: rhetoric of the Arab-Israeli conflict; intercultural communication. Publ: Contrib, Preaching in American history: selected issues in the American pulpit, Abingdon, 69, America in controversy: speaking on issues in American history, W.C. Brown, 73 & Intercommunication among nations and peoples, Harper, 73; auth, The rhetoric of the Arab-Israeli conflict, Quart. J. Speech, 2/70; Symbolism in the Middle East conflict, Acta Symbolica, fall 70; The Scottish tradition in pulpit rhetoric, South. Speech J, spring 71. Add: School of Speech, Kent State University, Kent, OH 44242.

HEISSENBUTTEL, ERNEST GERHARDT, b. New York, N.Y, Jan. 11, 03; m. 32; c. 2. ENGLISH. A.B, Columbia Univ, 26, M.A, 30; M.A, Gettysburg Col, 27; hon. D.Litt, Thiel Col, 73. Instr. ENG, Gettysburg Col, 26-28, asst. prof, 28-29; PROF, THIEL COL, 30-, chmn. dept. humanities, 45-55. Ed, Synod Monthly West. Pa-W.Va. Synod Lutheran Church Am, 46- American literature; Shakespeare; literary criticism. Publ: Pittsburgh Synod congregational histories, 59; co-auth, Pittsburgh Synod history, its auxiliaries and institutions, 1945-1962, 63. Add: 14 Ridgeway Ave, Greenville, PA 16125.

HEISSLER, JOHN M, JR. b. Chicago, Ill, Apr 12, 23. ENGLISH. A.B, Elmhurst Col, 51; M.A, Univ. Wyo, 54; Ph.D, Univ. Ill, 60. Teacher, High Sch, Ill, 51-53; Proviso W. High Sch, Hillside, 60-61; assoc. prof. ENG, ILL. STATE UNIV, 61-68, PROF, 68- Prof, Ill. State-wide Curriculum Stud. Ctr. for Prep. Sec. Sch. Teachers Eng, 65-70. U.S.A.A.F, 43-45. MLA; NCTE; NEA. George Herbert; teaching English in secondary schools. Add: Dept. of English, Illinois State University, Normal, IL 61761.

HEIST, WILLIAM WATTS, b. Orchard Park, N.Y, Mar. 29, 10; m. 39; c. 1. ENGLISH. B.A, Univ. Buffalo, 32, M.A, 33; A.M, Harvard, 38, Ph.D.(Eng), 42; Univ. Wis; Univ. Colo. Instr. ENG, Purdue Univ, 38-39; asst. prof, MICH. STATE UNIV, 46-53, assoc. prof, 53-61, PROF, 61- Sr. Comn. Relief in Belgium fel, 52-53; Am. Philos. Soc. res. grant, Belgium, 58-59; vis. lectr, Univ. Col, Galway, Ireland, 59-60; Am. Counc. Learned Soc. travel grant, 3rd Int. Congr. Celtic Stud, summer 67; Rhys fel. Celtic stud, Oxford, 71-72 & res. fel, Jesus Col, 71-72. U.S.N.R, 42-46, Lt. MLA; Am. Folklore Soc; Mediaeval Acad. Am. Old and Middle English language and literature; medieval Latin literature, especially religious legends; Celtic, Old French and English literature. Publ: The fifteen signs before doomsday; Vitae sanctorum Hiberniae, ex codice olim Salmanticensi nunc Bruxellensi; Sermon joyeux and Polemic: two sixteenth-century applications of the legend of the fifteen signs, Univ. N.C, 68; Dermot O'Donohue and the Codex Salmanticensis, Celtica, 60; Myth and folklore in the lives of Irish saints, Centennial Rev, spring 68; Sic(k) a dog on . . . , Am. Speech, spring 68. Add: Dept. of English, Michigan State University, East Lansing, MI 48824.

HEITNER, JOHN A, b. Brooklyn, N.Y, May 7, 31; m. 58; c. 3. AMERICAN LITERATURE. B.A, Hofstra Univ, 59; M.A, Cornell Univ, 60; Ph.D.(Eng), Univ. Rochester, 68. Instr. ENG, State Univ. N.Y. Albany, 62-65; ASST. PROF, CENT. CONN. STATE COL, 65- Consult, New Britain Pub. Schs, 68-; Equal Educ. Inst, Univ. Hartford, 71-; home group leader, Shanti Alternative High Sch, 72-73. U.S.M.C, 51-54, 1st Lt. Northeast Mod. Lang. Asn; Asn. Humanistic Psychol. Humanistic psychology and literature; humanistic education; mysticism and literature. Publ: The search for the real self: humanistic psychology and literature, 73. Add: Dept. of English, Central Connecticut State College, Stanley St, New Britain, CT 06050.

HELBERT, CLIFFORD L, b. Miles City, Mont, May 3, 20; m. 44; c. 5. JOURNALISM. Ph.B, Marquette Univ, 48, A.M, 56. Instr. JOUR, MARQUETTE UNIV, 48-51, asst. prof, 51-55, assoc. prof, 55-64, PROF, 64-, dean col. jour, 65-71. Design consult, St. Louis Rev, 55; The Reporter, Kansas City, 61-62; bus. consult, Boston Pilot, 58-59; design & bus. consult, Cath. Boy-Girl, 62-68; Newspaper Advert. Exec. Asn. fel, 63. Int. Craftsmen of the Year Benjamin Franklin Award, 61; Andrew Hamilton Award, 62; Wis. Graphic Arts man of year, 66. Sig.C, 42-46, 1st Lt. Am. Inst. Graphic Arts; Am. Acad. Advert; Soc. Typographic Arts; Asn. Educ. Jour; Printing Hist. Soc; Graphic Designer Can. Printing history; relation of printing history to development of journalism; research methods of advertising and communication media. Publ: Ed, Printing progress—a mid-century report, Int. Asn. Printing House Craftsmen, 59; auth, Printing, In: The Harper encyclopedia of science, Harper, 63. Add: College of Journalism, Marquette University, 1135 W. Kilbourn Ave, Milwaukee, WI 53233.

HELD, GEORGE, b. White Plains, N.Y, Jan. 28, 35. ENGLISH & AMERICAN LITERATURE. A.B, Brown Univ, 58; A.M, Univ. Hawaii, 62; Louis Bevier fel. & Ph.D.(Eng), Rutgers Univ, 67. Instr. ENG, Kamehameha Schs, 58-64; teaching asst, Rutgers Univ, 65-67; lectr, QUEENS COL.(N.Y), 67-68, ASST. PROF, 68- Fulbright lectr, Univ. Bratislava, 73-74. MLA; NCTE. Twentieth century British and American literature; writing. Publ: The second book of the Rhymer's Club, Rutgers Univ. Libr. J, 6/65; Jonson's Pindaric on friendship, Concerning Poetry, spring 70; Involving student tutors in teaching writing to disadvantaged students, In: Measure for measure: classroom practices in teaching English 1972-1973, NCTE, 72. Add: Dept. of English, Queens College, Flushing, NY 11367.

HELDMAN, JAMES M, b. Durham, N.C, July 15, 30; m. 52; c. 1. ENGLISH. B.A, Univ. N.C, 56, M.A, 58, Ph.D.(Victorian lit), 67. Instr. ENG, Roanoke Col, 58-60; Univ. Del, 64-66; asst. prof, Univ. Mo-Columbia, 66-72; PROF. & CHMN. DEPT, WEST. KY. UNIV, 72- U.S.A.F, 51-55, S/Sgt. MLA; S.Atlantic Mod. Lang. Asn; Asn. Depts. Eng. Victorian and British novel; Victorian prose and poetry; Edwardian novel. Publ: The last Victorian novel: technique and theme in Parade's end, Twentieth Century Lit, 72. Add: Dept. of English, Western Kentucky University, Bowling Green, KY 42101.

HELFAND, MICHAEL S, b. New York, N.Y, Mar. 20, 42; m. 65; c. 1. VICTORIAN & MODERN ENGLISH LITERATURE. B.A, Univ. Va, 64; Ph.D. (mod. lett), Univ. Iowa, 70. ASST. PROF. ENG, UNIV. PITTSBURGH, 70- Modern fiction. Publ: Contrib, The years work in Victorian literature, Victorian Poetry, 73; auth, Dickens at large, 1/72 & Architects of the self, 1/74. Novel: Forum on Fiction. Add: Dept. of English, University of Pittsburgh, Pittsburgh, PA 15213.

HELGERSON, RICHARD, b. Pasadena, Calif, Aug. 22, 40; m. 67; c. 1. ENGLISH LITERATURE. B.A, Univ. Calif, Riverside, 63; Wilson fel, Johns Hopkins Univ, 63-64; M.A, 64, NDEA fel, 67-69, Ph.D.(Eng), 70. ASST. PROF. ENG, UNIV. CALIF, SANTA BARBARA, 70- MLA; Renaissance Soc. Am; Shakespeare Asn. Am. Renaissance literature. Publ: Lyly, Greene, Sidney and Rich's Brusanus, Huntington Libr. Quart, 73; Two worlds of Goldsmith, Stud. Eng. Lit, 73. Add: Dept. of English, University of California, Santa Barbara, CA 93106.

HELLENGA, ROBERT RINER, b. Milwaukee, Wis, Aug. 5, 41; m. 63; c. 3. ENGLISH LITERATURE. B.A, Univ. Mich, Ann Arbor, 63; Queen's Univ. Belfast, 63-64; Univ. N.C, Chapel Hill, 64-65; Ph.D.(Eng), Princeton, 69. ASST. PROF. ENG, KNOX COL.(ILL), 68- Fac. fel, Newberry Libr. Sem. in Humanities, 73-74. AAUP. English Renaissance; English Romantic literature; death. Publ: Hamlet in the classroom, Col. Eng, 10/73; Russian dreams, Iowa Rev, 11/73; The tournaments in Malory's Morte Darthur, Forum Mod. Lang. Stud, (in press). Add: Newberry Library, 60 W. Walton St, Chicago, IL 60610.

HELLINGER, BENJAMIN, b. Brooklyn, N.Y, Nov. 11, 33; m. 69; c. 2. ENGLISH LITERATURE. B.A, Brooklyn Col, 55; M.A, N.Y. Univ, 57, Ph.D. (Eng), 69. Lectr. ENG, Lehman Col, 65-68; ASST. PROF, JOHN JAY COL. CRIMINAL JUSTICE, 69- U.S.A, 57-59. Eighteenth century English literature; history of criticism. Publ: The editing of Jeremy Collier's Short view of the immorality and profaneness of the English stage, Papers Bibliog. Soc. Am, 73. Add: Dept. of English, John Jay College of Criminal Justice, 445 W. 59th St, New York, NY 10010.

HELLMAN, HUGO E, b. Muenster, Tex, Aug. 18, 08; m. 32; c. 2. SPEECH. Ph.D, Marquette Univ, 40. Teacher, High Sch, Tex, 31-36; prof. SPEECH & dir. sch. speech, MARQUETTE UNIV, 36-73, EMER. DEAN, 73- Parliamentary consult, A.D.H.A, 64-; A.B.C, 65- Speech Commun. Asn; Am. Inst.

Parliamentarians (dir, 66-68). American group practice; the media and government credibility. Publ: Parliamentary procedure, Macmillan, 67; co-auth, Speaking in groups, Random, 68; auth, Good parish meetings, Franciscan Herald, 73. Add: 1530 Church St, Milwaukee, WI 53213.

HELLSTROM, WARD, b. Evanston, Ill, Feb. 2, 30; m. 53; c. 4. ENGLISH. B.S, Northwest, Univ, 52; M.A, Univ. Ill, 56, Ph.D.(Eng), 61. Asst. prof. ENG, UNIV. FLA, 61-67, assoc. prof, 67-71, PROF, 71-, summer humanities grants, 67, 68. Mem. bibliog. comt, MLA, 67- MLA; NCTE; Conf. Col. Compos. & Commun; S.Atlantic Mod. Lang. Asn. Literature of the Victorian and Romantic period; training junior college teachers. Publ: On the poems of Tennyson, Univ. Fla, 72; Time and type of Browning's Saul, ELH, 9/66; Jude the obscure as pagan self-assertion, Victorian Newsletter, spring 66; contrib, The English novel in the nineteenth century, Univ. Ill, 72; plus others. Add: Dept. of English, 200 Anderson Hall, University of Florida, Gainesville, FL 32611.

HELMER, WILLIAM FLOYD, b. Oneida, N.Y, Nov. 12, 26; m. 55; c. 4. ENGLISH, HISTORY. B.A, State Univ. N.Y. Albany, 53; A.M. Univ. Pa, 54, Ph.D.(Eng), 63. Asst. prof. ENG, STATE UNIV. N.Y. AGR. & TECH. COL. MORRISVILLE, 56-58, assoc. prof, 59-64, PROF, 65-, CHMN. LIB. ARTS DIV, 72-, chmn. dept, 66-72. State Univ. N.Y. Res. Found. grants-in-aid for proj. hist. abandoned railroads of N.Y. State, 57-59, 61-65 & res. fels, summers 62 & 65. C.Eng, U.S.A, 45-46, 50-51. MLA; Soc. Indust. Archaeol. Old English literature; New York State history. Publ: O. & W: the long life and slow death of the New York, Ontario & Western Railway, 59 & Rip Van Winkle Railroads, 70, Howell-North. Add: P.O. Box 157, Morrisville, NY 13408.

HELMICK, EVELYN THOMAS, b. McKeesport, Pa, July 20, 28; m. 50, 72; c. c. 3. ENGLISH. B.S, Carnegie Inst. Technol, 50; M.A, Univ. Miami, 64, Ph.D.(Eng), 69. Instr. ENG, Pa. State Univ, 55-56; UNIV. MIAMI, 64-69, asst. prof, 69-73, ASSOC. PROF, 73- MLA; S.Atlantic Mod. Lang. Asn. Willa Cather; myth and literature; literature of Florida. Publ: Myth in the works of Willa Cather, Midcontinent Am. Stud. J, fall 68; Emerson's Uriel as poetic theory, Am. Transcendental Quart, 69; Voltaire and Humphrey Clinker, Stud. Voltaire & Eighteenth Century, 69. Add: Dept. of English, University of Miami, Coral Gables, FL 33124.

HELMING, VERNON PARKER, b. Nutley, N.J, July 16, 04; m. 35, 68; c. 3. ENGLISH. A.B, Carleton Col, 25; Ph.D.(Eng), Yale, 37. Instr. Eng. & math, Am. Univ. Beirut, 25-28; ENG, Knox Col, 32-33; from instr. to PROF, UNIV. MASS, AMHERST, 33- Vis. prof, Amherst Col, 54-55; vis. lectr, Smith Col, 60-61. Medieval Acad. Am; MLA; Ling. Soc. Am. Middle English; Chaucer. Add: Dept. of English, University of Massachusetts, Amherst, MA 01002.

HELMSTADTER, THOMAS H, b. McKeesport, Pa, Aug. 23, 35; m. 58; c. 1. ENGLISH. B.A, Haverford Col, 57; M.A, Univ. Pa, 59, Ph.D, 63. Instr. ENG, WELLS COL, 62-65, asst. prof, 65-71, ASSOC. PROF, 71- MLA. Romantic movement; 20th century poetry. Add: Dept. of English, Wells College, Aurora, NY 13026.

HELTERMAN, JEFFREY ALEC, b. Brooklyn, N.Y, July 31, 42; m. 68; c. 4. ENGLISH, MEDIEVAL STUDIES. B.A, Univ. Rochester, 63, Ph.D.(Eng), 69; M.A, Northwest. Univ, Evanston, 64. ASST. PROF. ENG, Vanderbilt Univ, 67-71; UNIV. S.C, 71- Chaucer; Beowulf; medieval drama. Publ: Beowulf: the archetype enters history, 68 & The dehumanizing metamorphoses of the Knight's tale, 71, ELH; Satan as every shepherd: comic metamorphosis in The second shepherds' play, Tex. Stud. Lit. & Lang, 70. Add: Dept. of English, University of South Carolina, Columbia, SC 29208.

HELTON, TINSLEY, b. Kirksville, Ky, Feb. 22, 15. ENGLISH. B.A, Berea Col; M.A, State Univ. Iowa, 37; summer, Bread Loaf Sch. Eng, 41; Fulbright scholar, Univ. London, 50-51; Ph.D.(Eng), Univ. Minn, 52; summer, Oxford, 56. Teacher, High Sch, Iowa, 37-39; instr. Eng, speech & drama, Creston Jr. Col, 39-41; ENG, Univ. Minn, 41-45, 46-53; Col. St. Catherine, 45-46; assoc. prof, UNIV. WIS-MILWAUKEE, 53-73, PROF, 73- MLA; NCTE; AAUP; Shakespeare Asn. Am; Renaissance Soc. Am; Malone Soc. Publ: Ed, The Renaissance: a reconsideration of the theories and interpretations of the age, Univ. Wis, 60; auth, Renaissance, In: World Book Encyclopedia, Field, 63. Add: 2114 N. Summit Ave, Milwaukee, WI 53202.

HEMBY, JAMES BENJAMIN, JR, b. Ayden, N.C, Mar. 1, 34; m. 56; c. 3. ENGLISH. A.B, Atlantic Christian Col, 55; B.D, Vanderbilt Univ, 58; Duke Univ, 58-59; M.A, Tex. Christian Univ, 64, Ph.D.(Eng), 65. Instr. relig, Atlantic Christian Col, 59-62; dir. admis, 59-62; instr. ENG, Tex. Christian Univ, 62-64; Memphis State Univ, 64-65; assoc. prof, ATLANTIC CHRISTIAN COL, 65-68, PROF, 68-, CHMN. DEPT, 73- MLA. John Milton, a study of irony in Paradise lost; 17th century English literature; William Faulkner. Add: Dept. of English, Atlantic Christian College, Wilson, NC 27893.

HEMENWAY, ROBERT E, b. Sioux City, Iowa, Aug. 10, 41; m. 73; c. 3. ENGLISH, AMERICAN STUDIES. B.A, Univ. Omaha, 63; NDEA fel. & Ph.D. (Eng), Kent State Univ, 66. Asst. prof. Eng, Univ. Ky, 66-68; ASSOC. PROF. Eng. & Am. Stud, Univ. Wyo, 68-73; ENG, UNIV. KY, 73- MLA; Am. Stud. Asn; Col. Lang. Asn. Early American literature; Afro-American literature; American novel. Publ: Ed, The Black novelist, C.E. Merrill, 71; co-auth, Paul Allen's biography of Charles Brockden, Univ. S.C, 74; Enigmas of being in As I lay dying, Mod. Fiction Stud, 70; Zora Neale Hurston and the Harlem renaissance, In: The Harlem renaissance remembered, Dodd, 72; plus others. Add: Dept. of English, University of Kentucky, Lexington, KY 40506.

HEMLOW, JOYCE, b. Liscomb, Can, July 30, 11. ENGLISH LITERATURE. B.A, Queen's Univ.(Ont), 41, M.A, 42, LL.D, 67; Marty traveling scholar; A.M, Radcliffe Col, 44, Ph.D, 48; LL.D, Dalhousie Univ, 72. Now GREENSHIELDS PROF. ENG. LIT, McGILL UNIV. Can. Fed. Univ. Women fel; Guggenheim fel, 51-67. James Tait Black Mem. Book Prize best biog. in U.K, 58; Gov. Gen. Can. Medal acad. non-fiction, 58; Rose Mary Crawshay Prize, Brit. Acad, 60; Achievement Medal, Radcliffe Col, 69. MLA; fel. Royal Soc. Can. Publ: History of Fanny Burney, Oxford, 58; A catalogue of Burney family correspondence, 1749-1878, N.Y. Pub. Libr. & McGill-Queen's Univ, 71; ed, The Journals and letters of Fanny Burney (Madame d'Arblay), 1791-1840, Vol. 4, Clarendon, 73. Add: Dept. of English, McGill University, Montreal, P.Q, Can.

HEMMENS, THOMAS J, b. Chicago, Ill, Dec. 21, 31; m. 53; c. 3. ENGLISH. B.A, Univ. Ill, 57; M.A, Univ. Ark, 59; Ph.D.(Eng), Mich. State Univ, 68. Instr. Eng, Col. William & Mary, 58-60; assoc. prof, KANS. STATE COL. PITTSBURG, 63-72, PROF, 72- U.S.C.G, 51-54. NCTE; Conf. Col. Compos. & Commun. Rhetoric and composition; American drama. Publ: Co-auth, A preface to composition, Prentice-Hall, 68. Add: Dept. of English, Kansas State College of Pittsburg, Pittsburg, KS 66762.

HEMMER, JOSEPH JOHN, JR, b. Oshkosh, Wis, Sept. 24, 39; m. 67; c. 2. SPEECH COMMUNICATION. B.S, Wis. State Col-Oshkosh, 61; M.A, Bradley Univ, 62; Ph.D.(speech), Univ. Wis-Madison, 69. Instr. & dir. debate, Marquette Univ, 64-67; asst. prof. speech, Univ. Wis-Parkside, 69-70; PROF. SPEECH COMMUN, CARROLL COL, 70- U.S.A.R, 57, U.S.A, 57-64. Cent. States Speech Commun. Asn; Speech Commun. Asn. Civil War public address. Publ: Co-auth, How to debate labor management relations, 65 & How to debate foreign aid, 66, Marquette Debate Researchers; auth, Robert A. Toombs speaks for the South, South. Speech J, summer 63; The Charleston Platform Debate in rhetorical-historical perspective, Quart. J. Speech, 12/70; co-auth, May (or can) we be presumptuous, J. Wis. Commun. Asn, spring 72. Add: Dept. of Speech Communication, Carroll College, Waukesha, WI 53186.

HEMPHILL, GEORGE, b. Chicago, Ill, May 15, 22; m. 49; c. 4. ENGLISH LITERATURE. A.B, Kenyon Col, 47; M.A, Univ. Minn, 48, Ph.D, 54. Instr. ENG, UNIV. CONN, 54-60, asst. prof, 60-65, assoc. prof, 65-66, PROF, 66- Fulbright lectr. Am. lit, Univ. Hamburg, Ger, 56-57. U.S.A, 42-46. MLA. Publ: Discussions of poetry; rhythm and sound, Heath, 61; Allen Tate, Univ. Minn, 64; A mathematical grammar of English, Mouton, 73. Add: Dept. of English, University of Connecticut, Storrs, CT 06268.

HENAULT, MARIE JOSEPHINE, b. Oakland, Wash, July 16, 21; m. 52; c. 1. ENGLISH. B.A, Univ. Wash, 45, M.A, 46; Ph.D, Univ. Md, 52. Instr. ENG, Univ. Utah, 46-49; Univ. Md, 56-57; asst. prof, ST. MICHAEL'S COL.(VT), 65-70, assoc. prof, 70-73, PROF, 73-, chmn. dept, 69-72. Modern poetry; 20th century American literature. Publ: Peter Viereck, 69 & Stanley Kunitz (in prep), Twayne; Guide to Ezra Pound, 70, Checklist of Ezra Pound, 70 & ed, The Merrill studies in the Cantos, 71, C.E. Merrill; Henry James, lecturer, Am. Lit, 51; The saving of Father Urban, America, 63. Add: Dept. of English, St. Michael's College, Winooski, VT 05404.

HENCH, ATCHESON LAUGHLIN, b. Orange, N.J, Dec. 31, 91; m. 25; c. 2. ENGLISH LITERATURE. A.B, Lafayette Col, 12, Litt.D, 50; A.M, Harvard, 17, Ph.D, 21. Instr. Eng, Lafayette Col, 12-14; Eng. & Latin, Pa. Mil. Col, 14-16; asst. prof. ENG, Wesleyan Univ, 20-22; assoc. prof, UNIV. VA, 22-25, prof, 25-50, Kent Mem. prof, 40-62, EMER. PROF, 62- Mem. int. ed. adv. comt, World Book Encycl. Dictionary, 60-63; asst. to ed. & contrib, New Suppl. to Oxford Eng. Dictionary, 69-73. U.S.A, 18-19. MLA; Mediaeval Acad. Am; Am. Dialect Soc.(pres, 47); NCTE; Mod. Humanities Res. Asn, Gt. Brit; South. Folklore Soc. Textual studies of misunderstood words and passages in Middle English poetry; the growth of meanings, grammar, and forms in present day American English; manuscript collecting. Publ: Survival of start-naked in the South & Allegorical motif of conscience and reason counsellors from Bernard of Cluny to Gavin Douglas, Univ. Va. Stud; Notes on reading Webster III, Col. Eng, 5/63; plus others. Add: 2011 Lewis Mountain Rd, Charlottesville, VA 22903.

HENDERLIDER, CLAIR R, b. Onawa, Iowa, July 19, 18; m. 44. SPEECH. A.B, State Univ. Iowa, 40, A.M, 42, Ph.D, 45. Instr. SPEECH, West. Reserve Univ, 44-45, asst. prof, 45-46, assoc. prof, 46-68; prof, Miami Univ, 68-72; VIS. PROF, WITTENBERG UNIV, 72- Vis. prof, Univ. Md. Europ. Prog, 56-57; mem, Community Leaders in Am. Speech Commun. Asn; Cent. States Speech Asn. Rhetorical criticism; history of American public address; contemporary public address. Publ: Co-auth, Practical public speaking; auth, What Harry S Truman told us about his speaking, Quart. J. Speech; The persuasive techniques of Woodrow Wilson, Speech Monogr. Add: 1018 N. Limestone St, Springfield, OH 45503.

HENDERSON, ANNE MARIE, b. New York, N.Y, Nov. 4, 20; m. 46; c. 3. ENGLISH, EDUCATION. B.A, N.Y. Univ, 41; M.A, Columbia Univ, 42, 43, 44; Ed.D, George Wash. Univ, 54. Teacher, St. Monica's Sch, N.Y, 42-43; teacher & chmn. dept. Eng. pub. schs, N.Y. & Md. 43-51; guid. dir. Pub. Schs, Va, 51-52; dep. educ. off, Ft. Leslie J. McNair, Wash. D.C, 54-57; teacher Eng, Europ. Univ. Div, Univ. Md, Germany, 60-61; PROF. ENG. & CHMN. DEPT. MOD. LANG, ELIZABETH CITY STATE UNIV, 64- Dir. workshops, teaching the disadvantaged, pub. schs, Wash, Gates & Camden Counties, N.C, 66; reading consult, Elizabeth City-Pasquatank pub. schs, N.C, 66-67; consult, reading & teaching methodology, pub. schs, Martin, Tyrrell & Camden Counties, N.C, 67-69; Pasquatank County, N.C, 68-69. MLA; NCTE; Conf. Col. Compos. & Commun; Asn. Chmn. Depts. Eng. Learning disabilities as they relate to language arts—implications for approaches, techniques and materials; teaching the disadvantaged—location of major problem areas in classroom; construction of effective instructional materials. Add: Dept. of English, Elizabeth City State University, Elizabeth City, NC 27909.

HENDERSON, HANFORD MEAD, b. Toledo, Ohio, Aug. 1, 18; c. 1. COMPARATIVE LITERATURE, HISTORY OF ART. A.B, Haverford Col, 40; M.A, Univ. N.C, 47, Ph.D, 63; Fulbright fel, Italy, 49-51. Lectr. Am. poetry, Univ. Pisa, 51; Duncan Phillips Collection, Webster Jr. Col, 52-53; mem. fac. humanities, Am. Univ, 53-58; lectr. hist. art, U.S. Dept. Agr. Grad. Sch, 60-62; vis. prof. fine arts, Syracuse Univ, 62; Fulbright fel, Italy, 63-64; assoc. prof. Eng, East. Mich. Univ, 64-66; independent res. & tutoring, 66-67; prof. Eng, Kutztown State Col, 67-68; lectr. archit. hist, Am. Col. Paris, 69-70. Mem, Friends of Libr, Am. Acad. Rome, 64-; Wider Quaker fel, 68-; mem, Alliance Française, 74- Sig.C, U.S.A, 43-44. MLA; Mod. Humanities Res. Asn; Am. Soc. Aesthet; Col. Art Asn. Am; Am. Asn. Teachers Fr; Am. Asn. Teachers Ital; Shakespeare Asn. Am; Dante Soc; Milton Soc. Am; Soc. Archit. Hist; Bodley's Am. Friends. Renaissance, baroque and 18th century literature, art and music; Dante. Publ: Auth, Shakespeare in marble in colonial Annapolis, Shakespeare Quart, spring 61; contrib, Concordance to Dante's Commedia, Harvard Univ, 65 & Encycl. Poetry & Poetics, Princeton Univ, 65; plus others. Add: 3256 Martha Custis Dr, Alexandria, VA 22302.

HENDERSON, JERRY E, b. Cheatham Co, Tenn, May 19, 35; m. 62; c. 2. DRAMA. B.A, David Lipscomb Col, 57; M.A, South. Ill. Univ, 59; Ph.D, La. State Univ, 62. Instr. speech & drama, David Lipscomb Col, 60-62, asst. prof, 62-67; prof. speech, Murray State Univ, 67-68; David Lipscomb Col, 68-73; COORD. SPEECH & THEATRE, TENN. TECHNOL. UNIV, 73- Speech Commun. Asn; South. Speech Asn. Southern theatre history. Publ: Nashville in the decline of Southern legitimate theatre, South. Speech J, fall 63. Add: Box 5053, Tennessee Technological University, Cookeville, TN 38501.

HENDERSON, LOIS TAYLOR, b. Cedar Rapids, Iowa, Oct. 25, 05. ENGLISH & COMPARATIVE LITERATURE. B.A, Coe Col, 27; M.A, State Univ. Iowa, 28; Lydia Roberts fel, Columbia Univ, 34, 39. Instr. Eng. & French, Independence Jr. Col. Iowa, 28-32; Maquoketa Jr. Col, 33-34; asst. prof, Cornell Col, 35-53, 40; asst. prof. ENG, SAN JOSE STATE UNIV, 55-58, assoc. prof, 58-71, prof, 71-73, EMER. PROF, 73- Fulbright lectr, Univ. Mandalay, Burma, 58-59; vis. prof, New Col, San Jose State Univ, 74. NCTE; Am. Folklore Soc. Walter Savage Landor; Shelley; folktale. Add: Dept. of English, San Jose State University, San Jose, CA 95114.

HENDRICK, GEORGE, b. Stephenville, Tex, Mar. 30, 29; m. 55; c. 1. AMERICAN LITERATURE. B.A, Tex. Christian Univ, 48, M.A, 50; Ph.D.(Eng), Univ. Tex, 54. Asst. prof. Eng, Southwest Tex. State Col, 54-56; Univ. Colo, 56-60; prof. Am. stud, Frankfurt, 60-65; prof. ENG, Univ. Ill, Chicago, 65-67, PROF, UNIV. ILL, URBANA, 67-, HEAD. DEPT, 71-, assoc. dean grad. col, 67-71. Vis. prof. Eng, Univ. Ill, Chicago, 64-65. MLA; Mod. Humanities Res. Asn; Am. Stud. Asn. American transcendentalism; twentieth century American literature and culture; southern fiction. Publ: Directory of periodicals publishing articles in English and American Language and literature, 59, 65, 70 & co-auth, The American novel: a checklist of twentieth century criticism, Vol. I, 60 & Vol. II, 70, Swallow; auth, Katherine Anne Porter, 65 & Mazo de la Roche, 70, Twayne; Jesus and the Osiris-Isis myth; Lawrence's The man who died and Williams' The night of the iguana, Anglia, 3-4/66; American literary manuscripts in continental libraries, 5-8/67 & A checklist of American literary manuscripts in Australia, Canada, India, Israel, Japan, and New Zealand, 3/72; Bull. Bibliog; plus others. Add: Dept. of English, 100 English Bldg, University of Illinois, Urbana, IL 61801.

HENDRICKS, BEVERLY LUSTY, b. Milwaukee, Wis, Mar. 15, 34. SPEECH EDUCATION. B.S, Univ. Wis, Milwaukee, 56; M.A, Northwest. Univ, 58, Ph.D.(speech educ), 66. Teacher, high schs, Wis, Ill. & Calif, 56-64; instr. speech, Nat. Col. Educ, 65-66; ASST. PROF. speech & theatre, Univ. Ill, Chicago, 66-71; SPEECH COMMUN. & DRAMA, CALIF. STATE UNIV, LOS ANGELES, 71- Tri-univ. proj, Univ. Nebr, 68-69. West. Speech Commun. Asn; Speech Commun. Asn. Language acquisition; forms of oral interpretation for children; language and cognition. Publ: Co-auth, Effects of an NDEA institute upon attitudes of inner-city elementary teachers, 9/69, auth, The move to power: a philosophy of elementary speech education, 9/70 & Mythmaking with children through improvisation, 9/73, Speech Teacher; plus others. Add: Dept. of Speech Communication & Drama, California State University, 5151 State University Dr, Los Angeles, CA 90032.

HENDRICKS, GEORGE DAVID, b. Midlothian, Tex, Nov. 2, 13; m. 47; c. 4. ENGLISH. B.A, Univ. Tex, 35, M.A, 49, Ph.D, 51; Univ. Calif; Univ. Colo. Teacher, Pub. Schs, Tex, 35-45; mem. fac. ENG, N.TEX. STATE UNIV, 45-51, assoc. prof, 51-68, PROF, 68- U.S.A, 41-45, Res, 45-, Col. Am. Folklore Soc. Folklore; life and literature of the Southwest. Publ: The bad man of the West; Mirrors, mice, and mustaches, Tex. Folklore Soc, 66; Ranch country metaphors, Ariz. Quart; Misconceptions concerning western wild animals, West. Folklore. Add: 1819 Panhandle, Denton, TX 76201.

HENDRICKS, WALTER, b. Chicago, Ill, July 24, 92; m. 26; c. 4. ENGLISH LITERATURE. B.A, Amherst Col, 17; Univ. Grenoble, France, 26-27; M.A, Univ. Chicago, 30; Ph.D, Northwest. Univ, 40. Instr. Eng, Armour Inst. Technol, 22-23, asst. prof, 23-26, assoc. prof, 26-32, prof, 32-40, head dept. lang. & lit, 34-40; chmn. dept. humanities, Ill. Inst. Technol, 40-46; pres. & founder, Marlboro Col, 46-51; PRES, HENDRICKS HOUSE, INC, 51- Pres, Packard & Co, Chicago, 26-45; head dept, Biarritz Am. Univ, France, 45-46; v.pres. & gen. ed, Hendricks-Farrar-Straus, Inc, N.Y, 46-51; pres. & founder, Windham Col, 51-64; Mark Hopkins Col, 64-72; gen. ed, Univ. Classics. U.S.A.A.F, 17-18, 2nd Lt; Inform. & Educ. Div, U.S.A, 45-46, Col. NCTE. Medieval and Renaissance literature; life and works of John Dickinson; linguistics. Publ: Flames and fireflies, 26; Spires and spears, 28; Double dealer, Early Poems, 67; My quarrel with Robert Frost, 74. Add: Hendricks House, Inc, 103 Park Ave, New York, NY 10017.

HENDRICKSON, GEORGE WINDSOR, b. Glendale, N.Y, Oct. 16, 14; m. 43; c. 3. DRAMA. M.F.A, Yale, 42. Instr. theatre, TULANE UNIV, 46-48, asst. prof, 48-53, assoc. prof, 53-57, PROF. THEATRE, 57-, chmn. dept. theatre & speech, 67-69. Assoc. designer, Le Petite Theatre du Vieux Carre, 47-53; tech. consult, WTPS-TV; Xavier Univ; Monroe Little Theatre, La; Gallery Circle Theatre, La; Motion Picture Advertising Co, 50-65; vis. prof. design, Boston Univ, 66-67; assoc. producer, Tulane Summer Lyric Theatre, 69-, designer, Tulane Center Stage, 73. A.U.S, 42-46; U.S.A.R, Lt. Col. Am. Theatre Asn; South. Speech Asn. Stage lighting control. Publ: Designs for Winterset, Theatre Arts, 7/47; Source material for scene design, South. Speech J, winter 59; Design for Richard III, Am. Educ. Theatre Asn. J, 10/67. Add: Dept. of Theatre & Speech, Tulane University, New Orleans, LA 70118.

HENDRICKSON, RICHARD H, English, Linguistics. See Volume III, Foreign Languages, Linguistics & Philology.

HENDRIX, JERRY ALLEN, b. Dallas, Tex, July 12, 34. SPEECH. B.A, E.Tex. State Univ, 56; M.A, Univ. Okla, 57; Ph.D.(speech), La. State Univ, 64. Instr. SPEECH, Westmar Col, 58-60; Univ. Southwest. La, 63-65; asst. prof, AM. UNIV.(D.C), 65-67, assoc. prof, 67-72, PROF, 72- Speech Commun. Asn.(chmn. pub. add. div, 71-72). American public address. Publ: Co-auth, Rhetorical criticism: methods and models, W.C. Brown, 68; auth, A new look at textual authenticity of speeches in the Congressional record, 65, Presidential addresses to Congress: Woodrow Wilson and the Jeffersonian tradition, 66 & The Shivercrat Rebellion: a case study in campaign speaking strategies, 68, South. Speech J. Add: Dept. of Communication, American University, Massachusetts & Nebraska Aves, N.W, Washington, DC 20016.

HENDRIX, RICHARD GEORGE, b. New York, N.Y, Feb. 18, 42. ENGLISH LITERATURE, HISTORY. A.B, Oberlin Col, 64; Ford Found. fel. & M.A, Univ. Chicago, 65, Ford Found. & univ. fels. & Ph.D.(Eng), 70. Lectr. ENG, WILLIAMS COL, 68-69, ASST. PROF, 69- Nat. Endowment for Humanities Younger Humanist fel, 72-73. MLA. English Romantic poetry; political satire in the early 19th century; American social criticism. Add: Dept. of English, Williams College, Williamstown, MA 01267.

HENIG, SUZANNE, b. New York, N.Y, Jan. 12, 36. ENGLISH, POETRY. B.A, Wash. Sq. Col, N.Y. Univ, 57; fel, Univ. Iowa, 57-58; M.A, N.Y. Univ, 61, Dean Payne scholar. & Ph.D.(Eng), 68. Instr. Eng. & speech, City Univ. New York, 59-62; writer & teacher, 62-63; asst. prof. ENG, N.Y. State Univ, New Paltz, 63-68; SAN DIEGO STATE UNIV, 68-70, assoc. prof, 70-73, PROF, 73- Fel, Univ. Iowa, 57; N.Y. Univ, fel, 63-65; res. grants, Am. Philos. Soc, 69, 70 & 72, San Diego State Res. Found, 69, 71 & 72, Leopold Schepp Found, 69 & 72, Am. Counc. Learned Soc, 72; ed, Virginia Woolf Quart, 71- Thomas Wolfe Poetry Award, 57; Riverside Poetry Award, 58; Teaching Awards, City Univ. New York, 61 & 62. MLA; Poetry Soc. Am; Philol. Asn. Pac. Coast; AAUP. Twentieth century British literature; modern poetry; creative writing. Publ: Poetry anthologized by Marianne Moore in Riverside III, 58 & A critical study of John Lehmann, 74, Twayne; The literary criticism of Virginia Woolf, N.Y. Univ, 68; ed. & auth. introd, A Cockney's farming experience, San Diego State Univ, 72; ed. & auth. introd, Collected papers of the Second International Conference of Conrad Scholars, Mursia Editione, Italy, 74; auth, A TBA bibliography of Virginia Woolf, Pierian, 74; Hope Mirrlees: Queen of Lud, Virginia Woolf Quart, fall 72; Ulysses in Bloomsbury, James Joyce Quart, 1/73; Conversation with John Lehmann, J. Mod. Lit, summer 73. Add: Dept. of English, San Diego State University, San Diego, CA 92115.

HENINGER, SIMEON KAHN, JR, b. Monroe, La, Oct. 27, 22. ENGLISH. B.S, Tulane Univ, 43, B.A, 47, M.A, 49; Fulbright scholar, Oxford, 49-50, B.Litt, 52; Ph.D.(Eng), Johns Hopkins Univ, 55. Asst. prof. ENG, Duke Univ, 55-62, assoc. prof, 62-66, PROF, 66-67; Univ. Wis, Madison, 67-71, chmn. dept. 68-70; UNIV. B.C, 71- Guggenheim fel, 62-63; mem, Nat. Shakespeare Anniversary Comt, 63-64; fel, Southeast. Inst. Medieval & Renaissance Stud, 67; fel, Huntington Libr. U.S.A.A.F, 43-46, Capt. MLA; Mediaeval Acad. Am; Renaissance Soc. Am. Renaissance science and literature. Publ: A handbook of Renaissance meteorology, Duke Univ, 60; ed, Thomas Watson, the hekatompathia, Scholars Facsimiles, 64 & Edmund Spenser, selected poetry, Houghton, 68; auth, Touches of sweet harmony: Pythagorean cosmology and Renaissance poetics, Huntington Libr, 74; The implications of form for the shepheardes calender, Stud. Renaissance, 62; Tudor literature of the physical sciences, Huntington Libr. Quart, 69; The pattern of love's labour's lost, Shakespeare Stud, 73; plus others. Add: Dept. of English, University of British Columbia, Vancouver 8, B.C, Can.

HENINGHAM, ELEANOR KELLOGG, b. Brooklyn, N.Y, Aug. 28, 09; m. 36. ENGLISH, MEDIEVAL LATIN. B.A, Mt. Holyoke Col, 31; M.A, N.Y. Univ, 32, Mt. Holyoke & univ. fels, 33-35, Ph.D.(Eng), 37. Asst. & instr. ENG, Wash. Sq. Col, N.Y. Univ, 36-41; assoc, Sch. Gen. Stud, Columbia Univ, 59-66; ASST. PROF, SCH. LETT. & SCI, UNIV. IDAHO, 66- Sterling res. fel, Yale, 44-45; instr. Rutherford Campus, Fairleigh Dickinson Univ, 63-66. Shakespeare and the Medieval literature of death; the Vita AEduuardi Regis, earliest Anglo-Latin life of Edward the Confessor. Publ: An early Latin debate of the body and soul, privately publ, 37; co-auth, Ninth supplement to a manual of the writings in Middle English, 1050-1400, Conn. Acad, 51; auth, Bishop Brunton and the fable of the rats, 3/35 & Old English precursors of The Worcester fragments, 6/40, PMLA; The genuineness of the Vita AEduuardi Regis, Speculum, 10/46. Add: Dept. of English, University of Idaho, Moscow, ID 83843.

HENKE, JAMES THOMAS, b. Indianapolis, Ind, Apr. 26, 38; m. 66; c. 1. ENGLISH. A.B, Wash. Univ, 64; M.A, Univ. Mo-Columbia, 66; Ph.D.(Eng), Univ. Wash, 70. Instr. ENG, Univ. Mo-St. Louis, 66; ASST. PROF. YOUNGSTOWN STATE UNIV, 69- Mem, Woodrow Wilson Fel. Found. U.S.N, 56-60. AAUP; Renaissance Soc. Am. English Renaissance dramatic literature; modern dramatic literature. Publ: John Webster's motif of consuming: an approach to the dramatic unity and tragic vision of The white devil and The Duchess of Malfi, Neophilol. Mitt, (in press). Add: Dept. of English, Youngstown State University, Youngstown, OH 44503.

HENKEL, JULIA S, b. Grand Rapids, Mich, Nov. 23, 25; m. 50; c. 2. ENGLISH, RELIGIOUS EDUCATION. B.A, Hope Col; M.Ed, Univ. Pittsburgh, Ph.D, 62; B.D. & M.Th, Winona Lake Sch. Theol. Chmn. div. lang. & lit, Malone Col, 58-68; PROF. LIT. & RELIG. EDUC, GRAND RAPIDS BAPTIST COL, 68- Delta Kappa Gamma res. scholar, Univ. Oxford, Eng. & Utrecht, Netherlands, 65-66. NCTE; Nat. Educ. Asn; Relig. Educ. Asn. Educational contributions of the brethren of the common life. Publ: Co-auth, Dawn of modern civilization, Ann Arbor, 62. Add: 4531 Henkel Rd, Pierson, MI 49339.

HENLEY, ELTON F, b. Tallahassee, Fla, Oct. 29, 36. ENGLISH RENAISSANCE. B.A, Fla. State Univ, 58, M.A, 59, Ph.D, 62; Duke Univ, 59-60. Asst. prof. ENG, Northeast. La. State Col, 62-63; UNIV. S.FLA, 63-68, ASSOC. PROF, 68-, All-Univ. Res. Counc. res. grant, summer 68. MLA; NCTE; S.Atlantic Mod. Lang. Asn; Bibliog. Soc. Univ. Va; Renaissance Soc. Am; Shakespeare Soc. English Renaissance; bibliography; Shakespeare. Publ: Wordsworth criticism: an annotated bibliography, 60 & co-auth, Wordsworthian criticism 1945-1964, rev. ed, 65, N.Y. Pub. Libr; A check list of theses on William Wordsworth in the libraries of the United States, Bibliog. Soc. Univ. Va, 61. Add: Dept. of English, University of South Florida, Tampa, FL 33620.

HENLINE, RUTH, b. Chicago, Ill, Feb. 16, 02. ENGLISH. A.B, Ill. Wesleyan Univ, 24; B.Ed, Ill. State Norm. Univ, 26; A.M, Columbia Univ, 35; A.M, Northwest. Univ, 46, Ph.D, 47. Teacher, High Sch, Ill, 24-25; from instr. to PROF. ENG, ILL. STATE UNIV, 26-, mgr. bookstore, 26-43. Dir, Workshops in Lang, summers, 55-; Writing Lab, 63- Col. Eng. Asn; Conf. Col. Compos. & Commun; MLA; NCTE; Nat. Educ. Asn. Influence of Goethe on Matthew Arnold; college English education; American literature. Publ: Notes on Virginia as an evidence of Jefferson's reaction against the theories of the French naturalists, Va. Quart; Recent trends on methods of teaching English. Add: 902 Crestline Dr. Normal, IL 61761.

HENNEDY, HUGH L, b. Dorchester, Mass, Sept. 17, 29; m. 53; c. 4. ENGLISH. B.A, Univ. Notre Dame, 51; M.A, Columbia Univ, 56; fel, Boston Univ, 59-60; Ph.D.(Eng), 66. Instr. Eng, ST. FRANCIS COL.(MAINE), 55-59, assoc. prof, 60-66, PROF, 66-, chmn. div. humanities, 61-63 & 68-69. U.S.A, 52-54. MLA; Mediaeval Acad. Am; Shakespeare Asn. Am. English novel; Chaucer; Shakespeare. Publ: Unity in Barsetshire, Mouton, 71; The Friar's Summoner's dilemma, Chaucer Rev, 71; Shakespeare on screen, Commonweal, 71; Love and famine, family and country in Trollope's Castle Richmond, Eire-Ireland, 72. Add: Division of Humanities, St. Francis College, 605 Pool Rd, Biddeford, ME 04005.

HENNEDY, JOHN FRANCIS, b. Braintree, Mass, May 31, 36; m. 63; c. 5. ENGLISH. B.A, Univ. Notre Dame, 58; M.A, Boston Univ, 61; Ph.D.(Eng), Univ. Ill, Urbana, 65. Asst. prof. ENG, PROVIDENCE COL, 65-71, ASSOC. PROF, 71- MLA. Shakespeare; English Renaissance drama; 18th century. Publ: Ed, George Chapman's Sir Gyles Goosecappe, Knight, Vol. II, In: Illinois Edition of Chapman, Univ. Ill; auth, Launcelot Gobbo and Shylock's forced conversion, Tex. Stud. Lit. & Lang, fall 73. Add: Dept. of English, Providence College, Providence, RI 02918.

HENNEKE, BEN GRAF, b. St. Louis, Mo, May 20, 14; m. 40; c. 2. SPEECH. A.B, Univ. Tulsa, 35, hon. D.H.L, 67; Columbia Univ, 35; A.M, State Univ. Iowa, 41; Ph.D, Univ. Ill, 56. Reporter, Tulsa Daily World, Okla, 32-37; from instr. to prof. speech, UNIV. TULSA, 37-58, pres, 58-67, TRUSTEE'S PROF. HUMANITIES, 67-, dir. radio, 45-58, admin. v.pres, 52-58. Consult, Am. Petroleum Co, 47-58. Am. Soc. Theatre Res; Soc. Theatre Res, Eng. Theatre history; 19th century America. Publ: Radio announcer's handbook, 48, Reading aloud effectively, 53 & co-auth, Announcer's handbook, 59, Rinehart. Add: 3826 S. Birmingham Pl, Tulsa, OK 74105.

HENNING, STANDISH, b. Gregory, S.Dak, May 2, 32; m. 56; c. 2. ENGLISH. B.A, Univ. of the South, 53; M.A, Harvard, 57, Ph.D.(Eng), 60. Instr. ENG, UNIV. WIS-MADISON, 60-61, asst. prof, 61-65, assoc. prof, 65-72, PROF, 72- Am. Counc. Learned Soc. grant-in-aid, summer 64; Am. Philos. Soc. grant, winter 68. U.S.A.F, 54-56, 1st Lt. MLA; Renaissance Soc. Am; Shakespeare Asn. Am. Analytic bibliography; Jacobean drama. Publ: Ed, A mad world, my masters, Univ. Nebr, 65; Chauntecleer and Taurus, Eng. Lang. Notes, 9/65; The printer of Romeo and Juliet, Q1, Papers Bibliog. Soc. Am, 10/66; The printing of the Beaumont and Fletcher first folio, Stud. Bibliog, 69. Add: Dept. of English, Graduate Division, 213 Bascom Hall, University of Wisconsin-Madison, Madison, WI 53706.

HENNINGER, FRANCIS JOSEPH, b. Jamaica, N.Y, Oct. 17, 35; m. 57; c. 5. ENGLISH, AMERICAN STUDIES. B.A, St. John's Univ,(N.Y), 56; A.M, Univ. Notre Dame, 58; M.A, Univ. Pa, 62, Ph.D.(Am. civilization), 65. Instr. Eng, St. Bernardine of Siena Col, 58-61; res. archivist, nat. hist. site, Gunston Hall, 63-65; asst. prof. ENG, UNIV. DAYTON, 65-72, ASSOC. PROF, 72-, DIR, AM. STUD. PROG, 72- Consult, Civil Serv. Comn, 69-; Gen. Acct. Off, 72- Am. Stud. Asn; Popular Stud. Asn. Artifacts of popular culture, especially chairs; 19th century American authors; Camus. Publ: The bouquet of Poe's Amontillado, S.Atlantic Bull, 3/70; contrib, Popular culture and curricula, Popular Cult. Asn, 72; auth, Plot-theme fusion in The plague, Mod. Fiction Stud, summer 73. Add: American Studies Program, University of Dayton, Dayton, OH 45469.

HENRICKSEN, BRUCE CONLEY, b. Fairbault, Minn, Feb. 26, 41; m. 67; c. 1. RENAISSANCE LITERATURE. B.A, Univ. Minn, Minneapolis, 63; M.A, Univ. South. Calif, 67, Ph.D.(Eng), 70. Instr. ENG, Calif. State Col, Los Angeles, 67-68; assoc. Univ. Calif, Los Angeles, 68-70; ASST. PROF, LOYOLA UNIV.(LA), 70- MLA; Renaissance Soc. Am. Seventeenth century religious literature; John Donne. Publ: Donne's orthodoxy, Tex. Stud. Lit. & Lang, spring 72. Add: Dept. of English, Loyola University, New Orleans, LA 70118.

HENRIQUES, KENNETH EDMUND, b. San Francisco, Calif, Mar. 9, 19; m. 67. ENGLISH, THEOLOGY. B.A, San Luis Rey Col, 41; summer, Univ. Calif, Los Angeles, 45; M.A, Oxford, 61; Univ. N.Dak, 68. Instr. Eng. & Spanish, San Luis Rey Col, 45-46; asst. prof. ENG, BEMIDJI STATE COL, 65-66, ASSOC. PROF, 66-, CHMN. DEPT, 69- Mem. John Beard Res. Inst, 62- U.S.A.F, 53-58, Capt. MLA. Old English; Middle English; Chaucer. Add: Dept. of English, Bemidji State College, Bemidji, MN 56601.

HENRY, GEORGE H, b. Birdsboro, Pa, Sept. 20, 03; m. 53. ENGLISH, SECONDARY EDUCATION. A.B, Temple Univ, 26; M.A, Columbia Univ, 49, Ed.D.(curriculum), 53. Head dept. Eng, high sch, Del, 26-28, prin. high schs, Del, 28-49; prof. educ, UNIV. DEL, 49-64, ENG. & EDUC, 64-72, EMER. PROF, 72- Consult, Wilmington Pub. Schs, Del, 53-58; Albany State Dept. Educ, 63; Montgomery & Cumberland County Schs, Md, 64; Seaford Pub. Schs, Del, 65; Euclid Proj. Ctr, Cleveland, Ohio, 66; U.S. Off. Educ. grant, 66; lectr, Ind. Univ, 67; follow-up stud. NDEA Inst, 68. Cert. Merit Educ. TV Award, 64. NCTE (mem. res. comt, 66-68); Soc. Stud. Educ; Am. Theatre Asn.(mem. exec. bd, 61-66). Methods of teaching English; concept development in English; empirical inquiry into instruction in English. Publ: Co-auth, Short stories for our times, Houghton, 50 & General education in the high school, Asn. Supv. & Curriculum Develop. Yearbook, 50; auth, The idea of coverage, Eng. J, 65; English teaching encounters science, Col. Eng, 67; English education and the American dream, Eng. J, 73. Add: College of Education, University of Delaware, Newark, DE 19711.

HENRY, MABEL C. WRIGHT, b. Wilmington, Del, Feb. 14, 11; m. 53. ENGLISH, THEATRE ARTS. A.B, Rosemont Col, 34; M.A, Pa. State Univ, 41; dipl, Columbia Univ, 52. Teacher Eng. & drama, Bayard Jr. High Sch, Wilmington, Del, 34-44; teacher Eng. & speech & dir. dramatics, Baldwin Upper & Middle Schs, Bryn Mawr, Pa, 44-46; teacher Eng. & pub. speaking & dir. theatre activities, Wilmington High Sch, Del, 46-71; RETIRED. Ford Found. fel, 55; consult. children's theatre & creative speech arts, Wilmington Elem. Pub. Schs, 56- Am. Nat. Theatre & Acad; NCTE; Am. Theatre Asn; Children's Theatre Conf. Development of creativity through the speech arts; concept development; educational theatre at the secondary school level. Publ: Speech arts in the language arts program of the elementary schools, 64 & co-auth, Creative experience in oral language, 67, NCTE; auth, Creative dramatics, In: Teaching in America, Univ. Pa, 55. Add: 99 W. Park Pl, Newark, DE 19711.

HENRY, NATHANIEL H, b. Washington, N.C, Jan. 16, 09; m. 36; c. 2. ENGLISH. A.B, Univ. N.C, Chapel Hill, 29, M.A, 33, Ph.D.(Eng), 42. Teacher ENG. LIT, N.C. Pub. Schs, 29-32; fel. & asst. instr, Univ. N.C, Chapel Hill, 31-41; instr. Clemson Col, 36-38; Biarrite, France, 45-46; from instr. to PROF, Richmond Col, 46-68; VA. COMMONWEALTH UNIV, 68- Educ. adv, Fed. Civilian Conservational Corp, 34-35; vis. prof, Univ. N.C, Chapel Hill 52 & 66; prof, Medieval & Renaissance Lang. Coop. Prog, Univ. N.C, Chapel Hill & Duke Univ, 65-66. Ord.C, U.S.A, 42-46, Maj. MLA; Col. Eng. Asn; Renaissance Soc. Am. Seventeenth century English literature; theology and history. Publ: Milton's last pamphlet, In: Tribute to George Coffin Taylor, Univ. N.C, 52; The mystery of Milton's muse, 67 & John Milton, Anglican, 69, Renaissance Papers; plus others. Add: 3414 Noble Ave, Richmond, VA 23222.

HENRY, WILLIAM CLAUD, b. Altus, Okla, Jan. 9, 14; m. 40; c. 3. LITERARY CRITICISM. A.M, Univ. Okla, 37; tutorial fel, Northwest. Univ, 37, univ. fel, 38, Ph.D, 42. Instr. Eng, Northwest. Univ. 41-45, asst. prof, 45-46; assoc. prof, Univ. Omaha, 46-50, prof, 50; headmaster, Brownell Hall, Omaha, Nebr, 50-59; assoc. prof. ENG, COLO, STATE UNIV, 59-63, PROF, 63-, chmn. compos, 59-66. Mem, Colo, Adv. Counc. Lang. Arts, 61- NCTE. Composition; 19th century literary criticism. Publ: Co-auth, Teaching composition, Colo. State Dept. Educ, 64; auth, Applied rhetoric, Wadsworth, 68. Add: Dept. of English, Colorado State University, Ft. Collins, CO 80521.

HENRY, WILLIAM H. b. Philadelphia, Pa, May 10, 19. ENGLISH. A.B, Univ. Pa, 49; M.Ed, Temple Univ, 54, A.M, 57, Ph.D.(Eng), 70. Instr. econ, Taylor Sch, 51-52; ENG, Columbia Inst, 53-54; Phila. Textile Col, 54-55; Villanova Univ, 55-59; asst. prof, Moore Col. Art, 59-60; assoc. prof. WEST CHESTER STATE COL, 60-70, PROF. & ASST. CHMN. DEPT, 70- MLA. Modern American, British and French literature; modern drama. Publ: A French bibliography of W. Somerset Maugham, Bibliog. Soc. Univ. Va, 67. Add: Dept. of English, West Chester State College, West Chester, PA 19380.

HENSHAW, WANDALIE, b. Cincinnati, Ohio, Feb. 14, 35. THEATRE. B.A, Univ. Mich, 56; M.F.A, Yale, 59; Ph.D.(Restoration comedy), Univ. Pittsburgh, 67. Instr. acting & directing, Univ. Pittsburgh, 66-67, asst. prof, 67-68; Univ. Victoria (B.C), 68-73; ASSOC. PROF. THEATRE, UNIV. TENN, KNOXVILLE, 73- Assoc. dir, Victoria Fair Theatre, summers 69-71. Am. Theatre Asn. Directing and the training of directors; Restoration comedy; period movement and manners for modern production of period plays. Publ: Graphic sources for a modern approach to the acting of Restoration comedy, 5/68 & The open scene as a directing exercise, 10/69, Educ. Theatre J; Gilbert and Sullivan Through a glass brightly, Tex. Quart, 12/73. Add: Dept. of Speech & Theatre, University of Tennessee, Knoxville, TN 37916.

HENSLEY, CHARLES S. ENGLISH. A.B, Wash. Univ, 42, A.M, 43, univ. fel, 43-44; univ. fel, Columbia Univ, 45-47; Ph.D, Univ. Mo, 58. Instr. Eng, Univ. Minn, 47-50; asst. prof, Harris Teachers Col, 50-60; assoc. prof. Eng. & humanities, South. Ill. Univ, Alton Ctr, 60-63; asst. prof. ENG, Humboldt State Col, 63-65; Stanislaus State Col, 65-68; assoc. prof, CHICAGO STATE UNIV, 68-71, PROF, 71- Lectr, Wash. Univ, 48-51. Renaissance Soc. Am; MLA; NCTE; Conf. Col. Compos. & Commun; Col. Eng. Asn. Steel engravings used to illustrate English emblem poetry; student's guide for Shakespeare; Jacobean drama. Publ: The later career of George Wither, Mouton, The Hague, 68; Wither's career as a humanist, Seventeenth Century News, 61; Wither, Waller, Marvell: panegyrists for the protector, Ariel, 1/72; co-auth, Introd. to Wither's A collection of emblems (1635), Univ. S.C, 73. Add: Dept. of English, Chicago State University, 95th & King Dr, Chicago, IL 60628.

HENSLEY, DON HARPER, b. Steele City, Nebr, Aug. 8, 24. ENGLISH. B.A, Univ. Ore, 50. M.A, 55; Ph.D.(Eng), Univ. Wis, Madison, 64. Instr. ENG, High Sch, Ore, 51-52; Wis. State Univ, Whitewater, 59-62, ASST. PROF, Green Bay, 64-65; UNIV. WEST. ONT, 65- U.S.A, 44-45. MLA. Add: Dept. of English, University of Western Ontario, London, Ont, Can.

HENSON, CLYDE EUGENE, b. Xenia, Ill, June 30, 14; m. 49. ENGLISH. B.Ed, South. Ill, Univ, 37; M.A, State Univ. Iowa, 38; Ph.D, West. Reserve Univ, 50. With U.S. War Dept, 41-47; instr, MICH. STATE UNIV, 47-51, asst. prof, 51-57, assoc. prof, 57-62, PROF, 62-, dir. Am. Stud, 67-68. Fulbright lectr, State Univ. Leiden, 65-66. MLA; Am. Stud. Asn; Folklore Soc, London. American literature since 1871; poetry; comparative folklore; Henry James' Europe. Publ: Joseph Kirkland, 62 & Gist of poetics, 63, Twayne; plus others. Add: 1416 W. Michigan Ave, Lansing, MI 48915.

HENTZ, ANN LOUISE, b. Philadelphia, Pa, June 23, 21. ENGLISH LITERATURE, RENAISSANCE. B.A, Univ. Rochester, 50; univ. scholar, Ohio State Univ, 50-51, M.A, 51, teaching fel, 52-56, Ph.D, 56. Instr. ENG, LAKE FOREST COL, 56-58, asst. prof, 58-65, ASSOC. PROF, 65-, grant, 59. Ford grant, 69. MLA. Renaissance Soc. Am. Samuel Daniel; Shakespeare; Gerard Manley Hopkins. Publ: A senecan source for Samuel Daniel's verse epistle to Southampton, Notes & Queries, 6/62; Hamlet: the anatomy of a task, Col. Eng, 4/66; Language in Hopkins' Carrion comfort, Victorian Poetry, autumn 71. Add: Dept. of English, Lake Forest College, Lake Forest, IL 60045.

HENZE, RICHARD HAROLD, b. Evansville, Ind, Dec. 13, 39; m. 61. ENGLISH LITERATURE. B.A, Evansville Col, 61; M A, Univ. Nebr, 62, Ph.D. (Eng), 65. Instr. ENG, Univ. Nebr, 64-65; asst. prof, Univ. Ky, 65-70; ASSOC. PROF, COLO. STATE UNIV, 70- MLA; Renaissance Soc. Am;

Shakespeare Asn. Am. Shakespeare; Renaissance drama. Publ: Deception in Much ado about nothing, Stud. Eng. Lit, spring 71; The comedy of errors: a freely binding chain, winter 71 & The tempest: rejection of a vanity, fall 72, Shakespeare Quart. Add: Dept. of English, Colorado State University, Ft. Collins, CO 80521.

HEPBURN, JAMES GORDON, b. Montgomeryville, Pa, Dec. 13, 22; m. 47; c. c. 1. ENGLISH. B.A, Yale, 44; M.A, Univ. Pa, 49, Ph.D.(Eng), 57. Instr. ENG, Lafayette Col, 52-54; Cornell Univ, 57-61; asst. prof. Univ. R.I, 61-64; assoc. prof, 65-67; Am. Philos. Soc. grant, 67-72; DANA PROF. ENG. & CHMN. DEPT. BATES COL, 72-, TEMP. CHMN. DEPT. SPEECH & THEATRE, 73- Am. Counc. Learned Soc. grant-in-aid, 62, 66, 68, 70; vis. assoc. prof, Yale, 67. U.S.A, 44-46. MLA. Victorian and modern English literature. Publ: Co-ed, Robert Frost, Holt, 61; co-ed, Modern essays, 62, 68; auth, College composition, 64 & Poetic design, 66, Macmillan; The art of Arnold Bennett, Ind. Univ, 63; ed, Letters of Arnold Bennett (3 vols), 66, 68 & 70 & auth, The author's empty purse, 68, Oxford Univ; auth, Confessions of an American scholar, Univ. Minn, 71; Prod, Poor dumb animals, 6/71 & Time, life, sex, and you know what, 6/72, Questors Theatre, Ealing. Add: Dept. of English, Bates College, Lewiston, ME 04240.

HEPLER, JOHN CHISLETT, b. Pa, Nov. 8, 13; m. 42; c. 3. ENGLISH. B.S, Pa. State Teachers Col, 35; A.M, George Peabody Col, 37, fel, 40-42, Ph.D, 42; Harvard, 39; Vanderbilt Univ, 40-42. Instr. ENG, Dickinson Col, 42-46; from assoc. prof. to PROF, CENT. MICH. UNIV, 46-, head dept, 58-68. Guest, U.S. War Col, 69; chmn, Mich. State Competition of NCTE Achievement Awards Prog, 69-72. NCTE; MLA; Am. Stud. Asn. American culture of the 19th century; national literary magazines in America, 1850-1900. Publ: American and English periodicals in nineteenth century, In: Poole's Index to Nineteenth Century Periodicals. Add: 70 Cedar Dr, Route 7, Mt. Pleasant, MI 48858.

HEPWORTH, BRIAN E, b. Bawtry, U.K, Jan. 31, 31; U.S. citizen. ENGLISH. B.A, Univ. London, 55; M.A, Harvard, 62, Ph.D.(Eng), 65. Instr. ENG, Robert Col, Istanbul, 55-57; master, The Choate Sch, Conn, 57-61; teaching fel. & resident tutor, Harvard, 62-65; asst. prof, YORK UNIV, 65-72, ASSOC. PROF, 72- Instr, Royal Army Educ. Corps, U.K, 49-51. MLA. Augustan literature; mid-eighteenth century literature; the romantics. Add: Dept. of English, York University, 4700 Keele St, Toronto 12, Ont, Can.

HERBER, HAROLD L, b. Pontiac, Mich, Oct. 31, 29; m. 52. ENGLISH READING. B.A, Taylor Univ, 51; B.D, Gordon Sem, 55; Ed.M, Boston Univ, 57, Ed.D.(reading instr), 59; Hofstra Univ, 60-63. Teacher & coord, High Schs, N.Y. & Mass, 55-63; lectr. READING, SYRACUSE UNIV. SCH. EDUC, 63-66, assoc. prof, 66-71, PROF, 71- Coord. proj. Eng. demonstration ctr, Syracuse Univ, 63-66; chmn. visual aids comt, Int. Reading Asn, 65-67; mem. comn. Eng. curriculum, NCTE, 66-69, mem. reading comt, 67-; dir. experience teacher fel. prog. in reading, U.S. Off. Educ. grant, 67-68 & dir. demonstration ctrs. in secondary reading, 68- Int. Reading Asn.(ed, J. Reading, 67-); NCTE. Reading in content areas; critical thinking; classroom behavior. Publ: Success with words, Scholastic Bk. Serv, 64; Learning your language, Follett, Vol. I, 65, Vol. II, 66, Vol. III, 69; Reading through content, Prentice-Hall, 69; Concept association in physics, Reporter, 64; ed, Developing study skills in secondary schools, Int. Reading Asn, 65; auth, Study skills: reading to remember and use ideas, Educ. Rec. Bur, 68. Add: School of Education, Syracuse University, 732 Ostrom Ave, Syracuse, NY 13210.

HERBERGER, CHARLES FREDERICK, JR, b. Ilion, N.Y, Feb. 29, 20; m. 46; c. 1. ENGLISH. A.B, Dartmouth Col, 42; M.A, Univ. Cincinnati, 48; Ph.D. (Eng), Boston Univ, 60. Instr. ENG, Univ. Cincinnati, 48-50; Framingham State Col, 52-53; Colby Jr. Col, 53-54; Wayne State Univ, 54-58; asst. prof, NASSON COL, 58-60, assoc. prof, 60-64, PROF, 64-, COORD. HUMANITIES, 66-, dir. stud. abroad prog, Vienna, 70-71. U.S.N, 42-46, Res, 46-64, Comdr. Literary criticism; Chaucer; Renaissance literature; mythology and archetypes. Publ: The thread of Ariadne, Philos. Libr, 72. Add: Dept. of English, Nasson College, Springvale, ME 04083.

HERBERT, CHRISTOPHER CLARKE, b. New York, N.Y, Dec. 11, 41. ENGLISH LITERATURE. B.A, Yale, 63, Ph.D.(Eng), 70; C.E.S.(Fr. lit), Sorbonne, 64; M.A, Univ. Chicago, 65. ASST. PROF. ENG, NORTHWEST. UNIV, 69- Dickens; 19th century fiction. Publ: Converging worlds in Pickwick papers, 19th Century Fiction, 6/72; De Quincey and Dickens, Victorian Stud, 3/74. Add: Dept. of English, Northwestern University, Evanston, IL 60201.

HERBERT, EDWARD THOMAS, b. Milwaukee, Wis, Mar. 21, 19. ENGLISH & AMERICAN LITERATURE. B.A, Univ. Wis, 41, M.A, 42, Ph.D, 58. Asst. Univ. Minn, 43-44; lectr. Drama, Goodman Theatre, 51-52; instr. ENG, Duquesne Univ, 53-56; from asst. prof. to ASSOC. PROF, NORTH. ILL. UNIV, 57- Fulbright teacher, Netherlands, 56. Excellence in Teaching Award, Standard Oil Found, 69. NCTE (state chmn. achievement awards, 70). Twentieth century American literature. Publ: Var. arts, in: J. Am. Folklore, West. Folklore, Mod. Drama, Eng. J. & Psychoanal. Rev. Add: Dept. of English, Northern Illinois University, DeKalb, IL 60115.

HERBERT, LUCILLE OAKLANDER, b. New York, N.Y, Oct. 13, 29; m. 54; c. 1. ENGLISH. A.B, Cornell Univ, 49; Ph.D.(Eng), 58; M.A, Smith Col, 50; dipl, Univ. Rennes, 52. Instr. ENG, Carleton Col, 58-60, asst. prof, 60-62; lectr, Hunter Col, 62-63; asst. prof, Portland State Col, 66-67, YORK UNIV, 67-70, ASSOC. PROF, 70- MLA. English prose fiction; English romanticism. Publ: Hardy's views in Tess of the D'Urbervilles, ELH, 70; George Borrow and the forms of self reflection, Univ. Toronto Quart, 71; Tono-Bungay: tradition and experiment, Mod. Lang. Quart, 72. Add: Dept. of English, York University, Keele St, Toronto 12, Ont, Can.

HERBERT, THOMAS WALTER, b. Camden, S.C, Sept, 25, 08; m. 36; c. 3. ENGLISH LITERATURE. A.B, Wofford Col, 29; A.M, Emory Univ, 31; Ph.D, Princeton, 35. Teacher, High Sch, S.C, 29-30; instr. ENG, Clemson Agr. Col, 31-32; prof. & head dept, Berry Col, 35-41; adj. prof, Univ. S.C, 41-46; assoc. prof, UNIV. FLA, 46-51, PROF, 51-, President's medal for fac. lect, 67. U.S.N.R, 44-46, Lt. Comdr. MLA; S.Atlantic Mod. Lang. Asn.(pres, 67); Southeast. Renaissance Conf.(pres, 63); Renaissance Soc. Am. English literature and versification; Shakespeare studies. Publ: John Wesley as editor and author, Princeton, 40. Add: 13 S.W. 23rd Dr, Gainesville, FL 32601.

HERBERT, THOMAS WALTER, JR, b. Rome, Ga, Sept. 7, 38; m. 63; c. 2. AMERICAN LITERATURE. B.A, Harvard, 60; M.Div, Union Theol. Sem, 63; Ph.D.(Eng), Princeton, 69. Dir. exp. prog. ministry to grand. stud. & fac, Univ. Calif, Berkeley, 63-66; ASST. PROF. ENG, UNIV. KY, 69- Nat. Endowment for Humanities younger humanist fel, 73-74. MLA; S.Atlantic Mod. Lang. Asn; Soc. Relig. Higher Educ. Herman Melville; literature and religious thought. Publ: The movement: a view from Berkeley, Theol. Today, 68; Calvinism and cosmic evil in Moby Dick, PMLA, 69; The force of prejudice: Melville's attack on the missionaries in Typee, Border States, 73. Add: Dept. of English, University of Kentucky, Lexington, KY 40506.

HERBOLD, ANTHONY, b. Hollywood, Calif, Feb. 22, 33; m. 54; c. 7. ENGLISH, COMPARATIVE LITERATURE. A.B, Stanford Univ, 55; Univ. Vienna, 55-57; A.M, Univ. Mich, 59, Ph.D.(Eng), 63. Instr. Eng, Univ. Mich, 63; Dartmouth Col, 63-65; asst. prof, Univ. Calif, Berkeley, 65-70; ASSOC. PROF. ENG. & COMP. LIT, UNIV. MAINE, ORONO, 70- Univ. Calif, Berkeley, summer fel, 66. Shakespeare Asn. Am. Shakespeare; American literature; Spanish literature of the 17th century. Publ: Shakespeare, Calderón and Henry the Eighth, East-West, spring 65; Seeking secrets or poetiqueness: the dialectics of Donne's divine poems, Mod. Sprak, winter 66; Nature as concept and technique in the poems of Jones Very, New Eng. Quart, 6/67. Add: Dept. of English, University of Maine at Orono, Orono, ME 04473.

HERINGMAN, BERNARD, b. Baltimore, Md, Aug. 23, 23; m. 61; c. 3. ENGLISH. A.B, Johns Hopkins, 44; A.M, Columbia Univ, 48, Ph.D.(Eng), 55; Kenyon Col, summer, 48; Fulbright scholar, Univ. Paris, 49-50; Instr. Eng, & humanities, Mont. State Univ, 51-56, asst. prof, 56-57; asst. prof. ENG, Earlham Col, 57-60; Rockford Col, 60-62, ASSOC. PROF, 62-63; Baldwin-Wallace Col, 63-66; MOORHEAD STATE COL, 66- Poetry; modern literature; world literature. Publ: Which way I fly (poem), Noonday, 1/60; Wallace Stevens; the use of poetry, In: The act of the mind, Johns Hopkins Univ, 65; Roethke's poetry: the forms of meaning, Tex. Stud. Lit. & Lang, (in press); plus others. Add: Dept. of English, Moorhead State College, Moorhead, MN 56560.

HERMAN, DELDEE M, b. Watervliet, Mich, Aug. 2, 07; m. 31; c. 4. SPEECH. B.A, West. Mich. Univ, 28; M.A, Univ. Mich, 52; summers, Northwest. Univ. Teacher speech & hist, Stevensville High Sch, 26-27; teacher & debate coach, St. Joseph High Sch, 28-30; teacher & chmn. dept. Eng, Verona Jr. High Sch, 30-32; Southeast. Jr. High Sch, 32-35; teacher & debate coach, Battle Creek Cent. High Sch, 45-47; asst. prof. SPEECH, WEST. MICH. UNIV, 47-63, ASSOC. PROF, 63-, women's debate coach, 47-67. Vis. lectr, Univ. Mich, summer 62. Cert. consult, Mich. Speech Asn, 72-; consult, Mich. Dept. Educ, 72- Speech Commun. Asn; Cent. State Speech Asn; Am. Forensic Asn. Speech education; discussion; debate. Publ: Basic speech for high schools, Mich. Speech Asn, 57; co-auth, Speech in the junior high school, 68, Basic speech in the senior high school, 68, Discussion in the secondary school, 68 & Adventures in the looking glass: experiencing communication with your-self and others, 72, Nat. Textbk; co-auth, Speech communication in the process-centered curriculum, 69 & The status of speech teachers and/or teachers academically prepared to teach speech in Michigan Public High Schools, 72, Mich. Speech Asn. J; auth, The challenges we face, Mo. Speech J, spring 73; plus others. Add: 154 Bulkley, Kalamazoo, MI 49007.

HERMAN, GEORGE R, b. St. Joseph, Mich, Oct. 18, 25; m. 50; c. 5. ENGLISH COMPOSITION. B.S, Univ. Kans, 51, M.A, 56. Teacher ENG, De Soto High Sch, Kans, 53-54; instr, ARIZ. STATE UNIV, 56-60, asst. prof, 60-67, ASSOC. PROF, 67- U.S.A, 44-46; U.S.A.F, 51-53, 1st Lt. Creative writing. Publ: Let's go logging, Putnam, 62; co-auth, Modern grammar and composition, 1, 2 and 3, 65, 67, Resources for modern grammar and composition, 65, 67, Our language today 7 and 8, 66, Gains in our language today, 71, Experiences with our language today, 71, Operations in modern grammar and composition, 71, Procedures in modern grammar and composition, 71, Questions in modern grammar and composition, 71 & Resources in modern grammar and composition, 71, Am. Bk. Co; co-auth, Guide to American English, 4th ed, Prentice-Hall, 68; auth, The assassins, Colo. Quart, summer 61; The brief college career of Harry the Ape, Am. Asn. Univ. Profs. Bull, 9/61. Add: Dept. of English, Arizona State University, Tempe, AZ 85281.

HERMAN, HAROLD J, b. Huntingdon, Pa, Apr. 29, 29. MIDDLE ENGLISH LITERATURE & LANGUAGE. A.B, Univ. Md, 52; Ph.D, Univ. Pa, 60. Asst. instr. ENG, Univ. Pa, 52-57; instr, UNIV. MD, COLLEGE PARK, 57-61, asst. prof, 61-65, ASSOC. PROF, 65-, acting chmn. freshman Eng, 63, chmn. freshman Eng, 66-67, chmn. lower div. undergrad. Eng. prog, 68-70. Col. ed, Md. Eng. J, 63-66, ed-in-chief, 66- MLA; NCTE (dir, 65-). Rhetoric. Publ: Co-auth, Henry James' Washington Square and Daisy Miller: lessons in critical reading and writing, Harcourt, 68; English 1 in the pre-college summer session at the University of Maryland, Md. Eng. J, 63; introd, Write it right: a handbook of homonyms, Golden Press, 68. Add: Dept. of English, University of Maryland, College Park, MD 20742.

HERMAN, WILLIAM, b. New York, N.Y, Oct. 19, 26; div; c. 2. ENGLISH, WORLD DRAMA. B.S, City Col. New York, 48; M.F.A, Fordham Univ, 49, Ph.D.(Eng), 69. Lectr. ENG, CITY COL. NEW YORK, 67-69, ASST. PROF, 69- MLA; NCTE. Twentieth century British literature; English and world drama; Shakespeare. Publ: Theatre as enterprise, Tulane Drama Rev, fall 65; Pirandello and possibility, Tulane Drama Rev, spring 66 & In: Pirandello: a collection of critical essays, Prentice-Hall, 67; Richard Schechner descending a staircase: American theatre new'd in the seventies, Kans. Quart, spring 71. Add: 33 Bank St, New York, NY 10014.

HERNÁNDEZ, FRANCES BAKER, b. St. Louis, Mo, Apr. 6, 26; m. 51. COMPARATIVE LITERATURE, ENGLISH. B.S, Purdue Univ, 48, M.S, 58; M.A, Univ. N.Mex, 50, Ph.D.(comp. lit), 63, Teacher, Pub. Schs, N.Mex, 54-58; instr. Spanish, Purdue Univ, 58-59; teacher Eng, Univ. N.Mex, 59-61; asst. prof, Calvin Coolidge Col, 61-63; tutor world lit, St. John's Col.(Md), 63-64;

asst. prof. Eng, Boston Univ, 64; Northeast. Univ, 64-65; N.Mex, State Univ, 65-67; COMP. LIT, UNIV. TEX, EL PASO, 67-72, ASSOC. PROF, 72- Sr. Fulbright prof. Eng. & Am. lit, Cath. Univ. Santiago, 70; exchange prof, Univ. P.R, summer 73; vis. prof. Eng, Bogazici Univ, Turkey, 73-74. MLA; Col. Eng. Asn. South American literature, particularly Chilean; Spanish literature, particularly Catalan; world literature, particularly Russian and French. Publ: Raskolnikov's appraisal of Sofya Semyonovna: a problem in translation, CEA Critic, 10/67; Isaac Bashevis Singer: a new impact of an ancient tradition on modern fiction, Proc. Counc. Col. Teachers Eng, 3/68; Katherine Anne Porter and Julio Cortazar: the craft of fiction, Proc. Comp. Lit. Symp, Vol. V, 72; plus others. Add: P.O. Box 3196, Las Cruces, NM 88003.

HERNDON, GEORGE COLLINS, b. Louisville, Ky, Mar. 6, 16; m. 43; c. 2. ENGLISH LITERATURE. A.B, La. Col, 36; Th.M, South. Baptist Theol. Sem, 42; A.M, Univ. Ky, 47; Univ. South. Calif, 47-50; Th.D, New Orleans Baptist Theol. Sem, 59. Instr. ENG, Univ. Ky, 46-47; teaching asst, Univ. South. Calif, 47-48; prof. Calif. Baptist Theol. Col, 48-50; assoc. prof. & dean students, La. Col, 50-57; assoc. registr, NEW ORLEANS BAPTIST THEOL. SEM, 57-59, asst. prof, 59-63, ASSOC. PROF, 63-, REGISTR, 59- U.S.N.R, Chaplain. NCTE; South Col. Personnel Asn; Am. Asn. Col. Registr. & Admis. Off. Literature; John Donne; Charles Kingsley. Add: New Orleans Theological Seminary, 3939 Gentilly Blvd, New Orleans, LA 70126.

HERNDON, SARAH ELIZA, b. Glade Spring, Va, July 4, 02. ENGLISH. A.B, Salem Col, 24; A.M, Columbia Univ, 27; M.R.E, Biblical Sem. N.Y, 38; Ph.D, N.Y. Univ, 45. From instr. to assoc. prof. ENG, Fla. State Col. Women, 28-47, prof. FLA. STATE UNIV, 47-72, chmn. humanities, 50-67, EMER. PROF. ENG, 72- NCTE; MLA; Archaeol. Inst. Am. English literature; humanities in general education. Publ: Chaucer's five gildsmen, Fla. State Univ. Studs; Benjamin Whichcote; Cambridge Platonist, Fla. State Univ. Studs; co-auth, The humanities in contemporary life, 60 & The humanistic tradition, 64, Holt. Add: 1306 Betton Rd, Tallahassee, FL 32303.

HERNLUND, PATRICIA, b. Chicago, Ill, May 8, 30. ENGLISH. B.A, Carleton Col, 51; M.A, Univ. Chicago, 56, Ph.D.(Eng), 65. Instr. ENG, Chicago City Jr. Col, Wilson Br, 57-63, asst. prof, 63-66; WAYNE STATE UNIV, 66-68, ASSOC. PROF, 68- MLA; Bibliog. Soc. Univ. Va; Bibliog. Soc. Am. Eighteenth century bibliography and literature. Publ: William Strahan's ledgers: standard charges for printing, 1738-1785, 66 & William Strahan's ledgers II: charges for paper, 1738-1785, 68, Stud. Bibliog. Add: 431 State Hall, Wayne State University, Detroit, MI 48202.

HERRESHOFF, DAVID, b. New York, N.Y, Nov. 21, 21; m. 42; c. 3. ENGLISH. B.A, Univ. Akron, 52; Am. Counc. Learned Soc. fel, 51-52; M.A, Univ. Minn, 56, univ. fel, 58-59, Ph.D, 59. Instr. ENG, WAYNE STATE UNIV, 59-63, asst. prof, 63-69, ASSOC. PROF, 69- Carnegie fel. Am. stud, 57-58. U.S.A, 42-43. Am. Stud. Asn; MLA. Marxism in America; literary influence of the Bible; American studies and literature. Publ: American disciples of Marx: from the age of Jackson to the Progressive Era, Wayne State Univ, 67; Origins of American Marxism, Monad, 73; co-auth, American radicals 57 & American labor in midpassage, 59, Monthly Rev. Add: Dept. of English, Wayne State University, Detroit, MI 48202.

HERRIN, VIRGINIA (TOWNSEND), b. Jacksonville, Fla, Mar. 21, 12. ENGLISH. A.B, Agnes Scott Col, 32; M.S, Univ. South. Calif, 41; Ph.D.(Eng), Univ. N.C, 55. Dean, high sch, N.C, 37-46; dean women, Wesleyan Conserv, 46-49; asst. prof. ENG, Ala. Polytech. Inst, 53-56; E.CAROLINA UNIV, 56-60, assoc. prof, 60-63, PROF, 63-, DIR. GRAD. STUD. ENG, 67- MLA; Shakespeare Asn. Am; Mediaeval Acad. Am; Int. Fed. Theatre Res. Drama. Add: Dept. of English, Box 2707, East Carolina University, Greenville, NC 27834.

HERRING, HENRY DUNHAM, b. Florence, S.C, Apr. 26, 41. ENGLISH & AMERICAN LITERATURE. B.A, Univ. S.C, 61, M.A, 64; Ph.D.(Eng), Duke Univ, 68. Instr. ENG, Midwest. Univ, 63-65; asst. prof, Va. Polytech Inst, 66-69; ASSOC. PROF, COL. WOOSTER, 69- MLA; Twentieth century American literature; literature and psychology. Publ: Anthony Powell: a reaction against determinism, Ball State Forum, 68; Politics in the novels of Robert Penn Warren, Recherches Anglaises et Americaines, 71; Madness in At heaven's gate: a metaphor of the self in Robert Penn Warren's fiction, Four Quarters, 72. Add: Dept. of English, College of Wooster, Wooster, OH 44691.

HERRING, JACK W, b. Waco, Tex, Aug. 28, 25. ENGLISH. A.B, Baylor Univ, 47, M.A, 48; Ph.D.(Eng), Univ. Pa, 58. Instr. ENG, Howard Col, 48-50; asst. instr, Univ. Pa, 50-51; acting chmn, Grand Canyon Col, 51-55; instr, Ariz. State Univ, 55-56, asst. prof, 56-59; assoc. prof, BAYLOR UNIV, 59-61, prof, 61-73, MARGARET ROOT BROWN PROF. ROBERT BROWNING STUD, 73- Dir, Armstrong Browning Libr, 59- U.S.A, 44-46. NCTE; MLA; AAUP. Robert Browning; John Milton. Publ: Browning's Old schoolfellow, Beta Phi Mu, 72; ed, Studies in Browning and his circle, Armstrong Browning Libr, 73. Add: Armstrong Browning Library, Box 6336, Waco, TX 76706.

HERRING, PAUL DONALD, b. Clinton, N.C, May 26, 37; m. 68. ENGLISH. A.B, Univ. N.C, 59, Fulbright fel, Univ. Edinburgh, 59-60, Leverhulme fel, 64-65; M.A, Univ. Chicago, 61-64, Ph.D.(Eng), 64. Instr. ENG. & HUMANITIES, Univ. Chicago, 63-64, asst. prof, 65-72; ASSOC. PROF. & CHMN. DEPT, WABASH COL, 72- Am. Counc. Learned Soc. grant-in-aid, 64-65. Dickens; British social novel, 1800-1900; 19th century British taste. Publ: Co-ed, The arts and the public, Univ. Chicago, 67; auth, Dickens' monthly number plans for Little Dorrit, 66 & The number plans for Dombey and son, 70, Mod. Philol. Add: Dept. of English, Wabash College, Crawfordsville, IN 47933.

HERRING, PHILLIP F, b. Ft. Worth, Tex, June 30, 36; m. 62; c. 2. ENGLISH. B.A, Univ. Tex, 58, Ph.D.(Eng), 66. Instr. ENG, Univ. Tex, 64-65; asst. prof, Univ. Va, 65-70; assoc. prof, UNIV. WIS-MADISON, 70-74, PROF, 74- adv. ed, James Joyce Quart, 67-; Andrew Mellon fel, Univ. Pittsburgh, 68-69; Inst. Res. in Humanities fel, 73-74. U.S.N, 58-60. MLA. James Joyce. Publ: Joyce's Ulysses notesheets in the British Museum, Univ. Va, 72; The bedsteadfastness of Molly Bloom, Mod. Fiction Stud, 69; Joyce's politics, In: New light on Joyce from the Dublin Symposium, Ind. Univ, 72; The Lotus eaters, In: James Joyce's Ulysses, Univ. Calif, 73; plus others. Add: Dept. of English, Helen C. White Hall, 600 N. Park, University of Wisconsin-Madison, Madison, WI 53706.

HERRNSTADT, RICHARD L, b. New York, N.Y, Nov. 4, 26; m. 50; c. 3. ENGLISH. B.S, Univ. Wis, 48, M.S, 50; Ph.D.(Eng), Univ. Md, 60. Instr. Eng, IOWA STATE UNIV, 54-58, asst. prof, 58-61, assoc. prof, 61-65, PROF, 65-, chmn. freshman Eng, 60-72, U.S.N, 45-46. MLA; NCTE; Am. Stud. Asn.(exec. counc, 69-); Conf. Col. Compos. & Commun; Thoreau Soc; Mid-continent Am. Stud. Asn.(v.pres, 61-62, pres, 62-63). New England transcendentalism; 19th century American literature; Afro-American literature. Publ: Ed, The Letters of A. Bronson Alcott, Iowa State Univ, 69;Bronson Alcott: a new view from his letters, Bull. Cent. Miss. Valley Am. Stud.Asn, 59; co-auth, Amos Bronson Alcott: a bibliography, Bull. Bibliog, 54. Add: Dept. of English, 221 Ross Hall, Iowa State University, Ames, IA 50010.

HERRON, ARLIE EDWARDS, b. Gorgas, Ala, Nov. 17, 27; m. 50; c. 4. ENGLISH. B.S, Univ. Ala, 50; Tulane Univ, 51-52; M.A, Univ. Ga, 60; Sarah Moss fel, Johns Hopkins Univ, 60-61. Teacher high sch, Ga, 53-56; instr. ENG, Univ. Ga, 56-60; asst. prof, UNIV. TENN, CHATTANOOGA, 61-66, ASSOC. PROF, 66- MLA; Am. Stud. Asn. Henry James; Jonathan Edwards; American Southern writers. Add: Dept. of English, University of Tennessee, Chattanooga, Chattanooga, TN 37403.

HERRON, IMA HONAKER, b. Farmersville, Tex, Mar. 9, 99. AMERICAN LITERATURE. A.B, South. Methodist Univ, 21, A.M, 26; summer, Univ. Chicago, 24; Ph.D, Duke Univ, 35. Teacher high sch, Tex, 21-23; instr. Eng. Kidd-Key Jr. Col, 23-24, head dept, 26-27; instr, South. Methodist Univ, 27-31; asst, Duke Univ, 32-33; asst. prof, SOUTH. METHODIST UNIV, 34-42, assoc. prof, 42-46, prof, 46-63, chmn. dept, 51-53, E.A. Lilly prof, Am. lit, 62-64, EMER. PROF. ENG, 64-, prof. Eng, Naval V-5 & V-12 classes, 41-46. Mem. bibliog. comt, Am. Lit. Group, MLA, 32-53; res. grants, Sun Oil Co, 62 & Danforth Found, 62-63; post-retirement teaching, South. Methodist Univ, 64-66, mem. Friends of Libr. Comt, 68-; Dallas Asn. Phi Beta Kappa deleg, nat. triennial counc. meeting, Duke Univ, summer 67; lectr. symp, Sch. Continuing Educ, South. Methodist Univ, 70 & Am. Asn. Univ. Women, Dallas, 71; mem. Nat. adv. bd, Am. Security Counc, 72-73. South. Methodist Alumni Asn. fac. achievement award, 62, woman of achievement award, 65. S.Cent. Mod. Lang. Asn.(secy. Am. lit. group, 45-46, assoc. ed, bull, 48-50, v.pres, 52); S.Cent. Col. Eng. Asn.(secy, 57); MLA; Am. Stud. Asn. American criticism and drama; American regionalism. Publ: Co-auth, Better college English, Appleton, 50; auth, The small town in American literature, Pageant, reprinted 59; The small town in American drama, South. Methodist Univ, 69; O'Neill's comedy of recollection: a nostalgic dramatization of the real America, 1/68 & Young Washington Irving's Travel sketches, 4/72, CEA Critic; Changing United States literary canon, Southwest Rev, autumn 72; plus others. Add: 3001 University Blvd, Dallas, TX 75205.

HERSEY, JOHN, b. Tientsin, China, June 17, 14; m. 40, 58; c. 5. AMERICAN LITERATURE. B.A, Yale, 36, hon. M.A, 48; Clare Col, Cambridge, 36-37; hon. Litt.D, Wesleyan Univ, 54. WRITER, 42-; master, Pierson Col, YALE, 65-71, LECTR. ENG, 71- Fel, Berkeley Col, Yale, 50-65; mem, Yale Counc. Comt. Humanities, 51-56; bd. trustees, Putney Sch, 53-56; Nat. Citizens' Comn. Pub. Schs, 54-56; consult, Fund for Advan. Educ, 54-56; deleg, White House Conf. Educ, 55; trustee, Nat. Citizens' Counc. Pub. Schs, 56-58; deleg, PEN Cong, Tokyo, 58; mem, Yale Univ. Counc. Comt. on Yale Col, 59-64, chmn, 65-; mem. vis. comt, Harvard Grad. Sch. Educ, 60-65; trustee, Nat. Comt. Support Pub. Schs, 62-68; writer-in-residence, Am. Acad. in Rome, 70-71. Pulitzer Prize for fiction, 45; Sidney Hillman Found. Award, 50; Howland Medal, Yale, 52; Tuition Plan Award, 61; Sarah Josepha Hale Award, 63. War correspondent, World War II. Nat. Inst. Arts & Lett; Am. Acad. Arts & Lett; Auth. League Am.(v.pres, 49-55); Auth. Guild; PEN Club. Publ: Men on Bataan, 42, Into the valley, 43, A bell for Adano, 44, Hiroshima, 46, The wall, 50, The Marmot Drive, 53, A single pebble, 56, The war lover, 59, The child buyer, 63, Here to stay, 63, White Lotus, 65, Too far to walk, 66, Under the eye of the storm, 67, The Algiers Motel incident, 68, Letter to the alumni, 70, The conspiracy, 72 & ed, The writer's craft, 73, Knopf. Add: 420 Humphrey St, New Haven, CT 06511.

HERTZ, JOHN ATLEE, b. Lititz, Pa, June 16, 16; m. 41; c. 3. ENGLISH, MEDIAEVAL LITERATURE. A.B, Moravian Col, 38; Harvard, 38-39; M.A, Lehigh Univ, 47, Ph.D, 58. Instr. ENG, Moravian Col, 39-40; LEHIGH UNIV, 45-58, from asst. prof. to assoc. prof, 58-66, dir. adult educ, 63-66; dean, Keystone Jr. Col, Pa, 66-69; GRAD. CHMN. ENG, MARYWOOD COL, 69- Reader Eng, Col. Bds, Princeton, N.J, 50- MLA; NCTE. Chaucer; literary criticism; 20th century literature. Publ: Ed. & contrib, The idiot: analytic notes and review, 65, contrib. & auth, Introd, Crime and punishment: chapter notes and criticism, 64 & The Brothers Karamazov: chapter notes and criticism, 66, Am. R.D.M. Add: Dept. of English, Marywood College, Scranton, PA 18509.

HERUM, JOHN MAURICE, Rhetoric, Applied English Linguistics. See Volume III, Foreign Languages, Linguistics & Philology.

HERZBRUN, PHILIP INGRAM, b. Welch, V.Va, Jan. 10, 24; m. 61. ENGLISH & COMPARATIVE LITERATURE. A.B, George Wash. Univ, 46; fel, Johns Hopkins Univ, 47-50, Ph.D.(Eng), 55. Instr. ENG, George Wash. Univ, 46-47, 50-54; Univ. Md, 54-56; asst. prof, GEORGETOWN UNIV, 59-65, ASSOC. PROF, 65- Contrib. poetry ed, Wash. Star Papers, 60. Southwest poet of year, 58. U.S.N, 42-44. MLA; Col. Eng. Asn. Post-symbolist poetry; modern literary criticism; literature and the fine arts. Add: Dept. of English, Georgetown University, Washington, DC 20007.

HERZING, THOMAS WAYNE, b. St. Cloud, Minn, June 30, 39; m. 61; c. 4. BRITISH LITERATURE, ROMANTIC MOVEMENT. B.A, St. John's Univ. (Minn), 61; M.A, Marquette Univ, 63; Ph.D.(Eng), Univ. Wis-Madison, 72. Instr. ENG, St. Joseph's Col.(Ind), 62-67; ASST. PROF, UNIV. WIS-OSHKOSH, 67- MLA. Rhetorical analysis; the intellectual history behind Blake's poetry; the psychology of creativity. Publ: Reasoning for writing, Dickenson, 70; George Chapman and the rhetoric of obscurity, Eng. Notes,

68; co-auth, Games professors play, J. Higher Educ, 69; auth, Book I of Blake's Milton: natural religion as an optical fallacy, Blake Stud, 73. Add: Dept. of English, University of Wisconsin-Oshkosh, Oshkosh, WI 54901.

HERZOG, MICHAEL B, b. Bogdanesti, Rumania, Apr. 24, 44; U.S. citizen; m. 68; c. 1. COMPARATIVE LITERATURE. B.A, Gonzaga Univ, 66; M.A, Univ. Wash, 67, Ph.D.(comp. lit), 71. Teaching asst. Ger, Univ. Wash, 66-68; comp. lit, 68-70; ASST. PROF. ENG & MOD. LANG, GONZAGA UNIV, 70- MLA; Mediaeval Acad. Am. Medieval English and German literature; development of Gawain as Arthurian figure. Add: Dept. of English, Gonzaga University, 502 E. Boone, Spokane, WA 99202.

HESLA, DAVID H, b. Stevens Point, Wis, Oct. 14, 29; m. 56; c. 2. LITERATURE, THEOLOGY. B.A, St. Olaf Col, 51; A.M, Univ. Chicago, 56, Ph.D.(theol. & lit), 64. Instr. Eng, St. Olaf Col, 55-56; Cornell Col, 61-63, asst. prof, 63-65; lit. & theol, EMORY UNIV, 65-70, ASSOC. PROF. HUMANITIES, 70-, res. comt. summer grant, 66. Nat. Endowment for Humanities summer grant, 68; Fulbright lectr, U.S. Educ. Found, Finland, 72-73; consult, Miles Col, 71-72. U.S.M.C, 52-54, Sgt. Am. Acad. Relig; Soc. Relig. Higher Educ; MLA. Religious dimensions of literature; modern British and American literature; literary criticism and theory. Publ: The shape of chaos: an interpretation of the art of Samuel Beckett, Univ. Minn, 71; Theological ambiguity in the Catholic novels, In: Graham Greene, Univ. Ky, 63; The two roles of Normal Mailer, Adversity & Grace, 68. Add: Graduate Institute of the Liberal Arts, Emory University, Atlanta, GA 30322.

HESS, JUDITH WRIGHT, b. Schenectady, N.Y, Feb. 15, 43. AMERICAN LITERATURE, FILM. B.A, DePauw Univ, 65; M.A, Ind. Univ, 67, Ph.D. (comp. lit), 73. Instr. creative writing, Bay State Jr. Col, 67-68; compos. & lit, Univ. Md, Europ. Div, 68-70; film hist, Ind. Univ, 71-73; ASST. PROF. LIT. & FILM, CALIF. STATE COL, SONOMA, 73- MLA; Am. Comp. Lit. Asn. Folklore. Publ: Introduction to American folklore and literature, Hayden, 74; A morphology of the true love ballad, J. Am. Folklore, 1-3/72; Genre films and the status quo, Jump Cut, Vol. 1, No. 1; Traditional themes in Faulkner's The bear, Tenn. Folklore Soc. Bull, 6/74. Add: Dept. of English, California State College, Sonoma, 1801 E. Cotati Ave, Rohnert Park, CA 94928.

HESS, PHILIP JOSEPH, b. Chicago, Ill, Oct. 2, 35; m. 56; c. 3. RADIO-TELEVISION, JOURNALISM. B.A, Univ. Iowa, 56, M.A, 60. TV dir, KCRG-TV, Iowa, 56-57; KOIN-TV, Ore, 57-59; instr. television, Univ. S.Dak. & production dir, KUSD-TV, 60-62; ASSOC. PROF. RADIO-TV, & CHMN. DEPT, UNIV. MONT, 62- Ed, Mont. Broadcasters Directory, Univ. Mont, 63-72; consult, Mountain States Regional Med. Prog, 68-70 & Greater Mont. Found, 68- Fel. Nat. Acad. TV Arts & Sci; Broadcast Educ. Asn; West. Educ. Soc. Telecommun; Int. Broadcasters Soc.(educ. adv. bd, 66-69). Television production; broadcast journalism. Publ: Testing audience reactions, 63, Industry at the crossroads: CATV, 66 & Montana's ETV quandary, 71, Mont. Jour. Rev. Add: Dept. of Radio-Television, University of Montana, Missoula, MT 59801.

HESSER, DALE CAHILL, b. Glencoe, Okla, Oct. 21, 21; m. 41; c. 2. ENGLISH. B.A, Harding Col, 49; M.A, Okla. State Univ, 50; Ph.D.(Eng), Univ. Kans, 57. Instr. ENG, Harding Col, 50-52; asst, Univ. Kans, 53-57; assoc. prof, York Col, 57-60; Abilene Christian Col, 60-67; PROF, ANGELO STATE COL, 67- U.S.A, 45-46, Sgt. Conf. Col. Teachers Eng; Am. Stud. Asn; S.Cent. Mod. Lang. Asn. Walt Whitman and 19th century American poetry; modern American novel; Hebrew literature, particularly the Book of Job. Publ: The Book of Job, Sweet, 65. Add: Dept. of English, Angelo State University, Johnson & Ave. N, San Angelo, TX 76901.

HESTER, MARVIN THOMAS, b. Owensboro, Ky, July 22, 41; m. 68. RENAISSANCE LITERATURE. B.A, Centre Col, Ky, 63; M.A, Univ. Fla, 65, Ph.D.(Eng. lit), 72. Instr. Eng, Univ. Fla, 64-67; N.C. STATE UNIV, 71-72, ASST. PROF. ENG. LIT, 72-, fac. res. fel, 73-74. Nat. Endowment for Humanities fel, 72-73. Southeast. Renaissance Soc; Renaissance Soc. Am; S.Atlantic Mod. Lang. Asn. English Renaissance satire; Donne; Thomas More. Publ: Ed, The Martin Marprelate tracts, Scholars' Facsimiles & Reprints, (in press). Add: Dept. of English, Winston Hall, North Carolina State University, Raleigh, NC 27607.

HESTER, WAVERLY ERWIN, b. Spartanburg, S.C, Mar. 24, 31; m. 61; c. 3. ENGLISH. A.B, Univ. N.C, Chapel Hill, 52, fel, 52-53, M.A, 53, South. Fel. Found. fel, 60-61, Ph.D.(Eng), 61. Instr. ENG, Univ. Va, 61-64, asst. prof, 64-66; assoc. prof, E. CAROLINA UNIV, 66-67, PROF. & CHMN. DEPT, 68- MLA; NCTE; S.Atlantic Mod. Lang. Asn; S.Atlantic Asn. Dept. Eng. (pres, 71-72). English novel; Victorian period. Publ: A rhetoric reader, Prentice-Hall, 67; George Eliot's use of historical events in Daniel Deronda, Eng. Lang. Notes, 12/66; George Eliot's messengers, Stud. Eng. Lit, autumn 67. Add: Dept. of English, East Carolina University, Greenville, NC 27834.

HESTON, LILLA A, b. St. Helen, Mich, Oct. 1, 27. INTERPRETATION. B.S, Northwest. Univ, 49, M.A, 58, Ph.D.(interpretation), 65. Instr. Eng. & speech, Vassar Col, 58-60; INTERPRETATION, NORTHWEST. UNIV, EVANSTON, 61-65, asst. prof, 65-68, assoc. prof, 68-73, PROF, 73- Speech Commun. Asn.(secy. interpretation interest group, 66-67, chmn. interpretation div, 71-72); Cent. States Speech Asn. Henry James; 20th century novel. Publ: Ed, Man in the dramatic mode, Bks. 1-6, McDougal, Littel & Co, 70-71; contrib, Studies in interpretation, Ed. Rodopi, Netherlands, 72. Add: Dept. of Interpretation, Northwestern University, Evanston, IL 60201.

HETHMON, ROBERT H, b. Paducah, Ky, Oct. 19, 25; m. 52; c. 3. THEATRE, THEATRE HISTORY. B.A, Univ. Tenn, 46; M.A, Cornell Univ, 48; Fulbright fel, Univ. London, 53-54; Ph.D.(drama), Stanford Univ, 56. Instr. THEATRE, Univ. Colo, 48-51; Univ. Calif, Riverside, 55-56; asst. prof, Univ. Wis-Madison, 56-62; UNIV. CALIF, LOS ANGELES, 63-66, ASSOC. PROF, 66- U.S.A, 51-53. Publ: Ed, Strasberg at the Actors Studio, Viking, 65. Add: Dept. of Theatre Arts, University of California, 405 Hilgard Ave, Los Angeles, CA 90024.

HETTICH, BLAISE, O.S.B, b. LaPorte, Ind, Oct. 7, 24. ENGLISH LITERATURE. A.B, St. Meinrad Col, 47; Ph.D, Univ. Notre Dame, 57. From assoc. prof. to PROF. ENG. & SPEECH, ST. MEINRAD COL, 56- NCTE. Fourteenth century English mystics. Add: St. Meinrad College, St. Meinrad, IN 47577.

HETTICH, DAVID WILLIAM, b. La Porte, Ind, Oct. 9, 32. ENGLISH LITERATURE. B.S, Creighton Univ, 54; M.A, Marquette Univ, 56; Ph.D, Wayne State Univ, 61. Instr. ENG, Wayne State Univ, 59-61; asst. prof, UNIV. NEV, RENO, 61-67, ASSOC. PROF, 67-, chmn. freshman Eng, 62. MLA; NCTE; Conf. Col. Compos. & Commun. English literature of the Renaissance; English and American drama. Publ: Co-auth, Fundamentals of English, Allyn & Bacon, 66. Add: Dept. of English, University of Nevada, Reno, NV 89507.

HEUSER, ALAN, b. Montreal, Can, Mar. 5, 26; m. 62. ENGLISH LITERATURE. B.Sc, McGill Univ, 47, M.A, 49; Ph.D, Harvard, 53. Asst. instr. ENG, Princeton, 52-54; asst. prof, McGILL UNIV, 54-63, assoc. prof, 63-69, PROF, 69- Can. Counc. leave fel, 70-71. Hopkins Soc.(v.pres. Can. div, 69-). Nineteenth and 20th century literature, British and American; D.H. Lawrence; modern poetry. Publ: The shaping vision of G.M. Hopkins, Oxford Univ, 58. Add: Dept. of English, McGill University, Montreal, P.Q. H3C 3G1, Can.

HEUSTON, EDWARD F, b. Union City, N.J, Nov. 6, 32. ENGLISH. B.S, St. Peter's Col.(N.J), 55; M.A, Boston Col, 57; Ph.D(Eng), Univ. Wis, 65. Instr. ENG. LIT, Georgetown Univ, 62-65; asst. prof, Univ. Ill, Chicago, 65-68; ASSOC. PROF, STATE UNIV. N.Y. COL. PLATTSBURGH, 68- Co-founder & co-ed, Genre, Univ. Ill, Chicago, 67- U.S.A, 56, 1st Lt. MLA; Augustan Reprint Soc. Augustan literature; genre theory. Publ: The Chaucer sprig in Wordsworth's Liberty, Notes & Queries, 64; Gay's Bowzybeus and Thomas D'Urfey, Scriblerian, 68. Add: Dept. of English, State University of New York College at Plattsburgh, Plattsburgh, NY 12901.

HEVERIN, MARY ROSINA, C.C.V.I, b. Castlebar, Ireland, Feb. 2, 99; nat. ENGLISH. A.M, De Paul Univ, 39; Notre Dame Univ, 59; William Butler Yeats Int. Summer Sch, Sligo, 70. Chmn. dept. Eng, High Sch, 37-46; assoc. prof. Eng, Dominican Col, 46-70; RETIRED. Instr. lit, Immaculate Heart Col, 66-67. Col. Eng. Asn; MLA. Add: 1919 Crawford St, Houston, TX 77002.

HEWGILL, MURRAY, b. Clarksburg, Ont, Sept. 1, 25; m. 49; c. 2. SPEECH. B.A, East. Nazarene Col, 46; M.A, Univ. Mich, 53, Ph.D, 59. Teaching fel. speech, Univ. Mich, 53-56; instr, Mich. State Univ, 56-60, asst. prof, 60-63; assoc. prof, 63-67; prin. Cambrian Col. Arts & Technol, North Bay Campus, 67-72; PRES, CANADORE COL, 72- Speech Commun. Asn; Cent. States Speech Commun. Asn.(Outstanding Young Teacher Award, 57). Psychology of communication and persuasion; communication research; educational administration. Publ: Co-auth, The effect of variations in nonfluency on audience ratings of source credibility, Quart. J. Speech, 63, An experimental study of the effects of directing anxiety—arousing message cues at valued others, Speech Monogr, 6/65; & Some recent research on fear—arousing message appeals, Speech Monogr, 11/66. Add: Canadore College, Box 5001, North Bay, Ont, Can.

HEWITT, BARNARD (WOLCOTT), b. North Tonawanda, N.Y, Dec. 23, 06; m. 32; c. 1. THEATRE, DRAMA. A.B, Cornell Univ, 28, A.M, 29, Ph.D, 34. Instr. Eng, Univ. Colo, 31-32; from instr. to asst. prof, Mont. State Univ, 32-36; from instr. to asst. prof. speech, Brooklyn Col, 36-48; PROF. SPEECH & THEATRE, UNIV. ILL, URBANA, 48-, CHMN. DEPT. THEATRE, 67- Guggenheim fel, 62-63. Fel. Am. Theatre Asn.(ed, Educ. Theatre J, 49-51, pres, 53, sr. award, 62); Am. Soc. Theatre Res; Int. Fed. Theatre Res; Soc. Theatre Res, Eng; Theatre Libr. Asn. History of theater; theater aesthetics. Publ: Art and craft of play production, 40 & Play production: theory and practice, 52, Lippincott; ed, The Renaissance stage, Univ. Miami, 58; auth, Theatre U.S.A, 1668 to 1957, McGraw, 59; History of the theatre from 1800 to the present, Random, 70; pure repertory: New York theatre, 1809, Theatre annual, 52; Thornton Wilder says yes, Tulane Drama Rev, winter 59; The Americanism of American theater, In: The American theater today, Basic Bks, 67; plus others. Add: Dept. of Theatre, 4-122 Krannert Center, University of Illinois, Urbana, IL 61801.

HEWITT, CHRISTIAN B, b. New York, N.Y, Oct. 29, 09; m. 42; c. 2. ENGLISH. B.A, Columbia Col, 31; M.A, Boston Univ, 49, Ph.D.(Eng), 60; Fulbright & Coun. Am. Stud. Fel, Univ. Rome, 59-60. Instr. ENG, Pa. State Univ, 52-55, 57-60; Fulbright teacher, Denmark, 56-57, asst. prof, FAIRLEIGH DICKINSON UNIV, MADISON, 60-62, assoc. prof, 62-68, PROF, 68-, chmn. dept. lit. & lang, 65-68, chmn. dept. Eng, 69-72. Asst. prof. psychol. & Eng, New Eng. Col; Fulbright lectr, Univ. Trieste, 60-61. U.S.N, 42-45, Lt. Comdr. MLA; Col. Eng. Asn. Contemporary British literature; 19th and 20th century American literature. Add: Dept. of English, Fairleigh Dickinson University, Madison, NJ 07940.

HEWITT, RAY STORLA, b. Milton, Ore, Oct. 20, 12; m. 47; c. 1. ENGLISH LITERATURE. A.B, Univ. Ore, 41, M.A, 47; Ph.D.(Eng), Univ. Calif, 51. Part-time instr. ENG, Univ. Ore, 46-47; instr, Univ. Wyo, 51-53; ORE. STATE UNIV, 53-56, asst. prof, 56-62, assoc. prof, 62-69, PROF, 69- U.S.A, 42-45. NCTE; Shakespeare Asn. Am; AAUP. Foreshadowing of disaster in Elizabethan and Shakespearean tragedy; Spenser's Sir Guyon. Publ: Unit number two: paragraph cohesiveness, 67 & Sentence unity: a programmed text, 67, Ore. State Syst. Higher Educ; In loco parentis, Improv. Col. & Univ. Teaching, summer 70. Add: Dept. of English, Oregon State University, Corvallis, OR 97331.

HEWITT, RYLAND HUGH, JR, b. Elmira, N.Y, Aug. 21, 22; m. 49; c. 3. SPEECH, LINGUISTICS, PHONETICS. A.B, Cornell Univ, 48, A.M, 50, Ph.D, 61. Instr. Eng. & theatre, Colgate Univ, 49-50; speech & theatre, Mt. Union Col, 50-52; asst. prof. SPEECH, Bates Col, 52-58; PROF, STATE UNIV. N.Y. ALBANY, 58- Exec. dir, Northeast. N.Y. Speech Ctr, Inc, 66- Pronunciation of English in America in the 17th and 18th centuries. Add: Dept. of Speech Pathology & Audiology, State University of New York at Albany, Albany, NY 12222.

HEWSON, JOHN, Linguistics. See Volume III, Foreign Languages, Linguistics & Philology.

HEYMANN, HANS GERHARD, b. Berlin, Ger, Dec. 21, 15; m. 50; c. 2. ENGLISH, GERMAN. Referendar, Univ. Frankfort, Ger, 50, Assessor, 51, Ph.D.(Eng, hist), 52. Teacher, La. & Miss, 43-45; interpreter Ger. & Eng, Neumünster, Ger, 46-47; teacher Eng, Correspondence Sch, 48-53 & Fed. Govt, 50-51, Frankfort, Ger; Eng, Ger. & hist, woman's col. & univ. exten, Univ. Frankfort, 50-53; from asst. to assoc. prof. Eng. & Ger, Lenoir-Rhyne Col, 53-57, prof. Eng. & head dept, 57-69; PROF. ENG, APPALACHIAN STATE UNIV, 69- Deutscher Akademischer Austauschdienst fel, 66; vis. prof, Appalachian State Univ, summer 68. MLA; S.Atlantic Mod. Lang. Asn; NCTE; Asn. Depts. Eng. The later Wordsworth and Goethe; modern European history; Goethe and Byron. Publ: Englisch für Anfäger, Stimme der Arbeit, 48; Die dichterische Gestaltung von Ehe und Familie in der Dichtung des späteren Wordsworth, Univ. Frankfort, 52; Responsibility of education, 5/60 & Pursuit of excellence: honors program, 1/68, N.C. Eng. Teacher; Germany: from destruction to democracy, Vital Speeches, 8/67; plus others. Add: Dept. of English, Appalachian State University, Boone, NC 28607.

HEYWORTH, PETER LORRIMAN, b. Workington, Eng, Jan. 7, 31; m. 60; c. 3. ENGLISH, MEDIEVAL STUDIES. B.A, Oxford, 56, M.A, 60, B.Litt, 65. Instr. ENG, Univ. N.H, 56-60; asst. prof, UNIV. COL, UNIV. TORONTO, 62-66, assoc. prof, 66-71, PROF, 71- Can. Counc. sr. res. fel, 66-67; Am. Counc. Learned Soc. fel, 73-74. Chaucer; medieval scholarship of 17th and 18th centuries; textual criticism. Publ: Jack Upland, Friar Daw's reply, and Upland's rejoinder, Oxford Univ, 68; A lost Cistercian barn at Shilton, Oxoniensia, 71; Sir Gawain's crossing of Dee, Medium Aevum, 72; The -us abbreviation in Middle English manuscripts, Scriptorium, 72; plus others. Add: Dept. of English, University College, University of Toronto, Toronto 5, Ont, Can.

HIATT, DAVID, b. Richmond, Ind, July 6, 30; m. 52; c. 4. ENGLISH. B.A, Earlham Col, 52; M.A, Univ. N.Mex, 56, Ph.D, 59. Asst, Univ. N.Mex, 52-53, 55-56, teaching asst, 56-58, instr, 58-59; asst. prof. Eng, Carroll Col. (Wis), 59-63, assoc. prof, 63-68, prof, 68-70; acting dir. lower div. stud. Eng, Univ. Md, College Park, 70-71; ASSOC. PROF. AM. LIT, UNIV. SASK, 71- U.S.A, 53-55. Nineteenth century American literature; eighteenth century English literature; poetry; Emily Dickinson. Publ: Co-ed, William Dean Howells, Literary friends and acquaintance, Ind. Univ, 68; ed, British biography, In: College and adult reading list, Washington Square, 62; auth, Dickinson's Of bronze and blaze, Explicator, 62; plus others. Add: Dept. of English, University of Saskatchewan, Saskatoon, Sask. S7N 0W0, Can.

HIATT, RICHARD GORDON, b. La Grande, Ore, Nov. 28, 24; m. 53; c. 3. SPEECH & DRAMA. B.A, Univ. Ore, 52, M.A, 56; Iowa State Univ, 61-62. ASSOC. PROF. SPEECH & DRAMA, EAST. ORE. COL, 55- U.S.N, 43-46. Publ: Transl, An essay of dramatic renovation, the theatre du Vieux-Colombier, Educ. Theatre J, 12/67. Add: Dept. of Speech & Drama, Eastern Oregon College, La Grande, OR 97850.

HIBBARD, GEORGE RICHARD, b. Notts, England, May 31, 15; m. 39; c. 1. ENGLISH LITERATURE. B.A, Univ. London, 36, M.A, 38; Univ. Zurich, 38-39. Asst. lectr. ENG, Univ. Col. Southampton, 39-40; lectr, Univ. Nottingham, 46-54, sr. lectr, 54-62, reader, 62-70; PROF, UNIV. WATERLOO, 70- Brit. Army, 40-46. Mod. Humanities Res. Asn; Renaissance Soc. Am; Can. Asn. Univ. Teachers; Asn. Can. Univ. Teachers Eng; Int. Shakespeare Asn. Shakespeare; Elizabethan and Jacobean drama; Renaissance poetry and prose. Publ: Thomas Nashe: a critical introduction, Routledge & Kegan Paul, 62; ed, William Shakespeare's Coriolanus, 67, William Shakespeare's The taming of the shrew, 68 & William Shakespeare's Timon of Athens, 70, Penguin; auth, The country house poem of the seventeenth century, J. Warburg & Courtauld Inst, 56; Othello and the pattern of Shakespearean tragedy, Shakespeare Surv, 68. Add: Dept. of English, University of Waterloo, Waterloo, Ont. N2L 3G1, Can.

HIBBS, RICHARD PAUL, b. Ottumwa, Iowa, Oct. 21, 06. SPEECH, ENGLISH. A.B, Baker Univ, 28; A.M, Univ. Wis, 42; Univ. Ill, 48; South. Ill. Univ, 49-54. Chmn. dept. Eng. & dir. speech activities high sch, Ill, 28-47, asst. prin, 40-47, supt, 47-65; assoc. prof. SPEECH, SOUTH. ILL. UNIV, CARBONDALE, 65-72, PROF, 72-, COORD. SPEC. PROG. & CULT. EVENTS, 65, CHMN. DEPT. SPEECH, 73- Vis. dir. summer nat. high sch. inst, Northwest. Univ, 46; consult. & dir, summer debate inst, Univ. Ill, 48, 49; dir. musical shows, Egyptian Music Camp, Summers, 52, 54, 56-58; prod. dir. musical shows, South. Ill. Univ, summers 57, 58, 60-65, 72 & winters, 59-60. Award, Tau Kappa Alpha, 37, 48; Diamond Key award, Nat. Forensic League, 36, 47, Distinguished Serv. award, 36, 41, 46. Asn. Col. & Univ. Concert Mgr; Speech Commun. Asn. Publ: Auth. & ed, Speech for today, McGraw, 65; Extracurricular debating in secondary schools, Bull. Nat. Asn. Sec. Sch. Prin, 5/52; Diamonds in your own back yard, Ill. Banker, 5/62; Honestly, now, just how good is your high school speech program, Ill. J. Educ, 2/67. Add: Special Meetings & Speakers, Shryock Auditorium, Southern Illinois University, Carbondale, IL 62901.

HICKERSON, WILLIAM HOWARD, b. Louisville, Ky, Nov. 6, 02; m. 25; c. 2. ENGLISH LITERATURE. A.B, Univ. Ky, 23, A.M, 25; Univ. Chicago, 26; Ph.D, Univ. Mich, 32. Instr, Univ. Ky, 23-25; Agr. & Mech. Col. Tex, 25-26; asst. prof, Lake Erie Col, 26-29; asst. mem. staff, Mid. Eng. Dictionary, Univ. Mich, 30-31; mem. fac, Bradford Jr. Col, 31-35; PROF. ENG, LAKE ERIE COL, 35-, dir. sch. community educ, 42-51, acting dir. pub. relat, 48-51, chmn. area of lang. & lit, 51, dir. publ, 53-68. MLA; NCTE. English drama; significance of James Shirley's realistic plays in the history of English drama; the college woman in the modern world. Add: Dept. of English, Lake Erie College, Painesville, OH 44077.

HICKLIN, FANNIE ELLA FRAZIER, b. Talladega, Ala, div; c. 1. SPEECH THEATRE. B.A, Talladega Col, 39; M.A, Univ. Mich, 45; E.B. Fred fel, Univ. Wis, 63-64, Ph.D.(speech), 65. Teacher high sch, Miss, 40-42; Avery Inst, S.C, 42-44, asst. prof. Eng. & speech, Tuskegee Inst, 45-46; teacher high sch, S.C, 48-56, assoc. prof. Eng. & speech, Ala. A&M Col, 56-61; teaching asst. speech, Univ. Wis-Madison, 61-64; asst. prof. speech, UNIV. WIS-WHITEWATER, 64-65, assoc. prof. SPEECH & THEATRE, 65-66, PROF, 67- Am. Theatre Asn; Speech Commun. Asn. French Provincial folk costumes; American Negro playwrights 1920 to the present. Add: Dept. of Speech Communication & Theatre, 2078, Center of the Arts, University of Wisconsin-Whitewater, Whitewater, WI 53190.

HICKOK, BENJAMIN BLAKELY, b. Oneonta, N.Y, July 26, 14; m. 44; c. 4. COMMUNICATION, AMERICAN LITERATURE. A.B, Hamilton Col, 36; M.A, Univ. Iowa, 40; Ph.D.(Am. lit), Mich. State Univ, 53. Instr. Eng. lang, & lit, Athens Col, Greece, 36-39; Eng. & reading, Found. Sch, Berea Col, 40-41, Eng. compos, speech & theatre, 41-43; from instr. to PROF. AM. THOUGHT & LANG, MICH. STATE UNIV, 46-, CHMN. AM. HUMANITIES, 70-, dir. Eng. for for. stud, 46-47, writing clinic, 46-49. Fulbright lectr. Eng. as 2nd lang, Ecuador, 58-59 & Am. thought & lang, Univ. Iceland, 67-68; dir. NDEA inst. Eng. for sec. Eng. teachers of culturally deprived youth, Rust Col, 67, prof. Eng. comp. & Am. thought & lang, summer 65 & 66. U.S.A, 42-45. NCTE; Am. Stud. Asn; Col. Conf. Compos. & Commun; Thoreau Soc; Am. Civil Liberties Union; Nat. Asn. Advan. Colored People. Civil rights. Publ: National merit scholarship tests, Sci. Res. Assoc. Chicago, 58-62; Michigan State University English placement test; Political and literary careers of F.B. Sanborn; Iowa tests of educational development, 73- Add: Dept. of American Thought & Language, Michigan State University, East Lansing, MI 48824,

HICKS, ARTHUR CLARK, b. Canyon City, Ore, Dec. 28, 01; m. 25; c. 1. ENGLISH. B.A, Univ. Ore, 22, M.A, 27, Juilliard Exten. scholar, 27-30; piano teachers cert, Peabody Conserv. Music, 24; Ph.D.(Eng), Stanford Univ, 32. Instr. ENG, Univ. Ore, 27-30; asst. prof, San Jose State Teachers Col, 32-33; prof, WEST. WASH. STATE COL, 49-69, chmn. dept, 33-62, lectr, 70-72, EMER. PROF, 69- MLA; Col. Eng. Asn; Nat. Educ. Asn; NCTE. The Victorian novel; the English romantic period; Shakespeare and the Renaissance. Publ: The structure of Meredith's novels and the comic spirit, Univ. Ore. Monogr. Ser, 39; co-auth, A stage version of Shelley's Cenci, Caxton, 45; auth, The first fifty years, West. Wash. Col. Educ. Bull, 49; An American performance of The Cenci, Part II, Stanford Univ. Dramatists Alliance Bull, 41; A tribute to Mabel Zoe Wilson, Pac. Northwest Libr. Asn. Quart, 1/65; Western at 75, West. Wash. State Col. Found, 74. Add: 216 S. Forest, Bellingham, WA 98225.

HICKS, J. C, b. Calvin, Okla, Nov. 11, 22; m. 47; c. 3. SPEECH, DRAMA. B.S. & B.A, Southwest. State Col, 47; M.A, Univ. Okla, 49, Ph.D.(speech), 71. Instr. drama, Cameron Col, 67-68; spec. instr. SPEECH, Univ. Okla, 69-70; ASST. PROF, CAMERON COL, 71- U.S.A, 43-46. Speech Commun. Asn. Cherokee Indians speech and customs. Add: 1400 Scott Rd, Lawton, OK 73501.

HICKS, JOHN, b. Port Arthur, Tex, Aug. 11, 09; m. 39; c. 2. ENGLISH LITERATURE, COMPARATIVE ARTS. A.B, Univ. Louisville, 29, A.M, 31; Ph.D, Univ. Iowa, 39. Instr, Miss. State Col, 34-37; Eng, Purdue Univ, 37-40; asst. prof, Miami Univ, 40-46; assoc. prof, Lawrence Col, 46-49; prof. Eng. & humanities, Stetson Univ, 49-60, chmn. dept. Eng. stud, 56-60; prof. humanities & chmn. dept, Univ. S.Fla, 60-63; dean univ. col, SOUTH. METHODIST UNIV, 63-67, PROF. LIT. & ARTS, 67-, ASSOC. DEAN ACAD. AFFAIRS, MEADOWS SCH. ARTS, 71- South. Regional Educ. Bd. res. fel, 59-60. Asn. Higher Educ; Am. Soc. Aesthet; Col. Eng. Asn.(exec. dir, 60-63, treas, 63-65); Nat. Asn. Gen. & Lib. Stud.(pres, 68); MLA. Aesthetic and literary theory; 20th century arts & letters. Publ: Co-ed, Thought and experience in prose, Oxford, 2nd ed, 56; auth, Guide to the humanities, W.C. Brown, 63; Stoicism of Mathew Arnold, Iowa Humanistic Stud, 42. Add: 6964 Walling Lane, Dallas, TX 75231.

HICKS, JOHN (HARLAND), b. New York, N.Y, May 13, 19; m. 56. ENGLISH. A.B, Middlebury Col, 41; fel, Bread Loaf Sch. Eng, 41; Harvard, 46-47; M.A, Boston Univ, 52, Ph.D, 59. Instr. ENG, Tufts Univ, 47-50; Wesleyan Univ, 52-57; asst. prof, UNIV. MASS, AMHERST, 59-66, assoc. prof, 66-70, PROF, 71- Managing ed, Mass. Rev, 62-63, co-ed, 63-; mem, Eng. Inst. U.S.N.R, 41-46, Lt. Comdr. Col. Eng. Asn; MLA; New Eng. Col. Eng. Asn. Nineteenth century English and American literature; Joseph Conrad; modern novel. Publ: Ed. & contrib, Thoreau in our season, 66 & co-ed, Revolution and reaction: the Paris Commune of 1871, 73, Univ. Mass; Literacy and literature, J. Higher Educ, 1/60; ed, A centenary gathering for Henry David Thoreau, Mass. Rev, fall 63; Conrad's Almayer's folly, 19th Century Fiction, 3/64; plus others. Add: Enfield Rd, R.F.D. 2, Amherst, MA 01002.

HICKS, RONALD GRAYDON, b. Shongaloo, La, Nov. 29, 34; m. 55; c. 3. MASS COMMUNICATIONS, SOCIOLOGY. B.A.J, La. State Univ, 60, M.A.J, 61, Ph.D.(sociol), 70. Copywriter, Radio Sta. WXOK, 58-59; advert. salesman, Community Newspaper Rep, 59-60; newspaper ed. & publ, Baker Observer, 60-61; mgr, La. Press Asn, 62-73; dir, Jour. Exten. Serv, LA. STATE UNIV, 62-73, ASSOC. PROF. JOUR, 62- U.S.N, 54-57. Asn. Educ. in Jour; Am. Sociol. Asn; Newspaper Asn. Mgr. Communication theory; semantics. Publ: Semantics, Zen Buddhism and the protest movement, ETC, 3/72. Add: 16460 Fulwar Skipwith Rd, Baton Rouge, LA 70808.

HIEATT, ALLEN KENT, b. Indianapolis, Ind, Jan. 21, 21; m. 57; c. 2. ENGLISH. A.B, Univ. Louisville, 43; Cutting traveling fel, 47; Ph.D.(comp. lit), Columbia Univ, 54. Instr. ENG, Columbia Univ, 44-45, Col, 45-55, asst. prof, 55-60, assoc. prof, 60-69; PROF, UNIV. WEST. ONT, 69-, vis. prof, 68-69. MLA; Renaissance Soc. Am; Mod. Humanities Res. Asn; Asn. Can. Univ. Teachers Eng. English and comparative literature, 14th to 17th centuries. Publ: Short time's endless monument: the symbolism of the numbers in Epithalamion, Columbia Univ, 60, 72; co-auth, The golden book of The Canterbury tales, Golden Press, 60, Bantam Dual-Lang. Bks, 64 & The college anthology of British and American verse, Allyn & Bacon, 64, 71; co-ed, Selections from the poetry of Edmund Spenser, Appleton, 68; co-auth, The bird with four feathers: numerical analysis of a fourteenth-century lyric, Papers Lang. & Lit. 70; auth, Three fearful symmetries of The faerie queene, In: Theatre for Spenserians, Univ. Toronto, 73; A numerical key for Spenser's Amoretti and Guyon in the House of Mammon, Yearbook Eng. Stud, 73; plus others. Add: Dept. of English, University of Western Ontario, London, Ont, Can.

HIEATT, CONSTANCE, b. Boston, Mass, Feb. 11, 28; m. 58. ENGLISH. B.A, Hunter Col, 53, M.A, 57; univ. fel, Yale, 57-58, Lewis-Farmington fel, 58-

59, Ph.D, 59. Lectr. ENG, City Col. New York, 59-60, asst. prof, Queensborough Community Col, 60-64, assoc. prof, 64-65; St. John's Univ.(N.Y), 65-68, PROF, 68-69; UNIV. WEST. ONT, 69-, vis. prof, 68-69. Hunter Col. award, 59. MLA; Mediaeval Acad. Am; Int. Arthurian Soc; Soc. Advan. Scand. Stud. Language and literature of Old and Middle English; medieval comparative literature. Publ: Co-auth, Canterbury tales, Golden Press, 61, Bantam, 63; auth, The realism of dream visions, Mouton, 67; Beowulf and other Old English poems, 67 & ed, The Miller's tale of Geoffrey Chaucer, 70, Odyssey; auth, Essentials of Old English, Crowell, 68; co-auth, Selections from the poetry of Edmund Spenser, Appleton, 68; auth, Karlamagnus saga, I-III, Pontifical Inst. Mediaeval Stud, 73; A case for Dux Moraud as a play of the miracles of the Virgin, Medieval Stud, 70; Prosodic analysis of Old English poetry: a suggested working approach with sample applications, Rev. Univ. Ottawa, 72; Ogier the Dane in Old Norse, Scand. Stud, 73; plus others. Add: Dept. of English, University of Western Ontario, London, Ont. N6A 3K7, Can.

HIEBEL, WILLIAM RAYMOND, b. Chicago, Ill, Jan. 25, 36. ENGLISH. A.B, Loyola Univ.(Ill), 57; M.A, Northwest. Univ, 58, Ph.D.(Eng), 66. Instr. ENG, Ill. Inst. Technol, 61-62; Georgetown Univ, 62-64; Ill. Inst. Technol, 65-66, ASST. PROF, 66-68, LOYOLA UNIV. CHICAGO, 68- MLA; Am. Stud. Asn. Twentieth century American poetry, Robert Frost and T.S. Eliot; poetry of New England, Dickinson and Frost. Add: Dept. of English, Loyola University of Chicago, 820 N. Michigan Ave, Chicago, IL 60626.

HIEBERT, RAY ELDON, b. Freeman, S.Dak, May 21, 32; m. 55; c. 4. COMMUNICATIONS. B.A, Stanford Univ, 54; M.S, Columbia Univ, 57; M.A, Univ. Md, 61, Ph.D.(Eng. & hist), 62. Reporter, Long Island Press, 56-57; finance copy ed, Am. Banker, 57; instr. Eng. & jour, Univ. Minn, 57-58; asst. prof. commun, Am. Univ.(D.C), 58-62, from assoc. prof. to prof. jour, pub. relat. & broadcasting, 62-66, chmn. dept, 62-66; dir. jour, Wash. Jour. Ctr, 65-68; PROF. JOUR, UNIV. MD, COLLEGE PARK, 68-, DEAN, COL. JOUR, 73-, chmn. dept, 68-72. Ed. consult, Sigma Press, 58-60; ed. consult. & speech writer, U.S. Dept. Commerce, 60-; lectr. Am. civilization, Bus. Counc. Int. Understanding, Wash, D.C, 62-; Princeton & Found. Pub. Relat. Res. & Educ. res. grant, 63; ed, Govt. & Commun. Series, Wiley, 67-, Contemporary Issues in Jour. Series, Acropolis Bks, 69- & RTNDA Communicator, 71-; trustee, Found. Pub. Relat. Res. & Educ, 70-; consult, U.S. Civil Serv. Comn, 73-74. Sig.C, U.S.A, 54-56, pub. inform. specialist. Am. Stud. Asn; Pub. Relat. Soc. Am. Relationship between press and government; history of government-press relations; communication research. Publ: Courtier to the crowd, Iowa State Univ, 66; ed, The press in Washington, Dodd, 66; co-ed, The voice of government, Wiley, 68; co-auth, Franklin Delano Roosevelt, 68, Thomas Edison: American inventor. 69 & The stock market crash 1929, 70, Watts; co-ed, The political image merchants, Acropolis, 71; auth, Trends in public relations education, Found. Pub. Relat. Res. & Educ, 71; co-auth, Atomic pioneers (3 vols), Atomic Energy Comn, 71-73; ed, The super journalists, Acropolis, 74; co-auth, Mass media, McKay, 74. Add: College of Journalism, University of Maryland, College Park, MD 20742.

HIERS, JOHN TURNER, b. Pensacola, Fla, July 15, 45; m. 68; c. 2. AMERICAN LITERATURE. B.A, Emory Univ, 67, Ph.D, 74; M.A, Univ. Ga, 68. ASST. PROF. ENG, VALDOSTA STATE COL, 68- S.Atlantic Mod. Lang. Asn; Soc. Stud. South. Lit. Modern American poetry; modern Southern fiction. Publ: Wordsworth's poetic child: a call for reexamination, S.Atlantic Bull, 69; Robert Frost's quarrel with science and technology, Ga. Rev, 71. Add: Dept. of English, Valdosta State College, Valdosta, GA 31601.

HIGDON, BARBARA, b. Independence, Mo, May 18, 30; m. 50; c. 3. ENGLISH, SPEECH. B.A, Univ. Mo, 51, M.A, 52, Ph.D.(speech), 61. Instr. speech, Univ. Mo, 64-66; assoc. prof. ENG. & SPEECH, Tex. South. Univ, 58-62; PROF, GRACELAND COL, 62- NCTE; Speech Asn. Am. Mormon history; American literature. Publ: John Neihardt's oral interpretation of poetry, South. Speech J, 53. Add: Dept. of English, Graceland College, Lamoni, IA 50140.

HIGGINS, DAVID JAMES MONROE, b. Exeter, N.H, Feb. 16, 32. ENGLISH. B.A, Harvard, 53; M.A, Columbia Univ, 57, Ph.D.(Am. lit), 61. Instr. ENG, Univ. Mich, 60-61; Rutgers Univ, 61-63, asst. prof, 63-67, ASSOC. PROF, 67-73; MONMOUTH COL.(N.J), 73- U.S.A, 53-55. MLA. Nineteenth century American literature. Publ: A portrait of Emily Dickinson, Rutgers Univ, 67; Emily Dickinson's prose, In: Emily Dickinson, Prentice-Hall, 63; 25 poems by Emily Dickinson: unpublished variant versions, Am. Lit, spring 66. Add: Dept. of English, Monmouth College, West Long Branch, NJ 07764.

HIGGINS, THERESA, S.S.J, b. Winthrop, Mass, Sept. 29, 25. ENGLISH. A.B, Regis Col, 47; M.A, Boston Col, 57; Ph.D.(Eng), Univ. Wis, 63. Teacher, High Sch, Fontbonne Acad, 54-59; instr. ENG, REGIS COL.(MASS), 63-65, ASST. PROF, 65- Regional counr, Sisters of St. Joseph. MLA; Am. Asn. Univ. Women. Theology and literature. Add: Dept. of English, Regis College, 235 Wellesley St, Weston, MA 02193.

HIGGINSON, FRED HALL, b. Wichita, Kans, Nov. 8, 21; m. 46; c. 2. ENGLISH. A.B, Univ. Wichita, 42, M.A, 48; Ph.D.(Eng), Univ. Minn, 53. Instr. ENG, KANS. STATE UNIV, 50-51, asst. prof, 51-55, 57-58, assoc. prof, 58-65, PROF, 65-, CHMN. DEPT, 69- Ford Found. fac. fel, 55-56; vis. lectr, Univ. Minn, 56-57; ed, Nether Press, London, 65-; consult ed, James Joyce Quart, 69- Med. Dept, U.S.A, 42-45. Midwest Mod. Lang. Asn; MLA; NCTE; Am. Comt. Irish Stud. James Joyce; Robert Graves. Publ: Ed, Anna Livia Plurabelle, Univ. Minn, 60; auth, A bibliography of the works of Robert Graves, Archon Bks. & Vane, London, 66. Add: Dept. of English, Kansas State University, Manhattan, KS 66506.

HIGGS, ELTON DALE, b. Abilene, Tex, June 14, 37; m. 58; c. 2. ENGLISH. B.A, Abilene Christian Col, 61; Woodrow Wilson fel, Univ. Wash, 61-62; Andrew Mellon fel, Univ. Pittsburgh, 62-63, M.A, 63, Ph.D.(Eng), 65. Asst. prof. ENG, UNIV. MICH, DEARBORN, 65-70, ASSOC. PROF, 70-, Acting dean col. arts, sci. & lett, 73-74. MLA; Mediaeval Acad. Am; NCTE. Middle English literature; 16th and 17th century English literature. Add: Dept. of English, University of Michigan, Dearborn, MI 48128.

HIGGS, ROBERT JACKSON, b. Lewisburg, Tenn, Feb. 23, 32; m. 58; c. 2. AMERICAN LITERATURE. B.S, U.S. Naval Acad, 55; M.A, Univ. Tenn, 64, Ph.D.(Eng), 67. Asst. prof. ENG, East. Ky. Univ, 66-67; ASSOC. PROF, E.TENN. STATE UNIV, 67- U.S.A.F, 55-63, Capt. Col. Eng. Asn; Thoreau Soc; S.Atlantic Mod. Lang. Asn. Appalachian literature; American renaissance; athlete in American literature. Publ: Ed, Anne W. Armstrong's This day and time, E.Tenn. State Univ, 70; co-ed, Voices from the hills: selected readings of Appalachia, Ungar, 74; auth, Emily Dickinson's test of trouble, In: Essays in memory of Christine Burleson, E.Tenn. State Univ, 69. Add: Dept. of English, Box 2751, East Tennessee State University, Johnson City, TN 37601.

HIGHFILL, PHILIP HENRY, JR, b. Petersburg, Va, Aug. 12, 18; m. 43; c. 2. ENGLISH LITERATURE. B.A, Wake Forest Col, 42; M.A, Univ. N.C, Chapel Hill, 48, Ph.D.(Eng), 50. Instr. ENG, Univ. Rochester, 50-54, asst. prof, 54-55; assoc. prof, GEORGE WASHINGTON UNIV, 55-61, PROF, 61- Guggenheim Found. fel, 59-60; Henry E. Huntington Libr. grant, summer 59; consult. in lit, Folger Shakespeare Libr, 65-69, sr. fel, 69; Nat. Endowment for Humanities proj. grants, 67, 70; Washington Eve. Star grant, 68. U.S.A, 42-46. MLA; Brit. Soc. Theatre Res; Am. Soc. Theatre Res; Mod. Humanities Res. Asn; Int. Asn. Univ. Prof. Eng; S.Atlantic Mod. Lang. Asn. (chmn. dir. of grad. stud). Eighteenth century theatrical biography, 17th and 18th century drama; satire. Publ: Co-auth, A biographical dictionary of actors, actresses, musicians, dancers, managers, and other personnel in London, 1660-1800 (12 Vols), South. Ill. Univ, 73-; auth, Edmund Simpson's talent raid on England, Theatre Notebook, 58; Charles Surface in regency retirement, Stud. in Philol, 1/67; The British background of the American Hallams, Theatre Surv, 5/70. Add: Dept. of English, George Washington University, Washington, DC 20006.

HIGHLANDER, JAMES L, b. Galesburg, Ill, Aug. 27, 28; m. 58; c. 2. THEATRE. A.B, Eureka Col, 51; M.A, Univ. Ill, 52, Ph.D, 60. Instr. THEATRE, Moorhead State Col, 55-58; ASST. PROF, Chicago Teachers Col, 60-61; CENT. MO. STATE UNIV, 61-, CHMN. DEPT, 72- Theatre consult, 59, 60, 63, 67, 68. U.S.A, 52-54, T/Sgt. Speech Commun. Asn; Am. Theatre Asn. American theatre history. Add: Dept. of Theatre, Central Missouri State University, Warrensburg, MO 64093.

HIJIYA, YUKIHITO, b. Korea, Feb. 18, 42; Japanese citizen; m. 70. ENGLISH & MODERN JAPANESE LITERATURE. B.A, Shikoku Christian Col, Japan, 64; Davidson Col, 64-65; M.A, Wake Forest Univ, 67; Ph.D.(Eng), Univ. N.Mex, 71. ASST. PROF. ENG, BOISE STATE UNIV, 70- MLA; Keats-Shelley Asn. Am. English romanticism; 20th century Japanese novel; Milton and the English romantic poets. Publ: Ishikawa Takuboku, Twayne, (in press); Byron's Manfred: a critical study, 70 & Byron's skepticism, 71, Regard; A religion of humanity: a study of Dazai's No longer human, Critique, 74. Add: Dept. of English, Boise State University, 1907 Campus Dr, Boise, ID 83725.

HILBERRY, CONRAD ARTHUR, b. Melrose Park, Ill, Mar. 1, 28; m. 51; c. 3. ENGLISH LITERATURE. B.A, Oberlin Col, 49; M.S, Univ. Wis, 51, Ph.D. (Eng), 54. Teaching asst. Eng, Univ. Wis, 51-54; instr, DePauw Univ, 54-56, asst. prof, 56-60, assoc. prof, 60-61; prog. assoc, Assoc. Col. Midwest, 61-62; assoc. prof. ENG, KALAMAZOO COL, 62-67, PROF, 67- Eugene Saxton fel, 59; accrediting exam, N.Cent. Asn, 59-; assoc. dir, Stud. Future Lib. Arts Cols, 65-67; humanities coord, Great Lakes Col. Asn, 66- Seventeenth century English literature; 20th century poetry. Publ: Ed, Poems of John Collop, Univ. Wis, 62; auth, Encounter on Burrows Hill, 68 & Rust (poems), 74, Ohio Univ; co-auth, Struggle and promise: a future for liberal arts colleges, McGraw, 69; auth, Medical poems from John Collop's Poesia rediviva, 1656, J. Hist. Med. & Allied Sci; contrib, Prospect for renewal, Jossey-Bass, 72 & Youth in transition, Wayne State Univ, 72. Add: Dept. of English, Kalamazoo College, Kalamazoo, MI 49001.

HILBERT, BETSY SOKOLOF, b. New York, N.Y, Apr. 1, 41; m. 61; c. 1. COMMUNICATIONS, VISUAL LITERACY. A.B, Univ. Miami, 62, M.A, 65; Union Grad. Sch, 72-74. ASSOC. PROF. ENG, MIAMI-DADE COMMUNITY COL, 64- Nat. Asn. Media Educ. Mass Communications; educational media; psychology of perception. Publ: Co-auth, Toward better writing, Brown, 66; auth, Machines and the man, In: Classroom practices in teaching English, Nat. Counc. Teachers Eng, 68; Individualizing English: one model, Improving Col. & Univ. Teaching, spring, 73; Point and shoot: media projects in technical English, Am. Voc. J, 10/73. Add: Dept. of English, Miami-Dade Community College, 11380 N.W. 27th Ave, Miami, FL 33137.

HILDEBRANDT, HERBERT WILLIAM, b. Sheboygan, Wis, Jan. 25, 31; m. 54; c. 2. SPEECH, COMPARATIVE LITERATURE. B.A, Wartburg Col, 52; M.S, Univ. Wis, 54, Ph.D.(speech, comp. lit), 58. Lectr. speech, Univ. Wis, 58; from instr. to assoc. prof, UNIV. MICH, ANN ARBOR, 58-66, secy. univ. & asst. to pres, 66-70, PROF. BUS. ADMIN. & COMMUN, GRAD. SCH. BUS, 70- Outstanding Teacher Speech award, 60. U.S.A, 52-54. Speech Commun. Asn; Am. Inst. Parliamentarians; Int. Commun. Asn; Am. Bus. Commun. Asn. Organizational communication; international and intercultural communication; college administration. Publ: A treatise of schemes and tropes, Scholars Facsimiles, 61; Issues of our times: a summons to speak, Macmillan, 63; co-auth, Public speaking for college students, Am. Bk, 65; auth, Richard Sherry; Renaissance rhetorician, Cent. States Speech J, spring 60; co-auth, The critical edition in rhetorical scholarship, Speech Monogr, 3/61; auth, Communication barriers between German subsidiaries and parent American companies, Mich. Bus. Rev, 7/73; plus others. Add: School of Business Administration, University of Michigan, Ann Arbor, MI 48104.

HILEN, ANDREW R, JR, b. Mt. Vernon, Wash, Oct. 12, 13; m. 40; c. 3. ENGLISH & AMERICAN LITERATURE. A.B, Univ. Wash, 37; Ph.D, Yale, 43. From asst. prof. Eng. & Am. lit. to assoc. prof. Eng, UNIV. WASH, 45-59, PROF. ENG, 59- Lectr, Uppsala Univ, Sweden, 48-49; Guggenheim fel, 54-55; Smith-Mundt prof. Am. lit, Univs. Uppsala, Stockholm & Gothenburg, Sweden, 58-59; Nat. Endowment for Humanities fel, 72-73. U.S.N.R, 41-45, Lt. MLA; Am-Scand. Found. American literature, especially Longfellow. Publ: Longfellow and Scandinavia, Yale Univ, 47; Diary of Clara Crowninshield, Univ. Wash, 56; Letters of Henry Wadsworth Longfellow, Harvard Univ, Vols. I-IV, 66-72; Charley Longfellow goes to war, Harvard Libr. Bull, 60. Add: Dept. of English, University of Washington, Seattle, WA 98195.

HILL, ARCHIBALD ANDERSON, Linguistics. See Volume III, Foreign Languages, Linguistics & Philology.

HILL, CHARLES, b. Garnett, Kans, Sept. 22, 28; m. 55; c. 3. DRAMA & SPEECH. M.S, Kans. State Teachers Col, 55; Univ. Kans, 63-67. Instr. SPEECH & DRAMA, KANS. STATE TEACHERS COL, 55-62, asst. prof, 62-64, ASSOC. PROF, 64- U.S.A, 51-53. Am. Educ. Theatre Asn; Alliance Arts in Educ; Asn. Col. & Univ. Concert Mgr. American theatre; American film. Add: Dept. of Speech, Kansas State Teachers College, 1200 Commercial St, Emporia, KS 66801.

HILL, DONALD PHILLIP, b. Junction City, Ohio, Oct. 14, 26. THEATRE. B.A, Muskingum Col, 49; M.A, Case West. Reserve Univ, 57; M.F.A, Univ. Iowa, 67. Teacher drama & speech, pub. schs, Mich. & Ohio, 49-56; ASSOC. PROF. THEATRE & DIR, DRAMA THEATRE, MUSKINGUM COL, 59- Nat. Col. Players; Am. Theatre Asn; Speech Commun. Asn. Publ: Honors in Brecht, Speech Teacher, 67. Add: 119 Lakeside Dr, New Concord, OH 43762.

HILL, ERROL GASTON, b. Trinidad, West Indies, Aug. 5, 21; m. 56; c. 4. DRAMA. Dipl, Royal Acad. Dramatic Art, Eng, 51; dipl. dramatic art, Univ. London, 51; Rockefeller Found. fel, 58-60; Theatre Guild Am. fel, Yale, 61-62, B.A. & M.F.A, 62, D.F.A, 66; Rockefeller Found. fel, Univ. Ibadan, 65-67. Tutor drama, Univ. West Indies, 52-58, staff tutor creative arts, 62-65; assoc. prof. DRAMA, Richmond Col.(N.Y), 67-68; DARTMOUTH COL, 68-69, PROF, 69-, CHMN. DEPT, 71- Guest lectr. creative writing, Univ. B.C, summer 64; ed, Bull. Black Theatre, 71- Am. Theatre Asn; Asn. Commonwealth Lit. & Lang. Stud; Am. Soc. Theatre Res. Emergence of national Caribbean theatre; theatre of Black Africa. Publ: Ed, Caribbean plays, Vol. I, 58, Vol. II, 65 & auth, The artist in West Indian society, 64, Univ. West Indies; auth, The Trinidad Carnival, Univ. Tex, 72; Man better man (play), In: Three plays from the Yale School of Drama, Dutton, 64; Dance bongo (play), In: Caribbean literature: an anthology, Univ. London, 66. Add: Dept. of Drama, Dartmouth College, Hanover, NH 03755.

HILL, FORBES I, b. Berkeley, Calif, June 26, 28; m. 70; c. 1. RHETORIC, PUBLIC SPEAKING. A.B, San Diego State Col, 52; M.A, Univ. Ore, 55; Ph.D, Cornell Univ, 63. Instr. pub. speaking, Williams Col, 58-59; acting asst. prof. & dir. forensics, Univ. Calif, Santa Barbara, 59-64; from asst. prof. to ASSOC. PROF. COMMUN. ARTS & SCI, QUEENS COL.(N.Y), 64- Speech Asn. Am; Am. Forensic Asn; West. Speech Asn. Classical rhetoric. Add: Dept of Communication Arts & Sciences, Queens College, Flushing, NY 11367.

HILL, HAMLIN, b. Houston, Tex, Nov. 7, 31; m. 52; c. 4. AMERICAN LITERATURE. B.A, Univ. Houston, 53; M.A, Univ. Tex, 54; Ph.D, Univ. Chicago, 59. Instr. Eng, Univ. N.Mex, 59-61, vis. prof, summer 63, asst. prof, 63-65, assoc. prof, 65-68; asst. prof. Eng. & Am. stud, Univ. Wyo, 61-63; PROF. ENG, UNIV. CHICAGO, 68- Vis. lectr, Univ. Nebr, summer 60; Am. Counc. Learned Soc. grants-in-aid, 63, 65, 67; vis. asst. prof, Univ. Calif, Berkeley, spring 65; Fulbright prof. Am. lit, Copenhagen Univ, 66-67; vis. prof. Eng, Univ. N.Mex, summer 71; Guggenheim fel, 71-72; vis. prof. Eng, Stanford Univ, 72-73. Mil. Intel, U.S.A, 54-56. MLA. Mark Twain; American humor. Publ: Co-auth, The art of Huckleberry Finn, 62, 69, ed, Adventures of Huckleberry Finn, 62 & A Connecticut yankee in King Arthur's court, 63, Chandler Publ: auth, Mark Twain and Elisha Bliss, Univ. Mo, 64; ed, Mark Twain's letters to his publishers, Univ. Calif, 67; auth, Mark Twain: God's fool, Harper, 73; Mark Twain: audience and artistry, Am. Quart, 63; Modern American humor: the Janus laugh, Col. Eng, 63; Mark Twain, In Am. literary scholarship, an annual, Duke Univ, 69-72; plus others. Add: Dept. of English, University of Chicago, Chicago, IL 60637.

HILL, JOAN ANN, b. Cincinnati, Ohio, Sept. 11, 34. ENGLISH, EDUCATION. B.A, Mary Manse Col, 56; M.A, Univ. Toledo, 63, Ph.D.(higher educ. curriculum), 73. Teacher, high sch, Ohio, 56-59; instr. Eng, Mary Manse Col, 59-65; asst. prof, Univ. Toledo Community Col, 65-67; instr, Monroe County Community Col, Mich, 67-68; assoc. prof, Mary Manse Col, 68-69, dean, 69-73; CONSULT. EDUC, ST. VINCENT HOSP. & MED. CTR, 73- Am. Asn. Higher Educ; Am. Soc. Hosp. Educ. & Training. Curriculum improvement in higher education; allied health education; adult education. Publ: From here to there: a blueprint for curricular change, Critique, 11/73. Add: St. Vincent Hospital & Medical Center, 2213 Cherry St, Toledo, OH 43608.

HILL, JOHN STANLEY, b. Winfield, Kans, May 12, 29; m. 55; c. 2. AMERICAN LITERATURE. B.S, Univ. Kans, 51, M.A, 56; Ph.D.(Eng), Univ. Wis, 60. Instr. ENG, Ohio Univ, 59-62; assoc. prof, ILL. STATE UNIV, 62-67, PROF, 67-, DIR. GRAD. STUD, 72- Huntington Libr. res. grant, 67-68; chmn. acad. affairs counc, Conf. Midwest. Univ, 73- U.S.A, 51-53. MLA; Midwest Mod. Lang. Asn; NCTE. American literature 1830 to the present. Publ: Checklist of Frank Norris, C.E. Merrill, 70; Poe's Fall of the house of Usher, Southwest Rev, 63; Quest for belief: theme in the novels of John Updike, South. Humanities Rev, spring 69; The letters of Moses Herzog: a symbolic mirror, Stud. Humanities, summer 71; plus others. Add: Dept. of English, Illinois State University, Normal, IL 61761.

HILL, NANCY JOAN, b. St. Paul, Minn, June 22, 36; m. 59; c. 2. ENGLISH LITERATURE. B.A, Carleton Col, 58; Tozer Found. fel. & M.A, Columbia Univ, 62; univ. fel. & Ph.D.(Eng), Northwest. Univ, 72. Asst. prof. Eng, Yale, 72-73; RES. & WRITING, 73- MLA. Victorian literature and art. Add: 6648 S. Marion St, Littleton, CO 80121.

HILL, ORDELLE GERHARD, b. Brookings, S.Dak, Sept. 4, 35; m. 61. MEDIEVAL ENGLISH. B.A, Augustana Col, 57; M.A, Auburn Univ, 59; Ph.D.(14th century Eng), Univ. Ill, 65. Instr. ENG, Luther Col, 60-61; asst. prof, Merrimack Col, 65-66; assoc. prof, EAST. KY. UNIV, 66-68, PROF, 68- S.Atlantic Mod. Lang. Asn; MLA. Medieval English literature. Publ: The late-Latin De Jona as a source for patience, J. Eng. & Ger. Philol, 1/67; The audience of patience, Mod. Philol, fall 68; co-auth, Ursula Brangwen of the rainbow: Christian saint or pagan goddess, D.H. Lawrence Rev, fall 71. Add: Dept. of English, Eastern Kentucky University, Richmond, KY 40475.

HILL, PHILIP GEORGE, b. Christiansburg, Va, Sept. 19, 34; m. 57; c. 3. DRAMA. B.A, Univ. Fla, 56; M.A, Univ. N.C, Chapel Hill, 60; Ph.D.(theatre), Tulane Univ, 64. Instr. DRAMA & SPEECH, Allegheny Col, 60-62; asst. prof, FURMAN UNIV, 64-68, ASSOC. PROF, 68-, CHMN. DEPT, 64- Vis. instr, Univ. Ga, summers 66-67. U.S.A.F, 56-59, 1st Lt. Am. Theatre Asn; U.S. Inst. Theatre Technol; Southeast. Theatre Conf.(exec. secy-treas, 68-72, v.pres, 73-74). Publ: The living art, Holt, 71; Hallmarks of the American musical comedy, spring 67 & New play in a new playhouse, spring 70, South. Theatre; A reading of The firebugs, Mod. Drama, 9/70; plus others. Add: Dept. of Drama & Speech, Furman University, Greenville, SC 29613.

HILL, ROBERT WHITE, b. Anniston, Ala, Jan. 17, 41; m. 65; c. 2. ENGLISH & AMERICAN LITERATURE. A.B, Univ. N.C, Chapel Hill, 63, M.A, 64; Ph.D.(Eng), Univ. Ill, Urbana, 72. Instr. ENG, Converse Col, 64-65; CLEMSON UNIV, 65-69, ASST. PROF, 71- Host, Poetry Today, S.C. Educ. Radio Network, 72-; co-ed, S.C. Rev, 73- MLA; NCTE. Twentieth century English and American poetry; 19th century American literature. Publ: Contrib, James Dickey: the expansive imagination, Everett Edwards, 73. Add: Dept. of English, Clemson University, Clemson, SC 29631.

HILL, ROWLAND MERLIN, b. Westhampton Beach, N.Y, Apr. 20, 06; m. 26, 45; c. 5. ENGLISH. A.B, Dickinson Col, 28; A.M, Boston Univ, 29, Ph.D. (Eng), 41. Instr. Eng, Mich. State Univ, 29-39; Boston Univ, 39-40; L.I. Univ, 40-41; State Univ. N.Y. Teachers Col, Brockport, 41-42; asst. prof, The Citadel, 42-44, 46-48; prof. & head dept, Dickinson Jr. Col, 44-45; assoc. prof, Southwest. Col.(Kans), 45-46; prof, Memphis State Univ, 48-58; head div. lit, lang. & fine arts, Tenn. Wesleyan Col, 58-60; prof. Eng, Pa. Mil. Col, 60-62; prof. Eng, DEFIANCE COL, 62-71, chmn. div. lang. & lit, 62-68, chmn. dept. Eng, 68-71, EMER. PROF. ENG, 71- MLA. Setting in English fiction: 18th century novelists; topographical and environmental influences on British authors. Publ: Henry Fielding's use of setting, Bull. of The Citadel; Aphra Behn's use of setting, Mod. Lang. Quart; Historical and literary associations of some British castles and homes, Scholars J, 9/71. Add: 26 Lakeside Dr, Marstons Mills, MA 02648.

HILL, RUANE BURTON, b. Mondovi, Wis, May 27, 24; m. 49; c. 3. COMMUNICATION. B.A, Beloit Col, 48; M.A, Northwest. Univ, 49, fel, 51-52, Ph.D. (speech), 64; dipl, NBC summer TV inst, Chicago, Ill, 51. Asst. prof. speech & drama, Willamette Univ, 49-51; asst. prof. speech & dir. radio-TV, Beloit Col, 52-55; gen. mgr, Radio Station WFGM, Mass, 55-58; WMRC, Mass, 57-58; asst. prof. radio & TV & station mgr. WAER, Syracuse Univ, 58-63; assoc. prof. commun, UNIV. WIS-MILWAUKEE, 63-71, PROF. MASS COMMUN, 71-, DIR. INST. COMMUN, 63-, chmn. dept. mass commun, 70-73. Mem. fac. senate & chmn. univ. relat. comt, Univ. Wis-Milwaukee, 70-73; dir, Nat. Educ. Radio, 71-74; mem. budget adv. comt, Corp. Pub. Broadcasting, 72; mem, All-Channel Radio Legis. Comt, 72-73. Broadcast Educ. Asn; Nat. Asn. Educ. Broadcasters. Publ: Co-ed, The farther vision: educational television today, Univ. Wis, 67. Add: 3494 N. Frederick Ave, Milwaukee, WI 53211.

HILL, STEVEN PHILLIPS, Slavic Languages & Literatures. See Volume III, Foreign Languages, Linguistics & Philology.

HILL, THOMAS DANA, b. Boston, Mass, May 6, 40; m. 60; c. 3. ENGLISH. B.A, Harvard, 61; M.A, Univ. Ill, 63; Ph.D.(Eng), Cornell Univ, 67. Asst. prof. ENG, CORNELL UNIV, 67-72, ASSOC. PROF, 72- Soc. Humanities fac. fel, Cornell Univ, 70-71; Am. Counc. Learned Soc. fel, 73-74. Medieval Acad. Am. Old and Middle English literature; Old French and Old Icelandic literature. Publ: Some remarks on the The site of Lucifer's throne, Anglia, 69; Number and pattern in Lilja, J. Eng. & Ger. Philol, 70; Sapiential structure and figural narrative in the Old English Elene, Traditio, 71; plus others. Add: Dept. of English, Cornell University, Ithaca, NY 14850.

HILL, WILLIAM B, S.J, b. Pittsburgh, Pa, Dec. 11, 12. ENGLISH. A.B, Georgetown Univ, 38; A.M, Fordham Univ, 40, Ph.D.(Eng), 54; S.T.L, 46. Instr. ENG, Georgetown Univ, 40-42; asst. prof, Univ. Scranton, 46-47; assoc. prof, Novitiate St. Isaac Jogues, 51-59, prof, 59-66; assoc. prof, Fordham Univ, 66-69; PROF, UNIV. SCRANTON, 69-, CHMN. DEPT, 73-, ED, BEST SELLERS, 70- MLA; Renaissance Soc. Am; AAUP. Milton; drama of the English Renaissance; contemporary literature. Add: Dept. of English, University of Scranton, Scranton, PA 18510.

HILL, WILLIAM HENRY, JR, b. Nanticoke, Pa, Jan. 3, 12. ENGLISH. A.B, Pa. State Col, 33. Teacher, high sch, Pa, 39-43; Bullis Prep. Sch, Wash, D.C, 43-47; from instr. to ASSOC. PROF. ENG. COMPOS, POTTSVILLE CTR, PA. STATE UNIV, 47-, COORD. DEPT. ENG. & COMMONWEALTH CAMPUSES, 72- Add: Dept. of English, Pennsylvania State University, University Park, PA 16801.

HILL, WILLIAM SPEED, b. Louisville, Ky, Jan. 19, 35; m. 60; c. 3. RENAISSANCE. A.B, Princeton, 57; A.M, Harvard, 59, Ph.D.(Eng), 64. Asst. prof. ENG, Case West. Reserve Univ, 64-69; N.Y. Univ, 69-73; ASSOC. PROF, LEHMAN COL, 73- Am. Philos. Soc. grant-in-aid, summer 69; Am. Counc. Learned Soc. grant-in-aid, 69, sr. fel. humanities, 74-75; summer fel, Newberry Libr, Chicago, 69; Folger Shakespeare Libr, Wash, D.C, 69; gen. ed, Folger Libr. Ed. Works of Richard Hooker, 70-; Folger Libr-Brit. Acad. Exchange Prog. res. fel, 73. MLA; Renaissance Soc. Am; Renaissance Eng. Text Soc. Renaissance intellectual history; history of rhetoric and rhetorical theory; bibliography and textual criticism. Publ: Richard Hooker, Twayne, (in prep); Richard Hooker: a descriptive bibliography of the early editions, 1593-1724, 70 & ed. & contrib, Studies in Richard Hooker, 73, Case West. Reserve Univ; co-auth, Richard Hooker: a selected bibliography, Pittsburgh Theol. Sem, 71; auth, Biography, autobiography, and Volpone, Stud. Eng. Lit, spring 72; Order and joy in Spenser's Epithalamion, South. Humanities Rev, winter 72; Doctrine and polity in Hooker's Laws, Eng. Lit. Renaissance, spring 72; plus several others. Add: 47 Wildcliff Rd, New Rochelle, NY 10805.

HILLBRUNER, ANTHONY, b. Chicago, Ill, Feb. 10, 14; m. 42; c. 2. SPEECH. B.S, Northwest. Univ. 49, M.A, 50, Ph.D.(speech, hist, polit. sci), 53. Instr. speech, Univ. Denver, 50-51; instr. speech & dir. forensics, Univ. Ore, 51-

52; Stanford Univ, 52-54; from asst. prof. to PROF. SPEECH & AM. STUD, CALIF. STATE UNIV, LOS ANGELES, 54-, creative leave, spring 68. Calif. State Univ, Los Angeles Found. grant, 65-67; consult, Los Angeles County Adminr, 66-72; vis. scholar Am. lit, Cambridge, 72. Speech Commun. Asn; Am. Stud. Asn; West. Speech Asn; Ctr. Stud. Democratic Insts. History and criticism of American public address, especially history of ideas; language and thought, especially general semantics and group dynamics; classical and contemporary rhetorical theory, especially Plato and Wilson. Publ: Critical dimensions, Random, 66; Plato and Korzybski, South. Speech J; Word and deed: Jefferson's addresses to Indians, Speech Monogr, 11/63; The man of letters as critic, Quart. J. Speech, 4/73; plus 30 others. Add: Dept. of Speech, California State University, Los Angeles, CA 90032.

HILLEGAS, MARK R, b. Glendale, Calif, Dec. 26, 26; m. 51; c. 2. ENGLISH. A.B, Columbia Col, 49; M.A, Columbia Univ, 50, Ph.D, 57. Lectr. ENG, Columbia Sch. Gen. Stud, 52-57, instr, 57-58; Univ. Mich, 58-61; asst. prof, Colgate Univ, 61-65; assoc. prof, SOUTH. ILL. UNIV, CARBONDALE, 65-70, PROF, 70- Lucius N. Littauer Found, Alfred P. Sloan Found. & Res. Corp. summer res. fel, 63. Fantasy and science fiction; impact of science on literary and popular imaginations; history of science and technology. Publ: The future as nightmare: H.G. Wells and the anti-utopians, Oxford, New York, 67; ed, Shadows of imagination: the fantasies of C.S. Lewis, J.R.R. Tolkien and Charles Williams, 69 & Afterword to Kurd Lasswitz, Two planets, 71, South. Ill. Univ; Dystopian science fiction: new index to the human situation, N.Mex. Quart, autumn 61; introd, H.G. Wells, A modern utopia, Univ. Nebr, 67; plus others. Add: 1218 Carter St, Carbondale, IL 62901.

HILLER, CHARLES FRANCIS, b. Washington, D.C, May 24, 03. ENGLISH. A.B, Lehigh Univ, 24; A.M, Harvard, 30, Saltonstall scholar, 34, Ph.D, 35. Tutor Fr, Harvard, 32-34; bursar, UNIV. HOUSTON, 35-40, registr, 38-39, 44-45, dir. navy training sch, 41-44, dean col. arts & sci, 45-50, prof. Eng, 50-73, v.pres, 50-55, dean jr. col. div, 55-63, EMER. PROF. ENG, 73- MLA. Romance philology. Add: 5335 Carew, Houston, TX 77035.

HILLIARD, ADDIE SUGGS, b. Henderson, Tenn, Dec. 24, 06; m. 32; c. 3. ENGLISH, EDUCATION. B.A, Univ. Tenn, 32, Ed.D, 64; M.A, Memphis State Univ, 56; Ed.S, George Peabody Col, 62. Teacher, pub. schs, Tenn, 24-28, 41-43, 48-62, 63-64; assoc. prof. ENG, WEST. KY. UNIV, 64-71, EMER. ASSOC. PROF, 71- NCTE; NEA. Shakespeare's use of plants in his plays and poems; local folklore; teacher orientation. Publ: Applie warme at bedtyme, Ky. Folklore Rec, 10-12/66; I remember, I remember, 12/66 & co-auth, The Shakespeare teacher and folklore, 12/67, Tenn. Folklore Soc. Bull. Add: Dept. of English, Western Kentucky University, Bowling Green, KY 42101.

HILLIARD, ROBERT L, b. New York, N.Y, June 25, 25; m. 50; c. 2. COMMUNICATIONS. A.B, Univ. Del, 48; A.M, West. Reserve Univ, 49, M.F.A, 50; Ph.D.(educ), Columbia Univ, 59. Lectr. Eng, jour. & TV, Brooklyn Col, 50-56; asst. prof. speech & dramatic arts, Adelphi Univ, 56-60; assoc. prof. radio, TV & motion pictures, Univ. N.C, Chapel Hill, 60-64; CHIEF EDUC. BROADCASTING BR, FED. COMMUN. COMN, 64-; FOUNDER & CHMN, FED. INTERAGENCY BROADCAST COMT, 65- Chmn. TV proj, Am. Educ. Theatre Asn, 60-62; consult, N.C. Educ. TV Comn, 61; chmn. educ. TV comt, Southeast. Theatre Conf, 61-64; consult, N.C. Heart Asn, 62-64; radio & convention comt, Am. Asn. Educ. Broadcasters, 62-64; consult. TV in higher educ, N.Y. State Dept. Educ, 63; consult. TV, Counc. Higher Educ. Inst, New York, 63-64; planning comt, N.C. Advan. Sch, 64; chmn. radio-TV -film comt, South. Speech Asn, 64-65; exec. v.chmn, nat. Comt. for Full Develop. Instructional TV Fixed Serv, 65-; founder, Int. Univ. Commun, 69; mem. educ. comt, Am. Mgt. Asn, 69; consult, Open Univ, Japan, 70; lectr, Japan, Taiwan, Hong Kong, India & Nepal, 70. Broadcast Preceptor Award, San Francisco State Col, 69; Appreciation Award, Ohio Med. Educ. Network, 72. U.S.A, 44-46. Communications to solve critical problems in society; communications media as bases for formal and informal education. Publ: Writing for television and radio, 62 & rev. ed, 67, co-auth, & ed, Understanding television, 64 & Radio broadcasting, 67 & rev. ed, 74, Hastings; auth, Blue Rock Land, Publ. Affairs, 56; co-auth, TV facilities in higher education in N.Y. State, N.Y. State Educ. Dept, 64 & Instructional TV fixed service: what it is, how to plan, Nat. Educ. Asn, 67; Le radio: une carriere, Nouveaux Horizons, Strasbourg, 70; Radio, In: World Book Encycl, Field, 74; plus others. Add: 3747 Huntington St. N.W, Washington, DC 20015.

HILLIARD, STEPHEN SHORTIS, b. Framingham, Mass, June 20, 39. ENGLISH. A.B, Harvard, 61; M.A, Princeton, 64, Ph.D.(Eng), 67. Asst. prof. ENG, UNIV. NEBR, LINCOLN, 64-71, ASSOC. PROF, 71- MLA; Renaissance Soc. Am. Renaissance literature; critical theory. Add: Dept. of English, University of Nebraska, Lincoln, NE 68508.

HILLIER, RICHARD LIONEL, b. Burlington, N.J, Aug. 8, 07; m. 34; c. 2. ENGLISH. B.A, Haverford Col, 28; M.A, Univ. Colo, 32, Ph.D.(Eng), 44. Instr. ENG, Univ. Colo, 33-37; UNIV. WYO, 38-42, asst. prof, 42-46, assoc. prof, 46-50, PROF, 50- MLA. Color imagery in Elizabethan poetry; Shakespeare's Roman history plays; Raleigh's History of the world. Publ: The imagery of color, light and darkness in the poetry of Christopher Marlowe, In: Studies in honor of George F. Reynolds, Univ. Colo, 45; The bard in paper, Libr. J, 64; The dramatic structure of King Lear, Univ. Wyo. Publ, 64. Add: Dept. of English, University of Wyoming, Laramie, WY 82070.

HILTON, EARL RAYMOND, b. Beulah, Wyo, Dec. 22, 14; m. 47; c. 5. ENGLISH. B.A, Univ. Wyo, 38; Ph.M, Univ. Wis, 39; Ph.D, Univ. Minn, 50. Instr. ENG, Iowa State Col, 46-47; asst. prof, Cent. Wash. Col. Educ, 50; NORTH. MICH. UNIV, 50-55, assoc. prof, 55-59, PROF, 59- Fund Advan. Educ. fel, Oberlin Col, 51-52. U.S.A, 41-46, Lt. MLA. American literature, especially Sherwood Anderson, Mark Twain, Hawthorne. Publ: Co-auth, Exposition, Wadsworth, 67; The evolution of Sherwood Anderson's brother death, N.W. Ohio Quart; Browning's Sordello as a study of the will, PMLA; Hawthorne, the Hippie and the square, Stud. in the Novel, fall, 70. Add: 403 E. Arch St, Marquette, MI 49855.

HILTY, DEBORAH PACINI, b. Boston, Mass, July 23, 41; m. 65; c. 2. ENGLISH LANGUAGE & LITERATURE. A.B, Vassar Col, 63; M.A, Columbia Univ, 65; Ph.D.(Eng. lit), Case West. Reserve Univ, 69. Instr. ENG, Col. Wooster, 65-67; ASST. PROF, Bradley Univ, 69-70; COL. WOOSTER, 70- MLA; NCTE; Milton Soc. Am. Seventeenth century poetry; history of genres. Add: Dept. of English, College of Wooster, Wooster, OH 44691.

HILTY, PALMER A, b. Deepwater, Mo, Sept. 17, 04; m. 31; c. 1. ENGLISH, COMPARATIVE LITERATURE. B.A, Univ. Wis, 29, M.A, 30, Ph.D.(comp. lit), 50. Teacher high schs, Philippines, 31-33; teaching fel. comp. lit, Univ, Wis, 34-36, asst. Ger, 36-38; head dept. Eng, Ashland Jr. Col, 38-41; instr. radio mechanics, Truax Field, 42-46; teacher Eng, Farragut Col. & Tech. Inst, 46-49; prof. Eng. & humanities, Wash. State Univ, 49-71; admin. secy, Fel. Relig. Humanists, 71-74. Summers, Danforth grants, Pac. Sch. Relig, 57; Federated Theol. Fac, Univ. Chicago, 58. MLA. Greek literature and philosophy; Medieval literature; Bible as literature. Publ: Transl, J. Burckhardt, History of Greek culture, 63, Novalis, Henry of Ofterdingen, 64, J. Amery, Preface to the future, 64 & E. Compertz, The Bible & modern man, 65, Ungar; auth, Teaching the Bible as literature, Humanist, London, 61. Add: 371 Trailview Rd, Encinitas, CA 92024.

HILTY, PETER DANIEL, b. Fortuna, Mo, July 16, 21. ENGLISH LITERATURE. B.A, Univ. Mo, 50, M.A, 51, Ph.D, 58. Instr. Eng. lit, Univ. Mo, 51-57; assoc. prof. Eng. & chmn. dept, Park Col, 58-62; from assoc. prof. to PROF. ENG, SOUTHEAST MO. STATE UNIV, 62- MLA; S. Cent. Mod. Lang. Asn; Am. Stud. Asn; Col. Eng. Asn; Am. Name Soc. Comparative literature; creative writing; world drama. Publ: Kingsley Amis and modern prose, Discourse, 4/60; The rains came, Sat. Evening Post, 5-6/61; What's in a name—of the Governor, that is?, Mo. Hist. Rev, fall 72. Add: Dept. of English, Southeast Missouri State University, Cape Girardeau, MO 63701.

HILYARD, DELMER MANFORD, b. Braman, Okla, Feb. 21, 28; m. 50; c. 3. COMMUNICATION. A.B, Univ. Denver, 51; M.S, Kans. State Teachers Col, 58; Ph.D.(commun), Mich. State Univ, 66. Instr. speech, Kans. State Teachers Col, 56-62; asst. commun, Mich. State Univ, 62-65; asst. prof, SPEECH, Kans. State Univ, 65-67; BOWLING GREEN UNIV, 67-71, ASSOC. PROF, 71- Lectr-consult, Mich. State Univ-Agency Int. Develop. commun. seminars, 62- U.S.A, 46-47. Speech Asn. Am. Attitude and communication. Add: Dept. of Speech, Bowling Green University, Bowling Green, OH 43402.

HIMELICK, RAYMOND, b. Jonesboro, Ind, Oct. 7, 10; m. 40; c. 1. ENGLISH. A.B, Ball State Teachers Col, 32; A.M, Univ. Mich, 43; univ. fel, Ind. Univ, 46-47, Ph.D, 50. Instr, Ind. Univ, 47-50; ENG, PURDUE UNIV, WEST LAFAYETTE, 50-52, asst. prof, 52-59, assoc. prof, 59-64, PROF, 64- MLA; Midwest Mod. Lang. Asn; Renaissance Soc. Am. English Renaissance and American literature. Publ: Transl, Erasmus Enchiridion militis Christiani, Ind. Univ, 63; ed, Samuel Daniel's Musophilus, 65 & auth, Erasmus and the Seamless coat of Jesus, 71, Purdue Univ; Thoreau and Samuel Daniel, Am. Lit; Cabell and the modern temper, S.Atlantic Quart. Add: Dept. of English, Purdue University, West Lafayette, IN 47907.

HIMELSTEIN, MORGAN YALE, b. Lebanon, Conn, Sept. 19, 26; m. 58; c. 2. ENGLISH. B.A, Wesleyan Univ, 47, Winchester fel, 47-48; A.M, Columbia Univ, 48, Ph.D.(Eng. & comp. lit), 58. Instr. ENG, Univ. Rochester, 48-50; ADELPHI UNIV, 57-60, asst. prof, 60-64, assoc. prof, 64-68, PROF, 68-, dir. grad. stud, 65-74. U.S.A, 50-52. MLA; Col. Eng. Asn. History of drama and theater; drama and politics; literary and dramatic criticism. Publ: Drama was a weapon: the left-wing theatre in New York, 1929-1941, Rutgers Univ, 63; The pioneers of Bertolt Brecht in America, Mod. Drama, 9/66; Theory and performance in the Depression theatre, Mod. Drama, 2/72; contrib, Contemporary dramatists, St. James, 73; plus one other. Add: Dept. of English, Adelphi University, Garden City, NY 11530.

HINCHCLIFFE, PETER MICHAEL, b. Vancouver, B.C, Nov. 2, 36; m. 67; c. 2. ENGLISH LITERATURE. B.A, Univ. B.C, 58; M.A, Univ. Toronto, 60, Ph.D.(Eng), 67. Lectr. ENG, Huron Col, Univ. West. Ont, 62-66; ST. JEROME'S COL, UNIV. WATERLOO, 66-67, asst. prof, 67-73, ASSOC. PROF, 73- Can. Counc. leave fel, 72-73. Asn. Can. Univ. Teachers Eng. Nineteenth and 20th century English literature; Canadian literature. Publ: Fathers and children in the novels of Evelyn Waugh, Univ. Toronto Quart, 66; To keep the memory of so worthy a friend: Ethel Wilson as an elegist, J. Can. Fiction, 73. Add: Dept. of English, St. Jerome's College, University of Waterloo, Waterloo, Ont. N2L 3G3, Can.

HINCHEY, JOHN JOSEPH, b. Chelsea, Mass, July 8, 47; m. 68; c. 2. ENGLISH & AMERICAN LITERATURE. A.B, Georgetown Univ, 68; Ph.D.(Eng), Harvard, 74. ASST. PROF. ENG, SWARTHMORE COL, 73- Add: Dept. of English, Swarthmore College, Swarthmore, PA 19081.

HINCK, HENRY WILLIAM, b. Scranton, Pa, Apr. 15, 14. ENGLISH. B.A, St. Ambrose Col, 39; M.A, Univ. Iowa, 47, Ph.D, 55; Yale, 49-50. Asst. prof. hist, Hastings Col, 47; instr. Eng, Valparaiso Univ, 47-49; Iowa State Univ, 53-56; asst. prof, Mankato State Col, 56-59; assoc. prof, Southeast Mo. State Col, 59-61; S.Dak. State Univ, 61-64; prof. lang. & lit. & chmn. dept, Buena Vista Col, 64-67; assoc. prof. ENG, UNIV. WIS-LA CROSSE, 67-70, PROF, 70- U.S.A; U.S.A.F, S/Sgt. English literature, Medieval and Romantic. Add: Dept. of English, University of Wisconsin-La Crosse, La Crosse, WI 54601.

HINDEN, MICHAEL CHARLES, b. New York, N.Y, June 5, 41. ENGLISH & AMERICAN LITERATURE. A.B, Ohio Univ, 63; Dêgré Supérieur, Sorbonne, 62; Ph.D.(Eng), Brown Univ, 71. Instr. ENG, Brown Univ, 68-69; ASST. PROF, UNIV. WIS-MADISON, 70- Kiekhofer Distinguished Teaching Award, Wis, 72. MLA. Modern drama; nature of tragedy; contemporary literature. Publ: Yeats's symbolic farce: The player queen, Mod. Drama, 2/72; The wounds of Nessus: Sophocles' Trachiniae, Educ. Theatre J, 5/73; Lost in the funhouse: Barth's use of the recent past, 20th Century Lit, 4/73. Add: Dept. of English, University of Wisconsin-Madison, Madison, WI 53706.

HINDERYCKX, LESLIE ALPHONSE, b. Chicago, Ill, Jan. 7, 31; m. 70; c. 3. DRAMA, COMMUNICATIONS. B.A, Lake Forest Col, 54; M.A, Northwest. Univ, 58, Ph.D.(theatre), 68. Instr. dramatic arts, Rockford Col, 58-59, asst. prof, 59-61; speech & drama, Beloit Col, 61-63; THEATRE, NORTHWEST. UNIV, 63-71, ASSOC. PROF. & CHMN. DEPT, 71- U.S.M.C, 51-52, Sgt. Nat. Col. Players; Am. Theatre Asn. Elizabethan theatrical presentation; training of actors and directors; use of firearms in the theatre. Add: 814 Clinton Pl, Evanston, IL 60201.

HINDMAN, JENNIE LOUISE, b. Kaufman, Tex, Dec. 19. DRAMA, SPEECH. B.S, Tex. Woman's Univ, 33, M.A, 36; Ph.D.(drama, speech), La. State Univ, 50. Teacher, pub. sch, Tex, 36-42; PROF. SPEECH & DRAMA. & CHMN. DEPT, MIDWEST. UNIV, 42- Am. Educ. Theatre Asn; Speech Asn. Am. Theories and philosophies of acting; aesthetics; interpretation. Publ: Method in acting: whence and whither, Faculty Papers, Midwest. Univ, 66-67. Add: Dept. of Speech & Drama, Midwestern University, Wichita Falls, TX 76308.

HINDUS, MILTON, b. New York, N.Y, Aug. 26, 16; m. 42; c. 1. ENGLISH. B.A, City Col. New York, 36, M.S, 38; Columbia Univ, 38-39; Univ. Chicago, 47-48. Instr. Eng, Hunter Col, 43-46; asst. prof. humanities, Univ. Chicago, 46-48; assoc. prof. ENG, BRANDEIS UNIV, 48-62, PROF, 62- Lectr, New Sch. Soc. Res, 44-46; ed, Am. lit. sect, Encycl. Judaica, 68- Walt Whitman Prize, Poetry Soc. Am, 59. MLA; Col. Eng. Asn; NCTE; Jewish Publ. Soc. Am. Modern literature. Publ: The crippled giant, Boar's Head, 50; Céline tel que je l'ai vu, L'Arche, Paris, 51; Proustian vision, Columbia; ed, Leaves of grass: one hundred years after, Stanford, 55; auth, Reader's guide to Marcel Proust, Farrar, Straus, 62; F. Scott Fitzgerald: an introduction and interpretation, Holt, 68; The old east side, Jewish Publ. Soc. Am, 69; A world at twilight, Macmillan, 71; Whitman: the critical heritage, Routledge, London & Barnes & Noble, N.Y, 71. Add: Dept. of English, Brandeis University, Waltham, MA 02154.

HINE, DARYL, b. Burnaby, B.C, Feb. 24, 36. COMPARATIVE LITERATURE. McGill Univ, 54-58; M.A, Univ. Chicago, 65, Ph.D.(comp. lit), 67. Asst. prof. Eng, Univ. Chicago, 67-69; ED, POETRY MAG, 69-, vis. ed, 68-69. Vis. prof. Eng, Northwest. Univ, 71; Univ. Ill, Chicago Circle. Publ: The devil's picture book (poems), Abelard, 60; The wooden horse (poems), 65, Minutes (poems), 68 & transl, The Homeric hymns and the Battle of the frogs and the mice, 72, Atheneum; auth, The death of Seneca (drama), Chicago Rev, 70. Add: Poetry Magazine, 1228 N. Dearborn Pkwy, Chicago, IL 60610.

HINES, BEDE FRANCIS, T.O.R, b. Tamaqua, Pa, Feb. 25, 18. ENGLISH. B.A, St. Francis Col, 43; univ. fel, Pa. State Univ, 48-49, M.A, 51; M.Lit.Ed, Columbia Univ, 53; Ph.D, Univ. Montreal, 55. Instr. ENG, ST. FRANCIS COL. (PA), 47-48, asst. prof, 56-62, PROF, 62- NCTE; MLA; Cath. Poetry Soc. Creative writing; English; comparative-world literatures. Publ: Social world of Aldous Huxley, Mariale, 54, rev. 3rd ed, 62; English literary milieu, 58, rev. 2nd ed, 63, Communication in relation to the language arts, 59, rev. 2nd ed, 66, Dimensions of world literature, 61, rev. 2nd ed, 66 & Perspectives of world literature, 70, St. Francis Col. Bk. Store. Add: Dept. of English, St. Francis College, Loretto, PA 15940.

HINES, DONALD MERRILL, b. St. Paul, Minn, Jan. 23, 31; m. 61; c. 3. FOLKLORE, AMERICAN STUDIES. B.S. Lewis & Clark Col, 53; M.A.T, Reed Col, 60; Ford Found. fel, Ind. Univ, 65-66, Ph.D, 69. Teacher high schs, Wash, Ore, 57-61; instr, ENG, Yakima Valley Col, 62-65; asst. prof, WASH. STATE UNIV, 68-73, ASSOC. PROF, 73- Nat. Endowment for Humanities res. grant, 73. Intel.C, U.S.A, 53-55. Am. Folklore Soc; MLA; Int. Soc. Ethnol. & Folklore; Rocky Mountain Mod. Lang. Asn; Philol. Asn. Pac. Coast. American folklore; folklore in literature; material culture research. Publ: Odd customs and strange ways: the American Indian c. 1640, West. Rev, VII: 20-29; Wry wit and frontier humor—the Wellerism in the Inland Pacific Northwest, South. Folklore Quart, XXXV: 15-26; The development of folklife research in the United Kingdom: I, a brief history of folklife studies in England, Scotland, Wales and Northern Ireland, Pa. Folklife, XXI: 8-20; plus others. Add: Dept. of English, Washington State University, Pullman, WA 99163.

HINES, SAMUEL PHILIP, JR, b. Kinston, N.C, May 3, 24; m. 67. ENGLISH. B.A, Univ. N.C, Chapel Hill, 56, M.A, 59, Ph.D.(Eng), 67. Instr. Eng, Washington & Lee Univ, 63-65; asst. prof, OLD DOM. UNIV, 65-68, ASSOC. PROF. ENG, 68-, TEACHER GREEK, 66- U.S.A.A.F, 43-46, Sgt. MLA; S.Atlantic Mod. Lang. Asn; Milton Soc. Am. English translations of Aristophanes' and Sophocles' plays, 17th and 18th centuries; Restoration and 18th century drama. Publ: A translation of Aristophanes' Birds (1812), Notes & Queries, 10/71. Add: Dept. of English, Old Dominion University, Hampton Blvd, Norfolk, VA 23508.

HINGSTON, ALBERT CARDIFF, b. Index, Wash, Sept. 28, 12; m. 38; c. 1. SPEECH, DRAMA. B.A, State Col. Wash, 38; M.A, Univ. Wash, 42; Univ. South. Calif, summer 53; Univ. Hawaii, 59. Teacher speech, drama & Eng, Dalles High Sch, 38-42; asst. prof. SPEECH & DRAMA, PAC. UNIV, 42-45, assoc. prof, 45-51, PROF, 51-, CHMN. DEPT, 42-, CHMN. DIV. COMMUN, 63-, mem. bd. trustees, 73-76. Vis. lectr, Univ. Hawaii, 59. Am. Speech & Hearing Asn; Am. Theatre Asn; Speech Commun. Asn; West. Speech Asn; West. Forensic Asn.(secy-treas, 62-64, pres, 67-68). Radio and television; speech correction; rhetoric. Publ: Co-auth, Argumentation and debate, Dryden, 54, rev. ed, Holt, 63; & Communication through public speaking, Campus, 67. Add: Dept. of Speech, Pacific University, Forest Grove, OR 97116.

HINKEL, ROBERT CRAIG, b. Lynn, Mass. ENGLISH. B.A, Washington & Lee Univ, 60; Woodrow Wilson fel. & M.A, Northwest. Univ, 62, univ. fel. & Ph.D.(Eng), 67. Teaching asst. ENG, Northwest. Univ, 62-65; instr, Ill. Inst. Technol, 65-68; ASST. PROF, WEST. MICH. UNIV, 68- Modern literature; mythology; film interpretation. Publ: Co-auth, Auto neuroticism: the car as wreck symbol, Technol. & Human Affairs, fall 69. Add: Dept. of English, Western Michigan University, Kalamazoo, MI 49001.

HINKLE, DIANE LEONARD, b. Paintsville, Ky, Aug. 13, 44. COMPARATIVE LITERATURE. A.B, Marshall Univ, 65; Ph.D.(comp. lit), Univ. N.C, Chapel Hill, 71. Lectr. comp. lit, Univ. Wis-Madison, 68-69; ASST. PROF. Eng, N.C. Cent. Univ, 69-71; Stephens Col, 71-73; COMP. LIT, UNIV. N.C, CHAPEL HILL, 73- MLA; Women's Caucus Mod. Lang; Am. Comp. Lit. Asn; AAUP. Modern novel; literary theory and criticism. Add: Curriculum of Comparative Literature, Dey Hall, University of North Carolina, Chapel Hill, NC 27514.

HINKLE, OLIN ETHMER, b. Miller, Mo, Apr. 14, 02; m. 31; c. 2. JOURNALISM. A.B, W.Tex. State Col, 25; B.J, Univ. Mo, 26, A.M, 41. Ed, Pampa Daily News, Tex, 27-36; managing ed, Lexington Herald, Ky, 36-37; dir. jour, W. Tex. State Col, 37-43, 45-46; from assoc. prof. to prof, Univ. Tex, Austin, 46-73; RETIRED. U.S.A.A.F, 43-45, Capt. Asn. Educ. Jour. Offset printing of newspapers; techniques of column writing; news photography. Publ: Co-auth, How to write columns, Iowa State. Add: 303 E. 32nd, Austin, TX 78705.

HINMAN, CHARLTON, b. Ft. Collins, Colo, Feb. 10, 11; m. 36, 68; c. 1. ENGLISH LITERATURE. A.B, Cornell Univ, 33; Rhodes scholar, Oxford, 33-36, B.A, 36, M.A, 39; du Pont fel, Univ. Va, 39-41, Ph.D, 41. Instr. ENG, Univ. Mo, 37-39; asst. prof, Johns Hopkins Univ, 46-50; prof, UNIV. KANS, 60-63, UNIV. DISTINGUISHED PROF, 63- Folger res. fel, Folger Shakespeare Libr, Wash, D.C, 41-42, hon. fel, 53-59; Guggenheim fel, 54-55; Bollingen fel, 56-58; inventor, Hinman collating machine. U.S.N, 42-46, 50-52, Comdr. MLA; Shakespeare Asn. Am; Bibliog. Soc. London; Malone Soc. English Renaissance drama; analytical bibliography; text of Shakespeare. Publ: Printing and proof-reading of the first folio of Shakespeare (2 vols), Clarendon Press, 63; The first folio of Shakespeare, Norton, 68. Add: 1020 Crestline Dr, Lawrence, KS 66044.

HINMAN, MYRA MAHLOW, b. Saginaw Co, Mich, Jan. 11, 26; m. 48, 68; c. 1. ENGLISH. B.S, Columbia Univ, 47; M.A, Univ. Fla, 54, Ph.D.(Eng), 59. Asst. prof. ENG, Memphis State Univ, 59-61; instr, UNIV. KANS, 61-63, asst. prof, 63-68, ASSOC. PROF, 68- Am. Counc. Learned Soc. travel grant, Int. Arthurian Cong, France, summer, 66. MLA; Int. Arthurian Soc. Arthurian legend, Renaissance drama; Shakespeare. Publ: Lancelot at the Grail Castle, Folklore, 65; Morgan le Fay in Malory's Morte D'Arthur, Bibliog. Bull, Int. Arthurian Soc, 67; plus articles on Shakespeare. Add: 1020 Crestline Dr, Lawrence, KS 66044.

HINMAN, ROBERT B, b. Kans, Oct. 21, 20; m. 42; c. 4. ENGLISH. Ph.D. (Eng), Johns Hopkins Univ, 53. Instr. Eng, Univ. Rochester, 48-53, asst. prof, 53-59, assoc. prof, 59-64, prof, 64-69, dir. honors prog, 62-67; prof. ENG, Emory Univ, 69-73, chmn. dept, 70-73; PROF. & CHMN. DEPT, UNIV. PITTSBURGH, 73- Fund Advan. Educ. fel, 55-56; vis. prof, Univ. Hull, 59-60; assoc. ed, Seventeenth Century News, 74- U.S.N.R, 42-46. MLA; AAUP. English language and linguistics; English Renaissance; medieval literature. Publ: Abraham Cowley's world of order, Harvard, 60; The apotheosis of Faust: poetry and new philosophy in the 17th century, In: Metaphysical poetry, Univ. Ind, 70, 71; The Pindarique way: Abraham Cowley's . . . essays, In: Der Englische essay, Wissenschaftliche Buchgesellschaft, 74. Add: Dept. of English, University of Pittsburgh, Pittsburgh, PA 15260.

HINNANT, CHARLES HASKELL, b. Cleveland, Ohio, Mar. 18, 36; m. 68. ENGLISH. M.A, Columbia Univ, 60, Ph.D.(Eng), 66. Asst. prof. ENG, Univ. Mich, Ann Arbor, 65-72; ASSOC. PROF, UNIV. MO-COLUMBIA, 72- MLA. Interrelationship between literature and arts; 18th century English literature. Publ: Dryden Gallic Cock, Stud. Philol, 9/68; Marvell's Gallery of art, Renaissance Quart, 71; Dryden and Hogarth's Sigismunda, Eighteenth-Century Stud, 73. Add: Dept. of English, 231 Arts & Science, University of Missouri-Columbia, Columbia, MO 65201.

HINTON, BETTY JEAN, b. Ft. Smith, Ark, Dec. 20, 27. SPEECH. B.A, Univ. Ark, 52, M.A, 54; Univ. Iowa, 58-59; Ph.D.(rhetoric & pub. address), South. Ill. Univ, 65; LL.D, Geneva Col, 68. Instr. speech & drama, Ft. Smith Jr. Col, 51-53; teacher high sch, Ark, 54-55; therapist speech correction, Wichita pub. schs, 55-56; asst. prof. speech & drama, Upper Iowa Univ, 56-58; asst. prof. speech & drama & tech. dir. theatre, McNeese State Col, 59-63; assoc. prof. speech & dir. basic speech, Murray State Univ, 65-66, dir, speech & hearing, 66-67, prof. speech & dir. grad. stud, 67-70, inst. stud. & res. grants, 66, 67-68; RES. & WRITING, 70- Speech Commun. Asn. Astrology. Publ: The persuasive speech and delivery of Huey P. Long, Murray State Univ. Rev, fall 67. Add: 701 S. 16th St, Murray, KY 42071.

HINTON, MARGARET SCHOFIELD, b. Germantown, Pa. MIDDLE ENGLISH LITERATURE. A.B, Mt. Holyoke Col, 29; A.M, Radcliffe Col, 30; Ph.D, Univ. Pa, 36. Instr. ENG, Wheaton Col.(Mass), 30-33; asst. prof, BEAVER COL, 46-50, assoc. prof, 50-56, prof, 56-72, chmn. dept, 70-72, EMER. PROF, 72- MLA; Col. Eng. Asn; Renaissance Soc. Am. Eighteenth century English literature. Publ: The dicts and sayings of the philosophers, a Middle English version by Stephen Scrope, 38; Some existential aspects in modern literature, Newslett. Greater Phila. Counc. Teachers Eng, 1/67. Add: 830 Montgomery Ave, Bryn Mawr, PA 19010.

HINTON, NORMAN DEXTER, b. New York, N.Y, Aug. 25, 32; m. 54; c. 5. ENGLISH LITERATURE. B.A. & M.A, Univ. Tulsa, 54; Ph.D.(mediaeval lit), Univ. Wis, 57. Instr. Eng, Princeton, 57-61; asst. prof, St. Louis Univ, 61-64, assoc. prof, 64-71; PROF. LIT, SANGAMON STATE UNIV, 71- Asst. Univ. Wis, 57; Proctor & Gamble fel, Princeton, 59. MLA; Am. Dialect Soc. English and continental medieval literature; linguistics; aesthetics. Publ: The language of jazz musicians, Publ. Am. Dialect Soc; Anagogue and archetype: the phenomonology of Medieval literature, Annuale Medievale, 66; The black death and the Book of the Duchess, Univ. Tulsa Monogr. Ser, 67; plus others. Add: Literature Program, Sangamon State University, Springfield, IL 62708.

HINTON, VIRGINIA COOKSEY, b. Muscogee Co, Ga, Sept. 15, 23; m. 50; c. 1. ENGLISH. A.B.J, Univ. Ga, 42, Ph.D.(Eng), 67; M.S, Auburn Univ, 48. Instr. ENG, Cols, Ctr, Univ. Ga, 48-51; asst. prof, KENNESAW JR. COL, 66-73, ASSOC. PROF, 73- MLA. Southern literature; American humor. Publ: The Columbus Enquirer and literature, 1855-1872, Univ. Ga, 67. Add: 246 Normandy Dr, Marietta, GA 30060.

HINZ, JOHN PETER, b. New York, N.Y, May 24, 23. ENGLISH, AMERICAN STUDIES. A.B, City Col. New York, 44; A.M, Columbia Univ, 47, Ph.D, 59. Tutor Eng, City Col. New York, 47-67, lectr, 56-59, instr, 59-60, asst. prof, 60-66, asst. prof, 60-66, assoc. prof, 66-70; PROF. AM. STUD, RICHMOND COL.(N.Y), 70- Fulbright guest prof, Univ. Graz, Austria, 61-62; univ. prof. Am. stud, Univ. Innsbruck, 66-67. U.S.A.A.F, 43-46, Lt. MLA. American literature. Add: Humanities Division, Richmond College, Staten Island, NY 10301.

HIPKISS, ROBERT ARTHUR, b. Honolulu, Hawaii, Jan. 26, 35; m. 61. ENGLISH. A.B, San Jose State Col, 56; M.A, Univ. Calif, Los Angeles, 64, Ph.D.(Eng), 66. Asst. prof. ENG, CALIF. STATE UNIV, LONG BEACH, 66-72, ASSOC. PROF, 72- U.S.N.R, 57-, Comdr. American literature; the values of expatriation for major American novelists, 1914-1941. Publ: Djuna Barnes, a bibliography, Twentieth Century Lit, 10/68; Semantics of the generation gap, ETC, 9/70; Capable college frosh can skip composition, Calif. Eng. J, 12/72; plus others. Add: Dept. of English, California State University at Long Beach, 6101 E. Seventh St, Long Beach, CA 90801.

HIPPLE, WALTER JOHN, JR, b. Chicago, Ill, Mar. 14, 21. ENGLISH, PHILOSOPHY. B.A, Univ. Chicago, 47, M.A, 48, fel, 50-51, Ph.D, 54. Lectr. Eng, Roosevelt Univ, 48; instr. humanities, Univ. Chicago, 48-50; Eng, Univ. Ark, 51-52; asst. prof. humanities, Univ. Fla, 52-56; res, Courtauld Inst. Art, London, 56-57; assoc. prof. Eng. & Philos, Cornell Col, 57-61; Guggenheim fel, Cambridge, 61-62; vis. prof. Eng, Idaho State Univ, 63; prof. philos, Ind. State Univ, Terre Haute, 63-72, chmn. dept. humanities, 64-72; DEAN, SHIMER COL, 72- Summer vis. prof. Eng, Univ. South. Calif, 63. U.S.A, 42-45. MLA; Am. Soc. Aesthet; Nat. Asn. Humanities Educ; Am. Asn. Higher Educ. Aesthetic theory; British intellectual history; 18th century culture. Publ: Beautiful, sublime, and picturesque in eighteenth-century British aesthetic theory, South. Ill. Univ, 57; Alexander Gerard's essay on taste, Scholars' Facsimiles, 63; Matthew Arnold, dialectician, Univ. Toronto Quart, 10/62; Philosophical language and the theory of beauty in the eighteenth century, In: Studies in criticism and aesthetics, 1660-1800, Univ. Minn, 67. Add: 514 S. College St, Mt. Carroll, IL 61053.

HIRSCH, DAVID HARRY, b. Brooklyn, N.Y, Apr. 6, 30; m. 54; c. 2. ENGLISH & AMERICAN LITERATURE. B.A, N.Y. Univ, 51, M.A, 53; Ph.D.(Eng), Ohio State Univ, 61; hon. M.A, Brown Univ, 68. Instr. ENG, Ohio State Univ, 59-61; BROWN UNIV, 61-63, asst. prof, 63-68, assoc. prof, 68-72, PROF, 72- Vis. lectr, Bar-Ilan Univ, Israel, 66-67; Soc. Relig. Higher Educ. fel, 71-72. U.S.A, 51-53. MLA. Nineteenth century English and American literature; Poe; Melville; the Bible in English literature. Publ: Reality and idea in the early American novel, Mouton, The Hague, 71; John Barth's Freedom road, Mediter. Rev, spring 72; Linguistic structure and literary meaning, J. Lit. Semantics, fall 72; plus others. Add: Dept. of English, Brown University, Providence, RI 02912.

HIRSCH, E. DONALD, JR, b. Memphis, Tenn. Mar. 22, 28; m. 58; c. 3. ENGLISH LITERATURE. B.A, Cornell Univ, 50; M.A, Yale, 53, Fulbright fel, 55, Ph.D, 57. Instr. ENG, Yale, 56-60, asst. prof, 60-63, assoc. prof, 63-66; prof, UNIV. VA, 66-73, KENAN PROF, 73-, chmn. dept, 68-71. Morse fel, 60-61; Guggenheim fel, 64-65; Nat. Endowment for Humanities sr. fel, 71-72. U.S.N, 50-52. MLA; Keats-Shelley Asn. Am. Nineteenth century English and German literature; literary theory; theory of interpretation. Publ: Wordsworth and Schelling, 60, Innocence and experience: an introduction to Blake, 64 & Validity in interpretation in 67, Yale; Truth and method in interpretation, Rev. Metaphysics, 65; Literary evaluation as knowledge, Contemporary Lit, 68; Value and knowledge in the humanities, Daedalus, 71; plus others. Add: Dept. of English, Wilson Hall, University of Virginia, Charlottesville, VA 22901.

HIRSCH, KENNETH WILLIAM, Communication, Social Psychology. See 12th Edition, American Men & Women of Science, Social & Behavioral Sciences Section.

HIRSCH, LEOTA, b. Rock Island, Ill, Dec. 5, 20; m. 66; c. 2. ENGLISH. B.A, Drake Univ, 58, M.A, 59; Ph.D.(Eng), Univ. Minn, 67. Instr. ENG, Grand View Col, 59-63; Univ. Minn, 63-66; Col. St. Catherine, 64-65; asst. prof, ROSARY COL, 66-72, ASSOC. PROF, 72- Jane Arden Award, 59. MLA; Soc. Stud. South. Lit. Seventeenth century Southern literature. Add: Dept. of English, Rosary College, River Forest, IL 60305.

HIRSCH, LESTER MARTIN, b. New York, N.Y, July 5, 25; m. 49; c. 2. AMERICAN LITERATURE. B.S, City Col. New York, 48; M.A, N.Y. Univ, 49, Ph.D, 53. Asst. prof. Eng, Ala. Polytech. Inst, 53-55; Am. Int. Col, 55-59; assoc. prof. Eng. hist, WEST. NEW ENG. COL, 59-65, PROF. ENG, 65-, chmn. dept, 62-72. U.S.A, 44-46, Sgt. MLA; Col. Eng. Asn. English opinions of the American Revolution. Publ: Co-auth, Modern business communications, 63 & auth, Man and space, 66, Pitman; co-ed, All those voices, Macmillan, 71; auth, The autocrat of New England, New Eng. Galaxy, fall 71. Add: Dept. of English, Western New England College, 1215 Wilbraham Rd, Springfield, MA 01119.

HIRSCHFELD-MEDALIA, ADELINE G, b. Grand Rapids, Mich, Jan. 26, 21; m. 42; 72; c. 2. COMMUNICATION, THEATRE. B.A, Univ. Mich, 42; M.A, Wayne State Univ, 57, Ph.D.(videotape self-anal), 65. Instr. speech, Wayne State Univ, 58-65; asst. prof, OAKLAND UNIV, 66-71, ASSOC. PROF. SPEECH COMMUN, 71-, CHMN. DEPT, 72- NDEA exp. res. grant, 64-65; ESEA grant, 66-68. Speech Commun. Asn; Int. Commun. Asn. Utilization of videotape in teaching; extemporaction; semantics. Publ: Using video tape in the teaching of speech, Speech Teacher, 3/68; Extemporaction: an approach to speech education on all levels, Cent. States Speech J, spring 70. Add: Dept. of Speech Communication, 502 Vatner Hall, Oakland University, Rochester, MI 48063.

HIRSH, EDWARD L, b. Maplewood, N.J, Aug. 31, 10; m. 39; c. 6. ENGLISH LITERATURE. A.B, Yale, 32, Ph.D, 35. Instr. ENG, St. Joseph Col. (Conn), 35-39, asst. prof, 39-46; BOSTON COL, 46-48, PROF, 48- MLA. Chaucer; Milton; American literature. Publ: Henry Wadsworth Longfellow, Univ. of Minn, pamphlet ser, 63. Add: Dept. of English, Boston College, Chestnut Hill, MA 02167.

HIRSHBERG, EDGAR WALTER, b. Detroit, Mich; m. 47; c. 3. ENGLISH. A.B, Harvard Col, 38; A.B, Cambridge, 46, M.A, 51; M.A, Yale, 48, Ph.D. (Eng), 51. Instr. ENG, Ind. Univ, 46-47; N.Carolina State Univ, 50-51; Ohio Univ, 51-52; asst. prof, E.Carolina Univ, 52-55, assoc. prof, 55-60; UNIV. S.FLA, 60-67, PROF, 67- Danforth Found. fels, summers 54 & 56; Found. Econ. Educ. fel, summer 58; South. Fel. Fund. fel, summer 60; Duke Univ. Grad. Sch. fel, summer 65; Nat. Endowment for Humanities grant & proj. dir, Fla. Citizens' Comt. for Humanities, 73-74. U.S.A.A.F, 42-46. S.Atlantic Mod. Lang. Asn; Col. Eng. Asn. Nineteenth century English literature; English and American fiction. Publ: George Henry Lewes, Twayne, 70; Captain Bland on the New York stage, Bull. N.Y. Pub. Libr, 8/53; A glimpse of paradise, Humanist, 1-2/58; George Eliot and her husband, Eng. J, 9/67. Add: Dept. of English, University of South Florida, Tampa, FL 33620.

HIRTEN, WILLIAM JAMES, b. Brooklyn, N.Y, Oct. 5, 14. ENGLISH. A.B, Fordham Univ, 36; A.M. & Ph.D.(Eng), Yale, 43. Asst. instr. German, Fordham Univ, 37-38; Eng, Carnegie Inst. Technol, 43-44; Rutgers, 44-47, asst. prof, 47-53, lectr, 53-54; asst. prof, Canisius Col, 54-56; lectr. Yale, 56-58; assoc. prof. ENG, SIENA COL, 58-62, PROF, 62- Vis. fel, Princeton, 64-65. MLA; Mediaeval Acad. Am. English literature of the late Middle Ages and early Renaissance; works of Erasmus; English literature of the Victorian period. Publ: Ed, Erasmus' Complaint of peace, Scholars' Facsimiles, New York, 46; auth, introd, In: Eng. trans. Erasmus' De contemptu mundi, Scholars' Facsimiles, Gainesville, 67. Add: Dept. of English, Siena College, Londonville, NY 12211.

HISER, VELMA BISSELL, b. Anita, Iowa, July 10, 04. SPEECH. B.L, Northwest. Univ, 26, 34; A.M, State Univ. Iowa, 38. Teacher, high sch, Iowa, 32-37; instr. SPEECH, GRINNELL COL, 37-45, asst. prof, 45-55, from assoc. prof. to prof, 55-72, dir, Speech Clin, 37-72, EMER. PROF, 72- Speech Commun. Asn; Am. Speech & Hear. Asn. Iowa hand usage dextrality quotients of one hundred high school students; application of general semantics to a case of stage-fright. Add: Dept. of Communications, Grinnell College, Grinnell, IA 50112.

HISLOP, CODMAN, History, English. See Volume I, History.

HISSIGER, PAUL FREDERICK, b. New York, N.Y; m. 60; c. 5. MEDIEVAL LITERATURE. B.A, St. John's Univ.(N.Y), 63, M.A, 65; Ph.D.(medieval Eng), Univ. Pa, 69. Lectr. Eng, La Salle Col, 65-66, instr, 66-69; ASST. PROF. ENG. & WORLD LIT, MANHATTAN COL, 69- Adj. asst. prof. Eng, Queensborough Community Col, 70- MLA; Int. Arthurian Soc; Mediaeval Acad. Am; Early Eng. Text Soc. Arthurian literature; Chaucer. Publ: Using subordinate clauses, Educulture, 73; ed, Le Morte Arthur: a critical edition, Mouton, 74. Add: Dept. of English & World Literature, Manhattan College, Bronx, NY 10471.

HITCHCOCK, NED, II, b. Circleville, Ohio, Jan. 28, 41; m. 62; c. 1. THEATER, ENGLISH. B.A, West. Reserve Univ, 63, M.A, 65; M.F.A, Case West. Reserve Univ, 67, Ph.D.(theater), 73. Instr. ENG. & THEATER, COLGATE UNIV, 69-72, ASST. PROF, 72-, UNIV. THEATER DESIGNER, 69- Designer, Karamu Concert Dancers, 65-69; Portfolio Proj, 67-69. Aesthetics of theater and dance; cultural anthropology as it relates to performance; primitive thought forms. Add: Colgate University Theater, Colgate University, Hamilton, NY 13346.

HITCHCOCK, ORVILLE A, b. Hyndman, Pa, Apr. 9, 09; m. 33; c. 1. SPEECH. A.B, Pa. State Univ, 31; A.M, State Univ. Iowa, 32, Ph.D, 36. Instr. speech, Am. Univ.(D.C), 35-37; prof. & head dept, Univ. Akron, 37-43; mem. educ. serv. br, Off. War Inform. & Off. Price Admin, 43-44; mem, Town Hall, Inc, New York, N.Y, 44-46; PROF. SPEECH, UNIV. IOWA, 46-, asst. dean grad. col, 62-65. Speech Asn. Am(v.Pres, 49-51, secy, 51-54); Cent. States Speech Asn.(secy, 39-41, pres, 67). History of public address; discussion and public speaking. Publ: Contrib, Jonathan Edwards, In: History and criticism of American public address; co-auth, Ford Douglass' Fourth of July oration, 1860, In: Antislavery and disunion, 1858-1861, Harper, 63 & Views on the Army-McCarthy hearings, Quart. J. Speech. Add: 235 Jessup Hall, University of Iowa, Iowa City, IA 52240.

HITT, RALPH EUGENE, b. Savannah, Tenn, June 1, 23; m. 49; c. 3. ENGLISH. B.S, Mid. Tenn. State Col, 48; M.A, Vanderbilt Univ, 51, Ph.D, 55. Teaching fel. Eng, Vanderbilt Univ, 49-51; instr, Allegheny Col, 51-52; asst. prof, Miss. South. Col, 52-55, assoc. prof, 55-57; prof. Eng. & head div. langs. & lit, Delta State Col, 57-64; PROF. ENG. & HEAD DEPT, MISS. STATE COL. WOMEN, 64- Sig.C, U.S.A.A.F, 43-45. MLA; S-Cent. Mod. Lang. Asn; Am. Stud. Asn. Literature of Chaucer; the English 18th century literature. Publ: Chauntecleer as mock-hero of the Nun's priest's tale, 59 & Antiperfectionism as a unifying theme in Gulliver's travels, 62, Miss. Quart; Williams Ada Dallas, J. Miss. Hist, 60. Add: Dept. of English, Mississippi State College for Women, Columbus, MS 39701.

HIVELY, ROBERT WILLIAM, b. South Bend, Ind, May 31, 14. ENGLISH & AMERICAN LITERATURE. O.D, North. Ill. Col, 37; A.B, Univ. Miami, 51, M.A, 53; Duke Univ, 54; Ph.D.(Eng, ling), Univ. Fla, 58. PROF. ENG, UNIV. MIAMI, 56-, DIR. HONORS PROG. & PRIVILEGED STUD, 65-, DEAN, COL. ARTS & SCI, 72- U.S.N.R, 44-45. MLA; Col. Eng. Asn; AAUP. Add: Dept. of English, University of Miami, Coral Gables, FL 33124.

HNATKO, EUGENE, b. Cleveland, Ohio, Aug. 16, 31. LITERATURE. B.A, Bowling Green State Univ, 53, M.A, 55; Ph.D, Syracuse Univ, 62. Asst. prof. ENG, STATE UNIV. N.Y. COL. CORTLAND, 61-66, assoc. prof, 66-70, PROF, 70- Part time instr, Syracuse Univ, 55-61. MLA. Restoration and 18th century literature; style in prose. Publ: Sterne's whimsical syntax, Style, spring 69; The failure of 18th century tragedy, SEL, 70; contrib, The winged skull, Kent State Univ, 71; plus others. Add: Dept. of English, State University of New York College at Cortland, Cortland, NY 13045.

HOADLEY, FRANK M, b. Montpelier, Vt, July 18, 23; m. 46; c. 3. ENGLISH. B.A, George Peabody Col, 50, M.A, 51; Ph.D.(Eng), Univ. Okla, 55. Instr. ENG, Univ. Md, 55-59; asst. prof, La. State Univ, New Orleans, 59-65; Loyola Univ, 65-68; ASSOC. PROF, SOUTH. UNIV, NEW ORLEANS,

68- U.S.A, 43-46. Faulkner. Publ: Folk humor in the novels of William Faulkner, Tenn. Folklore Soc. Bull, 57. Add: Dept. of English, Southern University, New Orleans, LA 70126.

HOAG, GERALD BRYAN, b. Dallas, Tex, Oct. 30, 29; m. 63; c. 2. ENGLISH. A.B, Loyola Univ.(La), 51; Marquette Univ, 51-52; fel, Tulane Univ, 53-55, 57-61, M.A, 55, Ph.D.(Eng), 65. Instr. ENG, Marquette Univ, 55-57; Univ. Colo, 61-65, asst. prof, 65-67; ASSOC. PROF, WICHITA STATE UNIV, 67- MLA; NCTE; Midwest Mod. Lang. Asn; AAUP. The contemporary novel; the image of the hero and the growth of consciousness in literature. Publ: Coleridgean echos in Henry James's criticism, Univ. Colo. Stud. Lang. & Lit, 8/63; Malamud's trial: The fixer and the critics, West. Humanities Rev, 70; Henry James and the criticism of Virginia Woolf, Wichita State Univ. Bull, 8/72. Add: Dept. of English, Wichita State University, Wichita, KS 67208.

HOAGLAND, BARBARA M, b. Baton Rouge, La, Apr. 14, 35; m. ENGLISH. B.A, La. State Univ, 57; M.A, Univ. Md, 61, Ph.D.(Eng), 73. Instr. Eng, Univ. Southwest. La, 60-61; instr. Eng. & chmn. freshman Eng, St. Mary's Col. Md, 61-63; instr. Eng, McNeese State Col, 63-65; ASSOC. PROF. ENG, ST. MARY'S COL. MD, 66-, acting chmn. dept. Eng. & div. humanities, 66-67, chmn. freshman Eng, 66-69. Lectr. Eng, Va. Polytech. Inst. & State Univ, 73-74. AAUP; MLA. Medieval through 17th century prose fiction. Publ: The work of John Shirley, an early hack writer, Papers Bibliog. Soc. Am, 3rd quarter, 62; John Shirley's nonfiction: a study of a 17th century hack writer & his audience, McNeese Rev, 62. Add: P.O. Box 165 B15, Rte. 2, Hollywood, MD 20636.

HOARD, JAMES ELLSWORTH, Linguistics. See Volume III, Foreign Languages, Linguistics & Philology.

HOBBS, JOHN NELSON, b. St. Paul, Minn, Dec. 27, 40; m. 63; c. 2. ENGLISH & AMERICAN LITERATURE. A.B, Carleton Col, 62; M.A, Yale, 63, Ph.D.(Eng), 66. ASST. PROF. ENG, OBERLIN COL, 66- Midwest Mod. Lang. Asn. Contemporary American poetry; modern novel. Publ: The poet as his own interpreter, Col. Eng, 10/71; Love and time in Rossetti's The stream's secret, Victorian Poetry, winter 71; Judging contemporary poems: criteria and the editor, Iowa Rev, winter 74. Add: Dept. of English, Oberlin College, Oberlin, OH 44074.

HOBBS, ROBERT LOUIS, b. Framingham, Mass; m. 50; c. 1. THEATRE. B.A, Bates Col, 50; M.A, Univ. Wash, 54; Ph.D.(theatre), Northwest. Univ, 64. Dir. drama, Nat. Col.(Ill), 56-57; assoc. prof. theatre & chmn. dept, Barat Col. of the Sacred Heart, 59-63; vis. fac, Northwest. Univ, 63-65; assoc. prof. acting & directing & chmn. grad. directing prog, Boston Univ, 65-69; PROF. THEATRE & HEAD PROF. ACTOR TRAINING PROG, OHIO UNIV, 69- Vis. fac. & dir, Hunter Col. & Mannhardt Theatre Found, N.Y.C, 63-65; Tufts Univ, 65; founding mem, League Prof. Theatre Training Progs, 71-; artistic adminr, Nat. Endowment for Arts grants, 72-74; dir, Hobbs Studio, N.Y.C; Lake Sunapee Playhouse, N.H; guest artist, Actor's Lab, San Francisco, Calif; dir. & actor, Equity Libr. Theatre, N.Y.C; prod. & dir, Millbrook Playhouse, Mill Hall, Pa; actor, Weston Playhouse, Vt; Great Plays Co, Alta, Can; Poets Theatre, Cambridge, Mass; artistic dir, Spectator Co, N.Y.C. Distinguished teaching award, Ohio Univ, 73-74. Am. Theatre Asn.(v.chmn, theatre voice & speech proj, 70, chmn, 71-73, nat. chmn, Acting Ctr, 74). Publ: Is the liberal arts theatre obsolete?, Speech Teacher, 64; The A.R.T: primer for Lincoln Center, Theatre Annual, 66. Add: Professional Actor Training Program, School of Theatre, Ohio University, Athens, OH 45701.

HOBEN, JOHN BURTON, b. Chicago, Ill, May 30, 08; m. 35; c. 3. AMERICAN LITERATURE. A.B, Colgate Univ, 30; M.A, Univ. Mich, 31. Instr. speech, Kalamazoo Col, 34-37; COLGATE UNIV, 37-43, asst. prof. Eng. lit, 43-48, from assoc. prof. to PROF. ENG, 48-, dir. commun, 48-57. Lucius N. Littauer res. grant, 55, 60. AAUP. Mark Twain; contemporary American fiction; Ernest Hemingway. Publ: Co-auth, The American idea, Harpers, 42; auth, A pocket full of rye, 65 & A crooked stile, 70, Mid-York. Add: Dept. of English, Colgate University, Hamilton, NY 13326.

HOBGOOD, BURNET McLEAN, b. Belgian Congo, Africa, June 23, 22; U.S. citizen. DRAMA, SPEECH. A.B, Transylvania Col, 47; M.A, West. Reserve Univ, 49, M.F.A, 50; Drummond fel, Cornell Univ, 62, univ. fel, 63, Ph.D.(theatre arts), 65. Assoc. prof. drama & speech, Catawba Col, 50-57, prof, 57-64; assoc. prof. speech & theatre, SOUTH. METHODIST UNIV, 64-65, CHMN. DIV. DRAMATIC ARTS & CHMN. DEPT. THEATRE, 65-, PROF, 67- Ed, South. Theatre News; contrib, Princeton Conf. Theatre Res, 66-67; pres, Southwest Theatre Conf, 66-67; consult, Aesthet. Educ. Proj, Ohio State Univ, 68; dir. Oedipus the king, Kennedy Ctr, 72; originator & coord, Colloquium in Directing for Theatre Today, 73, 74. Sig.C, U.S.A, 42-46, T/Sgt. Am. Theatre Asn. (v.pres, 60-61, 2nd v.pres, 68, 1st v.pres, 69, pres, 70); Am. Soc. Aesthet; Am. Nat. Theatre & Acad; Southeast. Theatre Conf.(exec. secy-treas, 56-58). Aesthetics and criticism of drama and theater; curricula of the academic theater; theatre directing practice. Publ: Introduction to entertainment, Nat. Thespian Soc, 59; ed, Directory of American college theatre, Am. Educ. Theatre Asn, 60, 2nd ed, 67; The concept of experiential learning in the arts, 3/71 & Central conceptions in Stanislavski's system, 5/73, Educ. Theatre J; The development of theatre education in the U.S.A, In: Drama in education III, Pitman, U.K, 74. Add: Division of Dramatic Arts, Southern Methodist University, Dallas, TX 75275.

HOBSON, FRED COLBY, JR, b. Winston-Salem, N.C, Apr. 23, 43; m. 67; c. 1. AMERICAN LITERATURE. A.B, Univ. N.C, Chapel Hill, 65, Ph.D.(Eng), 72; M.A, Duke Univ, 67. Ed. writer, Journal & Sentinel, Winston-Salem, N.C, 69-70; ASST. PROF. ENG, Va. West. Col, 71-72; UNIV. ALA, 72- MLA; S.Atlantic Mod. Lang. Asn; Nat. Conf. Ed. Writers. Southern literature and history; modern American literature. Publ: Serpent in Eden: H.L. Mencken and the South, Univ. N.C, 74; Portrait of a black college, Commonweal, 5/68. Add: 3822 Fifth Ave, Tuscaloosa, AL 35401.

HOBSON, STANLEY PRESTON, b. Rich Mt, Ark, Feb. 1, 30. EDUCATION ADMINISTRATION, ENGLISH. B.A, Henderson State Col, 52, M.S.E, 56; Ph.D.(sch. admin. & Eng), E.Tex. State Univ, 67. Teacher, pub. schs, Ark, 51-63, prin, 63-65; fel. sch. admin, E.Tex. State Univ, 65-67; asst. prof. ENG, HENDERSON STATE COL, 67-72, ASSOC. PROF, 72- NEA; NCTE. Education; English. Publ: Homework gets A's from parents, teachers, Phi Delta Kappan, 1/66. Add: 507 N. 14th St, Arkadelphia, AR 71923.

HOCHBERG, IRVING, Audiology. See 12th Edition, American Men & Women of Science, Social & Behavioral Sciences Section.

HOCHBERGER, SIMON, b. York, Pa, Aug. 29, 12; m. 37; c. 1. JOURNALISM. B.J, Univ. Mo, 33, M.A, 35. Instr. jour. & Eng, UNIV. MIAMI, 37-41; asst. prof. jour, 41-45, assoc. prof, 45-46, prof. & chmn. dept, 47-66, PROF. MASS COMMUN, 66-, chmn. dept, 66-72. Assoc. & contrib. ed, Fla. Teacher, 37-42; ed, Alumni Record, Univ. Miami, 40-43, publicity writer, 41-42; manuscript ed, Glade House Publs, 42-45; writer & copy ed, Nashville Tennessean, 46-47, 53; vis. prof, Univ. Nev, Reno, 62, 69, 71-72, 73, summer 74. Am. Soc. Jour. Sch. Adminr.(secy-treas, 62-65); Asn. Educ. in Jour.(dep. secy-treas, 62-65); Inter-Am. Press Asn; Am. Acad. Polit. & Soc. Sci. History of journalism; law of press; mass communications and society. Publ: The student's Macbeth, Globe; Careers in photojournalism, Inst. Res, Chicago, 68; The Inter-American Press and the search for freedom, Jour. Quart; Common-law copyright, Writer's Digest. Add: Dept. of Communications, P.O. Box 8127, University of Miami, Coral Gables, FL 33124.

HOCHFIELD, GEORGE, b. Trenton, N.J, Sept. 15, 26; m. 57. ENGLISH. B.A, Univ. Calif, Berkeley, 49, M.A, 52, Ph.D.(Eng), 57; Univs. Aix Marseille & Paris, 49-50. Instr. ENG, Pa. State Univ, 55-57; Ohio State Univ, 57-61, asst. prof, 61-63; assoc. prof, STATE UNIV. N.Y. BUFFALO, 63-70, PROF, 70- Fulbright lectr, Univs. Bologna & Venice, 58-59; Univ. Ljubljana, 65-66. U.S.N, 44-46. AAUP. American literature; American transcendentalism. Publ: Ed, The great secession winter of 1860-61 and other essays of Henry Adams, Sagamore, 58; auth, Henry Adams: an introduction and interpretation, Barnes & Noble, 61; ed, Selected writings of American transcendentalists, New Am. Libr, 67. Add: Dept. of English, State University of New York at Buffalo, Buffalo, NY 14214.

HOCKEY, DOROTHY CORINNE, b. Cleveland, Ohio, June 9, 10. ENGLISH LITERATURE. A.B, West. Reserve Univ, 40, A.M, 41, Ph.D, 47. Instr. ENG, Fenn Col, 42-43; West. Reserve Univ, 43-47, asst. prof, 47-59; Univ. Akron, 59-62; assoc. prof, LAKE ERIE COL, 62-67, PROF, 67- MLA; NCTE; Shakespeare Asn. Am. Shakespeare. Publ: Note notes, forsooth, and noting, 57, Trial pattern in King Lear, 59 & A world of rhetoric in Richard II, summer 64, Shakespeare Quart. Add: Dept. of English, Lake Erie College, Painesville, OH 44077.

HOCKS, RICHARD ALLEN, b. Cincinnati, Ohio, June 30, 36; m. 57; c. 4. ENGLISH. A.B, Univ. Notre Dame, 57; Ph.D.(Eng), Univ. N.C, Chapel Hill, 67. Instr. ENG, UNIV. MO-COLUMBIA, 65-66, asst. prof, 66-71, ASSOC. PROF, 71- MLA; Midwest Mod. Lang. Asn. English and American literature. Publ: Henry James and pragmatistic thought: a study in the relationship between the philosophy of William James and the literary art of Henry James, Univ. N.C, 74; Defoe and the problem of structure, Lit. Wiss. & Unterricht, 70; Thoreau, Coleridge, and Barfield: reflections on the imagination and law of polarity, Centennial Rev, 73. Add: Dept. of English, University of Missouri-Columbia, Columbia, MO 65201.

HOCTOR, THOMAS MARION, S.S.J, b. Rochester, N.Y, May 1, 33. ENGLISH. B.A, Nazareth Col.(N.Y), 54; M.A, Cornell Univ, 55, Ph.D, 58; B.Litt, Oxford, 66. Instr. ENG, NAZARETH COL. ROCHESTER, 58-61, 63-67, assoc. prof, 67-72, PROF, V.PRES. ACAD. AFFAIRS & DEAN COL, 72- Mem, Eng. Inst; vis. prof, Russell Sage Col, 67-68. NCTE; Cath. Renascence Soc; MLA. Victorian literature; drama; literary criticism. Publ: Ed, Matthew Arnold's Essays in criticism, Univ. Chicago, 68. Add: Nazareth College of Rochester, 4245 East Ave, Rochester, NY 14610.

HODGE, FRANCIS RICHARD, b. Geneva, N.Y, Dec. 17, 15; m. 42; c. 1. DRAMA. A.B, Hobart Col, 39; A.M, Cornell Univ, 40, Ph.D, 48. Instr. Carroll Col.(Wis), 40-42; Cornell Univ, 46-48; vis. asst. prof. DRAMA, State Univ. Iowa, 48-49; from asst. prof. to PROF, UNIV. TEX, AUSTIN, 49- U.S.A.A.F, 42-45. Fel. Am. Theatre Asn.(ed, Educ. Theatre J, 66-68); Speech Commun. Asn; Am. Soc. Theatre Res; Theatre Libr. Asn. Drama and theatre production; history of the theatre. Publ: Yankee theatre, Univ. Tex, 64; Introd, Dramatic life as I found it, Blom, 66; Play directing, Prentice-Hall, 71; ed, Innovations in stage and theatre design, Am. Soc. Theatre Res, 72. Add: Dept. of Drama, University of Texas, Austin, TX 78712.

HODGES, MARGARET MOORE, b. Indianapolis, Ind, July 26, 11; m. 32; c. 3. LIBRARY SCIENCE. B.A, Vassar Col, 32; M.L.S, Carnegie Inst. Technol, 58. Librarian, Carnegie Libr. Pittsburgh, 53-64; lectr. CHILDREN'S LIT, GRAD. SCH. LIBR. & INFO. SCI, UNIV. PITTSBURGH, 64-68, asst. prof, 68-72, ASSOC. PROF, 72- Storyteller, Tell Me a Story, WQED-TV Ser, 65- Am. Libr. Asn.(mem. Newbery-Caldecott comt, 60); Am. Asn. Libr. Schs. Children's literature; folklore; history. Publ: The wave, Houghton, 64; The hatching of Joshua Cobb, 67, ed, Constellation, a Shakespeare anthology, 68, auth, Sing out, Charley!, 68, Lady Queen Anne, a biography of Queen Anne of England, 69, The making of Joshua Cobb, 71, Hopkins of the Mayflower, portrait of a dissenter, 72 & The other world, myths of the Celts, 73, Farrar, Straus; The Gorgon's head, 72, The fire bringer, 72, Persephone and the springtime, 73 & Baldur and the mistletoe, 74, Little. Add: Graduate School of Library & Information Sciences, University of Pittsburgh, 135 N. Bellefield Ave, Pittsburgh, PA 15260.

HODGES, RICHARD E, b. Los Angeles, Calif, Nov. 21, 28; m. 62; c. 2. ELEMENTARY EDUCATION. Ed.B, Ore. State Univ, 52; B.S, Ore. Col. Educ, 53, M.S, 58; Ed.D, Stanford Univ, 64. Asst. prof. ELEM. EDUC, UNIV. CHICAGO, 64-68, ASSOC. PROF, 68- Consult, Nat. Inst. Educ, 73- U.S.A, 46-47. Conf. Res. Eng.(pres, 73-74); Am. Educ. Res. Asn; Conf. Eng. Educ. (comt. prep. lang. arts for elem. teachers, 68-); NCTE(mem, comn. on reading, 71-); Int. Reading Asn.(chmn, psycholing. & reading comt, 71-73). American-English orthography; English language structure and language acquisition. Publ: Co-auth, Phonemegrapheme correspondences as aids to spelling improvement, U.S. Off. Educ, 66, Spelling: structure and strategies, 71 & co-ed, Language and learning to read: what teachers should know about language, 72, Houghton; auth, Linguistics, psychology and the teaching of English, 1/66 & The case for teaching sound-to-letter correspondences in spelling, 3/66, Elem. Sch. J; Theoretical frameworks for research in English orthography, Elem. Eng, 11/72; plus one other. Add: Graduate School of Education, University of Chicago, 5835 S. Kimbark Ave, Chicago, IL 60637.

HOENIGER, F. DAVID, b. Goerlitz, Ger, Apr. 25, 21; Can. citizen; m. 54; c. 2. ENGLISH. B.A, Univ. Toronto, 46, M.A, 48; Brit. Counc. scholar, Univ. London, 51-53, Ph.D.(Eng), 54. Lectr. ENG, Univ. Sask, 46-47; VICTORIA COL, UNIV. TORONTO, 48-51, 53-55, asst. prof, 55-61, assoc. prof, 61-63, PROF, 63-, dir. Ctr. Reformation & Renaissance Stud, 64-69. Humanities Res. Counc. Can. fel, 56-57; Folger Shakespeare Libr. fels, 59, 63; Guggenheim fel, 64-65; Can. Counc. fel, 73-74. Renaissance Soc. Am; Shakespeare Asn. Am. Shakespeare; Renaissance biology and bibliography; drama, 1500-1700. Publ: Co-ed, Representative poetry, 3 vols, Univ. Toronto, 62-63; ed, Shakespeare, Pericles, Methuen & Harvard, 63, rev. ed, 66 & Shakespeare, Henry VIII, Penguin, 66; ed, King Lear, Macmillan, Toronto, 68; co-auth, The development of natural history in Tudor England, 69 & The growth of natural history in Stuart England, from Gerard to the Royal Society, 69, 71, In: Folger Booklets, Univ. Va; gen. ed, The revels plays, Methuen, 71-; co-ed, Edward Topsell's The fowles of heaven or history of birdes, Univ. Tex, 72; auth, Irony and romance in Cymbeline, Stud. Eng. Lit, 1500-1900, spring 62; Thomas Dekker, The restoration of St. Paul's and J.P. Collier, The forger, Renaissance News, fall 63; co-auth, The Erasmus collection in the centre ... Toronto, a catalogue, Renaissance & Reformation, 71; plus one other. Add: Dept. of English, Victoria College, University of Toronto, Toronto 181, Ont, Can.

HOERR, WILLMER A, b. Johnstown, Pa, Feb. 25, 04; m. 51. ENGLISH. A.B, Washington & Jefferson Col, 25; M.A, Univ. Pittsburgh, 32. Teacher English, Garfield Jr. High Sch, Johnstown, 25-36, chmn. dept, 39-59; asst. prin, Cent. High Sch, 59-61; assoc. prof. Eng. & coord. audio-visual aids, Frederick Col, 61-68; assoc. prof. ENG, BAPTIST COL. CHARLESTON, 68-71, EMER. PROF, 71- Chmn. dept. Eng, Johnstown Jr. High Schs, 41-59; asst. prin, Garfield Jr. High Sch, 36-59; instr, Johnstown Ctr, Univ. Pittsburgh, 45. U.S.A.A.F, 42-43. The Victorian period; Gilbert and Sullivan; the detective story. Publ: The case of the curious slight, Baker Street J, 3/66 & Savoyard, 1/70; The case of the archetypical agent, Baker Street J, 3/68; The case of the sundry sources, Baker Street J, 12/72 & Abstr. Eng. Stud, 6/73; plus others. Add: 3312 S.E. 22nd Pl, Cape Coral, FL 33904.

HOEY, JOHN B, b. Manchester, N.H, June 10, 32. ENGLISH LITERATURE. B.A, Univ. N.H, 56; M.A, Univ. Nottingham, 58; Ph.D, Cambridge, 61. Instr. Eng. lit, Boston Univ, 61-63, asst. prof, 63-65; ASSOC. PROF. ENG, STATE UNIV. N.Y. COL. GENESEO, 65- U.S.N. Greek and Roman literatures; early English drama; 17th century English literature; Shakespeare. Publ: A study of Lord Herbert of Cherbury's poetry, Renaissance & Mod. Stud, 70. Add: Dept. of English, State University of New York College at Geneseo, Geneseo, NY 14454.

HOFER, ERNEST HARRISON, b. Morristown, N.J, July 10, 24. ENGLISH. B.A, Brown Univ, 46, Nat. Roster fel, 46-47, M.A, 47; Fulbright fel, Oxford, 50-52, B.Litt, 52; Ph.D.(Eng), Cornell Univ, 60. Master Eng, Taft Sch, 46-47; instr. freshman Eng, Cornell Univ, 47-50, 52-53; educ. adv, U.S. Air Force, Eng, 53-54; asst. dir. to dir, Univ. Md. Overseas Prog, Europ. div, 54-60; adminr. Ogilvy & Mather, London, 60-64; asst. prof. & asst. head dept. ENG, UNIV. MASS, AMHERST, 64-66, ASSOC. PROF. & ASSOC. HEAD DEPT, 66- Dir. summer sem, Trinity Col, Oxford, 66-73. Nineteenth century British literature; English novel; American literature. Publ: Dinner at All Souls, New Yorker, 10/53; Mid Atlantis, London Calling, 55; co-auth, 12 radio scripts, Süddutsche Rundfunk, 58, Add: Dept. of English, Bartlett Hall, University of Massachusetts, Amherst, MA 01002.

HOFFA, WILLIAM W, b. Detroit, Mich, Jan. 5. 39. ENGLISH. B.A, Univ. Mich, 61; A.M, Harvard, 62; Ph.D.(Eng), Univ. Wis, 67. Asst. prof. Eng, Vanderbilt Univ, 66-70; LIT, KIRKLAND COL, 70-74, ASSOC. PROF, 74-, DIR. AM. STUD, 70- MLA; AAUP; Am. Stud. Asn. Eighteenth and 19th century American literature. Publ: Norman Mailer in the fifties, In: The fifties, 71 & Norman Mailer in the sixties, In: The sixties, Edward Everett; Vorticist music and the Cantos: Ezra Pound and George Antheil, Am. Lit, spring 72; plus others. Add: Div. of Humanities, Kirkland College, Clinton, NY 13323.

HOFFMAN, ARNOLD R, b. Stillwater, Minn, Aug. 19, 38; m. 59; c. 2. AMERICAN LITERATURE. A.B, Univ. Kans, 63, M.A, 65; Ph.D.(Eng), Mich. State Univ, 70. Instr. ENG, ADRIAN COL, 65-68, asst. prof, 68-73, ASSOC. PROF. & HEAD DEPT, 73- Ed, Christianity & Lit, 73- MLA; NCTE; Col. Eng. Asn; Conf. Christianity & Lit; Popular Cult. Asn. Theology and literature. Publ: An element of structure in U.S.A, CEA Critic, 10/68; contrib, New dimensions in popular culture, Bowling Green Univ, 72. Add: Dept. of English, Adrian College, Adrian, MI 49221.

HOFFMAN, ARTHUR WOLF, b. Staten Island, N.Y, Mar. 13, 21; m. 49. ENGLISH LITERATURE. A.B, Wesleyan Univ, 42; A.M, Yale, 48, Ph.D, 51. Instr. ENG, Yale, 49-53; asst. prof, SYRACUSE UNIV, 53-56, assoc. prof, 56-61, PROF, 61-, CHMN. DEPT, 74-, dir. grad. stud. Eng, 71-74. Am. Counc. Learned Soc. fel, 61-62. MLA; Am. Soc. 18th Century Stud. Dryden; Pope; Congreve. Publ: John Dryden's imagery, Univ. Fla, 62; co-auth, Reading poetry, Harper, rev. ed, 68; Spenser and The rape of the lock, Philol. Quart, 70; plus others. Add: Dept. of English, Syracuse University, Syracuse, NY 13210.

HOFFMAN, C. FENNO, JR, b. Ardmore, Pa, June 24, 21; m. 47; c. 4. ENGLISH, HUMANITIES. A.B, Harvard, 43; A.M, Univ. Pa, 48, Ph.D.(Eng), 53; Oxford, 49-50. Instr. Eng, Univ, Vt, 50-54; Middlebury Col, 54-57; asst. prof. Eng. & humanities, Mass. Inst. Technol, 57-62; assoc. prof. humanities, R.I. SCH. DESIGN, 62-71, PROF. ENG, 71-, CHMN. DIV. LIB. ARTS, 69-, dir. Europ. honors prog. in Rome, 67-69. U.S.C.G.R, 43-46, Lt.(jg). MLA; Col. Eng. Asn. Sixteenth century English literature; Renaissance art and architecture; 20th century literature. Add: Dept. of English, Rhode Island School of Design, Providence, RI 02903.

HOFFMAN, DANIEL, b. New York, N.Y, Apr. 3, 23; m. 48; c. 2. ENGLISH. A.B, Columbia Col, 47; A.M, Columbia Univ, 49, fel, 51-52, Ph.D, 56. Lectr. ENG, Columbia Univ, 47-48; Rutgers Univ, 48-50; instr, Temple Univ, 50-52; Columbia Univ, 52-56; vis. prof. Am. lit. & hist, Univ. Dijon, 56-57; asst. prof. Eng. lit, Swarthmore Col, 57-60, assoc. prof. ENG, 60-65, PROF, 65-66; UNIV. PA, 66- Fel. sch. lett, Ind. Univ, 59; Am. Counc. Learned Soc. res. fels, 61-62, 66-67; Elliston lectr. poetry, Univ. Cincinnati, 64; lectr, Sixth Int. Sch. Yeats Stud, Sligo, Ireland, 65; Ingram Merrill Found. poetry grant, 71-72; chancellor, Am. Acad. Poets, 72-; Consult. poetry, Libr. of Congr, 73-74. Award, Yale Series of Younger Poets, 53; Clarke F. Ansley Award, 57; Medal excellence, Columbia Univ, 64; Award, Nat. Inst. Arts & Lett, 67. U.S.A.A.F, 44-46, Lt. MLA, PEN Club Am; Eng. Inst. Modern poetry; American literature. Publ: Paul Bunyan, last of the frontier demigods, Temple Univ, 52; An armada of thirty whales, Yale, 54; Poetry of Stephen Crane, Columbia Univ, 57; ed, American poetry and poetics, Anchor, 62; auth, Form and fable in American fiction, 61, City of satisfactions, 63, Barbarous knowledge, 67, Striking the stones, 68 & Broken laws: poems, 70 & A little geste: poems, 60, Oxford Univ; Poe Poe Poe Poe Poe Poe Poe, Doubleday, 72; The center of attention: poems, Random, 74. Add: Dept. of English, University of Pennsylvania, Philadelphia, PA 19174.

HOFFMAN, HARLAND LAMONT, b. Lyons, Kans, Jan. 19, 29; m. 61; c. 1. ENGLISH, SECONDARY EDUCATION. B.A, Ft. Hays Kans. State Col, 51, M.S, 55; Univ. Iowa, 53-54; Univ. Wyo, 57; Univ. Kans, 58; Ed.D.(Eng. educ), Univ. Nebr, Lincoln, 71. Head dept. ENG, Hoisington High Sch, 55-61; PROF, KEARNEY STATE COL, 61- U.S.M.C, 51-53, Sgt. NCTE; Conf. Eng. Educ; Conf. Col. Compos. & Commun. Responses to literature; film and literature; film and composition. Add: Dept. of English, Kearney State College, Kearney, NE 68847.

HOFFMAN, HARRY HOWARD, b. Garden City, Kans, Mar. 6, 22; m. 44; c. 3. ENGLISH, EDUCATION. A.B, Colo. State Col. Educ, 46, A.M, 47; Univ. Kans, 47-48; Ed.D, Univ. Wyo, 54. Asst. prof. Eng, Kearney State Col, 47-48, 49-53, assoc. prof, 55-56; instr, Univ. Kans, 48-49; educ, Univ. Wyo, 53-55; assoc. prof. lang. & lit, Kans. State Teachers Col, Pittsburg, 56-58; PROF. ENG. & CHMN. DIV. LANG. & LIT, KEARNEY STATE COL, 58- U.S.N, 42-45. NEA; NCTE; MLA; Col. Conf. Compos. & Commun. Communications in language arts; secondary school English teacher preparation; secondary school administration. Publ: English teaching through the years, Peabody J. Educ; A status of Nebraska English teachers, Nebr. Eng. Counselor; English teaching today. Add: Division of Language & Literature, Kearney State College, Kearney, NE 68847.

HOFFMAN, MICHAEL JEROME, b. Philadelphia, Pa, Mar. 31, 39; m. 72; c. 4. ENGLISH. A.B, Univ. Pa, 59, M.A, 60, Ph.D.(Eng), 63. Instr. ENG, Washington Col, 62-64; Univ. Pa, 64-66, asst. prof, 66-67; UNIV. CALIF, DAVIS, 67-71, ASSOC. PROF, 71- Univ. Pa. summer fac. res. grant, 67; Univ. Calif. Humanities Found. summer grants, 69, 70, 72, 73; vis. prof. Eng, Sorbonne, 72-73. U.S.A.R, 57-65. MLA; Am. Stud. Asn; Am. Lit. Group, MLA. Nineteenth and 20th century American literature; modern fiction; modernism. Publ: The development of abstractionism in the writings of Gertrude Stein, Univ. Pa, 65; The buddy system (novel), Holt, 71; The subversive vision: American romanticism in literature, Kennikat, 73; plus one other. Add: 942 Ponderosa Pl, Davis, CA 95616.

HOFFMAN, RICHARD LESTER, b. Philadelphia, Pa, Feb. 28, 37; m. 68. ENGLISH. A.B, Univ. Pa, 59; Woodrow Wilson fel, Princeton, 59-60, Danforth Found. fel, 59-63 & hon. Charles Scribner fel, 60-62, A.M, 61, Ph.D.(Eng), 64. Instr. ENG, Univ. Pa, 63-65, asst. prof, 65-68; assoc. prof, Queens Col.(N.Y), 68-71; PROF, VA. POLYTECH. INST. & STATE UNIV, 71- Mediaeval Acad. Am; MLA; Mod. Humanities Res. Asn; Early Eng. Text Soc. Chaucer; Old English; Middle English. Publ: Ovid and the Canterbury tales, Univ. Pa, 67; History of the English language: selected texts and exercises, 68 & co-auth, Companion to the roots of modern English, 72, Little; co-ed, Romantic and Victorian: studies in memory of William H. Marshall, Fairleigh Dickinson Univ, 71; auth, Guorinc astah: Beowulf 1118b, J. Eng. & Ger. Philol, 10/65; Jephthah's daughter and Chaucer's Virginia, Chaucer Rev, summer 67; The influence of the classics on Chaucer, In: A companion to Chaucer studies, Oxford, 68; plus others. Add: Dept. of English, Virginia Polytechnic Institute & State University, Blacksburg, VA 24061.

HOFFMAN, RUSSELL, b. Hackensack, N.J, Dec. 11, 27; m. 49; c. 3. ENGLISH. B.A, Univ. Calif, Berkeley, 50, M.A, 52, Ph.D.(Eng), 63. Teaching asst. Eng, Univ. Calif, Berkeley, 52-54; instr. humanities, Calif. Sch. Fine Arts, 54-56; ENG, Univ. Minn, Duluth, 57-63; asst. prof, ADELPHI UNIV, 63-70; ASSOC. PROF, 70- U.S.A, 46-47. Psychological theories influencing novelists; Emily Bronte's psychology of character. Add: Dept. of English, Adelphi University, Garden City, NY 11530.

HOFFMAN, STANTON, b. Philadelphia, Pa, Dec. 14, 34. ENGLISH LITERATURE. A.B, Temple Univ, 55; M.A, Pa. State Univ, 57, Ph.D, 62. Instr. Eng. & humanities, Univ. Chicago, 60-62; Eng, Northwest. Univ, 62-65; asst. prof. ENG. LIT, CONCORDIA UNIV, 65-72, ASSOC. PROF, 72- MLA. Medieval and grail literature; Conrad; American homosexual literature. Publ: Comedy and form in the fiction of Joseph Conrad, Mouton, The Hague, 68; The structure of the Conte del Graal, Romanic Rev, 4/61; Conrad's menagerie: animal imagery and theme, Bucknell Rev, 12/64; The hole in the bottom of the pail: comedy and theme in Heart of darkness, Stud. Short Fiction, winter 65. Add: Dept. of English, Concordia University, Montreal, P.Q, Can.

HOFFMANN, CHARLES GEORGE, b. Port Washington, Wis, Aug. 8, 21; m. 45. ENGLISH. Ph.B, Univ. Wis, 44, Ph.D.(Eng), 52; M.A, Univ. Iowa, 47. Assoc. prof. ENG, UNIV. R.I, 58-64, PROF, 64- Am. Counc. Learned Socs. grant-in-aid, 65-66. MLA. Modern American and English novel. Publ: The short novels of Henry James, Bookman Assocs, 57; Joyce Cary: the comedy of freedom, Univ. Pittsburgh, 64; Ford Madox Ford, Twayne, 67. Add: Dept. of English, University of Rhode Island, Kingston, RI 02881.

HOFFORD, JAMES LOVEDAY, b. Columbus, Ohio, Oct. 3, 28; m. 66; c. 5. SPEECH COMMUNICATIONS. B.S, Boston Univ, 52; M.A, Univ. Mich, 55; Ph.D.(speech), Syracuse Univ, 70. Ed. prom. publ, Detroit Steel Prod, Ill,

52-53; instr. speech, Univ. Toledo, 54-57; asst, Northwest. Univ, 57-58; field dir. theatre, U.S. Spec. Serv, W.Ger, 58-61; dir. pub. relat, Mass. Counc. Churches, 61-65; asst. prof. SPEECH, Boston State Col, 64-67; supvr. stud. teachers, Syracuse Univ, 67-69; ASSOC. PROF, BOSTON STATE COL, 69- Consult, Model Cities, Cohoes, N.Y, 68-72; Univ. Col. Adult Educ. Ctr, Syracuse Univ, 69-; dir, Ctr. Interpersonal Commun, Inc, Washington, N.H, 70- U.S.A, 46-48; U.S.A.F.R, 52-68, Capt. Speech Commun. Asn; Pan-Am. Soc. New Eng. Interpersonal communication; discussions and conference. Publ: A survey of radio-TV operations, U.S. Air Force Overseas Network, 61; Sidewalk America (poems), Carper, 64; Speech for the teacher in training, W.C. Brown, 67; Viva libido!, Christian Century, 2/64; The ivory tower is deserted, Publ. Auxiliary, 1/66; Report from Vietnam (5 part ser), Boston Globe, 1/66; plus many others. Add: Millen Pond Rd, Washington, NH 03280.

HOFFPAUIR, RICHARD, b. Bell, Calif, Oct. 8, 42; m. 70. ENGLISH LITERATURE. B.A, Univ. Calif, Berkeley, 65, M.A, 67; Ph.D.(Eng. lit), Univ. London, 69. ASST. PROF. ENG, UNIV. ALBERTA, 69- MLA; Can. Asn. Univ. Teachers; Keats-Shelley Asn. Am. Eighteenth century and Romantic epic poetry in England; Romantic narrative poetry; Robert Southey. Add: Dept. of English, University of Alberta, Edmonton, Alta. T6G 2G2, Can.

HOGAN, DONALD J, b. New York, N.Y, Jan. 3, 24; m. 54; c. 2. ENGLISH. B.A, Queens Col, 49; M.A, Univ. Minn, 50, Ford Found. fel, 55, Ph.D, 58; Johns Hopkins Univ, 50-52. Instr. ENG, Amherst Col, 56-58; UNIV. ILL, URBANA, 58-60, asst. prof, 60-71, ASSOC. PROF, 71- Instr, Johns Hopkins Univ, 50-52, teaching asst, 52-53; instr, Univ. Minn, 53-56, asst. dir. freshman Eng, 55-56; dir. Eng. prog, Dillard Univ, summer, 60. U.S.A, 43-45. MLA. Rhetoric; 19th century English and American literature. Add: Dept. of English, University of Illinois, Urbana, IL 61801.

HOGAN, ROBERT, b. Booneville, Mo, May 29, 30; m. 50; c. 5. ENGLISH. B.A, Univ. Mo, 53, M.A, 54, Ph.D.(Eng), 56. Instr. ENG, Univ. Mo, 54-56; Ohio Univ, 56-58; Purdue Univ, 58-59, asst. prof, 59-63; Univ. Calif, Davis, 63-66, assoc. prof, 66-68, PROF, 68-70; UNIV. DEL, 70- Guggenheim fel, 61-62; vis. prof, Univ. Rochester, 62-63; Fulbright vis. prof, Univ. Col, Dublin, 67-68; ed, J. Irish Lit, 72- U.S.A, 50-52. Anglo-Irish literature; modern drama. Publ: The experiments of Sean O'Casey, St. Martin's, 60; ed, Feathers from the green crow: Sean O'Casey, 1905-1925, Univ. Mo, 62; co-ed, Drama: the major genres, Dodd, 62; auth, Arthur Miller, In: Pamphlets on Am. Writers, 64, 2nd ed, 68, After the Irish Renaissance, 67 & ed, Seven Irish plays, 1946-1964, 67, Univ. Minn; auth, The independence of Elmer Rice, 65 & co-ed, Joseph Holloway's Abbey Theatre, 67, South. Ill. Univ; auth, Saint Jane (play), 67, Betty and the beast (play), 67, co-ed, Joseph Holloway's Irish theatre (3 vols), 68-70, auth, The fan club (play), 70 & co-ed, Lost plays of the Irish Renaissance, 70, Proscenium; co-ed, The plain style, Am. Bk. Co, 67; auth, Dion Boucicault, Twayne, 69; ed, The crows of Mephistopheles, 70 & Towards a national theatre, 70, Dolmen; auth, Eimar O'Duffy, 72 & Mervyn Wall, 72, Bucknell. Add: Dept. of English, University of Delaware, Newark, DE 19711.

HOGAN, ROBERT F, b. Oakland, Calif, Aug. 20, 27; m. 50; c. 4. ENGLISH EDUCATION. A.B, Univ. Calif, Santa Barbara, 50, M.A, Berkeley, 57. Supvr. Eng. teaching, Univ. Calif, Berkeley, 57-61; asst. dir. comn. on Eng, Col. Entrance Exam. Bd, 61-62; asst. exec. secy, NAT. COUNC. TEACHERS ENG, 62-68, EXEC. SECY, 68- Lectr. Eng, Univ. Ill, Urbana, 69- U.S.N.R, 45-46. School-college articulation; teaching of composition. Publ: Ed, Sch. edition, Koestler's Darkness at noon, 63; ed, The English language in the school program, 66 & co-auth, Obscenity, the law, and the English teacher, 66, NCTE; auth, On hunting and fishing and behaviorism, Media & Methods, 3/70; You'll like it—it's cannelloni!, Phi Delta Kappan, 4/71; For teachers of writing: some notes on the significance of prepositions, Eng. J, 2/72; plus three others. Add: National Council of Teachers of English, 1111 Kenyon Rd, Urbana, IL 61801.

HOGGARD, JAMES MARTIN, b. Wichita Falls, Tex, June 21, 41; m. 64; c. 2. ENGLISH, CREATIVE WRITING. B.A, South. Methodist Univ, 63; M.A, Univ. Kans, 65. Instr. ENG, MIDWEST. UNIV, 66-68, asst. prof, 68-72, ASSOC. PROF, 72- AAUP; S.Cent. Mod. Lang. Asn. Modern literature; tragedy and comedy. Publ: Contrib, The new breed, Prickly Pear, 73; auth, Mesquite, Southwest Rev, spring 69; But the daddy doesn't get to cry, Redbook Mag, 6/72; plus one other. Add: Dept. of English, Div. of Humanities, Midwestern University, 3400 Taft, Wichita Falls, TX 76308.

HOGREFE, PEARL, b. Holt Co, Mo. ENGLISH LITERATURE & COMPOSITION. A.B, Southwest. Col.(Kans), 10; A.M, Univ. Kans, 13; Ph.D, Univ. Chicago, 27. Instr, Iowa State Teachers Col, 21-25, prof, 25-28; prof. ENG. & head dept, La. Polytech. Inst, 28-31; assoc. prof, IOWA STATE UNIV, 31-44, PROF, 44- Folger Shakespeare Libr. fel, summer, 51, 61; Am. Asn. Univ. Women Founders fel, 52-53; Iowa State Univ. Alumni Achievement Award grant, 63, 71. Citation, Iowa State Univ, 69. MLA; Shakespeare Asn. Am; Renaissance Soc. Am; AAUP; Am. Asn. Univ. Women; Conf. Brit. Stud. Browning and Italian art and artists; artistic unity in Hamlet. Publ: The Sir Thomas More circle, Univ. Ill, 59; Process of creative writing, Harper, 3rd ed, 63; The life and times of Sir Thomas Elyot, Englishman, Iowa State Univ, 67; Legal rights of Tudor women and their circumvention by men and women, 16th Century J, 72; plus others. Add: Dept. of English, Iowa State University, Ames, IA 50010.

HOHENBERG, JOHN, b. New York, N.Y, Feb. 17, 06. JOURNALISM. B.Litt, Columbia Univ, 27; Pulitzer traveling scholar, Univ. Vienna, 28; hon. L.H.D, Wilkes Col, 71. Asst. city ed, N.Y. Evening Post, 28-33; polit. writer, N.Y. Jour. Am, 33-42; Washington, UN & for. correspondent, N.Y. Post, 46-50; PROF, GRAD. SCH. JOUR, COLUMBIA UNIV, 50- Consult, Secy. Air Force, 53-63; admin. & secy. adv. bd, Pulitzer Prizes, 54-; consult, Carnegie Endowment for Int. Peace, 56-57; U.S. Dept. State Am. specialist, Japan, Korea, Taiwan, Philippines, Hong Kong, India & Pakistan, 63-64; Counc. For. Relat. res. fel, Japan, Korea, Hong Kong, Philippines, S.Vietnam, Indonesia, Thailand, India & Pakistan, 64-65; speaker, Congr. Int. Press Inst, New Delhi, 66; discussant, Japanese-Am. Assembly, Shimoda, 67; sr. fel, East-West Ctr, Honolulu, 67; Knight Found. grant, Europe & Soviet Union, 68-69; Ford found. grant, Asia, 70-71; vis. prof. jour, Chinese Univ. Hong Kong, 70-71. U.S.A, 43-45. Counc. For. Relat; Asn. Educ. in Jour; Auth. League Am; Auth. Guild. Silurians; history of the Pulitzer Prizes. Publ: The Pulitzer Prize story, 59, Foreign correspondence: the great reporters and their times, 64, The new front page, 65 & Free press, free people—the best cause, 71, Columbia Univ; The professional journalist, 60, rev. ed, 68, 73 & the news media: a journalist looks at his profession, 68, Holt; Between two worlds: policy, press and public opinion in Asian-American relations, Praeger, 67; New era in the Pacific, Simon & Schuster, 72. Add: 702 Journalism Bldg, Columbia University, New York, NY 10027.

HOIG, STANLEY W, b. Duncan, Okla, June 24, 24; m. 53; c. 3. MODERN HISTORY. B.A, Okla. State Univ, 49; M.A, Univ. Okla, 64; Ph.D.(higher educ), 71. Teacher, Okla. State Univ, 52-53; tech. writer, Douglas Aircraft Co, 53-56; ed, Baroid Div, Nat. Lead Co, 56-64; PROF. JOUR, CENT. STATE UNIV, 64- Western America history, Cheyenne Indians; Oklahoma higher education history; western journalism history. Publ: Humor of the American cowboy, Caxton, 58, Signet, 60; The Sand Creek massacre, Univ. Okla, 61, 74, Univ. Nebr, 70; co-auth, In the shadows of Old North Tower, Cent. State Univ, 73; auth, The western odyssey of John Simpson Smith, Arthur H. Clark, 74; contrib, The bear went over the mountain, Macmillan, 64; auth, The Battle of Little Robe Creek, spring 67 & Covering the Oklahoma story, spring 68, Okla. Today; plus others. Add: Dept. of Journalism, Central State University, Edmond, OK 73034.

HOILMAN, DENNIS ROLAND, b. Denver, Colo, Dec. 13, 37; m. 66; c. 1. ENGLISH. B.A, Univ. N.Mex, 61; M.A, Univ. Utah, 64, Ph.D.(Eng), 68. Asst. ENG, Univ. Utah, 62-65, assoc, 65-66; instr. Univ. Ky, 66-67, lectr, 67-68; asst. prof, BALL STATE UNIV, 68-73, ASSOC. PROF, 73-, summer res. grant, 72. William Andrews Clark Mem. Libr. summer fel, 72. MLA; Midwest Mod. Lang. Asn; Am. Soc. 18th Century Stud; Johnson Soc. Cent. Region. Seventeenth century poetry; 18th century poetry; 18th century novel. Add: 1409 Briar Rd, Muncie, IN 47304.

HOK, RUTH CARTER, English as Foreign Language. See Volume III, Foreign Languages, Linguistics & Philology.

HOLADAY, ALLAN GIBSON, b. Grand Ledge, Mich, Jan. 16, 16; m. 45; c. 2. ENGLISH LITERATURE. A.B, Miami Univ, 38; A.M, Cornell Univ, 39; fel, George Washington Univ, 39-42, Ph.D, 43. Instr. ENG, UNIV. ILL, 42-47, asst. prof, 47-55, assoc. prof, 55-59, PROF, 59- Ed, Ill. Stud. Lang. & Lit, 71- MLA; Mod. Humanities Res. Asn, Gt. Brit; Cambridge Bibliog. Soc. English literature of the Renaissance. Publ: Ed, The rape of Lucrece, 50 & The plays of George Chapman, 70, Univ. Ill; plus others. Add: Dept. of English, 100 English Bldg, University of Illinois, Urbana, IL 61801.

HOLADAY, CLAYTON ALDRICH, b. Grand Ledge, Mich, July 20, 18; m. 44; c. 4. AMERICAN LITERATURE. A.B, Miami Univ, 41; M.A, West. Reserve Univ, 42; Ph.D, Ind. Univ, 49. Mem. fac, Ind. Univ, 42-46, 47-48; Ball State Teachers Col, 46-47; asst. prof, ENG, La. State Univ, 49-56; from asst. prof. to PROF, WEST. MICH. UNIV, 56- MLA. American novel. Publ: Kirkland's Captain of Company K, Am. Lit; A re-examination of Feathertop and RLR, New Eng. Quart; The Captain of Company K and the Twelfth Illinois Volunteers, Ill. Hist. Soc. Add: Dept. of English, Western Michigan University, Kalamazoo, MI 49001.

HOLAHAN, MICHAEL NORRIS, b. New York, N.Y, Aug. 21, 39; m. 63; c. 1. ENGLISH. B.A, Yale, 61, M.A, 63, Sterling fel, 64-65, Ph.D.(Eng), 67. Acting instr. ENG, Yale, 65-67, instr, 67-68, asst. prof, 68-73, Morse fel, 69-70; ASSOC. PROF, SOUTH. METHODIST UNIV, 73- MLA; Renaissance Soc. Am. Blanche Elizabeth MacLeish Billings Mem. Award, 67. Seventeenth century poetry, especially of Milton and Marvell; relationships of history and literature in the Renaissance; Spenser and Shakespeare. Add: Dept. of English, Southern Methodist University, Dallas, TX 75275.

HOLBEIN, WOODROW LEE, b. Gallipolis, Ohio, Jan. 1, 29; m. 56; c. 2. ENGLISH & AMERICAN LITERATURE. A.B, Baldwin-Wallace Col, 53; M.A, West. Reserve Univ, 54; Univ. S.C, 65-68. Instr. ENG, Marshall Univ, 55-56; Bethany Col, 56-57; asst. prof, THE CITADEL, 57-68, ASSOC. PROF, 68- U.S.M.C, 46-49. S.Atlantic Mod. Lang. Asn; MLA; AAUP; Shakespeare Asn. Am. Shakespeare; American stage history; Renaissance. Add: Dept. of English, The Citadel, Charleston, SC 29409.

HOLCOMB, KATHLEEN ANNE (DUGGAN), b. Ft. Huachuca, Ariz, June 22, 44; m. 69. EIGHTEENTH CENTURY ENGLISH LITERATURE. B.A, N.Mex. Highlands Univ, 64; Fulbright fel, Univ. Wurzburg, 64-65; M.A. & Woodrow Wilson fel, Tulane Univ, 66; NDEA fel, Univ. Colo, Boulder, 72, Ph.D.(Eng. lit), 72. ASST. PROF. ENG, ANGELO STATE UNIV, 71- MLA; Am. Soc. 18th Century Stud. Eighteenth century Scottish rhetorical theory; minor 18th century English satire. Add: Dept. of English, Angelo State University, San Angelo, TX 76901.

HOLCOMB, PHILLIP ANTHONY, b. Breckenridge, Tex, Feb. 10, 40; m. 69. ENGLISH LITERATURE. B.A, Univ. N.Mex, 63, M.A, 64; Ph.D.(Eng), Univ. Colo, Boulder, 71. ASST. PROF. ENG, ANGELO STATE UNIV, 70- Victorian prose; 19th century British novel; pre-Raphaelite writing and design. Add: Dept. of English, Angelo State University, San Angelo, TX 76901.

HOLDEN, EDMUND STANLEY, b. Chicago, Ill, Feb. 4, 20; m. 46; c. 2. ENGLISH. B.Ed, Chicago Teachers Col, 47; M.A, Northwest. Univ, 50, Ph.D. (18th century Eng. lit), 54. Instr. ENG, Palm Beach Jr. Col, 56-57; asst. prof, UNIV. FLA, 57-66, ASSOC. PROF, 66- U.S.A.F, 42-46, 1st Lt. MLA; S.Atlantic Mod. Lang. Asn. Eighteenth century English literature; George Crabbe. Add: Dept. of English, University of Florida, Gainesville, FL 32601.

HOLDER, ALAN, b. Brooklyn, N.Y, Sept. 19, 32. ENGLISH. A.B, Columbia Univ, 53, M.A, 55, Ph.D.(Eng), 62. Lectr. ENG, Columbia Univ, 56-57; instr, Univ. Vt, 58-60, 61-62; Univ. South. Calif, 62-63, asst. prof, 63-64; Williams Col, 64-67; HUNTER COL, 67-74, ASSOC. PROF, 74- MLA. American Literature. Publ: Three voyagers in search of Europe: a study of Henry James, Ezra Pound and T.S. Eliot, Univ. Pa, 66; Encounter in Alabama: Agee and the tenant farmer, Va. Quart. Rev, spring 66; Styron's slave: Confessions of Nat Turner, S.Atlantic Quart, spring 69; The flintlocks of the fathers: Robert Lowell's treatment of the American past, New Eng. Quart, spring 71. Add: Dept. of English, Hunter College, 695 Park Ave, New York, NY 10021.

HOLDER, GLENN, b. Oct. 9, 06; U.S. citizen; m. 34; c. 2. ENGLISH EDUCATION. A.B, DePauw Univ, 27; A.M, Ind. Univ, 35, Ed.D, 64. Dir. sec. educ, Richmond, Ind, Community Schs, 57-66; asst. prof. Eng, Ball State Univ, 66-73; WRITING, 73- Exec. secy, Midwest Eng. Conf, 66-73. Publ: Co-auth, Journeys in American literature, 58, & English on the job, I & II, 70, Globe; auth, Talking totem poles, Dodd, 73. Add: 101 N.W. 7th St, Richmond, IN 47374.

HOLDITCH, WILLIAM KENNETH, b. Ecru, Miss, Sept. 18, 33. AMERICAN LITERATURE. B.A, Southwest. at Memphis, 55; M.A, Univ. Miss, 57, South. fel. grant, 59-61, Ph.D, 61. Asst, Univ. Miss, 55-56, instr, 57-59; ENG, Christian Bros. Col.(Tenn), 61-63, asst. prof, 63-65; LA. STATE UNIV, NEW ORLEANS, 65-72, ASSOC. PROF, 72- S.Cent. Mod. Lang. Asn. Novels of Dos Passos; William Faulkner. Publ: Co-auth, Explorations of literature, La. State Univ, 67 & Westminster dictionary of Christian history, Westminster, 68; auth, Demigod and other poems, 70, Bitch (short story), 70 & Witch Dance (short story), 71, Miss. Writers; Circle (poem), Ga. Poetry Soc. Annual; plus others. Add: 732 Frenchmen St, New Orleans, LA 70116.

HOLLADAY, HOWARD PRESTON, b. El Dorado, Kans, July 30, 30; m. 64. RHETORICAL THEORY. B.S, Kans. State Col, 53, M.S, 56; Univ. Calif, Los Angeles, 59-66; Ph.D.(speech commun), Univ. South. Calif, 71. Instr. speech, Garden City Jr. Col, Kans, 52-54; Kans. State Col, 54-57; Fresno State Col, 57-59; asst. prof, Los Angeles State Col, 59-71; from assoc. prof. to PROF. SPEECH & CHMN. DEPT. SPEECH COMMUN; & DRAMA, CALIF. STATE UNIV, LOS ANGELES, 71- Lectr, Europ. Div, Univ. Md, 62-64; consult, Los Angeles City Schs, 66- Speech Commun. Asn; West. Forensic Asn.(pres, 60-61); West. Speech Commun. Asn. Intercultural communication. Add: Dept. of Speech Communication & Drama, California State University, Los Angeles, 5151 State University Dr, Los Angeles, CA 90032.

HOLLAHAN, EUGENE, b. Memphis, Tenn, Feb. 27, 33; m. 63; c. 2. ENGLISH & CONTINENTAL LITERATURE. A.B, Memphis State Univ, 59; M.A, Univ. Tenn, 61; Ph.D.(Eng), Univ. N.C, 69. Instr. ENG, N.C. State Univ, 62-69; ASST. PROF, GA. STATE UNIV, 69- U.S.N, 52-56. MLA. Novel; poetry; structuralism. Publ: Irruption of nothingness: sleep and freedom in Madame Bovary, Stud. Philol, 73; The concept of crisis, in Middlemarch, Nineteenth Century Fiction, 74. Add: Dept. of English, Georgia State University, 33 Gilmer St, Atlanta, GA 30303.

HOLLAND, CULLEN JOE, b. Blackwell, Okla, Aug. 31, 15; m. 47; c. 1. JOURNALISM. B.A, Univ. Okla, 37, M.A, 47, Ph.D.(hist), Univ. Minn, 56. Asst. press relat, UNIV. OKLA, 41-47, asst. prof. JOUR, 47-56, assoc. prof, 56-64, PROF, 64-, acting dir. Sch. Jour, 60-61, dir, 61-69. Vis. assoc. prof, Mich. State Univ, 56-57. U.S.A.A.F, 43-46, 2nd Lt. Asn. Educ. in Jour. Journalism history. Publ: Pronunciation guide to Oklahoma place names, Univ. Okla. Sch. Jour, 50. Add: 1003 Woodland Dr, Norman, OK 73069.

HOLLAND, DeWITTE T, b. Pelham, Ga, Sept. 27, 23; m. 49; c. 3. SPEECH, AMERICAN HISTORY. B.S, U.S. Merchant Marine Acad, 46; A.B, Howard Col, 49; M.A, Univ. Ala, 50; B.D, South. Baptist Theol. Sem, 53; Ph.D.(pub. address), Northwest. Univ, 56; Emory Univ, summer 65. Instr. speech, drama & Bible, Mars Hill Col, 53-54; speech & drama, Loyola Univ, 54-56; asst. prof. SPEECH, Denison Univ, 56-57; prof, La. Col, 57-59; Hardin-Simmons Univ, 59-66; asst. prof, Temple Univ, 66-71, dir, N.C.A.T.E. stud. & South. Asn. Schs. & Cols. univ. self stud, 62-64; PROF. SPEECH & CHMN. DEPT, LAMAR UNIV, 71- U.S.N.R, 44-52, Lt.(jg). Speech Commun. Asn; Cath. Homiletic Soc.(ed. bk. rev, Preaching, 68-); Christian Preaching Conf. (bk. rev. ed. & mem. bd, 68-). History of American public address; history of preaching in America; public speaking. Publ: Co-auth, Modern homiletical thought, 67, Preaching in American history, 69 & Sermons in American history, 71; co-ed. & contrib, A history of public speaking in Pennsylvania, Pa. Speech Asn, 71; ed. & contrib, America in controversy, Brown, 73; auth, Shared time, Vital speeches, 4/45; Televised debate tournaments, Forensic, 5/62; Humor in the pulpit, Today's Speech, 11/64. Add: 970 20th St, Beaumont, TX 77708.

HOLLAND, E. GRADY, b. Higden, Ark, July 22, 22; m. 56. ENGLISH. B.A, Univ. Ark, 48, M.A, 51; Coe Found. fel, Simpson Col, 61. Teacher ENG, high sch, Iowa, 53-60, Harmony Community Sch, 60-62; ASSOC. PROF, NORTHWEST. COL, 62-, DIR. REMEDIAL ENG, 64- Mem. Ark. State Commemorative Comn, 49-62. U.S.A.A.F, 42-46. Midcontinent Am. Stud. Asn. Add: Dept. of English, Northwestern College, Orange City, IA 51041.

HOLLAND, LAURENCE BEDWELL, b. Lincoln, Nebr, Oct. 21, 20; m. 50; c. 3. ENGLISH. B.A, Princeton, 42; M.A, Harvard, 50, Ph.D.(Am. civilization), 65. Teaching fel. & tutor, hist. & lit, Harvard, 46-50; from instr. & lectr. to assoc. prof. ENG, Princeton, 50-66, assoc. prof, 66-70, assoc. chmn. Am. civilization prog, 63-66, chmn, 66-70; PROF, ENG, JOHNS HOPKINS UNIV, 70- Vis. asst. prof, Haverford Col, 62-63; assoc. prof. Am. lit. Bread Loaf Sch. Eng, summers, 66-69, Robert Frost prof, 69, prof, 69-; vis. assoc. prof, Yale, 68-69; sr. res. fel, Inst. U.S. Stud, Univ. London, 69-70; mem. ed. bd, Am. Quart, 71- U.S.A.A.F, 42-46, Capt. MLA; Am. Stud. Asn; Eng. Inst. American literature and civilization. Publ: The expense of vision: essays on the craft of Henry James, Princeton, 64; co-auth, The literary heritage of New Jersey, Van Nostrand, 64; ed, Who designs America?, Anchor Bks, Doubleday, 66; co-auth, Blacks in America: bibliographical essays, Doubleday, 71; auth, Rhetoric and style in American literature. Yale Rev, spring 67. Add: 10 W. Highfield Rd, Baltimore, MD 21218.

HOLLAND, MARJORIE DILDY, b. Hope, Ark, Aug. 23, 22; m. 48; c. 1. ENGLISH EDUCATION. B.S, Univ. Ark, 45, M.S, 48, Ed.D.(Eng. educ), 63. Teacher, high sch, Tenn, 48-54, 56-59; instr. ENG, Ark. Agr. & Mech. Col, 59-61; assoc. prof, NORTHEAST. STATE COL, 63-66, PROF, 66-, acting chmn. div, commun, 71-72. MLA; Conf. Eng. Educ; NCTE. The preparation of public school teachers of English; merit pay for college teachers; honors courses in freshman English for superior students. Publ: An evaluation of an honors program in English, 65 & A study of methods of faculty evaluation, 67, Fac. Res. Bull. Add: 407 Janet, Tahlequah, OK 74464.

HOLLAND, NORMAN NORWOOD, JR, b. New York, N.Y, Sept. 19, 27; m. 54; c. 2. ENGLISH LITERATURE. S.B, Mass. Inst. Technol, 47; LL.B, Harvard, 50, Ph.D.(Eng. lit), 56. Teaching fel. & tutor, Harvard, 53-55; instr. ENG, Mass. Inst. Technol, 55-56, asst. prof, 56-62, assoc. prof, 62-66; PROF, STATE UNIV. N.Y. BUFFALO, 66-, chmn. dept, 66-68, Res. Found. fel, 68. Res. cand, Boston Psychoanal. Inst, 60-66, affiliate, 66-; mem. bd. suprv, Eng. Inst, 62-65; Old Dominion fel, 62; steering comt, Group Applied Psychoanal, 64-; joint awards counc. fel, State Univ. N.Y, 68-69; dir, Ctr. Psychol. Stud. Arts, 70-; vis. prof. Eng, Univ. Paris, 71-72; Am. Counc. Learned Soc. fel, 74-75. Shakespeare Asn. Am; MLA; Soc. Cinematologists. Literature and psychology; 17th century drama; cinema. Publ: First modern comedies, Harvard, 59; Shakespearean imagination, Macmillan, 64; Psychoanalysis and Shakespeare, McGraw, 66; The dynamics of literary response, Oxford, 68; Poems in persons, Norton, 73. Add: Dept. of English, State University of New York at Buffalo, Buffalo, NY 14214.

HOLLAND, REGINALD VALENTINE, b. Cadillac, Mich, June 4, 16; m. 41; c. 2. SPEECH, DRAMA. B.S, Northwest. Univ, 39; M.A, Mich. State Univ, 46; fel, Cornell Univ, 48-51, Ph.D, 51. Instr. speech, Mich. State Univ, 38-40, 46-48; Muskegon St. High Sch, 40-41; PROF. SPEECH & DRAMA & CHMN. DEPT, N.TEX. STATE UNIV, 51- U.S.N, 41-46, Res, 46-62. South. Speech Commun. Asn; Am. Theatre Asn; Speech Commun. Asn; Southwest Theatre Conf. Theatre; public address. Add: Dept. of Speech Communication & Drama, North Texas State University, Denton, TX 76203.

HOLLAND, T. SHANDY, JR, b. Clifton Forge, Va, Sept. 28, 27; m. 55; c. 2. DRAMATIC ART, SPEECH. A.B, Lynchburg Col, 49; George Wash. Univ, 50; M.Ed, Univ. Va, 54; Ph.D.(dramatic art), Univ. Iowa, 61. Instr, Jeter Jr. High Sch, 47-49; Falls Church High Sch, 49-50; high sch, Va, 52-53; chmn. dept. drama, Falls Church High Sch, 53-56; instr. commun. skills, Univ. Iowa, 56-58; CHMN. DEPT. SPEECH & DRAMA & CHMN. FINE ARTS DIV, CARTHAGE COL, 58- U.S.A, 50-52. Speech Asn. Am; Cent. States Speech Asn; Am. Educ. Theatre Asn; Children's Theatre Asn. Drama education; American drama; oral interpretation. Add: Dept of Speech & Drama, Carthage College, Kenosha, WI 53140.

HOLLAND, WILLIAM HOLMES, JR, b. Rosedale, Miss, June 10, 30; m. 64; c. 4. ENGLISH. B.A, Millsaps Col, 52; Univ. Miss, 55-56; dipl. Eng. Stud, Univ. Edinburgh, 57, Ph.D.(Spenser & Wordsworth), 66. Instr. Eng, Copiah-Lincoln Jr. Col, 57-58; teacher, High Sch, Miss, summer 58; instr. ENG, Kirknewton AFB, Scotland, 58-59; Southeast. La. Col, 59-62, asst. prof, 62-63; Troy State Col, 63-64; MID. TENN. STATE UNIV, 66-68, ASSOC. PROF, 68- U.S.N.R, 47-52; U.S.A, 52-55. Renaissance Soc. Am; Nat. Col. Honors Counc. Spenser and Wordsworth; John Buchan; Katherine Phillips. Publ: A proposed publication: an unpublished letter from Wordsworth to James Dyer, Eng. Lang. Notes, 2/69. Add: Box 202, Middle Tennessee State University, Murfreesboro, TN 37130.

HOLLANDER, JOHN, b. New York, N.Y, Oct. 28, 29; m. 53; c. 2. ENGLISH. A.B, Columbia Univ, 50, M.A, 52; Ph.D, Ind. Univ, 59. Lectr. ENG, Conn. Col, 57-59; instr. Yale, 59-61, asst. prof, 61-64, assoc. prof, 64-66; PROF. HUNTER COL. & GRAD. CTR, CITY UNIV. NEW YORK, 66- Jr. fel, Soc. of Fel, Harvard, 54-57; mem. Poetry Bd, Wesleyan Univ. Press, 59-62; Bollingen Poetry Transl. Prize Bd, 61-; Christian Gauss lectr, Princeton, 63; Nat. Inst. Arts & Lett. grant, 63; vis. prof, ling. inst, Ind. Univ, summer 64, fel, sch. lett; vis. prof, Salzburg Sem. in Am. civilization, summer 65; overseas fel, Churchill Col, Cambridge, 67-68; mem. Eng. Inst; sr. fel, Nat. Endowment for Humanities, 73-74. Yale Series Younger Poets Award, 58; Poetry Chap-Book Award, 61. MLA. Music and poetry; the Renaissance; romantic poetry. Publ: A crackling of thorns, Yale, 58; The untuning of the sky, Princeton, 61; Moviegoing, 62, Visions from the ramble, 65, Types of shape, 68 & The night mirror, 71, Atheneum; auth. & ed, Poems of our moment, Pegasus, 68, Modern poetry: essays in criticism, 68 & co-ed, The Oxford anthology of English literature, 73, Oxford Univ; ed, American short stories since 1945, Harper, 68; auth, Philomel, Turret, London, 69; Images of voice: sound and music in English romantic poetry, Heffer, Cambridge, 70; An entertainment for Elizabeth, ELR Monogr, Mass, 72; Town and country matters, 72 & The head of the bed, 74, Godine; Selected poems, Secker & Warburg, London, 72; co-ed, I.A. Richards: essays in his honor, Oxford, N.Y, 73; auth, Romantic verse form and the metrical contract, In: Romanticism and consciousness, Norton, 70; Wordsworth and the music of sound, In: New perspectives on Coleridge and Wordsworth, Columbia Univ, 72; Sense variously drawn out: some observations on English enjambment, In: Literary theory and structure, Yale Univ, 73; plus three others. Add: 88 Central Park W, New York, NY 10023.

HOLLATZ, EDWIN ARTHUR, b. Chicago, Ill, May 31, 30; m. 60; c. 2. SPEECH. A.B, Bob Jones Univ, 52; A.M, Northwest. Univ, 55, Ph.D. (speech), 65. Instr. SPEECH, WHEATON COL. (ILL), 54-58, asst. prof, 58-66, assoc. prof, 66-72, PROF, 72-, CHMN. DEPT. SPEECH COMMUN, 66- Spec. instr. Nat. High-Sch. Inst, 56-59; consult, Monarch Life Ins. Co, 59-60; deleg, N.Cent. Asn. Lib. Arts Workshop, 60; ed, Speech News, 62-64; consult, David C. Cook Publ. Co, 66-; Scripture Press, 67-; sr. prof, Inst. Management, Ill. Benedictine Col, 69- Speech Commun. Asn; Am. Acad. Polit. & Soc. Sci; Cent. State Speech Asn; Am. Forensic Asn. General speech; radio and television; debate. Publ: The development of literary societies in Illinois colleges, Univ. Microfilms, 65; Speech, a way of life, Wheaton Col. Bull, 56; Speech programs in Illinois junior and senior colleges, Speech News, 10/63 & 4/64; Literary societies at Wheaton College, Alumni J, 9/67. Add: Dept. of Speech Communication, Wheaton College, Wheaton, IL 60187.

HOLLENBACH, JOHN WILLIAM, b. Allentown, Pa, Feb. 10, 13. AMERICAN LITERATURE. A.B, Muhlenberg Col, 34; A.M, Columbia Univ, 35; Ph.D, Univ. Wis, 41; Univ. Chicago, 48; Univ. Minn, 49. Asst. prof. ENG, Northeast Mo. State Teachers Col, 41-45; PROF. HOPE COL, 45-, acad. v.pres, 57-65, chmn. dept. & dir. honors, 66-71. Dean undergrad. fac, Am. Univ. Cairo, 55-57; chmn. comt. lib. arts educ, N.Cent. Asn, 60-; vis. prof. cult. stud, Am. Univ. Beirut, 65-66; dir. Yugoslav-Am. Seminar, Great Lakes

Col. Asn, summer 68. Nat. Educ. Asn; MLA. Middle Eastern studies; 19th century American fiction; Mark Twain. Add: Dept. of English, Hope College, Holland, MI 49423.

HOLLERAN, JAMES V, b. Ashland, Pa, Sept. 28, 28; m. 61; c. 3. ENGLISH. A.B, St. Joseph's Col.(Pa), 55; M.A, Univ. Notre Dame, 57; Ph.D, La. State Univ, 61. Instr. Eng, Univ. Detroit, 57-58, ASST. PROF, 61-65; Renaissance, UNIV. MO-COLUMBIA, 65-72, PROF. ENG. & ASSOC. DEAN COL. ARTS & SCI, 72- MLA; Midwest Col. Eng. Asn; Renaissance Soc. Am; Midwest Mod. Lang. Asn. Shakespeare; Spenser; Sidney. Publ: Spenser's Braggadochio, La. State Univ, 62; Character transmutation in the alchemist, CLA J, 67; Pyramus-Thisbe theme in Midsummer's night dream, Calif. Eng. J, 67; A view of comedy in The faerie queen, In: Essays in honor of Esmond L. Marilla, La. State Univ, 70. Add: College of Arts and Sciences, University of Missouri-Columbia, Columbia, MO 65201.

HOLLIEN, HARRY, Experimental Phonetics, Underwater Speech Communication. See 12th Edition, American Men & Women of Science, Physical & Biological Sciences Section.

HOLLINGSWORTH, ALAN M, b. Westwood, Calif, Aug. 3, 20; m. 58; c. 2. ENGLISH. A.B, Univ. Calif, Berkeley, 48, M.A, 49, Ph.D.(Eng), 56. Instr. ENG, Ind. Univ, 54-57, asst. prof, 57-60, assoc. prof, 60-64, PROF, 65-67; MICH. STATE UNIV, 67-, CHMN. DEPT, 67- Ind. Univ. Found. res. grants, 57-58, 64-65; W.Europ. stud. grant, summer 67. Ulysses G. Weatherly Distinguished Teaching Award, 60. A.U.S, 42-45, M/Sgt. MLA; Midwest Mod. Lang. Asn.(v.pres, 68). Victorian and Edwardian literature. Publ: Last chance for English, 9/70 & Beyond literacy, 3/73, ADE Bull; plus two others. Add: Dept. of English, Michigan State University, East Lansing, MI 48823.

HOLLIS, CHARLES CARROLL, b. Needham, Mass, Oct. 27, 11; m. 36; c. 3. ENGLISH. Ph.B, Marquette Univ, 35; A.M, Univ. Wis, 37; fel, St. Louis Univ, 37-38; Ph.D.(Eng. & Am. lit), Univ. Mich, 54. Instr. Eng, Univ. Detroit, 38-43, asst. prof, 44-56, prof, 56-61, chmn. dept, 59-61; manuscript specialist Am. cult. hist, Libr. Congr, 61-63; PROF. AM. LIT, UNIV. N.C, CHAPEL HILL, 63-, CHMN. DIV. HUMANITIES, 72-, dept. Eng, 66-71. Vis. prof, Univ. Tulsa, 66-67. Am. Stud. Asn; Col. Eng. Asn; Manuscript Soc; MLA;NCTE;S.Atlantic Asn. Depts. Eng.(pres, 70-71). American literature; Walt Whitman; Orestes Brownson. Publ: Sinclair Lewis, In: Fifty years of American fiction; Huckleberry Finn, In: Great books, a Christian appraisal, Devin. Add: Dept. of English, University of North Carolina at Chapel Hill, Chapel Hill, NC 27514.

HOLLIS, JAMES R, b. Springfield, Ill, May 17, 40; m. 62; c. 2. ENGLISH. A.B, Manchester Col, 62; Ph.D.(Eng), Drew Univ, 67. Asst. prof. Eng, Manchester Col, 67-73; ASSOC. PROF. HUMANITIES; STOCKTON STATE COL, 73- MLA. Nineteenth and twentieth century English literature. Publ: Harold Pinter: the poetics of silence, South Ill. Univ, (in press); Modern life styles, Scott. Add: Dept. of English, Stockton State College, Pomona, NJ 08240.

HOLLOW, JOHN WALTER, b. McPherson, Kans, Mar. 2, 39; m. 62; c. 3. ENGLISH & AMERICAN LITERATURE. B.A, Fordham Univ, 61; M.A, Rice Univ, 63; Ph.D.(Eng), Univ. Rochester, 69. Instr. ENG, Univ. Va, 66-68; asst. prof, OHIO UNIV, 68-72, ASSOC. PROF, 72- U.S.A, 62-64, 1st Lt. MLA; William Morris Soc. & Kelmscott Fel. Nineteenth and 20th century English and American literature. Publ: William Morris's The haystack in the floods, Victorian Poetry, winter 69; William Morris and the judgment of God, PMLA, 5/71. Add: Dept. of English, Ohio University, Athens, OH 45701.

HOLLOWAY, EMORY, b. Marshall, Mo, Mar. 16, 85; m. 15; c. 2. AMERICAN LITERATURE. A.B, Hendrix Col, 06, hon. LL.D, 36; fel, Univ. Tex, 11-12, A.M, 12; grad. scholar, Columbia Univ, 13-14. Prin, High Sch, Ark, 07; prof. ENG. & head dept, Scarritt-Morrisville Col, 10-11; instr, Univ. Tex, 12-13; Adelphi Col, 14-16, asst. prof, 16-18, prof, 19-37; assoc. prof, QUEENS COL.(N.Y), 37-39, prof, 40-54, chmn. dept, 37-41, dir, Army Spec. Training Prog, 43-44, EMER. PROF, 54- Mem. fac, U.S. Army Univ. France, 19; lectr. workers univ, Int. Ladies Garment Workers Union, 24-26; assoc. ed, Am. Lit, 40-52; adv. ed, Collected writings of Walt Whitman, N.Y. Univ, 61- Pulitzer Prize, 27; Distinguished Serv. Medal, Brooklyn Col. Libr. Asn, 50. MLA. Biography, prose and poetry of Walt Whitman. Publ: Ed, The uncollected poetry and prose of Walt Whitman, 2 vols, Doubleday, N.Y, 21, Heinemann, London, 22, Peter Smith, N.Y, 32; ed, Leaves of grass, inclusive ed, 24 & abridged ed, 26, Doubleday; auth, Whitman: an interpretation in narrative, Knopf, 26; Pictures, an unpublished poem of Walt Whitman, June House, 27; Franklin Evans, or the inebriate, Random, 29; co-auth, I sit and look out, Columbia Univ, 32 & New York dissected, R.R. Wilson, 36; ed, Leaves of grass, Heritage, 36, Walt Whitman: complete poetry and selected prose and letters, Nonesuch, London, 38 & Leaves of grass, comprehensive ed, Dent, London & Dutton, N.Y, 47; auth, Free and lonesome heart, Vantage, 60; Aspects of immortality in Whitman, Kindle, 69; plus others. Add: 1013 E. 26th St, Brooklyn, NY 11210.

HOLLOWAY, MARCELLA MARIE, b. Dec. 1, 13; U.S. citizen. LITERARY CRITICISM. M.A, Univ. Mo, 43; Ph.D, Cath. Univ. Am, 47; Oxford, summer, 63. Prof. ENG. LIT, Col. St. Teresa (Mo), 47-63; MEM. FAC, FONTBONNE COL, 63- Prof, Cath. Univ. Am, summers, 48-68; mem, Int. Yeats Workshop, Sligo, Ireland, 63. Awards, Int. Clover Poetry Contest, 72 & St. Louis Poetry Ctr, 72. MLA; NCTE. Children's theater; writing, poetry and church drama. Publ: Prosodic theory of G.M. Hopkins, Cath. Univ. Am, 47; Last of the leprechauns, 52 & The little juggler, 66, Samuel French; The nun's role in The wreck of the Deutschland, Downside Rev, 7/70. Add: Dept. of English, Fontbonne College, St. Louis, MO 63105.

HOLLSTEIN, MILTON CLIFFORD, b. Salt Lake City, Utah, Sept. 6, 26; m. 48; c. 3. MASS COMMUNICATIONS. B.A, Univ. Utah, 48; M.S, Columbia Univ, 49; Ph.D.(mass commun), State Univ. Iowa, 55. Instr. jour, Univ. Utah, 51-52; State Univ. Iowa, 52-54; from asst. prof. to assoc. prof, Humboldt State Col, 54-61; from assoc. prof. to prof. & chmn. dept, UNIV. UTAH, 61-72, PROF. COMMUN, 72- Fulbright lectr, Univ. Rangoon, Burma, 60-61; Assoc. Bus. Publ. fel, summer 64; Mag. Publ. Asn. fel, 67. U.S.N, 44-46. Asn. Educ. in Jour. International communications; public opinion. Publ: Magazines in search of an audience: a guide to starting magazines, Mag. Publ. Asn, 69; chap, In: The Asian newspapers reluctant revolution, Iowa State Univ, 71. Add: 1072 Bonneville Dr, Salt Lake City, UT 84108.

HOLM, JAMES NOBLE, b. Ravenna, Ohio, Aug. 25, 09; m. 35; c. 3. SPEECH. B.S, Kent State Univ, 31; Ph.M, Univ. Wis, 37; Ph.D.(speech), West. Reserve Univ, 57. Teacher, High Schs, Ohio, 31-37; instr. SPEECH, Mont. State Univ, 37-39; KENT STATE UNIV, 39-42, asst. prof, 42-48, assoc. prof, 48-50, prof, 50-73, EMER. PROF, 73- Vis. prof, Mont. State Univ, summer 52; consult, B.F. Goodrich Co, 55-57; Ohio Bell Telephone Co, 61. Speech Commun. Asn; Cent. States Speech Asn. History of American public address; business and industrial communication. Publ: How to judge speech contests, 38, Successful discussion and debate, 14 editions, 47-60 & Tested methods of teaching speech, 62, Walch; Productive speaking for business and the professions, Allyn & Bacon, 67; A war-time approach to public speaking, Quart. J. Speech, 2/43; Human relations: a challenge to the teacher of speech, Today's Speech, 9/60; When Garfield debated Denton, Ohio Speech J, 63. Add: 7324 State Rte. 43, Kent, OH 44240.

HOLMAN, ALFRED P, b. Cincinnati, Ohio, Mar. 9, 09; m. 32; c. 2. ENGLISH. A.B, Centre Col, 30; M.A, Univ. Cincinnati, 32, Ed.D.(Eng. educ), 45; Columbia Univ, 44. From instr. to asst. prof. ENG, Buffalo State Teachers Col, 42-47; PROF, TRENTON STATE COL, 47-, chmn. dept, 47-68, mem. exec. comn, 68-73. Mem, nat. comt. int. educ, Counc. Cols. & Univs, 48-50; lectr, various cols, 50-65; chmn, Comt. Gen. Educ, N.J. Cols, 56-58; v.pres, fac. senate, Trenton State Col, 69-70. NCTE; MLA; AAUP. Modern communication; Faulkner; Japanese literature. Publ: Co-auth, Discussion manual for elementary teachers of English, NCTE Publ, 47; auth, British TV, 61 & Using the New York Times as a textbook in freshman English, 62, Eng. J. Add: 2 Brighton Rd, Trenton, NJ 08638.

HOLMAN, CLARENCE HUGH, b. Cross Anchor, S.C, Feb. 24, 14; m. 38; c. 2. AMERICAN LITERATURE. B.S, Presby. Col.(S.C), 36, A.B, 38, hon. Litt.D, 63; Ph.D, Univ. N.C, 49; hon. L.H.D, Clemson Univ, 69. Instr. Eng, Presby. Col.(S.C), 38-44, acad. dean, 44-46; asst. prof. ENG, UNIV. N.C, CHAPEL HILL, 49-52, assoc. prof, 52-56, prof, 56-59, KENAN PROF, 59-, dean grad. sch, 63-66, provost, 66-68. John Simon Guggenheim mem. fel, 67-68. MLA; S.Atlantic Mod. Lang. Asn; Am. Stud. Asn. American novel; William Gilmore Simms; Thomas Wolfe. Publ: Co-auth, Development of American literary criticism, Univ. N.C, 55; auth, Thomas Wolfe, 60 & John P. Marquand, 65, Univ. Minn; A handbook to literature, Odyssey, 60, 72; American novel through Henry James, Appleton, 66; Three modes of modern southern fiction, 66 & Roots of southern writing, 72, Univ. Ga; co-ed, Thomas Wolfe's letters to his mother, Univ. N.C, 68; auth, Thomas Wolfe, In: 15 modern American authors, Duke Univ, 68. Add: Dept. of English, University of North Carolina at Chapel Hill, Chapel Hill, NC 27514.

HOLMAN, HARRIET R, b. Anderson, S.C, Oct. 28, 12. ENGLISH. A.B, Winthrop Col, 34; A.M, Univ. Mich, 39; fel. & Ph.D.(Am. lit), Duke Univ, 48. Instr. Eng, Winthrop Col, 42-43, ref. librn, 49-52; Duke Univ, 44-49; prof. ENG. & chmn. dept, Erskine Col, 52-60; assoc. prof, CLEMSON UNIV, 60-71, PROF, 71- MLA. Add: 121 Lewis Rd. W, Clemson, SC 29631.

HOLMES, CHARLES MASON, b. North Dartmouth, Mass, Aug. 25, 23; m. 60; c. 3. ENGLISH. B.S, Cornell Univ, 44, A.B, 47; M.A, Columbia Univ, 50, Ph.D.(Eng), 59. Instr. ENG, Tufts Col, 50-52; Duke Univ, 53-55; Wash. Univ, 56-59; asst. prof, 59-60; assoc. prof, TRANSYLVANIA UNIV, 60-65; PROF, 65-, CHMN. DEPT, 71- Consult, Danforth Found, 65-67; Andrew Mellon fel, Univ. Pittsburgh, 67-68. U.S.N, 44-45. AAUP; MLA; S.Atlantic Mod. Lang. Asn; NCTE. Twentieth century interdisciplinary studies; modern British literature; 19th century literature. Publ: Aldous Huxley and the way to reality, Ind. Univ, 70; Aldous Huxley's struggle with art, West. Humanities Rev, 61; The early poetry of Aldous Huxley, Tex. Stud. Lit. & Lang, fall 66. Add: Dept. of English, Transylvania University, Lexington, KY 40508.

HOLMES, CHARLES S, b. Oberlin, Ohio, Jan. 13, 16; m. 37. ENGLISH. A.B, Oberlin Col, 38; Ph.D, Princeton, 41. Instr. ENG, POMONA COL, 41-43, asst. prof, 46-49, assoc. prof, 49-58, PROF, 58- Fulbright lectr, Graz Univ, 55-56; Univ. Vienna, 62-63; Am. Counc. Learned Soc. res. grant, 66-67. U.S.N.R, 43-45, Lt. MLA; Am. Stud. Asn; Philol. Asn. Pac. Coast. American literature; literary criticism; 17th century English poetry. Publ: Co-ed, The major critics; auth, The clocks of Columbus: the literary career of James Thurber, Atheneum, 72; A Connecticut yankee in King Arthur's court, S.Atlantic Quart, autumn 62; James Thurber and the art of fantasy, Yale Rev, fall 65; plus others. Add: Dept. of English, Pomona College, Claremont, CA 91711.

HOLMES, DORIS, b. Marshfield Hills, Mass, Mar. 1, 06. ENGLISH. A.B, Boston Univ, 27, A.M, 29, Ph.D, 31. Asst. ENG, col. lib. arts, BOSTON UNIV, 27-29, instr, col. music, 29-30, Sargent Col. Phys. Educ, 30-35, asst. prof, 35-44, assoc. prof, 44-54, COL. LIB. ARTS, 54-56, prof, 56-71, EMER. PROF, 71- Add: Dept. of English, Boston University, Boston, MA 02215.

HOLMES, EDWARD MORRIS, b. Montclair, N.J, Sept. 27, 10; m. 36; c. 3. AMERICAN LITERATURE. A.B, Dartmouth Col, 33; M.Ed, Univ. Maine, 54; M.A, Brown Univ, 56, Ph.D, 62. Instr. ENG, Farmington State Teachers Col, 54-55; UNIV. MAINE, ORONO, 56-68, PROF, 68- Vis. prof, Prince Wales Col, 68-69; state dir, NCTE Achievement Awards in Writing, 71-73. Emily Clark Balch Prize. MLA; Col. Eng. Asn. Hawthorne; Faulkner. Publ: Faulkner's Twice-told tales: his re-use of his material, Mouton, 66; Driftwood (short stories), Puckerbrush Press, 72; Drums Again, Va. Quart. Rev, summer 71 & In: Best American short stories 1972, 72; plus three others. Add: Dept. of English, 265 Stevens Hall, University of Maine at Orono, Orono, ME 04473.

HOLMES, FRANK LINCOLN DUANE, b. Pelican Rapids, Minn, Aug. 21, 91; m. 29; c. 2. SPEECH. A.B, Univ. Minn, 21; A.M, Univ. Wis, 25, Ph.D, 29. Teacher, High Sch, Minn, 21-24; instr. speech, Univ. Minn, 25-27; 28-29;

asst. prof, 29-32; lectr, Lawrence Col, 33-34; lectr. & instr. Univ. Wis, 34-35; prof. SPEECH, ILL. STATE UNIV, 35-59, head dept. & dir. div. speech educ, 35-59, EMER. PROF, 59- U.S.M.C, 17-19. Speech Commun. Asn; fel. Am Speech & Hear. Asn. Voice and voice improvement; auditory memory span; voice placement and resonance. Publ: Handbook of voice and diction; Covered wagon memories, 72. Add: 1301 W. Vista Ave, Phoenix, AZ 85021.

HOLMES, WILLIAM JAMES, JR, b. Cedar Rapids, Iowa, June 30, 27; m. 51; c. 3. ENGLISH. B.A, State Univ. Iowa, 51, Ph.D.(Eng), 62; Ohio Univ. res. grants, summers 60 & 62. Instr. Eng, State Univ. Iowa, 55-58; Ohio Univ, 58-62, asst. prof, 62-65, assoc. prof, 65-70; PRES, SIMMONS COL, 70- Dir, NDEA Inst. Eng, summer 67; fel, Am. Counc. Educ. Prog. Acad. Admin, 68-69. U.S.A.F, 45-49, Capt. MLA; NCTE. Composition and rhetoric; American literature; creative writing. Publ: Co-auth, American short fiction, 1800-1900, Scott, 69 & Survey at class sizes at freshman English programs, 60 & auth, The case for the fine arts magazine, 62, Col. Compos. & Commun. J. Add: Office of the President, Simmons College, Boston, MA 02115.

HOLS, EDITH JONES, Linguistics, Medieval English Literature. See Volume III, Foreign Languages, Linguistics & Philology.

HOLSINGER, RALPH LEE, b. Covington, Ohio, July 14, 18; m. 58; c. 1. JOURNALISM. A.B, Ohio Wesleyan Univ, 41. Reporter, Piqua Daily Call, 45-48, 50-51; admin. asst, Rep. William M. McCulloch, 48; reporter, Dayton J. Herald, 51-56, Wash. correspondent, 56-60; polit. ed, Cincinnati Enquirer, 60-61; managing ed, 61-65; assoc. prof. JOUR, IND. UNIV, BLOOMINGTON, 65-70, PROF, 70- Consult. pub. inform, Ohio-Ky-Ind. Transportation & Develop. Plan, Cincinnati, Ohio, 65-69; chmn. think tank comt, Assoc. Press Managing Ed. Asn, 67-, v.chmn. prof. standards comt, 71-72; mem. media task force, Nat. Comn. Causes & Prevention Violence, 69. Sig.C, U.S.A, 42-45. Asn. Educ. in Jour. The nature of news; freedom of the press. Publ: Reply to Cousin Alden, Bull. Am. Soc. Newspaper Ed, 4/71; Journalism...Is it a craft? an art? a skill? a calling? a trade? a job? a business? or is it a profession?, Prof. Standards, report by Assoc. Press Managing Ed. Comt, 11/72. Add: Dept. of Journalism, Indiana University, Ernie Pyle Hall, Bloomington, IN 47401.

HOLT, LEE ELBERT, b. Ann Arbor, Mich, Mar. 23, 12; m. 39; c. 2. ENGLISH. A.B, Swarthmore Col, 34; A.M, Columbia Univ, 36; Ph.D, Univ. Wis, 40. Asst. Eng, Univ. Wis, 36-40; instr, Ind. Univ, 40-42; Union Col, 42-43; physics, Williams Col, 43-45; tech. educ, underwater sound lab, U.S. Navy, 45-47; assoc. prof. ENG, AM. INT. COL, 47-49, PROF, 50- Vis. prof, Univ. Mass, 56-57. MLA; Col. Eng. Asn. Nineteenth century English literature; Samuel Butler and his Victorian critics; German use of sonic listening. Publ: Samuel Butler 1835-1902, Twayne, 64. Add: 40 Northumberland St, Springfield, MA 01109.

HOLTAN, ORLEY IVER, b. Duluth, Minn, Apr. 19, 33; m. 63. THEATRE. B.A, St. Olaf Col, 54; M.A, Univ. N.Dak, 60; Ph.D.(theatre), Univ. Minn, Minneapolis, 66. Teacher Eng. & speech, Broadview High Sch, Mont, 57-58; instr. theatre, Morehead State Col, 60-61; commun, Univ. Minn, Minneapolis, 65-67; assoc. prof. THEATRE, SLIPPERY ROCK STATE COL, 67-70, PROF, 70- Assoc. ed, Quart. J. Speech, 71-73. Med.Serv.C, U.S.A, 54-57. Speech Commun. Asn; Am. Theatre Asn. Dramatic literature; theory and criticism; theatre history. Publ: Mythic patterns in Ibsen's last plays, Univ. Minn, 70; The absurd world of Strindberg's The dance of death, Comp. Drama, 10/67; Eugene O'Neill and the death of the covenant, Quart. J. Speech, 10/70; Who's afraid of Virginia Woolf and the patterns of history, Educ. Theatre J, 3/73. Add: Dept. of Speech & Theatre, Slippery Rock State College, Slippery Rock, PA 16057.

HOLTON, SYLVIA WALLACE, b. Manchester, N.H, June 9, 36; m. 64. OLD & MIDDLE ENGLISH. B.A, Radcliffe Col, 58; M.A, Wayne State Univ, 59; Ph.D.(Eng), Yale, 63. Instr. ENG, Detroit Inst. Technol, 60-61; Hood Col, 62-63, asst. prof, 63-64; Univ. Md, 64-69; ASSOC. PROF, George Mason Col, 69-70; FED. CITY COL, 71- Vis. lectr. Eng, Univ. Skoplje, 70. MLA. Sir Orfeo; Old English dream vision; English as a foreign language. Add: Dept. of English, Federal City College, 425 Second St. N.W, Washington, DC 20001.

HOLTON, WILLIAM MILNE, b. Charlotte, N.C, Nov. 4, 31; m. 64. MODERN & AMERICAN LITERATURE. A.B, Dartmouth Col, 54; LL.B, Harvard, 57; M.A, Yale, 59, Ph.D.(Eng. lit), 65. Instr. ENG. LIT, UNIV. MD, COLLEGE PARK, 61-66, asst. prof, 66-72, ASSOC. PROF, 72- Fulbright lectr, Univ. Uppsala, 65-66; Fulbright prof, Univ. Skopje, 70. AAUP; MLA; S.Atlantic Mod. Lang. Asn. Modern poetry and fiction; American literature, 1900 to present; modern slavic literature. Publ: Co-auth, Private dealings: eight modern American writers, Almqvist & Wiksell, Stockholm, 69 & New Perspectives, 74; auth, Cylinder of vision: the fiction and journalistic writings of Stephen Crane, La. State Univ, 72; A baudelairesque thing: the directions of Hart Crane's Black tambourine, Criticism, 67; Sparrow's fall and sparrow's eye: Stephen Crane's Maggie, Stud. Neophilologica, 69; Notes on Macedonia, Contempora, 72. Add: Dept. of English, University of Maryland, College Park, MD 20742.

HOLTZ, WILLIAM VICTOR, b. Pontiac, Mich, Apr. 9, 32; m. 54; c. 3. ENGLISH. B.A, Univ. Mich, 54, Ph.D.(Eng), 64; M.A, Univ. Wash, 55. Instr. ENG, col. engineering, Univ. Mich, 59-65, asst. prof, 65-66; Univ. Calif, Santa Barbara, 66-70; ASSOC. PROF, UNIV. MO-COLUMBIA, 70- Stud. fel, Am. Counc. Learned Soc, 70-71. MLA; Brontë Soc. Eighteenth century English novel; painting and literature; literary theory and criticism. Publ: Image and immortality: a study of Tristram Shandy, Brown Univ, 70; Time's chariot and Tristram Shandy, Mich. Quart. Rev, summer 66; The journey and the picture: the art of Sterne and Hogarth, Bull. N.Y. Pub. Libr, 1/67; Field theory and literature, Centennial Rev, fall 67. Add: Dept. of English, University of Missouri-Columbia, Columbia, MO 65201.

HOLTZMAN, PAUL D, b. Los Angeles, Calif, Apr. 4, 18; m. 51; c. 1. SPEECH COMMUNICATION. B.A, La. State Univ, 41; M.A, Univ. South. Calif, 48, Ph.D.(clin. speech), 50. Instr. speech, San Francisco State Col, 48-51; Queens Col.(N.Y), 51-57; from assoc. prof. to PROF. SPEECH

COMMUN, PA. STATE UNIV, 57-, DIR, GRAD. SCH. LANG. TESTING CTR, 61- Vis. assoc. prof. speech, State Univ, N.Y. Albany, summer 56; consult, Pa. Dept. Educ, 65-68; vis. prof. speech, Univ. Hawaii, 67-68, consult, Hawaii Curriculum Ctr, 67-69. Speech Commun. Asn; Int. Commun. Asn. (ed, 71-73); Teachers Eng. to Speakers Other Lang; Asn. Teachers Eng. as Second Lang; Nat. Asn. For. Stud. Affairs; Am. Psychol. Asn. Persuasion; second language learning; testing of English language proficiency. Publ: Co-auth, Communicative speaking and listening, Holt, 68; auth, The psychology of speakers' audiences, Scott, 70. Add: Graduate School Language Testing Ctr, 305 Sparks Bldg, Pennsylvania State University, University Park, PA 16802.

HOLZBERGER, WILLIAM GEORGE, b. Chicago, Ill, Jan. 6, 32; m. 65; c. 2. ENGLISH. Ph.B, Northwest. Univ, Evanston, 60, M.A.(philos), 65, M.A. (Eng), 66, Ph.D.(Eng), 69. Asst. prof. ENG, BUCKNELL UNIV, 69-74, ASSOC. PROF, 74- Am. Philos. Soc. grant-in-aid, 70; Am. Counc. Learned Soc. grant-in-aid, 72 & 73. MLA; AAUP. American literature and intellectual history; 20th century literature. Publ: Ed, The complete poems of George Santayana: a critical edition, 74 & co-ed, Perspectives on Hamlet, 74, Bucknell Univ; co-ed, The complete letters of George Santayana, Univ. Ill, (in prep). Add: Dept. of English, Bucknell University, Lewisburg, PA 17837.

HOMAN, DELMAR C, b. Corning, Iowa, Jan. 10, 27. ENGLISH. B.A, State Univ. Iowa, 48, M.A, 49; Lydia Roberts fel, Columbia Univ, 54-56, Ph.D, 63. Instr. Eng, Red Oak High Sch. & Jr. Col, Iowa, 49-50; teacher jr. high sch, N.Mex, 52-53; instr. ENG, Iowa State Univ, 57-61; asst. prof, Bethany Col. (KANS), 61-64, assoc. prof, 64-69, PROF, 69-, HEAD DEPT. ENG. & SPEECH & CHMN. DIV. HUMANITIES, 65- Consult, Choice Mag, 64-; summer grant, Nat. Endowment for Humanities, Univ. Wis-Madison, 73. U.S.A, 50-52. Int. Arthurian Soc; NCTE; MLA; AAUP. Medieval romances; Arthurian and medieval drama. Publ: Merchant of Venice up-to-date: training ground for a President, Shakespeare Newslett, 11/65; Innovations in English at Bethany College, Bull. Kans. Asn. Teachers Eng, 2/69. Add: Dept. of English, Speech and Drama, Bethany College, Lindsborg, KS 67456.

HOMAN, SIDNEY RAMSDEN, JR, b. Philadelphia, Pa, May 21, 38; m. 60; c. 2. ENGLISH. A.B, Princeton, 60; M.A, Harvard, 62, Ph.D.(Eng), 65. Asst. prof. ENG, Univ. Ill, Urbana, 65-69; ASSOC. PROF, Boston Univ, 69-72; UNIV. FLA, 72- Vis. prof, George Washington Univ, summer 67; Nat. Endowment for Humanities award, summer 68; prog. dir. Florida's madding crowd, Nat. Endowment for Humanities & Fla. Citizens' Comt. Humanities grants, 74. MLA. Shakespeare, Renaissance and modern theatre. Publ: Ed, A midsummer night's dream, Blackfriars Shakespeare, 70; assoc. ed, Julius Caesar, S.Carolina Shakespeare, (in press); When the theatre turns to itself, New Lit. Hist, 71; The Tempest and Shakespeare's last plays: the aesthetic dimensions, Shakespeare Quart, 73; Dion, Alexander, and Demetrius—as mirrors for Julius Caesar, Shakespeare Stud, 74; plus others. Add: Dept. of English, University of Florida, Gainesville, FL 32611.

HONAKER, GERALD LEON, b. Huntington, W.Va, Sept. 5, 25; m. 51; c. 2. ENGLISH, SPEECH. A.B, Rollins Col; M.F.A, Univ. N.C, 54; Ph.D, Ind. Univ, 69. Master Eng. & drama, Asheville Sch. Boys, 53-56; instr. Eng. & speech, East. Ky. State Col, 56-61; teaching assoc. SPEECH & DRAMA, Ind. Univ, 61-64; CHMN. DEPT, CATAWBA COL, 64- U.S.A.A.F, 43-45. Am. Nat. Theatre & Acad; Southeast. Theatre Conf; Speech Commun. Asn. Dramatic art; playwriting and direction. Add: 1026 Highland Ave, Salisbury, NC 28144.

HONAN, PARK, b. Utica, N.Y, Sept. 17, 28; m. 52; c. 3. ENGLISH LITERATURE. M.A, Univ. Chicago, 51; Ph.D, Univ. London, 59. Instr. ENG, Conn. Col, 59-61, asst. prof, 61-62; Brown Univ, 62-65, assoc. prof, 65-68; from lectr. to SR. LECTR, UNIV. BIRMINGHAM, 68- Guggenheim fel, 62-63; managing ed, Novel: a forum on fiction, 67- MLA. Victorian poetry; English novel; stylistics. Publ: Browning's characters, Yale, 61; co-ed, Shelly, Dell, 62; co-auth, The book, the ring and the poet: a biography of Robert Browning, McGraw, 74; auth, 18th and 19th century English punctuation theory, Eng. Stud, 60; introd, In: Falkland, Cassell, 67. Add: Dept. of English, University of Birmingham, Birmingham B15 2TT, England.

HONE, RALPH E, b. Toledo, Ohio, July 27, 13; m. 44; c. 4. ENGLISH. A.B, Ohio State Univ, 43, A.M, 45; Penfield fel, N.Y. Univ, 47-49, Ph.D, 55. Assoc. prof. ENG, Gordon Col, 49-50, prof, 50-54; assoc. prof, Wheaton Col.(Ill), 54-56; UNIV. REDLANDS, 56-59, PROF, 59-, DEAN HUMANITIES, 73-, dir. div. lang. & lit, 60-73, dir, Redlands-in-Europe, Salzburg, Austria, 61-62. Fulbright prof, Univ. Helsinki, 65-66. MLA; Milton Soc; Renaissance Soc. Am; Philol. Asn. Pac. Coast. Edward and John Phillips, nephews and pupils of John Milton; 17th century English literature; Milton; history of drama. Publ: The voice out of the whirlwind: Job, 60 & John Milton's Samson Agonistes, 65, Chandler. Add: Dept. of English, University of Redlands, Redlands, CA 92373.

HONG, THEODORE NORMAN, b. Willmar, Minn, Mar. 15, 19; m. 53; c. 4. ENGLISH LITERATURE. B.A, St. Olaf Col, 40; Ph.D, Univ. Minn, 58. Instr. ENG, AUGUSTANA COL.(S.DAK), 47-48, 53-56, asst. prof, 56-58, assoc. prof, 58-61, PROF, 61-, acad. dean, 60-65. NCTE. Nineteenth century English literature; Newman; C.S. Lewis. Add: Dept. of English, Augustana College, Sioux Falls, SD 57102.

HONIG, EDWIN, b. New York, N.Y, Sept. 3, 19; m. 63; c. 2. ENGLISH. B.A, Univ. Wis, 41, M.A, 47; Guggenheim fel, 48-49; M.A, Brown Univ, 58. Instr. ENG, Purdue Univ, 42; Ill. Inst. Technol, 46; Univ. N.Mex, 47-48; Harvard, 49-52, Briggs-Copeland asst. prof, 52-57; assoc. prof, BROWN UNIV, 57-60, PROF, 60-, chmn. dept, 67-68. Guggenheim fel, 62; Bollingen Found.grant, 63; vis. prof, Univ. Calif, Davis, 64-65; Nat. Inst. Arts & Lett. grant, 66; Nat. Transl. Ctr. Grant, 66; grant, R.I. Comn. on Arts, 67, sr. poet, Poetry in Schs. Prog, 67-72, mem. spec. comt, Arts-in-Educ, 70-72, Arts Award Comt, 72-73; Amy Lowell traveling scholar, 68-69. Golden Rose Trophy, New Eng. Poetry Club, 61; Gov. Award for Distinction in Arts, R.I, 70. U.S.A, 43-46. Dante Soc. Am; PEN Club Am; Am. Transl. Asn; Poetry Soc. Am. Renaissance; theory of translation; theory of persona in literature and other disciplines. Publ: Dark conceit: the making of allegory, Northwest. Univ, 59, rev. ed, Oxford, 66 & Brown Univ, 72; The gazabos, 41 poems, Clarke & Way, 60; transl, Calderon, 4 plays, 61 & Calderon's Life is a dream, 70, Hill & Wang; co-auth, Mentor book of major American poets, 61 & transl, Cervantes Interludes, 64, New Am. Libr; auth, García Lorca, 63, rev. ed, Jonathan Cape, 68 & Orpheus below (verse play), In: New Directions annual, 72, New Directions; Survivals: poems, Oct. House, 65; Spring journal: poems, Wesleyan Univ, 68; Spenser, Laurel poetry ser. textbk, Dell, 68; co-auth, The major metaphysical poets of the seventeenth century, Wash. Square, 68; trans, Selected poems of Fernando Pessoa, 71 & auth, Four springs, 72, Swallow; Calderón and the seizures of honor, Harvard Univ, 72; Calisto and Melibea, Hellcoal, 72; Shake a spear with me: John Berryman, new poems, Copper Beech, 74; transl, F. Garcia Loca's Divan, Bonewhistle, 74; auth, The moral circus: poems, Contemporary Poetry, 55. Add: Dept. of English, Brown University, Providence, RI 02912.

HOOGESTRAAT, WAYNE E, b. Lennox, S.Dak, Mar. 7, 27; m. 57; c. 2. SPEECH. B.A, Sioux Falls Col, 51; M.A, Univ. S.Dak, 53; D.Ed, Pa. State Univ, 63. Grad. asst. speech, Univ. S.Dak, 51; instr. speech & drama, Idaho State Col, 53-55; grad. asst. speech, Pa. State Univ, 55; asst. prof. Eng, State Univ. N.Y. Col. Potsdam, 56; head dept. SPEECH & DRAMA, Dak. Wesleyan Univ, 56-60; assoc. prof, S.DAK. STATE UNIV, 60-68, PROF, 68-, HEAD DEPT. SPEECH, 67- Sig.C, U.S.A, 46-47. Speech Commun. Asn. Public address; speech education. Publ: Co-auth, Modern parliamentary practices, Burgess, 63; Memory: the lost canon? Quart. J. Speech, 4/60; Letters of evaluation: an exercise in speech criticism, Speech Teacher, 1/63. Add: Dept. of Speech & Drama, South Dakota State University, Brookings, SD 57006.

HOOK, FRANK SCOTT, b. Harrisonville, Mo, May 12, 22; m; c. 3. ENGLISH. A.B, Univ. Mo, 42, M.A, 47; Sterling fel, Yale, 51, Ph.D.(Eng), 52. Instr. ENG, Univ. Mo, 47-49; asst. prof, LEHIGH UNIV, 52-57, assoc. prof, 57-65, PROF, 65- U.S.A.A.F, 42-45, Sgt. NCTE; MLA; Malone Soc; Shakespeare Asn. Am. Elizabethan drama. Publ: The French Bandello; co-ed, Dramatic works of George Peele, Yale, 61 & 70. Add: 1849 Richmond Ave, Bethlehem, PA 18018.

HOOK, JULIUS N, b. Bunker Hill, Ill, Dec. 25, 13. ENGLISH. A.B, Univ. Ill, 33, A.M, 34, Ph.D, 41; Univ. Minn, 37. Teacher high sch, Ill, 34-36; assoc. prof. Eng, Minn. State Teachers Col, Mankato, 41-46; from assoc. prof. to prof. Eng. & counsel. teacher educ, UNIV. ILL, URBANA-CHAMPAIGN, 46-71, dir. Eng. curriculum stud. ctr, 64-69, EMER. PROF, 71- Coord, Proj. Eng, U.S. Off. Educ, 62-63. NCTE (exec. secy, 53-60, Distinguished Lectr. Award, 67). History of English language; teaching of high school English; modern English grammar. Publ: Teaching of high school English, 3rd ed, 65, 4th, 72 & co-auth, Modern English grammar for teachers, 70, Ronald; The story of American English, Harcourt, 72. Add: R.R. 1, Box 62, Waveland, IN 47989.

HOOKER, CHARLOTTE SCHRADER, b. Memphis, Tenn, Jan. 24, 32; m. 59; c. 1. ENGLISH, CHILDREN'S LITERATURE. B.A. & M.A, Tex. Woman's Univ, 53; fels, Tulane Univ, 53-55, Ph.D.(Eng), 59. Instr. ENG, Ga. State Col. Bus. Admin, 55-56; Arlington State Col, 56-58; La. State Univ, New Orleans, 59-60, asst. prof, 60-65; assoc. prof, LONGWOOD COL, 65-68, PROF, 68- Longwood Col. res. grant, Portugal, summer 67 & study grant, dept. cinema stud, New York Univ, 73-74. Am. Film Inst. Film aesthetics, history and criticism; English romantic poets. Publ: Dream vision in the poetry of Keats, Diss. Abstr, 60; The poet and the dreamer: a study of Keats' The fall of Hyperion, 66 & Byron's misadventures in Portugal, 71-72, McNeese Rev; Jean Vigo's A propos de Nice: documentary film and cinematic poem, (in press). Add: 1409 Lee Dr, Farmville, VA 23901.

HOOKER, KENNETH WARD, b. Niagara Falls, N.Y, Oct. 27, 08. ENGLISH. A.B, Columbia Univ, 31, A.M, 32, Ph.D, 38. Asst, Col. de Sidi-Bel-Abbes, Algeria, 32-33; instr. French & Eng, Carleton Col, 37-40, French, 40-42; from instr. to asst. prof. ENG, Univ. Rochester, 42-49; from assoc. prof. to PROF, BUCKNELL UNIV, 49-, acting chmn. dept, 68-69. Assoc. ed, Bucknell Rev, 58- MLA. Comparative literature; satire; contemporary French drama. Publ: The fortunes of Victor Hugo in England, Columbia Univ; Giraudoux's last play, Hudson Rev; Irony and absurdity, Kenyon Rev. Add: Dept. of English, Bucknell University, Lewisburg, PA 17837.

HOOPER, ALFRED GIFFORD, b. Nottingham, Eng, May 24, 07; m. 34; c. 2. ENGLISH. B.A, Leeds Univ, Eng, 29, M.A, 30, Ph.D, 32. Lectr. ENG, Univ, Witwatersrand, S.Africa, 35-37, asst. prof, 38-40, assoc. prof, 41-44; prof, & head dept, Univ. Stellenbosch, S.Africa, 45-61; PROF, LOYOLA COL. MONTREAL, 61-, chmn. dept, 65-69. Commonwealth Fund fel, Yale, 32-34; acting head dept. Eng, Potchefstroom Univ. Col, S.Africa, 2nd semester, 43; mem. Eng. lang. adv. comt, S.African Broadcasting Corp, 55-61. Eng. Asn; MLA; S.African Asn. Advan. Sci.(pres, sect. F, 47-48); Asn. Can. Univ. Teachers Eng. Sixteenth and 17th century poetry; Elizabethan and Jacobean drama; Chaucer. Publ: Co-auth, Poems for discussion, 55 & Talking of poetry, 61, Oxford; auth, Introduction to the study of language and literature, Longmans, 61; ed, Short stories from southern Africa, Oxford, 63. Add: Dept. of English, Loyola College, Sherbrooke St. W, Montreal 262, P.Q, Can.

HOOPES, NED EDWARD, b. Safford, Ariz, May 22, 32; div. BRITISH NOVEL, TEACHING SECONDARY ENGLISH. B.A, Brigham Young Univ, 56, M.A, 57; M.A, Northwest. Univ, 58, Ph.D.(Eng), 67. Instr. ENG, Hunter Col. & Hunter Col. High Sch, 63-67; ASSOC. PROF, PACE UNIV, 67- Host, C.B.S-TV Reading Room, 62-63; consult, Dell Publ. Co, 64-69. NCTE. Novel; biography; adolescent literature. Publ: Co-ed, Search for perspective, Holt, 65; co-ed, Incredible tales of Saki, 65 & Surprizes of O. Henry, 66, ed, Harte of the West, 66, Wonderful world of horses, 66 & Who am I?, 70 & auth, Ali Baba and other tales from Arabian nights, 68, Dell; co-auth, Greek gods, 66 & Heroes and monsters of Greek myth, 67, Scholastic; co-ed, Edge of awareness, Delacorte, 66; ed, Stories to enjoy, Macmillan, 67, 70. Add: Apt. 10U, 205 Third Ave, New York, NY 10003.

HOOPLE, ROBIN P, b. Syracuse, N.Y, Dec. 22, 30; m. 51; c. 4. ENGLISH, AMERICAN STUDIES. A.B, Syracuse Univ, 53, M.A, 54; Ph.D.(Am. stud), Univ. Minn, 63. Instr. ENG, S.Dak. State Col, 55-56; asst. prof, Iowa Wesleyan Col, 56-58; lectr, UNIV. MAN, 61-63, asst. prof, 63-68, ASSOC. PROF, 68-, chmn. grad. prog. eng, 72-74. Can. Coun. res. grant, summer 67 & 68-; Univ. Man. fac. grad. stud. grant, 67-68; ed, Mosaic, quarterly journal for the comparative study of literature & ideas. MLA; Can. Asn. Am. Stud. Nineteenth century American literature; origins of American Victorianism; sexual mores in 19th century American society. Publ: Chants democratic and native American: a neglected sequence in The leaves of grass, Am. Lit, 5/70; Walt Whitman and the City of Friends, Am. Transcendental Quart, spring 73. Add: Dept. of English, Argue Bldg, University of Manitoba, Winnipeg, Man, R3T 2N2, Can.

HOOVER, ANDREW GRAHAM. ENGLISH. A.B, Univ. Ky, 32; Ph.D, Yale, 39. Instr. ENG, Clark Univ, 36-39, asst. prof, 39-40; instr, OBERLIN COL, 40-48, asst. prof, 48-54, assoc. prof, 54-60, PROF, 60- The literary correspondence of Horace Walpole and Sir David Dalrymple. Add: Dept. of English, Oberlin College, Oberlin, OH 44074.

HOPFENSPERGER, JOSEPH ALLEN, b. Appleton, Wis, Sept. 2, 27. THEATRE, DRAMA. B.S, Lawrence Col, 52; Univ. Chicago, 54-55; M.A, Northwest. Univ, 60. Admin. asst. to pres, LAWRENCE UNIV, 52-54, dir. placement, 54-57, asst. prof. THEATRE & DRAMA, 61-63, ASSOC. PROF, 63-, CHMN. DEPT, 69-, TECH. DIR. & DESIGNER THEATRE, 57-, dir. radio, 56-65. Consult. design & sch. theatre planning; managing dir. summer stock company, Attic Theatre, 71- U.S.N, 45-48, Res, 48-65, Lt. U.S. Inst. Theatre Technol; Am. Theatre Asn. Educational broadcasting; theatre design; act of creation in theatre design. Add: Dept. of Theatre & Drama, Lawrence University, Appleton, WI 54911.

HOPKINS, HECTOR KENNETH, b. Bournemouth, Eng, Dec. 7, 14; m. 39; c. 1. ENGLISH. Vis. lectr. Eng, Univ. Tex, 61; writer in residence, South. Ill. Univ, 64, from assoc. prof. to prof. Eng, 65-72. Vis. prof, Winston-Salem State Col, spring 65, 66 & Colgate Univ, 66. R.A.O.C, 41-45. Powys Soc; fel. Royal Soc. Lit. U.K. English and American poetry; verse satire. Publ: Ed, Edmund Blunden: a selection, Hart-Davis, Eng. & Horizon, 50, Llewelyn Powys: a selection, Macdonald, Eng. & Horizon, 52 & H.M. Tomlinson: a selection, Hutchinson, Eng, 53; auth, Walter de la Mare, Brit. Counc, 53; The poets laureate, Bodley Head, Eng, Libr. Publ. & South. Ill. Univ, 54, rev. ed, E.P. Group, Eng. & Barnes & Noble, 73; The corruption of a poet, Barrie, Eng, 54; ed, Walter de la Mare: a selection, Faber, Eng, 56; auth, Portraits in satire, Barrie, Eng. & Barnes & Noble, 58; A trip to Texas, Macdonald, Eng, 62; English poetry: a short history, Phoenix House, Eng, South. Ill. Univ. & Lippincott, 62; ed, John Cowper Powys: poems, Macdonald, Eng. & Colgate Univ, 64 & The poetry of Railways, Frewin, Eng, 66; auth, Collected poems, 1935-1965, South. Ill. Univ, 66; The Powys brothers: a biographical appreciation, Warren House, Eng. & Fairleigh Dickinson Univ, 67; Poems English and American, Brick Row, 68; American poems and others, Rota, Eng, 70; ed, Marlow, Welsh ambassadors, Rota, Eng. & Colgate Univ, 71; Reflections on Satan Montgomery, Tex. Stud. Lit, fall 62; The second brother: a note on T.F. Powys, Rev. Eng. Lit, 1/63; E.H. Visiak: an appreciation, Aylesford Rev, summer 67; plus novels and others. Add: Warren House, Southrepps, Norwich NOR 35Y, England.

HOPKINS, JOHN EDWARD, b. Washington, D.C, Feb. 22, 43; m. 66; c. 3. SPEECH, COMMUNICATION. B.A, Marietta Col, 65; M.A, Ohio Univ, 66, Ph.D.(commun), 70. Instr. bus. commun, Ohio Univ, 67-68, speech & bus, 68-69; asst. prof. COMMUN, HOPE COL, 69-71, ASSOC. PROF. & CHMN. DEPT, 71- Consult, Donnelly Mirrors, Inc, 71-72; Herman Miller Inc, 73-; Educ. Comt. Int. Mgt. Counc, 72-; First Nat. Bank, Holland, Mich. Speech Commun. Asn; Cent. States Speech Asn. Presidential communication activities; effects of mass communication; small group decision-making. Publ: Co-ed, A bibliography of experimental studies in oral communication, N.C. Speech J, 70-73; co-auth, Who's sputtering: parents or teachers?, Sec. Educ Educ. Today, 73. Add: Dept. of Communication, Hope College, Holland, MI 49423.

HOPKINS, JON JAMES, b. Dekalb, Ill, Dec. 24, 18; m. 41; c. 3. SPEECH, COMMUNICATION. B.Ed, North. Ill. Univ, 41; M.A, Northwest. Univ, 50; Ph.D.(speech), Pa. State Univ, 61. Instr. SPEECH, Lehigh Univ, 48-51; Pa. State Univ, 51-52; asst. prof, Kent State Univ, 53-56; PROF, EAST. ILL. UNIV, 56- Commun. consult, U.S. Postal Serv, Southeast, 67; vis. prof, Univ. Ga, 67-68. U.S.A, 42-45, Sgt. Speech Commun. Asn. Persuasion; speech education; British rhetorical theory and practice. Publ: Co-auth, Successful discussion and debate, Walch, 54; auth, The national tape repository, 9/55 & The syntopicon and ideas for speeches, 11/67, Speech Teacher; William Penn and the rights of juries, Ohio Speech J, 4/65. Add: Dept. of Speech, Eastern Illinois University, Charleston, IL 61920.

HOPKINS, MARY FRANCES McKOY, b. Shreveport, La, Feb. 14, 32; m. 52; c. 2. SPEECH. B.S, La. State Univ, Baton Rouge, 52, M.A, 59, Ph.D. (speech), 68. Teacher Eng, Fair Park High Sch, 52-54; asst. prof. speech educ, LA. STATE UNIV, BATON ROUGE, 59-60, speech supvr, Lab. Sch, 62-63, instr. SPEECH, 63-65, 66-67, ASST. PROF, 68- Speech Commun. Asn.(secy. interpretation div, 72-74); South. Speech Commun. Asn. Linguistics; Russian poetry. Publ: Linguistic analysis as a tool for the oral interpreter, 9/69 & Interpreting Anglican illusions in English literature, 3/73, Speech Teacher; Russian poetry into English: linguistic analysis and poetry in translation, Speech Monogr, 3/71. Add: Dept. of Speech, Louisiana State University, Baton Rouge, LA 70803.

HOPKINS, MELVILLE, b. Loughor, Wales, June 9, 15; U.S. citizen; m. 54; c. 1. SPEECH. A.B, Bucknell Univ, 42, M.A, 46; Syracuse Univ, 47; Ph.D. (speech), Pa. State Univ, 51. Instr. SPEECH, Syracuse Univ, 47-48; Pa. State Univ, 48-51, asst. prof, 51-56; mgt. consult, Temple Univ, 56-57; assoc. prof. & chmn. dept, Marshall Univ, 57-60; PROF. & CHMN. DEPT, BLOOMSBURG STATE COL, 60- Ed, Bull. Debating Soc. Asn. Pa. Cols, 63-64. Speech Asn. Am; Am. Forensic Asn; Am. Arbit. Asn. Rhetoric and public address; argumentation; speech education. Publ: Semantics in industry, Today's Speech; plus others. Add: Dept. of Speech, Bloomsburg State College, Bloomsburg, PA 17815.

HOPKINS, ROBERT HAZEN, b. Buffalo, N.Y, Apr. 11, 30; m. 55; c. 3. ENGLISH. B.A, Kalamazoo Col, 51; M.A, Univ. Pa, 54, Ph.D, 61. Instr. ENG, Lehigh Univ, 59-60, asst. prof, 61-64; UNIV. CALIF, DAVIS, 64-68, ASSOC. PROF, 68- Founding ed, Eighteenth Century Stud, 67- U.S.A, 53-55. MLA; Am. Soc. 18th Century Stud. Eighteenth century and romantic literature;

poetic epistemology. Publ: The true genius of Oliver Goldsmith, Johns Hopkins, 69; The personation of Hobbism in Swift's Tale of a tub, Philol. Quart, 4/66; War and the pastoral design of Thomas De Quincey's English mail coach, Stud. Romanticism, spring 67; The function of the grotesque in Humphry Clinker, Huntington Lib. Quart, 69; plus others. Add: Dept. of English, University of California, Davis, Davis, CA 95616.

HOPKINS, THOMAS ALOYSIUS, b. U.S, Oct. 1, 24; m. 53; c. 1. SPEECH. B.A, Pa. State Univ, 48, M.A, 49, Ph.D.(speech), 54; summer, Northwest. Univ, 50. Instr. speech, Pa. State Univ, 49-52; asst. prof. SPEECH, CARLOW COL, 52-55, assoc. prof, 55-62, PROF, 62-, CHMN. DEPT. SPEECH, 52-, dean fac, 68. Consult, West. Pa. Speech Asn, 61-; Pa. High Sch. Speech League, 62-; Dept. Educ, Commonwealth Pa, 66-; assoc. ed, Speech Teacher, 73- U.S.A, 46-47. Speech Commun. Asn; Eastern Commun. Asn; Asn. Instnl. Res. Rhetoric; public address; debate. Publ: Rights for Americans: the speech of Robert F. Kennedy, Bobbs, 64; The speech that validated the Sherman Anti-Trust Act of 1890; Philander Chase Knox's address to the Supreme Court, Quart. J. Speech, 62; Pennsylvania's speech consultant system, Speech Teacher, 1/68; contrib, A history of public speaking in Pennsylvania, Pa. Speech Annual, 71; plus one other. Add: Dept. of Speech, Carlow College, 3333 Fifth Ave, Pittsburgh, PA 15213.

HOPKINS, VIVIAN C, b. Sept. 2, 09. ENGLISH & AMERICAN LITERATURE. B.A, Wellesley Col, 30; M.A, Univ. Mich, 31; Ph.D, 43; M.A, Radcliffe Col, 39. Teacher, Stafford Springs High Sch, Conn, 31-32; instr. Eng, Clinton High Sch, N.Y, 32-34; Russell Sage Col. & Emma Willard Sch, Troy, N.Y, 35-36; Medina Col. Ctr, N.Y, 36-37; Pine Manor Jr. Col, 37-38; asst. to dir, Hopwood Awards, Univ. Mich, 39-41; instr. Eng. & speech, STATE UNIV. N.Y. ALBANY, 41-48, asst. prof. ENG. & AM. LIT, 48-53, prof, 53-71, EMER. PROF, 71- Hopwood Award for play, Univ. Mich, 31; Am. Asn. Univ. Women fel, 48-49; Guggenheim fel, 56-57; State Univ. N.Y. Res. Found. summer fel, 60, 62; pres, Albany Gravel Co, N.Y, 72- MLA; Am. Lit. Group, Mod. Lang. Asn; Am. Stud. Asn. De Witt Clinton and the Empire state; Francis Bacon's influence on American thought: 1800-1865; the criticism of Margaret Fuller. Publ: Spires of form, a study of Emerson's aesthetic theory, 51 & Prodigal puritan, a life of Delia Bacon, 57, Harvard Univ; Margaret Fuller: American nationalist critic, Emerson Soc. Quart, 69; Emerson and the world of dream, 71 & Margaret Fuller: pioneer women's liberationist, 73, Am. Transcendental Quart; plus others. Add: 824 Second Ave, Troy, NY 12182.

HOPPE, HARRY RENO, b. Spokane, Wash, Dec. 1, 06; m. 32; c. 2. ENGLISH. B.A, Univ. Calif, 29, M.A, 30; Taussig traveling fel, 31; M.A, Kings Col, Univ. London, 33; Am. Field Serv. fel, 36; univ. fel, Cornell Univ, 39, Ph.D. (Eng), 42. Instr. ENG, Mont. State Univ, 34-35; Univ. Mo, 35-39; Cornell Univ, 40-42; from asst. prof. to prof, MICH. STATE UNIV, 42-74, EMER. PROF, 74- Belg. Am. Educ. Found. adv. fel, 46, summer, 59; Fulbright scholar, 50; Smith-Mundt vis. prof, Syrian Univ, 56; Fulbright lectr, Royal Univ. Malta & Am. Philos. Soc. res. grant, 59; Fulbright lectr, Univ. Jordan, 64- MLA; Bibliog. Soc, Eng; Soc. Theatre Res, Eng; Am. Soc. Theatre Res. Elizabethan literature; textual bibliography; history of printing. Publ: The bad quarto of Romeo and Juliet, Cornell Univ, 49; English actors in 17th century Belgium, Rev. Eng. Stud, 49, 54 & 55. Add: 6086 Abbott Rd, East Lansing, MI 48823.

HOPPER, STANLEY ROMAINE, Religion & Letters. See Volume IV, Philosophy, Religion & Law.

HOPPER, VINCENT FOSTER, b. West New York, N.J, Apr. 19, 06; m. 30, 45; c. 1. COMPARATIVE LITERATURE. A.B, Princeton, 27, A.M, 28; Ph.D, Columbia Univ, 38. Instr. GEN. LIT, N.Y. UNIV, 28-31, asst. prof, 31-41, assoc. prof, 41-47, PROF, 48-, asst. to head all-univ. dept. Eng, 64-72. Lectr, Newark, 36-39. U.S.A.A.F, 43-45. MLA; NCTE. Literature of Middle Ages and Renaissance; mediaeval number symbolism. Publ: Ed, Canterbury tales & co-auth, Essentials of European literature, Barron's; Backgrounds of European literature, Appleton. Add: Dept. of Literature, New York University, New York, NY 10003.

HORLACHER, AMOS BENJAMIN, b. Hazelton, Pa, Sept. 24, 02; m. 46; c. 3. ENGLISH LITERATURE. A.B, Wesleyan Univ, 26, D.D, 43; S.T.M, Union Theol. Sem.(N.Y), 29; M.A, Columbia Univ, 54, Ed.D, 57. Prof. Eng. lit, Dickinson Col, 47-73; RETIRED. Lindback Teaching Award, 61. Minister, Harrisburg, Pa. Unitarian Church, 54-64; trustee & chmn. comt. grants & awards, Nat. Alpha Chi Rho Educ. Found, 58-; fac. coord. self-study prog, Dickinson Col, 62-64. U.S.N, 43-47, Comdr. MLA. Comparative literature and religion. Publ: Guide to American social problems; Evaluation of counseling in the liberal arts college. Add: 681 W. Louther St, Carlisle, PA 17013.

HORN, ROBERT DEWEY, b. Traverse City, Mich, Nov. 13, 98; m. 26; c. 2. ENGLISH. A.B, Univ. Mich, 22, A.M, 24, Ph.D. 30. Teacher rhetoric, Univ. Mich, 22-25; instr. Eng, Univ. Ore, 25-28, asst. prof, 28-37, assoc. prof, 37-44, prof, 44-72; RETIRED. MLA; NCTE; Johnson Soc. Northwest. (v.pres, 67-68, pres, 68-69). Influence of English drama in Germany during the 18th century; English text-books; studies in Addison and Defoe and survey of Marlborough biography, panegyric and satire, 1689-1700. Publ: The early editions of Addison's campaign; Marlborough's first biographer, Dr. Francis Hare & Authorship of the first Blenheim panegyric, 8/61, Huntington Libr. Quart; Dickens and the patent Bramah lock, Dickensian, 66; plus others. Add: 1825 Fairmount Blvd, Eugene, OR 97403.

HORN, ROBERT LAWRENCE, b. Green Bay, Wis, Nov. 24, 37; m. 64; c. 2. ENGLISH. B.B.A, Univ. Notre Dame, 60, M.A, 63; Ph.D.(Eng), Univ. Wis, 68. Asst. prof. ENG, Col. Holy Cross, 67-68; St. Norbert Col, 68-71, assoc. prof, 71-72, chmn. dept, 68-72, dir. summer sessions, 70-72; PRES. ST. FRANCIS COL.(MAINE), 72- MLA. Nineteenth century American literature. Add: Office of the President, St. Francis College, Biddeford, ME 04005.

HORN, THOMAS DARROUGH, b. Iowa City, Iowa, June 26, 18; m. 41; c. 1. ENGLISH, EDUCATION. B.A, Univ. Iowa, 40, M.A, 46, Ph.D.(elem. educ, educ. psychol), 47; Cambridge, 45. Teacher pub. schs, Ill. & Colo, 40-43; asst. prof. & prin. ELEM. EDUC, Campus Elem. Sch, State Col. Iowa, 47-

51; assoc. prof, UNIV. TEX, AUSTIN, 51-59, PROF, 59-, chmn. dept. curriculum & instr, 62-73. Vis. prof. summers, Univ. Pittsburgh, 49, Harvard, 59 & Univ. Mich, 63; mem, elem. sect. comt, NCTE, 59-62, dir, 65-68, summer inst. teachers Span. speaking disadvantaged children, 65, 66; dir. U.S. Off. Educ. Proj, 64-65; bi-cultural sect, Col. Educ. Res. & Develop. Ctr, 65-67; San Antonio Lang. Res. Proj, 67- U.S.A, 43-46, U.S.A.F.R, 50-55, Capt. Am. Educ. Res. Asn; Asn. Teacher Educr.(pres, 57-58); Int. Reading Asn; Conf. Res. Eng.(pres, 58-59); NCTE; NEA; Nat. Soc. Stud. Educ. Language and reading; linguistically different learners. Publ: Co-auth, Spelling we use, grades 1-8, Lippincott, 59; Around the bend, 61, Above the clouds, 61 & Through the years, 61, Holt; ed, Reaching for the disadvantaged: problems of linguistically different learners, Harcourt, 70 & Research bases for oral language instruction, Nat. Counc. Teachers Eng, 71; Three methods of developing reading readiness in Spanish-speaking children in first grade, Reading Teacher, 10/66; Handwriting and spelling, Rev. Educ. Res, 4/67; Spelling, In: Encycl. Educ. Res, Macmillan, 69; plus one other. Add: Dept. of Curriculum and Instruction, University of Texas at Austin, Austin, TX 78712.

HORNBACK, BERT GERALD, b. Bowling Green, Ky, Dec. 22, 35. ENGLISH. A.B, Univ. Notre Dame, 57, A.M, 61, Ph.D.(Eng), 64; Rotary Found. fel, Trinity Col.(Dublin), 61-62. Instr. ENG, Univ. Notre Dame, 63-64; UNIV. MICH, ANN ARBOR, 64-65, ASST. PROF, 65- Horace H. Rackham Found. res. fels, 66, 71-72. MLA; Dickens Soc; Dickens Fel. Dickens and romanticism from Blake to Levi-Strauss; contemporary poetry; Irish theatre. Publ: Scenes from The dynasts by Thomas Hardy (prod. script), Univ. Mich, 68; The metaphor of chance: vision and technique in the works of Thomas Hardy, 71 & Noah's Arkitecture: a study of Dicken's mythology, 72, Ohio Univ; King Richard the catsup, Porridge, 72; Thoughts for food: minor meditations for campers, Am. Youth Found; 72; The moral imagination of George Eliot, Papers Lang. & Lit, 72; Five new Dickens letters, Mich. Quart. Rev, 72; plus three others. Add: Dept. of English, University of Michigan, 1601 Haven Hall, Ann Arbor, MI 48104.

HORNBACK, VERNON T, JR, b. Bowling Green, Ky, Oct. 3, 31; m. 62; c. 2. ENGLISH. B.S, St. Louis Univ, 53, M.A, 55, Ph.D.(Eng), 63. Instr. ENG, South. Ill. Univ, 59-63, asst. prof, 63-64; CALIF. STATE UNIV, SACRAMENTO, 64-68, assoc. prof, 68-72, PROF, 72-, CHMN. DEPT, 69- Pres. Eng. Counc, Calif. State Univs & Cols, 71-73. MLA; Asn. Depts. Eng; NCTE. Modern and contemporary American literature; history of ideas; modern British literature. Publ: The uses of time in Faulkner's The sound and the fury, Papers on Lang. & Lit, winter 65; Evaluations and open files in the California State Colleges, 5/71 & On building an effective regional professional association, 9173, Asn. Depts. Eng. Bull. Add: Dept. of English, California State University, Sacramento, 6000 Jay St, Sacramento, CA 95819.

HORNBERGER, THEODORE, b. Northville, Mich, Jan. 13, 06; m. 29; c. 2. AMERICAN LITERATURE. B.S, Univ. Mich, 27, Inglis for. fel, Univ. London, 27-28, A.M, 29, Ph.D, 34. Instr. ENG, Univ. Mich, 28-36, asst. prof, 36-37; prof, Univ. Tex, 37-46; Univ. Minn, 46-60, chmn. dept, 50-58; prof, UNIV. PA, 60-68, JOHN WELSH CENTENNIAL PROF. HIST. & ENG. LIT, 68-, grad. chmn. Eng, 65-67, acting chmn. dept, 68-69. Res. fel, Huntington Libr, Calif, 36-37; vis. lectr. Univ. Brazil, 52; Guggenheim fel, 67-68; Thord-Gray vis. lectr. Am. lit, Am-Scand. Found, Uppsala Univ, fall 73. MLA; Hist. Sci. Soc; NCTE; Am. Stud. Asn. Puritanism and science. Publ: Benjamin Franklin, Univ. Minn, 62; Scientific thought in the American colleges, 1638-1800, Univ. Tex; ed, Compendium Physicae, Publ. Colonial Soc. Mass. Add: Dept. of English, University of Pennsylvania, Philadelphia, PA 19104.

HORNBY, RICHARD, b. Paterson, N.J, Oct. 25, 38; m. 61; c. 2. DRAMA. B.S, Mass. Inst. Technol, 62; M.A, Tulane Univ, 65, Ph.D.(theatre), 66. Asst. prof. Eng. & dir. dramatics, Bowdoin Col, 66-70; theater, Univ. B.C, 70-71; ASSOC. PROF DRAMA, UNIV. CALGARY, 71- Mem. staff, Tulane Drama Rev, 63-66; vis. dir, Harvard Summer Players, 68. Am. Theatre Asn; Univ. & Col. Theatre Asn. Dramatic literature and criticism; directing. Publ: The symbolic action of Heartbreak house, Drama Surv, winter 68-69; Brecht versus Aristotle, Drama at Calgary, 3/69; Dramatic criticism and the contemporary theatre, Educ. Theatre J, 3/72. Add: Dept. of Drama, University of Calgary, Calgary, Alta, Can.

HORNE, ELINOR CLARK, Linguistics. See Volume III, Foreign Languages, Linguistics & Philology.

HORNE, LEWIS BENJAMIN, b. Mesa, Ariz, Apr. 14, 32; m. 60; c. 4. ENGLISH. B.A, Ariz. State Univ, 54; M.A, Univ. Mich, 60, Ph.D.(Eng), 66. ASST. PROF. ENG, Colo. Col, 66-71; UNIV. SASK, 71- U.S.A, 54-56. MLA. Nineteenth century literature; Thomas Hardy; contemporary poetry. Publ: The darkening sun of Tess Durbeyfield, Tex. Stud. Lit. & Lang, 71; The art of renunciation in Hardy's novels, Stud. Novel, 72. Add: Dept. of English, University of Saskatchewan, Saskatoon, Sask. S7N 0W0, Can.

HORNER, JOYCE MARY, b. Lofthouse, Eng. ENGLISH. B.A, Oxford, 26; A.M, Smith Col, 28. Mem. fac, Hood Col, 30-43; from assoc. prof. to prof. ENG, MT. HOLYOKE COL, 43-69, EMER. PROF, 69- Prize, Doubleday, Inc. & Curtis Brown, Ltd, 43. Novels; poems; articles. Add: Dept. of English, Mt. Holyoke College, South Hadley, MA 01075.

HORNSTEIN, LILLIAN HERLANDS, b. Brooklyn, N.Y, Mar. 20, 09; m. 35. ENGLISH LITERATURE. B.S, N.Y. Univ, 29, scholar, 29-30, A.M, 30, Ph.D, 40. From instr. to assoc. prof. ENG, WASH. SQ. COL, N.Y. UNIV, 30-59, PROF, GRAD. SCH. ARTS & SCI, 59- Congressional cert. merit, 45; N.Y. Univ. Great Teacher Award, 70. Emer. dir, N.Y. Univ. Alumni Fed, 73-; pres, Acad. Lit. Stud, Johns Hopkins Univ, 74. MLA; Mediaeval Acad. Am; Renaissance Soc. Am; Mod. Humanities Res. Asn. Medieval romance; folklore; Chaucer and Boccaccio. Publ: Reader's companion to world literature, Holt, Mentor, 56, 2nd ed, 73; Analysis of imagery: a critique of literary method, 42, King Robert of Sicily: a new manuscript, 12/63 & King Robert of Sicily: analogues and origins, 3/64, PMLA. Add: 37 Washington Square W, New York, NY 10011.

HOROWITZ, FLOYD R, b. New York, N.Y, Mar. 13, 30; m. 53; c. 2. ENGLISH, COMPUTER APPLICATION. B.A, Adelphi Col, 51; M.F.A, Univ. Iowa, 56, Ph.D.(Eng. & Am. lit), 60. Instr. Eng, South. Ore. Col, 59-61; UNIV. KANS, 61-63, asst. prof, 63-67, assoc. prof. & res. assoc. computation ctr, 67-72, PROF. ENG. & COMPUT. SCI. & CHMN. DEPT. COMPUT. SCI, 73- Chmn. conf. computing applications in humanities, MLA, 66; Summerfield res. grant, 66; mem. ed. bd, Int. Logic Rev, 67-; assoc. mem, spec. interest comt. lang. analysis & stud. in humanities, Asn. Computing Machinery, 67-; co-ed, Computer Stud. in Humanities & Verbal Behav, 67-; chmn. comt. computer educ, Am. Counc. Learned Soc, 68-; dir. summer training insts. humanistic comput, Nat. Endowment for Humanities & Nat. Sci. Found, 70 & 72. MLA. Computer analyses of natural language; development of symbolic motifs in the fiction of Henry James. Publ: The Christian time sequence in The American, Col. Lang. Asn. J, 3/66; Sublimating humanistic data into machine storage, Computer Stud, 1/68; Study of recall and acquisition of language forms in young children, Thought & Lang. in Operation, 4/70. Add: Dept. of Computer Science, University of Kansas, Lawrence, KS 66044.

HORSFORD, HOWARD CLARKE, b. Montezuma, Iowa, Nov. 26, 21. ENGLISH. B.A, Ripon Col, 43; State Univ. Iowa, 47; M.A, Princeton, 50, Ph.D.(Eng), 52. Instr. math, Ripon Col, 46-48; asst. prof. ENG, Princeton, 51-60; assoc. prof, UNIV. ROCHESTER, 60-66, PROF, 66-, dir. grad. stud, 63-70, acting chmn. dept, 63-64. Vis. prof. Am. lit, Bryn Mawr Col, 57-58; Bread Loaf Sch. Eng, 60, 61, 63, 64. U.S.A, 43-46, Lt. MLA; Melville Soc. Am. (pres, 57, mem. ed. bd, 69-72). American literature; English and American fiction; American civilization. Publ: Ed, Melville's journal of a voyage to Europe and the Levant, Princeton; asst. ed, Oxford anthology of English poetry, Oxford; The design of the argument in Moby Dick, Mod. Fiction Stud. Add: Dept. of English, University of Rochester, Rochester, NY 14627.

HORTON, ROD WILLIAM, b. White Plains, N.Y, June 28, 10; m. 37. AMERICAN LITERATURE, AMERICAN STUDIES. B.S, N.Y. Univ, 31, M.A, 35, Ph.D.(Eng), 45; Litt.D, Univ. Coimbra, 64. Instr. gen. lit, N.Y. Univ, 37-45, asst. prof, 45-49, assoc. prof, 49-57; cult. affairs off, U.S. Inform. Serv, Recife, Brazil, 57-59; Lisbon, Portugal, 59-64; PROF. ENG, COLO. WOMEN'S COL, 64- Smith-Mundt vis. prof, Univ. Brazil, 54-57; prof, Univ. Coimbra, 61-64; Dept. State Specialist's grant, Brazil, summer 66; mem. regional screening comt, Fulbright-Hays Prog. Am. Repubs, Area, 65-, mem. nat. screening comt, 66-; Fulbright lectr. Am. lit, Univ. Lisbon & Univ. Coimbra, 71. MLA; NCTE; Am. Stud. Asn. Edith Wharton; American literary thought and studies. Publ: Co-auth, Backgrounds of American literary thought, 52, 2nd ed, 66, 3rd ed, 74 & Backgrounds of European literature, 54, 2nd ed, 75, Prentice; transl, New Brazilian short stories, Rev. Branca, 54, The northeast of Brazil, Int. Geog. Union, 56 & Order and progress, Knopf. Add: Dept. of English, Colorado Women's College, Denver, CO 80220.

HOSEK, CHAVIVA MILADA, b. Czechoslovakia, Oct. 6, 46; Can. citizen. ENGLISH & AMERICAN LITERATURE. B.A, McGill Univ, 67; Ford Found. fel, Harvard, 67-73, A.M, 68, Ph.D.(Eng), 73. Lectr. ENG, VICTORIA COL, UNIV. TORONTO, 72-73, ASST. PROF, 73- MLA; Asn. Can. Univ. Teachers Eng. Nineteenth century and modern American literature, especially Franklin and Edwards; Canadian literature. Add: Dept. of English, Victoria College, University of Toronto, Queen's Park Crescent, Toronto, Ont. M5S 1K7, Can.

HOSKINS, HERBERT WILSON, JR, b. Springfield, Mass, Nov. 6, 20; m. 50; c. 3. ENGLISH & COMPARATIVE LITERATURE. Olin scholar, Wesleyan Univ, 37-41, A.B, 41; Alumni fel, Harvard, 41-42; Winchester fel, Columbia Univ, 46-47, M.A, 50, Ph.D.(Eng), 63. Instr. ENG, Rutgers Univ, 50-52; Wesleyan Univ, 53-57; from asst. prof. to ASSOC. PROF, CLAREMONT MEN'S COL. & CLAREMONT GRAD. SCH, 57- U.S.N.R, 42-46, Lt. MLA; Renaissance Soc. Am. Elizabethan and modern drama; 19th and 20th century intellectual history. Publ: A critical edition of John Ford's Love's sacrifice. Add: 1687 Shaw Place, Claremont, CA 91711.

HOSLEY, RICHARD, b. New York, N.Y, Mar. 13, 21; m. 45; c. 3. ENGLISH. B.A, Yale, 43, Ph.D.(Eng), 50. Instr. ENG, U.S. Naval Acad, 45-46; New Haven State Teachers Col, 50-52; Univ. Va, 52-55; from asst. prof. to assoc. prof, Univ. Mo, 55-63; PROF, UNIV. ARIZ, 63-, HEAD DEPT, 72- Folger Shakespeare Libr. fel, summer 53; Guggenheim fel, 57-58; hon. fel, Shakespeare Inst, 57-58; Huntington Libr. fel, 61-62; Princeton Humanities Counc. fel, spring 67. U.S.N.R, 43-46. MLA; Shakespeare Asn. Am; Malone Soc; Bibliog Soc. Univ. Va. Shakespeare; Elizabethan stage and dramatic texts; Renaissance Italian comedy. Publ: Romeo and Juliet, Yale Shakespeare, Yale Univ, 54; Essays on Shakespeare and Elizabethan drama in honor of Hardin Craig, Univ. Mo, 62; The taming of the shrew, Pelican Shakespeare, Penguin Bks, 64; Cymbeline, Signet Shakespeare, New Am. Libr, 68; Shakespeare's Holinshed, Putnam, 68; Shakespeare vzriorum handbook, 71; Revels history of the drama in English, 74; plus others. Add: Dept. of English, University of Arizona, Tucson, AZ 85721.

HOSMER, ELIZABETH RUTH, b. Fair Haven, Vt, Apr. 18, 14. ENGLISH. A.B, Mt. Holyoke Col, 35; Bardwell Mem. fel. from Mt. Holyoke Col. to Bryn Mawr Col, 35-36, A.M, 36; Class of 1905 fel. from Mt. Holyoke Col. to Univ. Ill, 39-40, Ph.D, 48; Bread Loaf Sch. Eng, Middlebury Col, summers, 49, 60. Asst. ENG, Univ. Ill, 36-42; instr, Mt. Holyoke Col, 44-45; Colby Jr. Col, 45-50; asst. prof, Hope Col, 51-52; ALBION COL, 52-60, ASSOC. PROF, 60- MLA; AAUP. Nathaniel Hawthorne; writers of the Concord Group; age of Chaucer. Publ: Science and pseudo-science in the writings of Nathaniel Hawthorne, Univ. Ill, 48. Add; Dept. of English, Albion College, Albion, MI 49224.

HOSMON, ROBERT STAHR, b. Ft. Jackson, S.C, Oct. 5, 43. VICTORIAN LITERATURE & ART. B.S, Spring Hill Col, 65; M.A, Ariz. State Univ, 67, Ph.D.(Eng), 69. Asst. prof. ENG, UNIV. MIAMI, 68-73, ASSOC. PROF. & CHMN. DEPT, 73- Mem. adv. comn, Res. Soc. Victorian Periodicals, 69-71. MLA; William Morris Soc; Victorian Soc.(mem. adv. bd, 71); Philol. Asn. Pac. Coast. Pre-Raphaelite literature and art; Edward Burne-Jones. Publ: Ed, The germ: a pre-Raphaelite little magazine, Univ. Miami, 70; The revolt of the pre-Raphaelites, Lowe Art Mus, 72; co-ed, Man: paradox and promise, Prentice-Hall, 73; Dante Gabriel Rossetti: the critical heritage, Routledge & Kegan Paul, 74; auth, The germ 1850, 69 & The Oxford and Cambridge magazine, 69, Victorian Periodicals Newsl. Add: Dept. of English, University of Miami, Coral Gables, FL 33124.

HOST, DAVID RICHARD, b. Milwaukee, Wis, Sept. 16, 11; m. 40; c. 5. JOURNALISM. A.B, Marquette Univ, 34, A.M, 37; Univ. Toronto, 37-39. Asst. prof. JOUR, MARQUETTE UNIV, 39-45, assoc. prof, 45-52, PROF, 52-, DIR. INST. CATH. PRESS. Asn. Educ. Jour; Cath. Press Asn; Nat. Conf. Ed. Writers; AAUP. The press' role in society; processes of communication; Catholic principles of journalism practice. Add: College of Journalism, Marquette University, Milwaukee, WI 53233.

HOSTETLER, PAUL SMITH, b. Butte, Mont, July 9, 21; m. 50; c. 3. SPEECH. B.A, Stanford Univ, 43, M.A, 49; Ind. Univ, summer 57; South. Fels. Fund fel, 58-59; Ph.D.(speech), La. State Univ, 64. Instr. theatre & speech, Tulane Univ, 49-53, asst. prof, 53-67, dir. univ. theatre, 60-67; prof. theatre & chmn. dept, Temple Univ, 67-74; PROF. DRAMA & EXEC. DIR. SCH. DRAMA, UNIV. WASH, 74- U.S.N.R, 43-46, Res, 46-60, Lt. Secy-treas, League Prof. Theatre Training Prog, 72. Am. Theatre Asn; Speech Commun. Asn.(assoc. ed, Quart. J. Speech, 65-); Am. Soc. Theatre Res; Nat. Theatre Conf; Int. Fed. Theatre Res. Early 19th century American theatre history and drama; theatre production. Publ: The influence of New Orleans on southern theatre history in the early 19th century, South. Speech J, fall 63; Elsslermania in New Orleans, Theatre Surv, 11/69. Add: School of Drama, University of Washington, Seattle, WA 98195.

HOSTETTLER, GORDON FLOYD, b. Kent, Ohio, Mar. 17, 18; m. 43; c. 2. SPEECH. A.B. & B.S, Kent State Univ, 40; A.M, Univ. Iowa, 42, Ph.D, 47. Instr. speech, Univ. Iowa, 43-44; Coe Col, 44-45; Temple Univ, 45-47, asst. prof, 47-52, assoc. prof. speech, 52-57, prof, 58-64, chmn. dept. speech & dramatic arts, 52-64; prof. speech, Ohio State Univ, 64-66; PROF. SPEECH & CHMN. DEPT. SPEECH ARTS, COLO. STATE UNIV, 66- Ed, Pa. Speech Annual, 49, 50, 61-62; assoc. ed, Speech Monogr, 66-69. Speech Commun. Asn; Speech Asn. East. States.(exec. secy, 51-54); Int. Soc. Gen. Semantics; AHA. Public address and rhetoric; oratorical careers of Jonathan P. Dolliver, Albert J. Beveridge and Robert M. La-Follette; history of rhetorical theory and criticism. Publ: The Brownlow-Pryne debate on slavery, In: Anti-slavery and disunion, Harper, 62; Speech as a liberal study, In: Speeches for illustration and example, Scott, 65; Trends in the history of rhetoric, In: The communicative arts and sciences of speech, Merrill, 67. Add: Dept. of Speech Arts, Colorado State University, Ft. Collins, CO 80521.

HOTCH, DOUGLAS RIPLEY, b. Brunswick, Ga, June 19, 42. ENGLISH LITERATURE. B.A, Univ. Mich, Ann Arbor, 64; M.A, Univ. Calif, Berkeley, 66, Ph.D.(Eng), 69. ASST. PROF. ENG, UNIV. ILL, URBANA-CHAMPAIGN, 69- MLA; Am. Soc. 18th Century Stud. Eighteenth century English literature; literature and psychoanalysis. Publ: Pope surveys his kingdom: an essay on criticism, Stud. Eng. Lit, 73. Add: Dept. of English, 100 English Bldg, University of Illinois, Urbana, IL 61801.

HOTSON, LESLIE, b. Delhi, Ont, Aug. 16, 97; nat; m. 19. ENGLISH LITERATURE. A.B, Harvard, 21, A.M, 22, Dexter traveling fel, summers 22, 25, Ph.D, 23; M.A, Cambridge, 54, Litt.D, 57. Sheldon traveling fel, Harvard, 23-24, instr. Eng, 24-25; asst, Yale, 25-26, Sterling sr. res. fel, 26-27; assoc. prof. Eng, N.Y. Univ, 27-29; Guggenheim fel, 29-31; prof. Eng, Haverford Col, 31-41; Folger Shakespeare mem. lectr, 40; Fulbright sr. res. fel, 49-50; res. assoc. Eng, Yale, 50-67, Shakespeare quatercentenary orator, 64. Lectr, Royal Soc. Lit, 38; fel, King's Col, Cambridge, 54-60. Sig.C, U.S.A, 43-46, Capt. MLA; fel. Royal Soc. Lit. U.K. English literary history; Shakespeare biography and chronology of plays; the Commonwealth and Restoration stage. Publ: Shakespeare's wooden O, 59 & Mr. W.H, 64, Hart-Davis; The first night of Twelfth night, Mercury, 61; Queen Elizabeth's master painter, Sunday Times Mag, London, 3/70. Add: Northford, CT 06472.

HOUCHIN, THOMAS D, b. Mattoon, Ill, July 15, 25. SPEECH PATHOLOGY & LINGUISTICS. B.A, State Univ. Iowa, 46, M.A, 50; fel, Harvard, 52-56, A.M, 55; Voc. Rehabilitation Admin. res. fel, 59-60; Ed.D, Columbia Univ, 63. Speech clinician, pub. schs, Fairmont, Minn, 46-48; speech psychologist, Minn. State Crippled Children Serv, St. Paul, 48-50; supvr. speech & hearing, Nebr. State Dept. Educ, Lincoln, 50-52; asst. prof. speech path. & ling, Emerson Col, 56-60; SPEECH PATH. & PHONETICS, ST. JOHN'S UNIV.(N.Y), 60-64, assoc. prof, 64-67, PROF, 67-, CHMN. DIV. HUMANITIES, STATEN ISLAND, 71-, chmn. dept. speech & theatre, Jamaica, 65-71, chmn. interdept. comt. ling, 68-71. Am. Speech & Hearing Asn; Ling. Soc. Am; Am. Dialect Soc; Int. Phonetic Asn; East. Commun. Asn.(2nd v.pres, 66-67, exec. secy, 69-71). Speech rehabilitation; aphasia; phonetics. Publ: Children with speech and hearing problems, Nebr. State Dept. Educ, 51, 52; Bibliographie critique de la statistique linguistique, Spectrum Ed, Utrecht, 54; Home exercises in language for aphasic patients, Holy Ghost Hosp, Cambridge, Mass, 57; How to help adults with aphasia, Pub. Affairs, 64. Add: Div. of Humanities, St. John's University, Staten Island, NY 10301.

HOUCK, JOSEPH KEMP, b. Lynchburg, Va, Aug. 15, 36; m. 61; c. 1. ENGLISH. B.A, Univ. Va, 58, M.A, 61; Ph.D.(Eng), Univ. N.C, 67. Instr. ENG, Duke Univ, 65-66; ASST. PROF, UNIV. KANS, 66- Consult. independent stud, Univ. Kans. Exten. Div. MLA; Renaissance Soc. Am; Shakespeare Asn. Am; Renaissance Eng. Text Soc. Early English drama; history of criticism. Publ: Francis Bacon: checklist of modern scholarship, Nether, London, 68; co-auth, Literature of the Renaissance: English, Stud. Philol, 67 & 68. Add: Dept. of English, University of Kansas, Lawrence, KS 66044.

HOUGH, GEORGE ANTHONY, III, Linguistics, Journalism. See Volume III, Foreign Languages, Linguistics & Philology.

HOUGH, ROBERT LEE, b. Los Angeles, Calif, May 19, 24; m. 52; c. 4. AMERICAN LITERATURE. B.A, Pomona Col, 49; M.S, Columbia Univ, 50; Ph.D, Stanford Univ, 57. Instr. jour, Whittier Col, 50-51; ENG, UNIV. NEBR, LINCOLN, 56-57, asst. prof, 57-61, assoc. prof, 61-64, PROF, 64-, asst. dean Col. Arts & Sci, 67, assoc. dean, 67-69, dean, 69-70. U.S.A.A.F, 42-46, Sgt. NCTE; AAUP. Publ: The quiet rebel: William Dean Howells,

59, ed, Literary criticism of Edgar Allan Poe, 65 & The West of Owen Wister, 72, Univ. Nebr; Howells' The rise of Silas Lapham, Bantam, 71; auth, W.D. Howells, In: The American novel, Basic Bks, 65; plus two others. Add: Dept. of English, University of Nebraska, Lincoln, NE 68508.

HOUGHTON, CHARLES NORRIS, b. Indianapolis, Ind, Dec. 26, 09. DRAMA. A.B, Princeton, 31; hon. D.F.A, Denison Univ, 59. Lectr. drama, Princeton, 41-42; adj. prof, Vassar Col, 59-60, prof, 62-67; DEAN THEATRE ARTS, STATE UNIV. N.Y. COL. PURCHASE, 67- Guggenheim Found. fels, 34-35, 60-61; Rockefeller Found. grant-in-aid, 40-41; lectr. comp. lit, Columbia Univ, 48-54; adj. prof. drama, Barnard Col, 54-58. U.S.N.R, 43-45, Lt. Nat. Theatre Conf.(pres, 68); Am. Theatre Asn; fel. Am. Acad. Arts & Sci; Am. Counc. Arts in Educ.(v.pres, 71-73, pres, 73-). Soviet theatre. Publ: Moscow rehearsals, 36 & Advance from Broadway, 41, Harcourt; Return engagement, Holt, 62; Masterpieces of continental drama (3 vols), Dell, 63; The exploding stage, Weybright & Talley, 72; plus one other. Add: State University of New York College at Purchase, Purchase, NY 10577.

HOUGHTON, DONALD EUGENE, b. Clark, S.Dak, May 22, 20; m. 41; c. 3. ENGLISH. B.A, Univ. Wash, 41; M.A, Columbia Univ, 47; Ph.D.(Am. stud), Univ. Minn, 55. Instr. ENG, Univ. Ore, 47-49; Centralia Jr. Col, 49-51; Univ. Minn, 53-55; asst. prof, CALIF. STATE UNIV, SACRAMENTO, 55-58, assoc. prof, 58-64, PROF, 64- Fulbright prof, Cairo & Ain Shams Univs, Egypt, 62-63. U.S.A.A.F, 42-45. Am. Stud. Asn. American novel; western American literature; film. Publ: Whores and horses in Faulkner's Spotted horses, Midwest Quart, summer 70; Two heroes in one: the popularity of The Virginian, J. Popular Culture, fall 70; The failure of speech in The ox-bow incident, Eng. J, 12/70. Add: 4241 Oterol Ct, Sacramento, CA 95821.

HOUGHTON, WALTER EDWARDS, b. Stamford, Conn, Sept. 21, 04; m. 29; c. 2. ENGLISH LITERATURE. Ph.B, Yale, 24, A.M, 27, Ph.D, 31. Instr. Eng, Hill Sch, Pa, 24-25; Phillips Acad.(Andover), 27-29; instr. & tutor hist. & lit, Harvard, 31-38, asst. prof. & tutor, 38-41; assoc. prof. Eng. lit, WELLESLEY COL, 42-48, prof. ENG, 48-69; EMER. PROF, 69- Lectr, Wheaton Col.(Mass), 39; Am. Counc. Learned Soc. grant, 64-65; Guggenheim fel, 65-66; Nat. Endowment for Humanities grants, 67-73. Am. Acad. Arts & Sci. Literature and intellectual history in the 19th century. Publ: The formation of Thomas Fuller's Holy and profane states, Harvard Univ, 37; The art of Newman's apologia, 45, The Victorian frame of mind, 1830-1870, 57 & The poetry of Clough, 63, Yale Univ; ed, The Wellesley index to Victorian periodicals, 1824-1900, Univ. Toronto, Vol. I, 66, Vol. II, 72; co-auth, Arthur Hugh Clough: a descriptive catalogue, N.Y. Pub. Libr, 67. Add: Wellesley College Library, Wellesley College, Wellesley, MA 02181.

HOUP, KENNETH WILTON, b. Jan. 18, 13; m. 40; c. 2. ENGLISH. A.B, Univ. Pittsburgh, 37, A.M, 39. Asst. Eng, Univ. Pittsburgh, 36-39; instr. ENG. COMPOS, PA. STATE UNIV. UNIVERSITY PARK, 39-45, asst. prof, 45-49, assoc. prof, 49-74, PROF, 74- Soc. Tech. Commun. Modern and historical English usage; literature of science. Publ: Elementary grammar and work-book, Appleton; Writer's resource book, Scott; co-auth, Reports for science and industry, Holt, 58 & Reporting technical information, Glencoe, 68, rev. ed, 73. Add: 220 E. McCormick, State College, PA 16801.

HOUPT, CHARLES THEODORE, b. Atlantic City, N.J, Sept. 14, 12; m. 41; c. 1. ENGLISH LITERATURE. A.B, Univ. Pa, 34, Ph.D, 44; A.M, Columbia Univ, 35. Instr. Eng, Univ. Pa, 35-42; mem. dept. Eng, hist. & govt, U.S. Naval Acad, 43-46; assoc. prof. ENG, PRINCIPIA COL, 46-55, PROF, 55-, asst. dean, 59-62, acting dean, 62-63, dean, 63-71. U.S.N.R, 42-46, Lt. MLA; fel. Royal Soc. Arts. The life and works of Julius Charles Hare and of Mark Akenside; the life and letters of John Flaxman. Add: Principia College, Elsah, IL 62028.

HOUPT, GARY L, b. Funkstown, Md, Jan. 9, 36; m. 59. ENGLISH, EDUCATION. A.B, Shepherd Col, 57; Johns Hopkins Univ, 59-60; M.Ed, Loyola Col, 64; Am. Univ, 66-67. Teacher, Baltimore County pub. schs, 57-64; instr. Eng. & lit, Essex Community Col, 60-61; Eng. compos. & speech, Univ. Baltimore, 64-65; STATE SUPVR. ENG. EDUC, DEL. STATE DEPT. PUB. INSTR, 65- Pangborn Found. scholar, 53-55; mem, Adv. Comt. Nat. Conf. Lang. Arts, 68-69; instr. Eng, Univ. Del, 71-72; supvr. Eng. & social stud, Am. Univ, 72. Veterans For. Wars Outstanding Serv. Award, 63-64. Hon. mem. Nat. Thespian Soc; NCTE; NEA. Preparation of English teachers; teacher self-evaluation; multiple elective programs in English. Publ: Co-auth, Speech arts, Baltimore County Pub. Schs, 60; English language arts curriculum supplement, 66, Dialogue with a teacher of listeners, speakers, readers, writers, 67 & ed, Strategies for teaching English in career education, 71, Del. Dept. Pub. Instr; auth, Grades—yes? or no!, Del. State Educ. Asn. J, 11/65; Planning for oral composition, spring 66 & Improving instruction through NDEA, title III, spring 67, Del. Eng. J. Add: State Dept. of Public Instruction, Townsend Bldg, Dover, DE 19901.

HOUSE, KAY SEYMOUR, b. Payson, Ill, May 19, 25; div; c. 2. ENGLISH & AMERICAN LITERATURE. B.A, Univ. Ill, 45; M.A, Wash. Univ, 46; Ph.D. (Eng. & Am. lit), Stanford Univ, 63. Instr. Eng. compos, Wash. Univ, 45-46; sci. writing & lit, Ohio State Univ, 46-47; advan. exposition, Stanford Univ, 61-63; asst. prof. lit, SAN FRANCISCO STATE UNIV, 63-67, assoc. prof, 67-71, PROF. AM. & ENG. LIT, 71-, RESIDENT DIR, INT. PROG, ITALY, 72- Fulbright-Hays lectr, Italy, 68-69; mem. adv. bd, definitive ed. works of James Fenimore Cooper, 70- MLA; Am. Stud. Asn. Italian-English comparative literature; James Fenimore Cooper; expatriate American writers. Publ: Cooper's Americans, Ohio State Univ, 66; ed, Reality and myth in American literature, Fawcett, 66; auth, Cooper's The pioneers, In: The American novel from James Fenimore Cooper to William Faulkner, Basic Bks, 65; contrib, History of literature in English (12 Vols), Sphere, Eng, 73; auth, Francesco Caracciolo, Fenimore Cooper, and Billy Budd, Stud. Am, Rome, 74. Add: Dept. of English, 220 Humanities Bldg, San Francisco State University, 1600 Holloway Ave, San Francisco, CA 94132.

HOUSER, DAVID JOHN, b. Ames, Iowa, Sept. 6, 42; m. 64; c. 2. ENGLISH LITERATURE. B.S, Iowa State Univ, 64; M.S, Univ. Wis-Madison, 66, Ph.D. (Eng), 70. ASST. PROF. ENG, KANS. STATE UNIV, 69- MLA. Shakespeare; Elizabethan and Jacobean drama. Publ: Armour and motive in Troilus and Cressida, Renaissance Drama, 71; Purging the Commonwealth: Marston's disguised dukes and A knack to know a knave, PMLA, 74. Add: Dept. of English, Kansas State University, Manhattan, KS 66506.

HOUSMAN, ARTHUR LLOYD, b. Missoula, Mont, June 8, 28; m. 53; c. 2. SPEECH, DRAMATIC ART. B.A, DePauw Univ, 50; M.A, State Univ. Iowa, 51, Ph.D, 56. Teaching asst, State Univ. Iowa, 51, 54-56; prof. speech, St. Cloud State Col, 56-68, chmn. dept. speech & dramatic art, 62-68; prof. theatre & chmn. dept, Ohio State Univ, 68-71; PROF. DRAMATIC ART & CHMN. DEPT, UNIV. N.C, CHAPEL HILL, 71- U.S. Dept. State Am. specialist grant, Turkey, 65-66, 69. U.S.A, 52-54, Lt. Am. Theatre Asn. Playwriting; theatre history and criticism; acting and directing. Add: Dept. of Dramatic Art, University of North Carolina at Chapel Hill, Chapel Hill, NC 27514.

HOUSTON, HOWARD ROGERS, b. Newfield, N.Y, June 28, 19. ENGLISH & AMERICAN LITERATURE. B.A, Cornell Univ, 39; M.A, Pa. State Univ, 50; fel, Claremont Grad. Sch, 57-60, Ph.D.(Eng. & Am. Lit), 67. Instr. ENG, Alfred Univ, 46-49; asst. prof, State Univ. N.Y. Brockport, 49; instr, Univ. Nev, 51-54; teaching assoc, Ind. Univ, Indianapolis, 55; instr, Univ. Colo, 55-56; Ore. State Col, 56-57; lectr, Univ. Calif, Riverside, 60-62; instr, Claremont Men's Col, 63-66; asst. prof, Calif. West. Univ, 67-68; ASSOC. PROF, NORTH. MICH. UNIV, 68- MLA. The novel; 19th century American literature, especially Thoreau; interdisciplinary approaches. Add: Dept. of English, Northern Michigan University, Marquette, MI 49855.

HOUSTON, NEAL BRYAN, b. Dallas, Tex, Aug. 7, 28; m. 56; c. 2. ENGLISH. B.S, Univ. Tex, 49, M.Ed, 53, M.A, 60; Ph.D.(Eng), Tex. Technol. Col, 65. Teacher, Independent Sch. Dist, Tex, 49-51; Mitsubishi Chem. Indust, Japan, 51-53; teacher, Independent Sch. Dist, Tex, 53-57; assoc. prof. ENG, Amarillo Col, 58-61, prof, 61-65; assoc. prof, Angelo State Col, 65-66; STEPHEN F. AUSTIN STATE UNIV, 66-67, PROF, 67-, fac. grants, 67, 68. Lectr, Kita-Kyushu Univ, 51-53; vis. prof, Tex. Technol. Col, summer 66; consult, Crockett Independent Sch. Dist, Tex, 68; vis. prof. Eng, Hilo Col, Univ. Hawaii, 70-71. U.S.A, 51-53. MLA; S.Cent. Mod. Lang. Asn; NCTE; Soc. Stud. South. Lit. American romanticism; 19th century British literature; Pacific literature. Publ: Ross Santee, Steck, 68; co-auth, Phonetikon, Scott, 70; auth, The mutiny on H.M.S. Bounty: an historical and literary bibliography, Bull. Bibliog, spring 70; co-auth, Holgrave: Hawthorne's antithesis to Carlyle's Teufelsdröckh, 3/70 & auth, Henry James's Maud-Evelyn: classic folie à deux, 3/73, Res. Stud; plus others. Add: Box 3007, Stephen F. Austin State University, Stephen F. Austin Station, Nacogdoches, TX 75961.

HOUSTON, RALPH HUBERT, b. Lewisville, Tex, Jun 17, 10; m. 33; c. 1. ENGLISH. B.A, N.Tex. State Univ, 30; M.A, Univ. Tex, 34, Ph.D.(Eng), 46. Teacher, High Sch, Tex, 30-36; from asst. prof. to PROF. ENG, SOUTHWEST TEX. STATE UNIV, 37-, DEAN SCH. LIB. & FINE ARTS, 65-, chmn. dept. Eng, 58-65. U.S.A.F.R, 42-46, 51-53. MLA; NCTE. Eighteenth century English; contemporary novel. Add: Dept. of English, Southwest Texas State University, San Marcos, TX 78666.

HOUTCHENS, CAROLYN WASHBURN, b. Taunton, Mass, Dec. 28, 06. ENGLISH. A.B, Mt. Holyoke Col, 27; A.M, Columbia Univ, 28; Ph.D, Univ. Ill, 37. Instr. ENG, Univ. Ill, 28-39, 41-46; MIAMI UNIV, 46-49, asst. prof, 49-58, assoc. prof, 58-69, PROF, 69- English prose fiction; 19th century British criticism of prose fiction; Charles Dickens. Publ: Co-ed, Leigh Hunt's literary criticism, & Leigh Hunt's political and occasional essays, 63, Columbia; co-ed. & contrib, English romantic poets and essayists: a review of research, Mod. Lang. Asn, rev. ed, 66. Add: 220 Upham Hall, Miami University, Oxford, OH 45056.

HOUTCHENS, LAWRENCE (HUSTON), b. Bloomfield, Ky, July 2, 98. ENGLISH LITERATURE. A.B, Univ. Mich, 23; A.M, Cornell Univ, 26, Ph.D, 31. Mem. dept. ENG, Bethany Col, 31-34; Univ. N.H, 34-37; Univ. Ill, 37-46; PROF, MIAMI UNIV, 46- Grant-in-aid, grad. sch, Univ. Ill. & Pforzheimer Fund; mem. summer fac, Univ. Vt, 45; Univ. Minn, 46. MLA; Soc. Advan. Educ. Charles Dickens and international copyright; 19th century English literature; Browning. Publ: Co-auth, Leigh Hunt's political and occasional essays, Columbia, 62; co-ed, Leigh Hunt's dramatic criticism, Columbia & Oxford; ed. dir. & contrib, English romantic poets and essayists: a review of research, MLA & N.Y. Univ. Add: Dept. of English, Miami University, Oxford, OH 45056.

HOVDE, CARL F, b. Meadville, Pa, Oct. 11, 26; m. 60; c. 2. ENGLISH. B.A, Columbia Univ, 50, Evans traveling fel, 50-51; M.A, Princeton, 54, Ph.D.(Eng), 56. Instr. Eng, Ohio State Univ, 55-58; vis. lectr. Am. lit, Univ. Münster, 58-60; asst. prof. ENG, COLUMBIA UNIV, 60-64, assoc. prof, 64-69, PROF, 69-, DEAN, COLUMBIA COL, 68- Vis. prof. Am. lit, Univ. Guanabara, 64. U.S.A, 44-46. MLA. Transcendentalists in American literature; American novel. Publ: Nature into art: Thoreau's use of his journal, Am. Lit, 5/58; Thoreau's literary sources in A week, PMLA, winter 62; Faulkner's democratic rhetoric, S.Atlantic Quart, spring 64. Add: Dept. of English, 423 Hamilton Hall, Columbia University, New York, NY 10027.

HOVE, HALDOR LAURITZ, b. Lakota, N.Dak, Jan. 23, 13; m. 67. ENGLISH. B.A, St. Olaf Col, 37; M.A, Univ. Chicago, 48, Ph.D.(cult. hist), 62. Asst. prof. ENG, ST. OLAF COL, 48-62, assoc. prof, 62-72, PROF, 72- U.S.N.R, 42-46, Lt. MLA. Victorian literature; Norwegian-American immigrant history. Add: Dept. of English, St. Olaf College, Northfield, MN 55057.

HOVE, JOHN, JR, b. Feb. 1, 16; U.S. citizen; m. 45; c. 3. AMERICAN STUDIES. B.A, Valley City State Col, 37; M.S, Univ. N.Dak, 46; Ph.D, Univ. Minn, 59. Teacher ENG, Jamestown High Sch, N.Dak, 37-42; asst, Univ. N.Dak, 45-46; from asst. prof. to PROF. & CHMN. DEPT, Mayville State Col, 46-59; N.DAK. STATE UNIV, 59- Mem. Rhodes scholar. comt. for N.Dak, 62-63; chmn, N.Dak. Counc. Arts & Humanities, 65-; mem. lit. adv. panel, Nat. Endowment for Arts, 72-75. U.S.N.R, 42-45, Lt.(jg). Am. Stud. Asn; NCTE; MLA. English curriculum; science, industry and technology in America; arts and humanities. Publ: Co-auth, North Dakota curriculum guide: English language arts, Dept. Pub. Instr, 49 & Conservation in North

Dakota, Webb Publ, 62; ed, Meeting censorship in the school, Nat. Counc. Teachers Eng, 67. Add: Dept. of English, North Dakota State University, Fargo, ND 58102.

HOVE, MARY RION, b. Lexington, Ky, Jan. 12, 23; m. 67. ENGLISH, AMERICAN LITERATURE. B.A, Univ. Ky, 43; A.M, Smith Col, 46; Ph.D.(Eng), Johns Hopkins Univ, 57. Transl. French, Span, Off. Censorship, 42-45; instr. Eng, Hood Col, 46-48; Mt. Holyoke Col, 51-54; asst. prof, Agnes Scott Col, 55-60, assoc. prof, 60-67. Various capacities up to asst. chief reader Eng. compos. exam. & advanced placement exam, Col, Bd, 47-, asst. chief reader, 65-66; mem. comt. lit. test, Col. Level Exam. Prog, Educ. Testing Serv, 64-72; mem. comt. area test humanities, Grad. Rec. Exam, 66-68. MLA; Am. Stud. Asn. Nineteenth century American literature; American novel; 19th century English novel. Add: 118 Madison St, Northfield, MN 55057.

HOVEY, RICHARD BENNETT, b. Cincinnati, Ohio, July 28, 17; m. 55; c. 1. ENGLISH. A.B, Univ. Cincinnati, 42; M.A, Harvard, 43, Ph.D.(Eng), 50. Instr. ENG, Univ. Cincinnati, 43-46; Univ, Pa, 49-55; asst. prof, West. Md. Col, 55-57, assoc. prof, 57-60; UNIV. MD, 60-68, PROF, 68- Ford fel, 51-52. U.S.War Dept, 43-44. NCTE; Col. Eng. Asn; AAUP; Counc. Basic Educ. Psychologically oriented criticism of American literature; Dreiser; Hawthorne. Publ: John Jay Chapman: an American mind, Columbia Univ, 59; Hemingway: the inward terrain, Univ. Wash, 68; co-auth, Dreiser's The genius, Hartford Stud. Lit, 70; auth, John Jay Chapman, Mod. Lang. J, 10/70; Our disposable past: a protest, Mod. Age, spring 73. Add: 4313 Knox Rd, College Park, MD 20740.

HOWARD, ALAN (BLAIR), b. Denver, Colo, Mar. 4, 39; m. 60; c. 2. ENGLISH. B.A, Princeton, 61; univ. fel, Stanford Univ, 64-66, M.A, 66, NDEA fel, 66-67, Ph.D,(Eng), 68. Asst. prof. ENG, UNIV. VA, 67-72, ASSOC. PROF, 72- Fulbright lectr. Am. stud, Australia, 69-70. Norman Forester Award, 72. Am. Stud. Asn; MLA; AAUP. American religious history; colonial American literature; historiography. Publ: Art and history in Bradford's Of Plymouth plantation, William & Mary Quart, 4/71; Huck Finn in the house of Usher: comic and grotesque in The hamlet, South. Rev, Australia, 6/72; The world as emblem: language and vision in the poetry of Edward Taylor, Am. Lit, 11/72. Add: Dept. of English, University of Virginia, Charlottesville, VA 22903.

HOWARD, ANNE BAIL, b. Albuquerque, N.Mex, Nov. 19, 27; m. 50; c. 2. AMERICAN LITERATURE, COMPOSITION. Univ. Colo, Boulder, 49; Univ. of the Americas, 50-51; M.A, Univ. N.Mex, 53, Ph.D, 66. Teacher ENG, Espanola High Sch, 54-55; Valley High Sch, Albuquerque, 55-57; instr. & dir. Eng. A, Univ. N.Mex, 59-63; instr, UNIV. NEV, RENO, 63-66, asst. prof, 66-71, ASSOC. PROF, 71- MLA; NCTE; AAUP. Hawthorne; Dickinson; women writers. Publ: Co-auth, A workbook for English A, Univ. N.Mex, 62. Add: Dept. of English, University of Nevada, Reno, NV 89507.

HOWARD, C. JERIEL, b. Wharton, Tex, Mar. 14, 39. ENGLISH. B.A, Union Coll, 61, M.A, Tex. Christian Univ, 62, Ph.D.(Eng), 67. Instr. Eng, Southwest. Union Col, 62-64; Union Col, 64-65, assoc. prof, 65-66; instr, Tex. Christian Univ, 66-67; guest instr, Tex. Wesleyan Col, 67; chmn. dept. Eng, Tarrant County Jr. Col, 67-68, chmn. dept. commun, 68-70; ASSOC. PROF. ENG, BISHOP COL, 70- Guest prof. Eng, E.Tex. State Univ, summer 68. MLA; NCTE; Conf. Col. Compos. & Commun; Conf. Col. Teachers Eng. Applied rhetoric; English methodology; American literature. Publ: Co-auth, Applied communications, 70 & co-auth, Contact. 2nd ed, 74, Prentice-Hall; co-auth, The responsible man, 70, co-auth, Tempo: themetic approach to sentence/paragraph writing, 71, co-auth, Desk copy: modern business communications, 71 & co-auth, Technique: studies in composition, 72, Canfield; co-ed, The age of anxiety, Allyn & Bacon, 72; co-auth, —30—A journalistic approach to freshman composition, Goodyear, 73. Add: 10027 Dale Crest Dr, Dallas, TX 75229.

HOWARD, DANIEL F, b. Waterbury, Conn, Mar. 30, 28; m. 54, 68; c. 3. ENGLISH. B.A, Yale Univ, 49, M.A, 51, Ph.D, 56. Instr. ENG, Carnegie Inst. Technol, 53-54; Williams Col, 54-58; asst. prof, Kenyon Col, 58-60; assoc. prof, RUTGERS UNIV, NEW BRUNSWICK, 60-66, PROF. & CHMN. DEPT, 66- Fulbright res. fel, Italy, 56-57; Am. Counc. Learned Soc. grants-in-aid, 59 & Am. Philos. Soc, 63-64, Eng. The novel; Victorian literature. Publ: The correspondence of Samuel Butler with his sister May, Univ. Calif, 62; Ernest Pontifex, or the way of all flesh, Houghton, 65; The modern tradition, Little, 68, 2nd ed, 72; The new criticism of the novel, Kenyon Rev, 59. Add: Dept. of English, Rutgers University, New Brunswick, NJ 08903.

HOWARD, DONALD ROY, b. St. Louis, Mo, Sept. 18, 27. ENGLISH. A.B, Tufts Univ; M.A, Rutgers Univ; Ph.D.(Eng), Univ. Fla. Instr. ENG, Univ. Fla, 54-55; Ohio State Univ, 55-63; assoc. prof, Univ. Calif, Riverside, 63-66; Univ. Calif, Los Angeles, 66-67; PROF, JOHNS HOPKINS UNIV, 67- Fulbright res. fel, Italy, 59-60; Am. Counc. Learned Soc. fel, 64; mem. ed. bd, Eng. Lit. Hist, 68-; fel, Guggenheim Found, 69-70; mem. ed. bd, Speculum, 70- MLA; Mediaeval Acad. Am; Renaissance Soc. Am. Medieval literature and history of ideas; De Contemptu Mundi writings; Chaucer. Publ: The three temptations: medieval man in search of the world, Princeton, 66; co-auth, Critical studies of Sir Gawain and the Green Knight, Univ. Notre Dame, 68; ed, Geoffrey Chaucer's The Canterbury tales: a selection, Signet, 69; Lothario dei Segni (Pope Innocent III), On the misery of the human condition, Bobbs-Merrill, 69; auth, The world of Mandeville's travels, Yearbk. Eng. Stud, 71; Lexicography and the silence of the past, In: New aspects of lexicography, South. Ill. Univ, 72; Medieval poems and medieval society, Medievalia et Humanistica, 72. Add: Dept. of English, Johns Hopkins University, Baltimore, MD 21218.

HOWARD, HUBERT WENDELL, b. Anderson, Ind, Sept. 22, 27; m. 56; c. 3. ENGLISH LITERATURE, MUSIC. A.B, DePauw Univ, 49; M.A, Stanford Univ, 52; dipl, Juilliard Sch. Music, 58; Ph.D.(Eng, music), Univ. Minn, Minneapolis, 70. Dir. relig. educ, First Methodist Church, Anderson, Ind, 49-50; plant mgr, Paglo Labs, N.Y, 58-60; instr. Eng, Univ. Minn, Minneapolis, 60-64; asst. prof. ENG. & MUSIC, ST. JOHN FISHER COL, 64-69, ASSOC. PROF, 69- Vis. prof, Eve. Sch, Monroe Community Col, 68-71 & 73-74; Univ. Rochester, summer 72. Winton Found. Excellence Award, 62. U.S.A, 52-54. MLA; Nat. Asn. Teachers Singing; NCTE. Renaissance British literature; 18th century British literature; Renaissance and Baroque music. Publ: He loved her (poem), Orphic Lute, spring 66; The mystic (poem), Roanoke Rev, fall 72; The parable, Col. Compos. & Commun, 12/73. Add: 46 Torrington Dr, Rochester, NY 14618.

HOWARD, LEON, b. Talladega, Ala, Nov. 8, 03; m. 31; c. 3. ENGLISH. A.B, Birmingham-South. Col, 23; M.A, Univ. Chicago, 26, L.H.D, 61; Ph.D.(Eng), Johns Hopkins Univ, 29; hon. Ph.D, Univ. Abo, 68. From instr. to asst. prof. ENG, Pomona Col, 30-37; from assoc. prof. to prof, Northwest. Univ, 38-50; prof. UNIV. CALIF, LOS ANGELES, 50-71, EMER PROF, 71- Huntington Libr. int. res. fel, 37-38; Guggenheim fel, 44-45; Newberry Libr. sr. res. fel, 66; vis. prof. Eng, Univ. N.M, 71- MLA; Am. Stud. Asn; fel. Am. Acad. Arts & Sci. American and English literature; American history. Publ: The Connecticut Wits; Herman Melville: a biography; Victorian knight-errant; a study of the early literary career of James Russell Lowell. Add: 1200 Calle del Sol N.E, Albuquerque, NM 87106.

HOWARD, MARTHA CUMMINS, b. Chicago, Ill, Mar. 6, 22; m. 47; c. 1. ENGLISH. A.B, Univ. Mich, 42, A.M, 47. Teacher ENG, Bd. Educ, Midland, Mich, 42-43; Ann Arbor, 48-50; instr, W.VA. UNIV, 60-67, asst. prof, 67-71, ASSOC. PROF, 71-, ASST. DEAN INSTR, COL. ARTS & SCI, 73-, asst. dean adv, 71-73. NCTE; Col. Counc. Commun. Linguistics; academic advising; undergraduate instruction. Publ: Orientation I. Finding your way around West Virginia University, W.Va. Univ. Mag, summer 73; A better way down the rabbit hole, Col. & Univ. J, 9/73. Add: College of Arts & Sciences, 103 Woodburn Hall, West Virginia University, Morgantown, WV 26506.

HOWARD, WILLIAM JAMES, b. Detroit, Mich, May 10, 33. ENGLISH. B.A, Univ. Toronto, 57, M.A, 61, S.T.B, 62; Ph.D.(Eng), Univ. Leeds, 65. Asst. prof. ENG. LIT, St. Michael's Col, UNIV. TORONTO, 65-72, ASSOC. PROF, SCARBOROUGH COL, 72- Am. Counc. Learned Soc. travel grant, summer 68; Can. Counc. res. grant, 68; convener, Toronto Ed. Conf, 68. Asn. Commonwealth Lit. & Lang. Stud. Early eighteenth century English literature; comparative literatures in English. Publ: Truth preserves her shape, Philol. Quart, 4/68; The mystery of the Cibberian Dunciad, Stud. Eng. Lit, summer 68; Literature in the law courts, 1770-1800, In: Editing eighteenth-century texts, Univ. Toronto, 68. Add: Dept. of English, Scarborough College, University of Toronto, Toronto, Ont, Can.

HOWARD, ZELMA INEZ TURNER, b. Indianola, Miss; m. 49; c. 1. ENGLISH. B.A, Tougaloo Col, 41; M.A, Atlanta Univ, 49; Ed.D.(Eng), Univ. North. Colo, 70. Teacher ENG, Drew High Sch, Miss, 41-43; Bowman High Sch, Vicksburg, 43-45; Indianola High Sch, 45-46; head dept, Voorhees Col, 47-54; MISS. VALLEY STATE COL, 54-68, PROF, 69- NCTE. Short fiction of Eudora Welty; remedial programs at state colleges; performance of student teachers. Publ: The rhetoric of Eudora Welty's short stories, Univ. & Col. Miss, 73. Add: Dept. of Communications, Mississippi Valley State College, Itta Bena, MS 38941.

HOWARD-HILL, TREVOR HOWARD, b. Wellington, N.Z, Oct. 17, 33; m. 67; c. 2. ENGLISH LITERATURE, BIBLIOGRAPHY. B.A, Victoria Univ. Wellington, 55, M.A, 57, Ph.D.(Eng), 60; dipl. librn, Nat. Libr. Sch, Wellington, 60; D.Phil.(Eng), Oxford, 71. Sr. cataloguer, Alexander Turnbull Libr, Wellington, N.Z, 61-63; Nat. Inst. Res. in Nuclear Sci. fel. comput. ling, Comput. Lab, Oxford, 65-67, sr. res. fel, 67-70; lectr. Eng. lang. & lit, Univ. Col. Wales, 70-73; ASSOC. PROF. ENG, UNIV. S.C, 73- Brit. Acad. res. grant, 65; N.Z. Libr. Asn. associateship 66; vis. assoc. prof. Eng. lang. & lit, Univ. S.C, 72-73; hon. lectr, Inst. Bibliog. & Textual Criticism, Univ. Leeds, 72- Bibliog. Soc, Eng; Bibliog. Soc. Am; N.Z. Libr. Asn; MLA; AAUP; Shakespeare Asn. Am; Int. Shakespeare Asn; Asn. Lit. & Ling. Comput. Shakespeare; computational linguistics; English bibliography and textual criticism. Publ: English printed books to 1700 in the Alexander Turnbull Library, 64 & Dutch printed books in the Alexander Turnbull Library, 64; Bibliography of British literary bibliographies, 69, ed, Oxford Shakespeare concordances (3 vols), 69-73 & auth, Shakespearian bibliography and textual criticism, 71; Clarendon; auth, Ralph Crane and some Shakespeare first folio comedies, Bibliog. Soc. Univ. Va, 72; Spelling and the bibliographer, Library, 63; The compositors of the Shakespeare first folio comedies, Stud. Bibliog, 73; A practical scheme for editing critical texts with a computer, Proof, 73. Add: Dept. of English, University of South Carolina, Columbia, SC 29208.

HOWARTH, WILLIAM LOUIS, b. Minneapolis, Minn, Nov. 26, 40; m. 63; c. 2. ENGLISH & AMERICAN LITERATURE. B.A, Univ. Ill, 62; NDEA fel, Univ. Va, 62-65, M.A, 63, Virginia-Wilson fel, 65-66, Ph.D.(Eng), 67. Instr. ENG, PRINCETON, 66-68, asst. prof, 68-70, bicentennial preceptor, 70-73, ASSOC. PROF, 73- Huntington Libr. res. grant & Princeton Univ. res. grant, summer 68; lectr, Humanities Ctr, Reed Col, 69; assoc. ed, Writings of Henry D. Thoreau, 69-70, textual ed, 71-72, ed-in-chief, 72. MLA; Thoreau Soc.(pres-elect, 73-74, pres, 74-75); Am. Stud. Asn. Autobiography and biography; descriptive bibliography and textual editing. Publ: Ed, A Thoreau gazetteer, 70 & co-ed, The Journal of Henry D. Thoreau, Vols. I & II, 74 & 75, Princeton Univ; auth, Twentieth-century interpretations of Poe's tales, Prentice-Hall, 71; The literary manuscripts of Henry David Thoreau, Ohio State Univ, 74; The Red badge of courage manuscript: new evidence for a critical edition, Stud. Bibliog, 65; Successor to Walden? Thoreau's Moonlight—a course of intended lectures, Proof, Univ. S.C, 72; Some principles of autobiography, New Lit. Hist, winter 74. Add: Dept. of English, Princeton University, McCosh 22, Princeton, NJ 08540.

HOWE, ANN R, b. Escanaba, Mich, Dec. 9, 28. ENGLISH. A.B, Radcliffe Col, 50; A.M, Yale, 52; Ph.D.(Eng), Boston Univ, 62. Teacher Jamaica Plain High Sch, 52-61; Girls Latin Sch, 62; PROF. ENG, BOSTON STATE COL, 62- Renaissance. Publ: Astrophel and Stella: why and how, Stud. in Philol, 4/64. Add: Dept. of English, Boston State College, Boston, MA 02115.

HOWE, CLARA, b. Apr. 29, 05; U.S. citizen; m. 35; c. 2. ENGLISH. A.B, Univ. Pittsburgh, 25, Ph.D.(Eng), 32; Columbia Univ, 25-26; A.M, Ohio State Univ, 27. Instr. ENG, East. Ky. State Teachers Col, 27, 28; Duquesne Univ, 46-47; assoc. prof, Gannon Col, 47-48; prof, Defiance Col, 48-56; assoc.

prof, Col. Steubenville, 56-59; Cent State Univ, 60-66, prof, 66-73. Res. assoc. Eng. vis. scholar prog, Univ. Calif, Berkeley, spring 67. NCTE; Renaissance Soc. Am; Shakespeare Asn. Am; MLA; Midwest Mod. Lang. Asn. Shakespeare; English novel. Publ: Composition principles in Shakespeare, fall 63 & Streaks of the tulip: Shakespeare's commentary on death, winter 64, Univ. S.Fla. Lang. Quart; Mild objection, Mr. Schulburg, Ohio Eng. Asn. Bull, 9/68. Add: Dept. of English, Central State University, Wilberforce, OH 45384.

HOWE, IRVING, b. New York, N.Y, June 11, 20; m. 47; c. 2. ENGLISH. B.Sc.S, City Col. New York, 40; Kenyon Rev. fel, 53. Assoc. prof. ENG, Brandeis Univ, 53-61; PROF, Stanford Univ, 61-63; HUNTER COL, 63- Lectr, Gauss Sem, Princeton, 53. Nat. Inst. Arts & Lett. Award, 59. U.S.A, 42-45. MLA. American 19th century prose; American 20th century literature; Yiddish literature. Publ: Sherwood Anderson: a critical biography; William Faulkner: a critical study; Politics and the novel; Steady work, 66 & Decline of the new, 70, Harcourt; Thomas Hardy, Macmillan, 67; The critical point, Horizon, 73. Add: Dept. of English, City University of New York, 33 W. 42nd St, New York, NY 10036.

HOWELL, ELMO, b. Tremont, Miss, Aug. 5, 18. ENGLISH. B.A, Univ. Miss, 40; M.A, Univ. Fla, 48, Ph.D, 55. Asst. prof. ENG, Jacksonville State Col, 55-57; MEMPHIS STATE UNIV, 57-60, ASSOC. PROF, 60- Southern literature. Publ: Eudora Welty's Comedy of manners, S.Atlantic Quart, autumn 70; Katherine Anne Porter as a Southern writer, S.C. Rev, 12/71; Faulkner and Scott and the legacy of the lost cause, Ga. Rev, fall 72; plus others. Add: Dept. of English, Memphis State University, Memphis, TN 38111.

HOWELL, JAMES, b. Wilkesboro, N.C, Mar. 20, 96; m. 29. ENGLISH. A.B, Guilford Col, 25; A.M, Univ. N.C, 31, Ph.D, 42. Prin, High Sch, 25-28; 29-30, 31-34, instr. Eng, Univ. N.C, 30-31, 34-35; supt. Schs, Red Springs, N.C, 35-37; assoc. prof. ENG, West. Carolina Teachers Col, 37-42; prof. & head dept, Greensboro Col, 42-45; prof. & chmn. dept, Tusculum Col, 45-46; Hardin-Simmons Univ, 46-47; prof. ELON COL, 47-68, chmn. dept, 47-60, EMER. PROF, 68- Prof. Eng, Methodist Col, 68-70, acting chmn. dept, 69-70; head dept. Eng, Harrells Christian Acad, 70-71. U.S.A, 17-18. MLA; Shakespeare Asn. Am; Renaissance Soc. Am; S.Atlantic Mod. Lang. Asn; Col. Eng. Asn; AAUP. Reniassance English literature and drama; medieval English literature; the rogue in non-dramatic English literature to Robert Greene. Publ: The rogue in English comedy to 1642. Add: Box 337, Elizabethtown, NC 28337.

HOWELL, JOHN MICHAEL, b. Oshawa, Ont, Mar. 2, 33; U.S. citizen; m. 63; c. 1. AMERICAN LITERATURE. B.A, Millsaps Col, 54; M.A, Univ. South. Calif, 60; Ph.D.(Eng), Tulane Univ, 63. Asst. prof, ENG, SOUTH. ILL. UNIV, CARBONDALE, 63-69, ASSOC. PROF, 69- MLA; NCTE; AAUP. American literature. Publ: Ed, Hemingway's African stories, Scribner, 69; Hemingway and Fitzgerald in The sound and the fury, Papers on Lang. & Lit, summer 66; Salinger in the waste land, Mod. Fiction Stud, fall 66; From Abercrombie & Fitch to The first forty-nine stories: the text of Ernest Hemingway's Francis Macomber, Proof, 72. Add: Dept. of English, Southern Illinois University, Carbondale, IL 62901.

HOWELL, RALPH DANIEL, b. Bonifay, Fla, Oct. 13, 38; m. 72; c. 3. LINGUISTICS, ENGLISH. B.A, Miss. Col, 60; M.A, Fla. State Univ, 64, Ph.D. (Eng, ling), 71. Teacher Eng. & Latin, Quincy High Sch, Fla, 60-62; ASST. PROF. ENG. & LING, MISS. COL, 68- MLA; NCTE; Conf. Col. Compos. & Commun. Linguistic geography, dialectology; sociolinguistics; English syntax, transformational. Add: Dept. of English, Mississippi College, Clinton, MS 39058.

HOWELL, WILBUR SAMUEL, b. Wayne, N.Y, Apr. 22, 04. RHETORIC, ORATORY. A.B, Cornell Univ, 24, A.M, 28, Ph.D, 31; Univ. Paris, France, 28-29. Instr. pub. speaking, Iowa State Col, 24-25; Wash. Univ, 25-27; Cornell Univ, 27-28; 29-30; Harvard, 30-33; asst. prof, Dartmouth Col, 33-34; PRINCETON, 34-40, assoc. prof, 40-55, PROF. RHETORIC & ORATORY, 55-72, EMER. PROF, 72- Guggenheim fel, 48-49, 57-58; Huntington Libr. fel, 51-52, 62-63; Counc. Humanities sr. fel, Princeton, 65-66; assoc. ed, Papers of Thomas Jefferson, 72- Speech Commun. Asn. (ed-in-chief, Quart. J. Speech, 54-56); MLA; Renaissance Soc. Am. History of British logic and rhetoric, 1500-1800; rhetoric and poetics; parliamentary writings of Thomas Jefferson. Publ: Fenelon's dialogues on eloquence, 51 & Eighteenth-Century British logic and rhetoric, 71, Princeton; Rhetoric of Alcuin and Charlemagne, 41 & Logic and rhetoric in England, 1500-1700, 56, Russell; Ramus, Petrus, In: Encycl. Britannica, 67; Literature as an enterprise in communication, In: Contemporary rhetoric, Scott, 72; John Locke and the new rhetoric, In: Philosophers on rhetoric, Nat. Textbk. Co, 73; plus four others. Add: 20 Armour Rd, Princeton, NJ 08540.

HOWELL, WILLIAM SMILEY, b. Footville, Wis, Apr. 13, 14; m. 35; c. 2. SPEECH. B.S, Univ. Wis, 35, A.M, 38, Ph.D, 42. Teacher, High Sch, Wis, 35-37; instr, Univ. S.Dak, 38-40; educ. consult, Air Force, U.S. Army, 42-45; asst. prof. SPEECH, UNIV. MINN, MINNEAPOLIS, 45-48, assoc. prof, 48-54, PROF, 54-, chmn. dept. speech & theatre arts, 54-59. Speech Commun. Asn.(pres, 70-72); Cent. State Speech Asn; Int. Stud. Asn; Soc. Int. Develop; Int. Commun. Asn. Intercultural communication; persuasion; task oriented small groups. Publ: Co-auth, Persuasion, a means of social control & co-auth, Interpersonal communication in the modern organization, 69, Prentice-Hall; co-auth, Discussion, Macmillan; Presentational speaking for business and the professions, Harper, 71. Add: Dept. of Speech-Communication, University of Minnesota, Minneapolis, MN 55455.

HOWELLS, ANNE BLACKMAN, b. St. Louis, Mo, Sept. 18, 41. ENGLISH. B.A, Swarthmore Col, 63; M.A, Univ. Wash, 66, Ph.D.(Eng), 68. Instr. Eng, OCCIDENTAL COL, 66-67, ASST. PROF. ENG. & COMP. LIT, 68- MLA. English Renaissance literature; 19th century English literature. Add: Dept. of English, Occidental College, Los Angeles, CA 90041.

HOWES, ALAN BARBER, b. St. Johnsbury, Vt, Sept. 20, 20; m. 58; c. 2. ENGLISH. B.A, Middlebury Col, 41, M.A, 43; Ph.D.(Eng), Yale, 55. Instr. ENG, Middlebury Col, 43-45; Univ. Conn, Hartford, 50-51; guest prof, Yokohama Nat. Univ, 51-53; instr, UNIV. MICH, ANN ARBOR, 55-58, asst. prof, 58-64, assoc. prof, 64-69, PROF, 69- U.S.A, 45-47, Sgt. Laurence Sterne; 18th century English novel; the teaching of English. Publ: Yorick and the critics, Yale Univ, 58; An outline of English composition, Doubleday, 62; Teaching literature to adolescents: plays, 68 & Teaching literature to adolescents: novels, 72, Scott; ed, Sterne: the critical heritage, Routledge, & Kegan Paul, London, 74; auth, A linguistic analogy in literary criticism, In: Introductory readings on language, Holt, rev. ed, 66. Add: Dept. of English, University of Michigan, Ann Arbor, MI 48104.

HOWLING, ROBERT TUNIS, b. N.J, Mar. 17, 21; m. 43; c. 2. ENGLISH LITERATURE. B.A, Rutgers Univ, 42; M.A, N.Y. Univ, 48; Ph.D.(Eng), Pa. State Univ, 54. Instr. ENG, Susquehanna Univ, 48-51; assoc. prof, Am. Univ. Beirut, 54-60; Guilford Col, 60-61; Am. Univ. Beirut, 61-63; prof, Univ. Riyadh, Saudi Arabia, 63-64; prof. & dir, Col. Petrol. & Minerals, Saudi Arabia, 64-65; PROF, UNIV. NEW HAVEN, 65- U.S.A, 42-46, 1st Lt; Bronze Star Medal; Silver Star. Col. Eng. Asn; Shakespeare Soc. Am; MLA; Teachers Eng. to Speakers Other Lang. Shakespeare; Tudor and Stuart drama. Publ: Contrib, English through patterns, Khayats, 63; auth, Browning's theory of art, Susquehanna Univ. Stud, 51. Add: Dept. of English, University of New Haven, New Haven,University, CT 06505.

HOY, CYRUS HENRY, b. St. Marys, W.Va, Feb. 26, 26. ENGLISH, RENAISSANCE LITERATURE. B.A, Univ. Va, 50, M.A, 51, DuPont jr, sr. & res. fels, Ph.D.(Eng), 54; Fulbright fel, Cambridge, 52-53. Instr. ENG, Univ. Va, 54-56; asst. prof, Vanderbilt Univ, 56-60, assoc. prof, 60-64; PROF, UNIV. ROCHESTER, 64- Folger Shakespeare Libr. fels, summer 61, 62 & spring 70, mem. ed. bd, Libr, 70-72; Guggenheim fel, 62-63; gen. ed, Regents Renaissance Drama Ser, 62-; mem. ed. bd, Shakespeare Quart, 67-; mem. ed. bd, Stud. Eng. Lit, 68- MLA; Shakespeare Asn. Am; Renaissance English literature; modern drama. Publ: The hyacinth room: an investigation into the nature of comedy, tragedy, and tragicomedy, Knopf, 64; co-ed, The dramatic works in the Beaumont and Fletcher Canon, Col. I, 66, co-ed, Vol. II, 70, & co-auth, Cambridge bibliography of English literature, Vol. I, I, 73, Cambridge; auth, The shares of Fletcher and his collaborators in the Beaumont and Fletcher Canon, Stud. in Bibliog, 57-62; Elizabethan and restoration dramatic plotting, In: Renaissance Drama, Vol. IX, Northwest. Univ, 66; Shaw's tragicomic irony, Va. Quart. Rev, 71. Add: Dept. of English, University of Rochester, Rochester, NY 14627.

HOYLE, JAMES F. b. Cornwall, N.Y, June 27, 31; m. 55; c. 3. ENGLISH LITERATURE. A.B, Kenyon Col, 53; Ph.D, Princeton, 61. Instr. ENG, Kenyon Col, 58-61, asst. prof, 61-63; Eastman Sch. Music, Univ. Rochester, 63-68; OAKLAND UNIV, 68-69, ASSOC. PROF, 69- U.S.A, 54-56. MLA; Shakespeare Asn. Am. Romantic poetry, especially S.T. Coleridge; Shakespeare. Publ: Kubla Khan as an elated experience, Lit. & Psychol, Winter 66. Add: Dept. of English, Oakland University, Rochester, MI 48063.

HOYLE, NORMAN EUGENE, b. Washington, Ill, Sept. 29, 34; m. 56; c. 1. ENGLISH. B.A, Univ. Redlands, 56; univ. scholar, Duke Univ, 57-58, M.A, 58, res. fel, 58-59, teaching fel, 59-60, Ph.D.(Eng), 60. Asst. prof. Eng, Linfield Col, 60-66; librn, Wash. State Univ, 66-67; ASSOC. PROF. LIBR. SCI, STATE UNIV. N.Y. ALBANY, 67- Shakespeare; Whitman; Melville. Add: School of Library Science, State University of New York at Albany, Albany, NY 12203.

HOYT, CHARLES ALVA, Middletown, Conn, Sept. 26, 31; m. 60; c. 3. ENGLISH LITERATURE. A.B, Wesleyan Univ, 53, M.A.T, 55; M.A, Columbia Univ, 56, Ph.D.(Eng), 61. Instr. ENG, Wayne State Univ, 57-60; asst. prof, BENNETT COL, 60-64, assoc. prof, 64-68, CHMN. DEPT, 68- Consult. humanities, U.S. govt, 72-; vis. prof, State Univ. N.Y. Col. New Paltz, 74. Ethnomusicology and jazz; English literature of the 19th century; contemporary English and American literature. Publ: Ed, Minor British novelists, 67 & Minor American novelists, 69, South. Ill. Univ; auth, Bernard Malamud and the new romanticism, In: Contemporary American novelists, South. Ill. Univ, 64; Novelist or historian?, Columbia Univ. Forum, 66; Contemporary British literature, In: Encyclopedia Americana, Grolier, 68. Add: Dept. of English, Bennett College, Millbrook, NY 12545.

HOYT, RICHARD DUANE, b. Hermiston, Ore, Jan 28, 41; m. 67. JOURNALISM, AMERICAN STUDIES. B.S, Univ. Ore, 63, M.S, 67; fel, Wash. Jour. Ctr, 67-68; Ph.D.(Am. stud), Univ. Hawaii, 72. Reporter, Honolulu Star-Bull, 68-69; Honolulu Advert, 69-72; vis. asst. prof. JOUR, UNIV. MD, COLLEGE PARK, 72-73, ASST. PROF, 73- Intel.C, U.S.A, 63-66, S/Sgt. Asn. Educ. Jour; Am. Stud. Asn. Mass media; popular culture; American literature. Add: College of Journalism, University of Maryland, College Park, MD 20742.

HOZESKI, BRUCE WILLIAM, b. Grand Rapids, Mich, Feb. 28, 41; m. 67; c. 1. ENGLISH LITERATURE, HISTORY OF LANGUAGE. B.A, Aquinas Col, 64; M.A, Mich. State Univ, 66, Ph.D.(medieval Eng. lit), 69. Asst. ENG, Mich. State Univ, 64-69; instr, Lansing Community Col, 68-69; ASST. PROF, BALL STATE UNIV, 69- AAUP; MLA; Midwest Mod. Lang. Asn; NCTE; Early Eng. Text Soc; Teachers Eng. to Speakers Other Lang. Medieval English literature; medieval drama; Hildegard of Bingen. Publ: Ordo Virtutum: Hildegard of Bingen's liturgical morality play, Annuale Medievale, 72; A review of Joseph Warren Beach's American fiction: 1920-1940, spring 72 & A review of John Steinbeck and Edward F. Ricketts' Sea of Cortez: a leisurely journal of travel and research, spring 73, Steinbeck Quart. Add: Dept. of English, Ball State University, Muncie, IN 47306.

HRUBY, JOHN FRANKLIN, b. Cleveland, Ohio, July 25, 14; m. 53; c. 2. DRAMA. A.B, Carnegie Inst. Technol, 38; M.A, West. Reserve Univ, 46, M.F.A, 47; Ph.D, Univ. Denver, 60. Instr, Allegheny Col, 48-49; asst. prof. drama, Wesleyan Col, 49-54; speech, Wagner Col, 55-61, assoc. prof. speech, head dept. speech & theatre & dean stud, 61-68; assoc. prof. theatre & dir. theatre, Rider Col, 68-72. Carnegie grant-in-aid, 51; gen. mgr, The Lost Colony, Roanoke Island Hist. Asn, 72-; mem, Inst. Outdoor Drama, 72- U.S.A.A.F, 41-46, Capt. Am. Theatre Asn; Children's Theatre Asn; Southeast. Theatre Conf. Add: The Lost Colony, P.O. Box 68, Manteo, NC 27954.

HUANG, RODERICK, b. May 15, 24; U.S. citizen; m. 53; c. 2. ENGLISH LITERATURE. B.A, Fukien Christian Univ, China, 47; M.A, Wesleyan Univ, 48; M.A, Northwest. Univ, 50, Ph.D.(Eng), 55. Lectr. ENG, Northwest. Univ, 52-53; instr, Valparaiso Univ, 53-55; lectr, Univ. Singapore, 55-59, sr. lectr, 59-66; PROF, UNIV. WINDSOR, 66- MLA; Johnson Soc; Humanities Asn. Can; Asn. Can. Univ. Teachers Eng. Eighteenth and nineteenth century English literature; the Romantic period. Publ: William Cowper: nature poet, Oxford, 57; William Blake's The tyger: a reinterpretation, Humanities Asn. Bull, fall 67; William Cowper and The rime of the ancient mariner, Univ. Windsor Rev, spring 68. Add: Dept. of English, University of Windsor, Windsor, Ont, Can.

HUBACH, ROBERT ROGERS, b. Kansas City, Mo, May 10, 16. ENGLISH. B.A, Univ. Kansas City, 38; univ. scholar, Univ. Colo, 38-39, M.A, 39; Ph.D, Ind. Univ, 43. Instr. ENG, Univ. Ill, 43-44; prof. Whitworth Col, 44-46; instr, Ill. Inst. Technol, 46-47; asst. prof, BOWLING GREEN STATE UNIV, 47-50, assoc. prof, 50-72, EMER. ASSOC. PROF, 72- MLA. Walt Whitman, middle western travel narratives. Publ: Walt Whitman and the West; Early midwestern travel narratives, Wayne, 61; A street beyond darkness, Phila, 68; Unpublished travel narratives on the early Midwest, Miss. Valley Hist. Rev. Add: 215 Beach St, Santa Cruz, CA 95060.

HUBBELL, JAY BROADUS, b. Smyth Co, Va, May 8, 85; m. 18; c. 2. AMERICAN LITERATURE. A.B, Univ. Richmond, 05, Litt.D, 56; A.M, Harvard, 08; Ph.D, Columbia Univ, 22; Litt.D, South. Methodist Univ, 51, Clemson Univ, 61. Instr. Latin & Greek, Bethel Col.(Ky), 05-06; Eng, Univ. N.C, 08-09; assoc. prof, Wake Forest Col, 11-14; asst. prof, South. Methodist Univ, 15-16; assoc. prof, 16-19, Lilly prof. & head dept, 21-27; prof, DUKE UNIV, 27-54, dir. grad. stud, 43-48, EMER. PROF. ENG, 54- Vis. prof, Univ. Vienna, 49, 50; Athens, Greece, 53; Univ. Va, 54-55; Clemson Univ, 56; Columbia Univ, 57-58; Tex. Tech. Univ, 60; Univ. Ky, 61; hon. consult, Am. cult. hist, Libr. Congr, 64-66; ed, Southwest Rev, 24-27; Am. Lit, 28-54. Mayflower Award, 55; Jay B. Hubbell Medallion, MLA, 64; Essays on Am. Lit. in Honor of Jay B. Hubbell, 67. U.S.A, 18-23, Lt. MLA (v.pres, 51). Literature of the South and New England; Poe. Publ: Co-auth, An introduction to poetry, 22 & An introduction to drama, 27, Macmillan; auth, The last years of Henry Timrod, 41, The South in American literature, 1607-1900, South and Southwest, literary essays and reminiscences, 65 & Who are the major American writers? a study of the changing literary canon, 72, Duke Univ; American life in literature, Harper; Southern life in fiction, Univ. Ga, 60; introd, Edgar Allan Poe's Tales and poems, C.E. Merrill, 68; co-auth, Essay on Edgar Allan Poe, In: Eight American authors; a review of research and criticism, MLA, 56 & Norton, 72; plus many articles & essays. Add: 121 Pinecrest Rd, Durham, NC 27705.

HUBBLE, THOMAS N, b. Pasadena, Calif, Oct. 15, 27; m. 52; c. 2. COMPARATIVE LITERATURE. B.A, Univ. South. Calif, 51, M.A, 54, Ph.D. (comp. lit), 62; Univ. Paris, 53-55. Teaching asst. COMP. LIT, Univ. South. Calif, 55-58; PROF, CALIF. STATE UNIV, LONG BEACH, 58- Fulbright lectr, Greece, 63-64; Tunisia, 67-68. U.S.N, 45-46. Am. Comp. Lit. Asn. The work of Albert Camus. Add: Dept. of Comparative Literature, California State University, Long Beach, 6101 E. Seventh St, Long Beach, CA 90801.

HUBENKA, LLOYD JOHN, b. Omaha, Nebr, Jan. 1, 31; m. 53; c. 4. ENGLISH. B.A, Creighton Univ, 52, teaching fel, 57-58, M.A, 59; Ph.D.(Eng), Univ. Nebr, 66. Instr. ENG, CREIGHTON UNIV, 58-61, asst. prof, 61-65, ASSOC. PROF, 66-, CHMN. DEPT, 65- Nat. Endowment for Humanities fel, summer 68. U.S.A, 52-54, Res, 54-, Lt. Col. MLA; Rocky Mountain Mod. Lang. Asn. Economic thought of John Ruskin; dramas and religious philosophy of Bernard Shaw. Publ: Ed, John Ruskins' Unto this last, Univ. Nebr, 67; co-auth, The design of drama, McKay, 73. Add: Dept. of English, Smith Hall, Creighton University, Omaha, NE 68131.

HUBER, ALBERTA, C.S.J, b. Rock Island, Ill, Feb. 12, 17. ENGLISH. B.A, Col. St. Catherine, 39; M.A, Univ. Minn, 45; Ph.D, Univ. Notre Dame, 54. Teacher high sch, 38-40; Instr. ENG, COL. ST. CATHERINE, 40-52, asst. prof, 52-57, assoc. prof, 57-63, PROF, 63-, PRES, 64-, acad. dean, 63-64. Consult-examr. comn. insts. of higher educ, N.Cent. Asn. Schs. & Cols, 71- Nat. Cath. Educ. Asn.(mem. comn. on purpose & identity, Higher Educ. Sect, 71-); Asn. Higher Educ. Linguistics; early Germanic languages, especially Gothic; American literature. Add: College of St. Catherine, St. Paul, MN 55105.

HUBER, JOAN R, b. Johnstown, Pa, July 5, 31. ENGLISH. A.B, Duquesne Univ, 59; A.M, Univ. Pittsburgh, 62, Ph.D.(Eng), 67. Asst. ENG, Univ. Pittsburgh, 60-61, teaching fel, 61-62, instr, Johnstown Col, 62-64; asst. prof, Pa. State Univ, New Kensington, 65-67; lectr, UNIV. PITTSBURGH, 68-74, ASST. PROF, 74- NCTE; MLA. Afro-American writing. Add: Dept. of English, 529 C.L, University of Pittsburgh, Pittsburgh, PA 15260.

HUBER, JOHN EDWARD, b. Watertown, Wis, Nov. 11, 39; m. 66; c. 2. ENGLISH LITERATURE. B.A, Notre Dame Univ, 62; Holy Cross Col, 62-63; M.A, Univ. Wis-Madison, 64, univ. fel, 69, Ph.D.(Eng), 73. Instr. ENG, Tex. South. Univ, 65-66; ASST. PROF, UNIV. NOTRE DAME, 69- NCTE; Col. Eng. Asn; Conf. Col. Compos. & Commun. Middle English literature; college composition; computer-assisted instruction. Publ: Troilus' predestination soliloquy, Neuphilol. Mitt, 65. Add: Dept. of English, University of Notre Dame, Notre Dame, IN 46556.

HUBER, PAUL, b. Akron, Ohio, Oct. 22, 19; m. 46; c. 1. SPEECH, RELIGION. A.B, Muskingum Col, 42; M.D, Emory Univ, 51; M.A, Univ. Mich, 53, Ph.D.(rhetoric & speech educ), 56. Instr. Eng. & speech, Ga. Inst. Technol, 53-54; asst. prof. SPEECH, Ariz. State Univ, 54-59; PROF, CALIF. STATE UNIV, SACRAMENTO, 59-, acting chmn. humanities div, 65-66, chmn. dept. speech, 65-66. Teaching asst. homiletics, Emory Univ, 49-51; dir, lay-speaking prog, Sacramento-Nevada Methodist Church, 61-62; consult. creative thinking & speaking, Calif. State Personnel Bd, 64; speaking & listening, oral commun, Aerojet Gen. Corp, 64-65; conf. leadership & written commun, Calif. Highway Patrol, 64-68; co-dir, NDEA Inst. Disadvantaged Children, summers 65-67; consult. psychol. of lang, Army Mid. Mgt. Sch, 66-68; consult, Mgt. of Time, Calif. Dept. Water Resources, 69-70 & Mgt. of Defensiveness, 70-71; Persuasion and Attitude Change, Sales Training Inst. Am, 70-72. Spec. agent, Internal Security & Intel. Div, U.S. War Dept, 42-44; agent in charge, Criminal Invest. Div, Austria, 44-46. Speech Commun. Asn; NEA. Creative thinking; listening; psychology of language. Publ: Co-auth, Speech: research, composition, delivery, Graphic Arts, 63 & Effective written communication: a multimedia approach, Calif. Dept. Water Resources, 70; auth, Discussion-progression sequence, In: Discussion and conference, Sattler & Miller & Prentice-Hall, 54. Add: Communication Studies, California State University, Sacramento, 6000 Jay St, Sacramento, CA 95819.

HUBER, ROBERT BRUCE, b. June 12, 09. SPEECH. A.B, Manchester Col, 30; A.M, Univ. Mich, 34; Ph.D, Univ. Wis, 42. Teacher high sch, Ind, 30-34; asst. prof, Manchester Col, 34-35; instr, Ind. Univ, 35-37, 38-41; asst. prof, Univ. Ore, 42-43; PROF. SPEECH & HEAD DEPT, UNIV. VT, 46- U.S.N.R, 43-46. Speech Commun. Asn; Speech Asn. East. States (pres, 50); New Eng. Speech Asn.(pres, 50); Am. Forensic Asn.(pres). Public address; Dwight L. Moody, salesman of salvation, a case study in audience psychology; rhetoric and public address. Publ: Influencing through argument, McKay, 63. Add: Dept. of Speech, University of Vermont, Burlington, VT 05401.

HUBERMAN, EDWARD, b. Newark, N.J, Jan. 30, 10; m. 39; c. 4. ENGLISH. A.B, Harvard, 29; A.M, Rutgers Univ, 30; Sorbonne, 31-32; Ph.D, Duke Univ, 34. Mem. fac, Essex Jr. Col; U.S. Dept. Agr. Grad. Sch; from assoc. prof. to PROF. ENG, RUTGERS UNIV, NEWARK, 47- Adv. to Am. del, Inter-Am. Conf. Indian life, Mex, 40; vis. prof, Grad. Sch, N.Y. Univ, 61-62; television lectr, New York, 62-63; conferee, Nat. Sci. Found. Conf. Honors Progs. Cols, June, 63; Fulbright prof. Am. lit, Univ. Innsbruck, Austria, 63-64. MLA; NCTE; Col. Eng. Asn.(dir, bur. appointments, 62-, treas, 64-67, v.pres, 67-69, pres, 69-70, dir, 70-71); Renaissance Soc. Am. Comparative and 20th century literature; the renaissance. Publ: Co-auth, Angles of vision, Houghton, 62; transl, Life is a dream, Great Bks. Found, 62; Fifty great essays, 64, 4th ed, 68, 8th ed, 72, Great British short stories, 68 & co-ed, Fifty great European short stories, 71, Bantam; co-ed, War: an anthology, Wash. Sq, 69; auth, Bibliographical note on James Shirley's The politian, Trans. Oxford Bibliog. Soc; Honors programs in colleges, Col. Eng. Asn. Critic, 3/63; Transl, Maruxa Vilalta's A mad day & Time's soliloquy, Latin-Am. Lit. Rev, 73. Add: Dept. of English, Rutgers University, Newark, NJ 07102.

HUBERMAN, ELIZABETH LYLE, b. Gloucester, Mass, Nov. 30, 15; m. 39; c. 4. ENGLISH & AMERICAN LITERATURE. A.B, Bryn Mawr Col, 37; M.A, New York Univ, 63, Ph.D.(Eng), 69. Asst. prof. ENG, KEAN COL. N.J, 68-69, assoc. prof, 69-73, PROF, 73-, CHMN. DEPT, 72- MLA; Col. Eng. Asn. Contemporary British and American poetry; the short story. Publ: Co-ed, Great British short stories, 68 & 50 great European short stories, 71, Bantam; co-ed, War: an anthology, Wash. Sq. Press, 69; auth, Hart Crane's use of symphonic form, Univ. Innsbruck, 70; The poetry of Edwin Muir, Oxford, 71; Initiation and tragedy: a new look at Edwin Muir's The gate, PMLA, 1/72. Add: Dept. of English, Kean College of New Jersey, Union, NJ 07083.

HUBLER, RICHARD G, b. Scranton, Pa, Aug. 20, 12; m. 41, 54; c. 4. ENGLISH. B.A, Swarthmore Col, 34. Pub. relat. consult, New York & Los Angeles, 38-60; instr. writing, Ventura Col, 55-60; asst. prof. Eng, San Fernando Valley State Col, 60-62; Univ. Calif, Santa Barbara, 62-63; ASST. PROF. WRITING & ENG, CALIF. STATE UNIV, NORTHRIDGE, 63-, asst. to pres, 64. Ed, El Crepusculo, N.Mex, 49; columnist, Santa Fe New Mexican, 50; ed, Ojai Valley News, Calif, 55; assoc. bk. reviewer, Los Angeles Times, Calif, 60; lectr. theatre arts, Univ. Calif, Los Angeles, 68. Harper's Best War Article Award, 41. U.S.M.C, 42-45, Capt. Fiction; biography; history. Publ: Lou Gehrig, 41; co-auth, I flew for China, 42 & Flying leathernecks, 44; auth, I've got mine, 45; The quiet kingdom, 48; The brass god, 52; The chase, 52; In darkest childhood, 54; The pass, 55; Man in the sky, 56; SAC: Strategic Air Command, 58; The shattering of the image, 59; True love, true love, 59; co-auth, St. Louis woman, 59; auth, Big eight, 60; Straight up: history of the helicopter, 61; The blue-and-gold man, 61; ed, The world's shortest stories, 61; co-auth, Trial and triumph, 65 & Where's the rest of me, 65; auth, The Cole Porter story, 65; The Cristianis, 66; South of the moon, 66; Soldier and sage, 66; Wheeler (3 vols), 70; Love and wisdom, 68; The itch of writing, Ed. Rodopi, Netherlands, 73. Add: P.O. Box 793, Ojai, CA 93023.

HUCKABAY, CALVIN, b. Bienville, La, Oct. 17, 28; m. 58; c. 1. ENGLISH, MILTON. B.A, La. Col, 49; scholar & M.A, Tulane Univ, 50; fel. & Ph.D.(Eng), La. State Univ, 55. Assoc. prof. Eng, Miss. State Univ, 58-61; prof. Hardin-Simmons Univ, 61-63; prof. Eng. & chmn. div. lang, HOUSTON BAPTIST UNIV, 63-73, DEAN COL. FINE ARTS & HUMANITIES, 73- South. Fels. Fund grant, 57. MLA; Renaissance Soc. Am; Milton Soc. Am; NCTE. Publ: John Milton: a bibliographical supplement, 1929-1957, Duquesne Univ, 60, AMS Press, 68; John Milton: an annotated bibliography, 1929-1968, Duquesne Univ, 69; Satan and the narrative structure of Paradise lost, Studia Neophilologica, 61; The Satanist controversy of the nineteenth century, La. State Univ. Stud. Renaissance, 62. Add: College of Fine Arts & Humanities, Houston Baptist University, 7502 Fondren Rd, Houston, TX 77036.

HUCKLEBERRY, ALAN WRIGHT, b. North Vernon, Ind, Sept. 27, 12; m. 36; c. 2. SPEECH. B.A, DePauw Univ, 35; M.A, La. State Univ, 40; Ed.D. (speech educ), Ind. Univ, 48. Teacher, high schs, Ind, 35-41; instr. SPEECH, Ind. State Univ, 41-43; from asst. prof. to PROF. & HEAD DEPT, BALL STATE UNIV, 43- Minn. Workshop on teacher educ, summer 57; mem. bd. dir, phonetics interest group, Speech Commun. Asn, 60-62, mem. legis. assembly, 61-64; consult. & lectr, div. speech, Univ. N.C, summer 68. Speech Commun. Asn.(assoc. ed, Jour, 60-62); Cent. States Speech Commun. Asn. Phonetics; public speaking; speech pathology. Publ: Beginning phonetics, W.C. Brown, 61, 67; co-auth, Speech education for the elementary teacher, Allyn & Bacon, 66 & The effective speaker, Houghton, 68; co-auth, The student teacher's speech, Quart. J. Speech, 12/43; auth, When you seek advice, Speech Teacher, 1/53; The disappearing r sound, Proc. Congr. Phonetics, Prague, 8/67. Add: Dept. of Speech, Ball State University, Muncie, IN 47306.

HUDDLESTON, EUGENE L, b. Ironton, Ohio, Jan. 29, 31; m. 61; c. 1. ENGLISH. A.B, Marshall Univ, 53; M.A, Ohio Univ, 56; Ind. Univ, 56-57; Ph.D, (Eng), Mich. State Univ, 65. Instr. Eng, Tri-State Col, 57-60; Kellogg Community Col, 60-61; asst. prof, Ind. State Univ, 62-66; AM. THOUGHT & LANG, MICH. STATE UNIV, 66-69, ASSOC. PROF, 69- Norman Foerster

Prize, 66. MLA. Poetry of early national period; agrarian idealism in American literature; 19th century feminist verse satire. Publ: Topographical poetry in the early national period, Am. Lit, 11/66; Indians and literature of the Federalist era: the case of James Elliot, New Eng. Quart, 6/71; Place names in the writings of Jesse Stuart, West. Folklore, 7/72. Add: Dept. of American Thought & Language, Bessey Hall, Michigan State University, East Lansing, MI 48823.

HUDNALL, CLAYTON E, b. East Bank, W.Va, Apr. 30, 36; m. 64; c. 1. ENGLISH. A.B, Wheeling Col, 59; Woodrow Wilson fel, 59-60; M.A, State Univ. Iowa, 61; Ph.D.(Eng), Univ. Ill, 66. Asst. prof. ENG, Vanderbilt Univ, 66-70; ASSOC. PROF, UNIV. HARTFORD, 70- Romanticism; later 18th century. Publ: Reynolds, Rice and Bailey in the Leigh Browne-Lockyer collection, Keats-Shelley J, 70; New lines by Keats, Eng. Lang. Notes, 70; Leigh Hunt on Keats: two new poems, South. Humanities Rev, 70. Add: Dept. of English, University of Hartford, 200 Bloomfield Ave, West Hartford, CT 06117.

HUDSON, CHARLES M, JR, b. Nashville, Tenn, Mar. 8, 12. ENGLISH LITERATURE. A.B, Vanderbilt Univ, 33, A.M, 34; Ph.D, Yale, 43. Instr. ENG, Lafayette Col, 38-39; UNIV. MO-COLUMBIA, 39-45, asst. prof, 45-48, assoc. prof, 48-54, PROF, 54-, chmn. dept, 56-60, 65-67. MLA; Keats-Shelley Asn. Am. Romantic period literature; humanities. Publ: Co-ed, English literature, 60. Add: Dept. of English, University of Missouri-Columbia, Columbia, MO 65201.

HUDSON, GERTRUDE REESE, b. Waco, Tex; m. 51. ENGLISH. A.B, Baylor Univ, 30, A.M, 35; Ph.D, Univ. Tex, 41. Instr. Baylor Univ, 36-37; assoc. prof, John Tarleton Col, 42-43; instr. ENG, Univ. Tex, 43-51, asst. prof, 51-52; assoc. prof, SOUTHWEST TEX. STATE UNIV, 63-67, PROF, 67- Univ. Tex. res. grant, 48; Am. Asn. Univ. Women Justin fel, Eng, 49-50; Am. Philos. Soc. res. grant, 57; Southwest Tex. State Coll. res. grant, 68-69. MLA; S-Cent. Mod. Lang. Asn. Sixteenth and nineteenth century English. Publ: Browning to his American friends, Bowes & Bowes, London, 65; Political import of the misfortunes of Arthur, Rev. Eng. Stud, 45; Robert Browning and his son, PMLA, 46. Add: 2401 Ridgeview, Austin, TX 78704.

HUDSON, RANDOLPH HOYT, b. Cleveland, Ohio, Apr. 12, 27; m. 51; c. 2. ENGLISH LITERATURE. A.B, Stanford Univ, 50, Ph.D, 62; A.M, Cornell Univ, 53; Univ. Paris, 47-48. Asst. prof. ENG, Humboldt State Col, 58-62; Col. Engineering, Univ. Colo, 62-64, assoc. prof, 64-67; prof. & chmn. dept, Cent. State Univ, 67-69; PROF, NORTHEAST. ILL. UNIV, 69- U.S.N, 45-56; U.S.A, 53-54. Conf. Col. Compos. & Commun.(ed.bd, 64-66); NCTE; MLA. History of the American short story; development of eighteenth-century English Gothicism. Publ: Technology, culture, and language, Heath, 66; A modern handbook of American English, Sci. Res. Assoc, 66; Teaching technical writing, Coll. Compos. & Commun. J, 12/61; Henry Mackenzie, James Beattie, et al. and the Edinburgh Mirror, Eng. Lang. Notes, 12/63; Atlantic monthly authorship, 1857-1861, Am. Notes & Queries, 9/64. Add: Dept. of English, Northeastern Illinois University, Chicago, IL 60625.

HUDSON, ROBERT J, b. Selma, Ala, June 11, 21; m. 44; c. 1. ENGLISH. B.A, Tenn. State Col, 46; M.A, N.Y. Univ, 47, Ph.D.(Eng), 62. Instr. ENG, TENN. STATE UNIV, 47-51, asst. prof, 51-55, assoc. prof, 55-63, PROF, 63-, CHMN. DEPT, 71-, DEAN SCH. ARTS & SCI, 74-, asst. dean, 68-74. Part-time prof. Eng, Fisk Univ, 64-65, lectr. Shakespeare & Elizabethan drama, 67- N.Y. Univ. Founder's Day Award, 63. MLA; CLA; NCTE; Shakespeare Asn. Am; Conf. Col. Compos. & Commun. Shakespeare; Elizabethan drama; sixteenth century non-dramatic literature. Add: Dept. of English, Tennessee State University, Nashville, TN 37203.

HUDSON, ROBERT VERNON, b. Indianapolis, Ind, Aug. 29, 32; m. 63; c. 1. HISTORY OF MASS COMMUNICATION. B.S, Ind. Univ, Bloomington, 54; M.S, Univ. Ore, 66; Ph.D.(mass commun), Univ. Minn, Minneapolis, 70. City ed, News-Sentinel, Rochester, Ind, 54; staff correspondent, United Press, Indianapolis, 54-56; reporter, Chicago Daily News, 56-57; Fairchild Publ, Chicago, 57-58; serv. exec, Pub. Relat. Bd, Chicago, 58-59; publ. asst, Traffic Inst. & Transp. Ctr, Northwest. Univ, 60-61, news bur. mgr, 61-63; asst. dir, News Bur, Ariz. State Univ, 63-65; asst. prof. JOUR, MICH. STATE UNIV, 68-73, ASSOC. PROF, 73-, ASST. CHMN, SCH. JOUR, 72-, ACTING ASST. DEAN COL. COMMUN. ARTS, 74- Freelance writer, 53-; staff writer, Traffic Dig. & Rev, 60-61; prod-writer-commentator, Dateline: ASU, TV Prog, Phoenix, Ariz, 64-65. U.S.N.R, 49-59. Asn. Educ. in Jour. Journalism biography; literary journalism. Publ: Co-auth, Johnson's information strategy for Vietnam: an evaluation, autumn 68, auth, Will Irwin's pioneering criticism of the press, summer 70 & Fo I crusade in perspective: three victories for the press, spring 73, Jour. Quart. Add: School of Journalism, Michigan State University, East Lansing, MI 48823.

HUDSON, SARA CARRUTH, b. Honolulu, Hawaii, Aug. 13, 22; m. 62; c. 2. ENGLISH LITERATURE. A.B, Univ. N.C, Chapel Hill, 43; M.A, Univ. Chicago, 47, Ph.D.(Eng), 58. Instr. ENG, Wilson Jr. Col, Chicago, 47-51; AUBURN UNIV, 52-58, asst. prof, 58-68, ASSOC. PROF, 68- MLA; S.Atlantic Mod. Lang. Asn; Res. Soc. Victorian Periodicals. Victorian fiction and periodicals. Add: Dept. of English, Auburn University, Auburn, AL 36830.

HUDSON, THEODORE R, b. Washington, D.C; m. 53; c. 2. AMERICAN & ENGLISH LITERATURE. B.S, Miner Teachers Col, 47; M.A, N.Y. Univ, 50; M.A, Howard Univ, 67, Ford Found. fel, 69-70, Ph.D.(Eng), 71. Lectr. ENG. D.C. TEACHERS COL, 62-63, instr, 64-68, asst. prof, 68-71, ASSOC. PROF, 71-, from asst. to acad. dean, 65-66. Adj. prof. Eng, Am. Univ, 68-69; lectr, Upward Mobility Col, U.S. Dept. Health, Educ. & Welfare, 71-73. MLA; Col. Lang. Asn; Asn. Study Afro-Am. Life & Hist; MLA (Am. Lit. Group). Afro-American literature; American literature. Publ: A LeRoi Jones (Amiri Baraka) bibliography, privately publ, 71; From LeRoi Jones to Amiri Baraka: the literary works, Duke Univ, 73; Langston Hughes' last volume of verse, Col. Lang. Asn. J, 6/68; Rhetoric for the Black power faith, J. Human Relat, 2nd quart, 70; Technical aspects of the poetry of Langston Hughes, Black World, 9/73. Add: 1816 Varnum St. N.E, Washington, DC 20018.

HUDSON, WILSON MATHIS, JR, b. Flatonia, Tex, Dec. 26, 07; m. 51. ENGLISH. A.B, Univ. Tex, 29, A.M, 30; fel, Univ. Chicago, 38-39, Ph.D, 47. Instr. ENG, Rice Inst, 30-37; Univ. Chicago, 39-42; asst. prof, UNIV. TEX, AUSTIN, 47-53, from assoc. prof. to PROF, 53- U.S.A.A.F, 42-46, Capt. MLA; Am. Stud. Asn; Am. Folklore Soc. Comparative literature and folklore. Publ: Texas folk and folklore & Andy Adams: his life and writings, South. Methodist Univ; Why the Chisholm Trail forks, Univ. Tex. Add: Dept. of English, University of Texas at Austin, Austin, TX 78712.

HUDSPETH, ROBERT N. b. Sweetwater, Tex, Nov. 21, 36; m. 59; c. 3. ENGLISH. A.B, Univ. Tex, 61; A.M, Syracuse Univ, 63, Ph.D.(Eng), 67. Asst. prof. ENG, Univ. Wash, 67-71, ASSOC. PROF, 71-72; PA. STATE UNIV, UNIVERSITY PARK, 72- MLA; Am. Stud. Asn. American transcendentalism; American fiction. Publ: Ellery Channing, Twayne, 73; A perennial springtime: Ellery Channing's friendship with Emerson and Thoreau, 69 & Ellery Channing's paradoxial muse, 69, Emerson Soc. Quart; A definition of modern nihilism: John Hersey's The war lover, Univ. Rev, 69; plus others. Add: Dept. of English, Pennsylvania State University, University Park, PA 16802.

HUELSBECK, CHARLES J, b. Dedham, Iowa, Jan. 29, 20. ENGLISH LITERATURE. B.A, Univ. North. Iowa, 46; M.A, Colo. State Col, 48; librn. cert, Kans. State Teachers Col, Emporia, 52; M.A, Univ. Wis, 53, summers 54-59. Instr. Eng, Pomeroy High Sch, Iowa, 46-57; Creighton Univ, 47-49; St. Ambrose Col, 49-51; librn, Parsons Jr. Col, 52-53; asst. prof. Eng. & librn, Aroostook State Teachers Col, 53-56; asst. prof. Eng, Merrimack Col, 56-62, assoc. prof, 62-71; DIR, AMES FREE LIBR, 73- U.S.A, 42-43. American literature of the 19th century, particularly Dickinson and Melville; 19th and 20th century English literature. Add: Ames Free Library, 53 Main St, North Easton, MA 02356.

HUENEMANN, CALVIN VICTOR, b. Plymouth, Wis, Jan. 26, 14; m. 40; c. 4. AMERICAN LITERATURE. A.B, Mission House Col, 37; A.M, Univ. Wis, 39, Ph.D, 53; Univ. Minn, summer 59. Teacher, High Sch, Wis, 37-38; instr. Eng. & German, Waukon Jr. Col, Iowa, 39-46; assoc. prof, Eng, Jamestown Col, 48-53, prof, 53-56; PROF. LIT, NORTHEAST MO. STATE UNIV, 56-, chmn. div. lang. & lit, 56-68. MLA; NCTE. Denton J. Snider. Publ: In defense of the invulnerable, Mo. Eng. Bull, 3/63. Add: 415 S. Halliburton, Kirksville, MO 63501.

HUFF, CHESTER CLARENCE, JR, b. Gary, Ind, Oct. 25, 24; m. 62; c. 3. ENGLISH & AMERICAN LITERATURE. B.S, Univ. Ind, Bloomington, 49; M.A, DePaul Univ, 55; Ph.D.(Eng), Univ. Colo, Boulder, 70. Instr. ENG, Univ. Colo, 55-61; UNIV. NORTH. COLO, 61-65, asst. prof, 65-71, ASSOC. PROF, 71-, CHMN. DEPT, 70- Eng.C, U.S.A, 50-52. NCTE. Victorian and Edwardian period; science fiction. Add: Dept. of English, University of Northern Colorado, Greeley, CO 80639.

HUFF, LAWRENCE, b. Athens, Ga, Sept. 10, 21; m. 45; c. 2. ENGLISH. A.B, Univ. Ga, 41, M.A, 48; Emory Univ, 50-51; Ph.D.(Eng), Vanderbilt Univ, 58. Instr. Eng. & French, High Sch, Ga, 41-42; French, Univ. Ga, 46-47, ENG, 47-50, asst. prof, 51-54; Ga. State Col, 56-58; asst. prof, GA. SOUTH; COL, 58-61, PROF, 61-, HEAD DEPT, 70- U.S.A, 42-45, Sgt. S.Atlantic Mod. Lang. Asn; MLA; Am. Stud. Asn. Southern literature. Publ: The literary publications of Joseph Addison Turner, 9/62 & Joseph Addison Turner and his quarterly, The plantation, winter 70, Ga. Hist. Quart; Joseph Addison Turner: southern editor during the Civil War, J. South. Hist, 11/63. Add: 103 Sherwood Ct, Statesboro, GA 30458.

HUFF, LLOYD DICKASON, b. Brownsville, Tex, Sept. 8, 17; m. 47; c. 2. ENGLISH LANGUAGE & LITERATURE. B.A, Trinity Univ, 39; Univ. Utah, 42-43; Whitworth Col, 43; Colo. Col, 43-44; A.M, Baylor Univ, 46; Ph.D, Ind. Univ, 49; M.A, Hardin-Simmons Univ, 63. Teaching fel, Baylor Univ, 42; Ind. Univ, 46-49; assoc. prof. ENG, McMurry Col, 49-51, prof. & head dept, 51-67; PROF. & CHMN. DEPT. HARDIN-SIMMONS UNIV, 67- U.S.A.F, 42-45. Chaucer; Milton; 19th century; English language and literature. Add: Dept. of English, Hardin-Simmons University, Abilene, TX 79601.

HUFF, ROBERT, b. Evanston, Ill, Apr. 3, 24; m. 58; c. 3. ENGLISH. A.B, Wayne State Univ, 49, A.M, 52; fel, Sch. Lett, Ind. Univ, 57. Instr. ENG, Univ. Ore, 52-53; Fresno State Col, 53-55; Ore. State Univ, 55-57 & 58-60; Wayne State Univ, 57-58; asst. prof, Univ. Del, 60-64; ASSOC. PROF, WEST. WASH. STATE COL, 64- Bread Loaf Writers Conf. scholar, 61; McDowell Colony writing fel, 63; manuscript collections poetry of Robert Huff, Wayne State Univ, Univ. Ky. & Carnegie Libr, Syracuse Univ, 61-; hon. trustee, Theodore Roethke Mem. Found, 68-; poetry ed, Concerning Poetry, 68- U.S.A.A.F, 43-46, Sgt. Modern poetry; creative writing. Publ: Colonel Johnson's ride, 59, The course, 66 & The Ventriloquist, 74, Wayne State Univ; poetry contrib. numerous literary magazines & journals, 47- Add: Dept. of English, Western Washington State College, Bellingham, WA 98225.

HUFFMAN, CLIFFORD CHALMERS, b. New York, N.Y, June 5, 40; m. 67. ENGLISH LITERATURE. B.A, Columbia Univ, 61, Woodrow Wilson fel, 61-62, E.J. Kellett fel, 61-63, Ph.D.(Eng), 69; M.A, Cambridge, 67. Instr. ENG, Brandeis Univ, 68-70; asst. prof, STATE UNIV. N.Y. STONY BROOK, 70-73, ASSOC. PROF, 73- Henry Huntington Libr. grant, summer 70. MLA; Shakespeare Soc. Am; Renaissance Soc. Am; Malone Soc. English Renaissance literature; history of ideas; Renaissance history. Publ: Coriolanus in context, Bucknell Univ, 72; Burgundy and France: a note on Shakespeare's sources, Eng. Lang. Notes, 71; Titus Andronicus: metamorphosis and renewal, Mod. Lang. Rev, 72; Tudor-Stuart drama: a bibliography, Educ. Theatre J, 72. Add: Dept. of English, State University of New York at Stony Brook, Stony Brook, NY 11790.

HUFFMAN, JAMES FLOYD, b. Kalamazoo, Mich, May 1, 22; m. 46; c. 2. SPEECH, HISTORY. B.S, Northwest. Univ, 48, M.A, 49; Ph.D.(speech & commun), Mich. State Univ, 66. Instr. speech, Iowa State Univ, 49-52; sr. specialist speech & commun, GEN. MOTORS INST, 52-64, PROF. HUMANITIES, 64-, COMMUN, 68- Consult. commun, Am. Inst. Banking, 56-; assoc. dir, Genesee Soil Conserv. Dist, 70-; trustee, Flint Inst. Music, 72- U.S.A.F, 43-46, Res, 46-52, Capt; Air Medal. Am. Asn. State & Local Hist; AHA. Political science and power; biographical history; psychohistory.

Film documentaries on the Civil War, privately prod. Add: Dept. of Humanities, General Motors Institute, Chevrolet & Third St, Flint, MI 48502.

HUFFMAN, JAMES RICHARD, b. Liberal, Kans, May 8, 44; m. 65; c. 2. ENGLISH, AMERICAN STUDIES. B.A, Harvard Col, 66; M.A, Mich. State Univ, 67, Alumni Distinguished fel, 66-69, Ph.D.(Eng), 70. ASST. PROF. ENG. & AM. LIT, STATE UNIV. N.Y. COL. FREDONIA, 70- State Univ. N.Y. Res. Found. Univ. Awards Comt-Joint Awards Counc. fac. res. fel, summers 71 & 72. MLA; Am. Stud. Asn; Pop. Cult. Asn; NEA. American literature; literary theory; popular culture. Publ: Jesus Christ Superstar: popular art and unpopular criticism, J. Pop. Cult, fall 72. Add: Dept. of English, State University of New York College at Fredonia, Fredonia, NY 14063.

HUFFMAN, MAXINE FISH, b. Decatur, Ill, Aug. 18, 28; m. 53. ENGLISH, ENGLISH AS SECOND LANGUAGE. A.B, Millikin Univ, 50; M.S, Kans. State Col. Pittsburg, 51; Ph.D.(botany), Kans. State Univ, 53; M.S, 58; Ed.D, (Eng. as 2nd lang), Columbia Univ, 67. Instr. biology, CENT. UNIV. IOWA, 53-55, asst. prof, 55-56, ENG, 56-59, assoc. prof, 59-66, PROF, 66-, CHMN. DEPT, 70- Prof. ling, NDEA Inst, Univ. Alaska, summer 67, vis. prof. Eng, univ, summer 68. NCTE; MLA; Am. Asn. Teachers Eng. As Second Lang. Publ: Tico tales, Exposition, 64. Add: Dept. of English, Central University of Iowa, Pella, IA 50219.

HUFFORD, ROGER A, b. Villa Grove, Ill, July 22, 34. PUBLIC ADDRESS. B.S, Ill. State Univ, 55, M.S, 56; Rotary Found. fel, Univ. Durham, 56-57; M.Litt, Univ. Durham, Eng, 58; Ph.D, South. Ill. Univ, 62. Mem. fac. math, Elgin Community Col, 57-58; from instr. to asst. prof. SPEECH, North. Ill. Univ, 58-63; assoc. prof, CLARION STATE COL, 63-66, PROF, 66- Speech Asn. Am; Am. Forensic Asn; Int. Soc. Gen. Semantics. Logic; language; general semantics. Add: Dept. of Speech, Clarion State College, Clarion, PA 16214.

HUGGARD, WILLIAM ALLEN, b. Colton, N.Y, Feb. 12, 98; m. 25; c. 2. ENGLISH. A.B, Middlebury Col, 20; Ph.D, State Univ. Iowa, 37. Instr. ENG, DePAUW UNIV, 23-25; asst. prof, 25-27, assoc. prof, 27-39, prof, 39-63, EMER. PROF, 63- Dir. summer sch, DePauw Univ, 26-29, secy. fac, 29-34. American literature, especially Emerson. Publ: The religious teachings of Ralph Waldo Emerson, Vantage, 72; Emerson and the problem of war and peace, Univ. Iowa Humanistic Stud; Emerson's philosophy of war and peace, Philol. Quart; Emerson's glimpses of the divine, Personalist. Add: Apt. 921, 4042 55th Way N, St. Petersburg, FL 33709.

HUGHES, CHARLES WILLIS, b. Dallas, Tex, July 24, 31; m. 58; c. 2. AMERICAN LITERATURE, LINGUISTICS. B.A, Univ. Tex, 57; M.A, Tex. Tech Univ, 68, Ph.D.(Eng), 71. Cryptanalyst, Nat. Security Agency, 57-60; chief of editing & publ, U.S. Air Force Security Serv, 60-66; instr. ENG, Tex. Tech Univ, 69-71; asst. prof, HENDERSON STATE COL, 71-73, ASSOC. PROF, 73-, Nat. teaching fel, 71-72. U.S.N, 48-52. South. Conf. Mod. Lang. Asn; Col. Eng. Asn; Conf. Col. Teachers Eng. Attitudes toward wild nature in American literature; behaviorism and art. Publ: Impact of evil on the poetry of Walt Whitman, Walt Whitman Rev, 12/69; Abstract of Impact of evil on the poetry of Walt Whitman, Am. Lit. Abstracts, 6/71. Add: Dept. of English, Henderson State College, Box 2902, Arkadelphia, AR 71923.

HUGHES, CHARLOTTE BRADFORD, b. Portland, Ore, Feb. 4, 27. ENGLISH, COMPARATIVE LITERATURE. B.A, Univ. Ore, 48; A.M, Brown Univ, 51, Ph.D.(Eng), 60. Instr. Eng, DePauw Univ, 56; Portland State Col, 56-63; asst. prof, Univ. Portland, 63-67; assoc. prof. ENG. & COMP. LIT, CALIF. STATE UNIV, FULLERTON, 67-72, PROF, 72- MLA. Nineteenth century novel. Publ: John Crowne's Sir Courtly Nice: a critical edition, Mouton, 66. Add: Dept. of English, California State University, Fullerton, Fullerton, CA 92631.

HUGHES, DANIEL JOHN, b. Dover, N.H, June 14, 29; m. 54. ENGLISH. B.A, Univ. N.H, 50; M.A, Brown Univ, 53, Ph.D.(Eng), 58. Teaching assoc. eng, Brown Univ, 53-56, instr, 56-59, asst. prof, 59-64; assoc. prof, WAYNE STATE UNIV, 64-70, PROF. ENG. LIT, 70-, fac. fel, 66. Brown Univ. summer res. grant, 62. Mil.Intel, U.S.A, 51-53, 1st Lt. MLA. English romanticism; modern British and American poetry; modern fiction. Publ: Waking in a tree (poems), Clark & Way, 63; Pieties and giant forms in The lord of the rings, In: Shadows of imagination, South. Ill. Univ, 69; Blake and Shelley: beyond the Uroboros, In: Essays for S. Foster Damon, Brown Univ, 69; John Berryman and the Poet's Pardon, Am. Poetry Rev, 7/73. Add: Dept. of English, Wayne State University, Detroit, MI 48202.

HUGHES, JEROME WILLIAM, b. Muscatine, Iowa, Jan. 3, 05. ENGLISH. A.B, Grinnell Col, 29; A.M, State Univ. Iowa, 34, Ph.D, 48. Instr. ENG, Foundation Jr. High Sch, Berea Col, 29-39, BEREA COL, 40-45, assoc. prof, 45-47, PROF, 48- Carnegie intern gen. educ, Univ. Chicago, 52-53. MLA; S.Atlantic Mod. Lang. Asn. Elizabethan drama; a textual study of Beaumont and Fletcher's Philaster. Add: Dept. of English, Berea College, Berea, KY 40403.

HUGHES, JOHN PAUL, Modern Languages. See Volume III, Foreign Languages, Linguistics & Philology.

HUGHES, LEO, b. Carlyle, Ill, Nov. 20, 08; m. 36; c. 2. ENGLISH LITERATURE. A.B, Univ. Ill, 33, A.M, 34, Ph.D, 38. Asst. instr. ENG, Univ. Ill, 35-38; instr, UNIV. TEX, AUSTIN, 38-42, asst. prof, 42-46, assoc. prof, 46-56, PROF, 56-, assoc. dean Grad. Sch, 60-66. Vis. prof, Rice Univ, 61-62. Folger fel, 53; Guggenheim fel, 56-57. MLA; S-Cent. Mod. Lang. Asn. Novel, drama and theatre; 18th century English literature. Publ: Ten English farces; A century of English farce; ed, Plain dealer, Univ. Nebr, 67; auth, The drama's patrons, Univ. Tex, 71. Add: Dept. of English, University of Texas at Austin, Austin, TX 78712.

HUGHES, NINA EDWARDS, b. Sulphur Springs, Ark, Aug. 1, 15. ENGLISH, SPEECH. A.B, Fla. State Col. Women, 36; M.A, Cath. Univ. Am, 46; Ed.D, Teachers Col, Columbia Univ, 70. Teacher, High Sch, Fla, 36-42, Md, 42-44; Eng, speech & dramatics, Atlantic Christian Col, 44-46; asst. prof. forensics & speech, Winthrop Col, 46-47; assoc. prof. ENG. & SPEECH, TOWSON STATE COL, 47-71, PROF, 71- Mem. comn. sec. schs. Mid. States Asn. Cols. & Sec. Schs; Danforth Found. summer scholar, 61. MLA; NEA; NCTE; Col. Eng. Asn; S.Atlantic Mod. Lang. Asn. Drama; theatre; novel. Add: Dept. of English & Speech, Towson State College, Baltimore, MD 21204.

HUGHES, PETER A. M, b. London, Ont, Dec. 11, 40; m. 66. ENGLISH. B.A, Oxford, 63, M.A, 66; Ph.D.(Eng), Yale, 65. Lectr. ENG, VICTORIA COL, 65-66, asst. prof, 66-68, ASSOC. PROF, 68- Can. Counc. res. fel, 67-, French Govt. Exchange fel, 71; Am. Philos. Soc. res. grant, 71-72; Soc. Humanities res. fel, Cornell Univ, 74-75. MLA; Johnson Soc. Seventeenth and eighteenth century English literature; literary theory; modern literature. Publ: Spots of time, Can. Broadcasting Corp, 69; co-ed, The varied pattern: studies in the 18th century, Am. Hakkert, 71; auth, George Woodcock, McClelland, 74; Language, history and vision: an approach to 18th century literature, In: The varied pattern, 71; The expressive validity of minor prose forms, Bucknell Rev, 71; Restructuring literary history: implications for the 18th century, New Lit. Hist, 74. Add: Dept. of English, Victoria College, Toronto, Ont, Can.

HUGHES, RAYMOND GROVE, b. Waynesburg, Pa, May 29, 02. ENGLISH. A.B, Univ. W.Va, 28, A.M, 29; Ph.D, Univ. Pittsburgh, 42; Duke Univ; Columbia Univ; Univ. N.C. Telegraph ed, Wheeling News Register, 23-24; prof. Eng. & chmn. dept, W.Liberty State Col, 42-70; RETIRED. American literature; McGuffey readers. Publ: McGuffey and his readers; Ray and his arithmetics; Alexander Campbell, W.Va. Rev. Add: Dept. of English, West Liberty State College, West Liberty, WV 26074.

HUGHES, RICHARD EDWARD, b. Amsterdam, N.Y, July 11, 27; m. 50; c. 5. ENGLISH. A.B, Siena Col, 49; A.M, Boston Col, 50; Ph.D, Univ. Wis, 54. Teaching asst. ENG, Univ. Wis, 50-53; instr. Ohio State Univ. 53-55; asst. prof, BOSTON COL, 55-63, PROF, 63-, CHMN. DEPT, 67-, dean col. arts. & sci, 68-71. MLA. Seventeenth century English literature. Publ: John Joyne's journal, Univ. Calif, 60; Rhetoric: principles and usage, 63, co-auth, Persuasive prose, 64, Literature: form and function, 65 & Principles of rhetoric, 66, Prentice-Hall; auth, Interior career of John Donne, William Morrow, 68; Pope's Essay on man; rhetorical structure, Mod. Lang. Notes; John Donne's Anniversaries, Eng. Lit. Hist, 9/68. Add: Dept. of English, Boston College, Chestnut Hill, MA 02167.

HUGHES, SHAUN FRANCIS DOUGLAS, Mediaeval English Language & Literature. See Volume III, Foreign Languages, Linguistics & Philology.

HUGHEY, JIM DUFF, b. Cherokee, Okla, Dec. 21, 38. SPEECH. B.A, Okla. State Univ, 61; M.S, Purdue Univ, 64, Ph.D.(speech), 66. Asst. prof. speech, Univ. N.Mex, 66-70; ASSOC. PROF. SPEECH COMMUN, OKLA. STATE UNIV, 70- Speech Commun. Asn; West. Speech Commun. Asn; Int. Commun. Asn. Communication sensitivity; instructional methods; interpersonal communication variables. Publ: Co-auth, Speech communication: foundations and challenges, Macmillan, 75. Add: Dept. of Speech Communication, Oklahoma State University, Stillwater, OK 74074.

HUGHEY, RUTH W, b. Gentry, Ark, Sept. 11, 99. ENGLISH LITERATURE. A.B, Hendrix Col, 20, D.Litt, 39; A.M, Columbia Univ, 21; scholar, Cornell Univ, 31, Yardley Found, fel, 31-32, Ph.D, 32. Teacher Latin, St. Mary's Sch, Memphis, Tenn, 21-23; assoc. prof. Eng, Henderson-Brown Col, 23-24; prof, Grenada Col, 24-26; instr, Univ. Mo, 26-29; Am. Asn. Univ. Women Maltby fel, 32-33; Am. Counc. Learned Soc. grant-in-aid, 34; Guggenheim fel, 35-36; instr. Eng. lit, Mt. Holyoke Col, 37-38; Howald fel, OHIO STATE UNIV, 38-39, asst. prof. ENG, 39-47, assoc. prof, 47-57, prof, 57-69, EMER. PROF, 69- Res. grants, Ohio State Univ, 58, 62-63 & 65. MLA; Renaissance Soc. Am; Bibliog. Soc. Univ. Va. Literary women of the English Renaissance; textual and literary criticism of Tudor poetry; John Harington of Stepney. Publ: The correspondence of Lady Katherine Paston, 1603-1625, Norfolk Rec. Soc, 41; The Arundel Harington manuscript of Tudor poetry, 2 vols, 60 & John Harington of Stepney: Tudor gentleman, 71, Ohio State Univ. Add: 2951 Neil Ave, Columbus, OH 43202.

HUGO, HOWARD EPPENS, b. Weehawken, N.J, May 26, 20; m. 49. ENGLISH. A.B, Williams Col.(Mass), 41; M.A, Harvard, 42, Ph.D.(comp. lit), 49. Instr. Eng, Williams Col.(Mass), 46; teaching fel. gen. educ, Harvard, 46-49, instr, 49-51, asst. prof. gen. educ. & comp. lit, 51-56, lectr, 56-57, sr. tutor, Eliot House, 49-52, chmn. tutors, dept. hist. & lit, 51-54; Fulbright res. grant, Univ. Vienna, 54-55; mem. faculty, Brooklyn Col, 57-58; assoc. prof. ENG, UNIV. CALIF, BERKELEY, 58-71, PROF, 71- Vis. lectr. humanities, Mass. Inst. Technol, 64. U.S.N, 42-46, Lt. MLA; Mediaeval Acad. Am; Dante Soc. European romanticism; metrics; modern novel. Publ: Viking portable romantic reader; Aspects of fiction; Varieties of English and American prose. Add: Dept. of English, University of California, Berkeley, CA 94720.

HUGUELET, THEODORE LONG, b. Hamlet, N.C, Sept. 7, 28; m. 52; c. 4. ENGLISH. A.B, Univ. N.C, 50, Ph.D, 59; M.A, Univ. Tenn, 51. Instr. ENG, Univ. N.C, 55-56; asst. prof, N.Tex. State Col, 56-59; assoc. prof, WEST. CAROLINA UNIV, 59-64, PROF, 64-, CHMN. DIV. HUMANITIES, 68-73. Coop.prog. in humanities fel, 65-66; exchange prof, Univ. P.R, Mayaguez, summer 73. MLA; Southeast. Renaissance Conf; Milton Soc. Am; Col. Eng. Asn. Milton's theology; English romanticism; Italian literature of the renaissance. Publ: Ed, David Hartley's observations on man (1749), Scholars' Facsimilies & Reprints, 66; The rule of charity in Milton's Divorce tracts, In: Milton Studies, Vol. VI, Univ. Pittsburgh, 74. Add: Box 201, Cullowhee, NC 28723.

HUGUENIN, CHARLES ARTHUR, b. New York, N.Y, May 19, 06. ENGLISH. B.S, N.Y. Univ, 29, A.M, 32; Ph.D, St. John's Univ.(N.Y), 40; A.M, Columbia Univ, 52. Teacher, high sch, N.Y, 30-38, jr. high sch, 38-43, 45-47; instr, Manhattan Col, 46-47, asst. prof, 47-51; instr, Corlears Jr. High Sch, 51-58; assoc. prof. ENG, IONA COL, 58-72, EMER. ASSOC. PROF, 72- Asst. prof, Hunter Col, 47-49; Pace Col, 56- Publ: Bronteana at Princeton University, Trans, 55; Kipling and Brattleboro, Vt. Hist, 56; MacMonnies' Civic virtue, N.Y. Hist, 56. Add: Dept. of English, Iona College, New Rochelle, NY 10804.

HULL, RAYMONA E, b. Petoskey, Mich, July 16, 07. ENGLISH. B.A, West. Reserve Univ, 29; M.A, Cornell Univ, 32; Ed.D, Columbia Univ, 51. Demonstration teacher Eng, Glenville High Sch, Cleveland, Ohio, 33-43; Dodge fel. & dept. asst, Teachers Col, Columbia Univ, 43-44; assoc. prof, State Univ. N.Y. Agr. & Tech. Col. Canton, 45-58; PROF. ENG, IND. UNIV. PA, 58- NCTE; Thoreau Soc; Emerson Soc; Melville Soc. Am; AHA. American renaissance, especially Thoreau, Hawthorne, and Melville; Greek and Roman literature in translation; Hawthorne family in England. Publ: Abstract of London & Melville's Israel Potter, Am. Lit. Abstracts, winter 68; The cairn at Walden pond, Thoreau Soc. Bull, winter 68; 19th century British periodical printings of Hawthorne, Hawthorne J, 73; plus others. Add: Dept. of English, Indiana University of Pennsylvania, Indiana, PA 15701.

HULL, WILLIAM DOYLE, b. Westminster, S.C, Apr. 13, 18. ENGLISH. A.B, Furman Univ, 38; A.M, Univ. Va, 40, Ph.D, 41. Instr. Howard Col, 41-42; N.C. State Col, 46; ENG, HOFSTRA UNIV, 46-47, asst. prof, 47-50, assoc. prof, 50-63, PROF, 63- Fulbright prof, Univ. Ceylon, 55-56 & Patna Univ, 59-60. Distinguished Teaching Award, Hofstra Bd. Trustees, 64-65. Cryptographer, U.S.A.A.F, 43-45. Medieval and modern literature; renaissance. Publ: Selected poems: 1942-1952, Brigant, 55; Dandy Brown, A. Swallow, 59; The Catullus of William Hull, Exp. Press, 60; The other side of silence, 65 & The mastery of love, 67, Swallowtree; A canon of the critical writings of Edgar A. Poe, Univ. Microfilms, 67; Collected poems, P.Lal, 70; Visions of Handy Hopper, I Flood, 70, II, Churn, 71, III, Park, 72, IV, Post, 73, V, Hinge, 74, P.Lal; Scholarship and criticism; the goose and the ass, Hofstra Rev, summer 66. Add: Dept. of English, Hofstra University, Hempstead, NY 11550.

HULSMAN, JOHN FRANCIS, b. Pittsburgh, Pa, Oct. 4, 45. ENGLISH LITERATURE. B.A, St. Vincent Col, 67; Ph.D.(Eng. lit), Ohio Univ, 72. ASST. PROF. ENG. LIT, RIDER COL, 72- MLA. Modern fiction; Victorian poetry. Publ: Co-ed, The complete works of Robert Browning, Ohio Univ, 72. Add: Dept. of English, Rider College, Trenton, NJ 08602.

HULTENG, JOHN LINNE, b. Grand Forks, N.Dak, Apr. 1, 21; m. 47; c. 3. JOURNALISM. Ph.B, Univ. N.Dak, 43; M.S, Columbia Univ, 47, Pulitzer traveling fel, 47-48; Nieman fel, Harvard, 49-50. Reporter, Record, East Grand Forks, Minn, 41-42; Herald, Grand Forks, N.Dak, 42-43; ed. writer, page ed, Providence Journal & Bulletin, 47-55; assoc. prof. JOUR, UNIV. ORE, 55-61, PROF, 61-, dean sch. jour, 62-68. Pres, Am. Asn. Schs. & Dept. Jour, 66-67; vis. prof. commun, Stanford Univ, 70-71. Ersted Award for Distinguished Teaching, Univ. Ore, 61; Sigma Delta Chi Award for Distinguished Teaching, 70. U.S.A.A.F, 43-46, 1st Lt. Asn. Educ. in Jour. Publ: Co-auth, The fourth estate, 71 & auth, The opinion function, 73, Harper; Chap, In: Journalists in action, Channel, 63; plus others. Add: School of Journalism, University of Oregon, Eugene, OR 97403.

HULTIN, NEIL, b. Kenmare, N.Dak, Apr. 11, 34; m. 56; c. 2. ENGLISH, PHILOLOGY & LINGUISTICS. B.A, Concordia Col.(Moorhead, Minn), 55; Univ. Marburg, 55-56; M.A, Univ. Chicago, 57; Ph.D.(Eng), Johns Hopkins Univ, 65. Instr. ENG, Concordia Col.(Moorhead, Minn), 58-59; Univ. Ariz, 63-64; lectr, Univ. West. Ont, 64-65, asst. prof, 65-69; UNIV. WATERLOO, 69-70, ASSOC. PROF, 70- U.S.A, 57-58, Res, 58-63. Mediaeval Acad. Am; Can. Ling. Asn; Ling. Soc. Am. Old English language and literature; folklore; Middle English literature. Publ: Anti-courtly elements in Chaucer's Complaint of Mars, Annuale Mediaevale, 68; Canadian views of American English, Am. Speech, 69; Inchiquin and Cobbett: American letters and British politics, Notes & Queries, 72; plus others. Add: Dept. of English, University of Waterloo, Waterloo, Ont. N2L 3G1, Can.

HUME, CHARLES VERNARD, b. Excelsior Springs, Mo, Apr 12, 13; m. 43; c. 2. SPEECH, DRAMA. B.S, Emporia State Col, 36; M.A, Iowa, 47; Ph.D. (drama), Stanford Univ, 54. Asst. prof. SPEECH, Ore. State Univ, 45-48; PROF, CALIF. STATE UNIV, SACRAMENTO, 49- U.S.N, 41-45, Lt. Speech Asn. Am; Am. Educ. Theatre Asn. Early California theatre, especially on gold rush days; history of mining camps. Add: 5918 Shepard Ave, Sacramento, CA 95819.

HUME, ROBERT ARTHUR, b. Urbana, Ill, Oct. 11, 07; m. 34; c. 3. ENGLISH A.B, Stanford Univ, 29, LL.B, 32, A.M, 35; Ph.D, Cornell Univ, 40. Instr. ENG, Idaho State Col, 35-37; asst. prof, Purdue Univ, 40-44; assoc. prof, Univ. B.C, 45-46; UNIV. NEV, RENO, 44-45, 46-51, PROF, 51- NCTE. American literature; life and thought of Henry Adams. Publ: Runaway star, an appreciation of Henry Adams, Cornell, 51. Add: Dept. of English, University of Nevada, Reno, NV 89507.

HUME, ROBERT DAVID, b. Oak Ridge, Tenn, July 25, 44; m. 66. ENGLISH LITERATURE. B.A, Haverford Col, 66; Ph.D.(Eng), Univ. Pa, 69. Asst. prof. ENG, CORNELL UNIV, 69-74, ASSOC. PROF, 74- MLA; Am. Soc. Aesthet; Brit. Soc. Aesthet; Soc. Theatre Res; Am. Soc. 18th Century Stud. English drama, 1660-1800; 18th century novel and aesthetics; theory of literary criticism. Publ: Dryden's criticism, Cornell Univ, 70; Development of English drama in the late seventeenth century, Clarendon, (in press); Gothic vs. Romantic: a revaluation of the Gothic novel, PMLA, 69; Restoration comedy 1660-1679, 18th Century Stud, 72; Theory of comedy in the Restoration, Mod. Philol, 73. Add: Dept. of English, Cornell University, Ithaca, NY 14850.

HUMMA, JOHN BALLARD, b. Rosiclare, Ill, Feb. 16, 40; m. 68; c. 2. NINETEENTH CENTURY AMERICAN LITERATURE. B.A, George Washington Univ, 63; M.A, South. Ill. Univ, Carbondale, 65, Ph.D.(Eng), 69. ASST. PROF. ENG, GA. SOUTH. COL, 69- MLA. Romanticism and its 20th century manifestations; modern British fiction. Publ: Young Goodman Brown and the failure of Hawthorne's ambiguity, Colby Libr. Quart, 12/71; Poe's Ligeia: Glanvill's will or Blake's will, Miss. Quart, winter 72-73; The art and meaning of Sarah Orne Jewett's The courting of Sister Wisby, Stud. Short Fiction, winter 73. Add: 110 Green Briar Trail, Statesboro, GA 30458.

HUMPHERYS, ANNE, b. Lehi, Utah, Feb. 25, 37; m. 67. ENGLISH LITERATURE. B.A, Stanford Univ, 59; M.A, Columbia Univ, 62, Ph.D.(Eng), 68. Lectr. ENG, Brooklyn Col, 62-67; preceptor, Columbia Col, 67-68; ASST. PROF, LEHMAN COL, 68- MLA, Res. Soc. Victorian Periodicals. Victorian literature; history of the English novel. Publ: Ed, Voices of the poor, 71 & ed, Library of Victorian times, Frank Cass. Add: Dept. of English, Herbert H. Lehman College, Bedford Park Blvd. W, Bronx, NY 10468.

HUMPHREY, CHARLES ROBERT, b. Windsor, Mo, Aug. 23, 30; m. 55; c. 4. ENGLISH. B.A, Baylor Univ, 51, M.A, 54; Ph.D.(Eng), Univ. Tex, 65. Instr. ENG, Tex. A&M Univ, 57-60; Univ. Fla, 60-61; teaching asst, Univ. Tex, 61-62; instr, Trinidad State Jr. Col, 62-64; ASSOC. PROF, SOUTH. COLO. STATE COL, 64- Fulbright lectr. Am. lit, Nat. Univ. Asuncion, Paraguay, 68. MLA; Rocky Mt. Mod. Lang. Asn. Contemporary American literature; Latin American fiction. Publ: B. Traven, Twayne U.S. Auth. Ser, 69. Add: Dept. of English, Southern Colorado State College, Pueblo, CO 81001.

HUMPHREY, STEPHEN BENEDICT, b. Minneapolis, Minn, July 25, 06. ENGLISH. B.A, St. John's Univ.(Minn), 29; M.A, Univ. Minn, 36. Instr. ENG, St. John's Univ.(Minn), 36-38; Univ. Minn, 38-42, 45-46; asst. prof, ST. JOHN'S UNIV.(MINN), 46-50, assoc. prof, 50-66, PROF, 66- U.S.A, 42-45, M/Sgt. NCTE. 18th century English literature; contemporary English and American literature. Add: Dept. of English, St. John's University, Collegeville, MN 56321.

HUNGERFORD, E. ARTHUR, b. Oak Park, Ill, Oct. 4, 11; m. 37; c. 1. SPEECH, BROADCASTING. S.B, Mass. Inst. Technol, 33; M.A, N.Y. Univ, 59. Asst. prof. mgr, Nat. Broadcasting Co, 33-42; acting dir. res. & develop, Inst. Technol, U.S. Navy Training Devices Ctr, 42-50; sales mgr, Gen. Precision Labs, 50-55; exec. dir. & dir. oper, Metropolitan Educ. TV Asn, N.Y, 55-61; assoc. prof. speech & chmn. broadcast options comn, Pa. State Univ, University Park, 61-72; CONSULT, 72- Consult, Educ. & Cult. Br, U.S. State Dept, Educ. TV for Algeria, 65, Educ. Radio Honduras, 66, Agency Int. Develop-State Dept, Regional Educ. TV for S.E. Asia, 66; Inst. Technol, Ford. Found, Pakistan, 68. Mass Media Award, Fund Adult Educ, 58. U.S.N, 42-46, Res, 46-67, Comdr. Speech Commun. Asn; Asn. Prof. Broadcasting Educ.(pres, 68); Nat. Asn. Educ. Broadcasters. Instructional technology; education problems of developing countries; systems analysis of training. Publ: Co-auth, Chap. 2, In: Understanding TV, Hastings, 65; ETV's financial dilemma, J. Broadcasting, spring 64; Formal adult education in broadcasting TV in USA, EBU Rev, 11/65; Education is the great society, Torch, 7/68. Add: 418 W. Ridge Ave, State College, PA 16801.

HUNGERFORD, EDWARD ARTHUR, b. Bremerton, Wash, Sept. 24, 21; m. 50; c. 2. ENGLISH. B.A, Univ. Puget Sound, 47, M.A,Cornell Univ, 48; Penfield fel, N.Y. Univ, 50-51, Ph.D.(Eng), 60. Instr. commun, Univ. Idaho, 48; ENG, Univ. Puget Sound, 49-50; Univ. Del, 52-56; asst. prof, Cent. Wash. State Col, 59-66; assoc. prof, SOUTH. ORE. COL, 66-67, PROF, 67-, chmn. dept, 66-70, MLA; Col. Eng. Asn; Philol. Asn. Pac. Coast. Modern British fiction. Publ: Mrs. Woolf, Freud and J.D. Beresford, Lit. & Psychol, 55; The method of Mrs. Dalloway, Mod. Fiction Stud, 57. Add: Dept. of English, Southern Oregon College, Ashland, OR 97520.

HUNGERFORD, EDWARD BUELL, b. New Britain, Conn, Jan. 19, 00; m. 31; c. 2. ENGLISH LITERATURE. A.B, Trinity Col.(Conn), 21; A.M, Harvard, 22, Ph.D.(Eng. lit), 28. Instr. ENG, Beloit Col, 22-23; tutor, Harvard, 25-26, 27-28; from asst. prof. to prof, NORTHWEST. UNIV, 28-68, EMER. PROF, 68- Ed, Northwest. Univ. Tri-Quart, 58-64; mem. adv. bd, Friends of Lit. Award, Friends of Lit, 68. U.S.N.R, 42-45, Lt. Shakespeare. Publ: Shores of darkness, Columbia Univ; Fighting frigate, forge for heroes, Follett; ed, Poets in progress, Northwest. Univ; auth, Recovering the rhythms of poetry, Scott, 64; Hamlet, the word at the center, Tri-Quart, 69. Add: 156 Virginia Ave, New Britain, CT 06052.

HUNGERFORD, HAROLD ROE, JR, b. Philadelphia, Pa, Aug. 25, 31; m. 66; c. 2. MEDIEVAL LITERATURE, ENGLISH LINGUISTICS. A.B, Univ. Calif, Berkeley, 54, M.L.S, 56, M.A, 60, Ph.D, 63. Instr. ENG, Cornell Univ, 62-63; asst. prof, Northwest. Univ, 63-69, dir, NDEA Inst. Eng, summer 66; PROF. ENG, ILL. WESLEYAN UNIV, 69- Consult, Ling. Res. & Demonstration Ctr, Rome, Ga, 66-69; vis. asst. prof. Eng, Univ. Calif, Berkeley, 68. MLA; NCTE; Ling. Soc. Am; Early Eng. Text. Soc. Medieval literature and culture; linguistic theory; structural and systems theory. Publ: Co-ed, English linguistics: an introductory reader, Scott, 70; auth, That was at Chancellorsville: the factual framework of The red badge of courage, Am. Lit, 62; Change in language, High Sch. J, 66. Add: Dept. of English, Illinois Wesleyan University, Bloomington, IL 61701.

HUNGIVILLE, MAURICE NEILL, b. Bradford, Pa, July 10, 36. ENGLISH & AMERICAN LITERATURE. B.A, St. Bonaventure Univ, 59; M.A, West. Reserve Univ, 62; Ph.D.(Eng), Univ. Tenn, 69. Instr. Eng, Marshall Univ, 63-65; ASST. PROF. AM. LIT, MICH. STATE UNIV, 66- MLA. British Victorian literature. Publ: Ezra Pound, educator, Am. Lit, 72; Ezra Pound's letters to Olivet, Tex. Quart, 73; A choice of critics: Eliot's edition of Kipling's verse, Dalhousie Rev, 73; plus one other. Add: Dept. of American Thought & Language, Michigan State University, East Lansing, MI 48823.

HUNSAKER, KENNETH BURNICE, b. Elwood, Utah, June 5, 32; m. 53; c. 6. AMERICAN LITERATURE. B.A, Utah State Univ, 57, M.A, 59; Ph.D, Pa. State Univ, 68. Asst. Eng, Utah State Univ, 57-58; instr, 58-59; asst, Pa. State Univ, 59-61; instr. Am. lit, UTAH STATE UNIV, 61-63, asst. prof, 63-66, assoc. prof. ENG, 67-71, PROF, 71-, GRAD. CHMN. DEPT, 72-, dir. Am. Stud, 66-70. U.S.N, 51-54. West. Lit. Asn. Twentieth century Mormon novels; Western American literature. Add: Dept. of English, Utah State University, Logan, UT 84322.

HUNSINGER, PAUL, b. Findlay, Ohio, Mar. 23, 19; m. 43; c. 3. SPEECH. B.A, N.Cent. Col, 41; B.D, Evangel. Theol. Sem, 44; M.A, Northwest. Univ, 46, Ph.D, 51. Instr. speech, N.Cent. Col, 41-44; lectr. oral interpretation, Northwest. Univ, 46-48; asst. prof. pub. speaking & debate, Morningside Col, 48-49; assoc. prof. oral interpretation & chief acad. adv, Univ. South. Ill, 49-58; assoc. prof, Occidental Col, 58-62; PROF. SPEECH, UNIV. DENVER, 62- Res. consult, Am. Bible Soc, 49; trustee, Inst. Gen. Semantics, 67-; prof. oral interpretation, Univ. Hawaii, Manoa, 72. Speech Commun. Asn; Int. Soc. Gen. Semantics. Semantics; oral interpretation; forensics. Publ: Co-auth, Contest speaking manual, 64 & Managing forensic tournaments, 67, Nat. Textbks; auth, Communicative interpretation, W.C. Brown, 67; co-auth, Technique of Fundamentals of story telling, Eihosha, Tokyo, 73; Public reading of poetry, British Speech & Drama J, 72; Storytelling and public speaking, Pac. Commun. J, 72; contrib, Studies in interpretation, Rodupi, Amsterdam, 73. Add: Dept. of Speech, University of Denver, Denver, CO 80210.

HUNT, EFFIE N, b. Waverly, Ill, June 19, 22. ENGLISH LITERATURE. A.B, MacMurray Col, 44; univ. scholar, Univ. Ill, 44-45; A.M, 45, univ. fel, 46-47, 48-49, Ph.D.(Eng), 50; Fulbright fel, Univ. London, Eng, 49-50; Columbia Univ, 52. Asst. Eng, Univ. Ill, 45-46, 47-48, instr, 50-51; librn, Harvard, 47; Univ. Pa, 48; Libr. Congr, 51-52; asst. prof. ENG, Mankato State Col, 52-59; prof, Radford Col, 59-63, chmn. dept, 61-63; assoc. prof, IND. STATE UNIV, TERRE HAUTE, 63-67, PROF, 67- MLA; NCTE. Ben Jonson and the tribe of Ben; Renaissance drama, particularly Shakespeare; 17th century literature. Add: Dept. of English, Indiana State University, Terre Haute, IN 47809.

HUNT, JAMES CLAY, b. Lexington, Ky, Jan. 28, 15. ENGLISH LITERATURE. A.B, Univ. Ky, 34, A.M, 35; Ph.D, Johns Hopkins Univ, 41. Instr. ENG, Wayne Univ, 39-41; WILLIAMS COL.(MASS), 41-42, 46-47, asst. prof, 47-53, assoc. prof, 53-58, PROF, 58- Am. Counc. Learned Soc. fac. stud. fel, 53. U.S.N.R, 42-45. MLA; Renaissance Soc. Am. Renaissance English literature; 20th century literature; Dante. Publ: Donne's poetry. Add: Dept. of English, Williams College, Williamstown, MA 01267.

HUNT, JOHN WESLEY, b. Tulsa, Okla, Jan. 19, 27; m. 51; c. 3. ENGLISH. B.A, Univ. Okla, 49; univ. fel, Univ. Chicago, 52-53, Ph.D.(lit. & theol), 61; Kent fel, Nat. Counc. Relig. Higher Educ, 52, 53, 54. Asst. prof. Eng, Earlham Col, 56-61, assoc. prof, 62-65, prof, 66-72, Bain-Swiggett prof. Eng. lang. & lit. & chmn. dept. Eng, 68-71, assoc. dean, 71-72; PROF. ENG. & DEAN, COL. ARTS & SCI, LEHIGH UNIV, 72- Asst. ed, Bull. Ill. Soc. Med. Res, 54-56; Lilly study grant, 58; Danforth teacher study grant, 60; Lilly fel, 64-65; mem, Annual Conf. Stud. 20th Century Lit, 66-; Carnegie Found. humanities prog. grant, 67-68; Ira Doan distinguished teacher travel award, 70; Ford Found. humanities develop. fund grant, summers 70, 71. E. Harris Harbison Distinguished Teaching Award, 66. U.S.N, 44-46, Res, 51-53, Ens, Fel. Soc. Relig. Higher Educ; NCTE; MLA; Soc. Stud. South. Lit. The novel; modern American literature; contemporary British novel. Publ: William Faulkner: art in theological tension, Syracuse Univ, 65; The journey back: the early novels of Wright Morris, Critique, summer 62; Comic escape and anti-vision: the novels of Joseph Heller and Thomas Pynchon, In: Adversity and grace: studies in recent American literature: Univ. Chicago, 68; The theological complexity of Faulkner's fiction & The theological center of Absalom, Absalom, In: Religious perspectives in Faulkner's fiction, Univ. Notre Dame, 72; plus others. Add: Springtown, PA 18081.

HUNT, JOSEPH ANTHONY, b. Philadelphia, Pa, Dec. 3, 38; m. 64; c. 2. ENGLISH & AMERICAN LITERATURE. B.S, St. Joseph's Col.(Pa), 60; M.A, Univ. Hawaii, 66; Ph.D.(Eng), Univ. N.Mex, 71. Instr. ENG, Colby Col, 68-71, ASST. PROF, 71-72; UNIV. P.R, MAYAGÜEZ, 72- MLA; NCTE. Twentieth century poetry and drama. Publ: Maine winter (poem), Maine Poets & Their Poems, 70; Composition for William Carlos Williams (poem), Atenea, spring 73; Gary Snyder's After work, Explicator, 74. Add: Dept. of English, University of Puerto Rico, Mayagüez, PR 00708.

HUNT, KELLOGG WESLEY, English Linguistics. See Volume III, Foreign Languages, Linguistics & Philology.

HUNT, TIMOTHY EARLE, b. Des Plaines, Ill, Oct. 7, 42; m. 64; c. 2. INTEGRATED HUMANITIES, ENGLISH. B.S, North. Ill. Univ, 66, M.A, 67, Ph.D. (Eng), 71; Univ. Toulouse, 71. Teacher Eng, Lyons Twp. High Sch. & Jr. Col, 66; ASST. PROF. HUMANITIES, NORTH. ARIZ. UNIV, 71- Consult, Univ. Nebr. Comp. Arts Workshop, summer 72. MLA; Nat. Asn. Humanities Educ.(publ. chmn, 71-). Humanities education; American literature. Publ: Humanities news, column in Humanities J, 71-; contrib. abstr. of articles, Abstr. Eng. Stud, 71-73; auth, Humanities in higher education: an option, Horizons, 12/72. Add: Dept. of Humanities, Box 6031, Northern Arizona University, Flagstaff, AZ 86001.

HUNTER, ARMAND LEE, b. Humboldt, Nebr, May 27, 14; m. 35; c. 2. SPEECH. A.B, Univ. Nebr, 35, M.A, 37; Ph.D, Northwest. Univ, 47. Asst. instr. speech, Univ. Nebr, 36-38, instr. speech & drama, 38-41, dir. univ. theatre, 40-41; instr. speech & radio, Northwest. Univ, 42-43, asst. prof, 43-46, chmn. dept. radio, 43-46; assoc. prof, chmn. dept. radio, speech & theatre & educ. dir, Sta. WFIL, Phila, Temple Univ, 47-51; prof. & dir. TV develop, MICH. STATE UNIV, 51-62, dir. TV develop, WKAR-TV, 51-62, acting head dept. speech, 56-62, acad. admin. broadcasting serv, Cent. Admin, 62-64, DIR. CONTINUING EDUC. SERV, 64- Consult. educ, TV, Joint Counc. Educ. TV & Nat. Asn. Educ. Broadcasters, 51-56; Fund Adult Educ. & Ford Found. grant, 53; mem. adv. comt. on new educ. media to comnr. & U.S. Off. Educ, under Title VII, NDEA, 60-63, anal. & eval. spec. res. stud. & reports, 61; off. U.S. rep, Int. Sem. Instr. TV, Ind, 61; spec. consult. to comnr. & U.S. Off. Educ, new educ. media develop, summers 61 & 62; spec. consult, Mich. State Univ-Agency in Develop. contract on potential educ. broadcasting, Brazil, summer 62; off. U.S. rep, Int. Sem. Univ. Today, Yugoslavia, summer 63; participant, Int. Conf. Use New Educ. Tech. in Developing Countries, Ditchley Found, Eng, 66; Nat. Univ. Exten. Asn. off. rep, Educ. Media Coun, 69- & Joint Counc. Educ. Telecommun, 71-; chmn. gen. adv. counc. on community servs. & continuing educ, Mich. State Bd. Educ, 70-; chmn. joint comt. relat, Adult Educ. Asn. U.S-Nat. Univ. Exten. Asn, 71-72; spec. consult, USAID, Brazil, 73; v.pres, Joint Counc. Educ. Telecommun, 73-74; mem. adv. comt. prog. continuing educ, Educ. Testing Serv. Nat. Asn. Educ. Broadcasters (secy, 53); Adult Educ. Asn. U.S; Nat. Univ. Exten. Asn.(secy, 70-71, pres-elect, 71-72, pres, 72-73); Nat. Asn. State Univs. & Land Grant Cols.(mem. exec. comt, Counc. on Exten, 69-73, mem. educ. telecommun. comt, 72-74). Radio; television; adult education. Publ: Television must educate, In: TV manual; Mid-term report, Spectator, 12/72; The education of everyone, Proc. Nat. Univ. Exten. Asn, 5/73; plus others. Add: Continuing Education Service, 114 Kellogg Center, Michigan State University, East Lansing, MI 48823.

HUNTER, CHARLES STUART, b. Kitchener, Ont, May 16, 41; m. 67; c. 1. ENGLISH LITERATURE. B.A, Univ. Waterloo, 64; Ont. grad. fel, McMaster Univ. & Univ. Toronto, 64-66; M.A, McMaster Univ, 65; Can. Counc. fel, Univ. Toronto, 66-67, Ph.D.(Eng), 69. Lectr. ENG, UNIV. GUELPH, 67-69, ASST. PROF, 70- Can. Asn. Univ. Teachers; Asn. Can. Univ. Teachers Eng. Seventeenth century English Literature; history and philosophy of science; relationship between literature and theology in the Renaissance. Publ: A new use of deiformed, Notes & Queries, 10/69. Add: Dept. of English Language & Literature, University of Guelph, Guelph, Ont. N1G 2W1, Can.

HUNTER, FREDERICK JAMES, b. Denver, Colo, May 31, 16; m. 45; c. 3. DRAMA. B.A, Univ. Calif, 40; M.A, Univ. N.C, 42; Ph.D.(theatre & drama), Stanford Univ, 54. Instr. Eng. & speech, Iowa State Col, 46; asst. prof. drama & Eng, Whitman Col, 46-48; speech & theatre, Univ. Ore, 50-57; assoc. prof. DRAMA, UNIV. TEX, AUSTIN, 57-70, PROF, 70-, cur, Theatre Libr, 60-70. U.S.A.A.F, 42-46, Capt. Am. Theatre Asn; Am. Soc. Theatre Res; Int. Fed. Theatre Res. Dramatic literature; dramatic theory and criticism; theatre history. Publ: A guide to theatre and drama collections at The University of Texas, Humanities Res. Ctr, Univ. Tex, 67; Drama bibliography, 71 & Catalog of Norman Bel Geddes theatre collection, 73, G.K. Hall; The power of dramatic form, Expo. Press, 74; plus others. Add: Dept. of Drama, University of Texas at Austin, Austin, TX 78712.

HUNTER, J. PAUL, b. Jamestown, N.Y, June 29, 34; m. 54; c. 3. ENGLISH LITERATURE. A.B, Ind. Cent. Col, 55; M.A, Miami Univ, 57; Ph.D, Rice Univ, 63. Instr. Eng. lit, Univ. Fla, 58-59; Williams Col, 62-64; asst. prof. ENG, Univ. Calif, Riverside, 64-66; assoc. prof, EMORY UNIV, 66-68, PROF, 68-, CHMN. DEPT, 73- MLA; Am. Soc. 18th Century Stud. Theory of fiction; 18th century poetics; intellectual history. Publ: The reluctant pilgrim: Defoe's emblematic method and quest for form in Robinson Crusoe, Johns Hopkins Univ, 66; ed, A critical edition of Moll Flanders, Crowell, 70; The Norton introduction to literature: poetry, Norton, 73; auth, Satiric apology as satiric instance, J. Eng. & Ger. Philol, 69; Response as reformation: Tristram Shandy and the art of interruption, Novel: A Forum on Fiction, 71; Fielding's reflexive plays and the rhetoric of discovery, Stud. Lit. Imagination, 72. Add: Dept. of English, Emory University, Atlanta, GA 30322.

HUNTER, JOHN NORMAN, b. Long Beach, Calif, Feb. 20, 39; m. 62; c. 1. ENGLISH & AMERICAN LITERATURE. A.B, Univ. Calif, Berkeley, 60, M.A, 64, Ph.D.(Eng. lit), 71. Instr. ENG. LIT, UNIV. COLO, BOULDER, 68-71, ASST. PROF, 71- Vis. instr, Columbia Univ, summer 70; summer res. initiation fac. fel, Univ. Colo, Boulder, 71. U.S.A.R, 61-67. Philol. Asn. Pac. Coast; MLA. History of utopias; Victorian fiction; Shakespeare. Add: Dept. of English, University of Colorado, Boulder, CO 80302.

HUNTER, KATHRYN MONTGOMERY, b. Wharton, Tex, June 23, 39; c. 2. ENGLISH. B.A, Tulane Univ, 60; M.A, Univ. Calif, Berkeley, 62; Ph.D. (Eng), Emory Univ, 68. Woodrow Wilson intern & instr. ENG, Clark Col, 64-65; instr, MOREHOUSE COL, 67-68, ASST. PROF, 68- Instr, Atlanta Univ, summer 68; Nat. Endowment for Humanities Younger fel, 71-72; Am. Philos. Soc. travel grant, summer 72. MLA; Am. Soc. 18th Century Stud. John Dryden; restoration and 18th century satire; graphic satire. Publ: Sun and water imagery in Richard II: its dramatic function, Shakespeare Quart, 70; Occasions so few: satire as strategy of praise in Swift's early odes, Mod. Lang. Quart, 70; The informing word: verbal strategies in visual satire, Stud. 18th Century Cult, Vol. 4. Add: Dept. of English, Morehouse College, Atlanta, GA 30314.

HUNTER, ROBERT GRAMS, b. Milbank, S.Dak, Nov. 12, 27; m. 56; c. 2. ENGLISH. B.A, Harvard, 49; M.A, Columbia Univ, 58, Ph.D.(Eng), 63. Instr. ENG, Robert Col, Istanbul, 49-52; Dartmouth Col, 59-63, asst. prof, 63-64, assoc. prof, 64-70, fac. fel, 64-65; KENAN PROF, VANDERBILT UNIV, 70- Ansley Award, 63. U.S.A, 52-54. Shakespeare and Elizabethan drama. Publ: Shakespeare and the comedy of forgiveness, Columbia Univ, 65. Add: Dept. of English, Vanderbilt University, Nashville, TN 37203.

HUNTER, WILLIAM BRIDGES, JR, b. Louisville, Ky, June 7, 15. ENGLISH. A.B, Princeton, 37; A.M, Vanderbilt Univ, 39, Ph.D, 46. Instr. Eng, Vanderbilt Univ, 42-44; assoc. prof, Mary Baldwin Col, 44-46; prof. & head dept, Wofford Col, 46-57; prof, Baylor Univ, 57-59; prof. & acting chmn. Eng. & head dept. humanities, Univ. Idaho, 59-65; chmn. dept. Eng, Macalester Col, 65-68; PROF. ENG, UNIV. N.H, 68- MLA; Northeast Mod. Lang. Asn; Milton Soc. Am.(secy). Milton; Jonson; Shakespeare. Publ: Complete poetry of Ben Jonson, Anchor, 63; co-auth, Bright essence, Univ. Utah, 71. Add: Dept. of English, University of New Hampshire, Durham, NH 03824.

HUNTING, ROBERT STILWELL, b. July 1, 15; U.S. citizen; m. 48; c. 2. ENGLISH. B.A, Boston Univ, 38, M.A, 39; Ph.D.(Eng), Brown Univ, 51. Instr. ENG, Duke Univ, 48-51; Purdue Univ, 51-52, asst. prof, 52-57, assoc. prof, 57-67; PROF. & CHMN. DEPT, UNIV. MAINE, ORONO, 68- Ed, Maine Eng. Notes, 68-; ed. asst, Paiduma, 72- U.S.A.F, 42-46, Sgt. MLA; NCTE; Col. Eng. Asn; New Eng. Asn. Teachers Eng.(publ. comt, 72-). English prose and poetry of the 18th century; Pope; development of the English novel. Publ: Jonathan Swift, Twayne, 67; ed, Boswell's life of Johnson, Bantam, 68; ed, Boswell's Dorando, Puckerbrush, 74; auth, Studies of writing frequency, Res. Teaching Eng, spring 67; A lodging for the knight, New Eng. Asn. Teachers Eng, 11/72; The poems in The vicar of Wakefield, Criticism, summer 73. Add: Dept. of English, University of Maine, Orono, ME 04473.

HUNTLEY, FRANK LIVINGSTONE, b. Hanyang, China, Oct. 10, 02; nat; m. 26; c. 5. ENGLISH LITERATURE. A.B, Oberlin Col, 24; A.M, Univ. Chicago, 26, Ph.D, 42; Japanese Lang. Sch, Tokyo, 29. Instr. Eng, Wash. Univ, 25-27; Oberlin Col, 27-29; prof, Doshisha Univ. & Univ. Kyoto, Japan, 29-35; chmn. dept. ENG, Stout Inst, 38-43; assoc. prof, Carleton Col, 43-44; UNIV. MICH, ANN ARBOR, 44-55, prof, 55-72, secy. Barbour Scholar Orient. Women, 46-72, EMER. PROF. ENG, ENG. LANG. & LIT, 72- Fulbright fel, Japan, 57-58, fel, Folger Libr, 70- & Clark Libr, 72. Renaissance Soc. Am; MLA. Seventeenth century English literature; Japanese literature. Publ: Sir Thomas Browne: a biographical and critical study, 62;

An essay on Dryden's essay of dramatic poesy, 51; Jeremy Taylor and the great rebellion, Univ. Mich, 70. Add: 1048 Martin Place, Ann Arbor, MI 48104.

HUNTLEY, H. ROBERT, b. Virginia, Minn, Sept. 13, 28; m. 53; c. 2. ENGLISH. B.A, Wis. State Univ, 53; M.A, Univ. Wis, 56, Ph.D.(Eng), 65. Instr. ENG, North. Ill. Univ, 56-59; WASHINGTON & LEE UNIV, 62-65, asst. prof, 65-67, assoc. prof, 67-70, PROF, 70- Fel. coop. prog. humanities, Duke Univ-Univ. N.C, 66-67. MLA; S.Atlantic Mod. Lang. Asn. Edwardian novel; myth and literature; 20th century British novel. Publ: The alien protagonist, Oxford & Univ. N.C, 70; Ford, Holbein and Dürer, S.Atlantic Bull, 5/65; The good soldier and Die Wahlverwandtschaften, Comp. Lit, spring 67; Flaubert and Ford: the fallacy of Le Mot Juste, Eng. Lang. Notes, 6/67. Add: Rte. 1, Lexington, VA 24450.

HUNTLEY, JOHN FARINGDON, b. Oberlin, Ohio, May 16, 27; m. 53; c. 5. ENGLISH LITERATURE. B.A, Univ. Chicago, 48, Ph.D, 61; B.A, Univ. Mich, 50; M.A, Univ. Conn. 52. Instr. Eng. lit, Univ. Cincinnati, 56-57; UNIV. IOWA, 57-61, asst. prof, 61-66, assoc. prof. ENG, 66-73, PROF, 73-, DIR. CORE LIT. PROG, SCH. LETT, 69- William R. Harper fel, 53; Carnegie teaching fel, 54; Fulbright fel, London, 55-56; vis. prof, Wash. Univ, summer 66. U.S.N, 45-46. MLA; Col. Eng. Asn; Milton Soc. Am; NCTE; AAUP. Milton; lyric and dramatic literature of the renaissance; literary and critical theory. Publ: The poet-critic and his poem-culture in L'allegro and Il penseroso, Tex. Stud. Lit. & Lang, winter 72; The images of poet and poetry in Milton's The reason of church govt . . . , In: Achievement of the left hand: essays on the prose of John Milton, Univ. Mass, 73; Milton's chorus, In: The Milton Encycl, Univ. Wis, (in press); plus others. Add: Dept. of English, English-Philosophy Bldg, University of Iowa, Iowa City, IA 52242.

HUNTRESS, KEITH GIBSON, b. South Portland, Maine, May 6, 13; m. 40; c. 5. ENGLISH. A.B, Wesleyan Univ, 35, A.M, 36; Ph.D, Univ. Ill, 42. Instr. ENG, IOWA STATE UNIV, 41-42, asst. prof, 42-44, assoc. prof, 44-46, PROF, 46- Vis. assoc. prof, Wesleyan Univ, 46, vis. prof, 51-52. Alumni award, Wesleyan Univ, 65; Distinguished prof. sci. & humanities, Iowa State Univ, 66. MLA. American and English literature; poems. Publ: Co-auth, Analysis of propaganda, Holt, 49 & Essentials of good writing, Heath, 59; auth, Murder of an American prophet, Chandler, 63; co-auth, Design for reading, 64 & Ideas and backgrounds, 64, Am. Bk; ed, Narratives of shipwrecks and disasters, 1586-1860, Iowa State Univ, 74; auth, Governor Thomas Ford and the murders of Joseph Smith, Dialogue, summer 69; Melville, Henry Cheever and The lee shore, New Eng. Quart, 9/71; Guinea of Whitejacket and Chief Justice Shaw, Am. Lit, 1/72. Add: Dept. of English & Speech, Iowa State University, Ames, IA 50010.

HUNTSBERRY, WILLIAM EMERY, b. Cleveland, Ohio, Dec. 13, 16; m. 44; c. 1. ENGLISH. B.A, Mich. State Norm. Col, 42; M.A, Univ. Hawaii, 49; State Univ. Iowa, 51-54. Instr, High Sch, Mich, 42-44; Culver Mil. Acad, Ind, 44-45; Kamehameha Sch. Boys, Hawaii, 45-46; ENG, UNIV. HAWAII, 46-63, asst. prof, 57-63, assoc. prof, 63-69, PROF, 69- Publ: Harbor of the little boats, 58 & Oscar Mooney's head, 61, Holt; The big wheels, 67 & The big hang up, 70, Lothrop. Add: Dept. of English, University of Hawaii, Honolulu, HI 96822.

HUPPE, BERNARD FELIX, b. New York, N.Y, Aug. 1, 11. ENGLISH LITERATURE. A.B, Amherst Col, 33; Ph.D, N.Y. Univ, 40. Asst. Eng, Duke Univ, 35-36; Wash. Sq. Col, N.Y. Univ, 36-40, instr, 40-42; asst. prof, Princeton, 45-50; from assoc. prof. to PROF. ENG, STATE UNIV. N.Y. BINGHAMTON, 50-, CO-DIR. CTR. MEDIEVAL & RENAISSANCE STUD, 68-, chmn. dept. Eng. & chmn. grad. comt, 50-68. Fulbright lectr, Univ. Vienna, 55-56; mem. ed. bd, State Univ. N.Y, 56-; mem, Bd. For. Scholars, 58-61; mem. selection bd, Nat. Endowment Humanities, 66- U.S.A, 42-45, Capt. MLA; Mediaeval Acad. Am. Old and Middle English literature; language. Publ: Co-auth, Piers Plowman and scriptural tradition, 51 & Fruyt and chaff, 63, Princeton; auth, Doctrine and poetry, 59, A reading of the Canterbury tales, 64, 67 & Web of words, 70, State Univ. N.Y. Add: Dept. of English, State University of New York at Binghamton, Binghamton, NY 13901

HURLEY, PAUL JOSEPH, b. Aliquippa, Pa, Aug. 30, 31. AMERICAN LITERATURE, DRAMA. B.A, Univ. Pittsburgh, 53, M.A, 54; Ph.D.(Eng), Duke Univ, 62. Instr. ENG, Kent State Univ, 56-58; teaching asst, Duke Univ, 59-60; asst. prof, U.S. Naval Acad, 61-65; SOUTH. ILL. UNIV, 65-68, assoc. prof, 68-72, PROF, 72- U.S.A, 54-56. MLA; NCTE. Modern drama; contemporary American literature; 19th century American literature. Publ: Young Goodman Brown's Heart of darkness, Am. Lit, 1/66; Suddenly last summer as morality play, Mod. Drama, 2/66; Law and the dramatic rhetoric of The way of the world, S.Atlantic Quart, spring 71. Add: Dept. of English, Southern Illinois University, Carbondale, IL 62901.

HURRELL, JOHN DENNIS, b. London, Eng, Nov. 8, 24; m. 49; c. 2. ENGLISH. B.A, Univ. London, Eng, 49; Ph.D.(Eng), Univ. Birmingham, 54. Instr. ENG, State Univ. Iowa, 54-55; lectr, Williams Col, 55-56; Ryerson Inst, Can, 56-57; UNIV. MINN, MINNEAPOLIS, 57-58, asst. prof, 58-61, from assoc. prof. to PROF, 61-, chmn. grad. prog. comp. lit, 63. Ed, Drama Survey, 61- R.N, 43-46. Am. Theatre Asn. Drama and dramatic theory; Elizabethan prose fiction. Publ: Ed, Two modern American tragedies, Scribners, 61. Add: Dept. of English, University of Minnesota, Minneapolis, MN 55455.

HURSEY, RICHARD C, b. Coshocton, Ohio, Dec. 4, 33; m. 58; c. 4. ENGLISH B.A, Ohio State Univ, 59; NDEA fel. & Ph.D.(Eng), Ohio Univ, 67. Asst. prof. Eng, Wayne State Col, 66-71; news ed, Maverick Media, Inc, 71-73; ASST. PROF. ENG, RAYMOND WALTERS GEN. & TECH. COL, UNIV. CINCINNATI, 73- Publicity consult, Southeast Nebr. Community Action Prog, 73. U.S.A, 55-57. MLA. Victorian fiction; John G. Neihardt; film. Publ: A cycle of the west: John G. Neihardt's tragedy of the American frontier, Wayne State Col. Soc. Sci. Rev, 70; Black elk speaks: the Indian value system, Wayne State Col. Rev, 71. Add: Dept. of English, Raymond Walters General & Technical College, University of Cincinnati, 9555 Plainfield Rd, Cincinnati, OH 45236.

HURT, JAMES RIGGINS, b. Ashland, Ky, May 22, 34; m. 58; c. 3. ENGLISH. A.B, Univ. Ky, 56, M.A, 57; Ph.D.(Eng), Ind. Univ, 65. Instr. ENG, Univ. Ky, 59-61; resident lectr, Ind. Univ, 63-66; asst. prof, UNIV. ILL, URBANA, 66-70, assoc. prof, 70-73, PROF, 73- U.S.A, 57-59. MLA. Dramatic literature. Publ: Aelfric, Twayne, 72; Catiline's dream: an essay on Ibsen's plays, Univ. Ill, 72; Focus on film and theatre, Prentice, 74; Inverted rituals in Webster's the White devil, J. Eng. & Ger. Philol, 62; The fantastic scenes in Peer Gynt, Mod. Drama, 62; Prometheus unbound and Aeschylean dramaturgy, Keats-Shelley J, 66. Add: 129 English Bldg, University of Illinois, Urbana, IL 61801.

HURWITZ, HAROLD M, b. Boston, Mass, Feb. 7, 29; m. 54; c. 2. ENGLISH. B.A, Boston Univ, 52, M.A, 54; Ph.D.(Eng), Univ. Ill, 59. Asst. prof. ENG, Humboldt State Col, 58-65; Univ. Hawaii, 65-67; ASSOC. PROF, WINDHAM COL, 67- Fulbright lectr. Am. lit, Seoul Nat. Univ, 63-64. U.S.A, 46-47. MLA. Twentieth century American and British literature; Indian literature—Rabindranath Tagore. Publ: Yeats and Tagore, Comp. Lit, winter 64; Ezra Pound and Rabindranath Tagore, Am. Lit, 3/64; Whitman, Tagore, and Passage to India, Walt Whitman Rev, 6/67. Add: Dept. of English, Windham College, Putney, VT 05346.

HUSBAND, JOHN DILLON, b. River Forest, Ill, Dec. 2, 09. ENGLISH. B.S, Northwest. Univ, 32, A.M, 38, Ph.D, 45. Teacher ENG, high sch, Ill, 37-45; chmn. dept, Shimer Col, 45-46; from asst. prof. to PROF, TULANE UNIV, 46- Assoc. teacher training, Northwest. Univ, 42-45. Modern American and British literature; intercultural education; fact and opinion. Add: Dept. of English, Tulane University, New Orleans, LA 70118.

HUSEBOE, ARTHUR R, b. Sioux Falls, S.Dak, Oct. 6, 31; m. 53. ENGLISH. B.A, Augustana Col.(S.Dak), 53; M.A, Univ. S.Dak, 56; Strauss fel, Ind. Univ, 57-59, Ph.D, 63. Asst, Univ. S.Dak, 55-56, instr. Eng. lang. & lit, 60-61; AUGUSTANA COL.(S.DAK), 56-57, summers, 58-59, asst. prof. ENG, 61-64, assoc. prof, 64-71, PROF. & CHMN. DIV. HUMANITIES, 71-, dir. NDEA Eng. Inst, summer 68, dir, Educ. Professions Develop. Act, Eng. Inst, 69. Teaching fel, Ind. Univ, 59-60; Am. Philos. Soc. grant, 65-66; ed-in-chief, Eng. Notes, 66-72; field reader, NDEA Eng. Inst. proposals, Bur. Elem & Sec. Educ, Dept. Health, Educ. & Welfare, Off. of Educ, 67-; Nat. Endowment for Humanities fel, summer 71; Am. Philos. Soc. grant, 73-74. Fac. Growth Award, Am. Lutheran Church, 65-66 & 73. U.S.A, 53-55. MLA; Augustan Reprint Soc; Norweg-Am. Hist. Asn; NCTE; West. Lit. Asn. Pope and Johnson; Restoration and 18th century drama; Western American literature and history. Publ: Ed, Robert Frost's Chicken feathers and other lectures, Augustana Col, 69 & And gladly teach, S.D. Counc. Teachers Eng, 71; co-ed, Restoration and eighteenth century theatre research: a bibliographical guide, South. Ill. Univ, 71; auth, Sir John Vanbrugh, Eng. auth. ser, Twayne, (in press); Pope's critical views of the London stage, Restoration & 18th Century Theatre Res, 5/64; Two songs in satire, Col. Eng, 4/70; Vanbrugh: additions to the correspondence, Philol. Quart, 1/74; plus others. Add: 813 E. 38th St, Sioux Falls, SD 57105.

HUSS, ROY G, b. New Orleans, La, June 26, 27. ENGLISH, FILM. B.A, Tulane Univ, 47, M.A, 49; Ph.D.(Eng), Univ. Chicago, 59. Instr. Eng, Chicago City Jr. Col, Wilson, 52-56; Wayne State Univ, 57-62; Queens Col.(N.Y), 62-66, asst. prof, 67-71; psychotherapist, Theodor Reik Consult. Ctr, 71- Fulbright prof, Athens Col, Greece, 56-57; Univ. Messina, Sicily, 59-60; lectr. film, N.Y. Community Col, 66-67; mem. ed. staff, Psychoanal. Rev, 72-; ed, Psychol. & Humanities, 73- Auth. Guild; Am. Fed. Film Soc; Asn. Appl. Psychoanal. Drama and film; psychoanalytic approaches to art and literature. Publ: Co-auth, Understanding film, Queens Col, 67 & The film experience, Harper, 68; ed, Focus on blow-up, 71 & co-ed, Focus on the horror film, 72, Prentice-Hall; auth, Max Beerbohm's drawings of theatrical figures (3 parts), Theatre Notebook, winter 66-67, spring 67 & summer 67; Social change and moral decay in the novels of Thomas Hardy, Dalhousie Rev, spring 67; Adler, Oedipus and the tyranny of weakness, Psychoanal, Rev, fall 73. Add: 130 E. 24th St, New York, NY 10010.

HUSSMAN, LAWRENCE EUGENE, JR, b. Dayton, Ohio, Mar. 20, 32; m. 59; c. 2. ENGLISH. B.A, Univ. Dayton, 54, M.A, Univ. Mich, 57, Ed.D, 64. Instr. Eng, Univ. Portland, 61-62, asst. prof, 62-63, acting chmn. dept, 63-65; asst. prof. ENG, WRIGHT STATE UNIV, 65-67, ASSOC. PROF, 68-, asst. chmn. dept, 61-67, acting chmn. dept, 67-72. U.S.A, 54-56. MLA; NCTE. Religious thought of Theodore Dreiser. Publ: Foreward, The bulwark, Chives, London, 73. Add: 508 Otterbein Ave, Dayton, OH 45406.

HUSTON, JOHN DENNIS, b. New York, N.Y, Sept. 21, 39; m. 64; c. 2. ENGLISH LITERATURE. B.A, Wesleyan Univ, 61; M.A, Yale, 64, Ph.D.(Eng), 66. Instr. ENG, Yale, 66-67, asst. prof, 67-69; ASSOC. PROF, RICE UNIV, 69- S.Cent. Mod. Lang. Asn. Elizabethan drama; Spenser; English Renaissance drama and poetry. Publ: Co-ed, Classics of the Renaissance theater, Harcourt, 69; auth, The function of the mock hero in Spenser's Faerie Queene, Mod. Philol, 2/69; Twelfth night and problems of identity, Mod. Lang. Quart, 9/72; Bottom waking, Stud. Eng. Lit. 1500-1900, spring 73. Add: Dept. of English, Rice University, Houston, TX 77001.

HUTCHENS, ELEANOR NEWMAN, b. Huntsville, Ala, Oct. 9, 19. ENGLISH. B.A, Agnes Scott Col, 40; Quennelle Harrold fel, 44; M.A, Univ. Pa, 44, Frances S. Pepper fel, 55, Ph.D, 57. Asst. prof, ENG, Univ. Ala, 57-61; assoc. prof, Agnes Scott Col, 61-67; PROF, UNIV. ALA, HUNTSVILLE, 67- MLA; Am. Soc. 18th Century Stud. English novel; 18th century English literature; literary criticism. Publ: Irony in Tom Jones, Univ. Ala, 65; Writing to be read, Prentice-Hall, 69; The identification of irony, J. Eng. Lit. Hist, 12/60; Verbal irony in Tom Jones, Publ. Mod. Lang. Asn, 3/62; The novel as chronomorph, Novel: a forum on fiction, 4/72; plus others. Add: 300 Williams Ave. S.E, Huntsville, AL 35801.

HUTCHESON, HAROLD RANDOLPH, b. Sandwich, Mass, June 24, 04; m. 34, 48; c. 3. ENGLISH LITERATURE. A.B, Yale, 26, Ph.D, 42; A.B, Swarthmore Col, 27. Instr. Eng, Hobart & William Smith Cols, 27-29; lit, Juilliard Sch. Music, 34-38; Eng, Amherst Col, 38-40; Univ. Conn 40-41; assoc. historian, Nat. Hq, Am. Red. Cross, 46-49; assoc. prof. Eng, Lake Forest Col, 49-50, prof, 50-66; prof. Eng. & chmn. div. humanities, BRIS-

TOL COMMUNITY COL, 66-68, sr. prof. ENG, 68-74, EMER. PROF, 74- Great Teacher Award, Lake Forest Col, 66. U.S.A, 42-43. Keats-Shelley Asn. Am. Lord Herbert of Cherbury; musical sonnets and poems. Add: Box 643, Sandwich, MA 02563.

HUTCHISON, EARL R, SR, b. Kincaid, Ill, July 11, 26; m. 47; c. 1. ENGLISH, MASS COMMUNICATIONS. B.S, Ed, Univ. Ill, Urbana, 51; B.J. & A.M, Univ. Mo-Columbia, 55; Ph.D.(Eng. & jour), Univ. Wis-Madison, 66. Lab. instr. news & reporting, Univ. Mo, 53-55; asst. prof. Eng, State Univ. N.Y. Col. Potsdam, 55-60, 62-63; instr. jour, Univ. Wis-Madison, 64-65; PROF. ENG, GEORGE PEABODY COL, 65- U.S.A, 44-46, 49-50, 51-53, Res, 53-66, Capt. Am. Civil Liberties Union. American literature; creative writing. Publ: Tropic of cancer on trial: a case history of censorship, Grove, 68; co-auth, Media and the law, Wiley, 69; auth, Literary giftbooks and annuals: mass communications ornaments, Jour. Quart, autumn 67; The sargasso sea of censorship, Sou'wester Quart, spring 68; co-auth, Self-censorship in broadcasting—the cowardly lions, N.Y. Law Forum, summer 72; plus two others. Prod: A peace-time episode (play), Univ. Wis, 64; TKO (play), CBS-TV & East. Educ. Network, 65. Add: Dept. of English, George Peabody College, Nashville, TN 37203.

HUTMAN, NORMA LOUISE, b. Buffalo, N.Y, Sept. 7, 34. COMPARATIVE LITERATURE, HUMANITIES. B.A, D'Youville Col, 56; M.A, West. Reserve Univ, 57; Univ. Madrid, Spain, 59; Andrew Mellon fel, Univ. Pittsburgh, 60-61, Ph.D, 61. Instr. Spanish, Chatham Col, 57-60; asst. prof, Wilson Col, 61-64; assoc. prof. mod. lang, HARTWICK COL, 64-70, PROF. COMP. LIT, 70-, CHMN. DIV. HUMANITIES, 64- West. Reserve Univ. grad. fel, 56-57; Cleveland Hispanic Soc. grad. award, 57; summers, lectr. Spanish, Univ. Pittsburgh, 60; Wilson Col, Warfield travel & res. grant, 62; mem, Nat. Scholar. Comt, Am. Asn. Teachers Span. & Port, 65-68. MLA; Am. Comp. Lit. Asn; Keats-Shelley Asn. Am; AAUP. Mythopoeics; comparative study of classic, Renaissance and Baroque drama; theories of literary criticism. Publ: Machado: a dialogue with time, Univ. N.Mex, 69; Universality and unity in the Lazarillo de Tormes, Mod. Lang. Asn, 61; Within the circle: on rereading Blood wedding, Mod. Drama, 73; Disproportionate doom: tragic irony in modern fiction, Mod. Fiction Stud, spring 73; plus others. Add: 395 Main St, Oneonta, NY 13820.

HUTSON, ARTHUR EUGENE, b. Los Angeles, Calif, Dec. 22, 06; m. 38; c. 1. ENGLISH. A.B, Univ. Calif; Los Angeles, 28; A.M, Univ. Calif, 29, Ph.D, 33. Instr. ENG, UNIV. CALIF, BERKELEY, 33-40, asst. prof, 40-41, assoc. prof, 48-58, PROF, 58-, secy. acad. senate, 59-68. U.S.A, 41-46, Res, 57-62; Col; Bronze Star Medal; Breast Order of Yün Hui. MLA; Mediaeval Acad. Am; Am. Folklore Soc; Am. Name Soc. Mediaeval vernacular and Latin literature. Add: 806 San Luis Rd, Berkeley, CA 94707.

HUTSON, RICHARD EUGENE, b. Sparta, Wis, May 18, 34; m. 56. AMERICAN LITERATURE. B.A, Univ. Ill, 57, M.A, 59, Ph.D.(Eng), 68. Acting asst. prof. ENG, UNIV. CALIF, BERKELEY, 64-67, asst. prof, 67-70, ASSOC. PROF, 70- Bruern fel, Univ. Leeds, 67-68. MLA. American poetry and culture. Add: Dept. of English, University of California, Berkeley, CA 94720.

HUTTAR, CHARLES ADOLPH, b. Austin, Tex, July 8, 32; m. 52; c. 7. ENGLISH. B.A, Wheaton Col, 52; M.A, Northwest. Univ, 53, Ph.D.(Eng), 56. Asst. prof. ENG, Gordon Col, 55-59, assoc. prof, 59-66, acting chmn. dept, 55-56, chmn. dept, 56-66; PROF, HOPE COL, 66-, CHMN. DEPT, 71- Bd. editors, Gordon Rev, ed, 57, 59, chmn, 65-66; Folger Shakespeare Libr. grant-in-aid, 61; Am. Philos. Soc. Penrose grant, 67. MLA; Renaissance Soc. Am; Conf. Christianity & Lit.(secy, 58-60, pres, 66-68); AAUP. Popular religious literature 1500-1700; Renaissance poetry; science, fiction and fantasy. Publ: Ed, Imagination and the spirit, Eerdmans, 71; auth, Poems by Surrey & others in a printed miscellany circa 1550, Eng. Miscellany, 65; Wyatt & the several editions of The Court of Venus, Stud. Bibliog, 66; The Christian basis of Shakespeare's Sonnet 146, Shakespeare Quart, 68; plus others. Add: Dept. of English, Hope College, Holland, MI 49423.

HUTTER, ALBERT DAVID, b. New York, N.Y, Dec. 16, 41. ENGLISH, COMPARATIVE LITERATURE. A.B, Antioch Col, 64; Woodrow Wilson fel, 64; Schepp fel, Cambridge, 64-66, M.A, 66; univ. fel, Univ. Calif, Berkeley, 66-70, Ph.D.(Eng), 71. Teaching asst. ENG, Univ. Calif, Berkeley, 67-69; ASST. PROF, UNIV. CALIF, LOS ANGELES, 70-, COMP. LIT, 72- Res. clin. fel, South. Calif. Psychoanal. Inst, 72-76. Dickens; psychoanalysis and literature; 19th century fiction. Publ: Contrib, Psychoanalysis and literary process, Winthrop, 70; auth, The Detective, Mystery & Detection Annual, 73. Add: Dept. of English, University of California, 405 Hilgard Ave, Los Angeles, CA 90024.

HUTTON, VIRGIL RALPH, b. Darjeeling, India, May 11, 31; U.S. citizen; m. 62. ENGLISH. B.A, Southwest. Col.(Kans), 52; M.A, Univ. Mich, 55, Ph.D.(Eng), 66. Asst. prof. ENG, ILL. STATE UNIV, 60-67, ASSOC. PROF, 67- U.S.A, 52-54, T/Sgt. Restoration comedy. Publ: Keats' Ode on a Grecian urn, Explicator, 3/61; The short happy life of Macomber, Univ. Rev, 6/64; James Joyce's The dead, East-West Rev, winter 65-66. Add: Dept. of English, Illinois State University, Normal, IL 61761.

HUX, SAMUEL H, b. Pitt Co, N.C, Apr. 12, 34; m. 56; c. 2. ENGLISH. A.B, Univ. N.C, 58; Ph.D.(Eng), Univ. Conn. Lectr. ENG, Queens Col.(N.Y), 63-65, INSTR, 65-67; YORK COL.(N.Y), 67- U.S.A, 53-55. American literature; literature and political ideology. Publ: Old Southern magic: some notes on tragedy, Mod. Occasions, spring 72; Liberal education and radical values, Dissent, fall 72; The English journals and the specialy syndrome, Change, 5/73. Add: Dept. of English, York College, 150-14 Jamaica Ave, Jamaica, NY 11432.

HVISTENDAHL, J.K, b. Sioux Falls, S.Dak, Dec. 3, 18; m. 45; c. 3. JOURNALISM. B.A, Augustana Col.(S.Dak), 41; M.A, Univ. Ore, 50; Ph.D, Univ. Minn, 68. Teacher, high schs, Ore, 50-56; ASSOC. PROF. JOUR, S.Dak. State Univ, 56-67; IOWA STATE UNIV, 67- Vis. lectr, Univ. Minn, 66-67; mem. adv. counc, J. Typographic Res, 68- Asn. Educ. in Jour. Typographic research. Publ: Co-auth, Producing the duplicated school paper,

Iowa State Univ, 2nd ed, 66; The effect of subheads on reader comprehension, spring 68 & Publishers' power: functional or dysfunctional?, fall 70, Jour. Quart; The reporter as activist, Quill, 2/70. Add: Dept. of Journalism, Iowa State University, Ames, IA 50010.

HWOPEK, DOROTHY ANN, b. Chicago, Ill. ENGLISH EDUCATION. B.A, DePaul Univ, 63, M.A, 69; Educ. Prof. Develop. Assistance fel, Univ. Ill, Urbana, 69-71, Ph.D.(Eng), 71. Elem. teacher, Mich, Ill, Ind. & Colo, 49-61; jr. & sr. high sch, Ill. & Nebr, 61-67; prin, Our Lady of Snows Sch, Chicago, 67-69; ASST. PROF. ENG, YOUNGSTOWN STATE UNIV, 71- NCTE; MLA; Conf. Eng. Educ; Conf. Col. Compos. & Commun. Student teaching. Publ: The use of creative dramatics to stimulate inter-cultural study, In: The world: context for teaching in the elementary school, W.C. Brown, 70. Add: Dept. of English, Youngstown State University, 410 Wick Ave, Youngstown, OH 44503.

HYDE, WILLIAM JAMES, b. Milwaukee, Wis, Nov. 28, 24; m. 50. ENGLISH. B.S, Univ. Wis, 46, Adams fels, 46, 50-52, M.A, 47, Knapp fel, 52-53, Ph.D, 53. Instr. ENG, Univ. Wis, Milwaukee, 46-47; West. Reserve Univ, 47-48; State Univ. Wash, 48-50; asst. prof, Trinity Univ, 53-56; PROF, UNIV. WIS-LA CROSSE, 56-, chmn. dept, 60-64, 67-72. MLA; Midwest Mod. Lang. Asn. English novel; Victorian literature and history. Publ: George Eliot and the climate of realism, PMLA, 3/57; Hardy's view of realism, Victorian Stud, 9/58; Thomas Hardy: the poor man and the deterioration of his ladies, Victorian Newslett, fall 69; Hardy's spider webs, Victorian Poetry, fall 70. Add: Dept. of English, University of Wisconsin-La Crosse, La Crosse, WI 54601.

HYDER, CLYDE KENNETH, b. W. Plains, Mo, Jan. 4, 02; m. 41; c. 1. ENGLISH LITERATURE. A.B, Drury Col, 23; A.M, Harvard, 26, Austin traveling fel, 30, Ph.D, 33. Instr. Eng, Univ. Tex, 26-27; asst. prof, UNIV. KANS, 30-37, assoc. prof, 37-47; ed, Univ. Press, 46-67, prof. ENG, 47-68, EMER. PROF, 68- Adv. bd, Victorian Poetry. U.S.A, 42-44. MLA. Nineteenth century English literature; concordances to the poems of A.E. Housman and Oliver Goldsmith. Publ: Swinburne's literary career and fame, Duke Univ; George Lyman Kittredge: teacher and scholar, Univ. Kans; Swinburne replies, Syracuse Univ, 66; ed, Swinburne: the critical heritage, 70 & ed, Swinburne as critic, 72, Routledge, London. Add: 233 Dakota St, Lawrence, KS 66044.

HYMAN, LAWRENCE W, b. New York, N.Y, Jan. 5, 19; m. 49; c. 1. ENGLISH LITERATURE. B.S.S, City Col. New York, 40; M.A, Columbia Univ, 47, Ph.D, 51. Instr. ENG, BROOKLYN COL, 52-60, asst. prof, 60-68, assoc. prof, 68-70, PROF, 70- U.S.A.A.F, 42-46. MLA; Am. Soc. Aesthet; NCTE. Seventeenth century English literature; literary criticism. Publ: Andrew Marvell, Twayne, 64; The quarrel within: art and morality in Milton's poetry, Kennikat, 72; Moral values and the literary experience, J. Aesthet. Art Criticism, summer 66; Literature and political action, Dissent, 7-8/67; Poetry and dogma in Paradise lost, Col. Eng, 4/68; plus others. Add: Dept. of English, Brooklyn College, Bedford Ave, Brooklyn, NY 11210.

HYMES, DELL HATHAWAY, Folklore, Linguistics. See Volume III, Foreign Languages, Linguistics & Philology.

HYNES, JOSEPH ANTHONY, JR, b. Detroit, Mich, Jan. 9, 27; m. 51; c. 3. ENGLISH LITERATURE. A.B, Univ. Detroit, 51; A.M, Univ. Mich, 52, Ph.D.(Eng. lit), 61. Instr. ENG. LIT, UNIV. ORE, 57-61, asst. prof, 61-65, assoc. prof, 65-72, PROF, 72- U.S.A, 45-46. MLA. Modern literature; the novel; Henry James. Publ: The middle way of Miss Farange: a study of James's Maisie, ELH, 12/65; The facts at The heart of the matter, Tex. Stud. in Lit, Winter 72; Varieties of death wish: Evelyn Waugh's central theme, Criticism, winter 72; plus others. Add: Dept. of English, University of Oregon, Eugene, OR 97403.

HYNES, SAMUEL L, b. Chicago, Ill, Aug. 29, 24; m. 44; c. 2. ENGLISH. A.B, Univ. Minn, 47; A.M, Columbia Univ, 48, Ph.D, 56. Instr. ENG. Swarthmore Col, 49-52, asst. prof, 54-61, assoc. prof, 61-65, PROF, 65-68; NORTHWEST. UNIV, 68- Fulbright fel, U.K, 53-54; Guggenheim fel, 59-60; Bollingen fel, 64-65; Am. Counc. Learned Soc. fel, 69; Nat. Endowment for Humanities sr. fel, 73-74; mem. Eng. Inst. Explicator Award, 62. U.S.M.C, 43-46, 52-53, Maj. English literature since 1900. Publ: Further speculations by T.E. Hulme, Univ. Minn, 55; Pattern of Hardy's poetry, Univ. N.C, 61; William Golding, Columbia Univ, 64; The Edwardian turn of mind, 68 & ed, Romance and realism, by Christopher Caudwell, 71; Princeton; ed, The authors craft and other critical writings by Arnold Bennett, Univ. Nebr, 68; auth, Edwardian occasions, Oxford, 72. Add: Dept. of English, Northwestern University, Evanston, IL 60201.

HYSHAM, JULIA HELEN, b. Red Oak, Iowa, Aug. 13, 01. ENGLISH LITERATURE. A.B, State Univ. Iowa, 22; A.M, Columbia Univ, 24, Roberts fel, 31-32, Ph.D, 50. Asst. prof. ENG, Wesleyan Col, 26-28; prof, SKIDMORE COL, 28-69, EMER. PROF, 69- Vis. prof. Eng, Pierce Col, Athens, Greece, 69-71. MLA. Publ: Joseph Warton, a biographical and critical study; Joseph Warton's reputation as a poet, Stud. Romanticism, 62. Add: Plymouth Harbor Apt. 1508, 700 John Ringling Blvd, Sarasota, FL 33577.

I

IANNI, LAWRENCE ALBERT, b. New Kensington, Pa, Apr. 19, 30; m. 52; c. 2. ENGLISH LINGUISTICS, LITERARY CRITICISM. B.S, Clarion State Col, 52; M.A, West. Reserve Univ, 57, scholar, 59, Ph.D.(Eng), 62. Teacher, Conneaut Valley Joint Schs, 52-54; Mentor Pub. Schs, 54-59; assoc. prof. ENG, IND. UNIV. PA, 60-63, PROF, 63-, ASSOC. DEAN GRAD. SCH, 71- Lectr, NDEA Insts. Eng, summers 66, 67; Comn. Eng,

Col. Entrance Exam. Bd, 67. NCTE; Ling. Soc. Am. English linguistics; the relationship of literature and science; psycholinguistics and language games. Publ: A linguistic approach to rhetoric, Col. Entrance Exam. Bd, 68; An answer to doubts about the usefulness of the new grammar, Eng. J, 11/64; Lawrence Ferlinghetti's fourth person singular and the theory of relativity, Wis. Stud. Contemporary Lit, summer 67; Sinclair Lewis as a prophet of black pride, Sinclair Lewis Newslett, 71; plus others. Add: Dept. of English, Indiana University of Pennsylvania, Indiana, PA 15701.

IDOL, JOHN LANE, JR, b. Deep Gap, N.C, Oct. 28, 32; m. 55. ENGLISH & AMERICAN LITERATURE. B.S, Appalachian State Univ, 58; M.A, Univ. Ark, 61, NDEA fels, 61-65, Ph.D.(Eng), 65. Teacher ENG, Blowing Rock Union Sch, 58-59; ASSOC. PROF, CLEMSON UNIV, 64- Teacher Eng, Converse Col, 65 & 67. U.S.A.F, 51-54. MLA; Renaissance Soc. Am; Southeast. Renaissance Soc; Soc. Stud. South. Lit. Seventeenth century English poetry; American novel; satire. Publ: The plays of Thomas Wolfe and their links with his novels, Miss. Quart, 69; Thomas Wolfe and painting, RE: Arts & Lett, 69; How much writing is Johnny doing?, S.C. Educ. J, 73. Add: Dept. of English, Clemson University, Clemson, SC 29631.

IGO, JOHN N, JR, b. San Antonio, Tex, May 29, 27. ENGLISH. M.A, Trinity Univ.(Tex), 52. Instr. English, St. Mary's Hall, 50-51; instr. & acquisitions librn, Trinity Univ.(Tex), 52-53; instr. ENGLISH, SAN ANTONIO COL, 53-56, asst. prof, 56-64, assoc. prof, 64-71, PROF, 71- Nat. Soc. Arts & Lett. Lit. Award, 54. S.Cent. Mod. Lang. Asn. The 1890's in England, the decadents; the sonnet in English; pre-Raphaelites. Publ: God of gardens, Am. Weave, 62; A chamber Faust, Wake-Brook, 64; Igo on poetry, Philippi, San Antonio, Tex, 65; The tempted monk, Hors Commerce, Calif, 67; Los pastores, San Antonio Col. Libr, 67; No harbor, else, 72 & Golgotha, 73, Et Cetera; A calendar of Fausts, Bull. N.Y. Pub. Libr, 1/67; Books for the new breed, Sch. Libr. J, 4/67; plus others. Add: 12505 Woller Rd, San Antonio, TX 78228.

IHRIG, MARY ALICE, b. Hannibal, Mo, June 4, 27. AMERICAN & ENGLISH LITERATURE. A.B, Shurtleff Col, 49; M.A.Ed, Wash. Univ, 56; B.D, Southeast. Baptist Theol. Sem, 60; Alida W. Parker Int. scholarship, Univ. N.C, Chapel Hill, 68-69, Ph.D.(Eng), 73. Teacher, Athens Community Unit Dist, Ill, 49-56; ENG, Streator Township High Sch, 56-57; from instr. to ASSOC. PROF, MARS HILL COL, 60- MLA; NEA; NCTE; AAUP. Ralph Waldo Emerson; literature by and about women. Add: Dept. of English, Mars Hill College, Mars Hill, NC 28754.

ILKO, DONALD WILSON, b. Philadelphia, Pa, Dec. 2, 43. THEATRE. B.A, Emerson Col, 65; M.A, West. Reserve Univ, 66, M.F.A, 67, Ph.D.(theatre), 69. Instr. speech, Worcester State Col, 69-70; ASST. PROF. THEATRE, COL. OF THE HOLY CROSS, 70- Am. Theatre Asn; Speech Commun. Asn. American musical theatre; American stage design; theatre architecture. Add: Dept. of Theatre, College of the Holy Cross, Worcester, MA 01610.

IMHOOF, MAURICE, English, Linguistics. See Volume III, Foreign Languages, Linguistics & Philology.

INCE, ROBERT LEE, b. Marysville, Kans, July 9, 36; m. 58; c. 2. SPEECH. B.A, Univ. Kans, 59, M.A, 63; fel, Northwest. Univ, 64, Ph.D.(speech), 65. Teacher Eng, Wichita S. High Sch, 59-62; instr. SPEECH, Chicago City Jr. Col. & Chicago Teachers Col, 62-64; asst. prof, UNIV. ILL, URBANA, 64-70, ASSOC. PROF, 70- Nat. Endowment for Humanities fel, 67. Speech Commun. Asn. Effects of criticism on oral performance; sociocultural influences on communication skill development; teacher-student interaction. Add: Dept. of Speech Communication, 244 Lincoln Hall, University of Illinois, Urbana, IL 61801.

INFANTE, DOMINIC A, b. Youngstown, Ohio, Feb. 23, 40; m. 63; c. 2. COMMUNICATION. B.S, Bowling Green State Univ, 62; M.S, Westminster Col, (Pa), 67; M.A, Kent State Univ, 69, Ph.D.(commun), 71. Teacher COMMUN, Austintown Fitch High Sch, Youngstown, Ohio, 62-69; ASST. PROF, State Univ. N.Y, Albany, 71-73; UNIV. S.FLA, 73- Commun. consult, N.Y. State Police Acad, summer 72. Speech Commun. Asn; Cent. States Speech Commun. Asn; Int. Commun. Asn. Attitude theory; persuasion theory; communication anxiety. Publ: The function of perceptions of consequences in attitude formation and communicator image formation, Cent. States Speech J, fall 72; Forewarnings in persuasion: effects of opinionated language and forewarner and speaker authoritativeness, West. Speech J, summer 73; The perceived importance of cognitive structure components: an adaptation of Fishbein's theory, Speech Monogr, 3/73; plus others. Add: Dept. of Speech Communication, University of South Florida, Tampa, FL 33620.

INGALLS, MILDRED DODGE JEREMY, b. Gloucester, Mass, Apr. 2, 11. AMERICAN, CHINESE & JAPANESE LITERATURE, CONTEMPORARY POETRY. A.B, Tufts Col, 32, A.M, 33; Univ. Chicago, 38-39, 41, 45, Chinese Ministry Educ. scholar, 46-47; Guggenheim fel, 43; Am. Acad. Arts & Lett. grant, 44; Ford fac. fel, 52-53; L.H.D, Rockford Col, 60; Litt.D, Tufts Univ, 65. Asst. prof, West. Col, 41-43; res. assoc. Chinese, Univ. Chicago, 47; res. poet & asst. prof. arts & lit, Rockford Col, 48-53, chmn. div. arts, 50-53, prof. Eng. & Asiatic stud. & chmn. dept. Eng, 53-60; RES. & WRITING, 60- Bates lectr, Wellesley Col, 43; ed, Common Cause, 47; vis. lectr, Ewha Women's Univ, Korea, 57; Fulbright prof. Am. lit, Kobe Col, Japan, 57-58; Rockefeller Found. lectr. Am. poetry, Kyoto & Doshisho Univs, 58; Steinman Found. lectr, Tufts Univ, 60; lectr, Univ. Ariz. Poetry Ctr, 64. Yale Ser. Younger Poets Award, 41. MLA; Asn. Asian Stud; Poetry Soc. Am.(Shelley Mem. Award, 50). Classical Greek and Chinese poetry and their relation to contemporary in the West. Publ: The metaphysical sword (poetry), Yale, 41; Tahl, Knopf, 45; The Galilean way, Longmans Green, 53; transl. & ed, A political history of China, 1842-1928, Van Nostrand, 56; auth, The woman from the island (poetry), Regnery, 58; These islands also (Poetry), Charles Tuttle, 59; The malice of empire (transl, Yao Hsin-nung, Ch'ing-Kung Yuan), Univ. Calif. & Allen & Unwin, 70; Nakagawa's Tenno Yūgao, Twayne, 74; Mr. Ch'ing-Yin and the Chinese erotic novel, Yearbook Comp. & Gen. Lit, 64; The epic tradition, East-West Rev, Japan, Vol. I, Nos. 1, 2 & 3. Add: 6269 E. Rosewood, Tucson, AZ 85711.

INGE, MILTON THOMAS, b. Newport News, Va, Mar. 18, 36; m. 58; c. 1. ENGLISH & AMERICAN LITERATURE, AMERICAN STUDIES. B.A, Randolph-Macon Col, 59; Col. Teaching Career fel, South. Fel. Fund, 59-62; M.A, Vanderbilt Univ, 60, Ph.D.(Eng, Am. lit), 64. Instr. Eng, Vanderbilt Univ, 62-64; asst. prof. Am. thought & lang, Mich. State Univ, 64-68, assoc. prof, 68-69; ENG, VA. COMMONWEALTH UNIV, 69-73, PROF, 73-, CHMN. DEPT, 74- Bk. reviewer, Nashville Tennessean, 61-; consult, Choice, 64-; all-univ. res. grants, Mich. State Univ, 65-67; Fulbright lectr. Am. lit, Univ. Salamanca, 67-68; mem, founding junta, Inst. Hisp-Norteam. Salamanca, 67-68; reader, col. bd. Eng. compos. test, Educ. Testing Serv, 67-; vis. assoc. prof. Eng, Vanderbilt Univ, summer 69; Am. Philos. Soc. grant, 70; gen. ed, Am. Critical Tradition series, David Lewis, 70-; bk. reviewer, Richmond Times-Dispatch & Menomonee Falls Gazette, 70, 73-; Fulbright lectr. Am. lit, Buenos Aires, Arg, 71; founding ed, Resources for Am. Lit. Stud, 71-; mem. bd. dirs, Friends of Richmond Pub. Libr, 72-; gen. ed, Research Guides in Eng, St. Martin's, 73-; mem. bd. dirs, Nat. Newspaper Arch. & Acad. Comic Art, San Francisco, Calif, 73- MLA; S.Atlantic Mod. Lang. Asn; Am. Stud. Asn; Soc. Stud. South. Lit; Am. Asn. Teachers Span. & Port; Popular Cult. Asn; Melville Soc. Am; Thoreau Fel; Soc. Stud. Midwest. Lit. Ethnic American literature; literature and culture of the American South; American humor, satire and comic art. Publ: Co-auth, Donald Davidson: an essay and a bibliography, 65 & ed, High times and hard times, 67, Vanderbilt Univ; ed, Sut Lovingood's yarns, Col. & Univ. Press, 66; auth, Agrarianism in American literature, Odyssey, 68; ed, Augustus Baldwin Longstreet by J.D. Wade, Univ. Ga, 69; co-ed, The black experience: readings in Afro-American history and culture, Mich. State Univ, 69; ed, Faulkner's A rose for Emily, 70 & Studies in Light in August, 71, C.E. Merrill; ed, William Byrd of Westover by R.C. Beatty, Archon Bks, 70; co-auth, Donald Davidson, Twayne, 71; plus others. Add: Dept. of English, Virginia Commonwealth University, Richmond, VA 23284.

INGLIS, WILLIAM HEARD, b. Toronto, Ont, June 7, 37; U.S. citizen; m. 62; c. 2. MODERN DRAMA, ARTS ADMINISTRATION. B.S, Univ. Rochester, 63; M.A, Univ. Wash, 66, Ph.D.(drama arts), 74. Admin. asst. to exec. v.pres. cent. univ. admin, Univ. Wash, 68-69; acting exec. dir, Am. Theatre Asn, 69-70, assoc. exec. dir, 70-72; gen. mgr, The Lost Colony, 72; ASST. PROF. SPEECH & THEATRE & DIR. THEATRE, ARIZ. STATE UNIV, 72- Managing ed, Educ. Theatre J, 69-70; contrib. ed, Theatre News, 69-72; consult, Arts Impact, U.S. Off. Educ. & J.D.R. III Fund, 70-72. Eng.C, U.S.A, 56-58, Res, 58-60. Am. Theatre Asn; Univ. & Col. Theatre Asn. Dramatic expressionism; relations between government and the arts; imaginative constructs of acting. Add: Dept. of Speech & Theatre, Arizona State University, Tempe, AZ 85281.

INGRAHAM, VERNON LELAND, b. Milford, N.H, Oct. 1, 24; m. 60; c. 3. ENGLISH. B.A, Univ. N.H, 49; M.A, Amherst Col, 51; Ph.D.(Eng), Univ. Pa, 65. Instr. ENG, Univ. Del, 60-62; Haverford Col, 62-63; Gettysburg Col, 63-65; asst. prof, SOUTHEAST. MASS. UNIV, 65-67, assoc. prof, 67-70, PROF, 71-, chmn. dept, 68-72. U.S.A, 43-45, Sgt. MLA. Nineteenth and twentieth century American literature; twentieth century British literature. Publ: Survival: readings on environment, Holbrook, 71. Add: 78 Pleasant St, Marion, MA 02738.

INGRAM, REGINALD W, b. Coventry, Eng, Oct. 3, 30. ENGLISH. B.A, Univ. Birmingham, Eng, 52, M.A, 53; Ph.D, Univ. London, Eng, 55; Beaverbrook scholar, St. Andrews Univ, Scotland, 55-56. Lect. Eng. & drama, Univ. Baghdad, Iraq, 56-58; res, Shakespeare Inst, Eng, 58-59; instr. Eng, Kokomo exten, Ind. Univ, 59-60; humanities & Eng, Univ. Chicago, 60-61, asst. prof, 61-62; ENG, UNIV. B.C, 62-64, assoc. prof, 64-69, PROF, 69- Can. Counc. sr. fel, 67-68 & 73-74. MLA; Renaissance Soc. Am; Soc. Theatre Res, Eng; Royal Musical Asn. Renaissance drama, use of music in the theatre; mediaeval drama, staging, production, popularity; relationship of types of drama and music-drama and opera. Publ: Music and poetry, St. Martins, 61; Music as structural cement in Shakespeare, In: Shakespeare 1971: proceedings World Shakespeare Conference, Univ. Toronto, 72; Shakespeare and music, Rev. Nat. Lit, fall 72. Add: Dept. of English, University of British Columbia, Vancouver 8, B.C, Can.

INGRAM, WILLIAM H, b. Chicago, Ill, Nov. 23, 30. RENAISSANCE LITERATURE & SOCIETY. B.A, Grinnell Col, 53; M.A, Columbia Univ, 56; Ph.D. (Eng), Univ. Pa, 66. Instr. ENG, Drexel Inst. Technol, 57-65; asst. prof, UNIV. MICH, ANN ARBOR, 66-70, ASSOC. PROF, 70-, DIR. MEDIEVAL & RENAISSANCE COLLEGIUM, 73- Am. Counc. Learned Soc, Folger Libr, Huntington Libr. & Univ. Mich. grants. Sig.C, U.S.A, 53-55. Elizabethan drama; Renaissance cultural history; computer-aided research. Publ: Co-ed, Concordance to John Milton's English poetry, Clarendon, 73. Add: Dept. of English, Haven Hall, University of Michigan, Ann Arbor, MI 48104.

INMAN, BILLIE JO (ANDREW), b. Thurber, Tex, May 16, 29; m. 50; c. 2. ENGLISH. B.A, Midwest. Univ, 50; M.A, Tulane Univ, 51; Tex. Technol. Col, summer 54; univ. fels, Univ. Tex, 58-60, Ph.D.(Eng. lit), 61. Teacher, High Schs, Tex, 51-54; instr. ENG, W.Tex. State Col, 55-57; spec. instr, Univ. Tex, 61-62; instr, UNIV. ARIZ, 62-63, asst. prof, 63-68, assoc. prof, 68-72, PROF, 72-, DIR. GRAD. STUD, 73-, dir. freshman Eng, 67-71. Dir, NDEA Inst. Eng, summer 65. NCTE; MLA. Victorian prose, especially the writings of Walter Pater and John Ruskin. Publ: Co-auth, Aspects of composition, Harcourt, 70; The organic structure of Marius the epicurean, Philol. Quart, 4/62; Tucson, Arizona: a British city, Col. Eng, 5/68; Pater's appeal to his readers: a study of two of pater's prose styles, Tex. Stud. Lit. & Lang, winter 73; plus others. Add: Dept. of English, University of Arizona, Tucson, AZ 85721.

IORIO, JOHN J, b. Casandrino, Italy, Jan. 1, 25; U.S. citizen; m. 50; c. 3. ENGLISH, AMERICAN LITERATURE. B.A, Columbia Univ, 50, M.A, 51; Univ. Minn, 54; Univ. Pa, 55. Instr. ENG, Dickinson Col, 52-53; Ford Found. intern & instr, Vassar Col, 53-54; asst. prof, Colby Col, 55-63; PROF, UNIV. S.FLA, 63- Vis. asst. prof, Univ. Miami, 61; fiction ed, Northeast, 63-68; assoc. prof, Fla. State Ctr, Florence, Italy, 70. U.S.A, 42-45, S/Sgt. American literature; 20th century literature; writing since World War II. Publ: Co-ed, Love, sex, and identity, 70 & Violence in modern literature, 71, Boyd & Fraser; The white wall, Prairie Schooner, spring 65; The man in the black apron, South. Rev, fall 67; Beckett, In: Cross-currents, Kendall/Hunt, 72; plus others. Add: Dept. of English, University of South Florida, Tampa, FL 33620.

IREY, EUGENE F, b. Boulder, Colo, Aug. 6, 12; m. 42; c. 1. AMERICAN LITERATURE. A.B, Univ. Colo, 34, M.Educ, 39, M.A, 46; Am. Counc. Learned Soc. fel, Univ. Minn, 47, Ph.D.(Am. stud), 48. Instr. Eng, high sch, Colo, 34-39; Stephens Col, 39-43; meteorology & navigation, Spartan Sch. Aeronautics, Okla, 43-44; ENG, UNIV. COLO, BOULDER, 45-52, asst. prof, 52-59, assoc. prof, 59-69, PROF, 69-; res. fel, spring 63. Emerson; frontier literature. Publ: Contrib. ed, Annual bibliography of English language & literature, Vols. XXXIV-XLII, Mod. Humanities Res. Asn, 59-63; auth, A note on the Tabor opera house, West. Speech, 50; Leadville's inglorious Miltons, Colo. Quart, 52. Add: Dept. of English, University of Colorado, Boulder, CO 80302.

IRMSCHER, WILLIAM F, b. Louisville, Ky, Apr. 11, 20; m. 42; c. 3. ENGLISH. B.A, Univ. Louisville, 41; M.A, Univ. Chicago, 47; Ph.D, Ind. Univ, 50. Asst. eng, Ind. Univ, 47-50; dir. freshman Eng, Univ. Ariz, 50-60; assoc. prof. ENG, UNIV. WASH, 60-66, PROF, 66-, DIR. FRESHMAN ENG, 60- Ed, Col. Compos. & Commun, 65-74. U.S.A, 42-45, T/Sgt. NCTE; Conf. Col. Compos. & Commun; MLA. John Donne; current rhetorical theory. Publ; Co-auth, The language of ideas, Bobbs, 63; auth, Man and warfare, Little, 64; Ways of writing, McGraw, 69; The Holt guide to English, Holt, 72. Add: Dept. of English, University of Washington, Seattle, WA 98195.

IRSFELD, JOHN HENRY, b. Bemidji, Minn, Dec. 2, 37; m. 65; c. 1. ENGLISH & AMERICAN LITERATURE & LANGUAGE. B.A, Univ. Tex, Austin, 59, M.A, 66, Ph.D.(Eng), 69. Asst. prof. ENG, UNIV. NEV, LAS VEGAS, 69-73, ASSOC. PROF, 73- U.S.A, 61-64, Sgt. Twentieth century English and American literature; poetry and poetics; fiction. Publ: They come in threes (story), Red Neck Rev, spring 69; The use of military language in Hamlin Garland's The return of a private, West. Am. Lit, summer 72; Stop, rewind, and play (story), S.Dak. Rev, 3/74. Add: Dept. of English, University of Nevada, 4505 S. Maryland Pkwy, Las Vegas, NV 89154.

IRVIN, FREDRIC BRINKER, b. Mt. Pleasant, Pa, Oct. 13, 13; m. 39. ENGLISH LITERATURE. B.A, Temple Univ, 36; M A, Univ. Pittsburgh, 42, Ph.D, 47, LL.D, 55, D.H.L, 60. Teacher, Bellevue Pub. Schs, Pittsburgh, 38-42; Temple Univ, 42-45; v.pres, Andhra Christian Col, India, 47-52; pres, Thiel Col, 52-60; cult. attache, U.S. Inform. Agency, 60-71; PRES, NEWBERRY COL, 71- English literature and education in India, Europe and United States. Add: Office of the President, Newberry College, Newberry, SC 29108.

IRVINE, PETER L, b. Washington, D.C, Mar. 13, 32; m. 57; c. 1. ENGLISH. B.A, Swarthmore Col, 53; M.A, Harvard, 55; Ph.D.(Eng), Columbia Univ, 65. Instr. ENG, Beloit Col, 62-64; asst. prof, UNIV. CINCINNATI, 64-70, ASSOC. PROF, 70- MLA; NCTE. Victorian and American literature; English novel. Add: Dept. of English, University of Cincinnati, Cincinnati, OH 45221.

IRVINE, ROSE ABERNETHY, b. Kingston, N.Y, Nov. 14, 24; m. 65. SPEECH. B.A, Col. St. Rose, 45; M.A, Columbia Univ, 46; Ph.D.(speech), Northwest. Univ, 64. Teacher Eng, Kingston High Sch, N.Y, 46-47; Eng. & speech, Croton-Harmon High Sch, N.Y, 46-47; from instr. to assoc. prof. SPEECH, STATE UNIV. N.Y. COL. NEW PALTZ, 49-64, PROF, 64- Evaluator, Oral Interpretation Festival, Orange County Community Col, 62, 63; res. paper presented, Nat. Convention, Speech Asn. Am, Chicago, 64, chmn. panel, Nat. Convention, N.Y, 65, mem. legis. assembly, 68-71; vis. prof, Yonsei Univ, Korea, summer 70. Speech Commun. Asn; Am. Speech & Hearing Asn. Oral interpretation of literature; story-telling as a communicative art form; kinesthetic approach to speech. Publ: A preliminary investigation of storytelling in the United States, Speech Teacher, 11/59; Oral interpretation in the humanities today, Educ. Forum, 3/63. Add: 164 Huguenot St, New Paltz, NY 12561.

IRVING, DONALD C, b. Watseka, Ill, Mar. 11, 38; m. 64; c. 1. AMERICAN LITERATURE & STUDIES. B.A, Univ. Ill, Urbana, 60; M.A, South. Ill. Univ, 62; Ph.D.(Eng), Ind. Univ, 69. Instr. Eng, Cent. Mo. State Col, 62-64; GRINNELL COL, 68, asst. prof. ENG. & AM. STUD, 69-73, ASSOC. PROF, 73- MLA; Am. Stud. Asn; AAUP. Nineteenth century American fiction and poetry; American film; preservation of American monuments. Publ: The whale and the corset, Midwest Educ. Rev, 72. Add: Dept. of English, Grinnell College, Grinnell, IA 50112.

IRVING, EDWARD BURROUGHS, JR, b. Philadelphia, Pa, Feb. 5, 23; m. 46; c. 3. ENGLISH. B.A, Haverford Col, 43; M.A, Yale, 47, Ph.D.(Eng), 51. Instr. ENG, Yale, 49-54, asst. prof, 54-60; assoc. prof, UNIV. PA, 60-70, PROF, 70- Morse fel, Yale, 53-54; vis. lectr, Bryn Mawr Col, 67. U.S.M.C, 43-46. MLA; Mediaeval Acad. Am. Old English; the epic; Middle English. Publ: The Old English Exodus, 53 & A reading of Beowulf, 68, Yale; Introduction to Beowulf, Prentice-Hall, 69; The heroic style in The Battle of Maldon, Stud. Philol, 7/61; Image and meaning in the elegies, In: Old English poetry: fifteen essays, Brown Univ, 67; New notes on the Old English exodus, Anglia, 12/72. Add: Dept. of English, University of Pennsylvania, Philadelphia, PA 19174.

IRVING, GEORGE W, b. New York, N.Y, Oct. 24, 27; m. 53; c. 4. SPEECH, THEATRE. B.A, Univ. Mich, 51, M.A, 52; Ph.D, Stanford Univ, 66. Instr. commun. skills, Mich. State Col, 52-54; asst. prof. Eng. & speech, State Univ. N.Y. Col. Oneonta, 56-58; Eng, BALL STATE UNIV, 58-66, assoc. prof. SPEECH, 66-69, PROF, 69- Med.Dept, U.S.A, 46-47, Spec.Serv, 51. Speech Commun. Asn; Am. Theatre Asn; U.S. Inst. Theatre Technol. Theatre administration; technical theatre techniques. Add: Dept. of Speech, Ball State University, Muncie, IN 47306.

IRVING, ROBERT FRANCIS EDWARD, b. New York, N.Y, June 30, 31. ENGLISH LITERATURE. B.A, N.Y. Univ, 53; M.A, Yale, 58, Ph.D.(Eng), 61. Instr. Eng, Miami Univ, 60-62; asst. prof, Georgetown Univ, 62-68; ILL. INST. TECHNOL, 68-73, ASSOC. PROF. HUMANITIES & DIR. FRESHMAN HUMANITIES, 73- MLA; NCTE. Romantic and Victorian literature; English novel. Add: Dept. of English, Illinois Institute of Technology, Chicago, IL 60616.

IRWIN, BETTY JEAN, b. Moline, Ill, June 27, 25. ENGLISH, LINGUISTICS. B.S.E, North. Ill. Univ, 58, M.A, 60; fel, Univ. Wis-Madison, summer 66, Ph.D.(Eng), 67. ASST. PROF. ENG, Ball State Univ, 66-68; UNIV. GA, 68- MLA; AAUP; Am. Name Soc; Am. Dialect Soc; NCTE; Ling. Soc. Am. Old and Middle English language and literature; 20th century English grammar. Add: Dept. of English, University of Georgia, Athens, GA 30601.

IRWIN, EDWARD EUGENE, b. Birmingham, Ala, Nov. 14, 30; m. 54; c. 2. ENGLISH & AMERICAN LITERATURE. A.B, Memphis State Univ, 56; A.M, Univ. Fla, 58, Ph.D, 61. Instr. ENG, Univ. Fla, 59-61, asst. prof, 61-62; AUSTIN PEAY STATE UNIV, 62-63, assoc. prof, 63-66, PROF, 66-, chmn. dept, 66-71. U.S.A, 51-53. Freshman English; British and contemporary fiction. Add: Dept. of English, Austin Peay State University, Clarksville, TN 37040.

IRWIN, ELEANOR CHIMA, b. Ellwood City, Pa. SPEECH, DRAMA. B.S, Univ. Pittsburgh, 57, M.Ed, 59, fel, 59-63, Ph.D.(speech), 63. Elem. teacher, Edgewood Sch. Dist, Pittsburgh, Pa, 57-59; EXPRESSIVE ARTS THERAPIST, PITTSBURGH CHILD GUID. CTR, 64-; INSTR. SPEECH, THEATRE & COMMUN, CARLOW COL, 67- Lang. therapist, Home for Crippled Children, Pittsburgh, Pa, 63-68; res. assoc. creative drama, Cleft Palate Res. Ctr, Univ. Pittsburgh, 64-69, consult. child drama & ment. health, 69-; consult. expressive ther, Speech Clin, Children's Hosp, Pittsburgh, 70-; assoc. fac. mem, Workshop in Living-Learning, 71-; film dir, Pittsburgh Model Cities grant, 73. Am. Theatre Asn; Children's Theatre Asn.(chairperson drama for except. child, 67-69); Am. Soc. Psychopathol. of Expression; Int. Soc. Psychopathol. Expression; Am. Orthopsychiat. Asn; Inst. Arts in Educ. Assessment of drama therapy in work with disturbed children; children's reactions to hospitalizations as measured by questionnaires, drawings and spontaneous stories; inter-relationships between art and drama as diagnostic tools with disturbed children and adolescents. Publ: Co-auth, Countdown for listening (record series), Educ. Activities, 69; co-auth, Children with oral-facial clefts: a contribution to the psychological development of handicapped children, J. Am. Acad. Child Psychiat, 73 & Parents working with parents: the cleft palate program, Cleft Palate J, 73; auth, Puppetry as a diagnostic and therapeutic tool, In: Art and psychiatry, 74; plus others. Add: Pittsburgh Child Guidance Center, 201 De Soto St, Pittsburgh, PA 15213.

IRWIN, JOHN THOMAS, b. Houston, Tex, Apr. 24, 40. AMERICAN & ENGLISH MEDIEVAL LITERATURE. B.A, Univ. St. Thomas, 62; Yale, 62-63; Danforth fel, M.A. & Ph.D.(Eng), Rice Univ, 70. Suprv. pub. affairs libr, Ling-Temco-Vought, NASA Manned Spacecraft Ctr, 66-67; ASST. PROF. ENG, JOHNS HOPKINS UNIV, 70- U.S.N, 63-66, Res, 66-70, Lt. Modern American poetry; 19th century American novel; 14th century English. Publ: Co-auth, The structure of Cleanness: parable as effective sign, Medieval Stud, 73; auth, A nest of tuneful persons, South. Rev, summer 73; The crisis of regular forms, Sewanee Rev, winter 73. Add: Dept. of English, Johns Hopkins University, Baltimore, MD 21218.

IRWIN, JOSEPH JAMES, b. Clinton, Iowa, Oct. 29, 08; m. 37; c. 3. ENGLISH LITERATURE. A.B, Grinnell Col, 31; A.M, State Univ. Iowa, 34, Ph.D, 42. PROF. Eng, Buena Vista Col, 34-36; ENG, ALBION COL, 37-, chmn. dept. eng, 49-71. MLA; NCTE; AAUP. Shakespeare and Elizabethan drama; modern and contemporary British and American literature; Anglo-American literary relations. Add: 416 E. Erie St, Albion, MI 49224.

IRWIN, RUTH ELIZABETH, Speech & Hearing Science, Speech Pathology. See 12th Edition, American Men & Women of Science, Social & Behavioral Sciences Section.

IRWIN, VERA RUSHFORTH, b. Yonkers, N.Y, Nov, 4, 13; m. 51. DRAMA. B.S, N.Y. Univ, 40, M.A, 47; Univ. Colo, 42; Columbia Univ, 45. Teacher Eng. & drama, Croton-Harmon High Sch, 37-47; asst. prof, STATE UNIV. N.Y. COL. NEW PALTZ, 47-51, assoc. prof. drama, 51-69, PROF. DRAMA LIT. & THEATRE ART, 69-, dir. drama, 51-62, chmn. dept, 69-70. Ford fel, study inter-relat. theatre & drama in U.S. acad. & prof. theatre, 55-56; fel, Inst. Advan. Stud. Theatre Arts, 61, 62-63. Am. Theatre Asn; Am. Nat. Theatre & Acad; Am. Soc. Theatre Res; NEA. Theories and style of presentation of world theatre classics as discussed and demonstrated by outstanding foreign directors; critical edition of American production of Ikkaku Sennin, labanotated. Publ: Ed, Four classical Asian plays, Penguin, 72. Add: Dept. of Theatre Arts, College Theatre Bldg. 130, State University of New York College at New Paltz, New Paltz, NY 12561.

IRWIN, WILLIAM ROBERT, b. Shenandoah, Iowa, Sept. 17, 15; m. 39, 54; c. 1. ENGLISH LITERATURE. A.B, Grinnell Col, 36; Roberts fel, Columbia Univ, 36-39, A.M, 37, Ph.D, 41. Instr, L.I. Univ, 38-42; Cornell Univ, 42-47; asst. prof. ENG, UNIV. IOWA, 47-51, assoc. prof, 51-62, PROF, 62-, DIR. GRAD. STUD, 64- Fulbright prof. Eng. & Am. lit, Univ. Tübingen, Ger, 58-60. MLA; Midwest Mod. Lang. Asn; Int. Asn. Univ. Prof. Eng; Deut. Ges. Amerikastud. English literature of the 18th century; English and American prose fiction. Publ: Making of Jonathan Wild: a study in the literary method of Henry Fielding, 41 & Challenge: an anthology of the literature of mountaineering, 50, Columbia Univ; co-auth, Comic style of Beaumarchais, Univ. Wash, 61. Add: 308B English-Philosophy Bldg, University of Iowa, Iowa City, IA 52240.

ISAAC, DAN BERT, b. Chicago, Ill, Mar. 13, 30. ENGLISH, DRAMA. B.A, Univ. Chicago, 51, Noyes scholarship, 60-62, M.A, 61, Ph.D, 68; B.H.L, Hebrew Union Col.(Ohio), 54, M.H.L, 57. Mem. fac, Roosevelt Univ, 63-64; Univ. Chicago, 64-65; lectr. ENG, Queens Col.(N.Y), 65-68; ASST. PROF, MANHATTANVILLE COL, 68- Prog. dir, Eugene O'Neill Mem. Theater Ctr, Critics Inst, summers 68, 69; contrib. ed, Dimensions Mag, 68-72; dramatic producer, Performance Group, 71-72; prog. consult, Manhattanville Improvisational Arts Inst, 72; adj. asst. prof, State Univ. N.Y. Col. Purchase, 72-73; moderator & coord, Playwrights Unit, Actors Studio, 72-73; lit. adv, Circle in the Square, 72-; adj. asst. prof. Eng, N.Y. Univ, 73-74. U.S.A, 57-59, 1st Lt. Am. Theatre Asn; Northeast Mod. Lang. Asn. (chmn. sect. lit. & film, 73). Publ: The O'Neill Memorial Theatre Center: a place for playwrights, Educ. Theatre J, 3/72; The playwright as auteur,

Village Voice, 8/72; Komentarz nie kiem z Boku, Dialog, 6/73; plus numerous others. Add: Dept. of English, Manhattanville College, Purchase, NY 10577.

ISAACS, EMILY ELIZABETH, b. Sioux Falls, S.Dak, Sept. 25, 17. ENGLISH LITERATURE. A.B, Cornell Col, 39; A.M, Columbia Univ, 40; Univ. Chicago, 42; Univ. Wash, 44; St. Louis Univ, 46; Breadloaf Sch. Eng, Middlebury Col, 48; Ph.D, Wash. Univ, 57. Instr, Lindenwood Col, 43-48; PROF. ENG, CORNELL COL, 48-, chmn. dept, 64-72. MLA. Francis Stewart Flint and the imagist poets; Robert Frost, the man and his art. Publ: An introduction to Robert Frost, A. Swallow, 62. Add: Dept. of English, Cornell College, Mt. Vernon, IA 52314.

ISAACS, NEIL D, b. New York, N.Y, Aug. 21, 31; m. 53; c. 4. ENGLISH LITERATURE. A.B, Dartmouth Col, 53; A.M, Univ. Calif, Berkeley, 56; univ. fel, Brown Univ, 56-57, Ph.D, 59. Instr. ENG, City Col. New York, 59-62, asst. prof, 63; Univ. Tenn, 63-66, assoc. prof, 66-71; PROF, UNIV. MD, 71- S.Atlantic Mod. Lang. Asn. Old English and Middle English poetry; fiction; film. Publ: Ed, Approaches to the short story, Howard Chandler, 63; ed, Tennessee studies in literature, Vol. XI, 66 & auth, Structural principles in Old English poetry, 68, Univ. Tenn; ed, Tolkien and the critics, Univ. Notre Dame, 68; auth, Eudora Welty, Steck-Vaughn, 69; co-auth, Fiction into film: a walk in the spring rain, Univ. Tenn, 70 & Dell, 72; auth, Life for Phoenix, Sewanee Rev, 1/63; Six Beowulf cruces, J. Eng. & Ger. Philol, 1/63; The convention of personification in Beowulf, In: Old English poetry, Brown Univ, 67. Add: Dept. of English, University of Maryland, College Park, MD 20742.

ISAACSON, CARL LEONARD, b. Comertown, Mont, June 14, 20; m. 46; c. 1. ENGLISH, COMMUNICATION. B.A, Univ. Mont, 43; M.A, Univ. Denver, 49, Ph.D.(rhetoric, commun), 54; summers, Univ. South. Calif, 51 & 52. Instr. speech debate, Idaho State Univ, 47-50, asst. prof. speech, 50-53; asst. forensics, Univ. Denver, 53-54; assoc. prof. speech, Idaho State Univ, 54-59; prof. speech & drama, 59-63, head dept. speech & drama, 56-61, head div. commun, 61-63; PROF. ENG. & DIR. INFORM, MONT. STATE UNIV, 63- Asst. TV writing, Univ. South. Calif, summer 52. U.S.A, 43-46, Res, 46-, Maj. Am. Col. Pub. Relat. Asn; Speech Commun. Asn; Nat. Soc. Stud. Commun. Psychology of emotion; public relations; emotional proof. Publ: Co-auth, Planned, (TV movie), Tee Vee Co, Calif, 53. Add: Office of the Director of Information, Montana State University, Bozeman, MT 59715.

ISAACSON, NORMAN, b. Bronx, N.Y, July 25, 35; m. 71. SPEECH COMMUNICATION. B.S.Ed, Fredonia State Univ, 61; M.A, N.Y. Univ, 64, Ph.D. (speech commun), 68. Dept. rep, Sch. Gen. Stud, LEHMAN COL, 65-70, chmn. AV dept, 69-71, ASST. PROF. SPEECH COMMUN, 68-, dir. debate, 66-70. Consult, Am. Fed. State, City & Munic. Employees, 67-68; dir, Seek Prog, Lehman Col, 68-70; coord, Eng. & speech prog, Martin Luther King Health Ctr, Montefiore Hosp, 69; consult, Suffolk County Police Acad, N.Y, 70-; vis. prof. speech, Iona Col, 71-72. U.S.A, 54-56. Int. Soc. Gen. Semantics; Speech Commun. Asn; Int. Commun. Asn. Persuasion. Publ: Co-auth, Phonetic symbolism and speaker credibility, South. Speech J, 1/69; auth, The traffic summons as persuasive communication, Law & Order, 11/73. Add: Dept. of Speech & Theatre, Herbert H. Lehman College, Bedford Park Blvd. W, Bronx, NY 10468.

ISAACSON, PAULINE, b. Spring Valley, Wis. SPEECH HISTORY. M.A, Univ. Wis, 42; Ph.D.(speech), Univ. Minn, 57. Teacher, High Sch, Minn, 36-44; head recreation worker, Am. Red Cross, 45-46; curator II & ed, II, State Hist. Soc. Wis, Madison, 46; instr. hist. speech, UNIV. WIS-STEVENS POINT, 46-58, chmn. dept. speech & drama, 58-65, PROF. COMMUN, 65-, DIR. INT. PROGS, 69- Speech Commun. Asn; Cent. States Speech Asn. Add: 1649 Clark St, Stevens Point, WI 54481.

ISBELL, THOMAS, b. S.C, Oct. 7, 14; m. 44; c. 1. ENGLISH. A.B, Berry Col, 36; B.D, Andover Theol. Sem, 40; M.A, Boston Univ, 40, Ph.D, 50; Harvard, 46-47. Head dept. philos. & relig, Berry Col, 46-50; pres, Maunaolu Col, 50-54; prof. ENG. & head dept, BRENAU COL, 54-72, EMER. PROF, 72- U.S.N.R, 42-46, Lt. Comdr. NCTE; S.Atlantic Mod. Lang. Asn. The romantic poets; creative writing. Add: Dept. of English, Brenau College, Gainesville, GA 30501.

ISHAK, FAYEK, b. Sharkia, A.R.E, Oct. 29, 22; m. 58; c. 2. MODERN & SEVENTEENTH CENTURY LITERATURE. B.A, Cairo Univ, 45, dipl. educ. & psychol, 47, dipl. Eng. lang, 51; dipl. Eng. lit, Univ. Exeter, 54; Ph.D. (mod. Eng. lit), Univ. Liverpool, 62. Teacher Eng, govt. sec. schs, Egypt, 47-52; lectr. ENG. LIT, Higher Teachers Col, Cairo, 54-63, asst. prof, 63-66; Notre Dame Univ.(B.C), 66-67; LAKEHEAD UNIV, 67-69, ASSOC. PROF, 69- Chancellor's Fund, Lakehead Univ, 69-73; co-ed, Art & Lit. Rev, 73. Asn. Can. Univ. Teachers Eng; Renaissance Soc. Am; Am. Orient. Soc; Northeast Mod. Lang. Asn. Modern British literature; the impact of the oriental mystical tradition on the modern European world of letters; Renaissance non-dramatic literature. Publ: Co-auth, Comprehension practice and precis writing, 57 & Literary terms, 63, Darel Fikr, Cairo; auth, The theories of literary criticism from the time of the Greeks to the modern age, Anglo-Egyptian Publ, Cairo, Vols. I & II, 64; T.S. Eliot: the critic, the poet and the playwright, Maaref Publ. House, Cairo, 65; The mystical philosophy of T.S. Eliot, Conn. Col. & Univ. Press Serv, 70; A complete English translation of the coptic orthodox mass and the liturgy of St. Basil, Toppan, Hong Kong, 73; The music of English verse, The Bulletin, Cairo, autumn 57; Studies in English poetry, Teachers Col. Mag, 59; Forty minutes with T.S. Eliot, The Forum, B.C, 4/67. Add: Dept. of English, Lakehead University, Oliver Rd, Thunder Bay, Ont. P7B 5E1, Can.

ISLE, WALTER WHITFIELD, b. Ponca City, Okla, Dec. 3, 33; m. 58; c. 2. ENGLISH. A.B, Harvard, 55; M.A, Univ. Mich, 57; Ph.D, Stanford Univ, 61. Asst. prof. ENG, RICE UNIV, 61-67, ASSOC. PROF, 67-, CHMN. DEPT, 73- Fulbright scholar, Univ. London, 61-62; vis. prof, Stanford Univ, 69. U.S.A, 55-63, Capt. MLA; NCTE. Modern novel and poetry; American literature. Publ: Experiments in form: Henry James's novels, 1896-1901, Harvard, 68. Add: Dept. of English, Rice University, Houston, TX 77001.

ISLER, ALAN DAVID, b. London, Eng, Sept. 12, 34; U.S. citizen. ENGLISH RENAISSANCE LITERATURE, SHAKESPEARE. B.A, Hunter Col, 61; M.A, Columbia Univ, 62, Ph.D.(16th century lit), 66. Asst. prof. ENG. LIT, Huron Col, Univ. West. Ont, 65-67; ASSOC. PROF, QUEENS COL.(N.Y), 67- Vis. sr. lectr, Tel-Aviv Univ, 71-72. Renaissance Soc. Am. Sir Philip Sidney; Renaissance heroic poetry; Shakespeare. Publ: Sidney, Shakespeare, and the Slain-notslain, Univ. Toronto Quart, 1/68; The allegory of the hero and Sidney's two Arcadias, Stud. Philol, 4/68; Heroic poetry and Sidney's two Arcadias, PMLA, 5/68. Add: Dept. of English, Queens College, Kissena Blvd, Flushing, NY 11367.

ITALIA, PAUL GREGORY, b. New York, N.Y, July 17, 42; m. 65; c. 2. ENGLISH ROMANTIC POETRY. B.A, Hunter Col, 64; Woodrow Wilson fels, Columbia Univ, 64-65 & 67-68, M.A, 65, Ph.D.(Eng), 71. ASST. PROF. ENG, STATE UNIV. N.Y. COL. ONEONTA, 71- Nat. Endowment for Humanities grant, summer 73. Twentieth century fiction. Publ: Love and lust in James Dickey's Deliverance, Mod. Fiction Stud, 74; On Adela Quested's given name in Forster's A passage to India, Eng. Lang. Notes, 73. Add: 90 Clinton St, Oneonta, NY 13820.

IVANOFF, JULIA SCAIFE, European History, American Literature. See Volume I, History.

IVES, ALMON BINGHAM, b. Bloomington, Ill, July 12, 09; m. 36; c. 4. SPEECH. A.B, Ill. Wesleyan Univ, 31; B.Ed, Ill. State Norm. Univ, 32; A.M, Northwest. Univ, 36; Univ. Wis, 41; Nat. Broadcasting Co. fel, Dartmouth Col, 43, hon. A.M, 50. Dir. speech & drama, dept. Eng, Stout Inst, 37-39; instr. pub. speaking, DARTMOUTH COL, 39-42, asst. prof. speech, 42-50, PROF. SPEECH & CONSULT. IN RADIO & TV, 50-, CHMN. DEPT. SPEECH, 67-, asst. dean col, 62-63, dir. gen. reading prog, 63-65. Pub. serv. prog. off, radio br, civil inform. & educ. sect, gen. hq, Supreme Comdr. Allied Powers, Tokyo, Japan, 50-51; mem. fac. seminar Japanese lit, Columbia Univ, summer 64; fac. seminars Japanese civilization & Chinese lit, Dartmouth Col, 64-65; Inst. Asian Stud, E.W. Ctr, Univ. Hawaii, 65; Comp. Stud. Ctr. travel-stud. grant, Taiwan & Japan, 65- U.S.N.R, 43-46, Lt. Speech Commun. Asn; Asn. Asian Stud. Oral study of literature; Japanese literature; Chinese literature. Publ: Ready room. Add: Dept. of Speech, Dartmouth College, Hanover, NH 03755.

IVES, CHAUNCEY B, b. New York, N.Y, Mar. 16, 07; m. 49. ENGLISH. B.A, Yale, 28; LL.B, Harvard, 31; M.A, Univ. N.C, 53, Ph.D, 57. Assoc. prof. ENG, Guilford Col, 57-60; asst. prof, Douglass Col, Rutgers Univ, 60-70, assoc. prof, 70-72; RETIRED. MLA. American literature. Publ: The realists, Dodd, 47; James's ghosts in the turn of the Screw, Nineteenth Century Fiction, 63; The little regiment of Stephen Crane, Midwest Quart, spring, 67; Symmetrical design in four of Stephen Crane's stories, Ball State Univ. Forum, 69; plus others. Add: Kingston, NJ 08528.

IVES, EDWARD DAWSON, b. White Plains, N.Y, Sept. 4, 25; m. 51; c. 3. FOLKLORE. A.B, Hamilton Col, 48; M.A, Columbia Univ, 50; summer res. & travel grant, Ind. Univ, 60; fel, 60-61, Ph.D.(folklore), 62. Instr. Eng, Ill. Col, 50-53; lectr, City Coll. New York, 53-54; instr, UNIV. MAINE, ORONO, 55-62, asst. prof, 62-64, assoc. prof, 64-67, FOLKLORE, 67-70, PROF, 70-, Coe Res. Fund grants. Guggenheim fel, 65-66; lectr, Univ. N.B, summer 65; lectr. N.Y. State Hist. Asn; Sem. Am. Cult, Cooperstown, N.Y, 67; assoc. ed, J. Am. Folklore, 68-; dir. Northeast Arch. of Folklore & Oral Hist, 72- U.S.M.C, 43-46. Am. Folklore Soc; Int. Folk Music Counc; Can. Folk Music Coun; Northeast Folklore Soc.(ed, Northeast Folklore); Oral Hist. Asn. All aspects of the folklore of the Northeast; the authorship of folksongs. Publ: Larry Gorman: the man who made the songs, Ind. Univ, 64; co-auth, Folksongs and their makers, Bowling Green Univ, 70; auth, Lawrence Doyle: farmer poet of Prince Edward Island, Maine Stud, 71; Ben Deane and Joe Scott: a ballad and its probable author, 59 & The man who plucked the Gorbey: a Maine woods legend, 61, J.Am. Folklore; Twenty one folksongs from Prince Edward Island, Northeast Folklore, 63; plus others. Add: Dept of Anthropology, South Stevens Hall, University of Maine, Orono, ME 04473.

IVES, SUMNER (ALBERT), b. Arkadelphia, Ark. Dec. 11, 11; m. 45; c. 1. ENGLISH LANGUAGE. A.B, Furman Univ, 32, A.M, 38; fel, Univ. Tex, 49-50, Ph.D, 50. Instr. Eng, Okla. Agr. & Mech. Col, 46; asst. prof, Tulane Univ, 50-54, assoc. prof, 54-59; PROF, N.Tex. State Univ, 59-61; Syracuse Univ, 61-66; Eng. educ, N.Y. Univ, 66-68; ENG, Hunter Col, 68-69, N.Y. UNIV, 69- Carnegie Found. res. grant-in-aid, 51; Ford Found. fel, 53-54; Am. Counc. Learned Soc. grant-in-aid, 57; contrib. & mem. steering comt, Nat. Soc. Stud. Educ, 1970 Yearbk, 66; dir, Comn. Eng. Lang, NCTE, 71-73. U.S.A, 42-45. MLA; Ling. Soc. Am; NCTE; Can. Ling. Asn; Am. Dialect Soc.(secy-treas, 66-67); Conf. Col. Compos. & Commun. English grammar; American dialects; applied linguistics. Publ: A new handbook for writers, Knopf, 60; Linguistics in the classroom, Col. Eng, 12/55; Grammar and Style, Eng, J, 5/63. Add: Dept. of English, New York University, New York NY 10003.

IZSAK, EMILY K, English, American Literature. See DALGARNO, EMILY K.

J

JAARSMA, RICHARD J, b. Amsterdam, Netherlands, Dec. 23, 39; U.S. citizen; m. 62; c. 2. ENGLISH. A.B, Hope Col, 61; Woodrow Wilson fel. & M.A, Rutgers Univ, 62, Woodrow Wilson & univ. fels, 63, Ph.D.(Eng), 66. Instr. ENG, Fairleigh Dickinson Univ, Teaneck Campus, 64-66, asst. prof, 66-69, ASSOC. PROF, WILLIAM PATERSON COL, 69- Esso humanities & Fairleigh Dickinson Univ. grants, 67-68. Shakespeare Soc. Am. Eighteenth century English literature; Shakespeare; science fiction. Publ: The tragedy of Banquo by William Shakespeare, Lit. & Psychol, summer 67; Satiric intent in The vicar of Wakefield, Stud. Short Fiction, summer 68; Ethics in the wasteland: image and structure in Goldsmith's The deserted village, Tex. Stud. Lit. & Lang, fall 71; plus others. Add: 565 Doremus Ave, Glen Rock, NJ 07452.

JABUSCH, DAVID M, b. Fortuna, Calif, Oct. 4, 33; c. 2. SPEECH. B.S, Ore. State Univ, 55; M.A, Pa. State Univ, 59, Ph.D, 62. Instr. speech, Pa. State Univ, 58-62; asst. prof, UNIV. UTAH, 62-66, assoc. prof, 66-69, PROF. SPEECH COMMUN, 69-, asst. dean summer sch, 65-67, dean summer sch, 67-70. U.S.N.R, 55-63, Lt. Speech Commun. Asn. Speech pedagogy; contemporary public address. Publ: Co-auth, Debater's guide, Pa. High Sch. Speech League, 62; Speech criticism handbook, Univ. Utah, 66; The rhetoric of civil rights, West. Speech, summer 66; auth, Effects of filmed speech models in beginning speech instruction, Cent. States Speech J, fall 69. Add: Dept. of Communication, University of Utah, Salt Lake City, UT 84112.

JACK, WILLIAM TERRY, b. Corsicana, Tex, Aug. 24, 22; m. 47; c. 2. AMERICAN LITERATURE & DRAMA. B.A, Univ. Tex, 47; M.A, Univ. Wash, 49; Ph.D.(Eng), Univ. Tex, 56. Chmn. dept. speech, Kilgore Col, 49-53; PROF. ENG, E.TEX. STATE UNIV, 65- Bk. reviewer, Dallas Times-Herald, 62-68; staff reviewer, New York Times, 66-68. U.S.A.A.F, 42-46. MLA; S.Cent. Mod. Lang. Asn; South. Lit. Festival Asn. American theatre; Herman Melville; contemporary novel. Add: Dept. of English, East Texas State University, Commerce, TX 75428.

JACKSON, AGNES L. MORELAND, b. Pine Bluff, Ark, Dec. 2, 30; m. 64. ENGLISH, AMERICAN LITERATURE. A.B, Univ. Redlands, 52; M.A, Univ. Wash, 53; Ph.D, Columbia Univ, 60; Danforth fel, 52-53, 55-59; South. Fel. Fund Award, 55-56. Instr. Eng, Spelman Col, 53-55; commun. & Am. lit, col. basic stud, Boston Univ, 59-61, asst. prof, 61-63; ENG, Calif. State Univ, Los Angeles, 63-69; ASSOC. PROF, PITZER COL, 69- Summers, instr, Atlanta Univ, 55, asst. prof. Eng. & Am. lit, Univ. Redlands, 63. MLA; Soc. Relig. Higher Educ. Twentieth century American literature; Afro-American literature. Add: Dept. of English, Pitzer College, Claremont, CA 91711.

JACKSON, ALAN S, b. Alhambra, Calif, Oct. 3, 30; m. 57; c. 2. ENGLISH. B.A, Univ. Redlands, 52, M.A, Univ. South. Calif, 58, Ph.D.(Eng), 65. Instr. ENG, Univ. Colo, 61-65, asst. prof, 65-67; assoc. prof, UNIV. WIS-EAU CLAIRE, 67-72, PROF, 72- U.S.A, 52-54, Sgt. MLA. The American novel. Add: Dept. of English, University of Wisconsin-Eau Claire, Eau Claire, WI 54701.

JACKSON, ALLAN STUART, b. Pittsburgh, Pa, Apr. 24, 34. THEATER. B.A, Univ. Colo, 56; M.A, Ohio State Univ, 59; Ph.D.(theater), 62. Instr. THEATER, Ohio State Univ, 62; asst. prof, STATE UNIV. N.Y. BINGHAMTON, 64-69, ASSOC. PROF, 69- U.S.A. Am. Educ. Theater Asn; Am. Soc. Theater Res; Class. Asn. Am; Int. Fed. Theater Res. Theater. Publ: Co-ed, Max Reinhardt exhibit, 68 & Max Reinhardt exhibit centennial, 73, Max Reinhardt Archive; auth, Evangeline the forgotten musical, 10/68, Players Mag. Add: Dept. of Theater, State University of New York at Binghamton, Binghamton, NY 13901.

JACKSON, BERNETTA M, b. O'Fallon Twp, Ill, May 14, 13; m. 44. ENGLISH. A.B, McKendree Col, 35; M.A, Univ. Ill, 49. Asst. ENG, Univ. Ill, 49-50; Instr, South. Methodist Univ, 50-55; from instr. to ASST. PROF, WASH. UNIV, 55- MLA; Col. Eng. Asn; NCTE. Charles Lamb in English literature. Publ: Co-auth, English composition, Barnes & Noble, 61. Add: Dept. of English, Washington University, St. Louis, MO 63130.

JACKSON, BLYDEN, b. Paducah, Ky, Oct. 12, 10; m. 58. ENGLISH. A.B, Wilberforce Univ, 30; A.M, Univ. Mich, 38, Rosenwald fel, 47-49, Ph.D, 52. Teacher, pub. schs, Ky, 34-45; from asst. to assoc. prof. Eng, Fisk Univ, 45-54; prof. Eng. & chmn. dept, South. Univ, 54-62, dean grad. sch, 62-69; PROF. ENG, UNIV. N.C, CHAPEL HILL, 69-, ASSOC. DEAN GRAD. SCH, 73- NCTE (chmn. col. sect, 71-73); MLA; Col. Lang, Asn.(pres, 57-59, ed. bull, 59-); Col. Eng. Asn; Speech Commun. Asn. Negro literature. Publ: Essay in criticism, Phylon; Case for American Negro literature, Mich. Alumni Rev; College Language Association, PMLA, 12/58; plus others. Add: Dept. of English, University of North Carolina, Chapel Hill, NC 27514.

JACKSON, BRUCE, b. Brooklyn, N.Y, May 21, 36; c. 3. FOLKLORE, SOCIOLOGY. B.A, Rutgers Univ, 60, Woodrow Wilson fel, 60; univ. fel, Ind. Univ, 61, M.A, 62. Asst. prof. ENG, COMP. LIT. & FOLKLORE, STATE UNIV. N.Y. BUFFALO, 67-68, assoc. prof, 68-71, PROF, 71-, DIR, CTR. STUD. AM. CULT, 72- Sr. consult, President's Crime Comn, Arthur D. Little Co, 66; dir, Newport Folk Found, 66-72; Guggenheim Found. fel, 71-72. U.S.M.C, 53-56. Am. Folklore Soc. Afro-American folklore; criminology; documentary photography. Publ: Ed, Folklore and society, Folklore Assocs, 66 & The Negro and his folklore in 19th century periodicals, Univ. Tex. & Am. Folklore Soc, 67; auth, A thief's primer, Macmillan, 69; Wake up dead man: Afro-American worksongs from Texas prisons, 72 & Get your ass in the water and swim like me: narrative poetry from Black oral tradition, 74, Harvard; ed, In the life: versions of the criminal experience, Holt, 72. Add: Center for Studies in American Culture, State University of New York at Buffalo, Butler Annex A, Buffalo, NY 14209.

JACKSON, ESTHER MERLE, b. Pine Bluff, Ark, Sept. 3, 22. DRAMA. B.S, Hampton Inst, 42; M.A, Ohio State Univ, 46, Whitney fel, 56-57, univ. fel, 57-58, Ph.D, 58. Instr. Eng, Agr. Mech. & Norm. Col, Ark, 42-44; asst. prof. drama, Hampton Inst, 46-49; Clark Col.(Ga), 49-56; prof. Eng, Agr. & Tech. Col, N.C, 58-59; vis. prof. humanities, Tuskegee Inst, 59-60; Fulbright drama res. fel, Eng, 60-61; prof. Eng, Clark Col.(Ga), 61-62, prof. & chmn. dept. speech & drama, 62-64; specialist theatre educ, U.S. Off. Educ, 64-65; dir. educ, New York Shakespeare Festival, 65-66; prof. dramatic art, Adelphi Univ, 66; vis. prof. dramatic lit, Shaw Univ, 66-67; Fulbright lectr. Am. drama, John F. Kennedy Inst. Am. Stud, Free Univ. Berlin, 67-68; Guggenheim fel. Am. drama, 68-69; PROF. THEATRE & DRAMA, UNIV. WIS-MADISON, 69- Asst. to producer, New York Shakespeare Festival, 63. MLA; Speech Commun. Asn.(assoc. ed, Quart. J. Speech, 66-69, 71-74); Am. Theatre Asn.(assoc. ed, Educ. Theatre J, 70-73, v.pres. res, 72-74); Am. Soc. Theatre Res; Int. Fed. Theatre Res; Col. Lang. Asn. History of the Western theatre; dramatic literature and criticism. Publ: The broken world of Tennessee Williams, Univ. Wis, 66; The American theatre and the speech professions, In: Representative American speeches, Wilson, 67; contrib, Das Amerikanische Drama von den Anfängen bis zur Gegenwart, Wissenschaftliche Buchgesellschaft, 72; auth, Maxwell Anderson: poetry and morality in the American drama, Educ. Theatre J, 3/73. Add: Dept. of Theatre & Drama, 6008 Vilas Hall, University of Wisconsin-Madison, Madison, WI 53706.

JACKSON, GABRIELE BERNHARD, b. Berlin, Ger, Nov. 17, 34; U.S. citizen; m. 61; c. 2. ENGLISH LITERATURE. B.A, Bard Col, 55; Fulbright fel, Lady Margaret Hall, Oxford, 55-56; univ. scholar, Yale, 57-58, M.A, 58, Smith-Farmington fel, 58-59, Sterling fel, 59-60, Ph.D, 61. Instr. Eng, Yale, 60-63; asst. prof, Wellesley Col, 63-68; assoc. prof, TEMPLE UNIV, 68-70, PROF. ENG. & GRAD. CHMN, 70- Lectr. lit, adult educ. prog, YWCA, New Haven, Conn, 62-63; Wellesley Col. jr. leave grant, 66-67; vis. assoc. prof. Eng, Univ. Pa, summer 70; Am. Counc. Learned Scc. fel, 71-72; mem, Comt. Eng. & Am. Lit. Selection Fulbright-Hays Lectr. & Res. Fels, 72-75. English Renaissance poetry and drama; 19th century English literature; Chaucer. Publ: Vision and judgment in Ben Jonson's drama, In: Yale studies in English, 68 & ed, Every man in his humor, In: The Yale Ben Jonson, Yale. Add: Dept. of English, Temple University, Philadelphia, PA 19122.

JACKSON, GEORGE STUYVESANT, b. Portland, Maine, Feb. 22, 06; m. 33; c. 2. ENGLISH & AMERICAN LITERATURE. A.B, Bowdoin Col, 27; M.A, Harvard, 31; Columbia Univ, 40-41. Teaching fel, Univ. Tenn, 27-28; instr, Harvard, 28-31; asst. prof. Eng, Wash. & Lee Univ, 31-41; with Cent. Intel. Agency, 46-58; asst. prof. Eng, Univ. Maine, 58-65, assoc. prof, Portland, 65-68, prof, 68-71; RETIRED. Exten. work, Georgetown Univ. & Univ. Va, 48-58. U.S.N, 42-45, Res, 45-68, Lt. Comdr. American history and biography. Publ: Early songs of Uncle Sam, 32, 63, Uncommon scold, 35 & Hamlet scene by scene, 64, Humphries; A Maine heritage, the history of the Union Mutual Life Insurance Company, 63; co-auth, Peoples and places in the United States of America, Country Women's Counc. U.S.A, 68. Add: Surf Rd, Cape Elizabeth, ME 04107.

JACKSON, JACQUELINE DOUGAN, b. Beloit, Wis, May 3, 28; div; c. 4. LITERATURE, CLASSICS. B.A, Beloit Col, 50; M.A, Univ. Mich, Ann Arbor, 51. Lectr. LIT, Kent State Univ, 66-68; ASSOC. PROF, SANGAMON STATE UNIV, 70- Consult, Rockford Teacher Develop. Ctr, Ill, 68-70; radio lectr, Univ. Wis, WHA Sch. of the Air, 69- Dorothy Canfield Fisher Award, 67. MLA. Creativity in children and adults; oral history; children's literature, current and historical. Publ: Julie's secret sloth, 53, auth. & illusr, The paleface redskins, 58, 68, auth, The taste of spruce gum, 66, Missing Melinda, 67, Chicken ten thousand, 68, auth. & illusr, The ghost boat, 69 & auth, Turn not pale, beloved snail, 74, Little; spring song, Kent State Univ, 69; The orchestra mice, Reilly & Lee, 70; co-auth, The endless pavement, Seabury, 73; auth, The Dougan variations, J. Nat. Fed. Music Clubs, 1/60; Making a book, Instructor, 11/71; How (maybe) to write a book, Publ. Weekly, 2/72. Add: Dept. of English, Sangamon State University, Capital Campus, Springfield, IL 62708.

JACKSON, JAMES HARVEY, b. Stroll, S.Dak, June 24, 20; m. 44; c. 2. PUBLIC ADDRESS. A.B, Pasadena Col, 41, M.A, 43; Pac. Sch. Relig, 43-44; M.A, Univ. South. Calif, 55, Ph.D, 57. Assoc. prof. SPEECH, POINT LOMA COL, 49-57, PROF, 57-, DEAN STUD, 60-, chmn. lett, 57-63. Danforth Found. teacher stud. grant, 55; mem. acad. counc, West. Personnel. Inst, 60- West. Speech Commun. Asn. Evaluation of speech delivery and content; speaking of Clarence Darrow. Publ: I believe, Nazarene Publ. House, 49; co-auth, Too young for love?, Beacon Hill, 68. Add: Dept. of Speech, Point Loma College, 3900 Lomaland Dr, San Diego, CA 92106.

JACKSON, JAMES L, b. Bloomington, Ill, Feb. 9, 16; m. 39; c. 2. ENGLISH LITERATURE. Ph.D, Univ. Ill, 49. Instr. Eng, Univ. Ill, 47-48; asst. prof, Univ. Ark, 49-51; lectr. commun. skills, Air Command & Staff Col, Maxwell Air Force Base, Ala, 51-54, assoc. prof, Air Force Acad, 54-60, chief precomn. schs. br, profess. educ. div, Wash, D.C, 60-67; PROF. ENG, GEORGE MASON COL, UNIV. VA, 67- Lectr. Eng, George Wash. Univ, 60-62; Univ. Md, 62-67. U.S.A.F, 40-46, 51-67, Lt. Col. English literature of the Renaissance; Shakespeare's dramatic structure and his use of fencing. Add: Dept. of English, George Mason College, University of Virginia, Fairfax, VA 22030.

JACKSON, JAMES ROBERT DE JAGER, b. St. Andrew's, Scotland, July 14, 35; Can. citizen; m. 69; c. 1. ENGLISH. B.A, Queen's Univ.(Ont), 57, M.A, 58; A.M, Princeton, 60, Ph.D.(Eng), 61; fel, Univ. London, 62-63, Ph.D.(Eng), 63. Asst. prof. ENG, McMaster Univ, 63-64; VICTORIA COL, UNIV. TORONTO, 64-67, assoc. prof, 67-73, PROF, 73- Can. Counc. sr. fel, 67-68; Guggenheim fel, 72-73. MLA. History of Shakespearean criticism, 1660-1840; Coleridge; Romantic poetry. Publ: Method and imagination in Coleridge's Criticism, Routledge & Kegan Paul & Harvard, 69; ed, Coleridge: the critical heritage, Routledge & Kegan Paul and Barnes & Noble, 70. Add: Dept. of English, Victoria College, Toronto 5, Ont, Can.

JACKSON, MARGARET YOUNG, b. Selma, Ala, Mar. 20, 18; m. 48; c. 1. ENGLISH COMPOSITION & LITERATURE. B.S, Tuskegee Inst, 39; M.A, Iowa Univ, 47, 49; Univ. Calif, Los Angeles, 49-50; Ph.D, Cornell Univ, 54. Teacher Eng. & librn, Fairfield High Sch, Ala, 39-42; teacher ENG, Garfield High Sch, Chillicothe, Mo, 42-43; instr, Tuskegee Inst, 47-49; Tenn. Agr. & Indust. State Univ, 50-51; assoc. prof, Del. State Col, 54-55; Md. State Teachers Col, Bowie, 55-56; prof, Cent. State Col.(Ohio), 56-59; Agr. & Tech. Col. N.C, 59-62; from assoc. prof. to PROF, D.C. TEACHERS COL, 62- W.A.C, 43-46. NCTE; AAUP; Am. Asn. Univ. Women; Am. Civil Liberties Union; MLA; Col. Lang. Asn; Conf. Col. Compos. & Commun. Nineteenth century American literature; fugitive slave narratives. Publ: Melville's use of a real slave narrative in Benito Cereno, 12/61 & High comedy in Shakespeare, spring 67, Col. Lang. Asn. J; A transcendental friendship: Ralph W. Emerson and Thomas Carlyle, World Order, 70. Add: 1990 Shepherd St. N.W, Washington, DC 20011.

JACKSON, PAUL JOSEPH, b. Seattle, Wash, June 8, 05; m. 30; c. 2. ENGLISH. A.B, Univ. Wash, 29, Ph.D, 40; Stanford Univ, 29-30; Columbia Univ, 30-31. Teaching fel. ENG, Univ. Wash, 32-34; instr, 34-36; WHITMAN COL, 36-39, asst. prof, 39-42, assoc. prof, 42-48, from prof. to Mary A. Denny prof, 48-70, dean fac, 54-63, EMER. PROF, 70- MLA; Am. Soc. Aesthet. Renaissance English literature; Chaucer; Jonathan Swift. Publ:

The Countess of Pembroke: an Elizabethan translator; Selecting students differently; Intervals (libretto). Add: 811 Statesman St, Walla Walla, WA 99362.

JACKSON, PAUL RUSSELL, b. Bristol, Conn, Oct. 9, 32; m. 55; c. 2. ENGLISH. B.A, Colgate Univ, 54; Danforth fel. & M.A, Columbia Univ, 59, Ph.D.(Eng), 67. Instr. ENG, Columbia Univ, 61-62; Northwest. Univ, 63-66; TEMPLE UNIV, 66-67, asst. prof, 67-72, ASSOC. PROF. & CHMN. DEPT, 72- U.S.A.F, 54-57, 1st Lt. MLA. American literature. Add: Dept. of English, Temple University, Philadelphia, PA 19122.

JACKSON, RICHARD EUGENE, b. Helena, Ark, Feb. 25, 41; m. 67; c. 1. THEATRE, PLAYWRITING. B.S, Memphis State Univ, 63; M.A, Kent State Univ, 64; Ohio State Univ, 65-67; Ph.D.(drama), South. Ill. Univ, Carbondale, 71. Teacher Eng. & speech, Antwerp High Sch, Ohio, 64-65; instr. speech & drama, Wis. State Univ-Eau Claire, 67-68; ASST. PROF. DRAMA, San Francisco State Col, 68-70; UNIV. S.ALA, 71- Atlanta Playwriting Contest Award, 66; Kansas City Children's Theatre Playwriting Contest Award, 73. Am. Theatre Asn; Children's Theatre Conf; Speech Commun. Asn; Southeast. Theatre Conf. Playwriting; children's theatre and creative drama. Publ: Ferdinand and the dirty knight, Pioneer Drama Serv, 66; Little Red Riding wolf, Stage Magic Plays, 73; Children's theatre is a seed, Theatron, 70 & Children's Theatre Rev, 70; plus others. Add: Theatre U.S.A, University of South Alabama, 307 University Dr, Mobile, AL 36688.

JACKSON, ROBERT SUMNER, b. New York, N.Y, Jan. 25, 26; m. 50; c. 4. ENGLISH LITERATURE. B.A, Beloit Col, 49; Middlebury Col, summer 48; Rotary fel, Oxford, 53-54; Rockefeller Bros. Theol. fel, Harvard, 55-56, S.T.B, 56; Ph.D, Univ. Mich, 58. Instr. relig, Yale, 57-58, Eng, 58-61; asst. prof, Kent State Univ, 61-70, res. fels, 64, 66, 67; PROF. HUMANITIES, SANGAMON STATE UNIV, 70-, consult. & planner, 70. Am. Philos. Soc. grant, summer 65; vis. assoc. prof, Rockford Col, 68-69; Newberry Libr. fel, 73-74. U.S.N.R, 44-46. MLA; Am. Acad. Relig. Seventeenth century English literature; relation of religion to literature; humanities in business and political life. Publ: John Donne's Christian vocation, Northwest. Univ, 70; A parabolic reading of James Joyce's Grace, Mod. Lang. Notes, 12/61; The prophetic vision: the nature of the utterance in Isaiah: 40-55, Interpretation, 1/62; plus others. Add: Dept. of Humanities, Sangamon State University, Springfield, IL 62708.

JACKSON, ROBIN CAROL, b. Ross, Calif, May 18, 33. THEATRE ARTS. B.A, San Francisco State Univ, 55, M.A, 66. Instr. drama & chmn. dept. Jefferson Sch. Dist, 61-65; instr, Col. Marin, 65-69; ASSOC. PROF. THEATRE ARTS, CALIF. STATE COL, SONOMA, 69- Adv, San Quentin Prison Theatre Workshop, 65; dir, Mountain Play Asn, 68-70; dir, Mill Valley Ctr. Performing Arts, 69-73; assoc. dir, Exp. Theatre Glej, Yugoslavia, 72-73. U.S.M.C, Maj. Experimental theatre. Add: 330 Montford Ave, Mill Valley, CA 94941.

JACKSON, THOMAS H, b. Detroit, Mich, Aug. 19, 30; m. 61. ENGLISH. B.A, Wayne State Univ, 54; Woodrow Wilson fel, 56-57; M.A, Univ. Mich, 57; Col. R.R. McCormick fel, 57-59; Ph.D.(Eng), Yale, 60. Instr. ENG, Yale, 59-63; asst. prof, Mass. Inst. Technol, 63-67; Brandeis Univ, 67-68; ASSOC. PROF, BRYN MAWR COL, 68- U.S.A, 54-56. Literary theory and criticism; modern American and British poetry. Publ: The early poetry of Ezra Pound, Harvard, 68; 20th century interpretations of Miss Lonelyhearts, Prentice-Hall, 71; Wordsworth's Thought and his verse, Col. Eng, 1/63; Adventures of Messire Wrong-Head, ELH, 6/65; Poetic politics of Ezra Pound, J. Mod. Lit, spring 74. Add: 4433 Spruce St, Philadelphia, PA 19104.

JACKSON, WALLACE, b. Philadelphia, Pa, Nov. 23, 30; m. 59; c. 1. ENGLISH. B.A, Bard Col, 53; M.A, Brandeis Univ, 58; Ph.D.(Eng), Univ. Pa, 64. Instr. ENG, Col. William & Mary, 60-61; asst. prof, Cath. Univ. Am, 63-65; DUKE UNIV, 65-71, ASSOC. PROF, 71- U.S.A, 53-55. Eighteenth century English literature and criticism. Publ: John Ogilvie, an essay on the lyric poetry of the ancients (1762), Augustan Reprint Soc, 70: Immediacy: the development of a critical concept from Addison to Coleridge, Ed. Rodopi N.V, Amsterdam, 73; Satire: an Augustan idea of disorder, Proc. MLA Neoclassicism Conf. 1967-68, AMS, 70; The country wife: the premises of love and lust, S.Atlantic Quart, 73; Gainsborough and Turner: the problem of stylistic continuity, J. Aesthetics & Art Criticism, 74. Add: Dept. of English, Duke University, Durham, NC 27706.

JACOBI, PETER PAUL, b. Berlin, Ger, Mar. 15, 30; U.S. citizen; m. 56; c. 2. JOURNALISM, MAGAZINE & ARTS CRITICISM. B.S.J, Northwest. Univ, 52, M.S.J, 53. News ed, ABC, 52-53; news assignment ed, reporter & arts critic, NBC, 55-61; ed, Music Mag/Musical Courier, 61-62; lectr. JOUR. NORTHWEST. UNIV, 63, asst. prof, 63-66, assoc. prof, 66-69, PROF, 69-, ASSOC. DEAN, MEDILL SCH. JOUR, 66-, asst. dean, 64-66. Ed, Lyric Opera News, 57-61; opera commentator, WFMQ-FM, 57-64; Chicago arts correspondent, Christian Sci. Monitor, 61-; theatre critic, Hollister Newspapers, 63-70; theatre, film & music commentator, WMAQ-TV, 65-; mem. mus. adv. comt, Ill. Arts Counc, 66-68, theatre panel, 69; mem. arts-humanities plan comt, Ill. Bd. Higher Educ, 71-72. U.S.A, 53-55. Radio-TV News Dir. Asn; Asn. Educ. Jour; AAUP; Nat. Acad. TV Arts & Sci. Creative and performing arts; United States culture; magazine and radio-television journalism. Publ: Numerous articles & criticisms in var. nat. & area publ. Add: 2042 Wilmette Ave, Wilmette, IL 60091.

JACOBS, BRIANT S, b. Mt. Pleasant, Utah, Dec. 15, 18; m. 39; c. 5. AMERICAN LITERATURE. B.A, Brigham Young Univ, 39; Ph.D, State Univ. Iowa, 44. PROF. AM. LIT, BRIGHAM YOUNG UNIV, 46- U.S.N.R, 44-46, Lt. Rocky Mountain Mod. Lang. Asn; Am. Stud. Asn. Nineteenth century American literature. Add: 1650 Willow, Provo, UT 84601.

JACOBS, CHARLES JUAN STEPHEN RICHARD, b. Rochester, N.Y, Apr. 19, 02; m. 34. ENGLISH. A.B, Univ. Rochester, 26; M. Div, Boston Univ, 33; Iliff Sch. Theol, 36-37; M.A, Univ. Denver, 38. Instr. Eng, Wood Jr. Col, Miss, 38-39; factory training, prod. cost accountant, Victor Insulators, N.Y, 39-44; instr. ENG, DeVeaux Sch, 44-46; UNIV. BRIDGEPORT, 46-48, asst. prof, 48-57, assoc. prof, 57-73, EMER. PROF, 73- Prof. poetry writer & genealogist; registr. gen, Order Founders & Patriots of Am, 58-60, genealogist gen, 60-69; chancellor, Nat. Fed. State Poetry Soc, 60-61; hon. grant of arms, Col. Arms, London, 60; hon. citizen Korea, 67; mem, Nat. Slavic Honor Soc; Knight Comdr. of Justice, Sovereign Order of St. John of Jerusalem, 62; mem. int. comt, Ctr. Stud. e Scambi, 64-72; Comdr, Sovereign Mil. Order of Temple of Jerusalem, 67; Inst. San Martiniano, Mex, 68-; Comdr, Int. Constantinian Order, 73. Am. Poetry League; New Eng. Hist. Geneal. Soc.(v.pres, 58-67); fel. Augustan Soc; Nat. Huguenot Soc; Royal Soc. St. George. Genealogy; parapsychology; Spanish Moslem backgrounds. Publ: Tables for teachers, Littlefield, 53; The violent universe (poems), Pageant, 67; A suggested Moslem descent for Eleanor of Provence and Eleanor of Castile, Augustan, 7-8/69; A reexamination of the Franklin Square, Math. Teacher, 1/71; Queen Clemencia, mother of Joan, princess of North Wales, Am. Genealogist, 7/72. Add: Apt. 6, 20 Rowsley St, Bridgeport, CT 06605.

JACOBS, DOROTHY HIERONYMUS, b. Hinsdale, Ill, Mar. 13, 28; m. 50; c. 2. ENGLISH LANGUAGE & LITERATURE. A.B, Univ. Mich, Ann Arbor, 50, A.M, 60, Ph.D.(Eng), 68. ASST. PROF. ENG, UNIV. R.I, 68- MLA; AAUP; Renaissance Soc. Am. Seventeenth century literature; modern drama; Renaissance drama. Add: Dept. of English, University of Rhode Island, Kingston, RI 02881.

JACOBS, ELIJAH LAWRENCE, b. Tryon, Okla, Nov. 4, 93; m. 21; c. 2. ENGLISH. A.B, Univ. Kans, 20; A.M, Univ. Chicago, 22; Ind. Univ, 36; Ph.D, Univ. South. Calif, 49. Asst. prof. ENG, Denison Univ, 22-25; prof, N.Mex. State Teachers Col, 25-28; assoc. prof, Cent. Mo. State Col, 28-47; prof, FRANKLIN COL, 47-64, head dept, 47-59, chmn. div. humanities, 55-59, EMER. PROF, 64- Teaching asst, Univ. South. Calif, 37-38; vis. lectr, summers, Univ. S.Dak, 49 & 59, Bradley Univ, 52, Evansville Col, 54, Col. Puget Sound, 55, Northeast. Univ, 63 & 64; prof, West. Ill. Univ, 64-67; vis. prof, Ind. Cent. Col, 67-68; adj. prof, Ind. State Univ, 68-69; Nat. Endowment for Arts & Ind. State Arts Comn. poet in residence, Paoli Ctr, Ind, 71. U.S.A, 17-19. English, American and comparative literature. Publ: Farewell to romance, Empire Publ. Co, 34; co-auth, Missouri writers, a literary history of Missouri, State Publ. Co, 55; auth, The artillery horse, VFW Mag, 4/71; The war in Texas, Southwest Rev, spring 73; Say now Shibboleth, Christian Sci. Monitor, 5/73; plus others. Add: 1220 E. Jefferson St, Franklin, IN 46131.

JACOBS, MORTON YALE, b. New Haven, Conn, Mar. 5, 30; m. 58; c. 1. ENGLISH. A.B, Cornell Univ, 50; Columbia Univ, 52-53; teaching fel, Univ. N.C, 54-55, Ph.D, 63; South. Fel, 56-57; Am. Counc. Learned Soc. Ling. Inst. grant, summer, 56. Instr. ENG, Univ. Wash, 56-61, asst. prof, 61-67; ASSOC. PROF, LEWIS & CLARK COL, 67- U.S.A, 50-52, Sgt. Mediaeval Acad. Am; MLA; Am. Folklore Soc; Philol. Asn. Pac. Coast; Soc. Advan. Scand. Stud. Chaucer; heroic literature of the Middle Ages; mediaeval Latin, English and Norse paleography. Add: Dept. of English, Lewis & Clark College, Portland, OR 97219.

JACOBS, PAUL HULAND, b. Nahunta, Ga, Dec. 25, 28; m. 51; c. 2. LINGUISTICS, RHETORIC. B.S, Ga. South. Col, 49; M.A, George Peabody Col, 55; Univ. Fla, 57-58. Teacher Eng, High Schs, Ga, 49-51, Fla, 55-59; asst. prof, Fla. State Univ. High Sch, 59-60; coord. lang. arts, Duval County Pub. Schs, Jacksonville, 60-61; consult, Fla. State Dept. Educ, Tallahassee, 61-64; res. assoc. ENG, UNIV. ILL, URBANA, 64-66, asst. prof, 66-70, ASSOC. PROF, 70- Consult, Nat. Assessment Educ. Progress, 66-67 & Nat. Study Sec. Sch. Eval, 67-68; assoc. dir, Ill. State-Wide Curriculum Study Ctr. in Prep. Sec. Sch. Eng. Teachers, 66-69; co-dir, Tri-Univ. Proj. Behav. Objectives in Eng, 69-71. U.S.A.F, 51-54. Conf. Col. Compos. & Commun; Conf. Eng. Educ; NCTE (mem. comt. supv. Eng. teaching in state & large-city sch. systs, 60-64, dir-at-large, 63-67, chmn. comt. Eng. prog. for slow learners, 66-70); Am. Asn. Cols. Teacher Educ. Modern American literature; supervision and evaluation of instruction in English; oral and written language usage. Publ: Co-auth, Illinois state-wide curriculum study center in the preparation of secondary school English teachers: final report, 69 & The competency of Illinois secondary school English teachers in educational measurement and evaluation, 69, Ill. State-Wide Curriculum Study Ctr; co-auth, What every English teacher should know, NCTE, 69, Representative performance objectives for high school English, Ronald, 72 & Illinois tests in the teaching of English (battery of 4 tests with manual), South. Ill. Univ, 73; auth, Criteria for evaluating high school English programs, Eng. J, 12/68; contrib, Evaluative criteria, Nat. Study Sec. Sch. Eval, 69; co-auth, Some implications of ISCPET, Eng. Educ, spring 70; plus others. Add: Dept. of English, 109 English Bldg, University of Illinois at Urbana, Urbana, IL 61801.

JACOBS, ROBERT DURENE, b. Vicksburg, Miss, Oct. 1, 18; m. 45; c. 1. AMERICAN LITERATURE. A.B, Univ. Miss, 37, A.M, 38; La. State Univ, 39-41; Ph.D.(Am. lit), Hopkins Univ, 53. Instr. Eng. writing, Hopkins Univ, 48-49, asst. prof, 49-53; AM. LIT, Univ. Ky, 53-58, assoc. prof, 58-67, PROF, 67-71; GA. STATE UNIV, 71- Am. Counc. Learned Soc. fel, 60-61. U.S.M.C.R, 41-, Col. MLA; S.Atlantic Mod. Lang. Asn; AAUP; Am. Stud. Asn. Literature of the South; contemporary American fiction; 19th century American literature. Publ: Co-ed, Southern Renascence, Hopkins Univ, 53 & South; modern southern literature, Doubleday, 61; auth, Poe: journalist and critic, La. State Univ, 69; plus others. Add: Dept. of English, Georgia State University, Atlanta, GA 30303.

JACOBS, ROBERT G, b. Bedford, Ind, Sept. 19, 27; m. 51; c. 2. ENGLISH. B.A, Grinnell Col, 50; M.F.A, Univ. Iowa, 52, Ph.D.(Eng), 65; B.D, Univ. Chicago, 54. Assoc. prof. ENG, Iowa Wesleyan Col, 58-63; asst. prof, Univ. Calif, Los Angeles, 65-69; PROF. & CHMN. DEPT, WEST. ILL. UNIV, 69- U.S.A, 46-47. MLA. American literature; English and American novel; Biblical literature. Publ: The literature of the Bible, W.C. Brown, 69; Nathanael West: the Christology of unbelief, Iowa Eng. Yearbk, fall 64; Comrade Ossipon's favorite saint: Lombroso and Conrad, Nineteenth Century Fiction, 6/68; Gilgamesh: the Sumerian epic that helped Lord Jim to stand alone, Conradiana, Vol. IV, No. 2. Add: Dept. of English, Western Illinois University, W. Adams St, Macomb, IL 61455.

JACOBS, RODERICK ARNOLD, Comparative & Diachronic Linguistics. See Volume III, Foreign Languages, Linguistics & Philology.

JACOBS, WILBUR R, History. See Volume I, History.

JACOBS, WILLIS DANA, b. Chicago, Ill, Aug. 21, 14. ENGLISH & COMPARATIVE LITERATURE. A.B, Univ. N.Mex, 36, A.M, 37; Ph.D. Univ. N.C, 45. From instr. to asst. prof, UNIV. N.MEX, 37-46, assoc. prof. Eng, 46-54, prof. ENG. & COMP. LIT, 54-72, EMER. PROF, 72- Vis. prof. humanities, Univ. Zaragoza, Spain, 57-58. Las Campanas prize for outstanding teaching, 62. Intel.C, U.S.A.F, 42-45, Res, 45-, Maj. MLA; NCTE. Contemporary English and American poetry; contemporary drama; comparative literature. Publ: William Barnes, linguist, Univ. N.Mex, 52; W.C. Williams' To awaken an old lady, 9/70, The hunter, 3/71 & A coronal, 4/71, Explicator; plus others. Add: Dept. of English, University of New Mexico, Albuquerque, NM 87106.

JACOBSEN, BRUCE C, b. Miles City, Mont, June 4, 40; m. 62; c. 1. THEATRE ARTS. B.S, Mont. State Univ, 62, M.S, 66; B.F.T, Thunderbird Grad. Sch. Int. Mgt, 63; Ph.D.(theatre arts), Univ. Minn, 69. Asst. prof. THEATRE ARTS, MONT. STATE UNIV, 69-73, ASSOC. PROF, 73-, CHMN. DEPT, 69-, CHMN. CULT. AFFAIRS, 71- Mem, Alliance West. Cols. for Cult. Presentations, 71- U.S.A.F, 63-65, Res, 65-73, Capt. Am. Theatre Asn; Univ. & Col. Theatre Asn; Rocky Mountain Theatre Conf.(pres, 73-74); Asn. Col. & Univ. Concert Mgr. Add: Dept. of Theatre Arts, Montana State University, Bozeman, MT 59715.

JACOBSEN, WILLIAM HORTON, JR, Linguistics. See Volume III, Foreign Languages, Linguistics & Philology.

JACOBSON, EUGENE H, b. Sauk Centre, Minn, July 6, 28; m. 53; c. 2. THEATRE, SPEECH. B.A, St. Olaf Col, 50; M.A, Univ. Colo, Boulder, 55; Ph.D. (theatre), Univ. Denver, 69. Instr. Eng. & speech, Mt. Lake High Sch, Minn, 50-51; Kerkhoven High Sch, 53-54; Trinidad State Jr. Col, Colo, 55-60; from asst. prof. to assoc. prof, Moravian Col, 61-70; ASSOC. PROF. THEATRE, JACKSONVILLE UNIV, 70- U.S.A, 51-53. Am. Theatre Asn; Speech Commun. Asn; AAUP. Modern Norwegian drama; Ibsen; Strindberg. Add: 6311 Sprinkle Dr. N, Jacksonville, FL 32211.

JACOBSON, HARVEY KENNETH, b. Langdon, N.Dak, Sept. 19, 30; m. 62; c. 2. MASS COMMUNICATION. B.A, Univ. N.Dak, 52, M.A, 56; Ph.D.(mass commun), Univ. Wis-Madison, 67. Reporter, Fargo Daily Forum, N.Dak, 52; dir. news & pub. inform, UNIV. N.DAK, 56-68, asst. prof. JOUR, 63-68, assoc. prof, 68-71, PROF, 71-, DIR. UNIV. RELAT, 68-, dir. commun. res. ctr, 68-71. Sears-Roebuck Found. Award, 67. Sig.C, U.S.A, 52-54. Int. Commun. Asn; Asn. Educ. in Jour; Educ. Writers Asn; Nat. Asn. State Univs. & Land Grant Cols.(secy. counc. univ. relat, 71-72). Source credibility; education news. Publ: Co-auth, Instructional television and student attitudes toward teacher, source and medium, Audiovisual Commun. Rev, 5-6/63; auth, Mass media believability: a study of receiver judgments, Jour. Quart, spring 69. Add: Dept. of Journalism, University of North Dakota, Grand Forks, ND 58201.

JACOBSON, RICHARD JOSEPH, b. Ft. Benning, Ga, July 12, 43; m. 66; c. 1. NINETEENTH CENTURY ENGLISH LITERATURE. A.B, Harvard, 65, Ph.D. (Eng), 70. ASST. PROF. ENG, UNIV. VA, 70- MLA; S.Atlantic Mod. Lang. Asn. Nineteenth century English poetry; critical theory. Publ: Hawthorne's conception of the creative process, Harvard Univ, 65; The two voices: a view of Wordsworth's poetic development, Va. Quart. Rev, winter 72. Add: Rte. 1, Box 6, Fork Union, VA 23055.

JACOBSON, RODOLFO, English, Linguistics. See Volume III, Foreign Languages, Linguistics & Philology.

JACOBSON, SIBYL CHAFER, b. Waukon, Iowa, Sept. 30, 42. ENGLISH & AMERICAN LITERATURE. B.A, St. Olaf Col, 64; M.A.T, Northwest. Univ, 65; Ph.D.(Eng), Univ. Wis-Madison, 72. Instr. Eng, Iowa Wesleyan Col, 65-66; Quinsigamond Community Col, 66-68; Univ. Wis-Whitewater, 70-71, asst. prof, 72-73; Fulbright sr. lectr, Univ. Jyväskylä, Finland, 73-74. MLA. Nineteenth century English literature; the novel; poetry. Publ: Co-auth, Concordance to Joseph Conrad's Heart of darkness, South. Ill. Univ, 73; The narrative framing of history: a discussion of Old mortality, J. Narrative Tech, 1/73; Image patterns in Edward Taylor: prayer and proof, Concerning Poetry, spring 73; co-auth, Computer assisted editorial work on Conrad, Conradiana, 11/73. Add: 22 Fourth Ave. N.W, Waukon, IA 52172.

JACOBUS, LEE ANDRE, b. Orange, N.J, Aug. 20, 35; m. 58; c. 2. ENGLISH, PHILOSOPHY. A.B, Brown Univ, 57, A.M, 59; Danforth grant, 66-68, Ph.D. (Eng), Claremont Grad. Sch, 68. Instr. ENG, West. Conn. State Col, 60-68; ASSOC. PROF, UNIV. CONN, 68- MLA; James Joyce Soc; Milton Soc. Am; Am. Soc. Aesthet. Milton; 17th century English authors; modern Irish literature. Publ: Ed, Aesthetics and the arts, 68 & auth, Humanities through the arts, (in press), McGraw; ed, Developing college reading, 70 & auth, Poetry in context, (in press), Harcourt; Sudden apprehension: aspects of knowledge in Paradise lost, Mouton, (in press); John Cleveland: a critical study, Twayne, (in press); Thaumaturgike in Paradise lost, Huntington Libr, Quart, 70; Self-knowledge in Paradise lost, Milton Stud. III, 71; Imamu Amiri Baraka: the quest for moral order, In: Modern black poets, Prentice 73. Add: Dept. of English, U-25, University of Connecticut, Storrs, CT 06268.

JACOBY, GORDON A, b. New York, N.Y, Nov. 8, 34; m. 63; c. 2. SPEECH, DRAMA. B.A, City Col. New York, 63; M.A, Ohio State Univ, 64, Ph.D. (theatre), 67. Assoc. prof. speech & drama, Mansfield State Col, 67-71; ASST. PROF. SPEECH & THEATRE, CITY COL. NEW YORK, 71- Speech Commun. Asn; Am. Theatre Asn. Dialects for the stage; acting and directing. Add: Dept. of Speech & Theatre, City College of New York, Convent Ave. at 138th St, New York, NY 10031.

JAFFE, DAN, b. Elizabeth, N.J, Jan. 24, 33; m. 60; c. 2. ENGLISH, HISTORY. B.A, Rutgers Univ, 54; M.A, Univ. Mich, 58. Instr. ENG, Univ. Nebr, 58-60; asst. prof, Willamette Univ, 60-61; instr, UNIV. MO-KANSAS CITY, 61-65, asst. prof, 65-68, ASSOC. PROF, 68- Fel, Breadloaf Writers Conf, 58; ed-in-chief, BKMK Press, 72-; poetry ed, Focus Midwest, 73- Jules & Avery Hopwood Poetry Award, Univ. Mich, 58; 1st & 2nd Prizes, Kansas City Star Contest, Kansas City Poetry Contests, 64. U.S.A.F, 55-57, 1st Lt. Midwestern history; modern poetry; jazz. Publ: Dan Freeman, Univ. Nebr, 67; The first Tuesday in November, BKMK 71; An all American muse, Saturday Rev, 10/66; Archibald MacLeish: mapping the tradition the thirties, Everett Edward, 67; Gwendolyn Brooks: an appreciation from the white suburbs, Black Am. Writer, 72. Add: 5725 Wyandotte, Kansas City, MO 64113.

JAFFE, HAROLD, b. Bronx, N.Y, July 8, 38. ENGLISH. B.A, Grinnell Col, 60; Ph.D.(Eng), N.Y. Univ, 68. Asst. prof. ENG, LONG ISLAND UNIV, 65-70, ASSOC. PROF, 70- Fulbright prof. Am. lit, Univ. Kerala, 71-72; guest lectr. visionary lit, New Sch. Social Res, 72-73. Founder's Day Award, N.Y. Univ, 68. U.S.A.R, 62. MLA. Publ: Co-ed, American experience: a radical reader, Harper, 69; co-ed, Affinities: a short story anthology, Crowell, 70; Whitman on Markham, Edwin Markham Rev, 5/68; Richard Maurice Burke's Walt Whitman, Walt Whitman Rev, 2/69; poems, Windsor Rev, 72, Confrontation, 73, Beloit Poetry J, 73 & Poetry Northwest, 73. Add: 58 Jane St, New York, NY 10014.

JAFFE, NORA CROW, b. Los Angeles, Calif, Feb. 12, 44; m. 71. EIGHTEENTH CENTURY ENGLISH LITERATURE. A.B, Stanford Univ, 65; M.A, Harvard, 68, Ph.D.(Eng), 72. ASST. PROF. ENG, SMITH COL, 71- Eighteenth century literature; Jonathan Swift; satire. Add: Dept. of English, Smith College, Northampton, MA 01060.

JAHN, JERALD DUANE, b. Onawa, Iowa, Mar. 17, 45; m. 71. ENGLISH RENAISSANCE. B.A, Univ. Iowa, 67; NDEA fel, Ind. Univ, 67-69, Ph.D. (Eng), 72. ASST. PROF. ENG, VANDERBILT UNIV, 71- Renaissance poetry and prose. Publ: The lamb of lust: the role of Adonis in Shakespeare's Venus and Adonis, Shakespeare Stud, 6/72. Add: Dept. of English, Vanderbilt University, Nashville, TN 37235.

JAIN, NEMI CHAND, b. Barwa Sagar, Uttar Predesh, India, Mar. 31, 42; m. 64; c. 2. SPEECH & INTERCULTURAL COMMUNICATION. B.S, Agra Univ, 61, M.S, 63; Ph.D.(commun), Mich. State Univ, 70. Asst. prof. agr. exten, Balwant Rajput Col, Agra Univ, 63-65; Uttar Pradesh Agr. Univ, 65-66; res. teaching asst. commun, Mich. State Univ, 66-69; ASST. PROF. COMMUN, UNIV. WIS-MILWAUKEE, 69- Mem. staff, U.S. Agency Int. Develop. Commun. Workshops, Mich. State Univ, 67-73. Speech Commun. Asn.(mem. intercult. & int. commun. comn, 74-76); Int. Commun. Asn; Asn. Educ. in Jour. Intercultural and international communication; dissemination and utilization of speech communication knowledge; speech communication in formal organizations. Publ: Co-auth, chap, In: Research implications for educational diffusion, Mich. Dept. Educ, 68 & chap, In: Communication of innovations: a cross-cultural approach, Free Press, 71; auth, chap, In: Perspectives on criminal justice, Ctr. Twentieth Century Stud, Univ. Wis-Milwaukee, 74. Add: Dept. of Communication, University of Wisconsin-Milwaukee, Milwaukee, WI 53201.

JAKOBOVITS, LEON ALEX, Psychology, Psycholinguistics. See 12th Edition, American Men & Women of Science, Social & Behavioral Sciences Section.

JAMES, CHARLES LYMAN, b. Poughkeepsie, N.Y, Apr. 12, 34; m. 60; c. 2. AMERICAN LITERATURE. B.S, State Univ. N.Y. Col. New Paltz, 61; M.S, State Univ. N.Y. Albany, 69; Danforth fel, Yale, 71-72. Teacher, Spackenkill Union Free Schs, Poughkeepsie, N.Y, 61-67; instr. ENG, Dutchess Community Col, 67-69; ASSOC. PROF, State Univ. N.Y. Col. Oneonta, 69-73; SWARTHMORE COL, 73- U.S.A, 55-57, Sgt. MLA; Black American literature; African literature. Publ: Black literature in America: resources for high school and college English, State Univ. N.Y, 69; ed, From the roots: short stories by Black Americans, Dodd, 70; auth, Bigger Thomas in the seventies: a twentieth century search for significance, Eng. Rec, fall 71; Batouala: René Maran and the art of objectivity, Stud. Black Lit, summer 73. Add: Benjamin West House, Swarthmore, PA 19081.

JAMES, ELEANOR, b. Belton, Tex, Oct. 22, 12. ENGLISH. B.A, Mary Hardin-Baylor Col, 33; M.A, Univ. Tex, 34; Ph.D, Univ. Wis, 42. Teaching fel. ENG, Univ. Wis, 38-42; instr, Univ. Tex, 42-44; assoc. prof, TEX. WOMAN'S UNIV, 45-62, PROF, 62- NCTE; S.Cent. Mod. Lang. Asn; MLA; Renaissance Soc. Am. Seventeenth century English poetry, especially the metaphysical poets; folklore and literature of the Southwest; comparative literature. Publ: The emblem as an image pattern in certain metaphysical poets; The imagery of Frances Quarles, Univ. Tex. Stud; The sanctificationists of Belton, Texas, Am. West, fall 65; Roy Bedichek, In: Southwest Writers Series, Steck-Vaughn, 70. Add: Box 23543, Texas Woman's University, Denton, TX 76204.

JAMES, EUGENE NELSON, b. Chicago, Ill, Aug. 31, 19; m. 50; c. 4. ENGLISH LITERATURE. B.A, Univ. Chicago, 40, M.A, 48; Ph.D, State Univ. Iowa, 58. Instr. ENG, Purdue Univ, 47-48; NORTH. ILL. UNIV, 48-52, asst. prof, 52-58, assoc. prof, 58-65, PROF, 65-, DIR, PROF. PUBL, 61- U.S.A, 41-45, Sgt. NCTE; MLA. Restoration, modern and Elizabethan drama. Publ: The critic as dramatist: Bernard Shaw, 1895-1898, Shaw Rev, 9/62; The burlesque of restoration comedy in Love and a bottle, Stud. Eng. Lit. 1500-1900, summer 65. Add: Dept. of English, Northern Illinois University, DeKalb, IL 60115.

JAMES, MAX HUBERT, b. Kennett, Mo, July 11, 25; m. 49; c. 2. ENGLISH, LINGUISTICS. B.A, Bob Jones Univ, 48, M.A, 50; M.A, Univ. Mich, 57; Ford Found. Intercol. Prog. Grad. Stud. grant, Claremont Grad. Sch. & Univ. Ctr, 61-64, Ph.D.(Eng), 67. Instr. Eng. lit, Bob Jones Univ, 48-50; dir, Eng as Second Lang, Eng. Lang. Inst, Japan, 51-55; chmn. dept. Eng, Japan Christian Col, 57-59, asst. to pres, 59-60, acting pres, 60, v.pres, 60-61; assoc. prof. Eng, Bethel Col, 64-67, PROF. ENG. & DIR. FRESHMAN ENG, 67-68; NORTH. ARIZ. UNIV, 68-, CHMN. DEPTS. ENG. & PHILOS, 70- U.S.A.A.F, 43-44. MLA; Ling. Soc. Am; NCTE; Am. Asn. Teachers Eng. as Second Lang; Asn. Depts. Eng. Japanese and English linguistics; Chaucer. Publ: The intonation of Japanese, Lang. Learning, 4/57; Leave their minds alone, Col. Eng, 5/73. Add: 908 W. Anderson, Flagstaff, AZ 86001.

JAMES, OVERTON PHILIP, b. Walnut Grove, Ark, Aug. 10, 12; m. 37; c. 1. ENGLISH. A.B, Arkansas Col, 39; A.M, Univ. Chicago, 45; Ph.D, Vanderbilt Univ, 62. From instr. to asst. prof. Eng, Memphis State Univ, 57-64; head dept. Eng, Northeast La. State Col, 64-67; dean col. lib. arts, Ark.

State Univ, 67-73; DIR, ACAD. PRESS, 73- MLA. Eighteenth century novel. Publ: Relation of Tristram Shandy to the life of Sterne, Mouton, 66; Game in bride comes to Yellow Sky, Xavier Univ. Stud, 65. Add: 905 Marjorie Dr, Jonesboro, AR 72401.

JAMES, RICHARD H, b. Chicago, Ill, May 22, 31. DRAMA. B.S, Northwest. Univ, 53, M.A, 58. Instr. speech & drama, Wis. State Univ, Eau Claire, 58-59; UNIV. MONT, 59-60, DRAMA, 60-64, asst. prof, 64-67, assoc. prof, 67-71, PROF, 72-, CHMN. DEPT, 69- Theater consult, 58-; bd. dir, Nat. Asn. Schs. Theatre, 71-, comptroller, 72- U.S.A, 54-56. Am. Theatre Asn; U.S. Inst. Theatre Technol. Design and technical theater; stage lighting; theater architecture. Add: Dept. of Drama, University of Montana, Missoula, MT 59801.

JAMIESON, KATHLEEN MARY, b. Minneapolis, Minn, Nov. 24, 46; m. 68; c. 2. SPEECH. B.A, Marquette Univ, 67; Knapp fel, Univ. Wis-Madison, 67-68, M.A, 68, Ford Found. fel, 69-71, Ph.D.(commun. arts), 72. Lectr. SPEECH, UNIV. MD, COLLEGE PARK, 71-72, ASST. PROF, 72-, grad. res, bd. award, summer 73. Speech Commun. Asn. (dissertation award, 72). Rhetorical criticism; rhetorical theory; political communication. Publ: Generic constraints and the rhetorical situation, summer 73 & Natural law as warrant, winter 73, Philos. & Rhet; Interpretations of natural law in the conflict over humanae vitae, Quart.J. Speech, 4/74. Add: Dept. of Speech & Dramatic Art, 1110 Tawes Fine Arts, University of Maryland, College Park, MD 20742.

JAMIESON, PAUL FLETCHER, b. Des Moines, Iowa, Aug. 1, 03; m. 31. ENGLISH. B.A, Drake Univ, 25; Roberts fel. & M.A, Columbia Univ, 26; Ph.D, Cornell Univ, 50. Instr. Eng, Drake Univ, 26-28; St. Lawrence Univ, 29-36, asst. prof, 36-52, assoc. prof, 52-59, prof, 59-65; RETIRED. Ed. consult, Adirondack Mus, 66- Romantic movement; Victorian age; Adirondack region. Publ: Adirondack reader, Macmillan, 64; ed, Man of the woods, Syracuse Univ. & Adirondack Mus, 72; auth, Tennyson and his audience in 1832, Philol. Quart, 10/52; Adirondack Mountains and state park, In: Encyclopedia Americana, 70; Lapsed paradise, Adirondac, 5-6/71. Add: 13 Jay St, Canton, NY 13617.

JANDOLI, RUSSELL JEROME, b. Orange, N.J, Aug. 16, 18; m. 47. JOURNALISM, ENGLISH. B.A, Univ. Notre Dame, 40; M.S, Columbia Univ, 41; M.A, St. Bonaventure Univ, 53; Ph.D.(social stud), N.Y. Univ, 56. Instr. jour, Univ. P.R, 42-43; wire ed. & correspondent, Stars & Stripes, Pac. area, 45-46; writer, U.S. Dept. War, 46-47; instr. Eng, ST. BONAVENTURE UNIV, 47-49, from asst. prof. to assoc. prof. JOUR, 49-53, PROF, 53-, FAC. SENATE, 73- Reporter & city ed, P.R. World Jour. & correspondent, Time Mag, 41-43; consult, Gebbie Press, New York, N.Y, 56-60; Found. Econ. Educ. fel, 58; chmn, Mark Hellinger Award Comt, 59-; managing ed, Cithara, 61-64, mem. ed. bd, 61-, supvr. judging newspaper awards competition, Cath. Press Asn, 64-73; chmn. ed. bd. Jour. Educator, 66-69; chmn. awards comt, Nat. Counc. Col. Publ. Adv, 67-68; bd. judges, Columbia Scholastic Press Asn, 67-; mem. stud. comt, Assoc. Press Managing Eds, 69-; coord, N.E. Press Adv. Asn, 73- Founders' Day Distinguished Scholar Award, N.Y. Univ, 56; Nat. Medal Merit, Pi Delta Epsilon, 69. U.S.A, 43-46, T/Sgt. Asn. Educ. in Jour; Am. Soc. Jour Sch. Adminr.(pres, 69-70); Am. Acad. Advert; Nat. Counc. Col. Publ. Adv. Catholic college education for journalism; education for journalism in the United States, especially social studies; college and high school journalism. Publ: Catholic journalism education in the U.S, St. Bonaventure Univ, 62; co-auth, Advertising principles, Pitman, 63; Undergraduate education for journalism, Jour. Educator, spring 67; The living legacy of Mark Hellinger, Quill, 2/68; Adventures in the groves of academe, monthly column in Olean (N.Y) Times Herald. Add: Dept. of Journalism, St. Bonaventure University, St. Bonaventure, NY 14778.

JANIS, JACK HAROLD, b. New York, N.Y, May 23, 10; m. 38; c. 2. BUSINESS WRITING. B.S, N.Y. Univ, 32, A.M, 42. Instr. BUS. WRITING, N.Y. UNIV, 34-42, asst. prof, 42-46, assoc. prof, 46-50, PROF, 50-, CHMN. DEPT. BUS. WRITING & SPEAKING, 63-, v.chmn. dept. bus. admin, 65-70. Consult, lett. & reports, City of New York, 42-44; consult. & lectr, Manufacturers Hanover Trust Co, New York, 49-; liaison ed, J. Commun, 62-65; consult. & lectr. Fed. Reserve Bank of New York, 67-72. Fel. Am. Bus. Commun. Asn.(assoc. ed, Bull, Am. Bus. Writing Asn, 47-49, v.pres, 48, pres, 49); NCTE; Int. Commun. Asn.(ed, Newslett, 65-68, dir-at-lg, 68-71); Speech Commun. Asn. Publ: Co-auth, Business writing, Barnes & Noble, 56, 2nd ed, 72; auth, Business communication reader, Harper, 58; Writing and communicating in business, 64, 2nd ed, 73 & co-auth, New standard reference for secretaries and administrative assistants, 72, Macmillan; auth, The business research paper, Hobbs, 67; contrib, Write better, speak better, Reader's Digest Bks, 72; auth, The writing behavior of businessmen, J. Commun, 6/65; A rationale for the use of common business-letter expressions, J. Bus. Commun, 10/66. Add: Dept. of Marketing, 437 Tisch Hall, New York University, Washington Square, New York, NY 10003.

JANN, REID, German, English. See Volume III, Foreign Languages, Linguistics & Philology.

JANSEN, WILLIAM HUGH, b. Stamford, Conn, Mar. 2, 14; m. 37; c. 2. COMPARATIVE FOLKLORE. A.B, Wesleyan Univ, 35; Columbia Univ, 35-36; fel, Ind. Univ, 37-41, Ph.D.(Eng. & folklore), 48. Instr. Eng. & French, Williston Acad, 36-37; Eng. & folklore, Ind. Univ, 41-49, dir. Eng. lang. orientation inst, 45-49; asst. prof. ENG. & FOLKLORE, UNIV. KY, 49-55, assoc. prof, 55-73, PROF, 73- Fulbright prof. folklore, Univ. Ankara, 51-52, vis. prof, 52-53; dir, Turkish-Am. Asn, 52-53; Ford fac. fel, 55-56; prof. Eng. as for. lang, Bandung Technol. Inst, 58-61; assoc. dir, Ky. Res. Found, 62-65; Nat. Endowment for Humanities sr. fel, 72-73; del, Am. Counc. Learned Soc, 72- Am. Folklore Soc.(v.pres, 61-62, publ. ed, 68-73); Folklore Soc. London; South. Folklore Soc.(pres, 51-52, 62-63); S.Atlantic Mod. Lang. Asn; Int. Soc. Folk Narrative Res. Folklore as a means of interpreting societies; folk narrative performance; the oral local legend. Publ: Co-auth, Folklore around the world, Ind. Univ, 61; auth, A culture's stereotypes and their expression in folk cliches, Southwest. J. Anthrop, 57; The esoteric-exoteric factor in folklore, Fabula, 59; Riddles: do-it-your-self oracles, In: Our living traditions, Basic Bks, 68. Add: Dept. of English, University of Kentucky, Lexington, KY 40506.

JANSSEN, JAMES GEORGE, b. Phlox, Wis, May 16, 34; m. 61; c. 2. AMERICAN LITERATURE. B.A, Marquette Univ, 60, M.A, 62; Ph.D.(Eng), Univ. Wis-Madison, 67. Instr. ENG, Lawrence Univ, 65-66, ASST. PROF, 66-68; ARIZ. STATE UNIV, 68- MLA. Nineteenth century American literature. Publ: Dimmesdale's Lurid playfulness, Am. Transcendental Quart, 69; Hawthorne's Seventh Vagabond: the outsetting bard, Emerson Soc. Quart, 71. Add: 1041 E. Wesleyan Dr, Tempe, AZ 85282.

JANUSKO, ROBERT JOHN, b. Cleveland, Ohio, Mar. 8, 39; m. 60; c. 3. ENGLISH. B.A, Kent State Univ, 64, M.A, 66, NDEA fel. & Ph.D.(Eng), 67. ASSOC. PROF. ENG, ASHLAND COL, 67- MLA. Twentieth-century literature, especially James Joyce; Afro-American literature. Add: Dept. of English, Ashland College, Ashland, OH 44805.

JANZOW, FREDERICK SAMUEL, b. Calgary, Alta, July 17, 13; U.S. citizen; m. 39; c. 2. ENGLISH. Grad, Concordia Theol. Sem, 36; M.A, Univ. Minn, 48; summer, Oxford, 65; Ph.D, Univ. Chicago, 68. Parish minister, London, Eng, 36-47 & Minn, 48-54; ASSOC. PROF. ENG, CONCORDIA TEACHERS COL.(ILL), 54-, ED, MOTIF: A LIT. J, 60- Mem. bd. dir, Minn. Dist. Lutheran Church-Mo, Synod, 52-54. NCTE; MLA; Lutheran Educ. Asn; Midwest Mod. Lang. Asn. Romantic movement; Thomas De Quincey, attribution problems. Publ: De Quincey enters journalism: his contributions to the Westmorland Gazette 1818-1819 (microfilm), Univ. Chicago, 68; Psalms and Canticles, Concordia Teachers Col.(Ill), 73; Worship in the scriptures and the confessions, Lutheran Educ, 11/59; Religious values in English literature and drama, In: The campus pastor, Comn. Col. & Univ. Work, Lutheran Church-Mo. Synod, 64-65; De Quincey's Danish origin of the Lake Country dialect republished, In: Vol. 1 & Philadelphus, a new essay by De Quincey, In: Vol 9, Costerus: Essays in English & American language & literature; plus others. Add: Dept. of English & Philosophy, Concordia Teachers College, 7400 Augusta St, River Forest, IL 60305.

JAQUES, JOHN FREDERICK, b. Portland, Maine, Sept. 3, 21; m. 51; c. 3. AMERICAN LITERATURE. A.B, Bowdoin Col, 43; A.M, Columbia Univ, 46, Ph.D.(Am. lit), 71. Instr. ENG, Drew Univ, 44-46; Portland Jr. Col, 46-48, chmn. dept, 48-58; asst. prof, UNIV. MAINE, PORTLAND, 58-66, assoc. prof, 66-72, PROF, 72-, asst. dir. undergrad. stud, asst. dean & acting dean of men, 58-66, consult, team teaching proj, 64-66. State judge, NCTE, 73. Thoreau Soc; Thoreau Fel. Thoreau; Maine writers. Publ: An enthusiastic newspaper account of Thoreau's second lecture in Portland, Maine, January 15, 1851, Am. Lit, 11/68; Ktaadn—record of Thoreau's youthful crisis, Thoreau J, 10/69. Add: 312 Pine St, South Portland, ME 04106.

JARRELL, MACKIE LANGHAM, b. Tex, Dec. 31, 14; m. 38. ENGLISH. B.A, Univ. Tex, 34, M.A, 35, Ph.D, 54. Instr. ENG, CONN. COL, 53-57, asst. prof, 57-63, assoc. prof, 63-66, PROF, 66-, chmn. dept, 66-69. Am. Asn. Univ. Women fel, 60-61; scholar in residence, Bellagio Study & Conf. Ctr, Rockefeller Found, 70. MLA; AAUP. Eighteenth-century English literature; W.B. Yeats; James Joyce. Publ: Co-auth, Eighteenth-century English minor poets, In: Laurel poetry series, Dell, 68; auth, The proverbs in Swift's Polite conversation, Huntington Libr. Quart, 56; Swiftiana in Finnegans wake, ELH, 59; Jack and the Dane: Swift traditions in Ireland, In: Fair liberty was all his cry: a tercentenary tribute to Jonathan Swift, Macmillan & St. Martin's, 67. Add: Box 1464, Connecticut College, New London, CT 06320.

JARRETT, HOBART SIDNEY, b. Arlington, Tex, Nov. 1, 15; m. 39. ENGLISH. A.B, Wiley Col, 36; M.A, Syracuse Univ, 37, Ph.D, 54. Instr. Eng, Langston Univ, 37-39, asst. prof, 39-41, assoc. prof, 41-43, prof, 43-49, dean men, 43-46, chmn. dept. lang, 46-49; chmn. div. humanities, Bennett Col, 49-61; assoc. prof. ENG, BROOKLYN COL, 61-70, PROF, 71- Mem, Brooklyn Col. Fac. Counc, 63-, Appointments Comt, Eng. Dept, 67-; mem. Univ. Senate, City Univ. New York, 73- Distinguished Teacher Award, Brooklyn Col, 73. NCTE (mem. comt. comp. & world lit, 71-, resolutions comt, 73); MLA; Col. Eng. Asn; Col. Lang. Asn; Renaissance Soc. Am; Shakespeare Asn. Am; Mod. Humanities Res. Asn; Int. Fed. Mod. Lang. & Lit. Shakespeare; humanities; 17th century British literature. Publ: Concerning brotherhood: an essay in five parts, Coun. Christians & Jews, 69; Some exceptional allusions to the Negro in non-dramatic literature of seventeenth-century England, CLA J, 9/62. Add: Dept. of English, Brooklyn College, Bedford at Ave. H, Brooklyn, NY 11210.

JARRETT, THOMAS DUNBAR, b. Union City, Tenn, Aug. 30, 13; m. 39; c. 1. ENGLISH. A.B, Knoxville Col, 33; A.M, Fisk Univ, 37; Ph.D.(Eng), Univ. Chicago, 47. Instr, high sch, Tenn, 33-37; asst. prof. Eng, Knoxville Col, 37-40; assoc. prof, Louisville Munic. Col, 41-43; asst. prof, ATLANTA UNIV, 47-50, assoc. prof, 50-55, prof, 55-67, chmn. dept, 57-67, acting dean, Sch. Arts & Sci, 57-60, dean, Grad. Sch. Arts & Sci, 60-67, acting pres. univ, 67-68, PRES, 68- Bk. rev. & poetry ed, Phylon, 48-67; ed, Lang. & Lit, 59-64; mem. comt, Carnegie Found. grants-in-aid: Ford Found, fel, England, 53-54; chmn. for. stud-travel awards comt. & adv, Fulbright Fels. & Woodrow Wilson Scholars, Atlanta Univ, 60-67; consult, prospective teachers fel. prog, Dept. Health, Educ. & Welfare, 66-; mem. adv. comt, Nat. Defense Lang. Develop. Prog, 66-; mem, Ga. Sci. & Technol. Comn, 69; bd. trustees, Knoxville Col, 71-; mem, Counc. Grad. Educ; Ga. State Adv. Counc; chmn. gov. bd, Educ. Improv. Proj, Urban Lab. Educ. U.S.A, 42-46, Lt. Col. Lang. Asn; NCTE (dir, 63-69, mem. comn. Eng, 68-); Nat. Asn. Col. Deans & Registr.(pres, 68-69); AAUP; Counc. Grad. Schs. U.S. William J. Grayson; novels of T.S. Stribling; 19th century English and American literature. Publ: The novels of Nicholas Monsarrat, Col. Eng, 3/56; New dimensions in curriculum structuring, J. Col. Deans & Registr, 3/60; contrib, Informing the public about the English language arts, NCTE, 61; plus others. Add: Atlanta University, Atlanta, GA 30314.

JARROTT, CATHERINE ANNA LOUISE, b. Los Angeles, Calif, Aug. 6, 25. ENGLISH. B.A, Univ. Calif, Los Angeles, 47; M.A, Stanford Univ, 49, Ph.D. (Eng), 54. Instr. ENG, St. Mary Col.(Kans), 52-54, asst. prof, 54-63; LOYOLA UNIV. CHICAGO, 63-66, ASSOC. PROF, 66- Fulbright exchange fel, Netherlands, 59-60; lectr, Rome Ctr. Lib. Arts, Loyola Univ, 67-68 & 73. MLA; Renaissance Soc. Am. Renaissance humanism, especially of Erasmus, Colet, and More; Chaucer. Publ: The vocation of St. Thomas More, Am. Benedictine Rev, 9/61; Erasmus in Principio erat sermo—a controversial translation, Stud. Philol, 1/64; Erasmus' Biblical humanism, Stud. Renaissance, 70. Add: Dept. of English, Loyola University of Chicago, 6525 N. Sheridan Rd, Chicago, IL 60626.

JARVI, RAYMOND, Modern Swedish Literature, Swedish Theater. See Volume III, Foreign Languages, Linguistics & Philology.

JARVIS, JOSEPH BOYER, b. Springville, Utah, June 1, 23; m. 55; c. 3. SPEECH. B.A, Univ. Ariz, 47; M.A, Ariz. State Univ, 50; Ph.D.(speech), Northwest. Univ, 58. Instr. speech, Univ. Ariz, 50-52; Dartmouth Col, 54-55; asst. to dean col. lett. & sci, UNIV. UTAH, 56-58, asst. dean, 58-60, acting dean, 61-62, asst. prof. SPEECH, 56-63, assoc. prof, 63-68, PROF, 68-, ASSOC. V.PRES. ACAD. AFFAIRS, 67-, asst. to pres, 62-64, dean summer sch, 62-67, dean admis. & registr, 65-71. Assoc. prog. dir, KUED-ETV, 58-61; spec. asst. to comnr. educ, U.S. Dept. Health, Educ. & Welfare, 61-62; mem. U.S. deleg, UNESCO Conf. Asian Ministers Educ, Tokyo, 62. Speech Commun. Asn. Public address; history. Add: Dept. of Communication, University of Utah, Salt Lake City, UT 84112.

JAUCH, CLEVELAND EDWARD, JR, b. Buffalo, N.Y, Mar. 9, 14. ENGLISH. A.B, Princeton, 37; M.A, Columbia Univ, 39; M.A, Yale, 49, Ph.D, 55. Instr. ENG, Univ. Buffalo, 46-48; Hamilton Col.(N.Y), 53-55; Lafayette Col, 55-66; ASSOC. PROF, STATE UNIV. N.Y. COL. BUFFALO, 66- U.S.A, 42-46. Modern fiction; D.H. Lawrence. Add: 107 Oakland Pl, Buffalo, NY 14222.

JAVITCH, DANIEL GILBERT, b. Cannes, France, June 13, 41; m. 68. ENGLISH, COMPARATIVE LITERATURE. A.B, Princeton, 63; B.A, Cambridge, 65, M.A, 70; M.A, Harvard, 66, Ph.D.(comp. lit), 70. ASST. PROF. COMP. LIT, COLUMBIA UNIV, 70- Dir, New Directions Publ. Corp, 72- MLA; Renaissance Soc. Am. Renaissance Europe, English, French, Italian literatures. Publ: The philosopher of the court, Comp. Lit, 71; Rival arts of conduct in Elizabethan England, Yearbk, Ital. Stud. I, 71; Poetry and court conduct, Mod. Lang. Notes, 72. Add: Dept. of English, 416 Hamilton Hall, Columbia University, New York, NY 10027.

JAYE, BARBARA H, b. Rapid City, S.Dak, Nov. 17, 30; m. 61; c. 2. ENGLISH LITERATURE. B.A, City Col. New York, 62; NDEA fel, Rutgers Univ, New Brunswick, 65-70, M.A, 65, Ph.D.(Eng. lit), 70. ASST. PROF. ENG, MONMOUTH COL.(N.J), 66- MLA; Mediaeval Acad. Am. Medieval drama; iconography. Add: Dept. of English, Monmouth College, Cedar Ave, West Long Branch, NJ 07764.

JAYE, MICHAEL C, b. New York, N.Y, Mar. 1, 41. ENGLISH LITERATURE. B.A, City Col. New York, 62; M.A, N.Y. Univ, 63, Ph.D.(Eng), 69. ASST. PROF. ENG, RUTGERS UNIV, NEWARK, 64-, fac. fel, 70-71. Pforzheimer Found. grant, 71. MLA; AAUP. Romantic period; Victorian period. Publ: John Carter and the dating of Ms. C of Wordsworth's Prelude, Notes & Queries, 68. Add: Dept. of English, Rutgers University, Newark, NJ 07102.

JAYNE, SEARS, b. Phoenix, Ariz, Aug. 11, 20; m. 41; c. 3. ENGLISH LITERATURE. A.B, Univ. Mo, 41, A.M, 42; Ph.D.(Elizabethan drama), Yale, 48. Instr, Univ. Mo, 41-42; asst. prof. Eng, Univ. Calif, 48-56; assoc. prof, Univ. Va, 56-59; Arensberg vis. prof, Claremont Grad. Sch, 59-60; prof, Pomona Col, 60-63; Queens Col.(N.Y), 63-67, assoc. dean fac, 67-68; PROF. Eng, Hunter Col, 68-69; ENG. & COMP LIT, BROWN UNIV, 69- Fulbright res. fel, Eng, 54-55; Guggenheim fel, 54-55; Am. Counc. Learned Soc. fel, Italy, 62-63; Harvard Res. Ctr. fel, Florence, Italy, 62-63; Guggenheim fel, 69-70. MLA; Renaissance Soc. Am. Renaissance Platonism; Elizabethan literature; comparative literature. Publ: Marsilio Ficino's commentary on Plato's Symposium, Univ. Mo; Library catalogues of the English Renaissance, Univ. Calif; John Colet and Marsilio Ficino, Oxford. Add: Dept. of English, Brown University, Providence, RI 02912.

JAYNES, BRYSON LESTER, b. Grand Junction, Colo, Nov. 5, 05; m. 26; c. 1. ENGLISH. B.A, Reed Col, 29; M.A, Wash. State Univ, 39, Ed.D, 51. Instr. algebra & Latin, jr. high sch, Hood River, Ore, 29-31; supt. & instr. Eng. & hist, Thornton, Wash, 31-33; instr. Eng. & drama, high sch, Clarkston, 33-38; N.Cent. High Sch, Spokane, 38-49; dir. freshman compos, Wash. State Univ, 49-57, assoc. prof. grammar & dir. scheduling for Eng. dept, 57-64, prof. Eng, 64-71; RETIRED. Life mem, Nat. Educ. Asn; NCTE. Problems of educational personnel; American humor; English grammar. Publ: Public attitudes toward teachers, 52 & Artemus Ward among the Mormons, 3/57, Res. Stud, Wash. State Univ; Remedial English and college graduation, Col. Compos. & Commun, 2/58. Add: 2341 Chambers Lake Dr. S.E, Lacey, WA 98503.

JAZAYERY, MOHAMMAD ALI, Linguistics. See Volume III, Foreign Languages, Linguistics & Philology.

JEDYNAK, STANLEY LOUIS, b. Lackawanna, N.Y, July 3, 22; m. 51; c. 3. ENGLISH. B.A, Univ. Buffalo, 49, M.A, 54; Ph.D, Syracuse Univ, 61. Instr. Eng, Univ. Buffalo, 52-54; asst. instr, Syracuse Univ, 55-60, instr. ENG, 60-61; asst. prof, SIENA COL.(N.Y), 61-66, assoc. prof, 66-73, PROF, 73-, head dept, 71-73. U.S.M.C, 43-46, 50-51, Sgt. Eng. Inst; MLA; NCTE. Linguistics; modern British literature. Publ: Under the volcano: an existentialist tragedy, Thoth, spring, 59; Epiphany as structure in Dubliners, Greyfriar, 71. Add: Dept. of English, Siena College, Loudonville, NY 12211.

JEFCHAK, ANDREW TIMOTHY, b. East Chicago, Ind, Jan. 25, 36; m. 59; c. 3. AMERICAN LITERATURE, FILM STUDY. A.B, Ind. Univ, Bloomington, 59; M.A, DePaul Univ, 65; Ph.D.(Eng), Mich. State Univ, 70. Instr. Eng, Am. Inst. Banking, Chicago, 64-65; grad. asst. & asst. to dir. inquiry & expression, Justin Morrill Col, Mich. State Univ, 65-68; ASST. PROF. ENG. & FILM STUD, AQUINAS COL, 68- Kellogg Found-Asn. Independent Cols. & Univs. of Mich. fel, 71-72. Admin.C, U.S.A, 59-62. Am. Civil Liberties Union; Am. Film Inst; AAUP; Univ. Film Asn. Family relationships in modern fiction; literature and motion pictures, comparative art forms; structure and irony in motion pictures. Add: Dept. of English, Aquinas College, 1607 Robinson S.E, Grand Rapids, MI 49506.

JEFFREY, DAVID LYLE, b. Ottawa, Ont, June 28, 41; m. 61; c. 3. ENGLISH LITERATURE, ART HISTORY. Wheaton fel & B.A, Wheaton Col.(Ill), 65; M.A, Princeton, 67, Woodrow Wilson fels, 65 & 68, Can. Counc. fel. & Ph.D.(Eng), 68. Asst. prof. ENG, Univ. Victoria (B.C), 68-69; Univ. Rochester, 69-72; ASSOC. PROF. & CHMN. DEPT, UNIV. VICTORIA (B.C), 73- Can. Counc. fac. res. award, 69; Reckitt & Coleman vis. prof. Eng, Univ. Hull, 71-72. MLA. Conf. Christianity & Lit; Mediaeval Acad. Am. Medieval literature and art history; modern literature. Publ: The early English lyric and Franciscan spirituality, Univ. Nebr, 73; The Friar's Rente, J. Eng. & Ger. Philol, 71; English saint's plays, Stratford-upon-Avon Stud, 73; Bosch's Haywain: communion, community, and the theatre of the world, Viator, 73. Add: Dept. of English, University of Victoria, Victoria, B.C. V8W 2Y2, Can.

JEFFREY, LLOYD NICHOLAS, b. Temple, Okla, Nov. 26, 18; m. 45; c. 2. ENGLISH. B.A, Univ. Tex, M.A, fel. & Ph.D.(Eng), 51. Instr. ENG, Univ. Tex, 46-50; assoc. prof, E.Cent. Okla. State Col, 51-55; PROF, N.TEX. STATE UNIV, 55-, res. grants, 62-64, 66-68. U.S.A, 41-46, Capt. S.Cent. Mod. Lang. Asn; MLA; Am. Class. League; Keats-Shelley Asn. Am. English Romantic poets; natural history in literature; classics. Publ: Thomas Hood, Twayne, 72; Reptile lore in Shelley: a study in the poet's use of natural history, Keats-Shelley J, winter 58; A Freudian reading of Keats's Ode to psyche, Psychoanal. Rev, summer 68; plus others. Add: Dept. of English, Box 6239, North Texas State University, Denton, TX 76203.

JEFFREY, ROBERT CAMPBELL, b. San Antonio, Tex, Nov. 11, 27; m. 47; c. 4. SPEECH. B.A, State Univ, Iowa, 49, M.A, 50, Ph.D.(speech), 57. Asst. prof. speech, Cornell Col, 50-53; instr. commun. skills, State Univ. Iowa, 53-54; asst. prof. SPEECH, Univ. Va, 54-59; Ind. Univ, 59-66, assoc. prof, 66-68; PROF. & CHMN. DEPT, UNIV. TEX, AUSTIN, 68- U.S.N.R, 45-46. Speech Commun. Asn.(exec. secy, 60-63, 2nd v.pres, 71-72, 1st v.pres, 72-73, pres, 73-74); NEA; Int. Commun. Asn. Speech criticism; contemporary American public address; modern rhetorical theory. Publ: co-auth, Speech: a text with adapted readings, Harper, 71; auth, Convention speaking: preface, 60 & History of the Speech Association of America, 1914-1964, 64, Quart. J. Speech; Republican credentials committee debates, 1952, Speech Monogr, 61. Add: Dept. of Speech Communication, School of Communication, University of Texas at Austin, Austin, TX 78712.

JEHLEN, MYRA, b. Paris, France, Mar. 3, 40; U.S. citizen; m. 62; c. 1. ENGLISH, AMERICAN STUDIES. B.A, City Col. New York, 61; Ph.D.(Eng), Univ. Calif, Berkeley, 68. Instr. ENG, N.Y. Univ, 66-69; ASST. PROF, COLUMBIA UNIV, 69- Nat. Endowment for Humanities jr. fel, 72-73; vis. lectr. Am. stud, Yale, spring 74. MLA; Asn. Am. Stud. The American novel; comparative fiction of Europe in the 18th and 19th centuries; critical theory. Publ: American epic: the novel and the middle-class in America, Columbia Univ, (in press); co-auth, Concepts of history and myth in the Iliad and Oddyssey, Lit. Na Swiecie, 74. Add: Dept. of English, Columbia University, 116th St. & Broadway, New York, NY 10027.

JELLEMA, RODERICK HARTIGH, b. Holland, Mich, Aug. 11, 27; m. 50; c. 3. ENGLISH. B.A, Calvin Col, 51; dipl. Eng, Univ. Edinburgh, 54, Ph.D.(Victorian lit), 62. Instr. ENG, West. Acad.(Iowa), 52-53; Univ. Md. Overseas Prog, 55-56; UNIV. MD, COLLEGE PARK, 56-64, asst. prof, 64-67, ASSOC. PROF, 67-, grad. sch. summer res. grants, 64, 66, creative & performing arts grant, summer 68. Vis. lectr, West. Md. Col, 61-62; gen. ed, Contemporary Writers in Christian Perspective Ser, Eerdmans, 65-; essayist, Valparaiso Coloquium Christianity & Humanism, 67; consult. poetry grants, Nat. Endowment Arts, 67; mem, Acad. Am. Poets, 68- U.S.N, 45-47. Poetry Soc. Am; Conf. Christianity & Lit, 61. Modern poetry; religious and theological implications of English and American literature since 1860. Publ: Peter de Vries, 66 & ed, Dorothy Sayers, Christian letters to a post-Christian world; 68, Eerdmans; In defense of being modern, 11/65 & Who is twentieth-century man?, 12/66, Reformed J. Add: Dept. of English, University of Maryland, College Park, MD 20740.

JELLICORSE, JOHN LEE, b. Bristol, Tenn, Nov. 1, 37; m. 61; c. 1. COMMUNICATIONS, PUBLIC COMMUNICATIONS HISTORY. B.A, Univ. Tenn, Knoxville, 59; Ph.D.(speech), Northwest. Univ, 67. From instr. to assoc. prof. speech, Northwest. Univ, 62-69, acting chmn. pub. address & group commun, 69; ASSOC. PROF. SPEECH, THEATRE & COMMUN, UNIV. TENN, KNOXVILLE, 69- Vis. instr. speech, Appalachian State Univ, summers 61-62; assoc. ed, South. Speech Commun. J, 69-72; Bibliog. Annual Speech Commun, 73-75. Speech Commun. Asn.(mem. comt. arch. of recorded materials, 67-); South. Speech Commun. Asn; MLA; Am. Film Inst; Int. Commun. Asn. Rhetoric of film; communication theory; Walt Whitman. Publ: Whitman and modern literary criticism, Am. Transcendental Quart, 71; Some historical essentials of teaching free speech, Free Speech Yearbook, 72; Audiovisual archives: uses and as evidence, Hist. Teacher, 73. Add: 1101 Dartmouth Rd, Knoxville, TN 37914.

JELLIFFE, REBECCA RIO, b. Iloilo, Philippines, Aug. 9, 22; U.S. citizen; m. 50; c. 2. ENGLISH. A.B. & B.S, Cent. Philippines Univ, 46; Fulbright scholar. & M.A, Oberlin Col, 50; Danforth grant, 60-64; Ph.D.(Eng), Univ. Calif, Berkeley, 64. Vis. lectr. ENG, Cent. Philippines Univ, 50-51; Kobe Col, 53-56; instr, UNIV. REDLANDS, 58-60, asst. prof, 64-68, assoc. prof, 68-73, PROF, 73-, CHAIRPERSON, 74- Danforth summer res. grant, 64; Univ. Redlands fac. res. grants, summer 66 & 68-69. Conf. Col. Teachers Eng. Nature in American literature; history of American criticism; poetic theory and practice of William Cullen Bryant. Add: Dept. of English, University of Redlands, Redlands, CA 92373.

JEMIELITY, THOMAS J, b. Cleveland, Ohio, Dec. 17, 33; m. 65; c. 3. ENGLISH. M.A, John Carroll Univ, 58; Allen Seymour Olmsted fel, Cornell Univ, 60-61, Ph.D, 65. Lectr. ENG, Carleton Univ,(Can), 62-63; instr, UNIV. NOTRE DAME, 63-65, asst. prof, 65-70, ASSOC. PROF, 70- Nat. Endowment for Humanities summer stipend, 67, Fel. Soc. Relig. Higher Educ. Restoration and 18th century English literature; Samuel Johnson; satire. Publ: More in notions than facts; Samuel Johnson's journey to Western Islands, Dalhousie Rev, fall 69; Dr. Johnson and the uses of travel, Philol. Quart, 4/73; Samuel Johnson, the second sight, and his sources, Stud. Eng. Lit, summer 74. Add: Dept. of English, University of Notre Dame, Notre Dame, IN 46556.

JENKINS, ANNIBEL, b. Shubuta, Miss, Mar. 4, 18. ENGLISH. B.A, Blue Mountain Col, 38; M.A, Baylor Univ, 43; Ph.D, Univ. N.C, Chapel Hill, 65. Instr. music & Eng, Blue Mountain Col; instr. ENG, Wake Forest Col, 50-56; asst. prof, Belhaven Col, 59-60; Miss. Col, 60-62; GA. INST. TECHNOL, 63-69, ASSOC. PROF, 69- Ga. Inst. Technol. Found. grant, summer 67. MLA; S.Atlantic Mod. Lang. Asn; Southeast. Renaissance Conf; Am. Soc. 18th Century Stud. Nicholas Rowe and 18th century drama; 18th century periodical press. Publ: Nicholas Rowe, Twayne, (in press); A second Astrophel and Stella cycle, Renaissance Papers, 70; Essays on Authur Calder-Marshall, Penelope Gilliatt, Jim Hunter, Emma Smith & Monica Stirling, In: Contemporary novelists, St. James, 72. Add: Dept. of English, Georgia Institute of Technology, Atlanta, GA 30332.

JENKINS, ANTHONY WHITE, b. Sutton Coldfield, Warwickshire, July 8, 36; m. 60; c. 2. ENGLISH. B.A, Cambridge, 59, M.A, 63; Can. Counc. fel, Univ. Calif, Berkeley, 65-66, Wheeler fel, 66, Ph.D.(Eng), 67. Instr. ENG, Univ. Victoria (B.C), 60-62; tutor, Corpus Christi Col, Cambridge, 62-63; instr, UNIV. VICTORIA (B.C), 63-64, asst. prof, 66-72, ASSOC. PROF, 72- Royal Corps Sig, 54-56. Fifteenth century English literature. Publ: Henryson's Fox, wolf and cadger again, Stud. Scottish Lit, 10/66. Add: Dept. of English, University of Victoria, Victoria, B.C, Can.

JENKINS, DAVID CLAY, b. Birmingham, Ala, June 1, 26. ENGLISH. B.A, Univ. Ala, 48, M.A, 51; Fulbright scholar, Univ. Wales, 49-51; Ph.D, Univ. Iowa, 56. Instr. ENG, Auburn Univ, 52-53; COL. WILLIAM & MARY, 56-58, asst. prof, 58-64, assoc. prof, 64-67, PROF, 68- Fels, summer inst. Asian stud, Univ. Va, 65 & coop. prog. humanities, Duke Univ. & Univ. N.C, 67-68; mem, Nat. Screening Comt. for Fulbright-Hays grants, Inst. Int. Educ, 70-72, chmn. South. Regional Selection Comt. for United Kingdom and Ireland applicants. U.S.A, 44-46, Sgt. Maj. MLA; AAUP. Modern American and British literature; Celtic literature; 18th century drama and poetry. Publ: A defense of the Anglo-Welsh, Univ. Microfilms, 56; The James Street Theatre at the old tennis court, Theatre Notebk, autumn 69; The shrine of the Boily Boy: the Dylan Thomas notebooks at Buffalo, Anglo-Welsh Rev, autumn 70; Flies in amber: John Payne Collier's falsifications of Pope, Huntington Libr. Quart, 8/71; plus others. Add: Dept. of English, College of William & Mary, Williamsburg, VA 23185.

JENKINS, JOSEPH HENRY, JR, b. Brooklyn, N.Y, Sept. 9, 06; div. ENGLISH. A.B, Hamilton Col, 28; A.M, Harvard, 33; Whitney Found. fel, 50-51. Instr. ENG, laboratory high sch, W.Va, State Teachers Col, Bluefield, 29-30; teacher, Atlanta Univ, 30-32; instr, Spelman Col, 33-42; asst. prof, Va. State Col, 45-46, ASSOC. PROF, 47-73, acting head dept, 62-69, head, 69-72, chmn. dept, 72-73; VA. COMMONWEALTH UNIV, 73- Exchange teacher, Morehouse Col. & Atlanta Univ, 33-42; consult, sec. sch. workshop, Hampton Inst, 41; instr, Va. Union Univ, 42; consult, lang. & lit. workshop, South. Univ, summer 62; bk. reviewer, Richmond Times-Dispatch, 70-71 & The Afro-American, 72-; self-syndication, Blacks in Books, 73. Qm.C, U.S.A, 42-45, S/Sgt. Col. Eng. Asn; Col. Lang. Asn.(treas, 41); NCTE; MLA; South. Mod. Lang. Asn. American literature; fiction; American studies. Add: 1501 Halifax St, Petersburg, VA 23803.

JENKINS, OWEN, b. Chicago, Ill, Dec. 10, 27; m. 54; c. 4. ENGLISH. A.B, Univ. Chicago, 45, A.M, 50; Ph.D, Cornell Univ, 54. Instr. ENG, Ga. Inst. Technol, 50-52; from asst. prof. to PROF, CARLETON COL, 54- U.S.A, 45-46. MLA. Concept of art in classical and modern criticism; Richardson and Fielding; Scott's criticism of 18th century fiction. Add: 514 E. Sumner St, Northfield, MN 55057.

JENKINS, RALPH EUGENE, b. Decatur, Tex, Aug. 6, 38. ENGLISH LITERATURE. B.A, Univ. Tex, Arlington, 63; M.A, Purdue Univ, W. Lafayette, 65; Ph.D.(Eng), Univ. Tex, Austin, 68. ASST. PROF. ENG, TEMPLE UNIV, 68- Eighteenth century English literature. Publ: The structure of Roxana, Stud. Novel, fall 70; Rhetorical structure in The man of feeling, Stud. Scottish Lit, 71; Johnson and Pennant in Scotland, Tex. Stud. Lang. & Lit, 72. Add: Dept. of English, Temple University, Philadelphia, PA 19122.

JENKINS, STARR, b. Chicago, Ill, June 1, 25; m. 50; c. 3. ENGLISH, AMERICAN STUDIES. B.A, Univ. N.Mex, 48, Ph.D.(Am. stud), 72; M.A, Stanford Univ, 59. Teacher Eng. & hist, Albuquerque Pub. Schs, N.Mex, 50-57; inform. specialist, Southwest. Region, U.S. Forest Serv, 57-61; asst. prof. ENG, CALIF. POLYTECH. STATE UNIV, SAN LUIS OBISPO, 61-66, assoc. prof, 66-73, PROF, 73- Free-lance writer, 61-; contrib, Calif. Polytech. AV Prod, 66- U.S.N.R, 43-44, 45-46; U.S.A, 44-45. Am. Stud. Asn; West. Lit. Asn. American statesmen as men of letters; Western regional literature; adventure nonfiction writing. Publ: Profiles of creative political leaders: American statesmen who were great writers, Whitmore, 74; We jump into fire, In: Man against nature, Harper, 54; Down with Yosemite City, San Francisco Mag, 8/65; The rugged return of Lewis and Clark, Nugget, 3/71. Add: Dept. of English, California Polytechnic State University, San Luis Obispo, CA 93407.

JENKINS, WILLIAM A, b. Scranton, Pa, Nov. 18, 22; m. 44; c. 2. ENGLISH EDUCATION. B.S, N.Y. Univ, 48; M.S, Univ. Ill, 49, Ph.D.(Eng. educ), 54. Res. asst. educ, Univ. Ill, 48-51; teacher, Jr. High Sch, Ill, 51-53; asst. prof. Eng, Univ. Wis-Milwaukee, 53-55, assoc. prof. Eng. educ, 55-58, secy. fac, 58-61; prof. & chmn. dept. sec. educ, 61-63, assoc. dean sch. educ, 63-70; DEAN SCH. EDUC, PORTLAND STATE UNIV, 70- Feature ed, The Educational Scene, Elem. Eng. Mag, 49-61; consult. & testing assoc, Educ. Testing Serv, 53, 54, 55, 57; mem, Comt. Children's Lit—Old & New, NCTE, 60-63; evaluator, NDEA Inst. proposals Eng. & reading, U.S. Off. Educ, 64-67; mem, Comt. Guidelines Eng. NDEA Insts, MLA & NCTE, 65; vis. prof. educ, Univ. Hawaii, summer 69; secy, City of Portland Develop. Comn, 72- C.Eng, 43-46, 1st Lt. NCTE (pres, 68-69); Nat. Conf. Res. Eng. Language arts, reading; teacher education. Publ: Co-auth, Elem. sch. reading & lang. texts, 63- & In other words—a beginning thesaurus, 68, Scott; auth, How to write compositions, Compton, 67; Language and communication, In: Coordinating reading instruction, 70 & The language arts, In: Handbook for teachers, 71, Scott; The state of the art of teaching language, In: A forum for focus, Nat. Counc. Teachers Eng, 73. Add: School of Education, Portland State University, P.O. Box 751, Portland, OR 97201.

JENKINSON, EDWARD B, b. Muncie, Ind, Oct. 23, 30; m. 54; c. 2. ENGLISH, SPEECH. A.B, Ball State Univ, 51; M.A, Ind. Univ, 56. Teacher, high schs, Ind, 51-56; alumni exec. secy, dir. stud. & sports publicity & mag. ed, North. Ill. Univ, 56-58; instr. jour, American Univ. Beirut, 58-60; from lectr. to assoc. prof. EDUC, 60-73, PROF, 73-, COORD. SCH. ENG. LANG. ARTS, IND. UNIV, BLOOMINGTON, 60-, DIR. ENG. CURRICULUM STUD. CTR, 63- Wall Street Jour. Newspaper Fund grant for prep. jour. course for teachers in Ind, 63-65; U.S. Off. Educ. grant for Eng. curriculum stud. ctr, 63-69; Cummins Engine Found. grant for prep. stud. courses, 63-69; mem. comt. pub. & prof. relat, NCTE, 63-69, state chmn. achievement awards prog, 68; co-dir. tri-univ. proj. behav. objectives in Eng, U.S. Off. Educ, 69-71. NCTE (v.pres, 71-); MLA. Teaching of language, composition and literature in secondary school and college. Publ: Ed, Two units on journalism for English classes, 64, Teacher's guide to high school journalism, 65 & Teacher's guide to high school speech, 66, Ind. State Dept. Pub. Instr; co-ed, On teaching literature: essays for secondary school teachers, 67, Teaching literature in grades seven through nine, 67, Two approaches to teaching syntax, 67, Teaching literature in grades ten through twelve, 68, Books for teachers of English: an annotated bibliography, 68, auth, What is language? And other teaching units for grades seven through twelve, 68, co-auth, Writing as a process of discovery, 70, co-ed, Essays on teaching speech in the high school, 71, co-ed, On teaching speech in elementary and junior high schools, 71 & co-auth, Teaching the Old Testament in English classes, 73, Ind. Univ; auth, A student guide to the Random House dictionary of the English language, Random, 68, sch. ed, 70; People, words and dictionaries, 72 & co-auth, Points of view in writing, 72, Harcourt; co-auth, Representative performance objectives for high school English: a guide for teaching, evaluating and curriculum planning, Ronald, 72; auth, One step toward alleviating the crisis of meaning, Hoosier Schoolmaster, 5/64; How words are formed, Ind. Univ. Eng. Curriculum Stud. Ctr. Newslett, 9/65; Report on Indiana University English curriculum study center, In: New materials for the teaching of English, PMLA, 9/66. Add: 3609 Longview Dr, Bloomington, IN 47401.

JENKS, JOSEPH B, b. Long Island City, N.Y, Nov. 18, 15; m. 38; c. 5. ENGLISH. A.B, Marquette Univ, 41; M.A, Mich. State Univ, 51, Hineman fel, 52, Ph.D.(Eng), 56. Teacher, high sch, Mich, 46-48, 52-54; asst. prof. ENG, Mankato State Teachers Col, Minn, 54-56; Cent. Mich. Col, 56-62; PROF, STATE UNIV. N.Y. COL. BROCKPORT, 62- Smith-Mundt prof, Univ. Huê, Vietnam, 61-62; Fulbright-Hays lectr, Univ. Saigon, 64-65 & Univs. Saigon & Delat, 66-67. U.S.A, 42-45. MLA; Mediaeval Acad. Am; Asn. Asian Stud. Middle English language and literature; comparative Indo-European linguistics; history of ideas and Vietnamese literature and language. Publ: Co-auth, Teacher personalities—a mirror of self, Vantage, 74. Add: 712 Ellis Dr, Brockport, NY 14420.

JENKS, MARY HATHAWAY, b. Cannonsville, N.Y, June 13, 06; m. 21. ENGLISH LITERATURE. B.A, Maryville Col.(Tenn), 42; univ. fel. & M.A, Univ. Tenn, 45, South. Regional fel. & Ph.D, 57. Teacher, elem. sch, N.Y, 36-39, 40-41; ed, Oxford Review-Times, N.Y, 42-43; instr. Eng, Univ. Tenn, 45-49, engineering librn, 54-55; asst. tech. ed, McGraw-Hill Book Co. contract, Atomic Energy Comn, Oak Ridge, Tenn, 51-54; prof. ENG, TENN. TECHNOL. UNIV, 55-71, EMER. PROF, 71- Drama critic, Cookeville Herald-Citizen, 70- Counc. Basic Educ; S.Atlantic Mod. Lang. Asn. Nineteenth century English literature, Greek literature and mythology; Scott, Cooper, Dumas literary relationship. Publ: The Quarterly Review appraises contemporary literature, Tenn. Technol. J, spring 67. Add: 1057 Mitchell Ave, Cookeville, TN 38501.

JENNINGS, EDWARD MORTON, III, b. Boston, Mass; Apr. 2, 36; m. 57; c. 3. ENGLISH. A.B, Dartmouth Col, 57; M.A, Univ. Wis, Madison, 61, fel, 64-65, Ph.D.(Eng), 65. ASST. PROF. ENG, Duke Univ, 65-68; STATE UNIV. N.Y. ALBANY, 68- Am. Counc. Educ. fel, Amherst Col, 71-72. U.S.N, 57-60, Res, 60-65, Lt. Am. Soc. 18th Century Stud; MLA; NCTE. English 18th century; theory of fiction; literature and computers. Publ: Ed, Science and literature, Anchor, 71; A paradigm for discovery, Col. Compos. & Commun, 10/68. Add: Dept. of English, State University of New York at Albany, Albany, NY 12222.

JENNINGS, LAWRENCE CHARLES, b. Exeter, Mo, Nov. 10, 12; m. 38; c. 3. ENGLISH LITERATURE, ENGLISH LANGUAGE. B.S, Southwest Mo. State Col, 34; B.D, Nazarene Theol. Sem, 48; M.S, Northwest. Mo. State Col, 60; Ed.D.(Eng), Univ. Okla, 71. Teacher Eng, Midway High Sch, Mo, 35-41; prin, Butterfield High Sch, 41-43; teacher bus, Maryville High Sch, 54-55; asst. prof. ENG, Can Nazarene Col, 55-63; BETHANY NAZARENE COL, 64-66, assoc. prof, 66-69, PROF, 69-, HEAD DEPT, 72- S.Cent. Mod. Lang. Asn; S.Cent. Renaissance Conf. Southwest Lit. Asn. Image of the professor in English literature from Carlyle to Snow; literary figures of the Mississippi River South. Add: Dept. of English, Bethany Nazarene College, Bethany, OK 73008.

JENNINGS, RUSSELL WAYNE, b. Deer Lodge, Mont, Sept. 29, 36; c. 2. INTERPERSONAL COMMUNICATION. B.S, West. Mont. Col, 59; M.A, Univ. Mont, 66; Ph.D.(rhetoric), South. Ill. Univ, Carbondale, 68. Instr. SPEECH, Northwest Community Col, 63-65; asst. prof, Chicago City Col, 67-68; ASSOC. PROF, SOUTH. ILL. UNIV, CARBONDALE, 68- Int. Commun. Asn; Speech Commun. Asn; Int. Transactional Anal. Asn. Field studies in volunteer organizations; phenomenological studies of small groups; phenomenological studies of personal growth and consciousness raising. Publ: Field studies in the urban situation, Proc. Speech Asn. Am, summer 69; co-auth, The situational analysis of urban communication, In: Research designs in general semantics, 73 & co-auth, A simulated communication model of community action organizations, In: General systems theory and general semantics, 74, Gordon & Breach. Add: Dept. of Speech, Southern Illinois University, Carbondale, IL 62901.

JENSEN, ARTHUR EUGENE, b. Gloucester, Mass, Feb. 12, 03. ENGLISH LITERATURE. A.B, Brown Univ, 26, A.M, 28, hon. L.H.D, 56; Ph.D, Univ. Edinburgh, 33; hon. Litt.D, L.I. Univ, 61; hon. LL.D, Windham Col, 68. Instr. Eng, Brown Univ, 26-31; asst. prof, Univ. Maine, 33-37; DARTMOUTH COL, 37-45, prof, 45-71, dean fac, 55-71, dir. great issues course, 49-52, chmn. Eng. dept, 51-55, EMER. PROF. ENG, 71- Vis. prof, Bread Loaf Sch. Eng, 48-55; dir. inst. mgt. develop, Am. Telephone & Telegraph

Co, 56-61; trustee, Col. Entrance Exam. Bd, 59-62; consult, mgt. develop, Int. Bus. Machines Corp, 60-; Nationwide Insurance Co, 62-; consult, Nat. Counc. Sch-Col. Relat, 65-66. U.S.N.R, 42-46, Lt. Comdr. Eighteenth and 19th century English literature; the romantic movement in England; Thomas Percy. Add: Dept. of English, Dartmouth College, Hanover, NH 03755.

JENSEN, DANA OLAF, b. St. Louis Co, Mo, June 20, 03. ENGLISH. A.B, Wash. Univ, 26; A.M, Univ. Ill, 27. Asst. ENG, Univ. Ill, 26-27; instr, WASH. UNIV, 27-40, asst. prof, 40-47, chmn. freshman Eng, acting alumni rep. & dir. alumni off, 41-44, assoc. prof, 47-67, asst. dean col. lib. arts, 44-59, assoc. dean, 59-68, prof, 67-69, EMER. PROF, 69- MLA. Contemporary usages in writing; English communication; modern composition and rhetoric. Add: 107 Coastal Highway, St. Augustine, FL 32084.

JENSEN, EJNER JACOB, b. Omaha, Nebr, Jan. 28, 37; m. 59; c. 2. ENGLISH. B.A, Carleton Col, 59; M.A, Tulane Univ, 60, Ph.D.(Eng), 65; King's Col, London, 60-61. Instr. ENG, UNIV. MICH, ANN ARBOR, 64-65, asst. prof, 65-70, ASSOC. PROF, 70- MLA; Midwest Mod. Lang. Asn; Renaissance Soc. Am. English Renaissance drama. Publ: Theme and imagery in The malcontent, Stud. Eng. Lit, 70; The wit of Renaissance satire, Philol. Quart, 72; The changing faces of love in English Renaissance drama, Comp. Drama, 73. Add: Dept. of English, University of Michigan, Ann Arbor, MI 48104.

JENSEN, HARVEY JAMES, b. Albert Lea, Minn, June 7, 33; m. 62; c. 2. ENGLISH LITERATURE. B.A, Univ. Minn, 55, M.A, 62; Ph.D.(Eng), Cornell Univ, 66. Asst. prof, Eng, IND. UNIV, BLOOMINGTON, 66-69, ASSOC. PROF. ENG. & COMP. LIT, 69- U.S.N, 55-59, Lt.(jg). MLA; Midwest Mod. Lang. Asn.(secy. Eng. lit. before 1800, 70-71, chmn, 71-72); Am. Soc. 18th Century Stud. English Restoration and 18th century literature; European 17th and 18th century cultural history; history of rhetoric, aesthetics and criticism. Publ: A glossary of John Dryden's critical terms, Univ. Minn, 69; co-ed, The satirist's art, Ind. Univ, 73; auth, Comparing the arts in the Baroque Era, 18th Century Stud, spring 73; plus others. Add: R.R. 3, Box 357, Bloomington, IN 47401.

JENSEN, J. VERNON, b. Scandia, Minn, Sept. 29, 22; m. 54; c. 2. SPEECH. B.A, Augsburg Col, 47; Univ. Ky, 43-44; Shrivenham Am. Univ, Eng, 45; M.A, Univ. Minn, 48, Ph.D.(speech & hist), 59. Instr. speech & hist, Augsburg Col, 48-51; teaching asst. hist, UNIV. MINN, MINNEAPOLIS, 51-53, instr. commun, 53-59, asst. prof. SPEECH & COMMUN, 59-64, assoc. prof, 64-67, PROF, 67-, dir. commun. prog, 70-73. Danforth Found. grant, 58-59; Fulbright lectr, State Training Col. Teachers, Rangoon, Burma, 61-62. U.S.A, 43-46. Speech Commun. Asn; AAUP; Rhetoric Soc. Am; Am. Hist. Asn; Asn. Asian Stud; NCTE; Conf. Col. Compos. & Commun. Rhetorical criticism; British and Commonwealth public speaking; Thomas Henry Huxley as a communicator. Publ: Perspectives on oral communication, Holbrook, 70; Clement R. Attlee and twentieth century parliamentary speaking, Parliamentary Affairs, London, 70; Interrelationships within the Victorian X Club, Dalhousie Rev, 72; Attempts to televise Parliament, J. Broadcasting, 72; plus others. Add: Dept. of Speech Communication, 122 Klaeber Ct, University of Minnesota, Minneapolis, MN 55455.

JENSEN, JAMES P, b. Spokane, Wash, Dec. 26, 27; m. 53; c. 2. ENGLISH. B.A, Univ. Wash, 53, M.A, 57, Ph.D.(Eng), 64. Asst. prof. ENG, CALIF. STATE COL, STANISLAUS, 61-65, assoc. prof, 65-72, PROF, 72-, chmn. dept, 64-72. U.S.A, 46-48. MLA; NCTE. Modern British literature; literary criticism; Shakespeare. Publ: The construction of Seven types of ambiguity, Mod. Lang. Quart, 9/66; Some ambiguous preliminaries, Criticism, fall 66. Add: Dept. of English, California State College, Stanislaus, 800 Monte Vista Ave, Turlock, CA 95380.

JENSON, SIDNEY LaMARR, b. Logan, Utah, Nov. 25, 38; m. 63; c. 4. ENGLISH. B.A, Utah State Univ, 63, M.A, 66; Ph.D.(Eng), Univ. Utah, 72. ASST. PROF. ENG, South. Utah State Col, 65-68; CHURCH COL. HAWAII, 71- Nat. Guard, 59-65. West. Lit. Asn. Western American literature; Mormon literature. Publ: The golden savage West of Jean Stafford, West. Am. Lit, winter 73; The compassionate seer: Wallace Stegner's literary artist, Brigham Young Univ. Stud, winter 74. Add: Dept. of English, Box 132, Church College of Hawaii, Laie, HI 96762.

JENTOFT, CLYDE WILLARD, b. Hancock, Mich, Apr. 13, 40; m. 71; c. 3. ENGLISH LITERATURE. B.A, Capital Univ, 62, fac. fel, Am. Lutheran Church, 64-65; M.A, Ohio State Univ, 64, univ. fel, 68-69, Ph.D.(Eng), 69. Instr. ENG, Capital Univ, 64-65; ASST. PROF, KENT STATE UNIV, 69-, summer res. fel, 72. MLA. Sixteenth and 17th century English poetry; classical and Renaissance rhetoric. Publ: Henryson as authentic Chaucerian: narrator, character, and courtly love in The Testament of Cresseid, Stud. Scottish Lit, 10/72; Surrey's four Orations and the influence of rhetoric on dramatic effect, Papers Lang. & Lit, summer 73. Add: Dept. of English, Kent State University, Kent, OH 44242.

JEPSEN, LAURA PAULINE, b. Clay Co, Iowa, Oct. 30, 07. COMPARATIVE LITERATURE. B.A, State Univ. Iowa, 29, M.A, 36, Ph.D.(Eng), 46. Instr. ENG, MacMurray Col. Women, 45-46; FLA. STATE UNIV, 46-47, asst. prof, 47-71, ASSOC. PROF, 71- S.Atlantic Mod. Lang. Asn; Archaeol. Inst. Am. European novel; theory of tragedy; contemporary literature. Publ: Ethical aspects of tragedy, Univ. Fla, 53 & AMS Press, 72. Add: Dept. of English, Florida State University, Tallahassee, FL 32306.

JERMAN, BERNARD ROBERT, b. Geneva, Ohio, Feb. 6, 21; div; c. 3. ENGLISH. B.A, Ohio State Univ, 46, M.A, 48, Ph.D.(Eng), 51. Instr. ENG, Univ. Ky, 51-52; Pa. State Univ, 52-55, asst. prof, 55-59, assoc. prof, 59-60; Univ. Md, 60-65; PROF, KENT STATE UNIV, 65-, chmn. grad. stud, 66-68. Fulbright-Hays lectr, Univ. Ljubljana, 71-72. U.S.A.A.F, 42-46. MLA. Nineteenth century English literature. Publ: The young Disraeli, Princeton, 60; Browning's witless duke, PMLA, 57; The production of Disraeli's trilogy, Papers Bibliog. Soc. Am, 64; The death of Robert Browning, Univ. Toronto Quart, 65; The passing of Tennyson, Acta Neophilologica, 72. Add: Dept. of English, Kent State University, Kent, OH 44242.

JERNIGAN, E. JAY, b. Emporia, Kans, Dec. 9, 35; m. 72. ENGLISH LANGUAGE & LITERATURE. B.A. & B.S, Kans. State Teachers Col, 57; M.S,

Kans. State Univ, 59, Ph.D.(Eng), 66. Teacher, high sch, Kans, 57-58; teaching asst. ENG, Univ. Nebr, Lincoln, 59-60; instr, Kans. City Jr. Col, 60-62; Kans. State Univ, 62-65; asst. prof, EAST. MICH. UNIV, 65-70, ASSOC. PROF, 70- MLA; NCTE. Nineteenth century British fiction and poetry. Publ: The forgotten serial version of George Moore's Esther Waters, Nineteenth Century Fiction, 6/68; The phoenix as thematic symbol in W.B. Yeat's Byzantium, Mich. Academician, fall 68; The bibliographical and textual complexities of George Moore's A mummer's wife, Bull. New York Pub. Libr, 6/70. Add: Dept. of English, Eastern Michigan University, Ypsilanti, MI 48197.

JERNIGAN, JACK JULIAN, b. Pensacola, Fla, Aug. 19, 23; m. 48; c. 2. ENGLISH. B.A, Miss. Col, 48; M.A, Univ. Miss, 49; Ph.D.(Eng), Vanderbilt Univ, 55. Instr. ENG, E.Miss. Jr. Col, 49-50; Columbia Mil. Acad, 52-53; asst. prof, Belmont Col, 53-55; prof, Tift Col, 55-59; La. Col, 59-65; assoc. prof, Calif. State Col. San Bernardino, 65-67; PROF, AUSTIN COL, 67- U.S.N.R, 43-46, Lt.(jg). English linguistics; literary criticism; English neo-classicism. Add: Dept. of English, Austin College, Sherman, TX 75090.

JERNIGAN, JESSE STEWART, b. Van Alstyne, Tex, Mar. 24, 12; m. 39; c. 2. ENGLISH. B.A, N.Tex. State Univ, 33; M.A, South. Methodist Univ, 46; M.A, Univ. Calif, Berkeley, 50. Instr. ENG, Okla. State Univ, 46-47; assoc, Univ. Calif, Berkeley, 51-52; instr, TEX. A&M UNIV, 52-54, asst. prof, 54-67, ASSOC. PROF, 67- Dir. NDEA Title XI Inst. Eng, 65-68. MLA; NCTE. Add: Dept. of English, Texas A&M University, College Station, TX 77843.

JEROME, JUDSON, b. Tulsa, Okla, Feb. 8, 27; m. 48; c. 5. ENGLISH. M.A, Univ. Chicago; Ph.D.(Eng), Ohio State Univ. Prof. Eng, Antioch Col, 53-73, asst. to pres, 54-55, dir. inner col, 68-69, dir. field study ctrs, Union Res. & Experimentation in Higher Educ, 68-69. Huntington Hartford Found. fel, summer 60; Amy Lowell Poetry traveling scholar, 60-61; prof, Col. Virgin Islands, 63-65; mem. staff, Bread Loaf Writer's Conf, 67-68. U.S.A.A.F, 45-46. Educational reform; modern poetry; communes. Publ: Light in the West, Golden Quill, 62; The ocean's warning to the skin diver and other love poems, 64 & Serenade (poems), 67, Crown Point Press; The fell of dark (novel), 66 & Poetry: premeditated art, 68, Houghton; Culture out of anarchy: the reconstruction of American higher learning, Herder, 70; Families of Eden, Seabury, 74; The system really isn't working, Life, 11/68; Radical premises in collegiate reform, Annals Am. Acad. Polit. & Soc. Sci, 11/72; After Illich, what?, In: After deschooling, What?, Perennial Libr, Harper, 73. Add: Downhill Farm, Hancock, MD 21750.

JESSEE, JACK W, b. Pulaski, Va, Oct. 17, 15; m. 47. ENGLISH. A.B. Emory & Henry Col, 36; M.A, George Peabody Col, 40; Ph.D, Univ. Ky, 55. Teaching fel, Univ. Ky, 49-54; instr. ENG, Emory Univ, 54-55; asst. prof, Univ. Ala, Mobile Ctr, 55-58, assoc. prof, 58-60; WEST. ILL. UNIV, 60-65, PROF, 65- U.S.N, 42-46, Res, 46-, Lt. Comdr. NCTE; MLA. Renaissance, specifically Edmund Spenser. Add: 3 Hickory Grove, Macomb, IL 61455.

JEWETT, MIKE, b. Jefferson, S.C, Nov. 4, 38; m. 64. ENGLISH LITERATURE. B.S, Appalachian State Teachers Col, 60; M.A, Univ. Ky, 67; Ph.D. (Eng), Univ. Mo-Columbia, 72. Asst. prof. ENG, NORTHWEST MO. STATE UNIV, 69-73, ASSOC. PROF, 73- Shakespeare Asn. Am. Shakespeare; 17th century poetry; Renaissance intellectual backgrounds. Add: Dept. of English, Northwest Missouri State University, Maryville, MO 64468.

JISHA, HENRY JERRY, b.Houston, Tex, Sept. 1, 32; m. 62; c. 1. SPEECH, THEATER ARTS. A.B, Univ. Houston, 54; A.M, Baylor Univ, 55; fel, Wayne State Univ, 57-60, Ph.D.(speech), 65. Instr. SPEECH, Univ. Md. Overseas Div, Tokyo, 57; UNIV. CINCINNATI, 60-65, asst. prof, 65-67, ASSOC. PROF, 67- Vis. lectr. speech, Univ. Hawaii, 70-71. U.S.A, 55-57. Speech Commun. Asn. Oral interpretation of literature; voice and articulation; public speaking. Publ: Development of imagery in interpretative reading 1890-1960, Speech Monogr, 3/66; Oral interpretation: a communication perspective, Ohio Speech J, 4/66. Add: 8539 Cavalier Dr, Cincinnati, OH 45231.

JOCHUMS, MILFORD CYRIL, b. Minonk, Ill, Feb. 23, 12; m. 42; c. 3. ENGLISH. A.B, Univ. Ill, 38, A.M, 40, Ph.D, 48. Teacher, primary sch, Ill, 33-36; high sch, 38-40; asst. ENG, Univ. Ill, 40-42, 46-48; asst. prof, ILL. STATE UNIV, 48-49, assoc. prof, 49-57, PROF, 57- U.S.A. & U.S.A.A.F, 42-46; U.S.A.F, 50-52, Capt. MLA; Shakespeare Asn. Am; Milton Soc. Am. Sixteenth and seventeenth century English literature. Publ: John Milton's An apology, a critical edition, Univ. Ill, 50; As ancient as Constantine, Stud. Eng. Lit. 1500-1900, winter 64; The legend of the voice from heaven, 2/64 & Antiquity re-invoked, 9/64, Notes & Queries; plus others. Add: 810 W. Division St, Normal, IL 61761.

JOEL, HELMUTH WULF, JR, b. Yonkers, N.Y, Dec. 13, 40; m. 64. ENGLISH LITERATURE. B.S, Dickinson Col, 62; M.A, Univ. Pa, 63, Ph.D.(Eng), 67. ASST. PROF. ENG, UNIV. R.I, 67- MLA. Eighteenth century British literature. Add: Dept. of English, University of Rhode Island, Kingston, RI 02881.

JOHANNESEN, RICHARD LEE, b. Davenport, Iowa, Aug. 14, 37. SPEECH COMMUNICATION. B.A, Augustana Col.(Ill), 59; M.A, Univ. Kans, 60, Ph.D.(speech), 64. Instr. SPEECH, Univ. Kans, 61-62; Ind. Univ, Bloomington, 64-66, asst. prof, 66-71, ASSOC. PROF, NORTH. ILL. UNIV, 71- Speech Commun. Asn.(mem. comt. freedom of speech, 64-); Cent. States Speech Asn; Nat. Soc. Stud. Commun. Contemporary theories of rhetoric; rhetorical criticism; ethical problems in communication. Publ: Ed, Ethics and persuasion, Random, 67; co-ed, Language is sermonic: Richard M. Weaver on the nature of rhetoric, La. State Univ, 70; ed, Contemporary theories of rhetoric, Harper, 71; co-ed, Contemporary American speeches, 3rd ed, Wadsworth, 72; auth, Richard Weaver's view of rhetoric and criticism, South. Speech J, winter 66; The emerging concept of communication as dialogue, Quart J. Speech, 12/71; Perspectives on ethics in persuasion, In: Persuasion: reception and responsibility, Wadsworth, 73. Add: Dept. of Speech Communication, Northern Illinois University, DeKalb, IL 60115.

JOHNSON, ALAN P, b. Norwood, Mass, Nov. 9, 31; m. 55; c. 3. ENGLISH. A.B, Amherst Col, 53; M.A, Univ. Mich, 54; univ. fel, Univ. Minn, 61-62,

Ph.D.(Eng), 67. Instr. ENG, Knox Col, 62-67; asst. prof, ARIZ. STATE UNIV, 67-72, ASSOC. PROF, 72- U.S.A, 54-56. MLA. Italian Renaissance in 19th century English literature. Publ: The Italian Renaissance and some late Victorians, Victorian Newsletter, 69; Sordello: Apollo, Bacchus, and the pattern of Italian history, Victorian Poetry, 69. Add: Dept. of English, Arizona State University, Tempe, AZ 85281.

JOHNSON, ALBERT EDWARD, b. Brooklyn, N.Y, Sept. 6, 12; m. 43. ENGLISH, SPEECH, DRAMA. A.B, Univ. Va, 34, A.M, 36; Ph.D, Cornell Univ, 48. Dir. sch. & community drama, Univ. Va, 39-42; teacher, high sch, Va, 42-46; prof. drama, Univ. Tex, 48-55, chmn. dept, summers 52, 54; prof. speech & chmn. dept, Tex. A&I Univ, 55-66; PROF. SPEECH & DRAMA, MEMPHIS STATE UNIV, 66- Ed, Va. Drama News, 39-42; drama dir, Univ. Va, summers 45 & 46. Speech Commun. Asn; Am. Theatre Asn; South. Speech Commun. Asn; Southeast. Theatre Conf. Dramatic criticism; bibliography; American theatre. Publ: Fabulous Boucicault & Greatest of Juliets, Theatre Arts; Dictionary of American drama critics, 1850-1910, Theatre Annual. Add: Dept. of Speech & Drama, Memphis State University, Memphis, TN 38152.

JOHNSON, ALICE E, b. Hartford, Conn. ENGLISH. A.B, Boston Univ, 45, M.A, 47; Ph.D.(Eng), Univ. Wis, 57. Instr. ENG, Boston Univ, 53-55; Wellesley Col, 55-58; asst. prof, CONN. COL, 58-65, assoc. prof, 65-74, PROF, 74-, ASSOC. DEAN COL, 69-, dean freshmen, 58-69. MLA; Am. Stud. Asn. Mathew Carey, 1760-1839. Add: Dept. of English, Connecticut College, New London, CT 06320.

JOHNSON, BRUCE M, b. Chicago, Ill, Apr. 29, 33; m. 57. ENGLISH. A.B, Univ. Chicago, 52; B.A, Northwest. Univ, 54, M.A, 55, Ph.D.(Eng), 59; Eli Lilly fel, Ind. Sch. Lett, summer 57. Instr. ENG, Northwest. Univ, 57-58; Univ. Mich, 58-62; asst. prof, UNIV. ROCHESTER, 62-67, ASSOC. PROF, 67- Nat. Endowment for Humanities sr. fel, 74-75. MLA. English novel, especially Joseph Conrad; modern British and American literature. Publ: Conrad's Models of mind, Univ. Minn, 71; Conrad's Karain and Lord Jim, 3/63 & Conrad's Falk: Ms. and meaning, 6/65, Mod. Lang. Quart; Heart of darkness and the problem of emptiness, Stud. Short Fiction, fall 72. Add: Dept. of English, University of Rochester, Rochester, NY 14627.

JOHNSON, CAROL VIRGINIA, b. Rockford, Ill, Sept. 7, 28. LITERATURE. B.A, Col. St. Catherine, 50; M.A, Marquette Univ, 58; M.F.A, Univ. Iowa, 59; Fulbright scholar, Bristol Univ, 61-63, Ph.D.(Eng), 63. Lectr. ENG, Univ. N.C, Greensboro, 59-60, 63-65; asst. prof, UNIV. VICTORIA, 68-69, ASSOC. PROF, 69- Modern literature. Publ: Reason's double agents, Univ. N.C, 65; John Berryman: the dream songs, Harvard Advocate, 69; Paul Valery: the art of concealment, 71 & Mrs. Wharton's profession: The reef reconnoitered, 73, Art. Int. Add: Dept. of English, University of Victoria, Victoria, B.C, Can.

JOHNSON, CHARLES EVEREST, b. Montgomery, Ala, Oct. 20, 25; m. 59; c. 4. ENGLISH. B.A, Univ. of the South, 47; Union Theol. Sem, 47-48; M.A, Univ. Ala, 50; Ph.D.(Eng), Duke Univ, 58. Instr. ENG, Duke Univ, 52-53; Newcomb Col, Tulane Univ, 53-60; assoc. prof, Radford Col, 60-61, PROF, 61-67; JACKSONVILLE STATE UNIV, 67- Danforth assoc, 64-68. U.S.N, 43-46, Lt.(jg). MLA; S.Atlantic Mod. Lang. Asn. Victorian literature; contemporary literature and theology. Publ: Browning's humor, 65 & The radical theology of William Hamilton, 66, Radford Rev. Add: Dept. of English, Jacksonville State University, Jacksonville, AL 36265.

JOHNSON, CLAUDIA DURST, b. Gastonia, N.C, Jan. 11, 38; m. 56; c. 2. AMERICAN LITERATURE. B.S, West. Ill. Univ, 59; M.A, George Peabody Col, 62; NDEA fel, Univ. Ill, 71, Ph.D.(Eng), 73. Instr. humanities, Shimer Col, 68-70; asst. ENG, Univ. Ill, Urbana, 71-72, instr, 73; ASST. PROF, UNIV. ALA, 73- MLA; Women's Caucus Mod. Lang. Nineteenth century and Puritan American literature. Publ: Hawthorne and 19th century perfectionism, Am. Lit, 2/73; Justification and Young Goodman Brown, Stud. Short Fiction. Add: Dept. of English, Morgan Hall, University of Alabama, University, AL 35486.

JOHNSON, CLIFFORD ROSS, JR, b. Alexandria, Va, May 30, 45; m. 65; c. 2. EIGHTEENTH CENTURY ENGLISH LITERATURE. A.B, Duke Univ, 66; M.A, Univ. Va, 67, Ph.D.(Eng. lit), 70. ASST. PROF. ENG, UNIV. PITTSBURGH, 70- MLA; Am. Soc. 18th Century Stud; Northeast Mod. Lang. Asn. Daniel Defoe; Jonathan Swift; Samuel Pepys. Publ: Defoe's reaction to enlightened secularism: the journal of the plague year, Enlightenment Essays, 3/74. Add: Dept. of English, University of Pittsburgh, Pittsburgh, PA 15260.

JOHNSON, DAVID MARCUS, b. River Falls, Wis, Jan. 23, 39; m. 64; c. 2. ENGLISH. B.A, St. Olaf Col, 60; M.A, Univ. Conn, 62, Ph.D.(criticism), 68; Rockefeller fel, Union Theol. Sem, 62-63. Asst. prof. ENG, UNIV. N.MEX, 65-70, ASSOC. PROF, 70- Myth; criticism; poetry. Add: Dept. of English, University of New Mexico, Albuquerque, NM 87106.

JOHNSON, DeWAYNE BURTON, b. Newman Grove, Nebr, Apr. 18, 20; m. 42; c. 3. JOURNALISM. B.A, Univ. Calif, Berkeley, 48, M.A, Los Angeles, 50; Ed.D, 55. Correspondent, United Press Asn, Tacoma, Wash, 48-49; res. assoc, Univ. Calif, Los Angeles, 51; instr. Eng, El Camino Col, 52-53; asst. prof. Eng. & dir. pub. relat, South. Ore. Col, 53-55; asst. prof. jour, San Diego State Col, 55-59; pub. relat. dir, La Mesa-Spring Valley Sch. Dist, Calif, 59-60; instr. Eng, San Diego City Col, 60; asst. prof. to PROF. JOUR. CALIF. STATE UNIV, NORTHRIDGE, 61- Copy ed, San Diego Union, 55-59; Los Angeles Times, 61-, mem. freedom of inform. comt, Sigma Delta Chi, 73- Outstanding Prof. Jour, Calif. Newspaper Publ. Asn, 73. U.S.A, 46-47. Asn. Educ. Jour. Photojournalism; future of the mass media; problems in mass communication. Publ: Historical analysis of the criticisms concerning teaching about the United Nations Educational, Scientific and Cultural Organizations in the Los Angeles city schools. Add: 10118 Aldea Ave, Northridge, CA 91324.

JOHNSON, DONALD DODGE, JR, b. Glen Ridge, N.J, Feb. 27, 37; m. 62; c. 2. ENGLISH. A.B, Princeton, 59; M.A, Univ. N.C, 64, Ph.D.(Eng), 70. Teacher Eng. & French, Milton Acad, 59-61; Eng. Haverford Sch, 60-61; instr, ST. LAWRENCE UNIV, 67-69, asst. prof, 69-73, ASSOC. PROF. ENG. & ASST. DEAN COL, 73- MLA; Mediaeval Acad. Am. Medieval English; teaching of composition. Add: Dept. of English, St. Lawrence University, Canton, NY 13617.

JOHNSON, E. BOND, III, Comparative Literature, German. See Volume III, Foreign Languages, Linguistics & Philology.

JOHNSON, ED H, b. Boulder, Colo, Sept. 21, 14; m. 38. COMMUNICATIONS. A.B, Univ. Colo, 36; M.A, Univ. Mo, 38. Asst. prof. JOUR, S.Dak. State Col, 46-48; PROF, UNIV. TULSA, 48- Mem. Am. Fed. Advert. U.S.A.A.F, 43-46. Pub. Relat. Soc. Am; Am. Acad. Advert; Am. Soc. Jour. Sch. Adminr; Int. Counc. Indust. Ed. Communication; public relations. Add: Dept. of Journalism, University of Tulsa, Tulsa, OK 74104.

JOHNSON, EDGAR, b. Brooklyn, N.Y, Dec. 1, 01; m. 33; c. 2. ENGLISH, COMPARATIVE LITERATURE. A.B, Columbia Univ, 22, 22-24, 26-27; hon. D.Litt, City Col. New York, 72. Instr, Columbia Univ, 22-24; Wash. Univ, 24-26; tutor, Hunter Col, 26-27; from tutor & instr. to prof. ENG, CITY COL. NEW YORK, 27-70, chmn. dept, 49-64, distinguished prof, 70-72, DISTINGUISHED EMER. PROF, 72- Lectr, New Sch. Social Res, 32-45; vis. assoc. prof, Vassar Col, 43; lectr, N.Y. Univ, 46-50; Carnegie vis. prof, Univ. Hawaii, 55; Fulbright sr. scholar, 56-57; Guggenheim fel, 57-58, 66-67; Frederic Ives Carpenter vis. prof, Univ. Chicago, 56; mem. Eng. lit. adv. comt, Comt. on Int. Exchange of Persons, 61-; vis. prof, Princeton, 68; Kenan distinguished vis. prof. Eng, Vanderbilt Univ, 69-70. Off, Palmes Acad, 66; Am. Heritage Biog. Award, 70. Dickens Fel.(v.pres, 72-75); fel. Royal Soc. Arts; MLA; PEN Club (v.pres, 59-61, pres, 61-63, hon. v.pres, 63-). Biography; satire; literary criticism. Publ: One mighty torrent; A treasury of satire; Charles Dickens: his tragedy and triumph; co-auth, The Dickens theatrical reader, Little, 64; auth, Sir Walter Scott: The great unknown, Macmillan, 70. Add: 320 Central Park W, New York, NY 10025.

JOHNSON, EDWARD ANDREW, b. Brooklyn, N.Y, Feb. 11, 15; m. 49. ENGLISH, AMERICAN LITERATURE. B.A, St. Francis Col.(N.Y), 36; M.A, St. John's Univ.(N.Y), 40, Ph.D, 50. Instr. hort. & bot, Brooklyn Botanic Garden, 32-38; Eng, biol. & hist, Bishop Loughlin Mem. High Sch, 36-42; PROF. ENG. LIT, ST. JOHN'S COL, ST. JOHN'S UNIV.(N.Y), 46-, GRAD. SCH, 50-, chmn. dept. Eng, 58-61. Lectr. undergrad. course, Rep. Plays of Shakespeare, closed-circuit instr. TV, 64- U.S.A, 42-46, Capt. MLA; NCTE; Shakespeare Asn. Am; Cath. Renascence Soc; Nat. Cath. Educ. Asn; AAUP; Browning Inst. Closed circuit instructional television; teacher education, especially observation of practice teaching; 19th century and medieval literature and Shakespeare. Publ: The vision of Shakespeare, St. John's Univ, 68; Poetry of Francis Thompson, Poetry of Ernest Dowson & Newman's Idea of university, In: Masterpieces of Catholic literature, Salem Press, 64. Add: Dept. of English, St. John's University, Jamaica, NY 11439.

JOHNSON, EDWARD DUDLEY HUME, b. Alton, Ohio, Nov. 29, 11; m. 47; c. 3. ENGLISH LITERATURE. A.B, Princeton, 34; Rhodes scholar, Oxford, 35-36, B.A, 36; Mitchell fel, Yale, 38-39, Ph.D, 39. Instr. ENG, PRINCETON, 39-42, asst. prof, 46-52, assoc. prof, 52-61, prof, 61-73, HOLMES PROF. BELLE-LETT RES, 73-, Freneau preceptor, 50-52, chmn. dept. Eng, 68-74. Nat. Endowment for Humanities sr. fel, 74-75. U.S.N.R, 42-46, Lt. Comdr. MLA. English Victorian literature; Victorian poetry; British painting in 18th and 19th centuries. Publ: Alien vision of Victorian poetry, Princeton, 52; ed, The world of the Victorians, Scribners, 64; ed, The poetry of earth, Atheneum, 65; auth, Charles Dickens: an introduction to his novels, Random, 69. Add: Dept. of English, 22 McCosh Hall, Princeton University, Princeton, NJ 08540.

JOHNSON, EVERETT ORVILLE, b. Straughn, Ind, Dec. 29, 11; m. 37; c. 5. SPEECH. A.B, Earlham Col, 33; A.M, Univ. Mich, 37, Ph.D, 57, Field secy, EARLHAM COL, 34-36, asst. to pres, 37-39, 43-45, instr. SPEECH, 37-42, asst. prof, 42-49, assoc. prof, 49-59, PROF, 59-, DEVELOP. ASSOC, 73-, dean men col, 45-47, dir, East. Ind. Ctr, 62-68. Teaching fel, Univ. Mich, 47-48; admin. asst. to Congressman D. W. Dennis, Ind, 69-72. Speech Commun. Asn. Rhetoric and public address; Oliver Perry Morton, Indiana's Civil War governor. Add: Alumni-Development, Earlham College, Richmond, IN 47374.

JOHNSON, FALK SIMMONS, English Linguistics. See Volume III, Foreign Languages, Linguistics & Philology.

JOHNSON, GEORGE W, b. Jamestown, N.Dak, July 5, 28; m. 55; c. 2. ENGLISH. B.A, Jameston Col, 50; M.A, Columbia Univ, 53, Ph.D.(Eng), 60. Instr. Eng, Univ. Mo, 54-56; TEMPLE UNIV, 57-61, asst. prof, 61-65, assoc. prof, 65-68, PROF. ENG. & DEAN COL. LIB. ARTS, 68- U.S.A, 51-52. NCTE; MLA; Col. Eng. Asn. American literature. Publ: Frank Norris and romance, Am. Lit, 61; Harold Frederic's young Goodman, Mod. Fiction Stud, 63; Stephen Crane's metaphor of decorum, PMLA, 63. Add: College of Liberal Arts, Temple University, Philadelphia, PA 19122.

JOHNSON, GERALD DAVID, b. Muscadine, Ala, Sept. 30, 37. ENGLISH LITERATURE, RENAISSANCE. B.A, Auburn Univ, 60; M.A, Univ. Va, 62; Ph.D.(Eng), Univ. Ala, 72. Instr. Eng, Auburn Univ, 63-64; Rollins Col, 64-66; Am. lit, Fulbright-Hayes Exchange, Denmark, 66-68; lectr. ENG, UNIV. ALA, BIRMINGHAM, 69-72, ASST. PROF, 72- Bibliog. Soc, Eng. Analytical bibliography; Renaissance drama; Shakespeare. Publ: Co-ed, Five by five: American short stories, Gyldendal, Copenhagen, 69; auth, Trollope's note on A fair quarrel, Notes & Queries, 71; The printer of Cooke's Tu Quoque, Library, 74. Add: Dept. of English, University of Alabama, University Station, Birmingham, AL 35294.

JOHNSON, GLORIA E, b. New York, N.Y, Oct. 24, 22; m. 54; c. 4. ENGLISH. B.A, Barnard Col, Columbia Univ, 44, M.A, Columbia Univ, 46, Ph.D.(Eng), 54; Fulbright fel, Univ. London, 49-51. Lectr. ENG, Barnard Col, Columbia Univ, 44-49; instr, Cornell Univ, 52-54; asst. prof, UNIV. ORE, 63-72, ASSOC. PROF, 72- MLA (Eng. Teaching Award, 70); NCTE; Am. Soc. Theatre Res; Renaissance Soc. Am. English drama and cultural history; melodrama. Publ: Shakespeare at Ashland, Shakespeare Quart, 58; Review of Waith's Ideas of greatness, Renaissance Quart, spring 73. Add: 2324 Olive St, Eugene, OR 97405.

JOHNSON, IRMGARD, b. Waverly, Iowa, Mar. 5, 16; m. 36; c. 3. HUMANITIES. B.A, Univ. Mo, 37; Ph.D.(Eng), Univ. Denver. Asst. instr. HUMANITIES, Univ. Denver, 53-54, instr, univ. community col, 54-55; asst. prof, UNIV. FLA, 55-60, assoc. prof, 60-67, PROF, 67- Summers, Univ. Fla. Grad. Sch. grant stud. nature of learning, 60, Fulbright grant, sem. on Indian civilization, 62, Rockefeller grant, alternate tour dir. Stephens Col. Asian sem, 65, Ford Found. grant, Univ. Mich. sem. on E.Asia, 67; lectr, NDEA summer inst. advan. stud. in Asian hist, July 68; past assoc. ed, J. Gen. Educ; past assoc. ed, Talisman. Nat. Asn. Gen. & Lib. Stud; Asn. Asian Stud. Peking opera in Taiwan; classical Noh drama in Japan today; Asian culture. Publ: Religion as a deterrent to learning, 69 & Mao among the classics, 73, J. Gen. Educ; The reform of Peking Opera in Taiwan, China Quart, 74; plus others. Add: 404 Little Hall, University of Florida, Gainesville, FL 32601.

JOHNSON, JAMES ROBERT, b. Rhinelander, Wis, Dec. 9, 37. SPEECH DRAMA. B.A, Wis. State Univ, Eau Claire, 59; M.A, Cornell Univ, 60, Ph.D.(speech, pub. address), 64. Instr. SPEECH, Cornell Univ, 62-63; BROOKLYN COL, 63-66, ASST. PROF, 66-, DEP. CHMN. SUMMER SESSION, DEPT. SPEECH & THEATRE, 72-, supvr. children's theatre & dir. speakers bur, 68-69. Dir. placement bur, Am. Theatre Asn, 64-65. Speech Commun. Asn; Am. Theatre Asn; Speech Asn. East. States.(2nd v. pres, 68-69); East. Forensic Asn. Rhetoric and public address; discussion and debate. Publ: Co-auth, Introduction to theatre courses, Today's Speech, 2/68. Add: Dept. of Speech & Theater, Brooklyn College, Brooklyn, NY 11201.

JOHNSON, JAMES WILLIAM, b. Birmingham, Ala, Mar. 1, 27; m. 57; c. 2. ENGLISH LITERATURE. Am. Counc. Learned Soc. fel, 49-50; A.B, Birmingham-South. Col, 50; A.M, Harvard, 50; Ph.D.(Eng), Vanderbilt Univ, 54. Instr. ENG, Vanderbilt Univ, 52-54; UNIV. ROCHESTER, 55-58, asst. prof, 58-61, assoc. prof, 61-65, PROF, 65- Fulbright scholar, U.K, 54-55; Folger Libr. fel, 63; Am. Counc. Learned Soc. fel, 66-67; Guggenheim fel, 70-71; ed. adv, Stud. in Burke & His Times, 71-73. U.S.N, 45-46. Eng. Inst; MLA; Conf. Brit. Stud. Eighteenth century English literature; Restoration literature and British novel; history of ideas. Publ: Logic and rhetoric, Macmillan, 62; The formation of English neo-classical thought, Princeton, 67; Utopian literature, Random, 68; Concepts of literature, Prentice-Hall, 71; Prose in practice, Harcourt, 72; Walpole and Burke, Stud. Burke & His Times, 70; What was neo-classicism?, 71 & Gibbon's architectural metaphor, 73, J. Brit. Stud; plus others. Add: Dept. of English, University of Rochester, Rochester, NY 14627.

JOHNSON, LEE ANN, b. Corpus Christi, Tex, May 21, 45; m. 67. AMERICAN LITERATURE. B.A, Univ. Tex, Austin, 67; M.A, Univ. Calif, Los Angeles, 68, Ph.D.(Eng), 72. ASST. PROF. ENG, MICH. STATE UNIV, 72- MLA. Nineteenth century American literature; continental fiction; novel. Publ: The relationship of The church militant to The temple, Stud, Philol, 4/71; A dog in the manger: James's depiction of Roger Lawrence in Watch and ward, Ariz. Quart, summer 73; James's Mrs. Wix: the dim, crooked reflector, Nineteenth Century Fiction, 9/74. Add: Dept. of English, Morrill Hall, Michigan State University, East Lansing, MI 48824.

JOHNSON, LEE MILFORD, b. Alexandria, Minn, Apr. 22, 44; m. 66; c. 3. ENGLISH LITERATURE. B.A, Hamline Univ, 66; Ph.D.(Eng), Princeton, 70. ASST. PROF. ENG, UNIV. B.C, 70- Prosody; Romantic poetry, 17th century poetry. Publ: Wordsworth and the sonnet, Anglistica, 73; Milton's blank verse sonnets, Milton Stud, 73. Add: Dept. of English, University of British Columbia, Vancouver 8, B.C, Can.

JOHNSON, LOLA VIDA, b. San Francisco, Calif, Apr. 28, 30. ENGLISH & AMERICAN LITERATURE. B.A, Col. Pac, 56, fel, 57-58, M.A, 59; Univ. London, summer 68. Instr. ENG, Col. Pac, 59-60; CALIF. STATE COL, STANISLAUS, 60-61, asst. prof, 61-70, ASSOC. PROF, 70-, chmn. dept, 60-62. Mem, Nat. Trust Hist. Preserv. Distinguished Teaching Award, Calif. State Univs. & Cols, 70. Nurse C, U.S.A, 52-54, 1st Lt. NCTE; Dickens Soc; AAUP. Victorian literature; 19th century American novel; English literature in transition. Add: Dept. of English & Foreign Languages, California State College, Stanislaus, 800 Monte Vista Ave, Turlock, CA 95380.

JOHNSON, LOWELL EDWARD, b. Minn, Jan. 17, 30; m. 53; c. 5. ENGLISH. B.A, St. Olaf Col, 52; M.A, Univ. Chicago, 53; Ph.D.(Middleton), Univ. Wis, 64. Instr. Eng-Am. lit, U.S. Naval Acad, 57-59; teaching asst. to freshmen, mod. lit, Univ. Wis, 59-62; asst. prof. RENAISSANCE, ST. OLAF COL, 63-67, ASSOC. PROF, 67-, humanities res. grant, 68. U.S.N, 53-59, Res, 60-, Comdr. MLA; Shakespeare Asn. Am; AAUP. Shakespeare; Jacobean drama; 16th century English literature. Publ: A liturgical drama, 66 & On the origins of modern drama, 67, Response; co-auth, Intelligence organizations, In: Intelligence for naval officers, Bur. Naval Personnel, 68. Add: Dept. of English, St. Olaf College, Northfield, MN 55057.

JOHNSON, LUCILLE MARGUERITE, b. Hatton, N.Dak, Apr. 3, 19; m. 48. ENGLISH LITERATURE, RHETORIC. B.A, Concordia Col.(Moorhead, Minn), 40; M.A, Wash. State Univ, 43; Univ. Colo, Boulder, 45 & 57; Univ. Wash, 47; Univ. Oslo, 48; Stanford Univ, 63; Ed.D.(rhetoric & hist. & philos. of educ), Univ. Mont, 67. Teaching fel. Eng. compos, Wash. State Univ, 41-43; chmn. dept. ENG, Austin Col.(Minn), 43-46; asst. prof, Ohio Univ, 46-48; Univ. Wash, 48-50; chmn. dept, Centralia Col, 50-53; assoc. prof, PAC. LUTHERAN UNIV, 53-67, PROF. & CHMN. DEPT, 67- Consult, Teacher Educ. Liaison Comt, Wash, 69-72. Am. Asn. Univ. Women; MLA; NCTE (Conf. Eng. Educ); Conf. Col. Compos. & Commun. Chauceriana, Canadian literature. Publ: The inner life of Henry Vaughan as revealed in his religious verse, Wash. State Univ, 43; A Neo-Aristotelian study of resources and qualities of descriptive writing, Univ. Mont, 67; Teach them, 47 & The World's slow stain, 47, Lutheran Herald. Add: Dept. of English, Pacific Lutheran University, Park Ave, Tacoma, WA 98447.

JOHNSON, MANLY, b. Gardner, Kans, Dec. 23, 20; m. 44; c. 2. ENGLISH. B.A, Univ. Mich, 46; M.A, Hopkins Univ, 50; Fulbright scholar, Univ. London, 53-54; Ph.D.(Am. stud), Univ. Minn, 57. Instr. ENG, Williams Col, 50-53, 54-55; Univ. Mich, 57-58; asst. prof, UNIV. TULSA, 58-63, assoc. prof, 63-68, PROF, 68-, dir. grad. stud, 66-69. U.S.A, 43-45. MLA; Am. Stud. Asn. Modern poetry; the novel. Publ: Virginia Woolf, Ungar, 73. Add: Dept. of English, University of Tulsa, Tulsa, OK 74104.

JOHNSON, MARY ELIZABETH, b. Powhatan Point, Ohio, Mar. 10, 05. SPEECH. A.B, Muskingum Col, 26; A.M, Univ. Mich, 33; Univ. Pittsburgh, 36; Ohio State Univ, summer, 47, 61, winter, 68; Northwest. Univ, 56, 60. Teacher Eng. & head dept, high sch, W.Va, 26-37, dean girls, 35-37; head dept, Eng, Ohio, 37-44; assoc. prof. speech, Muskingum Col, 44-72, chmn. dept. commun, 50-53, acting chmn. dept. speech, 65-67; RETIRED. Mem, Comp. Educ. Soc. Sem. & Field Stud, E.Europe, 67. Am. Speech & Hear. Asn; Alexander Graham Bell Asn. Deaf; AAUP. Speech correction; interpretation; general speech. Add: 174 Montgomery Blvd, New Concord, OH 43762.

JOHNSON, MARY LYNCH, b. Greensboro, N.C, May 13, 97. OLD ENGLISH. A.B, Meredith Col, 17; A.M, Columbia Univ, 21; Ph.D, Cornell Univ, 27; L.H.D, Wake Forest Col, 57. Instr. ENG, MEREDITH COL, 18-21, assoc. prof, 21-47, prof. & head dept, 47-69, EMER. PROF, 69-, COL. HISTORIAN, 71- Browning Prize, Cornell Univ, 26. Col. Eng. Asn; MLA. Publ: Elizabeth Avery Colton, Am. Asn. Univ. Women, N.C. Div; History of Meredith College, rev. ed, Meredith Col, 72. Add: 1906 Smallwood Dr, Raleigh, NC 27605.

JOHNSON, MARY LYNN, b. Corpus Christi, Tex, Sept. 28, 37; m. 74. ENGLISH. B.A, Univ. South. Miss, 56; M.A, Tulane Univ, 58, Ph.D.(Eng), 62. Instr. ENG, Delta State Col, 60; La. State Univ, Baton Rouge, 60-62; from instr. to asst. prof, Univ. Ill, Urbana, 62-69; ASSOC. PROF, GA. STATE UNIV, 69- MLA; AAUP. English Romantic poetry. Publ: Wordsworth's symbolic vale, Stud. Romanticism, 68; Beulah . . . and Blake's Thel, J. Eng. & Ger. Philol, 70; Emblem and symbol in Blake, Huntington Libr. Quart, 74. Add: Dept. of English, Georgia State University, Atlanta, GA 30303.

JOHNSON, MAURICE O, b. Rosemont, Nebr, July 18, 13; m. 45; c. 4. ENGLISH LITERATURE. A.B, Univ. Nebr, 35, A.M, 36; Ph.D, Columbia Univ, 49. Instr, Univ. Nebr, 36-38; Carnegie Inst. Technol, 39-42; asst. prof, Syracuse Univ, 48-50; vis. asst. prof. ENG. LIT, UNIV. PA, 50-51, asst. prof, 51-53, assoc. prof, 53-62, PROF, 62-, grad. chmn. Eng, 62-65. Adv. ed, Satire Newslettr, 64- U.S.A, 42-46, Sgt. MLA. Augustan prose fiction; late 17th century and early 18th century English literature; satire. Publ: Walt Whitman as a critic of literature, Univ. Nebr, 38; Sin of wit: Jonathan Swift as a poet, Syracuse Univ, 50; Fielding's art of fiction: eleven essays, Univ. Pa, 61; contrib, Swift's poetry reconsidered, In: English writers of the eighteenth century, Columbia Univ, 71; auth, Text and possible occasion for Swift's Day of judgement, PMLA 3/71; A note on Swift's Meditation on a broom-stick and A tale of a tub, Libr. Chronicle, spring 71. Add: Dept. of English, University of Pennsylvania, Philadelphia, PA 19104.

JOHNSON, MICHAEL LILLARD, b. Springfield, Mo, June 29, 43; m. 65. ENGLISH. B.A, Rice Univ, 65, Ph.D.(Eng), 68; M.A, Stanford Univ, 67. Lectr. ENG, Rice Univ, 68-69; asst. prof, UNIV. KANS, 69-72; ASSOC. PROF, 72- New journalism; lyric poetry; technology and literature. Publ: The new journalism, Univ. Kans, 71. Add: Dept. of English, University of Kansas, Lawrence, KS 66045.

JOHNSON, RAOUL FENTON, b. Nashville, Tenn, Jan. 2, 36; m. 57; c. 3. DRAMA. B.A, Austin Peay State Col, 57; M.A, Univ. Ill, 59, Ph.D.(drama), 65. Asst. prof. drama, Univ. Ga, 61-66; Univ. Ill, Chicago, 66-70; ASSOC. PROF. DRAMA, TECH. DIR. & DESIGNER, LOYOLA UNIV. CHICAGO, 70- U.S. Inst. Theatre Technol; Am. Theatre Asn. Scenic design for theatre; theatre architecture; stage machinery. Add: Dept. of Theatre, Loyola University of Chicago, 6525 N. Sheridan Rd, Chicago, IL 60626.

JOHNSON, RICHARD AUGUST, b. Washington, D.C, Apr. 18, 37; m. 60; c. 2. ENGLISH, AMERICAN STUDIES. B.A, Swarthmore Col, 59; Woodrow Wilson fel, Yale, 59-60; Ph.D.(Eng), Cornell Univ, 65. Instr. ENG, Univ. Va, 63-65; asst. prof, MT. HOLYOKE COL, 65-71, assoc. prof, 71-74, PROF. & CHMN. DEPT, 74- MLA. Modern literature; American literature; criticism. Publ: Man's place, an essay on Auden, Cornell Univ, 73; Auden's architecture of humanism, Va. Quart, 72; Auden and the art of clarification, Yale Rev, 73. Add: Dept. of English, Mt. Holyoke College, South Hadley, MA 01075.

JOHNSON, RICHARD BYRON, b. Pocatello, Idaho, July 23, 34; m. 58; c. 6. THEATRE, DRAMATIC LITERATURE. B.A, Idaho State Univ, 59; Long Beach State Col, summer 60; M.F.A, Ohio Univ, 62; Fulbright Hays fel. in Finland, South. Ill. Univ, Carbondale, 67-68, Ph.D.(theatre, speech), 70. Instr. & dir. speech & drama, Twin Falls Sr. High Sch, 59-61; instr, tech. dir. & designer, R.I. Col, 62-64; instr. play directing & speech, South. Ill. Univ, 66-67; asst. prof. oral interpretation & dir. reader's theatre, State Univ. N.Y. Col. Oneonta, 68-70; ASST. PROF. THEATRE, DIRECTING & DRAMATIC LIT, GA. SOUTH. COL, 70-, DIR. THEATRE, 71-, tech. dir, 70-71. Co-dir, Inst. Finnish Teachers Eng, Finnish-Am. Soc. & State Univ. N.Y. Col. Oneonta, summer 70. Am. Theatre Asn; Speech Commun. Asn; Southeast. Theatre Conf; South. Speech Commun. Asn. Drama of Aleksis Kivi and Finland; reader's theatre; play directing. Publ: Esko on Oppinut Englantia, Juhlaviesti, 12/67. Add: Dept. of Speech & Drama, Landrum Box 8091, Georgia Southern College, Statesboro, GA 30458.

JOHNSON, ROBERT CARL, b. Chicago, Ill, May 8, 38; m. 59; c. 2. ENGLISH. B.A, Monmouth Col.(Ill), 59; M.A, Univ. Ill, 60, Ph.D.(Eng), 64. Asst. prof. ENG, MIAMI UNIV, 64-69, assoc. prof, 69-73, PROF, 73- MLA; NCTE; Shakespeare Asn. Am; Renaissance Soc. Am; Midwest Mod. Lang. Asn.(chmn. bibliog. sect, 73). Renaissance drama; Shakespeare; textual and descriptive bibliography. Publ: Christopher Marlowe, 1946-1965, 68, Minor Elizabethans: Elizabethan bibliographies supplements, 68 & Greene, Lodge, Lyly, Nashe, Peele: Elizabethan bibliographies supplements, 68, Nether Press; John Heywood, Twayne, 70; Roderigo, that poor trash of Venice, Univ. Rev, 69; Audience involvement in the Tudor interlude, 70 & Stage directions in the Tudor interlude, 71, Theatre Notebk. Add: Dept. of English, Miami University, Oxford, OH 45056.

JOHNSON, ROBERT EUGENE, b. Springfield, Ohio, Dec. 19, 26; m. 51. DRAMA, DRAMATIC LITERATURE. B.S, Ohio State Univ, 49, M.A, 50; Ind. Univ, 54-58. Chmn. speech & drama, St. Bernard High Sch, Ohio, 50-54; teaching assoc. speech & theatre, Ind. Univ, 54-58; ASSOC. PROF.

THEATRE ARTS, & CHMN. DIV, MURRAY STATE UNIV, 58- Managing dir. Kenlake Summer Amphitheatre, Hardin, Ky, 67- U.S.N.R, 44-46. Am. Theatre Asn; Children's Theatre Conf; Am. Nat. Theatre & Acad; Southeast. Theatre Conf. Directing theatre productions with regard to historical period, social customs, costumes and setting. Add: Dept. of Theatre Arts, Murray State University, Murray, KY 42071.

JOHNSON, ROBERT GARRETT, b. Mount Harris, Colo, Sept. 27, 20; m. 47; c. 1. SPEECH, DRAMA. A.B, Brigham Young Univ, 42; B.S, U.S. Merchant Marine Acad, 45; M.A, Columbia Univ, 50; Ph.D.(commun. methodology), Denver Univ, 63. Teacher, high sch, Va, 50-54; Colo, 55-58; asst. prof. speech, WAYNE STATE COL, 58-62, assoc. prof, 63-65, PROF. SPEECH & HEAD DEPT. COMMUN. ARTS, 66-, dir, Danish Exchange Prog, 72. Curriculum specialist Title III prog, 67; exchange prof, Denmark, 69. Award, Wayne State Found, 68. U.S. Merchant Marine, 43-47. Int. Soc. Gen. Semantics; Inst. Gen. Semantics; Speech Commun. Asn; Cent. States Speech Commun. Asn. General semantics; communication and methodology; fine arts curriculum. Add: Faculty Apt. A, Wayne State College, Wayne, NE 68787.

JOHNSON, ROBERT GORDON, b. Jersey City, N.J, Aug. 7, 36; m. 63; c. 2. AMERICAN LITERATURE. B.S, St. Peter's Col, 60; M.A, Purdue Univ, W.Lafayette, 63; fel, Bowling Green State Univ, 68-71, Ph.D.(Am. lit), 71. Instr. ENG, Univ. Victoria, 63-65; Big Bend Community Col, 66-68; ASSOC. PROF, INDIANA UNIV. PA, 71- Pa. State grant, summer 73. U.S.A, 54-56. MLA; AAUP; NEA; Nat. Fac. Asn. Community & Jr. Cols. The genre of the novel; American literature; modern fiction. Publ: Co-auth, Criticism of Ford Madox Ford: a select checklist, Mod. Fiction Stud, summer 63; auth, The Daedalus myth in Joyce's A portrait of the artist as a young man, Stud. Humanities, 6/73. Add: Dept. of English, Indiana University of Pennsylvania, Armstrong Ctr, Kittanning, PA 16201.

JOHNSON, ROBERT OWEN, b. Englewood, N.J, July 16, 26; m. 52; c. 2. ENGLISH. A.B, Yale, 50; B.S, U.S. Merchant Marine Acad, N.Y, 50; M.A, Univ. Wash, 55, Ph.D.(Eng), 64. Instr. ENG. WASH. STATE UNIV, 57-65, asst. prof, 65-71, ASSOC. PROF, 71- U.S.N, 50-53, Res, 53-, Lt. Comdr. Philol. Asn. Pac. Coast; Rocky Mountain Mod. Lang. Asn; Am. Stud. Asn. Pac. Northwest (pres, 72-); Am. Stud. Asn. Contemporary fiction; contemporary drama; New Yorker magazine. Publ: An index to literature in The New Yorker (3 vols), 69-71 & An index to profiles in The New Yorker, 72, Scarecrow; Mr. Marquand and Lord Tennyson, 3/64 & Mary Monahan: Marquand's sentimental slip?, 12/65, Res. Stud; Hemingway's How do you like it now, gentlemen?: a possible source, Am. Lit, 3/73. Add: Dept. of English, Washington State University, Pullman, WA 99163.

JOHNSON, ROBERTA LEE, Peninsular Spanish & Comparative Literature. See Volume III, Foreign Languages, Linguistics & Philology.

JOHNSON, ROGER BARTON, JR, Comparative Literature, German. See Volume III, Foreign Languages, Linguistics & Philology.

JOHNSON, RONALD CONANT, b. Joliet, Ill, Dec. 14, 30; m. 55; c. 3. ENGLISH. B.A, Univ. Ill, 52, M.A, 57, Ph.D.(Eng), 64. Instr. ENG, Iowa State Col, 56-58; asst, Univ. Ill, 58-64; ASST. PROF, UNIV. B.C, 64- U.S.N, 52-55, Lt.(jg). MLA. Mid-sixteenth century poetry; non-Shakespearean sixteenth century drama. Publ: George Gascoigne, Twayne, 72. Add: Dept. of English, University of British Columbia, Vancouver, 8, B.C, Can.

JOHNSON, RUE CORBETT, b. Bancroft, Idaho, May 3, 27; m. 52; c. 5. SPEECH & THEATRE, COMPARATIVE LITERATURE. B.A, Brigham Young Univ, 53, M.A, 54; Ph.D.(speech & theatre), Ind. Univ, 67. Teaching asst. pub. speaking, Brigham Young Univ, 53-54; prin. & instr. New Testament & church hist, Dept. Educ, Church of Jesus Christ of Latter-day Saints, 54-55; instr. speech & theatre, Ricks Col, 55-57; lectr, Ind. Univ. Ft. Wayne, 59-66, asst. to dean, 64-66, asst. prof. & asst. dean Ft. Wayne Campus, 66-73; PROF. SPEECH & THEATRE & CAMPUS DEAN, UNIV. WIS-FOX VALLEY CTR, 73- Consult. higher educ. coord, Ala. Comn. Higher Educ, summer 72. U.S.A.F, 46-48. Speech Commun. Asn; Am. Theatre Asn. American theatre history; dramatic literature; theatre aesthetics. Publ: Theatre in Zion: the Brigham City Dramatic Association, Utah Hist. Quart, 65. Add: Office of the Dean, University of Wisconsin-Fox Valley Center, Menasha, WI 54952.

JOHNSON, SAMUEL FREDERICK, b. Pittsburgh, Pa, July 22, 18. ENGLISH LITERATURE. A.B, Haverford Col, 40; A.M, Harvard, 41, Ph.D, 48. Tutor ENG, Harvard, 46-48, instr, 48-49; asst. prof, N.Y. Univ, 49-54; COLUMBIA UNIV, 54-57, assoc. prof, 57-66, PROF, 66- Guggenheim fel, 54-55; assoc. ed, Renaissance Quart, 67-; Huntington Libr. summer res. grant, 72. U.S.A, 42-46. Eng. Inst; MLA; Renaissance Soc. Am; Shakespeare Asn. Am; Malone Soc. Elizabethan drama. Publ: Ed, Julius Caesar, In: Pelican Shakespeare, Penguin, 60, rev. ed, 71; auth, Regeneration of Hamlet, Shakespeare Quart; Critics and criticism: a discussion, J. Aesthet. & Art Criticism. Add: 618 Philosophy Hall, Columbia University, New York, NY 10027.

JOHNSON, STANLEY LEWIS, b. Garland, Utah, Oct. 6, 20. ENGLISH. B.A, Univ. Utah, 42; Ph.D.(Eng), Univ. South. Calif, 55. From instr. to asst. prof. ENG, PORTLAND STATE UNIV, 50-70, ASSOC. PROF, 70- U.S.A, 42-45. Contemporary American literature; English novel; continental novel. Publ: The contemporary American novel; co-ed, The dramatic experience; co-auth, The play and the reader, Prentice-Hall, 66; co-ed, Discovery and response: the strategies of fiction, Winthrop, 72; Thomas Wolfe and the northwest, Northwest Mag, 4/73. Add: 2222 N.W. Johnson St, Portland, OR 97210.

JOHNSON, THOMAS H, b. Bradford, Vt, Apr. 27, 02; m. 34; c. 2. ENGLISH. A.B, Williams Col, 26, L.H.D, 49; A.M, Harvard, 29, Ph.D, 34; hon. Litt.D, Marlboro Col, 55, Rutgers Univ, 56, Middlebury Col, 67. Instr. ENG, Rutgers Univ, 28-29; Williams Col, 29-31; teacher, Lawrenceville Sch, 37-72, chmn. dept, 44-67; RETIRED. Lectr, New Sch. Soc. Res, 43-44; Guggenheim vis. prof. Am. lit, Univ. Copenhagen, 51-52; vis. prof, Univ. Pa, 58-59; Berg prof, N.Y. Univ, 59-60; summers, lectr, Rutgers Univ, 30-32, State Univ. Iowa, 36, Chautauqua Univ, 37, Columbia Univ, 48, Harvard, 50. Fel. Soc. Am. Hist; Am. Stud. Asn; Bibliog. Soc. Am; MLA; Grolier Club. Publ: Ed, Poetical works of Edward Taylor, Princeton, 39; co-ed, Literary history of the United States, 48; Poems of Emily Dickinson (3 vols), 55; ed, The letters of Emily Dickinson (3 vols), Harvard, 58; Oxford companion to American history, Oxford, 67. Add: Lawrenceville, NJ 08648.

JOHNSON, VERNON E, b. Baskin, La, Nov. 19, 21; m. 58; c. 2. AMERICAN & DRAMATIC LITERATURE. B.A, George Peabody Col, 48, M.A, 49, Ph.D, 62; Danforth Found. grant, summer 60. Instr, Lander Col, 53-56; Huron Col, 56-57; asst. prof. Eng, West. Ill. Univ, 57-63; assoc. prof, Paterson State Col, 63-64; Eng. & theatre, Tenn. Technol. Univ, 64-65; Eng, Eastern Ill. Univ, 65-67; humanities, Shimer Col, 67-70; prof. Eng, Olivet Col, 70-73; RES. & WRITING, 73- U.S.A.A.F, 42-45. MLA. American literature; dramatic literature. Add: 3302 Loop Rd, Tuscaloosa, AL 34501.

JOHNSON, WENDELL STACY, b. Kansas City, Mo, Dec. 27, 27. ENGLISH. B.A, Univ. Mo, 48; M.A, Ohio State Univ, 49, Ph.D.(Eng), 52; Fulbright award, Univ. London, 52. Instr. ENG, Smith Col, 52-56, asst. prof, 56-61, assoc. prof, 61-62; HUNTER COL, 62-68, PROF, 68-, assoc. dean grad. stud, 66-68. Am. Counc. Learned Soc. grant-in-aid, 61; Elizabeth Howald fel, 61-62, assoc. ed, Victorian Poetry, 62-; Guggenheim fel, 65-66. MLA. Victorian poetry; romantic poetry; the religious lyric. Publ: Voices of Matthew Arnold, Yale, 61; co-auth, Introduction to literary criticism, Heath, 62; A poetry anthology, Random, 68; auth, Gerard Manley Hopkins; the poet as Victorian, Cornell Univ, 68; Words, things and celebrations, Harcourt, 72; Imagery and diction of the pearl, J. Eng. Lit. Hist; Parallel imagery in Arnold and Clough, Eng. Stud, 2/56; Browning's music, J. Aesthet, winter 63. Add: 360 E. 72nd St, New York, NY 10021.

JOHNSTON, ALBERT S, JR, b. Smithfield, N.C, Dec. 16, 20; m. 54; c. 3. ENGLISH. A.B, Univ. N.C, 41; M.A, Univ. Fla, 48, Ph.D.(Eng), 51. Teacher, pub. schs, N.C, 41-42; instr. ENG, Univ. Fla, 46-48; prof. & acting head dept, Georgetown Col, 50-54; PROF, FLORENCE STATE UNIV, 54-, CHMN. DIV. LANG. & LIT, 73-, chmn. dept. Eng. & mod. for. lang, 58-73. U.S.A.F, 42-46, S/Sgt. S.Atlantic Mod. Lang. Asn. Seventeenth century English literature; Shakespeare; complete plays of William D'Avenant. Add: Div. of Language & Literature, Florence State University, Florence, AL 35630.

JOHNSTON, EDNA LONG, b. Bristol, Fla, May 11, 21; m. 53; c. 3. ENGLISH. A.B, Atlantic Christian Col, 40; A.M, E.Carolina Col, 53; Univ. N.C, 62, 63, 67, 68. Instr. Eng. & Romance Lang, ATLANTIC CHRISTIAN COL, 53-54, asst. prof. ENG, 54-64, ASSOC. PROF, 64- NCTE; MLA; S.Atlantic Mod. Lang. Asn. British Romantic period; British and American literature of the 20th century. Add: Dept. of English, Atlantic Christian College, Wilson, NC 27893.

JOHNSTON, GEORGE BURKE, b. Tuscaloosa, Ala, Sept. 8, 07; m. 36; c. 4. ENGLISH LITERATURE. A.B, Univ. Ala, 29; A.M, Columbia Univ, 30, fel, 39-40, Ph.D, 43. Instr. Eng, Va. Polytech. Inst, 30-33; Univ. Ala, 35-41, asst. prof, 41-46, assoc. prof. & asst. dean, 46-50, prof. & asst. dean arts & sci, 50; dean arts & sci, VA. POLYTECH. INST. & STATE UNIV, 50-65, PROF. ENG, 65- U.S.A, 41-45, Lt. Col. MLA. English literature of the Renaissance. Ben Jonson, poet; ed, Poems of Ben Jonson. Add: Virginia Polytechnic Institute & State University, Blacksburg, VA 24061.

JOHNSTON, JOHN H, b. Norfolk, Va, Jan. 18, 21; m. 48; c. 7. ENGLISH. B.A, 47; M.A, Univ. Chicago, 50; Ph.D, Univ. Wis, 60. Instr. ENG, W.VA. UNIV, 54-56, 57-60, asst. prof, 60-64, ASSOC. PROF, 64- South. Fel. Fund fel, 56-57. U.S.A, 43-45. MLA; NCTE. English poetry of World War I; Georgian poetry; British poetry, 1920-1939. Publ: English poetry of the first World War, Princeton, 64; Charles Sorley's Bright promise, W.Va. Univ. Philol. Papers, 12/61; David Jones: the heroic vision, Rev. Politics, 1/62. Add: 306 Armstrong Hall, West Virginia University, Morgantown, WV 26506.

JOHNSTON, KENNETH R, b. Marquette, Mich, Apr. 20, 38; m. 61; c. 3. ENGLISH. B.A, Augustana Col.(Ill), 59; Rockefeller Bros. fel. & M.A, Univ. Chicago, 61; Danforth Found. fel. & A.M, Yale, 62, Ph.D.(Eng), 66. Instr. ENG, Augustana Col.(Ill), 62-63; asst. prof, IND. UNIV, BLOOMINGTON, 66-70, ASSOC. PROF, 70-, ASSOC. DEAN COL. ARTS & SCI, 73-, dir. undergrad. stud, 68-70. MLA; Keats-Shelley Asn. English and American romantic poetry; Wordsworth; teaching of English. Publ: Ed, The rhetoric of conflict, Bobbs, 69; contrib, Blake's visionary forms dramatic, Princeton, 70; contrib, New perspectives on Coleridge and Wordsworth, Columbia Univ, 72; Wordsworth's Home at Grasmere': reclusive song, Stud. Romanticism, 75. Add: Dept. of English, Indiana University, Bloomington, IN 47401.

JOHNSTON, ROBERT A, b. Lincoln, Nebr, July 23, 19; div; c. 2. DRAMA. A.B, Univ. Nebr, 39, M.A, 40; Carnegie Inst. Technol, summer 39; Ph.D. (theater), Northwest. Univ, 51. Asst. instr. THEATER, Univ. Nebr, 39-40; instr, Morgan Park Jr. Col, 40-42; CITY COLS. CHICAGO, Wright Campus, 47-62, PROF, 62-66, LOOP CAMPUS, 66- U.S.A, 42-46, Capt. Am. Nat. Theatre & Acad; Am. Theatre Asn. Publ: The Oresteia, an acting version, 56, 63 & The theater of Belize, 73, Christopher House; co-auth, Great Christian plays, Seabury, 57,& Improve your speech, Cefalu, 63. Add: Dept. of Drama, City Colleges of Chicago, 180 N. Michigan Ave, Chicago, IL 60601.

JOHNSTON, WILMA MONTGOMERY, b. Kaplan, La, Dec. 11, 04; m. 31. ENGLISH. B.A, La. State Univ, 28, M.A, 39. Instr. ENG, LA. STATE UNIV, 41-45, 47-66, asst. prof, 66-70, dir. writing lab, 60-70; RETIRED. Consult. lang, Justice Supreme Court, La, 63-64. NCTE; S.Cent. Mod. Lang. Asn; AAUP. Language and current American usage; composition. Add: 333 Louisiana State University Ave, Baton Rouge, LA 70808.

JOHNSTONE, CORAGREENE, b. Knoxville, Tenn, Sept. 26, 08. ENGLISH. A.B, Talladega Col, 32; M.A, Univ. Mich, 35, Ph.D, 52; Gen. Educ. Bd. fel, 40-41, 49-50. Instr. ENG, Tillotson Col, 35-36; Bennett Col, 36-40, 41-43; Spelman Col, 45-47, 48-54; assoc. prof, Ga. State Col, 47-48; Fisk Univ, 54-57; Dillard Univ, 57-60; prof. & chmn. dept, Elizabeth City State Teachers Col, 60-64; PROF, CHEYNEY STATE COL, 64-, DIR, DIV. HUMAN-

ITIES, 70- Carnegie Fund grant, summer, 53; NDEA Eng. Inst, S.C. State Col, summers 65-66. NCTE; MLA; Col. Lang. Asn; Int. Soc. Gen. Semantics; Ling. Soc. Am. Eighteenth century English literature. Add: Division of Humanities, Cheyney State College, Cheyney, PA 19319.

JOHNSTONE, JOHN KEITH, b. Ferintosh, Alta, Feb. 12, 23; m. 52; c. 4. ENGLISH LITERATURE. B.A, Univ. Alta, 48, M.A, 50; Imp. Order, Daughters of the Empire scholar, Univ. Leeds, 50-52, Ph.D. (Eng. lit), 52. Instr. Eng. & humanities, Col. Gen. Educ, Boston Univ, 53-55, asst. prof, 55-57, assoc. prof. ENG, Univ. N.B, 57-62, PROF, 62-67; UNIV. SASK, 67-, CHMN. DEPT, 69-, chmn, Fac. Asn, 73-74. Fel. Royal Soc. Lit. U.K; Can. Counc. & Nuffield Found. grants, 66. Can. Asn. Univ. Teachers; Asn. Can. Univ. Teachers Eng; MLA. Student travel, 20th century English literature; English novel. Publ: Bloomsbury group, Secker & Warburg, London & Noonday, 54; World War I and the novels of Virginia Woolf, In: Promise of greatness: the war of 1914-1918, Day, 68; E.M. Forster, In: The politics of twentieth-century novelists, Hawthorn, 71. Add: Dept. of English, University of Saskatchewan, Saskatoon, Sask. S7N 0W0, Can.

JOLLIFFE, HAROLD RICHARD, b. Winnipeg, Man, Feb. 26, 04; nat; m. 36. JOURNALISM. B.A, Queen's Univ, Can, 24; fel, Univ. Chicago, 26-27, 33-34, Ph.D, 36. Master classics, Albert Col, 24-26; lectr, Brandon Col, 27-28; spec. lectr, Victoria Col, Univ. Toronto, 28-29; reporter, feature writer & ed, Toronto Daily Star, 29-32; lectr, Tulane Univ, 35-36; mgt. res, West. Electric Co, 36-37; asst. prof. class. lang, Ohio Univ, 37-46, assoc. prof, 46-47; jour, Ohio State Univ, 47-49; prof, MICH. STATE UNIV, 49-69, EMER. PROF. JOUR, 69- Copy ed, Detroit Free Press, summers 45-58 & world desk, Wash. Post, 59; Smith-Mundt exchange prof, Afghanistan, 60. History of 16th century science; reviewing and criticism; semantics. Publ: Critical methods and influence of Bentley's Horace, Univ. Chicago, 39; Basics of journalism (in Persian), Royal Afghan Dept. Press, 61; Tales from the Greek drama, Chilton, 62; co-auth, English translation and commentary on Agricola's Bermannus (1530), Chamber Mines, Johannesburg. Add: 1274 Fairway Dr, Dunedin, FL 33528.

JONES, ALAN KENT, b. San Angelo, Tex, Apr. 19, 37. ENGLISH. B.A, Tex. Technol. Col, 60, NDEA fel, 60-63, M.A, 62, Ph.D.(Eng), 68. Instr. ENG, Southeast Mo. State Col, 63-65; Tex. Technol. Col, 65-67; asst. prof, Southeast Mo. State Col, 67-68, ASSOC. PROF, 68-69; SAM HOUSTON STATE UNIV, 69- Add: Dept. of English, Sam Houston State University, Huntsville, TX 77340.

JONES, ALEXANDER ELVIN, b. Independence, Mo, Oct. 11, 20; m. 46; c. 2. ENGLISH. A.B, DePauw Univ, 42, LL.D, 64; M.A, Univ. Minn, 49, Ph.D. (Eng), 50; LL.D, Univ. Ark, 67; hon. L.H.D, Ind. Cent. Col, 70. Instr. ENG, Univ. Minn, 49-50; Univ. Ark, 50-52, asst. prof, 52-55, assoc. prof, 55-56; MacMurray Col. Women, 56-59; PROF, BUTLER UNIV, 59-, PRES, 63-, dean col. lib. arts & sci, 59-63. Chmn. bd, Independent Cols. & Univs. Ind, Inc, 72- U.S.N.R, 42-45. MLA; Am. Lit. Group; Col. Eng. Asn; NCTE. Mark Twain; American literature; creative writing. Publ: Mark Twain and sexuality; Creative exposition; co-auth, Writing good prose, Scribner, 61, 2nd ed, 68, 3rd ed, 71. Add: Butler University, Indianapolis, IN 46208.

JONES, ANDREW MELVIN, b. McCool, Miss, Mar. 10, 32; m. 59; c. 2. SPEECH. A.B, Miss. Col, 52; M.A, Miss. South. Col, 54; South. Baptist Theol. Sem, 54-55; Ed.D, Univ. Miss, 69. Teacher, French Camp Acad, Miss, 52-53, teacher & prin, 55-57; speech therapist, Letterman Army Hospital, 57-58; teacher, Weir High Sch, Miss, 58; instr. educ, Univ. Miss, 58-59; SPEECH, Miss. State Col. Women, 59-62, asst. prof, 62-69; ASSOC. PROF, DELTA STATE COL, 69- Vis. instr. speech & educ, Miss. State Univ, summers 60-62. U.S.A, 57-58. Speech Commun. Asn; South. Speech Commun. Asn; NEA. Communication; education; mathematics. Publ: A course in Communication and its evaluation, Miss. South. Col, 54; Better Restroom care (film), Univ. Miss, 68; A survey of industrial enterprises in Mississippi to ascertain the desirability of offering fundamental training courses through the media of television to upgrade employees, Univ. Microfilms, 69. Add: Dept. of Speech, Delta State College, Cleveland, MS 38732.

JONES, ARCHIE H, American History & Literature. See Volume I, History.

JONES, ARTHUR E, JR, b. Orange, N.J, Mar. 20, 18; m. 43; c. 1. ENGLISH, LIBRARIANSHIP. A.B, Univ. Rochester, 39; M.A, Syracuse Univ, 41, Ph.D. (Eng), 50; M.L.S, Rutgers Univ, 64. Instr. ENG, Syracuse Univ, 46-49; DREW UNIV, 49-51, asst. prof, 51-53, assoc. prof, 53-60, PROF, 60-, LIBR, 56- Lilly Endowment scholar, 63-64; exec. bd, Counc. Nat. Libr. Asn, 72-75. U.S.A, 41-46, 1st Lt. NCTE; MLA; Am. Theol. Libr. Asn. (pres, 67-68); Am. Libr. Asn. William Faulkner; Darwinism and American thought; Emily Dickinson. Publ: Darwinism in American fiction, Drew Univ, 51; The years of disagreement, Hist. Am. Methodism, 64. Add: 24 Rose Ave, Madison, NJ 07940.

JONES, BARBARA SCHINDLER, b. Blue Lake, Calif, May 21, 21; div. SPEECH & COMMUNICATION. B.A, Univ. Calif, Berkeley, 42; M.A, Univ. Colo, 59, Ph.D.(speech), 68. Secy, Foote, Cone & Belding, advert. agency, San Francisco, 47-49; asst. advert. mgr, Gen. Paint Corp, San Francisco, 49-51; free lance writer, 51-55; asst. dir. Bur. Speech Serv, UNIV. COLO, BOULDER, 54-58, instr. speech & dir. bur. speech serv, 58-71, ASSOC. PROF. COMMUN, 71-, DIR, AFFIRMATIVE ACTION PROG, 72- Mem, Creative Educ. Found; commun. consult, var. bus, orgns & clubs. W.A.A.C. & W.A.F, 43-46, 1st Lt. Nat. Univ. Exten. Asn; Speech Commun. Asn; Am. Asn. Humanistic Psychol. Group communication and leadership; discussion as a teaching tool. Publ: Introduction to communication, Univ. Colo. Exten. Div, 63; co-auth. & ed, Speech and drama: a guide for secondary schools in Colorado, 63 & co-auth, Learning by discussing, 66, Colo. State Dept. Educ; auth, The high school speech institute story, 63 & The Colorado State Speech League and how it grew, 68, Bull. Nat. Univ. Exten. Asn. Comt. Discussion & Debate Rostrum; co-auth, An in-service alternative to the summer institute program, Mod. Lang. J, 64. Add: Affirmative Action Office, 914 Broadway, University of Colorado, Boulder, CO 80302.

JONES, CHARLES ASA, b. Charter Oak, Iowa, Feb. 4, 14; m. 47; c. 2. SPEECH. B.A, Drake Univ, 35; M.A, State Univ. Iowa, 38; Ph.D.(speech), Northwest. Univ, 53. Teacher, high sch, Iowa, 38-42; instr. speech & Eng, Mesa Col, 46; from assoc. prof. to PROF. SPEECH & DRAMA, WASH. STATE UNIV, 46- U.S.A, 42-46. Speech Commun. Asn; Am. Theatre Asn. Children's theater and creative dramatics; educational theater. Add: N.E. 1005 Duncan Lane, Pullman, WA 99163.

JONES, CHARLES WILLIAMS, b. Lincoln, Nebr, Sept. 23, 05; m. 28; c. 4. ENGLISH LITERATURE. A.B, Oberlin Col, 26, hon. Litt.D, 51; M.A, Cornell Univ, 30, Ph.D, 32. Rep, Allyn & Bacon, 26-29; instr. ENG, Oberlin Col, 32-35; Cornell Univ, 36-38, asst. prof, 38-41, PROF, 48-54; UNIV. CALIF, BERKELEY, 54- Am. Counc. Learned Soc. fel, 35-36; Guggenheim fels, 39-40, 45-46. Dir, U.S. Mil. Acad. Prep, 43-45. Mediaeval Acad. Am; Mod. Humanities Res. Asn, Gt. Brit; Philol. Asn. Pac. Coast. Patristic and Carolingian culture. Publ: Bedae Opera de Temporibus, Mediaeval, 43; Medieval literature, McKay, 48; St. Nicholas liturgy, Univ. of Calif, 63. Add: 766 Spruce St, Berkeley, CA 94707.

JONES, CLIFFORD REIS, History of South Asian Art, Classical Indian Theatre. See Volume I, History.

JONES, DAVID EDWARDS, b. Crosskeys, Gt. Brit, July 18, 24; m. 68. ENGLISH, DRAMA. B.A, Univ. Wales, 49, M.A, 53; Ph.D.(Shakespeare), Univ. Minn, 63. Educ. off, Risca Educ. Settlement, Gt. Brit, 52-57; instr. Eng, Univ. Minn, 57-64, asst. prof, 64-65; PROF. THEATRE, UNIV. UTAH, 65- R.N.V.R, 43-47, Sub-Lt. Shakespeare; Eliot; modern drama, especially absurdist. Publ: The plays of T.S. Eliot, Routledge & Kegan Paul, London & Univ. Toronto, 60; Mad idolatry: love in Troilus and Cressida, Drama Critique, VII: 8-14. Add: 205 Pioneer Memorial Theatre, University of Utah, Salt Lake City, UT 84112.

JONES, DAVID LLEWELLYN, b. Newburyport, Mass, Dec. 30, 27. ENGLISH, COMPARATIVE LITERATURE. A.B, Harvard, 50, M.A, 51, Ph.D.(Eng), 58; Fulbright fel, Univ. Innsbruck, 51-52. Instr. ENG, Auburn Univ, 53-55; Rutgers Univ, 58-60; UNIV. AKRON, 61-62, asst. prof, 62-67, ASSOC. PROF, 67- MLA. Publ: Hazlitt and Hunt at the opera house, 62 & Dolorès Disparue, Proust's influence on Nabokov, 66, Symposium; Proust and Doderer: themes and techniques, Bks Abroad, 63. Add: Dept. of English, University of Akron, Akron, OH 44304.

JONES, DENNIS M, b. Meridian, Tex, Aug. 2, 32; m. 52; c. 3. ENGLISH. B.A, Baylor Univ, 53; M.A, Univ. Iowa, 57, Ph.D.(Eng), 66. Asst. prof. ENG, Sam Houston State Col, 58-62; instr, Coe Col, 64-65; asst. prof, LUTHER COL.(IOWA), 65-68, assoc. prof, 68-73, PROF, 73-, DIR. FRESHMAN STUD. PROG, 72-, dir. & lectr, Nat. Endowment for Humanities Black Stud. Inst, summer 71 & proj. dir, Humanities Develop Prog, 73-76. Vis. prof, Univ. Ore, summer 60; Ariz. State Univ, summer 66; Danforth assoc, 68-, Black stud. fel, Yale, 69-70; Nat. Endowment for Humanities fel, summer 69. U.S.A, 53-55, Sgt. MLA; NCTE. Hawthorne; Faulkner; Black literature. Add: Dept. of English, Luther College, Decorah, IA 52101.

JONES, DOROTHY CAMERON, b. Detroit, Mich, Feb. 5, 22. ENGLISH LITERATURE, RENAISSANCE HUMANISM. A.B. & A.M, Wayne State Univ, 43; Ph.D.(Eng), Univ. Colo, 65. Attendance off, Detroit Bd. Educ, 43-44; teacher high sch, Mich, 46-56 & 57-58; exchange teacher dept. pub. instr, Hawaii, 56-57; instr. ENG, Colo. Women's Col, 62-64, asst. prof, 64-66; UNIV. NORTH. COLO, 66-69, assoc. prof, 70-74, PROF, 74- W.A.V.E.S, 44-46. MLA; Rocky Mountain Mod. Lang. Asn. Shakespeare; Thomas Starkey; Tudor humanism. Add: Dept. of English, Michener Library, University of Northern Colorado, Greeley, CO 80639.

JONES, DOROTHY RICHARDSON, b. Flushing, N.Y, Jan. 28, 11; m. 54. ENGLISH. A.B, Hood Col, 31; A.M, Columbia Univ, 32; Ph.D, Univ. Mich, 38. Hopwood asst. & librn, Univ. Mich, 36-37; instr. Eng, Carroll Col.(Wis), 37-39; QUEENS COL.(N.Y), 39-47, asst. prof, 47-57, assoc. prof, 57-69, prof, 69-73, chmn. dept, 49-54, EMER. PROF. ENG, 73- Vis. lectr, Univ. Leicester, 58-59; Am. Counc. Learned Soc. grant-in-aid, 62-63. MLA; Mod. Humanities Res. Asn; AAUP. English literature and criticism; Victorian decorative arts; English ceramics. Add: 345 E. 73rd St, New York, NY 10021.

JONES, DOUGLAS GORDON, b. Bancroft, Ont, Jan. 1, 29; div; c. 4. CANADIAN & MODERN LITERATURE. B.A, McGill Univ, 52; M.A, Queen's Univ.(Ont), 54. Lectr. ENG, Royal Mil. Col, 54-55; asst. prof, Ont. Agr. Col, 55-61; lectr, Bishop's Univ.(Pa), 61-63; ASSOC. PROF. UNIV. SHERBROOKE, 63- Mem. & consult, Arts Adv. Panel, Can. Counc, 70-73; chmn, Governor General's Award Juries, 73. Asn. Can. Univ. Teachers Eng; League Can. Poets. Canadian poetry in French and English. Publ: The sun is axeman (poetry), 61 & Butterfly on rock: a study of themes and images in Canadian literature, 70, Univ. Toronto; Phrases from Orpheus (poetry), Oxford, 67; Adam's inventory: aspects of contemporary Canadian literature, Social Educ, 10/71; Myth, Frye and some Canadian writers, Can. Lit, winter 73; In search of America, Boundary, 74. Add: Dept. of English, Faculty of Arts, University of Sherbrooke, Sherbrooke, P.Q, Can.

JONES, E. WINSTON, b. Karuizawa, Japan, July 6, 11; m. 37. SPEECH. A.B, Ind. Univ, 33; B.D, Garrett Theol. Sem, 36; M.A, Northwest. Univ, 37, Ph.D. (speech), 50; Th.D.(homiletics), Iliff Sch. Theol, 47. Minister, Methodist Churches, Ill. & Ohio, 36-48; teaching fel, Northwest. Univ, 48-50; asst. prof. SPEECH, BOSTON UNIV, 50-55, assoc. prof, 56-61, PROF, 61-, CHMN. DEPT, 56- Speech Commun. Asn. Publ: Preaching and the dramatic arts, Macmillan, 48; Guide to effective speech, Longmans, Green & Co, 61. Add: Bolton Rd, Harvard, MA 01451.

JONES, EVERETT L, b. Huron, S.Dak, Mar. 29, 15; m. 40; c. 2. ENGLISH, AMERICAN STUDIES. B.A, Antioch Col, 38; fel, Lehigh Univ, 39-41, M.A, 41; Univ. Calif, Los Angeles. 47-52. Writer, Time, Inc, 34-36; Penton Publ. Co, 37-38; Antioch Col, 38-39; instr. Eng, Lehigh Univ, 41-44; writer, Univ. Calif. & U.S. Navy, 44-46; teaching asst. ENG, UNIV. CALIF, LOS ANGELES, 47-48, INSTR. SUPVR, 48- Nat. Endowment for Humanities grant, 67-69. Auth. Guild; Auth. League Am. Seventeenth century English literature; American studies. Publ: Co-auth, An approach to college writing, Holt, 56, 2nd ed, 57, The Harbrace college reader, Harcourt, 59, 2nd ed, 64, 3rd ed, 68; The Negro cowboys, Dodd, 65 & The adventures of the Negro cowboys,

Dodd, 66; auth, Robert Hooke and The virtuoso, Mod.Lang. Notes, 51; co-auth, Negro cowboys, Am. West, 11/64 & Slaves on horseback, Pac. Hist. Rev, 11/64. Add: Dept. of Subject A, University of California, Los Angeles, CA 90024.

JONES, FRANK WILLIAM, b. Liverpool, Eng, Jan. 5, 15; nat; m. 43; 58, 66; c. 3. COMPARATIVE LITERATURE. B.A, Univ. Man, 34; B.A, Oxford, 37, M.A, 55; Ph.D, Univ. Wis, 41. Instr. classics, Yale, 42-43, 46; humanities, Col. of Univ. Chicago, 46-48; from asst. prof. to prof. lit. & humanities, Reed Col, 48-54, chmn. div. lit. & lang, 51-53; assoc. prof. ENG. & COMP. LIT, UNIV. WASH, 55-70, PROF, 70-, chmn. comp. lit, 55-67. Fund Advan. Educ. fac. fel, 54-55. Nat. Bk. Award for transl, 71. U.S.A, 43-46. MLA; Philol. Asn. Pac. Coast; Am. Comp. Lit. Asn. Greek tradition in modern poetry and drama; relations between literature and politics; East-West literary relations. Publ: Transl, Bertolt Brecht, Saint Joan of the stockyards, Ind. Univ, 70; Scenes from the life of Antigone, Yale Fr. Stud, 50; Tragedy with a purpose: Bertolt Brecht's Antigone, Tulane Drama Rev, 57; The yes and noh of sacrifice, Pac. Coast Philol, 66. Add: Dept. of English, University of Washington, Seattle, WA 98195.

JONES, FRED G, JR, b. Jacksonville, Fla, Oct. 5, 38; m. 61; c. 2. ENGLISH LITERATURE. B.A, Univ. of the South, 60; Ph.D.(Old Eng), Univ. Fla, 67. Instr. ENG, Univ. Fla, 65-67; ASST. PROF, STATE UNIV. N.Y. BINGHAMTON, 67- Fac. fel, State Univ. N.Y, 68. MLA. Old English literature; Chaucer; Old Norse literature. Add: Dept. of English, State University of New York at Binghamton, Binghamton, NY 13901.

JONES, GRANVILLE HICKS, b. Jefferson, Tex, Apr. 8, 32. ENGLISH & AMERICAN LITERATURE. B.A, Baylor Univ, 54; M.A, Columbia Univ, 61; Ph.D.(Eng), Univ. Pittsburgh, 69. Instr. ENG, CARNEGIE-MELLON UNIV, 60-64, lectr, 66-68, asst. prof, 68-72, ASSOC. PROF, 72- Teaching Award, MLA, 70. U.S.A, 55-57. Nineteenth and 20th century American literature; 20th century novel. Publ: Henry James's psychology of experience, Mouton, 74; Jack Kerouac and the American conscience, Carnegie Series in Eng, 63; Post mortem: student-directed courses I and II, Col. Eng, 71; Henry James's Georgina's reasons: the underside of Washington Square, Stud. Short Fiction, 74. Add: Dept. of English, Carnegie-Mellon University, Pittsburgh, PA 15213.

JONES, HATTIE, b. Burlington Junction, Mo, Sept. 4, 02. SPEECH. B.S, Northwest Mo. State Col, 29; M.A, Univ. Minn, 46; summers, Univ. Mo, 60, Univ. Minn, 47, 52. Teacher, schs, Mo, 25-40; teaching asst, Univ. Minn, 40-42; teacher SPEECH, Col. St. Catherine, 42-46; from instr. to asst. prof, DRAKE UNIV, 46-73, EMER. PROF, 73- Speech Commun. Asn. Public address; parliamentary procedure. Add: 1331 63rd St, Des Moines, IA 50311.

JONES, HAZEL JAMES, b. Eckert, Colo, Feb. 3, 15; m. 42; c. 1. ENGLISH. B.A, West. State Col. Colo, 37; M.A, Univ. Calif, Berkeley, 41; M.S.Ed, Univ. South. Calif, 57, Ed.D.(educ. psychol), 63. Teacher, pub. schs, Colo, 37-40, 41-42, 43-50; Japanese relocation camp, Calif, 42-43; high sch, Calif, 50-53, dean girls, 53-54; dir. in-serv. educ, Whittier Union High Sch. Dist, Calif, 54-59; asst. prof. educ, Calif. State Col, Los Angeles, 59-60; CALIF. STATE UNIV, FULLERTON, 60-63, assoc. prof. ENG, 63-67, PROF, 67-, DEAN, SCH. LETT, ARTS. & SCI, 69-, assoc. dean, 68-69. Consult, Orange Unified Sch. Dist, Montebello Unified Sch. Dist, Univ. Hawaii, NDEA in Eng, State Calif. & Anaheim High Sch. Dist, Calif, 59-67; Delta Kappa Gamma fel, 62-63; res. grant stud. prep. teachers of compos, 66-67. NCTE; NEA; Asn. Supv. & Curriculum Develop. Criteria for grading student work; preparation of teachers of English in composition. Publ: Co-auth, World trade, 63 & auth. all teacher & stud. materials & consult. to publ, Area studies in economic progress (8 vols), 63, Curriculum Resources; contrib, New reading ladders for human relations, NCTE, 64; auth, Myths and realities, Calif. Eng. J, spring 66. Add: California State University, 800 N. State College Blvd, Fullerton, CA 92634.

JONES, HENRY BROADUS, b. Wingate, N.C, Nov. 1, 86; m. 15; c. 2. ENGLISH. A.B, Wake Forest Col, 10; A.M, Univ. Chicago, 20, Ph.D.(Eng), 24. Instr. ENG, Cullowhee Norm. Sch, 12-20; prof. & head dept, Simpson Col, 21-24; prof, Wake Forest Univ, 24-59, head dept, 38-57, EMER. PROF, 59- Prof, Appalachian State Teachers Col, 59-62; prof. & head dept, Campbell Col.(N.C), 63-69. Nineteenth century English literature. Add: 1938 Faculty Dr, Winston-Salem, NC 27106.

JONES, HORACE RODMAN, b. Dallas, Tex, Jan. 27, 21; m. 44; c. 2. SPEECH, THEATRE. B.A, Univ. Tulsa, 41; M.A, State Univ. Iowa, 42; Ford Found. fel, 51-52; Ph.D.(speech educ), Northwest. Univ, 52. Teacher, high schs, Okla, 42-43; instr. Eng. & hist, UNIV. TULSA, 46-47, asst. prof. SPEECH & THEATRE, 47-53, assoc. prof, 54-62, PROF, 62-, dir. eve. div, 60-69, dean freshmen, 66-70, acting dean, Col. Fine & Prof. Arts, 70-71. Consult, citizenship training prog, Stanolind Oil Co. & Serv. Pipe Line Co, 52-54; speech consult, Dowell, Inc, 57-60; Jersey Prod. Res. Co, 59-63; Skelly Oil Co, 63-65. U.S.A.F, 43-45, 1st Lt. Speech Commun. Asn. Speech education and dramatics; dramatic literature; history of the theatre. Publ: The present status of beginning speech courses in colleges and universities in the United States, Cent. States Speech J, spring 55. Add: Dept. of Communication, University of Tulsa, 600 S. College, Tulsa, OK 74104.

JONES, HOWARD MUMFORD, b. Saginaw, Mich, Apr. 16, 92; m. 18, 27; c. 1. ENGLISH. B.A, Univ. Wis, 14, hon. Litt.D, 48; M.A, Univ. Chicago, 15; hon. Litt.D, Harvard, 36, Univ. Colo, 38, West. Reserve Univ, 48, Clark Univ, 52; hon. L.H.D, Tulane Univ, 38; hon. D.H.L, Ohio State Univ, 60, Hebrew Union Col, 60, Northwest. Univ, 66, Clarkson Col. Technol, 68, N.Y. Univ, 69; hon. LL.D, Colby Col, 62, Univ. Utah, 66, Univ. Windsor, 69. Adj. prof. Eng. & gen. lit, Univ. Tex, 16-17, assoc. prof. comp. lit. & head dept, 19-24; asst. prof. Eng, Mont. State Univ, 17-19; assoc. prof, Univ. N.C, 24-27, prof, 27-30; Univ. Mich, 30-36; HARVARD, 36-60, Lowell prof. HUMANITIES, 60-62, LOWELL EMER. PROF, 62- Guggenheim fel; Am. Univ. Union lectr, Bristol Univ, 33; Am. Inst, Munich, 50; chmn, Am. Counc. Learned Soc, 55-59; chmn, Weil Inst, 59-61; Carnegie vis. prof, Mass. Inst. Technol, 62-63; Knapp distinguished prof, Univ. Wis, 63. Pulitzer & Emerson Prizes, 64. MLA (pres); AHA (Jusserand Medal, 34); Am. Philos. Soc; Am. Acad. Arts & Sci.(pres, 44-51); Am. Antiq. Soc. American and English literary and cultural history; American and French culture; plays of the Restoration and the 18th century. Publ: A little book of local verse, 15; Gargoyles (poems), 18; co-auth, A bibliography of works and MSS. of Byron, 24; auth, America and French culture 1750-1848, 27; co-auth, The Romanesque lyric, 28; ed, The poems of Edgar Allan Poe, 29; co-ed, Plays of the Restoration and the eighteenth century, 30; auth, The life of Moses Coit Tyler, 33; co-ed, Major American writers, 35 & The college reader, 36; auth, They say the forties, 37; The harp that once, 37; co-ed, Oliver Wendell Holmes, 39; auth, Ideas in America, 44; Education and world tragedy, 46; The theory of American literature, 48; co-auth, Modern minds, 49; ed, Primer of intellectual liberty, 49; co-ed, Modern minds, 49 & Letters of Sherwood Anderson, 53; auth, The frontier in American fiction, 56; ed, American humanism, 57, Reflections on learning, 58 & One great society, 59; co-ed, Treasury of scientific prose, 63; auth, History and the contemporary, 64; O strange new world, 64; Jeffersonianism and the American novel, 66; The age of energy, 71; co-auth, Guide to American literature and the backgrounds since 1890, 4th ed. rev, 72; Revolution and romanticism, 74. Add: Widener 115, Harvard University, Cambridge, MA 02138.

JONES, JAMES H, b. Wheeling, W.Va, July 31, 29; m. 59; c. 5. ENGLISH. A.B, Kenyon Col, 51; M.A, Univ. Buffalo, 57; Harvard, summer 56; Ph.D. (Eng), Ind. Univ, 65. Asst. prof. ENG, NORTH. MICH. UNIV, 62-68, assoc. prof, 68-70, PROF, 70- Nat. Endowment for Humanities fel, 67-68. U.S.A, 51-53, 1st Lt. Shakespeare Asn. Am; MLA. Shakespeare; ballads; Renaissance Soc. Am; Conf. Christianity & Lit. Publ: Commonplace and memorization in the oral tradition of the English and Scottish popular ballad, J. Am. Folklore, 61; Lear and Leir: Matthew V: 30-37, the turning point and the rescue theme, Comp. Drama, 70. Add: Dept. of English, Northern Michigan University, Marquette, MI 49855.

JONES, JOEL MACKEY, b. Millersburg, Ohio, Aug. 11, 37; m. 63; c. 1. AMERICAN LITERATURE & HISTORY. B.A, Yale, 60; M.A, Miami Univ, 63; fel, Univ. N.Mex, 63-66, Ph.D.(Am. stud), 66. Dir. Am. stud. Univ. Md, Baltimore County, 66-69; ASSOC. PROF. AM. STUDIES & CHMN. DEPT, UNIV. N.MEX, 69- Univ. Md. summer res. grant, 68; mem. bd. ed, Am. Lit. Realism. Am. Stud. Asn; Popular Cult. Asn; Orgn. Am. Hist; Am. Asn. Higher Educ; Southwest Popular Cult. Asn.(pres). Scholarship and methodology; American literary regionalism and ecology; innovation in higher education. Publ: To feel the Heartland's pulse: the writing of Walter Havighurst, Kans. Quart, spring 70; What's good for Harvard may not be good for humanity, Am. Teacher, 6/71; Term papers, textbooks, toilet tissue and trees, J. Environ. Educ, spring 74. Add: Dept. of American Studies, Humanities Bldg, University of New Mexico, Albuquerque, NM 87131.

JONES, JOHN A, b. Williamsport, Tenn, Oct. 25, 22; m. 45; c. 4. ENGLISH & AMERICAN LITERATURE. A.B, Univ. Ky, 52, M.A, 57; South. Fels. Fund grant, Univ. Fla, 58-59, Ph.D.(Eng), 61. Instr. ENG, Univ. Ky, 54-57; Univ. Fla, 57-58, 59-61; asst. prof, OHIO UNIV, 61-66, assoc. prof, 66-71, PROF, 71- MLA. Eighteenth century English literature; twentieth century American and British literature. Publ: Pope's couplet art, Ohio Univ, 69; Hemingway: the critics and the public legend, West. Humanities Rev, autumn 59. Add: 54 Woodward Ave, Athens, OH 45701.

JONES, JOHN BUSH, b. Chicago, Ill, Aug. 3, 40; m. 68; c. 1. DRAMATIC LITERATURE, THEATRE HISTORY. B.S, Northwest. Univ, 62, M.A, 63, Ph.D.(Eng), 70. Instr. ENG, Northwest. Univ, 65-68; asst. prof, UNIV. KANS, 68-72, ASSOC. PROF, 72- Newberry Libr. grant-in-aid, summer 71; adj. drama critic, Kansas City Star, 71-; Am. Philos. Soc. grant, 72. MLA; Am. Theatre Asn; Malone Soc. Twentieth century British and American drama, theatrical production and theatre criticism; W.S. Gilbert and the Gilbert and Sullivan operas; 19th century printing history. Publ: Ed, W.S. Gilbert: a century of scholarship and commentary, N.Y. Univ, 70 & Readings in descriptive bibliography, Kent State Univ, 74; auth, In search of Archibald Grosvenor: a new look at Gilbert's Patience, Victorian Poetry, 65; Impersonation and authenticity: the theatre as metaphor in Kopit's Indians, Quart. J. Speech, 73; Shakespeare as myth and the structure of Winterset, Educ. Theatre J, 73. Add: Dept. of English, University of Kansas, Lawrence, KS 66045.

JONES, JOHN P, b. Tyler, Tex, Mar. 1, 15; m. 44; c. 2. ENGLISH. A.B, Tex. Col, 35; A.M, Univ. Chicago, 41; Rockefeller fel, Columbia Univ, 51, Southern fel, 57, United Col. fel, 60; Litt.D, Tex. Col, 72; Hum.D, Phillips Univ, 73; LL.D, Tex. Christian Univ, 73. From instr. to prof. Eng, Tex. Col, 35-62; assoc. prof. Eng. & admin. asst, JARVIS CHRISTIAN COL, 62-71, PRES, 71- A.U.S, 42-45, S/Sgt. MLA; NCTE; NEA; Int. Reading Asn. (counc. pres, 67-68). English literature; English language. Add: Office of the President, Jarvis Christian College, Hawkins, TX 75765.

JONES, JOHN PAUL, b. Micanopy, Fla, Mar. 3, 12; m. 38; c. 3. JOURNALISM. B.A.J, Univ. Fla, 37; M.A, Univ. Wis, 39. Instr. jour, Univ. Fla, 37-38; Univ. Ill, 39-43, asst. prof, 46-48; assoc. prof, UNIV. FLA, 48-51, prof, 51-68, DEAN COL. JOUR. & COMMUN, 68- Secy-mgr, Fla. Press Asn, 52-68; ed, The Fla. Press, 58-68. U.S.N.R, 43-46, Lt. Newspaper Asn. Mgrs; Asn. Educ. Jour. Newspaper law; advertising; reporting. Publ: The modern reporter's handbook, Rinehart, 49; co-auth, News beat, Macmillan, 49 & Radio and television reporting, Rinehart, 54; plus others. Add: College of Journalism & Communications, University of Florida, Gainesville, FL 32601.

JONES, JOSEPH J, b. Peru, Nebr, June 29, 08; m. 35; c. 3. AMERICAN & WORLD ENGLISH LITERATURE. B.S, Univ. Nebr, 30; Ph.D, Stanford Univ, 34. Instr. ENG, Colo. State Col, 34-35; UNIV. TEX, AUSTIN, 35-42; asst. prof, 42-46, assoc. prof, 46-58, PROF, 58- Ed, Libr. Chronicle, 44-53; Fulbright lectr, Univ. N.Z, 53, Univ. Hong Kong, 65-66; Smith-Mundt prof, Univ. S.Africa, 60; ed, WLWE Newsletter, 62-70. MLA; Asn. Commonwealth Lit. & Lang. Stud. American transcendentalism; comparative literature in English. Publ: Cradle of Erewhon: Samuel Butler in New Zealand: ed, American literary manuscripts; auth, Terranglia: the case for English as world literature, 65 & ed, Canada, Africa, Australia, New Zealand & West Indies sects, Twayne's world authors series, 70, Twayne; co-auth, Canada, Vol. I, Australia, Vol. II & West Indies, Vol. III, In: People and places in world English literature series, Steck, 70; Commonwealth literature: developments and prospects, In: The historiography of the British empire—commonwealth, Duke Univ, 66. Add: Dept. of English, University of Texas at Austin, Austin, TX 78712.

JONES, KIRKLAND C, b. Beaumont, Tex, Oct. 16, 38. ENGLISH LANGUAGE & LITERATURE. B.A, Univ. Wash, 59; M.A, Tex. South. Univ, 66; univ. fel, Univ. Wis-Madison, 68-69, South. Fel. Fund grant, 69-70, Ph.D. (Eng), 71. Instr. Span. & speech, Beaumont Independent Sch. Dist, Tex, 61-63, Span. & Eng, Tyler Pub. Sch, 63-64, speech, drama & Eng, Galveston Pub. Schs, 64-65 & Eng. & speech, Tex. South. Univ, 65-70; assoc. prof. & head dept, J.C. Smith Univ, 70-73; ASSOC. PROF. ENG. & DIR. FRESHMAN STUD, LAMAR UNIV, 73- Danforth fel, Conf. Higher Educ, Colorado Springs, Colo, summer 71. NCTE; Col. Lang. Asn; Conf. Col. Compos. & Commun; South. Speech Asn; Col. Conf. Teachers Eng. Middle English language and literature; classical rhetoric; dialectology. Publ: Co-ed, The English-language-arts in Wisconsin (a curriculum guide), Wis. Dept. Pub. Instr, 68; auth, Proverbs, proverbial wisdom, and medieval Topoi in the Paston letters, Univ. Microfilms, 71; What do teachers of composition want?, Wis. Eng. J, spring 68; The language of the black in-crowd, CLA J, 9/71; On the rhetoric of Martin Luther King, Sphinx Mag, 6/73; plus others. Add: Dept. of English, Box 10003, Lamar University, Beaumont, TX 77710.

JONES, LEO MONROE, b. Bloomington, Ind, Dec. 21, 22; m. 46; c. 5. DRAMA, MODERN THEATRE. B.S, Ind. Univ, 47, M.A, 48, Ph.D.(theatre), 73. Instr. theatre & speech & drama coach, Univ. Buffalo, 48-51; ASSOC. PROF. THEATRE ARTS, MARQUETTE UNIV, 53- U.S.A, 43-45. Add: Dept. of Theatre Arts, Marquette University, 1210 W. Michigan, Milwaukee, WI 53233.

JONES, LEONIDAS MONROE, b. Atmore, Ala, Feb. 19, 23; m. 51; c. 2. ENGLISH. A.B, Univ. Ala, 47; M.A, Harvard, 48, Ph.D.(Eng), 53. Instr. ENG, UNIV. VT, 51, asst. prof, 55-60, assoc. prof, 60-65, PROF, 65- Prof. Eng, summer sch, Harvard, 73. U.S.M.C, 42-46. MLA; Keats-Shelley Asn. Am. (mem, ed. bd, 67). Romantic period; John Hamilton Reynolds. Publ: Ed, Selected prose of J.H. Reynolds, Harvard, 66; ed, Letters of J.H. Reynolds, Univ. Nebr, 73; Keats' theatrical reviews & New letters, poems, and articles by J.H. Reynolds, Keats-Shelley J; The Ode to psyche: an allegorical introduction to Keat's great odes, Keats-Shelley Mem. Bull, 58. Add: 32 Fern St, Burlington, VT 05401.

JONES, LINDA BUNNELL, b. Dallas, Tex, Oct. 22, 42; m. 64. ENGLISH LITERATURE. B.A, Baylor Univ, 64; M.A, Univ. Colo, Boulder, 67, Woodrow Wilson fel, 69, Ph.D.(Eng), 70. ASST. PROF. ENG, UNIV. CALIF, RIVERSIDE, 70- MLA; Res. Soc. Victorian Periodicals. Nineteenth-century periodicals; 19th century fiction; history of publishing. Add: Dept. of English, University of California, Riverside, CA 92502.

JONES, LLOYD S, b. Glenwood, Iowa, May 13, 17; m. 43. SPEECH. B.A, Hastings Col, 39; M.A, Univ. Denver, 46, Ph.D.(oral interpretation), 55. Teacher, high schs, Nebr. & Colo, 41-44; head dept. speech, Friends Univ, 45-47; dir. drama, Willamette Univ, 47-48; CALIF. STATE UNIV, CHICO, 48-53, asst. prof. SPEECH, 55-59, assoc. prof, 59-64, PROF, 64-, CHMN. DEPT. SPEECH, DRAMA & DANCE, 70- Speech Commun. Asn; West. Speech Commun. Asn. Oral interpretation; forensics. Add: Dept. of Speech, Drama & Dance, California State University, Chico, First & Normal St, Chico, CA 95926.

JONES, MADISON PERCY, JR, b. Nashville, Tenn, Mar. 21, 25; m. 51; c. 5. FICTION. A.B, Vanderbilt Univ, 49; M.A, Univ. Fla, 51. Instr. ENG, Miami Univ, 53-54; Univ. Tenn, 55-56; asst. prof, AUBURN UNIV, 56-66, assoc. prof, 66-68, PROF, 68-, ALUMNI WRITER-IN-RESIDENCE, 68- Sewanee Rev. fel, 54-55; Rockefeller Found. writing fel, 68-; Guggenheim fel, 73-74. Mil. Police, U.S.A, 45-46. PEN Club. Creative writing; fiction. Publ: The innocent (novel), 57 & Forest of the night (novel), 60, Harcourt; A buried land (novel), 63 & An exile (novel), 67, Viking; A cry of absence, Crown, 71; The fiction of Robert Penn Warren, S.Atlantic Quart, fall 73. Add: 800 Kuderna Acres, Auburn, AL 36830.

JONES, MARY PATRICIA, b. Indianapolis, Ind, Mar. 25, 25; m. 49; c. 4. ENGLISH. B.A, Univ. Mich, 46, M.A, 61. Teacher High Schs, Mich, 46-58; instr. Eng, Adrian Col, 62-70, lectr. children's lit, 70-72, GRAD. ASST. FRESHMAN COMPOS, TOLEDO UNIV, 72- Modern grammar; early anti-slavery poetry; local history. Publ: A slanguage of Shakespeare, Clearing House, 12/64; An annucleazation of some typical student creations, Eng. J, 12/65. Add: Box 66, Tipton, MI 49287.

JONES, NANCY CAROL, b. Pittsburgh, Pa, June 15, 34. JOURNALISM. B.A, Univ. Pittsburgh, 56; M.S, Northwest. Univ, 59; Ph.D.(jour), Univ. Mo-Columbia, 67. Reporter, Daily Press, Newport News, Va, 56-58; reporter & bur. chief, Miami Herald, Fla, 59-61; ed, Assoc. Press, Louisville, Ky, 61-65; asst. prof. JOUR, Pa. State Univ, 67-71; ASSOC. PROF, DUQUESNE UNIV, 71- Women in Commun.(scholarship chairperson, 72-73). Reporting; editing; international communications. Publ: Well run libraries assist reporters, Ed. & Publ, 1/60; U.S. news in the Soviet press, Jour. Quart, winter 66; contrib, International communication, Hastings House, 70; plus others. Add: Dept. of Journalism, Duquesne University, Pittsburgh, PA 15219.

JONES, PUTNAM FENNELL, b. Amsterdam, N.Y. Aug. 22, 02; m. 35, 51; c. 1. ENGLISH LANGUAGE & LITERATURE. A.B, Cornell Univ, 24, A.M, 26, Ph.D.(lit. criticism), 27. Instr. ENG, Cornell Univ, 24-26; asst. prof, UNIV. PITTSBURGH, 27-32, assoc. prof, 32-46, prof, 46-68, prof-at-large, 68-72, EMER. DEAN GRAD. FAC, 68-, chmn. dept, 47-55, assoc. dean grad. sch, 53-54, assoc. dean col, 54-56, acting dean 55-56, dean grad. fac, 56-68. Mem, comn. insts. higher educ, Mid. States Asn. Cols. & Sec. Schs, 65-71. MLA; Milton Soc. Am; Mediaeval Acad. Am. Anglo-Latin culture of the Old English period; Chaucer; Milton. Publ: The constitution of the United States, 1787-1962, Univ. Pittsburgh, 62; Concordance to the Historia ecclesiastica of Bede, Mediaeval Acad. Am. Add: 346 Churchill Rd, Pittsburgh, PA 15235.

JONES, ROBERT CHARLES, b. Greeley, Colo, Sept. 12, 36; m. 59; c. 1. ENGLISH. B.A, Univ. Calif, Riverside, 58; M.A, Columbia Univ, 59; Ph.D. (Eng), Harvard, 64. Instr. ENG, Smith Col, 63-65; asst. prof, OHIO STATE UNIV, COLUMBUS, 65-71, ASSOC. PROF, 71- English Renaissance drama. Publ: Italian settings and the world of Elizabethan tragedy, Stud. Eng. Lang, spring 70; The stage world and the real world in Medwall's Fulgens and lucres, Mod. Lang. Quart, 6/71; Jonson's Staple of news gossips and Fulwell's Like will to like, Yearbk, Eng. Stud, 73. Add: Dept. of English, Ohio State University, Columbus, OH 43210.

JONES, ROBERT CLAUDE, b. Troup, Tex, July 20, 31; m. 53; c. 3. ENGLISH. B.J, Univ. Tex, 52, M.J, 53, Ph.D.(Eng), 58. Teaching fel. jour, Univ. Tex, 53-54, asst. ENG, 54-56, instr, 56-57; Univ. Colo, 57-58; asst. prof, William Jewell Col, 58-61; CENT. MO. STATE UNIV, 61-71, PROF, 71- Participant elem. educ. & Eng. Training Teachers Trainers Proj, 70-71. American literature, 1850-1900; American, English and European contemporary comparative literature; American humor. Publ: Co-auth, Grubstreet anthology, Astrolabe Press, 56; Generative English handbook, Wadsworth, 67; auth, The stress-hover, Col. Eng, 58. Add: Dept. of English, Central Missouri State University, Warrensburg, MO 64093.

JONES, SHIRLEY JEAN, b. McAlester, Okla, Oct. 17, 36. OLD & MIDDLE ENGLISH. A.B, Okla. Baptist Univ, 58; M.A, Cornell Univ, 59; Ph.D.(Eng), Univ. Okla, 66. Asst. prof. ENG, OKLA. BAPTIST UNIV, 64-73, PROF, 73-, CHMN. DEPT, 71- MLA; NCTE; AAUP; S.Cent. Mod. Lang. Asn. Medieval romance. Add: Dept. of English, Oklahoma Baptist University, Shawnee, OK 74801.

JONES, SIDNEY C. ENGLISH LITERATURE. B.A, State Univ, Iowa, 56; Woodrow Wilson fel, 56-57; M.S, Univ. Wis, 59. Asst, Dept. Polit. Sci, State Univ, Iowa, 55-56; Dept. Integrated Lib. Stud, Univ. Wis, 57-61; asst. prof. ENG, CARROLL COL.(WIS), 61-70, ASSOC. PROF, 70- NCTE; MLA; AAUP. Nineteenth and 20th century philosophy. Add: 603 E. Roberta Ave, Waukesha, WI 53186.

JONES, W. MELVILLE, b. Homestead, Pa, Sept. 29, 01; m. 27; c. 1. ENGLISH LITERATURE. A.B, Allegheny Col, 23, hon. Litt. D, 72; M.A, Ohio State Univ, 25; Ph.D, Harvard, 53. Instr. ENG, Univ. Richmond, 25-28; assoc. prof, COL. WILLIAM & MARY, 28-53, prof, 53-71, dir, John Marshall Bicentennial, 54-55, dean fac, 58-64, dean col, 64-68, v.pres, 68-71, EMER. CHANCELLOR PROF, 71- Prog. dir, Jamestown 350th Anniversary, 56-57. MLA. Fiction in the 18th century English chapbook. Publ: Ed, John Marshall—a reappraisal, Cornell Univ, 55. Add: 141 Indian Springs, Rd, Williamsburg, VA 23185.

JONES, WALTER PAUL, b. Larwill, Ind, Aug. 22, 91; m. 16; c. 2. ENGLISH. A.B, Wabash Col, 13; Univ. Calif, 19-20; Ph.D, Cornell Univ, 26. Instr, Telluride Asn, 13-17; Vincennes Univ, 17-18; Potter Sch. Boys, San Francisco, Calif, 18-20; Cornell Univ, 20-26; assoc. prof, Univ. Louisville, 26-31; Eng, Iowa State Univ, 31-32, prof, 32-63; RETIRED. Am. Soc. Engineering Educ; NCTE; Conf. Col. Compos. & Commun. Modern English usage; scientific and technical writing; report writing. Publ: Writing scientific papers and reports; 6th ed, 71; Essays on thinking and writing; co-ed, Ideas and backgrounds; co-auth, Design for reading, Am. Bk, 64. Add: 211 Beach Ave, Ames, IA 50010.

JONES, WARREN SAUNDERS, b. Williamston, N.C, May 28, 21; m; c. 4. SPEECH. B.A, David Lipscomb Col, 48; M.A, Wayne State Univ, 54, Ph.D, 60. PROF. SPEECH, PEPPERDINE UNIV, 58- Speech Commun. Asn. Public address: dialect. Add: Dept. of Speech, Pepperdine University, Los Angeles, CA 90044.

JONES, WILLIAM CLOUGH, b. Los Angeles, Calif, Feb. 1, 37; m. 59; c. 4. AMERICAN LITERATURE, U.S. SOCIAL HISTORY. B.S, Santa Clara Univ, 58; M.A, Creighton Univ, 62; Danforth fel, Univ. Minn, 67-69, Ph.D.(Am. stud), 70. Instr. Eng, Dominican Col.(Wis), 62-64; Wis. State Univ-Eau Claire, 64-67; asst. prof. ENG. & AM. CULT, UNIV. MO-KANSAS CITY, 69-73, ASSOC. PROF, 73-, CHMN. PROG. AM. CULT, 71-, ACTING CHMN. DEPT. ENG, 73- U.S.A, 59-61, Res, 61-67, Capt. Am. Stud. Asn. American 17th century Indian captivity narratives; social and intellectual history of U.S. 1840-1860; violence in American culture. Add: Dept. of English, University of Missouri-Kansas City, 5315 Holmes, Kansas City, MO 64110.

JONES, WILLIAM MCKENDREY, b. Dothan, Ala, Sept. 19, 27; m. 52; c. 3. ENGLISH. A.B, Univ. Ala, 49, fel, 49-50, M.A, 50; fel, Northwest. Univ, 50-52, Ph.D.(Eng), 53. Assoc. prof. ENG, Wis. State Col, 53-55; asst. prof, Univ. Mich, 55-59; UNIV. MO-COLUMBIA, 59-60, assoc. prof, 60-65, PROF, 65- Folger Shakespeare Libr. res. fel, 55. U.S.A, 45-46. MLA; Renaissance Soc. Am; Shakespeare Asn. Am. English Renaissance. Publ: Stages of composition, 64 & ed, Fiction: form and experience, 69, Heath; Two learned Italian in Elizabethan England, Italica; Foreign teachers in sixteenth century England, The Historian, 59; William Shakespeare as William in As you like it, Shakespeare Quart, 60. Add: Dept. of English, University of Missouri-Columbia, Columbia, MO 65201.

JONES, WILLIS KNAPP, Spanish American Literature. See Volume III, Foreign Languages, Linguistics & Philology.

JONES, WINONA STEVENS, b. Hartford, Ky, May 14, 90. ROMANCE LANGUAGES. A.B, Georgetown Col, 10; A.M, Transylvania Col, 26; cert, Sorbonne, France, 12, 24, 35; Ph.D, Univ. Ky, 43. Head depts. mod. lang. & English, Hartford Col, 10-12; mod. lang, Hamilton Col, 24-26; instr, TRANSYLVANIA UNIV, 26-30, dean women, 30-35, prof. Romance lang, 35-43, head dept, 43-55, EMER. PROF. MOD. LANG, 55- Carnegie grant-in-aid, 48; ed. & pub, Bicentennial Mag, Ky, 50; instr. semantics & Eng, Episcopal Theol. Sem. Ky, 54-57; head Eng. dept, Campbellsville Col, 57-60. Sovereign Order St. John of Jerusalem, Knights of Malta. Am. Asn. Teachers Fr. Marcel Proust and the modern novel; the modern French novel; genealogy. Publ: Our Royal ancestors, 71; Remembrance of the past, 72. Add: 448 W. Third St, Lexington, KY 40508.

JOOST, NICHOLAS TEYNAC, b. Jacksonville, Fla, May 28, 16; m. 43; c. 3. ENGLISH. B.S.S, Georgetown Univ, 38; M.A, Univ. N.C, 39, Ph.D.(Eng), 47. Instr. Eng, Univ. Miami, 40-41; Northwest. Univ, 47-49; asst. prof, Loyola Univ.(Ill), 49-54; assoc. prof, Assumption Col, 54-59; PROF. ENG, SOUTH. ILL. UNIV, 58-, ED, PAPERS ON LANG. & LIT, 64-, head div. humanities,

58-63. Acting ed, Poetry, 53-54, assoc. ed, 54; res. consult, Worcester Art Mus, 57-58; Fulbright lectr, Cath. Univ. Nijmegen, 63-64; Chapelbrook Found. grant, 70-71. Award Excellence Scholar, Fac. Eng. Lang. & Lit, 72. U.S.A.A.F, 42-45. Cath. Renascence Soc. Periodicals; modern poetry; American studies. Publ: The pertinence of the notes to Marianne Moore's The jerboa; Scofield Thayer and The dial, 64 & co-auth, D.H. Lawrence and The dial, 70, South. Ill. Univ; co-auth, Papers on the art and age of Geoffrey Chaucer, 67 & co-ed & co-auth, Toward the modern: some portents of the movement, 1880-1920, 72, Suppl. to Papers on Lang. & Lit; auth, Years of transition: The dial, 1912-1920, 67 & Ernest Hemingway and the little magazines, 68, Barre; co-auth, The dial, Two author indexes, Vol. 6, In: Bibliographic contributions, South. Ill. Univ, 71; auth, Ernest Hemingway and The dial, Neophilologus, 68; The dial collection: tastes and trends of the twenties, Apollo, 12/71; Some primitives in The dial of the twenties, Forum, winter-spring 73; plus others. Add: 1703 Liberty St, Alton, IL 62002.

JORDAN, FRANK, JR, b. Charlotte, N.C, Jan. 18, 37. ENGLISH. B.A, Duke Univ, 59, M.A, 60, Ph.D.(Eng), 65. Instr. ENG, Univ. N.C, 64-65; asst. prof, MIAMI UNIV, 65-71, ASSOC. PROF, 71- MLA; Midwest Mod. Lang. Asn. Walter Scott; English romantic period; English Victorian period. Publ: Ed, The English Romantic poets: a review of research and criticism, MLA, 72. Add: Dept. of English, Miami University, Oxford, OH 45056.

JORDAN, GRETCHEN GRAF PAHL, b. Cleveland, Ohio, Dec. 12, 15; m. 50; c. 1. ENGLISH LITERATURE. A.B, Ohio State Univ, 37, univ. scholar & M.A, 38; univ. fel, Univ. Calif, Los Angeles, 38-39, 40-41, Ph.D.(Eng. lit), 47. Dir. bus, Indust. Girls Clubs, YWCA, Akron, Ohio, 42-43; instr. ENG, Univ. Akron, 43-44; lectr, Univ. Calif, Los Angeles, 46, Berkeley, 47; instr, POMONA COL, 47-48, asst. prof, 48-53, assoc. prof, 53-65, PROF, 65- MLA. Late 17th and early 18th century English literature; 19th century American literature. Publ: Introduction to two 18th century essays, Augustan Reprints, 49; John Locke as literatry critic, In: Essays dedicated to L.B. Campbell, Univ. Calif, 50; Hawthorne's Bell, Nineteenth-Century Fiction, 63. Add: Dept. of English, Pomona College, Claremont, CA 91713.

JORDAN, HOOVER HARDING, b. Minneapolis, Minn, Sept. 13, 13; m. 40; c. 2. ENGLISH LITERATURE. A.B, Yale, 34; A.M, Cornell Univ, 35, Ph.D, 37. Instr. Univ. Kans, 37-39; from instr. to asst. prof. ENG. LIT, EAST. MICH. UNIV, 39-42, assoc. prof, 46-51, PROF, 51-, head dept, 63-68. U.S.N, 42-46, Lt. MLA; Shakespeare Asn. Am; Col. Eng. Asn; NCTE; Keats-Shelley Asn. Am. Publ: Elements of good writing; Unified English composition; Thomas Moore and Thomas Campbell, In: The English romantic poets and essayists, PMLA, 57. Add: Dept. of English Language & Literature, Eastern Michigan University, Ypsilanti, MI 48197.

JORDAN, JOHN EMORY, b. Richmond, Va, Apr. 8, 19; m. 43; c. 3. ENGLISH LITERATURE. B.A, Univ. Richmond, 40; M.A, Johns Hopkins Univ, 42, Ph.D, 47. Jr. instr. ENG, John Hopkins Univ, 46-47; instr, UNIV. CALIF, BERKELEY, 47-49, asst. prof, 49-53, assoc. prof, 53-59, PROF, 59-, v.chmn. dept, 61-69, chmn, 69-73, acad. asst. to chancellor, 62-65. Ford fel, 54-55; Guggenheim fel, 58-59; consult, Armed Forces Inst, 65-; Off. Educ, Eng. Inst, 65-; humanities res. prof, 67-68 & 73. U.S.N.R, 42-46, Lt. Comdr.(Ret). MLA; NCTE. Nineteenth century literature; rhetoric. Publ: Thomas De Quincey: literary critic, 52 & 73 & De Quincey to Wordsworth, a biography of a relationship, 62, Univ. Calif; Robert Louis Stevenson's Silverado journal, Bk. Club Calif, 54; Using rhetoric, Harper, 65; ed, Shelley, A defence of poetry & Peacock, The four ages of poetry, 65, Bobbs; co-ed, Some British romantics, Ohio State Univ, 66; ed, Questions of rhetoric, Holt, 71; ed, De Quincey as critic, Routledge & Kegan Paul, 73; co-auth, De Quincey, In: The English romantic poets and essayists, MLA, 57, rev. ed, 64; auth, Wordsworth's humor, PMLA, 3/58; The hewing of Peter Bell, Stud. Eng. Lit, autumn 67. Add: Dept. of English, University of California, Berkeley, CA 94720.

JORDAN, MOREEN ELIZABETH CRUMLEY, b. Ennis, Tex, Apr. 15, 24; m. 54. ENGLISH. B.A, N.Tex. State Col, 44; M.A, Univ. Tex, 46; Ph.D. (Eng), Univ. Chicago, 54. Teaching fel, Eng, Univ. Tex, 45; instr. Eng. & Spanish, Tex. Col. Arts & Indust, 46-48; Eng, Univ. Richmond, 50-52; instr, UNIV. ILL, CHICAGO CIRCLE, 53-55, asst. prof, 55-62, ASSOC. PROF, 62- MLA. American literature, especially Henry James and Emily Dickinson; English novel, 1860-1960. Add: 909 Raleigh Rd, Glenview, IL 60025.

JORDAN, RAYMOND JOSEPH, b. Chicago, Ill, Apr. 18, 30; m. 53; c. 5. ENGLISH. B.A, Loyola Univ.(Ill), 52, M.A, 57; Univ. Iowa, 60-68. ASSOC. PROF. ENG, MARYCREST COL, 57-, ASST. TO PRES, 70-, chmn. dept, 65-70, acting acad. dean, 68-70. U.S.M.C, 54-57, 1st Lt. NCTE; Am. Asn. Higher Educ; AAUP; Am. Col. Pub. Relat. Asn. Nineteenth century American literature; Nathaniel Hawthorne. Publ: Taylor's The ebb and flow, 4/62 & Dickinson's Bustle in the house, 2/63, Explicator. Add: Marycrest College, Davenport, IA 52804.

JORDAN, ROBERT MAYNARD, b. Chicago, Ill, June 16, 24; m. 55; c. 3. ENGLISH. B.A, Colo. Col, 49; M.A, Univ. Calif, Berkeley, 52, Ph.D, 55. Instr. Eng, Amherst Col, 55-58; asst. prof, Univ. B.C, 58-63; assoc. prof, State Univ. N.Y. Stony Brook, 63-66, prof. Eng. & grad. dean, 66-68; prof. Eng, Univ. Wis, Madison, 68-69; PROF. ENG. & HEAD DEPT, UNIV. B.C, 69- Can. Counc. res. fel, 61-62 & 72-73; ed. bd. Chaucer Variorum, 69- U.S.A.A.F, 42-45, Sgt. Asn. Can. Univ. Teachers Eng; Mediaeval Acad. Am; MLA (chmn. Chaucer group, 67). Chaucer; mediaeval aesthetics; theory and history of criticism. Publ: Chaucer and the shape of creation, Harvard, 67; The non-dramatic disunity of the Merchant's tale, PMLA, 63; Chaucerian narrative, In: Companion to Chaucer studies, Oxford, 68; Chaucerian romance, Yale Fr. Stud, 74; plus others. Add: Dept. of English, University of British Columbia, Vancouver 8, B.C, Can.

JORGENSEN, ELING SEJR, b. Minneapolis, Minn, Mar. 30, 23; m. 50; c. 3. EDUCATION, INSTRUCTIONAL MEDIA. B.A, Univ. Iowa, 47; M.A, Univ. Wis, 49, Ph.D.(speech), 55. Instr. speech, Univ. Nebr, 49-52; asst. prof, Mich. State Univ, 52-57; dir. radio & TV & assoc. prof. jour, Univ. Mont, 57-62; dir. course develop, Midwest Prog. Airborne TV Instr, 62-65; PROF. EDUC, RADIO & TV, ASSOC. DIR. INSTR. MEDIA CTR. & DIR. ITV, MICH. STATE UNIV, 65- Dir, Mont. educ. TV stud, Ford Found. grant, 60-61; consult, Midwest Prog. Airborne TV Instr, 65-68; consult. & evaluator, Educ. Media Inst. Evaluation Proj, U.S. Off. Educ, 66-67; consult, Ford Motor Co, 67-68; consult. & lectr, Ky. State TV Utilization Insts, 67-68; chmn. Comn. Radio & TV, Dept. Audiovisual Instr, Nat. Educ. Asn, 67-70; ed. bd, Int. J. Instr. Media, 73- U.S.A, 43-46. Asn. Educ. Commun. & Technol; Nat. Asn. Educ. Broadcasters. Instructional television utilization; instructional systems development; attitudinal changes in students and faculty in instructional development. Publ: Television for Montana education, Mont. State. Univ, 62; Television institutes, In: Educational Media Institute Evaluation Project report, 66 & Preface, In: Survey of instructional TV, 1967, Dept. Audiovisual Instr, NEA, 67; Closed-circuit TV in the U.S.A, Bull. Inter-Univ. Res. Unit, Cambridge, 4/68. Add: 116 Linton Hall, Michigan State University, East Lansing, MI 48824.

JORGENSEN, PAUL ALFRED, b. Lansing, Mich, Feb. 17, 16; m. 42; c. 2. ENGLISH LITERATURE. A.B, Santa Barbara State Col, 38; A.M, Univ. Calif, 40, Ph.D, 45. Instr. ENG, col. agr, Univ. Calif, 46-47; UNIV. CALIF, LOS ANGELES, 47-49, asst. prof, 49-55, assoc. prof, 55-60, PROF, 60- Guggenheim fel, 56; vis. prof, Univ. Wash, summer 66; mem. adv. bd. ed, Huntington Libr. Quart, 66-; Col. Eng, 66-70; mem. humanities inst, Univ. Calif, 67-69; Univ. Calif. regents' fac. fel. humanities, 73-74. MLA; Shakespeare Asn. Am; Philol. Asn. Pac. Coast; Renaissance Soc. Am. Shakespeare; renaissance literature and philosophy. Publ: Shakespeare's military world, 56, Redeeming Shakespeare's words, 62, Lear's self-discovery, 67 & Our naked frailties: sensational art and meaning in Macbeth, 71, Univ. Calif; ed, Comedy of errors, Penguin, 64; co-auth, The art of prose, Scribner's, 65; auth, Antony and the protesting soldiers: a renaissance tradition for the structure of Antony and Cleopatra, Essays on Shakespeare, 65; Shakespeare's dark vocabulary, In: The drama of the Renaissance: essays for Leicester, Bradner, 70; Foreign sources for the Elizabethan notion of the Spaniard, Viator, 70; plus others. Add: Dept. of English, University of California, Los Angeles, CA 90024.

JOSEPH, BERTRAM L, b. Maesteg, Gt. Brit, July 1, 15; m. 39; c. 2. ENGLISH, DRAMA. B.A, Univ. Wales, 36, M.A, 44, fel, 46-49; D.Phil.(Eng), Oxford, 46, B.A. & M.A, 47. Lectr. Eng, Bristol Univ, 49-60, reader Renaissance Eng. lit, 60-64; sr. prof. Eng, Univ. West. Ont, 64-65; prof. drama, Univ. Wash, 65-70; PROF. DRAMA & CHMN. DEPT. DRAMA & THEATRE, QUEENS COL.(N.Y), 70- Consult. teacher, Drama Sect, Juilliard Sch. Am. Soc. Theatre Res; Am. Theatre Asn. Shakespeare; English Renaissance literature and life; appreciation of poetry in junior and senior colleges. Publ: Elizabethan acting, Oxford, 51, rev. ed, 64; Conscience and the king, Chatto & Windus, 53; The tragic actor, 59 & Acting Shakespeare, 60, Routledge; ed, King Lear, Univ. London, 66; auth, Shakespeare's Eden, Blandford, Eng. & Barnes & Noble, 71; A rehearsal of Macbeth (film), Holt, 73; Chaucer's Troilus and Criseyde, Essay & Stud, 54; Scenes invented merely to be spoken, 5/61 & Character and plot, fall 64, Drama Surv. Dir, Five films on Macbeth, Holt. Add: Dept. of Drama & Theatre, Queens College, Flushing, NY 11368.

JOSEPH, GERHARD JOSEPH, b. Frankfurt, W.Germany, Dec. 22, 31; U.S. citizen; m. 57; c. 3. VICTORIAN LITERATURE. A.B, Univ. Conn, 53, M.A, 55; Fulbright fel, Univ. Frankfurt, 55-56; Ph.D.(Eng. lit), Univ. Minn, Minneapolis, 66. Teaching assoc. ENG, Univ. Conn, 53-55; from teaching assoc. to instr, Univ. Minn, Minneapolis, 56-60; instr, Georgetown Univ, 60-66; asst. prof, Univ. Minn, Minneapolis, 66-67, assoc. prof, 67-68; LEHMAN COL, 68-70, PROF, 70- MLA. Victorian literature; Chaucer; American literature. Publ: Tennysonian love: the strange diagonal, 69 & John Barth, 70, Univ. Minn; Tennyson's concept of knowledge, wisdom and Pallas Athene, Mod. Philol, 5/72; Poe and Tennyson, PMLA, 5/73; Recent studies in the nineteenth century, Stud. Eng. Lit, fall 73. Add: Dept. of English, Herbert H. Lehman College, Bedford Park Blvd. W, Bronx, NY 10468.

JOSEPHS, LOIS, English. See FOWLER, LOIS JOSEPHS.

JOSEPHSON, CLIFFORD A, b. New York, N.Y, July 23, 22; m; c. 2. ENGLISH LANGUAGE & LITERATURE. B.S, Franklin & Marshall Col, 44; M.A, Columbia Univ, 51, Ph.D.(Eng), 55; Fulbright scholar, Cambridge, 53-54. Instr. ENG, City Col. New York, 55-58; Hunter Col, 58-59; asst. prof, SAN FRANCISCO STATE UNIV, 59-63, assoc. prof, 63-68, PROF, 68-, V.CHMN. DEPT, 73- Dir. training in Eng, Peace Corps Proj. Philippines VI, 62 & Philippines IX, 63; curriculum consult, Katharine Branson Sch, Ross, Calif, 63; consult, Educ. Develop. Corp, Palo Alto, Calif; consult. ed, St. Martin's Press, N.Y; lectr, Univ. Hawaii, summer 66. U.S.M.C, 42-46, 1st Lt. NCTE; Conf. Col. Compos. & Commun. Contemporary British literature; language; applied linguistics. Publ: Reading for rhetoric, Macmillan, 62, 2nd ed, 67, 3rd ed, 74. Add: Dept. of English, San Francisco State University, 1600 Holloway, San Francisco, CA 94132.

JOST, EDWARD FRANKLIN, b. St. Louis, Mo, Nov. 9, 32; m. 55; c. 6. ENGLISH. B.A, St. Louis Univ, 54, fel, 58-60; scholar, Univ. Notre Dame, 54-55, M.A, 55. Instr. ENG, Marquette Univ, 57-58; Univ. Mo, 60-62; Col. St. Thomas, 62-63; asst. prof, Canisius Col, 63-66; assoc. prof, St. Vincent Col, 66-67; assoc. prof. & chmn. dept, Medaille Col, 67-68. Lectr, St. Louis Univ, summers 55, 57, 59, 60; Webster Col, 59. U.S.A, 55-57. Nineteenth century English and American literature; modern literature; the arts and the media. Publ: Newman and liberalism: the later phase, Victorian Newslett; American literature, In: Catholic encyclopedia for school and home, McGraw, 65; Love and two kinds of existentialism, Eng. Rec, 2/66. Add: 24 Crescent Ave, Buffalo, NY 14214.

JOYNER, CHARLES W, History, American Studies. See Volume I, History.

JOYNER, NANCY CAROL, b. Asheville, N.C, July 27, 36. ENGLISH. B.A, Meredith Col, 58; M.A, Columbia Univ, 59; Ph.D.(Eng), Univ. N.C, Chapel Hill, 66. Instr. ENG, Univ. N.C, Chapel Hill, 64-65; Univ. Ky, 65-66, asst. prof, 66-70; ASSOC. PROF, WEST. CAROLINA UNIV, 70- MLA; Am. Stud. Asn. American literature; twentieth century literature; E.A. Robinson. Publ: Robinson's Pamela and Sandburg's Agatha, Am. Lit, 69; E.A. Robinson's concessions to the critics, Res. Stud, 72; Robinson's poets, Colby Lit. Quart, 72. Add: Dept. of English, Western Carolina University, Cullowhee, NC 28723.

JUDD, LARRY R, b. Ashton, Idaho, May 30, 37. SPEECH. B.S, Idaho State Univ, 59; M.A, Univ. Okla, 64, Ph.D.(speech), 65. Instr. SPEECH, UNIV. HOUSTON, 64-66, asst. prof, 66-69, ASSOC. PROF, 70- Med. Serv.C, U.S.A.R, 59-60, Capt. Speech Commun. Asn; South. Speech Commun. Asn; Nat. Soc. Stud. Commun. Studies in attitude change and measurement. Publ: A guide to fundamentals of speech, McCutchan, 68; Toward a systematic approach to evidence, Today's Speech, 11/64. Add: Dept. of Speech, University of Houston, Houston, TX 77004.

JUDSON, JOHN I, b. Stratford, Conn, Sept. 9, 30; m. 59; c. 3. CREATIVE WRITING, ENGLISH. A.B, Colby Col, 58; Univ. Maine, Orono, 63-64; M.F.A, Univ. Iowa, 65. Teacher Eng, Grinnell Jr. & Sr. High Sch, Iowa, 61-62; head dept, Coburn Class. Inst, 62-64; fac. asst. rhet. & reading, Univ. Iowa, 64-65; asst. prof. AM. LIT. & CREATIVE WRITING, UNIV. WIS-LA CROSSE, 65-67, ASSOC. PROF, 67- Ed, Northeast/Juniper Bks, Juniper Press, 62- Hart Crane Mem. Award, 69; Wis. Writers Award, 71; Earplay Award, Corp. Pub. Broadcasting, 73. U.S.A.F, 51-55. AAUP. Publ: Co-auth, Two from where it snows, Northeast Chapbk. Series, 64; auth, Surreal songs, Juniper, 68; ed, Voyages to the inland sea (Vols. I-IV), Univ. Wis, 69-73; auth, Within seasons, Colby Col, 70; Finding words in winter, Elizabeth Press, 73; plus numerous poems & arts. in var. anthologies & jour. Add: Dept. of English, Grandview Hall, University of Wisconsin-La Crosse, La Crosse, WI 54601.

JUDSON, LYMAN SPICER VINCENT, b. Plymouth, Mich, Mar. 27, 03. SPEECH, VOICE SCIENCE. A.B, Albion Col, 25; M.S, Univ. Mich, Ann Arbor, 29; Ph.D.(med. sci), Univ. Wis-Madison, 33; dipl. art, Univ. San Francisco, Spain, 65. Prof. speech & dir. speech clin, Kans. State Teachers Col, summers 28, 29; res. assoc. speech path, Univ. Iowa, 29-30; prof. speech & drama & chmn. dept, Auburn Univ, 30-31; asst. prof. Eng, Univ. Ill, 33-35; prof. speech & drama & chmn. dept, Kalamazoo, Col, 36-42; chief visual educ. div, Orgn. Am. States, 46-50; chmn. dept. speech, dir. pub. relat. & dir. extension div, Babson Inst. Bus. Admin, 50-55; asst. to pres, Alfred Univ, 55-57; coord. develop. & dir. pub. relat, Ripon Col, 57-63; prof. speech, Winona State Col, 64-71; PRES. & TREAS, AM. FINE ARTS FOUND, 71- Mem, White House Comt. Speech Disorders, 33-34; liaison off, NATO, Paris, France, 55; lectr. anat. & physiol, Univ. Wis, 63-64. U.S.N, 42-46, Res, 46-59, Comdr. Fel. Explorers Club (ed, Log, 50-). Nerve impulse conduction; brain waves; pseudo-nation corporations. Publ: Co-auth, Basic speech and voice science, Col. Printing, 33 & Voice science, F.S. Crofts; auth, A manual of group discussion, Univ. Ill, 36; Public speaking for future farmers, 36, rev. ed, 39, 45, 55 & Winning future farmer speeches, 39, Interstate; co-auth, Modern group discussion, 37, 38, ed, The student congress movement, 40 & The Monroe Doctrine and the growth of western hemisphere solidarity, 41, Wilson; co-auth, After-dinner speaking, Noble, 37 & Voice science, Appleton, 42, rev. ed, 65; co-auth, The Judson guides to Latin America, Let's go to Colombia, 49, Let's go to Guatemala, 50, Let's go to Peru, 51 & Your holiday in Cuba, 52, Harper; ed, Operation inland seas, U.S. Navy, 59; auth, Conference methods, 67 & The interview, 68, Winona State Col; Vincent Judson: the island series, Castle-Pierce, 73; Solution: PNC and PNCland, Apex Univ, 73; co-auth, Electrodynamic recorder, Science, 30 & The vegetative versus the speech use of biological systems, Quart. J. Speech, 4/32; auth, Combining the breathing undae of speaker and listener with the dictaphone record of the speech, Am. J. Psychol, 1/32. Add: American Fine Arts Foundation, P.O. Box 1338, Oshkosh, WI 54901.

JUERGENSEN, HANS, b. Ger, Dec. 17, 19; nat; m. 45; c. 1. HUMANITIES. B.A, Upsala Col, 42; univ. fel, Johns Hopkins Univ, 46-51, Ph.D.(Ger), 51. Instr. Ger, Univ. Kans, 51-53; assoc. prof. Eng. & chmn. dept, Quinnipiac Col, 53-61, asst. prof. HUMANITIES, UNIV. S.FLA, 61-63, assoc. prof, 63-68, PROF, 68- Mem. bd. dir, Silvermine Col. Art, Conn, 60-61; coord, Poetry in Elem. Schs. Proj, Nat. Found. Arts, 72- C.W.S, U.S.A, 42-45. Fel. Int. Poetry Soc; AAUP; Poetry Soc. Am; Nat. Fed. State Poetry Soc. (pres, 68, ed, Annual Prize Poems, 69-73). Art and philosophy of the 17th century; contemporary poetry; American Civil War. Publ: I feed you from my cup (poems), Quinnipiac Col, 58; In need for names (poems), Linden, 61; Existential canon and other poems, 65 & Florida montage (poems), 66, South & West; Sermons from the ammunition hatch of the ship of fools, Vagabond, 68; From the divide (poems), 4 eds, 71-72, Hebraic modes (poems), 72 & Points of departure (poems), 74, Olivant; Monsoon season, In: Where is Vietnam?, Doubleday, 67; poem in Diamond anthology, Poetry Soc. Am, 71; Geul: George H. Thomas, a summary in perspective, Weid, 6/72; plus others. Add: 7815 Pine Hill Dr, Tampa, FL 33610.

JULEUS, NELS GEORGE, b. Cleveland, Ohio, Feb. 16, 26; m. 47; c. 2. SPEECH. A.B, Cleveland Col, 50; M.A, West. Reserve Univ, 51, Ph.D, 63. Lectr. speech, West. Reserve Univ, 51-55; instr, ALLEGHENY COL, 55-59, asst. prof, 59-65, assoc. prof. SPEECH & DRAMATIC ARTS, 65-70, PROF, 70-, CHMN. DEPT, 66- Actor, Penn Playhouse, summers 55-63; res. fel, Ling. Inst, Ohio State Univ, summer 70; mem. Creative Educ. Found. U.S.N, 44-46. Speech Commun. Asn. Linguistics; communication; public address. Publ: Perspectives on public speaking, Am. Bk, 66; The fabulous for-instance, Today's Speech, 60; Aram's defense, Gavel, 61; A plan for teaching speech preparation, In: Listening and speaking, Macmillan, 71; Voices of social reform, In: History of public speaking in Pennsylvania, Pa. Speech Asn, 71; The micro-language lab, Social Change, 72. Add: Dept. of Speech & Dramatic Art, Allegheny College, Meadville, PA 16335.

JUMPER, WILL CARRAGHER, b. Sacramento, Calif, Nov. 19, 16. AMERICAN LITERATURE, CREATIVE WRITING. B.S, Univ. Calif, Berkeley, 37; M.A, Stanford Univ, 51, univ. scholar, 54, Ph.D.(Am. lit), 58. Instr, high sch, Modesto, Calif, 38-42, 46-53, 54-59; asst. prof. CREATIVE WRITING & ENG, IOWA STATE UNIV, 59-60, assoc. prof, 60-66, PROF, 66- Asst, Stanford Univ, summer 56. Clarence Urmy Poetry Award, Stanford Univ, 53, 54; San Francisco Browning Soc. Poetry Award, 54. U.S.N, 42-46, Res, 46-53, Lt. Comdr. NCTE; Am. Stud. Asn; MLA; Am. Acad. Polit. & Soc. Sci. Stephen Crane and the late 19th century American realists; recent and contemporary American poetry; impact of impressionism on literary theory. Publ: The gifted child in the high school, Calif. J. Sec. Educ, 2/51; Whom seek ye? A note on Robert Lowell's poetry, Hudson Rev, 56; Language of Wallace Stevens, Iowa Eng. Yearbk, 61. Add: Pearson Hall, Iowa State University, Ames, IA 50010.

JUNEJA, MAN MOHAN KRISHNA, b. Rangpur, Punjab, India, Aug. 11, 36; m. 64; c. 3. DRAMA, THEATRE. B.A, Panjab Univ, India, 57; M.A, Univ. Delhi, 60; P.D.E.S, Univ. Leeds, 65; univ. scholar, Univ. Leicester, 66-68, Ph.D.(drama & Eng), 68; dipl. film, Ryerson Polytech. Inst, 74. Lectr. Eng, Univ. Delhi, 60-64; Waterloo Lutheran Univ, 68-69; ASST. PROF. ENG. & DRAMATIC ARTS, McMASTER UNIV, 69- Chmn, Camera Can. Col, 74. N.C.C, India, 62-64, 2nd Lt. Can. Asn. Univ. Teachers; Asn. Can. Univ. Teachers Eng; MLA; Can. Asn. Photographic Art (dir. contemporary & stud. div, 73-). Modern American drama; Hindu theatre of 200 B.C. to 900 A.D; cinema and photography and the relationship between visual and verbal culture. Publ: Truth alone will last, Foto Flash, 6/73; Dassehra: Hindu festival of morality drama, Artifact, 10/73; Photography in education, Camera Can, 11/73; plus three others. Add: Dept. of English, McMaster University, Hamilton, Ont. L8S 4L9, Can.

JUNKINS, DONALD A, b. Saugus, Mass, Dec. 19, 31; m. 58; c. 3. AMERICAN LITERATURE, CREATIVE WRITING. B.A, Univ. Mass, 53; S.T.B, Boston Univ, 56, S.T.M, 57, A.M, 59, Ph.D.(Am.lit), 63; Breadloaf poetry scholar, Breadloaf Writer's Conf, summer 59. From instr. Eng. to asst. prof, Emerson Col, 61-63; Chico State Col, 63-66; UNIV. MASS, AMHERST, 66-70, assoc. prof. ENG, 70-74, PROF, 74-, DIR. MFA GRAD. PROG, 70- Assoc. poetry ed, Mass. Rev, 68- Jennie Tane Award for poetry, 67; Nat. Endowment for the Arts award, 68. Poetry Soc. Am.(John Masefield Mem. Award, 72). Colonial and 19th century American literature; creative writing, poetry; contemporary world poetry. Publ: The sunfish and the partridge, Pym-Randall, 65; The graves of Scotland Parish (poems), Heron, 69; Walden, 100 years after thoreau (poems), Yorick, 69; And sandpipers she said (poems), Univ. Mass, 70; Edward Taylor's revisions, Am. Lit, 5/65; Hawthorne's House of seven gables: a prototype of the human mind, Lit. & Psychol, 67; Should stars woo and lobster claws?: Edward Taylor's poetic theory, Early Am. Lit, 11/68. Add: Dept. of English, Bartlett Hall, University of Massachusetts, Amherst, MA 01002.

JURICH, JOSEPH, b. Chicago, Ill, Dec. 14, 26; m. 57; c. 1. ENGLISH. Ph.B, Univ. Chicago, 46, M.A, 51; Ph.D.(Eng), Univ. Ill, 64. Asst. Eng, Univ. Ill, 53-57; instr, Univ. Fla, 57-58; Washburn Univ, 58-59; Univ. Ariz, 60-63; ASST. PROF. rhetoric, Col. Basic Stud, Boston Univ, 63-70; ENG, BOSTON STATE COL, 70- Conf. Col. Compos. & Commun; NCTE (mem. comt. bibliog. col. teaching of Eng, 65-); AAUP. Mark Twain and American literature; freshman and advanced composition; preparation of English teachers. Add: Dept. of English, Boston State College, 174 Ipswich St, Boston, MA 02115.

JUSTICE, DONALD RODNEY, b. Miami, Fla, Aug. 12, 25; m. 47; c. 1. WRITING. B.A, Univ. Miami, 45; M.A, Univ. N.C, 47; Stanford Univ, 48-49; Ph.D, State Univ. Iowa, 54. Instr. ENG, Univ. Miami, 47-48, 49-51; vis. asst. prof, Univ. Mo, 55-56; asst. prof, Hamline Univ, 56-57; vis. lectr, Univ. Iowa, 57-59, asst. prof, 59-63, assoc. prof, 63-66; Syracuse Univ, 66-67, PROF, 68-71, UNIV. IOWA, 71- Rockefeller fel, 54-55; poet in residence, Reed Col, 62; Elliston lectr, Univ. Cincinnati, 67; Nat. Counc. Arts fel, 67-68; vis. prof. Eng, Univ. Calif, Irvine, 70-71. Lamont Poetry Selection Award, 59; Inez Boulton Prize, 60; Harriet Monroe Mem. Prize, 60. PEN Club. Modern poetry. Publ: The summer anniversaries, 60 & Night light, 67; Wesleyan Univ; ed, The collected poems of Weldon Kees, Stonewall, 60; Univ. Nebr. 62; co-ed, Midland, Random, 61; auth, A local storm, 63 & Sixteen poems, 70, Stonewall; co-ed, Contemporary French poetry, Univ. Mich, 65; auth, Departures, Atheneum, 73. Add: Dept. of English, University of Iowa, Iowa City, IA 52242.

JUSTUS, JAMES HUFF, b. Newport, Tenn, Apr. 22, 29. ENGLISH. A.B, Univ. Tenn, 50, A.M, 52; Ph.D, Univ. Wash, 61. Instr. ENG, IND. UNIV, BLOOMINGTON, 61-62, asst. prof, 62-65, assoc. prof, 65-69, PROF, 60- Contrib, American literary scholarship, an annual 1968-, Duke Univ, 70- U.S.A, 54-56. MLA; Soc. Stud. South. Lit. Twentieth century American novel; American literature, 1800-1900. Publ: The mariner and Robert Penn Warren, Tex. Stud. Lit. & Lang, spring 66; All the burdens of All the King's men, In: The forties, Everett/Edwards, 69. Add: Dept. of English, Indiana University, Bloomington, IN 47401.

K

KABATCHNIK, AMNON, b. Tel-Aviv, Israel, May 24, 29; U.S. citizen; m. 67; c. 2. THEATRE. B.S, Boston Univ, 54; M.F.A, Yale, 57. Asst. prof. acting & directing, State Univ. N.Y. Binghamton, 68-71; Stanford Univ, 71-72; assoc. prof. acting & directing & head prof. acting prog, Ohio State Univ, 72-73; ASSOC. PROF. ACTING & DIRECTING & DIR. PROG. IN DIRECTING, SCH. THEATRE, FLA. STATE UNIV, 73- Dir, Off-Broadway Productions, 59-65, Nat. Rd. Companies, 62-68; Habimah Nat. Theatre, Israel, Zavit Theatre, Godik Productions & New London Players, N.H. Soc. Stage Directors & Choreographers; Univ. & Col. Theatre Asn. Theatre in Israel. Add: School of Theatre, Florida State University, Tallahassee, FL 32306.

KABEALO, THYRA BEVIER, b. Iola, Kans, Aug. 3, 05; m. 31, 62; c. 2. LINGUISTICS, LITERATURE. A.B, N.Y. State Col. Teachers, Albany, 26; Syracuse Univ, summers 28, 29; M.A, Ohio State Univ, 30. Teacher Eng. & librarian, Pub. Schs, N.Y, 26-29, 30-31; instr. ENG, OHIO STATE UNIV, 46-63, asst. prof, 63-71, asst. to ed, 48-53, res. assoc, univ. res. found, summer 60, EMER. PROF, 71- Instr. libr. sci, Sch. Libr. Sci, Syracuse Univ, summers 30, 31; assoc. ed, Ohio Archaeologist, 59-63; consult. ed, Ohio State Mus, 63-; tech. ed. & indust. consult. NCTE; Am. Correctional Asn; Col. Eng. Asn; Soc. Tech. Writers & Publ; MLA; AAAS; Mediaeval Acad. Am. Medieval moral and ethical subjects; criminology. Publ: Latin incipts from 10th to 13th century with Bloomfield, Howard & Guyot; American use of the subjunctive, Am. Speech, 2/31; co-auth, Rivolte carcerzire negli U.S.A, 1951-1971, Quaderni di Criminologia Clinica, 9/73. Add: 65 Nottingham Rd, Columbus, OH 43214.

KABLE, JUNE PRENTICE, b. Shreveport, La, June 22, 28; div; c. 2. RHETORIC, COMMUNICATION. B.Mus, Baylor Univ, 49; M.Ed, Sul Ross State Univ, 59; Ed.D.(educ, speech), N.Tex. State Univ, 71. Teacher, Archer City Pub. Schs, Tex, 52-53; Rankin Pub. Schs, 53-62; Wichita Falls Pub. Schs, 62-68; asst. prof. PUB. ADDRESS, MIDWEST. UNIV, 68-73, ASSOC. PROF. & CHMN. DEPT, 73- South. Speech Commun. Asn; Speech Commun. Asn. Add: Dept. of Public Address, Midwestern University, 3400 Taft, Wichita Falls, TX 76308.

KACHRU, BRAJ BEHARI, South Asian English, Dardic Languages. See Volume III, Foreign Languages, Linguistics & Philology.

KAGLE, STEVEN EARL, b. New York, N.Y, Sept. 15, 41; m. 65; c. 2. ENGLISH. A.B, Cornell Univ, 63; Rackham fel, Univ. Mich, 65, M.A. & Ph.D. (Am. cult), 67. Asst. prof. ENG, Richmond Col. (N.Y), 67-69; ASSOC. PROF, ILL. STATE UNIV, 69- Chmn, seminar speculative fiction, Midwest Mod. Lang. Asn, 70-71; seminar lit. exploration, Mod. Lang. Asn, 72- MLA; Am. Stud. Asn; Sci. Fiction Res. Asn. Autobiographical literature; American literary history; creative writing. Publ: Diary of John Adams & the motive of achievement, Hartford Stud. Lit, 71; Societal quest, Extrapolation, 71; Heroism and the Scouring of the shire, Muirgheal, 73; plus others. Add: Dept. of English, Illinois State University, Stevenson Hall, Normal, IL 61761.

KAHAN, GERALD, b. New York, N.Y, Nov. 28, 23; m. 67. DRAMA, THEATER. B.A, Univ. Wis, 47, M.A, 48, Ph.D, 54. Dir, Community Players, Sheboygan, Wis, 48-52; asst. prof, West. Wash. Col. Educ, 54-56; THEATER, Reed Col, 56-59; assoc. prof, UNIV. GA, 59-68, PROF, 66- Ed, Wis. Idea Theatre Quart, 54; guest prof. & dir, Univ. Colo. summers 58 & 60; co-chmn, Am. Educ. Theatre Asn. Prod. Lists Proj, 67-69. U.S.A.F, 45-48, Lt. Am. Theatre Asn; Southeast. Theatre Conf.(pres, 68-69); Am. Soc. Theatre Res; Int. Fedn. Theatre Res. Theatre history; dramatic literature and criticism. Publ: Critical edition of The mysterious father, Univ. Ga, 65; Graduate curriculum for community theatre directors, Educ. Theatre J, 10/62; Produce or 'produce', Educ. Record, Vol. 49, No. 3; The wayfarer: an American religious pageant, Players, 4-5/72; plus others. Add: Dept. of Drama, University of Georgia, Athens, GA 30602.

KAHAN, STANLEY, b. New York, N.Y, Apr. 21, 31; m. 57; c. 2. THEATER ARTS, DRAMATIC LITERATURE. B.A, City Univ. New York, 53; M.A, Univ. Wis, 54, Ph.D.(Eng. melodrama), 59. Instr. speech & radio, Iowa State Univ, 55-58; speech & drama, Bowling Green State Univ, 58-61; asst. prof. THEATER ARTS, CALIF. STATE UNIV, LONG BEACH, 61-65, assoc. prof, 65-69, PROF, 69-, chmn. dept, 69-72. Am. Theatre Asn; Speech Commun. Asn. History and techniques of acting; opera and musical comedy production; theater history. Publ: Introduction to acting, 62 & An actor's workbook, 67, Harcourt. Add: Dept. of Theater Arts, California State University at Long Beach, Long Beach, CA 90840.

KAHN, FRANK J, b. New York, N.Y, Apr. 3, 38; m. 68; c. 1. MASS COMMUNICATIONS, SPEECH. B.A, Queens Col.(N.Y), 58; M.S, Syracuse Univ, 61; Ph.D.(commun), N.Y. Univ, 67. Asst. speech & broadcasting, Queens Col. (N.Y), 57-58; radio-TV, Syracuse Univ, 60-61; acting dir. broadcasting, Queens Col.(N.Y), 63-64, lectr. & prod. supvr. speech & broadcasting, 63-66; asst. prof. speech & theatre & dir. TV, LEHMAN COL, 67-70, ASSOC. PROF. & DIR. MASS COMMUN, 71- Broadcast Preceptor Award, San Francisco State Col, 69. U.S.A.R, 62-68. Broadcast Educ. Asn; Speech Commun. Asn. Broadcasting law; history of broadcasting; public policy and mass media. Publ: Ed, Documents of American broadcasting, Appleton, 68 & Prentice, 73; auth, Compensation of faculty engaged in ITV, NAEB Jour, 1-2/65; Jazz radio: milestones and millstones, Jazz & Pop, 8/67; Economic injury and the public interest, Fed. Commun. Bar J, 69-70; plus many others. Add: Dept. of Speech & Theatre, Lehman College, Bedford Park Blvd. W, Bronx, NY 10468.

KAHN, SHOLOM J, b. New York, N.Y, Oct. 5, 18; m. 51; c. 2. ENGLISH, PHILOSOPHY. B.A, Columbia Univ, 38, M.A, 42, Ph.D.(philos), 50; B.H.L, Sem. Col. Jewish Stud, 50. Tutor ENG, Queens Col.(N.Y), 46-48; instr, HEBREW UNIV, ISRAEL, 51-57, lectr, 57-65, sr. lectr, 65-72, ASSOC. PROF, 72-, CHMN. DEPT. AM. STUD, 73- Rockefeller fel, 57-58; hon. for. mem, ed. counc, J. Aesthet. & Art Criticism; distinguished vis. prof, San Fernando Valley State Col, 66-67; vis. prof, Univ. Calif, Davis, 73. U.S.A.A.F, 43-46, Sgt. Col. Eng. Asn; MLA; Am. Philos. Asn; Am. Soc. Aesthet. Aesthetics and literary criticism; American literature; American studies. Publ: Science and aesthetic judgment, Columbia Univ, 53; ed, A whole loaf: stories from Israel, Grosset, 63; co-auth, Saul Tchernichowsky, London, E. & W. Libr, 68; auth, Pioneering and frontier life in American literature, (in Hebrew), Yachdav, Tel Aviv, 62. Add: Dept. of American Studies, Hebrew University, Jerusalem, Israel.

KAHN, SY M, b. New York, N.Y, Sept. 15, 24; m. 63; c. 1. ENGLISH. B.A, Univ. Pa; M.A, Univ. Conn; Ph.D.(Eng), Univ. Wis, 57. Instr. ENG, Univ. Conn, 49-51; teaching asst, Univ. Wis, 51-55; instr, Beloit Col, 55-57, asst. prof. Eng, 57-58, 59-60; Fulbright prof. Eng. & Am. lit, Univ. Salonica, Greece, 58-59; asst. prof. Eng. & humanities, Univ. S.Fla, 60-63; assoc. prof, RAYMOND COL, UNIV. OF THE PAC, 63-66, prof, 66-68, PROF. ENG. & DRAMA & DIR. UNIV. THEATRE, 68-, CHMN. DEPT. DRAMA, 70- Fulbright prof. Am. lit, Univ. Warsaw, 66-67; Univ. Vienna, 70-71. U.S.A, 43-45. MLA; AAUP; Am. Theatre Asn. Nineteenth and 20th century English and American literature; modern drama and poetry; humanities. Publ: Our separate darkness, Crosby Continental Ed, Italy, 63; co-auth, Triptych, Raymond Col, 64; A later sun, 66 & auth, Another time, 68, Sydon; The fight is with phantoms, South-West, 66; Through a glass menagerie darkly: the world of Tennessee Williams, In: Modern American drama, Everett Edwards, 67; Hart Crane and Harry Crosby: a transit of poets, J. Mod. Lit, 70; The games God plays with man: a discussion of JB, In: The fifties: poetry, fiction, drama, Everett Edwards, 71; plus others. Add: Dept. of Drama, University of the Pacific, Stockton, CA 95204.

KAHRL, GEORGE MORROW, b. Fairmont, W.Va, Feb. 17, 04; m. 29; c. 3. ENGLISH LITERATURE. A.B, Wesleyan Univ, 26; A.M, Princeton, 30; Ph.D, Harvard, 36. Instr, Am. Univ. Beirut, 26-28; acting asst. prof, Kenyon Col, 30-31, asst. prof, 36-37; curator poetry room, Widener Libr, Harvard, 33-36; prof. ENG, ELMIRA COL, 37-71, chmn. div. lang. & lit, 37-64, EMER. PROF, 71- Res. fel, Harvard, 46-47, Ford fac. fel, 53-54, res. assoc, fac, 68-69; Guggenheim fel, 64-65; res. dir, Elmira Col. Jr. Year Abroad Prog, Paris, 65-66; Folger & Huntington fels, 69; Am. Philos. Soc. & Am. Counc. Learned Soc. grants; vis. prof, Kenyon Col, 71-73. MLA; Mod. Humanities Res. Asn; Bibliog. Soc, Eng. Teaching and publication; English literature and drama of the 18th century. Publ: Tobias Smollett, traveler-novelist; co-auth, The letters of David Garrick; auth, The Garrick collection of English drama in the British Museum, Brit. Mus, (in press); Captain Robert Stobo, Va. Mag. Hist. & Biog, 4-7/41; Garrick, Johnson and Lichfield, New Rambler, London, 6/66; Smollett as a caricaturist, In: Tobias Smollett, Bicentenial Essays presented to Lewis M. Knapp, Oxford, 71; plus others. Add: Wolf Pen Springs, 30515 Rabbit Ridge Rd, Howard, OH 43028.

KAHRL, STANLEY JADWIN, b. Mt. Vernon, Ohio, June 30, 31; m. 54; c. 4. MEDIEVAL ENGLISH. A.B, Harvard, 53, Ph.D.(Eng), 62; B.A, Cambridge, 58, M.A, 62. Teaching fel. ENG, Harvard, 60-62; instr, Univ. Rochester, 62-65, asst. prof, 65-69, PROF. DIR. CTR. MEDIEVAL & RENAISSANCE STUD, OHIO STATE UNIV, 69-, assoc. dean. col. humanities, 70-72. Summer res. grant, Univ. Rochester, 66; secy, Eng. Group I, Mod. Lang. Asn, 67-68, chmn, 68-69, mem. exec. comt, 69-; ed, Old Eng. Newsletter, 69-; mem, vis. comt. bd. overseers, Harvard Univ. Libr, 72; chmn, Ctrs. & Regional Asns, Medieval Acad, 72-; consult, Nat. Endowment for Humanities. U.S.N, 53-56, Res, 56-66, Lt.(jg). MLA; Mediaeval Acad. Am; Mod. Humanities Res. Asn; Renaissance Soc. Am. Medieval drama; Middle English, including Chaucer; Old English. Publ: Ed, Merry tales of the mad men of Gotham, Northwest. Univ, 65; co-ed, Essential articles for the study of Old English poetry, Shoestring Press, 68; auth, Traditions of Medieval English drama, Hutchinson Univ. Libr, 74; Medieval origins of the sixteenth century jestbooks, Stud. in Renaissance, 66; Feuds in Beowulf: a tragic necessity?, Mod. Philol, 72; Chaucer's Squire's tale and the decline of chivalry, Chaucer Rev, 73; plus others. Add: Center for Medieval and Renaissance Studies, Ohio State University, 320 Main Library, 1858 Neil Ave, Columbus, OH 43210.

KAIN, RICHARD MORGAN, b. York, Pa, Dec. 19, 08; m. 31; c. 3. ENGLISH LITERATURE. A.B, Swarthmore Col, 30; A.M, Univ. Chicago, 31, Ph.D, 34; Harvard, 31-32. Assoc. prof. ENG, Augustana Col, 33-34; asst. prof, Ohio Wesleyan Univ, 34-40; assoc. prof, UNIV. LOUISVILLE, 40-47, PROF, 47-, acting head, 48-49, 53, chmn. div. humanities, 63-69. Summers, vis. prof. Northwest. Univ, 48, Harvard, 50, Univ. Colo, 59, N.Y. Univ, 63 & Univ. Wash, 66; res, Yale & Brit. Mus, 53-54; lectr, Yeats Int. Summer Sch, Ireland, 61 & 67; Fulbright lectr, Univ. Inst, Venice, Italy, 61-62; lectr, Am. Stud. Sem, Rome, 62; centennial lectr, Univ. Mass, 63; adv. ed, Joyce Quart, 63-; lectr. Univ. Col. Dublin, 72. MLA; Mod. Humanities Res. Asn, Gt. Brit; Am. Comt. Irish Stud; Int. Asn. Stud. Anglo-Irish Lit; James Joyce Soc. English and continental fiction; James Joyce; modern Irish history and literature. Publ: Fabulous voyager: James Joyce's Ulysses, Univ. Chicago & Viking; co-auth, Joyce: the man, the work, the reputation, N.Y. Univ, John Calder, Collier; auth, Dublin in the age of W.B. Yeats and James Joyce, Univ. Okla, 62 & Smythe, 72; co-auth, The workshop of Daedalus, Northwest. Univ, 65; auth, Susan Mitchell, Bucknell Univ, 72; contrib, Sunshine and the moon's delight: a centenary tribute to J.M. Synge, Smythe & Univ. Beirut, 72; Litters from aloft, Univ. Tulsa, 71; Ulysses and The waste land, fifty years after, Univ. Man, 72; plus others. Add: Dept. of English, University of Louisville, Louisville, KY 40208.

KAISER, ALVIN RICHARD, b. Preston, Nebr. SPEECH, DRAMA. B.A, N.Cent. Col, 29; M.A, State Univ. Iowa, 38; Ed.D, Univ. Ore, 55. Instr, High Sch, Kewanee, Ill, 29-30, head Eng. dept, 31-37; instr. SPEECH & DRAMA, EAST. ORE. STATE COL, 37-39, asst. prof, 39-47, assoc. prof, 47-55, prof, 55-69, head div. humanities, 56-69, EMER. PROF, 69- Am. Theatre Asn; NCTE. Free lance writing. Publ: Doctor, in buckskin clad, 59; Grande Ronde romance, 62. Add: 503 Washington, La Grande, OR 97850.

KAISER, WALTER JACOB, b. Bellevue, Ohio, May 31, 31; m. 66. ENGLISH & COMPARATIVE LITERATURE. A.B, Harvard, 54, Ph.D, 60; Fulbright fel, Univ. Paris, 54-55, Tower fel, Ecole Norm. Supér, 55-56. Instr. ENG. & COMP. LIT, HARVARD, 60-62, asst. prof, 62-65, ASSOC. PROF, 65-, CHMN. DEPT. COMP. LIT, 70- Am. Counc. Learned Soc. fel, Rome, 64-65. Mod. Greek Stud. Asn; Am. Comp. Lit. Asn; Renaissance Soc. Am. Renaissance comparative literature. Publ: Praisers of folly: Erasmus, Rabelais, Shakespeare, Harvard, 63 & Victor Gollancz, London, 64; ed, Essays of Montaigne translated by John Florio, Houghton, 64; transl, Three secret poems by George Seferis, Harvard, 69. Add: 401 Boylston Hall, Harvard University, Cambridge, MA 02138.

KAKONIS, THOMAS E, b. Long Beach, Calif, Nov. 13, 30; m. 58; c. 2. ENGLISH. B.A, Univ. Minn, 52; M.S, S.Dak. State Univ, 58; Ph.D.(Eng), Univ. Iowa, 65. Instr. ENG, Univ. Idaho, 58-59; Mankato State Col, 59-60; North. Ill. Univ, 64-66; assoc. prof, Wis. State Univ-Whitewater, 66-68, 69-72; S.Dak. State Univ, 68-69; HEAD DEPT. LANG. & LIT, FERRIS STATE COL, 72- Educ. consult, Film Counselors, Inc, 70-; ed. consult, Brevet Int, Inc, 70- U.S.A, 53-55, 1st Lt. MLA. Rhetoric and composition; 18th century English literature; popular culture. Publ: Co-ed, The short story: ideas and backgrounds, 67, Language, rhetoric, and idea, 67 & Plays by four tragedians, 68, C.E. Merrill; co-ed, The literary artist as social critic, Glencoe, 69, Forms of rhetoric, McGraw, 69, Strategies in rhetoric, Harper, 71, Statement and craft, Prentice-Hall, 71, From language to idea, Holt, 71, Now and tomorrow, 71 & Crossroads, 72, D.C. Heath & Scene seventy, Houghton, 72; auth, Beknighted healer, Med. Opinion, 8/72. Add: Dept. of Languages & Literature, School of General Education, Ferris State College, Big Rapids, MI 49307.

KALE, PRAMOD KESHAV, b. May 31, 34; Indian citizen; m. 61; c. 2. SPEECH & DRAMA, MASS COMMUNICATION. B.A, Univ. Poona, 54, M.A, 57; Fulbright-Smithmundt fel, Yale, 63-64; Ford fel. & M.A, Univ. Wis-Madison, 66, Ph.D.(speech), 67. Lectr. Eng, Khalsa Col, Univ. Bombay, 57-61, Mithibai Col, 61-63; asst. prof. literatural theatre & films, Univ. Minn, Minneapolis, 67-71; PROG. SPECIALIST FILMS & TV EDUC, FORD FOUND, 71- Dramatic theory; sociology of performing arts; interrelationship of mass media and society. Publ: The theatric universe: a study of the Natyasastra, Pop. Prakashan, Bombay, 74; contribr, P.S. Rege: Universal-personal, Bks. Abroad, 69, Whatever happened to Marathi cinema, Quest, 72 & Epic to Polemic: social change in Marathi drama—1843-1879, Sangeet Natak, 72. Add: Ford Foundation, 55 Lodi Estate, New Delhi 3, India.

KALISS, BERNARD STANLEY, b. Waterbury, Conn, Feb. 19, 19. ENGLISH. B.S, Mt. St. Mary's Col, 51; Fulbright scholar, Sorbonne & Univ. Bordeaux, 51-52; M.A, Fordham Univ, 55. Instr. ENG, MT. ST. MARY'S COL.(MD), 53-55, asst. prof, 55-68, ASSOC. PROF, 68-, DEAN ACAD. AFFAIRS, 69-, asst. dean & registr, 55-56. Consult. Eng. lit, CHOICE. U.S.A.A.F, 43-46. MLA; Col. Eng. Asn; Conf. Col. Compos. & Commun; NCTE; Am. Asn. Teachers Fr; Asn. Higher Educ; Am. Conf. Acad. Deans. Nineteenth century English. Add: Mt. St. Mary's College, Emmitsburg, MD 21727.

KALLICH, MARTIN, b. Brooklyn, N.Y, Jan. 19, 18; m. 43; c. 2. ENGLISH. Ph.D, Johns Hopkins Univ, 45. Instr, Johns Hopkins Univ, 43-44; Brooklyn Col, 45; Wayne Univ, 45-49; assoc. prof. ENG, S.Dak. State Col, 49-56, prof, 56-58; assoc. prof, NORTH. ILL. UNIV, 58-62, PROF, 62- U.S.A, 42-43. MLA. English literature; 18th century critical theory. Publ: Psychological milieu of Lytton Strachey, 61 & co-ed, A book of the sonnet: poems and criticism, 73, Twayne; co-auth, American Revolution through British eyes, Harper, 62; auth, Heaven's first law: rhetoric and order in Pope's essay on man, North. Ill. Univ, 67; The association of ideas and critical theory in 18th century England, Mouton, 70; The other end of the egg: religious satire in Swift's Gulliver's travels, N.Y. Univ, 70; Samuel Johnson's principles of criticism, J. Aesthet. & Art Criticism, fall 66; Pegasus on the seesaw: balance and antithesis in Pope's essay on criticism, Tenn. Stud. Lit, 67; Horace Walpole against Edmund Burke, Stud. Burke & His Time, summer-fall 68. Add: Dept. of English, Northern Illinois University, DeKalb, IL 60115.

KALLSEN, THEODORE JOHN, b. Jasper, Minn, Mar. 27, 15; m. 39; c. 2. AMERICAN LITERATURE. B.S, Mankato State Col, 36; M.A, State Univ. Iowa, 40, Ph.D, 49. Prin, Pub. Schs, Magnolia, Minn, 36-40; teacher, Lakefield, 40-41; head dept. Eng, New Ulm High Sch, 41-42; instr. educ, St. Louis Univ, 42-43; instr. Eng, State Univ. Iowa, 46-49; from asst. prof. to assoc. prof, W.Va. Univ, 49-55; PROF. ENG, STEPHEN F. AUSTIN STATE UNIV, 55-, DEAN LIB. ARTS, 65-, head dept. Eng, 55-65. U.S.N.R, 44-46, Lt.(jg). NCTE; South. Humanities Conf; AAUP. American literature; pedagogy in literature and composition. Publ: Modern rhetoric and usage, Henry Holt, 55; co-auth, Rhetoric and reading: order and idea, Dodd, 63; auth, Teachers' use of dictating machines, Austin State Univ, 65; Yeat's Byzantium poems—for teenagers?, Leaflet, 2/73; The Red badge of courage, Wis. Eng. J, 4/73; The undeserved degeneration of Babbitt, Names, fall 73; plus others. Add: School of Liberal Arts, Stephen F. Austin State University, Nacogdoches, TX 75961.

KALMAR, ELAINE BUSH, b. Brady, Tex, Sept. 8, 33; m. 55; c. 5. ENGLISH & COMPARATIVE LITERATURE. B.S, Univ. N.Mex, 55, M.A, 65, Ph.D. (Eng), 71. Teaching asst. ENG, Univ. N.Mex, 65-68; instr, Univ. S.Ala, 68-71; ASST. PROF, UNIV. NORTH. IOWA, 71-, res. grant, summer 73. Co-ed, Inscape, 59-63; participant, Afro-Am. Inst, Univ. Iowa, 70. AAUP; MLA; Milton Soc; Shakespeare Asn. Am. English Renaissance literature; comparative drama and dramatic theory; the depiction of women in literature. Add: Dept. of English, University of Northern Iowa, Cedar Falls, IA 50613.

KALMEY, ROBERT POHL, b. Lansdowne, Pa, July 3, 36; m. 59; c. 2. ENGLISH. B.A, Lehigh Univ, 59; M.A, Rice Univ, 61; Ph.D.(Eng), Univ. Fla, 70. NDEA fel. ENG, Rice Univ, 59-61; asst, Univ. Fla, 61-62, univ. fel, 62-64; instr, Univ. Ill, 64-67; ASSOC. PROF, SHIPPENSBURG STATE COL, 67- MLA; Am. Soc. 18th Century Stud. Alexander Pope. Publ: Pope's Eloisa to Abelard and those celebrated letters, Philol. Quart, 4/68; The struggles of grace and nature in the poems of Alexander Pope, Shippensburg State Col. Rev, 10/68; Rhetoric, language and structure in Eloisa to Abelard, Eighteenth Century Stud, winter 71-72. Add: Dept. of English, Shippensburg State College, Shippensburg, PA 17257.

KALSTONE, DAVID MICHAEL, b. McKeesport, Pa, July 25, 32. ENGLISH LITERATURE. B.A, Harvard, 54, Fulbright fel, 54-56, Ph.D.(Eng), 61. Instr. ENG, Harvard, 61-63, asst. prof, 63-67; assoc. prof, RUTGERS UNIV, NEW BRUNSWICK, 67-69, PROF, 69- Vis. Hurst prof, Wash. Univ, 73. MLA. Renaissance Soc. Am. English and Italian Renaissance literature; modern American poetry. Add: Dept. of English, Rutgers University, New Brunswick, NJ 08903.

KAMINSKY, ALICE R, b. New York, N.Y; m. 47; c. 1. LITERATURE. B.A, N.Y. Univ, 46, univ. scholar, 46-47, M,A, 47, Ph.D, 52. Teaching fel, N.Y. Univ, 47-49; instr. ENG, Hunter Col, 52-53; Cornell Univ, 54-57, 59-63; asst. prof, STATE UNIV. N.Y. COL. CORTLAND, 63-64, assoc. prof, 64-68, PROF, 68- State Univ. N.Y. fel. award, summer 65; State Univ. N.Y. Res. Found. summer fel, 69. MLA. Philosophy of literature; Chaucer; Shakespeare. Publ: The literary criticism of George Henry Lewes, Univ. Nebr, 64; George Henry Lewes as literary critic, Syracuse Univ, 68; co-auth, Logic: a philosophical introduction, Addison-Wesley, (in press); George Eliot, George Henry Lewes and the novel, PMLA, 55; On literary realism, In: The theory of the novel, new essays, Oxford (in press). Add: Dept. of English, State University of New York College at Cortland, Cortland, NY 13045.

KAMPF, LOUIS, b. Vienna, Austria, May 12, 29; U.S. citizen. COMPARATIVE LITERATURE, HISTORY. B.A, Long Island Univ, 51; Univ. Iowa, 54-58; Soc. of Fels Jr. fel, Harvard, 58-61. Asst. prof. LIT, MASS. INST. TECHNOL, 61-66, assoc. prof, 66-70, PROF, 70-, HEAD LIT. SECT, 67- Old Dom. grant, 64; mem. steering comt, New Univ. Conf, 68. U.S.A, 51-53. MLA (pres, 71); New Univ. Conf. Enlightenment; American ideologies. Publ: On modernism, Mass. Inst. Technol, 67; co-ed, The politics of literature, Pantheon, 72; auth, The scandal of literary scholarship, In: The dissenting academy, Pantheon, 68; plus others. Add: Dept. of Humanities, Massachusetts Institute of Technology, Cambridge, MA 02139.

KANE, HAROLD JOSEPH, b. Milwaukee, Wis, Aug. 12, 23; m. 60; c. 9. MEDIAEVAL LANGUAGE & LITERATURE, LINGUISTICS. A.B, Marquette Univ, 48; A.M, Univ. Pa, 50, Ph.D, 68. Instr. ENG, UNIV. COLO, BOULDER, 51-56, from asst. prof. to assoc. prof, 57-71, PROF, 71- Danforth Found. teaching fel, 60. U.S.A, 43-46, Sgt. MLA; Mediaeval Acad. Am. Fourteenth century devotional literature; structural linguistics. Add: Dept. of English, University of Colorado, Boulder, CO 80302.

KANE, M. FRANZITA, C.S.C, b. Idaho, Jan. 20, 09. ENGLISH. B.A, Immaculate Heart Col, 42; M.A, Cath. Univ. Am, 52; Ph.D, Univ. Notre Dame, 58. Teacher Eng. & prin, Holy Rosary Acad, Calif, 44-47; Col. St. Mary-of-the-Wasatch, 47-50; instr. ENG, Dunbarton Col, 53; ST. MARY'S COL.(IND), 53-58, assoc. prof, 58-63, PROF, 63-, CHMN. DEPT, 60- Guest lectr, Holy Names Col, summer 63; Elizabeth Olsen stud. grant, Oxford, 67; Calouste Gulbenkian res. grant, Portugal, summer 68; Europ. res. grants, 69, 70, 72 & 73. MLA; Int. Comp. Lit. Asn; Am. Comp. Lit. Asn; Col. Eng. Asn; AAUP; Int. Lang. & Lit. Asn. Comparative literature—heroic drama, Dante; Ezra Pound. Add: Dept. of English, St. Mary's College, Notre Dame, IN 46556.

KANE, PATRICIA L, b. St. Paul, Minn, June 23, 26; m. 47; c. 2. ENGLISH. B.A, Macalester Col, 47; M.A, Univ. Minn, 50, Danforth fel, 58-59, Ph.D. (Am. stud), 61. Instr. ENG, MACALESTER COL, 47-54, asst. prof, 54-67, assoc. prof, 67-71, PROF, 71- Proj. coord, Health, Educ. & Welfare Region V Grant, 72-73; humanist, Minn. Humanities Comn. grant, 72-73; vis. humanist, Nat. Humanities Ser, Midwest. Ctr, 73. Am. Stud. Asn.(pres, Minn. & Dakotas Region, 67-68); MLA. American literature; Twin City metropolitan region as case study of quality of urban life; career aspirations of undergraduate women. Publ: Place of abomination: a reading of Fitzgerald's Valley of ashes, Eng. Lang. Notes, 6/64; An irrepressible conflict: Allen Tate's The fathers, Critique, 68; Perry Mason: modern culture hero, In: Heroes of popular culture Bowling Green Univ, 72; plus others. Add: Dept. of English, Macalester College, St. Paul, MN 55101.

KANE, PETER E, b. Beverly Hills, Calif, Feb. 27, 32; m. 55; c. 4. PUBLIC ADDRESS. B.A, Univ. Calif, Santa Barbara, 54; Kellogg fel. Univ. Ore, 55-57; M.A, Univ. Calif, Los Angeles, 60; Ph.D.(speech), Purdue Univ, 67. Instr. SPEECH, Occidental Col, 57-60; Purdue Univ, 60-61; asst. prof, St. Joseph's Col.(Ind), 61-65; State Univ. N.Y. Binghamton, 65-68; ASSOC. PROF, STATE UNIV. N.Y. COL. BROCKPORT, 68- Ed, Free Speech, 73-76. Speech Commun. Asn.(mem. Freedom of Speech Comn, 70-); Speech Asn. East. States; West. Speech Asn; AAUP. Freedom of speech; contemporary American public address; rhetorical studies and criticism. Publ: Dictamen: the Medieval rhetoric of letter-writing, Cent. States Speech J, winter 70; Freedom of speech for public school students, Speech Teacher, 1/71; Extended debate and the rules of the United States Senate, Quart. J. Speech, 2/71; plus others. Add: Dept. of Speech, State University of New York College at Brockport, Brockport, NY 14420.

KANE, SEAN, b. Toronto, Ont, Jan. 9, 43. ENGLISH LITERATURE. B.A, Carleton Univ, 65; M.A, Univ. Toronto, 67, Ph.D.(Eng), 72. Instr. ENG, York Univ, 66-67; lectr, Univ. Toronto, 72-73; ASST. PROF, TRENT UNIV, 73- Medieval and Renaissance allegory; literary theory; Canadian literature. Add: Dept. of English, Trent University, Peterborough, Ont, Can.

KANJO, EUGENE RICHARD, b. Jeannette, Pa, Oct. 25, 25; m. 59; c. 3. AMERICAN LITERATURE. B.A. & M.A, Univ. Chicago, 56; Ph.D.(Am. lit), Claremont Grad. Sch, 67. Asst. prof. Am. lit, Carthage Col, 57-59; Pomona Col, 60; Eng, Calif. State Col, Los Angeles, 60-62; ASSOC. PROF. AM. LIT, UNIV. REDLANDS, 63-, fac. res. grants, summers 66, 70, 73. U.S.N, 43-46. MLA; AAUP. Walt Whitman; Edgar A. Poe. Publ: Poe's dark comedy of art and death, Poe Newslett, 10/69; Time and eternity in Crossing Brooklyn Ferry, Walt Whitman Rev, 9/72. Add: Dept. of American Literature, University of Redlands, Redlands, CA 92373.

KANTNER, CLAUDE EDGAR, b. Woodland, Mich, May 9, 07. COMMUNICATION. A.B, Albion Col, 28; A.M, Univ. Wis, 31, Ph.D, 33. Instr. high sch, Mich, 28-29; instr. speech & dir. speech clin, Stevens Col, 33-34; asst. prof. & dir. speech clin, La. State Univ, 34-44, assoc. prof, 37-44; speech pathologist, med. sch, Univ. Ore, 44-46, acting dir. crippled children's div, 46; PROF. COMMUN. & ASSOC. DEAN COL. COMMUN, OHIO UNIV, 47- Speech Commun. Asn; fel. Am. Speech & Hearing Asn; Cent. States Speech Asn. Phonetics; a study of speech sounds from the standpoint of neurology and anatomy. Publ: Co-auth, Phonetics, Harper, rev. ed, 60; auth, Language and ethics, Mod. Speech, 47; All the king's horses and all the king's men couldn't, Speech Teacher, 1/54; Nature, functions and problems of language, Speech for Everday Use, 60. Add: College of Communication, Ohio University, Athens, OH 45701.

KANTRA, ROBERT ANDREW, b. Perth Amboy, N.J, Feb. 19, 28; m. 52; c. 2. ENGLISH. B.S, Muhlenberg Col, 50; prof. dipl, Columbia Univ, 55; M.A, Fordham Univ, 58; Ph.D.(Eng. lit), Ohio State Univ, 64. Teaching intern & instr, Teachers Col, Columbia Univ, 54-55; asst, Ohio State Univ, 56-58, asst. instr, 58-62; asst. prof. ENG, VILLANOVA UNIV, 62-66, ASSOC. PROF, 66- Vis. prof. Eng, Mt. St. Mary's Col.(Md), 70. U.S.A, 50-52, Res, 52-58. Renaissance Soc. Am; MLA. Renaissance and 17th century English literature; literary theory; religious satire. Publ: Satire on the socialization of religion, Univ. Microfilms, 64; The legitimate but unchristened genre of tragisatire, Centennial Rev, 71; Beckett's little voices of conscience, J. Popular Cult, spring 73; Jerome and Erasmus: holy orders, literary talent, and intellectual revolution, In: Wisdom and knowledge: Festschrift in honour of Joseph Papin, Abbey Press, 74; plus others. Add: Dept. of English, Villanova University, Villanova, PA 19085.

KANTROWITZ, JOANNE SPENCER, b. Marquette, Mich; m. 58; c. 2. ENGLISH, DRAMA. B.A, Univ. Mich, Ann Arbor, 53; M.A, Univ. Chicago, 57, H.J. Lamson scholar, 57, vis. comt. fel, 58-59, Ph.D.(Eng), 67. Instr. ENG, Colby Jr. Col, 57-58; lectr, Vassar Col, 65-67; asst. prof, Marymount Col, 67-69; VIS. ASST. PROF, KENT STATE UNIV, 72- Secy, Russel M. Seeds Advert. Co, Chicago, 53-54; assoc. ed, Hardware & Housewares, 54-56; Am. Counc. Learned Soc. grant, 71-72. MLA; Medieval Acad. Am. Medieval and Renaissance English; allegory; critical theory. Publ: Dramatic allegory, Univ. Nebr, 74; co-auth, Meet Mr. Franklin: an example of usage, In:

Motherwit from the laughing barrell: readings in Afro-American folklore, Prentice-Hall, 72; auth, Palsgrave's translation of scaena, 1540, Neo-Latin News, 72; Dramatic allegory, or, exploring the moral play, Comp. Drama, 73; plus two others. Add: Dept. of English, Kent State University, Kent, OH 42240.

KAOUGH, RICHARD JAMES, b. Pasadena, Tex, Nov. 28, 37; m. 65; c. 2. SPEECH COMMUNICATION. B.A, Sacramento State Col, 65; M.S, South. Ill. Univ, Carbondale, 66, NDEA fel. & Ph.D.(speech), 71. Instr. SPEECH, SOUTH. ORE. COL, 66-69, ASST. PROF, 69- AAUP; Speech Commun. Asn; West. Speech Commun. Asn. American public address; Texas annexation to the United States. Add: Dept. of Speech Communication, Southern Oregon College, Siskiyou Blvd, Ashland, OR 97520.

KAPLAN, CHARLES, b. Chicago, Ill, May 15, 19; m. 43; c. 3. AMERICAN LITERATURE. A.B, Univ. Chicago, 40; A.M, Northwest. Univ, 42, Ph.D, 52. Instr. Eng, Roosevelt Col, 46-49, asst. prof, 49-53; Los Angeles State Col, 54-56, chmn. dept. lang. arts, 56-57; assoc. prof. ENG, CALIF. STATE UNIV, NORTHRIDGE, 57-59, PROF, 59-, chmn. div. lang. & lit, 57-63. Fulbright lectr. Am. lit, France, 63-64. U.S.N. 41-46. NCTE; MLA; Am. Stud. Asn; Col. Eng. Asn. Literary criticism; 19th century fiction; American studies. Publ: Co-auth, Technique of composition, 60 & auth, Guided composition, 68, Holt; Criticism: 20 major statements, Chandler, 64; The over-wrought urn, Pegasus, 69; Literature in America: the modern age, Free Press, 71. Add: Dept. of English, California State University Northridge, 18111 Nordhoff St, Northridge, CA 91324.

KAPLAN, FRED, b. New York, N.Y, Nov. 4, 37; m. 59; c. 3. ENGLISH. B.A, Brooklyn Col, 59; M.A, Columbia Univ, 61, Ph.D.(Eng), 66. Instr. ENG, Lawrence Col, 62-64; asst. prof, Calif. State Col. Los Angeles, 64-67; QUEENS COL.(N.Y), 67-70, ASSOC. PROF, 70- City Univ. New York fac. res. grant, 68-69; Fulbright lectr, Univ. Copenhagen, 73-74. MLA. Romantic poetry; Victorian poetry; 18th and 19th century English novel. Publ: Miracles of rare device: the poet's sense of self in nineteenth-century poetry, Wayne State Univ, 72; Dickens and mesmerism: the hidden springs of fiction (in press); The mesmeric mania: the early Victorians and animal magnetism, J. Hist. Ideas, 73; plus others. Add: Dept. of English, Queens College, Flushing, NY 11367.

KAPLAN, HAROLD, b. Chicago, Ill, Jan. 3, 16; m. 62; c. 3. ENGLISH & AMERICAN LITERATURE. B.A, Univ. Chicago, 37, M.A, 38. Instr. Eng, Rutgers Univ, 46-49; fac. lit, Bennington Col, 49-72; PROF. ENG, NORTHWEST. UNIV, 72- Fulbright-Hays lectr, Univ. Bari, 56-57, Univ. Clermont-Ferrand, 60, Univ. Poitiers, 61 & Univ. Aix-Marseille, 67-68. U.S.A.F, 42-46, Capt. MLA; Am. Stud. Asn. Problem of modern knowledge in modern literature; American literature and democratic values; literature and belief. Publ: The passive voice, Ohio Univ, 66; Democratic humanism and American literature, Univ. Chicago, 72. Add: Dept. of English, Northwestern University, Evanston, IL 60201.

KAPLAN, ISRAEL, b. Brooklyn, N.Y, Oct. 5, 07; m. 39; c. 2. ENGLISH, ANGLO-IRISH LITERATURE. A.B, State Univ. N.Y. Col. Albany, 30, M.A, 36; Ph.D.(Am. lit), Cornell Univ, 50. PROF. ENG, STATE UNIV. N.Y. COL. POTSDAM, 49- Consult, Armed Forces Inst, 57 & 60; judge, NCTE, 60-61; reader, Nat. Libr. & Trinity Col, Dublin, 63-64. U.S.M.C, 42-45. MLA; Am. Comt. Irish Stud. Irish literary revival; Kipling's Indian period. Publ: Kipling's America notes and Mark Twain interview, Papers Bibliog. Soc. Am, 50; Kipling's first visit to America, Dalhousie Rev, 59. Auth, When I was a boy in Brooklyn (L.P. record), Folkway Records, 61. Add: Dept. of English, State University of New York College at Potsdam, Potsdam, NY 13676.

KAPLAN, JUSTIN, b. New York, N.Y, Sept. 5, 25; m. 54; c. 3. AMERICAN LITERATURE. B.S, Harvard, 44. Free-lance work with various N.Y. publ, 46-54; ed, Simon & Schuster, 54-59; WRITER, 59- Vis. lectr, Harvard, 69 & 73. Pulitzer Prize in Biography, 67; Nat. Bk. Award in Arts & Lett, 67. Publ: Ed, Dialogues of Plato, 50, The pocket Aristotle, 58, Pocket Bks; With malice toward women, Dodd, 52 & Mark Twain, the gilded age, Trident, 64; auth, Mr. Clemens and Mark Twain, 66, Lincoln Steffens, a biography, 74 & Mark Twain and his world, 74, Simon & Schuster; ed, Great short works of Mark Twain, Harper, 67 & Mark Twain: profile, Hill & Wang, 67. Add: 16 Francis Ave, Cambridge, MA 02138.

KAPLAN, MILTON A, b. New York, N.Y, Mar. 6, 10; m. 39; c. 2. ENGLISH EDUCATION. B.S.S, City Col. New York, 29, M.S, 34; M.A, Columbia Univ, 37, Ph.D.(Eng), 46. Chmn. Eng. dept, High Sch, 54-64; vis. assoc. prof. ENG, TEACHERS COL, COLUMBIA UNIV, 64-65, assoc. prof, 65-66, PROF, 66- Asst. exam, New York City Bd. Educ, 50-64; lectr, Teachers Col, Columbia Univ, 59-64, speaker work conf. leaders in supv. & curriculum, summer 66. NCTE; MLA. Contemporary poetry; teaching of English; composition. Publ: Radio and poetry, Columbia Univ, 46; co-ed, World of poetry, Globe, 65; In a time between wars, Norton, 73; Radio and poetry, Poetry: A Mag. of Verse, 8/44; Before they write, Col. Compos. & Commun, 10/66; Substitution in the teaching of poetry, Eng. J, 9/67. Add: Dept. of Languages, Literature, Speech & Theatre, Teachers College, Columbia University, New York, NY 10027.

KAPLAN, MORT S, b. Passaic, N.J, Nov. 16, 33; m. 57; c. 2. DRAMA. B.A, Emerson Col, 57; M.A, N.Y. Univ, 58; Yeshiva Univ, 60-70. Instr. Eng, East Paterson High Sch, N.J, 59; instr. Eng. & speech & dir. drama, Irvington High Sch, N.J, 59-62; instr. speech, Col. Ins, N.Y.C, 63; ASSOC. PROF. THEATRE, ASSOC. DIR. & ADMIN. OFF, DEPT. DRAMA & SPEECH, NORTHEAST. UNIV, 63- Lectr. acting & dramatic lit, Eve. Div, Northeast. Univ, 64; guest instr, Premiere Playhouse, Lexington, Mass, 66; guest lectr, Contemporary Theatre Sem, Yeshiva Univ, 67; ser. six half-hour radio prog, Contemporary Trends in Theatre, WEEI, Boston, 68; theatre consult, East. Opera Consortium, Boston, 72-73; guest lectr, New Eng. Writer's Conf, Cambridge, 73; dir. & adaptor of numerous productions. U.S.A, 53-54. New Eng. Theatre Conf.(v.pres, 67-68, pres, 69-70, founder & exec. publ, New Eng. Theatre); Am. Theatre Asn; Speech Commun. Asn; Speech Commun. Asn. East. States. Audience analysis; character and characterization in the theatre of the absurd. Publ: Co-ed, The American playwright: his problems and prospects, 66 & auth, Stick-to-it-tiveness in Shakespearean characters, 68, New Eng. Theatre Conf. J. Add: Dept. of Drama & Speech, 409 EL, Northeastern University, 360 Huntington Ave, Boston, MA 02115.

KAPLAN, NATHANIEL, b. Camden, N.J, Feb. 8, 20; m. 46; c. 2. AMERICAN & ENGLISH LITERATURE. A.B, Randolph-Macon Col, 41; M.S, South. Conn. State Col, 66. ASSOC. PROF. ENG, UNIV. NEW HAVEN, 65- U.S.A, 42-46, Capt. American transcendentalism; contemporary American drama. Publ: Co-auth, The Western mystical tradition, 69 & co-auth, The mystical origins of American transcendentalism, 74, Col. & Univ. Press. Add: 28 Anthony St, New Haven, CT 06515.

KAPLAN, ROBERT B, Linguistics, English as a Second Language. See Volume III, Foreign Languages, Linguistics & Philology.

KAPLAN, SIDNEY, b. New York, N.Y, Mar. 1, 13; m. 33; c. 2. AMERICAN STUDIES. B.A, City Col. New York, 42; M.A, Boston Univ, 48; Ph.D.(Am. civilization), Harvard, 59. PROF. ENG, UNIV. MASS, AMHERST, 46- Fulbright lectr. Am. Lit, Univ. Thessaloniki, 63-64, Univ. Zagreb, 67-68. Bancroft Award, 48. U.S.A, 42-46, Lt. Am. Stud. Asn. American culture. Publ: Poe's Pym, Hill & Wang, 60; The portrait of the Negro in American painting, Bowdoin Col, 64; ed, Melville's Battle-pieces, Univ. Mass, 72; auth, Black presence in era of American Revolution, N.Y. Graphic Soc, 73. Add: Dept. of English, University of Massachusetts, Amherst, MA 01002.

KAPPEN, CHARLES VAUGHAN, b. Eureka Springs, Ark, May 25, 10; m. 31; c. 2. JOURNALISM. B.A, Univ. Ark, 33; Ark. State Teachers Col, 33; M.A, Univ. Wis, 47. Asst. prof. JOUR, Shrivenham Am. Univ, 45-46; Univ. Wis, 46-47; Univ. Tulsa, 47-48; SAN JOSE STATE UNIV, 48-51, assoc. prof, 51-59, prof, 59-72, EMER. PROF, 72- Ed, Calcoin News Mag, 50-62. U.S.A, 42-46, Maj. Asn. Educ. Jour. English regal copper and bronze coinage; so-called dollars, silver dollar-size medals of the United States; money of the merchants, scrip. Publ: Co-auth, Reprints from the numismatist, 4 vols, Whitman, 60; Depression scrip of the United States, Globe Printing Co, Calif, 61; So called dollars, Coin & Currency Pub. Inst, New York, 63; chaps, In: Money talks in 1970, Calif. State Numismatic Asn, 70; A survey of curricula in international communications, In: International communication as a field of study, Univ. Iowa, 70. Add: 2201 Peachtree Lane, San Jose, CA 95128.

KAPSTEIN, ISRAEL JAMES, b. Fall River, Mass, Jan. 16, 04; m. 28; c. 2. ENGLISH LITERATURE. A.B, Brown Univ, 26, A.M, 29, Ph.D, 33. Instr. ENG, BROWN UNIV, 28-35, asst. prof, 35-42, assoc. prof, 42-51, prof, 51-69, EMER. PROF, 69- Guggenheim fel, 44-45; Smith-Mundt vis. prof, Univ. Saigon, 60-61. MLA. English romantic period; modern English and American fiction; creative writing. Publ: The song the summer evening sings, Harper, 37; Something of a hero, Knopf, 42; Expository prose, Harcourt, 55; The symbolism of the wind and the leaves in Shelley's Ode to the west wind, 12/36 & The meaning of Shelley's Mont Blanc, 12/47; PMLA; A painting by Matisse, Art J, summer 73; plus others. Add: 63 Dexterdale Rd, Providence, RI 02906.

KARANIKAS, ALEXANDER, b. Manchester, N.H, Sept. 23, 16; m. 49; c. 3. AMERICAN LITERATURE. A.B, Harvard, 39; M.A, Northwest. Univ, 50, Ph.D.(Eng), 53. Asst. ENG, Northwest. Univ, 50-52; instr, Kendall Col, 52-53; Northwest. Univ, 53-54, bus. Eng, eve. div, 57-59; from asst. prof. to PROF, UNIV. ILL, CHICAGO CIRCLE, 54- Chmn. midwest meeting, Col. Eng. Asn, 57; consult, Peter D. Gianukos Scholar. Fund, Inc, 66- Friends of Literature Award, 67. U.S.A.A.F, 42-45, S/Sgt. MLA; Mod. Greek Stud. Asn; Soc. Stud. South. Lit. American literature; literary criticism; modern Greek literature. Publ: In praise of heroes (poetry), Clarke, 45; Tillers of a myth, Univ. Wis, 66 & 69; co-auth, Elias Venezis, Twayne, 69; auth, An approach to freshman writers, Col. Compos. & Commun, 60; contrib. poems, Port Chicago poets, Chicago Int. Manuscripts, 66; Hold fast to dreams, Follett, 69; plus others. Add: Dept. of English, University of Illinois at Chicago Circle, Chicago, IL 60680.

KARCHMER, SYLVAN N, b. Dallas, Tex, Dec. 31, 14. CREATIVE WRITING. M.F.A, Univ. Tex, 50. PROF. CREATIVE WRITING, Univ. Ore, 50-69; UNIV. HOUSTON, 69- Prof. Banff Sch. Fine Arts, summers 52-65. U.S.A.A.F, 42-46. Publ: Many short stories & plays in wide variety of lit. journals. Add: Dept. of English, University of Houston, Houston, TX 77004.

KARL, FREDERICK R, b. Brooklyn, N.Y, Apr. 10, 27; m. 51; c. 3. ENGLISH. A.B, Columbia Col, 48; M.A, Stanford Univ, 49; Ph.D, Columbia Univ, 57. Asst. prof. ENG, CITY COL. NEW YORK, 57-65, assoc. prof, 65-69, PROF, 69-, DIR. GRAD. ENG, 70- Am. Counc. Learned Soc. & Am. Philos. Soc. grants, 61 & 62; Fulbright lectr. Am. Lit, France, 65-66; Guggenheim fel, 66-67. U.S.N, 44-45. MLA. Nineteenth and twentieth century literature; letters of Joseph Conrad. Publ: Reader's guide to Joseph Conrad, Noonday, 60; Contemporary English novel, 62, An age of fiction: nineteenth century British novel, 64 & The adversary literature: the 18th century English novel, 73, Farrar, Straus; C.P. Snow: the politics of conscience, South. Ill. Univ, 63. Add: Dept. of English, City College of New York, New York, NY 10031.

KARL, THEODORE OSCAR HENRY, b. Marinette, Wis, Oct. 27, 12; m. 53. SPEECH. A.B, Gustavus Adolphus Col, 34, A.M, 36. Instr. speech & mem. pres. adv. counc, Los Angeles City Col; PROF. SPEECH & CHMN. DEPT. COMMUN. ARTS, PAC. LUTHERAN UNIV, 40-42, 48- West. Speech Asn. (2nd v.pres, 1st v.pres. & pres, 56-60); Speech Commun. Asn. Oral communication; public address; drama; telecommunications. Add: Dept. of Communication Arts, Pacific Lutheran University, Tacoma, WA 98447.

KARNIS, MICHAEL V, b. Jackson Co, Minn, Nov. 26, 21; m. 51; c. 2. SPEECH, INTERNATIONAL EDUCATION. B.S.Ed, Univ. Minn, Duluth, 47; Inst. Int. Educ. & Pan Am. travel grants, Univ. Chile, 47-48 & San Marcos Univ, 48; M.A, Northwest. Univ, 49, Ph.D.(speech educ), 53; Soc. Sci. Res. Counc. & Braniff travel grant, Univ. Buenos Aires, 51-52. Dir. courses Eng. binat. ctr, Centro-Colombo-Am, Bogota, 49-50 & Medellin, 50-51; instr. speech & head Eng. lang. prog. for. stud, Univ. Calif, Berkeley, 52-55; cult. attache Am. Embassy, U.S. Dept. State, Quito, 55-58, Santiago, 58-63 & Montevideo, 63-64, chief spec. exchanges, 64-67; dir. int. off. & prof.

speech, La. State Univ, 67-70; prof. speech & dean col. arts & sci, Univ. Bridgeport, 70-72; DEAN, UNIV. WIS. CTR-MANITOWOC, 72- Consult, Nat. Asn. For. Stud. Affairs, 69-73; founder & mem, Int. World Univ, 72- U.S.N.R, 42-46, Lt.(jg). Speech Commun. Asn.(mem. comt. int. liaison, 67-, mem. comn. int-intercult. speech commun, 70-); Nat. Asn. For. Stud. (chmn. Southwest. region, 68-69, v.pres, 70-71); Asn. Higher Educ; Teachers of Eng. to Speakers of Other Lang; Am. Theatre Asn. Latin American theatre; Latin American studies; international education. Publ: The crisis in the Argentine theatre, 12/53 & The role of the River Plate in colonial hispanic American drama, 5/55, Educ. Theatre J; Latin America's resurgent theatre, Quart. J. Speech, 12/54. Add: 310 Waldo Blvd, Manitowoc, WI 54220.

KARNS, CHARLES FRANKLIN, b. Loveland, Colo, Dec. 10, 21; m. 44; c. 7. SPEECH. B.A, Cincinnati Bible Sem, 43; B.A, Ashland Col, 44; M.A, Univ. Pittsburgh, 62, NDEA fel, 60-63, Ph.D.(speech), 64. Asst. prof. speech, Univ. Fla, 64-68, assoc. prof, 68-71; PROF. SPEECH & PHILOS, CINCINNATI BIBLE SEM, 71- Speech Commun. Asn; South. Speech Commun. Asn. (archivist, 70-71). Rhetorical theory; homiletics; psycholinguistics. Publ: The usefulness of Mill's Canons of causation to rhetoric, Pa. Speech Annual, 9/64; Causal analysis and rhetoric: a survey of the major philosophical conceptions of cause prior to John Stuart Mill, 3/65 & Speaker behavior to nonverbal aversive stimuli from the audience, 6/69; Speech Monogr. Add: Dept. of Speech, Cincinnati Bible Seminary, 2700 Glenway Ave, Cincinnati, OH 45204.

KAROLIDES, NICHOLAS J, b. Albany, N.Y, Aug. 5, 28; m. 62; c. 2. ENGLISH. B.S, N.Y. Univ, 50, M.A, 51, fel, 59-60, Ph.D.(Eng), 63. Teacher & guidance counsel. jr. high schs, N.Y, 54-64; asst. prof. ENG, UNIV. WIS-RIVER FALLS, 64-66, assoc. prof, 66-69, PROF, 69- Instr. part-time, N.Y. Univ, 60-64; ed, Wis. Eng. J, 65- & JM Newslett, 72- John W. Withers Mem. Award, N.Y. Univ. Sch. Educ, 63; Distinguished Teacher Award, Univ. Wis-River Falls, 71; Chisholm Award for Meritorious Serv, Wis. Counc. Teachers Eng, 72. U.S.A, 51-53, Res, 53-64, Capt. NCTE (co-chmn, Comt. Minority Lit, 73-); Conf. Eng. Educ. Literature; American pioneer related to American history and culture; teaching of minority literature in Wisconsin. Publ: The pioneer in the American novel, 1900-50, Univ. Okla, 67; Changing conceptions of the pioneer in the contemporary American novel, Wis. Stud. Lit, 67. Add: Dept. English, University of Wisconsin-River Falls, River Falls, WI 54022.

KARP, LILA, b. New York, N.Y, June 7, 33; m. 68. LITERATURE. B.A, Syracuse Univ, 54, M.S, 55. Vis. lectr. sociol, Bryn Mawr Col, 71-72; PROF. LIT, NEW SCH. SOC. RES, 73- Studio leader lit. & female stud, Univ. New World, summer 71; vis. lectr. sociol, State Univ. N.Y. Col. New Paltz, 71-; lectr, U.S. Off. Educ, summer 72; scholar-in-residence, St. Lawrence Univ, 73. The sociology of women's literature; 20th century women's literature. Publ: The queen is in the garbage (novel), Vanguard & W.H. Allen, Eng, 69. Add: 114 Spring St, New York, NY 10012.

KARP, MARK, b. Brockton, Mass, Oct. 15, 09; m. 36; c. 2. ENGLISH, READING. B.A, City Col. New York, 32; M.A, Columbia Univ, 35; Ph.D. (Eng), N.Y. Univ, 42. Instr. ENG, WILLIAM PATERSON COL, 36-40, asst. prof, 40-46, assoc. prof, 46-54, PROF, 54-, COORD. LANG. ARTS & READING, 67-, CHMN. DEPT. READING & LANG. ARTS, 73-, ASSOC. DEAN, 73- Int. Reading Asn. English communication; writing; reading. Publ: An evaluation of two methods of teaching of college freshmen English composition, J. Exp. Educ, 9/42; Silent before oral reading, Elem. Sch. J, 10/43; Is poetry for the gifted only?, Eng. J, 5/46. Add: Dept. of English, William Paterson College, 300 Pompton Rd, Wayne, NJ 07473.

KARRFALT, DAVID HERBERT, b. Erie, Pa, Jan. 30, 39. ENGLISH. B.A, Johns Hopkins Univ, 60; M.A, South. Ill. Univ, 63. Instr. ENG, Marshall Univ, 63-65; Ohio Univ, 66-68; asst. prof, EDINBORO STATE COL, 68-69, ASSOC. PROF, 69- NCTE; Conf. Col. Compos. & Commun; Rhet. Soc. Am; MLA. Nineteenth-century English literature; modern theory of rhetoric. Publ: The generation of paragraphs and larger units, Col. Compos. & Commun, 10/68; Accepting Lord Jim on his own terms: a structural approach, Conradiana, fall 69; The social theme in Osborne's plays, Mod. Drama, 5/70; plus others. Add: Dept. of English, Edinboro State College, Edinboro, PA 16412.

KARSTETTER, ALLAN BOYD, b. Williamson, N.Y, May 19, 27; m. 57; c. 2. SPEECH. B.E, State Univ. N.Y. Col. Brockport, 49; M.A, Northwest. Univ, 53; Univ. Buffalo, 59-61; Ph.D.(speech), Pa. State Univ, 63. Teacher, Northville Cent. Sch, 49-53; asst. prof. speech, State Univ. N.Y. Col. Brockport, 55-64; res. assoc, Pa. Dept. Pub. Instr, 64-66; prog. dir, East. Regional Inst. Educ, 66-68; prof. speech & chmn. dept, Tex. Woman's Univ, 68-71, dean arts & sci, 71-72; PRES, UNITY COL, 72- Consult, Marymount Col, 65-67; State of Vt, 66-67; ed, Today's Speech, 66-68; mem, Counc. on Humanities, 72- U.S.A, 45-46. Speech Commun. Asn; Am. Asn. Higher Educ. Publ: Toward a theory of rhetorical irony, Speech Monogr, 64. Add: Unity College, Unity, ME 04988.

KARTIGANER, DONALD M, b. Brooklyn, N.Y, May 29, 37; m. 64, 67; c. 3. ENGLISH. B.A, Brown Univ, 59, Grand Army Repub. fel. & Ph.D.(Eng), 64; M.A, Columbia Univ, 60. Asst. prof. ENG, UNIV. WASH, 64-69, ASSOC. PROF, 69- Fulbright lectr, Ljubljana, 67-68; Nat. Endowment Humanities summer stipend, 73. MLA. American literature chiefly modern. Publ: Co-ed, Theories of American literature, Macmillan, 72; auth, Absalom, Absalom!: discovery of values, Am. Lit, 11/65; The sound and the fury and Faulkner's quest for form, Eng. Lit. Hist, 12/70; Process and product: a study of modern literary form, Mass. Rev, spring & fall 71; plus others. Add: Dept. of English, University of Washington, Seattle, WA 98105.

KARWAND, ELWOOD C, b. Fargo, N.Dak, Jan. 12, 31; m. 57; c. 4. JOURNALISM, ENGLISH. B.A, Hamline Univ, 57; Wall St. J. fel, Univ. Minn, 61, M.A, 64. Teacher, High Sch, Minn, 57-60; teacher & jour. supvr, High Sch, Wis, 60-64; ASST. PROF. JOUR. & CHMN. DEPT, UNIV. WIS-EAU CLAIRE, 64- Pres, Wis. Jour. Teacher-Adv. Counc, 64-66; mem, Nat. Comt. Freedoms & Responsibility Col. Press Am, 67- Pioneer Award, Nat. Scholastic Press Asn, 70. U.S.A.F, 51-55. Jour. Educ. Asn.(exec. secy, 64-, Carl Towley Award, 69); Asn. Educ. in Jour; NCTE (dir, 64-); Nat. Counc. Col. Publ. Adv; Am. Soc. Jour. Sch. Adminr. Secondary school journalism education in America; scholastic press in America; history of journalism. Publ: What we may expect from high school journalism, Wis. J. Educ, 12/62; Recruiting future journalists, Nat. Publ, 10/66; Literature in journalism myth of reality, Wis. Eng. J, 10/67. Add: 3105 State St, Eau Claire, WI 54701.

KASE, CHARLES ROBERT, b. Lewistown, Pa, June 27, 05; m. 30; c. 2. DRAMATICS. A.B, Gettysburg Col, 26; A.M, N.Y. Univ, 30, Ph.D, 35. Instr. high sch, N.J, 26-27; N.Y. Univ, 27-30; asst. prof, UNIV. DEL, 30-41, assoc. prof. dramatics, 41-46, prof, 46-70, dir. dramatics, 30-66, chmn. dept. DRAMATIC ARTS & SPEECH, 46-66, EMER. PROF, 70- Nat. coord, First Am. Col. Theatre Festival, 68-69, chmn. cent. comt, 69-71; adv, title III proj. performing arts Del. schs, ESEA. Theatrical adv, U.S.A, 42-44. Fel. Am. Theatre Asn.(pres, 47; Silver Medallion Award of Excellence, 73); Nat. Theatre Conf; Am. Nat. Theatre & Acad.(mem, bd. dir, 46-). Theatre; speech; educational television. Publ: Three Chaucer studies, Oxford; Children's theatre comes of age & Stories for creative acting, Samuel French. Add: 606 Vanderbaker Rd, Temple Terrace, FL 33617.

KASKE, CAROL VONCKX, b. Elgin, Ill, Feb. 5, 33; m. 58; c. 1. ENGLISH & COMPARATIVE LITERATURE. A.B, Wash. Univ, 54; M.A, Smith Col, 55; Ph.D.(Eng), Johns Hopkins Univ, 64. Instr. ENG, Duke Univ, 59-60; Women's Col, Univ. N.C, 61; Univ. Ill, Urbana, 61-64; lectr, CORNELL UNIV, 64-68, sr. lectr, 68-73, ASST. PROF, 73- MLA; Renaissance Soc. Am. Renaissance literature; theology; Edmund Spenser. Publ: The dragon's spark and sting and the structure of Red Cross's dragon fight, Stud. Philol, 69; Mount Sinai and Dante's Mount Purgatory, Dante Stud, 71. Add: Dept. of English, Cornell University, Ithaca, NY 14850.

KASKE, ROBERT EARL, b. Cincinnati, Ohio, June 1, 21; m. 58; c. 1. ENGLISH, COMPARATIVE LINGUISTICS. A.B, Xavier Univ,(Ohio), 42; M.A, Univ. N.C, 47, Ph.D.(Eng. & comp. ling), 50. Instr. Eng, Mediaeval lit. & comp. ling, Wash. Univ, 50-52, asst. prof, 52-57; MEDIAEVAL LIT, Pa. State Univ, 57-58; assoc. prof, Univ. N.C, 58-61; PROF, Univ. Ill, 61-64; CORNELL UNIV, 64- Am. Counc. Learned Soc. grants-in-aid, summers, 60, 65, 68, fel, 71-72; Guggenheim fel, 62-63; assoc. mem, Ctr. Advan. Stud, Univ. Ill, 62-63; Am. Philos. Soc. grant, summer 65; Soc. for Humanities fel, Cornell Univ, 72-73. U.S.A, 42-46, Lt. Acad. Lit. Stud; MLA; Mediaeval Acad. Am; Dante Soc. Am; Int. Asn. Univ. Prof. Eng. Old and Middle English language and literature; Medieval Biblical exegesis and mythography; Dante. Publ: Sapientia et Fortitudo as the controlling theme of Beowulf, Stud. Philol, 58; Patristic exegesis in the criticism of Medieval literature: The defense, In: Critical approaches to Medieval literature, Eng. Inst, 60; Dante's DXV and Veltro, Traditio, 61. Add: Dept. of English, Cornell University, Ithaca, NY 14850.

KASTER, BARBARA JEANNE, b. El Paso, Tex, June 27, 34. COMMUNICATION, FILM. B.A, Tex. West. Col, 57; M.Ed, Univ. Tex, El Paso, 67, Ph.D. (commun), Univ. Tex, Austin, 70. Asst. prof. speech, Univ. S.Fla, 66-67; teaching assoc. Ind. Univ, 67-68; Univ. Tex, Austin, 68-70; asst. prof, Fla. Atlantic Univ, 70-73; ASSOC. PROF, COMMUN, BOWDOIN COL, 73- Producer & dir, Making policy, not coffee (film), Fla. Atlantic Univ, 73. Speech Commun. Asn; South. Speech Commun. Asn; Speech Asn. New Eng. Film; women's studies; rhetoric. Publ: Co-auth, Teaching through real debates, Ind. Speech J, fall 68; auth, Massaging the message: McLuhan and oral interpretation, South. Speech Commun. J, 71; contrib, Introduction to speech communication, Addison-Wesley, 73. Add: Dept. of English, Division of Communication, Sills Hall, Bowdoin College, Brunswick, ME 04011.

KASTOR, FRANK SULLIVAN, b. Evanston, Ill, Aug. 19, 33; m. 54; c. 2. ENGLISH & AMERICAN LITERATURE. B.A, Univ. Ill, 55, M.A, 56; Ph.D.(Eng. & Am. lit), Univ. Calif, Berkeley, 63. Asst. prof. Eng. & Am. lit, Univ. South. Calif, 63-68; assoc. prof, North. Ill. Univ, 68-69; PROF. ENG. & CHMN. DEPT, WICHITA STATE UNIV, 69- Univ. South. Calif. res. grant, 64-65 & assoc. res. fel, 65; Fulbright lectr, Spain, 66-67; Nat. Endowment for Humanities Younger Humanist award, 71. U.S.A.F, 56-59, Capt. MLA; Philol. Asn. Pac. Coast; Milton Soc. Am; AAUP; Renaissance Soc. Am. Milton and the English Renaissance; English drama; American literature. Publ: Giles and Phineas Fletcher, Twayne, 70; Modern tragicomedy: Genre, vision, myth?, Kans. Quart, spring 71; By force of guile eternal war: Paradise lost, IV, 776-1015, J. Eng. & Germanic Philol, Vol. LXX, No. 2; Milton and the Fletchers, In: Milton Encycl, Univ. Wis, 73. Auth, dir. & producer, The challenge of history: migration and community in Kansas, (TV documentary), Nat. Endowment for Humanities, 73. Add: Dept. of English, Wichita State University, Wichita, KS 67207.

KATOPE, CHRISTOPHER, b. Lowell, Mass, Apr. 1, 18; m. 42; c. 2. ENGLISH. Univ. Ind. & Univ. Louisville, 37-41; M.A, Univ. Chicago, 47; Ph.D. (Eng), Vanderbilt Univ, 54. Asst. prof. ENG, Westminster Col.(Mo), 47-50; instr, ALLEGHENY COL, 52-54, asst. prof, 54-62, assoc. prof, 62-69, PROF, 69- Fulbright scholar, Anatolia Col. & Athens Col, Greece, 59-61. U.S.N, 41-45. Nineteenth century English literature; literary criticism; student activism. Publ: Co-auth, Beyond Berkeley: sourcebook in student values, World, 66 & Rhetoric of revolution, Macmillan, 70; auth, Herbert Spencer and Dreiser's Sister Carrie, Am. Lit, 3/69; C.P. Cavafy and Durrell's Alexandria quartet, Comp. Lit, spring 69. Add: Dept. of English, Allegheny College, Meadville, PA 16335.

KATT, ARTHUR F, b. Jan. 20, 26; U.S. citizen; m. 48; c. 4. PRACTICAL MINISTRY, SPEECH. A.B, Cincinnati Bible Sem, 50, A.M, 51, B.D, 53; M.S, Ft. Hays Kans. State Col, 54; Ph.D.(rhet. & pub. address), Ind. Univ, 63. Assoc. prof. SPEECH & HOMILETICS, CINCINNATI BIBLE SEM, 57-58, PROF, 58-, MEM. FAC. PRACTICAL THEOL, CINCINNATI CHRISTIAN SEM, 65- U.S.A, 44-46, Sgt. Speech Commun. Asn. Homiletical techniques of G. Campbell Morgan; travel to Biblical sites in Israel, Turkey, Greece, Italy. Publ: G. Campbell Morgan: sermon preparation, Sem. Rev, fall 60. Add: Dept. of Practical Theology, Cincinnati Christian Seminary, 2700 Glenway Ave, Cincinnati, OH 45204.

KATTER, NAFE EDMUND, b. Saginaw, Mich, Oct. 25, 28. DRAMATIC ARTS. B.A, Univ. Mich, Ann Arbor, 50, M.A, 51, Ph.D.(theatre), 63. Asst. prof. THEATRE, Tex. Wesleyan Univ, 56-57; UNIV. CONN, 58-60, assoc. prof,

61-69, PROF, 70-, ACTING HEAD DEPT. DRAMATIC ARTS, 74- Guest prof. theatre, Univ. Mich, 64, 66, 67. Am. Theatre Asn; Speech Commun. Asn. Modern American theatre history. Publ: Contrib, Theatre Arts Mag, Univ. Mich, 63. Add: Dept. of Dramatic Arts, U-127, University of Connecticut, Storrs, CT 06268.

KATZ, ALBERT M, b. New York, N.Y, May 20, 38; m. 62; c. 2. SPEECH, THEATRE. B.A, Union Col, 58; M.A, Univ. Mich, 60, Ph.D.(theatre), 66. Instr. speech, Univ. Mich, 60-62; asst. prof. THEATRE, Alma Col, 62-65; ASSOC. PROF, UNIV. WIS-SUPERIOR, 66- Speech Commun. Asn; Am. Theatre Asn. Twentieth century European theatre: stage violence. Publ: Educational theatre in a small liberal arts framework, Cue, winter 72; Training the director, Onstage, 1/72; Copeau as regisseur: an anlysis, Educ. Theatre J, 5/73; plus others. Add: 2105 Harvard Ave, Duluth, MN 55803.

KATZ, JOSEPH, b. New York, N.Y, Aug. 14, 37; m. 63; c. 1. ENGLISH & AMERICAN LITERATURE. A.B, Brooklyn Col, 58; A.M, N.Y. Univ, 62; Ph.D.(Eng), Ind. Univ, 67. Assoc. ENG, Ind. Univ, 61-64; instr, Wright State Univ, 64-66; Ohio State Univ, 66, asst. prof, 66-68; assoc. prof, Kent. State Univ, 68-69; UNIV. S.C, 69-71, PROF, 71- Gen. ed, Calendars of American Lit. manuscripts, 64-; ed, Stephen Crane Newsletter, 66-; ed. consult. Am. lit, C.E. Merrill Publ. Co, 68-; ed, The Yearbook Am. Bibliog. & Textual Stud, 71; Guggenheim Mem. Found. fel, 72-73; consult, G.K. Hall & Co, 73. U.S.A.R, 58-65. MLA; Bibliog. Soc. Am; Grolier Club. Analytical bibliography and textual studies; American literature; literary realism and naturalism. Publ: The poems of Stephen Crane: a critical edition, Cooper, 66; Maggie: a girl of the streets (1893), 66 & The red badge of courage: syndicate versions, 67, Scholars' Facsimiles; The Viking portable Stephen Crane, Viking, 69; The blue battalions and the uses of experience, Stud. Neophilol, 66; The Maggie nobody knows, Mod. Fiction Stud, 66; Scholarship and mere artifacts, Stud. Bibliog, 69. Add: Dept. of English, University of South Carolina, Columbia, SC 29208.

KATZ, LEON, b. Bronx, N.Y, July 10, 19; m. 42; c. 2. ENGLISH, DRAMA. B.S.S, City Col. New York, 40; M.A, Columbia Univ, 46, Ford Found. fel, 52-53, Ph.D.(Eng), 62. Instr. Eng, Cornell Univ, 46-47; Hunter Col, 47-49; asst. prof. drama, Vassar Col, 49-58; lectr. playwrighting, Columbia Univ, 58-60; assoc. prof. Eng, Manhattanville Col, 60-64; vis. assoc. prof. drama, Stanford Univ, 64-65; prof. drama, Eng. & comp. lit, San Francisco State Col, 65-68; PROF. DRAMA, CARNEGIE-MELLON UNIV, 69-, vis. Andrew Mellon prof, 68-69. Nat. Endowment for Humanities res. fel, 72-73. U.S.A.F, 42-46, Capt. Gertrude Stein; avant garde theater; commedia dell arte. Publ: Co-transl, The trial, Gide-Barrault adaptation, Schocken, 62; co-ed, Gertrude Stein's Fernhurst, QED and other early writings, Liveright, 70; The three cuckolds, In: The classic theatre, Vol. I, Anchor Bks, 58. Add: Dept. of Drama, Carnegie-Mellon University, Pittsburgh, PA 15213.

KATZ, SEYMOUR, b. Newark, N.J, July 16, 26; m. 54; c. 2. ENGLISH & AMERICAN STUDIES. B.A, Rutgers Univ, 49; Ph.D.(Am. stud), Harvard, 61. Asst. prof. ENG, Grinnell Col, 58-66; UNIV. MASS, BOSTON, 66-68, ASSOC. PROF, 68- U.S.A, 44-46, Sgt. MLA; Am. Stud. Asn. Hawthorne; nineteenth-century American fiction. Publ: Character and nature in The scarlet letter, 19th-Century Fiction, 6/68; Culture and literature in American studies, Am. Quart, summer 68. Add: Dept. of English, University of Massachusetts, Boston, MA 02116.

KAUFFMAN, CORINNE ELIZABETH, b. Jerusalem, Jan. 17, 24; U.S. citizen. ENGLISH. B.A, Olivet Nazarene Col, 47; M.A, Mich. State, 50; South. Fels. Found. fel, Univ. Tex, Austin, 59-60, Ph.D.(Eng), 63. Instr. ENG, Bethany Col, 50-53; spec. instr, Univ. Tex, Austin, 56-59 & 62-63; asst. prof, Kans. State Teachers Col, 61-62; UNIV. TEX, ARLINGTON, 63-72, ASSOC. PROF, 72- MLA. Chaucer. Publ: We who kneel at the manger, Mich. Educ. J, 47; Adam in paradox, Arlington Quart, 68. Add: Dept. of English, University of Texas at Arlington, Arlington, TX 76010.

KAUFFMANN, ROY C, b. Brooklyn, N.Y, Feb. 27, 26; m. 59; c. 1. AMERICAN LITERATURE. B.A, Univ. Wis, 48; M.A, Univ. Houston, 60; Ph.D, Univ. Pa, 63. Asst. prof. ENG, GROVE CITY COL, 62-68, PROF, 68- U.S.A, 44-45. MLA. German philosophy, especially Nietzsche; American literature, 19th and 20th centuries. Add: Dept. of English, Grove City College, Grove City, PA 16127.

KAUFKE, PIERRE H.G, English, Foreign Languages. See Volume III, Foreign Languages, Linguistics & Philology.

KAUFMAN, ALVIN S, b. New York, N.Y, Aug. 31, 23; m. 51; c. 1. DRAMA, THEATRE ARTS. B.A, Ohio Wesleyan Univ, 46; M.A, Univ. Wash, 53; univ. fel, Stanford Univ, 59-60, Danforth fel, 62-63, Ph.D.(drama), 65. Instr. speech & drama, Culver-Stockton Col, 53-56; asst. prof, Fresno State Col, 56-65; dean instr, Pasadena Playhouse, 65-66; assoc. prof, coord. theatre & dir. acad. affairs, Sch. Performing Arts, U.S. Int. Univ, 66-68; assoc. prof. drama, East. Mich. Univ, 68-72; PROF. DRAMA & DIR. SCH. OF THEATRE, OHIO UNIV, 72- Artistic dir, San Diego Civic Light Opera Asn, 68. U.S.A, 44-46. Am. Theatre Asn; Speech Commun. Asn. Drama as history; theatre games in teaching acting. Add: 097 RTVE Bldg, School of Theatre, Ohio University, Athens, OH 45701.

KAUFMAN, ANTHONY DAVID, b. Minneapolis, Minn, July 31, 38; m. 72. ENGLISH LITERATURE. B.A, Carleton Col, 60; Fulbright fel, Univ. Reading, 60-61; Woodrow Wilson fel. & M.A, Yale, 62, Ph.D.(Eng), 68. Instr. ENG, Miami Univ, 63-65; asst. instr, Yale, 66-67; instr, UNIV. ILL. URBANA, 67-68, asst. prof, 68-73, ASSOC. PROF, 73- MLA; AAUP. Restoration and 18th century drama; restoration literature. Publ: Southerne's The wives' excuse, Mod. Lang. Quart, 3/73; Language and character in Congreve's The way of the world, Tex. Stud. Lit. & Lang, fall 73; introd, The life and death of Doctor Faustus, Clark Mem. Libr, 73. Add: Dept. of English, 100 English Bldg, University of Illinois, Urbana, IL 61801.

KAUFMAN, GLORIA (SHAPIRO), b. Danbury, Conn, Apr. 5, 29; m. 60; c. 1. ENGLISH & AMERICAN LITERATURE. B.A, Russell Sage Col, 50; M.A, Brooklyn Col, 52; Fulbright fel, Univ. Munich, Ger, 56-57; Ph.D.(Eng. & Am. lit), Brandeis Univ, 61. Instr. ENG, Oakland Univ, 60-62, asst. prof, 62-63; IND. UNIV, SOUTH BEND, 65-71, ASSOC. PROF, 71- Mem. int. comt, Centro Studi e Scambi Internazionale, Rome, Italy, 61, Medal of Honor, 66. Shakespeare Asn; MLA. Shakespeare; Elizabethan drama; modern literature. Publ: Which witch is which?, Willis Music Co, 53; auth, Sixteen poems, Centro Studi e Scambi Internazionale, 62; Dame Alice as deceptive narrator, Chaucer Rev, fall 71. Add: Dept. of English, Indiana University, South Bend, IN 46615.

KAUFMAN, MARJORIE RUTH, b. Milwaukee, Wis, May 24, 22. ENGLISH. B.S, Wis. State Teachers Col, Milwaukee, 44; M.A, Univ. Wash, 47; Ph.D, Univ. Minn, 54. Teacher high sch, Wis, 44-46; from teaching asst. to teaching assoc. ENG, Univ. Wash, 46-47; instr, Univ. Minn, 47-54; MT. HOLYOKE COL, 54-56, asst. prof, 56-62, assoc. prof, 62-71, PROF, 71- Am. Asn. Univ. Women Gladys Murphy Graham fel, 61-62; Mt. Holyoke Col. faculty fel, 68-69. Am. Stud. Asn; MLA. American literature; modern fiction; 18th century English literature. Publ: William James's Letters to a young pragmatist, J. Hist. Ideas, summer 63; Ellen Glasgow & Katharine Fullerton Gerould, In: Notable American women, 1607-1950, Radcliffe Col. Add: Dept. of English, Mt. Holyoke College, South Hadley, MA 01075.

KAUFMAN, MICHAEL WILLIAM, b. Brooklyn, N.Y, Nov. 1, 38; m. 63; c. 1. ENGLISH. B.S, Tulane Univ, 61; M.A, Univ. Mich, 62, Ph.D.(Shakespeare), 66. Instr. ENG. LIT, Univ. Mich, 65-66; CORNELL UNIV, 66-67, ASST. PROF, 67- Add: Dept. of English, 341 Goldwin Smith Hall, Cornell University, Ithaca, NY 14850.

KAUFMAN, PAUL, b. Providence, R.I, July 29, 86; m. 12, 47; c. 2. ENGLISH LITERATURE. A.B, Yale, 09, A.M, 10; Ph.D, Harvard, 18. Instr. Eng, Yale, 16-18; prof. Eng. lit, Am. Univ.(D.C), 20-30; educ. specialist, U.S. Dept. War, 41-47; private res. & travel, 47-58; CONSULT. BIBLIOG, UNIV. WASH, 58- Ed, Bull, Shakespeare Asn. Am, 24-33; res. grants, Am. Counc. Learned Soc, 59, Am. Philos. Soc, 60, 61 & Asn. Col. & Res. Libr, 63, Great Brit. Romantic period; library history in Great Britain. Publ: Outline guide to Shakespeare, Century House, 24; Heralds of original genius, Harvard, 26; Borrowings from the Bristol Library, Bibliog. Soc. Va, 60; Libraries and their users, Libr. Asn, London, 69; The community library: a chapter in English social history, Trans. Am. Philos. Soc. Vol. 57, Part 7. Add: University of Washington Library, Seattle, WA 98195.

KAUFMANN, DONALD L, b. Pittsburgh, Pa, Mar. 20, 27; m. 65. ENGLISH. B.A, Univ. Pittsburgh, 55, M.Litt, 57; Ph.D.(Eng), Univ. Iowa, 66. Asst. prof. ENG, Univ. Alaska, 64-68; UNIV. S.FLA, 68-72, ASSOC. PROF, 72- Consult, Upward Bound, Off. Econ. Opportunity, 67. MLA; Col. Eng. Asn. Twentieth century American and English literature; literary criticism. Publ: Norman Mailer; the countdown (the first twenty years), South. Ill. Univ, 69. Add: Dept. of English, University of South Florida, Tampa, FL 33620.

KAUFMANN, RALPH JAMES, b. Grand Forks, N.Dak, Aug. 2, 24; m. 69; c. 6. ENGLISH & COMPARATIVE LITERATURE. B.A, Grinnell Col, 47; Woodrow Wilson fel & M.A, Princeton, 49, Ph.D, 53; Fulbright fel, Univ. London. Instr. Eng, Princeton, 49-53; asst. prof, Wesleyan Univ, 53-55; Univ. Rochester, 55-60, assoc. prof, 60-63, prof, 63-64, hist. & Eng, 64-69, chmn. dept. hist, 66-68, assoc. dean arts & sci, 61-63; prof, UNIV. TEX, AUSTIN, 69-73, STILES PROF. HUMANITIES & COMP. LIT, 73-, assoc. dean humanities, 71-73. Folger summer fel, 62; mem. exec. bd, Eng. Inst, 63-64; Guggenheim fel, 64-65; mem. bd. dirs, Nat. Humanities Fac, 72- Harbison Teaching Prize, 68. U.S.N.R, 42-46. Renaissance literature; modern criticism; European intellectual history. Publ: Elizabethan drama, Oxford, 61; G.B. Shaw, Prentice-Hall, 65; Tragedy and its validating conditions, Comp. Drama, 67; plus others. Add: Dept. of English, University of Texas at Austin, Austin, TX 78712.

KAUFMANN, U. MILO, b. Cleveland, Ohio, Aug. 27, 34; m. 56; c. 3. ENGLISH. B.A, Greenville Col, 56; fel, Univ. Ill, 56-57, M.A, 57; Danforth fel, Yale, 56-60, Jr. Sterling fel, 58-59, Sr. Sterling fel, 59-60, Ph.D, 60. Asst. prof. ENG, Greenville Col, summer 61; instr. N.Park Col, 61-62; UNIV. ILL, URBANA, 62-63, asst. prof, 63-67, ASSOC. PROF, 67- Fac. summer fel, Univ. Ill, 63 & 66; ed, Light & Life, 69-; consult. humanities, Spring Arbor Col, 72- Soc. Relig. Higher Educ; Conf. Christianity & Lit. (treas, 66-68). Literary theory; Milton; devotional poetry of the English Renaissance. Publ: The Pilgrim's progress and traditions in Puritan meditation, Yale, 66; Expostulation with the divine, Interpretation, 64; Brave new improbable worlds, Extrapolation, 64. Add: Dept. of English, University of Illinois, Urbana, IL 61801.

KAULBACH, ERNEST NORMAN, b. Bridgeport, Conn, Jan. 3, 35; m. 70; c. 2. MEDIEVAL STUDIES & PHILOSOPHY. A.B, St. Mary's Univ, 57, S.T.L, 61; M.A, Fairfield Univ, 61; Ph.D.(medieval stud), Cornell Univ, 70. Instr. Eng, St. Joseph's Col, 61-62; Eng. & theol, St. Mary's Col, 63-66; vis. assoc. prof. Eng, classics & philos, UNIV. TEX, AUSTIN, 70-73, ASSOC. PROF. ENG. & CLASSICS, 73- Mediaeval Acad. Am; Dante Soc. Am. Medieval philosophy, literature and theology. Publ: Inferno XIX, 45: the Zanca of temporal power, Dante Stud, 68; Piers Plowman B. IX, 18, 52: further refinements of Inwit, Festschrift for A.A. Hill, 73. Add: Dept. of English, University of Texas at Austin, Austin, TX 78712.

KAUVAR, GERALD BLUESTONE, b. Denver, Colo, Mar. 16, 38; m. 72. ENGLISH. B.A, Univ. Colo, 61, M.A, 62; Ph.D.(Eng), Duke Univ, 66. Instr. ENG, Univ. Ill, Chicago, 65-66, asst. prof, 66-70, asst. dean grad. sch, 67-70; ASST. PROF. ENG, CITY COL. NEW YORK, 70- MLA; Mod. Humanities Res. Asn. Nineteenth and twentieth century literature; criticism; psychoanalytic criticism. Publ: Co-auth, The Victorian mind, Putnam & Cassell's, 69; The other poetry of Keats, 70 & co-ed, Nineteenth century English verse drama, 73, Fairleigh Dickinson Univ; auth, Coleridge, Hawkesworth, and the willing suspension of disbelief, Papers Lang. & Lit, autumn 68; Marlow as liar, Stud. Short Fiction, summer 68; Chapter 54 of Moby Dick Arlington Quart, winter 69. Add: Dept. of English, City College of New York, 138th St. at Convent Ave, New York, NY 10031.

KAVANAGH, PETER, b. Inniskeen, Ireland, Mar. 19, 16; m. 63; c. 2. ENGLISH. B.A, Univ. Col, Dublin, 40, H.D.E. & M.A, 41; Ph.D.(Eng), Trinity Col.(Dublin), 44. Master, Dublin Nat. Schs, 37-45; asst. prof. Eng, St.

Francis Col.(N.Y), 46-47; Loyola Univ.(Ill), 47-49; assoc. prof, Gannon Col, 49-50; ed. & writer, Encycl. Americana, 50-53; engineering, Cementation Co, London, 53-57; prof. Eng, Fairleigh Dickinson Univ, 57-58; publ, N.Y, 58- Assoc. prof. Eng, Stout State Univ, 66-68. Assoc. Brit. Soc. Engineers; MLA; Int. Fed. Journalists. Publ: The Irish theatre, Kerryman, 46; The story of the Abbey theatre, N.Y, 50; A dictionary of Irish Mythology, N.Y, 59; plus others; contrib. numerous lit. publ, encycl. & engineering journals. Add: Peter Kavanagh Hand Press, 250 E. 30th St, New York, NY. 10016.

KAY, CAROL McGINNIS, b. Gadsden, Ala, Jan. 14, 41; m. 68. ENGLISH LITERATURE. A.B, Univ. Ala, 62, M.A, 63; cert. stud, Shakespeare Inst, Eng, summer 65; Ph.D.(Eng), Univ. Tenn, 67. Asst. prof. ENG, UNIV. ALA, 67-72, ASSOC. PROF, 62-, CHMN. INSTR, 72- MLA; S.Atlantic Mod. Lang. Asn; Southeast. Renaissance Soc; Renaissance Soc. Am; Col. Eng. Asn. Renaissance drama; modern drama. Publ: Traps, slaughter, and chaos: a study of Shakespeare's Henry VI plays, Stud. Lit. Imagination, 4/72; Hawthorne's use of clothing in his short stories, Nathaniel Hawthorne J, 72; co-auth, Literary periodicals from 1790 to 1830, Bull. Bibliog, 10-12/72; plus others. Add: Dept. of English, Drawer AL, University of Alabama, University, AL 35486.

KAY, W. DAVID, b. Phila, Pa, Mar. 28, 39; m. 59. ENGLISH LITERATURE. B.A, Univ. Pa, 61; M.A, Princeton, 63, Ph.D.(Eng), 68. Instr. ENG, UNIV. ILL, URBANA, 65-68, ASST. PROF, 68- Danforth fel, Yale Div. Sch, 69-70. MLA; Renaissance Soc. Am. Renaissance humanism; Elizabethan and Jacobean drama; Ben Jonson. Publ: Shaping of Ben Jonson's career, Mod. Philol, 2/70; Christian wisdom on Ben Jonson's On my first sonne, Stud. Eng. Lit, winter 71. Add: Dept. of English, University of Illinois, Urbana, IL 61801.

KAY, WALLACE GRANT, b. Jena, La, Nov. 10, 39; m. 61; c. 2. COMPARATIVE LITERATURE, AESTHETICS. B.A, South. Methodist Univ, 62; M.A, Emory Univ, 63, Ph.D.(comp. lit), 65. ASSOC. PROF. ENG. & LIT, UNIV. SOUTH. MISS, 65- Nat. Col. Honors Counc; S.Atlantic Mod. Lang. Asn. Contemporary fiction and drama. Publ: Machine and metaphor: a study in communication, 1/67, The observer and the voyeur: theories of fiction in James and Robbe-Grillet, 10/70 & Blake, Baudelaine, Beckett: the romantics of nihilism, 4/71, South. Quart. Add: University Honors Program, University of Southern Mississippi, Box 5162, Southern Station, Hattiesburg, MS 39401.

KAY, WAYNE DONALD, b. Anderson, S.C, Aug. 30, 39; m. 68. ENGLISH LITERATURE. A.B, Presby. Col.(S.C), 61; M.A, Univ. Tenn, 63, Ph.D. (Eng), 67. Asst. prof. ENG, UNIV. ALA, 67-72, ASSOC. PROF, 72-, DIR. GRAD. ENG, STUD, 73-, asst. chmn. dept. Eng, 70-71. MLA; S.Atlantic Mod. Lang. Asn; South. Humanities Conf.(secy-treas, 70-72); Col. Eng. Asn; Boswell Auchinleck Soc. Eighteenth century fiction; Boswell and Johnson; Restoration drama. Publ: Short fiction in the Spectator, Univ. Ala, 74; Defoe's sense of history in A journal of the plague year, Xavier Univ. Stud, 72; Appearance-reality theme in Marlowe's The Jew of Malta, Stud. Eng. Lit, 72; Pamela and the poultry, Satire Newsletter, 72; plus others. Add: Dept. of English, Drawer AL, University of Alabama, University, AL 35486.

KAYE, HOWARD, b. Los Angeles, Calif, Dec. 26, 42. ENGLISH. B.A, Stanford Univ, 64; Woodrow Wilson fel. & M.A, Columbia Univ, 65, pres. fel, 66-67, Woodrow Wilson fel. & Ph.D.(Eng), 68. ASST. PROF. ENG, CORNELL UNIV, 68- Modern American literature; creative writing. Add: Dept. of English, Cornell University, Ithaca, NY 14850.

KAYE, JULIAN B, b. Brooklyn, N.Y, Aug. 24, 25. ENGLISH LITERATURE. B.A, City Col. New York, 44; M.A, Columbia Univ, 45, Ph.D, 54. Lectr. ENG, City Col. New York, 47-50, tutor, 50-53; instr, Hunter Col, 53-55; lectr, BROOKLYN COL, 56-58, instr, 58-64, asst. prof, 64-70, assoc. prof, 70-74, PROF, 74- Ford Found. publ. grant, 58. MLA; NCTE; Mod. Humanities Res. Asn, Gt. Brit. Modern British literature. Publ: Bernard Shaw and the nineteenth century tradition, Univ. Okla, 58; Simony, the three Simons, and Joycean myth, In: A James Joyce miscellany, James Joyce Soc. Press, 57; A portrait of the artist as Blephen-Stoom, In: A James Joyce miscellany, 2nd ser, South. Ill. Univ, 59; The awkward age, The sacred fount, The ambassadors: another figure in the carpet, 19th Century Fiction, 3/63. Add: Dept. of English, Brooklyn College, Brooklyn, NY 11210.

KAYE, PHILIP ALBERT, b. Highmore, S.Dak, July 3, 20; m. 45; c. 2. SPEECH. A.B, Dakota Wesleyan Univ, 42; Th.M, Iliff Theol. Sem, 45, M.R.E, 51; A.M, Univ. Denver, 47, Ph.D, 55. Prof. speech & head dept. speech & dramatic arts, Dakota Wesleyan Univ; from assoc. prof. SPEECH & head dept. to PROF. & HEAD DEPT, NEBR. WESLEYAN UNIV, 56- U.S.N.R, 45-46. Add: Dept. of Speech, Nebraska Wesleyan University, Lincoln, NE 68504.

KAZIN, ALFRED, b. Brooklyn, N.Y, June 5, 15; m. 52; c. 2. AMERICAN STUDIES. B.S.S, City Col. New York, 35; M.A, Columbia Univ, 38; Guggenheim fels, 40, 47; Rockefeller Found. fel, 45; Carnegie grant, 41-42; hon. M.A, Amherst Col, 56; Litt.D, Adelphi Univ, 64. Tutor Eng, City Col. New York, 39-42; lectr. Eng. & gen. lit, New Sch. Social Res, 41-42, 48-49, 51, 52-53; vis. lectr, Harvard, 53; Neilson res. prof, Smith Col, 54-55; prof. Am. Stud, Amherst Col, 55-58; lectr, New Sch. Social Res, 58-63; DISTINGUISHED PROF. ENG, STATE UNIV. N.Y. STONY BROOK, 63- Vis. lectr, Ger, Eng, France, Sweden & Norway; Black Mountain Col, 44; Berg Prof, N.Y. Univ, 57-58; vis. prof, Univ. P.R, 59; Gauss lectr, Princeton, 62; Gallagher Prof, City Col. New York, 63; Beckman Prof, Univ. Calif, Berkeley, 63; vis. prof. Am. Lit, Univ. Mich, summer 72; distinguished prof. Eng. lit, Hunter Col, 73-74. Am. Acad. Arts & Sci; Am. Stud. Asn; Nat. Inst. Arts & Lett. American literature; English literature; modern European literature. Publ: On native ground, 42, A walker in the city, 51 & The inmost leaf, 55, Harcourt; Contemporaries, 62 & Starting out in the thirties, 65, Little; Bright book of life: American novelists & storytellers from Hemingway to Mailer, Atlantic Monthly, 73. Add: 440 West End Ave, New York, NY 10024.

KEANE, PATRICK JOSEPH, b. New York, N.Y, Nov. 28, 39. ENGLISH, AMERICAN LITERATURE. B.S.S, Fordham Univ, 61; univ. scholar, N.Y. Univ, 68-69, M.A, 69, univ. fel, 69-70, Ph.D.(Eng. lit), 71. Advertising copywriter, Ronald Press, 65-68; from instr. to ASST. PROF. ENG. LIT, SKIDMORE COL, 70- Nat. Endowment for Humanities, summer stipend, 73. U.S.A, 62-65. MLA. English Romanticism; modern Irish literature; modern English and American poetry. Publ: Ed. & contrib, W.B. Yeats: contemporary studies in literature, McGraw, 73; auth, Luminous glimpse, New Republic, 1/73. Add: Dept. of English, Skidmore College, Saratoga Springs, NY 12866.

KEANE, ROBERT NORWOOD, b. New York, N.Y, June 27, 33; m. 60; c. 1. ENGLISH LITERATURE. A.B, Dartmouth Col, 55; A.M, Columbia Univ, 57, Ph.D.(Eng), 65. Instr. ENG, HOFSTRA UNIV, 59-66, asst. prof, 66-72, ASSOC. PROF, 72- Nat. Endowment for Humanities younger scholar fel, 69. MLA. Victorian English literature; pre-Raphaelitism; Dante Gabriel Rossetti. Publ: D.G. Rossetti's Poems 1870, Princeton Univ. Libr. Chronicle, spring 72 & In: Essays on the Rossettis; The Rossettis at Princeton, Manuscripts, spring 73; Rossetti's Jenny: moral ambiguity and the Inner standing point, Papers Lang. & Lit, summer 73. Add: Dept. of English, Hofstra University, Hempstead, NY 11550.

KEARNEY, FLORA McLAUGHLIN, b. New Orleans, La, Oct. 10, 20. ENGLISH LITERATURE. A.B, Col. William & Mary, 41; A.M, Radcliffe Col, 42; Ph.D, Univ. Md, 54; M.S, Univ. Ill, 67. Asst. prof. lang. & lit, Northeast Mo. State Teachers Col, 54-56; instr. Eng. lit. & compos, Univ. Tenn, 56-61; asst. prof, BALL STATE UNIV, 61-68, ASSOC. PROF. ENG, 68- MLA; Renaissance Soc. Am; Renaissance Eng. Text Soc; Am. Soc. 18th Century Stud. Eighteenth century English literature, bibliography; Renaissance English literature. Publ: James Hervey and eighteenth century taste, Ball State Univ, 69; Sacred versus secular in French books of hours, Ball State Univ. Forum, spring 68. Add: Dept. of English, Ball State University, Muncie, IN 47306.

KEARNEY, KEVIN EMMETT, b. Bogota, N.J, Jan. 19, 29; m. 67; c. 2. SPEECH. B.S, Univ. Vt, 54; M.A, Univ. Fla, 55, Ph.D.(speech), 60. Instr. SPEECH, Butler Univ, 58-60; asst. prof, Univ. Ala, 60-64; UNIV. S.FLA, 64-66, ASSOC. PROF, 66-, DIR. BACHELOR OF INDEPENDENTS STUD. DEGREE PROG, 68- Consult, speaker's bur, Gen. Telephone Fla, 68- U.S.N, 46-48, Res, 50-52. Nat. Univ. Exten. Asn.(chmn. div. spec. degree progs. & mem. comt. discussion & debate, 72-73); South. Speech Commun. Asn.(exec-secy, 66-69). Southern oratory; public address; innovative degree programs. Publ: Ed, Proceedings of a national conference on special adult degree programs, Ctr. Continuing Educ, Univ. S.Fla, 70; auth, Innovative higher education for adults, Compact, 10/72. Add: 1905 E. 114th Ave, Tampa, FL 33612.

KEARNS, FRANCIS EDWARD, b. Brooklyn, N.Y, Aug. 10, 31; m. 60; c. 2. AMERICAN LITERATURE. A.B, N.Y. Univ, 53; Noyes scholar, Univ. Chicago, 53-54, M.A, 54; univ. fel, Univ. N.C, 54-55, Smith travel grant, 58, Ph.D.(Eng), 61. Ed, Chicago Rev, 53-54; case off, U.S. Cent. Intel. Agency, 55-56; instr, Univ. N.C, 56-60; asst. prof. Am. lit, Georgetown Univ, 60-65; LEHMAN COL, 65-68, assoc. prof, 68-72, PROF. AM. LIT. & CHMN. DEPT. ENG, 72- Asst. dir. univ. writers conf, Georgetown Univ, 61, faculty res. grant, summer 62; lectr, Int. Teacher Develop. Prog, U.S. Off. Educ, Dept. of Health, Educ. & Welfare & Dept. State, 62; Am. Philos. Soc. res. grant, summer 62; Fulbright lectr, Univ. Bergen, 65-66; City Univ. N.Y. fac. res. grant, summer 62 & 71-72; vis. prof, Univ. Nancy, 69-70; lectr. tour, U.S. Inform. Serv, 70. Edward Douglas White Award, Georgetown Univ, 65. MLA. American Romantic period; modern American novel; American race relations. Publ: ed, The black experience in American literature, Viking, 70; Black identity, Holt, 70; Campus activism, autumn 68 & The un-angry Langston Hughes, autumn 70, Yale Rev; The theme of experience in Hawthorne's Blithedale romance, In: Geschichte und fiktion: Amerikanische prosa im 19 jahrhundert, Vandenhoeck & Ruprecht, 72; plus others. Add: Dept. of English, Herbert H. Lehman College, Bedford Park Blvd. W, Bronx, NY 10468.

KEARNS, ROBERT JOHN, S.J, b. Detroit, Mich, Aug. 9, 19. ENGLISH LITERATURE. A.B, Loyola Univ.(Ill), 44, A.M, 46; Ph.D, Univ. Mich, 58. ASST. PROF. ENG, UNIV. DETROIT, 58- Dir. libr, Univ. Detroit, 60- MLA; NCTE; Am. Libr. Asn; Cath. Libr. Asn. English Renaissance literature; recusant prose. Add: University of Detroit, Detroit, MI 48221.

KEAST, WILLIAM REA, b. Malta, Ill, Nov. 1, 14; m. 38; c. 3. ENGLISH LITERATURE. A.B, Univ. Chicago, 36, Rockefeller fel, 46-47, Ph.D, 47; LL.D, Univ. Mich, 67. Instr. Eng, Univ. Chicago, 38-47, asst. prof, 47-51, secy. dept, 49-51; assoc. prof, Cornell Univ, 51-57, prof. & chmn. dept, 57-62, dean col. arts & sci, 62-63, v.pres. acad. affairs, 63-65; pres, WAYNE STATE UNIV, 65-71, chmn. comn. acad. tenure, 71-72; PROF. ENG. & CHMN. DEPT, UNIV. TEX, AUSTIN, 72-, DIR. SPEC. COLLECTIONS, CTR. HIGHER EDUC, 74-, dir. ctr, 72-74. Fund Advan. Educ. fac. fel, 55-56; Guggenheim fel, 58-59; mem, President's Adv. Comt. on Developing Insts, 65-67. A.U.S, 41-46, Maj. Am. Acad. Polit. & Soc. Sci; MLA; Am. Asn. Higher Educ. History of criticism; Samuel Johnson; 18th century literature. Add: Dept. of English, University of Texas at Austin, Austin, TX 78712.

KEEFE, KATHRYN, C.D.P, b. Robstown, Tex, June 23, 27. SPEECH, DRAMA. B.A, Our Lady of the Lake Col, 51; Univ. Tex, Austin, 52-53; M.A, Northwest. Univ, 57, Ph.D.(speech), 65. Instr. St. Anthony Elem. Sch, Tex, 48-52; Providence High Sch, Tex, 53-60; SPEECH & DRAMA, OUR LADY OF THE LAKE COL, 60-61, asst. prof, 61-67, ASSOC. PROF, 68-, CHMN. DEPT, 66- Lectr. oral interpretation of scriptures, Ill, 65. Am. Theatre Asn; Speech Commun. Asn; AAUP. Adaptations of literature for the stage: Aldous Huxley's Brave new world, poetry of T.S. Eliot, The little prince, Saint-Exupéry. Add: Dept. of Speech, Our Lady of the Lake College, San Antonio, TX 78285.

KEEFE, ROBERT, b. Framingham, Mass, Mar. 11, 38; m. 60. ENGLISH. A.B, Brandeis Univ, 64; Woodrow Wilson fel, Princeton, 64-65, Danforth fel, 64-68, Ph.D.(Eng), 68. ASST. PROF. ENG, UNIV. MASS, AMHERST, 67- U.S.A.F, 56-61. Soc. Relig. Higher Educ; MLA. Victorian literature; Matthew Arnold; 19th century concepts of time. Add: Dept. of English, University of Massachusetts, Amherst, MA 01002.

KEEFER, TRUMAN FREDERICK, b. Frederick, Md, Feb. 25, 30; m. 65; c. 3. ENGLISH. A.B, West. Md. Col, 51; M.A, Duke Univ, 53, Ph.D, 60. Instr. Eng, W.Va. Univ, 55-56; asst. prof, Ga. South. Univ, 56-58; State Univ. N.Y. Col. Fredonia, 58-60; assoc. prof, Transylvania Col, 60-61; asst. prof, Univ. Cincinnati, 61-66; ASST. PROF. ENG, MIAMI UNIV, 66-, coord. humanities, 66-73. Conf. Col. Compos. & Commun. Ernest Poole; Philip Wylie. Publ: Ernest Poole, Twayne, 66; William Faulkner's Sanctuary: a myth examined, Twentieth Century Lit, 7/69; Emily Dickinson's Van Diemen's land, Explicator, 11/70; In pursuit of the copulative verb, Col. Compos. & Commun, 5/71; plus others. Add: 730 Kensington Court, Middletown, OH 45042.

KEELER, CLINTON CLARENCE, b. Lamont, Okla, Nov. 14, 19; m. 41; c. 2. ENGLISH. B.A, Okla. State Univ, 40; Johns Hopkins Univ, 41-42; Ph.D, Univ. Minn, 54. Jr. instr. Eng, Johns Hopkins Univ, 41-42; instr. commun. & humanities, Univ. Minn, 47-52; assoc. prof. ENG, State Univ. Col, Cortland, 52-56; PROF, OKLA. STATE UNIV, 56-, HEAD DEPT, 68- Ed-in-chief, Cimarron Rev, 69- U.S.N.R, Lt. Am. Stud. Asn; MLA; NCTE. Reform ideas in American literature, 1880-1900; 20th century American fiction and poetry; visual arts and American literature, 1860-1960. Publ: Narrative without accent: Willa Cather and Puvis De Chavannes, Am. Quart, spring 65; A Farewell to arms: Hemingway and Peele, Mod. Lang. Notes, 11/61; Sir William Osler visits Whitman, Calamus, 10/70. Add: Dept. of English, Oklahoma State University, Stillwater, OK 74074.

KEELEY, EDMUND LeROY, b. Damascus, Syria, Feb. 5, 28; U.S. citizen; m. 51. ENGLISH. A.B, Princeton, 49; Wilson fel, Oxford, 51-52, D.Phil. (comp. lit), 52. Fulbright teacher Eng, Thessalonica Agr. & Indust. Inst, 49-50; instr, Brown Univ, 52-53; Fulbright lectr. Eng. & Am. lit, Univ. Salonica, Greece, 53-54; instr. Eng, PRINCETON, 54-57, asst. prof, 57-62, assoc. prof, 63-70, PROF. ENG. & CREATIVE ARTS, 70-, DIR. PROG. CREATIVE WRITING & THEATRE, 71-, co-dir, comp. lit. prog, 64-65, dir. creative arts prog, 66-71. Counc. Humanities fel, 56-57; fel, Am. Acad. Rome, 59-60; Guggenheim fels, 59-60 & 73; vis. lectr. mod. Greek, Oxford, 60; Eng, Univ. Iowa, 62-63; writer-in-residence, Knox Col, spring 63; lectr, Hellenic-Am. Inst, Athens, 65-66; McCosh Fac. fel, 69-70; mem. bd. ed. dir, Princeton Alumni Weekly, 64- U.S.N.R, 45-46; U.S.A.F.R, 52-56, T/Sgt. Auth. Guild; Am. Comp. Lit. Asn; Am. Acad. Arts & Lett.(Prix de Rome, 59); Mod. Greek Stud. Asn.(pres, 69-73); PEN Club. Creative writing; English and American literature; modern Greek literature. Publ: The libation, Scribner, 58; The gold-hatted lover, Little, 61; co-auth, Six poets of modern Greece, 61, V. Vassilikos: the plant, the well, the angel, 64, Knopf; co-auth, George Seferis: collected poems, 1924-1955, 67, C.P. Cavafy: selected poems, 72, 74 & co-ed, Modern Greek writers, 72, Princeton; auth, The impostor, Doubleday, 70; co-auth, C.P. Cavafy; passions and ancient days, Dial, 71; auth, To a dark island, Curtis, 72; co-auth, Odysseus Elytis: the Axion Esti, Pittsburgh, 74; Seferis's Elpenor: a man of no fortune, Kenyon Rev, 6/66; George Seferis and the Mythical method, Comp. Lit. Stud, 6/69; George Seferis, Encounter, 3/72; plus others. Add: Creative Writing Program, Princeton University, 185 Nassau St, Princeton, NJ 08540.

KEEN, JOE J, b. Tonkawa, Okla, Oct. 2, 27; m. 54; c. 1. ENGLISH. B.A, Northwest Nazarene Col, 54; M.A, Univ. Colo, 56, fac. fel, Eng, 65-66, Ph.D. (Eng. lit), 66. Asst. adminr. admis. & rec, UNIV. COLO, DENVER, 54-57, asst. dean summer session, 57-62, asst. prof. ENG, 62-68, assoc. prof, 68-69, PROF, 69-, ASSOC. DEAN COL. ARTS & SCI, 66-, V.PRES, 69-, asst. dean col. arts & sci, 62-66. U.S.A, 45-47. Mod. Humanities Res. Asn. (Am. treas, 60-); MLA; Asn. Higher Educ. Eighteenth century English literature. Add: College of Arts & Sciences, University of Colorado at Denver, Denver, CO 80202.

KEENAN, CHARLES, S.J, b. Belfast, Ireland, July 12, 04; U.S. citizen. ENGLISH LANGUAGE & LITERATURE. A.B, Gonzaga Univ, 30, M.A, 31; B.A, Oxford, 40, M.A, 44. Instr. Eng, Gonzaga Univ, 31-33; managing ed, America, 43-56, feature ed, 56-58; asst. prof. ENG, GONZAGA UNIV, 58-60, assoc. prof, 60-70, EMER. PROF, 71-, REF. LIBRN, 71- Add: Dept. of English, Gonzaga University, Spokane, WA 99202.

KEENAN, JOHN JOSEPH, b. Bryn Mawr, Pa, Feb. 2, 31; m. 54; c. 4. AMERICAN LITERATURE. B.A, La Salle Col, 52; M.A, Univ. Pa, 57. Asst. prof. ENG, LA SALLE COL, 59-66, ASSOC. PROF, 66- Lindback Award for Distinguished Teaching, 67-68; ed, Four Quarters. NCTE; MLA. The American musical; American literature since 1870. Publ: Co-auth, Adventures in American literature, teachers manual, Harcourt, 62; Teaching the American musical, Col. Eng, 4/63. Add: Dept. of English, La Salle College, Philadelphia, PA 19141.

KEENER, FREDERICK M, b. New York, N.Y, Dec. 28, 37; m. 61; c. 2. ENGLISH. A.B, St. John's Univ.(N.Y), 59; M.A, Columbia Univ, 60, Ph.D.(Eng), 65. From instr. to asst. prof. ENG, St. John's Univ.(N.Y), 61-66; asst. prof, COLUMBIA UNIV, 66-71, ASSOC. PROF, 71- Lectr, Hunter Col, 66. MLA; Conf. Brit. Stud. Eighteenth century British literature; Milton; contemporary literature. Publ: English Dialogues of the dead, 73 & An essay on Pope, 74, Columbia Univ; The emergence of the dialogue of the dead in England, Bull. New York Pub. Libr, 1/69. Add: 102 Low Library, Columbia University, New York, NY 10027.

KEESEY, RAY EDWARD, b. Cadiz, Ohio, July 3, 14. SPEECH. A.B, Ohio Univ, 37, A.M, 38; Ph.D, Ohio State Univ, 50. Instr, High Sch, Ohio, 38-39; Eng, Univ. N.H, 40-43; asst. prof, Whitman Col, 45-46; asst. prof. speech & dir. speech clinic, Dartmouth Col, 48-51; assoc. prof. dramatic arts & speech, UNIV. DEL, 51-, PROF. DRAMATIC ARTS & SPEECH & CHMN. DEPT. SPEECH-COMMUN, 73-, assoc. dean col. arts & sci, 63-71, acting dean, 71-73. Speech Commun. Asn; East. Commun. Asn.(pres, 62-63); Am. Inst. Parliamentarians. Public address; rhetoric theory of John Lawson; 18th century rhetoric. Publ: Modern parliamentary procedure, Houghton, 73. Add: Dept. of Speech-Communication, University of Delaware, Newark, DE 19711.

KEETCH, BRENT HARRIS, b. Vernal, Utah, Aug. 23, 40; m. 64. AMERICAN LITERATURE. B.A, Utah State Univ, 66, M.A, 67; Ph.D.(Eng), Univ. Utah, 71. Newsman, Salt Lake Tribune, Utah, 63-65; newsman & ed, Assoc. Press, 65-67; ASST. PROF. Jour, CALIF. POLYTECH. STATE UNIV, SAN LUIS OBISPO, 67-69, ENG, 71- MLA. American novel. Publ: It's autumn in the country I remember, summer 69 & F. Scott Fitzgerald, spring 72, West. Humanities Rev. Add: Dept. of English, California Polytechnic State University, San Luis Obispo, CA 93407.

KEGEL, CHARLES HERBERT, b. Chicago, Ill, Aug. 16, 24; m. 50; c. 2. ENGLISH. A.B, Alma Col, 47; M.A, Northwest. Univ, 49; Ph.D, Mich. State Univ, 55. Instr, High Sch, Mich, 49-51; commun, Mich. State Univ, 51-56; asst. prof. ENG, IDAHO STATE UNIV, 56-62, PROF, 62-, ACAD. V.PRES, 68-, dean col. lib. arts, 63-66, dean faculties, 66-68, acting co-adminr, 72. U.S.N, 43-46. MLA. Romantic period; Victorian period; American studies. Publ: Co-auth, Communication: principles and practice, Wadsworth, 59 & A glossary for college English, McGraw, 66; co-auth, Lyric poems on twelve themes, Scott, 70; transl, Harald Grieg, Out fishing with Hemingway, Idaho State Univ, 72; auth, An undergraduate magazine, 1856 style, Basis Col. Quart; Ruskin's St. George in America, Am. Quart; plus others. Add: Box 63, Idaho State University, Pocatello, ID 83209.

KEHL, DELMAR GEORGE, b. Mt. Carroll, Ill, Sept. 12, 36; m. 63; c. 2. AMERICAN LITERATURE. B.A, Bob Jones Univ, 57; M.S, Univ. Wis-Madison, 58; Fordham Univ, 59; Univ. Pa, 59; Occidental Col, 60; Ph.D.(Eng), Univ. South. Calif, 67. Instr. ENG, Roosevelt Sch, Conn, 58-59; Pasadena High Sch, Calif, 60-61; teaching asst. Univ. South. Calif, 61-63, lectr, 63-65; asst. prof, ARIZ. STATE UNIV, 65-70, ASSOC. PROF, 70-, fac. grants-in-aid, 69, 70, 72 & 74. Consult, Critical Reports. Elizabeth K. Pleasants Award excellence in teaching, Univ. South. Calif, 62. NCTE; MLA; Rocky Mountain Mod. Lang. Asn. Twentieth century American literature; poetry, fiction and the visual arts; literature and theology. Publ: Ed, The literary style of the old Bible and the new, Bobbs, 70; auth, Love's difinition: dream as reality in Warren's fiction, Four Quarters, 5/72; Writing in the Apocalypse: rhetorical lessons from Walter Van Tilburg Clark, Col. Compos. & Commun, 2/74; Steinbeck's string of pictures in The grapes of wrath, Image, 3/74; plus others. Add: Dept. of English, Arizona State University, Tempe, AZ 85281.

KEHLER, HAROLD F, b. Philadelphia, Pa, Jan. 25, 30; m. 63; c. 2. ENGLISH. B.S, Albright Col, 51; M.A, Ohio Univ, 57, Ph.D.(Eng), 68; Danforth fels, Univ. Minn, Minneapolis, 61-63. Instr. ENG, MacMurray Col, 57-61, asst. prof, 63-65; Ohio Univ, 67-68; SAN DIEGO STATE UNIV, 68-72, ASSOC. PROF, 72- U.S.A.F, 51-55, S/Sgt. MLA; NCTE. American literature, especially 19th century and Poe, Melville and Hawthorne; 20th century British literature, especially Eliot and Yeats. Publ: Howells's Editha, 3/61, Dostoevski's Crime and punishment, 11/65 & James's The real thing, 5/67, Explicator. Add: Dept. of English, San Diego State University, San Diego, CA 92115.

KEHOE, CONSTANCE DeMUZIO, b. Malden, Mass, July 25, 33; m. 59; c. 2. ENGLISH. A.B, Mt. Holyoke Col, 55; M.A, Yale, 56; M.A, Bread Loaf Sch. Eng, 59; Ph.D.(W.B. Yeats), Trinity Col.(Dublin), 67. Instr. ENG, Bay Path Jr. Col, 56-59; ASSOC. PROF, WHEELOCK COL, 60- Col. Eng. Asn. Modern Irish literature; W.B. Yeats. Publ: Co-auth, Enjoying Ireland, Devin-Adair, 66. Add: 13 Rock Glen Rd, Medford, MA 02155.

KEIM, CHARLES JOSEPH, b. Judith Gap, Mont, Nov. 2, 22; m. 50; c. 3. ENGLISH, JOURNALISM. B.A, Univ. Wash, 48, M.A, 50. Correspondent, United Press, 40; news ed, Port Angeles Evening News, Wash, 50-54; instr. ENG. & JOUR, UNIV. ALASKA, FAIRBANKS, 54-55, asst. prof, 55-57, assoc. prof, 57-61, PROF, 61-, dean Col. Arts & Lett, 62-69. Mem. comn. arts & sci, Nat. Asn. State Univs. & Land-grant Cols, 65-67; mem. bd. dirs, Counc. Col. Arts & Sci, 67-; mem. steering comt, Pac. Northwest Regional Conf. Higher Educ, 68- U.S.A, 40-45, Sgt. Fiction and factual writing; exploration. Publ: Aghvook, white Eskimo, Univ. Alaska, 68; co-auth, Archaeological discoveries on the Denali Highway, Alaska, Anthrop. Papers Univ. Alaska, 58; auth, The gallant try, Alatna Press 71; co-auth, Fair chase with Alaskan guides, Alaska Northwest Publ, 72; auth, Arctic fossil exploration, Explorers, J, 62; Change, In: Alaskan reader, Meredith, 67. Add: Dept. of English, University of Alaska, Fairbanks, AK 99701.

KEISER, GEORGE ROBERT, b. Pottsville, Pa, Feb. 26, 41. ENGLISH & AMERICAN LITERATURE. B.A, Lehigh Univ, 62, M.A, 64. Ph.D.(Eng), 71. Instr. ENG, Canisius Col, 67-69, ASST. PROF, 69-73, KANS. STATE UNIV, 73- MLA; AAUP; Mediaeval Acad. Am. Medieval English literature. Publ: Edward III and the alliterative Morte Arthure, Speculum, 1/73. Add: Dept. of English, Kansas State University, Manhattan, KS 66506.

KEISTER, DON ADAM, b. Barberton, Ohio, Feb. 26, 11; m. 33; c. 2. ENGLISH & AMERICAN LITERATURE. A.B, Univ. Akron, 31, Pixley fel, 31-33, A.M, 33; Ph.D, West. Reserve Univ, 47. Instr. Eng, UNIV. AKRON, 33-37, asst. prof, 37-46, assoc. prof, 46-47, prof, 47-72, dean Buchtel Col. Lib. Arts, 68-72, chmn. div. humanities, 47-50, head dept. gen. stud, 60-67, EMER. DISTINGUISHED PROF. ENG, 72- MLA. Seventeenth century English literature; Edward Herbert. Add: 44 Orchard Rd, Akron, OH 44313.

KEITH, PHILIP MYRON, b. Washington, D.C, Nov. 5, 42; m. 71; c. 1. AMERICAN LITERATURE, AMERICAN STUDIES. A.B, Amherst Col, 64; M.A, Bryn Mawr Col, 68; Ph.D.(Eng), Univ. Pa, 71. Master ENG, Hebron Acad, Maine, 64-66; instr, Swarthmore Col, 70-71, WASHINGTON & LEE UNIV, 71-72, ASST. PROF, 72. Nat. Endowment Humanities summer stipend, 73. MLA. Quakerism and American literature; American poetics and critical thought; rhetoric in American prose. Publ: Whittier and Warren, Shenandoah, fall 72. Add: Dept. of English, Washington & Lee University, Lexington, VA 24450.

KEITH, QUENTIN G, b. Bethlehem, Pa, Aug. 14, 19; m. 45; c. 2. ENGLISH. B.A, Lehigh Univ, 40; Univ. Paris, France, 45; B.A.(Hons), Cambridge, 47, M.A, 52. Researcher, Gt. Brit, Columbia Univ. Press, 47-48; instr. Eng, Rutgers Univ, 48-51; lectr. Eng. lit, MONMOUTH COL.(N.J), 54-55, speech & drama, 55-56, dir. develop, 56-59, ASSOC. PROF. ENG, 59- Ed, Far East Intel. Digest, UN, Tokyo, Japan, 51-52; Brit. Schs. & Univs. Quart, 53-55; pub. inform. off, U.S. Army, New Brunswick, N.J, 53; dir. creative advert, James Gray, Inc, N.Y, 54-55; rare bk. appraiser &

consult; owner & dir, Keith Libr, N.J; consult. fac, U.S. Army Command & Gen. Staff Col, 70-73; spec. asst. to the chief, U.S. Army Reserve, Wash, D.C, 72; pres, Monmouth County, N.J, Eng. Speaking Union U.S. Mil. Intel, U.S.A.R, 40-73, Col;(Ret); Legion of Merit. Col. Eng. Asn; MLA; Am. Mil. Inst. Drama. Publ: Co-auth, The army wife, Harper, 53; auth, A short history of communications, James Gray, 54; Medical benefits for Army reservists, Dept. of Army, 73; The Oxford and Cambridge Honours B.A. degree, Bull. Int. Inst. Educ, 2/61. Add: Dept. of English, Wilson Hall Annex, Monmouth College, West Long Branch, NJ 07764.

KEITHLEY, GEORGE FREDERICK, b. Chicago, Ill, July 18, 35; m. 60; c. 3. MODERN POETRY & CREATIVE WRITING. A.B, Duke Univ, 57; Stanford Univ, 57-58; M.F.A, Univ. Iowa, 60. Asst. business writing, Univ. Iowa, 61-62; instr. ENG, CALIF. STATE UNIV, CHICO, 62-65, asst. prof, 65-69, assoc. prof, 69-73, PROF, 73- State Univs. & Cols. Calif. chancellor's leave, 66. Wrangler Award, West. Heritage Ctr, 72; Alice Faye di Castagnola Award, Poetry Soc. Am, 73. Poetry Soc. Am. Modern poetry; verse drama; versification. Publ: Co-ed, Themes in American literature, Heath, 72; auth, The Donner party, 72 & Song in a strange land, 74, Braziller; How Crazy Horse was killed (poem), 4/72 & Buster Keaton and the cops (poem), 3/73, Harper's Mag; Flesh and dust (story), N.Am. Rev, winter 72-73. Add: Dept. of English, California State University, Chico, First & Normal St, Chico, CA 95926.

KELL, KATHARINE TOLLE, b. Indianapolis, Ind, Sept. 18, 23; m. 44; c. 3. MODERN AMERICAN LITERATURE, FOLKLORE. B.A, Wayne State Univ, 54, M.A, 64, Ph.D.(Am. lit), 72. Asst. ENG, Wayne State Univ, 65-71, instr, 71-73; RES. & WRITING, 73- Modern American literature; folklore; social history. Publ: The folklore of the daisy, 56, Tobacco in folk cures in Western society, 65 & Folk names for tobacco, 66, J. Am. Folklore. Add: 1810 Oak, Birmingham, MI 48009.

KELLEHER, JAMES P, b. Ireland, May 24, 14; U.S. citizen. ENGLISH, LITERATURE, COUNSELING. A.B, St. Mary's Col.(Ill), 40; A.M, Boston Univ, 47, Ph.D.(Eng. lit), 66; Ed.M, Harvard, 48. Instr. Eng. lit, ST. AMBROSE COL, 53-54, asst. prof, 55-60, assoc. prof, 60-68, PROF. ENG, 68- MLA; NCTE. Psychology and counselling; pastoral renewal. Add: Dept. of English, St. Ambrose College, Davenport, IA 52804.

KELLEHER, JOHN J, b. Brockton, Mass, Apr. 7, 29; m. 62; c. 1. ENGLISH. B.A, Stonehill Col, 52; M.A, Boston Col, 55; Ph.D, Univ. Pittsburgh, 64. Instr. ENG, St. Joseph's Col, 54-56; Kent State Univ, 60-63; assoc. prof, EAST. ILL. UNIV, 64-72, PROF, 72- U.S.A, 46-48. MLA. American and British fiction. Add: Dept. of English, Eastern Illinois University, Charleston, IL 61920.

KELLER, JOSEPH R, b. Wash, Jan. 4, 22; m. 61. MEDIAEVAL LITERATURE. B.A, Syracuse Univ, 47, M.A, 48; Ph.D, Columbia Univ, 58. Instr. ENG, Syracuse Univ, 48-50; ASST. PROF, IND. UNIV, 58- U.S.A, 42-45. MLA. Mediaeval Acad. Am. Mediaeval social protest; Black American literature; Black English linguistics. Publ: Crossing by caution, Pageant, 66; The Sibyl: prophetess of antiquity and medieval fay, Dorrance, 67; Black patterns in American English, Ind-Purdue Univ, 71; The triumph of vice: a formal approach to the medieval complaint against the times, Medium Aevum, 69; Black writing and editorial unbelief, 69 & Black writing and the white critic, 70, Negro Am. Lit. Forum. Add: Dept. of English, Indiana University, Indianapolis, IN 46204.

KELLER, KARL, b. Manti, Utah, May 29, 33; m. 56; c. 5. ENGLISH. A.B, Univ. Utah, 58, M.A, 59; Ph.D.(Eng), Univ. Minn, 64. Instr. ENG, Univ. Minn, 59-64; asst. prof, State Univ. N.Y. Col. Cortland, 64-66; PROF, SAN DIEGO STATE UNIV, 66- MLA (secy. Am. lit. group I). Publ: The stairway of surprise: the metaphysical strain in 19th century poetry, Mouton; co-auth, The Bible in literature; co-auth, American literature: post 1945, Future Resources & Develop, 70; auth, The world slickt up in types: Edward Taylor as a version of Emerson, Early Am. Lit. 5/70; John Greenleaf Whittier, In: Twelve American authors: a review of research and criticism, 69; The words of Edward Taylor, In: A concordance to the poems of Edward Taylor, N.C.R, Wash, D.C, 72; plus others. Add: Dept. of English, San Diego State University, San Diego, CA 92115.

KELLER, PAUL WATSON, b. Chicago, Ill, Jan. 6, 13. SPEECH. A.B, Manchester Col, 35; Ph.M, Univ. Wis, 40; Ph.D, Northwest. Univ, 55; Stanford Univ, 62. Instr. SPEECH, Bridgewater Col, 40-42; Pa. State Univ, 47-48; from asst. prof. to assoc. prof, MANCHESTER COL, 48-55, PROF, 55-, HEAD DEPT, 48- Vis. prof, San Jose State Col, fall 61; West. Mich. Univ, 67-68. Speech Commun. Asn; Int. Commun. Asn; Int. Soc. Gen. Semantics; Cent. State Speech Asn. Publ: Co-auth, Monologue to dialogue: an exploration of interpersonal communication, Prentice-Hall, 73. Add: Dept. of Speech, Manchester College, North Manchester, IN 46962.

KELLER, THEODORE DONALD, b. Lebanon, Pa, June 25, 26. ENGLISH. B.A, Lebanon Valley Col, 48; A.M, Columbia Univ, 49. Instr. Eng, Lebanon Valley Col, 49-51, dean men, 52-55, asst. prof. ENG, 55-65; ASSOC. PROF, EAST STROUDSBURG STATE COL, 65-, coord. freshman Eng, 66-70. U.S.A, 44-46. NCTE; MLA; Col. Eng. Asn; Conf. Col. Compos. & Commun. Eighteenth century satire; nineteenth century poetry; life and works of Swift. Add: Dept. of English, East Stroudsburg State College, East Stroudsburg, PA 18301.

KELLEY, ALICE van BUREN, b. Abilene, Tex, Sept. 26, 44; m. 69. ENGLISH LITERATURE. B.A, Smith Col, 66; Ph.D.(Eng), City Univ. New York, 71. Lectr. ENG, UNIV. PA, 71-72, ASST. PROF, 72- MLA. Modern British and Irish novel. Publ: The novels of Virginia Woolf: fact and vision, Univ. Chicago, 73; The bleak houses of Bleak House, Nineteenth Century Fiction, 12/70. Add: Dept. of English, University of Pennsylvania, Philadelphia, PA 19174.

KELLEY, MARGARET TERESA, S.S.J, b. Ithaca, N.Y, Aug. 8, 03. ENGLISH. A.B, Cornell Univ, 25, Ph.D, 38; Fordham Univ, 24; A.M, Columbia Univ, 26; Cath. Univ. Am, 33. Instr. French & Eng, NAZARETH COL, 29-33, ENG, 33-38, PROF, 38-, MEM. FAC. GRAD. SCH, 74-, continuing Adult Educ. Br, 71-73. MLA; Dante Soc. Am; Soc. Christian Commonwealth. John Milton; Dante; world literature. Add: Dept. of English, Nazareth College, Rochester, NY 14610.

KELLEY, MAURICE, b. Okeene, Okla, May 22, 03; m. 26; c. 3. ENGLISH. A.B, Univ. Okla, 27; A.M, Univ. Maine, 29; Ph.D, Princeton, 34. Teacher, high sch, Okla, 23-28; instr. ENG, Univ. Maine, 28-29; W.Va. Univ, 29-31; PRINCETON, 34-38, asst. prof, 38-44, assoc. prof, 44-51, prof, 51-71, acting librn, 51-53, EMER. PROF, 71- Mem. ed. comt, PMLA, 61-66; mem. ed. bd, The complete prose works of John Milton, Yale. MLA. John Milton and 17th century Renaissance theology. Publ: Additional chapters on Thomas Cooper, Univ. Maine; This great argument, Princeton; ed, John Milton, Two books of investigations into Christian doctrine, Yale, 73. Add: Dept. of English, Princeton University, Princeton, NJ 08540.

KELLEY, MICHAEL ROBERT, b. Washington, D.C, Aug. 20, 40; m. 67; c. 1. ENGLISH LITERATURE, LINGUISTICS. B.A, Cath. Univ. Am, 62, M.F.A, 65, Ph.D.(Eng), 70. ASST. PROF. ENG, GEORGE MASON UNIV, 70- MLA; Mediaeval Acad Am. Medieval English drama; Chaucer; literary aesthetics. Publ: Fifteenth century flamboyant style and the Castle of perseverance, Comp. Drama, spring 72; English for foreign speakers—a television solution, Audiovisual Instr, 11/72. Add: 5118 Arrit Court, Burke, VA 22015.

KELLEY, ROBERT EMMETT, b. Waterloo, Iowa, Mar. 1, 38; m. 59; c. 3. ENGLISH LITERATURE. B.A, Creighton Univ, 60; Ph.D.(Eng), Ind. Univ, Bloomington, 68. Instr. ENG, UNIV. IOWA, 66-67, asst. prof, 67-71, ASSOC. PROF, 71- U.S.A.F.R, 61-67. Am. Soc. 18th Century Stud; Johnson Soc. Cent. Region; Midwest Mod. Lang. Asn. Eighteenth century English literature; biography and autobiography; novel. Publ: Ed, William Hayley's Two dialogues...comparative view of...Chesterfield and...Johnson, Scholars' Facsimiles & Reprints, 70; co-auth, Samuel Johnson's early biographers, 71 & co-ed, Early biographies of Samuel Johnson, 74, Univ. Iowa; contrib, Studies in Eighteenth century autobiography and biography: a selected bibliography, In: Essays in eighteenth century biography, Ind. Univ, 68; ed, John Courtenay's A poetical review of the literary and moral character of Samuel Johnson, Augustan Reprint Soc, 69; auth, This chance glimpse: the narrator in Under Western eyes, Univ. Rev, 71. Add: Dept. of English, University of Iowa, Iowa City, IA 52242.

KELLING, HAROLD DUNHAM, b. Cleveland, Ohio, Feb. 16, 16. ENGLISH LITERATURE. A.B, Yale, 37, Ph.D, 48. Instr, Univ. Mo, 40-42; Yale, 45-47; asst. prof. Eng. lit, Univ. Calif, 47-55; Ft. Wayne Ctr, Ind. Univ, 55-62; assoc. prof. ENG, UNIV. COLO, BOULDER, 62-64, PROF, 64-, CHMN. DEPT, 67- MLA; Conf. Col. Comp. & Commun. Augustan period; Jonathan Swift. Add: Dept. of English, University of Colorado, Boulder, CO 80302.

KELLNER, BRUCE, b. Indianapolis, Ind, Mar. 17, 30; m. 61; c. 2. ENGLISH. B.A, Colo. Col, 55; M.F.A, Univ. Iowa, 58. Asst. prof. Eng, Coe Col, 56-60; Hartwick Col, 60-69, ASSOC. PROF. SHAKESPEARE & MOD. POETRY, MILLERSVILLE STATE COL, 69- U.S.N, 51-54. MLA. Twentieth century American culture; dramatic readings arranged from non-dramatic literature; Van Vechten and Black culture. Publ: Carl Van Vechten and the irreverent decades, Univ. Okla, 68; Wormwood poems of Thomas Kinsella, West. Humanities Rev, 72; The poet as translator, Contemporary Poetry, 73; The fifth interpreter: Caruso, Am. Record Guide, 73. Add: Dept. of English, Millersville State College, Millersville, PA 17551.

KELLOGG, ALFRED LATIMER, b. Cleveland, Ohio, Apr. 24, 15; m. 41; c. 2. ENGLISH. A.B, West. Reserve Univ, 37; hon. fel, Yale, 40, Ph.D, 41. Instr. ENG, Yale, 41-42; Cornell Univ, 42; Yale, 45-47; asst. prof, RUTGERS UNIV, NEW BRUNSWICK, 47-51, assoc. prof, 51-60, PROF, 61- Ford fel, 51-52; Guggenheim fel, 53-54; Am. Philos. Soc. Penrose Fund grant, summer 65; Rutgers Univ. study fel, 73. MLA; Mediaeval Acad. Am; Dante Soc. Am; Int. Arthurian Soc. Intellectual backgrounds of mediaeval literature; Arthurian tradition. Publ: Chaucer, Langland, Arthur: essays in Middle English literature, Rutgers Univ, 72; Susannah and the Merchant's tale, Speculum, 60; co-auth, The Wyclifite Pater Noster and Ten Commandments with special reference to the English manuscripts 85 and 90 of the John Rylands Library, Bull. John Rylands Libr, 60; auth, Chaucer, In: New Catholic encyclopedia, McGraw, 66; plus others. Add: Dept. of English, Rutgers University, New Brunswick, NJ 08903.

KELLOGG, ROBERT LELAND, b. Ionia, Mich, Sept. 2, 28; m. 51; c. 2. ENGLISH. A.B, Univ. Md, 50; A.M, Harvard, 52, Am-Scand. Found. fel, 56, Ph.D, 58. Instr. ENG, UNIV. VA, 57-60, asst. 60-64, assoc. prof, 64-67, PROF, 67- Guggenheim fel, 68-69. U.S.A, 54-56, Res, 56-, 2nd Lt. Mediaeval Acad. Am; Renaissance Soc. Am; Soc. Advan. Scand. Stud; MLA. Medieval and Renaissance English; Medieval Scandinavian. Publ: Co-ed, Faerie Queene, bks, I & II, Odyssey, 64; co-auth, The nature of narrative, Oxford, 66; auth, Thought's astonishment and the dark conceits of Spenser's Amoretti, In: The prince of poets: essays on Edmund Spenser, N.Y. Univ, 68. Add: Dept. of English, University of Virginia, Charlottesville, VA 22904.

KELLY, CHARLES M, b. Pittsburg, Kans, Feb. 26, 32. SPEECH. B.S, Cent. Mo. State Col, 58; Ph.D, Purdue Univ, 62. Asst, Purdue Univ, 58-62; asst. prof. lang. & lit, State Univ. N.Y. Col. Plattsburgh, 62-63, assoc. prof, 63-66; asst. prof. speech, Syracuse Univ, 66-68; San Diego State Col, 68-70; assoc. prof, Calif. State Univ, Long Beach, 70-74; dir. personnel develop, Fiber Industs, Inc, 74- U.S.N, 51-55. Speech Commun. Asn; Nat. Soc. Stud. Commun. Interpersonal communications; listening; industrial communications. Publ: Mental ability and personality factors in listening, Quart. J. Speech, 4/63; The myth of the key communicator, Personnel J, 1/66; Listening: complex of activities and a unitary skill?, Speech Monogr, 11/67. Add: Fiber Industries, Inc, P.O. Box 10038, Charlotte, NC 28237.

KELLY, EDWARD HANFORD, b. Yonkers, N.Y, Aug. 9, 30; m. 54; c. 3. ENGLISH. A.B, State Univ. N.Y. Albany, 62, M.A, 63; fel, Univ. Rochester, 65-67, Ph.D.(18th century Eng. lit), 69. Instr. ENG, State Univ. N.Y. Albany, 63-65; asst. prof, Monroe Community Col, 67-68; assoc. prof, STATE

UNIV. N.Y. COL. ONEONTA, 68-73, PROF, 73- Transp.C, U.S.A.R, 50-56, Sgt. MLA; Northeast Mod. Lang. Asn. Eighteenth century English literature; classical and neo-classical literature. Publ: Ed, Moll Flanders (critical edition), Norton, 73; auth, By mouth of innocentz: the prioress vindicated, Papers Lang. & Lit, fall 69; plus others. Add: Dept. of English, State University of New York College at Oneonta, Oneonta, NY 13820.

KELLY, ELLIN MARGARET, b. Grand Forks, N.Dak, Aug. 11, 24. ENGLISH LITERATURE. B.A, St. Mary of the Woods Col, 45; M.A, Cath. Univ. Am, 48; M.S, Univ. Wis-Madison, 64, Villas fel, 67-68, Ph.D.(Eng), 70. Instr. ENG, DePAUL UNIV, 68-69, asst. prof, 69-74, ASSOC. PROF, 74- MLA; AAUP; Medieval Acad. Am. Medieval drama; medieval literature and art; 20th century British literature. Publ: Parallels between the Middle English Patience and Hymnus Ieiunantium in Prudentius, Eng. Lang. Notes, 6/67; Ludus Coventriae play 4 and the Egerton Genesis, Notes & Queries, 12/72. Add: Dept. of English, DePaul University, 2323 N. Seminary, Chicago, IL 60614.

KELLY, FAYE LUCIUS, b. Ocala, Fla, Nov. 22, 14; m. 36; c. 2. ENGLISH, LINGUISTICS. B.A, Univ. Fla, 41, M.A, 50, fel, 56, Ph.D.(Eng, ling), 65. Teacher, high sch, Fla, 44-53; asst. prof. Eng. lit, Stetson Univ, 56-57, Eng. & humanities, 59-61; Eng. & world lit, Univ. Md, 57-59; Eng. & ling, AM. UNIV, 62-65, ASSOC. PROF. ENG. LIT, 65-, DIR. GRAD. STUD, 68-, dir. freshman Eng, 64-68. MLA; Shakespeare Asn. Am; S.Atlantic Mod. Lang. Asn. Medieval drama; Elizabethan drama, especially religious and cultural backgrounds; interrelations between arts of poetry, painting and music. Publ: Prayer in sixteenth century England, a study in Elizabethan culture, Univ. Fla. Monogr. Ser, 66. Add: Dept. of English, American University, Massachusetts & Nebraska Aves. N.W, Washington, DC 20016.

KELLY, HELEN (MARIE TÉRÈSE), b. Cambridge, Mass. THEATRE, ORAL INTERPRETATION. B.B.A, Boston Univ, 40; M.A, Boston Col, 47; Ph.D. (theatre), Univ. Mich, 65. Children's librn, Cambridge Pub. Libr, 37-49; instr. speech & theatre, Mercyhurst Col, 49-52, asst. prof, 52-56, assoc. prof, 56-60; asst. prof, Bloomsburg State Col, 60-62; instr. speech & oral interpretation, Univ. Mich, 62-64; assoc. prof. SPEECH & THEATRE, WEST LIBERTY STATE COL, 64-67, PROF, 67- Part-time instr. speech & drama, Emmanuel Col.(Mass), 41-49. Am. Theatre Asn; Speech Commun. Asn. Theatre history. Publ: His people (play), Baker Co, 46; Successful sacrifice (play), Queen's Work, 55. Add: Dept. of Speech, West Liberty State College, West Liberty, WV 26074.

KELLY, HENRY ANSGAR, b. Fonda, Iowa, June 6, 34; m. 68; c. 2. MEDIEVAL RENAISSANCE LITERATURE, INTELLECTUAL HISTORY. A.B, St. Louis Univ, 59, Ph.L. & A.M, 61; Weston Col, 64-66; univ. fel, Harvard, 64-67, Ph.D.(Eng), 65. Asst. prof. ENG, UNIV. CALIF, LOS ANGELES, 67-69, assoc. prof, 69-72, PROF, 72- Guggenheim res. fel, 71-72. Mediaeval Acad. Am. Narrative poetry; drama; history of religion. Publ: The devil, demonology, and witchcraft, Doubleday, 68; Divine Providence in the England of Shakespeare's histories, Harvard Univ, 70; Canonical implications of Richard III's plan to marry his niece, Traditio, 67; The metamorphoses of the Eden serpent during the Middle Ages and Renaissance, 71 & Clandestine marriage and Chaucer's Troilus, 73, Viator. Add: Dept. of English, University of California, 405 Hilgard Ave, Los Angeles, CA 90024.

KELLY, LOUISE KLINE, b. Wilkes Barre, Pa, Jan. 7, 12; wid. ENGLISH. A.B, Skidmore Col, 36; scholar, Pa. State Univ, 37-38, M.A, 38, Ph.D.(Eng. lit), 51. Instr. Eng, Elizabethtown Col, 52-54, assoc. prof, 57-58, prof. & head dept, 58-62; cur, Penn State Collection, Pa. State Univ, 62-74; RETIRED. MLA; Col. Eng. Asn. Literary remains of Lady Jane Grey; concordance to Emily Dickinson's poetry. Add: 238 S. Gill St, State College, PA 16801.

KELLY, RICHARD MICHAEL, b. New York, N.Y, Mar. 16, 37; m. 61. ENGLISH, VICTORIAN PERIOD. B.A, City Col. New York, 59; M.A, Duke Univ, 61, Ph.D.(Eng), 65. Instr. ENG, Univ. N.C, Chapel Hill, 64-65; asst. prof, UNIV. TENN, KNOXVILLE, 65-70, ASSOC. PROF, 70- Ed, Tenn. Stud. Lit. MLA. Victorian humor, especially Punch magazine; Victorian poetry. Publ: Ed, The best of Mr. Punch: the humorous writings of Douglas Jerrold, Univ. Tenn, 70; Douglas Jerrold, Twayne, 72; Johnson among the sheep, Stud. Eng. Lit, summer 68; The dramatic relationship between By the fireside and Any wife to any husband, Victorian Newslett, spring 71; The haunted house of Bulwer-Lytton, Stud. Short Fiction, fall 71; plus others. Add: Dept. of English, University of Tennessee, Knoxville, TN 37916.

KELLY, ROBERT GLYNN, b. San Diego, Calif, Aug. 20, 20; m. 46; c. 5. ENGLISH. A.B, San Diego State Col, 46; M.A, Stanford Univ, 49, Ph.D, 52. Instr. ENG, San Jose State Col, 50; from assoc. prof. to PROF, IND. UNIV, BLOOMINGTON, 52- Vis. lectr. in charge courses Am. lit, Istanbul Univ, Turkey, 54-55. U.S.A, 43-46. American literature; modern British literature; literary criticism. Publ: The strange philosophy of Dorothy M. Richardson, Pac. Spectator; A lament for Barney Stone, Holt, 61. Add: Dept. of English,Indiana University, Bloomington, IN 47401.

KELLY, ROBERT GORDON, American Civilization. See Volume I, History.

KELLY, ROBERT LEROY, b. Shelton, Nebr, Feb. 6, 37; m. 64; c. 2. MEDIEVAL & RENAISSANCE LITERATURE. A.B, St. Benedict's Col, 59; M.A, Univ. Kans, 62; Ph.D.(Eng), Univ. Ore, 69. Instr. ENG, Idaho State Univ, 59-61; Mt. Angel Col, 66-68; ASST. PROF, UNIV. N.C, GREENSBORO, 68- Mediaeval Acad. Am; AAUP; MLA. Arthurian romance; Shakespeare; Spenser. Publ: Dactyls and curlews: satire in A grammarian's funeral, Victorian Poetry, summer 67; Shakespeare's Scroops and the spirit of Cain, Shakespeare Quart, winter 69; Arthur, Galahad and the scriptural pattern in Malory, Am. Benedictine Rev, 3/72. Add: Dept. of English, University of North Carolina at Greensboro, Greensboro, NC 27412.

KELLY, THOMAS DANIEL, b. Scranton, Pa, Sept. 13, 42; m. 72. ENGLISH LITERATURE. A.B, Univ. Calif, Berkeley, 63; Woodrow Wilson fels, Princeton, 63-64, 66-67, Mitchell fel, 64-65, Ph.D.(Eng), 67; Pontifical Inst. Mediaeval Stud, Toronto, 65-66. ASST. PROF. ENG, RICE UNIV, 67- Mediaeval Acad. Am; MLA; S.Cent. Mod. Lang. Asn; AAUP. Middle English literature; Chaucer; the Pearl poet. Publ: Co-auth, The meaning of cleanness: parable as effective sign, Mediaeval Stud, 73 & The way and the end are one: Patience as a parable of the contemplative life, Am. Benedictine Rev, 74. Add: Dept. of English, Rice University, Houston, TX 77001.

KELLY, WILLIAM WATKINS, b. Asheville, N.C, Sept. 21, 28; m. 53; c. 1. ENGLISH. B.A, Va. Mil. Inst, 50; univ. scholar, Duke Univ, 54-55, M.A, 55, Ph.D, 57. Instr. Eng, Va. Mil. Inst, 52-53; U.S. Air Force Acad, 57-58, asst. prof, 58-60; Va. Mil. Inst, 60-62; Am. thought, Mich. State Univ, 62-65, assoc. dir. honors col, 65-68, dir, 68-69; PRES, MARY BALDWIN COL, 69- Danforth Found. fel, 53-57; vis. prof, Univ. Ark, summer 61; Ellis L. Phillips Found. intern. acad. admin, Rutgers Univ, 64-65. U.S.A.F, 57-62, Res, Lt. Col. MLA; Am. Stud. Asn; Soc. Relig. Higher Educ; Nat. Col. Honors Counc. American literature, particularly literature of the South. Publ: Ellen Glasgow: a bibliography, Univ, Va, 63; Ellen Glasgow, Steck, 68. Add: Mary Baldwin College, Staunton, VA 24401.

KELSON, JOHN HOFSTAD, b. Pierre, S.Dak, Nov. 14, 27; m. 66. ENGLISH. B.A, Cornell Col, 49; M.A, Univ. Minn, Minneapolis, 53; Norweg. Govt. Scholar, Univ. Oslo, summer 57; Ph.D.(Eng), Univ. Kans, 63. Instr. ENG, Univ. Utah, 58-60; asst. prof, Dickinson State Col, 60-62; assoc. prof, East. Mont. Col, 62-66; S.Dak. State Univ, 66-67; MANKATO STATE COL, 67-71, PROF, 71- Irish and Norwegian drama; Medieval drama; English Renaissance drama. Publ: Myth and allegory in The cherry orchard, West. Humanities Rev, summer 59; The Serventois in the Cange Manuscript, Philol. Quart, 10/68; Abstract of Allegory and myth in The cherry orchard, In: Drama: a critical collection, Harper, 71. Add: Dept. of English, Mankato State College, Mankato, MN 56001.

KELTCHER, WESLEY, b. Farmington, N.Mex, Nov. 13, 15; m. 39; c. 2. ENGLISH. Emporia State Teachers Col, 40; Sorbonne, 45; M.S, Univ. Kans, 53. Teacher rural sch, Kans, 38-40; prin. grade sch, Scandia, Kans, 40-43 & jr. high sch, Humboldt, 43; teacher-coach, Yates Ctr, 45-49; TEACHER ENG, Yates Ctr. High Sch, 49-56; SR. HIGH SCH, LAWRENCE, 56- Participant, Comn. Eng. Planning Inst. for 1962 insts, 61; Kans. state chmn, Writing Awards Prog, NCTE, 65-68, mem, nat. adv. bd, achievement awards, 68-70. U.S.A, 43-45. NCTE; NEA. Publ: What do the maps say, teacher?, Instructor, 4/49; Student writing with a purpose, NEA J, 2/60; Correlation between a student's knowledge of rhetorical principles and writing ability, Bull. Educ, Univ. Kans, 5/61. Add: Rte. 5, Lawrence, KS 66044.

KELTNER, JOHN WILLIAM, b. Literberry, Ill, June 20, 18; div; c. 2. SPEECH COMMUNICATION. B.Ed, Ill. State Norm. Univ, 40; A.M, Northwest. Univ, 43, Ph.D, 47. Instr. elem. schs, Ill, 40-43, high sch, 43-44; lectr. speech, Northwest. Univ, 44-46; asst. prof, Iowa State Teachers Col, 46-48; Univ. Okla, 48-51, assoc. prof, 51-54; prof. & head dept, Kans. State Col, 54-58, lab. coord, human relat. training lab, 56-58; mediator, training off. & nat. off. rep, Fed. Mediation & Conciliation Serv, 58-63; prof. speech & CHMN. DEPT, ORE. STATE UNIV, 63-71, PROF. SPEECH COMMUN, 71- Speech Commun. Asn; Cent. States Speech Asn.(pres, 51); Nat. Soc. Stud. Commun.(2nd v.pres, 55-); Am. Arbit. Asn.(mem. pub. employment dispute panel, 70); Am. Soc. Training & Develop; West. Speech Commun. Asn.(pres, 71-72). Discussion and conference methods; human relations; labor-management and mediation. Publ: Group discussion processes, McKay, 57; co-ed, Labor in America, Ore. State Univ, 70; auth, Interpersonal speech communication, 70 & Interpersonal communication, 73, Wadsworth; The U.S. Federal Mediation and Conciliation Service, catalyst to collective bargaining, Int. Labour Rev, 63. Add: Dept. of Speech Communication, Oregon State University, Corvallis, OR 97331.

KELTY, JEAN McCLURE, b. Warren, Ohio, Mar. 13, 26; m. 51. ENGLISH LITERATURE. A.B, Youngstown Univ, 58; M.A, West. Reserve Univ, 59, Ph.D.(Eng), Case West. Reserve Univ, 69. Instr. ENG, YOUNGSTOWN STATE UNIV, 59-62, asst. prof, 62-70, ASSOC. PROF, 70- Dir. bibliog. res, Humane Soc. U.S, 70-72. NCTE; Col. Eng. Asn. Victorian literature; children's literature; humane education. Publ: If you have a duck, Nat. Humane Educ. Ctr, 69; Once theirs alone: a bibliographic study of animal rights, their protection and defense, Humane Soc. U.S, 71; The modern tone of Charles Dickens, Dickensian, Vol. LVII; The frontispiece of Ben Jonson's 1616 Folio: a critical commentary on the Elizabethan stage, Theatre Annual, 60; plus others. Add: 4038 Sunset Blvd, Youngstown, OH 44512.

KELVIN, NORMAN, b. New York, N.Y, Aug. 27, 24; m. 56. ENGLISH LITERATURE. A.B, Columbia Univ, 48, M.A, 50, Ph.D, 60. From instr. to PROF. ENG, CITY COL. NEW YORK, 60- Chapelbrook Found. grant, 66-67; Nat. Endowment for Humanities sr. fel, 67-68; vis. prof, Birkbeck Col, Univ. London, 67-68. U.S.A, 43-46. MLA. Nineteenth and 20th century British literature; letters of William Morris. Publ: A troubled Eden: nature and society in the works of George Meredith, Stanford, 61; E.M. Forster, South. Ill. Univ, 67; co-auth, An introduction to fiction, Random, 67; plus articles. Add: Dept. of English, City College of New York, Convent Ave. at 138th St, New York, NY 10031.

KEMBLE, C. ROBERT, b. Oskaloosa, Iowa, Aug. 17, 25; m. 49; c. 5. AMERICAN LITERATURE & HISTORY. B.S, U.S. Mil. Acad, 49; M.A, Univ. Pa, 56; Univ. Denver, 58; Columbia Univ, 58; Ph.D.(Am. stud), George Washington Univ, 68. Instr. Eng, U.S. Mil. Acad, U.S. Army, 56-58, asst. prof. Eng. & Am. stud, 58-60, instr. Eng. & speech, Univ. Md, Overseas Div, 61-62, assoc. prof. Eng. & Am. stud, U.S. Mil. Acad, 66-70, dir. Am. stud. prog, 70-72; PRES, N.MEX. MIL. INST, 72- Res. fel, Nat. War Col, 68-69. U.S.A, 49-72, Col. Am. Stud. Asn; MLA. Image of the military leader in the United States; Stephen V. Benét and John Brown's body; Clarence Stedman-Whitlaw Reid correspondence. Publ: Co-ed, John Brown's body, Holt, annotated ed, 68; auth, The image of the army officer in America, Greenwood, 73. Add: New Mexico Military Institute, Roswell, NM 88201.

KEMP, HOMER DALE, b. Kenton, Tenn, Jan. 25, 41; m. 64; c. 1. EARLY AMERICAN LITERATURE & CULTURE. A.B, Univ. Tenn, Martin, 66; NDEA fel, Univ. Tenn, Knoxville, 66, Colonial Williamsburg Found. grant-in-aid, John C. Hodges fel. & M.A, 71, Ph.D.(Eng), 72. ASST. PROF. ENG,

TENN. TECHNOL. UNIV, 71- Am. Philos. Soc. grant-in-aid, 74. U.S.N, 60-61; U.S.A.F, 61-62. Am. Lit. Group, Mod. Lang. Asn; Am. Stud. Asn; S.Atlantic Mod. Lang. Asn. Southern Colonial polemical literature; Colonial American satire. Publ: John Camm: to raise a flame and live in it, Stud. in honor of Richard Beale Davis, 74. Add: Dept. of English, Tennessee Technological University, Cookeville, TN 38501.

KEMP, JAMES WILLIAM, JR, b. Carthage, Miss, Dec. 7, 42; m. 64; ENGLISH RENAISSANCE LITERATURE, FILM. B.A, Millsaps Col, 64; M.A, Miss. State Univ, 67; NDEA fel. & Ph.D.(Eng), Univ. S.C, 70. ASST. PROF. ENG, MARY WASHINGTON COL, 70- Va. Univ. Ctr, Inc. grant, 71- MLA; Shakespeare Soc. Am. Shakespeare; Renaissance non-dramatic literature; 17th century English poetry. Add: Dept. of English, Mary Washington College, Fredericksburg, VA 22401.

KENDALL, CALVIN B, b. Bronxville, N.Y, Feb. 13, 35; m. 59; c. 2. ENGLISH. B.A, Bowdoin Col, 56; M.A, Univ. Calif, Berkeley, 61, Ph.D.(Eng), 66. Asst. prof. ENG, UNIV. MINN, MINNEAPOLIS, 67-71, ASSOC. PROF, 71- Am. Philos. Soc. grant-in-aid, 68- U.S.A, 57, 2nd Lt. Mediaeval Acad. Am; MLA. Bede; medieval Latin poetic and rhetoric; old English. Add: Dept. of English, University of Minnesota, Minneapolis, MN 55455.

KENDALL, KATHLEEN EDGERTON, b. Madison, Wis, June 17, 37; m. 67. RHETORIC & COMMUNICATION. B.A, Oberlin Col, 58; M.A, Univ. South. Miss, 60; Ph.D.(rhet, pub. address), Ind. Univ, Bloomington, 66. Instr. speech. Allegheny Col, 60-62, ASSOC. PROF. RHET. & COMMUN, STATE UNIV. N.Y. ALBANY, 64-, chmn. dept, 69-70. N.Y. State res. fels, summers 67, 70; asst. to speechwriter, Speechwriting Off, Friends of Rockefeller, 70; instr. N.Y. State Police Acad, Albany, 73. Speech Commun. Asn. American public address; rhetoric of political campaigns. Publ: Education as 'the balance wheel of social machinery'; Horace Mann's arguments and proofs, 2/68 & co-auth, Frances Wright on women's rights: eloquence versus ethos, 2/74, Quart J. Speech; co-auth, Oratory and learning: Horace Mann at Brown, R.I. Hist, 2/71. Add: R.D. 1, New Salem South Rd, Voorheesville, NY 12186.

KENDALL, KENNETH EVERETT, b. Oshkosh, Wis, July 2, 13. ENGLISH. Ph.D.(Eng), Univ. Fla, 65. ASSOC. PROF. ENG, UNIV. FLA, 65- U.S.A, 42-46, Res, 46-73, Command Sgt. Maj. MLA. Early work of Leigh Hunt. Publ: Leigh Hunt's Reflector, Mouton, The Hague, 71; An index to Leigh Hunt's Reflector, privately publ, 71; Some words in the poetry of Shelley and Wordsworth, Notes & Queries, 11/62. Add: Dept. of English, University of Florida, Gainesville, FL 32601.

KENDALL, LYLE HARRIS, JR, b. Kingsville, Tex, Feb. 3, 19; m. 41; c. 2. ENGLISH. Ph.D.(Eng), Univ. Tex, 52. Teaching fel, Univ. Tex, 47-49, instr. ENG, 49-52; asst. prof, U.S. Naval Acad, 52-56; Tex. Christian Univ, 56-58, assoc. prof, 58-62, PROF, 62-66; UNIV. TEX, ARLINGTON, 66- Res. fel, Folger Shakespeare Libr, 55; textbk. consult, Am. Counc. Educ, 61; assoc. ed, Am. Lit. Realism, 66-; dictionary consult, Eng-Lang. Inst. Am, 72-73. U.S.A.A.F, 43-46; Naval Air Res, 49-60, Lt. Bibliog. Soc, Eng; Bibliog. Soc. Am; Cambridge Bibliog. Soc; Oxford Bibliog. Soc. Publ: Co-auth, Shakespeare 1964, 65 & auth, The W.L. Lewis collection, Part I, 70, Tex. Christian Univ; co-auth, Suppressed critique of Wise's Swinburne transactions, Univ. Tex, 70; John Taylor's piracy of The pack-mans Paternoster, 63 & The not-so-gentle art of puffing, 68, Papers Bibliog. Soc. Am; Two further footnotes to An enquiry, Tex. Stud. Lit. & Lang, 65; contrib, Twentieth century interpretations of The fall of the House of Usher, Prentice-Hall, 69; plus others. Add: Dept. of English, University of Texas at Arlington, Arlington, TX 76019.

KENDALL, PAUL MURRAY, b. Philadelphia, Pa, Mar. 1, 11; m. 39; c. 2. ENGLISH LITERATURE. A.B, Univ. Va, 32, A.M, 33, Ph.D.(Eng), 39; hon. L.H.D, Ohio Univ, 71. Instr. Eng, Ohio Univ, 37-42, asst. prof, 42-49, assoc. prof, 49-54, prof, 54-59, distinguished prof, 59-66, regents prof, 66-70; PROF. ENG, UNIV. KANS, 70- Ford Found. fel, 52-53; Guggenheim fel, 57-58, 61-62; grants, Am. Philos. Soc, 60, Rockefeller Found, 61. U.S.A, 43-44. Renaissance Soc. Am; Am. Hist. Asn; Conf. Brit. Stud; MLA. Fifteenth century English, French and Italian history. Publ: Richard the Third, 55, Warwick the kingmaker, 57, The Yorkist age, 62, The art of biography, 65, ed, The great debate, 66 & auth, Louis XI, 71, Norton. Add: 928 Holiday Dr, Lawrence, KS 66044.

KENDALL, ROBERT E, b. Parlin, N.J, June 21, 11; m. 45; c. 2. THEATRE ARTS, DRAMATIC LITERATURE. B.A, Columbia Univ, 34; M.A, Pa. State Univ, 48; M.A, Middlebury Col, 51; Ph.D.(theatre arts), Univ. Denver, 52. Teacher Eng. & drama, Kamehameha Schs, Honolulu, Hawaii, 37-38; Out-of-Door Sch, Sarasota, Fla, 39-40; East Hampton High Sch, N.Y, 40-42; lectr. stagecraft, Univ. Mich, 46; instr. dramatics, Pa. State Univ, 46-50; PROF. ENG. & THEATRE ARTS, SOUTH. CONN. STATE COL, 52-, CHMN. DEPT. THEATRE, 67- Sig.C, U.S.A, 42-45, M/Sgt. Am. Theatre Asn. The plays of Eugene O'Neill, Eduardo de Filippo and Shakespeare. Add: Dept. of Theatre, Southern Connecticut State College, New Haven, CT 06515.

KENDIG, PERRY FRIDY, b. Mountville, Pa, July 7, 10; m. 47; c. 3. ENGLISH. A.B, Franklin & Marshall Col, 32; summer, Pa. State Teachers Col, Millersville, 33; A.M, Univ. Pa, 36, Ph.D, 47. Prin, high sch, Pa, 32-34; asst. instr. Eng, Univ. Pa, 36-38; instr. Muhlenberg Col, 38-42, asst. prof, 46-49, assoc. prof. & acting head dept, 49-51, prof. Eng, 51-63, head dept, 51-52, dean stud, 46-49; dean & prof. Eng, ROANOKE COL, 52-63, PRES, 63- Spec. instr, Drexel Inst. Technol, 37-38. U.S.N, 42-46, Lt. Comdr. MLA; Newcomen Soc. Publ: Trinity Reformed Church: an historical sketch, 38; The poems of Saint Columban translated into English verse, 49; Some notes on a little known American novel, 56; plus others. Add: Roanoke College, Salem, VA 24153.

KENDRIS, THOMAS, b. Albany, N.Y, Apr. 21, 21; m. 47; c. 1. ENGLISH. B.A, Cornell Univ, 46; M.A, Columbia Univ, 49, Ph.D.(Eng), 64. Instr. ENG, Ripon Col, 51-53; assoc. prof, WAGNER COL, 53-72, PROF, 72- U.S.A.A.F, 43-45, Capt. English literature since 1900; the novel; poetry. Add: Dept. of English, Wagner College, Staten Island, NY 10301.

KENNEDY, ADELE, b. Montrose, Iowa, Aug. 31, 07. ENGLISH. A.B, State Univ. Iowa, 27, A.M, 38, 30; Columbia Univ, 37. Instr, Britt Jr. Col, 28-29; Bloomfield Jr. Col, 29-44; head dept. ENG, William Woods Col, 44-46; ASSOC. PROF, MONMOUTH COL, 46- Tudor period English drama; certain contrasts between public and private early Tudor plays. Add: Dept. of English, Monmouth College, Monmouth, IL 61462.

KENNEDY, ARTHUR AFTON, JR, b. Clarks, Nebr, Apr. 17, 21. ENGLISH. B.A, Nebr. State Teachers Col, 42; M.A, Univ. Wis, 47. Instr. ENG. & SPEECH, Wash. State Univ, 47-50; WORCESTER POLYTECH. INST, 52-54, asst. prof, 54-60, assoc. prof, 60-67, PROF, 67- U.S.A, 42-45, S/Sgt. AAUP. Eighteenth and 19th century English literature; Elizabethan dramatic literature. Add: Dept. of English, Worcester Polytechnic Institute, Worcester, MA 01609.

KENNEDY, DENNIS EDWARD, b. Cincinnati, Ohio, Nov. 1, 40; m. 70. ENGLISH LITERATURE, THEATRE. B.A, Univ. San Francisco, 62; M.A, Univ. Calif, Santa Barbara, 68, Ph.D.(Eng), 72; Wadham Col, Oxford, 68-69. ASST. PROF. ENG, GRAND VALLEY STATE COL, 70- Fulbright lectr, Univ. Karachi, 73. U.S.N, 63-66, Lt. Theatre, history and production: modern poetry. Add: Dept. of English, Grand Valley State Colleges, Allendale, MI 49401.

KENNEDY, GEORGE ALEXANDER, Classics. See Volume III, Foreign Languages, Linguistics & Philology.

KENNEDY, JAMES GETTIER, b. New York, N.Y, May 30, 32; m. 54; c. 3. ENGLISH. A.B, Kenyon Col, 54; Wilson fel, Univ. Minn, 54-55, M.A, 55, Ph.D, 61; Martin Luther fel, Upsala Col, 60-61. Lectr. ENG, Hofstra Col, 57-58; instr, Upsala Col, 58-62, asst. prof, 62-64, ASSOC. PROF, 64-69; NORTH. ILL. UNIV, 69- Mem. res. & bibliog. comt, Eng. Lit. in Transition (1880-1920), 63-; Upsala Col. fac. fel, Cambridge, Eng, spring 67. MLA; NCTE. Literary conventions; modern fiction; history and the novel. Publ: Arnold Bennett: Künstler and Bürger, 62 & Reassuring facts ... in modern novels, 64, Eng. Lit. in Transition (1880-1920); the content and form of Native son, Col. Eng, 34: 2; plus others. Add: Dept. of English, Northern Illinois University, DeKalb, IL 60115.

KENNEDY, JAMES KEITH, b. Littlefield, Tex, Feb. 2, 30; m. 68. THEATER. B.A, Southwest. Tex. State Col, 57; M.A, Univ. Fla, 58, fel, 61-62, Ph.D. (theater), 63. Asst. prof. theater, Tex. A&I Univ, 58-61; instr. Eng, Univ. Fla, 62-63; assoc. prof. THEATER, Stephen F. Austin State Col, 63-65; MEMPHIS STATE UNIV, 65-68, PROF, 68- U.S.A.F, 47-50, S/Sgt. Am. Theatre Asn; Speech Commun. Asn; South. Speech Commun. Asn. (chmn. theater div, 65-68). Restoration theater; art history of theater. Add: Dept. of Speech & Drama, Memphis State University, Memphis, TN 38111.

KENNEDY, JOYCE DEVEAU, b. Boston, Mass, July 2, 37; m. 67; c. 2. ENGLISH & AMERICAN LITERATURE. B.S, Boston Col, 62; M.A, Univ. Del, 63, Ph.D.(Eng), 67. Asst. prof. Eng, Univ. Bridgeport, 66-68; Univ. Alta, 68-73. MLA; Thoreau Soc; Am. Soc. 18th Century Stud. Early 18th century British literature; modern American literature. Publ: Co-ed, Defoe's Consolidator & Essay upon projects, South. Ill. Univ, 74; auth, Defoe's Essay upon projects: the order of issues, Stud. in Bibliog, 70; The case for Defoe's authorship of the Consolidator pamphlets, Huntington Libr. Quart, 74. Add: 22 Woodlawn Rd, Dartmouth, N.S, Can.

KENNEDY, JUDITH MARY, b. Kasauli, India, Apr. 17, 35; m. 59; c. 3. ENGLISH. B.A, Oxford, 57, M.A, 61, B.Litt, 65. Instr. ENG, Goucher Col, 57-58; St. Thomas More Col, Univ. Sask, 60-63, sessional lectr, 64-66; assoc. prof, ST. THOMAS UNIV.(N.B), 66-71, PROF, 71- Cor. ed, Spenser Newslett. Asn. Can. Univ. Teachers Eng; MLA; Renaissance Soc. Am. Fourteenth and sixteenth century English literature. Publ: A critical edition of Yong's translation of Montemayor's Diana and Gil Polo's Enamoured Diana, Clarendon, Oxford, 68; co-ed, A theatre for Spenserians, Univ. Toronto & Univ. Manchester, 73. Add: Dept. of English, St. Thomas University, Fredericton, N.B, Can.

KENNEDY, L. D, b. Marston, Mo, Oct. 17, 24; m. 56; c. 4. ENGLISH & AMERICAN LITERATURE. A.B, Union Univ, 49; B.D, Southwest. Baptist Theol. Sem, 55, M.Div, 68; M.A, Memphis State Univ, 65; Univ. Ky, 67-68; Morehead Univ, 70. Instr. ENG, CAMPBELLSVILLE COL, 65-67, asst. prof. & acting chmn. dept, 67-69, ASSOC. PROF. & CHMN. DEPT, 69- MLA; S.Atlantic Mod. Lang. Asn; NCTE. The Bible as literature; 19th century English and American literature. Publ: Freedom and the college press, 68 & ed, SACS self-study report, 73, Campbellsville Col; auth, The new morality of our sexy sixties, Home Life, 3/67; Freedom of the press on a Christian campus, South. Baptist Educ, 2/69. Add: Dept. of Literature, Languages & Library Science, Campbellsville College, Hoskins Ave, Campbellsville, KY 42718.

KENNEDY, RICHARD FREDERICK, b. Chatham, Ont, Apr. 19, 33; m. 59; c. 3. ENGLISH. B.A, Univ. Windsor, 55; M.A, Univ. West. Ont, 56; B.Litt, Oxford, 68. Instr. ENG, St. Thomas More Col, Univ. Sask, 60-63, asst. prof, 64-66, PROF. & HEAD DEPT, ST. THOMAS UNIV.(N.B), 66- MLA; Renaissance Soc. Am. Sixteenth and seventeenth century English literature. Publ: Another Davies manuscript, Rev. Eng. Stud, 5/64; Swift and Suetonius, 69 & Words from Owen Felltham, 71, Notes & queries. Add: Dept. of English, St. Thomas University, Fredericton, N.B, Can.

KENNEDY, RICHARD SYLVESTER, b. St. Paul, Minn, Oct. 13, 20; m. 43; c. 3. ENGLISH. B.A, Univ. Calif, Los Angeles, 42; M.A, Univ. Chicago, 47; Ph.D.(Eng), Harvard, 53. Teaching fel. ENG, Harvard, 48-50; instr, Univ. Rochester, 50-55, asst. prof, 55-57; assoc. prof, Univ. Wichita, 57-63, PROF, 63-64; TEMPLE UNIV, 64- U.S.N.R, 42-46, Lt. Northeast Mod. Lang. Asn; MLA; Am. Stud. Asn. American literature; Victorian literature; the novel. Publ: Window of memory, the literary career of Thomas Wolfe, 62 & ed, The notebooks of Thomas Wolfe, 70, Univ. N.C; Working out salvation with diligence: the plays of T.S. Eliot, Univ. Wichita Stud; Aldous Huxley: the final wisdom, Southwest Rev, winter 65; Edward Cummings, the father of the poet, Bull. N.Y. Pub. Libr, 9/66. Add: Dept. of English, Temple University, Philadelphia, PA 19122.

KENNEDY, ROBERT MARTIN, b. Escanaba, Mich, Apr. 27, 22. VOICE SCIENCE. Ph.B, Marquette Univ, 51, M.A, Northwest. Univ, 53. Instr. SPEECH, MARQUETTE UNIV, 52-58, ASST. PROF, 58-, dir. radio workshop, 55-62, speech proficiency testing prog, 59-61. Speech consult, Greater Milwaukee Dent. Asn, 59. U.S.A, 42-45. Speech Commun. Asn. Effect of radio-television on political activity in the United States: 1928-1952; grade distribution in undergraduate courses; dramatic radio programming for children. Publ: Co-auth, The speech arts, Lyons & Carnahan, 66. Add: College of Speech, Marquette University, Milwaukee, WI 53233.

KENNEDY, SIGHLE AILEEN, b. New York, N.Y. MODERN LITERATURE. B.A, Manhattanville Col, 40; M.A, Columbia Univ, 64, Ph.D.(mod. lit), 69. ASST. PROF. MOD. LIT, HUNTER COL, 68- City Univ. New York Res. Found. fac. fel, 73-74. MLA; James Joyce Soc. Modern literature and drama; work of Samuel Beckett. Publ: Murphy's bed: a study of real sources and surreal associations in Samuel Beckett's first novel, Bucknell Univ, 71; contrib, Modern Irish literature, Iona Col, 72 & Yeats, Joyce and Beckett, Bucknell Univ, (in press). Add: Dept. of English, Hunter College, 695 Park Ave, New York, NY 10021.

KENNEDY, THEODORE R, b. Center Point, Ind, May 16, 19; m. 46; c. 3. RHETORIC. A.B, Wabash Col, 41; M.A, Univ. Wis, 43, Ph.D, 53. Instr. commun. skills, MICH. STATE UNIV, 45-53, asst. prof, 53-59, assoc. prof, AM. THOUGHT & LANG, 59-67, PROF, 67- Asst, U.S. House of Rep, 57. Speech Commun. Asn; NCTE; Conf. Col. Compos. & Commun. American public speaking and history; American studies. Add: Dept. of American Thought & Language, Michigan State University, East Lansing, MI 48823.

KENNEDY, VERNE RAY, b. Monroe, La, Nov. 24, 41; m. 63; c. 2. SPEECH COMMUNICATION. B.A, Belhaven Col, 63; M.A, La. State Univ, 65, Ph.D. (speech), 68; Univ. Wis-Madison, summer 73. Asst. prof. SPEECH, Univ. S.Ala, 67-68; Univ. Ga, 68-69; ASSOC. PROF. & CHMN. DEPT, LA. COL, 69- Consult, Republican Party La, 72-; Kraft Paper Co, Pineville, 73. Speech Commun. Asn; Am. Counc. Better Broadcasts (past pres); South. Speech Commun. Asn. Rhetoric and communication theory; political and campaign communication. Publ: Co-auth, Let the facts speak, Speech Teacher, 3/67; auth, Amplification: a central theme in late medieval rhetoric, Cent. States Speech J, fall 68; Auxesis: a concept of rhetorical amplification, South. Speech Commun. J, fall 71. Add: 4816 Westgarden Blvd, Alexandria, LA 71301.

KENNER, (WILLIAM) HUGH, b. Peterborough, Can, Jan. 7, 23; m. 47, 65; c. 7. ENGLISH. B.A, Univ. Toronto, 45, M.A, 46; Am. Counc. Learned Soc. fel, 49-50; Ph.D.(Eng), Yale, 50. Asst. prof, Assumption Col.(Can), 46-48; instr. Eng, Univ. Calif, Santa Barbara, 50-51, asst. prof, 51-56, assoc. prof, 56-58, prof, 58-73, chmn. dept, 56-62; PROF. ENG, JOHNS HOPKINS UNIV, 73- Am. Philos Soc. grant, 56; Guggenheim fel, 56, 63; vis. prof, Univ. Va, 63-64. Porter Prize, Yale, 50; Christian Gauss Prize, Phi Beta Kappa, 72. Fel. Royal Soc. Lit. U.K. Contemporary prose and verse. Publ: Wyndham Lewis, New Directions, 54; The invisible poet: T.S. Eliot, Oblensky, 59; Samuel Beckett, Grove, 62; Dublin's Joyce, 62 & The Stoic comedians, 63, Beacon; The counterfeiters, Ind. Univ, 68; The pound era, Univ. Calif, 72; Bucky: a guided tour of Buckminster Fuller, William Morrow, 73. Add: Dept. of English, Johns Hopkins University, Baltimore, MD 21218.

KENNEY, BLAIR GATES, b. New York, N.Y, Jan. 15, 34; m. 62. ENGLISH LITERATURE. B.A, Vassar Col, 55; Fulbright fel, Oxford, 55-56; Ph.D, Radcliffe Col, 61. Reader written anal. cases, Harvard Bus. Sch, 59-60; instr. ENG, Clark Univ, 61-62; UNIV. MD, 62-64, ASST. PROF, 64- Hon. fel, Vassar Col, 55; Univ. Md. res. grant, summer 65. Col. Eng. Asn; MLA. Victorian literature, especially the novel; Anthony Trollope; George Eliot. Publ: Nelly Dean's witchcraft, Lit. & Psychol, 68; Keats' Ode to a Grecian urn, Explicator, 5/69; Carlyle and Bleak House, Dickensian, 1/70; plus others. Add: St. Francis Farm, Orlean, VA 22128.

KENNEY, EDWIN JAMES, JR, b. Hoboken, N.J, Jan. 9, 42; m. 64. ENGLISH. B.A, Hamilton Col, 63; M.A, Cornell Univ, 64, Martin Sampson fel. & Ph.D. (Eng), 68. Instr. ENG, Hamilton Col, 66-68; asst. prof, COLBY COL, 68-74, ASSOC. PROF, 74- Vis. jr. fel, Cornell Soc. for Humanities, 74-75. MLA. Nineteenth century; novel. Publ: Elizabeth Bowen, Bucknell Univ, 74; George Eliot: through the looking glass, In: critical ed. George Eliot's Middlemarch, Norton, 74. Add: Dept. of English, Colby College, Waterville, ME 04901.

KENNEY, WILLIAM, b. Boston, Mass, June 18, 27. ENGLISH. B.S. & A.M, Boston Univ, 49, Ph.D, 56; scholar, Johns Hopkins Univ, 53-54. Instr. Eng. lit, Univ. N.Dak, 50-53, asst. prof. Eng, 56-57; teaching fel, Boston Univ, 54-55, instr, 55-56; asst. prof. ENG, BOSTON STATE COL, 57-64, assoc. prof, 64-65, PROF, 65- U.S.N, 45-46. MLA. Eighteenth century; Samuel Johnson. Publ: Co-auth, The world of ideas, Holt, 64 & The unity of literature, Addison-Wesley, 68; auth, Addison, Johnson and the Energetick style, Stud. Neophilol, 61; Dr. Slopers double in Washington Square, Univ. Rev, 70; The death of Morgan in James's The pupil, Stud. in Short Fiction, 71; plus others. Add: Dept. of English, Boston State College, Huntington Ave, Boston, MA 02115.

KENNEY, WILLIAM PATRICK, b. Newton, Mass, Jan. 29, 33; m. 64; c. 2. ENGLISH. B.A, Boston Col, 54, M.A, 56; Ph.D.(Eng), Univ. Mich, Ann Arbor, 64. Instr. ENG, Univ. Mich, 62-64; ASST. PROF, St. John's Univ, 64-66; MANHATTAN COL, 66- Nineteenth century American literature; Afro-American literature; cinema. Publ: How to analyze fiction, Monarch, 66. Add: Dept. of English & World Literature, Manhattan College, Bronx, NY 10471.

KENNY, SHIRLEY STRUM, b. Tyler, Tex, Aug. 28, 34; m. 56; c. 5. ENGLISH. Borden scholar, B.J. & B.A, Univ. Tex, 55; Woodrow Wilson fel. & M.A, Univ. Minn, 57; Fulbright grant, Univ. London, 57-58; W.H. Rainey & Sr. Vis. Comt. grants & Ph.D, Univ. Chicago, 64. Instr. ENG, Univ. Tex, 55-56 & 58-59; from asst. prof. to assoc. prof, Gallaudet Col, 62-66; Cath. Univ. Am, 66-71; from assoc. prof. to PROF, UNIV. MD, COLLEGE PARK, 71-, CHMN. DEPT, 73- Nat. Endowment for Humanities summer stipend, 67; Folger Shakespeare Libr. sr. fel, 70-71. MLA; S.Atlantic Mod. Lang. Asn; Am. Soc. 18th Century Stud; Anglo-Am. Assocs; Bibliog. Soc. Univ. Va. Eighteenth century drama; bibliography and editing. Publ: Ed, The conscious lovers, Univ. Nebr, 68 & The plays of Richard Steele, Clarendon, 71; auth, Eighteenth century editions of Steele's Conscious lovers, Stud. Bibliog, 68; Richard Steele and the Pattern of genteel comedy, Mod. Philol, 72; Theatrical warfare, 1695-1710, Theatre Notebook, 73; plus others. Add: Dept. of English, University of Maryland, College Park, MD 20742.

KENT, GEORGE E, b. Columbus, Ga, May 31, 20; m. 42; c. 2. ENGLISH & AMERICAN LITERATURE. B.A, Savannah State Col, 41; M.A, Boston Univ, 48, Ph.D.(Eng), 53. Asst. prof. ENG, Del. State Col, 49-53, prof, 53-60; assoc. prof, Quinnipiac Col, 60-62, PROF, 62-70; UNIV. CHICAGO, 70- Vis. lectr, Grambling State Col, summer 55; Fla. A&M Univ, summer 56; Univ. Conn, Stamford, summers 61 & 62, Hartford, summer 63; Wesleyan Univ, summer 65; Univ. Chicago, 69-70; contrib. ed, Black Bks. Bull, 71-; adv. ed, Col. Lang. Asn. J, 71- & Negro Lit. Forum, 71- U.S.A, 42-44, 2nd Lt. Col. Lang. Asn.(chmn. Black stud. comt, 70-); MLA; Am. Stud. Asn; NCTE (mem. comn. lit, 71-73). Black literature; southern literature; 20th century American literature. Publ: Blackness & the adventure of western culture, Third World, 72; Patterns of the Harlem Renaissance, In: Harlem Renaissance remembered, 72; Richard Wright, In: Twentieth century views, Prentice-Hall, 72; Self-conscious writers, Black folk tradition, In: The humanity of English, NCTE, 72; plus others. Add: Dept. of English, University of Chicago, 1050 E. 59th St, Chicago, IL 60637.

KENT, LEONARD J, b. Brooklyn, N.Y, Dec. 21, 27; c. 4. ENGLISH. B.A, L.I. Univ, 53; M.A, N.Y. Univ, 55; Ph.D.(comp. lit), Yale, 65. Instr. ENG, QUINNIPIAC COL, 60-64, asst. prof, 64-65, assoc. prof, 65-67, PROF, 67-, PRES, 71-, chmn. dept, 65-71. Nineteenth century Russian literature; literary criticism; eighteenth and nineteenth century English literature. Publ: Ed, The collected tales and plays of Nikolai Gogol, Pantheon, 64; co-ed, Anna Karenina, Random, 65; auth, The subconscious in Gogol and Dostoevski, Mouton, 69; co-ed. & transl. The best of E.T.A. Hoffmann, Univ. Chicago, 69. Add: Dept. of English, Quinnipiac College, Hamden, CT 06518.

KENVIN, ROGER LEE, b. New York, N.Y, May 26, 26; m. 52; c. 2. DRAMA. A.B, Bowdoin Col, 49; M.A, Harvard, 56; M.F.A, Yale, 59, D.F.A, 61. Teaching fel. Eng, Bowdoin Col, 49-50; prof. Eng. & Latin, Inst. Le Rosey, Switz, 53-55; instr. Eng, Northeast. Univ, 55-56; asst. prof, Mary Washington Col, Univ. Va, 59-65, assoc. prof, drama, 65-68, prof, 68-69; PROF. DRAMA & CHMN. DEPT, St. Mary's Col.(Ind) & Univ. Notre Dame, 69-72; MARY WASHINGTON COL, 72- Vis. lectr. Eng. & drama, Isabella Thoburn Col, Lucknow, India, 65-66. Am. Theatre Asn. Drama. Publ: The singing in a lonely cage (play), Joseph Jefferson Theatre Co, New York, 73; Krishnalight (play), Mary Washington Players, Mary Washington Col, 74. Add: Dept. of Dramatic Arts & Speech, Mary Washington College, Fredericksburg, VA 22401.

KEPKE, ALLEN NEAL, b. Cleveland, Ohio, Jan. 14, 35; m. 58; c. 3. SPEECH, THEATRE. B.A, Otterbein Col, 57; M.A, Ohio State Univ, 59; United Theol. Sem, 59-60; Ph.D.(speech, theatre), Mich. State Univ, 63. Instr. SPEECH, Col. Wooster, 62-63; BOWLING GREEN STATE UNIV, 63-65, asst. prof, 65-68, assoc. prof, 68-72, PROF, 72-, ASST. DEAN COL. ARTS & SCI, 70- Am. Theatre Asn; Speech Commun. Asn. Empirical research in theatre; criticism. Publ: Theatre with a purpose, Fine Arts, 7/66; The AETA Conference on Theater Research: a commentary, Cue, fall 67; co-auth, Reliability of judgements of directing techniques, Empirical Res. in Theatre, 71. Add: 718 Birch St, Bowling Green, OH 43402.

KEPPLER, CARL FRANCIS, b. Hillside, N.J, Dec. 17, 09; m. 36. ENGLISH. B.A, Princeton, 30; M.A, Univ. Ariz, 51, Ph.D.(Eng), Univ. Mich, 56. Instr. ENG, UNIV. ARIZ, 49-52, 54-58, asst. prof, 58-65, assoc. prof, 65-70, PROF, 70- Symbolism, particularly the second self, or doppelganger, in world literature. Publ: The other, Houghton, 64 & Victor Gollancz, 64; The literature of the second self, Univ. Ariz, 72. Add: Dept. of English, University of Arizona, Tucson, AZ 85721.

KERBY-MILLER, SINCLAIR, b. Bel Air, Md, Feb. 16, 99; m. 27; c. 1. COMMUNICATION. A.B, Univ. Ore, 20; M.A, Columbia Univ, 21; Ph.D.(philos), Oxford, 31. Instr. philos, Univ. Ore, 23-24; Harvard, 25-29; assoc. prof, Univ. Mo, 28-35; prof. philos. & hist. & dir. summer inst, Reed Col, 35-39; gen. mgr. agr. workers, Health Asn, Farm Security Admin, 39-47; lectr. speech, Univ. Calif, 48-52; asst. prof. lang. arts, SAN FRANCISCO STATE UNIV, 52-58, assoc. prof. ENG, 58-64, prof, 64-69, EMER. PROF, 69- Am. Philol. Asn. Philosophical analysis; communication theory. Publ: On causality, In: Philosophical essays for Alfred North Whitehead, Russell, 36. Add: P.O. Box 974, Carmel, CA 93921.

KERN, ALEXANDER C, b. Erie, Pa, Sept, 23, 09; m. 36; c. 2. AMERICAN LITERATURE & CIVILIZATION. A.B, Yale, 30; M.A, Univ. Wis, 33, fel, 34-35, Ph.D.(Am. hist), 36. Instr. ENG, Univ. Iowa, 36-42; Univ. Wis, 42-43; Allegheny Col, 43-44; asst. prof, UNIV. IOWA, 44-46, assoc. prof, 46-51, PROF, 51, CHMN. DEPT. AM. CIVILIZATION, 66- Vis. prof, Univ. Md, summer 49; Ford fel, 54-55; Rockefeller prof, Univ. Ankara, 58-60; summer vis. prof, Univ. Wis, 59; Univ. Wyo, 62; Huntington Libr. grant-in-aid, 63; prof, Am. Univ. Cairo, 64-66; mem. ed. comt, Thoreau edition, 64-72. MLA; Am. Stud. Asn; Midwest Mod. Lang. Asn; Archaeol. Inst. Am; Orgn. Am. Hist; Am. Hist. Asn. American transcendentalism; Thoreau; American civilization. Publ: Co-auth, Rise of transcendentalism, Duke, 54, Sources of the American republic, Scott, 60-61 & Myth and symbol in Faulkner's The bear, Univ. Nebr, 63; auth, Two fragments of Thoreau's journals, 68 & Preface to Huckleberries, 70, Windhover; Dreiser and Fitzgerald as social critics, Papers Midwest Mod. Lang. Asn, 72. Add: Dept. of English, University of Iowa, Iowa City, IA 52242.

KERN, ALFRED, b. Alliance, Ohio, Aug. 8, 24; m. 47; c. 3. AMERICAN LITERATURE. A.B, Allegheny Col, 48; A.M, N.Y. Univ, 54. Instr. ENG, ALLEGHENY COL, 49-53, asst. prof, 53-60, assoc. prof, 60-67, PROF, 67- U.S.A.A.F, 42-46, Sgt. Auth. Guild. Writing of fiction; modern novel. Publ:

The width of waters, 59 & Made in USA, 66, Houghton; The trial of Martin Ross, Norton, 71. Add: Dept. of English, Allegheny College, Meadville, PA 16335.

KERN, JEAN B, b. Bristol, Ind, Apr. 30, 13; m. 36; c. 2. ENGLISH. B.A. & M.A, Univ. Wis, 33, fel, 34-35, Ph.D, 36. Instr. ENG, Univ. Wis, 42-43; State Univ, Iowa, 46-47, 57-58; asst. prof, Georgetown Univ. in Ankara, 58-60; lectr, Grinnell Col, 60-61; asst. prof, Coe Col, 61-64, assoc. prof, Am. Univ, Cairo, 64-66, COE COL, 66-70, PROF, 70- Newberry Libr. fel, summer 62; Huntington Libr. grant-in-aid, summer 63. MLA; Midwest Mod. Lang. Asn. Eighteenth century English literature; English as a second language; Victorian literature. Publ: Introd. to Charles Macklin's Covent Garden Theatre, 65, A will and no will & The new play criticized, 67, Augustan Reprint Soc; auth, Satire: the elusive muse, West. Humanities Rev, 60; Thomson's revisions of Agamemnon, In: Essays in honor of Charles B. Woods, Philol. Quart, 66. Add: Dept. of English, Coe College, Cedar Rapids, IA 52402.

KERN, RONALD CHESTER, b. Sandusky, Ohio, Oct. 12, 24; m. 46; c. 2. SPEECH & DRAMA. B.S, Bowling Green State Univ, 49; M.A, Miami Univ, 49; West. Reserve Univ, summers 50, 52, 53; Ph.D.(drama), Bristol Univ, Eng, 58. Asst. speech & drama, Miami Univ, 48-49; instr, Univ. Idaho, 49-51; Miami Univ, 51-54, asst. prof, 54-55, 57-61, assoc. prof. speech, 61-68; prof. & chmn. dept, Ashland Col, 68-72; PROF. SPEECH & DRAMA & DIR. THEATRE, UNIV. SOUTHWEST. LA, 72- U.S.A, 43-46, Res, 48-53, 2nd Lt. Speech Commun. Asn; Soc. Theatre Res, Eng; Am. Theatre Asn. History of the English theatre; interpretation of literature; English theatrical documents. Publ: Documents relating to company management, 1705-1711, winter 59 & Two designs by the Elder Thomas Greenwood in 1777, autumn 60, Theatre Notebk; contrib, Ohio, a personal portrait of the 17th State, Doubleday, 69. Add: 103 Saxon Dr, Lafayette, LA 70501.

KERNAN, ALVIN BERNARD, b. Manchester, Ga, June 13, 23; m. 49; c. 4. ENGLISH. B.A, Williams Col.(Mass), 49; Moody fel, Oxford, 49-51, B.A, 51; M.A, Yale, 53, Ph.D.(Eng), 54. Instr. Eng, Rensselaer Polytech. Inst, 53-54; from instr. to prof, Yale, 54-73, assoc. provost, 65-68; DEAN GRAD. SCH, PRINCETON, 73- Morse fel. from Yale, 57-58; Am. Counc. Learned Soc. fel, 61-62; Nat. Endowment for Humanities sr. fel, 68-69. U.S.N, 41-45. Elizabethan drama; Shakespeare; satire. Publ: Cankered muse, 59, ed, Volpone, 62, auth, The plot of satire, 66 & ed, The alchemist, 74, Yale; Character and conflict, 63 & co-auth, Man and his fictions, 73, Harcourt; ed, Othello, Signet, 63; auth, Modern American theatre, Prentice-Hall, 67; The miracles in King Lear, In: Renaissance drama, Northwest. Univ, 66. Add: Graduate School, Princeton University, Princeton, NJ 08540.

KERNAN, ANNE, b. Chicago, Ill, Sept. 14, 35; m. 59; c. 2. MEDIEVAL LITERATURE. B.A, Col. St. Teresa (Minn), 57; Fulbright grant, Univ. Lyon, 57-58; NDEA fel, Cornell Univ, 68-69, Ph.D.(Eng), 70. ASST. PROF. ENG. & MEDIEVAL STUD, UNIV. CALIF, SANTA BARBARA, 70- Mediaeval Acad. Am; Medieval Asn. Pac; MLA. Medieval English literature; Old French; Old Norse. Publ: The archwife and the eunuch, ELH, 74; Theme and structure in The parlement of the thre ages, Neuphilol. Mitt, 74. Add: Dept. of English, University of California, Santa Barbara, CA 93106.

KERNER, DAVID, b. Philadelphia, Pa, Apr. 13, 20; m. 50; c. 1. ENGLISH. A.B, Univ. Pa, 40; A.M, Columbia Univ, 48. Tutor ENG, City Col. New York, 46-49; lectr, Rutgers Univ. Col. & Exten, Camden, 50-55; instr, PA. STATE UNIV, OGONTZ CAMPUS, 55-60, asst. prof, 60-70, ASSOC. PROF, 70- U.S.A.A.F. & U.S.A, 42-46, Sgt. NCTE. American and European fiction; humanities; Jewish literature in English and translation. Publ: A note on The beast in the jungle, Univ. Kansas City Rev, winter 50; Psychodrama in Eden, Chicago Rev, winter-spring 59; Thanksgiving, Commentary, 7/69; plus others. Add: Dept. of English, Pennsylvania State University, Ogontz Campus, Abington, PA 19001.

KERNODLE, GEORGE RILEY, b. Camp Hill, Ala, Mar. 17, 07. DRAMATICS. B.S, St. Lawrence Univ, 26; Carnegie Inst. Technol, 26-28; Columbia Univ, 28-29; A.M, Univ. Chicago, 30; Ph.D, Yale, 37. Instr. Eng. & dramatics, Ball State Teachers Col, 30-32; asst. prof. Eng. & dir. dramatics, Cleveland Col, West. Reserve Univ, 36-45; assoc. prof. dramatic arts, State Univ. Iowa, 45-50; speech, Univ. Tulsa, 50-52; PROF. DRAMATIC ARTS, UNIV. ARK, 52- Sterling fel, Europe, 38-39; Rockefeller Found. fel, 39; lectr, Shakespeare Inst, Eng, 56; vis. prof, State Univ. Iowa, spring 62; summer vis. prof, Univ. Calif, Los Angeles, 47, Univ. Colo, 51, Mich. State Univ, 52, San Francisco State Col, 59, Univ. B.C, 63 & Univ. Hawaii, 67. Am. Theatre Asn; Am. Soc. Theatre Res. Theatre history and criticism; art and society. Publ: From art to theatre, Univ. Chicago, 44; co-auth, The Renaissance stage, Univ. Miami, 59; auth, Invitation to the theatre, Harcourt, 67, brief ed, 71; The open stage: Elizabethan or existentialist?, Shakespeare Surv, 59. Add: 420 Rebecca St, Fayetteville, AR 72701.

KERR, ELIZABETH MARGARET, b. Sault Ste. Marie, Mich, Jan. 25, 05. ENGLISH. B.A, Univ. Minn, 26, M.A, 27, Ph.D, 41. Instr. ENG, Tabor Col, 29-30; Univ. Minn, 30-37, 38-43; Col. St. Catherine, 37-38; asst. prof, Rockford Col, 43-45; instr, UNIV. WIS-MILWAUKEE, 45-55, assoc. prof, 55-59, prof, 59-70, EMER. PROF, 70- Mod. Lang. Asn. res. grant, 42; Univ. Wis. Salary Support res. grants, summer 59, 1st semester, 62-63 & summer 64. Am. Stud. Asn; MLA; NCTE; James Joyce Found; Dickens Fel; Soc. Stud. South. Lit. Eighteenth and 19th century English novel; American, English & continental sequence novel; the Yoknapatawpha fiction of William Faulkner; Gothic elements in the novels of Charles Dickens. Publ: Bibliography of the sequence novel, Univ. Minn, 50 & 73; Yoknapatawpha; Faulkner's little postage stamp of native soil, Fordham Univ, 69; Polarity of themes in All the King's men, spring 60 & The Reivers: the golden book of Yoknapatawpha County, spring 67, Mod. Fiction Stud. Add: 4259 N. Sercombe Rd, Milwaukee, WI 53216.

KERR, HOWARD HASTINGS, b. Los Angeles, Calif, Nov. 23, 31; m. 63; c. 3. AMERICAN & ENGLISH LITERATURE. B.A, Univ. Calif, Berkeley, 53; M.A, Univ. Calif, Los Angeles, 63, Regents fel, 63-64, Ph.D.(Eng), 68. Instr. ENG, UNIV. ILL, CHICAGO CIRCLE, 66-68, asst. prof, 68-72, ASSOC. PROF, 72- MLA. Nineteenth century American literature; the novel. Publ: Mediums and spirit-rappers and roaring radicals; spiritualism in American literature 1850-1900, Univ. Ill, 72. Add: Dept. of English, University of Illinois at Chicago Circle, Box 4348, Chicago, IL 60680.

KERR, JOHN FAY, b. Monette, Ark, May 28, 30. AMERICAN LITERATURE, POETRY. B.A, Ark. State Univ, 53; M.A, Univ. Mich, Ann Arbor, 56; Univ. Iowa, 56; Univ. Mo-Columbia, 57-58; Ph.D.(Am. lit), Univ. Tex, Austin, 65. Teacher speech & jour, Kennett High Sch, Mo, 54-55; asst. prof. Am. lit. & fiction writing, Westminster Col.(Mo), 56-57; instr. narrative writing, Univ. Mo-Columbia, 57-58; Univ. Tex, Austin, 58-63; asst. prof. Am. lit. & fiction writing, La. State Univ, Baton Rouge, 65-67; assoc. prof. AM. LIT. & CREATIVE WRITING, CALIF. POLYTECH. STATE UNIV, SAN LUIS OBISPO, 73-74, PROF, 74-, DIR. GRAD. STUD. ENG, 73- Excellence in Teaching Award, Univ. Tex, Austin, 61. U.S.M.C, 46-49. MLA; AAUP; Am. Stud. Asn; NCTE; Poetry Soc. Am. American fiction since 1865; the aesthetics of fiction and poetry; contemporary poetry. Publ: Cast iron horse (poem), Cafe Solo, spring 71; Hemingway's posthumous novel, Shoreline, fall 71; Two poems, Calif. State Poetry Quart, summer 73; plus others. Add: 245-D N. Oak Park Blvd, Grover City, CA 93433.

KERSHNER, AMMON GEORGE, JR, b. Philadelphia, Pa, Dec. 20, 20. ENGLISH, SPEECH. B.S, Univ. Pa, 43, M.S, 44, A.M, 47, Ph.D.(Eng), 52; Temple Univ, 45-64. Instr. ENG, Ursinus Col, 47-52, asst. prof, 52-65; assoc. prof, WEST CHESTER STATE COL, 65-68, PROF, 68- MLA; NCTE; Col. Eng. Asn; Speech Commun. Asn; Nat. Asn. Parliamentarians; Am. Inst. Parliamentarians. Contemporary British literature; American literature; parliamentary procedure. Publ: Ralph Hodgson: a biographical and critical study, Univ. Microfilms, 52; Trees—an Ursinus College campus tradition, Pa. Forests, spring 55; John Dolman, Jr, Speech Teacher, 11/62. Add: 510 Swede St, Norriston, PA 19401.

KERSHNER, RICHARD BRANDON, JR, b. Cumberland, Md, Nov. 17, 44; m. 66; c. 1. MODERN BRITISH LITERATURE. B.A. & M.A, Johns Hopkins Univ, 66; M.A, Stanford Univ, 68, Ph.D.(Eng. & comp. lit), 71. Teaching asst. ENG, Stanford Univ, 68-69; ASST. PROF, UNIV. FLA, 70- MLA; S.Atlantic Mod. Lang. Asn.(mem. Irish Stud. Circle, 73-); Am. Comt. Irish Stud. Anglo-Irish literature; modern British literature; modern French novel. Add: Dept. of English, University of Florida, Gainesville, FL 32601.

KERSNOWSKI, FRANK LOUIS, b. Washington, D.C, May 6, 34; div; c. 1. ENGLISH, DRAMA. B.A, Univ. Tenn, 57, M.A, 59; Ph.D.(Eng), Univ. Kans, 62. Asst. ENG, Univ. Tenn, 57-59; Univ. Kans, 59-62; asst. prof, Ohio Univ, 62-64; ASSOC. PROF, TRINITY UNIV.(TEX), 64-, res. grants, 66, 69 & 71. Nat. Found. Arts & Humanities summer stipend, 68. MLA; Am. Comt. Irish Stud; S.Cent. Mod. Lang. Asn.(chmn. Anglo-Irish Lit. Sect, 73). Publ: The portrayal of the hero in Yeats's poetic drama, Renascence, 65; Exit the anti-hero, Critique, 68; To Adam (poems), 72, Darkness in the subways, 73 & Always and other poems, 73, Sisterdale, John Montague, Bucknell Univ, (in prep); Spring morning (poem), Chesapeake Rev, 70; The fabulous reality of Denis Devlin, Sewanee Rev, 72; The poet and politics: John Montague, Stud. by Mem. S.Cent. Mod. Lang. Asn, 72. Add: Box 115, 715 Stadium Dr, San Antonio, TX 78284.

KESSLER, CAROLYN LOUISE, Linguistics, English as a Second Language. See Volume III, Foreign Languages, Linguistics & Philology.

KESSLER, JASCHA FREDERICK, b. New York, N.Y, Nov. 27, 29; m. 50; c. 2. ENGLISH LITERATURE. B.A, N.Y. Univ, 50; M.A, Univ. Mich, 51, Ph.D, 55. Instr. Eng, N.Y. Univ, 54-55; Hunter Col, 55-56; dir. instructional res, Harcourt, Brace & Co, 56-57; asst. prof. ENG, Hamilton Col, 57-61; UNIV. CALIF, LOS ANGELES, 61-65, assoc. prof, 65-71, PROF, 71- Writing fels, Danforth Found, 60; D.H. Lawrence fel, Univ. N.Mex, 61; Wurlitzer Found. fel, 61; Fulbright res. scholar, Italy, 63-64, fel. inst. creative arts, Univ. Calif, 63-64, res. assoc, inst. govt. & pub. affairs, 66-; fel. playwrighting, Am. Place Theatre, N.Y.C, 67; Fulbright lectr Am. lit, Italy, 70; mem. adv. counc, West. Ctr, Nat. Ser. for Humanities, Nat. Endowment for Humanities, 73-, lectr, West. U.S, Alaska & Hawaii, 73- Maj. Hopwood Poetry Award, Univ. Mich, 52. MLA; Am. Soc. Composers, Auth. & Publ. Problems of culture; arts in urban society; Los Angeles playwrighting. Publ: Ed, American poems: a contemporary collection, South. Ill. Univ, 64; Perfect days (play), In: Modern occasions, Farrar, Straus, 66; Egyptian bondage and other stories, Harper, 67; Whatever love declares (poems), Plantin, 69; After the armies have passed (poems), N.Y. Univ, 70; auth. & ed, American poems: a contemporary collection, South. Univ, 2nd printing, 70; auth D.H. Lawrence's primitivism, Tex. Stud. Lit. & Lang, 64; Death comes for the behaviorist (novella), 9/70 & The gestalt doctor in the Elysian Fields, 10/72, Encounter, London. Add: Dept. of English, University of California, Los Angeles, CA 90024.

KESSLER, MILTON, b. Brooklyn, N.Y, May 9, 30; m. 52; c. 3. ENGLISH. B.A, Univ. Buffalo, 57; Robert Frost fel, Bread Loaf Sch, 61; M.A, Univ. Wash, 62; Ohio State Univ, 59-63; Harvard, 57. Lectr. ENG, Queens Col. (N.Y), 63-65; assoc. prof, STATE UNIV. N.Y. BINGHAMTON, 65-74, PROF, 74-, dir. creative writing prog, 73-74. Yaddo fel, 65-73; Edward MacDowell Found. fel, 66; Nat. Found. Arts grant, 67; Distinguished fel, State Univ. N.Y. Res. Found, 69; vis. prof, Univ. Negev, 71-72; co-ed, Choice, A Magazine of Poetry and Graphics, 73- Nineteenth and 20th century poetry in English. Publ: A road came once, Ohio State Univ, 63; Called home, Black Bird, 67; Woodlawn north, Impressions Workshop, 70; Sailing too far, Harper, 73; co-auth, Love songs and tomb songs of Ancient Egypt, In: Alcheringa, summer 73. Add: Dept. of English, State University of New York at Binghamton, Binghamton, NY 13901.

KESTERSON, DAVID BERT, b. Springfield, Mo, Feb. 19, 38; m. 63; c. 2. ENGLISH. B.S.E, Southwest Mo. State Univ, 59; M.A, Univ. Ark, 61, Ph.D. (Eng), 64. Asst. prof. ENG, N.C. State Univ, 64-68; N.TEX. STATE UNIV, 68-69, ASSOC. PROF, 69-, fac. res. grants, 68-73. N.C. State Univ. Fac. Res. & Develop. Fund res. grant, 67-68. U.S.A.R, 56-60. MLA; S.Cent. Mod. Lang. Asn.(secy, chmn, Am. Lit I, 72-73); S.Atlantic Mod. Lang. Asn; Soc. Stud. South. Lit; Southwest. Am. Lit. Asn. Nineteenth century American literature, especially Hawthorne and the novel; eighteenth century English literature; American humor. Publ: Ed, Studies in The marble faun, Merrill, 71; auth, Josh Billings, Twayne, 73; ed, Critics on Mark Twain, 73 & Critics on Poe, 73, Miami; Hawthorne and nature: Thoreauvian influence?, Eng. Lang. Notes, winter 67; Josh Billings and his burlesque Allminax, Ill. Quart, 72; Journey to Perugia: Dantean echoes in The marble faun, ESQ, 73; plus others. Add: Dept. of English, North Texas State University, Denton, TX 76203.

KESTERTON, WILFRED HAROLD, b. Regina, Sask, July 22, 14. JOURNALISM. B.A, Queen's Univ.(Ont), 42; B.J, Carleton Univ, 49. Lectr. JOUR, CARLETON UNIV, 49-54, asst. prof, 54-62, assoc. prof, 62-71, PROF, 71- Humanities Res. Counc. grant, summer 53; mem. lit. & media comt, Can. Exhibit, Brussels, 56; Can. Found. Assessment Comt. for Can. Counc. Scholarships, 61-68; Nat. Press Centennial Comt, 64-68. Coronation Medal, 53. Can. Army, 42-47, Capt. Can. Hist. Asn. History of Canadian journalism; law of the press in Canada. Publ: A history of journalism in Canada, McClelland & Stewart, 67; co-ed, A century of reporting—UnSiècle de Reportage, Clarke, Irwin, 67; auth, Journalism, 61-64 & Mass media, 65-67 & 68-70, Can. Annual Rev, Univ. Toronto; co-auth, Communications, In: The Canadians, 1867-1967, Macmillan, 67; plus others. Add: School of Journalism, Arts I Tower, Carleton University, Colonel By Dr, Ottawa, Ont. K1S 5B6, Can.

KESTNER, JOSEPH, b. Horton, Kans, Sept. 12, 43. ENGLISH NOVEL, ROMANTICISM. B.A, State Univ. N.Y. Albany, 65; regents fel, Columbia Univ, 65-67, M.A, 66, president's fel, 67-68, Woodrow Wilson fel. & Ph.D. (Eng. & classics), 69. Preceptor ENG, Columbia Univ, 68; ASST. PROF, Princeton, 69-73, BARUCH COL, 73- MLA; Keats-Shelley Asn. Am. English and European novel; romanticism. Publ: Jane Austen: spatial structure of thematic variation, Univ. Salzburg, 74; Tolstoy and Joyce: Resurrection and Penelope, James Joyce Quart, 6/72; Defoe and Madame de La Fayette: Roxana and La Princesse de Monpensier, Papers Lang. & Lit, 6/72; Pindar and Saint-Exupery: the heroic form of space, Mod. Fiction Stud, 12/73. Add: Dept. of English, Baruch College, 17 Lexington Ave, New York, NY 10010.

KETCHAM, CARL H, b. Ossining, N.Y, Oct. 3, 23; m. 50; c. 1. ENGLISH LITERATURE. B.A, Williams Col, 44; M.A, Harvard, 47, Ph.D, 51; Oxford, 60. Instr. ENG, Ga. Inst. Technol, 45-46; N.Y. Univ, 48-50; from instr. to assoc. prof, UNIV. ARIZ, 50-67, PROF, 67-, assoc. dean grad. col, 70-74. MLA. English literature of the romantic movement; Victorian literature. Publ: The letters of John Wordsworth, Cornell Univ, 69; Meredith and the Wilis, Victorian Poetry, 63; Meredith at work: The tale of Chloe, Nineteenth Century Fiction, 66; plus others. Add: Dept. of English, University of Arizona, Tucson, AZ 85721.

KETTERER, DAVID ANTHONY THEODOR, b. Leigh-on-Sea, Eng, June 13, 42; m. 72. ENGLISH & AMERICAN LITERATURE. B.A, Univ. Wales, 64; fel, Carleton Univ, 64-65, M.A, 65; Ph.D.(Am. lit), Univ. Sussex, 69. Lectr. ENG, McGill Univ, 65-66; SIR GEORGE WILLIAMS UNIV, 67-70, asst. prof, 70-73, ASSOC. PROF, 73- Can. Counc. leave fel, 73-74. Northeast Mod. Lang. Asn.(secy, 19th century Am. lit. sect, 72-73); MLA; Asn. Can. Univ. Teachers Eng; Can. Asn. Univ. Teachers; Sci. Fiction Res. Asn; Poe Stud. Asn; Can. Asn. Am. Stud. American literature; science fiction and allied literature; critical theory. Publ: New worlds for old: the apocalyptic imagination, science fiction, and American literature, Anchor Bks. & Ind. Univ, 74; Poe's usage of the hoax and the unity of Hans Pfaall, Criticism, 10/71; contrib, The novel and its changing form, Univ. Man, 72; auth, Epoch-eclipse and apocalypse: special effects in A Connecticut Yankee, PMLA, 10/73; plus others. Add: Dept. of English, Sir George Williams University, Montreal, P.Q. 25, Can.

KEY, HOWARD CRESAP, b. Waco, Tex, Nov. 16, 06; m. 47; c. 1. ENGLISH. B.A, Univ. Tex, 28, M.A, 35; Ph.D.(Eng), Stanford Univ, 52. Asst. prof. ENG, Stephen F. Austin State Col, 36-41; assoc. prof, N.TEX. STATE UNIV, 47-56, PROF, 56- Vis. prof, Istanbul Univ, Turkey, 53-54. U.S.A.A.F, 41-46, Capt. American novel; folklore and weather phenomena; prose style. Publ: World of William Faulkner, Istanbul Philol. J; Water and the West, Southwest Rev; Twister tales, Tex. Folklore Soc, 58. Add: Dept. of English, North Texas State University, Denton, TX 76203.

KEY, MARY RITCHIE, Linguistics. See Volume III, Foreign Languages, Linguistics & Philology.

KEYES, DANIEL, b. New York, N.Y, Aug. 9, 27; m. 52; c. 2. ENGLISH. A.B, Brooklyn Col, 50, M.A, 61. Assoc. fiction ed, Mag. Mgt. Co, N.Y, 50-52; Teacher ENG, Thomas Jefferson High Sch, N.Y. Bd. Educ, 55-62; instr, Wayne State Univ, 62-66; lectr, OHIO UNIV, 66-72, PROF, 72-, dir. creative writing, 73-74. PEN Club. The novel; contemporary fiction. Publ: Flowers for Algernon, 66 & The touch, 68, Harcourt. Add: Dept. of English, Ohio University, Athens, OH 45701.

KEYISHIAN, HARRY, b. New York, N.Y, Apr. 9, 32; m. 66; c. 4. ENGLISH LITERATURE. B.A, Queens Col.(N.Y), 54; M.A, N.Y. Univ, 57, Ph.D.(Eng. lit), 65. Asst. instr. ENG, Univ. Md. Overseas Prog, Nfld, 57-58; lectr, City Col. New York, 59-60; instr, Bronx Community Col, 61; Univ. Buffalo, 61-64; asst. prof, FAIRLEIGH DICKINSON UNIV, MADISON, 65-69, ASSOC. PROF, 69-, CHMN. DEPT, 72- Asst. Eng. Col. Engineering, N.Y. Univ, 59. U.S.N.R, 50-58. MLA; Renaissance Soc. Am; Northeast Mod. Lang. Asn; Soc. Theatre Res, Eng; Col. Eng. Asn. Elizabethan drama and Shakespeare; revenge themes in literature; 20th century fiction. Publ: William Saroyan: rebel or holdout?, winter 61 & The Armenian side of Michael Arlen, autumn 70, Ararat; Dekker's Whore and Marston's Courtesan, Eng. Lang. Notes, 6/67. Add: Dept. of English, Fairleigh Dickinson University, Madison Ave, Madison, NJ 07940.

KEYSER, BARBARA YARBROUGH, b. Sheffield, Ala, Mar. 25, 45. MODERN BRITISH & AMERICAN LITERATURE. A.B, Florence State Univ, 67; NDEA fel, Tulane Univ, 67-70, M.A, 70, Ph.D.(Eng), 71. INSTR. COMMUN. SKILLS, BARUCH COL, 73- MLA. Twentieth century British literature; the novel; contemporary American literature. Add: Dept. of English, Baruch College, 17 Lexington Ave, New York, NY 10010.

KHANNA, SATENDRA, b. Lahore, India, Dec. 22, 41. SEVENTEENTH CENTURY & MODERN INDIAN LITERATURE. A.B, Harvard, 64; Ph.D,(Eng), Univ. Calif, Los Angeles, 69. ASST. PROF. ENG. LIT, UNIV. MICH, ANN ARBOR, 69- William Andrews Clark Libr, jr. fel, summer 71; Rackham fel, Horace H. Rackham Sch. Grad. Stud, Univ. Mich, summer 73. Bibliog. Soc; Asn. Asian Stud. The application of psycholinguistics to literary studies; stylistics; the anthropology of literary forms in Asia and the West. Add: Dept. of English, University of Michigan, Ann Arbor, MI 48104.

KHER, INDER NATH, b. Gujrat, Panjab, India, Oct. 12, 33; Can. citizen; m. 63; c. 1. ENGLISH & AMERICAN LITERATURE. B.A, Panjab Univ, 54, M.A, 59; M.A, McMaster Univ, 66; Can. Counc. fel, Univ. Alta, 68-69; Ph.D.(Eng), 69. Lectr. Eng, D.A.V. Col, Jullundur, India, 60-65; asst. prof, ENG. & AM. LIT, UNIV. CALGARY, 69-74, ASSOC. PROF, 74- Can. Counc. res. grant, 70; Folger Shakespeare Libr, grant-in-aid, 71. MLA; Can. Asn. Am. Stud; Can. Asn. S.Asian Stud; Philol. Asn. Pac. Coast (chmn, Asian Sect, 73-); Can. Asn. Commonwealth Lit. & Lang. Stud; Asn. Can. Univ. Teachers, Eng. American poetry of the 19th and 20th centuries; modern European novel; Indo-Anglian poetry and novel. Publ: The landscape of absence: Emily Dickinson's poetry, Yale, 74; An abyss's face: the structure of Emily Dickinson's poem, Pluck, fall 68 & Emily Dickinson Bull, 6/69; That message from another shore: the esthetic vision of Nissim Ezekiel, Mahfil: A Quart. of S.Asian Lit, winter 72; Hermann Hesse's Siddhartha: the landscape of the inner self, Lit. Half-Yearly, 1/73. Add: Dept. of English, University of Calgary, Calgary, Alta. T2N 1N4, Can.

KIBLER, JAMES EVERETT, JR, b. Prosperity, S.C, June 24, 44. AMERICAN LITERATURE. B.A, Univ. S.C, 66, Woodrow Wilson fel, 69-70, Ph.D. (Eng), 70. Instr. ENG, Univ. S.C, 66-69; ASST. PROF, UNIV. GA, 70- MLA; Am. Lit. Group, Mod. Lang. Asn; Soc. Study South. Lit.(bibliogr, 69-). Romantic poetry; textual bibliography; modern Southern novel. Publ: The library of Stephen and Cora Crane, In: Proof: the yearbook of American bibliographical and textual studies, Univ. S.C, 71; William Faulkner and Provincetown drama, Miss. Quart, 6/69; A new Simms letter: on the advancement of Southern literature, Am. Lit, 1/73. Add: Dept. of English, Park Hall, University of Georgia, Athens, GA 30602.

KIBLER, ROBERT JOSEPH, b. Dayton, Ohio, Oct. 6, 34; m. 54; c. 3. COMMUNICATION, EDUCATIONAL PSYCHOLOGY. B.S, Ohio State Univ, 57, M.A, 59, Ph.D.(speech commun. & psychol), 62. Instr. speech & commun, Ohio State Univ, 59-61, res. assoc. & assoc. dir. psycholing. res. proj, 61-62; asst. prof. commun, South. Ill. Univ, 62-64, educ. psychol, 64-66, assoc. prof, 66-67, dir. exp. freshman year, 62-64, admin. asst. to v.pres. oper, 63-64, dir. educ. res. bur, 64-67; assoc. prof. speech & assoc. dir. Commun. Res. Ctr, Purdue Univ, 67-69; PROF. COMMUN, FLA. STATE UNIV, 69- Cent. Midwest. Regional Educ. Lab—U.S. Off. Educ. grants, 66-67; field reader, Bur. Res, U.S. Off. Educ, 66-; distinguished vis. prof. commun, Univ. Mont, summer 69; co-ed, Speech Commun. Ser, Prentice-Hall, 69- Outstanding Young Teacher Award, Cent. States Speech Asn, 64. Speech Commun. Asn; Am. Psychol. Asn; Am. Educ. Res. Asn; Int. Commun. Asn; Nat. Counc. Measurement Educ. Acquisition and evaluation of communication behaviors; assessment of instructional communication effects; development of and relationships among measures of communications effects. Publ: Co-ed, Conceptual frontiers in speech-communication, Speech Commun, Asn, 69; co-auth, Behavioral objectives and instruction, Allyn & Bacon, 70 & 74; co-ed, Speech communication behavior: perspectives and principles, Prentice-Hall, 71; plus others. Add: Dept. of Communication, Florida State University, Tallahassee, FL 32306.

KIDDER, RUSHWORTH MOULTON, U.S. citizen; m. 66; c. 2. TWENTIETH CENTURY ENGLISH & AMERICAN LITERATURE. B.A, Amherst Col, 65, Simpson fel, 65-66; M.A, Columbia Univ, 66, Ph.D.(Eng), 69. ASST. PROF. ENG. & DIR. HONORS PROG, WICHITA STATE UNIV, 69- Nat. Endowment for Humanities summer stipend, 73. MLA; Soc. Relig. Higher Educ. Modern poetry and religious thought; history of drama. Publ: Dylan Thomas: the country of the spirit, Princeton, 73; An introduction to the study of poetry: five assignments, Col. Eng, 3/73. Add: Dept. of English, Wichita State University, Wichita, KS 67208.

KIEFER, HARRY CHRISTIAN, b. Brooklyn, N.Y, July 14, 23; m. 49; c. 3. HUMANITIES. B.A, Villanova Col, 47; M.A, Columbia Univ, 48, Ph.D.(Eng, comp. lit), 61; Shakespeare Inst, Eng, 49. Instr. Eng, Long Island Univ, 48-50; Eng. & humanities, Univ. Ariz, 50-60; asst. prof. humanities, UNIV. S.FLA, 60-62, assoc. prof, 62-64, PROF, 64-72, ENG, 72-, CHMN. DEPT. HUMANITIES, 63- Phillips Found. fel. acad. admin, 64-65. U.S.N.R, 42-46, Lt.(jg). Am. Asn. Higher Educ; Asn. Gen. & Lib. Stud.(pres, 73-75). Shakespeare; Renaissance arts and letters; 20th century arts and letters. Publ: Co-auth, Forum, Appleton, 56; co-ed, The western humanities, Holt, 71; auth, Music and Marston's The malcontent, Stud. Philol, 4/54. Add: 129 Carlyle Circle, Palm Harbor, FL 33563.

KIELY, JAMES JOSEPH, b. Boston, Mass, Sept. 15, 20; m. 47; c. 5. ENGLISH LANGUAGE & LITERATURE. A.B, Boston Col, 41, A.M, 47; Ph.D. (Eng), Boston Univ, 67. Instr. ENG, Boston Col, 41-48; PROF. & CHMN. DEPT, BENTLEY COL, 48-, dean admis, 70-71. Instr, Groton Div, U.S. Coast Guard Acad, 43-45; educ. consult, U.S. Civil Serv. Training Div, 67-; mem. fac, Henderson House management prog, Northeast. Univ, 67-; dir. report writing sem, educ. & training prog, John Hancock Ins. Co, 68-; lectr. & dir. sem. auditing comt, N.E. Inst. Internal Auditors, 70. U.S.C.G, 42-46. MLA; NCTE; Conf. Col. Compos. & Commun; Am. Bus. Commun. Asn; Am. Acad. Polit. & Soc. Sci. Comparative and historical linguistics; theories of historical, political, literary biography; business and technical communication. Publ: Manual and workbook for English, 56, Report writing for accountants, 57, ed, Widening horizons for accountants, 57 & co-auth, Advanced communication in business, 62, Bentley. Add: 2 Forest Lane, South Hingham, MA 02043.

KIELY, ROBERT J, b. New York, N.Y, July 10, 31; m. 62; c. 3. ENGLISH. A.B, Amherst Col, 53; Dexter Prize, Harvard, 60, Fels fel, 61, Ph.D.(Eng), 62. Instr. ENG, HARVARD, 62-63, lectr, 63-64, asst. prof, 64-65, assoc. prof, 66-68, PROF, 68-, ASSOC. DEAN FAC. ARTS & SCI. UNDERGRAD. EDUC, 72- Soc. Relig. Higher Educ. vis. fel, St. Edmund's House, 71-72; master, Adams House, Harvard, 73- MLA. The Literature of Christianity;

the novel after World War II. Publ: Robert Louis Stevenson and the fiction of adventure, 64 & The romantic novel in England, 72, Harvard; ed, Man and nature, Little, 66. Add: University Hall 19, Harvard University, Cambridge, MA 02138.

KIERNAN, MICHAEL TERENCE, b. Brooklyn, N.Y, June 14, 40; m. 64; c. 1. ENGLISH LITERATURE. B.A, Fairfield Univ, 62; M.A, Marquette Univ, 64; Univ. Ill, Urbana, 64-67; Charles Dexter travelling fel, Harvard, 70, Ph.D.(Eng), 71. Ed. asst, Renascence, 62-64; teaching fel. ENG, Harvard, 67-71; ASST. PROF, PA. STATE UNIV, UNIVERSITY PARK, 71-, ASSOC. MEM. GRAD. FAC, 73- Res. fel, Inst. Arts & Humanistic Stud, Pa. State Univ, 72; Am. Counc. Learned Soc. grant-in-aid, 72. MLA; Malone Soc; Renaissance Soc. Am; Amici Thomae Morae. Francis Bacon; English Renaissance drama; analytical bibliography. Publ: Co-ed, The plays of George Chapman: the comedies: a critical edition, Univ. Ill, Urbana, 70; auth, The order and dating of the 1613 editions of Bacon's Essays, Library, London, 9/74. Add: Dept. of English, Pennsylvania State University, University Park, PA 16802.

KIESSLING, NICOLAS KARL, b. Watertown, Wis, Sept. 6, 36; m. 63; c. 1. OLD AND MIDDLE ENGLISH. B.A, Northwest. Col, 58; M.A, Univ. Wis, 61, Ph.D.(Eng), 67. Asst. prof. ENG, WASH. STATE UNIV, 67-73, ASSOC. PROF, 73- Am. Counc. Learned Soc. grant-in-aid, summer 73. MLA; Mediaeval Acad. Am. Beowulf studies; Chaucer; dark figures in Medieval and Early Renaissance literature. Publ: Antecedents of the medieval dragon in sacred history, J. Bibl. Lit, 70; The wife of Bath's Tale: D878-881, Chaucer Rev, 73; Dr. Faustus and the sin of demoniality, Stud. Eng. Lit, (in press); plus others. Add: Dept. of English, Washington State University, Pullman, WA 99163.

KIFER, DEVRA ROWLAND, b. New York, N.Y, May 20, 27; m. 66; c. 1. ENGLISH. B.S, City Col. New York, 50; A.M, Harvard, 52, Ph.D.(Eng. lang. & lit), 57. Instr. Eng, Univ. Ky, 56-58; Fairleigh Dickinson Univ, Teaneck, 60-61, asst. prof, 61-62; Col. Eng. Ed, D.C. Heath & Co, 62-64; asst. prof. Eng. Skidmore Col, 64-68. Dept. Health, Educ. & Welfare res. grant, 62-63. MLA; NCTE; Col. Eng. Asn. Elizabethan drama; Jacobean drama; computer programing. Publ: Ed, Ben Jonson's Staple of news, Univ. Nebr, 75; auth, The staple of news: Jonson's festive comedy, Stud. Eng. Lit, spring 72; Too many cokes, Eng. Lang. Notes, 74. Add: 208 Lake Ave, Saratoga Springs, NY 12866.

KIFFER, THEODORE EDWIN, English, Linguistics. See Volume III, Foreign Languages, Linguistics & Philology.

KILBY, CLYDE SAMUEL, b. Johnson City, Tenn, Sept. 26, 02; m. 30. ENGLISH LITERATURE. A.B, Univ. Ark, 29; fel, Univ. Minn, 30-32, A.M, 31; Ph.D, N.Y. Univ, 38. Registr, John E. Brown Col, 27-30, supt. educ. & chmn. dept. Eng, 32-34; registr, Rochester Jr. Col, 34-35; asst. prof. ENG, WHEATON COL.(ILL), 35-38, assoc. prof, 38-45, PROF, 45-, CUR. LEWIS COLLECTION, 73-, asst. dean men, 35-38, exam, 38-40, chmn. div. lang. & lit, 45-46 & 52-58, chmn. dept. Eng, 51-66. Exten. instr, Univ. Ark, 34; contrib. ed, Christianity Today, 56-; consult. ed, His Mag, 58- & Eternity Mag. MLA; Conf. Christianity & Lit.(pres, 56-59). Criticism; romantic period; aesthetics. Publ: Poetry and life, Odyssey; Minority of one, Eerdmans; Christianity and aesthetics, Inter-Varsity; The Christian world of C.S. Lewis, Eerdmans, 64, Marcham Manor, 65; ed, Letters to an American lady, Eerdmans, 67 & A mind awake: an anthology of C.S. Lewis, Geoffrey Bles, London, 68 & Harcourt, New York, 69; co-auth, C.S. Lewis: images of his world, Eerdmans, 73; David Brainerd, In: Heroic colonial Christians, Lippincott, 66; contrib, Meaning in In: Shadows of imagination, South. Ill. Univ, 69 & The creative logician speaking, In: C.S. Lewis, speaker and teacher, Zondervan, 71. Add: Dept. of English, Wheaton College, Wheaton, IL 60187.

KILCOYNE, FRANCIS P, b. Lawrence, Mass, June 28, 02. BRITISH & AMERICAN LITERATURE. A.B, Boston Col, 24, A.M, 26; Ph.D, N.Y. Univ, 45; hon. L.H.D, St. Francis Col.(N.Y), 73. Instr, Hunter Col, 28-30; Eng, BROOKLYN COL, 30-37, asst. prof, 37-51, assoc. prof, 51-54, prof. & dean, 54-66, pres, 66-68, EMER. PROF, 68- Vis. prof, Teachers Col, Fordham Univ, 30-37; St. Joseph's Col.(N.Y), 28-47; educ. consult, Nat. Counc. Cath. Men, 68; dean, Fordham Univ, 68- Col. Eng. Asn; Cath. Comn. Intellectual & Cult. Affairs; Newman Hon. Soc. Emergence and growth of social and political expression in John Gallsworth; 20th century British and American literature. Add: 633 E. 24th St, Brooklyn, NY 11210.

KILDAHL, ERLING EUGENE, b. Minneapolis, Minn, Mar. 20, 17; m. 43; c. 2. THEATRE, ORAL INTERPRETATION. B.A, Jamestown Col, 40; M.T.A, Pasadena Playhouse Col. Theatre Arts, 46; Purdue Univ, 49-50. Asst. dir, Pasadena Playhouse Col. Theatre Arts, 46-47, assoc. dir. & acting dean men, 47-48; instr. speech PURDUE UNIV, WEST LAFAYETTE, 48-53, asst. prof, 53-58, assoc. prof, 58-65, PROF. speech & theatre, 65-66, theatre & creative arts, 66-72, COMMUN, 72-, SR. DIR, UNIV. THEATRE, 65-, assoc. dir, 48-65. Mem, President's Nat. Shakespeare 400th Anniversary Comt, 64; Int. Comt, Shakespeare Birthplace Fund, Inc, 66- Am. Theatre Asn; Speech Commun. Asn. Ibsenian and Shakespearian drama and criticism; oral interpretation of prose, poetry and drama; readers theatre. Publ: Directing Shakespeare's plays, Speech Teacher, 11/56; The social conditions and principles of Hedda Gabler, 10/61 & Ibsen's contrasting clergy, 12/63, Educ. Theatre J. Add: Dept. of Communication, Heavilon Hall, Purdue University, West Lafayette, IN 47907.

KILDAHL, PHILLIP ANDREW, b. Chicago, Ill, June 13, 12. ENGLISH, HISTORY. A.B, Augsburg Col, 35; Luther Theol. Sem, 35-37; A.M, Univ. Minn, 41, Ph.D, 59. Assoc. prof. hist, Augsburg Col, 40-51, head dept, 47-51; assoc. prof, Concordia Col.(St. Paul, Minn), 51-53; asst. prof. Eng, Hastings Col, 56-61; assoc. prof. Eng. & chmn. freshman prog, WARTBURG COL, 61-65, PROF. ENG. & HEAD DEPT, 65- Wartburg Col. res. grant, 65-66; Am. Lutheran Church res. grant, 68-69. U.S.A, 43-46. MLA; Asn. Depts. Eng; NCTE. Latin epigraphy; Roman chronology; life of Dionysius I of Syracuse. Publ: Caius Marius, Twayne, 68; Freedom and authority in Christian education, Christian Educ; A solution to the chronological problem of the year 238 A.D, Historian, 5/62; Quality versus quantity in the teaching of literature, Iowa Eng. Yearbk, 62. Add: Dept. of English, Wartburg College, Waverly, IA 50677.

KILEY, FREDERICK S, b. Fall River, Mass, Aug. 4, 22; m. 46; c. 6. ENGLISH. B.S, R.I. Univ, 49; M.A, Univ. Conn, 51; Rutgers Univ, 57-63. Instr, Univ. Conn, 48-51; Killingly High Sch, Conn, 51-57; asst. prof. ENG, TRENTON STATE COL, 57-67, ASSOC. PROF, 67- Consult, Educ. Testing Serv, Princeton, N.J, 62. U.S.A, 42-46. NCTE. Eighteenth century satire; 19th century American fiction; thematic variations of wanderer image in Western literature. Publ: Co-auth, Literature of the world, McGraw, 63; auth, The public arts, Eng. J, 61-62; Literary art in Boswell's London Journal, Col. Eng, 5/62; Baedeker for Beckett, Eire-Ireland, winter 71. Add: Dept. of English, Trenton State College, Trenton, NJ 08625.

KILEY, FREDERICK THOMAS, b. Waltham, Mass, Jan. 4, 32; m. 54; c. 3. ENGLISH, LINGUISTICS. B.A, Univ. Mass, 53; M.A, Trinity Univ.(Tex), 59; Ph.D.(Eng), Univ. Denver, 65. Organizer adult educ. courses, Dept. Educ, State Mass, 54; U.S. AIR FORCE, 54-, instr. Eng. & chem, U.S. Naval Prep. Sch, 57-61, ENG, U.S. Air Force Acad. Prep. Sch, 61-62, U.S. AIR FORCE ACAD, 62-65, asst. prof, 65-66, assoc. prof, 66-74, PROF, 74- Lectr, Univ. Colo, 64-67. U.S.A.F, 54-, Lt. Col; Bronze Star Medal. Col. Eng. Asn; NCTE; Rocky Mountain Mod. Lang. Asn; MLA. Satire; modern poetry. Publ: Workbook in English grammar and vocabulary, U.S. Air Force Acad. Prep. Sch, 61; co-auth, Standards: handbook of rhetoric and composition, U.S. Air Force Acad, 66, 2nd ed, 67 & A satire reader, Odyssey, 69; ed. & transl, Satire from Aesop to Buchwald, Bobbs, 71; ed, A Catch-22 casebook, Crowell, 73; ed. & contrib, Listen. . .the war (poetry anthology), Johnson, 73; auth, Sir George Etherege: Restoration code hero, E-W. Rev, winter 67-68; A larger reading of Donne's A lecture upon the shadow, CEA Critic, 4/68; contrib, Vols. 3, 4, 5 & 6, New directions in English, Harper, 73; plus one other. Add: Dept. of English & Fine Arts, U.S. Air Force Academy, CO 80840.

KILGORE, ROCHELLE PHILMON, b. Reynolds, Ga, July 25, 87; m. 29. ENGLISH. A.B, Union Col, 20; M.A, Univ. Ga, 22; Prin, Graysville Acad, 15-19; mem. fac. ENG, Union Col, 20-29; prof, ATLANTIC UNION COL, 36-72, EMER. PROF, 72- MLA. Backgrounds of American literature. Add: Dept. of English, Atlantic Union College, South Lancaster, MA 01561.

KILLAM, GORDON DOUGLAS, b. New Westminster, B.C, Aug. 26, 30; m. 59; c. 2. ENGLISH & COMMONWEALTH LITERATURE. B.A, Univ. B.C, 55; Ph.D.(Eng), Univ. London, 64. TV producer, C.B.C, 56-60; lectr. Eng, Fourah Bay Col, Sierra Leone, 63-65; asst. prof, Univ. Alta, 65-66; lectr, Univ. Ibadan, 66-67; sr. lectr, Univ. Lagos, 67-68; assoc. prof, York Univ, 68-70; prof. lit. & head dept, Univ. Dar es Salaam, 70-71; assoc. prof. Eng. & master, Bethune Col, York Univ, 71-73; PROF. ENG. & HEAD DEPT, ACADIA UNIV, 73- MLA; Can. Asn. Univ. Teachers; Asn. Commonwealth Lit. & Lang. Stud. African and Canadian literature. Publ: Africa in English fiction, Ibadan Univ, 68; Novels of Chinua Achebe, 69 & ed, African writers on African writing, 73, Heinemann Educ; ed, Fiction of eastern Africa, Routledge, Kegan Paul; auth, Bruce Ohabrakpaya's art, Black Orpheus, 69; Chinua Achebe's fiction, Sewanee Rev, 71; Novels of Cyprian Ekwensi, In: Introduction to Nigerian writing, 72; plus others. Add: Dept. of English, Acadia University, Wolfville, N.S. B0P 1X0, Can.

KILPATRICK, RACHEL SARGENT HARRIS, Linguistics. See Volume III, Foreign Languages, Linguistics & Philology.

KILROY, JAMES F, b. Chicago, Ill, Sept. 7, 35; m. 61; c. 3. ENGLISH. B.A, DePaul Univ, 57; M.A, Univ. Iowa, 61; Ph.D.(Eng), Univ. Wis, 65. Asst. prof. ENG, VANDERBILT UNIV, 65-70, ASSOC. PROF, 70-, ASSOC. DEAN GRAD. SCH, 73- Nat. Endowment Humanities summer fel, 67; Am. Counc. Learned Soc. stud. fel, 67-68. MLA; Am. Comt. Irish Stud. Victorian literature; modern Irish literature. Publ: Ed, The autobiography of James Clarence Mangan, Dolmen, Dublin, 68; auth, James Clarence Mangan, Bucknell Univ, 70; co-ed, Lost plays of the Irish Renaissance, Proscenium, 70; auth, The playboy riots, Dolmen, 71; Conrad's Succès de curiosité, Eng. Lit. Transition, 5/67; Narrative techniques in The master of Ballantrae, Stud. Scottish Lit, 10/67; The playboy as poet, PMLA, 5/68. Add: Dept. of English, Vanderbilt University, Nashville, TN 37235.

KIM, MYUNG WHAN, b. Seoul, Korea; m. 67; c. 2. COMPARATIVE LITERATURE. B.A, Korea Univ, 60; Dartmouth Col, 60-61; M.A, Wayne State Univ, 63; Ford Found. fel. & Ph.D.(comp. lit), Ind. Univ, 69. Lectr. E.Asian lang. & lit, Ind. Univ, 68-69; ASST. PROF. ENG. & COMP. LIT, UNIV. S.C, 69- MLA; S.Atlantic Mod. Lang. Asn; Asn. Asian Stud. Yeats's drama; Noh drama; Japanese poetry. Publ: The vision of the spiritual world in Yeats's plays and the Noh, Phoenix, spring 70; Dance and rhythm: their meaning in Yeats and the Noh, Mod. Drama, 9/72; Zenchiku's philosophy of the wheels and the Yeatsian parallel, Lit. East & West, 12/72. Add: Dept. of English, University of South Carolina, Columbia, SC 29208.

KIMBALL, ARTHUR GUSTAF, b. Minneapolis, Minn, July 2, 27; m. 48; c. 5. ENGLISH. B.A, Pac. Lutheran Col, 54; B.D, Chicago Lutheran Theol. Sem, 57; NDEA fels, Claremont Grad. Sch, 60 & 63, M.A, 62, Ph.D.(Am. lit), 65. Instr. LIT, Willamette Univ, 63-64; asst. prof, LINFIELD COL, 64-66, ASSOC. PROF, 66-, CHMN. DEPT. ENG, 70- Fulbright-Hays res. grant, 67-68; vis. prof, Women's Christian Col, Tokyo & Kanto Gakuin Univ, Yokohama, 68-69. U.S.N, 45-46, Res, 61-64, Lt. MLA; Johnson Soc. Northwest; Asn. Asian Stud. Early American fiction; post-World War II Japanese fiction; contemporary American fiction. Publ: Rational fictions: a study of Charles Brockden Brown, Linfield Res. Inst, 68; Crisis in identity and contemporary Japanese novels, Charles E. Tuttle, 73; Sears Roebuck and regional terms, Am. Speech, 8/63; Benjamin Rush, prescribing for the nation, Pa. Med, 67; Brockden Brown's dramatic irony, Stud. in Romanticism, 8/67. Add: Dept. of English, Linfield College, McMinnville, OR 97128.

KIMBALL, CLARK DOUGLAS, b. Canton, Ohio, Aug. 12, 44; m. 66. COMMUNICATION THEORY. B.A, Butler Univ, 66; Ph.D.(pub. address, Am. stud), Ind. Univ, Bloomington, 71. ASSOC. PROF. COMMUN. ARTS & COORD. SPEECH COMMUN, MADISON COL, 70- Speech Commun. Asn; Am. Civil Liberties Union; South. States Speech Commun. Asn. History of free speech in America; due process and alien internment during World War I. Publ: Co-auth, Elements of tournament debate, Walch, 74 & Negative approach to the criteria case, In: Modern debate case strategies, Nat. Textbk, 70; auth, Patriots vs. dissenters: the rhetoric of intimidation in Indiana during the First World War, Free Speech Yearbk, 12/72; The internment of enemy aliens in Indiana during the First World War, Madison Col. Stud. & Res, 3/72. Add: Dept. of Communication Arts, Madison College, Harrisonburg, VA 22801.

KIMBALL, STANLEY BUCHHOLZ, Modern History. See Volume I, History.

KIMBROUGH, JOE ARTHUR, b. Stuttgart, Ark, Nov. 18, 31; m. 54; c. 2. ENGLISH. A.B, Univ. Mich, 53, A.M, 58; Ph.D.(Eng), Univ. Ill, 65. Instr. ENG, Lincoln Jr. Col, Ill, 58-60; asst, Univ. Ill, 60-64; instr, Univ. Houston, 64-65, ASST. PROF, 65-71; SAM HOUSTON STATE UNIV, 71- U.S.N, 53-57. MLA. Seventeenth-century English literature. Add: Dept. of English, Sam Houston State University, Huntsville, TX 77340.

KIMBROUGH, ROBERT ALEXANDER, III, b. Philadelphia, Pa, June 26, 29; m. 53; c. 3. ENGLISH LITERATURE. B.A, Williams Col.(Mass), 51; M.A, Stanford Univ, 55; Ph.D, Harvard, 59. Instr. ENG, UNIV. WIS-MADISON, 59-60, asst. prof, 60-64, assoc. prof, 64-68, PROF, 68-, CHMN. DEPT. INTEGRATED LIB. STUD, 70- Fel, Inst. Res. in Humanities, 65-66. U.S.M.C, 51-54, Res, 48-, Col. MLA; Shakespeare Asn. Am; Renaissance Soc. Am. Elizabethan literature; drama, prose and poetry. Publ: Shakespeare's Troilus and Cressida and its setting, Harvard, 64; ed, Critical edition of Conrad's Heart of darkness, 63 & Henry James, The turn of the screw, 66, Norton; auth, Selected works of Sir Philip Sidney, Holt, 69; Sir Philip Sidney, Twayne, 71; Discipline the saving grace: Winter's critical position, Renascence, winter 63; 1 Tamburlaine: a speaking picture in a tragic glass, Renaissance Drama, 64; Calm between crises; pattern and direction in Ruskin's Mature thought, In: Victorian literature; recent revaluations, N.Y. Univ, 68; plus others. Add: Dept. of Integrated Liberal Studies, University of Wisconsin-Madison, 228 N. Charter St, Madison, WI 53706.

KIMMEY, JOHN LANSING, b. Albany, N.Y, Nov. 17, 22; m. 43; c. 4. ENGLISH. A.B, Dartmouth Col, 46; M.A, Columbia Univ, 47, Ph.D.(Eng), 55. Instr, ENG, Univ. Va, 48-52; Va. Mil. Inst, 52-56; asst. prof, UNIV. S.C, 56-61, assoc. prof, 61-67, PROF, 67- Dir, NDEA Summer Inst, 66; dir, EPDA Prog. Eng, 70-74. U.S.A, Off. Strategic Serv, 43-45, Sgt. MLA; S.Atlantic Mod. Lang. Asn. Seventeenth century literature; the American novel; stylistics. Publ: Co-auth, Modes of literature, C.E. Merrill, 69; auth, Brief guide to freshman writing, Allyn & Bacon, 73; The tragic muse and its forerunners, Am. Lit, 1/70; Robert Herrick's persona, Stud. Philol, 4/70; Order and form in Herrick's Hesperides, JEGP, 4/71; plus others. Add: Dept. of English, University of South Carolina, Columbia, SC 29208.

KIMPEL, BEN (DREW), b. Ft. Smith, Ark, Nov. 6, 15. ENGLISH. A.B, Harvard, 37, M.A, 39; Ph.D.(Eng), Univ. N.C, 42. Asst. prof. ENG, UNIV. ARK, FAYETTEVILLE, 52-55, from assoc. prof. to PROF, 55- U.S.A, 42-46. MLA. Medieval literature; modern novel; 18th century literature. Publ: John Gould Fletcher in retrospect; co-transl, Goethe's Tasso; co-auth, The informal reader. Add: Dept. of English, University of Arkansas, Fayetteville, AR 72701.

KINAHAN, FRANCIS XAVIER, b. Bayonne, N.J, July 30, 44; m. 68; c. 1. MODERN LITERATURE & DRAMA. B.A, Fordham Univ, 66; M.A, Harvard, 69, Ph.D.(Eng), 74. Instr. ENG, UNIV. CHICAGO, 72-73, ASST. PROF, 73- Anglo-Irish literature; modern drama; Romantic poetry. Publ: F. Scott Fitzgerald's Tender is the night, In: American dreams, American nightmares, Univ. South. Ill, 70; The melancholy of anatomy: voice and theme in Swift's A tale of a tub, J. Eng. & Ger. Philol, 4/70. Add: 5706 S. Drexel Ave, Chicago, IL 60637.

KINCAID, GERALD L, b. Palestine, Ill, Mar. 1, 14; m. 44; c. 3. LANGUAGE ARTS, SOCIAL SCIENCE. B.Ed, East. Ill. State Teachers Col, 39; M.A, Univ. Ill, 42; Ed.D.(commun), Mich. State Univ, 53. Teacher, Pekin Community High Sch, 45-46; instr. Eng, Mich. State Univ, 46-50, educ. res, bd. exam, 50-53; dir. commun. skills, Hillsdale Col, 53-57; asst. prof, Moorhead State Col, 57-59; CONSULT. LANG. ARTS, MINN. STATE DEPT. EDUC, 59- C.Eng, U.S.A, 41-45, M/Sgt. NCTE; Conf. Eng. Educ; Asn. State Eng. & Reading Supvr; NEA; Am. Educ. Res. Asn; Asn. Supv. & Curriculum Develop; Int. Soc. Gen. Semantics; AAUP. Language in interpersonal communication; creativity; learning. Publ: A title I short course for reading teachers, Reading Teacher, 1/67; Innovations in language arts, Curriculum Leadership, 10/68; Curriculum for the 70's: cooperation is the name of the game, Eng. J, 5/72; plus one other. Add: Elementary & secondary Section, Div. of Instruction, Minnesota State Department of Education, Capitol Square Bldg, 550 Cedar, St. Paul, MN 55101.

KINCAID, JAMES RUSSELL, b. East Liverpool, Ohio, Aug. 31, 37; m. 62; c. 2. ENGLISH LITERATURE. B.S, Case Inst. Technol, 59; M.A, West. Reserve Univ, 62, Ph.D.(Eng), 65. Proj. engineer, Union Carbide Corp, 59-61; asst. prof. ENG, OHIO STATE UNIV, 65-69, assoc. prof, 69-71, PROF, 71- Nat. Endowment for Humanities fel, 71, conductor summer sem, 73; Guggenheim fel, 73-74. MLA (mem. publ. adv. comt, 73-76); Dickens Fel; Tennyson Soc. Anthony Trollope's novels; Tennyson; generic criticism. Publ: Dickens and the rhetoric of laughter, Clarendon, 71; Barchester Towers and the nature of conservative comedy, ELH, 70; Tennyson's Gareth and Lynette, Tex. Stud. Lit. & Lang, 72; Alice's invasion of Wonderland, PMLA, 73. Add: Dept. of English, Ohio State University, 164 W. 17th Ave, Columbus, OH 43210.

KINCHELOE, HENDERSON GRADY, b. Crewe, Va, Sept. 20, 09; m. 39; c. 1. AMERICAN LITERATURE. A.B, Univ. Richmond, 31; A.M, Harvard, 34; Ph.D, Duke Univ, 48. Instr. Eng. & French, Fork Union Mil. Acad, Va, 31-32; E.Carolina Training Sch, N.C, 33-34; teacher, High Sch, N.C, 34-35; instr. Eng, Univ. Richmond, 35-37; asst. prof, Furman Univ, 37-38; instr, N.C. State Univ, 39-42, asst. prof, 42-49, assoc. prof, 49-61, prof, 61-74; RETIRED. S.Atlantic Mod. Lang. Asn. Plot sketches; character sketches; essay reviews. Add: 210 Furches, Raleigh, NC 27607.

KINDER, MARSHA, b. Los Angeles, Calif, Feb. 20, 40; m. 59. ENGLISH, CINEMA. A.B, Univ. Calif, Los Angeles, 61, M.A, 63, Clark fel, 64-65, Ph.D.(Eng), 67. Teaching asst. Eng, Univ. Calif, Los Angeles, 62-64; instr, OCCIDENTAL COL, 65-67, asst. prof. Eng. & cinema, 67-71, ASSOC. PROF. ENG. LIT. & CINEMA, 71- Fac. Achievement Award, Occidental Col, 66; contrib. ed, Women & Film, 73- MLA. Eighteenth century English literature; cinema. Publ: Co-auth, Close-up: a critical perspective on film, Harcourt, 72; contrib, Focus on Blow-up, Prentice-Hall, 71; auth, The improved author's farce: an analysis of the 1734 revisions, Costerus, 6/72; co-auth, Bertolucci & the dance of danger: Last tango in Paris, Sight & Sound, fall 73; plus others. Add: Dept. of English, Occidental College, Los Angeles, CA 90041.

KINDRICK, ROBERT LeROY, b. Kansas City, Mo, Aug. 17, 42; m. 65. MEDIEVAL LITERATURE, LINGUISTICS. B.A, Park Col, 64; Coe fel, Univ. Wyo, 64; M.A, Univ. Mo-Kansas City, 67; univ. fel. & Ph.D.(Eng), Univ. Tex, Austin, 71. Asst. librn, Kansas City Col. Surg, 64-65; instr. ENG, CENT. MO. STATE UNIV, 67-69, asst. prof, 69-73, ASSOC. PROF. & DIR. FRESHMAN ENG, 73- Consult, NDEA Inst. Ling, 68; regional correspondent, Medieval & Renaissance Newslett, 73- MLA; Early Eng. Text Soc; Mediaeval Acad. Am; Soc. Rencesvals; Int. Arthurian Soc. Medieval romances and satires; the poetry of Robert Henryson; computer-assisted concordances. Publ: Contrib, Edward Dahlberg, Beacham, 68; auth, The beast of great renown, Satire Newslett, spring 73; The literature of medieval England, Medieval & Renaissance Newslett, 12/73. Add: Dept. of English, Central Missouri State University, Warrensburg, MO 64093.

KING, ANDREW ARTHUR, b. Glenview, Ill, Mar. 17, 37; m. 61; c. 3. RHETORIC, PUBLIC ADDRESS. Ph.D, Univ. Minn, 68. Instr. SPEECH, Univ. Minn, 63-68; ASST. PROF, State Univ. N.Y. Col. Buffalo, 68-69; UNIV. ARIZ, 69- U.S.A, 60-62, Cpl. Speech Commun. Asn; Rhetoric Soc. Am. Rhetorical criticism. Publ: Black Salt (poems), Cornish Soc, 64; The rhetorical legacy of the Black Church, Cent. States Speech J, fall 71; Nixon, Agnew, and the silent majority, West. Speech, fall 71. Add: Dept. of Speech Communication, University of Arizona, Tucson, AZ 85721.

KING, ARTHUR HENRY, b. Gosport, Eng, Feb. 20, 10; m. 66. ENGLISH LITERATURE. B.A, Cambridge, 31; Ph.D.(Eng), Univ. Lund, 41. Lectr. Eng, Univ. Lund, 31-41, assoc. prof, 41-43; mem, Brit. Counc, 43-71; PROF. ENG, BRIGHAM YOUNG UNIV, 71- Assoc. prof. Eng, Univ. Stockholm, 43-; consult, Ford Found, 68. Comdr, Order Brit. Empire, 65. Hon. fel, Inst. Ling, Eng; hon. fel, Col. Preceptors, Eng; Asn. Teachers Eng. as For. lang; Teachers Eng. to Speakers Other Lang; Am. Counc. Teaching For. Lang. English stylistics, 1597-1612; socio-political approach to the teaching of English as a second or foreign language. Publ: The language of satirized characters in Poetaster, Gleerups, Lund, 41; Notes on Coriolanus, 37 & 38 & Some notes on Andrew Marvell's Garden, 38, Eng. Stud; Some notes on ambiguity in Henry IV Part I, Stud. Neophilol, 41. Add: 771 Sunny Lane, Orem, UT 84057.

KING, CARLYLE ALBERT, b. Cooksville, Ont, Nov. 25, 07; m. 31; c. 1. ENGLISH. B.A, Univ. Sask, 26; M.A, Univ. Toronto, 27, Ph.D, 31; Univ. London, 27-28. Teaching fel. ENG, Univ. Toronto, 28-29; from instr. to assoc. prof, UNIV. SASK, 29-49, prof. & head dept, 50-64, BATEMAN PROF, 64-, V.PRIN, 70-, dir. summer sessions, 59-71, dean acad. serv, 64-70. Humanities Asn. Can; Can. Libr. Asn. American and Canadian literature. Publ: Saskatchewan harvest, 55, First fifty, 59 & A book of Canadian poems, 63, McClelland & Stewart, Toronto; Saskatchewan: the making of a university, Univ. Toronto, 59; Extending the boundaries, Univ. Sask, 67. Add: Administration Bldg, University of Saskatchewan, Saskatoon, Sask. S7N 0W0, Can.

KING, ELEANOR CAMPBELL, b. Middletown, Pa, Feb. 8, 06. DANCE, DRAMA. Instr. dance, Carleton Col, 42-43; head dept. dance, Cornish Sch, Seattle, Wash, 43-44; private studio, Seattle, 44-52; asst. prof. speech & dramatic art, UNIV. ARK, 52-60, assoc. prof, 60-71, dir. theatre imagination, 59-71, EMER. PROF, 71- Study class. dance & drama, Japan, 58, 60-61; dir. dance workshop, Int. Inst. Arts, Tokyo, 60; Fulbright res. scholar, Japan, 67; lectr-recital master classes, U.S. Inform. Serv, fifteen Japanese cities; dir. workshop, China Dance Arts Inst, Taipei, summer 67; vis. artist, Well Tempered Dancer Workshop, Les Rencontres Int. Danse Contemporaine, Paris, 73; lectr, Univ. Ariz, Univ. of Maine, Wilmington Col, Earlham Col, Lindenwood Col. & Mus. Int. Folk Art, New Mexico. Comt. Res. Dance; Am. Dance Guild. Publ: Influence of Doris Humphrey, Focus on Dance V, Am. Asn. Health, Phys. Educ. & Recreation J, spring 69; Sumiyoshi rice planting festival, CORD News, 71; Kagura: the search, Dance Res. Monogr, Comt. Res. Dance, 71-72. Add: 865 Don Diego, Santa Fe, NM 87501.

KING, GRACE HAMILTON, b. Philadelphia, Pa, July 27, 03; m. 29; c. 2. ENGLISH. A.B, Barnard Col, Columbia Univ, 25; A.M, N.Y. Univ, 40, Ph.D, 43. Teacher Eng, Bryant High Sch, New York, N.Y. 25-26, 28-29; Newtown High Sch, 27; Scarsdale High Sch, 27-28, dir. guid, Newburgh Jr. High Sch, 42-44; prof. Eng, Westmont Col, 44-49; instr. Eng. & counr, Glendale Col, 49-69, chmn. div. lang. arts, 61-69; dean women, Los Angeles Baptist Col, 70-71; RETIRED. Lectr. Bible, Eteri Bible Classes & Conf, 66- NCTE. Publ: Anthology of Christian literature, 47. Add: 22020 Placerita Canyon Rd, Newhall, CA 91321.

KING, JAMES, b. Springfield, Mass, June 14, 42; Can. citizen; m. 70. ENGLISH LITERATURE. B.A, Univ. Toronto, 67; Woodrow Wilson fel, Princeton, 67-68, M.A, 69, Can. Counc. fel, 69-70, Ph.D.(Eng), 70. ASST. PROF. ENG, McMASTER UNIV, 71- Am. Philos. Soc. fel, 71; Can. Counc. res. fel, 72- Am. Soc. 18th Century Stud. Cowper's correspondence; the sister arts, especially Blake; 18th century English poetry. Publ: In the lost boyhood of Judas: Graham Greene's early novels of hell, Dalhousie Rev, summer 69; The Meredith family, Thomas Taylor, and William Blake, Stud. Romanticism, spring 72; Pope's Windsor-Forest, 65-72, Explicator, 5/73. Add: Dept. of English, McMaster University, Hamilton, Ont. L8S 4L9, Can.

KING, JAMES BOYD, b. Braddock, Pa, Sept. 14, 40. ENGLISH. B.A, Adrian Col, 62; fel. & M.A, Univ. Pittsburgh, 63; Ph.D, Univ. Mich, 70. Instr. ENG. & chmn. dept, Addison High Sch, 63-65; asst. prof, HILLSDALE COL, 65-67, assoc. prof. & chmn. dept, 67-72, EZRA L. KOON PROF. ENG. & CHMN. DIV. HUMANITIES, 72- Part-time instr. Eng, Adrian Col, 63-65.

MLA; NCTE. Academic fiction; Shakespeare; Victorian literature. Add: Dept. of English, Hillsdale College, Hillsdale, MI 49242.

KING, JAMES KIMBALL, b. Trenton, N.J, Feb. 5, 34; m. 55; c. 3. ENGLISH. B.A, Johns Hopkins Univ, 56; M.A, Wesleyan Univ, 60; Ph.D.(Eng), Univ. Wis, 64. Asst. prof. ENG, UNIV. N.C, CHAPEL HILL, 64-68, ASSOC. PROF, 68- Publ: Satirical portraits by Thomas Nelson Page, Miss. Quart, spring 65; Regionalism in the three Souths, Proc. Wis. Acad, 65; Theory and practice in the plays of Henry James, Mod. Drama, 67. Add: Dept. of English, University of North Carolina, Chapel Hill, SC 27514.

KING, JOHN NORMAN, b. Feb. 2, 45; U.S. citizen. ENGLISH LITERATURE. B.A, Randolph-Macon Col, 65; M.A, Univ. Chicago, 66, Ph.D.(Eng), 73. Asst. lectr. ENG, Ahmadu Bello Univ, 67-68, lectr, 68-69; instr, BATES COL, 71-73, ASST. PROF, 73- MLA. English poetry of the Middle Ages, Renaissance and Enlightenment; 16th and 17th century English literature, history and culture. Publ: Contrib, Westminster dictionary of church history, Westminster, 71. Add: Dept. of English, Bates College, Lewiston, ME 04240.

KING, LAUREN ALFRED, b. Avilla, Ind, Apr. 17, 04. ENGLISH. A.B, Asbury Col, 27; Ph.D, Ohio State Univ, 30. Instr. Eng, Asbury Col, 27-28, prof. & chmn dept, 32-35; asst, Ohio State Univ, 30; prof. & head dept, Houghton Col, 30-31; Peru State Teachers Col, Nebr, 31-32; assoc. prof, Wheaton Col.(Ill), 35-42, prof, 42-46; Houghton Col, 46-50, dean, 47-50; prof. & chmn dept, Muskingum Col, 50-66; prof. Eng, Malone Col, 66-74, v.pres. acad. develop, 66-69; RETIRED. Consult, Salem Col.(W.Va), 67-68. NCTE; Conf. Col. Compos. & Commun; MLA. Verse technique of Alfred Lord Tennyson; building good sentences. Add: Cherry Lane, New Concord, OH 43762.

KING, MONTGOMERY WORDSWORTH, b. Yonkers, N.Y, Dec. 28, 09; m. 49; c. 2. ENGLISH. A.B, Howard Univ, 34, fel, 35-38, A.M, 37; Univ. Pittsburgh, 42; La. State Univ, 62-64. Instr. Eng, Va. Theol. Sem. & Col, 34-35; consult, curriculum construction, Wash, D.C, 35-38; instr. Eng. & hist, Huntington High Sch, 38-41; asst. prof. Eng, speech & drama, Morgan State Col, 43-45; PROF. ENG, SOUTH. UNIV, BATON ROUGE, 46-, HEAD DEPT, 51-54, 73- Consult, core curriculum, Va, 38-41; Avery Award, Univ. Pittsburgh, 41-43; ed, South. Univ. Bull, 54- CLA; MLA. American literature; the Manichaean impulse in the American Gothic novel. Publ: Born nude and modern, Vantage, 74. Add: Dept. of English, Southern University, Baton Rouge, LA 70813.

KING, RALPH F. B, b. Vancouver, B.C, July 16, 21; m. 43; c. 2. ENGLISH. B.A, Univ. B.C, 48; M.A, Univ. Toronto, 52, Ph.D, 60. Lectr. Eng, Univ. B.C, 48-49; Royal Mil. Col, 55-58; prof, Can. Serv. Col, Royal Roads, 58-63; PROF. ENG, BRANDON UNIV, 63-, assoc. dean arts, 63-65, dean, 65-72. Can. consult, Crowell-Colliers Young People's Encycl, 62- R.C.A.F, 42-46, Flying Off. Humanities Asn. Can; Asn. Can. Univ. Teachers Eng. Conception of genius in English thought. Add: Dept. of English, Brandon University, Brandon, Man. R7A 6A9, Can.

KING, ROBERT GENE, b. Caneyville, Ky, Oct. 4, 29. COMMUNICATION, RHETORIC. A.B, Georgetown Col, 51; M.A, Columbia Univ, 58, Ph.D. (speech), 64. Lectr. speech, Hunter Col, 58; instr, Columbia Univ, 58-62; Queens Col.(N.Y), 62-65; prof, East. Ky. Univ, 65-69; ASSOC. PROF. COMMUN. ARTS, BRONX COMMUNITY COL, 69- Mem, Comt. Int. Discussion & Debate, 67-70. South. Speech Asn; Am. Forensic Asn; East. Commun. Asn; Speech Commun. Asn. American public address; argumentation; group and interpersonal communication. Publ: Co-auth, Improving articulation and voice, Macmillan, 66; Forms of public address, Bobbs, 69. Add: Dept. of Communication Arts & Sciences, Bronx Community College, Bronx, NY 10468.

KING, ROBERT WENDELL, b. Denver, Colo, Dec. 7, 37; m. 59; c. 3. ENGLISH, CREATIVE WRITING. B.A, Univ. Iowa, 59, Ph.D.(Eng), 65; M.A, Colo. State Univ, 61. Asst. prof. Eng, Univ. Alaska, 65-68; UNIV. N.DAK, 68-72, ASSOC. PROF. CREATIVE WRITING, 72- Consult, Educ. Assoc, Inc, 67. Writing of poetry; teaching of writing; creative writing in elementary education. Add: Center for Teaching & Learning, University of North Dakota, Grand Forks, ND 58201.

KING, ROMA ALVAH, JR, b. Sanger, Tex, Dec. 30, 14; m. 42; c. 3. ENGLISH & COMPARATIVE LITERATURE. A.B, Baylor Univ, 36; A.M, Univ. Mich, 49, Ph.D.(Eng. drama), 53. Assoc. prof, ENG, Baylor Univ, 45-53; instr. Univ. Mich, 53-54; prof, Univ. Kansas City, 54-63, chmn. dept, 56-63; PROF, OHIO UNIV, 63- Vis. Prof, Univ. Colo, summer 67. Sig.C, U.S.A, 39-45, Maj. MLA. The works of Robert Browning; the nineteenth century; the development of the modern period. Publ: Robert Browning's finances, Baylor Univ, 47; The bow and the lyre: the art of Robert Browning, Univ. Mich, 57; The focusing artifice: the poetry of Robert Browning, 68 & gen. ed, The complete works of Robert Browning, 13 vols, Vol. I, 68, Ohio Univ; The Janus symbol in As I lay dying, Univ. Kansas City Rev, summer 55; Time and structure in the early novels of Robert Penn Warren, S.Atlantic Quart, autumn 57; Browning: Mage and Maker—a study in poetic purpose and method, Victorian Newsletter, fall 61. Add: Dept. of English, Ohio University, Athens, OH 45701.

KING, STEPHEN WILLIAM, b. San Francisco, Calif, Jan. 31, 47; m. 67. COMMUNICATION. B.A, Univ. Wash, 68, M.A, 64; Ph.D.(commun), Univ. South. Calif, 71. ASST. PROF. SPEECH, SAN DIEGO STATE UNIV, 71- Speech Commun. Asn; West. Speech Commun. Asn. Attitude change; group dynamics; intercultural communication. Publ: Social influence and communication, Addison-Wesley, (in press); Source appropriateness: a pedagogic model, Speech Teacher, 9/72; Theory testing: an analysis and extension, West. Speech, winter 73. Add: Dept. of Speech Communication, San Diego State University, San Diego, CA 92115.

KING, TERRANCE JOSEPH, b. Syracuse, N.Y, Mar. 17, 41. AMERICAN LITERATURE. A.B, LeMoyne Col, 64; M.A, Wayne State Univ, 67; Ph.D.(Eng), Univ. Mich, Ann Arbor, 70. ASST. PROF. ENG, WAYNE STATE UNIV, 70- MLA; Midwest Mod. Lang. Asn. American literature; lyric poetry; philosophy of language. Add: Dept. of English, State Hall, Wayne State University, Detroit, MI 48202.

KING, THOMAS JAMES, b. Philadelphia, Pa, July 25, 25; m. 50; c. 5. ENGLISH, DRAMA. A.B, Princeton Univ, 48; M.A, Columbia Univ, 58, Ph.D. (Eng), 63. Instr. ENG, Columbia Col, 61-65; asst. prof, Dartmouth Col, 65-67; vis. asst. prof, grad. sch, Columbia Univ, 67-68; ASST. PROF, CITY COL. NEW YORK, 68- Columbia Univ. Counc. Res. Humanities res. grant, summer 65. U.S.A.F, 43-45, 51, 1st Lt. MLA; Bibliog. Soc. Univ. Va; Shakespeare Asn. Am. Bibliography; theatrical history; stage conditions. Publ: Shakespearean staging 1599-1642, Harvard Univ, 71; Shirley's Coronation and Love will find out the way: erroneous title-pages, Stud. Bibliog, 65; Staging of plays at the Phoenix In Drury Lane, 1617-1642, Theatre Notebk, 65; The stage in the time of Shakespeare: a survey of major scholarship, Renaissance Drama, 71. Add: Dept. of English, City College of New York, New York, NY 10031.

KING, THOMAS ROY, b. Selma, Ala, June 11, 34; m. 58. SPEECH, COMMUNICATIONS. A.B, Howard Col, 56; M.A, Fla. State Univ, 58; Ph.D. (speech), La. State Univ, 64. Instr. SPEECH, Memphis State Univ, 58-60; FLA. STATE UNIV, 63-65, asst. prof, 65-71, ASSOC. PROF, 71- Instr. Memphis Div, Univ. Tenn, 59-60; asst. dir, NDEA Speech Inst, Fla. State Univ, summer 66, instr. grant, summer 68. South. Speech Asn.(assoc. ed, South. Speech J, 66-69); Speech Asn. Am; Nat. Soc. Stud. Commun. Effect of source credibility on recall; use of programmed instruction in speech; visible symptoms of stage fright. Publ: Co-auth, A factor analysis of visible symptoms of stage fright, Speech Monogr, 11/61; auth, An experimental study of the effect of ethos upon the immediate and delayed recall of information, Cent. States Speech J, 2/66; Programmed textbooks in communications, J. Commun, 3/67. Add: Dept. of Speech, Florida State University, Tallahassee, FL 32306.

KING, WALTER NEIL, b. Corvallis, Mont, May 14, 19; m. 59; c. 3. ENGLISH. B.A, Univ. Mont, 46; M.A, 48; Jr. Sterling fel. & Ph.D, Yale, 52. Instr. ENG, Yale, 51-55; asst. prof, UNIV. MONT, 55-58, assoc. prof, 58-64, PROF, 64- MLA. Publ: Ed, Twentieth century interpretations of Twelfth night, Prentice-Hall, 68; The rhetoric of Candida, Mod. Drama, 9/59; Much ado about something, Shakespeare Quart, summer 64; Shakespeare and Paramenides: the metaphysics of Twelfth night, Stud. Eng. Lit, spring 68. Add: Dept. of English, University of Montana, Missoula, MT 59801.

KING, WILLIAM W, b. Los Angeles, Calif, July 11, 28; m. 52; c. 4. ENGLISH, COMPARATIVE LITERATURE. A.B, Oberlin Col, 52; M.A, Univ. Redlands, 63, Ph.D.(comp. lit), 65; NDEA fel, Univ. Redlands & Claremont Grad. Sch, 63. Instr. ENG, Univ. Vt, 64-66; asst. prof, MIAMI UNIV, 66-72, ASSOC. PROF, 72- U.S.N, 46-48. MLA; Am. Soc. Aesthet. Comparative literature; 19th century; modern poetry; modern novel. Publ: Baudelaire and Mallarmé: metaphysics or aesthetics?, J. Aesthet, fall 67. Add: Dept. of English, Miami University, Oxford, OH 45056.

KINGHORN, NORTON DEAN, b. Beatrice, Nebr, Mar. 8, 33; m. 53; c. 3. AMERICAN LITERATURE, RHETORIC. A.B, Doane Col, 56; M.A, Univ. Nebr, Lincoln, 62, Ph.D.(Eng), 70. Instr. ENG, Univ. Nebr, Lincoln, 62-70, asst. prof, UNIV. N.DAK, 70-72, ASSOC. PROF. & DIR. FRESHMAN ENG, 72- U.S.A, 53-55, Cpl. MLA; NCTE; Conf. Col. Compos. & Commun. Nineteenth century American literature; the novel; rhetoric. Publ: E.W. Kemble's misplaced modifier: a note on the illustrations for Huckleberry Finn, Mark Twain J, summer 73. Add: Dept. of English, University of North Dakota, University Station, Grand Forks, ND 58201.

KINLOCH, A. MURRAY, b. Greenock, Scotland, Apr. 18, 23; m. 50. ENGLISH. M.A, Univ. St. Andrews, 44; M.A, 50, Ph.D.(Eng), 56. Asst. ENG, Univ. Hull, 52-54; Univ. Col. Wales, 54-55, lectr, 55-59; assoc. prof, UNIV. N.B, FREDERICTON, 59-72, PROF, 72- Assoc. ed, Am. Speech, 71- Brit. Army, 43-47, Capt. Asn. Can. Univ. Teachers Eng; Am. Dialect Soc; Am. Name Soc; Can. Ling. Asn; Ling. Soc. Am; MLA. Anglo-Saxon; dialects of English in New Brunswick; Canadian English. Publ: The Anglo Saxon period, Our Lit. Heritage, 66; Survey of Canadian English: possible evidence for pronunciation, 71 & Survey of Canadian English: a first look at New Brunswick results, 72-73, Eng. Quart; plus others. Add: Dept. of English, University of New Brunswick, Fredericton, N.B. E3B 5A3, Can.

KINNAIRD, JOHN WILLIAM, b. Nelsonville, N.Y, Dec. 5, 24; m. 60; c. 2. ENGLISH. B.A, Univ. Calif, Berkeley, 44; M.A, Columbia Univ, 49, Ph.D. (Eng. lit), 59; Fulbright fel, Oxford, 53-55. Instr. ENG, Bucknell Univ, 49-51; Rutgers Univ, 56; lectr, City Col. New York, 58-59; asst. prof, Vassar Col, 59-65; ASSOC. PROF, UNIV. MD, COLLEGE PARK, 65- Lectr, Hunter Col, 56-, mem. Ford Found. Sem. Col. Teaching, 57; instr, Adelphi Col, 57-58; Am. Counc. Learned Soc. grant-in-aid, 65. Off. Strategic Serv, U.S.A, 43-46. MLA; Keats-Shelley Asn. Am. Nineteenth century English literature, especially William Hazlitt; American literature; English curriculum. Publ: Leaves of grass and the American paradox, Partisan Rev, summer 58 & reprint in Whitman, 20th Century Views Series, Prentice-Hall, 62; Hazlitt as poet, Stud. Romanticism, winter 73; What's happening to the English curriculum, Col. Eng, 3/73; plus others. Add: 4612 Beechwood Rd, College Park, MD 20740.

KINNAMON, KENETH, b. Dallas, Tex, Dec. 4, 32; m. 53; c. 3. AMERICAN LITERATURE. B.A, Univ. Tex, 53; A.M, Harvard, 54, Ph.D.(Eng), 66. Instr. ENG, Boston Conserv. Music, 56; Tex. Technol. Col, 56-62; UNIV. ILL, URBANA-CHAMPAIGN, 65-66, asst. prof, 66-70, assoc. prof, 70-73, PROF, 73-, fac. summer fel, 68, assoc, Ctr. Advan. Stud, 74. Mem, comt. bibliog, Am. Lit. Group, MLA, 59-60, 67-; Nat. Endowment for Humanities summer stipend, 69. Col. Lang. Asn; Am. Stud. Asn; MLA. Afro-American literature; modern fiction; Richard Wright. Publ: The emergence of Richard Wright: a study in literature and society, Univ. Ill, 72; co-ed, Black writers of America: a comprehensive anthology, Macmillan, 72; ed, James Baldwin: a collection of critical essays, Prentice-Hall, 74; auth, Hemingway, the Corrida, and Spain, Tex. Stud. Lit. & Lang, summer 59; The man who created Simple, Nation, 12/4/67; Native son: the personal, social and political background, Phylon, 69. Add: Dept. of English, University of Illinois, Urbana-Champaign, Urbana, IL 61801.

KINNEAVY, GERALD B, b. Boise, Idaho, Aug. 18, 38; m. 61; c. 5. ENGLISH. B.A, Univ. San Francisco, 60; M.A, Univ. Notre Dame, 61; Ph.D.(Eng), Pa.

State Univ, 67. Instr. ENG, Univ. Dayton, 61-64; Pa. State Univ, 66-67; asst. prof, UNIV. COLO, BOULDER, 67-72, ASSOC. PROF, 72-, asst. dean arts & sci, 68-69. Fulbright lectr, Finland, 71-72. MLA. Chaucer; Middle English literature; 20th century poetry. Publ: Fortune, providence and the owl, Stud. Philol, 67; The poet in The Palice of Honour, Chaucer Rev, 69; An analytical approach to literature in the late Middle Ages, Neuphilol. Mitteilungen, 74; plus others. Add: Dept. of English, University of Colorado, Boulder, CO 80302.

KINNEAVY, JAMES LOUIS, b. Denver, Colo, June 26, 20; m. 61; c. 2. ENGLISH, EDUCATION. B.A, Col. Santa Fe, 42; M.A, Cath. Univ. Am, 51, Ph.D.(Eng), 56. Asst. Eng, De La Salle Col, 49-53; teacher high sch, La, 53-55; chmn. dept. Eng, Col. Santa Fe, 55-58; asst. prof, West. State Col, 58-63; assoc. prof. eng. & educ, UNIV. TEXAS, AUSTIN, 63-71, PROF. ENG. & CURRICULUM & INSTR, 71- Consult, State Dept. Educ, N.Mex, 57-58, Colo, 61-63, Southwest. Region Col. Conf. Compos. & Commun, 66, 73. NCTE; Conf. Col. Compos. & Commun. Literary theory; rhetorical history and theory; teaching composition. Publ: A study of three contemporary theories of the Lyric, Cath. Univ. Am, 56; A program for high school English, St. Paul's Col, 57; A theory of discourse, Prentice-Hall; Objective tests and the English teacher, Tex. J. Sec. Educ. XIX, 66; The functions of language, In: Foreign language teaching: an anthology, Macmillan, 67. Add: Dept. of English, University of Texas at Austin, Austin, TX 78712.

KINNEY, ARTHUR FREDERICK, JR, b. Cortland, N.Y, Sept. 5, 33. ENGLISH LANGUAGE & LITERATURE. A.B, Syracuse Univ, 55; M.S, Columbia Univ, 56; Rackham fel. & scholar, Univ. Mich, 60-61, Ph.D, 63; scholar, Bread Loaf Sch, 62. Teaching fel, Univ. Mich, 58-63; instr. ENG, Yale, 63-66; asst. prof, UNIV. MASS, AMHERST, 66-68, assoc. prof, 68-74, PROF, 74- Sr. lectr. Eng, Hotchkiss Sch, 65-66; lectr. fiction writing, Chatauqua Writers Conf, 68; ed, Eng. Lit. Renaissance, 68-; affil. prof. Eng, Clark Univ, 72-; chmn. conf. eds. learned jour, MLA, 71-73; Huntington Libr. fel, 73; fel, Medieval & Renaissance Inst, Univ. Calif, Los Angeles, 73-74; Folger Shakespeare Libr. sr. fel, 74. Hopwood Major Award in Essay, Univ. Mich, 61. Chaplain C, U.S.A, 56-58. MLA; NCTE; Am. Stud. Asn; Renaissance Soc. Am; Northeast Mod. Lang. Asn.(exec. secy, 70-73); New Eng. Col. Eng. Asn.(dir, 70-); Col. Eng. Asn; Bibliog. Soc. Am; Bibliog. Soc, Eng; Milton Soc. Am; Shakespeare Asn. Am. Renaissance English language and literature; Modern English and American literature; bibliography and textual editing. Publ: Co-auth, Bear, God and man: seven approaches to Faulkner's The bear, Random, 63, 2nd ed, 70; auth, On seven Shakespearean tragedies, Scarab, 68, 69; Symposium, 69 & Symposium on love, 70, Houghton; Rouges, vagabonds, and sturdy beggars, Imprint Soc, 73; Titled Elizabethans, 73 & Elizabethan backgrounds, 74, Archon; Markets of Bawdrie: the dramatic criticism of Stephen Gosson, Univ. Salzburg, 74; Thomas Dekker's Twelfth night, Univ. Toronto Quart, autumn 71; Paradoy and its implications in Sidney's Defense of poesie, Stud. Eng. Lit, winter 72; The Essex Rebellion: a new MS account, Papers Bibliog. Soc. Am, 72; plus others. Add: Dept. of English, University of Massachusetts, Amherst, MA 01002.

KINNEY, JOSEPH ALOYSIUS, JR, b. Philadelphia, Pa, May 14, 36; m. 57; c. 4. ENGLISH. B.A, Villanova Univ, 58, M.A, 59; Ph.D.(Eng, Am. lit), Bryn Mawr Col, 67. Instr. ENG, VILLANOVA UNIV, 59-63, asst. prof, 63-69, ASSOC. PROF, 69- John F. Kennedy mem. lectr. humanities, 66-68. MLA. Shakespeare; Elizabethan and Jacobean drama; methods of literary research. Publ: Auth, Educating your child, weekly column in South. Phila. Rev. & Chronicle, 70- Add: Dept. of English, Villanova University, Villanova, PA 19085.

KINNEY, STANLEY NEWELL, b. St. Johns, Mich, June 6, 18; m. 45. ENGLISH, SPEECH. A.B, Mich. State Univ, 40, M.A, 46; educ. dept. fel, Univ. Mich, 44, univ. fel, 55-56, Ph.D.(higher educ. & speech), 57. Instr. High Sch, Mich, 40-44, chmn. dept, 44-45; coord. radio activities, Pub. Schs, 45-46; instr. speech, Mich. State Univ, 46-49; from asst. prof. to ASSOC. PROF. ENG. & DIR, FORENSICS, COLGATE UNIV, 49-, DIR. CAREER COUNSELING & PLACEMENT CTR, 59- Dir. educ. prog, Radio Sta. WJIM, Lansing, Mich, 46-47; consult. discussion tech, Mich. State Community Sch. Conf, 48. East. Col. Personnel Off.(pres, 66-67); Col. Placement Coun; Speech Commun. Asn. Discussion methods; teaching methods; student government. Publ: The selection of outside speakers by student organizations at the University of Michigan, 1854-1935. Add: Dept. of English, Colgate University, Hamilton, NY 13346.

KINNEY, THOMAS L, b. Detroit, Mich, Mar. 28, 28; m. 54; c. 2. ENGLISH. B.A, Swarthmore Col, 50; M.A, Univ. Mich, 54, Henry A. Parker fel. & Ph.D.(Eng), 59. Instr. ENG, BOWLING GREEN STATE UNIV, 59-63, asst. prof, 63-67, assoc. prof, 67-73, PROF, 73-, acting chmn. dept, 69-70. A.U.S, 51-53. MLA. Middle English verse of social protest complaint; Chaucer; 14th century literature; edition: Pierce the Ploughmans crede. Publ: The temper of fourteenth century English verse of complaint, Annuale Mediaevale, 66. Add: Dept. of English, Bowling Green State University, BowlingGreen, OH 43403.

KINOIAN, VARTKIS, b. Pawtucket, R.I, Mar. 5, 31; m. 53; c. 2. AMERICAN & COMPARATIVE CONTEMPORARY LITERATURE. B.Ed, R.I. Col, 52; M.A, Columbia Univ, 57, Ph.D.(Eng), 71. Instr. ENG, FAIRLEIGH DICKINSON UNIV, 59-60, asst. prof, 60-68, assoc. prof, 68-72, PROF, 72-, deputy chmn. dept, 60-63, 67-69, asst. to dean col. lib. arts, 63-67. U.S.A, 52-55. AAUP; MLA; Armenian Lit. Soc. History of ideas in modern American literature; American poets and novelists in 20th century; Armenian history and literature. Publ: Study guides and notes to Faulkner's The sound and the fury, 64 & Henry James's The ambassadors, 65, The portrait of a lady, 65, The American, 65, Daisy Miller, 66 & The turn of the screw, 66, Monarch. Add: Dept. of English, Fairleigh Dickinson University, River Rd, Teaneck, NJ 07666.

KINSLEY, WILLIAM BENTON, b. Montpelier, Vt, Sept. 11, 34; m. 64; c. 3. ENGLISH. B.A, Univ. Toronto, 58; Ph.D.(Eng), Yale, 65. Instr. ENG, St. Michael's Col.(Vt), 58-59; Univ. Rochester, 63-64; asst. prof, UNIV. MONTREAL, 65-71, ASSOC. PROF, 71- Can. Counc. fel, 72-73. Am. Soc. 18th Century Stud; Can. Comp. Lit. Asn; MLA. Eighteenth century English literature; satire; allusion. Publ: Meaning and format: Mr. Spectator and his folio half-sheets, ELH, 12/67; The malicious world and the meaning of satire, Genre, 6/70; The Dunciad as mock-book, Huntington Libr. Quart, 11/71. Add: Dept. of English, University of Montreal, C.P. 6128, Montreal 101, P.Q, Can.

KINSMAN, ROBERT STARR, b. Jamaica Plains, Mass, Mar. 22, 19; m. 43; c. 3. ENGLISH. A.B, Dartmouth Col, 40; A.M, Yale, 42, Ph.D, 49; Univ. N.C, 41-42; Instr. ENGLISH, Univ. N.C, 46; UNIV. CALIF, LOS ANGELES, 48-50, asst. prof, 50-56, assoc. prof, 56-63, PROF, 63-, DEAN ACAD. SERV, 70-, DEAN PRO TEM GRAD. DIV, 72-, assoc. dean grad. div, 61-72. Fund Advan. Educ. fel, 52-53; Guggenheim fel, 56-57; mem. Woodrow Wilson Nat. Fel. Found, 60-70; regional chmn, 60-63; mem. comt. Martin Luther King, Jr. Fels, 68-71; mem. ed. bd. Grad. Admissions manual, Educ. Testing Serv, 71- U.S.M.C, 43-46, Lt. MLA; Renaissance Soc. Am; Renaissance Eng. Text Soc; Mediaeval Acad. Am. Tudor literature; poetical works of John Skelton; dramatic literature of the English Renaissance. Publ: Co-auth, Sketon: canon and census, Renaissance Soc. Am. 67; auth, Skelton, selections, Medieval & Tudor Ser, Clarendon, 68; ed, The darker vision, Univ. Calif, 74. Add: Dept. of English, Rolfe Hall, University of California, Los Angeles, CA 90024.

KINTER, WILLIAM L, b. St. Thomas, Pa, Oct. 21, 15. MEDIAEVAL COMPARATIVE LITERATURE. A.B, Lafayette Col, 38; A.M, Yale, 40; Ph.D, Columbia Univ, 58. Master Latin & Eng, Westminster Sch, Hartford, Conn, 44-46; asst. prof. Eng, Muhlenberg Col, 46-62; ASSOC. PROF, LOYOLA COL.(MD), 62-; CHMN. DIV. HUMANITIES, MD. INST. COL. ART, 66- Assoc. ed, Damascus Rd. Press. Contemporary American poetry. Publ: Prophetess and Fay, Xerox, 58; Introduction to Dante's Comedy, 64, Beowulf: an introduction, 65, T.S. Eliot major poems: introductions, 66 & Milton: Paradise lost: introductions, 67, Ivy Notes, Boston; Visio Pacis, the beat generation, Frontiers Mag, 61; co-ed, Window, 62. Add: Division of Humanities, Maryland Institute College of Art, 1300 W. Mt. Royal, Baltimore, MD 21217.

KINZER, WILLIAM EDWARD, b. Cleveland, Ohio, May 10, 21; m. 50; c. 4. THEATRE, DRAMA. A.B, West. Reserve Univ, 46, M.A, 47, M.F.A, 49. Instr. speech & threatre, Univ. Ala, 49-50; theatre, Fla. State Univ, 51; ASSOC. PROF. ACTING & DIRECTING, IND. UNIV, BLOOMINGTON, 51- Add: Dept. of Theatre & Drama, Indiana University, Bloomington, IN 47401.

KIPLING, GORDON LEE, b. Aurora, Ill, Jan. 4, 43; m. 65; c. 2. ENGLISH RENAISSANCE LITERATURE. B.A, Beloit Col, 65; Ford Found fel, Univ. Chicago, 65-66, Danforth grad. fel, 65-69, A.M, 66, Ph.D.(Eng), 71. Instr. ENG, North Park Col, 68-69; ASST. PROF, UNIV. CALIF, LOS ANGELES, 69- Nat. Endowment for Humanities Younger Humanist fel, 72-73. MLA Drama, 1300-1660; English-Netherlandic cultural relationships in the 15th and 16th centuries; pageantry, triumphs and Lord Mayors's shows in England. Add: Dept. of English, University of California, Los Angeles, CA 90024.

KIRALIS, KARL, b. Binghamton, N.Y, June 25, 23; div; c. 4. ENGLISH. A.B, Hamilton Col, 47; A.M, Brown Univ, 48, Ph.D.(Eng), 54. Instr. ENG, Brown Univ, 47-50; Carleton Col, 50-52; assoc. prof, St. Lawrence Univ, 52-67; Univ. Houston, 67-70; PROF, CALIF. STATE COL.(PA), 70- Am. Philos. Soc. grant, 57; mem, Eng. Inst; adv. reader, Stud. Romanticism, 66-; mem. adv. bd. ed, Blake Stud, 68- U.S.N.R, 43-46; Lt.(jg). MLA; Col. Eng. Asn.(mem. bd. dir, 66-68). William Blake; John Donne; Geoffrey Chaucer. Publ: Co-auth, The divine vision, bicentenary volume of studies in the poetry and art of William Blake, Gollancz, London, 57; auth, Joyce and Blake: a basic source for Finnegans wake, Mod. Fiction Stud, 58-59; The theme and structure of William Blake's Jerusalem, ELH, 6/56; William Blake as an intellectual and spiritual guide to Chaucer's Canterbury Pilgrims, Blake Stud, spring 69. Add: 420 Fourth St, California, PA 15419.

KIRBY, DAVID K, b. Baton Rouge, La, Nov, 29, 44; m. 69; c. 1. AMERICAN LITERATURE, CREATIVE WRITING. B.A, La. State Univ, 66; Ph.D.(Eng), Johns Hopkins Univ, 69. ASST. PROF. ENG, FLA. STATE UNIV, 69-, DIR. WRITING PROG, 73- Asst. ed, Abstracts Eng. Stud, 71-73. MLA; S.Atlantic Mod. Lang. Asn; NCTE. Writings of Henry James; late 19th century American literature; modern poetry. Publ: Two modern versions of the quest, South. Humanities Rev, fall 71; Henry James: art and autobiography, Dalhousie Rev, winter 72-73; The princess and the frog: the modern American short story as fairy tale, Minn. Rev, spring 73. Add: Dept. of English, Florida State University, Tallahassee, FL 32306.

KIRBY, JOHN PENDY, b. Hoosick Falls, N.Y, Jan. 20, 05; m. 32. ENGLISH. A.B, Hamilton Col, 27; Columbia Univ, 28-29; Mitchell fel, Yale, 36, Ph.D, 37. Instr. ENG, Pa. State Univ, 29-34; asst. prof, Lake Forest Col, 37-39, assoc. prof, 39-41; prof, Mary Washington Col, 41-47; prof. & head dept, RANDOLPH-MACON WOMAN'S COL, 47-73, EMER. PROF, 73- Ed, The Explicator, 42-; vis. prof. Eng, Univ. Va, 64-65. MLA; NCTE; Am. Soc. 18th Century Stud; Soc. Theatre Res, Eng. English drama; English novel; 18th century and 19th century English literature. Publ: Co-ed, Bibliography of detached pieces, Literature of western civilization. Add: Dept. of English, Randolph-Macon Woman's College, Lynchburg, VA 24504.

KIRBY, THOMAS (AUSTIN), b. Albion, N.Y, Sept. 7, 04; m. 37; c. 2. ENGLISH. A.B, Cath. Univ. Am, 27, fel, 27-28, A.M, 28; Univ. Munich, 29-30; Ph.D, Johns Hopkins Univ, 33. Prof. ENG. & head dept. St. Thomas Col, 33-34; prof, Manhattan Col, 34-35; asst. prof, LA. STATE UNIV, BATON ROUGE, 35-39, assoc. prof, 39-43, prof, 43-73, acting chmn. dept, 40-42, head, 42-73, EMER. PROF, 73- Mem. Ed. Bd, Chaucer Rev; mem. adv. bd, Variorum Ed. of Chaucer, 68- Col. Eng. Asn; NCTE; MLA; Mediaeval Acad. Am; Mod. Humanities Res. Asn, Gt. Brit; hon. mem. S.Cent. Mod. Lang. Asn.(v.pres, 47); Int. Arthurian Soc. Mediaeval literature. Publ: Studies for William A. Read, 40, Chaucer's Troilus, 40, reprint, 58 & co-ed, Essays in honor of Esmond Linworth Marilla, 70, La. State Univ; co-ed, Philologica: The Malone anniversary studies, Johns Hopkins Univ, 49; Chaucer and Arnold, In: Studies presented to Tauno F. Mustanoja on the occasion of his sixtieth birthday, Helsinki, 72; Chaucer research, 1972: report no. 33, Chaucer Rev, VIII: 71-85, Chaucer research in progress, 1972-1973, Neuphilol. Mitteilungen, 74: 534-540; plus others. Add: 6347 Moss Side Lane, Baton Rouge, LA 70808.

KIRBY-SMITH, HENRY TOMPKINS, JR, b. Sewanee, Tenn, Jan. 11, 38; m. 70. ENGLISH, CREATIVE WRITING. B.A, Univ. of the South, 59; Fulbright fel, Univ. Paris, 59-60; cert. French, Univ. Dijon, 60; Woodrow Wilson fel, Harvard, 60-61, M.A, 61, univ. fel, 63-65; Stegner writing fel, Stanford Univ, 62-63. Instr. ENG, UNIV. N.C, GREENSBORO, 67-71, ASST. PROF, 71-, COORD. GRAD. WRITING PROG, 70- Instr, NDEA Inst. Writing, 68; dir, Guilford Col-Univ. N.C, Greensboro Summer Sch. in Eng, 72. S.Atlantic Mod. Lang. Asn; Royal Astron. Soc. Can; Am. Asn. Variable Star Observers. Contemporary poetry; U Geminorum and Z Camelopardalis type variable stars. Publ: Contrib. poems in var. jour, 65-73; contrib, variable star observations, J. Royal Astron. Soc. Can, 72-; Miss Bishop and others, Sewanee Rev, summer 72. Add: Dept. of English, University of North Carolina at Greensboro, Greensboro, NC 27412.

KIRK, CLARA MARBURG, b. Philadelphia, Pa, May 10, 98; m. 30; c. 2. ENGLISH, AMERICAN LITERATURE. A.B, Vassar Col, 20, fel, 20-21, 26-27; A.M, Univ. Pa, 21; Comn. Relief in Belgium fel, Brussels, 21-23; fel, Univ. Chicago, 27-28, Ph.D, 29. Instr. Eng, Vassar Col, 23-26, 28-29, asst. prof, 29-33; assoc. prof, Bryn Mawr Col, 33-36; lectr, Rutgers Univ, 37-49, 54, Douglass Col, 56-63; vis. prof. Eng, Univ. Ill, Chicago, 67-69; RETIRED. Fulbright res scholar, Univ. Liège, Belgium, 55-56. MLA. Seventeenth century literature; Sir W. Temple, J. Evelyn & S. Pepys; American literature. Publ: Life of Howells; co-ed, William Dean Howells: representative selections, rev. ed, Hill & Wang; co-auth, Criticism and fiction and other essays, N.Y. Univ, 59; auth, W.D. Howells, traveler from Altruria, 62 & W.D. Howells and art in his time, 65, Rutgers; co-ed, Charlotte Temple, 64 & auth, Oliver Goldsmith: critical biography, 67, Twayne; co-ed, The Altrurian romances of William Dean Howells, Ind. Univ, 68; auth, Reality and actuality... in Howells, PMLA, 3/59; co-auth, Niagara revisited, In: Essays in literary history, Rutgers 60; auth, Toward a theory of art..., New Eng. Quart, 9/63. Add: 402 Balcones Apts, San Marcos, TX 78666.

KIRK, ELIZABETH DOAN, b. Philadelphia, Pa, Sept. 5, 37; m. 59. MIDDLE ENGLISH LITERATURE. B.A, Earlham Col, 59; Fulbright fel, Birkbeck Col, London, 63-64; Woodrow Wilson, Kent & Sterling fels. & Ph.D.(Eng), Yale, 64. Instr. ENG, Yale, 64-67; asst. prof, BROWN UNIV, 67-72, ASSOC. PROF, 72- Chaucer; Piers Plowman; Pearl-poet. Publ: The dream thought of Piers Plowman, Yale, 72; Tolkien's Elvish, Novel, fall 71. Add: Homstead Ave, R.D. 3, Rehoboth, MA 02769.

KIRK, GERALD A, b. Beaumont, Tex, Sept. 29, 21; m. 53; c. 2. ENGLISH LITERATURE. B.A, N.Tex. State Col, 50; M.A, Univ. Houston, 55; Ph.D.(Eng), Rice Univ, 59. Instr. ENG, Univ. Kans, 59-61; asst. prof, N.TEX. STATE UNIV, 61-63, assoc. prof, 63-70, PROF, 70- Managing ed, Stud. in the Novel, 69- U.S.N, 42-45. MLA; Am. Soc. 18th Century Stud. Eighteenth century English literature; novel. Add: Dept. of English, North Texas State University, Denton, TX 76201.

KIRK, JOHN W, b. Sewickley, Pa, Mar. 30, 32; m. 53; c. 3. SPEECH, THEATRE. B.A, Col. Wooster, 54; M.A, Ohio State Univ, 55; Ph.D.(speech), Univ. Fla, 62. Instr. speech, Univ. Fla, 57-63; asst. prof. & dir. theatre, Kearney State Col, 63-66; assoc. prof. THEATRE, ILL. STATE UNIV, 66-70, PROF, 71- Adminr, Title III grant, 67-70; bd. dirs. & founder, Univ. Resident Theatre Asn, 69-71. U.S.A, Spec. Serv, 55-57, Entertainment Specialist. Am. Theatre Asn; Speech Commun. Asn; Am. Nat. Theatre & Acad. Drama theory; directing; acting. Publ: Kenneth Burke and identification, Quart. J. Speech, 12/61; On teaching acting, Fla. Alligator, 2/63; Dramatism and the theatre, Kenneth Burke's dramatistic criticism, South. Speech J, spring 68. Add: Dept. of Theatre, Illinois State University, Normal, IL 61761.

KIRK, RUDOLF, b. Washington, D.C, Jan. 20, 98; m. 30; c. 2. ENGLISH & AMERICAN LITERATURE. A.B, Princeton, 22, 25-28, Scribner fel, 27-28, A.M, 28, Ph.D.(Elizabethan drama), 32; A.M, State Univ. Iowa, 25. Instr. Eng, State Univ. Iowa, 22-25; RUTGERS UNIV, NEW BRUNSWICK, 28-29, asst. prof, 29-40, assoc. prof, 40-45, prof, 45-63, acting chmn. dept, 56-57, chmn, 60-63, ed, Univ. Libr. Jour, 37-48, EMER. PROF, ENG, 63- Chmn, Col. Conf. Eng. Cent. Atlantic States, 33; mem, Eng. Inst, ed, Annual, 40-43; chmn. 17th century group, MLA, 44, Howells group, 50; Fulbright lectr, Univ. Ghent, Belgium, 55, annual sem. Am. lit, Rome, 56; Fulbright prof, Univ. Liege, 55-56; distinguished prof. Eng, Southwest. Tex. State Col, 63-67; vis. prof, Univ. Wis, 64; vis. prof, Univ. Ill, Chicago, 67-69. Summers, vis. prof, Univ. N.Mex, 48, N.Y. Univ, 49, Univ. Mo, 50, 53 & Huntington Libr. grant-in-aid, 64. Medal, Univ. Ghent, 55; Silver Medal, Univ. Liege, 56. U.S.A, 18. MLA. English literature; Stoicism; studies of Milton, Pepys, Massinger. Publ: Co-ed, Criticism and fiction and other essays by Howells, N.Y. Univ, 59; co-auth, Letters of Altrurian traveler, Scholars' Facsimiles, 61; co-auth, William Dean Howells, 62 & co-ed, Charlotte Temple, 64, Twayne; co-ed, Essays in literary history, Rutgers Univ, 63; co-auth, Altrurian romances, Ind. Univ, 68, Howells and Church of the Carpenter, New Eng. Quart, 6/59 & Abraham Cahan and W.D. Howells, Am. Jewish Hist. Quart, 9/62; auth, Seventeenth century controversy, Tex. Stud. Lit. & Lang, spring 67. Add: 402 Balcones Apts, San Marcos, TX 78666.

KIRK, RUSSELL, History. See Volume I, History.

KIRKCONNELL, WATSON, b. Port Hope, Ont, May 16, 95; m. 24, 30; c. 5. COMPARATIVE LITERATURE. M.A, Queen's Univ, Can, 16; Oxford, 21-22; Ph.D, Debrecen Univ, Hungary, 40; LL.D, Univ. Ottawa, 45, Univ. N.B, 50; D.P.Ec, Ukrainian Free Univ, 50; Litt.D, McMaster Univ, 52, Assumption Col, 55, Univ. Man, 57; D. es Let, Laval Univ, 62; D.Litt, Acadia Univ, 64, St. Francis Xavier Univ, 66; D.C.L, St. Mary's Univ, 64. Lectr. Eng, Wesley Col, Univ. Man, 22, asst. prof, 23, assoc. prof, 24-30, prof, 30-33, classics, United Col, 33-40; prof. Eng. & head dept, McMaster Univ, 40-48; pres, ACADIA UNIV, 48-64, prof. Eng, 64-68, EMER. PRES, 68- Chmn, Writer's War Comt, Can, 42-44; chmn, Humanities Res. Counc, Can, 44-47; hon. fel, Univ. Winnipeg, 68. Knight Officer, Order of Polonia Restituta, 36; Silver Laurel, Polish Acad. Lit, 37; Knight Comdr, Order of Falcon, Iceland, 63; Officer, Order Can, 68. Fel. Royal Soc. Can.(Pierce Gold Medal, 42); hon. fel. Icelandic Soc. Lit; hon. fel. Ukrainian Free Acad. Sci. Magyar literature; Milton studies. Publ: The celestial cycle, That invincible Samson, 64 & Awake the courteous echo, 73, Univ. Toronto; plus others. Add: Box 460, Wolfville, N.S, Can.

KIRKHAM, EDWIN BRUCE, b. White Plains, N.Y, Jan. 11, 38; m. 60; c. 3. ENGLISH, AMERICAN LITERATURE. B.A, Lehigh Univ, 61, M.A, 63; Ph.D.(Eng), Univ. N.C, Chapel Hill, 68. ASST. PROF. ENG, BALL STATE UNIV, 68- Mem, Am. Lit. Group, MLA. MLA; Am. Stud. Asn; Soc. Stud. South. Lit. Nineteenth century American literature. Publ: The building of Uncle Tom's cabin, Univ. Tenn, 74; co-auth, Index to American literary gift books and annuals, Res. Publ, 74; auth, The first editions of Uncle Tom's cabin: a bibliographical study, Papers Bibliog. Soc. Am, 71; plus others. Add: Dept. of English, Ball State University, Muncie, IN 47306.

KIRKLAND, JAMES WILTON, b. Miami, Fla, Oct. 9, 42; m. 64; c. 2. NINETEENTH CENTURY AMERICAN LITERATURE. A.B, Univ. Fla, 64, M.A, 65; Ph.D.(Eng), Univ. Tenn, 69. ASST. PROF. AM. LIT, E.CAROLINA UNIV, 69-, DIR. FRESHMAN COMPOS, 72- S.Atlantic Mod. Lang. Asn; Melville Soc. Am. Old English literature; American fiction. Publ: Co-auth, The art of Azarias, Medium AEvum, 72. Add: Dept. of English, East Carolina University, Greenville, NC 27834.

KIRKPATRICK, MARTIN SMITH, b. Roseville, Ark, Nov, 28, 22; m. 68; c. 1. CREATIVE WRITING. B.S.J, Univ. Fla, 53, M.A, 55; Sewanee Rev. fel, 58-60. Instr. WRITING, UNIV. FLA, 56-61, asst. prof, 61-68, ASSOC. PROF, 68-, DIR. CREATIVE WRITING PROG, 61- Dir. Fla. Writers' Conf, 70- Nat. Endowment for Arts Award, 73; Order of the South, South. Acad. Lett, Arts & Sci, 73. Writing and reading fiction. Publ: The sun's gold (novel), Houghton, 74; Silence, South. Rev, winter 68; Painting the ship, Sewanee Rev, summer 71; The wheel, In: Craft and vision, Delacorte, 71; plus others. Add: 1655 N.W. 10th Ave, Gainesville, FL 32601.

KIRSCH, ARTHUR CLIFFORD, b. New York, N.Y, Aug. 22, 32; m. 67. ENGLISH. B.A, Cornell Univ, 53; Fulbright fel, 53-55; B.Litt, Oxford, 55; Ph.D, Princeton, 61. Instr. ENG, Princeton, 60-63, asst. prof, 63-66; assoc. prof, UNIV. VA, 66-70, PROF, 70- Folger Shakespeare Libr. fel, 67, mem. ed. bd, 70-; Guggenheim fel, 70; mem. bd. ed, New Lit. Hist, 70-; mem. ed. bd. Shakespeare Quart, 70; mem. comt. lit. achievement test, Col. Entrance Exam. Bd, 71- Qm.C, 55-57, 1st Lt. MLA. Shakespeare; Renaissance and 17th century drama. Publ: Dryden's heroic drama, Princeton Univ, 65; co-auth, Restoration, Dell-Laurel, 65; ed, Literary criticism of John Dryden, Univ. Nebr, 66; auth, Jacobean dramatic perspectives, Univ. Va, 72; Cymbeline and coterie dramaturgy, ELH, 9/67. Add: Dept. of English, University of Virginia, Charlottesville, VA 22901.

KIRTLEY, BACIL F, b. Brownwood, Tex, Oct. 15, 24; m. 53; c. 3. ENGLISH, FOLKLORE. A.B, Univ. Tex, Austin, 49, M.A, 55; Ph.D.(Eng), Ind. Univ, Bloomington, 55. Instr. ENG, Univ. W.Va, 55-57; asst. prof, Univ. Maine, 57-61; Okla. State Univ, 61-62; Univ. Hawaii, 62-64, assoc. prof, 64-68, PROF, 68-69; Univ. Idaho, 69-72; UNIV. HAWAII, MANOA, 72- Vis. prof, Univ. Calif, Los Angeles, summer 61; orientation lectr. sr. scholars, Fulbright grants from Japan, E-W. Ctr, Honolulu, summer 64; vis. prof, Univ. Wyo, summer 66; consult, Hawaii Curriculum Ctr, 68-; summer res. grant, 71; vis. prof, World Campus Afloat, summer 73. U.S.A, 43-46. MLA; Am. Folklore Soc. Folk narrative; oceanic folklore; literary-folklore relationships. Publ: A motif-index of selected Polynesian narratives, Univ. Hawaii, 71; The slain eel-god and the origin of the coconut, with satellite themes in Polynesian mythology, In: Folklore international, essays in traditional literature, belief, and custom in honor of Wayland Debs Hand, Folklore Asn, 67; Some exotic affiliations of traditional Polynesian narratives, Bishop Mus, 73; co-auth, Animal tales from Rennell and Bellona, J. Polynesian Soc, 73; plus others. Add: Dept. of English, University of Hawaii at Manoa, Honolulu, HI 96822.

KIRWIN, WILLIAM JAMES, b. Newport, R.I, Jan. 23, 25. ENGLISH. A.B, Bowdoin Col, 50; M.A, Univ. Chicago, 51, Ph.D.(Eng), 64. Master ENG, Wilbraham Acad, Mass, 51-52; instr, Univ. Nebr, 52-54; Ripon Col, 56-58; asst. prof. MEM. UNIV. NFLD, 59-64, assoc. prof, 64-71, PROF, 71- Can. Counc. sr. fel. stud. dialect origins of Nfld. speech, 66-67; ed, Regional Lang. Stud . . . Nfld, 68- U.S.A, 43-46. Ling. Soc. Am; Am. Dialect Soc; MLA; Can. Ling. Asn. Middle English grammar; phonetics; Newfoundland dialectology. Publ: Co-auth, The Avalon peninsula of Newfoundland: an ethno-linguistic study, Nat. Mus. Can, 68; auth, Lines, coves, and squares in Newfoundland names, Am. Speech, 65. Add: Dept. of English, Memorial University of Newfoundland, St. Johns, Nfld, Can.

KISER, JOHN EDGAR, b. Lincolnton, N.C, Nov. 3, 42. ENGLISH LITERATURE. B.A, Cent. Wesleyan Col, 65; M.A, Appalachian State Univ, 69; Ph.D.(Eng), Univ. S.C, 72. Teacher ENG, Myers Park High Sch, N.C, 65-69; instr, UNIV. ALA, HUNTSVILLE, 72-73, ASST. PROF, 73- AAUP. Medieval English literature. Add: Dept. of English, University of Alabama in Huntsville, Huntsville, AL 35807.

KISH, DOROTHY, b. Pittsburgh, Pa. AMERICAN LITERATURE. B.A, Univ. Pittsburgh, 60, M.A, 61, M.L.S, 63, Ph.D.(Eng), 70. Librn, Carnegie Libr, Pittsburgh, Pa, 63-64; instr. ENG, POINT PARK COL, 64-66, asst. prof, 66-71, ASSOC. PROF, 71- AAUP; MLA. American novel; American women writers. Publ: Teacher without text, Am. Mercury, 5/59; Eva Tanguay, In: Dictionary of American biography, (in press). Add: Dept. of English, Point Park College, Wood Street, Pittsburgh, PA 15222.

KISSANE, JAMES, b. Pocatello, Idaho, June 21, 30; m. 52; c. 4. ENGLISH. A.B, Grinnell Col, 52; Ph.D.(Eng), Johns Hopkins Univ, 56. Jr. instr. ENG, Johns Hopkins Univ, 54-56; asst. prof, GRINNELL COL, 56-60, assoc. prof, 60-65, PROF, 65- MLA. Victorian literature. Publ: Co-auth, A preface to literary analysis, 64 & The practice of criticism, 66, Scott; auth, Alfred Tennyson, Twayne, 70; Victorian mythology, Victorian Stud, 9/62; Tennyson: the passion of the past and the curse of time, ELH, 3/65; P.G. Hamerton: Victorian art critic, Burlington Mag, 1/72; plus others. Add: 1327 Main St, Grinnell, IA 50112.

KISSANE, LEEDICE, b. Denison, Iowa, May 26, 05. ENGLISH LITERATURE. A.B, Cornell Col, 26; A.M, Univ. Idaho, 37; Ph.D.(Am. stud), Univ. Minn, 67. Instr, pub. schs, Idaho, 33-41; Eng, south. br, Univ. Idaho, 37-46; asst. prof, IDAHO STATE UNIV, 46-62, assoc. prof, 62-67, prof. Eng. & dir. Am. stud, 67-70, mem. adv. comt. Eng, 66-67, EMER. PROF. ENG, 70- Fulbright lectr. Am. lit. & insts, Univ. Iceland, 70-72. Am. Asn. Univ. Women. American novel since 1900; literary achievement of Halldor Laxness. Publ: Ruth Suckow, Twayne, 69; Interpretation through language: a study of metaphors in Stephen Crane's The open boat, Rendezvous, spring 66; An American reader looks at Laxness, Iceland Rev, summer 72; plus others. Add: 249 S. Seventh Ave, Pocatello, ID 83201.

KISSEL, BERNARD CHARLES, b. Grand Rapids, Mich, Sept. 1, 29; m. 51; c. 4. SPEECH COMMUNICATIONS. B.A, Univ. Mich, 51, M.A, 55, Ph.D.(speech), 59. Instr. speech, Univ. Mich, 55-59; asst. prof, Univ. Tex, 59-65, assoc. prof, 65-68; chmn. dept. commun, FLA. TECHNOL. UNIV, 70, DEAN COL. SOC. SCI, 70- Lectr, Episcopal Sem. Southwest, Tex, 60-68; advert. mgr, South. Speech Asn, 64-68; consult, Austin Presby. Theol. Sem, Tex, 65-68; mem, Creative Educ. Found. Teaching Excellence Award, Univ. Tex, 66. U.S.A, 51-53, Lt. Speech Commun. Asn.(mem. exec. counc, 67-70); Int. Commun. Soc. Communications; rhetoric and public address; behavioral science. Publ: Co-auth, Perspectives in communication, Holbrook, 73; auth, Impact of a visual public figure; a study of the diffusion of the death of General Eisenhower, Jour. Quart, summer 70; plus others. Add: College of Social Sciences, Florida Technological University, P.O. Box 25000, Orlando, FL 32816.

KISTLER, JONATHAN HIPPERLING, b. Tamaqua, Pa, Dec. 26, 09; m. 38; c. 4. ENGLISH & AMERICAN LITERATURE. A.B, Swarthmore Col, 32; A.M, Univ. Mich, 33, 34-37. Teaching asst, Univ. Mich, 36-37; instr, Iowa State Col, 37-38; prof. ENG, Doane Col, 38-47; asst. prof, COLGATE UNIV, 47-51, assoc. prof, 51-58, PROF, 58-, chmn. dept, 66-67. Ford Found. Asian fel, 65-66. MLA; NCTE. Shakespeare; the novel; Japanese and Indian fiction. Add: Dept. of English, Colgate University, Hamilton, NY 13346.

KISTLER, SUSAN WOOFTER, b. Salem, W.Va, Nov. 6, 07; m. 30; c. 1. SPEECH, HUMANITIES. B.A, Salem Col, 28; M.A, W.Va. Univ, 59. Teacher, Adamston Jr. High Sch, 28-32; teacher, dir. music & prin, Johnston Grade Sch, 33-45; instr. Eng. & Speech, SALEM COL.(W.VA), 48-49, asst. prof. Eng, 49-57, assoc. prof, 57-60, assoc. prof. speech, 60-73, PROF. ORAL COMMUN, 73-, DIR. INST. RES. & PLANNING, 72-, chmn. dept. speech, 60-72, chmn. div. humanities, 68-70. Study of humanities, London, summer 68. Speech Commun. Asn; Asn. Instnl. Res. Metaphysical poets; systems approach to planning; human communication. Add: Office of Institutional Research & Planning, Salem College, Salem, WV 26426.

KITCH, JOHN IRA, JR, b. Chicago, Ill, Apr. 10, 34; m. 55; c. 3. ENGLISH. A.B, Univ. Ill, 55, A.M, 56, Ph.D.(Eng), 65. U.S. AIR FORCE, 56-, instr. Eng, U.S. Air Force Acad, 59-60, asst. prof, 60-66, assoc. prof, 66-72, prof, 72-73; prof. aerospace stud. & adj. prof. Eng, Davis & Elkins Col, 73-75. U.S.A.F, 56-, Lt. Col. MLA; NCTE. American literature and history, especially the American historical novel. Add: Dept. of Aerospace Studies, Davis & Elkins College, Elkins, WV 26241.

KITZHABER, ALBERT RAYMOND, b. Cedar Rapids, Iowa, July 29, 15; m. 40; c. 3. ENGLISH. B.A, Coe Col, 39; M.A, Wash. State Col, 41; Am. Counc. Learned Soc. scholar, Univ. Iowa, 42-43; Ph.D, Univ. Wash, 53. Instr. Eng, Iowa State Col, 41-42, 46; Eng. & Russ, Wash. State Col, 46-48; asst. prof, Utah State Col, 50-52; from asst. prof. to prof. Eng, Univ. Kans, 52-60; prof. Eng. & dir. study stud. writing, Dartmouth Col, 60-62; PROF. ENG, UNIV. ORE, 62- Dir. High Sch. Curriculum Stud, Portland, Ore, 58-60; chmn. compos. planning comt, comn. on Eng, Col. Entrance Exam. Bd, 60-61, mem. writing sample comt, 62-67; dir. Ore. Curriculum Stud. Ctr, 62-67; panelist, White House Conf. Educ, 65; mem. Eng. Prog. Adv. Comt, MLA, 66-70. U.S.A, 43-45. NCTE (1st v.pres, 62-63, pres, 63-64); Conf. Col. Compos. & Commun.(chmn, 59); MLA. Rhetoric; improvement of English curriculum in schools; improvement of English composition in college. Publ: A bibliography on rhetoric in American colleges, 1850-1900, Denver Bibliog. Ctr, 54; Themes, theories, and therapy: the teaching of writing in college, McGraw, 63; co-auth, Education for college: improving the high school curriculum, Ronald, 61. Add: Dept. of English, University of Oregon, Eugene, OR 97403.

KIVETTE, RUTH M, b. Union City, N.J, Jan. 10, 26; m. 54. ENGLISH LITERATURE. A.B, Barnard Col, 48; A.M. Columbia Univ, 50, Ph.D, 60; B.D, Union Theol. Sem.(N.Y), 54. Asst. prof. ENG, Davis & Elkins Col, 50-52; lectr, BARNARD COL, 52-61, asst. prof, 61-67, ASSOC. PROF, 67- Kent. fel, 55-57; Lilly Found. fel. in relig, 63-64. Milton Soc. Am; MLA; Renaissance Soc. Am; Soc. Relig. Higher Educ. Milton's theology. Publ: The ways and wars of truth, Milton Quart 12/73. Add: Dept. of English, Barnard College, New York, NY 10027.

KLAMMER, THOMAS PAUL, b. Detroit, Mich, Jan. 8, 45; m. 66; c. 1. ENGLISH LINGUISTICS. B.A, Concordia Teachers Col.(Ill), 66; M.A, Univ. Mich, 67, NDEA & univ. fels, 68-69, Rackham Prize fels, 69-70, 70-71, Ph.D.(Eng. lang), 71. ASST. PROF. ENG, CALIF. STATE UNIV, FULLERTON, 71- Ling. Soc. Am; MLA; Am. Dialect Soc; Col. Eng. Asn; NCTE; AAUP. Discourse analysis; theory of literature. Publ: Co-auth, Some recent contributions to tagmemic analysis of discourse, Glossa, 70; auth, Multihierarchical structure in a Middle English Breton lay, Lang. & Style, 71; Foundations for a theory of dialogue structure, Poetics, 73. Add: Dept. of English, California State University, Fullerton, CA 92634.

KLAUS, CARL H, b. Cleveland, Ohio, May 24, 32; m. 67; c. 3. ENGLISH. B.A, Univ. Mich, 53, M.A, 54; Ph.D.(Eng), Cornell Univ, 66. Teaching fel. ENG, Cornell Univ, 54-59; instr. Bowdoin Col, 59-62; UNIV. IOWA, 62-65, asst. prof, 65-68, assoc. prof, 68-73, PROF, 73- Dir. NDEA Inst. Eng, Univ. Iowa, summer 66 & 67. Midwest Mod. Lang. Asn.(exec. secy, 66-69, 69-72); MLA; NCTE. Seventeenth century drama; theory of drama; stylistics and rhetorical theory. Publ: Style in English prose, Macmillan, 68; co-auth, Elements of the essay, 69, Elements of drama, 71 & Elements of writing, 72, Oxford Univ. Add: Dept. of English, University of Iowa, Iowa City, IA 52240.

KLEE, BRUCE B, b. Rochester, N.Y, Mar. 23, 28; m. 52; c. 3. THEATRE. A.B, Heidelberg Col, 50; M.A, Miami Univ, 51; Ph.D.(theatre), Ohio State Univ, 61. Instr. speech, Hobart & William Smith Cols, 53-54; THEATRE, Univ. Conn, 54-57; asst. prof, Elmira Col, 57-61; PROF, STATE UNIV. N.Y. COL. GENESEO, 61- Am. Theatre Asn. Repertory theatre; governmental involvement in the arts. Publ: The arts: American culture or foreign policy, 2/61 & Repertory New England style, 4/61, Today's Speech; Shubert vs. Woollcott: dramatic criticism on trial, Educ. Theatre J, 12/61. Add: Dept. of Dramatic Arts, State University of New York College at Geneseo, Geneseo, NY 14454.

KLEIN, KAREN WILK, b. Fargo, N.Dak, Dec. 3, 36; m. 59; c. 3. MEDIEVAL COMPARATIVE LITERATURE, ENGLISH. B.A, Radcliffe Col, 58; M.A, Columbia Univ, 59, Ph.D.(medieval comp. lit), 63. Teaching asst. ENG, Hunter Col, 60-61; preceptor, Columbia Univ, 62-63; instr, BRANDEIS UNIV, 64-67, ASST. PROF, 68- AAUP; Mediaeval Acad. Am. Troubadour poetry; Old English poetry; autobiography. Publ: The partisan voice, Mouton, 71; The political message of Bertran de Born, Stud. Philol, 68; Autobiography: the person between myth and history, Nat. Women's Comt. Stud. Group Prog, Brandeis Univ, 70. Add: Dept. of English, Brandeis University, Waltham, MA 02154.

KLEIN, MARCUS, b. Cleveland, Ohio, Apr. 19, 28; m. 60; c. 1. AMERICAN LITERATURE. B.A, West. Reserve Univ, 50; M.A, Columbia Univ, 52, univ. fel, 60-61, Ph.D.(Eng. & comp. lit), 62; Fulbright fel, Univ. Munich, Ger, 56-57. Instr. ENG, Barnard Col, Columbia Univ, 57-62, asst. prof, 62-65; assoc. prof, STATE UNIV. N.Y. BUFFALO, 65-68, PROF, 68- Barnard Col, Columbia Univ. res. grant, 60-61; Fulbright fel. for lecturing Am. lit, Univ. Toulouse, 66-67; vis. prof, Univ. Paris, 72-73. U.S.A, 46-47, S/Sgt. Modern American literature. Publ: After alienation: American novels at mid-century, World Publ, 64; co-auth, Innocence and experience, 66 & Short stories: classic, modern, contemporary, 67, Little; ed, The American novel since World War II, Fawcett, 70; auth, San Francisco and her hateful Ambrose Bierce, Hudson Rev, autumn, 54; Saul Bellow: a discipline of nobility, Kenyon Rev, spring 62; The roots of radicals: experience in the thirties, In: Proletarian writers of the thirties, South. Ill. Univ, 68. Add: Dept. of English, State University of New York at Buffalo, Buffalo, NY 14214.

KLEIN, MAXINE MAE, b. Blue Earth, Minn, Mar. 25, 34; div. THEATRE. B.A, Tex. West. Col, 56; M.A, Univ. Conn, 58; Ph.D.(theatre), Cornell Univ, 63. Instr. THEATRE, Keuka Col, 60-62; asst. prof, Univ. Minn, 62-69; ASSOC. PROF, BOSTON UNIV, 69- Resident dir, La Mama Exp. Theatre, 69-; dir. Off-Broadway plays, Martinique Theatre, N.Y. & Berkshire Theatre Festival, Mass. Obie Award, 72. Mayan theatre; acting. Publ: The philosopher dramatist, spring 68 & A country of cruelty and it's theatre, winter 69, Drama Surv; Mayan theatre, Educ. Theatre J, fall 71; plus other articles & plays. Add: Dept. of Theatre Arts, Boston University, 855 Commonwealth Ave, Boston, MA 02215.

KLEIN, THOMAS DICKER, b. Chicago, Ill, Oct. 25, 41; m. 69. ENGLISH, EDUCATION. B.A, Tufts Univ, 63; M.A.T, Harvard, 64; Ph.D.(Eng. educ), Northwest. Univ, 71. Teacher ENG, Evanston Twp. High Sch, 64-69; ASST. PROF, BOWLING GREEN STATE UNIV, 71- Consult, Educ. Coord, Inc. & Kansas City Schs, 67-68; Chicago Comt. on Urban Opportunity, summer 68. AAUP; NCTE. Creativity in English writing; group dynamics in the teaching of English. Publ: Co-auth, Spinach is good for you: a call for change in the American schools, Popular Press, 73; Personal growth in the classroom, Eng. J, 2/70; Personal reflections of a college teacher, New Directions in Teaching, fall 72. Add: Dept. of English, Bowling Green State University, Bowling Green, OH 43403.

KLEINAU, MARVIN DALE, b. Geneseo, Ill, Aug. 31, 29; m. 62. SPEECH. B.S, Ill. State Univ, 52, M.S, 60; South. Ill. Univ, 61-63. Teacher, Saybrook High Sch, 54-57; Geneseo High Sch, 57-61; ASST. PROF. SPEECH, SOUTH. ILL. UNIV, CARBONDALE, 63-, dir. forensics, 63-72. U.S.A, 52-54. Speech Commun. Asn. Argumentation and debate; contemporary public address. Publ: The judging of debate, Springboards, Inc, rev. ed, 63; co-auth, Scene location in readers theatre: static or dynamic, Speech Teacher, 9/65; auth, Speech in a free society, Ill. J. Educ, 2/67. Add: Dept. of Speech, Southern Illinois University, Carbondale, IL 62901.

KLEINBERG, SEYMOUR, b. New York, N.Y, Jan. 5, 33. ENGLISH LITERATURE. B.A, City Col. New York, 53; fel, Univ. Conn, 53-55, M.A, 55; fel, Univ. Mich, 55-59, Ph.D, 63. Instr. ENG, Flint Jr. Col, 59-62; asst. prof, LONG ISLAND UNIV, 62-67, assoc. prof, 67-72, PROF, 72- MLA. Renaissance literature. Add: Dept. of English, Long Island University, Brooklyn, NY 11201.

KLEINER, ELAINE LAURA, b. Portland, Ore, May 2, 42. ENGLISH & CONTINENTAL LITERATURE. B.A, Ore. State Univ, 64; M.A, Univ. Chicago, 66, Ph.D.(Eng), 71; Univ. Wis-Madison, 67. Teaching asst. ENG, Univ. Wis-Madison, 67-68; ASST. PROF, IND. STATE UNIV, 69- Instr, Upward Bound Prog, Wis. State Univ, summers 67 & 68; managing ed, Sch. Rev, 68-70; Ind. rep, Regional Comt, Nat. Endowment Humanities, 72-73; managing ed, Sci-Fiction Stud, 72-74. MLA; Mod. Humanities Res. Asn; William Morris Soc. & Kelmscott Fel; Pop. Cult. Asn; Midwest Mod. Lang. Asn. Literary theory and criticism; modern literature; the 19th century popular book. Publ: Contrib, Modern Humanities Research Association Annual bibliography of English language and literature, 71-73; auth, Conrad's forgotten role in the emergence of science fiction as literary genre, Extrapolation, 5/73. Add: Dept. of English, Indiana State University, Parsons Hall 236, Terre Haute, IN 47805.

KLEINFIELD, HERBERT L, b. New York, N.Y, July 4, 21. ENGLISH & AMERICAN STUDIES. A.B, Johns Hopkins Univ, 41; fel, Harvard, 53-56, Ph.D, 56. Instr. Eng, Temple Univ, 56-62; asst. prof. Eng. & Am. civilization, C.W. POST COL, LONG ISLAND UNIV, 62-64, assoc. prof. ENG. & AM. STUD, 64-68, PROF, 68- Assoc, fac. sem. Am. civilization, Columbia Univ, 65-; sr. ed, Complete Works of Washington Irving, 73- U.S.A, 42-43, 1st Lt. Am. Stud. Asn; MLA; Am. Soc. Theatre Res. American literature; theatre history. Publ: Co-auth, Washington Irving, a bibliography, 68 & auth, A census of Washington Irving manuscripts, 68, Kennikat; Infidel on Parnassus: Lord Byron and the North American Review, New Eng. Quart, 6/60; Irving as a journal writer, Am. Transcendental Quart, 1st quart. 70; Irving: as seen through his letters, In: Washington Irving: a tribute, 72; plus others. Add: Dept. of English & American Studies, Long Island University, Greenvale, NY 11548.

KLENE, MARY JEAN, C.S.C, b. Hannibal, Mo, Sept. 8, 29. RENAISSANCE LITERATURE & ART. B.A, St. Mary's Col.(Ind), 59; Cath. Univ. Am, 59; M.A, Notre Dame Univ, 66; Ph.D.(Eng), Univ. Toronto, 70. Instr. ENG, ST. MARY'S COL.(IND), 65-66, asst. prof, 70-74, ASSOC. PROF, 74-, CHMN. DEPT, 72- Fel. Soc. Religion Higher Educ. Shakespearean drama; editing Elizabethan entertainments. Publ: Othello: a fixed figure for the time of scorn, Shakespeare Quart, (in press). Add: Dept. of English, St. Mary's College, Notre Dame, IN 46556.

KLIESCH, RALPH ERNEST, b. Chicago, Ill, Jan. 3, 30; m. 61; c. 3. JOURNALISM. B.S.J, Ohio Univ, 56, M.S, 61; Ph.D.(mass commun), Univ. Minn, Minneapolis, 68. Tech. ed, Gen. Elec. Co, 56-57, sales engineer, 57-58, press relations specialist, 58-60; instr. JOUR, Univ. Minn, Minneapolis, 63-64; asst. prof, OHIO UNIV, 65-69, ASSOC. PROF, 69- Vis. lectr, Mara Inst. Technol, Malaysia, 71; vis. sr. lectr, New S.Wales Inst. Technol, 71-72. U.S.A.F, 51-52; Air Nat. Guard, 48-51, S/Sgt. Asn. Educ. in Jour; Int. Commun. Asn. Journalism history; international communication; photojournalism. Publ: The Chicago fire myth: Times's version lives, Publ. Auxiliary, 1/65; co-auth, Which readers are reached if paper expands coverage, Jour. Quart, summer 66; auth, Professionals return to the campus—and students love it, Quill, 7/68. Add: School of Journalism, Ohio University, Athens, OH 45701.

KLIEWER, WARREN, b. Mountain Lake, Minn, Sept. 20, 31; m. 60. ENGLISH, THEATER ARTS. B.A, Univ. Minn, 53, M.F.A, 67; M.A, Univ. Kans, 59; Danforth grant, Union Theol. Sem, 65-66. Instr. Eng. & drama, Bethany Col, 59-61; asst. prof. Eng, Earlham Col, 61-65; assoc. prof. Eng, speech & drama, Wichita State Univ, 66-70; prod. dir, Nat. Humanities Series, Princeton, N.J, 70-73; ARTISTIC DIR, CAROLINA READERS' THEATRE, 73- Co-ed, Relig. Theatre, 64-, pres, Relig. Theatre Publ, Inc; guest-lect. & readings at numerous cols; vis. prof, Univ. N.C, 73-74. Kenneth Rockwell award, Univ. Kans, 59. Dramatists Guild; Am. Theatre Asn. Directing, playwriting, poetry. Publ: Red rose and gray cowl, Omega Bks, 60; Moralities and miracles (poems & short plays), 62 & Liturgies, games, farewells, 74, Golden Quill; The violators (short stories), Marshall Jones, 64; Round the cherry tree, Motive, 11/62 & produced, Am. Educ. Theatre Asn. Convention, 8/63. Prod: Seventy times seven, Eagles Mere Playhouse, 7/65 & In: Relig. Theatre, winter 66; A lean and hungry priest, Scorpio Rising Theatre, 9/73. Add: 14 Dorann Ave, Princeton, NJ 08540.

KLIGERMAN, JACK, b. Atlantic City, N.J, Aug. 28, 38; m. 60; c. 2. ENGLISH, LINGUISTICS. B.A, Syracuse Univ, 60, M.A, 62; fels, Univ. Calif, Berkeley, 64-66, Ph.D.(Eng), 67. ASST. PROF. ENG, LEHMAN COL, 67- MLA. American and English literature; stylistics; style and form in 19th century American prose fiction. Publ: Co-auth, Invention: a course in prewriting and composition, Winthrop, 73; auth, A stylistic approach to Hawthorne's Roger Malvin's burial, Lang. & Style, summer 71; co-auth, Invention, composition, and the urban college, Col. Eng, 3/72; auth, Dress or Incarnation of thought: nineteenth century American attitudes toward language and style, Proc. Am. Philos. Soc, 2/73. Add: Dept. of English, Herbert H. Lehman College, Bedford Park Blvd. W, Bronx, NY 10468.

KLINCK, CARL FREDERICK, b. Elmira, Ont, Mar. 24, 08; m. 34; c. 1. ENGLISH. B.A, Univ. West. Ont, 27; hon. Litt.D, 74; A.M, Columbia Univ, 29, Ph.D, 43. Instr. Eng, Waterloo Col, UNIV. WEST. ONT, 28-29, asst. prof, 29-31, assoc. prof, 31-32, prof, 32-47, librn, 36-42, dean, 42-47, assoc. prof. Eng, univ, 47-49, prof. & head dept, 49-56, from prof. to sr. prof. CAN. LIT, 56-72, EMER. PROF, 73- Vis. commonwealth lectr, Univ. Leeds, 65. Officer, Order Can, 74. Fel. Royal Soc. Can. Canadian, American and commonwealth literature. Publ: Wilfred Campbell, 42, William Tiger Dunlop, 58 & co-auth, Canadian writers/ Ecrivains Canadiens, 64, rev. ed, 66, Ryerson; co-auth, Canadian anthology, W.J. Gage, Toronto, 55, rev. ed, 66, 74; auth, Tecumseh, Prentice-Hall, 61; co-auth. & ed, Literary history of Canada, Univ. Toronto, 65; The journal of Major John Norton, 1816, Champlain Soc, Toronto, 70. Add: Dept. of English, University of Western Ontario, London, Ont. N6A 3K7, Can.

KLINE, EDWARD ALTON, Linguistics, English. See Volume III, Foreign Languages, Linguistics & Philology.

KLINE, H. CHARLES, b. Macomb, Ill, Feb. 24, 29; m. 54; c. 1. THEATRE. B.S.Ed, Cent. Mo. State Col, 51; M.F.A, Yale, 54; Ph.D.(theatre), Univ. Denver, 63. Asst. prof. theatre & speech, Cent. Mo. State Col, 56-57; theatre, Wheaton Coll, 57-58; fel, Univ. Denver, 58-59; asst. prof. speech, Colo. State Col, 60-62; assoc. prof. drama & speech & head dept, Drake Univ, 63-64; PROF. THEATRE DRAMA & DIR. DRAMA, STATE UNIV. N.Y. COL. PLATTSBURGH, 64- Dir. summer theatre, Cent. Mo. State Col, summer 58; res. assoc. ctr. res. frontier theatre, Univ. Denver, 63-; exec. consult, Adirondack & Champlain Festival Performing Arts, 66-; cult. consult, N. Country Econ. & Cult. Counc, Inc, N.Y, 66-; chmn. exec. bd. dirs, Clinton-Essex County Counc. Arts, 69-72; theatre assoc, Adirondack Correctional Treatment & Eval. Ctr, Clinton Prison, Dannemora, N.Y, 68- U.S.A, 54-56, Res, 56-62. Nat. Educ. Asn; Am. Theatre Asn; Speech Commun. Asn. History of frontier theatre; college community relation in the performing arts; television in education. Publ: ETV: Where will it lead?, Colo. Speech J, fall 61; co-auth, A contest workshop in television speaking, Speech Teacher, 3/63; auth, Four boards and a passion, Des Moines Chamber Commerce Mag, spring 63. Add: Dept. of Speech & Drama, State University of New York College of Arts & Science, Plattsburgh, NY 12901.

KLINE, HERBERT W, b. Muskegon, Mich, May 26, 36; m. 63. SPEECH, THEATRE. A.B, Univ. Mich, 58, M.A, 63; Ph.D.(theatre), Univ. Ill, 67. Instr, Univ. Ill, 65-66; asst. prof. speech, Ball State Univ, 66-69; ASSOC. PROF. THEATRE ARTS & CHMN. DEPT, CALIF. STATE UNIV, SACRAMENTO, 69- Vis. asst. prof, Univ. Ore, 68-69. Intel.C, U.S.A, 58-60. Am. Theatre Asn. American theatre history; 19th century British theatre. Publ: Dramatic literature in the social sciences, Ind. Soc. Sci. Quart, fall 68; The Jew that Shakespeare drew?, Am. Jewish Arch, 4/71. Add: Dept. of Theatre Arts, California State University, Sacramento, 6000 J St, Sacramento, CA 95819.

KLINE, JOHN ALVIN, b. Marshalltown, Iowa, July 24, 39; m. 58; c. 2. SPEECH COMMUNICATION. B.S, Iowa State Univ, 67; NDEA fel, Univ. Iowa, 67-70, M.A, 68, Ph.D.(speech), 70. Asst. prof. speech commun, Univ. N.Mex, 70-71; DIR. GRAD. STUD. SPEECH & DRAMATIC ART, UNIV. MO-COLUMBIA, 71- Speech Commun. Asn; Int. Commun. Asn. Persuasion; problem-solving, small groups; language variables. Publ: Interaction of evidence and readers' intelligence of effects of short messages, Quart. J, Speech, 12/69; A Q-analysis of encoding behavior in the selection of evidence, Speech Monogr, 8.71; co-auth, Computer analysis of verbal behavior in the classroom, Speech Teacher, 1/73. Add: Dept. of Speech & Dramatic Art, University of Missouri-Columbia, Columbia, MO 65201.

KLINE, JUDD WILLIAM, b. Ft. Buford, N.Dak, July 21, 11; m. 39; c. 3. ENGLISH. B.S, Univ. Minn, 38, M.A, 39, Ph.D.(Eng), 47. Instr. ENG, Univ. Minn, 40-42; asst. prof, West. State Col. Colo, 47-48; PROF, EAST. ILL. UNIV, 48- U.S.A.A.F, 42-46, Maj. Eighteenth century English novel. Add: Dept. of English, Eastern Illinois University, Charleston, IL 61920.

KLINE, RICHARD BURTON, b. Cleveland, Ohio, May 15, 29; m. 63; c. 1. ENGLISH. A.B, Harvard, 53; M.A, West. Reserve Univ, 58; Ph.D.(Eng), Duke Univ, 65. Asst. prof. ENG, STATE UNIV. N.Y. COL. FREDONIA, 63-67, ASSOC. PROF, 67- State Univ. N.Y. Res. Found. grants-in-aid, 64-73, summer fel, 66; Am. Philos. Soc. summer fels, 65, 67; Nat. Endowment for Humanities summer stipend, 68; Am. Counc. Learned Soc. fel, 69-70. MLA; Am. Soc. 18th Century Stud. Matthew Prior; 18th century English literature; satire. Publ: Matthew Prior and John Dennis, Notes & Queries, 6/66; Matthew Prior and dear Will Nuttley: an addition to the canon, Philol. Quart, 4/68; Matthew Prior and Richard Steele: a measure of respect?, Stud. Eng. Lit, summer 69. Add: Birchwood Apt. A-1, Fredonia, NY 14063.

KLINGER, MARY FRANCES, b. Albany, N.Y. ENGLISH LITERATURE. B.A, Brooklyn Col, 65; M.A, N.Y. Univ, 66, Penfield fel, 69-70, Ph.D.(Eng. lit), 70. Instr. ENG, Brooklyn Col, 70-72; ASST. PROF, CALIF. STATE UNIV, NORTHRIDGE, 72- N.Y. Univ. Founders' Day Award, 71. MLA; Soc. Theatre Res, Eng; Am. Soc. Theatre Res.(asst. secy-treas, 69-70); Am. Soc. 18th Century Stud. Eighteenth century English drama and art; images of woman in literature; 18th century English literature. Publ: Music and theatre in Hogarth, Musical Quart, 7/71; The rake's progress: a new theatrical version of William Hogarth's prints, Notes & Queries, 10/72. Add: Dept. of English, California State University, Northridge, 18111 Nordhoff St, Northridge, CA 91324.

KLINKER, HARRIETTE GRAYSON, b. Vincennes, Ind, Aug. 13, 19; m. 70. ENGLISH. A.B, Franklin Col, 41; M.S, Ind. State Univ, 56, M.A, 60; Ph.D.(Eng. educ), Purdue Univ, West Lafayette, 73. Teacher, high sch, Ill, 44-46; Ind, 46-52; instr. ENG, VINCENNES UNIV, 56-57, assoc. prof, 57-62, PROF. & CHMN. DEPT, 62-, HEAD HUMANITIES DIV, 68- Co-chmn. jr. col. sect, nat. conf, NCTE, 67; examr. & consult, N.Cent. Asn. Cols. & Sec. Schs, 72- NCTE. Teaching English composition by television; teaching composition with an audio-tutorial approach. Publ: A study guide for a course in basic composition with an audio-tutorial approach, Burgess, 67. Add: 1516 Old Wheatland Rd, Vincennes, IN 47591.

KLOECKNER, ALFRED JOSEPH, b. New York, N.Y, Nov. 3, 26; m. 55; c. 3. ENGLISH & AMERICAN LITERATURE. A.B, Columbia Univ, 49; M.A, 50; Fulbright fel, Univ. Hamburg, 54-55; Ph.D, Ind. Univ, 56. Instr. ENG, Univ. Rochester, 56-59; asst. prof, Loyola Univ.(Ill), 59-60; from asst. to ASSOC. PROF, NORWICH UNIV, 60- U.S.N.R, 44-46. American transcendentalism: 19th century American novel. Publ: English text for Marcel Marceau by Pawlikowski, Hoeppner, Hamburg, 55; Intellect and moral sentiment in Emerson's opinions of The meaner kinds of men, 11/58 & The flower and the fountain: Hawthorne's chief symbols in Rappaccini's daughter, 11/66, Am. Lit. Add: Dept. of English, Norwich University, Northfield, VT 05663.

KLOPF, DONALD WILLIAM, b. Milwaukee, Wis, Jan. 22, 23; m. 54; c. 1. SPEECH. B.A, Univ. Hawaii, 53, M.A, 55; Ph.D.(speech), Univ. Wash, 58. Instr. SPEECH, Seattle Univ, 55-57; asst. prof, UNIV. HAWAII, MANOA, 58-62, assoc. prof, 62-69, PROF, 69-, dir. courses & curricula, col. gen. stud, 66-68. Consult, U.S. Air Force, 62; hon. fel, Univ. Wis, 64; vis. scholar, Northwest. Univ, 64-65. U.S.A.A.F, 43-46, S/Sgt. West. Speech Asn; Cent. States Speech Asn; South Speech Asn; East. States Speech Asn; Speech Asn. Am; Am. Forensic Asn.(bk. rev. ed, 66-68); Commun. Asn. Pac.(pres, 70-74). Publ: Co-auth, Forensic manual, 62; Individual speaking contests, Burgess, 67; Coaching and directing forensics, Nat. Textbk, 67; Elements of debate, Arco, 68; co-auth, Effective academic debate, 72 & Winning debates, 73, Gaku Shobo. Add: Dept. of Speech, University of Hawaii at Manoa, Honolulu, HI 96822.

KLOPSCH, RAYMOND ALBERT, b. Chicago, Ill, Apr. 27, 24; m. 49; c. 5. ENGLISH. B.S, Ill. Inst. Tech, 49; M.A, Univ. Ill, 50, Ph.D, 62. Instr. ENG, PAC. LUTHERAN UNIV, 53-56, asst. prof, 56-59, ASSOC. PROF, 59- U.S.A.A.F, 43-46. MLA; Pac. Northwest Col. Eng. Asn.(pres, 73-74). English novel; modern drama; prose fiction. Add: 764 S. 117th St, Tacoma, WA 98444.

KLOTEN, EDGAR L, b. Buffalo, N.Y, May 21, 12; m. 52; c. 1. SPEECH, DRAMA. Ph.D, Canisius Col, 34; M.A, Cath. Univ. Am, 41; Columbia Univ, 50-52, 65-68. Asst. prof. theatre arts, Fordham Univ, 46-52; actor-dir, theatre, 52-56; ASSOC. PROF. SPEECH & DRAMA, UNIV. HARTFORD, 56- Drama columnist, West Hartford News, 61- U.S.C.G, 42-46, Lt. Am. Nat. Theatre & Acad; Nat. Cath. Theatre Conf.(ed, Cath. Theatre, 51, 56, 57); Am. Theatre Asn; New Eng. Theatre Conf. Professional theatre and its religious aspects; synthesis of drama and theatre as art form. Publ: Contrib. to N.Y. Times & Players; auth, Kelly in New York, Miller in Hartford, Drama Critique, fall 67. Add: Dept. of Communication & Theater, University of Hartford, West Hartford, CT 06117.

KLOTMAN, PHYLLIS RAUCH, b. Galveston, Tex; m; c. 2. AMERICAN LITERATURE. B.A, Case West. Reserve Univ, 61, M.A, 63, Ph.D.(Eng, Am. & Afro-Am. lit), 69. Instr. Eng, Lawrence Inst. Technol, 67-68; asst. prof, Ind. State Univ, Terre Haute, 69-70; AFRO-AM. STUD, IND. UNIV, BLOOMINGTON, 70-73, ASSOC. PROF, 73- MLA; Midwest Mod. Lang. Asn; Col. Lang. Asn; Col. Eng. Asn; Popular Cult. Asn; AAUP. Afro-American literature, fiction, drama, biography and autobiography; blacks in films. Publ: Co-auth, The black family and the black woman: a bibliography, Ind. Univ,

72; auth, The white bitch archetype in contemporary Afro-American literature, Midwest Mod. Lang. Asn. Bull, spring 73; Jesse B. Semple and the narrative art of Langston Hughes, J. Narrative Technique, spring 73; The confidence man in two black novels: William M. Kelley's dem and John A. Williams' The man who cried I am, Am. Lit, 1/73. Add: Dept. of Afro-American Studies, Indiana University, Bloomington, IN 47401.

KLOTZ, MARVIN, b. New York, N.Y, Feb. 6, 30; m. 53, 68; c. 2. AMERICAN LITERATURE. B.S, Columbia Univ, 51; M.A, Univ. Minn, 52; Ph.D, N.Y. Univ, 59. Instr. ENG, N.Y. Univ, 56-59; asst. prof, CALIF. STATE UNIV, NORTHRIDGE, 59-63, assoc. prof, 63-69, PROF, 69- Fulbright lectr, Saigon, South Vietnam & Taipei, Taiwan, 67-68. U.S.A.F, 48-49, Res, 49-55. Faulkner; fictional realism; American prose style. Publ: Co-auth, Faulkner's people: index to his characters, Univ. Calif, 63; co-ed, Literature: the human experience, St. Martin's, 73; auth, Stephen Crane: tragedian or comedian: The blue hotel, Univ. Kans. City Rev, 9/61; The triumph over time: narrative form in William Faulkner and William Styron, Miss. Quart, 3/64; Procrustean revision in Faulkner's Go down, Moses, Am. Lit, 3/65. Add: Dept. of English, California State University, Northridge, CA 91324.

KLOUCEK, JEROME W, b. Milwaukee, Wis, Sept. 25, 13. AMERICAN LITERATURE. B.A, Univ. Chicago, 35, M.A, 40; Ph.D.(Am. lit), Northwest. Univ, 58. Teacher, private sec. schs, 38-43; instr. Eng. & registr, Montgomery Jr. Col, Md, 46-50, 53-56; instr. ENG, UNIV. TOLEDO, 57-58, asst. prof, 58-61, assoc. prof, 61-63, PROF. 63-, asst. dean col. arts & sci, 59-61, dean, 61-67. U.S.A, 43-46, M/Sgt. MLA; Am. Stud. Asn; Nat. Asn. Gen. & Lib. Stud. Nineteenth and 20th century American poetry and fiction. Add: Dept. of English, University of Toledo, Toledo, OH 43606.

KLUKOFF, PHILIP J, b. Brooklyn, N.Y, Feb. 27, 38; m. 63; c. 1. ENGLISH. B.A, Allegheny Col, 59; M.A, Mich. State Univ, 61, Ph.D.(Eng), 65. Instr. Eng, Univ. Cincinnati, 63-65; asst. prof, Wayne State Univ, 65-67; Univ. Md, Baltimore, 67-71; PROF. ENG. & CHMN. DIV. ARTS & HUMANITY, STOCKTON STATE COL, 71- Summer res. fel, Univ. Md, Baltimore, 68. MLA. Eighteenth century English literature; English romantic poetry. Publ: Smollett and the Critical Review: criticism of the novel, 1756-1763, Stud. Scottish Lit, 10/66; New Smollett attributions in the Critical Review, Notes & Queries, 11/67; Smollett and the Sackville Controversy, Neuphilologische Mitteillungen, 68. Add: Div. of Arts & Humanity, Stockton State College, Pomona, NJ 08240.

KNAPP, EDGAR H, b. Waltham, Mass, Feb. 19, 22; m. 42; c. 8. ENGLISH, EDUCATION. B.A, Wesleyan Univ, 43; M.A, Boston Univ, 50; Ed.D, Columbia Univ, 60. Teacher, Groton Sch, Mass, 46-47; Browne & Nichols Sch, 47-50; Natick High Sch, 50-51; Kingswood Sch, Conn, 51-53; Manhasset High Sch, N.Y, 53-60; curriculum coord, W. Essex High Sch, N.J, 60-62; ASSOC. PROF. ENG. & EDUC, PA. STATE UNIV, 62- U.S.N.R, 44-46, Lt. (jg). English education; literary criticism; American literature. Publ: Introduction to poetry, McCormick-Mathers, 65; co-auth, Ideas and patterns in literature, III, Harcourt, 70; auth, Poetry in the curriculum: introduction and consummation, In: Classroom Practices Teaching Eng, 66-67, NCTE, 66; Discussion strategies in teaching G.M. Hopkins' The windhover, Eng. Rec, 12/68; Found in the Barthhouse: novelist as savior, Mod. Fiction Stud, winter 68-69; Reading imaginative literature, High Sch. J, 4/69. Add: 451 Sierra Lane, State College, PA 16801.

KNAPP, JAMES FRANKLIN, b. Chicago, Ill, Oct. 10, 40; m. 67; c. 3. MODERN POETRY, MYTH. B.A, Drew Univ, 62; Ph.D.(Eng), Univ. Conn, 66. Asst. prof. ENG, UNIV. PITTSBURGH, 66-71, ASSOC. PROF, 71- MLA; Mediaeval Acad. Am. Modern British and American poetry; contemporary poetry; myth theory. Publ: The meaning of Sir Orfeo, Mod. Lang. Quart, 68; Delmore Schwartz: poet of the orphic journey, Sewanee Rev, 70; The poetry of R.S. Thomas, Twentieth Century Lit, 71. Add: Dept. of English, University of Pittsburgh, Pittsburgh, PA 15213.

KNAPP, JOSEPH GEORGE, S.J, b. St. Louis, Mo, Mar. 5, 24. ENGLISH, HISTORY. A.B, St. Louis Univ, 49, Ph.L, 50; A.M, Marquette Univ, 53; Ph.D, Univ. Minn, 62. Instr. Eng. & hist, ST. LOUIS UNIV, 61-67, assoc. prof, 67-73, PROF. ENG. & AM. STUD, 73-, chmn. freshman rhetoric, 64-68, dir. interdisciplinary film prog, 71-73. NDEA fels, 63-64; consult. merit awards, NCTE, 67-68; Fulbright-Hays sr. lectr, Fed. Univ. Rio de Janiero, 73- MLA; Am. Stud. Asn; AHA; Mid-Continent Am. Stud. Asn.(pres, 69-70); NCTE. Herman Melville, William Faulkner; relationship between literature and cinema. Publ: Ed, Rhetoric, St. Louis Univ, 63; auth, Tortured synthesis: the meaning of Melville's Clarel, Philos Libr, 71; The dynamics of the American dream 1776-1976: notes toward an interdisciplinary synthesis, Nat. Endowment for Humanities, 72; Dreiser, In: New Cath. Encycl, McGraw, 67. Add: Dept. of English, St. Louis University, 221 N. Grand, St. Louis, MO 63103.

KNAPP, LEWIS MANSFIELD, b. Groton, Mass, Mar. 4, 94; m. 22, 38; c. 2. ENGLISH. A.B, Amherst Col, 16; A.M, Columbia Univ, 20; Sterling fel. & Ph.D, Yale, 28; Litt.D, Colo. Col, 66. Master, Bishop's Col. Sch, Lennoxville, Can, 16-17; teacher, Hopkins Grammar Sch, New Haven, Conn, 20-23; instr. ENG, Univ. Colo, 22-25; instr. & asst. prof, Williams Col, 28-38; from asst. prof. to prof, COLO. COL, 39-61, chmn. dept, 47-59, EMER. PROF, 62- Grant-in-aid, Am. Counc. Learned Socs; Williams Col; Carnegie vis. prof, Univ. Alaska, 62-63; Am. Philos. Soc. grant, 66-67. U.S.A, 17-19. MLA; Mod. Humanities Res. Asn, Gt. Brit. Eighteenth century literature; Tobias Smollett and other 18th-century figures. Publ: Tobias Smollett, doctor of men and manners, Princeton Univ; ed, Tobias Smollett's Humphrey Clinker, 49 & The letters of Tobias Smollett, 70 & contrib, Student guides to the novel, 71, Oxford Univ; auth, Tobias Smollett, In: Cambridge bibliography of English literature, Cambridge Univ, 71. Add: 115 E. Del Norte St, Colorado Springs, CO 80907.

KNAPP, MARY E, b. New Canaan, Conn, Oct, 4, 02. ENGLISH LITERATURE. A.B, Columbia Univ, 31, A.M, 32; Ph.D, Yale, 42. Teacher, high sch, Conn, 35-44; chmn. dept. ENG, Albertus Magnus Col, 44-48; assoc. prof, WEST. COL, 48-56, prof, 56-68, EMER. PROF, 68-; EMER. PROF, ALBERTUS MAGNUS COL, 72-, prof, 68-72. Sterling fel, Yale, 43-44; Am. Philos. Soc. grant-in-aid, 50; Huntington Libr. grant, 53. MLA; Conn. Acad. Arts. & Sci. English literature of the 18th century; David Garrick. Publ: Checklist of verse by David Garrick, Univ. Va; Prologues and epilogues of the eighteenth century, Yale Univ, 61. Add: 120 Dwight St, New Haven, CT 06511.

KNAPP, PEGGY ANN, b. Brainerd, Minn, July 6, 37; m. 67; c. 3. ENGLISH & AMERICAN LITERATURE. B.S, Univ. Wis-Madison, 59, M.A, 61; Ph.D. (Eng), Univ. Pittsburgh, 65. Lectr. ENG, Mt. Mercy Col, 65-66; Univ. Pittsburgh, 66-68; ASST. PROF, Univ. Conn, 68-69; CARNEGIE-MELLON UNIV, 70- Mediaeval Acad. Am; MLA. Middle English prose; Shakespeare; drama. Publ: The style of John Wyclif's English sermons, Mouton, (in press); John Wyclif as a Bible translator, Speculum, 10/71; The orphic vision of Pericles, Tex. Stud. Lit. & Lang, winter 74. Add: Dept. of English, Carnegie-Mellon University, Pittsburgh, PA 15213.

KNAPP, ROBERT STANLEY, b. Alamosa, Colo, Mar. 29, 40; m. 65. ENGLISH. B.A, Univ. Colo, 62; M.A, Univ. Denver, 63; fel, Cornell Univ, 63-64 & 65-66, Ph.D.(Eng), 68. Instr. ENG, Princeton, 66-68, asst. prof, 68-74, Donald A. Stauffer bicentennial preceptor, 70-73; ASST. PROF, REED COL, 74- MLA. Renaissance drama; modern theatre. Publ: Samuel Beckett's Allegory of the uncreating word, Mosaic, winter 73; Horestes: the uses of revenge, ELH, summer 73. Add: Dept. of English, Reed College, Portland, OR 97202.

KNAPP, TERENCE RICHARD, b. London, Eng, Feb. 14, 32. DRAMA, THEATRE. Dipl. distinction & Bancroft Medallist, Royal Acad. Dramatic Art, 54. Mem. & scholar, Liverpool Playhouse, 54-58; mem. Chichester Festival Theatre, 62-64; inaugural player, Nat. Theatre of Gt. Brit, 64-66; mem, Nottingham Playhouse, 66-68; Churchill mem. fel, Japanese Classical Theatre Arts, 68-69; ASSOC. PROF. DRAMA & THEATRE, UNIV. HAWAII, 70- Brit. Counc. Bursary, Kumo Shingekidan, Tokyo, 66; Performer-choreographer, Naboth's vineyard, London Festival, 68 & Shadow play two, 69; assoc. dir, Anthony and Cleopatra, Shingeki Kumo, Tokyo, 68 & Macbeth, 71; dir-performer, Joan at the stake, Honolulu Symphony Soc, 73. R.A.F, 50-53. Shakespeare in Japanese performance; avant garde music theatre. Add: Dept. of Drama & Theatre, University of Hawaii, 1770 E. West Rd, Honolulu, HI 96822.

KNAUB, RICHARD K, b. Springfield, Mo, July 7, 28; m. 53; c. 2. SPEECH & DRAMA. A.B, Ind. Univ, 50; M.F.A, State Univ. Iowa, 55; Ph.D, Ind. Univ, 62. Instr. speech & drama & tech. dir, Allegheny Col, 55-57; lectr. speech & theatre & tech. dir, Ind. Univ, 57-62; ASSOC. PROF. SPEECH & DRAMA, UNIV. COLO, BOULDER, 62-, dir. theatre, 65-72. Fulbright lectr, Univ. Col, Wales, 73-74. Gold Medal, Am. Oil Co. & Am. Col. Theatre Festival, 73. U.S.A, 50-52, Sgt. Am. Theatre Asn.(pres, Rocky Mt. dist, 71-72). Technical theatre developments; American theatre history. Publ: Ed, On Shakespeare's stage, Univ. Colo, 67; co-auth, The art of play production, Harper, 72. Add: University Theatre, University of Colorado, Boulder, CO 80302.

KNEDLER, JOHN WARREN, JR, b. Elmhurst, Pa, Apr. 29, 01. ENGLISH PHILOLOGY. A.B, Harvard, 24, A.M, 27, Ph.D, 37. Instr. ENG, UNIV. COL, N.Y. UNIV, 29-38, asst. prof, 38-46, assoc. prof, 46-51, prof, 51-71, asst. dean, 46-57, assoc. dean, 57-60, dean, 60-67, exec. secy. dept, 44-46, chmn. exec. comt, Univ. Heights, 67-68, EMER. PROF. & DEAN, 71- Lectr. & adv. in charge lib. arts stud, Manhattan Sch. Music, 44-61, acad. consult, 67-69, chmn. admis. comt, 69-; ed, Masterworks in Sci. MLA; Renaissance Soc. Am; Asn. Higher Educ; NCTE; East. Asn. Col. Deans. Medieval romance and folklore; Shakespeare; contemporary British literature. Add: 215 Church St, Moscow, PA 18444.

KNEPLER, HENRY WILLIAM, b. Vienna, Austria, May 8, 22, nat. ENGLISH. B.A, Queen's Univ.(Can), 45, M.A, 46; Ph.D.(Eng), Univ. Chicago, 50. Lectr. ENG, Queen's Univ.(Can), 46; instr, ILL. INST. TECHNOL, 47-52, asst. prof, 52-58, assoc. prof, 58-61, PROF. ENG. & CHMN. DEPT. HUMANITIES, 61- Vis. prof Am. lit. & civilization, Sorbonne, 71-73; consult, UNESCO, 72-73. MLA; NCTE. English drama, especially Restoration and modern; American drama; relationship of engineering and humanities. Publ: Range of writing, Prentice-Hall, 59; Anglo-German cross currents, Vol. II, Univ. N.C, 62; co-ed, What is the play?, Scott, 67; auth, The gilded stage, William Morrow & Constable, London, 68; Man about Paris, William Morrow, 70 & Gollancz, London, 72; ed, The humanities and social sciences in engineering education, UNESCO, Paris, 73; Edward Albee: conflict of traditions, Mod. Drama, 12/67; plus others. Add: Dept. of Humanities, Illinois Institute of Technology, Chicago, IL 60616.

KNEPPER, BILL GARTON, b. Sioux City, Iowa, Sept. 5, 22; m. 45; c. 4. ENGLISH. B.A, Univ. Minn, 46, M.A, 48; Regent's tuition fel, Univ. Nebr, 62-64, Ph.D.(Eng), 67. PROF. ENG. & CHMN. DEPT, MORNINGSIDE COL, 59- Mem, Am. Inter-Prof. Inst. U.S.M.C.R, 42-45. Midwest Mod. Lang. Asn; MLA; NCTE; AAUP. Bernard Shaw. Publ: Shaw rewriting Shaw: a fragment, Shaw Rev, 9/69; Shaw's debt to the coming race, J. Mod. Lit, 3/71; J. Glen Gray, The warriors, considered, Morningside Rev, 7/72; plus others. Add: 3400 Dodge Ave, Sioux City, IA 51106.

KNICKERBOCKER, KENNETH LESLIE, b. Dallas, Tex, May 19, 05; m. 28; c. 2. ENGLISH LITERATURE. A.B, South. Methodist Univ, 25, A.M, 27; Univ. Chicago, 27; Ph.D, Yale, 33. Instr, Tex. Tech. Col, 26-29, 32-34; asst. prof. Eng, R.I. State Col, 34-36, assoc. prof, 36-38, prof. & head dept, 38-46; prof. & chmn. freshman Eng, UNIV. TENN, KNOXVILLE, 46-58, dean col. lib. arts, 58-63, PROF. ENG, 63-71, 73-, head. dept, 63-71, v.pres. acad. affairs, 71-73. Am. Counc. Learned Soc. grant-in-aid, 34; co-ed, Tenn. Stud. Lit, 63-73. U.S.N.R, 43-45, Lt. MLA; Col. Eng. Asn; Asn. Depts. Eng. Literature of the 19th century; Browning. Publ: Selected poetry of Robert Browning, Mod. Libr, 51; Ideas for writing, 51, 56, 62, co-auth, Interpreting literature, 55, 60, 65, 69, 74, Reading and assignments, 61 & Writing about poetry, 67, Holt; co-auth, New letters of Robert Browning, Yale Univ. & John Murray, 50. Add: 3524 Bluff Point Dr, Knoxville, TN 37920.

KNICKERBOCKER, MAXIMILIAN ROBERT, JR, b. Providence, R.I, Jan. 13, 22; m. 45; c. 5. ENGLISH. A.B, Providence Col, 48; M.A, Brown Univ, 50. Instr. ENG, ROCKHURST COL, 50-54, asst. prof, 54-63, assoc. prof, 63-73, PROF, 73-, CHMN. DEPT, 67- U.S.A.F, 42-46. American poetry from

Whitman to present; American literary criticism,1865-1900. Add: Dept. of English, Rockhurst College, Kansas City, MO 64110.

KNIEGER, BERNARD (MARTIN), b. New York, N.Y, Oct. 9, 22; m. 46. ENGLISH. A.B, N.Y. Univ, 48; M.A, Harvard, 49, Ph.D.(Eng), 52. Asst. prof. ENG, Ark. State Teachers Col, 53-54; instr, Univ. Baltimore, 54-55; asst. prof, Ripon Col, 55-56; Univ. Wis, Milwaukee, 56-61; Wash. State Univ, 61-64; SR. LECTR, HAIFA UNIV, 64- U.S.A, 43-46. Univ. Teachers Eng. Israel. Metaphysical poetry; contemporary short story; philosophy in literature. Publ: Humpty Dumpty and symbolism, Col. Eng, 2/59; Moral essays of Dr. Johnson, Personalist, 61; The purchase-sale: patterns of business imagery in the poetry of George Herbert, Stud. Eng. Lit, winter 66; plus others. Add: Dept. of English, Haifa University, Mt. Carmel, Haifa, Israel.

KNIES, EARL ALLEN, b. White Haven, Pa, July 11, 36; m. 59; c. 3. ENGLISH. B.A, Muhlenberg Col, 58; M.A, Lehigh Univ, 60; Ph.D.(Eng), Univ. Ill, 64. Asst. prof. ENG, OHIO UNIV, 64-70, ASSOC. PROF, 70- MLA. Victorian novel. Publ: The art of Charlotte Brontë, Ohio Univ, 69; Art, death and the composition of Shirley, Victorian Newsletter, fall 65; The artistry of Charlotte Brontë, Ohio Univ. Rev, 65; The I of Jane Eyre, Col. Eng, 4/66. Add: Dept. of English, Ohio University, Athens, OH 45701.

KNIGHT, CHARLES ANTHONY, b. San Francisco, Calif, Sept. 3, 37; m. 58; c. 4. ENGLISH. B.A, Haverford Col, 58; M.A, Univ. Pa, 60, Ph.D.(Eng), 64. Instr. ENG, Cath. Univ. Am, 61-62; Univ. Mass, Amherst, 62-65; asst. prof, UNIV. MASS, BOSTON, 65-69, ASSOC. PROF, 69-, ASSOC. DEAN ACAD. AFFAIRS, 72- MLA. Eighteenth century English literature; British fiction. Publ: Richardson's use of wills in Clarissa, Tex. Stud. Lit. & Lang, 69; Argument in Rochester's Satire against mankind, Mod. Lang. Rev. 70; Multiple structures and the unity of Tom Jones, Criticism, 72. Add: Dept. of English, University of Massachusetts, Harbor Campus, Boston, MA 02125.

KNIGHT, DOUGLAS MAITLAND, b. Cambridge, Mass, June 8, 21; m. 42; c. 4. ENGLISH. A.B, Yale, 42, M.A, 44, Ph.D, 46; LL.D, Ripon Col, 55, Knox Col, 63, Davidson Col, 63, Univ. N.C, Chapel Hill, 65, Emory Univ, 65; Litt.D, St. Norbert Col, 63, Wake Forest Col, 64, Ohio Wesleyan Univ, 70, Centre Col. Ky, 73; L.H.D, Lawrence Univ, 64, Carleton Col, 66. Instr. Eng, Yale, 46-47, asst. prof, 47-54; pres, Lawrence Col, 54-63; prof. Eng. & pres, Duke Univ, 63-69; div. v.pres. educ. develop, RCA Corp, 69-71, div. v.pres. educ. serv, 71-72, staff v.pres. educ. & community relat, 72-73; PRES, SOCIAL ECON. & EDUC. DEVELOP. INC, N.Y.C, 73- Morse res. fel, 51-52; mem. bd. dirs, Rockefeller Bros. Theol. Fel. Prog, 60-67; bd. trustees, Woodrow Wilson Nat. Fel. Found, 60-; bd. dirs, Nat. Merit. Scholar. Corp, 63-67; bd. trustees, Educ. & World Affairs, 63-71; mem. corp, Found. Arts, Relig. & Cult, 64-67; adv. comt. inst. relat, Nat. Sci. Found, 64-67; Nat. Comn. UNESCO, 65-67; Mass. Inst. Technol, 65-70; bd. trustees, United Negro Col. Fund, 66-67; mem, 67-; mem. Adv. Comn. Spec. Stud. Educ. Educr, 66-67; chmn, Nat. Adv. Comn. Libr, 66-68; Mid.S. Regional Educ. Lab. Develop. Comt, 66-69; educ. adv. comt, Esso Educ. Found, 66-70; bd. vis, Air Univ, 67; mem. bd. dirs, RCA Inst, 69-; pres, RCA Iran, Ltd, 71-72, mem. bd. dirs, 72-73; Random House, 71-73. MLA; Soc. Relig. Higher Educ; Newcomen Soc. Publ: Pope and the heroic tradition, Yale; ed, Federal government and higher education, Prentice-Hall, 60; co-ed, Iliad and Odyssey, Methuen, 67; co-auth, Medical ventures and the university: new values and new validities, Asn. Am. Med. Cols, 67; ed, Libraries at large, tradition, innovation and the national interest, Bowker, 70; auth, The dark gate (poetry), Univ. Tex, Austin, 71; The dramatic center of Paradise lost, S.Atlantic Quart, winter 64; The future of graduate education in the U.S, Educ. Record, spring 65. Add: Ridge Farm, R.D, 1, Box 156, Stockton, NJ 08559.

KNIGHT, IONE KEMP, b. Greensboro, N.C, Dec. 9, 22. MIDDLE ENGLISH. A.B, Meredith Col, 43; M.A, Univ. Pa, 49; Ph.D, Univ. N.C, 54. Prof. ENG. & head dept, Shorter Col, 53-56; assoc. prof, MEREDITH COL, 56-73, PROF, 73- Res, Bodleian Libr, Oxford Univ, 72. Col. Eng. Asn; S.Atlantic Mod. Lang. Asn; MLA. Old and Middle English; 19th century English literature. Publ: Wimbledon's sermon, Duquesne Univ, 67. Add: Dept. of English, Meredith College, Raleigh, NC 27611.

KNIGHT, JOSEPH ELWOOD, b. San Francisco, Calif, Oct. 4, 41; m; c. 2. ENGLISH LITERATURE. B.A, Univ. San Francisco, 64; M.A. & Arts D, Univ. Ore, 70, Ph.D.(Eng), 72. ASST. PROF. ENG, UNIV. IDAHO, 70-, summer fac. res. grant & res. assoc, 73. Wordsworth Circle; Byron Soc. Romantic movement; composition and rhetoric. Add: Dept. of English, University of Idaho, Moscow, ID 83843.

KNIGHT, KARL FREDERICK, b. Iredell Co, N.C, July 3, 30; m. 59; c. 2. AMERICAN LITERATURE. A.B, Univ. N.C, 56, M.A, 57; fel, Emory Univ, 58-60, Ph.D.(Eng), 62. Instr. ENG, Berry Col, 57-58; Univ. Ala, 60-62; asst. prof, OLD DOM. UNIV, 62-64, assoc. prof, 64-67, PROF, 67-, chmn. dept, 69- Humanities fel, coop. prog. humanities, Duke Univ-Univ. N.C, 65-66. U.S.A.F, 50-54, S/Sgt. MLA; S.Atlantic Mod. Lang. Asn. Herman Melville; John Crowe Ransom; William Faulkner. Publ: Auth, The poetry of John Crowe Ransom, Mouton, The Hague, 64; co-auth, Writer to writer: readings on the craft of writing, Houghton, 66 & A concise handbook of English composition, Prentice-Hall, 72; auth, Love as symbol in the poetry of Ransom, In: John Crowe Ransom: critical essays and a bibliography, La. State Univ, 68. Add: Dept. of English, Old Dominion University, Norfolk, VA 23508.

KNIGHT, WILLIAM NICHOLAS, b. Mt. Vernon, N.Y, Apr. 18, 39; m. 61; c. 4. MEDIEVAL & RENAISSANCE ENGLISH. B.A, Amherst Col, 61; M.A, Univ. Calif, Berkeley, 63; Ph.D.(Eng), Ind. Univ, 68. Instr. ENG, WESLEYAN UNIV, 66-68, ASST. PROF, 68-, asst. chmn. dept, 70-71, fel, Ctr. Humanities, 71-72. Consult. Renaissance lit, Choice; Ford Found. fel, 70-71; excellence in teaching award, Asn. Depts. Eng. & MLA, 72-73. MLA; NCTE; Renaissance Soc. Am. Shakespearean revenge tragedy; Shakespearean biography; equity in law and drama. Publ: Shakespeare at the law: a hidden life, 1585-1595, Mason & Lipscomb, 73; Equity and mercy in English drama 1400-1641, Comp. Drama, 72; Spenserian chivalric influence in Paradise regained, In: Costerus essays, 72; Toward archetype in the Joseph Colombo shooting, Brit. J. Soc. Psychiat. & Community Health, 72; The death of J.K. (play), London Rev, 70 & prod, Wesleyan, Amherst, Smith, Univ. Mass, Inns of Court, London & Cubiculo; plus others. Add: 227 Atkins St, Middletown, CT 06457.

KNIGHTON, ROBERT TOLMAN, b. Bountiful, Utah, Feb. 23, 35; m. 58; c. 3. ENGLISH & AMERICAN LITERATURE. B.S, Utah State Univ, 61, M.S, 62; Ph.D.(Eng), Univ. Colo, Boulder, 72. Instr. ENG, Utah State Univ, 61-62; ASST. PROF, UNIV. OF THE PAC, 67- Restoration and 18th century English literature; English Romantic poetry; modern existential literature. Add: Dept. of English, University of the Pacific, Stockton, CA 95204.

KNIPP, THOMAS RICHARD, b. Chicago, Ill, Feb. 27, 29; m. 52; c. 6. ENGLISH. A.B, DePaul Univ, 51, M.A, 55; Ph.D.(Eng), Mich. State Univ, 66. Asst. prof. Eng, Univ. Col, Ethiopia, 56-61; asst. instr, Mich. State Univ, 61-63; asst. prof, Kent State Univ, 63-69, assoc. prof, 69-73, asst. dean arts & sci, 66-73; PROF. ENG. & DEAN COL. ARTS & SCI, ST. LOUIS UNIV, 73- Regional Counc. Int. Educ. Stud. grant African lit, 66, chmn. publ. comt, 66-68; Fulbright lectr. Eng, Haile Sellassie I Univ, 68-69. African Stud. Asn. American literature; African literature. Publ: James Ngugi: the novel in Kenya, Bks. Abroad, fall 67; Richard Wrights letters to Joe C. Brown, Kent State Univ. Libr, 10/68; Lenrie Peters: poet as lonely African, Stud. Black Lit, fall 72. Add: College of Arts & Sciences, St. Louis University, 200 N. Grand Blvd, St. Louis, MO 63103.

KNITTEL, FRANK ALVIN, b. Shafter, Calif, Sept. 30, 27; m. 56; c. 2. ENGLISH. B.A, Union Col.(Nebr), 47; M.A, Univ. Colo, 55, Ph.D.(Eng. lang), 60. Dean men, Enterprise Acad, Kans, 47-51; Campion Acad, Loveland, Colo, 53-55; asst. to dean men, Univ. Colo, 55-59; assoc. prof. Eng, Andrews Univ, 59-64, dean students, 63-64, v.pres, 64-67; acad. dean, SOUTH. MISSIONARY COL, 67-71, PRES, 71- U.S.A, 51-53, Res, 53-, 1st Lt. MLA. Mediaeval language and literature. Add: Box 484, Collegedale, TN 37315.

KNODT, KENNETH SIMMS, b. Darby, Pa, Oct. 4, 40; m. 64. ENGLISH & AMERICAN LITERATURE. B.A, Northwest. Univ, 62; M.A, Mich. State Univ, 63; Ph.D.(Eng), Purdue Univ, West Lafayette, 72. Instr. ENG, Valparaiso Univ, 63-67; Col. William & Mary, 67-70; teaching asst, Purdue Univ, West Lafayette, 70-71; ASST. PROF, LA SALLE COL, 71- Ed. assoc, Four Quarters, 72- MLA; AAUP; Am. Stud. Asn. American studies; 20th century English literature; novel. Publ: Ed, American dreams, Prentice-Hall, 75. Add: Dept. of English, La Salle College, Philadelphia, PA 19141.

KNOEPFLE, JOHN IGNATIUS, b. Cincinnati, Ohio, Feb. 4, 23; m. 56; c. 2. ENGLISH, RENAISSANCE. Ph.B, Xavier Univ.(Ohio), 47, M.A, 49; Ph.D. (Eng), St. Louis Univ, 67. Asst. instr. Eng, Ohio State Univ, 56-57; instr, South. Ill. Univ, 57-61; honors prog, high sch, St. Louis, Univ, 61-62; ASST. PROF. ENG, Maryville Col. Sacred Heart, 62-66; St. Louis Univ, 66-72; SANGAMON STATE UNIV, 72- Consult, Educ. Assoc, Inc, 66-; Rockefeller Found. fel, 67-68. U.S.N, 42-46, Lt.(jg). MLA; Renaissance Soc. Am; Shakespeare Asn. Am; Am. Stud. Asn. American poetry, practitioner and publishing poet; studies in Macbeth; translations from Spanish poets. Publ: Co-auth, Twenty poems of Cesar Vallejo, Sixties, 62; auth, Rivers into islands, Univ. Chicago, 65. Add: Dept. of English, Sangamon State University, Springfield, IL 62703.

KNOEPFLMACHER, U. C, b. Munich, Ger, June 26, 31; U.S. citizen; m. 59; c. 3. ENGLISH LITERATURE. A.B, Univ. Calif, Berkeley, 55, M.A, 57; Ph.D, Princeton, 61. Instr. ENG, UNIV. CALIF, BERKELEY, 61-62, asst. prof, 62-66, assoc. prof, 66-69, PROF, 69- Am. Counc. Learned Soc. fel, 65; Humanities Res. Prof, 66-67; Guggenheim fel, 69-70; vis. prof. Eng, Harvard, summer 71; Nat. Endowment for Humanities sr. fel, 72-73. MLA; NCTE; Medieaval Acad. Am. Nineteenth century English literature; English novel. Publ: Religious humanism and the Victorian novel, Princeton, 65; George Eliot's early novels: the limits of realism, 68 & Laughter and despair: readings in ten novels of the Victorian era, 71, Univ. Calif; ed, Francis Newman: Phases of faith, Leicester Univ, 70; auth, Dover revisited: the Wordsworthian matrix in the poetry of Matthew Arnold, Victorian Poetry, 1/69, O rare for Strether!: Antony and Cleopatra and The Ambassadors, In: Nineteenth-Century Fiction, 3/65; The poet as physician: Pope's Epistle to Arbuthnot, Mod. Lang. Quart, 12/70; plus others. Add: Dept. of English, 322 Wheeler Hall, University of California, Berkeley, CA 94720.

KNOLL, ROBERT EDWIN, b. Liberty, Nebr, Feb. 3, 22; m. 53; c. 3. ENGLISH. B.A, Univ. Nebr, 43; M.A, Univ. Minn, 47, Ph.D, 50; Yale, 47-48. Asst. prof. ENG, UNIV. NEBR, LINCOLN, 50-62, PROF, 62-, Sr. fel, centennial educ. prog, 68-71. Woods Found. fel, London, 59-60; Fulbright teaching fel, Graz, Austria, 66-67; trustee, Shakespeare Asn. Am, 72- U.S.A, 43-46, Lt. MLA; NCTE; Cent. Renaissance Conf.(pres, 61-62, 65-66); AAUP. Sixteenth century English literature; Shakespeare; teaching of undergraduates. Publ: Contrasts, idea and technique, Harcourt, 55 & 59; Robert McAlmon, expatriate writer and publisher, 59, ed, McAlmon and the lost generation: a self portrait, 62 & auth, Ben Jonson's plays, an introduction, 64, Univ. Nebr; Christopher Marlowe, Twayne, 68; co-auth, Experiment in Nebraska: the first two years of a cluster college, Univ. Nebr. Stud, 72. Add: Dept. of English, University of Nebraska, Lincoln, NE 68508.

KNOPP, JOSEPHINE ZADOVSKY, b. Chicago, Ill. AMERICAN & EUROPEAN LITERATURE. B.A, Univ. Ill, 61, M.A, 65; Ph.D.(Comp. lit), Univ. Wis, 71. ASST. PROF. ENG. LIT. & HUMANITIES, UNIV. ILL, CHICAGO CIRCLE, 71- AAUP; MLA; Midwest Mod. Lang. Asn; Asn. Jewish Stud. Holocaust studies of the Nazi period; modern European literature; modern Jewish writers. Publ: Trial of Judaism in the contemporary novel, Univ. Ill, spring 74; Wiesel and the absurd, Wis. Stud. Contemporary Lit, spring 74; The ways of Mentshlekhayt in fiction of Bernard Malamud and Philip Roth, Tradition, winter 73. Add: Dept. of English, University of Illinois at Chicago Circle, Box 4348, Chicago, IL 60680.

KNOTT, A. KIRK, b. Blue Ridge, Tex, July 19, 03; m. 24; c. 2. ENGLISH. A.B. & A.M, Baylor Univ; fel, Univ. Ore, 37-38, D.Ed, 40. Teacher, pub. schs, Colo, 26-40; PROF. ENG, W.TEX. STATE UNIV, 40-, chmn. div. humanities, 40-72. Romantic poets; Shakespeare. Add: Dept. of English, West Texas State University, Canyon, TX 79015.

KNOTT, JOHN RAY, JR, b. Memphis, Tenn, July 9, 37; m. 59; c. 4. ENGLISH. B.A, Yale, 59; Ph.D.(Eng), Harvard, 66. Instr. ENG, Harvard, 66-67; asst. prof, UNIV. MICH, ANN ARBOR, 67-71, ASSOC. PROF, 71- Nat. Endowment for Humanities jr. fel, 74. Milton Soc. Am; MLA. Renaissance and seventeenth century English literature. Publ: Co-ed, The triumph of style, Houghton, 69; auth, Milton's pastoral vision, Univ. Chicago, 71; co-ed, Mirrors: an introduction to literature, Canfield, 72; Symbolic landscape in Paradise lost, Milton Stud, 3/70; Milton's heaven, PMLA, 70; Bunyon's gospel day, Eng. Lit. Renaissance, 73; plus others. Add: Dept. of English, University of Michigan, Ann Arbor, MI 48104.

KNOUSE, MARGARET LIVESAY, b. Rogersville, Tenn, Dec. 20, 05; m. 34; c. 2. ENGLISH. B.A, Carson-Newman Col, 29; M.A, State Univ. N.Y. Albany, 57. Instr. Eng, Bluefield Col, 29-34; TEACHER, Albany Acad. Girls, 51-54; ENG, GUILDERLAND HIGH SCH, 54- NCTE; NEA; Am. Asn. Univ. Women. Academically gifted child. Add: 40 Thorndale Rd, Slingerlands, NY 12159.

KNOWLES, ALBERT SIDNEY, JR, b. Savannah, Ga, Dec. 11, 26; m. 48; c. 3. ENGLISH. B.A, Univ. Va, 49, M.A, 51; Univ. N.C, Chapel Hill, 57-58. Instr. ENG, Ohio Univ, 52-55; N.C. STATE UNIV, 55-60, asst. prof, 60-67, assoc. prof, 67-68, alumni distinguished prof, 68-73, PROF, 73- U.S.A, 45-46, S/Sgt. MLA; Renaissance Soc. Am; Col. Eng. Asn. Eighteenth and nineteenth century and contemporary British and American literature. Publ: Spenser's natural man, Renaissance Papers, 58, 59 & 60, Southeast. Renaissance Conf, 61; The need for loners: nine novels of the sixties, South. Rev, summer 68; Six bronze petals and two red: Carson McCullers in the Forties, In: The Forties, Everett Edwards, 69; Defoe, Swift, and Fielding: notes on retirement, In: Quick springs of sense, Univ. Ga, 74; plus others. Add: Dept. of English, North Carolina State University, Raleigh, NC 27607.

KNOWLES, RICHARD ALAN JOHN, b. Southbridge, Mass, May 17, 35; m. 58; c. 2. ENGLISH RENAISSANCE. B.A, Tufts Univ, 56; M.A, Univ. Pa, 58, Samuel S. Fels fel, 61-62, Ph.D.(Eng), 63. Instr. ENG, UNIV. WIS-MADISON, 62-65, asst. prof, 65-68, ASSOC. PROF, 68- Folger Shakespeare Libr. fel, 68; vis. lectr, George Washington Univ. & Am. Univ, summer 69. MLA (mem. variorum Shakespeare comt, 72-76). Shakespeare; Renaissance mythography. Publ: Co-auth, Shakespeare variorum handbook, MLA, 71; Myth and type in As you like it, Eng. Lit. Hist, 66; Unquiet and the double plot of 2 Henry IV, Shakespeare Stud, 66; Rough notes on editions collated for As you like it, Shakespearean Res. & Opportunities, 68-69. Add: Dept. of English, University of Wisconsin-Madison, Madison, WI 53706.

KNOX, GEORGE A, b. Everett, Wash, May 9, 18; m. 47; c. 3. ENGLISH. A.B, Reed Col, 43; M.A, Univ. Ore, 49; Ph.D, Univ. Wash, 53. PROF. ENG. & AM. LIT, UNIV. CALIF, RIVERSIDE, 54-, CHMN. DEPT. ENG, 66- Fulbright lectr, Univ. Vienna, 57-58, Univ. Erlangen-Nürenberg, 64-65; ed. & contrib, Sadakichi Hartmann Newsletter, 69-73. U.S.N.R, 43-45. Am. Stud. Asn; Philol. Asn. Pac. Coast; MLA. Nineteenth and twentieth century American literature. Publ: Critical moments, Kenneth Burke's critiques and categories, Univ. Wash, 57; co-auth, Treaty trip, Univ. Mich, 60 & Dos Passos and The revolting playwrights, Upsala, 64; co-ed, Sadakichi Hartmann's White chrysanthemums: literary fragments and pronouncements, 71 & Buddha, Confucius, and Christ: three prophetic plays by Sakakichi Hartmann, 71, Herder & Herder. Add: Dept. of English, University of California, Riverside, CA 92502.

KNUDSON, KEITH DEAN, b. Osage, Iowa, Nov. 14, 32; m. 58; c. 3. ENGLISH. B.A, Luther Col, 55; M.A, Wash. State Univ, 57; Evangel. Lutheran Church scholar, George Peabody Col, 59-60, Martin Luther fels, 59-60, 60-61, Am. Lutheran Church future fac. fel, 61-62, Ph.D, 62. Teaching asst, Wash. State Univ, 55-57; instr. Eng. & speech, Waldorf Col, 58-59; teaching asst, George Peabody Col, 59-60, res. asst. Ford Found. prog, 60-62; asst. prof. ENG, MIDLAND LUTHERAN COL, 62-66, assoc. prof, 66-70, PROF, 70-, CHMN. DEPT, 72-, CHMN. DIV. MOD. LANG, 73- Vis. prof, Nev. South. Univ, summer 66; mem, NDEA Inst. for Col. & Univ. Prof. Eng. & Eng. Educ, Univ. Nebr, Lincoln, summer 68. U.S.A.R, 57-58. NCTE; MLA; AAUP; Col. Eng. Asn. Realism in the novel; science fiction; Plains literature. Publ: Co-auth, Teaching machines and programmed textbooks in the high school English curriculum, High Sch. J, 2/62; Norse mythology, Tenn. Folklore Soc. Bull, 3/70; Sci-fi, Midland Mag, 1st quart. 72. Add: Dept. of English, Midland Lutheran College, Fremont, NE 68025.

KNUDSON, RICHARD LEWIS, b. Newton, Mass, June 4, 30; m. 56; c. 2. ENGLISH. B.S, Gorham State Teachers Col, 57; M.Ed, Univ. Maine, Orono, 60; Fulbright grant, Netherlands, 62; D.Ed.(Eng. ed), Boston Univ, 70. Teacher Eng, Maine schs, 57-66; dir. Title III, Sch. Admin. Dist. 17, Paris, Maine, 66-70; ASSOC. PROF. ENG. EDUC, STATE UNIV. N.Y. COL. ONEONTA, 70- Consult. Eng, Maine State Dept. Educ, 65-66; ed, N.Y. State Eng. Counc, 73- Pacesetter's Award, President's Nat. Adv. Comt, 72; Spec. Citation, State of Maine Legis, 72. NCTE; Asn. Teacher Educ; Int. Reading Asn. English education. Publ: The effect of pupil-prepared videotape dramas upon the language development of selected rural children, Res. Teaching Eng, spring 71; What can the colleges change?, Eng. Educ, winter 73; Developing language skills with rural children, Rural Educ. News, 5-6/73; plus others. Add: Dept. of English, State University of New York College at Oneonta, Oneonta, NY 13820.

KNUST, HERBERT, German, Comparative Literature. See Volume III, Foreign Languages, Linguistics & Philology.

KNUTSON, WAYNE SHAFER, b. Sisseton, S.Dak, June 1, 26; m. 50; c. 3. THEATER. B.A, Augustana Col, 50; M.A, Univ. S.Dak, 51; Ph.D.(Eng, theater), Univ. Denver, 56. Instr. DRAMATIC ART, UNIV. S.DAK, 51-53, asst. prof, 56-59, assoc. prof, 59-63, PROF, 63-, DEAN, COL. FINE ARTS, 73, assoc. dir. univ. theater, 56-57, dir, 57-66, chmn. dept. Eng, 66-71, dir. merger, Univ. S.Dak-Univ. S.Dak, Springfield, summer 71. Assoc. dir. & bus. mgr, Black Hills Playhouse & Sch. Theater, Custer, S.Dak, 52-57, 59-62; chmn, S.Dak. Fine Arts Counc, 71-; mem, Inst. Educ. Mgt, Harvard, summer 73. U.S.N.R, 44-46; U.S.A, 46-47. Nat. Col. Players; MLA; NCTE. Modern drama, tragedy and comedy. Publ: A narrow escape into faith, Univ. S.Dak, 70. Add: 1153 Valley View, Vermillion, SD 57069.

KOBAN, CHARLES, b. Johnstown, Pa, Apr. 20, 33; m. 58; c. 4. ENGLISH. A.B, Pa. State Univ, 58; M.A, Columbia Univ, 60; fel, Univ. Ill, summer 61, Ph.D.(Eng), 63. Teaching asst. ENG, Univ. Ill, 60-63; asst. prof, STATE UNIV. N.Y. ALBANY, 63-71, ASSOC. PROF, 71- Res. Found. State Univ. N.Y. summer fels, 66 & 68. U.S.A, 54-56. Mediaeval Acad. Am; MLA. Geoffrey Chaucer's poetry; late medieval literature and culture; history of ideas. Add: Dept. of English, State University of New York at Albany, Albany, NY 12222.

KOBLER, JASPER FRED, b. Niagara Falls, N.Y, Apr. 6, 28; m. 52; c. 2. ENGLISH, AMERICAN LITERATURE. B.S, La. State Univ, 49, B.A, 51; M.A, Univ. Houston, 59; Ph.D.(Eng), Univ. Tex, 68. Reporter, Shreveport La. Times, 51-52; res. analyst, Defense Dept, Wash, D.C, 52-54; reporter, United Press, New Orleans, 55-56; indust. ed, Shell Oil Co, Houston, 56-59; instr. ENG, Univ. Houston, 59-61; from instr. to asst. prof, N.TEX. STATE UNIV, 64-70, ASSOC. PROF, 70- U.S.A.F, 53-55, 1st Lt. AAUP; Col. Eng. Asn; NCTE. Nineteenth century American short story; American writers of '20's and '30's, especially Hemingway and Faulkner. Publ: Hemingway's The sea change: a sympathetic view of homosexuality, winter 70 & Lena Grove: Faulkner's Still unravish'd bride of quietness, winter 72, Ariz. Quart; Francis Macomber as four-letter man, Fitzgerald-Hemingway Annual, 72; plus others. Add: P.O. Box 13561, North Texas Sta, North Texas State University, Denton, TX 76203.

KOBLER, TURNER SPENCER, b. Shreveport, La, Sept. 1, 30; m. 52; c. 2. ENGLISH. B.A, La. State Univ, 51; M.A, Univ. Houston, 61; Ph.D.(Eng), Univ. Tex, 68. Instr. ENG, Univ. Tex, Arlington, 64-68; from asst. prof. to ASSOC. PROF, TEX. WOMAN'S UNIV, 68- AAUP; Col. Eng. Asn; NCTE. Rhetoric; stylistics; linguistics. Publ: Alice Marriott, Steck-Vaughn, 69; The eclecticism of Rebecca West, Critique, 71; Alice Marriott: the anthropologist as artist, Southwest. Am. Lit, 5/71; plus one other. Add: Dept. of English, Texas Woman's University, Denton, TX 76204.

KOCH, CHRISTIAN HERBERT, b. St. Paul, Minn, June 27, 38; m. 72. COMMUNICATION THEORY. B.A, Northwest. Col, 59; M.A, Univ. Minn, Minneapolis, 64; M.F.A, South. Methodist Univ, 67; Ph.D.(speech & drama), Univ. Iowa, 70. Instr. music, Dr. Martin Luther Col, 59-60, 61-62; Wis. Lutheran Col, 62-66; ASST. PROF. COMMUN. STUD, OBERLIN COL, 70- Dir, Oberlin Int. Conf. Film Stud, 71-73; Nat. Endowment for Humanities younger humanists summer stipend, 72. Speech Commun. Asn.(chmn. res. comt, mass commun. div, 72-73); Int. Asn. Semiotic Stud; Am. Anthrop. Asn; Soc. Anthrop. Visual Commun; Soc. Cinema Stud. Semiotics; general systems theory; non-mechanistic cybernetics. Publ: Ed, Semiotics and cinema, Mouton, The Hague, 74; auth, Cinéma, discours, événement, In: Cinéma: théorie, lectures, Klincksieck, Paris, 73. Add: Dept. of Communication Studies, Oberlin College, Oberlin, OH 44074.

KOCH, CLAUDE F, b. Philadelphia, Pa, Nov. 28, 18; m. 41; c. 6. ENGLISH. B.S, La Salle Col, 40; fel, Niagara Univ, 41, Dodd-Mead fel, 49; Univ. Pa; M.A, Univ. Fla, 55. Asst. prof. ENG, LA SALLE COL, 46-58, assoc. prof, 58-66, PROF, 66- Sewanee Rev. fel, 56; lectr, Rosemont Col. & Holy Family Col.(Pa), 56-; Rockefeller Found. fel, 66. Lindbach Award for distinguished teaching, La Salle Col, 63; La Salle Col. Centennial Medal, 63. U.S.M.C.R, 41-45, Maj. Modern poetry; creative writing; Shakespeare. Publ: Island interlude, 51 & Light in silence, 58, Dodd; The kite in the sea, 64 & A casual company, 65, Chilton; A matter of family, In: Craft and vision, Delacorte, 72; Three poems, Sewanee Rev, Vol. LXXX, No. 2; plus others. Add: 128 W. Highland Ave, Philadelphia, PA 19118.

KOCH, DONALD ARTENIUS, b. Lykens, Pa, Jan. 5, 16; m. 41; c. 3. ENGLISH. A.B, Baldwin-Wallace Col, 42; M.A, West. Reserve Univ, 45, Ph.D. 54; Danforth scholar, Boston Univ, 53. Teaching fel. Eng, West. Reserve Univ, 46-47, instr, 47-50; asst. prof, Baldwin-Wallace Col, 50-55, assoc. prof, 55-60; PROF. ENG, CHMN. DEPT. & DIR. AM. STUD, SIMPSON COL, 60-, CHMN. DIV. HUMANITIES, 65- Fulbright vis. lectr. Am. lit, Univ. São Paulo, Brazil, 59; mem. educ. adv. comt, Iowa Civil War Centennial Comn, 63; vis. prof, Augustana Col.(Ill), fall 67; Mundelein Col, 69. Berea, Ohio pub. serv. cert, 59. MLA; Am. Stud. Asn; AAUP. Nineteenth century popular American literature; cultural history of 17th century New England; medical lore and practice in colonial New England. Publ: Ed, Ten nights in a bar-room, Harvard Univ, 64 & Tempest and sunshine, 68 & The lamplighter, 68, Odyssey; co-ed. & contrib, Popular American literature, Bowling Green State Univ, 72. Add: 810 W. Iowa Ave, Indianola, IA 50125.

KOCH, KENNETH, b. Cincinnati, Ohio, Feb. 27, 25; m. 54; c. 1. ENGLISH, COMPARATIVE LITERATURE. A.B, Harvard, 48; Fulbright fel, Univ. Aix-Marseilles & Sorbonne, France, 50; M.A, Columbia Univ, 53, Ph.D, 59. Asst, Univ. Calif, Berkeley, 51; instr. ENG. & COMP. LIT, COLUMBIA UNIV, 59-61, asst. prof, 61-66, assoc. prof, 66-71, PROF, 71- Guggenheim fel, 61. Harbison Award, Danforth Found, 70. U.S.A, 43-46. Twentieth century American poetry; modern European literature. Publ: Poems, De Nagy, 53; Ko, or a season on earth, 59, Thank you and other poems, 62, Bertha and other plays, 66 & The pleasures of peace (poems), 69, Grove; When the sun tries to go on (long poem), Black Sparrow Press, 69; Wishes, lies, and dreams: teaching children to write poetry, Chelsea House-Random, 70; A change of hearts (plays), 73 & Rose, where did you get that red?—teaching great poetry to children, 73, Random. Add: Dept. of English, Columbia University, New York, NY 10027.

KOCH, WILLIAM ERNEST, b. Hecla, S.Dak, Oct. 11, 10; m. 40; c. 2. ENGLISH. B.A, N.Dak. State Teacher's Col, 38; M.S, Kans. State Univ, 49; Ind. Univ, 52-54. Instr. Eng, KANS. STATE UNIV, 46-47, asst. prof, 47-73, ASSOC. PROF. ENG. & FOLKLORE, 73- Consult, Kans. 4-H Club Music Camps, summers, 50, 51, 55, 56; film consult, Nebr. Wheat Asn, 58; consult. & participant, Books & Songs of the Central Plains, Univ. Nebr, 61; music consult. & participant, Charles C. Howes' The Santa Fe Trail, 61. U.S.A, 42-46, Capt. Am. Folklore Soc; Am. Dialect Soc; Am. Name Soc. Folklore and folksong of central plains; place names of Kansas. Publ: Co-auth, Kansas folklore, Univ. Nebr, 61; Wellerisms from Kansas, West. Folklore, 60; Kansas history and folksongs, In: Heritage of Kansas, Kans. State Teachers Col, 61; Retention of Swedish folk festival and custom in central Kansas, In: Actes du Premier Congres International d'Ethnologie Europeenne, G.P. Maisonneuve & Larose, Paris, 73. Add: Dept. of English, Kansas State University, Manhattan, KS 66502.

KOCHER, PAUL HAROLD, b. Trinidad, B.W.I, Apr. 23, 07. ENGLISH. A.B, Columbia Univ, 26; J.D, Stanford Univ, 29, M.A, 32, Ph.D, 36. Instr, Stanford Univ, 36-37; from instr. to asst. prof, Univ. Wash, 38-46; prof. Eng, Univ. Nebr, 47-48; Claremont Grad. Sch, 48-57; ENG. & HUMANITIES, STANFORD UNIV, 60-73, EMER, PROF, 73-; WRITER, 73- Res. fel, Folger Shakespeare Libr, Wash, D.C, 40-41; Guggenheim fel, 46-47; fel, Henry E. Huntington Libr, 50-51, asst. ed, Quart, 50-; Guggenheim res. fel, 56-57. MLA; Cath. Hist. Soc. California missions; Renaissance literature and thought. Publ: Christopher Marlowe: his thought and learning, 46, 62; ed, Marlowe's Dr. Faustus, 50; auth, Science and religion in Renaissance England, 53; Mission San Luis Obispo 1772-1972, Blake Publ, 72; Master of Middle-earth: the fiction of J.R.R. Tolkien, Houghton, 73; Francis Bacon on the science of jurisprudence, J. Hist. Ideas. Add: Dept. of English, Stanford University, Stanford, CA 94305.

KOCHMAN, ANDREW J, JR, b. Akron, Ohio, Dec. 3, 18; m. 43; c. 3. SPEECH, THEATRE. B.A, Univ. Akron, 43; M.A, Univ. Wis, 47, Ph.D. (speech, theatre), 56. Assoc. prof. speech, Univ. N.Dak, 47-55; Ala. Col, 55-60; prof. speech & theatre, South. Ill, Univ, 60-70, dean fine arts div, SOUTH. ILL. UNIV, EDWARDSVILLE, 61-70, v.chancellor acad. affairs, 70-71, V.PRES. & PROVOST, 71- U.S.N.R, 42-46. Speech Commun. Asn; Am. Theatre Asn. British Restoration drama; 19th century British drama. Add: 120 Westridge Ct, Collinsville, IL 62234.

KOCHMAN, THOMAS MICHAEL, Anthropological Linguistics. See Volume III, Foreign Languages, Linguistics & Philology.

KOEHLER, G. STANLEY, b. West Orange, N.J, Mar. 27, 15; m. 51; c. 5. ENGLISH. B.A, Princeton, 36, M.A, 38, Ph.D, 42; M.A, Harvard, 37. Instr. ENG, Okla. State Univ, 38-40, Univ. Kans, 46; Yale, 46-50; asst. prof, UNIV. MASS, AMHERST, 50-58, assoc. prof, 58-62, PROF, 62- U.S.N.R, 42-46, Lt. MLA; Milton Soc. Am. Publ: The fact of fall (poems), Univ. Mass, 69; A curious quire, Univ. Mass, 63; The art of poetry: William Carlos Williams, Paris Rev, fall 64; Milton's milky stream, J. Am. Folklore, 4-6/69; Milton's use of color and light, Milton Stud. III, Pittsburgh Univ spring 71; plus others. Add: Dept. of English, University of Massachusetts, Amherst, MA 01002.

KOENIG, ALLEN E, b. Los Angeles, Calif, Feb. 11, 39. SPEECH. A.B, Univ. South. Calif, 61; A.M, Stanford Univ, 62; Ph.D.(speech), Northwest. Univ, 64. Asst. prof. speech, East. Mich. Univ, 64-65; Univ. Wis, Milwaukee, 65-67; Ohio State Univ, 67-69; dir. commun, Am. Asn. Univ. Prof, 69-70; V.PRES. UNIV. RELAT, CAPITAL UNIV, 70- Ed, Educ. Broadcasting Rev, 67-69. Broadcast Preceptor Award, Broadcast Indust. Conf, 69, San Francisco State Col, 71. Am. Col. Pub. Relat. Asn; Am. Asn. Higher Educ; Broadcast Educ. Asn; Speech Commun. Asn; Am. Alumni Counc. Educational broadcasting; broadcasting labor relations; higher education development and public relations. Publ: Co-ed, The farther vision: educational television today, 67 & ed, Broadcasting and bargaining: labor relations in radio and television, 70, Univ. Wis; plus others. Add: 5491 Pheasant Dr, Orient, OH 43146.

KOERNER, JAMES D, b. Cedar Rapids, Iowa, Feb. 3, 23; m. 49. AMERICAN STUDIES. Fel, Wash. Univ, 51-52, Ph.D, 52. Asst. prof. Eng, Kans. State Univ, 52-54; Ford fel, Harvard, 54-55; asst. prof. humanities, Mass. Inst. Tech, 55-57; exec. dir, Counc. Basic Educ, 57-59; Relm Found. stud. grant. prof. educ. Am. cols. & univs, 60-62; ed-in-chief, Educ. Develop. Ctr, Newton, 67-70; PROG. OFF, ALFRED P. SLOAN FOUND, 70- Pres, Counc. Basic Educ, 62- U.S.A.A.F, 42-45. Publ: Ed, Case for basic education, Little, 59; co-ed, Craft of writing, Harper, 61; auth, Miseducation of American teachers, Houghton, 63; Reform in education: England and the U.S, Delacorte, 67; Who controls American education? A guide for laymen, Beacon, 68; The Parsons College bubble: a tale of higher education in America, Basic Bks, 70; Hoffer's America: Eric Hoffer talks to James Koerner, Libr. Press, 73; plus others. Add: 60 Maple Ave. S, Westport, CT 06880.

KOGAN, BERNARD ROBERT, b. Chicago, Ill, May 16, 20; m. 62; c. 4. ENGLISH. A.B, Univ. Chicago, 41, A.M, 46, Ph.D, 53. Instr. Eng, Ind. Univ, 46-48; humanities, Univ. Chicago, 49-51; from instr. to assoc. prof, ENG, UNIV. ILL, CHICAGO CIRCLE, 53-66, PROF, 66-, exec. secy. dept, 65-70. U.S.N.R, 41-45. MLA; NCTE; Col. Conf. Compos. & Commun. English and American literature of mid-19th century; Charles Dickens; the Victorian novel. Publ: The Chicago hay market riot, Heath, 59; Darwin and his critics, Wadsworth, 60. Add: Dept. of English, University of Illinois at Chicago Circle, Box 4348, Chicago, IL 60680.

KOHLER, CHARLOTTE, b. Richmond, Va, Sept. 16, 08. ENGLISH, B.A, Vassar Col, 29; M.A, Univ. Va, 33, Ph.D.(Eng), 36; Litt.D, Smith Col, 71. Instr. Eng, Women's Col, Univ. N.C, 36-41, asst. prof, 41-42; managing ed, VA. QUART. REV, 42-46, ED, 46- Publ: Ed, Poems from the Virginia Quarterly Review, 1925-1967, Univ. Va, 69. Add: One West Range, Charlottesville, VA 22903.

KOINM, ALBERT J, JR, b. Houston, Tex, Jan. 27, 39; m. 67; c. 3. MEDIEVAL & RENAISSANCE LITERATURE. B.A, Tex. A&M Univ, 61, M.A, 63; Ph.D.(Eng), Univ. Tex, Austin, 68. Asst. prof. ENG, Colo. State Univ, 68-71; ASSOC. PROF, SAM HOUSTON STATE UNIV, 71- Conf. Col. Teachers Eng; MLA; Renaissance Soc. Am. History of science; 16th century English literature. Add: Dept. of English, Sam Houston State University, Huntsville, TX 77340.

KOKJOHN, JOSEPH EUGENE, b. Ft. Madison, Iowa, Dec. 11, 28. ENGLISH. A.B, St. Ambrose Col, 50; M.A, Cath. Univ. Am, 54; Ph.D.(Eng), Univ. Iowa, 61. PROF. ENG, ST. AMBROSE COL, 61-, V.PRES, 64- Vis. prof, Univ. San Francisco, summers 68, 69, 71 & Chaminade Col. Honolulu, summer 72. MLA. Creative writing. Publ: If winter comes, 5/64 & A hell of a good question, 1/71, Commonweal; contrib, A funny thing happened to the Church, Macmillan, 69; plus others. Add: Dept. of English, St. Ambrose College, Davenport, IA 52803.

KOLB, ALFRED, b. Vienna, Austria, July 5, 35; U.S. citizen. ENGLISH, GERMAN. B.A, Washington & Jefferson Col, 57; M.A, Syracuse Univ, 60, fel. & Ph.D, 66; dankstipendium, Univ. Freiburg, 62-64. Asst. prof. Am. thought & lang, Mich. State Univ, 66-70, all-univ. res. grant, 66-69; assoc. prof. Ger, Washington & Jefferson Col, 70-73; ASSOC. PROF. ENG, FOR. LANG. & MUSIC & CHMN. DEPT, MERCER COUNTY COMMUNITY COL, 73- Am. Asn. Teachers Ger; NCTE; Northeast Mod. Lang. Asn; MLA; Am. Stud. Asn. Nineteenth and twentieth century Anglo-German and German literature; American studies. Publ: Gerstäcker's America, Thoth, winter 66; transl, Nikolaus Happel's article on W. Faulkner's A rose for Emily, C.E. Merrill, 70. Add: 521 Spring Valley Dr, Somerville, NJ 08876.

KOLB, GWIN JACKSON, b. Aberdeen, Miss, Nov. 2, 19; m. 43; c. 2. ENGLISH. A.B, Millsaps Col, 41; A.M, Univ. Chicago, 46, Ph.D, 49. Instr. ENG, UNIV. CHICAGO, 49-53, asst. prof, 53-56, assoc. prof, 56-61, PROF, 61-, chmn. dept, 63-72. Guggenheim fel, 56-57; vis. assoc. prof. Northwest. Univ, 58; Stanford Univ, 60; Am. Counc. Learned Soc. grant-in-aid, 61-62; vis. prof, Univ. Wash, summers 67, 73; chmn. comt. advan. test. in lit, Educ. Testing Serv, 69-; co-ed, Mod. Philol, 73- U.S.N, 42-45. MLA; NCTE; Midwest Mod. Lang. Asn.(pres, 64-65); Asn. Depts. Eng.(pres, 67-68); Johnson Soc. Midwest (pres, 65-66); Am. Soc. 18th Century Stud. English literature of the 18th century. Publ: Co-auth, Dr. Johnson's dictionary, Univ. Chicago, 55; ed, Samuel Johnson's Rasselas, Appleton, 62; co-ed, English literature, 1600-1800: A bibliography of modern studies, 1951-1965 (3 vols), Princeton Univ, 62, 72. Add: Dept. of English, University of Chicago, 1050 E. 59th St, Chicago, IL 60637.

KOLB, GWIN JACKSON, II, b. Chicago, Ill, Oct. 9, 46. ENGLISH LITERATURE. B.A, Univ. Chicago, 67; Yale Univ, 67-68; Ph.D.(Eng), Univ. Va, 71. Prof. asst. ENG, Univ. Va, 70-71; ASST. PROF, UNIV. CALIF, LOS ANGELES, 71- MLA; Tennyson Soc. Arthur Henry Hallam; Alfred Tennyson's poetry; Victorian prose and poetry. Publ: Contrib, Victorian bibliography for 1972, Victorian Stud, 6/73; auth, The hero and his worshippers: the letters of Arthur Henry Hallam, John Rylands Libr. Bull, fall 73. Add: Dept. of English, University of California, Los Angeles, CA 90024.

KOLB, HAROLD HUTCHINSON, JR, b. Boston, Mass, Jan. 16, 33; m. 57; c. 2. ENGLISH, AMERICAN LITERATURE. A.B, Amherst Col, 55; M.A, Univ. Mich, 60; fels, Ind. Univ, 65-67, Ph.D.(Eng), 68. Instr. ENG, Valparaiso Univ, 60-62; teaching assoc, Ind. Univ, 62-65; asst. prof, UNIV. VA, 67-70, ASSOC. PROF, 70- Guggenheim fel, 70-71. U.S.N, 55-59, Res, 59-, Comdr. MLA. American literature; American studies. Publ: The illusion of life: American realism as a literary form, Univ. Va, 69. Add: Dept. of English, Wilson Hall, University of Virginia, Charlottesville, VA 22901.

KOLIN, PHILIP CHARLES, b. Chicago, Ill, Nov, 21, 45; m. 68; c. 1. ENGLISH LITERATURE. B.S, Chicago State Univ, 66; M.A, Univ. Chicago, 67; fel, Northwest. Univ, 71-73; Ph.D.(Eng), 73. Instr. ENG, West. Ill. Univ, 67-68; Ill. State Univ, 68-70; ASST. PROF, MILTON COL, 73- MLA; Am. Dialect Soc. Renaissance drama; modern drama; English linguistics. Publ: Milton's Samson Agonistes, Explicator, 72; A supplementary Edward Albee checklist, Serif, 73; co-auth, A bibliography of scholarship on the Elizabethan stage since Chambers, RORD, 74. Add: Dept. of English, Milton College, Milton, WI 53563.

KOLKER, DELPHINE, C.PP.S, b. Dayton, Ohio, Apr. 12, 18. ENGLISH. B.S, Univ. Dayton, 42; M.A, Cath. Univ. Am, 44, Ph.D.(Eng), 52; Univ. Notre Dame. Instr. Eng. & chmn. dept, Immaculata Col.(Ohio), 44-59; asst. prof. Eng. & humanities, St. Joseph Col.(Ind), 59-61; from asst. prof. to assoc. prof. ENG. & PHILOS, ST. JOHN COL. CLEVELAND, 61-69, PROF, 69- Consult, Choice, 64- MLA; Am. Cath. Philos. Asn. Translations; philosophy; children's literature. Publ: Spanish legends in English and American literature, 1800-1860, Cath. Univ. Am; Aspects and attitudes—poetry, Pageant, 65; Poet's wife, The Critic, 10/62; Inter-relation of the arts, Rev. Metaphysics, 12/62. Add: Div. of Liberal Arts, St. John College, Cathedral Sq, Cleveland, OH 44114.

KOLLER, KATHRINE (MRS. WILLIAM DIEZ), b. Hudson, N.Y, Jan. 25, 02; m. 50. ENGLISH. A.B, Wittenberg Col, 24, D.Litt, 50; Ph.D, Johns Hopkins Univ, 32. Teacher, High Sch, Plymouth, Ohio, 24-26, Tiffin, Ohio, 26-28; instr. ENG, Bryn Mawr Col, 32-37, asst. prof, 37-42; UNIV. ROCHESTER, 42-44, assoc. prof, 44-46, Joseph H. Gilmore prof, 46-67, chmn. dept, 46-58, EMER. PROF, 67- Mem. bd. dirs, Lewis Street Settlement, Rochester, N.Y, 43-; Guggenheim fel, 52; vis. Phi Beta Kappa scholar, 57-58; mem. comt. stud. pers, Am. Counc. Educ, 56-58; summer vis. prof, Univ. Minn, 57; President Kennedy's Nat. Shakespeare Comt, 64; trustee, Keuka Col, 68-; vis. prof, Nazareth Col. Rochester, 71-74. MLA; Col. Eng. Asn.(pres, 55). Renaissance literature. Add: 76 Oliver St, Rochester, NY 14607.

KOLODNY, ANNETTE, b. New York, N.Y, Aug. 21, 41. AMERICAN LITERATURE, WOMEN'S STUDIES. B.A. & N.Y. State Regents fel, Brooklyn Col, 62; advan. univ. grad. fel, Univ. Calif, Berkeley, 65-69, M.A, 65, Ph.D.(Am. lit), 69. Consult, Rand Corp, Calif, summer 68; asst. prof. Eng, Yale, 69-70; Univ. B.C, 70-74, admin. coord. women's stud. prog, 72-74; ASST. PROF. ENG, UNIV. N.H, 74- Univ. B.C. sr. res. grants, 70-; Can. Counc. sr. res. grant, 73-74; mem. adv. bd, Am. Lit, 74- MLA; Am. Stud. Asn; Am. Soc. 18th Century Stud; Can. Asn. Am. Stud; Can. Asn. Univ. Teachers. Early and contemporary American literature; women writers. Publ: Imagery in the sermons of Jonathan Edwards, Early Am. Lit, fall 72; co-auth, Pynchon's The crying of lot 49: the novel as subversive experience, Mod. Fiction Stud, spring 73; The land-as-woman: literary convention and latent psychological content, Women's Stud, 73. Add: Dept. of English, University of New Hampshire, Durham, NH 03824.

KOMECHAK, MICHAEL, O.S.B, b. Gary, Ind, Aug. 19, 32. ENGLISH & AMERICAN LITERATURE, JOURNALISM. M.A, Univ. Notre Dame, 61; Newspaper Fund, Inc. Wall St. J. fel, Univ. Minn, 62; Marquette Univ, 63 & 64; Univ. Ill, 65; Univ. San Francisco, 71. Chmn. dept. Eng, St. Procopius Acad, 59-65; CHAPLAIN, BLDG. COORD. & ENG. TEACHER, ILL. BENEDICTINE COL, 65- Nineteenth century American and English literature; contemporary journalism. Publ: Portfolio format, 12/62 & Raise funds via attractive ad book, 12/66, Scholastic Ed; Organize student press bureau for better public relations, Bull. Columbia Scholastic Press Adv. Asn, 1/66; plus others. Add: Dept. of English, Illinois Benedictine College, Lisle, IL 60532.

KONICK, MARCUS, b. Philadelphia, Pa, Oct. 22, 14; m. 40; c. 2. ENGLISH, COMMUNICATIONS. B.S.Ed, Temple Univ, 36; M.A, Univ. Pa, 37, Gimbel scholar, 45-46, univ. scholar, 45-46, Ph.D.(Eng), 53. PROF. ENG. & CHMN. DIV. HUMANITIES, LOCK HAVEN STATE COL, 66-, DIR. ACAD. SERV, 73-, chmn. dept. Eng, 66-73. Mem, Asn. Chief State Sch. AV Off, 60-62, exec. comt, 62-67, v.pres, 65, pres, 66; dir, Bur. Instr. Materials & Serv, Pa. Dept. Pub. Instr, 60-66; co-recipient, NDEA grants, 62-64 & 65-66; mem, Fed. Commun. Comn. Comt. Instruct. TV Fixed Serv, 65-66; v.chmn, Asn. State Educ. TV Authorities, 65-66; lectr. sensory aids to instr, grad. sch. arts & sci, Univ. Pa, summer 66; utilization educ. technol. teaching humanities, Cath. Univ. Am, summer 67; chmn. col. prog. comt, Allegheny Educ. Broadcasting Counc, 67-; mem, U.S. Off. Educ. Adv. Comt. on Title VI-A of Higher Educ. Act, 68; consult, Keystone Cent. Sch. Dist, 72-; chmn, Arts in Educ. Comt, Pa. Intermediate Unit 10, 73-; writer, dir. & actor numerous plays, Stage, Radio & TV. Citation for distinguished serv. to educ, Pa. Dept. Pub. Instr, 64; spec. award, Pa. Learning Resources Asn, 66. NCTE; MLA; NEA; AAUP; Am. Asn. Univ. Adminr. Medieval English literature; educational media; adult education. Publ: Co-auth, Guide to play selection, NCTE, 58 & The study of literature, Student's handbook, Bk. V, Holt, 59; co-auth. & ed, Plays for modern youth, 61, Tales in verse, 63 & Six complete world plays, 63, Globe & The Rubaiyat of Omar Khayyam, Avon, 67; auth, Exeter book riddle 41 as a continuation of riddle 40, Mod. Lang. Notes, 4/39; A regional instructional materials center, Educ. Screen & Audio-Visual Guide, 2/66; co-auth, The regional instructional materials center in Pennsylvania, Audiovisual Instr, 9/66. Add: Office of Academic Services, Lock Haven State College, Lock Haven, PA 17745.

KONIGSBERG, EVELYN, b. New York, N.Y, May 13, 05. SPEECH & DRAMA, ENGLISH. B.A, Hunter Col, 26; M.A, N.Y. Univ, 49. Teacher, high sch, N.Y, 26-41, acting chmn. dept. speech, 41-49, chmn. dept. speech, 49-52; asst. dir. bur. speech improv, pub. schs, N.Y, 52-56; prin, high sch, N.Y, 56-65; assoc. prof. speech & educ, ADELPHI UNIV, 65-66, assoc. prof. EDUC, 66-72, PROF, 72-, chmn. dept, 66-71, interim dean, grad. sch. arts & sci, 71-72. Part-time instr. educ, N.Y. Univ, 44-56; rep, White House Conf. on Children & Youth, 50; part-time instr. speech & educ, Adelphi Univ, 51-65; prof. lectr. educ, George Washington Univ, summer 54; mem, lib. arts adv. counc, Pace Col, 61, adv. comt, Sch. Nursing, Manhattan State Hospital, N.Y, 61-68, youth adv. comt, N.Y. Chap, Am. Red Cross, 63-65. Am. Speech & Hearing Asn; Nat. Asn. Admin. Women in Educ; Nat. Asn. Sec. Sch. Prin; Nat. Educ. Asn; Speech Commun. Asn.(rep, U.S. Dept. Health Educ. Welfare, 56); Speech Asn. East. States (pres, 56-57). Education; speech; theatre. Publ: Outline course of study in dramatics, Speech Teacher, 1/55; Fallacy of the first name, Today's Speech, 1/57; A candle of understanding, Eng. Rec, winter 61. Add: 95 Grand Ave, Rockville Centre, NY 11570.

KONIGSBERG, IRA, b. New York, N.Y, May 30, 35; m. 57. ENGLISH. B.A, City Col. N.Y, 56; M.A, Columbia Univ, 57; Ph.D.(Eng), Stanford Univ, 61. Instr. Eng. & Am. lit, Brandeis Univ, 61-63; asst. prof, 63-68, assoc. prof. ENG. LANG. & LIT, UNIV. MICH; ANN ARBOR, 68-74, PROF, 74- Fulbright-Hays lectr. Am. lit, Univ. Vienna, 66-67. U.S.A.R, 57-63. MLA. Restoration and 18th century English literature; fiction. Publ: Samuel Richardson and the dramatic novel, Univ. Ky, 68; co-ed, Critical thinking—an anthology for composition, Macmillan, 69; ed, The classic short story, Harper, 71; auth, The tragedy of Clarissa, Mod. Lang. Quart, fall 66; The dramatic background of Richardson's characters, PMLA, 3/68. Add: Dept. of English, University of Michigan, Ann Arbor, MI 48104.

KOOB, C. ALBERT, b. Philadelphia, Pa, Sept. 22, 20. ENGLISH. B.A, St. Norbert Col, 42; M.A, Cath. Univ. Am, 48, hon. LL.D, 73; hon. D.Ped, La Salle Col, 61; hon. L.H.D, Lewis Col, 70. Teacher Eng, speech & drama, Southeast Cath. High Sch, Phila, Pa, 42-48, v.prin, 49-54; prin, Bishop Neumann High Sch, 54-61; assoc. secy. sec. dept, NAT. CATH. EDUC. ASN, 61-67, exec. secy, 67-79, PRES, 69- Mem, Mayor's Comt. Human Relat, Phila, 57-61; adv. bd, Nat. Merit Scholar. Prog, 61-68, bd. dir, 68-; Proj. Eng. Res. Sem, Carnegie Inst. Technol, 62; adv. comt, teacher exchange prog, U.S. Dept. State & U.S. Off. Educ, 62-, chmn, 68-; mem. adv. bd, Ford Found. Coop. Plan for Guid. & Admis, Educ. Testing Serv, 63-, comt. tests & measurements, 68, adv. comt. progs. continuing educ, 72; comput. educ. comt, Nat. Asn. Sec. Sch. Prin, 67-; Comt. on Assessing Progress of Educ, 68-; bd. trustees, Joint Counc. Econ. Educ, 68- Nat. Asn. Sec. Sch. Prin; Nat. Cath. Educ. Asn.(ed, High Sch. Quart. Bull & Pointers for Prin, 61-67); Am. Asn. Sch. Adminr. Teaching of speech; curriculum improvement; school administration. Publ: Co-auth, Catholic secondary school administration, 68 & A handbook for Catholic high school administrators, Bruce; ed. & contrib, What is happening to Catholic education, 66 & co-ed, Shaping the future, 67, Washington; co-auth, S.O.S. for Catholic schools, Holt, 70; plus var. arts. in prof. jour. Add: National Catholic Educational Association, One Dupont Circle N.W, Washington, DC 20036.

KOON, GEORGE WILLIAM, b. Columbia, S.C, June 1, 42; m. 64; c. 2. ENGLISH LITERATURE. A.B, Newberry Col, 64; M.A, Auburn Univ, 66; Ph.D. (Eng. lit), Univ. Ga, 73. Instr. ENG. LIT, Univ. Ga, 66-68, 70-72; CLEMSON UNIV, 72-73, ASST. PROF, 73- Managing ed, S.C. Rev, 73- S.Atlantic Mod. Lang. Asn; Johnsonian Soc. Eighteenth century British literature; modern short fiction. Publ: William Price Fox (rev), Ga. Rev, 73; The over-production of Freshman English (abstract), S.Atlantic Mod. Lang. Asn. Bull, 74. Add: Dept. of English, Clemson University, Clemson, SC 29631.

KOON, HELEN WICKHAM, b. Minneapolis, Minn, Oct. 14, 25; m. 46; c. 5. ENGLISH LITERATURE, DRAMA. B.A, Univ, Iowa, 46; M.A, Pasadena Playhouse, 48; M.A, Immaculate Heart Col, 65; Ph.D.(Eng), Univ. Calif, Los Angeles, 69. Instr. ENG, Calif. State Col, Northridge, 69-71; asst. prof, CALIF. STATE COL, SANBERNARDINO, 71-73, ASSOC. PROF, 73- MLA; Am. Soc. 18th Century Stud; Am. Soc. Theatre Res; Soc. Theatre Res, Eng. Eighteenth century literature; Colley Cibber. Publ: Transl, Eugene Scribe's Feu Lionel, Baker's Plays, 65; ed, Colley Cibber's Letter to Mr. Pope, Univ. Calif, 73; auth, A Lilliputian poem, Mod. Lang. Notes, 69; Pope's first editors, Huntington Libr. Quart, 71. Add: Dept. of English, California State College, San Bernardino, 5500 State College Pkwy, San Bernardino, CA 92407.

KOON, WILLIAM HENRY, b. Columbus, Ga, Oct. 4, 38; m. 63; c. 2. ENGLISH, FOLKLORE. A.B, Belmont Abbey Col, 60; M.A, Appalachian State Univ, 61; Ph.D.(Eng), Univ. Ga, 66. Instr. ENG, Ga. Mil. Col, 61-62; teaching asst, Univ. Ga, 62-65; asst. prof, West. Ky. Univ, 65-70; ASSOC. PROF, CALIF. STATE UNIV, FULLERTON, 70- MLA; NCTE; Am. Folklore Soc. Ballads and folksongs of southern Appalachians; commercial country recordings of the 1920's and 1930's; bluegrass and popular culture. Publ: Ed, American ballads and folksongs, Foundation, 73; auth, American folklore, Harper, 74; Grassroots commercialism, John Edwards Mem. Found, 9/71; Darby and Taleton and Sam McGee, J. Ethnomusicol, 1/72; Songs of Ken Maynard, John Edwards Quart, 6/73; plus others. Add: Dept. of English, California State University, Fullerton, 800 N. State College Blvd, Fullerton, CA 92631.

KOONCE, BENJAMIN GRANADE, b. Hertford, N.C, Mar. 13, 22. ENGLISH. A.B, Univ. N.C, 43, M.A, 48; Ph.D, Princeton, 59. Instr. ENG, Tulane Univ, 48-50; N.C. STATE UNIV, 52-57, asst. prof, 57-63, assoc. prof, 63-67, PROF, 67- Mediaeval Acad. Am; MLA. Chaucer and mediaeval literature. Publ: Chaucer and the tradition of fame, Princeton Univ, 66; Satan the fowler, Mediaeval Stud, 59. Add: Dept. of English, North Carolina State University, Raleigh, NC 27607.

KOONTZ, THOMAS WAYNE, b. Ft. Wayne, Ind, July 9, 39; m. 59; c. 4. AMERICAN LITERATURE & FOLKLORE. B.A, Miami Univ, 61; Woodrow Wilson fel, Ind. Univ, Bloomington, 61-62, M.A, 65, Ph.D.(Eng), 70. Instr. ENG, George Washington Univ, 65-67; ASST. PROF, BALL STATE UNIV, 67- Nat. Endowment for Humanities educ. grant & proj. dir, Ball State Univ, 72-73. MLA; Am. Stud. Asn; Am. Folklore Soc. American studies and poetry; Black American literature. Add: Dept. of English, Ball State University, Muncie, IN 47306.

KOPERSKI, RONALD JOSEPH, b. Chicago, Ill, Oct. 30, 38; m. 61; c. 3. SPEECH. B.A, St. Mary's Col.(Minn), 60; M.A, St. Louis Univ, 62; Ph.D. (speech), Univ. Mo, Columbia, 66. Instr. SPEECH, St. Louis Univ, 60-61; St. Mary's Col.(Kans), 61-62; Univ. Mo, 62-66; asst. prof, BRADLEY UNIV, 66-71, ASSOC. PROF, 71- Cent. States Speech Asn. Award, 68. Speech Commun. Asn. Oral interpretation of literature; literary theory. Publ: Dylan Thomas reading his complete recorded poetry, Speech Teacher, 9/67; Buchwald Barometer of the times: readers theatre, Ill. Speech News, fall 67. Add: Dept. of Speech, Bradley University, Peoria, IL 61606.

KOPP, JANE BALTZELL, b. El Paso, Tex, Mar. 13, 35; m. 69; c. 1. ENGLISH. A.B, Brown Univ, 55; B.A, Cambridge, 57; M.A, Univ. Calif, Berkeley, 62, Ph.D.(Eng), 65. Asst. prof. ENG, Univ. N.Mex, 64-69, assoc. prof, 69-70; vis. assoc. prof, Kenyon Col, 71-72; assoc. prof, Univ. Utah, 72-73. MLA; Philol. Asn. Pac. Coast. Medieval literature; history of rhetoric and poetry; Chaucer. Publ: Rhetorical amplification and abbreviation and the structure of medieval narrative, Pac. Coast Philol, 4/67; contrib, Three medieval rhetorical arts, Univ. Calif, 71. Add: P.O. Box 632, Clarksville, AR 72830.

KOPPENHAVER, ALLEN J, b. Valley View, Pa, Oct. 21, 31; m. 55; c. 3. ENGLISH. B.S.Ed, Lebanon Valley Col, 53; M.A, Ohio Univ, 58; Ph.D.(Eng), Duke Univ, 64. Instr. Eng, WITTENBERG UNIV, 61-63, asst. prof, 63-66, assoc. prof, 66-73, PROF. ENG. & AM. STUD, 73-, DIR. HONORS PROG, 66- Fulbright lectr, Univ. Exeter, 71-72; BBC-TV performance of music-drama excerpts, No Easy Miracle, 73; Nat. Found. Arts grant, 74. U.S.A, 54-56. MLA; AAUP. Contemporary British and American literature; creative writing in music-drama and poetry. Publ: The fall and after, Mod. Drama, 9/66; The cask of Amontillado (libretto), Papers on Poe, 1/72; Young Goodman Brown (libretto), Studi Americani, 5/73; plus others. Add: 2538 Casey Dr, Springfield, OH 45503.

KOPPER, EDWARD ANTHONY, JR, b. Philadelphia, Pa, May 8, 37; m. 66; c. 1. ENGLISH. B.S, St. Joseph's Col.(Pa), 58; M.A, Temple Univ, 61, Ph.D.(Eng), 63. Asst. Eng, Lehigh Univ, 58-59; teacher high sch, Pa, 59-61; instr. ENG, Temple Univ, 61-63; asst. prof, Villanova Univ, 63-66, assoc. prof, 66-67; from asst. prof. to assoc. prof, Ind. Univ, South Bend, 67-69; PROF, SLIPPERY ROCK STATE COL, 69-, chmn. dept, 70-71. MLA; James Joyce Found; Col. Eng. Asn; Northeast Mod. Lang. Asn.(chmn, Early 20th Century Brit. & Am. Lit. Sect, 72, James Joyce Sect, 73, secy, Mod. & Contemporary Poetry Sect, 74). Twentieth century British literature; contemporary European literature and philosophy; languages. Publ: Reviser, Lady Gregory, Twayne; auth, Ulysses and James Joyce's use of comedy, Mosaic, fall 72; Lady Gregory and Finnegans Wake, A Wake Newslett, 12/72; contrib, A conceptual guide to Finnegans Wake, Pa. State Univ, 74. Add: 108 Farmington Dr, Butler, PA 16001.

KORENMAN, JOAN SMOLIN, b. Brooklyn, N.Y, Sept. 5, 41; m. 68; c. 1. AMERICAN LITERATURE. B.A, Brandeis Univ, 63; A.M, Harvard, 64, Ph.D.(Eng), 70. ASST. PROF. ENG, UNIV. MD. BALTIMORE COUNTY, 69- Soc. Study South. Lit; MLA; NCTE. American fiction; women's studies. Add: Dept. of English, University of Maryland Baltimore County, 5401 Wilkens Ave, Baltimore, MD 21228.

KORETSKY, ALLEN C, b. Boston, Mass, Nov. 12, 37; m. 64; c. 1. ENGLISH. A.B, Harvard, 59; M.A, Univ. Toronto, 61, Ph.D.(Eng), 67; Fulbright scholar. & Can. Counc. fel, 64-65. Lectr. ENG, YORK UNIV.(ONT), 65-67, asst. prof, 67-72, ASSOC, PROF, 72- MLA; Mediaeval Acad. Am. Medieval rhetoric; Chaucer's use of rhetoric; Middle English romances. Publ: Chaucer's use of the apostrophe in Troilus and Criseyde, Chaucer Rev, 71. Add: Dept. of English, Founders College, York University, 4700 Keele St, Downsview 463, Ont, Can.

KORG, JACOB, b. New York, N.Y, Nov. 21, 22; m. 53; c. 1. ENGLISH. B.A, City Col. New York, 43; M.A, Columbia Univ, 47, Ph.D, 52. Instr. ENG, Bard Col, 47-49; City Col. New York, 51-55; asst. prof, Univ. Wash, 55-62, assoc. prof, 62-67, PROF, 67-68; Univ. Md, 68-70; UNIV. WASH, 70- Exchange prof, Nat. Taiwan Univ, 60. MLA; Int. Asn. Univ. Prof. Eng. Victorian contemporary and comparative literature. Publ: An introduction to poetry, Holt, 59; George Gissing: a critical biography, Univ. Wash, 63; ed, London in Dickens' day, 60 & Twentieth century interpretations of Bleak House, 68, Prentice-Hall; auth, Dylan Thomas, Twayne, 65; ed, The poetry of Robert Browning, Bobbs, 71; contrib, Victorian fiction: a guide to research, Harvard Univ, 64; auth, The music of lost dynasties: Browning, Pound and history, Eng. Lit. Hist, 72; Language change and experimental magazines, 1910-1930, Contemporary Lit, 72. Add: Dept. of English, University of Washington, Seattle, WA 98195.

KORINKO, STEPHEN JOHN, b. Mahanoy City, Pa, Dec. 23, 30; m. 55; c. 5. ENGLISH, LINGUISTICS. A.B, Concordia Sem, 50, M.Div, 56; M.A, Wash. Univ, 62; Ph.D.(Eng), Univ. Nebr-Lincoln, 70. Instr. Eng, Concordia Col. Inst, 53-55; parish pastor, Hope & Concordia Congr, Mo, 56-59; asst. prof. Eng. & chmn. dept, St. Paul's Col.(Mo), 59-63; asst. prof, CONCORDIA TEACHERS COL.(NEBR), 63-67, ASSOC. PROF. ENG. & CHMN. DIV. HUMANITIES, 67- Lectr. ling. & reading, NDEA Reading Inst, Concordia Teachers Col.(Nebr), 67. Asn. Depts. Eng; MLA; Col. Eng. Asn; NCTE. Eighteenth and 19th century English, especially Arnold; Renaissance humanities. Publ: Ed, A bend on the river: a history of Seward County, Service, 66; The interminable conflict, 4/72 & Up the New and the Old English, 9/72, Lutheran Educ. Add: Dept. of English, Concordia Teachers College, Seward, NE 68434.

KORNBLUTH, MARTIN LEONARD, b. New York, N.Y, June 11, 25; m. 61; c. 5. ENGLISH. A.B, Univ, Mo, 50, A.M. 52; Ph.D.(Eng), Pa. State Univ, 56. Instr. Eng, Univ. Mo, 52-53; Univ. Tenn, 55-57; commun. skills, Mich. State Univ, 57-59; asst. prof. ENG, Univ. Idaho, 59-60; Monmouth Col, 60-62, assoc. prof, 62-64; Tex. Technol. Col, 64-65; PROF, Bradley Univ, 65-66; EAST. MICH. UNIV, 66-, DIR. GRAD. STUD, 73- Abstr. ed, Abstr. Eng. Stud, 61-; vis. prof. Eng, Univ. Nev. Las Vegas, summer 69. U.S.M.C, 43-46. MLA; NCTE. Restoration and 18th century drama; 18th century prose and poetry; Johnson and Boswell. Publ: Shaw and restoration drama, Shaw Rev, 1/58; Twentieth-century Everyman, Col. Eng, 10/59; Longfellow's Hyperion & Goethe's Wilhelm Meister, Emerson Soc. Quart, 2/63; plus others. Add: Dept. of English, Eastern Michigan University, Ypsilanti, MI 48197.

KORNFELD, MILTON HERBERT, b. New York, N.Y, Mar. 10, 42; m. 68; c. 2. AMERICAN LITERATURE. B.A, Brooklyn Col, 63; M.A, Cornell Univ, 64; Ph.D.(Am. lit), Brandeis Univ, 70. ASST. PROF. HUMANITIES, BOSTON UNIV, 69- The nature of evil as portrayed in American literature. Publ: Villainy and responsibility in The wings of the dove, Tex. Stud. Lit. & Lang, 7/72; Surgeing: some memoirs, Spectrum, 3/74. Add: College of Basic Studies, Boston University, 871 Commonwealth Ave, Boston, MA 02115.

KORSHIN, PAUL J, b. New York, N.Y, July 24, 39; m. 61. ENGLISH. A.B, City Col. New York, 61; Woodrow Wilson fel, Harvard, 61-62, A.M, 62, Dexter traveling scholar, 65, Ph.D.(Eng), 66. Asst. prof. ENG, UNIV. PA, 66-71, ASSOC. PROF, 71- Am. Philos. Soc. grant-in-aid, 70; Am. Counc. Learned Soc. grant-in-aid, 71. MLA; Mod. Humanities Res. Asn; Am. Soc. 18th Century Stud.(exec. secy, 73-); AAUP. Eighteenth century English literature and intellectual history; poetry and poetics; Samuel Johnson, 1709-1784. Publ: Auth. Introd. & ed, Proceedings of Neoclassicism conferences, 1967-1968, AMS Press, 70; Introduction to Meric Casaubon's A treatise concerning enthusiasme, 2nd ed, 1656, Scholars' Facsimiles, 70; ed. & contrib, Studies in change and revolution: aspects of English intellectual history, 1640-1800, 72 & auth, From concord to dissent: major themes in English poetic theory, 1640-1700, 73, Scolar Press, Eng; contrib, The interpretation of narrative: Harvard English studies, Harvard Univ, Vol. I, 70 & 18th century studies in memory of Donald Hyde, Grolier Soc, 71; auth. Introd, Robert Anderson's Life of Samuel Johnson, 3rd ed, 1815, Georg Olms, Verlag, 73; plus others. Add: Dept. of English, University of Pennsylvania, Philadelphia, PA 19174.

KORTE, DONALD MacCOULL, b. Teaneck, N.J, Nov. 7, 33; m. 58; c. 2. ENGLISH. B.A, State Univ. N.Y. Albany, 60, M.A, 63; Ph.D.(Eng), Syracuse Univ, 67. Asst. ENG, Syracuse Univ, 62-67; asst. prof, UNIV. GUELPH, 67-70, ASSOC. PROF, 70- U.S.N, 52-54. Humanities Asn. Can; MLA. Smollett; 18th century English literature. Publ: An annotated bibliography of Smollett scholarship 1946-1968, Univ. Toronto, 69; Johnson on Pope, Johnsonian Newslett, 6/68; Smollett's Advice and Reproof: apprenticeship in satire, Stud. Scottish Lit, 4/71; Johnson's Rasselas, PMLA, 1/72; plus others. Add: Dept. of English, University of Guelph, Guelph, Ont, Can.

KORTE, WALTER FRANCIS, JR, b. Roanoke, Va, Sept. 18, 43; m. 71. FILM AESTHETICS. B.A, Univ. Va, 65, M.A, 67; Univ. Milan, 65-66; Ph.D.(film), Northwest. Univ, 70. Instr. FILM, Univ. Ill, Chicago Circle, 69-70; ASST. PROF, UNIV. VA, 70- Soc. Cinema Stud; Univ. Film Asn; MLA; AAUP. Italian cinema; film history. Publ: Contrib, Man and the movies, La. State Univ, 67; auth, The stranger as film, December, 68; Marxism and formalism in the films of Visconti, Cinema J, 71. Add: Dept. of English, University of Virginia, Charlottesville, VA 22901.

KOSKENLINNA, HAZEL M, b. Kenosha, Wis, Feb. 11, 21. ENGLISH. B.S, Univ. Wis, 42, M.S, 60, Ph.D.(Eng), 68. Teacher high sch, Wis, 57-61; instr. ENG, UNIV. WIS-STEVENS POINT, 61-66, asst. prof, 66-68, ASSOC. PROF, 68- MLA; NCTE. Publ: Flying to Byzantium, 10/63 & What have our college freshmen read?, 1/65, Wis. Eng. J; Setting, image and symbol in Scott and Hawthorne, ESQ, 1/73. Add: Dept. of English, University of Wisconsin-Stevens Point, Stevens Point, WI 54481.

KOSOKOFF, STEPHEN, b. Seattle, Wash, May 9, 38; m. 62; c. 3. SPEECH. B.A, Univ. Wash, 61; A.M, Univ. Ill, 63; Ph.D.(speech), Univ. Ore, 66. Asst. prof. SPEECH, PORTLAND STATE UNIV, 66-72, ASSOC. PROF, 72- U.S.N.R, 55-63. Speech Asn. Am. Rhetorical theory; rhetoric of protest; rhetoric of song. Add: Dept. of Speech, Portland State University, Portland, OR 97207.

KOSSMANN, RUDOLF R, b. Jakarta, Indonesia, Dec. 1, 34; m. 62; c. 3. ENGLISH. Annan fel, Princeton, 59-60; Dr.Litt, Leyden Univ, 69. Assoc. prof. ENG. & AM. LIT, STATE UNIV. N.Y. COL. NEW PALTZ, 62-72, PROF, 72- Royal Netherlands Army, 54-56, 1st Lt. MLA; Am. Stud. Asn; AAUP. Twentieth century English and American drama; Chaucer. Publ: Henry James: dramatist, Wolters-Noordhoff, Groningen, 69. Add: Dept. of English, State University of New York College at New Paltz, New Paltz, NY 12561.

KOSTE, VIRGINIA GLASGOW, b. Akron, Ohio, Oct. 6, 24; m. 67; c. 6. THEATRE & DRAMA. A.B, Vassar Col, 45; A.M, Wayne State Univ, 47; Northwest. Univ, summer 48; Cornell Univ, summer 49; Ind. Univ, 49-50. Instr. speech. Albion Col, 47-49; specialist drama & speech, Durham Acad, 59-62; asst. prof, CHILDREN'S THEATRE, EAST. MICH. UNIV, 62-66, assoc. prof, 66-72, PROF, 72-, DIR. THEATRE OF THE YOUNG, 62-; ACTRESS, 27- Dir. Jr. League Children's Theatre, Durham, N.C, 51-53; dance specialist, Durham, N.C. YWCA, 53-61; lectr, Duke Univ, 56-60; drama consult, Birmingham, Mich. pub. schs, 65-66; dir. festival theatre, Mott Found. Flint, Mich, summer 66; drama consult, Oakland Univ, 71-72; lectr. summit drama conf, Univ. Tenn, Knoxville, 72. Children's Theatre Asn.(mem. nat. judges panel awards, 72-, mem. pres. comn, 72-); Int. Asn. Theatres Children & Youth (Am. del. Paris Cong, 65); Am. Theatre Asn. New plays for young and mixed-age audiences; dramatic play and theatre games; documentary theatre of involvment. Publ: The Old Country's young Vic, 71 & A bibliography of British books on child drama and theatre of the young, 72, Children's Theatre Rev; Dramatic experiencing: catalyst in learning, élan, winter 73. I open the door (recording ser), Univ. Mich, 63-66; Of plays and playmaking (film), Univ. Mich. TV, 65. Add: Dept. of Speech & Dramatic Arts, Quirk Theatre, Eastern Michigan University, Ypsilanti, MI 48197.

KOSTELANETZ, ANNE TIDABACK, English, Literature & Visual Arts. See MELLOR, ANNE KOSTELANETZ.

KOSTER, DONALD NELSON, b. New York, N.Y, Aug. 4, 10; m. 30; c. 2. ENGLISH. A.B, Univ. Pa, 31, M.S, 32, Ph.D.(Eng), 42. Instr. Eng, Univ. Pa, 36-46, asst. dir. cult. olympics, 43-46; asst. prof. ENG, ADELPHI UNIV, 46-54, assoc. prof, 54-59, PROF, 59-, res. grants, 49, 57, 69, & 72-73. Assoc. ed, Pa. Gazette, Phila, 45-46; lectr, exten. div, State Univ. N.Y, 47-62; ser. ed, Res. Guides Am. Stud, Gale Res. Co, 72- MLA; Am. Stud. Asn.(bibliographer, 62-); Col. Eng. Asn; AAUP. Transcendentalism; American literature and civilization; drama. Publ: Theme of divorce in American drama, 1871-1939, Univ. Pa; co-auth, Modern journalism, Pitman, 62; auth, Abstracting services and American studies, summer 65 & co-auth. & ed, Annual review of books, 68-72, Am. Quart; auth, Poe, romance and reality, Am. Transcendental Quart, summer 73; plus one other. Add: Dept. of English, Adelphi University, Garden City, NY 11530.

KÖSTER, PATRICIA, b. Victoria, B.C, Sept. 25, 32; m. 58; c. 4. ENGLISH. B.A, Univ, B.C, 53; M.A, Univ. Calif, Berkeley, 55; fel, Univ. Toronto, 55-56. Ph.D.(Eng), Univ. London, 58. Teaching asst. ENG, Univ. Calif, Berkeley, 53-55; instr. UNIV. VICTORIA (B.C), 58-60, asst. prof, 66-72, ASSOC. PROF, 72- Can. Counc. leave fel, 69-70; Can. adv, The Scriblerian & The Kit-Cats, 73- Johnson Soc. Northwest (treas, 72-73); Can. Soc. 18th Century Stud; Augustan Reprint Soc. Augustan satire; history of ideas; humanism. Publ: Ed, The novels of Mrs. Manley (2 vols), Scholars' Facsimiles, 71 & Arbuthnotiana: the story of the St. Albans ghost and A catalogue of Dr. Arbuthnot's library, Augustan Reprint Soc, 72; auth, Topical allusions in the Art of political lying, Trans. Johnson Soc. Northwest, 68; Arbuthnot's use of quotation and parody in his account of the Sacheverell affair, Philol. Quart, 69; Computer stylistics; Swift and some contemporaries, In: The computer in literary and linguistic research, Cambridge Univ, 71; plus others. Add: Dept. of English, University of Victoria, Victoria, B.C. V8W 2Y2, Can.

KOTT, JAN K, b. Warsaw, Poland, Oct. 27, 14; stateless; m. 39; c. 2. DRAMA, COMPARATIVE LITERATURE. L.L.M, Univ. Warsaw, 36; Ph.D. (French lit), Univ. Lodz, 47. Prof. romance lit, Univ. Wroclaw, 49-52; Polish lit, Univ. Warsaw, 52-56; vis. prof. drama, Yale, 66-67, 68-69; Univ. Calif, Berkeley, 67-68; PROF. COMP. LIT, STATE UNIV. N.Y. STONY BROOK, 69- Guggenheim fel, 72-73. Herder Award, Vienna, 64. Hon. mem. MLA. Shakespeare; Greek tragedy; modern drama. Publ: Shakespeare our contemporary, 64 & The theatre notebook, 68, Doubleday; Spektakel-Spektakel, Serie Piper, Ger, 72; The eating of the gods, Random, 73. Add: Dept. of Comparative Literature, State University of New York at Stony Brook, Stony Brook, NY 11790.

KOTTLER, BARNET, b. New York, N.Y, Jan. 17, 25; m; c. 2. ENGLISH. B.A, Queens Col.(N.Y), 46; jr. Sterling fel, Yale, 48, Ph.D.(Eng), 53. Instr. ENG, Yale, 49-53; Duke Univ, 53-57; asst. prof, PURDUE UNIV, WEST LAFAYETTE, 57-65, ASSOC. PROF, 65-, ASST. HEAD DEPT, 69-, dir. compos, 63-69. Andrew Mellow fel, Univ. Pittsburgh, 60-61. U.S.A.A.F, 43-45. MLA; NCTE; Mediaeval Acad. Am. Chaucer; medieval literature; linguistics. Publ: Co-auth, A concordance to five Middle English poems, Univ. Pittsburgh, 66; The vulgate tradition of the Colsolatio philosophiae in the fourteenth century, Mediaeval Stud. Add: Dept. of English, Purdue University, West Lafayette, IN 47907.

KOUWENHOVEN, JOHN A, b. Yonkers, N.Y, Dec. 13, 09; m. 35; c. 2. ENGLISH. A.B, Wesleyan Univ, 31; A.M, Columbia Univ, 33, Ph.D, 48. Instr, Harvey Sch, 32-36; Columbia Col, 37-39; mem. lit. fac, Bennington Col, 39-41; asst. ed, Harper's Mag, 41-43, assoc. ed, 44-46; assoc. ENG, BARNARD COL, COLUMBIA UNIV, 46-48, assoc. prof, 48-50, PROF, 50-, chmn. dept, 50-54. Contrib. ed, Harper's Mag, 46-53; trustee, R.I. Sch. Design, 61-67, 68-70; dir. hist. file, Brown Bros. Harriman & Co, 64-68; mem. adv. comt, Arch. Am. Art, Smithsonian Inst, 67- Off. Cross, Order Orange-Nassau, Netherlands. Am. Stud. Asn; Soc. Hist. Technol; Benjamin Franklin fel. Royal Soc. Arts; Soc. Archit. Hist. Interrelations of the arts and technology. Publ: Made in America, 48, Columbia historical portrait of New York, 53, The beer can by the highway, 61 & Partners in banking: an historical portrait of a great private bank, 68, Doubleday; American studies: words or things?, In: American studies in transition, Univ. Pa, 66; Design and chaos: some heretical conjectures about the artist and the public in America, In: The shaping of art and architecture in nineteenth century America, Metrop. Mus. Art, 72; Democracy, machines, and vernacular design, Ohio Rev, winter 73. Add: Dept. of English, Barnard College, Columbia University, New York, NY 10027.

KOVISARS, JUDITH FIORELLO, American Civilization, Urban Culture. See Volume I, History.

KOWAL, MICHAEL, b. Berlin, Ger, Apr. 2, 32; U.S. citizen. ENGLISH & COMPARATIVE LITERATURE. B.A, Queens Col.(N.Y), 53; Ph.D.(comp. lit), Yale, 62. Instr. Ger, Hofstra Col, 59-60; tutor ENG, QUEENS COL. (N.Y), 60-62, instr, 62-66, asst. prof, 66-74, ASSOC. PROF, 74- MLA; Am. Comp. Lit. Asn. Modern European literature; Kafka. Publ: Transl, E.R. Curtius' Essays on European literature, Princeton Univ, 73; auth, Kafka and the emigres, Ger. Rev, 11/66. Add: Dept. of English, Queens College, Flushing, NY 11367.

KOWALCZYK, RICHARD L, b. Detroit, Mich, Mar. 18, 35; m. 60; c. 4. ENGLISH. M.A, Wayne State Univ, 61, Ph.D.(Eng), 64. Instr. ENG, UNIV. DETROIT, 61-64, asst. prof, 65-67, assoc. prof, 67-71, PROF, 71- Kellogg Found. fel, 73-74. MLA; Midwest Mod. Lang. Asn; Mod. Humanities Res. Asn. Victorian literature; the aesthetic movement and the decadence; popular literature and English curriculum. Publ: Contrib. ed, Annual bibliography of English language and literature, Mod. Humanities Res. Asn, 65-; Horatian tradition and pastoral mode in Housman's A Shropshire lad, Victorian Poetry, fall 66; Moral relativism and the cult of love in Meredith's Modern love, Res. Stud, 3/69; Marie Corelli and Arthur Severn's reputation as an artist, Mod. Philol, 5/69; plus others. Add: Dept. of English, University of Detroit, College Park Station, Detroit, MI 48221.

KOZELKA, EDWIN PAUL, b. Chicago, Ill, Sept. 11, 09; m. 43; c. 1. SPEECH. A.B, Lawrence Col, 32; A.M, Northwest. Univ, 37; Ph.D, Yale, 43. Asst, Rosary Col, 37-40; asst. prof, Allegheny Col, 45-47; assoc. prof. speech, TEACHERS COL, COLUMBIA UNIV, 47-57, PROF, 57-63, THEATRE, 63-, acting chmn. dept. speech & theatre, 63-67. Founders Award, Sec. Sch. Theatre Conf, 71. Am. Red Cross, 43-45, Field Dir. Fel. Am. Theatre Asn.(Eaves Award, 61, v.pres, 62-64, pres, 65); Am. Nat. Theatre & Acad; Am. Soc. Theatre Res. (secy-treas, 56-60). Publ: Glossary to the plays of Bernard Shaw, T.C, 59; ed, Fifteen American one act plays, Washington Square, 61; Directing, & ed-in-chief, The theatre student (18 vols), Rosen. Add: Dept. of Languages, Literature, Speech & Theatre, Teachers College, Columbia University, New York, NY 10027.

KOZICKI, HENRY, b. Detroit, Mich, Mar. 20, 24; m. 50; c. 2. ENGLISH. B.A, Wayne State Univ, 62, M.A, 63, Ph.D.(Eng), 69. Instr. ENG, Wayne State Univ, 65-69, ASST. PROF, 69-70; UNIV. WIS-PARKSIDE, 70- MLA; Midwest Mod. Lang. Asn. Victorian literature, especially poetry; literature and history; Tennyson. Publ: Tennyson's Idylls of the King as tragic drama, Victorian Poetry, 66; Myths of redemption in Hardy's Tess of the d'Urbervilles, Papers Lang. & Lit, 74; Philosophy of history in Tennyson's poetry to the 1842 volume, ELH, 74. Add: Dept. of English, University of Wisconsin-Parkside, Kenosha, WI 53140.

KRABBE, JUDITH, Classical Languages. See Volume III, Foreign Languages, Linguistics & Philology.

KRAFT, JAMES, b. Washington, D.C, Jan. 12, 35; m. 62; c. 2. ENGLISH. A.B, Princeton, 57, Woodrow Wilson fel, 57; King's Col, Cambridge, 58-59; M.A, Fordham Univ, 62, Ph.D.(Eng), 67. Teacher Eng, Philips Acad, Andover, 57-58; instr, Univ. Va, 65-68; asst. prof, Wesleyan Univ, 68-72; MEM. STAFF, NAT. ENDOWMENT FOR HUMANITIES, 72- Vis. lectr, Laval Univ, 71-72. American literature; novel. Publ: The early tales of Henry James, South. Ill. Univ, 70; Change in Quebec; notes on Pierre Vallieres and Marie-Claire Blais, Novel, fall 72; On reading The American scene, Prose, spring 73; Provisional bibliography of works of Paul Horgan, In: Approaches to writing, Farrar, Straus, 73; plus several others. Add: National Endowment for the Humanities, 806 15th St. N.W, Washington, DC 20506.

KRAFT, QUENTIN GUILD, b. Hyannis, Mass, Jan. 3, 34; m. 56. ENGLISH & AMERICAN LITERATURE. A.B, Brown Univ, 56; M.A, Duke Univ, 58, Ph.D. (Eng), 63. Instr. ENG, DENISON UNIV, 61-63, asst. prof, 63-67, assoc. prof, 67-71, PROF, 71- American literature; the novel; literary criticism. Publ: Freedom in James's fiction, Col. Eng, 2/65; Life against death in Venice, Criticism, summer 65; The central problem of James's fictional thought: from The scarlet letter to Roderick Hudson, ELH. Add: Dept. of English, Denison University, Granville, OH 43023.

KRAMER, AARON, b. Brooklyn, N.Y, Dec. 13, 21; m. 42; c. 2. ENGLISH. B.A, Brooklyn Col, 41, M.A, 51; Ph.D.(Eng), N.Y. Univ, 66. Instr. ENG, Adelphi Univ, 61-63, asst. prof, 63-66, assoc. prof, 66-70; PROF, DOWLING COL, 70- Chmn. Ficke Award Comt, Poetry Soc. Am, 56, chmn, Reynolds Award Comt, 57; lectr, Queens Col.(N.Y), 66-69. MLA; Asn. Poetry Ther; Am. Soc. Composers, Auth & Publ.(awards, 72 & 73). World poetry, past and present; American history; aesthetic philosophy. Publ: Co-auth, The poetry and prose of Heinrich Heine, Citadel, 48; auth, The tune of the calliope: poems & drawings of New York, 58 & Rumshinsky's hat and house of buttons, 64, Yoseloff; co-auth, Rilke: visions of Christ, Univ. Colo, 67; auth, The prophetic tradition in American poetry, 1835-1900, 68 & Melville's poetry: toward the enlarged heart, 72, Fairleigh Dickinson Univ; co-auth, Poetry therapy, 69 & Poetry the healer, 73, Lippincott; ed, On freedom's side: American poems of protest, Macmillan, 72; auth, On the way to Palermo, A.S. Barnes, 73; The link between Heinrich Heine and Emma Lazarus, Publ. Am. Jewish Hist. Soc, Vol. XLV, No. 4; Robert Burns and Langston Hughes, Freedomways, Vol. VIII, No. 2; co-auth, Poetry as a means of group facilitation, J. Humanistic Psychol, 74; plus others. Add: Dept. of English, Dowling College, Oakdale, NY 11769.

KRAMER, DALE VERNON, b. Mitchell, S.Dak, July 13, 36; m. 60; c. 2. ENGLISH. B.S, S.Dak. State Univ, 58; M.A, West. Reserve Univ, 60, Ph.D. (Eng), 63. Instr. ENG, Ohio Univ, 62-63, asst. prof, 63-65; UNIV. ILL, URBANA, 65-67, assoc. prof, 67-71, PROF, 71- Ohio Univ. summer fel, 64; Univ. Ill. fac. study grant, 67; Am. Philos. Soc. res. grant, 69; assoc. fel, Ctr. Advan. Stud, Univ. Ill, 71-72; chmn. bd. ed, J. Eng. & Ger. Philol, 72- U.S.A, 58, Capt. MLA; AAUP. Textual scholarship; Victorian literature; aesthetics of fiction. Publ: Charles Robert Maturin, Twayne, 73; Marlow, myth and structure in Lord Jim, Criticism, 66; Revisions and vision: Thomas Hardy's The woodlanders, Bull. N.Y. Pub. Libr, 71; Hardy's prospects as a tragic novelist, Dalhousie Rev, 71; plus others. Add: Dept. of English, University of Illinois, Urbana, IL 61801.

KRAMER, JEROME A, b. Barberton, Ohio, Feb. 9, 36; m. 64; c. 1. ENGLISH. A.B, John Carroll Univ, 58; Ph.D.(Eng), Ohio State Univ, 66. Teaching asst. ENG, Ohio State Univ, 59-66; ASST. PROF, King's Col, Univ. West. Ont, 66-68; UNIV. OTTAWA, 68- U.S.A, 58-59, Res, 60-65, Capt. Add: Dept. of English, University of Ottawa, Ottawa, Ont, Can.

KRAMER, JOSEPH ELLIOT, b. New York, N.Y, Dec. 21, 34. ENGLISH LITERATURE, BRITISH & AMERICAN DRAMA. B.A, Princeton, 56, M.A, 58, Ph.D.(Eng), 64. Asst. prof. ENG, Univ. Calif, Berkeley, 61-69; ASSOC. PROF, BRYN MAWR COL, 69- Shakespeare; British drama to 1642; modern drama. Publ: Damon and Pithias: an apology for art, ELH, 12/68; Titus Andronicus: the Flykilling incident, Shakespeare Stud, 69. Add: Dept. of English, Bryn Mawr College, Bryn Mawr, PA 19010.

KRAMER, KENNETH P, Religion, Poetry. See Volume IV, Philosophy, Religion and Law.

KRAMER, MARY DUHAMEL, b. Columbus, Wis, June 12, 44; m. 68. ENGLISH LITERATURE. B.A, Univ. Wis-Madison, 66; NDEA fel, Univ. Kans, 66-69, M.A, 67, Ph.D.(Eng), 69. ASST. PROF. ENG, LOWELL STATE COL, 69- Fiction book reviewer, Boston Sunday Herald-Advertiser, 65- AAUP. Medieval and Renaissance literature. Publ: The Roman Catholic Cleric on the Jacobean stage, 71 & The American Wild West Show and Buffalo Bill Cody, 72, Costerus. Add: Dept. of English, Lowell State College, Lowell, MA 01854.

KRAMER, MAURICE, b. Philadelphia, Pa, Apr, 4, 30; m. 59. ENGLISH. A.B, Univ. Pa, 51, A.M, 53; Ph.D.(Eng), Harvard, 58. Instr. ENG, Rutgers Univ, 57-61; BROOKLYN COL, 61-66, asst. prof, 66-71, assoc. prof, 71-73, PROF, 73-, CHMN. DEPT, 70- MLA. American literature. Publ: Co-ed, Library of literary criticism: modern American literature, Ungar, 69 & Concordance to the poems of Hart Crane, Scarecrow Press, 73; auth, Hart Crane's Reflexes, Twentieth Century Lit, 10/67; plus others. Add: Dept. of English, Brooklyn College, Brooklyn, NY 11210.

KRAMER, VICTOR ANTHONY, b. Youngstown, Ohio, Oct. 21, 39; m. 63; c. 1. AMERICAN LITERATURE, LITERARY CRITICISM. A.B, St. Edward's Univ, 61; M.A, Univ. Tex, Austin, 63, Ph.D.(Eng), 66. ASST. PROF. ENG, Marquette Univ, 66-69; GA. STATE UNIV, 69- Participant, Afro-Am. Inst, Univ. Iowa, summer 70; Am. Philos. Soc. grant, 73. MLA; S.Atlantic Mod. Lang. Asn; Am. Stud. Asn; Am. Soc. Aesthet; NCTE; AAUP. Modern American literature; American studies and poetry. Publ: James Agee, Twayne (in press); Agee's Let us now praise famous men: image of tenant life, Miss. Quart, 72; Contemplative need in Horace Gregory's poetry, Mod. Poetry Stud, 73; A death in the family and Agee's projections, Proof, 73; plus ten others. Add: Dept. of English, Georgia State University, 33 Gilmer St. S.E, Atlanta, GA 30303.

KRANIDAS, THOMAS, b. Seattle, Wash, June 18, 27; m. 51; c. 4. ENGLISH. B.A, Univ. Wash, 49, Ph.D.(Eng), 62; A.M, Columbia Univ, 53. Instr. ENG, Ore. State Col, 57-60; lectr, Univ. Calif, Riverside, 60-61, acting asst. prof, 61-62, asst. prof, 62-66; assoc. prof, Univ. Del, 66-68; PROF, STATE UNIV. N.Y. STONY BROOK, 68- Fulbright res. grant, Greece, 64-65; vis. prof. Am. lit, Nat. Univ. Athens, 64-65; Am. Philos. Soc. grant-in-aid, 65; vis. part-time assoc. prof, Eng, Johns Hopkins Univ, 67-68; Guggenheim fel, 72-73. U.S.N, 45-46. MLA; Milton Soc. Am; Renaissance Soc. Am. Seventeenth century English literature, especially Milton. Publ: Co-ed, Oregon signatures, Ore. State Univ, 59; auth, The fierce equation, Mouton, The Hague, 65; ed, New essays on Paradise lost, Univ. Calif, 69; Milton and the rhetoric of Zeal, Tex. Stud. Lit. & Lang, 65; Dalila's role in Samson Agonistes, Stud. Eng. Lit, 66; A view of Milton and the traditional, Milton Stud, 69. Add: Dept. of English, State University of New York at Stony Brook, Stony Brook, NY 11790.

KRATINS, OJARS, b. Riga, Latvia, Jan. 11, 34; U.S. citizen; m. 57; c. 2. ENGLISH. B.A, Univ. Calif, Berkeley, 57, M.A, 59; fel, Harvard, 59-61, Ph.D.(comp. lit), 65. Instr. Germanic lang, Univ. Colo, 62-63; asst. prof. ENG, UNIV. CALIF, BERKELEY, 63-69, ASSOC. PROF, 69- faculty summer fel, 66, res. fel, 67-68. John S. Guggenheim Mem. fel, 67-68. Asn. Advan. Baltic Stud; Int. Arthurian Soc. Medieval Arthurian literature; Latvian literature; psychology of learning. Publ: Treason in Middle English metrical romances, Philol. Quart, 66; The Middle English Amis and Amiloun—chivalric romance or secular hagiography, PMLA, 66; Recent developments in Latvian fiction, Slavic & E.Europ. J, 72. Add: Dept. of English, University of California, Berkeley, CA 94720.

KRAUS, SIDNEY, b. Chicago, Ill, Mar. 10, 27; m. 52; c. 3. MASS MEDIA COMMUNICATION. B.F.A, Sch. of Art Inst. Chicago, 53, M.F.A, 54; grad. fel, State Univ. Iowa, 57-58; Ph.D, Univ. Iowa, 59. Teaching asst, State Univ. Iowa, 57-59; asst. prof. radio & TV, Roosevelt Univ, 60-64, asst. to pres, 64-65; prof. mass commun, Univ. Mass, 70-72; PROF. COMMUN. & CHMN. DEPT, CLEVELAND STATE UNIV, 72- Lectr, DePaul Univ, 59-66; Ford fel, Rutgers Univ, summer 60; res. asst, Ind. Univ, 61, grant, 62 & 63, ed. adv, Commun. Publs, 62-65; Nat. Asn. Broadcasters grant, 72; vis. lectr, Univ. Md. Sem. Mass Commun, 72; John & Mary Markle Found. grants, 73. Acad. Polit. Sci; Am. Asn. Pub. Opinion Res; Am. Fed. Film Soc; Cent. States Speech Commun. Asn; Int. Commun. Asn; Speech Commun. Asn; Int. Commun. Asn; Pub. Relat. Soc. Am. Political communication; mass communication and the political process. Publ: Ed, The great debates: background, perspective, effects, Ind. Univ, 62; co-auth, Fear threat appeals in mass communication: an apparent contradiction, Speech Monogr, 3/66; Mass communication and the election process: a reassessment of two decades of research, Quart. J. Speech, 12/73; Kennedy and the mass media: an election night survey 16 months after the Chappaquiddick television address, Jour. Quart, autumn 74. Add: Dept. of Communication, Cleveland State University, Cleveland, OH 44115.

KRAUSE, DAVID, b. Paterson, N.J, July 17, 17; m. 66; c. 4. ENGLISH. B.A, N.Y. Univ, 49, Ph.D, 54; M.A, Univ. Minn, 50. Assoc. prof. ENG, BROWN UNIV, 60-72, PROF, 72- Howard fel, 59; Am. Counc. Learned Soc. fel, 62; Bronson fel, 69; Nat. Endowment for Humanities fel, 74-75. U.S.A.A.F, 42-45. MLA; Am. Comt. Irish Stud. Sean O'Casey; Irish drama. Publ: Sean O'Casey: the man and his work, Macmillan, 60; ed, The Irish plays of Dion

Boucicault, Dolmen, 63; ed, Letters of Sean O'Casey, Vol. I, 74, Vol. II, 75, Vol. III, 76. Add: Dept. of English, Brown University, Providence, RI 02912.

KRAUSE, HERBERT, History, English. See Volume I, History.

KRAUSE, SYDNEY JOSEPH, b. Paterson, N.J, July 22, 25; m. 52. ENGLISH & AMERICAN LITERATURE. B.A, Univ. Mo, 49; M.A, Yale, 51; Ph.D.(Eng), Columbia Univ, 56. Instr. Eng, Univ. Mo, 50-52; asst. dir. Eng. prog. for for. stud, Col. William & Mary, 53; instr. Eng, Ohio State Univ, 53-55, dir. continuity, WOSU, 55; asst. prof. Eng, Univ. Akron, 55-62; assoc. prof, KENT STATE UNIV, 62-66, PROF. ENG, 66-, dir. bibliog. & textual ctr, 66-69. Summer res. grants, Am. Philos. Soc, 59, 60, 62; Am. Counc. Learned Soc, 61; gen. ed. C.B. Brown edition, Kent State Univ, & MLA, 66-; Fulbright lectr, Copenhagen, 68-69. U.S.A, 43-46. MLA. American literature; Mark Twain; Charles Brockden Brown. Publ: Henry James's revisions of The portrait of a lady: a study of literary portraiture and perfectionism; auth. & ed, Essays on determinism in American literature, Kent State Univ, 64; auth, Mark Twain as critic, Johns Hopkins, 67; Mark Twain's method and theory of composition, Mod. Philol, 2/59; Cooper's literary offences: Mark Twain in Wonderland, New Eng. Quart, 9/65; Ormond: seduction in a new key, Am. Lit, 1/73. Add: Dept. of English, Kent State University, Kent, OH 44242.

KREIDER, THOMAS McROBERTS, b. Wadsworth, Ohio, Mar. 2, 22; m. 52; c. 2. ENGLISH. A.B, Univ. Cincinnati, 46, Taft fel, 48-52, M.A, 49, Ph.D.(Eng), 52; M.A, Harvard, 47; summers, Oxford, 47 & Union Theol. Sem, 54; Cert. theol. stud, Pac. Sch. Relig, 68. Asst. prof. ENG, BEREA COL, 52-56, assoc. prof, 56-61, PROF, 61-, CHMN. DEPT, 71-, acting assoc. dean, 65-66. Instr, Univ. Cincinnati, summer 47, vis. prof, summer 61; dir. radio & TV publicity, Wilderness Road, 55, v.pres, 73-; Europ. tour leader, Bur. Univ. Travel, 56-62; Fulbright lectr. & prof. Am. lit, Univ. Karachi, 59-60; Lilly Found. grant, 61-63; consult, Nat. Asn. Standard Med. Vocabulary, 63-; Atomic Energy Comn-Nat. Sci. Found. grant, Seminar on Impact of Sci. on Soc, Oak Ridge, Tenn, summer 65; dir. Columbia Univ. sect, Harvard-Yale-Columbia Intensive Summer Stud. Prog, summer 67; Clarence Prouty Shedd fel, Pac. Sch. Relig, 67-68; mem. Danforth Conf, Colorado Springs, summer 68; mem. state bd, Proj. Opportunity, Ky, 69-; mem. bd. dirs. & v.pres, Ky. Humanities Counc, 72-; mem. bd. dirs, Berea Publ. Co, 73- U.S.A, 43-46. MLA; Asn. Gen. & Lib. Stud; Am. Stud. Asn; Col. Eng. Asn. American literature; European novel. Publ: Aristocratic tradition in Southern literature, Venture, 60. Add: Dept. of English, Berea College, Berea, KY 40403.

KREISEL, HENRY, b. Vienna, Austria, June 5, 22; Can. citizen; m. 47; c. 1. ENGLISH. B.A, Univ. Toronto, 46, Reuben Wells Leonard fel, 46-47, M.A, 47, Royal Soc. Can. fel, 53; Ph.D, Univ. London, Eng, 54. Lectr. ENG, UNIV. ALTA, 47-50, asst. prof, 50-55, assoc. prof, 55-59, PROF, 59-, V.PRES, 70-, head dept. Eng, 61-67, sr. assoc. dean grad. stud, fac. grad. stud. & res, 67-69, acting dean, 69-70. Chmn, scholar. comt, Can. Counc, 63-; mem, awards jury, Gov-Gen. Prizes in Lit, 66-68; mem. bd. gov, Univ. Alta, 66-69. Asn. Can. Univ. Teachers Eng.(pres, 62-63); MLA; fel. Int. Inst. Arts & Lett. Early 20th century British literature; history of the novel; Canadian literature. Publ: The rich man, 48 & The betrayal, 64, McClelland & Stewart; The broken globe, In: Best American short stories 1966, 67; Two sisters in Geneva, Mod. Can. Stories, 67; The prairie: a state of mind, In: Contexts of Canadian criticism, Univ. Chicago, 71; plus others. Add: Office of Vice President, University of Alberta, Edmonton, Alta. T6G 2J9, Can.

KREISMAN, ARTHUR, b. Cambridge, Mass, June 7, 18; m. 40; c. 4. ENGLISH, HUMANITIES. A.B, Brigham Young Univ, 42; A.M, Boston Univ, 43, Ph.D.(Eng), 52. Instr. Eng, SOUTH. ORE. COL, 46-47, asst. prof, 47-51, assoc. prof, 51-55, PROF. HUMANITIES & CHMN. DIV, 55-, DIR. GEN. STUD, 60-, DEAN ARTS & SCI, 66- Ford Found. scholar, Harvard, 54; Gresham lectr, Inst. Renaissance Stud, 56; dir. proj. exp. teaching humanities, Ore. State Syst. & U.S. Off. Educ, 56-58; consult. Eng, State Dept. Educ, Ore, 56-; dir, NDEA Inst. Advan. Stud. Eng, South. Ore. Col, 66-67; mem, Gov. Adv. Comt. Arts & Humanities, 66-68; examr, Northwest Asn. Sec. & Higher Schs, 69-, mem. comn. higher schs, 71-; examr, West. Asn. Schs. & Cols, 70- Ore. State Syst. Higher Educ. Excellent Teaching Prize, 66. Sig.C, U.S.A, 43-45. NCTE; fel. MLA; Philol. Asn. Pac. Coast. History of ideas; Oriental philosophy; aesthetics. Publ: Reader's guide to the classics of the literature of western civilization, Ore. State Univ, 61; Some thoughts on teaching method, Improving Col. & Univ. Teaching; For my students and for Joyce Kilmer, Col. Eng; The Oregon Shakespearean festival, J. Gen. Educ, 4/64. Add: Southern Oregon College, Ashland, OR 97520.

KREMPEL, DANIEL SPARTAKUS, b. Brooklyn, N.Y, July 26, 26; m. 48; c. 2. THEATRE. B.A, Brooklyn Col, 47; M.A, Ohio State Univ, 48; Ph.D.(speech & theatre), Univ. Ill, 53. Instr. speech & designer & asst. dir. theatre, Univ. Ore, 54-57, asst. prof, 57-58; theatre, Elmira Col, 58-62; Franklin Col, 62-63; DRAMA, Skidmore Col, 63-66; assoc. prof, SYRACUSE UNIV, 66-74, PROF, 74- Summers, vis. prof, State Univ. N.Y. Col. Geneseo, 62; Syracuse Univ, 63. Speech Commun. Asn; Am. Theatre Asn; Int. Fed. Theatre Res. Play direction and scene design; theatre history and aesthetics; motion pictures, history and aesthetics. Publ: Co-auth, The theatrical image, McGraw, 67; Oliver's Henry V, design in motion pictures, Educ. Theatre J; The theatre of the absurd and the art of scene design, Players Mag; Imaginary forces in the audience: a minority report, Quart. J. Speech. Add: Dept. of Drama, Syracuse University, Syracuse, NY 13210.

KREPS, LESLIE R, b. Powell, Wyo, Oct. 9, 24; m. 46; c. 3. SPEECH. B.A, Nebr. Wesleyan Univ, 47; A.M, Harvard, 49; Methodist Mission Bd. fel, Drew Univ, 49-50; Ph.D, Northwest. Univ, 57. Instr. speech & polit. sci, Aoyama Gakuin Univ, Japan, 50-52, asst. prof, 52-55; speech, Okla. State Univ, 57-59, assoc. prof, 59-60, prof, 63-69, head dept, 60-69; V.PRES. ACAD. AFFAIRS, TEX. WOMAN'S UNIV, 69- Asst, for. univ, Speech Asn. Am, 58-62; admin. asst, Senator Fred R. Harris, 67-69. U.S.N, 43-46, Res, 46-61, Lt.(jg). Speech Commun. Asn. Rhetoric and public address; Japanese history and political science. Publ: Image of Japan in speaking of United States congressmen, Speech Monogr, 58; Forensic program for a land grant university, Forensic, 59. Add: 2016 Mistywood, Denton, TX 76201.

KREUGER, WILLIAM EDWARD, b. Wheeling, W.Va, Sept. 17, 21; m. 51; c. 4. ENGLISH. A.B, Washington & Jefferson Col, 49; M.A, Ohio State Univ, 51; Univ. Ill, 52-56. Asst. Freshman Eng, Univ. Ill, 52-56; instr. ENG, MILLIKIN UNIV, 56-59, from asst. prof. to ASSOC. PROF, 59-, acting chmn. dept, 68-70. Qm.C, U.S.A, 42-45. Add: Dept. of English, Millikin University, Decatur, IL 62522.

KRIEGEL, LEONARD, b. New York, N.Y, May 25, 33; m. 57; c. 2. ENGLISH. B.A, Hunter Col, 55; M.A, Columbia Univ, 56; Penfield fel, N.Y. Univ, 58-59, Fels fel, 59-60, Ph.D.(Am. civilization), 60. Asst. prof. ENG, L.I. Univ, 60-61; instr, CITY COL. NEW YORK, 61-65, asst. prof, 65-69, assoc. prof, 69-72, PROF, 72- Fulbright lectr, Netherlands, 64-65, 68-69; City Univ. New York summer res. grant, 67; Guggenheim fel, 71-72. MLA; Am. Stud. Asn. Politics and literature; creative writing; writing on education. Publ: The long walk home, Appleton, 64; ed, Essential works of the founding fathers, Bantam, 64; auth, Edmund Wilson, South. Ill. Univ, 71; Working through: a teacher's journey in the urban university, Saturday Rev. Press, 72; Iris Murdoch: everybody through the looking glass, In: Contemporary British novelist, South. Ill. Univ, 65; Uncle Tom and Tiny Tim, summer 69 & Last stop on the D train, spring 70, Am. Scholar; plus others. Add: Dept. of English, City College of New York, New York, NY 10031.

KRIEGER, MURRAY, b. Newark, N.J, Nov. 27, 23; m. 47; c. 2. ENGLISH LITERATURE. Scholar, Univ. Chicago, 47-48, A.M, 48; scholar, Kenyon Sch. Eng, 49; univ. fel, Ohio State Univ, 49-51, Ph.D.(Eng), 52. Instr. ENG, Kenyon Col, 48-49; Ohio State Univ, 51-52; asst. prof, Univ. Minn, 52-55, assoc. prof, 55-58, prof, Univ. Ill, 58-63; Carpenter prof. lit. criticism, Univ. Iowa, 63-67; PROF. ENG. & COMP. LIT. & DIR. PROG. LIT. CRITICISM, UNIV. CALIF, IRVINE, 67-; PROF. ENG, UNIV. CALIF, LOS ANGELES, 73- Guggenheim fel, 56-57, 61-62; assoc. mem, Ctr. Advan. Stud, Univ. Ill, 61-62; Am. Counc. Learned Soc. fel, 66-67; Nat. Endowment for Humanities res. grant, 71-72. U.S.A, 42-46. MLA; AAUP. Poetics and literary theory; renaissance lyric; the tragic and the comic. Publ: The new apologists for poetry, Univ. Minn, 56; The tragic vision, Holt, 60; A window to criticism: Shakespeare's sonnets and modern poetics, Princeton, 64; The play and place of criticism, 67 & The classic vision, 71, Johns Hopkins Univ. Add: Dept. of English & Comparative Literature, University of California, Irvine, CA 92664.

KRIEGHBAUM, HILLIER, b. South Bend, Ind, Nov. 2, 02; m. 45; c. 1. JOURNALISM, CURRENT HISTORY. A.B, Univ. Wis, 26; M.S, Northwest. Univ, 39. Correspondent, United Press Asn, 27-38, 42; from asst. prof. to assoc. prof, Kans. State Col, 38-42; assoc. prof, Univ. Ore, 46-47; JOUR, N.Y. UNIV, 48-50, prof, 60-73, chmn. dept, 57-63, EMER. PROF, 73- Inform. off, Veteran's Admin, 45-46; consult, State Dept. Civil Serv, N.Y, 52-63; Josiah Macy, Jr. Found, 52-56; Nat. Sci. Found, 63-65; proj. dir, seminars sci. writers, N.Y. Univ, 60-62; vis. lectr. sci. writing, Japan, summer 60, Chile, 62; Elihu Stout lectr, Vincennes Univ, 73; vis. prof. jour, Manhattanville Col, 73-74; U.S. participant, First Ibero-Am. Cong. Sci. Jour, Caracas, Venezuela, 74. Pioneer Award, Nat. Scholastic Press Asn, 70. U.S.N.R, 42-45, Comdr.(Ret). Asn. Educ. in Jour.(pres, 71-72); Nat. Conf. Educ. Writers; Int. Press Inst; AAAS; Am. Soc. Jour. Sch. Adminr.(pres, 60-61); life mem. Nat. Asn. Sci. Writers. Specialized and investigative reporting; media and government relations; journalism education. Publ: American newspaper reporting of science news, Kans. State Univ, 41; Facts in perspective, Prentice-Hall, 56; ed, When doctors meet reporters, 57; Science, the news, and the public, 58, co-auth, Student journalist, 63, auth, Science and the mass media, 67 & co-auth, An investment in knowledge, 69, N.Y. Univ; co-auth, To improve secondary school science and mathematics teaching, Govt. Printing Off, 68; auth, Pressures on the press, Crowell, 72. Add: 731 River St, Mamaroneck, NY 10543.

KRING, HILDA ADAM, b. Munich, Ger, Jan. 3, 21; U.S. citizen; m. 46. FOLKLORE & FOLKLIFE, ENGLISH. B.S, Millersville State Col, 42; Pa. State Univ, 43-44; M.Litt, Univ. Pittsburgh, 52; Kent State Univ, summers 62-65; Ph.D.(folklore, folklife), Univ. Pa, 69. Teacher Eng, social stud. & Ger, Salisbury Twp. High Sch, Gap, Pa, 42-46; ENG, Westmont-Upper Yoder High Sch, Johnstown, 46-47; Adams Twp. High Sch, Sidman, 47-48; Conemaugh Twp. High Sch, Davidsville, 48-56; suprv, Slippery Rock State Col, 56-58; teacher, Slippery Rock Area Joint High Sch, 58-64, 66-67; PROF, GROVE CITY COL, 67- Pa. Teacher of the Yr, 67. Publ: The bird that couldn't sing (playette), Plays, 57; The harmonists: a folk cultural approach, Scarecrow, 73; Another approach to poetry, Eng. J, 1/61; The mountain wreath, Delta Kappa Gamma J, winter 65; Mary goes over the mountain, Pa. Folklife, summer 70; plus others. Add: Dept. of English, Grove City College, Grove City, PA 16127.

KROEBER, KARL, b. Oakland, Calif, Nov. 24, 26; m. 53. ENGLISH. A.B, Univ. Calif, 47; M.A, Columbia Univ, 51, Ph.D.(Eng), 56. Lectr. & instr, Columbia Univ, 52-56; instr. Eng, Univ. Wis, 56-59, asst. prof, 59-61, assoc. prof, 61-63, PROF, 63-70, assoc. dean grad. sch, 63-65; ENG. & COMP. LIT, COLUMBIA UNIV, 70-, CHMN. DEPT. ENG, 73- Kiekhofer Teaching Award, 59; Fulbright res. fel, Italy, 60-61; U.S. Off. Educ. grant, 65-66; Guggenheim fel, 66-67; vis. prof. Eng, Univ. Wash, 68. U.S.N, 44-46, Ens. MLA; Mod. Humanities Res. Asn, Gt. Brit; Am. Asn. Teachers Ital; Int. Asn. Univ. Prof. Eng. Nineteenth century English literature; continental romantic literature; theory and history of fiction. Publ: Romantic narrative art, 61 & The artifice of reality, 64, Univ. Wis; Styles in fictional structure, Princeton, 71; plus others. Add: Dept. of English & Comparative Literature, Columbia University, New York, NY 10027.

KROEGER, FREDERICK PAUL, b. Minneapolis, Minn, Apr. 25, 21; m. 46; c. 2. ENGLISH. B.A, Grinnell Col, 43; M.A, Univ. Minn, 49; Oxford, 53-54; Ph.D.(Am. lit), Univ. Mich, 67. Instr. Eng, North Mont. Col, 49-52; Univ. N.Dak, 54-56; mem. fac, Flint Community Jr. Col, 56-68; from assoc. prof. to prof, Ill. State Univ, 68-73, dir. freshman Eng, 68-69; PROF. ENG, TEX. A&I UNIV, 73- Dir. two-yr. col. Eng. Educ. Prof. Develop. Assistance fel. prog, Ill. State Univ, 68-73. U.S.N.R, 43-45, Lt. MLA; NCTE; Conf. Col. Compos. & Commun; AAUP; Am. Educ. Res. Asn. American literature; humanities in the two-year college; higher education. Publ: co-auth, English in the two year college, NCTE, 65; auth, Uncle Toby's pipe and whistle, Mich. Acad. Sci. & Arts, 61; The effect of a negotiated contract on the relations of the faculty to the administrator, CCC J, 5/67; Report on the survey of humanities courses taught in the occupational curricula in two year colleges in the U.S, Educ. Resources Inform. Ctr, 73. Add: Dept. of English, Texas A&I University, 6300 Ocean Dr, Corpus Christi, TX 78411.

KROESE, IRVIN B, b. Hull, Iowa, July 1, 36; m. 61; c. 1. ENGLISH. A.B, Calvin Col, 59; M.A, Ohio Univ, 63, Ph.D, 66. ASST. PROF. ENG, Humboldt State Col, 66-68; CALVIN COL, 68- U.S.A, 55-57. MLA; Keats-Shelley Asn; Wordsworth Circle. English romantic poetry, especially Shelley. Publ: Chatterton's Aella and Chatterton, Stud. Eng. Lit, summer 72. Add: Dept. of English, Calvin College, Grand Rapids, MI 49506.

KROETSCH, ROBERT PAUL, b. Heisler, Alta, June 26, 27; m. 56; c. 2. ENGLISH. B.A, Univ. Alta, 48; M.A, Middlebury Col, 56; fel, Univ. Iowa, 60-61; Ph.D.(Eng), 61. Asst. prof. ENG, STATE UNIV. N.Y. BINGHAMTON, 61-65, assoc. prof, 65-68, PROF, 68- Fel. fiction, Breadloaf Writers' Conf, summer, 66; mem, YADDO, N.Y, 66; Can. Counc. bursary, 67-68; summer fel, State Univ. N.Y, 64, 66, 68. Modern literature; American literature; creative writing. Publ: But we are exiles, 65 & The words of my roaring, 66, St. Martin's; The studhorse man, Simon & Schuster, 70. Add: Dept. of English, State University of New York at Binghamton, Binghamton, NY 13901.

KROHN, ROBERT KARL, Linguistics, English as a Second Language. See Volume III, Foreign Languages, Linguistics & Philology.

KROITOR, HARRY PETER, b. Regina, Sask, Mar. 2, 24. ENGLISH LITERATURE. B.A, Univ. Sask, 46, B.A, 49, M.A, 50; fel, Univ. Md, 50-53, Ph.D. (Eng), 57. Instr. ENG, Univ. Buffalo, 53-58; asst. prof, TEX. A&M UNIV, 58-63, assoc. prof, 63-67, PROF, 67- MLA; Am. Stud. Asn; NCTE; S.Cent. Mod. Lang. Asn; Conf. Col. Compos. & Commun; Am. Soc. 18th Century Stud. Rhetoric and rhetorical analysis; science fiction, history of ideas in science and literature; English literature of the 18th century. Publ: Co-auth, The unity of English, Harper, 70 & The five-hundred-word theme, Prentice-Hall, 74; Cowper, deism and the divinization of nature, J. Hist. Ideas, 60; The influence of popular science on William Cowper, Mod. Philol, 63. Add: 1217 Glade St, College Station, TX 77840.

KRONENBERGER, LOUIS, b. Cincinnati, Ohio, Dec. 9, 04; m. 40; c. 2. ENGLISH DRAMA. Hon. Litt.D, Univ. Cincinnati, 52. Lectr. Eng, Columbia Univ, 50; prof. theatre arts, Brandeis Univ, 52-70; WRITER & CRITIC, 70- Vis. prof, City Col. New York, 53, Stanford Univ, 54, 63 & Harvard, 59; vis. lectr, Oxford, 59; Christian Gauss Sem. lectr, Princeton, 61; adj. prof, Columbia Univ, 61; regents' prof, Univ. Calif, Berkeley, 68; Guggenheim fel, 69-70. Nat. Inst. Arts & Lett.(secy, 53-56); fel. Am. Acad. Arts & Sci. Eighteenth century English literature; drama; contemporary United States culture. Publ: Kings and desperate men: life in eighteenth century England, 41, The thread of laughter: English stage comedy, 52 & The republic of letters, 55, Knopf; ed, The cutting edge, Doubleday, 70; auth, No whippings, no gold watches, 70, ed, Atlantic brief lives, 71 & auth, A mania for magnificence, 72, Atlantic Monthly; ed, Animal, vegetable, mineral, Viking, 72; auth, The last word, Macmillan, 72; plus others. Add: 1514 Beacon St, Brookline, MA 02146.

KROPF, CARL R, b. Canton, Ohio, Sept. 7, 39. EIGHTEENTH CENTURY ENGLISH LITERATURE. B.A, Otterbein Col, 61; M.A, Kent State Univ, 63; Ph.D.(Eng), Ohio State Univ, 68. Teaching asst. ENG, Ohio State Univ, 63-68; asst. prof, GA. STATE UNIV, 68-72, ASSOC. PROF, 72- MLA; S.Atlantic Mod. Lang. Asn; Am. Soc. 18th Century Stud. Restoration drama; 18th century novel and poetry. Publ: The sale of Defoe's Library, Papers Bibliog. Soc. Am, 71; The thematic structure of Defoe's Roxana, Stud. Eng. Lit, 72; Educational theory and human nature in Fielding's works, PMLA, 74. Add: Dept. of English, Georgia State University, 33 Gilmer St, Atlanta, GA 30303.

KROUSE, AGATE NESAULE, b. Riga, Latvia, Jan. 23, 38; U.S. citizen; m. 58; c. 1. MODERN LITERATURE, WOMEN'S STUDIES. A.B, Ind. Univ, 61, M.A, 63; Ph.D.(Eng), Univ. Wis-Madison, 72. Teaching asst. ENG, Ind. Univ, 60-61; instr, Univ. Wis, 62-63; from instr. to ASST. PROF, UNIV. WIS-WHITEWATER, 63- Women's Caucus Mod. Lang; Midwest Mod. Lang. Asn.(mem. mod. lit. adv. comt, 72-74); Popular Cult. Asn. Modern British and American literature; women writers; feminist literary criticism. Publ: A feminist in every classroom, Female Stud, 72; Women in American culture, In: American studies and American women, KNGW, Inc, 72; A Doris Lessing checklist, Contemporary Lit, 73. Add: Dept. of English, University of Wisconsin-Whitewater, 800 W. Main, Whitewater, WI 53190.

KRUEGEL, EILEEN HELENANNE, b. Spokane, Wash, Oct. 30, 27; m. 66. ENGLISH, PHILOSOPHY. Service scholar, Marylhurst Col, 48-50, B.A, 50; Univ. Portland, 55-57; fel. & Ph.D.(Eng), St. Louis Univ, 62; Univ. Birmingham, Eng, summer 62. Teacher Eng, hist. & theol, Sacred Heart High Sch, Salem, Ore, 52-54; St. Mary's High Sch, Portland, 54-57; instr. Eng, Marylhurst Col, 59-60; Ft. Wright Col, 62-64; asst. prof. Eng. & supvr. stud. teachers, Univ. Wash, 64-66; teacher ENG, Edmonds High Sch, Edmonds, Wash, 66-67; Renton Sr. High Sch, Renton, 67-68; CHMN. DEPT, HAZEN SR. HIGH SCH, 68- Lectr, Portland Area Lit. Conf, spring 60; res. contrib, Cent. Renaissance Conf, spring 62; grant, Stratford-upon-Avon, Eng, summer 62; lectr, Inland Empire Educ. Asn, 62-64; Wash. Orgn. Reading Develop, 63- NCTE; Nat. Educ. Asn; MLA. Shakespeare's history plays; Albert Camus' concept of the hero; Jean-Paul Sartres' concept of honor. Publ: The concept of honor in four of Shakespeare's history plays, Univ. Microfilms, 62; The rebel hero of Albert Camus, Univ. Portland Rev, spring 60; Bliss (poem), Fleur de Lis, spring 62. Add: 14515 S.E. 170th Pl, Renton, WA 98055.

KRUEGER, ROBERT CHARLES, b. New Braunfels, Tex, Sept. 19, 35. ENGLISH. B.A, South. Methodist Univ, 57; M.A, Duke Univ, 58; Nottingham Univ, 58-59; B.Litt, Oxford, 61, D.Phil.(Eng), 64. Instr. Eng, Duke Univ, 61-64, asst. prof, 64-69, assoc. prof, 69-73, dir. curriculum rev, 67-68, v. provost & dean, Trinity Col. Arts & Sci, 72-73; chmn. bd, Comal Hosiery Mills, 73- Southeast. Renaissance Soc. Renaissance English literature. Publ: Ed, The complete poems of Sir John Davies, Clarendon, 74; Orchestra, complete Epigrams, unpublished poems, 62 & John Donne's sermons, 64, Rev. Eng. Stud; Samuel Daniel's Civil wars, Stud. Philol, 66. Add: P.O. Box 667, New Braunfels, TX 78130.

KRUEGER, SIDNEY, b. Newark, N.J, Aug. 3, 20; m. 48; c. 2. ENGLISH. B.S, Newark State Teachers Col, 41; M.A, George Peabody Col, 47; Wall St. Fund fel, Pa. State Univ, 60. Elem. teacher, Avon Ave. Sch, Newark, 47-54; teacher ENG, Robert Treat Jr. High Sch, 54-56; Cent. High Sch, 56-62; ASSOC. PROF, KEAN COL. N.J, 62- U.S.A, 41-45, S/Sgt. Add: Dept. of English, Kean College of New Jersey, Union, NJ 07083.

KRUGER, ARTHUR N, b. Boston, Mass, Feb. 4, 16; m. 41; c. 2. SPEECH, PHILOSOPHY. A.B, Univ. Ala, 36; Ph.D.(Eng), La. State Univ, 41. Instr. Eng, Essex Jr. Col, 40-41; N.C. State Univ, 41-42; asst. prof. Eng. & speech, Wilkes Col, 47-54, assoc. prof, 54-59, 59-62; PROF. SPEECH, C.W. POST COL, LONG ISLAND UNIV, 62-, CHMN. DEPT, 65- Sig.C, U.S.A, 1st Lt. Speech Commun. Asn; Am. Forensic Asn. Argumentation and debate; logic; speech. Publ: Modern debate: its logic and strategy, McGraw, 60; co-auth, Championship debating, Walch, Vols. I & II, 61 & 67; auth, A classified bibliography of argumentation and debate, 64 & Counterpoint: debates about debate, 68, Scarecrow; co-auth, Essentials of logic, 68 & Workbook for essentials of logic, 68, Am. Bk. Co; auth, Effective speaking: a complete course, Reinhold, 70; The inherent need: further clarification, 9/65 & The comparative advantage case: a disadvantage, 9/66, J. Am. Forensic Asn; The ethics of persuasion: a re-examination, Speech Teacher, 11/67. Add: Dept. of Speech, C.W. Post College, Long Island University, Greenvale, NY 11548.

KRUGLAK, THEODORE EDWARD, b. New York, N.Y, Feb. 5, 11; m. 36; c. 3. JOURNALISM, POLITICAL SCIENCE. B.A, Long Island Univ, 32; M.A, Univ. Iowa, 33; Dr. Polit. Sci, Univ. Geneva, 55. Prof. jour. & govt. & v.pres, Long Island Univ, 48-59; prof. polit. sci. & pres, Am. Col. Switz, 60-64; PROF. JOUR. & DIR. SCH, UNIV. SOUTH. CALIF, 64- Fulbright prof. int. commun, Univ. Rome, 58-59; vis. prof, Univ. Aix-Marseille, 59-60; Univ. Ankara, 68-69. Sigma Delta Chi Award; Frank Luther Mott Award; George Polk Mem. Award. Am. Counc. Educ. Jour.(accrediting comt, 72-); Asn. Educ. in Jour; Int. Commun. Asn; Inter-Am. Press Asn; Int. Asn. Mass. Commun. Res; Int. Press Inst. International communication; international and national communication systems; U.S.S.R. and Eastern European press systems. Publ: The foreign correspondents, Libr. Droz, Geneva, 55, Greenwood, 73; The international news channels, Univ. Rome, 59; The two faces of TASS, Univ. Minn, 62, McGraw, 63, Greenwood, 72. Add: School of Journalism, University of Southern California, University Park, Los Angeles, CA 90007.

KRUMMEL, REGINA POMERENZ, b. New York, N.Y, Dec. 30, 30; m. 62; c. 1. ENGLISH, EDUCATION. A.B, N.Y. Univ, 50; M.A, Columbia Univ, 52, prof. dipl. educ, 59, Ed.D.(Eng. & educ), 66. ASST. PROF. ENG, Bronx Community Col, 62-66; EDUC, QUEENS COL.(N.Y), 66- Mem. adult educ. degree prog, N.Y. Univ, 64-67; Eng. consult, high schs, New York, N.Y, 68. MLA; NCTE. Contemporary American literature, especially 1950's and 1960's; existentialism and education. Publ: The hell of not loving: Purdy's modern tragedy, Renascence, spring 64; Self-betrayal in modern American fiction, 4/64 & Two quests in two societies, 4/67, Eng. Rec. Add: Dept. of English, Queens College, Flushing, NY 11367.

KRUMP, JACQUELINE, b. Chicago, Ill. ENGLISH. Univ. fel, Northwest. Univ, 50, Ph.D, 51. Teacher Eng, South Campus, Chicago Teachers Col, 50-53; pers. dir, Sheil Inst, 53-54; from mem. fac. to assoc. prof. Eng. & chmn. dept, NORTHEAST. ILL. UNIV, 54-61, assoc. prof. ENG, 61-65, PROF, 65-, chmn. lit. dept, 65-66. MLA. Victorian literature; women's studies; children's literature. Publ: No better satires: Thackeray's use of letters in Vanity Fair, 12/71 & Thackeray nods over the piano in Vanity Fair, 9/71, Res. Stud; plus others. Add: Dept. of English, Northeastern Illinois University, Bryn Mawr at St. Louis, Chicago, IL 60625.

KRUPAT, ARNOLD, b. New York, N.Y, Oct. 22, 41. ENGLISH. B.A, N.Y. Univ, 62; Univ. Strasbourg, 62-63; M.A, Columbia Univ, 64, Woodrow Wilson & Fulbright fels, 62-63, President's fel, 64-66, Woodberry fel, 66-67, Ph.D. (Eng), 67. Instr. Eng, Rutgers Univ, 65-67, asst. prof, 67-68; MEM. FAC. LIT, SARAH LAWRENCE COL, 68- Nat. Endowment for Humanities fel, summer 70. Contemporary novel; theory of literature; irony in fiction. Publ: The strangeness of Wuthering Heights, 19th Century Fiction, 12/70. Add: Faculty of Literature, Sarah Lawrence College, Bronxville, NY 10708.

KRUPP, KATHLEEN McCOY, English. See McCOY, KATHLEEN.

KRUSE, ALICE MARIE, b. Clay Center, Nebr, Mar. 2, 07. ENGLISH. B.A, West. Union Col, 29; M.A, Univ. Ky, 43. PROF. ENG, WESTMAR COL, 46- NCTE. Hawthorne and children; literature by American Negro. Add: Dept. of English, Westmar College, Le Mars, IA 51031.

KRÜÜNER, MARTA REGINA, Sangaste, Estonia, Mar. 18, 25; Can. citizen. AMERICAN & COMPARATIVE LITERATURE. B.A, Univ. Man, 52; Ford Found. scholar, 54-61; M.A, Claremont Grad. Sch, 55; Ph.D.(comp. lit), Occidental Col, 61. Instr. Eng. & hist, Occidental Col, 60-61; lectr. ENG. UNIV. WINNIPEG, 61-64, asst. prof, 64-67; ASSOC. PROF, 67- MLA; Asn. Can. Univ. Teachers Eng. American and comparative literature; William Carlos Williams and modern American poetry; Southern renascence in American literature. Add: Dept. of English, University of Winnipeg, 515 Portage Ave, Winnipeg, Man. R3B 2E9, Can.

KUBAL, DAVID LAWRENCE, b. Cleveland, Ohio, Sept. 6, 36; m. 70; c. 4. ENGLISH LITERATURE. B.A, Univ. Notre Dame, 58, Ph.D.(Eng), 68; M.A, Northwest. Univ, 60. Instr. ENG, Loyola Univ. Chicago, 60-62; lectr, Ind. Univ. South Bend, 62-64; instr, Univ. Notre Dame, 64-65; Mich. State Univ, 65-68; asst. prof, CALIF. STATE UNIV, LOS ANGELES, 68-72, ASSOC. PROF, 72- The relationship between the imagination and culture in 18th, 19th and 20th century English literature. Publ: Outside the whale: George Orwell's art and politics, Univ. Notre Dame, 72; Lionel Trilling's The middle of the journey: an American dialectic, 3/66 & The secret agent and the mechanical chaos, 12/67, Bucknell Rev; Henry James and the supreme value, Ariz. Quart, summer 67. Add: Dept. of English, California State University, Los Angeles, 5151 State University Dr, Los Angeles, CA 90032.

KUBLY, HERBERT OSWALD, b. New Glarus, Wis, Apr. 26, 15; div; c. 1. ENGLISH, SPEECH. B.A, Univ. Wis, 37. Reporter, Pittsburgh Sun-Tel, 37-40, art critic, 40-42; reporter, N.Y. Herald Tribune, 42-44; music ed, Time Mag, 45-47; assoc. prof. speech, Univ. Ill, 49-54; writer travel & music, Life Mag. & Holiday Mag, 55-63; assoc. prof. Eng, San Francisco State Col, 64-68; PROF. ENG. & WRITER-IN-RESIDENCE, UNIV. WIS-PARKSIDE, 69- Rockefeller grant, 47-49; MacDowell Asn. fel, 47-62; Fulbright res. grant, Italy, 50-51; vis. lectr. creative writing, New Sch. Social Sci, 61-63; Columbia Univ, 62-63. Nat. Bk. Award, 56; Distinguished Serv. Citation, Univ. Wis, 62. Dramatists Guild (secy, 46-48); Edward A. MacDowell Asn. Italian theater; contemporary social and political issues in Italy, Greece and Switzerland. Publ: American in Italy (travel memoir), 55, Easter in Sicily (travel memoir), 56, Varities of love (short stories), 58 & The whistling zone (novel), 63, Simon & Schuster; Italy, 61 & Switzerland, 64, Life World Libr; At large (essays), 64, Gods and heroes (travel memoir), 68 & The Duchess of Glover (novel), 74, Doubleday; The vanishing novel, Saturday Rev, 5/64; plus several hundred articles on music, lit, travel & theatre in Time, Life, Holiday, Atlantic, Vogue, Venture, Town & Country & other mag. Men to the sea (play), produced in New York, 44; Inherit the wind (play), produced in London, 48; The Virus, produced at Univ. Wis-Parkside, 73; plus others. Add: Dept. of English, University of Wisconsin-Parkside, Wood Rd, Kenosha, WI 53140.

KUEHL, JOHN RICHARD, b. Davenport, Iowa, Mar. 19, 28; m. 74. AMERICAN LITERATURE, CREATIVE WRITING. B.A, State Univ. Iowa, 52; M.A, Univ. Calif, Los Angeles, 55; Ph.D.(Eng), Columbia Univ, 58. From instr. to asst. prof. ENG, Princeton, 58-66; ASSOC. PROF, N.Y. UNIV, 66- Asst. judge, G.J. Nathan Drama Critics' Award Comt, 61-65. U.S.M.C, 46-47, Res, 47-52, Sgt. American literature; creative writing. Publ: The apprentice fiction of F. Scott Fitzgerald, 1909-1917, 65 & The craft of John Hawkes, (in press), Rutgers Univ; Write and rewrite: a study of the creative process, Meredith, 67, also publ. as Creative writing and rewriting: contemporary novelists at work, A.C.C, 67; The fool-spy, For Now Press, 67; co-ed, Dear Scott/Dear Max: the Fitzgerald-Perkins correspondence, 71 & F. Scott Fitzgerald's The Basil and Josephine stories, 73, Scribner; Scott Fitzgerald: romantic and realist, Tex. Stud. Lit. & Lang, 59; Scott Fitzgerald's critical opinions, Mod. Fiction Stud, 61; A la Joyce, James Joyce Quart, 64. Add: Dept. of English, New York University, Washington Square, New York, NY 10003.

KUEHN, ROBERT E, b. Kohler, Wis, Aug. 17, 32; m. 55; c. 3. ENGLISH. B.A, Univ. Mich, 55; M.A, Univ. Wis, 57, Ph.D, 62. Instr. ENG, YALE, 62-65, asst. prof, 65-68, LECTR, 68-, ASST. DIR. YALE CTR. BRIT. ART & BRIT. STUD, 74-, dean, Jonathan Edwards Col, 65-73. Univ. Wis. distinguished teaching fel, 61. MLA. Twentieth century British and American literature. Publ: Ed, Twentieth century interpretations of Lord Jim, 69, co-ed, This powerful rime, 71 & ed, Aldous Huxley: a collection of essays, 74, Prentice-Hall. Add: 2120 Yale Station, New Haven, CT 06520.

KUHLMAN, THOMAS A, b. Cleveland, Ohio, May 24, 39; m. 64; c. 2. ENGLISH, AMERICAN CIVILIZATION. A.B, Xavier Univ.(Ohio), 61; Woodrow Wilson fel, Brown Univ, 61, univ. fel, 62, A.M, 63, Ph.D.(Am. civilization), 67. Instr. ENG, Georgetown Univ, 64-67; asst. prof, CREIGHTON UNIV, 67-70, ASSOC. PROF, 70-, COORD. AM. STUD. PROG, 67-, COORD. CONTINUING ED, 73- Lectr, Omaha Pub. Schs. V.I.P. prog. for ghetto teachers, 69-72; Creighton Univ. res. grant, 69; Rotary Int. Exchange fel. to Eng, 74. MLA. Contemporary American literature; Midwestern social history; American architecture. Publ: Book review consensus on The poetry of Theodore Roethke by Karl Malkoff, Am. Lit. Abstracts, 12/68; Note Bene, book review column, Triumph Mag, 71-; Warner's History of Dakota County, Nebraska: the western county history as a literary genre, West. Rev, winter 72. Add: Office of the Coordinator of Continuing Education, Creighton University, Omaha, NE 68178.

KUHLMANN, SUSAN, b. Goshen, N.Y, June 23, 42. AMERICAN LITERATURE. A.B, Radcliffe Col, 64; M.A, Stanford Univ, 66; Ph.D.(Am. lit), N.Y. Univ, 70. Vis. asst. prof. ENG, Ohio State Univ, 72-73; ASST. PROF, UNIV. IOWA, 73- MLA; Am. Stud. Asn. Nineteenth century American literature. Publ: Knave, fool, and genius, Univ. N.C, 73. Add: Dept. of English, University of Iowa, Iowa City, IA 52240.

KUHN, ALBERT J, b. Dowell, Ill, Apr. 4, 26; m. 49; c. 2. ENGLISH. A.B, Univ. Ill, 50; Ph.D, Johns Hopkins Univ, 54. Instr. ENG, OHIO STATE UNIV, 54-56, asst. prof, 57-61, assoc. prof, 61-65, PROF, 65-, PROVOST & V.PRES. ACAD. AFFAIRS, 71-, univ. traveling fel, England, 56, chmn. dept. Eng, 64-71. Woodrow Wilson fel. comt, 63-; chmn. Comt. Inst. Coop, 73-; pres, Res. Found, Ohio State Univ, 73- U.S.N, 44-46. MLA. Eighteenth and nineteenth century primitivism and poetry; influence of science on poetry, and of poetry on science. Publ: Ed, Three sentimental novels, Holt, 70; auth, Deism and romantic mythography, PMLA, 57; The anti-Newtonian Hutchinsonians, J. Hist. Ideas, 60; Christopher Smart: prophetic poet, Eng. Lit. Hist, 63. Add: 35 Webster Park, Columbus, OH 43214.

KUHN, HOWARD FREDERICK, b. Minn, July 9, 38; m. 65; c. 1. ENGLISH, AMERICAN LITERATURE. B.A, Col. St. Thomas, 65; NDEA fel, Univ. Ore, 65-68, M.A, 66, Ph.D.(Eng), 70. ASST. PROF. ENG, Franklin Col, 70-72; W.VA. INST. TECHNOL, 72- MLA; NCTE; Nat. Asn. For. Stud. Affairs. American fiction; English as a second language; creative writing. Add: Dept. of English, West Virginia Institute of Technology, Montgomery, WV 25136.

KUHN, JOHN GOTTLIEB, b. Philadelphia, Pa, June 2, 35; m. 60; c. 4. LITERATURE, THEATER. B.S, St. Joseph's Col.(Pa), 57; univ. res. grant, Purdue Univ, Lafayette, 58, scholarship, 59-60, M.S, 60; Gilman fel, Johns Hopkins Univ, 58-59; Ph.D.(Eng, dramatic lit), Univ. Pa, 69. Asst, Purdue Univ, Lafayette, 57-58; instr. Eng, N.Mex. State Univ, 60-62; playwright-in-residence, Hamlet Theater, Houston, Tex, 62; scriptwriter TV series, WCAU-TV, Phila, Pa, 63; instr. ENG. & DRAMATIC LIT, ROSEMONT COL, 63-64, asst. prof, 64-69, ASSOC. PROF, 69-, DIR. THEATER, 63- Lectr, Contemporary Arts Mus, Houston, Tex, 62; Univ. on the Air, Univ. Pa-WCAU-TV, 65; dir, theater workshop, Operation Discovery, Phila-Rosemont, summer 68; Josephine C. Connelly grant, 69; scriptwriter-dir, Response Street Theater, 71; lectr. grad. theatre dept, Villanova Univ, 73. U.S. Merchant Marine, 53-57. MLA; Am. Theatre Asn; Am. Soc. Theatre Res. Criticism. Publ: Lawrence Osgood, In: Contemporary dramatists, St. James Press, London, 73, St. Martin's, New York, 74; Then reproduce all in my own form: the cyclic artistry of Walt Whitman's verse, Walt Whitman Rev, fall 62; I morti (poem) & Santa Lucia in Tuscany (poem), Denver Quart, summer 73; Tony Pastor, Nineteenth Century Theatrical Res, spring 73. Add: 15 Pennock Terr, Lansdowne, PA 19050.

KUHN, SHERMAN McALLISTER, b. Alexandria, S.Dak, Sept. 15, 07; m. 26, 35; c. 4. ENGLISH. B.A, Park Col, 29; M.A, Univ. Chicago, 33, fel, 34-35, Ph.D.(Eng), 35. Teacher, high sch, 29-32; asst. prof. ENG, Okla. Agr. & Mech. Col, 35-41, assoc. prof, 41-47, prof, 47-48; assoc. prof, UNIV. MICH, ANN ARBOR, 48-55, PROF, 55- Assoc. ed, Mid. Eng. Dictionary, 48-61, ed, 61-; mem. adv. bd, Speculum, 68-70; mem. ed. bd, Stud. in Medieval Cult, 71- U.S.A, 44-45. MLA; Ling. Soc. Am; fel. Medieval Acad. Am; Early Eng. Text Soc; Am. Dialect Soc. English linguistics; medieval literature; lexicography. Publ: A grammar of the Mercian dialect, Univ. Chicago Libr, 38; collab, A functional grammar, Farrar & Rinehart, form A, 38, form B, 40; auth, The Vespasian Psalter, Univ. Mich, 65; On the consonantal phonemes of Old English, Philol. Essays, Univ. Pa, 70; The authorship of the Old English Bede revisited, Neuphilol. Mitt, 72; Cursus in Old English: rhetorical ornament or linguistic phenomenon?, Speculum, 72; plus others. Add: 225 Buena Vista, Ann Arbor, MI 48103.

KUHR, MANUEL I, b. Philadelphia, Pa, July 25, 28; m. 54; c. 3. SPEECH. B.A, Temple Univ, 49, M.A, 52; Ph.D.(speech), Univ. Mo, 63. Asst. prof. speech, Bradley Univ, 57-58; instr. speech & dir. forensics, Temple Univ, 58-61; PROF. SPEECH, SLIPPERY ROCK STATE COL, 61- Speech consult, Pa. Dept. Pub. Instr, 65- Speech Commun. Asn. American public address, rhetorical theory. Publ: Conducting a two-week debate institute, Speech Teacher, 3/63; How George Vest came to Missouri, Mo. Hist. Rev, 7/65; contrib, A history of public speaking in Pennsylvania, Pa. Speech Asn, 71. Add: Dept. of Speech & Theatre, Slippery Rock State College, Slippery Rock, PA 16057.

KUIPER, JOHN B, b. Ann Arbor, Mich, June 22, 28; m. 53; c. 4. SPEECH, MASS MEDIA. A.B, Univ. Ky, 50; Ill. Inst. Technol, 50-51; M.A, Univ. Iowa, 57, Ph.D.(film-TV), 60. Motion picture dir, Reela Films, Inc, Fla, 53-55; asst. prof. radio, TV & film, Univ. Iowa, 60-65, assoc. prof, 65-66; HEAD MOTION PICTURE SECT, LIBR. CONGR, 65- Lectr, Peace Corps, Univ. Nebr, 64; consult, Columbia Univ, 66; adj. prof. commun, Am. Univ. (D.C), 66-; cinema, N.Y. Univ, 72- Soc. Cinema Stud.(secy, 63-65; pres, 65-68, sr. councilor, 68-); Univ. Film Asn.(chmn. curriculum comt, 65-72); Speech Commun. Asn; Soc. Am. Archivist. Motion pictures and television communication; history of mass media; history and criticism of art. Publ: Cinematic expression: a look at Eisenstein's Silent montage, Art J, fall 62; Eisenstein's Strike: a study in cinematic allegory, J. Soc. Cinematologist, fall 63; D.W. Griffith and the development of film narrative, Quart. J. Libr. Congr, 1/68. Add: 3801 Underwood St, Chevy Chase, MD 20015.

KULKARNI, HANMANT B, b. Kadapur, India, Nov. 25, 16; m. 41; c. 4. ENGLISH, PHILOSOPHY. B.A, Univ. Bombay, 37, M.A, 39; Fulbright fel, 58; Ph.D.(Eng), Univ. Utah, 62. Asst. prof. Eng, Willingdon Col, India, 42-47; prof, Vijay Col, India, 47-50; reader, Osmania Univ, India, 50-58; teaching asst, Univ. Utah, 58-60, lectr, 61-63; reader, Osmania Univ, India, 63-67; asst. prof. Eng. & philos, UTAH STATE UNIV, 67-69, ASSOC. PROF. ENG, 69- Poetry Soc, Eng. Stephen Spender, poet in crisis; Melville, an Oriental approach. Publ: Moby Dick: a Hindu Avatar, Utah State Univ, 70; Stephen Spender: poet in crisis, Blackie & Son, Eng, 70; Exploring roots (poems), Omni-Press, 72; Poetic theory of Stephen Spender, 64 & Sound and significance in Macbeth, 65, Osmania J. Eng. Stud; Significance of sacrifice in Moby Dick, In: Indian response to American literature, 68. Add: 1510 E. 1100 North, Logan, UT 84321.

KULLY, ROBERT DELMAR, b. Hastings, Nebr, Feb. 27, 27. SPEECH. B.A, Hastings Col, 50; M.A, Univ. Ore, 54; summer fel. & Ph.D, Univ, Ill, 56. Teacher, high sch, Nebr, 50-52; assoc. prof. speech, CALIF. STATE UNIV, LOS ANGELES, 56-65, dor. forensics, 56-64, chmn. dept. speech & drama, 64-65, PROF. SPEECH COMMUN, 65-, assoc. dean acad. affairs, sch. lett. & sci, 65-70. Lectr, Europ. overseas prog, Univ. Md, 60-62. U.S.A, 45-46. Speech Commun. Asn; Am. Forensics Ans; West. Speech Commun. Asn. Rhetoric; American public address; argumentation. Publ: Co-auth, An exercise in audience analysis, Cent. States Speech J, 11/63; auth, Rabbi Isaac Mayer Wise: his language of anti anti-semitism, Quart. J. of Speech, 4/64; The 1962 California gubernatorial compaign: the new Brown, West. Speech J, spring 66. Add: Dept. of Speech Communication, California State University, Los Angeles, 5151 State University Dr, Los Angeles, CA 90032.

KULSETH, LEONARD IRVIN, b. Valley City, N.Dak, Sept. 24, 18; m. 46; c. 2. ENGLISH. B.S, Mankato State Col, 41; M.A, Univ. Minn, Minneapolis, 50; Mich. State Univ, 61-62. Instr. ENG, Brainerd Jr. Col, 52-57; asst. prof, Ball State Univ, 57-66; ASSOC. PROF, KUTZTOWN STATE COL, 66- Danforth grant, summer 61. U.S.A, 42-46, Sgt. MLA. Modern drama; Shakespeare; drama from beginnings to present. Publ: Cincinnatus among the Snopses: the role of Gavin Stevens, Ball State Univ. Forum, winter 69; Abstract of Cincinnatus among the Snopses: the role of Gavin Stevens, Am. Lit. Abstracts, 6/69. Add: Dept. of English, Kutztown State College, Kutztown, PA 19530.

KUMMER, GEORGE, b. Uhrichsville, Ohio, Aug. 11, 05; m. 32. ENGLISH. B.S, Ohio State Univ, 26; M.A, Harvard, 31; Ph.D, N.Y. Univ, 47. Instr. ENG, Seton Hall Col, 38-42; asst. prof, Bowling Green State Univ, 46-47; CASE WEST. RESERVE UNIV, 47-63, assoc. prof, 63-69, PROF, 69- U.S.A.A.F, 42-45. MLA; Am. Stud. Asn. American literature; folklore; aesthetics; bibliography. Publ: Harry Leon Wilson, West. Reserve Univ, 63; ed, The Leatherwood God, Scholars' Facsimilies, 66. Add: Dept. of English, Case Western Reserve University, Cleveland, OH 44106.

KUMMINGS, DONALD D, b. July 28, 40; U.S. citizen; m. 63; c. 2. ENGLISH & AMERICAN STUDIES. A.B, Purdue Univ, West Lafayette, 62, M.A, 64; Ph.D.(Eng. & Am. stud), Ind. Univ, Bloomington, 71. Instr. ENG, Adrian Col, 64-66; assoc. instr, Ind. Univ, 66-70; ASST. PROF, UNIV. WIS-PARKSIDE, 70- Acad. Am. Poets Prize, 69. Am. Stud. Asn; MLA (Am. Lit. Group); Col. Eng. Asn.(ed. reading comt, 72-). American studies with emphasis on the relationships between American poetry and culture; Walt Whitman; American nonfiction prose. Publ: Whitman's voice in Song of myself: from private to public, Walt Whitman Rev, 71; Hawthorne's The custom house and the conditions of fiction in America, CEA Critic, 71; A note on the Americanness of Walt Whitman, Calamus: An Int. Whitman Quart, 73. Add: Div. of Humanistic Studies, University of Wisconsin-Parkside, Kenosha, WI 53140.

KUNER, MILDRED CHRISTOPHE, b. New York, N.Y, Feb. 10, 22. ENGLISH, DRAMA. A.B, Hunter Col, 43, fel, 48-50; M.F.A, Yale, 47; Ph.D, Columbia Univ, 53. Instr. ENG. & DRAMA, Yankton Col, 47-48; lectr, HUNTER COL, 50-53, instr, 53-60, asst. prof, 60-66, assoc. prof, 66-72, PROF, 73- Anderson Award, Stanford Univ, 50; Sergel Award, Univ. Chicago, 51; Huntington Hartford grant, 52; part-time instr, New Sch. Soc. Res, 55-56; auth, Capacity for wings, three-act play produced off-Broadway, 56; Fulbright res. grant theatre hist, Univ. Vienna, Austria, 59-60. Int. Soc. Theatre Res; MLA; Dramatists Guild. Creative writing; theatre history; modern British literature. Publ: The mistress of Mellyn (adaptation of Victoria Holt's novel), Dramatic Publ. Co, 61; Thornton Wilder: the bright and the dark, Crowell, 72; Of actors & playwrights and makers of dreams, Drama Critique, 9/65; The New York Shakespeare festival, Shakespeare Quart, autumn 66 & 67; plus others. Add: Dept. of English, Hunter College, 695 Park Ave, New York, NY 10021.

KUNITZ, STANLEY, b. Worcester, Mass, July 29, 05; m. 30, 39, 58; c. 1. ENGLISH. A.B, Harvard, 26, A.M, 27; Lit.D, Clark Univ, 61. Mem. fac. lit, Bennington Col, 46-49; prof. ENG, State Univ. N.Y. Teachers Col, Potsdam, 49-50; lectr. Eng, New Sch. Soc. Res, 50-57; vis. prof, Brandeis Univ, 58-59, Danforth vis. lectr, 61-63; lectr, COLUMBIA UNIV, 63-66, ADJ. PROF. WRITING, SCH. ARTS, 67- Guggenheim fel, 45; Lowell Poetry Traveling fel, 54; vis. prof, Univ. Wash, 55-56; Queens Col.(N.Y), 56-57; Ford. Found. grant, 58-59; ed, Yale Series of Younger Poets, 69-; chancellor, Acad. Am. Poets, 70-; vis. prof, Yale, 72; Rutgers Univ, 74. Garrison Medal, Harvard, 26; Blumenthal Prize, 41; Levinson Prize, 56; Harriet Monroe Award, Univ. Chicago, 58; Pulitzer Prize, poetry, 59; Brandeis Univ. Creative Arts Medal for poetry, 65; fel. award, Acad. Am. Poets, 68. U.S.A.A.F, 43-45. Nat. Inst. Arts & Lett. Creative writing; modern British and American literature. Publ: Intellectual things, 30; ed, Twentieth century authors, 42, 55 & European authors, 1000-1900, 67, Wilson; auth, Selected poems, 1928-1958, 58, The testing-tree, 71 & co-auth, Poems of Akhmatova, 73, Atlantic Monthly Press. Add: 157 W. 12th St, New York, NY 10011.

KUNKEL, FRANCIS LEO, b. New York, N.Y, Oct. 23, 21; m. 51. ENGLISH. B.A, Notre Dame Univ, 43; M.A, Columbia Univ, 48, Ph.D, 59. Instr. ENG, Notre Dame Univ, 47-48; ST. JOHN'S UNIV.(N.Y), 49-53, asst. prof, 53-59, assoc. prof, 59-62, PROF, 62-, ED. DIR, UNIV. PRESS, 62-, rep. Eng. Dept, 60-62. U.S.C.G, 43-46. Cath. Renascence Soc. Contemporary literature. Publ: The labyrinthine ways of Graham Greene, Sheed, 60, Paul Appel, 73. Add: Dept. of English, St. John's University, Jamaica, NY 11432.

KUNKEL, ROBERT RAYMOND, b. Collinsville, Ill, Dec. 26, 27; m. 52; c. 3. RHETORIC, PUBLIC ADDRESS. B.A, Ill. Col, 52; M.A, Univ. Wis-Madison, 56; La. State Univ, Baton Rouge, 72-74. Teacher Eng. & speech, Postville Community High Sch, Iowa, 52-55; instr. SPEECH, Pensacola Jr. Col, 55-56; Furman Univ, 56-58; teaching asst, La. State Univ, Baton Rouge, 58-60; instr, Univ. N.Dak, 60-65; asst. prof, Kearney State Col, 65-71; ASSOC. PROF, UNIV. MONTEVALLO, 71- U.S.A, 45-48, Sgt. Speech Commun. Asn. Southern oratory; interpersonal speech. Add: 28 Vine St, Montevallo, AL 35115.

KUNTZ, JOSEPH MARSHALL, b. Lehighton, Pa, Feb. 1, 11. ENGLISH LITERATURE. A.B, Univ. N.Mex, 33, A.M, 34; Univ. Tex, 38-41; Ph.D, Univ. Denver, 60. Instr, Waldorf Jr. Col, 34-35; auditor, U.S. Forest Serv, 35-38; tutor, Univ. Tex, 38-41; dir. pubs, U.S. Army schs, Tex. & N.Mex, 41-43; instr. Eng, UNIV. N.MEX, 43-47, asst. prof, 47-61, assoc. prof. Eng. lit. & lang, 61-70, PROF. SHAKESPEARE & CHAUCER, 70- Contrib. bibliographer, Mod. Humanities Res. Asn, Gt. Brit, 47-50; contrib. ed, Explicator Checklist, 49-56. Linguistics. Publ: Co-ed, Poetry explication: a checklist of interpretation since 1925 of British and American poems past and present, Swallow, 50, ed, rev. ed, 62 & 3rd ed, (in press). Add: Dept. of English, University of New Mexico, Albuquerque, NM 87131.

KUNZ, DON R, b. Kansas City, Mo, Nov. 23, 41; m. 65; c. 1. ENGLISH LITERATURE. B.A, Kans. State Univ, 64; M.A, Univ. Tex, Austin, 65; Ph.D (Eng), Univ. Wash, 68. ASST. PROF. ENG. UNIV. R.I, 68-, summer fac. fel, 70. MLA; AAUP. British drama 1660-1780; 20th Century American novel; North American Indian literature. Publ: The drama of Thomas Shadwell, Inst. Eng. Sprache & Literatur, Univ. Salzburg, 72; Shadwell's A true widow; promis'd a play and dwindled to a farce?, 5/71 & Shadwell and his critics: the misuse of Dryden's Macflecknoe, 5/73, Restoration & 18th Century Theatre Res. Add: Dept. of English, University of Rhode Island, Kingston, RI 02881.

KURMAN, GEORGE, Comparative & Estonian Literature. See Volume III, Foreign Languages, Linguistics & Philology.

KURRIK, MAIRE JAANUS, b. Tartu, Estonia, Jan. 22, 40; U.S. citizen; m. 70; c. 1. ENGLISH & GERMAN LITERATURE. B.A, Vassar Col, 61; Fulbright grant, Cambridge, 61-62; Ph.D.(comp. lit), Harvard, 68. ASST. PROF. ENG, BARNARD COL, COLUMBIA UNIV, 68- Nat. Endowment for Humanities younger humanist fel, 73-74. First Prize, Nat. Humanities Ser. Proposal Competition, 72. Am. Comp. Lit. Asn; AAUP. Publ: Georg Trakl, Vol. 72, In: Columbia essays on modern writers, Columbia Univ, 74; coauth, Erich Auerbach's Philologie und Weltliteratur, Centennial Rev, winter 69; auth, Juhan Smuul's moral propaganda, J. Baltic Stud, fall 73. Add: 422 Barnard Hall, Barnard College, Columbia University, New York, NY 10027.

KURTH, BURTON OLIVER, b. Winnipeg, Man, Dec. 29, 23; m. 49; c. 2. ENGLISH. B.A, Univ. B.C, 45; M.A, Univ. Calif, Berkeley, 50, Ph.D, 55. Lectr. ENG, Univ. B.C, 46-48; Univ. Calif, Berkeley, 52-53, 54-55; instr, Univ. South. Calif, 55-57, asst. prof, 57-61; UNIV. VICTORIA, 61-62, ASSOC. PROF, 62- Can. Counc. sr. fel, 66-67. Renaissance Soc. Am; MLA; Humanities Asn. Can; Philol. Asn. Pac. Coast. Renaissance poetry and lyric; Milton; Shakespeare. Publ: Milton and Christian heroism, Univ. Calif, 59; co-auth, Writing from experience, Harper, 60. Add: Dept. of English, University of Victoria, Victoria, B.C, Can.

KURTZ, KENNETH, b. Frazer, Mont, Aug. 16, 07; m. 45. ENGLISH & AMERICAN LITERATURE. A.B, Jamestown Col, 29; B.A, Oxford, 33, M.A, 40; Ph.D, Yale, 47. From instr. to assoc. prof. Eng, West. State Col. of Colo, 33-36; asst. prof. Eng. & Am. lit, Black Mountain Col, 38-44; PROF. ENG, OCCIDENTAL COL, 46-, chmn. dept, 46-49. Ford Found. fel, 53-54. MLA; Melville Soc. Am; Col. Eng. Asn; Am. Stud. Asn. Emerson and transcendentalist thought. Publ: Literature of the American Southwest, a selected bibliography; The sources and development of Emerson's Representative men, Univ. Microfilms, 66. Add: Dept. of English, Occidental College, Los Angeles, CA 90041.

KUSHNER, EVA M, French Literature. See Volume III, Foreign Languages, Linguistics & Philology

KUSSROW, VAN CARL, JR, b. Miami Beach, Fla, Oct. 31, 26; m. 52; c. 4. SPEECH, DRAMA. A.B, Stanford Univ, 49, M.A, 50; Univ. Chicago, 55; Danforth fel, Ind. Univ, 55, Ph.D.(theatre hist), 59. Assoc. prof. SPEECH & DRAMA, VALPARAISO UNIV, 60-64, PROF, 64- Fulbright res. grant, Spain, 64; dir Valparaiso Univ-Coventry Cathedral Drama Proj, Eng, 65-66, 68-69, 70-72; Ind. Comt. for Humanities grant, 73-74. Am. Theatre Asn; Speech Commun. Asn; Conf. Christianity & Lit. Eighteenth century American theatre history; drama and the church; creativity and community, new theatrical forms. Add: Dept. of Speech & Drama, Valparaiso University, Valparaiso, IN 46383.

KUYK, DIRK ADRIAAN, JR, b. Roanoke, Va. Apr. 27, 34. NINETEENTH CENTURY ENGLISH LITERATURE. A.B, Univ. Va, 55; Ph.D.(Eng), Brandeis Univ, 70. ASST. PROF. ENG, TRINITY COL.(CONN), 70- Faulkner; Yeats; genre. Add: Dept. of English, Trinity College, Hartford, CT 06106.

KVAM, WAYNE EUGENE, b. Webster, S.Dak, July 20, 38; m. 73. AMERICAN LITERATURE. B.A, Augustana Col.(S.Dak), 60; Univ. Hamburg, 60-61; M.A, Fla. State Univ, 63; Univ. Grenoble, 64; Ford Found. grant, Univ. Wis-Madison, 67-68, Ph.D.(Eng), 69. Instr. ENG, Warstade Gym, Ger, 60-61; teaching asst, Fla. State Univ, 61-63; Univ. Wis-Madison, 63-68; asst. prof, KENT STATE UNIV, 68-73, ASSOC. PROF, 73- MLA. Twentieth century American fiction and poetry; literary criticism. Publ: Hemingway in Germany, Ohio Univ, 73; Hemingway's Banal story, Fitzgerald/Hemingway Annual, 73. Add: Dept. of English, Kent State University, Kent, OH 44240.

KWIAT, JOSEPH J, b. New York, N.Y, June 3, 12; m. 42; c. 2. AMERICAN LITERATURE & STUDIES, HUMANITIES. Ph.B, Univ. Chicago, 35; M.A, Northwest. Univ, 40; Ph.D, Univ. Minn, 50. Instr. Eng, jr. cols, Chicago, Ill, 36-42; Univ. Nebr, 43-44; from instr. to PROF. ENG, AM. STUD. & HUMANITIES, UNIV. MINN, MINNEAPOLIS, 44- Fulbright lectr, Univ. Tübingen, Ger, 53-54; Fulbright res. scholar, Ger, 54-55; Fulbright lectr, Univ. Innsbruck, Austria, 62-63, Univ. Stuttgart, 70-71; mem, Am. Counc. Learned Soc. Comt. on Res, 64-; adv. comt. Am. stud, Fulbright Prog, Comt. Int. Exchange Persons, 64-; lectr. Japan & India, 66-67; ed-in-chief, Series in Am. Stud, Johnson Reprint Corp, 66- U.S.A.A.F, 42-43. Am. Counc. Learned Soc. res. fel, 47-48. MLA; Am. Stud. Asn; Europ. Asn. Am. Stud; Ger. Soc. Am. Stud. Interrelationships between literature, the other arts and society in the United States; European literary and cultural images of the United States; American social, intellectual and cultural literature and thought since 1890. Publ: Co-ed and contrib, Studies in American culture, Univ. Minn; Robert Henri and the Emerson-Whitman tradition, PMLA; Dreiser and the graphic artists, Am. Quart; America's cultural coming of age: an American studies approach to art and literature in the U.S, 1890-1915, Am. Stud. Monogr. Series, 67. Add: Dept. of English, University of Minnesota, Minneapolis, MN 55455.

KYTE, ELINOR CLEMONS, Linguistics, English. See Volume III, Foreign Languages, Linguistics & Philology.

L

LA BAN, FRANK K, b. New York, N.Y, July 15, 30; m. 53; c. 2. SPEECH, PHONETICS. B.A, Univ. Kans, 55, M.A, 59; Ph.D.(speech), La. State Univ, 65. Instr. speech, radio & TV, Univ. N.Dak, 59-61; mem. staff TV, La. State Univ, 64-65; ASST. PROF. speech & drama, Wayne State Col, 65-66; SPEECH & PHONETICS, UNIV. ARIZ, 66-, CONSULT. & SCRIPT ADV. ENG. LANG. TV PROJ, 68-, HEAD. DEPT. SPEECH COMMUN, 72- Speech Commun. Asn. Phonetics and dialect studies; English as a second language; television. Publ: Contrib, A various language: perspectives on American dialects, Holt, 71. Add: Dept. of Speech Communication, University of Arizona, Tucson, AZ 85721.

LaBARBERA, VINCENT JAMES, b. Brooklyn, N.Y, May 3, 16; m. 61; c. 1. ENGLISH, JOURNALISM. B.A, Grove City Col, 43; M.Ed, Univ. Pittsburgh, 66. Ed. co. mag, Metro-Goldwyn-Mayer, N.Y.C, 46-48; mag. writer, Tex. Co, N.Y.C, 48-50; ed-in-chief, Allied Newspapers, Grove City, Pa, 50-53; ed. chief & prod. mgr, Pittsburgh Suburban Community Newspapers, 53-64; PROF. JOUR. & CHMN. DEPT. JOUR. & COMMUN, POINT PARK COL, 64- Ed. consult, Robinson Newspapers, Monongahela, Pa, 67-69. U.S.N, 42-46, Res, 46-48, Lt. AAUP; Nat. Counc. Col. Publ. Adv. Publ: Co-auth, Copy editing symbols, 67 & Journalism—a practical glossary, 67, Point Park

Press; auth, Art of copy editing—a practical workbook, Moten, 73. Add: Dept. of Journalism & Communications, Point Park College, 201 Wood St, Pittsburgh, PA 15222.

LaBELLE, MAURICE MARC, b. Seattle, Wash, June 7, 39. COMPARATIVE LITERATURE. B.A, Wash. State Univ, 61; M.A, 65; cert, Univ. Montreal, 61; cert, Sorbonne, 69; Ph.D.(comp. lit), Univ. Wash, 71. Teaching asst. Eng, Wash. State Univ, 63-65; asst. prof, West. Wash. State Col, 65-70; ASST. PROF. ENG. & COMP. LIT, DRAKE UNIV, 70-, Res. Counc. grants, 71, 72, res. fel, 73. U.S. Inform. Serv. grant, 73. MLA; Am. Comp. Lit. Asn; Int. Comp. Lit. Asn; Philol. Asn. Pac. Coast. Theater of the absurd; transition from romanticism to surrealism; pessimism. Publ: Artaud's use of Shelley's The Cenci: the experiment in the Theatre de la Cruaute, Rev. Lit. Comp, 10/69; H.L. Mencken's comprehension of Friedrich Nietzsche, Comp. Lit. Stud, 3/70; Artaud's use of language, sound, and tone, Mod. Drama, 3/73. Add: Dept. of English, Drake University, Des Moines, IA 50311.

LABOR, EARLE G, b. Tuskahoma, Okla, Mar. 3, 28; m. 52; c. 4. AMERICAN LITERATURE. A.B, South. Methodist Univ, 49, M.A, 52; Mary M. Adams fel, Univ. Wis, 58, summer fel, 59, Ph.D.(Am. lit), 61. Instr. Eng, South. Methodist Univ, 50-52, summer lectr, 61; asst. sales mgr, Haggar Co, Tex, 54-55; instr. Eng, Centenary Col, 55-56, asst. prof, 59-62; chmn. dept. Eng. & humanities, Adrian Col, 62-66; PROF. ENG, CENTENARY COL, 66- Managing ed, CEA Critic, 67-70; participant, Vis. Fac. Prog, Harvard, 71; Huntington Libr. grants, 72 & 73; Am. Philos. Soc. grant, 73; Fulbright lectr, Aarhus Univ, 73-74; Nat. Endowment for Humanities sr. fel, 74-75. U.S.N, 52-54. MLA; Col. Eng. Asn.(ed. publ, 70-); NCTE; Am. Stud. Asn. Literary criticism; American intellectual history and literary naturalism. Publ: Ed, Great short works of Jack London, 65, co-auth, A handbook of critical approaches to literature, 66 & co-ed, Mandala: literature for critical analysis, 70, Harper; auth, Jack London, Twayne, 74; James's The real thing: three levels of meaning, Col. Eng, 2/62; Fish and a wheelbarrow: an experiment in criticism, CEA Critic, 5/67; Jack London's Mondo Cane, The call of the wild and White fang, Jack London Newslett, 7-12/67; plus others. Add: Dept. of English, Centenary College, Shreveport, LA 71104.

LaBRANCHE, ANTHONY SPAHR, b. New York, N.Y, Sept. 23, 31; m. 60. ENGLISH LITERATURE. B.A, Williams Col, 52; M.A, Yale, 53, Ph.D, 58. Instr. Eng, Univ. Mich, 56-58, 59-60; Univ. Mass, 60-63; researcher, Newberry Libr, 63-64; ASSOC. PROF. ENG, LOYOLA UNIV. CHICAGO, 64- MLA; Renaissance Soc. Am. Elizabethan historical poetry and drama; classical background to 17th century; pastoral poetry. Publ: Blanda elegeia: Donne's Elegies, Mod. Lang. Rev, 7/66; Poetry, history, and oratory: the Renaissance historical poem, Stud. Eng. Lit, winter 69; Imitation: getting in touch, Mod. Lang. Quart, 9/70; plus others. Add: Dept. of English, Loyola University of Chicago, Chicago, IL 60626.

LaBRANT, LOU, b. Hinckley, Ill, May 28, 88. ENGLISH, LANGUAGE GROWTH. A.B, Baker Univ, 11, hon. D.Litt, 41; fel, Univ. Kans, 24-25, M.A, 25; fel, Northwest. Univ, 30-31, Ph.D, 32. Asst. prof. Eng. & educ, Univ. Kans, 25-30; assoc. prof, Ohio State Univ, 32-33, prof, 33-42; ENG, N.Y. UNIV, 42-53, EMER. PROF, 53- Vis. prof. Eng. & educ, Atlanta Univ, 53-55; Univ. Kans. City, 55-58; prof. Eng, Dillard Univ, 58-65, chmn, div. humanities, 65-69, emer. prof. Eng, 69- NCTE (v.pres, 52-53; pres, 53-54; Hatfield award, 62); Am. Psychol. Asn; Conf. Res. Eng. Growth of language in the child; development of reading habits; relations of language structure to experience. Publ: We teach English, Harcourt, 51; co-auth, Your language (6 vols), McGraw, 56-62; Study of certain language developments of children, Genetic Psychol. Monogr, 11/33. Add: 14 Chatham Dr, New Orleans, LA 70122.

LABRIE, E. ROSS, b. Montreal, P.Q, Oct. 17, 36; m. 66; c. 2. ENGLISH. B.A, Loyola Col. Montreal, 57; M.A, McGill Univ. 60; Ph.D.(Eng), Univ. Toronto 66. Instr. ENG, Univ. Sask, 62-63; instr. II, UNIV. B.C, 63-66, ASST. PROF, 66- Can. Counc. res. grant, 69-70. Asn. Can. Univ. Teachers Eng; Philol. Asn. Pac. Coast; Can. Asn. Am. Stud. Henry James; the twenties. Publ: Sirens of life and art in Henry James, Lakehead Univ. Rev, fall 69; The morality of consciousness in Henry James, Colby Libr. Quart, 12/71; The power of consciousness in Henry James, Ariz. Quart, summer 73; plus others. Add: Dept. of English, University of British Columbia, Vancouver 8, B.C, Can.

LABRIOLA, ALBERT CHRISTY, b. Pittsburgh, Pa, Oct. 22, 39; m. 66; c. 2. RENAISSANCE & SEVENTEENTH CENTURY ENGLISH LITERATURE. B.Ed, Duquesne Univ, 61; M.A.T, Columbia Univ, 62; M.A, Univ. Va, 63, Ph.D.(Eng), 66. Asst. prof. ENG, Col. William & Mary, 68-70; ASSOC. PROF, DUQUESNE UNIV, 70- Fel, Huntington Libr, summer 73. U.S.A, 66-68, Capt. MLA; Milton Soc. Am. Seventeenth century English literature; Christian iconography. Publ: The doctrine of charity and the use of homiletic figures in The man of Law's tale, Tex. Stud. Lang. & Lit, 70; Divine urgency as a motive for conduct in Samson Agonistes, Philol. Quart, 71; Donne's The Canonization: its theological context and its religious imagery, Huntington Libr. Quart, 73. Add: Dept. of English, Duquesne University, Pittsburgh, PA 15219.

LACASSE, RODOLPHE ROMEO, Contemporary French & Comparative Literature. See Volume III, Foreign Languages, Linguistics & Philology.

LACEY, JAMES, b. New York, N.Y, Oct. 15, 33; m. 58; c. 2. AMERICAN STUDIES. A.B, St. Peter's Col, 55; Inst. Int. Educ. fel, Univ. Berne, Switz, 55-56; M.A, Boston Col, 58; Ph.D.(Am. civilization), N.Y. Univ, 68. Instr. Eng, St. Francis Col.(N.Y), 58-62, asst. prof, 62-68; assoc. prof. AM. LIT. & AM. STUD, EAST. CONN. STATE COL, 68-71, PROF, 71- Ger. Acad. Exchange Serv. res. grant, Am. Inst, Univ. Munich, 65-66. U.S.A.R, 57-, 1st Lt. MLA; Am. Stud. Asn; Thoreau Soc. Am. American literature and history; Henry David Thoreau in German criticism, 1881-1965. Publ: Walden: analytic notes & review, 65, The last of the Mohicans: analytic notes & review, 66, The Deerslayer: analytic notes & review, 66 & co-auth, The prairie: analytic notes & review, 66, Am. R.D.M; auth, United States & entries on many Am. auth, Readers' encyclopedia of Shakespeare, 66. Add: Dept. of English, Eastern Connecticut State College, Willimantic, CT 06226.

LACEY, WILLIAM ROBERT, b. Kosciusko, Miss, Mar. 11, 21; m. 60. ENGLISH & AMERICAN LITERATURE. B.S, Miss. State Univ, 47, M.A, 59; Ph.D.(Eng), La. State Univ, 67. Mem. fac. ENG, Wood Jr. Col, 59-60; instr, La. State Univ, 65-66; UNIV. TEX, EL PASO, 66-67, ASST. PROF, 67- U.S.A, 41-45, M/Sgt. Nondramatic Renaissance poetry, especially Spenser and Sidney; 17th century English literature; medieval English literature. Add: Dept. of English, University of Texas at El Paso, El Paso, TX 79999.

LACHMANN, VERA REGINA, b. Berlin, Ger, June 23, 04; U.S. citizen. GREEK LITERATURE, POETRY. Ph.D.(Icelandic), Univ. Berlin, 31, staatsexamen, 33. Lectr. Ger, Vassar Col, 40-41; Greek & Latin, Brearley Sch, 42-43; instr. Greek, Bryn Mawr Col, 45-46; speaker Ger, Yale, 46-48; Ger. & classics, City Col. New York, 48-56; asst. prof. CLASSICS, BROOKLYN COL, 49-70, ASSOC. PROF, 70- Dir, Catawba Summer Camp, Blowing Rock, N.C, 43-70. Latin translations of Greek authors before 1600; Greek landscape reflected in ancient Greek lyrical poetry. Publ: Golden tanzt das Licht im Glas, Castrum Peregrini, Amsterdam, 68; co-auth, Aeschylus in Catalogus translationum, Union Acad. Int, 71; Das Alter der Hartarsaga, Palaestra, 31. Add: 47 Barrow St, New York, NY 10014.

LACY, EDGAR WILSON, b. Lexington, Ky, Feb. 18, 14; m. 52; c. 3. ENGLISH LANGUAGE & LITERATURE. A.B, Vanderbilt Univ, 36, A.M, 37; Ph.D, Univ. Ill, 39. Instr, Univ. Ala, 39-40, asst. prof, 40-41; instr. ENG, UNIV. WIS-MADISON, 41-42, 45-46, asst. prof, 46-48, assoc. prof, 48-52, PROF, 52-, ASSOC. CHMN. DEPT, 62-, dir, freshman Eng, 48-68. MLA; Mod. Humanities Res. Asn, Gt. Brit; NCTE. History of ideas; patterns in writing; guide for good writing. Add: Dept. of English, University of Wisconsin-Madison, Madison, WI 53706.

LACY, GERALD MORRIS, b. Greenville, Tex, Sept. 18, 40; m. 64; c. 2. ENGLISH LITERATURE. B.A, E.Tex. State Univ, 63; Ph.D.(Eng), Univ. Tex, Austin, 71. Teacher math, Grand Prairie Pub. Schs, 63-64; ENG, Deer Park Pub. Schs, 64-65; asst. prof, Angelo State Univ, 69-71; tutor, Univ. Manchester, 71-72; ASST. PROF, ANGELO STATE UNIV, 72- Leverhulme vis. fel, Univ. Manchester, 71-72. U.S.M.C, 64-65, Sgt. MLA; AAUP. D.H. Lawrence; 20th century English and American poetry; bibliography. Publ: Ed, The escaped cock, Black Sparrow, 73. Add: Dept. of English, Angelo State University, San Angelo, TX 76901.

LACY, JAMES MAXWELL, b. Wolfe City, Tex, Feb. 6, 13; m. 36; c. 2. CLASSICAL & AMERICAN LITERATURE. B.A, E.Tex. State Teachers Col, 36, M.A, 40; Ph.D.(Eng), Univ. Denver, 56. Teacher & prin, Hunt County Common Sch, Wolfe City, Tex, 34-36; teacher geog, elem. schs, Greenville, 36-39; Eng. & chem, Greenville High Sch, 39-42; flight instr, U.S. Army Air Corps, 43-44; flight inspector, Douglas Aircraft, 44-45; TEACHER chem, Highland Park High Sch, Dallas, 45-46; ENG, Tex. A&I Univ, 46-47; E.TEX. STATE UNIV, 47- MLA. American minority affairs; reading improvement. Publ: Reading laboratory handbook, E.Tex. State Univ, 56-63; co-auth, Read with speed, W.C. Brown, 68-; auth, New Mexican in early American writings, N.Mex. Hist. Rev, 1/59; Folklore of the South and racial discrimination, Tex. Folklore Soc, 64; The dark and tangled path: race in America, Mifflin, 71. Add: Dept. of Literature & Languages, East Texas State University, Commerce, TX 75428.

LADD, JAMES MATHON, b. Alta, Can, Apr. 7, 14. SPEECH. Th.B, Gordon Col, 37; Gordon Divinity Sch, 38-40; Univ. Hawaii, 46; A.B, Univ. Mo, 49; D.Ed, Okla. State Univ, 60. Pastor, New Eng, 37-42; instr. SPEECH, Univ. Mo, 47-49; from asst. prof. to assoc. prof, Phillip Univ, 49-61, prof. & chmn. dept, 61-66; assoc. prof, MANKATO STATE COL, 66-67, PROF, 67- Chaplain, U.S.A.F, 42-47, 51-53, Res, 53, Lt. Col; Bronze Star Medal. Speech Commun. Asn. Public address; homiletics; theory and practice of preaching of Dwight L. Moody. Add: 704 Byron, Mankato, MN 56001.

LA DRIERE, JAMES CRAIG, b. Grand Rapids, Mich, July 28, 10. COMPARATIVE LITERATURE. Ph.B, Univ. Detroit, 30; A.M, Univ. Mich, 32, Ph.D, 38; Harvard, 36-39. Instr. Eng, Univ. Detroit, 30-32; St. Louis Univ, 33-34; jr. fel, Soc. Fels, Harvard, 36-39, acting sr. fel, 68-69; instr, Grad. Sch, Cath. Univ. Am, 39-42, asst. prof, 42-46, assoc. prof, 46-52, prof, 52-65; PROF. COMP. LIT, HARVARD, 65- Exchange prof, Louvain, Belgium, 49; Guggenheim fel, 49-50; Richard lectr, 53; ed. consult, Webster's Third New Int. Dictionary, 57; vis. prof, Harvard, 52, 59, 64; mem, Eng. Inst; Nat. Endowment for Humanities, sr. fel, 68-69. Benemerenti, Papal Medal, 64. MLA; Am. Soc. Aesthet; Ling. Circle N.Y; Am. Comp. Lit. Asn; Int. Comp. Lit. Asn. Literary theory and criticism; history of aesthetics and criticism; prosody. Publ: Directions in contemporary criticism and literary scholarship, Bruce, 55; co-auth, Sound and poetry, Columbia Univ, 57; auth, Literary form and form in the other arts, In: Stil- und Formprobleme in der Literatur, FILLM Proc, Winter, Heidelberg, 59; Prosody, In: Encycl. of poetry and poetics, Princeton, 65; plus others. Add: 402 Boylston Hall, Harvard University, Cambridge, MA 02138.

LaFRANCE, MARSTON, b. Binghamton, N.Y, June 25, 27; m. 53; c. 4. ENGLISH & AMERICAN LITERATURE. B.A, Harpur Col, 53; M.A, Cornell Univ, 55; Ph.D.(Eng), Univ. Wis, 65. Instr. ENG, Clarkson Technol. Col, 56-58, asst. prof, 58-62; CARLETON UNIV, 63-65, assoc. prof, 65-69, PROF, 69- Humanities Res. Counc. Can. MLA; Can. Asn. Am. Stud; Can. Asn. Univ. Teachers. Eighteenth century English literature; irony. Publ: Ed, Patterns of commitment in American literature; Univ. Toronto, 67; A reading of Stephen Crane, Clarendon, 71; Context and structure of Evelyn Waugh's Brideshead revisited, 20th Century Lit, 4/64; Fielding's use of the humor tradition, Bucknell Rev, 12/69; plus others. Add: Dept. of English, Carleton University, Ottawa, Ont. K1S 5B6, Can.

LAGO, MARY McCLELLAND, b. Pittsburgh, Pa, Nov. 4, 19; m. 44; c. 2. MODERN ENGLISH & BENGALI LITERATURE. B.A, Bucknell Univ, 40; M.A, Univ. Mo-Columbia, 65, Ph.D.(Eng), 69. Instr. ENG, UNIV. MO-COLUMBIA, 64-70, LECTR, 70-, res. grants, 71, 72, 73-74. Am. Philos. Soc. res. grant, 67, 68, 70; Am. Counc. Learned Soc-Ford Found. Joint S.Asia Prog. grant, 72-73. MLA; Midwest Mod. Lang. Asn; Asn. Asian Stud; Asn. Commonwealth Lang. & Lit. Stud. Late 19th and early 20th century English literature and art history. Publ: Transl, Tagore's The housewarming, New Am. Libr, 65 & Tagore's The broken nest, Univ. Mo, 71, Macmillan, India,

73; ed, Imperfect encounter (William Rothenstein-R. Tagore letters), Harvard Univ, 72; auth, Tagore in translation: a case study in literary exchange, Books Abroad, 72; Rothenstein, Tagore, and Bangla Desh, Cornhill Mag, spring 72; Restoring Rabindranath Tagore, Encounter, 74. Add: Dept. of English, Arts & Sci. Bldg, University of Missouri-Columbia, Columbia, MO 65201.

LAGORIO, VALERIE M, b. Iowa City, Iowa, Sept. 8, 25; MEDIEVAL ENGLISH LITERATURE. B.A, San Francisco Col. Women, 63; M.A, Stanford Univ, 64, Ph.D.(Eng), 66. Asst. prof. ENG, San Francisco Col. Women, 66-67; Univ. Mo, St. Louis, 67-72; ASSOC. PROF, UNIV. IOWA, 72- Adv. ed, Manuscripta, 70-; mem. ed. adv. bd, Philol. Quart, 73- MLA; Mediaeval Acad. Am; Int. Arthurian Soc; Midwest Mod. Lang. Asn. Hagiographic considerations in the Arthurian legend; Latin paleography. Publ: Pan-Britonic hagiography and Arthurian grail cycle, Traditio, 70; The evolving legend of St. Joseph of Glastonbury, Speculum, 71; The Clementina in the Vulgate cycle, Studia Patristica, 72. Add: Dept. of English, University of Iowa, Iowa City, IA 52240.

LAHEY, GERALD, b. Middleport, N.Y, Dec. 13, 06. ENGLISH LITERATURE. B.A, Canisius Col, 28; M.A, Univ. Buffalo, 32; B.Litt, Oxford, 49, D.Phil, 63. Instr. ENG. LIT, Univ. Buffalo, 33-38; N.Y. UNIV, 46-50, asst. prof, 50-55, ASSOC. PROF, 55- Lectr, Buffalo Acad. Fine Arts, 33-38. Nineteenth century English literature; English dramatic comedy. Publ: Biographical and critical introductions to Theatre classics (10 vols), Barron's, 58-63. Add: Dept. of English, Washington Square College of Arts & Sciences, New York University, New York, NY 10003.

LaHOOD, MARVIN JOHN, b. Auburn, N.Y, Mar. 21, 33; m. 59; c. 3. ENGLISH. B.S, Boston Col, 54; M.A, Univ. Notre Dame, 58, Ph.D.(Eng), 62. Instr. Eng, Niagara Univ, 60-61, assoc. prof, 62-64; State Univ. N.Y. Col. Buffalo, 64-67, prof, 67-71, assoc. acad. develop, 68-71; prof. Eng. & acad. dean, Col. Misericordia, 71-72; PROF. ENG. & ACAD. DEAN, SALEM STATE COL, 72- State Univ. N.Y. fac. res. fel, summers 67 & 68. MLA. American fiction; modern fiction. Publ: Co-ed, Latvian literature, Dauqavas, Toronto, 64; ed, Tender is the night: essays in criticism, Ind. Univ, 69; auth, Conrad Richter's America, Mouton, The Hague, 74; Richter's early America, Univ. Rev, 6/64; The light in the forest: history as fiction, Eng. J, 3/66; Huck Finn's search for identity, Mark Twain J, winter 66. Add: Salem State College, Salem, MA 01970.

LAING, ROBERT CUTTER, b. Manchester, N.H, Nov. 3, 19. ENGLISH. B.A, Yale, 43; M.A, Univ. Pittsburgh, 55, Ph.D.(Eng), 61. Master, Kiski Sch, Pa, 46-52; Valley Sch. Ligonier, Pa, 52-54; asst. ENG. Univ. Pittsburgh, 55-57, lectr, 57-58, instr, 58-61, asst. prof, 61-64; UNIV. PITTSBURGH, BRADFORD, 64-67, assoc. prof, 67-71, PROF, 71-, CHMN. DIV. HUMANITIES, 73- Qm.C, U.S.A, 43-46, S/Sgt. NCTE; MLA. Victorian, medieval and American literature. Add: Dept. of English, University of Pittsburgh at Bradford, Bradford, PA 16701.

LAIR, ROBERT LELAND, b. Gloversville, N.Y, June 21, 32; m. 56; c. 2. ENGLISH, RELIGION. A.B, Bob Jones Univ, 54, A.M, 56; A.M, Middlebury Col, 61; Miami Univ, 62-63; Ph.D.(Eng), Ohio State Univ, 66. Prof. ENG, Bob Jones Univ, 56-62, 65-68; assoc. prof, Ohio State Univ, Mansfield, 68-69; PROF, MALONE COL, 69-, CHMN. DIV. LANG. & LIT, 70- MLA. American poetry; Emily Dickinson. Publ: T.S. Eliot, 68 & Emily Dickinson, 71, Barron's Educ. Ser; Hemingway and Cezanne: an indebtedness, Mod. Fiction Stud, 56; Emily Dickinson's As by the dead we love to sit, Explicator, 67. Add: 3413 27th St. N.W, Canton, OH 44708.

LAIRD, DAVID, b. Marshfield, Wis, Oct. 16, 27; m. 55; c. 1. ENGLISH LITERATURE. B.A, Univ. Wis, 50, Uhrig Found.fel. & M.A, 51, Ph.D, 55; Courtauld Inst, Univ. London, 53-54; U.S. Govt. grant, U.K, 53-54. From instr. to asst. prof. ENG, Oberlin Col, 55-58; asst. prof, CALIF. STATE UNIV, LOS ANGELES, 58-62, assoc. prof, 62-68, PROF, 68-, chmn. dept. 69-72. Henry E. Huntington Libr. grant-in-aid, summer 65; Calif. State Univ, Los Angeles fac. res. & creative leave award, spring 67; participant, West. Shakespeare Sem. MLA; Philol. Asn. Pac. Coast; Am. Stud. Asn. Shakespeare; rhetoric and style; form and tradition in contemporary American Indian art. Publ: The generation of style in Romeo and Juliet, J. Eng. & Ger. Philol, 4/64; Hieronimo's dilemma, Stud. Philol, 4/65. Add: Dept. of English, California State University, Los Angeles, 5151 State University Dr, Los Angeles, CA 90032.

LAKAS, ROBERT RAYMOND, S.J, b. Denver, Colo, Apr. 23, 17. ENGLISH LITERATURE, RENAISSANCE. B.A, St. Louis Univ, 39, Ph.L, 42, M.A, 45; S.T.L, St. Mary's Col.(Kans), 48; Ph.D.(Eng), Yale, 57. Instr. ENG. LIT, Campion High Sch, Prairie du Chien, Wis, 42-45; Creighton Univ, 54-55; asst. prof, ROCKHURST COL, 57-62, assoc. prof, 62-68, PROF, 68-, CHMN. HONORS PROG, 63-, DIR, THOMAS MORE ARTS CTR, 65- V.pres, Kans. City Philharmonic, 65-; chmn. film comt, Mo. Arts Counc, 72. MLA; NCTE. The rhetorical tradition of styles from Cicero to Dryden; the philosophical and symbolic values in modern fiction. Publ: Co-auth, Thomas More anthologies for high school, Singer Co. Add: Dept. of English, Rockhurst College, Kansas City, MO 64110.

LAKIN, BARBARA HOLBEACH, b. Denver, Colo, Aug. 6, 30; m. 52; c. 2. ENGLISH LITERATURE. B.A, Kans. State Col, 61; M.A, Colo. State Univ, 63; M.A, Colo. State Univ, 63; Ph.D.(Eng), Univ. Colo, Boulder, 70. Instr. ENG, Foothill Col, 63-66; COLO. STATE UNIV, 66-70, ASST. PROF, 70- MLA; Renaissance Soc. Am. Early 17th century English literature; Shakespearean drama; Renaissance Neo-Platonism. Add: Dept. of English, Colorado State University, Ft. Collins, CO 80521.

LAKOFF, ROBIN TOLMACH, Linguistics. See Volume III, Foreign Languages, Linguistics & Philology.

LAMACCHIA, GRACE A, b. New York, N.Y, Nov. 7, 39. ENGLISH. B.A, Pace Col, 61; M.A, Bowling Green State Univ, 62; fel, N.Y. Univ, 65-66, Ph.D.(Eng), 66. Teaching asst. ENG, Bowling Green State Univ, 61-62; Wash. Sq. Col. Arts & Sci, N.Y. Univ, 63-65; asst. prof, South. Conn. State Col, 66-67; NOTRE DAME COL, ST. JOHN'S UNIV. (N.Y), 67-74, ASSOC. PROF, 74- Nineteenth and 20th century British literature; 20th century American literature. Publ: Collision, Washington Irving, 74; Textual criticism in act IV of The admirable Crichton, Mod. Drama, spring 70. Add: Div. of Humanities, Notre Dame College, St. John's University, 300 Howard Ave, Staten Island, NY 10301.

LAMB, ARTHUR CLIFTON, b. Muscatine, Iowa, May 5, 09; m. 37; c. 2. DRAMATICS. A.B, Grinnell Col, 31; fel, State Univ. Iowa, 39-40, M.A, 40, fel, 53-54; cert. radio-TV, N.Y. Univ, 48. Instr. Eng. & drama, Shaw Univ, 35-36; asst. prof, Prairie View State Col, 37-42; prof. Eng, Spanish, speech & drama, Johnson C. Smith Univ, 42-46; ASSOC. PROF. ENG, SPEECH & DRAMA, MORGAN STATE COL, 46- Dir. & guest artist, Atlanta Univ. Summer Sch. Theatre, 41, 43, 46. Henry York Steiner Prize in playwriting, 31; Sergel Prize in regional playwriting, 39. Nat. Asn. Dramatics & Speech Arts (v.pres, 63-); Speech Commun. Asn; Am. Theatre Asn; Col. Lang. Asn. Playwriting and radio-TV production and writing; the Latin-American educational theater; Spanish-American drama. Publ: The two gifts: a Christmas play for Negroes, Dramatic Publ, 35; Portrait of a pioneer, Negro Hist. Bull, 4/49; Christy's citadel, Intercollegian, 4/56. Add: Dept. of English, Morgan State College, Baltimore, MD 21212.

LAMB, JACK HALL, b. Yuma, Colo, May 23, 21; m. 52. SPEECH. B.A, Hastings Col, 42; M.A, Univ. Iowa, 49, Ph.D, 64. Instr. speech & Eng, Colo. A&M Col, 43-44, 46-47; vis. instr, Iowa State Teachers Col, summer 49; instr. SPEECH, UNIV. CONN, 50-60, asst. prof, 60-65, ASSOC. PROF, 65- Vis. prof, Cleveland State Univ, 67-68. U.S.N, 44-46. Speech Commun. Asn; AAUP; Cent. States Speech Asn. Rhetorical theory; parliamentary practice; semantics. Publ: Co-auth, Speech as communication, Allyn & Bacon, 66; auth, John Walker and Joshua Steele, Speech Monogr, 11/65. Add: Dept. of Speech, University of Connecticut, Storrs, CT 06268.

LAMBERT, BYRON C, Philosophy of Education, American Cultural History. See Volume IV, Philosophy, Religion & Law.

LAMBERT, EDWARD CHARLES, b. What Cheer, Iowa, Jan. 29, 10; m. 36; c. 2. JOURNALISM. A.B, Iowa State Teachers Col, 33; A.M, State Univ. Iowa, 38; Ph.D, Univ. Mo, 52. Mem. circulation dept, Eagle, Wichita, Kans, 28; reporter, Patriot, Peabody, 28-30, Daily Record, Cedar Falls, Iowa, 33-35; supvr. stud. pubs, High Sch, Iowa, 35-37; instr. jour. & dir. publicity & radio activities, High Sch, Ill, 37-40; spec. events announcer & news ed, Radio Sta, WMRO, 40-43; dir. JOUR, Stephens Col, 46; asst. prof, UNIV. MO-COLUMBIA, 46-48, assoc. prof, 48-52, PROF, 52-, CHMN. DEPT. BROADCASTING, 72-, asst. to pres. in charge TV, 52-66, asst. to chancellor in charge TV, 66-71. News dir, Radio Sta, KFRU, 47-52; consult, KMOX-CBS Radio Network, 60-67; mem, Gov. Educ. TV Comt, Mo, 63-64. U.S.N.R, 43-46. AAUP; Asn. Educ. in Jour; Broadcast Educ. Asn; Nat. Asn. Educ. Broadcasters; Nat. Asn. Broadcasters. Educational uses of television; television news techniques; educational television in the United States. Publ: Radio's first entertainer, TV Guide, 70. Add: 4112 Faurot Dr, Columbia, MO 65201.

LAMBERT, JOSEPH PATRICK, b. Monticello, Miss, Feb. 20, 38. ENGLISH. B.A, Miss. Col, 60, M.A, 61; Ph.D.(Eng), Auburn Univ, 71. Instr. ENG, Gulf Coast Jr. Col, 61-65; Auburn Univ, 67-70; ASSOC. PROF, MO. SOUTH. STATE COL, 70- Nat. Endowment for Humanities fel, summer 73. AAUP; MLA. Eighteenth century British literature. Add: Dept. of English, Missouri Southern State College, Newman & Duquesne, Joplin, MO 64801.

LAMBERT, NEAL ELWOOD, b. Fillmore, Utah, Dec. 15, 34; m. 58; c. 8. ENGLISH. B.A, Univ. Utah, 61, Ph.D.(Eng), 66. Instr. ENG, Weber State Col, 65-66; asst. prof, BRIGHAM YOUNG UNIV, 66-72, ASSOC. PROF, 72- U.S.A, 57-63, Sgt. West. Lit. Asn; Rocky Mount Mod. Lang. Asn. Literature of the American West; American literature 1865-1915; literary problems of American historians. Publ: Owen Wister—the real incident & the thrilling story, In: The American West: an appraisal, Mus. N.Mex, 63; A cowboy writes to Owen Wister, Am. West, fall 65; Bishops blood & bandits: a look at Mormons in fiction, Utah Hist. Quart, winter 68. Add: Dept. of English, Brigham Young University, Provo, UT 84602.

LAMBERT, ROY EUGENE, Linguistics, Cybernetics. See Volume III, Foreign Languages, Linguistics & Philology.

LAMBERTS, JACOB J, English, LINGUISTICS. See Volume III, Foreign Languages, Linguistics & Philology.

LAMBETH, EDMUND BARRY, b. Birmingham, Ala, June 4, 32; wid; c. 2. JOURNALISM, POLITICAL SCIENCE. B.S, Northwest. Univ, 54, M.S, 55. Reporter, Atlanta J, 53; writer, Radio Sta, WLS, Chicago, 54; Chicago Sun-Times, 55; reporter, Binghamton Press, N.Y, 57-59; Milwaukee J, 59-62; Wash. correspondent, Gannett Newspapers, 62-68; ASSOC. PROF. & DIR. WASHINGTON REPORTING PROG, UNIV. MO-COLUMBIA, 68- Am. Polit. Sci. Asn. congressional fel, 61-62; Nieman fel. jour, Harvard, 67-68. Intel.C, U.S.A, 55-57, Sgt. Asn. Educ. in Jour. Media and government; urban affairs; education. Publ: Off campus education, Quill, 11/70; New towns: can they work?, Washington Monthly, 10/69; Gish: Kentucky editor, Grassroots Ed, 1-2/71; plus others. Add: 132 N. Columbus St, Arlington, VA 22203.

LAMM, ROBERT CARSON, Philosophy, Humanities. See Volume IV, Philosophy, Religion & Law.

LAMSON, ROY, b. New Haven, Conn, Feb. 7, 08; m. 33; c. 2. ENGLISH. A.B, Harvard, 29, M.A, 30, Dexter scholar, 33-35, Ph.D, 36. Instr. Eng. & tutor, div. mod. langs, Harvard, 35-38; asst. prof. Eng, Williams Col. (Mass), 38-42, assoc. prof, 46-49, prof, 50-57, dean freshmen, 53-57; prof, MASS. INST. TECHNOL, 57-72, dir. humanities & sci. course, 58-72, EMER. PROF. LIT, SR. LECTR. & SPEC. ASST. TO PRES. FOR ARTS, 72- Historian, Supreme Hdqrs. Allied Powers, Europe, 51-53. U.S.A, 42-46, Res, 46-, Col. MLA; Am. Hist. Asn; Inst. Jazz Stud. Elizabethan literature; English ballads and music; military history. Publ: Co-auth, Golden hind, 42, 56, Critical reader, 49, 62 & Renaissance England, 56, Norton. Add: Dept. of Humanities, Massachusetts Institute of Technology, Cambridge, MA 02139.

LANCASHIRE, ANNE, b. Montreal, P.Q, Nov. 23, 41; m. 68. ENGLISH LITERATURE, DRAMA. B.A, McGill Univ, 62; A.M, Harvard, 63, Ph.D.(Eng), 65. Lectr. ENG, UNIV. COL, UNIV. TORONTO, 65-67, asst. prof, 67-71, ASSOC. PROF, 71- Can. Counc. leave fel, 71-72. MLA; Asn. Can. Univ. Teachers Eng; Malone Soc; Renaissance Soc. Am. Renaissance drama; editing. Publ: Ed, John Lyly, Gallathea and Midas, Univ. Nebr, 69; auth, Look about you as a history play, Stud. Eng. Lit, 69; Timon of Athens: Shakespeare's Dr. Faustus, Shakespeare Quart, 70; contrib, The predecessors of Shakespeare: a survey and bibliography of recent studies in English Renaissance drama, Univ. Nebr, 73; plus others. Add: Dept. of English, University College, University of Toronto, Toronto, Ont. M5S 1A1, Can.

LANCASTER, ROBERT VAUGHAN, b. Wilmington, Del, Feb. 23, 21; m. 43; c. 4. ENGLISH LITERATURE, THEOLOGY. A.B, Univ. Del, 45, A.M, 49; Th.B, Phila. Divinity Sch, 55; Syracuse Univ, 66-73. Continuity writer, Radio Sta. WDEL, Wilmington, Del, 47-52; newspaper writer, Wilmington Jour-Every Eve, 53-55; vicar & dean, Diocese of Spokane, Wash, 55-60; rector, Diocese of West. N.Y, 61-65; asst. prof. ENG, STATE UNIV. N.Y. AGR. & TECH. COL. MORRISVILLE, 65-69, ASSOC. PROF, 69- Vis. instr. philos, Univ. Idaho, 57-60. AAUP; MLA; Am. Church Union; Am. Asn. Irish Stud. W.B. Yeats; time in modern literature; science fiction. Publ: Ella Middleton Tybout: Delaware writer, Del. Hist, spring 49; Symbols of the journey in T.S. Eliot's Four quartets, Philobiblon, spring 72. Add: 18 Charles St, Hamilton, NY 13346.

LANCE, DONALD MAX, English Linguistics. See Volume III, Foreign Languages, Linguistics & Philology.

LANDA, LOUIS A, b. Hallettsville, Tex, Nov. 6, 01. ENGLISH LITERATURE. A.B, Univ. Tex, 23, Oldright fel, 24; A.M, Columbia Univ, 26; Ph.D, Univ. Chicago, 41. Instr. ENG, Univ. Tex, 26-28; St. John's Col.(Md), 28-29; Univ. Chicago, 33-41, asst. prof, 41-45; assoc. prof, PRINCETON, 46-54, prof, 54-70, EMER. PROF, 70- Guggenheim fel, 47-48, 67-68; Fulbright lectr, Oxford & hon. lectr, Univ. Col, London, 52-53; ed, Annual 18th century bibliog; adv. ed, Huntington Libr. Quart, 62-; vis. lectr, Australian-Am. Educ. Found, Australian univs, 70. MLA (mem. ed. comt, 63-68); Mod. Humanities Res. Asn; fel. Royal Hist. Soc. English literature from 1660-1800; 18th century English literature. Publ: Pope and his contemporaries & ed, Defoe's Journal of the plague year, 69, Oxford Univ; auth, Swift and the Church of Ireland, Clarendon; ed, Gulliver's travels and other writings, Houghton, 60. Add: Dept. of English, Princeton University, Princeton, NJ 08540.

LANDAR, HERBERT (JAY), Linguistics. See Volume III, Foreign Languages, Linguistics & Philology.

LANDER, CLARA, b. Prince Albert, Sask, Apr. 9, 16; m. 39; c. 3. ENGLISH, ANCIENT GREEK. B.A, Univ. Sask, 38; M.A, Univ. Man, 56, Ph.D.(Eng), 68. Lectr. Eng, Univ. Man, 65-66; Balmoral Hall, 66-73. Lectr. Eng, Eve. Inst, Univ. Man, 72-73. Women writers of the 20th century; comparative literature. Publ: Winter scene: 1887 social conditions in post-Riel Manitoba, Queen's Quart, winter 62; A dangerous sickness which turned to a spotted fever, Stud. Eng. Lit, winter 71; The circle: a direct line to John Donne, Classmate, 6/73. Add: 1368 Mathers Bay E, Winnipeg, Man. R3M 2J9, Can.

LANDINI, RICHARD GEORGE, b. Pittsburgh, Pa, June 4, 29; m. 52; c. 5. ENGLISH. A.B, Univ. Miami, 54, M.A, 56; Ph.D, Univ. Fla, 59. Asst. prof. Eng, Ariz. State Univ, 59-68, prof. Eng. & asst. to pres, 68-70, dean Litchfield Col, 67-70, PROF. ENG. & ACAD. V.PRES, UNIV. MONT, 70- U.S.A, 48-51, Sgt. MLA. Twentieth century English and American poetry; literary criticism; aesthetics. Publ: Vorticism and the Cantos of Ezra Pound, West. Humanities Rev, 60; Confucianism and the Cantos of Ezra Pound, Topic 12, Perspectives in Am. Lit, autumn 66; Metaphor and imagery in E.A. Robinson's Credo, Colby Libr. Quart, 3/68. Add: President's Office, University of Montana, Missoula, MT 59801.

LANDMARK, NORA, b. Benson, Minn, Sept. 13, 09. ENGLISH. B.A, La. State Univ, 37, M.A, 38; Ph.D, Mich. State Univ, 54. Asst. prof. speech & radio, Ala. Col, 38-43; dir. broadcasting, La. State Univ, 43-46; prof. AM. THOUGHT & LANG, MICH. STATE UNIV, 46-72, EMER. PROF, 72- Add: 1421 Albert St, East Lansing, MI 48823.

LANDON, PHILIP J, b. Springfield, Mass, Aug. 1, 34; m. 59; c. 2. ENGLISH LITERATURE. A.B, Univ. Mass, 56; M.A, Univ. Md, 64, Ph.D.(Eng. lit), 67. Instr. ENG, Univ. Md, College Park, 64-67; asst. prof, UNIV. MD, BALTIMORE COUNTY, 67-72, ASSOC. PROF, 72- Mem. int. bibliog. comt, MLA, 66-; Univ. Md. res. grant, summer 68. Intel.C, U.S.A, 56-59, Sgt. MLA. Victorian literature; nineteenth century American literature. Add: Dept. of English, University of Maryland, Baltimore County Campus, 5401 Wilkins Ave, Baltimore, MD 21228.

LANDRUM, GRAHAM GORDON, b. Dallas, Tex, Dec. 1, 22; m. 55. ENGLISH. B.A, Univ. Tex, 43, M.A, 48; A.M, Princeton, 53, Ph.D, 54. Instr. ENG, Rice Inst, 48-50; prof, Austin Col, 54-64; assoc. prof, KING COL, 64-67, PROF, 67- U.S.N.R, 43-46. Chaucer; local history. Publ: An illustrated history of Grayson County, Texas, Univ. Supply & Equip. Co, Ft. Worth, Tex, 60- Add: 2115 Edgemont Ave, Bristol, TN 37620.

LANDRUM, LARRY N, b. Huntington, Ind. ENGLISH, POPULAR CULTURE. B.A, Purdue Univ, 65, M.A, 67; fel, Bowling Green State Univ, 67-70, Ph.D. (Eng), 73. Teaching asst. ENG, Purdue Univ, 65-67; instr, Ctr. Stud. Popular Cult, Bowling Green State Univ, 70-73; ASST. PROF, MICH. STATE UNIV, 73- MLA; Am. Stud. Asn; Popular Cult. Asn.(bibliogr, 73-). American literature and studies. Publ: Co-ed, Challenges in American culture, Bowling Green State Univ, 71; contrib, J. Popular Cult, 67- & J. Popular Film, 70-; co-auth, Popular literature, In: Children and books, Scott, 72; auth, Recent books in popular culture, Ind. Social Stud. Quart, winter 74. Add: Dept. of English, Michigan State University, East Lansing, MI 48824.

LANDRY, HILTON J, b. Waltham, Mass, July 27, 24; m. 47; c. 4. ENGLISH. B.A, Harvard, 50, M.A, 51, Ph.D, 58. Instr. ENG, Univ. Calif, Davis, 58-60, asst. prof, 60-66; PROF, KENT STATE UNIV, 66- Am. Philos. Soc. grant, 62; Soc. Relig. Higher Educ. cross-disciplinary fel, 64-65. U.S.A, 44-46. MLA; fel. Soc. Religion Higher Educ; Shakespeare Asn. Am. Shakespeare; Renaissance literature; theology. Publ: Interpretations in Shakespeare's sonnets, Univ. Calif, 63; Malone as editor of Shakespeare's sonnets, Bull. N.Y. Pub. Libr, 9/63; The leaven of wickedness: Hamlet, I.iv.1-38, In: Pacific Coast studies in Shakespeare, Univ. Ore, 66; The marriage of true minds: truth and error in Sonnet 116, Shakespeare Stud, III, 67. Add: Dept. of English, Kent State University, Kent, OH 44242.

LANDRY, LOWELL, b. New Orleans, La, Dec. 22, 32. MODERN LITERATURE. B.A, Rockford Col, 55; M.A, Tulane Univ, 63, Ph.D.(Eng), 70. Instr. ENG, Va. Polytech Inst. & State Univ, 66-69; prof. & chmn. dept, Am. Col. Switz, 70-71; ASST. PROF, SOUTHEAST. LA. UNIV, 72- Instr. NDEA inst. advan. lit. stud, Va. Polytech. Inst. & State Univ, summer 68. MLA. Henry James; the novel; 20th century literature. Add: Dept. of English, Southeastern Louisiana University, P.O. Box 664, Hammond, LA 70401.

LANDY, MARCIA, b. Cleveland, Ohio, June 24, 31; m. 53; c. 2. ENGLISH. A.B, Ohio Univ, 53; Fulbright fel, Univ. Munich, 53-54; Brown Univ, 54-55; M.A, Univ. Rochester, 61, Ph.D, 62. Instr. ENG, Univ. Rochester, 63-65, asst. prof, 66-67; UNIV. PITTSBURGH, 67-70, ASSOC. PROF, 70- Ed, Milton Stud, 67- MLA. Milton; women studies; literary criticism. Publ: The silent woman, Avon, 74; Gide's pastoralism and the new novel, Fr. Rev, 1/74; Language and mourning in Lycidas, Am. Imago, 74; plus five others. Add: Dept. of English, University of Pittsburgh, 509 E. Court, Pittsburgh, PA 15213.

LANE, LAURIAT, JR, b. Boston, Mass, Feb. 12, 25; m. 57; c. 2. ENGLISH. A.B, Harvard, 47, M.A, 48, Ph.D, 53. Tutor & fel, Harvard, 49-53; instr. ENG, Cornell Univ, 53-57, asst. prof, 57-60; UNIV. N.B, FREDERICTON, 60-62, assoc. prof, 62-66, PROF, 66-, ASSOC. DEAN GRAD. STUD, 71- Grant, Can. Counc, 62, sr. res. fel, 66-67. Sig.C, U.S.A, 43-45. MLA; Asn. Can. Univ. Teachers Eng; Can. Asn. Am. Stud; Melville Soc. Am; Thoreau Soc; Dickens Soc. Am. English fiction, especially Charles Dickens; American literature, especially Henry Thoreau. Publ: Approaches to Walden, Wadsworth, 61; co-ed, The Dickens critics, Cornell Univ, 62 & The stature of Dickens, Univ. Toronto, 71; auth, Dickens' archetypal Jew, PMLA, 3/58; Walden: the second year, Stud. Romanticism, 69; Dickens and Melville, Dalhousie Rev, 71; plus others. Add: Dept. of English, University of New Brunswick, Fredericton, N.B, Can.

LANE, PINKIE GORDON, b. Philadelphia, Pa, Jan. 13, 23. ENGLISH. B.A, Spelman Col, 49; M.A, Atlanta Univ, 56; Ph.D.(Eng), La. State Univ, 67. PROF. ENG, SOUTH. UNIV, BATON ROUGE, 67- Poetry Soc. Am. Publ: Wind Thoughts (poems), 72, ed, Discourses on Poetry, VI, 72 & Poems by Blacks, III, 73, South & West; articles in Phylon, J. Black Poetry, Negro Am. Lit. Forum, Jeopardy, La. Rev, Hoo Doo I, South & West, Voices Int, Energy W, Pembroke Mag, Poet: India, Last cookie; plus others. Add: 2738 77th Ave, Baton Rouge, LA 70807.

LANE, RALPH L, b. Eldorado, Ill, Nov. 30, 27; m. 54; c. 2. SPEECH, DRAMA. B.S.Ed, South. Ill, Univ, 49; M.A, Northwest. Univ, 56, Ph.D. (speech), 67. Teacher & dir. speech & drama, High Sch, Ill, 49-68; assoc. prof. speech & theatre, ILL. STATE UNIV, 68-72, PROF. THEATRE & SPEECH COMMUN, 72- Teacher & dir. speech, Nat. High Sch. Inst, Northwest. Univ, summers 56-60; ed, Ill. Speech Theatre Asn, 60-62, 70-72; consult, State Off. Supt. Pub. Instr, 61; ed, Ill. Speech News, 61-63; creative arts consult, Northbrook Civic Asn. & Northbrook Park Dist, 67; reader consult, Off. Educ, Dept. Health, Educ. & Welfare, 68. U.S.A, 51-54. Speech Commun. Asn; Am. Theatre Asn; NEA. Speech education; theatre; oral interpretation. Publ: Co-auth, Communication in the high school curriculum, State Supt. Pub. Instr, Ill, 61. Add: Dept. of Theatre, Illinois State University, Normal, IL 61761.

LANE, RICHARD LEE, b. Kansas City, Mo, Nov. 17, 27; m. 48; c. 2. MEDIEVAL ENGLISH LANGUAGE & LITERATURE. B.A, Univ. Mo-Kansas City, 54, M.A, 56; Ph.D.(Eng), Univ. Ark, 68. Asst. prof. ENG, Culver-Stockton Col, 59-62; UNIV. NEBR. AT OMAHA, 64-68, assoc. prof, 68-70, PROF, 70-, ASSOC. DEAN, COL. ARTS & SCI, 72-, ACTING DIR, AFGHANISTAN STUD. & RES. PROG, 73-, acting dean col. arts & sci, 71-72. U.S.M.C, 45-46, 50-52. Scottish Chaucerians; 14th century English poets; Icelandic sagas. Add: Dept. of English, University of Nebraska at Omaha, Omaha, NE 68101.

LANE, ROBERT P, b. Newark, N.J, July 22, 14; m. 52; c. 3. ENGLISH LITERATURE. A.B, Columbia Univ, 35; M.A.T, Harvard, 41; Ph.D, Univ. N.C, 56. Instr. ENG, Thayer Acad, Braintree, Mass, 39-42; Univ. Mass, 45-49, asst. prof, 49-56, assoc. prof, 56-62; PROF. & CHMN. DEPT, WINTHROP COL, 62- Summer fel, Folger Shakespeare Libr, 64. U.S.A.A.F, 42-45, T/Sgt. MLA; S.Atlantic Mod. Lang. Asn. Elizabethan drama 1583-1593; literary associations of Gabriel Harvey; 17th and 18th century editions of Gayton's Festivous notes. Add: Dept. of English, Winthrop College, Rock Hill, SC 29730.

LANE, WILLIAM GUERRANT, b. Reidsville, N.C, June 15, 19; m. 53; c. 1. ENGLISH. A.B, Furman Univ, 39; Dexter traveling scholar, Harvard, 52, Ph.D, 53. Instr. ENG, Tufts Univ, 47-50; Duke Univ, 52-56; assoc. prof, Southwest Mo. State Col, 56-60; Univ. Colo, 60-64; prof, 64-69, chmn. dept, 64-67; PROF. & HEAD DEPT, UNIV. N.C, GREENSBORO, 69- Gen. ed, Eng. Lang. Notes, 63-68. U.S.N.R, 41-47, Lt. Comdr. MLA; Keats-Shelley Asn. Am; Res. Soc. Victorian Periodicals. Bentley's Miscellany; R.H. Barham; 19th century English literature. Publ: Richard Harris Barham, Univ. Mo, 68; ed, Poetry: an introduction, Heath, 68; Primitive muse of Thomas Ingoldsby, Harvard Libr. Bull, 58; Relationships between some of Fielding's major and minor works, Boston Univ. Stud. in Eng, 61; A chord in melancholy: Hood's last years, Keats-Shelley J, winter 64. Add: Dept. of English, University of North Carolina at Greensboro, Greensboro, NC 27412.

LANG, CECIL Y, b. N.C, Sept. 18, 20; m. 52; c. 1. ENGLISH LITERATURE. A.B, Duke Univ, 41, M.A, 42; Ph.D, Harvard, 49. Instr. ENG, Yale, 49-54, asst. prof, 54-57; assoc. prof, Claremont Grad. Sch, 57-59; prof, Syracuse Univ, 59-65; Univ. Chicago, 65-67; Ctr. Advan. Stud. UNIV. VA, 67-70, COMMONWEALTH PROF, 70- Guggenheim & Fulbright fels, 51-52; Morse fel, Yale, 56-57; mem. adv. bd, Victorian Poetry, 63-, ed, spring-summer 71; mem. adv. bd, Victorian Stud, 64-66; mem. ed. comt, PMLA, 68-73. U.S.A.F, 42-46, 1st Lt. MLA. Nineteenth century English literature. Publ: Ed, The Swinburne letters, 6 vols, Yale, 59-62, New writings by Swinburne, Syracuse Univ, 64; The pre-Raphaelites and their circle, Houghton, 68; introd, Tennyson in Lincoln, Tennyson Res. Ctr, Lincoln, Eng, 71. Add: 1820 Edgewood Lane, Charlottesville, VA 22903.

LANG, JOVIAN PETER, O.F.M, b. Sioux City, Iowa, June 2, 19. SPEECH & HEARING THERAPY. A.B, Quincy Col, 43; M.S, in L.S, West. Reserve Univ, 50, M.A, 55. Asst. prof. speech & librarianship, Quincy Col, 47-55; speech, St. Joseph Sem, Westmont, Ill, 55-57; speech & relig, Villa St. Joseph Prov. Libr, St. Louis, Mo, 57-60; assoc. prof. speech & hearing & asst. prof. librarianship, Quincy Col, 60-71; ASST. PROF. LIBRARIANSHIP, UNIV. S.FLA, TAMPA, 71- Ed, Ordo, 58-; panel mem, Libr. Gen. Inform. Surv. Rev. Panel for Nat. Ctr. Educ. Statist, U.S. Off. Educ, 73- Counc. Except. Children; Am. Libr. Asn; Cath. Libr. Asn; Christian Preaching Conf; Asn. Coop. Libr. Orgn; Libr-Col. Assoc. Counseling of parents of handicapped; college librarianship; liturgy. Publ: Co-auth, Supplementary materials for lipreading teachers, Cleveland Hearing & Speech Ctr, 51; auth, Guide for the Liturgy, O.F.M, Franciscan Press, annually, 58-; Guide for the priest during parish services, 65 & co-auth, The liturgy of Vatican II (2 vols), 66, Franciscan Herald; Pray together, monthly, 70- & Ordo for the celebration of divine office and the mass, annually, 71-, Sunday Missal Serv; Evaluating a college library, Cath. Libr. World, 11/59; Curriculum and instruction, In: The library college, Drexel, 66; Library tools, Cath. Libr. J, 72. Add: 10110 Central Ave, Tampa, FL 33612.

LANG, PHYLLIS MARTIN, b. Norfolk, Nebr, Oct. 31, 38; m. 59. ENGLISH & AMERICAN LITERATURE. B.A, Nebr. Wesleyan Univ, 60; M.A, Univ. Nebr-Lincoln, 62; Ph.D.(Eng), Univ. Ill, Urbana, 72. Asst. ENG, Univ. Nebr, 60-61, 61-62; instr, MacMURRAY COL, 62-68, asst. prof, 68-73, ASSOC. PROF, 73- MLA; Col. Lang. Asn; NCTE; AAUP; Am. Asn. Higher Educ. Twentieth century Afro-American fiction; American short story; American southern fiction. Publ: An English teacher looks at oral interpretation, Ill. Speech & Theatre J, fall 69; Claude McKay: evidence of a magic pilgrimage, CLA J, 6/73; Developing the personal voice, In: Language activities, NCTE, 73. Add: Dept. of English, MacMurray College, Jacksonville, IL 62650.

LANG, ROBERT ALFRED, b. Cleveland, Ohio, June 22, 18; m; c. 2. SPEECH. A.B, West. Reserve Univ, 41, A.M, 47; Ph.D, Northwest. Univ, 50. Lectr, West. Reserve Univ, 46-47, instr. pub. speaking, 47-48; asst. prof. pub. speaking & dir. debate, 49-58; teaching fel, Northwest. Univ, 48-49; EXEC. SECY, ACAD. MED. OF CLEVELAND, OHIO, 58- Speech consult. U.S.A. U.S.A.A.F, 41-46, Capt. Speech Commun. Asn; Am. Soc. Asn. Exec; Am. Asn. Medical Soc. Exec. Rhetoric in continental Europe, 1550-1800; small group leadership; public speaking for adults. Add: 10525 Carnegie Ave, Cleveland, OH 44106.

LANGBAUM, ROBERT, b. New York, N.Y, Feb. 23, 24; m. 50; c. 1. ENGLISH. A.B, Cornell Univ, 47; M.A, Columbia Univ, 49, Ph.D.(Eng), 54. Instr. ENG, Cornell Univ, 50-55, asst. prof, 55-60; assoc. prof, UNIV. VA, 60-63, prof, 63-67, JAMES BRANCH CABELL PROF, 67- Am. Counc. Learned Soc. grant-in-aid, summer 61; fel, Ctr. Advan. Stud. Behav. Sci, 61-62; mem. ed. bd, Victorian Poetry, 63-; vis. prof, Harvard, summer 65; Columbia Univ, 65-66; mem. ed. bd, Style, 67- & New Lit. Hist, 69-; Guggenheim fel, 69-70; sr. fel, Nat. Endowment for Humanities, 72-73. U.S.A, 42-46, Lt. MLA; AAUP. Nineteenth and 20th century English literature; literary criticism. Publ: The poetry of experience: the dramatic monologue in modern literary tradition, Random & Chatto & Windus, London, 57, 2nd ed, 72 & Norton, 63, 2nd ed, 71; ed, Shakespeare's The tempest, New Am. Libr, 64 & In: Complete signet classic Shakespeare, Harcourt, 72; auth, The gayety of vision a study of Isak Dinesen's art, Chatto & Windus, London, 64, Gyldendal, Copenhagen, Danish transl, 64, Random, 65; ed, The Victorian age, Fawcett, 67; auth, The modern spirit: essays on the continuity of 19th and 20th century literature, Oxford Univ, 70, Chatto & Windus, London, 70. Add: Dept. of English, University of Virginia, Charlottesville, VA 22901.

LANGER, LAWRENCE L, b. New York, N.Y, June 20, 29; m. 51; c. 2. LITERATURE. B.A, City Col. New York, 51; A.M, Harvard, 52, fel, 54-57, Ph.D, 61. Instr. ENG, Univ. Conn, 57-58; SIMMONS COL, 58-61, asst. prof, 61-66, assoc. prof, 66-72, PROF, 72-, dir, Freshman Exp. Educ. Discovery, 71-74. Howard M. Jones Eng. prize, Harvard, 61; Fulbright lectr. Am. lit, Univ. Graz, Austria, 63-64. MLA; AAUP. American and Russian literature; literature of the holocaust. Publ: To make freedom real: James Baldwin and the conscience of America, In: Americana-Austrica: Festschrift des Amerika, Inst. Univ. Innsbruck, Wien, 66. Add: Dept. of English, Simmons College, 300 The Fenway, Boston, MA 02115.

LANGFORD, ALLIE GERALD, b. Bandera, Tex, Jan. 27, 23; m. 51; c. 3. MUSIC, ENGLISH LITERATURE. B.M, Univ. Tex, 48; Inst. Meschini, Rome, 49-50; M.A, Columbia Univ, 52, Ed.D.(music), 64. ASSOC. PROF. ENG, UNIV. FLA, 53- Thomas Jefferson Award for Excellence in Teaching, 68. U.S.A.A.F, 43-45; Air Medal. S.Atlantic Mod. Lang. Asn; MLA. Methodology of Italian music conservatories; biography of Ernesto Boezi, director of the Cappella Julia, San Pietro, 1902-1946. Add: 600 N.E. 7th Terr, Gainesville, FL 32601.

LANGFORD, GERALD, b. Montgomery, Ala, Oct. 20, 11; m. 38; c. 2. ENGLISH. A.B, Univ. Va, 33, A.M, 34, Ph.D, 40. Instr, Univ. Ky, 36-38; N.C. State Col, 38-40; assoc. prof, Winthrop Col, 40-43; asst. prof. ENG, UNIV. TEX, AUSTIN, 46-50, assoc. prof, 50-62, PROF, 62- U.S.M.C, 43-46. MLA. Creative writing; modern English and American literature. Publ: Alias O. Henry, a biography of William Sidney Porter, Macmillan, 57; The Richard Harding Davis years, Holt, 61; The murder of Stanford White, Bobbs, 62; Ingenue among the lions: the letters of Emily Clark to Joseph Hergesheimer, 65, Faulkner's revision of Absalom, Absalom!, 71 & Faulkner's revision of Sanctuary, 72, Univ. Tex. Add: Dept. of English, University of Texas at Austin, Austin, TX 78712.

LANGFORD, RICHARD EVERETT, b. Pensacola, Fla, Jan. 4, 26. ENGLISH. A.B, Univ. Fla, 51; M.A, Stetson Univ, 59. Instr. ENG, STETSON UNIV, 59-61, asst. prof, 62-67, ASSOC. PROF, 67- Pres, Everett-Edwards, Inc. DeLand, Fla, 64- U.S.N, 43-46. MLA; Int. Soc. Gen. Semantics; S.Atlantic Mod. Lang. Asn. American literature; general semantics. Publ: Ed. & contrib, Essays in modern American literature, Stetson Univ, 63 & The twenties/poetry and prose, Everett-Edwards, 66; auth, Books and authors, weekly column in DeLand Sun-News, 67- Add: Dept. of English, Stetson University, DeLand, FL 32720.

LANGHAM, NORMA, b. California, Pa. SPEECH, DRAMA. B.S, Ohio State Univ, 42; B.T.A, Pasadena Playhouse Col. Theatre Arts, 44; M.A, Stanford Univ, 56. Instr. SPEECH & DRAMA, Westminster Col, 57-58; CALIFORNIA STATE COL.(PA), 59-60, asst. prof, 60-61, ASSOC. PROF, 61- Co-founder & head, California State Col. Theatre for Children & Youth, 63- Freedoms Found. Award for children's play, John Dough, 68. Am. Theatre Asn; Int. Asn. Theatre Children & Young People; AAUP; Am. Asn. Univ. Women. Playwriting; children's theatre; television. Publ: Magic in the sky, Coach House, 63; Public speaking: the science of the art, privately publ, 67. Add: Dept. of Theatre, California State College, California, PA 15419.

LANGHANS, EDWARD A, b. Warren, Pa, Mar. 11, 23. DRAMA, THEATER. A.B, Univ. Rochester, 48, M.A, 49; M.A, Univ. Hawaii, 51; Stirling fel, Yale, 53-54, Ph.D.(theater hist), 55; Fulbright res. grant, Eng, 54-55. Asst. prof. DRAMA, Univ. Tex, 55-57; assoc. prof, UNIV. HAWAII, MANOA, 57-74, PROF, 74-, res. grants, 63, 68. Vis. assoc. prof, Tufts Univ, 67-68; Folger Shakespeare Libr. fels, summers 70, 72, 73. U.S.A.A.F, 42-47, Maj. Am. Soc. Theatre Res; Soc. Theatre Res, Eng; Malone Soc; Shakespeare Asn. Am; MLA; Am. Theatre Asn. Restoration and 18th century theatre research; bibliography and research methods; biography. Publ: Co-auth, A biographical dictionary of actors, actresses, musicians, dancers, managers, and other stage personnel in London, 1660-1800, South. Ill, Univ, 73; auth, Three early 18th century promptbooks, Mod. Philol, 11/67; New Restoration manuscript casts, Theatre Notebk, summer 73; A conjectural reconstruction of the Dorset Garden Theatre, Theatre Surv, 11/72. Add: Dept. of Drama & Theatre, University of Hawaii at Manoa, 1770 East-West Rd, Honolulu, HI 96822.

LANGHOLZ, ARMIN, b. St. Paul, Minn, June 25, 29; m. 55; c. 2. SPEECH. B.S. in Educ, Capital Univ, 51; A.M, Ohio State Univ, 55, Ph.D.(speech), 65. Instr. SPEECH, CAPITAL UNIV, 54-57, asst. prof, 57-66, assoc. prof, 66-71, PROF, 71-, CHMN. DEPT, 70- Dir. radio & TV, Columbus Area Counc. Churches, 59-70. U.S.A, 52-54, Sgt. Broadcast Educ. Asn; Speech Commun. Asn. Qualitative audience research in radio and television; measurement of listening comprehension. Add: Dept. of Speech, Capital University, Columbus, OH 43209.

LANGLAND, JOSEPH THOMAS, b. Spring Grove, Minn, Feb. 16, 17; m. 43; c. 3. ENGLISH. M.A, State Univ, Iowa, 41. Head dept. ENG, Dana Col, 41-42; from asst. prof. to assoc. prof, Univ. Wyo, 48-59; PROF, UNIV. MASS, AMHERST, 59- Fund Advan. Educ. fel, 53-54; Amy Lowell traveling poetry fel, Italy, 55-56; summers, guest lectr, Univ. B.C, 60; Poetry Ctr, San Francisco State Col, 61; guest prof, Univ. Wash, 64; Nat. Counc. Arts poetry grant, 66-67. Melville Cane Award in Poetry, 64. A.U.S, 42-46, Capt. Creative writing; poetry; contemporary authors. Publ: The green town, Scribner, 56; co-ed, Poet's choice, 62 & auth, The wheel of summer, 63, Dial; co-transl, Poetry from the Russian underground, Harper, 73; auth, Adlai Stevenson (poems), Stone Wall, 74; An interview and 14 poems, Clark Univ, 74. Add: Dept. of English, University of Massachusetts, Amherst, MA 01002.

LANGLEY, STEPHEN G, b. Gardner, Mass, Dec. 25, 38. THEATRE, SPEECH. B.A, Emerson Col, 60, M.A, 61; Ph.D.(theatre), Univ. Ill, Urbana, 65. Lectr. speech, BROOKLYN COL, 63-65, instr. SPEECH & THEATRE, 65-67, asst. prof, 67-72, ASSOC. PROF, 72-, BUS. MGR. & EXEC. OFF, OFFICE PERFORMING ARTS, 66-, GEN. MGR, 68-, bus. mgr. theatre div, 66. Managing dir, Falmouth Playhouse, Mass, summers 59-74. Dramatists Guild; Am. Theatre Asn; Am. Nat. Theatre & Acad. Puritanism and the American drama; performing arts administration. Publ: Theatre management in America: principle and practice, Drama Bk. Specialists, 73. Add: Performing Arts Center, Brooklyn College, Brooklyn, NY 11210.

LANGVARDT, ARTHUR LeROY, b. Junction City, Kans, June 16, 18. AMERICAN RURAL FICTION. A.B, & B.S, Kans. State Teachers Col, 40; A.M, Univ. Colo, 49, Ph.D, 56. Teacher high sch, Kans, 40-42, 46-47; asst. prof. ENG, Kans. State Univ, 47-61, assoc. prof, 61-63; PROF, HASTINGS COL, 63-, ACAD. DEAN, 72-, chmn. dept. Eng, 63-72, dean col, 66-72. U.S.A.R, Lt. Col. NEA. Add: Office of the Academic Dean, Hastings College, Hastings, NE 68901.

LANHAM, RICHARD ALAN, b. Washington, D.C, Apr. 26, 36; m. 57. ENGLISH. A.B, Yale, 56, M.A, 60, Ph.D.(Eng), 63. Instr. ENG, Dartmouth Col, 62-64, asst. prof, 64-65; UNIV. CALIF. LOS ANGELES, 65-68, assoc. prof, 68-71, PROF, 71- U.S.A, 56-58, Res, 58-62. MLA. Sir Philip Sidney; Renaissance prose; prose style. Publ: Sidney's Old Arcadia, publ. with a map of Arcadia, under title, Sidney's Arcadia, Yale Univ, 65; A handlist of rhetorical terms, 68 & Tristram Shandy: the games of pleasure, 73, Univ. Calif; Style: an anti-textbook, Yale Univ, 74; The literal Britomart, Mod. Lang. Quart, 12/67; Sidney: the ornament of his age, South. Rev, Australia, winter 68; Astrophil and Stella: pure and impure persuasion, Eng. Lit. Renaissance, winter 72. Add: Dept. of English, University of California, Los Angeles, Los Angeles, CA 90024.

LANICH, LLOYD J, JR, b. Grafton, W.Va, Aug. 29, 22; m. 50; c. 3. THEATRE ARTS. B.A, Washington & Lee Univ, 47; M.A, Hopkins Sch. Advan. Int. Stud; Ph.D.(theatre hist), Yale, 59. From instr. to asst. prof. fine arts, Washington & Lee Univ, 48-51, assoc. prof, 55-60; THEATRE ARTS, Pomona Col, 60-62; prof, State Univ. N.Y. Col. New Paltz, 62-64; assoc. prof, EMERSON COL, 64-67, PROF, 67-, chmn. dept. dramatic arts, 68-72. U.S.A.F, 43-45. Speech Commun. Asn; Am. Theatre Asn. Theatre history. Add: Dept. of Dramatic Arts, Emerson College, 130 Beacon St, Boston, MA 02116.

LANIER, RENE PARKS, JR, b. Athens, Ga, Jan. 4, 44; m. 68. ENGLISH & AMERICAN LITERATURE. B.A, Pfeiffer Col, 66; M.A, Univ. Tenn, Knoxville, 68, Ph.D.(Eng), 72. Instr. ENG, RADFORD COL, 71-72, ASST. PROF, 72- MLA; S.Atlantic Mod. Lang. Asn. English romanticism. Add: 5 South Dr, Radford, VA 24141.

LANSBURY, CORAL, b. Melbourne, Australia. ENGLISH LITERATURE, MODERN HISTORY. M.A, Univ. Auckland, 67, Ph.D.(Eng), 69. Tutor hist, Univ. New South Wales, 64-66; sr. lectr. Eng, Univ. Waikato, N.Z, 67-69; assoc. prof, Rosemont Col, 70-73; VIS. PROF. ENG. & HIST, DREW UNIV, 73- Am. Counc. Learned Soc. grant, 72-73. MLA; Northeast Mod. Lang. Asn; Royal Australian Hist. Soc. Victorian literature; modern British history; history of women. Publ: Arcady in Australia, Melbourne Univ, 71; Elizabeth Gaskell, Elek, London, 74; Terra Australis Dickensia, Mod. Lang. Stud, 71; Dickens' romanticism domesticated, Dickens Stud, 72; The feminine frontier, Meanjin Quart, 72. Add: 200 Radnor Chester Rd, Villanova, PA 19085.

LAPPERT, WILLIAM GRAYSON, b. Barnesville, Ohio, Oct. 16, 20; m. 42; c. 2. ENGLISH LITERATURE. A.B, Mt. Union Col, 42; A.M, West. Reserve Univ, 47, Ph.D, 51. Instr, West. Reserve Univ, 48-50; asst. prof. ENG. LIT, BALDWIN-WALLACE COL, 50-55, assoc. prof, 55-61, PROF, 61-, chmn. dept. Eng, 66-73. MLA; Milton Soc. Am. Milton's Comus; 17th century English literature; Browning. Publ: Edmund Yates: his life and works; Rebecca West's Black lamb and grey falcon. Add: Dept. of English, Baldwin-Wallace College, Berea, OH 44017.

LARDAS, KONSTANTINOS, b. Steubenville, Ohio, Aug. 3, 27; m. 51; c. 3. ENGLISH, MODERN GREEK. B.A, Univ. Pittsburgh, 50; M.A, Columbia Univ, 51; fel, Univ. Mich, 61-63, Ph.D.(comp. lit), 66. Instr. ENG, Univ. Mich, 64-66; asst. prof, CITY COL. NEW YORK, 66-69, ASSOC. PROF, 69- U.S.A, 46. Publ: And in him, too: in us (poems), Generation, Univ. Mich, 64; Five poems, Tex. Quart. Rev, winter 72; The cypress trees, the sun (short story), Hawaii Rev, 5/73; The broken wings, In: Best short stories of 73, Houghton, 73; plus others. Add: 68 Wakefield Ave, Yonkers, NY 10704.

LARNER, DANIEL, b. Olean, N.Y, Apr. 15, 39; m. 64. DRAMATIC LITERATURE, HISTORY OF SCIENCE. A.B, Harvard, 60; M.S, Univ. Wis, 62, Ph.D.(speech), 68. Tutor humanities, St. John's Col.(Md), 62-65; ASST. PROF. ENG, WEST. WASH. STATE COL, 68- MLA; Speech Commun. Asn. Publ: The death of Christopher Marlowe (play), Golliards, 73. Add: Dept. of Speech, Western Washington State College, Bellingham, WA 98225.

LARRABEE, CARLTON H, b. Leominster, Mass, Aug. 14, 06; m. 31. ENGLISH. A.B, Clark Univ, 27; A.M, Harvard, 30; D.Ed, N.Y. Univ, 46. Teacher, high schs, Mass, Conn. & Calif, 27-43; lectr. ENG, Univ. South. Calif, 46-47; from asst. prof. to prof, FRESNO STATE UNIV, 47-69, EMER. PROF, 69- Summer vis. prof, Univ. Maine, 49-50, 54 & 61; Univ. Vt, 52-53, 55, 58 & 60. AAUP. English language and literature; mass communication media in relation to the teaching of English; preparation of teachers of English. Add: P.O. Box 5712, Fresno, CA 93755.

LARSEN, ERLING LAURITZ, b. Cresco, Iowa, Sept. 7, 09; m. 33; c. 3. ENGLISH. B.A, St. Olaf Col, 30; M.A, State Univ, Iowa, 32. Instr. ENG, CARLETON COL, 57-59, asst. prof, 59-67, assoc. prof, 67-71, PROF, 71- Hill Family Found. grant, 62-63; assoc. ed, Carleton Miscellany, 60-64, ed, 64-70. U.S.N, 43-45, Lt. Comdr. NCTE. Modern English and American fiction; the writing of short stories and regional history. Publ: Minnesota trails, a sentimental history, Denison, 58; James Agee, Univ. Minn, 71; Little Finland, Farm Quart, 46; The geography of Fitzgerald's Saint Paul, Carleton Miscellany, 73. Add: Rte. 3, Box 243, Northfield, MN 55057.

LARSEN, FRANCIS KEVIN, b. Irvington, N.J, Dec. 19, 25; m. 50; c. 4. ENGLISH & AMERICAN LITERATURE. B.S, Seton Hall Univ, 49; M.A, Montclair State Col, 51; N.Y. Univ, 55-58; Ed.D.(Eng. educ), Rutgers Univ, New Brunswick, 72. Instr. ENG, KEAN COL. N.J, 57-60, asst. prof, 60-64, ASSOC. PROF, 64-, ASST. CHMN. DEPT, 72- Lectr, Fairleigh Dickinson Univ, 56-59; Seton Hall Univ, 57-58; consult. new freshman Eng. prog, Essex County Community Col, summer 68. U.S.A, 44-46. MLA; NCTE; Col. Eng. Asn. Aldous Huxley; 20th century English literature; interdisciplinary studies in English and American literature. Add: 32 N. Hillside Ave, Chatham, NJ 07928.

LARSEN, GOLDEN LAVON, b. Oakley, Idaho, June 16, 22; m. 46; c. 3. ENGLISH. B.S, Utah State Univ, 51, M.S, 53; Ph.D, Univ. Wash, 62. From asst. prof. to ASSOC. PROF. ENG, WEST. WASH. STATE COL, 56- U.S.A, 44-46. Am. Philol. Asn. English novel, especially the 20th century; Mormons as an ethnic group. Publ: The dark descent: social change and moral responsibility in the novels of Joyce Cary, Michael Joseph, London, 64. Add: Dept. of English, Western Washington State College, Bellingham, WA 98225.

LARSON, BARBARA A, b. La Grange, Ill. RHETORIC & PUBLIC ADDRESS. B.A, Univ. Wis, 48; M.A, Cornell Univ, 53; Northwest. Univ, summer 60; Ph.D.(speech commun), Univ. Minn, 69. Dir. drama & forensics, High Schs, Ill, Calif. & Wis, 48-60; pub. relat. dir, Wander Co, Chicago, Ill, 60-61; instr. speech & oral interpretation, Morton Col, 61-65, 66-67; teaching assoc. SPEECH COMMUN, Univ. Minn, 65-66; asst. prof, North. Ill. Univ, 67-69; UNIV. WIS-MILWAUKEE, 69-73, ASSOC. PROF, 73- Consult. ed. rhet. theory & criticism, Cent. States Speech J, 73-76. Speech Commun. Asn; Int. Commun. Asn; Cent. States Speech Asn. Rhetorical theory and criticism; contemporary public address and political persuasion; history and criticism of American public address. Publ: Samuel Davies and the rhetoric of the new light, Speech Monogr, 8/71; The election eve address of Edmund Muskie: a case study in method, summer 72 & Criticism and the campaign concept of persuasion, spring 73, Cent. States Speech J. Add: Dept. of Communication, University of Wisconsin-Milwaukee, Milwaukee, WI 53201.

LARSON, CLINTON F, b. American Fork, Utah, Sept. 22, 19; m. 42; c. 2. ENGLISH. B.A, Univ. Utah, 43, M.A, 47, Ph.D.(Eng), Univ. Denver, 56. Instr. ENG, BRIGHAM YOUNG UNIV, 47-49, asst. prof, 49-56, assoc. prof, 56-62, PROF, 62- Publ: Coriantumr and Moroni (plays), 62 & The Lord of experience (poems), 67, Brigham Young Univ; The mantle of the prophet and other plays, Deseret Bk, 66; Preface to Contemporary poetry of the United States, Paris, 64; transl, Jean de la Ceppède's poems, In: Renaissance and baroque lyrics, Northwest. Univ, 64. Add: Dept. of English, Brigham Young University, Provo, UT 84601.

LARSON, ESTHER ELISABETH, b. Williamsport, Pa, Oct. 20, 08. AMERICAN LITERATURE & CIVILIZATION. B.S, W.Chester State Col, 31; M.A, Columbia Univ, 45; Am-Scand. Found. fel, 49-50; Ph.D, N.Y, Univ, 59. Instr. ENG, High Sch, Jamestown, N.Y, 34-44; lectr, Columbia Univ, 52-54; instr, Bennett Col, 54-56; N.Y. Univ, summer 57; assoc. prof, E. STROUDSBURG STATE COL, 59-60, PROF, 60-, head dept, 60-69. Founders Day Award, N.Y. Univ, 59. MLA; Am. Stud. Asn; Conf. Col. Compos. & Commun; NCTE (regional judge, achievement awards prog, 63-); Col. Eng. Asn; Scand. Stud. Soc; Am-Scand. Found; Swed. Pioneer Hist. Soc; Am. Swed. Hist. Found. American and Swedish intercultural relations. Publ: Swedish commentators on America, 1638-1865, N.Y. Pub. Libr, 63; Svenskar on Amerika, Bokvännen, Stockholm, 63; Swedish commentators on America, 1638-1865: an introduction, N.Y. Pub. Libr. Bull, 6/63. Add: 584 E. Broad St, East Stroudsburg, PA 18301.

LARSON, GALE K, b. Ekalaka, Mont, Aug. 31, 37; m. 62; c. 1. ENGLISH. B.A, Carroll Col.(Mont), 60; M.A, Creighton Univ, 63; Ph.D.(Eng), Univ. Nebr, Lincoln, 68. Teacher high sch, 61-63; instr. ENG, Univ. Nebr, Lincoln, 66-67; asst. prof, CALIF. STATE UNIV, NORTHRIDGE, 67-70, ASSOC. PROF, 70-, ASSOC. DEAN SCH. HUMANITIES, 72- NCTE; Conf. Col. Compos. & Commun. George Bernard Shaw. Publ: Ed, Bernard Shaw's Caesar and Cleopatra, Bobbs-Merrill, 74; auth, Caesar and Cleopatra: the making of a history play, Shaw Rev, 5/71. Add: School of Humanities, California State University, Northridge, 18111 Nordhoff, Northridge, CA 91324.

LARSON, GEORGE STANLEY, b. Willmar, Minn, July 28, 39; m. 71. NINETEENTH CENTURY ENGLISH LITERATURE. B.A, Augsburg Col, 61; Woodrow Wilson fel, Duke Univ, 61-62, M.A, 62; NDEA fel, Univ. Mass, Amherst, 66-68, Ph.D.(Eng), 69. Instr. ENG, CONCORDIA COL,(MOORHEAD, MINN), 62-66, ASST. PROF, 68- MLA; NCTE. Charles Dickens; religion in 19th century England. Add: Dept. of English, Concordia College, Moorhead, MN 56560.

LARSON, HAROLD C, b. Beresford, S.Dak, Oct. 8, 24; m. 47; c. 2. RHETORIC & PUBLIC ADDRESS, COMMUNICOLOGY. B.S.Ed, Univ. S.Dak, 48, M.A, 49; Ph.D.(speech), Univ. Wis-Madison, 69. Chmn. dept. SPEECH, Huron Col.(S.Dak), 49-57; Carroll Col.(Wis), 57-68; PROF, NORTH. ARIZ. UNIV, 68- Consult. lay preaching, United Methodist Church, 64-65; consult. sales, Readers Dig. Spec. Prod, Inc, 66-68; consult. commun, United Auto Workers, 66-68; consult. mkt, ESB, Co, 67-68. Speech Commun. Asn; Int. Commun. Asn; Am. Forensic Asn. Rhetorical criticism; nonverbal communication. Publ: Auth, Speech communication: an academic discipline—some proposals, spring 72 & co-auth, Rejection-acceptance of stuttered speech in telephone conversation, fall 73, J. Ariz. Speech & Drama Asn. Add: Dept. of Speech, Northern Arizona University, Box 5687, Flagstaff, AZ 86001.

LARSON, ORVILLE K, b. Chicago, Ill, Mar. 7, 14; m. 46; c. 4. DRAMA. B.S, Univ. Wis, 41; M.A, West. Reserve Univ, 42; Ph.D.(speech), Univ. Ill, 56. Instr. speech & theatre, Univ. Md, 46-49; speech & drama, Univ. Conn, 51-56; asst. prof. speech, Mich. State Univ, 56-59; assoc. prof. fine arts, Ohio Univ, 59-61; assoc. prof. speech & theatre & head div. theatre, Univ. Mass, 61-65; prof. speech & theatre & chmn. dept, Univ. Bridgeport, 65-67; PROF. SPEECH & THEATRE, KENT STATE UNIV, 69- U.S.A, 43-46, T/Sgt. Am. Soc. Theatre Res; Am. Theatre Asn.(chmn. transl. & publ. rare bks. proj, 58-60); Col. Art Asn. Am; Speech Commun. Asn. Stage machinery and spectacle in the theatre of the Renaissance; history of theatrical art in 20th century American theatre; relationship between art and theatre of the Renaissance. Publ: Contemporary American science design, Univ. Conn, 55; ed, Scene design for stage and screen, Mich. State Univ, 61; auth, Sebastiano Serlio: an inquiry, Quart. J. Speech, 4/61; Spectacle in the Florentine Intermezzi, Drama Survey, winter 63; Robert Edmond Jones and his art, Theatre Design & Technol, 5/69. Add: Theatre Div, Dept. of Speech, Kent State University, Kent, OH 44242.

LARSON, PAUL MERVILLE, b. Denmark, Kans, Mar. 26. 03; m. 27; c. 3. SPEECH. B.S, Kans. State Univ, 27, M.S, 30; Ph.D, Northwest. Univ, 42. Teacher, pub. schs, Colo, 22-25; high sch, Kans, 27-30; instr. speech, Hutchinson Jr. Col, 30-39; N.Park Col, 39-42; acting head dept, East. Ill. Univ, 42-43; Southwest Tex. State Teachers Col, 43-45; head dept, Tex. Col. Arts & Indust, 45-46; South. Ill. Univ, 46-48; coord. forensics, Univ. Denver, 48-50; prof. SPEECH & head dept, TEX. TECH UNIV, 50-73, EMER. PROF, 73- Instr, Moorhead State Teachers Col, summer 39; Fulbright lectr. Am. civilization, 57-58; pres, Lubbock Little Theatre, 58-61. Nat. Col. Players; NEA; Speech Commun. Asn. Publ: Co-auth, Helping the Bible speak, Asn. Pres, 54, Speech for today, McGraw, 65, Speech for the creative teacher, 68 & Communicating effectively through speech, 71, W.C. Brown; plus one other. Add: 3120 21st St, Lubbock, TX 79410.

LARSON, RICHARD LESLIE, b. Stevens Point, Wis, Jan. 19, 29; m. 62. ENGLISH. A.B, Harvard, 49, A.M, 50, Ph.D.(Eng), 63. Instr, Harvard Grad. Sch. Bus. Admin, 56-59, lectr, 59-63; asst. prof. Eng, Univ. Hawaii, 63-66, assoc. prof, 66-69, prof, 69-73; PROF. & ASSOC. DEAN TEACHER EDUC, LEHMAN COL, 73- Consult, Off. Lang. Arts, State Dept. Educ, Hawaii, 63-66. NCTE (chmn. comt. teacher prep. & cert, 72-); Nat. Conf. Res. Eng; MLA; Conf. Col. Compos. & Commun.(chmn, 73-74); Speech Commun. Asn; Rhetoric Soc. Am.(exec. secy, 72-). Rhetoric; stylistics; evaluation of teaching in English. Publ: Rhetorical guide to the Borzoi college reader, Knopf, 67; Rhetoric (a collection of essays), Bobbs, 68; The evaluation of teaching college English, MLA, 71; Discovery through questioning: a plan for teaching rhetorical invention, Col. Eng, 11/68; Toward a linear rhetoric of the essay, Col. Compos. & Commun, 5/71; Process or product: the evaluation of teaching or the evaluation of learning, Bull, Asn. Depts. Eng, 12/72; plus others. Add: 7 Macy Ave, White Plains, NY 10605.

LaRUSSO, DOMINIC ANTHONY, b. New Rochelle, N.Y, Dec. 29, 24; m. 45; c. 2. RHETORIC. A.B, Univ. Wash, 50, A.M, 52; Ph.D, Northwest. Univ, 56. Instr. speech, Univ. Wash, 51-54; Northwest. Univ, 55-56; asst. prof, Univ. Wash, 56-64, assoc. prof. RHETORIC, 64-68; PROF, UNIV. ORE, 68-

U.S.A, 42-46. Speech Commun. Asn; Int. Commun. Asn; Am. Asn. Teachers Ital. Renaissance rhetoric and politics; experimental public address; nonverbal communication. Publ: Co-auth, Anatomy for speech and hearing, Harper, 65; auth, Basic skills of oral communication, 67, Mind the Shadows, 71 & Concepts and skills of oral communication, 73, W.C. Brown; co-auth, Oral communication in the secondary school classroom, Prentice-Hall, 70; auth, A neo-platonic dialogue: is rhetoric an art, Speech Monogr, 11/65; Visible communication: bodily action, In: Basic speech improvement, Harper, 65. Add: Dept. of Speech, University of Oregon, Eugene, OR 97403.

LARY, NIKITA MICHAEL, b. Washington, D.C, July 6, 40; m. 65; c. 2. COMPARATIVE LITERATURE. B.A, Haverford Col, 60; B.A, Cambridge, 63, M.A, 67; D.Phil.(comp. lit), Univ. Sussex, 69. ASST. PROF. HUMANITIES, YORK UNIV, 69- Cross-influences in 19th century English and Russian literature; Victorian studies; Russian literature and the problem of revolution. Publ: Dostoevsky and Dickens: a study of literary influence, Routledge & Kegan Paul, 73. Add: Faculty of Arts, Div. of Humanities, York University, 4700 Keele St, Toronto, Ont, Can.

LASATER, ALICE ELIZABETH, b. Chattanooga, Tenn, Aug. 18, 36. MEDIEVAL ENGLISH. B.A, Univ. Chattanooga, 67; M.A, Univ. Tenn, Knoxville, 68, Woodrow Wilson fel, 70-71, Ph.D.(Eng), 71. ASST. PROF. ENG, UNIV. SOUTH. MISS, 71- S.Atlantic Mod. Lang. Asn; MLA. Medieval comparative literature; English romantic period; Middle English literature. Publ: Spain to England: a study of Arabic, European and English literature of the Middle Ages, Univ. Col. Miss, 74; Wolfram's Flegetanis, 1/73 & The breakdown in communication in the twentieth century novel, 10/73, South. Quart. Add: Dept. of English, Box 382, University of Southern Mississippi, Hattiesburg, MS 39401.

LASER, MARVIN, b. Chicago, Ill, Nov. 2, 14; m. 48; c. 2. ENGLISH. Ph.B, Univ. Chicago, 35, M.A, 37; Ph.D, Northwest. Univ, 49. Teacher, Pub. Schs, Chicago, 37-38; instr. Eng, Wilson Jr. Col, Chicago, 38-42, 46-54; prof, Chicago Teachers Col, 54-56; prof, Calif. State Col. Los Angeles, 56-65, chmn. div. lang. arts, 56-63; PROF. ENG. & DEAN SCH. HUMANITIES & FINE ARTS, CALIF. STATE COL, DOMINGUEZ HILLS, 65- Lectr, Northwest. Univ, 47-49; Fund Advan. Educ. fac. fel, 53-54; spec. consult. educ. TV, Calif. State Cols, 61. Outstanding Prof. Award, Calif. State Col. Los Angeles, 65. U.S.A.A.F, 42-46, Capt. MLA; Am. Stud. Asn; NCTE. American literature, 19th and 20th century; literary criticism. Publ: Co-auth, Ideas and issues, Ronald, 63, Studies in J.D. Salinger, Odyssey, 63, Scope/reading, Vols. I, II, III & IV, 65-68 & Language in your life, Vols. I, II, III & IV, 65-68, Harper; Channel one, Dickenson, 70; auth, The growth and structure of Poe's concept of beauty, ELH, 48; Head, heart, and will in Hawthorne's psychology, Nineteenth Century Fiction, 55; Character names in The catcher in the rye, Calif. Eng. J, 65. Add: School of Humanities & Fine Arts, California State College, Dominguez Hills, 1000 E. Victoria St, Dominguez Hills, CA 90747.

LASH, KENNETH, b. New Britain, Conn, July 27, 18. ENGLISH. B.A, Yale, 39; M.A, Univ. N.Mex, 48; Fulbright scholar, Univ. Lille, France, 50-51; Rockefeller grant, Latin Am, 54. Instr. Eng, Univ. N.Mex, 48-53, ed, N.Mex. Quart, 51-55; teacher Eng. & art hist, San Francisco Art Inst, 59-63, chmn. dept. humanities, 63-70; PROF. ART & HEAD DEPT, UNIV. NORTH. IOWA, 70- Supvr, Carnegie grant in aid of experiment in teaching humanities, 64-67; consult. humanities prog, Am. Indian Sch. Arts, Santa Fe, 72; humanist, Nat. Humanities Ser, Midwest. Ctr, 73-; contrib. ed. & columnist, N.Am. Rev, 74- U.S.N, 43-46. Curriculum innovation; arts and letters. Publ: Ed, Report on a three-year experiment in the teaching of humanities, San Francisco Art Inst, 68; Children of turmoil, In: TLE Six, Holt, 72; It's ridiculous to give money to artists, Arts in Soc, fall-winter 73. Add: Dept. of Art, University of Northern Iowa, Cedar Falls, IA 50613.

LASHLEY, WARREN L, b. Akron, Ohio, May 27, 25; m. 51. SPEECH, DRAMA. B.A, Kent State Univ, 49, M.A, Northwest. Univ, 50, Ph.D. (speech), 66. Instr. SPEECH, Univ. Wash, 50-55; ASST. PROF, Calif. State Col. Long Beach, 58-63; UNIV. CINCINNATI, 63- Lectr. Mgt. Develop. Prog, Boeing Airplane Co, 53-55. U.S.A, 43-46. Speech Commun. Asn. History of American public address; rhetorical criticism; general speech. Publ: The debate over imperialism in the United States: 1898-1900, Speech Monogr, 8/67. Add: Dept. of Speech & Theater Arts, University of Cincinnati, Cincinnati, OH 45221.

LASS, ROBERT N, b. Denison, Iowa, Apr. 13, 13; m. 43; c. 5. ENGLISH. Ph.D, Univ. Iowa, 42. Instr. ENG, Purdue Univ, 45-46; U.S. Dept. War, Japan & Korea, 46-47; PROF, EAST. WASH. STATE COL, 47-, CHMN. DEPT, 58-, ASSOC. DEAN FAC. AFFAIRS, 66- Instr, U.S. Naval Postgrad. Sch, Monterey, Calif, 61-64. U.S.N.R, 42-45, 61-64, Lt. Comdr. NCTE; Conf. Col. Compos. & Commun. Composition; fiction; 18th century literature. Add: Dept. of English, Eastern Washington State College, Cheney, WA 99004.

LASS, ROGER GEORGE, Linguistics. See Volume III, Foreign Languages, Linguistics & Philology.

LATHAM-PFEIFER, MURIEL, b. New York, N.Y, Oct. 6, 21; m. 71; c. 3. ENGLISH. B.S, Columbia Univ, 48; M.A, East. N.Mex. Univ, 64; Royal Holloway Col, Univ. London, 64-65; Ph.D.(Eng), Univ. N.Mex, 73. Instr. ENG, East. N.Mex. Univ, 62-64; Univ. N.Mex, 65-66; ASST. PROF, UNIV. ALBUQUERQUE, 67- Ed, Albuquerque Archaeol. Soc. Newslett, 66-68; consult, Upward Bound Prog, Univ. Albuquerque, 73; lectr, N.Mex. Humanities Counc. AAUP (mem. nat. counc, 73-76); Am. Asn. Univ. Women. Literature and culture of the Southwest; Chaucer and the Middle Ages. Publ: The sound of a wind, N.Mex. Folklore Record, 63-64. Add: Dept. of English, University of Albuquerque, St. Joseph's Place N.W, Albuquerque, NM 87140.

LATT, DAVID JAY, b. Los Angeles, Calif, Feb. 2, 45. ENGLISH LITERATURE. B.A, Univ. Calif, Los Angeles, 66, Ph.D.(Eng), 71. Lectr. ENG, Calif. State Col, San Bernardino, 71-72; ASST. PROF, R.I. COL, 72- Milton Soc. Am; MLA; Augustan Reprint Soc. Seventeenth and 18th century English literature; Milton and Dryden; American film. Publ: Co-auth, John Dryden; a list of critical studies published from 1895-1972, Univ. Minn, rev. ed, 75. Add: Dept. of English, Rhode Island College, Providence, RI 02908.

LAUBENTHAL, PENNE J, b. Athens, Ala, Aug. 2, 44; m. 61; c. 2. ENGLISH, SPEECH. B.A, Athens Col.(Ala), 65, M.A.T, 68; Ph.D.(Eng), George Peabody Col, 72. Tutor & instr. ENG, ATHENS COL.(ALA), 65-68, asst. prof, 68-72, ASSOC. PROF, 73- MLA; AAUP. Modern drama; comparative literature; modern French literature. Add: Dept. of English, Athens College, Athens, AL 35611.

LAUBER, JOHN, b. Des Moines, Iowa, June 17, 25; m. 56; c. 3. ENGLISH. B.A, Univ. Wash, 48, M.A, 50, Ph.D, 57. Instr. ENG, Univ. N.Mex, 56-58; asst. prof, Univ. Idaho, 58-65; UNIV. ALTA, 65-67, assoc. prof, 67-73, PROF, 73- MLA. English Romantic period; American literature. Publ: Sir Walter Scott, Twayne, 67; Scott on the art of fiction, fall 63 & Don Juan as anti-epic, fall 68, Stud. Eng. Lit; Byron's concept of poetry, Dalhousie Rev, winter 67. Add: Dept. of English, University of Alberta, Edmonton, Alta. T6G 2E1, Can.

LAUERMAN, DAVID ANTHONY, b. Hammond, Ind, June 13, 31; m. 55; c. 5. ENGLISH LITERATURE. B.S, Univ. Notre Dame, 53, M.A, 58; Ph.D.(Eng), Ind. Univ, Bloomington, 72. Instr. ENG, North. Ill. Univ, 60-62; asst. prof, CANISIUS COL, 62-72, ASSOC. PROF, 72- U.S.A, 53-56. American literature; Willa Cather. Publ: Co-auth, Concise guide for student writers, Holt, 63. Add: Dept. of English, Canisius College, Buffalo, NY 14208.

LAUFE, ABE, b. Pittsburgh, Pa, May 25, 06. ENGLISH. B.A, Univ. Pittsburgh, 28, M.A, 35, Ph.D, 52; Columbia Univ, summers 35-36. Teacher ENG, Arnold Pub. Schs, 28-42; lectr, UNIV. PITTSBURGH, 47-49, instr, 49-53, asst. prof, 53-56, assoc. prof, 56-67, prof, 67-72, EMER. PROF, 72- Univ. Pittsburgh Int. Stud. Prog, grant to study theater in London, sponsored by Ford Found, summer 67. U.S.A, 42-45, M/Sgt, Legion of Merit, 46. MLA. American literature and drama; American musical theater. Publ: Ed, An army doctor's wife on the frontier: letters from Alaska and the Far West, Univ. Pittsburgh, 62; auth, Anatomy of a hit, Hawthorn, 66; Broadway's greatest musicals, Funk, 69, 70 & 73. Add: 122 S. Lang Ave, Pittsburgh, PA 15208.

LAUGHBAUM, ANNA BELLE, b. Galion, Ohio, Mar. 14, 15. ENGLISH. A.B, Greenville Col, 43; scholar, Univ. Ill, 43-44, A.M, 44, fel, 44-46, Ph.D, 48; Univ. Birmingham, 53. Asst. prof, Bethany-Peniel Col, 46-50; ASSOC. PROF. ENG, Seattle Pac. Col, 50-55; BETHANY NAZARENE COL, 55- MLA; NCTE; Am. Soc. Training Dir. The Crimean War and the English novel. Add: Dept. of English, Bethany Nazarene College, Bethany, OK 73008.

LAUGHNER, CARL L, b. Pittsburgh, Pa, July 1, 17; m. 48; c. 2. SPEECH. B.S, Slippery Rock State Col, 49; M.A, Univ. Pittsburgh, 55; Pa. State Univ, 58-61. Teacher Eng, Pittsburgh Pub. Schs, 49-51, activities dir, 51-55; ASSOC. PROF. SPEECH, SLIPPERY ROCK STATE COL, 55-; exec. dir, Slippery Rock State Alumni Asn, 72- Dir. lay speaking, West. Pa. Conf. Methodist Church, 65-68; ed, The Rock Mag, 72- U.S.A.A.F, 42-46, S/Sgt. Speech Commun. Asn; NEA. Communications theory; discussion; industrial communications. Publ: Classification of speech subjects, Pa. Speech Asn, 63. Add: Alumni Association, Slippery Rock State College, Slippery Rock, PA 16057.

LAUN, EDWARD CARL, b. Scranton, Pa, Oct. 23, 35; m. 59; c. 2. ENGLISH. B. A, Hobart Col, 57; M.A, Univ. Conn, 59; Ph.D.(Eng), Univ. Wis-Madison, 68. Lectr. ENG, Univ. Alta, 61-62; from instr. to asst. prof, Wis. State Univ-Whitewater, 62-66; from asst. prof. to ASSOC. PROF, WASHINGTON & JEFFERSON COL, 66- MLA. Victorian fiction, the novel. Add: Dept. of English, Washington & Jefferson College, Washington, PA 15301.

LAUREN, BARBARA, b. New York, N.Y, May 22, 47. ENGLISH & AMERICAN LITERATURE. B.A, Smith Col, 69; Woodrow Wilson fel, 69; M.A, Yale, 72, M.Phil, 71, Ph.D.(Eng), 73. Teaching asst. Eng, Yale, 72; ASST. PROF. ENG. LIT, BOWDOIN COL, 73- MLA; AAUP; Am. Asn. Univ. Women. Restoration and the 18th century; Jacobean drama. Publ: Pope's Epistle to Bolingbroke: satire from the vantage of retirement, Stud. Eng. Lit, summer 75. Add: Dept. of English, Bowdoin College, Brunswick, ME 04011.

LAURENCE, DAN H, b. New York, N.Y, Mar. 28, 20. ENGLISH LITERATURE. B.A, Hofstra Col, 46; M.A, N.Y. Univ, 50. Instr. Eng, Hofstra Col, 53-58; assoc. prof, N.Y. Univ, summer, 61, 62-67, prof, 67-70; LIT. ADV, GEORGE BERNARD SHAW ESTATE, 73- Guggenheim fels, 60, 61, 72; vis. prof, Univ. Tex, Austin, 74-75. U.S.A.A.F, 42-45. Bernard Shaw; Edwardian literature; modern British literature. Publ: Co-auth, A bibliography of Henry James, Rupert Hart-Davis, 57, rev. ed, 61; ed, Uncollected writings of Bernard Shaw, Hill & Wang, 61-; ed, Collected letters of Bernard Shaw, Dodd, Vol. I, 65, Vol. II, 72; Bodley Head Bernard Shaw: collected plays with their prefaces (7 vols), Reinhardt, London, 70-73. Add: Dodd, Mead & Co, 79 Madison Ave, New York, NY 10016.

LAURENCE, FRANK MICHAEL, b. Cincinnati, Ohio, Dec. 24, 42. AMERICAN & ENGLISH LITERATURE. B.A, Yale, 64; M.A, Univ. Toronto, 65; Ph.D.(Eng), Univ. Pa, 70. ASST. PROF. ENG, MISS. UNIV. WOMEN, 70- Hemingway; film; popular culture. Publ: Hollywood publicity and Hemingway's popular reputation, J. Popular Cult, summer 71; Hemingway's $5,000,000 plagiarism suit, Fitzgerald/Hemingway Annual, 74; Death in the matinee: the film endings of Hemingway's fiction, Lit/Film Quart, 74; plus one other. Add: Dept. of English, Mississippi University for Women, Columbus, MS 39701.

LAURITIS, JOSEPH A, C.S.Sp, b. Shenandoah, Pa, June 10, 09. ENGLISH. B.A, St. Mary's Sem.(Conn), 36, B.D, 40; A.M, Univ. Pa, 42, Ph.D, 58. Dir. pub. relat, DUQUESNE UNIV, 46-50, chmn. dept. Eng, 47-48, founder & chmn. dept. jour, 48-50, PROF. ENG, 58-, V.PRES. UNIV. RELAT. & SECY, 62-, dean col. arts & sci, 65-68. MLA; Mediaeval Acad. Am; Renaissance Soc. Am; NCTE. English literature, journalism, radio and television; public relations, fund-raising, development and college publications;

mediaeval language, linguistics and literature. Publ: Co-ed, Life of Our Lady, Duquesne, 61. Add: Dept. of English, Duquesne University, Pittsburgh, PA 15219.

LAUTERBACH, CHARLES EVERETT, b. Denver, Colo, Mar. 8, 34; m. 62. DRAMA. B.A, Univ. Colo, 56, M.A, 61; Ph.D.(theatre), Mich. State Univ, 66. Instr. drama, Univ. Colo, 61; asst. instr, Mich. State Univ, 63-64; asst. prof, Cent. Wash. State Col, 64-66; Univ. Calif, Riverside, 66-71; ASSOC. PROF. THEATRE, BOISE STATE UNIV, 71- Speech Commun. Asn; Am. Theatre Asn. The drama of Thornton Wilder; trends in dramatic styles in American drama of the 1920's; romantic drama. Add: Dept. of Theatre Arts, Boise State University, 1910 College Blvd, Boise, ID 83725.

LAUTZ, RICHARD, b. Buffalo, N.Y, June 28, 35. ENGLISH. B.S, State Univ. N.Y. Col. Buffalo, 56; M.A, Univ. Ark, 61; Ph.D.(Eng), Univ. Pa, 67. Instr. ENG, Univ. Pa, 64-67; asst. prof, State Univ. N.Y. Col. Brockport, 67-68; LA SALLE COL, 68-74, ASSOC. PROF, 74- U.S.A, 57-58, 61-62. MLA; NCTE. Nineteenth century novel; contemporary poetry. Add: Dept. of English, La Salle College, Philadelphia, PA 19141.

LAVERS, NORMAN CECIL, b. Albany, Calif, Apr. 21, 35; m. 67. ENGLISH LITERATURE, CREATIVE WRITING. B.A, San Francisco State Col, 60, M.A, 63; Ph.D.(Eng), Univ. Iowa, 69. Instr. ENG, North. Ill. Univ, 63-65; ASST. PROF, WEST. WASH. STATE COL, 70- The novel; 18th century English literature. Publ: Freud, The Clerkes tale, and literary criticism, Col. Eng, 12/64; The structure of Second skin, Novel: Forum on Fiction, spring 72; The action of Wuthering Heights, S.Atlantic Quart, winter 73. Add: Dept. of English, Western Washington State College, Bellingham, WA 98225.

LAVERTY, CARROLL DEE, b. Omaha, Nebr, Nov. 3, 06; m. 35; c. 2. ENGLISH. B.A, Univ. Colo, 33, M.A, 34; Ph.D, Duke Univ, 51. Instr, ENG, Univ. Colo, 34-37; from instr. to prof, TEX. A&M UNIV, 39-73, EMER. PROF, 73- U.S.N, 44-45. MLA; Hist. Sci. Soc; Am. Stud. Asn. American literature, especially Poe; the relations between science and literature; modern British literature—Yeats, Joyce, Eliot and Woolf. Publ: The death's head on the goldbug, Am. Lit; co-ed, The unity of English, Harper, 71; auth, Some touchstones of Hawthorne's style, Emerson Soc. Quart, 70; Vanity fair: the voice of the twenties, 72 & Edgar Allan Poe's vision of the future, 73, J. Am. Stud. Asn. Tex; plus others. Add: 503 Angus St, College Station, TX 77840.

LAVIN, HENRY ST. C, S.J, b. Richmond, Va, Jan. 4, 21. ENGLISH LITERATURE. A.B, Loyola Univ.(Ill), 44, M.A, 49; Ph.D, Fordham Univ, 58. Instr. Eng, St. Joseph's Col.(Pa), 53-54; assoc. prof. & chmn. dept, Loyola Col. (Md), 58-67; prof, Univ. Scranton, 67-70; St. Joseph's Col, 70-73; PRES, GEORGETOWN PREP. SCH, 73- MLA; NCTE; Col. Eng. Asn. Novels and plays of Henry Fielding. Publ: Transl, The heart of Ignatius, Helicon, 61. Add: Georgetown Preparatory School, Rockville, MD 20852.

LAVIN, JOSEPH ANTHONY, b. Wigan, Eng, Jan. 20, 32. ENGLISH. B.A, Univ. Birmingham, 54, Ph.D.(Eng), 63. Instr. ENG, Univ. Iowa, 56-60; lectr, Mt. Allison Univ, 61-62; asst. prof, UNIV. B.C, 62-64, assoc. prof, 64-72, PROF, 72- Can. Counc. leave fel, 68. MLA; Bibliog. Soc, Eng. Elizabethan drama; early printed books. Publ: Ed, James IV, 67, Friar Bacon & Friar Bungay, 69, Ernest Benn & Twelfth night, Macmillan, Can, 68; auth, Three owl blocks 1590-1640, 6/67 & Additions to McKerrow's Devices, 9/68, Library; William Barley, draper and stationer, Stud. Bibliog, 69. Add: Dept. of English, University of British Columbia, Vancouver 8, B.C, Can.

LAW, RICHARD ALEXANDER, b. Philadelphia, Pa, Apr. 4, 33; m. 55; c. 5. ENGLISH LITERATURE. B.S, W.Chester State Col, 58; M.A, Lehigh Univ, 61; Ph.D.(Eng), Temple Univ, 74. Asst, Lehigh Univ, 58-59; asst. prof. ENG, State Univ. Col, Fredonia, 60-62, KUTZTOWN STATE COL, 62-66, assoc. prof, 66-74, PROF, 74-, asst. dean lib. arts & sci, 70-73. Northeast Mod. Lang. Asn. Eighteenth century English. Publ: The respiration motif in Song of myself, Walt Whitman Rev, 12/64; The tragic vision of life in Macbeth, Stud. in Humanities, 12/69; Mock evangelism in Beckett's Watt, Mod. Lang. Stud, 8/72; plus others. Add: Dept. of English, Kutztown State College, Kutztown, PA 19530.

LAWALL, SARAH (SALLY) NESBIT, French, Comparative Literature. See Volume III, Foreign Languages, Linguistics & Philology.

LAWLER, DONALD LESTER, b. New York, N.Y, Mar. 19, 35; m. 57; c. 4. VICTORIAN & MODERN ENGLISH LITERATURE. B.S, Georgetown Univ, 56; M.A, Columbia Univ, 60; Ph.D.(Eng), Univ. Chicago, 69. Instr. ENG, Ill. Benedictine Col, 60-64, Loyola Univ. Chicago, 64-68; asst. prof, E.CAROLINA UNIV, 68-72, ASSOC. PROF, 73- MLA; James Branch Cabell Soc; Victorians Inst. Oscar Wilde bibliography; Wilde and the aesthetic movement; modern fantasy and science fiction. Publ: Ed, Bibliography of Oscar Wilde: a supplement to Stuart Mason, Kent. State Univ, 76; auth, Oscar Wilde's first manuscript of The picture of Dorian Gray, Stud. Bibliog, 72; Oscar Wilde in the new Cambridge bibliography of English literature, Papers Bibliog. Soc. Am, 73; The revisions of Dorian Gray, Victorians Inst. J, 74. Add: Dept. of English, East Carolina University, Greenville, NC 27834.

LAWLER, JOHN MICHAEL, Linguistics. See Volume III, Foreign Languages, Linguistics & Philology.

LAWLER, TRAUGOTT, b. Nyack, N.Y, Mar. 8, 37; m. 58; c. 4. ENGLISH. A.B, Col. Holy Cross, 58; M.A, Univ. Wis, 62; Woodrow Wilson & Danforth fels, Harvard, Ph.D.(Eng), 66. Instr. ENG, Yale, 66-67, asst. prof, 67-72; ASSOC. PROF, NORTHWEST. UNIV, EVANSTON, 72- U.S.M.C, 58-61, Res, 61-66, Capt. Medieval Acad. Am. Old and middle English; medieval Latin. Publ: Ed. & transl, Parisiana poetria of John of Garland, Yale Univ, 74. Add: Dept. of English, Northwestern University, Evanston, IL 60201.

LAWLESS, DONALD STEWART, b. Vernon, N.Y, Dec. 1, 18. ENGLISH. B.S, State Univ. N.Y. Col. Buffalo, 40; M.A, Niagara Univ, 42; Oxford, summer 48; M.L.S, Univ. Okla, 62; Ph.D.(Eng), Univ. Birmingham, 65. Instr. ENG, Purdue Univ, 46-50; asst. prof, LeMoyne Col, 56-58; vis. prof, St. Mary's Col, 65-66; ASST. PROF, Ball State Univ, 66-68; Niagara Univ, 68-69; AUBURN UNIV, 72- Ball State Univ. res. grant, 68; res. scholar Eng, Harvard, 71-72. U.S.A, 43-46. Malone Soc; MLA. The life and works of Philip Massinger; the plays of Shakespeare; Renaissance. Publ: Philip Massinger and his associates, 67 & ed, The poems of Philip Massinger, with critical notes, 68, Ball State Univ; Dante and Aquinas: a comparative study, Univ. Microfilms, 68; auth, Shakespeare's indebtedness to Homily XVII?, Shakespeare Newslett, 20: 13; The burial of Philip Massinger, 1/71 & Massinger's Secretary, 12/72, Notes & Queries; plus others. Add: 222 E. Tichenor Ave, Auburn, AL 36830.

LAWLIS, MERRITT EUGENE, b. Columbus, Ind, Nov. 22, 18; m. 46; c. 3. ENGLISH. A.B, Wabash Col, 40; M.A, Harvard, 47, Dexter fel, 51, Ph.D, 51. Instr. ENG, IND. UNIV, BLOOMINGTON, 51-53, asst. prof, 53-58, assoc. prof, 58-65, PROF, 65- U.S.A.A.F, 41-46, Lt. Col. MLA; Col. Eng. Asn. The Renaissance, especially the novel and Shakespeare. Publ: Apology for the middle class: the dramatic novels of Thomas Deloney, 60 & ed, Novels of Thomas Deloney, 61, Ind. Univ; ed, Elizabethan prose fiction, Odyssey, 67. Add: Dept. of English, Indiana University, Bloomington, IN 47401.

LAWN, BEVERLY BURGHARDT, b. New York, N.Y, Mar. 12, 38; m. 57; c. 2. AMERICAN & ENGLISH LITERATURE. B.A, Adelphi Univ, 59, M.A, 65; assistantship, State Univ. N.Y. Stony Brook, 67-68, summer res. grants & NDEA fel, 68-69, Ph.D.(Eng), 70. ASST. PROF. ENG, ADELPHI UNIV, 69- Lectr, Nassau Community Col, 72-73; Danforth assoc, 74- MLA; NCTE; Conf. Col. Compos. & Commun. Philosophy; psychology; women's studies. Publ: From temple to streets: the style of pragmatism, New Eng. Quart, 12/72. Add: Dept. of English, Adelphi University, South Ave, Garden City, NY 11530.

LAWNICZAK, DONALD ALOYSIUS, b. Toledo, Ohio, Feb. 26, 29; m. 49; c. 5. ENGLISH. B.A, Univ. Toledo, 56, M.A, 61; Ph.D.(Eng), Kent State Univ, 67. Instr. ENG, Kent State Univ, 61-67; asst. prof, EAST. MICH. UNIV, 67-71, ASSOC. PROF, 71- MLA. Seventeenth century English literature; history of literary criticism. Add: Dept. of English, Eastern Michigan University, Ypsilanti, MI 48197.

LAWRENCE, ELWOOD P, b. Detroit, Mich, July 7, 01; m. 26; c. 2. ENGLISH & AMERICAN LITERATURE. B.A, Kenyon Col, 26; Ph.D, West Reserve Univ, 40. Instr. ENG, Lehigh Univ, 26-27; MICH. STATE UNIV, 27-38, asst. prof, 38-41, assoc. prof, 42-57, prof, 57-72, EMER. PROF, 72- Rockefeller grant, 40-41; Smith-Mundt prof, 59-60; Agency Int. Develop. grant, 62-64. English and American literature, 1850-1930. Publ: Co-auth, Readings for today, Ronald, 51; auth, Henry George in Great Britain, Mich. State Univ, 58; The happy land: W.S. Gilbert as political satirist, Victorian Stud, 12/71; The banned Mikado: a topsy-turvey incident, Centennial Rev, 74. Add: Dept. of English, Michigan State University, East Lansing, MI 48824.

LAWRENCE, LARRY LEE, b. Red Lodge, Mont, May 23, 27; m. 49; c. 4. ENGLISH LITERATURE. B.A, Mont. State Univ, 51; M.A, Stanford Univ, 54, Ph.D.(Eng), 70. Instr. ENG, Univ. Ore, 56-63; asst. prof, CENT. WASH. STATE COL, 63-70, assoc. prof, 70-72, PROF, 72-, CHMN. DEPT, 72- AAUP; Col. Eng. Asn; Renaissance Soc. Am; NCTE. Shakespeare; Biblical literature; Elizabethan poetry. Publ: The library of English literature, Microform Rev, 4/73. Add: Dept. of English, Central Washington State College, Ellensburg, WA 98926.

LAWRENCE, LESLIE ANDREW, b. Bozeman, Mont, May 11, 22; m. 45; c. 2. ENGLISH. B.A, Mont. State Univ, 52, M.A, 56. Instr. ENG. & SPEECH, High Sch, Mont, 53-56; West. Mont. Col, 56-57, asst. prof, 57-58; instr, MONT. STATE UNIV, 58-61, asst. prof, 61-69, ASSOC. PROF, 69-, DIR. FORENSICS, 74- Assoc. ed, The Forensic, 59-63, ed, 63-67; pres, Mus. of Rockies, 65-68. U.S.A.A.F, 42-46, Sgt. West. Speech Commun. Asn; Am. Forensic Asn. Nineteenth century English literature; debate and argumentation. Add: Dept. of Speech Communication, Montana State University, Bozeman, MT 59715.

LAWRENCE, LIONEL HOUSTON, b. Millport, Scotland, June 21, 36; m. 59; c. 3. THEATRE. B.A, Queen's Univ.(Ont), 62; M.A, Univ. Ill, Urbana, 63. ASSOC. PROF. THEATRE & CHMN. DEPT, DALHOUSIE UNIV, 72- Canadian theatre history. Add: Dept. of Theatre, Dalhousie University, Halifax, N.S, Can.

LAWRENCE, ROBERT GILFORD, b. St. John, N.B, June 20, 23; m. 50. ENGLISH. B.A, Univ. N.B, 46, fel, 46-47, M.A, 47; Beaverbrook overseas scholar, 53; Humanities Res. Counc. Can. fel, 55-56; Ph.D.(Eng), Univ. Wis, 56. Asst. prof. ENG, Univ. West. Ont, 49-50; Univ. N.B, 50-52; United Col, Man, 54-55; instr, UNIV. VICTORIA (B.C), 56-57, asst. prof, 57-60, ASSOC. PROF, 60- MLA; NCTE; Humanities Asn. Can. Elizabethan and Jacobean drama; literary criticism; Canadian literature. Publ: Ed, The early seventeenth century drama, J.M. Dent, London, 63. Add: Dept. of English, University of Victoria, Victoria, B.C, Can.

LAWRY, JON S, b. Gas City, Kans, Dec. 3, 24; m. 49; c. 2. ENGLISH LITERATURE. B.S, Northwest. Univ, 48, M.A, 51, Ph.D, 55. Instr. ENG, Wesleyan Univ, 52-56; asst. prof, Ball State Univ, 56-60, assoc. prof, 60-65, PROF, 65-67; E.Carolina Univ, 67-68; Westminster Col.(Pa), 68-71; LAURENTIAN UNIV, 71- Res. grant, Ball State Univ, 62; Danforth Found. summer grant, 63; Fulbright-Hays lectr. Am. lit, Greece, 64-65. U.S.N.R, 43-46. MLA; Milton Soc. Am; Renaissance Soc. Am; Am. Soc. 18th Century Stud; Hopkins Soc. Renaissance; Milton; Ben Jonson. Publ: The shadow of heaven, 68 & Sidney's two arcadias, 72, Cornell; Twelfth night and Salt waves fresh in love, Shakespeare Stud, 72. Add: Dept. of English, Laurentian University, Sudbury, Ont. P3E 2C6, Can.

LAWS, GEORGE MALCOLM, JR, b. Philadelphia, Pa, Jan. 4, 19; m. 50; c. 4. ENGLISH. A.B, Univ. Pa, 42, A.M, 46, Ph.D, 49. Asst. instr. ENG, UNIV. PA, 42-44, instr, 44-55, asst. prof, 55-59, assoc. prof, 59-66, PROF, 66- MLA; Am. Folklore Soc.(secy-treas, 56). Nineteenth century English poetry and fiction; Victorian humor; British and American ballads and folksongs. Publ: Native American balladry, 50, rev. ed, 64, American balladry from British broadsides, 57 & Anglo-Irish balladry in North America, 62, Am. Folklore Soc; The British literary ballad: a study in poetic imitation, South. Ill. Univ, 72; Stories told in song: the ballads of America, In: Our living traditions, Basic Bks, 68; Death and Browning's dying bishop, In: Romantic and Victorian: studies in memory of William H. Marshall, Fairleigh Dickinson Univ, 71. Add: Dept. of English, University of Pennsylvania, Philadelphia, PA 19104.

LAWSON, HAROLD LEWIS, b. Pittsburg, Kans, Aug. 14, 40; m. 65. SPEECH, COMMUNICATION. B.S.E, Kans. State Teachers Col, 62, M.S, 63; Ph.D. (commun), Ohio State Univ, 67. Teacher, high sch, Kans, 62-64; instr. speech & debate, Southwest Mo. State Col, 64-65; teaching assoc, Ohio State Univ, 65-67, asst. prof, 67-69; SPEECH, West. Ill. Univ, 69-71; ASSOC. PROF, CAPITAL UNIV, 71- Mem, Dist. V Nat. Debate Tournament Comt, 66-; judge, Nat. Interstate Oratory Contest, 67. Speech Commun. Asn; Am. Forensic Asn; Nat. Soc. Stud. Commun; Midwest. Forensic Asn. Debate and forensics; rhetoric and public address: administration. Publ: An objective comparison of Kansas high school debate programs, Kans. State Speech J, 3/64. Add: Dept. of Speech, Capital University, Columbus, OH 43209.

LAWSON, JONATHAN N, b. Latrobe, Pa, Mar. 27, 41; m. 66; c. 2. ENGLISH LITERATURE. B.F.A, Tex. Christian Univ, 64, NDEA fel. & M.A, 66, univ. fel. & Ph.D.(Eng), 70; Tex. Christian Univ. Res. Found. grant, Brit. Mus, London, 69. Instr. Eng, Tex. Christian Univ, 69-70; ASST. PROF. ENG. & DIR. FRESHMAN ENG, ST. CLOUD STATE COL, 70- Minn. State Col. Fac. Res. Fund grant, England, summer 72. MLA; NCTE; Col. Eng. Asn; Rhet. Soc. Am; Am. Soc. 18th Century Stud. Eighteenth century British literature; pastoral and rural poetry; teaching of college English. Publ: Ed, Robert Bloomfield: collected poems 1800-1822, Scholars' Facsimiles, 71. Add: Dept. of English, St. Cloud State College, St. Cloud, MN 56301.

LAWSON, LEWIS ALLEN, b. Bristol, Tenn, Nov. 13, 31; m. 57; c. 2. ENGLISH. B.S, E.Tenn. State Col, 57, M.A, 59; Ph.D.(Eng), Univ. Wis, 64. Instr. ENG, E.Tenn. State Col, 59-60; UNIV. MD, COLLEGE PARK, 63-65, asst. prof, 65-67, assoc. prof, 67-71, PROF, 72- U.S.N, 51-54. MLA; S.Atlantic Mod. Lang. Asn. Southern and American literature. Publ: The added dimension, Fordham Univ, 66; The grotesque—comic in the Snopes trilogy, In: Hidden patterns, Macmillian, 66; Portrait of a culture in crisis, Tex. Quart, spring 67; The grotesque in recent Southern literature, In: Patterns of commitment in American literature, Univ. Toronto, 67. Add: Dept. of English, University of Maryland, College Park, MD 20742.

LAWSON, RICHARD ALAN, b. Saginaw, Mich, Sept. 26, 34; m. 63; c. 1. ENGLISH. B.A, Albion Col, 56; M.S.Ed, Bowling Green State Univ, 58, M.A, 59; Ph.D.(Eng), Tulane Univ, 66. Instr. ENG, SOUTH. ILL. UNIV, CARBONDALE, 63-66, asst. prof, 66-71, ASSOC. PROF, 71- MLA; Midwest Mod. Lang. Asn. Add: Dept. of English, Southern Illinois University, Carbondale, IL 62901.

LAWSON, RICHARD G, b. Durham, Ore, Feb. 18, 29; m. 50; c. 3. SPEECH, MASS COMMUNICATION. B.A, Wash. State Univ, 51; M.F.A, Yale, 57; Ph.D.(commun), Univ. Ill, 64. TV prod. coord, Univ. Ill, 54-60; ASST. PROF. TV & radio, Univ. Calif, Los Angeles, 64-66; TV, RADIO & FILM, UNIV. WIS-MADISON, 66- Instr, Univ. Ill, 57-66; commun. consult, Ascon Mgt, 65-66; consult. in educ. TV, Lockheed Aircraft Corp. & McCann-Erickson Advert, 66; prin. invest, Educ. Via Space Satellite Proj, Univ. Wis, 67- Nat. Asn. Educ. Broadcasters; Speech Commun. Asn; Asn. Prof. Broadcasting Educ. Instruction via space satellite; aesthetic aspects of television and film production. Publ: Teleconferencing in Wisconsin, Edsat Ctr, Madison, Wis, 71; A little perspective, please, J. Broadcasting, winter 70-71; On errorless communication, Wis. Libr. Bull, 3/71. Add: Dept. of Communication Arts, Vilas Hall, University of Wisconsin-Madison, Madison, WI 53706.

LAWSON, ROBERT NICHOL, b. Woodstock, Ill, Sept. 7, 28; m. 50; c. 4. ENGLISH. B.A, Univ. Kans, 56, M.A, 61, Ph.D.(Eng), 66. Instr. ENG, WASHBURN UNIV, 63-66, asst. prof, 66-68, assoc. prof, 68-72, PROF, 72- Danforth assoc, 68. U.S.A.F, 50-54, 61-62, Res, 62-, Maj. MLA; Bibliog. Soc. Univ. Va. Shakespeare bibliography. Add: Dept. of English, Washburn University of Topeka, Topeka, KS 66621.

LAWTON, DAVID LLOYD, English Creolized Languages. See Volume III, Foreign Languages, Linguistics & Philology.

LAWTON, ROBERT OSWALD, b. Greenwood, S.C, Dec. 28, 24; m. 46; c. 2. ENGLISH. A.B, Duke Univ, 46, M.A, 47, Ph.D.(Eng), 52; hon. Litt.D, Wofford Col, 69. Instr. ENG, FLA. STATE UNIV, 49-57, assoc. prof, 57-64, PROF, 64-, assoc. dean Col. Arts & Sci, 57-66, dean, 66-72. U.S.A, 42-44. S.Atlantic Mod. Lang. Asn; Shakespeare Asn. Am; Col. Eng. Asn. Shakespeare. Add: Dept. of English, Florida State University, Tallahassee, FL 32306.

LAYMAN, BEVERLY JOSEPH, b. Roanoke, Va, Sept. 20, 19; m. 48; c. 3. ENGLISH. B.A, Roanoke Col, 41; M.A, Univ. Va, 43; M.A, Harvard, 45, univ. fel, 45-49, Rosenwald fel, 48-49, Ph.D.(Eng), 53. Instr. ENG, WELLESLEY COL, 49-53, asst. prof, 53-59, assoc. prof, 59-65, PROF, 65- Mediaeval Acad. Am; Renaissance Soc. Am. Shakespeare; Elizabethan and Jacobean drama; English and Italian Middle Ages and Renaissance. Publ: Co-ed, British literature (2 vols), Heath, 3rd ed, 74; auth, The equilibrium of opposites in The white devil: a reinterpretation, PMLA, 9/59; Eloquence of pattern in Boccaccio's Tale of the falcon, Italica, 12/68; Tourneur's artificial noon: the design of The revenger's tragedy, Mod. Lang. Quart, 3/73. Add: 29 Dover Rd, Wellesley, MA 02181.

LAZARUS, ARNOLD LESLIE, b. Revere, Mass, Feb. 20, 14; m. 38; c. 4. ENGLISH. B.A, Univ. Mich, 35; M.A, Univ. Calif, Los Angeles, 41, Ford Found. fel, 54, Ed.D.(Am. stud. & Eng. educ), 57. Instr. Eng, Chaffey High Sch. & Jr. Col, Calif, 44-48; pub. schs, Santa Monica, Calif, 48-53; coord. freshman compos, Santa Monica City Col, 53-58; lectr. Eng. educ, Los Angeles State Col, 58-59; assoc. prof, Univ. Tex, 59-62; PROF. ENG. & EDUC, PURDUE UNIV, 62- Mem. Summer Insts. Planning Sect, Col. Entrance Exam. Bd. Eng. Comn, 61; co-ed, Quartet; consult. ed, Mod. Fiction Stud, 63; mem. exec. bd, Conf. Eng. Educ, 66-72; mem. bd. judges, Bk-of-Month Club writing fels, 68-71. U.S.A, 42-44. MLA; Conf. Res. Eng; Poetry Soc. Am. Currents of thought in modern fiction; contextual curricula in English. Publ: Co-auth, Adventures in modern literature, Harcourt, 56, 62, 70; Selected objectives for the English language arts, Houghton, 67; auth, Entertainments and valedictions (poetry), Windfall, 70; co-auth, Representative performance objectives in English, Ronald, 71; A glossary of literature and language, Grosset, 71, 72, 73; ed, Purdue project English literature units, Nat. Textbk, 71, 72, 73; co-auth, A suit of four (poetry), Purdue Univ, 73; auth, By the light of the lovely bookburning, New Repub, 3/61; Educational thought in modern literature, In: Foundations of education, Wiley, 63, 67; A house named Sylvia, Sat. Rev, 4/66. Add: Dept. of English, Purdue University, Lafayette, IN 47907.

LAZENBY, WALTER SYLVESTER, JR, b. Del Rio, Tex, Oct. 8, 30; m. 58; c. 3. ENGLISH, DRAMA. B.A, Southwest. at Memphis, 51; M.A, Yale, 53; Ph.D, Ind. Univ, 62. From instr. to asst. prof. Eng, Ky, Wesleyan Col, 54-56; instr, high sch, Tex, 56-57; from instr. to PROF. ENG, N.Tex. State Univ, 57-69; EAST. ILL. UNIV, 69- Fulbright lectr, Univ. Damascus, 65-66. U.S.N, 52-54, Ens. Midwest Mod. Lang. Asn. American stage adaptations of Dickens's novels; late Victorian and Edwardian drama; modern drama, continental, British and American. Publ: Arthur Wing Pinero, Twayne, 72; Paul Green (pamphlet), Steck-Vaughn, 70; Idealistic realist on the platform: Hamlin Garland, 63 & Exhortation as exorcism: Cotton Mather's sermons to murderers, 71, Quart. J. Speech. Add: Dept. of English, Eastern Illinois University, Charleston, IL 61920.

LAZIER, GILBERT NEIL, b. Pittsburgh, Pa, Jan. 31, 39; m. 61. THEATRE & DRAMATIC LITERATURE. B.A, Univ. Pittsburgh, 61, M.A, 63; Ph.D. (dramatic theory), South. Ill. Univ, 65. Asst. prof. speech & theatre & dir. theatre, Kans. State Teachers Col, 65-66; asst. prof. theatre, Univ. Fla, 66-67; Teachers Col, Columbia Univ, 67-69, assoc. prof, 69-70; THEATRE & DOCTORAL STUD, FLA. STATE UNIV, 70-73, PROF, 73- Consult, coop. prog. for cult. enrichment of stud. in isolated rural commun. in Kans, U.S. Off. Educ, 65-66; proj. youth theatre for disadvantaged, William C. Whitney Found, 68-69; educ. adv. proj. on develop. drama for low income areas of New York City, N.Y. State Arts Counc, 68-69; prin. investr, Health, Educ. & Welfare res. grant, Title IV, 69-71; mem. cent. comt, Am. Col. Theatre Festival, 70-73; consult, Rockefeller Found, 72-73; proj. dir, Nat. Ctr. Educ. Res. & Develop grant, 72-73. Am. Theatre Asn.(regional chmn, 68-69); Speech Commun. Asn.(prog. chmn, 66); Nat. Col. Players. Dramatic theory and criticism; empirical studies in theatrical aesthetics; directing theory. Publ: Co-auth, Psychology and drama, Empirical Res. in Theatre, 71 & A systematic analysis of developmental differences in dramatic behavior, Speech Monogr, 71; auth, Living newspaper 1970, Educ. Theatre J, 71; plus others. Add: Dept. of Theatre, Florida State University, Tallahassee, FL 32306.

LEACH, ELSIE, b. Santa Barbara, Calif, June 11, 25; m. 51. ENGLISH. B.A, Univ. Calif, Los Angeles, 45, M.A, 47, Ph.D, 51. Instr. ENG, Mt. St. Mary's Col.(Claif), 50-51; Univ. Calif, Los Angeles, 52-53; from instr. to asst. prof, Univ. Calif, Santa Barbara, 53-56; asst. prof, SAN JOSE STATE UNIV, 56-60, assoc. prof, 60-65, PROF, 65- Ford Fund Advan. Educ. fel, 51-52. MLA; NCTE. Seventeenth century literature; modern and American literature. Publ: Co-ed, Moral issues today, Wadsworth, 69; auth, Dylan Thomas' Ballad of the long-legged bait, Mod. Lang. Notes, 12/61; Alice in Wonderland in perspective, In: Aspects of Alice, 71; T.S. Eliot and the school of Donne, Costerus essays, Eng. & Am. Lang. & Lit, 72. Add: 12475 Briones Way, Los Altos Hills, CA 94022.

LEACH, JOSEPH, b. Weatherford, Tex, May 2, 21. AMERICAN LITERATURE. A.B, South. Methodist Univ, 42; Ph.D, Yale, 48. Assoc. prof. ENG, UNIV. TEX, EL PASO, 47-55, PROF, 55-, HEAD DEPT, 60- U.S.A, 46-47, Sgt. Am. Folklore Soc; Rocky Mountain Mod. Lang. Asn; NCTE; Col. Conf. Compos. & Commun; MLA. American cultural history. Publ: The typical Texan; Farewell to horseback, muleback, footback and prairie schooner; Bright particular star, Yale Univ, 70. Add: Dept. of English, University of Texas at El Paso, El Paso, TX 79968.

LEAKE, JANE ACOMB, Medieval History, Anglo-Saxon Studies. See Volume I, History.

LEARY, LEWIS, b. Blauvelt, N.Y, Apr. 18, 06; m. 32; c. 2. AMERICAN LITERATURE. B.S, Univ. Vt, 28, hon. LL.D, 63; A.M, Columbia Univ, 31, Ellis fel, 37-38, Ph.D, 40. Instr. ENG, Am. Univ. Beirut, 28-31; Univ. Miami, 35-37, asst. prof, 37-40, assoc. prof, 40-41; asst. prof, Duke Univ, 41-47, assoc. prof, 47-50, prof, 50-52; vis. prof, Columbia Univ, 51-52, prof, 52-68, chmn. dept. Eng. & comp. lit, 62-68; WILLIAM RAND KENAN, JR. PROF. ENG, UNIV. N.C, CHAPEL HILL, 68- Off. Strategic Serv, 42-45; consult. Eng, U.S. Off. Educ, 65-66. MLA; NCTE; Am. Stud. Asn; Century Asn; Grolier Club; PEN Club; Bibliog. Soc. Am; Eng. Inst. American literature to 1820; the transcendantalists; Mark Twain. Publ: That rascal Freneau: a study in literary failure, Rutgers Univ, 41 & Octagon, 66; Articles on American literature, 1900-1950, 54 & Articles on American literature, 1950-1968, 70, Duke Univ; Mark Twain, Univ. Minn, 60; John Greenleaf Whittier, Twayne, 62; Norman Douglas, Columbia Univ, 68; Mark Twain's Correspondence with Henry Huttleston Rogers, 1893-1909, Univ. Calif, 69; Southern excursion: essays on Mark Twain and others, La. Univ, 71; William Faulkner of Yoknapatawpha County, Crowell, 73. Add: 375 Tenney Circle, Chapel Hill, NC 27514.

LEARY, WILLIAM G, b. Minneapolis, Minn, Mar. 26, 15; m. 40; c. 2. ENGLISH. A.B, Univ. Calif, Los Angeles, 36, fel, 36-37, M.A, 38; Ph.D, Stanford Univ, 53. Teacher ENG, Kern County Union High Sch, Bakersfield, Calif, 38-41; assoc, Univ. Wash, 41-42; asst. prof, Calif. State Polytech. Col, 47-53; assoc. prof, CALIF. STATE UNIV, LOS ANGELES, 53-57, PROF, 57-, assoc. dean instr, 55-57. Vis. assoc. humanities, Educ. Testing Serv, Princeton, summer 63; vis. prof. Eng. educ, Stanford Univ, summer 64. Outstanding Prof. Award, Calif. State Univ, Los Angeles, 64-65. U.S.N.R, 42-47, Lt. American literature; Shakespeare; poetry. Publ: Co-auth, Think before you write, 51, Thought and statement, 56, 2nd ed, 60, 3rd ed, 69, co-ed, Ideas and patterns in literature (4 vols), 70 & co-auth,

From word to story, 71, Harcourt; Your language, McGraw, Bk. 5, 60, Bk. 6, 62. Add: Dept. of English, California State University, Los Angeles, Los Angeles, CA 90032.

LEASE, BENJAMIN, b. New York, N.Y, Apr. 29, 17; m. 57; c. 1. ENGLISH. B.A, Ind. Univ, 39; M.A, Univ. Chicago, 43, Ph.D.(Eng), 48. Instr. ENG, Ill. Inst. Technol, 46-48; asst. prof, Univ. Ill, Chicago, 48-55; from assoc. prof. to PROF, NORTHEAST. ILL. UNIV, 55-, chmn. humanities div, 61-63, assoc. chmn. dept. Eng, 68-70. Am. Philos. Soc. res. grant, 67; regional judge, Bk-of-the-Month Writing Fel. Prog, 68-69. MLA; Melville Soc. Nineteenth century American literature; Anglo-American literary relations. Publ: That wild fellow John Neal and the American literary revolution, Univ. Chicago, 73; The whole is a prose poem: an early review of The scarlet letter, Am. Lit, 3/72; John Bull versus Washington Irving: more on the Shakespeare Committee controversy, Eng. Lang. Notes, 6/72; plus others. Add: Dept. of English, Northeastern Illinois University, Bryn Mawr at St. Louis Ave, Chicago, IL 60625.

LEASKA, MITCHELL A, b. Putnam, Conn, Sept. 8, 34. ENGLISH LITERARY CRITICISM. B.A, Brown Univ, 56; M.A, Emerson Col, 58; Ph.D, N.Y. Univ, 68. Lectr. ENG, Brooklyn Col, 64-66; PROF, N.Y. UNIV, 66- MLA; NCTE. Linguistic stylistics, especially of Virginia Woolf and William Faulkner; rhetorical analysis in contemporary fiction. Publ: The voice of tragedy, Speller, 64; Virginia Woolf's lighthouse: a study in critical method, Columbia Univ. & Hogarth, 70; Virginia Woolf's The voyage out: character deduction and the function of ambiguity, Virginia Woolf Quart, winter 73. Add: 310 E. 55th St, New York, NY 10022.

LEATHERS, LYMAN LEE, b. Toledo, Ohio, Mar. 22, 29. AMERICAN STUDIES & LITERATURE. A.B, Cornell Univ, 52; M.A, Univ. Pa, 54, Ph.D. (Am. civilization), 63. Instr. Eng, Northeast. Univ, 56-59; ENG. & HUMANITIES, OHIO WESLEYAN UNIV, 61-63, asst. prof, 63-67, assoc. prof, 67-71, PROF, 71-, CHMN. DEPT. HUMANITIES, 73- Am. Stud. Asn; MLA; Midwest Mod. Lang. Asn; AAUP. Modern American poetry; poetry of Walt Whitman; novels of Herman Melville. Add: Dept. of Humanities, Ohio Wesleyan University, Delaware, OH 43015.

LEAVELL, FRANK HARTWELL, b. Memphis, Tenn, June 16, 28; div; c. 2. ENGLISH. B.A, Baylor Univ, 50, M.A, 53; South. Baptist Theol. Sem, 52-53, 55-56; Ph.D.(Eng), Vanderbilt Univ, 65. Instr. ENG, Campbellsville Col, 53-55; asst. prof, La. Col, 56-60; Ky. South. Col, 63-65; assoc. prof, BAYLOR UNIV, 65-71, PROF, 71- Soc. Stud. South. Lit; S.Cent. Mod. Lang. Asn. Mark Twain; Jesse Stuart; literature of the South. Publ: Desiderata in Jesse Stuart studies, Am. Bk. Collector, 2/66. Add: Dept. of English, Baylor University, Waco, TX 76703.

LEAVITT, CHARLES LOYAL, b. Randolph, Maine, Apr. 30, 21; m. 51, 69. ENGLISH. B.S, Gorham State Col, 46; M.A, Boston Univ, 47; Ph.D, Univ. Wis, 61; M.L.S, Columbia Univ, 69. Teacher jr. high sch, Vanceboro, Maine, 41-42; prin. & teacher, elem. sch, York Village, 45-47; instr. Eng. & hist, Endicott Jr. Col, 47-48; ENG, Lyndon Teachers Col, 48-53, 54-55, assoc. prof, 55; instr, Wayne State Univ, 59-61; asst. prof, Montclair State Col, 61-67, assoc. prof, 67-68; v.pres, secy, mem. bd. dir. & dir. educ, Universal Learning Corp, New York, 68-69; assoc. dir. admis, Sarah Lawrence Col, 70-71; ASST. PROF. ENG, BLOOMFIELD COL, 71-, ASST. DEAN SPEC. PROGS, 73- Scholar, Nat. Audubon Camp, 47; teaching asst. Eng, Univ. Wis, 53-54, 55-59; mem. ed. bd. of consult, Monarch Press, 64-; lectr. theater, 73- U.S.A, 42-45. MLA; NEA. Nathaniel Hawthorne; theater; travel. Publ: Literature study guides for: Scarlet letter, 64, The house of the seven gables and The marble faun, 65, Ethan Frome, 65, The deerslayer, 65, The last of the Mohicans, 65, The pathfinder, 66, The pioneers, 66, The prince and the pauper, 66, A Connecticut Yankee in King Arthur's court, Life on the Mississippi, and The mysterious stranger, 66 & co-auth, Literature study guide for The return of the native, 64, Monarch; London, Universal Learning Corp, 69; Leatherstocking: an existentialist? Quarterly, fall 66. Add: Office of Continuing Education, Bloomfield College, Bloomfield, NJ 07003.

LeBEL, EUGENE CARLISLE, b. Sarnia, Ont, July 27, 99. ENGLISH. B.A, Univ. Toronto, 24; A.M, Univ. Chicago, 31; hon. LL.D, Univ. West. Ont, 61, Univ. Windsor, 66. Lectr. Eng, St. Michael's Col, Ont, 31-36, prof, 36-39; Univ. Sask, 39-40, Eng. & medieval hist, 40-41; prof. Eng. & hist. & dean, Univ. Windsor, 47-52, pres. & v.chancellor, 52-63, pres, 63-64; prin, St. Mark's Col, Univ. B.C, 64-71; RETIRED. Asn. Univs. & Cols. Can. Medieval theology in Spenser's Hymnes; the conversion of John Dryden. Add: St. Michael's College, University of Toronto, 50 St. Joseph St, Toronto 5, Ont, Can.

LEBOFSKY, DENNIS STANLEY, Linguistics, History & Structure Of English. See Volume III, Foreign Languages, Linguistics & Philology.

LEBOWITZ, NAOMI GORDON, b. Feb. 6, 32; U.S. citizen; m. 53; c. 2. ENGLISH, COMPARATIVE LITERATURE. B.A, Wellesley Col, 53; M.A, Wash. Univ, 55, Ph.D.(Eng), 62. Asst. Eng, WASH. UNIV, 58-59, instr, 60-65, asst. prof. ENG. & COMP. LIT, 65-66, assoc. prof, 67-72, PROF, 72- Am. Asn. Univ. Women fel, 66-67; Guggenheim Found. fel, 73- The modern novel; the novel of France, England, America, Italy, and Germany; Russia from the middle of the 19th century to the present day. Publ: Auth, The imagination of loving: Henry James, Wayne State Univ, 65; Humanism and the absurd in the modern novel, Northwest. Univ, 71; Balzac and Dickens, In: Essays on European literature, Washington Univ, 72; plus four others. Add: Dept. of English, Washington University, St. Louis, MO 63130.

LECHNER, JOAN MARIE, O.S.U, b. Nebraska City, Nebr, July 25, 13. ENGLISH. B.A, Loras Col, 50; Ph.D, St. Louis Univ, 60. Instr. Eng. & Latin, St. Joseph High Sch, Owensboro, Ky, 36-48; commercial Eng, St. Catherine High Sch, New Haven, 48-50; prin, St. Francis High Sch, Loretto, 50-53; PRES, BRESCIA COL.(KY), 60-, treas, 53-56. MLA. English literature. Publ: Renaissance concepts of the commonplaces, Pageant, 62; E.E. Cummings and Mother Nature, Renascence Mag, 60. Add: Brescia College, 120 W. Seventh, Owensboro, KY 42301.

LECKY, ELEAZER, b. Mars, Pa, Dec. 28, 03. ENGLISH LITERATURE. A.B, Univ. Pittsburgh, 23, LL.B, 27; A.M, Harvard, 24; Ph.D, Cornell Univ, 38. Instr, Univ. Pittsburgh, 25-29; Columbia Univ, 31-36; from asst. prof, to prof. ENG, UNIV. SOUTH. CALIF, 38-70, EMER. PROF, 70- Col. Eng. Asn; NCTE. Semantics; drama; literary criticism. Publ: New theatre, Mod. Drama, 12/63; The enduring Shakespeare, Teachers Col. Rec, 4/64; Rhetoric, semantics, and composition, In: Rhetoric: theories for application, Nat. Counc. Teachers Eng, 67. Add: 7029 Senalda Rd, Los Angeles, CA 90068.

LeCLAIR, MARGARET FOSTER, b. Elmora, Pa, Sept. 7, 11; m. 45. ENGLISH. B.A, Ohio Wesleyan Univ, 33; M.A, Ohio State Univ, 34, Ph.D.(Eng), 40. Librn, Eng. Dept, Ohio State Univ, 34-41, instr. Eng, 41-44; asst. prof, N.Y. State Col. Teachers, Buffalo, 44-46; instr, Carnegie Inst. Technol, 46-47, asst. prof, 47-53, assoc. prof, 53-60, head dept. gen. stud, 55-56, dean Margaret Morrison Carnegie Col, 56-60; PROF. ENG, BEAVER COL, 60-, DEAN GRAD. STUD, 73-, dean col, 60-73. Ford Found. fel, 52-53. MLA; NCTE; Col. Eng. Asn. Twentieth century American and English poetry; Rimbaud; Melville. Publ: Hart Crane: poet of the machine age, Carnegie Press; A book for freshmen, J. Higher Educ. Add: Dept. of English, Beaver College, Easton and Church Rd, Glenside, PA 19038.

LE COMTE, EDWARD SEMPLE, b. New York, N.Y, May 28, 16; m. 45; c. 1. ENGLISH LITERATURE. A.B, Columbia Univ, 39, Proudfit fel, 39-42, A.M, 40, Ph.D, 43. Instr. ENG, Columbia Univ, 43-45; asst. prof, Univ. Calif, 45-48; Columbia Univ, 48-56, assoc. prof, 56-64; PROF, STATE UNIV. N.Y. ALBANY, 64- State Univ. N.Y. Res. Found. fac. fel, 65-67. Auth Guild; Milton Soc. Am. Interrelation of classical and English literature; Milton; biography. Publ: Endymion in England: the literary history of a Greek myth, King's Crown Press, 44; Yet once more: verbal and psychological pattern in Milton, Lib. Arts, 53; Dictionary of last words, Philos. Libr 55; The long road back, Beacon, 57 & Gollancz, London, 58; He and she, Obolensky, 60; Milton dictionary, Philos. Libr, 61, Peter Owen, London, 61; Grace to a witty sinner: a life of Donne, Walker, 65 & Gollancz, London, 65; The notorious Lady Essex, Dial, 69 & Robert Hale, London, 70; The man who was afraid, Crown, 69; Milton's unchanging mind, 73 & Poets' riddles: Shakespeare, Donne, Milton, Marvell, 74, Kennikat; New light on the Haemony passage in Comus, Philol. Quart, 42; Homer transprosed, Class. J, 50; Jack Donne: from rake to husband, In: Just so much honor, Penn. State Univ, 72. Add: Box 113, North Egremont, MA 01252.

LEDBETTER, KENNETH LEE, b. Willow Springs, Mo, Dec. 3, 31; m. 53; c. 3. AMERICAN LITERATURE. A.B, Cent. Methodist Col, 56; M.A, Univ. Ill, 57, Ph.D.(Eng), 63. Asst. Eng, Univ. Ill, 56-59; assoc. prof, Ill. State Univ, 59-66; PROF. AM. LIT, UNIV. WATERLOO, 66- Vis. prof. Am. lit, Am. Univ. Cairo, 69-71. U.S.A, 53-55. MLA; Can. Asn. Am. Stud. Publ: Henry Roth's Call it sleep: the revival of a proletarian novel, Twentieth Century Lit, fall 66; The journey of John Dos Passos, Humanities Asn. Bull, fall 67; Marxism and American literature, In: The great depression, Copp-Clark, 69; plus two others. Add: Dept. of English, University of Waterloo, Waterloo, Ont. Can.

LEDERER, KATHERINE, b. Trinity, Tex, Mar. 19, 32; m. 61; c. 2. ENGLISH. B.A, Sam Houston State Col, 52; M.A, Univ. Ark, 58, Ph.D.(Eng), 67. Teacher, pub. schs, Tex, 54-56; asst. ENG, Univ. Ark, 56-59, instr, 59-60; SOUTHWEST MO. STATE UNIV, 60-65, asst. prof, 65-67, assoc. prof, 67-68, PROF, 68- MLA; AAUP. American drama and novel. Publ: Lillian Hellman, Twayne. Add: Dept. of English, Southwest Missouri State University, 901 S. National, Springfield, MO 65802.

LEDERMAN-BIRNBAUM, MARIE JEAN, b. Brooklyn, N.Y, Dec. 28, 35; m. 70; c. 1. CONTEMPORARY LITERATURE. B.S, N.Y. Univ, 57, fel, 63-65, Ph.D, 66; M.A, Brooklyn Col, 63. Teacher ENG, N.Y.C. Bd. Educ, 57-59; instr, N.Y. Univ, 65-66; lectr, City Univ. Ctr, New York City Community Col, 66-67, asst. prof, 67-68; Univ. Ctr. Search Educ, Elevation & Knowledge Prog, 68-69; BARUCH COL, 69-72, ASSOC. PROF, 73- NCTE; Am. Comt. Irish Stud. Teaching remedial composition and writing; short stories and essays on general topics. Publ: Hip language and urban college English, Col. Compos. & Commun, 10/69; A comparison of student projections: magic and the teaching of writing, Col. Eng, 2/73; Open admissions and teaching English: birds caged and uncaged, Educ. Forum, 3/73; plus others. Add: Dept. of English, Baruch College, 17 Lexington Ave, New York, NY 10010.

LE DUC, DON RAYMOND, b. Milwaukee, Wis, Apr. 7, 33; m. 59; c. 2. MASS COMMUNICATION & INTERNATIONAL COMMUNICATION LAW. B.S, Univ. Wis, 59, Ph.D.(mass commun), 70; J.D, Marquette Univ, 62. Pvt. pract. law, Arnold, Murray & O'Neill, 62-66; chief counsel, Dept. Ins, State of Wis, 66-68; asst. prof. COMMUN, Univ. Md, 70-71; ASSOC. PROF, Ohio State Univ, 71-73; UNIV. WIS-MADISON, 73- Ford fel, 63-64; res. award, col. social & behav. sci, Ohio State Univ, 72; legal consult, Battelle Mem. Labs, 72-; mem. cable-TV adv. comt, Fed. Commun. Comn, 72- Mil.Intel, U.S.A, 54-57. Fed. Commun. Bar Asn.(mem. pub. comt, 70-); Broadcast Educ. Asn.(chmn. regulation comt, 72-). Law and communications policy; comparative media systems; innovation and media functions. Publ: Cable television and the FCC, Temple Univ, 73; ed, Issues in broadcast regulation, Broadcast Educ. Asn, 74; auth, Cable TV: evolution or revolution in electronic mass media?, Annals, 3/72; Broadcast legal documentation: a four dimensional guide, J. Broadcasting, spring 73; Communication revolution and the European press: after us the deluge?, Jour. Quart, summer 74. Add: Dept. of Communication Arts, Vilas Communication Hall, University of Wisconsin-Madison, Madison, WI 53706.

LEE, ALFRED MATTHEW, b. Louisville, Ky, July 1, 38; m. 70; c. 1. POETRY, MODERN AMERICAN NON-FICTION. B.A, Yale, 60; M.F.A, Univ. Iowa, 63. Sr. master, T.I. Ahmadiyya Sec. Sch, Ghana, 62-63; master, Oda Sec. Sch, 63-64; instr. ENG, NEWARK COL. ENGINEERING, 67-71, ASST. PROF, 71- MLA; Col. Eng. Asn. Publ: Ed, The major young poets, World Publ, 71; auth, Time, Ecco, 74. Add: Dept. of Humanities, Newark College of Engineering, 323 High St, Newark, NJ 07102.

LEE, ALVIN A, b. Woodville, Ont, Sept. 30, 30; m. 57; c. 5. ENGLISH LANGUAGE & LITERATURE. B.A, Univ. Toronto, 53, M.A, 58. Can. Counc.

fel, 60-61, Ph.D, 61; B.D, Victoria Univ, 57. Asst. prof. ENG, McMASTER UNIV, 60-67, assoc. prof, 67-70, PROF, 70-, V.PRES. ACAD, 74-, dean grad. stud, 71-73. Can. Counc. sr. fel, 66-67. Mediaeval Acad. Am; MLA; Asn. Can. Univ. Teachers Eng. Old English poetry; contemporary Canadian poetry. Publ: James Reaney, Twayne, 68; auth, The guest-hall of Eden; four essays on the design of Old English poetry, Yale Univ, 72; co-auth, Wish and Nightmare, 72, Circle of Stories, one, 72; Circle of stories, two, 72: The garden and the wilderness, 73, The temple and the ruin, 73 & The peaceable kingdom, 74, Harcourt; auth, Heorot and the guest-hall of Eden, Mediaeval Scand, 70. Add: Dept. of English, McMaster University, Hamilton, Ont. L8S 4M4, Can.

LEE, BERTA GRATTAN, b. Iola, Kans. ENGLISH, LINGUISTICS. B.S, Okla. State Univ, 34; M.A, Univ. Miami, 66; fel, Univ. Nev, Reno, 67-70, Ph.D. (Eng), 70. Instr. humanities, Univ. Miami, 65-66; Eng, Miami-Dade Jr. Col, 66-67; ASST. PROF. LING. & ENG, IND. STATE UNIV, TERRE HAUTE, 70- Mediaeval Soc. Am; MLA; AAUP; Ling. Soc. Am. Medieval and Renaissance literature; medieval language; linguistics, semantics. Publ: Co-auth, A storage and retrieval system for documents in educational technology, Univ. Miami, 64; auth, Linguistic evidence for the priority of the French text of the Ancrene Wisse, Mouton, The Hague, (in press); William Bartram: naturalist or poet, Early Am. Lit, fall 72. Add: Dept. of English, Parsons Hall 212, Indiana State University, Terre Haute, IN 47809.

LEE, BRIANT HAMOR, b. New Haven, Conn, May 6, 38; m. 62; c. 2. DRAMA, HISTORY OF THEATRE. A.B, Adelphi Univ, 61; cert, Acad. Belle Arti, Rome, 61; M.A, Indiana Univ, 62; Ph.D.(theatre), Mich. State Univ, 70. Instr. theatre, Am. Int. Col, 62-63; consult, Kliegl Bros, Stage Lighting, New York, 63-64; ASST. PROF. THEATRE, Bradley Univ, 67-68; BOWLING GREEN STATE UNIV, 68- Am. Soc. Theatre Res; U.S. Int. Theatre Technol; Speech Commun. Asn; Am. Theatre Asn. History of theatre; theatrical production; scenic design. Publ: Anything can be made of corrugated, 3/73 & Protection and preservation of theatre graphics, 10/73; Theatre design & Technol; The box set, late eighteenth scenic convention, J. Ohio Univ. Theatre Collection, 73-74. Add: Dept. of Speech, University Theatre, Bowling Green State University, Bowling Green, OH 43403.

LEE, CHARLES, b. Philadelphia, Pa, Jan. 2, 13; m. 52; c. 2. ENGLISH. B.A, Univ. Pa, 33, M.A, 36, Ph.D, 55. Lit. ed, Boston Herald Traveler, 37-40; Phila. Rec, 40-46; contrib. ed, Phila. Evening Bull, 47-49; from assoc. prof. to PROF. ENG. & DIR. UNDERGRAD. JOUR. PROG, UNIV. PA, 49-, prof. commun. & v.dean, Annenberg Sch, 59-65. Contemporary short story; feature writing; reviewing and criticism. Publ: The hidden public, Doubleday, 58; ed, The state of the nation, Univ. Pa, 62; auth, Sevens come eleven, Livingston, 72. Add: Dept. of English, University of Pennsylvania, Philadelphia, PA 19104.

LEE, CHARLOTTE IRENE, b. Denver, Colo, Aug. 13, 09. SPEECH. B.A, Univ. Wichita, 30, M.A, 32; Ph.D.(interpreation), Northwest. Univ, 45. Instr. French & speech, Monte Cassino, 32-36; speech, St. Mary-of-the-Woods Col, 36-40; chmn. dept, William Woods Col, 40-41; teaching asst. INTERPRETATION, NORTHWEST. UNIV, 42-45, instr, 45-48, asst. prof, 48-53, assoc. prof, 53-60, PROF, 60- Speech Commun. Asn. Modern poetry, especially prosody, structure and sound pattern. Publ: Oral interpretation, Houghton; Choric dramas, Baker; Speech in action, Scott. Add: 1822 Sheridan Rd, Evanston, IL 60201.

LEE, CLARENCE PENDLETON, b. Varner, Ark, May 26, 13. COMPARATIVE LITERATURE. A.B, Washington & Lee Univ, 32, A.M, 33; Rhodes scholar, Oxford, 33-35, B.A, 35, M.A, 72; Univ. Heidelberg, 35. Asst. prof. ENG, Southwest. at Memphis, 36-40; instr, Harvard, 40-44; assoc. prof, Clark Univ, 45; asst. U.S. cult. relat. attache, Brussels, 45-46; asst. prof. Univ. Tenn, 46-55; Fulbright prof, Univ. Athens, 55-56; assoc. prof, JACKSONVILLE UNIV, 62-65, PROF, 65- MLA; S.Atlantic Mod. Lang. Asn. Novels and short stories. Publ: The unwilling journey, 40 & High noon, 43, Macmillan; co-auth, Readings for citizens at war, Harper, 43; Athenian adventure, Knopf, 57; Library resources, Prentice-Hall, 72. Add: Dept. of English, Jacksonville University, Jacksonville, FL 32211.

LEE, GRACE FARRELL, b. Providence, R.I; m. 69. ENGLISH & AMERICAN LITERATURE. B.A, Emmanuel Col.(Mass), 69; M. A, Brown Univ, 70, Ph.D.(Eng), 73. Asst. ENG, Brown Univ, 70-72; ASST. PROF, HOLLINS COL, 73- MLA; Poe Stud. Asn; Col. Eng. Asn; Am. Asn. Univ. Women. Myth and folklore; fiction; literature and painting. Publ: The quest of Arthur Gordon Pym, South. Lit. J, spring 72; The hidden god of Isaac Bashevis Singer, Hollins Critic, 12/73. Add: Dept. of English, Hollins College, VA 24020.

LEE, HECTOR, b. Decatur, Tex, May 16, 08. AMERICAN FOLKLORE. A.B, Univ. Utah, 35; A.M, Univ. Calif, 38; Rockefeller fel, 44; Ph.D, Univ. N.Mex, 47. Instr. Eng, Univ. Utah, 37-43, asst. prof. & dir. Utah Humanities Res. Found, 45-47; prof. Eng. & dean instr, Chico State Col, 47-61; CALIF. STATE COL, SONOMA, 61-74, EMER. PROF. ENG, 74- Chmn. sr. comn. accreditation, West. Col. Asn, 66-69; pres, West. Asn. Schs. & Cols, 67-69. Am. Folklore Soc. The three nephites in American folklore; American literature. Publ: Co-auth, Lore of our land, Harper, 63; auth, Folklore of the Mormon country (rec), Folk-Legacy Rec, 64. Add: California State College, Sonoma, Rohnert Park, CA 94928.

LEE, HENRY GLENN, b. Fremont, Nebr, May 8, 22; m. 47; c. 2. THEATRE ARTS, SPEECH. B.A, Univ. Nebr, 47; M.A, State Univ. Iowa, 49; Univ. Wis, summers 51-53; Ph.D.(theatre arts), Tulane Univ, 67. Instr, Lincoln Col, 49-52; assoc. prof. SPEECH & THEATRE, Cent. Mo. State Col, 52-55; asst. prof, Univ. N.Dak, 55-58, ASSOC. PROF, 58-68; TEMPLE UNIV, 68- U.S.N.R, 43-46, Lt.(jg). Am. Theatre Asn; Am. Soc. Theatre Res. Theatre aesthetics; Maxwell Anderson. Publ: Introd, Volpone, Chandler Ed. Drama, 61. Add: 637 Old Lancaster Rd, Bryn Mawr, PA 19010.

LEE, HERBERT GRANT, b. Lockhart, S.C, Mar. 11, 10; m. 70. ENGLISH. B.S, West. Carolina Teachers Col, 41; M.A, Univ. N.C, 47; Northwest. Univ, 47-50. Part-time lectr, Northwest. Univ, 47-49; head dept. Eng, UNIV, 55- Amicus Award, Ind. Univ. Kokomo, 69. U.S.A.A.F, 42-45. Shakespeare Asn. Am. Shakespeare; Milton. Add: Dept. of English, Taylor University, Upland, IN 46989.

LEE, JAMES WARD, b. Birmingham, Ala, Feb. 12, 31; m. 52; c. 2. ENGLISH. B.S, Mid. Tenn. State Univ, 56; M.A, Auburn Univ, 57, Ph.D.(Eng), 64; Univ. Ark, 58-59. Instr. ENG, N.TEX. STATE UNIV, 58-64, asst. prof, 64-66, assoc. prof, 66-70, PROF, 70- Ed, Stud. in Novel, 66; gen. ed, Southwest writers ser, 66; South. writers ser, 67; mem, Nat. Humanities Fac, 73-74. U.S.N, 50-54. MLA; Southwest. Am. Lit. Asn.(secy, 69-). Contemporary British literature; the novel; folklore. Publ: Co-auth, J.D. Salinger and the critics, 62 & Poetry: a thematic approach, 68, Wadsworth; auth, William Humphrey, Steck, 67; John Braine, Twayne, 68; co-auth, Joyce Cary: a selected checklist, Mod. Fiction Stud, 63; auth, The penny dreadful as a folksong, Publ: Tex. Folklore Soc, 65; Trollope's clerical concerns, Hartford Stud, 69; plus one other. Add: Dept. of English, North Texas State University, 7801 North Texas Station, Denton, TX 76203.

LEE, LAWRENCE, b. Gadsden, Ala, Jan. 3, 03; m. 33; c. 1. LITERATURE. B.S, Univ. Va, 24; M.A, Harvard, 38. Instr. Eng. & French, Univ. Va, 30-38, asst. prof. French, 38-42; assoc. prof. Eng, Univ. Pittsburgh, 49-53, prof, 53-73; RETIRED. Mem. fac, Yeats Int. Summer Sch, Sligo, Ireland, 67. U.S.N.R, 42-45, Lt. Comdr. European fiction; 20th century poetry; comparative literature; the concept of tragedy. Publ: Tomb of Thomas Jefferson and other poems & Monticello and other poems, Scribner; American as Faust, 65, The voice of the Furies, 69 & Cockcrow at night, The heroic journey and 18 other stories, 73, Boxwood; The Cretan flute and other poems, Dolmen, Dublin, 68; La dame a la licorne, Cathedral Imprints, 72. Add: 510 Roslyn Pl, Pittsburgh, PA 15232.

LEE, LAWRENCE LYNN, b. Vernal, Utah, Mar. 4, 24; m. 55. ENGLISH. B.A, Univ. Utah, 50, M.A, 52, Ph.D.(Eng), 59. Instr. ENG, N.Mex. Highlands Univ, 55-56; asst. prof, Defiance Col, 58-62; from assoc. prof. to PROF, WEST. WASH. STATE COL, 62- Ed, Concerning Poetry. U.S.A, 43-46. Modern American novel; 20th century English and American poetry. Publ: Walter Van Tilburg Clark, In: Western writer ser, Boise State Col, 73; W.V.T. Clark's American dream, Col. Eng. 2/65; Nabokov's political dream, Wis. Stud. Cont. Lit, spring 67. Add: Dept. of English, Western Washington State College, Bellingham, WA 98225.

LEE, MARK W, b. Akron, Ohio, Jan. 23, 23; m. 43; c. 4. GENERAL SPEECH. B.A, Wheaton Col, 46, fel, 46-48, M.A, 52; Univ. Minn, 55-56; fel, Univ. Wash, 61-62, Ph.D.(rhetoric, pub. address), 66. Chmn. dept. speech, Northwest. Col, 48-57; assoc. prof. SPEECH & DRAMA, Whitworth Col.(Wash), 57-67, prof, 67-70, chmn. dept, 63-70; PRES, SIMPSON COL.(CALIF), 70- Consult, Standard Oil, Credit Union League, Oil Heat Inst. & Off. Emergency Planning, 67-70. Speech Commun. Asn; Am. Forensic Asn; West. Speech Commun. Asn. Pastoral theology. Publ: The minister and his ministry, 60 & Marriage is a family affair, 70, Zondervan. Add: Office of the President, Simpson College, 801 Silver Ave, San Francisco, CA 94134.

LEE, RICHARD RUSSELL, b. Minneapolis, Minn, Jan. 30, 25; m. 55; c. 3. ENGLISH EDUCATION. B.A, San Diego State Col, 60, M.A, 61; Ph.D.(Eng. educ), Stanford Univ, 68. Educ. off. II, Ministry Educ, Govt. Tanzania, 61-63; teacher, high sch, Calif, 63-64; instr. Eng, Palomar Col, 64-65; res. assoc, Inst. Human Learning, FLA. STATE UNIV, 67-68; ASST. PROF. COMMUN, 68- Speech Commun. Asn. Language behavior; instructional development. Publ: Co-auth, Physiological responses to feedback, 6/70 & auth, Performance criteria for teachers, 6/73, T.E.S.O.L. Quart; Dialect perception: a review and re-evaluation, Quart. J. Speech, 12/71. Add: Dept. of Communication, Florida State University, Tallahassee, FL 32306.

LEE, ROBERT CHARLES, b. Columbia, S.C, Nov. 7, 03. ENGLISH. B.S, Catawba Col, 33; A.B, Ouachita Col, 36; A.M, Univ. Fla, 38; Ph.D, George Peabody Col, 43. Instr. Eng, Univ. Tenn, 38-41; head dept, Asheville Col, 42-43; instr. Navy V prog, Univ. S.C, 43-44; head dept. ENG, Tift Col, 44-47; asst. prof, UNIV. FLA, 47-56, ASSOC. PROF, 56- Mem, Baltimore Symphony Orchestra, 26. NCTE; S.Atlantic Mod. Lang. Asn. Portrayal of the college in modern American novels; treatment of religion in the novels of Sinclair Lewis. Add: Dept. of English, University of Florida, Gainesville, FL 32601.

LEE, ROBERT EDSON, b. Sac City, Iowa, May 4, 21; m. 49; c. 2. ENGLISH. B.S, Iowa State Col, 43; M.A, Univ. Chicago, 49; Ph.D.(Am. stud), State Univ. Iowa, 55. Instr. ENG, Vassar Col, 49-51; teaching assoc, State Univ. Iowa, 53-55; instr, UNIV. COLO, BOULDER, 55-59, asst. prof, 59-61, assoc. prof, 61-66, PROF, 66- Univ. Colo. fac. fel, 65; Fulbright-Hays lectr, Univ. Warsaw, 67-68. U.S.N.R, 43-46, Lt. MLA. American literature. Publ: From West to East, Univ. Ill, 66; To the war, Knopf, 68. Add: Dept. of English, University of Colorado, Boulder, CO 80302.

LEE, RONALD JAMES, b. Austin, Minn, Feb. 8, 38; m. 61; c. 2. ENGLISH, HUMANITIES. B.A, St. Olaf Col, 59; Rhodes scholar, Oxford & M.A, 61; Danforth fel, Stanford Univ. & Ph.D.(Eng, humanities), 67. Instr. ENG, St. Olaf Col, 61-62; asst. prof, Trinity Col.(Conn), 65-69; ASSOC. PROF, ST. OLAF COL, 69- MLA. Medieval and Renaissance drama; drama and religion; modern dance. Add: Dept. of English, St. Olaf College, Northfield, MN 55057.

LEE, WARREN MARION, b. Mt. Etna, Iowa, Oct. 24, 08; m. 33; c. 2. CREATIVE PLAYWRITING. A.B, State Univ. Iowa, 31, A.M, 32, Rockefeller fel, 36-38, Ph.D, 41. Theatre tech. dir. Univ. Minn, 33-36; instr. DRAMATIC ART, UNIV. S.DAK, 38-39, asst. prof, 39-41, assoc. prof, 41-44, PROF, 44-, dean col. fine arts, 52-68; dir, Black Hills Fine Arts Ctr, 68-74. Vis. lectr, State Univ. Iowa, 36. Am. Theatre Asn; Am. Nat. Theatre & Acad; Nat. Theatre Conf. Contemporary and historic material. Publ: Troubleshooter; Shave and a haircut; The legend of Devil's Gulch. Add: College of Fine Arts, University of South Dakota, Vermillion, SD 57069.

LEECH, CLIFFORD, b. London, Eng, Jan. 16, 09; m. 61. ENGLISH. B.A, Univ. London, 30, M.A, 32, Ph.D.(Eng), 35; hon. Dr, Univ. Clermont-Ferrand, 62; hon. Litt.D, Acadia Univ, 69. Lectr. ENG, Univ. Durham, 36-54; PROF, 54-63, UNIV. TORONTO, 63- Ed, The Revels plays, Harvard, 58-70; vis. prof, Univ. Toronto, 62-63; George F. Reynolds lectureship, Univ. Colo, 63; Commonwealth fel, Univs. N.Z, summer 68; Commonwealth vis. prof, U.K, spring 69. Fel, Royal Soc. Can. Elizabethan, Jacobean drama; twentieth century drama; literary theory. Publ: Shakespeare's tragedies and other studies in seventeenth century drama, Oxford, 50; John Ford and the drama of his time, Chatto, 57; The John Fletcher plays, Harvard, 62; Shakespeare: the chronicles, 62 & John Ford, 64, Longmans; Comedy in the grand style, Univ. Col. Swansea, 65; Tragedy, Methuen, 69; The dramatist's experience with other essays in literary theory, Chatto & Windus, 70; co-ed, Shakespeare 1971, Univ. Toronto, 72. Add: Dept. of English, University College, University of Toronto, Toronto, Ont. M5S 1A1, Can.

LEECH, ROBERT MILTON, b. Cameron, Tex, June 23, 21; m. 42; c. 2. DRAMA, SPEECH. B.F.A, Univ. Tex, Austin, 48, M.F.A, 49, Ph.D.(drama, educ), 62. Instr. drama & speech, Lon Morris Jr. Col, 48-49; asst. prof, UNIV. TEX, EL PASO, 49-56, assoc. prof, 48-62, prof, 62-63, head dept, 48-63, asst. to pres, 63-64, dean admin, 65-66, v.pres. acad. affairs, 66-68, acting pres, 68-69, v.pres. acad. affairs, 69-71, PROF. DRAMA & SPEECH, 71- U.S.A.F, 42-45, 51-53, Capt. Nat. Asn. Mental Health. Publ: Education through theatre for children, Univ. Microfilms, 62; ed, Mission '73: a ten year plan proposed by citizens of El Paso for Texas Western College, 63 & co-ed, Texas sketchbook, a sheaf of prose poems, 67, Tex. West. Col. Add: Dept. of Drama & Speech, University of Texas at El Paso, P.O. Box 180, El Paso, TX 79999.

LEED, JACOB R, b. Lititz, Pa, Sept. 26, 24; m. 52; c. 2. ENGLISH. A.B, Harvard, 46; M.F.A, Univ. Iowa, 52; Ph.D, Univ. Chicago, 58. Instr. Eng. compos, Pa. State Univ, 52-55; ENG, Northwest. Univ, 58-62; asst. prof, KENT STATE UNIV, 63-67, assoc. prof, 67-71, PROF, 71- U.S.A, 46-47. MLA. Eighteenth century English literature. Publ: Ed, The computer and literary style, Kent State Univ, 66; auth, Two new pieces by Samuel Johnson, Mod. Philol, 57; Issues of the Gentleman's magazine, Stud. Bibliog, 63; Patronage in the rambler, Stud. Burke & his time, 72; plus others. Add: Dept. of English, Kent State University, Kent, OH 44242.

LEEDS, BARRY HOWARD, b. New York, N.Y, Dec. 6, 40; m. 68; c. 2. ENGLISH & AMERICAN LITERATURE. B.A, Columbia Univ, 62, M.A, 63; Ph.D.(Eng), Ohio Univ, 67. Lectr, ENG, City Univ. New York, 63-64; instr, Univ. Tex, El Paso, 64-65; teaching fel, Ohio Univ, 65-67; asst. prof, CENT. CONN. STATE COL, 68-71, ASSOC. PROF, 71- AAUP. Contemporary American fiction; 20th century literature; American literature. Publ: The structured vision of Norman Mailer, N.Y. Univ, 69; The test of manhood in Hemingway, Columbia Rev, spring-summer 62; The proselytizer, by D. Keith Mano, Saturday Rev, 7/72; American book review, Mod. Fiction Stud, winter 73-74. Add: Jerome Ave, RFD 1, Bristol, CT 06010.

LEEDY, PAUL FRANCIS, b. Battle Creek, Mich, May 10, 03; m. 25. ENGLISH LITERATURE. A.B, Univ. Mich, 30, A.M, 31, fel, 39-40, Ph.D, 40, A.B.L.S, 46; hon. LL.D, Bowling Green State Univ, 71. Instr, Univ. Mich, 32-37; instr. Eng, BOWLING GREEN STATE UNIV, 38-39, asst. prof, 40-43, assoc. prof, 43-46, prof, 46-68, trustee prof, 68-69, univ. librn, 43-56, dir. univ. libr, 56-61, provost, 61-67, v.pres. & provost, 67-68; EMER. PROF. ENG. & EMER. PROVOST, 69- MLA; Am. Libr. Asn. The overthrow of Alexander Pope's reputation as poet; genres criticism and the significance of Warton's essay on Pope. Add: 865 Parker St, Bowling Green, OH 43402.

LEEMAN, RICHARD KENDALL, b. Galesburg, Ill, Aug. 21, 26; m. 56; c. 5. ENGLISH, COMPARATIVE LITERATURE. B.A, Univ. Wis, 50, M.A, 53, Ph.D.(Comp. lit), 61. Instr. world lit, St. Mary's Col.(Calif), 56-57; asst. prof. Eng, Col. St. Catherine, 57-62; Eng. & comp. lit, Univ. Santa Clara, 62-66; assoc. prof, Parsons Col, 66-71, DEAN ACAD. AFFAIRS, ILL. BENEDICTINE COL, 71- MLA; NCTE; AAUP. Theory of literature; 17th century French and English drama; Platonism in modern literature. Publ: Corneille's first period & the modernist notion of poetic originality, Forum Mod. Lang. Stud, 1/66. Add: Office of Academic Affairs, Illinois Benedictine College, Lisle, IL 60532.

LEEMING, DAVID ADAMS, b. Peekskill, N.Y, Feb. 26, 37; m. 67; c. 2. ENGLISH, COMPARATIVE LITERATURE. A.B, Princeton, 58; fel. & M.A, N.Y. Univ, 64, fel. & Ph.D.(comp. lit), 70. Teacher Eng, Robert Col, Istanbul, 58-63, chmn. dept, 60-63; secy-asst. to James Baldwin, 64-67; teacher Eng. & chmn. dept, Robert Col, Istanbul, 66-69, instr. humanities, 67-69, ASST. PROF. ENG, UNIV. CONN, 69- MLA. Mythology; religion and literature; American literature. Publ: Auth. & ed, Mythology: the voyage of the hero, Lippincott, 73 & Flights: readings in Fantasy, magic, mysticism and myth, Harcourt, 74; auth, Henry James and George Sand, Rev. Lit. Comp, 69. Add: Dept. of English, University of Connecticut, Storrs, CT 06268.

LEER, NORMAN ROBERT, b. Chicago, Ill, Feb. 25, 37. ENGLISH, COMPARATIVE LITERATURE. A.B, Grinnell Col, 58; M.A, Ind. Univ, 60, fel, 62, Ph.D.(Eng), 64. Instr. ENG, State Univ. N.Y. Stony Brook, 63-65; asst. prof, Beloit Col, 65-67; ASSOC. PROF, ROOSEVELT UNIV, 67- Mem. acad. adv. bd, St. Mary's Ctr. Learning, 68-; mem. bd, Urban Life Ctr, 72- Asn. Humanistic Psychol.(ed, Educ. Network Newslett, 72-). Modern literature in the light of existential philosophy and humanistic psychology; writing poetry; application of some of the techniques of humanistic psychology to college teaching. Publ: The limited hero in the novels of Ford Madox Ford, Mich. State Univ, 67; Escape and confrontation in the stories of Philip Roth, Christian Scholar, summer 66; The double theme in Malamud's Assistant: Dostoevsky with irony, Mosaic, spring 71; Innovation and power struggles: an experiential deadlock, J. Humanistic Psychol, winter 73; plus others. Add: Dept. of English, Roosevelt University, 430 S. Michigan Ave, Chicago, IL 60605.

LEES, CHARLES J, S.M, b. South Fork, Pa, Mar. 26, 19. ENGLISH. B.A, Univ. Dayton, 43; M.A, Univ. Pittsburgh, 50; Ph.D.(Eng), Ohio State Univ, 61. Asst. prof. Eng, UNIV. DAYTON, 62-65; PROF. ENG, 65-, V.PRES. ACAD. AFFAIRS, 73- Am. Counc. Educ; NCTE; Renaissance Soc. Am; Nat. Cath. Educ. Asn. Literature of Renaissance in England, especially that written in Latin; philosophy; theology. Publ: The poetry of Walter Haddon, Mouton, 67. Add: Office of Academic Affairs, University of Dayton, Dayton, OH 45469.

LEFEVRE, CARL ANTHONY, SR, b. Cedar Rapids, Iowa, Jan. 14, 13; m. 37; c. 2; m. 46; c. 2. ENGLISH, LINGUISTICS. B.A, West. Mich. Univ, 34; M.A, Univ. Mich, 37; Ph.D.(Eng. lang. & lit), Univ. Minn, 43. Instr. Eng. & speech, Univ. Minn, 37-44; asst. prof, Wash. Univ, 46-49; assoc. prof. Eng, Minn. State Teachers Col, Mankato, 49-51; prof. Eng. & commun. & chmn. dept, Pace Col, 51-55; assoc. prof. Eng, Chicago Teachers Col-South, 55-61; prof. Eng. & chmn. commun. skills prog, Northeast. Ill. State Univ, 61-66; PROF. ENG. EDUC, COL. EDUC, TEMPLE UNIV, 66- Int. Reading Asn; MLA; Conf. Col. Compos. & Commun; NCTE; Ling. Soc. Am; Nat. Educ. Asn; Am. Educ. Res. Asn; Conf. Eng. Educ; Nat. Reading Conf. Psycholinguistics; language structure and reading comprehension; programed instruction. Publ: Linguistics and the teaching of reading, McGraw, 64; co-auth, Writing by patterns, forms A and B, Knopf, 65-67 & English writing patterns, Random, Singer, 68; auth, Linguistics, English, and the language arts, Teachers Col, Columbia Univ, 73; The simplistic standard word-perception theory of reading, Elem. Eng, 3/68; Language and critical reading: the consummate reader, 70 & Reading by patterns: a psycholinguistic remedial tutorial program for young adults, 72, Yearbook Nat. Reading Conf; plus others. Add: 114 Clemens Ct, Lansdale, PA 19446.

LEFEVRE, HELEN E, b. Grand Forks, N.Dak, Aug. 3, 13; m. 46; c. 4. ENGLISH. Ph.D.(Eng), Univ. Minn, 46. Prof. Eng, Chicago City Col, 56-66; PROF. ENG, COMMUNITY COL. PHILA, 67- NCTE; Conf. Col. Compos. & Commun; Int. Reading Asn. Publ: Co-auth, Writing by patterns, 65 & Oral/written practice in standard English forms, 69, Knopf; English writing patterns, Singer, 68; auth, Materials for teaching remedial reading in college, Jr. Col. J, 59. Add: Dept. of English, Community College of Philadelphia, 34 S. 11th St, Philadelphia, PA 19107.

LEFFORGE, ORLAND S, b. Pettisville, Ohio, July 31, 15; div; c. 3. SPEECH. B.A, Manchester Col, 37; Ph.M, Univ. Wis, 40, Ph.D.(speech), 53. Teacher, Chester Ctr. High Sch, 37-39; Howe Mil. Acad, 40-41; Auburn High Sch, 45-46; instr. speech, Manchester Col, 46-48; assoc. prof. speech, Univ. Hawaii, 48-66; admin. asst. to U.S. Sen. Daniel K. Inouye, 66-69; DIR. CURRICULA, HAWAII SYST. COMMUNITY COLS, 70- U.S.A, 41-45, Capt. Speech Commun. Asn. Rhetoric; public address. Add: Community College System Office, University of Hawaii, 2444 Dole St, Honolulu, HI 96822.

LEGGATT, ALEXANDER MAXWELL, b. Oakville, Ont, Aug. 18, 40; m. 64; c. 3. ENGLISH. B.A, Univ. Toronto, 62; M.A, Univ. Birmingham, 63, Ph.D. (Eng), 65. Lectr. ENG, Scarborough Col, UNIV. TORONTO, 65-67, asst. prof, 67-68, UNIV. COL, 68-71, ASSOC. PROF, 71- Assoc. ed, Mod. Drama, 72- Asn. Can. Univ. Teachers Eng; Renaissance Soc. Am. Renaissance drama; modern drama. Publ: Citizen comedy in the age of Shakespeare, Univ. Toronto, 73; Shakespeare's Comedy of love, Methuen, 74; The suicide of Volpone, Univ. Toronto Quart, 10/69; Shakespeare and the borderlines of comedy, Mosaic, fall 71; Tamburlaine's sufferings, Yearbk. Eng. Stud, 73. Add: Dept. of English, University of Toronto, Toronto, Ont. M5S 1A1, Can.

LEGGETT, B. J, b. Alamo, Tenn, Feb. 25, 38; m. 60; c. 2. MODERN LITERATURE. B.A, Lambuth Col, 60; M.A, Univ. Fla, 62, Ph.D.(Eng), 65. Asst. prof. ENG, UNIV. TENN, KNOXVILLE, 65-70, ASSOC. PROF, 70- Nat. Found. Arts. & Humanities fel, 67. S.Atlantic Mod. Lang. Asn. Modern poetry. Publ: Housman's Land of lost content, Univ. Tenn, 70; The Miltonic allusions in Housman's Terence, this is stupid stuff, Eng. Lang. Notes, 68; Dante, Byron and Tennyson's Ulysses, Tenn. Stud. Lit, 70; The limits of the intellect: Housman's Name and nature of poetry, Mod. Lang. Quart, 71. Add: Dept. of English, University of Tennessee, Knoxville, TN 37916.

LEGGETT, GLENN, b. Ashtabula, Ohio, Mar. 29, 18; m. 41, 73; c. 6. ENGLISH. A.B, Middlebury Col, 40, hon. LL.D, 71; M.A, Ohio State Univ, 41, Ph.D.(Eng), 49; hon. L.H.D, Rockford Col, 67, Ripon Col, 68; hon. Litt.D, Lawrence Univ, 68. Instr. Eng. & debate, Mass. Inst. Technol, 42-44; Eng. Ohio State Univ, 46-50, asst. prof. Eng. & asst. dir. freshman Eng, 51-52; assoc. prof. & dir. Univ. Wash, 52-58, spec. asst. to pres, 58-60, vice provost, 61-63, provost, 63-65; PRES, GRINNELL COL, 65- Mem. comn. Eng, Col. Entrance Exam Bd, 59-65, mem. bd. trustees, 65-, exec. comt, 68-, chmn. bd. trustees, 72-74; mem. adv. counc, Pres. Asn. Governing Bds. Univs. & Cols, 66-69; chmn, Assoc. Cols. Midwest, 71-73. U.S.N.R, 44-46. MLA; NCTE; Conf. Col. Compos. & Commun. Seventeenth century and modern literature; teaching of rhetoric and composition; English composition and modern poetry. Publ: Co-auth, Handbook for writers, 51, 54, 60, 65, 70 & Workbook for writers, 54, 58, 62, 67, 70 & co-ed, Theme and form, an introduction to literature, 56, 62, 69 & The written word, 60, Prentice-Hall; co-auth, Writing your papers, Ronald, 55; co-ed, Twelve poets, Holt, 59, 67; co-auth, Plain English please, Random, 66. Add: Grinnell College, Grinnell, IA 50112.

LEGLER, PHILIP, b. Mar. 7, 28; U.S. citizen; m. 50; c. 2. ENGLISH. B.A, Denison Univ, 51; M.F.A, State Univ. Iowa, 53. Instr. Eng. compos, Ohio Univ, 53-56; asst. prof. lit, Cent. Mo. State Col, 56-59; N.Mex. Highlands Univ, 59-60, Coe Found. guest-lectr, summer 63; ASST. PROF. lit, Ill. Wesleyan Univ, 60-63; WRITING & LIT, Sweet Briar Col, 63-66; NORTH. MICH. UNIV, 68- Annie Mary MacNeill Poetry Prize, Denison Univ, 51; N.Mex. Quart. Helene Wurlitzer Poetry Award, 67. U.S.M.C, 46-47, Sgt. Contemporary poetry; American literature. Publ: A change of view, Univ. Nebr, 64; The intruder, Univ. Ga, 72; Marianne Moore and the idea of a freedom, 12/53 & O yellow eye, 5/67, Poetry. Add: Dept. of English, Northern Michigan University, Marquette, MI 49855.

LEHAN, RICHARD D, b. Brockton, Mass, Dec. 23, 30; m. 60; c. 1. AMERICAN LITERATURE. B.A, Stonehill Col, 52; M.A, Boston Col, 53; Ph.D. (Am. lit), Univ. Wis, 58. Asst, Univ. Wis, 53-57; instr. Am. lit, Univ. Tex, 58-61, asst. prof, 61-62; UNIV. CALIF, LOS ANGELES, 62-66, assoc. prof, ENG, 66-69, PROF, 69-, chmn. dept, 71-73. Assoc. & co-ed, Nineteenth-Century Fiction, 66-71. Distinguished teaching awards, Univ. Tex, Austin, 61 & Univ. Calif, Los Angeles, 70. MLA; NCTE. History of the novel. Publ: F. Scott Fitzgerald and the craft of fiction, 66, Theodore Dreiser: his world and his novels, 69 & A dangerous crossing: French literary existentialism and the modern American novel, 73, South. Ill. Univ; Hemingway among the moderns, Ore. State Univ, 74; plus many others. Add: Dept. of English, University of California, 405 Hilgard Ave, Los Angeles, CA 90024.

LEHMAN, ALAN D, b. Coldspring, N.Y, Mar. 25, 20; m. 49; c. 2. ENGLISH. B.S, City Col. New York, 40; M.A, State Univ. Iowa, 46, Ph.D, 50. Instr. Eng, State Univ. Col. Plattsburgh, 48-49, prof. Eng. & Philos, 62-63; assoc. prof. ENG, Nebr. State Teachers Col, Wayne, 50-55; PROF, Wis. State Col, Eau Claire, 55-62, UNIV. WIS-STEVENS POINT, 63- U.S.A.A.F, 42-46, Res, 46-, Lt. Col. NCTE; MLA; Shakespeare Asn. Am. Shakespeare; Oriental literature; writing. Publ: Readable rhetoric, Burgess, 60; The Coriolanus story in antiquity, Class. J, 5/52. Add: Dept. of English, University of Wisconsin-Stevens Point, Stevens Point, WI 54481.

LEHMAN, ANNE KERNAN, Medieval Literature. See KERNAN, ANNE.

LEHMANN, MARGARET GRENNAN, b. New York, N.Y, Sept. 30, 12; m. 54. ENGLISH. Cone fel. & A.B, Hunter Col, 34; A.M, Columbia Univ, 35, univ. fel, 42, Ph.D, 43. From assoc. prof. to prof. Eng, LEHMAN COL, 35-72, EMER. PROF, MEDIEVAL & VICTORIAN LIT, 72- Anglo-Irish literature; Irish history; Victorian literature, especially Morris and Newman. Publ: The heart of Newman's Apologia, Longmans, Green & Co, 34; ed, Shakespeare's Julius Caesar, Loyola Univ, 42; auth, William Morris, mediaevalist and revolutionary, King's Crown, 45, 3rd ed, Russell, 70; co-ed, English voices, Sadlier, 46; auth, The heart of Newman's apologia, 2nd ed, Russell, 70. Add: 2420 Sedgwick Ave, New York, NY 10468.

LEHMANN, RUTH PRESTON, b. Ithaca, N.Y, Feb. 18, 12; m. 40; c. 2. ENGLISH, CELTIC. B.A, Cornell Univ, 32, M.A, 34; scholar, Bryn Mawr Col, 35-36; Gorham fel, Univ. Wis, 37-38, Ph.D, 42; Chapel Hill Inst, 42; Univ. Oslo, 50-51. Teacher, high sch, N.Y, 36-37; asst. Eng, Univ. Wis, 38-42, Markham fel, 42-43; instr, George Washington Univ, 44-46, instr. & lectr, 46-47; instr. Georgetown Eng. Lang. Prog, Univ. Ankara, 55-56; assoc. prof, Huston-Tillotson Col, 56-58; McHale traveling fel, 53-54; lectr, UNIV. TEX, AUSTIN, 62-68, assoc. prof, 68-73, PROF, 73- MLA; Mediaeval Acad. Am. English literature, especially the Middle Ages and the Renaissance; Celtic, especially of the old and middle periods. Publ: A study of the Buile Shuibhne, Etudes Celtiques, 55, 56; Fled Dúin na nGéd, Mediaeval & Mod. Irish Stud, Dublin Inst. Advan. Stud, 64; Some examples of early Irish storytelling, Tex. Folklore Soc, 68. Add: Dept. of English, University of Texas at Austin, Box 8148, University Station, Austin, TX 78712.

LEHR, WILSON, b. Brooklyn, N.Y, May 8, 13. PHILOSOPHY, DRAMA. B.A, Harvard, 34; M.F.A, Yale, 39. Instr. SPEECH & DRAMA, Packer Col. Inst, 40-42; City Col. New York, 46-51; Columbia Univ, 57-58; assoc. prof, BROOKLYN COL, 58-67, PROF, 67- Instr, New Sch. Social Res, 58-59. U.S.N.R, 42-45, Lt.(jg). Am. Theatre Asn. Playwriting; directing; acting. Publ: Co-auth, Fundamentals of play direction, Farrar & Rinehart, 40. Add: Dept. of Theatre, Brooklyn College, Brooklyn, NY 11210.

LEIB, AMOS PATTEN, b. New London, Conn, Dec. 8, 17; m. 50. ENGLISH. B.S, Haverford Col, 38; M.A, Univ. Hawaii, 47; Honolulu Community Found. scholar, Tulane Univ, 57, Ph.D.(Eng), 63. Instr. math. & Eng, Iolani Sch, Honolulu, Hawaii, 38-41; math. & gen. sci, physics, band, Punahou Sch, 41-45; ENG, UNIV. HAWAII, MANOA, 45-50, asst. prof, 50-61, assoc. prof, 61-71, PROF, 71- Vet. and selective serv. adv, Univ. Hawaii, Manoa, 56-59, ed, univ. catalogue, 61-62, univ. marshal, 63- Melville Soc. Am. Pacific literature; American literature, especially Nathaniel Hawthorne; mediaeval English literature. Publ: Hawaiian legends in English, Univ. Hawaii, 49; The many islands of Polynesia, Scribner, 72; History and setting in Michener's story of Norfolk Island, Mutiny, Australian Lit. Stud, 10/70. Add: Dept. of English, University of Hawaii at Manoa, 1733 Donaghho Rd, Honolulu, HI 96822.

LEIBLE, ARTHUR BRAY, b. Bloomington, Ind, Dec. 5, 24; m. 48; c. 4. ENGLISH. A.B, Ind. Univ, 46, M.A, 53; Ph.D, Univ. Mo, 61. Asst. math, Ind. Univ, 46-47, Eng, 52; teacher, High Sch, Ind, 47-48; instr. ENG, William Woods Col, 52-57; instr, Univ. Mo, 57-58; UNIV. WIS-OSHKOSH, 58, asst. prof, 59-62, assoc. prof, 62-66, PROF, 66- Vis. lectr, Westminster Col, 54-57. Midwest Mod. Lang. Asn; Int. Arthurian Soc; Mediaeval Acad. Am. Elizabethan; Arthurian; Middle English literature. Add: Dept. of English, University of Wisconsin-Oshkosh, Oshkosh, WI 54901.

LEICESTER, HENRY MARSHALL, JR, b. Palo Alto, Calif, Mar. 17, 42; div; c. 1. ENGLISH LITERATURE, MEDIEVAL STUDIES. B.A, Yale, 63, M.A, 65, Ph.D.(Eng), 67. Instr. ENG, Yale, 66-67; ASST. PROF, UNIV. CALIF, SANTA CRUZ, 67- Medieval Acad. Am. Chaucer; theory of narrative; literary interpretation, theory and practice. Publ: The dialectic of Romantic historiography: prospect and retrospect in The French Revolution, Victorian Stud, 9/71; The harmony of Chaucer's Parlement: a dissonant voice, Chaucer Rev, (in press); co-auth, Social structure as doom: the limits of heroism in Beowulf, In: Festschrift for John C. Pope, Univ. Toronto, 74. Add: Crown College, University of California, Santa Cruz, CA 95064.

LEIGH, DAVID JOSEPH, b. Seattle, Wash, Apr. 16, 37. ENGLISH. A.B, Gonzaga Univ, 61, M.A, 63; M.A. & lic. theol, Regis Col.(Ont), 69; Ph.D.(Eng), Yale, 72. Instr. Eng. & classics, Gonzaga Prep. Sch, 62-65; ASST. PROF. ENG, GONZAGA UNIV, 72- Religious roots of English romanticism; eschatological literature; Jonathan Swift. Publ: The Doomsday mystery play, Mod. Philol, 70; contrib, Medieval English drama, Univ. Chicago, 73; auth, In our time: interchapters, Stud. Short Fiction, 74; plus others. Add: Dept. of English, Gonzaga University, Spokane, WA 99202.

LEIGH, THOMAS WATKINS, b. South Boston, Va, Mar. 16, 18; m. 46; c. 3. ENGLISH. B.A, Hampden-Sydney Col, 39; M.A, Univ. Mich, 47. From asst. prof. to ASSOC. PROF. ENG, MADISON COL.(VA), 50- U.S.A.A.F, 42-46. Col. Eng. Asn. Shakespeare; English and American novel; contemporary literature. Add: Dept. of English, Madison College, Harrisonburg, VA 22801.

LEINAWEAVER, RICHARD E, b. Lancaster, Pa, July 20, 30; m. 60; c. 1. THEATER. B.A, Univ. Colo, 61, M.A, 63; Ph.D.(Am. drama), Mich. State Univ, 67. Teacher high sch, Ecuador, 61-62; Colo, 62-63; asst. prof. drama, CENT. WASH. STATE COL, 65-74, ASSOC. PROF. DRAMA. & CHMN. DEPT. THEATRE & DRAMA, 74- Fulbright lectr, Asn. Colombian Univs, Bogota, 68. U.S.A.F, 50-53. Am. Nat. Theatre & Acad; Am. Theatre Asn. American indigenous and primitive drama; Latin American theatre; theatre production, especially acting and directing. Publ: Transl, Rabinal Achí, spring 68, auth, Rabinal Achí: commentary and analysis, spring 68 & Mexico's second city: the 71-72 season, fall 72, Latin Am. Theatre Rev; Un Aspecto de la disciplina en el ensayo de teatro, Pliegos Teatro Universitario, Bogota, fall 68. Add: Dept. of Theatre & Drama, Central Washington State College, Ellensburg, WA 98926.

LEISHER, JOHN F. b. Mercer, Pa, Aug. 11, 15; m. 41; c. 2. ENGLISH. A.B, Allegheny Col, 37; A.M, Harvard, 42, Ph.D.(Eng. lang. & lit), 53. Teaching fel. ENG, Harvard, 42-44, 45-47; instr, BOSTON UNIV, 47-53, asst. prof, 53-57, ASSOC. PROF, 57- Vis. prof. Eng. & Am. Lit, Univ. Hamburg, 59-60. MLA; AAUP. English language and literature of the 16th and 18th centuries; Renaissance iconography. Add: 236 Bay State Rd, Boston, MA 02215.

LEITCH, VINCENT BARRY, b. Hempstead, N.Y, Sept. 18, 44; m. 70; c. 1. ENGLISH LITERATURE. B.A, Hofstra Univ, 66; M.A, Villanova Univ, 67; Ph.D.(Eng), Univ. Fla, 72. Res. asst. Eng, Villanova Univ, 67; instr, North Babylon Sr. High Sch, 68; teaching asst, Univ. Fla, 69-72, instr, summer 72, ASST. PROF. humanities, 72-73; ENG, MERCER UNIV, 73-, univ. res. grant, 74. Am. Philos. Soc. res. grant, 74. NCTE (mem. staff, Abstr. Eng. Stud, 72-); MLA; S.Atlantic Mod. Lang. Asn; Renaissance Soc. Am; AAUP; Southeast. Renaissance Conf. Religious poetry in England; poetry in Renaissance England. Publ: Ed, Marie Magdalens funeral teares, Scholars Facsimiles & Reprints, 74; auth, The landscape of hell in Paradise Lost, Bk. 1, Xavier Univ. Stud, fall 70; Herbert's influence in Dylan Thomas's I see the boys of summer, Notes & Queries, 9/72; Myth in Ulysses: the whirlwind and Hosea-Bloom, James Joyce Quart, winter 73. Add: Dept. of English, Mercer University, Coleman Ave, Macon, GA 31207.

LEITER, LOUIS H, b. Cleveland, Ohio, Feb. 22, 21. ENGLISH. A.B, State Univ, Iowa, 50, M.A, 53; Ph.D, Brown Univ, 60. Instr. ENG, Univ. Idaho, 53-55; Ripon Col, 55-56; Brown Univ, 58-59; asst. prof, Univ. Nebr, 59-63; res. grant, summer 60; assoc. prof, UNIV. PAC, 63-67, PROF, 67- Fulbright prof, Univ. Jyväskylä, Finland, 67-68. U.S.A. & U.S.A.A.F, 40-45, S/Sgt. MLA; Am. Soc. Aesthet. Shakespeare; European novel; English and European drama; film. Publ: Co-auth, Approaches to short story, Chandler, 63 & Seven short novels, Scott, 68; auth, A problem in analysis, J. Aesthet. & Art Criticism, 60; Patterns of transformation in The dream of the rood, In: Anglo-Saxon poetry, Brown Univ, 68. Add: Dept. of English, University of the Pacific, Stockton, CA 95204.

LEITER, SAMUEL LOUIS, b. Brooklyn, N.Y, July 20, 40; m. 63; c. 2. THEATRE. B.A, Brooklyn Col, 62; M.F.A, Univ. Hawaii, 64; Ph.D.(dramatic art), N.Y. Univ, 68. Lectr. THEATRE, BROOKLYN COL, 65-68, asst. prof, 68-72, ASSOC. PROF, 73- Ed, Asian Theatre Bull. Japan Soc; Am. Soc. East. Arts; Speech Commun. Asn; Am. Soc. Theatre Res; Am. Theatre Asn. Japanese theatre; theatre history; performance technique. Publ: Theatre in the city of churches, Players, 8-9/69; The depiction of violence on the Kabuki stage, Educ. Theatre J, 5/69; Onoe Kikugoro VII, Asian Theatre Bull, 73; plus several others. Add: Dept. of Theatre, Brooklyn College, Bedford Ave, Brooklyn, NY 11210.

LELAND, LOWELL POND, b. Sangerville, Maine, Feb. 22, 07; m. 47; c. 2. ENGLISH. B.A, Colby Col, 29; M.A, Univ. Maine, 33; Ph.D.(Eng), Ohio State Univ, 40. Instr. ENG, Wayne State Univ, 38-39; Westminster Col, 40-41, asst. prof, 45-46; from asst. prof. to ASSOC. PROF, BOWLING GREEN STATE UNIV, 46- U.S.A, 42-45. MLA; NCTE. Victorian literature. Add: Dept. of English, Bowling Green State University, Bowling Green, OH 43402.

LELAND, VIRGINIA EVERETT, b. Robersonville, N.C, Feb. 12, 08; m. 47; c. 2. ENGLISH. A.B, Carson-Newman Col, 25; A.M, Univ. Chicago, 27, fel, 35-36, Ph.D.(Chaucer), 40. From instr. to assoc. prof. ENG, Westminster Col.(Pa), 36-48; instr, BOWLING GREEN STATE UNIV, 48-62, asst. prof, 62-67, assoc. prof, 67-72, PROF, 72- Acting head dept, Tusculum Col, 44-45; assoc. prof, Carson-Newman Col, 46-48; assoc. chmn. elem. booklist comt, NCTE, 65- MLA; NCTE; Int. Reading Asn. Chaucer; American literature; children's literature. Add: Dept. of English, Bowling Green University, Bowling Green, OH 43402.

LELCHUK, ALAN, b. Brooklyn, N.Y, Sept. 15, 38. LITERATURE. B.A, Brooklyn Col, 60; M.A, Stanford Univ, 63, Ph.D.(Eng), 65; Univ. London, 63-64. ASST. PROF. ENG. & AM. LIT, BRANDEIS UNIV, 66- Assoc. ed, Mod. Occasions, 70-72. Publ: American mischief (novel), Farrar, Straus, 73; contrib, Partisan Rev, New Am. Rev, Mod. Occasions, Dissent, N.Y. Rev. Bks, Victorian Stud, Transatlantic Rev, and others. Add: Dept. of English, Brandeis University, Waltham, MA 02154.

LELL, VIRGIL GORDON, b. Delta, Colo, Feb. 10, 35; m. 55; c. 2. ENGLISH LITERATURE. B.A, West. State Col. Colo, 57; M.A, Colo. State Univ, 64; Ph.D.(Eng), Univ. Nebr-Lincoln, 70. Instr. ENG, Univ. Nebr, 64-70; ASST. PROF, CONCORDIA COL.(MOORHEAD, MINN), 70- Nat. Endowment for Humanities res. grant, summer 73. U.S.N, 57-62, Res, 62-, Comdr. AAUP; MLA. Shakespeare; Chaucer. Publ: English proficiency at U.S. Naval Officer Candidate School, Col. Eng, 11/65; Ganymede on the Elizabethan stage: homosexual implications of the use of boy actors, Aegis, spring 73. Add: Dept. of English, Concordia College, Moorhead, MN 56560.

LeMASTER, JIMMIE R, b. Pike County, Ohio, Mar. 29, 34; m. 66; c. 3. ENGLISH LANGUAGE & LITERATURE. B.S, Defiance Col, 59; M.A, Bowling Green State Univ, 62, Ph.D.(Eng), 70. Teacher ENG, Stryker High Sch, 59-61; Bryan High Sch, 61-62; PROF, DEFIANCE COL, 62- U.S.N, 51-55. MLA; AAUP. Twentieth century American literature; Jesse Stuart. Publ: Poets of the Midwest, Young, 66; co-ed, Symposia poets (poetry), South & West, 69; co-ed, There comes a time (poetry), 71, co-ed, Certain reconciliations (poetry), 72 & co-ed, On weighing a pound of flesh (poetry), 73, Defiance Col; auth, Ionesco's pictures, Paper, 1-3/72; The genitive: an empirical study, fall 72 & Jesse Stuart's Album of destiny: in pursuit of Whitman's parallels, winter 72, Ball State Univ. Forum; plus others. Add: Dept. of English, Defiance College, N. Clinton St, Defiance, OH 43512.

LEMAY, JOSEPH ALBERIC LEO, b. Bristow, Va, Jan. 17, 35; m. 65. ENGLISH. A.B, Univ. Md, 57, A.M, 62; Ph.D.(Eng), Univ. Pa, 64. Instr. ENG,

George Washington Univ, 63-64; asst. prof, 64-65, UNIV. CALIF, LOS ANGELES. 65-70, ASSOC. PROF, 70- Colonial Williamsburg, Inc. grant, summer 64; Am. Philos. Soc. grant, summer 65; fac. fel, Univ. Calif, Los Angeles, summer 67; mem. ed. bd, Eighteenth Century Stud, 67- U.S.A, 57-59. MLA; Am. Stud. Asn; Bibliog. Soc. Am; Am. Antiq. Soc. Early American literature; Benjamin Franklin; Edgar Allan Poe. Publ: Ebenezer Kinnersley, Franklin's friend, Univ. Pa, 64; A poem by John Markland of Virginia, William Parks Club, 65; A calendar of American poetry in the colonial newspapers and magazines and in the major English magazines through 1765, Am. Antiq. Soc, 72; Men of letters in colonial Maryland, Univ. Tenn, 72; Richard Lewis and Augustan American poetry, PMLA, 68; Robert Bolling and the bailment of Colonel Chiswell, Early Am. Lit, 71; Benjamin Franklin, In: Major writers of early American literature, Univ. Wis, 72; plus others. Add: Dept. of English, University of California, Los Angeles, CA 90024.

LEMELIN, ROBERT E, b. Holyoke, Mass, Aug. 8, 34; m. 57; c. 1. ENGLISH, AMERICAN STUDIES. B.S, South. Conn. State Col, 59; M.A, Univ. Md, 63, Ph.D, 67. Instr. ENG, Univ. Md, 63-65; UNIV. MAINE, ORONO, 65-67, ASST. PROF, 67- MLA; Am. Stud. Asn. Nineteenth century American culture and literature. Add: Dept. of English, 158 Little Hall, University of Maine, Orono, ME 04473.

LeMIRE, EUGENE D, b. Burton Twp, Mich, May 18, 29. ENGLISH. Ph.B, Univ. Detroit, 51, M.A, 54; fel, Wayne State Univ, 55-58, Ph.D, 62. Teaching fel, Univ. Detroit, 51-54, instr. ENG, 54-55, asst. prof, 61-62; instr, Wayne State Univ, 58-59, 60-61; asst. prof, Univ. Windsor, 62-66, assoc. prof, 66-69, prof, 69-70; sr. lectr, FLINDERS UNIV. S.AUSTRALIA, 70-71, READER, 72- Can. Counc. fel, 68-69. William Morris Soc. & Kelmscott Fel; Australian Univs. Lang. & Lit. Asn; Eng. Asn, Gt. Brit. Victorian literature; William Morris; the decadence. Publ: Ed, The unpublished lectures of William Morris, Wayne State Univ, 69; Irony in Erewhon, Humanities Asn.Bull, fall 65; H.G. Wells and the world of science fiction, Univ. Windsor Rev, spring 67; plus others. Add: School of Humanities, Flinders University of South Australia, Bedford Park, South Australia 5042.

LEMKE, FREDERICK DANIEL, b. Wabasha, Minn, Aug 6, 03. ENGLISH. A.B, Univ. Wis, 26, scholar, 26-27, A.M, 27; res. fel, Univ. Ill, 31-32, Ph.D, 33; hon. D.Litt, Heidelberg Col, 73. Asst. Eng, Univ. Ill, 27-31; prof. & chmn. dept, HEIDELBERG COL, 33-73, dean, 40-63, acting pres, 47-48, assoc. dean, 63-70, EMER. PROF. ENG, 73- MLA; NCTE. George Eliot and her predecessors in village literature. Add: Dept. of English, Heidelberg College, Tiffin, OH 44883.

LEMON, LEE THOMAS, b. Kansas City, Kans, Feb. 5, 31; m. 53; c. 4. LITERATURE, ENGLISH. B.S, St. Louis Univ, 51; M.A, South. Ill. Univ, 52; Ph.D, Univ. Ill, 61. Asst. ENG, Univ. Ill, 54-61; from asst. prof. to PROF, UNIV. NEBR, LINCOLN, 61- Assoc. ed, Prairie Schooner, 69- U.S.A, 52-54. MLA; NCTE. Literary theory; development of the novel; Russian literature. Publ: Partial critics, 65, Approaches to literature, 67 & A glossary for the study of English, 71, Oxford; co-auth, Russian formalist criticism, Univ. Nebr, 65; auth, Alexandrea quartet: form and fiction, Wis. Stud. Contemporary Lit, autumn 63; Billy Budd: the plot against the story, Stud. Short Fiction, 6/64; Portrait of the artist as a young man: motif as motivation and structure, Mod. Fiction Stud, winter 67; plus others. Add: Dept. of English, University of Nebraska, Lincoln, NE 68508.

LENAGHAN, ROBERT THOMAS, b. Clinton, Iowa, May 24, 27; m. 53; c. 1. ENGLISH LITERATURE. B.A, Univ. Iowa, 49; Yale Law Sch, 49-50; A.M, Harvard, 52, Dexter traveling fel, 56, Ph.D, 57. Instr. ENG, Univ. N.H, 54; Univ. Calif, Los Angeles, 57-59, asst. prof, 59-61; UNIV. MICH, ANN ARBOR, 61-65, assoc. prof, 65-73, PROF, 73- Rackham fac. fel, 63; Huntington Libr. grant-in-aid, 67. U.S.N, 45-46. MLA. Medieval English literature. Publ: Ed, Caxton's Aesop, Harvard, 67; co-ed, The Norton reader, Norton, 73; auth, Steinhowel's Esopus and early humanism, Monatshefte, 1/68; Chaucer's General prologue as history and literature, Comp. Stud. Soc. & Hist, 1/70; Irony in the Friar's tale, Chaucer Rev, 12/72; plus others. Add: Dept. of English, University of Michigan, Ann Arbor, MI 48104.

LENEHAN, WILLIAM THURMAN, b. Winnsboro, Tex, May 25, 30; m. 62; c. 1. AMERICAN LITERATURE. B.A, Univ. Okla, 55, Ph.D.(Eng), 63. Instr. ENG, UNIV. WIS-MADISON, 62-64, asst. prof, 64-67, assoc. prof, 67-70, PROF, 70- U.S.A.F, 51-53, S/Sgt. MLA; NCTE; AAUP. American fiction, 1880-1914; rhetorical theory and the teaching of composition. Publ: Co-auth, The writer's reader, Scott, 68; ed, Washington Irving's The Alhambra, Ctr. Editions Am. Authors, (in press). Add: 3526 Tally Ho Lane, Madison, WI 53705.

LENFEST, DAVID STANLEY, b. Portland, Maine, July 9, 36. ENGLISH. A.B, Haverford Col, 58; A.M, Univ. Mich, 62, Rackham travel grant, 65, Ph.D. (Eng. lang. & lit), 66. Admin. asst. to grad. dean, Horace H. Rackham Sch. Grad. Stud, Univ. Mich, 66; ASST. PROF. ENG, Univ. Ill, Chicago, 66-72; LOYOLA UNIV. CHICAGO, 72-, fac. summer grant, 73. Univ. Ill. summer fac. fel, 67, Ill. Arts Counc. Film & Poetry grants, 71, 72. U.S.A, 58-61. MLA. Eighteenth century satire; contemporary American poetry; experimental film making. Publ: The great odor of summer (film), Radim Films, 72; A checklist of illustrated Gulliver's travels, 1727-1914, Papers, Bibliog. Soc. Am, 68; Lefebvre's illustrations for Gulliver's travels, Bull. New York Pub. Libr, 73. Add: Dept. of English, Loyola University of Chicago, 6525 N. Sheridan Rd, Chicago, IL 60626.

LENNIG, ARTHUR, b. East Williston, N.Y, Feb. 22, 33; m. 55; c. 1. CINEMA, ENGLISH. B.A, State Univ. N.Y. Albany, 55, M.A, 56; Ph.D. (Eng), Univ. Wis, 61. Instr. Eng, Russell Sage Col, 62-64, asst. prof, 64-67; ART IN CINEMA, STATE UNIV. N.Y. ALBANY, 67-71, ASSOC. PROF. 71- Lectr, Inst. Man & Sci, Rensselaerville, 67. Soc. Cinema Stud. The silent and sound cinema; English and American literature. Publ: Co-auth. & ed, Film notes, Univ. Wis. Film Soc, 60 & Classics of the film, Wis. Film Soc, 65; auth, The silent voice, State Univ. N.Y. Albany, 66; Queen Kelly, Film Heritage, 66; The silent voice: a sequel, 67, The silent voice: a text, 69 & co-auth. & ed, The sound film: an introduction, 69, Snyder; auth, The Count: the life and film of Bela "Dracula" Lugosi, Putnam, 74; From the talkies to today, Hopkinson & Blake, 74; Broken blossoms, 72 & The raven, 73, Film J; Dream street, Silent Picture, 73. Add: Dept. of Art, State University of New York at Albany, Albany, NY 12222.

LENSON, DAVID ROLLAR, b. Kearny, N.J, June 28, 45. COMPARATIVE LITERATURE. A.B, Princeton, 67, M.A, 70, Ph.D.(comp. lit), 71. ASST. PROF. COMP. LIT, UNIV. MASS, AMHERST, 71- Co-ed, Panache Mag, 70-; Book Mag, 72-; Nat. Endowment for Humanities younger humanist fel, 73-74. Tragedy; poetics; American poetry. Add: Box 77, Sunderland, MA 01375.

LENTRICCHIA, FRANK, b. Utica, N.Y, May 23, 40; m. 67; c. 2. ENGLISH. B.A, Syracuse Univ, 62; M.A, Duke Univ, 63, Ph.D.(mod. poetry), 66. Asst. prof. ENG. & COMP. LIT, Univ. Calif, Los Angeles, 66-68, UNIV. CALIF, IRVINE, 68-70, ASSOC. PROF, 70- Nat. Humanities Found. fel, summer 68. MLA. Modern literature; literary theory; aesthetics. Publ: The gaiety of language: an essay on the radical poetics of W.B. Yeats and Wallace Stevens, Univ. Calif, 68; Wallace Stevens: the ironic eye, Yale Rev, 67; Four types of nineteenth-century poetic, 68 & The place of Cleanth Brooks, 70, J. Aesthet. & Art Criticism. Add: Dept. of English & Comparative Literature, University of California at Irvine, Irvine, CA 92664.

LENTZ, SALLY PALMER, b. Denver, Colo, May 1, 44; m. AMERICAN LITERATURE. B.A, Colo. Col, 66; Woodrow Wilson fel. & Ph.D.(Eng), Rutgers Univ, 71. Lectr. ENG, Brooklyn Col, 70-71; ASST. PROF, Univ. N.H, 71-73; COLO. COL, 73- Col. Eng. Asn. Expository writing; women's studies. Publ: Writing for understanding, Winthrop, 74. Add: Dept. of English, Colorado College, Colorado Springs, CO 80903.

LEONARD, NEIL, b. Cambridge, Mass, Dec. 3, 27; m. 54; c. 4. AMERICAN CIVILIZATION. A.B, Colby Col, 50; Ph.D, Harvard, 60. Instr. Eng, Northwest. Univ, 60-61; asst. prof. AM. CIVILIZATION, UNIV. PA, 61-66, ASSOC. PROF, 66- U.S.A, 50-52. Am. Stud. Asn. Modern American civilization; literature and the other arts in the United States since 1885; psychological implications of art. Publ: Edward MacDowell and the realists, Am. Quart, summer 66; Alfred Stieglitz and realism, Art Quart, fall 66; Jazz and the other arts, In: American Music, Transactions, 72. Add: Dept. of American Civilization, University of Pennsylvania, Philadelphia, PA 19174.

LEONDAR, BARBARA, b. New York, N.Y, Jan. 19, 28; m. 47; c. 3. LITERARY CRITICISM, AESTHETICS. B.A, N.Y. Univ, 47; M.A, Calif. State Univ, Northridge, 64; Kent fel, Danforth Found, Harvard, 66-68, Ed.D, 68. Teaching fel, Eng. & educ, Harvard, 64-67, asst. prof, 67-68; Eng, Univ. Mass, Boston, 68-69; Harvard, 69-72, ASSOC. PROF. ENG. & ASST. DEAN, DOUGLASS COL, RUTGERS UNIV, NEW BRUNSWICK, 72- Instr, NDEA Eng. Inst. Clark Univ, summer 66; asst. prof, NDEA Inst. Psycholinguistics & Sociolinguistics, Harvard, summer, 68. MLA; NCTE; Am. Asn. Univ. Adminr. Poetics; narrative structure; literature and linguistics. Publ: Metaphor in the classroom, In: Aesthetic concepts and education, Univ. Ill, 70; The counter-school approach, New Leader, 11/71; Metaphor and infant cognition, Poetics: Int. Rev. Theory of Lit, 74. Add: Dept. of English, Douglass College, Rutgers University, New Brunswick, NJ 08930.

LEONE, LEONARD, b. Highland Park, Mich, Sept. 13, 14; m. 38; c. 2. SPEECH, DRAMA. B.A, Wayne State Univ, 36, M.A, 37; Univ. Florence, Italy, 36; Univ. Wis, 40. Instr. SPEECH, WAYNE STATE UNIV, 41-45, asst. prof, 45-51, assoc. prof, 51-57, prof, 57-62, DISTINGUISHED PROF, 62-, DIR, UNIV. THEATRES, 46- Chmn. cent. comt, Am. Col. Theatre Festival, 73- Recognition Award, Italian-Am. Soc, 56; Cert. of Esteem, U.S. Dept. Defense, 62; Gold Medal Award, Mich. Acad. Arts & Sci, 72. Fel. Am. Theatre Asn; Int. Soc. Theatre Res; Am. Soc. Theatre Res. Renaissance Italian theatre. Add: University Theatres, Wayne State University, 4743 Cass, Detroit, MI 48202.

LEOPOLD, SARA ELLEN, b. Pa, Mar. 29, 27; m. 48; c. 1. ENGLISH LITERATURE. B.A, Wayne State Univ, 55, M.A, 56, fel, 56-59, Ph.D, 61. Instr. Eng. & humanities, WAYNE STATE UNIV, 59-60, asst. prof. HUMANISTIC STUD, MONTEITH COL, 60-65, assoc. prof, 65-67, PROF, 67-, chmn. dept, 65-69. Ling. Soc. Am; Philol. Soc. Gt. Brit. Shakespeare criticism; linguistics. Add: Div. of Humanistic Studies, Monteith College, Wayne State University, Detroit, MI 48202.

LePAGE, PETER VanATTA, b. North Fairfield, Ohio, Mar. 5, 38; m. 62; c. 1. ENGLISH. B.A, Ohio Wesleyan Univ, 60; M.A, Bowling Green State Univ, 61, Ph.D.(Eng), 64. Asst. prof. ENG, UNIV. CINCINNATI, 64-71, ASSOC. PROF, 71- MLA. English novel; 18th century English poetry and prose; music and poetry, especially their complementation. Publ: The search for godhead in Marlowe's Tamburlaine, Col. Eng, 5/65; The prison and the dark beauty of Amelia, Criticism, fall 67. Add: Dept. of English, McMicken College, University of Cincinnati, Cincinnati, OH 45221.

LeROY, GAYLORD CLARKE, b. Aspinwall, Pa, Sept. 28, 10; m. 42; c. 2. ENGLISH LITERATURE. A.B, Oberlin Col, 30; A.M, Harvard, 31, Ph.D, 35. Instr, Univ. Maine, 34-38; Univ. Hawaii, 38-40, asst. prof, ENG, 41-46; TEMPLE UNIV, 46-53, assoc. prof, 53-60, PROF, 60- MLA. Nineteenth century English prose and poetry; 20th century literary criticism; Marxism and literature. Publ: Perplexed prophets: six nineteenth-century British authors, Univ. Pa, 53; Marxism and modern literature, Am. Inst. Marxist Stud, 67; co-ed, Preserve and create: essays in Marxist literary criticism, Humanities, 73. Add: Dept. of English, Temple University, Philadelphia, PA 19122.

LESLIE, ROY FRANCIS, b. Milngavie, Scotland, May 9, 22; m. 46; c. 2. ENGLISH. B.A, Univ. Manchester, Eng, 49, M.A, 51, Ph.D.(Eng), 55. Asst. lectr. ENG, Univ. Manchester, 50-53, lectr, 53-60, sr. lectr, 60-64; prof, Univ. Wis, Madison, 64-68; PROF, UNIV. VICTORIA, 68-, head dept, 68-73. Mem, bd. governors, Univ. Manchester, 56-64; Can. Counc. leave fel, 73-74. R.A.F, 40-46. Mod. Humanities Res. Asn; Philol. Soc, Eng; MLA; Mediaeval Acad. Am. Old and Middle English literature; history of the English language. Publ: Three Old English elegies, 61 & The wanderer, 66, Manchester Univ; co-auth, Lazamon's Brut, Vol. I, Oxford, 63; auth, Textual notes on The seasons for fasting, 10/53 & The integrity of riddle, 60, 7/68, J. Eng. & Ger. Philol; Analysis of stylistic devices and effects in

Anglo-Saxon literature, Stil-und Formproblem, Heidelberg, winter 59. Add: Dept. of English, University of Victoria, Victoria, B.C, Can.

LESOUSKY, CHRISTINE ALPHONSINE, Classical Languages. See Volume III, Foreign Languages, Linguistics & Philology.

LESTER, JAMES D, b. Ft. Smith, Ark, Mar. 5, 35; m. 58; c. 2. NINETEENTH CENTURY AMERICAN & BRITISH LITERATURE. B.A, E.Cent. State. Col, 57; M.A, Okla. State Univ, 63; Ph.D.(Eng), Univ. Tulsa, 70. Teacher ENG, Northside High Sch, Ft. Smith, Ark, 59-63; instr, Kans. State Teachers Col, 63-67; grad. asst, Univ. Tulsa, 67-70; ASST. PROF, AUSTIN PEAY STATE UNIV, 70- MLA; NCTE; Col. Eng. Asn; S.Atlantic Mod. Lang. Asn. Victorian poetry; nonfiction prose. Publ: Writing research papers, Scott, 67 & 70; Patterns: readings for composition, W.C. Brown, 74; Writing college papers: models and methods, Scribner, (in prep); Yeats' Crazy Jane poems & Melville's Bartleby: the quest for communication, Tenn. Philol. Quart. Add: 2316 Dogwood Lane, Clarksville, TN 37040.

LESTER, JOHN ASHBY, JR, b. Pottstown, Pa, Dec. 5, 15; m. 48; c. 3. ENGLISH LITERATURE. B.S, Haverford Col, 37; A.M, Harvard, 39, Ph.D.(Eng), 43. Asst. ENG, Haverford Col, 37-38; Harvard, 39-41, teaching fel. & asst, 41-42; instr, Rutgers Univ, 45-46; HAVERFORD COL, 46, asst. prof, 46-52, assoc. prof, 52-60, PROF, 60-, librn, 50-60. Volunteer ambulance driver, Am. Field Serv, Africa, Italy, India & Burma, 42-45; col. & libr. consult, 58, 66, 68; mem, Mid. States Comn. Insts. Higher Educ, 65-71. MLA. Nineteenth century literature, 1880-1920 period. Publ: Journey through Despair: 1880-1914, Princeton, 68. Add: Haverford College, Haverford, PA 19041.

LeSTOURGEON, DIANA E, b. Covington, Ky, Apr. 6, 27. ENGLISH. A.B, Univ. Pa, 49, A.M, 50, Ph.D.(Eng), 60. Instr. ENG, Ala. Polytech. Inst, 53-54; Univ. Mo, 54-55; asst. instr, Pa. State Univ, 55-56; Univ. Pa, 56-59, instr, 60-63; asst. prof, WIDENER COL, 65-68, ASSOC. PROF, 68- MLA. Twentieth century British fiction; psychological fiction; 18th century prose and poetry. Publ: Rosamond Lehmann, Twayne, 65. Add: Dept. of English, Widener College, Chester, PA 19013.

LESTRUD, VERNON A. C, b. Minneapolis, Minn, Sept. 30, 31; m. 55; c. 5. DRAMA, SPEECH. B.A, Pac. Lutheran Univ, 53; B.A, Univ. Wash, 56, M.A, 57; Ph.D.(speech, drama), Univ. Ore, 65. Instr. SPEECH & DRAMA, Wartburg Col, 57-61; Univ. Ore, 62-63; asst. prof, IDAHO STATE UNIV, 63-67, assoc. prof, 67-70, PROF. SPEECH & DRAMA & DIR. DEVELOP. & INSTNL. RES, 70-, asst. dean col. lib. arts, 68-70. Ed, Rendezvous, Idaho State Univ. Journal Arts & Letts, 64; mem, West. Speech Asn. Comt. Acad. Standards, 65-66. U.S.A, 53-55. Speech Commun. Asn; Am. Theatre Asn. Nineteenth century American theatre; the theories of Bertolt Brecht; faculty government. Publ: Faculty governance: the exploited generation, Intermountain Observer, 70. Add: Development & Institutional Research, Idaho State University, Pocatello, ID 83201.

LETENDRE, DONALD HENRY, b. Spencer, Mass, Oct. 21, 15; m. 48; c. 1. ENGLISH. A.B, Clark Univ, 38, A.M, 39; Boston Univ. Asst. prof. Eng, Clark Univ, 46-59; assoc. prof. Eng. & asst. dean fac, ASSUMPTION COL, 59-64, PROF. ENG, 64-, assoc. acad. dean, 64-70. Consult. letterwriting serv, State Mutual Life Assurance Co, Worcester, 59-; corporator, Bay State Savings Bank, Worcester, 66-, trustee, 69-; mem. bd. educ, Diocese of Worcester, 70- Off. Strategic Serv, 44-46. NCTE; Newman Hon. Soc; New Eng. Theatre Conf. American literature, speech, theater. Add: Dept. of English, Assumption College, 500 Salisbury St, Worcester, MA 01609.

LETTERMANN, HENRY, b. Pittsburgh, Pa, Feb. 28, 32; m. 53; c. 2. ENGLISH. B.S, Concordia Teachers Col.(Ill), 54; M.A, Univ. Chicago, 59. Instr. ENG, Lutheran High Sch, St. Louis, Mo, 56-59; CONCORDIA TEACHERS COL.(ILL), 59-61, asst. prof, 61-72, ASSOC. PROF, 72- Am. Folklore Soc; Lutheran Educ. Asn; Lutheran Soc. Worship, Music & Arts. American folk song; childrens songs and devotional poetry. Publ: Auth, Children's songs in Joyfully sing and in Vol. II, Sing Praise ser, 62, 63 & text, Who are these that earnest knock (Christmas anthem), 62, Concordia. Add: Dept. of English, Concordia Teachers College, River Forest, IL 60305.

LETTIS, RICHARD, b. Springfield, Mass, June 30, 28; m. 51; c. 5. ENGLISH. B.A, Univ. Mass, 52; M.A, Yale, 53, Ph.D.(Eng), 57. Instr. ENG, Ohio Univ, 56-60; asst. prof, C.W. POST COL, LONG ISLAND UNIV, 60-63, assoc. prof, 63-67, prof, 67-71, EXEC. DEAN, 71- Humanities ed, Pennant Stud. Guides, Educ. Res. Assoc. & Bantam, 66-67. U.S.A, 46-48. English novel of 18th and 19th centuries. Publ: Co-auth, Stephen Crane's The red badge of courage, Harcourt, 60, Wuthering heights handbook, Odyssey, 61, The Hungarian revolt, Scribner, 61 & Huck Finn and his critics, Macmillan, 62. Add: Office of the Executive Dean, C.W. Post College, Greenvale, NY 11548.

LETZRING, MONICA, b. Grafton, N.Dak, Feb. 1, 35. ENGLISH & COMPARATIVE LITERATURE. B.A, Col. St. Scholastica, 57; M.A, Univ. Md, 60, Ph.D, 63. Instr. Eng. lit, Col. Notre Dame (Md), 63; ENG, Ctr. Ling, Bergamo, Italy, 63-65; ASST. PROF, TEMPLE UNIV, 65- MLA; Am. Soc. 18th Century Stud. Eighteenth century English literature; Portuguese literature. Publ: Influence of Camoens in English literature, Rev. Camoneana, 64, 65, 71; Strangford's poems from the Portuguese of Camoens, Comp. Lit, fall 71. Add: Dept. of English, Temple University, Philadelphia, PA 19122.

LEVANT, HOWARD, b. Eveleth, Minn, Mar. 24, 29; m. 53; c. 2. AMERICAN LITERATURE, CREATIVE WRITING. B.A, Univ. Minn, 50, M.A, 54; fel, Univ. Iowa, 52-53; Ph.D.(Am. lit), Cornell Univ, 62. Instr. ENG, Univ. Wash, 57-60; from asst. prof. to assoc. prof, Morningside Col, 60-66; assoc. prof, Muskingum Col, 66-69; assoc. prof. & chmn. dept, Hartwick Col, 69-73; VIS. PROF. & RES. FEL, PEPPERDINE UNIV, MALIBU, 73- Nat. Found. Arts & Humanities-Ohio Arts Counc. grant, 68-69. MLA; Midwest Mod. Lang. Asn. Poetry; contemporary American literature; film aesthetics. Publ: The novels of John Steinbeck, Univ. Mo, 74; The unity of In dubious battle: violence and dehumanization, Mod. Fiction Stud, spring 65; Tortilla Flat: the shape of John Steinbeck's career, PMLA, fall 70; plus others. Add: Dept. of English, Pepperdine University, 24255 Pacific Coast Hwy, Malibu, CA 90265.

LEVENSON, JACOB CLAVNER, b. Boston, Mass, Oct. 1, 22; m. 46; c. 3. ENGLISH. A.B, Harvard, 43, Ph.D.(hist. Am. civilization), 51. Tutor hist. & lit, Harvard, 46-50, vis. lectr. Eng. & gen. educ, 51-52; instr. ENG, Univ. Conn, 50-54; asst. prof, Univ. Minn, 54-57, assoc. prof, 57-60, prof, 60-67, acting chmn. prog. Am. stud, 63; EDGAR ALLAN POE PROF, UNIV. VA, 67-, chmn. dept, 71-74. Mem. fac. Am. Stud. Sem, Salzburg, Austria, 47, 49; Am. Philos. Soc. Penrose grant, 56; fac. res. grant, Univ. Minn, 56; Guggenheim fel, 58-59; Am. Counc. Learned Soc. fel, 61-62; mem. Eng. Inst; mem. comt. consult, Notable American Women, 1607-1950, Radcliffe Col, 63-72; ed. bd, Am. Quart, 67-70, Va. Quart. Rev, 69- & New Lit. Hist, 69- E. Harris Harbison Distinguished Teaching Award, Danforth Found, 66. U.S.A, 43-45. MLA; Am. Stud. Asn. American literature; American cultural history. Publ: The mind and art of Henry Adams, Houghton, 57, Stanford Univ, 68; ed, Discussions of Hamlet, Heath, 60 & Life on the Mississippi, Dillon, 67; Introd. to The works of Stephen Crane, Vols, IV, V & VII, Univ. Va, 69-; auth, Henry Adams and the culture of science, In: Studies in American culture, Univ. Minn, 60; Stephen Crane, In: Major writers of America, Harcourt, 62; Thorstein Veblen's practical cats, Mass. Rev, 64; plus others. Add: Belvedere R.F.D. 8, Charlottesville, VA 22901.

LEVER, KATHERINE, b. St. Louis, Mo, Feb. 15, 16. ENGLISH & GREEK LITERATURE. A.B, Swarthmore Col, 36; A.M, Bryn Mawr Col, 37, Ph.D, 43. Instr, Univ. Rochester, 39-41; Eng. & Greek lit, WELLESLEY COL, 42-47, asst. prof, 47-56, assoc. prof, 56-62, PROF. ENG, 62-, dean class of 1950. Folger Shakespeare Libr. fel, 62-63. MLA; Am. Philol. Asn. English and Greek drama; Milton; English language. Publ: The art of Greek comedy, Methuen, 56; The novel and the reader, Methuen & Appleton, 61; The perfect teacher, Seabury, 64. Add: Dept. of English, Wellesley College, Wellesley, MA 02181.

LEVERETT, ERNESTINE, b. Cheyenne, Okla, May 2, 02; m. 21; c. 3. EDUCATION, ENGLISH SPANISH, SPEECH. A.B, East. Cent. State Col, 35; M.S, Okla. Agr. & Mech. Col, 42, Ed.D, 52. Teacher, high sch, Okla, 43-47; assoc. prof. Latin & educ, Okla. Baptist Univ, 47-60, prof. educ. & Latin, 60-67; Eng. & speech, Jarvis Christian Col, 67-73, chmn. div. humanities & head dept. Eng, 71-73; RETIRED. NCTE; AAUP; Am. Asn. Univ. Women. Remedial English, college level; speech patterns of black Americans. Publ: Foundations of Language, Bison Press; A different approach to remedial English, Baptist Educator, 5/51; Remedial English is camouflaged, Col. Eng, 11/51; Basic requirements in college curricula, Sch. & Society, 4/61. Add: Apt. 13323-11300 May Ave. N, Oklahoma City, OK 73120.

LEVIN, DAVID, b. York, Pa, Nov. 21, 24; m. 45; c. 2. ENGLISH, AMERICAN STUDIES. A.B, Harvard, 47, A.M, 49, Ph.D, 55. Teaching fel, Harvard, 48-52; instr. ENG, Stanford Univ, 52-55, asst. prof, 55-59, assoc. prof, 59-64, prof, 64-71; COMMONWEALTH PROF, UNIV. VA, 71-, mem, Ctr. Advan. Stud, 71-74. Fulbright exchange lectr, Univs. Strasbourg & Toulouse, France, 56-57; gen. ed. Harbrace Sourcebooks, Harcourt, Brace & World, Inc, 60-71; mem. Eng. exam. comt, Col. Entrance Exam. Bd, 61-64; fel, Ctr. Advan. Stud. Behavioral Sci, 62-63; Nat. Endowment Humanities sr. fel, 68-69; mem. ed. bd, Am. Quart, 69-72, Am. Lit, 70-73 & Clio, 71- U.S.A.A.F, 43-46, 2nd Lt. MLA; Am. Stud. Asn. American literature, especially historiography in the Colonial period and the 19th century. Publ: What happened in Salem?, Twayne, 52, Harcourt, 60; History as romantic art: Bancroft, Prescott, Motley and Parkman, Stanford Univ, 59, In defense of historical literature, Hill & Wang, 67. Add: Dept. of English, University of Virginia, Charlottesville, VA 22901.

LEVIN, GERALD H, b. Chicago, Ill, May 18, 29; m. 56; c. 2. ENGLISH. A.M, Univ. Chicago, 52; Ph.D, Univ. Mich, 56. Instr. ENG, Univ. Mich, 55-56; Univ. Colo, 56-57; asst. prof, East. Ill. Univ, 57-60; UNIV. AKRON, 60-65, assoc. prof, 65-68, PROF, 68- MLA. Twentieth century English fiction and poetry; Victorian literature. Publ: Prose models, 63, 2nd ed, 70, A brief handbook of rhetoric, 66, The short story, 67, ed, The art of rhetoric, 68, co-auth, The rhetoric case book, 3rd ed, 69 & auth, Styles for writing, 71, Harcourt; Lovelace's dream, Lit. & Psychol, 70; Richardson's Pamela: conflicting trends, Am. Imago, 71; Shaw, Butler and Kant, Philol. Quart, 73; plus others. Add: Dept. of English, University of Akron, Akron, OH 44304.

LEVIN, HARRY, b. Minneapolis, Minn, July 18, 12; m. 39; c. 1. ENGLISH, COMPARATIVE LITERATURE. A.B, Harvard, 33; Shaw traveling fel, Univ. Paris, 33-34, hon. Dr, 73; Guggenheim fel, 43-44; hon. Litt.D, Syracuse Univ, 53; hon. LL.D, St. Andrews Univ, Scotland, 62; hon. L.H.D, Union Col, & Clarkson Col. Technol, 70. Fac. instr. Eng, HARVARD, 39-44, assoc. prof, 44-48, prof, 48-55, Eng. & comp. lit, 55-60, BABBITT PROF. COMP. LIT, 60-, CHMN. DEPT, 46-51, 63-, jr. fel, Soc. Fels, 34-39, sr. fel, 46-67, chmn. univ. div. mod. langs, 51-52, 55-61. Am. Acad. Arts & Lett. grant-in-aid, 48; Lowell lectr, Boston, 52; vis. prof, Univ. Paris & Salzburg Sem, 53; Deneke lectr, Oxford, 53; vis. prof, Tokyo Univ, 55; chmn. Eng. Inst, 57; Beckman prof. Eng. lang. & lit, Univ. Calif, Berkeley, 57; Alexander lectr, Univ. Toronto, 58; mem, Nat. Shakespeare Anniversary Comt, 64; fel, H.E. Huntington Libr, 67; Patten lectr, Ind. Univ, 68; overseas fel, Churchill Col, Cambridge, 68-; Nat Endowment for Humanities sr. fel, 73-74; vis. fel, All Souls Col, Oxford Univ, spring 74. Chevalier, Legion of Honor, 53; Am. Counc. Learned Soc. Prize, 62; Nat. Bk. Award, fiction jury, 63. Fel. Am. Acad. Arts & Sci; fel. Nat. Inst. Arts & Lett; fel. Am. Philos. Soc; MLA; Am. Comp. Lit. Asn.(pres, 65-68); Int. Comp. Lit. Asn.(v.pres, 64-67); Acad. Lit. Stud.(v.pres, 73); PEN Club. Elizabethan drama; the modern novel; literary criticism. Publ: James Joyce: a critical introduction, 41 & The waste land from Ur to Echt, 72, New Directions; The overreacher: a study of Christopher Marlowe, 52, Contexts of criticism, 57 & Grounds for comparison, 72, Harvard Univ; The power of blackness; Hawthorne, Poe, Melville, Knopf, 58; The question of Hamlet, 59, The gates of horn: a study of five French realists, 63 & Refractions: essays in comparative literature, 66, Oxford Univ; Why literary criticism is not an exact science, Heffers, 68; The myth of the Golden Age in the Renaissance, Ind. Univ. 69. Add: Dept. of Comparative Literature, 400 Boylston Hall, Harvard University, Cambridge, MA 02138.

LEVIN, LAWRENCE LEE, b. Baltimore, Md, Dec. 16, 38; m. 67. LITERATURE OF THE RENAISSANCE. B.A, West. Reserve Univ, 62, M.A, 63;

Ph.D.(Eng), Univ. Wis-Madison, 69. ASST. PROF. ENG, UNIV. CALIF, SANTA BARBARA, 67- MLA; AAUP. Ben Jonson; Shakespeare. Publ: Justice and society in Sejanus and Volpone, Discourse, 70; Clement justice in Every man in his humor, Stud. Eng. Lit, 72; Replication as dramatic strategy in Ben Jonson's Comedies, Renaissance Drama, 72; plus others. Add: Dept. of English, University of California, Santa Barbara, CA 93106.

LEVIN, MILTON I, b. Milwaukee, Wis, Mar. 4, 25; m. 54; c. 1. ENGLISH & DRAMA. B.S, Univ. Wis, 48, M.S, 49; Ph.D.(Am. drama), Univ. Mich, 58. Instr. ENG, State Univ. N.Y. Col. Plattsburgh, 49-50; Univ. Wis, Milwaukee, 51-52; asst. prof, Wis. State Col, Whitewater, 58-60; assoc. prof, 60-61; asst. prof, TRENTON STATE COL, 61-63, assoc. prof, 63-66, PROF, 66- U.S.A, 44-46, S/Sgt. NCTE; MLA. American drama; modern British drama. Publ: Noel Coward, Twayne, 68; co-auth, A student's guide to 50 American plays, Washington Square, 69; contrib, Reader's Encycl. of World Drama, Crowell, 69; auth, Brian Friel: an introduction, Eire-Ireland, 72. Add: Dept. of English, Trenton State College, Trenton, NJ 08625.

LEVIN, RICHARD LOUIS, b. Buffalo, N.Y, Aug. 31, 22; m. 52; c. 2. ENGLISH. A.B, Univ. Chicago, 43, A.M, 47, Ph.D.(Eng), 57, Instr. Eng, Univ. Chicago, 49-53, asst. prof, 53-57, exam. humanities, 51-54; PROF. ENG, STATE UNIV. N.Y. STONY BROOK, 57-, acting chmn. dept, 61-63, 65-66. Fels, Res. Found. State Univ, N.Y, 61, 65, 67, 68, 71, 73 & Am. Counc. Learned Soc, 63-64; consult, M.A. prog. lib. stud, New Sch. Social Res, 66-67; Nat. Endowment for Humanities sr. fel, 74. Explicator Award, 71. U.S.N, 43-46, Lt.(jg). Malone Soc; NCTE; MLA; Shakespeare Asn. Am. Literary criticism; Elizabethan drama; Shakespeare. Publ: Tragedy; plays, theory, and criticism, 60, The question of Socrates, 61 & Tragedy, 65, Harcourt; Thomas Middleton's Michaelmas term, Univ. Nebr, 66; The multiple plot in English Renaissance drama, Univ. Chicago, 71; Some second thoughts on central themes, Mod. Lang. Rev, 72; Thematic unity and the homogenization of character, Mod. Lang. Quart, 72; No laughing matter: some new readings of The Alchemist, Stud. Lit. Imagination, 73. Add: Dept. of English, State University of New York at Stony Brook, Stony Brook, NY 11790.

LEVINE, BERNARD, b. Boston, Mass, July 15, 34; m. 63. ENGLISH LITERATURE. A.B, Harvard, 56; Ph.D.(Eng), Brown Univ, 65. Asst. ENG, Brown Univ, 61-63; instr, WAYNE STATE UNIV, 63-65, ASST. PROF, 65- MLA. Nineteenth and twentieth century romantic poetry; W.B. Yeats. Publ: Yeats' aesthetics and his concept of self, 66 & The dissolving image: Yeats' spiritual-aesthetic development, 69, Wayne State Univ; High talk: concentrative analysis of a poem by Yeats, James Joyce Quart, winter 66; Yeats' Leda and the swan: a psychopoetic analysis, Bucknell Rev, 69. Add: Dept. of English, Wayne State University, Detroit, MI 48202.

LEVINE, GEORGE, b. New York, N.Y, Aug. 27, 31; m. 56; c. 2. ENGLISH LITERATURE. A.B, N.Y. Univ, 52; M.A, Univ. Minn, 53, Ph.D, 59. Instr. ENG, Ind. Univ, 59-62, asst. prof, 62-65, assoc. prof, 65-68; prof. & chmn. dept, Livingston Col, Rutgers Univ, New Brunswick, 68-74; PROF, STATE UNIV. N.Y. COL. PURCHASE, 74- Co-ed, Victorian Stud, 59-68; Am. Counc. Learned Soc. grant-in-aid, 64; Guggenheim fel, 71-72. U.S.A, 53-55. MLA; Col. Eng. Asn. Theory of fiction; Victorian literature; non-fiction prose. Publ: Ed, The emergence of Victorian consciousness, Free Press Glencoe, 67; co-ed, The art of Victorian prose, Oxford, 68; auth, The boundaries of fiction, Princeton, 68. Add: Div. of Humanities, State University of New York College at Purchase, Purchase, NY 10577.

LEVINE, GEORGE RICHARD, b. Boston, Mass, Aug. 5, 29; m. 58; c. 2. ENGLISH. B.A, Tufts Col, 51; M.A, Columbia Univ, 52, fel, 58-59, Ph.D.(Eng), 61. Instr. ENG, Northwest. Univ, 59-63; asst. prof. STATE UNIV. N.Y. BUFFALO, 63-66, assoc. prof, 66-70, PROF, 70-, assoc. provost fac. arts & lett, 71-72. Fulbright lectr, Univ. Cologne, 69-70. Sig.C, U.S.A. 52-54. MLA. Eighteenth century English literature; English novel; dynamics of the teaching-learning process. Publ: Co-auth, Riverside readings, Columbia Univ, 58 & Readings in American English, Prenctice-Hall Int, 60; auth, Henry Fielding and the Dry mock: a study of the techniques of irony in his early works, Mouton, 67; co-auth, Poetic and pictorial design in Two songs of innocence, PMLA, 5/67; auth, Dryden's Inarticulate Poesy: music and the Davidic King in Absalom and Achitophel, 18th-Century Stud, summer, 68; Satiric intent and Baroque design in Donne's Go and catch a falling star, Neuren Sprachen, 71. Add: Dept. of English, Annex B, State University of New York at Buffalo, Buffalo, NY 14214.

LEVINE, JAY ARNOLD, b. New York, N.Y, Feb. 12, 32; m. 62. ENGLISH. A.B, Columbia Univ, 53, A.M, 54; Ph.D.(Eng), Johns Hopkins Univ, 61. Instr. ENG, Goucher Col, 60-61; Univ. Chicago, 61-62; asst. prof, Univ. Calif, Berkeley, 62-67; assoc. prof, Univ. Rochester, 67-69; PROF, UNIV. ILL, CHICAGO CIRCL, 69-, HEAD DEPT, 72- Grant-in-aid, Huntington Libr, 63. U.S.A, 54-56. MLA. English literature of 18th century. Publ: Dryden's Song for St Cecilia's day, 1687, Philol. Quart, 1/65; The design of A tale of a tub (with a digression on a mad modern critic), ELH, 6/66; Pope's Epistle to Augustus, lines 1-30, Stud. Eng. Lit, summer 67; plus others. Add: Dept. of English, University of Illinois at Chicago Circle, Chicago, IL 60680.

LEVINE, L. CARL, b. New York, Aug. 23, 07; m. 30. ENGLISH. B.S, City Col. New York, 30; M.A, Univ. Chicago, 56; Ed.D, Columbia Univ, 61. Pres, Carl Levine & Co, 30-46; dir. for. aid, Am. Friends Serv. Comt, 46-48; asst. prof. ENG, Ill. Wesleyan Univ, 56-58; lectr, Hebrew Univ, Israel, 58-59; assoc. prof, Pueblo Col, 61-63; South. Colo. State Col, 63-64; COLO. STATE UNIV, 64-70, prof, 70-73, EMER. PROF, 73- Lectr, Viittakivi Int. Folk Col, Finland, 59, Conf. Int. Educ, 64; asst. dir. orientation, Teachers for E.Africa, Teachers Col, Columbia Univ, 61; dir. Workshops NDEA Inst. High Sch. Eng. Teachers, Colo. State Univ, 65; U.S. Nat. Inst. Mental Health res. grants, 66, 68; consult, Colo. State Hospital, Pueblo, 66; co-chmn, Am. Lit. Sect, Rocky Mount. Mod. Lang. Asn, 67, chmn, 68; Colo. State Univ. res. found. grants, 67-71; consult. ed. comt, PMLA, 68. NCTE; MLA; Int. Soc. Gen. Semantics. American literature; social forces in contemporary literature; communication and mental illness. Publ: Social criticism in Shaw and Nietzsche, Shaw Rev, 1/67; Communication disjunction and mental illness, J. Human Relat, 68; The released mental patient and the community: a study in communication, ETC: Rev. Gen. Semantics, 9/72; plus others. Add: 817 Balsam Lane, Ft. Collins, CO 80521.

LEVINE, NORMAN, b. New York, N.Y, Feb. 21, 38; m. 63; c. 1. TUDOR LITERATURE. B.E.E, Cooper Union, 59; M.S.E.E, Newark Col. Eng, 65; M.A, Columbia Univ, 65, Ph.D.(Eng), 72. Microwave res. & develop. eng, Wheeler Labs, 59-62; instr. math, Newark Col. Eng, 62-71; ENG, CITY COL. NEW YORK, 71-72, ASST. PROF, 72- MLA; Renaissance Soc. Am; Bibliog. Soc. Sidney; Shakespeare. Add: Dept. of English, City College of New York, 138th St. & Convent Ave, New York, NY 10031.

LEVINE, PHILIP, b. Detroit, Mich, Jan. 10, 28; m. 45; c. 3. CREATIVE WRITING. B.A, Wayne State Univ, 50, M.A, 55; M.F.A, Univ. Iowa, 57; Stegnar fel, Stanford Univ, 57-58. Instr. ENG, Univ. Iowa, 55-57; PROF, CALIF. STATE UNIV, FRESNO, 58- Guggenheim fel, 73. Joseph Henry Jackson Award, 63; Chaplebrook Award, 68; Frank O'Hara Mem. Award, 72; Nat. Inst. Arts & Lett. Award, 73. Poetry; contemporary Spanish and Spanish American poetry; translation. Publ: On the edge (poems), Stone Wall Press, 63; Not this pig (poems), Wesleyan Univ, 68; Pili's wall (poems), Unicorn Bks, 71; Red dust (poems), Kayak Bks, 71; They feed they lion (poems), 72 & 1933 (poems), 74, Atheneum; plus numerous others. Add: Dept. of English, California State University, Fresno, CA 93710.

LEVINE, RICHARD ALLAN, b. Malden, Mass, May 13, 32; m. 54; c. 2. ENGLISH. B.A, Univ. Mass, 53; fel, Univ. Conn, 53-55, M.A, 55; Ph.D, Ind. Univ, 61. Assoc. Ind. Univ, 55-57, resident lectr. ENG, 57-59; instr, Miami Univ, 59-61, asst. prof, 61-64; Univ. Calif, Riverside, 64-69, summer fac. fel, 65; assoc. prof, ENG, STATE UNIV. N.Y. STONY BROOK, 69-72, PROF, 72-, dir. grad. stud, 70-73. Res. asst, Miami Univ, 62; vis. prof. Eng, Univ. South. Calif, summer 72. MLA; NCTE; Int. Asn. Univ. Prof. Eng. Victorian literature; the English novel. Publ: Backgrounds to Victorian literature, Chandler, 67; Benjamin Disraeli, Twayne, 68; The Victorian experience, Ohio Univ, (in press); Disraeli's Tancred and The great Asian mystery, Nineteenth Century Fiction, 6/67; Dickens, The two nations and Individual possibility, Stud. Novel, summer 69; Three Dombeys, Dickens Stud, 7/72; plus others. Add: Dept. of English, State University of New York at Stony Brook, Stony Brook, NY 11790.

LEVINE, ROBERT, b. New York, N.Y, May 9, 33; m. 58; c. 3. ENGLISH. B. B.A, City Col. New York, 54; M.A, Columbia Univ, 58; Ph.D, Univ. Calif, Berkeley, 63. Instr. Eng, Rensselaer Polytech. Inst, 58-59; Cornell Univ, 62-64; asst. prof, BOSTON UNIV, 64-70, ASSOC. PROF. Eng. & CLASSICS, 70- U.S.A, 54-56. MLA. Old English; Middle English; Medieval Latin. Publ: Ingeld + Xrist, a medieval problem, In: Viator, Vol. II, Univ. Calif, 71. Add: Dept. of English, Boston University, 176 Bay State Rd, Boston, MA 02215.

LEVINE, STUART GEORGE, b. New York, N.Y, May 25, 32; m. 58, 63. AMERICAN STUDIES. A.B, Harvard, 54; univ. scholars, Brown Univ, 54, 55, 57, M.A, 56, univ. fel, 56-57, dissertation fel, 57-58, Ph.D, 58. Instr. Eng. & Am. civilization, UNIV. KANS, 58-61, asst. prof. Eng, 61-65, assoc. prof, 65-66, AM. STUD, 66-69, PROF, 69-, ED. AM. STUD. SER, 68-, univ. res. grants, 58-68. Fulbright lectr. Am. stud, La Plata Nat. Univ, Argentina, 62, Univ. Costa Rica, 65, 67 & Nat. Univ. Mex, 72; lectr. lit, NDEA Summer Inst, Univ. S.Dak, 65; vis. prof. Am. lit, Univ. Mo, Kansas City, 66-67 & Calif. State Univ, Los Angeles, 69 & 71; scholar-in-residence, Univ. Ariz, 71-72. Am. Stud. Asn.(ed, Am. Stud, 59-); MLA; NCTE. Music, painting and literature in America; American history. Publ: Co-auth, The American Indian today, 68 & auth, Edgar Poe: seer and craftsman, 72, Everett Edwards; Scholarly strategy: the Poe case, spring 65 & Art, values, institutions and culture; an essay in American studies methodology and relevance, 5/72, Am. Quart; Our Indian minority, Colo, Quart, winter 68. Add: Dept. of American Studies, University of Kansas, Lawrence, KS 66045.

LEVITSKY, RUTH MICKELSON, b. Freeman, Mo, Mar. 16, 13; m. 52; c. 1. ENGLISH. B.S, Cent. Mo. State Col, 45; M.S, Ill. State Norm. Univ, 47; Ph.D, Univ. Mo, 58. Teacher, elem. & high schs, Mo. & Ill, 30-35, 42-49; instr. ENG, Univ. Mo, 50-54; Douglass Col. & Univ. Col, Rutgers Univ, 55-56; asst. prof. Ont. Federated Cols, 62-64; ST. JEROME'S COL, UNIV. WATERLOO, 64-66, ASSOC. PROF, 67- Can. Counc. Humanities & Soc. Sci. grant, 69; Can. Counc. grant, 72-74. Shakespeare Asn. Am; MLA; Int. Shakespeare Soc. Richard Hooker as spokesman for the Anglican view of self-mastery; self-mastery as a virtue in Shakespeare's England; stoicism versus Christianity in Shakespeare. Publ: Rightly to be great, 65 & All-in-all sufficiency in Othello, 72, Shakespeare Stud; The elements were so mix'd, PMLA, 73. Add: Dept. of English, St. Jerome's College, University of Waterloo, Ont, Can.

LEVITT, MORTON PAUL, b. Brooklyn, N.Y, Dec. 22, 36; m. 63. ENGLISH. B.A, Dickinson Col, 58; Columbia Law Sch, 58-59; M.A, Columbia Univ, 60; Ph.D.(Eng), Pa. State Univ, 65. Instr. ENG, Pa. State Univ, 60-62; TEMPLE UNIV, 62-65, asst. prof, 65-71, ASSOC. PROF, 71- Assoc, Ctr. Neo-Hellenic Stud, 72- MLA; Mod. Greek Stud. Narrative innovations in modern fiction; the novels and verse of Nikos Kazantzakis; fiction of James Joyce. Publ: Co-auth, Bloomsday: an interpretation of James Joyce's Ulysses, N.Y. Graphic Soc, 72, McClelland & Stewart, 72 & Bodley Head, 73; Disillusionment and epiphany: the novels of Claude Simon, Critique, 69-70; The cretan glance: the world and art of Nikos Kazantzakis, J. Mod. Lit, 71-72; A hero for our time: Leopold Bloom and the myth of Ulysses, James Joyce Quart, 72; plus others. Add: Dept. of English, Temple University, Philadelphia, PA 19122.

LEVITT, PAUL M, b. Newark, N.J, Dec. 21, 35; m. 58; c. 3. ENGLISH. B.A, Univ. Colo, 57, M.A, 60; M.A, Univ. Calif, Los Angeles, 62, Ph.D.(Eng), 66. Instr. ENG, UNIV. COLO, BOULDER, 64-66, asst. prof, 66-69, ASSOC. PROF. & CHMN. DEPT, 69-, fac. fel, Counc. Res. & Creative Work, 69-70. MLA. Contemporary drama; development of British drama. Publ: A structural approach to the analysis of drama, Mouton, The Hague, 71; J.M. Synge: a bibliography of published criticism, Irish Univ. Press, Dublin, 74; The structural craftmanship of J.M. Synge's Riders to the sea, Eire-Ireland, spring 69; An analogue for Faulkner's A rose for Emily, Papers on Lang. & Lit, spring 73; An approach to bridging classical and modern drama, J. Eng. Teaching Technique, summer 73; plus others. Add: Dept. of English, Hellems 101, University of Colorado, Boulder, CO 80302.

LEVY, ALFRED J, b. Boston, Mass, Nov. 15, 26. ENGLISH & AMERICAN LITERATURE. A.B, Clark Univ, 49; A.M, Univ. Wis, 50, Ph.D.(Eng), 57. Assoc. ENG, Ind. Univ, 55-57, instr, 57-60, asst. prof, 60-61; UNIV. HAWAII, MANOA, 61-66, assoc. prof, 66-71, PROF, 71-, ASSOC. DEAN ARTS & SCI, 68- Lectr, Coe Found. Am. Stud. Inst, Hawaii, summer 64; NDEA Inst, Univ. Hawaii, summer 66. Sig.C, 45-46. AAUP. American prose fiction; world literature. Publ: Co-auth, Manuscripts of Hawthorne's short stories, Stud. Bibliog, 61; auth, Ethan Brand and the unpardonable sin, Boston Univ. Stud. Eng, autumn 61; The house of the seven gables: the religion of love, 19th-Century Fiction, 12/61. Add: Dept. of English, University of Hawaii at Manoa, Honolulu, HI 96822.

LEVY, BERNARD S, b. Northampton, Mass, Dec. 1, 27; m. 52; c. 8. ENGLISH. B.A, State Univ. Iowa, 52; M.A, Univ. Mich, 54; Ph.D, Univ. Calif, Berkeley, 61. Instr, Univ. Colo, 54-55; asst, Univ. Calif, Berkeley, 55-58, instr. freshman Eng, 58-61; asst. prof. ENG, HARPUR COL, STATE UNIV. N.Y. BINGHAMTON, 61-68, ASSOC. PROF, 68- State Univ. N.Y. fac. fels, 63, 66, 68-69. A.U.S, 46-48. MLA; Mediaeval Acad. Am. Middle English literature, especially Chaucer and the Gawain poet. Publ: Gawain's spiritual journey: Imitatio Christi in Sir Gawain and the Green Knight, Annuale Mediaevale, 65; Chaucer's Wife of Bath, the loathly lady and Dante's siren, Symposium, winter 65; Biblical parody in the Summoner's tale, Tenn. Stud. in Lit, 66. Add: Dept. of English, Harpur College, State University of New York at Binghamton, Binghamton, NY 13901.

LEVY, CHARLES SAMUEL, b. New York, N.Y, Aug. 15, 31; m. 56; c. 2. ENGLISH. A.B, Hamilton Col, 53; Fulbright grant, Oxford, 57-59; univ. fel, Cornell Univ, 59-60, teaching fel, 61-62, Ph.D,(Eng), 62. Asst. prof. ENG, Univ. Minn, Minneapolis, 62-67; ASSOC. PROF, CORNELL UNIV, 67- Am. Counc. Learned Soc. fel, 65-66. U.S.A.F, 53-57, Res, 57, Capt. MLA; Am. Philol. Asn; Renaissance Soc. Am; AAUP. Classical influence upon Renaissance English literature; Sir Philip Sidney; John Milton. Publ: Antigone's motives: a suggested interpretation, Trans. Am. Philol. Asn, 63; A supplementary inventory of Sir Philip Sidney's correspondence, Mod. Philol, 69; The Sidney-Hanau correspondence, Eng. Lit. Renaissance, 72. Add: Dept. of English, Goldwin Smith Hall, Cornell University, Ithaca, NY 14850.

LEVY, HERMAN MITTLE, JR, b. Charleston, S.C, Feb. 18, 35; m. 57; c. 2. FICTION. B.A, Tulane Univ, 57, M.A, 60; Ph.D.(Eng), Univ. Fla, 65. Instr. Eng, Univ. Fla, 60-65, asst. prof, 65-68; Loyola Univ.(La), 68-70; INSTR. ENG. & HUMANITIES, SANTA FE COMMUNITY COL.(FLA), 70- Contemporary humanities; sociology of liberation. Publ: Modern novel writing and Azemia, two novels by William Beckford, Scholars' Facsimiles, 68; An omission unnoticed: Nickleby forgotten, 68 & co-auth, Who tells the story of a queer client, 68, Dickensian; The interpolated tales in Pickwick papers, a further note, Dickens Stud, 68. Add: Dept. of Humanities, Box 1530, Santa Fe Community College, 3000 N.W. 83rd St, Gainesville, FL 32601.

LEVY, LEO B, b. Oakland, Calif, Dec. 21, 16; m. 53; c. 3. ENGLISH & AMERICAN LITERATURE. A.B, Univ. Calif, Berkeley, 45, M.A, 47, Ph.D, 54. Lectr. ENG, Univ. Calif, Berkeley, 54-55; instr, La. State Univ, 55-57; asst. prof, 57-58; Ind. Univ, 58-59; ARIZ. STATE UNIV, 59-61, assoc. prof, 61-64, PROF, 64- American novel; American civilization; American literature. Publ: The marble faun: Hawthorne's landscape of the fall, Am. Lit, 5/70; Fanshawe: Hawthorne's world of images, Stud. in Novel, winter 70; Times portraiture, Hawthorne's theory of history, Nathaniel Hawthorne J, 71. Add: Dept. of English, Arizona State University, Tempe, AZ 85281.

LEVY, WILLIAM TURNER, b. Far Rockaway, N.Y, Nov. 3, 22. ENGLISH. B.A, City Col. New York, 42; M.A, Columbia Univ, 47, Ph.D.(Eng), 52. From instr. to ASSOC. PROF. ENG, BARUCH COL, 46- Priest, Protestant Episcopal Church, 52-; sr. ed, The Churchman, 59- U.S.A, 43-45, Lt. Publ: William Barnes: the man and the poems, Longmans Ltd, Dorchester, 60; co-auth, Affectionately, T.S. Eliot, Lippincott, 68; auth, Jeffers as prophet, In: Robinson Jeffers, Grabhorn Press, 62; The idea of the church in T.S. Eliot, Christian Scholar, 58. Add: Dept. of English, Baruch College, 17 Lexington Ave, New York, NY 10010.

LEWALSKI, BARBARA KIEFER, b. Chicago, Ill, Feb. 22, 31; m. 56; c. 1. ENGLISH LITERATURE. B.S, Ed, Kans. State Teachers Col, Emporia, 50; A.M, Univ. Chicago, 51, William Rainey Harper fel, 52-53, Ph.D, 56; Am. Asn. Univ. Women fel, Brit. Mus, 53-54. Instr. ENG. LIT, Wellesley Col, 54-56; BROWN UNIV, 56-58, asst. prof, 58-63, assoc. prof, 63-68, PROF, 68-, dir. grad. stud. Eng, 68-72. Am. Asn. Univ. Women fel, 61-62; Guggenheim fel, 67-68; spec. lectr, Hebrew Univ. & Bar-Ilan Univ, Israel, 68, Milton Tercentenary Series, Univ. West. Ont, 71 & Clark Libr. 17th Century Series, 72; Huntington Libr. fel, summer 72; Am. Counc. Learned Soc. grant, summer 73; Nat. Endowment for Humanities sr. fel, 74-75. MLA (mem. Parker Prize comt, 72-74); Milton Soc. Am.(pres, 70); Renaissance Soc. Am; Acad. Lit. Stud. Seventeenth century poetry and prose; Milton studies; Renaissance literature. Publ: Milton's brief epic: the genre, meaning and art of Paradise regained, Methuen & Brown Univ, 66; ed, Much ado about nothing, Blackfriars Shakespeare, Brown, 69; co-ed, Major poets of the earlier seventeenth century, Odyssey, 73; auth, Donne's Anniversaries and the poetry of praise: the creation of a symbolic mode, Princeton, 73; Innocence and experience in Milton's Eden, In: New essays of Paradise lost, Univ. Calif, 69; Samson Agonistes and the Tragedy of the Apocalypse, PMLA, 70; Typology and poetry: a consideration of Herbert, Vaughan and Marvell, In: Clark library series, Univ. Calif, 73; plus others. Add: Dept. of English, Brown University, Providence, RI 02912.

LEWARS, KENNETH, b. Philadelphia, Pa, Mar. 5, 22. ENGLISH. B.S, Swarthmore Col, 40-42; B.S, Columbia Univ, 46, M.A, 47. Instr. ENG, Conn. Col, 49-51; Univ. Rochester, 51-53; Dartmouth Col, 53-55; Univ. Wis, 55-59; ASST. PROF, Carroll Col.(Wis), 59-61; SOUTH. CONN. STATE COL, 61- U.S.A.A.F, 42-45, 1st Lt. MLA. Contemporary British literature. Add: Dept. of English, Southern Connecticut State College, New Haven, CT 06515.

LEWELS, FRANCISCO J, b. El Paso, Tex, Apr. 10, 44. MASS COMMUNICATION, EDUCATION. B.A, Tex. West. Col, 66; M.S, Troy State Univ, 71; Ph.D.(jour), Univ. Mo, 73. Ed, Army Aviation Dig. Mag, 68-70; Freedom of Inform. Ctr. Publns, 70-72; consult. commun, U.S. Dept. Justice, 72; ASST. PROF. JOUR. & CHMN. DEPT, UNIV. TEX, EL PASO, 73- Eng.C, U.S.A, 66-69, Capt; Bronze Star Medal, Air Medal & Oak Leaf Cluster. Asn. Educ. in Jour. Minorities in communication; communications and society; international communication. Publ: Uses of the news media by the Chicano movement, Praeger, 74; The newspaper preservation act, 1/71 & Critical attitudes toward the media, 5/72, Freedom Inform. Dig; Critical attitudes toward the media, Educ. Broadcasting Rev, 10/72; plus others. Add: Dept. of Journalism, University of Texas at El Paso, El Paso, TX 79968.

LEWES, ÜLLE ERIKA, b. Tallinn, Estonia, Mar. 22, 42; U.S. citizen; m. 67. MEDIEVAL & COMPARATIVE LITERATURE. A.B, Cornell Univ, 64; M.A, Harvard, 65, Ph.D.(comp. lit), 72. Instr. ENG, TEMPLE UNIV, 71-72, ASST. PROF, 72- MLA; Mediaeval Acad. Am. The Tristran legend; mutual influences between medieval romances and Saints' lives; folklore. Add: 31 Hawthorne Ave, Princeton, NJ 08540.

LEWIS, ALBERT LUTHER, b. Portales, N.Mex, June 12, 39; m. 68; c. 2. SPEECH COMMUNICATION. B.A, Stanford Univ, 61; M.A, Univ. Ore, 63, Ph.D.(rhet, pub. address), 67. Teaching asst. speech, Univ. Ore, 63-65; asst. prof, CENT. WASH. STATE COL, 65-68, ASSOC. PROF. SPEECH COMMUN, 69-, CHMN. DEPT, 73- Mem. wording comt, Nat. Comt. Discussion & Debate, 65-67; vis. prof. rhet, Univ. Calif, Davis, 68-69. Speech Commun. Asn; West. Speech Commun. Asn.(chmn. interest group, 72-74); AAUP. Public address; communication and conflict resolution. Publ: Contrib, Landmarks in western oratory, Univ. Wyo, 68; auth, Stephen Toulmin: a reappraisal, Cent. States Speech J, spring 72; Every man his own orator: the impact of frontier on American public address, In: Rhetoric of the people, Rodopi, Netherlands, 74; plus four others. Add: Dept. of Communication, Central Washington State College, Ellensburg, WA 98926.

LEWIS, ALLAN, b. New York, N.Y, June 30, 08; m. 41; c. 2. CONTEMPORARY DRAMA. B.A, City Univ. New York, 28; M.A, Columbia Univ, 30; Ph.D.(Eng), Stanford Univ, 40; Dr. Lett.(contemporary drama), Nat. Univ. Mex, 55. Exec. dir. theatre, New Dramatists Comt, 46-48; chmn. dept. theatre, Bennington Col, 48-50; prof. comp. drama & dir, Univ. Theatre, Univ. Mex, 52-56; chmn. dept. drama, Briarcliff Col, 56-60; DIR, SHAKESPEARE INST, UNIV. BRIDGEPORT, 65- Sr. lectr. contemporary theatre, New Sch. Soc. Res, 52-; res. fel, Folger Shakespeare Libr, 65-66; drama critic, New Haven Register, 66-; res. fel, Aspen Inst. Humanistic Stud, 67-70. U.S.A.A.F, 41-45, 1st Lt. AAUP; MLA; Int. Asn. Univ. Prof. Shakespeare interpretation in contemporary terms; the contemporary theatre. Publ: The contemporary theatre, 63 & American plays and play-wrights, 65, Crown; Ionesco, Twayne, 73; But it's not Shakespeare, Arts in Soc, Vol. VII, No. 1; Shakespeare's comedies, Queens Quart, summer 71; Broadway's ill, Guardian, 8/73. Add: Shakespeare Institute, University of Bridgeport, Bridgeport, CT 06602.

LEWIS, ARTHUR ORCUTT, JR, b. Wellsville, Pa, Oct. 8, 20; m. 45; c. 3. AMERICAN LITERATURE. A.B, Harvard, 41, A.M, 42; Ph.D.(Eng), Pa. State Univ, 51. Instr. Eng, Rice Inst, 46-48; asst. Eng. lit, PA. STATE UNIV, UNIVERSITY PARK, 48-50, instr, 50-52, asst. prof, 52-55, assoc. prof, 55-60, PROF. ENG, 60-, ASSOC. DEAN COL. LIB. ARTS, 65-, chmn. Eng. grad. stud, 58-60, assoc. head dept. Eng, 60-65, acting dean, Col. Lib. Arts, 68-69. Vis. asst. prof. Eng, Sam Houston State Teachers Col, summer 48. Sig.C, 42-46, Lt. MLA; Col. Eng. Asn; Am. Stud. Asn; Soc. Hist. Technol. American-German literary relations; utopian novels; technology and society. Publ: Co-auth, The case for poetry, Prentice-Hall, 54, 2nd ed, 65 & Anglo-German and American-German crosscurrents, Univ. N.C, Vols. I, II & III, 57, 62 & 67; co-auth, Visions and revisions in modern American literary criticism, 62, auth, Of men and machines, 63 & co-auth, The world of Japanese fiction, 73, Dutton; ed, Utopian literature (41 vols), 71 & auth, American utopias; selected short fiction, Arno & N.Y. Times, 71; plus others. Add: 691 Westerly Pkwy, State College, PA 16801.

LEWIS, EARL E, b. Red Wing, Minn, Jan. 14, 22; m. 43; c. 4. ENGLISH, AMERICAN STUDIES. B.S, Wis. State Univ, La Crosse, 52; M.A, Univ. Iowa, 54; Ph.D.(Am. stud), Univ. Minn, Minneapolis, 66. Teacher, high sch, Wis, 54-59; PROF. ENG, UNIV. WIS-RIVER FALLS, 59- Publ: Co-auth, Readings in literature, W.C. Brown, 62; auth, Structural grammar in the classroom, Wis. Eng. J, 61; four biog. articles, In: Notable American Women, Harvard Univ, 69. Add: Dept. of English, University of Wisconsin-River Falls, River Falls, WI 54022.

LEWIS, ELSIE BRICKETT, b. New Bedford, Mass, Oct. 2, 03; m. 45. ENGLISH. A.B, Bates Col, 25; A.M, Univ. Maine, 29; Univ. Pa, 25-28; Univ. Vt, 26, 27; Ph.D, Yale, 37. Teacher jr. high sch, Pa, 25-28; teaching fel. ENG, Univ. Maine, 28-29, instr, 29-30; Colby Col, 30-32; asst. prof, JUDSON COL, 35-36, assoc, prof, 37-38, prof, 38-72, head dept, 35-72, chmn. div. humanities, 38-72, EMER. PROF, 72- MLA; NCTE; S.Atlantic Mod. Lang. Asn. The imagist school in modern poetry; the poets and poetry of New England transcendentalism. Add: Dept. of English, Judson College, Marion, AL 36756.

LEWIS, GEORGE L, b. Treasureton, Idaho, Dec. 3, 16; m. 41; c. 3. SPEECH, EDUCATION. B.A, Brigham Young Univ, 41, M.A, 47; Ph.D.(theatre, speech), Univ. Denver, 54. Teacher, Pub. Schs, 41-42; head educ. speech, War Relocation Authority, 42-43; instr. speech & Eng, Brigham Young Univ, 46-47, from asst. prof. to assoc. prof. SPEECH & EDUC, 48-56; asst. prof. OHIO STATE UNIV, 56-60, assoc. prof, 60-65, PROF, 65- Educ. consult, South. Utah Col, 59; Jewish Theol. Sem, 60-; educ. adv, Columbus Childrens Theatre Arts, 60-; assoc. ed, Ohio Speech J, 60- U.S.A.A.F, 43-45, Sgt. Speech Commun. Asn; Am. Theatre Asn. Publ: Co-auth, Communicative arts and sciences of speech, 66 & Teaching speech, 69, C.E. Merrill; auth, Secondary school speech textbooks: a bibliographical analysis, Ohio Speech J, 65; Courses in radio and television, Bull. Sec. Sch. Prin, 10/66; Creative drama problems and processes, Cent. States Speech J, 72. Add: 239 Arps Hall, Ohio State University, Columbus, OH 43210.

LEWIS, JANET ELIZABETH, b. Ottawa, Ont, Aug. 6, 40; m. 66; c. 1. ENBLISH LITERAUTRE. B.A, Carleton Univ, 62; M.A, Univ. Toronto, 64, Can.

Counc. fel. & Ont. Grad. fel, 64-67, Ph.D.(Eng), 70. Lectr. ENG, YORK. UNIV; 68-70, ASST. PROF, 70- MLA; Medieval Acad. Am; Asn. Can. Univ. Teachers Eng.(secy-treas, 70-72); Humanities Asn. Can; Can. Counc. Teachers Eng. Modern literature; the novel; Chaucer. Publ: Fitzgerald's Philippe, Count of darkness, Fitzgerald-Hemingway Annual, 75. Add: Dept. of English, York University, 4700 Keele St, Downsview, Ont. M5N 1K2, Can.

LEWIS, JOHN SAMUEL, b. Amarillo, Tex, Nov. 12, 29; m. 61. ENGLISH. B.S, Kans. State Univ, 52; Ph.D.(Eng), Univ. Kans, 68. Instr. Eng. & Correspondence stud, Univ. Kans. 60-61; ENG, Kans. State Teachers Col, 62-65; UNIV. TEX, ARLINGTON, 65-68, asst. prof, 68-71, ASSOC. PROF, 71- Asst. ed, Conradiana, 70- U.S.A, 52-54, Lt. MLA; AAUP; Malone Soc; Renaissance Soc. Am. Elizabethan Drama; Shakespeare; Joseph Conrad. Publ: Conrad's principal sources for The lagoon, UNISA Eng. Stud, 71. Add: Dept. of English, University of Texas at Arlington, Box 19475 University Station, Arlington, TX 76019.

LEWIS, JOHN SMITH, b. South Windham, Conn, July 9, 08. AMERICAN LITERATURE. A.B, Harvard, 29; A.M, Brown Univ, 30; Ph.D, N.Y. Univ, 41. Instr. Eng, Univ. Ga, 30-33; asst. ed. univ. press, Harvard, 33-35; teacher, sec. schs, R.I, 35-38; instr. Eng, N.Y. Univ, 38-41; mem. staff pers. dir, West. Elec. Co, 44-47; prof. ENG. & chmn. div, Wilson Teachers Col, 47-54; vis. lectr, Univ. Nev, 54-55; assoc. prof, East. Ky. State Col, 55-57; PROF, TOWSON STATE COL, 57- Instr, City Col. New York, 44. U.S.A, 41-44, Capt. MLA; NCTE. History of instruction in American literature in colleges and universities of the United States 1827-1939; English novel and American prose fiction; dramatic works, especially Shakespeare. Publ: Co-auth, Teaching English: 7/12, Am. Bk. Co, 63; auth, A note on Robinson's Forestalling, Am. Notes & Queries, 3/67. Add: Dept. of English, Towson State College, Baltimore, MD 21204.

LEWIS, KATHERINE ANN, b. Seattle, Wash, Sept. 16, 36. ENGLISH CONTEMPORARY AMERICAN LITERATURE. B.Ed, Seattle Univ, 62; M.A, San Diego Col. Women, 64; Ph.D.(Eng, Am. lit), Stanford Univ, 68. From asst. prof. to PROF. ENG, WAYNE STATE COL, 67- MLA. Edith Wharton; modern American drama; Eugene O'Neill. Add: Dept. of English, Wayne State College, Wayne, NE 68787.

LEWIS, LEON E, b. Boston, Mass, Dec. 30, 28; m. 57; c. 2. ENGLISH. B.S, Boston Col, 53, M.A, 55; Ph.D.(Eng), Univ. Wis, 62. Instr. ENG, Holy Cross Col, 59-62, asst. prof, 62-65; assoc. prof, UNIV. WIS-STEVENS POINT, 65-68, PROF. & CHMN. DEPT, 68- U.S.M.C, 45-47. MLA; Ling. Soc; Am; Am. Name Soc. English medieval drama; English philology. Publ: The complexion of English medieval drama, S.Dak. Drama Festschriften, fall 68; The English department and the Depression, 3/73 & English and the liberal arts, 9/73, ADE Bull. Add: Dept. of English, University of Wisconsin-Stevens Point, Stevens Point, WI 54481.

LEWIS, MARJORIE DUNLAVY, b. Childress, Tex, Nov. 12, 29; m. 61. ENGLISH. B.A, Tex. Woman's Univ, 49; M.A, Univ. N.C, 51; M.A, Tex. Christian Univ, 55; Ph.D.(Eng), Univ. Kans, 67. Instr. ENG, Arlington State Col, 54-56, 59-61; Tex. Woman's Univ, 61-63; TEX. CHRISTIAN UNIV, 65-66, asst. prof, 67-72, ASSOC. PROF, 72- MLA; Renaissance Soc. Am. Publ: The ingenious compliment: consideration of some devices and episodes, In: The merry wives of Windsor, studies in Medieval, Renaissance, and American literature, a festschrift, 71. Add: Dept. of English, Texas Christian University, Ft. Worth, TX 76129.

LEWIS, MERRILL EMBERT, b. Baldwin Park, Calif, Mar. 21, 32; m. 54; c. c. 4. NINETEENTH CENTURY AMERICAN LITERATURE, AMERICAN STUDIES. B.A, Univ. Ore, 54, M.A, 59; Ph.D.(Eng, Am. stud), Univ. Utah, 68. Instr. ENG, Cent. Ore. Col, 58-61; WEST. WASH. STATE COL, 62-66, asst. prof, 66-68, ASSOC. PROF, 68-, summer res. grants, 66, 69. Fel. Am. stud, Yale, 70-71; Huntington Libr. & Art Gallery fel, 72-73. Am. Stud. Asn; West. Hist. Asn; West. Lit. Asn. The writing of history; literature of the American West; late nineteenth century American intellectual history. Publ: Co-auth, Wallace Stegner, Caxton, 72; Organic metaphor and Edenic myth in George Bancroft's History of United States, J. Hist. Ideas, 10-12/65; Lost—and found—in the wilderness: the desert metaphor in Cooper's The prairie, West. Am. Lit, fall 70; The art of Frederic Jackson Turner, Huntington Libr. Quart, 5/72. Add: Dept. of English, Western Washington State College, Bellingham, WA 98225.

LEWIS, NANCY ELOISE, b. Covington, Ky, Dec. 10, 10. ENGLISH. A.B, Denison Univ, 32; M.A, Duke Univ, 45; Ph.D.(Eng), Ohio State Univ, 57. Teacher ENG, Pub. High Schs, Canton, Ohio, 32-46; instr, DENISON UNIV, 46-54, asst. prof, 54-58, assoc. prof, 58-63, PROF, 63-, chmn. dept, 60-63. Asst. instr, Ohio State Univ, 52-53. MLA; NCTE. Restoration drama; Shakespeare; Milton. Add: Dept. of English, Denison University, Granville, OH 43023.

LEWIS, RICHARD B, b. Mt. View, Calif, Feb. 8, 06; m. 32; c. 2. ENGLISH. B.A, Pac. Union Col, 27; M.A, Univ. South. Calif, 37; Ph.D.(Eng), Stanford Univ, 49. Prin, San Diego Acad, Calif, 27-35; Pac. Union Col. Prep. Sch, Angwin, Calif, 35-38; asst. prof. speech, Walla Walla Col, 38-45; prof. Eng, Pac. Union Col, 45-55; bk. ed. & prod. mgr. Chapel Records, Pac. Press Publ. Asn, Mt. View, Calif, 55-61; acad. dean, La Sierra Col, 61-67; PROF. ENG, LOMA LINDA UNIV, 67- Instr. speech, Seventh Day Adventist Theol. Sem, summer 43. MLA; Milton Soc. Am. Renaissance; Milton. Publ: Streams of light, 58 & Protestant dilemma, 61, Pacific Press; Ignatius and the Lord's day, Andrews Univ. Sem. Stud, 1/68. Add: Dept. of English, Loma Linda University, Riverside, CA 92505.

LEWIS, ROBERT ENZER, b. Windber, Pa, Aug. 12, 34; m. 61; c. 2. ENGLISH LANGUAGE & LITERATURE. B.A, Princeton, 59; M.A, Univ. Pa, 62, Ph.D.(Eng. lang), 64. Teacher ENG, Mercersburg Acad, 59-60; teaching fel, Univ. Pa, 61-63; lectr, IND. UNIV, BLOOMINGTON, 63-64, asst. prof, 64-68, ASSOC. PROF, 68- Am. Philos. Soc. res. grant, 66-67, 70; gen. ed, Chaucer Libr, 70-; Am. Counc. Learned Soc. res. grant, 73-74; vis. res. fel, Inst. Advan. Stud. Humanities, Univ. Edinburgh, 73-74. U.S.A, 54-56. MLA; Mediaeval Acad. Am. Medieval English literature; medieval manuscripts; English language. Publ: Handbook for contributors to the Chaucer Library, Univ. Ga, 73; Chaucer's artistic use of Pope Innocent III's De miseria humane conditionis in the Man of law's prologue and tale, PMLA, 12/66; Glosses to the Man of law's tale from Pope Innocent III's De miseria humane conditionis, Stud. Philol, 1/67; What did Chaucer mean by Of the wreched engendrynge of mankynde?, Chaucer Rev, winter 68. Add: Dept. of English, College of Arts & Sciences, Graduate School, Indiana University, Bloomington, IN 47401.

LEWIS, ROBERT JOHN, b. Philadelphia, Pa, Aug. 18, 42; m. 66; c. 3. ENGLISH RENAISSANCE LITERATURE. B.A, St. Joseph's Col.(Pa), 66; univ. fel, Woodrow Wilson fel. & Ph.D.(Eng. Renaissance), Univ. Notre Dame, 71. Teaching asst. ENG, Univ. Notre Dame, 67-69; ASST. PROF, POINT PARK COL, 70- Woodrow Wilson fel, 70- English Renaissance prose and drama. Publ: Co-auth, Annotated bibliography of the Renaissance, Notre Dame Eng, J, spring 70. Add: 2347 Rochester Rd, Pittsburgh, PA 15237.

LEWIS, ROBERT WILLIAM, JR, b. Elrama, Pa, Dec. 15, 30; m. 55; c. 2. ENGLISH. B.A, Univ. Pittsburgh, 52; M.A, Columbia Univ, 58; summer fel, Univ. Ill, 61, Ph.D, 63. Asst, Columbia Univ, 55; instr. ENG, Univ. Nebr, 55-58; asst, Univ. Ill, 58-63; instr, Univ. Tex, Austin, 63-65, asst. prof, 65-69; assoc. prof, UNIV. N.DAK, 69-71, PROF, 71-, CHMN. DEPT, 69- Asst. ed, Abstr. Eng. Stud, 64-66; coord. Peace Corps, Univ. Tex, 65-66; Fulbright-Hays lectr, Italy, 67-68; consult, Nat. Endowment for Humanities, 71-; res. prof, Univ. N.Dak, 71. U.S.A, 52-54, Res, 54-, Lt. Col. MLA; NCTE; West. Lit. Asn; AAUP; Conf. Col. Compos. & Commun.(mem. exec. comt, 69-73, affiliate speaker, 72-73); Am. Indian Hist. Soc.(mem. comt. 100 scholars, 71-). American literature; literary criticism; American Indian literature. Publ: Hemingway on love, Univ. Tex, 65; co-auth, The Texas manuscript of The snows of Kilimanjaro, Tex. Quart, winter 66; auth, Ernest Hemingway, In: Encycl. World Lit. in 20th Century, Ungar, 68; Hemingway's Sense of place, In: Hemingway: in our time, Ore. State Univ, 73. Add: Dept. of English, University of North Dakota, Grand Forks, ND 58201.

LEWIS, RUTH B, b. Louisville, Ky, Apr. 13, 33. SPEECH. B.S, Wittenberg Univ, 56; res. fel. & M.A, Ohio State Univ, 60, Ph.D, 62. Asst. SPEECH, Ohio State Univ, 58-62; asst. prof, Oberlin Col, 62-66; ASSOC. PROF, GRAD. FAC, UNIV. AKRON, 66- Speech Commun. Asn. Rhetorical analysis of Adolph Hitler, his speeches and times; analysis of the speeches of Angelina Grimke Weld, reformer. Add: Dept. of Speech, University of Akron, Akron, OH 44304.

LEWIS, THOMAS ROBERT, b. Cape Girardeau, Mo, Nov. 23, 06; m. 29; c. 2. SPEECH. B.A, Southeast Mo. State Teachers Col, 29, B.S, 32; M.A, State Univ. Iowa, 38, Ph.D.(speech), 48. Instr. speech, State Univ. Iowa, 44-48; assoc. prof, Univ. Miami, 48-49; prof. Fla. State Univ, 49-72, assoc. grad. dean, 58-72; RETIRED. Speech Commun. Asn; Nat. Soc. Stud. Commun. (pres, 57); South. Speech Asn.(pres, 58). Publ: Oral communications, E.O. Painter Co, 53; co-auth, Listening and speaking, 54 & auth, Speaking and listening, 64, W.C. Brown. Add: 1911 Old Fort Dr, Tallahassee, FL 32301.

LEWIS, THOMAS SPOTTSWOOD WELLFORD, b. Philadelphia, Pa, May 29, 42; m. 64; c. 2. ENGLISH & AMERICAN LITERATURE. B.A, Univ. New Brunswick, 64; fac. fels, Columbia Univ, 64-65, 65-68, M.A, 65, Paul Klingenstein fel, 65-66, Ph.D.(Eng), 70; Woodrow Wilson fel, Princeton, 68. Res. asst. ENG, Columbia Univ, 67-68; instr, SKIDMORE COL, 68-70, ASST. PROF, 70- Am. Philos. Soc. res. grant, 71. MLA. Biography; modern British and American literature; linguistics. Publ: Ed, Virginia Woolf: a collection of criticism, McGraw-Hill, 74 & The letters of Hart Crane and his family, Columbia Univ, 74; ed, Hart Crane and his mother: a correspondence, Salmagundi, 69; auth, Some new letters of John Butler Yeats, In: Modern Irish literature, Twayne, 72. Add: Dept. of English, Skidmore College, Saratoga Springs, NY 12866.

LEWIS, WILMARTH SHELDON, b. Alameda, Calif, Nov. 14, 95. ENGLISH, SOCIAL HISTORY. B.A, Yale, 18, hon. M.A, 37, LL.D, 65; Litt.D, Brown Univ, 45, Univ. Rochester, 46, Univ. Del, 61, Univ. Melbourne, 72; L.H.D, Trinity Col.(Conn), 50, Bucknell Univ, 58; D.Litt, Nat. Univ. Ireland, 57, Cambridge, 62; LL.D, Univ. Hartford, 72. Res. assoc, Yale, 33-38; AUTHOR & ED, 38- Assoc. fel, Calhoun Col, Yale Univ, 33-, trustee, Univ, 38-64; Avon Old Farms, 40-46; Thacher Sch, 41-47, 54-; Watkinson Libr, 41-; Miss Porter's Sch, 41-65; Brooks Sch, 45-48; Inst. Advan. Stud, 45-; Redwood Libr, 46-; John Carter Brown Libr; chmn. librn. counc, Libr. Congr, 42-47; mem, Winterthur Mus, 55-; Am. Heritage Found, 62- Chief Cent. inform. div, Off. Strategic Serv, 41-43. MLA; Bibliog. Soc. Am; Am. Acad. Arts & Sci; Am. Philos. Soc; fel. Royal Soc. Lit. U.K. Eighteenth century English. Publ: Horace Walpole's fugitive verses, 31; ed, Horace Walpole's correspondence (36 vols), 37-73 & A selection of Horace Walpole's letters, 73, Yale Univ; auth, Three tours through London, 1748, 1776, 1797, 42; Collector's progress, 51; Horace Walpole's library, 58; Horace Walpole, 60; One man's education, 67; See for yourself, Harper, 71. Add: Farmington, CT 06032.

LEYASMEYER, ARCHIBALD I, b. Riga, Latvia, Dec. 15, 35; U.S. citizen; m. 64. ENGLISH. B.A, Harvard, 57; M.R.E, East. Baptist Theol. Sem, 60; M.A, Princeton, 64, Ph.D.(Eng), 67. Instr. ENG, UNIV. MINN, MINNEAPOLIS, 64-66, asst. prof, 66-68, ASSOC. PROF, 68- MLA. Eighteenth century; Chaucer; modern drama. Add: Dept. of English, University of Minnesota, Minneapolis, MN 55455.

L'HOMME, CHARLES EDMUND, b. Pittsfield, Mass, June 4, 25; m. 49. ENGLISH & COMPARATIVE LITERATURE. A.B, Tufts Col, 49, M.A, 50; Ph.D.(Eng, comp. lit), Columbia Univ, 65. Instr. ENG, Tufts Col, 50-54; SIMMONS COL, 54-58, asst. prof, 58-66, assoc. prof, 66-72, PROF, 72- U.S.N.R, 43-46. Modern British and comparative literature: 1890-1950; comparative medieval literature; Victorian English literature and comparative symbolism and realism. Add: Dept. of English, Simmons College, Boston, MA 02115.

LIBBEY, EDWIN BISSELL, b. Bedford, Ohio, Dec. 1, 08; m. 41; c. 1. ENGLISH. A.B, Rollins Col, 33; A.M, Stetson Univ, 39; Univ. Chicago, 34-35,

40-41; Okla. Agr. & Mech. Col, 52-53. Teacher high sch, Fla, 41-42; Eng, Culver Mil. Acad, 42-46; humanities, Stephens Col, 46-49; PROF. ENG. & HUMANITIES, PANHANDLE STATE COL, 49-, CHMN. DEPT, 73- AAUP; Int. Reading Asn; NCTE. Correlation of the visual arts with music and literature; proverbs and proverbial phrases in Sidney's Arcadia. Publ: General course in humanities at Panhandle State College, West. Humanities Rev. Add: P.O. Box 52, Goodwell, OK 73939.

LIBBY, ANTHONY PETER, b. Jacksonville, Fla, May 19, 42; m. 65; c. 2. ENGLISH & AMERICAN LITERATURE. A.B, Holy Cross Col, 63; Woodrow Wilson fels, Stanford Univ, 63-64, 66-67, Ph.D.(Eng), 69. Asst. prof. ENG, OHIO STATE UNIV, 67-74, ASSOC. PROF, 74- MLA. Twentieth century American poetry; mystical poetry; short fiction. Publ: Claritas: William Carlos Williams' Epiphanies, Criticism, winter 72; Robert Bly alive in darkness, summer 72 & Fire and light, four poets to end and beyond, spring 73, Iowa Rev. Add: Dept. of English, Ohio State University, 164 W. 17th Ave, Columbus, OH 43210.

LIBBY, NANCY DOROTHEA, b. Caribou, Maine, Mar. 23, 14. ENGLISH & AMERICAN LITERATURE. A.B, Colby Col, 36; M.A, Columbia Univ, 42; fels, Duke Univ, 51-53, Ph.D.(Eng), 55. Teacher, Aroostook Cent. Inst, 36-38; Berwick Acad, 38-39; Traip Acad, 39-43; instr. ENG, Univ. Maine, 46-51; asst. prof, STATE UNIV. N.Y. COL, FREDONIA, 55-59, assoc. prof, 59-63, PROF, 63-, chmn. dept. Eng. & speech, 62-67. U.S.N.R, 43-46, Lt.(jg). MLA; AAUP; NCTE; Asn. Higher Educ; NEA. Milton; Browning; Victorian literature. Publ: Milton's harapha, S.Atlanta Quart, fall 72. Add: 14 Holmes Pl, Fredonia, NY 14063.

LICHTY, LAWRENCE WILSON, b. Pasadena, Calif, June 14, 37; m. 62. MASS COMMUNICATIONS. A.B, Univ. South. Calif, 59; M.A, Ohio State Univ, 61, Ph.D.(speech), 64. Asst. prof. SPEECH, Calif. State Col, Long Beach, 63-64; asst. prof, UNIV. WIS-MADISON, 64-67, assoc. prof, 67-72, PROF, 72- Staff dir, Governor's Task Force on cable TV, 71-73. Speech Commun. Asn; Broadcast Educ. Asn. Broadcasting history; TV journalism; cable TV. Publ: Co-auth, American broadcasting—introduction and analysis, Am. Printing, 69; auth, World and international broadcasting, a bibliography, Asn. Prof. Broadcasting Educ, 71; co-auth, Rough justice on a Saigon street: a gatekeeper study of NBC's test execution film, Jour. Quart, summer 72. Add: Dept. of Communication Arts, University of Wisconsin-Madison, 821 University Ave, Madison, WI 53706.

LICKLIDER, PATRICIA MINICHINO, b. New Haven, Conn, Mar. 20, 43; m. 71. COMPARATIVE RENAISSANCE LITERATURE. B.A, Regis Col. (Mass), 65; Woodrow Wilson fels, Columbia Univ, 65-66, 69-70, M.A, 66, Margaret Pickel fel, 66-67, univ. fel, 67-68, Ph.D.(Renaissance lit), 71. From instr. to ASST. PROF. ENG, JOHN JAY COL. CRIMINAL JUSTICE, 70-, deputy chmn. dept, 73-74. Renaissance Soc. Am; AAUP. Latin in the Renaissance; the poetry of Spenser; Renaissance lyrics. Publ: Three books of poetry: a review, Commonweal, 3/73. Add: Dept. of English, John Jay College of Criminal Justice, 455 W. 59th St, New York, NY 10019.

LID, RICHARD W, b. Marinette, Wis, Oct. 27, 28; m. 54; c. 1. ENGLISH. Ph.B, Univ. Chicago, 48, M.A, 52; Ph.D.(Eng), Univ.Mich, 59. Instr. ENG, Univ. Calif. Santa Barbara, 58-60, asst. prof, 60-64; CALIF. STATE UNIV, NORTHRIDGE, 64-66, assoc. prof, 66-68, PROF, 69-, chmn. dept, 70-73, res. grant, spring 67. Dir, Experienced Teacher Fel. Prog. Eng, 69-70; dir, Protocol Materials Eng, 70- U.S.A, 52-54, Sgt. MLA; NCTE; Col. Conf. Comp. & Commun.(mem. exec. comt, 72-74). Twentieth century British and American fiction. Publ: Ford Madox Ford: The essence of his art, Univ. Calif, 64; The innocent eye, Critique, winter 63; Philip Marlowe speaking, Kenyon Rev, winter 69; The passion of F. Scott Fitzgerald, Fitzgerald-Hemingway Annual, 70. Add: Dept. of English, California State University, Northridge, Northridge, CA 93124.

LIDDIE, ALEXANDER S, b. Newark, N.J, Nov. 1, 33; m. 55; c. 3. ENGLISH. B.S. Lehigh Univ, 55; A.M, Rutgers Univ, 58, Ph.D.(Eng), 67. Asst, Rutgers Univ, 55-60; instr. ENG, Univ. S.C, 60-61; asst. prof, TRENTON STATE COL, 61-64, assoc. prof, 64-68, PROF, 68-, CHMN. DEPT, 71- Essay Prize, Lehigh Univ, 55. MLA; NCTE; AAUP. Publ: Wallace Stevens' Metaphors of a magnifico, Explicator, 62. Add: Dept. of English, Trenton State College, Trenton, NJ 08625.

LIEB, MICHAEL J, b. Newark, N.J, Oct. 21, 40; m. 63; c. 2. ENGLISH LITERATURE. A.B, Rutgers Univ, New Brunswick, 62, A.M, 64, Ph.D.(Eng), 67. Asst. prof. ENG, Col. William & Mary, 67-70; ASSOC. PROF, UNIV. ILL. CHICAGO CIRCLE, 70- Summer fels, Col. William & Mary, 68, Folger Shakespeare Libr, 70 & 74, Huntington Libr, 72 & Univ. Ill, 72 & 74; Nat. Endowment for Humanities younger humanist, 74-75. MLA; Milton Soc. Am.(treas, 72-). Milton; 16th and 17th century English literature. Publ: The dialectics of creation, 70 & co-ed, Achievements of the left hand: essays on the prose of John Milton, 74, Univ. Mass; Milton and the Kenotic Christology, 70 & Holy rest: a reading of Paradise lost, 72, ELH; Milton and the organicist polemic, Milton Stud, 72. Add: Dept. of English, University of Illinois at Chicago Circle, Box 4348, Chicago, IL 60680.

LIEB-BRILHART, BARBARA, b. Brooklyn, N.Y, Oct. 11, 36; c. 1. SPEECH, EDUCATION. B.A, Queens Col.(N.Y), 58; M.A, Pa. State Univ, 60, Ph.D.(speech & psychol), 66. Instr. speech, Pa. State Univ, 60-65; Univ. Nebr, Lincoln, 65-66; Nat. Teacher Corps team leader, Omaha Pub. Schs, 66-67; asst. prof. educ, Univ. Nebr. at Omaha, 67-71, assoc. prof. speech & educ, 71-73; ASSOC. EXEC. SECY. EDUC, SPEECH COMMUN. ASN, 73- Consult, Nat. Teacher Corps, 67-68; pres. fac. senate, Univ. Nebr. at Omaha, 72-73; mem. adv. counc, Asn. Orgns. Teacher Educ, 73. Am. Asn. Univ. Women; Speech Commun. Asn.(mem. career educ. task force, 72-; v.chmn. instr. develop. div, 72-73); Int. Commun. Asn; Asn. Teacher Educ; Am. Educ. Res. Asn; Cent. States Speech Asn. Communication research and education; instructional systems; applied communication. Publ: Training classroom teachers for supervision, III and IV, Educ. Resources Inform. Ctr, 69; Various communication curricula, Nebr. State Educ. Dept, 72-73; Oral communication for the Indian student, Eng. J, 5/71; Paragon of animals, Phi Kappa Phi J, fall 72; co-auth, Field-independence and academic achievement of engineering students, Perceptual & Motor Skills, 32: 443-446; plus others. Add: Speech Communication Association, Statler Hilton Hotel, New York, NY 10001.

LIEBER, TODD MICHAEL, b. Philadelphia, Pa, Nov. 30, 44; m. 67; c. 1. ENGLISH, AMERICAN STUDIES. A.B, Duke Univ, 66; M.A, Case West. Reserve Univ, 67, fel, 68-69, Ph.D.(Am. stud), 69. Instr. Am. stud, Case West. Reserve Univ, 69; ASST. PROF. ENG. & AM. STUD, SIMPSON COL, 69-, consult. curriculum rev, 73. MLA; Am. Stud. Asn. Romanticism; 20th century American literature; literary criticism. Publ: Endless experiments: essays on the heroic experience in American romanticism, Ohio State Univ, 73; Design and movement in Cane, Col. Lang. Asn. J, 9/69; Talismanic patterns in the novels of John Steinbeck, Am. Lit, 5/72; Ralph Ellison and the metaphor of invisibility in black literary tradition, Am. Quart, 3/72. Add: Dept. of English, Simpson College, Indianola, IA 50125.

LIEBERMAN, LAURENCE, b. Detroit, Mich, Feb. 16, 35; m. 56; c. 3. ENGLISH, MODERN POETRY. B.A, Univ. Mich, 56, M.A, 58; fel, Univ. Calif, Berkeley, 58-60. Instr. ENG, Orange Coast Col, 60-64; asst. prof, Col. Virgin Islands, 64-66, assoc. prof, 66-68; UNIV. ILL, URBANA, 68-70, PROF, 70- Fel, YADDO, N.Y, 63 & 67; Huntington-Hartford Found fel, 64; consult, & poetry ed, Univ. Ill. Press, 70-; poetry reviewer, Yale Rev, 71-; assoc. fel, Univ. Ill. Ctr. Advan. Study, Japan & Hawaii, 71-72. Major Hopwood Award poetry writing, 58; Nat. Endowment for Arts Award for poem, 67. MLA. Contemporary American poetry; poetry criticism. Publ: The unblinding (a volume of poems), Macmillan, 68; The achievement of James Dickey, Scott, 68; The osprey suicides (a volume of poems), Macmillan & Collier, 73; The osprey suicides (poem), New Yorker, 11/73; Exiles and disinterments, fall 71, Survivor: a last oak leaf, the critic in the poet, winter 73 & The church of ash: the poetry of W.S. Merwin, summer 73, Yale Rev. Add: Dept. of English, University of Illinois, Urbana, IL 61801.

LIEBERT, HERMAN WARDWELL, b. New York, N.Y, Mar. 24, 11; m. 36; c. 2. ENGLISH LITERATURE. A.B, Yale, 33. Mem. exec. ed. staff, Paul Block Newspapers, 33-41; econ. ed, Off. Strategic Serv, 41-45; researcher on Dr. Samuel Johnson, 46-47; asst. exec. secy, President's Comt. For. Aid, 47; FEL, DAVENPORT COL, YALE, 47-, MEM. ED. COMT, YALE EDITIONS PRIVATE PAPERS JAMES BOSWELL & CHMN. ED. COMT, WORKS SAMUEL JOHNSON, 49- Consult, Econ. Coop. Admin, 48-50; res. asst, Yale Libr, 48-51, res. assoc. & asst. to librn, 51-58, cur, rare bk. room, 58-63, librn, Beinecke Rare Bk. & Manuscript Libr, 63-72; mem. adv. comt, Yale ed, Horace Walpole's Correspondence, 63- Bibliog. Soc. Am.(pres, 64-66); Am. Libr. Asn. Bibliography and biography of Dr. Samuel Johnson and Austin Dobson; rare book collection. Add: 210 St. Ronan St, New Haven, CT 06511.

LIEBLER, MARK C, Humanities, English. See Volume IV, Philosophy, Religion & Law.

LIEBMAN, SHELDON WAYNE, b. Pittsburgh, Pa, Nov. 17, 40; m. 65. ENGLISH. B.S, Univ. Pa, 62, Ph.D.(Eng), 72; M.A, Univ. Pittsburgh, 65. Instr. ENG, Glassboro State Col, 64-66; Lafayette Col, 66-72, ASST. PROF, 72-73; UNIV. ILL, CHICAGO CIRCLE, 74- Am. Stud. Asn. American literature; short story; 19th century. Publ: The body and soul metaphor in Moby-Dick, Emerson Soc. Quart, 68; Point of view in The portrait of a lady, Eng. Stud, 71; The forsaken maiden in Hawthorne's stories, Am. Transcendental Quart, 73; plus others. Add: Dept. of English, University of Illinois at Chicago Circle, Chicago, IL 60680.

LIECHTI, HARRIS NELSON, b. Des Moines, Iowa, Aug. 20, 35; m. 70; c. 1. SPEECH, COMMUNICATIONS. B.A, Univ. Mich, Ann Arbor, 57, M.A, 58, Ph.D.(speech), 68. Writer-producer-dir, Armed Forces Radio & TV Serv, Hollywood, Calif, 59-60; reports asst, U.S. Off. Educ, 62-63, asst. reports officer, 66-68; asst. prof. SPEECH, UNIV. WIS-OSHKOSH, 68-73, ASSOC. PROF, 73-, DIR. TV SERV, 69- U.S.A, 58-60. Nat. Asn. Educ. Broadcasters; Broadcast Educ. Asn; Asn. Educ. Commun. & Technol; Speech Commun. Asn; Am. Film Inst; Univ. Film Asn. Radio-television-film writing; educational broadcasting and telecommunications. Publ: The scene today: improving campus communications with a student-produced TV news program, Educ. Broadcasting, 11-12/72; Student TV news: the scene today, Futures Conditional, 8/73. Add: Dept. of Speech, University of Wisconsin-Oshkosh, Oshkosh, WI 54901.

LIEDLICH, RAYMOND DEAN, b. Greenport, N.Y, Feb. 21, 26; m. 55; c. 2. ENGLISH. B.S.Ed, Bowling Green State Univ, 53; M.A, Calif. State Col, Los Angeles, 60; Calif. State Col, Fullerton, 60-65; Calif. State Col, Long Beach, summers 61-62. Instr, high sch, N.Y, 53; elem. sch, Calif, 55-56; intermediate sch, 56-57; high sch, 57-60; Eng, Fullerton Jr. Col, 60-67; De Anza Col, 67-71, chmn. div. lang. arts, 71; instr. Eng, Portland Community Col, 71-73; ASSOC. DEAN INSTR. ARTS & SCI, CONTRA COSTA COL, 73- Asst. prof. Eng, Calif. State Col, Fullerton, 61-67; mem. exec. comt, Pac. Coast Regional Conf. Eng. in Two-Yr. Col, 66-67, 67-69, 70-72, NCTE-Conf. Col. Compos. & Commun, 69-71, Pac. Northwest Regional Conf. Eng. Two-Yr. Col, 71-72; adv. ed. community col. Eng, John Wiley & Sons, 68- NCTE (mem. comt. pub. doublespeak, 72-); Conf. Col. Compos. & Commun; Col. Eng. Asn; Int. Soc. Gen. Semantics; NEA. The teaching of English, especially in the community college; composition; mass media and popular culture. Publ: Co-auth, From thought to theme: a rhetoric and reader for college English, 65, 68, 71 & 74 & Rhetoric for today, 68, 71 & 74, Harcourt; auth, Coming to terms with language: an anthology, Wiley, 73; The state of our knowledge of terminal English, J. Conf. Col. Compos. & Commun, 12/66; contrib, Teaching basic English courses, Van Nostrand, 71. Add: Div. of Arts & Sciences, Contra Costa College, 2600 Mission Bell Dr, San Pablo, CA 94806.

LIEDMAN, JEAN ESTHER, b. Pittsburgh, Pa, Jan. 23, 05. SPEECH. A.B, Monmouth Col, 27; A.M, Univ. Wis, 35, Ph.D, 49. Teacher pub. schs, Pa, 28-35; instr. speech, MONMOUTH COL, 36-46, DEAN WOMEN, 46-, PROF. SPEECH, 48-, head dept, 46-63. Nat. Col. Players. Certain factors in the discrimination of vowels and vowel-like sounds. Add: Monmouth College, Monmouth, IL 61462.

LIEVSAY, JOHN LEON, b. Whitesboro, Tex, Feb. 20, 06; m. 26; c. 1. ENGLISH. Fel. & Ph.D, Univ. Wash, 37. Instr. ENG, Stanford Univ, 37-43, asst. prof, 43-47; assoc. prof, Univ. Tenn, 47-52, PROF, 52-62; DUKE UNIV, 62-, CO-CHMN, SOUTHEAST. INST. MEDIEVAL & RENAISSANCE STUD, DUKE UNIV-UNIV. N.C, 64-, sr. fel, 65. Res. fel, Folger Shakespeare Libr, 46-47, spec. consult, 59-60; Fulbright res. fel, Italy, 53-54; Guggenheim fel, 68-69; Rosenbach lectr, Univ. Pa, 68-69. MLA; Am. Asn. Teachers Ital; Renaissance Soc. Am; Dante Soc. Am; Renaissance Eng. Text Soc. English and comparative literature of the Renaissance; 17th century English and Italian literature. Publ: Stefano Guazzo and the English Renaissance, Univ. N.C, 61; Elizabethan image of Italy, Cornell Univ, 64; The sixteenth century: Skelton to Hooker, Appleton, 68; The Englishman's Italian books, 1550-1700, Univ. Pa, 69; ed, Essays of Daniel Tuvill, Univ. Va, 71; auth, Venetian Phoenix: Paolo Sarpi, Univ. Kans, 73. Add: 2725 Montgomery St, Durham, NC 27705.

LIFSON, DAVID S, b. New York, N.Y; m. 32. DRAMA, ENGLISH. B.S, Wash. Sq. Col, N.Y. Univ, 31; Cornell Univ, 54; M.A, N.Y. Univ, 57, Ph.D.(drama & lit), 62. Asst. prof. Eng, Univ. Md, 57-58; Eng. & drama, Pratt Inst, 58-63; Eng. & speech, Jersey City State Col, 63-64; PROF. ENG, MONMOUTH COL.(N.J), 64- Scholar, N.Y. Univ, 63; Fulbright-Hays res. fel, 70-71. Am. Theatre Asn. Yiddish drama and theatre; World drama and theatre; naturalism in the novel. Publ: Yiddish theatre in America, Yoseloff, 65; co-auth, A history of the theatre, Crown, 68; auth, Epic and folk plays of the Yiddish theatre, Assoc. Univ. Press, 73; auth. introd, Separate voices, an anthology of New Jersey shore poets, Bradley Beach, N.J, 66; dept. ed, Jews in drama and theatre, In: Encycl. Judaica, Jerusalem, 66; contrib, Arts of Jewish peoples; dance and theatre, Encycl. Britannica, 73; plus others. Add: 40 E. Tenth St, New York, NY 10003.

LIGHT, JAMES FOREST, b. Memphis, Tenn, Nov. 5, 21; m. 48, 59; c. 3. ENGLISH & AMERICAN LITERATURE. B.A, Univ. Chicago, 45, M.A, 47; Ph.D, Syracuse Univ, 53. Instr. ENG, Univ. Ky, 47-48; Syracuse Univ, 48-53; assoc. prof, Radford Col, 53-56; asst. prof, Ind. State Univ, 56-59, assoc. prof, 59-61, prof, 61-65, Bernhard prof. & chmn. dept, Univ. Bridgeport, 65-71; dean humanities, Calif. State Univ, 71-72; dean fac, LEHMAN COL, 71-73, PROVOST, 73- Fulbright prof. Am. lit, Univ. Keele, 63-64. Col. Eng. Asn; Am. Stud. Asn; MLA. Nineteenth and 20th century American literature. Publ: Nathanael West: an interpretative study, Northwest. Univ, 61, rev. ed, 71; John William De Forest, Twayne, 65; co-ed, The modern age, Holt, 69, rev. ed, 72; ed, Studies in All the king's men, Merrill, 71; auth, The religion of death in A farewell to arms, Mod. Fiction Stud, 61, 63; Political conscience in the novels of Scott Fitzgerald, Ball State Teachers Col. Forum, 63; John W. De Forest, Am. Lit. Realism, fall 67. Add: Dept. of English, Herbert H. Lehman College, Bedford Park Blvd, Bronx, NY 10468.

LIGHT, MARTIN, b. Pittsburgh, Pa, Apr. 5, 27; m. 51; c. 4. AMERICAN LITERATURE. B.A, Pa. State Univ, 49; M.A, Univ. Chicago, 51; Ph.D, Univ. Ill, 60. Instr. ENG, Forest Sch, Pa. State Univ, 49; Wayne State Univ, 51-52; asst, Univ. Ill, 52-60; instr, PURDUE UNIV, 60-61, asst. prof, 61-67, ASSOC. PROF, 68- Instr. article writing, Chautauqua Writer's Workshop, summers 63-67; lang. stud. in compos, NDEA Inst, Univ. Iowa, summer 68 & 69. U.S.N, 45-46. NCTE; MLA; Midwest Mod. Lang. Asn; Conf. Col. Compos. & Commun. American literature, language, composition and folklore. Publ: Co-auth, Critical approaches to American literature, 2 vols, Crowell, 65 & The world of words: a language reader, Houghton, 67; ed, Studies in Babbitt, C.E. Merrill, 71; Sinclair Lewis and the Quixotic hero, Purdue Univ, 74; auth, H.G. Wells and Sinclair Lewis, Eng. Lit. in Transition, 62; Of wasteful deaths: Hemingway's stories about the Spanish War, West. Humanities Rev, winter 69; Quixotic motifs in Main street, Ariz. Quart, 73. Add: 701 N. Chauncey Ave, West Lafayette, IN 47906.

LIGHTFOOT, MARJORIE JEAN, b. Oak Park, Ill, Apr. 24, 33. CONTEMPORARY ENGLISH, AMERICAN LITERATURE. A.B, Brown Univ, 55; fel, Northwest. Univ, 55-56, M.A, 56, Ph.D.(Eng), 64. Instr. freshman Eng, Univ. Ariz, 60-63; ASST. PROF. AM. LIT. & HUMANITIES, ARIZ. STATE UNIV, 64-, summer res. grants, 66, 68, 72 & 73. NCTE; MLA; Prosody; T.S. Eliot; women novelists. Publ: Charting Eliot's course in drama, Educ. Theatre J, 5/68; The uncommon cocktail party, Mod. Drama, 2/69; Numerical, sequential, and temporal patterns in English verse, Quart, J. Speech, 4/71; plus others. Add: Dept. of English, Arizona State University, Tempe, AZ 85281.

LIGOCKI, LLEWELLYN, b. Hammond, Ind, Aug. 25, 41; m. 63; c. 2. ENGLISH LITERATURE. B.A, Ohio Wesleyan Univ, 63; M.A, Ind. Univ, 64; Ph.D.(Eng), Univ. Kans, 68. ASST. PROF. ENG, WASH. STATE UNIV, 68- MLA; Conf. Brit. Stud. The historical novel; Victorian fiction; 19th century British literature. Publ: Ainsworth's historical accuracy reconsidered, Albion, spring 72; Ainsworth's Tudor novels: history as theme, Stud. in the Novel, fall 72; The imitators and the imitated: Scott, Ainsworth, and the critics, Papers Bibliog. Soc. Am, 4th quarter, 73. Add: Dept. of English, Washington State University, Pullman, WA 99163.

LIGON, JOHN FRANK, JR, b. Reidville, S.C, Oct. 10, 17; m. 43; c. 4. ENGLISH & AMERICAN LITERATURE. B.A, Vanderbilt Univ, 38; M.A, George Peabody Col, 41; Ph.D, Univ. Wash, 60. Instr. ENGLISH, ORE. STATE UNIV, 46-53, asst. prof, 53-57, assoc. prof, 57-66, PROF, 66-, CURRICULUM COORD, 62- Lectr. & consult, Region I, U.S. Bur. Mines, 58; Cornell, Howland, Hayes & Merifield, Engrs, 58-; consult, Flomatcher Co, 62. U.S.A, 41-46, Capt. AAUP. Shakespeare; 19th century American literature; cirricular development in higher education. Publ: An introduction to report writing, Ore. State Univ; The craft of writing, Proc. Summer Conf. Sci. Writing, 66; ed, Confrontations, Proc. Pac. Northwest Conf. Higher Educ, 70. Add: Curriculum Coordination, AdS A600F, Oregon State University, Corvallis, OR 97331.

LILES, BRUCE LYNN, b. Longview, Tex, May 27, 34. LINGUISTICS, MEDIEVAL LITERATURE. B.A, N.Tex. State Univ, 53, M.A, 54; Ph.D.(Eng), Stanford Univ, 67. Instr. ENG, Lon Morris Col, 54-57; Sam Houston State Univ, 62-63; San Antonio Col, 63-65; teaching asst, Stanford Univ, 65-66; asst. prof, N.Tex. State Univ, 66-70; UNIV. MO-ST. LOUIS, 70-73, ASSOC. PROF, 73- U.S.A.F, 57-61. MLA; Ling. Soc. Am. Old English syntax and phonology. Publ: An introductory transformational grammar, Prentice-Hall, 71; Linguistics and the English language, Goodyear, 72. Add: Dept. of English, University of Missouri-St. Louis, 8001 Natural Bridge Rd, St. Louis, MO 63121.

LILIEN, DAVID, b. Harrison, N.J, Dec. 9, 16; m. 42. ENGLISH. A.B, Rutgers Univ, 37, A.M, 39; Columbia Univ, 40; M.Ed, Seton Hall Univ, 42. Instr. speech, City Col. New York, 41-46; asst. prof. ENG, RUTGERS UNIV, 46-54, assoc. prof, 54-62, PROF, 62- MLA; NCTE. The drama. Publ: Experiment in adult education, Rutgers Univ. Add: 845 Hoe's Lane, Piscataway, NJ 08854.

LILLARD, RICHARD GORDON, English, American Civilization. See Volume I, History.

LILLIE, VERNELL AUDREY, b. Hempstead, Tex, May 11, 31; m. 51; c. 2. ENGLISH, CONTEMPORARY BLACK DRAMA. B.A, Dillard Univ, 52; Tex. South. Univ, summers 52-54; M.A, Carnegie-Mellon Univ, 70, D.A, 72. Group work specialist, Julia C. Hester House, 52-56; chmn. drama, speech, debate, Eng, Phillis Wheatley High Sch, Houston Sch. Dist, Tex, 56-69; Workshop substitute teacher Eng, Upward Bound Proj, Pittsburgh Bd. Educ, 69-70; dir. student activities, Carnegie-Mellon Univ, 70-71; proj. dir. res. design for comprehensive urban sch, UNIV. PITTSBURGH, 71-72, ASST. PROF. HUMANITIES, BLACK STUD, 72- Eng. coord. & dir. drama, Proj. Upward Bound, Tex. South. Univ, 66-69; consult, Carnegie-Mellon Univ. Action Prog, 69-71; African Am. Inst, Wesleyan Univ, summer 72; coord. curriculum develop, Ctr. Educ. Action, Univ. Pittsburgh Model Cities Proj, 72- NCTE. Urban education; contemporary black drama; psychodrama. Publ: Community Institute an educational alternative for minority youth and adults in Pittsburgh, Govt. Res. Report, 1/73. Add: 7126 Wiltsie St, Pittsburgh, PA 15206.

LIMBACHER, JAMES L, b. St. Marys, Ohio, Nov. 30, 26. DRAMA, FILM. B.A, Bowling Green State Univ, 49, M.A, 54; M.S, Ind. Univ, 55; M.S. in L.S, Wayne State Univ, 72. MEM. AUDIO-VISUAL DIV, DEARBORN DEPT. LIBR, 55-; INSTR. FILM HIST, WAYNE STATE UNIV, 73- Pres, Am. Fed. Film. Soc, 62-65, pres, Educ. Film Libr. Asn, 66-69. Soc. Cinema Stud. History and appreciation of the motion picture; audio-visual media. Publ: Ed, Using films, Educ. Film Libr. Asn, 67 & Feature films on 8 and 16, Bowker, annually; auth, Film music: from violins to video, Scarecrow, 73; Reference guide to audio-visual information, Bowker, 73; Four aspects of the film, Brussel, 68. Add: Morley Manor, Dearborn, MI 48124.

LIMBACHER, KARL, b. Columbus, Ohio, Jan. 5, 15; m. 53. ENGLISH, LINGUISTICS. B.E, N.Y. State Teachers Col, Albany, 46, M.S, 47; State Univ. Iowa, 47-49; Ed.D.(teaching Eng. as for. lang), Columbia Univ, 68. Instr. Eng, N.Y. State Teachers Col, Albany, 47; State Univ, Iowa, 48-49; UNESCO liaison off. to Korean Govt. & dir. For. Lang. Inst, Korea, 52-60; assoc. prof. ENG, CALIFORNIA STATE COL.(PA), 61-68, PROF, 68- Asst. prof, Univ. Kans, 49-51; for. serv. off, U.S. Agency for Int. Develop, State Dept, 65-67. Sig.C, U.S.A, 40-45, 51-52, Res, 52-68, Lt. Col. NEA; Asn. Higher Educ. The teaching of English as a foreign language; far eastern languages, literature and culture. Publ: An elementary Korean-English grammar, 58, co-auth, Middle school English readers, (3 vols), 55 & Basic English-Korean dictionary, 56, Korean Publ. Co. Add: Dept. of English, California State College, California, PA 15419.

LIMPUS, ROBERT MOORE, b. Indianapolis, Ind, June 8, 07; m. 37; c. 2. ENGLISH. A.B, Northwest. Univ, 29; M.A, Univ. Chicago, 31, Ph.D, 37. Instr. Eng. S.Dak. State Col, 34-37; Mich. State Col, 37-38; assoc. prof, Muskingum Col, 38-39; asst. prof, Mich. State Norm. Col, 39-43; from assoc. prof. to prof, WEST. MICH. UNIV, 47-72, humanities, 72-73, dir. basic stud, 56-65, dean sch. gen. stud, 65-72, EMER. PROF. HUMANITIES, 73- U.S.A.A.F, 43-46, Capt. MLA; NCTE. Linguistics; communication; American literature. Publ: Collab, Unified English composition. Add: 5141 On Ave. W, Kalamazoo, MI 49009.

LIN, PAUL J, Philosophy, English. See Volume IV, Philosophy, Religion & Law.

LIN, SAN-SU C, b. June 3, 16; m. 39; c. 2. ENGLISH, EDUCATION. B.A, Nat. Peking Univ, 39; M.A, Teachers Col, Columbia Univ, 50, Ed.D.(Eng), 53. Instr. Eng, Prov. Teachers Col, Formosa, 48-49; prof, Claflin Col, 55-64, head dept, 57-64, dir. proj. Eng, U.S. Off. Educ. grant, 61-64; PROF. ENG, SOUTH. UNIV, 64-, DIR. FRESHMAN ENG, 70-, dir. NDEA Insts, 66-68 & 69-70. Mem, NCTE spec. task force teaching Eng. to disadvantaged, 65; mem. comn. on humanities, Asn. Supv. & Curriculum Develop, 70-72. NCTE (mem. col. sect. comt, 72-75); MLA; Am. Dialect Soc. English grammar and usage; Chinese languages and dialects; education for disadvantaged youth. Publ: Pattern practice in the teaching of standard English to students with a non-standard dialect, Teachers Col, Columbia Univ, 65; A developmental English program for the culturally disadvantaged, Col. Compos. & Commun, 12/65; Disadvantaged student? Or disadvantaged teacher?, Eng. J, 5/67; The use of contrastive analysis in teaching English to Chinese speakers, On Teaching Eng. Speakers Other Lang, 67. Add: Dept. of English, Southern University, Baton Rouge, LA 70813.

LINCK, CHARLES E, JR, b. Lowemont, Kans, June 6, 23; m. 54; c. 1. ENGLISH. A.B, St. Benedict's Col, 51; M.S, Kans. State Univ, 53; Ph.D, Univ. Kans, 62. Asst. instr. ENG, Univ. Kans, 52-58; instr, E. Tex. State Univ, 58-60; asst. prof, Purdue Univ, Indianapolis, 62-63; E.TEX. STATE UNIV, 63-66, assoc. prof, 66-71, PROF, 71-, COORD. INTERNS, 72-, COORD. GRAD. STUD, 73- Adv. ed, Evelyn Waugh Newslett, 67- U.S.N.R, 43-46. MLA; NCTE. World literature and criticism in translation; bibliography and methods of literary study; modern novel and poetry. Publ: Edgar Rye, north central Texas cartoonist and journalist, E.Tex. State Univ, 72; co-auth, Evelyn Waugh: a checklist of primary and secondary material, Whitston, 72. Add: Box 3002, Commerce, TX 75428.

LINCK, ORVILLE FRANCIS, b. Detroit, Mich, Nov. 15, 06; m. 43. ENGLISH. A.B, Wayne State Univ, 27; A.M, Univ. Wis, 29; Ph.D.(Eng), Northwest.

Univ, 41. Asst. Eng, Univ. Wis, 29-30; teacher high sch, 30-34; instr. ENG, Wayne State Univ, 34-37; asst. & instr, Northwest. Univ, 37-40; instr. WAYNE STATE UNIV, 40-42, asst. prof, 43, assoc. prof, 48-58, prof, 58-69, EMER. PROF, 69- Asst. to chief gasoline rationing br, Off. Price Admin, 42-43; Fulbright prof, Pakistan, 56-57; part-time prof, Col. Santa Fe, fall 71 & State Penitentiary of N.Mex. Col. Prog, fall 72. U.S.A.A.F, 43-45, S/Sgt. MLA. English literature, 1660-1800; Shakespeare; the comic spirit in English and American literature. Publ: The American achievement in literature: 1900-1956, U.S. Educ. Found, Pakistan, 57 & U.S. Inform. Agency, 58; A passage through Pakistan, 59 & Kelsey the commentator: the affirmations and dissents of a distinguished columnist, 63, Wayne State Univ. Add: 429 Delgado, Santa Fe, NM 87501.

LINCOLN, ELEANOR H, b. Minneapolis, Minn, May 13, 24. ENGLISH. B.S, Col. St. Catherine, 46, B.A, 50; M.A, Univ. Minn, 55, Ph.D, 58. Libr. asst, Col. St. Catherine, 49-50; instr. Eng, Acad. Holy Angels, Minn, 50-51; libr. sci, COL. ST. CATHERINE, 51-56, asst. prof, 58-59, chmn. dept, 59-62, from asst. prof. to assoc. prof. ENG, 62-72, PROF, 72-, CHMN. DEPT, 71- Am. Stud. Asn; NCTE; Midwest Mod. Lang. Asn. Cultural history of American libraries; American literature. Add: Dept. of English, College of St. Catherine, St. Paul, MN 55105.

LINCOLN, ELEANOR TERRY, b. Fergus Falls, Minn, June 14, 03. ENGLISH LITERATURE. B.S, Univ. Minn, 25; A.M, Radcliffe Col, 29; Ph.D, Yale, 38. Teacher, High Sch, Austen, Minn, 25-27; instr. Eng, Univ. Del, 29-31; Vassar Col, 31-33; SMITH COL, 34-38, asst. prof, 38-44, assoc. prof, 44-58, prof. ENG. LIT, 58-68, chmn. dept, 60-63, chmn. comt. social responsibility, 68-70, EMER. PROF, 68- MLA; Renaissance Soc. Am. English literature of the 17th century; John Milton. Publ: Prose for comparison, 55 & Eight topics, 60, Norton; Pastoral and romance, Prentice-Hall, 69. Add: 54 Prospect St, Northampton, MA 01060.

LINCOLN, KENNETH ROBERT, b. Lubbock, Tex, July 22, 43. ENGLISH & AMERICAN LITERATURE. A.B, Stanford Univ, 65; M.A, Ind. Univ, Bloomington, 67, Ph.D.(Eng. lit), 69. ASST. PROF. ENG. LIT, UNIV. CALIF, LOS ANGELES, 69- Joseph Conrad; 19th and 20th century British literature; American Indian literature. Publ: Co-ed, Buffalo Bill's wild west, Filter Press, 71; auth, Comic light in Heart of darkness, Mod. Fiction Stud, 72; Wordsworth's Mortality ode, J. Eng. & Ger. Philol, 72; The poetics of learning, Col. Eng, 74. Add: Dept. of English, University of California, Los Angeles, CA 90024.

LIND, ILSE DUSOIR, b. Ger, June 25, 17. ENGLISH. A.B, N.Y. Univ, 39, A.M, 40; Ph.D, Univ. Pa, 45. Asst. prof. ENG, WASH. SQ. COL, N.Y. UNIV, 47-58, ASSOC. PROF, 58- Ford fac. fel, 53-54; Am. Philos. Soc. grant Faulkner res, summer, 63; vis. prof, Univ. Hawaii, Manoa, summer 70. MLA; AAUP; Northeast Mod. Lang. Asn; Am. Asn. Univ. Women. William Faulkner; women in American literature; contemporary American fiction. Publ: Co-auth, Henry James' Parisian sketches, N.Y. Univ, 57; ed, Quality fiction by 20th century American women writers, Johnson Reprint, 72; auth, The inadequate vulgarity of Henry James & Design and meaning of Absalom! Absalom!, PMLA; contrib, William Faulkner: four decades of criticism, Univ. Mich, 73. Add: Dept. of English, Washington Square College, New York University, 19 University Pl, New York, NY 10003.

LIND, SIDNEY EDMUND, b. New York, N.Y, June 6, 14; m. 42; c. 1. ENGLISH. B.S, City Col. New York, 37; M.A, N.Y. Univ, 39, Ph.D.(Eng), 49. Instr. ENG, N.Y. Univ, 46; Rutgers Univ, 47-50; from instr. to PROF, BROOKLYN COL, 50- U.S.A, 41-45, Capt. MLA; Am. Stud. Asn. American literature; 19th century British literature; comparative literature. Publ: Poe and mesmerism, PMLA; Edward Taylor: a revaluation, New Eng. Quart; James's The private life and Browning. Add: Dept. of English, Brooklyn College, Brooklyn, NY 11210.

LINDBERG, GARY H, b. Minneapolis, Minn, June 16, 41; m. 61. ENGLISH. B.A, Harvard, 63; NDEA fel, Stanford Univ, 63-66, M.A, 66, Woodrow Wilson fel, 66-67, Ph.D.(Eng. & Am. lit), 67. ASST. PROF. ENG, UNIV. VA, 67- MLA. Style in prose fiction; manners, social forms, and the novel in America. Add: Dept. of English, University of Virginia, Charlottesville, VA 22903.

LINDBERG, JOHN, b. Warren, Pa, Feb. 3, 31; m. 53; c. 3. ENGLISH LITERATURE. B.A, State Univ. N.Y. Col. Educ, Albany, 52; M.A, Univ. Wis, 53, univ. scholar, 53-54, Ph.D, 56. Asst. ENG, Univ. Wis, 52-56; instr, Carthage Col, 56-57, asst. prof, 57-58; instr, Univ Maine, 58-62, asst. prof, 62-63; State Col. Iowa, 63-66; assoc. prof, Univ. North. Iowa, 66-69; SHIPPENSBURG STATE COL, 69-72, PROF, 72- NCTE; Speech Commun. Asn; Ling. Soc. Am. Rhetorical theory and practice; stylistics; freshman composition in college. Publ: Individual conscience and social injustice in Great expectations, Col. Eng, 11/61; The decadence of style, Stud. Scottish Lit, 9/63; A semester of inductive stylistics, or one solution to advanced exposition, Iowa Eng. Yearbk, 64. Add: Box 487, Shippensburg State College, Shippensburg, PA 17257.

LINDBERG, LUCILE, b. Essex, Iowa, June 10, 13. ENGLISH, HISTORY. B.S, Northwest. Mo. State Col, 36; M.A, Northwest. Univ, 41; Ed.D.(Am. hist), Columbia Univ, 52. Teacher pub. schs, Iowa, Ill. & Mo, 32-47; lectr. EDUC, QUEENS COL.(N.Y), 47-53, asst. prof, 53-57, assoc. prof, 57-60, PROF, 60- World Comt. Early Childhood Orgn. Mondial Educ. Presch, UNESCO, 59-; assoc. ed, New Era Mag, 62-67; consult, Headstart, 64-; mem. UN Observer, U.S. Comt. Early Childhood Educ, 65-; Fulbright lectr, Australia, 66; ad hoc comt, 1970 White House Conf. for Children & Youth, 67. Am. Educ. Res. Asn; Asn. Childhood Educ. Int.(v.pres, 59-61, pres, 61-63); Soc. Prof. Educ. (pres, 74-75). American history; early childhood education; elementary English. Publ: The democratic classroom, Teachers Col, Columbia Univ, 54 & in Spanish, La Democracia in La Escuela, Ed. Letras, D.F, 61; co-auth, Teaching primary children, 57 & Exploring beginnings, 60, Beacon; co-auth, Kindergarten for todays children, Follett, 67, The flexible school, Elem. Prin, 57, Those first school years, Dept. Elem. Sch. Prin, 60 & Impact and improvement of school testing programs, Nat. Soc. Stud. Educ, 63. Add: Dept. of English, Queens College, Flushing, NY 11367.

LINDBLAD, WILLIAM E, b. Chicago, Ill, Dec. 21, 28; m. 52; c. 5. ENGLISH LITERATURE. Ph.D, Univ. Ill, 62. Asst. prof. ENG, BALL STATE UNIV, 62-72, ASSOC. PROF, 72- U.S.A, 51-53, 2nd Lt. MLA. English education; English novel; Victorian literature. Add: Dept. of English, Ball State University, Muncie, IN 47306.

LINDEMAN, RALPH DONALD, b. Pittsburgh, Pa, June 15, 25; m. 49, 69; c. 2. ENGLISH. A.B, Univ. Pittsburgh, 49, Ph.D, 56; A.M, Columbia Univ, 50. PROF. ENG, GETTSBURG COL, 52- Med.C, U.S.A, 43-46. Contemporary literature; poetic theory; history of ideas. Publ: Norman Douglas: a critical study, Twayne, 65; Let art be art: a theological rationale, Lutheran Quart, spring 64. Add: 249 Ridge Ave, Gettysburg, PA 17325.

LINDEMANN, ERIKA CAROLINE, b. Valparaiso, Ind, Feb. 14, 46. ENGLISH LITERATURE, PHILOLOGY. A.B, Univ. Ga, 68; M.A, Univ. N.C, Chapel Hill, 69, Ph.D.(Eng), 72. ASST. PROF. ENG, UNIV. S.C, 72- MLA; Mediaeval Acad. Am. Old and Middle English literature; English historical linguistics. Publ: Co-ed, English essays literary and linguistic, Scholar's Guild, 74; auth, Analogues for Latin quotations in Langland's Piers Plowman, Neuphilologische Mitteilungen, (in press). Add: Dept. of English, University of South Carolina, Columbia, SC 29208.

LINDENBERGER, HERBERT (SAMUEL), b. Los Angeles, Calif, Apr. 4, 29; m. 61; c. 2. COMPARATIVE LITERATURE. A.B, Antioch Col, 51; Fulbright fel, Austria, 52-53; Ph.D, Univ. Wash, 55. Instr. comp. lit. & Ger, Univ. Calif, Riverside, 54-56, asst. prof. comp. lit. & Eng, 56-62, assoc. prof, 62-65, prof, 65-66; prof. Ger. & Eng. lit. & chmn. prog. comp. lit, Wash. Univ, 66-69; AVALON FOUND. PROF. HUMANITIES IN COMP. LIT. & ENG. & CHMN. PROG. COMP. LIT, STANFORD UNIV, 69- Guggenheim fel, 68-69. MLA. English and European 19th and 20th century literature; historical drama; critical theory and method. Publ: On Wordsworth's Prelude, Princeton, 63; Georg Buechner, South. Ill. Univ, 64; Georg Trakl, Twayne, 71; co-ed, Essays on European literature in honor of Liselotte Dieckmann, Wash. Univ, 72; Danton's death and the conventions of historical drama, Comp. Drama, summer 69; The idea of a critical approach, In: Essays on European literature in honor of Liselotte Dieckmann, Wash. Univ, 72; The idyllic moment: on pastoral and romanticism, Col. Eng, 12/72; plus others. Add: Committee on Comparative Literature, Stanford University, Stanford, CA 94305.

LINDGREN, CHARLOTTE HOLT, b. Ipswich, Mass, Jan. 5, 24. ENGLISH. A.B, Boston Univ, 45, A.M, 47, Ph.D, 61; hon. M.A, Emerson Col, 67. Teacher Eng. & hist, Pinkerton Acad, Derry, N.H, 45-46; Medfield High Sch, 47-49; admin. asst, col. lib. arts, Boston Univ, 49-60; asst. prof. ENG, EMERSON COL, 60-63, assoc. prof, 63-66, PROF. & CHMN. DEPT, 66- Col. Eng. Asn; MLA; Melville Soc. Nineteenth century American sea fiction; mythology. Add: Dept. of English, Emerson College, 130 Beacon St, Boston, MA 02116.

LINDLEY, DANIEL ALLEN, JR, b. New Haven, Conn, Aug. 28, 33; m. 60; c. 2. ENGLISH. B.A, Yale, 55; Ed. M, Harvard, 59; Ph.D.(Eng. educ), Fla. State Univ, 70. Teacher Eng, Groton Sch, Mass, 59-60; instr, Lab. Sch, Univ. Ill, Urbana, 60-64; chmn. dept, Lab. High Sch, Univ. Chicago, 64-66; instr. Eng. educ, Fla. State Univ, 66-69; lectr. Eng, Yale, 69-70; asst. prof, educ, Dartmouth Col, 70-72; ASSOC. PROF. ENG, UNIV. ILL, CHICAGO CIRCLE, 72- Lectr. Eng, Bread Loaf Sch. English, summers 61, 62; coord. Eng, Ill. Demonstration Proj. Gifted Youth, 62-64; consult, U.S. Off. Educ, 65-66; consult. Title III, Vt. Dept. Educ, 72; mem. prof. standards bd, State of N.H. NCTE; Conf. Eng. Educ. History and criticism of still photography; non-print media and the teaching of English. Publ: Teaching, learning, and the learning of teaching, In: Method in the teaching of English, NCTE, 67; Heretical questions, 1/69 & The curriculum of fusion, Las Vegas, and what is happening to our heads, 4/72, Eng. J. Add: Dept. of English, University of Illinois at Chicago Circle, Box 4348, Chicago, IL 60680.

LINDLEY, DWIGHT N, b. Glen Ridge, N.J, July 4, 20; m. 44; c. 3. ENGLISH LITERATURE. A.B, Hamilton Col, 42; A.M, Columbia Univ, 47. Ph.D. (Eng. & comp. lit), 58. Instr. Eng, Bowdoin Col, 50-52; asst. prof, HAMILTON COL, 52-58, assoc. prof, 58-65, prof, 65-73, HAMILTON B. TOMPKINS PROF. ENG. LIT, 73-, CHMN. DEPT, 68- Class of 1916 fel, Cornell Univ, summer 61, 62, 67, spring & summer, 64. C.Engrs, 42-46, M/Sgt. MLA; AAUP. Victorian literature and its relationship to historical events. Publ: Co-ed, Adventures in English literature, Harcourt, 68 & The later letters of John Stuart Mill 1849-1873, Univ. Toronto, 72. Add: Dept. of English, Hamilton College, Clinton, NY 13323.

LINDQUIST, CAROL A, b. Newton, Mass, Sept. 11, 29; c. 2. RENAISSANCE & RESTORATION LITERATURE. B.A, Colby Col, 61; M.A, Bowling Green State Univ, 62; Ph.D.(Eng), Univ. Md, College Park, 70. Instr. ENG, Bowling Green State Univ, 62-63; Towson State Col, 63-64; Univ. Md, 65-69; ASST. PROF, UNIV. ARK, FAYETTEVILLE, 69- Bus. mgr, D.H. Lawrence Rev, 72- MLA; AAUP. Restoration and Renaissance prose fiction. Add: Dept. of English, University of Arkansas, Fayetteville, AR 72701.

LINDQUIST, WAYNE PAUL, b. Chicago, Ill, May 10, 38; m. 59; c. 1. ENGLISH. B.A, Elmhurst Col, 59; M.A, Univ. Iowa, 63, Ph.D.(Eng), 68. Instr. humanities, Univ. Miami, 60-61; asst. rhetoric, Univ. Iowa, 64-65; instr. ENG, UNIV. WIS-EAU CLAIRE, 65-68, asst. prof, 68-72, ASSOC. PROF, 72- MLA; NCTE. Tobias Smollett; English novel from its beginnings; 19th century English literature. Add: Dept. of English, University of Wisconsin-Eau Claire, Eau Claire, WI 54701.

LINDSAY, CRAWFORD BERNARD, b. Birmingham, Ala, Oct. 19, 05; m. 27; c. 3. ENGLISH & AMERICAN LITERATURE. A.B, Talladega Col, 27; A.M, Univ. Mich, 31, Gen. Educ. Bd. fel, 36-37; univ. scholar & Gen. Educ. Bd. fel, Cornell Univ, 48-49, Ph.D, 50; LL.B, Tenn. Evening Law Sch, 58. Instr, High Sch, N.C, 27-30; ENG, Morehouse Col, 31-41; prof, Fla. Agr. & Mech. Col, 43-46; PROF. & CHMN. DEPT, TENN. STATE UNIV, 46- Law pract, Tenn, 58- NCTE; Col. Lang. Asn.(pres, 54-56); Am. Bar Asn. English and American literature; needs of teachers of language arts in the Negro schools of Tennessee; Ruskin's quarrel with J.S. Mill. Add: Dept. of English, Tennessee State University, Nashville, TN 37203.

LINDSEY, ALFRED J, b. Macomb, Ill, July 7, 31; m. 51; c. 1. ENGLISH EDUCATION. B.S.Ed, West. Ill. Univ, 54, M.S.Ed, 60; Ed.D.(Eng), Univ. Ill, Urbana, 69. Teacher Eng, Malden High Sch, Ill, 55-56; Jamaica High Sch, 56-57; auto dealer, Robinson, Ill, 57-60; teacher Eng, Lyons Twp. High Sch, 60-61, Lyons Twp. Jr. Col, 61-63; from instr. to assoc. prof. & dir. freshman compos, WEST. ILL. UNIV, 63-72, from assoc. prof. to PROF. EDUC. FOUND, 72- NCTE; Col. Eng. Asn; Conf. Eng. Educ. Written composition; attitude and performance change in English teachers; values. Publ: Co-auth, The student speaks out, Brown, 72; auth, Should freshman composition be a required sequence?, Ill. Educ. Rev, summer 72; The authority to interfere in students' lives, 1/73, Should the methods teacher be an agent of social change?, spring 73, Educ. Dig; plus others. Add: Dept. of Education, Stipes 451, Western Illinois University, Macomb, IL 61455.

LINDSTRAND, GORDON, b. Chicago, Ill, Dec. 21, 27; m. 56; c. 2. ENGLISH LITERATURE. B.S, Univ. Ill, 58, A.M, 59, Ph.D.(Eng), 67. Instr. ENG, UNIV. S.C, 66-67, ASST. PROF, 67- U.S.C.G, 51-54. MLA; NCTE; Bibliog. Soc. Am. Modern British and American literature; poetics; undergraduate teaching. Publ: Conrad's literary manuscripts: a bibliographical survey (3 parts), Conradiana, 69-70; Fairley's checklist of Fergusson: a problem in analytical bibliography, Stud. Scottish Lit, 70; Mechanized textual collation, Stud. Bibliog, 71. Add: 8121 Fairglen Lane, Columbia, SC 29204.

LINEBARGER, JAMES M, b. Abilene, Tex, July 6, 34; m. 58; c. 2. ENGLISH. A.B, Columbia Col, 56; M.A, Columbia Univ, 57; fels. & Ph.D, Emory Univ, 63. Instr. ENG, Ga. Inst. Technol, 57-59, asst. prof, 60-62; N.TEX. STATE UNIV, 63-65, assoc. prof, 65-70, PROF, 70- MLA; Poetry Soc. Am; AAUP. Contemporary American and English literature; poetry, especially modern. Publ: John Berryman, Twayne, 74; Symbolic hats in The sun also rises, Fitzgerald-Hemingway Annual, 72; Oppa (poem), Southwest Rev, spring 69; Wallace Stevens' Gubbinal, Wallace Stevens Newslett, 4/72. Add: Box 5132, North Texas Station, Denton, TX 76201.

LINFORD, ERNEST H, b. Afton, Wyo, Mar. 7, 07; m. 31; c. 3. JOURNALISM. Ed, Laramie Daily Boomerang, Wyo, 37-48; ed, ed. page, Salt Lake Tribune, 48-67; PROF. JOUR, UNIV. WYO, 67-, head dept, 67-72. Nieman fel, Harvard, 46-47; dir, Am. Forestry Asn, 70-72. Sigma Delta Chi Courage in Jour. Award, 47; Am. Forestry Asn. Award, 53; Am. Motors Award, 61; Utah State Univ. Bridger Award, 61. Journalism and history. Publ: Utah, contrary state, In: Our sovereign state, Vanguard, 49; Crusading in a small town, In: Reporting the news, Harvard, 65; Weekly column on environmental problems, Salt Lake Tribune, 55-67, 73- Add: 1308 Steele St, Laramie, WY 82070.

LINK, S. GORDDEN, b. Chicago, Ill, Apr. 9, 07; m. 36. ENGLISH. B.S, N.Y. Univ, 29, M.A, 30; fel, Yale, summer 31; M.Ed, Harvard, 32; fel, Columbia Univ, summer 35; Ph.D, George Peabody Col, 38. Dir. sch. jour. & univ. chaplain, Oglethorpe Univ, 38-39; vis. prof. civilization, St. Lawrence Univ, 39-40; prof. writing & methods of teaching, Drury Col, 40-41; dir. personnel & training, Microstat Corp, 41-42; dir. writing workshop, McCoy Col, Johns Hopkins Univ, 47-51; dir, Link Assoc, 51-62; prof. Eng. & poet in residence, Anne Arundel Community Col, 62-66, chmn. div. humanities, 62-64; prof. Eng. & humanities, dir. lib. arts & writer in residence, SOUTHEAST. UNIV, 66-71, EMER. PROF. ENG, 71-; PRES, AMOS R. KOONTZ MEM. FOUND. CTR. ADVAN. STUD, 71- Consult, War Prod. Bd, 41-42; off. chief staff, U.S. Dept. Army, 48-49; off. adminr, Fed. Security Agency, 49; U.S. Off. Educ, 50; U.S. Comnr. Food & Drugs, 51; adminr, Econ. Stabilization Agency, 51; prof. lectr. poetry, drama & lit. criticism, Grad. Div, Loyola Col, 62-64; exec. dir, Orgn. Advan. Col. Teaching, 64-; Off. Educ. fel, Ctr. Educ. Technol, Cath. Univ. Am, summer 68; dir, Community Col. Press, 68-; trustee, Amos R. Koontz Mem. Found, 69-; dir, Dellbrook-Shenandoah Col. Writers' Conf, 69-; writer in residence, Shenandoah Col. & Shenandoah Conservatory Music, 71-; bd. mem, Am. Security Counc, 72- Jacob Sandler Award, Southeast. Univ, 70. U.S.A, 42-47, Res, 48-62, Lt. Col; Bronze Star Medal, 46; Spec. Breast Order, Yun Hi, China, 45, Breast Order, Pau Tang, 47. MLA; Poetry Soc. Am; Poetry Soc, Eng.(Am. v.pres, 31); fel. Am. Asn. Social Psychiat; Victorian Inst. Modern poetry; Victorian literature; place of humanities in professional and business curricula. Publ: A pocket guide to Germany, Dept. Defense, 52; Three poems for now: a book of verse on the atomic age, 53, 57, 68 & 72 & co-auth, Quartet from the golden year, 61, Univ. Press, Wash, D.C. Add: Amos R. Koontz Memorial Foundation Center for Advanced Studies, Dellbrook Campus, Riverton, VA 22651.

LINKLETTER, CHARLES M, b. Winnipeg, Man, Jan. 26, 20; U.S. citizen; m. 47; c. 2. ENGLISH NOVEL. M.F.A, Univ. Iowa, 50. Instr. commun. skills, Mich. State Univ, 50-58; from asst. prof. to ASSOC. PROF. ENG, UNIV. N.DAK, 58- U.S.N.A.F, 42-46. Novels and short stories. Publ: Cricket Smith, Harper, 59. Add: Dept. of English, University of North Dakota, Grand Forks, ND 58201.

LINN, IRVING, b. Newark, N.J, Jan. 24, 12; m. 39; c. 2. ENGLISH. B.B.A, City Col. New York, 33; A.M, N.Y. Univ, 34, Ph.D, 41. From reader to instr. ENG, City Col. New York, 33-39; instr, YESHIVA UNIV, 36-42, asst. prof, 42-46, assoc. prof, 46-53, PROF, 53-, secy. col. fac, 45-49, chmn. div. lang. & lit, 54-56. Consult, Nat. Refugee Serv. & adult educ. prog, Bd. Educ, New York, N.Y; United Serv. New Americans, 49; vis. prof. Am. lit, Fed. Univ. Santa Maria, Rio Grande do Sul, Brazil, 68. MLA; Ling. Soc. Am; Am. Folklore Soc. Early English literature and comparative folklore. Publ: Arming of Sir Thopas, Mod. Lang. Notes; Dean Swift, Pope Innocent and Oliver Wendell Holmes, Philol. Quart; If all the sky were parchment, PMLA. Add: Dept. of English, Yeshiva University, New York, NY 10033.

LINN, JOHN GAYWOOD, b. New York, N.Y, Jan. 18, 17; m. 53; c. 1. ENGLISH. A.B, Hamilton Col, 38; M.A, Columbia Univ, 39; Ph.D.(Eng), Cornell Univ, 51. Instr. ENG, Am. Univ. Beirut, 39-41; Robert Col. Turkey, 41-46; Cornell Univ, 46-53, asst. prof, 53-57; QUEENS COL.(N.Y), 58-67, ASSOC. PROF, 67- MLA; NCTE. Dramatic literature; prose fiction; theatre. Publ: The theater in the fiction of Marcel Proust, Ohio State Univ, 66. Add: Dept. of English, Queens College, Flushing, NY 11367.

LINNEMAN, WILLIAM RICHARD, b. Bloomington, Ill, Oct. 13, 26; m. 57; c. 2. ENGLISH, LINGUISTICS. A.B, Park Col, 50; M.A, Univ. Ill, 54, Ph.D, 60. Asst. rhetoric, Univ. Ill, 56-60; asst. prof. ENG, Fla. South. Col, 60-64; ASSOC. PROF, ILL. STATE UNIV, 64-, CHMN. DEPT, 73-, dir. honors prog, 70-73. U.S.N, 45-46. MLA; NCTE; Conf. Col. Compos. & Commun. American humor and dialects. Publ: Col. Bill Snort, Southwest. Hist. Quart, 60; Satires of American realism, Am. Lit, 62. Add: Dept. of English, Illinois State University, Normal, IL 61761.

LINSLEY, WILLIAM ALLAN, b. Peoria, Ill, Sept. 22, 33; m. 56; c. 2. SPEECH. B.S, Bradley Univ, 55, M.A, 61; Univ. Ill, 54-55; Northwest. Univ, 55; J.D, Ind. Univ, 56; Ph.D.(speech), Univ. Okla, 63. Assoc. prof. speech & dir. grad. stud. speech, UNIV. HOUSTON, 63-72, PROF. SPEECH & CHMN. DEPT, 72- U.S.A.F, 56-59, Capt. Speech Commun. Asn; South. Speech Commun. Asn; AAUP. American public address. Publ: Speech criticism: methods and materials, W.C. Brown, 68; The ambiguity of etc. in legal symbolism, South. Speech J, 65; The deliberative dogma and devices of a demagogue, Forum, 66; The Supreme Court and the First Amendment: 1971-1972, 72 & The Supreme Court and the First Amendment: 1972-1973, 73, Free Speech Yearbk. Add: Dept. of Speech, University of Houston, Houston, TX 77004.

LINT, ROBERT GLEN, English Linguistics, Stylistics. See Volume III, Foreign Languages, Linguistics & Philology.

LINTON, BRUCE ALLEN, b. Ottawa, Ill, Dec. 3, 23. SPEECH, JOURNALISM. A.B, Muskingum Col, 47; M.A, Northwest. Univ, 43, Ph.D, 53. Asst. instr, Northwest. Univ, 48-50; asst. prof. radio & dir. radio activities, Univ. Omaha, 50-55, head dept. speech & radio, 55; assoc. prof. SPEECH & JOUR, UNIV. KANS, 55-61, PROF, 61-, CHMN. RADIO & TV DEPT, 55- Speech Commun. Asn; Broadcast Educ. Asn.(pres, 60-62); Univ. Film Producers Asn. History of radio programming in Chicago. Publ: Self-regulation in broadcasting: a three-part study guide, Nat. Asn. Broadcasters, 67. Add: Dept. of Speech & Journalism, University of Kansas, Lawrence, KS 66044.

LINTON, CALVIN DARLINGTON, b. Kensington, Md, June 11, 14; m. 51. ENGLISH LITERATURE. A.B, George Washington Univ, 35; A.M, John Hopkins Univ, 39, Ph.D, 40. Jr. instr. Eng, John Hopkins Univ, 39-40, instr, 40; prof. & head dept, Queens Col.(N.C), 40-41; PROF. ENG, GEORGE WASHINGTON UNIV, 47-, DEAN, COLUMBIAN COL. ARTS & SCI, 57-, asst. dean, 45-56, assoc. dean, 56-57. Consult. report writing, Nat. Security Agency, U.S. Air Force, U. S. Civil Serv. Comn. & U.S. Army Chem. Corps; comnr, comn. insts. of higher educ, Mid. States Asn. Cols. & Sec. Schs, 62-71, v.chmn, 67-71; lectr, Folger Inst. Renaissance & 18th Century Stud. U.S.N.R, 41-45, Lt. Comdr. MLA; Mod. Humanities Res. Asn, Gt. Brit. (Am. secy, 63-); East. Asn. Deans; Am. Conf. Acad. Deans. Milton; government writing; T.S. Eliot. Publ: How to write reports: Effective revenue writing, U.S. Govt. Printing Off, 61; The Bible as literature, In: The expositor's commentary, Zondervan, 74. Add: 5216 Farrington Rd, Westmoreland Hills, Washington, DC 20016.

LIPA, CHARLES BUELL, b. Frankfort, N.Y, Feb. 6, 05. ENGLISH & AMERICAN LITERATURE. A.B, Cornell Univ, 27, A.M, 28, Ph.D, 40. Instr. ENG, Univ. Kans, 28-32; Cornell Univ, 34-40; IOWA STATE UNIV, 40-45, asst. prof, 45-49, assoc. prof, 49-58, PROF, 58- MLA. Literary criticism; critical theory of William Blake. Add: Dept. of English, Iowa State University, Ames, IA 50010.

LIPKING, LAWRENCE IRWIN, b. New York, N.Y, Apr. 28, 34; m. 65. ENGLISH. A.B, West. Reserve Univ, 55; A.M, Cornell Univ, 56, Ph.D, 62. From instr. to PROF. ENG, PRINCETON, 60- Fel, Ctr. for Humanities, Wesleyan Univ, 72-73; Am. Counc. Learned Soc. grant, 72-73. MLA; Eng. Inst; Am. Soc. 18th Century Stud. Eighteenth century English literature; literary criticism; poet critics. Publ: The ordering of the arts in eighteenth century England, Princeton, 70; co-ed, Modern literary criticism 1900-1970, Atheneum, 72 & The Norton anthology of English literature, Norton, 74; The dialectic of Il cortegiano, PMLA, 10/66; R.S. Crane and The idea of the humanities, Philol. Quart, 7/68. Add: Dept. of English, Princeton University, Princeton, NJ 08540.

LIPP, FRANCES RANDALL, b. Boston, Mass, Jan, 25, 30; m. 56. ENGLISH, MEDIAEVAL STUDIES. A.B, Univ. Mich, 54; M.A, Univ. Calif, Berkeley, 56; univ. fel, Yale, 58-59, univ. scholar, 59-60, Sr. Sterling fel, 60-61, Ph.D, 62. Teaching asst, Univ. Calif, Berkeley, 55-56, 57-58; instr. ENG, Elmhurst Col, 61-62, asst. prof, 62-64; Wash. Univ, 64-68; ASSOC. PROF, COLO. STATE UNIV, 69- MLA; Mediaeval Acad. Am. Old English literature; medieval Latin literature; Middle English literature. Publ: Aelfric's Old English prose style, Stud. Philol, 69; Contrast and point of view in The Battle of Brunanburh, Philol. Quart, 70; Guthlac A: an interpretation, Mediaeval Stud, 71. Add: Dept. of English, Colorado State University, Ft. Collins, CO 80521.

LIPPERT, ANNE, Comparative & African Literature. See Volume III, Foreign Languages, Linguistics & Philology.

LIPPERT, DAVID JAMES, b. Milwaukee, Wis, May 23, 19; m. 60; c. 4. JOURNALISM. B.A, Univ. Wis-Madison, 41, M.A, 47; Ph.D.(jour), South. Ill. Univ, Carbondale, 69. Reporter, Kenosha News, Wis, 46; Capital Times, Madison, 47-50; chief, State Capital Bur, Milwaukee Sentinel, 50-62; lectr. JOUR, Univ. Wis-Madison, 62-64; asst. prof, UNIV. WIS-OSHKOSH, 66-69, assoc. prof, 69-73, PROF, 73-, CHMN. DEPT, 70- Assoc. ed, Wis. State Employee Mag, 46-53. U.S.A, 42-46. Asn. Educ. in Jour; Am. Soc. Jour. Sch. Adminr.(chmn. awards comt, 66-); Nat. Counc. Col. Publ. Adv. Journalism history; access to public records and proceedings. Publ: Co-auth, The news magazines and the 1960 conventions, Jour. Quart, fall 63. Add: Dept. of Journalism, University of Wisconsin-Oshkosh, Oshkosh, WI 54901.

LIPPMAN, MONROE, b. Virginia, Minn, Dec. 10, 05; m. 30. THEATER. A.B, Univ. Mich, 26, M.A, 29, Ph.D, 37. Instr. speech, Southwest Tex. State Teachers Col, 29-30, asst. prof, 30-32, assoc. prof, 32-35; teaching fel, Univ. Mich, 35-37; instr. theater & speech, Tulane Univ, 37-38, asst. prof, 38-41, assoc. prof, 41-47, prof, 47-67, head dept, 39-67; prof. theatre & head dept. drama & cinema, N.Y. Univ, 67-70; prof. THEATRE & chmn. dept, UNIV. CALIF, RIVERSIDE, 70-73, EMER. PROF, 73- Guggenheim fel, 56; Ford Found. travel stud. grant, 65; mem. drama panel cult exchange prog, U.S. Dept. State, 65-70; consult. theatre prog, Nat. Endowment for Arts, 73-; vis. artist, Hamline Univ, 74. Fel. Am. Theatre Asn.(v.pres, 49, pres, 50); Nat. Col. Players (pres, 46-47); Nat. Theatre Conf; Theatre Libr. Asn; Am. Soc. Theatre Res; Int. Fed. Theatre Res. American theatre and drama; theatre production. Publ: American playwright looks at business, Educ. Theatre J; Battle for bookings; independents challenge the trust, Tulane Drama Rev; Death of the saleman's monopoly, Theatre Surv. Add: 1631 Ransom Rd, Riverside, CA 92506.

LIPPMANN, WALTER, b. New York, N.Y, Sept. 23, 89. PUBLIC AFFAIRS. A.B, Harvard, 10; hon. degrees from 15 insts. in U.S. Founder & ed, New Republic, 14; ed, New York World, 23-31; COLUMNIST, 31- Knights Cross the First Class, Order of St. Olav, Norway, Comdr, Legion d'honneur; Order of Leopold, Belgium; Order of Orange-Nassau, Netherlands; Pulitzer Prize Spec. Citation, 57; Pulitzer Prize, 62; Gold Medal, Nat. Inst. Arts & Lett, 65. Am. Acad. Arts & Lett; Nat. Inst. Arts & Lett; Am. Philos. Soc. Philosophy; political science; foreign policy. Publ: Ed, The Poems of Paul Mariett, 13; auth, A preface to politics, 13; Drift and mastery, 14; The stakes of diplomacy, 15; The political scene, 19; Liberty and the news, 20; Public opinion, 22; The phantom public, 25; Men of destiny, 27; American inquisitors, 28; A preface to morals, 29; co-auth, The United States in world affairs, 31, 32, 33; auth, Interpretations, 32; Interpretations, 33-35; The method of freedom, 34; The new imperative, 35; The good society, 37; Some notes on war and peace, 40; U.S. foreign policy: shield of the Republic, 43; U.S. war aims, 44; The cold war, 47; Isolation and alliances, 52; The public philosophy, 55; The communist world and ours, 59; The coming test with Russia, 61; Western unity and the Common Market, 62; The essential Lippmann, 63. Add: The Lowell, 28 E. 63rd St, New York, NY 10021.

LISCA, PETER, b. Sardinia, Feb. 1, 25, nat; m. 48; c. 2. ENGLISH. B.A, Univ. Calif. Santa Barbara, 50; M.S, Univ. Wis, 51, grant, 53, Ph.D.(Eng), 55. Teaching fel, Univ. Wis, 51-54; instr. Eng, Woman's Col. Univ. N.C, 54-56; Univ. Wash, 56-58; asst. prof. ENG, UNIV. FLA, 58-66, ASSOC. PROF, 66- Smith-Mundt lectr. Am. Lit, Univ. Zaragosa, 59-60; consult. & participant, U.S. Inform. Serv. film John Steinbeck, 70; Fulbright lectr, Am. lit, Univ. Warsaw, 73-74. MLA; S.Atlantic Mod. Lang. Asn. Modern American literature. Publ: The wide world of John Steinbeck, Rutgers Univ; ed, The grapes of wrath critical edition, Viking, 72; co-ed, From Irving to Steinbeck, Florida, 72; auth, Nick Carraway and the imagery of disorder, Twentieth Century Lit, 4/67; Escape and commitment: two poles of the Steinbeck hero, In: Steinbeck: the man and his work, 71; the dynamics of community in The grapes of wrath, In: From Irving to Steinbeck, Florida, 72. Add: Dept. of English, University of Florida, Gainesville, FL 32601.

LISENBY, WILLIAM E, b. Woodhull, Ill, Sept. 8, 22; m. 48. ENGLISH, SPEECH. B.S, West. Ill. State Univ, 46, M.S, 48; Univ, Iowa, 51-52; Univ. Wis, 55-56; San Jose State Col, 67. Instr, High Sch, Ill, 46-48; ASSOC. PROF. ENG. & SPEECH & CHMN. DEPT. SPEECH, NORTH. MONT. COL, 48- U.S.A.F, 43-46, S/Sgt. Speech Commun. Asn; AAUP. Undergraduate speech education; communication. Add: Dept. of Speech, Northern Montana College, Havre, MT 59501.

LISLE, MARGERY LILLIAN CUNNINGHAM MACOUBRIE, b. Portland, Ore, Apr. 21, 41; m. 72. COMPARATIVE LITERATURE, DRAMA. B.A, Univ. Minn, 63, M.A, 66, Ph.D.(comp. lit), 70. Teaching asst. French, Univ. Minn, 63-67, teaching assoc. I Ital, 67-68, teaching assoc. II French, 68-70, instr. ENG, 70-71; ASST. PROF, UNIV. CINCINNATI, 71- MLA. Comparative drama of all periods, especially drama of England, France and Italy, and European drama since 1887. Add: 2920 Scioto St, Cincinnati, OH 45219.

LISTER, ROTRAUD, b. Iserlohn, W.Ger, Jan. 9, 28; Can. citizen; div; c. 2. ENGLISH, DRAMA. B.A, Univ. Toronto, 62, M.A, 64, Can. Counc. fel, 69, Ph.D.(Eng), 71. Lectr. ENG, UNIV. WATERLOO, 66-71, ASST. PROF, 72- Can. Asn. Univ. Teachers; Asn. Can. Univ. Teachers Eng; MLA; Can. Counc. Teachers Eng. Jacobean and Caroline drama; Canadian drama; women's studies. Add: Dept. of English, University of Waterloo, Waterloo, Ont, Can.

LISTON, WILLIAM THOMAS, b. Mt. Kisco, N.Y, Oct. 7, 30; m. 58; c. 5. ENGLISH. B.A, State Univ. N.Y. Albany, 57; M.A, Univ. Ill, 60, Ph.D.(Eng), 65. Instr. ENG, Univ. Ill, 64-65; asst. prof, BALL STATE UNIV, 65-71, ASSOC. PROF, 71- U.S.A, 51-53. MLA; Renaissance Soc. Am; Renaissance Eng. Text Soc. Add: Dept. of English, Ball State University, Muncie, IN 47306.

LITTLE, ARTHUR, b. Thomasville, Ga, Oct. 31, 11; m. 40; c. 1. DRAMA. Univ. N.C, 27-30; Univ. Wash, 48. From instr. speech & drama to assoc. prof. DRAMA, EARLHAM COL, 47-65, PROF, 65- Ford stud. grant Japanese theatre, 62-63; Fulbright-Hays grant stud. noh theatre, Japan, 66-67. Civilian Pub. Serv, 42-46. Am. Theatre Asn. Add: Dept. of Drama, Earlham College, Richmond, IN 47374.

LITTLE, EDWARD GRANT, b. McKeesport, Pa, Dec. 13, 21; m. 56. COMPARATIVE LITERATURE, MODERN LANGUAGES. A.B, Hiram Col, 49; M.A, Univ. Mich, Ann Arbor, 50; fel, Duke Univ, 51; dipl. Russian stud, Syracuse Univ, 54; Ph.D.(comp. lit), Mich. State Univ, 69. Instr. French, Hiram Col, 51; asst. prof. Eng, Gen. Motors Inst, 57-58; Tri-State Col, 58-60; Eng, French & Ger, Lansing Community Col, 60-64; from asst. prof. to ASSOC. PROF. COMP. LIT, ENG. & FRENCH, GA. SOUTH. COL, 64- Med.C, U.S.A, 42-45, Sgt. Intel.C, U.S.A.F, 51-57, T/Sgt; Bronze Star Medal. MLA; Southeast. Mod. Lang. Asn; AAUP. Cultural and literary relations of European nations; modern European novel; Medieval literature. Add: Dept. of English, Georgia Southern College, Landrum Box 8023, Statesboro, GA 30458.

LITTLE, HELEN, b. Moline, Ill; m. 36. ENGLISH. B.A, Union Col.(Nebr), 37; M.A, Univ. Nebr, 38. Instr. ENG, Union Col.(Nebr), 38-40; asst. prof, Walla Walla Col, 40-49; assoc. prof, LOMA LINDA UNIV, 60-72, PROF, 72- NCTE; Conf. Col. Compos. & Commun. Add: Dept. of English, Loma Linda University, Riverside, CA 92505.

LITTLEFIELD, DANIEL FRANKLIN, JR, b. Salina, Okla, May 23, 39; c. 1. AMERICAN LITERATURE. B.A, Okla State Univ, 60, Ph.D.(Eng), 71; M.A, Univ. Ark, Fayetteville, 62. Instr. ENG, Okla. State Univ, 61-63, 64-67; Bemidji State Col, 63-64; Southwest Mo. State Col, 67-68; ASST. PROF, UNIV. ARK, LITTLE ROCK, 70- Fel, Inst. South. Hist, Johns Hopkins Univ, 73-74. Blacks in trans-Mississippi west, 1830-1900; five civilized tribes. Publ: Co-auth, Concise rhetoric, Dickenson, 68; auth, Flannery O'Connor's Wise blood, Miss. Quart, 70; co-auth, Negro marshals in the Indian territory, J. Negro Hist, 71; auth, Utopian dreams of the Cherokee fullbloods, J. West, 71. Add: 3104 Eureka Garden Rd, North Little Rock, AR 72117.

LITTLEFIELD, DAVID J, b. Tupper Lake, N.Y, Aug. 22, 28; m. 53; c. 4. ENGLISH. A.B, Spring Hill Col, 51; M.A, Yale, 53, Ph.D, 61. Instr. Eng, MIDDLEBURY COL, 53-56 & 59-61, asst. prof, 61-65, assoc. prof, 66-69, prof, 69-71, STEWART PROF. ENG. & CHMN. DEPT. ENG. & DRAMA, 71-, dir. freshman Eng, 64-65 & 66-68, chmn. div. humanities, 67-70. Vis. fel. classics, Princeton, 65-66; educ. consult, Kinney Nat. Serv, Inc, 68-; chmn, Vt. Counc. on Humanities & Pub. Issues, 72- U.S.A, 51-52, Sgt. MLA; Am. Philol. Asn. Aristophanes; Ovid; English neoclassical literature. Publ: Ed, Twentieth century interpretations of The frogs, Prentice-Hall, 68; auth, Pomona and Vertumnus: a fruition of history in Ovid's Metamorphoses, Arion, 65; Metaphor and myth: the unity of Aristophanes' Knights, Stud. Philol, 68. Add: Dept. of English, Middlebury College, Middlebury, VT 05753.

LITTLEFIELD, ROBERT L, b. Burkburnett, Tex, Sept. 15, 21; m. 63; c. 1. ENGLISH. B.A, N.Tex. State Univ, 49, M.A, 53; Ph.D.(Eng), Tex. Technol. Col, 65. Instr. ENG, UNIV. TEX, ARLINGTON, 52-56, asst. prof, 56-57, assoc. prof, 57-69, PROF, 69- Fulbright lectr, Nat. Univ. Nicaragua, Managua, 68-69. Classical and Elizabethan tragedy; translation of poems of Medardo Angel Silva, Ecuadorian poet, 1898-1918. Publ: Knowledge and opinion in Romeo and Juliet, Stud. & Critique, 66; transl, Poems from Ecuador, Arlington Quart, 67. Add: Dept. of English, University of Texas at Arlington, Arlington, TX 76010.

LITTLEFIELD, THOMSON HASTINGS, b. Springfield, Mass, Apr. 19, 20; m. 46; c. 2. ENGLISH. A.B, Dartmouth Col, 41; Campbell fel, Univ. Edinburgh, Scotland, 47-48; M.A, Harvard, 51; Ford fac. fel, Rensselaer Polytech. Inst; Ph.D.(Eng. & comp. lit), Columbia Univ, 63. Instr. ENG, Rensselaer Polytech. Inst, 48-56; asst. prof, STATE UNIV. N.Y. ALBANY, 56-62, ASSOC. PROF, 62- Fulbright prof, Univ. Jyväskylä, Finland, 64-65. U.S.A, 42-46, Lt. MLA. Tudor poetry; relations of literature and science; fine arts. Publ: Before Spencerian; Teaching analogies in literature and science, Col. Eng; Song of the interrupted session, Epoch, Add: 150 Chestnut St, Albany, NY 12210.

LITTLEFIELD, WALTER A, b. New Rochelle, N.Y, July 18, 33; m; c. 2. COMMUNICATIONS, THEATRE. B.A. & M.A, Mich. State Univ, 60; Ed.D, Boston Col, 73. ASSOC. PROF. COMMUN, EMERSON COL, 66-; DEAN, AM. CTR. PERFORMING ARTS, 71- Dir. advert. & promotion, Landscaped Interiors, 72- U.S.A.F, 52-56, Sgt. Speech Commun. Asn. Chinese propaganda techniques. Add: 7 Clive St, Boston, MA 02130.

LITTLEJOHN, DAVID, b. San Francisco, Calif, May 8, 37; m. 63; c. 2. ENGLISH, JOURNALISM. B.A, Univ. Calif, Berkeley, 59; Woodrow Wilson fel, Harvard, 59-60, M.A, 60, Ph.D.(Eng), 63. Asst. prof. Eng, UNIV. CALIF, BERKELEY, 63-68, Eng. & jour, 68-69, JOUR, 69-71, ASSOC. PROF, 71-, weekly critic, KQED-TV. Fulbright lectr, Univ. Montpellier, 66-67; critic-at-large, PBS Network, 71-72; Am. Counc. Learned Soc. fel, London & Paris, 72-73. Eighteenth and 20th century literature, especially Samuel Johnson; American Negro writers and André Gide; contemporary culture. Publ: Ed, Dr. Johnson: his life in letters, 65 & ed, Gide: a collection of critical essays, 70, Prentice-Hall; auth, Black on white: a critical survey of writing by American Negroes, 66 & Interruptions, 69, Grossman; ed, The André Gide reader, Knopf, 71; auth, Dr. Johnson & Noah Webster, Bk. Club Calif, 71; The anti-realists, Daedalus, spring 63; The permanence of Durrell, Colo. Quart, summer 65. Add: 719 Coventry Rd, Kensington, CA 94707.

LITTLETON, BETTY J, b. Shawnee, Okla, Dec. 16, 29. ENGLISH. B.A, Lindenwood Col, 51; M.A, Stanford Univ, 53; Ph.D.(Eng), Univ. Mo, 62. Instr. ENG, Lindenwood Col, 53-54; Univ. Mo, 54-57; asst. prof, Carroll Col, 58-60; INSTR, STEPHENS COL, 62- MLA; Auth. Guild. Elizabethan drama. Publ: In Samson's eye, Atheneum, 65; Clyomon and Clamydes, Mouton, 68. Add: Dept. of English, Stephens College, Columbia, MO 65201.

LITTLETON, TAYLOR DOWE, b. Birmingham, Ala, Mar. 14, 30; m. 54; c. 4. ENGLISH LITERATURE OF ELIZABETHAN PERIOD. B.S, Fla. State Univ, 51, M.A, 52, Ph.D.(Eng), 60. Asst. ENG, Fla. State Univ, 54-57; instr, AUBURN UNIV, 57-59, asst. prof, 59-63, assoc. prof, 63-68, PROF, 68-, V.PRES. ACAD. AFFAIRS, 72-, asst. dean grad. sch, 64-68, dean undergrad. stud, 68-71. U.S.A, 52-54. S.Atlantic Mod. Lang. Asn; Renaissance Soc. Am. English literature of the 16th century. Publ: Ed, To prove a villain: the case of King Richard III, Macmillan, 64 & The Spanish Armada, Am. Bk. Co, 64; co-auth, The idea of tragedy, Scott, 65; ed, Approaching the benign environment, Vol. I, 70, The shape of likelihood: relevance and the university, Vol. II, 71 & Our secular cathedrals: change and continuity in the university, Vol. III, 73, In: The Franklin lectures in science and humanities, Univ. Ala. Add: Dept. of English, Auburn University, Auburn, AL 36830.

LITTO, FREDRIC MICHAEL, b. Brooklyn, N.Y, Jan. 8, 39; m. 61. THEATRE HISTORY & BIBLIOGRAPHY. B.A, Univ. Calif, Los Angeles, 60; Ph.D. (theatre hist), Ind. Univ. Bloomington, 69. Lectr. Eng. Ind. Univ, Indianapolis, 62-64; instr. & dir. dramatics, Bowdoin Col, 64-65; asst. prof. drama, Univ. Kans, 65-70, assoc. prof, 70-71; PROF. THEATRE & CHMN. DEPT, UNIV. SÃO PAULO, 71- Ed, Afro-Asian Theatre Bull, 65-70; workshop theatre librarianship, Lincoln Ctr, Columbia Univ, summer 66; vis. prof, Univ. Brasilia, summer 67; ed, Latin Am. Theatre Rev, 67-71 & Theatre Documentation, 68-73; participant, Am. Counc. Learned Soc. Conf. Comput. Technol. in Humanities, Lawrence, Kans, 69 & Univ. South. Calif. Conf. Black Lit, Los Angeles, Calif, 70; Soc. Sci. Res. Counc-Am. Counc. Learned Soc. Joint Comt. Latin Am. Stud. grant for res. on contemporary Brazilian theatre, Brazil, 70-71. Theatre Libr. Asn.(v.pres, 66-70); Am. Theatre Asn; Am. Folklore Soc; Am. Soc. Theatre Res; Int. Fed. Theatre

Res; Soc. Theatre Res, Eng. Early American theatre history; African and Brazilian theatre and drama; bibliographic tools for theatre research. Publ: Ed. with introd, Plays from Black Africa, Hill & Wang, 68; auth, American dissertations on drama and theatre, Kent State Univ, 69; Addison's Cato in the colonies, William & Mary Quart, 7/66; contrib, Abstracts of Folklore Stud, 64-; auth, São Paulo theatre 1970, Educ. Theatre J, 3/71. Add: Dept. of Theatre, School of Communications & Arts, University of Sao Paulo, University City, Sao Paulo, Brazil 05508.

LITZ, ARTHUR WALTON, b. Nashville, Tenn, Oct. 31, 29. ENGLISH. B.A, Princeton, 51; D.Phil, Oxford, 54. Assoc. prof, ENG, PRINCETON, 56-67, PROF, 67- Am. Counc. Learned Soc. fel, 60-61. Danforth Gifted Teaching Award, 72. MLA; Eng. Inst. James Joyce; 19th century novel; modern poetry and fiction. Publ: The art of James Joyce, 61, Modern American fiction: essays in criticism, 63, Jane Austen, 65 & The poetic development of Wallace Stevens, 72, Oxford; ed, Modern Literary criticism, 1900-1970, Atheneum, 72 & Eliot in his time, Princeton, 73. Add: 22 McCosh Hall, Princeton University, Princeton, NJ 08540.

LITZINGER, BOYD ANTHONY, JR, b. Johnstown, Pa, Apr. 2, 29; m. 61. ENGLISH. B.S, Univ. S.C, 51, M.A, 55; Ph.D.(Eng), Univ. Tenn, 56. Instr. ENG, Univ. Tenn, 52-56; Tex. Technol. Col, 56-57; dept. head, Lander Col, 57-58; asst. prof, Univ. S.C, 58-59; assoc. prof, ST. BONAVENTURE UNIV, 59-65, PROF, 65-, DEAN ARTS & SCI, 69-, assoc. dean, 66-69, head dept. Eng, 61-62. Vis. assoc. prof, Univ. Tenn, 62-63; vis. prof, Univ. Wis, summer 66; mem. ed. bd, Cithara, 60-, Victorian Poetry, 65- & Stud. Browning & His Circle, 72- MLA; Northeast Mod. Lang. Asn. Victorian literature; Modern poetry; future of private education. Publ: Robert Browning and the Babylonian woman, Armstrong-Browning Libr, 62; Time's revenges: Browning's reputation as a thinker, Univ. Tenn, 62; co-auth, The Browning critics, Univ. Ky, 66 & Robert Browning: our critical heritage, Routledge, London, 69. Add: School of Arts & Sciences, St. Bonaventure University, St. Bonaventure, NY 14778.

LIVINGSTON, JAMES L, b. Detroit, Mich, Oct. 21, 40; m. 62; c. 4. RENAISSANCE LITERATURE. A.B, Univ. Detroit, 62; M.A, Univ. N.C, Chapel Hill, 65; Ph.D.(Eng), Univ. Buffalo, 70. Instr. ENG, Detroit Country Day Sch, 65-66; Clemson Univ, 66-67; Fredonia State Col, 67-68; asst. prof, NORTH. MICH. UNIV, 69-73, ASSOC. PROF, 73- Consult, Nat. Humanities Series, 71- Poetry and science; Ben Jonson; poetry and ritual. Publ: Walt Whitman's Epistle to the Americans, Am. Lit, 1/69; With Whitman around the campfire, Walt Whitman Rev, 6/70; Names in Twain's Mysterious stranger, Notes & Queries, 6/71. Add: Dept. of English, Northern Michigan University, Marquette, MI 49855.

LIVINGSTON, JAMES T, b. San Angelo, Tex, Mar. 16, 31; m. 57; c. 2. LITERATURE, THEOLOGY. A.B, Tex. Christian Univ, 52, M.A, 53; Fulbright & Ger. Acad. Exchange Serv. fels, Heidelberg Univ, 55-56; B.D, Univ. Chicago, 59, Ph.D.(theol. & lit), 63. Asst. prof. ENG, DRURY COL, 62-63, assoc. prof, 63-68, PROF, 68-, CHMN. DEPT, 66- Danforth Found. fel. black stud, Howard Univ. & Libr. of Congr, 70-71. MLA; Midwest Mod. Lang. Asn; NCTE; Am. Acad. Relig. Caribbean literature; the relation of Christian theology and modern literature; literary theory and criticism. Publ: Caribbean rhythms, the emerging English literature of the West Indies, Washington Square, 74; The artist's struggle to stand on holy ground: J.D. Salinger, In: Adversity and grace in recent American fiction, Univ. Chicago, 68. Add: Dept. of English, Drury College, Springfield, MO 65802.

LIVIX, MARY JOANNA (FINK), b. Outlook, Mont, May 6, 33; m. ENGLISH. B.A, Col. Great Falls, 56; M.S, Creighton Univ, 57; fel, Univ. Notre Dame, 63-65, Ph.D.(Eng), 65. Asst. prof. Eng, Col. Great Falls, 61-63; asst. to dean grad. sch, Univ. Notre Dame, 64-65; assoc. prof. Eng, Col. Great Falls, 65-66; acting assoc. dean & admin. intern, Beloit Col, 66-67; acad. v.pres, Col. Great Falls, 67-69; assoc. prof. Eng, Univ. Mich, 69-71; DEP. ASSOC. SUPT. EDUC. ADMIN, ARIZ. STATE DEPT. EDUC, 71- Ford Found. Am. Counc. Educ. fel. grant, 66-67; Inst. Int. Educ. scholar. grant, Oxford, 67. Am. Asn. Sch. Adminr. American literature, 1890 to present; contemporary British poetry; educational administration and management. Publ: The concept of the artist and creative genius in American naturalistic fiction, Univ. Microfilms, 65; co-auth. & ed, Reading performance objectives: a model, Ariz. Dept. Educ, 72; auth, The view of man in naturalistic fiction, Counc. Lett, Mont. Counc. Col. & Univ. Teachers Eng, spring 66. Add: 208 W. El Caminito Dr, Phoenix, AZ 85021.

LLEWELLYN, ROBERT HALL, b. Philadelphia, Pa, May 29, 17. MEDIEVAL LITERATURE & LANGUAGE. A.B, Dickinson Col, 39; A.M, Harvard, 42, Ph.D, 46. Instr. ENG, Dickinson Col, 41-42; Sheldon fel, Harvard, 46-47; instr, TEMPLE UNIV, 47-48, asst. prof, 48-60, assoc. prof, 60-68, PROF, 68- MLA. Publ: Co-auth, Basic writer and reader, Am. Bk. Co, 61, alternate forms, 63, 72. Add: Dept. of English, Temple University, Philadelphia, PA 19122.

LLOYD-JONES, RICHARD, b. Mason City, Iowa, Aug. 25, 27; m. 51; c. 4. ENGLISH. B.A, Univ. N.Mex, 49; A.M, Univ. N.C, 50; Ph.D, State Univ. Iowa, 56. Instr. ENG, UNIV. IOWA, 51-58, asst. prof, 58-62, assoc. prof, 62-65, PROF. & DIR. UNDERGRAD. STUD. ENG, 65-, IN CHARGE ADVAN. COMPOS, 56-, admin. asst. dept. Eng, 63-65. Mem. staff, Ind. Inst. Teachers Eng. in Predominately Negro Cols, summer, 65; mem, Midwest Regional Exec. Comt. Eng. in Two Year Cols, 67-69; consult, Nat. Assessment of Educ. Progs, 72- U.S.A, 45-46. NCTE (comn. compos, 68-73, publ. comt, 72-75); Conf. Col. Compos. & Commun. Poetry; Victorian literature; rhetorical theory and stylistics. Publ: Co-auth, Research in writing composition, NCTE, 63; auth, Romantic revels, Col. Compos. & Commun, 10/72. Add: Dept. of English, 308 English-Philosophy Bldg, University of Iowa, Iowa City, IA 52242.

LOACKER, GEORGINE, O.S.F, b. Chicago, Ill, May 27, 26. ENGLISH LITERATURE & LANGUAGE, EDUCATION. B.S.E, Alverno Col, 47; M.A, Marquette Univ, 56; Ph.D.(Eng), Univ. Chicago, 71. Instr. ENG, Pius XI High Sch, 46-57; ALVERNO COL, 57-62, asst. prof, 65-69, assoc. prof, 69-74, PROF, 74-, CHMN. DEPT, 69- Guest instr. Eng, St. Mary Col, summer 50; Sperry & Hutchinson grant, 70; Robert Pooley Found. res. grant, 73. Uhrig Found. Teacher of Yr. Award, 69, 73. MLA; NCTE; Midwest Mod. Lang. Asn; Women's Caucus Mod. Lang. Curricular design and implementation for the education of women; teaching Shakespeare; assessment of competence. Add: Dept. of English, Alverno College, 3401 S. 39th St, Milwaukee, WI 53215.

LOCHHEAD, DOUGLAS GRANT, b. Guelph, Ont, Mar. 25, 22; m. 49; c. 2. ENGLISH. B.A, McGill Univ, 43, B.L.S, 51; M.A, Univ. Toronto, 47. Librn. & lectr. sociol, Univ. Victoria (B.C), 51-52; librn. cataloguer, Cornell Univ, 52-53; chief librn. & prof, Dalhousie Univ, 53-60; chief librn. & prof. Eng, York Univ.(Ont), 60-63; LIBRN. MASSEY COL, UNIV. TORONTO, 63-, PROF. ENG, BIBLIOG. & PALAEOGRAPHY, UNIV, COL, 65-, spec. lectr, Eng. bibliog, 64-65. Consult. libr. planning, Trent Univ, 63-67; sr. fel, Massey Col, Univ. Toronto, 64-, spec. lectr. fac. libr. sci, 65-; Can. Counc. res. grants, 67 & 68. Can. Army, 43-45, Lt. Bibliog. Soc. Can; Bibliog. Soc. Eng; Bibliog. Soc. Am; Oxford Bibliog Soc; League Can. Poets (v.chmn, 68-72). History of printing in Canada; bibliography, especially printing and papermaking; Elizabethan handwriting. Publ: The heart is fire, 59 & It is all around, 60, Ryerson, Toronto; Poet talking, Apollo, Halifax, 64; Millwood Road poems, Ascham, Toronto, 70; co-ed, Made in Canada: new poems of the 70's, Oberon, Ottawa, 70; ed, Bibliography of Canadian Bibliographies, 2nd ed. rev, 72, ed, Literature of Canada series, gen. ed, 72 & ed, Toronto reprint library of Canadian prose and poetry (25 vols), 73, Univ. Toronto; co-ed, 100 Canadian poems of the 19th century, Macmillan, Toronto, 74; plus others. Add: Massey College, 4 Devonshire Pl, Toronto, Ont. M5S 2E1, Can.

LOCKE, LOUIS GLENN, b. Woodstock, Va, May 3, 12; m. 40; c. 2. ENGLISH PHILOLOGY. A.B, Bridgewater Col, 33; A.M, George Washington Univ, 34; Sanger scholar, Harvard, 36-37, Dexter traveling fel, 37, A.M, 37, univ. fel, 37-38, Ph.D, 38. Acting prof. ENG, Univ. N.B, 38-39; asst. prof, Mary Washington Col, Univ. Va, 39-43; assoc. prof, Southwest. at Memphis, 43-47; prof, Mary Baldwin Col, 47-56; prof, MADISON COL.(VA), 56-72, JAMES MADISON DISTINGUISHED PROF, 72-, head dept. Eng, 56-67, dir. humanities, 56-69, dean sch. humanities, 69-72. Ed, The Explicator, 42-; Ford fel, Harvard & Yale, 53-54. Eng. Inst; MLA. World literature; the humanities; 17th and 18th century English literature. Publ: Co-auth, Literature of western civilization, Ronald, 52, auth, Tillotson: a study in 17th century literature, Rosenkilde & Bagger, Copenhagen, 54; co-auth, University Handbook, 66, Readings for liberal education, 67, co-ed, Toward liberal education, 5th ed. & co-ed, TLE Six: options for the 1970's, 72, Holt. Add: Madison College, Harrisonburg, VA 22802.

LOCKE, MIRIAM (AUSTIN), b. Mobile, Ala, Apr. 9, 07. ENGLISH. A.B, Univ. Ala, 26, A.M, 31; fels, Northwest. Univ, 37-39 & 44-45, Ph.D, 45. Asst. ENG, UNIV. ALA, 29-31, instr, 31-37, 39-44, asst. prof, 45-47, assoc. prof, 47-59, PROF, 59-, res. comt. grants, summers 46-48, 50, 56, 59, 61-63. Col. Eng. Asn; MLA; S.Atlantic Mod. Lang. Asn; Milton Soc. Am; Southeast Renaissance Conf; NCTE; Am. Soc. 18th Century Stud. Seventeenth and 18th century English literature; Henry Fielding; Milton. Publ: An annotated edition of Henry Fielding's True patriot, Univ. Ala, 64. Add: Box 1484, University, AL 35486.

LOCKERBIE, DONALD BRUCE, b. Capreol, Ont, Aug. 25, 35; U.S. citizen; m. 56; c. 3. ENGLISH, AMERICAN CIVILIZATION. A.B, N.Y. Univ, 56, M.A, 63; Wheaton Col.(Ill), 56-57. Instr. ENG, Wheaton Col.(Ill), 56-57; MASTER, STONY BROOK SCH, 57-, chmn. dept, 61-73. Fel, Col. Entrance Exam. Bd. summer inst. Eng, 62; consult, NDEA summer insts, summer 67; advan. placement prog. consult, Northeast Regional Off. Col. Entrance Exam. Bd, 67-; Thomas J. Staley Distinguished Christian Scholar lectureship, Univ. Miss, 72; consult, Consortium of Christian Cols, Wheaton, Ill, summer 73; examr, Int. Baccalaureate Off, Geneva, Switz, 73- NCTE (mem. comn. Eng. curriculum, 69-72). Rhetoric; 19th century American literature; Christian aesthetics. Publ: Billy Sunday, Word Bks, 65, Patriarchs and prophets, 68 & ed, Major American authors, 70, Holt; co-auth, Macmillan English series, Bks. 10 & 12, Macmillan, 68; co-auth, Success in writing, Bk. II, 68 & auth, Purposeful writing, 72, Addison-Wesley; auth, The way they should go, Oxford Univ, 72; The liberating word: creation and the mystery of the Gospel, Eerdmans, 74; The conscious rhetorician, Eng. J, 10/69; The theater of deceit, Christianity Today, 7/70; What best sellers tell us about ourselves, Christian Herald, 3/73; plus others. Add: Dept. of English, Stony Brook School, Stony Brook, NY 11790.

LOCKLIN, GERALD IVAN, b. Rochester, N.Y, Feb. 17, 41; m. 61, 65; c. 5. ENGLISH. B.A, St. John Fisher Col, 61; M.A, Univ. Ariz, 63, Ph.D.(Eng), 64. Instr. ENG, Calif. State Col, Los Angeles, 64-65; ASST. PROF, CALIF. STATE UNIV, LONG BEACH, 65- Borestone Mt. Best Poem Award, 67. Twentieth century literature; poetry. Publ: Poop and other poems, MAG Press, 72; co-auth, Edward Field: stand-up poet, Minn. Rev, Vol. IV, No. 1, & Some observations on A Confederate General from Big Sun, Critique, Vol. XIII, No. 2; auth, The monopoly story (short story), In: Best little magazine fiction, N.Y. Univ, 70; plus several poems & short stories in numerous mags. & journals. Add: Dept. of English, California State University, Long Beach, Long Beach, CA 90801.

LOCKRIDGE, ERNEST HUGH, b. Bloomington, Ind, Nov. 28, 38; m. 60; c. 2. ENGLISH. A.B, Ind. Univ, 60; M.A, Yale, 61, Ph.D.(Eng), 64. Instr. ENG, Yale, 63-66, asst. prof, 66-71; ASSOC. PROF, OHIO STATE UNIV, 71- Fel, Ctr. Advan. Stud, Univ. Ill, 69-70. MLA. English and American novel; modern poetry; English romantic poets. Publ: Hartspring blows his mind, New Am. Libr, 68; Twentieth century interpretations of the Great Gatsby, Prentice-Hall, 68; Prince Elmo's Fire, Stein & Day, 74; A vision of the sentimental absurd: Sterne and Camus, Sewanee Rev, 64; A vision of art: Henry James's The tragic Muse, Mod. Fiction Stud, 66. Add: Dept. of English, Denney Hall, Ohio State University, Columbus, OH 43210.

LOCKRIDGE, LAURENCE SHOCKLEY, b. Bloomington, Ind, July 1, 42. ENGLISH LITERATURE. A.B, Ind. Univ, 64; Woodrow Wilson fel, Harvard, 64-65, Danforth Found. fel, 64-69, M.A, 68, Ph.D.(Eng), 69. ASST. PROF. ENG, RUTGERS UNIV, NEW BRUNSWICK, 69- MLA. Samuel Taylor Coleridge; 18th and 19th century moral philosophy; literature and philosophy. Add: 68 Carmine St, New York, NY 10014.

LOCKWOOD, PATTON, b. Madura, India, Feb. 16, 30; U.S. citizen; m. 54; c. 1. THEATRE, SPEECH. B.A, Oberlin Col, 53; M.Ed, Univ. Va, 55; Ph.D, Mich. State Univ, 62. Instr. THEATRE & SPEECH, Univ. Conn, 60-63; from asst. prof. to ASSOC. PROF, LONGWOOD COL, 63-, CHMN. DEPT. SPEECH & DRAMATIC ARTS, 68- Ed, South. Theatre, 73- Sig.C, U.S.A. Am. Theatre Asn; Speech Commun. Asn. William Inge's plays. Add: Dept. of Speech & Dramatic Arts, Longwood College, Farmville, VA 23901.

LOCKWOOD, THOMAS FRANK, b. Houston, Tex, Aug. 22, 42; m. 63; c. 2. ENGLISH LITERATURE. B.A, Rice Univ, 64, Ph.D.(Eng), 67. Asst. prof. ENG, UNIV. WASH, 67-73, ASSOC. PROF, 73- MLA. Restoration and 18th century satire and comedy; the English novel; literary illusion and convention. Publ: Co-ed, Fielding: the critical heritage, Routledge & Kegan Paul, 69; auth, The Augustan author-audience relationship: satiric vs. comic forms, ELH, 69; On the relationship of satire and poetry after Pope, Stud. Eng. Lit, 74; Swift's Modest proposal: a reinterpretation, Papers Lang. & Lit, 74. Add: Dept. of English, University of Washington, Seattle, WA 98195.

LODGE, EVAN ABEL, b. Columbiana, Ohio, Aug. 9, 05; m. 41; c. 2. ENGLISH. A.B, Mt. Union Col, 30; M.A, West. Reserve Univ, 45. Teacher, high schs, Cleveland, Ohio, 30-38, chmn. dept. Eng, 38-46, supvr. Eng, jr. & sr. high schs, 46-57, directing supvr, 57-63; ASSOC. PROF. ENG, KENT STATE UNIV, 63- Gen. consult, Adventures in Reading, Harcourt, Brace & World, 68; chmn, Eng. Conf, Kent State Univ, 64- NCTE. Methods of teaching English. Publ: Co-auth, Steps to language power, Harper, 49 & Adventures in Reading, Harcourt, 52, 58, 63; auth, A garland for Ohio, Partridge, 72, 2nd ed, privately publ, 73; What's wrong with a little grammar?, Ohio Eng. Bull, 3/71; Great symbolic needle hunt, Eng. J, 11/72. Add: 1506 Prospect Rd, Hudson, OH 44236.

LOEFFLER, DONALD LEE, b. Piqua, Ohio, May 30, 30. THEATRE, SPEECH. B.S, Univ. Dayton, 52; M.A, Columbia Univ, 53; State Univ. Iowa, 58-60; Ph.D.(theatre), Bowling Green State Univ, 69. Teacher speech, Durand Pub. Schs, Mich, 55-57; Arlington Pub. Schs, Va, 57-58; chief speech therapist, Barney Children's Med. Ctr, Dayton, Ohio, 60-64; asst. prof. speech, Worcester State Col, 64-67; speech therapist, New Reigel Pub. Schs, 67-68; ASSOC. PROF. THEATRE & HEAD DEPT. SPEECH & THEATRE ARTS, WEST. CAROLINA UNIV, 69- U.S.A, 53-55. Speech Commun. Asn; Am. Theatre Asn; Am. Speech & Hearing Asn; Southeast. Theatre Conf. An analysis of the treatment of the homosexual character in drama produced on the New York stage from 1950 to 1968. Add: Dept. of Speech & Theatre Arts, Western Carolina University, Cullowhee, NC 28723.

LOESCH, KATHARINE TAYLOR, b. Berkeley, Calif, Apr. 13, 22; m. 48; c. 1. SPEECH. B.S, Columbia Univ, 44, M.A, 49; Ind. Univ, Bloomington, 53; Ph.D.(speech), Northwest. Univ, 61. Instr. speech, Wellesley Col, 49-52; asst. prof. speech & Eng, Roosevelt Univ, 62-65; SPEECH, UNIV. ILL, CHICAGO CIRCLE, 68-70, ASSOC. PROF, 70- Speech Commun. Asn; Ling. Soc. Am; MLA; Am. Soc. Aesthet. Prosody; linguistics and literature; Dylan Thomas. Publ: Literary ambiguity & oral performance, Quart J. Speech, 10/65; The shape of sound: configurational rime in the poetry of Dylan Thomas, Speech Monogr, 11/68; Empirical studies in oral interpretation: the text, West. Speech, fall 69. Add: 2129 N. Sedgwick St, Chicago, IL 60614.

LOESSIN, EDGAR RAY, b. Thrall, Tex, Nov. 4, 28; m. 66. DRAMA. B.A, Univ. N.C, 49; M.F.A, Yale, 54. CHMN. DEPT. DRAMA & PRODUCER-DIR, SUMMER THEATRE, E.CAROLINA UNIV, 64- Stage mgr. & dir, several Broadway and stock productions, 63- U.S.A, 55-57. Am. Theatre Asn; Univ. Resident Theatre Asn. Add: Dept. of Drama, East Carolina University, Greenville, NC 27834.

LOEWE, RALPH ELIAS, b. Cleveland, Ohio, July 26, 23; m. 50; c. 2. ENGLISH. B.A, Ohio Univ, 47; M.A, Columbia Univ, 51. Teacher, East Tech. High Sch, 51-60; ed. humor, Am. Greetings Corp, 60-61; teacher, John Adams High Sch, 61-63; head dept. Eng, Glenville High Sch, 63-64; instr. ENG, CUYAHOGA COMMUNITY COL, 64-66, asst. prof, 66-67, ASSOC. PROF, 67-, head dept, 71-72. Sig.C, U.S.A, 43-45, Sgt. Mod. Lang. Asn; AAUP; Conf. Col. Compos. & Commun; NCTE. English composition and grammar; history of India; playwriting. Publ: The practical writer, Harcourt, 68; The writing clinic, Prentice-Hall, 73; Who makes a menace out of Johnny?, Saturday Rev, 6/63. Add: Dept. of English, Cuyahoga Community College, Community College Ave, Cleveland, OH 44115.

LOEWEN, PETER F, b. Mountain Lake, Minn, Feb. 1, 05; m. ENGLISH. B.A, Carleton Col, 28; M.A, Univ. Chicago, 31; Ph.D, Univ. Denver, 52. Instr. Eng. & debate, Lafayette High Sch, Red Lake Falls, Minn, 28-30; Moorhead State Teachers Col, Minn, 31-36; Eng, Compton Jr. Col, Calif, 38-39; asst. prof, Univ. S.Dak, 43-46; speech, Univ. Denver, 46-50; prof. ENG, MISS. STATE UNIV, 53-72, EMER. PROF, 72- Sir Thomas Pope Blount; the historical novel; comparative literature. Add: 1402 Third Ave. N, Columbus, MS 39701.

LOFTIS, JOHN, b. Atlanta, Ga, May 16, 19; m. 46; c. 3. ENGLISH LITERATURE. A.B, Emory Univ, 40; A.M, Princeton, 42, Ph.D, 48. Instr. ENG, Princeton, 46-48; Univ. Calif, Los Angeles, 48-50, asst. prof, 50-52; assoc. prof, STANFORD UNIV, 52-58, PROF, 58-, CHMN. DEPT, 73- Co-ed, Augustan Reprint Soc, 49-52; Ford Found. fel, 55-56; Fulbright lectr. Am. stud, Peru, 59-60; Guggenheim Mem. Found. fel, 66-67; mem. ed. bd, Stud. Eng. Lit, 66-; Folger Shakespeare Libr. fel, 67; mem. ed. bd, Huntington Libr. Quart, 68- U.S.N, 42-46, Lt. MLA; Philol. Asn. Pac. Coast. History of drama; 18th century English literature; Dryden. Publ: Steele at Drury Lane, Univ. Calif, 52; Comedy and society from Congreve to Fielding, Stanford Univ, 59; gen. ed, Regents restoration drama series (29 vols), Univ. Nebr, 62-; auth, The politics of drama in Augustan England, Clarendon, 63; co-ed, Works of John Dryden, Vol. IX, Univ. Calif, 66; ed, Restoration drama: modern essays in criticism, Oxford, 66 & Lucius Junius Brutus, Univ. Nebr, 67; auth, The Spanish plays of neoclassical England, Yale Univ, 73; co-ed, Restoration and eighteenth-century literature: a bibliography of modern studies, Philol. Quart, 51-56. Add: Dept. of English, Stanford University, Stanford, CA 94305.

LOFTIS, JOHN EDGAR, III, b. Sioux City, Iowa, Feb. 28, 45; m. 66; c. 1. ENGLISH LITERATURE. B.A, Univ. of the South, 66; M.A, Emory Univ, 69, Ph.D.(Eng), 71. Teaching asst. ENG, Emory Univ, 68-69; instr, UNIV. NORTH. COLO, 70-72, ASST. PROF, 72- Eighteenth century English literature; the novel; satire. Add: Dept. of English, University of Northern Colorado, Greeley, CO 80639.

LOGAN, BARRY L, b. Phila, Pa, Apr. 1, 30. ENGLISH LITERATURE. B.A, Syracuse Univ, 52, M.A, 56; scholar, Yale, 57, Ph.D.(Eng), 60. Instr. ENG, Duke Univ, 58-61; from asst. prof. to PROF, CALIF. STATE UNIV, FRESNO, 61- U.S.A.F, 52-54, Res, 54-, Maj. MLA. English romantic period; literature of English novel. Add: Dept. of English, California State University, Fresno, Fresno, CA 93726.

LOGAN, EUGENIA, S.P, b. Ft. Wayne, Ind. ENGLISH. A.B, St. Mary-of-the-Woods Col, 19; M.A, Ind. Univ, 25; Cath. Univ. Am, 26-27. Teacher, High Sch, Schs. Sisters of Providence, 11-22; dean, Immaculata Jr. Col, Wash, D.C, 22-27; ST. MARY-OF-THE-WOODS COL, 27-50, HISTORIAN & ARCHIVIST, 53-, for. stud. adv, 52-68, v.pres, 54-60. MLA; Nat. Asn. For. Stud. Adv. Romanticism; American church history. Publ: Concordance to poetry of S.T. Coleridge, Providence Press, 40; transl, Pere Ronsin's Gouverner c'est aimer, 52 & Pere Ronsin's Obeir c'est regner, 61, Alba Press; auth, History of foundation of St. Mary-of-the-Woods and Sisters of Providence in Indiana & Biography of Mother Theodore Guerin, In: Dizionario Enciclopedico dei Religiosi, Ed. Paolina, Rome, 66. Add: Providence Convent, St. Mary-of-the-Woods, IN 47876.

LOGAN, HARRY MILLARD, b. Norristown, Pa, Dec. 17, 33; m. 58; c. 2. LINGUISTICS, MEDIEVAL LITERATURE. A.B, Franklin & Marshall Col, 55; teaching asst, Univ. Pa, 57-59, Ph.D.(Eng), 66. Instr. ENG, Allegheny Col, 60-65, asst. prof, 65-66; UNIV. WATERLOO, 66-69, ASSOC. PROF, 69-, summer grants, 67-68, res. grants, 69, 71. Allegheny Col. summer grant, 65; vis. asst. prof, Univ. Waterloo, summer 66; Can. Counc. res. grant, 71. MLA; Can. Ling. Asn; Mediaeval Acad. Am; Asn. Can. Univ. Teachers Eng. Medieval, Old and Middle English dialects; computer research in linguistic and literary studies; stylistics. Publ: The dialect of the Life of St. Katherine, Mouton, The Hague, 73; The computer and Middle English dialectology, Can. J. Ling, fall 67; Some applications of linguistic theory to poetry, Humanities Asn. Bull, 71. Add: Dept. of English, University of Waterloo, Waterloo, Ont, Can.

LOGAN, JAMES VENABLE, JR, b. Ky, June 25, 01. ENGLISH LITERATURE. A.B, Washington & Lee Univ, 24; A.M, Princeton, 27, Ph.D, 32. Instr. ENG, East. Ky. State Teachers Col, 25-26; Univ. Pittsburgh, 27-30; asst. prof, Kans. State Teachers Col, 32-33; instr. Princeton, 33-35; OHIO STATE UNIV, 35-39; asst. prof, 39-46, assoc. prof, 46-62, PROF, 62- Am. Counc. Learned Soc. grant-in-aid, Europe, 34. MLA. Wordsworth and 19th century English literature. Publ: Poetry and esthetics of Erasmus Darwin; Wordsworthian criticism, a guide and bibliography, Ohio State Univ; co-auth, English romantic poets, Mod. Lang. Asn, 56. Add: Dept. of English, Ohio State University, Columbus, OH 43210.

LOGAN, LILLIAN M, b. Sykeston, N.Dak, Dec. 14, 09; m. 46. ENGLISH, SOCIAL STUDIES. B.S, East. Mich. Univ, 39; M.S, Univ. Wis, 51; Ph.D. (Eng, music), 53. Assoc. prof. educ, Union Col.(Nebr), 48-54; Univ. Evansville, 54-62; Eng, BRANDON UNIV, 65-70, PROF. EDUC, 70- Mem. U.S. nat. comt, World Orgn. Early Childhood Educ, 48- & mem. Can. nat. comt, 65-; summer vis. lectr, Univ. Alta, 62 & 72, Univ. Calgary, 64, Univ. Victoria (B.C), 66, 67 & 68. Int. Reading Asn; Music Educ. Nat. Conf; NCTE; Nat. Asn. Educ. Young Children; Nat. Counc. Social Stud; World Counc. Curriculum & Instr; Can. Speech Asn. Childhood education; language arts; social studies. Publ: Teaching the young child, 60 & co-auth, Teaching the elementary school child, 62, Houghton; co-auth, A dynamic approach to language arts, 67 & Man and his world: social studies, 69, McGraw; co-auth, Creative teaching, McGraw, Can, 71; co-auth, Creative communication, 72 & auth, Educating young children, (in press), McGraw-Ryerson, Can, 72; auth, Kindergarten education in Mexico, Educ. Horizons, summer 53; The first day, Childhood Educ, 8/62. Add: 602 15th St, Brandon, Man, Can.

LOGAN, ROBERT ALEXANDER, III, b. Syracuse, N.Y, Mar. 28, 35. ENGLISH LITERATURE. A.B, Williams Col, 56; A.M, Harvard, 57, teaching fel, 58-62, Ph.D, 62; traveling fel, Eng, summer, 59. Instr. Eng. lit, Williams Col, 62-65, asst. prof, 65-71; ASSOC. PROF. ENG, UNIV. HARTFORD, 71- MLA; Renaissance Soc. Am. Renaissance poetry; Marlowe, Shakespeare and Drayton; Shakespeare's plays. Add: Dept. of English, University of Hartford, Hartford, CT 06117.

LOGAN, SAMUEL TALBOT, JR, b. Vicksburg, Miss, Oct. 26, 43; m. 66; c. 1. LITERATURE, THEOLOGY. B.A, Princeton, 65; M.Div, Westminster Theol. Sem, 68; Ph.D.(theol. & lit), Emory Univ, 72. Asst. prof. ENG, BARRINGTON COL, 70-74, ASSOC. PROF, 74-, CHMN. DIV. HUMANITIES, 73- Core fac, Summer Inst. Early New Eng. Stud, 73- MLA; Am. Acad. Relig. New England and puritan theology and culture; 19th century American literature; theological and poetic language. Publ: Theology and literature: a linguistic relationship, Westminster Theol. J, spring 74. Add: Division of Humanities, Barrington College, Barrington, RI 02806.

LOGAN, SUSAN H, b. Chattanooga, Tenn, Apr. 14, 27; m. 48; c. 1. ENGLISH. A.B, Univ. Ga, 48, M.A, 52; Ph.D.(Eng. educ), Fla. State Univ, 66. Instr. Eng, Norman Col, 61-62; Eng. & reading, Fla. State Univ, 65-66; asst. prof. ENG, APPALACHIAN STATE UNIV, 66-68, ASSOC. PROF, 68- Add: Dept. of English, Appalachian State University, Boone, NC 28607.

LOGAN, TERENCE PATRICK, b. Boston, Mass, Nov. 6, 36; m. 65; c. 1. RENAISSANCE ENGLISH LITERATURE. A.B, Boston Col, 59; Dartmouth Col, 59-60; M.A, Univ. Wis-Madison, 61; fel. & Ph.D.(Eng. lit), Harvard, 66. Res. asst. Eng. lit, Univ. Wis-Madison, 61; asst. prof. ENG, Univ. Md, College Park, 65-68; UNIV. N.H, 68-71, ASSOC. PROF, 71-, fac. fel, summer 71, asst. to v.pres. res, 72-73. Fel, Southeast Inst. Medieval & Renaissance Stud, summer 66; vis. asst. prof. comp. lit, Univ. Wis-Milwaukee, summer 67; section ed, Eng. Lit. Renaissance, 70-; Shakespeare Newslett, 71- Dante Soc. Am.(Prize, 64); MLA. Renaissance English drama; Dante; bibliography. Publ: The variant issues of the 1704 edition of John Dennis's Liberty asserted, Library, 12/70; John Dennis's selected works, 1718, 1721, Papers Bibliog. Soc. Am. 4/71; Robert Wilson and the O.E.D, Notes & Queries, 12/68; plus others. Add: Dept. of English, University of New Hampshire, Durham, NH 03824.

LOGAN, VIRGIL GLENN, b. Rochester, Ind, June 21, 04; m. 46. SPEECH. A.B, West. Mich. Col, 28; M.A, Univ. Ala, 41; Ph.D.(speech), Univ. Wis, 51. Teacher high sch, Mich, 28-36; prin, Deer Lodge Acad, Tenn, 39-40; instr. speech, Exten, Univ. Ala, 41; employee utilization spec, U.S. War Dept, 42-47; asst. prof. speech, Union Col.(Nebr), 48-50, prof. & chmn. dept, 50-54; prof, Evansville Col, 54-62, chmn. dept. Eng, 57-62; prof. speech & head dept, Findlay Col, 62-65; prof. speech & creative arts, Brandon Univ, 65-72; RETIRED. Lectr, Col. Educ, Univ. Alta, 62; Univ. Calgary, summer 64; Univ. Victoria (B.C), summers 66, 67 & 68; vis. prof. commun, Univ. Prince Edward Island, summer 73. Speech Asn. Am; Asn. Supv. & Curriculum Develop; NCTE; Can. Speech Asn.(founding pres); Can. Counc. Teachers Eng; NCTE; World Counc. Curriculum & Instruct. Speech education in foreign countries; oral interpretation of literature. Publ: Co-auth, Teaching the elementary school child, Houghton, 61 & A dynamic approach to language arts, McGraw, Can, 67; co-auth, Design for creative teaching, 71, Communication skills: teaching the language arts, 72 & Educating young children, 74, McGraw-Hill Ryerson, Can; auth, Speech training in Mexico's kindergartens and elementary schools, Speech Teacher; Mexico's unified school system. Add: 602 15th St, Brandon, Man, Can.

LOGANBILL, G. BRUCE, b. Newton, Kans, Sept. 6, 40. SPEECH. B.A, Bethel Col, 56; M.A, Univ. Kans, 58; Ph.D, Mich. State Univ, 61. Asst. prof. speech, Kalamazoo Col, 61-63; clinic coord. speech path, Calif. State Col. Fresno, 66-68; ASSOC. PROF. SPEECH COMMUN, CALIF. STATE UNIV, LONG BEACH, 68- Res. grant, Inst. Logopedics, Wichita, Kans, summers 62-66; mem. participant, World Congr. Logopedics & Phoniatrics, 71. West. Speech Asn; Speech Commun. Asn; Am. Speech & Hearing Asn; Int. Asn. Logopedics & Phoniatrics; Norsk Logopedlag; Interpreters Theatre Asn.(v.pres, 73-74). Oral interpretation; interpreters theatre; logopedic pathology. Publ: A comparative investigation of speech concepts of mongoloid girls, Fonoaudiologica, 72 & Int. Trabajos Logopedia y Foniatria, 72. Add: 101 Claremont Ave, Belmont Shore, Long Beach, CA 90803.

LOGUE, CAL McLEOD, b. Bay Minette, Ala, July 14, 35; m. 59; c. 2. SPEECH COMMUNICATION. B.A, Auburn Univ, 60; M.S, Fla. State Univ, 61; Ph.D.(speech), La. State Univ, 67. Instr. SPEECH, Birmingham-South. Col, 61-64; asst, La. State Univ, 64-66; asst. prof, Univ. Ark, 66-67; UNIV. GA, 67-71, ASSOC. PROF, 71- U.S.M.C, 56-59, Sgt. Speech Commun. Asn. Rhetorical theory and criticism; contemporary American public address. Publ: The speaking of Ralph McGill, South. Speech J, summer 67; The political rhetoric of Ralph McGill, Speech Monogr, 6/68; Ralph McGill: more like a teacher, Nieman Reports, 6/68. Add: Dept. of Speech, University of Georgia, Athens, GA 30604.

LOHMAN, WILLIAM JOHN, JR, b. Jacksonville, Fla, Aug. 13, 38. ENGLISH LITERATURE. A.B, Davidson Col, 60, M.A, Duke Univ, 66, Danforth fel, 68-70, Ph.D.(Eng), 72. Tutor ENG, Duke Univ, 68-70; ASST. PROF, UNIV. TAMPA, 70- U.S.M.C, 60-64, 66-67, Res, 64-66, 67-, Maj. AAUP; MLA. Rudyard Kipling. Add: Div. of Humanities, English Area, University of Tampa, 401 W. Kennedy Blvd, Tampa, FL 33606.

LOHMANN, CHRISTOPH KARL, b. Berlin, Ger, Oct. 6, 35; U.S. citizen; m. 61; c. 2. ENGLISH, AMERICAN STUDIES. B.A, Swarthmore Col, 58; M.A, Columbia Univ, 61; George Leib Harrison Found. fel, Univ. Pa, 65-67, Ph.D.(Am. civilization), 68. Asst. prof. ENG, IND. UNIV, BLOOMINGTON, 68-73, ASSOC. PROF, 73- Assoc. ed, A selected edition of W.D. Howells, Ind. Univ, 72- MLA; Am. Stud. Asn. Nineteenth century American literature; American studies. Publ: The burden of the past in Hawthorne's American romances, S.Atlantic Quart, winter 67; The agony of the English romance, Nathaniel Hawthorne J, 72; Jamesian irony and the American sense of mission, Tex. Stud. Lit. & Lang, 74. Add: Dept. of English, Indiana University, Bloomington, IN 47401.

LOHRLI, ANNE, b. Bake Oven, Ore, Feb. 9, 06. ENGLISH LANGUAGE & LITERATURE. A.B, Occidental Col, 27, A.M, 28; A.M, Columbia Univ, 32; Ph.D, Univ. South. Calif, 37. Res. & collaboration, 27-37; teacher, City Schs, Calif, 37-45; prof. ENG, N.MEX. HIGHLANDS UNIV, 45-65, EMER. PROF, 65- Vis. prof, Univ. Trieste, 54. MLA. Victorian periodicals. Publ: Compiler, Household Words, a weekly journal . . . conducted by Charles Dickens: table of contents, list of contributors and their contributions, Univ. Toronto, 73; auth, American English in Trieste, Inst. Int. Educ. News Bull, 3/56; Household Words and its office book, Princeton Univ. Libr. Chronicle, autumn 64. Add: 790 Baylor Ave, Claremont, CA 91711.

LOKENSGARD, HJALMAR O, b. Hanley Falls, Minn, Nov. 9, 06; m. 38; c. 3. ENGLISH. B.A, St. Olaf Col, 28; M.A, State Univ, Iowa, 32; Ph.D, Univ. Minn, 44. Assoc. prof. ENG, St. Olaf Col, 28-48; asst. prof. Cent. Wash. State Col, 48-49; PROF, MANKATO STATE COL, 49- Smith-Mundt lectr, Univ. Iceland, 57-58; vis. prof. Eng, Col. Guam, 66-67. U.S.A.F, 42-45, Res, 45-, Lt. Col. NEA. Thomas Jefferson and Dr. Oliver Wendell Holmes. Publ: Holmes quizzes the professors, Am. Lit, 40; Oliver Wendell Holmes's phrenological study, New Eng. Quart, 41; Vachel Lindsay on the art of poetry, Col. Eng, 54. Add: Dept. of English, Mankato State College, Mankato, MN 56001.

LOMAS, CHARLES WYATT, b. Green Bay, Wis, Dec. 27, 07; m. 32; c. 3. SPEECH. A.B, Carroll Col, 29; A.M, Northwest. Univ, 34, Ph.D, 40; Univ. Wis, 36; Univ. Pittsburgh, 36. Instr. high sch, Wis, 29-35; speech, Univ. Pittsburgh, 35-38, 39-43; asst. prof, Stanford Univ, 43-44; chief propaganda anal. sect, Off. War Inform, San Francisco, Calif, 44-45; asst. prof. SPEECH, Univ. Mich, 45-47; Brooklyn Col, 47; UNIV. CALIF. LOS ANGELES, 47-52, assoc. prof, 52-64, PROF, 64- Speech Commun. Asn; West. Speech Asn.(ed. jour, 51-55). American and British public address; rhetorical and communication theory. Publ: Co-auth, Basic voice training for speech, McGraw & Speech: idea and delivery, Houghton; auth, The agitator in American society, Prentice-Hall, 68; co-auth, The rhetoric of the British peace movement, Random House, 71. Add: Dept. of Speech, University of California, Los Angeles, CA 90024.

LOMBARDI, BETTY RITCH, b. Seminole, Okla, Feb. 7, 31; m. 71. BRITISH & AMERICAN LITERATURE. B.A, Northeast. State Col, 53; M.A, Okla. State Univ, 56. Instr. Eng, Wyandotte High Sch, Okla, 53; Eng. & drama, Wagoner High Sch, 53-56; Eng, Northeast. A&M Col, 56-57; Northeast. State Col, 57-60, asst. prof, 60-64; ASSOC. PROF, Ind. State Col.(Pa), 64-65; ENG. & FOLKLORE, NORTHEAST. STATE COL, 65- Am. Folklore Soc; Soc. Asian Folklore; NCTE; Folklore Soc, London. Folklore among the Cherokee Indians; folklore of the Ozarks; analysis of motifs and epitaphs of old gravestones and the study of grave yard lore. Publ: Cherokee Indian lore in Adair, Cherokee, and Delaware counties, 9/69 & An analysis of some nineteenth and twentieth century gravestones, 9/73, Fac. Res. Publ. Northeast. State Col. Add: Dept. of English, Northeastern State College, Tahlequah, OK 74464.

LONDO, RICHARD JOSEPH, b. Green Bay, Wis, Feb. 5, 33; m. 55; c. 6. LITERATURE, LINGUISTICS. B.A, St. Norbert Col, 55; M.A, Univ. Wis, 60, Ph.D, 74. Instr. high schs, Wis, 55-58; ENG, ST. NORBERT COL, 58-63, asst. prof, 63-70, ASSOC. PROF, 70- Lectr, Univ. Wis-Green Bay, 73- Adj.Gen.C, U.S.A.R, 56-62, Capt. Am. Soc. 18th Century Stud. Arthur Maynwaring's Medley papers; early 18th-century British satire; prose writing. Publ: The false dilemma in Book IV of Gulliver's travels, 3/67 & The knight's tale as allegory, 3/71, Delta Epsilon Sigma Bull. Add: 1118 Biemeret St, Green Bay, WI 54304.

LONDON, NORMAN THEODORE, b. New York, N.Y, May 19, 34; m. 55; c. 2. COMMUNICATION. A.B, N.Y. Univ, 55, M.A, 57, Ed.D, 62. Instr. speech, N.Y. Univ, 56-57, Bowdoin Col, 57-60; UNIV. VT, 60-62, asst. prof, 62-66, assoc. prof. speech & chmn. dept. speech & drama, 66-70, PROF. COMMUN. & CHMN. DEPT. COMMUN. & THEATRE, 70-, asst. dean col. arts & sci, 64-66. Danforth Found. fac. res. grant, 59; consult. commun, State of Vt, 67- Speech Commun. Asn; Am. Forensic Asn; Speech Asn. East. States; New Eng. Speech Asn.(pres, 65-66); New Eng. Forensic Conf.(pres, 62-63); AAUP. Communication education; administrative structure; mass and instructional media. Publ: Motivating the academically gifted, Education, 2/61; Professional attitudes toward a first-course in speech and its requirement in American colleges, 1/64 & The administrative structure of departments of speech in American colleges and universities, 9/68, Speech Teacher; plus others. Add: Dept. of Communication & Theatre, University of Vermont, Burlington, VT 05401.

LONEY, GLENN MEREDITH, b. Sacramento, Calif, Dec. 24, 28. THEATRE & SPEECH. A.B, Univ. Calif, Berkeley, 50; M.A, Univ. Wis-Madison, 51; Stanford fel. & Ph.D.(dramatic lit), Stanford Univ, 54. Instr. lang. arts, San Francisco State Col, 55-56; Eng. & speech, Univ. Nev, Las Vegas, 56; lectr, Univ. Md, Europe, 56-59; instr. speech & drama, Hofstra Univ, 59-61; asst. prof. SPEECH & THEATRE, BROOKLYN COL, 61-66, assoc. prof, 67-70, PROF, 70-; THEATRE, GRAD. CTR, CITY UNIV. NEW YORK, 70- Hon. fel, Am. Scand. Found, 60. U.S.A, 53-55. Speech Commun. Asn; Am. Theatre Asn; Am. Soc. Theatre Res; Theatre Libr. Assocs; Int. Fed. Theatre Res; U.S. Inst. Theatre Technol. Subsidized European theatre; American theatre past and present; opera as theatre. Publ: Briefing and conference techniques, McGraw, 59; co-ed, Tragedy: an anthology, 71, Comedy: An anthology, 71 & The forms of drama, 72, Houghton; ed, Peter Brook's production of Midsummer night's dream, Dramatic Publ, 74; American theatre (1954-1967), In: History of the theatre, 68 & auth. introd. & ed, Dramatic soundings, 68, Crown; contrib, Reader's encycl. of world drama, Crowell, 69. Add: 187 Hicks St, Brooklyn Heights, NY 11201.

LONG, CHARLES (E), (JR), b. Seymour, Tex, June 16, 31; m. 55; c. 2. ENGLISH, GERMAN. M.A, Univ. Ark, 55, M.A, 56, Ph.D, 62; Univ. Tex, 57. Instr. German, MEMPHIS STATE UNIV, 57-59, asst. prof. & chmn, 59-61, assoc. prof, 61-66, PROF. ENG. & GERMANIC PHILOL, 66-, chmn. dept. mod. lang, 63-65. U.S.A.F, 47-48; U.S.A, 51-53, Res, 53-, Col. MLA; Am. Asn. Teachers Ger; S.Cent. Mod. Lang. Asn; S.Atlantic Mod. Lang. Asn; Am. Asn. Teachers Slavic & E.Europ. Lang. Tristan legend. Publ: Co-auth, Mustersätze und Grammatik, Memphis State Univ, 61. Add: Dept. of English, Memphis State University, Memphis, TN 38111.

LONG, CHARLES HOWARD, b. Schenectady, N.Y, Aug. 29, 38; m. 58; c. 3. ENGLISH. B.A, Rutgers Univ, 60; M.A, Univ. Calif, Berkeley, 62, Ph.D. (Eng), 67. Instr. ENG, YALE, 66-68, ASST. PROF, 68- Morse stud. fel, Eng, 71-72. MLA. Eighteenth century literature; the novel. Add: Dept. of English, Yale University, New Haven, CT 06520.

LONG, CHESTER CLAYTON, b. Salem Co, N.J, Mar. 7, 32; m. 58; c. 2. DRAMA, SPEECH. B.A, Univ. Wash, 57; Woodrow Wilson fel, 57-58; M.A, Northwest. Univ, 58, Ph.D.(drama), 62. Lectr. speech, Univ. Calif, Berkeley, 58-59; asst, Northwest. Univ, 59-61, instr, 61-62; asst. prof, Univ. Ill, Urbana, 62-64; Univ. Wash, 64-67; assoc. prof. SPEECH & THEATER, UNIV. ILL, CHICAGO, 67-70, PROF, 70-, grad. sch. res. grant, 63. Univ. Wash. Grad. Sch. Agnes H. Anderson Mem. Fund res. grant, 65-66; guest lectr, Univ. Denver, 66; consult. ed. drama, West. Speech J, 67- U.S.A.F, 51-54. Speech Commun. Asn; Poetry Soc. Am; Nat. Theatre Asn. Drama; film; electromyographical studies of speech behavior. Publ: The role of nemesis in Eugene O'Neill, Mouton, 68; This running sleep (poems), Windfall, 68; The liberal art of interpretation, Harper, 73; Cocteau's Orphée: from myth to drama & film, Quart. J. Speech, 10/65; Long day's journey as aesthetic object, In: The oral study of literature, Random, 66; Poem's text as technique of performance, West. Speech J, winter 67. Add: Dept. of Speech, University of Illinois, Chicago, IL 60680.

LONG, ELEANOR RUTH, b. Seattle, Wash, Feb. 8, 23; div; c. 2. MEDIEVAL LITERATURE, FOLKLORE. B.S, Portland State Univ, 57; M.A, Univ, Portland, 58; Univ. Ore, 61-63; Ph.D.(Eng), Univ. Calif, Los Angeles, 68; Dublin Inst. Advan. Stud, 69; Sch. Irish Stud, 71. Instr. ENG, Univ. Portland, 58-60; assoc, Univ. Calif. Santa Barbara, 63-64; ASST. PROF, UNIV. SANTA CLARA, 68- Res. grant, Univ. Santa Clara, 70; Nat. Endowment for Humanities summer stipend, 72. Folklore Prize, Univ. Chicago, 72. MLA; Am. Folklore Soc.(chmn. comt. status of women, 71-73); Int. Arthurian Soc; Folklore Soc. Ireland; Medieval Acad. Am. Folklore; medieval studies; Celtic studies. Publ: The maid and The hangman, Univ. Calif, 71; Thematic classification and Lady Isabel, J. Am. Folklore, 72; Aphrosidiacs, charms and philtres, 73 & Ballad singers and ballad etiology, 74, West. Folklore. Add: Dept. of English, University of Santa Clara, Santa Clara, CA 95053.

LONG, EMMETT THADDEUS, b. Kaufman, Tex, Dec. 31, 23; m. 46; c. 2. SPEECH, HIGHER EDUCATION. B.A, Pepperdine Col, 45; B.A, Univ. Calif, Berkeley, 46, M.A, 48; Ed.D.(higher educ), Univ. South. Calif, 65. Dir. admis. & assoc. prof. speech, Pepperdine Col, 54-57; registr. & admis. off, Calif. State Polytech. Col, 57-59; assoc. dean stud, Calif. State Col. Fullerton, 59-72, dir. admis. & assoc. prof. speech, 59-66, dir. relat. with schs. & prof. speech, 66-72; ASSOC. DEAN STUD. AFFAIRS & COORD. RELAT. WITH SCHS. & COLS, CALIF. STATE UNIV. & COLS, 72- Chmn, Calif. Articulation Conf, 73-74. Higher education; public address. Publ: A comparison of the standards for judgement of the debate with those of the rhetorical critic, 10/55 & Speech activities in the Western states, 10/58, West. Speech; The chief weakness and the chief strength of American higher education, Improving Col. & Univ. Teaching, autumn 67. Add: Office of the Chancellor, California State University & Colleges, 5670 Wilshire Blvd, Los Angeles, CA 90036.

LONG, HOWARD RUSK, b. Columbia, Mo, July 30, 09; m. 31; c. 2. JOURNALISM. B.J. & B.A, Univ. Mo, 30, M.A, 41, Ph.D, 48. Instr. JOUR, Univ. Mo, 41-43, asst. prof, 43-45, assoc. prof, 45-48, prof, 48-50; PROF. & CHMN. DEPT, SOUTH. ILL. UNIV, 53- Mgr. Mo. Press Asn, 41-49; consult, Brit. Ministry Inform, 45; secy, Int. Conf. Weekly Newspaper Ed, 55-, ed, Grassroots Editor, 60-; Smith-Mundt grant & vis. prof, Nat. Chengchi Univ, Taiwan & guest ed, China Post, Taipei, 57-58; U.S. State Dept. grant, North. Europ, 64; ed, New Horizons Jour, South. Ill. Univ. Press, 67-; consult, Nat. Chengchi Univ, Taipei, 68. Academician, China Acad. Am. Soc. Jour. Sch. Adminr.(pres, 60); Asn. Educ. Jour; Inst. Journalists; Royal Photographic Soc. Gr. Brit; Nat. Conf. Ed. Writers; Int. Press Inst; Inter-Am. Press Inst. Public opinion; community newspaper; international press. Publ: Co-auth, Fifty years of community service, Missourian Publ. Co, 54; auth, The people of Mushan, Univ. Mo, 60; co-auth, Recalling the Battle of Britain, Kent Messenger, Maidstone, 65. Add: Dept. of Journalism, Southern Illinois University, Carbondale, IL 62901.

LONG, JESSE RAYMOND, b. Lafayette, Ohio, Oct. 23, 06; m. 30; c. 3. JOURNALISM. A.B, Ohio North. Univ, 28, hon. Ed.D, 53; A.M, Columbia Univ, 34; Univ. Minn, 46. Prin, high sch, Ohio, 28-35, teacher, 35-41; instr. jour, UNIV. TOLEDO, 41-42, asst. prof, 42-44, assoc. prof, 44-53, prof, 53-73, head dept, 44-51, dir. summer sessions & pub. relat, 49-52, admin. asst. to pres, 51-62, provost, 62-64, exec. v.pres, 64-73, EMER. PROF. JOUR, 73- Trustee, Ohio North. Univ, 50-55; ed, Col. Pub. Relat. Quart, 54-55. Pub. Relat. Soc. Am. Editing and headline techniques. Publ: Ed. & co-auth, The tower builders—the centennial history of the University of Toledo, Univ. Toledo, 72; auth, Cracks in the ivory tower, Torch, 1/73. Add: 2328 Valleybrook Dr, Toledo, OH 43615.

LONG, JOHN HENDERSON, b. Carthage, Miss, Apr. 8, 16. ENGLISH. A.B, Univ. Fla, 38, A.M, 48, Ph.D, 51; Georgetown Univ, 39; res. fel, Folger Shakespeare Libr, 51. Asst. instr, Univ. Fla, 46-48; assoc. prof. ENG, Morehead State Col, Ky, 50-59; GREENSBORO COL, 59-63, PROF, 63- Guggenheim fel, 57; fel, Southeast. Inst. Medieval & Renaissance Stud, summer 66. S.Atlantic Mod. Lang. Asn; Renaissance Soc. Am; Am. Musicol. Soc. Shakespeare; Elizabethan drama and music. Publ: A study of the music and its performance in the original production of Seven comedies, Vol. I, 55, The final comedies, Vol. II, 61 & Histories and tragedies, Vol. III, 71, In: Shakespeare's use of music, Univ. Fla; ed, Music in English Renaissance drama, Univ. Ky, 68. Add: Dept. of English, Greensboro College, Greensboro, NC 27420.

LONG, JOHN M, b. Conway, S.C, Sept. 5, 37; m. 61; c. 2. ENGLISH. B.A, Furman Univ, 59; M.A, Northeast. Univ, 61; Ph.D.(Eng), Univ. N.C, Chapel Hill, 67. ASST. PROF. ENG, Va. Mil. Inst, 65-66; EAST. KY. UNIV, 67- MLA; NCTE; S.Atlantic Mod. Lang. Asn. English and American nineteenth century poetry and fiction. Add: 710 Hycliffe Dr, Richmond, KY 40475.

LONG, LITTLETON, b. Evanston, Ill, Feb. 28, 18; m. 44; c. 4. ENGLISH. A.B, Princeton, 39; M.A, Yale, 42, Ph.D, 49. Instr. ENG, Yale, 47-49; UNIV. VT, 49-51, asst. prof, 51-57, assoc. prof, 57-68, PROF, 68- U.S.A, 42-46, Res, 46-64, Maj. MLA; Renaissance Soc. Am; Col. Eng. Asn. Victorian literature; popular literature of the English Renaissance; Renaissance poetry. Add: Dept. of English, University of Vermont, Burlington, VT 05401.

LONG, RICHARD ALEXANDER, b. Philadelphia, Pa, Feb. 9, 27. ENGLISH, HUMANITIES. A.B, Temple Univ, 47, M.A, 48; D. es L, Univ. Poitiers, 65. Instr, W.Va. State Col, 49-50; asst. prof. Eng, Morgan State Col, 51-64; lectr, Univ. Poitiers, 64-65; PROF. Eng. & French, Hampton Inst, 66-68; ENG, ATLANTA UNIV, 68- Fulbright scholar, Univ. Paris, 57-58; vis. lectr, Harvard, 70-71; assoc. dir, Ling. Inst, Univ. N.C, summer 72. U.S.A, 44-45. MLA; Mod. Humanities Res. Asn; African Stud. Asn; Am. Asn. Mus; Col. Lang. Asn.(pres, 69-71); Southeast. Conf. Ling.(pres, 72-73); Ling. Soc. Am; Am. Dialect Soc; AAUP; Mediaeval Soc. Am; African Heritage Stud. Asn; S.Atlantic Mod. Lang. Asn; Am. Stud. Asn. Theory of art; Afro-American culture; medieval literature. Publ: Co-auth, Negritude: essays and studies, Hampton Inst, 67; co-ed, Afro-American writing, N.Y. Univ, 72. Add: Dept. of English, Atlanta University, Atlanta, GA 30314.

LONG, THOMAS R, b. Payne, Okla, Oct. 18, 28; m. 61; c. 2. SPEECH, DRAMA. B.F.A, Univ. Okla, 50, M.F.A, 51; Danforth scholar, Drew Univ, 56; Ph.D.(speech), Mich. State Univ, 66. Instr. speech & drama, Miss. South. Col, 54-56; Mich. State Univ, 56-60; asst. prof. dramatic art, Richmond Prof. Inst, 61-65; assoc. prof. speech & drama, Hiram Scott Col, 66-67, prof. & dir. theatre, 67-68; vis. assoc. prof, Univ. Kans, 68-72; PROF. THEATRE ARTS & CHMN. FAC, UNIV. W.FLA, 72- U.S.A, 52-54, Sgt. Am. Theatre Asn; Speech Commun. Asn; Am. Nat. Theatre & Acad. Play directing; acting; courtroom drama. Publ: Co-auth, Oral communication, W.C. Brown, 56; auth, The modern theatre audience: its plight and promise, Image, winter 64; Directing Seventy times seven, Relig. Theatre, winter 66-67. Add: Dept. of Theatre Arts, University of West Florida, Pensacola, FL 32504.

LONG, WILLIAM IVEY, b. Seaboard, N.C, July 2, 11; m. 46; c. 3. DRAMA. A.B, Univ. N.C, 32, M.A, 40. Teacher Eng, Aulander High Sch, N.C, 35-37; Aurelian Springs High Sch, 37-39; instr. drama, Marion Col, 40-42; instr, McGill Univ, 46-47; tech. dir, Raleigh Little Theatre, 47-52; Carolina Playmakers, Univ. N.C, 52-54; from assoc. prof. to PROF. DRAMA, WINTHROP COL, 54- Founder & adv. dir, S.C. High Sch. Drama Festival, Winthrop Col, annually, 54-; auth. & producer, Kah-Woh, Catawba, York County Hist. Asn, 61; producer, The other four & Courtship, Billy-Ditch style (full length plays) & Lost in the dark of night & A little boy grows up (one act plays). Raleigh Little Theatre Award, 52; Carolina Playmakers Alumnal Award, 54. C.Eng, 43-46, 1st Sgt. Am. Theatre Asn; Southeast. Theatre Conf. Catawba Indians of North and South Carolina. Publ: Ed, Twelve half-hours with the Winthrop Theatre, Winthrop Col, 59. Add: Box 5052, Dept. English & Drama, Winthrop College, Rock Hill, SC 29730.

LONGAKER, JOHN MARK, b. Newport, Ky, Aug 17, 00. ENGLISH. A.B, Lenoir Col, 19; Ph.D, Univ. Pa, 24. From asst. prof. to PROF. ENG. & ASSOC. DIR. ADMIS, UNIV. PA, 20- English biography in the 18th century; contemporary biography. Publ: English biography in the XVIIIth century, 31, Contemporary biography, 34, Ernest Dowson, a critical biography, 44, 3rd ed, 67 & ed, The poems of Ernest Dowson, 62, Univ. Pa; ed, The stories of Ernest Dowson, Univ. Pa, 47, A.S. Barnes, 60; co-auth, Contemporary English literature, Appleton, 53. Add: Dept. of English, University of Pennsylvania, Philadelphia, PA 19104.

LONGENECKER, MARLENE BLANEY, b. Santa Monica, Calif, Aug. 24, 45. ENGLISH & AMERICAN LITERATURE. B.A, Univ. Calif, Riverside, 67; Ph.D.(Eng), State Univ. N.Y, Buffalo, 73. ASST. PROF. ENG, OHIO STATE UNIV, 72- MLA; NCTE. English romanticism; 19th century American literature; 20th century poetry and poetics. Publ: Co-auth, Writing about experience: a report on freshman English, Col. Eng, 10/70. Add: Dept. of English, Ohio State University, 164 W. 17th Ave, Columbus, OH 43210.

LONGEST, GEORGE CALVIN, b. Richmond, Va, Feb. 17, 38. NINETEENTH CENTURY AMERICAN LITERATURE. B.A, Univ. Richmond, 60, M.A, 61; Ph.D.(Am. lit), Univ. Ga, 69; Cambridge, summer 71. Instr. Eng, Va. Polytech. Inst. & State Univ, 62-63; ASST. PROF. AM. LIT, VA. COMMONWEALTH UNIV, 63- Teaching Excellence Award, Asn. Dept. Eng. & MLA, 73. S.Atlantic Mod. Lang. Asn; Soc. Stud. South. Lit; Soc. Stud. Midwest Lit. Southern and midwestern literature. Add: 708 Forest Ave, Richmond, VA 23229.

LONGINI, PETER RICHARD, b. Pittsburgh, Pa, June 4, 44; m. 66; c. 1. COMMUNICATION, SPEECH. B.A, Col. Wooster, 66; M.S, Univ. Pittsburgh, 68, Ph.D.(commun), 70. ASST. PROF. COMMUN, UNIV. PITTSBURGH, 70- Int. Commun. Asn. Mass media; communication theory; conflict analysis. Publ: TV access: a Pittsburgh experiment, J. Broadcasting, spring 74. Add: Dept. of Speech, University of Pittsburgh, Pittsburgh, PA 15260.

LONGLEY, JOHN LEWIS, JR, b. Columbia, S.C, July 21, 26; m. 42; c. 3. LITERARY CRITICISM, HUMANITIES. A.B, Univ. Tenn, 48, M.A, 49; Ph.D, (Eng), N.Y. Univ, 57. Instr. Eng, N.Y. Univ, 49-52; Wayne State Univ, 52-56; from asst. prof. to PROF. HUMANITIES, UNIV. VA, 56- Vis. prof, N.Y. Univ, Univ. Freiberg & City Univ. New York; Old Dom. Found. fel, 58; Fulbright prof, Univ. Freiburg, 61-62; consult, Space Conditioning, Inc, summer 65; Humanities Res. grant, Univ. Va, summer 67; consult, Melpar, Inc, Tehran, 68 & summer 69. MLA. Literary criticism; contemporary fiction; creative writing. Publ: The tragic mask: a study of Faulkner's heroes, Univ. N.C, 63; Smith Island and the Cape Fear Peninsula, N.C. Acad. Sci, 64; Robert Penn Warren: a collection of critical essays, N.Y. Univ, 65; Robert Penn Warren, Steck-Vaughan, 69; Joe Christmas: the hero in the modern world, Va. Quart. Rev, spring 57; At Heaven's gate: the major themes, Mod. Fiction Stud, spring 60; Robert Penn Warren: the deeper rue, South. Rev, fall 65. Add: 232 Thornton Hall, University of Virginia, Charlottesville, VA 22903.

LONGO, JOSEPH ANTHONY, b. Tusa, Sicily, Nov. 20, 27; U.S. citizen; m. 56; c. 2. ENGLISH. B.S.Ed, Rutgers Univ, 52, M.Ed, 54, fel. & A.M, 56, fel. & Ph.D, 63. Instr. rhetoric, BOSTON COL, 59-63, asst. prof. ENG, 63-68, ASSOC. PROF, 68- U.S.N, 45-48. MLA; Shakespeare Asn. Am. Late mediaeval literature; Elizabethan drama; Shakespeare. Publ: The double time-scheme in Book II of Chaucer's Troilus and Criseyde, Mod. Lang. Quart; Dynamic equilibrium in Coriolanus, Ball State Univ. Forum, summer 69; Symmetry and symbolism in the Secunda Pastorum, Nottingham Mediaeval Stud, 69; plus others. Add: Dept. of English, Boston College, Chestnut Hill, MA 02167.

LONGSWORTH, ROBERT MORROW, b. Canton, Ohio, Feb. 15, 37; m. 58; c. 3. ENGLISH. A.B, Duke Univ, 58; M.A, Harvard, 60, Ph.D.(Eng), 65. Asst. prof. ENG, OBERLIN COL, 64-70, ASSOC. PROF, 70- Am. Counc. Learned Soc. fel, 70-71. MLA; Mediaeval Acad. Am. Medieval literature. Publ: The Cornish Ordinalia, Harvard, 67; The doctor's dilemma: a comic view of the Physicians tale, Criticism, XIII: 223-233. Add: Dept. of English, Oberlin College, Oberlin, OH 44074.

LONGTIN, RAY CHARLES, b. Otter Creek, Alaska, Mar. 26, 18. ENGLISH & AMERICAN LITERATURE. B.A, Univ. Wash, 39; M.A, Columbia Univ, 48, Ph.D.(Eng), 56. From asst. prof. to PROF. ENG, LONG ISLAND UNIV, 48- U.S.A, 42-46, Capt. NCTE; MLA. Literature of the Far West. Publ: Image of paradise in Oregon; co-ed, Modern critical temper, Ungar, 69. Add: Dept. of English, Long Island University, Brooklyn, NY 11201.

LONGWELL, ROBERT LEROY, b. Denver, Colo, Mar. 24, 26; m. 46; c. 3. SPEECH COMMUNICATION, ENGLISH. A.B, Kearney State Col, 50; M.A, Colo. State Col, 61; Ph.D.(commun), Univ. Colo, Boulder, 71. Instr. speech, Eng. & drama, Stanton Pub. Sch, Nebr, 50-51; Minden Pub. Schs, 51-52; Elm Creek Pub. Schs, 52-53; Mitchell Pub. Schs, 53-55; Gothenburg Publ Schs, 55-62; from instr. to ASSOC. PROF. SPEECH, ENG. & COMMUN, UNIV. NORTH. COLO, 62- Mgt. consult, Monfort of Colo, Int, 71- U.S.N, 44-46. Speech Commun. Asn; Int. Commun. Asn; AAUP. Management communication; organizational communication. Add: Dept. of Communication, University of Northern Colorado, Greeley, CO 80639.

LOOFBOUROW, JOHN W, b. Cincinnati, Ohio, Sept. 16, 27. ENGLISH. A.B, Harvard, 49, Ph.D.(Eng), 59; Oxford, 49-50; M.A, Columbia Univ, 55. Fel.

Eng, Harvard, 56-58, advertising, Harvard Press, 59-63; asst. prof. ENG, BOSTON COL, 63-65, ASSOC. PROF, 65- U.S.A, 46-47. MLA. English novel; Victorian literature. Publ: Thackeray and the form of fiction, Princeton, 64. Add: Dept. of English, Boston College, Chestnut Hill, MA 02167.

LOOK, ARNOLD EVERT, b. Bath, N.Y, Oct. 6, 96; m. 20; c. 3. ENGLISH. B.Th, South. Baptist Theol. Sem, 17; B.A, McMaster Univ, 19; M.A, Univ. Pa, 20; B.D, Crozer Theol. Sem, 20, Th.M, 22; fel, Dropsie Col, 24-25; Ph.D, Yale, 27. Prof. relig, Int. YMCA Col, 27-31; pres, Ellis Sch. Girls, Newton Sq, Pa, 31-61; vis. prof. hist. & polit. sci. & chmn. dept. hist, Talladega Col, 61-62, prof. Eng, chmn. dept. commun. & acting pres, 62-67; LECTR, ENG, EDISON JR. COL, 67- Lectr. hist. of YMCA, Univ. Pa, 51, 54, 56. Religion; history. Publ: Abba Marcus of Mount Tharmaka, Oxford, 27. Add: 8B Azalea Dr, Orange City, FL 32763.

LOOMIS, CHAUNCEY CHESTER, JR, b. New York, N.Y, June 1, 30. ENGLISH. A.B, Princeton, 52, Ph.D.(Eng), 63; A.M, Columbia Univ, 56. Instr. ENG, Univ. Vt, 56-59, asst. prof, DARTMOUTH COL, 61-67, assoc. prof, 67-70, PROF, 70- Smithsonian Inst. fel, 67-68. U.S.A, Arctic Inst. N.Am. Nineteenth century arctic exploration; Charles Francis Hall, arctic explorer. Publ: Weird and tragic shores, Knopf, 71; Structure and sympathy in Joyce's The dead, PMLA, 3/61; C.F. Hall: Cincinnati in the Arctic, Cincinnati Hist. Soc. Bull, fall 67; Thackeray and the Plight of the Victorian satirist, Eng. Stud, 2/68. Add: Dept. of English, Dartmouth College, Hanover, NH 03755.

LOOMIS, EDWARD W, b. Newport News, Va, Aug. 8, 24; m. 45; c. 3. AMERICAN LITERATURE. A.B, West. Reserve Univ, 47; M.A, Stanford Univ, 50, Ph.D, 59. Instr. ENG, Deep Springs Col, 50-52; Univ. Ariz, 55-59; UNIV. CALIF, SANTA BARBARA, 59-60, asst. prof, 60-62, from assoc. prof. to PROF. ENG. & CHMN. DEPT, 62- A.U.S. French fiction. Publ: Heroic love, Knopf, 60; The mothers, 62 & Men of principle, 63, Viking; The art of lying (textbook on creative writing), Cummings, 71. Add: Dept. of English, University of California, Santa Barbara, CA 93106.

LOOMIS, EMERSON ROBERT, b. Danville, Va, Oct. 5, 27; m. 55. ENGLISH. B.S, Wofford Col, 49; M.A, Emory Univ, 51; Ph.D.(Eng), Fla. State Univ, 57. Asst. prof. ENG, Wofford Col, 55-57; Univ. Houston, 57-58; UNIV. ALA, 58-63, assoc. prof, 63-68, PROF, 68-, univ. res. comt. grants, 59-63, Thompson lectr. Am. stud, 66. MLA; S.Atlantic Mod. Lang. Asn; Keats-Shelley Asn. Pre-romantic and romantic English literature; 19th century English novel. Publ: The Godwins in The letters of Shahcoolen, Nineteenth-Century Fiction, 6/62; The new philosophy satirized in American fiction, Am. Quart, fall 62; The turning point in Pope's reputation, Philol. Quart, 4/63. Add: Dept. of English, University of Alabama, University, AL 35486.

LOPRETE, NICHOLAS J, JR, b. Brooklyn, N.Y, Dec. 6, 32. AMERICAN LITERATURE, NOVEL. A.B, Col. Holy Cross, 54; M.A, Columbia Univ, 56; Ph.D.(Eng), 65. Teacher high sch, 55-58; instr. ENG, St. John's Univ, 58-60, ASST. PROF, 60-61; FORDHAM UNIV, 61- MLA; NCTE. The Irving family; the American novel and 19th century subliterature; 19th century American literature in Europe. Add: Dept. of English, Fordham University, Rose Hill Campus, Bronx, NY 10458.

LORD, CHARLOTTE VIRGINIA, b. Dorranceton, Pa. ENGLISH, DRAMA. B.S, N.Y. Univ, 40; M.A, Bucknell Univ, 46; M.A, Middlebury Col, 53; Fulbright grants, Univ. Siena, 54-55; Ph.D.(Eng), Univ. Pa, 70. Teacher Eng, Wilkes-Barre City Schs, 29-54, coord. TV educ, 56-58, dean activities & Eng, 61-62; teacher speech, Eng. & drama, Abington Sr. High Sch, 58-61; PROF. ENG, WILKES COL, 62- Instr. Eng, Wilkes Col. Exten, 48-58; Fulbright exchange prof, Rome, 54-55; fine arts consult. academically talented prog, Wilkes-Barre Area Schs, 74- U.S.N.R, 43-46, Lt. MLA; AAUP. American drama in Italy; British contemporary; translation of Italian. Publ: Transl, Amabile Ranucci's No love without sorrow, Pageant, 54; contrib, Venice 1954, Films in Rev, 10/54; auth, Local theatre criticism, In: Wilkes-Barre, Pa, Times Leader-Eve. News, 62-63. Add: Dept. of English, Wilkes College, Wilkes-Barre, PA 18703.

LORD, GEORGE deFOREST, b. New York, N.Y, Dec. 2, 19; m. 47; c. 3. ENGLISH. B.A, Yale, 42, Ph.D.(Eng), 51. From asst. prof. to assoc. prof. ENG, YALE, 61-66, PROF, 66-, master, Trumbull Col, 63-66. Morse fel, 54-55. U.S.M.C, 42-46, Capt. MLA; Renaissance Soc. Am; Eng. Inst. 17th century poetry; Homeric epic; mock epic. Publ: Homeric Renaissance: the Odyssey of George Chapman, 56 & ed, Poems on affairs of state, (7 vols, in ser), Yale, 63-75; ed, Andrew Marvell, Prentice-Hall, 68; Andrew Marvell: complete poetry, Random, 68. Add: Dept. of English, Yale University, New Haven, CT 06520.

LORD, JOHN BIGELOW, b. Evanston, Ill, Mar. 5, 17; m. 46; 60; c. 6. ENGLISH. A.B, Univ. Ill, 39, M.A, 48, Ph.D.(Shakespeare), 50. Instr. ENG, WASH. STATE UNIV, 51-54, asst. prof, 54-61, assoc. prof, 61-68, PROF, 68- Dir. workshop, NDEA summer inst. Eng, Wichita State Univ, 66. U.S.A, 40-45, 1st Lt. MLA; Am. Civil Liberties Union; Philol. Asn. Pac. Coast. English linguistics; stylistics; the grammar of poetry, especially prosody. Publ: Experiments in diction, rhetoric and style, 55 & The paragraph: structure and style, 65, Holt; Paragrammatical structure in a poem of E. E. Cummings, Pac. Coast Philol, 66; Two phonological analyses of Poe's To Helen, Lang. & Style, spring 70; Sequence in clusters of pre-nominal adjectives and adjectivals in English, J. Eng. Ling, 3/70; plus others. Add: Dept. of English, Washington State University, Pullman, WA 99163.

LORDI, ROBERT JOSEPH, b. Rockland, Mass, Oct. 18, 23; m. 55; c. 2. ENGLISH LITERATURE. A.B, Col. Holy Cross, 50; univ. fel, Univ. Wis, 51-52; M.A, Boston Col, 55; fels, Univ. Ill, summers 56, 57, Ph.D, 58. Asst. Eng, Univ. Ill, 52-58; instr, UNIV. NOTRE DAME, 58-59, asst. prof, 59-64, assoc. prof. Eng. lit, 64-70, PROF. ENG, 70-, univ. grant-in-aid, summers 62, 65 & 66, asst. dir. sophmore year abroad prog, 65-66, acad. fel, 67-68. Assoc. ed, Neo-Latin News, 61-65; Folger Shakespeare Libr. fel, summer 62; Am. Philos. Soc. summer grant-in-aid, 63 & 64; lectr. Shakespeare, Univ. Innsbruck, 66; Univ. Notre Dame fac. res. grant & Am. Philos. Soc. grant-in-aid, summer 71. U.S.A.A.F, 43-45. MLA; NCTE. Renaissance drama, including editing of dramatic texts and textual bibliography. Publ: Bussy D-Ambois, Univ. Nebr, 64; co-auth, Richard III: analysis and commentary, American R.D.M, 66; The relationship of Richardus Tertius to the main Richard III plays, Boston Univ. Stud. Eng, 61; Proofreading of The revenge of Bussy D'Ambois, Eng. Lang. Notes, 3/73; plus others. Add: Dept. of English, University of Notre Dame, Notre Dame, IN 46556.

LORENTZEN, ARTHUR ANDREAS, b. Vashon, Wash, Aug. 3, 28; m. 57. ENGLISH. B.A, Wash. State Univ, 50, B.A, 51; M.Ed, Univ. Wash, 60; fel, Univ. Ore, 67-68, M.A, 68. Teacher Eng, Seattle Pub. Schs, 53-70; chmn. div. humanities, Seattle Cent. Community Col, 70-71; INSTR. ENG, S.SEATTLE COMMUNITY COL, 71- Fulbright exchange teacher, Rotterdam, The Netherlands, 60-61; instr, Univ. Ore. NDEA Insts, summers 65-67; mem, Comn. Eng. Lang, NCTE, 66-69. U.S.A, 51-53, 1st Lt. NCTE; Nat. Educ. Asn. English grammar, a transformational-generative model; English composition. Publ: Co-auth, Language I, the Oregon curriculum, Holt, 68; auth, Problems of teaching linguistics in the secondary school, Eng. J. Add: 927 22nd Ave. E, Seattle, WA 98112.

LORENZ, ALFRED LAWRENCE, JR, b. Lakeland, Fla, Apr. 3, 37; m. 70; c. 1. JOURNALISM. B.S, Marquette Univ, 58; M.A, South. Ill. Univ, Carbondale, 65, Ph.D.(jour), 68. Reporter-ed, United Press Int, 62-64; instr. bus. writing, South. Ill. Univ, Carbondale, 67-68; asst. prof. JOUR, MARQUETTE UNIV, 68-71, ASSOC. PROF, 71- U.S.A, 59-62, Res, 62-70, Capt. Asn. Educ. in Jour; Broadcast Educ. Asn. History of American journalism. Publ: Hugh Gaine: a colonial printer-editor's odyssey to loyalism, South. Ill. Univ, 72; Lincoln, Medill and the Republican nomination of 1860, Lincoln Herald, 66; Truman and the broadcaster, J. Broadcasting, 69; Origins of Pan American copyright protection, Jour. Quart, 72; plus others. Add: College of Journalism, Marquette University, Milwaukee, WI 53233.

LORENZINI, AUGUST PETER, b. Staunton, Ill, Apr. 2, 22. SPEECH, COMMUNICATIONS. B.S, Ill. State Univ, 46; M.A, Univ. Denver, 50, Ph.D. (speech), 62. Speech therapist pub. schs, Ill, 46-49; instr. high sch, Colo, 50-55; speech therapist pub. schs, Ariz, 55-56; instr. high sch, Ariz, 56-63; PROF. SPEECH & DRAMA & CHMN. DEPT, GLENDALE COMMUNITY COL, 63- Am. Speech & Hearing Asn; Speech Commun. Asn. Speech pathology; linguistics. Add: 9251 N. 35th Dr, Phoenix, AZ 85021.

LORETTA, MARIA (TENBUSCH), I.H.M, b. Detroit, Mich, June 15, 24. ENGLISH, PHILOSOPHY. A.B, Marygrove Col, 50; Loyola Univ. Chicago, summer 50; Univ. Toronto, 52-53; Ph.D.(Eng), St. Louis Univ, 55. Instr. Eng. & philos, Marygrove Col, 50-51, 54-59, asst. prof, 59-65, assoc. prof, 65-68, acting chmn. dept. ENG, 63-64, chmn. 64-68; assoc. prof, IMMACULATA COL.(PA), 68-72, PROF, 72- Scholarship, Shakespeare Inst, Univ. Birmingham, summer 62; Shakespeare Inst, Univ. Bridgeport, summer 73. NCTE; Nat. Col. Honors Counc; AAUP; Children's Lit. Asn. Thomas More; Shakespeare; Christian humanism. Publ: Take Thomas More to the PTA, Cath. Educr, 61; The sister and self-fulfillment, Mich. Cath, 65; Faculty check of library expectations, Cath. Libr. World, 72; plus others. Add: Dept. of English, Immaculata College, Immaculata, PA 19345.

LORIMOR, E. S, b. Frankfort, Ind, June 11, 40. MASS COMMUNICATIONS, JOURNALISM. A.B, Univ. Calif, Berkeley, 58; Ph.D.(mass commun), Univ. Wis-Madison, 66; cert. Span. stud, Univ. Barcelona, 69. Res. asst. mass commun, Univ. Wis-Madison, 62-66, lectr. writing, 66-67; teacher Eng. as for. lang, Inst. N.Am. Stud, 67-69; ASST. PROF. MASS COMMUN. & JOUR. E.TEX. STATE UNIV, 70- Fel, Int. Commun. Sem, 72. Am. Acad. Advert; Asn. Educ. in Jour; Women in Commun.(fac. adv, 70-). Cross-cultural and international communication; process and effects of persuasive communication; the relationship of personality and national characteristics to communications. Publ: Effects of source and certain other factors on cross-cultural communication, Univ. Wis, 66; co-ed, NNTEP report of progress (6 vols), North. Nigeria Teacher Educ. Proj, 66; co-auth, Four measures of cross-cultural advertising effectiveness, J. Advert. Res, 12/67, Use of the mass media in France and Egypt, Pub. Opinion Quart, winter 68-69 & Reference groups, congruity theory and cross-cultural persuasion, J. Commun, 12/68; plus others. Add: Dept. of Journalism & Graphic Arts, East Texas State University, Commerce, TX 75428.

LORRAH, JEAN, b. Canton, Ohio. MEDIEVAL LITERATURE, LINGUISTICS. B.A, West. Reserve Univ, 62, M.A, 63; Ph.D.(Eng), Fla. State Univ, 68; summers, Univ. Birmingham, 69, Univ, London, 70 & Univ. Col, Galway, 72. Instr. ENG. & chmn. dept, Montverde Acad, Fla, 63-66; asst. prof, MURRAY STATE UNIV, 68-72, ASSOC. PROF, 72- AAUP; MLA; S.Atlantic Mod. Lang. Asn. Chaucer; medieval literature; linguistics. Add: Dept. of English, Murray State University, Murray, KY 42071.

LOSO, MARY JANE, b. St. Joseph, Minn, Jan. 29, 20. ENGLISH LITERATURE. B.A, Col. St. Benedict, 40; M.A, Univ. Minn, 47, Ph.D, 57. Teacher ENG, Belgrade Pub. Schs, 41-43; Worthington High Sch, 43-46; head dept, Col. Great Falls, 47-51; asst, Univ. Minn, 54-55, instr, 56-57; asst. prof, EAST. ORE. STATE COL, 57-61, from assoc. prof. to PROF, 61-, HEAD DIV. HUMANITIES, 73-, chmn. dept. Eng. & speech, 69-73. MLA; Col. Eng. Asn; Pac. Northwest Col. Eng. Asn; AAUP; Conf. Eng. Educ; NCTE. Victorian literature; Italian Renaissance. Add: Dept. of English, Eastern Oregon State College, La Grande, OR 97850.

LOSS, ARCHIE KRUG, b. Hanover, Pa, Jan. 31, 39; m. 67; c. 2. MODERN LITERATURE, ART HISTORY. B.S, Millersville State Col, 60; M.A, Pa. State Univ, 66, Ph.D.(Eng), 70. ASST. PROF. ENG, Behrend Col, Pa. State Univ, 70-72; WAYNE STATE UNIV, 72-, res. award, summer 73. Am. Counc. Learned Soc. grant-in-aid, summer 72. MLA; Am. Soc. Aesthetics; James Joyce Found. Modern literature, modern art, and relations between the two. Publ: The black figure in the Baltimore copy of Piero della Francesca's lost Ferrara frescoes, L'Arte, 3/68; The Pre-Raphaelite ideal, the symbolist femme-enfant and the girl with long flowing hair in the earlier work of Joyce, J. Mod. Lit, 73. Add: Dept. of English, Wayne State University, Detroit, MI 48202.

LOTHERS, WILLIAM T, b. Wichita, Kans, Jan. 8, 28; m. 56; c. 2. SPEECH. A.B, Okla. State Univ, 49; B.D, Faith Theol. Sem, 54; M.A, Univ. Okla, 59; Ph.D.(speech), Mich. State Univ, 66. Instr, high sch, Okla, 49-50; asst.

speech, Univ. Okla, 56-57; asst. prof, Greenville Col, 57-60; ASSOC. PROF, Dordt Col, 61-69; SPEECH COMMUN, WHEATON COL, 69- Acting prog. dir, KDCR-FM, Sioux Center, Iowa. Cent. States Speech Commun. Asn. Rhetoric and public address; speech science. Add: Dept. of Speech Communication, Wheaton College, Wheaton, IL 60187.

LOTT, JOHN BERTRAND, b. Aberdeen, Miss, June 27, 33; m. 61; c. 3. ENGLISH. B.A, Millsaps Col, 55; M.A, Vanderbilt Univ, 56, South Fels. Fund fel, 59, Ph.D, 61. Asst. prof. ENG, UNIV. MONTEVALLO, 59-62, assoc. prof, 62-64, PROF, 64-, CHMN. DEPT, 62- MLA; NCTE; S.Atlantic Mod. Lang. Asn. Victorian literature. Add: Dept. of English, University of Montevallo, Montevallo, AL 35115.

LOTT, (JOHN) RAYMOND, b. Orlando, Fla, July 7, 36; m. 58; c. 2. ENGLISH LITERATURE. B.A, Univ. Miami, 58, M.A, 59; Ph.D, Duke Univ, 62. Res. asst. Duke Univ, 61; instr. ENG, FLA. SOUTH. COL, 61-63, asst. prof, 63-65, assoc. prof, 65-73, PROF, 73- NCTE; Col. Eng. Asn; MLA. Shakespeare; English, American and French novel; modern drama. Publ: Herbert Gold: the novelist as son and lover, 5/67 & Coriolanus: how to fail by being very, very good, 5/68, Colleague; Romeo and Juliet (filmscript), Imperial Film Corp, 69. Add: 504 W. Beacon Rd, Lakeland, FL 33803.

LOTT, ROGER RICHARD STANLEY, O.S.B, b. St. Paul, Minn, Mar. 18, 22. ENGLISH. A.B, Spring Hill Col, 47; Vanderbilt Univ, 47-49; M.A. & M.A.L.S, George Peabody Col, 57. ASSOC. PROF. ENG, ST. BERNARD COL, 59-, DIR. ADMIS. & FINANCIAL AID, 73-, asst. prof. bus. law, 53-60, registr. & admis. off, 57-60. Mem. bd, Nat. Scholastic Aptitude Test, Princeton, 57-; Am. Col. Tests, 58-; hosp. chaplain supvr, Nat. Asn. Cath. Chaplains. U.S.A, 42-45, Sgt. MLA; Am. Libr. Asn; Am. Folklore Soc; NCTE. Add: Dept. of Language, St. Bernard College, St. Bernard, AL 35138.

LOUCKS, JAMES FREDERICK, b. Lakewood, Ohio, Feb. 7, 36. ENGLISH. B.A, Yale, 57; M.A, Ohio State Univ, 65, Ph.D.(Eng), 67. Teacher ENG, Columbus Sch. Girls, 60-63; asst. Ohio State Univ, 63-67; asst. prof, Univ. Va, 67-70; ASSOC. PROF, Drexel Univ, 70-71; VALPARAISO UNIV, 71- U.S.N, 57-60, Res, 60-, Lt. Comdr. MLA. Victorian literature. Publ: Co-auth, Browning's Roman murder story: a reading of The ring and the book, Univ. Chicago, 68. Add: Dept. of English, Valparaiso University, Valparaiso, IN 46383.

LOUGHLIN, RICHARD LAWRENCE, b. Brooklyn, N.Y, Oct. 29, 07; m. 50; c. 1. ENGLISH, SPEECH. B.S, St. John's Col.(N.Y), 29; M.A, Columbia Univ, 31; Ph.D, N.Y. Univ, 47. Chmn. & teacher ENG. & SPEECH, Prep. & High Schs, New York, N.Y, 29-60; assoc. prof, BRONX COMMUNITY COL, 60-61, prof, 61-73, head dept, 60-64, EMER. PROF, 73- Lectr. educ, Brooklyn Col, eve, 48-50; mem, NCTE comt. liaison with Speech Asn. Am. & Am. Educ. Theatre Asn, 67-72. U.S.A.F, 43-45, Med.Admin.C, 45-46, Res, 46-52, 1st Lt. Col. Eng. Asn. Eighteenth century English literature; Oliver Goldsmith. Publ: Co-ed, Journeys in science fiction & Four complete world novels, Globe, 61; co-auth, Macmillan English series, Vol. 8, Macmillan, 63, rev. ed, 73; auth, Spotnotes: Moby Dick, Dell, 67; The community colleges and civilization, Sch. & Soc, 3/68; The perils of publishing, CEA Forum, 12/71; Laugh and grow wise with Oliver Goldsmith, Costerus, Amsterdam, 72; plus 173 others. Add: 83-57 118th St, Kew Gardens, NY 11415.

LOUGY, ROBERT E, b. San Francisco, Calif, Sept. 11, 40; m. 62; c. 2. ENGLISH. A.B, Univ. Calif, Davis, 62, M.A, 64, Ph.D.(Eng), 66. Asst. ENG, Univ. Calif, Davis, 62-65, fel, 65-66; asst. prof, PA. STATE UNIV, UNIVERSITY PARK, 66-72, ASSOC. PROF, 72- Asst. ed, Seventeenth-Century News, 66-67, abstr. ed, 67-68; jr. fel, Inst. Arts & Humanistic Stud, Pa. State Univ, 70-73; Nat. Endowment for Humanities fel, 73-74. MLA. Nineteenth century British novel and theory of the novel; aesthetics and poetic theory of the 19th and 20th centuries; industrialization and the 19th century artist. Publ: Swinburne and twentieth-century criticism, Dalhousie Rev, autumn 68; Imagery and meaning in Atalanta in Calydon, Victorian Poetry, winter 69; contrib, Dickens' Hard Times: the romance as radical literature, In: Dickens studies annual, South. Ill. Univ, Vol. II, 72. Add: Dept. of English, Pennsylvania State University, University Park, PA 16802.

LOUIS, WILLIAM JOSEPH, b. Castorland, N.Y. SPEECH, DRAMA. A.B, Boston Col, 57, assistantship, 57-58, M.A, 59; univ. fel, Stanford Univ, 60-62, Ph.D.(speech, drama, humanities), 69; Fr. Govt. fel, Univ. Nice, 67-68. Instr. Eng, French & gymnastics, LeMoyne Col, 58-60; dir. residence hall, Stanford Univ, 62-66, admin. asst, Stanford Repertory Theatre, 66-67; asst. prof. acting & theatre hist, Univ. B.C, 68-70; drama coach & teacher Eng. & drama, Mexico Acad, 70-71; asst. prof. drama & chmn. dept, West. N.Mex, Univ, 71-73; ASSOC. PROF. DRAMA & CHMN. FINE ARTS DEPT, AVILA COL, 73- Can. Counc. for Arts grant, Univ. Nice, summer 69; dir. & scene designer, Ibsen's Ghosts, 71, Inge's Bus Stop, 72 & Rodgers & Hammerstein's Oklahoma, 73 & dir, scene designer & actor, Prometheus Bound, 72, West. N.Mex. Univ; dir, Paul Zindel's The Effect of Gamma Rays on Man-in-the-Moon Marigolds, 73 & Gershwin's Of Thee I Sing, 74, Avila Col; U.S. Govt. grant, Mexico, summer 73. Am. Theatre Asn. Humanities; education. Add: Dept. of Fine Arts, Avila College, 1901 Wornall Rd, Kansas City, MO 64145.

LOUISE, ROBERT, O.P. See PICHE, PRISCILLA M.

LOUKIDES, PAUL, b. Plainfield, N.J, Sept. 5, 37; m. 62; c. 2. AMERICAN LITERATURE, FILM. A.B, Univ. Pittsburgh, 61; M.A, Univ. Iowa, 62. Instr. ENG, ALBION COL, 62-69, asst. prof, 69-72, ASSOC. PROF, 72- Carnegie fel, 67-69; media consult, Asn. Independent Cols. & Univs, Mich, 71-73; Ctr. Programmed Learning, Univ. Mich, 72-73; Kellogg fel, 73. MLA; Col. Eng. Asn; Popular Cult. Asn; Am. Film Inst; AAUP. Contemporary American fiction; film and American culture; instructional design and programmed learning. Publ: Throwing on the wheel: centering, opening and raising (film), Validated Instr. Assoc, 72; co-auth, The personnel relations series (TV script), Dept. Social Serv. Mich, 73; auth, Some notes on the novel of the absurd, CEA Critic, 1/68; The radical vision, Mich. Academician, 4/73. Add: Dept. of English, Albion College, Albion, MI 49224.

LOUNSBURY, MYRON O, b. New York, N.Y, Feb. 9, 40; m. 63; c. 2. AMERICAN STUDIES. B.A, Duke Univ, 61; Woodrow Wilson fels, Univ. Pa, 62-66, M.A, 62, Ph.D.(Am. civilization), 66. Asst. prof. AM. STUD, UNIV. MD, COLLEGE PARK, 65-71, ASSOC. PROF, 71-, CHMN. AM. STUD. PROG, 74-, fac. res. award, summer 68. Popular Cult. Asn; Am. Stud. Asn. The intellectual's response to technology, popular culture and national identity crises. Publ: The origins of American film criticism, 1909-1939, Arno, 73; Flashes of lightning: the moving picture in the Progressive Era, J. Popular Cult, spring 70. Add: 4204 Underwood St, Hyattsville, MD 20782.

LOVE, GEORGE JOHN, b. Marine City, Mich, Aug. 24, 21; m. 62; c. 1. ENGLISH LANGUAGE & LITERATURE. B.S, Columbia Univ, 53, M.A, 57. ASST. PROF. ENG, Am. Univ, 57-64; MICH. TECHNOL. UNIV, 64- Franklin T. Baker citation, Teachers Col, Columbia Univ, 57. U.S.N, 42-45. MLA; Col. Eng. Asn; Midwest Mod. Lang. Asn; NCTE; Col. Compos. & Commun. Conf. English literature of 17th century; the short story as an art form; comparative literature. Add: 1123 E. Sixth Ave, Houghton, MI 49931.

LOVE, GLEN A, b. Seattle, Wash, July 4, 32; m. 56; c. 2. ENGLISH. B.A, Univ. Wash, 54, M.A, 59, Ph.D.(Am. lit), 64. Teacher pub. schs, Seattle, Wash, 55-59; asst. Eng, Univ. Wash, 59-60, asst. dean stud, 60-63; asst. prof. Eng, San Diego State Col, 63-65; asst. prof. ENG, UNIV. ORE, 65-68, ASSOC, PROF, 68-, dir. compos, 65-70, 73-74, assoc. dean grad. sch, 70-71. NCTE; Conf. Col. Compos. & Commun; Am. Stud. Asn. American literature; English teacher preparation; rhetoric. Publ: Co-ed, Contemporary essays on prose style, Scott, 69, The Oregon curriculum: rhetoric, Holt, Vols. I-VI, 70 & 74, Freshman composition manual, Univ. Ore, 66 & Ecological crisis, Harcourt, 70; auth, Winesburg, Ohio and the rhetoric of silence, Am. Lit, 3/68; World views and the teaching of composition, CCC J, 2/71; New pioneering on the prairies, Am. Quart, 12/73; plus others. Add: Dept. of English, University of Oregon, Eugene, OR 97403.

LOVE, WILLIE NELL STALLINGS, b. Grayson, La; m. 37. ENGLISH. M.A, Loyola Univ.(Ill), 43; M.A, Northwest. Univ, 53; Ph.D.(Eng. lang. & lit), Univ. Md, 60. Instr. Eng. & Latin, High Schs, La. & Chicago, Ill, 30-46; ENG, UNIV. ILL, CHICAGO CIRCLE, 46-60, asst. prof, 60-70, ASSOC. PROF, 70-, dir. Eng. teacher training prog, 65-70. Illuminated manuscripts; use of the epyllion by Greek and Roman satirists and its influence on Colonial writers. Publ: Eunice Tietjens: a biographical and critical study, 60. Add: Dept. of English, University of Illinois at Chicago Circle, Chicago, IL 60680.

LOVELL, ERNEST JAMES, JR, b. Roanoke, Va, Aug. 28, 18; m. 42; c. 2. ENGLISH LITERATURE. A.B, Duke Univ, 39; A.M, Cornell Univ, 40; Hunt fel, Princeton, 45-46, Ph.D, 46. Instr, Cornell Univ, 40-41; Univ. Miss, 41-42; asst. prof. ENG, UNIV. TEX, AUSTIN, 47-51, assoc. prof, 51-62, PROF, 62- Vis. Carnegie prof, Columbia Univ, 55-56; exec. ed, Tex. Stud. Lit. & Lang, 66- U.S.A, 42-45. MLA (mem. comt. res. proj, 51-); Byron Soc; Keats-Shelley Asn. Am. English literature of the early 19th century; English and American literature of the 20th century. Publ: Byron: the record of a quest, Univ. Tex, 49, Archon Bks, 63; His very self and voice: collected conversations of Lord Byron, Macmillan, 54; Captain Medwin, Friend of Byron and Shelley, Univ. Tex. & MacDonald & Co, Ltd, 62; co-auth, Modern drama: an anthology of nine plays, Ginn, 63; auth, Thomas Medwin's conversations of Lord Byron, 66 & Lady Blessington's conversations of Lord Byron, 69, Princeton & Oxford; Irony and image in Don Juan, In: English romantic poets: modern essays in criticism, Oxford, 60; The heretic in the sacred wood: or, the naked man, the tired man, and the romantic aristocrat: William Blake, T.S. Eliot, and George Wyndham, In: Romantic and Victorian, Assoc. Univ. Presses, 71; co-auth, Byron, In: The English romantic poets: a review of research and criticism, MLA, 72; plus others. Add: Dept. of English, University of Texas at Austin, Austin, TX 78712.

LOVELL, JAMES HENRY, JR, b. Dallas, Tex, Feb. 28, 29; m. 59; c. 1. ENGLISH. B.A, Tex. Christian Univ, 51, M.A, 53, Ford fel, 55-57; Ph.D.(philol, Eng), Vanderbilt Univ, 63. Instr. ENG, Tex. Christian Univ, 53-54; Vanderbilt Univ, 56-60; Memphis State Univ, 60-61; asst. prof, Queens Col.(N.C), 61-63, assoc. prof, 63-65, prof. & chmn. dept, 65-72; PROF, UPSALA COL, 72- MLA. Aesthetics; modern poetry; learning and perception theory in relation to literature. Add: Dept. of English, Upsala College, East Orange, NJ 07019.

LOVELL, JOHN, JR, b. Asheville, N.C, July 25, 07; m. 40, 54; c. 1. DRAMA, AMERICAN LITERATURE. A.B, Northwest. Univ, 26, A.M, 27; Univ. Pa, 28-30; Gen. Educ. Bd-Rockefeller Found. fel. & Ph.D, Univ. Calif, 38. Instr. ENG, W.Va. State Col, 27-28; from asst. prof. to PROF, HOWARD UNIV, 30-, ACTING HEAD DEPT, 68-, CHMN. COL. LIB. ARTS, 72-, assoc. dean, 64-68. Vis. prof. for Am. Friends Serv. Comt, Iowa & Calif, 48; Fulbright lectr, Osaka Univ, 60-61; summers, vis. instr, Prairie View State Col, 30, 31; lectr. Am. lit, Pendle Hill Sch, 43; vis. prof, Col. Pac, 50, 56; lectr. & consult, sem. for exec. develop, U.S. Dept. Agr, 64-; mem. founding group & mem. exec. comt, Nat. Col. Honors Counc, 66-68; contrib. annotator, Am. Lit. Realism, 66- U.S.A, 43-46, 1st Lt. MLA; Am. Stud. Asn; Am. Nat. Theatre & Acad; Int. Theatre Inst; Am. Soc. Theatre Res; Auth. Guild; Col. Lang. Asn; Am. Theatre Asn; Asn. Asian Stud; Asn. Stud. Afro-Am. Life & Hist; NCTE; Nat. Col. Honors Counc. American and international drama; Whitman; Afro-American folklore. Publ: Digests of great American plays, Crowell, 61; Black song: the forge and the flame, Macmillan, 72; Eugene O'Neill's darker brother, Theatre Arts, 2/48; Appreciating Whitman: Passage to India, Mod. Lang. Quart, 6/60; Some common ground between American and Japanese drama, Theatre Annual, 64. Add: Box 703, Howard University, Washington, DC 20001.

LOVENHEIM, BARBARA IRENE, b. Rochester, N.Y, July 19, 40. ENGLISH VICTORIAN LITERATURE. B.A, Barnard Col, 62; M.A, Univ. Wis-Madison, 63; Univ. London, 63-64; Ph.D.(Eng), Univ. Rochester, 70. Lectr. Eng, Queens Col.(N.Y), 66-70; pub. relat. asst, City of New York, 70-71; free lance writer, Appleton-Century-Crofts, N.Y.C, 71-72; ASST. PROF. ENG, BARUCH COL, 72- MLA. Apocalyptic literature; remediation; single life in the seventies. Publ: Co-auth, There was the word (play), Barnard Col,

61 & American government, Appleton, 71; auth, Disintegration and resumption of order in Hamlet, Barnard Undergrad. J, 62; contrib, Social Science, Appleton, 72. Add: 142 E. 16th St, New York, NY 10003.

LOVERING, JOSEPH PAUL, b. Calais, Maine, Feb. 16, 21; m; c. 5. ENGLISH. A.B, Col. of Holy Cross, 43; M.A, Boston Univ, 48. Instr. ENG, St. Anselm's Col, 46-48; asst. prof, St. Michael's Col, 48-56; assoc. prof, CANISIUS COL, 56-60, PROF. & CHMN. DEPT, 60-, CHMN. FAC. SENATE, 73- U.S.N, 43-45. Col. Eng. Asn. American novel and poetry. Publ: S. Weir Mitchell, Twayne, 71; Dorothy Canfield Fisher, Vt. Hist. Add: Dept. of English, Canisius College, 2001 Main St, Buffalo, NY 14208.

LOVING, JEROME MacNEILL, b. Philadelphia, Pa, Dec. 25, 41. AMERICAN LITERATURE. B.A, Pa. State Univ, 64; fel, Duquesne Univ, 69-70, M.A, 70; Ph.D.(Eng), Duke Univ, 73. Teaching asst. ENG, Duke Univ, 71-73; ASST. PROF, TEX. A&M UNIV, 73- U.S.N, 64-67, Res, 67-70, Lt. MLA; AAUP. Nineteenth century American literature, especially Whitman and Melville; the Civil War letters of George Washington Whitman. Publ: The rocking chair structure of Sister Carrie, Dreiser Newsletter, 71; ed, Civil War letters of George Washington Whitman from North Carolina, N.C. Hist. Rev, 73; Melville's pardonable sin, New Eng. Quart, 74. Add: Dept. of English, Texas A&M University, College Station, TX 77840

LOW, ANTHONY, b. San Francisco, Calif, May 31, 35; m. 61; c. 5. ENGLISH LITERATURE. A.B, Harvard, 57, M.A, 59, Ph.D.(Eng), 65. Asst. prof. ENG, Seattle Univ, 65-68; N.Y. UNIV, 68-71, ASSOC. PROF, 71- Asst. ed, Seventeenth-Century News, 68- U.S.A, 62-65. MLA; Milton Soc. Am; Mod. Humanities Res. Asn; Renaissance Soc. Am. Milton; Renaissance and 17th century literature; modern literature. Publ: Augustine Baker, Twayne, 70; The blaze of noon: a reading of Samson Agonistes, Columbia Univ, 74; Action and suffering: Samson Agonistes and the irony of alternatives, PMLA 5/69; The image of the tower in Paradise lost, Stud. Eng. Lit, winter 70; Milton's God: authority in Paradise lost, Milton Stud, 72; plus others. Add: Dept. of English, New York University, 19 University Pl, New York, NY 10003.

LOWANCE, MASON IRA, JR, b. Atlanta, Ga, June 2, 38; m. 63; c. 2. AMERICAN LITERATURE & STUDIES. A.B, Princeton, 60; Columbia Univ, 61; B.A, Oxford, 64, M.A, 67; Ph.D.(lit), Emory Univ, 67. Instr, Punahou Sch, Hawaii, 60-61; ENG, Morehouse Col, 65-67; asst. prof, UNIV. MASS, AMHERST, 67-70, ASSOC. PROF, 70- Consult, Educ. Serv, Inc, 65-66, Educ. Proj, Inc, 66-67, Educ. Assocs, Inc, 67- & U.S. Off. Educ, 70- Managing ed, Early Am. Lit, 69-; Am. Antiq. Soc. fel, 72; Huntington Libr. fel, 73. MLA (treas, Early Am. Lit. Group, 70-74); Am. Stud. Asn. Puritan and Colonial American literature; American studies, especially American religion and transcendentalism; 17th-century literature. Publ: Ed, Figures or types of the Old Testament, Johnson Reprint, 69; Increase Mather, Twayne, 74; The language of Canaan, Doubleday, 74; Veils and illusion in Benito Cereno, Ariz. Quart; Cotton Mather's Magnalia, In: Typology and early American literature, Univ. Mass, 72; From Edwards to Emerson and Thoreau: a revaluation, Am. Transcendental Quart, 73; plus others. Add: Dept. of English, University of Massachusetts, Amherst, MA 01002.

LOWDON, JEANNIE ELIZABETH, b. Lincoln, Nebr. ENGLISH LITERATURE. B.A, Hastings Col, 22; M.A, Univ. Nebr, 29; summers, State Univ. Iowa, 29, Univ. Birmingham, Eng, 59, 61, 64. Course writer & ed, Univ. Nebr. Exten. Div, 35-52; asst. prof. Eng, York Col, 52-53, prof. & chmn. dept, 53-55; assoc. prof, Buena Vista Col, 55-62; prof, Aurora Col, 62-69; RES. & WRITING, 70- NCTE; Am. Guild Organists. The Elizabethan Age in English literature; Shakespeare's interest in witchcraft and demonology; the Lowdon Clan in Scotland. Publ: Citizenship education for aliens, U.S. Immigration & Naturalization Serv, 44; A course in normal training music, Univ. Nebr, 45; Social studies via the mailbox, Social Educ, 12/49. Add: 2232 S. 15th St, Lincoln, NE 68502.

LOWE, ALMA LOUISE, b. Mabank, Tex, Feb. 23, 09; m. 46. ENGLISH & AMERICAN LITERATURE. B.A, Tex. Christian Univ, 34, M.A, 38; fel, Univ. Tex, 43-44; fel, Rice Univ, 52-55, Ph.D, 55. Teaching fel. Eng, Tex. Christian Univ, 36-38, instr, 38-44, asst. prof, 44-46; Mid-Town Ctr, City Col. New York, 50-51; Univ. St. Thomas, 55-60; Col. Nursing, Tex. Woman's Univ, 61-62; lectr. Eng. & dean women, Rice Univ, 62-67; DISTINGUISHED PROF. ENG, HOWARD PAYNE COL, 71- Asst. prof, Univ. P.R, summer 49; lectr. Am. Lang. Ctr, Columbia Univ, summer 51; Dental Br, Univ. Tex, 55-62. Conf. Col. Teachers Eng; Renaissance Soc. Am; S.Cent. Mod. Lang. Asn; MLA. Nineteenth century American literature; 18th century English literature; linguistics. Publ: Ed, Henry James' English hours, Heinemann, London & Orion, 60, 62, Mercury Paperback Ed, London, 63. Add: Dept. of English, Box 413, Howard Payne College, Brownwood, TX 76801.

LOWE, CLARICE PIERSON, b. West Point, Miss, July 14, 25; m. 58; c. 3. SPEECH, ENGLISH. A.B, Wiley Col, 43; B.S.L.S, Atlanta Univ, 44; M.A, Northwest. Univ, 50; Carnegie Found. fel, Ford Found. fel, univ. fel. & Ph.D.(speech), Univ. Wis-Madison, 70. Librn, Xavier Prep. Sch, 44-45; asst. librn, Talladega Col, 46-47; from instr. to assoc. prof. SPEECH & ENG, TEX. SOUTH. UNIV, 47-72, PROF. & HEAD DEPT, 72- Vis. prof. speech pathol, Fla. A&M Univ, summer 55; consult. teacher corps, Tex. South. Univ, 70-71; assoc. dir. facilities planning grant, Dept. Health, Educ. & Welfare, 71; consult. eval. team, Nat. Citizens Participation Conf, 73. Int. Commun. Asn; Speech Commun. Asn; Nat. Asn. Educ. Broadcasters; AAUP. Instructional methods; rhetorical criticism. Publ: Co-auth, Reaching out: linking the inner-city community and the university, 71 & Toward an urban university, 72, Tex. South. Univ. Add: Dept. of Speech & Drama, Texas Southern University, 3201 Wheeler, Houston, TX 77004.

LOWE, FREDERICK WILLIAM, JR, b. Newark, N.J, Sept. 27, 23; m. 46; c. 3. AMERICAN LITERATURE. A.B, Williams Col, 44; M.A, Columbia Univ, 47, Ph.D, 57; LL.D, Laurence Univ, 71- Instr. Eng, Colgate Univ, 47-50; from asst. prof. to assoc. prof, Danbury State Col, 53-60; prof. & chmn. dept, Glassboro State Col, 60-63; dean, MANCHESTER COMMUNITY COL, 63-65, PRES, 65- U.S.M.C, 43-46, 1st Lt. Am. Asn. Jr. Cols. American literature, especially the 1920's; the Paris expatriate group; film. Publ: Breadth and depth in a monuments of culture program, J. Teacher Educ, 59; An experience technique for introducing drama, N.J. Eng. Leaflet, 4/61; guest ed, The New English issue, Teacher Educ. Quart, fall 64. Add: Manchester Community College, Manchester, CT 06040.

LOWE, IRVING, b. New York, N.Y, July 18, 07; m. 47. ENGLISH. B.A, Univ. Wis, 35; M.A, 36; Ph.D.(Eng), Stanford, 57. Asst. prof. ENG, UNIV. SAN FRANCISCO, 57-61, ASSOC. PROF, 62- Henry James. Publ: John Donne: the middle way, J. Hist. Ideas, 7-9/61. Add: Dept. of English, University of San Francisco, San Francisco, CA 94117.

LOWE, LARRY VEAZEY, b. Warrenton, Ga, July 19, 31; m. 58; c. 3. SPEECH, DRAMA. A.B, Mercer Univ, 52; M.F.A, Univ. Ga, 59; Ph.D. (speech), Mich. State Univ, 65. Instr. speech, High Point Col, 59-61; asst. instr, Mich. State Univ, 61-63; asst. prof. SPEECH & THEATRE, MID. TENN. STATE UNIV, 63-65, ASSOC. PROF, 65-, CHMN. DEPT, 68- U.S.N, 52-57, Lt. Speech Commun Asn. History of public address; speech criticism. Add: 1915 Hamilton Dr, Murfreesboro, TN 37130.

LOWE, MERVIN R, b. York Co, Pa, Apr. 11, 20. ENGLISH. B.A, Pa. State Univ, 40; M.A, Univ. Pa, 48, Ph.D, 51. Asst. instr. ENG, Univ. Pa, 46-50; instr. Pa. State Univ, 50-53, asst. prof, 53-62; assoc. prof, WIDENER COL, 62-66, PROF, 66- Reader's Digest Found. lectr. grant. Am. lit, Univ. Dijon, 53-54; U.S. Dept. State lectr, Univ. Saigon, 58-59; bibliographer, Mod. Lang. Asn, 60-63; consult. & writer, U.S. Inform. Serv, 62; ed. consult, J.B. Lippincott Co, Pa, 63. U.S.A, 42-46, Capt. MLA; NCTE; Am. Stud. Asn; AAUP. American literature; comparative literature; creative writing. Publ: Co-auth, Annual bibliography, Mod. Lang. Asn, 61, 62 & 63; auth, La Rotonde (poem), Pivot, spring 57; co-auth, Symposium on the teaching of creative writing, Four Quarters, 3/61. Add: Humanities Group, Widener College, Chester, PA 19013.

LOWE, ROBERT LIDDELL, b. Cameron, Tex, Oct. 25, 08. ENGLISH. A.B, Baylor Univ, 27; A.M, Univ. Colo, 29; Harvard, 36-37; A.M, Princeton, 42, Ph.D, 47. Instr, Purdue Univ, 29-36, asst. prof, 37-40; off-instr, U.S. Naval Acad, 42-46; vis. asst. prof, Williams Col, 47-48; assoc. prof, ENG, PURDUE UNIV, 48-52, PROF, 52- Vis. prof, Univ. Pac, summers 57 & 62. Nineteenth century and modern English literature; Matthew Arnold. Add: Dept. of English, Purdue University, West Lafayette, IN 47906.

LOWE, WILLIAM JOHN, b. Newark, N.J, Dec. 24, 09; m. 34; c. 2. LIBERAL STUDIES, ENGLISH. A.B, Rutgers Univ, 31, M.Ed, 34; summers, Pa. State Univ, 48-55. Teacher High Sch, N.J, 31-36; Pa, 36-42; asst. prof. mil. sci, Rutgers Univ, 42-43; commandant, Army Specialized Training Prog, Pratt Inst, 43-44; prof. mil. sci, CLARKSON COL. TECHNOL, 44-45, from assoc. prof. Eng. to PROF. HUMANITIES, 45-, dean stud, 67-72. A.U.S, 42-46, U.S.A.R, 31-42, 46-60, Lt. Col. NCTE; Am. Stud. Asn. American literature; applied psychology. Publ: Like I said, Word Study, 4/61; The mountain shakes, 10/61 & It is with genuine regret, 4/65, Col. Eng. Add: Dept. of Humanities, Clarkson College of Technology, Potsdam, NY 13676.

LOWERS, JAMES K, b. Columbus, Ohio, Sept. 6, 06; m. 55; c. 2. ENGLISH. B.A, Univ. Calif, Los Angeles, 35, fel, 35, M.A, 37, Ph.D.(Eng), 50. Supvr. instr, Univ. Calif, Los Angeles, 38-42, 46-48, lectr, ENG, 48-50; asst. prof, Chico State Col, 50-51; prof, UNIV. HAWAII, MANOA, 51-72, EMER. PROF, 72- Correspondent, Am. Counc. Learned Soc, 62-64. U.S.A, 42-46, Capt. MLA. English literature of the Renaissance. Publ: Co-auth, Essentials for writing, Am. Bk, 45, rev, 55; auth, Mirrors for rebels, Univ. Calif, 53; auth, High comedy elements in Medwall's Fulgens and lucres, ELH, 41. Add: 2916 Oxford Ct, Ft. Collins, CO 80521.

LOWERS, VIRGINIA BELLE, b. Parkersburg, W.Va, Oct. 11, 01. ENGLISH. A.B, Stanford Univ, 22; Univ. Calif, 23, 26, 34, 35; Univ. South. Calif, 47, 48; M.A, Los Angeles State Col, 61. Teacher bus. educ, Madera Union High Sch, Calif, 22-24; Eng, Covina Union High Sch, 24-25; Los Angeles City Schs, 26-47, consult. sec. reading, 47-48, supvr. Eng, Curriculum Br, 48-67. Training teacher Eng, Univ. High Sch, Los Angeles & Univ. Calif, Los Angeles, 31-47; mem, Stanford Lang. Arts Invest, 38-40; instr. children's lit, Los Angeles State Col, 54; consult, Immaculate Heart Col. Libr. Sem, Los Angeles, 57-58; lectr. Eng. curriculum, grammar & reading, Colo. State Col, 61, 62; San Fernando Valley State Col, 67-71. Int. Reading Asn; NCTE (citation, 59). Secondary English curriculum; teaching reading in secondary school; team teaching of secondary English. Publ: Contrib, The English language arts in the secondary school, Appleton, 56; co-auth, Vanguard, 61, 63, 67, Perspectives..., 61, 63 & Accent: U.S.A, 65, Galaxy Sers, Scott. Add: 322 N. Flores St, Los Angeles, CA 90048.

LOWERY, THOMAS VINCENT, b. Providence, R.I, Dec. 22, 19. ENGLISH. Ed.B, R.I. Col. Educ, 41; Ph.B, Providence Col, 46; fel, Univ, Notre Dame, 47-48, M.A, 48. Teacher ENG, LA SALLE ACAD, 42-47, INSTR, 51-, CHMN. DEPT, 61-, ASST. PRIN, 69- Instr. Am. civilization, Exten, R.I. Col, 51-61; Exten, Univ. R.I, 63-72. MLA; Nat. Cath. Educ. Asn; NCTE. American intellectual history; rhetoric and composition. Publ: Co-auth, American literature, beginnings to 1900, 70 & Modern American poetry, 70, In: The perspective series, Harcourt. Add: La Salle Academy, 612 Academy Ave, Providence, RI 02908.

LOWREY, SARA, b. Nov. 14, 97. SPEECH. B.Litt, Blue Mt. Col, 17; dipl, Columbia Col. Expression, 19; A.M, Baylor Univ, 23; Univ. Wis, 30; La. State Univ, 34; Univ. Iowa, 35; Cent. Sch. Speech Training & Dramatic Art, 38. Mem. fac, Ouachita Col, 19-20; Blue Mt. Col, 20-21; chmn. dept. speech, Baylor Univ, 23-49; prof, Furman Univ, 49-63, chmn. dept, 55-63; producer & teacher educ. TV prog. lang. arts & lit, How do you say it? WFBC-TV, 59-63, S.C. Educ. TV Sta, 61- Summer lectr, Univ. Calif, Berkeley, 48, Northwest. Univ, 50, Univ. Fla, 53 & Univ. Utah, 65; vis. prof. oral interpretation, Univ. Utah. Speech Asn. Am; South. Speech Asn. Effect of study of speech on vocabulary. Publ: Co-auth, Interpretative reading, Appleton, 41, rev. ed, 53; auth, How do you say it? Furman Univ, 62; Theodosia, gift of God, Carlton, 72; Interpretative reading as an aid in acting, speech correction and radio, Quart. J. Speech, 12/45; Speech science or art?, Speech Teacher, 1/53; McGuffey of the sixties, South. Speech J, winter 61. Add: 23 W. Hillcrest Dr, Greenville, SC 29609.

LOWRIE, JAMES A, b. Braddock, Pa, July 31, 14; m. 46; c. 3. ENGLISH. A.B, Lafayette Col, 35; Ph.D.(Eng), Univ. Pittsburgh, 43. Instr. ENG, Univ. Pittsburgh, 43-46; asst. prof, IOWA STATE UNIV, 46-54, assoc. prof, 54-62, PROF, 62- MLA; NCTE. British, American and world drama. Publ: Co-auth, Writing from experience, Iowa State Univ, 54 & Experience and expression, Scribner, 60. Add: Dept. of English, 253 Ross Hall, Iowa State University, Ames, IA 50010.

LOXTERMAN, ALAN SEARING, b. Pittsburgh, Pa, May 21, 37; m. 65. ENGLISH. A.B, Kenyon Col, 59; M.A, Univ. Chicago, 60; Ph.D.(Eng), Ohio State Univ, 71. Instr. ENG, RICHMOND COL.(VA), 70-71, ASST. PROF, 71- MLA; Brontë Soc. Emily Brontë, Wuthering Heights; 17th century English poetry; literary criticism. Add: Dept. of English, Richmond College, University of Richmond, Richmond, VA 23173.

LOY, HAROLD W, b. Lincoln, Kans, June 2, 24; m. 48; c. 2. SPEECH COMMUNICATION, SPEECH EDUCATION. B.S, Kans. State Teachers Col, 48, M.A, Univ. Denver; 51; fel, Univ. Kans, 65-66, Ph.D.(speech commun), 68. Teacher, High Schs, Kans, 48-53; supvr. speech, drama & debate, Col. High Lab. Sch, KANS. STATE COL, PITTSBURG, 53-64, acting chmn. DEPT. SPEECH & THEATRE, 66-67, CHMN, 67- U.S.N.R, 43-46, Ens. Speech Commun. Asn. Speech education. Add: Dept. of Speech & Theatre, Kansas State College of Pittsburg, Pittsburg, KS 66762.

LOYD, ALLEN DENNIS, b. Nashville, Tenn, June 16, 36; m. 58; c. 3. AMERICAN LITERATURE. B.A, David Lipscomb Col, 58; M.A, George Peabody Col, 63, Ed.S, 66, Ph.D.(Eng), 68. Teacher Eng, Maplewood High Sch, Nashville, 58-59; David Lipscomb High Sch, 59-67; asst. prof, David Lipscomb Col, 68-70, assoc. prof, 70-73; ED, NASHVILLE, 74- S.Atlantic Mod. Lang. Asn; NCTE (Conf. Eng. Educ). Publ: The legend of Granny White, 68 & Tennessee's mystery woman novelist, 70, Tenn. Hist. Quart. Add: 1508 Woodmont Blvd, Nashville, TN 37215.

LUCAS, ALEC, b. Toronto, Ont, June 20, 13; m. 39; c. 2. ENGLISH. B.A, Queen's Univ.(Ont), 43, M.A, 45; A.M, Harvard, 47, fel, 47-50, Ph.D, 51. Asst. prof. ENG, Univ. N.B, 50-51, assoc. prof, 51-57; asst. prof, McGILL UNIV, 57-58, assoc. prof, 58-64, PROF, 64- Can. Counc. summer grants, 56, 63, 66, 67, 68 & leave fel, 73-74; vis. lectr. Am. lit, Laval Univ, 65; univ. exchange lectr, Univ. Toronto, 67. Asn. Can. Univ. Teachers Eng. Nineteenth century English fiction; Canadian literature. Publ: Co-auth, Archives des Lettres Canadiennes, Vol. II, Ed. Fides, 62 & Literary history of Canada, Univ. Toronto, 65; auth, Hugh MacLennan, McClelland & Stewart, 70; ed, Great Canadian short stories, Dell, 71; auth, Missing! Canadian literature, Can. Forum, 71; Curriculum crisis in English literature, Can. Dimension, 72; The anthology, a notable but unacclaimed achievement of Canadian literature, Lit. Half-Yearly, 72; plus others. Add: Dept. of English, McGill University, Montreal, P.Q, Can.

LUCAS, THOMAS EDWARD, b. Chicago, Ill, June 24, 19; m. 55; c. 1. AMERICAN LITERATURE. M.A, Univ. Chicago, 48; Univ. Ill, 49-50; Univ. Chicago, 50-51; Ph.D.(Eng), Univ. Denver, 63. Assoc. prof. ENG, U.S. Air Force Acad, 60-69; PROF, SETON HALL UNIV, 69- Contrib. ed, Vols. 40-45, Annual Bibliog. Mod. Humanities Res. Asn, 65-70; lectr, Univ. Colo, 66-69. U.S.A.F, 42-45, 52-69, Maj.(Ret). AAUP; Mod. Humanities Res. Asn; Melville Soc; Eng. Inst; Col. Eng. Asn. Literary theory; Herman Melville; literary criticism. Publ: Elder Olson, Twayne, 72; Herman Melville: the purpose of the novel, Tex. Stud. Lang. & Lit, 72. Add: Dept. of English, Seton Hall University, South Orange Ave, South Orange, NJ 07079.

LUCHT, WILLIAM EDWARD, b. Davenport, Iowa, May 29, 22; m. 46; c. 2. ENGLISH. B.A, Harvard, 47; M.A, Boston Univ, 48; fel. & Ph.D.(Eng), State Univ. Iowa, 54. Instr. ENG, Minn. State Teachers Col, Mankato, 48-50; State Univ. Iowa, 54-55; Univ. Ore, 55-59; from asst. prof. to ASSOC. PROF, LEWIS & CLARK COL, 59- U.S.A, 43-46. MLA. English renaissance and 17th century literature. Add: Dept. of English, Lewis & Clark College, Portland, OR 97219.

LUCID, ROBERT FRANCIS, b. Seattle, Wash, June 25, 30; m. 54; c. 1. ENGLISH. B.A, Univ. Wash, 54; M.A, Univ. Chicago, 55, Ph.D, 58. Instr. ENG, Univ. Chicago, 57-59, asst. prof, Wesleyan Univ, 59-64; UNIV. PA, 64-68, ASSOC. PROF, 68- MLA; Am. Stud. Asn.(exec. secy, 64-69). American literature; American civilization. Publ: Ed, The journal of Richard Henry Dana, Jr, Harvard, 68, Norman Mailer, the man and his work, Little, 71 & The long patrol: 25 years of writing from the work of Norman Mailer, World Publ, 71; plus others. Add: Dept. of English, University of Pennsylvania, Philadelphia, PA 19174.

LUCK, EDWARD GRAHAM, b. New Orleans, La, June 30, 22; m. 51; c. 3. SPEECH, JOURNALISM. B.A, La. State Univ, 50, M.A, 53. Instr. speech, Grinnell Col, 54-57; asst. prof, La. Polytech. Inst, 57-62, ASSOC. PROF. speech & dir. instr. TV, film & radio, 62-72; JOUR, GA. STATE UNIV, 72- U.S.N.R, 42-46, Lt. Speech Commun. Asn. Broadcasting; film; public address. Publ: Co-auth, Handbook for speaking, W.C. Brown, 62. Add: Dept. of Journalism, Georgia State University, Atlanta, GA 30303.

LUCOW, BENJAMIN JOHN, b. Winnipeg, Man, Feb. 7, 21; U.S. citizen. ENGLISH. A.B, Univ. Calif, Berkeley, 49, M.A, 50; Ph.D.(Eng), Univ. Wash, 64. Instr. ENG, Univ. Calif. Far East Command Prog, 53-54; San Jose State Col, 55-56; Ga. Inst. Technol, 57-58; Pa. State Univ, 58-59; Univ. Wash, 61-62; Univ. Colo, 62-64; ASSOC. PROF, Keene State Col, 64-65; ST. JOHN'S UNIV.(N.Y), 65- U.S.A.A.F, 42-46, S/Sgt. Renaissance Soc. Am; Malone Soc; MLA. Elizabethan, Jacobean, and Caroline drama. Publ: The peasant marey, 66 & The sad horn blowers, 66, Stud. Short Fiction. Add: Dept. of English, St. John's University, Jamaica, NY 11432.

LUDINGTON, CHARLES T, JR, b. Philadelphia, Pa, Jan. 31, 36; m. 58; c. 4. ENGLISH, AMERICAN STUDIES. B.A, Yale, 57; M.A, Duke Univ, 64, Ph.D. (Eng), 68. Instr. ENG, UNIV. N.C, CHAPEL HILL, 66-67, asst. prof, 67-71, ASSOC. PROF, 71- Fulbright lectr, Univ. Lyons, 71-72. U.S.M.C.R, 57-60, Capt. S.Atlantic Mod. Lang. Asn; Am. Stud. Asn. American literature, especially John Dos Passos; American studies. Publ: Ed, The fourteenth chronicle: letters and diaries of John Dos Passos, Gambit, 73; auth, The neglected satires of John Dos Passos, Satire Newslett, spring 70; Protest and anti-protest: Ralph Ellison, South. Humanities Rev, winter 70. Add: Dept. of English, University of North Carolina, Chapel Hill, NC 27514.

LUDLUM, CHARLES DANIEL, b. Albany, N.Y, Oct. 4, 26; m. 48; c. 3. ENGLISH PHILOLOGY. A.B, Cornell Univ, 48; Ph.D, Stanford Univ, 54. Instr. ENG, Ohio State Univ, 53-54; Ore. State Col, 54-56; from assoc. prof. to PROF, SAN JOSE STATE UNIV, 56- U.S.A, 44-46. MLA. Old and Middle English. Add: Dept. of English, San Jose State University, San Jose, CA 95114.

LUDWIG, JACK, b. Winnipeg, Man, Aug. 30, 22; m. 46; c. 2. ENGLISH LITERATURE. B.A, Univ. Man, 44; Ph.D, Univ. Calif, Los Angeles, 53. Instr. Eng. & humanities, Williams Col, 49-53; from asst. prof. to assoc. prof. Eng. & Eng. comp. lit, Bard Col, 53-58; vis. lectr, Eng. & lectr. humanities, Univ. Minn, 58-61; PROF. ENG, STATE UNIV. N.Y. STONY BROOK, 61- Chmn. humanities group, Harvard Int. Sem, 63-66; consult, Comn. on Col. Physics Films, 65-66; Can. Arts Counc. fiction fel, 67-68; writer-in-residence, Univ. Toronto, 68-69; play consult, Stratford Shakespeare Festival, Ont, spring 69; playwright in residence, summer 70, play consult. for Bust-out, Nat. Arts Centre, winter 70; consult, TV Film Joyceville, Can. Broadcasting Corp, winter 71. Atlantic Monthly First, 60; Longview Found. Fiction Award, 60; Best. Am. Short Stories Award, 61; O. Henry Prize Stories Award, 61 & 65. Contemporary fiction and poetry; humanities; international relations in arts and philosophy. Publ: Recent American novelist, Univ. Minn, 62; Confusions, N.Y. Graphic Soc, 63; Above ground, Little, 68; co-ed, Soundings, House of Anansi, Toronto, 70; auth, Hockey night in Moscow, 72 & A woman of her age, 73, McClelland & Stewart, Toronto; The great hockey thaw, Doubleday, 74; James Joyce's Dubliners, In: Stories: British and American, Houghton, 53, Sons and lovers, 69 & The dispossessed, 72, Partisan Rev; plus two others. Add: Dept. of English, State University of New York at Stony Brook, Stony Brook, NY 11790.

LUDWIG, JAY FERRIS, b. Bogota, N.J, Aug. 21, 30; m. 57; c. 2. SPEECH, THEATER. B.A, Montclair State Col, 52; M.A, Bowling Green State Univ, 53; Ph.D.(theatre), Univ. Ill, 58. Instr. speech, Russell Sage Col, 57-61; asst. prof. WILLIAM PATERSON COL. N.J, 61-66, assoc. prof, 66-69, PROF. THEATRE, 69-, DEAN COL. ARTS & SCI, 70- Consult, Choice Mag, 71- U.S.A, 53-55. Counc. Cols. Arts & Sci; Am. Theatre Asn. American theatre history; history of the theatre; acting. Publ: James H. McVicker and his theatre, Quart. J. Speech, 1/60; Shakespeare with few males, Players Mag, 1/61; A review of the Craftsmen of Dionysus, Speech Teacher, 1/67. Add; College of Arts & Sciences, William Paterson College, 300 Pompton Rd, Wayne, NJ 07470.

LUDWIG, RICHARD MILTON, b. Reading, Pa, Nov. 24, 20. ENGLISH. A.B, Univ. Mich, 42; A.M, Harvard, 43, fel, 46-50, Ph.D.(Eng), 50. Instr. ENG, PRINCETON, 50-53, asst. prof, 53-59, assoc. prof, 59-68, PROF, 68, ASST. LIBRN. RARE BKS. & SPEC. COLLECTIONS, 74- Dexter traveling fel, Harvard, summer 50; Princeton preceptor, 54-57, Eng, 55-56, McCosh fac. fel, 67-68. U.S.A, 44-46, 2nd Lt. MLA; Am. Stud. Asn. American and English novel; American poetry; American drama. Publ: Co-ed, Major American writers, Harcourt, 52; ed, Aspects of American poetry, Ohio State Univ, 63 & Letters of Ford Madox Ford, Princeton, 65; auth, Guide to American literature and its backgrounds since 1890, Harvard, 72; co-ed, Literary history of the United States, Macmillan, 74. Add: 143 Hartley Ave, Princeton, NJ 08540.

LUDWIGSON, KATHRYN, b. York, Pa, July 30, 21; m. 47; c. 1. ENGLISH, THEOLOGY. B.A, Columbia Col, 43; B.A, Wheaton Col, 44, fel. & M.A, 46; M.S, North. Ill. Univ, 58; Chicago Lutheran Theol. Sem, 56-57; Ph.D.(Eng), Northwest. Univ, 63. Instr. Greek, Wheaton Col, 45-47; teacher, elem. sch, Ill, 57-58; high sch, 58-59; instr. Eng, Wheaton Col, 59-63; asst. prof, North. Ill. Univ, 63-65; prof. & chmn. dept, Trinity Col.(Ill), 65-72, chmn. div. lang. & lit, 68-72; CHMN. DIV. HUMANITIES, KING'S COL.(N.Y), 72- Clement Stone Found. writer grant, 68-69; res. scholar & ed, New Int. Bible: New Testament; co-chmn, E.Coast Christian Educators' Conf; chmn. & founder, Community Speakers' Bur, King's Col.(N.Y). NCTE; NEA; MLA. Edward Dowden, literary critic in Ireland in late 19th century; preparation of overhead projector materials to be used in junior colleges and lower division classes of senior colleges. Publ: Achievement motivation for college students, Trinity Col, 68; Edward Dowden, Vol. 148, In: Twayne English authors series, 73; Christianity and literature (21 cassette recordings), King's Col.(N.Y), 73; co-auth, A survey of Bible prophecy, Zondervan, 73; auth, Samuel Beckett's view of man in Waiting for Godot and Endgame, In: Literature and religion: Albee and Beckett, Clarkson Col. Technol, 71; To motivate students, In: Improving college and university teaching, Univ. Ore, 73. Add: Div. of Humanities, King's College, Briarcliff Manor, NY 10510.

LUECKE, JANE MARIE, O.S.B, b. Okeene, Okla, Apr. 24, 24. ENGLISH. B.A, Benedictine Heights Col, 48; Univ. Okla, summer 48; M.A, Marquette Univ, 56; Ph.D, Univ. Notre Dame, 64. Teacher, parochial sch, 45-56; instr. Eng. & jour. & dir. pub. relat, Benedictine Heights Col, 56-57, asst. prof. Eng. & acad. dean, 57-61; dir. res. stud, St. Joseph Convent, 64-66; assoc. prof. ENG, OKLA. STATE UNIV, 66-70, PROF, 70- Mem, Nat. Comt. Res. in Renewal Relig. Life, 65-; consult, Int. Secretariat Eng. in Liturgy, 65-; mem. certification comt. & comn. diocesan structure, Okla. Diocesan Little Counc, 66-; chmn. lang. & lit. sect, Am. Benedictine Acad, 67-69. MLA; NCTE; Col. Eng. Asn. Rhythm and meter in English poetry; Old and Middle English literat; novels and novelists. Publ: The Princess Casamassima: Hyacinth's fallible consciousness, Mod. Philol, 5/63 & In: Modern judgements: Henry James, Macmillan, London, 69; Measuring the rhythmic variation of Old English meter, Lang. & Style, 73; The meter and rhythm of Beowulf, In: De Proprietatibus litterarum, Mouton, 73; plus others. Add: Dept. of English, Oklahoma State University, Stillwater, OK 74075.

LUECKE, RICHARD HENRY, Philosophy, Religion. See Volume IV, Philosophy, Religion & Law.

LUEDERS, EDWARD GEORGE, b. Chicago, Ill, Feb. 14, 23; m. 46; c. 3. AMERICAN STUDIES. A.B, Hanover Col, 47; M.A, Northwest. Univ, 48; Ph.D.(Am. stud), Univ. N.Mex, 52. Instr. Eng. & speech, Univ. N.Mex, 50-

53, asst. prof. Eng, 53-57, dir. freshman compos, 54-57; asst. prof. ENG, Long Beach State Col, 57-60, assoc. prof, 60-61; prof. & chmn. dept, Hanover Col, 61-66; PROF, UNIV. UTAH, 66-, chmn. dept, 69-72. U.S.A.A.F, 43-46. NCTE; Am. Stud. Asn. American literature; language arts; modern poetry. Publ: Carl Van Vechten and the twenties, Univ. N. Mex, 55; ed, College and adult reading list of books in literature and the fine arts, Washington Sq, 63; auth, Carl Van Vechten, In: United States authors series, Twayne, 65; co-auth, Reflections on a gift of watermelon pickle . . . and other modern verse, 66 & Some haystacks don't even have any needle and other complete modern poems, 69, Scott; auth, Teaching writing today, 1/67 & The McLuhan thesis, 4/68, Eng. J; plus others. Add: 3840 San Rafael Ave, Salt Lake City, UT 84109.

LUEDTKE, LUTHER STEPHEN, b. Hutchinson, Minn, Nov. 17, 43; m. 67; c. 1. ENGLISH & AMERICAN LITERATURE. B.A, Gustavus Adolphus Col, 65; NDEA fel. & Ph.D.(Am. civilization), Brown Univ, 71. Lectr. Am. stud, Univ. Kiel, 68-69; ASST. PROF. ENG, UNIV. SOUTH. CALIF, 70-, CO-DIR, AM. STUD. & DIR. AM. STUD. INST, 72- Nat. Endowment for Humanities younger humanist grant, summer 72; Graves Award, summer 74. MLA; Am. Stud. Asn. Nineteenth and 20th century American literature; American social and intellectual history; 19th century British literature. Publ: Structural dialectic of Dickens' Bleak House, Lit. Wiss. & Unterricht, 70; The Catcher in the rye, 70 & Sherwood Anderson's Tandy, 74, Mod. Fiction Stud. Add: Dept. of English, University of Southern California, Los Angeles, CA 90007.

LUKE, HUGH JAY, b. Kilgore, Tex, Feb. 26, 32; m. 54, 69; c. 2. ENGLISH LITERATURE. B.A, Univ. Tex, 56, M.A, 57, fel, 58-60, Ph.D, 63. Asst, Univ. Tex, 56-57; instr. ENG, San Antonio Col, 57-58; Agr. & Mech. Col. Tex, 60-62, asst. prof, 62-63; UNIV. NEBR, LINCOLN, 63-66, assoc. prof, 66-71, PROF, 71- Assoc. ed, Prairie Schooner, 68- MLA. Early 19th century English literature. Publ: Ed, Mary Shelley's The last man, 65 & A.C. Swinburne, William Blake: a critical essay, 70, Univ. Nebr; auth, The publishing of Byron's Don Juan, PMLA, 6/65; Sir William Lawrence: physician to Shelley and Mary, summer 65 & William Blake: pictor notus, summer 66, Papers Eng. Lang. & Lit. Add: 4640 Bryan Circle, Lincoln, NE 68506.

LUMIANSKY, ROBERT MAYER, b. Darlington, S.C, Dec. 27, 13; m. 46. ENGLISH. A.B, The Citadel, 33; A.M, Univ. S.C, 35, D.Hum, 65; Ph.D.(Eng), Univ. N.C, 42. Teacher high sch, S.C, 34-38; instr. Eng, Univ. N.C, 38-41; asst. prof, Tulane Univ, 46-47, assoc. prof, 47-49, prof, 49-63, head dept, 48-54, dean grad. sch, 54-63, provost, 60-63; PROF. ENG, Duke Univ, 63-65; UNIV. PA, 65-, AVALON FOUND. PROF. HUMANITIES, 66- Ford fac. fel, 51-52; chmn, Am. Counc. Learned Soc, 59-73, (pres, 73-); mem. counc, Nat. Endowment Humanities, 66-68; mem. bd, Cumulative Retirement Equities Fund, 67-; Guggenheim fel, 68-69. U.S.A, 42-45, Maj; Bronze Star medal; Croix de Guerre, France; Chevalier, Fr. Legion Honor. MLA; fel. Mediaeval Acad. Am; Ling. Soc. Am; Am. Dialect Soc; NCTE; Mod. Humanities Res. Asn; Int. Asn. Univ. Prof. Eng. Medieval English literature. Publ: Chaucer's Troilus and Criseyde in modern English, Univ. S.C; The Canterbury tales in modern English, Simon & Schuster, 48; Of sondry folk: the dramatic principle in the Canterbury tales, Univ. Tex, 55; co-auth, Malory's originality: critical essays concerning Le morte Darthur, Johns Hopkins, 64; co-ed, Critical approaches to six early English works: Beowulf through Paradise lost, Univ. Pa, 68; co-ed, The Chester Mystery Cycle, Oxford Univ, 74. Add: Dept. of English, University of Pennsylvania, Philadelphia, PA 19104.

LUMPKIN, BEN GRAY, b. Holly Springs, Miss, Dec. 25, 01. ENGLISH. A.B, Univ. Miss, 25, A.M, 35; Ph.D, Univ. N.C, 44. Instr. ENG, Univ. Miss, 35-37; Univ. N.C, 37-44; asst. prof, UNIV. COLO, BOULDER, 46-61; assoc. prof, 62-67, prof, 68-69, EMER. PROF, 69- Univ. Colo. Counc. res. grants, 59, 61. Cert. of Commendation, Am. Asn. State & Local Hist, 63, U.S.A, 44-46. Rocky Mountain Mod. Lang. Asn; West. Folklore Soc; Am. Folklore Soc. Folksongs of the United States; collection of Colorado folksongs. Publ: Words and sentence patterns, Univ. Colo. Bookstore, 59; ed, Colorado folksong bulletin, Vol. I, 61-62, Vol. II, 63 & Vol. III, 64, Univ. Colo; auth, Mr. Fox (Baughman type 955C): Cante fable, J. Am. Folklore, 1-3/68; Folksongs of the early 1830's, 6/69 & Folksongs from a Nebraska family, 3/72, South. Folklore Quart. Add: Rte. 3, Box 441, Clarksville, TN 37040.

LUNDQUIST, JAMES CARL, b. Duluth, Minn, Sept. 24, 41; m. 61; c. 3. ENGLISH. B.A, Westminster Col.(Mo), 64; NDEA fel, Univ. Fla, 64-67, Ph.D. (mod. lit), 67. ASSOC. PROF. MOD. ENG. & AM. LIT, ST. CLOUD STATE COL, 67- Ed, Sinclair Lewis Newslett, 68-; hon. dir, Sinclair Lewis Found, 72- MLA; Midwest Mod. Lang. Asn; NCTE. American literature of the 1920's; the American social and political novel. Publ: Guide to Sinclair Lewis, 70 & A Sinclair Lewis checklist, 70, Merrill; Sinclair Lewis, 73 & Theodore Dreiser, 74, Ungar; Moral of the avented descent: Poe's Pit and the pendulum, Poe Newslett, 4/69; World so wide and Sinclair Lewis' rewritten life, Sinclair Lewis Newslett, 70. Add: Dept. of English, St. Cloud State College, St. Cloud, MN 56301.

LUNZ, ELISABETH, b. Charleston, S.C, Apr. 16, 39. ENGLISH LITERATURE. B.A, Agnes Scott Col, 60; M.A, Duke Univ, 61; Ph.D.(Eng), Tulane Univ, 69. Teacher Eng. & Bible, Lausanne Sch, Memphis, Tenn, 61-64; instr. ENG, Dillard Univ, 64-67; asst. prof, Southwest. at Memphis, 67-72, ASSOC. PROF, 72-73; SAVANNAH STATE COL, 73-, res. & creative activities comt. summer grants, 69-72. Consult. & teacher, LeMoyne-Owen High Sch. Scholars Prog, summer 71. S.Atlantic Mod. Lang. Asn; Mediaeval Acad. Am; MLA. Medieval literature; communication skills; modern poetry. Publ: Count it all joy, Southwest. News, 71; Robert Lowell and Wallace Stevens on Sunday morning, Univ. Rev, 71; The Valley of Jehoshaphat in Piers Plowman, Tulane Stud. Eng, 72. Add: Dept. of English, Savannah State College, Savannah, GA 31404.

LURIA, MAXWELL SIDNEY, b. Trenton, N.J, Feb. 5, 32. ENGLISH, MEDIEVAL STUDIES. A.B, Rutgers Univ, 53; Univ. Bordeaux, 54-55; M.A, Univ. Pa, 55; Ph.D.(Eng), Princeton, 65. Instr. ENG, Univ. Md, 57-58; Rutgers Univ, 58-59; asst. prof, TEMPLE UNIV, 65-69, ASSOC. PROF, 69- U.S.A, 56-58. Mod. Humanities Res. Asn; MLA; Mediaeval Acad. Am. Middle and Old English literature; comparative medieval romance. Publ: The A-B-C-D of successful college writing, Kendall-Hunt, 71; ed, Middle English lyrics, Norton, 74; The storm-making spring and meaning of Chrêtien's Yvain, Stud. Philol, 67; Some literary implications of Hugh of St. Victor's Didascalicon, Proc. Fourth Int. Congr. Medieval Philos, 68. Add: Dept. of English, Temple University, Philadelphia, PA 19122.

LUSARDI, JAMES P, b. Morristown, N.J, Sept. 3, 31; m. 53; c. 2. ENGLISH. A.B, Lafayette Col, 55; M.A, Yale, 57, Ph.D.(Eng), 63. Instr. ENG, Williams Col, 58-61; asst. prof, Wesleyan Univ, 62-66; ASSOC. PROF, LAFAYETTE COL, 66- Am. Counc. Learned Soc. grant, 65; Wesleyan Univ. summer fel, 64; Lafayette Col. summer fel, 67; Am. Philos. Soc. grant, summer 68. U.S.A.F, 51-52, Sgt. Renaissance Soc. Am; MLA. English Renaissance; dramatic and non-dramatic literature, especially Thomas More, Shakespeare and Milton. Publ: Ed, Complete works of St. Thomas More, Yale. Add: Dept. of English, Lafayette College, Easton, PA 18042.

LUSCHEI, MARTIN LOUIS, b. Gordon, Nebr, Jan. 26, 30; m. 57; c. 4. AMERICAN LITERATURE & STUDIES. B.A, Nebr. Wesleyan Univ, 52; M.F.A, Univ. Iowa, 60; NDEA fel, Univ. N.Mex, 68-69, Ph.D.(Am. stud), 70. Instr. Eng, Univ. Tex, El Paso, 61-64; asst. cult. affairs off, U.S. Inform. Agency, Colombia, 64-67; ASSOC. PROF. ENG, CALIF. POLYTECH. STATE UNIV, SAN LUIS OBISPO, 69- MLA; Am. Studies Asn. Twentieth century American fiction; the novel. Publ: The sovereign wayfarer: Walker Percy's diagnosis of the malaise, La. State Univ, 72. Add: Dept. of English, California Polytechnic State University, San Luis Obispo, CA 93407.

LUSE, ELEANOR MERRIFIELD, b. Chicago, Ill, Dec. 31, 04. SPEECH. B.S, Northwest. Univ, 28, M.S, 34, Ph.D.(speech pathology), 48. Instr. SPEECH, Coe Col, 28-29; Boston Sch. Phys. Educ, 29-30; Wells Col, 30-34, asst. prof, 34-40, assoc. prof, 40-47; asst. prof, UNIV. VT, 47-50, assoc. prof, 50-54, PROF, 54- Pub. Health Serv. grant, 57-58; Vt. Cancer Soc. grant, 58-59. Fel. Am. Speech & Hearing Asn; Speech Commun. Asn; Int. Asn. Logopedics & Phoniatrics; Am. Cleft Palate Asn. Voice problems; cleft palate speech; laryngectomees. Publ: Something to do with speech, J. Educ, 50; The child who is slow to talk, Elem. Sch. J, 59; co-auth, The vocal approach in the correction of cleft palate speech, Folia Phoniatrica, 64. Add: Dept. of Communication & Theatre, University of Vermont, Burlington, VT 05401.

LUST, ANNETTE BERCUT, b. San Francisco, Calif, Feb. 22, 24; m. 54; c. 3. FRENCH, DRAMATIC ART. B.A, Pomona Col, 45; M.A, Univ. Calif, Berkeley, 47; D.Univ, Univ. Paris, 51. Lectr. FRENCH, Univ. Calif, Berkeley, 51-54; from instr. to ASSOC. PROF, DOMINICAN COL. SAN RAFAEL, 61- Lectr. French, Mills Col, summer 53; from instr. to assoc. prof, Univ. Calif. Exten, 61-; mem, Fulbright Grants Far West Screening comt, 73. Acad. Award for Teaching & Cult. Serv, Palmes Académiques, 72. French theatre, especially classical and modern and the history of mime. Publ: French present day mime, Theater World, London, 56; Etienne Decroux and the French School of Mime, Quart. J. Speech, 10/71. Add: Dept. of French, Dominican College of San Rafael, 1520 Grand Ave, San Rafael, CA 94901.

LUSTIG, IRMA S, b. Philadelphia, Pa, Aug. 31, 21; m. 46; c. 1. ENGLISH. A.B, Temple Univ, 46, teaching fel. & M.A, 49; summer, Univ. Birmingham, 50; Ph.D.(Eng), Univ. Pa, 63. Instr. Eng, Temple Univ, 48-49; asst. prof, West Chester State Col, 62-63; instr, Univ. Pa, 63-65, asst. prof, 65-68; ED. JOUR, YALE ED. PRIVATE PAPERS OF JAMES BOSWELL, 68- Univ. Pa. res. grant, summer 66; consult. fac. workshop curriculum develop, Gwynnedd-Mercy Col, 68; lectr, Bryn Mawr Col, 69-72; Am. Philos. Soc. res. grants, 71-72 & 72-73; Am. Counc. Learned Soc. grant-in-aid, 73-74; vis. lectr, Yale, 73-74; Nat. Endowment for Humanities res. grant, 73-74. MLA (chmn. sem. biog. & autobiog. eighteenth century, 74); Am. Soc. 18th Century Stud; Boswell Auchinleck Soc; Women's Caucus Mod. Lang. Asn. Eighteenth century British literature; especially Boswell and Johnson; biography and autobiography. Publ: Co-ed, Yale Editions Boswell Papers, Journals 1782-1785, (in prep) & Vol. II, 1786-1789, (in prep), McGraw-Hill; auth, Boswell at work: the animadversions on Mrs. Piozzi, Mod. Lang. Rev, 1/72; Boswell and the descendants of the venerable Abraham, Stud. Eng. Lit, summer 74; The manuscript as biography: Boswell's Letter to the people of Scotland 1785, Papers Bibliographical Soc. Am, 74; plus six others. Add: Yale Editions Private Papers of James Boswell, 331-A Yale University Library, New Haven, CT 06520.

LUSTY, BEVERLY L, Speech Education. See HENDRICKS, BEVERLY LUSTY.

LUTER, JOHN, b. Knoxville, Tenn, Jan. 17, 19; m. 48, 66; c. 1. JOURNALISM. B.A, St. Mary's Univ. San Antonio, 39; Time, Inc. fel, Sch. Advan. Int. Stud, Johns Hopkins Univ, 44. Writer, ed. & for. correspondent, Time & Life Mags, 44-56; CBS News, 57-58; Newsweek Mag, 58-61; lectr. jour. & coord. Advan. Int. Reporting Prog, COLUMBIA UNIV, 61-72, DIR. MARIA MOORS CABOT PRIZE PROG, 61- Adv. ed, Columbia Jour. Rev, 62-72; trustee, Overseas Press Club Found, 62-, chmn, 64-65; chmn. int. affairs comt, New York Protestant Counc, 67-70; mem. adv. screening comt. jour, Sr. Fulbright-Hays Prog, 68-70, chmn. adv. screening comt. commun, 70-73; mem, Press Ctr. Korea, 71-; mem, Ctr. Inter-Am. Relat; mem. fac, Bank St. Col. Educ, 73- Distinguished Alumnus Award, St. Mary's Univ. San Antonio, 62. Asn. Educ. in Jour; Overseas Press Club Am.(pres, 60-62); Asia Soc; Japan Soc. International journalism; international affairs; history. Add: Graduate School of Journalism, Columbia University, New York, NY 10027.

LUTHY, MELVIN JOSEPH, Linguistics, English Language. See Volume III, Foreign Languages, Linguistics & Philology.

LUTWACK, LEONARD, b. Hartford, Conn, Apr. 18, 17; m. 46; c. 1. ENGLISH. Winchester fel. & M.A, Wesleyan Univ, 40; Ph.D.(Eng), Ohio State Univ, 50. Instr. ENG, Univ. Maine, 46; asst, Ohio State Univ, 46-50; instr, UNIV. MD, COLLEGE PARK, 50-54, asst. prof, 55-61, assoc. prof, 62-70, PROF, 70- Fulbright lectr, Univ. Oslo, 54-55; NDEA Inst. Advan. Stud, Loyola Col.(Md), summer 68. U.S.A, 43-46. MLA. American literary criticism; stylistics; literary structure. Publ: Heroic fiction: the epic tradition and American novels of the twentieth century, South. Ill. Univ, 71; Mixed and uniform prose styles in the novel, J. Aesthet. & Art Criticism; Raintree Country and the epicising poet in American fiction, winter 72 & Melville's struggle with style, Forum; plus others. Add: Dept. of English, University of Maryland, College Park, MD 20742.

LUYBEN, HELEN LOUISE, b. Omaha, Nebr, July 26, 32. ENGLISH. B.A, Pa. State Univ, 54; M.A, Ind. Univ, 57; Ph.D.(Eng), Univ. Pa, 61. Instr. ENG, Purdue Univ, 61-62, asst. prof, 62-63; ST. JOHN'S UNIV.(N.Y), 64-68, ASSOC. PROF, 68- Adv. ed, Drama & Theatre, 64- MLA. Modern drama. Publ: James Bridie: clown and philosopher, Univ. Pa, 65; Bridie's last play, 2/63 & Bridie and the prodigal son story, 5/64, Mod. Drama; The dramatic method of James Bridie, Educ. Theatre J, 12/63. Add: Dept. of English, St. John's University, Jamaica, NY 11432.

LYDE, MARILYN JONES, b. Titusville, Pa, June 5, 28; m. 52; c. 1. ENGLISH. A.B, West. Col. Women, 50; A.M, Univ. Chicago, 51, Ph.D, 56. Asst, Univ. Fla, 51-52; instr. ENG, Ga. State Col, 55-57, asst. prof, 57-61; JACKSONVILLE UNIV, 61-64, assoc. prof, 64-74, PROF, 74- MLA; NCTE. American literature; Henry James. Publ: Edith Wharton, Univ. Okla, 59. Add: Div. of Humanities, Dept. of English, Jacksonville University, Jacksonville, FL 32211.

LYDENBERG, JOHN, b. White Plains, N.Y, Mar. 22, 13; m. 40; c. 2. ENGLISH, AMERICAN STUDIES. A.B, Oberlin Col, 34; Cambridge; Univ. Marburg, Ger; A.M, Harvard, 38, Ph.D, 46. Teaching fel. Am. civilization, Harvard, 39-40, Eng, 40-42; mem. fac. Am. hist, Bennington Col, 42-44; assoc. prof. ENG. & AM. STUD, HOBART & WILLIAM SMITH COLS, 46-54, PROF, 54- Vis. lectr, Scripps Col, 50-51; Univ. Minn, 53-54; Fulbright prof, Aix-en-Provence, Univ. Strasbourg, France, 60-61; vis. prof, Stanford Univ, 64-65; Fulbright lectr, Univ. Aix-Marseille, 68-69. War Prod. Bd, 44-45; For. Econ. Admin, 45-46. MLA; Am. Stud. Asn; AHA. American Civilization; American social literature; intellectual history; Publ: Ed, Dreiser, a collection of critical essays (Twentieth Century Views ser), Prentice-Hall, 71; auth, Henry Adams and Lincoln Steffens, S.Atlantic Quart; Nature myth in Faulkner's The bear, Am. Lit; Theodore Dreiser: Ishmael in the jungle, Monthly Rev. Add: Dept. of English, Hobart & William Smith Colleges, Geneva, NY 14456.

LYELL, FRANK HALLAM, b. Jackson, Miss, Aug. 7, 11. ENGLISH LITERATURE. A.B, Univ. Va, 30; A.M, Columbia Univ, 31; Ph.D, Princeton, 38. Instr, N.C. State Col, 35-36, 37-40, asst. prof, 40-42; ENG, UNIV. TEX, AUSTIN, 46-52, ASSOC. PROF, 52- U.S.A, 42-46. MLA. English novel; Shakespeare; modern drama. Publ: A study of the novels of John Galt, Princeton, 42. Add: Dept. of English, University of Texas at Austin, Austin, TX 78712.

LYERLY, RALPH HENRY, b. Granite Quarry, N.C, Apr. 15, 12. ENGLISH. A.B, Catawba Col, 32; A.M, Univ. N.C, 47. Teacher pub. schs, N.C, 32-42; ASSOC. PROF. ENG, LENOIR RHYNE COL, 47- U.S.A, 42-45. MLA; S.Atlantic Mod. Lang. Asn. Hawthorne's treatment of nature in his three American romances. Publ: Essential requirements for the college research paper, Lenoir Rhyne Col, 62, World Publ, 66, 67. Add: Dept. of English, Lenoir Rhyne College, Hickory, NC 28601.

LYFORD, JOSEPH PHILIP, b. Chicago, Ill, Aug. 4, 18; m. 63; c. 2. JOURNALISM. A.B, Harvard, 41. Reporter, Int. News Serv, 46-47; asst. ed, New Republic Mag, 47-48; admin. asst. to Gov. Chester Bowles, Conn, 49-50; exec. secy. to U.S. Senator William Benton, 50; dir. staff, Pub. Educ. Asn, N.Y, 53-55; staff mem, Ctr. Stud. Democratic Insts, Fund for Republic, 55-66; regents prof. JOUR, UNIV. CALIF, BERKELEY, 66-67, PROF, 67- Consult, Ctr. Stud. Democratic Insts, 66-; U.S. Senate Subcomt. Exec. Reorganization, 66-67; Pub. Broadcast Lab, 67-; pres, Fund for Peace, Inc, N.Y.C, 69-71, trustee, 69-; dir. alumnia counc, Phillips Acad, Mass, 71-; Ford Found. grant for stud. city of Berkeley, Calif, 73-74. Sidney Hillman Found. award for lit, 67. U.S.N, 41-46, U.S.N.R, Lt. Counc. For. Rels. Urban affairs; journalism. Publ: Candidate, McGraw, 59; The agreeable autocracies, Oceana, 61; The talk in Vandalia, 64 & The air tight cage, 66, Harper; Social science teachers and the difficult years, Bull. Am. Asn. Univ. Prof, 12/57; In defense of life, Fund for Peace, Inc, 1/70; The pacification of the press, Ctr. Mag, 3/73. Add: 216 Crestview Dr, Orinda, CA 94563.

LYLE, CORNELIUS RAILEY, II, b. Pittsburgh, Pa, June 24, 21; m. 46; c. 1. ENGLISH, JOURNALISM. B.A, Amherst Col, 43; M.Ed, Keene State Col, 61; Ph.D.(jour), Northwest. Univ, Evanston, 72. Reporter, Keene Evening Sentinel, N.H, 46-48, ed, 48-51, ed. writer, 51-55; managing ed, Freedom & Union Mag, D.C, 55-56; assoc. ed, Fla. Times Union, 56-57; ed, Orlando Sentinel, 57-58; publ, Monadnock Ledger, N.H, 58-59; instr. Eng, KEENE STATE COL, 60-65, ENG. & JOUR, 65-69, assoc. prof, 69-73, PROF, 73- Dir. develop. stud. grant, N.H. Col. & Univ. Counc, 73- A.U.S, 43-46, M/Sgt. Asn. Educ. in Jour; AAUP. New Hampshire journalistic history; Arthurian fact and archaeology. Publ: America discovers Vinland: scholarly controversy in the period 1830-1850, Swedish Pioneer Hist. Quart, 7/68. Add: Dept. of English, Keene State College, Main St, Keene, NH 03431.

LYLE, JACK, Communication Research. See 12th Edition, American Men & Women of Science, Social & Behavioral Sciences Section.

LYLES, ALBERT MARION, b. Kendrick, Fla, July 28, 26; m. 55; c. 2. ENGLISH. A.B, Union Col.(N.Y), 48; A.M, Univ. Pa, 49; Ph.D.(Eng), Rutgers Univ, 57. Instr. ENG, Univ. Mo, 49-51; fel, Rutgers Univ, 51-53; instr, Univ. Tenn, 53-56; asst. prof, Auburn Univ, 56-57; Univ. Tenn, 57-64, assoc. prof, 64-70; PROF, VA. COMMONWEALTH UNIV, 70- Am. Counc. Learned Soc. grant-in-aid, 66; Univ. Tenn. Grad. Sch. fac. grant, 68. U.S.A, 44-46. MLA; Am. Soc. 18th Century Stud. Eighteenth century English religious satire; Johnson and Boswell; Congreve bibliography. Publ: Methodism mocked, Epworth, London, 60; co-ed, John C. Hodges collection of William Congreve, Univ. Tenn. Libr, 70; Historical perspective in Gray's Eton College ode, Tenn. Stud. Lit, 64; Pamela's trials, CLA J, 3/65. Add: Dept. of English, Virginia Commonwealth University, Richmond, VA 23284.

LYNCH, BARBARA FURBER, b. Lubbock, Tex, Dec. 5, 40. ENGLISH RENAISSANCE LITERATURE. B.A, Univ. Tex, 63; M.A, Tex. Tech Univ, 66; Ph.D.(Eng), Univ. Pa, 71. Instr. ENG, E.Tex. State Univ, 66-68; ASST. PROF, MEMPHIS STATE UNIV, 71- Milton and Shakespeare studies. Publ: Contrib, Mod. Humanities Res. Asn. Annual Bibliog, 73. Add: Dept. of English, Memphis State University, Memphis, TN 38111.

LYNCH, JAMES JOSEPH, b. New York, N.Y, Sept. 12, 16; m. 42; c. 7. ENGLISH. B.S, Fordham Univ, 38; A.M, Columbia Univ, 41; Ph.D, N.Y. Univ, 61. Instr. ENG, Sampson Col, 46-48; Butler Univ, 48-51; teaching fel, Cornell Univ, 51-52; teacher high schs, Sherburne & Pelham, N.Y, 52-62; PROF, STATE UNIV. N.Y. COL. BROCKPORT, 62- Lect. bilingualism, Nat. Security Agency. Intel.C, U.S.A, 41-46, Mil. Intel, Res, 46-, Lt. Col. Nineteenth century Victorian literature; literature and language; sociolinguistics. Publ: The right to read—and not to read, Mod. Age, winter 65; Disorder, power, and the student, winter 67 & The curse of Babel, autumn 70, Va. Quart. Rev; plus others. Add: Dept. of English, State University of New York College at Brockport, Brockport, NY 14420.

LYNCH, JAMES JOSEPH, b. Brooklyn, N.Y, May 20, 44; m. 66; c. 3. ENGLISH RENAISSANCE LITERATURE. B.A, L.I. Univ, 65; M.A, Univ. Calif, Davis, 68, Ph.D.(Renaissance lit), 72. Teaching asst. Eng. comp, Univ. Calif, Davis, 65-68, assoc. ENG. LIT, 69-70, ASST. PROF, ORE. STATE UNIV, 70- MLA; Shakespeare Soc. Am; Philol. Asn. Pac. Coast. Shakespearean drama; theory of tragedy. Add: Dept. of English, Moreland Hall, Oregon State University, Corvallis, OR 97331.

LYNCH, ROBERT EDWARD, b. Brooklyn, N.Y, Dec. 17, 40; m. 65; c. 2. ENGLISH & AMERICAN LITERATURE. A.B, St. Francis Col.(N.Y), 62; M.A, N.Y. Univ, 63, Ph.D.(Eng), 71. Lectr. Eng, Brooklyn Col, 64-67; instr. HUMANITIES, NEWARK COL. ENG, 67-72, ASST. PROF, 72- MLA; Shakespeare Asn. Am. Elizabethan drama; historical literature. Publ: Contrib, The reader's encyclopedia of Shakespeare, 66 & The reader's encyclopedia of world drama, 69, Crowell; contrib, Contemporary novelists of the English language, St. James, London, 72. Add: Dept. of Humanities, Newark College of Engineering, Newark, NJ 07102.

LYNCH, VERNON EUGENE, b. Leona, Tex, June 26, 16; m. 42; c. 2. ENGLISH. B.A, Sam Houston State Col, 36; M.A, Univ. Tex, 39, Ph.D.(Eng), 51. Instr. ENG, Univ. Tex, 46-51; chmn. dept, Del Mar Col, 51-59, prof, 60-63; assoc. prof, Northeast La. State Col, 59-60; SOUTHWEST TEX. STATE UNIV, 63-65, PROF, 65- U.S.A.A.F, 42-45, S/Sgt. S.Cent. Mod. Lang. Asn; AAUP; NCTE. Modern British and American drama; materials and methods of teaching English; American literature. Publ: George Bernard Shaw and the comic, Univ. Tex. Microfilm, 58; ed, Selected workshop papers, San Felipe, Vols. I & II, 64 & 66; auth, 1879 in The echo: a year at Fort Griffin of the Texas frontier, W.Tex. Hist. Asn. Yearbk, 10/65. Add: Dept. of English, Southwest Texas State University, San Marcos, TX 78666.

LYNCH, WILLIAM JAMES, b. Philadelphia, Pa, June 28, 30; m. 54; c. 5. AMERICAN LITERATURE. A.B, St. Joseph's Col.(Pa), 52; M.A, Boston Col, 58; Ph.D.(Eng), Univ. Pa, 66. Asst. ENG, Boston Col, 52-53; instr, St. Joseph's Col.(Pa), 55-60, asst. prof, 60-66, assoc. prof, 66-68, chmn. dept, 67-68; assoc. prof, MONTGOMERY COUNTY COMMUNITY COL, 68-71, PROF, 71, chmn. dept, 68-74. MLA; NCTE. American drama; the American novel. Add: 117 W. Mt. Airy Ave, Philadelphia, PA 19119.

LYNEN, JOHN FAIRBANKS, b. Ridgewood, N.J, Mar. 2, 24. ENGLISH. B.A, Amherst Col, 48; M.A, Yale, 49, Ph.D, 54. Instr. Eng, Univ. Del, 49-50; Wesleyan Univ, 52-54; Am. lit, Univ. Dijon, 54-55; ENG, Yale, 55-59; assoc. prof, Univ. Ill, 59-67, PROF, 67-68; UNIV. COL, UNIV. TORONTO, 68- Guggenheim fel, 62-63; Can. Counc. fel, 73-74. Modern and American literature. Publ: The pastoral art of Robert Frost, 60 & The design of the present: essays on time and form in American literature, 69, Yale Univ; The poet's meaning and the poem's world, South. Rev, autumn 66; Three uses of the present, Col. Eng, 11/66. Add: F305 University College, University of Toronto, Toronto, Ont. M5S 1A1, Can.

LYNGSTAD, SVERRE, b. Norway, Apr. 30, 22; m. 53; c. 1. ENGLISH. B.A. (Eng), Univ. Oslo, Norway, 43, B.A.(hist), 46; M.A, Univ. Wash, 49; Ph.D. (Eng), N.Y. Univ, 60. Asst. Eng. compos, N.Y. Univ, 49-53; lectr. Eng. compos. & lit, City Col. New York, 54-55; instr. ENG, Hofstra Col, 55-60; Queens Col.(N.Y), 60-62; asst. prof, NEWARK COL. ENG, 62-65, assoc. prof, 65-68, PROF, 68- Ed. consult. Scand. lit, Grove Press, N.Y, 63-68. MLA; Am. Comp. Lit. Asn; Soc. Advan. Scand. Stud. The novel, especially British, Scandinavian and Russian; time in literature; translation. Publ: Encyclopedia of poetry and poetics, Princeton; transl, Sven Hassel's Comrades of war, Fawcett Publ, 63; co-transl, Lev Tolstoy's Childhood, boyhood, and youth, Washington Sq, 68; co-auth, Ivan Goncharov, Twayne, 71; plus others. Add: Dept. of Humanities, Newark College of Engineering, 323 High St, Newark, NJ 07102.

LYNN, KLONDA, b. Linton, N.Dak, June 21, 98. SPEECH, ENGLISH. B.A, Univ. N.Dak, 20; B.L.I, Emerson Col. Oratory, 22; M.A, Boston Univ, 25; Ph.D, La. State Univ, 40. Instr. SPEECH, Emerson Col. Oratory, 22-27; asst. prof, North. Ariz. Univ, 28-45; assoc. prof, UNIV. ARIZ, 45-53, head dept, 53-64, prof, 64-73, EMER. PROF, 73- Speech Asn. Am; Am. Speech & Hearing Asn. Bilingualism. Publ: Bilingualism in Arizona, Speech Asn. Am, 43. Add: 2001 E. Copper St, Tucson, AZ 85719.

LYON, EARL DeWITT, b. Los Angeles, Calif, Dec. 5, 10. ENGLISH. A.B, Univ. Calif, Los Angeles, 32; A.M, Univ. Calif, 33, Ph.D, 37. Instr. ENG, Univ. Utah, 37-38; from asst. prof. to PROF, CALIF. STATE UNIV, FRESNO, 38-, chmn. dept, 56-63, head humanities div, 56-60. U.S.A.A.F, 42-46, Maj. Add: Dept. of English, California State University, Fresno, CA 93726.

LYON, MELVIN ERNEST, b. Escondido, Calif, Dec. 24, 27; m. 53; c. 4. ENGLISH. A.B, Univ. Calif, Berkeley, 49; M.A, Univ. Calif, Los Angeles, 54; Ph.D, Univ. Wis, 60. Instr. Am. lit, Univ. N.Dak, 58-59; asst. prof, 59-61; George Washington Univ, 61-64; UNIV. NEBR, LINCOLN, 64-67, assoc. prof, 67-72, PROF. ENG, 72- Teaching fel, Univ. Wis, 55-59. U.S.A, 50-52. Am. Stud. Asn; MLA. American non-fiction prose; autobiography;

Edward Dahlberg. Publ: Symbol and idea in Henry Adams, Univ. Nebr, 70; The centrality of Hart Crane's The broken tower, 72, Univ. Nebr; Walden Pond as a symbol, PMLA, 5/68. Add: Dept. of English, University of Nebraska, Lincoln, NE 68508.

LYON, RICHARD COLTON, b. Los Angeles, Calif, June 20, 26; m. 52; c. 4. ENGLISH, AMERICAN STUDIES. B.A, Univ. Tex, 51; B.A, Cambridge, 53, M.A, 58; M.A, Univ. Conn, 58; Ph.D.(Am. stud), Univ. Minn, 64. Asst. prof, Eng, Univ. N.C, Chapel Hill, 62-66, assoc. prof, 66-68; PROF. ENG. & AM. STUD, HAMPSHIRE COL, 68-, dean col, 68-72. Univ. N.C. Fac. Res. Counc. grant, 65; consult, N.C. Dept. Pub. Instr, 66-67; Duke Univ-Univ. N.C. Coop. Humanities Prog. scholar, 67; contrib. ed, Mass. Rev. 68-U.S.N, 44-46. MLA; Am. Stud. Asn. American literature of the 19th century; American cultural history, 1865-1920. Publ: Santayana on America, Harcourt, 68; Santayana and the real thing, Shenandoah, spring 66; Normal madness, South. J. Philos, summer 72. Add: Dept. of English, Hampshire College, West St, Amherst, MA 01002.

LYONS, CHARLES R, b. Glendale, Calif, Apr. 29, 33; m. 56; c. 2. DRAMATIC LITERATURE & CRITICISM. A.B, Stanford Univ, 55, A.M, 56, Ph.D. (drama), 64. Instr. drama & speech, Principia Col, 60-64, asst. prof, 64-67, assoc. prof, 67-68, chmn. dept. drama, 64-68; assoc. prof. dramatic arts, Univ. Calif, Berkeley, 68-72, prof. dramatic arts & assoc. dean, Col. Lett. & Sci, 72-73; PROF. DRAMA & COMP. LIT. & CHMN. DEPT. DRAMA, STANFORD UNIV, 73- Summers, participant, Shakespeare Inst, 60, instr. speech, Stanford Univ, 64, participant, NEA-Nat. Training Labs. Summer Training Lab, Maine, 66, assoc. prof. Eng. & comp. lit, Wash. Univ, 67; Nat. Found. Arts & Humanities younger scholar award, 68-69. Samuel Stark Theatre Award, 64. U.S.N.R, 56-60, Lt. MLA; Midwest Mod. Lang. Asn; Rocky Mountain Mod. Lang. Asn; Renaissance Soc.Am; Cent. Renaissance Conf; Am. Theatre Asn. Critical theory; dramatic structure; the dramaturgy of Pirandello. Publ: Bertolt Brecht: the despair and the polemic, 68 & Henrik Ibsen, 72, South. Ill. Univ; Shakespeare and the ambiguity of love's triumph, Mouton, The Hague, 69; Congreve's Miracle of love, criticism, fall 64; some variations of Kindermord as dramatic archetype, Comp. Drama, 1/66; Ibsen's Master builder as drama of self, Scand. Stud, 11/67. Add: Dept. of Drama, Memorial Hall, Stanford University, Stanford, CA 94305.

LYONS, CLIFFORD PIERSON, b. Chicago, Ill, Oct. 5, 04; m. 28. ENGLISH LITERATURE. A.B, Cornell Col, 25, Litt.D, 53; summers, Univ. Chicago, 26, 27, 28; Ph.D, Johns Hopkins Univ, 32. Instr, sec. schs, Berea Col, 25-28; Lincoln Mem. Univ, 28-29; Johns Hopkins Univ, 30-36; prof. ENG. & head dept, Univ. Fla, 36-46; prof, UNIV. N.C, CHAPEL HILL, 46-61, KENAN PROF, 61-, head dept, 46-52, dean col. arts & sci, 51-54, secy. of fac, 66-69. Assoc. ed, Eng. Lit. Hist, 34-50; mem. Eng. Lit. Selection Comt, Fulbright Fund, 54-57. U.S.N.R, 42-45, Lt. Comdr. MLA.(exec. counc, 53-56); Southeast. Renaissance Conf.(pres, 64); Renaissance Soc. Am; S.Atlantic Mod. Lang. Asn.(pres, 39); Shakespeare Asn. Am. Renaissance; Shakespeare; criticism. Publ: It appears so by the story; notes on narrative-thematic emphasis in Shakespeare, Shakespeare Quart, summer 58; Stage images in Shakespeare's plays, In: Essays on Shakespeare and Elizabethan drama in honor of Hardin Craig, Univ. Mo, 62; The trysting scenes in Troilus and Cressida, In: Shakespearean essays, Tenn. Stud. in Lit, Knoxville, 64; and others. Add: Dept. of English, University of North Carolina, Chapel Hill, NC 27514.

LYONS, EUGENE, b. Elizabeth, N.J, Sept. 20, 43; c. m. 67; c. 2. ENGLISH & AMERICAN LITERATURE. B.A, Rutgers Univ, New Brunswick, 65; Ford Found. fel. & M.A, Univ. Va, 66, Ph.D.(Eng), 69. Instr. ENG, Univ. Va, 68-69; asst. prof, Univ. Mass, 69-72; UNIV. ARK, LITTLE ROCK, 72-74, ASSOC. PROF, 74- Bk. reviewer, Ark. Gazette; consult. lit, Nat. Endowment Arts. AAUP. Contemporary American and English fiction; English colonial fiction. Publ: Co-ed, An interview with Lawrence Durrell, Shenandoah, winter 71; auth, John Updike: the beginning and the end, Critique, winter 72; Walker Percy: the sovereign voyager, Southwest Rev, spring 74. Add: Dept. of English, University of Arkansas, Little Rock, AR 72207.

LYONS, JOHN O, b. Detroit, Mich, Sept. 3, 27; m. 56; c. 5. ENGLISH. A.B, Kenyon Col, 51; M.S, in L.S, Columbia Univ, 52; M.A, Univ. Fla, 54, Ph.D, 60. Humanities librn, Univ. Fla, 55-56; instr. ENG, Dartmouth Col, 57-58; Bowdoin Col, 58-60; asst. prof, UNIV. WIS-MADISON, 60-64, ASSOC. PROF, 64- Fulbright prof, Univ. Baghdad, 64-65 & Univ. Tehran, 70-72. U.S. Merchant Marine, 45-46, Ens; U.S.A, 46-47. MLA. Contemporary American fiction; James Joyce; Milton and the metaphysical poets. Publ: The college novel in America, 62, South. Ill. Univ; co-auth, Studying poetry, Harper, 65; auth, The man in the macintosh, In: A James Joyce miscellany, 2nd ser, South. Ill. Univ, 59; James Joyce and Chaucer's Prioress, Eng. Lang. Notes, 64; Pale fire and the fine art of annotation, Wis. Stud. Contemporary Lit, 67. Add: Dept. of English, White Hall, University of Wisconsin-Madison, Madison, WI 53706.

LYONS, KATHLEEN VIRGINIA, b. Louisville, Ky, Aug. 14, 32. ENGLISH LITERATURE. A.B, Nazareth Col, 54; M.A, Fordham Univ, 56, Ph.D, 70. Asst. prof. ENG, Nazareth Col, 58-60; Univ. Colo, 60-61; ASSOC. PROF, BELLARMINE COL.(KY), 63- MLA. Elizabethan drama; Renaissance literature of England; 20th century literature in English. Add: Dept. of English, Bellarmine College, 2000 Norris Pl, Louisville, KY 40205.

LYONS, NATHAN R, b. Brooklyn, N.Y, June 5, 32; m. 57; c. 4. ENGLISH. B.S,Univ. Pa, 53; A.M, Univ. Mich, 59, Ph.D.(Eng), 63. Teaching fel. ENG, Univ. Mich, 59-61; instr. HUNTER COL, 61-66, asst. prof, 66-72, ASSOC. PROF, 73- Exec. ed, Crown Publ, Inc, 64-72. U.S.A, 53-55. American literature; the seventeenth century. Publ: Ed, Jones Very: selected poems, Rutgers Univ, 66 & Fisherman's bounty, Crown, 69; auth, The seasonable angler, Funk & Wagnalls, 69; Kafka and Poe—and Hope, Minn. Rev, 65; Chrétien's Lancelot and Percival, Univ. Rev, 65; The figure of William Ellery Channing, 68 & Thomas Nashe: the antic stylist, 72, Mich. Quart. Add: Dept. of English, Hunter College, 695 Park Ave, New York, NY 10021.

LYONS, RICHARD EUGENE, b. Detroit, Mich, June 9, 20; m. 42; c. 2. ENGLISH, AMERICAN STUDIES. B.A, Miami Univ, 42, M.A, 47; Ind. Univ, 48-50; Univ. Minn, 59-60. Instr. ENG, Miami Univ, 47-48; N.DAK. STATE UNIV, 50-57, asst. prof, 57-65, assoc. prof, 65-74, PROF, 74- dir, Poetry North, N.Dak. State Univ, 66-69. Col. Eng. Asn; Am. Stud. Asn. Sociology of art; cultural history; creative writing. Publ: Men and tin kettles, Swallow, 56; One squeaking straw, 58, Paintings in taxicabs, 65, Above time, 66 & ed, Poetry north, 70, N.Dak. Inst. Regional Stud; Rune Boc, Rourke Art Gallery, 68; Walking wide, 70 & Public journal, 1941-1971, 72, Scopcraeft; November 4, 1956, In: From the Hungarian Revolution, Cornell Univ, 66; Garden of the (dead) gods, In: Enough of dying, Dell, 72; plus others. Add: 1314 Tenth St. N, Fargo, ND 58102.

LYTLE, ANDREW (NELSON), b. Murfreesboro, Tenn, Dec. 26, 02; m. 38; c. 3. ENGLISH. B.A, Vanderbilt Univ, 25; Yale, 27-29; Guggenheim fel, 41-42; Kenyon fel, 56; hon. Litt.D, Kenyon Col, 65, Univ. Fla, 70 & Univ. of the South, 73. Prof. hist, Southwest. Col, 36; Am. & Europ. hist, Univ. of the South, 42-43, ed, Sewanee Rev, 43; prof. creative writing, State Univ. Iowa, 47, 48; lectr. Eng, Univ. Fla, 48-61; ed, Sewanee Rev. & Prof. Eng, Univ. of the South, 61-73; RETIRED. Guggenheim fel, 60-61; Nat. Found. Arts & Lett. fel, 66-67. Writing and criticism of fiction. Publ: Bedford Forrest and his critter company, Minton, Balch & Co, rev. ed, Obolensky, 60; The long night & At the moon's inn, Bobbs; The velvet horn, 57 & Novel, novella and four stories, 58, Obolensky; The hero with the private parts, La. State Univ, 66; A wake for the living, Sewanee Rev, 67; plus others. Add: Monteagle, TN 37356.

LYTTLE, DAVID JANES, b. Brooklyn, N.Y, Mar. 9, 24; m. 46; c. 2. ENGLISH, AMERICAN LITERATURE. B.A, Earlham Col, 49; M.A, Claremont Grad. Sch, 50; M.F.A, Univ. Iowa, 55; Ph.D.(Am. lit), Pa. State Univ, 65. Instr. Eng, W.Va. Univ, 55-60; asst. prof, Bloomsburg State Col, 60-61; Univ. Cincinnati, 64-66; AM. LIT, SYRACUSE UNIV, 66-74, ASSOC. PROF, 74- Danforth fel, 65-66. MLA; AAUP. Colonial and 19th century American literature; writing of poetry. Publ: The case against Carwin, Nineteenth-Century Fiction, winter 71; Giovanni! My poor Giovanni!, Stud. Short Fiction, spring 72; Jonathan Edwards on personal identity, Early Am. Lit, fall 72. Add: Dept. of English, 206 C Hall of Languages, Syracuse University, Syracuse, NY 13210.

M

MABEY, MARION K, b. New York, N.Y, July 22, 03; wid. VICTORIAN ENGLISH. B.A, Vassar Col, 24; M.A, Radcliffe Col, 29; Ph.D, Yale, 38. Instr. Eng. & Latin, South Orange High Sch, N.J, 24-28; Eng, N.Y. State Col. Teachers, Albany, 29-34, asst. prof, 34-39; prof. & acad. dean, Lake Erie Col, 39-40; asst. prof, Fairleigh Dickinson Col, 53-55; instr. ENG, Univ. Conn, 46-47, 55-62; asst. prof, WELLS COL, 62-64, assoc. prof, 64-67, prof, 67-70, EMER. PROF, 70- Mem. staff, South. Conn. State Col, 70-73. Eng. Inst; MLA. Victorian literature, especially John Sterling, Carlyle and Meredith. Add: 76 Judson Ave, Woodbury, CT 06798.

McADAMS, JAMES R, b. Fall River, Mass, Aug. 17, 31; m. 62. ENGLISH. A.B, Colgate Univ, 53; A.M, N.Y. Univ, 60, Ph.D.(Eng), 66. Lectr. Eng, City Col. New York, 62-63; instr. Eng. & world lit, Manhattan Col, 64-65; 66-67; ASST. PROF. ENG, PA. STATE UNIV, UNIVERSITY PARK, 67- MLA. Milton; seventeenth century verse and prose (non-dramatic); Renaissance European literature. Publ: Asst. ed. & contrib, Seventeenth Century News; auth, The pattern of temptation in Paradise regained, Milton Stud, 72. Add: Dept. of English, Pennsylvania State University, University Park, PA 16802.

McAFEE, JAMES THOMAS, b. May 13, 38; U.S. citizen. CREATIVE WRITING, MODERN LITERATURE. A.B, Univ. Mo-Columbia, 49, M.A, 50, Instr. ENG, UNIV. MO-COLUMBIA, 45-49, asst. prof, 60-64, assoc. prof, 64-72, PROF, 72- Ed, Contempora Mag. Authors League Am; Authors Guild. Publ: Poems and stories, 60 & I'll be home late tonight, 67, Univ. Mo; Rover Youngblood, Richard Baron, 69; contrib, Four Poets, Cent. Col. Iowa, 67; Lady of the World (story), Am. Lit. Anthology, 69; Four poems, Sou'wester, winter 69. Add: Dept. of English 217 A & S Bldg, University of Missouri-Columbia, Columbia, MO 65201.

McALEER, EDWARD CORNELIUS, b. Haverhill, Mass, Apr. 18, 11. ENGLISH LITERATURE. A.B, Boston Col, 31; A.M, Harvard, 32; fel, Univ. Tenn, 48-50, Ph.D, 50. Instr, Athens Col, Greece, 37-40; Berea Col, 41-42; R.I. State Col, 46-47; Univ. Tenn, 47-48; Fulbright fel, Univ. Rome, 50-51; Am. Counc. Learned Soc. fel, 51-52; asst. prof. ENG, Univ. Va, 52-58; assoc. prof, La. State Univ, 58-59; HUNTER COL, 59-64, PROF, 64-, chmn. dept, 61-66. Pforzheimer Found. grant-in-aid, 63. U.S.N.R, 42-46, Lt. MLA; NCTE; Col. Eng. Asn. Nineteenth century English writers in Italy; 19th and 20th century English literature. Publ: Dearest Isa: Robert Browning's letters to Isabella Blagden, Univ. Tex; The sensitive plant: a life of Lady Mount Cashell, Univ. N.C; Learned lady: letters from Robert Browning to Mrs. Thomas FitzGerald, Harvard, 66. Add: Dept. of English, Hunter College, 695 Park Ave, New York, NY 10021.

McALEER, JOHN JOSEPH, b. Cambridge, Mass, Aug. 29, 23; m. 57; c. 6. ENGLISH. A.B, Boston Col, 47, M.A, 49; fel, Harvard Prize Found, 52-53; Dexter traveling fel, Europe, 54; Ph.D, Harvard, 55. Teaching fel, Boston Col, 47-48, instr, 48-50; teaching fel, Harvard, 53-55; instr, BOSTON COL, 55-56, asst. prof, 56-61, assoc. prof. ENG. LIT, 61-65, PROF. 65- Res. fel, Boston Col, 63, fac. fel, 64-65; assoc. ed, Shakespeare Newslett. Best Piece of Literary Criticism Award, Nat. Cath. Press Asn, 69. U.S.A, 43-46. MLA; NCTE; Thoreau Soc; Emerson Soc; Am. Transcendental Soc. Shakespeare; American literature; balladry. Publ: Songs and ballads loyal to the Hanoverian succession, Univ. Calif, 62; Theodore Dreiser: an introduction and interpretation, Holt, 68; ed, Artist and citizen Thoreau, Am. Transcendental Soc, 71; co-ed, Dreiser's Notes on life, Univ. Ala, 73; auth, Biblical analogy in the Leatherstocking tales, nineteenth Century Fiction,

12/62; Ballads on the Spanish Armada, Tex. Stud. Lit. & Lang, 63; Thoreau's epic Cape Cod, Thought, 68. Add: 121 Follen Rd, Lexington, MA 02173.

McALEXANDER, HUBERT HORTON, JR, b. Holly Springs, Miss, Oct. 27, 39; m. 70. ENGLISH & AMERICAN LITERATURE. B.A, Univ. Miss, 61, M.A, 66; Ph.D, Univ. Wis-Madison, 73. Instr. ENG, Univ. Miss, 66-69; ASST. PROF, TEX. A&M UNIV, 73- MLA; S.Cent. Mod. Lang. Asn. Twentieth century English and American literature; William Faulkner. Publ: William Faulkner—the young poet in Stark Young's The torches flare, Am. Lit, 1/72. Add: Dept. of English, Texas A&M University, College Station, TX 77843.

McALISTER, FLOYD L, b. Cash, Ark, Aug. 11, 28; m. 56; c. 2. ENGLISH LITERATURE. B.S, Univ. Ark, 48, M.A, 54; Ph.D, Univ. Minn, 58. Instr. ENG, Tulane Univ, 58-61; asst. prof, CALIF. STATE UNIV, SACRAMENTO, 61-66, assoc. prof, 66-71, PROF, 71- Chem.C, U.S.A. Milton; 17th century English literature. Add: Dept. of English, California State University, Sacramento, Sacramento, CA 95819.

McALLASTER, ELVA ARLENE, b. Marienthal, Kans, Aug. 30, 22. ENGLISH. A.B, Greenville Col, 44; A.M, Univ. Ill, 45, fel, 46-48, Ph.D, 48; Univ. London, Eng, 48. Teacher, pub. schs, Kans, 40-42; asst. ENG, Univ. Ill, 45-46; assoc. prof, Seattle Pac. Col, 48-50; PROF. & HEAD DEPT, 50-56; GREENVILLE COL, 56- Poet-in-residence, Westmont Col, 71-72. MLA; NCTE; Conf. Christianity & Lit.(secy, 56-58, dir, 72-75); Milton Soc. Am; Poetry Soc, Eng; Wilderness Soc. Contemporary poetry; 19th century English literature; the Oxford movement and Victorian poetry. Publ: My heart hears Heaven's reveille; Echoes from intercession, 66 & Here and now, 68, Moody Press; Strettam, Zondervan, 72; plus many poems. Add: Dept. of English, Greenville College, Greenville, IL 62246.

MacANDREW, ELIZABETH, b. Tonbridge, Eng, May 21, 24; U.S. citizen. ENGLISH LITERATURE. B.S, Columbia Univ, 66, Woodrow Wilson fel, 66-67, M.A, 67, univ. fel, 67-68, Ph.D.(Eng), 70. Asst. prof. ENG. LIT, CLEVELAND STATE UNIV, 70-73, ASSOC. PROF, 73- MLA; Am. Soc. 18th Century Stud. The novel; the Gothic novel; 18th century English literature. Publ: Fielding's use of names in Joseph Andrews, Names, 16: 362-370; A splacknuck and a dung-beetle: realism and probability in Swift and Kafka, Col. Eng, 70. Add: Dept. of English, Cleveland State University, Cleveland, OH 44115.

MACARE, HELEN HANKS, b. Monroe, Utah, Sept. 27, 23; m. 54; c. 1. ENGLISH & AMERICAN LITERATURE. B.A, Univ. Utah, 49, M.A, 55; Univ. Kans, 53-54; Ph.D, Univ. Calif, Los Angeles, 61. Asst. prof. ENG, SAN JOSE STATE UNIV, 60-70, ASSOC. PROF, 70-, fac. res. grant, 61-63. Critical re-evaluation of Dickens' novels; study of the Mormon hymnal, 1835 to the present; hymns in special collections. Add: 500 Magnolia Lane, Santa Clara, CA 95051.

McARTHUR, HERBERT CHRISTIAN, b. Atlanta, Ga, Sept. 25, 24; m. 44; c. 4. ENGLISH. B.A, Harvard, 47, Ph.D.(Eng), 53. Instr. ENG, Univ. Vt, 50-54, asst. prof, 54-59, assoc. prof, 59-65, prof. Eng. & assoc. dean arts & sci, 65-70; prog. off, Educ. & Pub. Prog, Nat. Endowment for Humanities, 68-69, dir. educ. prog, 69-72; ASST. V.CHANCELLOR ACAD. PROG, STATE UNIV. N.Y, 73- U.S.A.R, 42-63, Lt. Col. Publ: Romeo's loquacious friend, Shakespeare Quart, 59; Tragic and comic modes, Criticism, 61; In search of the Indian novel, Mass. Rev, 61. Add: Office of the Vice Chancellor for Academic Programs, State University of New York, Albany, NY 12210.

McAULEY, JAMES JOHN, b. Dublin, Ireland, Jan. 8, 36; m. 68; c. 2. MODERN POETRY, POETICS. B.A, Nat. Univ. Ireland, 62; M.F.A, Univ. Ark, 71. Asst. prof. ENG, Lycoming Col, 68-70; EAST. WASH. STATE COL, 70-73, ASSOC. PROF, 73- Lectr, Queen's Univ. Belfast, spring 66; Munic. Gallery Mod. Art, Dublin, 64-65; Nat. Endowment for Arts fel. creative writing, 72-73. Col. Eng. Asn. Contemporary American poetry and poetics; influence of the bardic system on contemporary Irish poetry. Publ: Observations, Mt. Salus, 60; A new address, 65 & Draft balance sheet, 70, Dolmen/Oxford; co-ed, Poetry Ireland (vols. 1-6), Dolmen, 63-66; contrib, Love poems of the Irish, Mercier, 67 & Penquin book of Irish verse, Penguin, 70; plus others. Add: Dept. of English, Eastern Washington State College, Cheney, WA 99004.

MACAULEY, ROBIE MAYHEW, b. Grand Rapids, Mich, May 31, 19; m. 48; c. 1. ENGLISH. A.B, Kenyon Col, 41; M.F.A, State Univ. Iowa, 50. Instr. Eng, Bard Col, 46-47; State Univ. Iowa, 47-50; asst. prof, Woman's Col, Univ. N.C, 50-53; assoc. prof, Kenyon Col, 59-61, prof, 61-66, ed, Kenyon Rev, 59-66; VIS. PROF. ENG. UNIV. ILL, CHICAGO CIRCLE, 70- Kenyon Rev. & Rockefeller Found. fel, 58; U.S. deleg, Congr. Cult. Freedom Gen. Assembly, Berlin, 60; mem. exec. comt, Am. Ctr. Int. PEN, 60-63; U.S. Dept. State lectr, Australia, 62; Fulbright res fel, Univ. London, 64-65; Guggenheim fel, 64-65. Benjamin Franklin Mag. Award, 57. U.S.A, 42-46. Asn. Lit. Mag. Am. The modern novel. Publ: The disguises of love, Random, 52; The end of pity, McDowell, Obolensky, 57; co-auth, The techniques of fiction, Harper, 64; co-ed, America and its discontents, Xerox Col, 71. Add: 1323 N. Sandburg Terrace, Chicago, IL 60610.

McAVOY, WILLIAM CHARLES, b. Cleveland, Ohio, Jan. 28, 21; m. 45; c. 9. ENGLISH. A.B, John Carroll Univ, 46; A.M, Univ. Ill, 48; Ph.D.(Eng), 52. Asst. prof. ENG, ST. LOUIS UNIV, 52-56, assoc. prof, 56-63, PROF, 63-, chmn. dept, 70-73. Ed, Year's work in Renaissance textual studies, Manuscripta, 57- U.S.A, 42-45. MLA; Shakespeare Soc. Am; Cent. Renaissance Soc. Am. Shakespeare; English Renaissance. Publ: Co-auth, American college handbook, Am. Bk, 60; ed, The new variorum Shakespeare: Twelfth night, MLA, 70; auth, Dramatic tragedy, McGraw, 71. Add: 6248 Washington Ave, St. Louis, MO 63130.

McBATH, JAMES HARVEY, b. Watertown, S.Dak, Oct. 24, 22; m. 63; c. 3. SPEECH. B.S, Northwest. Univ, 47, M.A, 48, Ph.D.(speech), 50; dipl, London Sch. Econ, 53. Asst. prof. speech, Univ. N.Mex, 50-52; fel, London Sch. Econ, 52-53; asst. prof. SPEECH, Univ. Iowa, 53-54; Europ. prog, Univ. Md, 54-56; UNIV. SOUTH. CALIF. 56-57, assoc. prof, 57-63, PROF, 63-, CHMN. DEPT, 65-, acting chmn. dept, summer 63, chmn. Fac. Senate, 70-71. Consult, Univ. Hawaii Forensic Workshop, summers 61, 62; consult, Am. Stud. Found, 61-64; moderator, Championship Debate Ser, NBC-TV, 62; commun. consult, Hughes Aircraft Co, 62-63; assoc. ed, Quart. J. Speech, 65-; consult, Calif. Off. Econ. Opportunity, 72; City of Hope Med. Ctr, 73; Rand Corp, 73-; consult, Nat. Endowment for Humanities, 73- U.S.A.A.F, 43-46, Sgt. Am. Forensic Asn.(pres, 60-62, ed, jour, 66-); Speech Commun. Asn; West. Speech Commun. Asn; (v.pres, 67-68, pres, 68); Int. Commun. Asn; Brit. Hist. Asn; AAUP; Am. Asn. Pub. Opinion Res; Commun. Asn. Pac. History and criticism of public communication; communication and social change. Publ: Co-auth, Guidebook for speech practice, 61 & Guidebook for speech communication, 73, Harcourt; ed, Argumentation and debate, Holt, 63 & Essays in forensics, Am. Forensic Asn, 70; co-auth, British Public addresses, 1828-1960, Houghton, 71; auth, Parliamentary reporting in the nineteenth century, Speech Monogr, 70; contrib, Encyclopedia of education, Macmillan, 71. Add: Dept. of Speech Communication, University of Southern California, Los Angeles, CA 90007.

McBRIDE, OTIS, b. Sanger, Tex, Aug. 20, 05; m. 47; c. 2. ENGLISH. B.S, N.Tex. State Teachers Col, 26, A.B, 29; A.M, George Peabody Col, 31, Ph.D, 41. Prin. high sch, Tex, 26-27, teacher, 27-31; Okla, 31-37; dir. placement, George Peabody Col, 37-42; dean men, Fla. State Univ, 46-53, dir. audio-visual ctr, 53-59, prof. & head dept. audio-visual educ, 59-62, prof. Eng. educ, 62-66; prof. educ. & dir. grad. prog. in educ. media-librarianship, UNIV. COLO, BOULDER, 66-73, EMER. PROF, 73- U.S.A.A.F, 42-46. NEA; NCTE; Am. Libr. Asn; Am. Asn. Sch. Libr; Asn. Hosp. & Inst. Libr; Spec. Libr. Asn; Asn. Educ. Commun. & Technol.(mem. comt. nat. legis, 63-). Compressed speech; super 8 film and projected materials. Publ: Lecture series and workship guide, 3M Co, 65; Materials and technology for adult basic education in corrections, Univ. Hawaii, 71; Libraries have developed into media centers since World War II, Sch. & Univ. Rev, 71; Compatibility, 71 & Compatibility and creativity—both are needed, 72, Am. Libr. Add: Graduate Program in Library Media, School of Education, Stadium 140, University of Colorado, Boulder, CO 80302.

McBRIDE, THOMAS EUGENE, b. Waco, Tex, Mar. 12, 45. ENGLISH LITERATURE. B.A, Baylor Univ, 66; M.A, Purdue Univ, West Lafayette, 68; Ph.D.(Eng), Univ. Ill, Urbana, 72. Instr. ENG, BELOIT COL, 73-74, ASST. PROF, 74- MLA. Jacobean tragi-comedy; Shakespeare. Add: Dept. of English, Beloit College, Beloit, WI 53511.

McBRIEN, WILLIAM AUGUSTINE, b. Huntington, N.Y, Nov. 20, 30. ENGLISH. B.A, St. John's Univ.(N.Y), 52, M.A, 54, Ph.D, 59. From instr. to assoc. prof. Eng, St. John's Univ.(N.Y), 58-65, coordinator freshman honors prog, 61-63, dir. univ. honors prog, 63-65; ASSOC. PROF. ENG, HOFSTRA UNIV, 65- Mem, Eng. Inst, 62-; ed, Twentieth Century Lit. MLA. Modern English poetry; 17th century literature; modern American poetry. Add: Dept. of English, Hofstra University, Hempstead, NY 11550.

McBROOM, ROBERT LOUIS, b. Wichita Falls, Tex, May 19, 28; m. 50; c. 4. MODERN AMERICAN & COMPARATIVE LITERATURE. B.A, Univ. Tex, Austin, 51; M.A, Midwest. Univ, 66; Ph.D.(Eng), Tex. Tech Univ, 70. Teacher ENG, Hirschi High Sch, Wichita Falls, Tex, 63-65; teaching asst, Midwest. Univ, 65-66; Tex. Tech Univ, 66-67; teacher & chmn. dept, Estacado High Sch, Lubbock, 67-68; instr, MIDWEST. UNIV, 68-70, ASSOC. PROF, 70-, DIR. DIV. CONTINUING EDUC, 73- Consult, Carl T. Anderson Oil Co, 70-74. Ord.C, U.S.A, 50-51. S.Cent. Mod. Lang. Asn; Col. Conf. Teachers Eng. Humanities; E.E. Cummings; petroleum geology of north Texas and southern Oklahoma. Add: Div. of Continuing Education, Midwestern University, Wichita Falls, TX 76308.

McBRYDE, DONALD M, b. Columbia, Miss, May 27, 37; m. 60; c. 1. THEATRE, SPEECH. B.A, Miss. Col, 58; M.A, Univ. Miss, 60; Ph.D.(theatre), Univ. Denver, 64. Instr. THEATRE, UNIV. MISS, 60-62, asst. prof, 62-64, assoc. prof. & chmn. dept, 64-68, PROF, 68- Building consult, Auditorium, Wood Col, 64-65; theatre, Laurel Little Theatre, Miss, 64-67; Cleveland Little Theatre, Miss, 65-67; Natchez Little Theatre, 67-; auditorium, Lander Col, 67- U.S.A, 59-60; Nat. Guard, 60-65, Res, 65-67. U.S. Inst. Theatre Technol.(mem. bd. dir, 68-); Southeast. Theatre Conf.(mem. adv. counc. & chmn. theatre archit. comt, 64-); Am. Theatre Asn. Theatre architecture; theatre equipment design; plastic and paper products for stage scenery. Publ: Metal theatre buildings, South. Theatre, spring 68. Add: Dept. of Speech, University of Mississippi, University, MS 38677.

McBURNEY, JAMES HOWARD, b. Tyndall, S.Dak, June 19, 05; m. 29; c. 3. SPEECH. A.B, Yankton Col, 25, Litt.D, 62; A.M, Univ. S.Dal, 29; Ph.D, Univ. Mich, 35; Columbia Univ, 36. Instr. SPEECH, Univ. S.Dak, 28-29; Univ. Mich, 29-35; asst. prof, Columbia Univ, 36; assoc. prof, NORTHWEST. UNIV, 36-40, prof, 40-73, dean sch. speech, 42-73, EMER. PROF. & EMER. DEAN, 73- Sesquicentennial Award, Univ. Mich, 67. Speech Commun. Asn.(pres, 49). History and criticism of rhetoric and public address. Publ: Guide to good speech; co-auth, Art of good speech & Discussion in human affairs. Add: 116 Meadowlark Dr, Tryon, NC 28782.

McCABE, BERNARD, b. Middlesbrough, Eng, Aug. 9, 23; m. 52; c. 8. ENGLISH. LL.B, Univ. Manchester, 45; M.A, Stanford, 59, Ph.D.(Eng), 61. Asst. prof. ENG, TUFTS UNIV, 61-66, ASSOC. PROF, 66-, CHMN. DEPT, 72- MLA. Novel of social protest; modern fiction; the eighteen-thirties and forties. Publ: Ivy Compton-Burnet: an English eccentric, Critique, spring 60; Francis Bacon and the natural law tradition, Natural Law Forum, 64; Benjamin Disraeli, In: Minor British novelists, Univ. South. Ill, 67. Add: Dept. of English, Tufts University, Medford, MA 02155.

McCABE, BERNARD P, JR, b. Portsmouth, N.H, Mar. 14, 33; m. 56; c. 1. RHETORIC & PUBLIC ADDRESS. B.A, Emerson Col, 56, M.A, 57; Ph.D. (rhetoric & pub. address), N.Y. Univ, 61. Instr. PUB. ADDRESS & RHETORIC, Brooklyn Col, 56-58; asst. prof, St. John's Univ.(N.Y), 61-66; Mt. Holyoke Col, 66-67; assoc. prof, SOUTH. CONN. STATE COL, 67-70, PROF. & DIR. UNDERGRAD. PROG, 70- Speech Commun. Asn; Speech Asn. East. States (2nd v.pres, 65-66). Communications theory; communication behavior. Publ: Co-auth, Speaking is a practical matter, 68 & 73, auth, Everyday speech for students, 69 & Communicative voice and articulation, 70, Holbrook. Add: Dept. of Speech, Southern Connecticut State College, New Haven, CT 06515.

McCABE, JOHN CHARLES, III, b. Detroit, Mich, Nov. 14, 20; m. 62; c. 3. DRAMA. Ph.B, Univ. Detroit, 47; M.F.A, Fordham Univ, 48; Ph.D, Birmingham Univ, 54. Instr. speech & theater, Wayne Univ, 49-51; speech, City Col. New York, 55-56; asst. prof. theater, N.Y. Univ, 56-58, assoc. prof, 58-63, prof, 63-67, chmn. dept. dramatic art, 61-67; sr. fel. drama & chmn. dept. drama & theatre arts, Mackinac Col, 67-70; AUTHOR-IN-RESIDENCE, LAKE SUPERIOR STATE COL, 70- U.S.A.A.F, 43-45, Sgt. Am. Theatre Asn; Cath. Actors Guild. Theatre history; Elizabethan stagecraft; dramatic humor. Publ: Mr. Laurel and Mr. Hardy, Doubleday, 61, Mus. Press, Eng. & U.K, 62, Grossett, 67 & New Am. Libr, 68; George M. Cohan: the man who owned Broadway, Doubleday, 73. Add: Box 363, Mackinac Island, MI 49757.

McCAFFREY, DONALD W, b. Muscatine, Iowa, Mar. 27, 26; m. 48; c. 2. THEATRE, CINEMA. B.A, Univ. Iowa, 49, Ph.D.(theatre, cinema), 62; M.A, Denver Univ, 50; Northwest. Univ, 50-51. Asst. prof. speech & theatre, Friends Univ, 51-53; Emporia Col, 53-57; instr. commun, Univ. Iowa, 57-60; asst. prof. THEATRE, UNIV. N.DAK, 60-65, assoc. prof, 65-71, PROF, 71- U.S.N.R, 44-46. Soc. Cinematologists (secy, 67-); Speech Commun. Asn; Am. Theatre Asn. Critical-historical research in the fields of comic drama and cinema. Publ: Four great comedians: Chaplin, Lloyd, Keaton, Langdon, Zwimmer & A.S. Barnes, 68; The use of comic theory in the study of silent screen comedy, Cent. State Speech J, 8/63; The mutual approval of Keaton and Lloyd, Cinema J, spring 67; Adaptation problems of the two unique media: the novel and the film, Dickinson Rev, spring 67. Add: Dept. of English, University of North Dakota, Grand Forks, ND 58201.

MacCAFFREY, ISABEL GAMBLE, b. Baltimore, Md, Aug. 2, 24; m. 56. ENGLISH LITERATURE. B.A, Swarthmore Col, 46; Fulbright fel, Cambridge, 50-51; Ph.D, Radcliffe Col, 54; hon. Litt.D, Holy Cross Col, 72. Instr. Eng, Bryn Mawr Col, 49-50, 52-54, asst. prof, 54-60, assoc. prof, 60-66, prof, 66-69; Tufts Univ, 69-71; KENAN PROF. HIST. & LIT, HARVARD, 71- Mem. supv. comt, Eng. Inst, 67-70; Guggenheim fel, 71-72. MLA; Renaissance Soc. Am. Publ: Paradise lost as myth, Harvard, 59; ed, Samson Agonistes and shorter poems of Milton, New Am. Libr, 66; co-auth, Lycidas: the poet in a landscape, In: The lyric and dramatic Milton, Columbia Univ, 65. Add: Holyoke Center 952, Cambridge, MA 02138.

McCALL, DAN ELLIOTT, b. Stockton, Calif, Jan. 14, 40; m. 64. ENGLISH. B.A, Stanford Univ, 62; Danforth fel, Columbia Univ, 62-66, M.A, 63, Ph.D. (Eng), 66. Preceptor ENG, Columbia Univ, 64-66; asst. prof, CORNELL UNIV, 66-71, ASSOC. PROF, 71- Guggenheim fel, 72-73. Nineteenth and twentieth century English and American literature. Publ: The example of Richard Wright, Harcourt, 69; The man says yes, Viking, 69; Jack the bear, Doubleday, 74; The quicksilver sparrow of M.B. Tolson, Am. Quart, 9/67; The meaning in darkness, a response to a psychoanalytical reading of Conrad, Col. Eng, 5/68; Hawthorne's familiar kind of preface, ELH, 9/68. Add: Dept. of English, Cornell University, Ithaca, NY 14850.

McCALL, (JOSEPH) DARRYL, JR, b. Miami, Fla. Oct. 15, 29. ENGLISH. A.B, Univ. Fla, 50, M.A, 52; Oxford, 55-56; Ph.D.(Eng), Univ. Fla, 58. Instr. ENG, Ga. State Col, 54-55; Univ. Ky, 58-60; asst. prof, De Pauw Univ, 60-64; assoc. prof, UNIV. N.C, CHARLOTTE, 64-70, PROF, 70- Commun. consult, Gulf Oil Co, Pittsburgh, 62. MLA; S.Atlantic Mod. Lang. Asn; Col. Eng. Asn. Criticism; Milton; Romantic period. Publ: Introduction to drama, Ind. Univ, 62; Communications at Gulf Oil Co, Gulf Oil Co, 62. Add: Dept. of English, University of North Carolina at Charlotte, Charlotte, NC 28223.

McCALL, JOHN PATRICK, b. Yonkers, N.Y, July 17, 27; m. 57; c. 4. ENGLISH. A.B, Holy Cross Col, 49; M.A, Princeton, 52, Ph.D, 55. Instr. ENG, Georgetown Univ, 55-58, asst. prof, 58-62, assoc. prof, 62-66; PROF, UNIV. CINCINNATI, 66-, HEAD DEPT, 70- Fel, Am. Counc. Learned Soc, 62-63; Fulbright grant, 62-63. Sig.C, U.S.A, 52-54. MLA; Mediaeval Acad. Am; AAUP (mem. counc, 71-74). Medieval literature; classical traditions. Publ: The Clerk's tale and the theme of obedience, Mod. Lang. Quart, 9/66; The writings of John of Legnano with a list of manuscripts, Traditio, 67; Chaucer and the pseudo origen De Maria Magdelena, Speculum, 71. Add: Dept. of English, University of Cincinnati, Cincinnati, OH 45221.

MacCALLUM, HUGH R, b. Toronto, Ont, Apr. 13, 28; m. 53; c. 2. ENGLISH. B.A, Univ. Toronto, 51, M.A, 54, Ph.D.(Eng), 59. Lectr. ENG, Univ. West. Ont, 55-59; UNIV. TORONTO, 59-60, asst. prof, 60-66, ASSOC. PROF, 66-, CHMN. GRAD. ENG. DEPT, 72- Can. Counc. fel, 64-65. Seventeenth-century English literature; Canadian poetry. Publ: Co-ed, Discourse of the light of nature, Univ. Toronto, 71; auth, Milton and the figurative interpretation of the Bible, Univ. Toronto Quart, 62; Milton and sacred history, In: Essays in English literature, Univ. Toronto, 64; plus one other. Add: Dept. of English, New College, University of Toronto, Toronto, Ont. M5S 1A1, Can.

McCANDLISH, GEORGE EDWARD, b. Seattle, Wash, May 31, 14; m. 50; c. 3. AMERICAN LITERATURE & CIVILIZATION. Ph.D.(hist. Am. civilization), Harvard, 62. PROF. ENG, GEORGE WASHINGTON UNIV, 71- Add: Dept. of English, George Washington University, Washington, DC 20006.

McCANLES, MICHAEL F, b. Kansas City, Mo, Mar. 8, 36; m. 67; c. 1. ENGLISH. B.S, Rockhurst Col, 57; M.A, Univ. Kans, 59, Ph.D.(Eng), 64. Instr. ENG, Univ. Cincinnati, 62-64; asst. prof, MARQUETTE UNIV, 64-68, ASSOC. PROF, 68-, res. comt. grants, 66-67, 68- MLA; Renaissance Soc. Am; Malone Soc; Shakespeare Soc. Am. Renaissance literature; Renaissance history of ideas; relations between philosophy and literary criticism. Publ: The dialectic of transcendence in Shakespeare's Coriolanus, PMLA, 67; Mythos and Dianoia: a dialectical methodology of literary form, In: Literary monographs, Univ. Wis, 71; Increasing store with loss: some themes of Shakespeare's sonnets, Tex. Stud. Lit. & Lang, 71; plus others. Add: Dept. of English, Marquette University, Milwaukee, WI 53233.

McCANN, GARTH A, b. Logan, Utah, May 26, 40. CRITICISM, LITERATURE. B.A, Univ. Hawaii, 63; M.A, Miami Univ, 65; NDEA fel. & Ph.D.(Eng), Ohio State Univ, 71. Lectr. ENG, Ohio State Univ, 67-70; ASST. PROF, COLO. STATE UNIV, 70- MLA; Col. Eng. Asn; West. Lit. Asn. Literary theory; romanticism; contemporary and Western American literature. Publ: Dryden and poetic continuity, S.Atlantic Quart, spring 73; Chaucer's first three tales, Bull. Rocky Mountain Mod. Lang. Asn, 3/73; contrib, Halkett and Laing Dictionary, Oliver & Boyd, Edinburgh, 74. Add: Dept. of English, Colorado State University, Ft. Collins, CO 80521.

MacCANN, RICHARD DYER, b. Wichita, Kans, Aug. 20, 20; m. 57. FILM HISTORY & CRITICISM. A.B, Univ. Kans, 40; M.A, Stanford Univ, 42; Ph.D, (govt), Harvard, 51. Staff correspondent, Los Angeles Bur, Christian Sci. Monitor, 51-57; asst. prof. cinema, Univ. South. Calif, 57-62; mem. prog. dept, Subscription TV, Calif, 64; vis. prof. speech & drama, Univ, Kans, 65-66, from assoc. prof. to prof. jour. & speech, 66-70; PROF. FILM, UNIV. IOWA, 70- Am. specialist & film consult, Repub. Korea, U.S. Embassy, Seoul, 63; mem. steering comt, Aspen Film Conf, Aspen Inst. Humanistic Stud, Colo, 63-65; vis. prof, Harvard, summer 67; co-adminr, Rockefeller grant film & Am. civilization, Univ. Iowa, 72-75; Nat. Endowment for Humanities sr. fel, Eng, 73. U.S.A, 42-45. Univ. Film Asn.(assoc. ed, Jour, 61-67); Soc. Cinema Stud.(ed, Cinema J, 67-). Mass communications; film writing; political science. Publ: Hollywood in transition, Houghton, 62; Film and society, Scribners, 64; Film: a montage of theories, 66 & co-ed, The new film index, 74, Dutton; auth, The people's films, Hastings, 73. Add: Broadcasting & Film Division, University of Iowa, Iowa City, IA 52242.

McCANTS, DAVID ARNOLD, b. Dinwiddie Co, Va, June 2, 37; m. 60; c. SPEECH. B.A, Univ. Richmond, 58; univ. fel, Northwest. Univ, 58-59, Danforth fel, 58-62, M.A, 59, Ph.D.(pub. address & group commun), 64. Instr. SPEECH, Amherst Col, 62-65; asst. prof, Univ. Ky, 65-68; ASSOC. PROF, PURDUE UNIV, FT. WAYNE, 68-, CHMN. COMMUN. SECT, 70- Univ. Ky. summer fac. res. fel, 66, summer fac. teaching improvement fel, 67. Speech Commun. Asn; AAUP. Late 19th century American homiletics; public address in the United States Colonial period. Publ: The lost Yale lectures on preaching by John A. Boradus, South. Speech J, fall 70. Add: Dept. of Communication, Purdue University, 2101 Coliseum Blvd. E, Ft. Wayne, IN 46805.

McCARTHY, B. EUGENE, b. Grand Haven, Mich, May 3, 34; m. 62; c. 3. ENGLISH. A.B, Univ. Detroit, 58, fel. & M.A, 61; fel. & Ph.D.(Eng), Univ. Kans, 66. Instr. ENG, Univ. Detroit, 60-61; COL. OF THE HOLY CROSS, 65-66, asst. prof, 66-72, ASSOC. PROF, 72- MLA. Milton; literary criticism of Restoration drama. Publ: A seventeenth century borrowing from Milton's A brief history of Moscovia, Notes & Queries, 3/68. Add: Dept. of English, College of the Holy Cross, Worcester, MA 01610.

McCARTHY, HAROLD T, b. Salem, Mass, Mar. 26, 20. ENGLISH. A.B, Univ. Mass, 41; M.A, Harvard, 42, Ph.D, 50. Instr. ENG. & AM. LIT, Northwest. Univ, 51-55; lectr, Europ. Prog, Univ. Md, 55-59; assoc. prof, UNIV. MASS, AMHERST, 59-73, PROF, 73- Lectr. Am. lit, Univ. Copenhagen, 64-65; Fulbright-Hays lectr, Italy, 67-68. U.S.N.R, 42-46, Lt. MLA; Col. Eng. Asn. Nineteenth and 20th century British and American fiction. Publ: Henry James: the creative process, Yoseloff, 58; The expatriate perspective, Fairleigh-Dickinson Univ, 73. Add: Dept. of English, University of Massachusetts, Amherst, MA 01002.

McCARTHY, JAMES S, b. New York, N.Y, Apr. 18, 32; m. 55; c. 3. SPEECH. B.A, St. John's Univ.(N.Y), 54; M.A, Columbia Univ, 58, Ed.D.(speech), 64. Teacher, high sch, N.J, 58-59; prof. speech, Paterson State Col, 59-70; DIR, SCH. CONTEMPORARY ARTS, RAMAPO COL. N.J, 70- U.S.A, 54-56. Speech Commun. Asn; NEA. Rhetoric; communications; speech education. Publ: College level speech, 65 & College level public speaking, 66, Monarch. Add: 45 Catherine Ct, Ringwood, NJ 07456.

McCARTHY, JOHN F, b. Newton, Mass, Feb. 25, 30. ENGLISH. B.A, Harvard, 51; M.A, Yale, 53, Ph.D.(Eng), 63. Instr. ENG, Univ. N.H, 56-59; BOSTON COL, 59-63, asst. prof, 63-69, ASSOC. PROF, 69- U.S.A, 53-55. MLA. Nineteenth century English poetry. Publ: The conflict in books I-II of The prelude, Mod. Lang. Quart, 9/69; The Wordsworthian imagination in poetry, Discourse, autumn 69; Browning's Waring: the real subject of the Fancy portrait, Victorian poetry, winter 71. Add: Dept. of English, Boston College, Chestnut Hill, MA 02167.

McCARTHY, KEVIN MICHAEL, Linguistics, American Literature. See Volume III, Foreign Languages, Linguistics & Philology.

McCARTHY, PATRICK JOSEPH, b. New York, N.Y, Aug. 6, 22; m. 51. ENGLISH. A.B, Fordham Univ, 44; A.M, Columbia Univ, 47, Ph.D, 60. Instr. ENG, Univ. Ariz, 52-60, asst. prof, 60-64, assoc. prof, 64-66; UNIV. CALIF, SANTA BARBARA, 66-70, PROF, 70-, acting head dept, 69-70, head, 70-71. Vis. asst. prof, Univ. Wash, summer 63; vis. assoc. prof, Harvard, summer 67; grant, Humanities Inst, summer 68. U.S.A, 43-46, 1st Lt. MLA; Mod. Humanities Res. Asn; Philol. Asn. Pac. Coast. Interaction of 19th century English literature and politics; history and development of English novel. Publ: Matthew Arnold and the three classes, Columbia Univ, 64. Add: Dept. of English, University of California, Santa Barbara, CA 93106.

McCARTHY, PAUL EUGENE, b. Des Moines, Iowa, Apr. 18, 21; m. 48; c. 5. ENGLISH. B.A, Univ. Iowa, 48, M.F.A, 51; Ph.D.(Eng), Univ. Tex, 62. Instr. ENG, Iowa State Univ, 51-53; Univ. Tex, Austin, 56-58; Univ. Idaho, 58-60; Univ. N.Dak, 60-62; asst. prof, Univ. Ala, 62-65, ASSOC. PROF, 65-67; KANS. STATE UNIV, 67- Grant-in-aid, Univ. Ala, summers 64-67. Sig.C, A.U.S, 42-45. MLA; NCTE; Melville Soc. Am; Soc. Stud. Midwestern Lit. Fiction of Herman Melville; literature of American romantic period; American novel. Publ: Ed, Long fiction of the American renaissance: a symposium on genre (essays), Am. Transcendental Quart, spring 74; auth, Symbolic elements in White jacket, Midwest Quart, 7/66; City and town in Melville's fiction, Res. Stud, 9/70; Elements of anatomy in Melville's fiction, Stud. in Novel, spring 74; plus others. Add: 1621 Browning Ave, Manhattan, KS 66502.

McCARTY, EDWARD CLAYTON, b. Louisville, Ky, Aug. 14, 01; m. 27; c. 3. SPEECH, DRAMA. A.B, Univ. Colo, 24; Univ. Calif, 25-27; summers, Univ. South. Calif, 27, Univ. Calif, Los Angeles, 32, Stanford Univ, 40, 42, 44; A.M, Claremont Cols, 38; Northwest. Univ, 38-39. Teacher drama & Eng, Joint Union High Sch. & Jr. Col, Reedley, Calif, 27-29, jr. high sch,

29-38; asst, Northwest. Univ, 39; instr. Eng, Pa. State Teachers Col, Calif, 39-42; asst. prof. drama & Eng, N.Mex. Col, 42-44; assoc. prof. speech & drama & chmn. dept, Trinity Univ, 44-62; asst. prof. speech & chmn. dept. speech & drama, Sul Ross State Col, 65-73; RETIRED. Auth. League Am; Sci. Fiction Writers Am. Critique of English composition; structural history of the one-act play; plays, radio manuscripts and short stories. Publ: Moon's still yellow & The kiss of death, Samuel French; Behind this mask, Baker, 60. Add: Box 6058, Alpine, TX 79830.

McCASLIN, NELLIE, b. Cleveland, Ohio, Aug. 20, 14. DRAMA & THEATRE. B.A, West. Reserve Univ, 36, M.A, 37; Ph.D, N.Y. Univ, 57. Instr. drama & speech, Tudor Hall, Indianapolis, Ind, 37-44; dir. dramatic arts, Nat. Col. Educ, 44-56; MILLS COL. EDUC, 57-64, DIR. STUD. PERSONNEL SERV, 64- Lectr. speech, Teachers Col, Columbia Univ, 60-63; summers, creativity workshop, Rockford Col, 62, 63; lang. arts workshop, Univ. N.C, 63; adj. assoc. prof. dramatic arts, N.Y. Univ, 72- Am. Theatre Asn; Children's Theatre Conf; Speech Commun. Asn; Children's Theatre Asn.(v.pres, 71-73, pres, 73-75). Children's theatre; creative drama. Publ: Legends in Action; More Legends in action, 50 & Pioneers in petticoats, 60, Row-Peterson & Baker Co; Tall tales and tall men, MacRae-Smith, 56; Creative dramatics in the classroom, McKay, 68, 2nd ed, 74; Children's theatre in the United States: a history, Univ. Okla, 71; Children and drama: perspectives, McKay, 74. Add: 40 E. Tenth St, New York, NY 10003.

McCAUGHEY, GERALD SHELDON, b. Montreal, P.Q, Oct. 4, 25; m. 50; c. 5. ENGLISH LITERATURE. B.A, McGill Univ, 51; M.A, Univ. Wash, 58. Asst. prof. ENG, Can. Serv. Col, 52-63; ASSOC. PROF, UNIV. ALTA, 63- Vis. prof. Shakespeare, Univ. Victoria, 62-63; reader, Col. Bd. Exam, Educ. Testing Serv, 64-69; U.S. For. Serv. Exam, 67-69; vis. prof. Eng. Calif. State Univ, Northridge, 67-69; Univ. Ore, summer 69; Univ. Waterloo, summer 70; res. consult, Can. Counc, 72-73. R.C.A.F, 42-44, Res, 48-52; R.C.N, 44-46, Res, 54-64, Maj; Can. Forces Decoration. Can. Asn. Univ. Teachers; Asn. Can. Univ. Teachers Eng. History of Canadian theatre; Shakespeare; literary criticism. Add: Dept. of English, University of Alberta, Edmonton, Alta, Can.

McCAY, DALE, b. Adams Co, Iowa, Dec. 21, 08; m. 40; c. 5. ENGLISH LANGUAGE & LITERATURE. B.A, Grinnell Col, 32, M.A, 37; Ph.D, State Univ. Iowa, 53. Teacher, high sch, Iowa, 36-42; Eng. & hist, West. Mil. Acad, 42-45; instr. ENG, IOWA STATE UNIV, 45-50, asst. prof, 50-58, assoc. prof, 58-65, PROF, 65- Contemporary and American literature. Add: 2003 Ashmore Dr, Ames, IA 50010.

McCLARTY, WILMA KING (DOERING), b. July 21, 39; U.S. citizen; m. 62; c. 1. ENGLISH, ENGLISH EDUCATION. B.A, Andrews Univ, 61, M.A, 62; D.Ed, Univ. Montana, 68. Asst. prof. Eng. & educ, Southwest. Union Col, 68-72; ASSOC. PROF. ENG. & CHMN. DEPT, SOUTH. MISSIONARY COL, 72- Coord, Seventh-day Adventist Sec. Sch. Eng. Teachers Conv, South. Missionary Col, 73. NCTE. Publ: Why are you so peculiar?, Rev. & Herald, 8/71; Open-minded or just empty headed, J. Adventist Educ, 2-3/72; Urgency (poem), Ministry, 2/72; plus others. Add: Dept. of English, Southern Missionary College, Collegedale, TN 37315.

McCLARY, BEN HARRIS, b. Ocoee, Tenn, July 8, 32. ENGLISH. B.A, Univ. Tenn, 55, M.A, 57; Fulbright scholar, Univ. Sussex, 64-66, D.Phil.(Eng. & Am. Stud), 66. Teacher Eng, Bradley Cent. High Sch, Cleveland, Tenn, 56-58, Am. hist, 59-61; teaching asst, Univ. Tenn, 58-59; asst. prof. ENG, Tenn. Wesleyan Col, 61-64, assoc. prof, 66-67; prof. & chmn. dept, Wesleyan Col.(Ga), 67-69, Cobb prof. Eng. lit, 69-71; PROF. ENG. & CHMN. DIV. HUMANITIES, MID. GA. COL, 71- Nat. Trust fel, Colonial Williamsburg, Va, 60; Suffield Writer-Reader Conf. scholar, 60; Wesleyan Col. fac. grants, summers 67 & 68; ed, Lovingood papers, 62-65; Am. Counc. Learned Soc. grant & Am. Philos. Soc. grant, summer 67; Am. Philos. Soc. grant, summer 70. Tenn. Wesleyan Col. Fac. Award, 62, 63. U.S.A, 55-56. MLA. British romantic and Victorian literature; publishing history. Publ: Ed, American cultural history, 1607-1829, 61 & The letters of Shahcoolen, 1802, 62, Scholars' Facs; auth, Washington Irving and the house of Murray: a chapter in publishing history, Univ. Tenn, 68; Washington Irving in Brighton, 1824, Sussex Life, 7/66; Irving's literary midwifery, Philol. Quart, 4/67; Irving, Lockhart and the Quarterly Review, Bull. N.Y. Pub. Libr, 72. Add: Division of Humanities, Middle Georgia College, Cochran, GA 31014.

McCLARY, MACLYN HOWARD, b. Oakland, Calif, Nov. 29, 36; m. 57; c. 2. JOURNALISM. B.A, Pomona Col, 57; M.S, Univ. Calif, Los Angeles, 66; Univ. Minn, Minneapolis, summers 68-70. Reporter & ed, var. newspapers, 57-67; asst. prof. JOUR, CALIF. STATE UNIV, HUMBOLDT, 67-71, ASSOC. PROF, 71-, chmn. dept, 70-73. Asn. Educ. in Jour; Inter-Am. Press Asn. Press history; press responsibility. Publ: Law day next year, J. State Bar Calif, 5/61; Academic qualifications of California journalism professors, Jour. Educr, fall 69; One county's newspaper heritage, Pacifica, 5/72. Add: Dept. of Journalism, California State University, Humboldt, Arcata, CA 95521.

McCLEARY, JOHNNIE MARIE, b. Taylor, Tex, Jan. 29, 17; m. 50. ENGLISH, LINGUISTICS. B.A, Wiley Col, 38; M.A, Cornell Univ, 40; Gen. Educ. Bd. grants, Univ. Chicago, 49-51, Ford Found. South. Fel. Fund grants, summers 55-58, Ph.D.(ling), 58. Instr. Eng, grammar & educ, Wiley Col. Exten. Sch, 38-39; ENG, Houston Col. Negroes, 40-47; asst. prof, TEX. SOUTH. UNIV, 47-51, assoc. prof, 51-58, PROF. & HEAD DEPT, 58-, acting head dept, 55-58. Consult. developing lang. arts curriculum guide, Wright High Sch, Angleton, Tex, 61, 62; dir. NDEA Insts. Teachers Eng, 65, 66; reader, Nat. Advan. Placement Exams. Eng, Educ. Testing Serv, 67-68. Tex. South. Univ. Award, 65. MLA; NCTE; Asn. Eng. Dept. Chmn; Conf. Eng. Educ. Historical linguistics; lexicography. Publ: Co-auth, English 8, Vol. IX & English 11, Vol. X, In: The Texas transparency development series, Tex. Educ. Agency, 65. Add: Dept. of English, Texas Southern University, Houston, TX 77004.

McCLELLAND, BENJAMIN WRIGHT, b. Uniontown, Pa, Oct. 23, 43; m. 72; c. 1. ENGLISH. A.B, Grove City Col, 65; M.A, Ind. Univ, Bloomington, 67, Ph.D.(Eng), 72. ASST. PROF. ENG, Univ. Dubuque, 72-73; R.I. COL, 73- MLA. Prose fiction; colonial American and American Indian literature. Add: Dept. of English, Rhode Island College, Providence, RI 02908.

McCLENDON, PAUL I, b. Denver, Colo, June 10, 28; m. 52; c. 4. COMMUNICATIONS. B.A, Bob Jones Univ, 51; M.A, Northwest. Univ, 52; Ph.D. (commun), Univ. Iowa, 56. Instr. commun, Univ. Iowa, 53-56; speech & theatre, Ind. Univ, 56-60; assoc. prof. speech & commun, Westmont Col, 60-64; dir. learning resources, ORAL ROBERTS UNIV, 64-67, PROF. COMMUN, 68-, DIR. TELECOMMUN, 70-, dir. commun, 67-70, chmn. dept. commun. arts, 68-70. Lectr, Purdue Univ, 56-57; Butler Univ, 57-58; Univ. Calif, 62-64; dir, Int. Educ. Found, 66-; consult. commun, Far East Broadcasting Co, Manila, Philippines, 71, Go-Tell Commun, Johannesburg, Daystar Commun. Res, Rhodesia & Kenya & World Radio Fel, Quito, Ecuador, 72; vis. lectr. commun, South. Asia Col, Bangalore, India, 71-72. U.S.C.G, 53. NEA; Int. Commun. Asn; Nat. Relig. Broadcasters. Cross cultural communications; international radio and television; multi-media communications. Publ: Dial access audio video system, 3/67 & An integrated multi-media system, 5/67, AV Instr; Christian broadcasting in the Philippines, Int. Christian Broadcasters Bull, 7/73. Add: Dept. of Communications, Oral Roberts University, Tulsa, OK 74105.

McCLERREN, BERYL F, b. West Frankfort, Ill, May 30, 29; m. 51; c. 4. SPEECH, PHILOSOPHY. B.S, South. Ill. Univ, 59, M.S, 60, Ph.D, 63. Asst. speech, South. Ill. Univ, 59-60, lectr, 60-63; asst. prof. RHETORIC & PUB. ADDRESS, State Univ. N.Y. Col. New Paltz, 63-64; assoc. prof, EAST. ILL. UNIV, 64-73, PROF, 73- Speech Commun. Asn; Cent. States Speech Asn. The religious issues in presidential campaigns; general semantics; speeches on church-state separation. Publ: Religious rhetoric, 1981, Christianity Today, 11/61; Creative teaching, Speech Teacher, 9/66; Southern Baptists and the religious issue during the presidential campaigns of 1928 and 1960, Cent. States Speech J, 5/67. Add: Dept. of Speech, Eastern Illinois University, Charleston, IL 61920.

McCLINTOCK, MICHAEL WILLIAM, b. Manchester, Iowa, July 6, 42; m. 72. MODERN LITERATURE, LITERARY CRITICISM. B.A, Univ. Notre Dame, 64; Ph.D.(Eng), Cornell Univ, 70. ASST. PROF. ENG, UNIV. MONT, 69- MLA; AAUP; Sci. Fiction Res. Asn. Theory of fiction; science fiction; Joseph Conrad. Publ: Games and the players of games: old French fabliaux and The shipman's tale, Chaucer Rev, fall 70; Some preliminaries to the criticism of science fiction, Extrapolation, 12/73; A case of conscience and the ontology of fiction, Proc. Sec. Universe Conf, (in press). Add: Dept. of English, University of Montana, Missoula, MT 59801.

McCLOSKEY, FRANK HOWLAND, b. Pittsburgh, Pa, Sept, 15, 95; m. 27; c. 2. ENGLISH LITERATURE. A.B, Syracuse Univ, 16; A.M, N.Y. Univ, 25; Ph.D, Harvard, 29. Instr. ENG, N.Y. Univ, 23-27; Boston Univ, 28-29; asst. prof, N.Y. UNIV, 29-37, asst. dean, 31-36, assoc. prof, 37-45, from prof. & univ. dean stud. to EMER. PROF. & EMER. DEAN STUD, 45- Adj. prof. Eng, Fairleigh Dickinson Univ, 65. U.S.A, 18-19, Lt. MLA. Elizabethan literature; Chaucer. Publ: How to write clearly and effectively. Add: 14 Willard Ave, Madison, CT 06443.

McCLURE, ARETTA STEVENS, b. Tacoma, Wash, Mar. 10, 30. ENGLISH. B.A, Seattle Univ, 61; Arthur J. Schmitt scholar, Loyola Univ.(Ill), 64-65, Ph.D, 67. Asst. prof. ENG, Wash. State Univ, 67-71; VIS. ASST. PROF, ALASKA METHODIST UNIV, 71- MLA; Am. Stud. Asn. Herman Melville. Publ: Hopkins' That nature is a Heraclitean fire, Explicator, 11/63; The edition of Montaigne read by Melville, Papers Bibliog. Soc. Am, first quart, 68; Head imagery in Moby Dick, Res. Stud, 12/70. Add: Dept. of English, Alaska Methodist University, Anchorage, AK 99504.

McCLURE, DONALD STUART, b. South Bend, Ind, Feb. 23, 39; m. 62; c. 3. ENGLISH & AMERICAN LITERATURE. A.B, Kalamazoo Col, 60; M.A, West. Mich. Univ, 63; Ph.D.(Eng), Vanderbilt Univ, 70. Teacher Eng. & math, Sparta Area Sec. Schs, Mich, 61-64; asst. prof. ENG, IND. UNIV. PA, 67-70, ASSOC. PROF, 70- MLA; Renaissance Soc. Am. English Renaissance drama; 19th and 20th century American fiction; English novel. Publ: Versification in Dekker's Shoemakers' holiday, 69 & Commercialism in the York mystery cycle, 70, Stud. Humanities. Add: Dept. of English, Indiana University of Pennsylvania, Indiana, PA 15701.

McCLUSKEY, DONALD, b. Easton, Pa, Mar. 28, 15. ENGLISH LITERATURE. A.B, Lafayette Col, 36; Ph.D, Yale, 41. Instr. ENG, LAFAYETTE COL, 46-50, asst. prof, 50-58, ASSOC. PROF, 58- U.S.A, 41-45, Master Sgt. MLA; Col. Eng. Asn; Ling. Soc. Am. Add: 130 Pennsylvania Ave, Easton, PA 18042.

McCOARD, WILLIAM B(RINKERHOFF), b. Provo, Utah, Nov. 18, 07; m. 37; c. 2. SPEECH. A.B, Brigham Young Univ, 29; M.A, Univ. South. Calif, 33; Univ. Calif, 36; State Univ. Iowa, 37; Ph.D.(speech), Univ. Wis, 41. Teacher, high sch, Univ. Utah, 29-33; instr. speech, San Jose State Col, 33-38; pub. speaking, Univ. Wis, 38-40; asst. prof. pub. speaking, radio & phonetics & head dept, Cleveland Col, West. Reserve Univ, 40-46; asst. prof. SPEECH, Univ. Calif, 46-50; from assoc. prof. to PROF, UNIV. SOUTH. CALIF, 49- Specialist consult. speech for mil. off, 49-55; exchange prof, Univ. Hawaii, 54-55. U.S.N.R, 44-46, Lt. Speech Commun. Asn; West. Speech Commun. Asn. Relation of speech to teaching efficiency; speech intelligibility in noise. Publ: Speech factors as related to teaching efficiency & Oral reading evaluation of good and poor silent readers, Speech Monogr; Contributions from the military programs in voice communication, Quart. J. Speech. Add: Dept. of Speech, University of Southern California, Los Angeles, CA 90007.

McCOLLOM, WILLIAM G. b. Brooklyn, N.Y, Oct. 25, 11; m. 37; c. 2. ENGLISH, DRAMA. A.B, Cornell Univ, 33, A.M, 38, Ph.D, 44. Instr. Eng, Univ. Md, 40-44, asst. prof, 44-45; ENG. & DRAMATIC ARTS, CASE WEST. RESERVE UNIV, 45-48, assoc. prof, 48-59, PROF, 60- Ford Found. fel, 52-53. Am. Soc. Aesthet; MLA. Theory of drama; dramatic literature and production. Publ: Tragedy, Macmillan, 57; The divine average: a view of comedy, Case West. Reserve Univ, 71. Add: Dept. of English, Clark Hall, Case Western Reserve University, Cleveland, OH 44106.

McCOLLUM, JOHN ISAAC, JR, b. Conway, Ark, Oct. 13, 19; m. 47; c. 2. RENAISSANCE ENGLISH LITERATURE. A.B, Univ. Miami, 46, A.M, 49; Ph.D, Duke Univ, 56. Instr. Eng, UNIV. MIAMI, 46-49, asst. to dean, col. lib. arts, 50-53, asst. prof. Eng, 55-59, assoc. dean univ. col, 60-61, assoc.

prof. ENG, 60-64, PROF, 64-, chmn. dept, 61-73. Mem. regional selection comt, Woodrow Wilson Nat. Fel. Found. MLA; S.Atlantic Mod. Lang. Asn; Renaissance Soc. Am; Southeast Renaissance Conf; Asn. Depts. Eng. English Renaissance histories; John Dryden; Spenser. Publ: Ed, The age of Elizabeth, 60 & The restoration stage, 61, Houghton; auth, Essentials of grammar and style, World, 66; The House of fame revisited, In: A Chaucerian puzzle and other medieval essays, 62 & William Harrison, In: Sweet smoke of rhetoric, 64, Univ. Miami; The indebtedness of James Boswell to Edmond Malone, New Rambler, 66. Add: Dept. of English, University of Miami, Coral Gables, FL 33124.

McCOMBS, ATHEL VICTOR, b. Wabash, Ind, Sept. 14, 14; m. 41; c. 1. SPEECH. B.S, Purdue Univ, 57, M.S, 59; Ph.D.(pub. address), Evangelical Sem, Chicago, 70. Asst. SPEECH, Purdue Univ, 57-58, instr, 58-59; ASSOC. PROF, OLIVET NAZARENE COL, 59-, CHMN. DEPT, 74- Speech Commun. Asn. Religious speaking, debate and theatre. Add: Dept. of Speech, Olivet Nazarene College, Kankakee, IL 60901.

McCOMMAS, BETTY JO, b. Paragould, Ark, Aug. 29, 31. ENGLISH, PHILOSOPHY. B.A, Baylor Univ, 53, M.A, 54; Univ. Ark, 56-57, Rockefeller grant, 57; Ouachita Baptist Col. grant to Univ. Ore, 61-62. Instr. philos. & asst. to pres, OUACHITA BAPTIST UNIV, 54-55, asst. prof. philos. & Eng, 55-56, ASSOC. PROF. ENG, 57-, acting chmn. div. humanities & dept. Eng, 62-64. S.Cent. Mod. Lang. Asn. Contemporary world literature, especially drama; literary criticism. Add: 137 Evonshire Dr, Arkadelphia, AR 71923.

McCONKEY, DONALD LeMOYNE, b. Cincinnati, Ohio, Jan. 12, 29; m. 61. RHETORIC, PUBLIC ADDRESS. B.S, Ill. State Univ, 51; M.A, Ohio State Univ, 52, Ph.D, 70. Assoc. prof. speech, Col. William & Mary, 54-70; PROF. SPEECH & DRAMA & CHMN. DEPT. COMMUN. ARTS, MADISON COL, 70- Asst. speech, Ohio State Univ, 51-52, 56-57; training off. pub. speaking, U.S. Naval Weapons Sta, Yorktown, Va, 56; faculty mem, Am. Inst. Bankers, 58 & 59; consult. pub. speaking, Colonial Williamsburg, Inc, 60-; U.S. Nat. Park Serv, Yorktown, 62. U.S.A, 52-54, Sgt. Speech Commun. Asn; Am. Forensic Asn. Ancient rhetorical theory; Virginia debates, 1765-1776; Virginia constitutional convention of 1829-30. Publ: Elements of tournament debate, Walch, 74. Add: Dept. of Communication Arts, Madison College, Harrisonburg, VA 22801.

McCONKEY, JAMES R, b. Lakewood, Ohio, Sept. 2, 21; m. 44; c. 3. ENGLISH; B.A, West. Reserve Univ, 43, M.A, 46; Ph.D.(Eng), State Univ. Iowa, 53. Asst. prof. ENG, Morehead State Col, 50-53, assoc. prof, 53-56; asst. prof, CORNELL UNIV , 56-61, assoc. prof, 61-67, PROF, 67- Saxton Mem. Trust fel, 62-63; Guggenheim fel, 69-70. U.S.A, 43-45. PEN Club. Fiction and poetry, especially the 20th century. Publ: The novels of E.M. Forster, 57 & Night stand, 65, Cornell Univ; ed, The structure of prose, Harcourt, 63; auth, Crossroads, Dutton, 68; A journey to Sahalin, Coward, 71. Add: Dept. of English, 63 Goldwin Smith Hall, Cornell University, Ithaca, NY 14850.

McCONNELL, FRANK DeMAY, b. Louisville, Ky, May 20, 42; m. 64; c. 1. ENGLISH. B.A, Univ. Notre Dame, 64; M.A, Yale, 65; Ph.D.(Eng), 68. Asst. prof. ENG, Cornell Univ, 67-71; PROF, NORTHWEST. UNIV, EVANSTON, 71- Romantic poetry; modern fiction. Publ: William Burroughs, Mass. Rev, 67; Virginia Woolf's The waves, Bucknell Rev, 68-69; Shelley's Epipsychidion, Keats-Shelley J. Add: Dept. of English, Northwestern University, Evanston, IL 60201.

McCONNELL, RUTH E, b. Vancouver, B.C, July 12, 15. ENGLISH. B.A, Univ. B.C, 54, M.A, 58; Ph.D.(Eng), Univ. Calif, Berkeley, 67. Teacher, pub. schs, B.C, 34-58; asst. prof. EDUC. & ENG, UNIV. B.C, 58-62, assoc. prof, 62-70, PROF, 70- Can. Counc. award, 63-65; assoc. ed, Eng. Quart, 67-72; mem. dialect surv. comt, NCTE, 67-, lang. comn, 68-71. NCTE; Can. Counc. Teachers Eng. Fiction of Joseph Conrad; English language and grammar. Publ: Co-auth, Learning English, Macmillan, Toronto, 63; auth, A pencil for his thoughts, J. Educ, 1/66; co-auth, What's the usage & Fugitive language, In: Looking at language, Gage, 66. Add: Faculty of Education, University of British Columbia, Vancouver 8, B.C, Can.

McCORD, CLARENCE WILTON, b. Lawton, Okla, Sept. 14, 34; m. 55; c. 4. SPEECH, LINGUISTICS. B.A, La. Col, 56; B.D, Golden Gate Baptist Theol. Sem, 60; M.A, La. State Univ, 62, Ph.D.(speech), 68; Univ. Mich, summer 65. Asst. prof. SPEECH, Howard Payne Col, 61-63; GA. SOUTH. COL, 63-69, ASSOC. PROF. & HEAD DEPT, 69- Guest lectr, Baptist Missionary Orientation Ctr, 70-72. Speech Commun. Asn.(v.chmn. speech sci, 73-74); Ling. Soc. Am. Experimental phonetics; psycholinguistics; theoretical linguistics. Publ: On Sophists and philosophers, South. Speech J, 63; Phillips Brooks and the accepted speech standards, Ga. Speech J, 71. Add: Dept. of Speech & Drama, Georgia Southern College, Statesboro, GA 30458.

McCORD, HOWARD, b. El Paso, Tex, Nov. 3, 32; m. 53; c. 2. ENGLISH. B.A, Univ. Tex, El Paso, 57; Woodrow Wilson fel, Univ. Utah, 57-58, M.A, 58. Assoc. prof. Eng. & humanities, Wash. State Univ, 60-71; PROF. ENG. & DIR. CREATIVE WRITING PROG, BOWLING GREEN STATE UNIV, 71- Fulbright award, summer inst. Indian civilization, Univ. Mysore & New Delhi, 65; E.O. Holland fel. & travel grant, summer 67; D.H. Lawrence fel, Univ. N.Mex, 71; secy. exec. comn. bd. dir, Coord. Counc. Lit. Mag, 72-; adj. prof, Union Grad. Sch, 73- U.S.N, 51-53. Poetry. Publ: Precise fragments, Dolmen, 63; The Spanish dark and other poems, Wash. State Univ, 65; Fables and transfigurations, 67, & Longjaunes His Periplus, 68 & Maps, 71, Kayak; The fire visions, Twowindows, 70; Gnomonology: a handbook of systems, Sand Dollar, 71; The diary of a young girl, Lillabulero, 72. Add: Dept. of English, Bowling Green State University, Bowling Green, OH 43403.

McCORMACK, ERIC PATRICK, b. Bellshill, Scotland, Sept. 20, 38; m. 64; c. 2. RENAISSANCE ENGLISH LITERATURE. M.A, Univ. Glasgow, 62; Ph.D.(Eng), Univ. Man, 73. Lectr. ENG, ST. JEROME'S COL, UNIV. WATERLOO, 70-73, ASST. PROF, 73- Asn. Can. Univ. Teachers Eng. Robert Burton and 17th century English literature; Canadian literature; Scottish literature. Add: Dept. of English, St. Jerome's College, University of Waterloo, Waterloo, Ont. N2L 3G1, Can.

McCORMICK, ANNETTE M, b. Cambridge, Mass, Oct. 9, 19. ENGLISH. A.B, Smith Col, 40; A.M, Univ. Chicago, 41; Ph.D.(Eng), Univ. London, 51. Instr. ENG, West. Col, 45-47; Univ. Colo, 49-50; Bryn Mawr Col, 50-52; Univ. Kans, 52-54, asst. prof, 54-56; vis. asst. prof, State Univ. Iowa, 56-57; asst. prof, LA. STATE UNIV, BATON ROUGE, 59-67, ASSOC. PROF, 67- Mem. Comt. Eng. Comp, Col. Entrance Exam. Bd, 62-66. MLA. Nineteenth century English literature; Victorian travel literature. Publ: Hebrew parallelism in Charles M. Doughty's Travels in Arabia Deserta, In: Studies in comparative literature, La. State Univ, 60; An Elizabethan Victorian travel book: Doughty's Travels in Arabia Deserta, In: Essays in honor of Esmond Linworth Marilla, La. State Univ, 70. Add: Dept. of English, Louisiana State University, Baton Rouge, LA 70803.

McCORMICK, EDGAR LINDSLEY, b. Wadsworth, Ohio, Mar. 12, 14; m. 45; c. 1. ENGLISH. A.B, Kent State Univ, 36; M.A, Univ. Mich, 37, Ph.D.(Eng), 50. Teaching fel. eng, Univ. Mich, 38-41, 45-56; head dept, Ala. State Teachers Col, Florence, 46-50; Bethany Col, 50-54; asst. prof, KENT STATE UNIV, 54-58, chmn. freshman Eng, 56-60, assoc. prof. Eng, 58-64, PROF. ENG, 64-, COORD. AM. STUD, 70-, asst. dean col. arts & sci, 64-69, assoc. dean, 69-70. U.S.A.A.F, 42-45. MLA; NCTE; Am. Stud. Asn. American literature; T.W. Higginson as literary historian. Publ: Co-auth, Life on a whaler, Heath, 60; Imagination and intellect, Prentice-Hall, 62; Nantucket migration to Portage County, Ohio, Hist. Nantucket, 63. Add: 1106 Old Forge Rd, Kent, OH 44240.

McCORMICK, EDWARD ALLEN, German. See Volume III, Foreign Languages, Linguistics & Philology.

McCORMICK, JAMES PATTON, b. Chicago, Ill, Mar. 1, 11; m. 39; c. 3. ENGLISH LITERATURE. A.B, Northwest. Univ, 33, A.M, 34, Ph.D, 37. Instr, Evanston Col. Inst, 34-35; teaching fel, Northwest. Univ, 36-37; lectr. ENG. LIT, Alborz Col, Iran, 37-38; from instr. to PROF, WAYNE STATE UNIV, 38-, asst. to v.pres. acad. admin, 57-60, secy. bd. gov, 60-66, v.pres. stud. affairs, 65-68. Fund Advan. Educ. fel, 53-54; Fulbright prof, Japan, 54-55; Found. Econ. Educ. fel, 55; mem, N.Cent. Asn. Cols. & Sec. Schs; v.pres. civic & educ. affairs, Detroit Edison Co, 68. U.S.N.R, 43-45, Lt. MLA; Col. Eng. Asn; Am. Soc. Aesthet. Victorian English and contemporary American literature; English and industry; international English studies. Publ: As a flame springs, Scribner; Patterns in recent American literature, Hokseido Press; co-auth, Seven plays of the modern theatre, Am. Bk. Co. Add: 201 E. Kirby, Detroit, MI 48202.

McCOY, DONALD EDWARD, b. Stanberry, Mo, Nov. 7, 23; m. 46, 68; c. 4. ENGLISH LANGUAGE & LITERATURE. B.A, Univ. Kans. City, 46, M.A, 48; Ph.D.(Eng), Univ. Ill, 52. Instr. Eng, Univ. Kans, 47-49; from instr. to head dept. lit. & writing, gen. col, Univ. Minn, 52-56; asst. prof. humanities, div. gen. stud, Univ. Ill, 56-61, chmn. verbal commun, 57-61; assoc. prof. ENG, Principia Col, 61-67, prof, 67-68, asst. dir. summer session, 61-62, dir, 62-68; PROF. EVENING COL, UNIV. MO-ST. LOUIS, 68- Ed, Gen. Educ. Sounding Bd, 54-56; educ. consult, Shell Oil Co, N.Y, 56-; ed, Word Stud, 58-70; partner, Higginbotham, Parker & McCoy, Consult. to Mgt, St. Louis, 68-71; vis. prof. Eng, Univ. Mo-St. Louis, 70; prin, D.E. McCoy Assoc, Educ. & Mgt. Consults, 71-; dir. res. & develop, Dynamic Prods, 71- U.S.A, 43-46; U.S.A.F.R, 51-, Capt. NCTE; MLA; fel. Int. Inst. Arts & Lett; Conf. Col. Compos. & Commun; Am. Bus. Commun. Asn; Am. Soc. Training & Develop. Nineteenth century English and American literature; linguistics and philology; managerial communication. Publ: Keys to good instruction, Shell Oil Co, 57, 59, 68; co-auth, Rhetoric and reading, order and idea, Dodd, 63. Add: 1138 Westmoor Pl, St. Louis, MO 63131.

McCOY, DOROTHY SCHUCHMAN, b. Pittsburgh, Pa, June 28, 22; m. 46, 54; c. 2. RENAISSANCE & COMPARATIVE LITERATURE. B.A, Allegheny Col, 44; Carnegie Inst. Technol, summers 40, 42; M.A, State Univ. Iowa, 46; Univ. Minn, 48-49; Cornell Univ, 50; Ph.D.(Eng), Univ. Pittsburgh, 62. Instr. Eng, Geneva Col, 46-48; Carleton Col, 48-49; chmn. dept, Point Park Jr. Col, 62-65; asst. prof. philos. & Eng, POINT PARK COL, 65-66, ASSOC. PROF. ENG, 66- Lectr. dramatic lit, Univ. Pittsburgh, summers 66-68. MLA; AAUP; Int. Arthurian Asn. Literary transmission, 12th century England and northeastern France; women, a Chaucerian panorama; medieval presuppositions in Shakespearean character development. Publ: Tradition and convention: a study in periphrasis in English pastoral poetry from 1557-1715, Mouton, The Hague, 65; plus poems. Add: 208 Breading Ave, Ben Avon, Pittsburgh, PA 15202.

McCOY, KATHLEEN, b. Pittsburgh, Pa, July 29, 34; m. 69; c. 2. ENGLISH. B.A, Westminster Col, 56; M.A, Univ. Pittsburgh, 60; Ph.D.(Eng), Fla. State Univ, 66. Instr. ENG, Albright Col, 62-65; Fordham Univ, 66-67, ASST. PROF, 67-69; SETON HALL UNIV, 69- Eighteenth century English literature; restoration drama. Add: 46 Great Jones St, New York, NY 10012.

McCOY, RALPH EDWARD, Librarianship. See Volume I, History.

McCOY, SAMUEL JESSE, b. Columbus, Ga, Sept. 30, 05; m. 31; c. 3. ENGLISH. B.A, Wofford Col, 25; M.A, Duke Univ, 29; Ph.D, Univ. N.C, 33. Instr. Eng, Emory Univ. Acad, 25-27; Univ. N.C, 31-33; prof. Eng. & chmn. dept, Col. William & Mary, 33-47; dean, Winthrop Col, 47-59; prof. Eng, Wofford Col, 59-62; prof. Eng. & dean, Charlotte Col, 62-65; prof. Eng, The Citadel, 65-73; RETIRED. Gen. Educ. Bd. fel, Ling. Atlas of U.S, 34. MLA; S.Atlantic Mod. Lang. Asn; Am. Dialect Asn. History of the English language; American dialects. Add: 306 Marion Ave, Summerville, SC 29483.

McCRACKEN, HUGH THOMAS, b. Oswego, N.Y, May 17, 35; m. 68; c. 4. ENGLISH, EDUCATION. B.S, State Univ. N.Y. Oswego, 58, M.S, 62; M.A, Middlebury Col, 65; Ph.D.(Eng, educ), Univ. Ill, Urbana, 71. Teacher Eng, Adams Ctr. Cent. Sch, N.Y, 58-62; Union-Endicott High Sch, 62-65; asst. prof, State Univ. N.Y. Cortland, 65-68; grad. asst. Eng. & educ, Univ. Ill, Urbana, 68-70; asst. prof. ENG, YOUNGSTOWN STATE UNIV, 70-72, ASSOC. PROF, 72- Reader col. bds, Educ. Testing Serv, 64-69; asst. dir, NDEA Summer Inst. Lang. & Compos, State Univ. N.Y. Cortland, 68; teacher Eng, Parkland Community Col, Ill, 68-70. NCTE (Conf. Eng. Educ); MLA; Asn. Supv. & Curriculum Develop. Teaching of language in schools and universities; teaching of writing. Publ: Politics and the study of language, Eng. Educ, winter 74. Add: Dept. of English, Youngstown State University, 410 Wick Ave, Youngstown, OH 44503.

McCRACKEN, JAMES DAVID, b. Cincinnati, Ohio, May 7, 39. ENGLISH. B.A, Oberlin Col, 61; M.A, Univ. Chicago, 62, Ph.D.(Eng), 66. Asst. prof. ENG, UNIV. WASH, 66-71, ASSOC. PROF, 71- MLA; Johnson Soc. Northwest. Eighteenth century politics and literature; political novels of French Revolution. Publ: Ed, Caleb Williams, Oxford, 69; auth, Godwin's literary theory, Philol. Quart, 69; The drudgery of defining: Dr. Johnson's debt to N. Bailey, Mod. Philol, 69; Godwin's Caleb Williams: a fictional rebuttal of Burke, Stud. in Burke & His Time, 70. Add: Dept. of English, University of Washington, Seattle, WA 98105.

McCRACKEN, MILDRED LOUISE, b. Chickasha, Okla, Dec. 30, 08. ENGLISH. B.A, Okla. Col. Lib. Arts, 33; M.A, Univ. Okla, 34; Ph.D, Univ. Tex, 42. Assoc. prof. ENG, Southeast. State Col.(Okla), 37-46; OKLA. COL. LIB. ARTS, 46-50, PROF. & HEAD DEPT, 50-, CHMN. HONORS COURSE, 48-, div. lang. & lit, 54-56. NCTE; S.Cent. Mod. Lang. Asn; MLA. English literature. Add: Dept. of English, Oklahoma College of Liberal Arts, Chickasha, OK 73018.

McCRAY, WILLIAM EDWARD, b. Memphis, Tenn, Sept. 20, 30. ENGLISH, DRAMA, SPEECH. B.S, Le Moyne Col.(Tenn), 55; M.A, N.Y. Univ, 57, Ph.D.(Eng. & speech educ), 62; M.A.(dance educ), Columbia Univ, 71. Instr. speech & drama, Miss. Voc. Col, 57-58; Eng. & drama, St. Paul's Col, 58-59; asst. prof. Eng, Grambling Col, 63-64, ASSOC. PROF, 64-72; THEATRE & BLACK STUD, OHIO STATE UNIV, 72- U.S.A, 52-54. Am. Dance Guild; Comt. Res. Dance; Am. Theatre Asn; Am. Civil Liberties Union; AAUP. Theatre and contemporary dance. Publ: And still it comes, deadly or not, Grambling Col. Lib. Arts Bull, spring, 67; Nat Turner revisited, Viewfinder, 12/68. Add: 1651 Rozelle Cove, Memphis, TN 38114.

McCRIMMON, JAMES McNAB, b. Renton, Scotland, June 16, 08; nat; m. 39; c. 2. ENGLISH. B.A, Northwest. Univ, 32, M.A, 33, Ph.D.(Eng), 37. Asst. instr. Eng, Northwest. Univ, 35; instr, Univ. Toledo, 36-38, asst. prof, 38-43, assoc. prof, 43-47; humanities, UNIV. ILL, URBANA, 47-55, prof, 55-60, prof. humanities & educ. & dir. Eng. curriculum proj, 60-65, chmn. humanities div, Galesburg Div, 47-49, head div. gen. stud, 54-62, EMER. PROF, 65- Vis. prof, Fla. State Univ, 67-69, prof, 69- NCTE; Conf. Col. Compos. & Commun. Curriculum development in English; rhetoric. Publ: Writing with a purpose, 4th ed, 67, 5th ed, 74 & From source to statement, 68, Houghton; co-auth, Bibliography of the writings of John Stuart Mill & Open door to education, 51, Univ. Ill. Add: 1330 W. Indian Head Dr, Tallahassee, FL 32301.

McCRORY, JULIET (KEY), b. Guin, Ala, July 4, 11. SPEECH. B.S, Univ. Ala, 37; Ph.M, Univ. Wis, 41, scholar, 41-42; fac. scholar, Lindenwood Col, 44; summer, Columbia Univ, 47; Danforth scholar, Univ. South. Calif, 53, 55; summer, Univ. Mo, 66. Assoc. prof. SPEECH, Lindenwood Col, 43-68, chmn. dept, 47-64; asst. prof, WEST. KY. UNIV, 68-72, ASSOC. PROF, 72- Cent. States Speech Asn; Speech Commun. Asn; South. Asn. Commun. Arts. Speech education; interpretation; public address. Add: Apt. B-04, 1225 College, Bowling Green, KY 42101.

McCRORY, THOMAS EDWIN, b. New York, N.Y, July 1, 29. ENGLISH, LITERARY CRITICISM. A.B, Cath. Univ. Am, 51; M.A, Columbia Univ, 53; Fordham Univ, 53; Ph.D.(Eng), Univ. Pa, 58. Instr. rhetoric & drama, St. Joseph's Col.(Pa), 53-56; asst. prof. Eng, Univ. Detroit, 58-61; assoc. ed, Hawthorn Bks, Inc, 62, asst. ed, Data Guide Publ. Co, 63; content ed, Cath. Encycl. for School and Home, McGraw-Hill, 63-64; asst. prof. ENG, NIAGARA UNIV, 65-66, assoc. prof, 66-67, PROF, 67- MLA; Dante Soc. Literary criticism; 19th century Romantic and Victorian English literature; 18th century English literature. Publ: Ed, 14 vols, Complete library of world art, 62-64 & 14 vols, Twentieth century encyclopedia of Catholicism, 62-64, Hawthorn; ed. 1400 articles & auth, Population & Realism in literature, In: Catholic encyclopedia for school and home, McGraw, 65. Add: Dept. of English, Niagara University, Niagara, NY 14109.

McCROSSON, DORIS ROSS, b. Berkeley, Calif, Feb. 13, 23. ENGLISH LITERATURE. A.B, Univ. Pa, 49, A.M, 51, Ph.D, 59; Sorbonne, 50. From asst. prof. to prof. ENG, Shippensburg State Col, 59-62; asst. prof, WILSON COL, 62-64, ASSOC. PROF, 64- Consult. affirmative action, Pa. Dept. Educ, 73-; Pa. Insurance Dept, 73- W.A.V.E.S, 43-45. MLA; NCTE. Victorian and 20th century English literature; women's studies. Publ: Walter de la Mare, Twayne, 66. Add: Dept. of English, Wilson College, Chambersburg, PA 17201.

McCUE, DANIEL LAWRENCE, JR, b. Somerville, Mass, Nov. 14, 17; m. 54; c. 3. ENGLISH, COMPARATIVE LITERATURE. A.B, Boston Col, 40; M.A, Columbia Univ, 47, Ph.D, 74. O'Malley teaching fel, BOSTON COL, 40-41, instr. ENG, 53-58, ASST. PROF, 58- A.U.S, 42-46, U.S.A.R, 46-70, Lt. Col. MLA; Conf. Brit. Stud; AAUP; Am. Soc. 18th Century Stud. Science and literature, 1600-1800; 18th century English literature; the romantic movement in English literature. Publ: Co-auth, Edmund Burke: the enlightenment and the modern world, Univ. Detroit, 67; auth, Burke and Philip Francis: revolution versus friendship, Burke Newslett, winter 64-65; Science and literature: the virtuoso in English Belles Lettres, Albion, fall 71; plus others. Add: Dept. of English, Boston College, Chestnut Hill, MA 02167.

McCULLOUGH, BRUCE, b. Scottsburg, Ind, Jan. 19, 91; m. 21; c. 1. ENGLISH LITERATURE. A.B, Univ. Ind, 14, A.M, 15; Ph.D, Univ. Pa, 17; Sorbonne, 19. Instr. ENG, Grinnell Col, 17-18; Univ. Pa, 19-20; asst. prof, Univ. Akron, 20-21; prof, Univ. Chattanooga, 21-24; asst. prof, N.Y. UNIV, 24-27, assoc. prof, 27-40, prof, 40-70, EMER. PROF, 70- U.S.A, 18-19. MLA. Prose fiction. Publ: Life and writings of Richard Penn Smith, George Banta Pub. Co, 17; Representative English novelists: Defoe to Conrad, Harper, 46. Add: 56 N. Monroe St, Ridgewood, NJ 07450.

McCULLOUGH, CONSTANCE, b. Indianapolis, Ind, Jan. 15, 12. EDUCATION. A.B, Vassar Col, 32; M.S, Butler Univ, 34; Ph.D, Univ. Minn, 38; Columbia Univ, 39. Asst. educ, Univ. Minn, 33-35, res. instr, 37-38; teacher Eng. & math, Edison High Sch, Minneapolis, Minn, 35-37; statistician, Coop. Test Serv, New York, 38; asst. prof. Eng, Hiram Col, 38-39; educ. & Eng, West. Reserve Univ, 39-47; prof. educ, SAN FRANCISCO STATE UNIV, 47-73, EMER. PROF, 73- Specialist elem. educ, Tokyo Inst. Educ. Leadership, 48-49; mem. fac, Univ. Hawaii, summer 61; Univ. Chicago, summer 62; mem. bd, Res. Found, Nat. Counc. Teachers Eng, 62; specialist in curriculum reading, Teachers Col, Columbia Univ. Team in India, 63-65; lectr, Harvard, summer 66; consult. textbk. eval, South. Ill. Univ. Team in Katmandu, summer 70. NCTE; Conf. Res. Eng.(pres, 61); Int. Reading Asn. (Citation of merit, 67, Award for int. serv, 69, pres-elect, pres, 73-76); Am. Educ. Res. Asn; Nat. Soc. Stud. Educ; NEA. Teaching of reading; test construction. Publ: Co-auth, Improvement of reading, McGraw, 46, 55, 61 & 67; Ginn basic readers, 50 & revisions & Ginn 360 readers, 70, Ginn; Teaching elementary reading, Appleton, 62, 68, rev. ed, 74; auth, Preparation of textbooks in the mother tongue, Int. Reading Asn, 66; contrib, Language and learning to read, Houghton, 72. Add: 80 Vicente Rd, Berkeley, CA 94705.

McCUNE, MARJORIE WOLFE, b. Millerstown, Pa, Sept. 8, 21; m. 43. ENGLISH. A.B, Susquehanna Univ, 43; A.M, Bucknell Univ, 61; Lutheran Brotherhood fel. & Ph.D.(Eng), Pa. State Univ, 68. Teacher jr. high sch, 43-44; instr. ENG, SUSQUEHANNA UNIV, 59-63, asst. prof, 63-68, ASSOC. PROF, 68- MLA; NCTE; Eng. Inst. Puritan American literature. Add: Dept. of English, Susquehanna University, Selinsgrove, PA 17870.

McCURDY, FRANCIS LEA, b. Clifton Hill, Mo, Jan. 12, 06; m. 44. SPEECH & DRAMA. B.S.Ed, Univ. Mo, 35; M.A, 44, Ph.D, 57; Columbia Univ, summer 57. Teacher Eng. & speech, High Schs, Mo. & Okla, 25-52; instr. speech, UNIV. MO, COLUMBIA, 52-57, asst. prof, 57-60, assoc. prof. 60-65, prof, 65-73, EMER. PROF. SPEECH & DRAMATIC ARTS, 73- Vis. prof, Univ. Hawaii, 67; Univ. Colo, summer 72; Northwest. Univ, spring 74. Stephens Col. Outstanding Alumnae Award, 63. Speech Commun. Asn.(chmn. interpretation div, 70-71); Cent. States Speech Asn. Pioneer orators of Missouri; woman suffrage. Publ: Co-auth, Curriculum guide in speech, dramatics, television, State Dept. Educ; auth, Frontier rhetoric, Univ. Mo, 69; co-auth, The people's rhetoric, Rodopi, 74; auth, Frontier invective, Quart. J. Speech, 4/60; Courtroom oratory of the pioneer period, Mo. Hist. Rev, 10/61; plus others. Add: 304 W. Broadway, Columbia, MO 65201.

McCUTCHEON, ELIZABETH NORTH, b. New York, N.Y, Nov. 13, 32; m. 59; c. 2. ENGLISH. B.A, William Smith Col, 54; Knapp fel, Univ. Wis, 55-56, M.A, 56, Young fel, 58-59, Gen. Electric Educ. & Charitable Fund, 58-59 & Am. Asn. Univ. Women nat. fel, 59-60, Ph.D.(Eng), 61. Asst. prof. ENG, UNIV. HAWAII, 66-69, ASSOC. PROF, 69- MLA; Bibliog. Soc. Eng; Renaissance Soc. Am; NCTE; Amici Thomae Mori. English literature of the 16th and 17th centuries; Neo-Latin literature; art and literature. Publ: Lancelot Andrewes' Preces Privatae: a journey through time, Stud. Philol, 68; Thomas More, Raphael Hythlodaeus, and the Angel Raphael, Stud. Eng. Lit, 69; Bacon and the Cherubim: an iconographical reading of the New Atlantis, Eng. Lit. Renaissance, 72. Add: Dept. of English, University of Hawaii, 1733 Donaghho Rd, Honolulu, HI 96822.

McDADE, MARY DEMETRIA, R.S.M, b. Bordentown, N.J, Apr. 20, 08. ENGLISH LITERATURE. A.B, Georgian Court Col, 45; M.A, Villanova Univ, 55; summers, Notre Dame Univ, 57, Cath. Univ. Am, 60; Harvard, 63. Teacher Eng, Camden Cath. High Sch, 33-44; Cathedral High Sch, Trenton, 44-55; instr, GEORGIAN COURT COL, 55-58, asst. prof. Eng. & chmn. freshman Eng, 58-70, ASSOC. PROF. ENG. & AM. LIT, 70-, dean freshmen, 64-70. NCTE; Cath. Renascence Soc; Nat. Asn. Women Deans & Counsel. Nineteenth century English liteature. Add: Dept. of English, Georgian Court College, Lakewood, NJ 08701.

McDAVID, VIRGINIA GLENN, b. Minneapolis, Minn, Aug. 9, 26; m. 50; c. 4. ENGLISH. B.A, Univ. Minn, 46, M.A, 48, Ph.D, 56. Instr. Eng, Kent State Univ, 56-57; from assoc. prof. to PROF. ENG, CHICAGO STATE UNIV, 57- MLA; Ling. Soc. Am; NCTE. General linguistics; American English; college composition. Publ: Co-auth, 99 exercises for college composition, Scott, 62 & Basic writing, privately publ, 63; auth, The Random House English handbook, 64. Add: Dept. of English, Chicago State University, 95th St. at King Dr, Chicago, IL 60628.

McDAVITT, ELAINE E, b. Marseilles, Ill, Mar. 19, 10. SPEECH. B.A, Northwest. Univ, 30, M.A, 35; Trueblood fel, Univ. Mich, 43-44, Ph.D, 46. Teacher speech & Eng, Pub. Schs, Muncie, Ind, 30-34; speech, High Sch, South Bend, 35-37; speech & Eng, Liggett Sch, Detroit, Mich, 37-46; asst. prof, North. Mich. Col, 46-47; from asst. prof. to PROF. SPEECH, UNIV. NORTH. IOWA, 47- Speech Commun. Asn; Am. Theatre Asn; Cent. States Speech Commun. Asn. Add: Dept. of Speech, University of Northern Iowa, Cedar Falls, IA 50613.

McDERMOTT, DOUGLAS, b. Los Angeles, Calif, Sept. 25, 36; m. 58; c. 6. DRAMATIC ART. A.B, Pomona Col, 58; M.A, Univ. N.C, 60; Ph.D.(drama), Univ. Iowa, 63. Asst. prof. dramatic art, Univ. Calif, Davis, 63-69, assoc. prof, 69-70; PROF. DRAMA, CALIF. STATE COL, STANISLAUS, 70- Univ. Calif. summer fac. fel, 64, Humanities Inst. fel, summer 68. Am. Soc. Theatre Res; Am. Theatre Asn. Eighteenth and 19th century American and British theatre history; dramatic theory and criticism. Publ: Propaganda and art: dramatic theory and the American depression, Mod. Drama, 5/68; The Woodland Hershey Opera House: the end of an era in California theatre, Calif. Hist. Soc. Quart, 12/69; Touring patterns on California's theatrical frontier, 1849-1859, Theatre Surv, 5/74; plus others. Add: Dept. of Drama, California State College, Stanislaus, 800 Monte Vista Ave, Turlock, CA 95380.

McDERMOTT, FRANCES McCLELLAN, b. Warsaw, Ind; m. 39. ENGLISH. A.B, East. Mich. Univ, 30; M.A, Univ. Mich, 33; Ed.D.(Eng, sociol), Mich. State Univ, 63. Teacher, sec. schs, Mich, 30-32, 34-41 & 47-54; librn, Dow Chem. Co, 42-47; instr. ENG, FERRIS STATE COL, 54-56, asst. prof, 56-61, assoc. prof, 61-66, PROF, 66- Vis. prof, Col. William & Mary, summers, 61-65 & 67. Vocabulary used in economics; factors affecting success or failure in college English. Publ: Co-auth, Summer workshops for recent high-school graduates, Higher Educ, 5/56. Add: 1152 Highland, Mt. Pleasant, MI 48858.

McDERMOTT, FRANCIS JOSEPH, b. Dedham, Mass, Aug. 13, 17; m. 51; c. 1. ENGLISH A.B, Boston Col, 39, fel, 39-41, A.M, 41; A.M, Harvard, 49, Ph.D.(Eng), 65. Instr. ENG, Niagara Univ, 42; BOSTON COL, 46-47, ASST. PROF, 47- U.S.A, 42-46, Res. Lt. Col. MLA; NCTE; Col. Eng. Asn. American literature; British and American literature of war; Victorian literature. Add: Dept. of English, Boston College, Chestnut Hill, MA 02167.

McDERMOTT, JOHN FRANCIS, Cultural History. See Volume I, History.

McDERMOTT, JOHN J, b. Buffalo, N.Y, May 21, 33; m. 58; c. 3. ENGLISH. A.B, Univ. Notre Dame, 57; M.A, Columbia Univ, 58; Ph.D.(Eng), Univ. Calif, Los Angeles, 64. Instr. ENG, Gonzaga Univ, 62-64, asst. prof, 65-67, ASSOC. PROF, 68-69, chmn. dept, 67-69; CALIF. STATE UNIV, FRESNO, 69-, ASST. ACAD. V.PRES, 71- MLA; NCTE; Philol. Asn. Pac. Coast; Mediaeval Acad. Am; Renaissance Soc. Am; Asn. Depts. Eng. English Renaissance and medieval literature; contemporary literature. Publ: Henryson's Testament of Cresseid and Heywood's A woman killed with kindness, Renaissance Quart, spring 67; Symbolism and psychological realism in The red badge of courage, Nineteenth Century Fiction, winter 68. Add: Dept. of English, California State University, Fresno, Shaw & Cedar Aves, Fresno, CA 94719.

McDILL, JOSEPH MOODY, b. Aliceville, Ala, June 23, 11; wid; c. 2. ENGLISH LITERATURE. A.B, Erskine Col, 33; M.A, Univ. N.C, Chapel Hill, 34; B.D, Erskine Theol. Sem, 36; fel, Vanderbilt Univ, 36-38, Ph.D.(Eng, Milton), 38; cert, South. Baptist Sem, La, 58; D.D.(human relat), Southwest. at Memphis, 60; Columbia Theol. Sem, 63; Austin Theol. Sem, 65. Instr. Eng, Erskine Col, 34-36; asst. prof, Miss. State Col. Women, 38-40; prof. & chmn. dept, Belhaven Col, 40-43; minister & counr, Fondren Presby. Church, Jackson, Miss, 42-66; assoc. dir, div. family life, Bd. Christian Educ, Presby. Church U.S, Richmond, Va, 66-69; asst. prof. ENG, RICHMOND COL.(VA), 69-73, ASSOC. PROF, 73- Ed, Presby. Herald, 42-43. AAUP; MLA; S.Atlantic Mod. Lang. Asn; Col. Eng. Asn; NCTE; Milton Soc. Am. Dating of Milton's De Doctrina Christiana; an approach to literature from a theological perspective. Publ: Milton and the pattern of Calvinism, Joint Librs, Nashville, Tenn, 42; Ecclesiastical survey of the status of Calvinism in the southern region, In: American Calvinism, Baker Bk, 57; plus others. Add: Dept. of English, Richmond College, University of Richmond, P.O. Box 92, Richmond, VA 23173.

McDONALD, CHARLES OSBORNE, b. Middletown, Conn, Mar. 5, 29; m. 48, 62; c. 4. ENGLISH. B.A, Wesleyan Univ, 50, M.A, 51; univ. scholar & fel, Jr. Sterling fel. & Ph.D.(eng), Yale, 59. Instr. ENG, Duke Univ, 56-59; Bowling Green State Univ, 59-62; asst. prof, Ohio State Univ, 62-63; Univ. Mass, 63-66, assoc. prof, 66-67; PROF, UNIV. CINCINNATI, 67-, dir. grad. stud. Eng, 70-71. Co-dir, Images of police in the media, arts, and Cincinnati, Ohio Prog. Humanities & Univ. Cincinnati, summer 73. MLA; AAUP. Shakespeare, Elizabethan drama and the relationship of classical literature to English literature. Publ: The rhetoric of tragedy, Univ. Mass, 66; An interpretation of Chaucer's Parlement of foules, Speculum, 7/55; Decorum, ethos, and pathos . . . , J. Eng. & Ger. Philol, 62; Restoration comedy as drama of satire . . . , Stud. Philol, 64. Add: Dept. of English, University of Cincinnati, Cincinnati, OH 45221.

McDONALD, DENNIS K, b. Lytton, Iowa, Mar. 8, 20. DRAMATIC LITERATURE. B.A, Univ. North. Iowa, 41; M.A, N.Y. Univ, 65; Ph.D.(dramatic lit), Carnegie-Mellon Univ, 68. N.Y. news ed, Billboard Mag, 46-57; v.pres. & treas, Theatrical Interests Plan, Inc, N.Y.C, 57-62; asst. prof. ACTING & DIRECTING, Wagner Col, 62-66; City Col. New York, 68-71; ASSOC. PROF, MONTCLAIR STATE COL, 72- Adj. prof. theatre hist, N.Y. Univ, 71-72. Am. Theatre Asn; Speech Commun. Asn. Primitive ritual; comedy; theatrical styles. Add: Apt. 7A, 170 E. 78th St, New York, NY 10021.

MacDONALD, DONALD, b. Dalmuir, Scotland, Dec. 1, 17; U.S. citizen; m. 47. ENGLISH. B.A, Wayne Univ, 42, M.A, 43; Ph.D.(Eng), Northwest. Univ, 58. Instr. Eng, WAYNE STATE UNIV, 45-49, admin. asst. col. lib. arts, 51-63, asst. prof. ENG, 60-67, ASSOC. PROF, 67- Wayne State Univ. fac. res. fel, 65, summer 68. Mediaeval Acad. Am; MLA. Publ: Proverbs, sententiae, and exempla in Chaucer's comic tales: the function of comic misapplication, Speculum, 7/66; Henryson and the Thre prestis of Peblis, Neophilologus, 4/67; Chaucer's influence on Henryson's Fables: the use of proverbs and sententiae, Medium AEvum, 70. Add: Dept. of English, Wayne State University, Detroit, MI 48202.

MacDONALD, DONALD, b. Muskegon, Mich, Apr. 22, 23; m. 46; c. 3. COMMUNICATION. B.A, Mich. State Univ, 49, M.A, 61, Ph.D.(commun), 71. Dir. news & spec. events, WKAR-WKAR/FM Radio, Mich, 49-51; ASST. PROF. COMMUN, UNIV. WIS-MILWAUKEE, 70-, CHMN. DEPT, 72-, assoc. dir. grad. sch. grant, 73-74. Consult. commun. res, Berlo & Assocs, 69-70; consult, Milwaukee Regional Off, U.S. Vet. Admin, 72-73. U.S.A.F, 42-46, 51-67. Am. Bus. Commun. Asn; Int. Commun. Asn; Speech Commun Asn; Acad. Mgt; Pub. Relat. Soc. Am. Communication networks; interviewing; effects of message campaigns. Publ: Role-playing techniques in communication, Wis. Commun. J, spring 73; co-auth, New directions in the study of organizational communication, J. Personnel Psychol, winter 73-74. Add: Dept. of Communication, University of Wisconsin-Milwaukee, Milwaukee, WI 53201.

MacDONALD, JAMES CAMPBELL, b. Highland Park, Mich, Aug. 9, 18; m. 57. JOURNALISM. A.B, Univ. Mich, Ann Arbor, 47. Reporter & chief ed. writer, Battle Creek Enquirer & News, Mich, 47-51; from instr. to assoc. prof. jour, Univ. Mich, Ann Arbor, 51-59, res. assoc, Inst. Pub. Admin, summer 55; ed. writer, Toledo Blade Co, Ohio, 59-60, assoc. ed, 60-63, exec. city ed, 63, ed, 63-70; ASSOC. PROF. JOUR, OHIO STATE UNIV, 70- Lectr. jour, Univ. Toledo, 63-64; participant sem. prog. Europ-Am. relat, Europ-Atlantic Movement, Oxford, summer 70. U.S.A.F, 42-46, 51-53, Capt. Am. Soc. Newspaper Ed; Nat. Conf. Ed. Writers; Asn. Educ. in Jour.(mem. joint comt. jour. educ, Am. Newspaper Publ. Asn); Int. Press Inst. Relations between local and state governments and the press; impact of news on attitudes and behavior of public. Publ: Press relations for local officials, Univ. Mich, 58; co-auth, Newspaper editorial readership and length of editorials, Jour. Quart, 61; auth, What two newspapers are doing, Int. Press Inst. Report, 67; Turned-off readers, Bull. Am. Soc. Newspaper Ed, 72; plus others. Add: School of Journalism, Ohio State University, 242 W. 18th Ave, Columbus, OH 43210.

McDONALD, JAMES L, b. Cincinnati, Ohio, Apr. 30, 36; m. 58; c. 3. ENGLISH. B.A, Univ. Notre Dame, 58; M.A, Northwest. Univ, 59, Ph.D.(Eng), 65. Lectr. ENG, Loyola Univ.(Ill), 61-62; instr, UNIV. DETROIT, 62-65, asst. prof, 65-68, assoc. prof, 68-74, PROF, 74- Soc. Relig. Higher Educ. Contemporary fiction; 20th century English and American literature. Publ: Graham Greene: a reconsideration, Ariz. Quart, 71; The frame of Barth's Giles goatboy, Critique, 72; contrib, A catch-22 casebook, Crowell, 73; plus others. Add: Dept. of English, University of Detroit, Detroit, MI 48221.

McDONALD, JOHN JOSEPH, b. Williamsport, Pa, Apr. 21; 42; m. 63; c. 3. AMERICAN LITERATURE, THEORY OF CRITICISM. A.B, Harvard, 64; NDEA fel, Princeton, 68-71, M.A, 70, Ph.D.(Eng), 71. ASST. PROF. ENG, UNIV. NOTRE DAME, 71- Am. Counc. Learned Soc. stud. fel, 74. MLA. Nathaniel Hawthorne; 19th century American aesthetics; theory of prose fiction. Publ: Emerson and John Brown, New Eng. Quart, 9/71; The old manse period canon, Nathaniel Hawthorne J, 72; The old manse and its mosses: the inception and development of Mosses from an old manse, Tex. Stud. Lit. & Lang, spring 74. Add: Dept. of English, University of Notre Dame, Notre Dame, IN 46556.

MacDONALD, ROBERT HUGH, b. Manchester, U.K, June 15, 34; m. 59; c. 2. ENGLISH LITERATURE. A.B, N.Y. Univ, 59; Stanford Univ, 59-61; dipl. Eng. stud, Univ. Edinburgh, 63, fel, 63-66, Ph.D.(Eng), 69. Asst. prof. ENG, CARLETON UNIV, 68-71, ASSOC. PROF, 71- Royal Air Force, 52-54, Pilot Off. The novel. Publ: The library of Drummond of Hawthornden, Edinburgh Univ, 71; The frightful consequences of onanism, J. Hist. Ideas, 7/67; Amendments to L.E. Kastner's edition of Drummond's poems, Stud. Scottish Lit, 7/69; Drummond of Hawthornden: The season of Bourges, 1607, Comp. Drama, 6/70. Add: Dept. of English, Carleton University, Ottawa, Ont. K1S 5B6, Can.

McDONALD, WALTER ROBERT, b. Lubbock, Tex, July 18, 34; m. 59; c. 3. ENGLISH. B.A, Tex. Technol. Col, 56, M.A, 57; Ph.D.(Eng), Univ. Iowa, 66. Instr. ENG, U.S. Air Force Acad, 60-62, 65-66, asst. prof, 66, ASSOC. PROF, 67-71, TEX. TECH UNIV, 71- Lectr, Univ. Colo, 67-69. U.S.A.F, 57-71, Maj.(Ret). MLA; NCTE; Col. Eng. Asn; S.Cent. Mod. Lang. Asn; Rocky Mountain Mod. Lang. Asn. Modern American literature; creative writing; the novel. Publ: Co-ed, A Catch-22 casebook, Crowell, 73; auth, Faulkner's The bear: the sense of its structure, Eng. Rec, 12/67; Coincidence in the novel, Col. Eng, 2/68; The functional comedy of Catch-22, CEA Critic, 1/72. Add: Dept. of English, Texas Tech University, Lubbock, TX 79409.

McDONALD, WILLIAM (ULMA), JR, b. Meridian, Miss, June 10, 27. ENGLISH. B.A, Univ. Ala, 47, fel, 48-49, M.A, 49; univ. fel, Northwest. Univ, 52-54, Ph.D.(Eng), 56. Instr. ENG, Auburn Univ, 49-52; UNIV. TOLEDO, 55-57, asst. prof, 57-61, assoc. prof, 61-66, PROF, 66-, ASSOC. CHMN. ENG, 66-, asst. chmn. Eng, 60-62, chmn. freshman Eng, 62-66, dir, 68-72, dir. grad. stud. Eng, 66-68. Mem. NCTE Comt. Bibliog. Col. Eng. Teaching, 62-69. MLA; NCTE; Conf. Col. Compos. & Commun; Midwest Mod. Lang. Asn.(secy. & chmn. bibliog. sect, 68-70). Eudora Welty; bibliography; the teaching of college composition. Publ: Co-ed, Language into literature, Sci. Res. Assoc, 65; auth, Welty's Keela: irony, ambiguity and the Ancient Mariner, 63 & Eudora Welty's revisions of A piece of news, 70, Stud. Short Fiction; Eudora Welty manuscripts: an annotated finding list, Bull. Bibliog, 63 & 74; plus others. Add: Dept. of English, University of Toledo, Toledo, OH 43606.

McDONNELL, ROBERT FRANCIS, b. Velva, N.Dak, Jan. 6, 28; m. 52; c. 8. ENGLISH. B.A, St. John's Univ.(Minn), 51; Univ. Vienna, 50-51; M.A, Univ. Minn, 54, Ph.D, 58. Instr. ENG, Iowa State Univ, 52-53; Ohio Univ. 57-59, asst. prof, 59-64, assoc. prof, 64-67; PROF. & CHMN. DEPT, WEST. WASH. STATE COL, 67- Consult. ed, Concerning Poetry, 68- U.S.A.F, 46-48, Sgt. Shakespeare Asn. Am. Shakespeare. Publ: Co-auth, The red badge of courage: text, sources and criticism, 60 & King Lear: text, sources and criticism, 62, Harcourt & Huck Finn and his critics, Macmillan, 62. Add: Dept. of English, Western Washington State College, Bellingham, WA 98225.

McDONOUGH, GEORGE E, b. Bridgeport, Conn, Mar, 25, 24; m. 49; c. 2. ENGLISH, CONTEMPORARY LITERATURE. B.A, Univ. Calif, 49; fel. & M.A, Johns Hopkins Univ, 50; M.Libr, Univ. Wash, 63; fel, Univ. Chicago, 65-66. Assoc. prof. Eng, Cascade Col, 57-62; asst. prof, Seattle Pac. Col, 62-65; libr. sci, Chicago State Univ, 65-66; Univ. Md, 66-67; Univ. Wash, 67-68; prof. Eng. & dir. learning resources, Seattle Pac. Col, 68-71; prof. Eng. & univ. librn, Hamline Univ, 71-73; PROF. ENG. & DIR. LEARNING RESOURCES, SEATTLE PAC. COL, 73- Mem, Invitational Conf. Educ. for Health Sci. Librarianship, Nat. Libr. Med. & Univ. Wash, summer 67; lectr, poetry, Wash. Writers Asn, West. Wash. State Col, summer 68; ed. jour, Inst. Res, Seattle Pac. Col, 68-71; prin. co-investr, Nat. Sci. Found-Hamline Univ. Inform. Syst. Develop. & Implementation Prog, 71-73; treas, Col. Libr. in Consortium, St. Paul, Minn, 72-73; vis. honors examr. anthrop, Macalester Col, 73. U.S.A, 42-46, Sgt. Am. Libr. Asn.(mem. Bogle Mem. Fund comt, libr. educ. div, 67-70, comt. comp. libr. orgn, libr. admin. div, 70-73); AAUP; Spec. Libr. Asn. Philosophical and cultural anthropology; metaphysics; bibliography. Publ: Collected poems, Univ. Calif, 49; co-auth, Anthropology through literature: cross-cultural perspectives, Little, 73; contrib. to Saturday Rev; Johns Hopkins Rev; Directions; Poetry Australia; Cath. Educ. Rev; Cath. Libr. World. Add: Weter Memorial Library, Seattle Pacific College, Seattle, WA 98119.

McDOUGAL, STUART YEATMAN, b. Los Angeles, Calif, Apr. 10, 42; m. 67; c. 2. ENGLISH & COMPARATIVE LITERATURE. B.A, Haverford Col, 64; M.A, Univ. Pa, 65, Ph.D.(Eng), 70. Lectr. Am. lit, Univ. Lausanne, 65-66; ASST. PROF. Am. stud, Mich. State Univ, 70-72; ENG. & COMP. LIT, UNIV. MICH, ANN ARBOR, 72- Am. Counc. Learned Soc. fel, 74-75. MLA; Eng. Inst; Am. Soc. 18th Century Stud. Modern poetry; Medieval Romance poetry; film. Publ: Ezra Pound and the troubadour tradition, Princeton, 72. Add: Dept. of English, University of Michigan, Ann Arbor, MI 48104.

McDOUGALD, (WILLIAM) WORTH, b. Statesboro, Ga, July 26, 25; m. 48; c. 2. JOURNALISM. A.B, Emory Univ, 47; Moss fel. & M.A, Univ. Ga, 56; Ph.D, Ohio State Univ, 64. From asst. prof. to assoc. prof. jour, UNIV. GA, 49-64, PROF. JOUR. & HEAD, RADIO-TV-FILM, 64- U.S.N.R, 43-46, 51-53, Lt. Comdr. Radio and television audience research; political broadcasting. Publ: Control of political broadcasting in the United States. Add: Henry W. Grady School of Journalism, University of Georgia, Athens, GA 30601.

McDOUGALL, GORDON, b. Inverness, Scotland, May 4, 41. ENGLISH. B.A. & M.A, Cambridge, 63. Dir, Granada TV, 63-66; asst. dir, Barrow-in-Furness, 64; Royal Court Theatre, London, 65; artistic dir, Traverse Theatre, Edinburgh, 66-68; Stables Theatre, Manchester, 68-71; dir, Gardner Theatre, Brighton, 71; artistic dir, Gardner Arts Ctr, Univ. Sussex, 72; ASSOC. PROF. DRAMA, UNIV. WATERLOO, 73- Artist in residence, Univ. York, 71. Contemporary theatre. Publ: The theatrical metaphor, Univ. Toronto, 74. Add: Dept. of Drama, University of Waterloo, Waterloo, Ont. N2L 3G1, Can.

McDOUGALL, ROBERT L, b. Vancouver, B.C, July 28, 18; m; c. 3. ENGLISH, CULTURAL HISTORY. B.A, Univ. B.C, 39; M.A, Univ. Toronto, 48, Ph.D.(Eng), 50. Lectr. ENG, Univ. Toronto, 50-54, asst. prof, 54-57; assoc. prof, CARLETON UNIV, 58-62, PROF, 62- Rockefeller award advan. res, 56-57; vis. prof, Australian Nat. Univ, 65-66. Can. Army, Maj. Asn. Can. Univ. Teachers Eng; Asn. Commonwealth Lit. & Lang. Stud.(chmn, 68, 72-73). Canadian literature; comparative studies in the literatures of the Commonwealth; interdisciplinary studies. Publ: Co-auth, The undergraduate essay, 58 & ed, Our living tradition (3 vols), 59, 62, 65, Univ. Toronto; ed, The clockmaker, McClelland & Stewart, 58 & Life in the clearings, Macmillan, 59; gen. ed, Carleton library (42 vols), Carleton Univ, 63-68; plus others. Add: Dept. of English, Carleton University, Rideau River Campus, Ottawa 1, Ont, Can.

McDOWELL, FREDERICK PETER WOLL, b. Philadelphia, Pa, May 29, 15; m. 53; c. 5. ENGLISH. B.S, Univ. Pa, 37, M.A, 38; Ph.D.(Eng), Harvard, 49. Instr. ENG, Washington & Jefferson Col, 38-39; Univ. Del, 39-41; instr, UNIV. IOWA, 49-51, asst. prof, 51-58, assoc. prof, 58-63, PROF, 63- Mem. ed. bd, Philol. Quart, 64-68; Eng. Lit. Transition, 64-; Shaw Rev, 65-; Papers Lang. & Lit, 66-; Nat. Endowment for Humanities sr. fel, 73-74. U.S.A, 41-46, Res, 46-61, Lt. Col.(Ret). MLA; Shaw Soc, Eng; N.Y. Shavians; Midwest. Mod. Lang. Asn; Joseph Conrad Soc. British and American literature since 1850; George Bernard Shaw; Bloomsbury group. Publ: Ellen Glasgow and the ironic art of fiction, Univ. Wis, 60; Elizabeth Madox Roberts, 63 & E.M. Forster, 69, Twayne; Caroline Gordon, Univ. Minn, 66; ed, The poet as critic, Northwest. Univ, 67; auth, E.M. Forster: an annotated bibliography of writings about him, Northern Ill. Univ, 74; Auden in his American phase, In: Aspects of American poetry, Ohio State Univ, 62; The Shavian world of John Bull's other island, PMLA, 67; Recent British fiction: some established writers, Contemporary Lit, XI: 401-431. Add: Dept. of English, University of Iowa, Iowa City, IA 52242.

McDOWELL, JOHN H, b. Tiffin, Ohio, May 25, 03; m. 35; c. 3. THEATRE HISTORY & CRITICISM. B.S, Boston Univ, 29; M.A, Univ. Wash, 33; Ph.D. (theatre), Yale, 37. Instr. theatre speech, Cornish Sch. Theatre, Seattle, 30-34; asst. prof, Wellesley Col, 36; hist. theatre, Smith Col, 37-44; theatre speech, Manhattanville Col, 44-45; HIST. THEATRE, OHIO STATE UNIV, 45-48, assoc. prof, 48-52, prof, 52-73, EMER. PROF, 73- Nat. Theatre Conf. fel, 50; Ohio State Univ. res. found. grants-in-aid, 50-68; Folger Shakespeare Libr. grant, summer 52; Ohio State Univ. develop. fund grant, 55-65; mem, Int. Congr. Libr. Performing Arts, 61-; U.S. mem, Comn. Bibliog. Iconographique Opera, 65- Int. Soc. Theatre Res. The early history of the box set; Filippo Juvarra's theatre in the Palazzo della Cancelleria in Rome; Pierre Dumont's theatre in a Jesuit seminary in Rome. Publ: The Renaissance stage: documents of Serlio, Sabbattini, and Furttenbach, Univ. Miami, 58; Original scenery and documents for productions of Uncle Tom's Cabin, Rev. Hist. Theatre, Paris, 63; The Ottoboni Theatre: a research adventure, Ohio State Univ. Theatre Collection Bull, 64; The Ohio State University Theatre Collection: a working and teaching collection, Acts VIIIe Congres Int. Bibliot. Muses Arts Spectacle, Amsterdam, 65. Add: 1977 Gulf Shore Blvd, Naples, FL 33940.

McDOWELL, JUDITH HOBSON, b. Chicago, Ill, May 18, 32; m. 52; c. 1. ENGLISH. B.A, Univ. Ore, 53; M.A, Univ. Minn, 57; Univ. Brussels, 57-58; Ph.D.(Eng), Univ. Denver, 61. Instr. Eng, Univ. Colo, 60-61 & 62-63; asst. prof. humanities, Colo. Woman's Col, 63-65, assoc. prof, 65-66; Eng, Tex. Woman's Univ, 66-73. MLA; AAUP. Literature. Publ: Auth. introd. & transl, Jean-Jacques Rousseau's La Nouvelle Héloïse, Pa. State Univ, 68; The themes of self and selflessness in Carson McCullers' fiction, Dragonfly, fall 70; Translations, adaptations and imitations of Shakespeare in 18th century France, Arlington Quart, winter 70-71. Add: 408 Westview Terrace, Arlington, TX 76013.

MACE, DEAN TOLLE, b. Neosho, Mo, May 21, 22; m. 50; c. 2. ENGLISH. A.B, Wash. Univ, 48; M.A, Columbia Univ, 49, Ph.D, 52. Instr. ENG, Wash. Univ, 50-52; VASSAR COL, 52-54, asst. prof, 54-59, assoc. prof, 59-66, PROF, 66- Vis. reader Eng, Univ. York, Eng, 66-67. MLA. Renaissance; 18th century. Add: Dept. of English, Vassar College, Poughkeepsie, NY 12601.

MacEACHEN, DOUGALD BERNARD, b. N.S, Can, July 25, 13; nat; m. 46; c. 4. ENGLISH. B.A, Cath. Univ. Am, 36; M.A, Columbia Univ, 42; Ph.D, Univ. Cincinnati, 48. Instr. Eng. & Latin, Portsmouth Priory Sch, R.I, 37-42; instr. ENG, JOHN CARROLL UNIV, 48-50, asst. prof, 50-55, assoc. prof, 55-60, PROF, 60- U.S.A, 42-45. NCTE. Victorian age. Publ: Wilkie Collins and British law, Nineteenth-Century Fiction. Add: 5255 Lynd Ave, Cleveland, OH 44124.

MACEDO, CELESTINO D, b. New Bedford, Mass, Feb. 25, 26; m. 55; c. 4. ENGLISH. A.B, Stonehill Col, 53; fel, Boston Col, 53-54, A.M, 54; Boston Univ. Instr. Eng. compos, SOUTHEAST. MASS. UNIV, 55-59, asst. prof. Milton & Chaucer, 59-64, ASSOC. PROF. ENG, 64-, DIR. STUDENT AFFAIRS, 68-, chmn. world lit. sect, 64-68. Consult, New Bedford Pub. Libr, 60-61; lectr, Mass. State Col. Bridgewater, 63. MLA; Col. Eng. Asn. Probable source to Chaucer's Prioress's tale; Milton's debt to scholasticism. Add: Dept. of English, Southeastern Massachusetts University, North Dartmouth, MA 02747.

McELROY, BERNARD PATRICK, JR, b. Newark, N.J, Sept. 25, 38. ENGLISH LITERATURE. B.A, Univ. Notre Dame, 60; M.A, Cornell Univ, 69, Ph.D. (Eng), 71. Res. assoc, Basford Inc, N.Y.C, 64-66; ASST. PROF. ENG, LOYOLA UNIV. CHICAGO, 70- Sig.C, U.S.A, 60-64, Lt. MLA. Shakespeare; Renaissance English literature; modern fiction. Publ: Shakespeare's mature tragedies, Princeton Univ, 73. Add: Dept. of English, Loyola University of Chicago, 6525 Sheridan Rd, Chicago, IL 60626.

McELROY, CLYDE WAYNE, b. Waco, Tex, Jan. 6, 21. SPEECH, DRAMA. B.A, Baylor Univ, 42, M.A, 50; Ed.D, Univ. Va, 58. Asst, Baylor Univ, 49-50; instr. drama, Wake Forest Col, 51-56; part-time instr, Univ. Va, 56-58; asst. prof. speech & drama, MONTCLAIR STATE COL, 58-62, assoc. prof, 62-67, PROF. SPEECH, 67- U.S.A, 42-45. Speech Commun. Asn; Am. Theatre Asn; East. States Speech Asn. Drama; theatre history; public address. Add: Dept. of Speech & Theater, Montclair State College, Upper Montclair, NJ 07043.

McELROY, DAVIS DUNBAR, b. San Francisco, Calif, Aug 1, 17; m. 62; c. 1. ENGLISH LITERATURE. B.A, Univ. Calif, Berkeley, 49; Ph.D.(Eng), Univ. Edinburgh, 52. Asst. prof. Eng, Ore. State Univ, 60-62; Wash. State Univ, 62-66, assoc. prof, 68-70; CHMN. HUMANITIES, CENTRALIA COL, 70- U.S.N, 42-46, Lt. Publ: Existentialism and modern literature, 64 & The study of literature, 65, Philos. Libr; Scotland's age of improvement, Wash. State Univ, 70. Add: Dept. of Humanities, Centralia College, Centralia, WA 98531.

McELROY, MAURINE D, b. Eastland, Tex, Sept. 28, 13; m. 37; c. 2. ENGLISH, HISTORY. B.A, Tex. Tech Univ, 37; M.A, Hardin-Simmons Univ, 41; Ph.D.(Eng), Univ. Tex, 64. Teacher, High Schs, Tex, 51-57; instr. ENG, Del Mar Col, 57-59; teaching assoc, instr. & lectr, UNIV. TEX, AUSTIN, 63-69, ASSOC. PROF, 69- Renaissance Soc. Am; MLA; Col. Eng. Asn; S.Cent. Renaissance Conf; S.Cent. Mod. Lang. Asn. Literary patronage and propaganda during the English Renaissance; propaganda and literature on the western frontiers; philosophy and methods of biography. Publ: Colonial propaganda for northern Mexico, J. West, 10/70; Poe's last partner: E.H.N. Patterson of Oquawka, Illinois, Papers Lang. & Lit, 71. Add: Dept. of English, Parlin 110, University of Texas at Austin, Austin, TX 78712.

McEVOY, J. EDWARD, b. Syracuse, N.Y, July 14, 09. SPEECH. A.B, Syracuse Univ, 36, M.A, 40; Ph.D.(speech), Univ. South. Calif, 53; summer, Univ. Hawaii, 60. Freshman debate coach, Syracuse Univ, 36-40, instr. pub. address, 38-54, asst. dir. summer sessions, pub. address prog, 48-54, chmn, 60-63, dir. stud. speakers bur, 54-58, asst. prof. pub. address & dir. discussion & debate, 54-63; assoc. prof. pub. address, STATE UNIV. N.Y. COL. OSWEGO, 63-64, PROF. SPEECH & CHMN. DEPT. SPEECH & THEATRE, 64- Lectr, Univ. South. Calif, 52-53. U.S.A.F, 40-48, Res, 48-65, Lt. Col. Speech Commun Asn; Am. Forensic Asn; Speech Asn. East. States; Int. Soc. Gen. Semantics. Argumentation; semantics. Add: Dept. of Speech & Theatre, State University of New York College at Oswego, Oswego, NY 13126.

McEVOY, POYNTER, b. Ft. Wayne, Ind, Jan. 7, 08; m. 37; c. 2. JOURNALISM. A.B, DePauw Univ, 29. Assoc, McPherson Metropolitan Newspaper Survs, 30-36; asst. mgr, St. Petersburg Times, Fla, 36-39; co-pub, Roswell Morning Dispatch, N.Mex, 39-44; advertising mgr, Hickory Daily Record, N.C, 44-47; from asst. prof. to prof. jour, IND. UNIV. BLOOMINGTON, 47-73, gen. mgr, Daily Student, 47-69, EMER. PROF. JOUR, 73- Assoc. mem, Inst. Newspaper Controllers & Finance Off, 50- Asn. Educ. in Jour. Newspaper content analysis; economics of major media; computerized newspaper cost accounting. Add: Dept. of Journalism, Indiana University, Bloomington, IN 47401.

McEWEN, FRED BATES, b. Pittsburgh, Pa, Jan. 31, 29; m. 61. ENGLISH. A.B, Allegheny Col, 51; M.A, Univ. Pittsburgh, 55, Ph.D.(Eng), 61. Grad. asst. Eng, Univ. Pittsburgh, 55-57; asst. to the dean, sch. gen. stud, 57-58, instr. ENG, 58-61; asst. prof, Morris Harvey Col, 61-62; assoc. prof, WAYNESBURG COL, 62-65, PROF, 65-, CHMN. DEPT. 70- U.S.A, 51-53. MLA; NCTE. English language and literature; philosophy and literature; comparative literature. Publ: Phenomenology in literary criticism, Lock Haven Rev, 68; Phenomenological criticism: Kafka as example, Dasein, 69; Description in the reading and appreciation of novels, Ohio Eng. Bull, 5/73; plus one other. Add: Dept. of English, Waynesburg College, Waynesburg, PA 15370.

McEWEN, GEORGE MIDDLETON, b. Cook Co, Ill, Nov. 21, 08; m. 32; c. 2. ENGLISH. B.A, Park Col, 31; M.A, Northwest. Univ, 35; fel, Univ. Mich, 38-40, Ph.D.(Eng), 46. Instr. ENG, Colo, Agr. & Mech. Col, 31-34, asst. prof, 34-38; instr, Col. Engineering, Univ. Mich, Ann Arbor, 40-47, asst. prof, 47-50, assoc. prof, 50-55, prof, 55-74, chmn. dept, 64-66, secy, summer session, 48-53, univ. senate, 50-58; RETIRED. MLA; NCTE; Am. Stud. Asn. Impressionistic criticism; theories of tragedy and tragic sense; literature of American pioneer settlement. Add: 1706 Hanover Rd, Ann Arbor, MI 48103.

McEWEN, GILBERT D, b. Mason City, Iowa, Jan. 17, 16; m. 42; c. 2. ENGLISH. B.A, State Univ, Iowa, 37; Univ. Minn, 38-39; M.A, Yale, 41, Ph.D. (Eng), 50. Instr. ENG, State Univ. Iowa, 46; West. Reserve Univ, 46-50, asst. prof, 50-53; instr. Pasadena City Col, 53-55; asst. prof, WHITTIER COL, 55-58, assoc. prof, 58-65, PROF, 65-, chmn. dept, 65-71. Grants, Danforth Found, 60, Huntington Libr, 63, Am. Philos. Soc. 63 & 69. U.S.A, 43-46. MLA. Restoration prose and poetry; restoration journalism; contemporary novel. Publ: How to be a better speller, Crowell, 53; The oracle of the Coffee House: John Dunton's Athenian Mercury, Huntington Libr, 72. Add: Dept. of English, Whittier College, Whittier, CA 90608.

MACEY, SAMUEL L, b. London, Eng, Mar. 12, 22; m. 54; c. 2. ENGLISH LITERATURE. B.A, Univ. B.C, 64; Ph.D.(Eng), Univ. Wash, 66. Asst. prof. ENG, UNIV. VICTORIA (B.C), 66-72, ASSOC. PROF, 72- Can. Counc. fels, 67, 72; vis. scholar, Corpus Christi Col, Cambridge, 72. R.N.V.R, 41-46, Lt. Johnson Soc. Northwest (pres, 72-73); Am. Soc. 18th Century Stud; Brit. Horological Inst; fel. Inst. Work Stud. Practitioners, Gt. Brit. Eighteenth century English and comparative literature; impact of technology on literature. Publ: Ed, A learned dissertation on Dumpling (1726), together with Pudding and Dumpling burnt to pot (1727), Augustan Reprint Soc, 70; auth, Non-heroic tragedy: a pedigree for American tragic drama, Comp. Lit. Stud, 69; The introduction of Shakespeare into Germany during the second half of the eighteenth century, 18th Century Stud, 71-72; On dividing the loot: the delegation of power, Yale Rev, 72. Add: Dept. of English, University of Victoria, Victoria, B.C, Can.

McFADDEN, GEORGE, b. Brooklyn, N.Y, July 5, 16; m. 44. ENGLISH. A.B, St. Francis Col.(N.Y), 38; M.A, Brooklyn Col, 48; Ph.D, Columbia Univ, 52. Instr. ENG, Duquesne Univ, 48-52, asst. prof, 52-55; instr, TEMPLE UNIV, 55-57, asst. prof, 57-60, assoc. prof, 60-66, PROF, 66- U.S.A, 42-46. MLA; Int. Comp. Lit. Asn. Literary criticism; John Dryden. Publ: Dryden's Most barren period—and Milton, Huntington Libr. Quart, 61; Probings for an integration: color symbolism in Wallace Stevens, Mod. Philol, 61; Elkanah Settle and the genesis of Mac Flecknoe, Philol. Quart, 1/64. Add: Dept. of English, Temple University, Philadelphia, PA 19122.

McFADYEN, ALVAN ROBBINS, b. Fayetteville, N.C, Aug. 23, 06; m. 42; c. 1. ENGLISH. A.B, Univ. N.C, 31; M.A, Duke Univ, 41; fel, Univ. Fla, 50-52, Ph.D.(Eng), 55. Instr, Univ. Minn, 46; prof. ENG, Austin Col, 46-49; asst. prof, UNIV. TAMPA, 52-55, from assoc. prof. to PROF, 55- U.S.N.R, 42-46, Lt. MLA; NCTE; S.Atlantic Mod. Lang. Asn. American literature and linguistics. Add: 4001 Euclid Ave, Tampa, FL 33606.

McFARLAND, ALICE, b. Holyrood, Kans, Sept. 10, 13; m. 37; c. 1. ENGLISH, LITERATURE. B.S, Univ. Kans, 35; M.A, Ft. Hays Kans. State Col, 57. Instr. Eng. & speech, Spearville High Sch, 35-37; Wilson High Sch, 45-50; instr. Eng. & lit, FT. HAYS KANS. STATE COL, 55-57, ENG. COMPOS. & LIT, 57-60, asst. prof, 60-72, ASSOC. PROF, 72- Add: Dept. of English, Ft. Hays Kansas State College, Hays, KS 67601.

McFARLAND, GEORGE FOSTER, b. Philadelphia, Pa, Oct. 6, 21; m. 65; c. 3. ENGLISH LITERATURE. A.B, Wesleyan Univ, 46; M.A, Univ. Chicago, 50; Ph.D.(Eng), Univ. Pa, 64. Instr. ENG, ST. LAWRENCE UNIV, 52-58, asst. prof, 58-64, assoc. prof, 64-67, PROF, 67-, CHMN. DEPT, 71-, asst. to pres, 64-65. Am. Counc. Learned Soc. grant-in-aid, 67-68; Ford Found-St. Lawrence Univ. grant-in-aid humanities, 68, 71. Mil.Intel.Serv, 43-45, T/Sgt. MLA. Biography of J.C. Hare, especially his literary and intellectual associations; English Romanticism, especially Wordsworth and Coleridge, in the Victorian Age; 20th century fiction in America. Publ: Julius Charles Hare: his literary career from 1818-1834, John Rylands Libr, 64; J.C. Hare: Coleridge, DeQuincey, and German literature, 9/64 & Wordsworth and Julius Hare, spring 73, Bull. John Rylands Libr. Add: Box 76, R.D. 1, Norwood, NY 13668.

McFARLAND, RONALD EARL, b. Bellaire, Ohio, Sept. 22, 42; m. 66; c. 1. SEVENTEENTH CENTURY ENGLISH LITERATURE, POETRY. B.A, Fla. State Univ, 63, M.A, 65; Ph.D.(Eng), Univ. Ill, Urbana, 70. Instr. ENG, Sam Houston State Col, 65-67; asst. prof, UNIV IDAHO, 70-74, ASSOC. PROF, 74- MLA. Seventeenth century poetry and prose; American poetry, especially modern. Publ: Co-ed, American controversy, Scott, 68; auth, Vision and perception in the works of Eudora Welty, Markham Rev, 2/71; Jonson's Magnetic lady and the reception of Gilbert's De magnete, Stud. Eng. Lit, spring 71; The Rhodian Colossus in Renaissance emblem and poetry, Eng. Miscellany, 74. Add: Dept. of English, University of Idaho, Moscow, ID 83843.

McFARLAND, THOMAS (ALFRED, JR), b. Birmingham, Ala, Sept. 13, 26. ENGLISH LITERATURE. A.B, Harvard, 49; M.A, Yale, 51, Ph.D, 53. Fulbright scholar, Univ. Tübingen, 53-54; instr. Eng, Oberlin Col, 54-56; Univ. Va, 56-58; asst. prof, West. Reserve Univ, 58-62, assoc. prof, 62-64, prof, 64-67; ENG. & COMP. LIT, GRAD. SCH, CITY UNIV. NEW YORK & ENG, HUNTER COL, 67-73, DISTINGUISHED PROF, 73- Guggenheim fels, 64-65 & 74-75; vis. prof, Univ. Colo, summer 68; mem, Columbia Sem. on Romantic Movement & 19th Century, 71-; vis. prof, Univ. Va, spring 72; Am. Counc. Learned Soc. fel, 73-74; chmn. supv. comt, Eng. Inst, 74; vis. prof, Yale, spring 75. U.S.N.R, 44-46. MLA (chmn. Eng. 9, 74). English Renaissance, Romanticism; literary theory. Publ: Tragic meanings in Shakespeare, Random, 66; Coleridge and the pantheist tradition, Clarendon, 69; Shakespeare's pastoral comedy, Univ. N.C, 72; The origin and significance of Coleridge's theory of secondary imagination, In: New perspectives on Coleridge and Wordsworth: selected papers from the English Institute, Columbia Univ, 72; The symbiosis of Coleridge and Wordsworth, Stud. in Romanticism, 72; Poetry and the poem: the structure of poetic content, In: Literary theory and structure: essays in honor of William K. Wimsatt, Yale Univ, 73; plus others. Add: Dept. of English, City University of New York Graduate School, 33 W. 42nd St, New York, NY 10036.

McFATE, PATRICIA ANN, b. Detroit, Mich. MODERN LITERATURE, ANGLO-IRISH LITERATURE. B.A, Mich. State Univ, 58; M.A, Northwest. Univ, 60, Ph.D.(Eng), 65; Univ. Ill, Chicago Circle, 58-60; Columbia Univ, 60-62. Staff physiologist, Sch. of Engineering & Appl. Sci, Columbia Univ, 60-62; instr. humanities, Univ. ILL, CHICAGO CIRCLE, 62-64, asst. prof. ENG, 65-70, ASSOC. PROF, 70-, ASSOC. V.CHANCELLOR ACAD. AFFAIRS & EXEC. ASST. TO CHANCELLOR, 74-, asst. dean lib. arts & sci, 67-73, chancellor's admin. intern, 73-74. Lectr. Eng, City Col. New York, 62; staff mem, Sch. Engineering & Appl. Sci, Columbia Univ, 62-64, participant, U.S.A.F. proj, 64; consult. hemat, Presby-St. Luke's Hosp, Chicago, 66-67; attending, Rush-Presby. St. Luke's Med. Ctr, Chicago, 67-; Univ. Ill. fac. fel, 68; vis. assoc. prof. hemat, Rush Med. Col, 71-; Am. Counc. Educ. acad. admin. intern, 73-74. MLA; Int. Asn. Stud. Anglo-Irish Lit; Can. Asn. Irish Stud. Irish literary revival; modern Irish fiction; the creative arts. Publ: Ed, Edward Martyn's The dream physician, DePaul Univ, 72; auth, Education for the itinerant student, Comt. Inst. Cooperation, 73; James Stephens' Deirdre and its legendary sources, Eire-Ireland, 69; W.B. Yeats'

Where there is nothing: theme and symbolism, Irish Univ. Rev, 72; Deirdre and The wooing of Becfola, In: Toward the modern: portents of the movement, South. Ill. Univ, 72. Add: Office of the Chancellor, University of Illinois at Chicago Circle, Box 4348, Chicago, IL 60680.

McGALLIARD, JOHN CALVIN, b. Connelly Springs, N.C, Oct. 12, 06. ENGLISH. B.A, Univ. N.C, 24, M.A, 25; M.A, Harvard, 29, Ph.D, 30; Univ. Paris, France, 30-31. Instr. Eng, Northwest. Univ, 25-28; Sheldon traveling fel, Harvard, 30-31; asst. prof. ENG, UNIV. IOWA, 31-46, assoc. prof, 46-47, PROF, 47- Vis. prof, Univ. Colo, 49, 51, Univ. Va, 52-53, Univ. N.C, 52-56, Univ. Wis, summers, 57, 64, Duke Univ, 62, 65, 66 & Univ. Notre Dame, 65-66; off. vis. for U.S. Off. Educ, summer Eng. insts, Univ. Wash, Stanford Univ. & Univ. Nev, summer 62; mem. consult. bd, Mod. Humanities Res. Asn. U.S.A, 43-45. MLA (chmn. Old Eng. group, 57, Eng. sect. I, 65 & Chaucer group, 66); Ling. Soc. Am; Mediaeval Acad. Am; Midwest Mod. Lang. Asn. Old Norse; Mediaeval comparative literature; general linguistics. Publ: Co-auth, A college Bible, Appleton, 38, Literary scholarship, Univ. N.C, 41, Masterpieces of world literature, Norton, 56 & 65 & Life and thought in the Early Middle Ages, Univ. Minn, 67; auth, Chaucerian comedy: the Merchant's tale, Jonson, and Moliere, Philol. Quart, 1/46; The complex art of Beowulf, Mod. Philol, 5/62; Links, language, and style in The pearl, Univ. Tex. Stud. Lang, Lit, & Cult. Middle Ages & Later, 69; plus one other. Add: Dept. of English, University of Iowa, Iowa City, IA 52240.

McGANN, JEROME JOHN, b. Brooklyn, N.Y, July 22, 37; m. 60; c. 3. ENGLISH. B.S, LeMoyne Col, 59; M.A, Syracuse Univ, 61; Fulbright fel. & Fels Found. fel, Yale, 65-66, Ph.D.(Eng), 66. Assoc. prof. ENG, UNIV. CHICAGO, 66-72, PROF, 72- Guggenheim fel, 69-70. Am. Philos. Soc. Award, 67; Melville Cane Award, Am. Poetry Soc, 73. MLA; Byron Soc; Keats-Shelley Mem. Asn, Eng; Tennyson Soc. British and comparative literature; 19th & 20th centuries literature. Publ: Fiery dust: Byron's poetic development, 68 & Swinburne: an experiment in criticism, 72, Univ. Chicago; ed, Pelham, Univ. Nebr, 72; auth, The beauty of the Medusa: a study in romantic literary iconology, Stud. Romanticism, winter 72; Romanticism and the embarrassments of critical tradition, Mod. Philol, 2/73; contrib, The aims of Blake's prophecies and the uses of Blake criticism in Blake's Sublime allegory, Univ. Wis, 73. Add: 5301 S. University Ave, Chicago, IL 60637.

McGAUGHEY, FLORENCE HELEN, b. Roachdale, Ind, Mar. 1, 04. ENGLISH. A.B, DePauw Univ, 26; A.M, Middlebury Col, 32; Ind. Univ, 38; Ind. State Teachers Col, 49. Asst. prof. ENG, IND. STATE UNIV, TERRE HAUTE, 46-57, assoc. prof, 57-61, prof, 61-70, EMER. PROF, 70- Scholar, Ind. Univ. Writers Conf, 45-46; mem. int. comt. & dipl. signalazione, Centro Studi e Scambi Int, Rome, 61-62, poet laureat, 62, hon. rep; mem, Acad. Am. Poets. Awards, Int. Poets Corner, 48-60; Alumni Citation, DePauw Univ, 59; Dipl. Merit & Medal of Honor, Centro Studi e Scambi Int, Rome, 67. Mod. Poetry Asn; fel. Int. Poetry Soc. Poetry; essay. Publ: Spring is a blue kite, Emory Univ, 46; Reaching for the spring, Exposition, 58; Selected poems, 62 & Shadows, 65, Mondo-Rome, Italy; ed. & contrib, History of First Christian Church, 73; Petals from a plum tree, Am. Poet, 67; Post office, 66 & Privacy we do not have, 67, Christian Sci. Monitor. Add: 136 S. 25th St, Terre Haute, IN 47803.

McGAVOCK, INA BETH, b. Seguin, Tex; m. 38. ENGLISH. A.B, Southwest. Univ, 22, A.M, 23; A.M, Vanderbilt Univ, 24; Kidd-Key Conserv, 27. Instr. Ala. Col, 24-25; Kidd-Key Col. & Conserv, 26-27; prof. Eng. & chmn. dept, Westmoorland Col. & Univ. San Antonio, 28-38; 39-42; assoc. prof. Eng, Trinity Univ, 42-69; RETIRED. Mem. loan comt. & scholars comt, Minnie Stevens Piper Found, 74. MLA; Col. Eng. Asn; Mod. Humanities Res. Asn, Gr. Brit. Shakespeare; English literature, Victorian era; William Alexander Percy. Publ: Dramatic monologue (book), PMLA. Add: 1702 Waverly Ave, San Antonio, TX 78201.

McGAW, CHARLES JAMES, b. Grand Rapids, Mich, Aug. 30, 10; SPEECH. A.B, Univ. Mich, 32, A.M, Ph.D, 40. Asst. prof, Ithaca Col, 40-42; Univ. Mich, 46; speech, Ohio State Univ, 46-47, assoc. prof, 47-57; PROF. ACTING & DIRECTING & HEAD DEPT. EDUC, GOODMAN SCH. DRAMA, ART INST. CHICAGO, 57-, DEAN, 66- Vis. assoc. prof, sch. dramatic art, Columbia Univ, 56-57; lectr, Univ. Chicago, 57-62; Am. Spec. grant, Univ. Bahia, 61; vis. prof, Northwest. Univ, summers 62 & 63, Tulane Univ, 64-65, Univ. Minn, summer 65 & Univ. Hawaii, summer 68; mem. adv. comt. theatre arts & comt. int. exchange of persons, Conf. Bd. of Assoc. Res. Counc, 66- U.S.N.R, 42-46, Lt. Speech Commun. Asn; Am. Theatre Asn. (assoc. ed, Educ. Theatre J, 63-67). Theatre; analysis of the theatrical criticism of William Winter; against the illusionistic approach to directing. Publ: Acting is believing, 55 & rev. ed, 66, Holt. Add: Goodman School of Drama, Art Institute of Chicago, Chicago, IL 60603.

McGEHEE, JUDSON DODDS, b. Akron, Ohio, Apr. 20, 27; m. 56; c. 6. ENGLISH. B.A, Stanford Univ, 51, Arthur A. Newhouse scholar, 51, M.A, 52; San Jose State Col, 53-54; univ. fel, Univ. Mich, 54, 55, Ph.D.(Eng. lang. & lit), 58. Teaching fel. Eng. comp, Univ. Mich, 56-58; instr. ENG, Northwest. Univ, 58-61; asst. prof, NORTH. ARIZ. UNIV, 61-66, ASSOC. PROF. & DIR. CREATIVE WRITING PROG, 66- U.S.A, 46-47. Creative writing; English literature. Publ: Contrib, Poems Southwest, Prescott Col, 68; plus other poems in literary magazines. Add: Dept. of English, Northern Arizona University, Box 5656, Flagstaff, AZ 86001.

McGHEE, NANCY B, b. High Point, N.C, Mar. 19, 13; m. 55. ENGLISH, HUMANITIES. A.B, Shaw Univ, 30, hon. D.H, 73; M.A, Columbia Univ, 31; Rosenwald & Gen. Educ. Bd. fels, Univ. Chicago, 40-42, Ph.D, 42; Univ. London, 51-52. Instr. ENG, Louisville Munic. Col, 31-39, asst. prof, 39-42, assoc. prof, 42-45; prof, HAMPTON INST, 45-67, AVALON FOUND. PROF. HUMANITIES, 67-, CHMN. DEPT. ENG, 45- V.pres, Nat. Counc. Negro Women, 55-58; pres, Va. Humanities Conf, 72-73. Distinguished Alumni Award, Shaw Univ, 60; Distinguished Teaching Award, Hampton Inst, 65. NCTE; Am. Asn. Univ. Women (mem. comt. standards in higher educ, 71-); Asn. Depts. Eng.(mem. exec. comt, 73-76). Negro literature; Negro preacher; slave narratives. Publ: English critics and the Negro writers, Phylon, 54; ed, Hampton Institute and the humanities, Hampton Inst, 70; On the trail of Negro folksongs, J. Am. Folklore, 65; The folk sermon—

a facet of Black literary heritage, CLA J, 9/69; Langston Hughes, poet in the folk manner, In: Langston Hughes, Black genius, Morrow, 71; plus others. Add: Dept. of English, Hampton Institute, Hampton, VA 23668.

McGHEE, RICHARD DENNIS, b. Rogers Co, Okla, Apr. 26, 40; m. 58; c. 3. ENGLISH LITERATURE. B.A, Univ. Mo-Kansas City, 62; NDEA fel, Univ. Okla, 62-66, M.A, 64, Ph.D.(Eng), 67. Instr. ENG, Univ. Okla, 66-67; asst. prof, KANS. STATE UNIV, 67-71, ASSOC. PROF, 71- MLA; Midwest Mod. Lang. Asn. English Romantic poetry; English Victorian poetry; 19th century British nonfictional prose. Publ: Thalassius: Swinburne's poetic myth, Victorian Poetry, summer 67; A view of Wordsworth's Laodamia, Stud. Philol, 7/71. Add: Dept. of English, Kansas State University, Manhattan, KS 66502.

McGILL, BRUCE DAVIDSON, b. Chidester, Ark, July 4, 24. ENGLISH. M.A, Univ. Ark, 48; Columbia Univ. ASST. PROF. ENG, South. State Col, 49-56; SOUTHEAST. LA. UNIV, 56- U.S.A.A.F, 45-47. NCTE; NEA; S.Cent. Mod. Lang. Asn. Communication; world literature; 17th and 18th century English literature. Add: Box 409, College Station, Hammond, LA 70401.

McGILL, FREDERICK THOMAS, JR, b. Newton Highlands, Mass, May 6, 04; m. 31; c. 2. AMERICAN LITERATURE. A.B, Harvard, 25, A.M, 28. Instr. ENG, N.J. Law Sch, 28-30; asst. prof, Dana Col, 30-36; Univ. Newark, 36-46; assoc. prof, NEWARK CAMPUS, RUTGERS UNIV, 46-58, prof, 58-69, dir. div. humanities, 58-62, assoc. dean, 62-69, EMER. PROF, 69- Assoc. mgr, Star Island Conf. Ctr, 52-73. MLA; Thoreau Soc.(pres, 72-73); Col. Eng. Asn. Life and work of William Ellery Channing II; cultural history of the Isles of Shoals. Publ: Channing of Concord, Rutgers Univ, 67; ed, Letters to Celia, Star Island Corp, 72; co-ed, Ten miles out, Isles of Shoals Asn, 72. Add: 274 Old Short Hills Rd, Short Hills, NJ 07078.

McGILLEY, MARY JANET, S.C.L, b. Kansas City, Mo, Dec. 4, 24. ENGLISH. B.A, St. Mary Col.(Kans), 45; M.A, Boston Col, 51; Ph.D.(Eng), Fordham Univ, 56, summers, Univ. Notre Dame, 60; Columbia Univ, 64. Social worker, Cath. Welfare Bur, Mo, 45-46; teacher high sch, Kans, 48-50; Mont, 51-53; instr. Eng, ST. MARY COL.(KANS), 56-58, asst. prof, 58-60, assoc. prof, 60-64; prof, 64, PRES, 64- NCTE. English Renaissance and metaphysical literature; contemporary literature; literary theory and criticism. Publ: Contrib. to Univ. Rev; Col. Eng; West. Humanities Rev; plus others. Add: St. Mary College, Leavenworth, KS 66048.

MacGILLIVRAY, ARTHUR A, S.J, b. Boston, Mass, Sept. 10, 12. ENGLISH. M.A, Univ. Minn, 47. Chmn. dept. ENG, Fairfield Univ, 47-53; ASST. PROF, BOSTON COL, 53- ed, fac. newslett, 59-69. Col. Eng. Asn; NCTE. Contemporary poetry; fiction; drama. Publ: Sufficient wisdom. Add: Dept. of English, Boston College, Chestnut Hill, MA 02167.

McGINN, DONALD JOSEPH, b. Indian Lake, N.Y, Apr. 1, 05; m. 40; c. 2. ENGLISH LITERATURE. A.B, Cornell Univ, 26, A.M, 29; Ph.D, 30. Teacher, Rutgers Prep. Sch, N.J, 30-36; instr. ENG, RUTGERS UNIV, 36-40, asst. prof, 40-46, assoc. prof, 46-51, prof, 51-73, EMER. PROF, 73-; PROF, GEORGIAN COURT COL, 52- Lectr, Georgian Court Col, 45-52. Cath. Comn. Intellectual & Cult. Affairs (secy, 60-61); Cent. Atlantic Col. Coun.(pres, 56-58); Renaissance Soc. Am; MLA; Shakespeare Asn. Am. Shakespeare; Elizabethan drama; pamphlet literature. Publ: Shakespeare's influence on the drama of his age, Rutgers Univ, 38 & Octagon, 65; sr. ed, Literature as a fine art, Row, Peterson, 60, Gordian, 67; auth, John Penry and the Marprelate controversy, Rutgers Univ, 66; What is Baroque art?, America, 52; A quip from Tom Nashe, Stud. Eng. Renaissance Drama, (in memory of Karl Holzknecht), 59; Cleopatra's immolation scene, Essays Lit. Hist, (presented to J.M. French), 60; plus others. Add: 2 President Ave, Lavallette, NJ 08735.

McGINTY, CAROLYN, b. Chicago, Ill, Jan. 7, 21. LITERARY CRITICISM, AMERICAN LITERATURE. Ph.B, Loyola Univ. Chicago, 43, M.A, 49; Ph.D.(Eng), Cath. Univ. Am, 63. Instr. Eng, ROSARY COL, 63-65, ASST. PROF, 65-, resident dir. semester in London, 73-75. Consult, Scholastic Testing Serv, Bensenville, Ill, 67- AAUP; Col. Eng. Asn; MLA; NCTE. Linguistics and stylistics; Henry James' prose style. Publ: The Jamesian parenthesis, Univ. Microfilm, 64. Add: Dept. of English, Rosary College, 7900 W. Division St, River Forest, IL 60305.

McGLINCHEE, CLAIRE, b. Newtonville, Mass. ENGLISH. A.B, Radcliffe Col, 21; Longy Sch. Music, 22; A.M, Columbia Univ, 24, Ph.D, 40. Teacher Eng, Achard Sch. Girls, Brookline, Mass, 21-22; Eng. & choral music, Acad. Holy Child, N.Y, 22-23; from instr. to PROF. ENG, HUNTER COL, 24-, George N. Shuster Fund grant, 63. MLA; Renaissance Soc. Am; Soc. Theatre Res, Eng; Am. Soc. Theatre Res; Int. Fed. Theatre Res. American literature. Publ: The first decade of the Boston Museum: 1941-1951, Humphries, 40; James Russell Lowell, In: United States authors, series, Twayne, 67; James Russell Lowell, Am. Biog. Encycl; Julia Arthur, In: Notable Am. Women, Vol. I, Harper. Add: 30 E. 68th St, New York, NY 10021.

McGLON, CHARLES ADDIS, b. New Smyrna, Fla, June 27, 10; m. 33; c. 2. SPEECH. B.A.E, Univ. Fla, 36, fel. & M.A.E, 39; Ph.D, Columbia Univ, 51. Teacher high schs, Fla, 32-38; instr. reading, speaking & writing, Univ. Fla, 38-40; asst. prof. speech & drama, Peabody Col, 40-43; mem. fac. SPEECH, SOUTH. BAPTIST THEOL. SEM, 43-47, PROF, 47- Consult. speech rehabil, Veterans Admin, Ky, 48-51. Speech Commun. Asn; South. Speech Commun. Asn.(pres, 48). Speech in theological education; mass media of communications; drama in the church. Publ: Speech education in Baptist Theological Seminaries in the United States, 1819-1943. Add: Dept. of Speech, Southern Baptist Theological Seminary, Louisville, KY 40206.

McGLONE, EDWARD LEON, b. Athens, Ohio, Sept. 20, 41; m. 63; c. 2. SPEECH COMMUNICATION. B.A. & M.A, Ohio State Univ, 63; Ph.D.(interpersonal commun), Ohio Univ, 67. Asst. prof. speech, North. Ill, Univ, 64-68; Wash. State Univ, 68-70; ASSOC. PROF. SPEECH COMMUN, WAYNE STATE UNIV, 70- Consult. ed, Cent. States Speech J, 71-73; mem. ed. bd, Speech Teacher, 72- Speech Commun. Asn; AAUP; Int. Commun. Asn. Behavioral studies in speech communication; speech education; research methods. Publ: Co-auth, Understanding oral communication, 72 & Introductory readings in oral communication, 72, Cummings Publ; auth, Toward improved quantitative research in forensics, J. Am Forensic Asn, 69; Toward an operational definition and measurement of understanding, Cent. States Speech J, 70; co-auth, Dimensions of teacher credibility, Speech Teacher, 9/73. Add: Dept. of Speech Communication & Theatre, Wayne State University, Detroit, MI 48202.

McGLONE, ROBERT ERNEST, Experimental Phonetics, Acoustics. See 12th Edition, American Men & Women of Science, Physical & Biological Section.

McGLYNN, PAUL DUMON, b. Detroit, Mich, July 11, 37; m. 63; c. 2. ENGLISH. Ph.B, Univ. Detroit, 59, M.A, 61; Ph.D.(Eng), Rice Univ, 67. Instr. ENG, Univ. Detroit, 61-62; EAST. MICH. UNIV, 64-67, asst. prof, 67-71, ASSOC. PROF, 71- MLA; Midwest. Mod. Lang. Asn. Eighteenth century British literature; the novel; cinema. Publ: Innocence preserved in Blake's 1789 Chimney sweeper, Explicator, 68; Orthodoxy versus anarchy in Sterne's Sentimental journey, Papers on Lang. & Lit, summer 71; Point of view and the craft of cinema: notes on some devices, J. Aesthet. & Art Criticism, winter 73. Add: Dept. of English, Eastern Michigan University, Ypsilanti, MI 48197.

McGONIGLE, PAUL F, b. Boston, Mass, Jan. 17, 33; m. 65; c. 1. ENGLISH. B.A, Col. Holy Cross, 54; M.A, Univ. Chicago, 55; Ph.D, Boston Univ, 63. Instr. ENG, St. Anselm's Col, 59-62, asst. prof, 62-63; St. John's Univ, 63-66; ASSUMPTION COL.(MASS), 66-68, ASSOC. PROF, 68-, CHMN. DEPT, 72- U.S.A, 56-58. MLA. George Crabbe's poetic development; techniques of literary criticism; Emerson's aesthetic theory. Add: Dept. of English, Assumption College, Worcester, MA 01609.

McGOUN, RALPH CLELAND, b. New Castle, Pa, Dec. 5, 05. DRAMATIC ARTS. A.B, Amherst Col, 27, A.M, 29; Yale, 37-38. Asst. biol, AMHERST COL, 27-29, instr, 29-37, DRAMATIC ARTS, 38-46, asst. prof, 46-53, from assoc. prof. to prof, 53-72, EMER. PROF, 72- Instr, U.S. Army Univ, France, 45; Fordham Univ, 46. U.S.A, 43-46. Am. Soc. Theatre Res. Theatre; stage lighting. Add: 157 Columbia Dr, Amherst, MA 01002.

McGOVERN, ROBERT JOHN, b. Minneapolis, Minn, Dec. 2, 27; m. 64; c. 4. SEVENTEENTH CENTURY ENGLISH LITERATURE, CREATIVE WRITING. B.A, Univ. Minn, 51, M.A, 57; Univ. London, 60; Ph.D.(Eng), Case West. Reserve Univ, 68. Asst. prof. ENG, Radford Col, 57-65; PROF. ENG. & CREATIVE WRITING, ASHLAND COL, 65- U.S.A, 51-52. Contemporary poetry; history of literary criticism; 17th century poetry. Publ: Co-ed, 17 Collections & anthologies of poetry, 69-74 & auth, A feast of flesh and other occasions, 71, Ashland Poetry Press; auth. numerous poems, var. lit. jour, 63-; Re-But, Hiram Poetry Rev, 73; Towards a definition of poetry pollution, Camels Coming, 73; plus others. Add: R.D. 4, Box 131, Ashland, OH 44805.

McGRATH, EDWARD, b. Lockport, N.Y, Nov. 29, 01. FRENCH & ENGLISH LITERATURE. A.B, Cornell Univ, 23, Ph.D, 35; Univ. Montpellier, 25-27. Instr. Eng, Cornell Univ, 23-25, Romance langs, 27-31; assoc. prof. Eng. & French, Loyola Univ.(La), 36-37; asst. prof. mod. langs, VILLANOVA UNIV, 37-47, assoc. prof, 47-48, prof. ENG, 48-72, EMER. PROF, 72- Eighteenth century English literature; 19th century French literature. Add: Box 218, Olcott, NY 14126.

McGRATH, JAMES B, b. Dallas, Tex, Mar. 28, 17; m. 41; c. 2. ORAL COMMUNICATION. B.A, South. Methodist Univ, 39; M.A, Univ. Wis, 49; Ed.D, Columbia Univ, 57. Assoc. prof. speech, SOUTH. METHODIST UNIV, 46-67, PROF. BROADCAST FILM-ARTS & CHMN. DEPT, 65-, PRODUCER, TV WORKSHOP, 57- Play dir, Dallas Little Theater, 55; Dallas Civic Theater, 56; commun. consult, Southwest. Grad. Sch. Banking, 57-63; Int. Bus. Machines Corp, 59; Tex. Power & Light Co, 59-63; Lone Star Steel Co, 60; Geophysical Serv, Inc, 60; Dallas Power & Light Co, 61-63; Nat. Sci. Found. grant, 73. U.S.A, 42-45, Sgt. Speech Commun. Asn; Asn. Prof. Broadcasting Educ. Television and theatrical production. Publ: Co-auth, Technically speaking, McGraw, 63. Add: Dept. of Broadcast-Film Arts, Southern Methodist University, Dallas, TX 75222.

McGRATH, JULIET, b. Fargo, N.Dak, May 15, 42; m. 61; c. 1. RENAISSANCE ENGLISH LITERATURE. A.B, Univ. Calif, Berkeley, 63, M.A, 65; Ph.D.(Eng), Univ. Chicago, 70. ASST. PROF. ENG, Loyola Univ. Chicago, 68-71; UNIV. ROCHESTER, 71- Publ: James Shirley's uses of language, Stud. Eng. Lit, 66. Add: Dept. of English, Morey 419, University of Rochester, Rochester, NY 14627.

McGRAW, REX T, JR, b. Hornell, N.Y, Aug. 1, 30. THEATRE. B.A, Bowling Green State Univ, 58, M.A, 59; Ph.D.(theatre, dramatic lit), Ind. Univ, 65. Asst. prof. theatre, Muskingum Col, 62-64; Ohio Univ, 64-69; assoc. prof, Hiram Col, 69-70; HEAD, PROF. DIR. TRAINING, OHIO UNIV, 70- U.S.A, 51-53. Am. Theatre Asn. Directing; acting; American theatre history. Publ: The meaning in Colours in the dark, Fine Arts, 68; A definition of the villain in nineteenth-century melodrama, Prompt Book, 70. Add: School of Theatre, Ohio University, Athens, OH 45701.

McGRAW, WILLIAM R, b. Martins Ferry, Ohio, Dec. 15, 30; m. 53; c. 5. DRAMA. A.B, Col. Wooster, 52; M.A, Ohio State Univ, 53; Ph.D, Univ. Minn, 58. Instr. drama, Col. Wooster, 53-55; Univ. Minn, 58; asst. prof, Univ. Ore, 58-61; Univ. Mich, 61-64, assoc. prof. theatre, 64-66; assoc. prof, Ohio Univ, 66-72, assoc. dean off campus acad. prog, 66-68, assoc. dean univ. col, 68-72; PROF. DRAMA & CHMN. DIV, W.VA. UNIV, 72- Mem. cent. comt, Am. Col Theatre Festival, Kennedy Ctr. Performing Arts, D.C, 71- Am. Theatre Asn.(admin. v.pres, 63-65, v.pres. prog, 72, pres. elect, 73). Stage direction; British drama. Publ: Co-auth, Principles and styles of acting, Addison-Wesley, 70; auth, The company you keep, Dramatics Mag, 10/61; James M. Barrie's concept of dramatic action, Mod. Drama, 9/62; Barrie and the critics, Stud. Scottish Lit, 10/63. Add: 1469 Dogwood Ave, Morgantown, WV 26505.

McGREW, JULIA HELEN, b. Detroit, Mich, Sept. 1, 20. ENGLISH. B.A, Oberlin Col, 43, M.A, 45; Goodhart fel, 52-53; Ph.D, Bryn Mawr Col, 54; F.B. Workman traveling fel, Denmark & Eng, 53-54. Teacher, Laurel Sch,

Cleveland, Ohio, 45-47; instr. ENG, Smith Col, 54-55; from instr. to asst. prof, Mt. Holyoke Col, 55-58; VASSAR COL, 58-64, assoc. prof, 64-70, PROF, 70-, MARY AUGUSTA SCOTT PROF, 73- Am. Asn. Univ. Women Shirley Farr fel. for res. in Iceland, England & Scotland, 64-65; vis. lectr. Chaucer, Odense Univ, Denmark, 71. Mediaeval Acad. Am; Mod. Humanities Res. Asn; Int. Arthurian Soc; Soc. Scand. Stud; Am-Scand. Found. Icelandic saga; Chaucer; Old English literature. Publ: Transl, Sturlunga saga, Am-Scand. Found. & Twayne, vols. I & II, 71 & (in press); auth, Faulkner and the Icelanders, Scand. Stud, 2/59. Add: Dept. of English, Vassar College, Poughkeepsie, NY 12601.

McGRORY, M. KATHLEEN, b. New York, N.Y, Mar. 22, 33. MODERN IRISH & COMPARATIVE MEDIEVAL LITERATURE. B.A, Col. White Plains, 57; M.A, Univ. Notre Dame, 62; N.Y. State Regents fels, Columbia Univ, 64-69, Fels fel, stud. abroad, 66-67, Ph.D.(Eng, comp. lit), 69. Asst. prof. ENG, Col. White Plains, 58-69; ASSOC. PROF, WEST. CONN. STATE COL, 69- Assoc. ed, J. Sports Med, 72-; Nat. Endowment for Humanities-Soc. Relig. Higher Educ. summer fel, 73; chmn. fac. adv. counc, Bd. Trustees State Cols, Conn, 73- MLA; Mediaeval Acad. Am; NCTE. Irish literature, Joyce, Beckett, Yeats; legends of the Holy Grail in medieval Germany, France and Spain. Publ: Co-ed, Yeats, Joyce, Beckett, Bucknell Univ, 74; auth, Wallace Stevens, romantic rebel, Conn. Rev, 70; Medieval aspects of modern Irish literature, In: Modern Irish literature, Twayne, 73; arts. on Joyce, Yeats, Synge, Lady Gregory and James Stephens, In: McGraw-Hill encyclopedia of modern biography, 73. Add: Whisconier Hill, Brookfield Center, CT 06805.

McGUCKIN, HENRY E, JR, b. Lolita, Calif, Jan. 10, 30; m. 53; c. 2. SPEECH, COMMUNICATION. B.A, San Francisco State Col, 58, M.A, 59; Ph.D.(speech, commun. res), Stanford Univ, 65. From assoc. prof. to PROF. SPEECH, SAN FRANCISCO STATE UNIV, 61-, CHMN. DEPT. SPEECH COMMUN, 73- U.S.A, 51-53. Speech Commun. Asn; West. Speech Asn. Rhetorical theory; group dynamics; experimental research in social control. Publ: The persuasive force of similarity in cognitive style between advocate and audience, Speech Monogr, 6/67; Forensics in the liberal education, J. West. Speech, spring 70; Better forensics: an impossible dream, J. Am. Forensics Asn, spring 72; plus others. Add: Dept. of Speech Communication, San Francisco State University, San Francisco, CA 94132.

McGUFFIE, HELEN LOUISE, b. Washington, Pa, Sept. 11, 15. ENGLISH. A.B, Bethany Col.(W.Va), 36; A.M, Univ. Pittsburgh, 37; Ph.D, Columbia Univ, 61. Instr. ENG, Hunter Col, 47; asst. prof, BETHANY COL.(W.VA), 47-53, from assoc. prof. to PROF. & HEAD DEPT, 54- U.S.C.G.R, 46-69, Comdr. MLA; NCTE; S.Atlantic Mod. Lang. Asn; AAUP. Eighteenth century English literature. Publ: Samuel Johnson and the hostile press. Add: Dept. of English, Bethany College, Bethany, WV 26032.

McGUGAN, RUTH E, b. Coldwater, Mich, June 16, 28. ENGLISH LITERATURE. B.S, Loyola Univ. Chicago, 53, M.A, 58; Ph.D.(Eng), Univ. Ill, Urbana, 65. ASST. PROF. ENG, Univ. Ill, Urbana, 65-71; LOYOLA UNIV. CHICAGO, 72- Sr. fel, Folger Shakespeare Libr, 71-72. MLA (mem. new Shakespeare variorum comt, 73-77); Malone Soc.(treas, Am. div, 74-); Shakespeare Asn. Am; Renaissance Soc. Am. English Renaissance; Shakespeare; textual editing. Publ: Co-auth, Shakespeare variorum handbook, MLA, 71. Add: Dept. of English, Loyola University of Chicago, Chicago, IL 60626.

McGUINNESS, ARTHUR EDWARD, b. Providence, R.I, July 11, 36; m. 60; c. 3. ENGLISH. A.B, Holy Cross Col, 58; M.A, Univ. Wis, 59, Ph.D.(Eng), 64. Asst. prof. ENG, UNIV. CALIF, DAVIS, 64-70, ASSOC. PROF, 70- Ed, Eighteenth Cent. Stud. Eighteenth century intellectual history; Anglo-Irish literature. Publ: Ed, The rivals, Chandler Publ, 68; auth, Henry Home, Lord Kames, Twayne, 69; George Fitzmaurice, Bucknell Univ, 73; Lord Kames and the Ossian Poems, Tex. Stud, spring 68; Hume and Kames: burden of friendship, Stud. Scottish Lit, 4/68. Add: Dept. of English, University of California, Davis, CA 95616.

McGUIRE, ALLEN WAYNE, b. Mt. Grove, Mo, May 19, 37. ENGLISH. B.A, Univ. Denver, 58; M.A, Univ. Ore, 60; Ark. Found. Assoc. Col. grant, Univ. Wash, 62, 64-68. Asst, Univ. Ore, 59-60; asst. prof. ENG, Ouachita Baptist Col, 60-64; asst. prof, SHORELINE COMMUNITY COL, 64-67, assoc. prof, 67-71, PROF, 71-, CHMN. DIV. HUMANITIES, 66- NCTE; Conf. Col. Compos. & Commun; MLA (del. assembly, 73-76). Old and middle English; romanticism; linguistics. Add: Dept. of English, Shoreline Community College, 16101 Greenwood Ave. N, Seattle, WA 98133.

McGUIRE, JOHN FRANCIS, b. Apr. 12, 34; U.S. citizen; m. 64; c. 1. ENGLISH, SCIENCE EDUCATION. B.A, Carroll Col, 64; M.A, Univ. of the Pac, 66; Ph.D.(Eng), Univ. Utah, 72. Instr. ENG, Univ. Nebr, 66-67; ASST. PROF, MONT. COL. MINERAL SCI. & TECHNOL, 70- Writing consult, Mont. Tech. Res. Found, 71-73. AAUP; Col. Eng. Asn. Archetypes in literature; student writing. Publ: Co-auth, Nineteen student essays, Univ. Utah, 69. Add: Dept. of Humanities & Social Sciences, Montana College of Mineral Science & Technology, Butte, MT 59701.

McGUIRE, PHILIP CARROLL, b. Pittsburgh, Pa, Aug. 23, 40; m. 71; c. 1. ENGLISH. B.A, La Salle Col, 62; Danforth Found. fel, 62-66; M.A, Stanford Univ, 65, Stanford Univ. Wilson fel, 66, Ph.D.(Eng), 68. Asst. prof. ENG, MICH. STATE UNIV, 66-71, ASSOC. PROF, 71- MLA; AAUP; Renaissance Soc. Am. English poetry of the Renaissance; Shakespeare. Publ: A sweetnesse readie penn'd: the literary and devotional contexts of Herbert's Jordan (II), Mich. Academician, 69; Othello as an assay of reason, Shakespeare Quart, 73; Private prayer and English poetry in the early seventeenth century, Stud. in Eng. Lit, 74. Add: Dept. of English, Michigan State University, East Lansing, MI 48823.

McGUIRE, VERNON R, b. Wichita, Kans, May 10, 24; m. 66. SPEECH EDUCATION. B.A, Wichita State Univ, 46; M.S, Kans. State Univ, 50; Denver Univ, 51-52. Asst. prof. speech, Kans. State Univ, 47-53; pres, Myco Inc, Kans, 54-63; v.pres, Inter-Am. Ins. Co, 64-65; ASSOC. PROF. SPEECH, TEX. TECH UNIV, 65- Am. Forensic Asn.(mem, Nat. Debate Tournament, 70-72); Speech Commun. Asn. Forensic activities; argumentation and debate. Add: Dept. of Speech, Texas Tech University, Lubbock, TX 79409.

McHALE, MICHAEL JAMES, b. Pitcairn, Pa, Sept. 9, 18; m. 62. THEATRE, SPEECH. A.B, Univ. Pittsburgh, 40; M.A, West. Reserve Univ, 48; Pa. State Univ, University Park, 61-62; Univ. Bridgeport, 66. Instr. Eng. & speech, Univ. Pittsburgh, 46-47; dir, Yorkk Little Theatre, Pa, 47-53; asst. prof. speech & dir. theatre, Univ. Pittsburgh, 53-61; ASSOC. PROF. SPEECH, BLOOMSBURG STATE COL, 63-, DIR. THEATRE, 71-, dir. cult. affairs, 69-73. Pres, Bloomsburg Civic Music Asn, 71- U.S.A.F, 42-45, S/Sgt. Am. Theatre Asn; Irish Geneal. Soc. Public speaking; theatre production styles; Shakespeare and Shaw. Add: Dept. of Speech, Bloomsburg State College, Bloomsburg, PA 17815.

McHANEY, THOMAS LAFAYETTE, b. Paragould, Ark, Oct. 17, 36; m. 62; c. 3. AMERICAN LITERATURE. B.A, Miss. State Univ, 59; Woodrow Wilson fel, Univ. N.C, Chapel Hill, 60, M.A, 62; NDEA fel, Univ. S.C, 65-68, Ph.D.(Eng), 68. Instr. ENG, Univ. Miss, 63-65; asst. prof, GA. STATE UNIV, 68-73, ASSOC. PROF, 73- Mem. ed. bd, Costerus: a jour. of Eng. & Am. Lit, 72- Spec. Award for Fiction, Henry Bellaman Found, 70. MLA. American fiction; William Faulkner; economics of authorship. Publ: Sanctuary and Frazer's slain kings, Miss. Quart, summer 71; Anderson, Hemingway and Faulkner's The wild palms, PMLA, 5/72; William Gilmore Simms, In: The chief glory of every people, South. Ill. Univ, 73; plus others. Add: Dept. of English, Georgia State University, 33 Gilmer St, Atlanta, GA 30303.

McHENRY, ROBERT WILLIAM, JR, b. Panama City, Fla, Aug. 27, 43; m. 72. ENGLISH LITERATURE. A.B, Boston,Univ, 65, M.A, 67; Ph.D.(Eng), Univ. Mich, Ann Arbor, 72. Lectr. ENG, Univ. Mich-Flint, 69-70; ASST. PROF, UNIV. HAWAII, MANOA, 70- MLA; Am. Soc. 18th Century Stud; Philol. Asn. Pac. Coast. Dryden; Pope; history of ideas. Publ: Co-ed, Alexander Pope's The rape of the lock, Merrill, 69; Critics on Dryden, Allen & Unwin, 73; auth, Introd. to Charles Wolseley's The reasonableness of scripture-belief 1672, Scholars' Facsimiles & Reprints, 73. Add: Dept. of English, University of Hawaii at Manoa, 1733 Donaghho Rd, Honolulu, HI 96822.

McHUGH, RICHARD W, b. Rochester, N.Y, Oct. 31, 25. ENGLISH, PHILOSOPHY. B.S, Univ. Wis, 55, fel. & M.A, Univ. Md, 57; summers, Univ. Chicago, 57, Syracuse Univ, 58, 59, Univ. Buffalo, 61. Teacher Eng. & drama, Benjamin Franklin High Sch, N.Y, 55-63, chmn. dept, 63-68; V.PRIN, JOHN MARSHALL HIGH SCH, 68- Mem. final exam. comt, N.Y. State Educ. Dept, 65-66. U.S.A, 45-46, T/Sgt. NCTE; Nat. Asn. Sec. Sch. Prin; NEA. American philosophers; American intellectual and social history; twentieth century American and British literature. Add: 30 Clintwood Dr, Rochester, NY 14620.

McHUGH, RUTH NELSON, b. St. Louis, Mo; m. 66. ENGLISH, MUSIC. B.M, Northwest. Univ, 35, M.M, 40; scholar, New Sch. Soc. Res, 60; M.A, Columbia Univ, 61, grant, 65; grant, N.Y. Univ, 62. Teacher, Woodmere Acad, N.Y, 43-56; Eng. & creative writing, G.W. HEWLETT HIGH SCH, N.Y, 56-68, COORD. HUMANITIES, 68- Publ: Co-auth, Enjoying English, Bk. II, 64 & auth, Enjoying English, Teacher Ed. of Bk. 12, 65, Singer; co-auth, New dimensions in literature: Am. lit. bks. 2 & 5, 66 & New dimensions in literature: Eng. lit. bks. 3 & 4, 67, Am. Bk. Co; plus others. Add: 7 Beverly Rd, Douglaston, NY 11363.

McILVAINE, ROBERT MORTON, b. Vernon, Tex, Dec. 28, 43; m. 66. ENGLISH & AMERICAN LITERATURE. B.A, Davis & Elkins Col, 66; M.A, Univ. Pa, 67; Ph.D.(Eng), Temple Univ, 72. Teaching asst, ENG, Temple Univ, 68-72; ASST. PROF, SLIPPERY ROCK STATE COL, 72- MLA. American realism and naturalism; American novel; Victorian literature. Publ: Robert Herrick and Thorstein Veblen, Wash. State Univ. Res. Stud, 6/72; Dos Passo's reading of Thorstein Veblen, Am. Lit, 11/72; Edith Wharton's American beauty rose, J. Am. Stud, 12/73. Add: Dept. of English, Slippery Rock State College, Slippery Rock, PA 16057.

McINERNEY, THOMAS J, b. Lynn, Mass, July 6, 21; m. 46; c. 5. ENGLISH. B.A, Dartmouth Col, 46; M.A, Boston Col, 48; Ph.D, Univ. Wash, 59. Instr. ENG, Seattle Univ, 48-52, asst. prof, 52-56, assoc. prof, 56-61; asst. prof, Fairfield Univ, 61-63, assoc. prof, 63-64; Seattle Univ, 64-68; ASSOC. PROF. & CHMN. DEPT, FAIRFIELD UNIV, 68- Danforth teacher grant, 58-59. U.S.N, 42-45. MLA; Am. Lit. Group; New Eng. Col. Eng. Asn; Asn. Depts. Eng. Nineteenth century American literature; short story; popular culture in 19th century America. Add: Dept. of English, Fairfield University, Fairfield, CT 06430.

McINTOSH, JAMES HENRY, b. N.Y, Feb. 4, 34. ENGLISH, AMERICAN STUDIES. A.B, Harvard, 55; A.M, Yale, 59, Ph.D.(Eng), 66; Free Univ. Berlin, 59-60. Instr, Seattergood Sch, 60-61; Eng, Tufts Univ, 62-64, 65-66, asst. prof, 66-67; ENG. & AM. STUD, YALE, 67-72, ASSOC. PROF, 72- U.S.N, 55-57. American and English romanticism; Goethe. Publ: Thoreau as romantic naturalist, Cornell Univ, 74. Add: Dept. of English, Yale University, New Haven, CT 06520.

McINTOSH, RUSTIN CAREY, b. New York, N.Y, Feb. 4, 34; m. 60; c. 2. ENGLISH. A.B, Harvard, 55, Ph.D.(Eng), 64; B.A, Cambridge, 59. Instr. ENG, Harvard, 64-66, asst. prof, 66-69; UNIV. ROCHESTER, 69-72, ASSOC. PROF, 72- Canaday Humanities Fund res. grant, summer 67; assoc, Danforth Found, 70- MLA; Am. Soc. 18th Century Stud. Prose style; Samuel Johnson; novel. Publ: The choice of life: Samuel Johnson and the world of fiction, Yale Univ, 73; Pamela's clothes, ELH, 3/68; Reynold's portrait of The infant Johnson, 18th Cent. Stud. in Honor of Donald F. Hyde, 70; Nominal style in the novel, Proc. ASECS, 74. Add: Dept. of English, University of Rochester, Rochester, NY 14627.

MacINTYRE, JEAN ANN, b. Pittsburgh, Pa, Sept. 13, 34. ENGLISH. B.A, Bryn Mawr Col, 56; M.A, Yale, 57, Ph.D.(Eng), 63. Instr. ENG, Kent State Univ, 59-62; lectr, UNIV. ALTA, 62-63, asst. prof, 63-68, ASSOC. PROF, 68- MLA; Asn. Can. Univ. Teachers Eng. Spenser's Faerie Queene and its iconographic background; Shakespeare. Publ: Spenser's Herculean heroes, Humanities Asn. Bull, 64; Artegall's sword and the Mutabilitie Cantos, ELH, 12/66. Add: Dept. of English, University of Alberta, Edmonton, Alta, Can.

McINTYRE, JOHN PATRICK, b. Boston, Mass, Aug. 12, 30. ENGLISH LANGUAGE & LITERATURE. A.B, Boston Col, 52, S.T.L, 64; M.A, Weston Col, 57; M.A, Univ. Toronto, 60, Ph.D.(Eng), 68. Instr. ENG, Col. Holy Cross, 64-65; asst. prof, FAIRFIELD UNIV, 68-71, ASSOC. PROF, 71- MLA; Renaissance Soc. Am; Soc. Arts, Relig. & Contemporary Cult. Poetics and rhetoric; academic drama of the 16th century. Publ: Henry Adams and the unity of Chartres, Twentieth Century Lit, 62; Sidney's Golden world, Comp. Lit, 62; The word as dance: Eliot's Four quartets, In: Word in the world, Weston, 73. Add: Dept. of English, Fairfield University, Fairfield, CT 06430.

MacISAAC, WARREN JORDAN, b. Worcester, Mass, Dec. 31, 29; m. 58; c. 4. ENGLISH. A.B, Harvard, 54, fel, 60-62, M.A, 62, Ph.D.(Eng), 64. Instr. Eng, Brooks Sch, 54-58; headmaster & instr, Am. Sch, 58-59; instr, Calasanctius Sch, 59-60; Eng. & humanities, Mass. Inst. Technol, 62-64, asst. prof, 64-69, ASSOC. PROF. Eng, Fed. City Col, 69-71; DRAMA, CATH. UNIV. AM, 71- Old Dom. Found. grant, 66. U.S.A.F, 48-49. MLA; Shakespeare Asn. Am; AAUP; S.Atlantic Mod. Lang. Asn. Shakespeare; modern drama; linguistics and literature. Publ: The three cousins in Richard II, Shakespeare Quart, 68. Add: Dept. of Drama, Catholic University of America, Washington, DC 20017.

MACK, MATTIE SWAYNE, b. Springville, Tenn, Nov 27, 98; m. 46. ENGLISH. A.B, W.Tex. State Col, 22; A.M, Columbia Univ, 25; Univ. Wash, 29; Ph.D, Univ. Tex, 38. Teacher, rural sch, 15-17; high sch, Tex, 18-21; instr. Eng, W.Tex. State Col, 22-24, asst. prof, 35; instr, Univ. Tex, 35-38; assoc. prof, W.Tex. State Univ, 38-46, prof, 46-68; RETIRED. MLA. Whitman; Emerson; Thoreau. Publ: The progress piece in seventeenth century English poetry, Univ. Tex. Stud. Eng; Whitman's catalogue rhetoric, Stud. Eng; Henry VI as a pacifist, Col. Eng. Add: 811 14th St, Canyon, TX 79015.

MACK, MAYNARD, b. Hillsdale, Mich, Oct. 27, 09; m. 33; c. 3. ENGLISH. A.B, Yale, 32, Ph.D, 36; D.Litt, Duke Univ, 69, Kalamazoo Col, 73; D.H.L, Towson State Col, 71. Instr. ENG, YALE, 36-40, asst. prof, 40-45, assoc. prof, 45-48, prof, 48-65, STERLING PROF, 65-, dir. div. humanities, fac. arts & sci, 62-64, chmn. dept. Eng, 65-68. Guggenheim fel, 42-43, 65; Ford fac. fel, 52-53; Walker Ames vis. lectr, Univ. Wash, 56; Fulbright sr. res. fel, Univ. London, 59-60; Alexander vis. lectr, Univ. Toronto, 63; Beckman vis. prof, Univ. Calif, Berkeley, 64-65; mem. ed. bd, Stud. Eng. Lit, 62-; Nat. Endowment for Humanities sr. fel, 68-69; trustee, Hopkins Grammar Sch. & Berkeley Ctr, Yale Divinity Sch; fel, Ctr. Advan. Stud. Behav. Sci, Hartford, 71-72; mem. comn. fac. affairs, Am. Counc. Educ, 71-74; Lord Northcliffe lectr, Univ. London, 72; Williams Andrews Clark Libr. sr. res. fel, Los Angeles, 73-74. MLA (v.pres, 68, 1st v.pres, 69, pres, 70); NCTE; Malone Soc; Renaissance Soc. Am; Int. Asn. Univ. Prof. Eng; Am. Acad. Arts & Sci; corr. fel, British Acad; Shakespeare Asn; Am; Mod. Humanities Res. Asn. The Renaissance; the Augustan age; contemporary literature. Publ: Co-auth, Tragic themes in western literature, 53 & ed, Alexander Pope: an essay on man—the manuscripts of the Morgan and Houghton libraries, 62, Yale; co-auth, Jacobean theatre, Edward Arnold, London, 60 & Essays on Shakespeare and Elizabethan drama, Univ. Mo, 62; auth, King Lear in our time, Univ. Calif, 65; Poetical works of Alexander Pope: Twickenham edition, Vol. 3, part 2, 50, Vols. 7-10, Methuen & Yale, 68; The garden and the city: retirement and politics in the later poetry of Pope, Univ. Toronto, 69; The shadowy cave: some speculations upon a Twickenham grotto, In: Restoration and eighteenth century literature: essays in honor of Dugald McKillop, Univ. Chicago, 63; A poet in his landscape: Alexander Pope at Twickenham, In: From sense to sensibility: essays in honor of Frederick A. Pottle, Oxford, 65; Secretum iter: some uses of retirement literature in the poetry of Pope, In: Aspects of the eighteenth century, Johns Hopkins Univ, 65; plus others. Add: 273 Willow St, New Haven, CT 06511.

McKAY, JAMES WILLIAM, b. Washington, Pa, Dec. 10, 16; m. 70; c. 4. EDUCATION, READING & LANGUAGE ARTS. A.B, Waynesburg Col, 38; M.Litt, Univ. Pittsburgh, 48, Ph.D.(educ), 68. Teacher high sch, Pa, 38-42, 46; instr. Eng, Slippery Rock State Col, 47, mem. fac, 48-56, assoc. prof, 56-64; asst. & lectr. reading, Univ. Pittsburgh, 65-66; assoc. prof. SEC. EDUC, SLIPPERY ROCK STATE COL, 66-68, PROF, 68-, CHMN. DEPT, 72- U.S.A.A.F, 42-45, S/Sgt. NCTE; Int. Reading Asn. English teaching methods; reading in secondary schools; reading interests. Publ: The nature and extent of work-study skills, Proc. 22nd Annual Conf. & Course on Reading, Univ. Pittsburgh, 66; The components of a secondary reading program for the disadvantaged, Proc. Annual Conf. & Course on Reading, Univ. Pittsburgh, 67; Developing reading skills through literature, In: Reaching children and young people through literature, Int. Reading Asn, 71. Add: Dept. of Secondary Education, Slippery Rock State College, Slippery Rock, PA 16057.

MACKAY, LaMAR S, b. Gannett, Idaho, Jun 24, 20; m. 47; c. 3. JOURNALISM, MASS COMMUNICATION. B.S, Utah State Univ, 42; Ph.M, Univ. Wis, 47, Ph.D.(mass commun), 66. Teaching asst. jour, Univ. Wis, 46-47; writer, Portland Cement Asn, 47-48; instr. jour, San Francisco State Col, 48-49; asst, Univ. Wis, 49-50; asst. prof, Univ. S.Dak, 50-53; writer & bur. chief, Wall Street J, 53-59; PROF. JOUR, SAN JOSE STATE COL, 59- Lectr, Sch. Jour, Univ. Wis, 63-64; prof. mass commun. res, Univ. Guadalajara, 73-74. U.S.N.R, 42-68, Lt. Comdr. Am. Asn. Jour. Publ: Co-auth, Mysterious silence, lyrical scream: government information in World War II, Asn. Educ. in Jour. ser, 5/71; Media image survey of Santa Clara County, 72 & Media habits of minorities, 73, Calif. State Univ, San Jose. Add: 1124 Greenbriar Ave, San Jose, CA 95128.

McKAY, RUTH CAPERS, b. Ridgewood, N.J, Mar. 24, 02; m. 30; c. 3. ENGLISH LITERATURE. A.B, Wheaton Col.(Mass), 23, hon. Litt.D, 73; A.M, Univ. Pa, 24, Bennett fel, 24-25, Bennett scholar, 25-26, Ph.D, 27. Instr, Wheaton Col.(Mass), 27-28, asst. prof, 28-30; tutor & instr. Eng, Radcliffe Col, 38-41, 44-49; lectr. acad. dept, New Eng. Conserv. Music, 49-55; vis. lectr. ENG. & gen. lit, Smith Col, 55, 56-61; CHMN. ACAD. STUD, NEW ENG. CONSERV. MUSIC, 61-, dean grad. div, 63-68; exec. dir, Opera Co. Boston, 68-71. Trustee, Wheaton Col.(Mass), 46-; mem. fel. selection comt, Woodrow Wilson Found, 60-62. MLA. Comparative and 19th century English literature; Shakespeare and English novel; graduate field in music. Publ: George Gissing and his critic; ed, Hidden gardens of Beacon Hill, Cinamon Assoc, 72. Add: 5 Chestnut St, Boston, MA 02108.

McKEAN, KEITH F, b. Beaver Falls, Pa, Aug. 18, 15; m. 42; c. 2. ENGLISH & AMERICAN LITERATURE. A.B, Williams Col, 38, Clark fel, 38-39; univ. scholar, Univ. Chicago, 38-39, M.A, 39; Rackham fel, Univ. Mich, 48-49, Ph.D, 50. Instr. Eng, Univ. Toledo, 40-42; teaching fel, Univ. Mich, 46-48; assoc. prof. gen. stud, Univ. N.C, Raleigh, 49-55; prof, 55-61; Eng, Elmira Col, 61-68; PROF. ENG, UNIV. NORTH. IOWA, 68-, head dept. Eng. Lang. & lit, 68-71. Ford Found. fac. fel, Yale, 54-55; mem, TV Teaching Conf, Univ. Pa, 57; Res. & Develop. Comn. grant, Univ. N.C, Raleigh, 59-60; Inter-Univ, Comt. Econ. Develop. South grant, 61-62; mem, Am. Counc. Educ. U.S.A.A.F, 42-46, 1st Lt. MLA; NCTE. American literary criticism; Southern literature; television teaching. Publ: Cross currents in the South, Swallow, 60; The moral measure of literature, Swallow, 61 & Greenwood, 73; co-auth, Critical approaches to fiction, McGraw, 68; auth. introd, On modern poets, Meridian, 59; The world of informative and persuasive prose, Holt, 71; co-ed, Filmer versus Locke & The patriarchal society, In: Ideas in action, Vol. I, Am. Bk, 68; Mark the Twain, In: Revolt in the parlor, Parlor, 69. Add: 824 Hudson Rd, Cedar Falls, IA 50613.

McKEE, IRVING, b. Oakland, Calif, Nov. 11, 09; m. 37. ENGLISH. A.B, Yale, 31, A.M, 33, Ph.D.(Eng), 35. Instr, Storm King Sch, Cornwall, N.Y, 35-37; Culver Mil. Acad, 37-53; lectr, Univ. Calif, 46-47; assoc. prof. ENG, CALIF. STATE UNIV, SACRAMENTO, 48-53, prof, 53-71, chmn. dept, 57-64, faculty res. lectr, 64, EMER. PROF, 71- MLA res. grant, 60. U.S.N.R, 43-46, Lt. MLA; Nat. Asn. Advan. Colored People; Auth. Guild; Auth. Club London; Shaw Soc, Eng. George Bernard Shaw; Shakespeare; American literature, 1850-1900. Publ: Ed, Trail of death, Ind. Hist. Soc, 41; auth, Ben-Hur Wallace, Univ. Calif, 47; Alonzo Delano's California correspondence, Sacramento Bk. Collectors, 52. Add: Dept. of English, California State University, Sacramento, 6000 Jay St, Sacramento, CA 95819.

McKEE, JOHN D, b. Emporia, Kans, Dec. 22, 19; m. 56. AMERICAN STUDIES & ENGLISH. A.B, Kans. Wesleyan Univ, 43; M.A, Univ. N.Mex, 52, jr. fel, 53, Ph.D, 59. Asst, Univ. N.Mex, 54-58, instr. ENG, 58-59, vis. prof, summer 60; asst. prof, N.MEX. INST. MINING & TECHNOL, 59-66, assoc. prof, 66-70, PROF, 70- Publ. Ed, N.Mex. Bur. Mines & Mineral Resources, summer 61; chmn. N.Mex. Develop. Disabilities Planning & Adv. Counc, 73. Am. Stud. Asn; AAUP. William Allen White and the progressive era; writings in science as literature; the teaching of writing: methodology. Publ: Two legs to stand on, Appleton, 55; co-ed, Spanish times and boom times: toward an architectural history of Socorro, 72 & Life and death of a frontier fort: Fort Craig, New Mexico, 1845-1885, 73, Socorro County Hist. Soc; auth, The great academic sham battle, Colo. Quart, winter 67; Roughing it as retrospective reporting, West. Am. Lit, summer 70; The nightmare and the better dream, Colo. Quart, summer 71; plus two others. Add: Dept. of Humanities, New Mexico Institute of Mining & Technology, Socorro, NM 87801.

McKEEN, DAVID BRUCE, b. Hamilton, Ont, Jan. 21, 38. ENGLISH. B.A, Univ. N.B, 59, M.A, 60; Ph.D.(Eng), Univ. Birmingham, 64. Lectr. ENG, Middlesex Col, Univ. West. Ont, 63-64, Univ. Col, 64-65; asst. prof, SIR GEORGE WILLIAMS UNIV, 65-72, ASSOC. PROF, 72- MLA; Humanities Asn. Can. Shakespeare; Milton; 16th century British history. Add: Dept. of English, Sir George Williams University, 1435 Drummond St, Montreal, P.Q, Can.

McKEITHAN, DANIEL MORLEY, b. Florence. S.C, Nov. 9, 02; m. 27; c. 1. ENGLISH & AMERICAN LITERATURE. A.B, Col. Charleston, 24, A.M, 25; Univ. Va, 25, 26; Univ. N.C, 30; Ph.D, Univ. Tex, 35. Teacher, high sch, S.C, 24-26; instr. ENG, Furman Univ, 26-28; Univ. Tex, 28-35; assoc. prof, E.Tex. State Teachers Col, 35-36; instr, UNIV. TEX, AUSTIN, 36-38, asst. prof, 38-46, assoc. prof, 46-61, prof, 61-73, EMER. PROF, 73- Fulbright lectr, Univs. Strasbourg & Bordeaux, 57-58. MLA; Mod. Humanities Res. Asn; Am. Stud. Asn. American literature of the 19th century; Mark Twain. Publ: Ed, A collection of Hayne letters, Univ. Tex, 44, Traveling with the Innocents abroad: Mark Twain's original reports from Europe and the Holy Land, Univ. Okla, 58 & The Morgan manuscript of Mark Twain's Pudd'nhead Wilson, In: Essays and studies on American language and literature, Eng. Inst. Royal Univ. Uppsala, 61; plus others. Add: Box 7050, University Station, Austin, TX 78712.

MacKELLAR, WALTER, b. Blauvelt, N.Y, Nov. 19, 92. ENGLISH LITERATURE. A.B, Cornell Univ, 18, Ph.D, 23; Yale, 18-20. Instr. ENG, Univ. Minn, 20-21; N.Y. UNIV, 23-37, asst. prof, 37-47, assoc. prof, 47-53, prof, 53-58, EMER. PROF, 58- Asst. prof, Cornell Univ, 45-46; vis. prof, Wayne State Univ, 59-60; Queens Col.(N.Y), 62-63; lectr, N.Y. Univ, 64; teacher Latin, Rockland Country Day Sch, N.Y, 64-; mem. ed. bd, Variorum Commentary on Poems of John Milton. MLA; Mid. Atlantic Class. Asn; Milton Soc. Am.(pres, 54, ed). English literature and philosophy of the 17th and 18th centuries; the Latin poems of John Milton. Publ: Ed, Paradise regained, Vol. 4, In: A variorum commentary on the poems of John Milton, Columbia Univ. & Routledge & Kegan Paul, London, 73. Add: 335 Western Highway N, Blauvelt, NY 10913.

MacKENDRICK, LOUIS KING, b. Toronto, Ont, Feb. 1, 41; m. 66; c. 1. ENGLISH. B.A, Univ. West. Ont, 63, M.A, 65; Phil.M, Univ. Toronto, 66, Ph.D.(Eng), 71. Instr. ENG, Univ. Sask, 67-70: ASST. PROF, UNIV. WINDSOR, 71- Asn. Can. Univ. Teachers Eng. Nineteenth century Canadian literature; British literature 1880-1920. Publ: The New freewoman: a short story of literary journalism; Eng. Lit. in Transition, 72; Introd, Robert Barr's The measure of the rule, Univ. Toronto, 73. Add: Dept. of English, University of Windsor, Windsor, Ont. N9B 3P4, Can.

McKENZIE, ALAN TABER, b. Arlington, Mass, July 7, 40; m. 62; c. 2. ENGLISH LITERATURE. B.A, Harvard, 62; M.A, Univ. Pa, 66, Ph.D.(Eng), 68. Asst. prof. ENG, PURDUE UNIV, W.LAFAYETTE, 68-73, ASSOC. PROF, 73-, acting asst. head dept, 73-74. Intel.C, U.S.A, 63-65, Res, 65-67, Capt. Am. Soc. 18th Century Stud; MLA. Eighteenth century English literature; Samuel Johnson; expository prose. Publ: Proper words in proper places: syntax and substantive in The conduct of the allies, Eighteenth Century Stud, 68; The lamentation of Glumdalclitch: what we have been missing, Tex. Stud. Lit. & Lang, 71; Two letters from Giuseppe Baretti to Samuel Johnson, PMLA, 71. Add: Dept. of English, Purdue University, Heavilon Hall, West Lafayette, IN 47906.

McKENZIE, BARBARA, b. Mt. Vernon, N.Y, July 22, 34. ENGLISH LITERATURE. B.A, Univ. Miami, 56, M.A, 58; Ph.D.(Eng), Fla. State Univ, 63. Instr. Eng, Univ. Miami, 58-59; Dade County Jr. Col, 60-61; Fla. State Univ. Exten. prog, S.A.C. Base, Homestead, 63-64; asst. prof, Drew Univ, 64-68; asst. prof, RADIO-TV-FILM DIV, SCH. JOURNALISM, UNIV. GA, 68-71, ASSOC. PROF, 71- Am. Film Inst; Soc. Photog. Educ. Twentieth century American literature, especially the novel and short story; film history and criticism; the mass media, especially television. Publ: Mary McCarthy, Twayne, 66; ed, Modern American stories, 69, rev. ed, The process of fiction: contemporary stories and criticism, 74, Harcourt. Add: School of Journalism, University of Georgia, Athens, GA 30601.

McKENZIE, EMORY JARIEL, b. Lorraine, Kans, Jan. 23, 20; m. 45; c. 2. ENGLISH. A.B, Ottawa Univ, 45, hon. L.H.M, 70; A.M, Duke Univ, 47; Ph.D. (Eng. & philos), Univ. Nebr, 62. Instr, Duke Univ, 46-47; asst. prof. humanities, Ouachita Col, 47-48; ENG, OTTAWA UNIV, 48-61, assoc. prof, 61-64, PROF, 64-, chmn. dept, 61-68, chmn. div. lang. & lit, 68-71. NCTE; MLA. American Victorian literature; American Indian literature. Add: Dept. of English, Ottawa University, Ottawa, KS 66067.

McKENZIE, JAMES JEREMIAH, b. Buffalo, N.Y, Aug. 27, 18. ENGLISH. A.B, Canisius Col, 39; A.M, Harvard, 41, Ph.D, 49; Japanese fel, Am. Asn. Univ. Prof, 42. From instr. to asst. prof. ENG, Canisius Col, 49-53; instr, Univ. Buffalo, 53-54; from asst. prof. to PROF, GLASSBORO STATE COL, 54- Lectr, Columbia Univ, summer 49; TV lectr. Sig.C, U.S.A. Col. Eng. Asn. Shakespeare; Chaucer; Renaissance. Publ: Contrib, Notes and queries, Explicator; auth, Exit Ophelia, Notes & Queries, 4/70. Add: Dept. of English, Glassboro State College, Glassboro, NJ 08028.

MacKENZIE, NORMAN HUGH, b. Salisbury, Rhodesia, Mar. 8, 15; m. 48; c. 2. ENGLISH. B.A, Rhodes Univ. Col, 34, M.A, 35; Union scholar, Univ. S.Africa, 37-40; Ph.D, Univ. London, 40. Temporary lectr. ENG, Rhodes Univ. Col, 37; lectr, Univ. Hong Kong, 40-41; Univ. Melbourne, 46-48; sr. lectr-in-charge, Univ. Natal, 49-55; PROF. & HEAD DEPT, Univ. Col. Rhodesia & Nyasaland, 55-65; Laurentian Univ, 65-66; QUEEN'S UNIV. (ONT), 66-, dir. grad. stud. Eng, 67-73, chmn. counc. grad. stud. & res, 71-73. Dean, Fac. of Arts, Rhodesia. Coastal Defence, 40-46; Prisoner of War, Hong Kong & Japan, 41-45. MLA; Int. Asn. Prof. Eng; Eng. Asn, Gt. Brit; Hopkins Soc.(pres, 72-); Can. Asn. Irish Stud.(treas, 72-73, exec. mem, 72-74); Can. Asn. Commonwealth Lit. & Lang. Stud.(exec. 72-73). Modern poetry, especially Hopkins, Yeats and Eliot; seventeenth century literature and history; Victorian literature. Publ: The outlook for English in Central Africa, 60 & co-auth, The poems of Gerard Manley Hopkins, 4th ed, 67, Oxford; auth, Hopkins, Oliver & Boyd, Edinburgh, 68; ed, Poems by Gerard Manley Hopkins, Folio Soc, London, 74; auth, Sir Thomas Herbert of Tintern, Bull. Inst. Hist. Res, 56; English proficiency testing in the British Commonwealth, In: Testing the English proficiency of foreign students, Univ. Wash, 61; contrib, Hopkins in The Victorians, Cresset Press, 69. Add: Dept. of English, Queen's University, Kingston, Ont. K7L 3N6, Can.

McKEON, NEWTON FELCH, b. Paterson, N.J, Dec. 21, 04; m. 35; c. 4. ENGLISH LITERATURE. A.B, Amherst Col, 26; Cambridge, 33-34. Instr. Eng, Amherst Col, 31-37, asst. prof, 37-41, assoc. prof, 41-48, prof, 48-70, acting dean, 36-37, asst. to dir, Amherst Col. Libr, 35-37, asst. dir, 37-39, dir, 39-70; RETIRED. Bibliog. Soc. Am; Am. Libr. Asn. Add: Academy Hill, Conway, MA 01341.

MACKEY, MARY LOU, b. Indianapolis, Ind. COMPARATIVE LITERATURE, FILM. A.B, Radcliffe Col, 66; M.A, Univ. Mich, 67; Ph.D.(comp. lit), 70. Instr. ENG, Univ. Mich, 67-68; lectr, Sonoma State Col, 72; ASST. PROF. & WRITER IN RESIDENCE, CALIF. STATE UNIV, SACRAMENTO, 72- MLA. Modern literature, French, English, Spanish and Russian; poetry. Publ: Immersion, S.H. Press, 72; Split ends (poetry), Ariel, 74; Form and structure in Pickwick papers, Dickens Stud, 67; Kate Chopin writer unknown, Women: a Jour, 70; Women's poetry, Small Press Rev, 72; contrib. poetry, numerous lit. mag, 66. Silence (screenplay), Studio 16, 72; Eloise (screenplay), Hargrove Prod, 74. Add: Dept. of English, California State University, Sacramento, 6000 J St, Sacramento, Sacramento, CA 95819.

MACKIN, COOPER RICHERSON, b. Selma, Ala, Apr. 26, 33; m. 58; c. 3. ENGLISH LITERATURE. B.A, Troy State Col, 56; fel, Tulane Univ, 56-58, M.A, 58; fel, Rice Univ, 59-62, Ph.D, 62. Instr. ENG, Tex. South. Univ, 58-59; asst. prof. N.Tex. State Univ, 62-63; UNIV. NEW ORLEANS, 63-66, assoc. prof, 66-70, PROF, 70-, DEAN COL. LIB. ARTS, 69-, chmn. dept. Eng, 66-69. U.S.A, 53-55. S.Cent. Mod. Lang. Asn; S.Cent. Renaissance Conf; Renaissance Soc. Am; Milton Soc. Am. Seventeenth century and Restoration literature. Publ: Co-auth, Explorations of literature, La. State Univ, 66; auth, William Styron, Steck-Vaughn, 69; The satiric technique of John Oldham's Satyrs upon the Jesuits, Stud. Philol, 1/65. Add: Dept. of English, University of New Orleans, New Orleans, LA 70122.

MACKIN, JOHN H, b. Boardman, Wis, May 8, 21; m. 47; c. 4. ENGLISH. A.B, Univ. Wis, 43; A.M, Univ. Chicago, 47, Ph.D.(Eng), 62. Instr. Eng, Wilson Chicago City Jr. Col, 47-48; Wright Chicago City Jr. Col, 50-51; UNIV. ILL, CHICAGO CIRCLE, 51-62, asst. dean col. lib. arts, 62-67, asst. prof ENG, 67-68, ASSOC. PROF, 68- U.S.N, 43-46, Lt.(jg). MLA; NCTE. Shakespeare and classical rhetoric; Socrates, Plato and classical rhetoric. Publ: Classical rhetoric and modern discourse, Free Press, Macmillan, 69. Add: Dept. of English, University of Illinois at Chicago Circle, Box 4348, Chicago, IL 60680.

McKINLEY, JAMES COURTRIGHT, b. Omaha, Nebr, Dec. 8, 35; m. 59; c. 3. TWENTIETH CENTURY BRITISH & AMERICAN LITERATURE. B.A. & B.J, Univ. Mo-Columbia, 59, M.A, 68, Ph.D.(Eng), 70. Copy supvr, Procter & Gamble, Inc, 60-64; account exec, Young & Rubicam Advert, Inc, 64-66; ASST. PROF. ENG, UNIV. MO-KANSAS CITY, 70- Nat. Endowment for Humanities fel, 72-73. U.S.A, 60-61, 1st Lt. Twentieth century British poetry. Publ: Interview with Robert Graves, Playboy, 70; Interview with Jesse Hill Ford, Contempora, 71; plus numerous reviews, stories & poems. Add: Dept. of English, University of Missouri-Kansas City, 5315 Holmes Ave, Kansas City, MO 64110.

McKINNEY, EUGENE, b. Ft. Worth, Tex, Oct. 2, 22; m. 47; c. 1. DRAMA. B.A, Baylor Univ, 47, M.A, 48. Prof. playwriting, Baylor Univ, 48-63; PROF. PLAYWRITING & PLAYWRIGHT-IN-RESIDENCE, TRINITY UNIV, 63- Script consult, Radio & TV Comn, S.B.C, 55-; prof, Dallas Theatre Ctr, 59- U.S.A, 42-45, 2nd Lt. Am. Theatre Asn. Playwriting; film and television writing. Publ: A different drummer, produced on Omnibus, 55; The cross-eyed bear, produced by Dallas Theatre Ctr, 60; A different drummer, 68 & People in the glass paperweight, 73, French. Add: Dept. of Drama, Trinity University, San Antonio, TX 78212.

MacKINNON, MALCOLM HUGH MURDOCH, b. Regina, Sask, Feb. 5, 17; m. m. 41; c. 4. ENGLISH LITERATURE. B.A, Univ. Toronto, 38, M.A, 39, Leonard fel, 41-42, Ph.D, 48. Instr. Eng, Queen's Univ, Can, 39-41; asst. prof, Univ. West. Ont, 46-49, assoc. prof, 49-56, prof. & head dept, 56-, v.prin, Univ. Col, 63-64; DEAN COL. ARTS, UNIV. GUELPH, 64- Humanities Res. Counc. Can. summer res, grants, 49, 52; Royal Soc. Can. fel, 50-51. R.C.A.F, 42-45, Res, 49-58, Squadron Leader. MLA; Humanities Asn. Can. Elizabethan poetry; translations; education; life and writings of Sir John Harington. Publ: Sir Thomas Browne, Bull. Hist. Med; School books at Eton College 1600 A.D, J. Eng. & Ger. Philol; Sir John Harington and Bishop Hall, Philol. Quart. Add: College of Arts, University of Guelph, Guelph, Ont, Can.

McKNIGHT, HAVEN RAY, b. Charleston, W.Va, Aug. 19, 33; m. 60; c. 3. ENGLISH. A.B, Harvard, 55; M.A, Univ. N.C, 58, Ph.D.(Eng), 64. Instr. ENG, Univ. Ore, 60-64; asst. prof, 64-65; CALIF. STATE UNIV, FRESNO, 65-69, ASSOC. PROF, 69- Eighteenth century English literature; film. Add: Dept. of English, California State University, Fresno, Shaw & Cedar Ave, Fresno, CA 93710.

MACKSEY, RICHARD ALAN, Comparative Literature, English. See Volume III, Foreign Languages, Linguistics & Philology.

MACKSOUD, SALEEM JOHN, b. Brooklyn, N.Y, Aug. 13, 34; m. 58; c. 1. RHETORIC. B.A, Univ. Calif, Los Angeles, 57, M.A, 60, Ph.D.(rhetoric), 64. Asst. prof. speech, Univ. Calif, Santa Barbara, 64-72, fac. fel, summer 68; ASSOC. PROF. RHETORIC, STATE UNIV, N.Y. BINGHAMTON, 73- Humanities Inst. fel, 70. Speech Commun. Asn.(Golden Anniversary Monogr. Award, 71); West. Speech Commun. Asn. Theory of language; rhetorical criticism; oral interpretation of literature. Publ: Other illusions: inquiries toward a rhetorical theory of language, privately publ, 74; Anyone's how town: interpretation as rhetorical discipline, Speech Monogr, 3/68; Phenomenology, experience and interpretation, Philos. & Rhetoric, summer 71. Add: Dept. of English, State University of New York at Binghamton, Binghamton, NY 13901.

McLACHLAN, WILLIAM IAN, b. London, Eng, Oct. 20, 38; m. 60; c. 2. ENGLISH, COMPARATIVE LITERATURE. M.A, Oxford, 60. Lectr. Eng, Univ. Hong Kong, 60-66, sr. lectr. comp. lit, 66-70, chmn. mod. lang, 68-70; ASSOC. PROF. ENG, TRENT UNIV, 70- Mem. comt. stud. finance, Hong Kong Govt, 68-70. Australasian Univs. Lang. & Lit. Asn. Twentieth century English and American literature; The Asian influence on European literature; the translation of Chinese poetry. Publ: The orphan Chao, East. Horizon, 1-3/64; The translator as critic, Enquiry, 6/67; The Asian influence on American literature, In: The Asian response to American literature, Vikas, Delhi, India, 72. Add: Champlain College, Trent University, Peterborough, Ont, Can.

McLAIN, RICHARD LEE, b. Colorado Springs, Colo, Nov. 28, 39; m. 66; c. 2. ENGLISH LITERATURE. B.A, Univ. Calif, Berkeley, 65, M.A, 66, Ph.D. (Eng), 72. Instr. ENG, STATE UNIV. N.Y. BINGHAMTON, 71-72, ASST. PROF, 72- U.S.A, 58-61. MLA. Twentieth century English and American poetry; linguistics. Add: Dept. of English, State University of New York at Binghamton, Binghamton, NY 13901.

MacLAINE, ALLAN HUGH, b. Montreal, P.Q, Oct. 24, 24; m. 49. ENGLISH. B.A, McGill Univ, 45; Ph.D.(Eng), Brown Univ, 51. Instr. ENG, McGill, 46-47; Brown Univ, 47-50; Univ. Mass, 51-54; asst. prof, Tex. Christian Univ, 54-56, assoc. prof, 56-62, prof, 62; PROF, UNIV. R.I, 62-, DIR. GRAD. STUD. ENG, 71- Vis. prof, summer 62, chmn. dept. Eng, 66-67, acting dean div. univ. exten, 67-68, dean, 68-71. MLA; Col. Eng. Asn.(dir, 61-, pres, 65-66); Mod. Humanities Res. Asn; Int. Asn. Univ. Prof. Eng; fel. Nat. Univ. Exten. Asn. Scottish poetry, especially Burns; middle English literature, especially Chaucer; 18th century English literature. Publ: The student's comprehensive guide to the Canterbury tales, Barron's, 64; Robert Fergusson, Twayne, 65; Burn's use of parody in Tam O'Shanter, Criticism, 59; The Christis Kirk tradition: its evolution in Scots poetry to Burns, Stud. in Scottish Lit, 65-66; plus others. Add: Dept. of English, University of Rhode Island, Kingston, RI 02881.

McLANE, PAUL ELLIOTT, b. Spokane, Wash, July 17, 07; m. 47; c. 2. ENGLISH. M.A, Gonzaga Univ, 30; Ph.D.(Eng), Univ. Wash, 42. Prof. ENG, Univ. Seattle, 33-46; UNIV. NOTRE DAME, 46-72, EMER. PROF, 72- Huntington Libr. fel, 51-52. MLA; Renaissance Soc. Am. Spenser; Shakespeare. Publ: Spenser's Shepheardes calender: a study in Elizabethan allegory, Univ. Notre Dame, 61; plus others. Add: 1954 Beverly Rd, South Bend, IN 46616.

McLAUCHLAN, JULIET, b. Indianapolis, Ind. ENGLISH & AMERICAN LITERATURE. B.A, Principia Col. TEACHER ENG, AYLESBURY HIGH SCH. FOR GIRLS, 59- Participant, Int. Conrad Conf, London, 72; Int. Joseph Conrad Colloquy, Poland, 72; contrib. ed, Conradiana, 72-; mem. Eng. organizing comt, Int. Conf. Conrad, Canterbury, Eng, summer 74; participant, Int. Conf. Conrad Scholars, San Diego, 74. Joseph Conrad Soc. Joseph Conrad; Shakespeare; the novel. Publ: Conrad: Nostromo, 69, Shakespeare: Othello, Arnold, London, 71; Thomas Hardy, Tess of the D'Ubervilles, Basil Blackwell, Oxford, 71; The politics of Nostromo, 10/67 & Allusion in The waste land, 10/69, Essays in Criticism; The Prince of

Denmark—and Claudius' court, Shakespeare Surv, 11/74. Add: Dept. of English, Aylesbury High School for Girls, Walton St, Aylesbury, Buckinghamshire, England.

McLAUGHLIN, CARROL D, b. Bronson, Kans, Sept. 26, 24; m. 59; c. 2. ENGLISH. A.B, Baker Univ, 44; B.D, South. Methodist Univ, 49; M.A, Univ. Denver, 58, Ph.D.(Eng), 62. Asst. prof. ENG, Southwest. Col.(Kans), 60-63; assoc. prof, Baker Univ, 63-66; MORNINGSIDE COL, 66-72, PROF, 72- Consult. psychol. & lit, Larned State Hosp, Kans, 64-66. A.U.S, 44-46, M/Sgt. MLA; Soc. Stud. Midwest. Lit. Pilgrimage motifs in British and American literature; modern American fiction, particularly Robert Penn Warren and William Faulkner. Add: Dept. of English, Morningside College, Sioux City, IA 51106.

McLAUGHLIN, CHARLES ANGUS, b. Tumwater, Wash, Sept. 9, 20; m. 46; c. 3. ENGLISH. M.A, Univ. Chicago, 49, Ph.D.(Eng), 57. Instr. ENG, UNIV. CONN, 52-60, asst. prof, 60-64, assoc. prof, 64-69, PROF, 69-, res. found. stud. grant, 68-69. U.S.A, 43-46, Tech. Sgt. MLA. Literary criticism; satire; Ibsen. Publ: Co-auth, Poetry: an introduction to its form and art, Harper, 61; auth, Logic, rhetoric, and style, Little, 63; A note on Imitation and theme, J. Aesthet, 12/54; Two views of poetic unity, Univ. Kans. City Rev, summer 56. Add: Dept. of English, University of Connecticut, Storrs, CT 06268.

McLAUGHLIN, ELIZABETH TAYLOR, b. Washington, D.C, Aug. 30, 23; m. 47; c. 2. PHILOLOGY. B.A, Wellesley Col, 44; M.A, Radcliffe Col, 46, Ph.D, 49. Instr. Eng, George Washington Univ, 44-45, lectr, 57-58; instr. ENG, N.Y. Univ, 48-51; BUCKNELL UNIV, 58-60, asst. prof, 60-66, ASSOC. PROF, 66-, summer res. fel, 66. Scholar, Radcliffe Inst, 67-68. MLA; Mod. Humanities Res. Asn; Milton Soc. Am. Milton; 17th and 19th centuries. Publ: Ruskin and Gandhi, Bucknell Univ, (in press); Coleridge and Milton, Stud. Philol, 7/64; Milton and Thomas Ellwood, Milton Newsletter, 5/67; The extasie—deceptive or authentic?, Bucknell Rev, winter 70; plus others. Add: Dept. of English, Bucknell University, Lewisburg, PA 17837.

McLAUGHLIN, ROBERT GUY, b. St. Peter, Minn, June 26, 44; m. 66; c. 1. DRAMA. B.A, St. Olaf Col, 66; M.A, Univ. Wis, 68, Ph.D.(drama), 70. ASST. PROF. DRAMA, UNIV. VA, 70- Am. Theatre Asn; Southeast. Theatre Conf. Twentieth century American theatre history; actor training techniques. Publ: Auth, Broadway and Hollywood: a history of economic interaction, Arno, 74; co-auth, Broadway's financial dilemma, J. Producers Guild Am, 3/70; co-auth, The economic dilemma of the Broadway theatre, 3/69 & The introductory course in acting and directing, 12/73, Educ. Theatre J. Add: Dept. of Drama, University of Virginia, Charlottesville, VA 22903.

McLAUGHLIN, TED JOHN, b. Elkhart, Ind, Dec. 23, 21; m. 51. COMMUNICATION. B.A, Manchester Col, 47; M.A, Univ. Wis-Madison, 48, Ph.D. (speech), 52. Instr. speech, Milwaukee Exten. Div. Univ. Wis, 49-53, asst. prof, 53-56, UNIV. WIS-MILWAUKEE, 56-57, assoc. prof, 57-65, PROF, 65-67, COMMUN, 67-, ASSOC. DEAN GRAD. SCH, 71-, humanities, 62-69. Commun. consult, Louis Allis Co, 56-57. U.S.A.R, 42-43, A.U.S, 43-46, Sgt. AAAS; Int. Commun. Asn; Speech Commun. Asn. Industrial communication; governmental communication; parliamentary law. Publ: Co-auth, Communication, 64 & Cases and projects in communication, 65, C.E. Merrill; A study of context, content, and meaning in school board deliberations, J. Educ. Res, 1/66; auth, The responsibility of speech departments in a time of revolt, Speech Teacher, 1/67; The evolution of faculty government of the University of Wisconsin-Milwaukee, Transactions Wis. Acad. Sci, Arts & Lett, 72. Add: Graduate School, University of Wisconsin-Milwaukee, Milwaukee, WI 53201.

McLAY, CATHERINE MARGARET, b. Hamilton, Ont, Dec. 10, 34. ENGLISH LITERATURE. B.A, McMaster Univ, 57; M.A, Univ. Toronto, 61, Ph.D. (Eng), Univ. Alta, 70. Teacher geog. & Eng, Fisher Park High Sch, Ottawa, Ont, 57-59; instr. ENG, Lakehead Col, 62-63; from instr. to ASST. PROF, UNIV. CALGARY, 66- Asn. Can. Univ. Teachers Eng; MLA. American literature, 1820-1940; Canadian literature; fiction. Publ: Ed, Canadian anthology: the beginnings to 1910, McClelland & Stewart, Toronto, 74; auth, The dialogues of Spring and Winter: a key to the unity of Love's labour's lost, Shakespeare Quart, spring 67; Every man is an island: the theme of isolation in Laurence's A jest of God, Can. Lit, fall 71; W.O. Mitchell's The kite: a study in immortality, J. Can. Fiction, spring 73; plus others. Add: Dept. of English, Calgary Hall, University of Calgary, Calgary, Alta. T2N 1N4, Can.

MACLAY, JOANNA HAWKINS, b. Birmingham, Ala, Mar. 22, 38; m. 68. SPEECH, INTERPRETATION. A.B, Univ. Ala, 59, M.A, 60; Ph.D.(interpretation), Northwest. Univ, 65. Teaching asst. speech, Univ. Ala, 59-60; interpretation, Northwest. Univ, 61-64; asst. prof. SPEECH, North. Ill, Univ, 64-65; instr, UNIV. ILL, URBANA-CHAMPAIGN, summer 65, asst. prof, 65-71, ASSOC. PROF, 71- Speech Commun. Asn; Cent. States Speech Asn. Interpretation of contemporary fiction and literary criticism; readers theatre. Publ: Readers theatre: toward a grammar of practice, 69 & co-auth, Interpretation: an approach to the study of literature, 71, Random; auth, The interpreter and modern fiction, In: Studies in interpretation, Rodopi, 73. Add: Dept. of Speech, University of Illinois, Urbana-Champaign, Urbana, IL 61801.

McLEAN, ALBERT FORBES, b. Boston, Mass, July 2, 28; m. 52; c. 2. AMERICAN STUDIES. A.B, Williams Col, 51; M.A, Harvard, 53, Ph.D.(Am. civilization), 60. Instr. Eng, Tufts Univ, 56-60, asst. prof, 60-61; assoc. prof, Transylvania Col, 61-67; PROF. ENG, POINT PARK JR. COL, 67-, dean col, 67-69. Fulbright lectr, Univ. Iceland, 61-62; Am. Philos. Soc. res. grant, 63. Am. Stud. Asn; Mla; Melville Soc. Am. Nineteenth century literature and culture. Publ: William Cullen Bryant, Twayne, 65; American vaudeville as ritual, Univ. Ky, 66; Bryant's Thanatopsis: a sermon in stone, Am. Lit, 1/60; Addenda to the Thoreau correspondence, Bull. New York Pub. Libr, 4/67; Spouter Inn and Whaleman's Chapel, In: The cultural matrices of Moby Dick, Kent State Univ, 68; plus others. Add: Dept. of English, Point Park College, 201 Wood St, Pittsburgh, PA 15222.

McLEAN, ALVIN HUGH, b. Oct. 5, 36; U.S. citizen; c. 2. ENGLISH LITERATURE. B.A, Atlantic Union Col, 63; M.A, Univ. Mass, Amherst, 67, Ph.D. (Eng), 71. Lectr. Eng, Atlantic Union Col, 65-67; asst. prof, Clark Univ, 68-70; ASST. PROF. ETHNIC STUD. & CHMN. DIV, UNIV. SOUTH. CALIF, 71- Vis. asst. prof. Eng, Atlantic Union Col, 67-70; Clark Univ. & Holy Cross Col, 68-69; Assumption Col, 69-70; consult, Vandenburg AFB, 72; Martin Luther King Hosp, 72-; Probation Dept, Los Angeles County, 73- Afro-American literature; cultural determinants in illness and healing. Add: 4597 Northridge Dr, Los Angeles, CA 90043.

McLEAN, ANDREW MILLER, b. Brooklyn, N.Y, May 25, 41. ENGLISH RENAISSANCE LITERATURE & HISTORY. B.A, St. Olaf Col, 63; M.A, Brooklyn Col, 67; Ph.D.(Eng), Univ. N.C, Chapel Hill, 71. ASST. PROF. ENG, UNIV. WIS-PARKSIDE, 70- Rev. ed, CLIO: An Interdisciplinary Jour. of Lit, Hist, and Philos. of Hist, 71- MLA; Renaissance Soc. Am; Soc. Stud. Midwest. Lit; Col. Eng. Asn. Sixteenth century English literature; modern poetry and novel; interdisciplinary studies, film-Shakespeare. Publ: Emerson's Brahma, New Eng. Quart, 3/69; Joyce's Ulysses and Döblin's Alexanderplatz Berlin, Comp. Lit, spring 73. Add: Dept. of English, University of Wisconsin-Parkside, Kenosha, WI 53140.

MACLEAN, HUGH NORMAN, b. Aguilas, Spain, Mar. 24, 19; m. 49; c. 2. ENGLISH. B.A, Princeton, 40; M.A, Univ. Toronto, 47, Ph.D.(Eng), 50. Teaching fel. ENG, Univ. Toronto, 47-48, 48-49, lectr, 49-50; assoc. prof, Royal Mil. Col, 50-56; Univ. Cincinnati, 56-60; York Univ, 60-63; PROF, STATE UNIV. N.Y. ALBANY, 63- Can. Humanities Res. Counc. res. grant, 54; Huntington Libr. res. fel, 54-55; State Univ. N.Y. summer res. fels, 64, 68. Can. Army, 40-46. MLA; Renaissance Soc. Am; Renaissance Eng. Text. Soc. Literature of the English Renaissance. Publ: Ed, Edmund Spenser's poetry, Norton, 69; auth, Milton's revisions in Paradise lost, Bk. V, Milton Quart, 73; Ben Jonson's Timber and Falstaff, Papers Lang. & Lit, 73; plus others. Add: Dept. of English, State University of New York at Albany, Albany, NY 12222.

MacLEAN, KENNETH DUART, b. Berkeley, Calif, Aug. 17, 28; m. 54; c. 5. AMERICAN LITERATURE, WRITING. B.A, Univ. Wash, 52, M.A, 57. Instr. Eng, Cent. Wash. Col, 58-59; SEATTLE UNIV, 61-65, asst. prof. ENG. & WRITING, 65-71, ASSOC. PROF, 71- U.S.A, 46-48. AAUP. Publ: On the poetry of James Wright, fall 71 & Caliban's voices: the poetry of Theodore Weiss, fall 72, North Stone Rev; co-auth, The comics: art to wrap the garbage in?, Puget Soundings, 10-11/68. Add: Dept. of English, Seattle University, Seattle, WA 98122.

MacLEAN, MALCOLM SHAW, JR, b. St. Paul, Minn, June 28, 20; m. 48; c. 2. COMMUNICATION, JOURNALISM. B.A, Univ. Minn, 47, M.A, 49; Ph.D. (mass commun), Univ. Wis, 54. Instr. jour, Univ. Wis, 50-54, asst. prof, 54-56; from assoc. prof. to prof. commun. & assoc. dir, Commun. Res. Ctr, Mich. State Univ, 56-64; George H. Gallup prof. commun. res, UNIV. IOWA, 64-67, PROF. JOUR, 72-, dir. sch. jour, 67-72. From assoc. investr. to acting prin. investr. U.S. Off. Educ. grant, Nat. Ctr. Educ. Commun, 71-72; adv, Title VII, NDEA, U.S. Off. Educ, 72-; res. consult. advert. res, Ford Motor Co, 72-; consult, Assoc. Press, 72- Eng.C, U.S.A, 42-46. Int. Commun. Asn.(pres, 72-73); Am. Sociol. Asn; hon. mem. Women in Commun. Communication indicators; patterns of interest in mass communication content; systems and simulation. Publ: On the education of responsible newsmen, In: Learning and communication education, Simon & Schuster, 72; Communication strategy, editing games and Q, In: Science, psychology and communication: essays honoring William Stephenson, Teachers Col, Columbia Univ, 72; co-auth, Final report: pilot study 7, Simulation and knowledge utilization in education, Univ. Iowa, 72; plus others. Add: School of Journalism, University of Iowa, Iowa City, IA 52242.

MACLEAN, NORMAN FITZROY, b. Clarinda, Iowa, Dec. 23, 02; m. 31; c. 2. ENGLISH. A.B, Dartmouth Col, 24; Ph.D, Univ. Chicago, 40. Instr. ENG, Dartmouth Col, 24-26; from instr. to assoc. prof, UNIV. CHICAGO, 31-54, prof, 54-73, dean students, Col, 42-45, acting dir, inst. mil. stud, 43-45, chmn. comt. gen. stud. in humanities, 52-66, EMER. PROF, 73- MLA. Literary criticism; lyric poetry. Publ: Co-auth, Manual of instruction in military maps and aerial photographs & Critics and criticism; ancient and modern. Add: 5514 S. Woodlawn Ave, Chicago, IL 60637.

McLEAN, ROBERT COLIN, b. Chicago, Ill, Sept. 3, 27; m. 52; c. 1. ENGLISH & AMERICAN LITERATURE. B.S, Ind. Univ, 49, M.A, 52; univ. fels, Wash. Univ, 55-57, Ph.D, 61; Fulbright fel, Univ. Edinburgh, Scotland, 57-58. Teaching asst. Eng, Wash. Univ, 53-55; instr. Univ. Rochester, 58-61; asst. prof, WASH. STATE UNIV, 61-64, assoc. prof, 64-69, PROF. ENG. & AM. LIT, 69- Vis. lectr, Wash. Univ, summer 57; mem. ed. bd, ESQ: J. of Am. Renaissance, 72- & Poe Stud, 72- U.S.A, 46-47. MLA; Am. Stud. Asn; Soc. Stud. South. Lit. American studies. Publ: George Tucker: moral philosopher and man of letters, Univ. N.C, 61; The completed vision: a study of Madame de Mauves and The ambassadors, Mod. Lang. Quart, 67; The Bostonians: New England pastoral, 71 & Love by the doctor's direction: disease and death in The wings of the dove, 72, Papers on Lang. & Lit. Add: Dept. of English, Washington State University, Pullman, WA 99163.

McLEAN, ROBERT SIMPSON, b. New York, N.Y, Nov. 13, 28; m. 57; c. 3. ENGLISH. B.A, City Col. New York, 50; M.A, Columbia Univ, 52; Ph.D. (Eng), N.Y. Univ, 65. Newspaper reporter, Herald Statesman, 55-57; teacher high sch, 57-62; assoc. prof. ENG, QUEENSBOROUGH COMMUNITY COL, 62-73, PROF, 73- U.S.A, 52-54, Sgt. NCTE: MLA; Res. Soc. Victorian Periodicals. Victorian literature; folklore; the Bible. Publ: Putting Quilp to rest, Victorian Newslett, fall 68; Another source for Quilp, Nineteenth Century Fiction, 12/71; Altruistic ideals versus leisure class values: an irreconcilable conflict in John Ruskin, J. Aesthetics & Art Criticism, spring 73; plus two others. Add: 158 Willow St, Roslyn Heights, NY 11577.

McLEMORE, JOHN ANDERSON, b. Sturgis, Miss, Apr. 15, 21; m. 52. ENGLISH, HISTORY. B.A, Memphis State Univ, 56, M.A, 57, grants, summer 60 & 64-65; fel, Univ. Miss, 64-65, Ph.D.(Eng), 67. Instr. Eng, Memphis State Univ, 56-60, asst. prof, 60-65; NORTHEAST LA. UNIV, 65-66, assoc. prof, 66-67, head dept. Eng, 68-73, DEAN GRAD. SCH, 73- U.S.A, 42-45, T/Sgt. MLA; S.Cent. Mod. Lang. Asn; NCTE. Renaissance; Southern folklore, especially Faulkner, Tennessee and Mississippi; Louisiana linguistic atlas. Add: Graduate School, Northeast Louisiana University, Monroe, LA 71201.

MacLENNAN, DONALD WALLACE, b. Detroit, Mich, Aug. 23, 36; m. 59; c. 2. BROADCASTING, SPEECH. B.A, Univ. Mich, Ann Arbor, 58, M.A, 59; Ph.D.(speech), Univ. Mo-Columbia, 68. Instr. speech, Univ. Mo, 60-65; BROOKLYN COL, 65-68, asst. prof, 68-72, ASSOC. PROF. SPEECH & DIR, TV CTR, 72- Speech Commun. Asn.(chmn. mass. commun. div, 70-71); Nat. Asn. Educ. Broadcasters. Instructional film and television effectiveness. Publ: Co-auth, Research in instructional TV and film, U.S. Off. Educ, 65; co-ed, Teaching by television, Univ. Mo, 65. Add: TV Ctr, 018 Whitehead Hall, Brooklyn College, Brooklyn, NY 11210.

McLEOD, ALAN L, b. Sydney, Australia, Mar. 13, 28; U.S. citizen; m. 54; c. 2. ENGLISH, SPEECH. B.A, Univ. Sydney, Australia, 50, M.A, 52, Dip.Ed, 51; B.Ed, Univ. Melbourne, Australia, 56; Ph.D, Pa. State Univ, 57. Lectr. Eng. & speech, Wagga State Teachers Col, Australia, 52; asst. speech, Pa. State Univ, 52-53, 54-56; lectr. Eng. & speech, Balmain State Teachers Col, 56-57; asst. prof, State Univ. Col. Fredonia, 57-59, assoc. prof, 59-62; prof, Lock Haven State Col, 62-66; PROF. ENG. & SPEECH, RIDER COL, 66- State Univ. N.Y. res. fel, 62. Speech Commun. Asn; MLA; Book Collectors Soc, Australia. Seventeenth and eighteenth century poetry and drama; commonwealth literature; rhetorical criticism. Publ: Beyond the cresting surf, Boxwood, 59; co-auth, The commonwealth pen, 61 & The pattern of Australian culture, 63, Cornell; auth, Rex Warner: writer, 60, Walt Whitman in Australia and New Zealand, 64, co-auth, Achievement of Rex Warner, 65, & ed, Australia speaks, 69, Wentworth; co-auth, Patterns of New Zealand culture, Oxford, Cornell, 68; ed, The literature of Australia and New Zealand, Pa. State Univ, 70; Intentions in African literature, Asian Stud. Asn, 72; Walt Whitman; Wayne State Univ, 73. Add: Dept. of English, Rider College, Trenton, NJ 08618.

McLEOD, ARCHIBALD, b. Edinburg, Scotland, Nov. 5, 06; nat; m. 43; c. 1. DRAMA. B.A, Oberlin Col, 33; M.A, State Univ. Iowa, 34; Ph.D.(speech & drama), Cornell Univ, 42. Instr. SPEECH & DRAMA, Kans. State Teachers Col, 34-35; assoc. prof, Tex. State Col. Women, 35-39, 41-43; asst. prof, La. State Univ, 43-47; PROF, SOUTH. ILL. UNIV, CARBONDALE, 47-, CHMN. DEPT. THEATRE, 59- Fulbright lectr. dramatic art, Natya Sangh, Madras, India, 62-63. Am. Theatre Asn. Dramatic literature; theatre audience; aesthetics of the theatre. Publ: The actor's elocution, South. Speech J. Arena modification, Player's Mag. Add: 907 W. Schwartz St, Carbondale, IL 62901.

McLEOD, FREDERICK R, b. Sault Ste. Marie, Mich, Dec. 20, 17. ENGLISH. B.A, Bowling Green State Univ, 46; M.A, Univ. Detroit, 50; fel, Univ. Mich, 49-50. Instr. Eng, Bowling Green State Univ, 47-49, 50-53, dir. freshman Eng, 52-53; instr. ENG, UNIV. MO, KANSAS CITY, 57-61,asst. prof, 61-65; ASSOC. PROF, 65-71, PROF, 71-, DIR. FRESHMAN ENG, 57- NCTE; Conf. Col. Compos. & Commun; MLA; Rhetoric; Milton; teaching of English in college. Publ: Co-auth, Modern American writer, 61 & A reader for composition, 62, Am. Bk. Co. Add: Dept. of English, University of Missouri at Kansas City, Kansas City, MO 64110.

MACLEOD, NORMAN WICKLUND, b. Salem, Ore, Oct. 1, 06; m. 26; c. 3. ENGLISH. B.A, Univ. N.Mex, 30; Univ. South. Calif, 31-32; M.A, Columbia Univ, 36; summers, Univ. Okla, 34, Mt. Holyoke Col, 37, Univ. Colo, 41, Calif. State Col. Fullerton, 60. Teaching fel. Eng, Univ. N.Mex, 30-31; reader & circulation asst, Harper & Bros, winters 32-34; ed. asst, Univ. Okla. Press, summer 34; borough ed. Bronx, New York City Guide, 35-36; ed, N.Mex. Guide Bk, 36-37; prom. dir, Conn. Fed. Theatre, Hartford, 37-39; founder-dir. & instr. poetry, N.Y. Poetry Ctr, 39-42; asst. prof. Eng. & mem. grad. fac, Univ. Md, 42-44; head dept. Eng. & ed. & publ. dir. Briarcliff Quart, Briarcliff Jr. Col, 44-47; lectr. Eng, Ohio State Univ, 47; adult educ. in Eng, City Col. New York, 48-50; admin. asst. in charge pub. relat. for state dir, N.Mex. Dept. Pub. Welfare, 51-53; instr. humanities & lang. arts & asst. dir. poetry ctr, San Francisco State Col, 54-55; pub. relat. dir. juvenile delinquency correction, N.Mex. Boys Sch. Springer, 56-57; teacher, High Sch, Nev, 58-59; Calif, 59-61; Mont, 62; Calif, 62-63; head dept. Eng, Higher Inst. Lang, head unified Eng. dept. & head div. for. lang, Univ. Baghdad, 63-64; asst. prof. Eng, Chadron State Col, 64-65; teacher, High Sch, Alta, 65-66; asst. prof. Eng, Savannah State Col, 66-67; assoc. prof, PEMBROKE STATE UNIV, 67-72, COMMUNICATIVE ARTS, 72-, ED. & PUBL, DIR, PEMBROKE MAG. & DIR. CREATIVE WRITING PROG, 69-, POET-IN-RESIDENCE. Am. ed, Front, Amsterdam & Morada, Lago di Garda, Italy, 30-32; for. cor. & free lance writer, France, Holland, Ger, Eng, Latvia, Estonia & U.S.S.R, summers 32, 33; lectr. writing poetry & fiction, Writers Workshop, West. State Col. Colo, summer 42; ed. dir, Md. Quart, 42-44; lectr. Eng, Lehigh Univ, summer 46; poetry, writers conf, Univ. Mo-Columbia, 6/47; guest ed, Cronos, summer 47; teacher, Rhodes Prep. Sch, New York, 48-49; field rep. N.Mex, Div, Am. Cancer Soc, summer 54. Horace Gregory Award, New Sch. Social Res, 72. Col. Eng. Asn; AAUP. Professional writing; editing anthologies and magazines; public relations. Publ: Horizons of death (poetry), 34 & Thanksgiving before November (poems), 36, Parnassus; You get what you ask for, Harrison-Hilton, 39; ed, Calendar: an anthology of 1940 poetry, 40, Calendar: an anthology of 1941 poetry, 41 & Calendar: an anthology of 1942 poetry, 42, James A. Decker & Y.M.H.A. Poetry Ctr; auth, We thank you all the time (poetry), James A. Decker, 41; The bitter roots, Smith & Durrell, 41; A man in midpassage (poetry), Cronos Editions, Columbus, Ohio & Florence, Italy, 47; Pure as nowhere (poetry), Golden Goose, 52; Recollecting Sonja (poem), 73 & I never lost anything in Istanbul (1st chap. of memoirs), 73, Pembroke Mag; A girl on the green, (poem), The Lance, 73; plus many others. Add: P.O. Box 756, Pembroke, NC 28372.

McLEOD, STUART R, b. Eveleth, Minn, July 7, 24; div; c. 2. ENGLISH, COMPARATIVE LITERATURE. B.A, Univ. Mich, 48; Wayne State Univ, 51-52; M.F.S, Univ. Md, 55; Ph.D.(Eng), Univ. Fla, 61. Instr. ENG, Univ. Fla, 60-61; ASST. PROF, POLYTECH. INST. NEW YORK, 61- Sig.C, U.S.A, 43-46. Creative writing. Add: Dept. of English, Polytechnic Institute of New York, 333 Jay St, Brooklyn, NY 11201.

McLEOD, SUSAN HERMINGHAUS, b. Shreveport, La, Nov. 27, 42; m. 65; c. 1. ENGLISH & AMERICAN LITERATURE. B.A, Principia Col, 64; M.A, Univ. Wis-Madison, 65, NDEA fel, 69-70, Vilas fel, 70-71, univ. fel, 71-72, Ph.D.(Eng), 72. Instr. ENG, Tex. South. Univ, 65-66; LECTR, Haile Selassie Univ, 66-68; UNIV. CALIF, SAN DIEGO, 73- MLA; Renaissance Soc. Am. Renaissance drama; lyric poetry; Medieval literature. Add: 6358 Lambda Dr, San Diego, CA 92120.

McLUHAN, HERBERT MARSHALL, b. Edmonton, Alta, July 21, 11; m. 39; c. 6. ENGLISH LITERATURE. B.A, Univ. Man, 32, M.A, 34; B.A, Cambridge, 36, M.A, 39, Ph.D, 42; Univ. Wis, 36-37; nine hon. degrees from Am. Cols. & Can. Univs, 65-72. Asst, Univ, Wis, 36-37; instr, St. Louis Univ, 37-44; assoc. prof, Assumption Univ, 44-46; ENG. LIT, UNIV. TORONTO, 46-52, PROF, 52-, DIR. CENTRE CULT. & TECHNOL, 63- Chmn, Ford Found Sem. Cult. & Commun, 53-55; co-ed, Explor. Mag, 54-59; dir. media proj, Nat. Asn. Educ. Broadcasters & U.S. Off. Educ, 59-60; Albert Schweitzer prof. humanities, Fordham Univ, 67-68; Vatican appt. as consult, Pontif. Comn. Social Commun, 73. Lect, Univ. Pa, 66; Univ. Toronto, 67; Am. Inst. Archit, 67; Congr. Breakfast, Wash, D.C, 70; Univ. West. Ont, 70; State Univ. N.Y. Col. Geneseo, 70; St. Joseph Col.(Conn), 72. Gov. Gen. Award for Critical Prose, 63; Hon. Award Cult. & Commun, Niagara Univ, 67; Molson Award for Outstanding Achievement in Soc. Sci, 67; Pres. Award, Inst. Pub. Relat, Gt. Brit, 70; Companion, Order of Can, 70; Christian Cult. Award, Assumption Univ, 71; Gold Medal Award, Pres. Ital. Repub, Rimini, 71; Pres. Cabinet Award, Univ. Detroit, 72. Fel. Royal Soc. Can. Place of Thomas Nashe in the learning of his time. Publ: The mechanical bride: folklore of industrial man, Vanguard, 51; co-ed, Explorations in communications, Beacon, 60; auth, Gutenberg galaxy: the making of typographic man, Univ. Toronto, 62; Understanding media, 64, co-auth, War and peace in the global village, 68, auth, Literary criticism of Marshall McLuhan, 1943-62, 69 & Culture is our business, 70, McGraw; co-auth, Voices of literature, Holt, Vols. I, II & III, 64, 65 & 70; auth, The medium is the massage, Bantam, 67; co-auth, Through the vanishing point: space in poetry and painting, Harper, 68; auth, Counterblast, 69 & co-auth, Take today: the executive as dropout, 72, Harcourt; co-auth, From cliche to archetype, Viking, 70. Add: 3 Wychwood Park, Toronto, Ont. M6G 2U5, Can.

MacLURE, MILLAR, b. Dundas, P.E.I, July 23, 17; m. 45. ENGLISH. B.A, Acadia Univ, 39; M.A, Queen's Univ.(Ont), 44; Ph.D.(Eng), Univ. Toronto, 49. Prof. ENG, United Col, Winnipeg, 49-53; asst. prof, VICTORIA COL, UNIV. TORONTO, 53-56, assoc. prof, 56-61, PROF, 61- Can. Counc. fel, 58-59. MLA (chmn, Spenser discussion group, 63); Renaissance Soc. Am. Non-dramatic literature of the English Renaissance. Publ: The Paul's Cross sermons, 1534-1642, 58, co-ed, Essays in English literature from the Renaissance to the Victorian age presented to A.S.P. Woodhouse, 64 & auth, George Chapman: a critical study, 66, Univ. Toronto; ed, The poems of Christopher Marlowe, Methuen, London, 68; auth, Nature and art in The Faerie Queene, ELH, 3/61; Literary scholarship, In: A literary history of Canada, Univ. Toronto, 65; Spenser and the ruins of time, In: A theatre for Spenserians, 73. Add: Dept. of English, Victoria College, University of Toronto, Toronto 5, Ont, Can.

McMAHON, FRED RILEY, b. Springfield, Mo, Aug. 13, 20; m. 46; c. 2. SPEECH. B.A, State Univ. Iowa, 42; M.A, Univ. South. Calif, 54, Ph.D, 57. Instr. drama, Univ. Ariz, 42; Eng. & Speech, Glendale Col, 49-56; PROF. RHETORIC & SPEECH, CALIF. STATE UNIV, NORTHRIDGE, 56-, res. grant, 63. Consult, Los Angeles Pub. Employees' Speakers Club, 56-60; commun. consult, Lockheed Aircraft Corp, 63-65; U.S. Armed Forces, Europe, 67-68; assoc. ed, West. Speech, ed, 67-70. U.S.A, 42-46, 50-52, Capt. West. Speech Commun. Asn.(assoc. ed, West. Speech, 60-); Speech Commun. Asn; Conf. Brit. Stud; Col. Nat. Soc. Stud. Commun. Rhetoric and public address; 17th century church history; 17th century British history. Publ: Jacobean elocutio, West. Speech, 62; Sleight of speech, Calif. Asn. Sec. Schs, 63; Rhetoric of California rhetoricians, Speech Asn. Am, 63. Add: Dept. of Communication, California State University, Northridge, Northridge, CA 91324.

McMAHON, MARY AVILA, I.H.M, b. Syracuse, N.Y, May 31, 06. SPEECH, ENGLISH, DRAMA. A.B, St. Joseph's Col.(Md), 28; M.A, Columbia Univ, 49; Wayne State Univ, 45, 50-51, 57; Univ. Mich, 56; Northwest. Univ, 63; Oxford, 65. Teacher high sch, Mich, 32-33; Eng, speech, Latin & French, St. Mary Acad, Monroe, Mich, 33-38; instr. Eng, MARYGROVE COL, 38-43, asst. prof, 43-45, Eng. & speech, 45-48, assoc. prof. SPEECH, 48-62, PROF, 62-, CHMN. DEPT, 48-, summer dir. & team teacher, Film Stud. Inst, 66-67. Participant, NDEA Summer Inst, Univ. California, Santa Barbara, 68; vis. prof. Eng. lit. & mod. drama, Siena Heights Col, 69-71; lectr. mid. Eng, Duns Scotus College, 73. Speech Commun. Asn; Am. Speech & Hearing Asn; Am. Theatre Asn; Nat. Cath. Theatre Conf.(mem. bd, 65-69); NCTE. Phonetics; development of drama; speech and communications problems of the inner city. Publ: Poetry, Eng. Newslett, 44; French-without-fiction, Cath. Sch. J, 45; Radio passes Marygrove entrance exam, J. Educ. Radio & TV, 45. Add: 610 Elm Ave, Monroe, MI 48161.

McMANAWAY, JAMES GILMER, b. Fayette, Mo, Aug. 24, 99; m. 26; c. 1. SHAKESPEARE. A.B, Univ. Va, 19, A.M, 20; Ph.D, Johns Hopkins Univ, 31; D.Lit, Hofstra Univ, 60, Ripon Col, 64; D.H.L, George Wash. Univ, 63. Instr. & dean fac, Va. Jr. Col, 23, 27; assoc. prof. Eng, Miss. Agr. & Mech. Col, 27-28; secy. grad. dept. Eng, Johns Hopkins Univ, 28-36, instr. Eng, 30-33, res. assoc. sch. higher stud, 33-36; asst. to dir, Folger Shakespeare Libr, 36-43, asst. dir, 43-46, acting dir, 46-48, consult. lit. & bibliog, 48-68; PROF. ENG, UNIV. MD, COLLEGE PARK, 70- Am. Counc. Learned Soc. grants-in-aid, 34, 37 & 63; vis. prof, Univ. Md, 40-70; Pierpont Morgan Libr, 45; Rosenbach Found. Bibliog, 47; Hyde Mem. lectr, Valparaiso Univ, 48; gen. ed, New Variorum Shakespeare, 50-; ed, Shakespeare Quart, 51-72; Guggenheim fel, 53-54; Huntington Libr. grant, 61; vis. prof, Rice Univ, 66; Univ. Kans, 67; Univ. Tex, 68-69; Univ. Ariz, 69. U.S.N.R, 18. Bibliog. Soc. Univ. Va; Malone Soc; fel. Royal Soc. Lit. U.K; MLA; Shakespeare Soc. Am; Bibliog. Soc, Eng. Elizabethan literature; bibliography; Shakespeare. Publ: Co-auth, Check list of English plays: 1641-1700, Newberry Libr, 45; co-ed, Dick of Devonshire, Malone Soc, 55; ed, Pericles, Pelican Bks, 56, 69; auth, The authorship of Shakespeare, Folger Shakespeare Libr, 62; ed, Shakespeare 400, Holt, 64; auth, Studies in Shakespeare: bibliography and theater, Shakespeare Asn. Am, 69; L, heritage de la Renaissance dans la mise en scene en Angleterre: 1642-1700, In: Le lieu théatral a la Renaissance, Nat. Ctr. Sci. Res, Paris, 64; All's well with Lafeu, In: Shakespeare's art, Univ. Chicago, 73. Add: 5505 Center St, Chevy Chase, MD 20015.

McMANMON, JOHN JOSEPH, b. Evanston, Ill, June 26, 32; m. 66; c. 2. ENGLISH, HISTORY OF IDEAS. B.A, Univ. Notre Dame, 55, M.A, 61; M.A, Holy Cross Col.(D.C), 59; Ph.D.(Eng), Univ. Chicago, 65. Instr. ENG, Univ. Notre Dame, 64-65, asst. prof, 65-66; assoc. prof, Roosevelt Univ, summer 66; asst. prof, Univ. Calif, Los Angeles, 66-68; assoc. prof, State Univ. N.Y. Col. Geneseo, 68-69; Calif. State Univ, Northridge, 69-71; PROF, INDIANA UNIV. PA, 71- MLA. Eighteenth century history of ideas; critical theory; medieval ideas in philosophy and theology. Publ: Transl, Daniel Heinsius, De Constitutione tragedia, 72; auth, Correspondence between Gilbert Burnet and Francis Hutcheson, Stud. Scottish Lit, 65; Problem of a religious interpretation of Gulliver IV, J. Hist. Ideas, 66. Add: Dept. of English, Indiana University of Pennsylvania, Indiana, PA 15701.

McMANN, MARY A, b. Kansas City, Mo, Aug. 17, 17; m. 50; c. 1. ENGLISH, HUMANITIES. A.B, Univ. Mo, Kansas City, 38, fel, 58-60, Ph.D.(gen. educ, humanities), 64; A.M, Columbia Univ, 42. Instr. ENG, Harpur Col, 47-50; teacher pub. schs, Mo, 55-58; Sunset Hill Sch, Mo, 62-63; instr, UNIV. MO-KANSAS CITY, 63-65, ASST. PROF, 65- Part-time instr, Metropolitan Jr. Col, 53-58; Avila Col, 62-63; consult, Loretto in Kansas City, 66-; proj. communicate, Northwest Mo. State Col, 67; Mem, N.Cent. Eval. Comt, High Sch, 68; assoc. chmn. Educ. Resources Inform. Ctr. comt, NCTE, 68- NCTE; Conf. Eng. Educ; Midwest Mod. Lang. Asn; MLA. General education; English education; comparative literature; French novel, especially Francois Mauriac. Add: Dept. of English, University of Missouri-Kansas City, 5200 Rockhill Rd, Kansas City, MO 64110.

McMASTER, JULIET, b. Kisumu, Kenya, Aug. 2, 37; m. 68; c. 2. ENGLISH. B.A, Oxford, 59, M.A, 62; Mt. Holyoke Col, 59-60; M.A, Univ. Alta, 62, Ph.D. (Eng), 65. Asst. prof. ENG, UNIV. ALTA, 65-70, ASSOC. PROF, 70- Can. Counc. fel, 69-70. MLA; Asn. Can. Univ. Teachers Eng. John Ford; Thackeray and the 19th century novel; 18th and 19th century novel. Publ: Thackeray: the major novels, Univ. Toronto, 71; The continuity of Jane Austen's novels, Stud. Eng. Lit, fall 70; The unfortunate moth: unifying theme in The small house at Allington, Nineteenth-Century Fiction, 9/71; The portrait of Isabel Archer, Am. Lit, 3/73. Add: Dept. of English, University of Alberta, Edmonton, Alta, Can.

McMASTER, ROWLAND DOUGLAS, b. Sydney, Australia, Dec. 5, 28; Can. citizen. ENGLISH. B.A, Univ. Toronto, 53, fel, 53-54, M.A, 54, Can. Humanities Res. Counc. fel, 56-57, Ph.D.(Eng), 59. Part time instr, Univ. Toronto, 54-56; assoc. prof. ENG, Acadia Univ, 57-58; asst. prof, UNIV. ALTA, 58-62, assoc. prof, 62-67, PROF, 67- Asn. Can. Univ. Teachers Eng. rep, Humanities Res. Coun. Can, 73-76. Asn. Can. Univ. Teachers Eng.(pres, 72-74); MLA; Int. Asn. Univ. Prof. Eng. Victorian novel—Dickens; Victorian thought. Publ: Ed, Great expectations by Charles Dickens, 65 & ed, Little Dorrit, 69, Macmillan; auth, Dickens and the horrific, Dalhousie Rev, 58; Little Dorrit: experience and design, Queen's Quart, 61; Criticism of civilization in the structure of Sartor Resartus, Univ. Toronto Quart, 4/68. Add: Dept. of English, University of Alberta, Edmonton, Alta T6G 2G2, Can.

McMICHAEL, GEORGE, b. Tulsa, Okla, Aug. 20, 27; m. 53; c. 1. AMERICAN LITERATURE. B.S, Northwest. Univ, 50, M.A. & Ph.D.(Eng), 59. Instr. Eng, Roosevelt Univ, 57-59; asst. prof, Chico State Col, 59-62; prof. Am. lit, Calif. State Col. San Bernardino, 62-70, dean of fac, 62-67; PROF. ENG. & DEAN SCH. ARTS, LETT. & SOC. SCI, CALIF. STATE UNIV, HAYWARD, 72- Am. Philos. Soc. res. grant, 67; Fulbright vis. prof, Univ. Thessaloniki, 68-69. MLA; Am. Stud. Asn. Nineteenth century and Colonial American literature. Publ: Co-auth, Shakespeare and his rivals, Odyssey, 62; auth, Journey to obscurity, Univ. Nebr, 67; ed, Anthology of American literature (2 vols), Macmillan, 74. Add: School of Arts, Letters & Social Science, California State University, Hayward, Hayward, CA 94542.

McMILLAN, DOUGLAS JOSEPH, b. Cleveland, Ohio, July 2, 31; m. 57; c. 1. ENGLISH. A.B, De Paul Univ, 54; Fulbright fel, Frankfort Univ, 54-55; M.A, Univ. Md, 60, Ph.D, 63. Instr. ENG, Univ. Md, 60-65, asst. prof, 65-67, assoc. prof, 67-68; Univ. Ark, Fayetteville, 68-69; PROF. E.CAROLINA UNIV, 69- Fel, Southeast. Inst. Medieval & Renaissance Stud, summer 69. U.S.A, 56-62. MLA; Mediaeval Acad. Am. Medieval literature; Anglo-German literature; folk literature. Publ: A survey of theories concerning the oral transmission of the traditional ballad, 12/64 & Some popular views of four mediaeval battles, 6/66, South. Folklore Quart; The Phoenix in the Western world from Herodotus to Shakespeare, D.H. Lawrence Rev, fall 72; plus others. Add: Dept. of English, East Carolina University, P.O. Box 2707, Greenville, NC 27834.

McMILLAN, JAMES BENJAMIN, Linguistics, English. See Volume III, Foreign Languages, Linguistics & Philology.

McMILLAN, MARY EVELYN, b. Greensboro, Ala, Nov. 9, 26. ENGLISH. B.A, Birmingham South. Col, 49; M.A, Univ. Ala, 55, Ph.D, 60; South. fel, Shakespeare Inst, Univ. Birmingham, 58-59. Instr. ENG, Univ. Ala, 56-60; PROF, Athens Col, 60-63; JACKSONVILLE STATE UNIV, 63- MLA. English literature, Elizabethan Period. Add: Dept. of English, Jacksonville State University, Jacksonville, AL 36265.

McMILLAN, MONTAGUE, b. Florence Co, S.C, Aug. 29, 92. ENGLISH. A.B, Limestone Col, 11, D.Litt, 45; Columbia Univ; Univ. N.C; A.M, George Washington Univ, 27; Duke Univ, 29-30. Teacher pub. schs, S.C, 11-17; from instr. to prof. Eng, LIMESTONE COL, 17-72, EMER. PROF. ENG. & ARCHIVIST, 72- Dean women, summer sch, Furman Univ, 25-30. South Carolina life in fiction; Scottish vernacular poetry. Publ: A history of Limestone College, 1845-1970, Bryan, 70. Add: Limestone College, Gaffney, SC 29340.

McMILLAN, NORMAN ROBERT, b. Greensboro, Ala, Aug. 13, 42; m. 62; c. 2. ENGLISH LITERATURE. B.A, Univ. Ala, 64, M.A, 67; Ph.D.(Eng), Univ. Mich, 71. Teaching asst. ENG, Univ. Ala, 64-66, instr, 66-67; teaching fel, Univ. Mich, Ann Arbor, 67-70, lectr, Univ. Mich, Flint, 70-71; ASST. PROF, UNIV. MONTEVALLO, 71- Dept. of State Int. Study grant, summer 73. MLA; AAUP. Seventeenth century prose; metaphysical poetry; 17th century rhetoric. Publ: Donne's Biathanatos and the tradition of the paradox, Univ. Microfilms, 71; co-auth, Among the new words, Am. Speech, 65-66. Add: Dept. of English, University of Montevallo, Montevallo, AL 35115.

McMILLAN, SAMUEL H, JR, b. Galveston, Tex, Sept. 6, 35; m. 62; c. 2. MODERN DRAMA & AMERICAN LITERATURE. B.A, South. Methodist Univ, 57; Ph.D, Univ. Tex, 64. Teaching asst. Eng, Univ. Tex, 60-64; asst. prof, UNIV. TENN, KNOXVILLE, 64-72, ASSOC. PROF, 72- Danforth post-doctoral fel. black stud, Yale, 71-72. MLA; S.Atlantic Mod. Lang. Asn; Asn. Stud. Afro-Am. Life & Hist; AAUP. Modern drama; Black literature; American literature. Publ: John Crowe Ransom's Painted head, Ga. Rev, summer 68; Image and suggestion: James Wright and Andrew Wyeth, winter 68 & ed, Spring 71 Issue, Tenn. Poetry J. Add: Dept. of English, University of Tennessee, Knoxville, TN 37916.

McMILLIN, HARVEY SCOTT, JR, b. Pittsburgh, Pa, June 29, 34; m. 57; c. 3. ENGLISH LITERATURE. B.A, Princeton, 56; M.A, George Washington Univ, 60; fel, Univ. Col, London, 64; Ph.D.(Eng), Stanford Univ, 65. Instr. ENG, CORNELL UNIV, 64-66, asst. prof, 66-72, ASSOC. PROF, 72- Cornell Univ. grant-in-aid award, summer 66; Nat. Endowment for Humanities stipend, summer 68; Am. Philos. Soc. res. grant, 72-73. U.S.N, 57-60, Lt.(jg). MLA; Am. Soc. Theatre Res. Shakespeare; Elizabethan-Jacobean drama; dramatic literature. Publ: Ed, Restoration and eighteenth-century comedy, Norton, 73; auth, The book of Sir Thomas More: a theatrical view, Mod. Philol, 70; The figure of silence in The Spanish tragedy, Eng. Lit. Hist, 72; Casting for Pembroke's men: the Henry VI quartos and Taming of a shrew, Shakespeare Quart, 72. Add: Dept. of English, Cornell University, Ithaca, NY 14850.

McMUNN, WILLIAM ROBERT, Linguistics. See Volume III, Foreign Languages, Linguistics & Philology.

McMURRAY, WILLIAM J, b. Gardner, Mass, July 12, 28; m. 58; c. 1. ENGLISH. B.A, Middlebury Col, 57; M.A, Univ. Ill, 58; Ph.D, Univ. N.Mex, 61. Instr. ENG, Victoria Col.(B.C), 61-62; Univ. Ky, 62-65; PROF, MADISON COL.(VA), 65-, head dept, 70-74. U.S.A, 51-53. MLA. The fiction of William Dean Howells; the realism movement in American literature. Publ: The literary realism of William Dean Howells, South. Ill, Univ, 67; Pragmatic realism in The Bostonians, Nineteenth Century Fiction, 3/62; Point of view in Howells' The landlord at Lion's Head, Am. Lit, 12/62; The concept of complicity in Howells' fiction, New Eng. Quart, 12/62. Add: Dept. of English, Madison College, Main St, Harrisonburg, VA 22802.

McNALLY, JAMES J, b. Washington, D.C, Sept. 30, 24; m. 49; c. 2. ENGLISH, AMERICAN LITERATURE. B.A, Univ. Va, 51, Virginia M. Davidge fel, 52, M.A, 52, M.A, 54, Ph.D, 61. Instr. Eng, Pa. State Univ, 57-58; asst. prof, Morris Harvey Col, 58, acting head dept, 59, assoc. prof. Eng. & head dept, 61-63; asst. prof. ENG, OLD DOM. UNIV, 63-66, assoc. prof, 66-69, PROF, 69- Treas, Victorians Inst, 71-73. U.S.M.C.R, 43-46, Sgt. MLA; Col. Eng. Asn; Am. Comt. Irish Stud. Browning; Anglo-Irish literature; 19th century English and American literature. Publ: Suiting sight and sound to sense, autumn 67 & Two small verses of Browning, autumn 71, Victorian poetry: Browning's political thought, Queen's Quart, winter 70; plus two others. Add: 1035 Manchester Ave, Norfolk, VA 23508.

McNALLY, JAMES RICHARD, b. Council Bluffs, Iowa, July 28, 33; m. 63; c. 2. SPEECH. A.B, St. Louis Univ, 57, M.A, 60; Univ. Ill, 60-61; Ph.D. (speech), Univ. Iowa, 66. Teacher high sch, Marquette Univ, 58-60; Thomas Jefferson High Sch, 62-63; Lewis Cent. High Sch, 63-64; asst. prof. speech, Univ. Wis-Madison, 66-69; ASSOC. PROF. RHET. & COMMUN, STATE UNIV. N.Y. ALBANY, 69- Univ. Wis. fels, summers 66 & 68. Speech Commun. Asn. Medieval and Renaissance rhetoric; classical rhetoric and logic; speech communication. Publ: Dux illa directrizque artium . . ., Quart. J. Speech, 12/66; Rudolph Agricola's De inventione dialectica: a translation . . ., Speech Monogr, 11/66; Characteristics of art in the text of Aristotle, J. Aesthet. & Art Criticism, summer 71. Add: 2 Victoria Dr, Guilderland, NY 12084.

McNALLY, JOHN, b. Chicago, Ill, May 15, 24; m. 47; c. 4. ENGLISH. A.B, Loyola Univ.(Ill), 47, M.A, 50; Univ. Ore, 43-44; Ph.D.(Eng), Univ. Chicago, 61. Instr. ENG, State Col. Iowa, 50-53; teacher, Wright Jr. Col, 54-56; asst. prof, West. Mich. Univ, 56-61, ASSOC. PROF, 61-67; UNIV. MINN, MINNEAPOLIS, 67- Vis. Fulbright prof, Univ. Deusto, 65-66. U.S.A, 43-46. MLA; Mediaeval Acad. Am; NCTE. Medieval languages and literatures; linguistics; English as a foreign language. Publ: The useless wall, Univ. Deusto, 66; Courtly love and penitential literature in Gower's Confessio amantis, Stud. Medieval Cult, I, 64; Chaucer's topsy-turvy Dante, Stud. Medieval Cult, II, 66. Add: Dept. of English, College of Liberal Arts, University of Minnesota, Minneapolis, MN 55455.

McNALLY, TERRENCE JAMES, b. Cincinnati, Ohio, Jan. 5, 37; m. 64; c. 3. ENGLISH LITERATURE. B.A, Duns Scotus Col, 60; M.A, Xavier Univ, (Ohio), 63; fel, Loyola Univ. Chicago, 64-66, Ph.D.(Eng), 68. Instr. ENG, Marquette Univ, 63-64; DePaul Univ, 66-68; asst. prof, Xavier Univ.(Ohio), 68-70; ASSOC. PROF, NORTH. KY. STATE COL, 70- MLA; S.Atlantic Mod. Lang. Asn; NCTE; Conf. Col. Compos. & Commun. English literature of the 18th century; the theory and practice of tragedy from the Greeks to the moderns; the teaching of college composition courses. Add: Dept. of English, Northern Kentucky State College, Highland Heights, KY 41076.

McNAMARA, BROOKS B. b. Peoria, Ill, Feb. 1, 37; m. 62; c. 1. DRAMA. B.A, Knox Coll, 59; M.A, Univ. Iowa, 61; univ. grant, Tulane Univ, 64, Colonial Williamsburg grants, 64, 65, Ph.D.(drama), 65. Instr. DRAMA, Monmouth Col.(Ill), 61-63; asst. prof, Univ. Del, 65-68; assoc. prof, N.Y. UNIV, 68-71, PROF, 71- Univ. Del. res. grants, 66-68; contrib. ed, Drama Rev; consult, State Univ. N.Y. Stony Brook, Va. Polytech Inst. & State Univ, Univ. Del. & Col. White Plains. Adj.Gen.C, U.S.A.R, 59-67, 1st Lt. Am. Theatre Asn.(mem. bd. res, 71-74); Am. Soc. Theatre Res; Theatre Libr. Asn.(dir, 69-75); Univ. & Col. Theatre Asn.(secy-treas, 71-72). Eighteenth and 19th century British and American theatre; theatre architecture and scene design; popular entertainments. Publ: The American playhouse in the eighteenth century, Harvard, 69; The English playhouse in eighteenth century America, Connoisseur, 12/67; David Douglass and the beginnings of American theatre architecture, Winterthur Portfolio, 67; The Indian medicine show, Educ. Theatre J, 12/71. Add: Dept. of Drama, Press Bldg, New York University, New York, NY 10003.

McNAMARA, EUGENE JOSEPH, b. Oak Park, Ill, Mar. 18, 30; m. 52; c. 5. ENGLISH. B.A, DePaul Univ, 53, M.A, 55; Ph.D.(Eng), Northwest. Univ, 64. Instr. ENG, Univ. Ill, Chicago, 55-59; PROF, UNIV. WINDSOR, 59- Ed, Univ. Windsor Rev. MLA; NCTE; Can. Asn. Am. Stud; League Can. Poets. Modern novel; nineteenth century American literature; contemporary poetry. Publ: For the mean time (poems), Gryphon, 65; ed, Interior landscape: literary criticism of Marshall McLuhan, McGraw, 69; auth, Outerings (poems), Delta Can, 70; Love scenes (poems), Hellric, 70; Dillinger poems, Black Moss, 71; Hard words (poems), Fiddlehead Bks, 72; Passages and other poems, Sono Nis, 72; William Styron's Long march: absurdity and authority, West. Humanities Rev, summer 61; Post-modern American novel, Queen's Quart, summer 62, Blackfriars, Eng, 4/62; Note on the academic life (short story) Tex. Quart, spring 66; plus others. Add: Dept. of English, University of Windsor, Sunset Ave, Windsor, Ont, Can.

McNAMARA, ROBERT JEREMY, b. Portsmouth, Ohio, Jan. 25, 32; m. 53; c. 2. ENGLISH. B.A, Kenyon Col, 53; M.A, Univ. N.C, 54; Ph.D.(Eng), Mich. State Univ, 61. Instr. ENG, Idaho State Col, 56-57; Miami Univ, 61-63, asst. prof, 63-64; MONMOUTH COL, 64-68, ASSOC. PROF, 68-, chmn. dept, 67-72. U.S.A, 54-56. MLA; NCTE. English renaissance drama; Shakespeare. Add: Dept. of English, Monmouth College, Monmouth, IL 61462.

McNAMEE, LAWRENCE, b. Pittsburgh, Pa, Mar. 14, 17; c. 3. ENGLISH. B.A, Duquesne Univ, 46, M.A, 48; Univ. Cologne, Ger, 55-56; Ph.D, Univ. Pittsburgh, 57. Instr. Eng, Carnegie Inst. Tech, 47-49; assoc. prof. Eng. & German, E.TEX. STATE UNIV, 50-65, PROF. ENG, 65- German consult, Britannica World Lang. Dictionary, 54; jr. & high sch. German textbook selection, Tex, 62-63; U.S. Off. Educ. grant, 65-66; vis. prof, Univ. Pittsburgh, 74. U.S.A.A.F, 42-46, M/Sgt. Shakespeare Asn. Am; MLA; Renaissance Soc. Am; NCTE. Stage history of Shakespeare's plays; methods of teaching Shakespeare; bibliography. Publ: Heinrich Laube und sein Beitrag zu Julius Caesar, Maske u. Kothurn, Austria, 63; A bibliography of all English-literature dissertations accepted by German, British, and American universities since 1865, 68, English dissertations, 1964-1968, 69 & 1969-1973, 73, Bowker; Ninety-nine years of English dissertations, E.Tex. Univ, 69; The English doctorate in the United States, Col. Eng, 64; Graduate English study, Asn. Dept. Eng, 9/69; The computer and the theatre, Quart. J. Speech, 10/70; plus others. Add: Dept. of English, East Texas State University, East Texas Sta, Commerce, TX 75428.

McNAMEE, MAURICE BASIL, S.J, b. Montello, Wis, June 5, 09. ENGLISH. A.B, St. Louis Univ, 33, A.M, 34, S.T.L, 41, Ph.D, 45. Instr. Creighton Prep. Sch, Nebr, 36-37; asst. prof. ENG, ST. LOUIS UNIV, 44-54, assoc. prof, 54-60, CHMN. DEPT, 56-, CHMN. UNDERGRAD. ENG. COMT, 44-, HONORS COUNC, 50-, res. grant, 55. Fulbright res. fel, Belgium, 65-66; Am. Philos. Soc. res. grant, 65-66; Ford Found. Jesuit Fac. Fund res. grant, St. Louis Univ, 66-68. Renaissance Soc. Am; NCTE; MLA; Conf. Col. Compos. & Commun; Asn. Depts. Eng; Col. Art Asn. Am; Mediaeval Acad. Am; Cath. Comn. Intellectual & Cult. Affairs. Symbolism in Flemish painting; mannerism and surrealism in art and literature. Publ: Literary decorum in Francis Bacon, St. Louis Univ, 50; Reading for understanding, 58, 3rd ed, 68, Honor and the epic hero, 59 & Literary types and themes, 60, Holt; Essays by the masters, Bobbs, 67; Bacon's inductive method and humanistic grammar, Stud. Lit. Imagination, 4/71; The eucharist as a central theme in the Ghent altarpiece, Rev. Relig, 1/73; The origin of the Vested Angel as a eucharistic symbol in Flemish painting, Art Bull, 9/73. Add: Dept. of English & Art History, St. Louis University, 221 Grand Ave, St. Louis, MO 63103.

McNARON, TONI ANN HURLEY, b. Birmingham, Ala, Apr. 3, 37. ENGLISH. B.A, Univ. Ala, 58; Woodrow Wilson fel. & M.A, Vanderbilt Univ, 60; univ. fel. & Ph.D.(Eng), Univ. Wis, 64. Instr. Eng. & geog, All Saints' Episcopal Col, 59-61; asst. prof. ENG, UNIV. MINN, MINNEAPOLIS, 64-67, ASSOC. PROF, 67- Nat. Endowment for Arts & Humanities grant, summer 67; Univ. Minn. grad. sch. fel, summer 68. Distinguished Teacher Award, Univ. Minn, 67. MLA; Midwest Mod. Lang. Asn; NCTE; AAUP; Am. Asn. Higher Educ. Shakespeare's romances; early 17th century poetry, especially Herbert and Marvell; Virginia Woolf. Add: Dept. of English, University of Minnesota, Minneapolis, MN 55455.

McNEELY, JAMES TREVOR, b. Russell, Man, May 10, 34; m. 55; c. 4. ENGLISH & AMERICAN LITERATURE. B.S, Univ. Man, 55; M.A, Univ. Alta, 65. Geologist, Phillips Petrol. Co, 55-62; asst. prof. ENG, BRANDON UNIV, 66-71, ASSOC. PROF, 71- Can. Asn. Univ. Teachers. Nineteenth and 20th century British and American literature; Shakespeare. Publ: Norse heroic psychology and the Nifling lays of the poetic Edda, Discourse, fall 66; Religion, Marxist logic, and revisionism, Dalhousie Rev, spring 67; Matthew Arnold and the vision of sin: underground themes in the poetry, Mosaic, fall 71. Add: Dept. of English, Brandon University, Brandon, Man. R7A 6A9, Can.

McNEELY, JERRY C, b. Cape Girardeau, Mo, June 20, 28; m. 51; c. 3. SPEECH. B.A, Southeast Mo. State Col, 49; M.S, Univ. Wis, 50, univ. fel, 55, Ph.D, 56. Instr. speech, Southeast Mo. State Col, 50-51; UNIV. WIS-MADISON, 56-57, asst. prof, 57-61, assoc. prof, 61-64, PROF, 64-72, COMMUN. ARTS, 72- Exec. story consult, Universal Studios, 71-72, freelance TV dir, 73. Writers Guild Am. Award, 57; Hallmark Teleplay Competition Award, 61. U.S.A, 51-53. Speech Commun. Asn; Am. Soc. Composers, Auth. & Publ. Playwriting; dramatic criticism. Publ: The staring match, produced on Studio One, CBS-TV, 57; The joke and the valley, produced on Hallmark Hall of Fame, 61, Dr. Kildare (15 scripts), 62-66, The man from U.N.C.L.E (4 scripts), 65-66 & The Virginian, NBC-TV; Marcus Welby, M.D.(numerous scripts), 69-72, Owen Marshall, Counselor at law (pilot & numerous scripts), 71-73 & Streets of San Francisco, 73, ABC-TV; plus others. Add: 6054 Vilas Hall, University of Wisconsin-Madison, Madison, WI 53706.

McNEELY, SAMUEL SIDNEY, JR, b. New Orleans, La, May 24, 15; m. 53. ENGLISH. A.B, Loyola Univ.(La), 35; M.A, La. State Univ, 36, Ph.D.(Eng), 40; Litt.D, Univ. Rome, 39. Instr. Eng, Southwest. La. Inst, 40-42; civil educ. off. civil affairs, Gen. Hq, Japan, 46-51; asst. prof. Eng, La. State Univ, 51-55; Univ. Houston, 55-58; ASSOC. PROF. ENG. & DIR. INT. OFF, TULANE UNIV, 58- Consult, U.S. Educ. Found, India, 65-66; dir, Cordell Hull Found, 70-; consult, Inst. Int. Educ, 71- U.S.A, 42-46, S/Sgt. Soc. Am. Archaeol; Nat. Asn. For. Stud. Affairs (dir, 60-65). Philology. Publ: Co-auth, Student services for Indian universities and colleges, U.S. Educ. Found, India & Indraprastha Press, New Delhi, 66; auth, Education in the Caribbean countries, Nat. Asn. For. Stud. Affairs Prof. Papers, 59. Add: International Office, Tulane University, New Orleans, LA 70118.

McNEIL, NORMAN L, b. San Antonio, Tex, Oct. 3, 15; m. 41; c. 2. AMERICAN LITERATURE. B.A, Univ. Tex, 37, M.A, 44, Ph.D, 56. Instr. Eng, Univ. Tex, 46; asst. prof, Univ. Houston, 46-47; Trinity Univ, 47-52; Tex. Col. Arts & Industs, 56-58, assoc. prof, 58-60, prof, 60-65, for. stud. adv, 60-65; PRES, SUL ROSS STATE UNIV, 65- Univ. Tex. E.D. Farmer Int. fel. collecting folk ballads, Mex, 41; field collector folk music, Libr. Congr, Mex. & Southwest U.S, 41; asst. dir. orientation prog. foreign scholar. grantees, Orientation Ctr, Univ. Tex, summers 55-61, 63; Creole Oil Corp. & Nat. Asn. For. Stud. Adv. Creole Grant study higher educ, Cent. Am, Colombia & Venezuela, 61; U.S. Dept. State, Bur. Educ. & Cult. Affairs Am. Specialist grant, lectr. U.S. folksongs, S. Am, 62. U.S.A.A.F, 43-44. Am. Folklore Soc; S.Cent. Mod. Lang. Asn; Nat. Asn. For. Stud. Adv. British and American folk ballads; regional literature of the United States, especially of the West and Southwest; higher education in Latin America. Publ: Observations of education in the Caribbean countries, Nat. Asn. For. Stud. Adv, 62; The British ballad in the Middle West and Lower Mississippi Valley, Publ. Tex. Folklore Soc, 56; auth, Folksongs by Brownie McNeil, Sonic Records, 60. Add: Sul Ross State University, Alpine, TX 79830.

McNEIL, ROBERT HOOPER, b. Alton, Ill, Nov. 9, 02. JOURNALISM. A.B, George Wash. Univ, 24; A.M, Ohio State Univ, 25. Reporter, Washington Herald, 25; instr. ENG. & JOUR, Colgate Univ, 25-28, prof. & dir. pub. relat, VA. POLYTECH. INST, 28-64, EMER. PROF, 64- Assoc. ed, Montgomery County News Messenger, Va, 64- Add: P.O. Box 862, Blacksburg, VA 24060.

McNEIR, WALDO FOREST, b. Houston, Tex, Sept. 13, 08; m. 35; c. 1. ENGLISH LITERATURE. A.B, Rice Univ, 29; A.M, Univ. N.C, 32, Ph.D, 40. Instr. ENG, Univ. N.C, 34-40; asst. prof, N.Tex. State Univ, 40-42, 46; Univ. Chicago, 46-49; La. State Univ, 49-53, assoc. prof, 53-58, PROF, 58-61; UNIV. ORE, 61- Fulbright lectr, Univ. Marburg, 57 & 64, Univ. Münster, 68. U.S.N.R, 42-46, Comdr. MLA; Mod. Humanities Res. Asn, Gt. Brit; Renaissance Soc. Am; Shakespeare Asn. Am; Mediaeval Acad. Am; S.Cent. Mod. Lang. Asn.(secy-treas, 51-54); S.Cent. Renaissance Conf.(pres, 58-59); Philol. Asn. Pac. Coast; Pac. Northwest Renaissance Conf. Elizabethan literature. Publ: Studies in English Renaissance literature, La. State Univ, 62; co-auth, Annotated bibliography of Edmund Spenser, Duquesne Univ, 62, 2nd ed, 75; co-ed, Five plays of Shakespeare, Scott, 65; The merchant of Venice: an outline-guide to the play, Barnes & Noble, 65; Pacific Coast studies in Shakespeare, Univ. Ore, 66; contrib, Festschrift für Edgar Mertner, Fink, 69, Essential articles for the study of Edmund Spenser, Archon, 73; Pacific coast philology, Philol. Asn. Pac. Coast, 74. Add: Dept. of English, University of Oregon, Eugene, OR 97403.

McNELIS, JAMES IGNATIUS, b. Centralia, Pa, Oct. 23, 17; m. 56; c. 3. ENGLISH. A.B, Columbia Col, Columbia Univ, 42, M.A, Columbia Univ, 47, Ph.D.(Eng), 54. Instr. ENG, Stanford Univ, 51-56; asst. prof, HUMBOLDT STATE UNIV, 56-60, assoc. prof, 60-65, PROF, 65-, res. award, 59. Fulbright lectr, Hacettepe Univ, Turkey, 67-68. U.S.C.G.R, 43-45, Lt.(jg). MLA; Acad. Polit. Sci; NCTE; Am. Polit. Sci. Asn. Seventeenth and eighteenth century English literature; the imaginary voyage. Publ: Ed, Holberg, the journey of Niels Klim to the world underground, Univ. Nebr, 60; The perception of size in the first two books of Gulliver's travels, Timber, N.Coast J, 63. Add: Dept. of English, Humboldt State University, Arcata, CA 95521.

McNELLY, WILLIS EVERETT, b. Waupun, Wis, Dec. 16, 20; m. 44; c. 5. ENGLISH. B.A, Cent. YMCA Col, 42; M.A, Loyola Univ.(Ill), 48; Ph.D, Northwest. Univ, 57, Instr. ENG, Loyola Univ.(Ill), 47-52; chmn. dept, Rich Twp. High Sch, Park Forest, Ill, 52-58; instr, Santa Ana Col, 58-61; asst. prof, CALIF. STATE UNIV, FULLERTON, 61-63, assoc. prof, 63-68, PROF, 68- Vis. prof, St. Joseph's Col.(Calif), 59-65, dir. pub. lectr. ser, 61- Qm.C, 42-46, 50-51, 1st Lt. NEA; MLA; Col. Eng. Asn. Catholicism and Joyce; Yeats and Eliot; science fiction. Publ: Co-ed, Mars, we love you!, Doubleday, 71, Pyramid, 73 & Above the human landscape, Goodyear, 72; ed, Chapbook of science fiction, Col. Eng. Asn, 74; Linguistic relativity in middle high Martian, 5/68 & Science fiction and the academy, 10/72, 1/73 & 5/73, CEA Critic; Twenty years in search of a footnote, James Joyce Quart, summer 73. Add: Dept. of English, California State University, Fullerton, 800 N. State College Blvd, Fullerton, CA 92634.

McNICHOLS, DONALD, b. Burr Oak, Kans, Sept. 26, 15; m. 40; c. 1. ENGLISH. A.B, Los Angeles Pac. Col, 41; A.B, Univ. South. Calif, 47, M.A, 50; Univ. Wash. Dean men, Los Angeles Pac. Col, 40-42, 45-48; prin, high sch, 48-50; prof. Eng. & dean, George Fox Col, 50-55, fac. lectr, 55; PROF. ENG, SEATTLE PAC. COL, 55-, ASSOC. DEAN ACAD. AFFAIRS, 68-, chmn. dept. Eng, 55-68. Bd. trustees, George Fox Col. U.S.A, 43-45. Backgrounds to Quaker ideology; novels of Willa Cather; religious trends in 20th century American poetry. Publ: Optimism and academic respectability, Bull. Asn. Am. Cols; Studies in fulfillment: a consideration of the novels of Willa Cather; Folk poetry as biography, Seattle Genealogical Soc, 71. Add: 3207 Tenth Ave. W, Seattle, WA 98119.

MACOMBER, PHILIP A, b. Linworth, Ohio, July 11, 29; m. 51; c. 1. TELEVISION, DRAMA. B.A, Otterbein Col, 59; M.A, Ohio State Univ, 52, Ph.D. (theatre), 59. Tech. dir. theatre, Miss. South. Col, 52-54; instr, Ohio State Univ, 54-60; ASSOC. PROF. SPEECH, KENT STATE UNIV, 60- Consult, Parma Pub. Schs, 64; M.A. prog. commun. arts, Univ. Dayton, 67; Lake County Pub. Schs, 67-68. Speech Commun. Asn; Nat. Asn. Educ. Broadcasters; Univ. Film Producers Asn. Publ: Summer fair theatres, 56 & Production problems in prompt books, 57, Ohio State Univ. Collection Bull; Educational television distribution, View Mag, 8/66. Add: School of Speech, Kent State University, Kent, OH 44240.

McORMOND, G. GRANT, b. Saskatoon, Sask, Oct. 14, 22; m. 46; c. 3. ENGLISH. B.A, Univ. Sask, 42 & 43; M.A, 46; Univ. Wash. Instr. ENG, UNIV. VICTORIA, 46-49, asst. prof, 49-62, ASSOC. PROF, 62- R.C.A.F, 43-45, Res, 45- English poetry, 1750-1824. Add: Dept. of English, University of Victoria, Victoria, B.C, Can.

McPEEK, JAMES ANDREW SCARBOROUGH, b. New Concord, Ohio, Aug. 31, 99; m. 26; c. 1. ENGLISH LITERATURE. A.B, Harvard, 22, Ph.D, 32; M.A, Acadia Univ, 27. Asst. prof, Washington & Lee Univ, 23-26; Acadia Univ, 26-28; Washington & Jefferson Col, 28-30; Eng, UNIV. CONN, 32-40, assoc. prof, 40-46, prof, 46-69, res. found grant, 62, EMER. PROF. ENG, 69- Am. Counc. Learned Soc. grant, 68. MLA. Shakespeare; Elizabethan and medieval literature. Publ: Catullus in strange and distant Britain, Harvard, 39; co-auth, An introduction to philosophy through literature, 49 & Handbook of English, 56, Ronald; co-auth, Shakespeare's Twelfth night, Allyn & Bacon, 65; auth, The black book of knaves and unthrifts in Shakespeare and other authors, Univ. Conn, 69; Selected bibliography of myth in literature, Col. Eng. Asn, 69; Richard II and his shadow world, Am. Imago, 58; The thief deformed and much ado about 'noting', Boston Univ. Stud. Eng, 60; The psyche myth and A midsummer night's dream, Shakespeare Quart, 72. Add: Box 55, Storrs, CT 06268.

MacPHEE, LAURENCE EDWARD, b. Jersey City, N.J, Dec. 2, 34; m. 60; c. 3. ENGLISH. B.S, St. Peter's Col.(N.J), 56; Swiss govt. fel, Univ. Lausanne, 56-57; Woodrow Wilson fel. & M.A, N.Y. Univ, 59; Ph.D.(Eng), Rutgers Univ, 67. Instr. ENG, SETON HALL UNIV, 59-61, asst. prof, 61-68, ASSOC. PROF, 68- U.S.A, 57, 1st Lt. MLA; AAUP. J.F. Cooper; 19th century American novel. Publ: The Great Gatsby's Romance of motoring: Nick Carraway and Jordan Baker, Mod. Fiction Stud, summer 72. Add: Dept. of English, Seton Hall University, South Orange, NJ 07079.

McPHERSON, DAVID C, b. Jayton, Tex, Jan. 19, 35; m. 61; c. 2. ENGLISH. B.A, Hardin-Simmons Univ, 57; M.A, Univ. Tex, 62, Ph.D.(Eng), 66. Asst. prof. ENG, Univ. Calif, Santa Barbara, 66-72; ASSOC. PROF, UNIV. N.MEX, 72- MLA. Elizabethan drama; comedy; Elizabethan prose and poetry. Publ: Ed, Ben Jonson: selected works, Holt, 72; auth, Ben Jonson's library and marginalia (monogr), Stud. in Philol, 74; The origin and function of Mopsa in Sidney's Arcadia, Renaissance Quart, 68; Aretino and the Harvey-Nashe quarrel, PMLA, 69; Rough beast into tame fox: the adaptations of Volpone, Stud. Lit. Imagination, 4/73; plus others. Add: Dept. of English, University of New Mexico, Albuquerque, NM 87106.

McPHERSON, ELISABETH ALLEN, b. Vancouver, Wash, July 5, 14; m. 42; c. 3. ENGLISH. B.A, Wash. State Univ, 38; M.A, Reed Col, 59. Instr. ENG, Clark Col.(Wash), 56-64, head dept, 64-67; ASSOC. PROF, FOREST PARK COMMUNITY COL, 67-, CHMN. DIV. HUMANITIES, 73- Mem. adv. comt. gen. educ, Educ. Testing Serv, 67-69; mem. policy & standards comt, Nat. Fac. Asn. Community & Jr. Cols, 68-69. NCTE (mem. nat. jr. col. comt, 66-70, chmn, 67, ed. publ, 68-70); Conf. Col. Compos. & Commun.(chmn, 72); MLA (mem. Eng. adv. comt, 68-70). Non-transfer junior English. Publ: Plain English please, 66, Background for writing, 67 & Plain English reader and rhetoric (Eng. in plain words ser), 70, Random; Incompetence in composition: a realistic solution, Jr. Col. J, 9/64; auth, Will the real terminal student please stand up, 5/67 & Hats off—or on—to the junior college, 12/68, Conf. Col. Compos. & Commun. J. Add: 5287 Westminster Pl, St. Louis, MO 63108.

McPHERSON, HUGO, b. Sioux Lookout, Ont, Aug. 28, 21; m. 50. NORTH AMERICAN LITERATURE, COMMUNICATIONS. B.A, Univ. Man, 49, hon. LL.D, 70; M.A, Univ. West. Ont, 50; Ph.D.(Eng), Univ. Toronto, 56. Lectr. Eng, McGill Univ, 52-53; Univ. Man, 53-55, Univ. B.C, 55-56; asst. prof, Univ. Toronto, 56-60, assoc. prof, 60-65, prof, 65-66; Univ. West. Ont, 66-67; comnr, Nat. Film Bd, State Dept. Can, 67-70; PROF. COMMUN, McGILL UNIV, 70- Can. Counc. fel, 61-62; Commonwealth fel, Yale, 66; chmn, Soc. Art Publ, 68-69, v.chmn, 69-; mem. bd, Nat. Arts Ctr, 68-70; mem. counc, Theatre du Nouveau Monde, Montreal, 70-; mem. bd, Can. Film Develop. Corp. Canada Centennial Medal, 67. Can. Asn. Univ. Teachers; Asn. Can. Univ. Teachers Eng; Int. Commun. Asn; Humanities Asn. Can. Contemporary literature. Publ: Hawthorne as myth-maker, Univ. Toronto, 69; ed, Studies in Canadian literature series (11 vols), Copp Clark, McGill Univ. & Queen's Univ, 69-; auth, Fiction: 1940-1960, In: The literary history of Canada, Univ. Toronto, 65; Painting and sculpture, In: The Canadians, Macmillan, Can, 67; plus others. Add: Dept. of English, McGill University, P.O. Box 6070, Montreal 101, P.Q, Can.

MACPHERSON, (JEAN) JAY, b. London, Eng, June 13, 31; Can. citizen. ENGLISH. B.A, Carleton Col.(Ont), 51; B.L.S, McGill Univ, 53; fel, Victoria Col, Univ. Toronto, 54-57, M.A, 55, Ph.D.(Eng), 64. Lectr. ENG, VICTORIA COL, UNIV. TORONTO, 57, asst. prof, 58-67, assoc. prof, 67-73, PROF, 73- Asn. Can. Univ. Teachers Eng. Milton; Romantic poetry and fiction; Victorian poetry and fiction. Publ: The boatman and other poems, Oxford, Toronto, 57; Four ages of man (mythology text), Macmillan, Toronto, 62; co-ed, The hymn book of the Anglican Church of Canada and the United Church of Canada, 71; auth, Autobiography, In: Literary history of Canada, Univ. Toronto, 65. Add: Dept. of English, Victoria College, University of Toronto, Toronto, Ont. M5S 1K7, Can.

MacPHERSON, JOHN A, b. Windsor, Ont, June 1, 31. ENGLISH, CRITICISM. B.A, Univ. West. Ont, 53; M.A, Univ. Windsor, 55; dipl. guidance, Boston Univ, 57; dipl. Elizabethan stud, Univ. Birmingham, 58; fel, Univ. Ottawa, 63-65, Ph.D.(Eng), 66. Asst. registr, Univ. Windsor, 53-55; lectr. ENG, Xavier Col.(N.S), 55-58, asst. prof, 58-61; assoc. prof, ST. FRANCIS XAVIER UNIV, 61-74, PROF, 74-, SECY. DIV. GRAD. STUD, 71-, CHMN. FAC. ARTS, 72- Mem, Can. Centennial Decoration, 67; mem. bd, Col. Eng. Lang. Aptitude Test, 69-; 1st v.pres, Theatre-Can, 71- Knight Commander, Military & Hospitaller Order of St. Lazarus of Jerusalem, 69; Knight of Grace, Sovereign Military Order of Malta, 73. Fel. Royal Soc. Arts; fel. Royal Soc. Lett, U.K; Can. Conf. Christians & Jews; Humanities Asn. Can; Asn. Can. Univ. Teachers Eng; Can. Counc. Teachers Eng; MLA; Can. Asn. Univ. Teachers (mem. bd, 72-). Edwardian and Georgian novelists; minor Victorian poets and novelists; Canadian theatre history. Publ: A checklist of short films for catechetics, 67 & A checklist of feature films for catechetics, 67, St. Francis Xavier Univ; D.H. Lawrence's first novel, spring 64 & Father Faber's Sir Lancelot, summer 64, Inscape; introd, Comfort me with apples, St. Francis Xavier Univ, 66; The femme fatale in the novels of Iris Murdoch, 70 & Compton Mackenzie's theatre of youth novels, 73, Humanities Asn. Can; contrib, Love and whisky: the story of the Dominion Drama Festival (2 vols), McClelland & Stewart, 73. Add: Dept. of English, St. Francis Xavier University, Antigonish, N.S, Can.

McQUEEN, WILLIAM ASHLEY, III, b. Greenville, Ala, June 13, 26; m. 52; c. 3. ENGLISH LITERATURE. B.A, Vanderbilt Univ, 49; M.A, Univ. N.Mex, 52; Ph.D.(Eng), Univ. Ill, 62. Instr. ENG, Auburn Univ, 54-56; UNIV. N.C, CHAPEL HILL, 62-64, asst. prof, 64-66, ASSOC. PROF, 66- Summer grants, Coop. Prog. in Humanities, Univ. N.C, 65, Huntington Libr. & Art Gallery, 68. U.S.A.F, 44-45. S.Atlantic Mod. Lang. Asn; Southeast. Renaissance Conf. Seventeenth century English literature. Publ: Co-ed, The Latin poetry of Andrew Marvel, Univ. N.C, 64; auth, A short guide to English composition, Wadsworth, 67, 2nd ed, 72; ed, A selection of emblems, Augustan Reprint Soc, 72; The missing stanzas in Marvell's Hortus, Philol. Quart, 4/65; Point of view in Paradise lost I-IV, Renaissance Papers, spring 68; The hateful siege of contraries: satan's interior monologues in Paradise lost, Milton Quart, 12/70. Add: Dept. of English, University of North Carolina, Chapel Hill, NC 27514.

McQUITTY, ROBERT ALAN, b. Washington D.C, July 22, 33; m. 64. ENGLISH. B.S, Tex. Wesleyan Col, 55; M.A, Tex. Christian Univ, 63; Ph.D.(Eng), Syracuse Univ, 68. Teacher, Jr. High Sch, Tex, 55-58; Nuernberg Am. High Sch, Dependent Educ. Group, U.S. Army, 58-62; instr. ENG, N.Tex. State Univ, 63-65; Syracuse Univ, part-time, 65-68; asst. prof, George Peabody Col, 68-72; PROF. ENG. & CHMN. DIV. COMMUN, NORTHEAST. STATE COL, 72- MLA; NCTE. Teacher evaluation of student writing; freshman English; American fiction. Publ: Freshman English at Syracuse: what's worth watching, In: Freshman English at Syracuse, Wadsworth, 67; Contract grading with quality, Okla. Eng. Bull, fall 73. Add: 202 E. Seneca, Tahlequah, OK 74464.

MacRAE, CHRISTOPHER FREDERICK, b. Wardsville, Ont, Dec. 2, 09; m. 35; c. 3. ENGLISH. B.A, Univ. West. Ont, 30; M.A, McMaster Univ, 47; Ph.D, Univ. Toronto, 53. Teacher high sch, Ont, 31-47; teaching fel, univ. col, Univ. Toronto, 47-49; asst. prof. ENG, Mt. Allison Univ, 49-54, Tweedie prof, 54-63; PROF, UNIV. WATERLOO, 63- Humanities Res. Counc. Can. grant-in-aid, Brit. Dom, 55-56 & Australia, summer 64. MLA. Literature of the Victorian age and the British Commonwealth. Publ: Adam Lindsay Gordon, Twayne, 68; ed, French Canada today, 1962, Proc. Mt. Allison Summer Inst, 61. Add: 257 Stanley Dr, Waterloo, Ont, Can.

McREYNOLDS, RONALD WELDON, b. Cincinnati, Ohio, Jan. 26, 34; m. 57; c. 4. ENGLISH LITERATURE. B.S, Miami Univ, 55, M.A, 56; Ph.D, Univ. Tex, 59. Instr. ENG, Belleville High Sch, Mich, 56-57; PROF. CENT. MO. STATE UNIV, 59- MLA; Midwest Mod. Lang. Asn; Latter-Day Saints Prof. Teachers Asn. Early 19th century British poetry; William Wordsworth's poetry; modern British and American poetry. Publ: A time between and other poems, Mitre, London, 67; The poet's poetry, Cent. Mo. State Univ, 70; The artistry of Ivo Andric, Univ. Bull, 5/63; contrib, The Missouri poets, Eads Bridge, 71; plus others. Add: Dept. of English, Central Missouri State University, Warrensburg, MO 64093.

MACRORIE, KENNETH, b. Moline, Ill, Sept. 8, 18; m. 52; 65. ENGLISH. A.B, Oberlin Col, 40; M.A, Univ. N.C, 48; Ph.D.(Eng. & commun), Columbia Univ, 55. Instr. Eng, Univ. N.C, 46-48; from instr. to asst. prof. commun. skills, Mich. State Univ, 48-60; assoc. prof. ENG, San Francisco State Col, 60-61; WEST. MICH, UNIV, 61-66, PROF, 66- U.S.A, 42-46. NCTE; Conf. Col. Compos & Commun.(ed, jour, 62-64). Communication. Publ: The perceptive writer, reader, and speaker, Harcourt, 59; ed, Four in depth, Houghton, 63; auth, Writing to be read, 68, Telling writing, 70, Uptaught, 70 & A vulnerable teacher, 74, Hayden; Too many messages, 7/61 & Arriving and departing, 9/62, Reporter; The objectivity-subjectivity trap, Antioch Rev, winter 64-65. Add: Dept. of English, Western Michigan University, Kalamazoo, MI 49001.

MacSHANE, FRANK, b. Pittsburgh, Pa, Oct. 19, 27; m. 59; c. 1. WRITING, ENGLISH LITERATURE. A.B, Harvard, 49; M.A, Yale, 51; D.Phil.(Eng. lit), Oxford, 55. Lectr. Eng, McGill Univ, 55-57; vis. lectr, Vassar Col, 58-59; asst. prof, Univ. Calif, Berkeley, 59-64; assoc. prof, Williams Col, 64-67; WRITING, COLUMBIA UNIV, 67-69, PROF, 69-, dean sch. of arts, 71-72. Fulbright prof, Univ. Chile, 57-58; Tribhuvan Univ, Nepal, 63-64. Auth. League Am; PEN Club; MLA; Century Asn. English and American literature; Oriental art and letters; South American literature. Publ: Many golden ages, Tuttle, 63; Impressions of Latin America, Morrow, 63; Critical writings of Ford Madox Ford, Univ. Nebr, 64; transl, Miguel Serrano, The serpent of Paradise, Rider, 64 & Routledge & Kegan Paul & Harper, rev. ed, 72; auth, Life and work of Ford Madox Ford, Routledge & Horizon, 65; The American in Europe, 65 & co-ed, Borges on writing, 73, Dutton; transl, Miguel Serrano, C.G. Jung and Hermann Hesse, Schocken & Routledge, 66; ed, Ford Madox Ford: the critical heritage, Routledge, 72; transl, Miguel Serrano, The ultimate flower, 72, The visits of the Queen of Sheba, 72, Routledge & Harper & El/Ella, Harper, 72. Add: Div. of Writing, School of the Arts, Columbia University, New York, NY 10027.

McSHANE, JAMES ARTHUR, b. New York, N.Y, July 21, 38; m. 62; c. 5. ENGLISH. B.A, Georgetown Univ, 60; M.A, Emory Univ, 61, Ph.D.(Eng), 68. Instr. ENG, grad. sch, Atlanta Univ, 63-67; asst. prof, UNIV. NEBR-LINCOLN, 67-74, ASSOC. PROF, 74- Vis. instr, Clark Col, fall 64 & 65. Milton; Shakespeare. Add: Dept. of English, University of Nebraska-Lincoln, Lincoln, NE 68508.

McSLOY, DEAN FRANKLIN, b. Sturgis, S.Dak, Oct. 10, 02; m. 27, 48; c. 2. SPEECH. B.A, Yankton Col, 24; M.S, Northwest. Univ, 35; Univ. South. Calif, 29, 45, 51. Instr. high sch, Nebr, 24-25, S.Dak, 26-29; prof. speech, Garrett Inst, Northwest. Univ, 30-46; assoc. prof. speech & dir. forensics, Ariz. State Col, 47-54; from assoc. prof. speech & dir. forensics to prof. SPEECH, WHITMAN COL, 54-69, EMER. PROF, 69- Dir. music, churches, Ill, 39-46, Calif, 45, Ariz, 48-49. Speech Commun. Asn; West. Speech Commun. Asn; Am. Forensic Asn. Publ: Speech education in the graduate theological seminary. Add: 1912 E. Meadow Dr, Tempe, AZ 85282.

McTAGGART, WILLIAM JOSEPH, b. McKeesport, Pa, Jan. 22, 41. ENGLISH ROMANTIC POETRY. B.A, W.Va. Wesleyan Col, 62; M.A, Ohio Univ, 67, Ph.D.(Eng), 68. ASST. PROF. ENG, CARNEGIE-MELLON UNIV, 69- Fulbright scholar, Wadham Col, Oxford, 68-69. Keats-Shelley Mem. Asn. Eng. The editing of the works of Percy B. Shelley; sonnets of John Keats; American animated film. Publ: The major poems of Timothy Dwight, Scholars Facsimiles, 69; England in 1819, Keats Shelley Mem. Asn, 70; Some new enquiries into Shelley's Platonism, 70 & Theme and unity in the Alastor volume, 72, Keats Shelley Mem. Asn. Bull; contrib, movie revs, Pittsburgh Forum, 71- Add: Dept. of English, Carnegie-Mellon University, Pittsburgh, PA 15213.

McTEAGUE, JAMES H, b. Corning, Ohio, Sept. 20, 31; m. 52; c. 4. DRAMA. B.F.A, Carnegie Inst. Technol, 53, M.F.A, 54; Ph.D.(drama), Univ. Iowa, 62. Instr. DRAMA, Earlham Col, 54-55; guest dir, Ohio Univ, 55; asst. prof, Fairmont Col, 55-59; Emporia Col, 61-64; from assoc. prof. to PROF, WEST. ILL. UNIV, 64-, CHMN. DEPT. THEATRE, 73- Regional judge, Am. Col. Theatre Festival, 71-72. Speech Commun. Asn; Am. Theatre Asn; Cent. States Speech Asn. Improvisation; non-literary drama. Publ: Stanislavski: technique, Dramatics Mag, 59; Speech in the theatre, 10/59 & Stanislavski revisited, 11/60, Players' Mag. Add: Dept. of Theatre, Western Illinois University, Macomb, IL 61455.

McVEIGH, TERRENCE A, b. Bayonne, N.J, Sept. 24, 25. ENGLISH. A.B, Georgetown Univ, 50; M.A, Fordham Univ, 60, Ph.D, 64. Instr. ENG, Fordham Univ, 63-66, ASST. PROF, 66-70; CALIF. STATE UNIV, HAYWARD, 70- MLA. Mediaeval and Renaissance English literature; literary theory and criticism. Add: Dept. of English, California State University, Hayward, 25800 Hillary St, Hayward, CA 94542.

McWHORTER, H. BOYD, b. Cochran, Ga, May 8, 23; m; c. 4. ENGLISH. B.S, U.S. Naval Acad, 45; M.A, Univ. Ga, 49; Ph.D.(Eng), Univ. Tex, Austin, 60. Instr. Eng, UNIV. GA, 49-51, 53-54, asst. prof, 57-62, assoc. prof, 62-68, PROF. ENG. & DEAN COL. ARTS & SCI, 68- Spec. consult, Roper Hydraulics Co, summer 63; instr. exec. develop. prog, Univ. Ga. for Upper Mgt. Personnel, summer 64. U.S.N, 45-47, 51-53, Res, 53-, Capt. S.Atlantic Mod. Lang. Asn. Early 19th century English literature. Add: 208 Old College Bldg, University of Georgia, Athens, GA 30601.

McWILLIAMS, JOHN PROBASCO, JR, b. Cleveland, Ohio, July 22, 40; m. 67; c. 3. ENGLISH, AMERICAN LITERATURE. A.B, Princeton, 62; A.M, Harvard, 63, Woodrow Wilson fel, 63-64; teaching fel, 64-67, Ph.D.(Eng), 67. ASST. PROF. ENG, UNIV. CALIF, BERKELEY, 67- MLA; Am. Stud. Asn. Publ: Political justice in a Republic, Univ. Calif, 72; co-ed, James Fenimore Cooper: the critical heritage, Routledge & Kegan Paul, 73; auth, The orator and the Constitution, Tex. Stud. Lit, 71; Drum taps and Battle-pieces, Am. Quart, 71; The beacon and the gibbet, Dickens Stud. Annual, 72; plus others. Add: Dept. of English, University of California, Berkeley, CA 94720.

McWILLIAMS, RICHEBOURG GAILLARD, b. Oakhill, Ala, June 24, 01; m. 37; c. 3. ENGLISH. B.S, Univ. Ala, 22, A.M, 25; Univ. P.R, 23; Univ. Wis, 28; Univ. Munich, Ger, 32; A.M, Harvard, 33; Columbia Univ, 36. Teacher Eng, Continuation Sch, Cabo Rojo, P.R, 22; from instr. to asst. prof, Univ. Ala, 23-27; asst. prof, BIRMINGHAM-SOUTH. COL, 28-33, assoc. prof, 33-41, prof, 41-70, chmn. humanities, 39-55, head dept. ENG, 42-70, EMER. PROF, 70- Fel, Am. Counc. Learned Soc, 51; Officier d'Acad, 53. Eighteenth century culture in the Gulf States; fiction. Publ: Fleur de Lys and Calumet; Dramatic history of Dauphin Island. Add: Dept. of English, Birmingham Southern College, Birmingham, AL 35204.

MADDEN, EDGAR ALLEN, b. Merrill, Mich. Jan. 8, 33; m. 54; c. 5. ENGLISH. B.A, Cent. Mich. Univ, 55, M.A, 60; Univ. Mich, 56-57; summers, Dow Chem. Co. grant, Mich. State Univ, 56, NDEA grant, Univ. S.Dak, 59. Teacher high sch, Mich, 55-64, head dept. Eng. 61-64; instr. ENG, NORTHWOOD INST, 64-67, asst. prof, 67-70, ASSOC. PROF, 70-, HEAD DEPT, 68- Mem. steering comt. & treas, Midwest Regional Conf. Eng. in Two Year Col, 68-69; grant, Mich. State Univ, 68-69. Am. Security Counc. Excellence Award, 67. NCTE. Sequential curricula in English; the teaching of composition; the efficacy of methods of teaching English. Publ: Stimulating discriminate reading, Mich. Educ. J, 3/63; Evolution of a writing program, Eng, J, 1/64; The participation lecture, Record of Kappa Delta Pi, 10/67. Add: 16901 Gratiot Rd, Hemlock, MI 48626.

MADDEN, JERRY DAVID, b. Knoxville, Tenn, July 25, 33; m. 56; c. 1. ENGLISH. B.A, Univ. Tenn, 57; M.A, San Francisco State Col, 58; Yale Drama Sch, 59-60. Instr. Eng. & drama, Appalachian State Teachers Col, 58-59; Eng, Centre Col, 60-62; lectr. creative writing, Univ. Louisville, 62-64; Kenyon Col, 64-66; Ohio Univ, 66-68; WRITER-IN-RESIDENCE, LA. STATE UNIV, 68- Asst. ed, Kenyon Rev, 64-66; assoc. ed, Film Heritage, 65, Film J, 71 & Fiction Int, 73; Rockefeller grant fiction, 69. Nat. Counc. on Arts Selection in Fiction, 70. U.S.A, 53-55. MLA; Soc. Cinematologists; Am. Soc. Aesthet; Auth. Guild; Soc. Stud. South. Lit; Popular Cult. Asn. English, especially contemporary literature; drama; creative writing. Publ: The beautiful greed, Random, 61; Wright Morris, 64 & James M. Cain, Twayne, Tough guy writers of the thirties, 68, Proletarian writers of the thirties, 68, American dreams, American nightmares, 69 & The poetic image in six genres, 69, South. Ill. Univ; Cassandra singing (novel), 69, ed, Rediscoveries, 71 & Bijon, 74, Crown; auth, The shadow knows (short stories), La. State Univ, 70; Brothers in confidence, Avon, 72; co-ed, Popular culture explosion, Brown, 72; ed, Nathanael West: the cheaters and the cheated, Everett/Edwards, 74; auth, Harlequin's stick, Charlie's cane, Ctr. Stud. Popular Cult, 73; Ambiguity in Camus' The fall, Mod. Fiction Stud, winter 66; Form and life in the novel, J. Aesthet, spring 67; James M. Cain and the tough guy novelists of the '30's, In: The Thirties, Everett Edwards, 67. Add: 614 Park Blvd, Baton Rouge, LA 70806.

MADDEN, JOHN F, b. Detroit, Mich, Oct. 20, 21. ENGLISH. B.A, Univ. Toronto, 45, M.A, 47; Ph.D.(Eng), Harvard, 53. Lectr. ENG, St. Michael's Col, Univ. Toronto, 52-56, asst. prof, 56-58, assoc. prof, 58-62, prof, 62-72, chmn. dept, 62-65; ASSOC. PROF, UNIV. ST. THOMAS (TEX), 72- MLA. Old English poetry. Publ: Co-auth, A grouped frequency word-list of Anglo-Saxon poetry, Dept. Eng, Harvard, 54. Add: Dept. of English, University of St. Thomas, Houston, TX 77066.

MADDEN, ROBERT J, b. Detroit, Mich, June 18, 28. ENGLISH. B.A, Univ. Toronto, 52, M.A, 55, S.T.B, St. Michael's Col, 55; Ph.D.(Eng), Univ. London, 63. Tutor ENG, St. Michael's Col, Univ. Toronto, 53-54, lectr, 56-57; Univ. Windsor, 57-60; asst. prof, UNIV. ST. MICHAEL'S COL, 63-70, ASSOC. PROF, 70- Rector, St. Basil's Col, 73- Restoration and eighteenth century literature; historiography. Publ: Introd, An essay on criticism, Augustan Reprint Soc, 64. Add: Dept. of English, University of St. Michael's College, 50 St. Joseph St, Toronto, Ont. M5S 1J4, Can.

MADDEN, WILLIAM ANTHONY. ENGLISH. A.B, Univ. Notre Dame, 47; Ph.D.(Eng), Univ. Mich, 55. Instr. Eng, Ind. Univ, Bloomington, 55-58, asst. prof, 58-62, assoc. prof, 62-66, prof, 66-69, dean jr. div, 67-69; PROF. ENG, UNIV. MINN, MINNEAPOLIS, 69- Co-ed, Victorian Stud, 57-69. MLA; NCTE; Am. Civil Liberties Union. Victorian literature; literary criticism; Chaucer. Publ: Co-auth, 1859: entering an age of crisis, 59 & auth, Matthew Arnold, 67, Ind. Univ; co-auth, The art of Victorian prose, Oxford, 68; auth, The Victorian sensibility, Victorian Stud, 63; The search for forgiveness in some 19th century English novels, Comp. Lit. Stud, 66; Macaulay's style, Art Victorian Prose, 68; plus others. Add: Dept. of English, University of Minnesota, Minneapolis, MN 55455.

MADDOCK, LAWRENCE HILL, b. Ogden, Utah, July 14, 23. ENGLISH. B.A, George Peabody Col, 46, Ph.D.(Eng), 65; M.A, Univ. South. Calif, 49. Teacher, pub. schs, Fla, 49-52; instr. Eng, Univ. Fla, 52-53; asst. prof, California State Col.(Pa), 55-56, assoc. prof, 56-64; Northeast La. State Col, 64-67; ASSOC. PROF, UNIV. W.FLA, 67-, acting chmn. dept, 69-70. MLA; Col. Eng. Asn; NCTE. Conf. Col. Compos. & Commun. Nineteenth century English literature; Samuel Taylor Coleridge; Thomas Wolfe. Add: Alpha College, University of West Florida, Pensacola, FL 32504.

MADDOX, NOTLEY SINCLAIR, b. Carthage, Mo, June 12, 00; m. 31. ENGLISH. B.S, Ohio State Univ, 22, M.A, 25, Ph.D.(Eng), 40. Instr. educ, Ohio State Univ, 22-29, instr. Eng. & supvr. freshman compos, 37-42; teacher, high sch, Ohio, 30-31; dir. Eng, YMCA Schs, Columbus, Ohio, 32-33; dean evening col, Franklin Univ, 33-35; chmn. dept. ENG, Monticello Col, 42-47; prof, EAST. MICH. UNIV, 47-70, EMER. PROF, 70- Vis. prof, Conn. Col, summers, 47-48. U.S.A, 18. AAUP; Thomas Hardy Soc, Eng; MLA; Counc. Basic Educ. American literature; Biblical literature; English novel in the 19th century. Publ: Co-auth, College readings for inductive study, Dryden Press; Scribner workbook, Scribner; Irving Babbitt and the Emperor Shun, Am. Rev, 1/26; Literary nationalism in Putnam's Magazine, Am. Lit, 5/42; Whittier's Ichabod, Explicator, 4/60. Add: Dept. of English, Eastern Michigan University, Ypsilanti, MI 48197.

MADER, THOMAS FRANCIS, b. May 29, 30; U.S. citizen; m. 61. SPEECH. B.A, St. John's Univ.(N.Y), 52; M.A, N.Y. Univ, 56; Ph.D.(commun. stud), Northwest. Univ, 66. Instr, La Salle Acad, New York, 51-52, St. John's Prep, 54-55, Massapequa High Sch, 55-56; asst. prof. speech, St. John's Univ.(N.Y), 56-63; asst, sch. of speech, Northwest. Univ, 61-62; asst. prof. pub. speaking, Amherst Col, 63-66, res. assoc. Eng. & vis. fel. rhetoric, Princeton, 66-67; ASSOC. PROF. COMMUN, HUNTER COL, 67- Lectr, St. John's Univ.(N.Y), 55-56; speech consult, Pitman Pub. Corp, N.Y, 60-63; vis. asst. prof. educ, N.Y. Univ, 63- Ord.C, 52-54, Sgt. Speech Commun. Asn; Am. Forensic Asn. Argumentation; public address; linguistics. Publ: Death of a sale, Today's speech, 2/66; The inherent need to analyze stasis, J. Am. Forensic Asn, winter 67. On presence in rhetoric, Col. Compos. & Commun, 12/73. Add: 31 Camel Hollow Rd, Lloyd Harbor, NY 11724.

MADIGAN, MARY, I.B.V.M, b. Chicago, Ill, July 25, 22. MEDIEVAL ENGLISH. B.A, De Paul Univ, 52; M.A, Univ. Detroit, 58; Ph.D.(Eng), St. Louis Univ, 67. Asst. prof. ENG, St. Procopius Col, 65-69; ASSOC. PROF, Duquesne Univ, 69-72; UNIV. ST. MICHAEL'S COL, 72- Mediaeval Acad. Am; MLA; NCTE. Middle English prose; English drama; literary criticism. Add: Loretto College, 70 St. Mary's St, Toronto, Ont. M5S 1J3, Can.

MADSEN, HAROLD STANLEY, b. Salt Lake City, Utah, Apr. 23, 26; m. 52; c. 6. ENGLISH. B.A, Univ. Utah, 53, M.A, 60; Brigham Young Univ, 61-62; fels, Univ. Colo, 63-65, Ph.D.(Eng. educ), 65. Instr. Eng, Brigham Young Univ, 56-65, asst. prof, 65-68; educ, Haile Sellassie I Univ, 66-68, assoc. prof, 68-70; COORD. TEACHING ENG. AS FOR. LANG, BRIGHAM YOUNG UNIV, 70- Adv, Eng. as second lang, Ministry Educ. & Fine Arts, Ethiopia, 67-68; consult. Eng. as second lang, Adult Educ. Div, Calif. State Dept. Educ, 69-70; chief of party, U.S. Aid/Univ. Utah Contract Group, Ethiopia, 69-70; consult. teaching Eng. as second lang, Am. Univ. Cairo, summer 70. U.S.A, 44-46. NCTE; Teachers Eng. to Speakers Other Lang. Research oral and written Teaching English as Second Language Examinations; adaptation; intermediate teaching English as second language materials. Publ: Let's make room for reading instruction, J. Teachers Eng. Ethiopia, 5/67; English language testing in Ethiopia, 6/67 & The curriculum-ESLC seminar of 1967, 6/68, Ethiopian J. Educ. Add: 720 Sunny Lane, Orem, UT 84057.

MADSEN, WILLIAM GEORGE, b. St. Paul, Minn, Mar. 13, 18; m. 43; c. 3. ENGLISH LITERATURE. B.A, Univ. Minn, 39, M.A, 41; Ph.D, Yale, 52. Instr. ENG, Yale, 46-47, 52-55, Morse fel, 55-56; asst. prof, Wayne State Univ, 56-60, assoc. prof, 61-63; PROF, Emory Univ, 63-68; WASH. UNIV, 68- Vis. lectr, Eng, Univ. Minn, 60, 61. U.S.A.A.F, 42-45, Capt. MLA; Milton Soc. Am; Renaissance Soc. Am. Theories of Biblical interpretation; theories of language in the 16th and 17th centuries; Puritan aesthetics. Publ: The idea of nature in Milton's poetry, 58 & From shadowy types to truth, 68, Yale Univ, ed, Milton's Paradise Lost, Modern Libr, 68; plus two others. Add: Dept. of English, Washington University, St. Louis, MO 63130.

MADSON, ARTHUR L, b. Arlington, Iowa, June 21, 27; m. 50; c. 5. ENGLISH. B.A, Morningside Col, 50; M.A, Univ. S.Dak, 53; South. fel, Univ. Okla, 59-60, Ph.D, 66. Instr. ENG, Univ. S.Dak, 53-55; asst. prof, UNIV. WIS-WHITEWATER, 60-63, from assoc. prof. to PROF, 63- U.S.A, 45-47, Sgt. MLA. Publ: An explication of John Donne's The flea, Notes & Queries, 2/57; Melville's comic progression, Wis. Stud. Lit, 64; The rape of the rape, Satire Newsletter, spring 65. Add: Dept. of English, University of Wisconsin-Whitewater, Whitewater, WI 53190.

MADTES, RICHARD EASTMAN, b. Youngstown, Ohio, Dec. 3, 21; m. 41; c. 1. ENGLISH. A.B, Allegheny Col, 48; M.A, Cornell Univ, 49; Harvard, summer 50 & 51; Ph.D.(Eng), Columbia Univ, 61. Instr. ENG, State Univ. N.Y. Col. New Paltz, 49-55, asst. prof, 55-57, assoc. prof, 57-62; ALLEGHENY COL, 62-68, PROF, 68-, CHMN. DEPT, 71- U.S.A.A.F, 42-45, S/Sgt. MLA. James Joyce; Shakespeare. Publ: Joyce and the building of Ithaca, Eng. Lit. Hist, 12/64. Add: Dept. of English, Allegheny College, Meadville, PA 16335.

MAGALANER, MARVIN, b. New York, N.Y, Nov. 6, 20. ENGLISH. A.B, City Col. New York, 42; M.A, Columbia Univ, 47, Ph.D.(Eng), 51. From asst. prof. to assoc. prof. ENG, CITY COL. NEW YORK, 46-66, PROF, 66- Lectr, Columbia Univ, 48, 54; Ford Found. & N.Y. State Educ. Dept. grant, 63-64; Fulbright lectr, Univ. Saar, 65-66. U.S.A.A.F, 42-46. MLA. Contemporary English and Irish literature; Katherine Mansfield; fiction of Samuel Beckett. Publ: Time of apprenticeship: the fiction of young James Joyce, Abelard, 60; co-auth, Joyce: the man, the work, the reputation, N.Y. Univ, 56; ed, A James Joyce miscellany: second and third series, 59, 62 & auth, The fiction of Katherine Mansfield, 71, South. Ill. Univ. Add: 505 W. Broadway, New York, NY 10012.

MAGARET, HELENE, b. Omaha, Nebr, May 18, 06. ENGLISH. A.B, Barnard Col, 32; A.M, State Univ. Iowa, 38, Am. Asn. Univ. Women fel, 38-39, Ph.D, 40. Instr. creative writing, exten. div. Creighton Univ, 35; ENG, Rockford Col, 40-41; prof, Col. St. Teresa, 41-44; MARYMOUNT COL.(N.Y), 44-73, chmn. dept, 62-68, EMER. PROF, 73- Van Rensselaer Poetry Prize, 32. Col. Eng. Asn. Popular biographies; poems. Publ: The trumpeting crane, 34, The great horse, 37, Father DeSmet, 40 & Change of season, 41, Farrar; Who walk in pride, 45, Giant in the wilderness, 52, The head on London bridge, 56, Kingdom and a cross, 58 & Felipe, 62, Bruce; Gailhac of Beziers, Longmans, 46; English literature and the problem of education, Christian Educ, 3/42; The eye, the ear and the misspelled word, Col. Eng, 10/51; Barriers to the organic curriculum, America, 9/52. Add: 2922 N. 54th St, Omaha, NE 68104.

MAGAW, BARBARA LOUISE, English. See HOAGLAND, BARBARA M.

MAGAW, MALCOLM, b. Eden Valley, Minn, Jan. 28, 30; m. 57; c. 2. ENGLISH, AMERICAN LITERATURE. A.B, Duke Univ, 50; Univ. Tenn, 52; M.A, Emory Univ, 58; Ph.D.(Eng), Tulane Univ, 64. Instr. Eng. & hist, Glynn Acad, 50-57; ENG, LA. STATE UNIV, NEW ORLEANS, 61-64, asst. prof, 64-67, assoc. prof, 67-73, PROF, 73-, DIR. GRAD. STUD, 72- Consult, Cult. & Humanistic Insights into Crime & Corrections, Community Serv. Ctr, New Orleans, 73. Award for distinguished teaching on undergrad. level, Standard Oil Corp. of Ind, 67. MLA; S.Cent. Mod. Lang. Asn; Melville Soc. Am. Melville; current American novel. Publ: Yeats and Keats: the poetics of romanticism, Bucknell Rev, 12/65; The confidence-man and Christian deity: Melville's imagery of ambiguity, In: Explorations of literature, La. State Univ, 66; Apocalyptic imagery in Melville's The apple-tree table, Midwest Quart, summer 67. Add: Dept. of English, Louisiana State University at New Orleans, New Orleans, LA 70122.

MAGEE, WILLIAM HENRY, b. N.Battleford, Can, July 28, 24. ENGLISH. B.A, Univ. B.C, 45, M.A, 46; Ph.D, Univ. Toronto, 50. Instr. Eng, Univ. Alaska, 50-52, asst. prof, 52-53, assoc. prof, 53-57, prof, 57-61, dean arts & lett, 61-62; assoc. prof. ENG, UNIV. CALGARY, 62-72, PROF, 72- Rockefeller grant, Univ. Toronto, 54-55. MLA; Philol. Asn. Pac. Coast; Humanities Asn. Can. English novel, especially Jane Austen; English-Canadian novel; Shakespeare. Publ: Philip Child. a reappraisal, Can. Lit, spring 65; Romanticism on trial in Mansfield Park, Bucknell Rev, 3/66; Helena, a female Hamlet, Eng. Miscellany, 71; plus others. Add: Dept. of English, University of Calgary, Calgary, Alta. T2N 1N4, Can.

MAGILL, FRANK NORTHEN, b. Atlanta, Ga, Nov. 21, 07; m. 47; c. 3. ENGLISH & AMERICAN LITERATURE. B.S.C.E, Ga. Inst. Technol, 31; M.S.C.E, Columbia Univ, 34; Ed.D, Univ. South. Calif; hon. LL.D, Pepperdine Univ, 64. BK. ED. & AUTH, REF. WORKS IN HUMANITIES, SALEM PRESS, INC, 48- Adj. prof. libr. sci, Univ. South. Calif, 68-; mem. adv. panel, Secy. Comn. Med. Malpractice, Dept. Health, Educ. & Welfare, 72. U.S.A.F, 42-46, Maj. Publ: Ed, Masterplots, Series 1, 2, 3 & 4 (8 vols), 49-68, Cyclopedia of world authors (2 vols), 58, Masterpieces of world philosophy (2 vols), 61, Cyclopedia of literary characters (2 vols), 63, Masterpieces of Christian literature (2 vols), 63, Masterpieces of Catholic literature (2 vols), 65, Magill's quotations in context (2 vols), 65 & second series (2 vols), 69, Salem & Harper; ed, Masterplots annual (19 vols), 54-, Great events from history: Ancient and medieval series (3 vols), 72-73, Modern European series (3 vols), 73 & American series (3 vols), 74, Salem. Add: 607 Foxwood Rd, Flintridge, Pasadena, CA 91103.

MAGILL, LEWIS MALCOLM, b. Lexington, Ill, Apr. 30, 13; m. 42; c. 2. ENGLISH LITERATURE. A.B, Ill. Wesleyan Univ, 34; A.M, Univ. Ill, 43, Ph.D, 49. From asst. prof. to assoc. prof. ENG, WASH. STATE UNIV, 49-59, PROF, 59-, DIR. ACAD. STANDING OFF, 60- Am. Col. Personnel Asn.(chmn, Comn, XIV, 71-73); Acad. Affairs Asn.(pres, 71-73); Am. Personnel & Guid. Asn; MLA; Philol. Asn. Pac. Coast; NCTE. Contemporary fiction; 17th and 18th century English drama; English novel. Publ: Co-auth, Shakespeare's complete plays, Littlefield, 52 & Business letters, Howard Chandler, 56; auth, Get off Johnny's back, Saturday Rev, 2/64; auth, Joseph Conrad: Russia and England, Albion, spring 71. Add: 101 Administration Annex, Washington State University, Pullman, WA 99163.

MAGNER, JAMES EDMUND, JR, b. New York, N.Y, Mar. 16, 28; m. 57; c. 4. ENGLISH. B.A, Duquesne Univ, 57; M.A, Univ. Pittsburgh, 61, fel, 61-62, Ph.D.(Eng), 66. Teacher, High Sch, 57-61; instr. ENG, JOHN CARROLL UNIV, 62-65, asst. prof, 65-68, ASSOC. PROF, 68- John Carroll Univ. fac. fel, spring 70. U.S.A, 48-51, Sgt. MLA; NCTE. Modern poetry, creative writing and literary criticism. Publ: Toiler of the sea, 65 & Although there is the night, 68, Golden Quill; Gethsemane, Poetry Sem, 69; John Crow Ransom: critical principles and preoccupations, Mouton, 71; The dark is closest to the moon, Ryder, 73; plus others. Add: Dept. of English, John Carroll University, Cleveland, OH 44118.

MAGNUS, DOROTHY BARBARA, b. Winona, Minn, Nov. 15, 03. SPEECH & DRAMA. B.S, Univ. Minn, 25, M.A, 34; Univ. Iowa, 35-36; Northwest. Univ, summers 35, 48; Columbia Univ, summer 42. Teacher & dir. dramatics, High Sch, Long Prairie, Minn, 25-28; instr, Univ. Minn, 28-29; dir. theater, Wis. State Univ, La Crosse, 29-31; St. Mary-of-the-Woods Col, 32-35; asst. prof. speech & dir. theater, South. Ill. Univ, 36-43; prof. & head dept. speech & dir. theatre, WINONA STATE COL, 43-72, EMER. PROF. SPEECH & THEATRE ARTS, 72- Dir. first col. co. to play Guthrie Theatre, Minneapolis in Ibsen's Ghosts, 63; dir. first Minn. col. open stage prod. of Agamemnon, 71; panelist, Nat. Col. Players Prog, Am. Theatre Asn. Nat. Conv, 71. Dorothy B. Magnus Open Stage Theatre named, 71; Int. Personnel Res. Creativity Award Plaque, 72. Speech Commun. Asn; hon. life mem. Am. Theatre Asn. Theatre arts. Publ: A decade of arena theatre, 2/61, First venture in the Guthrie Theatre, 4/64 & Othello on the open stage, 10/65, Players Mag; plus others. Add: 111 W. Howard St, Winona, MN 55987.

MAGNUSON, PAUL ANDREW, b. Newton, Mass, Apr. 10, 39; m. 65; c. 2. ENGLISH LITERATURE. A.B, Brown Univ, 61; Wilson fel, Univ. Minn, 63-64, Ph.D.(Eng), 69. ASST. PROF. ENG, UNIV. PA, 69- U.S.N, 61-63, Lt.(jg). MLA; AAUP. English Romantic literature. Publ: The dead calm in the conversation poems, Wordsworth Circle, 72; Coleridge's nightmare poetry, Univ. Press Va, 74. Add: Dept. of English, University of Pennsylvania, Philadelphia, PA 19104.

MAGRUDER, MILDRED (ANDERSON), b. Kiester, Minn, May 5, 07; m. 40; c. 2. ENGLISH. B.A, Univ. Calif, Los Angeles, 29; M.A, Univ. Calif, Berkeley, 30; Ph.D.(Eng), Univ. South. Calif, 36. Admis, All Nations Clin, 31-37; instr. Eng. & French, Los Angeles Pac. Col, 37-40; Eng, Westmont Col, 41-42; prof. Eng. & chmn. div. humanities, Azusa Pac. Col, 47-72; RETIRED. MLA; NCTE. Stephen Hawes; children's literature; Allan A. Hunter. Publ: What is the professor's function, Universitas, 1/73. Add: 318 N. Hobart Pl, Los Angeles, CA 90004.

MAGUIRE, CATHERINE ELIZABETH, b. New York, N.Y, Jan. 19, 10. ENGLISH. B.A, Col. Mt. St. Vincent, 31; M.A, Columbia Univ, 36; Ph.D, Fordham Univ, 50. Asst. prof, Manhattanville Col. Sacred Heart, 45-50; PROF. ENG, NEWTON COL. SACRED HEART, 50-, acad, dean, 68-70. Am. Asn. Univ. Women fel, 65-66; Am. Counc. Learned Soc. res. grant, 65-66; mem. comn. higher educ, New Eng. Asn. Sec. Schs. & Cols, 69-73. MLA; Eng. Inst; NCTE; Col. Eng. Asn. Piers Plowman; modern literature; hagiography. Publ: Maria Goretti; Saint Madeleine Sophie, Sheed, 61; Henry James and Dumas Fils, Mod. Drama, spring 67. Add: Newton College of the Sacred Heart, Newton, MA 02159.

MAGUIRE, JAMES HENRY, b. Denver, Colo, Apr. 2, 44; m. 67; c. 1. AMERICAN LITERATURE & STUDIES. B.A, Univ. Colo, Boulder, 66; M.A, Ind. Univ, Bloomington, 69, Ph.D.(Eng. & Am. stud), 70. ASST. PROF. ENG. & AM. LIT, BOISE STATE UNIV, 70- Co-ed, Boise State Univ. West. Writers Ser, 72- MLA; Am. Stud. Asn; West. Lit. Asn. American realism; Western American literature; the novel. Publ: Mary Hallock Foote, Boise State Univ, West. Writers Ser, 72; Elysium and the wilds, Hist. N.H, 1/71. Add: Dept. of English, Boise State University, 1907 Campus Dr, Boise, ID 83707.

MAGUIRE, JOHN BERNARD, b. Chicago, Ill, Apr. 23, 30. ENGLISH LITERATURE. A.B, Univ. Notre Dame, 53; S.T.L, Pontif. Gregorian Univ, 57; Ph.D.(Eng), Stanford Univ, 70. Instr. theol, Univ. Notre Dame, 57-58; ENG, Univ. Portland, 67-69; vis. prof, Xavier Univ. La, 69-70; ASST. PROF, LOYOLA UNIV. CHICAGO, 70- Admin. consult, Priests of Holy Cross, Ind. Province, 73- Renaissance Soc. Am. Thomas More; Erasmus; Chaucer. Publ: William Roper's Life of More, Moreana, 8/69; Erasmus' biographical masterpiece: Heironymi Stridonensis Vita, Renaissance Quart, fall 73; The clandestine marriage of Troilus and Criscyde, Chaucer Rev, winter 74. Add: Dept. of English, Loyola University of Chicago, 6525 Sheridan Rd, Chicago, IL 60626.

MAGUIRE, ROBERT C, b. San Francisco, Calif, Apr. 9, 19. SPEECH, HISTORY. B.S, Univ. Dayton, 41; M.A, West. Reserve Univ, 49; Ph.D.(speech), Univ. Calif, Los Angeles, 67. Teacher, High Sch, Calif, 40-41; Ohio, 41-42, 44-50; P.R, 42-44; Calif, 50-67, v.prin, 62-64; acad. dean, CHAMINADE COL. HONOLULU, 67-69, PRES, 69- Valley Forge Freedom Found. Play Award, 54. Speech Commun. Asn. Publ: Teacher-centered English, Marianist Educator J, spring 62; What is the next curriculum breakthrough, J. Sec. Educ, 11/63; co-auth, Secondary schools speech course of studies, South. Calif. Speech Counc. Add: Chaminade College of Honolulu, Honolulu, HI 96816.

MAHAFFEY, KATHLEEN, b. Snyder, Okla, July 18, 17. ENGLISH. B.A, Univ. Okla, 39, M.A, 44, fel, 49-50; Ph.D.(Eng), Univ. Tex, 63. Film librn, Oklahoma City Air Depot, 42-43; instr. sec. schs, Okla. & Tex, 39-42 & 44-45; Eng, Univ. Okla, 45-49; asst. ed, Univ. Wis. Press, 50-51; ed, Univ. Tex. Press, 51-55; instr. ENG, Univ. Md. Overseas, Eng. & Ger, 55-57; spec. instr, Univ. Tex, 61-62; assoc. prof, Univ. Southwest. La, 62-67, prof, 67-69. South. Fels. Fund fac. grants, 59-61; vis. prof. Eng, Univ. Puerto Rico, Mayagüez, 69-70, prof, 70-73, acting chmn. dept, 71-72. MLA; AAUP; Am. Soc. 18th Century Stud; Augustan Reprint Soc. Eighteenth century English literature, especially Alexander Pope. Publ: Alexander Pope and his Sappho: Pope's relationship with Lady Mary Wortley Montagu and its influence on his work, Univ. Microfilms, 63; Timon's Villa: Walpole's Houghton, Tex. Stud. Lit. & Lang, summer 67; Pope's Artimesia and Phryne as personal satire, Rev. Eng. Stud, 11/70. Add: 1351 The High Rd, Austin, TX 78746.

MAHAN, RONALD GAIR, b. Springfield, Ohio, Mar. 12, 33; m. 52, 63; c. 2. ENGLISH, AMERICAN CIVILIZATION. A.B, Wittenberg Univ, 59; M.A, Univ. Tenn, 63. Instr. ENG, Wittenberg Univ, 60-63; Univ. Tenn, 65-68; LENOIR RHYNE COL, 68-71, ASST. PROF, 71- U.S.N, 52-54. MLA; Am. Stud. Asn. Letters of F.W. Thomas to Edgar Allan Poe; critical biography of Cornelius Mathews. Add: Dept. of English, Lenoir Rhyne College, Hickory, NC 28601.

MAHAN, ROSE SELKIS, b. Watertown, N.Y, May 19, 37; m. 63; c. 2. ENGLISH. A.B, St. Lawrence Univ, 58; univ. fels. & N.Y. State Regents fel, Univ. Rochester, 58-60, M.A, 63, Ph.D, 66. Instr. ENG, Wittenberg Univ, 62-63; Univ. Tenn, 63-67, asst. prof, 67-68; LENOIR RHYNE COL, 68-73, ASSOC. PROF, 73- MLA. Nineteenth-century American literature. Add: Dept. of English, Lenoir Rhyne College, Hickory, NC 28601.

MAHANEY, WILLIAM EARLE, b. Malden, Mass, Oct. 8, 40; m. 63; c. 1. ENGLISH. A.B, Dartmouth Col, 62; Dartmouth fel. & M.A, Univ. Conn, 63; Ph.D.(Eng), Ohio State Univ, 67. Teaching assoc. ENG, Ohio State Univ, 64-67; asst. prof, Univ. Md, Baltimore County, 67-70, ASSOC. PROF, SALEM STATE COL, 70- MLA; NCTE; Conf. Col. Compos. & Commun; Shakespeare Asn. Am; Col. Eng. Asn; AAUP. Renaissance drama; Shakespeare; medieval drama. Publ: John Webster: a classified bibliography, 73 & Deception in the John Webster plays, 73, Jacobean Drama Stud; co-ed, Two university Latin plays: Philip Parsons' Atalanta and Thomas Atkinson's Homo, Elizabethan Stud, 73; co-auth, Structure and dramatic tone in Othello and Otello, Stud. in Humanities, 73. Add: Dept. of English, Salem State College, Salem, MA 01970.

MAHL, MARY R, b. Paterson, N.J, Dec. 6, 14. ENGLISH LITERATURE. A.B, Wheaton Col.(Ill), 50; A.M, N.Y. Univ, 55, Ph.D, 61; res. fel, Pub. Welfare Found, Eng, 60. Lectr. ENG. LIT, UNIV. SOUTH. CALIF, 60-61, instr, 61-62, asst. prof, 62-65, ASSOC. PROF, 65- Am. Philos. Soc. res. award, Am. Counc. Learned Soc. award & Phi Delta Gamma hon. award, 68. MLA; Renaissance Soc. Am; NCTE; Col. Eng. Asn; Conf. Christianity & Lit; English-Speaking Union; Milton Soc. Am; Shakespeare Soc; Philol. Asn. Pac. Coast. Period of Chaucer; 16th century English literature; 17th century literature. Publ: Seventeenth-century English prose, Lippincott, 68; Gawdy Brampton: another Norfolk poet, Norfolk Archaeol, 10/62; ed, The Norwich MS of Sir Philip Sidney's Apology for poetry, Calif. State Univ. Found, Northridge, 69. Add: Dept. of English, University of Southern California, Los Angeles, CA 90007.

MAHLER, ANDREW JOHN, b. Wilmington, N.C, Feb. 23, 04; m. 47; c. 3. ENGLISH LITERATURE. Wagner Col, 21-25; A.M, Columbia Univ, 26; Ph.D, Univ. N.C, 36. Asst. Eng, Univ. N.C, 30-31, teaching fel, 31-33, instr, 33-36; asst. prof. ENG, Mary Baldwin Col, 36-38, assoc. prof, 38-42, prof, 46-47, head dept, 47-65; PROF, MADISON COL, 65- U.S.A, 42-45. Col. Eng. Asn. English humor in the Victorian period. Add: Dept. of English, Madison College, Harrisonburg, VA 22801.

MAHONEY, IRENE, O.S.U, b. Brooklyn, N.Y, May 5, 21. ENGLISH. B.A, Col. New Rochelle, 41; M.A, Fordham Univ, 48; Ph.D.(Eng), Cath. Univ. Am, 58. Assoc. prof. ENG, COL. NEW ROCHELLE, 62-69, PROF, 69-, WRITER-IN-RESIDENCE, 70- Franco-Am. Cult. Serv. & Educ. Aid stud. & travel grant, France, summer 67. French Renaissance; contemporary fiction. Publ: Marie of the incarnation: mystic and missionary, 64 & Royal cousin: life of Henry IV of France, 70, Doubleday; Life of Catherine de Medici, Coward, 74. Add: Dept. of English, College of New Rochelle, New Rochelle, NY 10801.

MAHONEY, JOHN FRANCIS, b. Detroit, Mich, May 19, 29; m. 52; c. 4. ENGLISH, CLASSICS. B.A, Univ. Detroit, 50, M.A, 52; Ph.D, Univ. N.C, 56. Instr. Eng, Univ. N.C, 53-56; Latin, Duke Univ, 54-56; asst. prof. Mid. Eng, Duquesne Univ, 56-59, assoc. prof. Eng. & chmn. grad. stud, 59-61; assoc. prof. Eng. & comp. lit, Univ. Detroit, 61-63, chmn. grad. comt, 61-64, dean col. arts & sci, 69-73, prof. Eng. & comp. lit. & chmn. dept, 64-73; dean, Walden Univ, 73-74; V.PRES. ACAD. AFFAIRS, WILLIAM PATERSON COL. N.J, 74- South. Fels. Fund fel, 56; mem. bd, Am. Grad. & Prof. Comn, 66-; consult, Higher Educ. Exec. Assoc, 68- MLA; Mediaeval Acad. Am; Dante Soc. Am. Mixed media; mediaeval languages; Dante. Publ: Co-auth, Studies in honor of V.T. Holmes, Jr, Univ. N.C. Chapel Hill, 66; ed, American authors and critics (12 vols), Holt, 62-; co-auth, The insistent present, Houghton, 70; co-ed, New poets, new music, Winthrop, 71; ed, The structure of Purgatorio, Dante Soc. Bull, 62; Chaucerian tragedy and the Christian tradition, Annuale Mediaevale, 62; Alice of Bathe: her sectc and gentil sectc, Criticism, 64. Co-auth, Early help (film), Medianovations, 73. Add: William Paterson College of New Jersey, 300 Pompton Rd, Wayne, NJ 07470.

MAHONEY, JOHN L, b. Somerville, Mass, Feb. 4, 28; m. 56; c. 3. ENGLISH. A.B, Boston Col, 50, A.M, 52; Ph.D, Harvard, 57. Teaching fel. ENG, Boston Col, 50-52; Harvard, 53-54; instr, BOSTON COL, 55-58, asst. prof, 58-61, assoc. prof, 61-65, PROF, 65-, chmn. dept, 62-67 & 69-70, dir. Ph.D. stud, 70-72. Vis. prof. summer sessions, Harvard, 63, 65, 67 & 71. C.Eng, U.S.A, 46-47. MLA; Conf. Brit. Stud; Mod. Humanities Res. Asn. Literary criticism; 18th century English literature; early 19th century English literature. Publ: Ed, An essay on original genius by William Duff, Scholars Facsimiles & Reprints, 64 & An essay of dramatic poesy and other critical essays by John Dryden, Bobbs, 65; Imitation and the quest for objectivity in English romantic criticism, Proc. Congr. Int. Comp. Lit. Asn, 66; Classical form and the oratory of Edmund Burke, Class. Folia, 70; The deadlock of the universities, Intellect, 72. Add: 8 Sutherland Rd, Lexington, MA 02173.

MAHONEY, MARY BERCHMANS, R.S.M, b. Troy, N.Y, May 28, 19. ENGLISH. B.A, St. John's Univ.(N.Y), 40; M.A, Cath. Univ. Am, 48; N.Y. Univ, 60; M.L.S, State Univ. N.Y. Albany, 72. Teacher classics, Cath. Cent. High Sch, Troy, 40-51; prin, St. Joseph's Acad, Albany, 51-57; St. Teresa Jr. High Sch, 57-62; teacher ENG, MARIA COL. ALBANY, 61-65, INSTR, 65-, PRES, 68- Mem, Mid. Atlantic States Evaluating Comt, 53-56. Outstanding Teacher Award, Freedoms Found, 60. NCTE; MLA; Renaissance Soc. Am; Cath. Renascence Soc; Am. Asn. Higher Educ; Nat. Cath. Educ. Asn; AAUP; Am. Asn. Community & Jr. Cols; Eng. Inst. Medieval period of English literature; library science. Add: Office of the President, Maria College of Albany, 700 New Scotland Ave, Albany, NY 12208.

MAHONY, PATRICK J, b. New York, N.Y, Jun 11, 32; m. 62; c. 1. ENGLISH LITERATURE. B.A, Iona Col, 54; M.A, N.Y. Univ, 57, Ph.D.(Eng), 63. Asst. Eng. lit, N.Y. Univ, 59-61; Fulbright lectr. Am. stud, Univ. Aix Marseille, 62-63; asst. prof. ENG. LIT, UNIV. MONTREAL, 63-71, ASSOC. PROF, 71- Can. Counc. judge & award, 68; France-Que. award, 68. U.S.A, 54-56. MLA; Renaissance Soc. Am. Thomas Browne and William Shakespeare, figures of English literary Renaissance. Publ: An analysis of Shelley's craftsmanship in Adonais, Stud. Eng. Lit, autumn 64. Add: Dept. of English, University of Montreal 101, P.Q, Can.

MAHOOD, SHARON MARIE, b. Springfield, Mo, Oct. 9, 45. SPEECH COMMUNICATION. Firestone scholar, Allen Craften scholar & B.A, Univ. Kans, 67, Ph.D.(speech commun), 71; M.A, Univ. Minn, Minneapolis, 69. ASST. PROF. speech, Univ. Okla, 71-72; SPEECH COMMUN, UNIV. ILL, URBANA, 72- Speech Commun. Asn; Cent. States Speech Commun. Asn. Interpersonal communication and impression formation; contemporary rhetorical theory; communication theory. Add: Dept. of Speech Communication, 244 Lincoln Hall, University of Illinois, Urbana, IL 61801.

MAIENKNECHT, GILBERT O, b. Chatham, Mich, Sept. 3, 19; m. 46; c. 2. JOURNALISM. B.A, North. Mich. Univ, 41; M.A, Univ. Iowa, 42, M.A, 48, Ed.D.(jour. educ), Univ. Ind, Bloomington, 52. Reporter, Green Bay Press-Gazette, Wis, 46-47; dir. publicity, CENT. MICH. UNIV, 48-58, PROF. JOUR. & CHMN. DEPT, 59-, dir. inform. serv, 59-68. U.S.A, 43-46, 1st Lt. Asn. Educ. in Jour; Am. Col. Pub. Relat. Asn. Public relations in higher education; journalism. Publ: Education for journalism—yes, Scholastic Educ, 12/61; Self-styled signs make buildings easy to identify, Col. & Bus, 8/62; New university plaza out of tragic fire, Col. Store J, 4-5/64; plus numerous others. Add: 1147 Eastwood, Mt. Pleasant, MI 48858.

MAIMON, ELAINE PLASKOW, b. Philadelphia, Pa, July 28, 44; m. 67; c. 2. ENGLISH & AMERICAN LITERATURE. A.B, Univ. Pa, 66, NDEA fel, 66-70, M.A, 67, Ph.D.(Eng. & Am. lit), 70. Asst. prof. ENG, Haverford Col, 71-73; LECTR, BEAVER COL, 73- MLA; NCTE; Am. Stud. Asn; AAUP. Women's studies; American writers of 1920's; rhetoric of the novel. Publ: F. Scott Fitzgerald's book sales: a look at the record, Fitzgerald Hemingway Annual, 73. Add: 402 Achille Rd, Havertown, PA 19083.

MAIN, CHARLES FREDERICK, b. Stacyville, Maine, Sept. 11, 21. ENGLISH. Ph.D, Harvard, 54. From instr. to assoc. prof. Eng, RUTGERS UNIV, NEW BRUNSWICK, 54-67, PROF. ENG. & ASSOC. DIR. RES. COUNC, 67- U.S.C.G.R, 42-46. Seventeenth century English civilization. Add: 800 W. Seventh St, Plainfield, NJ 07063.

MAIN, WILLIAM WESLEY, b. Scottsbluff, Nebr, Jan. 24, 19; m. 50. ENGLISH. B.A, Univ. Denver, 40, Yetter fel. & M.A, 41; Harvard, 46; Ph.D.(Eng), Univ. N.C, 54. Instr. Eng, Denver exten, Univ. Colo, 46-50; instr, Univ. N.C, 51-53, teaching fel, 53; instr, Rutgers Univ, 54-56; asst. prof, UNIV. REDLANDS, 56-60, assoc. prof, 60-64, PROF. LIT, 64- U.S.A.A.F, 41-45. MLA; Col. Eng. Asn. Renaissance, especially Shakespeare; comparative literature; cinema criticism and productions. Publ: Ed, Macbeth, 62, King Lear, 62, Hamlet, 63 & Odyssey, 64, intertextual ed, Odyssey; auth, Shakespeare re-viewed, Redlands Alumni Mag, winter 71. Add: Dept. of English, University of Redlands, Redlands, CA 92373.

MAIZITIS, MARA R, b. Riga, Latvia, Jan. 18, 32. ENGLISH. B.A, Wellesley Col, 55; M.A, Yale, 56, Selden, Lewis-Farmington & Fels Found. fels. & Ph.D, 60. Instr. Eng, Conn. Col. Women, 59-61; Temple Univ, 61-64, asst. prof, 64-68. Am. Philos. Soc. grant, summer 68; Mary E. Stevens fel, 68-69; lectr. Eng, Univ. Calif, Santa Barbara, 70, Univ. Mass, Boston, 70-71, & Morehouse Col, 72. MLA. Shakespeare; Chaucer. Add: 36 Ridge St, Greenwich, CT 06830.

MAJDIAK, DANIEL, b. Cleveland, Ohio, May 5, 37; m. 58; c. 2. ENGLISH. B.A, West. Reserve Univ, 59, M.A, 60, Ph.D.(Eng), 64. Instr. ENG, Case Inst. Technol, 62-65; asst. prof, UNIV. ILL, URBANA, 65-72, ASSOC. PROF, 72- MLA. Nineteenth and twentieth century English literature. Add: Dept. of English, University of Illinois, Urbana, IL 61801.

MAJOR, DIANA, b. Salt Lake City, Utah, Oct. 18, 38; c. 1. ENGLISH, LINGUISTICS. B.A, Lake Forest Col, 60; M.A, Longwood Col, 64; Ph.D.(Eng, ling), Univ. Utah, 71. Instr. ENG. & LING, UNIV. UTAH, 69-72, ASST. PROF, 72- Consult. third grade reading stud, Utah State Off. Educ, 69-70; creative lang. proj, Bur. Educ. Res, Univ. Utah, 70-71. Children's language; linguistic stylistics; teaching language effectively. Publ: The acquisition of modal auxiliaries, Mouton, 73; co-auth, Teaching transformational grammar, Eng. J, 3/73; auth, Review of teaching English as a second language, TESOL Quart, 9/73; contrib, Teacher's manual, English for today, Bk. III, McGraw-Hill, rev. ed, 73; plus others. Add: Dept. of English, University of Utah, Salt Lake City, UT 84112.

MAJOR, JOHN McCLELLAN, b. Rochester, N.Y, Oct. 20, 18. ENGLISH. A.B, Syracuse Univ, 39, fel, 40-41; Ph.D, Harvard, 54. Tutor & teaching fel. ENG, Harvard, 48-50; instr, Oberlin Col, 50-53; Duke Univ, 54-57; asst. prof, UNIV. COLO, BOULDER, 57-61, assoc. prof, 61-66, PROF, 66- U.S.A, 41-45, Lt. Col. MLA; Renaissance Soc. Am; Milton Soc. Am. Renaissance humanism; relationship of English and classics; 17th century English literature. Publ: Sir Thomas Elyot and renaissance humanism, Univ. Nebr, 64; The letters steal'd in Hamlet and the character of Claudius, J. Eng. & Ger. Philol, 7/58; The personality of Chaucer the pilgrim, PMLA, 6/60; Milton's view of rhetoric, SP, 10/67. Add: Dept. of English, University of Colorado, Boulder, CO 80302.

MAJOR, MABEL, b. Ogden, Utah, Sept. 20, 93. ENGLISH & AMERICAN LITERATURE. A.B, Univ. Mo, 14, B.S, 16, A.M, 17; Univ. Chicago, 25; Univ. Calif, 28; Columbia Univ, 46; Litt.D, Tex. Christian Univ, 64. Prof. ENG, TEX. CHRISTIAN UNIV, 19-63, acting head dept, 43-46, EMER. PROF, 63- Carnegie res. grant-in-aid, 49-51; vis. prof, Baylor Univ, 63-69; N.Mex. State Univ, summer 66; San Fernando State Col, summer 68; consult, S. Tex. Developing Jr. Col. Consortium, 69-70. Minnie Piper Award, 64; Theta Sigma Phi Award, 64; Univ. Mo. Distinguished Alumnae, 68. MLA; S.Cent. Mod. Lang. Asn; Am. Stud. Asn. Ballads; Southwest literature; Frank Desprez. Publ: Co-auth, Southwest in literature, Macmillan; co-auth, Southwest heritage & Signature of the sun, Univ. N.Mex; Mary Austin in Fort Worth, N.Mex. Quart, 11/34; The man who wrote Lasca, Southwest Rev, fall 51; A September Sunday '38, Descant, summer, 66. Add: P.O. Box 30798, Texas Christian University, Ft. Worth, TX 76129.

MAJOR, MINOR WALLACE, b. St. Louis, Mo, Sept. 13, 08; m. 39. ENGLISH. A.B, Wash. Univ, 32; M.A, Univ. Kans, 38; Ph.D.(Eng. lit), Univ. Colo, 57. Supt. schs, Augusta, Mo, 42-44; prin. high sch, Mo, 44-46; asst. prof. ENG, N.Mex. Highland Univ, 46-56; from assoc. prof. to PROF, CALIFORNIA STATE COL.(PA), 56- MLA; AAUP; Col. Eng. Asn. American literature. Publ: The Melville symbol that isn't there, Rocky Mountain Mod. Lang. Asn. Bull; A. St. Louisan's view of Prufrock, CEA Critic, 9/61; A new interpretation of Whitman's Calamus poems, Walt Whitman Rev, 6/67; William Bradford versus Thomas Morton, Early Am. Lit, fall 70. Add: Dept. of English, California State College, California, PA 15419.

MAKOSKY, DONALD ROBIN, b. Easton, Md, Mar. 2, 31; m. 57, 71; c. 2. AMERICAN LITERATURE & CIVILIZATION. A.B, West. Md. Col, 52; A.M, Univ. Pa, 54, Ph.D.(Am. civilization), 66. Instr. ENG, Kent State Univ, 58-60; from instr. to ASSOC. PROF. ST. LAWRENCE UNIV, 62- U.S.A, 56-58. MLA; Am. Stud. Asn. Literature of the mass culture, American fiction. Add: Dept. of English, St. Lawrence University, Canton, NY 13617.

MAKOSKY, JOHN DONALD, b. Buckeystown, Md, June 28, 03. ENGLISH. A.B, West. Md. Col, 25; A.M, Columbia Univ, 26, D.Ed, 49, hon. Litt.D, 73. Asst. prof, Wash. Col, 26-34; Eng, West. Md. Col, 34-43, assoc. prof, 43-48, prof, 48-73, dean fac, 49-69, 71-73; RETIRED. MLA; Col. Eng. Asn; NCTE. Classical influences on English prose; Ciceronianism; histories of Western Maryland College and Washington College. Add: 35 Ridge Rd, Westminster, MD 21157.

MALARD, SANDRA GENE, b. New Haven, Conn, May 28, 41. ENGLISH LITERATURE. B.A, Tufts Univ, 62; M.A.T, Yale, 63; Rackham Prize fel, Univ. Mich, 70-71, Ph.D.(Eng), 72. Teacher ENG, North Haven High Sch, Conn, 63-68; ASST. PROF, HAVERFORD COL, 72- AAUP; Mediaeval Acad. Am; MLA. Piers Plowman; Chaucer; tragedy. Add: Dept. of English, Haverford College, Haverford, PA 19041.

MALARKEY, STODDARD, b. Portland, Ore, July 9, 27; m. 56; c. 3. ENGLISH, EDUCATION. B.A, Reed Col, 55; M.Ed, Ore. State Univ, 60; Ph.D. (Eng), Univ. Ore, 64. Instr. ENG, Univ. Ore, 63-64; asst. prof, Univ. Calif, Santa Barbara, 64-65; UNIV. ORE, 65-68, ASSOC. PROF, 68-, DIR. COMPOS, 70- Fulbright lectr. Eng, Univ. Jordan, 73-74. U.S.N, 45-46. Philol. Asn. Pac. Coast; MLA; Mediaeval Acad. Am; NCTE. Publ: Co-auth, The Oregon curriculum; literature, Holt, 68; ed, Style: diagnoses and prescriptions, Harcourt, 72; co-auth, Gawain and the green girdle, J. Eng. & Ger. Philol, 1/64; auth, Sequence and literature: some considerations, Eng. J, 3/67; An experimental curriculum in literature, Elem. Eng, 73. Add: Dept. of English, University of Oregon, Eugene, OR 97403.

MALBONE, RAYMOND GATES, b. Christian Co, Ky, June 2, 28; m. 54; c. 1. ENGLISH. A.B, Univ. Louisville, 50; M.A, Univ. Minn, 51, univ. fel. & Ph.D, 59. Instr. ENG, Univ. Louisville, 55-56; asst. prof, STATE UNIV. N.Y. COL. CORTLAND, 59-62, assoc. prof, 62-66, PROF, 66-, summer res. fel, 61. U.S.N, 52-55, Res, 55-, Lt. MLA. Nineteenth century English novel; Victorian literature. Publ: How to be: Marlow's quest in Lord Jim, Twentieth Century Lit, 1/65; How shall we teach the new Bully Budd, sailor?, Col. Eng, 3/66; That blasted rose-acacia: a note on Browning's Soliloquy of the Spanish cloister, Victorian Poetry, summer 66. Add: Dept. of English, State University of New York College at Cortland, Cortland, NY 13045.

MALE, ROY RAYMOND, b. Brooklyn, N.Y, Mar. 15, 19; m. 44; c. 2. AMERICAN LITERATURE. B.S, Hamilton Col, 39; M.A, Columbia Univ, 40; Ph.D, Univ. Tex, 50. Instr. ENG, Univ. Tex, 46-50; asst. prof, Tex. Technol. Col, 50-54; assoc. prof, UNIV. OKLA, 55-60, prof, 61-69, BOYD PROF, 69- Ford Fel, 53-54; vis. prof. Eng, Univ. Wash, summer 67; Univ. Tex, Arlington, summer 71. Regents award for excellence in teaching, 66. U.S.A, 40-46, 1st Lt. MLA; S. Cent. Mod. Lang. Asn.(pres, 66-67). Hawthorne; Melville; types of American fiction. Publ: Hawthorne's tragic vision, Univ. Tex, 57; co-auth, Reading & writing, 60 & co-ed, American literary masters, 65, Holt; ed, Types of short fiction, Wadsworth, 61; auth, The two versions of The displaced person, Stud. Short Fiction, summer 70; Hawthorne, In: American literary scholarship, Duke Univ, 70; Hawthorne's fancy, Nathaniel Hawthorne J, 72. Add: Dept. of English, University of Oklahoma, Norman, OK 73069.

MALEK, JAMES STANLEY, b. Hampton, Nebr, Aug, 11, 41. ENGLISH LITERATURE. B.A, Earlham Col, 63; Woodrow Wilson fel, Univ. Chicago, 63-64, M.A, 66, Ph.D.(Eng), 68. Asst. prof. ENG, UNIV. IDAHO, 68-70, ASSOC. PROF, 70-, CHMN. DEPT, 73- Nat. Endowment for Humanities Younger Humanists fel, 71-72. Am. Soc. Aesthetics; MLA; Rocky Mountain Mod. Lang. Asn. Eighteenth century British aesthetic theory; British drama, 1660-1800; E.M. Forster. Publ: The arts compared: an aspect of 18th century British aesthetics, Wayne State Univ, 74; Physiology and art: Daniel Webb's aesthetics, Neuphilologische Mitteilungen, 70; Thomas Twining's analysis of poetry and music as imitative arts, Mod. Philol, 2/71; Adam Smith's contribution to eighteenth century British aesthetics, J. Aesthetics & Art Criticism, fall 72. Add: Dept. of English, University of Idaho, Moscow, ID 83843.

MALIN, IRVING, b. New York, N.Y, Mar. 18, 34; m. 55; c. 1. ENGLISH. B.A, Queens Col.(N.Y), 55; Ph.D, Stanford Univ, 58. Acting instr, Stanford Univ, 55-56, 57-58; instr, Ind. Univ, 58-60; ENG, CITY COL. NEW YORK, 60-64, asst. prof, 64-68, assoc. prof, 69-72, PROF, 72- YADDO grant, 63; Nat. Found. Jewish Cult. fel, 63-64. MLA; Am. Stud. Asn; Melville Soc; Soc. Stud. South. Lit; NCTE; PEN Club; Am. Jewish Hist. Soc; Popular Cult. Asn; Eng. Inst; Auth. Guild. American novel; literature and psychology; Jewish-American literature. Publ: William Faulkner: an interpretation, Stanford Univ, 57; New American gothic, 62, Jews and Americans, 65, Saul Bellow's fiction, 69 & Nathanael West's novels, 72, South. Ill. Univ; co-ed, Breakthrough: a treasury of contemporary American-Jewish literature, McGraw & Jewish Publ. Soc; ed, Psychoanalysis and American fiction, Dutton, 65; ed, Saul Bellow and the critics, 67 & ed, Critical views of Isaac Bashevis Singer, 69, New York Univ; ed, Truman Capote's In cold blood: a critical handbook, 68 & co-ed, William Styron's The confessions of Nat Turner: a critical handbook, 70, Wadsworth; auth, Isaac Bashevis Singer, Ungar, 72; ed, Contemporary American-Jewish literature, Ind. Univ, 73; ed, The achievement of Carson McCullers, Everett/Edwards, 74; co-ed, The achievement of William Styron, Univ. Ga, 74; auth, The elements of William Golding, In: Contemporary British novelists, 65 & The metaphysical falcon, In: Tough guy writers of the thirties, 68, South. Ill. Univ; Flannery O'Connor and the grotesque, In: The added dimension, Fordham, 66. Add: Dept. of English, City College of New York, New York, NY 10031.

MALIN, STEPHEN DURBORAW, b. Philadelphia, Pa, Dec. 20, 32; m. 64; c. 1. THEATRE, POETRY. B.A, Pa. State Univ, University Park, 57; M.A, Univ. Fla, 62, Ph.D.(speech & theatre), 68. Teacher Eng, West Islip High Sch, N.Y, 58-60; instr, Univ. Fla, 63-64; asst. prof. SPEECH & THEATRE, MEMPHIS STATE UNIV, 64-69, ASSOC. PROF, 69-, res. grant to Eng, 73. Consult. playwriting & poetry, Fla. Int. Univ, 74- U.S.A, 53-55. Folklore Soc, London; Speech Commun. Asn; South. Speech Commun. Asn. Folklore; theatre history; playwriting. Publ: Eye dialect in Li'l Abner, Am. Speech, 10/65; A Boston ballad and the Boston Riot, Walt Whitman Rev, 9/63; contrib, Poetry southeast: 1950-1970, Tenn. Poetry J, 68. Add: Dept. of Speech & Drama, Memphis State University, Memphis, TN 38111.

MALINA, MARILYN J, b. New York, N.Y, Oct. 9, 28. ENGLISH. A.B, Hiram Col, 49; M.A, Trinity Col.(Conn), 64; Ph.D.(Eng), Univ. Va, 67. Instr. ENG, Mass. State Col. Framingham, 66-67; ASST. PROF, UNIV. R.I, 67- Asst. prof. Eng, New Eng. Col, Eng, 71-72. MLA; Mediaeval Acad. Am; AAUP. Middle and Old English literature; dramatic literature. Publ: A note on Charles Donahue's Account of the exegetical tradition, Annuale Mediaevale, 72. Add: Dept. of English, University of Rhode Island, Kingston, RI 02881.

MALKIN, MICHAEL ROBERT, b. Huntington, N.Y, July 20, 43; m. 70; c. 1. THEATER HISTORY, DRAMATIC LITERATURE. B.A, Tufts Univ, 65, NDEA fel, 66-69, M.A, 70, Ph.D.(dramatic hist. & lit), 71. Sessional lectr. THEATER, Univ. Alta, 70-71; ASSOC. PROF, IND. UNIV. PA, 71- Am. Theater Asn; Speech Commun. Asn. History of puppet theater; acting theory; dramatic literature. Publ: Danton's death: Büchner's unidealistic Danton, Stud. Humanities, spring 73; Teaching improvisation with hand puppets, Dramatics, 11/73; A critical perspective on puppetry as theater art, Puppetry J, 1-2/74; plus others. Add: Dept. of English, Indiana University of Pennsylvania, Indiana, PA 15701.

MALKOFF, KARL, b. Bronx, N.Y, July 27, 38; m. 61; c. 2. ENGLISH. A.B, Columbia Univ, 59, A.M, 63, Ph.D.(Eng), 65. Instr. ENG, C.W. Post Col, L.I. Univ, 65-66; CITY COL. NEW YORK, 66-67, asst. prof, 67-72, ASSOC. PROF, 72- MLA. Contemporary American and British literature; contemporary American poetry. Publ: Theodore Roethke: an introduction to the poetry, 66 & Muriel Spark, 68, Columbia Univ; Crowell's handbook of contemporary American poetry, Crowell, 73; Allusion as irony, Minn. Rev, 67; contrib, William Styron's The confessions of Nat. Turner, Wadsworth, 70 & Contemporary Jewish American literature, Ind. Univ, 73; plus two others. Add: Dept. of English, City College of New York, 138th St. & Convent Ave, New York, NY 10031.

MALLINGER, ANITA ELLEN, b. Pittsburgh, Pa, Nov. 19, 45. ENGLISH, CREATIVE WRITING. B.A, Univ. Pittsburgh, 67; M.A, Carnegie-Mellon Univ, 68, fel, 69-70, D.A. (Eng), 72. Teacher ENG, Munhall High Sch, 68-69; ASST. PROF, UNIV. PITTSBURGH, 72- Add: Dept. of English, University of Pittsburgh, Pittsburgh, PA 15260.

MALLOCH, ARCHIBALD EDWARD, b. New York, N.Y, Sept. 20, 26; m. 48; c. 4. ENGLISH. B.A, Queens Univ, Can, 48; M.A, Univ. Toronto, 49, Ph.D, 58. Lectr. ENG, Univ. West. Ont, 52-53; McGILL UNIV, 53-54, asst. prof, 54-58, assoc. prof, 58-67, PROF, 67- Can. Counc. res. fel, 63-64. Can. Army, 44-45. MLA. Renaissance literature. Publ: Techniques and function of the Renaissance paradox, Stud. Philol; John Donne and the Casuists, Stud. Eng. Lit, 62. Add: Dept. of English, McGill University, Montreal 110, P.Q, Can.

MALLON, HUGH VINCENT, C.S.B, b. Toronto, Ont, July 5, 10. ENGLISH. B.A, Univ. Toronto, 31; Pontif. Inst. Medieval Stud, Toronto, 40-41; M.A, Univ. Mich, 42. Lectr. Eng, Assumption Col.(Ont), 35-38, asst. prof, 38-40; St. Michael's Col, Univ. Toronto, 40-47, prof, 47-61, chmn. dept, 55-58, registr, 58-61; prof, Univ. Windsor, 61-62, v.pres, 62-63; PROF. ENG. & V.PRES, ST. MICHAEL'S COL, UNIV. TORONTO, 63-, registr, 63-72. Can. Univ. Registr. Asn.(councillor, 59-61, 63-68). Add: Dept. of English, St. Michael's College, University of Toronto, Toronto, Ont. M5S 1J4, Can.

MALLORY, THOMAS OLIVER, JR, b. Dallas, Tex, Dec. 24, 23; m. 48; c. 3. ENGLISH LANGUAGE & LITERATURE. B.A, Southwest Tex. State Col, 47, M.A, 48; Ph.D, Univ. Ill, 57. Teacher, elem. sch, Tex, 42-43, High Sch, 47; asst, Southwest Tex. State Col, 47-48, instr, 48-49, asst. prof, 51-57; asst, Univ. Ill, 49-51; assoc. prof. ENG, N.MEX. HIGHLANDS UNIV, 57-62, PROF, 62- U.S. Merchant Marine, 43-46. Rocky Mountain Mod. Lang. Asn; NCTE; Conf. Eng. Educ. Nineteenth century prose fiction; the devil in fiction; science fiction. Add: Dept. of English, New Mexico Highlands University, Las Vegas, NM 87701.

MALMSHEIMER, LONNA MYERS, b. Tarentum, Pa, June 10, 40; m. 65; c. 2. AMERICAN LITERATURE & STUDIES. B.A, Pa. State Univ, 62, M.A, 65; Ph.D.(Am. stud), Univ. Minn, 73. ASST. PROF. AM. LIT, SAN DIEGO STATE UNIV, 73- Am. Stud. Asn; MLA. Colonial American culture; American literature. Add: School of Literature, San Diego State University, San Diego, CA 92115.

MALMSTROM, JEAN, b. St. Louis, Mo, June 19, 08; m. 29; c. 5. ENGLISH. B.A, Wash. Univ, 28, Barr fel, 28-29, M.A, 29; Ph.D, Univ. Minn, 58. Instr. ENG, WEST. MICH UNIV, 48-52, asst. prof, 52-58, assoc. prof, 58-64, PROF, 64- Award for Teaching Excellence, West. Mich. Univ, 71. Conf. Col. Compos. & Commun; Col. Eng. Asn; MLA; NCTE (mem. comn. Eng. lang, 62-66); Ling. Soc. Am; Am. Dialect Soc; Int. Ling. Asn; Int. Reading Asn; Asn. Machine Transl. & Computational Ling. American English dialects; teaching of English; applied linguistics. Publ: Dialects—U.S.A, NCTE, 63; Language in society, 65, 73 & An introduction to modern English grammar, 68, Hayden; co-auth, Teaching English linguistically: principles and practices for high school, Appleton, 71; co-auth, Transgrammar: English structure, style and dialects, Scott, 73; plus others. Add: Dept. of English, Western Michigan University, Kalamazoo, MI 49001.

MALOF, JOSEPH FETLER, b. Riga, Latvia, May 26, 34; U.S. citizen; m. 57; c. 3. ENGLISH. B.A, Kenyon Col, 56; M.A, Univ. Calif, Los Angeles, 57, Woodrow Wilson Nat. fel, 56-57, Ph.D.(Eng), 62. Asst. ENG, Univ. Calif, Los Angeles, 60-61; instr, UNIV. TEX, AUSTIN, 61-65, asst. prof, 65-68, assoc. prof, 68-73, PROF, 73- E. Harris Harbison Prize, Danforth Found, 70. MLA. Twentieth century poetry in English; American literature; English versification. Publ: A manual of English meters, Ind. Univ, 70; The native rhythm of English meters, Tex. Stud. Lit. & Lang, winter 64; Meter as organic form, Mod. Lang. Quart, 3/66; Haiku in heroics, Lit. East & West, 3/71; plus one other. Add: Dept. of English, University of Texas at Austin, Austin, TX 78712.

MALOFF, SAUL, b. New York, N.Y, Sept. 6, 22; m. 50; c. 1. ENGLISH, AMERICAN CIVILIZATION. B.A, City Col. New York, 43; fels, Univ. Iowa, 46-48, M.A, 47, Ph.D.(Eng), 52. Instr. Eng, Univ. Mich, 49-51; from instr. to asst. prof, Ind. Univ, 51-54; lectr, City Col. New York, 55-56; Pratt Inst, 56-59; assoc. prof, Univ. P.R, 59-60; lectr. lit, N.Y. Univ. & New Sch. Social Res, 60-62; mem. fac, Bennington Col, 62-64; lit. ed, Newsweek Mag, 64-68; PROF. ENG, HUNTER COL, 68- Juror, PEN Club transl. award, 65; Nat. Bk. awards, 66; vis. regents lectr, Univ. Calif, winter 67; Guggenheim fel, 68-69; consult, Guggenheim Found, 68- George Polk Mem. Award Lit. Criticism, 67. U.S.A, 43-46. PEN Club. Fiction writing—novels and short stories; literary criticism and journalism. Publ: Auth, Happy families, 68 & Heartland (novel), 73, Scribner; co-auth, chap, In: Modern British novel, South. Ill. Univ, 65; plus others. Add: Skyline Ridge, Bridgewater, CT 06752.

MALONE, DAVID HENRY, b. Washington, D.C, Aug. 9, 19. COMPARATIVE LITERATURE. A.B, Univ. N.C, 40, Ph.D, 48; La. State Univ, 40-41. Asst. prof. Eng, Auburn Univ, 48-52, assoc. prof, 52-57, prof, 57-62; PROF. COMP. LIT, UNIV. SOUTH. CALIF, 62-, DEAN HUMANITIES, 72-, chmn. dept. Eng, 64-68, chmn. dept. comp. lit, 62-72. FAE fel, Philipps Univ. & Sorbonne, 54-55; Fulbright lectr. Am. stud, Univ. Vienna, 58-60. MLA; Am. Comp. Lit. Asn; Philol. Asn. Pac. Coast; Am. Asn. Higher Educ; AAUP (chmn. comt, relat. higher educ. to state & fed. govts, 67-73); Int. Comp. Lit. Asn; NCTE; Comp. Lit. Asn. West. States (chmn, 67-68). European romanticism; realism and naturalism; symbolism. Publ: Collab, Outline of comparative literature, Univ. N.C, 54; contrib, Cambridge bibliography of English literature, Cambridge, 57; Mark Twain and the Literature of the Frontier, Die Neueren Sprachen, Beiheft, 61; Literature and comparative literature, In: Medieval epic to the epic theatre of Brecht, Univ. South. Calif, 68. Add: Div. of Humanities, University of Southern California, Los Angeles, CA 90007.

MALONEY, HENRY B, b. Detroit, Mich, Oct. 4, 27; m. 54; c. 4. EDUCATION, SECONDARY ENGLISH. A.B, Univ. Detroit, 49; M.A, Univ. Mich, 50; Ed.D. (teaching of Eng), Columbia Univ, 67. Supvr. sec. Eng, Detroit Pub. Schs, Mich, 64-67; assoc. prof. educ, Wayne State Univ, 67-68; dir. teacher educ, UNIV. DETROIT, 68-72, DEAN FAC, 72- Dir, U.S. Off. Educ. curriculum develop. project, Trenton High Sch, Mich, 64-67; mem. resolutions comt. NCTE, 67 & dir. spring insts. sponsored by sec. sect. comt, 69 & 72. U.S.A, 45-46, S/Sgt. Secondary English curriculum; teaching of literature; teaching of composition. Publ: Ed, Plays to remember, Macmillan, 66, rev. ed, 73; ed, Success in language and literature, Follett, Vols. B & C, 67 & 68; co-ed, Superboy, supergirl, 71 & co-ed, Inside story, 73, Scholastic; ed, Accountability and the teaching of English, 72 & ed, Goal making for English teaching, 73, NCTE. Add: 953 Hollywood, Grosse Pointe Woods, MI 48236.

MALONEY, LEO JAMES, b. Honeoye Falls, N.Y, Dec. 4, 18. ENGLISH, PHILOSOPHY. A.B, St. Bernard's Col. & Sem, 39; M.A, Univ. Notre Dame, 47; summers, Harvard, 58-61. Instr. ENG, NIAGARA UNIV, 47-50, asst. prof, 51-60, assoc. prof, 61-64, PROF, 65-, chmn. dept, 65-72. U.S.A.A.F, 43-45, Sgt. MLA; NCTE. Shakespeare; Victorian literature; Chaucer. Add: Dept. of English, Niagara University, Niagara, NY 14109.

MALPAS, EDWARD REGINALD HOWARD, b. Northampton, Eng, Aug. 25, 22; U.S. citizen; m. 59. ENGLISH, DRAMA. Grad, Royal Acad. Dramatic Art, 49; A.B, Wayne State Univ, 56; M.A, State Univ. Iowa, 60; Ph.D.(dramatic criticism), Univ. Wis, 65. Asst. prof. Eng. & drama, Cornell Col, 57-65; acting dir, Wis. Repertory Co, Univ. Wis, 65-66; ASSOC. PROF. DRAMA, MILLS COL, 66- R.A.F, 42-46. Am. Theatre Asn.(chmn. int. comn, Int. Artists & Scholars Serv, 71-). Contemporary and television drama. Add: Dept. of Drama, Box 9904, Mills College, Oakland, CA 94613.

MALTBY, JOSEPH, b. Long Beach, Calif, Sept. 22, 31; m. 58; c. 2. ENGLISH LITERATURE. B.A, Stanford Univ, 52, M.A, 57; Ph.D, Univ. Wis, 63. Asst. ENG, Univ. Wis, 55-60, instr, Manitowoc Ctr, 60-62; UNIV. HAWAII, 62-63, asst. prof, 63-68, assoc. prof, 68-73, PROF, 73-, chmn. dept, 70-73. MLA; NCTE; AAUP. Restoration and 18th century English literature; Shakespeare, modern literature. Add: Dept. of English, University of Hawaii, Honolulu, HI 96822.

MALTMAN, M. NICHOLAS, O.P, b. Los Angeles, Calif, June 16, 15. ENGLISH. B.A, Dominican Col.(Calif), 36; M.A, Cath. Univ. Am, 49; Ph.D. (Eng), Univ. Calif, Berkeley, 57. Instr. humanities, DOMINICAN COL. SAN RAFAEL, 45-48, from asst. prof. to assoc. prof, 49-57, PROF. ENG. & HUMANITIES, 57-, CHMN. DEPT. ENG, 58-, dean women, 45-52. Col. Eng. Asn; MLA. Medieval English literature; Corpus Christi plays; medieval literature and liturgy. Publ: Pilate—os malleatoris, Speculum, 61; contrib, New Catholic encyclopedia, McGraw, 67; auth, Meaning and art in the Croxton Play of the sacrament, ELH, 74. Add: Dept. of English, Dominican College of San Rafael, San Rafael, CA 94901.

MAMMEN, EDWARD WILLIAM, b. New York, N.Y, Oct. 2, 07; m. 32; c. 2. DRAMA, SPEECH. A.B, Columbia Univ, 28, A.M, 29, Ph.D, 45. Teacher, Tech. High Sch, Brooklyn, 29-30; from tutor to prof. SPEECH, City Col. New York, 30-57; prof, BARUCH COL, 57-71, gen. adv, 46-68, EMER. PROF, 71- Instr, Columbia Univ, 28-40. Speech Commun. Asn; AAUP; Auth. Guild. Interpretation; theater. Publ: The spoken word & Voice speech handbook, Prentice-Hall, 32, 55; Old stock company school of acting, Boston Pub. Libr, 45; The Buttons go walking, Harper, 40; co-auth, Art of speaking made simple, Made Simple Bks, 54. Add: 45 Elm St, Great Neck, NY 11021.

MANCHEL, FRANK, b. Detroit, Mich, July 22, 35; m. 58; c. 2. ENGLISH EDUCATION. B.A, Ohio State Univ, 57; M.A, Hunter Col, 60; Ed.D.(Eng), Columbia Univ, 66. Instr. High Sch, N.Y, 58-64; asst. prof. Eng, South. Conn. State Col, 64-67; assoc. prof, UNIV. VT, 67-72, PROF. COMMUN. & THEATRE, 72- Dir. grad. Eng. intern prof, Univ. Vt, 68, La Mancha proj, 68; Mem. Nat. Comt. Innovative Practices in Eng. Educ, 68. U.S.A, 57. Am. Fed. Film Soc.(chmn, 72-); MLA; NCTE; Asn. Stud. Teaching; Soc. Cinema Stud.(treas, 72-); Am. Film Inst; Brit. Film Inst. Motion picture; Black studies; comedy. Publ: Movies and how they are made, 68, When pictures began to move, 69, When movies began to speak, 69, Terrors of the screen, 70 & Cameras West, 71, Prentice-Hall; Film Study: a resource guide, Fairleigh Dickinson Univ, 73; Yesterday's clowns, Watts, 73; Teaching nothing but a man, 10/67 & Teaching Dr. Strangelove, 12/67, Media & Methods; Volunteers for La Mancha, Eng. Leaflet, 9/68. Add: Dept. of Communication & Theatre, University of Vermont, Burlington, VT 05402.

MANDEL, BARRETT JOHN, b. New York, N.Y, Dec. 22, 37; m. 61; c. 1. ENGLISH. B.A, Emerson Col, 60; M.A, Univ. Conn, 64, Ph.D.(Eng), 66. Teaching asst, Univ. Conn, 60-65; ASST. PROF. ENG, Carnegie-Mellon Univ, 66-67; Univ. Pittsburgh, 67-72; DOUGLASS COL, RUTGERS UNIV. NEW BRUNSWICK, 72- MLA. Art of autobiography; 18th century literature. Publ: Bogey, Today's Speech, 65; Pope's Eloisa to Abelard, Tex. Stud. Lit. & Lang, 67; Bunyan and the autobiographer's artistic purpose, Criticism, 68. Add: Dept. of English, Douglass College, Rutgers University, New Brunswick, NJ 08903.

MANDEL, JEROME HERBERT, b. Cleveland, Ohio, Nov. 17, 37; m. 64; c. 2. ENGLISH. A.B, Oberlin Col, 59; M A, Ohio State Univ, 61, Ph.D, 66. Asst. prof. ENG, Rutgers Univ, 66-72; ASSOC. PROF, CLEMSON UNIV, 72-, DIR. GRAD. STUD, 73- Summer res. grant, Rutgers Univ, 68, fac. fel, 69-70; Mellon fel, humanities, 69-70. Anthologist of Year, N.J. Asn. Teachers Eng, 72. MLA; Mediaeval Acad. Am; Int. Arthurian Soc; Mod. Humanities Res. Asn; Northeast Mod. Lang. Asn; S.Atlantic Mod. Lang. Asn. Old English poetry; medieval romance; Chaucer. Publ: Co-ed, Old English literature: twenty-two analytical essays, Univ. Nebr, 68; co-ed, Medieval literature and folklore studies: essays in honor of Francis Lee Utley, Rutgers Univ, 70; auth, Elements in the Charrette world: the father-son relationship, Mod. Philol, 12/64; The man of the hill and Mrs. Fitzpatrick: character and narrative technique in Tom Jones, Papers Lang. & Lit, 1/69; Contrast in Old English poetry, Chaucer Rev, 71. Add: Dept. of English, Clemson University, Clemson, SC 29631.

MANDEL, OSCAR, b. Antwerp, Belgium, Aug. 24, 26; nat. ENGLISH. M.A, Columbia Univ, 48; univ. fel, Ohio State Univ, 50-51, Ph.D.(Eng), 51. Asst. prof. Eng, Univ. Nebr, 55-61; assoc. prof. HUMANITIES, CALIF. INST. TECHNOL, 61-68, PROF, 68- Fulbright lectr, Holland, 60-61. U.S.A, 53-55. MLA. Comparative literature; drama; creative writing. Publ: A definition of tragedy, N.Y. Univ, 61; Chi Po and the sorcerer, Tuttle, 63; The theatre of Don Juan, Univ. Nebr, 64; Gobble-up stories, Humphries, 66; The fatal French dentist, French, 66; Seven comedies by Marivaux, Cornell Univ, 68; Five comedies of medieval France, Dutton 70; Collected plays, (2 vols), Unicorn, 70-72; The excesses of seriousness in literature, Antioch Rev, spring 68; Reactionary notes on the experimental theatre, Mass. Rev, winter 70; Dissonant music sixty years after, S.Atlantic Quart, winter 73. Add: Div. of Humanities, California Institute of Technology, Pasadena, CA 91109.

MANDEL, SIEGFRIED, b. Berlin, Ger, Dec. 20, 22; m. 46; c. 2. ENGLISH, COMPARATIVE LITERATURE. B.A, Brooklyn Col, 46; M.A, Columbia Univ, 47; Ph.D.(Eng, comp. lit), Univ. Denver, 67. Instr. ENG, Polytech. Inst. Brooklyn, 48-57, asst. prof, 57-59, assoc. prof, 59-62; UNIV. COLO, BOULDER, 62-65, PROF, 65- Lectr, exten. div, N.Y. Univ, 55; Univ. Colo. Grad. Sch. Counc. Res. & Creative Work fac. fel, 68-69. Intel.C, U.S.A, 43-46, T/Sgt. Col. Eng. Asn; MLA. Seventeenth century English, German and French Baroque literature; modern German fiction; comparative European and American 20th century literature. Publ: Co-auth, Rainer Maria Rilke: visions of Christ, Univ. Colo, 67; auth, Group 47: the reflected intellect, South. Ill. Univ, 73; Rainer Maria Rilke: the poetic instinct, 65 & ed. & contrib, The German novel: in the wake organized madness, In: Contemporary European novelists, 68, South. Ill. Univ. Add: Dept. of English, Hellems 101, University of Colorado, Boulder, CO 80302.

MANDELBAUM, BERNARD D, b. New York, N.Y, July 24, 27; m. 56; c. 2. ENGLISH, COMPARATIVE LITERATURE. B.A, Brooklyn Col, 50; M.A, N.Y. Univ, 53, Ph.D.(Eng), 62. Teacher high schs, New York, N.Y, 56-61; lectr. ENG, City Col. New York & Queens Col.(N.Y), 61-62; asst. prof, BRONX COMMUNITY COL, 62-67, assoc. prof, 67-70, PROF, 70- State Univ. N.Y. fac. res. fel, 66. U.S.A.A.F, 45-47. MLA; NCTE. Comparative drama; the monomyth in literature; literary criticism. Publ: Two lyric poems: a demonstration, Eng. Rev, 5/63; John Steinbeck's The snake: the structure of a dream, Eng. Rec, 2/66; plus twenty-five articles on comparative mythology and literature for Encycl. Am, 71-73. Add: Dept. of English, Bronx Community College, New York, NY 10453.

MANEIKIS, WALTER, b. Chicago, Ill, July 13, 08; m. 30. ENGLISH & AMERICAN LITERATURE. Ph.B, Univ. Chicago, 33, M.A, 36; Ph.D.(Eng), Northwest. Univ, 43. Teacher, Northwest. Univ, West. Ill. State Teachers Col, Univ. Idaho, Purdue Univ, De Paul Univ; ASSOC. PROF. ENG, CHICAGO STATE UNIV, 66- Nat. Guard, 24-37; A.U.S, 43-44. MLA; Col. Eng. Asn; Asn. Higher Educ; NEA. American literary criticism; Shakespeare. Publ: Short stories & articles. Add: Dept. of English, Chicago State University, Chicago, IL 60621.

MANFULL, LOWELL L, b. Ogden, Utah, Dec. 18, 27; m. 56; c. 2. THEATRE. B.S, Univ. Utah, 53, M.A, 55; univ. fel. & Ph.D, Univ. Minn, 61. Instr. speech, Univ. Minn, 55-60; asst. prof, Univ. Wis, 60-65; THEATRE ARTS, PA. STATE UNIV, UNIVERSITY PARK, 65-72, ASSOC. PROF, 72-, COORD. GRAD. STUD, 69- Res. fel, Univ. Wis, 63. U.S.A, 50-52, M/Sgt. Am. Theatre Asn; AAUP. Dramatic literature and theory; theatre history; graduate research. Add: Dept. of Theatre Arts, Pennsylvania State University, University Park, PA 16802.

MANGELSDORF, RUTH BRUNE, b. Lawrence, Kans, Sept. 12, 93; m. 56. ENGLISH. A.B, Baker Univ, 16; Univ. Chicago, summer 20; M.A, Columbia Univ, 24; scholar, Univ. Calif, Berkeley, 29-31; fel, Univ. Colo, 45-47, Ph.D, 49; Nat. Univ. Mex, 57. Teacher Eng, Latin & Ger, High Schs, Kans, 16-18, Eng, Latin & jour, 18-23; instr. Eng, Ger. & jour, Bemidji State Col, 24-47, prof. & chmn. Am. humanities, 50-62; RETIRED. Consult, North. Stud, 31-42; Minn. J. Educ; founder & ed, North. Minn. Educator, 40-64;

deleg. nat. meeting, Teachers Ethics & Profess. Standards, 60; ed, News Bull. Retired Teachers Asn. Minn. MLA; NCTE; Nat. Educ. Asn; Teachers Col. Nat. Scholar. Asn.(pres, 55-57, historian, 57-62). Biography of Edgar Watson Howe; development of American humanities programs; American goodwill ambassadors traveling in foreign countries. Publ: Birds and animals in poetry, 1750-1800, Columbia Univ, 24; Historical sketch of Bemidji Teachers College, 36 & Take a second look, 70, Pioneer Publ. Co; Early life of Edgar Watson Howe, Univ. Colo, 49. Add: 1121 Lake Blvd, Bemidji, MN 56601.

MANGIONE, JERRE, b. Rochester, N.Y, Mar. 20, 09; m. 57. ENGLISH. B.A, Syracuse Univ, 31; hon. M.A, Univ. Pa, 71. Writer, Time Mag, 31; ed, Robert M. McBride & Co, 34-37; nat. coord. ed, Fed. Writers Proj, 37-39; spec. asst. to U.S. Comnr. Immigration & Naturalization, 42-48; lectr. Eng. compos. & dir. freshman compos. courses, UNIV. PA, 61-63, assoc. prof, ENG, 63-68, PROF, 68-, DIR. WRITING PROG, 67- Free-lance writer, New Repub. Mag. & N.Y. Herald Tribune Bk. Sect, 31-36; Guggenheim fel, 45; Fulbright res. fel, 65; vis. lectr, Bryn Mawr Col, 66-67; Rockefeller Found. res. grant, 68-69; judge, Nat. Bk. Award in Fiction, 69; Am. Philos. Soc. res. grant, 72; vis. prof, Trinity Col, Rome, Italy Campus, summer 73. Friends of Rochester Pub. Libr. lit. award, 66; Commendatore, Order Ital. Solidarity, 71; Athenaem Lit. Award, 73. Auth. League Am; Conf. Col. Compos. & Commun; PEN Club. Creative writing; expository writing; 20th century literature. Publ: Mount Allegro, Houghton, 43, Knopf, 52 & Hill & Wang, 63, Crown, 72; The ship and the flame, Wyn, 48; Reunion in Sicily, Houghton, 50; Night search, Crown, 65; Life sentences for everybody, Abelard, 66; A passion for Sicilians - the world around Danilo Dolci, William Morrow, 68; America is also Italian, Putnam, 69; The dream and the deal: the Federal Writers' Project, 1935-1943, Little, 72; Authors on campus, Report Sch. & Col. Conf. Eng, 5/67; Federal Writers' Project, N.Y. Times Bk. Rev, 5/69; Let's resurrect Federal One, Chronicle Higher Educ, 5/73. Add: Dept. of English, University of Pennsylvania, Philadelphia, PA 19174.

MANGUM, ANTHONY BRYANT, b. Monroe, N.C, Jan. 12, 43; m. 66; c. 2. AMERICAN LITERATURE. A.B, Univ. N.C, Chapel Hill, 61; M.A, Univ. S.C, 69, Ph.D.(Eng), 74. INSTR. ENG, VA. COMMONWEALTH UNIV, 71- MLA; S.Atlantic Mod. Lang. Asn. American novel in the 1920's; F. Scott Fitzgerald; Ernest Hemingway. Publ: The reception of Dearly beloved, Fitzgerald/Hemingway Annual, 70. Add: Dept. of English, Hibbs Bldg, Virginia Commonwealth University, Richmond, VA 23220.

MANHEIM, LEONARD FALK, b. New York, N.Y, Apr. 22, 02; m. 27; c. 1. ENGLISH, COMPARATIVE LITERATURE. A.B, Columbia Univ, 21, J.D, 24, Ph.D.(comp. lit), 50. Lectr. ENG, City Col. New York, 46-65; vis. prof, Univ. Mass, Amherst, 65-67; prof, UNIV. HARTFORD, 67-72, EMER. PROF, 72- Practicing atty, 23-32; teacher Eng, high schs, New York, N.Y, 32-59; TV writer, 46-48; ed, Lit. & Psychol, 50-67; vis. lectr. Eng, George Peabody Col, 60-61; spec. lectr, lit. & psychol, Temple Univ. & State Univ. Col. New Paltz, 61, 62; Temple Univ, 67; ed, Hartford Stud. Lit, 68-; vis. prof. Eng, Emory Univ, 73. MLA. Psychoanalytic literary criticism; history of the novel; English and comparative literature. Publ: Co-ed, Hidden patterns: studies in psychoanalytic criticism, Macmillan, 66; The mythical joys of Shakespeare: or What you will, Shakespeare Encomium, 64; Floras and Doras: the women in Dickens' novels, Tex. Stud. Lang. & Lit, 65; Dickens' fools and madmen, Dickens Stud. Annual, 72; Metaphysical literary criticism—theory and practice: essays in honor of Leonard Manheim, 73; plus others. Add: Hartford Studies in Literature, University of Hartford, 200 Bloomfield Ave, Hartford, CT 06117.

MANHEIM, MICHAEL, b. New York, N.Y, Mar. 4, 28; m. 55; c. 2. ENGLISH. A.B, Columbia Col, 49; M.A, Columbia Univ, 51, grant, 52-53, Ph.D, 61. Instr. Eng, Univ. Del, 53-61; asst. prof, UNIV. TOLEDO, 61-63, assoc. prof. ENG, 63-67, PROF, 67-, assoc. dean humanities, 63-66, chmn. dept. Eng, 66-72. Danforth grant, 59-60; vis. prof. Eng, Dartmouth Col, summer 72. MLA; Midwest Mod. Lang. Asn; Am. Fed. Teachers. Shakespeare; Elizabethan drama; modern drama. Publ: The weak king dilemma in the Shakespearean history play, Syracuse Univ, 73; The weak king history play of the early 1590's, Renaissance Drama, 69; The construction of The shoemakers' holiday, Stud. Eng. Lit, spring 70; plus others. Add: Dept. of English, University of Toledo, Toledo, OH 43606.

MANION, FREDERICK PAUL, S.J, b. Freeport, Ill, Aug. 18, 16. ENGLISH LITERATURE. B.A, Loyola Univ.(Ill), 41; M.A, Univ. Detroit, 43; Cambridge, 49-50; Ph.D, Fordham Univ, 58. Instr. Eng, Latin & Greek, Loyola Acad, Chicago, Ill, 43-44; asst. prof. ENG, W.Baden Div. Loyola Univ.(Ill), 54-58; Xavier Univ.(Ohio), 58-62, assoc. prof. & assoc. dean, Milford Col, 62-65; vis. prof, Loyola Univ.(Ill) Rome Ctr. Lib. Arts, 65-66; ASST. PROF, LOYOLA UNIV.(ILL), 66- MLA; NCTE. English recusant literature of the 16th and 17th centuries; medieval English drama; Milton. Add: Dept. of English, Loyola University, 6525 N. Sheridan Rd, Chicago, IL 60626.

MANIQUIS, ROBERT MANUEL, b. Newark, N.J, Sept. 4, 40; m. 61; c. 2. NINETEENTH CENTURY ENGLISH LITERATURE, COMPARATIVE LITERATURE. B.A, Rutgers Univ, 62; Woodrow Wilson fel, Columbia Univ, 62-66, M.A, 63, Ph.D.(Eng), 67. ASST. PROF. ENG, UNIV. CALIF, LOS ANGELES, 66- Am. Counc. Learned Soc. fel, 72-73. MLA; Philol. Asn. Pac. Coast. Nineteenth century.Romanticism, English, French, and German; 19th century novel, English, French, and German. Publ: Comparison, intensity, and time in Tintern Abbey, Criticism, fall, 69; The puzzling Mimosa: sensitivity and plant symbols in Romanticism, Studies Romanticism, spring 69. Add: Dept. of English, University of California, Los Angeles, CA 90024.

MANLEY, FRANK, b. Scranton, Pa, Nov. 13, 30; m. 52; c. 2. ENGLISH. B.A, Emory Univ, 52, M.A, 53; Ph.D, Johns Hopkins Univ, 59. Instr. ENG, Yale, 59-62, asst. prof, 62-64; assoc. prof, EMORY UNIV, 64-67, PROF, 67- Morse fel, Yale, 63-64; Guggenheim fel, 66-67. U.S.A, 53-55. MLA. Renaissance drama; John Donne; St. Thomas More. Publ: John Donne: the anniversaries, Johns Hopkins Univ, 63; co-ed, Richard Pace's De fructu qui ex doctrina pericitur, Renaissance Soc. Am, 66; ed, George Chapman's All fools, Regents Renaissance Drama Ser, 68. Add: Dept. of English, Emory University, Atlanta, GA 30322.

MANLOVE, GEORGE KENDALL, b. Cleveland, Ohio, Nov. 26, 13; m. 45; c. 3. ENGLISH. B.A, Oberlin Col, 36, M.A, 46; Ph.D, Duke Univ, 60. Instr. ENG, UNIV. MAINE, ORONO, 49-54, asst. prof, 55-61, assoc. prof, 61-68, PROF, 68- Eighteenth century English literature; Goldsmith. Add: Dept. of English, 220 Stevens Hall, University of Maine, Orono, ME 04473.

MANN, CHARLES WILLIAM, b. Altoona, Pa, Dec. 29, 29; div; c. 1. ENGLISH, BIBLIOGRAPHY. B.A, Pa. State Univ, 52, M.A, 54; M.L.S, Rutgers Univ, 61. Bibliogr, PA. STATE UNIV. LIBR, UNIVERSITY PARK, 54-58, RARE BKS. LIBRN, 58-, ASSOC. PROF. ENG, PA. STATE UNIV, 71-, asst. prof, 66-71. Assoc. ed, Univ. Pittsburgh Ser. in Bibliog. Soc. Am; Milton Pa. State Univ. Press, 72- Grolier Club; MLA; Bibliog. Soc. Am; Milton Soc. Am. Modern American literature; rare books. Publ: Co-auth, The Hemingway manuscripts: an inventory, Pa. State Univ, 69; auth, The John O'Hara manuscripts at Pennsylvania State, Manuscripts, 69; co-auth, Fitzgerald's The sun also rises, Fitzgerald Hemingway Annual, 70; auth, The role of rare books in a university library, Courier, 72. Add: Rare Books & Special Collections, Pennsylvania State University Library, W342 Pattee, University Park, PA 16802.

MANN, DAVID DOUGLAS, b. Oklahoma City, Okla, Sept. 13, 34; m. 72. ENGLISH. B.S, Okla. State Univ, 56, M.A, 63; Ph.D.(Eng), Ind. Univ, 69. Teacher, Leelanau Schs, Mich, 62-63; instr, ENG, Wabash Col, 65-67; asst. prof, MIAMI UNIV, 68-73, ASSOC. PROF, 73- Folger Shakespeare Libr. fel, 70-71. U.S.N.R, 56-59, Lt. Comdr. MLA; NCTE; Midwest. Mod. Lang. Asn. Modern American poetry; Restoration and 18th century literature, Milton. Publ: Ed, A concordance to the complete plays of William Congreve, Cornell Univ, 73; co-auth, John Crowe Ransom's Poetic revisions, PMLA, 3/68. Add: Dept. of English, Miami University, Oxford, OH 45056.

MANN, JOHN STUART, b. Washington, D.C, Sept. 12, 45; m. 69. ENGLISH & AMERICAN LITERATURE. B.A, Col. Wooster, 67; Ford Found. fel, Univ. Pa, 67-71, M.A, 68, Ph.D.(Eng), 72. ASST. PROF. ENG, WEST. ILL. UNIV, 71- MLA; Col. Eng. Asn. Nineteenth century American fiction and poetry; contemporary American literature. Add: Dept. of English, Western Illinois University, Macomb, IL 61455.

MANN, KENNETH EUGENE, b. Winslow, Ariz, June 11, 39; m. 62; c. 4. SPEECH COMMUNICATION. B.S, Brigham Young Univ, 65, M.A, 66; Ph.D. (rhet, pub. address), Ind. Univ, 71. Asst. speech, Brigham Young Univ, 65-66; instr, Ind. Univ, Ft. Wayne, 66-67; Purdue Univ, Ft. Wayne, 67-68; teaching assoc, Ind. Univ, Bloomington, 68-71, instr. commun, Labor Educ. & Res. Ctr, 69-71; ASST. PROF. MASS COMMUN. & SPEECH, CHURCH COL. HAWAII, 71- Vis. lectr. intercult. commun, Ariz. State Univ, 73. Speech Commun. Asn; West. Speech Commun. Asn; Int. Soc. Gen. Semantics; Can. Speech Asn. Black American history; intercultural communication; intergroup relations. Publ: Oscar Stanton DePriest: persuasive agent for the black masses, 10/72 & John Roy Lynch: U.S. Congressman from Mississippi, (in press), Negro Hist. Bull; Intercultural communication training: a bridge for human understanding, Teaching Eng. Second Lang. Reporter, summer 73; plus others. Add: Dept. of Mass Communication & Speech, Church College of Hawaii, Laie, HI 96762.

MANN, LINDSAY ALFRED, b. Panama City, Repub. Panama, Nov. 11, 36; Can. citizen; m. 60; c. 3. ENGLISH. B.S, Univ. Santa Clara, 58; fels, Univ. Ill, Urbana, 58-59, spring 61, 61-62, summer 64, M.A, 59, Ph.D.(Eng), 65. Instr. ENG, Univ. Santa Clara, summers 60, 61; asst. prof, Univ. Calif, Davis, 65-69; CARLETON UNIV, 71-74, ASSOC. PROF, 74- Univ. Calif. regents fac. summer fel, 66. MLA; Renaissance Soc. Am; Milton Soc. Am. English literature of the 16th and 17th centuries; intellectual traditions and literary theory in relation to medieval and Renaissance literature; the idea of marriage and its analogues in medieval and Renaissance thought and literature, especially Donne and Milton. Publ: John Donne's doctrine of marriage in its historical context, Univ. Microfilms, 66; Gentilesse and the Franklin's tale, Stud. Philol, 1/66; The marriage analogue of letter and spirit in Donne's devotional prose, J. Eng. & Ger. Philol, 10/71; plus one other. Add: Dept. of English, Carleton University, Ottawa, Ont. K1S 5B6, Can.

MANNING, AMBROSE NUEL, b. Bailey, N.C, May 18, 22; m. 48; c. 4. ENGLISH. A.B, Atlantic Christian Col, 43; M.A, Univ. N.C, 47; Ed.S, George Peabody Col, 55. Instr. Eng. & French, Oak Ridge Mil. Inst, 47-48; ENG, E.TENN. STATE UNIV, 48-52, asst. prof, 52-56, assoc. prof, 56-61, PROF, 61- U.S.A, 43-45. MLA; NCTE; Conf. Col. Compos. & Commun, English romanticism; American folklore. Publ: Co-auth, Collection of folklore by students of East Tennessee State University, 66 & Folklore: folksongs, 67, E.Tenn. State Univ; auth, The present status of the freshman research paper, Col. Compos. & Commun, 5/61; railroad work songs, Tenn. Folklore Soc. Bull, 6/66. Add: Dept. of English, East Tennessee State University, Johnson City, TN 37601.

MANNING, CHARLES, b. Boston, Mass, Feb. 16, 09; m. 38; c. 2. ENGLISH. B.S, Tufts Col, 29; A.M, Harvard, 31; Ph.D, Univ. N.C, 50. Instr, Colby Col, 31-33; asst. prof, Centre Col. Ky, 36-46; Eng. UNIV. MD, COLLEGE PARK, 46-50, assoc. prof. & assoc. dean col, arts & sci, 50-62, PROF. ENG, 62-, acting dean col. arts & sci, 62-63, dean, 63-71. MLA. American literature. Add: 502 Apple Grove Rd, Silver Spring, MD 20904.

MANNING, PETER J, b. New York, N.Y, Sept. 27, 42; m. 67. ENGLISH. B.A, Harvard, 63; M.A, Yale, 65, Ph.D.(Eng), 68. ASST. PROF. ENG, UNIV. CALIF, BERKELEY, 67- MLA; Byron Soc. English romantic poetry. Publ: Byron's English bards and Scotch reviewers: the art of allusion, Keats-Shelley Mem. Bull, 70; Byron's English bards and Shelley's Adonais, Notes & Queries, 70; Edmund Kean and Byron's plays, Keats-Shelley J, 73. Add: Dept. of English, 322 Wheeler Hall, University of California, Berkeley, CA 94720.

MANNING, ROBERT NICKERSON, b. Boston, Mass, May 1, 38; m. 61; c. 2. CINEMA, COMMUNICATION. B.A, Univ. Vt, 61; M.A, Syracuse Univ, 64, Ph.D.(visual & performing arts), 72. Lectr. speech, Syracuse Univ, 62-63, asst. film, 63-64; instr. commun, LeMoyne Col, 64-66; ASST. PROF. film, St. Lawrence Univ, 66-69; film & TV, Wash. State Univ, 69-70; FILM, Cent. Mich. Univ, 70-72; BROOKLYN COL, 72- Dir, N.Y. Independent Film Exposition Int, 65-; producer, Filmscene (14 TV progs), KWSU-TV, Wash.

State Univ, 69; producer & dir, The Distance Runner, Cent. Mich. Univ, 71; Changes, Vision Quest, Chicago, 71; Cheesemaking, Films Inc, Chicago, 72; producer, Film Forum (26 TV progs), Brooklyn Col. TV Ctr. & WNYC-TV, N.Y, 72-73; lectr. & consult, U.S. Inform. Agency, 72-73. Univ. Film Asn; Speech Commun. Asn.(chmn. media forum, 72-). Television. Publ: An actor in academia, Speech Teacher, 9/66. Add: Office of Director Photography, Television Ctr, Brooklyn College, Brooklyn, NY 11210.

MANNING, STEPHEN, b. Indiana, Pa, Aug. 14, 30. ENGLISH, MEDIEVAL LITERATURE. A.B, Cath. Univ. Am, 52; univ. scholar, Johns Hopkins Univ, 52-55, spec. scholar, 54-56, Ph.D.(Eng), 56. Instr. ENG, Kent State Univ, 56-57; Univ. Colo, 57-60; asst. prof, Univ. Va, 60-64, assoc. prof, 64-67; PROF, UNIV. KY, 67- MLA; Mediaeval Acad. Am; S.Atlantic Mod. Lang. Asn.(v.pres, 72, pres, 73). Lyric; Chaucer; narrative literature. Publ: Wisdom and number, Univ. Nebr, 62; A psychological interpretation of Sir Gawain and the green knight, Criticism, spring 64; Game and earnest in the Middle English and Provencal love lyrics, Comp. Lit, summer 66; Scriptural exegesis and the literary critic, In: Typology and early American literature, Univ. Mass, 72. Add: Dept. of English, University of Kentucky, Lexington, KY 40506.

MANNING, SYLVIA P, b. Montreal, P.Q, Dec. 2, 43; m. 67. ENGLISH. B.A, McGill Univ, 63; Woodrow Wilson fels, Yale, 63, 66; M.A, 64; Ph.D, 67. Asst. prof. ENG, CALIF. STATE UNIV, HAYWARD, 68-71, ASSOC. PROF, 71- MLA. Publ: Dickens as satirist, Yale, 71. Add: 115 Parkside Dr, Berkeley, CA 94705.

MANSELL, DARREL LEE, JR, b. Canton, Ohio, Apr. 9, 34. ENGLISH LITERATURE. A.B, Oberlin Col, 56; Fulbright scholar, Oxford, 62-63; Ph.D. (Eng), Yale, 63. Instr. ENG. LIT, DARTMOUTH COL, 63-65, asst. prof, 65-68, ASSOC. PROF, 68- Dartmouth Col. fac. fel, 67-68. Literary theory. Publ: The novels of Jane Austen, Macmillan, London, 73; Ruskin and George Eliot's realism, Criticism, summer 65; George Eliot's conception of form, Stud. Eng. Lit, autumn 65; Seemers in Measure for measure, Mod. Lang. Quart, 9/66. Add: Dept. of English, Dartmouth College, Hanover, NH 03755.

MANSFIELD, LUTHER STEARNS, b. Arlington, Nebr, Apr. 25, 06. AMERICAN LITERATURE. A.B, Tex. Christian Univ, 27, fel, 27-28, A.M, 28; fel, Univ. Chicago, 32-33, Ph.D, 36. Head dept. ENG, Ill. Mil. Sch, 28-29; asst. prof, Jamestown Col, 29-36; instr, WILLIAMS COL, 36-39, asst. prof, 39-46, assoc. prof, 46-52, prof, 52-70, EMER. PROF. AM. HIST. & LIT, 71- Vis. prof, Swarthmore Col, 44-45; Nat. Univ. Buenos Aires, Argentina, 56; vis. lectr, Univ. Minn, Minneapolis, 64-65. MLA; Melville Soc.(pres, 47); Am. Stud. Asn; Emerson Soc. Herman Melville: Duyckinck literary circle in New York from 1840 to 1860; Henry Adams. Publ: Co-ed, Moby Dick, Hendricks House, 52 & Moby Dick centennial essays, South. Methodist Univ, 53; auth, Some patterns from Melville's loom of time, In: Essays on determinism in American literature, 64 & Melville and Hawthorne in the Berkshires, In: Melville Annual, 70, Kent State Univ; What's American about American literature, Descant, spring 67. Add: Stetson Ct, Williamstown, MA 01267.

MANSFIELD, MARGARET A, b. Baltimore, Md, Sept. 21, 39; m. 69. MEDIEVAL LITERATURE. B.A, Mt. St. Agnes Col, 60; M.A, Cath. Univ. Am, 63; Ph.D.(Eng), Cornell Univ, 68. Asst. dir. admis, Trinity Col.(D.C), 61-62; instr. ENG, Mt. St. Agnes Col, 62-65; asst. PROF, State Univ. N.Y. Col. Cortland, 68-69; BOSTON STATE COL, 69- MLA. Medieval English and European literature; 19th century American literature; teaching of writing skills. Publ: Dante and the Gorgon within, Italica, summer 70. Add: Dept. of English, Boston State College, Boston, MA 02115.

MAPP, ALF JOHNSON, JR, American History & Literature. See Volume I, History.

MARCETT, MILDRED ELIZABETH, b. Providence, R.I, Aug. 24, 06. ENGLISH. Ph.B, Brown Univ, 27; A.M, Bryn Mawr Col, 28; Ph.D, N.Y. Univ, 38. Asst. Eng, WASH. SQ. COL, N.Y. UNIV. 32-39, instr, 39-44, gen. lit, Sch. Commerce, Accounts & Finance, 44-45, asst. prof. GEN. LIT, 45-53, ASSOC. PROF, 53-, adv. women, 45-53. MLA; Col. Eng. Asn; NCTE. Great Western literature in translation; Mediaeval English literature. Publ: Uhtred de Boldon, Friar William Jordan and Piers Plowman, Banta, 38; co-auth, A complete guide to good English, Heath, 51; ed. & Introduction to The compact Homer, Barron, 63. Add: Dept. of English, Washington Square College of Arts & Science, New York University, Washington Square, New York, NY 10003.

MARCHAND, LESLIE ALEXIS, b. Bridgeport, Wash, Feb. 13, 00; m. 50. ENGLISH LITERATURE. A.B, Univ. Wash, 22, A.M, 23; Sorbonne, 27-28; Univ. Munich, 32; Ph.D, Columbia Univ, 40. Prof. Eng. & French, Alaska Agr. Col. & Sch. Mines, 23-37, 34-35; exten. instr. ENG, Columbia Univ, 28-34, lectr, Col. Pharmacy, 36-37; instr, RUTGERS UNIV, 37-42, asst. prof, 42-46, assoc. prof, 46-53, prof, 53-66, EMER. PROF, 66- Summer vis. prof, Univ. Calif. Los Angeles, 49; Univ. Ill, 54; Univ. Wash, 58; Fulbright prof. Am. life & civilization, Univ. Athens, Greece, 58-59; prof. lectr. Eng, Hunter Col, 60-62; Berg vis. prof, N.Y. Univ, 62-63; vis. prof, Ariz. State Univ, 66-67; Hofstra Univ, 67-68; Guggenheim fel, 68-69; Nat. Endowment for Humanities res. grant, 72-73. MLA; Keats-Shelley Asn. Am; PEN Club. Victorian and romantic literature; Byron. Publ: The Athenaeum; a mirror of Victorian culture, Univ. N.C, 41; ed, Letters of Thomas Hood, Rutgers Univ, 45; auth, Byron: a biography, (3 vols), 57 & Byron: a portrait, 70, Knopf; Byron's poetry: a critical introduction, Houghton, 65; ed, Complete letters and journals of Byron, Vols. I & II, John Murray & Harvard, 73. Add: 97 Lakeview Lane, Englewood, FL 33533.

MARCHANT, PETER L, b. London, Eng, May 14, 28; m. 61; c. 2. ENGLISH. B.A, Cambridge, 53, M.A, 56; Ph.D.(Eng), Univ. Iowa, 66. Lectr. ENG, Univ. B.C, 54-55; instr. Coe Col, 57-58; Pa. State Univ, 63-66, asst. prof, 66-68; STATE UNIV. N.Y. COL. BROCKPORT, 68-71, assoc. prof, 71-74, PROF, 74- Brit. Army, 47-49, Sgt. MLA. Fiction; the English novel; teaching English to the disadvantaged. Publ: Give me your answer, do, Michael Joseph, 60. Add: Dept. of English, State University of New York College at Brockport, Brockport, NY 14420.

MARCKWARDT, ALBERT HENRY, b. Grand Rapids, Mich, Dec. 1, 03. ENGLISH LANGUAGE. A.B, Univ. Mich, 25, A.M, 28, Ph.D, 32; hon. B.Litt, North. Mich. Univ, 73. Instr. Eng, Univ. Mich, 28-34, asst. prof, 34-39, assoc. prof, 39-46, prof, 46-63, dir, Eng. Lang. Inst, 60-63; prof. ENG. & LING, PRINCETON, 63-72, EMER. PROF, 72- Vis. lectr, Univ. Calif, Los Angeles, 39; dir, Eng. Lang. Inst, Mex, 43-45; Fulbright lectr, Univs. Vienna & Graz, Austria, 53-54; v.chmn. bd. dir, Am. Counc. Learned Soc, 61-64; chmn. adv. panel Eng. teaching, U.S. Inform. Agency, 61-; mem, res. adv. counc, U.S. Off. Educ, 63-67, bd. dir, Ctr. Applied Ling, 65-; vis. prof. Eng, Univ. Mich, Ann Arbor, 72- MLA; Ling. Soc. Am.(pres, 62); Am. Dialect Soc.(pres, 62-64); NCTE (pres, 67, David H. Russell Award, 70, Distinguished Serv. Award, 72); Am. Name Soc; Teachers Eng. Speakers Other Lang. History of the English language; American English; dialect geography. Publ: Introduction to the English language & American English, Oxford; Laurence Nowell's Vocabularium Saxonicum, Univ. Mich; co-auth, A common language, BBC & U.S. Govt, 64, Voice Am, 65; auth, Linguistics and the teaching of English, Ind. Univ, 66; ed, Linguistics in school programs, Nat. Soc. Stud. Educ, 70; co-auth, Old English: language and literature, Norton, 72. Add: 22 Harvard Pl, Ann Arbor, MI 48104.

MARCOTTE, PAUL, b. Quebec, P.Q, 29; m; c. 6. ENGLISH. B.A, St. John's Univ.(N.Y), 51, M.A, 53; Ph.D, Univ. Ottawa, 57. Asst. prof. ENG, UNIV. OTTAWA, 56-60, assoc. prof, 60-65, PROF, 65-, chmn. dept, 65-71. Literary criticism and Shakespeare. Publ: Notes towards an understanding of Aristotle's Poetics, 63 & The God within: essays in speculative literary criticism, 64, Runge, Ottawa; Priapus unbound: Shakespeare's concept of love inferred from six early works, Univ. Ottawa, 71; Quebec revisited and other poems, Hiamaska Press, 72; Pluralism and the Chicago Neo-Aristotelian, summer 63; Tradition and the individual talent: T.S. Eliot, spring 64 & On the intentional fallacy, summer 65, Inscape. Add: Dept. of English, University of Ottawa, Ottawa, Ont, Can.

MARCUS, FRED HAROLD, b. Brooklyn, N.Y, Oct. 17, 21; m. 48; c. 2. ENGLISH. B.A, Brooklyn Col, 42; M.A, N.Y. Univ, 47, Ph.D, 52. Instr. ENG, N.Y. Univ, 48-52; asst. prof, State Univ. N.Y. Col. Educ, Oneonta, 52-55; CALIF. STATE UNIV, LOS ANGELES, 55-58, assoc. prof, 58-63, PROF, 63- Summers, dir. inst. in composition, Univ. Kansas City & mem. Comn. on Eng. Planning Inst, Univ. Mich, 61; vis. prof, Victoria Col, Can, 61, 63 & Comn. on Eng. Prog, Univ. Calif, Los Angeles, 62; vis. prof, N.Y. Univ, 67; vis. prof. lit, Univ. Hawaii, summer 68. Sig.C, U.S.A, 43-46. NCTE. Teaching of composition and communication; training teachers of English and language arts; studies in the mass media. Publ: Co-auth, Ideas and issues, Ronald, 63 & Motion pictures and the teaching of English, Nat. Counc, 65; auth, Student, school and society, Chandler, 64; co-auth, Scope/reading 2, 65 & Language in your life 2, 66, Harper; auth, Perception and pleasure, Heath, 67; ed, Film and literature: contrasts in media, Intext, 71. Add: Dept. of English, California State University, Los Angeles, Los Angeles, CA 90032.

MARCUS, MITCHELL, b. Boston, Mass, Sept. 30, 17; m. 42; c. 2. ENGLISH. B.A, State Univ. Iowa, 40, M.A, 41; Ph.D, Stanford Univ, 50. Instr. ENG, Univ, Nebr, 46-47; Stanford Univ, 47-49; asst. prof, Univ. Calif, Los Angeles, 49-53; assoc. prof, Los Angeles State Col, 53-57; PROF, CALIF. STATE UNIV, NORTHRIDGE, 57- U.S.M.C.R, Maj. MLA; Soc. Tech. Writers & Publ. Literary criticism; technical publishing. Add: 12450 Deerbrook Lane, Los Angeles, CA 90049.

MARCUS, MORDECAI, b. Elizabeth, N.J, Jan. 18, 25; m. 55; c. 2. ENGLISH. B.A, Brooklyn Col, 49; M.A, N.Y. Univ, 50; Ph.D, Univ. Kans, 58. Asst, Rutgers Univ, 51-52; asst. instr, Univ. Kans, 52-53, instr, 53-58; ENG, Purdue Univ, 58-60, asst. prof, 60-65; UNIV. NEBR, LINCOLN, assoc. prof, 66-72, PROF, 72- MLA. Modern poetry; American literature since 1850; writing of poetry. Publ: Five minutes to noon (poems), Best Cellar, 71; What is an initiation story?, J. Aesthet. Art Criticism, winter 60; Walt Whitman and Emily Dickinson, Personalist, autumn, 62; Eugene O'Neill's debt to Thoreau in A touch of the poet, J. Eng. & Ger. Philol, 4/63. Add: Dept. of English, University of Nebraska-Lincoln, Lincoln, NE 68508.

MARCUS, PHILLIP L, b. Kansas City, Mo, Dec. 1, 41; m. 60; c. 3. ENGLISH. B.A, Univ. Mo, Kansas City, 63; Woodrow Wilson fel. & M.A, Harvard, 64, Woodrow Wilson fel & Ph.D.(Eng), 68. Asst. prof. ENG, CORNELL UNIV, 67-72, ASSOC. PROF, 72- MLA; Am. Comt. Irish Stud; Can. Asn. Irish Stud; Int. Asn. Stud. Anglo-Irish Lit. Irish literature; 20th century English literature. Publ: Yeats and the beginning of the Irish Renaissance; Cornell Univ, 70; Standish O'Grady, Bucknell Univ, 70; T.S. Eliot and and Shakespeare, Criticism, winter 67; George Moore's Dublin Epiphanies and Joyce, James Joyce Quart, winter 68; Myth and meaning in The death of Cuchulain, Irish Univ. Rev. autumn 72. Add: Dept. of English, Goldwin Smith Hall, Cornell University, Ithaca, NY 14850.

MARCUS, STEVEN, b. New York, N.Y, Dec. 13, 28; m. 50. ENGLISH. A.B, Columbia Univ, 48, A.M, 49, Ph.D, 61; scholar, Kenyon Sch. Lett, 49; Fulbright scholar, Pembroke Col, Cambridge, 52-54. Instr. ENG, Ind. Univ, 49-50; lectr, City Col. New York, 50-52; supvr, Cambridge, 53-54; instr, COLUMBIA UNIV, 56-61, asst. prof, 61-63, assoc. prof, 63-67, PROF, 67- Fel, Ind. Sch. Lett, 61; assoc. ed, Partisan Rev, 61-; Am. Counc. Learned Soc. grant, summer 66; Guggenheim fel, 67-68; vis. prof, Ctr. Victorian Stud, Univ. Leicester, 68; fel, Ctr. Advan. Stud. Behav. Sci, Stanford Univ, 72-73. U.S.A, 54-56. Nineteenth century English literature and culture. Publ: Dickens: from Pickwick to Dowbey, Basic Bks. & Chatto & Windus, 65; The other Victorians, Basic Bks. & Weidenfeld & Nicolson, 66. Add: Hamilton Hall, Columbia University, New York, NY 10027.

MARCUSE, MICHAEL JOSEPH, b. Ashland, Pa, Oct. 9, 44; m. 68. ENGLISH LANGUAGE & LITERATURE. B.A, Univ. Pittsburgh, 66; M.A. & Woodrow Wilson fel, Univ. Mich, 67, Rackham Prize fel, 69-70 & 70-71, Ph.D.(Eng), 71; Fulbright fel, Univ. Mainz, 67-68. ASST. PROF. ENG, Southeast. Mass. Univ, 71-72; CATH. UNIV. AM, 72- MLA; Am. Soc. 18th Century Stud; AAUP. Restoration and 18th century English literature; satire; English literary theory and literary criticism, 1660-1800. Add: Dept. of English, Catholic University of America, Washington, DC 20017.

MARCUSON, LEWIS R, b. Cleveland, Ohio, May 4, 29. DRAMA, ENGLISH. B.A, Antioch Col, 51; M.F.A, Yale, 54; Ph.D.(theatre), Univ. Denver, 66. Dir, Theatre St. Paul, Inc, 56-57; asst. prof. ENG. & THEATRE, WILMINGTON COL.(OHIO), 57-66, ASSOC. PROF, 66-, DIR. INSTNL. RES. & ASST. PROVOST, 72- U.S.A, 54-56, Sgt. Am. Theatre Asn. Dramatic literature; theatre history; stage direction. Add: Dept. of English, Wilmington College, Wilmington, OH 45177.

MARDER, DANIEL, b. Chicago, Ill, July 10, 23; m. 54; c. 3. AMERICAN LITERATURE, RHETORIC. B.A, Roosevelt Univ, 48; M.F.A, Univ. Iowa, 50; Ph.D.(Eng), Univ. Pittsburgh, 61. Sci. ed, W.L. Maxson Corp, 51-53; news ed, Spanish-American Courier, Madrid, 53-54; asst. prof. ENG, Univ. Pittsburgh, 56-61; assoc. prof, Pa. State Univ, 61-68; prof. & chmn. dept, Slippery Rock State Col, 68-70; PROF. & HEAD DEPT, UNIV. TULSA, 70- Correspondent, Time & Life, Madrid, 53-54; consult, Aberdeen Proving Ground, Md, 56-68; Fulbright prof, Univ. Skoplje, 66-67. Air Transport Command, U.S.A.A.F, 43-46. MLA; NCTE; AAAS; Nat. Asn. Sci. Writers. American literature; rhetoric and writing; science and human values. Publ: Craft of technical writing, Macmillan, 60; College English, Int. Col. Schs, 69; Hugh Henry Brackenridge, Twayne, 67; ed, Hugh Henry Brackenridge reader, Univ. Pittsburgh, 70; ed, Incidents of insurrection, Col. & Univ. Press, 72; auth, Szechwora variation, Accent, 55. Add: Dept. of English, University of Tulsa, 600 College St, Tulsa, OK 74104.

MARDER, HERBERT. ENGLISH. Ph.D.(Eng), Columbia Univ, 64. ASSOC. PROF. ENG, UNIV. ILL, URBANA, 65- Modern fiction; myth and literature; improvisation in contemporary poetry. Publ: Feminism and art: a study of Virginia Woolf, Univ. Chicago, 68; The revolutionary art of Isaac Babel, Novel: a Forum on Fiction, fall 73. Add: 100 English Bldg, University of Illinois, Urbana, IL 61801.

MARDER, LOUIS, b. New York, N.Y, Sept. 26, 15; m. 40; c. 2. ENGLISH. A.B, Brooklyn Col, 41; A.M, Columbia Univ, 47, Ph.D, 50. From instr. to lectr, ENG, Brooklyn Col, 46-53; chmn. dept, Pembroke State Col, 53-56; asst. prof, Kent State Univ, 56-60, assoc. prof, 60-65; PROF, UNIV. ILL, CHICAGO CIRCLE, 65- Ed. & publ, Shakespeare Newslett, 51-; res. fel, Folger Shakespeare Libr, Wash, D.C, summer 57; mem, ed. bd, The computer & the humanities, 67-68; chief consult, Library of Shakespeare Scholarship & Criticism, 67-; lectr, Ore. Shakespeare Festival Renaissance Inst, 68; vis. prof, Univ. Toledo, 68; mem, ed, bd, Computor Rev, 68-; consult, World Ctr. Shakespeare Stud, London, 72- U.S.A, 43-46. Col. Eng. Asn; MLA; Am. Theatre Asn; Am. Soc. Theatre Res; Shakespeare Asn. Am; Renaissance Soc. Am; Midwest Mod. Lang. Asn.(chmn. humanities sect, 72); Int. Shakespeare Asn. Shakespeare; English Renaissance; drama. Publ: His exits and his entrances: the story of Shakespeare's reputation, Lippincott, 63; ed, Study Master Shakespeare Series, Study Master, 64-; auth, Shakespeare scholarship, 20th century, In: Readers' encyclopedia of Shakespeare, Crowell, 66; An authenticated bust of Shakespeare, Notes & Queries, 4/67; plus many others. Add: Dept. of English, University of Illinois at Chicago Circle, Chicago, IL 60680.

MARDON, ERNEST GEORGE, b. Houston, Tex, Dec. 21, 28; Brit. citizen; m. 57; c. 3. ENGLISH LITERATURE, CANADIAN STUDIES. B.Ed, Univ. Alta, 61; M.A, Univ. Ottawa, 66, Ph.D.(Eng. lit), 67. Asst. prof. ENG, UNIV. LETHBRIDGE, 67-72; ASSOC. PROF, 72- Rep. Home & Sch. Fed, Alta. Govt. Rev. Sch. Act, 69-70; vis. prof. Eng, Univ. Calgary, summers, 70, 71, 74; treas, Confed. Alta Fac. Asns, 70-73; secy-treas, Can. Inst. Onomastic Sci, 73-74; exec. mem, Can. Conf. Scottish Stud, 73-74. Brit. Army, 51-53, Res, 53-55, Lt. Medieval English literature; origin and history of western Canadian place names; biographical sketches of Alberta politicians. Publ: The narrative unity of the Cursor Mundi, 70 & The conflict between the individual and society in the plays of James Bridie, 71, W. McLelland, Glasgow; Who's who in federal politics from Alberta, 72 & Community names of Alberta, 73, E.G. Mardon, Lethbridge; The history of place names in southern Alberta, Onomastica, 72. Add: Dept. of English, University of Lethbridge, 4401 University Dr, Lethbridge, Alta. T1K 3M4, Can.

MARESCA, THOMAS EDWARD, b. Jersey City, N.J, Feb. 5, 38. ENGLISH. B.A, St. Peter's Col, 59; M.A, Johns Hopkins Univ, 61, Ph.D.(Eng), 63. Asst. prof. ENG, Ohio State Univ, 63-68; ASSOC. PROF. STATE UNIV. N.Y. STONY BROOK, 68- Fel, humanities ctr, Johns Hopkins Univ, 67-68. MLA. Restoration and eighteenth-century English literature. Publ: Pope's Horatian poems, Ohio State Univ, 66. Add: Dept. of English, State University of New York at Stony Brook, Stony Brook, NY 11790.

MARGESON, JOHN MALCOLM RUSSELL, b. Trail, B.C, May 21, 20; m. 47; c. 3. ENGLISH. B.A, Univ. B.C, 42; fel, Univ. Col, Toronto, 46-48; M.A, Univ. Toronto, 47, Humanities Res. Counc. Can. res. fel, 49-50, Ph.D.(Eng), 52. Asst. prof, ENG, Acadia Univ, 48-50, assoc. prof. 50-53, prof, 53-56; dir. stud, Gonville & Caius Col, Cambrige, 56-59; vis. prof, Univ. Oslo, 60-61; lectr, Univ. Hull, 61-64; assoc. prof, SCARBOROUGH COL, UNIV. TORONTO, 64-66, PROF, 66- Royal Soc. Can. fel, 52-53; Bedford Col, Univ. London sr. res. fel, 55-56; Can. Counc. res. grant, 68-69. R.C.A.F, 42-46, Flying Off. Int. Asn. Univ. Prof. Eng. Sixteenth century humanism; English Renaissance drama; Canadian literature. Publ: The origins of English tragedy, Clarendon, 67; co-ed, Shakespeare 1971, Univ. Toronto, 72; auth, Franz Kafka: a critical problem, Univ. Toronto Quart, 10/48; English for scientists, Univs. Rev, 2/56; Practical criticism, Essays in Criticism, 7/60. Add: Dept. of English, Scarborough College, University Toronto, Toronto, Ont. M5S 1A1, Can.

MARGETTS, RALPH ELLIOT, b. Salt Lake City, Utah, Mar. 7, 09; m. 44; c. 2. SPEECH, THEATRE. B.A, Univ. Utah, 49, M.A, 50, Ph.D.(speech & theatre), 59. Teaching asst. theatre, Univ. Utah, 47-53, assoc. prof, 57-64; assoc. prof. & chmn. dept, Chico State Col, 53-57; campus coord. Mali Proj, South. Ill. Univ, 64-66; PROF. THEATRE, UNIV UTAH, 66-, assoc. chmn. dept, 66-74. U.S.N, 42-47. Theatre history; western history; theories of acting. Publ: Contrib, The business of show business, Harper, 61. Add: Dept. of Theatre, University of Utah, Salt Lake City, UT 84112.

MARGOLIES, ALAN, b. New York, N.Y, Oct. 12, 33. ENGLISH & AMERICAN LITERATURE. B.A, City Col. New York, 54; M.A, N.Y. Univ, 60, Ph.D. (Eng), 69. Lectr. ENG, Brooklyn Col, 61-68; City Col. New York, 69-70; ASST. PROF, JOHN JAY COL. CRIMINAL JUSTICE, 70- City Univ. New York fac. res. award, 71-74; Am. Counc. Learned Soc. grant-in-aid, 72. U.S.A, 54-56. MLA; Bibliog. Soc. Am; Am. Lit. Sect, MLA; NCTE; Am. Stud. Asn; Northeast Mod. Lang. Asn. American literature; bibliography; film. Publ: The editing and publication of The journal of Madam Knight, Papers Bibliog. Soc. Am, 64; F. Scott Fitzgerald's work in the film studios, Princeton Libr. Chronicle, winter 71; The Great Gatsby, The last tycoon, and the dramatic novel, Fitzgerald-Hemingway Annual, 71. Add: Dept. of English, John Jay College of Criminal Justice, 445 W. 59th St, New York, NY 10019.

MARGOLIES, EDWARD, b. Boston, Mass, Dec. 19, 25; m. 58; c. 3. AMERICAN CIVILIZATION & LITERATURE. B.A, Brown Univ, 50; M.A, N.Y. Univ, 59, Ph.D.(Am. civilization), 64. PROF. ENG, STATEN ISLAND COMMUNITY COL, N.Y, 59- Am. Counc. Learned Soc. fel, 65, U.S.A, 44-46. Am. Stud. Asn; MLA. Negro literature and culture; American studies. Publ: Native sons, 68 & ed, A Native sons reader, 70, Lippincott; auth, The art of Richard Wright, South. Ill. Univ, 69; Richard Wright, Bull. Bibliog; America's dark pessimism, Saturday Rev, 3/69; The image of the primitive in Black letters, Midcontinent Am. Stud. J, fall 70. Add: 141 E. Third St, New York, NY 10009.

MARGOLIS, JOHN DAVID, b. Pittsburgh, Pa, Sept. 16, 41. ENGLISH. A.B, Haverford Col, 63; Woodrow Wilson fel, 63-64; M.A, Princeton, 65, Ph.D. (Eng), 67; Theodore Whitefield Hunt fel, 65-66. Instr. ENG, Northwest. Univ, 66-68; asst. prof, Univ. Calif, Los Angeles, 68-69; NORTHWEST. UNIV, 69-71, ASSOC. PROF, 71- Soc. Relig. Higher Educ; MLA. Literary criticism; T.S. Eliot; 19th century literature. Publ: Ed, The campus in the modern world, Macmillan, 69; ed, W.H. Mallock, The new Paul and Virginia, Univ. Nebr, 70; auth, T.S. Eliot's intellectual development, 1922-1939, Univ. Chicago, 72; plus var. articles & rev. Add: Dept. of English, Northwestern University, Evanston, IL 60201.

MARIANI, JOHN FRANCIS, b. New York, N.Y, Aug. 27, 45. ENGLISH, FILM. B.A, Iona Col, 67; M.A, Columbia Univ, 68, Ph.D.(Eng), 73. INSTR. humanities, Katharine Gibbs Sch, 69-73; art, Bronx, N.Y, 68-69; ENG, MERCY COL, 73-; MARYMOUNT COL, 73-; FILM, COL. NEW ROCHELLE, 74- Nat. Proj. Ctr. for Film & Humanities acad. humanist, 73. MLA. Romantic literature; American cinema. Publ: The missing American hero, N.Y. Mag, 8/73; A man for all seasons and Joseph Schultz, Freedom & Responsibility, 74. Add: 294 Bronxville Rd, Bronxville, NY 10708.

MARIANI, PAUL LOUIS, b. New York, N.Y, Feb. 29, 40; m. 63; c. 3. MODERN POETRY & POETICS. B.A, Manhattan Col, 62; M.A, Colgate Univ, 64; univ. fel. & Ph.D.(Eng), City Univ. New York, 68. Lectr. ENG, Colgate Univ, 63; instr, John Jay Col, 66-67, asst. prof, 67-68; UNIV. MASS, AMHERST, 68-71, ASSOC. PROF, 71-, summer teaching fel, 70. Nat. Endowment for Humanities younger humanist fel, 73. MLA; Hopkins Soc. Twentieth century American poetry and poetics; Gerard Manley Hopkins; William Carlos Williams. Publ: A commentary on the complete poems of Gerard Manley Hopkins, Cornell Univ, 70; Towards the canonization of William Carlos Williams, autumn 72 & A Williams Garland: petals from the falls, 1945-1950, winter 73, Mass. Rev; The satyr's defense: Williams' Asphodel, Contemporary Lit, winter 73. Add: Dept. of English, University of Massachusetts, Amherst, MA 01002.

MARINELLI, PETER V, b. New York, N.Y, July 30, 33. ENGLISH. B.A, Fordham Univ, 55, M.A, 60; Ph.D.(Eng), Princeton, 64. ASSOC. PROF. ENG, UNIV. COL, UNIV. TORONTO, 63- Medieval period; English and Italian Renaissance. Publ: Pastoral, Methuen, 71; The Faerie Queene: book one, In: Studies of major works in English, Oxford, 68. Add: Dept. of English, University College, University of Toronto, Toronto, Ont. M5S 1A1, Can.

MARKELS, JULIAN, b. Chicago, Ill, June 24, 25; m. 63; c. 3. ENGLISH. B.S, Univ. Chicago, 48; M.A, Univ. Minn, 52, Ph.D.(Eng), 57. Instr. ENG, Univ. Minn, 52-56; OHIO STATE UNIV, 56-60, asst. prof, 60-63, assoc. prof, 63-67, PROF, 67- Elizabeth Clay Howald fel, 65-66. U.S.A, 43-46, Sgt. MLA; Am. Stud. Asn. Shakespeare; American literature; American cultural history. Publ: The pillar of the world: Antony and Cleopatra in Shakespeare's development, Ohio State Univ, 68; Dreiser and the plotting of inarticulate experience, spring 61 & King Lear and Moby Dick: the cultural connection, winter 68, Mass. Rev; Shakespeare's confluence of tragedy and comedy, spring 64, Shakespeare Quart; plus others. Add: Dept. of English, Ohio State University, Columbus, OH 43210.

MARKEN, JACK WALTER, b. Akron, Ohio, Feb. 11, 22; m. 46; c. 3. ENGLISH. B.A, Univ. Akron, 47; M.A, Ind. Univ, 50, Ph.D.(Eng), 53; Fulbright fel, Univ. London, 51-52. Instr, Univ. Ky, 52-54; asst. prof. Eng. & humanities, Ohio Wesleyan Univ, 54-55; Cent. Mich. Univ, 55-60; prof. ENG, Slippery Rock State Col, 60-67; PROF. & HEAD DEPT, S.DAK. STATE UNIV, 67- Am. Philos. Soc. grant, 59, res. grants, 65, 67; Fulbright lectr, Univ. Jordan, 65-66; U.S. Inform. Serv-Finnish-Am. Soc. lectr. Am. Indian lit, Finland, 70. U.S.A.A.F, 43-45. MLA; Charles Lamb Soc; NCTE. The late 18th century; literature of the American Indian. Publ: Bibliography of books by and about the American Indian in print in 1972, Dakota Press, 73; Joseph Bevan and William Godwin, Ga. Hist. Quart; Introd, Imogen: a pastoral romance (reprint from 1784 ed), N.Y. Pub. Libr, 63; co-auth, Introd, William Godwin's Uncollected writings, 1785-1822, Scholars' Facsimiles, 68. Add: 319 20th Ave, Brookings, SD 57006.

MARKER, FREDERICK JOSEPH, b. Medford, Mass, Oct. 28, 36; m. 59. ENGLISH LITERATURE, COMPARATIVE DRAMA. A.B, Harvard, 58; Fulbright fel, Univ. Copenhagen, 59; fel, Salzburg Sem. Am. Stud, 59; D.F.A. (drama), Yale, 67. Asst. prof. ENG, UNIV. COL, UNIV. TORONTO, 67-70, ASSOC. PROF, 70-, acad. secy, Grad. Ctr. Stud. Drama, 71-72, dir. tech. training, 72-73. Can. Counc. res. grants, 70, 71, 72, leave fel, 74-75; publ. grant, Humanities Res. Counc. Can, 71 & Nordisk Kulturfond, 74; managing ed, Mod. Drama, 72- Int. Fed. Theatre Res; Am. Soc. Theatre Res; MLA; Soc. Advan. Scand. Stud. Nineteenth century Scandinavian and English theatre; comparative modern drama; Shakespearean production in England and America. Publ: Transl, Johannes Allen's Tumult, Chatto & Windus, London, 69; auth, Hans Christian Andersen and the Romantic Theatre, Univ.

Toronto, 71; ed. & transl, The Heibergs, Twayne, 71; co-auth, Contemporary approaches to Ibsen, Universitetsforlaget, Oslo, 71, The Scandinavian theatre, a short history, Basil Blackwell, Oxford, 74 & Revels history of drama in English, VI (1750-1880), Methuen, London, 74; auth, Negation in the blond kingdom, the theatre criticism of Edvard Brandes, ETJ, 68; The first night of Charles Kean's The tempest, Theatre Notebook, 70; Fru Heiberg as Lady Macbeth, Scandinavica, 73. Add: Dept. of English, University College, University of Toronto, Toronto, Ont. M5S 2E1, Can.

MARKER, LISE-LONE, b. Aalborg, Denmark; m. 59. THEATRICAL HISTORY, DRAMA. Scand-Am. Found. scholar, Vassar Col, 53-54; Mag. artium, Univ. Copenhagen, 61, fel, 62-65; Ph.D.(hist. of theatre), Yale, 68. Librn, Theatre Collection, Danish Royal Theatre, Copenhagen, 55-61; asst. prof. THEATRE HIST, Inst. Theatre Res, Univ. Copenhagen, 61-66; GRAD. CTR. STUD. DRAMA, UNIV. TORONTO, 68-71, ASSOC. PROF, 71- Lectr. theatre hist, Teaterdirektorforeningens Skuespillerskole, Copenhagen, 57-65; Folkeuniversitet, 58-60; consult. arch. comt. bd. gov, Stratford Shakespeare Festival, Ont, 71-73; Can. Counc. res. grants, 71, 72, 73, leave fel, 74-75; assoc. ed, Mod. Drama, 72- & Scand. Stud, 73- Int. Fed. Theatre Res.(nat. del, 73); Am. Soc. Theatre Res; MLA. Nineteenth century English and American theatre; history and aesthetics of acting; Scandinavian theatre and drama. Publ: David Belasco: naturalism in the American theatre, Princeton Univ, 74; co-auth, The Scandinavian theatre, a short history, Basil Blackwell, Oxford, 74 & Revels history of drama in English, VI (1750-1880), Methuen, London, 74; auth, Nature and decorum in the theory of Elizabethan acting, In: The Elizabethan theatre, Macmillan, Toronto, Vol. II, 70; The first Nora: notes on the world premiere of A doll's house, In: Contemporary approaches to Ibsen, Universitetsforlaget, Oslo, 71; Fru Heiberg: a study of the art of the romantic actor, Theatre Res, 73. Add: Graduate Ctr. for Study of Drama, Massey College, University of Toronto, Toronto, Ont. M5S 2E1, Can.

MARKERT, LOUISE, b. Garrison, N.Dak, Apr. 15, 18. ENGLISH. B.A, Univ. Wash, 45 & 50; Columbia Univ, 60; Seattle Univ, 61-62. Teacher, SEATTLE PUB. SCHS, 45-55, curriculum consult, 55-59, asst. Eng. lang. arts, 59-70, ENG. SPECIALIST, 70- Mem, Comn. Eng. curriculum, NCTE, 63-66, mem. elem. sect, 64-67; mem. staff NDEA Eng. Inst, Univ. Wash, 65; field evaluator, NDEA Inst. prog. proposals Eng, U.S. Off. Educ, 67. NCTE; Int. Reading Asn; Asn. Childhood Educ. Int; NEA. Literature; composition; humanities. Publ: Co-auth, Along story trails, 62, auth, Manual for teaching Along story trails, 63 & Poetry keepsake, 64, Ginn; Children, culture, and community, Packet, 59; Curriculum developments in the language arts, Grade Teacher, 64; Literature in the kindergarten, Wash. State Dept. Pub. Instr, 71. Add: Administrative & Service Center, Seattle Public Schools, 815 Fourth Ave. N, Seattle, WA 98109.

MARKGRAF, BRUCE RICHARD, b. La Crosse, Wis, Feb. 17, 35. SPEECH COMMUNICATION, PLAYWRITING. Wis. fel. & B.A, Univ. Wis-Madison, 56, M.S, 57, State of Wis. Univ. scholar, 58, Ph.D.(speech, drama), 60. Teaching assoc. speech, Univ. Wis-Madison, 58-59; asst. prof. Eng. & speech, Wesleyan Univ, 59-66; PROF. SPEECH COMMUN. & CHMN. DEPT, DENISON UNIV, 66- Speech Commun. Asn. Interpersonal communication; dramatic criticism; film criticism. Publ: John Cage: ideas and practices of a contemporary speaker, Quart J. Speech, 4/62; contrib, Readings in listening, 66; auth, The passing of Francis Scott Key, Drama Rev, 9/70. Add: Dept. of Speech Communication, Denison University, Granville, OH 43023.

MARKGRAF, CARL, b. Portland, Ore, July 18, 28; m. 52; c. 7. ENGLISH LITERATURE, THEATRE ARTS. A.B, Univ. Portland, 51, M.A, 54, Ph.D.(Eng), 70; NDEA fel, Univ. Calif, Riverside, 63-66. Teacher, Eng. & chmn. dept, Hood River County Sch. Univ, Ore, 54-57; from instr. to asst. prof. drama, & head dept, Marylhurst Col, 57-63; from asst. prof. to ASSOC. PROF. ENG, PORTLAND STATE UNIV, 66-, asst. head dept, 72-73, acting head, 73-74. Consult, Phillips, Coughlin, Buell & Phillips, Attys-at-Law, 68. Eng.C, U.S.N.R, 46-49; U.S.A.R, 56-64, 1st Lt. AAUP. Victorian literary criticism; Victorian bibliography; Medieval and Renaissance drama. Publ: Ed, Problems in usage, State of Ore, 69; Oscar Wilde's anonymous criticism: an annotated edition, Xerox, 70; An annotated bibliography of writings about John Addington Symonds, Eng. Lit. Transition, 73; Co-auth, Making the point: challenge and response, Intext, 74. Add: Dept. of English, Portland State University, Portland, OR 97207.

MARKHAM, DAVID H, b. Stigler, Okla, Dec. 26, 36; m. 64; c. 3. SPEECH, BEHAVIORAL SCIENCE. B.S, Univ. Wis, 59; B.A, Northeast. State Col, 60; M.A, Univ. Okla, 62, Ph.D.(speech), 64. Asst. prof. speech, North. Ill. Univ, 62-66; speech & commun, SAN JOSE STATE UNIV, 66-67, tutorials, 67-69, ASSOC. PROF. SPEECH-COMMUN. & CYBERNET. SYSTS, 69- Consult. cybernet, Peerless Pomp, Los Angeles, 66-67. Cent. States Speech Asn; Speech Commun. Asn; West. Speech Commun. Asn. Source credibility of mass media sources; computer optimization and simulation; experimental higher education. Publ: A case history of subscription television: Bartlesville, Oklahoma, Cent. States Speech J, 11/63; Dimensions of source credibility of television newscasters, J. Commun, 4/68; Federal censorship of national open forum radio, In: Free speech yearbook: 1971, Speech Commun. Asn, 72; plus one other. Add: Dept. of Speech-Communication, San Jose State University, 125 N. Seventh St, San Jose, CA 95192.

MARKLAND, BEN CLIFFORD, b. Champaign, Ill, Nov. 14, 12; m. 38; c. 2. SPEECH, JOURNALISM. B.A, Univ. Ariz, 47; M.A, Northwest. Univ, 51; Ph.D, Univ. Mich, 55. Reporter & radio writer, Chicago Tribune & WGN, Chicago, Ill, 35-46; dir. radio-TV bur. & lectr. speech & jour, Univ. Ariz, 46-65; assoc. prof. speech & dir. educ. media, S.DAK. STATE UNIV, 66-70, PROF. SPEECH & JOUR, 70- Speech Commun. Asn; Am. Acad. Polit. & Soc. Sci. Radio and TV audience analysis. Add: Dept. of Speech, South Dakota State University, Brookings, SD 57006.

MARKLAND, MURRAY FAULDS, b. Decatur, Ill, Feb. 9, 21; m. 48; c. 2. ENGLISH. B.A, Univ. Mich, 43, M.A, 48; Ph.D, Univ. Calif, Los Angeles, 57. Instr. ENG, Wash. State Univ, 50-57, asst. prof, 57-62, assoc. prof, 62-67; PROF, CALIF. STATE UNIV, CHICO, 67-, head dept, 67-68. U.S.M.C.R, 42-45, Capt. MLA; Philol. Asn. Pac. Coast; Mediaeval Acad. Am. Late English Middle Ages. Publ: Humor and pathos in English mystery plays, Theater Annual, 70; The ending of Troilus and Criseyde, Mod. Lang. Quart, 70; The task set by valor, Costerus Essays in Eng. & Am. Lang. & Lit, 72; plus others. Add: Dept. of English, California State University, Chico, Chico, CA 95926.

MARKLE, JOYCE BONNERS, b. Chicago, Ill, Nov. 3, 42; wid; c. 2. MODERN AMERICAN LITERATURE. A.B, Marquette Univ, 64, M.A, 66; Ph.D.(Eng), Univ. Wis-Madison, 71. Instr. ENG, Marquette Univ, 65-66; Nat. teaching fel. & instr, Edgewood Col, 69-70; ASST. PROF, LOYOLA UNIV. CHICAGO, 70- MLA; Popular Cult. Asn; Midwest Mod. Lang. Asn; Rocky Mt. Mod. Lang. Asn. John Updike, American novelist; contemporary American novels. Publ: Fighters and lovers: theme in the novels of John Updike, N.Y. Univ, 73. Add: Dept. of English, Loyola University of Chicago, 6525 Sheridan Rd, Chicago, IL 60626.

MARKMAN, ROBERTA HOFFMAN, b. Toronto, Ont, Feb. 27, 25; m. 62; c. 2. ENGLISH, COMPARATIVE LITERATURE. B.A, Hunter Col, 45; M.A, Columbia Univ, 61; Ph.D.(comp. lit), Occidental Col, 69. Instr. Eng, Univ. Tex, El Paso, 55-62; assoc. prof, Pasadena City Col, 62-68; COMP. LIT, CALIF. STATE UNIV, LONG BEACH, 68-74, PROF, 74- William Faulkner as tragedian, Thomas Mann, especially Joseph und seine Brüder; the 19th century continental novel. Publ: Co-auth, 10 steps in writing the research paper, Barron's Educ. Ser, 65. Add: Dept. of English, California State University, Long Beach, 6101 E. Seventh St, Long Beach, CA 90840.

MARKOS, DONALD W, b. La Crosse, Wis, July 1, 33; m. 57; c. 4. AMERICAN LITERATURE. B.S, Wis. State Univ, La Crosse, 59; M.S, Mankato State Col, 60; Ph.D, Univ. Ill, 66. Teacher, high sch, 58-59; pub. schs, Iowa, 60-61; ASST. PROF. ENG, CALIF. STATE UNIV, HAYWARD, 66- U.S.A, 54-56. Nineteenth and 20th century American literature. Add: Dept. of English, California State University, Hayward, 25800 Hillary St, Hayward, CA 94542.

MARKS, ALFRED HARDING, b. Farmingdale, N.Y, July 18, 20; m. 42; c. 3. ENGLISH. Ph.D, Syracuse Univ, 53. Instr. ENG, Syracuse Univ, 49-53; Ohio State Univ, 53-56; assoc. prof, Ball State Teachers Col, 56-63, PROF, STATE UNIV. N.Y. COL. NEW PALTZ, 63- Fulbright sr. lectr, Kanazawa Univ, Japan, 65-66; vis. prof. Am. lit, Univ. Hawaii, Honolulu, 73-74; ed, Literature East & West. A.U.S, 42-46, 1st Lt. MLA; Japan Soc; Haiku Soc. Am. Hawthorne, Whitman; romantic irony; Japanese language and literature. Publ: Transl, Yukio Mishima's Forbidden colors, Knopf, 68; auth, Hawthorne's daguerreotypist: scientist, artist, reformer, Ball State Teachers Col. Forum; Whitman's triadic imagery, Am. Lit; Who killed Judge Pyncheon? PMLA. Add: Dept. of English, State University of New York College at New Paltz, New Paltz, NY 12561.

MARKS, BARRY ALAN, b. New York, N.Y, Feb. 1, 26; m. 48; c. 3. ENGLISH, AMERICAN CIVILIZATION. A.B, Dartmouth Col, 48; M.A, Univ. Minn, 49, Ph.D.(Am. civilization), 57; hon. A.M, Brown Univ, 63. Instr. gen. stud, Univ. Minn, 49-53; great issues & govt, Dartmouth Col, 53-54; Eng. & Am. civilization, Brown Univ, 55-58, asst. prof, 58-63, assoc. prof, 63-68; PROF. ENG. & CHMN. DEPT, AMERICAN UNIV, 68- Fulbright lectr, Univ. Lille, France, 63-64. U.S.M.C, 43-46. NCTE; Am. Stud. Asn; New Eng. Asn. Am. Stud.(pres, 61-62). American literature; American intellectual history. Publ: Mark Twain's Huckleberry Finn, Heath, 59; E.E. Cummings: poet of nowhere, Twayne U.S. Auth. Ser, 63. Add: Dept. of English, The American University, Washington, DC 20016.

MARKS, EMERSON ROBERT, b. New York, N.Y, Oct. 13, 18; m. 43; c. 2. ENGLISH. A.B, City Col. New York, 40; A.M, State Univ. Iowa, 42; Ph.D.(Eng), N.Y. Univ, 53. Instr. ENG, Newark Col, Rutgers Univ, 46-50, asst. prof, 50-56; lectr, South. Ill. Univ, 56-57; asst. prof, Wayne State Univ, 57-60, assoc. prof, 60-64, PROF, 64-69; UNIV. MASS, BOSTON, 69- Ed, Criticism, 62-68; Fulbright lectr. Am. lit, Univ. Montpellier, 64-65; vis. prof, Harvard Univ, summer 72. U.S.A, 42-46, Lt. Am. Comp. Lit. Asn; MLA; Am. Soc. Aesthet. History and theory of literary criticism; literary aesthetics. Publ: Relativist and absolutist: the early neoclassical debate in England; The poetics of reason: English neoclassical criticism, Random, 68; ed. & transl, Literary criticism of Sainte-Beuve, Univ. Nebr, 71; Poe as literary theorist: a reappraisal, Am. Lit, 11/61; plus others. Add: Dept. of English, College II, University of Massachusetts, Boston, MA 02125.

MARKS, SAMUEL MILTON, b. Chicago, Ill, Oct. 9, 17; m. 41; c. 1. SPEECH. B.S.M.E, Purdue Univ, 39, M.S, 41; Ph.D.(speech), Univ. Wis, 55. Instr. SPEECH & THEATRE, PURDUE UNIV, WEST LAFAYETTE, 41-42, 45-50, asst. prof, 50-55, assoc. prof, 56-59, PROF, 59-, ASST. TO ADMIN. DEAN FOR DEVELOP. REGIONAL CAMPUS ADMIN, 66-, asst. to dean sch. technol, 64-66. Theater consult. to archits, Walter Scholer & Assoc, 55; Hafner, Hafner & Stranckmeyer, 62 & Boyd Phelps, Inc, 62. U.S.A, 42-45, Maj. Speech Commun. Asn; Am. Theatre Asn. Theatre architecture, especially trends and buildings; space development for academic excellence; laboratory design. Publ: Settings by Joseph Urban; Industrial survey—201, Regional Campus Admin, Purdue Univ, 7/65. Add: 124 Seneca Lane, West Lafayette, IN 47906.

MARKS, SITA PATRICIA, b. New York, N.Y, Aug. 16, 43; m. 68. ENGLISH & AMERICAN LITERATURE. B.A, Douglass Col, 65; NDEA fel. & Ph.D.(Eng), Mich. State Univ, 70. Instr. ENG, VALDOSTA STATE COL, 71-72, ASST. PROF, 72- MLA; AAUP; Am. Asn. Univ. Women. Nineteenth century American literature; the Victorian novel; the short story. Publ: The sound and the silence: non-verbal patterns in The wings of the dove, Ariz. Quart, summer 71. Add: Dept. of English, Valdosta State College, Valdosta, GA 31601.

MARKS, WILLIAM S, III, b. Long Branch, N.J, Aug. 4, 33; m. 61; c. 2. ENGLISH. B.A, Rutgers Univ, 55; Ph.D.(Eng), Stanford Univ, 64. Asst. prof. ENG, UNIV. CALIF, SANTA BARBARA, 62-71, ASSOC. PROF, 71- U.S.A.R, 55-65, 1st Lt. MLA; Philol. Asn. Pac. Coast. Modern British and American literature. Publ: The psychology of the uncanny in Lawrence's The rocking horse winner, Mod. Fiction Stud, winter 65; Advertisements for Grace: Flannery O'Connor's A good man is hard to find, Stud. Short Fiction, fall 66; D.H. Lawrence and his rabbit Adolph: three symbolic permutations, Criticism, summer 68. Add: Dept. of English, University of California, Santa Barbara, CA 93106.

MARKUS, THOMAS BENJAMIN, b. Evanston, Ill, Oct. 28, 34; div; c. 1. THEATER. B.A, Pomona Col, 56; M.F.A, Tulane Univ, 58, Ph.D.(theater), 62. Asst. prof. dramatic art, Univ. Calif, Santa Barbara, 62-69; ASSOC. PROF. THEATER, Queens Col, 69-71; City Univ. New York, 70-71; TEMPLE UNIV, 71- Assoc. producer, Utah Shakespearean Festival, 64-67; Roundabout Theatre, N.Y.C, 70; pres, Am. Repertory Theatre of Phoenix & Santa Barbara, 66-67; ed, Callboard, 66-67; ed, Bks. in Print, Educ. Theatre J, 72-74. U.S.A, 58-60. Am. Theatre Asn; Univ. & Col. Theatre Asn. Modern French theater; Elizabethan theater production. Publ: Contrib, Miscellaneous contemporary dramatists, St. James, 73; auth, The theatre of the perverse, Educ. Theatre J, 62; contrib, The psychological universe of Jean Genet, In: The theatre of Jean Genet, Grove, 71 & Essays of Beaumarchais, Dramatic Criticism, 74. Add: Dept. of Theater, Temple University, Philadelphia, PA 19122.

MARKWARD, WILLIAM B, b. Kansas City, Mo. ENGLISH. A.B, Park Col, 30; A.M, Colo. State Col, 38; summers, Stanford Univ, 39 & 40; dipl. phonetics, Univ. Grenoble, 50; Ph.D.(Eng), Univ. Birmingham, 53. Teacher, high sch, Nebr, 30-35; Colo, 35-41; Kemper Mil Sch, Mo, 41-42; instr. Eng, UN UNIV. COLO, BOULDER, 45-50, PROF. ENG. & COMP. LIT, 53- Guest lectr, Alverno Col, autumn 67. Teaching Recognition Award, Univ. Colo, 70; Robert L. Stearns Award for Distinguished Serv, 71. Sig. Intel, U.S.A, 42-45, S/Sgt. Am. Soc. Theatre Res. Renaissance English literature; comparative literature; oral interpretation. Publ: Christopher Beeston, and the Phoenix Theatre, 1617-1638, Univ. Colo. Stud, 8/63. Add: Hellems 124, University of Colorado, Boulder, CO 80302.

MARLER, ROBERT FRANKLIN, JR, b. Winston-Salem, N.C, Apr. 18, 32; m. 59; c. 2. AMERICAN & ENGLISH LITERATURE. B.S.E, Princeton, 54; M.A, George Washington Univ, 61, Ph.D.(Am. lit), 70. Mech. engr, Shell Oil Co, 54-55, 57-58; H.D. Nottingham & Assocs, 58-61; instr. ENG, George Washington Univ, 63-66; TEMPLE UNIV, 66-70, asst. prof, 70-73, ASSOC. PROF, 74-, DIR. AM. STUD. PROG, 72- Consult, Nat. Am. Stud. Fac, 73- U.S.A, 55-57. MLA; Am. Stud. Asn; AAUP. American short fiction; 19th century American literature; American novel. Publ: Anne Charlotte Lynch Botta, In: Notable American women, Belknap, 70; Bartleby, the Scrivener and the American short story, Genre, 12/73. Add: Dept. of English, Temple University, Philadelphia, PA 19122.

MARLIN, CHARLES LOWELL, b. Naylor, Mo, Apr. 4, 36. SPEECH. B.S.Ed, Univ. Mo, 58; M.A, Ind. Univ, 61, Ph.D.(rhetoric, pub. address), 67. Teacher pub. schs, Mo, 58-60; assoc, Ind. Univ, 60-61 & 64-65; instr. Iowa State Univ, 61-64; ASSOC. PROF. RHETORIC & PUB. ADDRESS, CLARION STATE COL, 66- Speech Commun. Asn; Speech Commun. Asn. East States. Publ: Eisenhower before the press, Today's Speech, 61; Jemina Wilkinson: Errant Quaker divine, Quaker Hist, 63. Add: Dept. of Speech, Clarion State College, Clarion, PA 16214.

MARLOR, CLARK STRANG, b. Nov. 18, 22. SPEECH. B.F.A, Carnegie Inst. Technol, 41, scholar & M.A, 46; Columbia Univ, 51-53; Ed.D, N.Y. Univ, 61. Instr. speech & drama, Kalamazoo Col, 46-47; Miami Univ, 47-50; tutor speech, Queens Col.(N.Y), 50-56; asst. prof. SPEECH & DRAMATIC ART, ADELPHI UNIV, 56-62; ASSOC. PROF, 62- Speech Commun. Asn; Am. Theatre Asn; Speech Asn. East. States. Speech; drama; play directing. Publ: Co-auth, Bibliography of speech and allied areas, Chilton, 62. Add: Dept. of Speech & Dramatic Art, Adelphi University, Garden City, NY 11530.

MARLOW, JAMES ELLIOTT, b. Belle Rive, Ill, Feb. 14, 38; m. 65; c. 2. ENGLISH LITERATURE. B.A, Dartmouth Col, 60; M.A, Univ. Calif, Davis, 68, Ph.D.(Eng), 72. ASST. PROF. ENG, Col. William & Mary, 69-73, SOUTHEAST. MASS. UNIV, 73- Nat. Endowment for Humanities summer grant, 73. Sig.C, U.S.A, 60-62. MLA; Dickens Soc; Victorian Inst. Novels of Charles Dickens; theory of the novel; contemporary literature. Publ: Dickens and Carlyle's Way, Victorians Inst. J, 72; Hamlet: the acts that a man might play, Shakespeare Quart, 74; The solecism in Our mutual friend, Dickens Soc. Newslett, 3/74. Add: Dept. of English, Southeastern Massachusetts University, North Dartmouth, MA 02747.

MARNELL, WILLIAM H, b. Boston, Mass, May 22, 07; m. 58. ENGLISH. A.B, Boston Col, 27; A.M, Harvard, 29, Ph.D.(Eng), 38. Master classics, Boston Latin Sch, 28-50; prof. Eng, BOSTON STATE COL, 50-70, EMER. PROF. ENG, 70- Col. Eng. Asn; Am. Class. League. Religious history; development of philosophical thought. Publ: The first amendment, 64 & Man-made morals, 66, Doubleday; The good life of Western man & Once upon a store, Herder & Herder, 71; The right to know, Seabury, 73. Add: 7 Cutter Lane, West Yarmouth, MA 02673.

MAROLDO, WILLIAM JOHN, b. New York, N.Y, Apr. 16, 23; m. 48; c. 2. ENGLISH, PHILOSOPHY. A.B, Hofstra Univ, 48; A.M, Univ. Colo, 49; M.P.A, N.Y. Univ, 58; Ph.D.(Eng. & comp. lit), Columbia Univ, 64. Instr. Eng, Univ. Md, 53-55; asst. prof. world polit. geog, N.Y. Univ, 55-58; Eng. & philos, U.S. Air Force Acad, 60-64; instr. Eng, Univ. Md, 64-66; intel. staff off, HQ, Air Training Command, Randolph Air Force Base, Tex, 66-70; ASSOC. PROF. ENG. & COMP. LIT, TEX. LUTHERAN COL, 70- Lectr. Eng, Univ. Colo, Colorado Springs Ctr, 61-64; Gasthörer fel, Univ. Mainz, 65-66. U.S.A.F, 43-45, 51-70, Lt. Col. MLA; Am. Philos. Asn; Am. Comt. Irish Stud. Modern American and European drama and literature; medieval and Renaissance studies; comparative linguistics. Add: 1733 Rosewood Dr, Seguin, TX 78155.

MAROTTA, JOSEPH GERALD, b. New York, N.Y, Sept. 14, 42; m. 65; c. 2. MEDIEVAL ENGLISH LITERATURE, HISTORY OF RHETORIC. B.A, Manhattan Col, 64; M.A, Brooklyn Col, 65; Oxford, summer 69; Ph.D.(Eng), City Univ. N.Y, 72. Instr. ENG, ST. JOHN'S UNIV.(N.Y), 68-72, ASST. PROF, 72- AAUP; MLA; Richard III Soc. Medieval rhetorical theory; the poetry of Geoffrey Chaucer and John Lydgate; modern poetry. Add: Dept. of English & Communication Arts, St. John's University, Grand Central & Utopia Pkwys, Jamaica, NY 11432.

MAROTTI, ARTHUR FRANCIS, b. New York, N.Y, Apr. 3, 40; m. 64; c. 1. ENGLISH. A.B, Fordham Univ, 61; Woodrow Wilson fel, Johns Hopkins Univ, 61-62, univ. fels, 62-65, Ph.D.(Eng), 65. Asst. prof. ENG, Wash. Univ, 65-70, summer fac. fels, 66 & 68; ASSOC. PROF. WAYNE STATE UNIV, 70-, fac. res. grant, summer 73. Fel, Humanities Ctr, Johns Hopkins Univ, 70-71. MLA; Midwest Mod. Lang. Asn; Renaissance Soc. Am. Sixteenth and 17th century poetry and drama; John Donne's poetry; Ben Jonson's works. Publ: Fertility and comic form in A chaste maid in Cheapside, Comp. Drama, 69; The self-reflexive art of Ben Jonson's Sejanus, Tex. Stud. Lit. & Lang, 70; All about Jonson's poetry, ELH, 72. Add: Dept. of English, Wayne State University, Detroit, MI 48202.

MAROVITZ, SANFORD E, b. Chicago, Ill, May 10, 33; m. 64. ENGLISH. B.A, Lake Forest Col, 60; Woodrow Wilson fel. & M.A, Duke Univ, 61, univ. scholar. & Ph.D.(Eng), 67. Instr. ENG, Temple Univ, 63-65; Fulbright lectr Univ. Athens, Greece, 65-67; asst. prof, KENT STATE UNIV, 67-70, ASSOC. PROF, 70-, chmn. grad. stud, 72-74. U.S.A.F, 53-57, S/Sgt. MLA; Am. Stud. Asn; Melville Soc. Am; John Steinbeck Soc. Am. Nineteenth century American literature; American frontier and Western fiction; the work of Aldous Huxley. Publ: Roderick Hudson: James' Marble faun, Tex. Stud, winter 70; Howells and the ghetto: the mystery of misery, Mod. Fiction Stud, autumn 70; Aldous Huxley and the visual arts, Papers on Lang. & Lit, spring 73; plus others. Add: Dept. of English, Kent State University, Kent, OH 44242.

MARRE, K. E. DEBOO, b. Ahmedabad, India, Mar. 28, 39; m. 68. NINETEENTH & TWENTIETH CENTURY LITERATURE. B.A, Univ. Bombay, 58, M.A, 60; Bryn Mawr Col, 60-61; fel. & Ph.D.(Eng), State Univ. N.Y. Buffalo, 66. Asst. prof. ENG, UNIV. DAYTON, 66-72, ASSOC. PROF, 72- MLA. James Joyce; 20th century British and American poetry, especially Wallace Stevens; William Blake. Add: Dept. of English, University of Dayton, Dayton, OH 45409.

MARRINER, ERNEST CUMMINGS, b. Bridgton, Maine, Oct. 16, 91; m. 17; c. 2. ENGLISH LINGUISTICS. A.B, Colby Col, 13, L.H.D, 53; hon. L.H.D, Univ. Maine, 57. Head dept. Eng, Hebron Acad, Maine, 13-21, prin, 20-21; Maine rep, Ginn & Co, 21-23; librn, Colby Col, 23-29, prof. Eng, 29-60, dean men, 29-47, dean fac, 47-57; RETIRED. Pres, New Eng. Col. Entrance Cert. Bd, 38-45; mem. Col. Entrance Exam. Bd; State Bd. Educ, 49-72, chmn, 56-58; pres. of trustees, Thomas Col, Maine, 58-; consult, Keyes Fibre Co, 62; mem, State Arch. Bd, 66-, chmn, 66-68; trustee, Maine League Hist. Soc, 68- Acad. dean, U.S.A.A.F, 42-45. Am. Dialect Soc; Am. Asn. Acad. Deans; Am. Asn. State & Local Hist.(Award of Merit, 66). Administration in higher education; public education; Maine social history, including weekly radio programs since 1948. Publ: Kennebec yesterdays, 54, Remembered Maine, 57, History of Colby College, 62 & Man of Mayflower Hill, 67. Add: 17 Winter St, Waterville, ME 04901.

MARRONEY, PETER RAY, b. Pueblo, Colo, June 29, 13. DRAMA. B.F.A, Univ. Okla, 36; M.A, State Univ. Iowa, 39. Tech. supvr, Ore. Fed. Theatre, 37; tech. dir, UNIV. ARIZ, 39-41, from assoc. prof. to PROF. DRAMATICS, 41-, HEAD DEPT. DRAMATIC ARTS, 41- Founder, Ariz. Corral Theatre, Tucson; mem, Ariz. Comn. Arts & Humanities; mem. President's adv. comt, John F. Kennedy Ctr. Performing Arts. Outstanding Fac. Mem. Award, Univ. Ariz, 65-66; Tucson Trade Bur. Fac. Recognition Award, 66. Am. Theatre Asn. Add: Dept. of Drama, University of Arizona, Tucson, AZ 85721.

MARRS, EDWIN WILSON, JR, b. Harrisburg, Pa, Oct. 21, 28; m. 49; c. 3. ENGLISH. A.B, Syracuse Univ, 59, M.A, 61, Ph.D, 66; fel, Duke Univ, 63-64. Instr. ENG, Colgate Univ, 65-66, asst. prof, 66-67; UNIV. PITTSBURGH, 67-69, assoc. prof, 69-72, PROF, 72- Nat. Found. Arts & Humanities summer stipend award, 68; external Ph.D. examr, Univ. Edinburgh, 70; Univ. Pittsburgh Ctr. Int. Stud. res. award, 70; Guggenheim fel, 72-73. U.S.N, 51-54. Nineteenth-century British literature; letters of Charles and Mary Anne Lamb. Publ: The letters of Thomas Carlyle to his brother Alexander, with related family letters, Harvard, 68; Reminiscences of a visit with Carlyle in 1878 by his nephew and namesake, Thoth, spring 67; Carlyle, Bernardin de Saint-Pierre, and Madame Cottin, Victorian Newslett, spring 68; Some account of the publishing history of the Lambs' letters, with notes on a new edition in progress, Charles Lamb Bull, 4/74; plus others. Add: Dept. of English, University of Pittsburgh, Pittsburgh, PA 15213.

MARSDEN, MALCOLM MORSE, b. Plymouth, Mass, Nov. 6, 22; m. 48; c. 2. AMERICAN LITERATURE. B.A, Yale, 43; M.A, Harvard, 47; Ph.D, Syracuse Univ, 51. Instr. ENG, Syracuse Univ, 46-51; asst. prof, S.Dak. State Col, 51-55; from assoc. prof. to PROF, ELMIRA COL, 55- Study grant, Col. Ctr. Finger Lakes, 63-64. U.S.A, 43-45. MLA. Nineteenth century American taste in literature. Publ: If you really want to know: a catcher casebook, Scott, 63; Love as threat in Katherine Anne Porter's work, Twentieth Century Lit, 4/67. Add: Dept. of English, Elmira College, Elmira, NY 14901.

MARSH, DWIGHT CHANEY, b. Hall Co, Nebr, Oct. 2, 32; m. 55; c. 4. ENGLISH. B.A, Hastings Col, 54; M.A, Univ. Nebr, 56, Ph.D.(Eng), 68. Asst. prof. ENG, Nebr. Wesleyan Univ, 58-62; instr, Univ. Nebr, 62-65; asst. prof, HASTINGS COL, 66-68, ASSOC. PROF, 68- Conf. Col. Compos. & Commun; NCTE. Renaissance poets; modern rhetoric. Publ: Above heroic: a theological explication of Paradise regained as anti-epic, Univ. Microfilms, 68; A rationale for composition, Nebr. Eng. Counr, fall 71. Add: Dept. of English, Hastings College, Hastings, NE 68901.

MARSH, FLORENCE GERTRUDE, b. Rochester, N.Y, Sept. 15, 16. ENGLISH. B.A, Mt. Holyoke Col, 37; M.A, Columbia Univ, 39; M.A, Univ. Tenn, 43; univ. fel. & Jr. Sterling fel, Yale, Ph.D.(Eng), 51. Instr. ENG, West. Col. Women, 43-45; Mt. Holyoke Col, 48-49; CASE WEST. RESERVE UNIV, 50-51, asst. prof, 51-60, assoc. prof, 60-66, PROF, 66-, chmn. dept, 72-74. Ford Found. Award, 54-55. MLA; NCTE; Am. Soc. Aesthet. Romantic poets; Wordsworth and Coleridge. Publ: Wordsworth's imagery, Yale Stud. Eng; Wordsworth's Ode: obstinate questionings, Stud. Romanticism, 66. Add: Clark Hall, Case Western Reserve University, Cleveland, OH 44106.

MARSH, JOHN L, b. Morristown, N.J, Nov. 3, 27; m. 60; c. 1. AMERICAN LITERATURE. A.B, Syracuse Univ, 50; A.M, Univ. Pa, 53, Ph.D, 59. Instr. ENG, Univ. S.C, 55-57; master, Manlius Sch, N.Y, 57-60; assoc. prof, EDINBORO STATE COL, 60-66, PROF, 66- Mil. Intel, U.S.A.R, Lt. Col. Am. Stud. Asn. Nineteenth century American theatre. Publ: Co-auth, English literature, a televised approach, 65 & American literature, a televised approach, 66, W.C. Brown; ed, A student's bibliography of American literature, Kendall/Hunt, 71; auth, Of prescriptions and playbills: from the diaries of Michael V. Ball, M.D, 1884-86, Northwest. Pa. Hist. Stud, 73. Add: Dept. of English, Edinboro State College, Edinboro, PA 16412.

MARSH, PATRICK OTIS, b. Cordell, Okla, Mar. 14, 28; m. 53; c. 3. RHETORIC & PUBLIC ADDRESS. B.S, Ore. State Col, 52; Ford Found. scholar, Reed Col, summer 53; M.A, Univ. Wash, 56, Ph.D, 61. Instr. Eng. & speech, Benson Polytech. Sch, Portland, Ore, 52-54; asst. speech, Univ. Wash, 54-56, acting instr, 56-59; instr, Univ. Wyo, 59-62, asst. prof, 63-65; assoc. prof, Portland State Univ, 65-70; PROF. COMMUN. STUD, CALIF. STATE UNIV, SACRAMENTO, 70-, chmn. dept, 70-72. U.S.A, 46-48; U.S.A.F.R, 52-, Capt. Speech Commun. Asn; Am. Forensic Asn; West. Speech Commun. Asn. Communication theory and research; argumentation; rhetorical heritage. Publ: Persuasive speaking: theory—models—practice, Harper, 67; Is debate merely a game for conservative players?, 10/64, Terminological tangle, 1/65 & The terminal tangle, 5/65, Speaker & Gavel. Add: Dept. of Communication Studies, California State University, Sacramento, Sacramento, CA 95819.

MARSH, ROBERT HARRISON, b. San Diego, Calif, Sept. 17, 26; m. 53; c. 2. ENGLISH LITERATURE. A.B, San Diego State Col, 50; M.S. Univ. Ore, 51; Ph.D.(philos), Johns Hopkins Univ, 55. Instr. ENG, State Univ. N.Y. Teachers Col, Albany, 53-55; Harpur Col, 55-56, asst. prof, 56-59; Univ. Calif, Santa Barbara, 59-61; assoc. prof, State Univ. N.Y. Stony Brook, 61-66; PROF, UNIV. CHICAGO, 66- U.S.A.A.F, 45-47. MLA. History of literary criticism; history of ideas; aesthetics. Publ: Four dialectical theories of poetry, Univ. Chicago, 65; The fallacy of universal intention, 5/58 & Akenside and Addison: the problem of ideational dept, 8/61, Mod. Philol; Historical interpretation and the history of criticism, In: Literary criticism and historical understanding, Columbia Univ, 67; plus others. Add: Dept. of English, University of Chicago, 1050, E. 59th St, Chicago, IL 60637.

MARSH, THAD NORTON, b. Wichita, Kans, Aug. 25, 26; m. 55; c. 2. ENGLISH. A.B, Univ. Kans, 48; Rhodes scholar, Oxford, 49-51, 52-54, B.A, 51, M.A, 55, B.Litt, 57. Instr. Eng, Univ. Kans, 48-49; Kans. State Col, 51-52; asst. prof, Rice Univ, 54-62, asst. to the pres, 59-61; prof. Eng. & dean col, Muhlenberg Col, 62-66; Centenary Col. La, 66-73; LECTR. ENG. & PROVOST, UNIV. OF THE SOUTH, 73- Mem. nat. selection bd, Harbison Award Distinguished Teaching, 64-67. U.S.A, 45-46. MLA. History of travel; English literature of the 16th century. Publ: The heritage of freedom, Harper, 62; Anglo-American relations before 1580, Rice Inst. Pamphlet; An unpublished Hakluyt manuscript?, New Eng. Quart, 6/62. Add: Office of the Provost, University of the South, Sewanee, TN 37375.

MARSHALL, CARL LEROY, b. Dayton, Ohio, Aug. 23, 14; m. 36; c. 4. AMERICAN LITERATURE. B.S.Ed, Wilberforce Univ, 35; M.A, Ohio State Univ, 47, Ph.D.(Eng), 54. Asst. prof. ENG, Ark. AM&N Col, 47-51, prof, 54-55, chmn. dept, 47-55; prof, South. Univ, Baton Rouge, 55-69, chmn. dept, 62-69; PROF, OHIO STATE UNIV, 69- NDEA prof, Eng. Inst, South. Univ, summer 66. U.S.A, 41-46, 1st Lt. MLA; NCTE; Col. Lang. Asn; AAUP. Nineteenth century American literature; black literature. Publ: American critical attitudes toward the fiction of W.D. Howells, Col. Lang. Asn. J, autumn 55; Eliot's Sweeney erect, South. Univ. Bull, fall 56. Add: Dept. of English, Ohio State University, 164 W. 17th Ave, Columbus, OH 43210.

MARSHALL, DAVID FRANKLIN, English Linguistics. See Volume III, Foreign Languages, Linguistics & Philology.

MARSHALL, DONALD GLENN, b. Long Beach, Calif, Sept. 9, 43. ENGLISH. A.B, Harvard, 65; M.Phil, Yale, 69, Ph.D.(Eng), 71. ASST. PROF. ENG, UNIV. CALIF, LOS ANGELES, 69- Nat. Endowment for Humanities younger humanist fel, 73-74; Soc. Relig. Higher Educ; Am. Soc. Eighteenth Century Stud; MLA. Critical theory; modern narrative; poetic style from Milton to Wordsworth. Add: Dept. of English, University of California, Los Angeles, CA 90024.

MARSHALL, GEOFFREY, b. Lancaster, Pa, Feb. 6, 38; m. 61; c. 2. ENGLISH. B.A, Franklin & Marshall Col, 59; M.A, Rice Univ, 61, Ph.D.(Eng), 65. Asst. prof. ENG, UNIV. OKLA, 64-68, ASSOC. PROF, 68-, DIR. HONORS PROG, 70- Univ. Okla. Alumni Develop. Fund grant, 65; Couch Scholars Award, 66; Danforth assoc, 68- MLA; Am. Civil Liberties Union; Nat. Col. Honors Counc; NCTE. English tragedy, 1660-1800; English Restoration drama; John Dryden. Publ: Restoration serious drama, Univ. Okla, 74; Taking the Beatles seriously, J. Popular Cult, summer 69; The coherence of The orphan, Tex. Stud. in Lit. & Lang, summer 69; Comic worlds within worlds, Col. Eng, 1/71. Add: Dept. of English, University of Oklahoma, 760 Van Vleet Oval, Norman, OK 73069.

MARSHALL, GEORGE OCTAVIUS, JR, b. Americus, Ga, Feb. 27, 22; m. 56, 67. ENGLISH. A.B.J, Univ. Ga, 42, M.A, 51; Ph.D.(Eng), Univ. Tex, 55. Teaching fel, ENG, Univ. Tex, 53-54, instr, 54-55; UNIV. GA, 55-56, asst. prof, 56-61, assoc. prof, 61-66, PROF, 66- U.S.A, 43-45. Alfred Tennyson; Victorian literature. Publ: A Tennyson handbook, Twayne, 63. Add: 402 Riverview Rd, Athens, GA 30601.

MARSHALL, JAMES MORSE, b. Cleveland, Ohio, June 19, 24; m. 60. ENGLISH & AMERICAN LITERATURE. B.A, Denison Univ, 49; M.A, State Univ. Iowa, 52; fel, Syracuse Univ, 54-61, Ph.D, 61. Instr. ENG, Iowa State Col, 52-54; asst. prof, Wash. & Jefferson Col, 61-65; ASSOC. PROF, UNIV. R.I, 65-, summer fel, 64. Med.C, U.S.A, 43-46, Sgt. MLA. American literature and culture; 17th and 19th century English literature. Publ: The heroic adventure in A winter walk (Thoreau), Emerson Soc. Quart, 69. Add: Dept. of English, University of Rhode Island, Kingston, RI 02898.

MARSHALL, KENNETH B, b. Blackwood, N.J, Nov. 28, 22; m. 48; c. 3. ENGLISH. A.B, Univ. Mich, 47, M.A, 48, Ph.D.(Eng), 55; Univ. Edinburgh, 48-49. Instr. ENG, DENISON UNIV, 53-56, asst. prof, 56-59, assoc. prof, 59-63, PROF, 63-, CHMN. DEPT, 65- Consult, Alderson-Broaddus, W.Va, 66-; mem. future proj. comt, Asn. Depts. Eng, 68- Qm.C, U.S.A, 43-46. MLA; NCTE. Add: Dept. of English, Denison University, Granville, OH 43023.

MARSHALL, MADELEINE FORELL, b. New York, N.Y, Dec. 18, 46; m. 66; c. 2. COMPARATIVE LITERATURE. B.A, St. Olaf Col, 66; Univ. Iowa, 63-66; Univ. Hamburg, 66-67; univ. fel, univ. scholar, dissertation fel. & Ph.D. (comp. lit), N.Y. Univ, 73. ASST. PROF. ENG, UNIV. P.R, MAYAGUEZ, 73- MLA; Am. Comp. Lit. Asn. Eighteenth century sentimental drama in England, France and Germany; nature of the sentimental response; women in 18th century literature. Publ: Sentimental drama in England, France and Germany: a fresh view of the rational choice and moral conduct components, as reinforced by the theory and practice of natural acting in the eighteenth century, Univ. Microfilm, 73; assoc. ed. & contrib, The Mary Wollstonecraft newsletter, Vol. II, 73-74. Add: Dept. of English, University of Puerto Rico, Mayaguez, PR 00708.

MARSHALL, MARY HATCH, b. Scarborough, N.Y, May 21, 03. ENGLISH LITERATURE. A.B, Vassar Col, 24, Sutro fel, 26-27, Alumnae fel, 30-31; A.M, Yale, 28, Mitchell fel, 31-32, Ph.D, 32; hon. D.Litt, Colby Col, 73. Teacher Eng, Baldwin Sch, Bryn Mawr, Pa, 24-26; instr, Rockford Col, 27-29; Mont. State Col, 32-33; teacher, Hathaway-Brown Sch, Cleveland, Ohio, 33-35; instr. & asst. prof. ENG, Colby Col, 35-39, assoc. prof, 39-48; prof, SYRACUSE UNIV, 48-, Peck Prof. Eng. lit, 52-70, dir. honors prog, Col. Lib. Arts, 65-67; EMER. PROF, 70- Guggenheim fel. & hon. res. fel, Yale, 45-47; vis. prof, Barnard Col, Columbia Univ, summer 44; Bowling Green State Univ, summer 60; Conn. Col, 61-62; Colby Col, 71; Syracuse Univ, 72-74; mem, Nat. Humanities Fac, 69-70. MLA; Mediaeval Acad. Am; Renaissance Soc. Am; Mod. Humanities Res. Asn. Mediaeval drama; Shakespeare and Elizabethan drama; Spenser. Publ: Theatre in the middle ages: evidence from dictionaries and glosses, Symposium; Boethius, definition of persona and mediaeval understanding of the Roman theater, Speculum; Aesthetic values of the liturgical drama, Eng. Inst. Essays. Add: 520 Euclid Ave, Syracuse, NY 13210.

MARSHALL, ROBERT KOSSUTH, b. Mt. Airy, N.C, Oct. 31, 02. ENGLISH. A.B, Guilford Col, 25; A.M, Haverford Col, 26; Harvard; Univ. N.C; Northwest. Univ; Iowa State Col. Head dept. dramatics & speech, Guilford Col, 37-39; asst. prof. ENG, OHIO WESLEYAN UNIV, 39-49, assoc. prof, 49-56, prof, 56-69, EMER. PROF, 69- Ohioanna Medal, 49. MLA; Guild Am. Auth; Eng-Speaking Union (mem. nat. bd, 50-67); NEA; Soc. Authors, London. Novels. Publ: Little squire Jim; Julia Gwynn. Add: Dept. of English, Ohio Wesleyan University, Delaware, OH 43015.

MARSHALL, RODERICK, b. Altoona, Pa, Mar. 29, 03; m. 29, 54; c. 2. ENGLISH & COMPARATIVE LITERATURE. A.B, Columbia Univ, 23, M.A, 24, univ. traveling fel, 28-29, Ph.D.(comp. lit), 34. Instr. Eng, Barnard Col, Columbia Univ, 24-38, Columbia Col, 44-47; asst. prof. Eng. & comp. lit, BROOKLYN COL, 47-52, assoc. prof, 52-60, prof. ENG, 60-70, EMER. PROF, 70- Fel, Folger Shakespeare Libr, 55; Fulbright prof. Am. lit, India, 57-59; pres, The Tagore Soc, New York, 62-64. MLA; Am. Folklore Soc; Col. Eng. Asn; Asiatic Soc. Bengal. Anglo-Italian literary relationships; Indo-European folklore as it helps to explain English and European literature; Jungian psychology as it helps to explain the persistence of mythic and folkloristic personages and patterns in literature. Publ: Italy in English literature, Columbia Univ; Falstaff in the light of world myth and folklore, Asia Publishing House; Passage to more than India, Punjab Univ, 63. Add: Conant Rd, Lincoln, MA 01773.

MARSHALL, THOMAS FREDERIC, b. Waterbury, Conn, June 3, 08; m. 37. ENGLISH. A.B, Temple Univ, 31; A.M, Univ. Pa, 32, Ph.D, 41. Teacher, pub. schs, Pa. & Del, 32-36; prof, Valley Forge Mil. Acad. & Jr. Col, 36-43; Am. lit, West. Md. Col, 43-55; prof. ENG, KENT STATE UNIV, 55-72, head dept, 55-62, EMER. PROF, 72- Fulbright prof, Athens, 53-54; Fulbright-Hays vis. prof. Am. stud, Nat. Univ. Mex, 62, 63. MLA; Mod. Humanities Res. Asn; Am. Soc. Theatre Res.(pres, 70-73); Int. Fed. Theatre Res; Am. Stud. Asn. American studies; bibliography; American drama and theater. Publ: A history of the Philadelphia Theater, 1878-1890; Literature and society, 1955-60, a selective bibliography, Miami Univ, 62; An analytical index to American literature, 1929-1959, Duke Univ, 63; Charles W. Witham: scenic artist, In: Anatomy of an illusion, 69. Add: Skyfield, Emory Rd, Upperco, MD 21155.

MARTIA, DOMINIC FRANCIS, b. Canton, Ohio, May 9, 35; m. 54; c. 2. ENGLISH. B.A, Roosevelt Univ, 62; Woodrow Wilson fel. & M.A, Univ. Chicago, 63; Ph.D.(Eng), Loyola Univ. Chicago, 71. Instr. ENG, Univ. Ill, Chicago, 63-65; ROOSEVELT UNIV, 65-68, asst. prof, 68-72, ASSOC. PROF, 72-, ASST. TO PRES, 72- Eighteenth century British literature; teaching of English; administration of higher education. Publ: A response to Grade beans not themes, Eng. Educ, 10/70; Beyond schoolmarmism: the English teacher's responsibility to his language, Xerox Eng. Exchange, fall 73. Add: Office of the President, Roosevelt University, 430 S. Michigan, Chicago, IL 60605.

MARTIN, BRUCE KIRK, b. Jersey City, N.J, May 28, 41; m. 65; c. 1. ENGLISH & AMERICAN LITERATURE. A.B, Univ. Cincinnati, 63, M.A, 66, Ph.D.(Eng), 67. Asst. prof. ENG, DRAKE UNIV, 67-73, ASSOC. PROF, 73- MLA. Victorian literature; the novel; literary theory. Publ: Rescue and marriage in Adam Bede, Stud. Eng. Lit, 72; The dual structure of Silas Marner, Tex. Stud. Lit. & Lang, 72; Whatever happened to Eustacia Vye?, Stud. Novel, 73. Add: Dept. of English, Drake University, Des Moines, IA 50311.

MARTIN, CARTER WILLIAMS, b. Clover, S.C, Jan. 13, 33; m. 55; c. 2. ENGLISH, AMERICAN LITERATURE. A.B, Presby. Col.(S.C), 55; M.A, Vanderbilt Univ, 58, Ph.D.(Eng), 67. Instr. Eng, N.C. State Univ, 58-63, asst. prof, 63-64; UNIV. ALA, HUNTSVILLE, 64-68, assoc. prof, 68-71, PROF. AM. LIT, 71- Soc. Stud. South. Lit; MLA; NCTE. American literature; contemporary Southern fiction. Publ: The true country: themes in the fiction of Flannery O'Connor, Vanderbilt Univ, 69. Add: 2602 Scenic Dr, Huntsville, AL 35801.

MARTIN, CECILIA CUTTS, b. New Boston, Ill, Oct. 15, 03; m. 45; c. 1. ENGLISH, LANGUAGE ARTS. A.B, Univ. Wash, 23, A.M, 25, Ph.D, 38. Teacher Eng, Latin & Spanish, LaCrosse High Sch, Wash, 25-26; instr. French & Spanish, Gooding Col, 26-27; secy. dept. Romantic lang, Univ. Wash, 30-38; head dept. Eng. & lang, Wenatchee Jr. Col, 39-43; Univ.

Alaska, 43-45; assoc. prof. LANG. ARTS, GEORGE FOX COL, 57-61, prof. & chmn. div, 61-73, EMER. PROF, 73- MLA. Ancient Greek language and literature; ancient East; mediaeval English and French. Add: 1004 N. College St, Newberg, OR 97132.

MARTIN, CHARLES BASIL, b. Pittsburg, Kans, Aug. 9, 30; m. 61; c. 3. ENGLISH LITERATURE. B.A, Univ. N.Mex, 52; M.A, Univ. Fla, 54; Ph.D, Univ. Mo, 59. Instr. ENG, Univ. Mo, 54-59; assoc. prof, E.Cent. State Col, 59-64; N.TEX. STATE UNIV, 64-70, PROF, 70- Fulbright lectr. Eng. as for. lang, Univ. Seville, 67-68. MLA; NCTE. Linguistics; old and middle English language and literature; folklore. Publ: Co-auth, The English language: yesterday and today, Allyn & Bacon, 73; The English teacher's five-foot shelf, Okla. Eng. Bull, fall 64; auth, Shakespeare in paperback: a checklist, Bull. Bibliog, 7-9/71; Semana Santa in Seville, Publ. Tex. Folklore Soc, 72. Add: Dept. of English, North Texas State University, Denton, TX 76203.

MARTIN, DEXTER, b. New York, N.Y, Aug. 10, 15; m. 46; c. 3. ENGLISH. B.A, Dartmouth Col, 49; M.A, Univ. Pa, 51. Asst. instr. ENG, Univ. Pa, 52-56; instr, Princeton, 56-57; Univ. R.I, 57-58; Univ. Ala, 58-60; asst. prof, Madison Col.(Va), 60-61; assoc. prof, Calif. State Col.(Pa), 61-66; Frostburg State Col, 66-67; ASST. PROF, S.DAK. STATE UNIV, 67- Ed, D.H. Lawrence News & Notes. U.S.A, 43-44. MLA. American literature; D.H. Lawrence; J.D. Salinger. Publ: Contrib. to N.Y. Times; Sat. Rev; Am. Scholar. Add: Dept. of English, South Dakota State University, Brookings, SD 57006.

MARTIN, EDWARD ALEXANDER, b. New York, N.Y, June 12, 27; m. 57; c. 4. ENGLISH & AMERICAN LITERATURE. A.B, Princeton, 50; M.A, Columbia Univ, 52, Ph.D.(Eng), 62. Lectr. ENG, Hunter Col, 59-60; instr, MIDDLEBURY COL, 61-63, asst. prof, 63-67, ASSOC. PROF, 67- Asst. dir, Bread Loaf Writers' Conf, 64, Admin. dir, 72. U.S.N, 45-46; U.S.A, 52-54. MLA; Col. Eng. Asn; Eng. Inst. American literature; Chaucer. Publ: The ordeal of H.L. Mencken, S.Atlantic Quart, summer 62; H.L. Mencken's poetry, Tex. Stud. Lit. & Lang, autumn 64; Whitman's A Boston ballad (1854), Walt Whitman Rev, 9/65. Add: Dept. of English, Middlebury College, Middlebury, VT 05753.

MARTIN, HAROLD C, b. Raymond, Pa, Jan. 12, 17; m. 39; c. 4. ENGLISH, COMPARATIVE LITERATURE. A.B, Hartwick Col, 37, LL.D, 65; Columbia Univ, 41; M.A, Univ. Mich, 41; Ph.D, Harvard, 54; hon. Litt.D, Elmira Col, 66, Concord Col, 68, St. Bernardine Siena Col, 68; hon. L.H.D, Trinity Col. (Conn), 70. Teacher high schs, N.Y, 37-48; dir. gen. educ, Harvard, 51-65, lectr. comp. lit, 54-65; pres, Union Col. & chancellor, Union Univ, 65-74; PRES, AM. ACAD. ROME, ITALY, 74- Secy, Eng. Inst, 58-63; chmn, Mass. comt, Fulbright Found, 58-64; chmn. comn. Eng, Col. Entrance Exam. Bd, 60-63; mem. comn. lib. learning, Asn. Am. Cols, 69-72; chmn. regent's regional counc, Regents of State Univ. N.Y, 71- U.S.N, 44-46. MLA; NCTE; Am. Comp. Lit. Asn. Prose style in American literature; English, French and German romantic literature; critical theory. Publ: Co-auth, Inquiry and expression, 58, rev. ed, 63 & Logic and rhetoric of exposition, 58, rev. ed, 63, Holt; ed, Style in prose fiction, Columbia Univ, 60. Add: Office of the President, American Academy in Rome, Rome, Italy.

MARTIN, HOWARD HASTINGS, b. Madison, Wis, Nov. 19, 25; m. 47; c. 2. SPEECH. B.S, Northwest. Univ. 45, M.A, 48, Ph.D.(speech), 55. Instr. SPEECH, Allegheny Col, 49-52, asst. prof, 52-55, assoc. prof, 55-56; asst. prof, Pomona Col, 56-58, ASSOC. PROF, 58-64; UNIV. MICH, ANN ARBOR, 64- U.S.N.R, 43-46, Lt.(jg). Speech Commun. Asn.(chmn. contemporary pub. address comt, 68). American colonial rhetoric; style and language; contemporary public address. Publ: Co-auth, Speech communication: analysis and readings, Allyn & Bacon, 68; co-auth, Communication and consensus, Harcourt, 72; auth, Style in the golden age, 12/57, The Fourth of July oration, 12/58 & Puritan preachers on preaching, 10/64; Quart. J. Speech. Add: Dept. of Speech, University of Michigan, Ann Arbor, MI 48104.

MARTIN, HOWARD S, b. Cincinnati, Ohio, May 6, 25; m. 48. SPEECH. B.A, Olivet Col, 49; M.A, Univ. Wis, 54, Ph.D, 58. Teacher, high sch, Hesperia, Mich, 53-54; asst. prof. radio, speech & TV, Univ. Nebr, 58-62; RADIO & TV, Sacramento State Col, 62-65; assoc. prof, CALIF. STATE UNIV, LONG BEACH, 65-74, PROF, 74-, chmn. dept, 68-71. U.S.A, 43-46. Speech Commun. Asn; Nat. Asn. Educ. Broadcasters; Asn. Prof. Broadcast Educ; West. Educ. Soc. Telecommun. Broadcast education; radio station operation; broadcast audiences. Publ: Minority programming, 4-5/72 & How 10 watt stations function, 10/72, J. Col. Radio; Some changes in TV production courses, Today's Speech, spring 72; plus others. Add: Dept. of Radio & Television, California State University, Long Beach, Long Beach, CA 90801.

MARTIN, JAY H, b. Newark, N.J, Oct. 30, 35; m. 56; c. 3. ENGLISH, AMERICAN STUDIES. A.B, Columbia Col, 56; M.A, Ohio State Univ, 57, univ. fel, 59-60, Ph.D, 60. Instr. Eng, Pa. State Univ, 57-58; from instr. to assoc. prof. Eng. & Am. stud, Yale, 60-68; PROF. ENG. & COMP. LIT, UNIV. CALIF, IRVINE, 68-, DIR. EDUC. ABROAD, 71-, dir. prog. comp, cult, 68-71. Fel, Silliman Col, Yale, 61-; Yale fac. club lectr, 63, Morse fel, 63-64; Am. Philos. Soc. grant, 66; Guggenheim fel, 66-67. Eng. Inst; MLA; Auth. Guild. Biography; literary history; American literature. Publ: Conrad Aiken: a life of his art, Princeton, 62; Harvests of change: American literature, 1865-1914, 67, ed, A collection of critical essays on The waste land, 68 & ed, Twentieth century views of Nathanael West, 71, Prentice-Hall; auth, Nathanael West: the art of his life, Farrar, 70; ed, A singer in the dawn: reinterpretations of Paul Laurence Dunbar, 74 & The Dunbar reader, 74, Dodd; auth, Ambrose Bierce, In: Comic imagination in America, Rutgers Univ, 73. Add: Dept. of English & Comparative Literature, University of California, Irvine, CA 92664.

MARTIN, JO ANN, b. Indianapolis, Ind, Oct. 29, 19. ENGLISH LITERATURE. A.B, Earlham Col, 41; Friends' Col. scholar, Bryn Mawr Col, 41-42; M.A, Northwest. Univ, 49; Ph.D.(Eng. & humanities), Stanford Univ, 63. Teacher, High Sch, Ind, 42-43; mem. staff, dean's off, Col. Arts & Sci, Cornell Univ, 46-48; instr. Eng, Earlham Col, 50-54; Eng. & humanities, Stanford Univ, 55-57; ENG, San Jose State Col, 58-61, asst. prof, 61-65, assoc. prof, 65-70; acting chmn. dept, West. Col, Miami Univ, 70-71; ASSOC. PROF, MANCHESTER COL, 71- W.A.V.E.S, 43-46, Lt.(jg). MLA. Pre-Shakespearean drama; Renaissance literature. Add: Dept. of English, Manchester College, North Manchester, IN 46962.

MARTIN, JOHN SAYRE, b. Eng, Nov. 24, 21; U.S. citizen; m. 53; c. 3. ENGLISH. A.B, Univ. Calif, Berkeley, 43, M.A, 48, Ph.D.(Eng), 58. Lectr. ENG, Univ. Calif, Berkeley, 55-56; instr, Univ. Ill, Urbana, 57-62; asst. prof, Hiram Col, 62-65; ASSOC. PROF, UNIV. CALGARY, 65- Dir. pre-freshman stud, Dillard Univ, summer 61. U.S.N, 43-46, 50-52, Lt. MLA; Philol. Asn. Pac. Coast; Asn. Can. Univ. Teachers Eng. Nineteenth and twentieth century literature. Publ: Mrs. Moore and the Marabar Caves, Mod. Fiction Stud, winter 65-66; Peter Bayley and the lyrical ballads, Eng. Stud, 12/67; Wordsworth's echoes, Eng. Lang. Notes, 3/68. Add: Dept. of English, University of Calgary, Calgary, Alta, T2N 1N4, Can.

MARTIN, JOHN STEPHEN, b. New York, N.Y, Apr. 29, 33; m. 61; c. 2. ENGLISH, AMERICAN STUDIES. B.A, Hofstra Univ, 55; M.A, Univ. Ga, 61; fel, Univ. Wis, 62-63; Ph.D.(Eng), 65. Asst. prof, ENG. & AM. STUD, Univ. N.Mex, 65-68; ASSOC. PROF, UNIV. CALGARY, 70- Mem. Am. Lit. Group, MLA, 65-; Am. Philos. Soc. grant-in-aid, summer 67; Univ. N.Mex. alumni award & res. allocation, summer 67; Fulbright lectr, Univ. Salzburg, 68-69; reader Am. lit. & Am. stud, Free Univ, Amsterdam, 69-70; ed, Rocky Mountain Am. Stud. Newslett, 72-; assoc. ed, Ariel, 73- U.S.A, 56-58, Res, 58-62, 1st Lt. MLA; Am. Stud. Asn; Rocky Mountain Am. Stud. Asn.(secy-treas, 72-); Can. Asn. Am. Stud; Asn. Can. Univ. Teachers Eng. American literature since 1607; American studies; modern literature, English, American and continental. Publ: Rhetoric, society, and literature in the age of Jefferson, Midcontinent Am. Stud. J, spring 68; Henry Adams on war: the transformation of history into metaphor, Ariz. Quart, winter 68; Main street, U.S.A; changing conceptions of individualism in modern American literature, Am-Austriaca: Beitrage Amerikakunde, 73. Add: 3323 Breton Close, N.W, Calgary, Alta. T2L 1X3, Can.

MARTIN, MARGARET R, b. Davenport, Iowa, Oct. 3, 38. COMMUNICATIONS. B.A, Parsons Col, 59; M.S, Syracuse Univ, 61, Ph.D.(commun), 68. Instr. Eng. & dir. pub. inform, Parsons Col, 60-62; res. asst. jour, Syracuse Univ, 62-64; asst. prof. Eng, Cuyahoga Community Col, 64-67; res. coord, Educ. Develop. Labs, 67-68; mem. fac, Col. Found. Prog. ROCKLAND COMMUNITY COL, 68-72, ASSOC. PROF. & DIR, COL. SKILLS CTR, 72- Conf. Col. Compos. & Commun; NCTE; MLA; Soc. Appl. Anthrop; Int. Commun. Asn; Int. Reading Asn; Int. Asn. Soc. Psychiat; Am. Soc. Adlerian Psychol. Communications and linguistics, educational media and psychology. Add: College Skills Ctr, Rockland Community College, 145 College Rd, Suffern, NY 10901.

MARTIN, MILDRED ALICE, b. Cadwell, Ill, July 9, 04. ENGLISH. A.B, Univ. Ill, 29, A.M, 32, Ph.D, 40. Asst. ENG, Univ. Ill, 29-40; from instr. to assoc. prof, BUCKNELL UNIV, 40-55, PROF, 55-72, EMER. PROF, 72- MLA. English literature of the 17th century; annotated bibliography of criticism concerning T.S. Eliot; diction and figures of speech in Dryden's prose. Add: Dept. of English, Bucknell University, Lewisberg, PA 17837.

MARTIN, PETER EDWARD, b. Buenos Aires, Argentina, July 6, 40; U.S. citizen; m. 64; c. 1. ENGLISH. B.A, Principia Col, 62; M.A, Univ. Ill, 63; summer, Univ. Edinburgh, 65; Ph.D.(Eng), Syracuse Univ, 67. ASST. PROF. ENG, Miami Univ, 67-71; Fla. Atlantic Univ, 71-72; NEW ENG. COL, ENG, 72- MLA; Am. Soc. 18th Century Stud. Early 18th century English literature and gardening; 18th century drama; 17th century English literature. Publ: Some background to the rhetoric of blame in Pope's Epistle to Harley, S.Atlantic Bull, 72. Add: Dept. of British Studies, New England College, Arundel, Sussex, England.

MARTIN, RICHARD THOMAS, b. Chicago, Ill, Jan. 30, 31; m. 60; c. 2. ENGLISH ROMANTIC POETRY. B.A, Univ. Ill, 53, M.A, 59, Ph.D.(Eng), 64. Asst. prof. ENG, OHIO STATE UNIV, COLUMBUS, 64-73, ASSOC. PROF, 73- U.S.A, 53-55. MLA; Midwest Mod. Lang. Asn. English Romantic and Victorian poetry. Publ: Robert Southey's copy of Simon Browne's A defence of the religion of nature, BNYPL, 5/66; Coleridge's use of sermoni propriora, Wordsworth Circle, spring 72. Add: Dept. of English, Ohio State University, Columbus, OH 43210.

MARTIN, ROBERT BERNARD, b. La Harpe, Ill, Sept. 11, 18. ENGLISH. A.B, State Univ. Iowa, 43; A.M, Harvard, 47; B.Litt, Oxford, 50. Instr. Eng, PRINCETON, 51-55, asst. prof, 55-60, assoc. prof. ENG. LIT, 60-68, PROF, 68- Am. Counc. Learned Soc. fel, 66-67; Guggenheim fel, 72-73. U.S.A.A.F, 43-46. MLA. Victorian literature. Publ: Co-auth, A companion to Victorian literature, Scribner, 55; auth, Charles Kingsley's American notes, Princeton, 58; The dust of combat: a life of Charles Kingsley, 60, Enter rumour, 62 & The accents of persuasion: Charlotte Bronte's novels, 66, Faber & Faber, London & Norton; ed, Victorian poetry: ten major poets, Random, 64; auth, Death takes a sabbatical, 67 & Deadly Meeting, 70, Norton; Death takes the last train, Constable, London, 68; Illegal entry, Norton, 72 & Faber & Faber, London, 73. Add: 22 McCosh Hall, Princeton University, Princeton, NJ 08540.

MARTIN, ROBERT CARL, b. Gary, Ind, May 9, 17; m. 40; c. 2. SPEECH, SEMANTICS. B.S, Northwest. Univ, 40, M.A, 43, Ph.D.(rhetoric & pub. address), 53. Teacher, pub. schs, Ind, 40-43; PROF. speech, Lake Forest Col, 46-62; SPEECH & DRAMA, CALIF. STATE UNIV, HAYWARD, 62- Consult, Indust. Mgt. Inst, Ill, 50-62; Speech Assoc. Inc, 55-62; Pure Oil Co, 58-62; Motorola, Inc, 60-62; Shell Oil Co, Calif, 64-68. Speech Commun. Asn. History of American public address; semantics and linguistics; discussion. Publ: Co-auth, Practical speech for modern business, Appleton, 63; auth, Review business speech books, Quart. J. Speech, spring 59; Speech as an academic discipline, Cent. States Speech J, winter 66. Add: Dept. of Speech & Drama, California State University, Hayward, 25800 Hillary St, Hayward, CA 94542.

MARTIN, RONALD EDWARD, b. Chicago, Ill, June 30, 33; m. 56; c. 3. ENGLISH. B.A, Carroll Col.(Wis), 55; A.M, Boston Univ, 57, Ph.D.(Am. lit), 63. Instr. ENG, Boston Univ, 61-62; UNIV. DEL, 62-64, asst. prof, 64-68, ASSOC. PROF, 68-, summer fac. fel, 64, 68. Am. Counc. Learned Soc. grant-in-aid, 67-68; consult. comt. to establish a six-year med. curriculum,

Univ. Del, 72- AAUP. American literature since 1880; history of science; relationships of science, philosophy, and literature. Publ: The fiction of Joseph Hergesheimer, Univ. Pa, 65. Add: Dept. of English, University of Delaware, Newark, DE 19711.

MARTIN, SUE GILLESPIE, b. Detroit, Mich, Apr. 20, 40, M. 63; c. 2. SPEECH & EARLY CHILDHOOD EDUCATION. B.A, Wayne State Univ, 61, MA, 63, Ph.D.(speech & early childhood educ), 69. Prog. coord, Station WXYZ, 62-65; instr. speech, Wayne State Univ, 70-71; ASST. PROF. DRAMA, UNIV. WINDSOR, 71- Children's book reviewer, Detroit News, 70-71; asst. producer, Henry K. Martin Theatre for Children, 70-; children's literary ed, Detroit Free Press, 71- Am. Theatre Asn.(mem. children's theatre div); Speech Commun. Asn. Drama; children and creativity, first five years. Publ: Techniques for the more effective telling of stories to children, Elementary Eng. J, 5/68; contrib, Lang. Arts in the elementary school: reading's Lippincott, 72; How to raise a more creative child, Detroit Mag, 6/73. Add: Sch. of Dramatic Arts, University of Windsor, Windsor, Ont, Can.

MARTIN, TERENCE JOHN, b. Columbus, Ohio, Mar. 9, 25; m. 48; c. 2. ENGLISH. B.A, John Carroll Univ, 49; M.A, Ohio State Univ, 50, Ph.D.(Eng), 54. From instr. to PROF. ENG, IND. UNIV, BLOOMINGTON, 54- Vis. lectr. Am. lit, Univ. Dijon, 52-53, vis. prof, 59-60; Am. Counc. Learned Soc. study fel, 63-64. U.S.A.A.F, 43-46. MLA; Am. Stud. Asn. American literature. Publ: The instructed vision, Ind. Univ, 61; Nathaniel Hawthorne, Twayne, 65; Rip, Ichabod and the American imagination, Am. Lit, 59; Edgar Allen Poe: the imagination at play, Kenyon Rev, 3/66; plus others. Add: Dept. of English, Indiana University, Bloomington, IN 47401.

MARTIN, W. R, b. Durban, S.Africa, Apr. 6, 20; Can. citizen; m. 70; c. 3. ENGLISH. B.A, Univ. S.Africa, 41, M.A, 47, D.Litt. et Phil.(Eng), 65. Sr. lectr. ENG, Univ. Stellenbosch, 59-61; asst. prof, Ontario Agr. Col, 61-62; UNIV. WATERLOO, 62-65; assoc. prof, 65-69, PROF, 69-, dep. chmn. dept, 67-69. Royal Durban Light Infantry, 40-45, 1st Lt. Asn. Can. Univ. Teachers Eng; Can. Counc. Teachers Eng. Twentieth century British, especially W.B. Yeats, D.H. Lawrence and Conrad. Publ: Allegory in Conrad's The rover, 9/67 & Yeats' Heaven blazing into the head, 9/72, Eng. Stud. Africa; Beginnings and endings in Conrad, Conradiana, Vol. V, No. 1, plus two others. Add: Dept. of English, University of Waterloo, Waterloo, Ont. N2L 3G1, Can.

MARTIN, WALLACE DEAN, b. Hinsdale, Ill, Mar. 28, 33; m. 58. ENGLISH. B.A, Oberlin Col, 54; M.A, Stanford Univ, 57; Ph.D.(Eng), Univ. London, 61. Instr. ENG, UNIV. TOLEDO, 61-62, asst. prof, 62-65, assoc. prof, 65-70, PROF, 70- U.S.A, 54-56. MLA. Criticism; modern British and American literature. Publ: The new age under Orage: chapters in English cultural history, Manchester Univ, 67 & Barnes & Noble, 68; The sources of the imagist aesthetic, PMLA, 70; The hermeneutic circle and the art of interpretation, Comp. Lit, 72. Add: Dept. of English, University of Toledo, Toledo, OH 43606.

MARTIN, WENDY, b. Coral Gables, Fla, Mar. 15, 40. AMERICAN LITERATURE. B.A, Univ. Calif, Berkeley, 62; M.A, Univ. of the Pac, 65; Ph.D. (Am. lit), Univ. Calif, Davis, 68. ASST. PROF. AM. LIT, QUEENS COL. (N.Y), 68-, CHAIRWOMAN, AM. STUD. PROG, 71- MLA; Am. Stud. Asn. Early American literature; American novel and American studies; feminism in American intellectual life. Publ: Ed, The American sisterhood: feminist writings from the Colonial times to the present, Harper, 72; Women's studies: an interdisciplinary journal, Gordan & Breach, 73; auth, On the road with the philosopher and the profiteer: the picaresque, marginal experience, and upward mobility in Hugh Henry Brackenridge's Modern chivalry, Eighteenth Century Stud, spring 71; The rogue and the rational man: a study of a con man in Modern chivalry, Early Am. Lit; Seduced and abandoned in the New World: the image of woman in American literature, In: Woman in sexist society, Basic Bks, 71 & Bantam, 72; plus three others. Add: Dept. of English, Queens College, Flushing, NY 11367.

MARTIN, WILLARD EDGAR, JR, b. Somerville, Mass, Mar. 7, 06; m. 34; c. 2. ENGLISH. A.B, Boston Univ, 27; A.M, Harvard, 32; fel. Duke Univ, 34-35; Ph.D, 44. Instr. ENG, Millikin Univ, 36-37; Duke Univ, 37-42; Boston Univ, 42-43; Tufts Col, 43-44; lectr, Union Col, 45-46; assoc. prof. & resid. head dept, Champlain Col, 46-49; Babcock prof, HARTWICK COL, 49-71, chmn. dept, 49-65, chmn. div. humanities, 63-65, Coe Am. Stud. prog, summer 63, EMER. PROF, 71- MLA. American literature; life and works of Theodore Winthrop; a Chaucer bibliography. Add: South St, Box 143, West Oneonta, NY 13861.

MARTIN, WILLIAM BIZZELL, b. Waxahachie, Tex, May 12, 26; m. 50; c. 2. ENGLISH LITERATURE. B.A, South. Methodist Univ, 48; dipl, Univ. Edinburgh, Scotland, 50, Ph.D, 53. Instr. ENG, Tarleton State Col, 50-51; Agr. & Mech. Col. Tex, 52-54, asst. prof, 54-55; assoc. prof, Northeast Mo. State Teachers Col, 55-56; PROF. & HEAD DEPT, TARLETON STATE UNIV, 56- Smith-Mundt lect. Eng. & Am. lit, Lebanese Nat. Univ, 60-61; participant, U.S. Dept. Health, Educ. & Welf. Sem. on Stud. Involvement in Higher Educ, summer 69; Nat. Endowment for Humanities Sem. on New Directions in Literary Hist, summer 73. MLA; NCTE; AAUP; Asn. Depts. Eng. Eighteenth century English drama. Add: Dept. of English & Language, Tarleton State University, Stephenville, TX 76402.

MARTIN, WILLIAM JOHN, b. St. Louis, Mo, Feb. 10, 20; m. 46; c. 1. SPEECH, THEATRE. B.A, Univ. Mo, 46; M.F.A, Yale, 49. Instr. theatre, Middlebury Col, 49-50; Williams Col, 50-54, lectr, 55-59; instr, Sarah Lawrence Col, 54-55; dir. theater, Culver Mil. Acad, 59-66; PROF. DRAMATIC ART & DIR. CONCERT HALL, UNIV. N.MEX, 66- U.S.A, 45-49. Asn. Col. & Univ. Concert. Mgr. Add: Popejoy Hall, Univ. of New Mexico, Albuquerque, NM 87131.

MARTIN-TRIGONA, HELEN VASILIOU, b. Manchester, N.H, Sept. 12, 17; m. 45; c. 2. SPEECH, ENGLISH. B.A, Univ. N.H, 40; M.A, Cornell Univ, 42; Wesleyan Univ, spring 53; B.Litt. stud, Oxford, 58-60; Ph.D.(speech), Univ. Ill, Urbana, 68. Instr. speech & Eng, Cent. Conn. State Col, spring 51; Univ. Md, 59-62; asst. & instr. speech, Univ. Ill, 62-64; asst. prof, Rollins Col, 66-67; ASSOC. PROF. SPEECH & ENG, D.C. TEACHERS COL, 67- Off. Strategic Serv, 43-45. Speech Commun. Asn; Am. Acad. Polit. & Soc. Sci; Am. Asn. Univ. Women; Am. Philos. Soc. Greek and Roman studies; English literature of the 17th century; rhetoric from ancient Greece to the present. Publ: Logical proof and imaginative reason in selected speeches of Francis Bacon, Libr. Cong, 68; Katus and other poems, Vantage, 73; Sergeant Goodlow, 101st Airborne Division, In: New Voices in American poetry, Vantage, 72. Add: 1900 S. Eads St, Arlington, VA 22202.

MARTINE, JAMES JOHN, b. Philadelphia, Pa, July 23, 37; m. 61; c. 3. AMERICAN LITERATURE, ENGLISH. B.A, Temple Univ, 67; M.A, Pa. State Univ, 68, Ph.D.(Eng), 71. Teaching fel. Eng, Pa. State Univ, 67-71; asst. prof. AM. LIT, ST. BONAVENTURE UNIV, 71-74, ASSOC. PROF, 74- Reviewer, Philadelphia Sunday Bull. Bk. Sect, 71-; Libr. Jour, 73; adv. ed, Stud. Am. Fiction, 72- MLA (mem. Am. lit. sect); AAUP; Northeast Mod. Lang. Asn.(secy. bibliog. sect, 73-74). Twentieth century American fiction; 19th century American literature; history of American literature. Publ: Fred Lewis Pattee and American literature, Pa. State Univ, 73; ed, A history of American literature between the wars, 1918-1942, Cooper Sq, 74; A little light on Hemingway's The light of the world, Stud. Short Fiction, summer 70; Hemingway's Fifty grand: the other fight, J. Mod. Lit, 9/71; The courage to defy, In: Critical essays on Catch 22, Dickenson, 73. Add: Dept. of English, St. Bonaventure University, St. Bonaventure, NY 14778.

MARTINEAU, BARBARA HALPERN, b. New York, N.Y, Feb. 19, 43; m. 66; c. 1. CINEMA, WOMEN'S STUDIES. M.A, Univ. Edinburgh, 64; M.A, Columbia Univ, 65, Ph.D.(Eng), 70. Instr. ENG, SCARBOROUGH COL, UNIV. TORONTO, 67-68, lectr, 68-70, ASST. PROF, 70-, coord. interdisciplinary stud. women's course, 71-72. Can. Counc. res. grant, 72-73. Fictions. Publ: Some thoughts about the objectification of women constructed around a series of quotations from movies and books, Take One, 3/72; Portraits are murdered in the short fiction of Henry James, J. Narrative Technique, 2/72; Subjecting her objectification & Nelly Kaplan, an interview, Notes on Women's Cinema, 3/73. Add: Dept. of English, Scarborough College, University of Toronto, West Hill, Ont, Can.

MARTZ, LEONARD JOHN, JR, b. Sioux Rapids, Iowa, Nov. 5, 29; m. 65; c. 2. ENGLISH, SPEECH. B.A, Univ. Iowa, 50; A.M, Univ. S.Dak, 52; Ariz. State Univ, 52, 54; Ed.D.(Eng. educ), Univ. Nebr, 65. Teacher high sch, Iowa, 51-52; chmn. Eng. & speech, Emmetsburg Community Col, 52-54; dir. sec. educ, Emmetsburg Community Sch. Dist, 54-66; PROF. LANG. & LIT. & CHMN. DIV, North. State Col, 66-67; BUENA VISTA COL, 67- NEA; NCTE. Chaucer's use of profanity; instruction of talented and gifted students in secondary school English. Publ: The academically talented student in English, In: Iowa English yearbook, 65; Selected bibliography, In: English for the academically talented student in the secondary school, NCTE-NEA, 69. Add: 602 Peterson, Alta, IA 51002.

MARTZ, LOUIS LOHR, b. Berwick, Pa, Sept. 27, 13; m. 41; c. 3. ENGLISH. A.B, Lafayette Col, 35, Litt.D, 60; Ph.D, Yale, 39. Instr. Eng, YALE, 38-44, asst. prof, 44-48, assoc. prof, 48-54, prof, 54-57, Douglas Tracy Smith prof. Eng. & Am. Lit, 57-71, STERLING PROF. ENG, 71-, DIR. BEINECKE RARE BOOK & MANUSCRIPT LIBR, 72- Guggenheim fel, 48-49; William Lyon Phelps lectr, Yale, 67; Ward-Phillips lectr, Notre Dame Univ, 68. Am. Acad. Arts & Sci; MLA; Renaissance Soc. Renaissance; 17th and 20th centuries. Publ: The later career of Tobias Smollett, 42, The poetry of meditation, 54, The paradise within, 64 & co-ed, Thomas More's prayer book, 69, Yale; auth, The poem of the mind, Oxford, 66; The wit of love, Univ, Notre Dame, 69; ed, Marlowe's Hero and Leander, Folger Shakespeare Libr, 72; auth, A greenhouse Eden, In: Theodore Roethke, Univ. Wash, 65; The rising poet, In: Lyric and dramatic Milton, Columbia Univ, 65; Portrait of Miriam, In: Imagined words, Methuen, 68. Add: Beinecke Library, Yale University, 1603A Yale Station, New Haven, CT 06520.

MARTZ, WILLIAM J, b. Dec. 5, 28; U.S. citizen; m. 55; c. 2. ENGLISH. B.A, Univ. Rochester, 50; M.A, Northwest. Univ, 51; Ph.D, Yale, 57. Instr. ENG, Middlebury Col, 55-58; asst. prof, RIPON COL, 58-63, assoc. prof, 63-65, PROF, 66- Fel, Assoc. Cols. Midwest Fac, 62; gen. ed, Mod. Poets ser, 66- MLA. Modern poetry. Publ: Beginnings in poetry, 65 & 73, The distinctive voice, 66, The achievement of Theodore Roethke, 66, The achievement of Robert Lowell, 66 & ed, William Shakespeare's Hamlet, 70 Scott; auth, John Berryman, Univ. Minn, 69; Shakespeare's universe of comedy, David Lewis, 71. Add: Dept. of English, Ripon College, Ripon, WI 54971.

MARVIN, BURTON WRIGHT, b. Somerville, Mass, Dec. 23, 13; m. 38; c. 3. JOURNALISM. A.B, Univ. Nebr, 35; Hitchcock scholar, Columbia Univ, 36-37, M.S, 37; hon. D.Journ, Southwest. Col. (Kans), 64. Lectr, Northwest. Univ, Chicago, 45-46, asst. prof, 46-47; assoc. prof, Columbia Univ, 47-48; prof. jour. & dean, William Allen White Sch, Univ. Kans, 48-65; assoc. gen. secy. commun, Nat. Counc. Churches, New York, 66-68; PROF. JOUR, SYRACUSE UNIV, 68-, ASSOC. DEAN, S. I. NEWHOUSE SCH. COMMUN, 70- Avery Mem. lectr, Univ. Nebr, 50; chmn. accrediting comt, Am. Counc. on Educ. for Jour, 56-60; Fulbright lectr, Univ. Tehran, 60-61; vis. prof. Tel-Aviv Univ, 65-66. Asn. Educ. Jour. Reporting and interpretive reporting; editing and interpretive editing; religious journalism. Publ: Education for journalism in the U.S.A, UNESCO. Add: 307 Newhouse Communications Center, Syracuse University, Syracuse, NY 13210.

MARVIN, JOHN R, b. Ft. Morgan, Colo, Sept. 27, 23; m. 45; c. 2. MODERN LITERATURE. A.B, Univ. Denver, 49, M.A, 50. Teaching fel, Johns Hopkins Univ, 53; instr. ENG, Marshall Univ, 55-58; asst. prof, Idaho State Col, 58-60; Univ. Notre Dame, 60-65; UNIV. MASS, BOSTON, 65-66, ASSOC. PROF, 66- U.S.N, 43-45. MLA. Modern fiction; fiction writing; modern literary criticism. Publ: Co-ed. & contrib, Faulkner Stud, 52-53; auth, The wrath-bearing tree, 57 & Above the burning plain, 59, Hudson Rev; plus others. Add: Dept. of English, University of Massachusetts, 100 Arlington St, Boston, MA 02116.

MARX, LEO, b. New York, N.Y, Nov. 15, 19; m. 43; c. 3. AMERICAN STUDIES. S.B, Harvard Col, 41, Ph.D, Harvard, 50; hon. M.A, Amherst Col, 59. Teaching fel. hist. & lit, Harvard Col, 47-49; asst. prof. Eng, Univ. Minn, 49-54, assoc. prof, 55-58; prof. ENG. & AM. STUD, AMHERST COL, 58-71, KENAN PROF, 71- Fulbright lectr. Am. stud, Nottingham Univ, Eng, 56-57;

Guggenheim fel, 61-62; Fulbright lectr, Rennes, France, 65-66; vis. prof, Brandeis Univ, 69-70; mem, Nat. Humanities Fac, 71-73; vis. scholar, Phi Beta Kappa Vis. Scholar Prog, 72-73, bicentennial fel, 74-75. U.S.N.R, 41-45, Lt. Fel, Am. Acad. Arts & Sci; Am. Stud. Asn; MLA. American cultural history. Publ: The machine in the garden, Oxford, 64. Add: Dept. of English, Amherst College, Amherst, MA 01002.

MARX, PAUL, b. New York, N.Y, Dec. 24, 30; m. 55; c. 2. ENGLISH. B.A, Univ. Mich, 53; M.F.A, Univ. Iowa, 57; Ph.D, N.Y. Univ, 66. Lectr. ENG, South. Ill. Univ, 57-60; asst. prof, Lehigh Univ, 63-67; assoc. prof, UNIV. NEW HAVEN, 67-73, PROF. & CHMN DEPT, 73- U.S.A, 54-55. MLA; NCTE. Romantic, Victorian and modern British literature. Publ: Ed, Twelve short story writers, Holt, 70; auth, Eduora Welty, & Harvey Swados, In: Contemporary novelist, St. James, 72; plus two others. Add: Dept. of English, University of New Haven, New Haven, CT 06516.

MARZ, ROY, b. Bellevue, Ky, June 21, 11. ENGLISH. A.B, Univ. Cincinnati, 33, M.A, 34, Taft teaching fel, 35-37, Ph.D, 37. Instr. ENG, Univ. Cincinnati, 37-42, 46-48; asst. prof, BUTLER UNIV, 48-51, assoc. prof, 51-61, PROF, 61- Ford study & writing fel, Italy, 51-52; New York Poetry Ctr Award, 51; Oscar Blumenthal Poetry Award, 52; Fulbright lectr. Am. lit, Univ. Catania, 59-60. Intel.C, U.S.A, 42-45. MLA; Poetry Soc. Am. Shakespeare; modern poetry and drama. Publ: After closing, summer 62 & O'Fallon's cup, spring 66, First Stage. Add: Dept. of English, Butler University, Indianapolis, IN 46207.

MASBACK, FREDERIC JOSEPH, b. New York, N.Y, July 25, 26; m. 55; c. 2. ENGLISH. B.A, Cornell Univ, 49; M.A, Univ. Wis, 50; Columbia Univ, 51-52; Ph.D.(Eng), Syracuse Univ, 60. Teacher ENG, Harrisville Cent. Sch, 52-53; S. Huntington High Sch, 53-54; asst. instr, Syracuse Univ, 54-59, instr, 59-60; Bowling Green State Univ, 60-61; asst. prof, Trenton State Col, 61-64; CALIF. STATE UNIV, LONG BEACH, 64-67, assoc. prof, 67-72, PROF, 72- MLA; NCTE. American and world literature; teaching of English. Publ: The economics of evil: a study of John Woolman's thought, Am. Friends Serv. Comt, 59; Conrad's Jonahs, Col. Eng, 61; An approach to the novel in high school English, Eng. J, 61. Add: Dept. of English, California State University, Long Beach, 6101 E. Seventh St, Long Beach, CA 90840.

MASI, MICHAEL, b. Detroit, Mich, Sept. 1, 39; m. 63; c. 2. ENGLISH. B.A, Loyola Univ, 62; M.A, Northwest. Univ, 65, Ph.D.(Eng), 68. Instr. ENG, LOYOLA UNIV. CHICAGO, 65-68, ASST. PROF, 68- Fel, Inst. Res. Humanities, Univ. Wis-Madison, 71-72. MLA; Mediaeval Acad. Am. Medieval English literature; Medieval science and philosophy. Publ: Boethian number theory, Univ. Fla, 74; Troilus: a medieval psychoanalysis, Annuale Medievale, 70; Manuscripts containing the De Musica of Boethius, Manuscripta, 71; Newberry manuscript fragments, Mediaeval Stud, 72. Add: Dept. of English, Loyola University of Chicago, 6525 N. Sheridan, Chicago, IL 60626.

MASINTON, CHARLES G, b. La Veta, Colo, May 28, 38; m. 63; c. 2. ENGLISH & AMERICAN LITERATURE. B.A, Univ. Colo, 61; NDEA fel, Univ. Okla, 62-65, M.A. & Ph.D.(Eng), 66. Instr. ENG, Punahou Acad, Honolulu, 61-62; Univ. Okla, 65-66; asst. prof, Univ. N.Mex, 66-67; UNIV. KANS, 67-71, ASSOC. PROF, 71- Danforth assoc, 70. Elizabethan drama, especially Christopher Marlowe; modern American drama and novel. Publ: Christopher Marlowe's tragic vision: a study in damnation, Ohio Univ, 72; J.P. Donleavy: the style of his sadness and humor, Popular Press, (in press); Marlowe's artists: the failure of imagination, Ohio Univ. Rev, 69. Add: Dept. of English, University of Kansas, Lawrence, KS 66044.

MASON, DAVID JOSEPH, b. Beloit, Wis, Dec. 31, 24; m. 52; c. 1. ENGLISH, JOURNALISM. B.A, Beloit Col, 49; M.A, Columbia Univ, 50. Mem. ed. staff, Beloit Daily News, Wis, 50-53; asst. prof. Eng, BELOIT COL, 53-66, ASST. TO PRES, 66-, dir. pub. inform, 53-60, dir. pub. relat, 60-66. U.S.A, 43-45, S/Sgt. Add: 2110 W. Collingswood Dr, Beloit, WI 53511.

MASON, ELLSWORTH GOODWIN, b. Waterbury, Conn, Aug. 25, 17; m. 64; c. 3. MODERN LITERATURE. B.A, Yale, 38, M.A, 42, Ph.D.(Eng. lit), 48; hon. L.H.D, Hofstra Univ, 73. Instr. Eng. lit, Williams Col, 48-50; asst. prof, Marlboro Col, 51-52; serial librn, Univ. Wyo, 52-54; lectr. Eng. & librn, Colo. Col, 54-63; PROF. ENG. & DIR. LIBR, Hofstra Univ, 63-72; UNIV. COLO, BOULDER, 72- Consult. libr. bldgs, U.S, Colombia, P.R, & Can, 60-73; res. assoc, Univ. Calif, Berkeley, 65; guest lectr, Colo. Col, Syracuse Univ. Columbia Univ, Univ. Ill, Lincoln Univ, Univ. B.C, Univ. Toronto, Univ. Tulsa, Rutgers Univ. & Simmons Col, 65-73; ed, Focus on Robert Graves, 72- U.S.N, 43-46. Bibliog. Soc. Am; Libr. Asn, Eng; MLA; Private Libr. Asn; Grolier Club; James Joyce Found; Am. Libr. Asn. James Joyce; Robert Graves; 20th century literature. Publ: Ed, Recollections of James Joyce, James Joyce Soc, 51; co-ed, The early Joyce, Mamalujo Press, 55; co-ed, Critical writings of James Joyce, Viking, 59, 64, Macmillan, 59 & Faber, 59, Fr. ed, Gallimard, 66, Span. ed, Ed. Lumen, 73; auth, James Joyce's Ulysses and Vico's Cycle, Yale, 73. Add: University of Colorado Library, Boulder, CO 80302.

MASON, JULIAN DEWEY, JR, b. Washington, N.C, Mar. 25, 31; m. 54; c. 3. ENGLISH. A.B, Univ. N.C, Chapel Hill, 53, fel, 59-60, Ph.D.(Eng), 62; Carnegie fel, George Peabody Col, 53-54, M.A, 54. Teacher high sch, Tenn, 54-55; admin. asst. & teacher, Army Educ. Ctr, Ger, 56-57; instr. Eng, Univ. N.C, Chapel Hill, 60-62, asst. prof. & dir. stud. aid, 62-66; asst. prof. ENG, UNIV. N.C, CHARLOTTE, 66-68, assoc. prof, 68, 70-72, PROF, 72-, res. grants, summers 68 & 73, acting chmn. dept, summer 70. Specialist Am. cult. hist, Manuscript Div, Libr. Congr, 68-70. U.S.A, 55-57. MLA; Am. Stud. Asn; Col. Lang. Asn; Soc. Stud. South. Lit. American literature; American Negro literature; American studies. Publ: Search party, Pageant, 53; The poems of Phillis Wheatley, Univ. N.C, 66; Charles W. Chesnutt as Southern author, Miss. Quart, spring 67; David Humphrey's lost ode to George Washington, 1776, 1/71 & Owen Wister, champion of old Charleston, 7/72, Quart. J. Libr. Congr; plus many others. Add: Dept. of English, University of North Carolina at Charlotte, Charlotte, NC 28213.

MASON, MARY ELIZABETH, O.S.B, b. Richmond, Va, Sept. 13, 17. ENGLISH, NEO-LATIN. B.A, Immaculata Col.(Pa), 41; M.A, Marquette Univ, 59; Arthur J. Schmitt scholar, Loyola Univ.(Ill), 63-65, Ph.D.(Eng), 66. Prof. Eng, Mary Col, 65-73, parish worker adult educ, St. Anne's Parish, 73- Participant classification & anal, Monastic Manuscript Microfilm Libr, Collegeville, Minn, summers 68-70. MLA; NCTE. Latin poems of George Herbert; Neo-Latin and Medieval Latin manuscripts; the concept of vita activa and vita contemplativa, especially in Augustine, Gregory the Great and Thomas Aquinas. Publ: Active life and contemplative life: a study of the concepts from Plato to the present, Marquette Univ, 61. Add: Annunciation Priory, Apple Creek Rd, Bismarck, ND 58501.

MASON, RICHARD G, b. Montague, Mich, Sept. 15, 19; m. 50. ENGLISH LANGUAGE & LITERATURE. B.A, Univ. Mich, 48, M.A, 50, teaching fel, 50-55. Instr. ENG, MICH. TECHNOL. UNIV, 56-60, asst. prof, 60-66, ASSOC. PROF, 66- U.S.A.F, 42-46, Res, 46-, Lt. Col. MLA; Col. Eng. Asn; NCTE; Conf. Col. Compos. & Commun. Eighteenth century English literature; history of drama; modern novel. Add: Dept. of Humanities, Michigan Technological University, Houghton, MI 49931.

MASON, ROBERT L, b. Woodbury, Tenn, Feb. 17, 12; m. 40; c. 1. AMERICAN & SOUTHERN LITERATURE. B.S, Mid. Tenn. State Teachers Col, 36; M.A, George Peabody Col, 39, Ph.D.(Eng), 46. Teacher ENG, High Sch, Tenn, 37-39; instr, Castle Heights Mil. Acad, 41-42; PROF, U.S. NAVAL ACAD, 46-, Res. Counc. grant, summer 68. U.S.N.R, 43-46, Lt. William Faulkner; Civil War history; folklore. Publ: Ten Old-English ballads in Middle Tennessee, South. Folklore Quart, 6/47; A defense of Faulkner's Sanctuary, Ga. Rev, winter 68. Add: Dept. of English, History & Government, U.S. Naval Academy, Annapolis, MD 21402.

MASSA, RICHARD WAYNE, b. Carona, Kans, May 2, 32; m. 71; c. 3. ENGLISH, JOURNALISM. B.J. & M.A, Univ. Mo-Columbia, 54; Univ. Ark, Fayetteville, 64-65. Instr. jour, Univ. Mo, 55; Miss. State Col. Women, 57-58; assoc. prof. Eng, Okla. Col. Lib. Arts, 58-69; consult. & v.pres, Interpersonal Commun. Consults, 69-72; ASSOC. PROF. JOUR, MO. SOUTH. STATE COL, 72- Spec. instr. jour, Northeast Mo. State Univ, 71. U.S.A, 55-57, Res, 57-61. Communications; crime reporting. Publ: Co-auth. & co-ed, Contemporary man in world society, 69, co-ed, Aesthetic man, 69, Philosophical man, 69 & Inquisitive man, 70, McCutcheon. Add: Dept. of Journalism, Missouri Southern State College, Newman & Duquesne Rds, Joplin, MO 64801.

MASSEY, IRVING JOSEPH, b. Montreal, Can, June 15, 24; nat; m. 46; c. 2. COMPARATIVE LITERATURE. B.A, McGill Univ, 44; resid. scholar. & A.M, Columbia Univ, 45; Austen fel. & A.M, Harvard, 46, Ph.D.(comp. lit), 54. Instr. Eng, Wayne Univ, 46-50; teaching fel. humanities, Harvard, 50-54; instr. comp. lit, Brandeis Univ, 54-56, asst. prof, 56-60; asst. prof. Eng, McGill Univ, 60-64; assoc. prof. ENG. & COMP. LIT, STATE UNIV. N.Y. BUFFALO, 64-66, PROF. & DIR. GRAD. STUD. ENG, 66-, res. grant, Paris, summer 67. Summers, grants, Am. Philos. Soc. & French Govt, Paris, 59, Am. Philos. Soc, Am. Counc. Learned Soc. & Can. Counc, Oxford, 61; vis. prof. comp. lit, Univ. Wis, 63; McGill Univ, 69-70; Sir George Williams Univ, spring 71. MLA (chmn. Romanticism group & mem. comt. on transl, 72-73); Comp. Lit. Asn; Keats-Shelley Asn. Am. Poetry of the Romantic period. Publ: Transl, Stello, 63 & ed, Posthumous poems of Shelley, 69, McGill Univ; auth, The uncreating word, Ind. Univ. 70; Honte: form and content in a Rimbaud poem, Romanic Rev; Shelley's Music, when soft voices die, J. Eng. & Ger. Philol, 60; The Romantic movement: phrase of fact?, Dalhousie Rev, winter 64-65. Add: Dept. of English, State University of New York at Buffalo, Buffalo, NY 14214.

MAST, GERALD J, b. Los Angeles, Calif, May 13, 40. ENGLISH, DRAMA. A.B, Univ. Chicago, 61, M.A, 62, Ph.D.(Eng), 67. Instr. ENG, N.Y. Univ, 64-65; Oberlin Col, 65-67; from asst. prof. to ASSOC. PROF, RICHMOND COL.(N.Y), 67- Instr. & consult, New Sch. Col. & Sch. Soc. Res, 67- MLA; Soc. Cinema Stud. History and theory of film; contemporary drama; aesthetics. Publ: A short history of the movies, Pegasus, 71; The comic mind, Bobbs, 73; Filmguide to rules of the game, Ind. Univ, 73; Pinter's Homecoming, Drama Surv, spring 68; The logic of illogic: Ionesco's Victims of Duty, Mod. Drama, spring 70; Motion pictures, history of, In: Encycl. Britannica, 74. Add: Div. of Humanities, Richmond College, 130 Stuyvesant Pl, Staten Island, NY 10301.

MASTERSON, JOHN PATRICK, b. Chicago, Ill, Mar. 15, 25; m. 56; c. 4. ENGLISH, HUMANITIES. B.A, St. Mary of the Lake Sem, 47; M.A, DePaul Univ, 52; Ph.D.(Eng), Univ. Ill, 61. Instr. ENG, DePAUL UNIV, 59-61, asst. prof, 61-63, assoc. prof, 64-69, PROF, 69-, DEAN COL. LIB. ARTS & SCI, 70-, chmn. dept. Eng, 64-66, head humanities div, 66-69. Shell Oil Co. grant, summer 68; Am. Counc. on Educ. fel, Acad. Admin. Internship prog, 69-70. Am. Conf. Acad. Deans; Am. Asn. Higher Educ; MLA; NCTE. Written communications in industry; 17th century literature. Add: Office of the Dean, College of Liberal Arts & Science, Schmitt Academic Ctr, DePaul University, Chicago, IL 60614.

MASTON, ROBERT EDWARD, Linguistics, Psychology. See Volume III, Foreign Languages, Linguistics & Philology.

MATALENE, HENRY WILLIAM, III, b. New York, N.Y, June 13, 36; m. 69; c. 1. ENGLISH, COMPARATIVE LITERATURE. A.B, Princeton, 58; M.A, Univ. Pa, 62, Ph.D.(Eng), 70. Instr. ENG, UNIV. S.C, 69-70, ASST. PROF, 70- MLA. Seventeenth and 18th century literature; aesthetics. Publ: Information, expectancy, and the perception of fiction, Genre, 5/72; Marlowe's Faustus and the comforts of academicism, ELH, 72. Add: Dept. of English, University of South Carolina, Columbia, SC 29208.

MATCHETT, WILLIAM HENRY, b. Chicago, Ill, Mar. 5, 23; m. 49; c. 3. ENGLISH. A.B, Swarthmore Col, 49; M.A, Harvard, 50, Ph.D, 57. Teaching fel. gen. educ, Harvard, 53-54; instr. ENG, UNIV. WASH, 54-56, asst. prof. 56-60, assoc. prof, 60-66, PROF, 66- Ed, Mod. Lang. Quart. Hayes Prize, 48; Furioso Prize, 52. MLA. Poetry of any period; Elizabethan period; Shakespeare. Publ: Water Ouzel and other poems, Houghton, 55; The phoenix and the turtle: Shakespeare's poem and Chester's Loues martyr, Mouton, 65; co-auth, Poetry: from statement to meaning, Oxford, 65; ed, Shakespeare's King John, Signet, 66; auth, Dickinson's revisions of Two butterflies, PMLA, 9/62; What and why is a poem?, Col. Eng, 2/66; Some dramatic techniques in The winter's tale, Shakespeare Survey, 69; plus others. Add: Dept. of English, GN-30, University of Washington, Seattle, WA 98195.

MATERER, TIMOTHY JOHN, b. Chicago, Ill, Oct. 25, 40; m. 63; c. 3. MODERN & COMPARATIVE LITERATURE. B.S, Loyola Univ. Chicago, 62; M.A, Stanford Univ, 66, Ph.D.(Eng. & humanities), 68. Asst. prof. ENG, Univ. Pa, 67-73; ASSOC. PROF, UNIV. MO-COLUMBIA, 73- MLA. Modern British novel; modern British and American poetry. Publ: Short stories of Wyndham Lewis, Stud. Short Fiction, fall 70; Merton and Auden, Commonweal, 2/70; Wyndham Lewis, satirist of the machine age, Satire Newslett, fall 72; plus one other. Add: Dept. of English, University of Missouri-Columbia, Columbia, MO 65201.

MATES, JULIAN, b. New York, N.Y, June 24, 27; m. 51; c. 2. DRAMATIC LITERATURE. B.A, Brooklyn Col, 49; M.A, Columbia Univ, 50, Ph.D, 59; fac. fel, Hofstra Col, 57. Lectr. ENG, City Col. New York, 51-52; Hofstra Col, 52-53, instr, 53-58; asst. prof, C.W. POST COL, L.I. UNIV, 59-61, assoc. prof, 62-66, PROF, 67-, DEAN FINE ARTS DIV, 68- Oscar G. Sonneck Found. Libr. Congr. Mem. grant, 61; dir, Am. Theatre Festival, C.W. Post Col, 68- U.S.N, 45-47. MLA; Am. Soc. Theatre Res. American literature. Publ: The American musical stage before 1800, Rutgers Univ, 62; Style sheet, Barnes & Noble, 63; co-auth, Renaissance culture: a new sense of order, Braziller, 66; auth, Dramatic anchor: research opportunities in the American drama before 1800, Early Am. Lit, 71; American musical theatre: beginnings to 1900, In: American theatre: the sum of its parts, Samuel French, 72; Sam Harris, In: Dictionary of American biography, Scribner, 73. Add: Dept. of English, C.W. Post College, Long Island University, Greenvale, NY 11548.

MATHENY, DAVID LEON, b. El Reno, Okla, Oct. 15, 31; m. 54; c. 2. SPEECH. B.A, Kans. State Teachers Col, 53, M.S, 57; Ph.D.(speech), Univ. Okla, 65. Instr. SPEECH, Tex. Christian Univ, 57-59, asst. prof, 59-67; PROF. & ASSOC. CHMN, KANS. STATE TEACHERS COL, 67- U.S.A, 53-55. Speech Commun. Asn; Am. Forensic Asn; Cent. States Speech Asn. American public address; argumentation and debate. Publ: The new South: Grady's use of Hegelian dialectic, South. Speech J, fall 65; The comparative advantages debate case, In: The presumption on compulsory military service, State Teachers Col, fall 68. Add: Dept. of Speech, Kansas State Teachers College, Emporia, KS 66801.

MATHES, JOHN C, b. Toledo, Ohio, Jan. 3, 31; m. 59; c. 2. COMPARATIVE LITERATURE. A.B, Univ. Mich, 52, A.M, 53, fel, 56-60, Ph.D.(Eng), 65. Instr. Eng, San Diego State Col, 61-63; UNIV. MICH, ANN ARBOR, 63-66, asst. prof, 66-70, ASSOC. PROF. HUMANITIES, 70- U.S.A, 54-56. Am. Soc. Eng. Educ; Soc. Tech. Commun; Midwest Mod. Lang. Asn; Inst. Elec. & Electronics Engrs; Systs, Man & Cybernet. Soc. Modern drama; rhetoric; futures planning. Publ: Co-auth, Your future in naval architecture, Richards Rosen, 68 & Growth policy: population environment and beyond, Univ. Mich, 74; auth, The engineer's social responsibility, Phi Kappa Phi J, spring 71; Rhetoric and the engineering approach, J. Tech. Writing & Commun, 4/72. Add: Dept. of Humanities, College of Engineering, University of Michigan, Ann Arbor, MI 48104.

MATHESON, JOHN MORLEY, b. Duluth, Minn, Feb. 22, 23; m. 48; c. 1. JOURNALISM. B.A, Mich. State Univ, 48; M.A, South. Ill. Univ, 65, Ph.D.(jour), 67. Asst. prof. jour, South. Ill. Univ, Carbondale, 65-69; ASST. TO PRES. & SECY, BD. CONTROL, LAKE SUPERIOR STATE COL, 69-, DEAN SCH. ARTS & SCI, 73- U.S.N, 41-46. The press and Keynesian economics; history of election returns coverage in four Illinois cities, 1836-1928. Publ: Elections and magic lanterns, 1-2/68 & Instant elections, 3-4/68: Grassroots Ed. Add: Lake Superior State College, Sault Ste. Marie, MI 49783.

MATHEWS, FRANCIS X, b. Stamford, Conn, Nov. 10, 35; m. 62. ENGLISH. A.B, Fairfield Univ, 57; M.A, Univ. Wis, 58, Ph.D.(Eng), 64. Instr. ENG, Colby Col, 62-65, asst. prof, 65-67; UNIV. R.I, 67-69, ASSOC. PROF, 69- R.I. State Counc. on Arts grant, 73-74. Modern British literature; the English novel. Publ: The concrete judasbird, 68 & The frog at the bottom of the well, 71, Houghton. Add: Dept. of English, University of Rhode Island, Kingston, RI 02881.

MATHEWS, JAMES WILLIAM, b. East Point, Ga, June 27, 26; m. 49; c. 2. LITERATURE. B.A, David Lipscomb Col, 49; M.A, Emory Univ, 50; South. Fel. Fund fel, Univ. Tenn, 59-60, Ph.D, 60. Instr. ENG, Marion Inst, 50-54; Univ. Tenn, 56-59; PROF, W.GA. COL, 60-, CHMN. DEPT. ENG, 73-, chmn. div. humanities, 60-73. U.S.A, 44-46. MLA; S.Atlantic Mod. Lang. Asn; NCTE (dir-at-large, 67-71). Nineteenth century American and English literature. Publ: Hawthorne and the chain of being, Mod. Lang. Quart, 59; Howells and the Shakers, Personalist, 63; House of Atreus and House of seven gables, Emerson Soc. Quart, 71; plus others. Add: Dept. of English, West Georgia College, Carrollton, GA 30117.

MATHEWS, JOHN BELL, Biblical Studies, Theology & Literature. See Volume IV, Philosophy, Religion & Law.

MATHEWS, JOHNYE ELIZABETH, b. Pampa, Tex, Dec. 30, 30; m. 49; c. 2. ENGLISH, AMERICAN STUDIES. B.A, Univ. Ark, Fayetteville, 55, M.A, 57, Ph.D.(Eng), 69. Instr. Eng, UNIV. ARK, LITTLE ROCK, 60-61, asst. prof, 61-69, assoc. prof, 69-73, ASSOC. PROF. HUMANITIES & DIR. ORAL HIST. PROG, 73- Mem: bd. dir, Acad. Press Ark, 72-; mem adv. bd, Border States, 72- MLA; Am. Stud. Asn; Oral Hist. Asn. Women in society; regional cultural history; contemporary artists. Add: Oral History Office, University of Arkansas at Little Rock, 33rd & University, Little Rock, AR 72204.

MATHEWS, JOSEPH CHESLEY, b. Flemington, Fla, Nov. 19, 06; m. 32; c. 3. ENGLISH. A.B, Furman Univ, 27; A.M, Duke Univ, 29; Ph.D, Univ. Calif, 37. Instr. ENG, Univ. Tex, 37-44; asst. prof, UNIV. CALIF, SANTA BARBARA, 44-51, assoc. prof, 51-58, PROF, 58-, chmn. dept, 51-56. Fulbright lectr, Univ. Turin, 58-59. Dante Prize, Harvard, 38. MLA; Philol. Asn. Pac. Coast. American literature; Dante in America; American author's knowledge of Dante. Publ: Ed, Emerson's translation of Dante's Vita nuova, Univ. N.C, 59; suppl, Eight American authors, Norton, 62. Add: Dept. of English, University of California, Santa Barbara, CA 93106.

MATHEWSON, JEANNE THOMPSON, b. Cowen, W.Va, Nov. 22, 25; div; c. 2. ENGLISH. B.A, Wells Col, 47; Univ. St. Andrews, 59-60; Ph.D.(Eng), Stanford Univ, 68. Teacher high sch, Pa, 57-59; ASST. PROF. ENG, UNIV. WYO, 66- MLA. Twelfth and thirteenth century Latin tragedies and comedies; medieval literary theory and its influence on 14th century English literature. Add: Dept. of English, University of Wyoming, Laramie, WY 82071.

MATHEWSON, MARY ELIZABETH, b. Wakefield, Nebr, Mar. 2, 04. ENGLISH. A.B, Smith Col, 27; M.A, Univ. Colo, 40; Univ. Iowa, 62-63, 64-65, Ph.D.(Milton), 71. Teacher, Hosmer Hall, Mo, 27-29; high schs, Wyo, Minn, Ill, Ariz. & Wash, 29-46; instr. ENG, Grays Harbor Jr. Col, 46-48; CENT. WASH. STATE COL, 48-50, asst. prof, 50-59, assoc. prof, 59-71, prof, 71-72, EMER. PROF, 72- Fulbright grant, teacher of Eng. as for. lang, Spec. Training Inst. Women, Egypt, 53-54. MLA. Shakespeare in Moby Dick; irony, idea and image in Samson Agonistes. Publ: A case of inferior school work and personality maladjustment: a case study, Educ. Records Bull, 10/39. Add: 702 E. First Ave, Apt. B-6, Ellensburg, WA 98926.

MATHISON, JOHN KELLY, b. Chicago, Ill, May 1, 16; m. 43; c. 2. ENGLISH LITERATURE. A.B, Northwest Univ, 38; A.M, Princeton, 41, Ph.D. 43. Instr. ENG, Stanford Univ, 41-43, 46-48; asst. prof, UNIV. WYO, 48-53, assoc. prof, 53-58, PROF, 58-, chmn. dept, 66-73. Mem, Eng. Inst. A.U.S, 43-46, M/Sgt. MLA. Publ: Nelly Dean and the power of Wuthering Heights, 9/56 & The German sections of Vanity Fair, 12/63, Nineteenth-Century Fiction; Northanger Abbey and Jane Austen's Conception of the Value of fiction, ELH, 6/57; plus others. Add: Dept. of English, University of Wyoming, Laramie, WY 82070.

MATLACK, JAMES HENDRICKSON, b. Mt. Holly, N.J, Apr. 25, 38; m. 60; c. 3. ENGLISH, AMERICAN STUDIES. A.B, Princeton, 60; B.A, Oxford, 62, Fulbright scholar. & M.A, 65; Woodrow Wilson & Danforth fels. & M.A, Yale, 64, Ph.D.(Am. stud), 67. ASST. PROF. ENG, Cornell Univ, 67-71; UNIV. MASS, AMHERST, 71- MLA; Am. Stud. Asn; Soc. Relig. Higher Educ. American Negro literature and history; 19th century novel; Elizabeth Barstow Stoddard. Add: Dept. of English, University of Massachusetts, Amherst, MA 01002.

MATLAW, MYRON, b. Ger, May 21, 24, nat; m. 50; c. 2. ENGLISH. B.A, Hofstra Col, 49; Ph.D.(Eng), Univ. Chicago, 53. Instr. Eng, Univ. Ill, 53-55; lectr. humanities, col, Univ. Chicago, 54-55; asst. prof. ENG, Auburn Univ, 55-56; Hunter Col, 57-60; PROF, QUEENS COL. (N.Y) & GRAD. SCH, CITY UNIV. NEW YORK, 60- Am. Counc. Learned Soc. grant-in-aid, 59-60; ed, The Independent Shavian, 62-65; vis. prof. Eng. & drama, Univ. Hawaii, 67-68. U.S.A, 43-46, 2nd Lt. Am. Soc. Theater Res. Dramatic literature and theatre history. Publ: Co-auth, Pro and con, Houghton, 60; ed, The black crook and other nineteenth century American plays, 67 & auth, Modern world drama: an encyclopedia, 72, Dutton; plus one other. Add: Dept. of English, Queens College, Flushing, NY 11367.

MATLOCK, CHARLES MICHAEL, b. Atlantic City, N.J, Mar. 11, 45; m. 72. MIDDLE ENGLISH LITERATURE. B.A, Rutgers Univ, New Brunswick, 67; M.A, State Univ. N.Y, Albany, 68, Ph.D.(Eng), 72. Instr. ENG, UNIV. S.ALA, 71-72, ASST. PROF, 72. MLA; South. Mod. Lang. Asn; NCTE. The Middle English dream vision and Arthurian romances; historical development of the English language. Add: Dept. of English, University of South Alabama, Mobile, AL 36688.

MATLON, RONALD JOHN, b. Chicago, Ill, Oct, 5, 38; m. 64. RHETORIC, PUBLIC ADDRESS. B.A, Ind. State Univ, 60; M.S, Purdue Univ, 62, Ph.D. (speech), 66. Teaching asst. speech, Purdue Univ, 60-62; instr. speech & forensics, Univ. Ill, Chicago, 62-65; instr. debate, Purdue Univ, 65-66; from asst. prof. to ASSOC. PROF. RHETORIC, PUB. ADDRESS & DEBATE & DIR. FORENSICS, UNIV. MASS, AMHERST, 66- Chmn, Nat. Debate Tournament Site Selection & Finance Comt, 67-68; mem, Nat. Univ. Exten. Asn. Comt. Discussion & Debate, 70- Speech Commun. Asn.(pres, forensics div, 72-); Am. Forensic Asn; Cent. States Speech Asn; East. Commun. Asn; East. Forensic Asn. Methods and materials in the teaching of public speaking; argumentation and debate; history of speech education in America. Publ: Co-auth, Table of contents and index to journals in speech, 1915-1969, Speech Commun. Asn, 71; auth, Art of judging contest debates, 3/67 & co-auth, Prepared research materials and research habits in high school debate, 1/68, Educ. Serv. Report; The Jonathan Barber—James Rush relationship, Speech Monogr, 3/69; plus three others. Add: Dept. of Communication Studies, University of Massachusetts, Amherst, MA 01002.

MATONIS, ANN, b. Philadelphia, Pa, Apr. 23, 37; div; c. 1. ENGLISH. B.A, Adelphi Univ, 60; M.A, Univ. Pa, 63, fel, 63-66, Ph.D.(Eng), 66. ASST. PROF. ENG, TEMPLE UNIV, 66- MLA. Medieval and Old English literature. Add: Dept. of English, Temple University, Philadelphia, PA 19122.

MATSON, MARSHALL N, b. Chicago, Ill, Apr. 22, 31; m. 60; c. 2. ENGLISH, DRAMA. B.S, Northwest. Univ, 56, Ph.D.(Eng), 67; A.M, Harvard, 58. Instr. ENG, Northwest. Univ, 64-67; ASST. PROF, UNIV. GUELPH, 67- U.S.M.C, 51-53, Sgt. MLA; NCTE. English Renaissance drama; modern drama. Publ: The wisdom of Doctor Dodypoll, Malone Soc, 65. Add: Dept. of English, University of Guelph, Guelph, Ont, Can.

MATTES, ELEANOR BUSTIN, b. New York, N.Y, Aug. 29, 13; m. 43; c. 3. ENGLISH, AMERICAN LITERATURE. B.A, Smith Col, 35; B.A, Cambridge, 37, M.A, 42; M.Div, Yale, 42, Ph.D.(Eng), 45. Instr. Eng, New Haven Woman's Col, 38-39; relig, Mather Col, West. Reserve Univ, 42-43; lectr, Barnard Col, Columbia Univ, 45-46; instr. ENG, Conn. Col. Women, 47-48; asst. prof, WILSON COL, 62-67, assoc. prof, 68-73, PROF, 73- MLA. Tennyson; T.S. Eliot; American women writers. Publ: In Memoriam: the way of a soul, Exposition, 51. Add: Dept. of English, Wilson College, Chambersburg, PA 17201.

MATTESON, ROBERT STEERE, b. New Paltz, N.Y, Nov. 19, 31; m. 58; c. 3. ENGLISH. B.A, Haverford Col, 53; M.S, Univ. Pa, 59, M.A, 61; Ph.D.(Eng), Univ. Okla, 68. Spec. instr. ENG, Univ. Okla, 63-64; instr, ST. LAWRENCE UNIV, 65-67, asst. prof, 67-70, ASSOC. PROF, 70- U.S.N.R, 53-56. MLA; AAUP; Col. Eng. Asn. Restoration and 18th century literature; Irish literature. Publ: Arthur Machen: a vision of an enchanted land, Personalist, 4/65; Surprises in an old Irish attic, Bull. Friends Owen D. Young Libr,

12/72; Archbishop William King's library: some discoveries and queries, Long Room, spring 74. Add: Dept. of English, St. Lawrence University, Canton, NY 13617.

MATTHEISEN, PAUL FRANCIS, b. Minneapolis, Minn, Oct. 4, 25. ENGLISH. LITERATURE. B.A, Univ. Minn, 53; M.A, Rutgers Univ, 56, Ph.D, 58. Asst. prof. ENG, HARPUR COL, STATE UNIV. N.Y. BINGHAMTON, 60-65, ASSOC. PROF, 65- MLA. Victorian literature. Publ: Transatlantic dialogue, Univ. Tex, 65; Uproar in the echo, In: University of Wisconsin literary monographs, Univ. Wis, 70. Add: Dept. of English, Harpur College, State University of New York at Binghamton, Binghamton, NY 13901.

MATTHEWS, CHARLES EUGENE, b. Oxford, Miss, Sept. 28, 40; m. 69. ENGLISH LITERATURE. B.A, Univ. Miss, 62; Fulbright grantee, Univ. Tübingen, 62-63; M.A, Harvard, 64, Ph.D.(Eng), 68. ASST. PROF. ENG, SOUTH. METHODIST UNIV, 68- English literature 1800-present; Romantic, Victorian and modern poetry; Victorian non-fictional prose. Publ: Satire in the Alice books, Criticism, spring 70; Argument through metaphor in John Stuart Mill's On liberty, Lang. & Style, summer 71; co-auth, To the student of poetry; an essay on essays, CEA Critic, 1/73. Add: Dept. of English, Southern Methodist University, Dallas, TX 75275.

MATTHEWS, JOHN FLOYD, b. Cincinnati, Ohio, Apr. 8, 19; m. 66; c. 1. DRAMA. B.A, Univ. Cincinnati, 40. Lectr. playwriting, New Sch. Soc. Res, 48-50; chmn. fac. & head playwriting dept, Dramatic Workshop & Technol. Inst, 50-52; assoc. prof. dramatic lit, BRANDEIS UNIV, 52-70, PROF. AM. STUD, 70-, CHMN. DEPT, 73-, chmn. theatre dept, 56-58. Mem. prog. comt, Brandeis Creative Arts Festivals, 53-60, Creative Arts Awards Comn, 57-, chmn. theatre jury, 62, 69, 71 & film jury, 70, 72. Screenwriter, Warner Bros, 44-45; mem. play comt, New Stages, Inc, 46-48; lectr. playwriting, City Col. New York, 47-; contrib. ed, Libr. Living Painters & Dictionary of the Arts, 50-51; mem, New Dramatists Comt, 51-52; consult, script & prod. probs. plays & musicals, 53-; screenwriter, United Artists, 61; Assoc. Screen Prod, 63; vis. critic playwriting, Yale Sch. Drama, 65; mem, Sem. Am. Dramatic Lit, Cercle Culturel de Royaumont, France, summer 66. Arts of the Theatre Found. award, 50. Dramatists Guild; Authors League Am. American drama; American internal migrations; history of popular entertainment in America. Publ: Co-auth, The Old Vic in America, Theatre, Inc, 48; ed, El Greco, Abrams, 51, 52; ed. & auth. introd, Shaw's dramatic criticism, Hill & Wang, 59. Add: Dept. of American Studies, Brandeis University, Waltham, MA 02154.

MATTHEWS, JOHN PENGWERNE, b. Sydney, Australia, Oct. 22, 27; m. 55; c. 3. ENGLISH. B.A, Univ. Melbourne, 51; Dipl. Educ, Univ. London, 52, LL.B, 54; Carnegie traveling fel, 53; Leonard Wells sr. fel, Univ. Toronto, 54-55, Ph.D.(Eng), 57. Instr. ENG, Univ. Col, Univ. Toronto, 55-56; from asst. prof. to assoc. prof, St. John's Col, Univ. Man, 56-57, prof. & dean arts & sci, 57-62; PROF, QUEEN'S UNIV.(ONT), 62-, dir. inst. commonwealth & comp. stud, 62-67. Chmn. Can. Commonwealth exchange comt. of Humanities Res. Counc. Can, Soc. Sci. Res. Counc. Can. & Asn. Univs. & Cols. Can, 63-; chmn. acad. interchange prog, Brit. Commonwealth Conf, Leeds, 64. Royal Australian Air Force Reserve, 50-53; R.C.A.F.R, 53-58, Res, 58-, Flight Lt. MLA; Inst. Asn. Univ. Prof. Eng; Asn. Can. Univ. Teachers Eng; Humanities Asn. Can.(pres, 71-72). Canadian and commonwealth literature; Victorian literature. Publ: Tradition in exile, Univ. Toronto, 63; The Canadian experience, In: Commonwealth literature, Heinemann, 65; Charles Mair, In: Our living tradition, Univ. Toronto, 65; Abraham Klein and the problem of synthesis, J. Commonwealth Lit, 65. Add: Dept. of English, Queen's University, Kingston, Ont, Can.

MATTHEWS, WILLIAM, b. London, Eng, June 25, 05; nat; m. 48. ENGLISH. B.A, Univ. London, 29, M.A, 31, Ph.D.(Eng), 34; hon. D.Lett.(Eng), Claremont Grad. Sch, 67. Tutor, Diplomatic & Indian Civil Serv, Davies, London, 34-37; lectr. ENG, Westfield Coll, Univ. London, 36, Birkbeck Col, 37; instr, Univ. Wis, 38-39; asst. prof, UNIV. CALIF, LOS ANGELES, 39-43, assoc. prof, 43-48, prof, 48-72, EMER. PROF, 72- Vis. prof, Univ. Manchester, Eng, 51; Univ. London, 55; prof, Univ. Pittsburgh, 72- Ling. Soc. Am; Mediaeval Acad. Am; Int. Asn. Univ. Prof. Eng.(pres, 71-72); MLA; Am. Dialect Soc; Philos. Asn. Pac. Coast. History of English language; medieval literature; diaries and autobiographies. Publ: Cockney, past and present; American diaries; British autobiographies; The tragedy of Arthur, 60, The ill-framed knight, 67, British diaries, 50 & Charles II's escape from Worcester, 66, Univ. Calif; ed, Later Medieval English prose, 63 & auth, Old and Middle English literature, 68, Appleton; ed, Diary of Samuel Pepys, Vols. 1-8, Bell & Univ. Calif, 70-74; American diaries in manuscript, 74. Add: Dept. of English, University of California, Los Angeles, CA 90024.

MATTHEWS, WILLIAM R, JR, b. Chicago, Ill, Mar. 17, 20; m. 45; c. 2. ENGLISH LITERATURE. B.Ed, Univ. Toledo, 49, M.A, 50; Ph.D, Ohio State Univ, 60. Instr. ENG, Ohio State Univ, 58-59; asst. prof, Wittenberg Univ, 59-64, assoc. prof, 64-65, assoc. dean col, 65-67; V.PRES. ACAD. AFFAIRS, AUGUSTANA COL.(S.DAK), 68- Med.C, U.S.A, 41-45. MLA. Victorian literature; modern poetry. Publ: Co-auth, Guide to doctoral dissertations in Victorian literature, Univ. Ill, 60. Add: Augustana College, Sioux Falls, SD 57102.

MATTHIAS, JOHN EDWARD, b. Columbus, Ohio, Sept. 5, 41; m. 67; c. 2. ENGLISH LITERATURE. B.A, Ohio State Univ, 63; M.A, Stanford Univ, 66; Univ. London, 66-67. ASSOC. PROF. ENG, UNIV. NOTRE DAME, 67- Mem, London Poetry Secretariat, London Arts Asn, 70-; poets & writers prog, N.Y. State Counc. Arts, 70-; prog. poetry readings, Ill. Arts Counc, 70- Modern British poetry; modern American poetry; creative writing. Publ: Bucyrus, 70, ed, Twenty-three modern British poets, 71 & auth, Turns, 74, Swallow; ed, Contemporary British poetry, Northwest. Univ, 71. Add: Dept. of English, University of Notre Dame, Notre Dame, IN 46556.

MATTINGLY, ALETHEA, b. Chicago, Ill, May 27, 05; m. 35. SPEECH. B.A, Univ. Wis, 24, M.A, 31; Ph.D.(speech), Northwest. Univ, 54. Instr. speech & asst. dir. univ. theatre, Univ. Minn, 24-28; asst. prof. SPEECH, Fla. State Coll. Women, 28-34; instr, UNIV. ARIZ, 34-38, asst. prof, 38-43, assoc. prof, 43-55, PROF, 55- Vis. prof, Univ. Wis, summer 41; Univ. Colo, summer 48; Univ. Hawaii, 48-49, Northwest. Univ, summers 51, 52, 54; Univ. Utah, 63; Univ. Wash, 68; lectr. grad. symposium, Northwest. Univ, summer 58; Denver Univ, summer 64; dir. NDEA Inst. Advan. Stud. Eng, Univ. Ariz, 66-67; assoc. ed, Quart. Jour. Speech, 66-69. Speech Commun. Asn.(publ. chmn. interpretation div, 71-74); Nat. Col. Players; West. Speech Asn.(v.pres, 48); Am. Soc. Aesthetics. Dramatic literature; history and theories of interpretation; literary criticism. Publ: Interpretation: writer, reader, audience, Wadsworth, 2nd ed, 69; The playing time and manner of delivery of Shakespeare's plays in Elizabethan theatre, 3/54 & Follow nature: a synthesis of 18th century views, 3/64, Speech Monogr; contrib, Studies in interpretation, Rodopi, 72; plus others. Add: 1312 E. Adams St, Tucson, AZ 85719.

MATTINGLY, IGNATIUS G, Linguistics. See Volume III, Foreign Languages, Linguistics & Philology.

MAUD, RALPH NOEL, b. Bradford, Eng, Dec. 24, 28; U.S. citizen; m. 61; c. 1. ENGLISH. A.B, Harvard, 53, Dexter traveling fel. & Ph.D, 58. Teaching fel, Harvard, 54-58; instr. ENG, State Univ, N.Y. Buffalo, 58-59; asst. prof, 59-64, assoc. prof, 64-65; PROF, SIMON FRASER UNIV, 65- Am. Counc. Learned Soc. grant-in-aid, 61; Guggenheim fel, 66-67. R.A.F, 47-49. MLA. Modern British and American literature; Welsh history and literature. Publ: Entrances to Dylan Thomas' poetry, Univ. Pittsburgh, 63; ed, The notebooks of Dylan Thomas, 67 & Dylan Thomas in print, 71, New Directions. Add: Dept. of English, Simon Fraser University, Burnaby 2, B.C, Can.

MAULDIN, LLOYD WESLEY, b. Canton, Ga, Apr. 30, 23; m. 43; c. 2. ENGLISH, EDUCATION. B.A, Columbia Union Col, 45; M.A, George Peabody Col, 55, Ph.D.(educ. & Eng), 60. Educ. consult, Indonesia Union Mission of Seventh-Day Adventist, 52-58; PROF. ENG. & EDUC, COLUMBIA UNION COL, 64-, CHMN. DEPT. ENG, 72-, dept. educ, 60-72. Asn. Supv. & Curriculum Develop; NCTE. Linguistics and composition. Add: Dept. of Education, Columbia Union College, Carroll Ave, Takoma Park, MD 20012.

MAURER, A. E. WALLACE, b. Grenfell, Sask, Sept. 11, 21; U.S. citizen; m. 63; c. 2. ENGLISH. B.A, Univ. Man, 42, M.A, 48; Ph.D, Univ. Wis, 54. Teaching asst. ENG, Univ. Wis, 48-53; asst. instr, OHIO STATE UNIV, 53-54, instr, 54-59, asst. prof, 59-63, assoc. prof, 63-69, PROF, 69- U.S.A, 44-46, S/Sgt. MLA. John Dryden and the Restoration. Publ: Co-ed, The works of John Dryden: prose 1668-1691, Vol. XVII, Univ. Calif, 71; auth, Dryden's Balaam well hung?, Rev. Eng. Stud, 11/59; Who prompted Dryden to write Absalom and Achitophel?, Philol. Quart, 1/61; The design of Dryden's The medall, Papers Lang. & Lit, fall 66. Add: Dept. of English, College of Arts & Sciences, Ohio State University, 164 W. 17th Ave, Columbus, OH 43210.

MAURER, DAVID W, Linguistics. See Volume III, Foreign Languages, Linguistics & Philology.

MAURER, OSCAR EDWARD, b. New Haven, Conn, Jan. 29, 11; m. 39; c. 2. ENGLISH LITERATURE. A.B, Yale, 32, Ph.D, 35. Instr. ENG, Cornell Univ, 35-40, Univ. Buffalo, 40-41; Yale, 41-42; asst. prof. UNIV. TEX. AUSTIN, 42-49, assoc. prof, 49-62, PROF, 62- MLA. Nineteenth century English literature. Publ: William Morris and the poetry of escape; Anonymity versus signature in Victorian reviewing; Pope and the Victorians; plus others. Add: Dept. of English, University of Texas, Austin, TX 78712.

MAUSKOPF, CHARLES G, b. Cleveland, Ohio, Nov. 25, 34; m. 59. ENGLISH. B.A, N.Y. Univ, 56, fel, 59-61, Ph.D.(Eng), 64; M.A, Univ. N.C, 58. Instr. ENG, Harpur Col, 58-59; lectr, Brooklyn Col, 61-64; asst. prof, TEMPLE UNIV, 64-72, ASSOC. PROF, 72- MLA. Victorian novel; romantic poetry and prose. Publ: Thackeray's attitude towards Dickens' writings, Nineteenth Century Fiction, 66. Add: Dept. of English, Temple University, Philadelphia, PA 19122.

MAVEETY, STANLEY R, b. Oak Park, Ill, Oct. 16, 20; m. 48; c. 1. ENGLISH LITERATURE. B.S, Northwest. Univ, 43; M.A, Columbia Univ, 50; Ph.D, Stanford Univ, 56. Instr. ENG, UNIV. ORE, 55-57, from asst. prof. to assoc. prof, 57-73, PROF, 73-, asst. head dept. Eng, 57-72, dir. grad. stud, 71-73. U.S.N.R, 42-46, Lt.(jg). Col. Eng. Asn; MLA. Literature of the English Renaissance; Bible as literature. Publ: High style, strange words, and the answer to an old problem, Eng. Lang. Notes, 3/68; The Oregon campaign: the euphoria of the inexperienced doing the impossible, N.Mex. Quart, summer 68; A second fall of cursed man: the bold metaphor in Richard II, J. Eng. & Ger. Philol, spring 73. Add: Dept. of English, University of Oregon, Eugene, OR 97403.

MAXFIELD, JAMES F, b. Omaha, Nebr, Dec. 25, 36; m. 58; c. 3. ENGLISH. B.A, Knox Col, 59; M.A, Univ. Iowa, 61, Ph.D.(Eng), 67. Instr. ENG, Knox Col, 64-66; WHITMAN COL, 66-67, asst. prof, 67-71, ASSOC. PROF, 71- Graves Award, 70-71. Victorian novel, Dickens, Hardy; 20th century literature; cinema. Add: Dept. of English, Whitman College, Walla Walla, WA 99362.

MAXFIELD, MALINDA RUTH, b. Jackson, Miss, Dec. 22, 36. COMPARATIVE & ENGLISH LITERATURE. B.A, Vanderbilt Univ, 59, NDEA fel. & Ph.D.(comp. lit), 69; grant, Piedmont Univ. Ctr, summer 68. Assoc. prof. ENG. & chmn. dept, Queens Col.(N.C), 65-72; PROF. & CHMN. DEPT, ELIZABETHTOWN COL, 72- Eng. Speaking Union fel, summer 71; Nat. Endowment for Humanities fel, summer 73. MLA; AAUP; Col. Eng. Asn. Drama; religion and literature; comparative literature. Add: Dept. of English, Fairview 274, Elizabethtown College, Elizabethtown, PA 17022.

MAXWELL, DESMOND E. S, b. Londonderry, Ireland, July 6, 25; m. 55; c. 1. ENGLISH. B.A, Trinity Col.(Dublin), 47, Ph.D.(Eng), 50. Lectr. ENG, Univ. Ghana, 56-60, asst. dir. exam, Civil Serv. Comn, London, 60-63; prof. & chmn. dept, Univ. Ibadan, 63-67; PROF, YORK UNIV, 67-, MASTER, WINTERS COL, 70- Can. Asn. Irish Stud.(chmn, 73-74). Modern literature; American literature; Anglo-Irish literature. Publ: Poetry of T.S. Eliot, 52 & Melville, 68, Routledge; American fiction, Routledge & Columbia Univ, 63; Cozzens, Oliver & Boyd, 64; Poets of the thirties, Routledge & Barnes & Noble, 69; Swift's dark grove, In: Yeats centenary essays, Univ. Ibadan, 65; plus one other. Add: Dept. of English, York University, Downsview, Ont. M3J 1P3, Can.

MAXWELL, JOHN C, b. Brooklyn, N.Y, Dec. 9, 26; m. 48; c. 4. ENGLISH EDUCATION. B.S, Univ. Nebr, 50, M.A, 51; fel, Univ. Wis, 61-62, Ph.D. (educ), 66. Teacher, Westside Community Schs, 50-55; consult. lang. arts, pub. schs, Racine, Wis, 55-61; instr. Eng. & educ, Univ. Wis, 61-62, assoc. dir. teacher internships, 62-64; consult. Eng, Minneapolis Pub. Schs, Minn, 64-66; dir, Twin City Inst. for Talented Youth, St. Paul, Minn, 66; prog. coord, Upper Midwest Regional Educ. Lab, 66-72; DEP. EXEC. SECY, NCTE, 72- U.S.N, 44-46. NCTE (mem. exec. comt. & chmn. sec. sect, 66-68, chmn. curriculum comn, 68-71). In-service education of teachers; curriculum materials in English; the teaching of composition and language. Publ: Co-auth, Macmillan English series (text), Book 10, Macmillan, 64; auth, Ginn elementary English, Book V, 67, Book VII, 69, Ginn; co-auth, On writing behavioral objectives for English, NCTE, 70; auth, Part II: the study of language, In: Ends and issues: 1965-66, NCTE, 66; Preparing for new curriculum materials: councilletter, 12/67 & National assessment of writing: useless and uninteresting?, 12/73, Eng. J. Add: National Council of Teachers of English, 1111 Kenyon Rd, Urbana, IL 61801.

MAY, CHARLES EDWARD, b. Paintsville, Ky, Feb. 18, 41; m. 67; c. 1. ENGLISH & AMERICAN LITERATURE. B.A, Morehead State Univ, 63; M.A, Ohio Univ, 64, Ph.D.(Eng), 66. Asst. prof. ENG, Ohio Univ, 66-67; CALIF. STATE UNIV, LONG BEACH, 67-72; ASSOC. PROF, 72- MLA. Victorian literature; the short story; erotic literature. Publ: Thomas Hardy and the poetry of the absurd, Tex. Stud. Lit. & Lang, spring 70; The short story in the college classroom, Col. Eng, 1/72; Myth and mystery in Steinbeck's The snake, Criticism, fall 73. Add: Dept. of English, California State University, Long Beach, Seventh St, Long Beach, CA 90840.

MAY, CLARENCE EDWARD, b. Weyers Cave, Va, Apr. 12, 03; m. 28; c. 1. ENGLISH LITERATURE. A.B, Bridgewater Col, 24; A.M, Univ. Va, 31; summers, Columbia Univ, 39, 40, 41, Univ. Birmingham (Eng), 49. Prin. jr. high sch, W.Va, 25-30; high schs, Va, 31-41, 45-46; prof. ENG. & dir. publicity, BRIDGEWATER COL, 46-68, chmn. dept, 55-68, EMER. PROF, 68- S.Atlantic Mod. Lang. Asn. Elizabethan period in English literature; mental abnormality in revenge plays from Thomas Kyd to Shakespeare. Add: Dept. of English, Bridgewater College, Bridgewater, VA 22812.

MAY, JOHN RICHARD, Religious Studies, Literature & Theology. See Volume IV, Philosophy, Religion & Law.

MAY, LELAND CHANDLER, b. Purdy, Mo, June 11, 34; m. 57; c. 3. ENGLISH LITERATURE & EDUCATION. B.A, Okla. Baptist Univ, 57; M.Ed, Univ. Mo-Columbia, 62; Ed.D, Okla. State Univ, 69- Teacher ENG, Southwest High Sch, Washburn, Mo, 57-61; asst. prof, Southwest Baptist Col, 66-69; ASSOC. PROF, NORTHWEST MO. STATE UNIV, 69- MLA; Nineteenth century English literature; parodies of the Gothic novels. Publ: Way to teach spelling, Sch. & Community, 11/72; Thoughts about evaluating English compositions, Clearinghouse, 5/73; How to play educational games with a road map, Ford Times & Ford Outdoors, fall 73; plus others. Add: Dept. of English, Northwest Missouri State University, Maryville, MO 64468.

MAY, STEVEN WILLIAM, b. Indianapolis, Ind, Oct. 25, 41; m. 67; c. 1. RENAISSANCE ENGLISH LITERATURE. B.A, Rockford Col, 63; M.A, Univ. Chicago, 64, Ph.D.(Eng), 68. Instr. ENG, Augustana Col, 64-65; ASST. PROF, North. Ill. Univ, 68-69; GEORGETOWN COL, 69- Spec. consult. to Eng. dept, Carson Newman Col, 70. MLA; Renaissance Soc. Am; AAUP. Elizabethan court poets; textual criticism and bibliography; Renaissance poetry. Publ: The French primero: a study in Renaissance textual transmission and taste, Eng. Lang. Notes, 12/71; Spenser's amyntas: three poems by Ferdinando Stanley, Lord Strange, Fifth Earl of Derby, 8/72 & co-auth, An epilogue possibly by Shakespeare, 11/72, Mod. Philol. Add: Dept. of English, Georgetown College, Georgetown, KY 40324.

MAYER, MILTON (SANFORD), b. Chicago, Ill, Aug. 24, 08; m. 47; c. 4. ENGLISH. Univ. Chicago, 25-28; hon. Litt.D, Windham Col, 73. Instr. adult educ, Univ. Chicago, 37-45, asst. prof. educ. & soc. sci. & tutor comt. soc. thought, 45-48; acad. dir. CLASSICS, GREAT BKS. FOUND, 48-51, CONSULT, 51- Vis. lectr, U.S. & Europ. cols. & univs, 39-; contrib. & contrib. ed, numerous jour. & mag, 39-; consult, Great Bks. West. World, Encycl. Britannica, 45-; Am. Friends Serv. Comt, Fel. Reconciliation, Jewish Peace Fel, 45-; vis. prof. relig, William Penn Col, 48-51; soc. res, Univ. Frankfurt, 51-52; vis. tutor classics, Ecole d'Humanité, Switz, 55; vis. prof. relig. insts, Comenius Theol. Fac, Prague, 61-62; vis. prof. Eng, Univ. Mass, Amherst, 64-; fel, Ctr. Stud. Democratic Insts, 64-; mem, U.S. Comn. Christian Peace Conf, 64-; vis. prof. humanities, Windham Col, 69-; vis. prof. Am. stud, Univ. Paris, 74. Social issues; education; religion. Publ: They thought they were free: the Germans 1933-45, 55 & 66, co-auth, The revolution in education, 58 & auth, What can a man do?, 64, Univ. Chicago; co-auth, Humanistic education and Western civilization, Holt, 64; auth, If men were angels, Atheneum, 72; contrib, J. Pub. Law; Yale Law J; Communio Viatorum, Prague; Junge Kirche, Dortmund; plus others. Add: 119 Bay Rd, Hadley, MA 01035.

MAYHEW, GEORGE P, b. Boston, Mass, Oct. 25, 18; m. 41; c. 3. ENGLISH. A.B, Harvard, 41, fels, 46-49, M.A, 47, Ph.D, 53. Asst. dean, Harvard Col, 49-52, asst. to dean admis, 53-54; asst. prof. ENG, CALIF. INST. TECHNOL, 54-60, assoc. prof, 60-68, PROF, 68-, master stud. houses, 54-58. Am. Counc. Learned Soc. grant, summer 59; fel, Huntington Libr, 62-63; Inst. of Advan. Stud. in Humanities fel, Edinburgh, Scotland, 73. U.S.A, 41-46; Bronze Star Medal, 44. MLA; assoc. mem, Am. Counc. Learned Soc. Eighteenth century English literature; modern Anglo-Irish literature. Publ: Rage or raillery: the Swift manuscripts at the Huntington Library, Huntington Libr, 67; co-auth, A tower of polished black stone, Dolmen, Dublin, 71; Druid craft: the writing of the shadowy waters, Univ. Mass, 71 & Oxford, 72; auth, Swift's games with language in Rylands English ms. 659, Bull. John Rylands Libr, 54; Swift's first will and the first use of the provost's negative at T.C.D, Huntington Libr. Quart, 58; co-auth, Recent Swift scholarship, In: Jonathan Swift: a Dublin tercentenary tribute, Dolmen, 67; plus others. Add: 301 E. Baxter Hall, Div. of Humanities & Social Sciences, California Institute of Technology, Pasadena, CA 91109.

MAYHEW, JEAN BINKLEY, b. Gratiot Co, Mich, July 29, 19; m. 49; c. 2. SPEECH, DRAMA. B.A, Mich. State Univ, 41; M.A, Univ. Mich, 51. Instr. SPEECH & DRAMA, CENT. MICH. UNIV, 52-54, asst. prof, 55-61, assoc. prof, 62-69, PROF, 69-, LECTR. TV, 61-, DIR. BEGINNING COURSE, 62-, ASST. CHMN. DEPT, 70- Vis. lectr, Queens Col.(N.Y), summer 65. Speech Commun. Asn; Int. Commun. Asn; Cent. States Speech Asn. Voice and diction; oral interpretation; speech methods. Publ: Handbook for speech, 2 vols, Cent. Mich. Univ, 61, 62; Handbook for speech 101, Brown, 68; co-auth, Four methods of teaching improvement at the college level, J. Develop. Reading, 60, Faculty resistance to ITV, Nat. Asn. Educ. Broadcasters J, 9-10/66 & Televised testing in the beginning speech course, Mich. Speech J, spring 68; plus others. Add: Dept. of Speech & Dramatic Arts, Central Michigan University, Mt. Pleasant, MI 48858.

MAYNARD, TEMPLE JAMES, b. London, Eng, Dec. 22, 36; Can. citizen. ENGLISH LITERATURE. B.A, Univ. B.C, 59, M.A, 63; Univ. Toronto, 63-66; Ph.D. Univ. London, 70. Lectr. ENG, SIMON FRASER UNIV, 66-70, ASST. PROF, 70- Can. Counc. fel, 71-73. MLA; Johnson Soc. Northwest; Asn. Can. Univ. Teachers Eng. Development of 18th and 19th century novel; genre of the Oriental tale; the gothic in prose and architecture. Add: Dept. of English, Simon Fraser University, Burnaby 2, B.C, Can.

MAYNE, FREDERICK, b. London, Eng, Feb. 18, 14; m. 60; c. 1. ENGLISH. B.A, Univ. Witwatersrand, 40, B.A. Hons, 46, Ph.D.(Eng), 61. Teacher, Parktown Boys' High Sch, Johannesburg, S.Africa, 41-44, head dept. hist, 45-55; Johannesburg Col. Educ, 56-60; lectr. educ, Univ. Adelaide, 61-63; sr. lectr. ENG, Univ. Witwatersrand, 64-67; assoc. prof, UNIV. VICTORIA, 67-73, PROF, 73- Lectr. hist. educ, Univ. Witwatersrand, 57-60; Hugh le May fel, Rhodes Univ, 61; consult, Dictionary S.African Biog, 66-67. Bernard Shaw; theory of wit and humour. Publ: The slaughter of an innocent, Cent. News Agency, S.Africa, 55; The wit and satire of Bernard Shaw, Edward Arnold, 67; Consonance and consequence, 9/59 & Hamlet restated, 3/67, Eng. Stud. Africa; The real and the ideal, South. Rev, 63. Add: Dept. of English, University of Victoria, Victoria, B.C, Can.

MAYO, EDWARD LESLIE, b. Dorchester, Mass, July 26, 04; m. 36; c. 3. ENGLISH. A.B, Univ. Minn, 32, A.M, 36; Litt.D, Iowa Wesleyan Col, 60. Instr, N.Dak. Agr. Col, 36-42; Univ. Minn, 42-43; Phillips Acad, 43-45; head dept. Eng, Newburgh Prep. Sch, 45-47; asst. prof. ENG, Drake Univ, 47-51, assoc. prof, 51-66; Univ. Ore, 66-67; PROF, DRAKE UNIV, 68- Lowell poetry traveling scholar, 53, 54. Blumenthal Poetry Prize, 43. MLA. William Blake. Publ: The diver, 47 & Summer unbound, 58, Univ. Minn; The center is everywhere, Twayne, 54; Selected poems, Prairie Press, 73. Add: Dept. of English, Drake University, Des Moines, IA 50311.

MAYO, MARIANNE K, b. Vienna, Austria, Jan. 26, 21; U.S. citizen; m. 49; c. 2. ENGLISH. B.A, Jacksonville Univ, 62; M.A, Univ. Fla, 63, Ph.D. (Eng), 68. Instr. German, Univ. Fla, 66-67; asst. prof. ENG, VALDOSTA STATE COL, 67-70, ASSOC. PROF, 70- MLA; Col. Eng. Asn. Restoration and 18th century English literature. Add: Dept. of English, Valdosta State College, Valdosta, GA 31601.

MAYO, ROBERT D, b. Chicago, Ill, Aug. 4, 10; m. 47; c. 1. ENGLISH. A.B, Oberlin Col, 32; A.M, Univ. Chicago, 34; A.M, Princeton, 36, Ph.D, 38. Instr, Oberlin Col, 36-37, 38-41; ENG, NORTHWEST. UNIV, 41-42, asst. prof, 46-52, assoc. prof, 52-61, PROF, 61-, chmn. dept, 66-70. Ford fac. fel, 54-55; Guggenheim fel, 63-64. U.S.A, 42-46. MLA; AAUP; Res. Soc. Victorian Periodicals; Am. Soc. 18th Century Stud. English periodicals; 18th century novel; cantos of Ezra Pound. Publ: The English novel in the magazines, 1740-1815, Northwest. Univ. & Oxford, 62. Add: Dept. of English, Northwestern University, Evanston, IL 60201.

MAZZAFERRI, E. ANNETTE MONROE, b. Wheeling, W.Va, June 17, 32; m. 68. SPEECH. B.A, Muskingum Col, 54; scholar. & M.A, Northwest. Univ, 55; fel. & Ph.D.(speech), Univ. Wis, 63. Instr. SPEECH, Univ. Md, 55-57; acting adv, Miami Univ, 57-58; asst. prof, Mt. St. Joseph Col, 58-60; Hood Col, 63-65; PROF. KUTZTOWN STATE COL, 65-, CHMN. DEPT, 66-70, 74- Leader, Exp. Int. Living, summer 62; Fulbright grant, India, summer 64; Adv. Fine Arts Proj. Comt, Dept. Pub. Inst, Pa, 66-67, speech consult, 66- Speech Commun. Asn; Am. Asn. Univ. Women. Oral interpretation. Publ: The group reading: expression for drama of mental action, Cent. States Speech J, 8/64. Add: Dept. of Speech & Theatre, Kutztown State College, Kutztown, PA 19530.

MAZZARO JEROME, b. Detroit, Mich, Nov. 25, 34. RENAISSANCE & CONTEMPORARY LITERATURE. A.B, Wayne State Univ, 54, Ph.D.(Eng), 63; M.A, Univ, Iowa, 56. Instr. ENG, Univ. Detroit, 58-61; asst. prof, State Univ. N.Y. Col. Cortland, 62-64; from asst. prof. to PROF, STATE UNIV, N.Y. BUFFALO, 64- Guggenheim fel, 64-65. Dante Soc. Am. Contemporary poetry; Renaissance poetry. Publ: The achievement of Robert Lowell: 1939-1959, Univ. Detroit, 60; The poetic themes of Robert Lowell, 65 & transl, Juvenal's Satires, 65, Univ. Mich; auth, Changing the windows (poems), Ohio Univ, 66; Transformations in the Renaissance English lyric, 70 & William Carlos Williams: the later poems, 73, Cornell Univ; Modern American poetry: essays in criticism: David McKay, 70; Profile of Robert Lowell, 71 & Profile of William Carlos Williams, 71, C.E. Merrill. Add: Dept. of English, Annex B, State University of New York at Buffalo, Buffalo, NY 14214.

MAZZEO, JOSEPH A, b. New York, N.Y, June 25, 23; m. 48. ENGLISH, COMPARATIVE LITERATURE. A.B, Columbia Univ, 46, A.M, 47, Ph.D, 50; Am. Counc. Learned Soc. fel, Univ. Florence, Italy, 48-49. Lectr. Eng, Hunter Col, 47-48; Eng. & comp. lit, Columbia Univ, 48, instr, 49-53, asst. prof, 53-55; assoc. prof. Eng. & Italian lit, Cornell Univ, 55-59, prof, 59-60; ENG. & COMP. LIT, COLUMBIA UNIV, 60-73, PARR PROF, 73- Am. Philos. Soc. Grant, 54; Guggenheim fel, 59; Counc. of Humanities sr. fel, Princeton, 72-73. Gold Medal, Dante Soc. Florence, 59. U.S.A, 43-46, Res, 47-53, 2nd Lt. MLA; Renaissance Soc. Am; Am. Comp. Lit. Asn; Dante Soc. Am. Comparative literature of the Renaissance; science and the literary imagination; general theory of interpretation. Publ: Structure and thought in the Paradiso, 58 & ed, Medieval cultural tradition in Dante's comedy, 60, Cornell Univ; ed, Reason and the imagination, 62& auth, Renaissance & Seventeenth century studies, 64, Columbia Univ; Renaissance & revolution: the remaking of European thought, 66 & The design of life: major themes in the development of biological thought, 67, Pantheon; Machiavelli: the poetry of power, Rev. Nat. Lit, 71; some interpretations of the history of ideas, J. Hist. Ideas, 72; Seventeenth-century English prose style: the quest for a natural style, Mosaic, 73. Add: 604 Philosophy Hall, Columbia University, New York, NY 10027.

MEAD, CARL DAVID, b. Cadiz, Ohio, May 4, 13; m. 38; c. 2. ENGLISH LITERATURE. B.S, Ohio State Univ, 36, A.M, 38, Ph.D, 47. Instr. ENG, Denison Univ, 38-39; Ohio State Univ, 46-47; from asst. prof. to assoc. prof, MICH. STATE UNIV, 48-57, PROF, 57-, chmn. dept, 59-66. Consult. Eng, Univ. Ryukyus, 55-57. U.S.A, 42-46. MLA; Am. Stud. Asn. Oriental literature; middlewestern culture; yankee eloquence in the Middle West. Add: Dept. of English, Michigan State University, East Lansing, MI 48823.

MEADE, RICHARD A, b. Sutherland, Va, Dec. 13, 11; m. 37; c. 2. ENGLISH EDUCATION. A.B, Randolph-Macon Col, 31; M.A, Univ. Va, 36, Ph.D.(educ, Eng), 41. Teacher Eng, Greensville County High Sch, Va, 31-34; Lane High Sch, Va, 34-50; instr. sec. educ. & teaching of Eng, UNIV. VA, 34-42, asst. prof, 42-50, assoc. prof. EDUC, 50-57, PROF, 57-, chmn. dept. curriculum & instr, Sch. Educ, 67-72. Vis. lectr, Univ. Wis, summer 57; mem, Comt. Nat. Interest Teaching of Eng, 59-; Comn. on Eng. Curriculum, 60-66; Comt. Reading Ladders & Human Relat, 61-63; exec. comt, Nat. Conf. Eng. Educ, 62-70 & 73-; consult. Eng. curriculum, Va. Beach, Va, 62-65; dir. NDEA Inst. Eng, Univ. Va, 65, 66 & 68; consult, curriculum proj. for low-achieving pupils in Eng, Va. State Dept. Educ, 66-68; proj. opportunity, Nelson County, Va, 67, 68 & 69. NCTE (dir, 55-74); Conf. Eng. Educ. Grammar in the English curriculum; curriculum construction in English; instruction and developments in various phases of English as a school subject. Publ: Better English, I, II, III & IV, 45, 46, 48 & 49 & co-auth, Effective English, I, II, III, IV, 61, Allyn & Bacon; Spelling for everyday life, 2 through 8, Turner Smith, 56; auth, Fifth-year and five-year programs for the preservice education of teachers of English, NCTE 63; co-ed, Literature for adolescents, Merrill, 73; auth, Developments in honors programs in the public high school, Va. Eng. Bull, 3/60; Who can learn grammar?, 2/61 & Whatever happened to insights, 12/71, Eng. J. Add: School of Education, Ruffner Hall, University of Virginia, Charlottesville, VA 22903.

MEADOR, PRENTICE AVERY, JR, b. Portland, Tenn, Feb. 8, 38; m. 60; c. 2. SPEECH, CLASSICAL THEORY. B.A, David Lipscomb Col, 60; M.A, Univ. Ill, 61, Ph.D.(speech), 64. Asst. prof. SPEECH, Univ. Calif, Los Angeles, 63-71; ASSOC. PROF, UNIV. WASH, 71- Univ. Calif, Los Angeles fel, 63-64, res. grants, 64-71, mem. fac, Engineering & Mgt. Conf, 64-69; lectr, Am. Stud. Forum IX, Mem. Coliseum, Portland, Ore, 72-73. Speech Commun. Asn; Am. Philol. Asn; Am. Renaissance Soc; West. Speech Commun. Asn. Greek and Latin rhetorical theory; communication theory; homiletics. Publ: Co-auth, Preaching to modern man, Bibl. Res. Press, 68; auth, Quintilian and the Institutio oratoria, In: A synoptic history of classical rhetoric, Random, 72; Quintilian's Vir bonus, West. Speech, 70; Cicero on humanism and rhetoric, Philos. & Rhet, 70; plus several others. Add: 11821 N.E. 143rd St, Kirkland, WA 98033.

MEAGHER, JOHN CARNEY, b. St. Louis, Mo, Mar. 23, 35; m. 58; c. 5. ENGLISH, RELIGION. B.A, Univ. Notre Dame, 56; M.A, Princeton, 58, Ph.D.(Eng), 62; Ph.D.(Eng), Univ. London, 61; Cath. Inst. Paris, 65-66. Asst. prof. Eng, Univ. Notre Dame, 61-66, gen. prog, 64-66; assoc. prof. Eng, UNIV. ST. MICHAEL'S COL, UNIV. TORONTO, 66-70, PROF, 70-, THEOL, 73-, dir, Inst. Christian Thought, 73. Can. Counc. leave fel, 72-73. Soc. Relig. Higher Educ.(cross-disciplinary fel, 65-66); Church Soc. Col. Work; Malone Soc. Renaissance drama; literary criticism; Christian origins. Publ: Ed, The downfall of Robert Earl of Huntingdon, 65 & The death of Robert Earl of Huntingdon, 67, Malone Soc; auth, Method and meaning in Jonson's masques, Univ. Notre Dame, 66; The gathering of the ungifted, Herder & Herder, 72; John 1:14 and the new temple, J. Bibl. Lit, 69; Toward a moral theory of idioms, Soundings, 71; contrib, Shakespeare 1971, Univ. Toronto, 72; plus others. Add: University of St. Michael's College, 81 St. Mary St, Toronto, Ont. M5S 1J4, Can.

MEANS, MICHAEL H, b. Beloit, Wis, June 12, 32; m. 56; c. 6. ENGLISH. B.A, Wis. State Univ, Whitewater, 55; M.A, Ohio State Univ, 57; Ph.D.(Eng), Univ. Fla, 63. Instr. ENG, Univ. Fla, 57-60, 62-63; asst. prof, UNIV. DAYTON, 63-67, ASSOC. PROF, 67-, ASST. CHMN. DEPT, 68- MLA; NCTE; Mediaeval Acad. Am. Medieval English literature; literary criticism; teaching of English. Publ: The consolatio Genre in Medieval English literature, Univ. Fla, 72. Add: Dept. of English, University of Dayton, Dayton, OH 45409.

MEARS, RICHARD M, b. Chincoteague, Va, Oct. 5, 21; m. 46; c. 2. ENGLISH. B.A, Col. William & Mary, 42; M.A, Univ. Pa, 46; Ph.D.(Eng), Univ. N.C, 53. Instr. ENG, Univ. Del, 46-49; assoc. prof, Catawba Col, 52-58; assoc. prof, DRURY COL, 58-66, PROF, 66- U.S.A, 42-45. MLA. Drama; relations art and literature; comparative literature. Add: Dept. of English, Drury College, Springfield, MO 65802.

MEASELL, JAMES SCOTT, b. Cleveland, Ohio, Feb. 13, 42; m. 64; c. 3. SPEECH, PHILOSOPHY. B.A, Muskingum Col, 64; M.A, Univ. Ill, Urbana, 68, Ph.D.(speech), 70. ASST. PROF. SPEECH, WAYNE STATE UNIV, 70- Speech Commun. Asn; Cent. States Speech Asn. Publ: Classical bases of the concept of analogy, J. Am. Forensic Asn, fall 73; Development of the concept of analogy in rhetorical theory, In: Studies in rhetoric and communication: the University of Illinois tradition, Univ. Ill, 74; co-auth, Wallace and his ways: a study of the rhetorical genre of polarization, Cent. States Speech J, spring 74. Add: Dept. of Speech Communication & Theatre, 585 Speech & Language Bldg, Wayne State University, Detroit, MI 48202.

MEBANE, MARY ELIZABETH, b. Durham, N.C. AMERICAN & NINETEENTH CENTURY BRITISH LITERATURE. B.A, N.C. Col. Durham 55; M.A, Univ, N.C. Chapel Hill, 61, Ph.D.(Eng), 73. Teacher Eng. & soc. stud, Durham City Sch, N.C, 58-60; instr. ENG, N.C. Col. Durham, 60-64, ASSOC. PROF, S.C. STATE COL, 67- MLA; Col. Lang. Asn; NCTE; S.Atlantic Mod. Lang. Asn. Black literature. Publ: Contrib, A galaxy of Black writing, Moore, 70; The eloquence of protest, Houghton, 72. Add: Communications Ctr, South Carolina State College, Orangeburg, SC 29119.

MECKIER, JEROME THOMAS, b. Jersey City, N.J, Sept. 16, 41. ENGLISH LITERATURE. A.B, LeMoyne Col.(N.Y), 63; Woodrow Wilson fel, Harvard, 63-64, M.A, 64, fels, 64 & 65-67, Ph.D.(Eng), 68. Asst. prof. ENG, Univ. Mass, Amherst, 67-70; ASSOC. PROF, UNIV. KY, 70- Huntington Libr. fel, summer 71 & 73; Nat. Endowment Humanities younger humanist fel, 74; rev. ed, Dickens Stud. Newsletter, 72- Aldous Huxley; modern novel; 19th century novel. Publ: Aldous Huxley: satire and structure, Chatto & Windus, London, 69; Looking back at anger, Dalhousie Rev, spring 72; Dickens and King Lear: a myth for Victorian England, S.Atlantic Quart, winter 72; Quarles among the monkeys: Huxley's zoological novels, Mod. Lang. Rev, 4/73; plus others. Add: Dept. of English, Patterson Office Tower, University of Kentucky, Lexington, KY 40506.

MEDINE, PETER ERNEST, b. DeKalb, Ill, Mar. 30, 41; m. 68; c. 1. LITERATURE OF THE ENGLISH RENAISSANCE. B.A, Northwest. Univ, Evanston, 63; M.A, Univ. Wis-Madison, 65, Ph.D.(Eng), 70. Instr. ENG, UNIV. ARIZ, 69-70, ASST. PROF, 70- Huntington Libr. fel, summer 73. MLA; Renaissance Soc. Am. Renaissance poetry, prose and drama. Publ: Ed, Horace his arte of poetrie, 72 & De satyrica Graecorum poesi et Romanorum satira, 73, Scholars' Facsimiles & Reprints, 73; auth, Praise and blame in Renaissance satire, Pac. Coast Philol, 72. Add: Dept. of English, University of Arizona, Tucson, AZ 85721.

MEDLICOTT, ALEXANDER GUILD, JR, b. Springfield, Mass, May 15, 27; m. 49; c. 3. ENGLISH, AMERICAN LITERATURE. B.A, Dartmouth Col, 50; M.A, Trinity Col.(Conn), 58; Ph.D.(Eng), Univ. Wash, 62. Asst. ENG, Univ. Wash, 58-60, assoc, 60-61, instr, 61-62; master, Lakeside Sch, Wash, 62-64; asst. prof, UNIV. CONN, 64-67, assoc. prof, 67-73, PROF, 73- Vis. prof, Dartmouth Col, 72-73. U.S.A, 44-46. MLA. Colonial and 18th century American literature and history. Publ: Introd, The female marine, Da Capo, 66; Soldiers are citizens of death's gray land: William March's Company K, Ariz. Quart, autumn 72; An open letter on an open letter, Eng. Exchange, spring 73; plus others. Add: Dept. of English, University of Connecticut, Storrs, CT 06268.

MEECE, SHIRLEY BAKER, b. Berea, Ky, Oct. 2, 29; m. 65. ENGLISH. A.B, Berea Col, 50; Haggin fel, Univ. Ky, 50-51, M.A, 55, Ph.D.(Eng), 67; summer, Anglo-Am. Folk Arts Sch, Barford, Eng, 53. Instr. ENG, Berea Found. Sch, Berea Col, 51-54; ASSOC. PROF, CAMPBELLSVILLE COL, 67- NEA; NCTE; MLA. Elizabethan and contemporary drama; drama theory; linguistics and folklore. Add: Dept. of English, Campbellsville College, Campbellsville, KY 42718.

MEEHAN, VIRGINIA M, b. Chicago, Ill. ENGLISH. A.B, Univ. Miami, 58, M.A, 59; fel, Univ. Fla, 59-61, Ph.D.(Eng), 66. Instr. humanities, Univ. Miami, 61-65; asst. prof. Eng, Columbus Col, 65-67; W.GA. COL, 67-72, ASSOC. PROF. ENG. & THEATRE ARTS, 72- Col. Eng. Asn. Medieval English literature; Renaissance English literature; English poetry. Publ: Christopher Marlowe: poet and playwright, Mouton, 73; More on totalled, spring 67 & Walk-in restaurant and Temporary runaround, spring 67, Am. Speech. Add: Dept. of English, West Georgia College, Carrollton, GA 30117.

MEERS, GENEVA (MAE), b. Heyworth, Ill, Dec. 31, 20. ENGLISH. B.Ed, Ill. State Norm, 42; M.A, Northwest. Univ, 45, Ph.D, 53. Teacher high sch, Ill, 42-44, 47-50; Mich, 45-46; instr, Marquette Univ, 46-47; from asst. prof. to ASSOC. PROF. ENG, CORNELL COL, 53-, CHMN. DEPT, 71- Victorian literature. Publ: It was a good program, NEA J; Check sheet for errors, Eng. J; What can I do with an English major?, Asn. Depts. Eng. J, 9/72. Add: Dept. of English, Cornell College, Mt. Vernon, IA 52314.

MEERSMAN, ROGER L, b. Moline, Ill, Jan. 1, 31; m. 55; c. 4. DRAMA, SPEECH. B.A, St. Ambrose Col, 52; Cath. Univ. Am, 52-54; M.A, Univ. Ill, 59, Ph.D.(theatre), 62. Instr. Eng. & speech, Univ. Scranton, 61-62; dir. theatre, Jewish Community Ctr, Scranton, 62-63; instr. THEATRE & SPEECH, UNIV. MD, COLLEGE PARK, 63-65, asst. prof, 65-68, ASSOC. PROF, 68-, Gen. Res. Bd. res. grants, 68 & 73, Creative & Performing Arts Bd. grants, 69 & 74. Outstanding Fac. Mem. Award, Univ. Md, 65, Bd. Regents Award, 66. Intel.C, U.S.A, 54-58. Am. Theatre Asn; Speech Commun. Asn. Theatre history; theatre theory and aesthetics. Publ: The Meininger in America, 3/66 & Père René Rapin's Eloquence des Belles Lettres, 11/71, Speech Monogr; co-auth, The National Theatre in Washington: buildings and audiences, 1835-1972, Rec. Columbia Hist. Soc, 1971-1972, 73. Add: Dept. of Speech & Dramatic Arts, University of Maryland, College Park, MD 20740.

MEESE, ELIZABETH ANN, b. Norfolk, Va, Oct. 23, 43. AMERICAN LITERATURE, WOMEN'S STUDIES. B.A, Univ. Mich, Ann Arbor, 65, M.A, Wayne State Univ, 67, Ph.D.(Eng), 72. Instr. ENG, Wayne State Univ, 70-72; ASST. PROF, DOUGLASS COL, RUTGERS UNIV, 72- MLA; AAUP; Women's Caucus Mod. Lang. American transcendental theory; women's studies; folklore. Publ: The art of the tale teller: a study of the suprasegmental phonemes in a folktale, Ky. Folklore Rec, 4-6/68. Add: Dept. of English, Douglass College, Rutgers University, New Brunswick, NJ 08903.

MEGAW, ROBERT NEILL ELLISON, Ottawa, Ont, Oct. 7, 20; U.S. citizen; m. 47; c. 3. ENGLISH LITERATURE. M.A, Univ. Chicago, 47, Ph.D, 50. Instr. Eng. lit, Williams Col, 50-53, asst. prof, 53-60, assoc. prof, 60-65, PROF, 65-69; ENG, UNIV. TEX, AUSTIN, 69-, chmn. dept, 69-71. Carnegie interne gen. educ, Harvard, 55-56; consult. acad. planning, Univ. Calif, Santa Cruz, summer 62; Transylvania Col, 66-67; gen. consult. humanities, Fla. Atlantic Univ, summer 63; vis, Nat. Humanities Fac, 70-73; consult, Nat. Endowment for Humanities, 72-73. U.S.A.A.F, 42-45, 1st Lt. MLA; NCTE; AAUP. Modern drama; Shakespeare and Renaissance literature; college and university academic planning. Publ: A proposal for a new college of liberal arts, Am. Asn. Univ. Prof. Bull, winter 61. Add: 2805 Bowman Ave, Austin, TX 78703.

MEHOK, EDWARD EUGENE, b. Akron, Ohio, Sept. 25, 32. ENGLISH LITERATURE & SCRIPTURE. M.A, Cath. Univ. Am, 61; Ph.D.(Eng), West. Reserve Univ, 71. From instr. to PROF. ENG, BORROMEO COL. OHIO, 61-, CHMN. DEPT, 69-, V.PRES. & DEAN MEN, 67-, asst. dean men, 61-67. MLA; NCTE; Midwest Mod. Lang. Asn; Renaissance Soc. Am. Middle

English literature; Elizabethan recusants; Bible as literature. Add: Office of the Vice President, Borromeo College of Ohio, 28700 Euclid Ave, Wickliffe, OH 44092.

MEINDL, ROBERT JAMES, b. Wausau, Wis, Sept. 17, 36; m. 63; c. 1. ENGLISH. B.S, Univ. Wis, 58; M.A, Univ. Conn, 60; Ph.D.(Eng), Tulane Univ, 65. Instr. ENG, Univ. Wis, Green Bay, 63-65; asst. prof. CALIF. STATE UNIV, SACRAMENTO, 65-71, ASSOC. PROF, 71- U.S.N.R, 53-61. MLA; Mediaeval Acad. Am; Am-Scand. Found. Middle English; Old English; Old Norse. Publ: The artistic unity of Widsith, Xavier Univ. Stud, 3/64. Add: Dept. of English, California State University, Sacramento, Sacramento, CA 95819.

MEINERS, ROGER K, b. Forreston, Ill, Dec. 5, 32; m. 58; c. 2. ENGLISH. B.A, Wheaton Col.(Ill), 54; Westminster Sem, 54-56; M.A, Univ. Denver, 57, Ph.D, 61. Instr. ENG, Ariz. State Univ, 59-61, asst. prof, 61-64; Univ. Mo-Columbia, 64-65, assoc. prof, 66-70, dir. grad. study, 67-70; assoc. prof, MICH. STATE UNIV, 70-71, PROF, 71- MLA. American literature; literary criticism; 19th and 20th century philosophy, psychology and literature. Publ: The last alternatives: a study of the works of Allen Tate, A. Swallow, 63; Everything to be endured: an essay on Robert Lowell and modern poetry, Univ. Mo, 70; The end of history: Allen Tate's Seasons of the soul, Sewanee Rev, 62; Yvor Winters and the possibilities of a rational criticism, Papers Midwest Mod. Lang. Asn, 69; The poetry of Delmore Schwartz and others, South. Rev, 71; plus others. Add: Dept. of English, Michigan State University, East Lansing, MI 48823.

MEINKE, DARREL M, b. Plymouth, Nebr, June 19, 29; m. 52; c. 4. ENGLISH. B.Sc.Ed, Univ. Nebr, 51, M.Ed, 55, D.Ed, 66; M.A, Univ. Denver, 59. Teacher, Grace Lutheran Sch, Nebr, 51-54; librn, high sch, Nebr, 54-60; assoc. prof. Eng, Concordia Teachers Col, 60-73; PROF. LIBR. SCI. & DIR. INSTRUCT. RESOURCES, MOORHEAD STATE COL, 73- Head librn, Concordia Teachers Col, 60-73; participant, NDEA Advan. Media Summer Inst, Mich. State Univ, 67. Am. Libr. Asn; Mountain Plains Libr. Asn; Lutheran Acad. Scholarship; Asn. Educ. Commun. & Technol. Library science, school media centers and periodicals. Publ: From box to bookshelf, Concordia, 62; co-auth, Four steps to a learning center, Instructor, 6-7/67. Add: Dept. of Library Science, Moorhead State College, Moorhead, MN 56560.

MEINKE, J. PETER, b. Brooklyn, N.Y, Dec. 29, 32; m. 57; c. 4. ENGLISH. A.B, Hamilton Col, 55; M.A, Univ. Mich, 61; Ph.D.(Eng), Univ. Minn, 65. Instr. Eng. Lit, Hamline Univ, 61-65, asst. prof, 65-66, ECKERD COL, 66-68, assoc. prof, 68-72, PROF. ENG. LIT. & DIR. WRITERS' WORKSHOP, 72- Dir, Assoc. Mid-Fla. Cols. Prog, Neuchatel, Switz, 71-72; writer-in-residence, Hamline Univ, 73. Best Poems Award, 63; First prize, Olivet Sonnet Competition, 65, second prize, 66-67. U.S.A, 55-57. Modern poetry; criticism; original writing. Publ: Howard Nemerov, Univ. Minn. & Am. Writers Ser, 68; The legend of Larry the Lizard (children's verse), John Knox, 68; Very seldom animals, Possum, 69; The Monkey's paw, In: Best Poems of 1971, Borestone, 72 & New Republic; poems, In: Adam among the television trees, Word Bks, 71; poems, In: Sports poems, Dell Bks, 72; plus others. Add: Writers' Workshop, Eckerd College, St. Petersburg, FL 33733.

MEISEL, MARTIN, b. New York, N.Y, Mar. 22, 31; m. 57; c. 3. ENGLISH. B.A, Queens Col.(N.Y), 52; Cornell Univ, 52; M.A, Princeton, 57, Ph.D. (Eng), 60; Univ. Rome, 58-59. Instr. ENG, Rutgers Univ, 57-58; Dartmouth Col, 59-61, asst. prof, 61-64, assoc. prof, 64-65; PROF, Univ. Wis, 65-68; COLUMBIA UNIV, 68-, V.CHMN. DEPT. ENG. & COMP. LIT, 73- Guggenheim fel, 63-64; Am. Counc. Learned Soc. fel, 70-71. U.S.A, 54-56. Am. Soc. Theatre Res; MLA. European drama, 17th century to present; 19th century fiction; literary-pictorial relations. Publ: Shaw and the nineteenth century theater, Princeton & Oxford, 63. Add: Dept. of English & Comparative Literature, Columbia University, New York, NY 10027.

MEISTER, CELESTIA ANNE, b. Minneapolis, Minn, Dec. 30, 16. ENGLISH. B.A, Macalester Col, 38; B.S, Univ. Minn, 40, M.A, 41. Teacher & librn, Maywood Sch, Va, 41-44; high sch, Minn, 44-47; head librn, Upper Iowa Univ, 47-48; instr. ENG, MACALESTER COL, 48-52, asst. prof, 52-71, ASSOC. PROF, 71- Consult, McGraw-Hill Publ. Co, summer 73. NCTE; MLA; Am. Asn. Univ. Women. Survivals of the Gothic in modern novels; English education; adolescent and children's literature. Publ: The placement of Macalester College English majors in 1973, Minn. Eng. J, spring, 73. Add: 3420 33rd Ave. S, Minneapolis, MN 55406.

MEISTER, CHARLES WALTER, b. Chicago, Ill, Jan. 23, 17; m. 43; c. 2. ENGLISH & HUMANITIES. A.B, Cent. Y.M.C.A. Col, 41; Cook scholar, Univ. Chicago, 41-42, M.A, 42, Ph.D.(Eng), 48. Instr. Eng, Roosevelt Univ, 48-49; asst. prof, Ariz. State Col, 49-50, assoc. prof, 50-53, prof. Eng. & co-ord. gen. educ, 53-57, chmn. div. humanities, 49-57, dean of instr, 57-65; PRES, EAST. N.MEX. UNIV, 65- Exam. & consult, N.Cent. Asn. Cols, 60, comnr, 70- U.S.A, 42-46, Capt. NCTE. American literature; Russian literature; dramatic criticism. Publ: A year in Berlin education, Harvard Educ. Rev; Franklin as a proverb stylist, Am. Lit; Chekhov's reception in England and America, Am. Slavic & E.Europ. Rev. Add: 1600 W. Cherry, Portales, NM 88130.

MEIXNER, JOHN A, b. New York, N.Y, June 6, 25. ENGLISH. A.B, City Col. New York, 51; univ. fel, Brown Univ, 52-53, A.M, 53, Ph.D, 57. Reporter, New York Times, 47-48; instr. ENG, Brown Univ, 53-56; Clark Univ, 56-57; Univ. Kans, 57-60, asst. prof, 60-63, assoc. prof, 63-68; PROF, RICE UNIV, 68- MLA. Twentieth century literature; literary criticism; creative writing. Publ: Ford Madox Ford's novels: a critical study, Univ. Minn, 62; Frost four years after, South. Rev, autumn 66; The use of biography in criticism, Col. Eng, 11/66; Ford and Conrad, Canadiana, 9/74. Add: Dept. of English, Rice University, Houston, TX 77001.

MELDRUM, BARBARA RUTH, b. Albany, Ore, Apr. 13, 34; m. 60; c. 2. ENGLISH. B.A, Westmont Col, 56; scholar, Claremont Grad. Sch, 56-57, M.A, 57, Intercol. Prog. Grad. Stud, fel, 57-60, Ph.D, 64. Instr. ENG, Univ. Redlands, 59-61, 62; asst. prof, Ariz. State Univ, 62-65; UNIV. IDAHO, 65-67, assoc. prof, 67-73, PROF, 73- Lectr, Alaska Methodist Univ, summer 67. MLA; Am. Stud. Asn; West. Lit. Asn; AAUP; Melville Soc; Rocky Mountain Mod. Lang. Asn; Philol. Asn. Pac. Coast; Am. Stud. Asn. Pac. Northwest (secy-treas, 72-74). Nineteenth century American literature; literature of the American West; American studies. Publ: Melville on war, Res. Stud, 6/69; The artist in Melville's Mardi, Stud. in the Novel, winter 69; Structure and meaning in S.K. Winther's Beyond the garden gate, West. Am. Lit, fall 71; plus others. Add: Dept. of English, University of Idaho, Moscow, ID 83843.

MELDRUM, RONALD M, b. Penticton, B.C, Jan. 31, 27; U.S. citizen; m. 60; c. 2. ENGLISH. B.A, Univ. B.C, 49; M.A, Univ. Wash, 57; Ph.D, Ariz. State Univ, 65. Instr. ENG, Univ. Colo, 55-59; Mt. San Antonio Col, 60; Univ. Redlands, 61; assoc, Univ. Calif, Riverside, 61-62; asst. prof, WASH. STATE UNIV, 65-72, ASSOC. PROF, 72- Ariz. State Univ. res. found. fel. grant, 63-64; vis. prof, Alaska Methodist Univ, summer 67; Gresham lect, Inst. Renaissance Stud, Ore. Shakespearean Festival, 68 & 70, assoc. dir, 72; assoc. ed, Albion Renaissance Soc. Am; MLA; NCTE; Conf. Brit. Stud. English Renaissance literature; Shakespeare. Publ: The epistolary concerns of Henry Adams, 69 & Three of Henry James' dark ladies, 69, Res. Stud; Charles Dickens as a artist and reformer, Albion 71; plus others. Add: Dept. of English, Washington State University, Pullman, WA 99163.

MELE, JOSEPH CHARLES, b. Hammond, La, Jan. 29, 32; m. 54; c. 2. SPEECH. B.A, Southeast. La. Col, 55; M.A, La. State Univ, 56, Ph.D. (speech), 59. Asst. prof. speech, Univ. Southwest. La, 59-63; Univ. Ala, 63-64; ASSOC. PROF. SPEECH COMMUN, UNIV. S.ALA, 64-, HEAD DEPT, 67-, acting head dept, 64-67. Fund Adult Educ. scholar, Univ. Tenn, 63. Speech Commun. Asn; South Speech Commun. Asn. Public address; classical rhetoric; phonetics. Publ: Edward Douglas White's influence on the Louisiana anti-lottery movement, South. Speech J, fall 62. Add: Dept. of Speech Communication, University of South Alabama, Mobile, AL 36688.

MELI, SAMUEL SALVADOR, b. Badera, Pa, Nov. 26, 25; m. 69; c. 1. SPEECH COMMUNICATION, THEATRE. B.F.A, Carnegie-Mellon Univ, 51, M.F.A, 53. Announcer, WRYO, 48-51; instr. speech, DUQUESNE UNIV, 51-58, asst. prof. SPEECH THEATRE, 57-63, assoc. prof, 63-71, PROF. & CHMN. DEPT, 71- Technical dir, White Barn theatre, 52-59, dir, Rabbit Run Theatre, 54-55. U.S.A, 44-47. Speech Commun. Asn; Am. Theatre Asn; AAUP. Speech Communication education; theatre. Publ: Directing the one-act: a manual, Duquesne Univ, 69. Add: Dept. of Speech Communication & Theatre, Duquesne University, Pittsburgh, PA 15219.

MELL, DONALD CHARLES, b. Akron, Ohio, May 20, 31; m. 57; c. 2. ENGLISH LITERATURE. B.A, Yale, 53, M.A, 59; Ph.D.(Eng), Univ. Pa, 61. Instr. ENG, Rutgers Univ, 61-65; asst. prof, Middlebury Col, 65-68; UNIV. DEL, 68-73, ASSOC. PROF, 73- U.S.A, 53-55. MLA; Am. Soc. 18th Century Stud. Augustan satire; Milton; eighteenth-century elegy. Publ: Form as meaning in Augustan elegy: a reading of Thomas Gray's Sonnet on the death of Richard West, Papers Lang. & Lit, Vol. 4, No. 2; Pope's idea of the imagination and the design of elegy to the memory of an unfortunate lady, Mod. Lang. Quart, 69; Samuel Johnson's moral elegiacs: theme and structure in On the death of Dr. Robert Levet, Genre, 72. Add: Dept. of English, University of Delaware, Newark, DE 19711.

MELLARD, JAMES MILTON, b. West Monroe, La, Jan. 30, 38; m. 58; c. 3. ENGLISH, AMERICAN LITERATURE. B.A, Lamar Univ, 60; M.A, Univ. Okla, 61; Ph.D.(Eng), Univ. Tex, 64. Spec. instr. ENG, Univ. Tex, 63-64; asst. prof. Univ. South. Calif, 64-67; NORTH. ILL. UNIV, 67-71, assoc. prof, 71-73, PROF, 73- Nat. Endowment for Humanities summer stipend grant, 68. MLA. The fiction of William Faulkner; modern American fiction; form and technique in fiction. Publ: Four modes: a rhetoric of modern fiction, Macmillan, 73; Faulkner's golden book: The Reivers as romantic comedy, Bucknell Rev, 12/65; Narrative forms in Winesburg, Ohio, PMLA 10/68. Add: Dept. of English, Northern Illinois University, De Kalb, IL 60115.

MELLEN, JOAN, b. New York, N.Y, Sept. 7, 41. FILM, LITERATURE. B.A, Hunter Col, 62; M.A, City Univ. New York, 64, Ph.D.(Eng), 68. ASSOC. PROF. ENG, TEMPLE UNIV, 67, Soc. Cinema Stud; MLA; Film criticism; contemporary fiction. Publ: Marilyn Monroe, Pyramid, 73; The battle of Algiers, Ind. Univ, 73; Women and their sexuality in the new film, Horizon, 73; The film today: towards a socially conscious cinema, Arts in Soc, fall-winter 72; Film and style: the fiction documentary, Antioch Rev, spring 73; Bergman and women, Film Quart, fall 73. Add: Dept. of English, Temple University, Philadelphia, PA 19122.

MELLOR, ANNE KOSTELANETZ, b. Albany, N.Y, July 15, 41; m. 69; c. 1. ENGLISH, LITERATURE & VISUAL ARTS. B.A, Brown Univ, 63; Woodrow Wilson fels, Columbia Univ, 63-64, 65-66, M.A, 64, Ph.D.(Eng), 68; Fulbright fel, Courtauld Inst, Univ. London, 64-65. Asst. prof. ENG, STANFORD UNIV, 66-73, ASSOC. PROF, 73- Guggenheim fel, 72-73. Romanticism, especially poetry and art; modern literature. Publ: Blake's human form divine, Univ. Calif, 74; Wordsworth's conversations, ELH, 69; Blake's Book of Thel, Philol. Quart, 71; Blake's human form divine and the structure of Jerusalem, Stud. Eng. Lit, 72; plus others. Add: Dept. of English, Stanford University, Stanford, CA 94305.

MELLOWN, ELGIN WENDELL, b. Selma, Ala, Dec. 29, 31; m. 57; c. 2. ENGLISH LITERATURE. A.B, Emory Univ, 54; M.A, Univ. London, 58, Ph.D. (Eng), 62. Instr. ENG, Univ. Ala, 58-60, asst. prof, 62-65; DUKE UNIV, 65-68, ASSOC. PROF, 68- U.S.A, 54-56. MLA. Twentieth century British literature. Publ: Bibliography of the writings of Edwin Muir, Univ. Ala, 64, 2nd ed, Vane, London, 66; co-auth, A checklist of writings about Edwin Muir, Whitston, 71; auth, The reception of Hopkins' poetry, 1889-1930, In: G.M. Hopkins, Herder Bk, 69; A descriptive catalogue of the bibliographies of 20th century British Writers, Whitston, 72; Character and themes in the novels of Jean Rhys, Contemporary Lit, 72; plus others. Add: Dept. of English, Duke University, Durham, NC 27706.

MELNITZ, WILLIAM WOLF, b. Cologne, Ger, Apr. 14, 00. THEATER ARTS. Univ. Cologne, 20-22; Univ. Berlin, 24; A.M, Univ. Calif, Los Angeles, 44, Ph.D, 47. From asst. prof. & dean col. fine arts to prof. THEATER ARTS, UNIV. CALIF, LOS ANGELES, 47-67, EMER. PROF. & DEAN, 67-; EMER. PROF, STATE UNIV. N.Y. BINGHAMTON, 73- Prof. commun. & theater,

Annenberg Sch. Commun, Univ. Pa, 67-68; prof. theater & dir. Max Reinhardt Arch, State Univ. N.Y. Binghamton, 69-73. Am. Theatre Asn; Speech Commun. Asn. History of theater arts. Publ: Theatre pictorial: Living stage; co-auth, Golden ages of the theater, Prentice-Hall, 59. Add: 10370 Rochester Ave, Los Angeles, CA 90024.

MELTON, JOHN LESTER, b. Walsenburg, Colo, Aug. 11, 20; m; c. 4. ENGLISH. B.A, Univ. Utah, 48, M.A, 49; Ph.D.(Eng) Johns Hopkins Univ, 55. Lectr. ENG, Col. Notre Dame Md, 54-55; instr, John Carroll Univ, 55-57, asst. prof, 57-61, assoc. prof, 61-67, prof, 67-68, chmn. dept, 62-66; assoc. prof, ST. CLOUD STATE COL, 68-69, PROF, 69- Consult, Ctr. Doc. & Commun. Res, Case West. Reserve Univ, 57-62. U.S.A. 42-46. MLA; Int. Arthurian Soc; Mod. Humanities Res. Asn; Am. Soc. Aesthet; Brit. Soc. Aesthet; NCTE; Col. Eng. Asn. Middle Ages, especially medieval romance, American frontier. Publ: Literature of the American frontier, produced on KTCA-TV St. Paul, 70. Add: 1340 Ninth Ave. S, St. Cloud, MN 56301.

MELTZER, SHARON B, b. Brooklyn, N.Y, Feb. 22, 40; m. 60; c. 2. ENGLISH. A.B, Barnard Col, 61; A.M, Yale, 62, Ph.D.(Eng), 70. Lectr. Eng, City Univ. N.Y, 63; instr, Tufts Univ, 65-66; lectr. ENG. & HUMANITIES, UNIV. CHICAGO, 70-71, ASST. PROF, 71- MLA. Henry James; history and theory of criticism; 19th and early 20th century literature. Add: Dept. of English, University of Chicago, 1050 E. 59th St, Chicago, IL 60637.

MENCHER, MELVIN, b. New York, N.Y, Jan. 25, 27; m. 47; c. 3. JOURNALISM. B.A, Univ. Colo, 47; Nieman fel, Harvard, 52-53. Reporter, United Press Assocs, 47-50; statehouse correspondent, Albuquerque Jour, N.Mex, 50-54; investigative reporter, Fresno Bee, Calif, 54-58; ASST. PROF. JOUR, Univ. Kans, 58-62; GRAD. SCH. JOUR, COLUMBIA UNIV, 62- Exec. secy, Univ. Kans-Univ. Costa Rica Exchange Prog, 60-61; assoc. dir, Summer Prog. Minority Educ. Jour, 71; evaluator, New Eng. Daily Newspaper Surv, 73. Asn. Educ. Jour; Nat. Counc. Col. Publ. Adv. Newspaper performance; freedom of the student press; recruiting and training blacks and other minorities for journalism. Publ: Student journalists have constitutional rights, too, Quill, 10/72; Journalism teachers: a failure of nerve and verve, Nieman Reports, 12/72 & 3/73; Without fear or favor, Masthead, spring 73; plus others. Add: Graduate School of Journalism, Columbia University, New York, NY 10027.

MENDEL, SYDNEY, b. London, Eng, July 9, 25; m. 52. ENGLISH. M.A, Cambridge, 56; Univ. Calif, Berkeley. Lectr. ENG, Univ. B.C, 56-58; asst prof, West. Wash. State Col, 59-62; DALHOUSIE UNIV, 62-66, ASSOC. PROF, 66- Can. Counc. leave fel, 68. Can. Comp Lit. Asn; Asn. Can. Univ. Teachers Eng. Nineteenth century; Shakespeare. Publ: Roads to consciousness, Allen & Unwin, 74; The revolt against the father: the adolescent hero in Hamlet and The wild duck, Essays in Criticism, 4/64; Carlyle: notes towards a revaluation, Eng. Stud. in Africa, 4/67; plus others. Add: Dept. of English, Dalhousie University, Halifax, N.S, Can.

MENDELL, CHARLES, JR, b. Taunton, Mass, Mar. 7, 10; m. 32; c. 2. ENGLISH. A.B, Dartmouth Col, 31; A.M, Harvard, 34. From instr. to assoc. prof. Eng, Rollins Col, 36-46, chmn. dept, 46-51, 60-67, dean 51-52, prof, 46-74; RETIRED. Medallion of honor, Rollins Col, 48; cur, Mattapoisett Hist. Mus. S.Atlantic Mod. Lang. Asn; Col. Eng. Asn. Shipbuilders of Mattapoisett. Publ: Historical summary of Rollins College, Rollins Col. Mag, 73. Add: 178 Ward Dr, Winter Park, FL 32789.

MENDELSOHN, LEONARD R, b. Nashville, Tenn, Feb. 28, 37; m. 66; c. 4. ENGLISH. B.A, Brandeis Univ, 59; A.M, Harvard, 61; Ph.D.(Eng), Univ. Wis, 66. Asst. prof. ENG, Iowa State Univ, 64-67; SIR GEORGE WILLIAMS UNIV, 67-69, ASSOC. PROF, 69- MLA; Renaissance Soc. Am; Shakespeare Asn. Am. Renaissance; drama; modern. Publ: Kafka's in the penal colony and the paradox of enforced freedom, Stud. Short Fiction, spring 71; The player as director: an approach to character, Comparative Drama, summer 72. Add: Dept. of English, Sir George Williams University, Montreal, P.Q, Can.

MENDELSOHN, MICHAEL JOHN, b. Cleveland, Ohio, Jan. 30, 31; m. 52; c. 2. ENGLISH. B.A, Univ. Pittsburgh, 51; M.A, Trinity Univ, 54; Ph.D, Univ. Colo, 62. Instr. Eng. U.S. Air Force Acad, 58-59, asst. prof, 59-63, assoc. prof, 63-70, prof, 70-72, asst. dean fac, 67-69; V.PRES. ACAD. AFFAIRS & DEAN FAC, UNIV. TAMPA, 72- Lectr, overseas exten. prog, Univ. Calif, 56; overseas exten. prof, Univ. Md, 56-58; exten, Univ. Colo, 63-; Am. Counc. Educ. internship in acad. admin, Mass. Inst. Technol, 66-67. U.S.A.F, 51-72, Lt. Col. MLA; Rocky Mountain Mod. Lang. Asn. Modern American drama. Publ: Clifford Odets: humane dramatist, Everett-Edwards, 69; Odets at center stage, 2 parts, Theatre Arts, 5-6/63; The heartbreak houses of Shaw and Chekhov, Shaw Rev: Clifford Odets and the American family, Drama Surv. Add: University of Tampa, Tampa, FL 33606.

MENGELING, MARVIN EDWIN, b. Sycamore, Ill, Sept. 7, 37; m. 62; c. 2. AMERICAN LITERATURE. B.A, Rockford Col, 59; M.A, Univ. Wis-Madison, 61, Ph.D.(Am. lit), 74. From instr. to asst. prof. humanities, Clarkson Col. Technol, 62-66; ASST. PROF. ENG, UNIV. WIS-OSHKOSH, 66- MLA; NCTE; Sci. Fiction Res. Asn; Melville Soc. Am. Nineteenth century American prose; modern American prose; science fiction and fantasy. Publ: Other voices, other rooms: Oedipus between the covers, Am. Imago, winter 62; Moby-Dick: the fundamental principles, Emerson Soc. Quart, 65; Ray Bradbury's Dandelion wine: themes, sources, and style, Eng. J, 10/71. Add: Dept. of English, University of Wisconsin-Oshkosh, Oshkosh, WI 54901.

MENIKOFF, BARRY, b. Brooklyn, N.Y, Jan. 2, 39; m. 66; c. 3. ENGLISH. B.A, Brooklyn Col, 60; M.S, Univ. Wis, 62, Ph.D.(Eng), 66. Asst. prof. ENG, UNIV. HAWAII, 65-70, ASSOC. PROF, 70- Mem, Am. Lit. Group, MLA, 66-; Fulbright-Hays grant lectr, Univ. Santiago, 68-69. MLA; AAUP; Philol. Asn. Pac. Coast. Nineteenth and twentieth century American literature; modern British literature; Henry James and Robert Louis Stevenson. Publ: Co-auth, The short story; an introductory anthology, Little, 69; auth, Punctuation and point of view in the late style of Henry James, Style, 69; The subjective pronoun in the late style of Henry James, Eng. Stud, 71; Oliver Wendell Holmes, In: Fifteen American authors before 1900, Univ. Wis, 71. Add: Dept. of English, University of Hawaii, 1733 Donaghho Rd, Honolulu, HI 96822.

MERCER, CAROLINE G, b. Minneapolis, Minn, Apr. 13, 08. AMERICAN LITERATURE. A.B, Vassar Col, 29; A.M, Radcliffe Col, 32; Ph.D, Univ. Chicago, 48. From instr. to asst. prof, Vassar Col, 39-49, assoc. prof. ENG, 49-55, prof, 55-73, chmn. dept, 56-58, 61-73, asst. dean, 48-50; RETIRED. Henry James and contemporaries; English and American poetry 1789-1840. Add: 528 Belgravia Ct, Louisville, KY 40208.

MERCHANT, FRANK ELDREDGE, b. Providence, R.I, Dec. 20, 10; m. 48; c. 1. ENGLISH, LINGUISTICS. A.B, Brown Univ, 31, M.A, 32; Ph.D.(Eng. & Am. lit), Univ. Denver, 51. Inform. off. highways dept, State of Colo, 53-59; chmn. div. lang, Mayville State Col, 59-60; GRAD. PROF. ENG, UNION COL.(KY), 60-, head dept, 61-71. Ed, Smoke, Providence, R.I, 33-36. U.S.A, 42-45. South. Mod. Lang. Asn; NCTE; Conf. Col. Compos. & Commun. Composition and stylistics; the novel and 20th century verse; philology. Publ: Apparatus, Adult style, To Poiein & Blood all over (pamphlets), Union Col.(Ky), 67-68; auth. & ed, The Turner theory and the American novel, Union Col. Lects, 68. Add: Dept. of English, Union College, Barbourville, KY 40906.

MERCHANT, JERROLD JACKSON, b. Seattle, Wash, Nov. 2, 41; m. 64; c. 2. SPEECH COMMUNICATION. B.A, Pac. Lutheran Univ, 64; M.A, Univ. N.Mex, 65; NDEA fel, Univ. South. Calif, 67, Ph.D.(speech commun), 71. Asst. dir. debate Univ. N.Mex, 64-65; dir. forensics, Univ. Calif, Santa Barbara, 65-67; res. asst. & instr. speech, Univ. South Calif, 67-69; ASST. PROF. SPEECH COMMUN, SOUTH. ORE. COL, 71- Partner, M-3 Assocs, 70-; M-W Commun. Consults, 72- Int. Commun. Asn; Speech Commun. Asn; West. Speech Commun. Asn; Inst. Strategic Stud, Eng. International political communication; intercultural and interpersonal communication. Publ: Co-auth, Perceived differences between debaters and non-debaters, J. Am. Forensic Asn, 69. Add: Dept. of Speech Communication, Southern Oregon College, Ashland, OR 97520.

MERCIER, VIVIAN HERBERT SAMUEL, b. Dublin, Ireland, Apr. 5, 19; m.40, 50; c. 3. ENGLISH. B.A, Trinity Col, Dublin, 40, Ph.D.(Eng), 45. Instr. lit, Bennington Col, 47-48; Eng, City Col. New York, 48-54, asst. prof, 54-60, assoc. prof, 61-65; PROF. ENG. & COMP. LIT, UNIV. COLO, 65- Lectr, sch. gen. stud, Columbia Univ, 48-51; Ford Fund Advan. Educ. fel, 55-56; Am. Counc. Learned Soc. grant-in-aid, summer 58, fel, 64-65; vis. lectr, Univ. Calif, Berkeley, 59-60; John Simon Guggenheim Mem. Found. fel, 72-73. MLA; Am. Comt. Irish Stud. Irish literature in English; literature and society in Ireland; modern British and French literature. Publ: Irish comic tradition, Clarendon, 62; co-ed, 1000 years of Irish prose, part 1, Devin, 52; ed, Great Irish short stories, Dell, 64; auth, The new novel: from Queneau to Pinget, Farrar, Straus, 71; contrib, Perspectives on pornography, St. Martin's, 70; auth, Beckett's Anglo-Irish stage dialects, James Joyce Quart, summer 71; contrib, Sunshine and the Moon's delight: a centenary tribute to J.M. Synge, Smythe, Eng. & Am. Univ. Beirut, 72; plus others. Add: 4285 Aurora Ave, Boulder, CO 80303.

MEREDITH, ROBERT CHIDESTER, b. Boulder, Colo, Sept. 4, 21; m. 47; c. 2. ENGLISH. B.A, Oberlin Col, 43; M.A, Univ. Wis, 50; Ph.D.(Eng), 55. Instr. ENG, Mich. Col. Mining & Technol, 52-56; Butler Univ, 56-61, assoc. prof, 61-62; CHICAGO STATE UNIV, 62-66, PROF, 66-, acting dean, Div. Fine Arts & humanities, 72-73. U.S.A.A.F, 43-45, 2nd Lt. MLA; Auth. Guild. Seventeenth and eighteenth century Anglicanism; Henry Fielding and the novel; creative writing. Publ: Writing in action, 68 & An anthology for young writers, 68, Nat. Textbook Co; co-auth, The professional story writer and his art, Crowell, 63 & Structuring your novel: from basic idea to finished manuscript, Barnes & Noble, 72. Add: Dept. of English, Chicago State University, 95th & King Dr, Chicago, IL 60628.

MEREDITH, WILLIAM, b. New York, N.Y, Jan. 9, 19. ENGLISH. A.B, Princeton, 40, Woodrow Wilson fel, 47-48, univ. fel, 49-50; hon. L.H.D, Carnegie-Mellon Univ, 72. Instr. ENG, Princeton, 46; asst. prof, Univ. Hawaii, 50-51; lectr, CONN. COL, 55-56, asst. prof, 57-59, assoc. prof, 59-63, PROF, 64-, DIR. HUMANITIES-UPWARD BOUND PROG, 65- Instr. Eng, Breadloaf Sch. Eng, Middlebury Col, summers 57-62; chancellor, Acad. Am. Poets, 63-; writer in residence, Int. Poetry Forum, 70. U.S.A, 41-42; U.S.N, 42-46, 52-54, Lt. Comdr. Nat. Inst. Arts & Lett. Poetry; opera. Publ: Love letter from an impossible land, Yale Univ, 44; Ships and other figures, Princeton Univ, 48; The open sea and other poems, 58, The wreck of the Thresher, 63 & Earth walk: new and selected poems, 70, Knopf; transl, Guillaume Apollinaire, Alcools, Doubleday, 62; ed, Shelley, 62 & co-ed, Eighteenth century English minor poets, 68, Dell. Add: Connecticut College, New London, CT 06320.

MEREWETHER, JOHN ARMSTRONG, b. Detroit, Mich, May 3, 19; m. 43; c. 2. ENGLISH. A.B, Univ. Mich, 45, fel, 45-56, A.M, 46; fel, Wayne State Univ, 66-67, Ph.D.(Eng), 69. Instr. Eng, North. Mich. Univ, 46-47; Wayne State Univ, 47-51; teacher dir. & producer plays, High Sch, Mich, 51-52; engineer & designer, private business, 52-58; engineering, Thompson Ramo Wooldridge, Inc, 58-64; INSTR. ENG, HIGHLAND PARK COL, 64-66, 67- Dir. plays & amateur actor, Contemporary Theater, Detroit, Mich, 48-50; fac. adv-dir, col. lit. mag, Highland Park Col, 64-66. U.S.A, 41. Col. Eng. Asn; NCTE. Romantic poets; modern Black and white writers; parapsychology and literature. Publ: Contrib. (four poems), Harlo's anthology of modern day poets and authors, 73. Add: Dept. of English, Highland Park College, Highland Park, MI 48203.

MERITT, HERBERT DEAN, b. Durham, N.C, Feb. 28, 04. ENGLISH PHILOLOGY. A.B, Hamilton Col, 25; A.M, Princeton, 26, Ph.D, 31. Instr. Eng, Union Col.(N.Y), 26-28; Am. Counc. Learned Soc. fel, 31-33; Sterling fel, Yale, 33-34; instr. Eng, Hamilton Col, 34-36; asst. prof, STANFORD UNIV, 36-48, prof. ENG. PHILOL, 48-73, EMER. PROF, 73- MLA; Mediaeval Acad. Am. Old English glosses. Publ: Fact and lore about Old English words, 54, Old English Prudentius glosses at Boulogne-sur-Mer, 59 & Some of the hardest glosses in Old English, 68, Stanford Univ; Supplement of Hall's Anglo-Saxon dictionary, Cambridge, 60. Add: 1671 Miller Ave, Los Altos, CA 94022.

MERIVALE, PATRICIA, b. Derby, Eng, July 19, 34. ENGLISH, COMPARATIVE LITERATURE. B.A, Univ. Calif, Berkeley, 55; B.A, Oxford, 58, M.A, 62; Ph.D.(comp. lit), Harvard, 63. Instr. ENG, UNIV. B.C, 62-63, asst.

prof, 63-66, assoc. prof, 66-70, PROF, 70-, summer res. grants. Can. Counc. leave fel, 69-70. MLA; Asn. Can. Univ. Teachers Eng; Am. Comp. Lit. Asn. Thematics; the classical tradition in modern literature; artifice in contemporary fiction. Publ: Pan the goat-god: his myth in modern times, Harvard, 69; The death of Pan in Victorian literature, Victorian Newslett, spring 63; Wallace Stevens' Jar: the absurd detritus of romantic myth, Col. Eng, 4/65; The flaunting of artifice in Nabokov and Borges, In: Nabokov: the man and his work, Univ. Wis, 67; plus others. Add: Dept. of English, University of British Columbia, Vancouver, 8, B.C, Can.

MERIWETHER, FRANK T, b. Asheville, N.C, July 13, 25; m. 46; c. 3. ENGLISH, AMERICAN LITERATURE. A.B, Univ. N.C, 48; M.A, La. State Univ, 49, Ph.D.(Eng), 52. Asst. prof. ENG, UNIV. SOUTHWEST. LA, 52-55, assoc. prof, 55-58, PROF, 58-, CHMN. FRESHMAN ENG, 57- U.S.N, 43-46. MLA. Southwestern humor; Southern literature. Add: Dept. of English, Box 76, University of Southwestern Louisiana, Lafayette, LA 70501.

MERIWETHER, JAMES BABCOCK, b. Columbia, S.C, May 8, 28; m. 55; c. 5. ENGLISH, AMERICAN LITERATURE. B.A, Univ. S.C, 49; M.A, Princeton, 52, Jacobus fel, 57-58, Ph.D, 58. Asst. prof. Eng, Univ. Tex, 58-59; Univ. N.C, Chapel Hill, 59-62, assoc. prof, 62-64; prof, UNIV. S.C, 64-69, McCLINTOCK PROF. SOUTH.LETT, 69- Am. Counc. Learned Soc. fel, 60-61; Guggenheim fel, 63-64; mem. exec. comt, S.Atlantic Mod. Lang. Asn, 67-70; Ctr. Ed. Am. Auth, Mod. Lang. Asn, 68-72; South. Humanities Cong, 68-70. U.S.A, 53-56. MLA; Am. Stud. Asn; Bibliog. Soc. Am; S.Atlantic Mod. Lang. Asn. English and American fiction; Southern literature; William Faulkner. Publ: The literary career of William Faulkner, Princeton Libr, 61; ed, Essays, speeches and public letters of William Faulkner, Random, 66; plus others. Add: Dept. of English, University of South Carolina, Columbia, SC 29208.

MERKOWITZ, DAVID ROBERT, b. New York, N.Y, May 3, 42; c. 2. AMERICAN STUDIES & LITERATURE. B.A, N.Y. Univ, 63, 63-65; Ph.D.(Am. cult), Univ. Mich, Ann Arbor, 71. Instr. Eng, UNIV. COLO, BOULDER, 67-71, ASST. PROF. ENG. & AM. STUD, 71-, ED. SILVER & GOLD REC, 73- Am. Stud. Asn. Creative writing; journalistic writing; modern and contemporary American literature. Add: Silver & Gold Record, 366 Administrative Annex, University of Colorado, Boulder, CO 80302.

MERREN, JOHN JAY, b. Port Arthur, Tex, Sept. 30, 40. ENGLISH. B.S. & B.A, Lamar State Col, 62, M.A, 63; W.Tex. State Univ, 63-64, 67; Tex. Technol. Col, 64; Univ. Tex, 65. Instr. Eng, Amarillo Col, 63-67; instr. Eng. & audio-visual dir. dept. Eng, Univ. Ariz, 67-73; RES. & WRITING, 73- MLA; NCTE. Modern fiction; history of the short story; teaching English with audio-visual media. Publ: Some American writing, Critique, 1/68; Banked up on the side of redeemable error, Bull. Rocky Mountain Mod. Lang. Asn, 9/68; Character and theme in the Amarillo novels of Al Dewlen, West. Rev, 4/69; plus one other. Add: 1130 N. First Ave, Tucson, AZ 85719.

MERRIAM, HAROLD GUY, b. Westminster, Mass, Sept. 6, 83; m. 15; c. 2. BRITISH LITERATURE. A.B, Univ. Wyo, 05, hon. LL.D, 62; Rhodes scholar, Oxford, 04-07, B.A, 07, M.A, 12; Harvard, 10; Ph.D, Columbia Univ, 39; hon. D.Litt, Mont. State Univ, 63. Instr. ENG, Whitman Col, 08-10; Austin teaching fel, Harvard, 10; Beloit Col, 11-13; asst. prof, Reed Col, 13-19; prof, Univ. Ore, 39-40; MONT. STATE UNIV, 19-39, 40-54, chmn. dept, 19-54, chmn. div. humanities, 34-54, EMER. PROF, 54- Ed, The Frontier, 20-39; Northwest Verse, 31; Northwest Conf. Higher Educ, Bull; state dir. fed. writers proj, Works Progress Admin, Mont, 37; ed, Mont. Inst. Arts Quart, 57-64; lectr, Mont. State Univ, 67- AAUP. Nineteenth century British literature; creative writing; Northwest writing and writers. Publ: Edward Moxon, publisher of poets, 39, ed, Linderman's recollections of Charley Russell, 63 & ed, Way out west; reminiscences and tales, 69, Univ. Okla; co-auth, Readings for an air age, Macmillan, 43; ed, Western adventure, recollections of Frank B. Linderman, Univ. Nebr, 68; auth, History of the University of Montana; co-auth, Seed in the soil, Mountain, Press, 67; ed, Adventures of a frontier woman: 1850-1900, Univ. Mont.(in press), Best books about Montana, Pa. Northwest Libr. Asn. Quart, 73. Add: 304 Westview Dr, Missoula, MT 59801.

MERRILL, GEORGE JACKSON, b. Haverhill, Mass, July 11, 31; m. 66; c. 2. ENGLISH. A.B, Boston Univ, 53; Caleb Duston Hunking scholar, 53 & 55; Ph.D.(Eng), Univ. Birmingham, 63. Teacher ENG, High Sch, Mass, 58-61; lectr, LAKEHEAD UNIV, 63-65, asst. prof, 65-68, ASSOC. PROF, 68-, Chancellor's Fund award, 67 & 68. Can. Counc. grant, summer 64. U.S.A, 56-58. Asn. Can. Univ. Teachers Eng; MLA; Shakespeare Asn. Am. Elizabethan books and readers; Elizabethan printers and printing practices; Shakespeare. Publ: The pre-Armada years: literature of patriotic sentiment, Lakehead Univ. Rev, 68. Add: Dept. of English, Lakehead University, Thunder Bay, Ont, Can.

MERRILL, JOHN CALHOUN, b. Yazoo City, Miss, Jan. 9, 24; m. 49; c. 5. JOURNALISM, PHILOSOPHY. B.A, Miss. Delta State Col, 49; M.A, La. State Univ, Baton Rouge, 50; Ph.D.(mass commun), Univ. Iowa, 62. Instr. Eng. & jour, Southwest. Col.(Kans), 50-51; from instr. to asst. prof, Northwest. State Col.(La), 51-62; assoc. prof. JOUR, Tex. A&M Univ, 62-64; PROF, UNIV. MO-COLUMBIA, 64- Lectr, Int. Inst. Jour, Berlin, summer 68; U.S. Inform. Serv. lectr, S.Korea, summer 70; spec. chair, Grad. Sch. Jour, Nat. Chengchi Univ, Taiwan, 70-71; vis. prof. speech commun, Univ. Va, 74. Asn. Educ. in Jour; Inter-Am. Press Asn. International propaganda; national images; comparative press systems. Publ: Handbook of the foreign press, 59 & co-auth, The foreign press, 64 & 70, La. State Univ; auth, The elite press, Pitman, 70; co-auth, Dimensions of Christian writing, Zondervan, 70 & Media, messages, and men, McKay, 71; auth, The imperative of freedom, Hastings, 74. Add: School of Journalism, University of Missouri-Columbia, Columbia, MO 65201.

MERRILL, REED BALLIF, b. Provo, Utah, Oct. 28, 29; m. 51. COMPARATIVE LITERATURE. B.S, Univ. Utah, 61, M.A, 65; Ph.D.(comp. lit), Univ. Colo, Boulder, 70. Buyer, Purchasing Dept, Univ. Utah, 61-64, bus. mgr, Comput. Ctr, 64-65; asst. ed, Rocky Mountain Mod. Lang. Asn. Bull, Univ. Colo, Boulder, 67-68; lectr. ENG, WEST. WASH. STATE COL, 69-70, asst. prof, 70-74, ASSOC. PROF, 74-, res. fel, summer 74. Am. Comp. Lit. Asn; Int. Comp. Lit. Asn; MLA; Philol. Asn. Pac. Coast. Dostoevsky; modern novel; literary criticism and theory. Publ: Ivan Karamazov and Harry Haller: the consolation of philosophy, Comp. Lit. Stud, 71; The mistaken endeavor: Dostoevsky's Notes from Underground, Mod. Fiction Stud, winter 72-73; Undergraduate programs in comparative literature approached through studies in the humanities, Proc. VIIth Int. Comp. Lit. Asn. Congr, (in press). Add: Dept. of English, Western Washington State College, Bellingham, WA 98225.

MERRILL, RODNEY HARPSTER, b. Idaho Falls, Idaho, Mar. 24, 40. ENGLISH LITERATURE. B.A, Harvard, 62; Fulbright fel, Univ. Bristol, 62-63; M.A, Stanford Univ, 67, Ph.D.(Eng. lit), 70. ASST. PROF. ENG, UNIV. CALIF, BERKELEY, 68- Mediaeval Acad. Am. Medieval love literature; 15th century English literature. Publ: Chaucer's Broche of Thebes: the unity of The complaint of Mars and The complaint of Venus, Lit. Monogr, 73. Add: Dept. of English, University of California, Berkeley, CA 94720.

MERRILL, THOMAS F, b. Maplewood, N.J, Jan. 5, 32; m. 57; c. 4. ENGLISH. A.B, Princeton, 54; M.A, Univ. Nebr, 60; Ph.D.(Eng), Univ. Wis, 64. Asst. prof. Eng, Univ. Calif, Los Angeles, 64-66; Fulbright-Hays lectr. Am. lit, Univ. Bordeaux, 66-67; asst. prof. Eng, DePauw Univ, 67-69, ASSOC. PROF. ENG. & DIR. GRAD. STUD, UNIV. DEL, 69- U.S.A.F, 54-56, 63, Capt. MLA. Modern poetry; Renaissance literature; stylistics. Publ: William Perkins 1558-1602, De Graaf, Nieuwkoop, 66; Allen Ginsberg, Twayne, 69; Wrath and rhetoric and the Summoner's tale, Tex. Stud. Lit. & Lang. autumn, 62; John Donne and the word of God, Neuphilologische, Mitt, 68; The sacrifice and the structure of religious language, Lang. & Style, fall 69. Add: Dept. of English, University of Delaware, Newark, DE 19711.

MERRILL, WALTER M, b. Evanston, Ill, May 26, 15; m. 39, 59; c. 6. ENGLISH. B.S.L, Northwest. Univ, 37; A.M, Harvard, 41, Ph.D, 46. Master Eng, Loomis Sch, 42-43; instr, Amherst Col, 43-45; Temple Univ, 45; Swarthmore Col, 45-47; Northwest. Univ, 47-51; asst. prof, Bowdoin Col, 53-54; dir. Essex Inst, Salem, Mass, 54-59; PROF. ENG. & CHM. DEPT, WICHITA STATE UNIV, 59- Am. Counc. Learned Soc. fel, 51-53, grant-in-aid, 66-67; dir. Wichita Community Theatre, 60-64; Wichita City Libr, 63-64; Wichita Art Mus, 64-; treas, 68-; Wichita State Univ. grant-in-aid, 65-68; Am. Philos. Soc. grant-in-aid, 67-68. NCTE; MLA. Eighteenth century English literature; American literature and history; aesthetics of film. Publ: From statesman to philosopher, a study of Bolingbroke's deism, Philos. Libr, 49; Behold me once more, Houghton, 54; Against wind and tide, a biography of William Lloyd Garrison, 63 & co-ed, The letters of William Lloyd Garrison, Vol. I, 68, Harvard. Add: Dept. of English, Wichita State University, Wichita, KS 67208.

MERRIMAN, JAMES DOUGLAS, b. Wheeler, Tex, July 21, 26; m. 58; c. 2. ENGLISH LITERATURE. B.A, Tex. Tech. Col, 47; M.A, Columbia Univ, 50, univ. fel, 61, Ph.D.(Eng), 62. Lectr. ENG, Columbia Univ, 54-58, instr, 58-62, asst. prof, 62-66; assoc. prof, WICHITA STATE UNIV, 66-68, PROF, 68-, COORD. GRAD. STUD. ENG, 66- Counc. in Humanities grant, Columbia Univ, 65. MLA; Mod. Humanities Res. Asn; Am. Soc. Aesthet; Ling. Soc. Am. Literary and critical theory; Victorian and Arthurian literature. Publ: The flower of kings, Arthurian literature in England 1485-1835, Univ. Kans, 69; co-auth, Literary analysis with the aid of the computer, Computers & Humanities, 3/68. Add: Dept. of English, Wichita State University, Wichita, KS 67208.

MERRIN, JAMES, b. Atlanta, Ga, May 25, 15; m. 41; c. 2. ENGLISH. A.B, Southwest. Col.(Tenn), 37; A.M, Univ. Chicago, 40, Ph.D, 48. Instr. ENG, Wayne Univ, 40-43; Univ. Chicago, 45-47; Univ. Calif, Los Angeles, 47-50; asst. prof, Memphis State Col, 50-56; assoc. prof, Colo. Sch. Mines, 56-66; PROF. METROPOLITAN STATE COL, 66-, CHMN. DEPT, 73- AAUP; MLA. Elizabethan drama; Restoration comedy; 17th century English literature. Add: Rte 5, Golden, CO 80401.

MERRITT, FRANCINE, b. Ft. Worth, Tex, Oct. 4, 17. SPEECH. B.A, Hardin-Simmons Univ, 38; M.A, La. State Univ, 43, Ph.D, 53. Instr. speech & Eng, Hardin-Simmons Univ, 42-44; SPEECH, Univ. Mo, 44-47; LA. STATE UNIV, BATON ROUGE, 47-53, asst. prof, 53-57, ASSOC. PROF, 57- Speech Asn. Am.(deleg, 62); Am. Speech & Hearing Asn; Am. Theatre Asn; NCTE; South. Speech Commun. Asn. Interpretative reading; history of speech education; general speech. Publ: Contrib, Speech methods and resources, Harper, 61; West Texas pronunciation, 44 & A speech journal views original speaking, 57, South. Speech J. Add: Dept. of Speech, Louisiana State University, Baton Rouge, LA 70803.

MERRITT, FRANK WESTLEY, b. Brooklyn, N.Y, Sept. 12, 10; m. 40. ENGLISH. A.B, Hamilton Col, 39, A.M, 41; Ph.D, Cornell Univ, 51. Instr, Hamilton Col, 39-41; Cornell Univ, 42-45; asst. prof, Princeton, 45-48; assoc. prof. ENG, BUCKNELL UNIV, 48-56, PROF, 56-, DIR. DEBATE, 73- Speech. Commun. Asn. Rhetorical criticism of the speeches of Elihu Root; rhetoric and literature; argumentation and debate. Add: Dept. of English, Bucknell University, Lewisburg, PA 17837.

MERRITT, JAMES D, b. Lebanon, N.H, Sept. 13, 34. ENGLISH. B.A, Univ. N.H, 55; M.A, Univ. R.I, 58; Ph.D.(Eng), Univ. Wis, 63. Asst. prof. ENG, Univ. Pittsburgh, 63-66; BROOKLYN COL, 66-70, ASSOC. PROF, 70- City Univ. N.Y. Res. Found. res. grant, 72-73. Victorian Soc; Am. Civil Liberties Union. H.P. Lovecraft, American writer of macabre fiction; 19th and 20th century literature. Publ: Ed, the pre-Raphaelite poem, Dutton, 66; auth, Ronald Firbank, Twayne, 69; co-ed, Urban adventurer, McGraw, 71; The identity of the novelist St. Barbe in Disraeli's Endymion, Nineteenth Century Fiction, 6/68; Shaw and the pre-Raphaelites In: Shaw: seven essays, Univ. Toronto Press, 70; twelve articles for World Book Encyclopedia, Field; plus others. Add: Dept. of English, Brooklyn College, Brooklyn, NY 11210.

MERRITT, ROBERT G, b. Yonkers, N.Y, Feb. 1, 36. DRAMA. A.B, Cornell Univ, 58; M.A, Univ. N.C, 60; Ph.D, Tulane Univ, 63. ASST. PROF. DRAMA, Univ. Houston, 62-67; DALHOUSIE UNIV, 67- Nixon Theatre fel, Tulane Univ, 60-62; adv. ed, Tulane Drama Rev, 62-63, contrib. ed, 63-67. Directing; film; the Greek theatre. Add: Dept. of Theatre, Dalhousie University, Halifax, N.S, Can.

MERRITT, TRAVIS RHODES, b. Plattsburgh, N.Y, Nov. 20, 33; m. 57; c. 4. LITERATURE. B.A, Williams Col, 55; M.A, Univ. Chicago, 56, Ph.D.(Eng), 65. Instr. Eng, Wesleyan Univ, 58-64; asst. prof, MASS. INST. TECHNOL, 64-71, ASSOC. PROF. LIT, 71- Old Dom. Found. res. & travel grant, 67. Victorian and contemporary literature; prose style and stylistics. Publ: Ed, Style in substance, Harcourt, 69; auth, Taste, opinion and theory in the rise of Victorian prose stylism, In: The art of Victorian prose, Oxford, 68. Add: Dept. of Literature, Massachusetts Institute of Technology, Cambridge, MA 02139.

MERRIX, ROBERT PAUL, b. Princeton, W.Va, June 6, 26; m. 54; c. 4. ENGLISH & RENAISSANCE DRAMA. B.A, Butler Univ, 59, grant & M.A, 60; fels, Univ. Cincinnati, 60-63, Ph.D.(Eng), 66. Instr. ENG, Univ. Cincinnati, 63-65, asst. prof, 65-66; UNIV. AKRON, 66-73, ASSOC. PROF, 73- Dir. Higher Educ. Act fed. grant, 70-72; dir. & consult, Gov. Ohio comt, Dictionary Am. Regional Eng, 72-73; mem, Ohio Stud. Loan Comn, 72-74. Sig.C, U.S.A, 50-52. MLA; Shakespeare Asn. Am; Renaissance Soc. Am; Col. Eng. Asn. Shakespeare; Renaissance drama; historical criticism. Publ: Ed, Introduction to library for freshmen, Univ. Cincinnati, 65; auth, The Alexandrian allusion in Shakespeare's Henry V, Eng. Lit, Renaissance, autumn 72; var. arts. on higher educ, Ohio Academe, 72-73; Shakespeare's history plays, Shakespeare Stud, 74. Add: Dept. of English, University of Akron, Akron, OH 44325.

MERSAND, JOSEPH, b. Zbaraz, Austria, July 30, 07; nat. m. ENGLISH. B.S, N.Y. Univ, 28, univ. fel, 28-29, M.A, 29, Penfield fel, 29-30, Ph.D.(Germanic philol), 34. Instr. Eng. & speech, Brooklyn Boys High Sch, 43-53; curriculum coord, Acad. High Sch, New York, N.Y, 53-54; prin, Paulding Jr. High Sch, Bronx, 54-55; chmn. dept. Eng, Jamaica High Sch, Queens, N.Y, 55-72; lectr. educ, Fairleigh Dickinson Univ, 72-73. Adj. prof, Grad. Sch. Educ, Yeshiva Univ; summers, Cornell Univ, 55, Teachers Col, Columbia Univ, 57, 58; Syracuse Univ, 59; N.Y. Univ, 60, 61, N.Tex. State Univ, 61; Univ. Colo, 62; Johns Hopkins Univ. 63, Hofstra Univ, 70-72; consult, Audio-Visual Div, Popular Sci. Publ, 63-; chmn. liason comt, NCTE-Am. Educ. Theatre Asn, 64-, chmn. elem. educ. comt, Speech Asn. East. States, 64-71; mem, Nat. Educ. Comn, Am. Jewish Cong, 71-; Eng. consult, Bd. Jewish Educ. N.Y.C, 72- U.S.A, 43-45. MLA; Ling. Soc. Am; Mod. Humanities Res. Asn, Gt. Brit; Col. Eng. Asn; Speech Asn. Am; NCTE (pres, 58-59), Am. Educ. Theatre Asn; Nat. Soc. Stud. Commun; Conf. Col. Compos; & Commun; Asn. Supvr. & Curriculum Develop; Am. Educ. Res. Asn; Nat. Asn. Sec. Sch. Prin; Nat. Educ. Asn; Int. Reading Asn. Middle English language and literature; contemporary drama; English methodology and supervision. Publ: Attitudes toward English teaching, Chilton, 61; Great narrative essays, Washington Square, 68; Chaucer's romance vocabulary, Kennikat, 68; Eight American ethnic plays, Scribners, 74; plus others. Add: 166-05 Highland Ave, Jamaica, NY 11432.

MERSCH, ARNOLD ROY GORDON, b. St. Paul, Minn, Mar. 4, 38. ENGLISH & AMERICAN LITERATURE. B.A, St. Mary's Col.(Minn), 60, M.Ed, 64; M.A, DePaul Univ, 65; Ph.D.(Eng), St. Louis Univ, 69. Instr. ENG, St. Patrick High Sch, Chicago, Ill, 60-62; instr. & head dept, St. Francis High Sch, Wheaton, Ill, 62-64; La Salle High Sch, Cincinnati, Ohio, 64-65; Christian Brothers High Sch, Memphis, Tenn, 66-68; ASST. PROF, Memphis State Univ, 68-70; UNIV. WIS-CTR, SHEBOYGAN, 70- Lectr, Univ. Wis-Exten. MLA; NCTE. Walt Whitman; teaching of poetry; teaching composition. Publ: Teilhard de Chardin and Whitman's Noiseless, patient spider, 9/71 & Cosmic contrast: Walt Whitman and the Hindu philosophy, 6/73, Walt Whitman Rev; Student inertia: myth or reality, Midwest Educ. Rev, winter 72. Add: Dept. of English, University of Wisconsin Center, Sheboygan, WI 53081.

MERSMANN, JAMES F, b. Richmond, Kans, Dec. 25, 38; m. 59; c. 4. ENGLISH & AMERICAN LITERATURE. B.A, Univ. Mo-Kansas City, 65; Woodrow Wilson fel, Univ. Kans, 65-66, NDEA fels, 65-66, 67-68, 68-69, M.A, 67, Ph.D.(Eng), 72. Asst. instr. ENG, Univ. Kans, 66-67; instr, Mt. St. Scholastica, 69-71, ASST. PROF, Benedictine Col, 71-73; UNIV. ALA, BIRMINGHAM, 73- Mem, Nat. Endowment for Humanities summer sem, 73. U.S.M.C, 56-58. AAUP; MLA. Contemporary American poetry. Publ: Out of the Vietnam vortex: a study of poets and poetry against the war, Univ. Kans, 74. Add: 929 Shades Glen Dr, Birmingham, AL 35226.

MERTON, EGON STEPHEN, b. New York, N.Y, Nov. 26, 12. ENGLISH. B.A, Columbia Univ, 33, M.A, 35, Ph.D.(Eng), 48. Instr. ENG, N.Y. State Col. Teachers, 38-39; Colo. Col, 39-42; assoc. prof, Mary Baldwin Col, 42-43; asst. prof, Col. William & Mary, 43-46; instr, Cornell Univ, 46-50; PROF, CITY COL. NEW YORK, 50- Am. Philos. Soc. grant, 63. MLA; Hist. Sci. Soc. Seventeenth century English literature and science; poetry and religion; 19th century English fiction. Publ: Science and imagination in Sir Thomas Browne, Kings Crown, 48, Octagon & Farrar, Straus, 69; Mark Rutherford (William Hale White), Twayne, 67; The botany of Sir Thomas Browne, Isis; The personality of Mark Rutherford, 19th Century Fiction. Add: 395 Riverside Dr, Apt. 12D, New York, NY 10025.

MESEROLE, HARRISON TALBOT, b. Brooklyn, N.Y, July 25, 21; m. 43. ENGLISH. B.S, Wilson Col.(D.C), 42; M.A, Univ. Md, 54, univ. fel, 55-56, Ph.D, 60. Instr. ENG, Univ. Md, 56-57; PA. STATE UNIV, UNIVERSITY PARK, 57-59, asst. prof, 59-61, assoc. prof, 61-63, PROF, 63-, ASSOC. HEAD DEPT. ENG, 72- Co-ed, Seventeenth-Century News, 69- MLA (assoc. bibliogr, 63-66, bibliogr-in-chief & ed. annual MLA Int. Bibliog, 66); Am. Stud. Asn; Bibliog. Soc. Am; Bibliog. Soc. Univ. Va; Malone Soc; Mod. Humanities Res. Asn. American literature of the 17th, 18th & 19th centuries; bibliography. Publ: Co-auth, The critical question, Allyn & Bacon, 64; auth, Seventeenth century American poetry, Doubleday, 68 & Norton, 72; co-ed, American literature: tradition and innovation (3 vols), Heath, 69; auth, Charles Lamb's reputation and influence in America to 1835, J. Gen. Educ, 1/65; Shakespeare in New York, 1823-24: The Mirror, morals, and The merry wives of Windsor, In: Essays on Shakespeare, 65 & Edward Taylor's sources, In: Directions in literary criticism, 73, Pa. State Univ; plus others. Add: Dept. of English, 117 Burrowes, Pennsylvania State University, University Park, PA 16802.

MESERVE, WALTER J, JR, b. Portland, Maine, Mar. 10, 23; m. 47, 67; c. 4. THEATRE. A.B, Bates Col, 47; M.A, Boston Univ, 48; Ph.D, Univ. Wash, 52. Instr. Eng, Univ. Kans, 51-53, asst. prof, 53-58, assoc. prof, 58-63, prof, 63-68; vis. prof. dramatic art, Univ. Calif, Santa Barbara, 67-68; PROF. THEATRE & DRAMA, IND. UNIV, BLOOMINGTON, 68- Vis. lectr. Am. lit, Victoria Univ, Eng, 59-60; Am. Philos. Soc. grant, 60; assoc. ed, Mod. Drama, 60-; Nat. Humanities Found. grant, 66-67. MLA; Asn. Asian Stud; Asia Soc; Auth. Guild; Am. Theatre Asn; Am. Soc. Theatre Res. American drama and theatre; dramatic literature and theory; drama and theatre of China. Publ: Complete plays of W.D. Howells, N.Y. Univ, 60; An outline history of American drama, Littlefield, 65; Discussions of modern American drama, Heath, 66; Robert Sherwood reluctant moralist, Bobbs, 70; co-ed, Modern drama from Communist China, N.Y. Univ, 70; ed, W.D. Howells' The rise of Silas Lapham, Ind. Univ, 71 & Studies in Death of a salesman, C.E. Merrill, 72; co-auth, Satiric comedies, Vol. XXI, In: America's lost plays, Ind. Univ, 69; auth, Philip Barry: a dramatists search, Mod. Drama, 5/70; co-auth, Communist China's war theatre, J. Popular Cult, fall 72; plus others. Add: Dept. of Theatre & Drama, Indiana University, Bloomington, IN 47401.

MESSBARGER, PAUL ROBERT, b. Parnell, Mo, Oct. 8, 34; m. 59; c. 5. AMERICAN LITERATURE. B.A, St. Benedict's Col.(Kans), 56; M.A, Univ. Notre Dame, 58; Ph.D.(Am. stud), Univ. Minn, Minneapolis, 69. Instr. Eng, St. Ambrose Col, 60-61; asst. prof, Marquette Univ, 65-69; dir. honors prog, 66-69; assoc. prof. ENG. & chmn. dept, St. Mary's Col.(Ind), 69-73; ASSOC. PROF, LOYOLA UNIV. CHICAGO, 73- Nat. Endowment for Humanities summer fel, 72. Eng.C, U.S.A, 58-60. Am. Stud. Asn; Midwest Mod. Lang. Asn; AAUP. American literary history; American religious history. Publ: Fiction with a parochial purpose, Boston Univ, 71. Add: Dept. of English, Loyola University of Chicago, 6525 N. Sheridan Rd, Chicago, IL 60626.

MESSENGER, ANN P, b. Pittsburgh, Pa, May 31, 33; m. 60. ENGLISH LITERATURE, DRAMA. B.A, Oberlin Col, 55; B.A, Oxford, 57, M.A, 61; Ph.D.(Eng), Cornell Univ, 64. Lectr. ENG, Bucknell Univ, 60-61; instr, San Francisco State Col, 65-66; lectr, Univ. B.C, 66-68; asst. prof, SIMON FRASER UNIV, 68-73, ASSOC. PROF, 73- MLA; Asn. Can. Univ. Teachers Eng; Am. Soc. 18th Century Stud; Can. Soc. 18th Century Stud; Can. Asn. Univ. Teachers. Restoration and 18th century literature; modern drama, English and Canadian; Shakespeare. Publ: Blindness and the problem of identity in Pinter's plays, Die Neueren Sprachen, 8/72; John Arden's essential vision: tragical-historical-political, Quart. J. Speech, 10/72; contrib, Dramatists in Canada: selected essays, Univ. B.C, 72. Add: Dept. of English, Simon Fraser University, Burnaby 2, B.C, Can.

MESSENGER, WILLIAM EDMUND, b. Independence, Mo, Feb. 21, 31; m. 60. ENGLISH. B.A, Univ. Wash, 56; M.A, Cornell Univ, 59; Ph.D.(Eng), Univ. Calif, Berkeley, 68. Instr. ENG, Bucknell Univ, 59-61; UNIV. B.C, 66-68, ASST. PROF, 68- U.S.A.F, 50-54, S/Sgt. MLA; Asn. Can. Univ. Teachers Eng; Can. Asn. Univ. Teachers. Nineteenth and 20th century English and American literature; the novel; Joseph Conrad. Publ: Conrad and Melville again, winter 69-70 & Conrad and his sea stuff, 74, Conradiana; co-auth, One of us: a Biblical allusion in Conrad's Lord Jim, Eng. Lang. Notes, 12/71. Add: Dept. of English, University of British Columbia, Vancouver, B.C, Can.

METCALF, ALLAN ALBERT, b. Clayton, Mo, Apr. 18, 40; m. 66; c. 3. ENGLISH, LINGUISTICS. B.A, Cornell Univ, 61; Deutscher Akademischer Austauschdienst, Free Univ. Berlin, 61-62; M.A, Univ. Calif, Berkeley, 64, Ph.D.(Eng), 66. Asst. prof. ENG, Univ. Calif, Riverside, 66-73; ASSOC. PROF. & CHMN. DEPT, MacMURRAY COL, 73- Consult. reading & ling, Riverside Unified Sch. Dist, 68; ed, Calif. Ling. Newslett, 70-73; mem. fac, Univ. Calif, Santa Cruz summer prog. ling, 71 & 72, co-dir, 73. MLA; Ling. Soc. Am.(mem. comt. regional affairs, 71-, comt. ling. insts, 72); Mediaeval Acad. Am; Am. Dialect Soc; Tennyson Soc. Publ: Riverside English: the spoken language of a Southern California community, Univ. Calif, Riverside, 71; Poetic diction in the Old English Meters of Boethius, Mouton, The Hague, 73; Ornamentale Tiermotive in der altenglischen Versdichtung, In: Das Tier in der Dichtung, Carl Winter, Heidelberg, 70; Sir Gawain and you, Chaucer Rev, winter 71; Mexican-American English in Southern California, West. Rev, spring, 72; plus others. Add: Dept. of English, MacMurray College, Jacksonville, IL 62650.

METZGER, CHARLES REID, b. Spokane, Wash, May 22, 21; m. 50; c. 1. ENGLISH. B.A, Univ. Wash, 43, M.A, 50, Ph.D.(Eng), 54. Instr. ENG, Univ. Utah, 46-48; Bakersfield Col, 54; asst. prof, Portland State Col, 55-61; vis. assoc. prof. UNIV. SOUTH. CALIF, 61, assoc. prof, 62-68, PROF, 68- Vis. Fulbright prof. Am. lit, Univ. São Paulo, 60; co-moderator, Aspen Inst. Humanistic Stud, 2/59. Am. Stud. Asn; Philol. Asn. Pac. Coast; MLA. American literature; criticism; esthetics. Publ: Emerson and Greenough: transcendental pioneers of an American esthetic, Univ. Calif, 54; Thoreau and Whitman, Univ. Wash, 61; co-auth, Fifty songs from the Yüan: poetry of 13th century China, Allen & Unwin, 67; co-ed, Essays in American & English literature presented to Bruce Robert McElderry, Jr, Ohio Univ, 68. Add: 5648 Heatherdale Dr, Los Angeles, CA 90043.

METZGER, LORE, b. Frankfurt, Germany, May 8, 25; U.S. citizen. ENGLISH & COMPARATIVE LITERATURE. B.A, Hunter Col, 46; M.A, Columbia Univ, 47, Ph.D, 56. Instr. Eng, Mt. Holyoke Col, 56-59; Am. Asn. Univ. Women fel, 59-60; instr, Eng, Univ. Wash, 60-61, asst. prof, 61-64; assoc. prof. Eng. & comp. lit, Mich. State Univ, 64-68; PROF. ENG, EMORY UNIV, 68- Huntington Libr. res. grant, 63; fel. consult, Nat. Endowment for Humanities, 71-74. MLA; Am. Comp. Lit. Asn. Romanticism; literary theory. Publ: Ed, Coleridge's marginalia on 35 German authors, In: Complete works of S.T. Coleridge, Princeton, 69-; Gunter Grass' Rehearsal play, Contemporary Lit, spring 73; introd. to Aphra Behn's Oroonoko, Norton, fall 73; plus others. Add: Dept. of English, Emory University, Atlanta, GA 30322.

MEWS, SIEGFRIED, German, Comparative Literature. See Volume III, Foreign Languages, Linguistics & Philology.

MEYER, GERALD DENNIS, b. Rochester, N.Y, June 16, 15; div; c. 2. ENGLISH LITERATURE. B.A, Univ. Rochester, 42; Harvard, 43; M.A, Columbia Univ, 47, Ph.D, 51. Instr. ENG, Columbia Univ, 47-49; asst. prof, Univ.

Calif, Los Angeles, 49-55; PROF, STATE UNIV. N.Y. COL, CORTLAND, 55- Ford Found. fel, 51-52; summer fels, Univ. Calif, 50, 53, 55, State Univ. N.Y, 59, 62. U.S.N.R, 42-45, Lt.(jg). MLA. Early mineralogical theories and their popularization; the biographies of Dr. Samuel Johnson. Publ: Tom Tyers Life of Samuel Johnson, Augustan Reprint Soc, 53; The scientific lady in England: 1640-1750, Univ. Calif, 55; Fontenelle and the plurality of worlds, Hist. Ideas Quart, 60. Add: Dept. of English, State University of New York College at Cortland, Cortland, NY 13045.

MEYER, KENNETH JOHN, b. Manitowoc, Wis, Aug. 24, 30; m. 53; c. 4. ENGLISH, AMERICAN STUDIES. B.A, Lawrence Col, 53; M.A, Univ. Minn, 56, Ph.D.(Am. stud), 65. Instr. ENG, Monmouth Col.(Ill), 57-61; assoc. prof, HURON COL.(S.DAK), 64-67, PROF, 67-, CHMN. DEPT, 64-, coord, Res. & Planning Develop. Proj, 67-71. Am. Stud. Asn; NCTE; Conf. Col. Compos. & Commun; MLA; AAUP. American literature and cultures, 1800-1900; curriculum in the small liberal arts college; the teaching of composition. Add: 832 Wisconsin Ave, S.W, Huron, SD 57350.

MEYER, MARIE MALMIN, b. Leland, Iowa, Aug. 14, 98; m. 33. ENGLISH. B.A, Concordia Col.(Minn), 21, M.A, Univ. Minn, 23, Ph.D, 29. Teacher grade sch, Iowa, 15-17; prof. ENG, ST. OLAF COL, 23-68, EMER. PROF, 68- Fulbright res. fel, Norway, 50-51; mem. fac, N.Community Col, N.Y, 68-69. MLA; NCTE. Comparative literature, especially European drama. Publ: Co-ed. & transl, Ibsen studies; co-auth, A manual of examinations. Add: St. Olaf College, Northfield, MN 55057.

MEYER, RICHARD DeWITT, b. Springfield, Mo, Sept. 2, 28; m. 51; c. 4. DRAMA, THEATRE. A.B, Drury Col, 50; M.A, Northwest Univ, 52; Univ. Iowa, summers 59, 61; Columbia Univ, summer 60. Dir. theatre, Ark. State Univ, 52-56; asst. prof. speech & TV, Univ. Notre Dame, 56-57; assoc. prof. & dir. theatre, Grinnell Col, 57-67; prof. theatre & assoc. chmn. dept, Fla. State Univ, 67-73; PROF. THEATRE, DIR. THEATRE PROGS. & CHMN. DEPT, UNIV. MICH, ANN ARBOR, 73- Consult, Fed. Mediation & Conciliation Serv, 56-58; asst. to Elia Kazan, Lincoln Ctr, New York, 63-64; guest dir, Tent Theatre, Springfield, Mo, summer 66; Kalamazoo Repertory Theatre, Mich, summer 67; Asolo Theatre, Sarasota, Fla, summers 68-73. Am. Theatre Asn; U.S. Inst. Theatre Technol; Am. Nat. Theatre & Acad. Publ: Co-auth, A view from the director's notebook, In: Theatre, Vol. II, Hill & Wang, 64; auth, The paradox of Gordon Craig, West. Humanities Rev, 65; What the open stage means to the playwright, Educ. Theatre J, 66. Add: Professional Theatre Program, Mendelssohn Theatre, University of Michigan, Ann Arbor, MI 48104.

MEYER, ROBERT HOLT, b. Santa Ana, Calif, Sept. 22, 34; m. 61; c. 2. ENGLISH. A.B, Sacramento State Col, 60, M.A, 62; Ph.D.(Eng), Univ. Calif, Davis, 66. Instr. ENG, Am. River Col, 63-66; asst. prof, Univ. Santa Clara, 66-73; LECTR, SAN JOSE STATE UNIV, 73- U.S.A, 57; Nat. Guard & Res, 57-63. NCTE. Modern English literature; speculative literature; utopian literature. Publ: An anatomy of the theme, Glencoe, 69; co-auth, Borrowed time: literature on man and his environment, Wadsworth, 72; auth, Dylan Thomas: the experience, the picture, and the message, Eng. J, 2/71. Add: Dept. of English, San Jose State University, 125 S. Seventh St, San Jose, CA 95192.

MEYER, ROY WILLARD, b. Zumbrota, Minn, Jan. 20, 25; m. 55; c. 1. ENGLISH. B.A, St. Olaf Col, 48; summers, Univ. Maine, 47 & Univ. Minn, 48; M.A, Univ. Iowa, 49, Ph.D, 57. Mem. hist. fac, N.Dak. State Teachers Col, Valley City, 50-52, ENG, 52-54, 55-57; asst. prof, MANKATO STATE COL, 57-65, assoc. prof, 65-67, PROF, 67- Solon J. Buck award, Minn. Hist. Soc, 62; Am. Asn. State & Local Hist. grant-in-aid, 63; Fulbright lectr, Australian-Am. Educ. Found, Flinders Univ. S.Australia, 69; Am. Philos. Soc. res. grant, 73. U.S.A, 44-46. Am. Stud. Asn; West. Lit. Asn; West. Hist. Asn. (West. Hist. Award, 69); Thoreau Soc. American Indian; Western American literature; national and state parks. Publ: The Middle Western farm novel in the twentieth century, 65 & History of the Santee Sioux, 68, Univ. Nebr; The Canadian Sioux: refugees from Minnesota, Minn. Hist, spring 68; The Outback and the West: Australian and American frontier fiction, West. Am. Lit, spring 71; B.M. Bower: poor man's wister, J. Popular Cult, spring 74; plus others. Add: Dept. of English, Mankato State College, Mankato, MN 56001.

MEYERS, CAROLYN HODGSON, American Literature. See RHODES, CAROLYN HODGSON.

MEYERS, JOSEPH HENRY, b. Cincinnati, Ohio, June 6, 03; m. 57; c. 3. HUMANITIES. A.B, Xavier Univ.(Ohio), 25; M.A, Princeton, 26. Instr. ENG, Xavier Univ.(Ohio), 26-28; asst. prof, Purdue Univ, 46-51; ASSOC. PROF, ILL. WESLEYAN UNIV, 53- Publ: Skoblianka, Atlantic Monthly, 6/52; plus others. Add: Humanities Division, Illinois Wesleyan University, Bloomington, IL 61701.

MEYERS, ROBERT REX, b. Okmulgee, Okla, Aug. 7, 23; m; c. 3. ENGLISH. B.A, Abilene Christian Col, 48; M.A, Univ. Okla, 51; Ph.D, Wash. Univ, 57. Asst. prof. Eng, Harding Col, 52-54, assoc. prof, 57-60; assoc. prof. Eng. & chmn. div. humanities, Friends Univ, 60-67; assoc. prof. ENG, WICHITA STATE UNIV, 67- 70, PROF, 70- Teaching fels, Univ. Okla, 49-50, Wash. Univ, 54-57; summer vis. prof, early admis. prog, Stetson Univ, 62; consult, Choice (jour), 71-; ed. bd, Kans. Univ. Press, 71- U.S.A, 43-46. NCTE; Midwest Mod. Lang. Asn. Victorian prose and poetry; comparative religion; Milton. Publ: Voices of concern, Bethany Press, 66; George Borrow, Twayne, 66; Stephen Crane's The open boat, Explicator, 4/63; Will the real King James version please stand up?, Restoration Rev, 11/67; Was there a toad in the bower?, Mod. Lang. Quart, 3/72. Add: Dept. of English, Wichita State University, Wichita, KS 67208.

MEYERS, RONALD J, b. Mar. 1, 36; U.S. citizen; m. 59; c. 2. ENGLISH. B.A, Brooklyn Col, 57; M.A, Columbia Univ, 59; Ph.D.(Eng), N.Y. Univ, 63. Lectr. ENG, Pratt Inst, 59-60; instr, Brooklyn Col, 60-63; asst. prof, Temple Univ, 63-66; assoc. prof, EAST STROUDSBURG STATE COL, 66-70, PROF, 70- Lectr, Hunter Col, 62-63; Rutgers Univ, summer 69; Newark Col. Eng, summer 70. MLA; Northeast Mod. Lang. Asn; Auth. League; Dramatists Guild. Shakespeare; comedy; American literature. Publ: O'Neill's use of the Phedre legend in Desire under the elms, Revue de Lit. Comp, 1-3/67; The conflict of generations, APSCUF J, 5-6/70; Is symbiosis between technology and letters possible?, Dialogist, spring 71. Add: Dept. of English, East Stroudsburg State College, East Stroudsburg, PA 18301.

MEYERS, WALTER CAMERON, b. Spokane, Wash, Dec. 3, 16; m. 40. JOURNALISM. B.A, Wash. State Univ, 38; M.A, Northwest. Univ, 47, fels, 51-52, 56-57, Ph.D.(Am. stud), 59. Reporter, Spokane Daily Chronicle, Wash, 38-40; Portland Oregonian, Ore, 40-42; managing ed, McMinnville Ore. Telephone-Register, 42-43; asst. pub. relat, Am. Telephone & Telegraph Co, 43-46; asst. prof. JOUR, Pa. State, 47-48; Univ. Okla, 48-52; MICH. STATE UNIV, 52-59, assoc. prof, 59-71, PROF, 71- Pub. dir, Spokane Community Welfare Fed, Wash, 38-40; sports copyreader, Spokane Spokesman Rev, 39-40. Asn. Educ. Jour; Am. Acad. Polit. & Soc. Sci. Journalism history. Publ: Chicago newspaper hoax in the 36 election, Jour. Quart, 60; Footnote to a friendship—Henry Horner and Richard Finnegan, 62 & McCormick of Chicago: an unconventional portrait of a controversial figure, 68, J. Ill. State Hist. Soc. Add: School of Journalism, Michigan State University, East Lansing, MI 48823.

MEYERS, WALTER EARL, b. Pittsburgh, Pa, July 1, 39; m. 61; c. 3. MEDIEVAL ENGLISH LITERATURE, ENGLISH LINGUISTICS. B.A, Duquesne Univ, 64; Danforth & NDEA fels, Univ. Fla, 64-67, Ph.D.(Eng), 67. Asst. prof. ENG, N.C. STATE UNIV, 67-71, ASSOC. PROF, 71- U.S.A, 56-59. MLA; NCTE. Medieval drama; modern English usage. Publ: A figure given: typology in the Wakefield plays, Duquesne Univ, 70; Handbook of contemporary English, Harcourt, 74; A study of usage items based on an examination of the Brown Corpus, Col. Compos. & Commun, 5/72; Literary terms and Jakobson's theory of communication, Col. Eng, 4/69. Add: Dept. of English, North Carolina State University, Raleigh, NC 27607.

MEZEY, ROBERT, b. Philadelphia, Pa, Feb. 28, 35; m. 63; c. 3. AMERICAN & EUROPEAN POETRY. B.A, Univ. Iowa, 59, fel, Stanford Univ, 60-61. Instr. ENG, Western Res. Univ, 63-64; asst. prof, Franklin & Marshall Col, 65-66; Fresno State Univ, 67-68; ASSOC. PROF, UNIV. UTAH, 73- Vis. poet, Beaver Col, 64; Ingram-Merrill Found. grantee, 73-74. Lamont Poetry Award, 60. U.S.A, 53-55. Spanish poetry; Thomas Hardy. Publ: The lovemaker, 61, & White blossoms, 65, Cummington; co-ed, Naked poetry, Bobbs, 68; auth, The book of dying, Kayak, 70; The door standing open, Houghton, 70 & Oxford, 70; ed, Poems from the Hebrew, Crowell, 73. Add: Dept. of English, University of Utah, Salt Lake City, UT 84114.

MICHAEL, JAMES ELDER, b. Seattle, Wash, July 2, 10; m. 46; c. 3. DRAMATICS. A.B, Amherst Col, 32; M.F.A, Yale, 38. Instr. Eng, Sweet Briar Col, 38-40; instr. Eng. & asst. dir. theatre, Williams Col.(Mass), 40-42; asst. prof. dramatics, Amherst Col, 46-47; assoc. prof. speech & dramatics, KENYON COL, 47-55, PROF. DRAMA, 55- Auth, Rude Awakening, Kenyon Col, 49 & Red Two, Amherst Col, 52; Fund Advan. Educ. fac. fel, 54-55; Fulbright res. grant, Paris, France, 60-61. U.S.N, 42-46, Lt. Am. Theatre Asn. Production of plays in the classic repertory; dramatic literature and theatre. Add: Dept. of Drama, Kenyon College, Gambier, OH 43022.

MICHAEL, MARION C, b. Monroe, Ga, May 17, 30; m. 57; c. 2. ENGLISH. A.B, Univ. Ga, 50, Ph.D.(Eng), 63; M.A, Univ. Va, 55; res. fel, Univ. London, 57-59. Instr. ENG, Univ. Ga, 55-57, 59-61; asst. prof. Southeast. La. Col, 61-63, assoc. prof, 63-65; asst. prof, Auburn Univ, 65-67, assoc. prof, 67-71, chmn. freshman Eng, 66-71; PROF. & CHMN. DEPT, TEX. TECH UNIV, 71- Assoc. ed, Conradiana, Univ. Md, 68- U.S.A, 51-53. MLA; S.Atlantic Mod. Lang. Asn. Conrad. Publ: Conrad's definite intention in The secret agent, Conradiana, 5/68. Add: Dept. of English, Texas Tech University, Lubbock, TX 79409.

MICHAEL, MARY RUTH, b. Frederick, Md, Mar. 13, 05. ENGLISH. B.A, Hood Col, 27; M.A, Cornell Univ, 28; Columbia Univ, 29-30; Ph.D, Radcliffe Col, 42. Instr, Simmons Col, 38-39; ENG, WELLESLEY COL, 39-42, asst. prof, 42-48, from assoc. prof. to prof, 48-72, EMER. PROF, 72- Renaissance Soc. Am; Shakespeare Soc. Am. American literature and post-Civil War fine arts. Add: 8 Midland Rd, Wellesley, MA 02181.

MICHAELS, LEONARD, b. New York, N.Y, Jan. 2, 33; m. 65; c. 2. ENGLISH. B.A, N.Y. Univ, 53; M.A, Univ. Mich, 56, Ph.D.(Eng), 67; Univ. Calif, Berkeley, 58-60. Asst. prof. ENG, Paterson State Col, 62-63; Univ. Calif, Davis, 67-69; from asst. prof. to ASSOC. PROF, UNIV. CALIF, BERKELEY, 69- Mem, Univ. Calif. Inst. Creative Art, 68; Nat. Found. on Art, 68; Guggenheim fel, 70-71. Am. Acad. Arts & Sci. Romantic poetry and prose; modern literature. Publ: Going places, Farrar, Strauss, 69; Byron's Cain, PMLA, 69. Add: 607 San Miguel Ave, Berkeley, CA 94707.

MICHAELSON, LOUIS W, b. Denver, Colo, Mar. 27, 17; m. 48; c. 1. AMERICAN LITERATURE, CREATIVE WRITING. B.A, Univ. Denver, 54, Ph.D. (Eng), 69; Univ. Ariz, 54-55; M.A. Univ. Iowa, 56. Instr. ENG, Univ. Idaho, 56-58; ASST. PROF, COLO. STATE UNIV, 58- U.S.A, 40-41. Publ: Phoenix nest (satires), Doubleday, 51; Songs of my divided self (poems), Southwest, 69; New shoes on old man (poems), Pierian, 68; Bunny rabbit, Esquire, 38; The Ferrari, Prairie Schooner, 61; Literature of Acedia, In: Minority of One, 64. Add: Dept. of English, Colorado State University, Ft. Collins, CO 80521.

MICHEL, LAURENCE ANTHONY, JR, b. Charleston, S.C, Aug. 17, 16; m. 48; c. 4. ENGLISH. B.A, Col. Charleston, 37; M.A, Fordham, 39, Ph.D.(Eng), 42. Instr. ENG, Yale, 46-50, asst. prof, 50-55, fel, Timothy Dwight Col, 48-55; assoc. prof, Canisius Col, 55-60; Univ. Buffalo, 60-62; PROF, STATE UNIV. N.Y. BUFFALO, 62-, assoc. dean grad. sch, 65-67. U.S.N.R, 43-46, Comdr. MLA; Col. Eng. Asn; Renaissance Soc. Am. English Renaissance; works of Samuel Daniel; tragedy. Publ: Ed, Samuel Daniel: the civil wars, Yale, 57; The thing contained: theory of the tragic, Ind. Univ, 70; Shakespearean tragic poetry: critique of humanism from the inside, Mass. Rev, 61. Add: 175 Highland Ave, Buffalo, NY 14222.

MICHELSON, PETER FREDRICK, b. Chicago, Ill, Dec. 23, 36; m. 59; c. 2. ENGLISH. B.A, Whitman Col, 57; M.A, Univ. Wyo, 58; Univ. Chicago, 60-62. Instr. ENG, Jamestown Col, 58-60; Northwest. Univ, 62-65; Univ.

Notre Dame, 65-71; ASST. PROF, Northwest. Univ, Evanston, 71-74; UNIV. COLO, BOULDER, 74- History and theory of criticism; modern poetics; pop culture. Publ: The aesthetics of pornography, Herder & Herder, 71; The eater (poems), Swallow, 72; Quotidian radicalism, 71, Where did neighborhood go?, 72 & Armchair revolution, 73, New Republic. Add: Dept. of English, University of Colorado, Boulder, CO 80302.

MICKEL, JERE C, b. Lincoln, Nebr, Mar. 4, 05; m. 42; c. 3. SPEECH. A.B, Nebr. State Teachers Col, Peru, 26; Goodman Theatre, 28-29; A.M, Univ. Nebr, 31; univ. fel, Univ. Chicago, 32-33; fel. & Ph.D, Univ. Denver, 49. Instr. humanities, Mont. State Univ, 33-35; Univ. Chicago, 39-45; assoc. prof. SPEECH, Tex. State Col. Women, 45-47; Canterbury Col, 48-52; prof, MILLIKIN UNIV, 53-72, EMER. PROF, 72- Am. Theatre Asn; Nat. Col. Players. History of the theatre-mediaeval; dramatic production; history of the theatre, especially American midwestern rep show. Publ: Producing The little clay cart, In: Asian drama: festival papers, Univ. S.Dak, 5/65; The genesis of Toby: a folkhero of the American theater, J. Am. Folklore, 10/67. Add: Dept. of Speech, Millikin University, Decatur, IL 62522.

MICKEN, RALPH ARLINGTON, b. Minneapolis, Minn, Jan. 26, 07; m. 31; c. 2. SPEECH. A.B, Intermt. Union Col, 29; Univ. N.Dak, 32; M.A, Mont. State Univ, 36; Ph.D, Northwest. Univ, 48. Teacher speech & Eng, Cutbank High Sch, 30-32, prin, 32-36; teacher speech, Great Falls High Sch, 36-38, asst. prin, 39; instr. speech, Mont. Sch. Mines, 39-41, asst. prof, 41-44; Iowa State Univ, 44-46, assoc. prof, 46-49; Ill. State Norm. Univ, 49-51, prof, 51-57; PROF. SPEECH & CHMN. DEPT, SOUTH. ILL. UNIV, CARBONDALE, 57- Sales speech consult, Banker's Life Ins. Co, 46-49; lectr, Northwest. Univ, 47-48. Am. Forensic Asn; Am. Asn. Teacher Adult Educ; Speech Commun. Asn; NEA; Cent. States Speech Commun. Asn. Rhetoric and public address; persuasion; legislative debate. Publ: Speaking for results, Houghton, 58; America in controversy, Brown, 73; What a man is, Pantograph, 73. Add: Dept. of Speech, Southern Illinois University, Carbondale, IL 62903.

MIDDENDORF, JOHN HARLAN, b. New York, N.Y, Mar. 31, 22; m. 43; c. 2. ENGLISH. A.B, Dartmouth Col, 43; A.M, Columbia Univ, 47, Fund. Advan. Educ. fac. fel, 51-52, Ph.D, 53. Instr. ENG, COLUMBIA UNIV, 50-54, asst. prof, 54-59, assoc. prof, 59-65, PROF, 65-, dir. grad. stud. Eng. & comp. lit, 71-74. Co-ed, Johnsonian Newslett, 50-; Counc. Res. in Humanities res. grant, 58-59; Am. Philos. Soc. grant, 62; Am. Counc. Learned Soc. grant-in-aid, 62; mem, Eng. Inst, mem. supvry. comt, 63-66; Eng. compos. test comt, Col. Entrance Exam. Bd, 61-67, chmn, 67-; assoc. ed, Yale Ed. Works of Samuel Johnson, 62-66; gen. ed, 66-; chmn. Columbia Univ. Sem. eighteenth century cult, 73- U.S.N.R, 43-45, Lt.(jg). MLA; Conf. Brit. Stud; Econ. Hist. Soc; Oxford Bibliog. Soc; Am. Soc. 18th Century Stud. Samuel Johnson; economic theory and attitudes in 18th century English literature bibliography and editing. Publ: Ed, English writers of the eighteenth century, Columbia Univ, 71; Johnson on wealth and commerce, In: Johnson, Boswell and their circle, Clarendon, 65; Johnson as editor: some proofs of the Prefaces, In: Eighteenth century studies in honor of Donald F. Hyde, Grolier, 70; Ideas vs. words: Johnson, Locke and the edition of Shakespeare, In: English writers of the eighteenth century, Columbia, 71; plus others. Add: Dept. of English, Columbia University, New York, NY 10027.

MIDDLEBRO, THOMAS GALBRAITH, b. Owen Sound, Ont, Mar. 31, 32; m. 57; c. 3. ENGLISH LITERATURE. B.A, Univ. Toronto, 55, M.A, 58; Ph.D.(Eng), McGill Univ, 72. Lectr. ENG, Univ. Sask, 59-61; lectr, CARLETON UNIV, 63-66, asst. prof, 66-71, ASSOC. PROF, 71- Asn. Can. Univ. Teachers Eng.(secy-treas, 64-65). Canadian literature in English and French; 19th century English intellectual history, Burke to the Fabians; Victorian novel. Publ: Hell on earth: the structure of Orwell's 1984, Edge, fall 68; Esther Summerson: a plea for justice, Queen's Quart, summer 70; William Morris and the Paris commune, Communist Viewpoint, 5-6/71. Add: Dept. of English, Carleton University, Colonel By Dr, Ottawa Ont. K1S 5B6, Can.

MIDDLEBROOK, DIANE W, b. Pocatello, Idaho, Apr. 16, 39; c. 1. ENGLISH LITERATURE. B.A, Univ. Wash, 61; Ph.D.(Eng), Yale, 68. Instr. ENG, Olympic Col, 62-63; asst. prof, STANFORD UNIV, 66-73, ASSOC. PROF, 73- Alfred Cook Mem. Poetry Prize, Yale, 62, Theron Field Prize, 68; Acad. Am. Poets Prize, 65. MLA. American Romantic poetry. Publ: Walt Whitman and Wallace Stevens, Cornell Univ, 74. Add: 1524 Larkin St, San Francisco, CA 94109.

MIDDLEBROOK, JONATHAN, b. New York, N.Y, Oct. 6, 40; m. 73; c. 1. ENGLISH LITERATURE. B.A, Harvard, 61, M.A, Yale, 63, Ph.D, 65. Asst. prof. ENG, Univ. Calif, Berkeley, 65-69; ASSOC. PROF, SAN FRANCISCO STATE UNIV, 69- MLA; NCTE; Melville Soc. Am. Modern American literature; 19th century British and American literature. Add: Dept. of English, San Francisco State University, 1600 Holloway Ave, San Francisco, CA 94132.

MIDDLEBROOK, LEAH RUTH, b. New York, N.Y, Oct. 12, 03; m. 28; c. 2. ENGLISH. A.B. & A.M, Wash. Univ, 23. Instr. Eng, Iowa State Teachers Col, 23-24; asst, Univ. Ill, 24-28; instr, WASH. SQ. COL, N.Y. UNIV, 29-48, asst. prof, 48-54, assoc. prof, 54-63, prof, 63-71, asst. to chmn, 52-65, acting chmn, 63-64, EMER. PROF. ENG, 71- MLA. Platonism in Spenser; T.S. Eliot and the Victorians; literary criticism. Add: 450 Riverside Dr, New York, NY 10027.

MIDDLEBROOK, SAMUEL MARVIN, b. Wilton, Conn, Jan. 15, 05; m. 28; c. 2. AMERICAN LITERATURE. A.B, Wesleyan Univ, 25; Univ. Ill, 26-27; A.M, Columbia Univ, 37. Asst, Illinois, 26-27; instr. Eng, N.Y. Univ, 27-29; assoc. ed, E.P. Dutton & Co, Inc, 30-36; from tutor to assoc. prof. ENG, CITY COL. NEW YORK, 37-56, prof, 56-71, asst. dean, Col. Lib. Arts & Sci, 57-63, acting dean, 63-64, assoc. dean, 64-71, EMER. PROF, 71- Ed, Centennial addresses, 49. MLA; Am. Stud. Asn. English literature and its backgrounds. Add: 450 Riverside Dr, New York, NY 10027.

MIDDLETON, ANNE LOUISE, b. Detroit, Mich, July 14, 40. ENGLISH. B.A, Univ. Mich, 62; M.A, Harvard, 63, Ph.D.(Eng), 66. Asst. prof. ENG, UNIV. CALIF, BERKELEY, 66-72, ASSOC. PROF, 72- MLA; Mediaeval Acad. Am; Medieval Asn. Pac. Old and Middle English literature. Add: Dept. of English, University of California, Berkeley, CA 94720.

MIDDLETON, HERMAN DAVID, b. Sanford, Fla, Mar. 24, 25; m. 46; c. 2. THEATRE. B.S, Columbia Univ, 48, M.A, 49; summers, N.Y. Univ, 50, Northwest. Univ, 51; Ph.D.(speech), Univ. Fla, 63. Instr. drama & speech, Maryville Col, 49-50; Univ. Del, 50-55; assoc. prof. DRAMA & SPEECH, UNIV. N.C. GREENSBORO, 56-64, PROF, 64-, HEAD DEPT, 56- Asst. theatre, Univ. Fla, 56-57, summer 61; stage mgr, dir-designer & tech. dir, symphonic dramas, summers 53-59; consult, Jefferson Standard Life Ins, 67; N.C. Nat. Bank, 68; Gilbarco, Inc, 68. Award of Excellence Am. Col. Theatre, Am. Oil Co, 73. Southeast. Theatre Conf.(pres, 65-67); South. Speech Commun. Asn; Am. Theatre Asn; Speech Commun. Asn. Theatre aesthetics; theatre scenery design. Add: Dept. of Drama & Speech, University of North Carolina at Greensboro, Greensboro, NC 27412.

MIDDLETON, JOHN ALEXANDER, b. San Francisco, Calif, Oct. 4, 42; m. 65; c. 1. AMERICAN LITERATURE. B.A, Univ. Kans, 64; M.A, Ind. Univ, Bloomington, 68, Ph.D.(Eng), 69. ASST. PROF. ENG, GA. STATE UNIV, 69- Nat. Endowment for Humanities younger humanist fel, 72-73. MLA; Melville Soc. American prose fiction; 19th century American literature; the novel. Publ: Shreve McCannon and Sutpen's legacy, South. Rev, 1/74. Add: Dept. of English, Georgia State University, 33 Gilmer St. S.E, Atlanta, GA 30303.

MIDURA, EDMUND MICHAEL, b. Utica, N.Y, Oct. 25, 35; m. 61; c. 4. MASS COMMUNICATION, JOURNALISM. B.S, Syracuse Univ, 57; Marquette Univ, 62-63; M.A, Pa. State Univ, University Park, 66; Ph.D.(mass commun), Univ. Iowa, 69. Reporter, Syracuse Post-Standard, N.Y, 58-59; sports ed, Oneida Daily Dispatch, N.Y, 59-60; reporter & copy ed, Utica Daily Press, 60-62; copy ed, Milwaukee J, 62-63; teacher Eng, Ilion Cent. Sch, N.Y, 63-64; teaching asst. jour, Pa. State Univ, 64-65; instr, Univ. Iowa, 65-68; ASST. PROF, Univ. R.I, 68-69; Univ. Md, 69-72; MASS COMMUN, UNIV. WIS-MILWAUKEE, 72- Nat. Inst. Sci. fel, Inst. Polit Commun, Ohio Univ, 69; teaching improv. grant, Univ. Md, 70. Asn. Educ. in Jour.(chmn. mass commun. & soc. div, 72-73). Mass media performance; journalism history; analysis and criticism of press performance. Publ: Ed, Why aren't we getting through?: the urban communication crisis, Acropolis, 71; auth, The Press Council proposal—20 years later, Iowa Journalist, 3/68; The Press Council experience in Britain, Jour. Quart, spring 68; A.J. Liebling: the wayward pressman as critic, J. Monogr, 4/74. Add: Dept. of Mass Communication, Mitchell 214 E, University of Wisconsin-Milwaukee, Milwaukee, WI 53201.

MIESLE, FRANK L, b. Fremont, Ohio, May 13, 23; m. 48; c. 3. SPEECH & DRAMA. B.A, Bowling Green State Univ, 47, M.A, 47; Ohio State Univ. Found. grant & Ph.D, 55. Instr. speech & drama, BOWLING GREEN STATE UNIV, 48-50, asst. prof, 50-61, assoc. prof, 61-65, PROF. SPEECH, 65-, DIR. THEATRE, 51-, CHMN. DEPT. SPEECH, 62- Curator, Ohio State Univ, Theatre Collection, 52-53; chmn. Int. Theatre Celebration, State of Ohio, 56-61; dir. & consult, Huron Sesquicentennial, 59. U.S.A, 43-46. Speech Commun. Asn; Am. Theatre Asn; Cent. States Speech Asn. American and English 18th and 19th century drama; theater history; play direction. Publ: The Huron story, 59; Bench 18, Dramatic Publ, 61; Theatre research: methods, trends, ideas, In: The communicative arts and sciences of speech, Merrill, 67. Add: Dept. of Speech, Bowling Green State University, Bowling Green, OH 43402.

MIGNON, CHARLES WILLIAM, b. New York, N.Y, Dec. 11, 33; m. 59; c. 2. ENGLISH. B.A, Kenyon Col, 56; M.A, Univ. Conn, 59, Ph.D.(Eng), 63. Instr. ENG, Univ. Conn, summer 63; asst. prof, Univ. Ill, 63-67; UNIV. NEBR, LINCOLN, 67-68, assoc. prof, 68-73, PROF, 73- Am. Philos. Soc. Penrose Fund grant, summer 66; Fulbright lectr, Inst. Eng, Warsaw Univ, 72-73. U.S.A.F, 56-58. Ralph W. Emerson. Publ: Decorum of imperfection; Edward Taylor's Preparatory meditations, PMLA, 10/68; A principle of order in Edward Taylor's Preparatory Meditations, EAL, 70; Emerson to Chapman: four letters about publishing, ESQ, 7/73; plus two others. Add: Dept. of English, University of Nebraska, Lincoln, NE 68508.

MIHM, BRIAN LEE, b. Darby, Pa, Dec. 13, 43; m. 66. ENGLISH NOVEL, AMERICAN LITERATURE. B.A, St. Olaf Col, 65; Ford Found. fel. & M.A, Univ. Chicago, 66; Ph.D.(Eng), Univ. Pa, 71. Instr. ENG, Pahlavi Univ, Iran, 67-69; Denison Univ, 71-72; ASST. PROF, MILLIKIN UNIV, 72- MLA. Victorian novel; Harlem renaissance; modern American novel. Add: Dept. of English, Millikin University, Decatur, IL 62522.

MILBURN, DANIEL JUDSON, b. Milburn, Okla, Feb. 17, 13; m. 36; c. 3. ENGLISH. B.S. & M.A, Okla. State Univ, 35; Ph.D.(Eng), Univ. Okla, 53. Teacher high sch, Okla, 35-38; prof. in exten, Eng. & soc. sci, Northeast. State Col, 39-41; instr. ENG, OKLA STATE UNIV, 41-46, asst. prof, 46-54, assoc. prof, 54-60, PROF, 60- Dir, NDEA Insts, summers, 65, 66; dir, Title V fels, NDEA, 66-69. U.S.N, 44-46, Lt. NCTE. Seventeenth and 18th centuries English literature; Victorian literature. Publ: A first course in college English, Houghton, 61; ed, Oklahoma revised teaching guide for the language arts, Okla. Dept. Pub. Instr, 63; The age of wit, Macmillan, 66; The college English department and the teaching profession, Okla. Eng. Bull, spring 66. Add: Dept. of English, Oklahoma State University, Stillwater, OK 74074.

MILD, WARREN PAUL, b. Minneapolis, Minn, Mar. 22, 22; m. 43; c. 3. ENGLISH LITERATURE. A.B. & A.M, Univ. Minn, 47, Ph.D, 50. Instr, Bethel Col, 48-50; Eng. lit, Univ. Redlands, 50-51, asst. prof, 51-55, assoc. prof, 55-58; dir. dept. educ. serv, bd. educ. & pub, Am. Baptist Convention, 58-66; PRES, ELLEN CUSHING JR. COL, 66- Ford fel, 54-55. U.S.A, 42-46. Scholarship aid programs; 18th century English literature. Publ: Strangers outside the feast, 66 & Recording: look back and dream, 68, Friendship; Fractured questions, 66 & The drop-ins, 68, Judson; Johnson and Lauder: a reexamination, Mod. Lang. Quart. Add: Box 37, Bryn Mawr, PA 19010.

MILDENBERGER, KENNETH WARREN, English. See Volume III, Foreign Languages, Linguistics & Philology.

MILES, ELTON ROGER, b. Coryell, Tex, May 25, 17; m. 41; c. 2. AMERICAN LITERATURE. A.B, Baylor Univ, 39; A.M, N.Tex. State Col, 47; Ph.D, Univ. Tex, 52. Instr, U.S. Army Univ, Eng, 45; from assoc. prof. to PROF. AM. LIT. & CHMN. DIV. LANG. ARTS, SUL ROSS STATE UNIV, 49- U.S.A, 41-46. MLA; S.Cent. Mod. Lang. Asn. William Dean Howells; Big Bend folklore. Publ: Devil in the Big Bend, Chisos ghosts & Old Fort Leaton, Tex. Folklore Soc; ed, Lucky 7: a cowman's autobiography & The way I heard it, Univ. Tex; auth, Southwest humorists, Steck, 69. Add: Dept. of English, Sul Ross State University, Alpine, TX 79830.

MILES, JOSEPHINE, b. Chicago, Ill, June 11, 11. ENGLISH PHILOLOGY & CRITICISM. A.B, Univ. Calif, Los Angeles, 32; A.M, Univ. Calif, 34, Phelan fel, 37-38, Ph.D, 38; D.Litt, Mills Col, 66. From instr. to prof. ENG, UNIV. CALIF, BERKELEY, 40-73, UNIV. PROF, 73- Am. Asn. Univ. Women. res. fel, 39-40; Guggenheim fel, 48-49; Am. Counc. Learned Soc. fel, 64-65; Nat. Found. Arts fel, 67-68. Shelley award, 35; Nat. Inst. Arts & Lett. award for poetry, 56. MLA; Am. Soc. Aesthet; Philol. Asn. Pac. Coast; Am. Acad. Arts & Sci. Literary history; linguistics; modern poetry. Publ: Continuity of poetic language, 51, Eras and modes in English poetry, 57, 64 & Poetry and change, 74, Univ. Calif; Poems, 1930-1960, Ind. Univ, 60; Civil poems (poems), 66 & Fields of learning (poems), 68; Oyez; Style and proportion, Little, 67; Kinds of affection, Wesleyan Univ, 67; ed, Ways of poem, rev. ed, Prentice-Hall, 73; auth, To all appearances: poems new and selected, Univ. Ill, 74; American poet, 1965, Mass. Rev, spring 66; co-auth, Scholastic Folkways today's poets II, 12/67 & auth, Library of Congress recording in poetry, spring 68, (records); plus many articles. Add: Dept. of English, 454 Wheeler Hall, University of California, Berkeley, CA 94720.

MILES, LELAND (WEBER), b. Baltimore, Md, Jan. 18, 24; m. 49; c. 2. ENGLISH, HISTORY. A.B, Juniata Col, 46, hon. D.Litt, 69; M.A, Univ. N.C, 47, Ph.D.(Eng), 49; Duke Univ, 49; hon. L.H.D, Rosary Hill Col, 70. Assoc. prof. Eng, Hanover Col, 49-50, prof. & chmn. dept, 50-60; assoc. prof, Univ. Cincinnati, 60-63, prof, 63-64; dean col. arts & sci, Univ. Bridgeport, 64-67; PRES, Alfred Univ, 67-74; UNIV. BRIDGEPORT, 74- Danforth scholar, Union Theol. Sem, summer 56; producer & moderator, progs. on classics, WHAS-TV, 58-61; Lilly fel, Sch. Lett, Ind. Univ, summer 59; Am. Counc. Learned Soc. fel, Harvard, 63-64; Fulbright sr. res. scholar, King's Col, Univ. London, 64 & vis. scholar, 72; chmn. bd. trustees, Col. Ctr. Finger Lakes, 68-71; moderator, Aspen Inst. Humanistic Stud, 69-70; consult, Nat. Humanities Ser, 69-71; chmn. bd. dirs, Empire State Found, 71-73; consult, Mid. States Asn, 71- Rosa & Samuel Sachs Prize, Cincinnati Inst. Fine Arts, 61. U.S.A.A.F, 44-45, 1st Lt. Mod. Humanities Res. Asn; Renaissance Soc. Am; MLA; Conf. Brit. Stud; Amici Thomae Mori; Acad. Polit. & Soc. Sci; Royal Soc. Lit. U.K. Renaissance and Reformation. Publ: John Colet and the platonic tradition, Open Ct. Publ, 61 & Allen & Unwin, 62; ed, St. Thomas More's Dialogue of comfort against tribulation, Ind. Univ, 66; auth, John Colet: an appreciation, Moreana, 69; co-ed, Studies in British history and culture, Conf. Brit. Stud. & Wittenberg Univ, 68-; auth, Persecution and the dialogue of comfort: a fresh look at the charges against Thomas More, J. Brit. Stud, 11/65; The dialogue of comfort and More's execution, Mod. Lang. Rev, 10/66; The literary artistry of Thomas More, Stud. Eng. Lit, winter 66; plus others. Add: Office of the President, University of Bridgeport, Bridgeport, CT 06602.

MILES, THOMAS HARDY, b. Binghamton, N.Y, July 2, 43; m. 66; c. 1. MEDIEVAL LITERATURE, HISTORY OF RELIGION. A.B, Univ. Rochester, 65; M.A, State Univ. N.Y. Binghamton, 67, Ph.D.(Eng), 70. ASST. PROF. ENG, CARNEGIE-MELLON UNIV, 70- MLA. Medieval poetry; Oriental and mystical material in contemporary literature. Add: Dept. of English, Carnegie-Mellon University, Schenley Park, Pittsburgh, PA 15213.

MILEY, WILBERT HARLEY, b. Waldo, Ohio, May 30, 07; m. 30; c. 2. SPEECH. A.B, Otterbein Col, 30; A.M, Univ. Mich, 33; M.R.E, Bethany Bibl. Sem, 40; Northwest. Univ. 47; West. Reserve Univ, 57. Instr, high sch, Ohio, 30-37, 39-43, supt, 43-44; asst. prof, Bethany Bibl. Sem, 37-39; from asst. prof. to ASSOC. PROF. SPEECH, ASHLAND COL, 44-, head dept, 44-71. Consult. Nat. Resources Libr, Church of the Brethren, 68- Conducting public discussions; religious drama in the Church of the Brethren. Add: Dept. of Speech, Ashland College, Ashland, OH 44805.

MILHAUPT, JEAN, O.P, b. Norwalk, Ohio, July 30, 23. ENGLISH LANGUAGE & LITERATURE. A.B, Aquinas Col, 45; M.A, Cath. Univ. Am, 49; Rackham fel, Univ. Mich, 61-62, Ph.D, 63; Oxford, summer 64. Teacher, Marywood Acad, 49-51; from instr. to PROF. ENG, AQUINAS COL, 51- Renaissance Soc. Am. Renaissance literature, English and Latin; medieval literature; history of English language. Publ: The structure of Cynewulf's Christ II, In: Studies in medieval culture, IV/I, Medieval Inst, West. Mich. Univ. Add: Dept. of English, Aquinas College, Grand Rapids, MI 49506.

MILIC, LOUIS TONKO, b. Split, Yugoslavia, Sept. 5, 22; nat; m; c. 3. ENGLISH. A.B, Columbia Univ, 48, M.A, 50, Ph.D, 63. Instr. ENG, Mont. State Col, 52-54; lectr, Columbia Univ, 55-58, instr, 58-62, asst. prof, 63-67, assoc. prof, Teachers Col, 67-69; PROF. & CHMN. DEPT, CLEVELAND STATE UNIV, 69- Rev. ed, Comput. & Humanities, 66-71; Am. Counc. Learned Soc-Int. Bus. Mach. fel, 67-68; gen. ed, New Humanistic Res. Ser, Teachers Col. U.S.A.A.F, 43-46. MLA; Int. Asn. Univ. Profs. Eng; Asn. Comput. Ling; Midwest Mod. Lang. Asn; Am. Soc. 18th Century Stud. Stylistics and rhetoric; 18th century English literature; computer-assisted literary research. Publ: A quantitative approach to the style of Jonathan Swift, Mouton, The Hague, 67; Style and stylistics: an analytical bibliography, Free Press, 67; Stylists on style, Scribner, 69; ed, The modernity of the eighteenth century, Case West. Reserve Univ, 71; co-auth, The English language: form and use, McKay, 74; auth, Theories of style and their implications for the teaching of composition, 5/65 & Metaphysics in the criticism of style, 10/66, Col. Compos. & Commun; Against the typology of styles, In: Essays on the language of literature, Houghton, 67; plus others. Add: 1 Bratenahl Plaza, Bratenahl, OH 44108.

MILLAR, BRANFORD PRICE, b. Monroe, Conn, Mar. 20, 14; m. 39; c. 2. ENGLISH. A.B, Harvard, 35, A.M, 39, Ph.D. 46; hon. LL.D, Pac. Univ, 65. Instr. & tutor ENG, Harvard, 35-41; instr, Md. State Teachers Col, Towson, 41-43; asst. prof, Mich. State Univ, 46-51, asst. to dean, Sch. Grad. Stud, 50-55, assoc. prof, 51-56, prof, 57-59; pres, Portland State Col, 59-68; distinguished res. prof, Teaching Res. Div, Ore. State Syst. Higher Educ, 68-69; DISTINGUISHED SERV. PROF. ENG, PORTLAND STATE UNIV, 69- Ed, Centennial Rev. Arts & Sci, 56-59; mem, Asn. Am. Col, 59-68, comn. lib. learning, 65-68; Am. Counc. Educ, 59-68; Northwest Asn. Cols. & Sec. Schs, 59-61, comnr, 64-66. MLA. English literature; English and American ballads and songs; higher education research. Publ: Contrib. to prof. journals, lit. & educ. Add: Portland State University, P.O. Box 751, Portland, OR 97207.

MILLAR, DAN PYLE, b. South Bend, Ind, Mar. 29, 38; m. 63; c. 1. INTERPERSONAL & NONVERBAL COMMUNICATION. B.A, Wabash Col, 60; M.A, Northwest. Univ, Evanston, 62; Ph.D.(speech commun), Mich. State Univ, 69. Instr. speech & dir. debate, Port Huron Jr. Col, 62-64; staff announcer, WHLS Radio, Port Huron, 64; from instr. speech to asst. prof, Bowling Green State Univ, 66-70; ASSOC. PROF. INTERPERSONAL COMMUN, CENT. MICH. UNIV, 70- Speech Commun. Asn; Int. Commun. Asn; Am. Forensic Asn.(secy, 70-72); Midwest. Forensic Asn.(pres, 72-74). Speech education. Publ: Co-auth, Preference for remembrance at junior college, Mich. Asn. Col. Personnel, 65; contrib, Introduction to speech communication, Brown, 67. Add: Dept. of Speech & Dramatic arts, Central Michigan University, Mt. Pleasant, MI 48859.

MILLEDGE, LUETTA C, b. Savannah, Ga, Jan. 13, 29; m. 62; c. 1. LITERATURE. B.A, Ft. Valley State Col, 44; M.A, Atlanta Univ, 49; Breadloaf Sch. Eng, Middlebury, Vt, summer, 55; Univ. Kans. City, summer, 60; South. Educ. fel, George Peabody Col, 62. Instr. ENG, SAVANNAH STATE COL, 49-54, asst. prof, 54-71, ASSOC. PROF, 71- Col. Lang. Asn. Creative Writing Prize, 55; Freedoms Found. George Washington Honor Medal, 63. NCTE; Col. Lang. Asn; Conf. Col. Compos. & Commun. Contemporary fiction; creative writing; short story and poetry. Publ: Light eternal: an analysis of some folkloristic elements in Faulkner's Go down, Moses, Tenn. Folklore Soc. Bull. 12/63; A brief analysis of the nature of sin as evinced in selected Hawthorne works, Quart. Rev, 10/64. Add: Dept. of English, Savannah State College, Savannah, GA 31404.

MILLER, ARTHUR BURTON, b. Des Moines, Iowa, Jan. 22, 22; m. 42; c. 2. RHETORIC. A.B, Whitworth Col, 49, B.Ed, 50; fel, Univ. Ore, 61, A.M, 62, Ph.D.(rhetoric), 64. Teacher, Hermiston High Sch, 50-51; Springdale High Sch, 51-52; N.Cent. High Sch, 52-59 & 60-61; instr. speech, Univ. Ore, 62-63; asst. prof, State Univ. N.Y. Col. Oneonata, 63-65; Wash. State Univ, 65-67; assoc. prof, North. Mich. Univ, 67-68; prof, Park Col, 68-70; dir. rhet. & pub. address, Univ. Akron, 70-72; PROF. PASTORAL MINISTRY, CENT. BAPTIST THEOL. SEM, 72- U.S.C.G, 41-45. Speech Commun. Asn; Cent. States Speech Asn. Argumentation and debate; rhetorical theory; basic rhetoric. Publ: Co-auth, Elements of deliberative debating, 68 & auth, Modes of public speaking, 69, Wadsworth; Rhetorical exigence, spring 72 & co-auth, Enthymemes: body and soul, winter 72, Philos. & Rhetoric. Add: Central Baptist Theological Seminary, Seminary Heights, Kansas City, KS 66102.

MILLER, CLARENCE ADOLPH, b. Atlanta, Ill, July 12, 09. SPEECH, DRAMA. Ed.B, Ill. State Norm. Univ, 31; M.A, Northwest. Univ, 37; alumni fel, Columbia Univ, 52-53, Ed.D.(speech educ), 54. Teacher high sch, Ill, 31-38, dir. dramatics, 38-47; asst. prof. DRAMA, SAN FRANCISCO STATE UNIV, 47-52, assoc. prof, 54-59, PROF, 59-, ASSOC. DEAN, 65-, chmn. dept, 59-65, acting chmn, div. creative arts, summer session, 59, 63. Children's theatre consult, Asn. Jr. Leagues Am, 53-54. U.S.N.R, 42-46, Lt.(jg). AAUP. Speech and drama education. Add: 1241 Redwood Way, Millbrae, CA 94132.

MILLER, CLARENCE HARVEY, b. Kansas City, Mo, Aug. 4, 30; m; c. 4. ENGLISH LITERATURE. A.B, St. Louis Univ, 51; A.M, Harvard, 52, Ph.D. (Eng. lang. & lit), 55. Instr. ENG, ST. LOUIS UNIV, 57-59, asst. prof, 59-62, assoc. prof, 62-66, PROF, 66- Am. Counc. Learned Soc. grant-in-aid, 60; Fulbright guest lectr, Univ. Wurzburg, Ger, 60-61; Guggenheim fel, 66-67. U.S.A, 55-57, Res, 57- MLA; Midwest Mod. Lang. Asn; Mod. Humanities Res. Asn; Renaissance Soc. Am. Renaissance English literature; Erasmus; St. Thomas More. Publ: Ed, Sir Thomas Chaloner's translation of Erasmus' Praise of folie, Early Eng. Text Soc, 64; auth, The order of stanzas in Cowley and Crashaw's On hope, Stud, Philol, 1/64; Donne's A nocturnall upon S. Lucies Day and the nocturns of matins, Stud. Eng. Lit, winter 66; The holograph of More's Expositio Passionis, Festschrift for Elizabeth F. Rogers, Moreana, 67. Add: Dept. of English, St. Louis University, St. Louis, MO 63103.

MILLER, CLARENCE WILLIAM, b. Sunbury, Pa, June 5, 14. ENGLISH LITERATURE. A.B, Gettysburg Col, 36; A.M, Univ. Va, 38, Ph.D, 40. Instr. ENG, Univ. Va, 40-46; asst. prof, TEMPLE UNIV, 46-49, assoc. prof, 49-62, PROF, 62- MLA; Bibliog. Soc. Am; Renaissance Soc. Am. English and American critical bibliography. Add: 119 Gladstone Rd, Lansdowne, PA 19050.

MILLER, CRAIG WILLIAM, b. Prince Albert, Sask, June 9, 15; m. 47; c. 3. ENGLISH. B.A, Univ. Sask, 37, M.A, 42, B.Ed, 46; Humanities Res. fel, Univ. Wash, 48-56, Ph.D, 56. Instr. ENG, UNIV. B.C, 46-57, asst. prof, 57-63, ASSOC. PROF, 63- Can. Counc. res. grant, 64-65, 73-74. Can. Army, 42-44. MLA; Can. Humanities Asn. George Bernard Shaw; English romantics, especially Coleridge. Publ: Coleridge's concept of nature, J. Hist. Ideas, winter 64; plus others. Add: Dept. of English, University of British Columbia, Vancouver 8, B.C, Can.

MILLER, DAVID MERLIN, b. Citronelle, Ala, Sept. 5, 34; m. 72; c. 2. ENGLISH LITERATURE. B.S, Univ. Minn, Minneapolis, 58, M.A, 61; res. grant, Univ. Calif, Davis, summer 63, Ph.D.(Eng), 66. Instr. ENG, Mankato State Col, 64-66; ASSOC. PROF, PURDUE UNIV, WEST LAFAYETTE, 66- Summers, Purdue Res. Found. fels, 67, 69; Clark Libr. fel, Univ. Calif, Los Angeles, 68. U.S.A, 64-66. MLA. Milton; aesthetics; science fiction. Publ: The net of Hephaestus: modern criticism and metaphysical metaphor, Mouton, 71; Faulkner's women, Mod. Fiction Stud, 67; The location of verbal art, Lang. & Style, 70; From delusion to illumination: a larger structure for L'Allegro-Il Penseroso, PMLA, 71. Add: Dept. of English, Purdue University, West Lafayette, IN 47907.

MILLER, EDMUND GILLMORE, b. Milwaukee, Wis, Mar. 9, 22. ENGLISH. A.B, Dartmouth Col, 43; M.A, Columbia, 47, Ph.D.(Eng), 55. Instr. ENG, Dartmouth, 47-48; UNIV. N.H, 51-55, asst. prof, 55-61, assoc. prof, 61-72, PROF, 72- U.S.N.R, 43-46, Lt. MLA; Romantic and Victorian English literature. Add: 34 Oyster River Rd, Durham, NH 03824.

MILLER, EDWIN HAVILAND, b. Johnstown, Pa, Sept. 2, 18; m. 46; c. 1. ENGLISH LITERATURE. A.B, Lehigh Univ, 40; A.M, Pa. State Col, 42; Ph.D, Harvard, 51. Instr. ENG, Pa. State Col, 40-42, 45-46; from instr. to asst. prof, Simmons Col, 47-52, assoc. prof, 52-59, prof, 59-61; assoc. prof, N.Y. UNIV, 61-62, PROF, 62-, chmn. dept, 68-73. Res. fel, Folger Shakespeare Libr, 53; Am. Counc. Learned Soc. fel, 59-60; Guggenheim fel, 67-68. U.S.A, 42-45. MLA; Col. Eng. Asn. Elizabethan and American literature. Publ: Professional writer in Elizabethan England, Harvard, 59; The correspondence of Walt Whitman (5 vols), 61-69 & ed, The artistic legacy of Walt Whitman, 70, N.Y. Univ; Walt Whitman's poetry: a psychological journey, Houghton, 68; A century of Whitman criticism, Ind. Univ, 69; Whitman-Leaves of grass: selections, Appleton, 70. Add: Dept. of English, New York University, Washington Sq, New York, NY 10003.

MILLER, EDWIN SHEPARD, b. Newark, Ohio, Sept. 23, 04; m. 30; c. 1. ENGLISH LITERATURE. A.B, Bethany Col.(W.Va), 25; W.Va. Univ, 26; A.M, Ohio State Univ, 30; Ph.D, Univ. N.C, 43. Instr, Ore. State Col, 27-29; Gen. Motors Inst. Tech, 30-31; for. teacher, Wakayama Col. Commerce, Japan, 34-37; instr, Univ. N.C, 37-43; teacher lit, STEPHENS COL, 43-71, chmn. upper div, 67-71, chmn. dept. lit, 57-68, chmn. div. lang, lit. & philos, 61-67, EMER. PROF, 71- Vis. lectr, Univ. Minn, 46-47; Fulbright grants, Netherlands, 52-53, Italy, 58-59; summer vis. prof, Univs. Omaha, Pittsburgh & Mo. Mediaeval and Renaissance English literature; early 16th century drama. Publ: Selected poems, Open Places Poet Ser, 72. Add: 200 W. Blvd S, Columbia, MO 65201.

MILLER, EUGENE ERNEST, b. Akron, Ohio, Apr. 18, 30; m. 62; c. 2. ENGLISH. B.A, Univ. Notre Dame, 55; M.A, Ohio Univ, 62; Ph.D.(Eng), Univ. Ill, Urbana, 67. ASSOC. PROF. ENG, ALBION COL, 67- Nat. Endowment for Humanities fel, Howard Univ, 71-72. MLA; Col. Eng. Asn. English; Afro-American literature; aesthetics. Publ: Voodoo parallels in Native son, Col. Lang. Asn. J, 9/72; Some Black thoughts on Don L. Lee's Think Black, Col. Eng, 5/73. Add: 919 N. Berrien, Albion, MI 49224.

MILLER, FREDERICK DeWOLFE, b. Rogersville, Tenn, Aug. 2, 07. ENGLISH. A.B, Davidson Col, 30; A.M, Univ. Va, 35, DuPont sr. fel, 40-42, Ph.D, 42. Teaching fel, Univ. Va, 40-42; spec. agent, Fed. Bur. Invest, 42-45; instr, Bucknell Univ, 45-46; asst. prof. ENG, UNIV. TENN, KNOXVILLE, 46-51, assoc. prof, 51-62, PROF, 62- Am. Philos. Soc. grant, 54-55, 60; Am. Counc. Learned Soc. grant, 61; Fulbright lectr, Univ. Oslo, 63-64. MLA; S.Atlantic Mod. Lang. Asn; NEA. Emily Dickinson; Walt Whitman; American transcendentalism. Publ: Christopher Pearse Cranch, Harvard, 51; contrib, Melville and Hawthorne in the Berkshires, Kent State Univ, 69; auth, Russian response to American literature, Resources Am. Lit. Stud, 71; Emily Dickinson: self-portrait, New Eng. Quart, 73; plus one other. Add: Dept. of English, University of Tennessee, Knoxville, TN 37916.

MILLER, GERSON FREDERIC, b. New York, N.Y, Nov. 6, 26; m. 60; c. 2. JOURNALISM, ENGLISH. B.A, Univ. Calif, Berkeley, 48; M.A, Pa. State Univ, 64. Ed. asst, King Features Syndicate, 45-47; movie critic, Movie Stars on Parade, 48-50; asst. sales mgr, Harry F. Doehla Co, 50-52; area rep, Manchester Union Leader, N.H. 52-55; dir. pub. relat, San Mateo Times, Calif, 55-63, nat. advertising mgr, 62-63; teaching asst. jour, Pa. State Univ, 63-64; asst. prof. advertising, San Jose State Col, 64-67; PROF. ENG, WEST. WASH. STATE COL, 67-, DIR. JOUR. PROG, ADV. STUDENT PUBL. & CHMN. FAC. AFFAIRS COUNC, COL. ARTS & SCI, 73- Am. Bus. Press summer fel, 65. Five Ed. & Pub. Mag. & Nat. Newspaper Promotion Asn. awards, 55-63. Asn. Educ. in Jour. The right of privacy and the mass media, history of newspaper promotion in the United States; history of the New Zealand press. Publ: The story of the Times, 56 & the 5th richest county in the United States, 59, San Mateo Times; Newspaper promotion, Ed. & Publ. Mag, 8/64. Add: Journalism Program, 339 Humanities Bldg, Western Washington State College, High St, Bellingham, WA 98225.

MILLER, HAROLD A, b. Powell, Wyo, July 12, 31; m. 50; c. 2. SPEECH. B.A, Northwest. Col, 55; M.A, Univ. Minn, 57, Ph.D.(speech), 62. From asst. prof. speech to assoc. prof, Northwest. Col, 56-64; asst. prof. rhetoric, Univ. Minn, Minneapolis, 64-65; assoc. prof. commun, Westmont Col, 65-67; from asst. prof. to PROF. SPEECH, UNIV. MINN, MINNEAPOLIS, 67-, DEAN CONTINUING EDUC. & EXTEN, 71-, asst. dean summer session, 67-71. Nat. Soc. Stud. Commun; Speech Commun. Asn. Religious public address; communication for religious workers. Publ: The voice of God—natural or supernatural, Preaching in Am. Hist, spring 69. Add: 150 Wesbrook Hall, University of Minnesota, Minneapolis, MN 55455.

MILLER, HENRY KNIGHT, b. Brooklyn, N.Y, Apr. 25, 20. ENGLISH. B.A, Oberlin Col, 49; Scribner fel, 50-51; Procter fels, 51-53; Ph.D.(Eng), Princeton, 53. Instr. ENG, PRINCETON, 53-56, asst. prof, 56-61, assoc. prof, 61-69, PROF, 69- U.S.C.G, 41-46. John Annan bicentennial preceptorship, 58-61. MLA; Am. Soc. 18th Century Stud.(chmn. publ. comt, 73-). The English novel; 18th century English literature. Publ: Essays on Fielding's miscellanies, Princeton, 61; co-ed, The Augustan milieu, 70 & ed, Henry Fielding's Miscellanies, Vol. I, 72, Clarendon; co-ed, English literature, 1600-1800: a current bibliography, 58-64; & auth, Some functions of rhetoric in Tom Jones, 66, Philol. Quart; The Whig interpretation of literary history, Eighteenth-Century Stud, 72; plus others. Add: Dept. of English, 22 McCosh Hall, Princeton University, Princeton, NJ 08540.

MILLER, HENRY PRENTICE, b. Barnesville, Ga, Mar. 7, 05; m. 31; c. 1. AMERICAN LITERATURE. Ph.B, Emory Univ, 27, A.M, 28; Ph.D, Univ. Chicago, 42. From instr. to ASSOC. PROF. ENG. & DEAN ALUMNI, EMORY UNIV, 28- V.Chmn, Ty Cobb Educ. Found, 69-; chmn, Gordon Jr. Col, Found, 72- NCTE; S.Atlantic Mod. Lang. Asn. Life and works of William Tappan Thompson. Add: Alumni Memorial Bldg, Emory University, Atlanta, GA 30322.

MILLER, JAMES EDWIN, JR, b. Bartlesville, Okla, Sept. 9, 20; m. 44; c. 2. ENGLISH. B.A, Univ. Okla, 42; M.A, Univ. Chicago, 47, Ph.D.(Eng), 49. Instr. ENG, Univ. Mich, 49-50; asst. prof, Univ. Nebr, 53-56, prof. & chmn. dept, 56-62; PROF, UNIV. CHICAGO, 62- Fulbright lectr. Am. lit, Naples & Rome, Italy, 58-59; ed, Col. Eng, 60-66; mem, adv. counc, Am. Lit. Group, MLA, 61-62; lectr, Northwest. Univ, summer 62; Univ. Hawaii, summer 64; chmn, comn. lit, NCTE, 67-69; Fulbright lectr. Am. lit, Kyoto, Japan, 68; Guggenheim fel, 69-70. Sig.C, 42-46, 50-52, Capt. MLA (mem. ed. bd, PMLA, 68-72); NCTE (pres-elect, 69, pres, 70); Am. Stud. Asn. American literature; contemporary fiction. Publ: A critical guide to Leaves of grass, 57 & Quests surd and absurd; essays in American literature, 67, Univ. Chicago; co-auth, Start with the sun, Univ. Nebr, 60; auth, Reader's guide to Herman Melville, Noonday, 62; Walt Whitman, Twayne, 62; F. Scott Fitzgerald: his art and his technique, N.Y. Univ, 64; J.D. Salinger, Univ. Minn, 65; Theory of fiction: Henry James, Univ. Nebr, 72; Word, self, reality: the rhetoric of imagination, Dodd, 72. Add: 5536 Blackstone Ave, Chicago, IL 60637.

MILLER, JAMES HULL, b. Sewickley, Pa, June 21, 16; m. 42; c. 3. DRAMATIC ART. A.B, Princeton, 38. Tech. production, summer theatres, 37-42; Goodman Theatre Art Inst, Chicago, Ill, 45; prof. DRAMATIC ART, Univ. N.Mex, 46-55; CENTENARY COL, 55-58, VIS. PROF, 58-; DIR, ARTS LABORATORY, SHREVEPORT, LA, 58- Consult. theatre design. C.Eng, U.S.A, 41-46. Am. Theatre Asn; U.S. Inst. Theatre Technol. Publ: Self-supporting scenery for children's theatre ... and grown ups' too, privately publ, 71, 2nd ed, 73; The general auditorium, Am. Inst. Archit. J, 60; For everyman, a theatre, Tulane Drama Rev, 6/63; Stone age art in an IBM world?, Earlham Rev, Vol. 1, No. 2; plus others. Add: 3415 Reily Lane, Shreveport, LA 71105.

MILLER, JAMES IVAN, JR, b. Okmulgee, Okla, Oct. 8, 30; m. 50; c. 2. ENGLISH. B.A, Univ. Okla, 52, M.A, 53; Rotary fel, New Col. grant & B.A, Oxford, 55, M.A, 59; Dankstipendium, Univ. Munich, 56-57; Ph.D. (Eng), Harvard, 67. Instr. Eng, Univ. Md. Overseas, 54-57; Univ. Dayton, 58; U.S. Air Force Acad, 58-59, German, 59-60, ASST. PROF. ENG, 62-65; Morningside Col, 65-67; Univ. Tulsa, 67-70; NORTH. ILL. UNIV, 70- Nat. Endowment for Humanities summer stipend, 68; fel, Fifth Session Southeast. Inst. Medieval & Renaissance Stud, summer 69. U.S.A.F, 55-65, Capt. MLA; Mod. Humanities Res. Asn; Col. Eng. Asn; Mediaeval Acad. Am. John Lydgate; St. Edmund and St. Fremund; Saint's legend as genre. Add: Dept. of English, Northern Illinois University, De Kalb, IL 60115.

MILLER, JAMES WHIPPLE, Comparative & Chinese Literature. See Volume III, Foreign Languages, Linguistics & Philology.

MILLER, JIM WAYNE, German Language & Literature, American Literature. See Volume III, Foreign Languages, Linguistics & Philology.

MILLER, JOHN HAWKINS, b. Philadelphia, Pa, July 23, 43; m. 66; c. 1. ENGLISH LITERATURE. B.A, Yale, 65; fel, Univ. Pittsburgh, 66-70, M.A, 67, Ph.D.(Eng), 70. Teaching intern ENG, Univ. Pittsburgh, 66-70; Fulbright-Hays advan. teaching fel, Univ. Clermont-Ferrand, 70-71; ASST. PROF, ROBERT MORRIS COL, 71- MLA; AAUP. Matthew Arnold; 19th century British literature; prose nonfiction. Add: 5606 Woodmont St, Pittsburgh, PA 15217.

MILLER, JORDAN YALE, b. Manhattan, Kans, Sept. 2, 19; m. 45; c. 2. COMPARATIVE LITERATURE, DRAMA. B.A, Yale, 42; Ph.D, Columbia Univ, 57. Assoc. prof. ENG, Kans. State Univ, 50-67, prof, 67-69; PROF. & CHMN. DEPT, UNIV. R.I, 69- Fulbright lectr. drama, Natya Acad, Natya Sangh, Bombay, 64-65. U.S.A, 42-45. MLA; NCTE; Conf. Col. Composition & Commun. American drama; Eugene O'Neill. Publ: American dramatic literature, McGraw, 61; Eugene O'Neill and the American critic, Shoe String, 62; Playwright's progress: O'Neill & the critics, Scott, 65; ed, Twentieth century interpretations of a streetcar named desire, Prentice-Hall, 71; Camino real, In: The fifties, Everett-Edwards, 70; William Inge, Kans. Quart, spring 70; Expressionism: the wasteland enacted, In: The Twenties, Everett-Edwards, (in press); plus others. Add: Dept. of English, University of Rhode Island, Kingston, RI 02881.

MILLER, JOSEPH HILLIS, b. Newport News, Va, Mar. 5, 28; m. 49; c. 3. ENGLISH LITERATURE. B.A, Oberlin Col, 48; M.A, Harvard, 49, Ph.D. (Eng), 52; M.A, Yale, 72. Instr. Eng, Williams Col, 52-53; asst. prof, Johns Hopkins Univ, 53-59, assoc. prof, 59-63, prof, 63-68, Eng. & humanistic stud, 68-72; PROF. ENG, YALE, 72- Ed, Mod. Lang. Notes, 53-61; ELH, 53-; Col. Eng, 62, 63; teacher, Univ. Hawaii, summer 58; Guggenheim fels, 59-60, 65-66; Danforth seminar lectr, Univ. Chicago, 59; teacher, Harvard, summer 62; Am. Philos. Soc. res. grant, 64; chmn. dept. Eng, Johns Hopkins Univ, 64-68; vis. prof, Swarthmore Col, Ward-Phillips lectr, Notre Dame Univ, 67; vis. prof, Univ. Va, 68; mem. supv. comt, Eng. Inst, 68-71, chmn, 71-; ed, J. Am. Acad. Relig, 70-; fel, Humanities Inst, Wesleyan Univ, 71; vis. prof, Univ. Wash, summer 71; Univ. Zurich, summer 72. Danforth Found E. Harris Harbison Award, 68. MLA (mem. res. comt, 68-71); fel. Soc. Relig. Higher Educ; fel. Am. Acad. Arts & Sci. Nineteenth and twentieth century English and American literature. Publ: Charles Dickens: the world of his novels, 58, The disappearance of God: five nineteenth century writers, 63, Poets of reality: six twentieth-century writers, 65 & Thomas Hardy: distance and desire, 71, Harvard; The form of Victorian fiction, Univ. Notre Dame, 68. Add: Dept. of English, Yale University, New Haven, CT 06520.

MILLER, JOSEPH WASHBURN, b. Cape Girardeau, Mo, Aug. 11, 19; m. 57; c. 1. ENGLISH. B.S. in Ed, Southeast Mo. State Univ, 40, B.A, 41; M.A, Columbia Univ, 47; res. fel, Univ. Minn, 56-58, Ph.D, 58. Instr. math. & Eng, Kemper Mil. Sch, 42-46; asst. admis, Teachers Col, Columbia Univ, 46-47; instr. freshman Eng, Col. Sci. Lit. & Arts, Univ. Minn, 47-52; secy, charitable found, Minneapolis, 52-56; dir. freshman Eng, MOORHEAD STATE COL, 59-60, dir. field servs, 60-64, assoc. prof. ENG, 64-69, PROF, 69- Prog. specialist, U.S. Off. Educ, Wash, D.C, 65-67. Am. Asn. Higher Educ; NCTE (assoc. chmn. ad hoc comt. state of knowledge about compos, 61-63); NEA; Conf. Col. Compos. & Commun; Col. Eng. Asn; Conf. Eng. Educ; AAUP. Communication; freshman English, especially composition. Add: 1116 S. 16th St, Moorhead, MN 56560.

MILLER, KEITH ALLEN, b. Tiffin, Ohio, Mar. 16, 41; m. 60; c. 1. COMMUNICATION THEORY. B.S.Educ, Bowling Green State Univ, 66, M.A, 67, Ph.D.(commun), 70. ASST. PROF. COMMUN, Cornell Univ, 70-72; UNIV. WYO, 72- Int. Commun. Asn; Speech Commun. Asn. Therapeutic communication; conversational analysis; communication in performing arts. Publ: Paradigmatic scholar: the rhetorical method of Emerson, Ohio Speech J, 68; contrib, Words and things and other stuff: a general semantics perspective, Cornell Univ, 70. Add: Dept. of Communication & Theatre, University of Wyoming, Laramie, WY 82071.

MILLER, LEE WELLS, b. Waterbury, Vt, Nov. 29, 12; m. 43. ENGLISH, AMERICAN LITERATURE. B.A, Cedarville Col, 42; M.A, Rice Inst, 48; Ph.D.(Eng), La. State Univ, 51. Instr. ENG, N.TEX. STATE UNIV, 48-49, asst. prof, 51-52, assoc. prof, 53-57, PROF, 58- Mem, Am. Lit. Group, MLA. U.S.A, 42-46. Puritan period, especially Jonathan Edwards; transcendental group, especially Emerson and Thoreau; American novel. Add: Dept. of English, North Texas State University, Denton, TX 76203.

MILLER, LEWIS HOLMES, JR, b. New York, N.Y, Sept. 24, 37; m. 60; c. 2. ENGLISH LITERATURE. A.B, Amherst Col, 60; M.A, Cornell Univ, 61, Ph.D.(Eng), 64. Asst. prof. ENG, IND. UNIV, BLOOMINGTON, 64-68, ASSOC. PROF, 68-, summer res. grant, 66. MLA. Edmund Spenser and the English Renaissance; Robert Frost. Publ: Phaedria, Mammon, and Sir Guyon's education by error, J. Eng. & Ger. Philol, 1/64; Arthur, Maleger, and history in the allegorical context, Univ. Toronto Quart, 1/66; A secular reading of The faerie queene, book II, ELH, 6/66. Add: Dept. of English, Indiana University, Bloomington, IN 47401.

MILLER, MARY RUTH, b. Bartow, Fla, Dec. 22, 26. ENGLISH. A.B, Fla. State Univ, 48; M.A, George Peabody Col, 51; Cokesbury Award, Duke Univ, 59-60, 61-62, Woodrow Wilson Summer Award, 62, Ph.D.(Eng), 66. Teacher elem. schs, Fla, 48-49; high schs, 49-53; instr. Eng, Reinhardt Col, 53-59, dir. pub. relat, 56-59; asst. prof. ENG, Fla. South. Col, 62-67; PROF. & CHMN. DEPT, TENN. WESLEYAN COL, 67-, summer grant 68. MLA; S.Atlantic Mod. Lang. Asn; Col. Eng. Asn; Southeast. Renaissance Conf. Nineteenth century English literature; Thomas Campbell. Publ: The Crimean War: a perspective for the war in Vietnam?, Colleague, fall 67; English Education Conference, Bull. Asn. Depts. Eng, 2/71. Add: 422 Gettys Lane, Athens, TN 37303.

MILLER, MELVIN HULL, b. Flushing, Mich, Apr. 19, 20; m. 51. SPEECH. A.B, Albion Col, 42; M.A, Mich. State Univ, 49; Ph.D, Univ. Wis, 57. Instr. speech, Grinnell Col, 49-51; overseas prog, Univ. Md, 51-54; teaching asst, Univ. Wis, 54-56, instr. speech, UNIV. WIS-MILWAUKEE, 56-58, asst. prof, 58-63, assoc. prof, 63-66, PROF. COMMUN, 66-, chmn. dept. speech, 63-67, res. support grants, Grad. Sch, summers 60, 63. U.S.N, 42-47, Lt. Comdr. Speech (mem, legis. assembly, 68). Rhetoric and public address. Publ: Co-auth, A syllabus for public speaking, W.C. Brown, 62; Charles Dickens at the English charity dinner, Quart. J. Speech, 4/61; Charles Dickens and his audience, Cent. States Speech J, autumn 62; plus others. Add: 7332 Harwood Ave, Wauwatosa, WI 53213.

MILLER, NEWTON EDD, JR, b. Houston, Tex, Mar. 13, 20; m. 42; c. 2. SPEECH, ADMINISTRATION. B.S, Univ. Tex, 39, A.M, 40; Ph.D, Univ. Mich, 52. Instr, Univ. Tex, 41-45, asst. prof, 45-47; lectr. speech, Univ. Mich, 47-48, asst. prof, 50-55, assoc. prof, 55-59, prof, 59-65, asst. dir. summer session, 53-57, assoc. dir, 57-62, asst. to v.pres. acad. affairs, 62-65; chancellor & prof. speech, Univ. Nev, 65-68, PRES, 68-73; UNIV. MAINE, PORTLAND-GORHAM, 73- Dir. forensics, Univ. Tex, 42-47; res. asst, Navy Conf. Res. Proj, Univ. Mich, 47-49. Speech Commun. Asn; Am. Forensic Asn; AAUP. Discussion; debate; contemporary public address. Publ: First course in speech, Steck & Required arbitration of labor disputes, Univ. Tex, 46; co-auth, Discussion and conference, Prentice-Hall, 54, rev. ed, 68; The student in an age of unrest, N.Y. State Bar J, 2/71. Add: University of Maine at Portland-Gorham, 37 College Ave, Gorham, ME 04038.

MILLER, NOLAN, b. Kalida, Ohio, May 4, 12. ENGLISH. A.M, Wayne Univ, 40. Spec. instr, Wayne Univ, 40-45; from assoc. prof. to PROF. LIT, ANTIOCH COL, 46-, DIR. ANTIOCH CTR. ENG. STUD, 71- Ed, Antioch Rev. & New Campus Writing. Univ. Mich. Hopwood Prize, 43. Literature; 19th and 20th century fiction and poetry. Publ: A moth of time & The merry innocents, Harper; Why I am so beat, Putnam. Add: Antioch College Centre for English Studies, 110 Hemingford Rd, London, N.1, England.

MILLER, PAUL WILLIAM, b. Welland, Ont, June 6, 26; nat; m. 51; c. 3. ENGLISH. B.A, McMaster Univ, 47; M.A, Brown Univ, 48; fel, Univ. Mich, 48-53, Ph.D, 55. Teaching asst. ENG, Brown Univ, 48; instr, Univ. Wis, 55-58, assoc. prof, King Col, 58-61; WITTENBERG UNIV, 61-68, PROF, 68- Vis. prof, East. Mich. Univ, 65-66. MLA; Renaissance Soc. Am; AAUP. English Renaissance; criticism; 17th century London drama. Publ: The effectiveness of rhetorical devices in Elizabethan epyllia; Seven minor epics of the English Renaissance, Scholars' Facsimiles, 67; The provenience of death symbolism in Van Gogh's cornscapes, Psychoanalytic Rev, 12/65; The decline of the English epithalamion, Tex. Stud. Lit. & Lang, fall 70; The cyclical renewal of London, S.Atlantic Quart, summer 72; plus others. Add: 1122 Garfield Ave, Springfield, OH 45504.

MILLER, RALPH NORMAN. AMERICAN LITERATURE. A.B, Wayne State Univ, 38; A.M, Univ. Mich, 39; Ph.D, Northwest. Univ, 46. Instr. ENG, Wayne State Univ, 39-41; Northwest. Univ, 43-46; assoc. prof, WEST. MICH. UNIV, 46-53, PROF, 53- Ford fel, 52-53. NCTE; Col. Eng. Asn; Am. Soc. Aesthet; MLA. Eighteenth century American historiography; 19th century American aesthetics. Add: Dept. of English, Western Michigan University, Kalamazoo, MI 49001.

MILLER, ROBERT ALEXANDER, b. Moundsville, W.Va, Jan. 9, 23; m. 47; c. 2. ENGLISH. A.B, Washington & Jefferson Col, 44; M.A, Univ. Okla, 47; Univ. Minn, Minneapolis, 47-55. Grad. instr. ENG, Univ. Okla, 46-47; instr, Univ. Minn, 48-55; from instr. to ASSOC. PROF, PURDUE UNIV, WEST LAFAYETTE, 55-, DIR. COMPOS, 69- AAUP; MLA; Midwest Mod. Lang. Asn; NCTE; Conf. Col. Compos. & Commun; Col. Eng. Asn. English composition; English and American literature. Add: Dept. of English, Purdue University, West Lafayette, IN 47907.

MILLER, ROBERT HENRY, b. Defiance, Ohio, Aug. 10, 38; m. 60; c. 3. ENGLISH LITERATURE, BIBLIOGRAPHY. B.A, Bowling Green State Univ, 60, M.A, 61; Ph.D.(Eng), Ohio State Univ, Columbus, 68. Instr. humanities, Mich. Technol. Univ, 61-64; asst. prof. ENG, UNIV. LOUISVILLE, 68-72, ASSOC. PROF. & ASSOC. THEATRE ARTS, 72-, DIR. GRAD. STUD, 70- MLA; S.Atlantic Mod. Lang. Asn; AAUP; Renaissance Soc. Am. Sixteenth century English literature; English Reformation history; textual criticism. Publ: The publication of Raymond Chandler's The long goodbye, Papers Bibliog. Soc. Am, winter 69. Add: Dept. of English, University of Louisville, Louisville, KY 40208.

MILLER, ROBERT L, Linguistics. See Volume III, Foreign Languages, Linguistics & Philology.

MILLER, ROBERT PARSONS, b. Newark, N.J, Sept. 12, 23; m. 45; c. 2. ENGLISH. A.B, Princeton, 47, M.A, 49, Ph.D.(Eng), 54. Instr. ENG, Princeton, 50-53; asst. prof, QUEENS COL.(N.Y), 53-67, assoc. prof, 67-74, PROF, 74- U.S.N, 43-46. MLA; Mediaeval Acad. Am. Renaissance narrative poetry; Christian iconographic tradition; medieval literature. Publ: The wife of Bath's tale and medieval exempla, ELH, 65; Allegory in the Canterbury tales, In: A companion to Chaucer studies, Oxford, 68; plus others. Add: Dept. of English, Queens College, Flushing, NY 11367.

MILLER, RUTH, b. Chicago, Ill, Apr. 5, 21; div; c. 2. ENGLISH, AMERICAN CIVILIZATION. M.A, Univ. Chicago, 45; Ph.D.(Am. civilization), N.Y. Univ, 65. Lectr. Eng, Brooklyn Col, 45-55, humanities, 55-62; instr. Eng. STATE UNIV. N.Y. STONY BROOK, 62-65, asst. prof, 66-67, assoc. prof, 67-69, PROF. ENG. & COMP. LIT, 69-, CHMN. PROG. COMP. LIT, 72- Lectr. Am. lit, New Sch. Social Res, 61-62; Fund Adult Educ. fel, 61-62; Fulbright-Hays prof. Am. lit, India, 65-66; State Univ. N.Y. Stony Brook Projects, Grants & Res. Comt. grant, 67-68; vis. prof. Am. lit, Hebrew Univ. Jerusalem, 70-72. Melville Cane Award, Poetry Soc. Am, 68. MLA; Am. Comp. Lit. Asn.(ed, Newslett, 73-); Int. Comp. Lit. Asn. American poetry and drama; Emily Dickinson; Black American literature. Publ: The poetry of Emily Dickinson, Wesleyan Univ, 68; ed, Blackamerican literature: 1760 to the present, Glencoe & Macmillan, 71; co-ed, Race awareness: the nightmare and the vision, Oxford, 71; auth, The poetry of Stephen Crane, Bull. N.Y. Pub. Libr, 5/68; Invisible man: a parable for our time, Scripta Hierosolymitana, 73; preface to Mark Twain's Palestine journey, Lewensohn, Jerusalem, 73. Add: 6 Dogwood Dr, Stony Brook, NY 11790.

MILLER, VIRGINIA ROGERS, b. Brookline, Mass, Apr. 7, 09; div. SPEECH. A.B, Wheaton Col.(Mass), 31; A.M, Cornell Univ, 41. Teacher, Westford Acad, Mass, 35-36; Rogers Hall Sch, 36-38; spec. instr, Simmons Col, 39-44, instr, 44-46; Wellesley Col, 41-44, lectr, 46-48, asst. prof. speech, 48-65, chmn. dept, 55-65, teacher, Inst. For. Stud, 47-50; private practice, speech, speech path. & ther, 65- Private teaching, Lowell, Mass, 35-41; teacher, Abbot Acad, 36-41; Acad. of the Assumption, 46-48; dir, Children's Little Theatre Group, Young People's Little Theatre Group; All Souls Theatre Guild; speech therapist, Tynysborough Pub. Schs, 68. New Eng. Speech Asn.(secy-treas, 44-46, v.pres, 56, pres, 57). Theatre; psychology. Publ: Phonetic ed, General Speech, McGraw, 63 & A program for speech improvement, Electronic Futures, 64; correlator & co-auth, Audiometric tests of speech defective college students, J. Speech & Hearing Disorders, 3/48; auth, Present day use of the "broad A" in eastern Massachusetts, 11/53 & co-auth, A possible basis for the association of voice characteristics and personality traits, 11/58, Speech Monogr. Add: 16 Garden Rd, Lowell, MA 01852.

MILLER, WARD SEARING, b. Buffalo, N.Y, Apr. 19, 08; m. 42; c. 3. ENGLISH. B.A, Denison Univ, 29; M.A, Syracuse Univ, 36; Ph.D, State Univ. Iowa, 55. Teacher high sch, Ohio, 29-31, N.Y, 31-42; instr, Univ. Rochester, 46-48; from asst. prof. to assoc. prof. ENG, UNIV. REDLANDS, 49-64, prof, 64-73, EMER. PROF, 73-; PROF. & CONSULT, HONG KONG BAPTIST COL, 73-, vis. prof. & consult, 71-72. Fulbright lectr, Finland, 62-63; Fulbright prof, Univ. Jordan, 66-67. U.S.N.R, 42-46, Lt. Comdr. MLA; Conf. Christianity & Lit.(pres, 61-64). Old Testament poetry and modern critical methods; vocabulary research; English as a second language. Publ: Word wealth, 39, 48, 58, rev. ed, 67 & Word wealth jr, 50, 62, Holt; Write, Forest Lawn Found, 59, 61; co-auth, English for Chinese students, Hong Kong Baptist Col, 72; auth, The allegory in part I of Hudibras, Huntington Libr. Quart, 58; The writer that is to be, In: Imagination and the spirit, Eerdmans, 71. Add: Dept. of English, Hong Kong Baptist College, 224 Waterloo Rd, Kowloon, Hong Kong.

MILLER, WAYNE CHARLES, b. New York, N.Y, Nov. 3, 39; m. 73; c. 2. AMERICAN LITERATURE & STUDIES. B.A, St. John's Univ.(N.Y), 60; M.A, Columbia Univ, 61; Ph.D.(Eng), N.Y. Univ, 68. Instr. ENG, U.S. Air Force Acad, 63-66, asst. prof, 66-67; assoc. prof, State Univ. N.Y. Col. Oneonta, 67-70, fac. res. fel, summer 69; assoc. prof, UNIV. CINCINNATI, 70-72, PROF, 72-, fac. res. fel, summer 71. Lectr. Eng, Univ. Colo, 64-67; Taft fel, summer 72. U.S.A.F, 62-67, Capt. MLA; Am. Acad. Polit. & Soc. Sci; Inter-Univ. Sem. Armed Forces Soc. The American novel, 19th and 20th century; the literature of American minorities; the American military novel and the history of the American military. Publ: An armed America: its face in fiction, a history of the American military novel, 70 & Gathering of ghetto writers: Irish, Italian, Jewish, Black and Puerto Rican, 72, N.Y. Univ; contrib, Reader's encyclopedia of American literature, Crowell, 62; auth, Walt Whitman's Blue book: an evaluation, N.Y. Hist, 69; Southeast Asia: the war in fiction, Clifton, 73; plus others. Add: Dept. of English, University of Cincinnati, Cincinnati, OH 45221.

MILLER, WILLIAM CHARLES, b. Detroit, Mich, Jan. 3, 08; m. 33; c. 1. SPEECH, DRAMA. B.S, Univ. South. Calif, 31, M.A, 32, Ph.D, 47. From instr. to asst. prof. Eng, UNIV. NEV, RENO, 32-47, assoc. prof, 47-55, SPEECH & DRAMA, 55-57, prof, 57-73, acting chmn. dept, 71-72, EMER. PROF, 73- Vis. instr. & dir. dramatics, Univ. South. Calif, 39-40; assoc. prof. & chmn. dept. speech, Ala. Polytech. Inst, 47-48; chmn. bd. of rev, Employ. Security Dept, 56-71. Western American theatre; Nevada territorial papers, 1861-1864. Publ: Early western playbills; co-auth, Fundamentals of English, Allyn & Bacon, 66; co-ed, Letters from Nevada territory, 1861-1862, 72 & Reports of 1863 constitutional convention, Nevada Territory, 72, Legis. Counc. Bur, Nev; auth, Mark Twain at the sanitary ball, Calif. Hist. Quart; Mark Twain's source for the Latest sensation hoax?, Am. Lit, 3/60; Samuel L. and Orion Clemens vs. Mark Twain and his biographers (1861-1862), Mark Twain J, summer 73. Add: 615 Skyline Blvd, Reno, NV 89502.

MILLET, STANTON, b. New York, N.Y, Mar. 14, 31; m. 52. ENGLISH. A.B, Wabash Col, 52; M.A, Ind. Univ, 54, Ph.D.(Eng), 58. Asst. Eng, Ind. Univ, 52-56; instr, Oberlin Col, 56-58; Univ. Ill, Champaign, 58-61, asst. prof, 61-64, assoc. prof, 64-70, assoc. exec. secy. dept. Eng. & dir. grad. stud, 63-65, assoc. dean grad. col, 65-66, dean stud, 66-70, summer fel, 61; PROF. ENG. & FOR. LANG. & CHMN. DEPT, UNIV. W.FLA, 70- Consult, Nat. Stud. High Sch. Eng. Prog, 63-64. MLA; NCTE. Victorian and Edwardian literature; Rudyard Kipling. Publ: Co-auth, An introduction to literature, 66 & auth, The study of poetry, 67, World; co-auth, Rudyard Kipling: an annotated bibliography of writings about him, Eng. Fiction in Transition, 60; plus others. Add: Dept. of English and Foreign Languages, University of West Florida, Pensacola, FL 32504.

MILLETT, FRED BENJAMIN, b. Brockton, Mass, Feb. 19, 90. ENGLISH LITERATURE. A.B, Amherst Col, 12, hon. L.H.D, 57; Ph.D, Univ. Chicago, 31; hon. D.Litt, Wesleyan Univ, 67. Lectr. Eng, Queen's Univ.(Can), 12-16; asst. prof, Carnegie Inst. Technol, 19-26, assoc. prof, 26-27; asst. prof, Univ. Chicago, 27-32, assoc. prof, 32-37; vis. prof, WESLEYAN UNIV, 37-39, prof, 39-58, dir. honors col, 47-58, EMER. PROF. ENG. & EMER. DIR. HONORS COL, 58- Distinguished prof. Eng, State Univ. N.Y. Col. Albany, 61-62. MLA; Col. Eng. Asn; NCTE. Modern European fiction; literary criticism; contemporary English literary history. Publ: Contemporary American authors, 40 & Rebirth of liberal education, 45, Harcourt; Professor, Macmillan, 60; co-auth, Minor British novelists, 67 & Minor American novelists, 70, South. Ill. Univ. Add: 35 Washington St, Whitman, MA 02382.

MILLETT, ROBERT WALTER, b. Johnstown, N.Y, May 12, 31; m. 60; c. 4. ENGLISH. B.A, Mich. State Univ, 61; M.A, Univ. Ottawa, 63, Ph.D.(Eng), 65. Instr. humanities, Clarkson Col. Technol, 63-65, asst. prof, 65-66; ENG, UTICA COL, 66-67, ASSOC. PROF, 67- U.S.A, 51-53. AAUP; MLA. Writings and paintings of D.H. Lawrence; 20th century British novel; Christ-myth in literature. Publ: Great expectations: D.H. Lawrence's The trespasser, Twenty-seven to One, 70; Pornography, Newman Icon, 72. Add: 10 Laurelwood Dr, New Hartford, NY 13413.

MILLGATE, JANE, b. Leeds, Eng, June 8, 37; Can. citizen; m. 60. ENGLISH. B.A, Univ. Leeds, 59, M.A, 63; Ph.D.(Eng), Univ. Kent, 70. Instr. ENG, VICTORIA COL, UNIV. TORONTO, 64-65, lectr, 65-70, asst. prof, 70-72, ASSOC. PROF, 72- Can. Counc. res. grant, summer 72. MLA. Nineteenth century fiction; Victorian non-fiction prose; modern fiction. Publ: Macaulay, Routledge & Kegan Paul, 73; Narrative distance in Jane Eyre, Mod. Lang. Rev, 68; Quentin Compson as poor player, Revue Langues Vivantes, 68; Father and son: Macaulay's Edinburgh debut, Rev. Eng. Stud, 70. Add: Dept. of English, Victoria College, University of Toronto, Toronto, Ont. M5S 1K7, Can.

MILLGATE, MICHAEL (HENRY), b. Southampton, Eng, July 19, 29; Can. citizen; m. 60. ENGLISH & AMERICAN LITERATURE. B.A, Cambridge, 52, M.A, 56; Univ. Mich, Ann Arbor, 56-57; Ph.D.(Eng), Univ. Leeds, 60. Tutor Eng. & politics, Workers' Educ. Asn, Eng, 53-56; lectr. ENG, Univ. Leeds, 58-64; prof. & chmn. dept, York Univ, 64-67; PROF, UNIV. COL, UNIV. TORONTO, 67- Vis. prof, Univ. Peshawar, summer 61; Can. Counc. leave grant, 68-69; S.W. Brooks fel, Univ. Queensland, 71. MLA (mem. adv. counc, Am. lit. sect, 70-72, chmn, 72; mem. adv. comt, Ctr. Eds. Am. Auth, 71-74). William Faulkner; Thomas Hardy; Anglo-American literary relations. Publ: William Faulkner, Oliver & Boyd, Edinburgh, 61; American social fiction, Barnes & Noble, 64; co-ed, Transatlantic dialogue, Univ. Tex, 66; auth, The achievement of William Faulkner, 66, co-ed, Lion in the garden: interviews with William Faulkner, 1926-1962, 68 & auth, Thomas Hardy: his career as a novelist, 71, Random. Add: Dept. of English, University College, University of Toronto, Toronto, Ont. M5S 1A1, Can.

MILLHAUSER, MILTON, b. New York, N.Y, Nov. 3, 10; m. 38; c. 2. ENGLISH LITERATURE. B.A, City Col. New York, 31; M.A, Columbia Univ, 33, Ph.D, 51. Instr. ENG, City Col. New York, 31-46; L.I. Univ, 46-47; asst. prof, UNIV. BRIDGEPORT, 47-55, assoc. prof, 55-63, PROF, 63-, CHMN. DEPT, 71- Vis. prof, Wesleyan Univ, summer, 59. Tennyson Soc; MLA. Impact of science on Victorian literature; Tennyson. Publ: Just before Darwin, Wesleyan Univ, 59; Fire and ice: the influence of science on Tennyson's poetry, Tennyson Soc. Monogr, 71; The scriptural geologists, Osiris XI, 54; Tennyson, Artifice and image, J. Aesthet. & Art Criticism, 3/56; Great expectations: the three endings, In: Dickens Studies Annual, South. Ill. Univ, 72; plus one other. Add: Dept. of English, University of Bridgeport, Bridgeport, CT 06602.

MILLICHAP, JOSEPH ROBERT, b. Troy, N.Y, Feb. 14, 40; m. 67; c. 3. ENGLISH, AMERICAN LITERATURE. B.S, St. Peters Col, 61; NDEA fel, Notre Dame Univ, 61-64, M.A, 62, Ph.D.(Eng), 70. Instr. ENG, Sacred Heart Univ, 64-65; Univ. N.C, Greensboro, 65-68; ASST. PROF, Univ. Mont, 68-71; UNIV. TULSA, 71- MLA; Soc. Stud. South. Lit. Southern Renaissance; religion and literature. Publ: Narrative structure and symbolic imagery in Look homeward angel, South. Humanities Rev, 73; Carson McCullers literary ballad, Ga. Rev, 73; The Pauline old man in The comforts of home, Stud. Short Fiction, 74; plus others. Add: Dept. of English, University of Tulsa, 600 S. College, Tulsa, OK 74104.

MILLIGAN, BURTON ALVIERE, b. Toledo, Ohio, Oct. 19, 03. ENGLISH. B.S, Northwest. Univ, 26, A.M, 30, Ph.D, 39; Univ. N.C, 33-35. Instr. ENG, Univ. Mo, 30-32; asst, Univ. N.C, 34-35; asst. prof, Univ. Fla, 36-38; instr, UNIV. ILL, URBANA, 39-46, asst. prof, 46-48, assoc. prof, 48-55, prof, 55-72, EMER. PROF, 72- Chmn. ed. bd, Ill. Stud. Lang. & Lit, 62-71. U.S.N.R, 42-45, Lt. MLA; Renaissance Soc. Am; Malone Soc. Non dramatic literature of the English Renaissance. Publ: Three Renaissance classics; John Heywood's works and miscellaneous short poems; co-auth, Studies in honor of T.W. Baldwin, Univ. Ill, 58. Add: 2208 Pond St, Urbana, IL 61801.

MILLS, BARRISS, b. Cleveland, Ohio, Jan. 26, 12. ENGLISH. A.B, Dartmouth Col, 34; A.M, Univ. Chicago, 36; fel, Univ. Wis, 41-42, Ph.D, 42. Instr. ENG, Iowa State Col, 37-40, Mich. State Col, 42-44; from asst. prof. to assoc. prof, Iowa State Col, 44-47; prof. & chmn. dept, Univ. Denver, 47-50; PROF, PURDUE UNIV, 50-, head dept, 50-62. American Renaissance; modern poetry; translation of Greek and Latin poetry. Publ: Black and white geometry, 55 & Parvenus and ancestors, 59, Vagrom; Idylls of Theokritos, 63, The Carmina of Catullus, 65, Epigrams from martial, 69 & co-auth, A suit of four, 73, Purdue Univ; auth, Occasions and silences, 64 & Letter to Felix, 68, Scrip; Aftermath, Goosetree, 65; Domestic fables, Elizabeth, 71; Hawthorne and puritanism, New Eng. Quart, 3/48; Old times on the Mississippi as an initiation story, Col. Eng, 1/64; Motivation in Othello and The winter's tale, Univ. Rev, 12/66. Add: Dept. of English, Purdue University, Lafayette, IN 47907.

MILLS, DOROTHY HURST, Linguistics, Spanish & English As Foreign Languages. See Volume III, Foreign Languages, Linguistics & Philology.

MILLS, GLEN EARL, b. Minneapolis, Minn, May 10, 08; m. 37; c. 1. RHETORIC. B.S, East. S.Dak. Norm. Sch, 30; A.M, Univ. Mich, 35, fel, 40-41, Ph.D, 41. Instr, Univ. Mich, 41-42; assoc. prof. pub. speaking, Northwest. Univ, 49-57, prof. speech, 57-68, asst. dean sch. speech, 56-68; PROF. SPEECH, UNIV. CALIF, SANTA BARBARA, 68-, chmn. dept, 71-75. Ed, West. Speech, 73-76. Speech Commun. Asn; West. Speech Commun. Asn. Public address. Publ: Composing the speech, 51; Argumentation and debate, Macmillan, 51 & 64; Reason in controversy, Allyn & Bacon, 64 & 68; Message preparation, 66 & Putting a message together, 72, Bobbs; co-auth, Guidebook for student speakers, Ronald, 66; plus others. Add: Dept. of Speech, University of California, Santa Barbara, Santa Barbara, CA 93106.

MILLS, GORDON H, b. Mt. Pleasant, Mich, 14; m. 41; c. 1. ENGLISH. B.A, State Univ. Iowa, 39, M.A, 40, Ph.D, 42. Instr. ENG, UNIV. TEX, AUSTIN, 45-47, asst. prof, 47-55, assoc. prof, 55-66, PROF, 66- American literature. Add: 208 Calhoun Hall, University of Texas at Austin, Austin, TX 78712.

MILLS, JOHN, b. London, Eng, June 23, 30; Can. citizen; m. 60. ENGLISH. B.A. & Woodrow Wilson fel, Univ. B.C, 64; M.A, Stanford Univ, 65. Instr. ENG, SIMON FRASER UNIV, 65-68, asst. prof, 68-72, ASSOC. PROF, 72- Brit. Army, 50-52. The novel; Renaissance literature. Publ: The land of is, 72 & The October men, 72, Oberon, Ottawa; Chaucer's low seriousness, Paunch, 66; Love and anarchy in Sgt. Musgrave's dance, Drama Surv, 68; The courtship ritual of Hero and Leander, Eng. Lit. Renaissance, 72. Add: Dept. of English, Simon Fraser University, Burnaby 2, B.C, Can.

MILLS, JOHN ARVIN, b. Indianapolis, Ind, Dec. 3, 31; m. 61. ENGLISH. B.A, Butler Univ, 53; M.A, Ind. Univ, 59, Ph.D, 61. Lectr. speech & drama, Ind. Univ, 59-61; assoc. prof. drama, Univ. Ariz, 61-66; asst. prof. theater, State Univ. N.Y. Binghamton, 66-69, ASSOC. PROF, 69-74, ENG, UNIV. ARIZ, 74- State Univ. N.Y. Res. Found. grant-in-aid, 68-69; John Simon Guggenheim Mem. Found. res. fel, London, 72-73. U.S.A, 53-55, Res, 55-61. Am. Theatre Asn; Speech Commun. Asn; Int. Fed. Theatre Res; Am. Soc. Theatre Res; MLA. Dramatic criticism; modern drama; theatre history. Publ: Language and laughter: Shaw's comic diction, Univ. Ariz, 68; Shaw's linguistic satire, 1/65 & Acting is being: Bernard Shaw on the art of the actor, 5/70; Shaw Rev; The comic in words: Shaw's Cockneys, Drama Surv, summer 66; plus one other. Add: Dept. of English, University of Arizona, Tucson, AZ 85721.

MILLS, LLOYD L, b. New Orleans, La, Apr. 9, 27; m. 48; c. 3. ENGLISH. B.A, La. State Univ, 52, M.A, 58; Ph.D.(Eng), Univ. Wash, 65. Acting instr. ENG, Univ. Wash, 61-62; instr, Univ. Ariz, 62-65; asst. prof, KENT STATE UNIV, 65-69, ASSOC. PROF, 69- MLA. Publ: Ben Jonson's poetry; a caveat and two interpretations, Laurel Rev, 12/71; The English origin of still-born and dumb-born in Mauberley, Am. Notes & Queries, 1/72; The literary character of Donne's Reference's to specular stone, Humanities Asn. Can. Bull, 2/73; plus two others. Add: Dept. of English, Kent State University, Kent, OH 44242.

MILLS, MOYLAN C, b. Philadelphia, Pa, June 19, 29; m. 67. ENGLISH, DRAMA. B.A, Pa. State Univ, 52, M.A, 57; Ph.D, Univ. Pa, 74. Instr. ENG, PA. STATE UNIV, OGONTZ CAMPUS, 60-65, ASST. PROF. & CHMN. DEPT, 65- Intel.C, U.S.A, 54-56. MLA; NCTE; AAUP. Contemporary American literature; contemporary comparative drama; film study. Publ: Violence in Pinterland, 5/67 & The burden of the masks: Bergman's Persona, 9/67, Talisman. Add: 1000 Ivy Hill Rd, Philadelphia, PA 19150.

MILLS, RALPH JOSEPH, JR, b. Chicago, Ill, Dec. 16, 31; m. 59. ENGLISH. B.A, Lake Forest Col, 54; M.A, Northwest. Univ, 56, Ph.D.(Eng), 63; Eng. Speaking Union fel, Oxford, 56-57. Instr. Eng, Univ. Chicago, 59-61, comt. social thought, 61-62, asst. prof, 62-65; assoc. prof. ENG, UNIV. ILL, CHICAGO CIRCLE, 65-67, PROF, 67-, summer fac. fel, grad. col, 66. U.S.N.A.F.R, 51-55. Contemporary American and British poetry. Publ: Theodore Roethke, 63 & Richard Eberhart, 66, Univ. Minn; Contemporary American poetry, Random, 65; ed, On the poet and his craft: selected prose of Theodore Roethke, 65 & Selected letters of Theodore Roethke, 68, Univ. Wash; auth, Edith Sitwell, 66 & Kathleen Raine, 67, Eerdmans; Creation's very self, Tex. Christian Univ, 69; ed, The notebooks of David Ignatow, Swallow, 73; auth, Cry of the human: essays on contemporary American poetry, Univ. Ill, 74; Wallace Stevens: the image of the rock, In: Wallace Stevens, Prentice-Hall, 63; Theodore Roethke, In: Modern American poetry: essays in criticism, Everett Edwards, 72; Earth hard: the poetry of David Ignatow, Boundary Two, 74; plus one other. Add: Dept. of English, University of Illinois at Chicago Circle, Chicago, IL 60680.

MILLWARD, CELIA McCULLOUGH, Linguistics, English. See Volume III, Foreign Languages, Linguistics & Philology.

MILNE, WILLIAM GORDON, b. Haverhill, Mass, Mar. 17, 21. ENGLISH. A.B, Brown Univ, 41, A.M, 47; A.M, Harvard, 47, Ph.D.(Eng), 51. Instr. ENG, Univ. Kans. City, 47-48; Mass. Inst. Technol, 51; asst. prof, LAKE FOREST COL, 51-53, assoc. prof, 53-58, PROF, 58- Fulbright guest prof, Univ. Wurzburg, 58-59. U.S.N.R, 42-46, Lt. Comdr. MLA. Political fiction; novel of manners; Anglo-American literary relations. Publ: George William Curtis and the genteel tradition, Ind, Univ, 56; The American political novel, Univ. Okla, 66; Louis Auchincloss and the novel of manners, Univ. Kans. City Rev, 63; contrib, essay on John Dos Passos, In: The politics of twentieth century novelists, Hawthorn, 71; George William Curtis, inheritor of the transcendental mantle, Am. Transcendental Quart, spring 73; plus one other. Add: 501 Green Bay Rd, Lake Bluff, IL 60044.

MILNER, EDWARD WILLIS, b. Atlanta, Ga, June 12, 30; m. 54; c. 4. THEOLOGY, LITERATURE. B.S, Davidson Col, 51; B.D, Columbia Theol. Sem, 54; M.A, Univ. Chicago, 57, South. Fels. Found. fel, 61-62. Instr. Eng. & humanities, Austin Col, 59-61; asst. prof. relig. & chaplain, Skidmore Col, 62-65; ASSOC. PROF. ENG. & HUMANITIES & CHMN. AFRO-ASIAN STUD, J.C. SMITH UNIV, 65- Danforth summer fel, Seminar Relig. & Cult, 60; N.Y. Dept. Educ. fel, Sem. Asian Cult, 64-65. African Stud. Asn; Asn. Asian Stud; Soc. Sci. Stud. Relig; MLA. Vision of evil in fiction of Robert Penn Warren; Protestant, Catholic, Negro and Jew in American education; Afro-Asian studies in predominantly Negro institutions. Add: Dept. of English, Johnson C. Smith University, Charlotte, NC 28208.

MILNER, JOSEPH O'BEIRNE, b. June 18, 37; m. 63; c. 3. ENGLISH, EDUCATION. A.B, Davidson Col, 59; M.A, Univ. N.C, Chapel Hill, 65, Ph.D. (Eng), 71. Instr. Eng, N.C. State Univ, 65-66; Univ. N.C, Chapel Hill, 68-69; ASST. PROF. ENG. & EDUC, WAKE FOREST UNIV, 69- Dir, N.C. Gov. Sch. Inst, summer 72; ed, N.C, Eng. Teacher, 72-; consult, Winston-Salem-Forsyth County Schs, 73- Intel.C, U.S.A, 59-61, Res, 61-63, Capt. MLA; AAUP; Southeast. Mod. Lang. Asn. American literature, 1960-1973. Add: Dept. of English, Wake Forest University, Winston-Salem, NC 27109.

MILOSH, JOSEPH EDMUND, JR, b. Blue Island, Ill, Dec. 28, 36; m. 58; c. 2. MEDIEVAL ENGLISH LITERATURE. B.A, St. Edward's Univ, 58; M.A, Univ. Ill, 60, Ph.D, 63; res. fel, Brit. Mus, 62. Instr. ENG, Univ. Wis-Madison, 63-65, asst. prof, 65-66, assoc. prof, 66-70; NORTH. ILL. UNIV, 70-72, PROF. & COORD. ENG. EDUC, 72- Univ. Wis-Madison res. grants, 64 & 67; consult, Madison Pub. Schs, 67-68; Am. Counc. Learned Soc. stud. fel, 68-69; consult, Nat. Humanities Ser, Nat. Endowment for Humanities, 73. Kiekhofer Teaching Award, 66. MLA; Mediaeval Acad. Am; NCTE; Conf. Eng. Educ. Middle English literature; the history of the English language and linguistics; English education. Publ: The scale of perfection and the English mystical tradition, Univ. Wis, 66; Teaching the history of the English language in the secondary classroom, NCTE, 72; Sisam's structure of Beowulf and realism in criticism: a review essay, Cithara, 5/66; Chaucer's too-well told Franklin's tale, Wis. Stud. Lit, 68; Composing orally for image and sound, J. Eng. Teaching Tech, 72. Add: Dept. of English, Northern Illinois University, DeKalb, IL 60115.

MILOWICKI, EDWARD JOHN, b. Plains, Pa, Mar. 2, 32. ENGLISH. B.A, Wilkes Col, 58; M.A, Duquesne Univ, 63; Ph.D.(Eng), Univ. Ore, 68. Asst. ENG, Duquesne Univ, 59-61; instr, St. Vincent Col, 61-63; Univ. Ore, 63-68; ASSOC. PROF, MILLS COL, 68-, DIR. GRAD. STUD, 72- U.S.A, 51-54. MLA; Medieval Asn. Pac. Medieval literature, especially Chaucer. Add: Div. of Graduate Study, Mills College, Oakland, CA 94613.

MILSTEAD, JOHN, b. Mishawaka, Ind, July 31, 24; m. 45; c. 2. ENGLISH. B.A, Univ. N.Mex, scholar & M.A, State Univ. Iowa; Ph.D, Univ. Wis. Instr. ENG, Univ. Nev, 48-51; asst, Univ. Wis, 51-55; instr, Univ. Idaho, 55-58; ASSOC. PROF, La. Polytech. Inst, 58-65; OKLA. STATE UNIV, 65- MLA; Col. Eng. Asn. Romantic and Victorian poetry; modern drama. Publ: Co-auth, Readings for college writers, Ronald, 62, 67, Patterns in poetry, 68 & What the poem means, 70, Scott; auth, Freshman research paper, CEA Critic, 63; Communication and identity as structural principles in small classes, Liberal Educ, 12/73. Add: Dept. of English, Oklahoma State University, Stillwater, OK 74074.

MILTON, DOROTHY, b. Chicago, Ill, May 1, 18. ENGLISH. Ph.B, Loyola Univ.(Ill), 43, M.A, 50; Ph.D.(Eng), Univ. Chicago, 67. Instr. ENG, Bryant & Stratton Bus. Col, 45-52; Univ. Nebr, 53-55; FERRIS STATE COL, 55-57, asst. prof, 57-61, assoc. prof, 62-72, PROF, 72- MLA. Henry James. Add: Dept. of English, Ferris State College, Big Rapids, MI 49307.

MILTON, JOHN RONALD, b. Anoka, Minn, May 24, 24; m. 46. ENGLISH. B.A, Univ. Minn, 48, M.A, 51; Ph.D, Univ. Denver, 61. Instr. Eng. & philos, Augsburg Col, 49-56; prof. Eng. & chmn. dept, Jamestown Col, 57-63, chmn. humanities div, 62-63; PROF. ENG. & ED, S.DAK. REV, UNIV. S.DAK, 63-, DIR. CREATIVE WRITING, 65-, chmn. dept. Eng, 63-65. Mem, comt. bibliog. of Am. Lit. Group, MLA, 63-73; fel, Helene Wurlitzer Found. N.Mex, 65; consult, Librns. Inst, Ind. State Univ, 66; lectr. & vis. prof, N.Dak. State Univ, 66. U.S.A, 43-46. Am. Stud. Asn; West. Hist. Asn; West. Lit. Asn. (exec. & ed. bds, 65-, pres, 70-71); Rocky Mountain Mod. Lang. Asn. Western American and contemporary literature; creative writing. Publ: Western plains, Poet's Gallery, 64; The tree of bones, Verb Publ, 65; This lonely house, Thueson, 68; ed, The American Indian speaks, 69, Three west, 70 & American Indian II, 71, Dakota; auth, Oscar Howe: The story of an American Indian, Dillon, 71; Conversations with Frank Waters, Swallow, 72; American novel: the search for home, tradition, and identity, West. Humanities Rev, 62; Western novel, Chicago Rev, 63; The American West: a challenge to the literary imagination, West. Am. Lit, winter 67; plus others. Add: Dept. of English, University of South Dakota, Vermillion, SD 57069.

MINCHER, JOHN W, JR, b. Youngstown, Ohio, Apr. 30, 34; m. 55; c. 2. THEATRE, SPEECH. B.A,Kent State Univ, 61, M.A, 62; South. Ill. Univ, 65. Instr. design, STATE UNIV. N.Y. COL. OSWEGO, 62-64, asst. prof, 64-66, assoc. prof. STAGE DESIGN, 67-72, PROF, 72- U.S.A.F, 53-57, S/Sgt. Am. Theatre Asn; Speech Commun. Asn. Stage design and technical theatre; playwrighting. Add: R.D. 3, California Rd, Oswego, NY 13126.

MINCHEW, ELMER REID, b. Taylor, La, Jan. 26, 08; m. 34; c. 2. SPEECH. B.A, La. Col, 29; M.A, La. State Univ, 38, Ph.D.(speech), 55. Asst. prin, Bienville High Sch, 29-30; Lisbon High Sch, 30-32; prin, Castor High Sch, 32-64; PROF. SPEECH & HEAD DEPT, LA. TECH UNIV, 64- U.S.A.A.F, 43-45, 1st Lt. NEA; Speech Commun. Asn. Speech education. Publ: A high school principal looks at speech, Speech Teacher, 38. Add: Dept. of Speech, Louisiana Tech University, Box 4505, Tech Station, Ruston, LA 71270.

MINEKA, FRANCIS EDWARD, b. Caneadea, N.Y, July 26, 07; m. 34; c. 2. ENGLISH LITERATURE. A.B, Hamilton Col, 29, A.M, 31, hon. Litt.D, 58; fel, Columbia Univ, 41-42, Ph.D, 43. Instr. Eng, Hamilton Col, 29-32, 34-35, asst. prof. Eng. & pub. speaking, 35-42; instr. Eng. & Latin, St. Francis Col, 33-34; asst. prof. Eng, Univ. Tex, 42-46; CORNELL UNIV, 46-47, assoc. prof, 47-51, prof, 51-56, Class of 16 prof, 56-73, chmn. dept, 48-57, dean col. arts & sci, 57-62, EMER. PROF. ENG, 73- Ford fel, 52-53; Guggenheim fel, 62-63; Fulbright res. fel, Eng, 62-63; trustee, Hamilton Col, 63-69; Alexander lectr, Univ. Toronto, 68. MLA. John Stuart Mill; 19th century English literature. Publ: Dissidence of dissent: the monthly repository, 1806-1838, Univ. N.C, 44; ed, Earlier letters of John Stuart Mill, 63 & co-ed, The later letters of John Stuart Mill (4 vols), 72, Univ. Toronto; plus one other. Add: 110 Irving Pl, Ithaca, NY 14850.

MINER, EARL ROY, b. Marshfield, Wis, Feb. 21, 27; m. 50. ENGLISH. B.A, Univ. Minn, 49, M.A, 51, univ. fel, 52-53, Ph.D.(Eng), 55. Instr. ENG, Williams Col.(Mass), 53-55; Univ. Calif, Los Angeles, 55-57, asst. prof, 57-60, assoc. prof, 60-64, PROF, 64-72; PRINCETON, 72- Cor. ed, Orient/West, 60-64; Fulbright lectr, Japan, 60-61; Oxford, 66-67; Am. Counc. Learned Soc. fel, Eng, 62-63; gen. ed, Augustan Reprint Soc, 62-67, adv. ed, 67-; adv. ed, Lit. East & West, 67-, Eighteenth Century Stud, 70-; CLIO, 72-; William Andrews Clark Mem. Libr. Prof, 71-72. Interpreter, U.S.A, 44-46. MLA; Asn. Asian Stud; Eng. Lit. Soc. Japan; Int. Comp. Lit. Asn. English literature; Japanese literature; comparative literature. Publ: The Japanese tradition in English and American literature, Princeton, 58; Nihon o Utsusu Chiisana Kagami, Chikuma Shobo, 62; Works of John Dryden, 61, 66, 67, 69, 71, 72, auth, Japanese poetic diaries, 69, ed, Seventeenth century imagery, 71 & Stuart and Georgian moments, 72, Univ. Calif; co-auth, Japanese court poetry, 61, Fujiwara Teika's Superior poems of our time, 67 & auth, Introduction to Japanese court poetry, 68, Stanford Univ; John Ogilby, fables of Aesop, Augustan Reprint Soc, 65; ed, Restoration dramatists, Prentice-Hall, 66; Dryden's poetry, Ind. Univ, Selected poetry and prose of John Dryden, Random, 69; auth, The metaphysical mode from Donne to Cowley, 69, The cavalier mode from Jonson to Cotton, 71 & The restoration mode from Milton to Dryden, 74, Princeton; ed, English criticism in Japan, Univ. Tokyo, 72; John Dryden, Bell, 73; Some characteristics of Dryden's use of metaphor, Stud. Eng. Lit, 62; Felix Culpa in the redemptive order of Paradise lost, Philol. Quart, 68; Some thematic and structural features of the Genji monogatari, Monumenta Nipponica, 69. Add: Dept. of English, 22 McCosh, Princeton University, Princeton, NJ 08540.

MINER, THELMA SMITH, b. Ocean City, N.J, Jan. 15, 15; m. 50. ENGLISH. A.B, Dickinson Col, 35; summer, Univ. South. Calif, 40; A.M, Univ. Pa, 42, Moore fel, 43-45, Ph.D.(Am. civilization), 45. Teacher, Pub. Schs, N.J, 35-42; cur. Bibliog. Am. Lit, Univ. Pa, 43-45; instr. ENG, Temple Univ, 45-48; asst. prof, Dickinson Col, 48-51; res, France, 51-53; instr, Vassar Col, 53-55; Univ. Kans, 56-57; asst. prof, YOUNGSTOWN STATE UNIV, 57-59, assoc. prof, 59-65, PROF, 65- Am. Counc. Learned Soc. scholar, 51-52; Fulbright lectr, Int. People's Col, Denmark, 60-61. Distinguished Prof. Award, Youngstown State Univ, 72. MLA; Am. Stud. Asn; AAUP. American literature and civilization. Publ: The uncollected poems of James Russell Lowell, Univ. Pa, 50; co-auth, Transatlantic migration: the contemporary American novel in France, Duke Univ, 55. Add: Dept. of English, Youngstown State University, Youngstown, OH 44503.

MINER, WARD LESTER, b. Wellman, Iowa, Mar. 22, 16; m. 50. ENGLISH. A.B, Univ. Colo, 38; A.M, Univ. Chicago, 40; Ph.D.(Am. civilization), Univ. Pa, 51. Instr. Eng, S.Dak. State Col, 40-42; Colo. Sch. Mines, 45-46; Temple Univ, 46-51; asst. prof, Queens Col.(N.Y), 53-54; assoc. prof, YOUNGSTOWN STATE UNIV, 57-63, PROF. AM. STUD, 63-, IN CHARGE GRAD. STUD. ENG, 68-, chmn. dept. Eng, 63-68. Am. Counc. Learned Soc. fel, 51-52; Am. Philos. Soc. res. grant, 55; Fulbright lectr, Turku Univ, Finland, 55-56; vis. asst. prof, Univ. Kans, 56-57; Fulbright lectr, Int. People's Col, Elsinore, Denmark, 60-61 & Univ. Iceland, 66-67. U.S.A.A.F, 42-45. NCTE; MLA; Am. Stud. Asn; AAUP. Colonial printing, 20th century American novel; reception of American literature in Europ. Publ: The world of William Faulkner, 52, co-auth, Transatlantic migration: the contemporary American novel in France, 55 & auth, William Goddard, newspaperman, 62, Duke Univ. Add: Dept. of English, Youngstown State University, Youngstown, OH 44503.

MINEROF, ARTHUR F, b. New York, N.Y, Nov. 10, 29. ENGLISH. B.A, Brooklyn Col, 51, M.A, 53; Ph.D.(Thomas Hardy), N.Y. Univ, 63. Instr. ENG. & SPEECH, STATEN ISLAND COMMUNITY COL, 63-64, asst. prof, 64-66, assoc. prof, 66-68, PROF, 68- Asst. ed, Victorian Newsletter, 65-; State Univ. N.Y. fac. res. grant, 67; City Univ. New York doctoral fac. res. grant, 67, summer res. grant, 68. MLA. Add: Dept. of English, Staten Island Community College, Staten Island, NY 10301.

MINNICK, WAYNE, b. Logansport, Ind, Oct. 1, 15; m. 48; c. 2. SPEECH. A.B, Ind. Univ, 42; M.A, Northwest. Univ, 47, Ph.D, 49. Assoc. prof. speech, Fla. State Univ, 49-56; Northwest. Univ, 56-59; PROF. SPEECH & HEAD DEPT, FLA. STATE UNIV, 59-, ASSOC. DEAN ARTS & SCI, 67- Adv. ed. speech & dramatic arts, Houghton Mifflin Co, 63-; vis. prof. commun, Univ. South. Calif, summers 65 & 70. U.S.A, 43-45, Sgt. Speech Commun. Asn.(2nd v.pres, 65, 1st v.pres, 66, pres, 67); South. Speech Commun. Asn; Cent. States Speech Asn; Am. Theatre Asn. Persuasion; debate; public address. Publ: Art of persuasion, Houghton, 57, rev. ed, 68; The New England execution sermon, 1639-1800, 68 & A case study in persuasive effect: Lyman Beecher on duelling, 71, Speech Monogr; plus others. Add: Dept. of Speech, Florida State University, Tallahassee, FL 32306.

MINOT, STEPHEN, b. Boston, Mass, May 27, 27; m. 55; c. 3. LITERATURE & CREATIVE WRITING. A.B, Harvard, 53; M.A, Johns Hopkins Univ, 55. Instr. ENG, Bowdoin Col, 55-57, asst. prof, 57-58; vis. asst. prof, Univ. Conn, 58-59; TRINITY COL.(CONN), 59-61, vis. lectr, 61-63, asst. prof, 63-69, ASSOC. PROF, 69- Eugene F. Saxton Mem. fel, 63-64; contrib. ed, N.Am. Rev, 69- & New Story, 74- U.S.A.A.F, 45-46. Auth. Guild; AAUP. Creative writing; publications in fiction and poetry. Publ: Chill of dusk, Doubleday, 64; Three genres, Prentice-Hall, 65, 2nd ed, 72; co-ed, Three stances of modern fiction, Winthrop, 72; auth, Sausage and beer, Atlantic Monthly, 11/62; Crossings, Redbk, 2/67; Mars revisited, Va. Quart. Rev, winter 70 & In: O.Henry prize stories, 71; plus others. Add: 69 Hickory Hill Rd, Simsbury, CT 06070.

MINTER, DAVID LEE, b. Midland, Tex, Mar. 20, 35; m. 57; c. 2. MODERN & AMERICAN LITERATURE. B.A, N.Tex. State Univ, 57, M.A, 59; B.D, Yale, 61, Ph.D.(Am. stud), 65. Lectr. Am. lit, Univ. Hamburg, 65-66; Am. stud, Yale, 66-67; asst. prof. ENG, RICE UNIV, 67-69, ASSOC. PROF, 69- Nat. Endowment for Humanities Younger Humanists fel, 69-70; vis. assoc. prof. Eng, Columbia Univ, summer 71 & Wash. Univ, summer 73. MLA (Am. Lit. Group II, secy, 72, chmn, 73). American literature; modern fiction. Publ: The interpreted design as a structural principle in American prose, Yale, 69; ed, Twentieth century interpretations of Light in August, Prentice-Hall, 69; auth, The puritan jeremaid as a literary form, In: The American puritan imagination: recent essays in revaluation, 73; Conceptions of self in Black slave narratives, Am. Transcendental Quart, (in press); By dens of lions: notes on stylization in early Indian captivity narratives, Am. Lit, (in press); plus others. Add: Dept. of English, Rice University, Houston, TX 77001.

MINTZ, SAMUEL ISAIAH, b. New York, N.Y, Nov. 20, 23; m. 47; c. 2. ENGLISH. B.A, Brooklyn Col, 48; M.A, Columbia Univ, 49, Ph.D, 58; Fulbright scholar, Cambridge, 55-56. Instr. ENG, CITY COL. NEW YORK, 48-60, asst. prof. 60-65, assoc. prof, 65-69, PROF, 69- Co-ed, Hist. Ideas News lett; Fulbright res. scholar, Cambridge, 64-65; Guggenheim fel, 64-65; vis. fel, Wolfson Col, Oxford, 72-73. U.S.A.A.F, 43-46. MLA; Conf. Brit. Stud; Renaissance Soc. Am. History of ideas; history of science. Publ: The hunting of Leviathan: seventeenth century reactions to the materialism and moral philosophy of Thomas Hobbes, Cambridge, 62; Galilio, Hobbes, and the circle of perfection, Isis; the Duchess of Newcastle and the Royal Society, J. Eng. & Germanic Philol; Hobbes on the law of heresy: a new manuscript, J. Hist. Ideas, 7/68; Hobbes, In: Dictionary of scientific biography, Scribners, Vol. VI, 72. Add: Dept. of English, City College of New York, New York, NY 10031.

MIRABELLI, EUGENE, JR, b. Arlington, Mass, Feb. 3, 31; m. 59; c. 3. ENGLISH & AMERICAN LITERATURE. B.A, Harvard, 52, Ph.D.(Eng), 64; M.A, Johns Hopkins Univ, 55. Instr. & lectr. Eng, Williams Col, 60-64; asst. prof, STATE UNIV. N.Y. ALBANY, 65-69, ASSOC. PROF. ENG. & AM. LIT, 69-, res. fels, 66, 68. Creative writing grant, Rockefeller Found, 69-70. MLA; AAUP; Auth. Guild. The writing of novels. Publ: The burning air, Houghton, 59; The way in, 68 & No resting place, 72, Viking. Add: Dept. of English, State University of New York at Albany, Albany, NY 12203.

MIROLLO, JAMES V, b. New York, N.Y, Aug. 5, 28; m. 53; c. 2. ENGLISH. B.A, City Col. New York, 50; M.A, Columbia Univ, 51, Ph.D, 61. Instr. Eng, City Col. New York, 52-60, asst. prof, 61-66, assoc. prof, 66-67; COMP. LIT, COLUMBIA UNIV, 67-69, PROF, 69-, chmn. dept, 71-73. Fulbright fel, 68-69; vis. prof, N.Y. Univ, spring 70, Bread Loaf Sch, summers 72 & 73; adj. prof, Juilliard Sch, 72-; co-ed, Renaissance Quart. Ansley Award, Columbia Univ. Press, 61. U.S.A, 52-54. Renaissance Soc. Am; MLA; Dante Soc. Am; Am. Comp. Lit. Asn; AAUP. European Renaissance and Baroque literature. Publ: The poet of the marvelous Giambattista Marino, Columbia Univ, 63. Add: Dept. of English & Comparative Literature, Columbia University, New York, NY 10027.

MIRSKY, DAVID, b. Jerusalem, Israel, Sept. 7, 21; nat; m. 49; c. 3. ENGLISH. B.A, Yeshiva Col, 42; M.A, Columbia Univ, 48. Ed, Jewish Horizon, 45; asst. dir, Jewish Cult. Found, N.Y. Univ, 46-47; instr. Hebrew, YESHIVA UNIV, 48-52, asst. prof, 52-62, assoc. prof. Eng. & Hebrew, 62-67, PROF. ENG, 67-, DEAN, STERN COL, 68-, asst. registr, 54-63, dean admis, 63-68. Dir, NDEA summer lang. Inst. Hebrew, 61, 63, Overseas Inst, Jerusalem, 65. MLA; Hebrew Acad. Am. The Jew in English literature; Jewish source material in world literature; influence of English literature on Hebrew literature. Publ: The Jew in the plays of George Bernard Shaw, Perakim, 51; The Jew in English literature of the 20th century, Sura, 55; The beginnings of Hebrew in the United States, Herzl Yearbook, 63; The fictive Jew in the literature of England 1890-1920, Samuel K. Mirsky Mem. Vol, 70; plus others. Add: Stern College, Yeshiva University, New York, NY 10016.

MISENHEIMER, JAMES BUFORD, JR, b. Abilene, Tex, Dec. 7, 32; m. 52; c. 3. ENGLISH LITERATURE. B.A, Baylor Univ, 53; M.A, South. Ill. Univ, 54; Ph.D.(Eng. lit), Univ. Colo, 64. Asst. Eng, South. Ill. Univ, 52-54; teaching asst, Univ. Ill, 54-55; asst. prof, Baylor Univ, 57-60; teaching asst, Univ. Colo, 60-62; asst. prof, U.S. Air Force Acad, 62-65, assoc. prof. Eng. lit, 65-67; George Washington Univ, 67-68; N.Tex. State Univ, 68-70, prof, 70-72; PROF. ENG. LIT. & CHMN. DEPT. ENG, IND. STATE UNIV, TERRE HAUTE, 72- Outstanding Educator of America Award, 73. U.S.A.F, 55-57, 62-67, Capt. Johnson Soc. London; MLA; Mod. Humanities Res. Asn.(Am. ed, Annual Bibliog. Eng. Lang. & Lit, 65-); NCTE; Am. Soc. 18th Century Stud; Bibliog. Soc. Am; Bibliog. Soc. Univ. Va; Johnson Soc. Midwest. English Enlightenment, 1660-1800; English novel; romantic period. Publ: Leigh Hunt: a great introducer in English romanticism, 71 & Samuel Johnson's Christian humanism and the function of literature, 73, Yearbook of English Studies; Samuel Johnson's Life of savage: a survey, New Rambler, spring 71; plus three others. Add: Dept. of English, Indiana State University, Terre Haute, IN 47809.

MISH, CHARLES CARROLL, b. Williamsport, Pa, June 27, 13; m. 45. ENGLISH LITERATURE. A.B, Univ. Pa, 36, Ph.D, 51. Asst. ENG, Univ. Pa, 47-48; instr, UNIV. MD, COLLEGE PARK, 48-55, asst. prof, 55-60, assoc. prof, 60-65, PROF, 65- Fel, Newberry Libr, 53. MLA (asst. bibliogr, 55-66); Bibliog. Soc. Am; Bibliog. Soc. Univ. Va; Renaissance Soc. Am. Early prose fiction. Publ: English prose fiction, 1600-1700: a chronological checklist, Univ. Va. Bibliog. Soc, 52, 2nd rev. ed, 67; The Anchor anthology of short fiction of the seventeenth century, Anchor Bks, 63; ed, Restoration prose fiction: an anthology of representative pieces, Univ. Nebr, 70. Add: Dept. of English, University of Maryland, College Park, MD 20740.

MISHRA, VISHWA MOHAN, b. Nov. 12, 37; U.S. citizen; m. 60; c. 3. COMMUNICATION, MASS COMMUNICATION. B.A, Patna Univ, 54, M.A, 56; M.A, Univ. Ga, 57; fel, Univ. Minn, 64-68, Ph.D.(mass commun), 68. Staff reporter, Hindusthan Samachar, Ltd, India, 50-56; exec. dir. & minister, India for Christ, Inc, Minneapolis, Minn, 60-64; instr, Univ. Minn, 64-68; asst. prof. jour, Univ. Okla, 68-69; ASSOC. PROF. JOUR. & MASS COMMUN, MICH. STATE UNIV, 69- Nat. Sci. Found. fel. polit. commun, 69; vis. scholar, Inst. Social Res, Univ. Mich, 71; dir. res. projs. & consult, Lansing Community Col, 71-73; dir, Am. for Effective Law Enforcement media proj, Mich. State Univ, 72-, acting dir, Commun. Arts Res. Ctr, 73; consult, var. orgn. Asn. Educ. in Jour; Soc. Int. Develop; Int. Commun. Asn; AAUP; Radio-TV News Dir. Asn.(res. comt, 71-). Communication and modernization; television and crime; political mass communication, opinion, and attitudes. Publ: Communication and modernization in urban slums, 72 & Basic news media and techniques, 72, Asia Publ; Mass media variables related to urbanization and modernization in developing countries, Jour. Quart, 71; The broadcast media exposure and modernization in urban slums, Gazette, 73; Communication, culture and modernization in developing countries, Human Orgn, summer 73; plus others. Add: College of Communication Arts, 113 Auditorium, Michigan State University, East Lansing, MI 48824.

MISKIMIN, ALICE-AUGUSTA SCHWENK, b. Newark, N.J, Feb. 20, 32; m. 53; c. 2. MEDIEVAL LITERATURE. B.A, Vassar Col, 53; M.A, Yale, 54, Ph.D.(Eng), 63. Instr. ENG, YALE, 63-66, asst. prof, 66-72, SR. LECTR, 72-, dir. undergrad. stud, 68-72, Morse fel, 68-69. Pierson Col. fel, 67- Medieval and Renaissance literature; history of the English language. Publ: Susanna, a Medieval alliterative poem, 68 & The Renaissance Chaucer, 74, Yale Univ. Add: Dept. of English, Yale University, New Haven, CT 06520.

MISSEY, JAMES L, b. San Bernardino, Calif, July 9, 35; m. 65; c. 1. ENGLISH. B.A, Pomona Col, 57; M.A, Univ. Pa, 59, Ph.D.(Eng), 63. Instr. ENG, Beloit Col, 62-64; asst. prof, Denison Univ, 64-66; UNIV. WIS-STEVENS POINT, 66-68, ASSOC. PROF, 68- MLA. The fiction of E.M. Forster. Publ: Forster's redemptive siren, Mod. Fiction Stud, winter 64-65; The connected and the unconnected in Howards end, Wis. Stud. Lit, 69. Add: Dept. of English, University of Wisconsin-Stevens Point, Stevens Point, WI 54481.

MITCHAM, ELIZABETH ALLISON, b. Tisdale, Sask, June 9, 32; m. 55; c. 3. ENGLISH & NORTH AMERICAN LITERATURE. B.A, Univ. Sask, 52; Univ. Toronto, 52-53; M.A, Univ. N.B, 54, Ph.D.(Eng), 72. Dir. & teacher Eng, Univ. N.B, 54-56; lectr. French, Univ. Sask, 56-57; ASSOC. PROF. LIT, UNIV. MONCTON, 68-, dir. thesis prog. comp. Can. lit, 73-74. Humanities Asn. Can; Can. Comp. Lit. Asn; Can. Asn. Univ. Teachers. Canadian literature, comparative French-English; American literature; comparative American and British literature. Publ: Thoreau the ecologist, La Revue, 5/71; The isloation of protesting individuals who belong to minority groups, Wascana Rev, 72; The northern innocent in the fiction of Gabrielle Ray, Humanities Asn. Rev, winter 72-73. Add: Dept. of English, University of Moncton, Moncton, N.B, Can.

MITCHELL, BREON, Comparative Literature, German. See Volume III, Foreign Languages, Linguistics & Philology.

MITCHELL, EDWARD B, b. Aurora, Ill, Jan. 28, 37; m. 58; c. 2. ENGLISH. NDEA fel, Univ. Conn, 60-63, Ph.D.(Eng), 64. Asst. prof. ENG, St. Cloud State Col, 63-65; OHIO UNIV, 65-68, ASSOC. PROF, 68- John Calhoun Baker grant, summer 67. MLA. American fiction and poetry; technology and popular culture. Publ: Co-auth, Continental stories: the modern tradition, Norton, 68 & Nineteenth century American short stories, Scott, 70; ed, Henry Miller: three decades of criticism, N.Y. Univ, 71; Artists and artists: the aesthetics of Henry Miller, Tex. Stud. Lit. & Lang, 66; Themes in Elizabeth Bowen's short stories, Critique, 66; From action to essence: some notes on the structure of Melville's The confidence man, Am. Lit, 68; plus one other. Add: Dept. of English, Ohio University, Athens, OH 45701.

MITCHELL, ELEANOR DRAKE, b. Cookeville, Tenn, Mar. 23, 24; m. 49; c. 2. RENAISSANCE & EIGHTEENTH CENTURY ENGLISH LITERATURE. B.S, Tenn. Polytech. Inst, 46; M.A, Univ. Tenn, Knoxville, 49; Ph.D.(Eng), Univ. Md, College Park, 67. Teacher ENG, Ridgely High Sch, Tenn, 46-47; Brownsville High Sch, Tex, 51-52; instr, TENN. TECHNOL. UNIV, 50-51, 52-58, asst. prof, 58-67, assoc. prof, 67-71, PROF, 71- S.Atlantic Mod. Lang. Asn; Southeast. Renaissance Conf. Eighteenth century periodicals; biography; satire. Publ: A preliminary checklist of Tennessee imprints, 1861-1866, Bibliog. Soc. Univ. Va, 53; co-auth, Draper families in America, Parthenon, 64. Add: Buck Moutain Rd, Box 128, Rte. 6, Cookeville, TN 38501.

MITCHELL, JEROME, b. Chattanooga, Tenn, Oct. 7, 35. MIDDLE ENGLISH LITERATURE. B.A, Emory Univ, 57; Fulbright scholar, Univ. Bonn, 57, Ger. govt. grant, 61-62; Woodrow Wilson & James B. Duke fels, Duke Univ, 58-59, M.A, 59, James B. Duke fel, 62-63, Angier Duke mem. fel, 63-64, distinguished teaching fel, 64-65, Ph.D.(Eng), 65. Teacher, high sch, Tenn, 59-61; asst. prof. ENG, Univ. Ill, Urbana, 65-67; assoc. prof, UNIV. GA, 67-72, PROF, 72- Newberry Libr. grant-in-aid, summer 67; Southeast. Inst. Medieval & Renaissance Stud. fel, summer 69; Am. Counc. Learned Soc. travel grant, Sir Walter Scott Bicentenary Conf, Edinburgh, 71; Fulbright guest prof. Eng. & Am. lit, Univ. Bonn, 72-73. MLA; S.Atlantic Mod. Lang. Asn.(assoc. ed, S.Atlantic Bull, 70-); Mediaeval Acad. Am; Early Eng. Text Soc. Fourteenth and 15th century English literature; operatic versions of the Waverley novels. Publ: Thomas Hoccleve: a study in early fifteenth century English poetic, Univ. Ill, 68; co-ed, Hoccleve's minor poems, Early Eng. Text Soc-Oxford Univ, 70 & Chaucer the love poet, Univ. Ga, 73; auth, The autobiographical element in Hoccleve, Mod. Lang. Quart, 9/67; Hoccleve's tribute to Chaucer, In: Chaucer und seine Zeit: Symposion für Walter F. Schirmer, Niemeyer, Tübingen, 68; Operatic versions of the bride of Lammermoor, Stud. Scottish Lit, 73; plus others. Add: Dept. of English, University of Georgia, Athens, GA 30602.

MITCHELL, JOHN D, b. Rockford, Ill, Nov. 3, 17; m. 56; c. 3. SPEECH. B.S, Northwest. Univ, 39, A.M, 41; Ed.D, Columbia Univ, 56. Prod. dir, univ. theatre, Univ. Mo, 39-40; actor & stage mgr, Katharine Cornell-Guthrie McClintic, 42-43; radio producer, Am. Broadcasting Co, New York, N.Y, 43-46; asst. ed. & play agent, Samuel French, Inc, 46-48; from asst. prof. to assoc. prof. speech, Manhattan Col, 48-58; PRES, INST. ADV. STUD. IN THE THEATER ARTS, 58-; LECTR, POSTGRAD. CTR. PSYCHOTHERAPY, 58-; DIR, RUDOLPH STEINER SCH, 72- Leader, study tour theater arts of Europe, Columbia Univ, 50-51, 54 & 56; U.S. deleg, Int. Theater Inst, Holland, 53, Bombay, India, 56; bd. mem, Beneficia Found, Pa, 60-; pres, comt.

theater & youth, Am-Soviet Exchange in Arts, Inst. Int. Educ. Conf, 61; adj. prof, Univ. Denver, 66-; assoc. trustee, Univ. Pa. Adv. Comt. Performing Arts, 68; artistic dir, Your own thing, Inst. Advan. Stud. Theatre, Monte Carlo, summer 73. International styles of theatres; farces of Labiche and Feydeau; translation of Gozzi's The green bird from the Italian and Venetian dialect. Publ: Ed, The red pear garden: recent Peking operas, 73 & transl, Wild boar forest, 73, Godine; co-ed, Ye Ju Lin, a Peking opera Chinese text for advanced students, Northwood, 74; auth, Applied psychoanalysis and the director-actor relationship, Am. Imago; In search of Brecht, Player, 63. Add: Creek Rd, Bryn Athyn, PA 19009.

MITCHELL, JOHN H, b. West Hartford, Conn, Feb. 14, 21; m; c. 2. ENGLISH. B.S, Bowdoin Col, 43; A.M, Harvard, 47. Instr. Eng, Tufts Univ, 52-53, systs. anal, 53-54; ENG, UNIV. MASS, AMHERST, 54-59, assoc. prof, 59-67, PROF, 67-, DIR. WRITERS' WORKSHOPS, summers 66- Summers, consult, Boeing Airplane Co, 55; Standard Electric Time Co, 56; Hamilton-Standard, 61; U.S. Navy Mine Defense Lab, 63; vis. prof, Univ. Hawaii, 64-65; consult, Gen. Electric, summer 65; vis. prof, Ariz. State Univ, 65-66; consult, Harza Engineering, summer 66; Union Carbide, summer 68; assoc. ed, J. Tech. Writing & Commun, 71-; consult. tech. writing, Naval Underwater Systs. Ctr. & Xerox Corp, 72-73; vis. prof, Canberra Col. Advan. Educ, 73. U.S.N.A.F, 43-45. Soc. Tech. Commun; hon. fel, Tech. Publ. Asn, Eng; Inst. Sci. & Tech. Commun, London; Tech. Commun. Asn. Australia; Inst. Tech. Auth. & Illusr. Australia. Technical writing; information control systems. Publ: Handbook of technical communication, Wadsworth, 62; Writing for technical and professional journals, John Wiley, 68. Add: 120 Red Gate Lane, Amherst, MA 01002.

MITCHELL, JUNE HAMBLIN, b. Boston, Mass, July 19, 15. SPEECH, DRAMA. B.L.I, Emerson Col, 35, A.M, 44, hon. M.A, 55; Columbia Univ, 37; Tufts Univ, 67. Teacher children with defective speech, Pub. Sch, Revere, Mass, 36-44, supvr. speech & drama, 45-48; PROF. SPEECH, EMERSON COL, 48- Instr, Emerson Col, 44-48. Am. Theatre Asn; Am. Speech & Hear. Asn; Nat. Thespian Soc; New Eng. Speech Commun. Asn. (pres, 67-68); Speech Commun. Asn. East. States. Speech therapy; dramatic arts conferences, tournaments and festivals; speech arts. Add: Dept. of Speech, Emerson College, Boston, MA 02116.

MITCHELL, LEE, b. Washington, D.C, Oct. 24, 06. DRAMA. A.B, Carnegie Inst. Tech, 29; Ph.D, Northwest. Univ, 41. Instr. dramatic prod, Northwest. Univ, 29-38, asst. prof, 38-47, assoc. prof, 47-52, prof, 52-71, chmn. dept. theatre & dir, Univ. Theatre, 51-71; DISTINGUISHED PROF. THEATRE, WEST. KY. UNIV, 71- Chmn. grad. comt, Nat. Asn. Schs. Theatre, 71- Kahn Prize, 29. A.U.S, 42-46, Capt. Fel. Am. Theatre Asn; Speech Commun. Asn; AAUP; MLA. Conventions affecting the staging of Shakespeare; aesthetics of dramatic production; survey of doctoral programs in theatre. Publ: Co-auth, Principles of theater art, Houghton, 55, rev. ed, 68. Add: Dept. of Speech & Theatre, Western Kentucky University, Bowling Green, KY 42101.

MITCHELL, LOUIS DUVALO, b. New York, N.Y, June 30, 28. ENGLISH LITERATURE. B.A, Fordham Univ, 52, M.F.A, 54; Ph.D(Eng. lit); N.Y. Univ, 67. Teacher Braille, Eng, hist, Span, French & retarded, N.Y. Inst. for Educ. Blind, 54-61; PROF. LIT, UNIV. SCRANTON, 61-, fels, summer 69, 73. Am. Counc. Learned Soc. fel, summer 69; lectr, St. Joseph Col.(Vt), 72. MLA; Nat. Asn. Advan. Colored People. Renaissance literature, 18th century and music; Afro-American studies. Publ: Command performances during the reign of Queen Ann, Theatre Notebook, spring 70; Democracy, drugs or Disney, Crisis, 2/73; Command performances during the reign of George I, Eighteenth Century Stud, spring 74. Add: Dept. of English, University of Scranton, Scranton, PA 18510.

MITCHELL, LOYCE STANDLEE, b. Crisp, Tex, Nov. 14, 04. DRAMA, ENGLISH. A.B, Abilene Christian Col, 28; summers, Rocky Mount Artist Colony, 28, 29, Univ. Tex, 30, 31, Irvine Sch. for Theatre, 31, 32; A.M, Colo. Col. Educ, 38. ASSOC. PROF. DRAMA & ENG, UNIV. HOUSTON, 31-, head dept. drama, 31-70, from asst. dean men to dean men, 39-72. South Speech Commun. Asn. Add: Dept. of English, University of Houston, Houston, TX 77004.

MITCHELL, NANCY HEYROTH, b. Cincinnati, Ohio, Apr. 24, 31; m. 54; c. 2. ENGLISH. B.A, Swarthmore Col, 53; M.A, Yale, 54; Ph.D(Eng), Cath. Univ. Am, 65. Assoc. prof. ENG, MARY WASHINGTON COL, UNIV. VA, 56-73, PROF, 73-, asst. dean acad. counseling, 70-72. MLA. E.M. Forster; literary theory; linguistics. Add: 1701 College Station, Fredericksburg, VA 22401.

MITCHELL, OLIVE KIMBALL B, b. Tucson, Ariz, Feb. 20, 16; m. 34, 57; c. 3. ENGLISH, ART. B.A, Univ. Ariz, 33; M.A, Brigham Young Univ, 34. Teacher, Pub. Schs, Ariz, 30; instr, Alpine Sch. Dist, Utah, 36-47; ASSOC. PROF. ENG, BRIGHAM YOUNG UNIV, 47- Fulbright teaching grant & assoc. prof, Suan Suandha Teacher Col. & Prasarnmitr Teacher Col, Bangkok, Thailand, 52-53; French Govt. & Nat. Asn. For. Affairs, workshop grant, France, 66; teacher Eng. drama, Univ. Reading, 68. Nat. Asn. For. Affairs; NCTE; AAUP; Am. Asn. Univ. Women; West. Hist. Asn. Arizona southwestern American Indian cultural arts; pioneer history of Arizona and Utah. Publ: Life is a fulfilling, Brigham Young Univ, 67. Add: Dept. of English, A289 Jesse Knight Bldg, Brigham Young University, Provo, UT 84601.

MITCHELL, PAUL LEE, b. Steele, Mo, Aug. 30, 40; m. 61; c. 2. NINETEENTH CENTURY BRITISH LITERATURE. B.A. & M.A, N.Mex. Highlands Univ, 63; Univ. Tex, Austin, 66-67; Ph.D(Eng), Univ. South. Miss, 71. Off. mgr, Jefferson Standard Life Ins. Co, 64-65; instr. ENG, San Antonio Col, 65-67; Northeast La. Univ, 67-69; ASST. PROF, PAN AM. UNIV, 71- Ling. consult, Pascagoula Independent Sch. Dist, 70. Col. Eng. Asn; S.Cent. Mod. Lang. Asn; Conf. Col. Teachers Eng. John Henry, Cardinal Newman; educational and religious controversy in the 19th century; the rhetoric and prose styles of Victorian writers. Publ: North toward home: the quest for an intellectual home, Notes Miss. Writers, 70; The initiation motif in Benjamin Disraeli's Coningsby, South. Quart, 71. Add: Dept. of English, Pan American University, Edinburg, TX 78539.

MITCHELL, ROBERT EARL, b. Columbus, Ohio, July 1, 11; m. 54. ENGLISH & AMERICAN LITERATURE. A.B, Miami Univ, 34; M.A, Duke

Univ, 40; M.A, Harvard, 47, Ph.D.(Eng. lang. & let), 51. Instr. ENG, Emory Univ, 39-42; Queens Col.(N.Y), 48-51; asst. prof, DUQUESNE UNIV, 51-57, ASSOC. PROF, 57- Asst. field dir, Am. Nat. Red Cross, 42-46. MLA. Late 19th century American and English literature. Add: Dept. of English, Duquesne University, Pittsburgh, PA 15219.

MITCHELL, ROGER SHERMAN, b. Boston, Mass, Feb. 8, 35; m. 59; c. 1. ENGLISH & AMERICAN LITERATURE. A.B, Harvard, 57; M.A, Univ. Colo. 61; Ph.D.(Eng), Univ. Manchester, 63. Instr. ENG, Univ. Wis, 63-65, asst. prof, 65-68; MARQUETTE UNIV, 68-71, ASSOC. PROF, 71- Univ. Wis. Grad. Sch. summer res. grant, 65; Am. Counc. Learned Soc. grant-in-aid, 72-73; ed, Minn. Rev, 73- Borestone Mountain Poetry Award, 73. U.S.A, 58-59. MLA. Prosody; 20th century American literature; contemporary British literature. Publ: Co-auth, Another time (poetry), Sydon, 68; auth, Letters from Siberia and other poems, New Rivers, 71; co-ed, This book has no title: an anthology of Milwaukee poetry, Third Coast, 71; In a meantime (poetry), Albatross, 71; Edges (poetry), Sycamore, Eng, 73; A prosody for Walt Whitman?, PMLA 69; Toward a system of grammatical scansion, Lang. & Style, 70; co-ed, Injunction granted (play), Minn. Rev, 73; plus others. Add: Dept. of English, Marquette University, Milwaukee, WI 53233.

MITCHELL, SIDNEY HAMMOND, b. Baltimore, Md, Dec. 8, 26; m. 54; c. 2. ENGLISH. B.A, Swarthmore Col, 50; Philip Francis du Pont fel, Univ. Va, 50-53, M.A, 52, Philip Francis du Pont res. fel, 53-54, Ph.D.(Eng), 62. Instr. ENG, MARY WASHINGTON COL, UNIV. VA, 54-58, asst. prof, 58-62, assoc. prof, 62-67, PROF, 67-, chmn. dept, 67-70. U.S.A, 45-47. MLA. English novel; Joseph Conrad. Add: 1701 College Station, Fredericksburg, VA 22401.

MITCHELL, VICTOR EDWARD, b. Vancouver, B.C, Jan. 19, 29; m. 65. DRAMA. B.A, Univ. B.C, 51; L.G.S.M, Guildhall Sch. Music & Drama, 59; A.M, Stanford Univ, 64. Asst. prof. DRAMA, UNIV. CALGARY, 64-67, ASSOC. PROF. & HEAD DEPT, 67- Theatre history; directing; educational programs in theatre and drama teacher training institutes in England, Eastern Europe, and the United States. Publ: Blueprint for an integrated production-centered undergraduate drama programme, Drama at Calgary, 5/68. Add: Dept. of Drama, University of Calgary, Calgary, Alta, Can.

MITCHELL, W.J. THOMAS, b. Anaheim, Calif, Mar. 24, 42; m. 68; c. 2. EIGHTEENTH & NINETEENTH CENTURY LITERATURE. B.A, Mich. State Univ, 64; M.A, Johns Hopkins Univ, 66, Ph.D.(Eng), 68. Asst. prof. ENG, OHIO STATE UNIV, 68-73, ASSOC. PROF, 73-, humanities res. fel, 70-71. Am. Philos. Soc. grant, 70-71; ed. consult, Stud. Romanticism, 73- MLA; AAUP. Poetry and painting in romantic period; works of William Blake. Publ: Poetic and pictorial imagination in Blake, Eighteenth Century Stud, fall 69; Blake's composite art, In: Blake's visionary forms dramatic, Princeton Univ, 70; Blake's radical comedy, In: Blake's sublime allegory, Univ. Wis, 73. Add: Dept. of English, Ohio State University, Columbus, OH 43210.

MITCHELL, WILLIAM R, b. McLoud, Okla, Dec. 3, 30; m. 48; c. 3. LITERATURE. B.A, Okla City Univ, 52; M.A, Boston Univ, 57; Ph.D.(Eng), Univ. Okla, 69. Instr. Eng, OKLA. BAPTIST UNIV, 58-59, asst. prof, 59-69, assoc. prof, 69-73, PROF. ENG. & DEAN ARTS & SCI, 73- U.S.A, 53-55. Conf. Christianity & Lit; NCTE. Victorian poetry, theology and literature; 18th century English literature. Publ: Literature, In: Faith-learning ser, Broadman, (in press); Art and religion: some premises, Newslett. Conf. Christianity & Lit, summer 69; contrib, Adam among the television trees: an anthology of verse by contemporary Christian poets, Word Bks, 71. Add: Office of the Dean of Arts & Sciences, Oklahoma Baptist University, Shawnee, OK 74801.

MITCHNER, ROBERT WARREN, b. Holton, Kans, July 15, 10; m. 37; c. 1. ENGLISH. A.B, DePauw Univ, 33; Ph.D, Ind. Univ, 47. Instr. ENG, IND. UNIV, BLOOMINGTON, 45-49, asst. prof, 49-55, assoc. prof, 55-63, PROF, 63- MLA; NCTE; Mediaeval Acad. Am. Medieval English literature. Publ: Wynkyn de Worde's use of the Plimpton Manuscript of De Proprietatibus Rerum, The Libr. Add: Dept. of English, Indiana University, Bloomington, IN 47401.

MIX, CLARENCE REX, b. Greenville, Tex, Jan. 14, 35; m. 61; c. 2. SPEECH COMMUNICATION. B.A, Tex. Christian Univ, 57, B.D, 61; Ph.D.(speech commun), Univ. Denver, 72. Minister, Cent. Christian Church, Rosenburg, Tex, 61-62; assoc. dir. educ, Christian Church in Tex, Ft. Worth, Tex, 62-67; instr. SPEECH COMMUN, STATE UNIV. N.Y. COL. FREDONIA, 70-72, ASST. PROF, 72- Speech Commun. Asn; AAUP; Int. Commun. Asn. Communication theory; interpersonal and group communication; organizational communication. Publ: Co-auth, Toward effective teaching—youth, Warner, 70. Add: Div. of Speech Communication, Dept. of Theatre Arts, State University of New York College at Fredonia, Fredonia, NY 14063.

MIXON, HAROLD D, b. Enterprise, Ala, Aug. 27, 32; m. 58; c. 2. SPEECH. A.B, Howard Col, 54; M.A. & Ph.D.(speech), Fla. State Univ, 64. Asst. prof. SPEECH, Mobile Col, 64-65; LA. STATE UNIV, BATON ROUGE, 65-73, ASSOC. PROF, 73- Speech Commun. Asn. History and criticism of American public address: argumentation theory. Publ: Boston's artillery election sermons and the American Revolution, Speech Monogr, 3/67; Progressivism, In: American in controversy: history of American public address, W.C. Brown, 73. Add: Dept. of Speech, Louisiana State University, Baton Rouge, LA 70803.

MIYOSHI, MASAO, b. Tokyo, Japan, May 14, 28; U.S. citizen; m. 53; c. 2. ENGLISH. B.A, Univ. Tokyo, 51; Yale, 52-53; M.A, N.Y. Univ, 57, Ph.D.(Eng), 63. Instr. ENG, Peers' Col, Gakushuin Univ, Tokyo, 51-52, lectr, 54-55; asst. prof, UNIV. CALIF, BERKELEY, 63-69, assoc. prof, 69-73, PROF, 73-, summer fac. fel, 64, mem. Humanities Res. Inst, 66-67. Prof. humanities res, Univ. Calif, 71-72; Guggenheim fel, 71-72. MLA. Nineteenth century English; Japanese literature. Publ: The divided self: a perspective on 19th century English literature, N.Y. Univ, 69; Accomplices of silence: the modern Japanese novel, Univ. Calif, 74; plus various articles. Add: Dept. of English, University of California, Berkeley, Berkeley, CA 94720.

MIZENER, ARTHUR MOORE, b. Erie, Pa, Sept. 3, 07; m. 35; c. 1. ENGLISH LITERATURE. B.S, Princeton, 30, Ph.D, 34; A.M, Harvard, 32. Instr. Eng,

Yale, 34-40; asst. prof, Wells Col, 40-43, assoc. prof, 43-45; prof. & chmn. dept, Carleton Col, 45-51; prof, CORNELL UNIV, 51-64, OLD DOM. FOUND. PROF. HUMANITIES, 64- Fulbright lectr, Univ. London, 55-56; Guggenheim fel, 64-65; Nat. Endowment for Humanities sr. fel, 68. MLA; Century Asn. Shakespeare; literary criticism; 20th century literature. Publ: The far side of Paradise, 51, Houghton, Sentry & Avon; The Fitzgerald reader, Scribner, 63; Sense of life, Houghton, 64; Twelve great American novels, New Am. Libr, 67; The saddest story: a biography of Ford Madox Ford, World, N.Y. & Bodley Head, London, 72; Scott Fitzgerald and his world, Thames & Hudson, London & Putnam, N.Y, 73. Add: Dept. of English, Cornell University, Ithaca, NY 14850.

MIZER, RAYMOND EVERETT, b. Licking Co, Ohio, Sept. 29, 18; m. 44. ENGLISH. B.A, Muskingum Col, 40; M.A, Ohio State Univ, 46, Ph.D.(Eng), 52. Prin, Jersey Sch, Ohio, 41-42; instr. ENG, Grinnell Col, 47-50; DePAUW UNIV, 52-53, asst. prof, 54-62, assoc. prof, 62-69, PROF, 69- Dir. poetry workshop, Methodist Stud. Movement Quadrennial Conf, Univ. Ill, summer 61; lectr. Eng, Butler Univ, 62-63. Nat. relig. drama prod. award, Gen. Bd. Lay Activities, Methodist Church, 65; poetry award, Nat. Endowment for Arts, 69. U.S.A, 42-46. Victorian literature, the poetry of Thomas Edward Brown; modern poetry; creative writing. Publ: Co-auth, Indiana sesquicentennial poets, Ball State Univ, 67; auth, Dirge, In: A decade of southern poetry review, 69 & In: American literature III, Viking, 70; Guest of honor & Real is ideal, So. Poetry Rev, fall, 70; Chrysalis, Poet, summer 72; plus others. Add: 711 Highridge Ave, Greencastle, IN 46135.

MOAKE, FRANK B, b. Johnston City, Ill, Aug. 18, 23; m. 44; c. 3. ENGLISH. B.S, South. Ill. Univ, 48, M.A, 49; Ph.D.(Eng), Univ. Ill, 57. Instr. ENG, South. Ill. Univ, 55-57; asst. prof, UNIV. ILL, URBANA, 57-63, ASSOC. PROF, 63- U.S.A.A.F, 43-46, Sgt. Twentieth century American literature. Publ: Freshman composition courses in ten Illinois colleges, 12/60 & Criticism of freshman writing, 11/64, Ill. Eng. Bull; Training graduate students as teachers at University of Illinois, Col. Compos. & Commun, 12/63. Add: 100 English Bldg, University of Illinois, Urbana, IL 61801.

MOBLEY, LAWRENCE EUGENE, b. Holly, Mich, July 8, 25; m. 51. ENGLISH & AMERICAN LITERATURE. B.A, Andrews Univ, 50; M.A, Univ. Mich, 52; Ph.D.(Eng), Mich. State Univ, 61. Teacher & librn, Adelphia Acad, Holly, Mich, 50-52; PROF. ENG, LOMA LINDA UNIV, 52-, chmn. dept, 65-70. Prof. Eng. & chmn. dept, Saniku Gakuin Col, Japan, 70-72. U.S.A, 43-46, S/Sgt. MLA; NCTE; West. Lit. Asn. Faulkner; early California journalism. Add: Dept. of English, Loma Linda University, Riverside, CA 92505.

MOCKOVAK, PAUL WILLIAM, b. Danbury Conn, Apr. 19, 23; m. 52; c. 2. ENGLISH. B.S, West. Conn. State Col, 47; M.A, Columbia Univ, 48; N.Y. State Regents fel, Syracuse Univ, 66-67. Jr. instr. ENG, STATE UNIV. N.Y. AGR. & TECH. COL. MORRISVILLE, 48-53, instr, 58-61, asst. prof, 62-64, assoc. prof, 65-66, PROF, 67-, CHMN. DEPT, 72-75. U.S.A, 43-46. MLA. John Donne. Add: Dept. of English, State University of New York Agricultural & Technical College at Morrisville, Morrisville, NY 13408.

MODIC, JOHN LEONARD, b. Cleveland, Ohio, May 4, 20; m. 51; c. 4. ENGLISH. B.A. & M.A, Case West. Reserve Univ, 47, Ph.D.(Eng), 70; Stanford Univ, 48-49. Asst. instr. freshman rhetoric, Univ. Ill, 53-54, instr. Eng. compos, lit. & drama, Wayne State Univ, 54-57; asst. prof, State Univ. N.Y. Col. Oswego, 57-59; Ball State Univ, 59-66; ASST. PROF. ENG, LING. & DRAMA, PURDUE UNIV, FT. WAYNE, 66-, dir. freshman Eng, 66-67. Instr, Berlitz Sch. Lang, 51-53; Cleveland Col, West. Reserve Univ, summer 53. U.S.A.A.F, 42-45, Sgt. MLA. Dramatic comedy; the modern novel; linguistics. Publ: The eclectic Mr. Wilder, Ball State Forum, spring 61; Gascoigne and Ariosto again, Comp. Lit, summer 62; Thornton Wilder essay, In: Encycl. of world literature in the twentieth century, Ungar, 71. Add: Dept. of English, Purdue University, Ft. Wayne, IN 46805.

MOE, CHRISTIAN HOLLIS, b. New York, N.Y, July 6, 29; m. 52; c. 2. THEATRE. A.B, Col. William & Mary, 51; M.A, Univ. N.C, Chapel Hill, 55; Ph.D.(drama), Cornell Univ, 58. Asst. prof. theatre, SOUTHERN ILL. UNIV, CARBONDALE, 58-61, assoc. prof. & asst. dean sch. commun, 61-68, PROF. THEATRE, 68-, acting chmn. dept. 62-63, acting dean sch. commun, 64. Consult, Writing & Producing Hist. Drama, 57-; lectr, sem. Am. cult, N.Y. State Hist. Asn, 57; dir, Lincolnland Drama Festival, Ill, 65-69; mem. adv. bd, Inst. Outdoor Drama, 65-; participant, int. theatre sem, Brit. Drama League & Brit. Counc, London, 68; playwright & dir, Stranger in the land, off-Broadway, 57; Hark upon the gale, Jamestown Festival Celebration, Col. William & Mary, 57; The strolling players, 65; Make her wilderness like Eden, sesquicentennial drama, State of Ill, 68; Between the tower and the town, Miss. River Tri-Centennial Celebration, Grand Tower, Ill, 73; The day Santa Claus came to Simpson's crossing, 73. Joseph D. Feldman Award, 57; 1st prize, Encore Players Nat. Playwriting Contest, 57; 1st Prize, Humboldt State Col. Nat. Children's Play Contest, 66; Gov. of Ill. Spec. Citation, 68. U.S.N, 51-53. Am. Theatre Asn; Speech Commun. Asn. The dramatization of American history, research, writing and production; the comic theatre and comedic theories; children's theatre. Publ: Creating historical drama, 65 & co-ed, Six new plays for children, 71, South. Ill. Univ; co-auth, The William and Mary Theatre: a chronicle, Dietz, 68, auth, Are we really training studient actors?, spring 71 & Production standards in outdoor drama, fall 71, South. Theatre; contrib, Contemporary dramatists, St. James, 73; plus others. Add: Dept. Theatre, Southern Illinois University, Carbondale, IL 62901.

MOE, SIGRID, b. Lom, Norway, Dec. 28, 99; U.S. citizen. ENGLISH & NORWEGIAN LITERATURE. B.A, St. Olaf Col, 23; M.A, Univ. Chicago, 28; Ph.D.(Eng), N.Y. Univ, 51. Teacher & head dept. Eng, High Sch, Ill, 30-44; instr, Jacksonville Univ, 45-46; Univ. S.Dak, 46-47; prof, Col. Emporia, 50-54; Ottawa Univ.(Kans), 54-56; prof. & mem. grad. fac, UNIV. NEV, LAS VEGAS, 56-70, EMER. PROF. ENG, 70- Danforth summer study grants, 54 & 56; Univ. Nev. Desert-Res. Inst. res. grant, 66-67. MLA. Intercultural relations of Norway and America, especially in literature; the colonial period in American literature. Publ: Transl. Norweg. article on Walt Whitman, In: Walt Whitman abroad, Syracuse Univ, 47; auth, A reassessment of Cotton Mather's literary production, Am. Notes & Querie; An elegy on John Alden, Nat. Geneal. Soc. Publ. Add: 213 Fourth St, San Antonio, TX 78205.

MOEHL, ERNA, b. Thomasboro, Ill, May 27, 06. ENGLISH. B.S, Univ. Ill, 28, M.A, 35; Univ. Minn, summer, 50; grants, State Univ. Iowa, 54, 61; Bread Loaf Sch. Eng, 57. Teacher ENG, Herscher High Sch, Ill, 28-47; instr, WARTBURG COL, 47-51, asst. prof, 51-58, assoc. prof, 58-67, prof, 67-72, EMER. PROF, 72- Mem, NDEA Inst. teaching Eng, Univ. Minn, summer 66; participant, teacher trainers prog, Univ. Minn, 69. NCTE; NEA. English literature; literary criticism; teaching of English. Add: 307 Fourth Ave. N.W, Waverly, IA 50677.

MOELLER, LESLIE GEORGE, b. Everly, Iowa, Oct. 21, 04; m. 26; c. 2. MASS COMMUNICATIONS. B.A, Univ. Iowa, 25; Litt.D, Wartburg Col, 57. Advert. mgr, Spencer News-Herald, Iowa, 25-26; managing ed, New Hampton Gazette, 26-27; managing ed. & gen. mgr, Bremer County Independent, Waverly, 27-43, managing ed, Waverly Democrat, 32-43, gen. mgr, Bremer County Independent & Waverly Democrat, 45-46; assoc. prof. JOUR, UNIV. IOWA, 46-47, prof, 47-72, John H. Murray Prof, 72-73, dir, 47-67, EMER. PROF, 73- Chmn. accrediting comt, Am. Counc. Educ. for Jour, 53-56; consult, Am. Broadcasting Corp. TV News, 70-; J. Stewart Riley chair jour, Ind. Univ, 73. U.S.N, 43-45, Comdr. Asn. Educ. in Jour.(chmn. mass commun. & soc. div, 67-68, mem. prof. freedom & responsibility comt, 69-, chmn, 69-71 & 72-73); Int. Asn. Mass Commun. Res; World Asn. Pub. Opinion Res; Int. Commun. Asn; Am. Asn. Pub. Opinion Res. Mass communications and society; mass media and popular culture; mass media and social change. Publ: Co-ed, The government and the media, Asn. Educ. in Jour, 71; contrib, The web of international communication, Hastings 70; auth, A free press: how can we undo misunderstanding?, Quill, 3/70; contrib, Masskommunikationsforschung: 1. Produktion, Fischer Taschenbuch, Frankfurt, 72; plus others. Add: School of Journalism, University of Iowa, Iowa City, IA 52242.

MOERS, ELLEN, b. New York, N.Y, Dec. 9, 28; m. 49; c. 2. ENGLISH, COMPARATIVE LITERATURE. B.A, Vassar Col, 48; M.A, Harvard, 49; Ph.D.(Eng), Columbia Univ, 55. Lectr. ENG, Hunter Col, 56-57; COLUMBIA UNIV, 57-58, SR. RES. ASSOC, 65-, ADJ. ASSOC. PROF, BARNARD COL, 69- Guggenheim fel, 62-63; Nat. Endowment for Humanities sr. fel, 72-73 & res. grant, 73-74; mem. ed. bd, Dreiser Newslett. & Twentieth Century Lit. Nineteenth century English and comparative literature; history of novel; American literature. Publ: The dandy: Brummell to Beerbohm, Secker & Warburg & Viking, 60, transl, Rizzoli, Milan, 65; Two Dreisers, Viking, 69, Thames & Hudson, London, 70; Women's lit: a tradition, Columbia Forum, fall 72; S. Richardson, N.Y. Rev. Bks, 2/72; Bleak House: the agitating women, Dickensian, 1/73. Add: 33 East End Ave, New York, NY 10028.

MOFFATT, WALTER AUGUSTUS, JR, b. Monticello, Ark, Aug. 3, 11. ENGLISH LITERATURE. A.B, Hendrix Col, 32; A.M, Harvard, 34; Ph.D, Princeton, 41. Mem. dept. ENG, Ark. Agr. & Mech. Col, 35-46; assoc. prof, Ripon Col, 46-48; PROF, HENDRIX COL, 48-, CHMN. HUMANITIES AREA, 55-, CHMN. DEPT, 58- Med.Admin.C, U.S.A, 42-46, 1st Lt. MLA; S.Cent. Mod. Lang. Asn. The literary reputation of Robert Burns; social history of pioneer Arkansas. Publ: Arkansas schools, 1819-1840, First theatrical activities in Arkansas & Cultural and recreational activities in pioneer Arkansas, Ark. Hist. Quart. Add: Dept. of English, Hendrix College, Conway, AR 72032.

MOFIELD, WILLIAM RAY, b. Hardin, Ky, July 3, 21; m. 53; c. 1. SPEECH, JOURNALISM. A.B, Murray State Univ, 43; broadcast cert, Northwest. Univ, Evanston, 45; CBS News fel & M.A, Columbia Univ, 58; LL.D, Magic Valley Christian Col, 62; Ph.D.(speech), South. Ill. Univ, Carbondale, 64. Teacher speech & jour, Vienna High Sch, Ill, 44-45; mgr, WPAD-AM-FM, Paducah, Ky, 45-59; teacher & dir. broadcasting, South. Ill. Univ, Carbondale, 59-64; PROF. COMMUN, MURRAY STATE UNIV, 64-, CHMN. DEPT, 68-, exec. asst. to pres, 64-68. Participant, Am. Folklife Festival, Smithsonian Inst, 73. U.S.N.R, 42-43. Speech Commun. Asn; Asn. Educ. Jour; Nat. Asn. Educ. Broadcasters; Broadcast Educ. Asn. Economic development of an area through tourist promotion, Marshall County, Ky; broadcast audience surveys; local history. Publ: FM capital of the world, 49 & Silver anniversary of WPAD, 55, Young Printing; Development of an area by tourism, Ky. Dept. Parks, 65; Benton's big singing; Southern harmony, In: 150th Anniversary of the Jackson purchase, Mayfield, 59; The Jackson purchase in historical perspective, JPHS Jour, 73. Add: Dept. of Communications, Murray State University, Murray, KY 42071.

MOGAN, JOSEPH J, JR, b. Nashville, Tenn, Jan. 20, 24; m. 57; c. 3. ENGLISH LITERATURE. A.B, St. Mary's Sem. & Univ, 46; grant, Notre Dame Univ, 51-54, M.A, 54; Ph.D.(Eng. lit), La. State Univ, 61. Asst. prof. Eng, Lewis Col, 54-56; asst, La. State Univ, 56-61; asst. prof. ENG, St. Norbert Col, 61-63; South. Ill. Univ, 63-66; assoc. prof, TEX. TECH UNIV, 66-70, PROF, 70- Newberry fel, summer 66; Am. Philos. Soc. grant, summer 67. Mediaeval Acad. Am. Middle English. Publ: Chaucer and the theme of mutability, Mouton, The Hague, 68; Chaucer and the Bona Matrimonii, Chaucer Rev, 70. Add: Dept. of English, Texas Tech University, Lubbock, TX 79409.

MOHL, RONALD ALFRED, b. Grand Island, Nebr, Aug. 1, 38; m. 64; c. 4. ENGLISH. B.A, Univ. Nebr, 61, M.A, 62; Ph.D.(Eng), Univ. Conn, 67. Asst. prof. ENG, State Univ. N.Y. Col. Potsdam, 66-68; EAST. MICH. UNIV, 68-71, ASSOC. PROF, 71- Eighteenth-century English literature; English linguistics and stylistics. Add: Dept. of English, Eastern Michigan University, Ypsilanti, MI 48197.

MOHR, MARY HULL, b. Moline, Ill, Oct. 31, 34; m. 65; c. 1. ENGLISH LITERATURE. B.A, Augustana Col.(Ill), 56; M.A, Univ. Minn, Minneapolis, 61; Ph.D.(Eng), Univ. Colo, Boulder, 64. Instr. ENG, Augustana Col.(S.Dak), 57-59;Univ. Colo, Boulder, 59-61; teaching asst, 61-63; asst. prof, LUTHER COL.(IOWA), 63-70, ASSOC. PROF, 70- AAUP; MLA. Sixteenth century poetry; life of Lucy Harrington Countess of Bedford; modern literature about women. Add: Dept. of English, Luther College, Decorah, IA 52101.

MOLDENHAUER, JOSEPH JOHN, b. Rastatt, Ger, Feb. 9, 34; U.S. citizen; m. 57; c. 2. ENGLISH. B.A, Amherst Col, 56; Amherst Col. fel, Columbia Univ, 56-57, M.A, 57, South. Fel. Fund fac. fel, 59-60, Ph.D.(Eng), 64. Spec. instr. ENG, UNIV. TEX, AUSTIN, 57-59, 60-62, instr, 62-64, asst. prof, 64-68, assoc. prof, 68-72, PROF, 72-, res. inst. grants, summer 64 & 66-67. Guggenheim fel, 68-69; textual ed, The writings of Henry D. Thoreau, 72- MLA. Literary rhetoric; 19th century American literature; the Thoreau edition. Publ: Ed, H.D. Thoreau's The Maine woods, Princeton Univ, 72; Unity of theme and structure in The wild palms, In: William Faulkner: three decades of criticism, Mich. State Univ, 60; Murder as a fine art, basic connections between Poe's aesthetics, psychology, and moral vision, PMLA, 5/68. Add: Dept. of English, University of Texas, Austin, TX 78712.

MOLDSTAD, DAVID FRANKLYN, b. Cleveland, Ohio, Aug. 17, 23; m. 47; c. 4. ENGLISH LITERATURE. A.B, Hiram Col, 47; A.M, Brown Univ, 49; Ph.D, Univ. Wis, 54. Asst. prof. ENG, Univ. Tulsa, 53-57; assoc. prof, COL. WOOSTER, 57-67, PROF, 67- U.S.A.A.F, 43-45, 2nd Lt. MLA. Nineteenth century English literature. Add: Dept. of English, College of Wooster, Wooster, OH 44691.

MOLER, KENNETH LLOYD, JR, b. Baltimore, Md, Mar. 24, 38; m. 59; c. 2. ENGLISH. B.A, Johns Hopkins Univ, 58; M.A, Harvard, 60, Ph.D.(Eng), 64. Asst. prof. ENG, UNIV. NEBR-LINCOLN, 64-67, assoc. prof, 67-72, PROF, 72- Ord.C, U.S.A, 59, Res, 59-67, 1st Lt. MLA. Jane Austen; Thackeray. Publ: Jane Austen's art of allusion, Univ. Nebr, 68; Sense and sensibility and its sources, Rev. Eng. Stud, 11/66; Pride and prejudice: Jane Austen's patrician hero, Stud. Eng. Lit, summer 67; Evelina in Vanity Fair, Nineteenth Century Fiction, 9/72; plus others. Add: 1841 Pawnee St, Lincoln, NE 68502.

MOLETTE, CARLTON W, II, b. Pine Bluff, Ark, Aug. 23, 39; m. 60; c. 2. AFRO-AMERICAN DRAMA, THEATRE TECHNOLOGY. B.A. & Ford Found. scholar, Morehouse Col, 59; fel, Univ. Kansas City, 59-60; M.A, Univ. Iowa, 62; Carnegie Found. grant, Fla. State Univ, 66-68, Ph.D.(theatre), 68. Asst. dir, Little Theatre, Tuskegee Inst, 60-61; designer & tech. dir, Des Moines Community Playhouse, Iowa, 62-63; asst. prof. tech. prod. & design, Howard Univ, 63-64; asst. prof. drama & tech. dir, Fla. A&M Univ, 64-67, ASSOC. PROF. DRAMA, 67-69; SPELMAN COL, 69-, acting chmn. dept, 71-73. Consult, South. Speech J, 66-68; mem. adv. bd, J. Black Stud, 70-73; Atlanta Univ. Ctr. fac. res. grant, 70-71; Nat. Endowment for Arts grant, summer 73. Dramatists Guild; Am. Theatre Asn; Nat. Asn. Dramatic & Speech Arts (ed, Encore, 65-71); U.S. Inst. Theatre Technol. Afro-American theatre aesthetics; lighting and make-up for dark complexioned actors. Publ: The first Afro-American theatre, Negro Digest, 4/70; co-auth, Attitudes about Black Muslims, Encore, 70; auth, Afro-American ritual drama, Black World, 4/73; plus many others. Add: Dept. of Drama, Spelman College, Atlanta, GA 30314.

MOLIN, S. ERIC, b. Rochester, N.Y, May 12, 29; m. 69; c. 5. DRAMA, ENGLISH LITERATURE. B.A, Amherst Col, 50; M.A, Columbia Univ, 51; Ph.D, Univ. Pa, 56. Instr. ENG, Ohio Univ, 56-58; asst. prof, Randolph-Macon Woman's Col, 58-63, ASSOC. PROF, 63-71; GEORGE MASON UNIV, 71- Am. Counc. Learned Soc. res. fel, 64-65; Fulbright lectr. Eng, Univ. Jyvaskyla, Finland, 69-70. Am. Film Inst; AAUP; Am. Soc. 18th Century Stud. Eighteenth century English literature; sex in the 18th century; T.H. White. Publ: Co-auth, Drama: the major genres, Dodd, 62; auth, Appraisals: T.H. White, J. Irish Lit, 73. Add: Dept. of English, George Mason University, 4400 University Dr, Fairfax, VA 22030.

MOLLENHAUER, EMERY C, F.S.C, b. Philadelphia, Pa, Feb. 16, 28. ENGLISH. B.A, Cath. Univ. Am, 49; M.A, Univ. Pittsburgh, 51, Owens fel, 55-56, Ph.D, 57; Laval Univ, 58; Cath. Inst. Paris, 59; Casa Generalissa, Roma, 59-60. Teacher ENG, Cent. Dist. Cath. High Sch, 49-58; asst. prof, LA SALLE COL, 58-66, ASSOC. PROF, 66-, ACAD. V.PRES, 69-, dir. summer sessions, 60, dean evening div, 61-69. Scholar, restoration lit, Univ. London, 60; Connelly grant for study of evening col. adult educ. in Eng, spring 68; regional chmn, Asn. Univ. Evening Cols, 68-69, mem. exec. comt, 68- Nat. Cath. Educ. Asn.(chmn. mid. states region, 72-). Publ: 20th century writers, Macmillan, 60. Add: Dept. of English, La Salle College, Philadelphia, PA 19141.

MOLLENKOTT, VIRGINIA RAMEY, b. Philadelphia, Pa, Jan. 28, 32; m. 54; c. 1. ENGLISH LITERATURE. B.A, Bob Jones Univ, 53; M.A, Temple Univ, 55; Penfield fel, N.Y. Univ, 63-64, Ph.D.(Eng. lit), 64. Instr. Eng, Bob Jones Univ, 53-54; Shelton Col, 55-56, assoc. prof. Eng. & chmn. dept, 56-63; prof. ENG, Nyack Missionary Col, 63-67; ASSOC. PROF, WILLIAM PATTERSON COL. N.J, 67- Stylistic consult, New Int. Bible Transl. Comt, 71- Conf. Christianity & Lit.(chief bibliogr, 67-); MLA; Milton Soc. Am. Religion and literature; 17th century English literature. Publ: Milton and the apocrypha, Univ. Microfilms, 66; Adamant and stone chips: a Christian-humanist approach to knowledge, 67, In search of balance, 69 & ed, Adam among the television trees: an anthology of verse by contemporary Christian poets, 71, Word Bks; auth, The cycle of sins in Paradise lost, book XI, Mod. Lang. Quart, 3/66; Relativism in Samson Agonistes, Stud. Philol. 1/70; Milton's rejection of the fortunate fall, Milton Quart, 3/72; plus others. Add: Rte. 1, Box 16-C, Hewitt, NJ 07421.

MOLSON, FRANCIS JOSEPH, b. Whiting, Ind, Oct. 30, 32; m. 58; c. 4. ENGLISH. A.B, St. Joseph's Col.(Ind), 54; M.A, Univ. Notre Dame, 56, Ph.D. (Eng), 65. Lectr. Eng. Ind. Univ, South Bend, 59-65, asst. prof, 65-72, acad. counselor, 59-65, summer fel, 68; ASST. PROF. ENG, CENT. MICH. UNIV, 72- Danforth assoc, 68-74. MLA; NCTE; Childrens Lit. Asn. Nineteenth century American literature; fantasy; children's literature. Add: Dept. of English, Central Michigan University, Mt. Pleasant, MI 48858.

MOMADAY, NAVARRE SCOTT, b. Lawton, Okla, Feb. 27, 34; m. 59; c. 3. ENGLISH, AMERICAN STUDIES. A.B, Univ. N.Mex, 58; A.M, Stanford Univ, 60, Ph.D.(Eng), 63; hon. D.H.L, Cent. Mich. Univ, 70; hon. D.Litt, Lawrence Univ, 71. Asst. prof. Eng, Univ. Calif, Santa Barbara, 63-67, assoc. prof, 67-69; prof. Eng. & comp. lit, Univ, Calif, Berkeley, 69-72; distinguished vis. prof. humanities, N.Mex. State Univ, 72-73; PROF. ENG. & COMP. LIT, STANFORD UNIV, 73- Univ. Calif. Inst. for Humanities fel, 66-67; Guggenheim fel, 66-67; vis. lectr, Moscow State Univ, spring 74. MLA; Am. Stud. Asn. American literature; American studies; creative writing. Publ: Ed, The complete poems of Frederick Goddard Tuckerman, Oxford, 65; auth, House made of dawn, Harper, 68; The way to Rainy Mountain, Univ. New Mex, 69; Colorado: summer, fall, winter, spring (photography by D. Muench) McNally, 73; Angle of geese and other poems, D.R. Godine, 74. Add: Dept. of English, Stanford University, Stanford, CA 93105.

MOMBERGER, PHILIP, b. Philadelphia, Pa, Dec. 9, 39; m. 68. AMERICAN LITERATURE. B.A, Swarthmore Col, 61; M.A, Columbia Univ, 63; M.A, Johns Hopkins Univ, 63, Ph.D.(Eng), 70. Asst. prof. ENG, Towson State Col, 64-69; ASSOC. PROF, UNIV. W.FLA, 69- MLA. American fiction; Victorian fiction. Publ: Self and world in works of Charlotte Brontë, Eng. Lit. Hist, 65; Faulkner's country as ideal community, In: The individual and the community, Duke Univ, 74. Add: Faculty of English, University of West Florida, Pensacola, FL 32504.

MONAGHAN, MARY CHARLES, I.H.M, b. Philadelphia, Pa. ENGLISH. A.B, Univ. Pa, 29, A.M, 34. Chmn. ENG, Little Flower High Sch, 39-45; instr, IMMACULATA COL.(PA), 45-52, asst. prof, 52-60, assoc. prof, 61-73, COL. ARCHIVIST & EMER. ASSOC. PROF, 73- Mem, Eng. Inst. NCTE; Conf. Col. Compos. & Commun; Nat. Col. Honors Counc. Add: Dept. of English, Immaculata College, Immaculata, PA 19345.

MONAGHAN, ROBERT R, b. Dowagiac, Mich, Mar. 31, 28; m. 54; c. 1. MASS COMMUNICATION, HUMANISTIC SCIENCE. B.A, Olivet Col, 52; M.A, Stanford Univ, 59; Ph.D.(commun), Mich. State Univ, 64. From assoc. prof. to PROF. COMMUN, OHIO STATE UNIV, 64- Danforth assoc, 60-74. U.S.M.C, 46-48. Asn. Educ. in Jour; Asn. Humanistic Psychol; Speech Commun. Asn; Nat. Asn. Educ. Broadcasters; Int. Commun. Asn. (v.pres, 72-74). The media manager and influences on decision-making; philosophy of humanistic science; effects of media on audiences, especially child learning. Publ: A systematic way of being creative, J. Commun, 3/68; co-auth, EBR readership profile analysis, Educ. Broadcasting Rev, 69 & Researching the problems, In: Broadcasting and bargaining, 69; plus others. Add: Dept. of Communication, Ohio State University, Columbus, OH 43210.

MONAHAN, DEAN WRIGHT, b. Detroit, Mich, July 9, 35; m. 68; c. 1. ENGLISH. B.A, Wayne State Univ, 58, M.A, 63; Ph.D, Pa. State Univ, 68. ASST. PROF. ENG, SOUTHEAST MO. STATE UNIV, 65- U.S.A.F, Air Nat. Guard, U.S.A.F.R, 53-61. MLA. Edgar Allan Poe. Add: Dept. of English, Southeast Missouri State University, Cape Girardeau, MO 63701.

MONAHAN, (MARY) JOAN, b. Minneapolis, Minn, Dec. 23, 26; m. 69. COMPOSITION, ENGLISH EDUCATION. B.S.E, St. John Col.(Ohio), 55; M.A, John Carroll Univ, 63; Ph.D.(Eng), Kent State Univ, 71. Teacher, elem. schs, 48-59; ENG, St. Vincent High Sch, Akron, Ohio, 59-67; chmn. dept, Cardinal Mooney High Sch, Youngstown, 67-68; instr, BALDWIN-WALLACE COL, 70-71, asst. prof, 71-73, ASSOC. PROF, 73- MLA; NCTE; AAUP. Composition; English teacher education; modern literature. Publ: Billy Budd—Benito Cereno, Barnes & Noble, 68; Speaking of thinking, Cath. Educr, 2/62; News is everywhere, Scholastic Ed, 12/66; Teaching poetry by parody, Mo. Eng. Bull, 10/73. Add: Dept. of English, Baldwin-Wallace College, Berea, OH 44017.

MONDA, JOSEPH B, b. Wenatchee, Wash, Mar. 27, 29; m. 60; c. 3. ENGLISH. B.A, St. Martin's Col, 49; M.A, Marquette Univ, 51; NDEA fel, Univ. Colo, 67, Ph.D.(Eng), 68. Teacher high sch, Wash, 60-61; instr. ENG, SEATTLE UNIV, 55-58, asst. prof, 61-68, ASSOC. PROF, 69-74, PROF, 74-, DIR. SUMMER SCH, 73-, acting chmn. dept, 68-69, chmn, 69-73. Assoc. dir, NDEA summer inst, 65; teaching assoc. Eng, Univ. Colo, 65-67; Col. Entrance Exam. Bd. reader, 66- U.S.A, 51-54, Sgt. Mediaeval Acad. Am; MLA. Middle English devotional literature; folk-lore in literature. Publ: The sayings of St. Bernard, Mediaeval Stud, 6/71. Add: 1151 20th Ave. E, Seattle, WA 98102.

MONDALE, CLARENCE COWAN, b. St. James, Minn, July 12, 26; m. 51; c. 7. AMERICAN STUDIES. B.A, Macalester Col, 47; M.A, Univ. Minn, 54, Ph.D, 60. Instr. Eng, Univ. Minn, 54-60; asst. prof, Univ. Ala, 60-63, assoc. prof, 63-65, dir. Am. stud, 61-65; AM. CIVILIZATION, GEORGE WASHINGTON UNIV, 65-70, PROF, 70-, DIR. DIV. EXP. PROG, 74-, dir, Peace Corps Training progs, 65-66. Mem, panel on soc. indicators, Dept. Health, Educ. & Welfare, 67-68; Nat. Humanities fac, 71- U.S.N, 44-45. Am. Stud. Asn. Ceremonial oratory in antebellum United States; computer-stored bibliography; cultural change and technological impact in New England and the South. Publ: Daniel Webster and technology, in an anthology publ. by Houghton. Add: Div. of Experimental Programs, George Washington University, Washington, DC 20006.

MONK, SAMUEL HOLT, b. Selma, Ala, Mar. 25, 02; wid. ENGLISH LITERATURE & CRITICISM. A.B, Southwest. at Memphis, 22, hon. D.Litt, 63; A.M, Princeton, 24, Scribner fel, 28-29, Ph.D, 29; Univ. Chicago, 26. From asst. prof. to prof. Eng, Southwest. at Memphis, 24-42; Rockefeller Found. fel. humanities, 45-46; prof. Eng, UNIV. MINN, MINNEAPOLIS, 47-70, chmn. dept, 48-50, EMER. PROF. ENG, 70- Am. Counc. Learned Socs. res. fel, 30-31; Berg prof, N.Y. Univ, 54-55; Guggenheim fel, 56-57; Beckman vis. prof. Eng. lit, Univ. Calif, Berkeley, 61; res. fel, William A. Clark Libr, Los Angeles, Calif, 64. U.S.A.F, 42-45, Capt. MLA. Eighteenth century English literature and literary theory. Publ: Theories of the sublime in eighteenth century England, Mod. Lang. Asn. Am, 35, Univ. Mich, 60; Five miscellaneous essays by Sir William Temple, Univ. Mich, 63; ed, Defoe's Colonel Jack, Oxford, 65; auth, Restoration and eighteenth century, In: Norton anthology, Vol. I, 1126-1734, Norton, 62. Add: 800 Rugby Rd, Charlottesville, VA 22903.

MONROE, GEORGE KARL, Linguistics, German. See Volume III, Foreign Languages, Linguistics & Philology.

MONROE, HOWARD CHANDLER, b. Columbia, Mo, Aug, 5, 20; m. 53; c. 3. SPEECH, DRAMA. B.A, Principia Col, 50; M.A, Univ. Mo, Columbia, 54, Ph.D.(speech & drama), 65; summers, State Univ, Iowa, 55, 56. Radio announcer, KHMO, Hannibal, Mo, 52-53; teacher, High Sch, Mo, 50-53; instr. speech, Culver-Stockton Col, 53-54; teacher, High Sch, Iowa, 54-56; instr. pub. speaking, Univ. Mo, Columbia, 56-60; asst. prof. SPEECH, NORTHEAST MO. STATE UNIV, 60-65, assoc. prof, 65-67, PROF, 67-, CHMN. FAC. SPEECH, 71- Lectr. consult, Christian Sci. Bd. Lect, Boston, Mass,

66-68; parliamentarian, Mo. Dept. Classroom Teachers, 67; consult, Southwest Bell Telephone Col. Conf. Mo, 67; guest lectr, workshops, MINNEMAST, N.E. Mo. State Col, 68. Qm.C, U.S.N.R, 42-45, 50-52. NEA; Asn. High Educ; Speech Commun. Asn. Religious drama. Publ: Academic standards maintained by faculty, Vital Speeches of Day, 7/66. Add: Dept. of Speech, Northeast Missouri State University, Kirksville, MO 63501.

MONSMA, JOHN WILLIAM, JR, b. Muskegon, Mich, May 10, 36; m. 59; c. 5. SPEECH EDUCATION, PUBLIC ADDRESS. B.A, Calvin Col, 58; M.A, Bowling Green State Univ, 59; Ph.D.(speech), Ind. Univ, Bloomington, 66. Asst. prof. speech & dir. forensics, North. Mich. Univ, 61-66; Purdue Univ, West Lafayette, 66-70; ASSOC. PROF. SPEECH, NORTH. ARIZ. UNIV, 70- Speech Commun. Asn; Int. Commun. Asn; West. States Commun. Asn; Am. Forensic Asn. Speech pedagogy; public address and forensics. Publ: Co-auth, Contemporary forensic dialogue, J. Ariz. Speech & Drama Asn, winter 71; Teaching communication to Indian educators, J. Ariz. Speech & Drama Asn, fall 72 & Res. in Educ, 11/72; Report of action caucus on high school workshops, J. Am. Forensic Asn, fall 73; plus one other. Add: Dept. of Speech & Theatre, Box 6006, Northern Arizona University, Flagstaff, AZ 86001.

MONSMAN, GERALD CORNELIUS, b. Baltimore, Md, Mar. 3, 40; m. 66. ENGLISH. B.A, Johns Hopkins Univ, 61, M.A, 63, Ph.D.(Eng), 65. Instr. ENG, Johns Hopkins Univ, 62-65; asst. prof, DUKE UNIV, 65-72, ASSOC. PROF, 72- Summer fac. res. fel, 67. MLA. Fiction of Walter H. Pater; late 19th century literature; the Christian romantics, especially C.S. Lewis, Charles Williams and J.R.R. Tolkien. Publ: Pater's portraits, Johns Hopkins Univ, 67; Nicholai, Blackwood's Mag, 11/67. Add: Dept. of English, Duke University, Durham, NC 27706.

MONSON, ALLWIN DOUGLAS, b. Dunkirk, Mont, May 21, 17; m. 40; c. 2. SPEECH. A.B, Concordia Col.(Moorhead, Minn), 38; A.M, Univ. Denver, 41; Syracuse Univ, 41-42. Instr, Syracuse Univ, 41-45, 46-48; prof. speech & head dept, CONCORDIA COL.(MOORHEAD, MINN), 48-64, PROF. SPEECH & DRAMA, 64- Teacher humanities forum, Tri-Col. Univ, spring 74. U.S.N.R, 45-46. Speech Commun. Asn; Cent. States Speech Asn. Add: Dept. of Speech & Drama, Concordia College, Moorhead, MN 56560.

MONSON, LELAND HANS, b. Presto, Idaho; m. 20; c. 5. ENGLISH, SPEECH. B.A, Univ. Utah, 25, Ph.D.(Eng), 56; M.A, Univ. Chicago, 26; Henry Newell scholar, Stanford Univ, 45-46. Prof. ENG, WEBER STATE COL, 26-68, EMER. PROF, 68-, chmn. div. humanities, 43-67. Dir. facilities & res. development, David McKay Hospital, 68-72. NEA. Shakespeare and Bible as literature. Publ: Life in ancient America, 46, Ancient America speaks, 58, co-auth, Character and leadership, 64 & auth, Look to the Mount, 68, Deseret; Let's pull together, County Off, 3/45; plus others. Add: 2042 Jackson Ave, Ogden, UT 84401.

MONSON, SAMUEL CHRISTIAN, English. See Volume III, Foreign Languages, Linguistics & Philology.

MONTAGUE, GENE BRYAN, b. Santa Ana, Calif, Oct, 27, 28; m. 50; c. 4. LITERATURE. B.A, Cent. Wash. State Col, 50; M.A, Univ. Tex, 52, univ. fel. for stud. at Fla. State Univ, 52-53, scholar, 53 & 54, Ph.D.(lit), 57; dipl, Episcopal Theol. Sch, 67. Instr. ENG, Univ. Tex, 55-57; from instr. to assoc. prof, Ariz. State Univ, 57-68; PROF, UNIV. DETROIT, 67-, CHMN. DEPT, 70- Vis. prof, Cent. Wash. State Col, summer 61; lectr, Mass. Inst. Technol, 68-73. MLA. Nineteenth century British and American literature; literary criticism. Publ: Co-auth, Colloquium, Little, 62; co-ed, The experience of literature, 66, 2nd ed, 70, Man: paradox and promise, 72 & co-auth, Guide to American English, 5th ed, 72, Prentice-Hall; Poetry and a principle, Lippincott, 72; Melville's battle-pieces, Tex. Stud. Lit. & Lang, 56; A nowhere that goes somewhere, Col. Compos. & Commun. J, 62; Dylan Thomas and Nightwood, Sewanee Rev, 68. Add: Dept. of English, University of Detroit, Detroit, MI 48221.

MONTEIRO, GEORGE, b. Cumberland, R.I, May 23, 32; m. 58; c. 3. ENGLISH. A.B, Brown Univ, 54, Ph.D.(Eng), 64; A.M, Columbia Univ, 56. Instr. ENG, BROWN UNIV, 61-65, asst. prof, 65-68, assoc. prof, 68-72, PROF, 72-, co-chmn. Am. civilization, 71-73. Fulbright lectr. Am. lit, Univ. São Paulo, 69-70. MLA; Am. Folklore Soc. English and American literature; American studies; folklore. Publ: Henry James and John Hay: the record of a friendship, Brown Univ, 65; Poems (1890-1896), by Emily Dickinson, Scholars' Facsimiles, 67; co-ed, The scarlet letter, Chandler, 68; auth, Redemption through nature: a recurring theme in Thoreau, Frost and Richard Wilbur, Am. Quart, winter 68; The logic beneath the open boat, Georgia Rev, fall 72; The limits of professionalism: a sociological approach to Faulkner, Fitzgerald and Hemingway, Criticism, spring 73; plus others. Add: Dept. of English, Brown University, Providence, RI 02912.

MONTESI, ALBERT JOSEPH, b. Memphis, Tenn, Jan. 10, 21. ENGLISH. B.S, Northwest. Univ, 49; M.A, Univ. Mich, 50; grant-in-aid, Pa. State Univ, 54-55, Ph.D.(Eng), 55. Instr. Eng. compos, Pa. State Univ, 52-55; asst. prof. ENG, The Citadel, 55-57; ST. LOUIS UNIV, 55-62, assoc. prof, 62-71, PROF, 71- Am. Learned Soc. grant-in-aid, 61-62; summer vis. prof, Wesleyan Univ, 64; State Univ. N.Y. Buffalo, 68. U.S.A.A.F, 42-46. MLA; NCTE. Contemporary letters; American literature; English decadent period. Publ: Micrograms, Maryhurst Press, 70; The letters of Walt Whitman, Manuscripta, spring 63; Essays on Fabliau, surrealism, Fable, Parnassianism, Gongorism, In: New Cath. Encycl, World Publ, 67; Huey Long and the Southern Review, J. Mod. Lit, 6/73; plus others. Add: 22 Benton Pl, St. Louis, MO 63104.

MONTGOMERY, ALLENE DOROTHY, b. Mercer Co, Pa, Mar. 29, 06. DRAMA. A.B, Muskingum Col, 28; A.M, Univ. Mich, 32; N.Y. Univ, 37; Palmer scholar, Boston Univ, 40-41. Head dept. speech, debate, radio & drama, High Sch, Pa, 30-47;from asst. prof. to assoc. prof. SPEECH, CAPITAL UNIV, 47-63, PROF, 63-, DIR. DRAMA, 47- Asst. to dean women, Boston Univ, 40-41; outstanding prof. & counsel. award, Capital Univ, 65. Am. Theatre Asn. Relationship of directing in drama to television and radio; plays; monologues. Add: Dept. of Speech, Capital University, Columbus, OH 43209.

MONTGOMERY, KIRT EARL, b. Oshkosh, Wis, May 3, 07. SPEECH. A.B, Carroll Col, 30; fel, Inst. Econ. Res, 32-33; A.M, Northwest. Univ, 39, Ph.D, 48. Teaching fel, Northwest. Univ, 38-41; from asst. prof. to assoc. prof. SPEECH, UNIV. ORE, 46-71, EMER. ASSOC. PROF, 71- Consult. esophageal speech, Univ. Miami Med. Sch, summer 57. Speech Commun. Asn. Public speaking and rhetoric; speeches illustrating rhetorical principles; status of high school debating in the West. Publ: Criticizing speeches, Speech Teacher, 9/57. Add: 129 Elkay Dr, Eugene, OR 97404.

MONTGOMERY, LYNA LEE, b. Granby, Mo, Oct. 18, 25. ENGLISH LITERATURE. B.A, Southwest Mo. State Col, 64; M.A, Univ. Ark, 64, Ph.D. (Eng), 67. Asst. prof. ENG, UNIV. ARK, FAYETTEVILLE, 66-70, ASSOC. PROF, 70- Am. Soc. 18th Century Stud; S-Cent. Mod. Lang. Asn. Eighteenth-century and 19th-century English literature. Publ: The Phoenix: its use as a literary device from the seventeenth century to the twentieth century, D.H. Lawrence Rev, fall 72. Add: Dept. of English, University of Arkansas, Fayetteville, AR 72701.

MONTGOMERY, MARGARET BARRON, b. Clarendon, Tex, June 8, 04; m. 27. ENGLISH. B.A, South. Methodist Univ, 24, M.A, 26; Sorbonne, 27; Univ. London, 62; Oxford, 64. Instr. Eng, Texarkana Col, 57-62, prof. Eng. & chmn. div. lang. arts, 62-73; WRITER, 73- MLA; Vergilian Soc; NCTE. Greek epic; Dante; linguistics. Add: 2121 Glendale St, Texarkana, AR 75501.

MONTGOMERY, MARION, b. Upson Co, Ga, Apr. 16, 25; m. 51; c. 5. MODERN LITERATURE. A.B, Univ. Ga, 50, M.A, 52; State Univ, Iowa, 56-58. Asst. dir. univ. press, UNIV. GA, 50-52, instr. ENG, 54-60, asst. prof, 60-67, assoc. prof, 67-70, PROF, 70- Managing ed, West. Rev, 57-58; writer-in-residence, Converse Col, summer 63. Saxton Mem. Trust Award, Harper & Bros, 60. Contemporary literature, especially that of the South. Publ: Dry lightning, Univ. Nebr, 60; The wandering of desire, Harper & Bros, 62; Darrell, Doubleday, 64; Stones from the rubble, Argus Bks, 65; Ye olde bluebird, New Col, 67; The gull and other Georgia scenes, 69, T.S. Eliot: an essay on The American Magus, 70 & The reflective journey toward order: essays on Dante, Wordsworth, Eliot and others, 73, Univ. Ga; Ezra Pound: a critical essay, Eerdmans, 70; Fugitive, Harper, 74. Add: Dept. of English, University of Georgia, Athens, GA 30602.

MONTGOMERY, REID HOOD, b. Antreville, S.C, Nov. 27, 09; m. 35; c. 2. JOURNALISM. A.B, Wofford Col, 30; A.M, Univ. S.C, 38; Ph.D, N.Y. Univ, 55. Dir. pub. relat, Pub. Schs, Columbia, S.C, 40-43; asst. supt. Schs, Sumter, 43-45; prof. jour, head dept. & dir, inform, Winthrop Col, 46-55; prof. jour, Fla. State Univ, 55-65, dir. stud. publs, 55-65, dir. univ. union, 62-65; PROF. JOUR, UNIV. S.C, 65-; MGR. S.C. PRESS ASN, 65- Asst. city ed, State, Columbia, S.C, 42-43; news ed, Sumter Daily Item, 46; consult. & critic, Ala. Scholastic Press Asn, 61, 62; New Eng. Press Asn, 71, 72; Ind. Col. Press Asn, 73; dir, Carolinas Ed. Conf, Winthrop Col, 61-63; ed, South. Stud. Leader, 65-67; ed, S.C. Newspaper, 66-; adv, S.C. Col. Press Asn, 66- U.S.M.C, 44-45, Maj. Asn. Educ. Jour; Nat. Counc. Col. Publ. Adv. (pres, 69-71). Libel laws and South Carolina newspapers. Add: School of Journalism, University of South Carolina, Columbia, SC 29208.

MONTGOMERY, ROBERT LANGFORD, JR, b. Hartford, Conn, June 15, 27; m. 51; c. 3. ENGLISH. A.B, Harvard, 50, A.M, 51, Ph.D, 56; Fulbright fel, France, 51-52. Instr. Eng, Univ. Tex, 56-59, asst. prof, 59-61, assoc. prof, 61-66; vis. prof, Williams Col, 66-67; PROF. ENG. & COMP. LIT, UNIV. CALIF, IRVINE, 67- Summers, Folger Libr. fel, 59; Huntington Libr. fel, 61. U.S.N, 45-46. MLA; Dante Soc. Am; Mod. Humanities Res. Asn; Renaissance Soc. Am. English Renaissance poetry; Renaissance literary criticism. Publ: Symmetry and sense: the poetry of Sir Philip Sidney, Univ. Tex, 62; Shakespeare's gaudy: the method of The rape of Lucrece, In: Stud. in honor of Dewitt T. Starnes, Univ. Tex, 67; The dimensions of time in Richard II, Shakespeare Stud, IV, 69; William Caxton and the beginnings of Tudor critical thought, Huntington Libr. Quart, 73; plus two others. Add: Dept. of English & Comparative Literature, University of California, Irvine, CA 92664.

MOOD, ROBERT GIBBS, b. Dallas, Tex, May 19, 99; m. 31; c. 1. ENGLISH LITERATURE. A.B,Southwest. Univ.(Tex), 20; A.M, Columbia Univ, 25; Ph.D, Univ. Ill, 38. Instr. ENG, South. Methodist Univ, 21-23, asst. prof, 24-27; asst, Univ. Ill, 28-36; assoc. prof, WICHITA STATE UNIV, 36-41, prof, 41-69, head dept, 49-59, EMER. PROF, 69- Lectr. Eng, Sacred Heart Col.(Kans), 69-70. MLA. Add: 1603 Vassar, Wichita, KS 67208.

MOODIE, CLARA LEE REDWOOD, b. Atlanta, Ga, Nov. 22, 34. ENGLISH, EDUCATION. B.A, Emory Univ, 56; fel, Univ. Ga, summer 56; M.A, Univ. Colo, Boulder, 61; Ph.D.(Eng. & educ), Univ. Mich, Ann Arbor, 71. Teacher, North Fulton High Sch, Atlanta, Ga, 56-60; Baseline Jr. High Sch, Boulder, Colo, 60-61; instr. Eng. lang. & lit, East. Mich. Univ, 61-71; ASST. PROF. AM. LIT. & DIR. COMMUNITY COL. ENG. PROG, CENT. MICH. UNIV, 71- MLA; NCTE; Conf. Eng. Educ; Conf. Col. Compos. & Commun; Am. Asn. Community & Jr. Col. Teacher training for community colleges; community college movement in America; American literature, 1920-1930. Publ: The community college is where the action is!, Clearinghouse Reading & Commun. Skills, 72. Add: Community College English Program, Central Michigan University, Mt. Pleasant, MI 48859.

MOODY, PETER RICHARD, b. Dillon, S.C, Apr. 5, 17; m. 42; c. 5. ENGLISH. B.A, Wofford Col, 37; B.S, U.S. Mil. Acad, 42; M.A, Duke Univ, 47, Ph.D.(Eng), Cambridge, 63. Assoc. prof. Eng, U.S. Mil. Acad, 48-50; prof, U.S. Air Force Acad, 54-67, assoc. dean, 65-66, v.dean, 66-67; V.PRES. INSTR, EAST. ILL. UNIV, 67- U.S.A.F, 42-67, Brig. Gen. NCTE; MLA. Add: 1548 Fourth St, Charleston, IL 61920.

MOODY, RICHARD, b. Des Moines, Iowa, Sept. 30, 11; m. 37; c. 2. SPEECH, DRAMA. A.B, Drake Univ, 32, A.M, 34; Yale, 32-33, 34-35; Nat. Theatre Conf. fel, Cornell Univ, 40-42, Ph.D, 42. Instr. speech & drama, Univ. Ill, 36-40; Cornell Univ, 41-42; asst. prof. IND. UNIV, BLOOMINGTON, 42-43, 45-51, assoc. prof, 51-55, PROF. THEATRE & DRAMA, 55- Vis. prof, Univ. Hawaii, 52; Nat Endowment for Humanities sr. fel, 73-74. U.S.N.R, 42-44, Lt. Speech Commun. Asn; Am. Theatre Asn. Negro minstrelsy; 19th century American theatre; old American plays. Publ: America takes the stage, 55 & The Astor Place riot, 58, Ind. Univ; Edwin Forrest, Knopf, 60; Dramas from the American theatre, 1762-1909, World Publ, 66; Lillian Hellman: playwright, Bobbs, 72; Uncle Tom, the theatre and Mrs. Stowe, Am. Heritage. Add: Dept. of Theatre & Drama, Indiana University, Bloomington, IN 47401.

MOONEY, HARRY JOHN, JR, b. Pittsburgh, Pa, Apr. 14, 28. ENGLISH. B.A, Univ. Pittsburgh, 48, M.A, 54, Ph.D.(Eng), 62. Instr. ENG, UNIV. PITTSBURGH, 58-62, asst. prof, 62-67, assoc. prof, 67-70, PROF, 70- MLA. Milton and seventeenth century literature. Publ: The fiction: criticism of Katherine Anne Porter, 57, James Gould Cozzens: novelist of intellect, 63 & co-auth, The shapeless god, 68, Univ. Pittsburgh; auth, Leo Tolstoy: the epic voice, Univ. Tulsa, 68. Add: Dept. of English, University of Pittsburgh, Pittsburgh, PA 15213.

MOORADIAN, KARLEN, b. Boston Mass, Mar. 25, 35. JOURNALISM, MASS COMMUNICATION. B.S, Northwestern Univ, 56, M.S, 57, Ph.D.(jour), 63. Ed-in-chief, Am. Peoples Encyclopedia, 57-58; ed-in-chief, Defense Lang. Sch, Ft. Ord, Calif, 58-60; asst. prof. JOUR, Am. Univ, 63-65; prof. lectr, Northwest. Univ, 67; asst. prof, Ball State Univ, 67-70; ASSOC. PROF, UNIV. OKLA, 70- U.S. Dept. State researcher, Int. Commun. Res. Fel, Yugoslavia, 71; head int. commun. res. sect, Ctr. Mass Media Anal, Univ. Okla, 71- U.S.A, 58-60. Int. Asn. Mass Commun. Res; Asn. Educ. Jour. History of ancient mass communication; history of art; U.S.S.R-Near East. Publ: Use of the press for revolution, 1902-1920, Armenian Digest 1/73; The mystery of movable type in Crete, Visual Lang, winter 73; Arshile Gorky: image from Armenia, Monogr. Catalog, Okla. Art Ctr, 10/73; plus others. Add: School of Journalism, University of Oklahoma, Norman, OK 73069.

MOORE, ARTHUR KEISTER, b. Carrollton, Ky, Jan. 10, 14; m. 40; c. 4. ENGLISH. A.B, Morehead State Col, 35; Univ. N C, 38, 39, 41; A.M, Univ. Ala, 41; Ph.D, Vanderbilt Univ, 43. Instr, Vanderbilt Univ, 43-44; asst. prof, Tulane Univ, 46-49; Eng, Univ. Ky, 49-51, assoc. prof, 51-54, prof, 54-69; CALLAWAY PROF. ENG. LANG. & LIT, GA. STATE UNIV, 69- Ford fel, 53-54; vis. prof, Univ. Tex, 56. Sig.C, U.S.A, 44-45. MLA; S.Atlantic Mod. Lang. Asn. English language and medieval literature; modern poetry; critical theory. Publ: Secular lyric in Middle English & Frontier mind, Univ. Ky; Contestable concepts of literary theory, La. State Univ, 73. Add: Dept. of English, Georgia State University, Atlanta, GA 30303.

MOORE, DON DICK, b. Jackson, Tenn, May 13, 34; m. 58; c. 2. ENGLISH RENAISSANCE DRAMA. B.A, Vanderbilt Univ, 56, M.A, 57; Ph.D.(Eng), Tulane Univ, 63. Instr. ENG, Va. Polytech. Inst, 57-59; Dillard Univ, 62-63; LA. STATE UNIV, BATON ROUGE, 63-64, asst. prof, 64-66, ASSOC. PROF, 66- La. State Univ. res. counc. grant, Folger Libr, summer 67. Standard Oil Award Excellence in Teaching, 72. MLA; S.Cent. Mod. Lang. Asn. Elizabethan and Jacobean drama. Publ: John Webster and his critics, La. State Univ, 66; The Duchess of Malfi by Webster and Horne, In: Essays in honor of E.L. Marilla, La. State Univ, 70; The Merchant of Venice, Educ. Theatre J, 8/71; John Webster, In: Recent studies in Renaissance drama, Univ. Nebr, 74; plus others. Add: Dept. of English, Louisiana State University, Baton Rouge, LA 70803.

MOORE, DONALD EDWIN, b. Los Angeles, Calif, Aug. 8, 17; m. 42; c. 4. ENGLISH, EDUCATION. A.B, Univ. Calif, Los Angeles, 40, M.A, 47, Ed.D, 57. Teacher, John Adams Jr. High Sch, 45-51; Santa Monica High Sch, 51-52 & 53-57; instr. Eng, Santa Monica City Col, 52-53; asst. prof. educ, Sacramento State Col, 57-59; EDUC. & ENG, SOUTH. ORE. COL, 59-61, assoc. prof, 61-66, PROF, 66-, dir, NDEA Inst. Advan. Stud. Eng, summer 68. NCTE. History and philosophy of education; historical linguistics; regional dialects of Great Britain and the United States. Publ: Co-auth, Handbook for student teachers, 63 & Handbook for supervising teachers, 63, South. Ore. Col; auth, Wanted: a new humanism, Phi Delta Kappan, 4/58; co-auth, Point of view: language, In: Guide for Oregon secondary teachers of English, Ore. State Dept. Educ, 66. Add: Dept. of English, Southern Oregon College, Ashland, OR 97520.

MOORE, DWAIN EARL, b. Rossville, Ind, Sept. 6, 15; m. 45; c. 4. SPEECH. A.B, Wabash Col, 38; A.M, Boston Univ, 39; Ph.D, Univ. Ill, 55; summers, Columbia Univ, Univ. Mich. Teacher, High Sch, 40-52; from asst. prof. to PROF. SPEECH, CALIF. STATE UNIV, SACRAMENTO, 54- Consult, Aerojet-Gen. Corp, 60-66; Calif. State Personnel Bd, 60-; instr, Calif. Highway Patrol, 61-72. U.S.A.A.F, 42-45. Speech Commun. Asn. Rhetoric and public address. Publ: The history of Sacramento State College, Assoc. Stud. Sacramento State Col, 67; John Morley: critic of public address; Quart. J. Speech, 4/58; Morley's concepts of the nature and function of rhetoric, West. Speech, fall 68. Add: 2751 Huntington Rd, Sacramento, CA 95825.

MOORE, EDWARD MUMFORD, b. Macon, Ga, Jan. 19, 40; m. 64; c. 2. ENGLISH. B.A, Univ. of the South, 62; Fulbright scholar, Univ. Lille, 62-63; Woodrow Wilson fel. & M.A, Harvard, 64, Ph.D.(Eng), 68. Instr. ENG, GRINNELL COL, 67-68, asst. prof, 68-72, ASSOC. PROF, 72- Nat. Endowment for Humanities summer grant, 70. MLA. Shakespeare; modern literature; Renaissance literature. Publ: Ed, Uncollected prefaces by Harley Granville-Barker, 74; auth, Some recent southern things, Sewanee Rev, 70; William Poel, Shakespeare Quart, 72. Add: Dept. of English, Grinnell College, Grinnell, IA 50112.

MOORE, FRANK HARPER, b. Scranton, Pa, July 14, 20; m. 49; c. 3. ENGLISH LITERATURE. A.B, Univ. Fla, 43; M.A, Univ. N.C, 48, fel, 52, Ph.D, 53. Instr. ENG, Univ. Tenn, 53-55; N.C. STATE UNIV, 55-56, asst. prof, 56-62, assoc. prof, 62-67, PROF, 67-, Fac. Res. & Prof. Develop. Fund, grant, 62. U.S.N.R, 43-46, Lt.(jg). S.Atlantic Mod. Lang. Asn; MLA. Seventeenth century English literature; Milton. Publ: The nobler pleasure; Dryden's comedy in theory and practice, Univ. N.C, 63. Add: Dept. of English, North Carolina State University, Raleigh, NC 27607.

MOORE, HAMILTON FRAZIER, b. East Point, Ga, June 7, 13, m. 50; c. 1. ADVERTISING, MASS COMMUNICATIONS. A.B, Univ. Ga, 34, M.A, 35; Ph.D.(commun), Univ. Ill, Urbana, 65. Instr. Eng, Univ. Ga, 35-36, head news bur, 36-38, dir, Univ. Ga. Press, 38-50; ed, Tupper & Love Publ. Co, Atlanta, 50-54; copywriter, Liller, Neal, Battle & Lindsay, Atlanta, 54-55; asst. prof. JOUR, UNIV. GA, 55-58, assoc. prof, 58-64, PROF, 64- Consult. ed, Tupper & Love, Inc. & David McKay, Inc, 55-60; head advert-pub. relat. sequence, Univ. Ga, 55-; vis. prof. advert, Mich. State Univ, 68. U.S.C.G.R, 42-46, Capt. Am. Acad. Advert; Asn. Educ. in Jour.(pres. pub. relat. div, 72-74); Pub. Relat. Soc. Am.(ed. coord. counc, 72-74). Communications research methods; advertising effectiveness; public opinion and public relations. Publ: Charles Colcock Jones, Jr, romanticist, Univ. Ga, 35; An evaluation of the art and techniques of corporate public relations, Univ. Ill, 65; co-auth, Public relations: principles, cases and problems, R.D. Irwin, 73; co-auth, Advertising education: an appraisement, J. Advert, 73. Add: School of Journalism, Advertising-Public Relations Sequence, University of Georgia, Athens, GA 30602.

MOORE, HAROLD EUGENE, b. Montrose, Colo, Nov. 29, 23; m. 49; c. 3. ENGLISH. A.M, Univ. Chicago, 51; Ph.D.(Eng), Univ. Iowa, 60. Teaching asst, Univ, Iowa, 51-54; instr. ENG, Univ. Colo, 54-58; UNIV. UTAH, 58-60, asst. prof, 60-65, assoc. prof, 65-70, PROF, 70-, DIR. CREATIVE WRITING PROG, 70- U.S.N, 43-46, Lt.(jg). Modern American literature; the existential novel: fiction writing. Publ: My father's money, Tex. Quart, autumn 62; An American dilemma, Colo. Quart, autumn 66; Incident at Billy Springs, Esquire, 5/67; plus others. Add: Dept. of English, University of Utah, Salt Lake City, UT 84112.

MOORE, HARRY T, b. Oakland, Calif, Aug. 2, 08; m. 46; c. 2. HUMANITIES. Ph.B, Univ. Chicago, 34; M.A, Northwest. Univ, 42; Ph.D, Boston Univ, 51. Instr, Ill. Inst. Tech, 40-41; Northwest. Univ, 41-42; lectr, Air Univ, 46-47; assoc. prof. hist. & lit. & chmn. dept, Babson Inst, 47-57; res. prof. ENG, South. Ill, Univ, 57-62; prof, Univ. Colo, 62-63; RES. PROF SOUTH. ILL. UNIV, 63- Founding ed, Air Univ. Quart. Rev, 46; res. prof, Columbia Univ. & N.Y. Univ, summer 61. U.S.A.F, 42-47, Lt. Col. PEN Club; MLA; fel. Royal Soc. Lit. U.K; Col. Eng. Asn.(pres, 61). Seventeenth and 20th century England. Publ: Life and works of D.H. Lawrence, Twayne & Allen & Unwin, London, 51; The intelligent heart, Farrar Straus & Heinemann, 55; ed, Collected letters of D.H. Lawrence, Heinemann-Viking, 62; auth, Twentieth century French literature, South. Ill. Univ, Dell & Heinemann, 66; Twentieth century German literature, Basic Bks. & Heinemann, London, 67; The priest of love, Farrar, Straus, 73 & Heinemann, 74; Henry James and his world, Thames & Hudson, London, 74. Add: 922 S. Division, Carterville, IL 62918.

MOORE, HELEN JEAN, b. Falls Creek, Pa, div; c. 1. ENGLISH, LIBRARY SCIENCE. B.A, Univ. Pa, 38; M.A, Univ. Pittsburgh, 41, Ph.D.(Eng), 52; M.L.S, Carnegie Inst. Technol, 58. Teacher pub. schs, Pa, 38-43; instr. Eng, Univ. Pittsburgh, 41-43, 45-52, bibliogr. libr. sci, 55-62; instr. Eng, Newcomb Col, Tulane Univ, 43-44; Chatham Col, 44-45; PROF. ENG. & DIR. LIBR, POINT PARK COL, PA, 62- Indexer & ed. consult, Univ. Pittsburgh Press, 58-; lectr, Carnegie Libr. Sch, Carnegie Inst. Technol, 60-62; consult, Prentice-Hall Publ, 67-68; off. exec. counc, Pittsburgh Regional Libr. Ctr, 69- Am. Libr. Asn; MLA. American literary criticism; history of printing; history of the English novel. Publ: Library cooperation in Pittsburgh, Libr. Trends, 62; Friends of time and companions on the way, book column in Pa. Libr. Asn. Bull, 65-69. Add: Point Park College Library, 201 Wood St, Pittsburgh, PA 15222.

MOORE, HOWARD KIMBALL, b. Lynn, Mass, May 28, 16; m. 41; c. 2. ENGLISH & AMERICAN LITERATURE. A.B, Boston Univ, 39, A.M, 40, Ph.D. (Eng), 50; M.S.L.S, Simmons Col, 70. Teaching fel. ENG, Col. Lib. Arts, Boston Univ, 40-42; asst. prof, Clark Univ, 46-54; PROF, LOWELL TECHNOL. INST, 54- A.U.S, 42-45. MLA; Am. Soc. Engineering Educ; Am. Soc. Inform. Sci. Nineteenth century American literature. Publ: Exploding wires, Plenum, Vol. 1, 59, Vol 2, 62, Vol. 3, 64 & Vol. 4, 68. Add: Dept. of Languages & Literature, Lowell Technological Institute, Lowell, MA 01854.

MOORE, JACK BAILEY, b. Newark, N.J, Oct. 23, 33; m. 56; c. 4. AMERICAN LITERATURE. A.B, Drew Univ, 55; M.A, Columbia Univ, 56; Ph.D. (Eng), Univ. N.C, Chapel Hill, 63. Instr. Eng, W.Va. Univ, 56-58; asst. instr, Univ.N.C, 58-60; instr, Washington & Lee Univ, 60-62; asst. prof, UNIV. S.FLA, 62-64, assoc. prof, 64-69, PROF. AM. LIT, 69- Am. Philos. Soc. res. grant, summers 66, 71; Fulbright lectr, Sierra Leone, 68-69; Danforth fel, 68-; res. affil, Inst. African Stud, Univ.Ghana, 71. S.Atlantic Mod. Lang. Asn; Popular Cult. Asn; AAUP. American literature; popular culture; African-Afro-American studies. Publ: The literature of early America, C.E. Merrill, 67; Guide to Last of the Mohicans, Barnes & Noble, 69; Maxwell Bodenheim, Twayne, 70; Don't die, Jeff Chandler, Esquire, 4/66; The first Narrative of the unpardonable sin, Discourse, summer 67; Slave castles by the sea, Colo. Quart, autumn 72; plus others. Add: Dept. of English, University of South Florida, Tampa, FL 33620.

MOORE, JOHN EUGENE, b. Kalamazoo, Mich, May 17, 13. AMERICAN LITERATURE. A.B, Univ. Mich, 36, A.M, 37. Instr.ENG, Pa. State Col, 37-39; West. Mich. Col, 39-42; from instr. to prof, UNIV. MONT, 43-72, EMER. PROF, 72- Ford fel, 52-53. Creative writing; readings for an air age; exposition of ideas. Publ: Co-auth, Writing through revision, Harcourt, 64; auth, By Selkirk's Lake and other poems, Ithaca House, 72. Add: 314 Connell Ave, Missoula, MT 59801.

MOORE, JOHN REES, b. Washington, D.C, Oct. 15, 18; m. 54; c. 2. ENGLISH LITERATURE. B.A, Reed Col, 40; M.A, Harvard, 42; Ph.D, Columbia Univ, 57. Instr. ENG, Univ. Ga, 46; Carnegie Inst. Technol, 47; Lehigh Univ, 47-50; lectr, sch. gen. stud, Columbia Univ, 54-57; asst. prof, HOLLINS COL, 57-61, assoc. prof, 61-68, PROF, 68-, CHMN. DEPT, 71- Researcher on Marlowe, Harvard, 41-42; South. fel. & Danforth Found. study grant, Ireland, summer 60; researcher on W.B. Yeats, Dublin, 62-63; co-ed, Hollins Critic, 64-71, ed, 71- U.S.A.A.F, 42-45, Sgt. MLA; Am. Comt. Irish Stud. (v.pres, 69-72, pres, 72-); Asn. Depts. Eng. Modern poetry and drama; Renaissance and 17th century English literature; modern Irish literature. Publ: Co-auth, The idea of an American novel, Crowell, 61; auth, Masks of love and death, Cornell Univ, 71; co-ed, The sounder few, Univ. Ga, 71; auth, You must go home again: Robert Penn Warren, South. Rev, spring 68; The Janus face: Yeats' Player queen, Sewanee Rev, fall 68; contrib, Sunshine and the moon's delight, Colin Smythe, Eng, 72; plus others. Add: Dept. of English, Hollins College, VA 24020.

MOORE, LESTER LEE, b. Blackshear, Ga, July 14, 24. SPEECH, DRAMATIC ARTS. B.A, Univ. Miami, 48; M.A, Columbia Univ, 49, Ed.D.(theatre), 66. Instr. Eng. & humanities, Fla. State Univ, 49-52; dramatic art & speech, RUTGERS UNIV, NEWARK, 52-56, asst. prof, 56-66, assoc. prof. THEATRE ART & SPEECH, 66-69, PROF, 69-, CHMN. DEPT, 52-66, 69-. Assoc. dir, Parkway Playhouse & Art Ctr, 52-; dir, N.C. Tercentennial Prod, Prince of Parthia, 63; regional dir. pageant & mem. cent. steering & planning comt, N.J. Tercentennial Pageant, 64; dir. of over 150 theatre productions. U.S.A, 42-46. Speech Commun. Asn; Speech Asn. East. States; Japan Soc. Interpretation; Asian theatre; American theatre. Publ: Modern American poetry, Fla. State Univ, 51; Outside Broadway: a history of the professional theater in Newark, New Jersey to 1867, Scarecrow, 70; On the tragic view, Parkway Playbill, 63; The several languages of the classic Hindu theatre, J. Speech Asn. N.J, 72. Add: Dept. of Theatre Art & Speech, Rutgers University, Newark, NJ 07102.

MOORE, LITTLETON HUGH, b. Atlanta, Ga, Mar. 24, 35; m. 59; c. 2. ENGLISH. B.A, Emory Univ, 57, M.A, 58, Ph.D.(Eng), 64. Instr. ENG, Ga. Inst. Technol, 60-63; Emory Univ, 63-64; asst. prof, GA. INST. TECHNOL, 64-67, assoc. prof, 67-68, PROF, 68-, res. found. grant, summer 67. Nat. Endowment for Humanities res. fel, 69, summer sem, Univ. Calif, Berkeley, 73. MLA; S.Atlantic Mod. Lang. Asn; Am. Ornithol. Union; Nat. Audubon Soc. Study of early American explorers and nature writers; modern American and English literature. Publ: Robert Penn Warren and history, Mouton, The Hague, 68; co-auth, A concise handbook of English composition, Prentice-Hall, 72; auth, Mrs. Hirsch and Mrs. Bell in The killers, Mod. Fiction Stud, winter 65; Hawthorne's ideal artist, Stud. Short Fiction, winter 65; Siegfried Sassoon and Georgian realism, 20th Century Lit, 1/69. Add: Dept. of English, Georgia Institute of Technology, Atlanta, GA 30332.

MOORE, NANCY, b. Chicago, Ill, May 28, 12. ENGLISH. A.B, Butler Univ, 33, A.M, 34; Columbia Univ, 34-37. Instr. ENG, BUTLER UNIV, 37-40, asst. prof, 40-66, assoc. prof, 66-69, DEMIA BUTLER PROF, 69-, chmn. freshman Eng, 40-56. Chmn. bd. dir, Winona Mem. Hosp, 73. Baxter award distinguished teaching, Butler Univ, 63, Butler Medal, 68. MLA; Midwest Mod. Lang. Asn; Johnson Soc. London; Am. Soc. 18th Century Stud. Philosophical influences in the 18th century and early romantic period; Swift and Johnson; Dylan Thomas. Publ: Definitions, In: Dictionary of world literature, Philos. Libr, 43; David Hartley, Hibbert J, 49. Add: 3801 N. Meridian St, Indianapolis, IN 46208.

MOORE, NATHAN, b. Trinidad, W.I, June 26, 31; m. 67. ENGLISH. Dipl. lib. arts, Caribbean Union Col.(Trinidad), 58; B.A, Rockford Col, 63; M.A, Carleton Univ, 65; Ph.D.(Eng), Univ. B.C, 72. Teacher Eng. & social stud, Barrier High Sch, B.C, 66-67; ASSOC. PROF. ENG, WALLA WALLA COL, 67- Sessional lectr, Carleton Univ, summers 64-65. Am. Soc. 18th Century Stud; MLA. Hymnody in the 18th century; enthusiasm in England from the 16th to the 18th centuries. Add: Dept. of English, Walla Walla College, College Place, WA 99324.

MOORE, RAYBURN SABATZKY, b. Helena, Ark, May 26, 20; m. 47; c. 2. ENGLISH. B.A, Vanderbilt Univ, 42, M.A, 47; Ph.D.(Eng), Duke Univ, 56. Res. asst, Duke Univ, 52, asst, 52-54; asst. prof. ENG, Hendrix Col, 54-55; assoc. prof, 55-58, prof, 58-59; assoc. prof, UNIV. GA, 59-65, PROF, 65-, dir. grad. stud. Eng, 64-69. Summer vis. scholar grants, Grad. Sch, Duke Univ, 58 & 64; mem. bibliog. comt, Lit. & Soc. Sect, MLA, 61-; chmn, S.Atlantic Grad. Eng. Group, 71-72. Adj.Gen.C, U.S.A, 42-46; Res, 46-55, Capt. MLA; Am. Stud. Asn; South. Hist. Asn; S.Atlantic Mod. Lang. Asn. (secy, Am. lit. sect, 66-67, chmn, 67-68); Soc. Stud. South. Lit. Southern literature since 1820: American literary magazines, 1865-1890; 19th century American realism. Publ: Constance Fenimore Woolson, 63 & Paul Hamilton Hayne, 72, Twayne; ed, For the major and selected short stories of Constance Fenimore Woolson, Col. & Univ, 67; auth, Don Joaquin, a forgotten story by George W. Cable, Am. Lit, 11/54; The full light of a higher criticism, S.Atlantic Quart, winter 64; The Old South and the New: Paul Hamilton Hayne and Maurice Thompson, South. Lit. J, 12/72; plus others. Add: Dept. of English, University of Georgia, Athens, GA 30602.

MOORE, ROBERT ETHERIDGE, b. Macon, Ga, Dec. 31, 20. ENGLISH LITERATURE. A.B, Wash. Col, 40; Ph.D, Yale, 43. Inst. ENG, Yale, 43-45; from asst. prof. to assoc. prof, UNIV. MINN, MINNEAPOLIS, 46-61, PROF, 61- MLA. Dr. Johnson on Fielding and Richardson; 18th century English literature, architecture and painting. Publ: Hogarth's literary relationships, Univ. Minn, 48; Henry Purcell and the Restoration theatre, Harvard, 61; Reynolds & the art of characterization, In: Studies in criticism and aesthetics, 1660-1800, Univ. Minn, 67. Add: Dept. of English, University of Minnesota, Minneapolis, MN 55455.

MOORE, ROBERT HAMILTON, b. St. Matthews, Ky, Jan. 3, 13; m. 39. ENGLISH. A.B, Ind. Univ, 34, A.M, 38; Ph.D, Univ. Ill, 48. Asst. Eng, Ind. Univ, 35-38; Univ. Ill, 38-46, instr, 46-49; assoc. prof. ENG, COMPOS, GEORGE WASHINGTON UNIV, 49-58, PROF, 58-, CHMN. COMPOS, 49-. NCTE; Conf. Col. Compos. & Commun. Freshman English; linguistics; rhetoric. Publ: Plan before you write, 50, Effective writing, 55, 59, 65, 71, Elements of composition, 60, Handbook of effective writing, 66, 71 & The research paper, 67, Holt. Add: 314 Van Buren St, Falls Church, VA 22046.

MOORE, ROBERT HENRY, b. Madisonville, Ky, Sept. 16, 40; m. 64; c. 2. AMERICAN LITERATURE & HISTORY. A.B, Davidson Col, 62; M.A, Univ. N.C, Chapel Hill, 64; Ph.D.(Eng), Univ. Wis-Madison, 70. Instr. ENG, U.S. Mil. Acad, 68-70; ASST. PROF, UNIV. MD, COLLEGE PARK, 70- Contrib-reader, Dictionary Am. Regional Eng, 68-; exec. secy, Faulkner Concordance Proj, 70-, ed, Faulkner Concordance Newslett, 72-; reviewer, Nat. Endowment for Humanities, 72; fel, Inter-Univ. Sem. Armed Forces & Soc, 73- Adj.Gen.C, 68-70, Res, 70-72, Capt. MLA; Am. Stud. Asn; Am. Civil Liberties Union. Twentieth century American language and literature; American studies; armed forces and society. Publ: Co-auth, School for soldiers, Oxford, 74; co-auth, Black puritan, William & Mary Quart, 4/67; ed, Ellison at West Point, Contemporary Lit, spring 74. Add: Dept. of English Language & Literature, University of Maryland, College Park, MD 20742.

MOORE, ROBERTA J, b. Wallingford, Vt, Apr. 19, 20. JOURNALISM. B.A, Atlantic Union Col, 48; M.A, Boston Univ, 53; Ph.D.(commun), Syracuse Univ, 68. Head dept. Eng, Union Springs Acad, N.Y, 50-51; Can. Union Col, 51-57; asst. prof, Walla Walla Col, 57-59, from assoc. prof. to prof. JOUR, 59-73, head dept, 65-73; PROF, LOMA LINDA UNIV, 73- Asn. Educ. in Jour.(mem. res. comt, mag. div, 72-). History of religious journalism; role of women in education. Publ: If winter comes, Review & Herald, 73. Add: Dept. of Communication, Loma Linda University, Riverside, CA 92505.

MOORE, STEPHEN C, b. Wilkes-Barre, Pa, May 5, 31; m. 58; c. 3. ENGLISH. A.B, N.Y. Univ, 54, M.A, 55; fel. & Ph.D(Eng), Univ. Mich, 63. Teaching fel, ENG, Univ. Mich, 58-62, instr, 62-63; Univ. Del, 63-65, asst. prof, 65-68; UNIV. SOUTH. CALIF, 68-70, ASSOC. PROF, 70- U.S.A.F, 50-52. MLA; Philol. Asn. Pac. Coast. Modern poetry; modern criticism; Anglo-American literary relations. Publ: Contemporary criticism and the end of a literary revolution, Centennial Rev, spring 71; Politics and the poetry of Robert Lowell, Georgia Rev, summer 73; Literary studies and literature: the return of history, Mich. Quart, summer 73; plus others. Add: Dept. of English, University of Southern California, Los Angeles, CA 90007.

MOORE, WILLIAM HAMILTON, b. Kansas City, Mo, June 29, 37; m. 64; c. 1. ENGLISH. B.A, Southwest. Univ.(Tex), 59; Woodrow Wilson & Danforth fels. & M.A, Harvard, 60, Woodrow Wilson fel. & Ph.D.(Eng), 63. Instr. ENG, Duke Univ, 63-65, asst. prof, 65-67; AUSTIN COL, 67-69, ASSOC. PROF, 69- MLA. The poetry of Michael Drayton; Elizabethan drama. Publ: An allusion in 1593 to The taming of the shrew, Shakespeare Quart, winter 64; Sources of Drayton's conception of Poly-Olbion, Stud. Philol, 10/68. Add: Dept. of English, Austin College, Sherman, TX 75090.

MOORMAN, CHARLES, b. Cincinnati, Ohio, May 24, 25; m. 48; c. 2. ENGLISH. B.A, Kenyon Col, 49; M.A, Tulane Univ, 51, Ph.D.(Eng), 53. Teaching fel. Eng, Tulane Univ, 49-53; asst. prof, Ala. Polytech. Inst, 53-54; assoc. prof, UNIV. SOUTH. MISS, 54-56, prof. & chmn. dept, 56-68, assoc. grad. dean, 68-69, grad. dean, 69-70, UNIV. DEAN, 70- Guggenheim fel, 60-61; Am. Counc. Learned Soc. fel, 64-65. U.S.A, 43-45. Mediaeval Acad. Am; Royal Soc. Arts. Medieval literature; literary criticism; modern literature. Publ: Arthurian triptych, Univ. Calif, 60; The book of Kyng Arthur, 65, A knyght there was, 67 & Kings and captains, 71, Univ. Ky; The precincts of felicity, Univ. Fla, 66; The Pearl-poet, Twayne, 68; plus others. Add: Box 2, Southern Station, Hattiesburg, MS 39401.

MOOSE, ROY CLIFTON, b. Catawba, N.C, Sept. 1, 22. ENGLISH LITERATURE. B.A, Univ. N.C, Chapel Hill, 49, South. Found. fel. & Ph.D.(Eng), 65; Rotary Int. fel, Oxford, 49, B.A, 53, M.A, 57. Instr. ENG, Univ. N.C, Chapel Hill, 56-57; Fla. State Univ, 57-59, asst. prof, 60-62; assoc. prof, UNIV. N.C, CHARLOTTE, 63-72, PROF, 72- Found fel, summer 67. Thomas Wolfe Award in Creative Wrting, Univ. N.C, Chapel Hill, 49. U.S.A.A.F, 42-45, 1st Lt. S.Atlantic Mod. Lang. Asn.(chmn. Eng. dept. grad. dir, 73-74); Southeast. Renaissance Conf; AAUP. Shakespeare and the English Renaissance; 17th and 18th century studies; Renaissance Drama. Publ: Ed, O. Henry in North Carolina, Univ. N.C. Libr, Chapel Hill, 57; auth, The novels of W. Somerset Maugham, Carolina Quart, 3/50; America: the fantastic fifties, Cherwell, 10/9/50; Recent North Carolina poetry, Carolina Quart, fall 56. Add: Dept. of English, University of North Carolina at Charlotte, Charlotte, NC 28223.

MORAMARCO, FRED STEPHEN, b. Brooklyn, N.Y, July 13, 38; m. 64; c. 2. AMERICAN LITERATURE & STUDIES. B.A, L.I. Univ, 64; M.A, Univ. Utah, 66, Ph.D.(Eng) & cert. Am. stud, 69. Instr. Eng, Univ. Utah, 68-69; asst. prof. LIT, SAN DIEGO STATE UNIV, 69-71, ASSOC. PROF, 71-, chmn. Am. lit. sect, 70-72. Assoc. ed, West. Humanities Rev, 67-70; Fulbright lectr. Am. lit, Cath. Univ. Sacred Heart, Milan, 73. Am. Stud. Asn; Am. Film Inst. Modern and contemporary American poetry. Publ: Edward Dahlberg, Twayne, 72; Hamilton and the historians: the economic program in retrospect, Midcontinent Am. Stud. J, spring 67; Make him a legend in his own time: writing about Edward Dahlberg, Utah Papers Lang. & Lit, 69; A gathering of poets, column in West. Humanities Rev, winter 69-; plus others. Add: Sch. of Literature, San Diego State University, 5402 College Ave, San Diego, CA 92115.

MORAN, DENNIS V, b. Bayonne, N.J, Aug. 23, 32. ENGLISH, HUMANITIES. A.B, Univ. Notre Dame, 53; B.A, Oxford, 59, Rhodes scholar & M.A, 64; Ph.D.(Eng), Stanford Univ, 68. Instr. Eng, Stanford Univ, 61-63; asst. prof. ENG. & HUMANITIES, ARIZ. STATE UNIV, 64-71, ASSOC. PROF, 71- Mem, Ariz. State Comt. Rhodes Scholar, 64- U.S.A, 53-55. Am. Asn. Rhodes Scholars; Mediaeval Acad. Am. Medieval English literature and philosophy; philology. Add: 6795 E. Bluebird Lane, Scottsdale, AZ 85251.

MORAN, RONALD WESSON, b. Philadelphia, Pa, Sept. 9, 36; m. 59; c. 2. ENGLISH. B.A, Colby Col, 58; M.A, La. State Univ, 62, Ph.D.(Eng), 66. Instr. ENG, La. State Univ, 63-66; asst. prof, UNIV. N.C, CHAPEL HILL, 66-69, ASSOC. PROF, 69-, ASST. DEAN ARTS & SCI, 72-, summer study fel, 67. Fulbright lectr. Am. lit, Univ. Wurzburg, 69-70. MLA; S.Atlantic Mod. Lang. Asn. Modern American poetry; American literature. Publ: So simply means the rain (poems), Claitor's, 65; Louis Simpson, Twayne, 72; co-auth, The emotive imagination: a new departure in American poetry, 1/67, South. Rev; auth, Meaning and value in Luke Havergal, Colby Libr. Quart, 3/67; The Octaves of E.A. Robinson, In: Appreciation of Edwin Arlington Robinson, Colby Col, 69. Add: Dept. of English, University of North Carolina, Chapel Hill, NC 27514.

MORAN, WILLIAM CHARLES, b. Huntington, W.Va, July 12, 35; m. 60; c. 2. ENGLISH. B.A, Marshall Univ, 58, M.A, 59; Ph.D.(Eng), Univ. Tenn, 64. Instr, pub. schs, Md, 60-61; ENG, Marshall Univ, 61-62; from instr. to assoc. prof, Southeast Mo. State Col, 64-67; PROF. & HEAD DEPT, BERRY COL, 67-, ACAD. DEAN, 71-, Dana distinguished prof, 68, assoc. dean, 69-71. Participant, workshops for Teachers of Eng. in Sec. Schs, 64-67; dir. NDEA Inst, 67; participant, Educ. Instr. Materials Insts, 67. U.S.A, 60, Res, 60-65. MLA; NCTE; NEA; Am. Conf. Acad. Deans; S.Atlantic Asn. Depts. Eng.(secy-treas, 69-71). Victorian poetry; English education; 19th century English novel. Add: Dept. of English, Berry College, Mt. Berry, GA 30149.

MORAVCEVICH, NICHOLAS, Comparative Literature, Slavic Studies. See Volume III, Foreign Languages, Linguistics & Philology.

MOREHEAD, BARBARA, b. Evanston, Ill, Jan. 19, 12. ENGLISH. B.S, Carnegie Inst. Technol, 33; B.A, William & Mary Col, 34; M.A, Radcliffe Col, 35; Ph.D.(Eng), Univ. Chicago, 50. Instr. ENG, Fla. State Col. Women, 39-43; Shorter Col, 45-46; Temple Univ, 46-48; Glenville State Col, 48-49; S.Dak. State Col, 50-51; Curry Col, 59-60; asst. prof, Univ. Bridgeport, 60-62; Centenary Col, 62-64; asst. prof, Monmouth Col.(N.J), 64-66; ASSOC. PROF, THIEL COL, 66- MLA; NCTE; Col. Eng. Asn; Melville Soc. Am. American literature of 19th century; Melville. Add: Dept. of English, Thiel College, Greenville, PA 16125.

MOREHOUSE, WILLIAM MANTLE, b. Battle Creek, Mich, Mar. 14, 33; m. 59; c. 3. SPEECH COMMUNICATION, THEATRE. B.S, Purdue Univ, West Lafayette, 54, M.S, 58, Ph.D.(speech commun), 67. CHMN. DEPT. SPEECH & THEATRE, Radford Col, 58-68; WEST CHESTER STATE COL, 68- Consult, Carroll County Cult. Exchange Title III Proj, 67. Transp.C, U.S.A, 54-56, 1st Lt. Am. Theatre Asn; Speech Commun. Asn; Am. Arbit. Asn.(arbitrator, 69-). Publ: Butter your bread, Radford J, spring 59; auth. & ed, A look at love (dramatic reading), produced 62 & Tears of Mary (dramatic reading), produced 63; auth, Which of us (play), produced 64; Punch and Judy (play), produced 67. Add: Dept. of Speech & Theatre, West Chester State College, West Chester, PA 19380.

MORGAN, FRANK, JR, b. West, Miss, Jan. 14, 31; m. 53. ENGLISH. B.A, Miss. Col, 54; M.A, Univ. Miss, 57, Ph.D.(Eng), 66. Instr. Eng, Memphis State Univ, 58-61, 64-65; asst. prof, NORTHEAST LA. UNIV, 65-67, assoc. prof, dir. freshman Eng. & adminr. col. prog. superior high sch. stud, 67-68, PROF. ENG, 72-, DEAN COL. LIB. ARTS, 68- S.Cent. Mod. Lang. Asn; Am. Conf. Acad. Deans. Eighteenth century English aesthetics and rhetoric; restoration drama. Publ: Adam Smith and belles lettres, Univ. Microfilms, 67. Add: College of Liberal Arts, Northeast Louisiana University, Monroe, LA 71201.

MORGAN, GERALD, b. London, U.K, May 8, 25; Can. citizen; m. 57; c. 2. ENGLISH, PHILOSOPHY. B.A, Loyola Col.(Que), 51; M.A, Univ. Montreal, 55, M.A, 59, Ph.D.(Eng), 62. Lectr. lit. & lang, Royal Mil. Col.(Que), 55-57, lang. & philos, 57-60, asst. prof, 60-63, PROF. & HEAD DEPT, 63-65; LIT. & PHILOS, ROYAL ROADS MIL. COL, VICTORIA, 65- Mem. ed. comt, Can. Asn. Slavists, 67; mem. exec. comt, Humanities Research Counc. Can, 70-72; Can. Counc. leave fel, 71-72. R.N, 40-46, 2nd Off. Humanities Asn. Can.(pres, 69-71); Can. Asn. Slavists; Mod. Humanities Res. Asn; Int. Asn. Univ. Prof. Eng. Conrad and maritime history; analogy versus metaphor in literature and science; contingent being in Aristotle's Physics and Poetics. Publ: Co-auth, Of several branches, Part III, Univ. Toronto, 68; auth, Conrad, Madach et Calderon, Etudes Slaves et Est-Europeennes, spring 61; Narcissus afloat: myth and symbol in Conrad, autumn 64 & Harlequin Faustus: Marlowe's comedy of hell, spring 67, Humanities Asn. Bull. Add: Dept. of English, Royal Roads Military College, Victoria, B.C, Can.

MORGAN, JUNE J, b. Elkader, Iowa, Apr. 3, 00; wid. ENGLISH. B.A, State Univ. Iowa, 21, M.A, 25, Ph.D, 28. Instr. English, State Univ. Iowa, 28-29; prof. & head dept, Sterling Col, 29-30; assoc. prof, KANS. STATE TEACHERS COL, 30-32, part-time teacher & in charge correspondence work in English, 54-60, asst. prof. ENGLISH, 60-62, assoc. prof, 62-67, prof, 67-70, EMER. PROF, 70- Prof. Eng. & head dept, Col. Emporia, 70-73. MLA; Col. Eng. Asn; NCTE; Int. Arthurian Soc; Am. Comp. Lit. Asn; Shakespeare Asn. Am. Renaissance; Middle English. Publ: Toward a textual study of The wit of a woman, Emporia State Res. Stud, 9/66. Add: P.O. Box 602, Emporia, KS 66801.

MORGAN, KENNETH SCOTT, b. Ann Arbor, Mich, Apr. 27, 40. ENGLISH. B.A, Haverford Col, 62; Ph.D.(Eng), Princeton, 66. Instr. ENG, Bryn Mawr Col, 66-67, lectr, 67-68; asst. prof, UNIV. NEBR, LINCOLN, 68-72, ASSOC. PROF, 72- MLA; Renaissance Soc. Am. Spenser; Shakespeare; literary theory. Add: Dept. of English, University of Nebraska, Lincoln, NE 68510.

MORGAN, LEE, b. El Dorado, Ark, Sept. 20, 26; m. 60; c. 6. ENGLISH. B.A, Hendrix Col, 49; M.A, Univ. Tenn, 50; Ph.D.(Eng), Univ. Fla, 54. Teacher, High Sch, Ark, 50-51; asst. prof. ENG, CENTENARY COL, 54-57, assoc. prof, 57-63, PROF, 63-, CHMN. DEPT, 66- Vis. fac, Harvard-Yale-Columbia Univ. Intensive Summer Stud. Prog, 69; mem. La. state adv. comt, U.S. Comn. Civil Rights, 70- U.S.A, 45-46. MLA; Col. Eng. Asn.(interim ed, 73-); AAUP. Eighteenth century English literature, especially Samuel Johnson and his circle. Publ: Co-auth, A handbook of critical approaches to literature, 66 & co-ed, Mandala: literature for critical analysis, 70, Harper; auth, Boswell's portrait of Goldsmith, Tenn. Stud. Lit, 61. Add: 236 Gladstone Blvd, Shreveport, LA 71104.

MORGAN, MARY LOUIS, O.S.U, b. Louisville, Ky, Jan. 20, 96. ENGLISH LITERATURE, SPEECH, DRAMA. B.A, Creighton Univ, 22, M.A, 24; Ph.D, Cath. Univ. Am, 31. Instr. Eng. lit, Sacred Heart Jr. Col, 24-38; head dept. ENG, Ursuline Col, 38-66; prof, BELLARMINE COL.(KY), 66-70, EMER. PROF, 70- Vis. prof. Eng. lit. & consult. lit. studies, Incarnate Word Col, 59-60. Ursuline Col. teaching award, 62. NCTE; Poetry Soc. Am; S.Cent. Mod. Lang. Asn; Am. Stud. Asn. Mediaeval and modern English literature. Publ: Galahad in English literature, Cath. Univ. Am, 32. Add: Dept. of English, Bellarmine College, Louisville, KY 40205.

MORGAN, PETER FREDERICK, b. Stafford, Eng, Sept. 1, 30; m. 61; c. 4. ENGLISH. B.A, Univ. Birmingham, 51; M.A, Univ. London, 55, Ph.D.(Eng), 58. Lectr. ENG, Victoria Col, 58-59; UNIV. COL, UNIV. TORONTO, 59-66, asst. prof, 66-68, ASSOC. PROF, 68- R.A.F, 51-53, Pilot Off. Early 19th century periodicals; Romanticism; film and literature. Publ: Ed, Letters of Thomas Hood, Univ. Toronto, 73; Taylor and Hessey, Keats-Shelley J, winter 58; Wordsworth and Jeffrey, Humanities Asn. Bull, fall 68; plus others. Add: Dept. of English, University College, University of Toronto, Toronto, Ont. M5S 1A1, Can.

MORGAN, WILLIAM R, b. Indianapolis, Ind, June 30, 21; m. 42; c. 3. SPEECH, THEATRE. B.F,A, Univ. Tex, 42; M.F.A, State Univ. Iowa, 48, Ph.D, 51. Teaching asst. theatre & commun. skills, State Univ. Iowa, 46-48; instr. speech & radio, Univ. Calif, Santa Barbara, 48-49; commun. skills, State Univ. Iowa, 49-51; asst. prof. speech, Brooklyn Col, 51-53; assoc. prof. speech & drama, Carthage Col, 53-55, prof, 55-57, chmn. dept, 53-57; asst. prof. speech & theatre, Univ. Minn, Duluth, 57-59; assoc. prof, SPEECH & DRAMATIC ART, UNIV. NEBR, LINCOLN, 59-67, PROF, 67-, DIR. GRAD. STUD. THEATRE, 70-, dir. univ. theatre, 59-73. U.S.A, 42-45. Speech Commun. Asn; Am. Theatre Asn. Aesthetics; experimental audience response; 19th century American actors and directors. Add: 103A Temple Bldg, University of Nebraska, Lincoln, NE 68508.

MORGENSTERN, BARRY STEPHEN, b. New York, N.Y, Jan. 30, 45. MODERN BRITISH LITERATURE. A.B, Brooklyn Col, 65; M.A, Pa. State Univ, 67, Ph.D.(Eng), 71. Instr. ENG, Pa. State Univ, Beaver Campus, 67-68; ASST. PROF, MICH. TECHNOL. UNIV, 71- Acting dir. writing prog, Juniata Col, summer 72. The Bloomsbury group; biography. Publ: The self-conscious narrator in Jacob's Room, Mod. Fiction Stud, fall 72. Add: Dept. of Humanities, Michigan Technological University, Houghton, MI 49931.

MORILLO, MARVIN, b. Charleston, S.C, Sept. 6, 26; m. 57; c. 2. ENGLISH LITERATURE. A.B, Univ. N.C, 46, M.A, 48; Ph.D, Univ. Mich, 58. Instr. ENG, Emory Univ, 48-51; Carleton Col, 55-56; Univ. Mich, 56-58; asst. prof, NEWCOMB COL, TULANE UNIV, 58-63, ASSOC. PROF, 63-, Counc. on Res, res. grant, 60. Dir. Summer Inst. Eng, Col. Entrance Exam. Bd, 61-62; dir, NDEA Summer Inst, 65. MLA; Renaissance Soc. Am; S-Cent. Mod. Lang. Asn. Shakespeare; 17th century poetry and drama. Publ: James Shirley and the Court of Charles I, Stud. Eng. Lit, 61; Donne's Farewell to love, Tulane Stud. Eng, 63; Donne's compasses: circles and right lines, Eng. Lang. Notes, 3/66. Add: Dept. of English, Newcomb College, Tulane University, New Orleans, LA 70118.

MORIN, EDWARD A, b. Chicago, Ill, Feb. 25, 34; div; c. 3. ENGLISH, PHILOSOPHY. A.B, Maryknoll Col, 56; A.M, Univ. Chicago, 58; Ph.D.(Eng), Loyola Univ. (Ill), 67. Instr. Eng, Loyola Univ.(Ill), 58-59; Univ. Ky, 61-63; Univ. Cincinnati, 63-66; Wayne State Univ, 66-67, asst. prof, 67-70, fac. res. grant-in-aid, 68, part-time asst. prof. Eng, Urban Exten. Ctr, 71- Ed, Mich. State Univ. Press, 70-71; ed-exec. writer, Mich. Blue Shield, Detroit, 72-74, res. assoc, 74- Fourth Annual Sister Madeleva Poetry Contest 2nd Prize, 61; Poems for Peace Poetry Contest 3rd Prize, Newton-Wellesley Br, Women's Int. League Peace & Freedom, 63. MLA. Modern drama; creative writing; American literature. Publ: Co-auth, In the late, gnat light and other poems, Art Asn. Cincinnati, 65; auth, Joyce as Thomist, Renascence, spring 57; Séance (poem), Poetry Northwest, spring 70; Noblesse (poem), Prairie Schooner, autumn 72. Add: 255 E. Drayton, Ferndale, MI 48220.

MORISSET, GORDON RODNEY, b. Hanna, Alta, Jan. 24, 34. ENGLISH, ENGLISH EDUCATION. B.Ed, Univ. Alta, 58; M.A, Univ. London, 62. Prin, Alta. pub. schs, 54-57; master, Essex Educ. Counc, Eng, 61-62; from asst. prof. to assoc. prof. Eng, Univ. Calgary, 62-67, asst. dean fac. arts & sci, 62-67; asst. exec. secy, Nat. Counc. Teachers Eng, 67-73. Imp. Order Daughters Empire World War I mem. scholar, 59-61. MLA; Can. Counc. Teachers Eng; Asn. Can. Univ. Teachers Eng. Children's and adolescent's literature; 17th century prose. Publ: Co-auth, Points of view, Gage, 67; auth, Hero: book two of the theme sequence, Ginn, 72; co-auth, The professional load of secondary teachers of English, Alta. Teachers Asn, 66. Add: 1111 Kenyon Rd, Urbana, IL 61801.

MORLEY, PATRICIA ANN, b. Toronto, Ont, May 25, 29; m. 50; c. 4. CANADIAN & COMMONWEALTH LITERATURE. B.A, Univ. Toronto, 51; M.A, Carleton Univ, 67; Ph.D.(Eng), Univ. Ottawa, 70. Lectr. CAN. LIT, Univ. Ottawa, 71-72; ASST. PROF, SIR GEORGE WILLIAMS UNIV, 72- Humanities Res. Counc. Can. & Soc. Sci. Res. Counc. Can subventions, 71-72. Can. Asn. Commonwealth Lang. & Lit; MLA; Asn. Can. Univ. Teachers Eng; Humanities Asn. Can; Can. Stud. Asn. Fiction; humor. Publ: The mystery of unity: theme and technique in the novels of Patrick White, McGill-Queen's Univ, 72; The immoral moralists: Hugh MacLennan and Leonard Cohen, Clarke Irwin, 72; E.M. Forster's Temple: eclectic or visionary?, Univ. Toronto Quart, 4/70; Doppelganger's Dilemma: artist and man in The Vivisector, Queen's Quart, 8/72; Seton's Animals, J. Can. Fiction, summer 73. Add: Dept. of English, Sir George Williams University, 1455 de Maisonneuve Blvd. W, Montreal 107, P.Q, Can.

MORRAL, FRANK R, b. Vanersborg, Sweden, Apr. 7, 37; U.S. citizen; m. 61; c. 3. ENGLISH. A.B, Whitman Col, 59; A.M, Columbia Univ, 60, Ph.D. (Eng), 65. Instr. ENG, Whitman College, 62-64; CARLETON COL, 64-65, asst. prof, 65-70, ASSOC. PROF, 70- Shakespeare; 17th century literature; James Joyce. Add: 28 Fareway, Northfield, MN 55057.

MORRILL, ALLEN CONRAD, b. Shrewsbury, Mass, Nov. 20, 04; m. 33; c. 3. ENGLISH LITERATURE. A.B, Brown Univ, 26, A.M, 28; Ph.D, Harvard, 37. Asst. Eng, Brown Univ, 26-28, instr, 28-30; Washington & Jefferson Col, 32-37, asst. prof, 37-38; assoc. prof, Geneva Col, 38-41, prof. Eng. & dean fac, 41-49; prof. langs. & head dept, Mich. Col. Mining & Technology, 50-53; prof. ENG. & chmn. dept, Monmouth Col, 53-64; GENEVA COL, 64-69, EMER. PROF, 69- MLA; NCTE. English literature of the 17th century; Idaho history. Publ: Co-auth, The measuring woman and the cook, fall 63 & Talmaks, fall 64, Idaho Hist. Soc. Add: Dept. of English, Geneva College, Beaver Falls, PA 15010.

MORRIS, ALTON CHESTER, b. Forest City, Fla, Feb. 6, 03; m. 28; c. 2. ENGLISH. A.B.E, Univ. Fla, 27, M.A, 28; Gen. Educ. Bd. fel, 37-38; Rosenwald fel, 39-40; Ph.D, Univ. N.C, 41. Instr, Agr. & Mech. Col, Tex, 28-29; ENG, Univ. Fla, 29-35, asst. prof, 35-39; instr, Univ. N.C, 39-40; assoc. prof, UNIV. FLA, 40-46, prof, 47-73, EMER. PROF, 73- Ed, South. Folklore Quart, 36-66; vis. prof, Harvard, summers 49, 50; folklore consult, Fla. Folk Festival Asn, Stephen Foster Mem. Am. Folklore Soc; Southeast Folklore Soc.(pres, 40); MLA. Romantic period of English literature; folklore; Florida cultural history. Publ: Folksongs of Florida; collab, The meaning in reading; co-auth, College English: the first year, 4th ed, 60, 6th ed, 68, The modern essay, 2nd ed, 68 & Imaginative literature, 2nd ed, Harcourt; collab, Florida place names: a guide, Univ. Fla, 73; auth, The rolling stone: the way of a song, South. Folklore Quart, 73. Add: Dept. of English, 208 Anderson Hall, University of Florida, Gainesville, FL 32601.

MORRIS, ANN ROBERSON, b. De Land, Fla, Aug. 18, 30; m. 53; c. 2. ENGLISH & AMERICAN LITERATURE. B.A, Stetson Univ, 53; fel, Univ. S.C, 53-54, M.A, 56; fel, Fla. State Univ, 59-60, Ph.D, 61. From instr. to asst. prof. ENG, STETSON UNIV, 61-68, assoc. prof, 68-74, PROF, 74-; chmn. fac. senate, 72-74. MLA; NCTE; AAUP; Col. Eng. Asn; Am. Stud. Asn. Twentieth century fiction; literature by and about women. Publ: A short guide to writing better themes, Everett Edwards, 68; Notes on Winesburg, Ohio, Cliffs, 73. Add: Dept. of English, Stetson University, De Land, FL 32720.

MORRIS, DAVID BROWN, b. New York, N.Y, Aug. 11, 42; m. 66; c. 1. EIGHTEENTH CENTURY ENGLISH LITERATURE. B.A, Hamilton Col, 64; Ph.D.(Eng), Univ. Minn, Minneapolis, 68. Asst. prof. Eng, Univ. Va, 68-72; ASSOC. PROF. LIT, AM. UNIV, 72- Nat. Endowment for Humanities younger humanist fel, 72-73. MLA; Am. Soc. 18th Century Stud. Alexander Pope; history of criticism; eighteenth century literature. Publ: The religious sublime: Christian poetry and critical tradition in eighteenth century England, Univ. Ky, 72; The kinship of madness in Pope's Dunciad, Philol. Quart, 72; The visionary maid: tragic passion and redemptive sympathy in Pope's Eloisa to Abelard, Mod. Lang. Quart, 73; Virgilian attitudes in Pope's Windsor-Forest, Tex. Stud. Lit. & Lang, 73. Add: Dept. of Literature, American University, Washington, DC 20016.

MORRIS, GILBERT LESLIE, b. Forrest City, Ark, May 24, 29; m. 48; c. 3. ENGLISH. B.A, Ark. State Univ, 58, M.S.E, 62; Ph.D.(Eng), Univ. Ark, Fayetteville, 68. PROF. ENG, OUACHITA BAPTIST UNIV, 62- Dir, Eng. Stud, Upward Bound, 70-73; consult, N.Cent. Accreditation Agency, 72- MLA; NCTE. Eighteenth century poetry; medieval Romance. Publ: Can Johnnie learn to think?, Learning, 5/63; No time for fiction, Humanism Today, 11/66; Monopoly, Voices Int, 5/73; plus others. Add: Dept. of English, Ouachita Baptist University, Arkadelphia, AR 71923.

MORRIS, HARRY, b. New York, N.Y, Aug. 9, 24; m. 49; c. 2. ENGLISH. A.B, Univ. Miami, 49, A.M, 50; Ph.D, Univ. Minn, 57. Teaching fel. ENG, Ind. Univ, 52-55; instr, Ohio Univ, 55-56; Tulane Univ, 56-58, asst. prof, 58-61; FLA. STATE UNIV, 61-63, assoc. prof, 63-67, PROF, 67- Folger Libr. fel, 58. U.S.N.A.F, 43-45. MLA; S.Atlantic Mod. Lang. Asn. Renaissance and modern poetry. Publ: Co-auth, Poetry: a critical and historical introduction, Scott, 62; auth, Richard Barnfield: Colin's child, 63 & Birth and copulation and death, 69, Fla. State Univ; Sorrowful city, Univ. Fla, 65; The snake hunter, Univ. Ga, 69. Add: Dept. of English, Florida State University, Tallahassee, FL 32306.

MORRIS, JOHN ALLEN, b. Charleston, S.C, Apr. 25, 11; m. 34; c. 3. ENGLISH & AMERICAN LITERATURE. A.B, Col. Charleston, 33; M.A, Univ. N.C, 38, fel, 41-42; Univ. S.C, 67-68. Head dept. Eng, Murray Voc. Sch, 34-48; asst. prof, The Citadel, 48-56; circulation promotion adv, Eve. Post Publ. Co, 56-60; ASSOC. PROF. ENG, THE CITADEL, 60- Southern literature. Publ: The stories of William Gilmore Simms, Am. Lit, 3/42; Gullah in the stories and novels of William Gilmore Simms, Am. Speech, 2/47; Richard Topcliffe: a most humbell pursuivant of her majestie, Citadel Monogr. Series, 2/64. Add: Dept. of English, The Citadel, Charleston, SC 29409.

MORRIS, JOHN NELSON, b. Oxford, Eng, June 18, 31; U.S. citizen; m. 66; c. 3. ENGLISH. A.B, Hamilton Col, 53; M.A, Columbia Univ, 56, Ph.D.(Eng), 64. Instr. ENG, Univ. Del, 56-58; lectr, Columbia Univ, 58-60, instr, 60-61; lectr, San Francisco State Col, 61-62; instr, Columbia Univ, 62-64, asst. prof, 64-67; assoc. prof, WASH. UNIV, 67-71, PROF, 71- U.S.M.C, 53-55, 1st Lt. MLA. Eighteenth century English literature; Milton. Publ: Co-ed, Modern short stories; the fiction of experience, McGraw, 62; auth, Versions of the self: studies in English autobiography from John Bunyan to John Stuart Mill, Basic Bks, 66; Green business: poems, Atheneum, 70; Paradise lost now, Am. Scholar, winter 63-64; Wishes as horses: a word for the Houhynhynms, Yale Rev, 73; Samuel Johnson and the artists work, Hudson Rev, 73; plus others. Add: Dept. of English, Washington University, St. Louis, MO 63130.

MORRIS, JOHN WILLIAM, b. Clinton, S.C, Dec. 1, 25; m. 47; c. 2. ENGLISH LANGUAGE & LITERATURE. B.S, Univ. S.C, 46 & 47, M.A, 48; fel, Univ. Tenn, 48-50, Ph.D, 54. Asst. prof. ENG, Presby. Col, 50-54; assoc. prof, Ark. Agr. & Mech. Col, 54-56; UNIV. WIS-EAU CLAIRE, 56-61, PROF, 61-, V.CHANCELLOR ACAD. AFFAIRS, 72-, dean, Sch. Arts. & Sci, 65-72. U.S.N, 43-46, Res, 46-56, Lt.(jg). NCTE; Conf. Col. Compos. & Commun. English romanticism; English novel; history and structure of English language. Publ: Beauchamp's career: Meredith's acknowledgment of his debt to Carlyle, Tenn. Stud. Lit, 61; The germ of Meredith's Lucifer in starlight, Victorian Poetry, 63; Inherent principles of order in Richard Feverel, PMLA, 63. Add: Office of Vice Chancellor for Academic Affairs, University of Wisconsin-Eau Claire, Eau Claire, WI 54701.

MORRIS, ROBERT K, b. Greenwich, Conn, Apr. 28, 33; m. 60; c. 2. CONTEMPORARY BRITISH & AMERICAN LITERATURE. B.A, Cornell Univ, 54, M.A, 58; Ph.D.(Eng), Univ. Wis, 63. Asst. prof. ENG, CITY COL. NEW YORK, 63-68, assoc. prof, 68-73, PROF, 74- U.S.A, 54-56. Contemporary British and American literature. Publ: A guide to Gulliver's travels, 67 & A guide to Beowulf, 68, Educ. Res. Assoc; The novels of Anthony Powell, Univ. Pittsburgh, 68; Continuance and change: the contemporary British novel sequence, South. Ill. Univ, 72; The consolations of ambiguity: an essay on the novels of Anthony Burgess, Univ. Mo, 72; co-ed, The achievement of William Styron, Univ. Ga, 74. Add: Denmark, ME 04022.

MORRIS, ROBERT LEE, b. Ind, June 21, 03. ENGLISH & AMERICAN LITERATURE. B.A, Univ. Ark, 26; M.A, Univ. Chicago, 28; Ph.D, Univ. Iowa, 32. Asst, Univ. Iowa, 29-32; instr. writing, Ark. Col, Monticello, 32-33; PROF. LIT. & DIR. CREATIVE WRITING, UNIV. ARK, FAYETTEVILLE, 33-; LECTR, CRITIC & WRITER, 40- Fel, Univ. Colo, 36; lectr, Ark. Writer Ser, 46; consult, Bella Vista summer writers workshop, 63, 64. U.S.A.F, 43-45. MLA; S.Cent. Mod. Lang. Asn. Modern criticism; American folklore and humor; psychology of the creative mind. Publ: Transitional attitudes in the literary criticism of Joseph Addison, Univ. Iowa, 40; The mythos of anguish in Thomas Wolfe, Univ. Ark, 56; The psychology and creative disciplines in Thackeray's Barry Lyndon, Univ. Nebr, 64; Opie Read: American humorist, Helios, 66; A French drama in the deep South, 63, Success of Kit, the Arkansas traveler, 64 & Opie Read's unpublished play about Lincoln, 65, Ark. Hist. Quart. The story in the song (play), produced by Univ. Ark, 1/72. Add: 521 Olive Ave, Fayetteville, AR 72701.

MORRIS, VIRGINIA BAUMGARTNER, b. Ballston Spa, N.Y, Mar. 28, 42; m. 70; c. 2. ENGLISH & IRISH LITERATURE. B.A, Beaver Col, 64; M.A, Columbia Univ, 66, Ph.D.(Eng), 73. ASST. PROF. ENG, JOHN JAY COL. CRIMINAL JUSTICE, 67- MLA; Renaissance Soc. Am. Sixteenth century English literature; Irish literary Renaissance; Joseph Conrad. Add: Box 35 John Jay College of Criminal Justice, 445 W. 59th St, New York, NY 10019.

MORRIS, WILLIAM EDGAR, b. Wilmington, Del, Aug. 16, 26; m. 47; c. 2. ENGLISH LITERATURE. B.A, Univ. Del, 50, M.A, 53; Ph.D, Univ. N.C, 57. Part time instr. ENG, Univ. Del, 50-51; Univ. N.C, 52-55; instr, Duke Univ, 55-57; Ohio Univ, 57-59, asst. prof, 59-64; UNIV. S.FLA, 64-65, assoc. prof, 65-69, PROF, 69-, acting dean col. lang. & lit, 71-72. U.S.N, 45-46. MLA; S.Atlantic Mod. Lang. Asn; Milton Soc. Am. Fiction; English novel; 17th century English literature. Publ: Co-auth, The red badge of courage: text and criticism, 60 & auth, Form and focus 2, 64, Harcourt; co-auth, A Wuthering Heights handbook, 61 & Portraits of an artist, 62, Odyssey; co-auth, Huck Finn and his critics, Macmillan, 62; co-auth, Assessing Great expectations, Chandler, 63 & The Hungarian revolt, Scribner, 63; auth, The conversion of Scrooge, Stud. Short Fiction, fall 65; J.P. Donleavy's wild gingerbread man, Lang. Quart, spring-summer 68; Donne's use of enallage in The good-morrow, Am. Notes & Queries, 10/72. Add: Dept. of English, University of South Florida, Tampa, FL 33620.

MORRISON, JACK, b. Santa Barbara, Calif, Dec. 17, 12; m. 53; c. 4. THEATER. B.A, Univ. Calif, Los Angeles, 34, M.A, 52; Ed.D.(educ. psychol), Univ. South. Calif, 62. Lectr. theater arts, Univ. Calif, Los Angeles, 47-62, assoc. prof, 62-66; dean col. fine arts & prof. theater, Ohio Univ, 66-70; ASSOC. DIR, ARTS IN EDUC. PROG, JDR 3rd FUND, INC, 70- Dir-observer, new dramatics comt, Ford Found, 63; theater specialist, Arts & Humanities Prog, U.S. Off. Educ, 65-66; mem. adv. counc, Educ. Lab. Theater Proj, 66-; consult, Hofstra Univ, 71-72; Syracuse Univ; Univ. Md; Univ. Ky; Purdue Univ; Am. Nat. Theatre & Acad. Fel. Am. Theatre Asn.(pres, 57, 68, Award of Merit, 66); Nat. Counc. Art in Educ.(pres, 64-65); Latin Am. Stud. Asn; Am. Educ. Res. Asn; fel. Am. Counc. Arts Educ. Expressive behavior in the arts; directing. Publ: The rise of the arts on the American campus, McGraw, 73; Educational theater—a working myth, 12/57 & American educational theatre of the future, 3/68, Educ. Theatre J; The arts as early warning signals, Arts in Soc, 71. Add: Arts in Education Program, JDR 3rd Fund, Inc, Room 1034, 50 Rockefeller Plaza, New York, NY 10020.

MORRISON, JOHN WILSON, b. St. Paul, Minn, May 20, 15; m. 37; c. 2. ENGLISH. Fel. & Ph.D.(Eng), Univ. Wash, 48. Instr. ENG, Univ. Wash, 46-49; UNIV. NEV, RENO, 49-50, asst. prof, 50-56, assoc. prof, 56-64, PROF, 64-, CHMN. DEPT, 66- U.S.M.C, 42-43, Capt. MLA. Oriental literature; comparative literature; Japanese language and literature. Publ: In the world through literature; Modern Japanese fiction; In Indiana University conference on oriental-western literary relations. Add: Dept. of English, University of Nevada, Reno, NV 89507.

MORRISON, THEODORE, b. Concord, N.H, Nov. 4, 01; m. 27; c. 2. ENGLISH. A.B, Harvard, 23; Litt.D, Middlebury Col, 51. Asst. ENG, HARVARD, 30-31, instr. & tutor, 32-37, asst. prof, 37-39, dir. Eng. A, 39-51, lectr, 51-53, PROF, 63- Am. Acad. Arts & Sci. Chaucer; Shakespeare's Sonnets. Publ: The devious way, 44, ed. & transl, The portable Chaucer, 49, auth, The dream of Alcestis, 50 & The stones of the house, 53, Viking. Add: 6 Buckingham Pl, Cambridge, MA 02138.

MORRISSEY, BERNARD DELBERT, b. Farmersville, Ill, Mar. 20, 07. ENGLISH RENAISSANCE DRAMA & POETRY. A.B, St. Louis Univ, 28, A.M, 30; Ph.D.(Eng), Northwest. Univ, 57. Teaching fel. Latin, St. Louis Univ, 28-30; instr. Eng, French, Latin & hist, St. Louis Univ. High Sch, 30-42; instr. Eng, St. Louis Univ, 45-50; asst. prof, BELOIT COL, 55-58, assoc. prof, 58-63, prof, 63-72, chmn. div. humanities, 60-64, 66-69, acting chmn. dept. Eng, 61-62, 68-69, chmn. dept, 69-72, EMER. PROF, 72- Consult-examr, N.Cent. Asn. Col. & Sec. Sch, 70-; lectr, Univ. Wis-Rock County, 72- U.S.C.G.R, 42-45. MLA; Renaissance Soc. Am. Renaissance English translation from Latin classics; minor literary figures of English Renaissance; drama of English Renaissance. Add: 724 Chapin St, Beloit, WI 53511.

MORRISSEY, LEROY J, b. Brainard, Nebr, Apr. 26, 35; m. 59; c. 3. ENGLISH. B.A, Univ. Nebr, 58; Woodrow Wilson fel, Univ. Chicago, 58-59, M.A, 59; Ph.D.(Eng), Univ. Pa, 64. Instr. ENG, Pa. State Univ, 59-60; asst. instr, Univ. Pa, 60-63; instr, Dickinson Col, 63-65; asst. prof. Univ. West. Ont, 65-69; ASSOC. PROF, UNIV. SASK, 69- Can. Counc. grants, 67, 68, summer 71. Can. Soc. 18th Century Stud; Am. Soc. 18th Century Stud. Restoration and 18th century Britain. Publ: Ed, Henry Fielding's The tragedy of tragedies, 70 & Fielding's Grub Street opera, 73, Oliver & Boyd; auth, An anonymous ballad opera, Notes & Queries, Vol. 19, No. 6; English street theatre: 1655-1708, Costerus, IV: 105-137; Fielding's first political satire Anglia, 3: 325-48; plus others. Add: Dept. of English, University of Saskatchewan, Saskatoon, Sask. S7N 0W0, Can.

MORROW, PATRICK DAVID, b. Inglewood, Calif, Oct. 1, 40; m. 64; c. 2. AMERICAN LITERATURE & STUDIES. B.A, Univ. South. Calif, 63; M.A, Univ. Wash, 65, Ph.D.(Eng), 69. Prof. musician, 57-62; tech. writer, U.S. Vet. Admin. Property Mgt. Div, 63; teaching asst. Eng, Univ. Wash, 64-68, instr, 68-69; ASST. PROF. ENG. & AM. STUD, UNIV. SOUTH. CALIF, 69-, co-dir. Am. stud. prog, 69-72. Egan Found. Res. awards; Leo S. Bing Mem. Fel, 71; vis. assoc. prof, Univ. N.Mex, summer 72; TV acting & consult, 72-; mem. ed. bd, Pop. Mus. & Soc, 72- MLA; West. Am. Lit. Asn; Pop. Cult. Asn; Am. Stud. Asn. Western American literature; popular music; mass culture. Publ: Porcelain butterfly: five French symbolist poets in translation, Red Hill, 71; Bret Harte, Boise State Col, 72; The Greek nexus in Robert Frost's West-running brook, Personalist, 68; A writer's workshop: Hawthorne's The great carbuncle, Stud. Short Fiction, 69; Sgt. Pepper, hair and Tommy: forerunners of the Jesus-rock movement, In: Mystery, magic and miracle: religion in a post-aquarian age, Prentice-Hall, 73. Add: Dept. of English, University of Southern California, Los Angeles, CA 90007.

MORSBERGER, ROBERT E, b. Baltimore Md, Sept. 10, 29; m. 55; c. 1. ENGLISH. B.A, Johns Hopkins Univ, 50; M.A, Univ. Iowa, 54, Ph.D.(Eng), 56; Shakespeare Inst, summer 55. Instr. Eng, Miami Univ, 56-58, asst. prof, 58-59; Utah State Univ, 59-61; Am. thought & lang, Mich. State Univ, 61-64, assoc. prof, 64-68; PROF. ENG, East. Ky. Univ, 68-69; CALIF. STATE POLYTECH. UNIV, POMONA, 69- Vis. prof. & adv, Eng, Mich. State Univ—U.S. Agency for Int. Develop. team, Univ. Nigeria, 64-66; vis. assoc. prof, N.Mex. State Univ, 67-68; seasonal ranger, Mt. Rainier Nat. Park, summer 62; seasonal ranger-historian, Great Smoky Mountains Nat. Park, summers 63, 64, 68, 69, 70, 71 & 73; adv. Globeville proj, Nat. Am. Stud. Fac, 73. U.S.A, 51-53. Am. Stud. Asn; Rocky Mountain Mod. Lang. Asn; Col. Eng. Asn; John Steinbeck Soc. Am. American and African literature; motion pictures; popular culture. Publ: James Thurber, Twayne, 64; The language of composition, 65 & co-auth, Commonsense grammar and style, 65, rev. ed, 72, Crowell; ed, Essays in exposition: an international reader, Univ. Nigeria & U.S. Agency for Int. Develop, 66; Steinbeck's Zapata: rebel vs. revolutionary, In: John Steinbeck: the man and his work, Ore. State Univ, 71; The Wilkes expedition: 1838-1842, Am. Hist. Illus, 6/72; The minister's black veil: Shrouded in a blackness, ten times black, New Eng. Quart, 9/73; plus others. Add: Dept. of English, California State Polytechnic University, 3801 W. Temple Ave, Pomona, CA 91768.

MORSE, DONALD E, b. Boston, Mass, Mar. 3, 36; m. 62; c. 2. ENGLISH. A.B, Williams Col, 58; Union Theol. Sem.(N.Y), 58-60; Univ. London, summer 61; Roothbert Fund fel, Univ. Conn, 62-63; univ. fel. & M.A, 63, Ph.D. (Eng), 65. Asst. Eng, Univ. Conn, 60-62; asst. prof. lit, Babson Inst, 63-67; ENG, OAKLAND UNIV, 67-69, ASSOC. PROF, 69- MLA; Col. Eng. Asn. (exec. secy, 71-); Irish Am. Cult. Inst; Am. Soc. 18th Century Stud; AAUP. Satire; the poetry of W.H. Auden; Irish literature. Publ: The choices of fiction, Winthrop, 73; Time in Auden's For the time being, Renascence, winter 69; Two major revisions in W.H. Auden's For the time being, Eng. Lang. Notes, 6/70; Auden's concept and practice of Christian comedy, Mich. Academician, summer 71; plus two others. Add: Dept. of English, Oakland University, Rochester, MI 48063.

MORSE, JOSIAH MITCHELL, b. Columbia, S.C, Jan. 14, 12; m. 36; c. 2. ENGLISH. A.B, Univ. S.C, 32, M.A, 33; Am. Counc. Learned Soc. fel, 51; Ph.D. (Eng), Pa. State Univ, 52. Reporter, Columbia Record, S.C, 34; news ed, Am. Banker, 35-42; asst. ed, The Nation, 43-45; UN correspondent, Free Press India, 46-47; instr. ENG, Pa. State Univ, 48-56, asst. prof, 56-60, assoc. prof, 60-63, PROF, 63-67; TEMPLE UNIV, 67- Mem, Int. Fed. Mod. Lang. & Lit; bk. rev. ed, J. Gen. Educ, 60-67; mem. ed. comt, PMLA, 70-74. MLA; Int. Comp. Lit. Asn; Am. Comp. Lit. Asn. James Joyce; comparative literature; problems of teaching English. Publ: The sympathetic alien, N.Y. Univ, 59; Matters of style, Bobbs, 68; The irrelevant English teacher, Temple Univ, 72; plus others. Add: 115 Morris Rd, Ambler, PA 19002.

MORSE, LUCILE McCARTY, Linguistics, Composition. See Volume III, Foreign Languages, Linguistics & Philology.

MORSE, SAMUEL FRENCH, b. Salem, Mass, June 4, 16; m. 50; c. 1. ENGLISH. A.B, Dartmouth Col, 36; A.M, Harvard, 38; Ph.D.(Eng), Boston Univ, 42. Instr. ENG, Harvard, 38-42; Colby Col, 42; Univ. Maine, 46-49; from instr. to assoc. prof, Trinity Col.(Conn), 50-58; assoc. prof, Mt. Holyoke Col, 58-62; PROF, NORTHEAST. UNIV, 62- Am. Counc. Learned Soc. fel, 60-61; Fulbright prof, Univ. Canterbury, 66; Fulbright prof. & Megumi prof. Am. stud, Kobe Jogakuin, Japan, 69-70; lectr. U.S. Inform. Agency, Pakistan, summer 70. U.S.A.A.F, 43-46, Sgt. Poetry; American literature. Publ: Time of year, Cummington, 44; The scattered causes, 55 & The changes, 64, Swallow; ed, The opus posthumous and poems, W. Stevens, Knopf, 57-59; auth, Wallace Stevens: poetry as life, Pegasus, 70; Sea sums, Little, 70; Wallace Stevens, bibliography, Yale Libr, 54. Add: 41 Russell St, Milton, MA 02187.

MORTENSON, PETER, b. Manchester, N.H, Dec. 5, 37; m. 70. ENGLISH LITERATURE. B.S, Univ. N.H, 59, B.A, 60; M.A, Univ. Ore, 62, Ph.D.(Eng. lit), 66. Instr. ENG. LIT, Univ. Ore, 64-66; asst. prof, SYRACUSE UNIV, 66-73, ASSOC. PROF, 73- MLA; Renaissance Soc. Am. Renaissance literature; English romantic period. Publ: Image and structure in Shelley's longer lyrics, Stud. Romanticism, 65; Friar Bacon and Friar Bungay: festive comedy and three form'd luna, Eng. Lit. Renaissance, 72; The economics of joy in The shoemakers' holiday, Stud. Eng. Lit, 74; plus others. Add: Dept. of English, Syracuse University, Syracuse, NY 13210

MORTENSON, ROBERT LAWRENCE, b. Phila, Pa, Jan. 13, 38; m. 61; c. 2. ENGLISH. A.B, Univ. Pa, 59, A.M, 61, Ph.D.(Eng), 64. Instr. ENG, South. Ill. Univ, 63-64, asst. prof, 64-66; UNIV. WASH, 66-73; INSTR, EVERETT COMMUNITY COL, 73- Am. Philos. Soc. res. grant, 65. MLA; Mod. Humanities Res. Asn; Keats-Shelley Asn. Am. English Romantic literature; 19th century fiction; poetry. Publ: Another continuation of Don Juan, Stud. Romanticism, summer 63; Byroniana: remarks on Cain identified, Harvard Libr. Bull, 7/68; Abel: a mystery by Philip Dixon Hardy, an answer to Lord Byron's Cain: a mystery, Keats-Shelley Mem. Bull, 68. Add: 3710 Wallingford N, Seattle, WA 98103.

MORTON, BEATRICE KERR, b. Manti, Utah, m. 36; c. 3. ENGLISH EDUCATION. B.A, Univ. Utah, 34, M.A, 36, Ph.D.(Eng. educ), 71. Teacher Eng, Mounds View High Sch, Minn, 55-61; Jackson Hole High Sch, Wyo, 61-65; ASST. PROF. ENG. EDUC, BOWLING GREEN STATE UNIV, 69- Conf. Eng. Educ; NCTE. Creative dramatics; creativity in the classroom; creative and humanistic teaching of English. Publ: Creative dramatics—a visit to a class, Eng. J, 4/73. Add: Dept. of English Education, Bowling Green State University, Bowling Green, OH 43403.

MORTON, LENA BEATRICE, b. Ky, June 15, 01. ENGLISH LITERATURE. A.B, Univ. Cincinnati, 22, A.M, 25; Ph.D, West. Reserve Univ, 47; Univ. London, 56, Harvard, 59. Teacher pub. schs, Ohio, 22-48; prof. Eng, Langston Univ, 48-50; chmn. div. humanities & dean, Lane Col, 50-55, PROF. ENG, South. Univ, 55-62; HEAD DEPT. ENG. & DIV. HUMANITIES, TEX. COL, 62- Co-operating teacher, Univ. Cincinnati, 27-30, 35-42; vis. prof. Eng, E.Tex. State Univ, 70-72. Piper Award, 67. MLA; fel, Int. Inst. Arts & Lett. Influence of the sea upon English poetry from the Anglo-Saxon period to the Victorian period; English literature, especially Arnold's multiple editions; patterns of language usage in elementary schools; the Black student at the University of Cincinnati. Publ: Negro poetry in America, Stratford, 25; Farewell to the public schools—I'm glad we met, Meador, 52; Man under stress, 60 & My first sixty years—passion for wisdom, 65, Philos. Libr. Add: 3256 Beresford Ave, Cincinnati, OH 45206.

MORTON, LEONARD, b. New York, N.Y, Sept. 2, 19; m. 52; c. 1. ENGLISH. B.A, Brooklyn Col, 40; M.S.Ed, City Col. New York, 41; Univ. Genoa, Italy, 48-49; Columbia Univ, 50-54; Ed.D, Yeshiva Univ, 64. Teacher pub. schs, N.Y, 47-48, 49-55; chmn, jr. high sch, N.Y, 55-59; chmn. high schs, N.Y, 59-65; chmn. dept. Eng. & commun. arts, N.Y. INST. TECHNOL, 65-67, dir. spec. educ, 67-69, PROF. ENG. & CHMN. DEPT, 69- Dir, Ford Proj. Disadvantaged Stud, 67-68. U.S.A, 42-47, 1st Lt. Col. Eng. Asn; NCTE; MLA; AAUP. Innovative teaching techniques, TV, multi-media, automated instruction; socio-economically and academically disadvantaged students; reading and study skills instruction. Add: 138 S. Brush Dr, Valley Stream, NY 11581.

MORTON, RICHARD (EVERETT), b. Liverpool, U.K, Nov. 8, 30; m. 59; c. 2. ENGLISH. B.A, Univ. Wales, U.K, 52; B.Litt, Oxford, 54. Lectr. ENG, Univ. Witwatersrand, S.Africa, 56-59; asst. prof, Lake Erie Col, 60-62; McMASTER UNIV, 62-66, assoc. prof, 66-70, PROF, 70- Fel, Univ. Wales, 54-56; gen. ed, Lake Erie Col. Stud, 61-62; Am. Counc. Learned Soc. grant-in-aid, 62; lectr, Univs. Can. Shakespeare Sem, Stratford, Ont, 63; Can. Counc. grant-in-aid, 65, fel, 68-69; Can. Counc. fel, 71; lectr. Shakespeare sem, Univ. Birmingham, 71. MLA; Northeast. Mod. Lang. Asn. Sir Aston Cokayne; James Shirley; Thomas Southerne. Publ: Co-auth, John Gay's three hours after marriage, Lake Erie Col, 61; auth, Anne Killigrew's poems, Scholars' Facsimilies, 67; Boileau's Lutrin made English, Augustan Reprint Soc, 67; The poetry of W.B. Yeats, Forum House, 71; James Shirley's drama, Renaissance Drama, 66; contrib, Restoration and 18th century theatre research 1900-1968, Univ. South. Ill, 71; Eighteenth century play texts, In: The triumph of culture, Hakkert, 72; plus others. Add: Dept. of English, McMaster University, Hamilton, Ont. L8S 4M4, Can.

MOSELEY, EDWIN MAURICE, b. Orangeburg, S.C, Sept. 12, 16. ENGLISH & MODERN LITERATURE. A.B, Col. Charleston, 37; A.M, Syracuse Univ, 39, Ph.D, 47. Mem. fac. Eng, Syracuse Univ, 37-42, 44-45, 46-47; asst. prof, Evansville Col, 47-48; Washington & Jefferson Col, 48-49, from assoc. prof. to prof, 49-61; PROF. ENG. & DEAN FAC, SKIDMORE COL, 61-, PROVOST, 67- Instr, U.S.A.A.F, U.S.A, & Army Spec. Training Prog, 43-44; U.S.A, 45-46. MLA; Col. Eng. Asn; Am. Conf. Acad. Deans; East. Deans Asn. Renaissance; contemporary literature; history of the novel. Publ: Co-ed, Elizabethan fiction, Holt, 53; auth, Pseudonyms of Christ in the modern novel, Univ. Pittsburgh, 63; The outsider as hero and anti-hero, Skidmore Col, 67; F. Scott Fitzgerald—a critical essay, Eerdmans, 67. Add: Office of the Provost, Skidmore College, Saratoga Springs, NY 12866.

MOSELEY, VIRGINIA DOUGLAS, b. Gainesville, Tex, Jan. 31, 17. ENGLISH LITERATURE. B.A, Univ. Okla, 38, M.A, 48, Delta Kappa Gamma State fel, 55; Ph.D, Columbia Univ, 58. Instr. Eng. & bus, Gainesville High Sch. & Jr. Col, Tex, 38-44; asst. prof. ENG, Southeast. State Col, 47-55; North. Ill. Univ, 55-59, assoc. prof, 59-63, PROF, 63-66; Texas Woman's Univ, 66-69; UNIV. OTTAWA, 69- Vis. prof, Univ. Waterloo, summer 67; North. Ill. Univ, summer 68. W.A.V.E.S, 44-46, Lt. MLA; Am. Comn. Irish Stud. James Joyce; modern poetry; modern drama. Publ: Co-transl, Those Americans, Regnery, 62; auth, Joyce and the Bible, North. Ill. Univ, 67; The coincidence of contraries in Joyce's Grace, James Joyce Quart, 68; The dangerous paradox in Joyce's Eveline, Costerus: essays in English and American literature, 72; Joyce and the Bible: the external evidence, In: Essays commemorating the fiftieth anniversary of the publication of James Joyce's Ulysses in Paris, Marcel Didier, Paris, 73; plus others. Add: Dept. of English, University of Ottawa, Ottawa, Ont. K1N 0E8, Can.

MOSER, EDWIN, b. New York, N.Y, Jan. 8, 29; m. 54; c. 1. ENGLISH. A.B, N.Y. Univ, 50, A.M, 51, Penfield fel, 55-56, Ph.D, 59. Instr. Eng, N.Y. Univ, 51-58; teacher, Hicksville High Sch, N.Y, 58-61; instr, Univ. Mass, 61-62; supvr. lang. arts, Hicksville Pub. Schs, N.Y, 62-63; from instr. to asst. prof. ENG, Univ. Mass, 63-72; ASSOC. PROF, LAKEHEAD UNIV, 72- Vis. prof, Rand Sch. Soc. Sci, 54. Andiron Club Award, 59. MLA; NCTE; Col. Eng. Asn. American literature. Add: Dept. of English, Lakehead University, Thunder Bay, Ont, Can.

MOSER, THOMAS COLBORN, b. Connellsville, Pa, Nov. 22, 23; m. 52; c. 2. ENGLISH. Nat. scholar, Harvard, 47-50, A.B, 48, A.M, 49, Ph.D, 55. Teaching fel. ENG, Harvard, 50-52; instr, Wellesley Col, 52-56; STANFORD UNIV, 56-57, asst. prof, 57-60, assoc. prof, 60-64, PROF, 64-, dir. freshman Eng, 59-62, exec. head dept. Eng, 64-68. Am. Counc. Learned Soc. fel, 63. C.Eng, U.S.A, 43-46. MLA; NCTE. English and American novel; 20th century English and American literature. Publ: Joseph Conrad: achievement and decline, Harvard, 57; Wuthering heights: text, sources, criticism, Harcourt, 62; Lord Jim: text, backgrounds and sources, essays in criticism, Norton, 68; Towards the good soldier, Daedalus, spring 63; Thomas Wolfe: Look homeward, angel, In: The American novel, Basic Bks, 65. Add: 812 Esplanada Way, Stanford, CA 94305.

MOSES, ELBERT RAYMOND, JR, b. New Concord, Ohio, Mar. 31, 08; m. 33; c. 1. PHONETICS. A.B, Univ. Pittsburgh, 32; Northwest. Univ, summer 33; M.Sc, Univ. Mich, 34, Ph.D.(speech & gen. ling), 36; Ohio State Univ, 40; East. Ill. State Col, 55. Dir, Falk Speech Clin, Pittsburgh, Pa, 34-35; speech clin, Children's Hospital, 35-36; instr. Eng. & dir. speech improv, Woman's Col, Univ. N.C, 36-38; asst. prof. speech, Ohio State Univ, 38-46; assoc. prof. speech & dir. radio, East. Ill. State Col, 46-56; asst. prof. commun. skills, Mich. State Univ, 56-59; prof. speech & chmn. dept. speech & dramatic arts, CLARION STATE COL, 59-71, EMER. PROF. SPEECH, 71- Alumni Fund grant, Ohio State Univ, 41; Fulbright lectr, Cebu Norm. Sch,

Cebu City, P.I, 55-56; phonetic res. grant, Mich. State Univ, 57-58; deleg, Int. Congr. Phonetic Sci, Helsinki, 61; liaison rep, Peace Corps; mem. nat. adv. comt. for. stud. & teachers, Dept. Health, Educ. & Welfare, 64-; deleg. XIIIth Congr. Int. Soc. Logopedics & Phoniatrie, 65. Sig.C, 42-46, 52-53, Lt. Col. Overseas Educ. Asn.(past pres); Nat. Asn. For. Stud. Adv. Palatography and speech improvement; history of palatography techniques; palatograph changes with rates of articulation. Publ: Phonetics: history and interpretation, Prentice-Hall, 64; Parameters of palatography (paper presented at Speech Symposium), Akademiai Kiado, Budapest, 71. Add: 18 Fairview Ave, Clarion, PA 16214.

MOSES, WILLIAM ROBERT, b. Alexandria, Minn, Dec. 24, 11; m. 35; c. 1. ENGLISH. B.A, Vanderbilt Univ, 32, M.A, 33, fel, 33-35, Ph.D.(Eng), 39. Instr. ENG, Hendrix Col, 35-36; State Col. Wash, 36-39; Univ. Ill, 39-42; asst. prof, KANS. STATE UNIV, 50-51, assoc. prof, 51-54, PROF, 54- Ford fel, 52-53; vis. prof, Univ. Sask, Regina Campus, 66-67. U.S.N.R, 42-46, Lt. Comdr. MLA; Am. Stud. Asn. Twentieth century British poetry; 20th century American poetry and fiction. Publ: Identities, Wesleyan Univ, 65; The unity of the wild palms, Mod. Fiction Stud; Another reading of The bear, Accent; contrib, Arteries of morning, Five Young Am. Poets. Add: 314 Denison Ave, Manhattan, KS 66502.

MOSHER, HAROLD FREDERICK, JR, b. Pittsburgh, Pa, Aug. 20, 30; m. 71; c. 3. ENGLISH, COMPARATIVE LITERATURE. B.A, South. Methodist Univ, 52; Univ. Paris, 57-58; Ph.D.(Eng), Univ. Tex, 66. Instr. French, South. Methodist Univ, 56-57; ENG, Univ. Cincinnati, 61-66, asst. prof, 66-68, res. grant, 67-68, Taft res. & travel grants, 67-68; assoc. prof. Univ. Nice, 69-71; vis. assoc. prof, NORTH. ILL. UNIV, 70, ASSOC. PROF, 71-, acad. res. grants, 71-74. Fulbright-Hays lectr, Univ. Toulouse, 68-69; Am. lit. summer sem, Univ. Nice, 70; NDEA res. grant, 68-69; U.S. Inform. Serv. travel grants, 69-70; French govt. nat. educ. res. grants, 69-71. U.S.N, 52-56. MLA; Midwest Mod. Lang. Asn. British literature of the 19th and 20th centuries; comparative literature; stylistics. Publ: Co-ed, American literature: an anthology (2 vols), Hachette, Paris, 73-74; contrib, Joseph Conrad: an annotated bibliography of writings about him, North. Ill. Univ, 71; auth, The lyrics of American pop music, Popular Music & Soc, 72; La Metamorphose des symboles chez H. Crane et A. Rimbaud, Rev. Lang. Vivantes, 73; plus several others. Add: Dept. of English, Northern Illinois University, De Kalb, IL 60115.

MOSIER, JOHN FRIEDEL, b. Bentonville, Ark, July 9, 44; m. 62; c. 3. ENGLISH. B.A, Tulane Univ, 64, M.A, 66, Ph.D.(Eng), 68. Instr. music, Tulane Univ, 66-68; ENG, LOYOLA UNIV.(LA), 67-68, ASST. PROF, 68-, EXEC. SECY. ACAD. AFFAIRS, 71-, asst. dean, 69-71. Fac. res. grant, Loyola Univ, summer 68. MLA. History of science; 19th century English. Publ: Co-auth, Instit research: a review, Univ. Southwest. La, 72; auth, Machine intelligence and the arts, New Orleans Rev, 69. Add: 324 Pine St, New Orleans, LA 70118.

MOSKOVIT, LEONARD, b. New York, N.Y, Nov. 27, 22; m. 51; c. 1. ENGLISH. B.A, Univ. Calif, Berkeley, 57, Woodrow Wilson fel. & Wall Mem. scholar, 57-58, univ. fel, 58-59, M.A, 59, Ph.D.(Eng), 63. Instr. ENG, UNIV. COLO, BOULDER, 62-64, asst. prof, 64-67, assoc. prof, 67-72, PROF, 72- MLA. Restoration and 18th century English literature. Publ: Pope's purposes in Sober advice, Philol. Quart, 4/65; Maugham's outstation: a single, serious effect, Univ. Colo. Stud. Ser. Lang. & Lit, 2/66; Pope and the tradition of neoclassical imitation, Stud. Eng. Lit, summer 68. Add: Dept. of English, University of Colorado, Boulder, CO 80302.

MOSLEY, WALTER LYND, b. Hattiesburg, Miss, Nov. 28, 38; m. 60; c. 3. ENGLISH LITERATURE. B.A, Univ. South. Miss, 60; M.A, Tulane Univ, 61; Ph.D.(Eng), Tex. Christian Univ, 67. Instr. Eng, McNeese State Univ, 61-65; ASSOC. PROF. ENG. & HEAD DEPT. LANG, NORTHWEST. STATE UNIV, 67- MLA; Int. Phenomenol. Soc; Col. Eng. Asn. Modern British novel; modern poetry; aesthetics. Publ: Teacherness (poem), CEA Critic, 12/73; On a friend after analysis (poem), Twigs, spring 74; Chopin Mazurka (poem), Cottonwood Rev, spring 74; plus six others. Add: Dept. of Languages, Northwestern State University, Natchitoches, LA 71457.

MOSS, FREDERICK KEITH, b. Grand Rapids, Mich, Oct. 12, 39; m. 62; c. 2. ENGLISH & AMERICAN LITERATURE. A.B, Olivet Col, 61; M.A, Ohio Univ, 63; Ph.D.(Eng), Univ. Wis-Madison, 69. ASST. PROF. ENG, UNIV. WIS. CTR-SHEBOYGAN, 66- AAUP. Nineteenth century English novel; English and American fiction since World War II. Add: Dept. of English, University of Wisconsin Center-Sheboygan, Box 719, Sheboygan, WI 53081.

MOSS, HAROLD GENE, b. New Eagle, Pa, Jan. 24, 43; m. 66; c. 2. ENGLISH LITERATURE & LANGUAGE. B.A, Washington & Jefferson Col, 64; M.A, Univ. Wash, 66; Ph.D.(Eng), Univ. Mich, 69. Instr. ENG, East. Mich. Univ, 68-69; ASST. PROF, UNIV. FLA, 69-, ASSOC. DIR, CTR. STUD. HUMANITIES, 73-, humanities counc. planning proj, 72-73. MLA; S.Atlantic Mod. Lang. Asn; Am. Soc. 18th Century Stud; Col. Eng. Asn. Eighteenth century British drama; 18th century British popular song. Publ: Ballad opera and the popular song, J. Am. Musicol. Soc, 73; Silvia, my dearest: a Fielding ballad-opera tune and a biographical puzzle, S.Atlantic Bull, 73; Imitation and allusion in John Gay's The beggar's opera, Notes & Queries, 73; plus one other. Add: Ctr. of Studies in the Humanities, University of Florida, Gainesville, FL 32601.

MOSS, LEONARD JEROME, b. Paterson, N.J, Oct. 22, 31. COMPARATIVE LITERATURE. B.A, Univ. Okla, 53; M.A, Ind. Univ, 54, Ph.D, 59. Instr. Eng, Ft. Wayne Ctr, Ind. Univ, 58-60; asst. prof, Harpur Col, State Univ. N.Y. Binghamton, 60-67; assoc. prof, STATE UNIV. N.Y. COL. GENESEO, 67-71, PROF. COMP. LIT, 71-, DIR. COMP. LIT. PROG, 69- State Univ. N.Y. fac. fel, 66-67. Mil. Intel, U.S.A, 56, Res, 56-68, Capt. MLA; Am. Comp. Lit. Asn. Theory of tragedy; modern and classical drama. Publ: Arthur Miller, Twayne, 67; Rhetorical style of Samson Agonistes, Mod. Philol, 5/65; The influence of Hegel's theory of tragedy, J. Aesthetics & Art Criticism, 69; Plato and the Poetics, Philol. Quart, 71; plus others. Add: Dept. of English, State University of New York College at Geneseo, Geneseo, NY 14454.

MOSS, SIDNEY PHIL, b. Liverpool, Eng, Mar. 27, 17; nat; m. 46; c. 3. ENGLISH. B.S, Univ. Ill, 50, fel. & M.A, 51, Ph.D, 54. Res. asst. Am. lit, Univ. Ill, 50-51, asst. ed, 54-56; head res. dept, Champaign, Ill, off, Spencer Press, 52-53, ed, 53-54; from assoc. prof. to prof. ENG, Murray State Univ, 56-64; vis. prof, SOUTH. ILL. UNIV, CARBONDALE, 64, PROF, 65- Am. Philos. Soc. grant, 66; Fulbright lectr. Am. lit, Univ. Col, Dublin, 69-70. U.S.A, 41-45. American literature, especially of the nineteenth century. Publ: Co-auth, Thy men shall fall, Ziff-Davis, 48; auth, Poe's literary battles, 63 & Poe's major crisis, 70, Duke Univ; Composition by logic, 66 & Readings for composition by logic, 68, Wadsworth; Hawthorne and Melville: an inquiry into their art and the mystery of their friendship, Univ. Wis; & Cock-a-doodle-doo and some legends in Melville scholarship, Am. Lit; Hawthorne's Marble faun, Nineteenth Century Fiction. Add: Dept. of English, Southern Illinois University, Carbondale, IL 62901.

MOSSE, BASKETT, b. Henderson, Ky, Sept. 9, 17; m. 42; c. 2. JOURNALISM. B.A, Univ. Tulsa, 41; M.S.J, Northwest. Univ, 43. News ed, Nat. Broadcasting Co, Chicago, 41-46; PROF. JOUR, NORTHWEST. UNIV, 46- Exec. secy, Accrediting Comt, Am. Counc. Educ. Jour, 55-; exec. secy, 57-; consult, U.S. Weather Bur, 61-68. Radio-TV News Dir. Asn.(awards chmn, 46-68); Asn. Educ. in Jour. Radio and television news and public affairs. Publ: Radio news handbook, Studio Press, 46. Add: Sch. of Journalism, Northwestern University, Evanston, IL 60201.

MOSSNER, ERNEST CAMPBELL, b. New York, N.Y, Oct. 22, 07; m. 36; c. 1. ENGLISH LITERATURE. A.B, City Col. New York, 29, fel, 29-30; A.M, Columbia Univ, 30, univ. traveling fel, 34-35, Ph.D, 36. Tutor, City Col. New York, 30-34, instr, 34-37; assoc. prof. Eng, Syracuse Univ, 37-45, prof, 45-47, UNIV. TEX, AUSTIN, 47-72, mem. educ. comt, Stud. in Lit. & Lang, 48-72, ASHBEL SMITH EMER. PROF. ENG. & PHILOS, 72- Guggenheim fel, 39-40, 45-46; McMurray award, Tex. Inst. Lett, 55; vis. prof. summers, Columbia Univ, 47; Univ. Colo, 60; Fulbright Res. fel, Univ. Glasgow, 68-69. MLA; Mod. Humanities Res. Asn, Gt. Brit; NCTE; Augustan Reprint Soc. Literature and thought of the 18th century; Milton. Publ: Bishop Butler and the age of reason, Macmillan, 36; The forgotten Hume, Columbia, 43; The life of David Hume, Univ. Tex, 54; co-auth, David Hume: a letter from a gentleman, Edinburgh Univ, 67. Add: 3001 Glenview, Austin, TX 78703.

MOST, RALPH CHRISTIAN, b. Philadelphia, Pa, Oct. 22, 14; m. 47. ENGLISH. A.B, Haverford Col, 36; M.A, Univ. Pa, 37, Ph.D.(Eng), 51. Asst. instr. ENG, Univ. Pa, 37-42; instr, DREXEL UNIV, 46-52, asst. prof, 52-57, assoc. prof, 57-69, PROF, 69- U.S.A, 42-45. MLA; Am. Stud. Asn. American literature and civilization; American novel; fiction dealing with American Civil War. Add: Dept. of Literature & Language, Drexel University, 32nd & Chestnut Sts, Philadelphia, PA 19104.

MOSVICK, ROGER K, b. Eau Claire, Wis, Feb. 1, 31; m. 51; c. 2. SPEECH, COMMUNICATION. B.A, Macalester Col, 52; M.A, Univ. Minn, 59, Ph.D. (rhet. & pub. address), 66. Dir. speech, high sch, Minn, 52-56; instr. speech & drama, Macalester Col, 56-60; Univ. Minn, 61-62; asst. prof, SPEECH, MACALESTER COL, 62-68, ASSOC. PROF, 68-, CHMN. DEPT. SPEECH COMMUN. & DRAMATIC ARTS, 71- Commun. consult, Honeywell, Inc, 58-68; Minn. Mining & Mfg. Co, 70-73; Volkeswagen of Am, 71-72; dist. 5, U.S. Civil Serv, 67; Wallace fel. & summer grant, Brunel Univ, 67-68. U.S.A.R, S/Sgt. Speech Commun. Asn; Cent. States Speech Asn. Experimental evaluations of industrial human relations courses and communication laboratory instruction. Publ: Human relations training for scientists, technicians and engineers: a review of relevant experimental evaluations of human relations training, Personnel Psychol, 24: 275-292. Add: Dept. of Speech Communications & Dramatic Arts, Macalester College, St. Paul, MN 55101.

MOTLEY, FRANK WALLACE, b. Blairs, Va, Mar. 30, 25. ENGLISH, EDUCATION. A.B, Lynchburg Col, 49; M.A, E.Tenn. State Univ, 52; Ed.D.(Eng, educ), Univ. N.C, Chapel Hill, 65. Teacher pub. schs, Va, 49-52; high sch, N.C, 52-55; prin. jr. high sch, N.C, 55-61; dir. stud. teaching E.Tenn. State Univ, 61-65; COL. PROF. ENG, E.CAROLINA UNIV, 65- U.S.A, 43-46. Col. Eng. Asn; MLA; S.Atlantic Mod. Lang. Asn; NCTE. American literature; methods; student teaching. Add: P.O. Box 3105, Greenville, NC 27834.

MOTLEY, MICHAEL TILDEN, b. Salt Lake City, Utah, Jan. 4, 45. SPEECH COMMUNICATION, LINGUISTICS. B.A, Univ. Tex, Austin, 65, M.S, 67; Ph.D.(speech commun), Pa. State Univ, 70. Instr. speech commun, Pa. State Univ, 67-70; ASST. PROF. commun. disorders, Fresno State Col, 70-71; SPEECH COMMUN, CALIF. STATE UNIV, LOS ANGELES, 71- West. Speech Commun. Asn; Speech Commun. Asn.(secy, 72-73); Int. Commun. Asn; Am. Speech & Hearing Asn. Communication theory; psycholinguistics. Publ: An analysis of Spoonerisms as psycholinguistic phenomena, 73 & Verbal conditioning in encoding, (in press), Speech Monographs; co-auth, Heart rate changes during classroom public speaking, J. Psychophysiol, (in press). Add: Dept. of Speech Communication, California State University, Los Angeles, 5151 State University Dr, Los Angeles, CA 90032.

MOTT, SARA LOUISE, b. Charlotte, N.C, Jan. 1, 24. ENGLISH. B.A, Limestone Col, 44; M.A, Univ. N.C, 51; South. fel, Univ. S.C, 62-63, Ph.D.(Eng), 65. Teacher high sch, 45-50, teacher & counsel, 51-53; counsel, COLUMBIA COL.(S.C), 53-58, instr. ENG, 58-64, asst. prof, 64-67, assoc. prof, 67-70, PROF, 70- NCTE; S.Atlantic Mod. Lang. Asn; Soc. Stud. South. Lit. Modern American literature; linguistics and modern grammar. Add: Dept. of English, Columbia College, Columbia, SC 29203.

MOUAT, LAWRENCE H, b. Pasadena, Calif, Mar. 15, 09; m. 63; c. 5. RHETORIC. A.B, Stanford Univ, 34, M.A, 35; Ph.D, Cornell Univ, 42. Instr, Stanford Univ, 36-37; Occidental Col, 37-39; Cornell Univ, 39-46; from asst. prof. to PROF. SPEECH, SAN JOSE STATE UNIV, 46-, HEAD DEPT. SPEECH-COMMUN, 63- West. Speech Commun. Asn.(exec. secy, 49-52, 2nd v.pres, 56, 1st v.pres, 61, pres, 62). Publ: Guide to effective public speaking, Heath, 53, 59; Reading literature aloud, Oxford, 62; co-auth, To make a speech, Pac. Bks, 66; auth, An approach to criticism, In: The rhetorical idiom, Cornell Univ, 58. Add: Dept. of Speech-Communication, San Jose State University, San Jose, CA 95114.

MOULTON, EUGENE R, b. Mogadore, Ohio, Mar. 18, 16; m. 41; c. 4. SPEECH. B.A, West. Reserve Univ, 48, M.A, 49, Ph.D, 53. Pers. mgr, Porcelain Steel Co. & Van der Horst Corp; assoc. prof. speech, Carroll Col, 49-52; prof. speech & chmn. dept, Univ. Redlands, 52-67; chmn. dept. speech & drama, Madison Col.(Va), 67-70; PROF. SPEECH & CHMN. DIV. HUMANITIES, EAST. MONT. COL, 70- Int. Gen. Semantics Asn. grant, 61; instr, Creative Problem Solving Inst, State Univ. N.Y. Col. Buffalo, 62-63; commun. consult, Lockheed Propulson Co, 62-66; Creative Educ. Found. Counc, 62-, mem, leadership counc, 65-; speaker's bur, Nat. Manufacturer's Asn, 63-; vis. prof, Univ. Calif, 65-66. U.S.A.A.F, 42-44, Lt. Speech Commun. Asn; Rocky Mt. Mod. Lang. Asn; Nat. Humanities Asn; Nat. Soc. Commun; Nat. Asn. Col. Adminr. Creativity; innovations in education; interpersonal communication. Publ: Fundamentals of speech syllabus, Univ. Redlands, 59; The dynamics of debate, Harcourt, 66; Identity, to be or not to be, 68 & Roadblocks to communication, Madison Col. Fac. Res. Bull; plus others. Add: Division of Humanities, Eastern Montana College, Billings, MT 59102.

MOULTON, ROBERT DARRELL, b. Dodge Center, Minn, July 20, 22; m. 48; c. 2. THEATRE ARTS. B.A, Univ. Minn, 47, M.A, 49, Ph.D.(theatre), 56. Instr. THEATRE, UNIV. MINN, MINNEAPOLIS, 47-56, asst. prof, 56-58, assoc. prof, 58-64, PROF, 65- McMillan traveling grant, U.K, 65; Univ. Minn. grad. sch. res. grant. dance, 67-69; Minn. State Arts Counc. fel. in dance. U.S.A, 42-46. Am. Theatre Asn; Nat. Dance Guild; AAUP; Am. Asn. Health, Phys. Educ. & Recreation; Comt. Res. Dance. Dance, games, and choreography for theatre. Add: University Theatre, 249 Middlebrook Hall, University of Minnesota, Minneapolis, MN 55455.

MOUNTAIN, JOHN ANTHONY, b. Summit, N.J, Feb. 14, 39; m. 70. COMPARATIVE LITERATURE, PHILOSOPHY. B.A, Columbia Univ, 61; M.A, Univ. Wash, 66, Ph.D.(comp. lit), 70. ASSOC. PROF. LIB. STUD, ENG. & COMP. LIT, HUTCHINS SCH. LIB. STUD, CALIF. STATE COL, SONOMA, 70- U.S.A, 61-64, Sgt. MLA. History of philosophy; modern novel; nature of interdisciplinary studies. Publ: Eden, a modern myth, Dalhousie Rev, Vol. 52, No. 2. Add: Hutchins School of Liberal Studies, California State College, Sonoma, 1801 E. Cotati Ave, Rohnert Park, CA 94928.

MOUNTS, CHARLES EUGENE, b. Moravia, Iowa, Mar. 12, 06; m. 26; c. 2. ENGLISH LITERATURE. A.B, Univ. Fla, 26, A.M, 29; fel, Duke Univ, 36-37, Ph.D, 41. Asst, UNIV. FLA, 26-27, instr, 27-37, asst. prof. ENG, 37-45, assoc. prof, 45-57, prof, 57-60, EMER. PROF, 60- Instr, Duke Univ, 35-36; assoc. prof, Jacksonville State Col, 60-61; Univ. Idaho, 61-62; High Point Col, 62-64, prof, 64-74. MLA; S.Atlantic Mod. Lang. Asn; Southeast Renaissance Conf. Spenser; contemporary literature; creative writing. Publ: Spenser and the seven corporal works of mercy, PMLA; Spenser and the Countess of Leicester, J. Eng. Lit. Hist; Colin Clout, priest of Cupid and Venus, High Point Stud, 63. Add: 803 Montlieu Ave, High Point, NC 27262.

MOWRER, EDGAR A, English, Philosophy. See Volume IV, Philosophy, Religion & Law.

MOYES, NORMAN B, b. Fairmont, W.Va, Aug. 26, 31; m. 60; c. 3. JOURNALISM. A.B, W.Liberty State Col, 53; M.A, W.Va. Univ, 56; Ph.D.(commun), Syracuse Univ, 66. Instr. Eng. & jour, W.Liberty State Col, 56-59; JOUR, Syracuse Univ, 60-66; asst. prof, BOSTON UNIV, 66-69, ASSOC. PROF, 69- Sig.C, U.S.A, 53-55. Asn. Educ. in Jour. Newspaper; advertising; photography. Publ: Co-auth, Journalism in the mass media, 69 & Mass media journalism, 74, Ginn. Add: Dept. of Journalism, School of Public Communication, Boston University, Boston, MA 02215.

MOYNAHAN, JULIAN LANE, b. Cambridge, Mass, May, 21, 25; m. 45; c. 3. ENGLISH. A.B, Harvard, 47, A.M, 51, Ph.D, 56. Teaching fel. gen. educ, Harvard, 51-53; instr. Eng, Amherst Col, 53-55; asst. prof. Eng. lit, Princeton 55-63; assoc. prof, ENG, RUTGERS UNIV, 64-65, PROF, 65- Donald Stauffer Bicentennial Preceptor, Princeton, 60-63; Am. Counc. Learned Soc. grant-in-aid, 61; Fulbright-Hayes lectr, Univ. Col, Dublin Univ, 63-64; Am. Philos. Soc. grant-in-aid, 64; Nat. Endowment for Arts award, 67-68; Ingraham-Merrill Found. award for creative writing, 71-72; Nat. Endowment for Humanities vis. prof, Manhattanville Col, fall 72. MLA; Int. Asn. Univ. Prof. Eng. Anglo-Irish literature, 1880-1940; Charles Dickens; H.G. Wells. Publ: Sisters and brothers, Random, 60 & Heinemann, 61; Deed of life: the novels and tales of D.H. Lawrence, Princeton & Oxford, 63; Pairing off, Heinemann & William Morrow, 69; D.H. Lawrence: Sons and lovers, Viking, 68; Vladimir Nabokov, Univ. Minn, 70; Garden state, a novel, Little, 73; preface, Nabokov's Priglashenie ma Kazn (Invitation to a beheading), Victor, Paris, 67; From a view to a death: pastoralism as culture and counter-culture in the English novel, 1800-1927, Novel: Forum on Fiction, 72. Add: Scott Hall, Rutgers University, New Brunswick, NJ 08903.

MOYNE, ERNEST JOHN, b. Hanko, Finland, May 3, 16; nat; m. 43; c. 1. AMERICAN LITERATURE. A.B, Yale, 38, A.M, 40; Dexter traveling fel, Harvard, 47, Ph.D.(Eng. philol), 48. Instr. Eng, Williams Col, 42-43; UNIV. DEL, 48-51, asst. prof, 51-56, assoc. prof, 56-64, prof, 64-72, H.F. DU PONT WINTERTHUR PROF. AM. LIT, 72- U.S.A, 43-46. MLA; Am. Stud. Asn. Comparative literature; English literature. Publ: Transl. & ed, A half year in the New World, Univ. Del, 54; auth, A study of the relationship between Longfellow's Indian edda and the Finnish epic, Acad. Scientiarum Fennica, 63; ed, The journal of Margaret Hazlitt: recollections of England, Ireland, and America, Univ. Kans, 67; auth, Leaves of grass and Granite boulders: Walt Whitman and Finland, Neuphilol. Mitt, 1/72; Henry Adams and Peter Haggerstein, Scand. Stud, summer 73; Mark Twain and Baroness Alexandra Gripenberg, Am. Lit, 11/73; plus others. Add: Dept. of English, University of Delaware, Newark, DE 19711.

MOYNIHAN, ROBERT DUNCAN, b. Denver, Colo, June 26, 36; m. 62; c. 2. ENGLISH LITERATURE. B.A, Regis Col, 58; M.A, Univ. Colo, 61; Ph.D. (Eng), Univ. Ariz, 69. Instr. ENG, Univ. Ariz, 61-67; asst. prof, STATE UNIV. N.Y. COL, ONEONTA, 67-69, ASSOC. PROF, 69- Inst. Int. Educ. fel, 68 & 69; Nat. Endowment Humanities fel, 73. MLA; Northeast Mod. Lang. Asn; Am. Soc. 18th Century Stud; Eng. Inst. Eighteenth century English novel; contemporary philosophy and literature. Publ: Clarissa and the enlightened woman as literary heroine, J. Hist. Ideas, 74. Add: Dept. of English, State University of New York College at Oneonta, Oneonta, NY 13820.

MOYNIHAN, WILLIAM T, b. Haverhill, Mass, June 23, 27; m. 53; c. 5. LITERATURE. B.A, St. Bonaventure Univ, 52; M.A, Univ. Conn, 57; Beebe fel, Brown Univ, 60-61, Ph.D, 62; Kent fel, 59. Instr. ENG, UNIV. CONN, 56-59, 61, asst. prof, 62-65, assoc. prof, 65-67, PROF. & HEAD DEPT, 67- U.S.M.C, 46-49. MLA; Col. Eng. Asn. Modern British and American literature. Publ: Co-auth, Using prose, Dodd, 61 & Reading writing and rewriting, Lippincott, 64; auth, The craft & art of Dylan Thomas, Cornell Univ, 66; Joyce's The dead, Allyn & Bacon, 66; Essays today # 6, 68, # 7, 71, Harcourt. Add: Dept. of English, University of Connecticut, Storrs, CT 06268.

MUCHNIC, HELEN, Modern Comparative Literature. See Volume III, Foreign Languages, Linguistics & Philology.

MUCKLEY, ROBERT L, English as a Second Language. See Volume III, Foreign Languages, Linguistics & Philology.

MUDRICK, MARVIN, b. Philadelphia, Pa, July 17, 21; m. 46; c. 4. ENGLISH. A.B, Temple Univ, 42; M.A, Univ. Calif, Berkeley, 47, Ph.D.(Eng), 49. Instr. ENG, Temple Univ, 47; UNIV. CALIF, SANTA BARBARA, 49-51, asst. prof, 51-57, assoc. prof, 57-63, PROF, 63-, PROVOST, COL. CREATIVE STUD, 67- Guggenheim fel, 59-60; vis. prof, Queens Col.(N.Y), 60-61. U.S.A.A.F, 42-45. Chaucer; theory of fiction; writing of fiction. Publ: Jane Austen, Princeton, 52; On culture and literature, Horizon, 70; contrib, Hudson Rev. Add: Dept. of English, University of California, Santa Barbara, CA 93106.

MUELLER, HENRY LANCASTER, b. Cape Girardeau, Mo, Apr. 15, 15. SPEECH. A.B, Southeast. Mo. State Teachers Col, 37, B.S, 38; Syracuse Univ, 41-42; A.M, Univ. Mo, 42; Columbia Univ, 44-48. Instr, Syracuse Univ, 41-43; Univ. Mo, 43-44; instr, Teachers Col, Columbia Univ, 44-48; from asst. prof. to assoc. prof. speech, UNIV. ILL, URBANA-CHAMPAIGN, 48-62, PROF. SPEECH, 62- Lectr, Columbia Univ, 45-46, col. dent. & oral hygiene, 47; ed, Speech Teacher, 55-57. Speech Commun. Asn; NEA. Pronunciation of suffixes; film and television. Publ: Dusk or dawn: new books about film, Quart. J. Speech, 10/61; Teaching screen appreciation in English schools, 3/62 & The screen arts: no longer neglected, 9/67, Speech Teacher. Add: 244 Lincoln Hall, University of Illinois at Urbana-Champaign, Urbana, IL 61801.

MUELLER, IRIS WESSEL, b. St. Louis, Mo, Oct. 20, 28; m. 50; c. 1. ENGLISH. A.B, Wash. Univ, 48, M.A, 49; Ph.D.(Eng), Univ. Ill, 54. MEM. FAC. ENG, FINCH COL, 54-, DEAN COL, 70- MLA. Victorian romantic and modern American literature. Publ: John Stuart Mill and French thought, Univ. Ill, 55. Add: Finch College, 52 E. 78th St, New York, NY 10021.

MUELLER, JANEL M, b. Chicago, Ill, Nov, 26, 38; m. 60; c. 2. ENGLISH. A.B, Augustana Col.(Ill), 59; A.M, Radcliffe Col, 61; Ph.D.(Eng), Harvard, 65. ASST. PROF. Eng, Univ. Ill, Urbana, 66-67; ENG. & COL. HUMANITIES, UNIV. CHICAGO, 67- Sixteenth and seventeenth century English literature, especially poetry and prose of John Donne. Publ: Ed, Donne's Prebend sermons, Harvard, 71; auth, The exegesis of experience: Donne's Devotions, J. Eng. & Ger. Philol, 1/68; Ibsen's wild duck, Mod. Drama, 69; Donne's epic venture in the Metempsychosis, Mod Philol, 72. Add: Dept. of English, University of Chicago, Chicago, IL 60637.

MUELLER, JOAN EILEEN, b. Willmar, Minn, Jan. 2, 29. ENGLISH. B.A, Ohio Wesleyan Univ, 50, M.A, 51, grad. sch. res. grant, Ohio State Univ, 57-58, Ph.D, 59. Instr. Eng, Cottey Col, 52-53; lectr, South. Ill. Univ, 53-54; asst, Ohio State Univ, 54-57; instr. ENG, Lake Forest Col, 58-59; asst. prof, HOPE COL, 60-66, assoc. prof, 66-72, PROF, 72- Hope Col. res. grants, summer 62 & spring 69; Great Lakes Cols. Asn. grant film stud, 67-68; U.S. Dept. Labor grant, White Freedom Sch, 68-69, values definition & selection grant, 70-71. English Renaissance; American literature; interdisciplinary studies. Add: Dept. of English, Hope College, Holland, MI 49423.

MUELLER, MARTIN, b. Breslau, Ger, June 24, 39; m. 65. ENGLISH & COMPARATIVE LITERATURE. M.A, Ind. Univ, 62, Ph.D.(classics), 66. Instr. Eng, Brandeis Univ, 65-66, asst. prof, 66-67; Univ. Col, UNIV. TORONTO, 67-71, ASSOC. PROF. ENG. & COMP. LIT, 71- Can. Coun. leave fel, 72-73. MLA; Am. Comp. Lit. Asn. Epic tradition; influence of classical on European tragedy. Publ: Pathos and katharsis in Samson Agonistes, ELH, 64; Paradise lost and the Iliad, Comp. Lit. Stud, 69; Hermione's wrinkles, Comp. Drama, 71; plus others. Add: Graduate Program in Comparative Literature, University of Toronto, Toronto 181, Ont, Can.

MUELLER, ROGER C, b. Arlington, Minn, Aug. 14, 35; m. 58; c. 1. ENGLISH. B.A, Macalester Col, 57; M.A, Univ. Minn, 65, Ph.D.(Eng), 68. Teaching assoc. Eng, Univ. Minn, Minneapolis, 64-68; asst. prof. LIT, CALLISON COL, UNIV. OF THE PAC, 69-73, ASSOC. PROF, 73- Nat. Endowment for Humanities teaching resident, Bucknell Univ, 68-69, acting ed, Bucknell Rev, 68-69; Am. Philos. Soc. grant, 71. U.S.A, 57-58. MLA. American interest in the Orient. Publ: Transcendental periodicals and the Orient, Emerson Soc. Quart, 69; Samuel Johnson (1822-1882): university religion in 19th century, Aryan Path, 72. Add: Callison College, University of the Pacific, Stockton, CA 95204.

MUELLER, WILLIAM RANDOLPH, b. Baltimore, Md, July 10, 16; m. 45; c. 3. ENGLISH, THEOLOGY. A.B, Princeton, 39; M.A.(Eng), Harvard, 41, Ph.D.(Eng), 46; Ford fac. fel, 53-54; vis. fel, Yale, 53-54; M.A, Columbia Univ, 54. Instr. ENG, Williams Col.(Mass), 46-49; asst. prof, Univ. Calif, Santa Barbara, 48-51; Woman's Col. Univ. N.C, 51-56, assoc. prof, 56-59; Goucher Col, 59-61, prof, 61-73, chmn. dept, 59-64 & 71-72; DIR, HUMANITIES INST, BALTIMORE, 72- Guggenheim fel, 58-59; vis. prof, Princeton, 63-64; vis. prof, Princeton Univ. Theol. Sem, Drew Univ. Grad. Sch, Univ. Pa, Grad. Sch. Theol. Univ. of the South, St. Mary's Sem. & Univ. Sch. Theol. & Johns Hopkins Univ. Sch. Health Serv, 68-72. U.S.N.R, 42-46. Contemporary literature; theological and philosophic ideas in literature. Publ: The anatomy of Robert Burton's England, Univ. Calif, 52; Prophetic voice in modern fiction, Asn. Press, 59; John Donne: preacher, Princeton, 62; co-auth, The testament of Samuel Beckett, 64 & Ionesco and Genet: playwrights of silence, 68, Hill & Wang; Celebration of life: studies in modern fiction, Sheed & Ward, 72. Add: Director's Office, Humanities Institute, Box 515, Brooklandville, MD 21022.

MUELLERLEILE, MARY ALICE, b. St. Paul, Minn, Feb. 18, 37. ENGLISH. B.A, Col. St. Catherine, 61; M.A, Univ. Chicago, 63, Ph.D.(Eng), 67. Asst. prof. ENG, COL. ST. CATHERINE, 67-71, ASSOC. PROF, 71- Am. Philos. Soc. fel, summer 68; Nat. Endowment for Humanities fel, 71-72. Jane Austen. Add: Dept. of English, College of St. Catherine, St. Paul, MN 55105.

MUIR, ARTHUR LAURENCE, b. Holden, Mass, Nov. 11, 07; m; c. 2. LITERATURE. A.B, Oberlin Col, 29; Ph.D, Cornell Univ, 34. Instr. ENG, Adams State Teachers Col, Colo, 32-33, asst. prof, 33-35; UNIV. ARIZ, 35-41, assoc. prof, 41-48, PROF, 48-, head dept, 62-72. Vis. prof, Cornell Univ, summer 48; vis. prof, Univ. Ore, 54-55. U.S.N.R, 44-46, Lt. Comdr. MLA; Mediaeval Acad. Am; Philol. Asn. Pac. Coast (pres, 62-63). Old and middle English Biblical translations. Publ: Co-ed, Forum: a book of essays for college English; auth, Biblical translations, paraphrases, and commentaries, In: A manual of the writings in middle English, 1050-1500, Fascicule 2, 69. Add: Dept. of English, University of Arizona, Tucson, AZ 85721.

MULDER, JOHN RUDOLPH, b. Deventer, The Netherlands, Sept. 15, 32; Can. citizen. COMPARATIVE LITERATURE. B.A, Univ. West. Ont, 59, M.A, 60; Ph.D.(comp. lit), Univ. Mich, 63. Lectr. ENG, Univ. West. Ont, 61-64; asst. prof, N.Y. Univ, 64-70, assoc. prof, 70-73; A.W. MELLON FOUND. ASSOC. PROF. LIT, DREW UNIV, 73- Assoc. ed, Seventeenth Century News, 65-; ser. ed, Pegasus Press, 67- Sig.C, Royal Dutch Army. Renaissance Soc. Am. Milton; metaphysical poetry and prose; Pascal. Publ: The temple of the mind, Pegasus, 69; transl. & introd, Selections from the Latin Defenses of John Milton, In: The prose of John Milton, Doubleday, 67; auth, George Herbert's The Temple: design and methodology, Seventeenth Century News, 73. Add: Dept. of English, Box 176, Drew University, Madison, NJ 07940.

MULHAUSER, FREDERICK LUDWIG, b. Cleveland, Ohio, June 21, 11; m. 37; c. 1. ENGLISH LITERATURE. A.B, Col. Wooster, 32; A.M, Yale, 34, Ph.D, 37; Oxford, 49-50. Instr. ENG, Hiram Col, 35-36; Northwest. Univ, 36-41; from instr. to assoc. prof, POMONA COL, 41-52, PROF, 52- Mem. fac, U.S. Army Univ, Italy, 45; Guggenheim fel, 56-57; Fulbright res. fel, Italy, 63-64. MLA. Victorian literature; tradition of Burke. Publ: Poems of Arthur Hugh Clough, & Correspondence of Arthur Hugh Clough, Oxford. Add: Dept. of English, Pomona College, Claremont, CA 91711.

MULL, DOROTHY SIPE, b. Bayonne, N.J, Feb. 4, 39; m. 68; c.2. ENGLISH LITERATURE & LANGUAGE. B.A, Cornell Univ, 59; B.A, Cambridge, 61, M.A, 66; M.A, Yale, 62, Ph.D.(Eng), 64. Instr. ENG, Yale, 63-64; assoc. prof, South. Univ, 65-67; asst. prof, Univ. Wis-Madison, 67-69; ASSOC. PROF, UNIV. MASS, BOSTON, 69- Spec. lectr, La. State Univ, 66-67. MLA; AAUP. Historical English philology; Renaissance and medieval English literature. Publ: Shakespeare's metrics, Yale Univ, 68. Add: Dept. of English, University of Massachusetts, Boston, MA 02125.

MULLALY, COLUMBA, S.N.D, b. Washington, D.C, Apr. 28, 02. ENGLISH, EDUCATIONAL PSYCHOLOGY. A.B, Trinity Col.(D.C), 25; M.A, Cath. Univ. Am, 40, Ph.D.(educ. psychol), 52; summer, Oxford, 54. Secy. social action dept, Nat. Cath. Welfare Conf, 26-27; teacher, high schs, Pa, 30-40, supvr, Md, 40-41; instr. Eng, TRINITY COL.(D.C), 41-43, asst. prof. educ. & dean stud, 43-50, assoc. prof. ENG, 50-52, PROF, 52-, ARCHIVIST, 72-, v.pres. in charge acad. affairs, 53-65, v.pres, inst. res, 65-72. Dir. Sophomore Group, Oxford, 66-68. MLA; Col. Eng. Asn; NCTE; Nat. Cath. Educ. Asn. Middle and 19th century English; memory and reading problems; prediction of college success in a liberal arts curriculum. Publ: The retention and recognition of information learned from one reading of a prose article, Cath. Univ. Am; Notre Dame Child Guidance Clinic, Cath. Educ. Rev. Add: Dept. of English, Trinity College, Washington, DC 20017.

MULLALY, EDWARD JOSEPH, b. St. John, N.B, Feb. 16, 49; m. 70. AMERICAN LITERATURE, THEATRE HISTORY. B.A, Univ. Windsor, 63; M.A, Univ. N.B. Fredericton, 66, Ph.D.(Eng), 70. Lectr. ENG, St. Thomas Univ. (N.B), 69-70, ASST. PROF, 70-71; UNIV. N.B. FREDERICTON, 71- Asn. Can. Univ. Teachers Eng. Works of Archibald MacLeish; history of the London stage. Publ: Archibald MacLeish: a checklist, Kent State Univ, 73; O'Neill and the perfect pattern, Dalhousie Rev, winter 72; The rebirth of theatre in New Brunswick, In: Drama Canada, Univ. Toronto, 72. Add: Dept. of English, Carleton Hall, University of New Brunswick, Fredericton, N.B, Can.

MULLANY, PETER F, b. New York, N.Y, May 22, 33; m. 61; c. 2. ENGLISH RENAISSANCE, SHAKESPEARE. B.A, Fordham Univ, 55, M.A, 59, Ph.D.(Eng), 67. Instr. ENG, Fordham Univ, 60-65; Adelphi Univ, 65-67; ASST. PROF, Marquette Univ, 67-71; FAIRLEIGH DICKINSON UNIV, 71- U.S.A.R, 58-63. MLA. Medieval literature; Renaissance literature; Shakespeare. Publ: Co-auth, The Victorian poets: a review guide, 63 & auth, Marlowe's Dr. Faustus and other plays: a review guide, 65, Monarch; Chaucer's miller and Pilates voys, Am. Notes & Queries, 64; Religion in Massinger's The maid of honour, Renaissance Drama, 68. Add: Dept. of English, Fairleigh Dickinson University, Rutherford, NJ 07070.

MULLEN, RICHARD D, b. Mountain View, Mo, Sept. 30, 15; m. 38. ENGLISH. A.B, Univ. Ala, 49; M.A, Univ. Miss, 50; Ph.D, Univ. Chicago, 55. Instr. ENG, Univ. Miss, 50-51, 53-56; asst. prof, IND. STATE UNIV, TERRE HAUTE, 56-59, assoc. prof, 59-68, PROF, 68- U.S.A, 43-45, Capt; Silver Star, Bronze Star Medal. MLA; Sci. Fiction Res. Asn. English drama to 1642; English literature 1500-1660; science fiction. Publ: Ed, Science fiction studies, Ind. State Univ, 73-; Auth, Blish, van Vogt and the uses of Spengler, 8/68 & The prudish prurience of Haggard and Burroughs, 8/73, Riverside Quart; The undisciplined imagination: E.R. Burroughs and Lowellian Mars, In: Science fiction: the other side of realism, Bowling Green Popular Press, 71. Add: Dept. of English, Indiana State University, Terre Haute, IN 47809.

MULLEN, ROBERT WILLIAM, b. Melrose, Mass. Nov. 1, 37; c. 2. SPEECH COMMUNICATION. B.S, Emerson Col, 60, M.A, 62; Ph.D, Ohio State Univ, 71. ASST. PROF. SPEECH, NORTH. KY. STATE COL, 71- U.S.A, 62-68. Speech Commun. Asn. Publ: Blacks in America's wars, Pathfinder, 73. Add; Dept. of Speech, Northern Kentucky State College, Highlands Heights, KY 41076.

MULLER, GILBERT HENRY, b. Brooklyn, N.Y, Nov. 8, 41; m. 64; c. 2. AMERICAN LITERATURE. Ph.D.(Eng. & Am. lit), Stanford Univ, 67. Teaching asst. Eng. & Renaissance lit, Stanford Univ, 64-66; asst. prof. AM. & COMP. LIT, Pahlavi Univ, Iran, 67-71; from asst. prof. to ASSOC. PROF, LaGUARDIA COMMUNITY COL, CITY UNIV. NEW YORK, 71- Nat. Endowment for Humanities fel, 74. NEA; Am. Stud. Asn; MLA; Am. Fed. Teachers. Interdisciplinary studies; American studies; rhetoric and composition. Publ: Nightmares and visions: Flannery O'Connor and the Catholic grotesque, Univ. Ga, 72; Comparison and contrast, Harper, 74; Flannery O'Connor's Dantean vision, Ga. Rev, 6/69; Revolutionary romanticism, New Republic, 9/72; Faulkner's Red leaves and the garden of the south, Stud. Short Fiction, 74; plus others. Add: 23 Monfort Rd, Port Washington, NY 11050.

MULLER, HERBERT JOSEPH, b. Mamaroneck, N.Y, July 7, 05. LITERARY CRITICISM. A.B, Cornell Univ, 25, A.M, 26, Ph.D, 32; D.Litt, Purdue Univ, 60. Instr. Eng, Cornell Univ, 26-35; Guggenheim fel, 39-40; for. serv. auxiliary off, U.S. Dept. State, 43; ed, War Prod. Bd, 44; from asst. prof. to prof. Purdue Univ, 45-55; prof. ENG. & GOVT, IND. UNIV, 56-59, distinguished serv. prof, 59-73, EMER. PROF, 73- Vis. prof, Istanbul Univ, 46-47 & 51-52; distinguished vis. prof, N.Y. Univ, 58; Sloan vis. prof, Menninger Found, 63; distinguished vis. prof, Univ. Ala, 67. Phi Beta Kappa Award, 62; Frederic G. Melcher Book Award, 64. Am. Acad. Arts & Sci; World Acad. Arts & Sci. Philosophy of history; tragic drama; history of freedom. Publ: Modern fiction, 37; Science and criticism, 43; Thomas Wolfe, 47; The uses of the past, 52; The spirit of tragedy, 56; The loom of history, 58; Issues of freedom, 60; Freedom in the ancient world, 61; Freedom in the western world, 62; Religion and freedom in the modern world, 63; The individual in a revolutionary world, 64; Freedom in the modern world, 66; Adlai Stevenson: a study in values, 67; The uses of English, 67; The children of Frankenstein, 70 & In pursuit of relevance, 71, Ind. Univ. Add: Dept. of English, Indiana University, Bloomington, IN 47401.

MULLICAN, JAMES STANLEY, b. Elizabethtown, Ky, Sept. 3, 30; m. 58; c. 5. RHETORIC, ENGLISH. A.B, St. Bernard Col, 55; M.A, Ind. State Univ, Terre Haute, 58; fel, Purdue Univ. W.Lafayette, 65-66, Ph.D.(Eng), 68. Teacher, Decker Chapel High Sch, Ind, 55-57, teacher & libr, 57-58; Attica High Sch, Ind, 58-59; instr, ENG. & social stud, Lab. Sch, IND. STATE UNIV, TERRE HAUTE, asst. prof, 62-64, asst. prof, Univ, 64-69, assoc. prof, 69-71, PROF, 73-, ASSOC. CHMN. DEPT, 72-, acting chmn. dept. 71-72. NCTE; Col. Eng. Asn. Kenneth Burke's rhetorical theory; Emily Dickinson's poetry; teaching of English. Dickinson's Water makes many beds, 11/68 & Dickinson's Praise it—tis dead, 4/69, Explicator; Kenneth Burke's comic attitude: a corrective to propaganda analysis, Contemporary Educ, 11/71. Add: Dept. of English, Indiana State University, Terre Haute, IN 47809.

MULLIN, DONALD C, b. Nutley, N.J, Mar. 6, 24. DRAMA. B.A, State Univ. Iowa, 49, M.A, 50. Instr. DRAMA, Lehigh Univ, 50-51; St. Louis Univ, 51-52; asst. prof, San Diego State Col, 52-53; instr. W.Va. Univ, 55-56; asst. prof, Valparaiso Univ, 56-60; Tufts Univ, 60-65; assoc. prof, Col. St. Benedict, 65-67; UNIV. GUELPH, 67-72, PROF, 72- Humanities Asn. Can. Theatre architecture; theatre history; dramatic theory and criticism. Publ: Development of the playhouse, Univ. Calif, 70; Theatre architecture, In: Encycl. Americana, Grolier, 72; plus three others. Add: Dept. of Drama, University of Guelph, Guelph, Ont. Can.

MULLIN, MICHAEL, b. Chicago, Ill, Nov. 30, 44; m. 66; c. 2. ENGLISH LITERATURE, DRAMA. Whitehall Found. fel, Col. Holy Cross, 62-66, A.B, 66; Edward & Charles Suissman fel, Yale, 66-70, Danforth fel, 68-70, M. M.Phil, 70, Ph.D.(Eng), 72. Instr. ENG, UNIV. ILL, URBANA, 70-72, ASST. PROF, 72-, summer fac. fel, 73. Nat. Endowment for Humanities younger humanist fel, summer 73. Soc. Theatre Res. Eng; Am. Soc. Theatre Res; Shakespeare Asn. Am; MLA. Shakespeare in performance; theatre; stage history. Publ: Macbeth on the modern stage: performance as criticism, Univ. Microfilms, 73; Macbeth on film, Lit/Film Quart, winter 73; Auguries and understood relations: Theodore Komisarjevsky's Macbeth, Educ. Theatre J, 3/74. Add: Dept. of English, University of Illinois, Urbana, IL 61801.

MULLING, LEON CHARLES, b. Denver, Colo, Mar. 15, 14. SPEECH, DRAMA. A.B, Colo. State Col, 36, M.A, 40; Ph.D.(speech path), Stanford Univ, 60. Teacher, High Sch, Colo, 36-41; instr, Univ. Ore. High Sch, 41-42; speech & Eng, SOUTH ORE. COL, 46-49, asst. prof. SPEECH, 49-54, assoc. prof, 54-60, PROF, 60-, chmn. dept. speech & drama, 60-73. Guest lectr, Sacramento State Col, summer 51; vis. prof, Univ. Colo, summer 54; sabbatical study, Europe, 60, summer 67, 69, 73; coord, Cleft-palate Prog, Govt. of Guam, summers 63, 64. U.S.N. Am. Speech & Hearing Asn; Speech Commun. Asn; West. Speech Commun. Asn. Speech correction in the public schools; methodology in speech therapy; communicative disorders, etiology and treatment of. Publ: Rhymes for speech improvement, 68; Help your child to better speech. Add: Dept. of Speech Communication & Theatre, Southern Oregon College, Ashland, OR 97520.

MULLWEE, DELORIS ROBINSON, b. Tioga, W.Va, Oct. 24, 30; m. 61; c. 1. ENGLISH. B.A, Furman Univ, 55; M.A, Univ. S.C, 62, Ph.D.(Eng), 69. Instr. Eng. & dir. pub. relat, North Greenville Jr. Col, 56-60; pub. relat. asst, Furman Univ, 60-61; instr. Eng. & jour, Spartanburg Jr. Col, 61-65; ASST. PROF. ENG, Limestone Col, 65-66; NEWBERRY COL, 70- Pub. relat. consult, Mullwee Pub. Relat. & Advert, 73-; dir, Blue Ribbon Cooking Sch, 73-; dramatic monologist, Emily Dickinson's Reminiscences, 73- MLA; Col. Eng. Asn; AAUP. Water imagery in Tennyson's In Memoriam; the ballad tradition in Hardy's major novels; the role of the sun in Camus' The Stranger. Publ: Poems for fun and thought, Piedmont Publ, 64. Add: Dept. of English, Newberry College, Newberry, SC 29108.

MULRYAN, JOHN JAMES, b. New York, N.Y, May 19, 39; m. 63; c. 4. RENAISSANCE LITERATURE. B.A, Iona Col, 61; M.A, Marquette Univ, 63; fel, Southeast. Inst. Medieval & Renaissance Stud, summer 68; Ph.D.(Eng), Univ. Minn, 69. Asst. prof. ENG, ST. BONAVENTURE UNIV, 66-70, ASSOC. PROF, 70-, grant, summer 73. Summers, Col. Ctr. Finger Lakes grant, 70; grant, Newberry Libr, 71; Am. Philos. Soc. grants, 72, 73; fel, Huntington Libr, 73. MLA; Renaissance Soc. Am; S.Cent. Renaissance Soc; Northeast Mod. Lang. Asn. Classical and continental influences on English

Renaissance literature; post-classical mythology; neo-Latin studies. Publ: Vincenzo Cartari's Imagini: a translation with introduction, Renaissance, 74; The function of ritual in the marriage songs of Catullus, Spenser and Ronsard, Ill. Quart, 12/72; The occult tradition and English Renaissance literature, Bucknell Rev, winter 72; Aulus Gellius and Milton's Il Penseroso, Am. Notes & Queries, (in press); plus others. Add: Dept. of English, St. Bonaventure University, P.O. Box 85, St. Bonaventure, NY 14778.

MUNDAY, MILDRED BRAND, b. Lynchburg, Va, Apr. 16, 18. RENAISSANCE DRAMA. A.B, Randolph-Macon Woman's Col, 40, A.M, Smith Col, 47; Ph.D, Univ. Wis, 53. Instr. ENG, West. Col. Women, 47-49; from instr. to asst. prof, Bucknell Univ, 53-55; assoc. prof, Evansville Col, 59-63; Otterbein Col, 63-65; lectr, OHIO STATE UNIV, 67-68, ASST. PROF, 68- W.A.C, 43-46, Capt. MLA; Renaissance Soc. Am; Col. Eng. Asn; NCTE. Shakespeare; Renaissance drama; women in literature. Add: Dept. of English, Ohio State University, Columbus, OH 43210.

MUNFORD, HOWARD McCOY, b. Des Moines, Iowa, July 13, 12; m. 35; c. 2. AMERICAN LITERATURE. B.S, Middlebury Col, 34, A.M, Bread Loaf Sch. Eng, 39; Ph.D, Harvard, 51. Teacher, Clark Sch, 34-38; instr. AM. LIT, MIDDLEBURY COL, 41-43, asst. prof, 46-47, assoc. prof, 47-56, PROF, 56-, CHMN. DEPT, 67-, CHMN. HUMANITIES DIV, 70-71, 73-, COORD. AM. STUD. PROG, 71- Fund Advan. Educ. fel, 52-53; Fulbright lectr, Finland, 54-55 & Ger, 63-64; lectr, San Francisco State Col, summers 55, 63; U.S. specialist, Int. Educ. Exchange Serv, U.S. Dept. State, summers, India, 57, Soviet Union, 58. U.S.N.R, 43-46, Lt. MLA; Am. Stud. Asn. W.D. Howells; Henry Adams; Henry James. Publ: Henry Adams and the tendency of history, New Eng. Quart, 3/59; Henry James: the divided stream, Text & Kritik, Bremen, 12/66; Henry Adams: the limitations of science, South. Rev, 1/68. Add: Dept. of American Literature, Middlebury College, Middlebury, VT 05753.

MUNN, HARRY EUGENE, JR, b. Chicago, Ill, Feb. 28, 34; m. 67; c. 1. SPEECH COMMUNICATION, HUMAN RELATIONS. B.S, Univ. Wis-Eau Claire, 60; M.A, Bradley Univ, 62; Ph.D.(speech commun), Univ. Kans, 71. Teacher SPEECH, E.Peoria Community High Sch, 62-63; Chippewa Falls Sr. High Sch, 63-64; instr, Kent State Univ, 64-66; Univ. Fla, 66-67; asst. prof, Miami-Dade Jr. Col, 67-69; grad. asst, Univ. Kans, 69-71; ASST. PROF, N.C. STATE UNIV, 71- U.S.M.C, 53-56, Sgt. Speech Commun. Asn; South. Speech Commun. Asn; Int. Soc. Gen. Semantics. Speech education; organizational communication. Publ: One man's duck is another man's rabbit (words don't mean—people do), Persuader, winter 69; co-auth, The relationships between teachers task behavior, interpersonal maintenance behavior, student achievement, and student satisfaction, Speech Teacher, 11/73. Add: Speech Div, Box 5110, North Carolina State University, Raleigh, NC 27607.

MUNRO, BERTHA, b. Saugus, Mass, Feb. 19, 87. ENGLISH. A.B, Boston Univ, 07; A.M, Radcliffe Col, 16, 27-30. Teacher, high sch, Mass, 07-10; Col. Inst, North Scituate, R.I, 10-15; prof. Eng, Taylor Univ, 16-19; EAST. NAZARENE COL, 19-57, lit, 19-70, acad. dean, 23-57, EMER. DEAN, 57-, EMER. PROF. LIT, 70- NCTE; Col. Eng. Asn; MLA. Publ: Truth for today; The pilgrim's roadmap; Strength for today; Not somehow, but triumphantly; The years teach. Add: 90 Franklin Ave, Wollaston, MA 02170.

MUNSELL, PAUL EDWIN, English as a Second Language. See Volume III, Foreign Languages, Linguistics & Philology.

MUNSON, WILLIAM FREDERICK, b. Streator, Ill, Oct. 13, 37; m. 63; c. 2. ENGLISH. B.A, Oberlin Col, 58; M.A, Yale, 59, Ph.D.(Eng), 65. Instr. ENG, N.Y. UNIV, 63-66; ASST. PROF, UNIV. CALIF, RIVERSIDE, 66- Consult, humanities inst, Univ. Calif, 68. Medieval literature. Add: Dept. of English, University of California, Riverside, CA 92502.

MURDY, LOUISE BAUGHAN, b. Dover, N.H, Sept, 28, 35; m. 58; c. 2. ENGLISH. B.A, Univ. Fla, 57, Ph.D.(Eng), 62; M.A, Univ. N.C, Chapel Hill, 58. Instr. ENG, Fla. State Univ, 62-63; asst. prof, WINTHROP COL, 63-70, ASSOC. PROF, 70- South. Fel. Fund grant, 57-60. Victorian literature; modern poetry. Publ: Sound and sense in Dylan Thomas's poetry, Mouton, The Hague, 66; Dylan Thomas, In: Encycl. Americana, Grolier, 71. Add: Dept. of English, 224 Kinard Hall, Winthrop College, Rock Hill, SC 29730.

MURPHEY, JOSEPH COLIN, b. Lufkin, Tex, Dec. 13, 15; m; c. 2. COMPARATIVE LITERATURE, ENGLISH. B.S, Sam Houston State Col, 37; M.A, South. Methodist Univ, 53; summer, Univ. Ark, 55; Ph.D.(humanities in higher educ), Univ. Tex, 63. Teacher, Hurst-Euless Ind. Sch. Dist, 55-56. Corpus Christi Ind. Sch. Dist, 56-60; asst. prof. Eng. & humanities, Austin Col, 63-65; Eng. Ind. State Univ, 65-67; ASSOC. PROF. ENG. & HUMANITIES, SAM HOUSTON STATE UNIV, 67- Poetry ed, Southwest Rev, 64-66; lectr. rhet, NDEA Inst. Eng, Austin Col, summer 65; Ind. State Univ, summer 66; ed, Stone Drum lit. mag, 70. U.S.A.A.F, 42-46, S/Sgt. S.Cent. Mod. Lang. Asn; NCTE; Conf. Col. Compos. & Commun. Modern and contemporary poetry, British and American; modern and contemporary drama, European and American; 19th century poetry, European and British. Publ: Co-auth, Language arts curriculum guide, Sam Houston Curriculum Ctr, 68; auth, Trajectories, twelve space poems, Graphic Arts Dept. Sam Houston State Univ, 70; Eight poems, Ind. Sesquicentennial Poets, 67; Four steps of the creative act, Teachers Col. J, 3/67; Two sky diving poems, Antioch Rev, summer 67; plus over 100 poems in various literary quarterlies. Add: Box 2234, Sam Houston State University, Huntsville, TX 77340.

MURPHREE, ALBERT ALEXANDER, b. Tallahassee, Fla, Feb. 22, 08. ENGLISH LITERATURE. A.B, Univ. Fla, 29; Rhodes scholar, Oxford, 29, B.A, 33; Johns Hopkins Univ, 37-41. Instr, Univ. Fla, 34-37; Johns Hopkins Univ, 37-41; ASSOC. PROF. ENG. LIT, UNIV. FLA, 41- MLA. Critical opinions of John Dryden. Add: 202 Anderson Hall, University of Florida, Gainesville, FL 32601.

MURPHY, CHARLES DRISCOLL, b. New Diggings, Wis, Nov. 8, 08; m. 44; c. 3. ENGLISH LITERATURE. A.B, Univ. Wis, 29; A.M, Harvard, 30; Ph.D, Cornell Univ, 40. Instr. ENG, UNIV. MD, COLLEGE PARK, 31-40, asst. prof, 40-46, assoc. prof, 46-50, PROF, 50-, acting head dept, 49-58, head dept, 58-67. U.S.A, 42-46, Maj. MLA; Milton Soc. Am. Religious literature of the 17th century England; John Davies' versification of Sidney's prose; Milton. Add: Dept. of English, University of Maryland, College Park, MD 20740.

MURPHY, DANIEL J, b. New York, N.Y, Sept. 13, 21; m. 50; c. 3. ENGLISH. B.S, Columbia Univ, 49, M.A, 50, M.S. & Ph.D.(Eng), 61. Instr. ENG, Gen. Stud, Columbia Univ, 57-62; BARUCH COL, 62-65, asst. prof, 65-72, ASSOC. PROF, 72- Guggenheim fel, 65-66; Nat. Endowment for Humanities grant, 72-73. Anglo-Irish literature. Publ: Art of technical writing, Crowell & Bantam, 64; Writing and researching term papers and reports, 64 & Speed grammar, 67, Bantam; introd, Lady Gregory's Our Irish theatre, Capricorn, 67 & Gods and fighting men, Colin Smythe, 67; auth, College developmental reader, Free Press, 68; Practical grammar for writing, McGraw-Hill, 73; Letters of Lady Gregory to T.J. Kiernan, Bull. New York Pub. Libr, 12/67 & 1-2/68; Letters of Lady Gregory to G.B. Shaw, Mod. Drama, 2/68. Add: Dept. of English, Baruch College, 17 Lexington Ave, New York, NY 10010.

MURPHY, EDWARD FRANCIS, b. Pittsfield, Mass, Jan. 16, 19; m. 42; c. 6. ENGLISH. A.B, St. Michael's Col, 40, A.M, 47; M.Ed, Univ. Vt, 51; Boston Univ, 53; Ph.D, Univ. Ottawa, 59. Instr. Eng. & speech, ST. MICHAEL'S COL.(VT), 46-50, asst. prof, 50-59, assoc. prof, 59-63, PROF. ENG, 63-, chmn. dept, 60-70. Dir. prog. Eng. Int. Stud, 67-70. U.S.A, 43-45. MLA; Col. Eng. Asn; NCTE; Conf. Col. Compos. & Commun; Asn. Teachers of Eng. to Speakers of Other Lang. Bilingual education; Henry James; Katherine Anne Porter. Add: Dept. of English, St. Michael's College, Winooski, VT 05404.

MURPHY, FRANCIS, b. Springfield, Mass, Mar. 13, 32. ENGLISH & AMERICAN LITERATURE. B.A, Am. Int. Col, 53; M.A, Univ. Conn, 55; Ph.D. (Eng),Harvard Univ, 60. Assoc. prof. ENG, SMITH COL, 59-72, PROF, 72- Mem, Advan. Placement Exam. Comt, 68-69. Seventeenth, nineteenth, and twentieth century English and American literature. Publ: Ed, Poetry: form and structure, 64 & Major American poets to 1914, 67, Heath: Penguin critical anthology: Walt Whitman, Penguin, 69; Twentieth century views: Edward Arlington Robinson, Prentice-Hall, 69; Uncollected essays of Yvor Winters, Swallow, 73; The complete poetry of Walt Whitman, 74; Going it alone, Yale Rev, autumn 66. Add: Dept. of English, Language & Literature, Smith College, Northampton, MA 01060.

MURPHY, GEORGE DOUGLAS, b. Chicago, Ill, Aug. 24, 29; m. 56; c. 2. AMERICAN LITERATURE. B.A, Univ. Notre Dame, 49, M.A, 51; Ph.D. (Am. civilization), Univ. Pa, 64. Instr. ENG, VILLANOVA UNIV, 54-58, asst. prof, 58-64, ASSOC. PROF, 65- U.S.A, 52-54, Res, 54-68. Am. Stud. Asn. American biography; 19th century American fiction; modern American novel. Publ: Poe's ballistics, Am. Notes & Queries, 66; The theme of sublimation in Winesburg, Ohio, Mod. Fiction Stud, 67. Add: Dept. of English, Villanova University, Villanova, PA 19085.

MURPHY, GERALDINE, b. Cambridge, Mass, Apr. 13, 20. ENGLISH. A.B, Regis Col.(Mass), 41; M.A, Radcliffe Col, 42, Ph.D.(educ), 60. Teacher high sch, 44-54; asst. prof. educ. WESLEYAN UNIV, 57-60, assoc. prof, ENG. & EDUC, 62-70, PROF, 70- Fel, Harvard, 60-61. Massachusetts Bay Colony in the 17th century; the Irish Renaissance; development of the short story. Publ: The study of literature in high school, Blaisdell, Ginn, 68; ed, A momentary stay, Harper, 72; plus others. Add: 119 Wesleyan Station, Middletown, CT 06457.

MURPHY, JAMES JEROME, b. San Jose, Calif, Sept. 9, 23; m. 48; c. 2. ENGLISH & SPEECH. B.A, St. Mary's Col.(Calif), 47; M.A, Stanford Univ, 50, Ph.D.(Eng. lit), 57. Teacher, High Sch, 48-49; instr. speech & Eng. & dir. forensics, St. Mary's Col.(Calif), 50-53; instr. rhet. & pub. address, Stanford Univ, 54-57, asst. prof, 57-59, dir. forensics, 54-57; asst. prof. Eng, Princeton, 59-65; assoc. prof. speech, UNIV. CALIF, DAVIS, 65-66, PROF. RHET, 66-, ASSOC. DEAN COL. LETT. & SCI, 72-, chmn. dept, 66-72. Overseas res. grant, Princeton 60, bicentennial preceptor, 60-63; Am. Counc. Learned Soc. fel, 71-72; adv. ed, Biog. Dictionary Speech Educ; co-recipient grants Conf. Medieval Bibliog, Am. Counc. Learned Soc, Can. Counc. & UNESCO. U.S.A.A.F, 42-45, Maj. Speech Commun. Asn.(Golden Anniversary Award, 65); MLA; Mediaeval Acad. Am; Medieval Asn. Pac. (pres, 66-); West. Speech Commun. Asn; Philol. Asn. Pac. Coast. Humanities; classical and medieval rhetoric; Middle English literature. Publ: Co-auth, Debater's guide, 61 & auth, Quintilian on the early education of the citizen-orator, 65, Bobbs; Demosthenes on the crown: a case study, 67 & ed, A synoptic history of classical rhetoric, 71, Random; co-auth, Teaching urban youth, John Wiley, 67; auth, Medieval rhetoric: a select bibliography, Univ. Toronto, 71; ed. & contrib, Three medieval rhetorical arts, 71 & auth, Rhetoric in the Middle Ages: a history of rhetorical theory from Saint Augustine to the Renaissance, 74, Univ. Calif; auth, Arts of discourse, 1050-1400, Medieval Stud, 61; A new look at Chaucer & the rhetoricians, Rev. Eng. Stud, 2/64; Cicero's rhetoric in the Middle Ages, Quart. J. Speech, 4/67; plus others. Add: 915 Villanova Dr, Davis, CA 95616.

MURPHY, JOHN JOSEPH, b. Brooklyn, N.Y, Apr. 3, 33; m. 62; c. 4. ENGLISH, FOREIGN LITERATURE. B.A, St. John's Univ.(N.Y), 56, M.A, 61. Instr. ENG, Col. St. Teresa (Minn), 60-65; asst. prof, MERRIMACK COL, 65-69, ASSOC. PROF, 69- Delivered TV lect. ser, great ladies of Am. novel, KTCA-TV, St. Paul, Minn, fall 63, Hawthorne, fall 64; participant, NDEA Inst. Advan. Stud. Ling, Harvard, summer 68; coord. & participant, Willa Cather: a pre-centennial symposium, Merrimack Col, 10/72; participant int. sem, The art of Willa Cather, Univ. Nebr-Lincoln, 10/73. U.S.A, 58-60. American novel, particularly Hawthorne, James, Cather and Faulkner; French Canadian literature, especially Gabrielle Roy; American realism. Publ: The function of sin in Hawthorne's novels, Emerson Soc. Quart, 68; The satiric structure of Wharton's The age of innocence, Markham Rev, 5/70; The respectable romantic and the unwed mother: class consciousness in My Antonia, Colby Libr. Quart, 9/73; plus numerous others. Add: Dept. of English, Merrimack College, North Andover, MA 01845.

MURPHY, JOHN LEO, b. Calumet, Okla, July 27, 23. ENGLISH. B.A, St. Benedict's Col.(Kans), 43; Ph.D.(Eng), Univ. Okla, 63. Instr. ENG, Notre

Dame Univ, 57-59; UNIV. COLO, BOULDER, 60-64, asst. prof, 64-68, assoc. prof, 68-73, PROF, 73-, res. fel, 65-66. U.S.N.R, 43-46, Lt.(jg). MLA. Drama in the English Renaissance; non-dramatic Renaissance literature; 19th century criticism. Add: Dept. of English, University of Colorado, Boulder, CO 80302.

MURPHY, JOHN M, b. Chickasha, Okla, Apr. 11, 33. ENGLISH. B.A, Univ. Okla, 53, M.A, 56. Instr. Eng, Cent. State Col.(Okla), 58-59; spec. instr, Univ. Okla, 59-60 & 69-72; bus. mgr, NCTE, 61; asst. prof. ENG, Oklahoma City Univ, 62-67; vis. asst. prof, East. Ky. Univ, 67-68; prof. & chmn. dept, Cameron State Univ, 67-68; ADJ. PROF, OKLAHOMA CITY UNIV, 72- Consult, Tex. State Dept. Educ, spring 67; instr, Oscar Rose Jr. Col, 73- MLA; AAUP; NCTE (tour leader, Lit. through Brit. Isles, summer 72, ed. convention newslett, 73-75, chmn. nominating comt, 73, mem. Conf. Eng. Educ); charter mem. Renaissance Soc. Am; Conf. Col. Compos. & Commun: Milton Soc. Am. English literature of the Renaissance, especially Spenser; English pedagogy and interdisciplinary studies; linguistics. Publ: Co-auth, Literary map of Oklahoma, Okla. Counc. Teachers Eng, 60; auth, The fine print, Okla. Teacher, 3/61. Add: 501 N.W. 18th St, Oklahoma City, OK 73103.

MURPHY, JOHN VINCENT, b. Chicago, Ill, Oct. 12, 32; m. 63; c. 1. NINETEENTH CENTURY BRITISH LITERATURE. A.B, Wayne State Univ, 58; A.M, Univ. Mich, Ann Arbor, 63, fel, 64-66, 67-68, Ph.D.(Eng. lit), 69. Instr. ENG, Italian Ministry Aviation, 58-59; Eng. Lang. Serv, Congo, 61-63; teaching asst, Univ. Mich, Ann Arbor, 63-64, 66; asst. prof, Wis. State Univ-Oshkosh, 66-67; BUCKNELL UNIV, 68-74, ASSOC. PROF, 74- Reader & critic, Lock Haven Proj, Inst. Regional Affairs, 72-73, adv, Lewisburg Proj, 73; Nat. Endowment for Humanities summer sem. stipend, 74. U.S.N.R, 51-55, Res, 52-54. AAUP; MLA. Romantic poets; literature and human consciousness; modern European novel. Publ: The dark angel: Gothic elements in Shelley, 74 & Existentialism and mythic awareness, 75, Bucknell Univ; Don Quixote among the engineers, Bucknell Engr, summer 73. Add: Dept. of English, Bucknell University, Lewisburg, PA 17837.

MURPHY, KARL MICHAEL, b. Cambridge, Ohio, June 29, 14; m. 46; c. 3. ENGLISH. A.B, Kent State Univ, 41; A.M, Harvard, 47, Ph.D.(Eng), 49. Instr. ENG, Boston Univ, 47-48; N.Y. Univ, 49-51; asst. prof, GA. INST. TECHNOL, 51-56, assoc. prof, 56-62, PROF, 62-, acting dean grad. div, 67-68. Nat. Sci. Found. grant, 64-65; dir. Counc. Commun. Socs, 69- U.S.A.A.F, 42-46. Am. Bus. Commun. Asn.(dir, 69-73, pres, 70). English Renaissance; technical and business writing. Publ: Modern business letters, Houghton, 56; Business writing in the English department, Col. Eng, 3/62. Add: Dept. of English, Georgia Institute of Technology, Atlanta, GA 30332.

MURPHY, MARGARET SPARLING, b. Converse, Ind, May 30, 17; m. 55; c. 2. ENGLISH. A.B, Franklin Col, 39; M.A, Ind. Univ, 51. Teacher, pub. schs, Ind, 40-46; from asst. prof. to assoc. prof. ENG, Franklin Col, 46-59; ASSOC. PROF, ROCKY MT. COL, 61- NCTE. Development of Wordsworth's imagination, 1797-1807. Add: Dept. of English, Rocky Mountain College, Billings, MT 59102.

MURPHY, MICHAEL ANTHONY, b. Ireland, Sept. 4, 32; U.S. citizen; m. 64; c. 2. MEDIEVAL ENGLISH. B.A, Univ. London; Mellon fel, Univ. Pittsburgh, 62-64, Ph.D.(Eng), 65. Instr. ENG, Univ. Buffalo, 60-62; asst. prof, Duquesne Univ, 64-66; instr, BROOKLYN COL, 66-68, asst. prof, 68-72, ASSOC. PROF, 73- City Univ. N.Y. res. awards, 71-72, 73-74. Medieval English; history of language; pioneer scholars of Old English. Publ: John Foxe, martyrologist and editor of Old English, Eng. Stud, 68; Methods of study of Old English in the sixteenth and seventeenth centuries, Medieval Stud, 69; Religious polemic in the genesis of Old English studies, Huntington Libr. Quart, 69; plus three others. Add: Dept. of English, Brooklyn College, Brooklyn, NY 11210.

MURPHY, RICHARD, b. Marienville, Pa, Sept. 12, 03; m. 37; c. 2. SPEECH. A.B, Univ. Pittsburgh, 27, A.M, 28, Ph.D, 38; Cornell Univ, 34-35; State Univ. Iowa, summers, 29, 30; Univ. Edinburgh, Scotland, 31-32. Instr. Eng, Univ. Pittsburgh, 28-34; instr. rhet. & speech, Cornell Univ, 34-35; assoc. prof. Eng. & speech & dir. debate, Univ. Colo, 35-45; PROF. SPEECH, UNIV. ILL, URBANA, 45- Assoc. ed, Quart. J. Speech, 57-59, ed, 60-62; assoc. ed, Speech Teacher, 61-63; vis. prof, Cornell Univ, 65-66; Univ. N.C, Chapel Hill, summer 66. Rhetoric and literature. Publ: Debating, Theodore Roosevelt; Conference, forum and parliamentary procedure; co-ed, A course of lectures on oratory and criticism, South. Ill. Univ, 67 & An historical anthology of select British speeches, Ronald, 67; auth, The speech as literary genre, Quart. J. Speech, 4/58; Problems in speech texts, Rhetoric & Poetic, 65; Teaching rhetorical appreciation of literature, Eng. J, 5/66. Add: 244 Lincoln Hall, University of Illinois at Urbana, Urbana, IL 61801.

MURPHY, RICHARD ALLEN, Linguistics. See Volume III, Foreign Languages, Linguistics & Philology.

MURPHY, RICHARD JOSEPH, b. Chicago, Ill, Apr. 12, 37; c. 1. ENGLISH. B.A, Univ. Notre Dame, 59; M.A, Loyola Univ. Chicago, 64; Ph.D.(Eng), Duke Univ, 73. Instr. ENG, PROVIDENCE COL, 64-66, ASST. PROF, 68- U.S.A, 59, Res, 60-65. MLA; Northeast. Mod. Lang. Asn; Am. Soc. 18th Century Stud. Swift; novel; enlightenment. Add: Dept. of English, Providence College, Providence, RI 02918.

MURPHY, ROBERT PATRICK, b. Alexandria, Va, Mar. 25, 41; m. 64; c. 1. DRAMA, IRISH LITERATURE. B.A, Yale, 63; M.A, Univ. Va, 68, Ph.D. (Eng), 71. ASST. PROF. ENG, UNIV. IDAHO, 71- Nat. Endowment for Humanities summer stipend, 73. U.S.N, 63-67, Res, 67-, Lt. AAUP; MLA. Nineteenth century drama; 20th century drama. Publ: Sean O'Casey and The bald Primaqueera, James Joyce Quart, fall 70; Non-verbal communication and the overlooked action in Pinter's The caretaker, Quart. J. Speech, 2/72. Add: Dept. of English, University of Idaho, Moscow, ID 83843.

MURPHY, ROY DENNIS, b. Bellefontaine, Ohio, Feb. 2, 12; m. 39; c. 2. SPEECH. A.B, Wittenberg Col, 34, A.M, 38; Ohio State Univ, 37-39. Instr. SPEECH, Wittenberg Col, 35-37; asst, Ohio State Univ, 37-39; PROF, HEAD DEPT. & DIR. FORENSICS, UNIV. SOUTHWEST. LA, 39- Assoc. ed, The Forensic, 45-51. Am. Forensic Asn; Speech Commun. Asn; South. Speech Asn.(pres, 63-64). Forensics; rhetoric and public address; oratory and debate. Publ: Presidential acceptance speech - golden anniversary convention, Forensic, 5/63; A third of a century of Progress, South. Speech J, fall 64. Add: Dept. of Speech, University of Southwestern Louisiana, Lafayette, LA 70501.

MURPHY, WILLIAM MICHAEL, b. New York, N.Y, Aug. 6, 16; m. 39; c. 3. ENGLISH LITERATURE. A.B, Harvard, 38, A.M, 41, fel, 42-43, Ph.D, 47. Instr. Eng, Harvard, 38-40, secy, univ. comt. educ. relat, 40-42, asst. prof. ENG, UNION COL.(N.Y), 46-48, assoc. prof, 48-60, PROF, 60- Vis. prof, Univ. Freiburg, 53-54; Sem. Am. Stud, Univ. Frankfurt, 54; Am. Philos. Soc. grant, 67; Am. Counc. Learned Soc. fel, 68. U.S.N.R, 43-46, Lt. Am. Comt. Irish Stud; MLA; Int. Asn. Univ. Prof. Eng; Int. Asn. Stud. Anglo-Irish Lit; Can. Asn. Irish Stud. Irish Renaissance; Shakespeare; Chaucer. Publ: David Worcester, 1907-1947; co-auth, Challenges to thought; auth, The Yeats family and the Pollexfens of Sligo, Dolmen, Dublin, 71; ed, Letters from Bedford Park: a selection from the correspondence (1890-1901) of John Butler Yeats, Cuala, Dublin, 72; auth, Father and son: the early education of William Butler Yeats, Rev. Eng. Lit, 10/67; In memory of Alfred Pollexfen: W.B. Yeats and the theme of family, Irish Univ. Rev, fall 70; The ancestry of William Butler Yeats, Yeats Stud, spring 71; plus one other. Add: 1077 Glenwood Blvd, Schenectady, NY 12308.

MURRAY, BYRON D, b. Oregon, Mo, Sept. 19, 00; m. 25; c. 4. ENGLISH. A.B, Univ. Mo, 24, A.M, 26; B.S, Northwest Mo. State Col, 25; Ph.D.(Eng), State Univ. Iowa, 45. Instr. high schs, Clearmont, Mo, 21-23, Keithsburg, Ill, 24-25; Eng. & hist, Christian Col, 25-26; Eng. & jour, MOORHEAD STATE COL, 26-38, PROF. ENG, 39-, chmn. dept, 39-48, dir. upper div, 49-56, dir. grad. stud, 57-66. Lectr, summer ser, Moorhead State Col, 61, 65; Concordia Col. Ser, Moorhead, Minn, 62. Am. Stud. Asn; NEA. American intellectual history; James Russell Lowell. Publ: Commonwealth of Americans, Philos. Libr, 59; Lincoln and the mystic chords, Discourse, spring 61; Lincoln speaks, Contemporary Rev, 5/66; C.P. Snow: grounds for reappraisal, Personalist, winter 66. Add: 1516 S. 19½ St, Moorhead, MN 56560.

MURRAY, DIANE JOHNSON, b. Moline, Ill, Apr. 28, 34; m. 53; c. 4. NINETEENTH CENTURY NOVEL, VICTORIAN HISTORICAL BACKGROUND. B.A, Univ. Utah, 58; M.A, Univ. Calif, Los Angeles, 65, Am. Asn. Univ. Women pre-doctoral fel, 68-69, Ph.D.(Eng), 69. ASST. PROF. ENG, UNIV. CALIF, DAVIS, 68- MLA; PEN Club. Victorian biography; history of the novel; 19th century history. Publ: Fair game, 65, Loving hands at home, 68 & Burning, 71, Harcourt; Lesser lives, Knopf, 73. Add: 46 El Camino, Berkeley, CA 94705.

MURRAY, DONALD CHARLES, b. Buffalo, N.Y, Dec. 17, 35; m. 67. ENGLISH. B.A, Yale, 58; M.A, Duke Univ, 62; Ph.D.(Eng), Syracuse Univ, 66. ASST. PROF. ENG, Mary Washington Col, Univ. Va, 66-68; UNIV. SASK, REGINA, 68-, ACTING CHMN. DEPT, 73- MLA. Aldous Huxley; J.P. Donleavy; Djuana Barnes. Add: Dept. of English, University of Saskatchewan, Regina, Sask. S4S 0A2, Can.

MURRAY, DONALD M, b. Denver, Colo, Sept. 16, 17; m. 43; c. 2. ENGLISH. B.A, Syracuse Univ, 38; M.A, Univ. Ky, 40; Univ. Ill, 40-42; Ph.D, N.Y. Univ, 50. Instr. ENG, N.Y. Univ, 46-51; asst. prof, E.Carolina Col, 52-55; Univ. N.Dak, 55-57; assoc. prof, NORTH. ILL. UNIV, 57-60, PROF, 60- Fulbright lectr. Am. lit, Univ. Hong Kong, 67-68, 69-70. MLA. American literature. Publ: Co-auth, Horizon, Heath, 63; auth, Henry James in the advanced composition course, Col. Eng, 10/63; co-auth, Quality of Cathay: Ezra Pound's translations, Lit. E. & W, 9/66; auth, Candy Christian as pop art Daisy Miller, J. Popular Cult, fall 71. Add: Dept. of English, Northern Illinois University, De Kalb, IL 60115.

MURRAY, EDWARD JAMES, b. Brooklyn, N.Y, Apr. 8, 28; m. 54; c. 5. ENGLISH. B.A, Youngstown Univ, 62; Woodrow Wilson & NDEA fels, Univ. South. Calif, 65; Ph.D.(Eng), 66. Assoc. prof. ENG, West. Ill. Univ, 65-68; asst. prof, STATE UNIV. N.Y. COL. BROCKPORT, 68-72, ASSOC. PROF, 72- Lectr, West-Cent. Writers Conf, 67. Med.C, U.S.A, 51-53, Sgt. MLA. The modern novel; the modern drama; the motion picture. Publ: Arthur Miller, Dramatist, 67, Clifford Odets: the thirties and after, 68 & The cinematic imagination: writers and the motion pictures, 72, Ungar; Point of view in After the fall, CLA J, 12/66; Dramatic technique in The crucible, In: Twentieth century interpretations of The crucible, Spectrum Bks, 72; In cold blood: the filmic novel and the problem of adaptation, Lit/Film Quart, spring 73. Add: Dept. of English, State University of New York College at Brockport, Brockport, NY 14420.

MURRAY, EUGENE BERNARD, b. Chicago, Ill, Dec. 22, 27; m. 63. ENGLISH. A.B, Kenyon Col, 52; M.A, Columbia Univ, 57, Ph.D.(Eng), 65. Instr. ENG, Rutgers Univ, 61-62; resident lectr, Ind. Univ, Ft. Wayne, 62-65, asst. prof, 65-66; UNIV. MO-ST. LOUIS, 66-68, ASSOC. PROF, 68-, asst. prof. grant, 68. U.S.A, 46-47. MLA. P.B. Shelley; Gothic novel. Publ: Ann Radcliffe, Twayne, 72; Elective affinity in The revolt of Islam, J. Eng. & Ger. Philol, 10/68; Mont Blanc's Unfurled veil, 69 & Ambivalent mortality in the Elgin Marbles sonnet, 71, Keats-Shelley J. Add: Dept. of English, University of Missouri-St. Louis, St. Louis, MO 63121.

MURRAY, JOHN FRANKLIN, S.J, b. Axtell, Kans, Apr. 11, 11. ENGLISH. A.B, St. Louis Univ, 37, A.M, 42; S.T.L, 47; Ph.D, Univ. N.Mex, 57. From instr. to prof. Eng, SPRING HILL COL, 41-66, chmn. dept, 52-66, acad. v.pres, 66-72, PROF. ENG, 72- MLA; S.Atlantic Mod. Lang. Asn; NCTE (Ala. rep, 67-); Milton Soc. Am. Renaissance English literature; Renaissance criticism of Chaucer. Publ: Milton's conception of original justice and original sin; co-auth, Writing and research, Spring Hill Col, 61; auth, Jesuit place names in the United States, Names, 3/68. Add: Spring Hill College, Mobile, AL 36608.

MURRAY, JOHN RALPH, b. Alva, Okla, Apr. 17, 16; m. 36; c. 2. ENGLISH, ADMINISTRATION. A.B, Northwest. State Col, 37; A.M, Univ. South. Calif, 39; Ph.D, Univ. Fla, 52. Teacher Eng. & prin, Carrier & Gore High Schs, 36-38; teaching asst, Univ. Calif, 39-41; instr. Eng, Univ. Miami, 41-42, from asst. prof. to assoc. prof, 45-52, asst. dean, registr, acting dean & dir. South Campus, 46-50, asst. to pres, 48-50, 52; instr. Eng, Ohio Univ, 42-44, lectr. physics, 45; pres, Greenbrier Col, 52-54; ELMIRA COL, 54-72, CHANCELLOR, 72- Co-ed, Learning Today, Libr-Col. Asn, 71- U.S.N.R, 44-45. Int. Asn. Univ. Pres; Libr-Col. Asn. College and world affairs; non-western studies in the liberal arts colleges; Sir Edwin Arnold's Buddhism, Victorian period. Publ: Co-auth, College and world affairs, Comn. Col. & World Affairs, 64 & Non-western studies in the liberal arts colleges, Comn. Int. Understanding, 64. Add: Office of Chancellor, Elmira College, Elmira, NY 14901.

MURRAY, MICHAEL EDWARD, Philosophy, Literature. See Volume IV, Philosophy, Religion & Law.

MURRAY, MICHAEL H, b. New York, N.Y, Aug. 18, 38; m. 59; c. 4. ENGLISH. A.B, Fordham Univ, 60; M.A, N.Y. Univ, 63, Ph.D.(Eng), 72. Teacher ENG, Archbishop Stepinac High Sch, White Plains, N.Y, 61-63; Sachem Cent. Schs, Long Island, 63-66; PROF. ENG. & DIR. COOP. EDUC, COL. INS, N.Y.C, 66- MLA; Coop. Educ. Asn; NEA. Victorian; medieval drama. Publ: Liam O'Flaherty and the speaking voice, Stud. Short Fiction, winter 68; Insurance recruiting takes a step backward, J. Col. Placement, 2-3/69; A term paper alternative, Clearing House, spring 71. Add: Div. of Liberal Arts, College of Insurance, 123 William St, New York, NY 10038.

MURRAY, PETER BRYANT, b. New York, N.Y, Oct. 6, 27; m. 54, 70; c. 4. ENGLISH, DRAMA. A.B, Swarthmore Col, 50; A.M, Univ. Pa, 59, Ph.D. (Eng), 62. Res. chemist, Sun Oil Co, 50-57; instr. ENG, Univ. Pa, 61-63, asst. prof, 63-67; assoc. prof, Univ. Del, 67-68; PROF, MACALESTER COL, 68-, CHMN. DEPT, 71- Sig.C, U.S.A, 46-47. MLA; Mod. Humanities Res. Asn; AAUP. English Medieval and Renaissance drama; American literature; modern drama. Publ: A study of Cyril Tourneur, Univ. Pa, 64; A study of John Webster, Mouton, The Hague, 69; Thomas Kyd, Twayne, 69. Add: Dept. of English, Macalester College, St. Paul, MN 55105.

MURRAY, ROGER NICHOLAS, b. Fargo, N.Dak, June 26, 32; m. 56; c. 3. ENGLISH. B.A, Moorhead State Col, 54; M.A, Stanford Univ, 58; fel, Univ. Iowa, 64-65, Ph.D.(Eng), 65. Teacher, Pub. Schs, Minn, 54-55; instr. ENG, Univ. Colo, 58-61; ASST. PROF, Wis. State Univ-Eau Claire, 65-68; ARIZ. STATE UNIV, 68- Vis. prof. Eng, Univ. Minn, 70-71; poetry ed, West. Rev, 72- MLA; NCTE. English romantic period; 17th century British writers; criticism. Publ: Wordsworth's style, Univ. Nebr, 67; Wordsworth: the romantic poet as mental traveller, Wis. Stud. Lit, 67; Betty Foy: an early mental traveller, J. Eng. & Ger. Philol, 1/71; A case for the study of period styles, Col. Eng, 11/71; plus one other. Add: Dept. of English, Arizona State University, Tempe, AZ 85281.

MURRAY, THELMA TAYLOR, b. Salt Lake City, Utah; wid. ENGLISH, EDUCATION. A.B, Wilberforce Univ, 20; summers, Univ. Chicago & Ind. State Teachers Col; M.A, Atlanta Univ, 44; Gen. Educ. Fund scholar, N.Y. Univ. summer 45; Carnegie scholar, Northwest. Univ, 47-48, univ. fel, 48-49, Ph.D, 50. Teacher & head dept. Eng. high sch, Ky, 20-44; instr. ENG. & EDUC, FT. VALLEY STATE COL, 44-48, assoc. prof, 49-51, prof, 51-67, dir. reading lab, 51-67, dir. inst. testing, 59-67, acting head dept. educ, 51-52, head dept. Eng. & acting chmn. div. humanities, 57-60, chmn. div. humanities, 60-67, EMER. PROF, 68- Consult, Reading Clinic, Miles Col, 50 & 58; spec. consult. pre-convention meetings Eng. prog. disadvantaged, NCTE convention, Honolulu, Nov. 67; campus coord, Col. Educ. Achievement Proj, Birmingham, Ala, 67-68; chmn. div. humanities, Paul Quinn Col, 68-69. NCTE; Conf. Col. Compos. & Commun; Col. Lang. Asn; Nat. Asn. Dramatic & Speech Arts; Int. Reading Asn; Asn. Higher Educ. Reading, especially problems and methods of teaching; teaching of English on the secondary level; guidance. Add: 5665 Wenlock St, Los Angeles, CA 90016.

MURRAY, THOMAS JAMES, b. Big Rapids, Mich, Oct. 7, 31; m. 52; c. 3. SPEECH. B.A, Univ. Mich, 53, M.A, 55, Ph.D, 60. Fel. speech, Univ. Mich, 55-57, instr, 57-60; Univ. Wis, 60-61, asst. prof, 61-63; from assoc. prof. to PROF. SPEECH & DRAMATIC ARTS, EAST. MICH. UNIV, 63-, HEAD DEPT, 72- Consult, Agency Int. Develop. Commun. Seminars, 60-63. Cent. States Speech Asn. Award, 61. Speech Commun. Asn. Presidential campaign speaking; communication in small groups; audience analysis. Add: Dept. of Speech & Dramatic Arts, Eastern Michigan University, Ypsilanti, MI 48197.

MURRAY, WALLACE R, JR, b. San Jose, Calif, Feb. 5, 12; m. 39; c. 1. DRAMA, EDUCATION. B.A, San Jose State Col, 33; M.A, Stanford Univ, 47; Dr.Arts, Staley Col, 56. Teacher Eng, speech & drama & head dept, San Jose Unified Sch. Dept, 33-47; teacher speech & drama, SAN JOSE STATE UNIV, 47-50, PROF. DRAMA & EDUC. & COORD. SPEECH & DRAMA EDUC, 50- Lectr. & consult. speech & drama educ, 47- Field dir. army bases, Am. Red Cross, World War II. Adaptations of literary classics for storytelling and reading. Publ: Time to talk, (jr. high pub. speaking text), 36, Adaptation of House of seven gables, 47 & Adaptation of Benjamin Franklin's autobiography, 48, San Jose Unified Sch; ed, Sherlock Holmes adaptations, Globe, 47; auth, Teaching of diacritics, Spartan Shop, San Jose State Col, 48, rev. 61, 66 & 71; co-auth, Speech program requires good teaching, Bull. Nat. Asn. Sec. Sch. Prin, 1/54. Add: Dept. of Drama & Education, San Jose State University, San Jose, CA 95192.

MURRAY, WILLIAM MARTIN, b. Miltown Malbay, Eire, June 18, 29; U.S. citizen; m. 61; c. 4. ENGLISH. B.Sc, South. Conn. State Col, 56; M.A, Univ. Iowa, 58, Ph.D.(Eng), 64; Univ. Calif, Berkeley, 61. Asst. Eng, Univ. Iowa, 56-59; Univ. Calif, 60-61; instr, Univ. Iowa, 61-64; asst. prof, Univ. Iowa & Writers Workshop, 64-67; ASSOC. PROF. ENG, UNIV. IOWA, 67-, DIR. MOD. LETT. PROG, 70-, res. fel, fall 68. Meredith Publ. Writing Award, 67. U.S.A, 51-53. Modern British, American and continental novel; modern poetry; Irish literature. Publ: Michael Joe, Appleton, 65; A long way from home, (novel), Houghton, 74; The bearded sockless radical of Moo U, New York Times Mag, 4/67; Grasses, Am. Heritage, spring 68; Fight for rural America: NFO, N.Am. Rev, spring 68. Add: Box 227, Route 1, West Branch, IA 52358.

MURROW, WAYNE LEE, b. Alva, Okla, Jan. 23, 35; m. 56, 68; c. 4. SPEECH COMMUNICATION, SMALL GROUP COMMUNICATION. B.A, Bethany Nazarene Col, 56; M.Ed, Cent. State Univ.(Okla), 68; Ph.D.(speech), Okla. Univ, 72. Minister, Church of the Nazarene, 56-61; teacher speech & Eng, Choctaw Pub. Schs, Okla, 61-68, dept. head, 65-68; instr. SPEECH COMMUN, BETHANY NAZARENE COL, 68-70, asst. prof, 70-72, assoc. prof, 72-74, PROF, 74-, GRAD. COORD, 72- Speech Commun. Asn. Small group communication; study of the use of PROANA 5, a computerized technique for the analysis of small group interaction. Add: Dept. of Speech Communication, Bethany Nazarene College, Bethany, OK 73008.

MURSELINGAN, JEFFERSON O, b. Peoria, Ill, May 28, 09; m. 32; c. 1. SPEECH, COMMUNICATION. B.A, Univ. Ill, Urbana, 30, M.A, 32, Ph.D. (speech), 38. Instr. speech, Univ. Ill, Urbana, 30-32, asst. prof, 32-38, prof, 38-46; commun. adv, E.R. Stevens Co, 46-73; RETIRED. Speech Commun. Asn. Public speaking; rhetoric; pursuasive communication. Add: 6107 E. Rose Circle Dr, Phoenix, AZ 85018.

MURTAUGH, DANIEL MAHER, b. Evanston, Ill, May 8, 41; m. 68. ENGLISH. B.A, Col. Holy Cross, 63; Woodrow Wilson fel, Yale, 63-64, Danforth fel, 63-67, Ph.D.(Eng), 67. Instr. ENG, Northwest. Univ, 65-66; ASST. PROF, Boston Univ, 67-72; MANHATTANVILLE COL, 72- MLA; Mediaeval Acad. Am; Dante Soc. Am. Chaucer; allegory; Old French. Publ: Riming justice in the Friar's tale, Neuphilol. Mitt, spring 73; Oir et Entandre: figuralism and narrative structure in Chretien's Yvain, Romanic Rev, 5/73; The garden and the sea: the topography of The Faerie Queene, III, ELH, fall 73; plus others. Add: Dept. of English, Manhattanville College, Purchase, NY 10577.

MUSACCHIO, GEORGE LOUIS, b. Louisville, Ky, Nov. 1, 38; m. 62; c. 2. ENGLISH LITERATURE, MILTON. B.A, Calif. Baptist Col, 62; M.A, Univ. Calif, Riverside, 65, Ph.D.(Eng), 71. Instr. ENG, CALIF. BAPTIST COL, 64-65, asst. prof, 65-67, assoc. prof. 67-71, PROF, 71- MLA; Conf. Christianity & Lit; Renaissance Soc. Am; Milton Soc. Am. Reformation and Puritan theology in relation to Milton. Publ: Fallible perfection: the motivation of the fall in Reformation theology and Paradise lost, Univ. Microfilms, 71; A note on the fire-rose synthesis of T.S. Eliot's Four Quartets, Eng. Stud, 6/64; Milton's feminine pronouns with neuter antecedents J. Eng. Ling, 3/68; contrib, Milton Encyclopedia, Univ. Wis, (in press). Add: Dept. of English, California Baptist College, 8432 Magnolia Ave, Riverside, CA 92504.

MUSCATINE, CHARLES, b. Brooklyn, N.Y, Nov. 28, 20; m. 45; c. 2. ENGLISH. A.B, Yale, 41, A.M, 42, Ph.D, 48. Lectr. ENG, UNIV. CALIF, BERKELEY, 48, instr, 48-49, asst. prof, 49-55, assoc. prof, 55-60, PROF, 60-, asst. dean col. let. & sci, 56-60. Vis. asst. prof, Wesleyan Univ, 51-53; vis. prof, Univ. Wash, summer 61; Am. Counc. Learned Soc. fel, 58-59; Fulbright res. fels, Italy, 58-59 & France, 62-63; Guggenheim fel, 62-63; Nat. Endowment Humanities sr. fel, 68-69. U.S.N.R, 42-45, Lt. MLA; Mediaeval Acad. Am. Medieval literature and culture; Chaucer; old French literature. Publ: Chaucer and the French tradition, Univ. Calif, 57; The book of Geoffrey Chaucer, Book Club Calif, 63; co-ed, The Borzoi college reader, 66, 2nd ed, 71 & First person singular, 73, Knopf; co-auth. & ed, Education at Berkeley, Acad. Senate, Berkeley, 66, 2nd ed, Univ. Calif, 68; auth, Poetry and crisis in the age of Chaucer, Univ. Notre Dame, 72. Add: Dept. of English, University of California, Berkeley, CA 94720.

MUSGRAVE, MARIAN E, b. Cleveland, Ohio. ENGLISH. B.A, Howard Univ, 45, M.A, 46; Ph.D.(Eng), West. Reserve Univ, 60. Instr. Eng, Ark. Mech, Agr. & Norm. Col, 46-48; South. Univ, 48-51; prof. & chmn. dept, Alcorn Col, 59-64; assoc. prof, Ala. State Col, 64-66; Cent. State Univ, 66-69, dir. grad. Eng. prog, 67-69; ASSOC. PROF. ENG, MIAMI UNIV, 69- MLA; Milton Soc. Am. Germanic languages; linguistics. Publ: Program for regressed patients on chemotherapy, 6/59 & co-auth, History of auxiliary therapies at Cleveland State Hospital, 6/60, J. Recreational Therapy; auth, Teaching English as a foreign language to students with sub-standard dialects, J. Col. Lang. Asn, 9/63. Add: Dept. of English, Miami University, Oxford, OH 45056.

MUSTE, JOHN M, b. Mt. Kisco, N.Y, Jan. 21, 27; m. 50; c. 2. AMERICAN LITERATURE. A.B, Brown Univ, 49; M.A, Miami Univ, 53; Ph.D, Univ. Wis, 60. From instr. to asst. prof. ENG, OHIO STATE UNIV, 58-67, assoc. prof, 67-71, PROF, 71-, V.CHMN. DEPT, 72- Am. Counc. Learned Soc. grant-in-aid, 61; mem. ed. bd, Ohio State Univ. Press, 72- U.S.N, 44-46. Am. Stud. Asn; MLA. American literature of World War II; influence on the understanding of literature of sexual roles and sexual assumptions. Publ: Say that we saw Spain die, Univ. Wash, 66; The second major subwar: four novels by Vance Bourjaily, In: The shaken realist, La. State Univ, 70; Norman Mailer and John Dos Passos, Mod. Fiction Stud, 71. Add: Dept. of English, Ohio State University, 164 W. 17th Ave, Columbus, OH 43210.

MUTCH, GEORGE ERNEST, III, b. Rochester, N.Y, Feb. 17, 19. HUMANITIES, ENGLISH. A.B, Univ. Rochester, 45; M.A, Columbia Univ, 49. Lectr. & instr. humanities, Col. Men, Columbia Univ, 45-48; instr. Eng. & lit, Univ. Md, 48-50; guid. counr, U.S. Employ. Serv, N.Y, 50, 50-52; dir. Eng. & reading improv, N.Mex. Mil. Inst, 52-54; educ. specialist, Bolling AFB & The Pentagon, Wash, D.C, 54-57; Fulbright exchange prof, Palermo & Naples, Italy, 57-58; instr. speech & Eng. & specialist, reading & speech ther, Georgetown Univ, 58-61; asst. prof. Eng. & speech, Univ. Baltimore, 61-71; prof. humanities, Univ. Md-Morgan State Col, 72-73; EDUC. SPECIALIST, BD. OF EDUC, CITY OF BALTIMORE, 73- Instr. Eng. & humanities, Wash. Sq. Col, N.Y. Univ, 45-47; Fulbright scholar; mem, Nat. Counc. Guid. Counsel; Nat. Asn. Improv. Reading; Southwest. Reading Conf; Cornell Univ. Reading Improv. Asn; U.S. Govt. Employees Reading Improv; reading improv. specialist, U.S. Army, Ft. Belvoir, Va; chmn. psychol. testing, N.Mex. Mil. Inst; educ. counsel, U.S. Employ. Serv, Dept. Labor, N.Y, 58; asst. prof. lit, Univ. Md. & Towson State Col, 66-67. NCTE; Col. Eng. Asn. English and American literature; reading improvement. Publ: Improvement of college reading, Southwest. Conf. Reading, 52. Add: 714 Horizon House, 1101 Calvert & Chase, Baltimore, MD 21202.

MYERS, CHESTER JAMES, b. Ogden, Utah, May 5, 99; m. 22, 58; c. 1. SPEECH. B.S, Univ. Utah, 21; M.S, State Univ. Iowa, 25; Northwest. Univ, 28; Ph.D, Univ. South. Calif, 40. Teacher, High Sch, Utah, 21-25; Weber State Col, 25-26; from instr. to prof. SPEECH, UTAH STATE UNIV, 26-64, head dept, 26-59, EMER. PROF, 64- Teacher, Iowa & South. Calif; prof. speech, Dixie Col, summer 69. Groups of lessons for use in correcting certain minor speech difficulties; study of Brigham Young as a public speaker. Add: Apt. 4, 350 S. 200 East, St. George, UT 84770.

MYERS, DORIS EVALINE THOMPSON, b. Gilbert, Ark, Mar. 12, 34; m. 62; c. 2. CHAUCER, RHETORIC. B.S.Ed, State Col. Ark, 54; M.A, Ohio Univ, 56; Ph.D.(Eng), Univ. Nebr-Lincoln, 67. Teacher ENG, Newport High Sch, Ark, 54-55; Quantico Post High Sch, 56-59; instr, Univ. Nebr, 60-61, 64-66; UNIV. NORTH. COLO, 67-68, asst. prof, 68-72, ASSOC. PROF, 72-, res. grant, spring 71. Participant, Ling. Soc. Am. ling. inst, State Univ. N.Y. Buffalo, summer 71; Summer Ling. Inst, Univ. Okla, 72. NCTE; Ling. Soc. Am; AAUP. Discourse analysis. Publ: Brave new world: the status of women according to Tolkien, Lewis, and Williams, Cimarron Rev, 71; Justesse rationnelle: le Myrie tale in prose de Chaucer, Le Moyen Age, 72; Focus and moralite in the Nun's Priest's tale, Chaucer Rev, 73. Add: Dept. of English, University of Northern Colorado, Greeley, CO 80639.

MYERS, GAIL ELDRIDGE, b. Clark, S.Dak, Mar. 1, 23; m. 47, 69; c. 3. SPEECH. B.A, State Univ. Iowa, 48, M.A, 49; Ph.D.(commun. methodology), Univ. Denver, 59. Dir. publ. & alumni affairs, State Col. Iowa, 49-53; dir. publ. & tech. ed, Colo. Sch. Mines, 53-59; v.pres, Monticello Col, 59-63; asst. prof. speech, Univ. Denver, 63-66; pres, Monticello Col, 66-71; DEAN ARTS & SCI, TRINITY UNIV, 71- Mem, Inst. Gen. Semantics; pres, Lewis & Clark Community Col, 70-71. U.S.A.A.F. Speech Commun. Asn; Int. Commun. Asn; Int. Soc. Gen. Semantics. Publ: Co-ed, Language behavior, Mouton, The Hague, 70; co-auth, Dynamics of human communication, Mc-Graw, 73 & Effect of feedback in training groups, J. Appl. Behav. Sci, spring 69; auth, chap, In: Counselling and accountability, Pergamon, 73. Add: College of Arts & Sciences, Trinity University, 715 Stadium Dr, San Antonio, TX 78284.

MYERS, JOSEPH WILSON, b. Jackson, Mich, Apr. 10, 24; m. 48; c. 3. ENGLISH, AMERICAN STUDIES. B.A, Haverford Col, 58; Woodrow Wilson fel, Univ. Calif, Berkeley, 58, M.A, 60, Ph.D.(Eng), 66. Instr. HUMANITIES, MICH. STATE UNIV, 65-66, asst. prof, 66-70, ASSOC. PROF, 70- MLA; Archaeol. Inst. Am. Mark Twain; American popular culture in the 19th century; classical culture. Add: 518 Ardson Rd, East Lansing, MI 48823.

MYERS, LOUIS McCORRY, b. Jackson, Tenn, Nov. 16, 01; m. 30; c. 1. ENGLISH, LINGUISTICS. B.A, Bard Col, 25; M.A, Columbia Univ, 29; Ph.D. (Eng), Univ. Calif, Berkeley, 35. Instr. French, Univ. Ore, 29-32; Eng, West. Wash. Col, 35-36; Univ. Idaho, 36-37; prof, ARIZ. STATE UNIV, 37-72, chmn. dept, 37-57, head div. lang. & lit, 57-62, EMER. PROF. ENG, 72- Sig.C, 42-46, Lt. Col. MLA; NCTE; Conf. Col. Compos. & Commun.(mem, ed. bd, Col. Compos. & Commun, 67-70). English grammar; history of English language. Publ: American English: a twentieth century grammar, 52 & Guide to American English, 55, 59, 63, 68 & co-auth, 5th ed, 72, Prentice-Hall; auth, The roots of modern English, 66 & co-auth, Companion to The roots of modern English, 72, Little; Linguistics—but not quite so fast, Col. Eng, 61; Two approaches to languages, PMLA, 62; Generation and deviation, Col. Compos. & Commun, 67. Add: Dept. of English, Arizona State University, Tempe, AZ 85281.

MYERS, NEIL, b. Philadelphia, Pa, Oct. 31, 30; m. 62. ENGLISH LITERATURE. B.A, Univ. Wis, 52; M.A, Harvard, 54, teaching fel, 54-59, Ph.D, 59, Instr. ENG, Univ. Minn, 58-61; asst. prof, PURDUE UNIV, WEST LAFAYETTE, 61-67, ASSOC. PROF, 67- Founder & co-ed, Minn. Rev, 61, ed. spec. issue, War Crimes of World War II, winter 62. MLA. William Carlos Williams; 20th century poetry; problems in creative writing and composition. Publ: Williams' imitation of nature in The desert music, winter 70 & Decreation in Williams' The descent, fall 72, Criticism; Williams' Two pendants: for the ears, J. Mod. Lit, 5/71; plus three others. Add: 901 N. Chauncey, West Lafayette, IN 47906.

MYERS, NORMAN JERALD, b. Canton, Ohio, June 24, 35; m. 59; c. 2. THEATRE, SPEECH. A.B, Hiram Col, 57; M.A, Univ. Ill, Urbana, 59, Ph.D, 62. ASST. PROF. speech & drama, Lycoming Col, 59-61; theatre, Ky. Wesleyan Col, 62-63; State Univ. N.Y. Col. Oswego, 63-66; drama, La. State Univ, New Orleans, 66-70; SPEECH, BOWLING GREEN STATE UNIV, 70- Managing dir, Huron Playhouse, 71- Am. Theatre Asn; Univ. Resident Theatre Asn. American theatre history; British theatre history; dramatic theory and criticism. Publ: A season at the John Street: from The theatrical register, South. Speech J, winter 68; Early recognition of Gordon Craig in American periodicals, Educ. Theatre J, 3/70. Add: Dept. of Speech, Bowling Green State University, Bowling Green, OH 43403.

MYERS, ROBERT MANSON, b. Charlottesville, Va, May 29, 21. ENGLISH LITERATURE. A.B, Vanderbilt Univ, 41; A.M, Columbia Univ, 42, Ph.D, 48; A.M, Harvard, 43. Instr. ENG, Yale, 45-47; asst. prof, Col. William & Mary, 47-48; Newcomb Col, Tulane Univ, 48-54; Brearley Sch, N.Y, 54-56; chmn. dept, Osbourn High Sch, Manassas, Va, 56-59; asst. prof, UNIV. MD, COLLEGE PARK, 59-63, assoc. prof, 63-68, PROF, 68- Fulbright res. scholar, Univ. London, 53-54; Fulbright prof, Rotterdam, Netherlands, 58-59. Nat. Book Award Hist, 73. MLA; Am. Soc. 18th Century Stud. Eighteenth century English literature, especially as it relates to music; 19th century American social and cultural history. Publ: Handel's Messiah: a touchstone of taste, Macmillan, 48; From Beowulf to Virginia Woolf; an astounding and wholly unauthorized history of English literature, Bobbs, 52; Handel, Dryden, and Milton, Bowes & Bowes, London, 56; The children of pride: a true story of Georgia and the Civil War, Yale, 72. Add: Dept. of English, University of Maryland, College Park, MD 20742.

MYERSON, JOEL ARTHUR, b. Boston, Mass, Sept. 9, 45; m. 67. AMERICAN LITERATURE. A.B, Tulane Univ, 67; univ. fel, NDEA fel. & Woodrow Wilson dissertation year fel, Northwest. Univ, Evanston, 67-71, M.A, 68, Ph.D.(Eng), 71. ASST. PROF. ENG, UNIV. S.C, 71- Abstracter, Abstr. Eng. Stud, 70-; Am. Philos. Soc. res. grantee, 72-73. MLA. New England transcendentalism; American Renaissance; R.W. Emerson. Publ: Assoc. ed, The writings of Herman Melville, Northwest. Univ, 70-; auth, Margaret Fuller: bibliographies, Franklin, 75; co-auth, Melville dissertations: an annotated directory, Melville Soc, 72; auth, A calendar of transcendental club meetings, Am. Lit, 5/72; An annotated list of contributions to the Boston Dial, Stud. Bibliog, 73; Margaret Fuller's 1842 journal: at Concord with the Emersons, Harvard Libr. Bull, 7/73. Add: Dept. of English, University of South Carolina, Columbia, SC 29208.

MYLER, CHARLES B, b. Marshall, Tex, Sept. 3, 26; m. 51; c. 3. DRAMA, SPEECH. B.F.A, Univ. Tex, 51, M.F.A, 54, Ph.D.(drama hist), 68. Teacher, high sch, 56-59; instr. DRAMA & SPEECH, ST. MARY'S UNIV. (TEX), 59-60, asst. prof, 60-68, assoc. prof, 68-73, PROF, 73-, CHMN. DEPT, 66- U.S.N, 44-46. Am. Theatre Asn; Speech Commun. Asn. Dramatic production; local theater history in San Antonio; public speaking. Add: Dept. of Speech & Drama, St. Mary's University, San Antonio, TX 78284.

MYRBO, CALVIN L, b. Underwood, Minn, Feb. 18, 25; m. 47; c. 4. ENGLISH EDUCATION. B.A, Bob Jones Univ, 50; M.A, Univ. Minn, 56, Ph.D. (Eng. educ), 64. Assoc. prof. Eng, Northwest. Col.(Minn), 56-65; PROF. ENG. & DIR. FRESHMAN COMPOS, UNIV. WIS-PLATTEVILLE, 65- Consult. lang. arts, Monroe Pub. Schs, 66; Wis. Lang. Arts Curriculum Workshop, summer 66. NCTE; Conf. Col. Compos. & Commun. Add: Dept. of English, University of Wisconsin-Platteville, Platteville, WI 53818.

N

NABHOLTZ, JOHN R, b. Cleveland, Ohio, Jan. 6, 31. ENGLISH. A.B, Loyola Univ.(Ill), 51; M.A, Univ. Chicago, 52, univ. fel, 53, Carnegie fel, 55, Ph.D. (Wordsworth), 61; Fulbright fel, Univ. Durham, 54. Instr. ENG, Cornell Univ, 59-63, asst. prof, Univ. Rochester, 63-69; ASSOC. PROF, LOYOLA UNIV, CHICAGO, 69- AAUP; MLA. English romanticism. Publ: Ed, Selected essays of Charles Lamb, 67 & ed, Selected essays of William Hazlitt, 70, Appleton; ed, Essay on Principles of human action by William Hazlitt, Scholars' Facsimiles & Reprints, 69; ed, Prose of the British Romantic Movement, Macmillan, 74; auth, Wordsworth's Guide to the lakes, Mod. Philol, 64; The journeys homeward: book IV of The prelude, Stud. in Romanticism, 71; Drama and rhetoric in Lamb's essays, Stud. Eng. Lit, 72. Add: Dept. of English, Loyola University, 6525 N. Sheridan Rd, Chicago, IL 60626.

NABORS, D. J, JR, b. Emory, Tex, July 24, 07; m. 32; c. 3. SPEECH. A.B, E.Cent. State Col, 30; M.Ph, Univ. Wis, 31; Ed.D, Univ. Okla, 57. Prin, high sch, Okla, 27-30; chmn. dept. speech, Nebr. State Teachers Col, Peru, 31-37; prof. SPEECH & chmn. dept, E.CENT. STATE COL, 37-72, EMER. PROF, 72- Ed, Okla. Gideon. NEA; Am. Forensic Asn. Speech Commun. Asn. Intercollegiate forensic activities; educational radio and television. Publ: The affirmative case, Forensic. Add: Dept. of Speech, East Central State College, Ada, OK 74820.

NADEL, IRA BRUCE, b. Rahway, N.J, July 22, 43; m. 66. ENGLISH & AMERICAN LITERATURE. B.A, Rutgers Univ, New Brunswick, 65, M.A, 67; Ph.D.(Eng), Cornell Univ, 70. ASST. PROF. ENG, UNIV. B.C, 70- MLA; Victorian Stud. Asn. West. Can; Asn. Can. Univ. Teachers Eng. Victorian literature and thought; contemporary Canadian and American literature. Publ: Portraits and the artist: the poetry of A.M. Klein, Jewish Dialog, spring 73; What's Canadian about Canadian literature?, Event, spring 73; The later letters of J.S. Mill, Univ. Toronto Quart, summer 73; plus one other. Add: Dept. of English, University of British Columbia, Vancouver 8, B.C, Can.

NAESETH, HENRIETTE CHRISTIANE KOREN, b. Decorah, Iowa. AMERICAN LITERATURE. A.B, Grinnell Col, 22; A.M, Univ. Minn, 24; Ph.D, Univ. Chicago, 31; Litt.D, Luther Col, 61. Instr, Park Region Luther Col, 24-26; Univ. Chicago, 29-31; asst. prof, Goucher Col, 31-32; prof. ENG, Nebr. State Teachers Col, Chadron, 32-34; AUGUSTANA COL, 34-69, head dept, 35-68, chmn. div. humanities, 44-68, EMER. PROF, 69. On leave for res. on Marcus Thrane, sponsored by Norweg. Am. Hist. Asn, 68-69. St. Olaf Medal, Norway, 70. MLA; Swed. Pioneer Hist. Soc; Norweg-Am. Hist. Asn; Soc. Advan. Scand. Stud. Theatre, particularly foreign language theatre with emphasis in Norwegian theatre; Scandinavian immigrants. Publ: Swedish Theatre in Chicago, 1868-1950, Augustana Hist. Soc, 51; Early Norwegian dramatic societies, Stud. & Rec; Drama in early Deadwood, 1876, Am. Lit, 38; Early years of the Norwegian Folk High School, Scand. Stud, 53. Add: 1632 18th Ave, Rock Island, IL 61201.

NAGEL, JAMES EDWARD, b. St. Paul, Minn, May 20, 40; m. 67. ENGLISH & AMERICAN LITERATURE. B.A, Moorhead State Col, 62; M.A, Pa. State Univ, 64, Ph.D.(Eng), 71. ASST. PROF. ENG, NORTHEAST. UNIV, 71- Bibliogr, MLA, 70-74; ed, Studies in Am. Fiction, 73- MLA; Northeast Mod. Lang. Asn. American fiction; impressionism; the novel. Publ: Ed, Vision and value, 70 & Critical essays on Catch-22, 74, Dickenson; auth, Structure and theme in Crane's An experiment in misery, Studies in Short Fiction, 73; An annotated bibliography of selected recent books on American fiction, Studies in Am. Fiction, 73; The narrative method of The short happy life of Francis Macomber, Res. Studies, 73; plus others. Add: Dept. of English, Northeastern University, Boston, MA 02115.

NAGER, RAE ANN, b. Cheswick, Pa, Oct. 16, 39. ENGLISH, COMPARATIVE LITERATURE. B.A, Cath. Univ. Am, 61, M.A, 65; travelling fel, Harvard, 70-71. Res. analyst, Cent. Intel. Agency, 61-62; teacher, St. Anthony's Sch, Wash, D.C, 62-63; CUR. KEATS COLLECTION, HOUGHTON LIBR, HARVARD, 71- Assoc. ed, Keats-Shelley J, 71-72, bibliogr, 72-74, ed, 72- Keats-Shelley Asn. Am; Mediaeval Acad. Am. Prosody; literary theory and criticism. Publ: Co-auth, Annual bibliography to Vol. XIX, 70, Keats-Shelley Asn. Am, 74; auth, English II: bibliographical, In: Versification: major language types, N.Y. Univ. & MLA, 72. Add: Houghton Library, Harvard University, Cambridge, MA 02138.

NAGLER, ALOIS, b. Graz, Austria, Sept. 14, 07; nat; m. THEATER HISTORY. Ph.D, Univ. Graz, 30. Drama & music critic, Berlin, Ger, 30-32;

drama critic & lit. ed, daily newspaper, Vienna, Austria, 32-38; vis. lectr, U.S, 38-40; Rockefeller res. fel, 40-41; supvr. cross-cult. surv, U.S. Dept. Navy, 43-45; asst. prof. DRAMATIC HIST. & CRITICISM, YALE, 46-48, assoc. prof, 48-60, prof, 60-63, HENRY McCORMICK PROF, 63- Cross of Honor, first class, Repub. Austria, 66. Am. Soc. Theatre Res; Soc. Hist. Théâtre; Int. Fed. Theatre Res.(pres, 59-63); Austrian Acad. Arts & Sci. History of the drama and theater. Publ: Hebbel und die Musik, Bachem, Cologne, 28; Sources of theatrical history, Theatre Annual, N.Y, 52; Shakespeare's stage, 58 & Theatre festivals of the Medici, 63, Yale. Add: School of Drama, Yale University, New Haven, CT 06520.

NAGLER, MICHAEL NICHOLAS, Classics, Comparative Literature. See Volume III, Foreign Languages, Linguistics & Philology.

NAGY, GREGORY JOHN, Classics, Linguistics. See Volume III, Foreign Languages, Linguistics & Philology.

NAIDEN, JAMES RICHARD, b. Adel, Iowa, Feb. 2, 15. HUMANISTIC STUDIES. A.B, State Univ. Iowa, 35, A.M, 36; A.M, Columbia Univ, 41, Ph.D, 48; Ecole des Hautes Etudes, Paris. Instr, Middlebury Col, State Univ. Iowa, Univ. Mo, Rutgers Univ. & Columbia Univ, 39-48; asst. prof. humanistic social stud, Univ. Wash, 48-53; class. master, Lakeside Sch, Seattle, 53-68; PROF. ENG, SOUTH. ORE. COL, 68- Lectr. classics & Eng, Seattle Univ, 53-64; Eng, Univ. Wash, 64-68. Neo-Latin literature; world Black literature; comparative literature. Publ: Sphera of George Buchanan, privately publ, 53. Add: Dept. of English, Southern Oregon College, Ashland, OR 97520.

NALL, KLINE ALLEN, b. Canyon, Tex, Nov. 5, 13; m. 36; c. 2. ENGLISH. B.A, Tex. Technol Col, 37, M.A, 39; Ph.D, Univ. Tex, 52. Teacher high sch, Tex, 37-42; instr. ENG, Univ. Tex, 43-44; TEX. TECH UNIV, 44-52, asst. prof, 52-56, assoc. prof, 56-60, PROF, 60- NCTE; MLA; S.Cent. Mod. Lang. Asn. American literature; the short story; teaching by television. Publ: Co-auth, Technical writing, Houghton, 60; co-auth, History of Texas Tech University, 75; auth, Beefing up the T.A. program through ETV, Col. Compos. & Commun, 2/67. Add: Dept. of English, Texas Tech University, Lubbock, TX 79406.

NAM, SUNWOO, b. Chinchun, Korea, June 19, 38; m. 62; c. 3. JOURNALISM. B.A, Hankuk Univ. Foreign Stud, Korea, 61; Fulbright fel. & M.A.(commun), Stanford Univ, 65, M.A.(polit. sci), 67; Ph.D.(mass commun), Univ. Wis-Madison, 69. ASST. PROF. JOUR, UNIV. HAWAII, 69- For. news analyst, Dong-A Ilbo, Seoul, Korea, 59-64, correspondent, 64- Asn. Educ. in Jour. Press-government relationship; media-society interaction; historical aspects of the press. Publ: Editorials as an indicator of the press freedom in three far eastern countries, 71 & co-auth, Press freedom: function of subsystem autonomy, antithesis of development, 73, Jour. Quart; contrib, Broadcasting in Asia and the Pacific, Temple Univ, 74. Add: 658 Hahaione, Honolulu, HI 96825.

NAMJOSHI, SUNITI MANOHAR, b. Bombay, India, Apr. 20, 41. ENGLISH LITERATURE. B.A, Univ. Poona, 61, M.A, 63; M.S, Univ. Mo, 69; Ph.D. (Eng. lit), McGill Univ, 72. Lectr. Eng. lit, Fergusson Col, Univ. Poona, 63-64; officer, Indian Admin. Serv, Govt. of India, 64-69; lectr. ENG. LIT, UNIV. TORONTO, 72-73, ASST. PROF, 73- Ezra Pound; Canadian poetry; science fiction. Publ: Co-auth. & transl, Poems of Govindagraj, 69 & auth, Cyclone in Pakistan (poems), 70, Writers Workshop, Calcutta; contrib. poems, Descant, Antigonish Rev. & Illus. Weekly India. Add: Dept. of English, Scarborough College, University of Toronto, Toronto, Ont. M5S 1A1, Can.

NANCE, GUSTA BARFIELD, b. Atlanta, Tex, Nov. 9; wid. COMPARATIVE LITERATURE. B.A, South. Methodist Univ, 25, M.A, 27; Carnegie Found. grant, 51; scholar, Univ. Wis, 51-52, Ph.D.(comp. lit), 54. Instr. comp. lit, South. Methodist Univ, 29-33; Eng. & comp. lit, Hockaday Jr. Col, 34-37; comp. lit, South. Methodist Univ, 37-43, asst. prof, 43-54, assoc. prof, 54-56, prof, 56-68, chmn. dept, 56-63; CHMN. DEPT. ENG, DALLAS BAPTIST COL, 68- Founder & charter mem, Friends of Dallas Pub. Libr, 50- & Dallas Goethe Ctr, 64- Dallas Philol. Soc. honor award, 65. MLA; Conf. Col. Teachers Eng; Soc. Stud. Chinese Cult; S.Cent. Mod. Lang. Asn; NCTE; Dante Alighieri Soc. The Italian historical novel. Publ: The Paolo and Francesca story in literature; The tragic element in Moliere's plays; co-transl, History of Mexican literature, South. Methodist Univ, 68; Philosophy of Goethe's Faust, Goethe Festival, South. Methodist Univ. Add: 3637 Shenandoah Ave, Dallas, TX 75205.

NANCE, WILLIAM LESLIE, b. El Paso, Tex, Jan. 9, 33; m. 65; c. 2. AMERICAN LITERATURE. B.A, St. Mary's Univ.(Tex), 55; fel, Univ. Notre Dame, 62, Ph.D.(Eng), 63. Asst. prof. ENG, St. Mary's Univ.(Tex), 63-65; ASSOC. PROF, Univ. Tex, El Paso, 65-67; UNIV. TEX, AUSTIN, 68- Fulbright lectr, Univ. Lyon, 67-68. MLA. American fiction, especially Southern; literary criticism. Publ: Katherine Anne Porter and the art of rejection, Univ. N.C, 64; Satiric elements in Brackenridge's Modern chivalry, Tex. Stud. Lit. & Lang, autumn 67. Add: Dept. of English, University of Texas at Austin, Austin, TX 78712.

NAPIERALSKI, EDMUND ANTHONY, b. Buffalo, N.Y, Nov. 6, 37; m. 64; c. 3. DRAMATIC LITERATURE & THEORY. B.A, Canisius Col, 61; NDEA fel. & Ph.D.(Eng), Loyola Univ. Chicago, 67. From instr. to ASST. PROF. ENG, Georgetown Univ, 64-71; KING'S COL.(PA), 71- MLA. Tragedy; dramatic form; comparative literature. Publ: Restoration and 18th century theatre research bibliography, Restoration & 18th Century Theatre Res, 61-73; contrib, Restoration and eighteenth century theatre research: a bilbiographical guide, 1900-1968, South. Ill. Univ, 71; auth, The tragic knot: paradox in the experience of tragedy, J. Aesthetics & Art Criticism, 73; plus others. Add: Dept. of English, King's College, Wilkes-Barre, PA 18711.

NAPLES, DIANE CLARK, b. Independence, Mo, May 20, 47; m. 69. AMERICAN LITERATURE. B.A, Stanford Univ, 69; M.A, Univ. Calif, Los Angeles, 71, Ph.D.(Eng), 73. ASST. PROF. ENG, UNIV. IDAHO, 73- MLA. Early American literature; Jonathan Edwards. Publ: Roger Malvin's burial—a parable for historians?, Am. Transcendental Quart, winter 72. Add: Dept. of English, University of Idaho, Moscow, ID 83843.

NARDIN, JAMES THOMPSON, b. Columbia, Mo, Feb. 26, 21; m. 46; c. 4. AMERICAN DRAMA. A.B, Harvard, 41; A.M, Lehigh Univ, 47; Ph.D, Univ. Chicago, 49. Asst. ENG, Lehigh Univ, 41-42, 46-47; instr, Univ. Chicago, 48-49; asst. prof, North. Colo. Univ, 49-52, assoc. prof, 52-55, PROF, 55-62; LA. STATE UNIV, BATON ROUGE, 62- Fund for the Advan. Educ. fac. fel, 54-55; Fulbright lectr, France, 60-61; mem. pres. vis. comt, Lehigh Univ, 67-70; lectr, Am. civilization & lit, Univ. Dijon, 69-70; U.S.A, 42-45. MLA; NCTE. American and English drama; American literature; freshman compostion. Add: Dept. of English, Louisiana State University, Baton Rouge, LA 70803.

NARVESON, ROBERT D, b. Erskine, Minn, June 3, 30; m. 56; c. 3. ENGLISH. B.A, Concordia Col.(Minn), 53; M.A, Univ. Chicago, 54, Ph.D, 62. Instr. ENG, Concordia Col.(Minn), 54-55; Northwest. Univ, 58-62; asst. prof, UNIV. NEBR, LINCOLN, 62-68, ASSOC. PROF, 68- U.S.A, 51. NCTE; MLA; Midwest Mod. Lang. Asn. American literature, 1870 to present; Edgar Lee Masters; Ernest Hemingway. Add: Dept. of English, University of Nebraska, Lincoln, NE 68508.

NASH, JAMES F, b. Philadelphia, Pa, Mar. 15, 44; m. 66; c. 1. ENGLISH LITERATURE. B.A, La Salle Col, 66; NDEA fel, Univ. Va, 66-69, M.A, 67, du Pont fel, 69-70, Ph.D.(Eng), 71. Asst. ed, University Press Va, 70-72; ASST. PROF. ENG, MONTCLAIR STATE COL, 72- MLA; Am. Soc. 18th Century Stud. Eighteenth century English literature. Add: Dept. of English, Montclair State College, Upper Montclair, NJ 07043.

NASH, JOHN R, b. Royalton, Vt, Aug. 6, 38. ENGLISH & FRENCH LITERATURE. A.B, Dartmouth Col, 60; A.M, Stanford Univ, 63, Ph.D.(French), 67; NDEA fel, Stanford Univ. fel. & Fr. Govt. travelling fel, 63-64. RES. & WRITING, 67- Film-making techniques; writing. Publ: Jarry, Reverdy and Artaud: the abrupt path, Stanford Univ, 67. Add: Hanover, NH 03755.

NASH, RALPH (LEE), b. Sullivan, Ind, Feb. 22, 25; m. 49; c. 2. ENGLISH. A.B, Duke Univ, 45, M.A, 46; Ph.D.(Eng), Harvard, 51. Instr. ENG, Univ. Louisville, 48-50; Wash. Univ, 50-54; WAYNE STATE UNIV, 55-58, asst. prof, 58-61, assoc. prof, 61-64, prof. & asst. chmn, 64-68, chmn, 68-72, PROF, 72- Am. Asn. Teachers Ital; Renaissance Soc. Am. Publ: Transl, Sannazaro's Arcadia, Wayne State Univ, 66; auth, Ben Jonson's tragic poems, Stud. in Philol, 58; Chivalric themes in Samson agonistes, In: Studies in honor of John Wilcox, 58; plus others. Add: Dept. of English, Wayne State University, Detroit, MI 48202.

NASSAR, EUGENE PAUL, b. Utica, N.Y, June 20, 35. ENGLISH, CRITICISM. B.A, Kenyon Col, 57; M.A, Oxford, 60; fel. & Ph.D.(Eng), Cornell Univ, 62. Instr. ENG, Hamilton Col, 62-64; asst. prof, UTICA COL, 64-66, assoc. prof, 66-71, PROF, 71- Nat. Found. Arts & Humanities grant, summer 67, fel, 73-74; Rhodes scholar; Woodrow Wilson fel. Literary criticism. Publ: Wallace Stevens: an anatomy of figuration, Univ. Pa, 65; The Rape of Cinderella: essays in literary continuity, Ind. Univ, 70; Hopkins and Figura, spring 65 & Literary tone and the Rape of illusion, winter 66, Renascence; Ezra Pound's Pisan cantos, Paideuma, Vol. I, No. 2. Add: Dept. of English, Utica College, Utica, NY 13502.

NATHAN, EDWARD LEONARD, b. Los Angeles, Calif, Nov. 8, 24; m. 48; c. 3. RHETORIC. B.A, Univ. Calif, Berkeley, 50, M.A, 52, Ph.D.(Eng), 61. Instr. Eng, Modesto Jr. Col, Calif, 54-60; lectr. speech, UNIV. CALIF, BERKELEY, 61-62, asst. prof, 62-65, assoc. prof, 66-68, PROF. RHET, 68-, chmn. dept, 68-71. Univ. Calif. creative arts fel, 64-65; Am. Inst. Indian Stud. fac. training fel, 66-67. Longview Found. Award in Poetry, 60; Nat. Inst. Arts & Lett. Award for Creative Lit, 71. U.S.A, 43-46, Sgt. MLA. English Renaissance lyric; Sanskrit literature; W.B. Yeats. Publ: Western reaches (poetry), Talisman, 58; Glad and sorry seasons (poetry), Random 63; The tragic drama of W.B. Yeats, Columbia Univ, 65; The matchmaker's lament and other astonishments, Gehenna, 67; The day the perfect speakers left (poetry), Wesleyan Univ, 69; co-auth, The craft of writing, Prentice-Hall, 69 & The rhetoric of argumentation, Bobbs, 70; co-transl. & ed, First person, second person: a selection of poems from the work of Agyeya, Occasional Papers, Ctr. S. & Southeast Asia Stud, Univ. Calif, Berkeley, 71; auth, Flight plan, Cedar Hill, 71; chap. 4, In: The rhetoric of Renaissance poetry, Univ. Calif, Berkeley, 74. Add: Dept. of Rhetoric, University of California, Berkeley, CA 94720.

NATHAN, NORMAN, b. Brooklyn, N.Y, Nov. 19, 15; m. 40; c. 3. ENGLISH. A.B, N.Y. Univ, 36, A.M, 38, Ph.D.(Eng), 47. Instr. ENG, City Col. New York, 46-49; asst. prof, Utica Col, Syracuse Univ, 49-52, assoc. prof, 52-58, PROF, 58-68; FLA. ATLANTIC UNIV, 68- Lectr, univ. col, Rutgers Univ, 47-49; WKTV, 54-55; vis. prof, Univ. Mo, Kansas City, summers 64, 66; vis. prof. & chmn. humanities, Col. Virgin Islands, 65-66, vis. prof, Nev. South. Univ, summer 68; mem. Comt. Classroom Practices in Teaching Eng, NCTE, 71-; coord, ten progs, WPBT-TV, 71. Shakespeare; poetry; William Blake's philosophy. Publ: Though night remain, Golden Quill, 59; Judging poetry, Putnam, 61; The right word, 62 & Writing sentences, 64 Houghton; Short stories, Bobbs, 68; Pronouns of address in The Canterbury Tales, Mediaeval Stud, 59; Shakespeare: The play's the thing, Eng. J, 10/67; Leontes' Provocation, Shakespeare Quart, winter 68. Add: Dept. of English, Florida Atlantic University, Boca Raton, FL 33432.

NATHANSON, LEONARD, b. New York, N.Y, Sept. 22, 33. ENGLISH LITERATURE. B.A, Brooklyn Col, 54; M.A, Duke Univ, 55; Ph.D, Univ. Wis, 59. Instr. ENG, Northwest. Univ, 59-60; asst. prof, Univ. Cincinnati, 60-66; ASSOC. PROF, VANDERBILT UNIV, 66- Taft Mem. Fund res. grant, 62. MLA; Mod. Humanities Res. Asn; Renaissance Soc. Am; S.Atlantic Mod. Lang. Asn; Midwest Mod. Lang. Asn; Milton Soc. Am. Seventeenth century literature; Milton; Sir Thomas Browne. Publ: The strategy of truth: a study of Sir Thomas Browne, Univ. Chicago, 67; ed, Shakespeare, The tempest, W.C. Brown, 69; contrib. & co-ed, A Milton encyclopedia, Univ. Wis, 74; plus others. Add: Dept. of English, Vanderbilt University, Nashville, TN 37235.

NATTINGER, JAMES RALPH, b. Kansas City, Mo, July 29, 40. ENGLISH LANGUAGE, LINGUISTICS. B.A, Univ. Mo, 62; M.A, Univ. Mich, 64, Ph.D. (Eng. lang), 69. Prof. ENG, Inst. N.Am. Stud, Barcelona, Spain, 64-66; asst. prof, PORTLAND STATE UNIV, 70-73, ASSOC. PROF, 73- Co-investr,

Dept. Health, Educ. & Welfare grant, 71-72. Ling. Soc. Am; West. Conf. Ling. Teaching English as a second language; sociolinguistics. Publ: Co-auth, Language teaching in a bilingual environment, Lang. Learning, 65; Sociolinguistics and TESL, Proc. Int. AIMAV Conf, 73; It is not I and it is not me, either: the treatment of conversational English in TESL texts, Creativity, 74; plus others. Add: Dept. of English, Box 751, Portland State University, Harrison St, Portland, OR 97207.

NAUGLE, HELEN HARROLD, b. West Point, Miss, Aug. 11, 20; m. 42; c. 1. EIGHTEENTH CENTURY & ENGLISH LITERATURE. B.A, Miss. State Col. Women, 42; M.A, Univ. Miss, 48; Ph.D.(Eng), Univ. Ala, 68. Instr. Eng, Univ. Miss, 48-49; prof. Eng. & asst. adminr, U.S. Armed Forces Inst, Guam, 50-51; teacher ENG, Woodward Acad, College Park, Ga, 60-61; Atlanta City Sch. Syst, Ga, 61-63; PROF, GA. INST. TECHNOL, 64- Ga. Inst. Technol. Found. assoc. prof, 67-68. MLA; Am. Soc. 18th Century Stud; NCTE; Johnsonian Soc; Conf. Col. Compos. & Commun. Eighteenth century periodicals; Samuel Johnson's style and authorship of poems attributed to him; experimental teaching methods and aids. Publ: Ed, A concordance to the poems of Samuel Johnson, Cornell Univ, 73 & Georgia Institute of Technology self-study, Ga. Inst. Technol, 73. Add: Dept. of English, Georgia Institute of Technology, Atlanta, GA 30332.

NAULT, CLIFFORD ALBERT, JR, b. Marquette, Mich, Apr. 23, 26; m. 53; c. 4. LITERATURE. B.A, Univ. Kansas City, 52, M.A, 54; Ph.D, Wayne State Univ, 60. Instr. Eng, Univ. Vt, 57-59; Ohio Univ, 59-62; from asst. prof. to ASSOC. PROF. ENG. & HEAD DEPT, PURDUE UNIV, FT. WAYNE, 62- U.S.M.C.R, 44-46. MLA; Midwest Mod. Lang. Asn; Asn. Depts. Eng. Cultural, social and literary history of the United States, 1829-1865; Herman Melville; James Joyce. Publ: Co-auth, Portraits of an artist: a casebook on James Joyce's A portrait of the artist as a young man, Odyssey, 62. Add: Dept. of English, Purdue University at Ft. Wayne, Ft. Wayne, IN 46805.

NAUSS, GEORGE MURRAY, b. Altoona, Pa. ENGLISH & AMERICAN LITERATURE. B.A, Univ. Md, 48; M.A, Johns Hopkins Univ, 49; fel, Univ. Iowa, 50-51, Ph.D.(Eng), 53. Asst. ENG, Johns Hopkins Univ, 48-49; asst. prof, Univ. N.C. Greensboro, 56-62; Duquesne Univ, 62-64; ASSOC. PROF, ST. JOHN'S UNIV.(N.Y), 64- Fel, McDowell Colony, 54-56. Eng.C, U.S.A, 43-46, Res, 46-53, 1st Lt. AAUP; MLA. Leigh Hunt and English romanticism; modern poetry. Publ: Samurai and serpent poems, Scribner, 54; plus others. Add: Dept. of English, St. John's University, Jamaica, NY 11439.

NEAL, JULIA, b. Auburn, Ky, Aug. 15, 05. ENGLISH. B.S, West. Ky. State Col, 31, M.A, 33; Univ. Mich, 43-45. Teacher, Auburn Elem. Sch, 26-30; instr. Eng, West. Ky. State Col, 34-41; dean of residence, Kingswood-Cranbrook Sch. for Girls, 44-46; asst. prof. Eng, Florence State Col, 46-56, assoc. prof, 56-64; dir. Ky. Libr. & Mus, West. Ky. Univ, 64-72; RETIRED. South. Fel. Fund grant-in-aid, 60; participant, Hancock, Mass. Conf. Shaker Stud, 69. Hopwood Lit. Award, Univ. Mich, 45. Am. Asn. State & Local Hist; Am. Stud. Asn; Pace Soc. Am; Manuscript Soc. The Shakers; Kentuckiana. Publ: By their fruits: history of the South Union Shaker Society, Univ. N.C, 47 & Porcupine, 74; ed, The journal of Eldress Nancy, Parthenon, 63; auth, South Union Shakers, Filson Quart, 4/65; Regional characteristics of Western Shaker furniture, 10/70 & Shaker industries in Kentucky, 3/74; plus others. Add: 1523 Park St, Bowling Green, KY 42101.

NEALE, JAMES RALPH, JR, b. Princeton, N.J, Dec. 25, 19; m. 54; c. 3. ENGLISH, SPEECH. A.B, Westminster Col.(Pa), 41; B.D, Yale, 44; Univ. Fla, 47-49; Ed.D.(intergroup relat), Columbia Univ, 54. Instr. Eng. & speech, Tarkio Col, 44-46; comprehensive Eng, UNIV. FLA, 46-54, asst. prof, 54-63; ASSOC. PROF. COMPREHENSIVE ENG. & ACAD. ADV, 63- Consult. intergroup relat, Melrose area; minister, Presby. Church, Melrose, Fla, NCTE; Col. Conf. Compos. & Commun. Publ: Manual of intergroup relations, Nat. Conf. Christians & Jews, 54. Add: Box 301, Melrose, FL 32666.

NEBEKER, HELEN ELIZABETH, b. Indianapolis, Ind, Jan. 16, 27; m. 44; c. 2. ENGLISH, CONTEMPORARY AMERICAN LITERATURE. B.A, Ariz. State Univ, 56, M.A, 58, 61-62. Instr. ENG, ARIZ. STATE UNIV, 58-61, asst. prof, 62-71, ASSOC. PROF, 71- MLA; NCTE. Contemporary short story; American literature; 19th century English literature. Publ: Chronology revised, summer 71 & The great corrupter or Satan rehabilitated, fall 71, Stud. Short Fiction; The pear tree: sexual implications in Katherine Mansfield's bliss, Mod. Fiction Stud, winter 72-73; plus three others. Add: Dept. of English, Arizona State University, Tempe, AZ 85281.

NEBEL, JOYCE BEHM, b. Portage Co, Wis, July 5, 18; m. 62; c. 3. ENGLISH, PHILOSOPHY. B.S, Wis. State Univ, Oshkosh, 61; M.S, Univ. Wis-Madison, 63, Ph.D.(Eng), 67. ASST. PROF. ENG, UNIV. WIS-OSHKOSH, 67- Nineteenth century and contemporary literature. Add: Dept. of English, University of Wisconsin-Oshkosh, Oshkosh, WI 54901.

NEBERGALL, ROGER ELLIS, b. Davenport, Iowa, July 3, 26; m. 58; c. 1. SPEECH COMMUNICATION. A.B, Augustana Col, 49; M.A, Bradley Univ, 51; Ph.D.(speech), Univ. Ill, 56. From instr. to asst. prof. SPEECH, Bradley Univ, 51-55; from asst. prof. to prof, Univ. Okla, 55-69, chmn. dept, 59-69; PROF. & HEAD DEPT, UNIV. ILL, URBANA, 69- Lectr. sem. commun, Agency Int. Develop, 60-69; ed, Cent. States Speech J, 67-69; lectr, La. State Univ, summer 69; ed, Speech Monogr, 75- Chem.C, A.U.S, 46-47. Speech Commun. Asn.(Golden Anniversary Prize, 67). Persuasion, attitude structure and change. Publ: Ed, Dimensions of rhetorical scholarship, Univ. Okla, 63; co-auth, Attitude and attitude change, Saunders, 65; auth. of articles in Speech Monogr, Quart. J. Speech, Speech Teacher, Cent. States Speech J. & West. Speech. Add: Dept. of Speech, University of Illinois at Urbana, 244 Lincoln Hall, Urbana, IL 61801.

NEEB, MARTIN J, JR, b. Austin, Tex, Aug. 16, 33; m. 56; c. 3. MASS COMMUNICATION. B.A, Concordia Theol. Sem, 55, scholar. & B.D, 58; M.A, St. Louis Univ, 59; Concordia Teachers Col. fels, 64-66; univ. fel, Northwest. Univ, 65-66, Ph.D, 67. Sports dir. & staff announcer, KFUO Radio, St. Louis, 54-58, asst. to prog. dir, 54-56; instr. speech, Concordia Teachers Col, 59-62, asst. prof, 62-64, assoc. prof, 64-67, dir. pub. relat, 62-67; EXEC. SECY, LUTHERAN TV PROD, 67-; ASSOC. PROF. MASS COMMUN, CONCORDIA THEOL. SEM, 68- Announcer, KETC-TV, St. Louis, 56-58; asst. to pastor, Grace Lutheran Church, Willow Springs, Ill, 59-62; producer & host, Meet the Churchman, (weekly prog), WAAF Radio, Chicago, 60-64; asst. to pastor, Good Shepherd Lutheran Church, Maywood, Ill, 63-65; exec. producer, College with a Cause, (film), Concordia Col, 64; gen. mgr, WNUR Radio, Northwest. Univ, 64-65; asst. to pastor, St. Paul Lutheran Church, Melrose Park, Ill, 65-66; fac. res. grant, Northwest Univ, 67. San Francisco Int. Film Festival Cert. Meritorious Achievement. Nat. Asn. Educ. Broadcasters; Am. Col. Pub. Relat. Asn; Relig. Pub. Relat. Counc; Speech Commun. Asn. Add: Dept. of Mass Communication, Concordia Theological Seminary, St. Louis, MO 63105.

NEEDHAM, GWENDOLYN BRIDGES, b. Altus, Ark, Aug. 14, 06; div. ENGLISH, FICTION. A.B, Univ. Calif, Berkeley, 28, fel, 28-29, M.A, 30, Ph.D. (Eng), 37. Instr. ENG, Univ. Calif, Davis, 37-42; Univ. Calif, Berkeley, 43-44; asst. prof, UNIV. CALIF, DAVIS, 48-53, assoc. prof, 53-61, prof, 61-73, EMER. PROF, 73- Huntington Libr. grant-in-aid, summer 54; Am. Asn. Univ. Women Founders fel, 55-56. U.S.N.R, 44-48, Lt. AAUP; Am. Asn. Univ. Women; Am. Soc. 18th Century Stud; Jane Austen Soc; MLA. Women in literature; 18th century English life, literature; history and criticism of English novel. Publ: Co-auth, Pamela's daughters, Macmillan, 36, libr. ed, Russell & Russell, 72; auth, Mary de la Rivière Manley, Tory defender, Huntington Libr. Quart, 49; The undisciplined heart of David Copperfield, Nineteenth-Century Fiction, 52; Richardson's characterization of Mr. B. and double purpose in Pamela, Eighteenth Century Stud, 70. Add: 417 E St, Davis, CA 95616.

NEEDLEMAN, MORRISS HAMILTON, b. Brooklyn, N.Y, July 2, 07; m. 32; c. 4. ENGLISH, EDUCATION. B.A, City Col. New York, 31, M.S.Ed, 39; N.Y. Univ, 45-49. Teacher elem. schs, N.Y.C. Bd. Educ, 36-45; teacher & chmn. dept. Eng, jr. high schs, N.Y.C, 45-57, supvr. elem. & jr. high schs, 57-70; PRIN, ELEM. SCHS, N.Y.C, BD. EDUC, 70- Consult. ed, Barnes & Noble, Inc, N.Y, 39-47; chief consult, Facts on Dial, Inc, N.Y.C, 51-53; dir. res-writing, Educ. Res. Asn, 52-; coord. reading grades 3-10 & adults, Adult Educ, Brooklyn Col, 60-; chief consult. & dir, Growth: Prog. Remedial Educ, Brooklyn & N.Y.C, 61-; supvr. reading grades 3-10, Queens Col.(N.Y), 65-; mem, Counc. Supvrs. & Adminrs, N.Y.C, 65-; coord. written expression, Intensive Teacher Training Prog, City Col. New York, 66-67; consult. ed. & chmn. curriculum comt, Inst. Indust. Technol, New York, 67-; adj. asst. prof. reading, Continuing Educ. Prog, Queens & Brooklyn Cols, 69-73, adj. assoc. prof, 73- Am. Asn. Sch. Adminr; Asn. Supv. & Curriculum Develop; Int. Reading Asn; NCTE; Nat. Asn. Pub. Sch. Adult Educ; Educ. Aids Asn; Mark Twain Lit. Soc. American and English literature; American usage; how to teach reading. Publ: Co-auth, An outline-history of English literature, 2 vols, 36-38 & American literature, 45 & auth, A manual of pronunciation, 49, Barnes & Noble; co-auth, Biology for all, Barnes & Noble, 50; auth, Handbook for practical composition, McGraw, 68; Basic reading-spelling communication vocabulary of 1350 words, 71, Manual to accompany Morriss H. Needleman's Basic reading-spelling communication vocabulary of 1350 words, 71 & Basic reading communication vocabulary of 1850 words for adults, 71, privately publ; Basic reading-spelling communication vocabulary of 2000 words, 72; Las 2000 palabras usadas con mas frecuencia en ingles (bilingual dictionary), 74; co-auth, Pronunciation, In: Word-mastery for all, Barnes & Noble, 48; The Needleman integrating basic communication vocabulary of 1,000 words, Growth: Prog. Remedial Educ, 62. Add: 2367 E. 18th St, Brooklyn, NY 11229.

NEEL, HELEN McDONNELL, b. Toledo, Ohio, Feb. 27, 08; m. 53. COMPOSITION, LITERATURE. A.B, Dickinson Col, 28; Columbia Univ, 29; M.A, Northwest. Univ, 41; Ph.D.(Eng), Univ. Pittsburgh, 54. Teacher, high sch, Pa, 28-46; instr, ENG, Edinboro State Col, 46-54, prof, 54-56; Monmouth Col.(N.J), 56-64; asst. prof, Berkshire Community Col, 64-67; assoc. prof, NORTH ADAMS STATE COL, 67-69, PROF, 69- NCTE; MLA. Textbooks used in teaching the history of English literature in American schools; school publicity; history of language. Add: Ballou Lane, Williamstown, MA 01267.

NEESON, JACK (Mc) HENRY, b. Wilmington, Del, July 31, 18; m. 43. DRAMA. B.A, Univ. Del, 40; B.D, Va. Theol. Sem, 43; M.A, West. Reserve Univ, 46, TV fel, 54-55, M.F.A, 55, Ph.D, 59. Asst. prof. drama, Univ. Ga, 47-49; assoc. dir, Dock St. Theatre, Charleston, S.C, 49-52; dir, Circle at the Rowe, Grand Rapids, Mich, 53-54; ASSOC. PROF. DRAMA, Chatham Col, 56-58; San Jose State Col, 58-67; CHATHAM COL, 67- U.S. Merchant Marine, 43-45. Am. Theatre Asn; Am. Nat. Theatre & Acad. Theories of direction; criticism; history of theatre in Wilmington, Delaware. Publ: Theatre in Cleveland, In: Enciclopedia dello Spectacolo, Milano, 56; From schoolhouse to play house, 58 & co-auth, Favorite Wilmington plays before the Civil War, 57, Del. Hist. Soc. Add: Dept. of Drama, Chatham College, Woodland Rd, Pittsburgh, PA 15232.

NEFF, ERNESTINE ANDERSON, English As A Second Language, English. See Volume III, Foreign Languages, Linguistics & Philology.

NEILL, (JAMES) KERBY, b. Washington, D.C, Mar. 2, 06; m. 37; c. 6. ENGLISH LITERATURE. A.B, Georgetown Univ, 28; Ph.D, Johns Hopkins Univ, 35. Instr, St. Louis Univ, 34-37; assoc. prof, Col. New Rochelle, 37-38; asst. prof. ENG. LANG. & LIT, CATH. UNIV. AM, 38-48, assoc. prof, 48-52, prof, 52-70, acting head dept, 62-63, head dept, 63-70, EMER. PROF, 70- Lectr, Johns Hopkins Univ, 39-40. MLA. Edmund Spenser; Elizabethan sonnet; Milton. Publ: The degradation of the Red Cross Knight in That Soueraine light; Structure and symbol in Crashaw's Hymn in the Nativity, PMLA; More ado about Claudio: an aquittal for the slandered groom, Shakespeare Quart. Add: 7118 Glenbrook Rd, Bethesda, MD 20014.

NEILSON, GEORGE LOCKHART, b. Caputh, Scotland, Nov. 27, 41. DRAMA. Dipl. speech & drama, Royal Scottish Acad, 64; Rotary & Fulbright scholarships & M.F.A, Univ. Ga, 66. Asst. prof. THEATRE, Columbus Col, 66-67; ASSOC. PROF, UNIV. WINDSOR, 67- Speech Commun. Asn. Outdoor theatre; directors. Add: School of Drama, University of Windsor, Windsor, Ont. N9B 3P4, Can.

NEIMAN, FRASER, b. Brooklyn, N.Y, Apr. 9, 11; m. 50; c. 2. ENGLISH. A.B, Amherst Col, 32; Simpson fel, Trinity Col, Cambridge Univ, 32-33;

A.M, Harvard, 34, Ph.D.(Eng), 38. Instr. ENG, COL. WILLIAM & MARY, 38-42, asst. prof, 46, assoc. prof, 46-58, prof, 58-68, head dept, 64-70, HERITAGE FEL, 68- Ford fel, 54-55; Commonwealth Fund res. grants, 50, 53, 58 & 63; vis. prof, Univ. Hawaii, summer 62 & 70-71; mem. bd. dir, Univ. Press Va, 66-; Commonwealth Fund res. grant, summer 67; mem. ed. bd, Victorians Inst. J, 71- & Matthew Arnold Newslett, 73. U.S.A, 42-46, Res, 46-64, Col; Bronze Star Medal, 45. MLA; Dante Soc. Am. English literature, especially Romantic movement and Victorian period; Shakespeare; Romantic and Victorian poetry and criticism. Publ: Matthew Arnold, Twayne, 68; ed, Essays, letters and reviews by Matthew Arnold, Harvard, 60; auth, The letters of William Gilpin to Samuel Henley, Huntington Libr. Quart, 2/72. Add: Dept. of English, College of William & Mary, Williamsburg, VA 23185.

NEIMAN, GILBERT HOWARD, b. Whitewater, Kans, Nov. 24, 12; m. 50; c. 1. ENGLISH, ROMANCE LANGUAGES. B.A, Univ. Colo, 37; Ph.D.(Eng), Univ. N.Mex, 59. Instr. Span, Univ. Colo, 43-45; head dept. Eng. & Span, high sch, Colo, 50-52; asst. Eng, Univ. N.Mex, 55-57; assoc. prof, Inter-Am. Univ. P.R, 58-60, dir. ctr. creative writing, 61-63; assoc. prof. ENG, CLARION STATE COL, 63-67, PROF, 67- Lectr, Writers' Conf, Univ. Denver, summer 57. MLA. Publ: Transl, Federico Garcia Lorca, Blood wedding, New Directions, 39; auth, There is a tyrant in every country, Harcourt, 47; Charlie Chaplin, or the absurdity of scenery, N.Mex. Quart, spring 53; Thomas Hardy, existentialist, 1/56 & Was Hardy anthropomorphic?, 7/56, Twentieth Century Lit. Add: 55 Applewood Valley, Clarion, PA 16214.

NELMS, BEN FRANK, b. Pulaski, Tenn, May 12, 36; m. 62; c. 5. ENGLISH, EDUCATION. B.A, David Lipscomb Col, 58; Woodrow Wilson fel. & M.A, Univ. N.C, 59; Ph.D.(Eng. & educ), Univ. Iowa, 67. Instr. Eng, Abilene Christian Col, 59-63; educ, Univ. Iowa, 66-67; asst. prof. ENG. & EDUC, UNIV. MO-COLUMBIA, 67-70, ASSOC. PROF, 70- NCTE; Col. Eng. Asn; Conf. Eng. Educ.(ed, Eng. Educ, 73-); Midwest Mod. Lang. Asn; Conf. Christianity & Lit. Add: 2000 N. Allen Dr, Columbia, MO 65201.

NELSON, ALAN H, b. Boston, Mass, Nov. 4, 38; m. 61; c. 2. ENGLISH, ART HISTORY. B.A, St. Olaf Col, 60; Univ. Minn, 61-62; M.A, Univ. Calif, Berkeley, 63, Ph.D.(Eng), 66. ASST. PROF. Eng. & humanities, Univ. Chicago, 66-71; ENG, UNIV. CALIF, BERKELEY, 71- Inland Steel fel, summer 67. MLA; Mediaeval Acad. Am. Dramatic structure of English corpus Christi plays; staging of medieval religious drama; relationships of pictorial art and drama in the later middle ages. Publ: Sacred and secular currents in the Towneley Play of Noah, Drama Surv. III, winter 64. Add: Dept. of English, University of California, Berkeley, CA 94720.

NELSON, ALFRED LEWIS, JR, b. Chicago, Ill, June 19, 14; m. 39; c. 2. LITERATURE, THEATRE. A.B, Wayne State Univ, 38, A.M, 40; fel, George Washington Univ, 63-65, Ph.D.(Eng), 68. Instr. Eng, East. Mich. Univ, 65-67, asst. prof, 67-68; assoc. prof. Eng. & dir. grad. stud. Eng, Univ. Nev, Las Vegas, 68-69, chmn. dept, 69-70; assoc. prof. Eng. & dir. freshman Eng. courses, EAST. MICH. UNIV, 70-73, PROF. ENG, 73- Folger Libr. fel, 74. U.S.M.C, 42-45, 51-63, Maj. MLA; NCTE (dir, 68-70); Soc. Theatre Res. Eng; Int. Fed. Theatre Res. British provincial theatre, 18th and 19th century; British and American drama. Publ: Co-ed, Drury Lane journal; selections from the diaries of James Winston, Soc. Theatre Res.(London), 74; auth, James Winston in Paris, 1824, Theatre Res, 70; The Winston diaries, Theatre Notebook, 70; co-auth, Milton invents a matron, Am. Notes & Queries, 72. Add: Dept. of English, Eastern Michigan University, Ypsilanti, MI 48197.

NELSON, ARMOUR HALSTEAD, b. Smolan, Kans, Aug. 7, 13; m. 54. ENGLISH. B.A, Univ. Chicago, 48, M.A, 50. Instr. ENG, N.Park Col. & Ill. Inst. Technol, 51-52; asst. prof, Concordia Col.(Moorhead, Minn), 53-58, prof, 58-64; ASSOC. PROF, CALIF. LUTHERAN COL, 64, chmn. div. humanities, 64-67, acquisitions librn, 73-74. Folger Libr. fel, 54; ed, Discourse, 58-64. U.S.A, 41-45. MLA; Renaissance Soc. Am; Shakespeare Asn. Am; NCTE. Sixteenth and 17th century literature; Shakespeare's dramatic uses of supernatural; Milton. Publ: Co-auth, Introduction to research, Concordia Col, 57; Critics and the waste land, Eng. Stud, 2/55; College dictionaries, Discourse, 1/58. Add: Dept. of English, California Lutheran College, 60 W. Olsen Rd, Thousand Oaks, CA 91360.

NELSON, ARNOLD GERHARD, b. Stillwater, Minn, July 10, 18; m. 43; c. 3. ENGLISH. B.A, Hamline Univ, 41; M.A, Univ. Minn, 48, Am. Counc. Learned Soc. fel, 51-52, Ph.D.(Am. stud), 53. Instr. ENG, Univ. Minn, 50-53; asst. prof, Stout Inst, 53-54; PROF, WEST. MICH. UNIV, 54- Nat. Asn. Educ. Broadcasters grant, 61-62; Fulbright lectr. Am. lit, Turku, Finland, 64-65. U.S.A.A.F, 42-46, Sgt. American literature; American studies; linguistics. Add: 1218 W. North St, Kalamazoo, MI 49007.

NELSON, AUGUSTA CHARLOTTE, b. Manila, P.I, July 6, 08. ENGLISH, COMPARATIVE LITERATURE. B.A, Univ. Minn, 29, M.A, 30, Ph.D.(mod. langs. & Eng), 40; summer, Univ. Paris, 33. Asst. instr. French, Univ. Minn, 29-31, ed. asst, Univ. Press, 42-43, librn, geol. libr, 43; prof. Romance Langs, Col. St. Scholastica, 31-33; instr, Univ. Nebr, 35-39; Romance langs, Univ, Ore, 43-44; PROF. Eng, Col. St. Teresa, 44-47; LANG. & LIT, ENG. & HUMANITIES, WINONA STATE COL, 47-, acting chmn. div. lang. & lit, 52-53. MLA; NEA. Literary criticism; development of the dramatic form; modern poetry, novel and drama. Publ: Victor Hugo's dramatic theory and practice, Univ. Minn. Add: Dept. of English, Winona State College, Winona, MN 55987.

NELSON, CARY ROBERT, b. Philadelphia, Pa, May 15, 46. ENGLISH & AMERICAN LITERATURE. B.A, Antioch Col, 67; Ph.D.(Eng), Univ. Rochester, 70. ASST. PROF. ENG, UNIV. ILL, URBANA, 70- MLA. Modern English and American literature; critical theory. Publ: The incarnate word: literature as verbal space, Univ. Ill, 73; Suffused-encircling shapes of mind: inhabited space in Williams, J. Mod. Lit, 5/71. Add: Dept. of English, University of Illinois, Urbana, IL 61801.

NELSON, CONNY EDWIN, b. Seattle, Wash, Feb. 20, 33; m. 52; c. 8. ENGLISH, COMPARATIVE LITERATURE. A.B, Univ. Wash, 56, Ph.D.(Eng. & comp. lit), 64. Instr. Eng, Wash. State Univ, 61-64; asst. prof. Eng. & comp. lit, Purdue Univ, 64-67, assoc. prof, 67-68; assoc. prof. ENG. & chmn. prog. lit. stud, Wash. State Univ, 68-70; PROF. & ASST. TO V.CHANCELLOR, 70-, chmn. dept. commun. concentration, 70-72. Fel, Acad. Admin. Internship Prog, Am. Counc. Educ, 73-74. U.S.A, 52. MLA; Am. Comp. Lit. Asn; Renaissance Soc. Am. Renaissance drama; literary criticism and theory of literature; modern poetry. Publ: Co-auth, Drama and tradition, Am. Bk. Co, 68; auth, Homer's Odyssey: a critical handbook, Wadsworth, 69; Politics and passion in Phedre, Fr. Rev, 10/65; T.S. Eliot, Michaelangelo, and John Webster, Res. Stud, 70; St. John Perse, In: Encycl. World Lit. 20th Century, Ungar, 71; plus others. Add: Office of the Vice Chancellor, University of Wisconsin-Green Bay, Green Bay, WI 54302.

NELSON, DAVID ARTHUR, b. Amarillo, Tex, June 3, 29; m. 58; c. 2. ENGLISH. B.A, Univ. Chicago, 51, M.A, 54; Ph.D.(Eng), Cornell Univ, 65. Instr. ENG, Ga. Inst. Technol, 54-55; BATES COL, 59-65, asst. prof, 65-72, ASSOC. PROF, 72- U.S.A.F, 46-49, Sgt. MLA. English novel; 18th century English dramatic comedy. Add: Dept. of English, Bates College, Lewiston, ME 04240.

NELSON, DUNCAN MORSE, b. Durham, N.C, May 9, 30; div; c. 7. ENGLISH. B.A, Wesleyan Univ, 52; M.A, Harvard, 54, Ph.D.(Eng), 63. Asst. prof. humanities, Mass. Inst. Technol, 63-67; ENG, UNIV. MASS, BOSTON, 67-73, ASSOC. PROF, 73- Mass. Inst. Technol. summer res. grant, 66. Romantic, Victorian and modern literature; Thomas Hardy. Publ: The light that never was: book 23 of the Iliad, Class. J, 3/64. Add: Dept. of English, University of Massachusetts, Boston, MA 02116.

NELSON, FRANK G, b. St. Joseph, Mo, Oct. 28, 07; m. 45; c. 2. ENGLISH. A.B, Park Col, 30; M.A, Haverford Col, 31; Ph.D, Univ. Calif, Berkeley, 37; Univ. Oslo, 39. Prof. Eng, Polytech. Inst. P.R, 35-36; asst. prof, Univ. Wichita, 37-39; lectr. Eng. & Am. lit, Univ. Oslo, 40, 45-46; assoc. prof. Eng, Univ. Denver, 46-47; PROF, Univ. Ark, 47-49; William Jewell Col, 49-50; Calif. State Col. Long Beach, 50-63, Latin, 63-66; ENG, UNIV. HAWAII, HILO, 66- Smith-Mundt lectr, Nat. Univ. Chile & Cath. Univ. Chile, 56; Univ. Barcolona, 57; summer lectr, Caracas Cent. Libr, Venezuela, 60; lectr, int. summer session, Univ. Uppsala, Sweden, 63-67; vis. prof, Ariz. State Univ, 66; Am. coord. & co-dir. summer session Eng, Univ. Lund, Sweden, 68. Distinguished Teaching Award, Calif. State Cols, 65-66 & Hilo Col, 73. Soc. Advan. Scand. Stud. Troy tradition in Medieval Scandinavia; classical backgrounds of English literature; American literature of the 19th century. Publ: Literatura Norteamericana, 1607-1900, Univ. Chile, 56; transl, Brochmann, humanity and happiness, Viking, 50. Add: 1748 Waianuenue Ave, Hilo, HI 96720.

NELSON, HARLAND S, b. Hawley, Minn, Aug. 11, 25; m. 54; c. 3. ENGLISH. B.A, Concordia Col.(Minn), 49; M.A, Wash. State Univ, 51; Kent fel. Nat. Counc. Relig. Higher Educ, 56; univ. fel, Univ. Minn, 58, Ph.D, 59. Instr. ENG, Univ. Mo, 51-53; Univ. Conn, 59-62; asst. prof, LUTHER COL.(IOWA), 62-63, assoc. prof, 63-67, PROF, 67- Fulbright lectr, Univ. Bergen, 67-68 & Univ. Innsbruck, Austria, 72-73. U.S.A.A.F, 44-45. MLA; NCTE; AAUP; Soc. Relig. Higher Educ. Victorian literature; Dickens; modern and contemporary fiction. Publ: Stephen Crane's achievement as a poet, Tex. Stud. Lit. & Lang, winter 63; Steinbeck's politics then and now, Antioch Rev, spring 67; Stagg's gardens: the railway through Dickens' world, Dickens Stud. Annual, 73. Add: Dept. of English, Luther College, Decorah, IA 52101.

NELSON, HAROLD ELROY, b. Northwood, Iowa, Oct. 29, 12; m. 38; c. 3. SPEECH. B.A, State Univ. Iowa, 35, M.A, 40, Ph.D.(speech & educ. psychol), 47. Instr. speech, Iowa Wesleyan Col, 40-44; commun. skills, State Univ. Iowa, 44-47; asst. prof. SPEECH, PA. STATE UNIV, UNIVERSITY PARK, 47-54, assoc. prof, 54-64, PROF, 64- Mem. ed. bd. J. Commun, 56-58. Broadcast Educ. Asn; Speech Asn. East. States (exec. secy, 65-67); Speech Commun. Asn. Radio; television; speech. Publ: Two methods of presentation of Meet the Press compared, J. Broadcasting, summer 57; Teaching speech by television, Cent. States Speech J, winter 60; Videotaping the speech course, Speech Teacher, 3/68. Add: Dept. of Speech, 310 Sparks Bldg, Pennsylvania State University, University Park, PA 16802.

NELSON, HUGH ALAN, b. Erie, Pa, Mar. 21. 24; m. 52; c. 2. ENGLISH. A.B, Union Col, 47; M.A, Northwest. Univ, 48, Ph.D, 58. Instr. ENG, Valparaiso Univ, 48-49; ASSOC. PROF, UNION COL.(N.Y), 54- Lectr, Northwest. Univ, 52-53. U.S.N, 43-46, Lt.(jg). NCTE. Modern British poetry, linguistics. Add: Dept. of English, Union College, Schenectady, NY 12308.

NELSON, JAMES GRAHAM, b. Covington, Ky, Dec. 20, 29. ENGLISH LITERATURE. B.A, Univ. Ky, 52; M.A, Columbia Univ, 55, Ph.D, 61. Lectr. ENG, Columbia Univ, 58-61; instr, UNIV. WIS, MADISON, 61-62, asst. prof, 62-65, assoc. prof, 65-69, PROF, 69- Guggenheim fel, 65-66. U.S.A.F, 52-54, Res, 54-, Capt. MLA; Milton Soc. Am. Romantic poetry; Victorian literature; aesthetic and decadent movements in English literature. Publ: The sublime puritan: Milton and the Victorians, Univ. Wis, 63; Sir William Watson, Twayne, 67; The early nineties: a view from the Bodley Head, Harvard Univ, 71. Add: Dept. of English, University of Wisconsin, Madison, WI 53706.

NELSON, JAMES MALCOLM, b. Stratford, Ont, May 2, 28. ENGLISH, DRAMA. B.A, Univ. West. Ont, 51; cert. Eng, Ont. Col. Educ, 52; M.A, Univ. Toronto, 55, Ph.D.(Eng), 68. Instr. ENG, Univ. Sask, 57-59; lectr, UNIV. ALTA, 62-63, asst. prof, 63-72, ASSOC. PROF, 72- Asn. Can. Univ. Teachers Eng; Humanities Asn. Can. Theatre in England from 1820 to 1890; early modern drama, English, Irish, continental and American. Add: Dept. of English, University of Alberta, Edmonton, Alta, T6G 2G2, Can.

NELSON, JANE ARMSTRONG, b. New York, N.Y, Mar. 25, 27; m. 59. ENGLISH & AMERICAN LITERATURE. B.A, Mt. Holyoke Col, 48; M.A, Univ. Mich, Ann Arbor, 49, Ph.D.(Eng. lit), 66. From instr. to asst. prof. Eng, East. Mich. Univ, 52-58; lectr, Univ. Md, Munich, Ger, 59-61; instr. Am. stud, Mich. State Univ, 61-66; assoc. prof. ENG, Bradford Col, 66-69; from asst. prof. to ASSOC. PROF, NORTHEAST. UNIV, 69-, acting chmn. dept. psychol, 72-73. MLA; AAUP. Literary theory; 19th century English literature; 19th and 20th century American literature. Publ: Form and image in the fiction of Henry Miller, Wayne State Univ, 70; Ecstacy and transformation in Whitman's Lilacs, Walt Whitman Rev, 72; Circumambulation and descent in James' The jolly corner, Stud. Am. Fiction, fall 74. Add: Dept. of English, Northeastern University, Boston, MA 02115.

NELSON, LAWRENCE EMERSON, b. Clinton, Mo, July 25, 93; m. 16; c. 3. HISTORY OF CIVILIZATION, LITERATURE. A.B, William Jewell Col, 15; A.M, Univ. Kans, 21; Ph.D.(Eng), Stanford Univ, 30; hon. D.Litt, Univ. Redlands, 71; hon. L.H.D, Sioux Falls Col, 72. Prof. Eng, Sioux Falls Col, 18-25; prof. & chmn. dept, Univ. Redlands, 25-61, chmn. dept. hist. civilization, dir. div. langs & lit. & later grad. stud; prof. Eng. & chmn. dept. humanities, 61-73, CALIF. BAPTIST COL, CUR, BOOK OF LIFE MUS, 73- Chmn, educ. counc. intercol. prog, Ford Found, 54-55; chmn. dept. Eng, Judson Col, 68-69; Rike-Kummler Found. grant. Hon. Citation, Calif. Baptist Col, 72. Historical influence of the English Bible; local history. Publ: Our roving Bible, Abingdon; Redlands: biography of a college, Univ. Redlands, 58; Only one Redlands, Redlands Community Music Asn, 63; Trademarks show biblical influence, 65, Ships show biblical influence, 66, Rivers show biblical influence, 67; Medicines show biblical influence, 68, co-auth, The Prospect Park book, 68, Calif. Baptist Col; plus others. Add: 811 N. University St, Redlands, CA 92373.

NELSON, MALCOLM A, b. Carbondale, Ill, May 29, 34; m. 55; c. 4. ENGLISH. B.A, Williams Col, 55; M.A, Northwest. Univ, 57, Ph.D, 61. Asst, Northwest. Univ, 56-59; instr. ENG, Miami Univ, 59-61; asst. prof, 61-65; Grinnell Col, 65-68; assoc. prof, STATE UNIV. N.Y. COL. FREDONIA, 68-73, PROF, 73- State Univ. N.Y. Res. Found. grant, 69 & 71; Am. Philos. Soc. grant, 71. Renaissance Soc. Am; MLA; Catch Soc. Am.(exec. secy, 68-); Am. Soc. 18th Century Stud; Shakespeare Asn. Am; AAUP; Am. Fed. Teachers. Sixteenth through 18th century poetry and music—catches, canons and glees; Shakespeare; lyric poetry. Publ: Co-ed, A collection of catches, canons and glees, 1762-1793 (4 vols), Mellifont, 70; The Robin Hood tradition in the English Renaissance, Univ. Salzburg, 73; auth, The poet and the goddess, Nous, 3/67; Catches, glees and chaces: cantici bibendi et alii, Lyric & Song, 6/71. Add: Dept. of English, State University of New York College at Fredonia, Fredonia, NY 14063.

NELSON, MARY ANN, b. Tacoma, Wash, Aug. 7, 38. CHILDREN'S LITERATURE, ENGLISH EDUCATION. B.A, Univ. Puget Sound, 60; M.A, Univ. Wash, 65. Teacher, Tacoma Pub. Schs, 60-66, consult. teacher Eng. & spelling, 66-67; asst. prof. ENG, EAST. WASH. STATE COL, 67-72, ASSOC. PROF, 72-, CONSULT. ELEM. LANG. ARTS, 67- NCTE; Col. Eng. Asn. History of children's literature, 850-1800; excellence in contemporary children's literature. Publ: Ed, A comparative anthology of children's literature, Holt, 72. Add: Dept. of English, Eastern Washington State College, Cheney, WA 99004.

NELSON, NICOLAS HARDING, b. Nebraska City, Nebr, July 7, 40; m. 65; c. 2. ENGLISH LITERATURE. B.A, Stanford Univ, 62; Third degree, Alliance Francaise, Paris, 63; M.A, Univ. Wis-Madison, 65, Ph.D.(Eng), 71. Lectr. ENG, IND. UNIV, KOKOMO, 69-71, ASST. PROF. & CHMN. DIV. HUMANITIES, 71- Ind. Univ. Found. summer fac. fel, summer 72. MLA; Am. Soc. 18th Century Stud; Johnson Soc. Cent. Region; Augustan Reprint Soc. Samuel Bulter; Hudibras; 18th century English satire. Add: Div. of Humanities, Indiana University at Kokomo, 2300 S. Washington St, Kokomo, IN 46901.

NELSON, NORMAN EDWARD, b. Minneapolis, Minn, Jan. 1, 99; m. 21; c. 2. ENGLISH & COMPARATIVE LITERATURE. A.B. & A.M, Univ. Minn, 21; Univ. Ill, 21-24; Ph.D.(Eng), Harvard, 28. Teaching asst, Univ. Ill, 21-24; instr, Tufts Col, 24-28; asst. prof. ENG, UNIV. MICH, ANN ARBOR, 28-37, assoc. prof, 37-48, prof, 48-71, EMER. PROF, 71- Ford Found. fel, 54-55; Rockefeller cult. interchange fel, Kyoto Am. Stud. Ctr, Japan, 56-57. NCTE; Am. Soc. Aesthet. Literary criticism; relations of humanities to physical and social sciences. Publ: Science and the irresponsible imagination, Yale Rev; Popular arts and the humanities, Col. Eng; The two cultures, Ingenor III, 67. Add: Dept. of English, University of Michigan, Ann Arbor, MI 48104.

NELSON, PAULINE W, b. Dallas, Tex, Nov. 12, 13; div. SPEECH, DRAMA. B.A, South. Methodist Univ, 39; M.A, Univ. Ariz, 49; Ph.D.(speech & drama), Stanford Univ, 65. Oral interpreter mod. lit, Sanger-Harris, Dallas, Tex, 33-41; instr. Eng. & drama, Univ. Ariz, 43-45; asst. prof. drama & speech, Pac. Lutheran Univ, 49-50; SPEECH, San Jose State Col, 63-66; from asst. prof. to ASSOC. PROF, SAN FRANCISCO STATE UNIV, 66- W.A.V.E.S, 45. West. Speech Commun. Asn; Speech Commun. Asn. Oral interpretation; interpersonal communication; speech education. Add: 27040 Dezahara Way, Los Altos Hills, CA 94022.

NELSON, RAYMOND STANLEY, b. Brooklyn, N.Y, Oct. 11, 21; m. 43; c. 4. ENGLISH. B.Th, Trinity Sem, 44; B.A, Univ. Minn, 55, M.A, 57; Ph.D, Univ. Nebr, 68. Asst. prof. Eng, MORNINGSIDE COL, 57-62, assoc. prof, 62-68, PROF. ENG. & CHMN. DIV. HUMANITIES, 68-, V.PRES. ACAD. AFFAIRS, 72- Mem. Iowa bd, Nat. Endowment for Humanities, 72- MLA. Nineteenth century English literature; Bernard Shaw. Publ: Ed, Candida, Bernard Shaw, Bobbs, 72; auth, Wisdom and power in Androcles and the lion, Yearbk. Eng. Stud, 2/72; Measure for measure as satiric comedy, Iowa State Res. J, 5/73. Add: Morningside College, Sioux City, IA 51106.

NELSON, ROY CONRAD, b. Superior, Wis, July 5, 10; m. 39; c. 2. SPEECH. B.E, Wis. State Col, 31; M.A, Univ. Minn, 37, Ph.D, 55. Prin, high sch, Wis, 31-35, instr, 35-38; Waterloo, Iowa, 38-42; staff off. speech & Eng, West. Mil. Acad, Ill, 42-43; SPEECH, Univ. Colo, 46-48; ASSOC. PROF, COLO. STATE UNIV, 48-, CHMN. DEPT. ENG. & MOD. LANGS, 56-, ASSOC. DEAN COL. HUMANITIES & SOC. SCI, 68-, assoc. dean col. sci. & arts, 64-68. Consult. develop. prog, Univ. Guadalajara. U.S.A, 43-46. Speech Commun. Asn; NCTE. Public address; communication; persuasion. Publ: The nurse speaks, Davis, 58; And now to define the terms, The Gavel; Administrative practices in college forensic programs, West. Speech. Add; 738 Gregory Rd, Ft. Collins, CO 80521.

NELSON, ROY PAUL, b. Portland, Ore, June 17, 23; m. 60; c. 4. JOURNALISM, GRAPHIC ARTS. B.S, Univ. Ore, 47, M.S, 55; Art Ctr. Sch, Calif, 47-48. Copywriter, McCann-Erickson, Portland, 47; reporter, United Press, Salt Lake City, Utah, 48-49; asst. ed. dir, Am. Forest Prod. Indust, D.C, 49-53, dist. mgr, San Francisco, 54-55; assoc. prof. JOUR, UNIV. ORE, 55-68, PROF, 68- Lectr. pub. utilities exec. course, Univ. Idaho, 59; Mag. Publ. Asn. res. grant, 67. U.S.N.R, 43-47, Lt.(jg). Asn. Educ. Jour. Graphic design; biography. Publ: Fell's guide to the art of cartooning, 62 & co-auth, Fell's guide to commercial art, 66, Fel; auth, The design of advertising, 67 & 73 & Publication design, 72, W.C. Brown; co-auth, The fourth estate, Harper, 71. Add: School of Journalism, University of Oregon, Eugene, OR 97403.

NELSON, RUTH, English, Music. See McHUGH, RUTH NELSON.

NELSON, THEODORE F, b. St. James, Minn, Feb. 5, 06; m. 28; c. 2. SPEECH. B.A, Gustavus Adolphus Col, 27; M.A, Univ. Minn, 34; Ph.D.(speech), State Univ. Iowa, 44; San Francisco State Col, 67-68. Instr. high schs, Ill, 29-43; asst. prof. speech, Allegheny Col, 44-46; prof. & chmn. dept, ST. OLAF COL, 46-72, chmn. div. lang. & lit, 61-72, EMER. PROF. SPEECH, 72- Speech Commun. Asn; Cent. States Speech Commun. Asn. General semantics; voice science; argumentation and persuasion and public address. Publ: Personality through speech, Benjamin H. Sanborn Co; Speech and your personality, L.W. Singer & Co; Spurgeons theory and practice of preaching, Quart. J. Speech. Add: Dept. of Speech, St. Olaf College, Northfield, MN 55057.

NELSON, WILLIAM, b. New York, N.Y, Jan. 18, 08; m. 30; c. 2. ENGLISH. B.S, City Col. New York, 27; A.M, Columbia Univ, 28, Ph.D, 39. Teacher sec. schs, New York, N.Y, 28-42; ed-in-chief, America, U.S. Dept. State, 45-46; asst. prof, COLUMBIA UNIV, 49-51, assoc. prof, 51-56, prof. ENG, 56-73, W.P. TRENT PROF, 73- Field rep, Off. War Inform, Moscow, 44-45; Guggenheim fel, 56. Eng. Asn, Gt. Brit; Acad. Lit. Stud; Renaissance Soc. Am. Literature of the English Renaissance. Publ: John Skelton, Laureate, 39 & The poetry of Edmund Spenser, 63, Columbia; The life of St. George by Alexander Barclay, Early Eng. Text Soc, 55; A fifteenth century schoolbook, Clarendon, 56; Fact or fiction: dilemma of the Renaissance storyteller, Harvard, 73. Add: Dept. of English, Columbia University, New York, NY 10027.

NEMANIC, GERALD CARL, b. Biwabik, Minn, Sept. 18, 41. AMERICAN LITERATURE. B.A, Univ. Minn, 63; M.A, Univ. Ariz, 65, Ph.D.(Eng), 69. Instr. ENG, Calif. State Col, Long Beach, 65-67; NORTHEAST. ILL. UNIV, 67-70, ASST. PROF, 71- Co-ed, The Great Lakes Rev, 73- MLA; Midwest Mod. Lang. Asn; Soc. Stud. Midwest. Lit. Regional American literature; modern novel. Publ: The ripening eye: the fiction of Wright Morris, Mid. Am, fall 73. Add: Dept. of English, Northeastern Illinois University, Bryn Mawr & St. Louis, Chicago, IL 60625.

NEMANICH, DONALD DEAN, b. Joliet, Ill, July 2, 37; m. 68; c. 1. ENGLISH LANGUAGE & COMPOSITION. B.S, Ill. State Univ, 59, M.A, 62; Univ. Mo, 63; Univ. Calif, Los Angeles, 66; Univ. Mich, 67; Ph.D, Univ. Nebr, 68. Instr. Eng, Univ. Nebr-Lincoln, 64-65, 67-68; res. assoc, Curriculum Ctr, 65-67; ASST. PROF. ENG, Fla. State Univ, 68-69, UNIV. ILL, URBANA-CHAMPAIGN, 69- Vis. asst. prof. Eng, Univ. N.C, Chapel Hill, summer 69; co-ed, Ill. Eng. Bull, 72-73, ed, 73- MLA; NCTE; Ling. Soc. Am. Conf. Col. Compos. & Commun; Conf. Eng. Educ. English grammar and grammars; linguistic variation; child language. Publ: Co-auth, The Nebraska study of the syntax of children's compositions (3 vols), Nebr. Curriculum Develop. Ctr, 67; auth, Why they hate to write, Ill. Eng. Bull, 71; Passive verbs in children's writing, Elem. Eng, 72; Preparing the composition teacher, Col. Compos. & Commun, 74. Add: Dept. of English, University of Illinois at Urbana-Champaign, Urbana, IL 61801.

NEMSER, RUBY, b. Brooklyn, N.Y, Apr. 18, 33. ENGLISH. B.A, McGill Univ, 54, M.A, 56; Ph.D.(Eng), Harvard, 65. Part-time instr. ENG, Boston Col. Sch. Nursing, spring 59; lectr, UNIV. B.C, 60-64, instr, 64-65, ASST. PROF, 65- MLA. English novel; 16th century English poetry, especially Edmund Spenser. Publ: A reinterpretation of The unexpressive nuptial song, Milton Newsletter, 3/68. Add: Dept. of English, University of British Columbia, Vancouver, B.C, V6T 1W5, Can.

NERBONNE, GARY PATRICK, Speech, Hearing Science. See 12th Edition, American Men & Women of Science, Social & Behavioral Sciences Section.

NESBITT, GEORGE LYMAN, b. Davenport Twp, N.Y, Aug. 31, 03; m. 39; c. 2. ENGLISH LITERATURE. A.B, Hamilton Col, 24; A.M, Columbia Univ, 27, Ph.D, 34. Instr, Eng. compos, Hamilton Col, 24-26; Eng, Univ. Del, 27-28; assoc. prof, HAMILTON COL, 30-41, prof, 41-58, Hamilton B. Tompkins prof. ENG. LIT, 58-73, chmn. dept. Eng, 52-68, EMER. PROF, 73- Nineteenth century English literature and journalism. Publ: Benthamite reviewing, Columbia Univ; Wordsworth: the biographical background of his poetry, Pegasus, 70. Add: Dept. of English, Hamilton College, Clinton, NY 13323.

NESS, ORDEAN GERHARD, b. Buxton, N.Dak, Oct. 4, 21. SPEECH. B.A, Univ. N.Dak, 42; M.A, Univ. Wis, 47, fel. & Ph.D.(speech), 53. Instr. speech, Syracuse Univ, 47-49; consult. & personnel policies off, Off. Secy. Army, 50-52; asst. prof. SPEECH, Pa. State Univ, 53-55; UNIV. WIS, MADISON, 55-58, assoc. prof, 58-62, PROF, 62-, CHMN. DEPT. THEATRE & DRAMA, 73-, assoc. chmn. dept. & admin. grad. stud, 63-70, assoc. dir. articulated instr. media, 64-66. U.S.A, 42-46, 50-52. Speech Commun. Asn; Am. Theatre Asn; Cent. States Speech Asn; Nat. Educ. Broadcasters; Asn. Prof. Broadcasting Educ. Radio broadcasting; oral interpretation; theatre. Publ: Co-auth, An introduction to public speaking, 61 & Fundamentals and forms of speech, rev. ed, Odyssey, 63. Add: 4725 Sheboygan, Madison, WI 53705.

NESSELHOF, JOHN MORRISON, b. Kansas City, Mo, Oct, 15, 28. ENGLISH. A.B, Univ. Kans, 49, A.M, 50; A.M, Princeton, 54, Ph.D.(Eng), 55. Instr. ENG, WELLS COL, 55-57, asst. prof, 57-62, assoc. prof, 62-68, PROF, 68-, acting chmn. dept, 67-68, chmn, 68-71. MLA; Renaissance Soc. Am. Spenser and Chaucer; modern poetry; Jonson. Add: Dept. of English, Wells College, Aurora, NY 13026.

NESVIG, MILTON LUTHER, b. Chicago, Ill, July 16, 15; m. 42; c. 3. ENGLISH. A.B, St. Olaf Col, 37; C.T, Luther Theol. Sem, 42; A.M, Univ. Minn, 47. Pastor, Immanuel Lutheran Church, Tacoma, Wash, 42-45; ASST. PROF. ENG, PAC. LUTHERAN UNIV, 47-, V.PRES. FOR UNIV. RELAT, 63- Distinguished Serv. Award, Bd. Col. Educ, Am. Lutheran Church, 60. U.S.N, 45-46, 51-53, Res, Chaplain. Mil. Chaplains Asn. U.S; Am. Col. Pub. Relat. Asn. Religious journalism; Norwegian-American history. Publ: Ed. & contrib, The gladiators, Pac. Lutheran Univ, 72. Add: 1103 S. 121st St, Tacoma, WA 98444.

NETHERCOT, ARTHUR HOBART, b. Chicago, Ill, Apr. 20, 95; m. 22, 50; c. 2. ENGLISH LITERATURE. A.B, Northwest. Univ, 15, A.M, 16; Oxford, 19; Ph.D, Univ. Chicago, 22. Master, St. Alban's Sch, Ill, 16-17; instr. ENG, NORTHWEST. UNIV, 19-24, asst. prof, 24-31, assoc. prof, 31-39, prof, 39-60, Franklyn Bliss Snyder Prof, 60-63, chmn. dept, summers 58-62, EMER. PROF, 63- Fulbright res. scholar, India, 56-57; mem. ed. bd, Shaw Rev, 56-; prof, Northwest. Univ, summers 64, 67, 68; vis. prof, Univ. Kans, 64; Univ. Mont, 64-65; Fulbright lectr, Univ. Cologne, 65-66; vis. prof, Transylvania Col, 67; Colo. Col, 68; Pa. State Univ, 71. Alumni Merit Award, Northwest. Univ, 61; Chicago Friends of Lit. Award, 63. U.S.A, 17-19, 2nd Lt. MLA; Mod. Humanities Res. Asn. Eugene O'Neill, Bernard Shaw. Publ: Co-ed, Elizabethan and Stuart Plays, 32 & ed, Elizabethan plays, 71 & ed, Stuart plays, 71, Holt; auth, Road to Tryermaine, Chicago, 39 & Russell, 63; First five lives of Annie Besant, 60 & Last four lives of Annie Besant, 63, Chicago; Men and supermen: the Shavian portrait gallery, Harvard, 54 & Blom, 66; Sir William D'avenant, Chicago, 38 & Russell, 66; Abraham Cowley, Oxford, 31 & Russell, 66; Bernard Shaw, mathematical mystic, 1/69 & Who was Eugene Marchbanks?, 1/72, Shaw Rev; Bernard Shaw and psychoanalysis, 2/69 & The psychoanalyzing of Eugene O'Neill: P.P.S, 6/73, Mod. Drama; plus others. Add: 1202 W. High Point Lane, Colorado Springs, CO 80904.

NETTELS, ELSA, b. Madison, Wis, May 25, 31. ENGLISH, AMERICAN LITERATURE. A.B, Cornell Univ, 53; M.A, Univ. Wis, 55, Beatrice Bakrow Kaufman fel, 55-56, Am. Asn. Univ. Women fel, 58-59, Ph.D.(Eng), 60. Instr. ENG, Mt. Holyoke Col, 59-62, asst. prof, 63-67; COL. WILLIAM & MARY, 67-69, ASSOC. PROF, 69- Albert Markham travelling fel, 62-63. MLA; S. Atlantic Mod. Lang. Asn. American literature; modern fiction. Publ: The ambassadors and the sense of the past, Mod. Lang. Quart, 6/70; Action and point of view in Roderick Hudson, Eng. Stud, summer 72; James and Conrad on the art of fiction, Tex. Stud. Lit. & Lang, fall 72. Add: Dept. of English, College of William & Mary, Williamsburg, VA 23185.

NEUFELDT, LEONARD N, b. Yarrow, B.C, Nov. 3, 37; m. 61; c. 3. ENGLISH. B.A, Waterloo Univ. Col, 61; A.M, Univ. Ill, 62, Ph.D.(Eng), 66. Asst. prof. Eng, Univ. Wash, 66-73; ASSOC. PROF. AM. LIT, UNIV. TEX. OF THE PERMIAN BASIN, 73- Fulbright prof. Am. stud, Univ. Erlangen, 72-73. MLA. Emerson and Thoreau; Whitman; American poetry. Publ: A way of walking, Univ. N.B, 72; ed, Ralph Waldo Emerson: new appraisals, Transcendental Bks, 73; auth, The vital mind: Emerson's epistemology, Philol. Quart, 4/71; Time and man's possibilities in Light in August, Ga. Rev, spring 71; Emerson and the Civil War, J. Eng. & Ger. Philol, 10/72. Add: Dept. of English, University of Texas of the Permian Basin, Odessa, TX 79762.

NEUFELDT, VICTOR ALFRED, b. Yarrow, B.C, Dec. 28, 33; m. 58; c. 3. ENGLISH & AMERICAN LITERATURE. B.A, Univ. B.C, 57, teaching cert, 58; Can. Counc. fel, Univ. Ill, Urbana, 64-65, 66-68, grad. fel, 64-68, Ph.D. (Eng), 69. Teacher Eng. & hist, Mt. Elizabeth Jr-Sr. High Sch, 58-62, 63-64; instr. ENG, Univ. Ill, Urbana, 67-68; UNIV. VICTORIA, 68-69, ASST. PROF, 69- Can. Asn. Univ. Teachers; Asn. Can. Teachers Eng; Victorian Stud. Asn. West. Can. Victorian literature. Publ: Emily Brontë and the responsible imagination, Victorian Newslett, spring 73; Browning's Saul in the context of the age, J. Eng. & Germanic Philol, 73. Add: Dept. of English, University of Victoria, Box 1700, Victoria, B.C. V8W 2Y2, Can.

NEUFFER, CLAUDE HENRY, b. Abbeville, S.C, Nov. 2, 11; m. 53; c. 3. ENGLISH. A.B, Clemson Col, 33; M.A, Univ. S.C, 38; summers, Univ. Wis, 40, Univ. Va, 47. Mem. fac. ENG, Ga. Mil. Col, 39-42; Presby. Jr. Col, N.C, 46-47; assoc. prof, UNIV. S.C, 47-73, PROF, 73- U.S.A.A.F, 42-46, Sgt. Am. Name Soc; Am. Dialect Soc; S.Atlantic Mod. Lang. Asn. Onomastics; Southern literature. Publ: Ed, Names in South Carolina, (annually), Eng. Dept, Univ. S.C, 54-; auth, The Christopher Happoldt Journal, Charleston, S.C, Mus, 60; The name game: from Oyster Point to Keowee, Sandlapper, 72; Folk etymology in South Carolina place names, Am. Speech, 10/66; Havilah Babcock: Virginia Carolinian, Ga. Rev, 9/67; co-auth, Reprint with biographical sketch of Coogler's Purely original verse, 1897, Columbia, S.C, 4/74. Add: Dept. of English, University of South Carolina, Columbia, SC 29208.

NEUMAN, ROBERT MICHAEL, b. Washington, D.C, Feb. 5, 43; m. 68. ENGLISH LITERATURE, THEATRE. B.A, Villanova Univ, 65; M.A, Univ. Mich, Ann Arbor, 66, Ph.D.(Eng), 73. Instr. ENG, Tuskegee Inst, 67; ASST. PROF, CAPITAL UNIV, 73- MLA; NCTE; AAUP. Renaissance English literature; drama. Add: Dept. of English, Capital University, Columbus, OH 43209.

NEUMEYER, PETER F, b. Munich, Ger, Aug. 4, 29; U.S. citizen; m. 52; c. 3. ENGLISH. B.A, Univ. Calif, Berkeley, 51, M.A, 54, Ph.D, 63. Teacher pub. schs, Calif, 57-58, 60-61; assoc. supvr. dept. educ, Univ. Calif, Berkeley, 61-62, acting instr. Eng, 62-63; asst. prof. educ. & tutor Eng, Grad. Sch, Harvard, 63-69; ASSOC. PROF. ENG, STATE UNIV. N.Y. STONY BROOK, 69-, DIR. FRESHMAN ENG, 73-; fac. res. fels, summers 70, 74. NCTE; Philol. Asn. Pac. Coast. German-English literary relations; freshman English; children's literature. Publ: The faithful fish, Young Scott Bks, 71; Franz Kafka and England, Ger. Quart, 11/67; A structural approach to the teaching of literature to children, Elem. Eng, 12/67; plus others. Add: 15 North Rd, Stony Brook, NY 11790.

NEVILLE, MARGARET MARY, b. Chicago, Ill, Mar. 27, 07. ENGLISH. A.B, DePaul Univ, 29, A.M, 30; A.M, Northwest. Univ, 39; Ph.D.(Eng), Loyola Univ.(Ill), 50. From instr. to PROF. ENG, DEPAUL UNIV, 30- MLA; NCTE; Col. Eng. Asn. Medieval literature; history of English language. Add: Dept. of English, DePaul University, Chicago, IL 60604.

NEVILLE, MARY EILEEN, O.S.B, b. York, Nebr, July 11, 30. ENGLISH. A.B, Mt. Marty Col.(S.Dak), 53; M.A, St. Louis Univ, 56, Ph.D, 58. Instr. ENG, MT. MARTY COL.(S.DAK), 57-68, PROF, 68-, DIR. INTERCULT. EDUC, 73-, chmn. dept. Eng 65-69. Vis. prof. Eng. & educ, Univ. Nebr, 69-70, fel, 69-70. NCTE; Conf. Col. Compos. & Commun; Conf. Eng. Educ; Nat. Col. Honors Counc. Native American literature and culture; Afro-American literature; priorities in American values. Add: 1100 W. Fifth, Yankton, SD 57078.

NEVILLE, WILLIAM A, b. Manchester, N.H, Dec. 7, 24; m. 50; c. 3. ENGLISH. B.A, Univ. N.H, 49; M.A, Lehigh Univ, 52, Ph.D.(Eng), 61. Instr. Eng, Lehigh Univ, 51-61; asst. prof, STATE UNIV. N.Y. COL. FREDONIA, 61-63, assoc. prof. Eng, 63-73, PROF. & CHMN. DEPT. ENG, 73-, acting chmn, 72-73. MLA. Chaucer; the romantic period. Add: Dept. of English, State University of New York College at Fredonia, Fredonia, NY 14063.

NEVINS, THOMAS FREDERICK, b. Chicago, Ill, Dec. 19, 37; m. 65; c. 2. THEATRE. B.A, Quincy Col, 61; M.A, Villanova Univ, 62. Asst. prof. theatre, Villanova Univ, 62-66; counr, Vanguard Schs, 66-69; ASSOC. PROF. THEATRE, QUINCY COL, 69- Dir, Progressive Playhouse, 70-71; Quincy Little Theatre, 72; The Long Way Home (outdoor drama), 73. U.S. Inst. Theatre Technol; Theatre Hist. Soc; Inst. Outdoor Drama. History of theatre buildings. Publ: The Walnut Street Theatre, J. Theatre Hist. Soc, 73. Add: Dept. of Theatre, Quincy College, College Ave, Quincy, IL 62301.

NEVIUS, BLAKE REYNOLDS, b. Winona, Minn, Feb. 12, 16. AMERICAN LITERATURE. A.B, Antioch Col, 38; A.M, Univ. Chicago, 41, Ph.D, 47. Asst, Univ. Ill, 41-42; from instr. to assoc. prof. ENG, UNIV. CALIF, LOS ANGELES, 47-61, PROF, 61- Fulbright lectr, Ger, 53-54; Guggenheim fel, 62-63; ed, Nineteenth Century Fiction, 65-71, sr. adv. ed, 71-; adv. West. Humanities Ctr, Nat. Endowment for Humanities, 72. MLA; Int. Asn. Univ. Prof. Eng.(treas, 71-74). Early American fiction; Romantic landscape in American literature; theory of fiction. Publ: Edith Wharton: a study of her fiction, 53, Robert Herrick: the development of a novelist, 62 & co-ed, Dickens centennial essays, 71, Univ. Calif; ed, Edith Wharton's Ethan Frome: the story with sources and commentary, Scribner, 68; ed, The American novel: Sinclair Lewis to the present, Appleton, 70; auth, Ivy Compton-Burnett, In: Columbia essays on modern writers, Columbia Univ, 70; Saul Bellow and the theater of the soul, In: Studies presented to Tauno Mustanoja, Neuphilol. Mitt, 72. Add: 4009 Woodcliff Rd, Sherman Oaks, CA 91403.

NEW, GEORGE, b. Lebanon, Ill, Mar. 16, 15; m. 45; c. 1. SPEECH, DRAMA. B.S, Northwest. Univ, 45; M.A, Columbia Univ, 48, Ed.D, 64. Exec. dir, Pioneer Youth Am, Inc, 45-50; Infants Welfare League Camps, Inc, 50-54; Camp Madison-Felicia, Inc, 54-56; instr. speech, PRATT INST, 56-58, asst. prof. SPEECH & DRAMA, 58-65; ASSOC. PROF, 65-, CHMN. DEPT. & DIR. THEATRE, 72- Speech Commun. Asn; Children's Theatre Conf; Am. Theatre Asn; U.S. Inst. Theatre Technol. Educational theatre; small group processes. Add: Dept. of Performing Arts, Pratt Institute, Brooklyn, NY 11205.

NEW, MELVYN, b. New York, N.Y, Oct. 8, 38; m. 59; c. 2. ENGLISH. B.A, Columbia Univ, 59; M.A, Vanderbilt Univ, 62, Ph.D, 66. Instr. ENG, Univ. Tenn, Martin, 62-63; Vanderbilt Univ, 65-66; asst. prof, UNIV. FLA, 66-70, ASSOC. PROF, 70- Am. Philos. Soc. summer stud. grant, 68 & 71; Nat. Endowment for Humanities younger scholar fel, 73-74. U.S.N.R, 59-61, Lt. MLA; S.Atlantic Mod. Lang. Asn; Am. Soc. 18th Century Stud. Restoration and 18th century English literature; satire. Publ: Laurence Sterne as satirist: a reading of Tristram Shandy, Univ. Fla, 69; Sterne and Swift: sermons and satire, Mod. Lang. Quart, 69; Laurence Sterne and Henry Baker's The microscope made easy, Stud. Eng. Lit, 70; Sterne's Rabelaisian fragment: a text from the holograph manuscript, PMLA, 72. Add: Dept. of English, University of Florida, Gainesville, FL 32601.

NEW, WILLIAM HERBERT, b. Vancouver, B.C, Mar. 28, 38; m. 67. ENGLISH. B.Ed, Univ. B.C, 61, M.A, 63; Ph.D, Univ. Leeds, 66. Asst. prof. ENG, UNIV. B.C, 65-69, ASSOC. PROF, 69- Asst. ed, Can. Lit, 65-69, assoc. ed, 69-; ed. bd, Twentieth Century Lit, 70-; assoc. ed, World Lit. Written in Eng, 71- MLA; Asn. Can. Univ. Teachers Eng; Asn. Commonwealth Lit. & Lang. Stud. Commonwealth literature; the novel; Canadian literature. Publ: Malcolm Lowry, 71 & co-ed, Voice and vision, 72, McClelland & Stewart; ed, Four hemispheres, Copp Clark, 71; auth, Articulating west, New Press, 72; ed, Dramatists in Canada, Univ. B.C, 72; auth, Modern fiction, In: Read Canadian, Lewis & Samuel, 72. Add: Dept. of English, University of British Columbia, Vancouver 8, B.C, Can.

NEWBY, FRANK S, b. Glendale, Calif, Feb. 14, 14; m. 43; c. 1. ENGLISH. B.A, Univ. Redlands, 38; M.A, Univ. Calif, Berkeley, 49, Ph.D.(Eng), 66. Instr. remedial Eng, Univ. Calif, Berkeley, 48-53, lectr. ENG, 56-57; instr, San Francisco State Col, 53-56; UNIV. B.C, 57-62, ASST. PROF, 62- Asn. Can. Univ. Teachers Eng. Novels of D.H. Lawrence; contemporary poetry; 20th century fiction. Add: Dept. of English, University of British Columbia, Vancouver, B.C. V6T 1W5, Can.

NEWBY, RICHARD LEE, b. Bridgeton, Ind, June 15, 24; m. 50; c. 4. ENGLISH. B.A, South. Ill. Univ, 50, M.A, 53; Ph.D.(Eng), Univ. Colo, 70. ASST. PROF. ENG, ILL. STATE UNIV, 58- U.S.N, 43-46. MLA. Publ: Meredith as social reformer, McNeese Review, 10/71. Add: 1007 Porter Lane, Normal, IL 61761.

NEWCOMB, MARY JANE, b. Kansas City, Mo, July 10, 16; m. 60. ENGLISH & TWENTIETH CENTURY AMERICAN LITERATURE. B.S, Univ. Kans, 63, Ph.D.(Eng. educ), 70; M.A, Kans. State Univ, 64. Asst. instr. ENG, Kans. State Univ, 63-64; asst, Univ. Kans, 64-66; instr, RESIDENCE CTR, CENT. MO. STATE UNIV, INDEPENDENCE, 66-70, ASST. PROF, 70- Layout dir. & adv, Interplay Mag, Cent. Mo. State Univ. Residence Ctr, 67-; poetry ed, Fine Arts Discovery Mag, 68-72. Soc. Tech. Commun; Col. Eng. Asn; MLA; NCTE; Theosophical Soc. Am.(mem. nat. educ. comt). The work of John Gould Fletcher; the imagist movement; language arts curriculum and instruction. Publ: Co-ed, Solitary singers: an anthology of new poets, Fine Arts Discovery, 69. Add: Dept. of English, Central Missouri State University Residence Ctr, Independence, MO 64050.

NEWCOMB, ROBERT HOWARD, b. Saginaw, Mich, Apr. 11, 24; m. 48; c. 3. LITERATURE. B.A, Univ. Md, 48, M.A, 49, Ph.D, 57. Instr. ENG, Univ. Md, 51-52; asst. prof, Bridgewater Col, 52-56, assoc. prof, 56-58; asst. prof, BALL STATE UNIV, 58-62, assoc. prof, 62-67, PROF, 67- Am. Philos. Soc. grant, 62. U.S.A, 42-46, Lt.(jg). The English proverb; Benjamin Franklin; the English maxim and epigram. Publ: Poor Richard's debt to Lord Halifax, PMLA, 6/55; Franklin and Richardson, J. Eng. & Ger. Philol, 1/58; Poor Richard and the English epigram, Philol. Quart, 4/61. Add: Dept. of English, Ball State University, Muncie, IN 47306.

NEWCOMB, STANLEY SPENCER, b. Bellflower, Calif, July 9, 12. SPEECH. A.B, Univ. Redlands, 36, A.M, 48; B.D, Princeton Theol. Sem, 39; Univ. South. Calif, 60-61; summers, Univ. Wash, 43, Long Beach State Col, 54. Prof. speech & drama, Whitworth Col, 41-44; instr. speech, Princeton Theol. Sem, 44-46; prof. speech & drama, Univ. Dubuque, 48-52; assoc. prof, Hastings Col, 55-59; asst. prof. speech, Calif. West. Univ, 61-68, chmn. div. commun, 63-68; assoc. prof. & acad. dean, John F. Kennedy Col, 68-70; ADMIN. V.PRES, MILLER COMMUNITY COL, 73- Lectr, New Brunswick Sem, 44-46. Speech Commun. Asn. Publ: Rightly dividing the word, Presbyterian, 1/46; This is my talent, Presby. Outlook, 7/55; Excellence as a communicator, Improving Col. & Univ. Teaching, fall 66. Add: 292 Viejo St, Laguna Beach, CA 92651.

NEWCOMBE, PARK JUDSON, b. Grand Rapids, Mich, Dec. 14, 30. SPEECH, THEATRE EDUCATION. B.A, West. Mich. Univ, 53; M.A, Northwest. Univ, 57, Ph.D.(speech), 63. Prog. dir, Muncie Boys Club, Ind, 55-56; teacher high schs, Mich, 57-59; instr. speech & educ, West. Mich. Univ. & Paw Paw High Sch, 59-61; asst. prof. speech, Chaminade Col, 62-65; asst. prof. SPEECH EDUC. & chmn. dept, Northwest. Univ, 65-70; ASSOC. PROF, UNIV. S.FLA, 70- Consult, Nat. Metal Trades Asn, Chicago, 61-62, 65-66; Pres. & 1st v.pres, Pac. Speech Asn, 63-65, mem. legis. assembly & comt. fifty, 64-65; pres, Hawaii Asn. Stud. Teaching, 64-65; consult, Bank Pub. Relat. & Marketing Asn. summer schs, 65- U.S.A, 53-55. Speech Commun. Asn; Am. Theatre Asn; Asn. Stud. Teacher Educ. Preparation of speech teachers for high school and college; historical backgrounds of academic speech training; teaching spoken English to foreign students. Publ: Co-auth, Speech education in Canadian higher education, Speech Teacher, 11/68; Choose an objective in speech communication, Media Tronics, 73. Add: Dept. of Speech Education, University of South Florida, Tampa, FL 33620.

NEWCOMER, JAMES WILLIAM, b. Gibsonburg, Ohio, Mar. 14, 12; m. 46; c. 3. ENGLISH. Ph.B, Kenyon Col, 33; M.A, Univ. Mich, 38; Ph.D, State Univ. Iowa, 53. Asst. headmaster & head dept. Eng, Elgin Acad. & Jr. Col, 37-42; dean col. & head dept. Eng, Hockaday Jr. Col, 46; dean col. & prof. Eng, Olivet Col, 52-60; dean fac. & grad. studies, Tex. Woman's Univ, 60-65; v.chancellor, TEX. CHRISTIAN UNIV, 65-72, TRUSTEES PROF. ENG. & DIR. UNIV. PRESS, 72- Qm.C, 42-46, 1st Lt. MLA; Col. Eng. Asn; NCTE; Am. Comt. Irish Stud. Eighteenth and early 19th century English novel; Maria Edgeworth and Lady Morgan, Irish authors; history of Grand Duchy of Luxembourg. Publ: Co-auth, Liberal education and pharmacy, 60 & auth, Maria Edgeworth the novelist, 67, Tex. Christian Univ; Maria Edgeworth, Bucknell Univ, 73; The case for the ivory tower, J. Higher Educ, 12/66; With Johnson and Boswell in the Highlands, Scots Mag, spring 73. Add: Box 30783, Texas Christian University, Ft. Worth, TX 76129.

NEWELL, KENNETH BERNARD, b. Cohoes, N.Y, Apr. 18, 30. ENGLISH. B.S, Lowell Technol. Inst, 51; M.A, Columbia Univ, 53; Ph.D.(Eng), Univ. Pa, 64. Instr. ENG, Univ. Kans, 62-64, acting asst. prof, 64-65, asst. prof, 65-66; Univ. Calif, Los Angeles, 66-71; ASSOC. PROF, VA. COMMONWEALTH UNIV, 71- U.S.N, 53-56, Lt. MLA. British literature since 1875; Edwardian fiction; history of novel and short story. Publ: Structure in four novels by H.G. Wells, Mouton, 68; The destructive element and related dream passages in the Lord Jim manuscript, J. Mod. Lit, 70; The artist stories in George Moore's The untilled field, Eng. Lit. Transition, 71; Science fiction and the merging of romance and realism, Extrapolation, 12/72; plus others. Add: Dept. of English, Virginia Commonwealth University, Richmond, VA 23284.

NEWKIRK, GLEN A, b. Strawn, Kans, Aug, 23, 31; m. 57; c. 3. ENGLISH LITERATURE. A.B, Kans. State Col, 53, M.A, 56; Univ. Mo, 57; Ph.D.(Eng), Univ. Denver, 66. Asst. ed, Emporia Times, Kans, 53-54; instr. Eng, Kans. State Col, 55-57; Colo. State Univ, 57-58; Southwest Mo. State Col, 58-60; dir. publicity, Southwest. Col.(Kans), 60-61; instr. commun, Univ. Denver, 61-63; from asst. prof. to PROF. ENG, UNIV. NEBR. AT OMAHA, 63-, acting chmn. dept, 68, grad. coord, 69-72. Renaissance Soc. Am; MLA. Renaissance courtesy books; Milton. Publ: Ed, Contemporary Issues & auth, Instr. manual, Scott, 71. Add: Dept. of English, University of Nebraska at Omaha, 60th & Dodge, Omaha, NE 68101.

NEWLIN, PAUL A, b. Long Beach, Calif, Oct. 28, 30; m. 56; c. 3. ENGLISH. B.A, Earlham Col, 52; M.S, Ohio State Univ, 53; M.A, Univ. Calif, Los Angeles, 62, Ph.D.(Eng), 67. Teaching asst. ENG, Univ. Calif, Los Angeles, 61-65, assoc, 65-66; instr, Univ. Del, 66-67, ASST. PROF, 67-71; STATE UNIV. N.Y. STONY BROOK, 71- Improvement instr. grant Negro Am. lit, Univ. Del, summer 68. U.S.A, 54-55. MLA. Nineteenth century American and Negro American literature. Add: Dept. of English, State University of New York at Stony Brook, Stony Brook, NY 11790.

NEWMAN, ARNOLD EUGENE, b. New York, N.Y, June 20, 34; m. 59; c. 3. ENGLISH. B.A, State Univ. N.Y. Albany, 56, M.A, 57; Ph.D.(Eng), Univ. Wis, 65. Teacher high sch, N.Y, 58-60; instr. ENG, Chico State Col, 64, asst. prof, 64-67; PROF, KUTZTOWN STATE COL, 67- U.S.A, 57, Res, 58-63. NCTE. Literature and related arts; American literature; rhetoric of literature. Publ: Once upon an image, Calif, Eng. J, spring 67. Add: Dept. of English, Kutztown State College, Kutztown, PA 19530.

NEWMAN, CHARLES HAMILTON, b. St. Louis, Mo, May 27, 38. ENGLISH. B.A, Yale, 60; Woodrow Wilson fel, 60-61; Fulbright fel, Oxford, 61-62. Instr. ENG, NORTHWEST. UNIV, 63-65, asst. prof, 65-68, ASSOC. PROF, 68-, ED, TRIQUART. REV, 64- Bd. dirs, Northwest. Univ. Press, 67-69; Rockefeller fel. creative writing, 68-69; dir. coord. counc. lit. mag, Nat. Endowment for Arts, 68-, creative writing fel, 73; consult, Ill. Arts Counc, 69- Writing fiction; criticism of contemporary fiction. Publ: New axis, Houghton, 66; The promisekeeper, Simon & Schuster, 71; co-ed, New writing in Eastern Europe, Quadrangle, 68; ed, The art of Sylvia Plath, 70 & co-ed, New American writers under thirty, 70, Ind. Univ; co-ed, Nabokov: criticism, 70 & co-ed, Prose for Borges, 73, Northwest. Univ. Press; co-ed, Literature in revolution, Holt; auth, A little rumble through the remnants of literature culture, Tri-Quart. Rev, winter 63; The last Yank at Oxford, Yale Rev, fall 73; On being ahistorical, Prose, fall 73; plus many others. Add: Dept. of English, University Hall 101, Northwestern University, Evanston, IL 60201.

NEWMAN, FRANKLIN BALDWIN, b. West Chester, Pa, Feb. 1, 18. ENGLISH LITERATURE. A.B, Univ. Pa, 39; Ph.D, Harvard, 47. Instr, Amherst Col, 43-46; from instr. to asst. prof. Eng. & fac. counr, Univ. Mich, 47-57; lectr. ENG, UNIV. DEL, 58-61, asst. prof, 61-68, ASSOC. PROF, 68- MLA; Renaissance Soc. Am; Shakespeare Asn. Am; NCTE. Shakespeare; English Renaissance. Publ: Co-ed, Modern short stories. Add: 28 Norfolk Ave, West Chester, PA 19380.

NEWMAN, JOHN BENJAMIN, b. Lowell, Mass, May 3, 17; m. 44; c. 2. SPEECH. B.A, Brooklyn Col, 37; M.A, La. State Univ, 39; Ph.D.(speech educ), N.Y. Univ, 50. Tutor SPEECH, QUEENS COL.(N.Y), 46-50, instr, 50-57, asst. prof, 57-61, assoc. prof, 61-69, PROF, 69-, supvr. speech, sch. gen. stud, 56-67. Lectr, City Col. Intensive Bus. Training Ctr, 50-52. Speech Commun. Asn; Am. Speech & Hearing Asn; Ling. Soc. Am; Am. Dialect Soc; Int. Soc. Gen. Semantics. Sociolinguistics, semantics. Publ: The role of Joshua Steele in the development of speech education in America & The phonetic aspect of Joshua Steele's system of prosody, Speech Monogr; The area of semantics, Quart. J. Speech; Sound, syntax and sense—and meaning, In: Essays in honor of C.M. Wise, 70. Add: Dept. of Communication Arts & Sciences, Queens College, Flushing, NY 11367.

NEWMAN, KATHARINE D, b. Philadelphia, Pa, Aug. 17, 11; div; c. 2. ENGLISH. B.S.Ed, Temple Univ, 33; M.A, Univ. Pa, 37, Ph.D.(Eng), 61. Assoc. prof. ENG, Moore Col. Art, Pa, 61-63; WEST CHESTER STATE COL, 67-69, PROF, 69-, CO-DIR. ETHNIC CULT. INST, 71- Mem. ed. bd, Col. Lit, 73- MLA; NCTE; Col. Lang. Asn; Col. Eng. Asn; Northeast Mod. Lang. Asn. Victorian literature; multi-ethnic literature of the United States. Publ: The American equation; literature in a multi-ethnic culture, Allyn & Bacon, 71; Her very voice: American women poets, West Chester Rev, 73. Add: 845 Parkside Ave, West Chester, PA 19380.

NEWMAN, PAUL BAKER, b. Chicago, Ill, May 12, 19; m. 45; c. 3. AMERICAN LITERATURE. B.S, Univ. Chicago, 40, Ph.D, 58; M.F.A, State Univ. Iowa, 51. Lectr. ENG, UNIV. P.R, 56-58; asst. prof, Kans. State Univ, 59-62; assoc. prof, QUEENS COL.(N.C), 63-67, PROF, 67- Charlotte English-Speaking Union scholar, Exeter Col, Oxford, 67. Fiske poetry prize, Univ. Chicago, 55; Roanoke-Chowan Bk. Award, N.C. Lit. & Hist. Asn, 68 & 71. U.S.A.A.F, 40-45, Capt. MLA. Modern American fiction; modern poetry; English and American literature of the 1920's. Publ: The ladder of love, Smith-Horizon, 70; The cheetah and the fountain, 68 & Dust of the sun, 69, South & West; Hemingway's grail quest, Univ. Kans. City Rev, summer 62; The natural aristocrat in letters, Univ. Rev, autumn 64; Mailer: the Jew as existentialist, N.Am. Rev, 7/65. Add: Dept. of English, Queens College, Charlotte, NC 28207.

NEWMAN, ROBERT PRESTON, b. Hannibal, Mo, Jan. 26, 22; m. 62; c. 2. SPEECH, COMMUNICATIONS. B.A, Univ. Redlands, 42; Univ. Chicago, 42-43; B.A, Oxford, 49, M.A, 52; Ph.D.(educ), Univ. Conn, 56. Instr. SPEECH, Smith Col, 49-50; Univ. Conn, 50-52; asst. prof, UNIV. PITTSBURGH, 52-56, assoc. prof, 56-60, PROF, 60- Consult. commun, Exec. Training Conf, Bell Tel. Co, Pa, 57-59; vis. prof, Univ. Hawaii, spring 66. U.S.A, 43-45. Am. Forensic Asn.(pres, 58-60); Speech Commun. Asn; Am. Polit. Sci. Asn; Am. Hist. Asn. China policy; theory of evidence; intelligence-communication systems. Publ: Recognition of Communist China?, Macmillan, 61; co-auth, A handbook of debate, McMaster Union, 67; Evidence, Houghton, 69; auth, The future of Oxford, Am. Oxonian, 1/48; The four pillars of Chiang, Ilha Formosa, fall 63; The spectacular irrelevance of Mr. Bundy, Today's Speech, 9/65. Add: Dept. of Speech, University of Pittsburgh, Pittsburgh, PA 15213.

NEWMAN, ROBERT S, b. Utica, N.Y, Apr. 27, 35; m. 65; c. 1. ENGLISH & LITERATURE. B.A, Univ. Calif, Los Angeles, 56, M.A, 57, Ph.D.(Eng), 64. Asst. prof. ENG, San Fernando Valley State Col, 64-67; STATE UNIV. N.Y. BUFFALO, 67-71, ASSOC. PROF, 71- MLA. Literary criticism; 18th century literature; Restoration drama. Publ: Language and writing; Dickenson, 67; Irony in Dryden's Aureng-Zebe, Stud. Eng. Lit, 70. Add: Dept. of English, State University of New York at Buffalo, Buffalo, NY 14214.

NEWMAN, RONALD BRUCE, b. Uniontown, Pa, July 25, 41; m. 64; c. 2. ENGLISH. A.B, Univ. Mich, Ann Arbor, 63, A.M, 64, univ. fel, 65, Rackham fel, 68, Ph.D.(Eng), 72. Instr. ENG, Robert Morris Jr. Col, 64-65; ASST. PROF, UNIV. MIAMI, 69-, DIR. FRESHMAN ENG, 73- MLA; NCTE. British novel; American humor and folklore; rhetoric. Publ: Robert (Charles) Benchley, Dictionary Am. Biog, 73. Add: Dept. of English, University of Miami, P.O. Box 8145, Coral Gables, FL 33124.

NEWSTEAD, HELAINE, b. New York, N.Y, Apr. 22, 06. MEDIEVAL LITERATURE. A.M, Columbia Univ, 28, Ph.D, 39; hon. D.Litt, Univ. Wales, 69. Tutor ENG, HUNTER COL, 28-30, instr, 30-41, asst. prof, 41-48, assoc. prof, 48-54, prof, 54-71, DISTINGUISHED PROF, 71-; DISTINGUISHED PROF, GRAD. SCH, CITY UNIV. N.Y, 71-, EXEC. OFF. DOCTORAL PROG. COMP. LIT, 74- Guggenheim fel, 48-49; vis. prof. grad. sch, Columbia Univ, 52, adj. prof, 60-61, mem. Sem. Medieval Stud, 62-; exec. off, doctorate prog. Eng. lit, City Univ. New York, 62-69. Int. Arthurian Soc.(pres, 72-); Mediaeval Acad. Am; Am. Folklore Soc; MLA; Acad. Lit. Stud. Arthurian romances; Chaucer; Old English. Publ: Bran the Blessed in Arthurian romance, Columbia Univ, 39 & 66; ed, Chaucer and his contemporaries, Fawcett, 68; auth, Arthurian legends, In: A manual of writings in Middle English, 1050-1500, Conn. Acad. Arts & Sci, 67; The equivocal oath in the Tristan legend, in: Mélanges Rita Lejeune, J. Ducelot, Liège, 70; Malory and romance, In: Four essays in romance, Harvard, 71; plus others. Add: Dept. of Comparative Literature, Graduate School, City University of New York, 33 W. 42 St, New York, NY 10036.

NEWTON, RAY, b. Denver, Colo, Sept. 26, 35; m. 56; c. 3. ENGLISH, JOURNALISM. A.B, Ft. Hays Kans. State Col, 57; M.S, S.Dak. State Univ, 61. Head dept. Eng, high sch, Kans, 57-59; teaching asst. Eng. & speech, S.Dak. State Univ, 59-60, instr, 60-61; Eng, N.Mex. Highlands Univ, 61-63, asst. dean stud, 63-65, admin. asst. to pres, 70-71, dir. bilingual mass media prog, 72-73, assoc. prof. Eng. & jour, 65-73; PROF. JOUR, N.ARIZ. UNIV, 73- Assoc. fel, Danforth Found, 61-; consult, Ford Found. Small Schs. Proj, Wagon Mound, N.Mex, 62-64; Proj. Catch-up, U.S. Off. Educ, summer 65; Rotary Found. Group stud. fel, Australia, spring 68; grad. fel, Univ. Tex, Austin, 71-72; consult, Tex. Partners in Peru, 71-72; consult, El norte, El sol, newspapers, Mex, 71-72; mem. Assoc. Pres. Jour. Educ. Comt, 72-73. Rocky Mountain Mod. Lang. Asn. Communications, foreign and Latin American: media technology. Publ: TV as partner in teaching, N.Mex. Sch. Rev, 6/70; Journalism education—Mexican style, Ed. & Publ, 4/72; Markets for New Mexico writers, Highlands Univ, 12/72; plus others. Add: 3445 N. King, Flagstaff, AZ 86001.

NEY, JAMES WALTER, English, Linguistics. See Volume III, Foreign Languages, Linguistics & Philology.

NICHOL, JOHN WILLIAM, b. Mt. Vernon, Ohio, June 2, 21; m. 43; c. 1. ENGLISH. A.B, Denison Univ, 42; M.A, Ohio State Univ, 48, Ph.D.(Eng), 53. From asst. to instr. ENG, Ohio State Univ, 47-53; instr, Denison Univ, 53-55, asst. prof, 55-61; UNIV. SOUTH. CALIF, 61-66, ASSOC. PROF, 66- U.S.A.A.F, 43-47, Capt. MLA; Am. Stud. Asn; Philol. Asn. Pac. Coast; AAUP. American literature; economic and intellectual relationship of an author to his society; Jack London. Publ: Contrib, Challenges in American culture, Bowling Green Univ, 70; auth, Melville's Soiled fish of the sea, Am. Lit; Melville and the midwest, PMLA. Add: Dept. of English, University of Southern California, Los Angeles, CA 90007.

NICHOLAS, JAMES KARL, b. Cleveland, Miss, June 25, 39; m. 64; c. 3. ENGLISH LANGUAGE & LITERATURE. B.A, Univ. Miss, 61; M.A, Old Dom. Univ, 68; Ph.D.(Eng), Univ. South. Calif, 71. Instr. ENG, Norfolk State Col, 68; ASST. PROF, WEST. CAROLINA UNIV, 71- U.S.N, 61-67, Lt. MLA; Ling. Soc. Am; Southeast. Conf. Ling; West. Conf. Ling; S.Atlantic Mod. Lang. Asn. General linguistics; English education. Publ: Handbooks and horse sense, Freshman Eng. News, fall 73; Teaching black students to write standard English, Papers of SECOL, Vol. IX, 74. Add: Dept. of English, Western Carolina University, Cullowhee, NC 28723.

NICHOLL, GRIER, b. Boston, Mass, Apr. 20, 26; m. 56; c. 3. ENGLISH, AMERICAN STUDIES. A.B, Wesleyan Univ, 51; M.A, Columbia Univ, 54; Ph.D.(Am. stud), Univ. Minn, 64. Instr. Eng, South. Ore. Col, 55-57; ASSOC. PROF. ENG. & AM. STUD, AUGSBURG COL, 60, DIR, AM. STUD. PROG, 67- U.S.N.R, 44-46. Am. Stud. Asn; MLA. The Christian social novel in America, 1870-1920. Publ: The Christian social novel and social gospel evangelism, Religion in Life, fall 66; The image of the protestant minister in the Christian social novel, Church Hist, 9/68. Add: Dept. of English, Augsburg College, Minneapolis, MN 55404.

NICHOLL, JAMES ROBERT, b. Plainview, Tex, Dec. 11, 38; m. 67; c. 2. ENGLISH LITERATURE. B.A, Univ. Tex, Austin, 61, fel, 69-70, Ph.D. (Eng), 70. ASST. PROF. ENG, WEST. CAROLINA UNIV, 70- Mil.Intel, U.S.A, 61-64, Res, 65-69, 1st Lt. MLA; Shakespeare Asn. Am; NCTE; Conf. Eng. Educ. Shakespearean drama; English education; modern literature and films. Add: Dept. of English, Western Carolina University, Cullowhee, NC 28723.

NICHOLS, ALAN C, Speech Pathology. See 12th Edition, American Men & Women of Science, Social & Behavioral Sciences Section.

NICHOLS, ARTHUR RICHARD, b. Ionia, Mich, Oct. 1, 40; m. 63; c. 2. THEATRE. B.A, Mich. State Univ, 63; M.F.A, Ohio Univ, 65; Ph.D.(theatre), Univ. Wash, 71. Instr. THEATRE, Hiram Col, 65-67; ASST. PROF, OHIO STATE UNIV, 71-, res. fel, 73. Res. fel, Japan Found, 73. Am. Theatre Asn. Japanese theatre; movement training for actors. Add: Dept. of Theatre, Ohio State University, 1849 Cannon Dr, Columbus, OH 43210.

NICHOLS, DUANE CRESS, b. Pine Ridge, S.Dak, Sept. 10, 31; m. 52; c. 2. ENGLISH. B.S, Univ. S.Dak, 52, M.E, 57; Ph.D.(Eng), Univ. Kans, 64. Instr. ENG, Univ. S.Dak, 62-63; Kans. Univ, 63-64; asst. prof, State Col. Iowa, summer 64; asst. prof. & dir. freshman eng, Kans. State Univ, 64-71, assoc. prof, 71-72; PROF. & CHMN. DEPT, SALISBURY STATE COL, 72- U.S.A, 52-54, 1st Lt. MLA; NCTE; Malone Soc. English Renaissance drama; Shakespeare; rhetoric. Publ: Composition research, Kans. Univ. Bull. Educ, 5/65; The five paragraph essay, Eng. J, 10/66; The last NDEA institutes, KATE Bull, 2/68. Add: Dept. of English, Salisbury State College, Salisbury, MD 21801.

NICHOLS, FRED JOSEPH, b. Staten Island, N.Y, Mar. 24, 39; m. 65. ENGLISH, COMPARATIVE LITERATURE. A.B, Georgetown Univ, 61; Cath. Univ. Louvain, 61-62; M.A, N.Y. Univ, 66, Ph.D.(comp. lit), 67. Instr. ENG, YALE, 67-68, ASST. PROF, 68- MLA (chmn, Neo-Latin sem, 68); Renaissance Soc. Am; Am. Comp. Lit. Asn. Renaissance Latin literature. Add: Dept. of English, Yale University, New Haven, CT 06520.

NICHOLS, GEORGE EMORY, III, b. New Haven, Conn, Nov. 28, 16. DRAMA. B.A, Yale, 38, M.F.A, 41; Stanford Univ, 46-47. Instr. drama, Stanford Univ, 47-48; asst. prof, Fresno State Col, 48-49; instr. Eng. & drama, TRINITY COL.(CONN), 50-55, asst. prof. DRAMA, 55-60, assoc. prof, 60-68, PROF, 68-, CHMN. DEPT. THEATRE ARTS, 60- U.S.A, 42-45, Capt. Am. Theatre Asn; New Eng. Theatre Conf. Play production and direction; dramatic literature. Add: Dept. of Theatre Arts, Trinity College, 300 Summit St, Hartford, CT 01606.

NICHOLS, HAROLD JAMES, b. Mitchel Field, N.Y, July 27, 45; m. 67; c. 1. DRAMATIC LITERATURE, THEATRE HISTORY. B.S, Iowa State Univ, 67, NDEA fel, Ind. Univ, 67-69, M.A, 69, Ph.D.(theatre), 71. ASST. PROF. SPEECH, KANS. STATE UNIV, 71- Nat. Endowment for Humanities summer stipend, 72. Am. Theatre Asn; Speech Commun. Asn; Am. Soc. Theatre Res; Cent. States Speech Commun. Asn. Nineteenth century theatre; contemporary theatre; behavioral studies. Publ: Co-auth, Semantic differential stability as a function of meaning domain, J. Commun, 3/73; Perception of intensional and extensional meaning domains in a semantic differential application, Speech Monogr, 11/73; auth, The prejudice against native American drama from 1778 to 1830, Quart. J. Speech, 74. Add: Dept. of Speech, Kansas State University, E. Stadium, Manhattan, KS 66506.

NICHOLS, JAMES RICHARD, b. Troy, N.Y, June 29, 38; m. 63; c. 2. ENGLISH LITERATURE. B.A, Union Col.(N.Y), 61; M.A, Univ. N.C, Chapel Hill, 66, Ph.D.(Eng), 69. ASST. PROF. ENG, MUSKINGUM COL, 69- Co-ed, Ohio Eng. Bull, 70-73; coord. Commonwealth lit. prog, Nat. Endowment for Humanities, 71-; Freuhauff Found. grant, 73. U.S.M.C.R, 61-71, Res, 61-65, Capt. MLA; AAUP. Novel; Commonwealth literature; 20th century literature. Publ: The tale of Genji: novel of manners 1000 A.D, Japan Quart, 70; The bourgeosie hero in Chekov's Cherry Orchard, Stud. Twentieth Century, 72. Add: Dept. of English, Muskingum College, New Concord, OH 43762.

NICHOLS, JAMES WILLIAM, b. St. Louis, Mo, Dec. 26, 24; m. 61; c. 3. ENGLISH. A.B, Univ. Mo, 49; Vice-chancellor's scholar. & M.A, Univ. Birmingham, 51; scholar, Univ. Wash, 59-60, Ph.D.(Eng), 62. Instr. ENG, Wash. Univ, 52-56; Univ. Ariz, 56-58; from teaching asst. to instr, Univ. Wash, 58-62; asst. prof, Univ. South. Calif, 63-68; assoc. prof, WINONA STATE COL, 68-69, PROF, 69-, HEAD DEPT, 68- Fulbright lectr, Univ. Jordan, 66-67. A.U.S, 43-46. MLA; Mod. Humanities Res. Asn; AAUP. English and American satire; 18th century English literature; modern American literature. Publ: Insinuation: the tactics of English satire, Mouton, 71. Add: Dept. of English, Winona State College, Winona, MN 55987.

NICHOLS, MARIE HOCHMUTH, b. Dunbar, Pa, July 13, 08. SPEECH. A.B, Univ. Pittsburgh, 31, A.M, 36; Ph.D, Univ. Wis, 45. Instr, Mt. Mercy Col. Women, 35-38; UNIV. ILL, URBANA, 38-46, asst. prof. SPEECH, 46-52, assoc. prof, 52-58, PROF, 58- Assoc. ed, Quart. J. Speech, 42-45, ed, 63-65. Speech Commun. Asn.(2nd v.pres, 67, 1st v.pres, 68). American public address; rhetoric. Publ: Rhetoric and criticism, La. State, 63; ed, American speeches, 54 & A history and criticism of American public address, 55, Longmans, Green & Co. Add: Dept. of Speech, 123 Lincoln Hall, University of Illinois, Urbana, IL 61801.

NICHOLS, RALPH G, b. Oxford, Nebr, Mar. 1, 07; m. 33; c. 2. RHETORIC. B.A, State Col. Iowa, 29; M.A, State Univ. Iowa, 34, Ph.D, 48. Teacher speech & Eng, Pub. Schs, Elkader & Ft. Dodge, Iowa, 29-37; instr. RHETORIC, UNIV. MINN, MINNEAPOLIS, 37-43, asst. prof, 43-44, assoc. prof, 44-49, prof. & head dept, 49-72, EMER. PROF, 72- Spec. summer lect. series at Univ. Ala, 48, Univ. Denver, 49, Mich. State Univ, 50, Univ. Wis, 56, Ohio Univ, 57 & Northwest. Univ, 59; consult, State Univ. Iowa Mgt. Course, 50-60; chmn, Nat. Comt. Listening Comprehension, 52-58; mem. adv. comt, Air Force ROTC Communs. Instr, 55-58; consult. exec. develop. prog, Okla. State Univ, 55-; indust. consults, C.W. Wright & Assocs, Toronto, Can, 57-; mem. adv. bd. eds, Thorndike-Barnhart Int. Dictionaries, 60- Nat. Soc. Study Commun.(pres, 51); Speech Commun. Asn.(pres, 61); NCTE; NEA. Listening comprehension; the psychology of persuasion; communication problems in industrial management. Publ: Are you listening?, McGraw, 57; co-auth, Listening and speaking, W.C. Brown, 54; Learn to listen, speak and write, Scott, 61-63. Add: Dept. of Rhetoric, University of Minnesota, Minneapolis, MN 55455.

NICHOLS, ROBERT E, JR, b. Chicago, Ill, Oct. 10, 32; m. 56; c. 2. ENGLISH. B.S, Univ. Ill, 54; M.A, DePaul Univ, 60; Ph.D.(Eng), Univ. Wash, 65. Instr. ENG, PURDUE UNIV, CALUMET CAMPUS, 65, asst. prof, 65-68, ASSOC. PROF, 68-, res. found. XL & int. travel grants, summer 67. U.S.A, 54-56, Capt. MLA; NCTE; Mediaeval Acad. Am. Chaucer; Middle English; history of the English language. Add: Dept. of English, Purdue University, Calumet Campus, Hammond, IN 46323.

NICHOLS, WILLIAM WATSON, b. San Francisco, Calif, Aug. 14, 38; m. 60; c. 2. ENGLISH. B.A, Park Col, 60; M.A, Johns Hopkins Univ, 61; Ph.D. (Eng), Univ. Mo, 66. ASST. PROF. ENG, DENISON UNIV, 66-, assoc. dean, 71-73. Danforth fel. Afro-Am. stud, Yale, 69-70. Afro-American literature; 19th century American literature; autobiography. Publ: Ralph Ellison's Black American scholar, Phylon, 70; co-auth, Violence in Afro-American fiction: an hypothesis, Mod. Fiction Stud, 71; auth, Individualism and autobiographical art: Frederick Douglass and Henry Thoreau, CLA J, 72. Add: Dept. of English, Denison University, Granville, OH 43023.

NICHOLSON, LEWIS EDWARD, b. Hopkins, Mo, Jan. 9, 22. ENGLISH. B.A, State Univ. Iowa, 47, M.A, 48; M.A, Harvard, 51, Ph.D, 58. Instr. ENG, Ohio State Univ, 52-53; teaching fel, Harvard, 53-54; instr, Univ. Mich, 55-58; UNIV. NOTRE DAME, 58-60, asst. prof, 60-64, ASSOC. PROF, 64- Vis. lectr, Univ. Ill, 62-63. U.S.A, 43-46, S/Sgt. MLA. Anglo-Saxon language and literature; Old Norse, Gothic, and middle English. Publ: An Anthology of Beowulf criticism, Univ. Notre Dame, 63; The literal meaning and symbolic structure of Beowulf, Classica et Mediaevalia, 64. Add: Dept. of English, University of Notre Dame, Notre Dame, IN 46556.

NICHOLSON, NANCY SNIDER, b. Lachine, Mich, May 28, 23; m. 67. ENGLISH. A.B, Univ. Mich, 46, M.A, 47, Ph.D.(Eng), 61. Instr. Eng, Iowa State Teachers Col, 47-48; Alpena Community Col, 53-54; asst. prof, N.Y. State Teachers Col, Cortland, 55-56; instr. & supvr, Columbia Univ. Teachers Col. in Afghanistan, 56-57; instr, Tufts Univ, 58-61; assoc. prof, Clarion State Col, 63-66; Wis. State Univ, La Crosse, 66-67; prof. Eng. lit, South. Univ, Baton Rouge, 69-71; LECTR. CHILDREN'S LIT, CENT. MICH. UNIV, 72- Birla scholar, Banaras Hindu Univ, 54-55; sem. dir, Ford Found, Pa, 66-; lectr, East. Mich. Univ, 67-68. MLA; Midwest Mod. Lang. Asn; Col. Eng. Asn. Mosque education in Afghanistan; Afghan folklore; biblical images in modern literature. Publ: Mosque education in Afghanistan, Muslim World, 1/68. Add: Rte. 1, Lachine, MI 49753.

NICOLOFF, PHILIP LOVELESS, b. Indianapolis, Ind, Aug. 21, 26; m. 51; c. 6. AMERICAN LITERATURE. B.A, Univ. Calif, Los Angeles, 49; M.A, Columbia Univ, 52, Ph.D.(Eng), 59. Instr. ENG, UNIV. N.H, 54-58, asst. prof, 58-63, assoc. prof, 63-72, PROF, 72- Ansley Award, 59. U.S.N,

44-46. New England transcendentalism; 20th century American literature; Henry James. Publ: Emerson on race and history, Columbia Univ, 61. Add: Dept. of English, University of New Hampshire, Durham, NH 03824.

NICOLSON, MARJORIE HOPE, b. Yonkers, N.Y, Feb. 18, 94. ENGLISH. A.B, Univ. Mich, 14, A.M, 18; Ph.D.(Eng), Yale, 20; hon. Litt.D, Mt. Holyoke Col, 33, Univ. Mich, 37, Wilson Col, 40, Middlebury Col, 41, Princeton, 46, Mills Col, 56, George Washington Univ, 62, Columbia Univ, 63, Rutgers Univ, 64, Col. William & Mary, 66; hon. LL.D, Goucher Col, 40, Smith Col, 41, Elmira Col, 43; hon. L.H.D, Univ. Vt, 41, Wesleyan Univ, 43, Colby Col, 53, Yale, 63. Instr. Eng, Univ. Minn, 20-22, asst. prof, 22-23; Goucher Col, 23-26; Guggenhein fel, Europe, 26-27; assoc. prof, Smith Col, 27-28, prof, 28-41, dean, 29-41; prof. ENG. & COMP. LIT, COLUMBIA UNIV, 41-62, chmn. dept, 54-62, EMER. WILLIAM PETERFIELD TRENT PROF, 62- Vis. scholar, Johns Hopkins Univ, 23-26; mem, Guggenheim Found. Comt. Awards, 30-37, consult, 37-62; ed, Am. Scholar, 40-44; mem. ed. bd, J. Hist. Ideas, 40-62, hon. chmn, 62-; Luther J. Lee vis. prof. Renaissance stud, Claremont Grad. Sch, 62-63; mem, Inst. Advan. Stud, 63-68. John Addison Porter Prize, Yale, 20, Wilbur Lucius Cross Medal, 67; Rose Mary Crawshay Prize, Brit. Acad, 47; Achievement Award, Am. Asn. Univ. Women, 54; Distinguished Scholar Award, Am. Counc. Learned Soc, 62; Sesquicentennial Award, Univ. Mich, 67; Morton Zabel Award, Nat. Inst. Arts & Lett, 73. MLA (v.pres, 37-38, pres, 62-63); Am. Philos. Soc. Seventeenth and 18th century English literature. Publ: Conway letters, Yale, 30; Microscope and English imagination, 35 & A world in the moon, 37, Smith Col; Newton demands the muse, 46 & co-auth, This long disease, my life: Alexander Pope and science, 68, Princeton; Voyages to the moon, Macmillan, 48 & 60; Breaking of the circle, Northwest. Univ, 50 & Columbia Univ, 60; Science and imagination, 59 & Mountain gloom and mountain glory, 59, Cornell Univ; John Milton: a reader's guide to his poetry, 63; Pepys' diary and the new science, Univ. Va, 65. Add: Butler Hall 15 H, Columbia University, 400 W. 119 St, New York, NY 10027.

NIELSEN, ELIZABETH E, b. Raymond, Iowa, July 6, 12. ENGLISH, PHILOLOGY. B.A, Cornell Univ, 30; M.A, Boston Univ, 32; Oxford, 37-39; Mich. Univ, 39-40; Ph.D.(Eng), Northwest. Univ, 43. Assoc. prof. ENG, Stout Inst, Univ. Wis, 41-45; asst. prof, Univ. Calif, Santa Barbara, 45-49; assoc. prof, CALIF. STATE UNIV, LONG BEACH, 49-53, PROF, 53-, dean women, 49-52. Shakespeare; contemporary education. Publ: After 400 years of Shakespeare, Press-Tel, 64; Macbeth—the nemesis of the post-Shakespearean actor, 65 & Monarchy under Tanistry, Due of birth & Macbeth's conscience, plus others, 71, Shakespeare Quart. Add: 4315 E. Ocean Blvd, Long Beach, CA 90803.

NIELSEN, LUELLA KAEDING, b. Mankato, Minn, Aug. 23, 19. ENGLISH. B.A, Dana Col, 42; M.A, Univ. Minn, 51; summers, Coe fel, Univ. Wyo, 56, 57, 58, Univ. Vt, 63; West. State Col. Colo, 67; humanities sem, Oxford, 70. Instr. ENG, Pender High Sch, 42-43; Blair High Sch, 44-58; DANA COL, 58-61, asst. prof, 61-64, ASSOC. PROF, 64-, chmn. fac. senate, 65-67. NCTE; MLA; NEA. American studies. Add: Dept. of English & Humanities, Dana College, Blair, NE 68008.

NIELSEN, MARGARET ENGEL, b. Brooklyn, N.Y, June 27, 13; m. 31; c. 2. NINETEENTH CENTURY BRITISH LITERATURE. A.B, N.Y. Univ, 60; M.A, Syracuse Univ, 65. ASSOC. PROF. ENG, LOCK HAVEN STATE COL, 65- AAUP; MLA; Am. Asn. Teachers Ger; NCTE. British literature, 1880-1920; British romantic movement; detective fiction. Publ: A reading of W.B. Yeats's poem On a picture of a black centaur by Edmund Dulac, Thoth, spring 63. Add: Dept. of English, Lock Haven State College, Lock Haven, PA 17745.

NIELSEN, VENETA LEATHAM, b. Wellsville, Utah, Oct. 25, 09; c. 2. ENGLISH. B.A, Utah State Univ, 40, M.A. 50. Lectr. ENG, UTAH STATE UNIV, 45-50, PROF, 50-, fac. honor lectr, 74. Utah Inst. of Fine Arts Award, 72. MLA; Am. Asn. Univ. Women (Nat. Poetry Prize). Publ: To find the poem, Under Sound, 58, co-auth, Tree of fire, 63 & Insurgent form, 66, Utah State Univ; auth, Who's afraid of Samuel Twain?, Utah Acad. Arts & Lett, 66, Too sudden pilgrims, State Bd. Educ, Utah, 66. Add: 535 E. Fifth North, Logan, UT 84321.

NIEMEYER, CARL ANTHONY, b. Quincy, Ill, Nov. 18, 06. ENGLISH. A.B, Univ. Kans, 27, A.M, 29; A.M, Harvard, 31, Ph.D.(Eng. philol), 33. Instr. Eng, Univ. Kans, 28-30; Grinnell Col, 33-39; teacher, Chicago Munic. Jr. Cols, 39-42, 45-46; assoc. prof, UNION COL.(N.Y), 46-54, prof, 54-67, Thomas W. Lamont prof. ancient & mod. lit. & chmn. div. humanities, 67-72, chmn. div, 55-61, chmn. dept. Eng, 63-68, EMER. PROF. ENG, 72- Fulbright travel grant, St. Andrews Univ, 51-52. U.S.A, 42-45, S/Sgt. MLA. Modern English literature, American literature. Publ: Transl, Primal sound, Cummington Press, 43; co-auth, Challenges to thought, Stackpole; ed, Carlyle's on heroes, hero worship, Univ. Nebr, 66. Add: 1380 Valencia Rd, Schenectady, NY 12309.

NIEMEYER, GROVER CHARLES, b. Indianapolis, Ind, Jan. 29, 13. FILM, THEATRE. B.A, Depauw Univ, 33; M.A, Northwest. Univ, 35; Ph.D, Yale, 42. Instr. theatre & film, Ohio Univ, 41-43; asst. prof, Tex. Woman's Univ, 43-44; drama, Carnegie Inst. Technol, 44-45; FILM & THEATRE, UNIV. MD, 45-60, ASSOC. PROF, 60- Film consult, President's Counc. Arts, 65; Am. Counc. Educ, 65. Am. Theatre Asn; Nat. Col. Players; Speech Commun. Asn; Am. Film Inst. Film and film history. Publ: The Renaissance and Baroque theatre in France; the playhouses and the mise en scene, 1550-1700, Univ. Microfilms, 67; Hotel de Bourgogne: France's first popular playhouse, Theatre Annual; David Wark Griffith: in retrospect, 1965, Film Heritage, fall 65 & In: Focus on D.W. Griffith, Prentice, 71; plus others. Add: 1616 18th St. N.W, Washington, DC 20009.

NIERENBERG, EDWIN H, b. Syracuse, N.Y, July 6, 27; m. 52; c. 4. ENGLISH. B.A, Antioch Col, 55; M.F.A, State Univ. Iowa, 57; Andrew Mellon fel, Univ. Pittsburgh, 60-62, Ph.D, 62. Asst. Eng. & humanities, State Univ. Iowa, 55-57; instr. ENG, Ripon Col, 58-60; asst. prof, SAN FRANCISCO STATE UNIV, 62-66, assoc. prof, 66-70, PROF, 70-, v.chmn. lit, 69-71. Nat. Endowment for Humanities lectureship, 74. U.S.M.C, 45-49, S/Sgt. MLA; Philol. Asn. Pac. Coast; Am. Soc. 18th Century Stud. E.M. Forster; satire; 18th century interdisciplinary studies. Publ: The prophecy of E.M. Forster, Queen's Quart, summer 64; The withered priestess: Mrs. Moore's incomplete passage to India, Mod. Lang. Quart, 6/64; Art's own reason in an age of enlightenment; Pope's Essay on criticism, Enlightenment Essays, 8/71; plus others. Add: Dept. of English, San Francisco State University, 1600 Holloway Ave, San Francisco, CA 94132.

NIGGLI, JOSEFINA, b. Monterrey, Mex, July 13, 10; U.S. citizen. DRAMA. B.A, Incarnate Word Col, 31; M.A, Univ. N.C, 37; Rockefeller fels, Stanford Univ, 36-37 & Univ. N.C, 37-38. Instr. radio, Univ. N.C, 43-44; asst. prof. drama, Woman's Col, Univ. N.C, 54-55; ASSOC. PROF. SPEECH & THEATRE ARTS, WEST. CAROLINA UNIV, 56- Drama fel, Middlebury Col, summer, 33; New Play fel, Theatre Guild, New York, N.Y, 38-39; Mayflower Cup Award, 48; Rockefeller traveling fel, Dublin & London, 50; guest teacher playwriting, Bristol Univ, Eng, 55-56. Am. Theatre Asn. Directing; acting, period and styles. Publ: Mexican folk plays, 38 & Mexican village, 48, Univ. N.C; Step down, elder brother, Rinehart, 47; Grace of Guadalupe, 63 & Miracle for Mexico, 64, N.Y. Graphic; New pointers on playwriting, Writer, 67. Add: Dept. of Speech & Theatre Arts, Western Carolina University, Cullowhee, NC 28723.

NIGRO, AUGUST JOHN, b. Jersey City, N.J, Dec. 11, 34; m. 67. ENGLISH. B.A, Fairleigh Dickinson Univ, 58; M.A, Univ. Miami, 60; Ph.D.(Eng), Univ. Md, 63. Asst. ENG, Univ. Miami, 58-60; Univ. Md, 60-63; lectr, Univ. Md, Europe, 63-65; asst. prof, Niagara Univ, 65-67; PROF, KUTZTOWN STATE COL, 67- Modern poetry and American fiction; myth and psychological criticism. Publ: Co-auth, William Styron: a configuration, Minard, Rev. Lett. Mod, Paris, 68; auth, The long march: expansive hero in closed world, Critique, winter 67-68. Add: Dept. of English, Kutztown State College, Kutztown, PA 19530.

NILES, JOHN JACOB, b. Louisville, Ky, Apr. 28, 92; m. 36; c. 2. MUSIC. Hon. D.Mus, Cincinnati Conserv. Music, 49; Univ. Lyon, France; hon. D.F.A, Transylvania Col, 68; hon. M.F.A, Episcopal Theol. Sem.(Ky); hon. doctoral degrees, Univ. Louisville & Univ. Ky, 73. Lectr, Juilliard Sch. Music; Univ. Rochester; Curtis Inst; COMPOSER, CONCERT ARTIST & ARRANGER OF FOLK MUSIC. Nat. Citation, Nat. Fed. Music Clubs, 67. U.S.A.A.F, 17-19, Lt. Am. Folklore Soc; Am. Dialect Soc. Publ: The ballad book of John Jacob Niles, Houghton, 61; co-auth, Folk ballads for young actors, 62 & Christmas carols for young actors, 62, Holt; plus others. Hundreds of music publ. by G. Schirmer, Inc, Carl Fischer, Inc. & Mark Foster Music Co. Records by Tradition-Everest & RCA-Victor. Add: Boot Hill Farm, R.D. 7, Lexington, KY 40502.

NILSEN, DON LEE FRED, English Linguistics. See Volume III, Foreign Languages, Linguistics & Philology.

NILSEN, FRIDA R, b. May 30, 94. ENGLISH. A.B, St. Olaf Col, 16; Univ. Minn; Bread Loaf Sch. Eng; Columbia Univ; Int. Lang. Sch.(China), 18-20; M.S, Univ. N.Dak, 27. Teacher & dean girls, Acad. Scandinavia, Wis, 16-18; prin, I Kwang Mid. Sch, Sinyang, Honan, China, 19-25; teacher, Red Wing Sem, 27-29; dean women, Concordia Col.(Moorhead, Minn), 29-39, assoc. prof. Eng, 39-61; RETIRED. Lectr. sch, church & civic groups; Am-Scand. Found. Schaeffer fel, Univ. Oslo, 54-55; Oxford, summer 55; mem. panel judges educ. award, Delta Kappa Gamma Soc, 64-68, chmn, 66-68. NCTE. Present status of secondary education for girls in China; translating original source material of Norwegian immigrants to United States. Publ: Eyes of understanding; transl. & ed, Letters of longing, Augsburg, 70, addenda, 73. Add: 905½ Greenvale Ave, Northfield, MN 55057.

NILSEN, GEORGE HOWARD, b. Bergland, Mich, May 17, 25; m. 62; c. 4. ENGLISH LITERATURE. A.B, Colgate Univ, 47; M.A, Middlebury Col, 59; Ph.D.(Eng), Mich. State Univ, 72. Instr. ENG, E.Carolina Univ, 65-68; ASST. PROF, E.TENN. STATE UNIV, 72- U.S.M.C, 43-68, Lt. Col. Spenser; Chaucer; Medieval romance. Add: Dept. of English, East Tennessee State University, Johnson City, TN 37601.

NIMITZ, JACK, b. Berlin, Ger, Dec. 22, 24; U.S. citizen; m. 53; c. 1. ENGLISH. A.B, Univ. Calif, Berkeley, 51, M.A, 54; Columbia Univ, 52; Univ. Calif, Los Angeles, 53; Ph.D.(Eng), Univ. South. Calif, 67. PROF. ENG, LOS ANGELES VALLEY COL, 64- Vis. prof, Laval Univ, 68-69. Malone Soc. English Renaissance drama. Publ: Ecology in The grapes of wrath, Hartford Stud. Lit, summer 70. Add: Dept. of English, Los Angeles Valley College, 5800 Fulton Ave, Van Nuys, CA 91401.

NIMS, JOHN FREDERICK, b. Muskegon, Mich, Nov. 20, 13; m. 47; c. 3. ENGLISH LITERATURE. A.B, Univ. Notre Dame, 37, A.M, 39; Ph.D, Univ. Chicago, 45. Asst. prof, Univ. Toronto, 45-46; assoc. prof. Eng, Univ. Notre Dame, 39-45, 46-55, prof, 55-61; vis. writer in residence, Univ. Ill, Urbana, 61-62, PROF. ENG, 62-65; Univ. Ill, Chicago, 65-73; UNIV. FLA, 73- Fulbright lectr, Univ. Milan, 52-53 & Univ. Florence, 53-54; vis. prof, Univ. Madrid, 58-60; vis. ed, Poetry, Chicago, Ill, 60-61; vis. prof, Harvard, 64, 68-69; Nat. Found. on Arts & Humanities sabbatical grant, 67-68; Nat. Inst. Arts & Lett. grant, 68; Creative Arts Citation in Poetry, Brandeis Univ, 74. Creative writing; Elizabethan and Jacobean drama; comparative literature. Publ: The iron pastoral, 47 & A fountain in Kentucky, 50, Sloane; Poems of St. John of the Cross, Grove, 59, 68; Knowledge of the evening, 60, Of flesh and bone, 67 & Sappho to Valéry: poems in translation, 71, Rutgers Univ; ed, Arthur Golding's transl. of Ovid's Metamorphoses, Macmillan, 65; auth, Western wind: an introduction to poetry, Random, 74; plus others. Add: Dept. of English, University of Florida, Gainesville, FL 32601.

NIMS, MARGARET FRANCES, b. Muskegon, Mich, July 25, 16. ENGLISH. B.A, Univ. Toronto, 39, M.A, 40. Lectr. ENG, UNIV. ST. MICHAEL'S COL, 40-50, asst. prof, 50-58, assoc. prof, 58-65, PROF, 65- MLA. Anglo-Saxon; Middle English; Medieval poetics. Publ: Transl, Poetria nova of Geoffrey of Vinsauf, Pont. Inst. Mediaeval Stud, 67. Add: Dept. of English, University of St. Michael's College, Toronto 5, Ont, Can.

NISBET, ADA BLANCHE, b. Chicago, Ill, May 7, 07. ENGLISH. A.B, Dominican Col. San Rafael, 29; A.M, Univ. Calif, Los Angeles, 39, Am. Asn. Univ. Women Morrison fel, 45-46; Ph.D, Univ. Calif, 47. Instr. ENG, Mt. St. Mary's Col.(Calif), 37-39; Col. Holy Names, 39-41; UNIV. CALIF, LOS

ANGELES, 46-48, asst. prof, 48-54, assoc. prof, 54-61, prof, 61-74, EMER. PROF, 74- Am. Counc. Learned Soc. grant-in-aid, 46, 67 & fel, 63-64; Guggenheim fels, 48-49, 54-55; assoc. ed, Nineteenth-Century Fiction, 54-; mem. Calif. Comt. State Fulbright Scholar, 58-; Huntington Libr. grant-in-aid, 61; Ford Found. grant int. & comp. stud, 66-67; Inst. for Humanities grant-in-aid, 67. Fac. award, Theta Sigma Phi, 59; Carondelet award, Mt. St. Mary's Col.(Calif), 63. MLA. Victorian literature; Anglo-American relations in 19th century; Charles Dickens. Publ: Dickens and Ellen Ternan, 52 & co-ed, Dickens centennial essays, 72, Univ. Calif; Dickens, In: The Victorian novel: a guide to research, Harvard, 64; New light on the Dickens-Poe relationship, Nineteenth-Century Fiction, 3/51; Autobiographical matrix of Great expectations, Victorian Newsletter, spring 59. Add: Dept. of English, University of California, Los Angeles, CA 90024.

NIST, JOHN ALBERT, b. Chicago, Ill, Nov. 27, 25; m. 71; c. 5. ENGLISH LANGUAGE & LINGUISTICS, COMPARATIVE LITERATURE. A.B, DePauw Univ, 49; M.A, Ind. Univ, 50, Ph.D, 52. Asst. prof. Eng, East. Mich. Univ, 52-55, assoc. prof, 55-61; Fulbright lectr. Am. Lit, Univ. São Paulo, 58-59; Soc. Sci. Res. Counc. res. fel. Brazilian lit, Univ. Brazil, 61-62; vis. prof. ENG, Univ. Ariz, 62-63; prof. & chmn. dept, Austin Col, 63-65, Shoap prof, 65-66; PROF, AUBURN UNIV, 66- Dir. NDEA Inst. Eng, Austin Col, summer 65, Univ. Hawaii, summer 67 & N.C. Agr. & Technol. Univ, summer 68; vis. prof, Univ. Puget Sound summer 68; Fulbright-Hays sr. lectr. ling, Univ. Rome, 70-71. Machado de Assis Medal, Brazilian Acad. Lett, 64. U.S.N, 44-46. MLA; NCTE; Ling. Soc. Am; Conf. Col. Compos. & Commun. History of English language, linguistics, and literature; modern Brazilian literature; creative writing. Publ: The structure and texture of Beowulf, Univ. São Paulo, 59; Fui Crucificado, Ed. Anhambi, São Paulo, 60; Modern Brazilian poetry, Ind. Univ, 62; In the middle of the road, Univ. Ariz, 65; A structural history of English, 66 & Speaking into writing, 69, St. Martin's; The Modernist movement in Brazil, Univ. Tex, 67; Style in English, Bobbs, 69; Handicapped English: the language of the socially disadvantaged, C.C. Thomas, 73; The three major modes of literary art: comedy, tragedy, pathedy, South. Humanities Rev, winter 67; The short stories of Machado de Assis, Ariz. Quart, spring 68; English structures, In, The encyclopedia of education, Vol. 3, Macmillan & Free Press, 71. Add: 1034 Rudd Ave, Auburn, AL 36830.

NITCHIE, GEORGE WILSON, b. Chicago, Ill, May 19, 21; m. 47; c. 3. ENGLISH LITERATURE. B.A, Middlebury Col, 43; A.M, Columbia Univ, 47, Ph.D, 58. Instr. ENG, Polytech. Inst. Brooklyn, 47; SIMMONS COL, 47-50, asst. prof, 50-58, assoc. prof, 58-66, PROF, 66-, CHMN. DEPT, 72- U.S.A.A.F, 43-45, S/Sgt. Modern English and American poetry; seventeenth century English literature; Milton. Publ: Robert Frost; Human values in the poetry of Robert Frost, Duke Univ, 60; Marianne Moore: an introduction to the poetry, Columbia Univ. Press, 69; Frost as underground man, 10/66 & The importance of Robert Lowell, winter 72, South. Rev; Lycidas: a footnote, Notes & Queries, 10/66. Add: Dept. of English, Simmons College, Boston, MA 02115.

NIXON, HOWARD KENNETH, JR, b. New York, N.Y, Oct. 4, 27; m. 52. ENGLISH. A.B, Columbia Univ, 50; M.A, Univ. Ill, 52, Ph.D.(Eng), 61. Asst. ENG, Univ. Ill, 50-57, 60-61; asst. prof, North. Ill. Univ, 57-60; from asst. prof. to ASSOC. PROF, BALL STATE UNIV, 61-, co-dir, NDEA Insts. Ling. & Compos, 65, 66, 67. NCTE. Rhetoric. Publ: A reply to... Non Serviam..., 5/68 & Fragments, 12/68, Col. Compos. & Commun. Add: Dept. of English, Ball State University, Muncie, IN 47306.

NJOKU, BENEDICT CHIAKA, b. Owerri, Nigeria, Feb. 9, 22; m. 47; c. 4. ENGLISH. B.A, Wiley Col, 52; M.A, Cath. Univ. Am, 53, univ. fel, 54-56, Govt. scholar, 54-57, Ph.D, 57. Master, St. Charles Sch, Owerri, 45; headmaster, St. Joseph Sch, 46; St. Teresa's Sch, 47-51; instr. mod. lang, Wiley Col, 51-56, chmn. dept. Eng. & div. humanities, 57-70, acad. dean, 60-70; INSTR. ENG, RUST COL, 70- Brit. Empire res. fel, 55; consult, E.Tex. Comn. Reading, 60; fel, inst. col. & univ. admin, Univ. Mich, summer, 65. MLA; Col. Lang. Asn; NCTE; Nat. Asn. Col. Deans, Registr. & Admis. Off. Prosody of English Romanticism, literary theory and criticism; centralization in administrative structure as an obstacle to quality education; English literature in a non-English world. Publ: The pattern of retrospect and response in Wordsworth's prelude, 53 & Cadence patterns in the prose of Wordsworth, 60, Cath. Univ. Am; History of human dynamism, Pageant. Add: Dept. of English, Rust College, Holly Springs, MS 38635.

NOBLE, DONALD RUPERT, b. Portsmouth, Va, Dec. 11, 41; m. 64; c. 2. AMERICAN LITERATURE. B.A, State Univ. N.Y. Albany, 63, M.A, 64; Ph.D.(Eng), Univ. N.C, 74. Instr. ENG, UNIV. ALA, 69-73, ASST. PROF, 73-, res. grant, summer 73, dir. interim term, 74. MLA; S.Atlantic Mod. Lang. Asn; AAUP; Soc. Stud. South. Lit. American novel; southern literature; colonial literature. Publ: Ed. & auth, Introd, George Tucker's The valley of Shenandoah, Univ. N.C, 70; auth, Erskine Caldwell, In: A bibliographical guide to the study of southern literature, La. State Univ, 69; Lesson for the teacher, N.Y. Times, 72; Faulkner's Pantaloon in black: an Aristotelian reading, Forum, 73. Add: Dept. of English, Box 1832, University of Alabama, University, AL 35486.

NOBLE, PAULINA BUHL, b. Knoxville, Tenn, Dec. 12, 30. ENGLISH. A.B, Wesleyan Col, 52; M.A, Univ. N.C, 53; Ph.D, Univ. Tenn, 61. Instr. ENG, Univ. Tenn, 55-61; assoc. prof, SHORTER COL, 61-62, PROF. & HEAD DEPT, 62- MLA; NCTE; S.Atlantic Mod. Lang. Asn; Col. Eng. Asn. Browning; Victorian poetry; modern poetry. Add: Dept. of English, Shorter College, Rome, GA 30161.

NOBLE, YVONNE, b. Pittsburgh, Pa, Feb. 6, 35; m. ENGLISH. B.A, Colby Col, 56; univ. fel. & M.A, Yale, 57, Am. Asn. Univ. Women fel, 63-64, Ph.D.(Eng), 66; Rosenbach Soc. fel, 59; Woodrow Wilson fel, 61-62. Ed. asst, Papers of Benjamin Franklin, Yale, 57-58, res. asst. to Edwin Wolf, II, 59-60, staff mem, Libr. Co, Phila, 60; instr. Eng, Univ. Pa, 62-63, 64-66, asst. prof, 66-67; Univ. Ill, Urbana, 67-70, assoc. prof, 70-72. Univ. Pa. fac. res. grant, summer 67; Univ. Ill. fac. fel, summer 68; Guggenheim Found. fel, 70-71. MLA; Int. Soc. 18th Century Stud; Am. Soc. 18th Century Stud; Brit. Soc. 18th Century Stud. The imaginative influence of Paradise lost in the 18th century; comedy. Publ: John Gay, The beggar's opera; a critical edition, Princeton. Add: Box A, Finleyville, PA 15332.

NOBLES, WILLIAM SCOTT, b. Paris, Tex, July 15, 23; m. 46; c. 3. SPEECH. B.A, Southeast. Okla. State Col, 47; M.A, West. Reserve Univ, 48; Ph.D.(speech), La. State Univ, 55. Assoc. prof. speech, La. Col, 48-51; asst. prof, Univ. Ore, 55-60, assoc. prof, 60-67, PROF, 67-69; SPEECH & COMMUN, MACALESTER COL, 69- U.S.N, 42-46, 51-53, Lt. Comdr. Speech Commun. Asn; Am. Forensic Asn. Classical rhetoric; rhetorical American criticism. Add: Dept. of Speech, Macalester College, St. Paul, MN 55105.

NOEL, ELISABETH ANN, b. Oak Park, Ill, Nov. 24, 26. ENGLISH. B.A, Seton Hill Col, 48; M.A, Univ. Ill, 54, univ. fel, 54-56, Ph.D.(Eng), 56. Teaching asst, Yale, 48-50; Univ. Ill. traveling fel, England, 56-57; instr. ENG, Aquinas Col, 57-60; asst. prof, ST. MARY'S COL.(IND), 60-63, assoc. prof, 63-68, PROF, 68-, chmn. dept, 67-71. MLA. Victorian literature; the poetry of Cardinal John Henry Newman. Add: Dept. of English, St. Mary's College, Notre Dame, IN 46556.

NOID, BENJAMIN MAYNARD, b. Sacramento, Calif, Apr. 14, 28; m. 58; c. 4. THEATRE, SPEECH. B.A, Univ. Pac, 50; fel, Univ. Utah, 50, M.A, 56, Ph.D.(theatre), 68. Sales mgr, Pilot Products Co, 54-55; prin. elem. sch, Calif, 55-56; chmn. dept. theatre, Stockton Col, 56-63; ASSOC. PROF. SPEECH, WEBER STATE COL, 63-, head dept. speech & drama, 63-65, speech, 65-67, commun, 67-72, dir. fine arts ctr, 64-66. Bd. gov, Stockton Civic Theatre, 58-62; managing dir, Sacramento, Calif. Civic Opera Asn, 60-62; chmn, Easter sunrise serv, Stockton Counc. Churches, 61-62; educ. consult, U.S. Air Force, 64-66; dir. music, Ogden First Methodist Church, 64-67. U.S.A.F, 51-53, 1st Lt. Speech Commun. Asn; Am. Theatre Asn. Theatre history; communication theory and practice; non-pathological speech handicaps. Publ: No bed of roses, Utah Speech Teacher, 67. Add: Dept. of Communications, Weber State College, Ogden, UT 84403.

NOLAN, BARBARA, b. Indianapolis, Ind, Jan. 26, 41; m. 73. ENGLISH. B.A, Trinity Col.(D.C), 62; M.A, Univ. Wis, Madison, 63, Wis. Alumni Res. Found. fel, summer 65, Fulbright grant, 65-66, Wilson fel, summer 66, Ph.D.(Eng), 67. Teaching asst, Univ. Wis, Madison, 62-65, res. asst, dept. Chinese, summer 64; instr. ENG, WASH. UNIV, 66-67, asst. prof, 67-72, ASSOC. PROF, 72-, fac. fel, 67-68, summer res. grant, 68. Nat. Endowment for Humanities summer stipend, 69; Am. Counc. Learned Soc. grant-in-aid, 72; vis. prof, Univ. Ore, summer 74. MLA. Medieval Acad. Am; Dante Soc. Dante; 13th and 14th century vision poetry and art; Arthurian romance. Publ: The Vita nuova: Dante's book of revelation, Dante Stud, 70; The authorship of Pearl: two notes, Rev. Eng. Stud, 71. Add: Dept. of English, Washington University, St. Louis, MO 63130.

NOLAN, BARBARA SCHULER, b. Bronxville, N.Y, July 3, 30; m. 67. AMERICAN & MODERN BRITISH LITERATURE. B.A, Marymount Col.(N.Y), 52; Cath. Univ. Am, 57-59; Georgetown Univ, summer 59; M.A, Marquette Univ, 61; Ph.D.(Eng), Univ. Notre Dame, 64. Teacher & from asst. prin. to acting prin, Marymount Sch, Richmond, Va, 52-60; asst. prof. Eng, Marymount Manhattan Col, 63-64; fac. Eng. & math, Manatee Jr. Col, 65; asst. prof. ENG, Univ. S.Ala, 65-68; SPRING HILL COL, 68-71, ASSOC. PROF, 71- MLA; AAUP. Modern British and American literature; the short story. Publ: The house of Peter Taylor, Critique: Stud. Mod. Fiction, Vol. IX, No. 3. Add: Dept. of English, Spring Hill College, Mobile, AL 36608.

NOLAN, EDWARD FRANCIS, b. Fernandina, Fla, Mar. 30, 15. ENGLISH. B.A.E, Univ. Fla, 37, A.M, 38; Ph.D, Princeton, 41. Head dept. ENG, Presby. Jr. Col, 41-42; instr, Presby. Col, 42-44, assoc. prof, 46-47; adj. prof, UNIV. S.C, 47-48, assoc. prof, 48-63, PROF, 63- U.S.A, 44-46. Southeast Renaissance Conf; S.Atlantic Mod. Lang. Asn. Old English; Renaissance. Publ: Shakespeare's sonnet LXXIII; Verdi's Macbeth; The death of Bryan Lyndon; Barron's simplified approach to Shakespeare: Romeo and Juliet, 67, Barron's simplified approach to Shakespeare: Othello, 67, co-auth, Barron's simplified approach to Shakespeare: King Lear, 68 & auth, A simplified approach to Shakespeare: The merchant of Venice, 71, Barron's. Add: Dept. of English, University of South Carolina, Columbia, SC 29208.

NOLAN, EDWARD P, b. Appleton, Wis, Mar. 14, 37; m. 60. ENGLISH, COMPARATIVE LITERATURE. B.A, Yale, 62; Ph.D.(comp. lit), Ind. Univ, 66. Instr. ENG. & COMP. LIT, UNIV. COLO, BOULDER, 66-67, asst. prof, 67-71, ASSOC. PROF, 71- MLA; Am. Comp. Lit. Asn. Literary theory; Medieval narrative; lyric poetry. Add: Dept. of English, University of Colorado, Boulder, CO 80302.

NOLAN, PAUL THOMAS, b. Rochester, N.Y, Apr. 4, 19; m. 47; c. 3. ENGLISH. B.A, State Col. Ark, 47; M.A, Tulane Univ, 49; univ. fel. & fac. scholar from Centenary Col, 50-51, Ph.D.(Eng. & Brit. drama), 53. Publicity dir. & instr. Eng, State Col. Ark, 47-48; Centenary Col, 49-50, asst. prof. Eng. speech & jour, 53-54; instr. Eng, Tulane Univ, 50-53; Ford Found. assoc. prof, Ark. State Univ, 54-55; from assoc. prof. to prof, UNIV. SOUTHWEST LA, 55-67, DUPRE PROF. HUMANITIES, 67- Mem. bd. dir, Deep South Writers Conf, 62; ed. consult, Pioneer Drama Serv, 72-; reader, Edgemoor Publ. Co. U.S.A.A.F, 42-45. MLA; Am. Theatre Asn; Am. Stud. Asn; S.Cent. Mod. Lang. Asn. Drama; provincial literature; English literature. Publ: Chaucer for children, Eldridge, 63; Writing one act play for amateur stage, Pioneer Drama, 64; Provincial drama in America, Scarecrow, 67; Describing people, Heath, 68; Drama workshop plays, 69 & Round-the-world plays, 71, Plays, Inc; The loneliest game, Edgemoor, 73; Between hisses, Pioneer, 73; The other great plays (ser. 8), Dramatics, 10/67-5/68; plus others. Add: Box 552, University of Southwestern Louisiana, Lafayette, LA 70501.

NOLAN, PHILIP JEROME, Classics, Comparative Literature. See Volume III, Foreign Languages, Linguistics & Philology.

NOLAND, RICHARD WELLS, b. Atlanta, Ga, Jan. 8, 33; m. 56; c. 1. ENGLISH. B.A, Emory Univ, 54, M.D, 58; M.A, Columbia Univ, 61, Ph.D.(Eng), 68. Instr. ENG, Rutgers Univ, 62-64; preceptor, Columbia Univ, 64-66; asst. prof, UNIV. MASS, AMHERST, 66-71, ASSOC. PROF, 71- Nat. Endowment for Humanities fel, 73-74. MLA. Victorian and comparative contemporary literature; literature and psychology. Publ: T.H. Huxley on culture, Personalist, winter 64; John Barth and the novel of comic Nihilism, Wis.

Stud. Contemporary Lit, autumn 66; Medical education and psychoanalysis, Am. Scholar, summer 67. Add: Dept. of English, University of Massachusetts, Amherst, MA 01002.

NOLEN, ANNE DANIEL, b. Natchez, Miss, Mar. 13, 28; m. 61. DRAMA. B.S, Miss. State Col. Women, 50; M.A, Univ. Miss, 53; summers, Northwest. Univ, 58; Tulane Univ, 59. Asst, Univ. Miss, 53-54; instr. SPEECH & DRAMA, Pearl River Jr. Col, 54-58; asst. prof, UNIV. MISS, 58-70, ASSOC. PROF, 70- South. Speech Commun. Asn; Speech Commun. Asn. Speech and dramatic literature; oral interpretation; business and professional speech. Publ: Practical speech for the business student, Univ. Miss, 66; The frozen countenance, South. Speech J, 60. Add: Dept. of Speech & Theater, University of Mississippi, University, MS 38677.

NOLL, DOLORES LOUISE, b. Iowa City, Iowa. ENGLISH. B.A, Univ. Fla, 51; M.A, Univ. Ky, 54, Haggin fel, 58-61, Ph.D.(Eng), 65. Instr. ENG, St. Olaf Col, 54-56; KENT STATE UNIV, 61-65, asst. prof, 65-72, ASSOC. PROF, 72-, res. grant, fall 70. MLA; Mediaeval Acad. Am. Fifteenth century English and Scottish literature; Chaucer; gay studies. Publ: The romantic conception of marriage; some remarks on C.S. Lewis' discussion of The Kingis Quair, Stud. Medieval Cult, 71; The testament of Cresseid: are Christian interpretations valid ?, Stud. Scottish Lit, 71. Add: Dept. of English, Kent State University, Kent, OH 44242.

NOLL, LOU BARKER (BINK), b. Orange, N.J, Apr. 15, 27; div; c. 3. ENGLISH. A.B, Princeton, 48; M.A, Johns Hopkins Univ, 50; Ph.D.(Eng), Univ. Colo, 56. Instr. ENG, Beloit Col, 53-54; Dartmouth Col, 54-57, asst. prof, 57-61; BELOIT COL, 61-63, assoc. prof, 63-69, PROF, 69- Fulbright lectr, Univ. Zaragoza, 60-61; writer-in-residence, Princeton, 67-68; artist-in-residence, Juniata Col, 70. Pa. Maritime Acad, 45-47. Restoration and 18th century English literature and history; Milton; The Baroque. Publ: Center of the circle, 62 & The feast, 67, Harcourt. Add: Dept. of English, Beloit College, Beloit, WI 53511.

NOLTE, EUGENE ARCHE, JR, b. Matador, Tex, Oct. 8, 20; m. 47; c. 1. ENGLISH. B.A, Tex. Tech. Col, 48, Ph.D.(Eng), 55; M.A, Univ. Denver, 49. Instr. ENG, STATE COL. ARK, 49-51, asst. prof, 52-56, assoc. prof, 56-60, PROF. & HEAD DEPT, 60- Ford Found. fac. fel, Univs. London & Edinburgh, 55-56; Am. Philos. Soc. grant, 58. U.S.A.A.F, 42-45. MLA. Nineteenth century English literature; Blackwood's magazine. Publ: Co-auth, Pete Whetstone of Devil's Fork, Press-Argus, 57; Michael Scott and Blackwood's magazine, The Libr; Plagiarism of an Albert Pike poem, Ark. Hist. Quart. Add: Dept. of English, State College of Arkansas, Conway, AR 72032.

NOLTE, WILLIAM HENRY, b. Tulia, Tex, May 2, 28; m. 54; c. 1. ENGLISH. A.B, Univ. Mo, 51; M.A, Univ. Tex, 52; Ph.D, Univ. Ill, 59. Instr. Eng, Univ. Ill, 54-59; asst. prof, Univ. Ore, 59-65; assoc. prof. AM. LIT, Univ. Mo, St. Louis, 65-67; PROF, UNIV. S.C, 67- U.S.A.A.F, 46-47. American literature of the 19th and 20th centuries. Publ: H.L. Mencken, literary critic, Wesleyan Univ, 66; H.L. Mencken's smart set criticism, Cornell Univ, 68; Mencken on prose fiction, Tex. Quart, autumn 64; Hawthorne's Dimmesdale: a small man gone wrong, New Eng. Quart, 6/65; Robinson Jeffers as didactic poet, Va. Quart. Rev, spring 66; plus others. Add: Dept. of English, University of South Carolina, Columbia, SC 29208.

NOON, WILLIAM THOMAS, S.J, b. Utica, N.Y, May 17, 12. ENGLISH. A.B, Hamilton Col, 34; M.A, Loyola Univ.(Ill), 43; Ph.L, W.Baden Col, 43; S.T.L, Woodstock Col, 50; Ph.D.(Eng), Yale, 54. Instr, high sch, N.Y, 34-46; asst. prof. Eng, Canisius Col, 54-61, dir. grad. div, 54-55; assoc. prof. ENG, Col. Philos. & Lett, Fordham Univ, 59-64; PROF, LE MOYNE COL.(N.Y), 64- Eng. Inst; MLA; Col. Eng. Asn; Cath. Renascence Soc. English literature; aesthetics; criticism. Publ: Joyce and Aquinas, Yale, 57; Poetry and prayer, Rutgers Univ, 67; co-auth, James Joyce today, Ind. Univ, 67; auth, Yeats and the human body, Thought, 55; James Joyce: unfacts, fiction, and facts, PMLA, 6/61; Newman's Apologia, America, 5/65; Song the syrens sang, Mosaic, fall 72. Add: Loyola Hall, Le Moyne College, Syracuse, NY 13214.

NOONAN, JOHN PATRICK, b. Belvue, Kans, Feb. 8, 22; m. 47; c. 4. ENGLISH. B.S, Rockhurst Col, 47; M.S, Kans. State Univ, 48; Ph.D, Univ. Denver, 54. From asst. prof. Eng. & v.chmn. freshman compos. to prof. ENG, KANS. STATE UNIV, 53-70, PROF, 70-, ASSOC. DEAN GRAD. SCH, 66- U.S.A.A.F, 43-45. NCTE; Conf. Col. Compos. & Commun; Midwest Asn. Grad. Schs. American usage; linguistics; medieval literature. Publ: Co-ed, Planning Ph.D. programs in education, Univ. Tenn, 69. Add: Graduate School, Kansas State University, Manhattan, KS 66502.

NORBERG, JANET LOUISE, b. Sioux Falls, S.Dak, Apr. 5, 25. SPEECH, DRAMATIC ART. B.A, Sioux Falls Col, 47; M.R.E, Southwest. Baptist Theol. Sem, 51; Ph.D.(speech, drama), State Univ. Iowa, 64. Teacher high schs, S.Dak, 47-49, 51-52; youth dir, First Baptist Church, Waco, Tex, 52-54; instr. & dir. social activities, Hardin-Simmons Univ, 54-57; asst. commun. skills, State Univ. Iowa, 57-58, rhet, 62-63; from asst. prof. to assoc. prof. speech & drama, Cent. Methodist Col, 58-62; PROF. SPEECH, EAST. ILL. UNIV, 63- Dir. grad. staff, inst. teachers of gifted in speech & dramatic art, Div. Gifted, Ill. Dept. Educ, summer 66; vis. prof. speech educ, Ore. State Univ, summer 67. Speech Commun. Asn; Cent. States Speech Asn. American theater history; speech education; Southern Baptist convention and theology. Add: Box 185, Hebron Hills, Ashmore, IL 61912.

NORDLOH, DAVID JOSEPH, b. Cincinnati, Ohio, May 3, 42; m. 68; c. 1. AMERICAN LITERATURE, BIBLIOGRAPHY. A.B, Holy Cross Col, 64; Ph.D.(Eng), Ind. Univ, 69. Instr. ENG, IND. UNIV, BLOOMINGTON, 68-69, ASST. PROF, 69- Textual ed, A selected edition of W.D. Howells, Ind. Univ, 68-73, gen. ed, 74-; textual expert, Ctr. Eds. Am. Auth, MLA, 68- Nineteenth century American literature; bibliography and textual editing; W.D. Howells. Publ: Co-ed, The son of Royal Langbrith, 70, The shadow of a dream, 70, An imperative duty, 70, A chance acquaintance, 71, The rise of Silas Lapham, 71 & Indian summer 71, Ind. Univ. Add: Dept. of English, Indiana University, Bloomington, IN 47401.

NOREEN, ROBERT GERALD, b. Gresham, Ore, Jan. 2, 38; m. 61; c. 2. ENGLISH LITERATURE & COMPOSITION. B.A, Univ. Chicago, 60, M.A, 63, Ph.D.(Eng), 69. Instr. ENG, Northwest. Univ, 65-68; asst. prof, CALIF. STATE UNIV, NORTHRIDGE, 68-72, ASSOC. PROF, DIR. FRESHMAN ENG. & COORD. LIB. STUD, 72- Dir. innovative proj. individualized instrn. in freshman Eng, Calif. State Univ. Syst, 73. NCTE; Conf. Col. Compos. & Commun. Composition; the novel; Victorian literature. Publ: Ghetto worship: a study of the names of storefront churches, Names, 63; co-ed, Perspectives for the seventies, Dodd, 71. Add: Dept. of English, California State University, Northridge, 18111 Nordhoff St, Northridge, CA 91324.

NORLAND, HOWARD BERNETT, b. Palo Alto Co, Iowa, Mar. 1, 32; m. 54; c. 2. ENGLISH. B.A, St. Olaf Col, 54; Drake Univ, summer 52; M.S, Univ. Wis, 58, Ph.D.(Eng), 62. Instr. ENG, Univ. Kans, 61-63; asst. prof, UNIV. NEBR, LINCOLN, 63-67, assoc. prof, 67-71, PROF, 71- Fac. summer fel, Univ. Nebr, 64, res. grant, spring 67, Frank H. Woods fel. humanities, 74; Folger Shakespeare Libr. fel, 67; ed. bd, Genre, 67- U.S.A.F, 54-56, Res, 56-67, Capt. MLA; Renaissance Soc. Am. Renaissance drama and critical theory. Publ: Critical edition of Beaumont and Fletcher's The maid's tragedy, 68 & ed, Study of Ben Jonson, 69, Univ. Nebr; The text of The maid's tragedy, Papers Bibliog. Soc. Am, 67. Add: Dept. of English, University of Nebraska, Lincoln, NE 68508.

NORMAN, MARION, I.B.V.M, b. Strathroy, Ont, Apr. 29, 14. ENGLISH. B.A, Univ. Toronto, 39, M.A, 40; Ph.D.(Eng), Univ. Chicago, 55. ASSOC. PROF, ENG, St. Michael's Col, Univ. Toronto, 40-68; UNIV. ALTA, 68- Fac. res. grants, Univ. Toronto, 61 & 64; Can. Counc. res. grant, summers 66, 70-72; Int. Fed. Univ. Women grant, 66-67. Add: Dept. of English, University of Alberta, Edmonton, Alta. T6G 2G2, Can.

NORMAN, RICHARD A, b. Columbus, Ohio, July 11, 15. ENGLISH, SPEECH. B.A, George Washington Univ, 51; M.A, Columbia Univ, 52, Ph.D.(educ), 57. Instr. Eng, Columbia Col, COLUMBIA UNIV, 52-54, speech, Teachers Col, 54-57, asst. prof. ENG, BARNARD COL, 57-64, assoc. prof, 64-72, PROF, 73-, CHMN. DEPT, 71- Speech consult, CBS News, 71- U.S.A.A.F, 41-46, Capt. Int. Ling. Asn; NCTE; Speech Commun. Asn. Rhetorical criticism; 19th century American oratory; the origins of the speech of New York City. Publ: Co-auth, Guide to speech training, Ronald, 64. Add: 560 Riverside Dr, New York, NY 10027.

NORRELL, LEMUEL NATHANIEL, b. Abbeville, S.C, Nov. 11, 23; m. 70; c. 4. ENGLISH. B.A, Furman Univ, 48; Philip Francis DuPont fel. & M.A, Univ. Va, 49; summer, Univ. Iowa, 59; univ. fel. & Ph.D.(Eng), Fla. State Univ, 62. Teacher, Darlington Sch. for Boys, 49-51; agent-rep, Macmillan Co, 51-53; instr. ENG, Ga. State Col, 54-62; assoc. prof, Pfeiffer Col, 62-64, W.GA. COL, 64-67, PROF, 67- Vis. prof, Asheville-Biltmore Col, summer 63; coord. three-year master's degree prog, Ford Found. grant, 66-68; dir, NDEA Inst. Eng, W.Ga. Col, 67, mem. teaching staff, 68 & 69; consult, curriculum stud. comt, Ga. State Dept. Educ, 67-68. U.S.A, 43-45. S.Atlantic Mod. Lang. Asn. Restoration drama; modern poetry; contemporary criticism. Add: Dept. of English, West Georgia College, Carrollton, GA 30117.

NORRIS, DAVID, U.S. citizen. MODERN DRAMA. B.A, Columbia Col, 63; M.A, Columbia Univ, 65, Fulbright fel, 69-70, Ph.D.(Eng. & comp. lit), 71. Preceptor ENG, Columbia Col, 69-71; ASST. PROF, CITY COL. NEW YORK, 71- Bertolt Brecht; parapsychology; human energy fields and learning. Add: Dept. of English, City College of New York, Convent Ave. & 133rd St, New York, NY 10031.

NORRIS, MARGOT CHRISTA, b. Baden bei Vienna, Austria, Dec. 23, 44; U.S. citizen; div; c. 1. ENGLISH LITERATURE. B.A, Univ. Fla, 67; Ph.D.(Eng), State Univ. N.Y, Buffalo, 72. ASST. PROF. ENG, UNIV. TULSA, 72- MLA. James Joyce's Finnegans Wake; structuralist critical theory; linguistics and grammar. Add: 2207 E. 21st St, Tulsa, OK 74114.

NORRIS, WILLIAM EDWARD, Applied Linguistics, English as a Foreign Language. See Volume III, Foreign Languages, Linguistics & Philology.

NORSTEDT, JOHANN ALBERT, b. Kulpmont, Pa, July 9, 37; m. 65. ANGLO-IRISH LITERATURE. A.B, Univ. Pa, 59, A.M, 61; Ph.D.(Eng), Univ. Col. Dublin, 72. Instr. Eng, Temple Univ, 62-64; Am. Beirut, 64-67; tutor, Univ. Col. Dublin, 69-70; res. ed, Irish Univ. Press, 70-72; ASST. PROF. ENG, VA. POLYTECH. INST. & STATE UNIV, 72- Dean summer session, Sch. Irish Stud, Dublin, 69 & 70. Am. Comt. Irish Stud; Can. Asn. Irish Stud; Int. Asn. Stud. Anglo-Irish Lit; S.Atlantic Mod. Lang. Asn. Thomas MacDonagh; Anglo-Irish poetry and drama. Publ: Co-ed, Area studies series of British Parliamentary papers: United States, 71 & co-ed, Area studies series of British Parliamentary papers: China and Japan, 72, Irish Univ; co-ed, When the dawn is come, DePaul Univ, 73. Add: Dept. of English, Virginia Polytechnic Institute & State University, Blacksburg, VA 24061.

NORTH, HELEN FLORENCE, Classical Literature, Rhetoric. See Volume III, Foreign Languages, Linguistics & Philology.

NORTH, JOHN STANLEY, b. Vancouver, B.C, Sept. 1, 39; m. 63; c. 3. ENGLISH LITERATURE. B.A, Univ. B.C, 62, M.A, 65; Ph.D.(Eng), Univ. Alta, 69. ASST. PROF. ENG, UNIV. WATERLOO, 68- Killam fel, Univ. B.C, 71-72. Can. Counc. Teachers Eng.(ed, Eng. Quart, 72-74); Asn. Can. Univ. Teachers Eng; Victorian Stud. Asn. West. Can; Tennyson Soc; Res. Soc. Victorian Periodicals. Victorian periodical literature; Victorian history of ideas—Metaphysical Society; Tennyson. Publ: The Waterloo directory of Victorian periodicals, Victorian Periodicals Newslett, 6/71. Add: Dept. of English, University of Waterloo, Waterloo, Ont. N2L 3G1, Can.

NORTH, ROSS S, b. Abilene, Tex, Mar. 12, 30; m. 55; c. 4. SPEECH, RELIGION. B.A, Abilene Christian Col, 50; M.A, La. State Univ, 52; Ph.D. (speech), Univ. Fla, 57. Instr. speech, OKLA. CHRISTIAN COL, 52-54, asst. to pres, 56-58, dean instr, 58-70, DEAN COL, 70- Minister, Church of Christ, 48-; Bible lectr, Abilene Christian Col, 62; consult, Langston Univ, 67; mem, long range planning comt, Southwest. Regional Educ. Lab. 67; consult, Univ. San Carlos, Guatemala, 67; Pub. Schs, Dade County, Fla, 68; Tyler Jr. Col, summer 68. NEA; Speech Commun. Asn; Am. Asn. Col. Registr. & Admis. Off. Use of recordings in instruction; use of learning center. Publ: Ed, A road to faith (relig. educ. ser), Quality Printing, 70;

auth, Preaching: man and method, Okla Christian Col, 71; Learning center gives each student a study carrel, Col. & Univ. Bus, 5/66; Dial access retrieval system at Oklahoma Christian College, AV Instr, 5/67; Some lessons in innovation, CASC Newslett, 7/68. Add: Oklahoma Christian College, Oklahoma City, OK 73111.

NORTHROP, DOUGLAS ANTHONY, b. Ontario, N.Y, Apr. 12, 35; m. 56; c. 4. ENGLISH. B.A, Wesleyan Univ, 56; M.A, Univ. Chicago, 57, Ph.D.(Eng), 66. Instr. ENG, RIPON COL, 60-62, asst. prof, 62-68, assoc. prof, 68-74, PROF, 74- Severy Award for excellence in teaching, 66, Uhrig Award, 71. MLA; Renaissance Soc. Am. Edmund Spenser; Renaissance drama; Milton. Publ: Spenser's Defence of Elizabeth, Univ. Toronto Quart, 4/69; Mercilla's Court as parliament, Huntington Libr. Quart, 2/73. Add: Dept. of English, Ripon College, Ripon, WI 54971.

NORTHWALL, JOHN HOWARD, b. Kansas City, Mo, May 25, 27; m. 51; c. 4. RHETORIC, PHILOSOPHY. B.A, State Univ. Iowa, 48; B.D, Warthurs Sem, 51, S.T.M, 68; M.A, Univ. Denver, 67; Ph.D, Univ. Colo, 69. Pastor, Am. Lutheran Church, 51-68; ASSOC. PROF. SPEECH, DANA COL, 68- Add: Dept. of Speech, Dana College, Blair, NE 68008.

NORTON, ALOYSIUS A, b. N.J, July 31, 20; m. ENGLISH, LITERATURE AS HISTORY. B.S, U.S. Mil. Acad, 44; M.A, Columbia Univ, 50; Ph.D, Univ. Madrid, Spain, 54. Instr. ENG, U.S. Mil. Acad, 48-52; Fairleigh Dickinson Univ, 57-58; assoc. prof, Seton Hall Univ, 58-63; chmn. dept, Dickinson State Col, 63-64, prof, Incarnate Word Col, 64-65; assoc. prof, U.S. MERCHANT MARINE ACAD, 65-70, PROF, 70- Adj. assoc. prof, St. John's Univ, 65-; Consult-contrib, Choice, 64- U.S.A, 38-41; U.S.A.F, 41-52, Capt. Am. Forensic Asn; MLA; NCTE; Speech Commun. Asn. Literature and history of American southwest; Theodore Roosevelt. Publ: Co-auth, Christian approach to western literature, Newman, 60 & Literary craftsmanship, Florham Park Press, 61; auth, Huckleberry Finn: an analysis in depth, Barrister Publ, 66. Add: Dept. of English, U.S. Merchant Marine Academy, Kings Point, NY 11024.

NORTON, LAURENCE EUGENE, b. West Concord, Minn. Mar. 17, 06; m. 35; c. 2. SPEECH. A.B, Carleton Col, 27; A.M, State Univ. Iowa, 34; Ph.D, Univ. Wis, 47. Prof. Speech, Adrian Col, 34-35; Eureka Col, 35-43, 45-48; assoc. prof, BRADLEY UNIV, 48-53, prof, 53-73, dean men, 55-70, chmn. dept. speech, 60-71, acting dean, Col. Lang. & Speech, 71-73, EMER. PROF. SPEECH, 73- Speech Commun. Asn; Am. Forensic Asn. Public discussion and debate; semantics; parliamentary law. Publ: Planning the negative case, Forensic; Present status of intercollegiate discussion, Gavel, 57; Research directions in debate, Register, 60. Add: 1010 N. Heading Ct, Peoria, IL 61604.

NORTON, MAX C, b. Rigby, Idaho, Feb. 2, 20; m. 51; c. 3. SPEECH PATHOLOGY, COMMUNICATIONS. B.A, Univ. Pac, 51, M.A, 55; Stanford Univ, 55-56; fel, Univ. Denver, 60-61, Ph.D, 62. PROF. SPEECH. & COMMUN. SCI, CALIF. STATE COL, STANISLAUS, 67-, DIR. SPEECH, LANG. & HEARING CTR, 68- Consult. speech & hearing, Modesto City Schs, Calif, 52-60, dir. dept, 56-60. Outstanding Prof. Award, Calif. State Col, Stanislaus, 71 & 72. West. Speech Commun. Asn; Speech Commun. Asn; Am. Speech & Hearing Asn; Int. Soc. Gen. Semantics; Soc. Gen. Syst. Res. Publ: Double frequency audiometry in public schools, J. Speech & Hearing Disorders, 8/61; Levels of meaning: criteria for effective speech and hearing therapy, Voice, 5/63; Development and evaluation of specialized program for acceleration of language skills of pre-reading child, Speech Monogr, 8/63. Add: 5766 Stoddard Rd, Modesto, CA 95350.

NORVELLE, LEE. SPEECH. A.B, Ind. Univ, 21, Ph.D, 31; A.M, State Univ. Iowa, 23; Oxford, 27; Cornell Univ, 28. Instr. SPEECH, State Univ. Iowa, 21-23, assoc, 23-24; instr, Mont. State Univ, 24-25; asst. prof, IND. UNIV, BLOOMINGTON, 25-37, assoc. prof, 38-48, prof, 48-63, dir. radio broadcasting, 37-46, chmn. dept, 45-58, dir. univ. theatre, 30-58, EMER. PROF, 63- Dir, Nat. Theatre Conf. Touring Co, 47-49; Brown County Playhouse, 48-63; mem. bd. dir, All Ways Travel, Inc, 63-, pres, 65-73, chmn. bd. dirs, 73- Am. Col. Theatre Gold Medallion Award of Excellence, 73. U.S.A, 17-18; expert consult, U.S. War Dept, 41-43; U.S.N, 43-45. Speech Commun. Asn; Nat. Theatre Conf.(pres, 42-44, 53-57); Am. Theatre Asn.(pres, 39, Merit Award, 73). Effective speech; trend of the American theatre since 1920; responsibilities of the theatre director to his university; aesthetics in the theatre. Publ: Co-auth, History of the National Theatre Conference, Nat. Theatre Conf, 68; auth, Stanislaviski revisited—or what did he say his method was?, Educ. Theatre J, 3/62. Add: University Apts. 120-22, 1415 E. Third St, Bloomington, IN 47401.

NORVISH, FRANKLIN, b. Brockton, Mass, Oct. 25, 11; m. 45; c. 1. ENGLISH LITERATURE. B.S, Colby Col, 34; A.M, Yale, 36; Boston Univ, 39-40. Instr. ENG, NORTHEAST. UNIV, 36-42, asst. prof, 45-50, assoc. prof, 50-63, PROF, 63-, chmn. freshman Eng. prog, 47-67, acting chmn. Eng. dept, 60-61. Consult, var. publ; gen. ed, Bobbs-Merrill Compos. & Rhetoric Ser, 66; Eng. lang. ed, Encycl. Lituanica, 74. Counter-Intel.C, U.S.A, 43-45. Col. Eng. Asn; Speech Commun. Asn; New Eng. Col. Eng. Asn.(pres, 53-54); MLA. Essentials of modern speech; speech and conference techniques. Publ: Business writing (reports), Babenroth, 64. Add: Dept. of English, Northeastern University, Boston, MA 02115.

NORWOOD, FRANK WESLEY, b. New York, N.Y, May 15, 28; m. 57; c. 2. SPEECH. B.A, Queens Col.(N.Y), 50, M.A, 51; Univ. Mo, 51-52, 54-55; Ohio State Univ, 55-56. Producer-dir, KSLH, St. Louis Bd. Educ, 56-57; asst. prof. speech arts, San Diego State Col, 57-60, assoc. prof, 60-66; prog. assoc, Nat. Ctr. Sch. & Col. TV, Ind, 66-68; EXEC. SECY, JOINT COUNC. EDUC. TELECOMMUN, 68- Discovery res. grant, Am. Broadcasting Co, 62. U.S.A, 52-54. Nat. Asn. Educ. Broadcasters; Asn. Prof. Broadcasting Educ; Int. Broadcasting Inst. Educational communications; rhetoric of broadcasting. Add: Joint Council on Educational Telecommunications, 1126 16th St, N.W, Washington, DC 20036.

NOSSEN, ROBERT JOSEPH, b. San Francisco, Calif, Sept. 4, 20; m. 45. ENGLISH. A.B, Univ. Calif, 44; M.A, Northwest. Univ, 48, Ph.D, 51. Lectr. Eng, Northwest. Univ, 48-50; asst. prof, Creighton Univ, 50-54, head dept, 51-54; prof. & head dept, Lamar State Univ, 54-60; prof. Eng. & chmn. dept. Eng. & speech, State Univ. N.Y. Col. Fredonia, 60-62, dean lib. arts & sci, 62-66, v.pres. acad. affairs, 66-69; pres, Bloomsburg State Col, 69-72; PROF. HIGHER EDUC. & ASSOC. PROVOST REGIONAL CAMPUSES, UNIV. PITTSBURGH, 72- Mem. comt. acad. & stud. personnel, Am. Asn. State Cols. & Univs, 70- Seventeenth century religious writings; higher education administration; college evaluation. Publ: TV and the teaching of English, Improving Col. & Univ. Instr, 58; Jeremy Taylor: 17th century theologian, Anglican Theol. Rev, 60; Patterns for inter-institutional cooperation, Tri State Comt. Articulation & Coop, 72; plus others. Add: 3209 C.L, University of Pittsburgh, Pittsburgh, PA 15260.

NOSTWICH, THEODORE DANIEL, b. Akron, Ohio, Sept. 14, 25; m. 53; c. 5. AMERICAN LITERATURE, BIBLIOGRAPHY. B.A, Ohio State Univ, Columbus, 48, M.A, 50; Ph.D.(Eng), Univ. Tex, Austin, 68. Asst. prof. ENG, Ferris State Col, 55-59; instr, Univ. Tex, Austin, 61-62; Purdue Univ, W.Lafayette, 62-63; asst. prof, Del Mar Col, 63-68; ASSOC. PROF, IOWA STATE UNIV, 68- Soc. Stud. Midwest. Lit. American culture 1900-1925; literature of the Midwest; literature of the South. Add: Dept. of English, Iowa State University, Ames, IA 50010.

NOTEBOOM, ANN M, b. Wellsburg, Iowa, Jan. 23, 23; m. SPEECH. A.B, Calvin Col, 46; M.A, Northwest. Univ, 52, Ph.D, 57; Fulbright scholar, 54-55. Asst. Eng. & speech, CALVIN COL, 52-53, instr, 53-54, 55-57, asst. prof. SPEECH, 57-58, assoc. prof, 58-62, PROF, 62- Cent. States Speech Asn; Speech Commun. Asn. Old Dutch literature. Add: Dept. of Speech, Calvin College, Grand Rapids, MI 49506.

NOVAK, ELAINE ADAMS, b. West Milton, Ohio, July 3, 22; div; c. 2. SPEECH, THEATRE. A.B, Marshall Univ, 43; A.M, Columbia Univ, 50; Simon Lazarus Mem. scholar, Ohio State Univ, 62-63, Ph.D.(speech), 63. Instr. SPEECH, MARSHALL UNIV, 56-60, asst. prof, 60-63, assoc. prof, 63-68, PROF, 68- Benedum Found. res. grant, summer 64. U.S.N.R, 43-46, Lt. Am. Theatre Asn. Styles of acting. Add: Dept. of Speech, Marshall University, Huntington, WV 25701.

NOVAK, JANE DAILEY, b. Omaha, Nebr, Aug. 27, 17; m. 40; c. 4. MODERN ENGLISH LITERATURE. B.A, Carleton Col, 38; M.A, Univ. Miami, 64; Woodrow Wilson grant, Univ. Chicago, 69-70, Ph.D.(Eng), 70. Grad. asst. ENG, Univ. Miami, 63-64; asst, UNIV. ILL, CHICAGO CIRCLE, 67-69, instr, 69-70, ASST. PROF, 70- Leverhulme vis. fel, Univ. E.Anglia, Eng, 73-74. MLA. Modern British novel; 20th century literature; curriculum experiment in British universities. Publ: The razor edge of balance: a study of Virginia Woolf, Univ. Miami, 74; Verisimilitude and visions: Defoe and Blake as influences on Joyce's Molly Bloom, Carrell, 6/67; Virginia Woolf—a fickle Jacobean, Virginia Woolf Newslett, 11/71; Recent Virginia Woolf criticism, Virginia Woolf Quart, 10/72. Add: Dept. of English, Box 4348, University of Illinois at Chicago Circle, Chicago, IL 60680.

NOVAK, MAXIMILLIAN, b. New York, N.Y, Mar. 26, 30. ENGLISH LITERATURE. B.A, Univ. Calif, Los Angeles, 52, M.A, 54, Ph.D, 58; D.Phil, Oxford, 61. Instr. ENG. LIT, Univ. Mich, 58-61, asst. prof, 61-62; UNIV. CALIF, LOS ANGELES, 62-65, assoc. prof, 65-69, PROF, 69- Guggenheim fel, 65-66; prin. investr, Nat. Endowment for Humanities res. grant, 72-73; Clark prof, Clark Mem. Libr, 73-74. Augustan Reprint Soc.(gen. ed, 62-73); Am. Soc. 18th Century Stud; MLA. Daniel Defoe, Congreve and Dryden; 18th and 19th century fiction; Restoration drama. Publ: Economics and the fiction of Daniel Defoe, 62 & co-ed, Dryden, Works, Vol. X, 70 & Vol. XVII, 71; auth, Defoe and the nature of man, Clarendon, 63; co-auth, The uses of irony: Swift and Defoe, 66 & co-auth, Congreve consider'd, 71, Clark Mem. Libr; ed, The empress of Morocco and its critics, Augustan Reprint Soc, 68; auth, William Congreve, Twayne, 71; co-ed, The wild man within, Pittsburgh Univ, 72; auth, Crime and punishment in Defoe's Roxana, J. Eng. & Ger. Philol, 7/66. Add: Dept. of English, University of California, 405 Hilgard Ave, Los Angeles, CA 90024.

NOVAK, ROBERT LEE, b. Olney, Ill, Sept. 4, 33. ENGLISH. B.A, Wabash Col, 55; Univ. Ind, Bloomington, 55-56; M.A, Univ. Okla, 58, Ph.D.(Eng), 72. Asst. ENG, Univ. Okla, 56-60; instr, PURDUE UNIV, FT. WAYNE, 60-67, ASST. PROF, 67- Ed, Windless Orchard, 70-74. MLA; AAUP; Coop. Small Mag. Ed. & Publ. The novels of C.P. Snow and Pamela Johnson; the poetry of W.H. Auden. Publ: High afternoon, 71, At the splinter house, 71, Woman in the red skirt, 71, Machines for loving, 73 & Things to do in Fort Wayne, 73, Windless Orchard; A review of The New York anthology of poets, Happiness Holding Tank, 72. Add: Dept. of English, Purdue University, Ft. Wayne, IN 46805.

NOVARR, DAVID, b. Hartford, Conn, June 29, 17; m. 42; c. 2. ENGLISH LITERATURE. A.B, Yale, 39, A.M, 42, Ph.D, 49. Instr. Eng. lit, CORNELL UNIV, 46-49, fac. instr, 49-51, asst. prof, 51-56, assoc. prof, 56-63, PROF. ENG, 63- Ford fel, 51-52; mem. adv. screening comt. Eng. lang. & lit, Comt. Int. Exchange Persons, Fulbright-Hays Prog, 70-73; mem. ed. comt, Folger Libr. Ed. Works of Richard Hooker. U.S.N.R, 42-45. MLA. Seventeenth century literature; biography; Elizabethan and Jacobean drama. Publ: Making of Walton's Lives, Cornell Univ, 58; Seventeenth century English prose, Knopf, 67; Donne's Epithalamion made at Lincoln's Inn: context and date, Rev. Eng. Stud, 56; Dekker's gentle craft and the Lord Mayor of London, Mod. Philol, 60; Swift's relation with Dryden, and Gulliver's Annus mirabilis, Eng. Stud, 10/66. Add: Dept. of English, Goldwin Smith Hall, Cornell University, Ithaca, NY 14850.

NOVOSAL, PAUL PETER, b. St. Louis, Mo, Oct. 5, 18. ENGLISH, LIBRARY SCIENCE. B.S, Univ. Dayton, 40; B.S.L.S, Our Lady of the Lake Col, 41; M.A, St. Mary's Univ.(Tex), 65. Librn, teacher & athletic dir, Cath. & pub. high schs, Tex. & Mo, 41-47; librn. & asst. prof. Eng, ST. MARY'S UNIV. (TEX), 47-57, ASSOC. PROF. ENG, 67-, dir. libr, 58-73. Arch, St. Louis Prov. Soc. of Mary. Am. Libr. Asn; Cath. Libr. Asn; Southwest. Libr. Asn. Publ: Compiler, Union catalog of Marian books in San Antonio, Cath. Libr. Asn, 56. Add: Dept. of English, St. Mary's University, 2700 Cincinnati Ave. San Antonio, TX 78228.

NOXON, GERALD FORBES, b. Toronto, Ont, May 3, 10; m. 31, 51; c. 1. FILM & DRAMATIC WRITING. B.A, Cambridge, 31, M.A, 49; Univ. Paris,

28-30; Regia Univ, Perugia, 29-31. Asst. prof. radio writing, BOSTON UNIV, 47-52, assoc. prof. radio & TV, film writing & prod, 52-68, PROF. FILM THEORY & DRAMATURGY, 68- Pres. Univ. Film Stud. Ctr, Cambridge, Mass, 71-72, v.pres. & chmn. res. comt, 72- Best Radio Drama Award, Columbus, Ohio, 48; Can. Broadcasting Award. Soc. Cinema Stud. (treas, 59-62, pres, 62 & 63). Film production; film theory; dramaturgy and historical development of cinema narrative. Publ: Pictorial origins of cinema narrative in pre-historic and ancient art, Experiment, 68; The anatomy of the close-up, 60 & Cinema and cubism, 62, J. Soc. Cinematologists. Add: 10 Harborside Park, P.O. Box 266, Dennisport, MA 02639.

NOYES, CHARLES EDWARD, b. Natchez, Miss, July 19, 17; m. 43; c. 3. ENGLISH. A.B, Univ. Mo, 39, A.M, 40; Ph.D.(Eng), Univ. Tex, 50. Instr. ENG, Univ. Mo, 40-42; Univ. Tenn, 50-53; asst. prof, UNIV. MISS, 53-57; assoc. prof, 57-62; PROF, 62-, ASST. V.CHANCELLOR & DIR. SUMMER SESSION, 64-, provost, 63-64. U.S.A.A.F, 42-46, Maj. MLA; Asn. Univ. Summer Sessions. Eighteenth century English literature. Publ: Co-auth, Christopher Smart: a biographical and critical study, Univ. Mo, 43; auth, Hume's Umbrage to the Godly, 60 & Samuel Johnson: student of Hume, 62, Univ. Miss. Stud. Eng. Add: Vice Chancellor's Office, University of Mississippi, University, MS 38677.

NOYES, GERTRUDE ELIZABETH, b. New London, Conn, May 18, 05. ENGLISH. A.B, Conn. Col, 25; A.M, Yale, 26, Ph.D, 37. Asst. ENG, Univ. Ill, 26-29; instr, CONN. COL, 29-38, asst. prof, 38-45, assoc. prof, 45-54, prof, 54-69, dean freshmen, 45-58, dean col, 58-69, EMER. PROF. & EMER. DEAN, 69- MLA. English lexicography; history of drama. Publ: Co-auth, English dictionary from Cawdrey to Johnson, Univ. N.C. Add: 484 Montauk Ave, New London, CT 06320.

NOYES, JEANICE WILLIAMS, b. Milford, Iowa, Aug. 20, 14; m. 39; c. 1. SPEECH, DRAMA. B.E, Drake Univ, 35; M.A, State Univ. Iowa, 39. Teacher, Pocahontas High Sch, 35-37; dir. children's theatre, Drake Univ, 37-38; PROF. SPEECH & DRAMA & HEAD DEPT, GRAND VIEW COL, 45- Distinguished Serv. Award, Zeta Phi Eta. Cent. States Speech Asn; Speech Commun. Asn. Community theatre, especially children's theatre. Publ: Co-auth, Core knowledge for successful speech, Scott, 69. Add: 4027 Welker Ave, Des Moines, IA 50312.

NOYES, RUSSELL, b. Pittsfield, Mass, Dec. 16, 01; m. 28, 64; c. 2. ENGLISH LITERATURE. B.S, Univ. Mass, 24; univ. scholar, Harvard, 27-28, A.M, 28, Austin scholar, 29-32, Ph.D, 32. Prin. high sch, Vt, 24-26; instr. ENG, Ind. Univ, 28-29; Boston Univ, 30-31; asst, Harvard, 31-32; asst. prof, IND. UNIV, BLOOMINGTON, 32-41, assoc. prof, 41-48, prof, 48-72, chmn. dept, 41-51, EMER. PROF, 72- MLA; Col. Eng. Asn.(v.pres, 50); AAUP. English romanticism; Wordsworth. Publ: Influence and reputation of Michael Drayton; Wordsworth and Jeffrey in controversy, 41 & Wordsworth and the art of landscape, 68, Ind. Univ; English Romantic poetry and prose, Oxford, 56; William Wordsworth, Twayne, 71; Wordsworth and copyright, PMLA, 61; English Romanticism in retrospect, Review, 72. Add: 831 S. High St, Bloomington, IN 47401.

NUGENT, MARY LOUISE, b. London, Ont, Feb. 2, 14; m. 42; c. 2. ENGLISH, CLASSICS. B.A, Univ. West. Ont, 35; M.A, Univ. Ill, 38; Ph.D. (comp. lit), Cornell Univ, 42. ASST. PROF. ENG, UNIV. HOUSTON, 53-57, 64- Wordsworth, especially The Prelude; Greek drama. Add: Dept. of English, University of Houston, Houston, TX 77004.

NUNAN, JOSEPH CARLTON, b. Atlanta, Ga, Dec. 26, 08; m. 37; c. 4. ENGLISH. Ph.B, Emory Univ, 31, A.M, 32. Teacher, high schs, Ga, 32-46; ASST. PROF. ENG, EMORY UNIV, 46- Instr, eve. sch, Ga. Inst. Technol, 44-46. NCTE; Conf. Col. Compos. & Commun. Grammar; composition; English education. Add: Dept. of English, Emory University, Atlanta, GA 30322.

NURMI, MARTIN KARL, b. Duluth, Minn, Sept. 4, 20; m. 44; c. 3. ENGLISH. Wis. State Col, Superior; M.A, Univ. Chicago, 48; Ph.D.(Eng), Univ. Minn, 54; Columbia Univ. & Princeton, 54-55. Instr. ENG, Ala. State Teachers Col, Florence, 48-49; teaching & res. asst, Univ. Minn, 50-52; instr, Univ. N.Dak, 52-54; asst. prof, KENT STATE UNIV, 55-58, assoc. prof, 58-63, PROF, 63-, CHMN. DEPT, 71-, dean grad. sch, 64-68. Ford Found. Fund Advan. Educ. fac. fel, 54-55; vis. assoc. prof, Univ. Wash, summer, 62; vis. lectr, Univ. Minn, 62-63; vis. prof, Mich. State Univ, summer 66; Univ. B.C, summer 67. MLA. William Blake; English Romantic movement; history of ideas. Publ: Co-auth, A Blake bibliography, Univ. Minn, 64 & Poetry: an introduction and anthology, C.E. Merrill, 67; auth, William Blake, Hutchinson Univ. Libr, London, 74; Blake's Marriage of heaven and hell: a critical study, Kent State Univ. Res. Ser, 57; ed, The Romantic movement: a selective and critical bibliography, Philol. Quart, 57-61; plus others. Add: 1400 Ridgecrest Dr, Kent, OH 44240.

NUTKU, EMILY BOHNETT, b. Campbell, Calif, Apr. 21; m. 41, 66; c. 3. ENGLISH LANGUAGE & LITERATURE. B.A, San Jose State Col, 41; M.A, Univ. Calif, Berkeley, 43, Ph.D.(Eng. lang), 66. Asst. prof. ENG, San Jose State Col, 64-65; San Francisco State Col, 65-66; lectr, UNIV. MD, COLLEGE PARK, 71-72, ASST. PROF, 72- MLA; Col. Eng. Asn; Ling. Soc. Am; AAUP. Early Middle English literature; English grammar. Add: 8 H Plateau Pl, Greenbelt, MD 20770.

NUTLEY, GRACE STUART, b. Alameda, Calif, Nov. 8, 00; m. 25; c. 1. ENGLISH. B.E, Univ. Wash, 22; M.A, N.Y. Univ, 36, Ph.D.(Eng), 45; Austrian-Am. Inst, 30; Alliance Francaise, 31. Assoc. prof. ENG, Pratt Inst, 36-46; from asst. prof. to assoc. prof, Brooklyn Col, 46-70; EDUC. CONSULT. & LECTR, 70- Smith-Mundt prof, U.S. Dept. State, P.I, 50-52; Fulbright prof, Annamalai Univ, Madras, 59-61; dir. teacher training insts, S.E. Asia, 59-60, 64, 67, U.S. Dept. State Am. specialist grants, 64, 67 & 68; NDEA dir, 65-66; consult. workshops; consult, NDEA Inst, Phila. Bd. Educ, 69-72; lectr. Eng. as second lang, U.S. State Dept, 72. AAUP; Col. Eng. Asn. (chmn, status of women in the profession comt, 69-72); NCTE; Conf. Col. Compos. & Commun; MLA; fel. Am. Stud. Asn. The social criticism of Robert Herrick as reflected in his novels of American life; contemporary American poets, especially the work of the women poets; English as a second language. Add: 9407 109th Dr, Sun City, AZ 85351.

NYCE, BENJAMIN M, b. Buffalo, N.Y, Apr. 25, 32; m. 67. ENGLISH. A.B, Princeton, 54; Ph.D.(Eng), Claremont Grad. Sch, 67. Lectr. ENG, Scripps Col, 61-63; instr, Univ. Calif, Riverside, 63-64; ASST. PROF, Calif. State Polytech. Col, 64-67; UNIV. SAN DIEGO COL. MEN, 67- Fulbright-Hays prof. Am. stud, Univ. Mohammed V, Morocco, 69-70, Univ. Nairobi, 72-73. MLA. English and American novel, late 19th and 20th century; political fiction; African literature. Publ: Ignazio Silone's Political trilogy, New Orleans Rev, 68; Joyce Cary's Political trilogy: the atmosphere of power, Mod. Lang. Quart, 3/71; Joseph Conrad's Nostromo, Recovering Lit, spring 72. Add: 2228 Via Aprilia, Del Mar, CA 92014.

NYE, RUSSEL B, b. Viola, Wis, Feb. 17, 13; m. 38; c. 1. ENGLISH. A.B, Oberlin Col, 34; M.A, Univ. Wis, 35, Ph.D, 40; hon. L.H.D, North. Mich. Univ, 68; hon. LL.D, Ferris State Col, 69. Instr. ENG, Adelphi Col, 39-40; MICH. STATE UNIV, 41-43, asst. prof, 43-45, assoc. prof, 45-46, prof, 46-65, DISTINGUISHED PROF, 65- Chmn. adv. comt. Am. stud, Conf. Bd. Assoc. Res. Counc, 63. Pulitzer Prize, Biography, 45. MLA; Popular Cult. Asn; Am. Stud. Asn.(pres, 64). American literature and history. Publ: George Bancroft, Knopf, 45; Fettered freedom, Mich. State Univ, 47; Cultural life of the new nation, Harper, 60; Unembarrassed muse, Dial, 71; plus others. Add: Dept. of English, Michigan State University, East Lansing, MI 48823.

NYGARD, HOLGER OLOF, b. Vasa, Finland, Feb. 24, 21; U.S. citizen; m. 44; c. 4. ENGLISH, FOLKLORE. B.A, Univ. B.C, 44; M.A, Univ. Calif, Berkeley, 49, Ph.D.(Eng), 55; Can. Humanities Res. Counc. scholar, 52; Am. Counc. Learned Soc. grad. fel, 52-53. Instr. ENG, Univ. B.C, 45-47; Univ. Kans, 53-55, asst. prof, 55-57; assoc. prof, Univ. Tenn, 57-60; DUKE UNIV, 60-62, PROF, 62- Watkins fac. fel. & Endowment Asn. grant, Univ. Kans, 56; Guggenheim fel, 66-67. Chicago Folklore Prize, 59. MLA; Am. Folklore Soc; NCTE; Folklore League Denmark; Soc. Advan. Scand. Stud; Mediaeval Acad. Am. Balladry; Old and Middle English. Publ: The ballad of Heer Halewijn: a study of the history and nature of a ballad tradition, Acad. Sci. Fennica, 58; Ballad, folkevise, chanson populaire, Folklore Stud. in Honor of Arthur Palmer Hudson, 65; Popular ballad and medieval romance, Folklore Int, 67. Add: Dept. of English, Duke University, Durham, NC 27706.

O

OAKMAN, ROBERT LEE, III, b. Memphis, Tenn, Feb. 19, 41; m. 68. VICTORIAN LITERATURE. B.A, Univ. Miss, 63; Woodrow Wilson fel, Univ. Wis, 63-64, M.A, 64; NDEA fel, Ind. Univ, Bloomington, 65-68, M.A, 66, Ph.D.(Eng), 71. Instr. Eng, Univ. Miss, summer 66; ENG. & COMPUT. SCI, UNIV. S.C, 68-71, asst. prof, 71-73, ASSOC. PROF, 73- MLA; Asn. Comput. Mach. Computer applications in literary and linguistic research; Victorian prose and novel. Publ: The present state of computerized collation, 12/72 & Concordances from computers, 12/73, Proof. Add: Dept. of English, University of South Carolina, Columbia, SC 29208.

OAKS, HAROLD RASMUS, b. Provo, Utah, June 20, 36; m. 60; c. 4. THEATRE. B.A, Brigham Young Univ, 60, M.A, 62; Tozer Found. fel. & Ph.D. (speech, theatre arts), Univ. Minn, 64. Instr. speech & theatre arts, Univ. Minn, 62-64, admin. asst. off. adv. drama res, 63-64; asst. prof, speech & drama, Frostburg State Col, 64-66; assoc. prof. & dir. theatre, Kearney State Col, 66-68; ASSOC. PROF. DRAMATIC ARTS, Colo. State Univ, 68-70; BRIGHAM YOUNG UNIV, 70- U.S. Off. Econ. humanities & soc. sci. develop. prog. grant-in-aid, 66-68. Am. Theatre Asn.(treas, 72-73); U.S. Inst. Theatre Technol. Theatre administration; improvisation and role playing; child drama. Publ: Introduction to the theatre, Brigham Young Univ, 71; Theatre management and administration training in American colleges and universities, U.S. Inst. Theatre Technol, 9/67; co-auth, An evening of historical vignettes, Ensign, 10/72; plus others. Add: Dept. of Dramatic Arts, Brigham Young University, Provo, UT 84601.

OAKS, PRISCILLA (SHAMES), b. Boston, Mass, Apr. 15, 24; div; c. 4. AMERICAN LITERATURE. A.B, Radcliffe Col, 45; Patent Fund Awards, Univ. Calif, Los Angeles, 68, 69, Ph.D.(Am. lit), 69. ASST. PROF. AM. LIT, CALIF. STATE UNIV, FULLERTON, 69- Instr. exten, Univ. Calif, Los Angeles, 69-, vis. prof, Univ, 70-72, consult, Am. Indian Libr, 70-; vis. scholar, Radcliffe Inst, 72-73; assoc, Harvard Grad. Sch. Educ, 72-73; consult, Intercult. Stud. Group, 73- MLA; West. Lit. Asn; Philol. Asn. Pac. Coast; Am. Anthrop. Asn; Am. Folklore Asn. Native American literature; literature of ethnic peoples of the United States; women's literature. Add: Dept. of English, California State University, Fullerton, Fullerton, CA 92631.

OATES, MARY I, b. Los Angeles, Calif, Mar. 28, 38; m. 58; c. 3. ENGLISH. B.A, Stanford Univ, 59; M.A, San Jose State Col, 65; NDEA fel, Proctor fel. & Ph.D.(Eng), Princeton, 72. Instr. ENG, Princeton, 70-72; RIDER COL, 72-73, ASST. PROF, 73- Lectr. Romance lang, Princeton, 71-72. MLA; Shakespeare Soc. Am; AAUP. Renaissance drama; English lyric poetry. Publ: Economics of the Elizabethan theater, Swedish J. Econ, spring 72. Add: Dept. of English, Rider College, Trenton, NJ 08202.

OBEE, HAROLD BREHM, b. Catawba, Ohio, May 4, 15; m. 40; c. 4. SPEECH, THEATRE. A.B, Adrian Col, 38; M.A, Ohio State Univ, 46, Ph.D.(theatre), 61. Instr, high schs, Ohio, 38-42; speech, Bowling Green State Univ, 46-49, asst. prof, 49-63, assoc. prof. speech & theatre, 63-67, PROF. SPEECH & THEATRE & HEAD THEATRE AREA, 67-, dir. theatre, 63-67, res. grant, 63-65, res. leave, summer 68. Theatre prog. consult, Frederick Douglas Community Ctr, Ohio, 48-50 & 62; chmn. libr. comt, Am. Educ. Theatre Asn, 49-50; assoc. tech. dir. The 17th Star, Ohio Sesqui-Centennial Comn, summer 53; lectr. speech, Ohio State Univ, 56-57; vis. prof. theatre, Colo. State Col, summer 63. U.S.A, 42-45, T/Sgt. Speech Commun. Asn.(secy. theatre group, 63-65); Am. Theatre Asn; Am. Soc. Theatre Res; Soc. Theatre Res, Eng; Theatre Libr. Asn. High school speech education; theatre history; theatre curriculum, especially college. Publ: The high school and college theatre work together, Bull. Nat. Asn. Sec. Sch. Prin, 1/54; co-auth, A survey of theatre in four state universities, Cent. States Speech J, spring 57; auth, Stage lighting (ser. of 8 articles), Dramatics, 10/61-5/62. Add: Dept. of Speech, Bowling Green State University, Bowling Green, OH 43402.

OBER, WARREN UPTON, b. Smackover, Ark, May 2, 25; m. 51; c. 3. ENGLISH. B.A, Washington & Lee Univ, 48; Ph.D.(Eng. lit), Ind. Univ, 58. Instr. Eng, Ky. Mil. Inst, 48-50; teaching asst, Ind. Univ, 50-53; instr. Eng. & reading improvement, South. State Col, 53-55; asst. prof. ENG, North. Ill. Univ, 55-59, assoc. prof, 59-62, prof, 62-65, acting head dept, 61-62; PROF, UNIV. WATERLOO, 65-, CHMN. DEPT, 65-69, 73-, acting dean, fac. arts, 69-70, dir, inter-fac. prog. bd, 70-72. Mem, bd. ed. adv, Germano-Slavica, 73- U.S.N, 43-46, Res, 46-58, Lt.(jg). Can. Counc. Teachers Eng; Asn. Can. Univ. Teachers Eng; Mod. Humanities Res. Asn. English romantic poets; Russian translations of English poetry. Publ: Southey, Coleridge, and Kubla Khan, J. Eng. & Ger. Philol, 7/59; co-auth, Zukovskij's first translation of Gray's Elegy, Slavic & E.Europ. J, summer 66; auth, Nature, the imagination, and the conversion of Peter Bell, In: The yearbook of English studies, 73. Add: Dept. of English, University of Waterloo, Waterloo, Ont. N2L 3G1, Can.

OBERG, ARTHUR K, b. Jamaica, N.Y, Dec. 12, 38; m. 64; c. 2. ENGLISH. A.B, Columbia Univ, 60; fel, Harvard, 60-62, A.M, 61, Ph.D.(Eng), 66. Asst. prof. ENG, Univ. Calif, Santa Barbara, 65-68; UNIV. WASH, 68-71, ASSOC. PROF, 71- MLA. Contemporary literature. Publ: Krapp's last tape and the Proustian vision, Mod. Drama, 12/66; Death of a salesman and Arthur Miller's search for style, Criticism, fall 67; Modern British and American lyric: what will suffice, Papers Lang. & Lit, winter 72; plus one other. Add: Dept. of English, University of Washington, Seattle, WA 98105.

OBERLE, MARCELLA, b. Oct. 14, 21; U.S. citizen. SPEECH. B.E, North. Ill. Univ, 42; State Univ, Iowa, summers, 43, 44; M.A, Northwest. Univ, 48, Ph.D.(speech), 65. Teacher Eng. & drama, high sch, Hooppole, Ill, 42-43; Eng, speech & drama, twp. high sch, Dwight, 43-46; pub. schs, Chicago, 46-47; instr. Eng. & speech, State Univ. Col. Oswego, N.Y, 50-51; speech educ, Northwest. Univ, 54-60; asst. prof. SPEECH, CALIF. STATE UNIV, LOS ANGELES, 60-66, assoc. prof, 66-73, PROF, 73- Speech Commun. Asn. (AV aids ed, Speech Teacher, 61-63, chmn, instruct. develop div, 72); West. Speech Commun. Asn.(2nd v.pres, 66, exec. secy, 67-70, pres, 70); Am. Theatre Asn; Children's Theatre Conf; NCTE; Sec. Sch. Theatre Conf. Speech and drama education in secondary and elementary schools. Add: Dept. of Speech Communication and Drama, California State University, Los Angeles, Los Angeles, CA 90032.

OBLER, PAUL CHARLES. ENGLISH LITERATURE. B.A, Am. Univ.(D.C), 48; M.A, Columbia Univ, 50; Ph.D, Rutgers Univ, 55. Instr. Eng, Drew Univ, 53-55, ast. prof, 55-62; assoc. prof. ENG, CALIF. STATE UNIV, FULLERTON, 62-67, PROF. & DIR. INTERDISCIPLINARY CTR, 67- U.S.N.R, 43-46. Inter-relationships between literature and religion, philosophy, science and psychology; literary criticism. Publ: The new scientist, Doubleday, 62; Mirrors of man, Am. Bk. Co, 62; The world of Lawrence's Rainbow, Drew Studies, 55. Add: Dept. of English, California State University, Fullerton, 800 N. State College Blvd, Fullerton, CA 92631.

O'BRIEN, AUDREY, b. New York, N.Y, May 16, 21; m. 56. SPEECH. A.B, Hunter Col, 42; scholar, Fordham Univ, 42, M.S, 43; Ph.D, Columbia Univ, 60. Instr. SPEECH, Sch. Educ, Fordham Univ, 43-47, asst. prof, 47-59; assoc. prof, St. John's Univ.(N.Y), 60-65, prof, 66-67, chmn. dept, 61-65; PROF, TRENTON STATE COL, 67- Int. Asn. Logopedics & Phoniatrics; Int. Phonetic Asn; Int. Soc. Phonetic Sci; Am. Speech & Hearing Asn. Speech pathology; voice science; acoustic phonetics. Publ: Directory of speech and hearing clinic facilities in Kings and Queens Counties, Cath. Schs. Off, Diocese of Brooklyn, 65; Speech and hearing services in the Republic of Ireland, Dublin Col. Speech Ther, 73; Voice quality and chronic laryngitis, Proc. XIV Congr. Int. Asn. Logopedics & Phoniatrics, 70; Some acoustic aspects of chronic laryngitis, Proc. XI World Congr. Int. Soc. Rehabilitation of Disabled, 70; Toward a definition of hoarseness, J. Dublin Col. Speech Ther, 71; plus one other. Add: Dept. of Speech Pathology and Audiology, Trenton State College, Trenton, NJ 08625.

O'BRIEN, DARCY G, b. Los Angeles, Calif, July 16, 39; m. 61; c. 1. ENGLISH. A.B, Princeton, 61; Woodrow Wilson fel. & M.A, Univ. Calif, Berkeley, 63, Ph.D.(Eng), 65; Fulbright fel, Cambridge, 63-64. Instr. ENG. POMONA COL, 65-66, asst. prof, 66-70, ASSOC. PROF, CLAREMONT GRAD. SCH, 70- Res. fel. Irish lit, Ctr. Advan. Stud, Univ. Ill, 69-70; mem, bd. ed. consult, James Joyce Quart, 72- MLA; James Joyce Soc. Irish and contemporary literature and history. Publ: The conscience of James Joyce, Princeton Univ, 68; W. R. Rodgers, 71 & Patrick Kavanagh, 73, Burknell Univ; contrib, Approaches to Ulysses, Pittsburgh Univ, 70 & New light on Joyce, Indiana Univ, 72; plus one other. Add: Dept. of English, Pomona College, Claremont, CA 91711.

O'BRIEN, DOMINIC VINCENT, b. Philadelphia, Pa, Sept. 1, 37; m. 66; c. 1. ENGLISH. B.A, La Salle Col, 62; M.A, Univ. Pa, 63, Ph.D.(Eng), 68. Reader ENG, Univ. Pa, 63-65; instr, St. Joseph's Col.(Pa), 65-68; assoc. prof, Harcum Jr. Col, 68-70; SR. CONSULT. EDUC. PLANNING, PA. DEPT. EDUC, 70- Consult, Pa. Nurses Asn. & Pa. Comn. Prof. & Occup. Affairs, 70- MLA; Am. Asn. Higher Educ; Am. Soc. Planning Off. Professional and graduate education; educational planning; futuristics. Publ: Co-ed, The master plan for higher education in Pennsylvania, 71, co-auth, A design for regionalization & Program survey of educational programs in Pennsylvania, 72 & The reduced-time baccalaureate degree, 73, Pa. Dept. Educ; auth, Language training and public education, Pittsburgh Post-Gazette, 4/73; Health manpower: a new wrinkle, Pa. Med, 10/73. Add: Bureau of Planning, Pennsylvania Department of Education, P.O. Box 911, Harrisburg, PA 17126.

O'BRIEN, FRANK PATRICK, b. New York, N.Y, Nov. 10, 32; m. 56; c. 2. ENGLISH, IRISH LITERATURE. A.B, Fordham Univ, 54; A.M, N.Y. Univ, 59; Ph.D.(Irish), Univ. Dublin, 63. Instr. ENG, Wash. Sq. Col, N.Y. Univ, 63-65; asst. prof, HOLLINS COL, 65-68, ASSOC. PROF, 68- Danforth assoc, N.Y. Univ, 64-65; consult. ed, Irish-Am. Cultural Inst, 67-; Nat. Found. for Humanities young scholars grant, summer 68. U.S.A, 57-59. MLA; Am. Comt. Irish Stud.(ed, 67-). Irish literature in Irish; 18th and 20th century Irish literature in English. Publ: Modern poetry in Irish: a critique, 68 & Modern poetry in Irish: an anthology, 68, An Clochomhar TTA; Another Irish revolution, Arts & Sci, winter 67. Add: Dept. of English, Hollins College, VA 24020.

O'BRIEN, GORDON WORTH, b. Chicago, Ill, Feb. 3, 19; m. 42; c. 2. ENGLISH. A.B, Univ. Kans, 40, Whitcomb fel, 40-41, M.A, 41; Ph.D.(Eng), Ohio State Univ, 51. Instr. ENG, Pa. State Col, 41-42; Univ. Kans, 45-46; Ohio State Univ, 46-50; assoc. prof, Youngstown Univ, 50-57, PROF, 57-61; UNIV. MINN, MINNEAPOLIS, 61-, dir. grad. study Eng, 69-72. Resident fel, Folger Shakespeare Libr, 57, 62. U.S.A, 42-45. Shakespeare Asn. Am; Milton Soc. Am; MLA. Literature of the English Renaissance, especially aesthetics and the history of ideas. Publ: Renaissance poetics and the problem of power, 56; Hamlet IV. v. 156-157, Shakespeare Quart, spring 59; The Genius and the mortal instruments, Minn. Rev, fall 67. Add: Dept. of English, University of Minnesota, Minneapolis, MN 55455.

O'BRIEN, HAROLD JAMES, b. Locust Gap, Pa, Oct. 26, 12; m. 45; c. 2. SPEECH. B.S, Bloomsburg State Col, 35; M.A, Pa. State Univ, 48, Ph.D. (speech), 52. Teacher, pub. sch, Pa, 45-47; ASSOC. PROF. SPEECH, PA. STATE UNIV. UNIVERSITY PARK, 47-, from asst. to dean col. lib. arts to ASSOC. DEAN COMMONWEALTH CAMPUSES, 49- Speech Commun. Asn; East. Speech Commun. Asn. Rhetorical criticism; industrial communications. Publ: Collab, Management-employee communication in action; auth, How to think creatively, 11/57 & Slavery sentiments which led to war, 11/61, Today's Speech; David Wilmot and the rise of the Republican Party, In: A history of public speaking in Pennsylvania, Pa. Speech Asn, 71. Add: 123 Sparks Bldg, Pennsylvania State University, University Park, PA 16802.

O'BRIEN, JOHN EGLI, S.J, b. Montreal, P.Q, July 3, 24. COMMUNICATION, SOCIAL SCIENCES. B.A, Univ. Montreal, 45; S.T.B, St. Mary's Univ, 57; S.T.L, Regis Col, 58; Clune fel, Univ. South. Calif, 62-64, Ph.D.(commun. & soc. sci), 64. Asst. prof. COMMUN. ARTS, CONCORDIA UNIV, 64-68, ASSOC. PROF, 68-, CHMN. DEPT, 65- Chmn, prog. & bldg. comt, Christian Pavilion EXPO 67, Montreal, 64-67; consult, Europ. Secretariat Mass Media, Barcelona, 65; S.Am. Secretariat Commun, Mexico City, 66; mem, stud. comt. educ. TV, Dept. Educ, Que, 67-68; Sci. Comt. Can. Mental Health Assoc, Montreal, 67-68. Can. Army, 43-45, 2nd Lt. Broadcast Educ. Asn; Educ. TV & Radio Asn. Can.(bd. dir, 68). Communication research; film study programs; study of new approaches to perception. Add: Dept. of Communication Arts, Concordia University, Montreal, P.Q, Can.

O'BRIEN, MARGARET TOWNSEND, b. Albany, N.Y, Sept. 30, 17. ENGLISH LITERATURE, PHILOSOPHY. B.A, Smith Col, 38, trustee fel. & M.A, 42, Fanny Bullock Workman fel; tuition scholar, resid. fel. & M.A, Radcliffe Col, 43, Alice Freeman Palmer fel, Am. Asn. Univ. Women. & Ph.D, 51. Instr. Eng, Vassar Col, 44-46; Newton Col. Sacred Heart, 46, 49-51; asst. prof. Eng. & Philos, Col. Sacred Heart (La), 52-54; ENG, Manhattanville Col, 54-57; from assoc. prof. to PROF, WEST. STATE COL. COLO, 57- Lectr. philos, Dunbarton Col, 48. MLA. Seventeenth century; relations between science and literature and science and philosophy; comparative religion. Publ: Education through English to philosophy, New Scholasticism; An approach to wonder, Cath. Art Quart; A bird fell, Nat. Poetry Anthol. Add: Dept. of English, Western State College of Colorado, Gunnison, CO 81230.

OCHOJSKI, PAUL M, b. Brussels, Belgium, Nov. 21, 16; nat; m. 41; c. 2. ENGLISH. B.A, Long Island Univ, 47; M.A, Columbia Univ, 48, Ph.D, 60. Instr. ENG, Long Island Univ, 47-49; SETON HALL UNIV, 49-52, asst. prof, 52-58, assoc. prof, 58-60, PROF, 60-, dir. Eng. grad. stud, 56-60, chmn. dept. Eng, 60-68. Vis. prof. comp. lit, World Campus Afloat, Chapman Col, spring 69, 71, 73. U.S.A, 42-46. MLA; Col. Eng. Asn; AAUP; NCTE. Rockland County, New York, local history; Sir Walter Scott; German-English literary relations. Publ: Co-auth, Checklist of periodicals: English, McLaughlin Libr, 64; auth, Study guide to Dickens' David Copperfield, 64, Study guide to Dickens' Pickwick papers, 65 & Study guide to Dickens' Hard times, 66, Monarch; co-auth, Scott bicentenary essays, Scottish Acad. Press, 73; ed, Gleanings from Rockland history, 70, More gleanings from Rockland history, 71 & The way it was: an informal history of New City, 72, Rockland Co. Hist. Soc. Add: 24 College Rd, Monsey, NY 10952.

OCHS, DONOVAN JOSEPH, b. Charles City, Iowa, Oct. 2, 38; m. 62; c. 3. SPEECH. B.A, Loras Col, 60; M.A, Univ. Iowa, 62, Ph.D.(class. rhetoric), 66. Teacher, High Sch, Iowa, 60-61; instr. gen. supply, U.S. Army, 61-62; asst. prof. speech, Univ. Calif, 64-67; rhetoric, UNIV. IOWA, 68-70, ASSOC. PROF. SPEECH, 70-, COORD. RHET. PROG, 72, grad. col. res. grant, 67-68. Univ. Calif. regent's fel, 66-67; assoc. ed, Speech Mongr, 70-75. U.S.A, 61-62. Speech Commun. Asn.(assoc. ed, Speech Teacher, 63-); Cent. States Speech Commun. Asn.(chmn. awards comt, 72-73). Classical rhetoric and public address; speech education. Publ: Co-auth, Rhetoric of agitation & control, Addison-Wesley, 71; co-ed, Explorations in rhetorical criticism, Pa. State Univ, 73; auth, Speech education and videotape, Speech Teacher, 3/68; co-auth, Demosthenes use of argument, In: Demosthenes, 68 & contrib, A synoptic history of classical rhetoric, 72, Random; plus one other. Add: Dept. of Rhetoric, University of Iowa, Iowa City, IA 52240.

O'CLAIR, ROBERT M, b. Nashua, N.H, Feb. 28, 23; m. 69; c. 2. ENGLISH LITERATURE. B.A, Harvard, 49, M.A, 50, Ph.D, 56. Lectr. Eng. & Allston Burr Sr. Tutor, Kirkland House, Harvard, 56-61; asst. prof. ENG, MANHATTANVILLE COL, 61-62, assoc. prof, 62-68, PROF, 68- Publ: Co-ed, Norton book of modern poetry, Norton, 73. Add: Dept. of English, Manhattanville College, Purchase, NY 10577.

O'CONNELL, ADELYN, English. See DOUGHERTY, ADELYN (O'CONNELL).

O'CONNELL, MICHAEL WILLIAM, b. Seattle, Wash, Nov. 11, 43; m. 69; c. 2. ENGLISH LITERATURE, RENAISSANCE STUDIES. A.B, Univ. San Francisco, 66; Woodrow Wilson fel, 66; M.Phil, Yale, 69, Ph.D.(Eng), 71. ASST. PROF. ENG, UNIV. CALIF, SANTA BARBARA, 70- Nat. Endowment for Humanities younger humanist grant, 73-74. MLA; Renaissance Soc. Am. English Renaissance literature; poetry of Spenser; Shakespeare. Publ: Astrophel: Spenser's double elegy, Stud. Eng. Lit, 71; History and the poet's golden world, Eng. Lit. Renaissance, 74. Add: Dept. of English, University of California, Santa Barbara, CA 93106.

O'CONNELL, RICHARD JAMES, b. New York, N.Y, Oct. 25, 28; m. 53; c. 2. ENGLISH & AMERICAN LITERATURE, CREATIVE WRITING. B.S, Temple Univ, 56; M.A, Johns Hopkins Univ, 57. Instr. ENG, TEMPLE UNIV, 57-61, asst. prof, 61-69, ASSOC. PROF, 69- Fulbright lectr. Am Lit, Univ. Brazil, 60, Univ. Navarre, 62-63; guest lectr. poetry, Writing Sems, Johns Hopkins Univ, 61- U.S.N, 48-52. MLA; Assoc. Writing Prog. Modern British and American poetry; 17th century English poetry; modern Brazilian poetry. Publ: Terrane (poems), Contemporary Poetry, 67; ed, Apollo's day, Atlantis Eds, 69; contrib, Open Poetry (poems), Simon & Schuster, 73. Add: Dept. of English, Temple University, Philadelphia, PA 19122.

O'CONNELL, RICHARD LEO, JR, b. Syracuse, N.Y, Apr. 19, 12; m. 48; c. 1. DRAMA, ENGLISH. B.A, Syracuse Univ, 35; M.F.A, Yale, 38; Ph.D.(Eng. & drama), Univ. Birmingham, 58. Instr. drama, Univ. Tex, 38-40; Univ. Syracuse 40-41; civilian entertainment dir, Letterman Gen. Hosp, San Francisco, Calif, 46; assoc. dir, Pasadena Playhouse, Calif, 46-48; asst. prof. drama & Eng, N.MEX. HIGHLANDS UNIV, 50-52, assoc. prof, 54-58, PROF. SPEECH & DRAMA, 58-, DIR. SPEECH & DRAMA, 68-, drama dir, 58-68. Dir, Community Concerts Asn, 58-62, pres, 62-67, chmn. publicity & artists' reception, 67-; chmn, N.Mex. Counc. Am. Col. Theatre Festival, 68-69; pres, N.Mex. Theatre Guild, 68-70. A.U.S, 41-46, Capt; Bronze Star Medal. Am. Theatre Asn; Southwest Theatre Conf.(2nd v.pres, 65-66, 1st v.pres, 66-67, pres, 67-68). Publ: Co-transl, From Lorca's theatre, 41 & The horse and his shadow, 42, Scribner; Three tragedies of Lorca, 47, Five plays of Lorca: comedies and tragi-comedies, 64 & Short plays and theatre essays of Garcia Lorca, (in press), New Directions. Add: 1007 Eighth St, Las Vegas, NM 87701.

O'CONNOR, ANTONY CYRIL, b. Newport, R.I, May 28, 23. ENGLISH. B.A, Cath. Univ. Am, 45; M.A, Univ. Santo Tomas, Manila, 52, Ph.D.(Eng), 56. Instr. ENG, Col. Santa Fe, 62-66; asst. prof, De La Salle Col, Cath. Univ. Am, 66-73; PROF. & EXEC. V.PRES, BETHLEHEM UNIV, ISRAEL, 73- Fels, Oxford, 62; Shakespeare Inst, Univ. Birmingham, 63. Curriculum development; English as a second language. Publ: Co-auth, A second book of nonfiction, 65 & auth, Modern American prose, 2nd ed, 66, Macmillan. Add: Bethlehem University, West Bank, P.O. Box 9, Bethlehem, Israel.

O'CONNOR, JOHN JOSEPH, b. Waterbury, Conn, June 15, 18; m. 43; c. 3. ENGLISH. A.B, Clark Univ, 40; M.A, Harvard, 46, Ph.D, 51. Instr. ENG, RUTGERS UNIV, NEW BRUNSWICK, 48-52, from asst. prof. to assoc. prof, 52-66, PROF, 66- Fund Advan. Educ. fel, 54-55. U.S.A, 41-43; U.S.A.A.F, 43-45. MLA; Mediaeval Acad. Am. Sixteenth and 17th century fiction; mediaeval astrology; Spenser. Publ: Amadis de Gaule and its influence on Elizabethan literature, Rutgers Univ, 70; The astrological background of The miller's tale, Speculum; The astronomical dating of Chaucer's Troilus and Criseyde, J. Eng. & Ger. Philol. Add: 563 Mountain Ave, Bound Brook, NJ 08805.

O'CONNOR, JOHN REGIS, b. Louisville, Ky, Jan. 17, 41; m. 72. SPEECH, COMMUNICATION SCIENCE. B.A, Bellarmine Col.(Ky), 65; M.A, Ind. Univ, Bloomington, 66, Ph.D.(speech), 71. Instr. SPEECH, WEST. KY. UNIV, 69-71, ASST. PROF, 71-, STAFF ASST. TO DEAN, COL. ARTS & HUMANITIES, 74- Speech Commun. Asn. Small group leadership; kinesic communication; organizational communication. Publ: The objectivity of debate judges, Cent. States Speech J, 67; John Cabell Breckinridge's personal secession: a rhetorical insight, Filson Club Hist. Quart, 69; Parnell visits the Ireland of America, Register Ky. Hist. Soc, 71. Add: Dept. of Speech & Theatre, Western Kentucky University, Bowling Green, KY 42101.

O'CONNOR, LEO FRANCIS, b. Jersey City, N.J, July 24, 36; m. 61; c. 3. ENGLISH, AMERICAN STUDIES. B.S, St. Peter's Col, 58; U.S. State Dept. grant, Univ. Col, Dublin, 60; M.A, N.Y. Univ, 62, Ph.D.(Eng), 72. Admin. asst, CBS News, 59-60; dist. group serv. mgr, Prudential Insurance Co, 61-62; ASST. PROF. Eng, N.Y. Inst. Technol, 63-65, ENG. & AM. STUD, FAIRFIELD UNIV, 65- U.S.A, 58-59, Res, 60-65, Capt. MLA; AAUP. The image of religion in American fiction; the image of the businessman in American literature. Publ: Culture and anarchy: a study, New Frontiers, 66. Add: Dept. of English, Fairfield University, Gonzaga Hall, Fairfield, CT 06480.

O'CONNOR, MARY CATHARINE, b. Newark, N.J, Mar. 17, 96. ENGLISH. A.B, Col. St. Elizabeth, 17; A.M, Fordham Univ, 24; Ph.D, Columbia Univ, 40. Instr. ENG, COL. ST. ELIZABETH, 24-30, asst. prof, 30-35, prof, 35-70, chmn. dept, 52-70, EMER. PROF, 70- Trustee, Col. St. Elizabeth, 42-49, 62- MLA; NCTE; Col. Eng. Asn. Mediaeval literature. Publ: The art of dying well, Columbia, 42; The Kinderbeist prize, Sheed, 62; The rivals, Critic, 4-5/63. Add: Dept. of English, College of St. Elizabeth, Convent, NJ 07961.

O'CONNOR, PHILIP FRANCIS, b. San Francisco, Calif. ENGLISH, CREATIVE WRITING. B.S, Univ. San Francisco, 54; M.A, San Francisco State Col, 61; M.F.A.(creative writing), Univ. Iowa, 63. From instr. to asst. prof. humanities, Clarkson Col. Technol, 63-67; from asst. prof. to PROF. ENG, BOWLING GREEN STATE UNIV, 67- Mem. bd. dirs, Assoc. Writing Prog, 69-70. Iowa Sch. Lett. Prize, Univ. Iowa, 71. U.S.A, 54-56. Auth. Guild. Contemporary literature. Publ: Old morals, small continents, darker times, Univ. Iowa, 71. Add: Dept. of English, Bowling Green State University, Bowling Green, OH 43402.

O'DANIEL, THERMAN BENJAMIN, b. Wilson, N.C, July 9, 08. AMERICAN LITERATURE. A.B, Lincoln Univ.(Pa), 30; A.M, Univ. Pa, 32; Ph.D, Univ. Ottawa, 56. Instr. Eng. & head dept, Allen Univ, 33-34, prof. Eng. & chmn. div. lang. & lit, 34-37, dean col. lib. arts & ed. bull, 37-40, acting pres, 38, dir. stud. publ; assoc. prof. Eng, Ft. Valley State Col, 40-44, prof. & head dept, 44-45, 46-55, dir. stud. aid prog, 40-45, dir. Nat. Youth Admin. Prog, 40-55, acting dean & acting registr, 45-46, dir. summer sch, 46, registr. & dir. summer sch, 52-55; assoc. prof. ENG, Dillard Univ, 55-56; asst. prof, MORGAN STATE COL, 56-63, assoc. prof, 63-67, PROF, 67-, dir, summer sch, 62, 63. Dir, Teacher-Training Sch, Ft. Benning, Ga, 46; founder & ed, CLA Jour, 57- MLA; NCTE; Col. Lang. Asn.(ed. bull, 51); NEA; Melville Soc. Francis Bacon's literary theory; friendship of Irving and Dickens with a note on their views of England and America; Cooper's treatment of the Negro. Publ: Ed, Langston Hughes, Black genius: a critical evaluation, 71; auth, introd. to The blacker the berry, 70; A Langston Hughes bibliography, CLA Bull; Emerson as a literary critic, 64-65 & The image of man as portrayed by Ralph Ellison, 67, CLA J; plus others. Add: Dept. of English, Morgan State College, Baltimore, MD 21239.

ODEGARD, MARGARET, b. Charleston, W.Va, Nov. 20, 25; m. 51; c. 5. TWENTIETH CENTURY ENGLISH. B.A, Agnes Scott Col, 47; M.A, Univ. Wis, 49, Ph.D.(Eng), 56. Asst. Eng, Univ. Wis, 47-51, 52-53; instr, Rockford Col, 58-59, ASST. PROF, 59-60; Hamline Univ, 65-66; 20TH CENTURY LIT, UNIV. WIS-RIVER FALLS, 66-68, 70-; humanities, Moorhead State Col, 69-70. NCTE; AAUP. Twentieth century English literature. Add: Dept. of English, Fine Arts Bldg, University of Wisconsin-River Falls, River Falls, WI 54022.

ODELL, DANIEL W, b. Montour Falls, N.Y, Sept. 11, 25; m. 51; div; c. 3. ENGLISH. B.A, Univ. Rochester, 49, M.A, 51; Danforth Found. teacher grant, Cornell Univ, 59-60, Ph.D, 61. Instr. ENG, Miami Univ, 55-59; asst. prof, STATE UNIV. N.Y. ALBANY, 61-63, assoc. prof, 63-68, PROF, 68- U.S.A.A.F, 44-45. MLA; Col. Eng. Asn. Eighteenth century literature and history of ideas. Publ: Young's Night thoughts as an answer to Pope's Essay on man, Stud. Eng. Lit, 72. Add: Dept. of English, State University of New York at Albany, 1400 Washington Ave, Albany, NY 12222.

ODLE, ZELMA RUTH, b. Cooke Co, Tex, Aug. 19, 19. ENGLISH LITERATURE. B.A, N.Tex. State Univ, 42, M.A, 49; Ph.D, Univ. Ark, 60. Teacher, Grayson County Schs, Tex, 39-42, high sch, Woodson, 42-44, Collinsville, 44-46; campus sch, Abilene Christian Col, 46-53; grad. asst. ENG, Univ. Ark, 53-54; asst. prof, ABILENE CHRISTIAN COL, 54-61, assoc. prof, 61-67, PROF, 67- Grad. asst, Univ. Ark, 57-59. Annual Trustees Outstanding Teacher Award, 64. MLA. Shakespeare's imagery; contemporary novel and drama; 18th century. Publ: Land of pure delight, Christian Woman, 5/61. Add: Dept. of English, Abilene Christian College, Abilene, TX 79601.

ODOM, KEITH CONRAD, b. Healdton, Okla, Mar. 22, 31; m. 59; c. 2. ENGLISH. B.A, E.Cent. State Col, 52; M.A, Okla. State Univ, 56; Ph.D, Univ. Wis, 61. Instr, high sch, Tex, 52-55; grad. asst, Okla. State Univ, 55-56; teaching asst, Univ. Wis, 56-61; asst. prof. ENG, TEX. CHRISTIAN UNIV, 61-66, ASSOC. PROF, 67- Res. fel, Univ. Wis, summer 61. MLA; Conf. Col. Teachers Eng; Col. Eng. Asn. The English novel; the Brontës, Henry Green and Sir Walter Scott. Publ: Symbolism and diversion: birds in the novels of Henry Green, 62 & Selective bibliography of Cecil Brown Williams, spring 67, Descant; Nine types of ambiguity, CEA Critic, 2/68. Add: Dept. of English, Texas Christian University, Ft. Worth, TX 76129.

O'DONNELL, BERNARD, b. Teaneck, N.J, July 26, 29; m. 55; c. 4. ENGLISH, ENGLISH EDUCATION. B.S, St. Peter's Col.(N.J), 56; M.A, Columbia Univ, 57; fel, Harvard, 60-63, Ed.D.(Eng. educ), 63. Instr. Eng, W.Va. Univ, 57-59; asst, Univ. Ill, 59-60; asst. prof, Ball State Univ, 63-65; Eng. & rhetoric, Univ. Iowa, 65-67; dir. res. Eng, Clearinghouse on Teaching Eng, NCTE-ERIC, 67-72, DIR, CLEARINGHOUSE ON READING & COMMUN. SKILLS, ERIC, 72- Mem. adv. panel, ctr. applied ling, ERIC Clearinghouse, 68-70, adv. bd, Clearinghouse on Lang, MLA-ERIC, 70-, exec. comt, Counc. ERIC Dirs, 73-; adv. bd, Champaign Co. Opportunities Industrialization Ctr, 69- U.S.A, 51-53. NCTE; Conf. Res. Eng; Am. Educ. Res. Asn; Int. Reading Asn; Am. Dialect Soc. Teacher education in English; English prose style; computer applications in the humanities. Publ: An analysis of prose style to determine authorship, Mouton, 70; ed, Aids to curriculum planning: English language arts K-12, NCTE, 73; Stephen Crane's The O'Ruddy: a problem in authorship discrimination, In: The computer and literary style, Kent Univ, 66. Add: National Council of Teachers of English, 1111 Kenyon Rd, Urbana, IL 61801.

O'DONNELL, CHARLES PATRICK, JR, b. Cleveland, Ohio, Dec. 12, 45. ENGLISH & AMERICAN LITERATURE. B.A, Harvard Col, 68; M.A, Princeton, 70, Ph.D.(eng), 73. ASST. PROF. ENG, PRINCETON, 72- Renaissance drama; 16th century English history and literature. Add: Dept. of English, Princeton University, 22 McCosh Hall, Princeton University, Princeton, NJ 08540.

O'DONNELL, CHARLES ROBERT, b. Pittsfield, Mass, May 3, 26; m. 48, 65; c. 4. ENGLISH. A.B, Univ. Mich, 50, M.A, Univ. Conn, 52; Ph.D, Syracuse Univ, 57. Instr, Univ. Conn, 50-52; lectr. Eng, Syracuse Univ, 53-57; instr. Eng. & Am. lit, Univ. Mich. 57-60, asst. prof, 60-64, assoc. prof, 64-69; PROF. ENG, HOFSTRA UNIV, 69-, chmn. dept, 69-73. Consult. Am. Lit, Choice Mag, 64-; vis. assoc. prof, Hofstra Univ, 65-66; mem. comt. exam. for humanities test, Grad. Rec. Exams. Area Tests, Educ. Testing Serv, 66-; vis. prof. Am. stud, Williams Col, 69. U.S.A.A.F, 44-45. MLA. American literature and studies. Publ: Hawthorne and Dimmesdale: the search for the realm of quiet, Nineteenth-century Fiction, 3/60; Progress and property: the later Cooper, Am. Quart, fall 61; From earth to ether: Poe's flight into space, PMLA, 3/62. Add: 109 Elmwood Ave, Hempstead, NY 11550.

O'DONNELL, GERALD R, b. Elmira, N.Y, July 14, 07; m. 38; c. 1. ENGLISH. A.B, Georgetown Univ, 29; A.M, Harvard, 32; Ed.D, Univ. Buffalo, 59. Teacher, pub. schs, N.Y, 33-63; asst. prof. ENG, NIAGARA UNIV, 63-67, assoc. prof, 67-69, PROF, 69- Mem, Russ. Lang. Inst, Canisius Col, 60-62, fac. educ, col, 62-63; Eng. & educ, Niagara Univ, 62-63; moderator weekly radio prog, Niagara Univ. Presents, 63-; consult, Nat. Counc. Cath. Men, 66- NCTE; MLA. Communications, especially newspapers; English literature of the Victorian period; comparative literature and linguistics. Add: 654 Crescent Ave, Buffalo, NY 14216.

O'DONNELL, JOHN FRANCIS, b. Philadelphia, Pa, Aug. 23, 37; m. 67; c. 2. ENGLISH. B.S, Villanova Univ, 59; M.A, Harvard, 60; Univ. South. Calif,

61-62; Trinity Col.(Conn), 67; Univ. Pa, 63-64; Ed.D.(Eng. educ), Temple Univ, 74. Instr. ENG, Culver Mil. Acad, Ind, 60-61; Harvard Sch, Calif, 61-62; curriculum coord, Upper Merion Sch. Dist, Pa, 62-69; CHMN. DEPT, MILLERSVILLE STATE COL, 69- Instr. Eng, Pa. State Univ, 63-68; consult. educ. improv. prog, Int. Paper Co, 71-73; mem. nat. comt. in-serv. educ. & supv, NCTE-Conf. Eng. Educ, 71- AAUP; Conf. Col. Compos. & Commun; Conf. Eng. Educ; NCTE. English education; linguistics, psycholinguistics and the reading process; language development of high-risk college students. Publ: Co-auth, Annotated list of recommended elementary and secondary curriculum guides in English, 71 & Effective practices in supervision and in-service education, 74, NCTE; auth, The new English, Inscape, 69; The English methods course: an interpretation, ERIC Doc, 73. Add: Dept. of English, Millersville State College, Millersville, PA 17551.

O'DONNELL, KATHLEEN M, b. Montreal, P.Q, Apr. 5, 34. ENGLISH. B.A, McGill Univ, 55; M.A, Univ. West. Ont, 56; Ph.D.(Eng), Univ. Montreal, 59. Asst. prof. ENG, St. Patrick's Col.(Ont), 63-66; Univ. Windsor, 66-68; CARLETON UNIV, 68-72, ASSOC. PROF, 72- Can. Hist. Soc; Asn. Can. Univ. Teachers Eng; Humanities Asn. Can; Can. Comp. Lit. Asn. Canadian poetry; translations of French Canadian poetry; Canadian literature. Publ: The wanderer in Barometer rising, Univ. Windsor Rev, 68; D'Arcy McGee's Canadian ballads, Univ. Ottawa Rev, 72; Dorothy Livesay and Simone Routier: a parallel study, Humanities Asn. Rev, 73; plus one other. Add: Dept. of English, Carleton University, Ottawa, Ont, Can.

O'DONNELL, ROY C, b. Ashville, Ala, Mar. 5, 29; m. 54. ENGLISH. B.S, Auburn Univ, 55, M.Ed, 56; Ph.D.(Eng), George Peabody Col, 61. Instr, Lanett High Sch, Ala, 55-56; Eng, Free Will Baptist Bible Col, 56-57; asst. prof, West. Ky. State Col, 59-61; head dept, Mt. Olive Jr. Col, 61-65; asst. prof. ENG. EDUC, Univ. N.C, Greensboro, 65-66; assoc. prof, Fla. State Univ, 66-69, PROF, 69-72; UNIV. GA, 72- Dir. coop. res. proj. Eng, U.S. Off. Educ, 62-63; consult, Res. & Develop. Ctr, Univ. Ga, 67; mem. ed. bd, Fla. State Univ. Press, 67-72; Nat. Conf. Res. Eng. fel, 73- NCTE(assoc. chmn. comt. res, 72-73, mem. ed. bd, 72-73 & res. found. trustee, 72-75); Conf. Col. Compos. & Commun; Am. Dialect Soc; Am. Educ. Res. Asn. Linguistic structure; history of English language; children's language development. Publ: Co-auth, Syntax of kindergarten and elementary school children, NCTE, 67; auth, Does research in linguistics have practical applications?, Eng. J, 3/70; Psycholinguisticis, In: Encycl. Educ, Macmillan, 71; co-auth, An exploration of deep structure recovery and reading comprehension skills, Res. Teaching Eng, 10/74; plus others. Add: Dept. of Language Education, University of Georgia, Athens, GA 30602.

O'DONNELL, THOMAS FRANCIS, b. Oneida, N.Y, June 2, 15; m. 40; c. 2. ENGLISH. A.B, Hamilton Col, 42; M.A, Syracuse Univ, 47, Ph.D.(Eng), 57. Instr. ENG, Hamilton Col, 42-44; Syracuse Univ, 45-49, Utica Col, 49-57, asst. prof, 57-60, assoc. prof, 60-65, PROF, 65-70, chmn. div. langs, 62-70; STATE UNIV. N.Y. COL. BROCKPORT, 70- Ed, Frederic Herald, 67-70. MLA; Am. Stud. Asn; Milton Soc. Am. New York state literature; William Dean Howells; Harold Frederic. Publ: Three literary maps of New York State, F.E. Richards, 59; co-auth, Harold Frederic, Twayne, 61; Back home in Oneida, 65, ed, Harold Frederic's stories of York State, 66 & Description of the New Netherlands, 69, Syracuse Univ; The Dutchman's fireside, Col. & Univ, 66. Add: Dept. of English, State University New York College at Brockport, Brockport, NY 14420.

O'DONNELL, WILLIAM GREGORY, b. Milford, Mass, Dec. 11, 16; m. 46; c. 2. ENGLISH & AMERICAN LITERATURE. B.S, Mass. State Col, 38; Ph.D, Yale, 42. Instr. ENG, UNIV. MASS, AMHERST, 42-47, asst. prof, 47-49, assoc. prof, 49-54, PROF, 54- Vis. instr, Amherst Col, 46-47. Fund Advan. Educ. fac. fel, 52-53; Fulbright lectr, Univ. Vienna, 64-65. MLA; Am. Stud. Asn. Publ: Robert Frost and New England: a revaluation, Yale Rev, summer 48; Parable in poetry, Va. Quart. Rev, spring 49; Robert Frost at eighty-eight, Mass. Rev, autumn 62. Add: Dept. of English, University of Massachusetts, Amherst, MA 01002.

O'DONNELL, WILLIAM HUGH, b. San Diego, Calif, June 17, 40; m. 67; c. 2. TWENTIETH CENTURY BRITISH LITERATURE, ANGLO-IRISH LITERATURE. B.A, Univ. Wash, 62; M.A, Princeton, 69, Ph.D.(Eng), 71. ASST. PROF. ENG, PA. STATE UNIV, UNIVERSITY PARK, 71- U.S.N, 62-67, Lt. Comdr. MLA; Yeats; 20th century British poetry. Publ: Ed, The speckled bird, Cuala, 72. Add: Dept. of English, Pennsylvania State University, 117 Burrowes Bldg, University Park, PA 16802.

O'DRISCOLL, ROBERT, b. Nfld, May 3, 38; m. 66; c. 1. ENGLISH LITERATURE. B.A, Mem. Univ. Nfld, 58, B.A, 59, M.A, 60; Rothermere fel, Univ. London, 60-63, Ph.D.(Eng), 63. Res. fel. Eng, Univ. Reading, 63-64; vis. lectr, Univ. Col. Dublin, 64-66; asst. prof, ST. MICHAEL'S COL, UNIV. TORONTO, 66-69, ASSOC. PROF. ENG. LIT, 69- Lectr, Yeats Sch, Ireland, 64-; chmn, Irish Stud. Sem, Toronto, 67-; Can. Counc. grant, 68, leave fel, 69, 73 & res. fels, 70, 71, 72; Can. rep, Int. Asn. Stud. Irish Lit, 70- R.C.N.R, Lt. Royal Irish Acad; Can. Asn. Irish Stud.(chmn, 67-72); Irish Arts Can.(art dir, 71-). Irish literature; modern poetry and drama. Publ: Ed, Theatre and nationalism in twentieth-Century Ireland, Univ. Toronto & Oxford Univ, 71; co-ed, Yeats during the eighteen nineties, Vol. I, 71 & Theatre and the visual arts: Jack Yeats and John Synge, Vol. II, 72, In: Yeats Studies, Irish Univ; plus three others. Add: Dept. of English, St. Michael's College, University of Toronto, Toronto, Ont, Can.

OETTINGER, ELMER ROSENTHAL, JR, Law, English. See Volume IV, Philosophy, Religion and Law.

OGDEN, DUNBAR HUNT, b. Portsmouth, Ohio, Mar. 1, 35; m. 57; c. 1. DRAMATIC ART. A.B, Davidson Col, 55; M.A, Duke Univ, 56; Univ. Munich, 56-58; Free Univ. Berlin, 58-59; Ph.D, Yale, 62. Instr. Eng, Univ. Md. Overseas Prog, 58; Ger, South. Conn. State Col, 60-62; asst. prof. DRAMATIC ART, UNIV. CALIF, BERKELEY, 62-70, ASSOC. PROF, 70-, CHMN. GRAD. STUD, 72- Humanities Res. Prog. fel, Univ. Calif, 67-68; Am. Counc. Learned Soc. fel, 68-69. Int. Fed. Theatre Res; Am. Theatre Asn; Am. Soc. Theatre Res. Medieval and Renaissance theater and drama; German theater and drama of the 20th century; Italian Baroque scene design. Publ: The staging of drama within the medieval church, Yale Univ, (in press); The Italian baroque stage: documents, Miami, (in press). Add: Dept. of Dramatic Art, University of California, Berkeley, Berkeley, CA 94720.

OGDEN, HENRY VINING SETON, b. Milwaukee, Wis, Sept. 19, 05; m. 34; c. 2. ENGLISH. A.B, Harvard, 27; A.M, Univ. Chicago, 32, fel, 32-33, Ph.D, 37. Teaching fel. & sub-ed, Early Mod. Eng. Dictionary, UNIV. MICH, ANN ARBOR, 35-37, instr. ENG, 37-43, asst. prof, 43-49, assoc. prof, 49-56, PROF, 56- MLA. History of ideas and of taste from 1600 to 1800. Publ: English taste in landscape in the 17th century. Add: Dept. of English, University of Michigan, Ann Arbor, MI 48104.

OGDEN, JOHN TERENCE, b. Hinsdale, Ill, June 7, 38; m. 61; c. 2. ENGLISH LITERATURE. A.B, Princeton, 60; M.A.T, Johns Hopkins Univ, 61; Ph.D. (Eng), Univ. Ill, Urbana, 66. Asst. prof. ENG, State Univ. N.Y. Buffalo, 66-73; ASSOC. PROF, UNIV. MAN, 73- MLA. Romantic poetry. Publ: The power of distance in Wordsworth's Prelude, PMLA, 3/73; From spatial to aesthetic distance in the eighteenth century, J. Hist. Ideas, 1/74. Add: Dept. of English, University of Manitoba, Winnipeg, Man. R3T 2N2, Can.

OGDEN, MARGARET SINCLAIR, b. Asheville, N.C, Aug. 2, 09; m. 34; c. 2. ENGLISH, PHILOLOGY. A.B, Univ. Mich, 27, A.M, 28; Ph.D, Univ. Chicago, 35. Res. asst, MID. ENG. DICTIONARY, UNIV. MICH, 33-37, res. assoc, 40-44, ASST. ED, 44- Guggenheim fel, 60. MLA. History of medicine; English taste in landscape, 1600-1800; Middle English lexicography. Publ: The Liber de diversis medicinis in the Thornton manuscript, 38 & The Cyrurgie of Guy de Chauliac, 71, Early Eng. Text Soc; co-auth, English taste in landscape in the seventeenth century, 55 & Bibliography in Middle English dictionary, 54, Univ. Mich. Add: 4475 Ford Rd, Ann Arbor, MI 48105.

OGDEN, MERLENE, b. Lincoln, Nebr, June 10, 29. AMERICAN LITERATURE. B.A, Union Col, 50; M.A, Univ. Nebr, 54, Ph.D, 64. Instr. Eng, Platte Valley Acad, 51-54; asst. prof, Andrews Univ, 54-60; grad. asst, Univ. Nebr, 60-62; PROF. ENG, ANDREWS UNIV, 62-, DIR. HONORS PROG, 69- Vis. prof. Eng, Loma Linda Univ, 70. MLA; NCTE; Nat. Col. Honors Soc; Upper Midwest Honors Soc. Nathaniel Hawthorne; John Bunyan; American transcendentalists. Add: 740 Timberland, Berrien Springs, MI 49104.

OGILVIE, MARDEL, b. Middletown, N.Y, Feb. 2, 10. SPEECH. B.A, Cornell Univ, 31, M.A, 32; Ph.D.(speech), Columbia Univ, 42. Teacher math, Eng. & speech, South Fallsburg High Sch, N.Y, 34-36; Mex. Acad, Mexico, N.Y, 36-38; instr. SPEECH, State Univ. N.Y. Teachers Col, 38-42, asst. prof, 42-46, prof, 46-48; asst. prof, Queens Col.(N.Y), 48-57, assoc. prof, 57-62, PROF, 63-68; LEHMAN COL, 68- Speech Commun. Asn.(consult. ed, Speech Teacher, 52-61, 70-72); NEA. Speech education. Publ: Speech in the elementary school, 54 & co-auth, Communication skills: voice and pronunciation, 69, McGraw; auth, Teaching speech in the high school, Appleton, 61; co-auth, Speech correction in the schools, Macmillan, 3rd ed, 70. Add: Dept. of Speech and Theater, Lehman College, 695 Park Ave, New York, NY 10021.

OGILVY, JACK DAVID ANGUS, b. La Salle, Colo, June 18, 03; m. 40. ENGLISH. A.B, Univ. Colo, 25; A.M, Harvard, 26, Ph.D, 33. Instr, Northwest. Univ, 27-30; from instr. to assoc. prof. Eng. & speech, UNIV. COLO, 31-56, prof, 56-71, EMER. PROF. ENG, 71- Mediaeval Acad. Am; MLA. Sources used by early Anglo-Latin writers; Anglo-Saxon libraries; Anglo-Saxon culture. Publ: Books known to Anglo-Latin writers from Aldhelm to Alcuin, 36 & Books known to the English, 597-1066, 67, Mediaeval Acad. Am. Add: Dept. of English, University of Colorado, Boulder, CO 80302.

OGLE, ROBERT BERTRAM, b. Burlington, Vt, Oct. 23, 13; m. 37; c. 2. COMPARATIVE LITERATURE. B.A, Univ. Minn, 35; B.Mus, Am. Conserv. Music, Chicago, 36, M.Mus, 37; M.A, Univ. Chicago, 47; Ph.D.(19th century Eng. lit), Univ. Ill, 52. Instr. music, Univ. Ky, 39-41; Eng, Purdue Univ, 52-53, asst. prof, 53-57, assoc. prof, 57-63, summer res. grants, Res. Found, 59, 61; prof. & chmn. dept. humanities, Mansfield State Col, 63-64; PROF. ENG, UNIV. ILL, CHICAGO-CIRCLE, 64-, head dept, 64-71. U.S.M.C, 42-46, Res, 46-62, Maj. MLA. Byron and the Italian Bernesque satire; Italian and French literary historiography of the late 18th and early 19th centuries; English and Italian Renaissance. Publ: The Bernesque satire: a critical essay, Symposium, winter 54; A Byron contradiction, Stud. Romanticism, 73; Wyatt and Petrarch: a puzzle in prosody, J. Eng. & Germanic Philol, 74. Add: Dept. of English, University of Illinois at Chicago-Circle, Chicago, IL 60680.

OGLESBEE, RHEA SIMPSON, b. Feb. 14, 21; U.S. citizen; m. 45; c. 1. ENGLISH LITERATURE. B.A, Lamar Univ, 57, M.A, 65; Ph.D.(Eng. lit), West. Colo. Univ, 73. Instr. Eng, Lutcher Stark High Sch, Orange, Tex, 57-65; Lamar Univ, 65-66; INSTR. ENG. & DIR. FOR. STUD, SAN JACINTO COL, 66- Nat. Asn. For. Stud. Affairs. Christian theology; Anglo-Saxon literature; teaching English to foreign students. Add: San Jacinto College, 8060 Spencer Hwy, Pasadena, TX 77505.

O'GRADY, BRENDAN ANTHONY, b. New York, N.Y, Apr. 14, 25; m. 51; c. 7. ENGLISH. B.A, Univ. Notre Dame, 47; M.A, Columbia Univ, 50; Ph.D.(Eng), Univ. Ottawa, 54. Instr. Eng. lit, St. Dunstan's Univ, 48-50, asst. prof, 50-62, prof, 62-68, dean arts & v.pres, 67-69; PROF. ENG. LIT, UNIV. PRINCE EDWARD ISLAND, 69- Can. Asn. Am. Stud. American and Canadian literature. Add: Dept. of English, University of Prince Edward Island, Charlottetown, P.E.I, Can.

O'HALLORAN, BERNARD CHRISTOPHER, b. New York, N.Y, Dec. 20, 30; m. 61; c. 2. ENGLISH, VICTORIAN LITERATURE. B.A, Iona Col, 54; Danforth fel, 54; M.A, Loyola Univ.(Ill), 56; Univ. Stranieri, Italy, summer 59; Ph.D.(Eng), Columbia Univ, 65. Instr. ENG. LIT, St. John's Univ.(N.Y), 57-60; asst. prof, Marymount Col.(N.Y), 60-65; assoc. prof, INCARNATE WORD COL, 65-69, PROF, 69-, DIR. GRAD. STUD, 73-, chmn. dept. Eng, 70-73. Piper prof, Minnie Stevens Piper Found, 72. MLA; AAUP. Religious thought in Victorian England. Add: Dept. of English, Incarnate Word College, 4301 Broadway, San Antonio, TX 78209.

OHARA, DAVID MITSUGI, b. Hiroshima, Japan, Mar. 10, 27; U.S. citizen; m. 52; c. 2. ENGLISH LITERATURE. B.A, Ind. Univ, 49; M.A, Univ. Hawaii, 50; Ph.D, Univ. Pa, 57. Assoc. prof. ENG, ALFRED UNIV, 57-67, PROF, 67- U.S.A, 54-56. MLA. Sixteenth and 17th century English literature; restoration comedy. Add: Dept. of English, Alfred University, Alfred, NY 14802.

O'HARA, ROBERT C, b. Louisville, Ky, Aug. 11, 25; m. 52; c. 2. AMERICAN LITERATURE, LINGUISTICS. B.A, Univ. Louisville, 50, M.A, 51; Univ. Minn, 52-61. Instr. commun, Univ. Minn, 53-61; asst. prof. ENG, UNIV. S.FLA, TAMPA, 61-65, assoc. prof, 65-73, PROF, 73- Mem, Nat. Adv. Comt. Motion Picture & Teaching Eng, 63-; co-dir, Training Teacher Trainers Prog, Univ. S. Fla, 71-73. U.S.A.A.F, 43-46, Sgt. NCTE; Ling. Soc. Am; S.Atlantic Mod. Lang. Asn; Am. Dialect Soc. Mass communication theory; sociolinguistics; semiology. Publ: Media for the millions, Random, 61; A new perspective in teaching mass communication, Using Mass Media in Schs, 62; The role of sociolinguistics in a humanistic curriculum, Univ. S.Fla. Quart, 73; plus one other. Add: Dept. of Linguistics, College of Language and Literature, University of South Florida, Tampa, FL 33620.

O HEHIR, BRENDAN PETER, b. New York, N.Y, Apr. 11, 27; m. 57; c. 2. ENGLISH. B.S, Loyola Col, 54; M.A, Johns Hopkins Univ, 54; Gilman fel, 56-57, Samuel S. Fels Found. fel, 57-58, Ph.D, 59. Jr. instr, Johns Hopkins Univ. & instr, McCoy Col, 53-56; instr. ENG, UNIV. CALIF, BERKELEY, 58-60, asst. prof, 60-65, assoc. prof, 65-70, PROF, 70- Part-time instr, Loyola Col, 53-56; Guggenheim fel, 65. MLA; Mod. Humanities Res. Asn; Renaissance Soc. Am; Augustan Reprint Soc. Balance of opposites in 18th century poetry; classical aspects of English Augustanism; the place and concept of the Prince in English poetry of the 17th and 18th centuries. Publ: A Gaelic lexicon for Finnegan's wake, 67, Harmony from discords: a life of Sir John Denham, 68 & Expans'd hieroglyphicks: a critical edition of Sir John Denham's Coopers Hill, 68, Univ. Calif; Structure and symbol in Joyce's The dead, Twentieth Century Lit, 4/57 & In: Joyce's The dead, Allyn & Bacon, 65; Virtue and passion: the dialectic of Eloisa to Abelard, Tex. Stud. Lang. & Lit, summer 60 & In: Essential articles for the study of Alexander Pope, Archon Bks, 64; Lost, authorized and pirated editions of John Denham's Coopers Hill, PMLA, 6/64; plus others. Add: 1028 Mariposa Ave, Berkeley, CA 94707.

OHLIN, PETER HAKAN, b. Stockholm, Sweden, Apr. 3, 35; m. 64; c. 3. ENGLISH, FILM. Fil. Mag, Univ. Stockholm, 59; M.A, Univ. N.Mex, 62, univ. fel, 62-64; Ph.D.(Eng), 64. Lectr. ENG, McGILL UNIV, 64-66, asst. prof, 66-69, ASSOC. PROF, 69- Sig.C, Swedish Army, 55-56. MLA. American literature; film; 18th century English literature. Publ: Agee, Obolensky, 66; Cadenus and Vanessa: reason and passion, Stud. Eng. Lit, summer 64; plus others. Add: Dept. of English, McGill University, Montreal, P.Q. H3C 3G1, Can.

OHLMANN, GILBERT SYLVESTER, b. Louisville, Ky, Aug. 7, 12. ENGLISH, HUMANITIES. A.B, Univ. Louisville, 34; M.A, St. Louis Univ, 36; fel, Univ. N.C, 36-39; Univ. Birmingham, summer 48. Instr. Eng, Auburn Univ, spring 39; ed. Talking Bks, Am. Printing House for Blind, 39-46; from asst. prof. to PROF. ENG, UNIV. LOUISVILLE, 46- MLA. History of the drama, especially Medieval; early and Middle English literature; Medieval cultural history. Add: Dept. of English, College of Arts & Sciences, University of Louisville, Louisville, KY 40208.

OHMANN, RICHARD MALIN, b. Cleveland, Ohio, July 11, 31; m. 55; c. 2. ENGLISH. B.A, Oberlin Col, 52; M.A, Harvard Univ, 54, univ. fel, 54-58, jr. fel, Soc. of Fellows, 58-61, Ph.D, 60. Asst. prof. ENG, WESLEYAN UNIV, 61-63, assoc. prof, 63-66, PROF, 66-, assoc. provost, 66-69, chancellor, 69-70. Guggenheim fel, 64-65; ed, Col. Eng, 66-; consult, Am. Heritage Dictionary, 67-; Nat. Endowment for Humanities, 68. MLA; NCTE; Ling. Soc. Am. Stylistics; linguistics. Publ: Shaw: the style and the man, Wesleyan Univ, 62; co-auth, The logic and rhetoric of exposition, rev. ed, Holt, 63; auth, Generative grammars and the concept of literary style, Word, 12/64; Literature as sentences, Col. Eng, 2/66. Add: Dept. of English, Wesleyan University, Middletown, CT 06457.

OJALA, WILLIAM TRUMAN, b. Morgantown, W.Va, Sept. 26, 33; m. 51; c. 1. ENGLISH EDUCATION. B.S, Univ. Minn, Minneapolis, 58, M.A, 62; Ph.D. (Eng. educ), Fla. State Univ, 69. Instr. Eng, Univ. Minn, Minneapolis, 58-63; ENG. EDUC, Fla. State Univ, 63-69, asst. prof, 69-71; ARIZ. STATE UNIV, 71-73, ASSOC. PROF, 73- Consult. Eng, Amarillo, Tex. Sch. Dist, Mercer, W.Va. Schs, Kanawha County Schs, W.Va; county schs, Fla. & Ariz, 63-73; mem, Conf. Eng. Educ. Comt. Teacher training in Nonprint Media, 72- NCTE (Conf. Eng. Educ); Conf. Col. Compos. & Commun; Am. Educ. Res. Asn. Response to literature; teaching composition and literature. Publ: Co-auth, A survey of adolescent interests . . . , Ariz. Eng. Bull, 4/72; auth, On teaching poetry . . . , J. Eng. Teaching Tech, 2/73; co-auth, Films for English teacher preparation . . . , Eng. Educ, fall 73. Add: Dept. of English, Arizona State University, Tempe, AZ 85281.

O'KELLY, BERNARD, b. Winnipeg, Man, Aug. 10, 26; m. 57; c. 3. ENGLISH, RENAISSANCE STUDIES. B.A, Univ. Montreal, 50; Lic. Philos, Col. Immaculate Conception, 50; M.A, Harvard, 55, Dexter traveling fel, 56, Ph.D. (Eng), 60. Lectr. classics, St. Paul's Col, Univ. Man, 50-52; Eng. & French, Loyola Col. Montreal, 52-54; instr. Eng, Ohio State Univ, 57-61, asst. prof, 61-66; PROF. ENG. & DEAN COL. ARTS & SCI, UNIV. N.DAK, 66- Am. Philos. Soc. grant, res. in Eng, 62; res. assoc, Yale, 64-65. MLA; Renaissance Soc. Am; NCTE; Archaeol. Inst. Am; Counc. Cols. Arts & Sci.(v.pres, 73-74). Early Tudor philosophers and theologians, especially John Colet and Thomas More; Shakespeare; Spenser. Publ: Ed, The Renaissance image of man and the world, Ohio State Univ, 66. Add: College of Arts & Sciences, University of North Dakota, Grand Forks, ND 58201.

OKERLUND, ARLENE NAYLOR, b. Emmitsburg, Md, Oct. 13, 38; m. 59; c. 1. ENGLISH LITERATURE. B.A, Univ. Md, College Park, 60; Ph.D.(Lit), Univ. Calif, San Diego, 69. Sci. instr, Mercy Hosp. Sch. of Nursing, 59-63; teaching asst. humanities, Univ. Calif, San Diego, 64-69; asst. prof. ENG, SAN JOSE STATE UNIV, 69-73, ASSOC. PROF, 73-, fac. res. grant, 70-71. MLA; Philol. Asn. Pac. Coast. English Renaissance; Spenser and Shake-speare; phenomenological criticism. Publ: Spenser's wanton maidens: reader psychology and the bower of bliss, PMLA, 1/73. Add: Dept. of English, San Jose State University, 125 S. Seventh St, San Jose, CA 95114.

OLAFSON, ROBERT B, b. Dickinson, N.Dak, May 7, 32. ENGLISH. B.A, Pac. Lutheran Univ, 56; M.A, Univ. Wash, 58, Ph.D.(Eng), 66. Instr. ENG, Pac. Lutheran Univ, 59-62; ASST. PROF, Calif. State Col, San Bernardino, 65-67; EAST. WASH. STATE COL, 67- Assoc. prof, Pac. Lutheran Univ, summer 67. U.S.N, 51-53. Philol. Asn. Pac. Coast; Rocky Mountain Mod. Lang. Asn.(v-chmn. Am. stud. sect). American literary naturalism; B. Traven's Mexican fiction. Publ: B. Traven: two novels on the underdogs in Mexico, Mex. Life; The great Traven hunt, Organon, Vol. 3, No. 1; B. Traven's Norteamericanos in Mexico, Markham Rev, 10/73; plus one other. Add: Rte. 1, Box 48, Medical Lake, WA 99022.

OLANDER, JAMES H, b. Manitowoc, Wis, May 11, 30. SPEECH & DRAMA, ENGLISH. B.A, Lawrence Col, 52; M.A, Univ. Wis, 53, Ph.D.(speech), 63. Teacher high sch, 53-55; Univ. Sch, South. Ill. Univ, 58-59; instr. Eng, South. Ill. Univ, 59-60; supvr. stud. teachers, Univ. Wis, 60-62; lectr. speech & Eng, Europ. div, Univ. Md, 62-66, Far East div, 66-68; ASSOC. PROF. SPEECH & THEATRE, N.Y. INST. TECHNOL, 68- Speech Commun. Asn. Theatre; literature; music. Publ: Some notes on Angkor Wat, Marab, fall 67. Add: Dept. of English, New York Institute of Technology, Wheatley Rd, Old Westbury, NY 11568.

OLAUSON, C. RONALD, b. Bell, Calif, May 2, 37; div; c. 1. DRAMA, COMPARATIVE LITERATURE. B.S, Brigham Young Univ, 59; M.F.A, Univ. Utah, 63; Ph.D.(theatre), Univ. Minn, 57. Asst. prof. SPEECH & THEATRE, MANKATO STATE COL, 65-68, assoc. prof, 68-72, PROF, 72- Speech Commun. Asn; Am. Theatre Asn; Am. Nat. Theatre & Acad. Comparative analysis of the writing styles and philosophies of avante-garde playwrights; continuance of the creative process after initial formulation, acting and directing. Add: Box 23, Performing Arts Center, Mankato State College, Mankato, MN 56001.

OLDANI, LOUIS JOSEPH, b. St. Louis, Mo, Mar. 1, 33. AMERICAN & ENGLISH LITERATURE. A.B, St. Louis Univ, 57, Ph.L, 59, M.A, 62; S.T.B, 66; Ph.D.(Eng), Univ. Pa, 72. Instr. ENG, ROCKHURST COL, 71-73, ASST. PROF, 73- MLA. Dreiser, descriptive and textual bibliography; the novel. Publ: Muriel Spark's delightful and savage heroes, Current: Rev. Catholicism, summer 64; Bibliographical description of Dreiser's The genius, Libr. Chronicle, winter 73. Add: Dept. of English, Rockhurst College, 5225 Troost Ave, Kansas City, MO 64110.

OLDHAM, JANET BOCK, b. Chicago, Ill, Feb. 28, 11; m. 43. ENGLISH. B.S, N.Cent. Col.(Ill), 32; M.S, Univ. Ill, 35; Univ. Ky, 56-58. Teacher, high sch, Ky, 56-62; ASST. PROF. ENG, EAST. KY. UNIV, 62- State chmn. achievement awards, NCTE, 66-68, co-chmn. stud. group on rhetoric in schs, annual convention, fall 67; instr. poetry, NDEA Inst, 67-68. W.A.A.C, 42-43, 1st Lt. NCTE; MLA; South. Mod. Lang. Asn; NEA. Poetry and composition. Publ: Dr. Zhivago and Babbit, Eng. J, 5/59. Add: 432 Breck Ave, Richmond, KY 40475.

OLDSEY, BERNARD STANLEY, b. Wilkes-Barre, Pa, Feb. 18, 23; m. 46; c. 2. ENGLISH. A.B, Pa. State Univ, 48, A.M, 49, Ph.D, 55. From instr. to asst. prof. Eng. Pa. State Univ, 51-63, assoc. prof, 63-67, Eng. & comp. lit, 67-69; PROF. ENG, WEST CHESTER STATE COL, 69- Sr. Fulbright lectr, Univ. Zaragoza, 64-65; ed, Col. Lit, 73- U.S.A. MLA. American literature; comparative literature, especially the European novel; 19th and 20th century English novel. Publ: Co-auth, Visions and revisions in modern American literary criticism, Dutton, 62; From fact to judgment, Macmillan, 2nd ed, 63; The art of William Golding, 65 & auth, The Spanish season (novel), 70, Harcourt; plus others. Add: Dept. of English, West Chester State College, West Chester, PA 19380.

O'LEARY, KENNETH, b. Bayonne, N.J, Nov. 28, 24. ENGLISH. A.B, Seton Hall Col, 45; S.T.L, Cath. Univ. Am, 49; M.A, Fordham Univ, 61, Ph.D. (Eng), 65; M.S, St. John's Univ, 73. Asst. prof. ENG, SETON HALL UNIV, 65-73, ASSOC. PROF, 73- MLA; NCTE; Am. Soc. Theatre Res. Eighteenth century English literature. Add: Dept. of English, Seton Hall University, South Orange, NJ 07079.

O'LEARY, RONALD THOMAS, b. Mansfield, Ohio, Dec. 31, 38; m. 62; c. 2. DRAMA & SPEECH. B.S.Ed, Bowling Green State Univ, 60, M.A, 61; M.F.A, Univ. Wis, 64; Ph.D.(theater & TV), 66. Asst. prof. THEATRE, UNIV. MD, COLLEGE PARK, 66-72, ASSOC. PROF, 72- Am. Theatre Asn; Speech Commun. Asn. Contemporary dramatic criticism; theory and practice of teaching acting and directing in the university. Add: Dept. of Speech, University of Maryland, College Park, MD 20742.

OLESON, CLINTON WARREN, b. Mason City, Iowa, May 18, 28; m. 50; c. 3. ENGLISH LITERATURE. B.A, Luther Col, 52; M.A, Univ. Chicago, 53, Danforth fel, 53-56, Danforth teaching fel, 57, Ph.D, 68. From assoc. prof. to PROF. ENG. & DIR. DIV. HUMANITIES, GEORGE WILLIAMS COL, 58- U.S.N, 46-48. MLA; NCTE. Seventeenth century English literature; contemporary fiction. Add: Div. of Humanities, George Williams College, Downer's Grove, IL 60515.

OLIPHANT, ROBERT T, Linguistics. See Volume III, Foreign Languages, Linguistics & Philology.

OLIVE, WILLIAM JOHN, b. Fayetteville, N.C, May 8, 07; wid; c. 1. ENGLISH. A.B, Univ. N.C, 28, A.M, 29, Ph.D, 37. Asst. ENG, Univ. N.C, 28-29; instr, LA. STATE UNIV, BATON ROUGE, 29-35, asst. prof, 36-37, assoc. prof, 37-50, PROF, 51- MLA; Shakespeare Asn. Am; S.Cent. Mod. Lang. Asn; Renaissance Soc. Am. English literature; Renaissance literature; Elizabethan literature. Publ: Co-ed, Studies in honor of E.L. Marilla, La. State Univ, 70; contrib, A tribute to George Coffin Taylor. Add: Dept. of English, Louisiana State University, Baton Rouge, LA 70803.

OLIVER, EGBERT SAMUEL, b. Ore, Dec. 27, 02; m. 24; c. 2. AMERICAN LITERATURE. A.B, Univ. Wash, 27, A.M, 29, Ph.D, 39. Instr. ENG, Willamette Univ, 29-35, asst. prof, 35-39, assoc. prof, 39-43, prof, 43-50; asst.

prof, gen. exten. div, Ore. State Syst. Higher Educ, 50-51, assoc. prof, 51-55; prof, PORTLAND STATE UNIV, 55-72, head dept, 61-67, EMER. PROF, 72- Vis. prof, Ahmednager Col, India, 55; Fulbright lectr, col. arts & commerce, Osmania Univ, India, 56-57, Kurukshetra Univ, 64-65; lectr. sem. Am. Lit, U.S. Educ. Found. India, Naini Tal, 57, Mussoorie, 65 & Ootacamund, India, 71. Thoreau Soc; Melville Soc. Am. Publ: Readings for ideas and form, Doubleday, Doran, 35; How our Bible grew, Pilgrim, 52; ed, Giving form to ideas, Odyssey, 46 & Piazza tales, Hendricks, 62; auth, Studies in American literature, 65 & American literature 1890-1965, an anthology, 67, Eurasia, Delhi. Add: 1220 N.E. 17th Ave, Portland, OR 97232.

OLIVER, KENNETH ARTHUR, b. Sweet Home, Ore, Feb. 17, 12; m. 35; c. 1. COMPARATIVE LITERATURE & ENGLISH. A.B, Willamette Univ, 35; A.M, Univ. Wash, 39; scholar, Univ. Wis, 41-43, fel, 46-47, Ph.D, 47. Instr. comp. lit, Univ. Wis, 47-48; assoc. prof. ENG, OCCIDENTAL COL, 48-50, PROF, 50-, chmn. dept. Eng. & comp. lit, 49-65, div. humanities & fine arts, 62-68. Ford Found. grant, Intercol. Prog. Grad. Stud, 55-65; Fulbright lectr, Univ. Salonica, 56-57; fac. award lectr, Occidental Col, 58, res. grants, 70, 72. U.S.N.R, Lt. Comdr. NCTE (chmn, comp. lit. comt, 65-68); Int. Comp. Lit. Asn; Am. Comp. Lit. Asn; Counc. Basic Educ. Literary criticism; poetry. Publ: The road and the stars (poetry), Wings, 57; Our living language, Anderson, Ritchie, Simon, 62; transl. & contrib, Anthology of medieval lyrics, Mod. Libr, 62 & The medieval age, Dell, Phoenix, 63; ed, Walk the rugged earth (poetry), Metropolitan, 67; contrib, On writing well, Odyssey, 65 & Effective speech, Holt, 70; plus various articles. Add: Dept. of English & Comparative Literature, Occidental College, Los Angeles, CA 90041.

OLIVER, LESLIE M, b. Forman, N.Dak, Oct. 27, 99; m. 28. ENGLISH LITERATURE. B.Sc. in Ed, Ore. State Univ, 27; M.A, Harvard, 30, Ph.D, 46. Instr. Eng, Syracuse Univ, 28-30; U.S. Naval Acad, 30-33; from instr. to assoc. prof, Colo. Sch. Mines, 33-41; instr. Eng. & hist, Mass. Inst. Tech, 43-46; asst. prof, Eng, State Col. Wash, 46-48; asst. librn. bibliog, Houghton Libr, Harvard, 48-54; prof. ENG, LESLEY COL, 54-72, EMER. PROF, 72- MLA. Sixteenth century English literature and bibliography. Publ: Technical exposition, McGraw, 40; co-auth, A bibliography of the works of Max Beerbohm, Harvard Univ, 52; auth, A bookseller's account book, 1545, Harvard Libr. Bull, 4/68. Add: 61 Lila Rd, Jamaica Plain, MA 02130.

OLIVER, RAYMOND DAVIES, b. Arlington, Mass, Jan. 28, 36; m. 59; c. 2. ENGLISH. B.A, Oberlin Col, 57; M.A, Univ. Wis, 58; grant, Univ. Munich, 60-61; Ph.D.(Eng), Stanford Univ, 67. Acting asst. prof. ENG, UNIV. CALIF, BERKELEY, 65-67, asst. prof, 67-71, ASSOC. PROF, 71- Middle English literature; fourteenth and fifteenth century French and German culture. Add: 322 Wheeler Hall, University of California, Berkeley, CA 94720.

OLIVER, ROBERT TARBELL, b. Ore, July 7, 09. PUBLIC SPEAKING. A.B, Pac. Univ, 32, LL.D, 49; A.M, Univ. Ore, 32; Ph.D, Univ. Wis, 37. Dean, Clark Jr. Col, 33-35; asst. prof. speech, Bradley Polytech. Inst, 37; from asst. prof. to assoc. prof, Bucknell Univ, 37-42; assoc. prof. & head div. rhet. & pub. address, Syracuse Univ, 44-47; from prof. & head dept. speech to res. prof. INT. SPEECH, PA. STATE UNIV, 49-70, EMER. RES. PROF, 70- Consult, Republic of Korea & mgr, Korean Pac. Press, Wash, D.C, 47-60; educ. consult, Dept. State, Australia, 58; vis. prof, Los Angeles State Col, 60; lectr. commun, U.S. Army War Col, 67-68. Asst. chief, victory speakers bur, Off. Civilian Defense, 42; chief food conserv, War Foods Admin, 43-44. Speech Commun. Asn.(pres, 64); For. Policy Asn; E.Pub. Speaking Conf; East. Commun. Asn.(pres, 65). Influence of speech in shaping the course of human history; intercultural communications; problems and methods of diplomacy. Publ: Syngman Rhee: the man behind the myth; Four who spoke out; Psychology of persuasive speech; History of public speaking in America, Allyn & Bacon, 65; Communication and leadership (2 vols), Toastmasters Int, 70; Making your meaning effective, Holbrook, 71; Communication and culture in ancient India and China, Syracuse Univ, 71. Add: 601 Ridge Ave, State College, PA 16801.

OLIVER, WILLIAM I, b. Panama, Repub. Panama, Nov. 6, 26; U.S. citizen; m; c. 3. DRAMA. B.F.A, Carnegie Inst. Technol, 50; M.A, Cornell Univ, 55, Ph.D, 59. Co-dir, Fargo-Moorhead Community Theatre, N.Dak, 50-53; bus. & publicity mgr, Cornell Univ. Theatre, 53-58, instr. acting technique & asst. dir. studio prog, 55-57, instr. speech & drama & supvr. studio theatre prog, 57-58; PROF. DRAMA, UNIV. CALIF, BERKELEY, 58- Dir. Onteora Playhouse, Tannersville, N.Y, summers 55-56; dir. major & studio prod, Univ. Calif, Berkeley, 58-; Fine Arts fel, 65-66; dir. Medusa, Cornell Univ. Latin Am. Festival, 66; vis. prof, Univ. Chile, 66-67; dir. Marat-Sade, Chilean Nat. Theatre, 67. Dial Press Award, 49. U.S.N, 45-46. Am. Theatre Asn.(v.chmn, aesthet. sect, 61-68, chmn, 68-). Spanish, Jacobean and modern drama; theatre aesthetics; playwriting and theatre practice. Publ: Co-ed, Modern drama essays in criticism, Oxford Univ, 65; transl, The witches sabbath (play) & Morality in the theatre, In: Masterpieces of the modern Spanish theatre, Collier Bks, 67; auth, Voices of change in Spanish American theatre, Univ. Tex, 71; Marat-Sade in Santiago, Educ. Theatre J, 12/67; plus others. Add: 2647 Piedmont Ave, Berkeley, CA 94704.

OLLEY, FRANCIS R, b. Brooklyn, N.Y, Feb. 26, 28; m. 60; c. 2. DRAMA. A.B, St. Joseph's Col.(Pa), 48; M.A, Temple Univ, 55; Ph.D, Fordham Univ, 65. PROF. ENG. & DIR. DRAMA, ST. JOSEPH'S COL.(PA), 50- MLA; Am. Nat. Theatre & Acad. Shakespeare; modern and Renaissance drama. Publ: Claudius at prayer: Hamlet, 2/64, Last block on the Camino Real, 11/65 & Anouilh's The rehearsal, 5/68, Drama Critique. Add: Dept. of English, St. Joseph's College, Philadelphia, PA 19131.

OLMSTED, AUDREY PERRYMAN, b. Sioux Falls, S.Dak. PUBLIC ADDRESS, THEATRE HISTORY. B.A, Univ. North. Iowa, 62, M.A, 63; Ph.D.(rhetoric & publ. address), Ind. Univ. Bloomington, 71. Instr. SPEECH, BOSTON UNIV, 68-72, ASST. PROF, 72- Speech Commun. Asn; Speech Commun. Asn. East States. Radical rhetoric, especially 20th century. Publ: Foundations of education instructor's manual, Wiley, 67. Add: Dept. of Speech, College of Liberal Arts, Boston University, 232 Bay State Rd, Boston, MA 02215.

OLMSTED, CHARLES H, b. East Hartford, Conn, June 16, 21. ENGLISH. A.B, Amherst Col, 43; H.P. Field fel. from Amherst Col. to Harvard, 46-47, A.M, 47, teaching fel, 51-54, Ph.D, 59. Instr. Eng, State Univ. Iowa, 47-49; admin. asst, Harvard Col, 54-56; instr. ENG, Trinity Col.(Conn), 57-59; Univ. Mass, 59-62; asst. prof, MT. HOLYOKE COL, 62-65, LECTR, 65-, ASSOC. DEAN STUD, 73-, asst. acad. dean, 65-71, asst. dean stud, 71-73. U.S.A.A.F, 43-45. MLA; Mediaeval Acad. Am. Eighteenth century English satire and political journalism; Chaucer; Victorian period. Add: Dept. of English, Mt. Holyoke College, South Hadley, MA 01075.

OLMSTED, STERLING PITKIN, b. Hartford, Conn, Feb. 16, 15; m. 42; c. 1. ENGLISH. A.B, Rollins Col, 36; M.A, Yale, 38, Selden fel, 38-39, Ph.D. (Eng), 40. Instr. Eng, Rensselaer Polytech. Inst, 39-47, asst. prof, 47-52, assoc. prof, 52-53, prof. Eng. & head dept. lang. & lit, 53-68; PROF. LIT. & LANG, WILMINGTON COL.(OHIO), 68-, PROVOST, 70-, dean fac, 68-70. U.S.A, 42-45. MLA; NCTE; Am. Soc. Eng. Educ. Communication theory; general education. Publ: Co-auth, Language and literature, Harcourt, 62 & Exposition: technical and popular; Liberal learning for the engineer, J. Eng. Educ, 12/68. Add: Wilmington College, Wilmington, OH 45177.

O'LOUGHLIN, MICHAEL JEROME KEVIN, b. Forest Hills, N.Y, Oct. 22, 36; m. 60; c. 4. ENGLISH. A.B, Col. Holy Cross, 58; M.A, Yale, 60, Ph.D. (Eng), 65; Columbia Univ, summer 60. Acting instr. ENG, YALE, 63-65, instr, 65-66, asst. prof, 66-72, ASSOC. PROF, 72- Morse fel, 68-69. E. Harris Harbison Teaching Prize, 69. MLA; Soc. Relig. Higher Educ. Baroque and classical literature; pastoral-romance forms. Publ: Teaching the Odyssey: some weavings and unweavings, Yale Conf. Teaching Eng, 4/67; The sober frame: a reading of Marvell's Upon Appleton House, Andrew Marvell: twentieth century views, 9/68. Add: Dept. of English, 1142 Trumbull College, Yale University, New Haven, CT 06520.

OLSON, ELDER JAMES, b. Chicago, Ill, Mar. 9, 09; m; c. 4. ENGLISH. A.B, Univ. Chicago, 34, M.A, 35, Ph.D, 38. Instr. ENG, Armour Inst. Technol, 35-40, asst. prof, 40-42; UNIV. CHICAGO, 42-48, assoc. prof, 48-54, prof, 54-71, DISTINGUISHED SERV. PROF, 71- Rockefeller exchange prof, Univ. Frankfurt, 48; Powell prof, Ind. Univ, 55, vis. prof. lit. criticism, 58-59, sch. lett. fel, 62, Patten lectr, 64; Rockefeller Found. prof, Univ. Philippines, 66-67. Poetry Soc. Am. Award; award for best critical book on poetry, Acad. Am. Poets, 55; Llewellyn John & Harriet Manchester Quantrell Award for excellence in undergrad. teaching, Univ. Chicago, 66. MLA; Europ. Soc. Cult; PEN Club. History and theory of literary criticism, poetics and prosody; philosophy of David Hume. Publ: Co-ed, Critics and criticism, 52, 57, auth, The poetry of Dylan Thomas, 61, Collected poems, 63 & ed, Aristotle's poetics and English literature, 64, Univ. Chicago; auth, Tragedy and the theory of drama, Wayne State Univ, 61; ed, American lyric poems, Appleton, 63; auth, The theory of comedy, Ind. Univ, 69; ed, Major voices, McGraw, 73. Add: Dept. of English, University of Chicago, Chicago, IL 60637.

OLSON, ENID MARTELL, b. Centerville, S.Dak, Dec. 19, 20; m. 42; c. 2. ENGLISH. B.A, Gustavus Adolphus Col, 40; Univ. Mich, summer 38; M.A.T, Univ. Ill, 49. Teacher Eng, Warren High Sch, Minn, 40-43; hist, Bloomington High Sch, Minn, 43-44; Eng, Urbana High Sch, Ill, 54-60; assoc. publ, NCTE, 60-62, dir. pub. & pub. relat, 62-69, proj. dir. Eng. & adult educ, Educ. Div, Reader's Digest Serv, 69-71; SUBJECT MATTER ADV. ENG, TEACHING JOUR, 73- Asst. instr. rhetoric, Univ. Ill, 53. NCTE. Teaching of composition and literature. Publ: Poems of faith for the Christian year, Augsburg, 59; co-auth, Teaching world literature in the high school, Ill. Asn. Teachers Eng, 61; auth, What do the censors fear?, Teachers Col. Rec, 4/65. The growth of the city (ser. radio scripts), Nat. Asn. Educ. Broadcasters, 52. Add: Rte. 1, Box 76, Spicer, MN 56288.

OLSON, ERNEST LEROY, b. Salt Lake City, Utah, June 24, 16; m. 44; c. 4. ENGLISH. B.A, Univ. Utah, 48, M.A, 49; Univ. Calif, Los Angeles, 50-51. Instr. ENG, BRIGHAM YOUNG UNIV, 53-55, asst. prof, 54-71, ASSOC. PROF, 72-, DIR. UNIV. PRESS, 67-, chmn. off. univ. publ, 56-66. Finance C, A.U.S, 42-43, Med.Serv.C, U.S.A.R, 43-55, Chaplain C, 55-, Col. Am. Col. Pub. Relat. Asn; Mil. Chaplains Asn. U.S; NCTE. American literature; Mark Twain. Publ: American literature: poets, critics . . . , 61, America's literature, 62 & Understanding and enjoying literature, 65, Brigham Young Univ. Add: 101 E. 2120 North, Provo, UT 84601.

OLSON, ESTHER J, b. Belgrade, Minn, Feb. 8, 08; div; c. 3. SPEECH. B.S, Univ. Minn, 45, M.A, 48, Ph.D, 56. Coord. oral commun, gen. col, Univ. Minn, 45-56; assoc. prof. speech & dir. col. radio sta, Luther Col, 56-60; assoc. prof. SPEECH & DRAMA, AUGSBURG COL, 63-73, PROF, 73- Nat. Col. Players. Religious drama. Add: 809 Superior St. S.E, Minneapolis, MN 55414.

OLSON, GLENDING, b. Lake Placid, N.Y, Aug. 6, 42; m. 66; c. 1. ENGLISH LITERATURE. B.A, Lawrence Univ, 64; Woodrow Wilson fel, Stanford Univ, 64-65, NDEA fel, 65-68, Ph.D.(Eng), 68. Acting asst. prof. ENG, Lawrence Univ, 68-70; ASST. PROF, Macalester Col, 70-72; CLEVELAND STATE UNIV, 72- MLA; Mediaeval Acad. Am. Chaucer; Medieval literary theory. Publ: The Reeve's tale and Gombert, Mod. Lang. Rev, 9/69; Deschamps' Art de dictier and Chaucer's literary environment, Speculum, 9/73; The medieval theory of literature for refreshment, Stud. Philol, 74. Add: Dept. of English, Cleveland State University, Cleveland, OH 44115.

OLSON, PAUL A, b. Washburn, Wis, July 7, 32; m. 52; c. 3. ENGLISH. B.A, Bethany Col, 51; univ. fel, Princeton, 54-55, Theodore W. Hunt fel, 55-56, Counc. Humanities fel, 56-57, Ph.D.(Eng), 57. Asst. prof. ENG, UNIV. NEBR, LINCOLN, 57-61, assoc. prof, 61-63, prof, 63-68, FOUND. PROF. & DIR. TRI-UNIV. PROJ, 68- Guggenheim fel, 62-63; Fulbright scholar, Univ. London, 63-64; consult, U.S. Off. Educ. & dir, stud. comn. undergrad. educ, 71-75; co-dir, Nebr. Curriculum Develop. Ctr. NCTE; MLA; Mediaeval Acad. Am. Medieval literature; education; Indian literature. Publ: Several books on education. Add: Dept. of English, University of Nebraska, Tri-University Project, Andrews Hall, Lincoln, NE 68508.

OLSON, RICHARD DALE, b. Tacoma, Wash, Sept. 1, 32; m. 57; c. 3. ENGLISH. B.A, Seattle Pac. Col, 54; M.A, Univ. Wash, 58, Ph.D.(Eng), 67. TEACHER ENG, Cascade Jr. High Sch, Seattle, 58-62; Evergreen High Sch,

62-66; HIGHLINE COMMUNITY COL, 66- U.S.A, 54-56. NEA; NCTE. American and 19th century English literature. Publ: Whittier and the machine age, In: Memorabilia of John Greenleaf Whittier, Emerson Soc, 68. Add: 21304 Fifth St, Seattle, WA 98148.

OLSON, ROBERT C, b. Chicago, Ill, May 25, 17; m. 45; c. 3. ENGLISH. B.S, Northwest. Univ, 47; M.A, Univ. Colo, 50, Ph.D.(Eng), 51; Yale, 59. Teacher, high sch, Mich, 47-49; asst. prof. Eng, Adams State Col, 51-52; assoc. prof. & head dept, Tex. Lutheran Col, 52-55; from asst. prof. to prof, East. N.Mex. Univ, 55-61; dir. Inst. Eng. as For. Lang, Am. Lang. Ctr, Rabat, Morocco, 61-62; PROF. ENG, Lamas Univ, 62-67; Duquesne Univ, 67-68; LAMAR UNIV, 68- U.S.A, 41-45, S/Sgt. MLA. Eighteenth century English literature; linguistics; Old English. Publ: Swift's use of Philosophical transactions in A tale of a tub, Stud. Philol, 7/52; Othello, I, i, 25-26, Explicator, 3/64. Add: Dept. of English, Lamar University, Box 10023, Beaumont, TX 77710.

OLSON, THOMAS O, b. Oak Park, Ill, Feb. 7, 33; m. 55; c. 2. MASS COMMUNICATIONS, ORAL INTERPRETATION. A.B, Ill. Col, 55; M.S, Syracuse Univ, 56; Ph.D.(mass commun), Wayne State Univ, 66. Producer-dir. commercial TV, Cowles Broadcasting, 56-58; instr. radio-TV, Wayne State Univ, 58-59, producer-dir. educ. TV, 59-61 & prod. mgr, 61-64, assoc, 64-65, dir. TV, 65-68, asst. prof. mass commun, 68-71; ASSOC. PROF. RADIO-TV & CHMN. DEPT, SOUTH. ILL. UNIV, CARBONDALE, 71- Speech Commun. Asn; Nat. Asn. Educ. Broadcasters; Broadcast Educ. Asn. Mass media appreciation and criticism; television production. Add: Dept. of Radio-TV, Southern Illinois University, Carbondale, IL 62901.

O'MALLEY, GLENN E, b. Cleveland, Ohio, July 1, 18; m. 48. ENGLISH. B.A, West. Reserve Univ, 49, M.A, 50; Ph.D.(Eng), Princeton, 56. Instr. ENG, Princeton, 52-53; Northwest. Univ, 53-56, asst. prof, 56-63, assoc. prof, 63-68; PROF, ARIZ. STATE UNIV, 68- Med.C, U.S.A, 41-45. MLA. English literature of the 19th century; Percy Bysshe Shelley. Publ: Shelley and synesthesia, Northwest. Univ, 64; Literary synesthesia, J. Aesthet. & Art Criticism, 57; co-auth, Some new letters from W.B. Yeats to Lady Gregory, Rev. Eng. Lit, 63. Add: Dept. of English, Arizona State University, Tempe, AZ 85281.

O'MALLEY, JEROME FRANCIS, b. Scranton, Pa, Mar. 26, 25. ENGLISH, HISTORY. B.A, Boston Col, 48, M.A, 49; S.T.L, Woodstock Col.(Md), 55; Ph.D.(Eng), Duquesne Univ, 64. Teacher, high sch, Pa, 49-52; instr. Eng. & Greek, Wheeling Col, 57-62, asst. prof, 64-65; ENG, Loyola Col, (Md), 65-69, chmn. dept, 68-69; assoc. prof, SLIPPERY ROCK STATE COL, 69-72, PROF, 72- Northeast. Mediaeval & Renaissance Soc. fel, Univ. N.C, summer 65 & Duke Univ, 66; Nat. Humanities Found. grant, summer 67. MLA. Latin hymnology; history of religion; medieval theology. Publ: An introduction to the study of the hymns of St. James as literature, Traditio, 70. Add: Dept. of English, Slippery Rock State College, Slippery Rock, PA 16057.

OMAN, WILLIAM M, b. New York, N.Y, Dec. 30, 11; m. 42; 68; c. 3. ENGLISH. A.B, Princeton, 34. V.pres. & ed-in-chief, Oxford Univ. Press, N.Y, 49-57; V.PRES. & DIR, DODD, MEAD & CO, 57- Mem. adv. counc. dept. Eng, Princeton, 48-60; past treas. & dir, Franklin Bk. Prog. U.S.N.R, 42-45, Lt. Comdr. Add: Dodd Mead & Co, 79 Madison Ave, New York, NY 10016.

OMANS, GLEN A, b. Bay City, Mich, Apr. 24, 29; m. 52; c. 3. ENGLISH. B.A, Mich. State Univ, 51; M.A, Univ. Mich, 52; Ph.D.(Eng), Univ. Minn, 63. ASSOC. PROF. ENG, TEMPLE UNIV, 60- U.S.A, 52-54. Am. Comp. Lit. Asn; Eng-Speaking Union. Nineteenth century poetry—American, English and French. Publ: The Villon Cult in England, Comp. Lit, winter 66. Add: Dept. of English, Temple University, Philadelphia, PA 19122.

OMANS, STUART EARL, b. Chicago, Ill, July 31, 40; m. 62; c. 3. ENGLISH. A.B, Univ. Ill, Urbana, 62; M.A, Miami Univ, 64; Ph.D.(Eng), Northwest. Univ, 69. Teaching fel, ENG, Miami Univ, 63-64; Northwest. Univ, 65-66, ed, fel, 66-67; asst. prof, FLA. TECHNOL. UNIV, 68-70, ASSOC. PROF, 71- Asst. ed, Renaissance drama, 66, 67; Res. Opportunities in Renaissance Drama, 68, 69. MLA; S.Atlantic Mod. Lang. Asn; Col. Eng. Asn. Renaissance drama; Shakespeare; ethnic literature. Publ: Ed, The use of linguistics in the teaching of English, Cent. Fla. Conf. Teaching Eng, 74; auth, English Renaissance drama in the Silver collection at Newberry Library, Res. Opportunities Renaissance Drama, 68; Masked leaders: the literary relationship of Herman Melville and Ralph Ellison, J. S.Atlantic Bull, 70; Those troublesome little words in Shakespeare's plays, Exercise Exchange, (in press). Add: Dept. of English, Florida Technological University, Alafaya Trail, Orlando, FL 32816.

O'MARA, PHILIP FRANCIS, b. Brooklyn, N.Y, Feb. 24, 38. MODERN AMERICAN & AFRICAN LITERATURE. B.A, St. John's Univ.(N.Y), 60; M.A, Notre Dame Univ, 61, Ph.D.(Eng), 70; Kent fel, Univ. Chicago, 64-65. ASST. PROF. ENG, TOUGALOO COL, 66-72, ASSOC. PROF. & CHMN. DEPT, 72- MLA; Col. Eng. Asn; Conf. Col. Compos. & Commun; Soc. Relig. Higher Educ; Soc. Pentecostal Stud; AAUP. Recent African fiction; religious literature; modern poetry. Publ: Co-auth, No game for kids (opera), Tougaloo Col, 71; contrib, In the midst stands Jesus: a pastoral introduction to the new Testament, Alba; auth, The return of the Lord, 9/72 & Social action, 10-11/72, New Covenant. Add: Dept. of English, Tougaloo College, Tougaloo, MS 39174.

OMRCANIN, MARGARET S, b. Lexington, Ky, Apr. 7, 17; m. 66. ENGLISH. A.B, Univ. Ky, 37, M.A, 41; Ph.D.(Eng), Univ. Ill, 60. Teacher high sch, Ky, 39-47; asst. ENG, Univ. Ill, 47-51; prof, Ind. Univ. Pa, 51-56; instr, Univ. Ky, 56-62; PROF, INDIANA UNIV. PA, 62- MLA; Cath. Renascence Soc. American literature. Publ: Ruth Suckow: a study of her fiction, 72 & The American novel and political insurgency, 73, Dorrance. Add: Dept. of English, Indiana University of Pennsylvania, Indiana, PA 15701.

O'NEAL, COTHBURN MADISON, b. Wolfe City, Tex, July 29, 07; m. 27. ENGLISH. B.A, Trinity Univ, 27; M.A, Univ. Tex, Austin, 32, Ph.D.(Eng), 40. Teacher Eng. & music, High Schs, Tex, 27-38; prof. Eng, UNIV. TEX, ARLINGTON, 38-41, 45-56, head dept. fine arts, 56-60, asst. to pres, 60-63, PROF. ENG, 63- U.S.N, 41-45, Lt. Comdr. Authors League Am; S.Cent. Mod. Lang. Asn. Shakespeare; Poe; Tamerlane. Publ: Master of the world, 52, The dark lady, 54, The very young Mrs. Poe, 56, Untold glory, 57, Hagar, 58, The gods of our time, 60, Pa, 62 & The money hunters, 66, Crown. Add: Dept. of English, University of Texas at Arlington, Arlington, TX 76010.

O'NEAL, GLENN, Practical Theology, Speech. See Volume IV, Philosophy, Religion and Law.

O'NEILL, JOHN HIGBEE, b. Madison, Wis, Dec. 4, 41; m. 66; c. 2. ENGLISH LITERATURE. B.S, Wis. State Univ-La Crosse, 63; M.A, Univ. Minn, Minneapolis, 68, Ph.D.(Eng), 72. Instr. lit. & writing, Univ. Minn, 70-72; ASST. PROF. ENG, HAMILTON COL, 72- Nat. Endowment for Humanities younger humanist award, 73. MLA; Am. Soc. Eighteenth Century Stud; Augustan Reprint Soc. Restoration and eighteenth century literature. Add: Dept. of English, Hamilton College, Clinton, NY 13323.

O'NEILL, JOSEPH EUGENE, S.J, b. Hoboken, N.J, Mar. 29, 10. ENGLISH. B.A, Woodstock Col, 32, M.A, 33; S.T.L, Col. de St. Jean Berchmans, Louvain, Belgium, 40; M.A, Fordham Univ, 46; Ph.D.(Eng), Columbia Univ, 55. Instr. ENG. & AM. LIT, col, FORDHAM UNIV, 46-48, asst. prof, GRAD. SCH, 51-65, assoc. prof, 65-73, PROF, 73-, ED, THOUGHT, 56- MLA. American literature, especially 19th century; imagery and symbolism in literature. Publ: Ed, A Catholic case against segregation, 61 & The encounter with God, 62, Macmillan; Longfellow: poet and preacher, Thought. Add: Dept. of English, Fordham University, Bronx, NY 10458.

O'NEILL, MICHAEL JOSEPH, b. Dublin, Ireland, Mar. 1, 13; nat; m. 50. ENGLISH. B.A, Fordham Univ, 37; M.A, Univ. Dublin, Ireland, 50, Ph.D.(Eng), 52. Instr. Eng, LaSalle Acad, 39-42; asst. prof, St. Louis Univ, 46-58; assoc. prof. & chmn. dept, Bellarmine Col, 58-63; assoc. prof. ENG. LIT, UNIV. OTTAWA, 63-65, PROF, 65-, CHMN. CONTEMPORARY LIT. DOCTORAL PROG, 68- Vis. prof, Univ. Ottawa, summer 62; Can. Counc. res. award, summers 65, 66, leave fel, 70. Can. Asn. Univ. Teachers; Asn. Can. Univ. Teachers Eng; Soc. Theatre Res, Gt. Brit; fel. Royal Soc. Antiq. Ireland. Irish literary revival; Abbey theatre archives, Dublin; modern English and American drama. Publ: Co-auth, James Joyce miscellany, 59 & Joseph Holloway's Abbey theatre, 67, South. Ill. Univ; auth, Lennox Robinson, Twayne, 64; co-ed, Joseph Holloway's Irish theatre (3 vols), Proscenium, 68-70; auth, Irish poets of the nineteenth century, Univ. Rev; Memory in Joyce: its use in a mother, Mod. Lang. Notes; co-auth, An introduction to Joseph Holloway, Dublin Mag, winter 64. Add: Dept. of English, Faculty of Arts, University of Ottawa, 175 Waller St, Ottawa, Ont. K1N 6N5, Can.

ONG, WALTER JACKSON, S.J, b. Kansas City, Mo, Nov. 30, 12. ENGLISH. A.B, Rockhurst Col, 33, L.H.D, 68; M.A, St. Louis Univ, 41, S.T.L, 48; Guggenheim fels, 49-50, 51-52; Ph.D.(Eng), Harvard, 55; D.H.L, Univ. Mo-Columbia, 73; D.H, Creighton Univ, 73. Instr. ENG. & FRENCH, Regis Col. (Colo), 41-43; asst. ST. LOUIS UNIV, 44-47, instr, 53-54, asst. prof, 54-57, assoc. prof, 57-59, PROF, 59-, HUMANITIES IN PSYCHIAT, SCH. MED, 70- Res. & lectr, Europe, 50-54, 62; mem, Fulbright Nat. Selection Comt, France, 57-59, chmn, 58-59; regional assoc, Am. Counc. Learned Soc, 57-66; vis. prof. Eng, Univ. Calif, 60; fel, Ctr. Advan. Stud, Wesleyan Univ, 61-62; mem. adv. bd, Guggenheim Mem. Found, 62-; vis. lectr, Ctr. Advan. Renaissance Stud, Univ. Poitiers, 62; Terry lectr, Yale, 63-64; mem. comn. lit, NCTE, 64-68; fel, Sch. Lett, Ind. Univ, 65-; Berg prof, N.Y. Univ, 66-67; Presidential appointee, White House Task Force Educ, 66-67, Nat. Counc. Humanities, 68-74, v.chmn, 71-; McDonald lectr, McGill Univ, 68; Willett vis. prof, Univ. Chicago, 68-69; mem. bd, Nat. Humanities Fac, 68-; Phi Beta Kappa vis. scholar, 69-70; Ctr. Advan. Stud. Behav. Sci. fel, 73-74; Bd. For. Scholar. Lincoln lectr, Africa, 73-74. Chevalier, Palmes Académiques. Renaissance Soc. Am; MLA; Cambridge Bibliog. Soc; Mod. Humanities Res. Asn, Gt. Brit; Milton Soc. Am.(pres, 67); Cath. Comn. Intellectual & Cult. Affairs; NCTE; fel, Am. Acad. Arts & Sci. Renaissance literature and history of ideas; modern poetry and criticism; contemporary culture. Publ: Frontiers in American Catholicism, 57, American Catholic crossroads, 59, co-auth. & ed, Darwin's vision and Christian perspectives, 60, auth, The barbarian within, 62 & In the human grain, 67, Macmillan; Ramus, method, and the decay of dialogue, 58 & Ramus and Talon inventory, 58, Harvard; The presence of the Word, Yale, 67; co-auth. & ed, Knowledge and the future of man, Holt, 68; ed, Petrus Ramus and Audomarus Talaeus, collectanea praefationes, epistolae, orationes, 69 & Petrus Ramus, scholae in liberales artes, 70, Olms, Ger; auth, Rhetoric, romance, and technology, Cornell Univ, 71; Latin language study as a Renaissance puberty rite, Stud. Philol, 4/59; Oral residue in Tudor prose style, PMLA, 6/65; Evolution, myth, and poetic vision, Comp. Lit. Stud, 1/66. Add: Dept. of English, St. Louis University, St. Louis, MO 63103.

ONORATO, RICHARD JAMES, b. New York, N.Y, Mar. 8, 33; div; c. 2. ENGLISH & AMERICAN LITERATURE. A.B, Columbia Col, 54; Columbia Univ. Kellett fel. & A.B, Cambridge, 56; univ. fel. & A.M, Harvard, 59, univ. fel, 59-63, Ph.D.(Eng), 66. Instr. ENG. & AM. LIT, BRANDEIS UNIV, 63-66, asst. prof, 66-71, ASSOC. PROF, 71-, dean stud, 69-71. U.S.A, 56-58, Res, 58-61. AAUP. Romantic and modern literature; applied psychoanalysis. Publ: The character of the poet: Wordsworth in The Prelude, Princeton Univ, 71. Add: Dept. of English, Brandeis University, Waltham, MA 02154.

ONUSKA, JOHN THOMAS, JR, b. Port Chester, N.Y, Dec. 31, 37; m. 65; c. 1. ENGLISH. A.B, Col. Holy Cross, 59; Woodrow Wilson fels, Harvard, 63-66, M.A, 63, univ. fel. & Ph.D.(Eng), 66. Lectr. humanities, Mass. Inst. Technol, 66-67; asst. prof. ENG, UNIV. MO-ST. LOUIS, 67-72, ASSOC. PROF, 72-, res. grant, summer 68. U.S.N, 59-62, Lt. MLA; Midwest Mod. Lang. Asn; Shakespeare Asn. Am. Elizabethan and Jacobean drama; Shakespeare; Milton. Publ: The equation of action and passion in Samson Agonistes, Philol. Quart, 73; They also serve: the significance of Shakespeare's bit players, In: Literary studies: essays in memory of Francis A. Drumm, Cultura, 73. Add: Dept. of English, University of Missouri-St. Louis, 8001 Natural Bridge Rd, St. Louis, MO 63121.

ONWUEMENE, MICHAEL CHUKWUELOKE, b. Issele-Uku, Nigeria, May 24, 39. ENGLISH. B.A, Ottawa Univ, 65; M.A, Univ. Kans, 66, Ph.D.(Eng), 70. ASST. PROF. ENG, MILLIKIN UNIV, 69- AAUP; Mediaeval Acad. Am; NCTE; MLA. Add: Dept. of English, Millikin University, Decatur, IL 62522.

OOSTENDORP, JOHN ANTHONY, b. West Liberty, Iowa, Dec. 21, 26; m. 57; c. 3. SPEECH, HISTORY. B.A, State Univ. Iowa, 48, M.A, 49, Ph.D. (speech), 65. Instr. speech, Univ. R.I, 52-56, asst. prof, 56-57; Ill. State Norm. Univ, 57-58; UNIV. WIS-RIVER FALLS, 58-66, assoc. prof. SPEECH, 66-69, PROF, 69-, coord. res, 66-70. Speech Commun. Asn. Rhetorical criticism; behavioral research in speech. Add: Dept. of Speech, University of Wisconsin-River Falls, River Falls, WI 54022.

OPDAHL, KEITH MICHAEL, b. Chicago, Ill, Nov. 4, 34; m. 65; c. 2. ENGLISH. B.A, Denison Univ, 56; M.A, Univ. Ill, 57, Ph.D.(Eng), 61. Instr. ENG, Univ. Wis-Madison, 61-63, asst. prof, 63-67; DePAUW UNIV, 67-69, ASSOC. PROF, 69- Univ. Wis. res. grant, summer 62; DePauw Univ. res. grant, summer 68; res. grants, DePauw Univ-Ford Found. Humanities, summers 69, 70 & 71; Fulbright lectr, Univ. Coimbra, 72. American literature, especially modern; creative writing. Publ: The novels of Saul Bellow: an introduction, Pa. State Univ, 67; His stories lay quiet siege, Xian Sci. Monitor, 1/70; Bellow's planet, Commonweal, 2/70. Add: Dept. of English, DePauw University, Greencastle, IN 46135.

OPPENHEIMER, PAUL, b. New York, N.Y, May 1, 39; m. 69; c. 2. MEDIEVAL LITERATURE, WRITING. B.A, Princeton, 61; M.A, Columbia Univ, 62, Ph.D.(comp. medieval lit), 69. Lectr. Eng, Hunter Col, 64-67; CITY COL. NEW YORK, 67-69, ASST. PROF. MEDIEVAL LIT. & ENG, 70- Alfred Hodder fel, Princeton, 69-70. Comparative medieval literature; poetry; the theatre. Publ: Before a battle and other poems, Harcourt, 67; transl, A pleasant vintage of Till Eulenspiegel, Wesleyan Univ, 72; auth, Fantasy theatre: magicians, madmen and beauty, spring 71 & Classical theatre: some new productions of Shakespeare, summer 71, Dimensions; R.P. Blackmur and the poetics of the provisional, Castalian, fall 73. Add: Dept. of English, City College of New York, 133rd St. & Convent Ave, New York, NY 10031.

ORANGE, LINWOOD ELDEN, b. Hagerstown, Md, Apr. 22, 22. ENGLISH. B.A, Duke Univ, 47, M.A, 48, Ph.D.(Eng), 55. Instr. Eng, Davidson Col, 49-51; Duke Univ, 51-52; prof. Eng. & chmn. div. lang. & lit, Carey Col, 55-56; assoc. prof. Eng, UNIV. SOUTH. MISS, 56-59, PROF. ENG. & CHMN. DEPT, 68-, dir. freshman Eng, 59-67. Mem, Miss. Comt. Humanities, Nat. Endowment for Humanities, 70- U.S.A.A.F, 43-45, 2nd Lt. MLA; S.Cent. Mod. Lang. Asn; S.Atlantic Mod. Lang. Asn. Elizabethan drama; Milton, Spenser and Shakespeare. Publ: English: the pre-professional major, MLA, 72; Bussy D'Ambois: the web of pretense, South. Quart, 10/69; Non-teaching careers for English majors, Bull, Asn. Dept. Eng, 3/73; All bent to mirth: Spenser's humorous word play, S.Atlantic Quart, 73. Add: Dept. of English, University of Southern Mississippi, Hattiesburg, MS 39401.

ORAS, ANTS, b. Tallinn, Estonia, Dec. 8, 00. ENGLISH. Ph.M, Tartu Univ, Estonia, 23, Docent, 32; Univ. Leipzig, 23-24; B.Litt, Oxford, 28; Docent, Univ. Helsinki, 34. Instr. Eng, Tartu Univ, 28-34; personal prof, 34-38, prof, 38-43, acting head dept. west. lang. & lit, 40-41; lectr, bd. extramural stud, Cambridge, 45-46; vis. prof. ENG, UNIV. FLA, 49-50, prof, 50-72, EMER. PROF, 72- Vis. prof, Univ. Helsinki, 57-58; Am. specialist, Dept. State, Sweden & Finland, 65; chmn. discussion groups, MLA. Visnapuu prize for best book in Estonian, 62, 65; Annual Prize, Estonian Cult. Fund in Am, 71. MLA; S.Atlantic Mod. Lang. Asn; Estonian Learned Soc. Am; PEN Club (v.pres, Estonian Ctr, 67, 68, pres, 72-74); Nat. Asn. Lit. Hist. Finland. Comparative literature; Estonian literature; poetical translation. Publ: Milton's editors and commentators, 1695-1801, Oxford & Univ. Tartu, 31, 3rd ed, Haskell House, 68, Oxford Univ, 69; The critical ideas of T.S. Eliot, 32 & Shelleys poetic imagery, 38, Univ. Tartu; Baltic eclipse, Gollancz, London, 48; Pause patterns in Elizabethan and Jacobean drama, 60 & Blank verse and chronology in Milton, 66, Univ. Fla; ed. & transl, Bucolica-Kazjaselaulud of Vergil (Latin & Estonian), Estonian Learned Soc. Am, 70; auth, Lyrical instrumentation in Marlowe, In: Studies in Shakespeare, Univ. Miami, 53; The multitudinous orb; some Miltonic elements in Shelley, Mod. Lang. Quart, 55; Spenser and Milton: some parallels on the handling of sound, In: Sound and poetry, Columbia Univ, 57. Add: 1226 N.W. Fourth Ave, Gainesville, FL 32601.

ORBISON, THEODORE TUCKER, b. Albany, N.Y, Aug. 8, 25; m. 48; c. 4. ENGLISH DRAMA, RENAISSANCE LITERATURE. B.A, Yale, 49; M.A, Trinity Col.(Conn), 56; Ph.D.(Eng. lit), Boston Univ, 63. Instr. ENG, BUCKNELL UNIV, 61-64, asst. prof, 64-72, ASSOC. PROF, 72-, summer grants, 64, 71. Malone Soc; MLA. Renaissance drama; mythology. Publ: The tragic vision of John Ford, Univ. Salzburg, (in press); Traces of two Jacobean dramatic performances at the Middle Temple, Yearbk. Eng. Stud, 71; The case for the attribution of a Chapman letter, Stud. Philol, (in press); This distracted globe: self in Hamlet, In: Perspectives on Hamlet, Bucknell Univ, (in press). Add: Dept. of English, Bucknell University, Lewisburg, PA 17837.

ORDOUBADIAN, REZA, Linguistics. See Volume III, Foreign Languages, Linguistics & Philology.

OREL, HAROLD, b. Boston, Mass, Mar. 31, 26; m. 51; c. 2. ENGLISH LANGUAGE & LITERATURE. B.A, Univ. N.H, 48; M.A, Univ. Mich, 49, Ph.D, 52; Harvard, summer, 49. Instr. Eng, Univ. Md, 52-54, 55-56, overseas prog, 54-55; admin. assoc, applied phys. lab, Johns Hopkins Univ, 56; pub. specialist, Gen. Elec. Co, Evendale, Ohio, 57; assoc. prof. ENG, UNIV. KANS, 57-62, PROF, 62- Tech. consult, Midwest Res. Inst, Kans. City, Mo, 58-; Am. Philos. Soc. grant, 64; Am. Counc. Learned Soc. grant, 67. U.S.N, 44-46. MLA; Am. Comt. Irish Stud.(v.pres, 61-70, pres, 70-72); Int. Asn. Univ. Prof. Eng; Thomas Hardy Soc, Eng.(v.pres, 67-). Victorian and American literature; modern British literature. Publ: World of Victorian humor, 61 & co-ed, British poetry, 1880-1920, 69, Appleton; co-auth, Six studies in nineteenth century English literature and thought, 62, auth, The development of William Butler Yeats, 68 & co-ed, The nineteenth-century writer and his audience, 69, Humanistic Ser, Univ. Kans; Thomas Hardy's The Dynasts, Univ. Kans, 63; ed, Thomas Hardy's personal writings: prefaces, literary criticism, reminiscences, Univ. Kans, 66 & Macmillan, England, 67; auth, English Romantic poets and the Enlightenment: nine essays on a literary, Voltaire Found, 73; English critics and the Russian novel: 1850-1917, Slavonic & E.Europ. Rev, 6/55; Synge's last play, Mod. Drama, 12/61; The forgotten ambassadors: Russian fiction in Victorian England, Am. Slavic & E.Europ. Rev, 10/63. Add: Dept. of English, University of Kansas, Lawrence, KS 66045.

ORGEL, STEPHEN KITAY, b. New York, N.Y, Apr. 11, 33. ENGLISH. B.A, Columbia Univ, 54; Woodrow Wilson fel, Harvard, 54-55, Dexter fel. & Ph.D, 59. Instr. ENGLISH, Harvard, 59-60; asst. prof, UNIV. CALIF, BERKELEY, 60-66, assoc. prof, 66-72, PROF, 72- Am. Counc. Learned Soc. study fel, 67-68. MLA; Renaissance Soc. Am. Renaissance poetry, especially non-dramatic; the English court masque; Shakespearean drama. Publ: The Jonsonian masque, Harvard, 65; ed, Ben Jonson, complete masques, Yale, 69 & Marlowe, complete poems and translations, Penguin, 71; co-auth, Inigo Jones, Univ. Calif, 73; plus two others. Add: Dept. of English, University of California, Berkeley, Berkeley, CA 94720.

O'RILEY, MARGARET CATHERINE, b. Durant, Okla, Aug. 3, 13. ENGLISH & IRISH LITERATURE. A.B, Southeast. Okla. State Col, 33; M.A, Okla. State Univ, 37; Ph.D.(Eng), Univ. Wis, 55. Instr. ENG, Okla. high schs, 33-39; Cameron Col, 39-41; Lawton High Sch, 41-46; Univ. Mo, 46-49; asst. Univ. Wis, 49-50; asst. prof, Wis. State Col, Superior, 53-54; assoc. prof, Minn. State Col, Mankato, 55-57; PROF, SOUTHEAST. STATE COL, 57-, HEAD DEPT, 71- MLA; Col. Eng. Asn; NCTE; S.Cent. Col. Eng. Asn.(secy-treas, 71-72, pres, 72-73). Contemporary Irish drama; 20th century English literature; 19th century English literature. Add: Dept. of English, Southeastern State College, Durant, OK 74701.

ORLIK, PETER BLYTHE, b. Hancock, Mich, Sept. 30, 44; m. 67; c. 1. RADIO & TELEVISION. B.A, Wayne State Univ, 65, M.A, 66, Ph.D.(speech), 68. Intern & copywriter, Campbell-Ewald Co, 65; instr. mass commun, Wayne State Univ, 66-69; asst. prof. SPEECH, CENT. MICH. UNIV, 69-71; ASSOC. PROF, 71-, HEAD BROADCAST & CINEMATIC ARTS, 70- Consult, U.S. broadcasting, Univ. Leicester Ctr. for Mass Commun. Res, 70. Asn. Educ. Jour; Broadcast Educ. Asn.(co-chmn. course & curricula comt, 73-74, chmn, 74-75, course outline ed, writing & music course outlines, 72-); Nat. Asn. Educ. Broadcasters; Soc. Teachers Speech & Drama. Comparative and international broadcasting; music in broadcasting; theory of oral interpretation. Publ: A survey of public school radio in the United States, Wayne State Univ, 66; Under Damocles' sword: the South African press, Jour. Quart, summer 69; Three dailies' views of the United Nations, Journalisme, fall 71; contrib, Broadcasting in Africa: a continental survey of radio and television, Temple Univ, 74. Add: Broadcast & Cinematic Arts Area, Moore Hall 340, Central Michigan University, Mt. Pleasant, MI 48859.

ORLOSKY, ELIZABETH BROWN, b. Angola, Ind, Apr. 13, 20; m. 48; c. 2. SPEECH, ENGLISH. B.A, DePauw Univ, 42; M.A, Ball State Univ, 62; Ind. Univ, Ft. Wayne, 67. Teacher speech & Eng, Walkerton High Sch, Ind, 42-43; Fairmount High Sch, 43-44; Rochester High Sch, 44-48; prof. lectr. & interpretative reader, Beth Orlosky Prog. Bur, Angola, Ind, 48-56; ASSOC. PROF. SPEECH & ENG, TRI-STATE COL, 56- Speech Commun. Asn; Am. Forensic Asn; Cent. States Speech Asn. Publ: The glacier (poem), 61 & Thread of womanhood (poem), 63, Nat. Anthology Poetry; Royalties (poem), Col. Eng, 1/62; plus others. Add: 213 S. Kinney, Angola, IN 46703.

ORMES, ROBERT MANLY, b. Colorado Springs, Colo, Sept. 27, 04; m. 37; c. 2. ENGLISH, CLASSICS. A.B, Colo. Col, 26, A.M, 27. Lectr. Eng. & classics, COLO. COL, 50-56, instr, 56-57, asst. prof, 57-64, assoc. prof, 64-73, EMER. PROF. ENG, 73- Railroads of the Rocky Mountain region; the Colorado Rockies. Publ: Guide to the Colorado Rockies; Pike Peak atlas, 62 & Colorado skylines, 67, privately pub; Railroads and the Rockies, Sage Bks, 63; Ghost railroads of Colorado, 74. Add: 22 E. Del Norte, Colorado Springs, CO 80907.

ORNSTEIN, ROBERT, b. New York, N.Y, Nov. 3, 25; m. 51; c. 3. ENGLISH. A.B, N.Y. Univ, 48; A.M, Univ. Wis, 49, Ph.D.(Eng), 54; Fulbright scholar, Univ. London, 51-52. Instr. ENG, Oberlin Col, 52-54; Univ. Conn, 54-58; asst. prof, Univ. Ill, 58-61, assoc. prof, 61-63, PROF, 63-66; CASE WEST. RESERVE UNIV, 66-, chmn. dept, 66-68. Guggenheim fel, 61-62; Nat. Endowment for Humanities grant to make three educ. films, 71-72. Eng.C, U.S.A, 44-46. MLA (Eng. prog. adv. comt, 66-68, New Variorum Shakespeare Comt, 72-); Renaissance Soc. Am; NCTE. Elizabethan drama; Elizabethan intellectual history; Shakespeare. Publ: Moral vision of Jacobean tragedy, Univ. Wis, 60; Shakespeare in the classroom, Educ. Illustrators, 60; ed, Discussions of Shakespeare's problem comedies, 61 & co-auth, Elizabethan and Jacobean comedy, 64 & Elizabethan and Jacobean tragedy, 64, Heath; auth, A kingdom for a stage: the achievement of Shakespeare's history play, Harvard Univ, 72; The ethic of the imagination: love and art in Antony and Cleopatra, In: Later Shakespeare, E. Arnold Ltd, 66; Marlowe and God: the tragic theology of Dr. Faustus, PMLA, 10/68; Shakespeare and Jonsonian comedy, Shakespeare Surv, 69; plus one other. Add: Dept. of English, Case Western Reserve University, Cleveland, OH 44106.

O'ROURKE, JOSEPH, b. Davenport, Iowa, May 11, 28; m. 52; c. 1. SPEECH. A.B, Univ. Mo, 52, M.A, 54, Ph.D.(speech), 67. Instr. SPEECH, Univ. Hawaii, Hilo, 54-56; Univ. Mo, 56-60; ASSOC. PROF, WABASH COL, 60- U.S.A, 46-48, 52-53, 1st Lt. Speech Commun. Asn. Rhetoric; public address; Irish oratory. Add: Dept. of Speech, Wabash College, Crawfordsville, IN 47933.

ORR, GUSS, b. Coushatta, La, Mar. 15, 10; m. 55; c. 1. ENGLISH. B.A, Northwest. State Univ, 32; M.A, La. State Univ, 33, fel, 37-39, Ph.D.(Eng), 41. Teacher & asst. prin. high sch, La, 33-37; asst. instr. Eng, La. State Univ, 39-40; assoc. prof, Southeast. La. Univ, 40-42, prof, 46-70, head dept. Eng, 56-67, dean sch. humanities, 67-70; PROF. ENG. & AM. LIT, DELTA STATE UNIV, 70- U.S.N.R, 42-46, Res, 46-70, Comdr.(Ret). MLA; NCTE; S.Cent. Mod. Lang. Asn. Eighteenth century drama; 19th century prose and poetry; American literature. Add: 706 W. Colorado Ave, Hammond, LA 70401.

ORR, JOHN B, b. Jan. 22, 16; U.S. citizen; m. 41; c. 4. ENGLISH & AMERICAN STUDIES. M.A, Univ. Minn, 48. Instr. ENG, Aleppo Col, Syria, 37-40; Robert Col, Istanbul, 40-44; Univ. Minn, 45-54; ASSOC. PROF, WEST. MICH. UNIV, 55- U.S.N.R, 44-45, Lt. MLA; NCTE. Images of American in the modern French novel. Add: Dept. of English, Western Michigan University, Kalamazoo, MI 49001.

ORRELL, JOHN OVERTON, b. Maidstone, Eng, Dec. 31, 34; m. 56; c. 2. ENGLISH. B.A, Oxford, 58, M.A, 63; M.A, Univ. Toronto, 59, Can. Counc. fel, 59-61, Ph.D.(Eng), 64. Asst. prof. ENG, UNIV. ALTA, 61-68, assoc. prof, 68-74, PROF, 74- Elizabethan and Jacobean drama; British television drama. Publ: Ed, Studies of major works in English, Oxford Univ. Press, Toronto, 68. Add: Dept. of English, University of Alberta, Edmonton, Alta, Can.

ORSINI, GIAN NAPOLEONE (GIORDANO), b. Parma, Italy, Aug. 8, 03; m. 49. COMPARATIVE LITERATURE. D.Litt, Univ. Rome, 25, Ph.D, 28. Asst. prof. Eng, Univ. Florence, Italy, 27-37, prof, 44-50; Univ. Milan, 37-40; comp. lit, Univ. Wis-Madison, 49-74; RETIRED. Vis. prof, Duke Univ, 47-49; mem, Inst. Advan. Stud, 56-57; Inst. Res. Humanities, 62-63; Nat. Found. Arts & Humanities sr. award, 67-68. MLA; Eng. Asn, Gt. Brit. Literary criticism; English and Italian literary interrelations; Renaissance and Romantic period; philosophy. Publ: B. Croce, philosopher of art and literary critic, South. Ill. Univ, 61; The Italian Renaissance in England, Sansoni, 35; Coleridge and Schlegel reconsidered, Comp. Lit, spring 64; J.A. Symonds and F.De Sanetis, Stud. in Renaissance, 65. Add: 1815 Adams St, Madison, WI 53711.

ORTEGO, PHILIP D, b. Blue Island, Ill, Aug. 23, 26. LITERATURE, LINGUISTICS. B.A, Tex. West. Col, 59; M.A, Univ. Tex, El Paso, 66; Ph.D. (Eng. lang. & lit), Univ. N.Mex, 71; cert. mgt. planning, Columbia Univ, 73. Teacher Span. & French, Munhall Pub. Schs, Pa, 52-53, 62-63; French, El Paso Pub. Schs, Tex, 63-65; instr. Eng, N.Mex. State Univ, 65-69; teaching asst, Univ. N.Mex, 69-70; asst. prof. Eng. & dir. Chicano affairs, Univ. Tex, El Paso, 70-72; prof. urban stud. & asst. to pres, Metrop. State Col, 72-73; LECTR, ENG, MEX-AM. GRAD. STUD. & SOCIAL WORK, SAN JOSE STATE UNIV, 73- Fulbright lectr. Am. Stud, 71; consult, Educ. Comn. of States, 72; Counc. Social Work Educ, 73-74; Nat. Counc. Laraza, 73-74; West. Interstate Comn. Higher Educ, 74. U.S.M.C, 44-47, Res, 47-50; U.S.A.F, 53-62, Res, 52-53, Capt. AAUP; NCTE (chmn. minority affairs comt, 73-74); Ling. Soc. Am; Col. Eng. Asn; Chicano Teachers Eng.(pres, 72-73). Language, culture and behavior; literary history; bilingual education. Publ: Co-auth, Problems and strategies in teaching the language arts to Spanish speaking Mexican American children, U.S. Off. Educ, 69 & Issues in language and reading instruction of Spanish speaking children, Int. Reading Asn, 69; ed, The linguistic imperative in teaching English to speakers of other languages, Ctr. Appl. Ling, 70; co-auth, Montezuma's children, Amerex, 71; ed, Selective Mexican American bibliography, Border Libr. Asn, 72 & We are Chicanos: anthology of Mexican American literature, Washington Square, 73; Backgrounds of Mexican American literature, Marfel Publ, 74; co-ed, Chicano content and social work education, Counc. Social Work Educ, 74; auth, the minority on the border, Nation, 12/67; Schools for Mexican Americans, Saturday Rev, 4/71; The Mexican Americans, Encycl. Americana Annual, 71. Add: Dept. of Mexican American Graduate Studies, San Jose State University, San Jose, CA 95192.

ORTH, MELVIN FAY, b. Chester, Nebr, May 24, 21; m. 42; c. 2. ENGLISH. B.A, Nebr. State Teachers Col, 42; M.A, Colo. State Col. Educ, 48; Ph.D. (Eng. lit), Univ. Colo, 53. Teacher high sch, Nebr, 46-48; instr, Colo. State Col. Educ, 48-49; Univ. Colo, 49-52; asst. prof. & supvr. stud. teaching Eng, Cent. Mo. State Col, 52-53; instr. ENG, UNIV. WYO, 53-62, assoc. prof, 62-64, PROF, 64-, assoc. dean Col. Arts & Sci, 63-72. E.L. Phillips Found. internship, 63-64; ed. consult, U.S. Bur. Mines, Laramie Br, 66- U.S.A, 42-46. NCTE. Later 19th century literature; Western history and literature; scientific writing. Publ: Stevenson as a novelist; Abstracting for the writer, IEEE Trans. Prof. Commun, 6/72; An approach to better technical report writing, Engr. Educ, 1/74. Add: Dept. of English, University of Wyoming, Laramie, WY 82070.

ORTH, RALPH HARRY, b. New York, N.Y, Oct. 5, 30; m. 55; c. 3. ENGLISH. B.A, Queens Col.(N.Y), 56; fels, Univ. Rochester, 56-59, Ph.D, 60. Instr. ENG, UNIV. VT, 59-61, asst. prof, 61-66, assoc. prof, 66-70, PROF, 70- Res. grants, Univ. Vt, 62, 63, 66 & Ctr. Ed. Am. Authors, 67-71; mem. ed. bd, The journals and miscellaneous notebooks of Ralph Waldo Emerson; Vt. coord, Am. Lit. Manuscripts. U.S.A, 51-53. MLA; Thoreau Soc. Publ: Ed, Vol. VI, 66 & co-ed, Vol. IX, 71 & Vol. XIII, (in prep), In: Journals and miscellaneous notebooks of Ralph Waldo Emerson, Harvard Univ; auth, Emerson lectures in Vermont, Vt. Hist, 7/65; An early review of The confidence-man, Emerson Soc. Quart, 66; Emerson, Thoreau and transcendentalism, In: American literary scholarship 1972, Duke Univ, 74; plus others. Add: Dept. of English, University of Vermont, Burlington, VT 05401.

ORTOLANI, BENITO, b. Rome, Italy, Aug. 18, 28; m. 66; c. 1. DRAMA, JAPANESE. Lic. philos, Facoltá Filos. Aloisianum, Gallarate, Italy, 51; Univ. Turin, 51-52; dipl. Japanese lang. & cult, Eiko Japanese Lang. Sch, 54; Univ. Frankfurt, 56-58; lic. theol, Hochsch. Sankt Georgen, 59; Ph.D. (drama), Univ. Vienna, 61. Instr. Latin, Sophia Univ, Japan, 54-55, assoc. prof. drama, 62-66; vis. prof. Japanese drama, Univ. New S.Wales, 66; assoc. prof. drama & theatre, Univ. Hawaii, 66-69; theatre arts, Columbia Univ, 69-71; PROF. comp. lit, BROOKLYN COL, 71-73, THEATRE, 73- Judge, Int. Festival Relig. Film, Vienna; adv. Japanese rep, Int. Symp. Theatre in the E. & in the W, Japanese Ctr. Int. Theatre, Tokyo, 63; Vatican radio rep, 2nd Int. Conf. Broadcasting Orgns. Sound & TV Sch. Broadcasting, Tokyo, 64; organizer, performances Tokyo Noh Ensemble, Ger. & Ital, 65; Sophia Univ. exhib. Noh masks & costumes, Rome, Milan, Vienna, Madrid, New York, Mexico City, 65; Univ. Hawaii Res. Counc. & Lang. & Area Ctr. Overhead res. & writing grant, 67-68; State Found. Cult. & Arts State Hawaii grant, 68; lectr, Princeton, Harvard, Univ. Calif, Berkeley, Univ. Vienna, Free Univ. Berlin & Univ. Madrid. Japanese Soc. Theatre Res; Int. Fed. Theatre Res; Am. Theatre Asn; Asn. Asian Stud. The history of the Japanese theatre, classic theatre and modernization; sociological and religious background of the Japanese actor. Publ: Das Kabukitheater: kulturgeschichte der anfaenge, Sophia Univ, 64; co-auth, Teatro Nô, Costumi e Maschere, Inst. Giapponese Cult, Rome, 70; auth, Shingeki: the maturing new drama of Japan, In: Studies in Japanese culture, Sophia Univ, 63; Das Japanische theater, In: Fernöstliches Theater, Kröner, Stuttgart, 66; Fukuda Tsuneari: modernization and Shingeki, In: Tradition and modernization in Japanese culture, Princeton Univ, 71; plus others. Add: Dept. of Theatre, Brooklyn College, Brooklyn, NY 11210.

ORUCH, JACK B, b. Omaha, Nebr, Mar. 22, 37; m. 58; c. 2. ENGLISH. B.A, Univ. Nebr, 59; Woodrow Wilson fels, Ind. Univ, 59-60 & 62-63, univ. fel, 60-61, Ph.D.(Eng), 64. Instr. ENG, UNIV. KANS, 63-64, asst. prof, 64-69, ASSOC. PROF, 69- Elizabeth Watkins fac. scholar, summer 65. MLA; NCTE. English Renaissance literature; Chaucer. Publ: Chaucer's worldly monk, Criticism, summer 66; Spenser, Camden, and the poetic marriages of rivers, Stud. Philol, 7/67; Imitation and invention in the Sabrina myths of Drayton and Milton, Anglia, summer 72; plus one other. Add: Dept. of English, University of Kansas, Lawrence, KS 66045.

ORVELL, MILES DAVID, b. New York, N.Y, Jan. 9, 44. ENGLISH & AMERICAN LITERATURE. A.B, Columbia Univ, 64; Woodrow Wilson fel, Harvard, 64-65, M.A, 65, N.Y. State Regents fel, 66-69, Ph.D.(Eng), 70. ASST. PROF. ENG, TEMPLE UNIV, 69- Nat. Endowment for Humanities younger humanist fel, summer 72. MLA; AAUP; Am. Stud. Asn. Modern American literature; the novel. Publ: Invisible parade: the fiction of Flannery O'Connor, Temple Univ, 73; The messianic sexuality of Miss Lonelyhearts, Stud. Short Fiction, spring 73; The camera and the magic of self-transformation in Buster Keaton, West. Humanities Rev, summer 73; Entirely fictitious—the fiction of Flann O'Brien, J. Irish Lit, 74. Add: Dept. of English, Temple University, Philadelphia, PA 19122.

OSBORN, JAMES MARSHALL, b. Cleveland, Ohio, Apr. 22, 06; m. 29; c. 2. ENGLISH LITERATURE. A.B, Wesleyan Univ, 28; A.M, Columbia Univ, 34; B.Litt, Oxford, 37, D.Litt, 68; hon. L.H.D, Kenyon Col, 63; hon. D.Litt, McGill Univ, 73. With Guaranty Trust Co, New York, N.Y, 28-32; res. assoc. Eng, YALE, 38-74, fel, Silliman Col, 57-74, adv. 17th century manuscripts & cur, OSBORN COLLECTION, UNIV. LIBR, 57-72, EMER. CUR, 72- Vis. lectr, Wesleyan Univ, 39-40; dir. training progs, State War Counc, Conn, 41-44; fels, Pierpont Morgan Libr, 53-, Royal Soc. Arts, 62-; trustee, Eng. Inst. 57-; mem, Inst. Hist. Res, Univ. London; trustee, Yale Libr. Assocs; Conf. Brit. Stud, 65-; fel, St. Catherine's Col, Oxford, 67- MLA; Mod. Humanities Res. Asn, Gt. Brit; Bibliog. Soc. Am; Nat. Munic. League; Bibliog. Soc, Eng; fel. Soc. Antiq. London; fel. Royal Hist. Soc. Sir Philip Sidney; Joseph Spence and the Pope circle; Edmond Malone and the history of English scholarship. Publ: Dryden facts and problems, Univ. Fla; The beginnings of autobiography in England, Univ. Calif, 59; ed, The Quenes maiesties passage, 60, co-ed, Shakespeare's poems, 64 & auth, Young Philip Sidney, 72, Yale Univ; Autobiography of Thomas Whythorne, 1528-1596, 61 & Spence's observations, anecdotes and characters of books and men, 66, Oxford Univ. Add: Box 1914, Yale Station, New Haven, CT 06520.

OSBORN, LYNN ROBERT, b. Webb City, Mo, May 30; 30; m. 55; c. 3. SPEECH, EDUCATION. B.A, Univ. Kans, 52, univ. fel, 52-53, M.A, 55, Danforth Found. grant, 60-61, Ed.D, 62. Asst. instr. speech, Univ. Kans, 52-54, instr. speech & radio, 54-55; advertising & pub. relat, Norris Bros, Lawrence, Kans, 57-58; admin. asst. to chmn. speech & drama, Univ. Kans, 58-60; chmn. educ. & psychol, Graceland Col, 61-62; asst. prof. & asst. chmn. speech & drama, Univ. Kans, 62-66, assoc. prof. speech, 66-69, prof. speech commun, 69-71, asst. dean res. fac, 67-71; PROF. speech & drama, CENT. WASH. STATE COL, 71-72, COMMUN, 72-, chmn. dept. speech & drama, 71-72. Head Eng. conversation curriculum, U.S. Dept. State & Inst. Int. Educ, for. stud. orientation ctr, Univ. Kans, 59-; Univ. Kansas res. grants, 62-63, 65-68; Speech & Drama Serv. Ctr. grants, 63-64; consult, Bur. Indian Affairs, 63-; consult, Assoc. Credit Bur. Am, 64-; Danforth Found. grant, 66-67; U.S. Off. Educ. grants, 66-68; consult, Nat. Endowment for Humanities, 68; participant, Speech Asn. Am-U.S. Off. Educ. Conf. Res. & Instr. Develop, 68, Int. Conf. World Commun. Probs, 72 & Nat. Develop. Conf. Teacher Educators Speech Commun, 73. U.S.A.F, 55-57, Res, 57-65, Capt. Can. Speech Asn; Int. Commun. Asn; Speech Commun. Asn; assoc. Nat. Indian Educ. Asn. Speech education; communication problems of the American Indian; speech communication and human relations. Publ: Speakers training handbook, Advertising & Sales Exec. Club, Kans. City, 59; Commercial radio in Kansas: 1908-1945, Radio-TV Res. Ctr, Univ. Kans, 63; Speech communication problems of Indians and Eskimos, Can. Speech Commun. J, spring 69; co-auth, Relevant speech education for the American Indian, Cent. States Speech J, winter 70; auth, Language, poverty, and the North American Indian, In: Language and poverty: perspectives on a theme, Markham, 70; plus two others. Add: 2001 Parklane Ave, Ellensburg, WA 98926.

OSBORN, MICHAEL McDONALD, b. Dothan, Ala, Apr. 18, 37; m. 60; c. 3. SPEECH. B.A, Univ. S.C, 58, M.A, 59; univ. fel, Univ. Fla, 59, Ph.D. (speech), 63. Asst. prof. speech, Am. Univ, 61-63; Univ. Iowa, 63-66; assoc. prof, MEMPHIS STATE UNIV, 66-69, PROF. SPEECH & DRAMA, 69-, DIR. GRAD. STUD, 72-, summer res. fel, 68, acting chmn. dept, 69-70. Old Gold fac. res. fel, Univ. Iowa, 65; assoc. ed, Speech Monogr, 68-71; Memphis State Univ. Found. summer res. award, 71. U.S.N.R, 54-62. Speech Commun. Asn.(v.chmn. rhet. & commun. theory div, 73-74); South. Speech Commun. Asn. The rhetorical metaphor; rhetoric and poetics. Publ: Co-auth, The metaphor in public address, Speech Monogr, 8/62; Attitudinal effects of selected types of concluding metaphors in persuasive speeches, In: The psychology of language, Markham, 72; auth, Archetypal metaphor in rhetoric: the light-dark family, In: Methods of rhetorical criticism: a twentieth century perspective, Harper, 72. Add: Dept. of Speech & Drama, Memphis State University, Memphis, TN 38152.

OSBORNE, WILBUR J, b. Highland Park, Mich, July 17, 38; m. 63. SPEECH. B.A, Wayne State Univ, 60, M.A, 62; Ph.D.(speech), Pa. State Univ, 66. Part time instr. speech, Wayne State Univ, 62; asst, Pa. State Univ, 62-66; ASST. PROF. ENG, KENT STATE UNIV, 66- Speech Commun. Asn; Int. Commun. Asn; Am. Psychol. Asn. Persuasion theory; attitude change; communication process. Add: Dept. of English, School of Speech, Kent State University, Kent, OH 44242.

OSBORNE, WILLIAM STEWART, b. Nichols, N.Y, Dec. 21, 23; m. 50. AMERICAN LITERATURE. B.A, Univ. N.C, 47; M.A, Columbia Univ, 48, Ph.D.(Eng), 60. Instr. ENG, Elon Col, 49-50; from instr. to PROF, SOUTH. CONN. STATE COL, 54-, chmn. dept, 72-75. Ed, Masterworks of Lit. Ser, Col. & Univ. Press. U.S.A.A.F, 43-45. S.Atlantic Mod. Lang. Asn; Asn. Depts. Eng. Southern literature; 19th century American literature, minor figures, literary interests. Publ: Ed. & introd, A new home, 65, Rob of the bowl, 65 & The power of sympathy and the coquette, 70, Col. & Univ; auth, Caroline M. Kirkland, Twayne, 72; ed. and introd, Swallow barn, Hafner, 72; auth, John P. Kennedy's Horse shoe Robinson: a novel with the utmost historical accuracy, Md. Hist. Mag, 9/64. Add: Dept. of English, Southern Connecticut State College, New Haven, CT 06515.

OSTERMEIER, TERRY HARLAN, b. New London, Wis, Apr. 15, 37; m. 64; c. 1. SPEECH COMMUNICATION. B.S, Wis. State Univ-Oshkosh, 59; M.A, Marquette Univ, 61; Ph.D.(speech commun), Mich. State Univ, 66. Instr. SPEECH COMMUN, State Univ. N.Y. Buffalo, 63-66, asst. prof, 66-67; assoc. prof, UNIV. WIS-WHITEWATER, 67-69, PROF. & CHMN. DEPT, 69-, acting chmn. dept, 68-69. Int. Commun. Asn; Speech Commun. Asn. Cross cultural communication; interpersonal communication feedback; video tape and communication research. Publ: Co-auth, A rejoinder to Combs and Miller, 9/68; Speech Teacher; auth, Effects of type and frequency of reference upon perceived source credibility & attitude change, Speech Monogr, 6/67; contrib, Readings in intercultural communication, Univ. Pittsburgh, 72. Add: Dept. of Speech Communication, 465 Heide Hall, University of Wisconsin-Whitewater, Whitewater, WI 53190.

OSTRIKER, ALICIA, b. New York, N.Y, Nov. 11, 37; m. 58; c. 2. ENGLISH. B.A, Brandeis Univ, 59; M.A, Univ. Wis, 61, Ph.D.(Eng), 64. Asst. prof. ENG, RUTGERS UNIV, NEW BRUNSWICK, 65-68, ASSOC. PROF, 68- Am. Asn. Univ. Women fel, 64-65; Am. Counc. Humanities younger scholar summer grant, 68. MLA. Blake; metrics; English and American lyric poetry. Publ: Vision and verse in William Blake, Univ. Wis, 65; Songs: a book of poems, Holt, 69; Song and speech in the metrics of George Herbert, 65 & Tennyson's early prosody, 67, PMLA; The lyric, In: Vol. II, Sphere history of English literature, 70. Add: Dept. of English, Rutgers University, New Brunswick, NJ 08903.

OSTROM, ALAN B, b. New York, N.Y, Mar. 2, 25; m. 46; c. 2. ENGLISH. B.A, Bard Col, 48; M.A, Columbia Univ, 50, Ph.D.(Eng), 59. Asst. instr. Eng, Ohio State Univ, 52-55; instr. humanities, Stevens Inst. Technol, 59-61; ENG, BROOKLYN COL, 61-66, asst. prof, 66-73, ASSOC. PROF, 73- Choice Bk. Award, 67. U.S.N, 43-46. Poetry; modern American literature; relationship between 20th century poetry and painting theories of romanticism. Publ: The poetic world of William Carlos Williams, South. Ill. Univ, 66; Huck Finn and the modern ethos, Centennial Rev, 72; Interpretations, In: Die amerikanische lyrik von Edgar Allan Poe bis Wallace Stevens, Wissenschaftliche Buchgesellschaft, Darmstadt, 72. Add: Dept. of English, Brooklyn College, Bedford Ave. & Ave. H, Brooklyn, NY 11210.

OSTROM, JOHN WARD, b. Middletown, N.Y, June 20, 03; m. 29; c. 1. ENGLISH. A.B, Gettysburg Col, 26, M.A, 30, hon. Litt.D, 52; Ph.D, Univ. Va, 47. Adv. & instr. ENG, Japanese govt. schs, Nagoya, Japan, 27-28; instr, Gettysburg Col, 28-35; Augustana Col.(Ill), 36-38; asst. prof, The Citadel, 40-44; WITTENBERG UNIV, 45-47, assoc. prof, 48-49, prof, 49-71, head dept, 48-60, EMER. PROF, 71- Ohioana Libr. award, 48; lang. consult, Nat. Asn. Standard Med. Vocabulary, 63. NCTE. Improvement of English composition, especially in high schools; letters of Edgar Allan Poe. Publ: Letters of Edgar Allan Poe, Harvard, 48 & reprinted Gordian, 66; Craft of composition, Holt, 53; Better paragraphs, Chandler Publ, 61, rev. ed, 68 & 73; The letters of Poe: quest and answer, Baltimore Bull. Educ, Vol. XLIII, No. 1. Add: 823 Snowhill Blvd, Springfield, OH 45504.

OTT, FRIEDRICH PETER, Comparative Literature, German. See Volume III, Foreign Languages, Linguistics & Philology.

OTTEN, CHARLOTTE FENNEMA, b. Chicago, Ill, Mar. 1, 26; m. 48; c. 2. ENGLISH & AMERICAN LITERATURE. A.B, Calvin Col, 49; M.A, Univ. Mich, Ann Arbor, 69; Ph.D.(Eng), Mich. State Univ, 71. VIS. LECTR. ENG, GRAND VALLEY STATE COL, 72- Am. Counc. Learned Soc. grant-in-aid, 73. MLA; Milton Soc; Midwest Mod. Lang. Asn. Seventeenth century botanico-literary studies; contemporary American literature; poetry of John Milton. Publ: Homer's moly and Milton's rue, Huntington Libr. Quart, 8/70; Milton's daffadillies, Eng. Lang. Notes, 9/73; Milton's paradise and English gardens, Milton Stud, 73. Add: 48 Baynton, N.E, Grand Rapids, MI 49503.

OTTEN, TERRY RALPH, b. Dayton, Ky, Apr. 15, 38; m. 60; c. 2. ENGLISH. A.B, Georgetown Col, 59; M.A, Univ. Ky, 61; Ph.D.(Eng), Ohio Univ, 66. Instr. ENG, West. Ky. State Col, 61-63; Ohio Univ, 65-66; asst. prof, WITTENBERG UNIV, 66-70, ASSOC. PROF, 70- Abstracter, Abstracts Eng. Stud, 67-72; Nat. Endowment for Humanities summer stipend, 73. MLA; NCTE. Nineteenth century English literature; drama; relationship between tragedy and melodrama. Publ: The deserted stage: the search for dramatic form in 19th century England, Ohio Univ, 72; Christabel, Beatrice and the encounter with evil, Bucknell Rev, 69; Action in Wordworth's Lucy poems, Ill. Quart, 71; Macaulay's secondhand theory of poetry, S.Atlantic Quart, spring 73; plus others. Add: Dept. of English, Wittenberg University, Springfield, OH 45501.

OTTO, DON HENRY, b. Unionville, Mo, Sept. 1, 22; m. 46; c. 4. ENGLISH, EDUCATION. B.A, Quincy Col, 48; M.A, Drake Univ, 49; Ph.D.(Eng), Univ. South. Calif, 69. Teacher, high schs, Calif. & Iowa, 48-59; instr. ENG, Cerritos Col, 59-66; asst. prof, Univ. S.Dak, 66-67; PROF, Blackburn Col, 67-69, ST. CLOUD STATE COL, 69- Minn. State Col. res. grant, stud. imagery & teaching poetry, 72-74. NCTE(dir, 72-); Conf. Eng. Educ; NEA; MLA. English education, especially methods; teaching of poetry and film; 20th century British fiction. Publ: Co-auth, United States in literature, 63, 68, England in literature, 63, 68, Exploring life through literature, 63, 68 & Outlooks through literature, 63, 68, Scott; auth, Supervisory counseling and teacher morale, Teachers Col. J, 12/57; Junior high school publications, Clearing House, 10/58; Discovering persons in fiction, Education, 11/61. Add: R.F.D. 6, N. River Rd, St. Cloud, MN 56301.

OUELLETTE, EUGENE G, b. Lowell, Mass, Feb. 9, 29; m. 55; c. 2. SPEECH. B.A, Univ. Redlands, 57, M.A, 58; Ph.D.(speech), Univ. Wash, 60. Assoc. prof. speech therapy, San Diego State Col, 60-64; prof. speech therapy & chmn. dept. speech & drama, UNIV. REDLANDS, 64-71, CHANCELLOR, JOHNSTON COL, 71- Mem. int. bd. trustees, Asn. World Cols. & Univs. U.S.M.C, 53-56, 1st Lt. Am. Speech & Hearing Asn; Nat. Rehabil. Asn; Acoust. Soc. Am; AAUP; Am. Asn. Higher Educ. Audiology; voice therapy; stuttering. Add: Office of the Chancellor, Johnston College, University of Redlands, Redlands, CA 92373.

OWEN, CHAS. ABRAHAM, JR, b. Johnstown, Pa, June 5, 14; m. 46; c. 4. ENGLISH. A.B, Princeton, 35; B.Litt, Oxford, 39. Instr. ENG, Univ. Buffalo, 38-41; UNIV. CONN, 46-51, asst. prof, 51-59, assoc. prof, 59-63, PROF, 63- Mem. supv. comt, Eng. Inst, 66-, secy. comt, 69-74. U.S.A, 41-46, Capt. MLA; Mediaeval Acad. Am; New Eng. Col. Eng. Asn.(secy-treas, 57-66, 2nd v.pres, 66-67, 1st v.pres, 67-68, pres, 68-69). Publ: Discussions of the Canterbury tales, Heath, 61; The problems of free will in Chaucer's narratives, Philol. Quart, XLVI; Mimetic form in the central love scene of Troilus and Criseyde, Mod. Philol, 11/69; The tale of Melibee, Chaucer Rev, spring 73; plus others. Add: Dept. of English, University of Connecticut, Storrs, CT 06268.

OWEN, DAVID H, b. Chicago, Ill, Aug. 30, 11; m. 61; c. 4. ENGLISH. B.A, Lawrence Col, 35; M.A, Columbia Univ, 36; Ph.D, State Univ. Iowa, 49. PROF. ENG, SYRACUSE UNIV, 48- Ford fel, 55. U.S.N.R, 43-45, Lt. MLA. Twentieth century American novel. Add: Dept. of English, Syracuse University, Syracuse, NY 13210.

OWEN, GORDON RICHARD, b. Cincinnati, Ohio, Jan. 31, 24; m. 46; c. 5. PUBLIC SPEAKING. B.S, Univ. Minn, 48, M.A, 49; Ph.D.(speech), Purdue Univ, 62. Instr. speech & dir. forensics, N.MEX. STATE UNIV, 62-63, asst. prof. SPEECH, 63-65, assoc. prof, 65-71, PROF, 71- Sig.C, U.S.A, 43-46. NEA; Speech Commun. Asn; Am. Forensic Asn. Undergraduate speech instruction; history of public address; undergraduate instruction in communication. Publ: The beginning course: don't renovate, innovate, Speech Teacher, 1/70; Tijerina—agitator or demagogue?, Abstr, 12/71; N.C.D.A—an immodest proposal, Forensic, 10/72. Add: Dept. of Speech, New Mexico State University, Box 3W, Las Cruces, NM 88003.

OWEN, GUY, b. Clarkton, N.C, Feb. 24, 25; m. 52; c. 2. ENGLISH. A.B, Univ. N.C, Chapel Hill, 47, A.M, 49, Ph.D, 55. Instr. ENG, Davidson Col, 49-51; asst. prof, Elon Col, 54-55; assoc. prof, Stetson Univ, 55-62; N.C. STATE UNIV, 62-64, PROF, 64- Fel, Breadloaf Writer's Conf, 60; Yaddo fel, 67. U.S.A, 42-45. S.Atlantic Mod. Lang. Asn; Renaissance Soc. Am. Modern poetry; Southern literature. Publ: Season of fear, Random, 60; co-ed, Southern poetry today, Stetson Univ, 62; auth, The ballad of the flim-flam man, Macmillan, 65; Cape Fear country, New Athenaeum, 58; The white stallion and other poems, Blair, 69; Journey for Joedel (novel), 70 & The flim-flam man and the apprentice grifter (novel), 72, Crown; ed, Modern American poetry: essays in criticism, Everett Edwards, 72. Add: Dept. of English, North Carolina State University, Raleigh, NC 27607.

OWEN, JOHN ISAAC, b. Gilbertsville, Ky, Dec. 2, 00; m. 36. ENGLISH LITERATURE. A.B, Univ. Ky, 26, A.M, 27; Univ. Chicago, 29; Ph.D.(Eng), Univ. Ill, 52. Teacher, Pub. Schs, Ky, 20-22; asst. prof, Eng, The Citadel, 27-30; asst, Univ. Ill, 30-32, 33-45, 46-47; assoc. prof. Eng. & chmn. div. lang, lit. & arts, Ohio North. Univ, 47-50; assoc. prof. Eng, Anderson Col, 52-66; Taylor Univ, 66-67; RETIRED. MLA; AAUP. Shakespeare; the romantic movement; English novel. Publ: An edition of the rare triumphs of love and fortune, Diss. Abstr, 53. Add: Rte. 2, Box 112-B, Woodlawn, VA 24381.

OWEN, LAWRENCE S, b. Hereford, Tex, Feb. 1, 32; m. 58; c. 3. ENGLISH. B.A, Hardin-Simmons Univ, 53; M.A, Univ. Wyo, 61; Univ. Kans, 61-63, 66-67. Teacher high sch, Wyo, 56-57; instr. ENG, Univ. Mo. Sch. Mines, 58-59; West. Wyo. Jr. Col, 59-61; ASSOC. PROF, GUSTAVUS ADOLPHUS COL, 63-, chmn. dept, 73-76. U.S.A, 54-55. MLA. The poetry of Christopher Smart; modern drama; 18th century literature. Publ: Co-auth, A dialogue on teaching, New Directions in Teaching, spring 67. Add: Dept. of English, Gustavus Adolphus College, St. Peter, MN 56082.

OWEN, LEWIS J, b. Nanking, China, Apr. 2, 25; U.S. citizen; m. 58; c. 1. ENGLISH LITERATURE. A.B, Harvard, 49, A.M, 50; Fulbright fel, Univ. Edinburgh, 53-54; Ph.D, Univ. London, 58. Instr. Eng, Carnegie Inst. Technol, 50-53; Va. Mil. Inst, 54-56; Univ. Vt, 58-59; asst. prof, OCCIDENTAL COL, 59-63, assoc. prof, 63-67, prof, 67-73, PRICE PROF. ENG. LIT, 73-, chmn. dept. Eng. & comp. lit, 67-70. U.S.A.A.F, 43-46, S/Sgt. MLA; Renaissance Soc. Am; AAUP; Mediaeval Acad. Am. English medieval and Renaissance literature. Publ: Co-ed, Middle English poetry, Bobbs, 71; auth, The recognition scene in Sir Orfeo, Medium Aevum, 71; Mutable in eternity: Spenser's despair and the multiple forms of mutabilitie, J. Medieval & Renaissance Stud, spring 72; plus others. Add: Dept. of English, Occidental College, Los Angeles, CA 90041.

OWEN, WARWICK JACK BURGOYNE, b. Auckland, N.Z, May 12, 16; m. 45; c. 2. ENGLISH. M.A, Univ. Auckland, 38; B.A, Oxford, 41, M.A, 46; Ph.D, Univ. Wales, 56. Asst. lectr. ENG, Univ. Auckland, 38-39; Univ. Col. N. Wales, 46-49, lectr, 49-59, sr. lectr, 60-65; PROF, McMASTER UNIV, 65- Leave fel, Can. Counc, 73-74; fel, Inst. Advan. Stud. Humanities, Univ. Edinburgh, 73-74. R.A.O.C. & R.E.M.E, 42-46, Capt. MLA; Mod. Humanities Res. Asn; Asn. Can. Univ. Teachers Eng. Edmund Spenser; William Wordsworth. Publ: Wordsworth's preface to Lyrical ballads, Rosenkilde & Bagger, 57; Wordsworth & Coleridge, Lyrical ballads, 1798, Oxford Univ, 67; Wordsworth as critic, Univ. Toronto, 69; co-auth, Prose works of William Wordsworth, Clarendon, 74; auth, The structure of The faerie queene, PMLA, 53; Literary echoes in The prelude, Wordsworth Circle, 72; Annotating Wordsworth, In: Editing texts of the romantic period, Univ. Toronto, 72; plus two others. Add: Dept. of English, McMaster University, Hamilton, Ont. L8S 4M4, Can.

OWENS, CULLEN BRYANT, b. Dwarf, Ky, Apr. 24, 08. SPEECH. A.B, Berea Col, 31; M.S, Northwest. Univ, 35; Ph.D, Cornell Univ, 46. Instr. SPEECH, High Point Col, 35-38; Miami Univ, 38-40; Cornell Univ, 40-45; asst. prof, Univ. Ill, 45-52; ASSOC. PROF, UNIV. N.MEX, 52- Speech

Commun. Asn. British and American oratory; persuasion; rhetoric and public address. Add: Dept. of Speech, University of New Mexico, Albuquerque, NM 87106.

OWENS, CURTIS, b. Raven, Ky, Aug. 5, 07; c. 3. ENGLISH. A.B, Tusculum Col, 28; Yale, 29-30; M.A, Univ. Ky, 42. Teacher, pub. schs, Ky, 30-34, prin, 34-44; teacher ENG, PACE UNIV, 46-49, asst. prof, 49-55, assoc. prof, 55-70, PROF, 70- A.U.S, 44-45. Col. Eng. Asn. Education of the deprived; matters of political and social concern for use in creative writing. Publ: Preparation of the research theme, Pace Col, 49; A woman to remember, Reader's Scope, 6/47; Expanding educational opportunity, In: Instructional improvement through research, N.Y. State Educ. Dept, 65; Whose Dan Tucker?, J. Am. Folklore, 10-12/71. Add: Dept. of English, Pace University, Pace Plaza, New York, NY 10038.

OWENS, DAVID BENTON, b. Evans City, Pa, Sept. 28, 14. ENGLISH LITERATURE. B.Ed, Pa. State Col, 36, M.Ed, 37; Evangel. Lutheran Sem, 44-47. Ed. asst, The Butler Eagle, Pa, 37-44; instr. ENG, CAPITAL UNIV, 45-47, asst. prof, 47-54, assoc. prof, 54-58, PROF, 58-, univ. chaplain, 49-60, chmn. dept. Eng, 58-70. NCTE; MLA; Keats-Shelley Asn. Am. Percy Bysshe Shelley; a centennial history of Capital University; Greek drama. Publ: Co-auth, Modern journalism, Pitman, 62. Add: Dept. of English, Capital University, Columbus, OH 43209.

OWENS, ROBERT REILEY, b. York, Pa, Jan. 8, 20; m. 46; c. 3. ENGLISH. B.A, Dickinson Col, 41; M.A, Univ. Minn, 48, Ph.D.(Eng), 55. Instr. ENG, Univ. Tenn, 46, 49-51; teaching asst, Univ. Minn, Minneapolis, 46-47, 51-53, instr, 48-49, 53-55; asst. prof, UNIV. MINN, DULUTH, 55-60, assoc. prof, 60-67, PROF, 67-, dir. honors prog, 68-71, head dept, 69-71. Planning Off, Ministry Educ, Buganda, 64. U.S.A, 41-46, Res, 46-50, 1st Lt. Literature and science; Jonathan Swift; literature of travel and discovery in tropical Africa. Add: Dept. of English, University of Minnesota, Duluth, MN 55812.

OWENS, WILLIAM A, b. Blossom, Tex, Nov. 2, 05. ENGLISH. A.B, South. Methodist Univ, 32, A.M, 33; Ph.D, State Univ. Iowa, 41. Assoc. prof. ENG, Agr. & Mech. Col, Tex, 37-47; from asst. prof. to assoc. prof, COLUMBIA UNIV, 48-71, PROF, 71-, DIR. SUMMER SESSION, 59- Dir, Oral Hist. Tex. Oil, Univ. Tex, 52-58. MLA; Col. Eng. Asn.(treas, 48-50). American and folk literature; Texas folk music; Texas play party games. Publ: Walking on borrowed land, Bobbs, 54; Fever in the earth, Putnam, 58; Look to the river, Atheneum, 63; This stubborn soil, Scribner, 66. Add: Dept. of English, Columbia University, 420 Lewisohn Hall, New York, NY 10027.

OWINGS, MARVIN ALPHEUS, b. Rock Hill, S.C, Dec. 8, 09; m. 34; c. 3. ENGLISH. A.B, Wofford Col, 31; M.A, Vanderbilt Univ, 32, fels, 37 & 38, Ph.D. (Eng), 41. Instr. ENG, St. Johns, S.C, 33-36; asst. prof, Ga. South. Col, 39-40, assoc. prof, 41-42; CLEMSON UNIV, 46-50, prof, 51-66, alumni prof, 66-69, PROF. & HEAD DEPT, 69- U.S.A, 42-46, Col. MLA; Mediaeval Acad. Am; NCTE; Eng. Asn, Gt. Brit; Keats-Shelley Asn. Am; S.Atlantic Mod. Lang. Asn; Int. Arthurian Soc; Early Eng. Text Soc. Chaucer; medieval and metrical romances. Publ: The arts in the middle English romances, Bookman Assocs, 52. Add: Dept. of English, Clemson University, Clemson, SC 29631.

OWNBEY, EGBERT SYDNOR, b. Wilkesboro, N.C, July 11, 07; m. 30; c. 1. ENGLISH LITERATURE. A.B, Vanderbilt Univ, 27, A.M, 28, Ph.D, 32; Univ. Chicago, 29, 40. Asst. prof. ENG, BIRMINGHAM-SOUTH. COL, 30-39, assoc. prof, 39-47, PROF, 47- S.Atlantic Mod. Lang. Asn; MLA. Arthurian legend; Shakespeare; Victorian poetry. Publ: Robinson's Mr. Flood's party, 17-24, 4/50 & Shirley's The glories of our blood and state, 2/52, Explicator. Add: Dept. of English, Birmingham-Southern College, Birmingham, AL 35204.

P

PAANANEN, VICTOR NILES, b. Ashtabula, Ohio, Jan. 31, 38; m. 64; c. 2. ENGLISH. A.B, Harvard, 60; M.A, Univ. Wis, 64, Ph.D.(Eng), 67, Alumni Res. Found. & univ. fels. Instr. ENG, Wofford Col, 62-63; asst. prof, Williams Col, 66-68; MICH. STATE UNIV, 68-73, ASSOC. PROF, 73- MLA. Nineteenth and twentieth century British literature. Publ: Byron and the Caves of Ellora, Notes & Queries, 69. Add: Dept. of English, Michigan State University, East Lansing, MI 48824.

PACE, GEORGE B, b. Augusta, Ga, Nov. 9, 15; m. 58; c. 4. ENGLISH. B.A, Furman Univ, 37; M.A, Univ. Va, 39, DuPont res. fel, 41, Ph.D.(Eng), 42. Instr. ENG, Univ. Va, 46-47, asst. prof, 47-49; Univ. Mich, 50-51; UNIV. MO-COLUMBIA, 51-54, assoc. prof, 54-62, PROF, 62- Am. Counc. Learned Soc. award, 52, grant, summer 72; Fulbright lectr, 57-58. U.S.N.R, 42-46, Lt. Comdr. Ling. Soc. Am; Mediaeval Acad. Am; MLA. Chaucer; Middle English literature; English language. Publ: Co-auth, English literature, Macmillan, 60; Otho A. XVIII, Speculum, 4/51; auth, Adam's hell, 3/63 & co-auth, A new Chaucer MS, 3/68, PMLA. Add: Dept. of English, University of Missouri-Columbia, Columbia, MO 65201.

PACE, THOMAS JENNINGS, JR, b. Wichita Falls, Tex, June 22, 29; m. 51; c. 2. SPEECH. B.A, Southwest. Univ, 49, M.A, 53; Ph.D.(speech), Univ. Denver, 57. Teacher speech, Wichita Falls Sr. High Sch, Tex, 53-55; internship, Univ. Denver, 56-57, prof. rhetoric & pub. address, 58-59; PROF, speech, Midwest. Univ, 57-58, rhetoric & pub. address, 59-65; SPEECH, SOUTH. ILL. UNIV, CARBONDALE, 65- Vis. scholar, Northwest. Univ, 63-65; consult. group dynamics, Inst. Gen. Semantics, summer, 56. Speech Commun. Asn; Int. Commun. Asn. Philosophy of communication; interpersonal communication in small groups; image studies of political candidates. Add: Dept. of Speech, Southern Illinois University, Carbondale, IL 62901.

PACEY, DESMOND, b. Dunedin, N.Z, May 1, 17; m. 39; c. 7. ENGLISH LITERATURE. B.A, Univ. Toronto, 38; Massey traveling fel, Cambridge, 38-40, Ph.D, 41; hon. Litt.D, Mt. Allison Univ, 73; hon. D.Litt, Univ. N.B, Fredericton, 73. Prof. ENG, Brandon Col, 40-44; PROF. & HEAD DEPT, UNIV. N.B, FREDERICTON, 44-, ACAD. V. PRES, 70-, dean grad. stud, 60-73, acting pres, 72-73. Ed, Wartime Inform. Bd, 43; Can. Counc. sr. res. fel, Cambridge, 62-63; mem. acad. adv. panel, Can. Counc, 67-70; pres, Can. Asn. Grad. Schs, 66-68. Fel. Royal Soc. Can.(secy. sect. II, 66-69, Lorne Pierce Medal, 72); Asn. Can. Univ. Teachers Eng; Humanities Asn. Can. Canadian literature; comparative literature; 17th century English literature. Publ: Frederick Philip Grove, Ryerson, Toronto, 45 & ed, rev. ed, McGraw, Can. & Ryerson, Toronto, 70; ed, Book of Canadian stories, 47, rev. ed, 50, 52, 62, auth, Creative writing in Canada, 52, rev. ed, 62, Ten Canadian poets, 58 & Essays in Canadian criticism 1938-68, 69, Ryerson, Toronto; co-ed, Literary history of Canada, Univ. Toronto, 65; ed, Our literary heritage, Ryerson, Toronto & Macmillan, 66 & Tales from the margin, McGraw, Can. & Ryerson, Toronto, 71; auth, Ethel Wilson, Twayne, 68. Add: University of New Brunswick, Fredericton, N.B, Can.

PACK, ROBERT FREDERICK, b. Wheeling, W.Va, Feb. 13, 43; m. 65; c. 1. ENGLISH LITERATURE. B.A, W.Va. Univ, 65; Univ. Wis-Madison, 65-66; M.A, Univ. Pittsburgh, 67, Ph.D.(Eng), 70. ASST. PROF. ENG, DOUGLASS COL, RUTGERS UNIV, 70- MLA; Keats-Shelley Asn. Am; NCTE; Col. Eng. Asn; AAUP. English Romantic poetry; 19th century English social and political writing. Publ: Bryon's Ode to Napoleon, Rutgers Libr. J, 6/71. Add: Dept. of English, Douglass College of Rutgers University, New Brunswick, NJ 08903.

PACKARD, THEODORE HIRAM, b. Boston, Mass, Mar. 30, 11; m. 40; c. 5. ENGLISH, DRAMA. B.S, Tufts Col, 34; M.F.A, Yale, 41. Asst. Eng, Dartmouth Col, 37-38, instr, 38-42; teacher gen. sci, high sch, Mass, 42-46; asst. prof. ENG, Univ. Mass, Ft. Devens, 46-48; WORCESTER POLYTECH. INST, 48-55, ASSOC. PROF, 55- Am. Soc. Eng. Educ; Dramatists Guild. Playwriting. Add: Dept. of English, Worcester Polytechnic Institute, Worcester, MA 01609.

PADEN, WILLIAM DOREMUS, b. Parkersburg, W.Va, July 13, 03; m. 31; c. 2. ENGLISH LITERATURE. Ph.B, Yale, 25, A.M, 31, Ph.D, 35. Instr. mathematics, Univ. Tenn, 25-26; Trinity Col.(Conn), 29-31; ENG, Yale, 35-36; UNIV. KANS, 36-38, asst. prof, 38-45, assoc. prof, 45-51, prof, 51-74, EMER. PROF, 74- MLA. Nineteenth century English poetry. Publ: Tennyson in Egypt, 42; An investigation of Gondal, Bookman Assoc, 58; co-transl, Vilhelm Gronbech, Religious currents in the 19th century, Univ. Kans, 64; auth, Arthur O'Shaughnessy in the British Museum, Victorian Stud, 9/64; Tennyson's The lovers' tale, R.W. Shepherd, and T.J. Wise, Stud. in Bibliog, 65; The ancestry and families of Ford Madox Brown, Bull. John Rylands Libr, 3/68. Add: 838 Broadview Dr, Lawrence, KS 66044.

PADROW, BEN, b. New York, N.Y, Dec. 16, 27; m. 54; c. 2. SPEECH. B.S, Lewis & Clark Col, 49; M.S, Univ. Ore, 51. Dir. speech arts, high sch, Ore, 49-50; asst. dir. forensics, Univ. Ore, 50-52; dir. speech & drama, Palomar Col, 53-55; asst. prof. speech & dir. forensics, PORTLAND STATE UNIV, 56-63, assoc. prof. SPEECH, 63-68, PROF, 68-, HEAD DEPT, 67- Consult. commun, Int. Asn. Machinists, 62-65, Pac. Northwest Bell Telephone, 64-66, U.S. Forest Serv, 64-, Tektronix, Inc, Ore, 64-, U.S. Civil Serv. Comn, 66-, Volunteers Serv. Am, 66-, nursing serv, Veterans Hospital, Walla Walla, Wash, 67-, Northwest Mgt. Training Ctr, 68- & Omark Indust, 73; on leave, comnr, Multnomah County Govt, Ore, 71- Speech Commun. Asn; Nat. Soc. Stud. Commun; Am. Forensic Asn. American political public address; conference leadership and information briefing; interpersonal communication. Publ: Mark Hatfield: Oregonian orator, Today's Speech, 4/61; Oral briefing at Tektronix, Inst. Elec. & Electronics Engrs. Trans. on Educ, 9/70; Public hearings, public officials, and the hot seat, Nation's Cities, 2/74; plus others. Add: Board of County Commissioners, Multnomah County Courthouse, Portland, OR 97204.

PAFF, WILLIAM J, b. Wausau, Wis, Apr. 4, 07; m. 39; c. 2. ENGLISH. A.B, Univ. Wis, 28; A.M. & Ph.D, Harvard, 50. Instr. Eng, Northwest. Univ, 34-36; teaching fel, Harvard, 39-42; instr. ENG, Amherst Col, 42-45; Yale, 45-49; from asst. to assoc. prof, UNIV. IOWA, 50-59, PROF, 59- Mediaeval Acad. Am; MLA; Archaeol. Inst. Am; Soc. Advan. Scand. Stud. Germanic antiquities; mediaeval literature and language. Publ: Geographical and ethnic names in the Thrithriks saga, Harvard, 59. Add: Dept. of English, University of Iowa, Iowa City, IA 52240.

PAGE, ALEX, b. Czech, June 6, 23; nat. ENGLISH. B.A, Univ. Vt, 48; M.A, Harvard, 49, Ph.D, 53. Instr. ENG, Rutgers Univ, 53-56; UNIV. MASS, AMHERST, 56-57, asst. prof, 57-61, assoc. prof, 61-70, PROF, 70- Fulbright lectr. grant, Univ. Karachi, 61-62. U.S.A, 44-46. MLA; Am. Comp. Lit. Asn. The novel; 18th century literature; comparative literature. Publ: Transl. & introd, Three plays by Ernst Barlach, Univ. Minn, 64 & Goethe's West-Östlicher Divan, Gehenna, 73; co-ed, Masterpieces of western literature, W.C. Brown, 66; auth, Vater-Sohn Vergältnis in Barlach, Barlach Publs, 66; Faculty psychology and metaphor in 18th century Williams, Mod. Philol, 2/69; Origin of language and 18th century Williams, J. Eng. & Ger. Philol, 1/72; plus others. Add: Dept. of English, University of Massachusetts, Amherst, MA 01003.

PAGE, CORNELIUS ALBERT, b. Richmond, Va. OLD ENGLISH, LINGUISTICS. A.B, Va. Union Univ, 49; M.A, N.Y. Univ, 52; Ph.D.(Old & Middle Eng), Fordham Univ, 73. Instr. Eng, Fla. A&M Univ, 52; Tuskegee Inst, 52-55; Univ. Minn, 55-59; asst. prof, State Univ. N.Y. Col. Cortland, 59-64; dir. scholarship progs, Phelps-Stokes Fund, 64-69; dir. stud. activities, BARUCH COL, 69-72, ASST. PROF. LING, 72- AAUP; MLA. Medieval literature; general linguistics. Add: 490 Fourth St, Brooklyn, NY 11215.

PAGE, CURTIS CARLING, b. Roxbury, Mass, Dec. 21, 14; m. 42; c. 1. ENGLISH. A.B, Yale, 37, Ph.D.(Eng), 47, Instr. ENG, Lafayette Col, 41-43; asst. prof, Univ. Chattanooga, 46-49; assoc. prof, DRAKE UNIV, 49-56, PROF, 56-, asst. provost, 67-70. Ford fac. fel, 54-55; consult. training div, Peace Corps, 62, consult, 64-67. U.S.C.G.R, 43-46, Lt.(jg). MLA;

Am. Nat. Theatre & Acad; NCTE; Col. Conf. Compos. & Commun; AAUP. Drama; biographies of Stephen Phillips and Liberty Hyde Bailey. Publ: Chaucer's testimony concerning his sources; Drama: Synge's Riders to the sea, Ginn, 66. Add: Dept. of English, Drake University, Des Moines, IA 50311.

PAGE, MALCOLM, b. York, Eng, June 4, 35; m. 61; c. 4. ENGLISH. B.A, Cambridge, 58; dipl, Oxford, 59; M.A, McMaster Univ, 64; Ph.D.(Eng), Univ. Calif, Riverside, 66. ASSOC. PROF. ENG, SIMON FRASER UNIV, 66- Friends' Ambulance Unit Int. Serv, 53-55. MLA; NCTE; Asn. Can. Univ. Teachers Eng; Can. Counc. Teachers Eng. Twentieth century British drama and fiction, especially contemporary dramatists, Arnold Wesker and David Mercer. Publ: West Indian writers, Novel, winter 70; The early years at Unity, Theatre Quart, 10-12/71; The British television play, J. Popular Cult, spring 72; plus others. Add: Dept. of English, Simon Fraser University, Burnaby, B.C, Can.

PAGE, NORMAN, b. Kettering, Eng, May 8, 30; m. 58; c. 4. ENGLISH LITERATURE & LANGUAGE. B.A, Cambridge, 51, M.A, 55; Ph.D.(Eng), Leeds Univ, 68. Head dept. ENG, Ripon Col. of Educ, Eng, 60-69; from asst. prof. to ASSOC. PROF, UNIV. ALTA, 69- Victorian novel, especially Dickens and Hardy. Publ: Ed, Charles Dickens' Bleak House, Penguin, 71; auth, The language of Jane Austen, Blackwell, Oxford, 72; Speech in the English novel, Longman, London, 73; Convention and consistency in Dickens' cockney dialect, Eng. Stud, 70; Trollope's conversational mode, Eng. Stud. Africa, 72; Hardy's pictorial art in The mayor of Casterbridge, Etudes Anglaises, 72. Add: Dept. of English, University of Alberta, Edmonton, Alta. T6G 2E1, Can.

PAGE, W. E, JR, b. Trenton, N.C, Sept. 12, 31. ENGLISH LINGUISTICS. A.B, E.Carolina Col, 57; M.A, Fla. State Univ, 59; Pa. State Univ, 61-64. Instr. Eng, Towson State Col, 59-61; Pa. State Univ, 63-64; asst. prof, Fresno State Col, 64-67; ASSOC. PROF. ENG. LANG. & LING, WEST CHESTER STATE COL, 67- Mem, bibliog. comt, Gen. Ling. Sect, MLA, 65-; dir. summer inst. & workshop Teachers Eng. to Speakers Other Lang, West Chester State Col, 70, 71. U.S.A, 53-55. MLA; NCTE; Teachers Eng to Speakers Other Lang. English language and linguistics; American literature. Add: Dept. of English, West Chester State College, West Chester, PA 19380.

PAGE, WILLIAM DOUGLAS, b. Detroit, Mich, Oct. 7, 33; m. 59; c. 2. ENGLISH EDUCATION. B.F.A, Wayne State Univ, 59, M.Ed, 64, Ed.D.(curriculum), 70. Instr. READING, Wayne State Univ, 68-70; ASST. PROF, UNIV. CHICAGO, 70- Int. Reading Asn; NCTE; Am. Educ. Res. Asn. Oral reading miscues; psycholinguistics; clinical observation. Publ: Clinical uses of miscue research, In: Miscue analysis: applications in reading instruction, NCTE & ERIC/RCS, 73; Destructive myths that block the right to read, Reading World, 10/73; Are we beginning to understand oral reading, Reading World, 3/74. Add: Graduate School of Education, University of Chicago, 5835 Kimbark, Chicago, IL 60637.

PAGLIARO, HAROLD E, b. New York, N.Y, June 19, 25; m. 48, 66; c. 2. ENGLISH LITERATURE. A.B, Columbia Col, 47, M.A, Columbia Univ, 48, Ph.D.(Eng), 61. Lectr. Eng, Columbia Univ, 48-56, instr, 57-59, asst. prof, 60-64, dir. honors, sch. gen. stud, 62-64, fac. grant, 63; assoc. prof. ENG. LIT, SWARTHMORE COL, 64-71, PROF, 71-, CHMN. DEPT, 72-, PROVOST, 74- Old. Dom. grant, summer 68; Ford-Swarthmore & Mellon-Swarthmore grants, 69-70 & 73-74; mem, Sr. Common Rm, St. Edmund Hall, Oxford, 73-74. U.S.A, 43-45. MLA; Conf. Brit. Stud; AAUP; Am. Soc. 18th Century Stud. English Romantic poets; 18th century English. Publ: Henry Fielding's Journal of a voyage to Lisbon, Nardon Press, 63; Major English writers of the 18th century, Free Press & Macmillan, 68; ed, Studies in eighteenth-century culture, Proc. Am. Soc. 18th Century Stud, Vols. 2 & 3, Case West. Reserve Univ, 72 & 73 & Univ. Wis, 74; auth, Aphoristic paradox, PMLA, 3/64. Add: Dept. of English, Swarthmore College, Swarthmore, PA 19081.

PAIGE, HARRY W, b. Syracuse, N.Y, Sept. 25, 22; m. 46; c. 2. ENGLISH, AMERICAN INDIAN STUDIES. A.B, Union Col.(N.Y), 48; M.A, State Univ. N.Y. Albany, 51, fels, 64-65, Ph.D.(Eng), 67. Instr. lib. stud, Clarkson Col. Technol, 53-60, asst. prof, 55; assoc. prof. Eng, Rockland Community Col, 60-62; instr, State Univ. N.Y. Albany, 62-66; assoc. prof. HUMANITIES, CLARKSON COL. TECHNOL, 66-74, PROF, 74-, div. of res. fel, 68. Nat. Endowment Humanities fel, 68; vis. prof. creative writing, N.Mex. State Univ, 73-74. U.S.A.A.F, 43-45. MLA; Poetry Soc. Am; Int. Acad. Poets. Songs, myths and legends of the Teton Sioux Indians; creative writing; American Indian. Publ: Songs of the Teton Sioux, Westernlore Press, 70; Wade's place (novel), Scholastic Press, 73; The vision of Noah Jumping Eagle, 72, Reflections on a Catholic boyhood, 73 & Mass here, mass there, 9/73, Cath. Dig; plus others. Add: Dept. of Humanities, Clarkson College of Technology, Potsdam, NY 13676.

PAINE, ROBERT NELSON, b. New London, Conn, Jan. 16, 26. ENGLISH. B.S, Teachers Col. Conn, 49; M.A, George Peabody Col, 50, scholars, 53-55, Ph.D.(Eng), 56. Instr. high sch, Miss, 50-51, chmn. dept, 51-52, pub. schs, 52-53; asst. prof. ENG, Wash. Univ, 55-60; assoc. prof, Jacksonville Univ, 60-61; Chicago Teachers Col, South Campus, 61-67; NORTHEAST. ILL. UNIV, 67-72, PROF, 72- U.S.A, 44-46. MLA; NCTE. Eighteenth century English novel; literary criticism; English methods. Add: Dept. of English, Northeastern Illinois University, 5500 N. St. Louis Ave, Chicago, IL 60625.

PAINE, STEPHEN CURTISS, b. Mineola, N.Y, Apr. 27, 32; m. 60. ENGLISH. A.B, Amherst Col, 53; M.A, Duke Univ, 55, Ph.D, 61. Instr. ENG, Salem Col, 56-59, asst. prof, 60-66; BRADLEY UNIV, 66-68, ASSOC. PROF, 68- MLA; AAUP. American literature; literary criticism; popular culture. Add: Dept. of English, Bradley University, Peoria, IL 61606.

PAINTER, HELEN (WELCH), b. Covington, Ind, Sept. 25, 13; m. 33. ENGLISH. A.B, Ind. Univ, 35, A.M, 36, Ed.D, 41. Asst, Ind. Univ, 37-38, sch. psychologist, Univ. sch, 38-42, teacher Eng, 41-42; from instr. to prof, Univ. Akron, 45-67; PROF. ENG. EDUC, KENT STATE UNIV, 67- Vis. summer instr, N.Mex. Highlands Univ, 38; vis. summer prof, Colo. Col, 63; Ohio State Univ, 65; Kent State Univ, 66; dir, NDEA Inst. Advan, Stud. Eng, summer 68; summer vis. prof. & consult, Hawaii State Dept. Educ, 68. NEA; NCTE (mem. bk. list comt, 65-70, 70-75); Conf. Eng. Educ.(chmn. preparation teachers of children's lit, 71-); Int. Reading Asn.(mem. comt. int. bk. yr. 72, 71-72). Children's literature; reading tastes and interests. Publ: Co-auth, Mastering your language, grades 7, 8, Lyons & Carnahan, 66; auth, Poetry and children, 70 & ed, Reaching children and young people through literature, 71, Int. Reading Asn; auth, Elizabeth Yates—artist with words, 10/65 & Marcia Brown: a study in versatility, 12/66, Elem. Eng; Literary criticism: translations of traditional and modern material, Int. Reading Asn. Bull, 68. Add: Dept. of English, Satterfield Hall, Kent State University, Kent, OH 44242.

PALESTRANT, STEPHEN, b. New York, N.Y, July 1, 37; m. 60. SPEECH, DRAMA. A.B, N.Y. Univ, 57, M.A, 65; M.F.A, Yale, 60; Ed.D.(fine arts), Columbia Univ, 69. Instr. speech & drama, N.Y. UNIV, UNIV. HEIGHTS CTR, 61-65, asst. prof, 65-70, ASSOC. PROF. DRAMA, 70- Stage designer, various prod. in off Broadway, summer & community theatres, 56-; instr. speech & theatre, Teachers Col, Columbia Univ, summer 68; dir, Bronx Counc. Arts, 68; part-time lectr. theatre hist. & dramatic lit, Mercy Col. (N.Y), 72 & 73. Am. Theatre Asn; Illuminating Engineering Soc. Design for the stage; theatre history; dramatic literature. Publ: Commedia dell' arte in the Bronx, Drama Critique, 64; Electronic devices for the control of light in the theatre, 62 & Lighting New York's buildings, 66, Quadrangle. Add: Dept. of Drama, New York University School of Education, Washington Square, New York, NY 10003.

PALEY, MORTON D, b. New York, N.Y, July 27, 35. ROMANTIC POETRY. N.Y. State Regents Bd. scholar, City Col. New York, 52-57, B.A, 57; Woodrow Wilson fel, Brown Univ, 57-58, M.A, 58; Ph.D.(Eng), Columbia Univ, 64. Lectr. Eng, City Col. New York, 58-64; lit, New Sch. Soc. Res, 62-64; asst. prof. ENG, UNIV. CALIF, BERKELEY, 64-70, ASSOC. PROF, 70-, summer fel, 66, res. fel, 67-68. Am. Counc. Learned Soc. fel, 69-70; Guggenheim fel, 72-73; mem, Poets Workshop, London; exec. ed, Blake Newslett, Univ. N.Mex. MLA; Poetry Soc, Eng. Poetry and painting of William Blake; British art in relation to literature. Publ: Energy and the imagination, 69 & co-ed, William Blake: essays in honour of Sir Geoffrey Keynes, 73, Clarendon, Oxford; auth, Tyger of wrath, PMLA, 12/66; Cowper as Blake's spectre, 18th Century Stud, 3/68; plus others. Add: Dept. of English, 322 Wheeler Hall, University of California, Berkeley, CA 94720.

PALMATIER, ROBERT ALLEN, Linguistics, English. See Volume III, Foreign Languages, Linguistics & Philology.

PALMER, ERWIN, b. Sodus, N.Y, May 11, 08; m. 40; c. 2. ENGLISH. A.B, Syracuse Univ, 34, Ph.D.(Am. lit), 52; M.A, Middlebury Col, 46. Prof. compos. & lit. & chmn. dept. Eng, State Univ. N.Y. Col. Oswego, 46-72, res. found. grants-in-aid, 63, 65, fel, summer 67; RETIRED. N.Y. State Eng. Counc. fel, 68. U.S.A, 42-45, Sgt. MLA; NCTE; Thoreau Soc. Dreiser; imagery. Publ: Symbolic imagery in an American tragedy. Add: 156 W. Sixth St, Oswego, NY 13126.

PALMER, JOE DARWIN, Linguistics, English as a Second Language. See Volume III, Foreign Languages, Linguistics & Philology.

PALMER, JOHN A, b. Spokane, Wash, May 22, 26. ENGLISH. B.A, Univ. Wash, 50; M.A, Cornell Univ, 52, Martin Sampson fel, 55, sr. fel, 60, Ph.D.(Eng), 62. Teaching asst. philos, Cornell Univ, 50-52, ENG, 53-55, instr, 55-59, 60-62; asst. prof, CALIF. STATE UNIV, LOS ANGELES, 62-65, assoc. prof, 65-69, PROF, 69-, V.PRES. ACAD. AFFAIRS, 70-, chmn. dept, 67-69, dean letters & sci, 69-70. U.S.N, 44/46. MLA. American literature; theory of criticism; prose fiction. Publ: Joseph Conrad's fiction: a study in literary growth, Cornell Univ, 68; ed, Twentieth century interpretation of The nigger of the narcissus, Prentice-Hall, 69. Add: Office of the Vice President for Academic Affairs, California State University, Los Angeles, Los Angeles, CA 90032.

PALMER, JOHN JAMES ELLIS, b. Claiborne Parish, La, Dec. 13, 14. ENGLISH. A.B, La. Polytech. Inst, 35; A.M, La. State Univ, 37; Rhodes scholar, Oxford, 37-40, B.Litt, 40. Instr. Eng, La. State Univ, 40-42, asst. prof, 42-46; lectr. Eng. & ed, Sewanee Rev, Univ. of the South, 46-52; LECTR. ENG. & ED, YALE REV, YALE, 54-, DEAN, SILLIMAN COL, 63- Managing ed, South. Rev, 40-42. Restoration English literature; modern criticism. Add: Silliman College, Yale University, New Haven, CT 06520.

PALMER, JOYCE CORNETTE, b. Columbia, Tenn, Sept. 4, 41; m. 65. ENGLISH. B.A, David Lipscomb Col, 63; NDEA fel, Univ. Tenn, 63-66, M.A, 64, Ph.D.(Eng), 67. Instr. ENG, TEX. WOMAN'S UNIV, 67-68, ASST. PROF, 68- MLA; NCTE. James Boswell; Samuel Johnson; Thomas Hardy. Add: Dept. of English, Texas Woman's University, Denton, TX 76204.

PALMER, LESLIE H, b. Memphis, Tenn, Jan. 25, 41; m. 65. ENGLISH. B.A, Memphis State Univ, 62; non-serv. fel, Univ. Tenn, 63-65, M.A, 63, Ph.D. (Eng), 66. Instr. ENG, Univ. Tenn, 66-67; ASST. PROF. ENG, N.TEX. STATE UNIV, 67- MLA. English and American literature. Add: 1905 W. Oak, Denton, TX 76201.

PALMER, MELVIN DELMAR, Comparative Literature, Literary Criticism. See Volume III, Foreign Languages, & Linguistics & Philology.

PALMER, OSMOND ERNEST, b. Chicago, Ill, Sept. 14, 07; m. 36; c. 2. ENGLISH. Ph.D.(Eng. & Am. lit), Univ. Chicago, 52. Teacher, high sch; instr. Eng, St, Bernard's Sem; St. Louis Univ; Canisius Col; Univ. Chicago, 41-46; PROF, OFF. OF EVAL. SERVS, MICH. STATE UNIV, 46- Conf. Col. Compos. & Commun; NCTE. Teaching and measurement of reading and of writing. Publ: Co-auth, Critical thinking in reading and writing, Holt. Add: 805 Lantern Hill Dr, East Lansing, MI 48823.

PALMER, RICHARD E, b. Phoenix, Ariz, Nov. 6, 33; m. 56; c. 3. COMPARATIVE EUROPEAN LITERATURE. B.A, Univ. Redlands, 55, M.A, 56, Ph.D.(comp. lit), 59; Ford Found. fel, 55-59; Inst. Hermeneutics, Univ. Zurich, 64-65; Univ. Heidelberg, 65. Asst. prof. humanities, MacMURRAY COL, 59-64, assoc. prof. humanities & world lit, 64-69, PROF, 69-71, LIT.

& PHILOS, 72-, DIR. HUMANITIES CORE LIT. PROG, 65- Am. Counc. Learned Soc. fel, 64-65; Nat. Endowment for Humanities younger humanist fel. philos, Univ. Heidelberg, 71-72. Existentialism and phenomenology; Romantic literature and philosophy; philosophy of literary interpretation. Publ: Hermeneutics: interpretation theory in Schleiermacher, Dilthey, Heidegger, and Gadamer, Northwest. Univ, 69; Existentialism in T.S. Eliot's The family reunion, Mod. Drama, 9/62; Hermeneutics and methodology, Continuum, winter 69; Phenomenology as foundation for a post-modern philosophy of literary interpretation, Cult. Hermeneutics, 73; plus others. Add: Div. of Humanities, MacMurray College, Jacksonville, IL 62650.

PALMER, RUPERT ELMER, JR, b. Maryville, Tenn, Aug. 22, 26; m. 54; c. 1. ENGLISH LANGUAGE & LITERATURE. B.A, Univ. Tenn, 50, M.A, 52; Ph.D.(Eng. lang. & lit), Yale, 57. Instr. ENG, Yale, 57-60; asst. prof, VANDERBILT UNIV, 60-67, assoc. prof, 67-72, PROF, 72-, CHMN. DEPT, 73- A.U.S, 44-46. MLA; Ling. Soc. Am; Mediaeval Acad. Am. Old and Middle English literature. Publ: Thomas Whythorne's speech, Rosenkilde & Bagger, 69; The uses of character in Bishop Blougram's apology, Mod. Philol, 11/60. Add: Dept. of English, Vanderbilt University, Nashville, TN 37235.

PALMER, WINTHROP, b. New York, N.Y, Sept. 14, 99; m. 19; c. 4. ENGLISH. Litt.D, L.I. Univ, 56. Asst. prof. LIT. & FINE ARTS, C.W. POST COL, LONG ISLAND UNIV, 56-60, ASSOC. PROF, 60-, ASSOC. ED, CONFRONTATION LIT. MAG, 74- Publ: The invisible wife, and other poems, Fine Editions, 45; The new barbarian, Farrar, Straus, 51; Fables and ceremonies, Peter Pauper, 56 & Jean Grassin, Paris, 59; Like a shadow passing, Steamboat, 68; American kaleidoscope (chronicle play with music), Dramatic Publ, 72. Add: 435 East 52nd St, New York, NY 10022.

PANAGE, JOHN H, b. Cyprus, Oct. 24, 99. ENGLISH LITERATURE. A.B, Boston Univ, 23; A.M, Emory Univ, 31; Ph.D, Univ. Minn, 39. Prof. ENG. & head dept, JOHN BROWN UNIV, 39-73, EMER. PROF, 73- U.S.A, 42-45. Add: Dept. of English, John Brown University, Siloam Springs, AR 72761.

PANARA, ROBERT FREDERIC, b. New York, N.Y, July 8, 20; m. 47; c. 1. ENGLISH. B.A, Gallaudet Col, 45; M.A, N.Y. Univ, 48. Instr. Eng, N.Y. Sch. Deaf, 45-49; Gallaudet Col, 49-54, asst. prof, 54-58, assoc. prof, 58-67; chmn. Eng. dept, NAT. TECH. INST. FOR DEAF, ROCHESTER INST. TECHNOL, 67-70, PROF. ENG. & DRAMA, 70-, dir. educ. theatre, 70-72. Consult. captioned films for deaf, U.S. Off. Educ, 60-63; mem. secy. nat. adv. bd. for estab. of Nat. Tech. Inst. for Deaf, Dept. Health, Educ. & Welfare, 65-67; fac. lectr, Nat. Theatre of Deaf, Eugene O'Neill Theatre Ctr, Waterford, Conn, 67-73; mem. comt. pedag, VII World Congr. of Deaf, 72-75. Am. Instr. Deaf (citation teaching merit, 71, mem. exec. bd, counc. educ. deaf, 72-75); NCTE; Am. Theater Asn; AAUP. Deaf poets and writers; deaf characters in fiction and drama; sign language translations of Shakespeare and other plays. Publ: Co-auth, The silent muse: an anthology of poetry of the deaf, Gallaudet Col, 60; auth, The deaf: education of, In: New Catholic encyclopedia, Vol. 4, McGraw, 66; The deaf writer in America, parts I & II, Am. Ann. Deaf, 9 & 11/70; Deaf characters in fiction and drama, Deaf Am. Mag, 5/72. Add: National Technical Institute for the Deaf, Rochester Institute of Technology, Rochester, NY 14623.

PANICHAS, GEORGE ANDREW, b. Springfield, Mass, May 21, 30. ENGLISH LITERATURE. B.A, Am. Int. Col, 51; A.M, Trinity Col, 52; Ph.D, Nottingham Univ, Eng, 61. Instr. ENG, UNIV. MD, COLLEGE PARK, 62-63, asst. prof, 63-66, assoc. prof, 66-68, PROF, 68- Mem. ed. adv. bd, Modern Age: A Quart. Rev, 71- Fel, Royal Soc. Arts. British literature and culture between the two world wars; modern novel; interdisciplinary studies. Publ: Adventure in consciousness: the meaning of D.H. Lawrence's religious quest, Mouton, The Hague, 64; co-ed, Renaissance and modern essays, Routledge & Kegan Paul, 66; Epicurus, Twayne, 67; ed, Mansions of the spirit: essays in literature and religion, 67 & The politics of twentieth-century novelists, 71, Hawthorn; Promise of greatness: the war of 1914-1918, Day, 68; auth, The reverent discipline: essays in literary criticism and culture, Univ. Tenn, 74; contrib, The vision obscured: perceptions of some twentieth-century Catholic novelists, Fordham Univ, 70, Critics on D.H. Lawrence, Univ. Miami, 71 & In sight of the logos: Dostoevsky's Crime and punishment as spiritual art, St. Vladimir's Theol. Quart, Vol. 15, No. 3; plus others. Add: Dept. of English, University of Maryland, College Park, MD 20742.

PANZER, VERN ALBERT, b. Mundelein, Ill, July 20, 18; m. 42; c. 2. ENGLISH LINGUISTICS, LITERARY CRITICISM. A.B, Cornell Col, 40; B.D, Garrett Sch. Theol, 43; M.A, Univ. Mich, 50, Ed.D.(Eng), 63. Asst. prof. ENG, Kans. Wesleyan Univ, 56-58, assoc. prof, 58-66, prof, 66-71, chmn. humanities div, 70-71; PROF. & CHMN. DEPTS. ENG, SPEECH & DRAMA, IOWA WESLEYAN COL, 71- Consult. rating freshman themes, Univ. Kans, 66-67; participant, Educ. Prof. Develop. Act Inst. Urban Eng, Univ. Mich, summer 73. MLA; NCTE; Conf. Col. Compos. & Commun. English education, especially articulation between high school and college English; English linguistics, especially the contribution of linguistic study to literary criticism; American literature, especially modern period. Publ: Trends in the articulation of English between American high schools and colleges, Univ. Microfilms, 63. Add: 206 E. Madison, Mt. Pleasant, IA 52641.

PAPALEO, JOSEPH JR, b. New York, N.Y, Jan. 13, 25; m. 48; c. 2. COMPARATIVE LITERATURE, CREATIVE WRITING. A.B, Sarah Lawrence Col, 49; Dipl. di Profitto, Univ. Florence, Italy, 50; Grad. Sch. Lit, Columbia Univ, 50-51. Teacher lower sch, Fieldston, New York, N.Y, 51-54, Eng, upper sch, 54-60; PROF. LIT. & WRITING, SARAH LAWRENCE COL, 60- Fel, Lab di Cibernetica, Naples, Italy, 68-69; John Simon Guggenheim Mem. Found. grant in creative writing, 73-74. U.S.A.A.F, 43-46. Modern Italian poetry; translating. Publ: Arete, Dial, 61; All the comforts, 67 & Out of place, 71, Little; The word to go, Harpers Mag, 11/71; The end, Transatlantic Rev, 73; New flesh, Penthouse, 74; plus others. Add: Dept. of Literature & Writing, Sarah Lawrence College, Bronxville, NY 10708.

PAPINCHAK, ROBERT ALLEN, b. Pittsburgh, Pa, Jan. 1, 44; m. 73. CREATIVE WRITING, AMERICAN LITERATURE. B.A, Univ. Pittsburgh, 64, M.A, 65; Ford grant, Univ. Wis-Madison, 68, Ph.D.(Eng), 71. Teaching asst. Eng, Univ. Wis-Madison, 65-69; ASST. PROF, UNIV. PITTSBURGH, 69- Adv. ed, MSS: Writing at Univ. of Pittsburgh, 69-; contrib, Bread Loaf Writers' Conf, summer 72. The American short story; creative writing; graphology. Publ: Barron's profile of American colleges, an in-depth study of the University of Pittsburgh, Barron's, 73; Let the dead, Quixote, 4: 89-105; Maxine Kumin: an education in perception, 74 & Stephen Spender: the felt experience, 74, Pittsburgh Poetry Forum; plus others. Add: Faculty of Arts & Sciences, Dept. of English, University of Pittsburgh, Pittsburgh, PA 15260.

PAPOUSEK, MARILYN DEWEESE, b. Chicago, Ill, Aug. 8, 39. LITERATURE, DRAMA. B.A, Univ. North. Iowa, 66; NDEA fel, Univ. Iowa, 67-70, Ph.D. (Eng), 71. Teaching asst. ENG, Univ. Iowa, 69-71; ASST. PROF, UNIV. PITTSBURGH, 71- Folger fel, Folger Shakespeare Libr, summer 74. MLA; NCTE; Renaissance Soc. Am; Shakespeare Asn. Am; AAUP. Seventeenth century drama, poetry and society; women writers 1500-1800. Add: Dept. of English, University of Pittsburgh, Pittsburgh, PA 15260.

PAPPERT, EDWARD CECIL, C.S.B, b. Rochester, N.Y, Feb. 13, 14. ENGLISH. B.A, Univ. Toronto, 38; M.A, Univ. Detroit, 44; Ph.D, Univ. Ottawa, 54. Teacher ENG, St. Michael's High Sch, Toronto, Ont, 36-38; Cath. Cent. High Sch, Detroit, Mich, 38-41; Aquinas Inst, Rochester, 43-48; instr, Univ. Toronto, 48-50; lectr, UNIV. WINDSOR, 50-53, ASST. PROF, 53-, DEAN EXTEN. & CONTINUING EDUC, 70- Can. Asn. Dir. Exten. & Summer Sch. (secy, 60-61, treas, 61-62, v.pres, 62-63, pres, 63-64); Can. Asn. Adult Educ; Asn. Univ. Eve. Cols. English literature, especially the Renaissance; adult education. Add: 400 Huron Line, Windsor, Ont, Can.

PAREDES, AMERICO, b. Brownsville, Tex, Sept. 3, 15; m. 48; c. 4. LATIN AMERICAN FOLKLORE & CULTURAL HISTORY. B.A, Univ. Tex, 51, M.A, 53, Ph.D.(folklore), 56. Instr. ENG, Univ. Tex, El Paso, 56-57; asst. prof, UNIV. TEX, AUSTIN, 57-60, assoc. prof, 60-64, PROF, 64-, ANTHROP, 66-, dir. folklore arch, 57-67, dir. ctr. intercult. stud. folklore & oral hist, 67-70, dir. ctr. Mex-Am. stud, 70-73. Bibliog, South. Folklore Quart, 60-64; prof. Latin Am. stud, Univ. W.Va, 61, 62; Guggenheim fel, 62-63; vis. prof. anthrop, Univ. Calif, Berkeley, 67; ed, J. Am. Folklore, 68-73. U.S.A, 43-45, Sgt. Am. Folklore Soc.(v.pres, 64); Am. Anthrop. Asn. Mexican folklore, especially the corrido; folklore as indicator of attitudes, especially legends, jokes, names and ethnic labels; folklore theory. Publ: With his pistol in his hand, 58, co-auth, Corridos and calaveras, 61, transl, American extremes, 64, co-ed, The urban experience and folk tradition 71 & Toward new perspectives in folklore, 72, Univ. Tex; auth, Folktales of Mexico, Univ. Chicago, 70; co-ed, Mexican-American authors, Houghton, 72. Add: 324 Parlin Hall, University of Texas, Austin, TX 78712.

PARINS, JAMES WILLIAM, b. Green Bay, Wis, Nov. 19, 39; m. 63; c. 2. ENGLISH LITERATURE. B.S, St. Norbert Col, 64; M.A, Univ. Wis-Madison, 70, Ph.D.(Eng), 72. Asst. prof. ENG, Univ. Wis-Stevens Point, 71-72; ASST. PROF. & ACTING CHMN. DEPT, UNIV. ARK, LITTLE ROCK, 72- U.S.M.C.R, 57-62. MLA; S.Cent. Mod. Lang. Asn; AAUP; Hopkins Soc; Int. Asn. Comput. in Humanities. Victorian literature; English literature in transition; computers and the humanities. Add: Dept. of English, University of Arkansas, 33rd at University, Little Rock, AR 72204.

PARIS, BERNARD JAY, b. Baltimore, Md, Aug. 19, 31; m. 49; c. 2. ENGLISH. A.B, Johns Hopkins Univ, 52, Ph.D.(Eng), 59. Instr. ENG, Lehigh Univ, 56-60; asst. prof, MICH. STATE UNIV, 60-64, assoc. prof, 64-67, PROF, 67- Nat. Endowment for Humanities fel, 69-70; vis. prof, Victorian Stud. Ctr, Univ. Leicester, 72- MLA. The psychological study of fiction; aesthetics of fiction; Victorian literature. Publ: Experiments in life: George Eliot's quest for values, Wayne State Univ, 65; A psychological approach to fiction: studies in Thackeray, Stendhal, George Eliot, Dostoevsky, and Conrad, Ind. Univ, 74; A confusion of many standards: conflicting value systems in the Tess of the D'Urbervilles, Nineteenth Century Fiction, 6/69; plus others. Add: Dept. of English, Michigan State University, East Lansing, MI 48824.

PARISH, CHARLES, Linguistics, English as Foreign Language. See Volume III, Foreign Languages, Linguistics & Philology.

PARISH, JOHN EDWARD, b. Huntsville, Tex, July 18, 13. ENGLISH. B.A, Sam Houston Col, 34; M.A, Univ. Tex, 38; Ph.D.(Eng), Columbia Univ, 51. Instr. ENG, Southwest. Univ, 41-42; RICE UNIV, 46-48, asst. prof, 51-58, assoc. prof, 58-68, PROF, 68- U.S.A, 42-46, Capt. MLA. Sixteenth and seventeenth century English literature. Add: Dept. of English, Rice University, Houston, TX 77001.

PARK, BRUCE ROBERTSON, b. June 5, 22; m. 47; c. 2. ENGLISH. A.B, Bates Col, 44; M.A, Columbia Univ, 47, Ph.D, 52. Lectr. ENG, Columbia Univ, 51-52; instr, Cornell Univ, 52-56; from instr. to asst. prof, BROOKLYN COL, 56-68, ASSOC. PROF, 68-, lit, New Sch. Lib. Arts, 72-73. U.S.N.R, 43-46, Lt.(jg). Drama; literary criticism and theory; poetry. Publ: A mote in the critic's eye: Bernard Shaw and comedy, In: G.B, Shaw: a collection of critical essays, Prentice-Hall, 65; Give me back my ivory tower, Nat. Observer, 10/71; The cosmology of Mr. Bruffee and the new-men, Col. Eng, 10/73; plus others. Add: New School of Liberal Arts, Brooklyn College, City University of New York, 210 Livingston St, Brooklyn, NY 11201.

PARK, MARY CATHRYNE, b. Bellefonte, Pa, June 18, 18. HUMANITIES. B.A, Univ. Pa, 39, scholar. & M.A, 42, fel. & Ph.D, 47. Prof. Eng. & speech, King's Col.(Del), 46-47; asst. prof. Anderson Col, 47-50; assoc. prof. Eng. & Ger, Catawba Col, 50-52; Eng, Stetson Univ, 52-55; prof. Fla. South. Col, 55-60; PROF. ENG. & CHMN. DIV. HONORS, BREVARD COMMUNITY COL, 68-, chmn. div. soc. sci, 60-68; ADJ. PROF, SHELTON COL, 71- Col. Eng. Asn. judge, High Sch. competitions, 57-; appointment, Brevard Hist. Comn, 63-; Governor Claude Kirk's comn. hist. state Fla, 68-; consult, Proj. & Develop, U.S. & Latin Am, 70- Charles Lamb Soc, London; MLA; S.Atlantic Mod. Lang. Asn; Am. Stud. Asn; Southeast. Am. Stud. Asn.(secy-treas, 56); Am. Asn. Univ. Women. American literature and civilization; television classrooms in humanities, history and literature. Publ: Joseph Priestley and the problem of pantisocracy. Add: 450 Norwood St, Merritt Island, FL 32952.

PARK, WILLIAM, b. Philadelphia, Pa, Apr. 6, 30; m. 57; c. 4. ENGLISH. A.B, Princeton, 51; A.M, Columbia Univ, 54, Ph.D, 62. Instr. Eng, Hamilton Col, 54-57; Columbia Col, 59-62; FAC. MEM. LIT, SARAH LAWRENCE COL, 62-, dir, London Summer Sch, 66-70. Am. Counc. Learned Soc. grant-in-aid, 68-69. U.S.M.C, 51-53, 1st Lt. MLA. Eighteenth century; film. Publ: Co-auth, A college anthology of British and American poetry, Allyn & Bacon, 64; Fielding and Richardson, PMLA, 10/66; Fathers and sons—Humphry Clinker, Lit. & Psychol, 12/66; Change in the criticism of the novel since 1760, Philol. Quart, 1/67. Add: Dept. of Literature, Sarah Lawrence College, Bronxville, NY 10708.

PARKANDER, DOROTHY J, b. Chicago, Ill, Mar. 14, 25. ENGLISH. A.B, Augustana Col.(Ill), 46; A.M, Univ. Chicago, 47, Ph.D.(Eng), 62. Instr. ENG, AUGUSTANA COL.(ILL), 47-50, asst. prof, 50-58, assoc. prof, 58-63, PROF, 63- O.N. Olson fel, Lutheran Sch. Theol.(Ill), 63, lectr. relig. & lit, 63-64. Renaissance studies in rhetoric; Puritan literature, 1550-1640; contemporary drama. Publ: The sermons of Samuel Ward, Anglican Theol. Rev, 59; Dorothy L. Sayers: a passionate intellect, Frontiers, 59; Onstage: a new calling of the saints, Sem. Rev, 63. Add: Dept. of English, Augustana College, Rock Island, IL 61201.

PARKE, CATHERINE NEAL, b. Washington, D.C, Oct. 22, 47. ENGLISH. B.A, Wellesley Col, 65; fel, Stanford Univ, 69-73, M.A, 72, Ph.D.(Eng), 74. Teaching asst. ENG, Stanford Univ, 70-73; ASST. PROF, UNIV. MO-COLUMBIA, 73- MLA; Johnson Soc. Cent. Region; Am. Soc. 18th Century Stud. Eighteenth-century English literature; theory and practice of education in 17th and 18th centuries; literature and philosophy. Add: 231 Arts & Science, Dept. of English, University of Missouri-Columbia, Columbia, MO 65201.

PARKER, CHARLES ALEXANDER, b. Camden, N.J, May 19, 24; m. 50; c. 4. SPEECH. A.B, Muhlenberg Col, 50; M.A, Temple Univ, 53; Ph.D.(speech), La. State Univ, 58. Instr. speech, Ala. Polytech. Inst, 53-55; assoc. prof. & chmn. dept, Pfeiffer Col, 58-60; prof. & chmn. dept, La. Col, 60-65; assoc. prof, Appalachian State Teachers Col, 65-66; prof. & chmn. div, N.C. STATE UNIV, 66-72, DIR. COOP. EDUC, 72- Mem. ed. bd, South. Speech J, 66-70; ed, N.C. J. Speech, 67-; consult, Meter Div, Westinghouse Corp, 71-73. U.S.C.G, 42-46; U.S.N.R, Lt. South. Speech Asn; Speech Commun. Asn; Coop. Educ. Asn. Communication; cooperative education. Add: 4101 Huckleberry Dr, Raleigh, NC 27612.

PARKER, DOROTHY, b. Minneapolis, Minn; m. 58; c. 2. ENGLISH. B.A, Univ. Minn, 50, M.A, 51; Ph.D.(Eng), Univ. Tex, 60. Lectr. ENG, Am. Univ, Cairo, 51-54; Wesleyan Univ, 54-55; instr, Univ. Colo, 59-60; asst. prof, UNIV. TORONTO, 60-68, ASSOC. PROF, VICTORIA COL, 68- MLA; Victorian Stud. Asn; Asn. Can. Univ. Teachers Eng. Victorian novel; Dickens; Mrs. Gaskell. Publ: The time scheme of Pamela and the character of B, Tex. Stud. Eng, 68; George Ryga, In: Contemporary dramatists, St. James, 73; Allegory and the extension of Mr. Bucket's finger, Mod. Lang. Notes, 74. Add: Victoria College, University of Toronto, 78 Queen's Park Crescent, Toronto 5, Ont, Can.

PARKER, FRANK, b. Chicago, Ill, July 12, 91. FINE ARTS, DRAMA. Ph.B, Univ. Chicago, 22, A.M, 26; Sorbonne, Paris, 39. Prof. drama, PRINCIPIA COL, 22-27, 31-67, dir. Principia abroad, 59, 61, 63, stud. tour Japan, 72, EMER. PROF. DRAMA, 68- Anglo-French literary relations. Add: 2090 Broadway, San Francisco, CA 94115.

PARKER, HERSHEL, b. Comanche, Okla, Nov. 26, 35; m. 63; c. 2. ENGLISH. B.A, Lamar State Col, 59; Woodrow Wilson fels, Northwest. Univ, 59-60 & 62-63, M.A, 60, univ. fel, 60-61, asst, 61-62, Ph.D.(Eng), 63. Asst. prof. ENG, Univ. Ill, Urbana, 63-65; Northwest. Univ, 65-68; assoc. prof, UNIV. SOUTH. CALIF, 68-70, PROF, 70- Mem. adv. comt, Ctr. Ed. Am. Authors, 71-74; W.Coast rep, Melville Soc. Am. MLA. American literature; Melville; textual studies. Publ: Gansevoort Melville's 1846 London journal, New York Pub. Libr, 66; The recognition of Herman Melville, Univ. Mich, 67; co-auth, The Norton critical edition of Moby-Dick, 67, co-ed, Moby Dick as Doubloon, 70 & ed, The Norton critical edition of the confidence-man, 71, Norton; co-ed, The Northwestern-Newberry edition of the writings of Herman Melville, Northwest-Newberry, 68-; auth, The metaphysics of Indian-hating, Nineteenth-Century Fiction, 9/63; Gansevoort Melville's role in the campaign of 1844, N.Y. Hist. Soc. Quart, 4/65; Regularizing accidentals, In: Proof yearbook of American bibliographical & textual studies, 73; plus others. Add: Dept. of English, University of Southern California, Los Angeles, CA 90007.

PARKER, JAMES W, b. Farmville, Va, July 6, 34. DRAMA. B.A, Longwood Col, 56; M.A, Univ. Va, 57. ASSOC. PROF. DRAMA & HUMANITIES, CONVERSE COL, 57- Kosciuszko Found. fel, Inst. Arts, Polish Acad. Sci, 71-72. South. Speech Asn; Southeast. Theatre Conf; Am. Nat. Theatre & Acad. Polish theatre between the Wars: Stanislaw Ignacy Witliewicz, playwright; theory-criticism of theatre: surrealism; theatre history. Add: Box 514, Dept. of Humanities, Converse College, Spartanburg, SC 29302.

PARKER, JOHN W, JR, b. Palmer, Tex, Aug. 8, 18; m. 42; c. 3. ENGLISH LANGUAGE & LITERATURE. A.B, Tex. Christian Univ, 42; M.A, Columbia Univ, 48; Ford fel, George Peabody Col, 52-53, Ed.D, 53; Ed.D, Univ. Ky, 58. Instr, Univ. Nev, 46; Columbia Univ, 47-50; assoc. prof. ENG. & chmn. dept, Ky. Wesleyan Col, 50-61; prof. & chmn. dept, Methodist Col, N.C, 61-62; ASSOC. PROF, UNIV. S.FLA, 62- Vis. prof, West. Ill. Univ, 65. Music critic, Tampa Tribune, 63-68. Publ: Contrib, Together, Minn. Rev. Add: Dept. of English, University of South Florida, Tampa, FL 33620.

PARKER, JOHN WILLIAM, b. Murfreesboro, N.C, Oct. 16, 09; m. 36; c. 1. SPEECH, DRAMA. A.B, Univ. N.C, 30, Rockefeller fel, 34-36, A.M, 37. Instr. Eng. high schs, N.C, 30-34; DRAMATIC ART, UNIV. N.C, CHAPEL HILL, 34-39, asst. prof, 39-46, assoc. prof, 46-49, PROF, 49- Carolina Playmakers Mask Award, 30; natl. consult. outdoor drama, 38-; Carolina Dramatic Asn. Award, 62. U.S.A.A.F, 42-46, Capt. Southeast. Theatre Conf.(exec. secy-treas, 49-53); Am. Theatre Asn; Am. Nat. Theatre & Acad. theatre administration; outdoor drama; drama festivals. Publ: Sleep on, Lemuel (N.C. drama); ed, Adventures in playmaking, four plays by Carolina Playmakers, Univ. N.C, 68. Add: 1 Brierbridge Lane, Chapel Hill, NC 27514.

PARKER, REGINALD BRIAN, b. Bunbury, Cheshire, Eng, June 28, 31; m. 58; c. 2. ENGLISH, DRAMA. B.A, Univ. Liverpool, 53, M.A, 55; cert, Univ. London, 55; Ph.D.(Eng), Univ. Birmingham, 57. Vis. lectr. ENG, Univ. Tex, 57-58; Univ. Wis, 58-59; vis. asst. prof, Univ. Colo, 59-60; asst. prof, TRINITY COL, UNIV. TORONTO, 60-65, assoc. prof, 65-69, PROF, 69-, dir, grad. ctr. stud. drama, Sch. Grad. Stud, 67-72. Fulbright fel, 57-60; summer fels, Huntington Libr, 58, Folger Libr, 62 & Folger Shakespeare Libr, 72; Can. Counc. sr. fels, 66 & 72-73. President's Medal, 63. Can. Asn. Univ. Teachers; Malone Soc. Jacobean drama, especially Middleton; modern drama; history of American and Canadian drama. Publ: Ed, Thomas Middleton, A chaste maid in Cheapside, Methuen & Harvard, 69, The ecstacy of Rita Joe and other plays, 70 & Masques of childhood, 71, New Press, Toronto; auth, The themes and staging of Bartholomew Fair, Univ. Toronto Quart, 68; Somerset Maugham's The circle, In: Shaw: seven critical essays, 71; Richard III and the modernizing of Shakespeare, Mod. Drama, winter 72; plus others. Add: Dept. of English, Trinity College, University of Toronto, Hoskins Ave, Toronto 5, Ont, Can.

PARKER, ROBERT WESLEY, b. Watertown, N.Y, Mar. 19, 31; m. 55; c. 3. ENGLISH. A.B, Middlebury Col, 53; M.A, Columbia Univ, 59, Ph.D.(Eng), 65. Instr. ENG, Middlebury Col, 60-66; asst. prof, Univ. Rochester, 66-72; ASSOC. PROF, WITTENBERG UNIV, 72- Danforth Found. teacher fel, 64-65. U.S.N.R, 53-57, Lt. MLA; Renaissance Soc. Am. Sir Philip Sidney; Renaissance fiction; comedy. Publ: Terentian structure in Sidney's original Arcadia, Eng. Lit. Renaissance, winter 72. Add: Dept. of English, Wittenberg University, Springfield, OH 45501.

PARKER, STEPHEN JAN, Russian Literature, Comparative Literature. See Volume III, Foreign Languages, Linguistics & Philology.

PARKER, WILFORD OREN, b. Lansing, Mich, Dec. 1, 12; m. 37; c. 2. SCENE DESIGN, THEATRE ARCHITECTURE. B.S.D, Univ. Mich, 34; Rockefeller fel, Yale, 38-39, M.F.A, 40. Instr. scene design, Univ. Mich, 34-37; asst. prof, Univ. Tex, 41 & 47; scene design & theatre mgt, Williams Col, 42-44; tech. prod. & scene design, Yale, 46-63; PROF. SCENE DESIGN, CARNEGIE-MELLON UNIV, 63- Curriculum consult, grad. drama prog, Univ. Tex. 62; undergrad. drama prog, Union Col, 67; grad. & undergrad. prog, Tufts Univ, 67. Consult, War Dept, 44. U.S. Inst. Theatre Technol.(dir, 67-69); Am. Theatre Asn. Perspective in the theatre; history of theatre decor; mixed media and audio-visual theatre, especially technical and design aspects. Publ: Co-auth, Scene design and stage lighting, Holt, 63, rev. ed, 68, 3rd ed, 74; auth, Sceno-graphic techniques, Carnegie-Mellon Univ, Parts I & II, 64. Add: Dept. of Drama, Carnegie-Mellon University, 5000 Forbes Ave, Pittsburgh, PA 15213.

PARKER, WILLIAM HENRY, b. Phila, Pa, Sept. 20, 28; m. 53; c. 1. AMERICAN STUDIES, AMERICAN LITERATURE. B.A, Syracuse Univ, 52, M.A. Ed, 56, M.A, 60, Ph.D.(Am. stud), 68. Instr. pub. affairs, Syracuse Univ, 66-68, asst. prof. educ, Ithaca Col, 68-73; HEAD DEPT. ENG, ODESSA-MONTOUR CENT. SCHS, 73- Mem. adj. fac. sociol. Am. educ, Elmira Col, N.Y, spring 74. U.S.A, 46-48. Am. Stud. Asn. Impact of technology upon American pastoral utopianism and its relation to current educational romanticism. Publ: Jonathan Edwards: founder of the counter-tradition of transcendental thought in America, Ga. Rev, summer 73. Add: 232 Haller Blvd, Ithaca, NY 14850.

PARKERSON, JAMES WOODROW, b. Alexandria, La, Oct. 19, 16; m. 41; c. 2. RHETORIC, PUBLIC ADDRESS. B.A, La. Tech. Univ, 39; M.A, Univ. Iowa, 49; Ohio State Univ, Columbus, 51; Ph.D.(speech), La. State Univ, Baton Rouge, 71. Broker, Merrill, Lynch, Pierce, Fenner & Beane, 45-46; contact rep, Vet. Admin, 46-47; instr. SPEECH, NORTHEAST LA. UNIV, 47-71; HEAD DEPT, 71- U.S.A.F, 42-45, Res, 49-66, Maj; Air Medal & Oak Leaf. Speech Commun. Asn; South. Speech Commun. Asn. Oratory of the pre-Civil War period. Publ: What can be done to preserve freedom of speech: a symposium, South. Speech J, 5/54; Good men speaking well: America's urgent need, Vital Speeches of the Day, 5/68; Resources materials: Louisiana Speech Association, Speech Teacher, 3/69; plus one other. Add: Dept. of Speech, Northeast Louisiana University, 700 University Ave, Monroe, LA 71201.

PARKHURST, CHARLES EDWARD, b. Albion, Mich, Sept. 25, 26; m. 68. SPEECH. B.A, Albion Col, 46; Garrett Bibl. Inst, 48, 52; Ph.D.(speech), Northwest. Univ, 53. Lectr. speech, Ind. Univ, South Bend Exten, 52; instr. pub. speaking, Harvard Univ, 53-55; instr. SPEECH, BROOKLYN COL, 55-61, asst. prof, 61-72, ASSOC. PROF, 72- Lectr, New Sch, summer, 59; Univ. Md. Europ. Div, 59-61, 64-65 & summers, 62, 63, Far E. Div, 65; West. Electric Mgt. Training Prog, 68. U.S.A, 46-47. Speech Commun. Asn; Am. Forensic Asn. Intercollegiate debating. Add: Dept. of Speech & Theatre, Brooklyn College, Brooklyn, NY 11210.

PARKIN, ANDREW TERENCE LEONARD, b. Birmingham, Eng. ENGLISH, DRAMA. B.A, Cambridge, 61, M.A, 65; Ph.D.(drama), Bristol Univ, 69. ASST. PROF. ENG, UNIV. B.C, 70- Can. Asn. Univ. Teachers; Asn. Can. Univ. Teachers Eng; Int. Asn. Stud. Anglo-Irish Lit; Irish-Am. Cult. Inst. Anglo-Irish drama; dramatic theory and criticism; modern drama. Publ: Stage one: a Canadian scenebook, Van Nostrand, 73; Similarities in the plays of Yeats and Beckett, Ariel, 7/70. Add: Dept. of English, University of British Columbia, Vancouver 8, B.C, Can.

PARKIN, REBECCA P, b. Newton, N.C, May 7, 18; m. 49; c. 2. LITERATURE. Murray fel. & A.B, Barnard Col, 40; M.A, Columbia Univ, 42; Ph.D. (Eng), Yale, 48; Oxford, 66-67. Instr. ENG, Univ. Nev, 47-48; Univ. Houston, 48-49; Cornell Univ, 49-50; South. Methodist Univ, 50-51; asst. prof, CALIF. STATE UNIV, SACRAMENTO, 59-66, assoc. prof, 66-68, PROF, 68- MLA; Am. Soc. 18th Century Stud. Eighteenth century; modern poetry; criticism. Publ: Alexander Pope's poetic workmanship, Univ. Minn, 55; ed, The Augustans: Dryden, Pope, and Swift, Holt, 70; auth, Swift's Baucis and Philemon: a sermon in the burlesque mode, Satire Newslett, 70; The journey down the great scale reflected in two neoclassic elegies..., Enlightenment Essays, 70; Neoclassic defensive techniques in the verse of Swift and Johnson..., Trans. Int. Soc. 18th Century Stud, 71; plus others. Add: Dept. of English, California State University, Sacramento, 6000 J St, Sacramento, CA 95819.

PARKINSON, THOMAS FRANCIS, b. San Francisco, Calif, Feb. 24, 20; m. 48; c. 2. ENGLISH LANGUAGE & LITERATURE. A.B, Univ. Calif, 45, A.M, 46, Johnson fel, 47-48, Ph.D, 48. Teaching asst, UNIV. CALIF, BERKELEY, 46-47, instr. ENG, 48-50, asst. prof, 50-53, assoc. prof, 53-60, PROF, 60- Vis. asst. prof, Wesleyan Univ, 51-52; Fulbright lectr, Univs. Bordeaux & Toulouse, 53-54; Univ. Grenoble, 65-66; Guggenheim fel, 57-58; Am. Philos. Soc. travel grants, 57-59 & summer 68; fel. inst. creative art, Univ. Calif, 63-64; hon. fel. Eng, St. Peter's Col, Oxford, 69-70; vis. prof, Univ. York, Eng, 70; mem. lit. panel, Nat. Endowment for Arts, 70-73. MLA. Modern British literature; American literature. Publ: W.B. Yeats, self-critic, 51, W.B. Yeats, the later poems, 64 & both vols. in one, 72, Univ. Calif; Men, women, vines (verse), 59 & Homage to Jack Spicer (verse), 70, Ark Press; A casebook on the beat, Crowell, 61; Thanatos (verse), Oyez Press, 65; ed, Robert Lowell, Prentice-Hall, 68; auth, Protect the earth (verse & prose), City Lights, 70; Twenty-five years of the endless war (verse drama), Thorp Springs Press, 74; Forgeries (verse), Plain Wrappers Press, 74. Add: 1001 Cragmont, Berkeley, CA 94708.

PARKS, GEORGE BRUNER, b. Watkins, N.Y, Oct. 16, 90; m. 25. ENGLISH LITERATURE. A.B, Amherst Col, 11; A.M, Columbia Univ, 14, Ph.D, 29. From instr. to assoc. prof. ENG, Wash. Univ, 21-39; from assoc. prof. to prof, QUEENS COL.(N.Y), 39-61, EMER. PROF, 61- Guggenheim fel, 31-32; fel, Huntington Libr, Calif, 34-35; Fulbright Act grant, Italy, 49-50. MLA; Renaissance Soc. Am; Conf. Brit. Stud. English literature of the Renaissance, especially travel literature. Publ: Richard Hakluyt and the English voyages, 28, 2nd ed, Ungar, 61; The English traveler to Italy, 54 & ed, Gregory Martin, Roma Sancta, 69, Ed. Storia e Lett. Add: 121 Hollywood Ave, Douglaston, NY 11363.

PARKS, LLOYD C, b. Chicago, Ill, Jan. 30, 22; m. 50; c. 2. ENGLISH. B.A, Kenyon Col, 50; Fulbright res. grant, Sorbonne, France, 50-51; M.A, Univ. Wash, 53, Ph.D, 59. Asst. prof. ENG, Cortland State Teachers Col, 54-58; Ohio State Univ, 59-67; PROF, N.TEX. STATE UNIV, 67- Mem, YADDO, N.Y, summer 56; consult, Scott, Foresman & Co, 61; Ohio State Univ. Press; Fulbright lectr, Univ. Grenoble, 63-64; Univ. Lille, 64-65. U.S.N, 42-45. MLA. British and American modern poetry; symbolist French poetry; Victorian poetry. Publ: Transl, Stendhal, The red and the black, New Am. Libr, 70; auth, My father living, In: Best poems of 1957, Stanford Univ, 58; The hidden aspect of Sailing to Byzantium, Etudes Anglaises, 63; plus others. Add: 1517 Panhandle, Denton, TX 76201.

PARKS, MALCOLM GORDON, b. Petite Riviere, N.S, Apr. 7, 24; m. 50; c. 4. ENGLISH. B.A, Dalhousie Univ, 50, M.A, 51; Ph.D.(Eng), Univ. Toronto, 63. Teaching fel. ENG, Univ. Toronto, 52-53; lectr, Univ. King's Col, 53-54; asst. prof, DALHOUSIE UNIV, 56-62, assoc. prof, 62-68, PROF, 68-, chmn. dept, 69-72. Instr, Univ. Toronto, 54-56; assoc. ed, Dalhousie Rev, 56-67; Can. Counc. leave fel, 72-73. Can. Army, 43-46. Milton; 16th and 17th century English non-dramatic literature; Canadian literature. Publ: Sam Slick in pictures, Ryerson, Toronto, 56; ed, Western and eastern rambles: Joseph Howe's travel sketches of Nova Scotia, 73 & introd. to reprint of Joseph Howe's Poems and essays (1874), 73, Univ. Toronto; introd. to F.P. Grove's Fruits of the earth, McClelland & Stewart, Toronto, 65. Add: Dept. of English, Dalhousie University, Halifax, N.S, Can.

PARKS, STEPHEN ROBERT, b. Columbus, Ohio, July 18, 40. ENGLISH LITERATURE. B.A, Yale, 61; Ph.D.(Eng), Cambridge, 65. Librn, OSBORN COLLECTION, YALE LIBR, 67-68, assoc. cur, 68-71, CUR, 71- Jr. res. fel, Univ. Edinburgh, 64-65, sr. res. fel, 65-67. Bibliog Soc, Eng; Bibliog. Soc. Am; Grolier Club. English book-trade history; English gothic revival. Publ: Ed, Sale catalogues of libraries of eminent persons, Vol. 5, In: Men of letters, Sotheby-Mansell, 72. Add: Beinecke Library, 1603A Yale Station, New Haven, CT 06520.

PARLAKIAN, NISHAN, b. New York, N.Y, Aug. 11, 25; m. 52; c. 2. DRAMA & SPEECH. B.A, Syracuse Univ, 48; M.A, Columbia Univ, 50 & 52, Ph.D. (Eng. & drama), 67. Instr. Eng. & speech, Bronx Community Col, 61-63; ASSOC. PROF, SPEECH & DRAMA, Pace, Univ, 63-70, JOHN JAY COL CRIMINAL JUSTICE, 70-, DEPUTY CHMN. DEPT, 73- Artistic dir, Diocesan Players of Armenian Church of Am, 72-; mem. ed. bd, Ararat, 73- Excellence in Teaching Award, Pace Univ, 69. U.S.A, 44-46, S/Sgt; Bronze Star Medal. Speech Commun. Asn; MLA; Pirandello Soc. Am. Eighteenth century English drama; modern theatre; ethnic drama. Publ: The last Armenian (play), Armenian Rev, 7/59 & 10/59; Plagiarized (play), First Stage, summer 62; Evgeni Vakhtangov of the Moscow Art Theatre, Ararat, spring 69; Ancestral voices in Venice, Pace, spring 69. Add: John Jay College of Criminal Justice, 444 W. 56 St, New York, NY 10019.

PARLER, NETTIE P, b. Pittsburgh, Pa, Jan. 16, 16. ENGLISH LANGUAGE. A.B, Claflin Col, 36; A.M, Columbia Univ, 44; Gen. Educ. Bd. fel, N.Y. Univ, 48-49, Ph.D, 52. Teacher, high sch, S.C, 36-39, elem. sch, 39-43; state field worker, S.C. Tuberculosis Asn, 44; PROF. ENG, S.C. STATE COL, 44-, HEAD DEPT, 52- State chmn. achievement prog, Nat. Counc. Teachers Eng, 65-68. MLA; NCTE. Language skills of prospective English teachers; English today and tomorrow; socio-economic background of the State Agricultural and Mechanical College students. Publ: Significant steps in successful language teaching: the communications approach, Col. Lang. Asn, 58; The communications center at South Carolina State College, Palmetto Educ. Asn, 58; The nature of language: some aspects of language development in early childhood, Explorations in Educ, spring 66. Add: Dept. of English, South Carolina State College, Orangeburg, SC 29115.

PARNELL, PAUL E, b. Churchville, N.Y, Apr. 5, 17. ENGLISH. B.Ed, Brockport State Teachers Col, 46; M.A, N.Y. Univ, 47, Ph.D.(Eng), 51. Mem. faculty ENG, City Col. New York, 50-51; instr, Univ. Col, N.Y. Univ, 51-54, asst. prof, 54-60; BOWLING GREEN STATE UNIV, 60-64, assoc. prof, 64-68, PROF, 68-, stud. grant, spring 66. Midwest Mod. Lang. Asn; Johnson Soc. Cent. Region. Restoration and 18th century drama; early Elizabethan poetry and drama. Publ: Moral allegory in Lyly's Love's metamorphosis, 55 & Equivocation in Cibber's Love's last shift, 60, Stud. Philol; The sentimental mask, PMLA, 63; plus others. Add: 220 Baldwin Ave, Bowling Green, OH 43402.

PAROISSIEN, DAVID HARRY, b. Middlesbrough, Eng, Oct. 24, 39; m. 63; c. 2. VICTORIAN LITERATURE. B.A, Univ. Hull, 61; M.A, N.Mex. Highlands Univ, 65; Ph.D.(Eng), Univ. Calif, Los Angeles, 68. ASST. PROF. ENG, UNIV. MASS, AMHERST, 68- Vis. lectr. Eng, Univ. Kent, 73-74. MLA (mem. Victorian annual bibliog. comt, 68-); Dickens Soc; Dickens Fel. Dickens; Victorian fiction. Publ: Ed, Charles Dickens's pictures from Italy, Andre Deutsch, 73; auth, Mrs. Browning's influence on and contribution to A new spirit of the Age (1844): Eng. Lang. Notes, 71; Charles Dickens and the Weller family, Dickens Stud. Annual, 72. Add: 49 Kensington Ave, Northampton, MA 01060.

PARR, JOHNSTONE, b. Washington, D.C, May 5, 11; m. 35; c. 4. ENGLISH LITERATURE. A.B, Univ. Ala, 35, A.M, 36; Ph.D, Vanderbilt Univ, 41. Instr. ENG, Univ. Ala, 38-39, 41-44, asst. prof, 44-47, assoc. prof, 47-56, prof, 56-62; teaching fel, Vanderbilt Univ, 39-41; PROF, KENT STATE UNIV, 62- Fulbright fel, Eng, 58-59. MLA; Shakespeare Asn. Am. Chaucerian, Renaissance, Shakespearian and Victorian English literature. Publ: Tamburlaine's malady; Basic bibliographies for English studies, Univ. Ala, 53, 62; Robert Greene's classmates at Cambridge, PMLA, 62. Add: Dept. of English, Kent State University, Kent, OH 44240.

PARR, ROGER PHILLIP, b. Janesville, Wis, Aug. 2, 19; m. 45; c. 3. ENGLISH. B.S, Northwest. Univ, 45, M.A, 46; Ph.D.(medieval lit), Univ. Toronto. ASSOC. PROF. MEDIEVAL LIT, MARQUETTE UNIV, 53- Am. Philos. Soc. grant, 67-68. U.S.N.R, 42-45. MLA; Mediaeval Acad. Am; Speech Commun. Asn. Classical and medieval rhetoric and poetics; cinema theory; communication theory. Publ: The rhetorical tradition and Chaucer's narrative technique; transl, Geoffroi de Vinsauf's Documentum de modo et arte dictandi et versificandi, In: Medieval philosophical texts in translation, Marquette Univ, 68; Rhetoric and symbol in The pearl, Stud. Medieval Cult, spring 68. Add: 2721 N. Shepard Ave, Milwaukee, WI 53211.

PARRELLA, GILDA C, b. New Haven, Conn. INTERPRETATION OF LITERATURE, COMMUNICATION ARTS. B.A, Univ. R.I, 62; M.A, Univ. Denver, 64; Ph.D.(speech), Univ. Wash, 69. Assoc. speech & interpretation, Univ. Wash, 66-69; ASST. PROF. interpretation & theatre, Ill. State Univ, 69-73; INTERPRETATION, LOYOLA UNIV. CHICAGO, 73- Consult, Charles E. Merrill Publ. Co, 70- Speech Commun. Asn. Empathy; performance behavior; literary techniques. Publ: Projection and adoption: toward a clarification of the concept of empathy, Quart. J. Speech, 4/71; Image and mirror: empathy in language devices, West. Speech, fall 72. Add: Dept. of Communication Arts, Loyola University Lake Shore Campus, 6525 N. Sheridan Rd, Chicago, IL 60626.

PARRISH, BERYL MARGARET, b. Gnadenhutten, Ohio, Feb. 20, 12. ENGLISH. B.S, Ohio State Univ, 34, M.A, 39, 53-54, summers, Delta Kappa Gamma scholar, 48, 48-52; Delta Kappa Gamma scholar, Univ. Minnesota, 56-57, summers, 54-56. Teacher, high schs, Ohio, 34-44, pub. schs, 44-46; from asst. prof. to ASSOC. PROF. ENG, BOWLING GREEN STATE UNIV, 46-53, 54- Asst. instr, Ohio State Univ, 53-54; instr, Univ. Minn, 56-57. MLA; NCTE; Speech Commun. Asn; Int. Soc. Gen. Semantics. Eighteenth and 19th century English literature; linguistics. Publ: Education of the gifted, Twayne, 64; Teaching of composition for integration, Ohio Schs; Teaching of literature for social consciousness, High Sch. J; Providing an audience for freshman compositions, Col. Compos. & Commun. Add: Dept. of English, Bowling Green State University, Bowling Green, OH 43402.

PARRISH, JAMES ARTHUR, b. Auburn, Ala, July 12, 15; m. 47; c. 2. ENGLISH. B.S, Auburn Univ, 35; M.A, Fla. State Univ, 49, Ph.D.(Eng), 55. Educ. specialist, course materials, U.S. Air Force Exten. Course Inst, 52-57; assoc. prof, ENG, West. Ill. Univ, 57-60; UNIV. S.FLA, 60-62, PROF, 62-, chmn. dept, 62-73. U.S.A.A.F, 42-46, Maj. MLA; NCTE; Conf. Col. Compos. & Commun. American literature since 1865; modern drama; composition. Publ: James Gould Cozzens fights a war, Ariz. Quart, winter 62. Add: 3116 Samara Dr, Tampa, FL 33618.

PARRISH, STEPHEN MAXFIELD, b. Minneapolis, Minn, June 11, 21; m. 45, 69; c. 2. ENGLISH. A.B, Univ. Ill, 42; M.A, Harvard, 47, Ph.D, 54. Teaching fel, Harvard, 48-50, 52-54; instr. ENG, CORNELL UNIV, 54-56, asst. prof, 56-61, assoc. prof, 61-66, PROF, 66-, assoc. dean col. arts & sci, 65-69; Guggenheim fel, 59. U.S.N, 42-46, 50-52, Capt. MLA. Nineteenth century; Wordsworth; poetic theory. Publ: Co-auth, Keats and the Bostonians, 51 & auth, The art of the lyrical ballads, 73, Harvard; Concordances to Arnold & Yeats, Cornell Univ, 59 & 63. Add: Dept. of English, Cornell University, Ithaca, NY 14850.

PARROTT, FREDERICK JAMES, b. Poughkeepsie, N.Y, Aug. 22, 13. ENGLISH, SPEECH, DRAMA. B.A, St. Lawrence Univ, 35, M.A, 41; grant, Oxford, 42; fel, Cornell Univ, 46-48, Ph.D, 48; Columbia Univ, 51-52. Teacher, Poughkeepsie High Sch, 36-37; asst. in admin, St. Lawrence Univ, 37-40, dir, univ. radio workshop & instr. Eng, 40-42, instr. Eng. & speech, 45-46, asst. prof. Eng, 48-51; speech & theatre, Ind. Univ, 51-52; asst. prof. Eng. & in charge dramatics, Berea Col, 52-55, assoc. prof. Eng, 55-60, prof, 61-64; lectr. speech & Eng, Univ. Md. Far East Div, 64-68; ASSOC. PROF. SPEECH, FLA. A&M UNIV, 68- Asst. dir, Wilderness road (play), summers 55 & 57; stage mgr, Stephen Foster story, summers 58 & 59; hon. col. ed, Players Mag, 59-60; consult, Gekidan Tohai, Tokyo, Japan, 62; lectr, Far East Div, Univ. Md, Tokyo, Guam, Taiwan, 62-63; lectr, Am. Cult. Ctr, Tokyo, 64-65. Med.C, 42-45, Sgt. Am. Theatre Asn; Speech Commun. Asn. Intercultural humanities; costuming for the stage; theatre aesthetics. Publ: Mid-nineteenth century American theatre, Cornell Univ, 48; Introduction to African arts of Kenya, Zaire, Nigeria, ARCO, 73; Introduction & African art, In: The wind in a sieve, W.C. Brown, 69; Reappraisal: toward intercultural humanities, St. Andrews Rev, 71; How to cheat the cheaters, Improving Col. & Univ. Teaching, summer 72. Add: c/o Saltford, 30 Meyer Ave, Poughkeepsie, NY 12603.

PARSHALL, RAYMOND EDWARD, b. Salem, Ohio, Aug. 26, 06. ENGLISH. B.S, Col. Wooster, 28; Ph.D, Yale, 36. Teacher, High Sch, Ohio, 28-29; instr. Eng, Carnegie-Mellon Univ, 30-33, 35-38, asst. prof, 38-48, assoc. prof, 48-74, asst. to pres, 46-56, 58-74, dir. stud. personnel & welfare, 56-

58, secy. corp, 60-74; RETIRED. U.S.A.A.F, 44-45. The dramatic works of Edward Ravenscroft. Add: 4177 W. 11th Ave, Vancouver, B.C. V6R 2L5, Can.

PARSONS, COLEMAN OSCAR, b. Ripley, W.Va, Apr. 16, 05; m. 28; c. 1. ENGLISH & AMERICAN LITERATURE. A.B, Columbia Univ, 28; Ph.D, Yale, 31. Instr, L.I. Univ, 31-32, 37-41; Vassar Col, 33-34; Am. Univ.(D.C), 34-35; int. res. fel, Huntington Libr, Calif, 35-36; from lectr. to assoc. prof, CITY COL. NEW YORK, 41-62, prof. ENG, 63-72, supvr. Eng, eve. div, sch. gen. stud, 56-61, EMER. PROF, 72- Res. Nat. Libr, Scotland & Brit. Mus, 32-33, 61-62, 65-66; S.Africa, 67; lectr, Rand Sch, 39; Newark Sch. Soc. Sci, 40; grad. prof, grad. sch, City Univ. New York, 63-72, vis. prof. Eng. & Scottish lit, 72-75; prof, Columbia Univ, summers 65, 66; adv. Scottish lit, Yale Univ. Libr, 73-76. MLA; Grolier Club. Scottish fiction; romantic age; Mark Twain. Publ: Witchcraft and demonology in Scott's fiction, Oliver & Boyd, 64, ed. & introd, Joseph Glanvill's Saducismus triumphatus, 66 & George Sinclair's Satan's invisible world discovered, 69, Scholar's Facsimiles & Reprints; many articles in learned jour, 32- Add: 501 W. 123rd St, New York, NY 10027.

PARSONS, DAVID STEWART, b. Dec. 12, 25; Can. citizen; m. 56; c. 4. ENGLISH. B.A, Univ. Toronto, 48; M.A, 51; Ont. Col. Educ, 52. Instr. ENG, Meisterschaft Col, 48-51; Ryerson Instr. Technol, 52-56; S.Alta. Inst. Technol. & Art, 56-58; UNIV. SASK, 58-61, lectr, 61-65, asst. prof, 65-71, ASSOC. PROF, 71- Can. Counc. sr. scholar award, summer 67, post-doctoral res. award, 71. Can. Asn. Commonwealth Lang. & Lit. Stud; Can. Soc. 18th Century Stud. British literature between the wars; poetic drama. Publ: Childe Roland and the fool, Univ. Windsor Rev, 4/68; The odes of Drayton and Jonson, Queens' Quart, 4/68; Roy Campbell and Wyndham Lewis, Papers Lang. & Lit, 4/71. Add: Dept. of English, University of Saskatchewan, Saskatoon, Sask, S7N 0W0, Can.

PARSONS, J.E, b. Pittsburgh, Pa, Jan. 14, 37; m. 69. INTELLECTUAL HISTORY, AMERICAN LITERATURE. A.B, Kenyon Col, 58; Brandeis Univ, 58-59; fels, Univ. Rochester, 59-61, 64, Ph.D.(Eng), 64. Asst. prof. Eng. & tutor, col. lett, Wesleyan Univ, 65-72, dir. Am. stud. prog, 66-70; vis. prof. Eng, Fisk Univ, 71; prof. lett, Mohammed Univ, Morocco, 72-74. Ctr. Ed, Am. Authors, MLA & Nat. Endowment Humanities res. grant, 67-69; Fulbright sr. grant, 72-74. DeRothschild Found. poetry prize, 57, 58. MLA; Emerson Soc. Contemporary American culture; literature of decadence; intellectual history. Publ: Co-ed, The journals and miscellaneous notebooks of Ralph Waldo Emerson, Harvard, Vols. VII-XI. Add: Candlewood Hill, Jacoby Rd, Higganum, CT 06441.

PARSONS, ROGER L, b. Rochester, N.H, Nov. 28, 24; m. 59; c. 3. ENGLISH LITERATURE. B.S, Va. Polytech. Inst, 47, M.S, 49; B.A, Univ. Wis, 50, M.A, 51, Fulbright fel, 55-56, Ph.D, 59. Instr. elec. eng, Va. Polytech. Inst, 47-48; ENG, Univ. Wis-Milwaukee, 56-60; asst. prof, 60-61; UNIV. WIS- LA CROSSE, 61-63, assoc. prof, 63-65, PROF, 65-, chmn. dept, 64-67. U.S.A, 43-46. MLA; AAUP. English literature of the Renaissance. Add: Dept. of English, University of Wisconsin-La Crosse, La Crosse, WI 54601.

PARSONS, THORNTON HARRIS, b. Old Town, Maine, Sept. 7, 21; m. 49; c. 1. ENGLISH & AMERICAN LITERATURE. A.B, Ind. State Col, 50; M.A, Univ. Mich, 52, Ph.D, 59. Instr. lit. & compos, East. Mich. Univ, 56-58; Univ. Mich, 59; asst. prof. AM. LIT, SYRACUSE UNIV, 59-63, assoc. prof, 63-69, PROF, 69- Fulbright lectr. Am. lit, Charles Univ, Prague, 69-70. U.S.C.G, 43-46. MLA. Modern American poetry and fiction. Publ: Co-ed, Transcendentalism and its legacy, Univ. Mich, 66; auth, Hemingway's tyrannous plot, Univ. Kans. City Rev, summer 61; John Crowe Ransom, Twayne, 69; The civilized poetry of John Crowe Ransom, Perspective, autumn 64; Doing the best they can, Ga. Rev, autumn 69; plus others. Add: Dept. of English, Syracuse University, Syracuse, NY 13210.

PARTLOW, ROBERT B, JR, b. Boston, Mass, May 27, 19; m. 42; c. 2. ENGLISH. A.B, Harvard, 41, M.A.T, 48, A.M, 49, Ph.D, 55. Instr. ENG, Boston Univ, 46-49; from instr. to asst. prof, Univ. N.H, 49-57; from asst. prof. to PROF, SOUTH. ILL. UNIV, CARBONDALE, 57- U.S.A, 41-46, Maj. MLA; Dickens Soc. Victorian literature; theory of the novel. Publ: Liberal arts reader, Prentice-Hall, 63; ed, Papers Lang. & Lit, 65-69; Studies in American literature, 69, Dickens the craftsman, 70 & Dickens studies annual, Vols. I & II, 70 & 72, South. Ill. Univ; Dickens Stud. Newsletter, Vols. I-IV, 70- Add: Dept. of English, Southern Illinois University, Carbondale, IL 62901.

PARTRIDGE, COLIN J, b. Cardiff, Wales, Mar. 2, 34. ENGLISH. B.A, Univ. Nottingham, 59, Ph.D.(Eng), 65; Ford fel, Johns Hopkins Univ, 61-62; cert. educ, Univ. London, 63. Asst. lectr. Am. lit, Univ. Manchester, 63-66; lectr, 66-68; asst. prof. Eng. & Am. lit, UNIV. VICTORIA (B.C), 68-71, ASSOC. PROF. ENG. & DIR. AM. & COMMONWEALTH DIV, 71- Brit. Army Intel, 53-55. Asn. Commonwealth Lit. & Lang; Asn. Can. Univ. Teachers Eng. George Gissing; American fiction 1920-40; juvenile literature. Publ: Death of a salesman, a critical study, 69, Coriolanus: a critique, 70 & The crucible: a critique, 71, Blackwell; co-ed, George Gissing: the critical heritage, Routledge, 72; auth, Poetry of Robin Hyde, J. Commonwealth Lit, 7/68; Katherine Anne Porter and Mexico, Stud. Short Fiction, 70; Some functions of ideological satire, Lit. Half Yearly, 71; plus two others. Add: Dept. of English, University of Victoria, Victoria, B.C, Can.

PARTRIDGE, EDWARD BELLAMY, b. Phelps, N.Y, Mar. 21, 16; m. 43; c. 3. ENGLISH. A.B, Hobart Col, 38; M.A, Univ. Rochester, 39; Harvard, 40-41; univ. fel, Columbia Univ, 48-49; Ph.D, 50. Instr. ENG, Hobart Col, 39-40; Univ. Rochester, 42-46; Columbia Univ, 46-47; Cornell Univ, 49-53, asst. prof, 53-57; Bucknell Univ, 57-59, assoc. prof, 59-65; PROF, Tulane Univ, 65-67; Univ. Iowa, 67-68; TULANE UNIV, 68- Vis. prof, Calif. State Col. Los Angeles, 64-65. Col. Eng. Asn; MLA; Renaissance Soc. Am. Dramatic literature; English Renaissance; Ben Jonson. Publ: The broken compass: a study of the major comedies of Ben Jonson, Columbia Univ, 58; Ben Jonson: Bartholomew Fair, Univ. Nebr, 63; The allusiveness of Epicoene, J. Eng. Lit. Hist; Ben Jonson: the makings of the dramatist, Elizabethan theatre: Stratford-upon-Avon Stud, 66; plus others. Add: Dept. of English, Newcomb College, Tulane University, New Orleans, LA 70118.

PARTRIDGE, ELINORE HUGHES, b. Salt Lake City, Utah, Oct. 18, 37. AMERICAN LITERATURE, LINGUISTICS. A.B, Univ. Utah, 58; M.A, N.Y. Univ, 63; Ph.D.(Eng), Univ. Calif, Davis, 70. Teacher ENG, N.J. & N.Y. State Pub. Sch, 58-64; teaching assoc, Univ. Utah, 64-66; teaching asst, Univ. Calif, Davis, 66-70; ASST. PROF, UNIV. WIS-MILWAUKEE, 70- MLA. Nineteenth century American prose style; realistic American fiction; women in American literature. Publ: Contrib, Eight American authors, Duke Univ, 72. Add: Dept. of English, University of Wisconsin-Milwaukee, Milwaukee, WI 53201.

PASSLER, DAVID LUTHER, b. Boston, Mass, June 17, 41; m. 65. ENGLISH. B.A, Yale, 64; M.A, Univ. N.C, Chapel Hill, 66, Ph.D.(Eng), 68. ASST. PROF. ENG, EMORY UNIV, 68- MLA. Johnson and Boswell, specifically The life of Johnson; prose style. Add: Dept. of English, Emory University, Atlanta, GA 30322.

PASSLER, SUSAN MILLER, b. Washington, D.C, Dec. 10, 42. EIGHTEENTH CENTURY ENGLISH LITERATURE. Ph.D.(Eng), Univ. N.C, Chapel Hill, 71. ASST. PROF. ENG, GA. STATE UNIV, 69- MLA; S.Atlantic Mod. Lang. Asn; Am. Soc. 18th Century Stud. Publ: None has considered the audience, South. Humanities Rev, 73; Coleridge and Fielding: and Arthur Murphy, Wordsworth Circle, 74; Authur Murphy on Fielding and Tom Jones: re-evaluating a slighted critic, New Rambler, 74. Add: Dept. of English, Georgia State University, 33 Gilmer St, Atlanta, GA 30306.

PASSON, RICHARD HENRY, b. Hazelton, Pa, Aug. 18, 39; m. 65; c. 2. ENGLISH. B.A, King's Col.(Pa), 61; NDEA fel, Univ. Notre Dame, 61-64, M.A, 63, Ph.D.(Eng), 65. Instr. Eng, Univ. Scranton, 64-65, asst. prof, 65-68, assoc. prof, 68-72, prof, 72-73, chmn. dept, 70-73; DEAN COL. ARTS & SCI, CREIGHTON UNIV, 73- Nat. Asn. For. Stud. Affairs in-serv. training grant, 66-67. MLA; NCTE; AAUP; Am. Asn. Higher Educ; Am. Counc. Acad. Deans. Chaucer; 18th century English literature, especially satire and work of John Arbuthnot; satire, especially satiric theory. Publ: Legal satire in Gulliver from John Bull, Am. Notes & Queries, 3/67; Entente in Chaucer's friar's tale, Chaucer Rev, winter 68; Goldsmith and his vicar: another look, Mod. Lang. Stud, summer 73. Add: Office of the Dean, College of Arts & Sciences, Creighton University, Omaha, NE 68178.

PAST, RAYMOND EDGAR, b. Jamestown, N.Dak, Dec. 14, 18; m. 42; c. 2. ENGLISH. A.B, Univ. Pa, 41; M.A, Univ. Tex, Austin, 47, fel, 48, Ph.D, 50; Ling. Inst, Univ. Wash, 62. Instr. Eng, Univ. Tex, Austin, 50-51; asst. prof, Tex. A&M Univ, 51-52; UNIV. TEX, EL PASO, 52-57, assoc. prof, 57-61, prof, 61-67, Eng. & educ, 67-71, PROF. LING. & CHMN. DEPT, 71- Mem, Teaching Eng. to Non-Eng. Speakers Conf, 66; dir, NDEA Insts, 66-68; consult, Home Educ. Livelihood Prog, N.Mex, 66- U.S.N, 41-46, Lt. Teachers Eng. to Speakers Other Lang; NCTE. English linguistics; teaching English to speakers of other Languages. Publ: Co-auth, Say it in English, Vol. I, 68 & auth, Language as a lively art, 70, W.C. Brown; co-auth, Say it in English, Vols. II & III, Kendall/Hunt, 73; auth, Of cats and jays, Bull. Rocky Mountain Mod. Lang. Asn, 66; Border golf, Hispania, 70; Linguistics and oral language development, In: Early explorations, Denoyer-Geppert, 73; plus two others. Add: Dept. of Linguistics, University of Texas at El Paso, El Paso, TX 79968.

PATCH, GERTRUDE KEILEY, R.S.C.J, b. Brooklyn, N.Y, Oct. 28, 26. ENGLISH LITERATURE. B.A, San Francisco Col. Women, 47, M.A, 53; Ph.D.(Eng), Stanford Univ, 57. Instr. Eng. lit, San Francisco Col. Women, 56-58; San Diego Col. Women, 58-60, asst. prof, 60-62, assoc. prof, 62-66; acting pres, San Francisco Col. Women, 66, PRES, 66-70, LONE MOUNTAIN COL, 70- Asn. Am. Cols.(mem. comn. relig. higher educ, 72-). Medieval English literature, especially Piers Plowman; poetry of W.B. Yeats and his use of Irish folklore; modern American poetry. Add: Lone Mountain College, 2800 Turk Blvd, San Francisco, CA 94118.

PATEREK, JOSEPHINE DURKEE, b. Chicago, Ill, Dec. 9, 16; m. 36; c. 3. ENGLISH, SPEECH & DRAMA. B.S, Univ. Wis, 37; M.A, Univ. Minn, 55, Ph.D.(speech & theater), 61. Assoc. prof. ENG, UNIV. WIS-RIVER FALLS, 61-67, PROF, 67- Costumer, Hamline Univ. Theatre, St. Paul, 53-61; instr. commun, nursing educ. prog, KTCA-TV, St. Paul, 62-66. Am. Theatre Asn.(mem. tech. proj. comt); Speech Commun. Asn. Costuming, directing and acting for professional and educational theater; television teaching. Publ: Auth. & illustrator, Costuming for the theatre, Crown, 59. Add: Dept. of Speech, University of Wisconsin-River Falls, River Falls, WI 54022.

PATERSON, JOHN, b. Bathgate, Scotland, June 4, 23; m. 54; c. 6. ENGLISH. B.A, McGill Univ, 44; Ph.D, Univ. Mich, 54. Instr, Princeton, 53-56; assoc. prof. ENG, UNIV. CALIF, BERKELEY, 56-71, PROF, 71- MLA. The novel; prose fiction; modern British literature. Publ: The making of The return of the native, Univ. Calif; The novel as faith: the gospel according to James, Hardy, Conrad, Joyce, Lawrence and Virginia Woolf, Gambit, 73; The mayor of Casterbridge as tragedy, Victorian Stud, 59; The language of adventure in Henry James, Am. Lit, 60; introd. & notes, George Eliot's Adam Bede, Riverside Ed, 68. Add: Dept. of English, University of California, Berkeley, CA 94720.

PATON, FLORENCE ANN, b. New Castle, Pa, Dec. 12, 28. ENGLISH. B.A, Geneva Col, 50; M.Litt, Univ. Pittsburgh, 53; Ph.D.(Eng), Univ. Colo, 63. Teacher, High Sch, 50-58; instr. ENG, GENEVA COL, 58-60, asst. prof, 60-63, assoc. prof, 63-66, PROF, 66- NCTE; NEA; Mod. Humanities Res. Asn; MLA; Conf. Christianity & Lit. Middle English; literary criticism. Publ: It's only number two: a study of the Aunturs of Arthure, Pa. Counc. Teachers Eng. Bull, 8/67; contrib, Annual bibliography, Mod. Humanities Res. Asn, 69-72 & Halkett & Laing's dictionary of anonymous and pseudonymous literature, Oliver & Boyd, 73. Add: 3204 Sixth Ave, Beaver Falls, PA 15010.

PATON, JAMES, III, b. St. Louis, Mo, Sept. 17, 23; m. 46. ENGLISH. A.B, Kenyon Col, 47; M.A, West. Reserve Univ, 48, Ph.D.(Eng), 54. Instr. Eng, West. Reserve Univ, 49-51; Ohio Univ, 51-54; asst. prof, GROVE CITY COL, 54-55, from assoc. prof. & dir. debate to PROF. ENG. & CHMN. DEPT, 55- U.S.A, 43-46, Lt. MLA. English novel; Shakespeare; Victorians. Add: 435 W. Washington Blvd, Grove City, PA 16127.

PATRICK, JOHN MERTON, b. Georgetown, Tex, Mar. 11, 22; m. 46; c. 4. ENGLISH, HISTORY. A.B, Southwest. Univ, 42, A.M, 47; South. Asn. Am. Col. fel. & Ph.D.(hist), Georgetown Univ, 56; Univ. Tex, 56-57; Univ. Minn, 61. Instr. ENG, South. Methodist Univ, 47-48; asst. prof, Southwest. Univ. (Tex), 55-57, head dept, 56-57; asst. prof, UTAH STATE UNIV, 57-60, assoc. prof, 60-65, PROF, 65- Utah State Univ. res. grant, 60-62; col. Eng. rep. State of Utah, Utah Educ. Asn, 65-66; U.S. Dept. Health, Educ. & Welfare grant, 74-75. U.S.A, 41; U.S.N, 42-43; U.S.M.C, 43-46, 48-55, Res, 55-, Lt. Col. MLA; Rocky Mountain Mod. Lang. Asn; West. Asn. Mil. Hist; Geol. Soc. Am; Southwest. Asn. Mil. Hist. (pres). Romantic period of English literature; educational television; military history. Publ: Milton's conception of sin in Paradise lost, 60 & Artillery and warfare in the 13th and 14th centuries, 62, Utah State Univ; Buried astronomy, Hyperion Bks, 61; The great explosion: August, 1914, Proc. Utah Acad. Arts, 65. Auth. & producer TV ser, The art of war, 63, War and the waste land, spring 64 & The epic art of Homer, spring 66 & 67, KUSU-TV & KUED; Shakespeare radio series, KUSU-FM, spring 73. Add: 1566 E. 11th N, Logan, UT 84321.

PATRICK, JULIAN W. O, b. Winnipeg, Man, Dec. 28, 41. ENGLISH. B.A, Univ. Toronto, 64; M.A, Yale, 65, Woodrow Wilson fels, 64-65, 67-68. ASST. PROF. ENG, VICTORIA COL, UNIV. TORONTO, 68- Elizabethan and Jacobean drama; romantic poetry. Publ: Ed, A celebration of Ben Jonson, Univ. Toronto, 73. Add: Dept. of English, Victoria College, University of Toronto, 73 Queen's Park Crescent, Toronto, Ont. M5S 1K7, Can.

PATRICK, MICHAEL DAVIS, b. Lake Ozark, Mo, Jan. 12, 35; m. 59; c. 2. ENGLISH. B.S.Ed, South. Ill. Univ, 56, M.A, 57; Ph.D.(Eng), Univ. Mo-Columbia, 66. Instr. ENG, Univ. Mo, 59-63; ASST. PROF, West. Ky. State Col, 63-66; UNIV. MO-ROLLA, 66- Univ. Mo-Rolla summer res. grants, 67 & 68, asst. prof. traveling grant, summer 68; consult. state forum, Nat. Endowment for Humanities, summer 71. MLA; Mediaeval Acad. Am. The stage plays of Robert Browning; Browning's use of humor; English romantic poetry. Publ: Henry James' literary criticism, Ill. Quart, 12/72; Coleridge's Christabel, Romantic Reassessment, 2/73; Browning's dramatic techniques and The ring and the book, Costerus Essays Eng. Lit. & Philol, fall 73. Add: Dept. of Humanities, University of Missouri-Rolla, Rolla, MO 65401.

PATRICK, WALTON RICHARD, b. Collins, Miss, Sept. 9, 09; m. 37. AMERICAN LITERATURE. B.S, Miss. State Col, 33; A.M, La. State Univ, 34, Ph.D, 37. Instr, La. State Univ, 37-40, asst. prof, 40-45; assoc. prof. ENG, AUBURN UNIV, 46-47, PROF. & HEAD DEPT, 47- Fund Advan. Educ. fac. fel, 53-54. U.S.A, 42-46, Lt. Col. MLA; S.Atlantic Mod. Lang. Asn. American literature. Publ: Ring Lardner, Twayne, 63; co-auth, Southern literary culture: a bibliography of master's and doctors' theses, Univ. Ala, 55, What is the short story, 61 & American short stories: 1820 to the present, 64, Scott; auth, Poetic style in the contemporary short story, Col. Compos. & Commun, 5/67. Add: Dept. of English, Auburn University, Auburn, AL 36830.

PATRIDES, CONSTANTINOS APOSTOLOS, b. New York, N.Y, Apr. 20, 30. ENGLISH. B.A, Kenyon Col, 52; D.Phil, Oxford, 57. Instr. ENG, Univ. Calif. Berkeley, 57-59, asst. prof, 59-63, assoc. prof, 63-64; univ. lectr, UNIV. YORK, ENG, 64-66, sr. lectr, 66-70, READER, 70- Guggenheim fels, 60-61, 63-64; Am. Counc. Learned Soc. grant-in-aid, 63-64. Greek Underground Forces, 42-44; U.S.A, 52-54, Res, 54-, Sgt. MLA; Mod. Humanities Res. Asn; Renaissance Soc. Am; Milton Soc. Am.(exec. comt, 62-65); Eng. Asn, Gt. Brit; Soc. Renaissance Stud. Renaissance literature; Byzantine literature; patristic literature. Publ: Ed, Milton's Lycidas: the tradition and the poem, Holt, 61; auth, The phoenix and the ladder, Univ. Calif, 64; Milton and the Christian tradition, Clarendon, Oxford, 66; ed, Milton's epic poetry, Penguin, 67; Approaches to Paradise lost, E. Arnold Ltd, 68; ed, The Cambridge platonists, Harvard, 69 & Sir Walter Raleigh's history of the world, Temple Univ, 71; co-auth, Bright essence: studies in Milton's theology, Univ. Utah, 71; auth, The grand design of God, Univ. Toronto, 72; ed, Milton's poetry, Macmillan, 72-; ed, Milton's selected prose, Penguin, 74 & Herbert's poems, Everyman, 74- Add: Dept. of English, Langwith College, University of York, Heslington, York, England.

PATROUCH, JOSEPH FRANCIS, JR, b. Allentown, Pa, May 23, 35; m. 58; c. 4. ENGLISH. B.A, Univ. Cincinnati, 58, M.A, 60; Ph.D.(Eng), Univ. Wis, 65. ASSOC. PROF. ENG, UNIV. DAYTON, 64- Sci. Fiction Writers Am. Chaucer; Middle English literature; science fiction. Publ: The science fiction of Isaac Asimov, Doubleday, 74; Reginald Pecock, Vol. 106, In: English authors series, Twayne, 70; The gods themselves by Isaac Asimov, Extrapolation, 5/72. Add: Dept. of English, University of Dayton, Dayton, OH 45469.

PATTEN, KARL WATSON, JR, b. Beverly, Mass, Feb. 28, 27; m. 47; c. 2. ENGLISH. A.B, Williams Col, 47; M.A, Boston Univ, 49, Ph.D.(Eng. lit), 56. Instr. ENG, Boston Univ, 52-54; BUCKNELL UNIV, 56-59, asst. prof, 59-65, assoc. prof, 65-72, PROF, 72- Modern poetry and fiction; Renaissance poetry. Publ: The structure of The power and the glory, Mod. Fiction Stud, 57 & In: The power and the glory, Viking; plus numerous poems, 59- Add: Dept. of English, Bucknell University, Lewisburg, PA 17837.

PATTEN, ROBERT LOWRY, b. Oklahoma City, Okla, Apr. 26, 39; div; c. 2. ENGLISH LITERATURE, GRAPHIC ARTS. B.A, Swarthmore Col, 60; Woodrow Wilson fel, Princeton, 60-61, jr. fel, 61-62, M.A, 62, Theodore Whitefield Hunt fel, 62-63, Ph.D.(Eng), 65; Fulbright scholar, Univ. London, 63-64. Lectr. ENG, Bryn Mawr Col, 64-66; asst. prof, 66-69, RICE UNIV, 69-71, ASSOC. PROF, 71- Nat. Endowment for Humanities younger scholar, 68-69. Dickens Soc; MLA; AAUP; S.Cent. Mod. Lang. Asn; Victorian Soc. Am. Charles Dickens; Victorian publishing; George Cruikshank. Publ: Co-ed, Dickens' studies annual, South. Ill. Univ, 70-71, 73-; ed, Charles Dickens' The Pickwick papers, Penguin, 72; George Cruikshank: a revaluation, Princeton, 74; auth, The art of Pickwick's interpolated tales, ELH, 67; The fight at the top of the tree: Vanity fair versus Dombey and son, Stud. Eng. Lit, 70; Dickens time and again, Dickens Stud. Annual, 71. Add: Dept. of English, Rice University, Houston, TX 77001.

PATTERSON, CHARLES (IVEY), JR, b. Cooper, Ga, Apr. 26, 13. ENGLISH. A.B, Emory Univ, 34, A.M, 40; fel, Univ. Ill, 49-50, Ph.D, 50. Instr. ENG, Boys' High Sch, Atlanta, Ga, 34-36; Ga. Inst. Technol, 36-39; Auburn Univ, 41-46, asst. prof, 46-52, assoc. prof, 52-54, prof, 64; from asst. prof. to PROF, Univ. Ark, 55-64; North. Ill. Univ, 65-67; UNIV. GA, 67- Instr, Univ. Ill, 49-50; Ford fac. fel, Harvard, 52; Fulbright lectr. Am. lit, Univ. Erlangen, 58-59; prof. Eng, Univ. Ala, 59-60. MLA; S.Atlantic Mod. Lang. Asn. English Romantics; 19th century prose fiction; intellectual history. Publ: Ed, The Daemonic in the poetry of John Keats, Univ. Ill, 70; auth, The Keats-Hazlitt-Hunt copy of Palmerin of England in relation to Keats's poetry, J. Eng. & Ger. Philol, 1/61; Passion and permanence in Keats's Ode on a Grecian urn, ELH, XXI. Add: Dept. of English, University of Georgia, Athens, GA 30602.

PATTERSON, FRANK HARMON, b. New Britain, Conn, July 5, 12; m. 41. ENGLISH. A.B, Clark Univ, 36; A.M, Yale, 43, Ph.D, 44. Asst. prof. Eng, Norwich Univ, 39-42; dean & dir. admis, Becker Jr. Col, Mass, 46-49; assoc. prof. Eng. & chmn. dept, BOSTON UNIV, 49-50, prof. Eng. & humanities & chmn. dept, div. gen. educ, 50-67, PROF. HUMANITIES, 67- U.S.N.R, 42-45, Lt. Col. Eng. Asn. General education. Publ: Words in action, Am. Bk. Co, 4/68. Add: Dept. of Humanities, Div. of General Education, Boston University, Boston, MA 02215.

PATTERSON, FRANK MORGAN, b. Newark, N.J, Oct. 26, 31; m. 55; c. 1. ENGLISH. B.A, Park Col, 53; M.A, Univ. Iowa, 57, Ph.D.(Eng), 66. Instr. ENG, W.Va. Univ, 57-59; asst, Univ. Iowa, 59-63; asst. prof, CENT. MO. STATE UNIV, 63-67, assoc. prof, 67-71, PROF, 71- Danforth assoc, Danforth Found, 71- Sig.C, U.S.A, 53-55. NCTE. Restoration drama; Australian literature; police report writing. Publ: Co-auth, A manual of police report writing, C.C. Thomas, 68; auth, The brackets in To the lighthouse, Eng. Rec, 2/66; The revised scenes of The provok'd wife, Eng. Lang. Notes, 9/66; Weaknesses in police report writing instructions, Police Law Quart, 1/72. Add: Dept. of English, Central Missouri State University, Warrensburg, MO 64093.

PATTERSON, J. W, b. Stillwell, Okla, May 9, 28; m. 52; c. 1. SPEECH, COMMUNICATION. B.A, Northeast. State Col, 48; M.A, Univ. Mich, 54; Ph.D.(speech), Univ. Okla, 60. Instr. SPEECH, Univ. Okla, 58-59; asst. prof, Univ. Ariz, 59-60; ASSOC. PROF, UNIV. KY, 60-, acting chmn. dept, 67-72, centennial coordr, 63-66. Speech Commun. Asn. Rhetorical criticism and theory. Publ: Ethical obligations in a policy debate, Speech Teacher, 62; Speech in the South, South. Humanities Bull, 65. Add: Dept. of Speech, 117 Bradley Hall, University of Kentucky, Lexington, KY 40506.

PATTERSON, JOYE, b. Marvell, Ark, Dec. 28, 25. JOURNALISM. B.J, Univ. Tex, 47; M.A, Univ. Mo, 62, Ph.D.(jour), 66. Instr. JOUR, UNIV. MO-COLUMBIA, 66-67, asst. prof, 67-72, ASSOC. PROF, 72- Asn. Educ. in Jour; Nat. Asn. Sci. Writers. Science writing. Add: School of Journalism, University of Missouri-Columbia, Columbia, MO 65201.

PATTERSON, MARGARET C, b. Woburn, Mass, Apr. 13, 23; c. 2. ENGLISH. B.A, Wellesley Col, 44; M.Ed, Univ. Fla, 65, Ph.D, 70. Asst. Eng. & libr. sci, UNIV. FLA, 65-70, ASST. PROF. ENG, 70- NDEA grant, 69; Carnegie Prog. grant, 71 & 73; mem. bibliog. comt, MLA Int. Bibliog, 72- MLA; Am. Libr. Asn. Poetry; Hopkins; nineteenth century English literature. Publ: Carnegie program methodology manual, 71, 2nd ed, 73; Creative writers bibliography, Univ. Fla, 73; Literary research guide, Gale, 74; Lilacs: a sonata, Walt Whitman Rev, 67; V.I.P. publications, Bull. Bibliog, 73. Add: Dept. of English, Anderson Hall, University of Florida, Gainesville, FL 32601.

PATTERSON, MERRILL REEVES, b. Jersey City, N.J, Jan. 27, 02; m. 28; c. 2. ENGLISH. B.S, Wesleyan Univ, 25; A.M, Brown Univ, 30; Ph.D, Yale, 33; Litt.D, Marietta Col, 67. Managing ed, New Haven Union, Conn, 26-27; master, Tilton Sch, N.H, 27-28; asst. instr, Wesleyan Univ, 32-34; instr. Eng, MARIETTA COL, 34-36, asst. prof, 36-38, prof, 38-39, Hillyer prof. & chmn. dept, 39-63, dean col, 48-67, dir. acad. advising, 67-72, EMER. ACAD. DEAN, 67- Asst, Conn. Col, 33-34; mem, Inst. Col. & Univ. Adminrs, 58; pres, Nat. Conf. Acad. Deans, Stillwater, Okla, 58; mem. comn. cols. & univs, N.Cent. Accrediting Asn, 66-70; consult. on accreditation & instr. Eng, Parkersburg Community Col, W.Va, 72- MLA; NCTE; Col. Eng. Asn; Am. Conf. Acad. Deans (treas, 60-63); N.Cent. Asn. Acad. Deans; Inst. Europ. Stud.(distinguished serv. award int. educ, 72). Biography; Sumner Lincoln Fairfield. Publ: They are building still, Ohioana Libr. Quart. Mag, summer 71. Add: 411 Fifth St, Marietta, OH 45750.

PATTERSON, N. S, b. Bardwell, Tex, Apr. 20, 11; m; c. 2. JOURNALISM. A.B, Baylor Univ, 31; M.A, Univ. Tex, 35; fel, South. Methodist Univ, 38; Univ. Mo. Teacher pub. sch. adminr. & pub. relat. worker, schs, Tex, 31-40; from instr. to assoc. prof. jour, Univ. Houston, 40-53, head dept. jour. & publs, 40-50, dir. publs. & sch. jour, 50-53; PUBL. & ED, PHOTOLITH, 50-, dir, Nat. Sch. Yearbk. Asn, 50-73; dir, Nat. Newspaper Serv, 58-73. Fac. mem. sch. jour, Univ. Mo. & dir, Mo. Interscholastic Press Asn, 55-59; consult, Nat. Sch. Yearbook & Newspaper Asn, 73-; columnist, Photolith Mag. Pioneer Award, Nat. Scholastic Press Asn, 70. Hon. mem. Nat. Counc. Col. Publ. Adv.(outstanding serv. award, 70); Asn. Educ. in Jour. Scholastic and collegiate publications. Publ: Prize package, compilation and commentary on best yearbooks of 1971, 72 & Judging standards, rev. ed, Nat. Sch. Yearbk. Asn; numerous articles & eds, Photolith Mag, 50- Add: 418 Woodmere Lane, Memphis, TN 38117.

PATTERSON, REBECCA, b. Ola, Ark, Aug. 6, 11; m. 36; div. 53; c. 2. ENGLISH. B.A, Univ. Tex, 34, M.A, 35, fel, 35-38, Ph.D.(Eng), 38. Instr. Eng, Univ. Tex, 38-39; Amarillo Col, 45-46; Stanford Univ, 48-49; Univ. N.C, 50-51; PROF. AM. LIT, KANS. STATE COL. PITTSBURG, 54- Am. Asn. Univ. Women fel, 49; Houghton-Mifflin fel, 50; ed-in-chief, Midwest Quart, 67- MLA; NCTE. Eighteenth century English literature; 19th century American poetry; modern poetry. Publ: A study of Whitman's vocabulary; The riddle of Emily Dickinson; Emily Dickinson and Elizabeth Browning. Add: 2006 S. Stilwell, Pittsburg, KS 66762.

PATTERSON, REMINGTON PERRIGO, b. Nice, France, Dec. 16, 26. ENGLISH. B.A, Yale, 50, M.A, 53, Ph.D, 57. Instr. ENG, BARNARD COL, COLUMBIA UNIV, 55-58, asst. prof, 58-64, assoc. prof, 64-73, PROF, 73- Fulbright grant to U.K, 61-62; mem. regional selection comt, Woodrow Wilson Nat. Fel. Found, 62-67. U.S.A, 45-46. Malone Soc; MLA; Shakespeare Asn. Am. Shakespeare; Elizabethan drama. Add: Dept. of English, Barnard College, Columbia University, New York, NY 10027.

PATTERSON, THOMAS McEVOY, b. Silver Creek, Miss, July 14, 11; m. 36, 53; c. 4. DRAMATIC ART. A.B, Univ. Tex, 34, A.M, 36; Yale, 46-48; creative writing fel, Stanford Univ, 48-49. Instr. Eng, Univ. Tex, 35-41; head dept, pub. schs, Tex, 41-42; spec. agent, Fed. Bur. Invest, 42-44; PROF. DRAMATIC ART, Univ. Okla, 49-50; UNIV. N.C, CHAPEL HILL, 50-, CHMN. DEPT, 68- Yale grant-in-aid, 47; Fulbright exchange prof, Korea, 62-63; auth, Old Four-eyes, produced Theodore Roosevelt & Badlands Asn, 58- U.S.N, 44-46. Am. Educ. Theatre Asn; Southeast. Theatre Conf.(exec. secy, 54-56). Playwriting; sources of Elizabethan drama; plays. Add: Dept. of Dramatic Art, Graham Memorial, University of North Carolina at Chapel Hill, Chapel Hill, NC 27514.

PATTINSON, JOHN PATRICK, b. Windermere, Eng, Mar. 25, 26; m. 61; c. 2. ENGLISH. B.A, Cambridge, 47, M.A, 49; Penfield fel, N.Y. Univ, 63, Ph.D. (Eng), 68. Instr. ENG, Graham-Eckes Sch, Palm Beach, Fla, 51-54; Dickinson Col, 54-58; asst, N.Y. Univ, 58-60; substitute lectr, City Col. New York, 59-60; lectr, Queens Col.(N.Y), 60-63, 64-65; asst. prof, NEWARK COL. ENG, 65-68, assoc. prof, 68-72, PROF. & CHMN, 72- Adj. assoc. prof, Queens Col.(N.Y), 72- MLA. Contemporary poetry criticism; Greek and Latin classics; Italian literature. Publ: Transl, Pirandello's The art of humor, Mass. Rev, summer 65. Add: Dept. of Humanities, Newark College of Engineering, 323 High St, Newark, NJ 07102.

PATTISON, EUGENE HAMILTON, b. Pontiac, Mich, Jan. 8, 35. ENGLISH, RELIGION. B.A, Alma Col.(Mich), 56; M.A, Univ. Mich, 57, Ph.D.(Eng), 63; Union Theol. Sem, summer 59; S.T.B, Harvard, 64. Asst. prof. ENG, ALMA COL.(MICH), 64-71, ASSOC. PROF, 71- MLA; AAUP; Conf. Christianity & Lit. American culture, with emphasis on literature, William Dean Howells and religion. Publ: Ed, William Dean Howells, The leatherwood god, Ind. Univ. Add: Dept. of English, Alma College, Alma, MI 48801.

PATTISON, JOSEPH C, b. Boston, Mass, Aug. 11, 22; m. 43; c. 2. LITERATURE. B.S. in Ed, Boston Univ, 47; M.A, Columbia Univ, 49, Ed.D, 55. Instr, teachers col, Columbia Univ, 50-51, ENG, 51-55; asst. prof, CALIF. STATE UNIV, SACRAMENTO, 55-59, assoc. prof, 59-65, PROF, 65- U.S.A, 44-46, 1st Lt. NCTE; MLA. Nineteenth century American fiction; Hawthorne. Publ: The guilt of the innocent Donatello, Emerson Soc. Quart, 63; Point of view in Hawthorne, PMLA, 10/67; The celestial railroad as dream-tale, Am. Quart, summer 68; plus others. Add: 1744 Daphne Ave, Sacramento, CA 95825.

PATTISON, SHERON J. DAILEY, b. Indianapolis, Ind, Jan. 11, 40. SPEECH COMMUNICATION, POETRY. B.A, Wake Forest Univ, 61; M.A, Univ. Minn, 63, Ph.D.(speech commun), 69. Teaching asst. speech, Univ. Minn, 61-64; instr. speech & theatre, Wake Forest Univ, 64-65; asst. prof. SPEECH COMMUN, IND. STATE UNIV, TERRE HAUTE, 65-72, ASSOC. PROF, 72- Guest lectr, Slippery Rock State Col, 72; mem, Oral Interpretation Bibliog. Comt, 72-; guest speaker, Focus Forum Ser, Fed. Penitentiary. Speech Commun. Asn; Cent. States Speech Commun. Asn. Theatre theory and oral interpretation of literature; rhetoric and oral interpretation with special emphasis on Kenneth Burke. Publ: Listeners' theatre: perhaps naming is explaining, Oral Interpretation Newslett, fall 72; Indiana Speech Association: a plea for reform, fall 72 & Rhetoric and oral interpretation, spring 73, Ind. Speech Notes. Add: Dept. of Speech Communication, Indiana State University, Terre Haute, IN 47809.

PATTON, BOBBY RAY, b. Ft. Worth, Tex, Dec. 18, 35; m. 58. SPEECH. B.F.A, Tex. Christian Univ, 58; M.A, Univ. Kans, 62, Ph.D.(speech commun), 66. Instr. speech & forensics, high sch, Kans, 58-61; Univ. Wichita, 61-62, asst. prof. speech & forensics & dir. debate, 62-65, dir. speech educ, 65-66; asst. prof. speech commun. & human relat, UNIV. KANS, 66-68, assoc. prof. SPEECH & DRAMA, 68-74, PROF, 74-, CHMN. DEPT, 72-, dir. fundamentals of speech prog, 66-72, asst. chmn. dept. speech & drama, 66-72. Speech Commun. Asn; Int. Commun. Asn. Interpersonal communication, small group interaction; instructional communication. Publ: Descriptive analysis of high school debaters, Am. Forensic Asn, 62; co-auth, Fundamentals of interpersonal communication, 71, co-ed, Basic readings in interpersonal communication, 71, co-auth, Problem-solving group interaction, 73 & Interpersonal communication: basic text and readings, 74, Harper; Personal communication in human relations, C.E. Merrill, 74; auth, High school speech training in the United States, Nfld J. Educ, 4/68. Add: Dept. of Speech & Drama, University of Kansas, Lawrence, KS 66045.

PATTON, JOHN JOSEPH, b. Philadelphia, Pa, Sept. 4, 21; m. 59; c. 2. ENGLISH. A.B, Univ. Pa, 48, M.A, 49; fel, Univ. Colo, 60-61, Ph.D, 62. Instr. Eng, Villanova Col, 49-51; Univ. Colo, 53-57; Russell Sage Col, 57-60; asst. prof, Albright Col, 61-62; assoc. prof, Marshall Univ, 62-63; Ulster County Community Col, 63-66; prof. Eng. & asst. dean curriculum & instr, Newark State Col, 66-68; PROF. ENG, ATLANTIC COMMUNITY COL, 68-, CHMN. DIV. COMMUN. ARTS, 71-, chmn. dept. Eng, 68-71. Marshall Univ. Res. Bd. grant, 63; vis. prof, McMaster Univ, summer 65. A.U.S, 42-45. MLA; Col. Eng. Asn; NCTE; Am. Asn. Higher Educ; Northeast Mod. Lang. Asn; Nat. Fac. Asn. Twentieth century American poetry and drama. Publ: Variety of Rolfe Humphries, Eng. Rec, 4/67; Comprehensive bibliography of criticism of Edna St. Vincent Millay, The Serif, 9/68; Satiric fiction in Millay's Distressing dialogues, Mod. Lang. Stud, summer 72; plus others. Add: Div. of Communicative Arts, Atlantic Community College, Mays Landing, NJ 08330.

PATTON, MARY MILLER, b. Kalamazoo, Mich, Jan. 31, 15; m. 50. ENGLISH, SPEECH. Fel, Kalamazoo Col, 33-36, B.A, 36; West. Mich. Univ. summers 37-45; M.A, Columbia Univ, 40; Univ. Havana, summer 44; Stanford Univ, 50. Teacher high sch, Mich, 36-39; instr. Eng. & jour, Fairmount Jr. Col, 40-42; recreation specialist, Am. Red. Cross, New Orleans, 42-43; instr. speech & drama, AM. UNIV, 43-47, asst. prof, 47-51, dir. univ. theater, 43-54, assoc. prof. Eng, 51-73, EMER. PROF. ENG. & SPEECH, 73- Hodge Prize & Jones Prize, Kalamazoo Col, 36; Women's Counc. Kalamazoo Award, 62. Mem. bd. trustees, Kalamazoo Col, 72- Col. Eng. Asn; Eng. Speaking Union. Shakespearean comedy; Greek and Roman drama; Victorian prose and poetry. Add: Dept. of English, American University, Washington, DC 20016.

PAUL, ALDRICH K, b. Dallas Center, Iowa, July 28, 22; m. 46; c. 2. DRAMATIC ARTS. B.A, Iowa State Teachers Col, 47; M.S, Drake Univ, 51; Ph.D.(theatre & speech), Univ. Denver, 54. Prof. speech & dir. forensics, Iowa State Col, 54-56; from assoc. prof. to prof. speech & head dept, Univ. Omaha, 56-64; head dept. speech & theater arts, Univ. Cincinnati, 64-70; PROF. SPEECH & PRES. UNIV, UPPER IOWA UNIV, 70- U.S.A, 42-46, Capt. Speech Commun. Asn; Nat. Soc. Stud. Commun; Am. Counc. Better Broadcasts with TACT (treas, 67-68). Industrial communications. Publ: Speech management, W.C. Brown, 61, 63. Add: Office of the President, Upper Iowa University, Fayette, IA 52142.

PAUL, CHARLES B, Cultural History, History of Science. See Volume 1, History.

PAUL, SHERMAN, b. Cleveland, Ohio, Aug. 26, 20; m. 43; c. 4. AMERICAN LITERATURE. Ph.D.(Am. civilization), Harvard, 50. Instr. Eng, State Univ. Iowa, 46; Harvard, 50-52; asst. prof. AM. LIT, Univ. Ill, 52-55, assoc. prof, 55-57, prof, 57-66, Ctr. Advan. Stud, 66-67, assoc. mem, ctr. advan. stud, 61, 63-64; M.F. CARPENTER PROF, UNIV. IOWA, 67- Bowdoin Prize, 50; Ford fel, 52; Fulbright vis. prof, Univ. Vienna, 57-58; Guggenheim fel, 63-64; mem. adv. bd, Stud. Romanticism, 63-; ed. bd, Am. Lit, 64-66. U.S.A.A.F, 42-46, Capt. MLA (mem. adv. bd, PMLA, 73-). American poetry; American criticism and culture; the Emersonian tradition. Publ: Emerson's angle of vision, Harvard, 52; The shores of America, 58, Edmund Wilson: a study of literary vocation in our time, 65, The music of survival: a biography of a poem by W.C. Williams, 68 & Hart's bridge, 73, Univ. Ill; Louis Sullivan, Prentice-Hall, 62; Randolph Bourne, 66 & ed, Six class American writers, 71, Univ. Minn; auth, Harry Callahan, Mus. Mod. Art, 67; ed, Criticism and culture, Papers Midwest Mod. Lang. Asn, 72. Add: 903 E. College Ave, Iowa City, IA 52240.

PAUL, WILSON BENTON, b. Colfax, La, July 15, 05; m. 30; c. 1. SPEECH. A.B, Taylor Univ, 29; summers, Northwest. Univ, 28-30; A.M, State Univ. Iowa, 32, Ph.D, 40; Univ. Mich, 34-35. Instr, Taylor Univ, 29-31; high sch, Wis, 32-36; head dept. speech & dean men, Ill. Wesleyan Univ, 36-38; from asst. prof. to prof, Univ. Denver, 40-47; prof. speech, MICH. STATE UNIV, 47-71, head dept, 47-56, dir. lect-concert series, 56-71, CONSULT, OFF. DEAN COL. ARTS & LETT, 71- Exec. secy, Adult Educ. Counc, Denver, Colo, 45-46; mem. bd. trustees, Taylor Univ, 65-70. Am. Theatre Asn; Am. Nat. Theatre & Acad; West. Speech Asn.(exec. secy, 45, v.pres, 46); Asn. Col. & Univ. Concert Mgr.(v.pres, 57, pres, 60-62); Int. Asn. Concert Mgr. Public address; theater arts; educational administration. Publ: Basic communications; Early American rhetoric and history of American theatre; John Witherspoon's theory and practice of public speaking, Speech Monogr. Add: 940 Huntington Rd, East Lansing, MI 48823.

PAUL-EMILE, BARBARA TAYLOR, b. Montego Bay, Jamaica, Sept. 18, 37; U.S. citizen; m. 63; c. 2. ENGLISH LITERATURE. B.A, N.Y. Univ, 62, fel. & M.A, 63; fel. & Ph.D.(Eng), Univ. Colo, 71. Res. asst. Eng, Univ. Colo, Boulder, 63-65, teaching assoc, 65-67, instr, 67-70, ASST. PROF. ENG. & BLACK STUD, 71-74; VASSAR COL, 74- Summer fac. res. fel, Univ. Colo, Boulder, 73. MLA; NCTE. Nineteenth century English literature; Afro-American and Caribbean literature. Publ: Coleridge as abolitionist, Ariel, (in press). Add: Dept. of English, Vassar College, Poughkeepsie, NY 12601.

PAULEY, JOHN FRANCIS, b. Sioux City, Iowa, Jan. 31, 16. SPEECH, DRAMA. B.A, Trinity Col.(Iowa), 37; M.F.A, State Univ. Iowa, 49, Ph.D, 50. Asst. prof. speech & drama, Wis. State Col, Whitewater, 50-52; HUMBOLDT STATE UNIV, 52-55, acting chmn. div. fine & appl. arts, 55-56, from assoc. prof. SPEECH & DRAMA to PROF, 56-, CHMN. DEPT. THEATRE ARTS, 69-, chmn. div. lang. arts & asst. dean instr, 56-66, chmn. div. creative arts, 66-69. U.S.A, 42-46, 1st Lt. Speech Commun. Asn; Am. Theatre Asn. Playwriting. Publ: September tea (play) N.W. Drama Festival, 70; Honsea (play), Calif. State Univ, 71. Add: Dept. of Theatre Arts, Humboldt State University, Arcata, CA 95521.

PAULI, KENNETH W, b. Champaign, Ill, Apr. 17, 20; m. 68; c. 2. SPEECH, DRAMA. B.A, Wesleyan Univ, 41; M.A, Columbia Univ, 47; Newhouse Found. scholar, Stanford Univ, 53, Royall Victor fel, 54, Field Hotaling fel, 54-55, univ. honors scholar, 55, Ph.D.(speech), 60; South. Found. fel, Vanderbilt Univ, 56. From instr. to asst. prof. speech, Vanderbilt Univ, 55-61; assoc. speech & drama, Elmira Col, 61-63; asst. prof. speech, Univ. Conn, 64-65; Univ. Hartford, 65-67; prof. speech & head dept. speech & drama, PEMBROKE STATE UNIV, 67-72, MANAGING ED, PEMBROKE MAG, 71-, dir. forensics, dept. communicative arts, 72-73. Elmira Col. res. grant, 62; Citizen Exchange Corps travel grant, Soviet Union, 69. Mil.Intel, U.S.A, 45. Speech Commun. Asn. Speech education; creative writing; forensics. Add: R.D. 2, Red Springs, NC 28377.

PAULITS, WALTER JOHN, F.S.C, b. Westmont, N.J, Apr. 24, 23. ENGLISH LITERATURE. B.A, Cath. Univ. Am, 47; M.A, Univ. Pittsburgh, 50, univ. scholar, 54, Ph.D, 55. Instr. ENG. LA SALLE COL, 56-57, asst. prof, 57-66, ASSOC. PROF, 66- Emerson and transcendentalism; Shakespeare and drama; literature and theology interdiscipline. Publ: This is right; that must be wrong, America, 3/65; A paradox of love, 7/66 & More on prayer, 3/68, Rev. For Religious. Add: Dept. of English, La Salle College, Philadelphia, PA 19141.

PAULK, WILLIAM ESTON, JR, b. Rebecca, Ga, Mar. 7, 29. ENGLISH. A.B, Univ. Ga, 50, M.A, 54; Tulane Univ, summer 55; Darlington grant & cert, Oxford, 58. Instr. Eng, Univ. Ga, 54-57; master, Darlington Sch, Rome, Ga, 57-59; instr, WEST. CAROLINA UNIV, 59-61, ASST. PROF. ENG. & PROF. WRITING, 61-, DIR. PROF. WRITING PROG, 62- Carolina Dramatic Asn. Author Award, 62. U.S.A, 50-52, Sgt. S.Atlantic Mod. Lang. Asn; NEA; NCTE. Professional writing; pantisocracy, the pantisocrats, and their literature; the love poetry of John Donne. Publ: Green jade bowl, Persimmon Hill Press, 55; College preparation in the senior year, Eng. J, 10/60; White glove, In: Distinctive American short stories, 62; contrib, Christian Sci.

Monitor, Satire Newslett, Green River Rev, Georgia Rev, Motive; plus others. Add: Dept. of English, Western Carolina University, Cullowhee, NC 28723.

PAULSON, CLARA J, b. Buxton, N.Dak, June 10, 07. ENGLISH. A.B, Concordia Col.(Moorhead, Minn), 30; summers, Univ. Minn, 30-31; fel, Syracuse Univ, 35-37, A.M, 37; summers, Univ. Colo, 54, 56-58. Demonstration teacher, rural sch, 26-27; instr. Eng. & asst. dean women, Concordia Col. (Moorhead, Minn), 30-35, 37-39; dean women, LUTHER COL, 39-47, assoc. prof. ENG, 47-52, prof, 52-71, EMER. PROF, 71- Fulbright exchange teacher, Bergen, Norway, 51-52. NCTE; MLA; Col. Eng. Asn. American literature; freshman English. Add: Kimble Lake, Star Rte. 1, Pequot Lakes, MN 56472.

PAULSON, ELEANOR, b. Iron Mountain, Mich, Nov. 3, 25. SPEECH. A.B, Wheaton Col.(Ill), 47; A.M, Northwest. Univ, 52. Teacher, high sch, Mich, 47-52; instr. speech & Eng, Detroit Bible Col, 51-52; SPEECH, WHEATON COL.(ILL), 52-57, asst. prof, 57-68, ASSOC. PROF, 68- Speech Commun. Asn; NEA. Oral interpretation; speech education; speech in elementary school. Add: Dept. of Speech, Wheaton College, Wheaton, IL 60187.

PAULSON, RONALD HOWARD, b. Bottineau, N.Dak, May 27, 30; m. 57; c. 2. ENGLISH LITERATURE. B.A, Yale, 52, M.A, 55, Sterling fel, 57-58, Ph.D, 58. Instr. Eng, Univ. Ill, 58-59, asst. prof, 59-62, assoc. prof, 62-63; PROF, Rice Univ, 63-67; JOHNS HOPKINS UNIV, 67-, MELLON PROF. HUMANITIES, 73- Univ. Ill. summer fac. fel, 60, 62; Am. Philos. Soc. grants, 61, 67; Am. Counc. Learned Soc. grant, 65; Guggenheim fel, 65-66. U.S.A, 52-54, 1st Lt. MLA. Seventeenth and eighteenth century English literature. Publ: Theme and structure in Swift's Tale of a tub, 60, Hogarth's graphic works, 65, Satire and the novel, 67 & Hogarth: his life, art, and times, 71, Yale; Fielding: a collection of critical essays, Prentice-Hall, 62; The fictions of satire, Johns Hopkins Univ, 67; Rowlandson: a new interpretation, Oxford, 72. Add: Dept. of English, Johns Hopkins University, Baltimore, MD 21218.

PAULSON, STANLEY FAY, b. Atwater, Minn, Mar. 5, 20; m. 44; c. 2. SPEECH. B.A, Univ. Minn, 42, M.A, 49, Ph.D.(speech, psychol), 52; B.D, Bethel Theol. Sem, 44. Instr. speech & commun, Univ. Minn, 49-51, asst. prof, 53-56; res. assoc. stud. lang. & behav, Off. Naval Res, 51-52; assoc. prof. speech & commun, San Francisco State Col, 56-60, prof, 60-62, v.pres, acad. affairs, 63-66; prof. Am. lang, Kanazawa Univ, Japan, 62-63; PROF. SPEECH & CHMN. DEPT, PA. STATE UNIV, 66-, DEAN COL. LIB. ARTS, 69- Asst. prof, overseas div, Univ. Md, 52-53; Fulbright lectr. Am. lang. & lit, Japan, 62-63; pres, Counc. Cols. Arts & Sci, 72-73; mem. comn. arts & sci, Nat. Asn. State Univs. & Land Grant Cols, 73-75. U.S.N.R, 44-45, Lt.(jg). Int. Commun. Asn; Speech Commun. Asn. Experimental studies of communication including attitude change, related source credibility and message variables in connected discourse. Publ: Co-auth, Communication through speech, Burgess, 54; co-auth, Controversial statements in connected discourse, their form and politics, 53 & auth, Effects of speaker prestige and both sides presentation on retention and opinion, 54, Speech Monogr; Thaddeus Stevens: rapier of the opposition, In: A history of public speaking in Pennsylvania, Pa. Speech Asn, 71; plus others. Add: 108 Sparks Bldg, Pennsylvania State University, University Park, PA 16802.

PAULU, BURTON, b. Pewaukee, Wis, June 25, 10; m. 42; c 3. COMPARATIVE WORLD BROADCASTING. B.A, Univ. Minn, Minneapolis, 31, B.S, 32, M.S, 34; Ph.D.(mass. commun), N.Y. Univ, 49. Mgr. radio broadcasting, UNIV. MINN, MINNEAPOLIS, 38-56, dir. dept. radio & TV, 57-72, DIR, UNIV. MEDIA RESOURCES, 72- Fulbright res. grant, U.K, 53-54; Ford Found. res. fel, U.K, 58-59, Geneva, 64-65. Field rep, U.S. Off. War Inform, Eng. & Luxembourg, 44-45. Publ: British broadcasting: radio and television in the United Kingdom, 56, British broadcasting in transition, 61, Radio and television broadcasting on the European continent, 67 & Radio and television in Eastern Europe, 74, Univ. Minn. Add: 540 Rarig Ctr, University of Minnesota, Minneapolis, MN 55455.

PAULY, THOMAS HARRY, b. Missoula, Mont, Mar. 6, 40; m. 67; c. 1. AMERICAN LITERATURE. A.B, Harvard, 63; M.A, Univ. Calif, Berkeley, 65, Ph.D.(Am. lit), 70. ASST. PROF. AM. LIT, UNIV. DEL, 70- U.S.M.C, 62-63, Res, 63-67. MLA; Popular Culture Asn. Nineteenth century American literature; travel literature. Publ: J. Ross Brown: wine lobbyist and frontier opportunist, Calif. Hist. Soc. Quart, 72; Mr. Higginbothom's catastrophe: the story-teller's disaster, Am. Transcendental Quart, 72; The contents of Huckleberry Finn, Proof, 73. Add: Dept. of English, Univ. Delaware, Newark, DE 19711.

PAWLEY, THOMAS DESIRE, JR, b. Jackson, Miss, Aug. 5, 17; m. 41; c. 2. THEATRE & DRAMATIC ART. A.B, Va. State Col, 37; A.M, State Univ. Iowa, 39, Ph.D, 49. Instr. & dir. dramatics, Prairie View State Col, 39-40; Eng, LINCOLN UNIV.(MO), 40-43, asst. prof, 43-49, assoc. prof, 49-53, PROF. SPEECH & THEATRE, 53-, HEAD DEPT, 69-, CHMN. DIV. HUMANITIES & FINE ARTS, 67-, acting head, dept. Eng. & speech, 58-59, head, 59-69. Asst, State Univ. Iowa, 48-49; vis. prof, Univ. Calif, Santa Barbara, 68; theatre, North. Ill. Univ, 71; mem. centrol comt, Am. Col. Theatre Festival, 71- Am. Theatre Asn; Nat. Asn. Dramatic & Speech Arts. Writing of original plays; poetry; stagecraft in Negro colleges. Publ: Co-ed. & co-auth, The Black teacher and the dramatic arts, Negro Univ. Press, 70; auth, The Black theatre audience, Players Mag, 8-9/71; The first Black playwrights, Black World Mag, 4/72; The three P's: neo-stereotyped in Black theatre, Encore Mag, spring 73. Add: Dept. of Speech & Theatre, Lincoln University, Jefferson City, MO 65101.

PAXSON, OMAR M, b. Huntington Beach, Calif, Dec. 10, 23; m. 52; c. 2. ENGLISH LITERATURE. A.B, Occidental Col, 48; M.A, Northwest. Univ, 50, Ph.D, 60. Instr. THEATRE, OCCIDENTAL COL, 50-53, asst. prof, 53-61, assoc. prof, 61-66, PROF, 66-, chmn. dept. speech & drama, 70-74. U.S.A, 43-46. Am. Theatre Asn. Nineteenth century English literature. Add: Dept. of Speech & Drama, Occidental College, Los Angeles, CA 90041.

PAYNE, ALMA JEANETTE, b. Highland Park, Ill, Oct. 28, 18. AMERICAN STUDIES. B.A, Wooster Col, 40; M.A, West. Reserve Univ, 41, fel, 41, 54, Ph.D, 56. Instr. pub. schs, Ohio, 41-46; from instr. to assoc. prof. Eng, BOWLING GREEN STATE UNIV, 46-61, PROF. ENG. & AM. STUD, 61-CHMN. AM. STUD. PROG, 62-, DIR, CTR. AM. STUD, 73- Am. Counc. Learned Soc. grant, 67-68; Bowling Green State Univ. res. & travel grant, 67-68. Am. Stud. Asn; Mod. Lang. Asn; Col. Eng. Asn. William Dean Howells and the American family; changing image of American women in periodicals of late 19th century; The arena of Benjamin Orange Flower: mirror and shaper of American culture. Publ: The independent woman in the works of William Dean Howells, Midwest Rev, 63; Woman militant in The arena of Benjamin Orange Flower, In: Popular Literature in America, Bowling Green Univ, 72; Louisa May Alcott (1832-1888), Am. Lit. Realism, winter 73; plus two others. Add: Center for American Studies, Bowling Green State University, Bowling Green, OH 43403.

PAYNE, FRANCES ANNE, b. Harrisonberg, Va, Aug. 28, 32. ENGLISH, MEDIEVAL STUDIES. B.A. & B.Mus, Shorter Col, 53; M.A, Yale, 54, Ph.D. (Old Eng), 60; Middlebury Col, summer 62. Instr, Conn. Col. Women, 55-56; ENG, STATE UNIV. N.Y. BUFFALO, 58-60, lectr, 60, asst. prof, 61-68, ASSOC. PROF, 68-, assoc. dean grad. sch, 71-72. N.Y. Res. Found grants, 65, 67 & 68; Am. Asn. Univ. Women grant, 66-67; State Univ. N.Y. Res. Found. summer fels, 71, 72. Medieval Acad. Am. Old English; Chaucer; literary criticism. Publ: King Alfred and Boethius, Univ. Wis, 68; Three aspects of WYRD in Beowulf, In: Beowulf studies in honor of John C. Pope, Univ. Toronto, 74. Add: Dept. of English, State University of New York at Buffalo, Buffalo, NY 14214.

PAYNE, (CLYDE) LADELL, b. Birmingham, Ala, Dec. 6, 33; m. 54; c. 2. ENGLISH. B.A, Howard Col, 55; M.A, La. State Univ, 56; Ph.D.(Eng), Stanford Univ, 66. From instr. to ASSOC. PROF. ENG, CLAREMONT MEN'S COL, 60- Mem, compos. fac, NDEA Inst. Advan. Stud. Gen. Eng. for Sec. Sch. Teachers, Univ. Ky, summer 68; Fulbright lectr. Am. stud, Univ. Vienna, 71-72; Nat. Endowment for Humanities fel, 73. MLA. Southern writers, black and white; Dickens; British and American novel. Publ: Thomas Wolfe, Steck, 69; Willie Stark and Huey Long: atmosphere, myth or suggestion?, Am. Quart, fall 68; The trilogy: Faulkner's comic epic poem in prose, Stud. Novel, spring 69; contrib, Thomas Wolfe and the glass of time, Univ. Ga, 71; plus others. Add: Dept. of English, Bauer Center, Claremont Men's College, Claremont, CA 91711.

PAYNE, MICHAEL, b. Dallas, Tex, Jan. 17, 41; m. 73. ENGLISH. B.A, South. Ore. Col, 62; Ph.D.(Eng), Univ. Ore, 69. Asst. Eng, Univ. Ore, 63-65, instr, 65-69, asst. dir. Eng. compos, 66-69; asst. prof. ENG, BUCKNELL UNIV, 69-73, ASSOC. PROF, 73-, DIR. UNIV. PRESS, 72- Assoc. ed, Bucknell Rev, 70-; Folger Shakespeare Libr. fel, 73. MLA; Shakespeare Asn. Am; Col. Eng. Asn; AAUP. Shakespeare; Renaissance literature; literary theory. Publ: Co-ed, Contemporary essays on style, Scott, 69; auth, Irony in Shakespeare's Roman plays, Inst. Eng. Sprache & Lit, 73; Political myth and rhetoric in Julius Caesar, Bucknell Rev, 71; Do psychologists and critics speak the same language?, J. Gen. Educ, 72; La critique engagée: literature and politics, CEA Critic, 73; plus others. Add: Dept. of English, Bucknell University, Lewisburg, PA 17837.

PAYNE, MILDRED Y. ENGLISH, HISTORY. A.B, Athens Col, 39; M.A, Murray State Col, 52; Litt.D, Sussex Col. Technol, 72. Asst. prof. ENG, UNIV. TENN, MARTIN, 54-68, assoc. prof, 69-73, PROF. & CHMN. DEPT, 73- Mem. Folklore panel, Tenn. Arts Comn, 68-70. NCTE (judge, 71-74); NEA; Philol. Soc, Eng; S.Atlantic Mod. Lang. Asn; AAUP (secy, 69-70). Images of women in literature: Browning—feminist poet and Chekhov's women characters. Publ: Co-auth, Mounds in the mist, A.S. Barnes, 69; auth, Payne's notes on Milton, 70, Eighteenth century prose, 71, Western culture I, Renaissance to Romanticism, 72 & Western culture II, Realism to Multanimity, 73, Univ. Tenn; Folk elements in Milton's Comus, Tenn. Flore Bull, 6/68; The nun and the lesbian, Tenn. Philol. Bull, 72; Uncloseting Robert Browning's closet dramas, Costerus Essays, 6/72. Add: 216 Oxford St, Martin, TN 38237.

PAYNE, RICHARD CHAMP, b. Washington, D.C, Aug. 18, 46; m. 66; c. 2. OLD & MIDDLE ENGLISH LITERATURE. B.A, Univ. Va, 67, M.A, 68; M.A, Princeton, 70, Ph.D.(Eng), 72. Asst. ENG, Princeton, 71-72; ASST. PROF, UNIV. CHICAGO, 72- MLA; Medieval Acad. Am. Old English poetry; Middle English literature; history of the English language. Add: Dept. of English, University of Chicago, 1050 E. 59th St, Chicago, IL 60637.

PAYNE, ROBERT AUSTIN, b. Muskogee, Okla, Mar. 17, 32; m. 52; c. 3. SPEECH COMMUNICATION, MASS MEDIA. B.A, Okla. Baptist Univ, 53; M.Div, Southwest. Baptist Theol. Sem, 57; Ph.D.(speech commun), Univ. Okla, 70. Asst. prof. speech commun. & dir. debate, E.CENT. STATE COL, 66-70, ASSOC. PROF. SPEECH & THEATRE & CHMN. DEPT, 70- Pastor, New Bethel Baptist Church, 66-72. Speech Commun. Asn; Cent. States Speech Asn. Religious drama; rhetoric of social movements; dynamics of small groups. Publ: How small is too small, Church Recreation Mag, 63; Some thoughts on church drama, In: Rec-Lab manual, South. Baptist Convention, 72. Add: Dept. of Speech & Theatre, East Central State College, Ada, OK 74820.

PAYNE, ROBERT O, b. Hermiston, Ore, Dec. 4, 24; m. 46. ENGLISH. A.B, Univ. Ore, 48; A.M, Johns Hopkins Univ, 51, Ph.D.(Eng), 53. Instr. Eng, Univ. Cincinnati, 51-53, asst. prof, 53-58, assoc. prof, 58-64; PROF. ENG. LIT, Univ. Wash, 64-72; GRAD. CTR. & HERBERT H. LEHMAN COL, CITY UNIV. NEW YORK, 72- Vis. assoc. prof, Univ. Wash, 62-63; vis. prof, Univ. Ariz, 67. U.S.A, 42-45. MLA; Mediaeval Acad. Am; Int. Asn. Prof. Eng. Old and Middle English poetry; Chaucer; Mediaeval rhetoric and poetics. Publ: The key of remembrance: a study of Chaucer's poetics, Yale, 63; Boundaries of language and rhetoric, Col. Commun. & Compos, 5/68; Chaucer and the art of rhetoric, In: Companion to Chaucer studies, Oxford, 68. Add: Ph.D. Program in English, City University of New York, 33 W. 42nd St, New York, NY 10036.

PAYNTER, MARY, O.P, b. Madison, Wis, May 23, 31. ENGLISH. B.A, Rosary Col, 52; M.A, Univ. Wis-Madison, 53, Ph.D.(Eng), 65; Sorbonne, 53-54. Instr. Eng, Rosary Col, 56-60, asst. prof. & acad. dean, 65-70; PROF. ENG. & LIT, EDGEWOOD COL, 70- MLA; Am. Conf. Acad. Deans; NEA. Seventeenth century English metaphysical poetry; Renaissance art history in the Low Countries. Add: Dept. of English, Edgewood College, 855 Woodrow, Madison, WI 53711.

PEACOCK, GORDON BRUCE, b. Hanna, Alta, Apr. 28, 28. DRAMA. B.Ed, Univ. Alta, 50; M.F.A, Carnegie Inst. Technol, 52. Asst. prof. drama, Univ. Alta, 54-58; chmn. dept. theatre, Banff Sch. Fine Arts, 58-63; assoc. prof. DRAMA, UNIV. ALTA, 59-65, PROF, 65-, chmn. dept, 65-71. Vis. instr, Nat. Theatre Sch. Can, 63 & 64; chmn. & founder, West. Can. Educ. Theatre Conf, 63; chmn, Can. Univ. Centennial Comt, 66; vis. lectr, Allan Hancock Col, 68-73. Can. Drama Award, 62. Am. Theatre Asn.(dir, 65-68); Can. Theatre Ctr.(dir, 65-68); Int. Theatre Inst. Acting style; theatre aesthetics; media presentation. Publ: Co-auth, Adventures in acting, Inst. Press, 60. Add: Dept. of Drama, University of Alberta, Edmonton, Alta. T6G 2G2, Can.

PEACOCKE, CHARLES THOMAS, b. Lethbridge, Alta, Mar. 31, 33; m. 56; c. 3. DRAMA. B.Ed, Univ. Alta, 55, B.A, 59; M.F.A, Carnegie-Mellon Univ, 61. Asst. prof. DRAMA, Univ. Alta, 61-62; Carnegie-Mellon Univ, 62-63; UNIV. ALTA, 63-67, assoc. prof, 67-73, PROF, 73-, CHMN. DEPT, 71-, ARTISTIC DIR. STUDIO THEATRE, 73-, Torches Theatre, 65-73. Head drama div, Banff Sch. Fine Arts, 72-; mem, Prov. Comt. Rev. Training Fine & Performing Arts Alta, 73-74; ed. adv. bd, Can. Theatre Rev, 73- Can. Drama Award, 67. Can. Theatre Ctr.(mem. bd. dir, 68); Can. Univ. Theatre Asn.(pres, 67-69); Am. Educ. Theatre Asn. Stage direction; curriculum and instruction in acting and directing; drama in secondary education. Add: Dept. of Drama, University of Alberta, Edmonton, Alta. T6G 2G4, Can.

PEAKE, RICHARD HENRY, b. Norfolk, Va, Mar. 25, 34; m. 57; c. 2. ENGLISH. B.A, Univ. Va, 57, M.A, 58; Ph.D.(Eng), Univ. Ga, 66. Instr. ENG, Clemson Univ, 58-61; asst. prof, West. Carolina Univ, 63-65; instr. Univ. Ga, 65-67; asst. prof, 67-68, chmn. freshman Eng, 66-68; PROF. & CHMN. DEPT, CLINCH VALLEY COL, UNIV. VA, 68- MLA; Renaissance Soc. Am; Malone Soc. Renaissance drama; Renaissance lyric; contemporary lyric. Add: Dept. of English, Box 103, Clinch Valley College, Wise, VA 24293.

PEARCE, BESSIE M, b. Orange, Tex, Sept. 15, 15. ENGLISH. B.A, Daniel Baker Col, 36; M.A, Univ. Tex, 49, Ph.D.(Eng), 65. Teacher, pub. schs, Tex, 36-41; instr. Eng, Kilgore Col, 41-42; Span. transl, censorship & with Am. Red Cross, Eng. & France, 42-46; prin, High Sch, Catarina, Tex, 46-48; chmn. dept. Eng, Carrizo Springs, 48-50; teacher Eng, hist. & driver educ, San Antonio, 51-56; instr. ENG, SAN ANTONIO COL, 56-58, asst. prof, 58-64, assoc. prof, 64-66, PROF, 66-, ASST. TO DEAN, 73- Grant, Delta Kappa Gamma, 62. MLA; Col. Eng. Asn; Conf. Col. Teachers Eng; NCTE; S.Cent. Mod. Lang. Asn; Am. Stud. Asn. Frederick Law Olmsted—his life and work; Texas through women's eyes, 1823-1860. Publ: Economic and social history in certain Texas novels, J. Am. Stud. Asn. Tex, 6/70. Add: Dept. of English, San Antonio College, San Antonio, TX 78284.

PEARCE, DONALD R, b. Brantford, Ont, Apr. 14, 17; m. 64; c. 3. ENGLISH, CLASSICS. B.A, Univ. West. Ont, 40; M.A, Univ. Mich, 41, Ph.D.(Eng), 48. Instr. ENG, Univ. Mich, 48-51, asst. prof, 52-56; assoc. prof, UNIV. CALIF, SANTA BARBARA, 56-61, PROF, 62- Alfred H. Lloyd fel, Horace H. Rackham Sch. Grad. Stud, 49-50. Can. Army, 42-46, Capt. Romantic and modern poetry; classics; modern theatre. Publ: The Senate speeches of W.B. Yeats, Bloomington, London, 62; Journal of a war, Macmillan, Toronto, 65; In the Presidents' and my opinion, Prentice-Hall, 68; Horace and Cleopatra: thoughts on the entanglements of art history, winter 62 & The style of Milton's epic, spring 63, Yale Rev; Flames begotten of Flame, Sewanee Rev, summer 65. Add: Dept. of English, University of California, Santa Barbara, CA 93106.

PEARCE, HOWARD D, b. Orlando, Fla, Aug. 31, 31; m. 52; c. 2. AMERICAN LITERATURE. B.A, Univ. Fla, 58, M.A, 61; Univ. N.C, Chapel Hill, 63-65; Ph.D.(Eng), Fla. State Univ, 67. Asst. prof. ENG, Lander Col, 61-62; instr, N.C. State Univ, 63-65; from asst. prof. to ASSOC. PROF, FLA. ATLANTIC UNIV, 68- MLA; S.Atlantic Mod. Lang. Asn; AAUP. Modern American literature; dramatic literature. Publ: Synge's playboy as mock-Christ, In: The playboy of the Western world: Twentieth century interpretations, Prentice-Hall, 69; Steinbeck's The leader of the people: dialectic and symbol, Papers Lang. & Lit, fall 72; Transcending the folk: Paul Green's utilization of folk materials, In: From an ancient to a modern theatre, Univ. Man, 72. Add: Dept. of English, Florida State University, Boca Raton, FL 33432.

PEARCE, JOSEPHINE ANNA, b. Ottawa, Ont, Dec. 3, 18. ENGLISH. A.B, Univ. Wash, 40; M.A, Stanford Univ, 43; Ph.D.(Eng), Univ. Mo, 55. Lectr. Eng. lit. & compos, Victoria Col, 45-46; instr. compos. & lit, Univ. Miami, 46-49; Univ. Mo, 50-55; asst. prof. ENG, BRADLEY UNIV, 55-58, assoc. prof, 58-63, PROF, 63- Renaissance Soc. Am; MLA; Mod. Humanities Res. Asn. Renaissance history and literature; Shakespeare and English history plays; Milton. Publ: An earlier Talbot epitaph, Mod. Lang. Notes; Constituent elements in Shakespeare's English history plays, Stud. in Shakespeare. Add: Dept. of English, Bradley University, Peoria, IL 61606.

PEARCE, RICHARD A, b. New York, N.Y, Apr. 14, 32; m. 54; c. 2. AMERICAN LITERATURE. B.A, Hobart Col, 53; M.A, Columbia Univ, 57, Ph.D. (Eng), 63. Asst, Columbia Univ, 58; instr. ENG, Rutgers Univ, 58-59; Alfred Univ, 59-63, asst. prof, 63-64; WHEATON COL.(MASS), 64-68, assoc. prof, 68-72, PROF, 72- Am. Counc. Learned Soc. grant-in-aid, 67; Nat. Endowment for Humanities summer stipend, 69; Ford Found. fac. grant, 71. U.S.A, 54-56. MLA; AAUP. Modern literature; American literature; literature, art, and science. Publ: Stages of the clown: perspectives on modern fiction from Dostoyevsky to Beckett, South. Ill. Univ, 70; William Styron, Univ. Minn, 71; The limits of realism, Col. Eng, 1/70; Norman Mailer's Why are we in Vietnam: a radical critique of frontier values, Mod. Fiction Stud, fall 71; Enter the frame, In: Surfiction: fiction now and tomorrow, Swallow, 74 & TriQuart, spring 74. Add: Dept. of English, Wheaton College, Norton, MA 02766.

PEARCE, ROY HARVEY, b. Chicago, Ill, Dec. 2, 19; m. 47; c. 2. ENGLISH. A.B, Univ. Calif, Los Angeles, 40, A.M, 42; President's scholar, Johns Hopkins Univ, 44-45, Ph.D, 45. Instr. Eng, Ohio State Univ, 45-46; asst. prof, Univ. Calif, 46-49; assoc. prof, Ohio State Univ, 49-54, prof, 54-63; PROF. AM. LIT, UNIV. CALIF, SAN DIEGO, 63-, DEAN GRAD. STUD. & RES, 73-, chmn. dept. lit, 63-68, assoc. dean grad. stud. & res, 68-73. Am. Counc. Learned Soc. res. fel, 47, 58-59, fac. stud. fel, 50-51; Comt. Midwest Stud. res. fel, 49-50; Fund Advan. Educ. fel, 53-54; lectr, Salzburg Sem. Am. Stud, 54; vis. prof, Claremont Grad. Sch, summer 60; Fulbright lectr, Univ. Bordeaux, 61-62; vis. prof. & res. assoc, Teachers Col, Columbia Univ, 63; mem. ed. bd, ELH, 45-; gen. ed, Centenary Ed. Works of Nathaniel Hawthorne, Ohio State Univ, 62-; mem. comt, Int. Exchange of Persons, 63-66; mem. supv. comt, Eng. Inst, 66-68; mem. Am. consult. bd, Mod. Humanities Res. Asn, 66-68. Poetry Chap. Bk. Award, Poetry Soc. Am, 61. MLA; AHA; fel, Am. Anthrop. Asn; Am. Stud. Asn; NCTE; Int. Asn. Univ. Profs, Eng; Mod. Humanities Res. Asn, Gt. Brit; fel. Am. Acad. Arts & Sci. American literature and intellectual history; American studies; theory and method in intellectual and cultural history and criticism. Publ: Colonial American writing, Rinehart, 50; Savages of America, 53 & co-ed, The act of the mind: essays on the poetry of Wallace Stevens, 65, Johns Hopkins & The growth of American literature, Am. Bk. Co, 56; ed, Whitman: Leaves of Grass, 1860, Cornell Univ, 60; auth, Continuity of American poetry, 61 & Historicism once more, 69, Princeton; ed, Whitman: twentieth century views, Prentice-Hall, 62; Experience in the novel, Columbia Univ, 68. Add: Office of Graduate Studies and Research, University of California, San Diego, La Jolla, CA 92037.

PEARCE, THOMAS MATTHEWS, b. Covington, Ky, May 22, 02; m. 41; c. 2. RENAISSANCE STUDIES. A.B, Univ. Mont, 23; A.M, Univ. Pittsburgh, 25, Ph.D, 30; Univ. Calif, 28; Univ. Chicago, 29. Instr. Univ. Pittsburgh, 25-27; asst. prof, ENG, UNIV. N.MEX, 27-29, assoc. prof, 30-41, prof, 41-64, acting head dept, 39, head dept, 40-51, EMER. PROF, 64- Henry E. Huntington Libr. grant-in-aid, spring 68. MLA; Shakespeare Asn. Am; Am. Dialect Soc; Mod. Humanities Res. Asn, Gt. Brit; Col. Eng. Asn. Christopher Marlowe; literature of the Southwest; American English. Publ: Beloved house, Caxton, 40; Southwesterners write, 46, Signature of the sun, 50 & New Mexico place names, 65, Univ. N.Mex; Mary Austin, 65 & Oliver La Farge, 72, Twayne. Add: 1712 Sigma Chi Rd. N.E, Albuquerque, NM 87106.

PEARCE, WALTER BARNETT, b. Huntsville, Ala, July 25, 43; m. 65; c. 2. INTERPERSONAL & SPEECH COMMUNICATION. B.A, Carson-Newman Col, 65; Southwest. Baptist Theol. Sem, 65-67; NDEA fel, Ohio Univ, 67-69, M.A, 68, Ph.D.(interpersonal commun), 69. From asst. prof. to ASSOC. PROF. speech & jour, Univ. N.Dak, 69-72; SPEECH, UNIV. KY, 73- Speech Commun. Asn; Int. Commun. Asn. Nonverbal communication; philosophy of science. Publ: Co-auth, Communication behavior and coorientation relations, 71 & auth, Consensual rules in interpersonal communication, 73, J. Commun; co-auth, Vocalic communication and persuasion, Quart. J. Speech, 72. Add: Dept. of Speech, 1415 Patterson Office Tower, University of Kentucky, Lexington, KY 40506.

PEARCY, ROY JAMES, b. Parkstone, Dorset, Eng, June 27, 31; m. 55; c. 2. ENGLISH. B.A, Univ. London, 59; Ph.D, Ohio State Univ, 63. Asst. prof, ENG, Univ. Calif, Los Angeles, 63-68; UNIV. OKLA, 68-71, ASSOC. PROF, 71- Guest lect, Univ. Kent, 67; assoc. ed, Variorum Chaucer, 72- MLA; Mediaeval Acad. Am. Chaucer; English literature of the later Middle Ages; French literature of the 12th and 13th centuries. Publ: Relations between the D and A versions of Berenger au long cul, Romance Notes, 72; Logic and the folktale: The scholar and his imaginary egg, Fabula, 73; Realism and religious parody in the Fabliaux: Watriquet de Couvin's Les trois dames de Paris, Belg. Rev. Philol. & Hist, 73; plus others. Add: Dept. of English, University of Oklahoma, 760 Van Vleet Oval, Norman, OK 73069.

PEARSALL, ROBERT BRAINARD, b. Berkeley, Calif, Sept, 18, 20; m. 48; c. 6. HUMANITIES. B.A, Univ. Puget Sound, 48; M.A, Cornell Univ, 49, univ. fel, 50-51, Ph.D, 52. Instr. Eng, Univ. Tex, 52-56; asst. prof. humanities, Sacramento State Univ, 56-60; prof. ENG. & chmn. dept, Spelman Col, 61-64; prof, East. Mich. Univ, 64-67; prof. & chmn. dept, Univ. Nev, Las Vegas, 67-71; Fulbright vis. prof, Ger, 71-72; RES. PROF, COL. NOTRE DAME, 73- Vis. prof, San Francisco State Univ, 59-60; gen. ed, Melville Stud. Am. Cult, Amsterdam. U.S.A, 44-46. Nineteenth century literature. Publ: Co-auth, Robert Browning: a bibliography 1833-1950, Cornell Univ. & Oxford, 54; ed, The Californians: writings of their past and present, 2 vols, Hesperian, 61; auth, Frank Harris, 68, Robert Browning, Twayne, 73; Maxwell Anderson, Tübingen Univ, 72; Life and writings of Ernest Hemingway, 73, Rupert Brooke the man and poet, 74 & The Symbionese Liberation Army, 74, Rodopi; The values of Housman's soldiery, PMLA, 67; Robert Browning and Elizabeth Browning, New Cambridge Bibliog. Eng. Lit, 69; 250 chronological emendations to the letters of Thomas Moore, Papers Bibliog. Soc. Am, 70; plus many others. Add: 1129 Leavenworth St, San Francisco, CA 94109.

PEARSALL, THOMAS E, b. New York, N.Y, Oct. 28, 25; m. 46; c. 4. ENGLISH. A.B, Colgate Univ, 49; M.A, Univ. Tex, 56; Ph.D.(creative writing), Univ. Denver, 60. Assoc. prof. Eng, U.S. Air Force Acad, 56-64, Eng. & tech. writing, 64-65, tech. writing, 65-69; PROF. RHETORIC, UNIV. MINN, ST. PAUL, 69- U.S.N, 43-46; U.S.A.F, 49-69, Lt. Col. NCTE; Conf. Col. Compos. & Commun; Soc. Tech. Commun. Technical and scientific writing; computer assisted instruction. Publ: Co-auth, Reporting technical information, 68 & auth, Audience analysis for technical writing, 69, Glencoe; co-auth, Better spelling, Heath, 72. Add: Dept. of Rhetoric, University of Minnesota, St. Paul, MN 55101.

PEARSON, D'ORSAY WHITE, b. Crossnore, N.C, May 8, 33; m. 56; c. 1. RENAISSANCE ENGLISH. B.A, Univ. N.C, 55; M.A, Univ. Fla, 61; NDEA Inst, Ohio State Univ, 64; Ph.D.(Eng), Kent State Univ, 69. Instr. ENG, UNIV. AKRON, 66-69, ASST. PROF, 69- MLA; Mediaeval Acad. Am; Renaissance Soc. Am; AAUP. Occult sciences; theology. Publ: Unless I be relieved by prayer: The tempest in perspective, Shakespeare Stud, 74. Add: Dept. of English, University of Akron, Akron, OH 44304.

PEARSON, JUSTUS RICHARD, JR, b. Detroit, Mich, Jan. 2, 15; m. 53; c. 5. ENGLISH & AMERICAN LITERATURE. B.A, Yale, 40, M.A, 42; Ph.D.(Eng. & comp. lit), Columbia Univ, 55. Instr. ENG, Vassar Col, 46-47; Emory Univ, 55-58, asst. prof, 58-59; Mich. State Univ, Oakland, 59-62; PROF, ILL. WESLEYAN UNIV, 62-, chmn. dept. Eng. & chmn. div. humanities, 62-69. Ed. & writer, Encycl. Americana & Grolier Encycl, 53-57; prof. Am. lit, Univ. Uppsala, 72-73. MLA. Linguistics; Chaucer. Publ: The galaxy, 1866-1878, Edwards; co-auth, Project grammar: the linguistic and language preparation of secondary school teachers of English, Off. Educ, U.S. Dept. Health, Educ. & Welfare, 69. Add: Dept. of English, Illinois Wesleyan University, Bloomington, IL 61701.

PEARSON, MARY DEBORAH, b. St. Louis, Mo, May 19, 30. ENGLISH. A.B, Webster Col, 54; Woodrow Wilson fel, Fordham Univ, 58, M.A, 60, Ph.D. (Eng), 68. Instr. ENG, WEBSTER COL, 63-65, asst. prof, 65-68, assoc. prof, 68-73, PROF, 73-, chmn. dept, 65-70. MLA; NCTE. Chaucer and other medieval literature; Elizabethan drama; contemporary poetry. Add: Dept. of English, Webster College, Webster Groves, MO 63119.

PEARSON, NORMAN HOLMES, b. Gardner, Mass, Apr. 13, 09; m. 41; c. 2. AMERICAN STUDIES, ENGLISH. A.B, Yale, 32, Ph.D, 41; Univ. Berlin, 33; B.A, Oxford Univ, 34, M.A, 41. Instr. Eng, YALE, 41-42, asst. prof, 46-51, assoc. prof, 51-62, PROF. ENG. & AM. STUD, 62-, chmn. Am. stud, 58-67. Vis. fel, Huntington Libr, 48; Guggenheim fels, 48-49, 55-56; pres, Bryher Found, New York, N.Y, 49-52; chmn, Eng. Inst, 48; chancellor, Acad. Am. Poets, 65-; mem. Smithsonian counc, Smithsonian Inst, Wash, D.C, 66-; vis. prof, Eng, Kyoto Univ. & Doshisha Univ, Japan, 70. Knight, Order of St. Olaf, Norway; Knight, Order of Dannebrog, Denmark, 70. Off. Strategic Serv, 42-46; Medaille de la Reconnaissance, Chevalier, Legion d'honneur, France; Medal of Freedom, U.S. MLA; Col. Eng. Asn.(v.pres, 55-56); New Eng. Col. Eng. Asn.(pres, 51-52); Am. Stud. Asn.(pres, 68-69). Publ: Co-ed, Oxford anthology of American literature, Oxford, 38 & Poets of the English language, Viking, 50; auth, Four studies, Valdonega, Italy, 62; Some American studies, 64 & American literary fathers, 65, Apolon-sha, Kyoto; American literature, Eihōsha, Tokyo, 67; ed, Decade, Wesleyan Univ, 69, Hermetic definition, 72 & Trilogy, 73, New Directions. Add: 2731 H.G.S, Yale University, New Haven, CT 06520.

PEASE, MARILYN THERESA, b. New York, N.Y, July 13, 30. ENGLISH. B.A, Hunter Col, 53, M.A, 57; Ph.D.(18th century Brit. & early Am. lit), Fordham Univ, 67. TEACHER ENG, St. Helena High Sch, 53-57; Plainview-Old Bethpage Sr. High Sch, 57-68; REGIS HIGH SCH, 68- NEA; NCTE. Eighteenth century British and early American literature; Charles Brockden Brown; early American novel. Publ: Word analogies I & II, Educ. Aids Publ. Corp, 63. Add: 1133 Pugsley Ave, Bronx, NY 10472.

PEAVLER, JAMES MARTIN, b. Ada, Okla, Oct. 13, 40. MEDIEVAL ENGLISH LITERATURE & LANGUAGE. B.A, Univ. Colo, 62, M.A, 63; Ph.D. (Eng), Univ. Mo, 71. Instr. ENG, Univ. Mo, 63-68; ASST. PROF, NORTH. ILL. UNIV, 69-, dean's fund grant, 72-73. Bibliog. Soc, Eng; Medieval Acad. Am; MLA; Midwest Mod. Lang. Asn. Chaucer and other 14th century poets; manuscripts of 14th century poetry; computers and textual editing. Add: Dept. of English, Northern Illinois University, De Kalb, IL 60115.

PEAVLER, TERRY J, Latin American & Comparative Literature. See Volume III, Foreign Languages, Linguistics & Philology.

PEAVY, CHARLES DRUERY, b. Cuero, Tex, May 8, 31; m. 55; c. 2. ENGLISH, AMERICAN LITERATURE. B.A, La. State Univ, 53, M.A, 57; Ph.D. (Eng), Tulane Univ, 63. Teaching asst. ENG, La. State Univ, 56-58; instr, La. State Univ, New Orleans, 58-63; asst. prof, UNIV. HOUSTON, 63-66, assoc. prof, 66-70, PROF, 70- Nat. Found. Arts & Humanities summer stipend, 67; Fac. Res. Award Prog. grant, 67; Am. Philos. Soc. res. grant, 68, 72; mem. gov. bd, Nat. Am. Stud. Fac, 71-73; resident, Inst. Relig. & Human Develop, 72-73; Am. Counc. Learned Soc. grant, 73. U.S.A, 54-56, Res, Capt. Mod. Humanities Res. Asn; MLA; Col. Eng. Asn; Am. Stud. Asn; Popular Cult. Asn. American literature, particularly contemporary literature; William Faulkner. Publ: Charles A. Siringo: a Texas picaro, Steck, 67; ed, Two evil isms: Pinkertonism and anarchism, 67 & History of Billy the Kid, 67, Austin; auth, Go slow now: Faulkner and the race question, Univ. Ore, 71; Faulkner's use of folklore in The sound and the fury, J. Am. Folklore, fall 66; The eyes of innocence: Faulkner's The kingdom of God, Papers in Lang. & Lit, spring 66; Did you ever have a sister? Holden, Quentin, sexual innocence, Fla. Quart, spring 68; plus others. Add: Dept. of English, University of Houston, Cullen Blvd, Houston, TX 77004.

PEBWORTH, TED-LARRY, b. Shreveport, La, Apr. 19, 36. ENGLISH. B.A, Centenary Col, 57, M.A, Tulane Univ, 58; Ph.D.(Eng), La. State Univ, 66. Instr. Eng, Southeast. La. Col, 58-62; teaching asst, La. State Univ, 62-64, instr, 64-66; asst. prof, Univ. Ill, Chicago Circle, 66-70; Calif. State Univ, Northridge, 70-71; UNIV. MICH-DEARBORN, 71-72, ASSOC. PROF. ENG. & CHMN. DEPT. HUMANITIES, 72- Univ. Ill. fac. summer res. fel, Eng. & Netherlands, 67; asst. ed, 17th Cent. News, 72- Nat. Guard, 58-61; U.S.A.R, 61-64. MLA; Renaissance Soc. Am; Milton Soc. Am. Seventeenth century English prose and poetry; Biblical literature; 19th century American literature. Publ: Co-ed, The poems of Owen Felltham, 17th Cent. News Mongr, 73; auth, Owen Felltham, Twayne, 74; Jonson's Timber and the essay tradition, In: Essays in honor of Esmond Marilla, La. State Univ, 70; Real English evidence: stoicism and the English essay tradition, PMLA, 1/72; plus others. Add: Dept. of Humanities, College of Arts, Sciences and Letters, University of Michigan-Dearborn, Dearborn, MI 48128.

PECEK, LOUIS G, b. Euclid, Ohio, Oct. 6, 31; m. 57; c. 4. AMERICAN LITERATURE. A.B, Col. Holy Cross, 53; M.A, John Carroll Univ, 55; Ph.D, Ohio State Univ, 59. Lectr. ENG, John Carroll Univ, 54-55; asst, Ohio State Univ, 55-59; instr, JOHN CARROLL UNIV, 59-61, asst. prof, 61-67, assoc. prof, 67-72, PROF, 72-, CHMN. DEPT, 66- MLA; NCTE; Col. Eng. Asn; Conf. Col. Compos. & Commun. Western Americana in general; travels of Mark Twain; critical bibliography of William Faulkner. Add: Dept. of English, John Carroll University, Cleveland, OH 44118.

PECHEUX, CHRISTOPHER, O.S.U, b. Newburgh, N.Y, Oct. 9, 16. ENGLISH LITERATURE. B.A, Col. New Rochelle, 37; M.A, Fordham Univ, 46; Ph.D, Cath. Univ. Am, 51. From instr. to PROF. ENG. LIT, COL. NEW ROCHELLE, 43- MLA; Milton Soc. Am. Milton and the 17th century. Publ: The concept of the second Eve in Paradise lost, PMLA, 9/60; The second Adam and the church in Paradise lost, ELH, 6/67; Sin in Paradise regained, In: Calm of mind, Case West. Reserve Univ, 71. Add: Dept. of English, College of New Rochelle, New Rochelle, NY 10801.

PECHTER, EDWARD LEWIS, b. New York, N.Y. ENGLISH LITERATURE. B.A, Cornell Univ, 62; M.A, Univ. Calif, Berkeley, 64, Ph.D.(Eng), 68. ASST. PROF. ENG, SIR GEORGE WILLIAMS UNIV, 68- Can. Counc. leave fel, 70-71. MLA; Asn. Can. Univ. Teachers Eng. English Renaissance; Shakespeare. Publ: Dryden's classical theory of literature, Cambridge Univ, 75. Add: Dept. of English, Sir George Williams University, Montreal 107, P.Q, Can.

PECK, GEORGE AUGUST, b. Cleveland, Ohio, Sept. 30, 08; m. 37. ENGLISH LITERATURE. A.B, West. Reserve Univ, 29, M.A, 35, Ph.D, 43. Instr, West. Reserve Univ, 34-39; ENG, Wayne Univ, 39-43, asst. prof, 43-48, assoc. prof, 48-55; prof. & chmn. dept, BROOKLYN COL, 55-67, PROF, 71-, dean admin, 67-71, acting pres, 69. MLA; NCTE; Col. Eng. Asn; Milton Soc. Am. Seventeenth century English literature. Publ: Write: first principles of composition, Scott; ed, Writing from observation, Harcourt. Add: Dept. of English, Brooklyn College, Brooklyn, NY 11210.

PECK, HELEN MARGARET, C.S.J, b. DeGraff, Minn, Jan. 13, 02. ENGLISH. B.A, Col. St. Catherine, 24; M.A, Univ. Chicago, 27, Ph.D, 30. Instr. ENG, COL. ST. CATHERINE, 27-28, asst. prof, 30-37, assoc. prof, 37-45, PROF, 45-, registr, 37-62, chmn. dept, 63-64, acad. dean, 64-68. Add: Dept. of English, College of St. Catherine, St. Paul, MN 55116.

PECK, RICHARD E, b. Milwaukee, Wis, Aug. 3, 36; m. 60; c. 1. ENGLISH. B.A, Carroll Col.(Wis), 61; Woodrow Wilson fel. & M.S, Univ. Wis, Madison, 62, Knapp fel. & Ph.D.(Eng), 64. Asst. prof. ENG, Univ. Va, 64-67; TEMPLE UNIV, 67-72, ASSOC. PROF. & ASST. DEAN, 72-, res. grant, 68. Consult. Am. lit, Univ. Microfilms, 66. U.S.M.C, 54-59, Capt. MLA; NCTE. American literature, primarily 19th century. Publ: Ed, Poems/Nathaniel Hawthorne, Univ. Va, 67; auth, Stephen Crane and Baudelaire: a direct link, 5/65 & Two lost Bryant poems: evidence of Thomson's influence, 3/67, Am. Lit; Films, television, and tennis, In: Man and the movies, La. State Univ, 67. Add: Dept. of English, Temple University, Philadelphia, PA 19122.

PECK, RUSSELL ALBERT, b. Riverton, Wyo, Dec. 17, 33; m. 58; c. 3. MIDDLE ENGLISH LITERATURE. A.B, Princeton, 56; Ph.D.(Chaucer), Ind. Univ, 63. Instr. ENG, UNIV. ROCHESTER, 61-64, asst. prof, 64-69, assoc. prof, 69-72, PROF, 73- Reckitt-Colman prof. Eng, Univ. Hull, 67-68. E.Harris Harbison Award for Gifted Teaching, Danforth Found, 72; Edward Peck Curtis Award for Undergrad. Teaching, Univ. Rochester. MLA; Mediaeval Acad. Am. Middle English literature; medieval poetics and aesthetics; history of the English language. Publ: Confessio Amantis, Holt, 68; Theme and number in Chaucer's book of the duchess, In: Silent poetry, Routledge & Kegan Paul, 70; Number symbolism and Troilus and Criseyde, Mosaic, 72; The careful hunter in the parlement of the thre ages, Eng. Lit. Hist, 72; plus others. Add: Dept. of English, University of Rochester, Rochester, NY 14627.

PECKHAM, MORSE, b. Yonkers, N.Y, Aug. 17, 14. ENGLISH LITERATURE. A.B, Univ. Rochester, 35; A.M, Princeton, 38, Ph.D, 47. Asst. prof, The Citadel, 38-41; instr, Rutgers Univ, 47-48, asst. prof, 48-49; Eng, Univ. Pa, 49-52, assoc. prof. Eng. lit, 52-61, prof. Eng, 61-67, dir, inst. humanistic stud, 53-54, univ. press, 53-55; DISTINGUISHED PROF. ENG. & COMP. LIT, UNIV. S.C, 67- U.S.A.A.F, 41-46. MLA. Victorian literature; relation in the arts; 19th century comparative literature. Publ: Charles Darwin's The origin of species: a variorum text, Univ. Pa, 59; Beyond the tragic vision 62, Romanticism, 65 & Victorian revolutionaries, 70, Braziller; co-auth, Word, meaning, poem, Crowell, 61; auth, Man's rage for chaos, Chilton, 65; Art and pornography, Basic Bks, 69; co-ed, The collected works of Robert Browning, Ohio Univ, 69-73; auth, The triumph of romanticism: collected essays, Univ. S.C, 70. Add: Dept. of English, University of South Carolina, Columbia, SC 29208.

PECKHAM, ROBERT WILSON, b. Detroit, Mich, Nov. 8, 32. ENGLISH. B.A, Sacred Heart Sem, 54; St. John's Sem, 54-55; M.A, Univ. Detroit, 59; Ph.D. (Eng), Univ. Notre Dame, 6/65. Instr. ENG, Univ. Detroit, 59-61; SACRED HEART SEM, 63-65, ASST. PROF, 65- MLA; NCTE. Twentieth century poetry; Charles Williams; Oxford Christians. Add: Dept. of English, Sacred Heart Seminary, 2701 Chicago Blvd, Detroit, MI 48206.

PEDEN, WILLIAM, b. New York, N.Y, Mar. 22, 13; m. 38; c. 2. AMERICAN LITERARY & SOCIAL HISTORY. B.S, Univ. Va, 34, M.S, 36, Ph.D, 42. Instr. Eng, Univ. Md, 38-42, asst. prof, 42-44; assoc. prof. ENG, UNIV. MO-COLUMBIA, 46-50, PROF, 50-, dir, univ. press, 58-62. Ed, Story mag, 59-62; Guggenheim fel, 61-62; mem. ed. bd, Univ. Mo. Press, 62-; mem. ed. comt, Stud. in Short Fiction, 63-; vis. prof, Univ. Md, College Park, 71; mem. bd. dirs, Assoc. Writing Progs, 72- Thomas Jefferson Award, McConnell Found, 72. MLA; PEN Club; Auth. Guild. Contemporary fiction and writing of fiction; American literature; creative writing. Publ: Co-ed. & co-auth, Life and selected writings of Thomas Jefferson, Random, 44; ed, Selected writings of John and John Quincy Adams, Knopf, 46; ed, Notes on the State of Virginia, Univ. N.C, 54; Modern short stories from Story magazine, Grosset, 60; 29 stories, 60, 2nd ed, 67, auth, The American short story, 64, ed, Short fiction: shape and substance, 71 & auth, Twilight at Monticello, 73, Houghton; auth, Night in funland and other stories, La. State Univ, 68; ed, Collected stories of Hubert Crackanthorpe, Scholars' Facsimiles, 69; co-ed, New writing from South Carolina, Univ. S.C, 71; introd, Stories by John Cheever, Jean Stafford..., Noonday Press, 66, The golden shore, Platt & Munk, 67 & Jane Eyre, Mod. Libr. Col. Ed, 68. Add: Dept. of English, University of Missouri-Columbia, Columbia, MO 65201.

PEDERSEN, GLENN MALVERN, b. Pierson, Iowa, Nov. 10, 17. ENGLISH. B.S, North. State Teachers Col, 42; Ph.D, Univ. Wash, 54. Instr. compos, Univ. Idaho, 54-56; ed. oceanog. pubs, U.S. Dept. Interior, Seattle, Wash, 56-59; asst. prof. ENG, La. State Univ, New Orleans, 59-60; from assoc. prof. to PROF, SOUTHWEST MO. STATE UNIV, 60- U.S.N.R, 42-46, Lt. MLA. Identity of art and religion; the visionary in creativity; religion of William Blake. Publ: Blake's Urizen as Hawthorne's Ethan Brand, Nineteenth-Century Fiction, 3/58; Vision in To the lighthouse, PMLA, 12/58; Forster's symbolic form, Kenyon Rev, Spring 59. Add: Dept. of English, Southwest Missouri State University, Springfield, MO 65802.

PEDERSEN, MYRTLE EDITH, b. Fairdale, N.Dak, June 25, 09. ENGLISH. B.S, Univ. N.Dak, 31, M.A, 37; summers, Univ. Wash, 38; Univ. Minn, 39, 41, 48-49. Teacher, high schs, N.Dak, 31-34; instr. ENG, UNIV. N.DAK,

37-48, asst. prof, 48-68, ASSOC. PROF, 68-, freshman Eng, 57-70, dir. introd. to drama, 70-72. NCTE; MLA; AAUP. Add: Dept. of English, University of North Dakota, Grand Forks, ND 58201.

PEDERSON, LEE A, English Linguistics & Philology. See Volume III, Foreign Languages, Linguistics & Philology.

PEDICORD, HARRY WILLIAM, b. Benwood, W.Va, Mar. 23, 12; m. 39; c. 1. ENGLISH LITERATURE. A.B, Washington & Jefferson Col, 33, M.A, 34, hon. Litt.D, 61; Th.B, Princeton Theol. Sem, 37; Ph.D.(Eng), Univ. Pa, 49; hon. D.D, Waynesburg Col, 49. Asst. pastor, First Presby. Church, Bridgeport, Conn, 37-38; exec. minister, Church of Covenant, Erie, Pa, 38-42; pastor, First Presby. Church, Bridgeport, 42-47; Hiland Presby. Church, Pittsburgh, 47-63; prof. ENG, THIEL COL, 63-64, CHMN. DEPT, 64- Kansas City Regional Counc. Higher Educ. travel fel, India, summer 70; Folger fel, 73; Am. Philos. Soc. res. grant, 73; U.S. deleg, Int. Fed. Theatre Res. Am. Soc. Theatre Res.(chmn, exec. comt, 61-); MLA (chmn, sect. 14); NCTE. Eighteenth century English literature; drama and theatre history; modern drama and theatre history. Publ: The theatrical public in the time of Garrick, Columbia Univ, 54; Course of plays, 1740-2: an early diary of Richard Cross, prompter to the theatres, John Rylands Libr, 58; Mr. & Mrs. Garrick: some unpublished correspondence, PMLA, 9/45; The second chronicler: a tentative identification of the unknown hand in the MS. diaries of Drury Lane Theatre, Theatre Surv, 11/64; White gloves at five, Philol. Quart, 1/66. Add: Dept. of English & Speech, Thiel College, Greenville, PA 16125.

PEEK, GEORGE SHERMAN, b. Miami, Fla, Oct. 21, 45; m. 69. MEDIEVAL ENGLISH LITERATURE, DRAMA. A.B, Providence Col, 67; M.A, Univ. R.I, 71; Ph.D.(Eng), Case West. Reserve Univ, 72. ASST. PROF. ENG, ARK. STATE UNIV, 72- MLA; Mediaeval Acad. Am; NCTE; AAUP; Early Eng. Text Soc. Medieval English drama; Old English poetry; Chaucer. Add: Div. of English, Philosophy and Languages, Arkansas State University, State University, AR 72467.

PEEL, DONALD FRANK, b. Glenwood, Iowa, Sept. 30, 21; m. 49; c. 3. ENGLISH LITERATURE. A.B, Cincinnati Bible Sem, 47; A.M, Univ. Denver, 52; Coe fel, Univ. Wyo, 54, Carnegie fel, 58; Curators fel, Univ. Mo, 63-64; Ph.D.(ling), Univ. Denver, 70. Prof. Eng, Lincoln Christian Col, 55-57; asst. prof, Northwest Mo. State Col, 57-65; Renaissance, Mont. State Univ, 65-68; ling, North. State Col, 68-69, assoc. prof, 69-71; asst. prof. lang. & lit, West. N.Mex. Univ, 71-74. NCTE; Conf. Col. Commun. & Compos; MLA. North American Indian languages; psycholinguistics. Publ: A linguistic edition of The Emperor of the East, Univ. Denver, 70; A comparison of modern grammars, 71 & ed, Problems of freshman English, 72, West. N.Mex. Stud; Thirteen ways of looking at a beard, Mont. Eng. J, 68; plus others. Add: 1919 Main, Silver City, NM 88061.

PEER, LARRY HOWARD, Comparative Literature. See Volume III, Foreign Languages, Linguistics & Philology.

PEET, ALICE L, Speech, Drama. See FAUST, ALICE L. P.

PEET, CHARLES DONALD, b. St. Louis, Mo, July 8, 27. ENGLISH. A.B, Princeton, 48, Ph.D, 56; A.M, Wash. Univ, 49. Instr. ENG, IND. UNIV, BLOOMINGTON, 56-59, asst. prof, 59-64, ASSOC. PROF, 64-, dir. freshman lit, 60-66. U.S.A, 54-55. MLA; NCTE; Col. Eng. Asn; Malone Soc. Renaissance poetry and rhetoric; Chaucer; Shakespeare. Publ: Ed, Representative poems, Allyn & Bacon, 64; auth, The rhetoric of Tamburlaine, J. Eng. Lit. Hist, 59; On teaching biography, In: On teaching literature, Ind. Univ, 67. Add: Dept. of English, Indiana University, Bloomington, IN 47401.

PEGIS, ANTON GEORGE, b. Milwaukee, Wis, Feb. 21, 20; m. 49; c. 2. ENGLISH, PHILOSOPHY. A.B, West. State Col. Colo, 49; M.A, Univ. Denver, 51, Ph.D.(Eng), 56. Jr. Engr, N. Shore Gas Co, Waukegan, Ill, 46-47; instr. Eng, Ft. Lewis Col, 52-53; process control tech, Gates Rubber Co, Denver, 53-54; PROF. ENG, COLO. SCH. MINES, 54-, V.PRES. DEVELOP, 68-, V.PRES. EXTERNAL AFFAIRS, 72-, asst. to pres, 64-68. Consult, U.S. Bur. Mines, Area V, Denver, 58-68; Off. Mineral Reports, Washington, D.C, 62-; secy, Col. Sch. Mines Found, Inc, 64-73. U.S.A, 37-40; A.U.S, 40-46; U.S.A.R, 46-63, Maj. Am. Soc. Eng. Educ.(pres. Rocky Mt. sect, 67-68); MLA; Am. Alumni Counc. Classics; modern literature; history of ideas. Publ: Humanism and the practical order, Mines Mag, 4/65. Add: 415 Scenic Ct, Golden, CO 80401.

PEINS, MARYANN, Speech Pathology, Audiology. See 12th Edition, American Men & Women of Science, Social & Behavioral Sciences Section.

PEIRCE, BROOKE, b. Washington, D.C, Jan. 2, 22; m. 52. ENGLISH. B.A, Univ. Va, 43; M.A, Harvard, 47, Dexter traveling fel, 51, Ph.D, 54. Instr. ENG, Univ. Va, 51-54; from asst. prof. to assoc. prof, GOUCHER COL, 61-66, PROF, 66-, CHMN. DEPT, 64-68 & 72- U.S.A, 43-45. MLA; Renaissance Soc. Am; Southeast. Renaissance Conf. Shakespeare; 18th century literature; classical tradition. Add: Dept. of English, Goucher College, Towson, Baltimore, MD 21204.

PEIRCE, CAROL MARSHALL, b. Columbia, Mo, Feb. 1, 22; m. 52. ENGLISH. A.B, Fla. State Univ, 42; Dupont fel, Univ. Va, 42-43, M.A, 43; Ph.D.(Eng), Radcliffe Col, 51. Head dept. Eng, Fairfax Hall Jr. Col, 43-44; instr, Cedar Crest Col, 44-46; tutor, Harvard, 48-50, instr, 52-53; asst. dean instrn, Radcliffe Col, 50-53; head home study Eng, Univ. Va, 53-54; asst. dir. admis, Goucher Col, 56-62; PROF. ENG. & CHMN. DEPT, UNIV. BALTIMORE, 67-, CHMN. DIV. HUMANITIES, 72- Anne Radcliffe traveling fel, summer 51. MLA. Shakespeare; Romantics; Lawrence Durrell. Publ: English at Radcliffe, Radcliffe Col, 51; co-auth, An introduction to English literature from Chaucer to the eighteenth century, Vol. I & An introduction to English literature from the eighteenth century to the present, Vol. II, In: Study of literary types, Univ. Va, 54. Add: Dept. of English, University of Baltimore, 1420 N. Charles St, Baltimore, MD 21201.

PEIRCE, JAMES FRANKLIN, b. Edwardsville, Ill, July 27, 18; m. 47; c. 1. SPEECH, ENGLISH. A.B, Univ. Ill, 40; M.A, State Univ. Iowa, 42; summers, Agr. & Mech. Col. Tex, 49, 50. Instr. speech & Eng, TEX. A&M UNIV, 46-51, asst. prof, 51-72, ASSOC. PROF. SPEECH & CREATIVE WRITING, 72-, admin. asst. to head dept. Eng, 72. Mem. staff, Southwest Writers Conf, 59-62, 72 & 73; Nat. Endowment Arts creative writing fel, 73. Med. Dept, U.S.A, 42-46. S.Cent. Mod. Lang. Asn; Col. Eng. Asn; S.Cent. Eng. Asn. Creative writing; speech; Shakespeare. Publ: The devil to pay and other stories, South & West, 67; Organization and outlining, Arco, 71; The total portrait, In: The best detective stories of the year—1972, Doubleday, 72; The car as symbol in Hemingway's The short happy life of Francis Macomber, S.Cent. Bull, winter 72; 39 Shakespeares, CEA Critic, 3/73; plus others. Add: 906 North Ave, Bryan, TX 77801.

PELADEAU, MARIUS BEAUDOIN, b. Boston, Mass, Jan. 27, 35; m. 72. AMERICAN LITERATURE & HISTORY. B.A, St. Michael's Col.(Vt), 56; M.S, Boston Univ, 57; M.A, Georgetown Univ, 62. Assoc. ed, Pub. Utilities Fortnightly, Wash, D.C, 62-66; press secy. & admin. asst, U.S. Congressman Joseph P. Vigorito, 66-72; DIR, MAINE LEAGUE HIST. SOCS. & MUS, 72- Consult, Nat. Park Serv, 69-72. Co. Mil. Hist; Am. Asn. State & Local Hist. American history, especially of decorative arts, antique furnishings and accessories, the Civil War and the Shaker religious sect. Publ: The verse of Royall Tyler, Univ. Va, 68; The prose of Royall Tyler, Vt. Hist. Soc. & Charles Tuttle, 72; The Shaker meetinghouses of Moses Johnson, Antiques, 10/70; Corps badges of the Civil War, Mil. Collector & Hist, winter 71; Historic preservation in Maine, Hist. Preservation, 10-12/73. Add: Norris Hill, Monmouth, ME 04259.

PELFREY, CHARLES J, b. Olive Hill, Ky, Nov. 9, 25. LITERATURE. A.B, Morehead State Col, 49; M.A, Univ. Ky, 50, South. Teachers fel, 57-58, Ph.D, 58. Instr. ENG, Centre Col. Ky, 54-55; prof. & head dept, Abadan Inst. Technol, Iran, 58-62; assoc. prof, MOREHEAD STATE UNIV, 63-65, PROF, 65- U.S.A, 44-46. MLA; NEA. American literature; translation of the works of Ahmad Kasravi from the Farsi. Add: Dept. of English, Box 811, Morehead State University, Morehead, KY 40351.

PELL, CARROLL LEE, Modern Languages. See Volume III, Foreign Languages, Linguistics & Philology.

PELLMAN, HUBERT R, b. Richfield, Pa, Nov. 29, 18; m. 41; c. 2. ENGLISH & AMERICAN LITERATURE. A.B, Susquehanna Univ, 40; M.A, Bucknell Univ, 41; Ph.D, Univ. Pa, 58. PROF. ENG, EAST. MENNONITE COL, 41-43, 47- Vis. prof, Westmount Col, 64-65, Goshen Col, 69-70, Holsusei Col, Japan, 74-75. NCTE; MLA; Conf. Christianity & Lit. Colonial American literature. Publ: Eastern Mennonite College, 1917-1967, East. Mennonite Col, 67. Add: Dept. of English, Eastern Mennonite College, Harrisonburg, VA 22801.

PENCE, JAMES WORTH, JR, b. Staunton, Va, Dec. 10, 29; m. 54; c. 4. SPEECH. B.A, Univ. Va, 50, M.A, 51; Ph.D, Cornell Univ, 63. Asst. prof. SPEECH, Va. Mil. Inst, 56-66; UNIV. N.C, CHAPEL HILL, 66-73, ASSOC. PROF. & DIR. SPEECH DIV, 73- Exec. secy, N.C. High Sch. Debating Union; ed, Directory of Univs. & Cols. Conducting Summer High Sch. Speech Commun. Insts; assoc. ed, Quart. J. Speech. Speech Commun. Asn; South. Speech Commun. Asn. Public address; dialect. Publ: Nondebate activities in high school summer speech institutes, 72 & The campaign for the United States Senate in North Carolina: debate on educational television, 72 Speech Commun. Asn. Abstr; Vowel phonemes of Black dialect in Ahoskie, North Carolina, N.C. J. Speech & Drama, fall 72. Add: Speech Division, University of North Carolina at Chapel Hill, Chapel Hill, NC 27514.

PENDLETON, JAMES DUDLEY, b. Ft. Bragg, N.C, Dec. 12, 30; m. 51; c. 3. ENGLISH. B.S, Davidson Col, 52; M.A, Univ. N.C, 59. Instr. Eng. & asst. to dean, N.Y.C. Community Col, 54-56; instr. Eng, Richmond Prof. Inst, 58-61, asst. prof. Eng. & dean stud, 61-68; ASSOC. PROF. ENG, VA. COMMONWEALTH UNIV, 68- U.S.A, 52-54, Res, 54-60, Capt. S.Atlantic Mod. Lang. Asn; Southeast. Theatre Conf. Contemporary drama. Prod: The defender (play), Richmond Prof. Inst, 61; The oaks of Mamre (play), Va. Mus. Theatre & Baker Co, 63; Nightsong (play), Converse Col, 64; The brief and violent reign of Absalom (play), Hiram Scott Col, 68 & Relig. Theatre, 69; The trial of Judas (play), St. Paul's Episcopal Church, 68 & Chr. Kaiser Verlag, Munich, 74; The obscene verse of Magdalene Randallman (play), Clarion Col, 72; A last supper (play), N.C. Sch. Arts, 72 & WUNC-TV, Chapel Hill, 73. Add: Dept. of English, Virginia Commonwealth University, 901 W. Franklin St, Richmond, VA 23220.

PENN, JOHN S, b. Portage, Wis, Jan. 11, 14; m. 53; c. 3. SPEECH. B.A, Carroll Col, 35; M.A, Univ. Wis, 38, Ph.D, 59. Teacher hist, pub. schs, Wis, 36-38; SPEECH, pub. schs, Mich, 38-40; asst. prof, UNIV. N.DAK, 40-43, 46-47; assoc. prof, 47-54, PROF, 54-, DIR. SUMMER SESSIONS, 68-, DEAN & ASST. TO PRES, 73-, chmn. dept. speech, 48-67. Consult, Peabody awards, 42-43; lectr, Rockford Col, 50. U.S.N, 43-46, Res, 46-, Lt. Speech Commun. Asn; Cent. States Speech Asn. History of broadcasting; persuasion processes in society; mass media and persuasion. Add: University of North Dakota, Grand Forks, ND 58201.

PENNEL, CHARLES A, b. Memphis, Tenn, July 4, 34; m. 55; c. 5. ENGLISH. B.S, Memphis State Univ, 55, M.A, 56; South. Fac. Fel. Fund fel, Univ. Ill, 59-61, univ. summer fel, 62, Ph.D, 62. Teacher ENG, White Sta. High Sch, Memphis, Tenn, 55-57; instr, Auburn Univ, 57-59; asst. prof, Kans. State Univ, 62-67, assoc. prof, 67-71; PROF. & DIR. GRAD. STUD, NORTH. ILL. UNIV, 71- Univ. summer fel, 65, gen. ed, Elizabethan Biographies Supplements, Nether, 67- MLA; Bibliog. Soc, Eng; AAUP; Midwest Mod. Lang. Asn. Bibliography; drama, especially 16th and 17th century English Renaissance and 17th century English literature. Publ: Co-auth, George Chapman and John Marston, Vol. IV & Beaumont-Fletcher-Massinger, Ford and Shirley, Vol. VIII, In: Elizabethan bibliographies supplements, Nether, 68; auth, On introducing Shakespeare: Richard III, Col. Eng, 5/65; The authenticity of the George a Greene title-page inscriptions, J. Eng. & Ger. Philol, 10/65; The plays of Peter Shaffer: experiment in convention, Kans. Quart, spring 72. Add: Dept. of English, Northern Illinois University, DeKalb, IL 60115.

PENNELL, ARTHUR EMMET, b. Brooklyn, N.Y, Sept. 20, 23; m. 51; c. 5. ENGLISH LITERATURE. B.S, Univ. Ill, 49, M.A, 53, univ. fel. summer, 57, Ph.D.(Eng), 59. Instr. Eng, Univ. N.Mex, 58-61; asst. prof, NORTH. MICH.

UNIV, 61-62, assoc. prof. Eng. & asst. to dean arts & sci, 62-65, PROF. ENG, 65-, head dept, 65-73. Malone Soc; MLA; NCTE. Renaissance drama, especially Elizabethan; history and development of literary criticism; aesthetics of tragedy and comedy. Add: Dept. of English, Northern Michigan University, Marquette, MI 49855.

PENNER, ALLEN R, b. Chicago, Ill, Nov. 14, 36; m. 61; c. 2. ENGLISH. B.A, N.Tex. State Univ, 58, M.A, 61; Ph.D.(Eng), Univ. Colo, 65. ASSOC. PROF. ENG, UNIV. TENN, KNOXVILLE, 65- MLA; S.Atlantic Mod. Lang. Asn. English, American and European novel; modern fiction. Publ: Alan Sillitoe, Twayne, 72; Judgment in The ring and the book, Xavier Univ. Stud, 6/66; Edward Taylor's meditation one, Am. Lit, 5/67; Dantesque allegory in Sillitoe's Key to the door, Renascence, winter 68. Add: Dept. of English, University of Tennessee, Knoxville, TN 37919.

PENNER, JONATHAN G, b. Clinton, Mo, Sept, 27, 22; m. 43; c. 4. SPEECH. B.A, Emmanuel Missionary Col, 44; Ind. Univ, 55-56; M.S, Purdue Univ, 58, Ph.D, 62. Minister, Ind. & W.Va. Conf. Seventh-day Adventist, 44-58; assoc. prof. speech & chmn. dept, Walla Walla Col, 58-65; PROF. speech & relig, South. Missionary Col, 65-73; SPEECH & RADIO, LAKE MICH. COL, 73- Speech Commun. Asn. Rhetorical theory; speech analysis and homiletic techniques and content. Add: 74 Fourth St, Berrien Springs, MI 49103.

PENNINGER, FRIEDA ELAINE, b. Marion, N.C, Apr. 11, 27. MEDIAEVAL LANGUAGE & LITERATURE. A.B, Woman's Col, Univ. N.C, 48; M.A, Duke Univ, 50, Ph.D, 61. Asst. prof. ENG, Flora McDonald Col, 50-51; teacher, Barnwell High Sch, S.C, 51-52; Glynn Acad, Brunswick, Ga, 52-53; instr, Univ. Tenn, 53-56; Woman's Col, Univ. N.C, 56-58, 60-61, asst. prof, 61-63; WESTHAMPTON COL, 63-66, assoc. prof, 66-71, PROF, 71-, CHMN. DEPT, 70- Fel, Southeast. Inst. Medieval & Renaissance Stud, summers 65, 67. MLA; Mediaeval Acad. Am; Southeast Renaissance Conf; S.Atlantic Mod. Lang. Asn. Medieval-Renaissance drama; Chaucer; Caxton. Add: Dept. of English, Westhampton College, University of Richmond, VA 23173.

PENNINGTON, PAUL JORDAN, b. Deweyville, Tex, Apr. 20, 23; m. 48; c. 3. SPEECH. B.A, Henderson State Teachers Col, 48; M.A, Univ. Okla, 50; Ph.D, La. State Univ, 57. Teacher speech, Classen High Sch, Oklahoma City, Okla, 48-49; asst. SPEECH, Univ. Okla, 49-50; dept. head, Southeast. State Col, 50-51; asst, La. State Univ, 51-52; PROF, LA. POLYTECH. INST, 52-, DEAN SCH. ARTS & SCI, 64-, head dept. speech, 52-64. Pres, Conf. La. Cols. & Univs, 70-71. U.S.A.A.F, 42-46, S/Sgt. Speech Commun. Asn; South. Speech Asn. Franklin D. Roosevelt, gubernatorial speaking; group discussion and personality involvements. Publ: Handbook for speaking, W.C. Brown, 62. Add: College of Arts & Sciences, Louisiana Polytechnic Institute, Ruston, LA 71270.

PENNYBACKER, JOHN HOWARD, b. Philadelphia, Pa, Feb. 26, 30; m. 58; c. 2. SPEECH. B.A, Univ. Pa, 51; M.A, Temple Univ, 55; Ph.D.(speech), Ohio State Univ, 61. Instr. SPEECH, LA. STATE UNIV, BATON ROUGE, 60-63, asst. prof, 63-65, ASSOC. PROF, 65-, CCTV COORD, 66- U.S.A.F, 51-53, Res, 53-62, 1st Lt. Broadcast Educ. Asn.(ed, newsletter, Asn. Prof. Broadcasting Educ, 67-72, v.pres, 70-71, pres, 71-73); Speech Commun. Asn; South. Speech Asn. Television-radio; communications theory. Publ: Co-auth, Broadcasting and the public interest, Random, 69; auth, Working with universities, spring 65 & Leadership and the educator: the middle way, winter 66, J. Broadcasting; Teaching students to understand broadcast media & Teaching student to use broadcast media, In: Speech methods and resources: a textbook for the teacher of speech communication, Harper, 2nd ed, 72; plus others. Add: Dept. of Speech, Louisiana State University, Baton Rouge, LA 70803.

PENNYBACKER, RUTH, b. Palestine, Tex, Feb. 24, 97. LITERATURE, CREATIVE WRITING. B.A, Vassar Col, 18; M.A, Univ. Tex, 34; State Univ. Iowa, 41-44. Instr. ENG, Univ. Houston, 35-39, asst. prof, 39-41; asst, State Univ. Iowa, 42-43; asst. prof, UNIV. HOUSTON, 46-47, assoc. prof, 47-70, EMER. PROF, 70- Fac. sponsor, The Harvest, Univ. Houston. Matrix Award, Theta Sigma Phi, 59. MLA; Am. Stud. Asn; NCTE. Add: 2801-A Warren St, Austin, TX 78703.

PENROD, JAMES, b. Nashville, Tenn, Sept. 24, 16; m. 51; c. 2. FOLKLORE, AMERICAN LITERATURE. B.A, Vanderbilt Univ, 38, M.A, 40; Ph.D, George Peabody Col, 52. Teacher, Miami Country Day Sch, 41-42; employ. counsel, Tenn. Dept. Employ. Security, 46-48; pub. secy, Nashville Chamber of Commerce, Tenn, 48-49; assoc. prof. ENG, Ky. Wesleyan Col, 51-55; Troy State Col, 55-59; EAST. N.MEX. UNIV, 59-64, PROF, 64- U.S.A, 42-45. AAUP; Am. Stud. Asn; Am. Folklore Soc. American humor, folklore and fiction. Publ: Folk motifs in old southeastern humor, South. Folklore Quart, 6/55; Harden Taliaferro: folk humorist of North Carolina, Midwest Folklore, fall 56; Characteristic endings of southwestern yarns, Miss. Quart, winter 61-62. Add: Box 2058, Eastern New Mexico University, Portales, NM 88130.

PEPLE, EDWARD CRONIN, b. Richmond, Va, Dec. 12, 11; m. 36; c. 2. ENGLISH PHILOLOGY. B.A, Univ. Richmond, 32; A.M, Harvard, 34, Ph.D, 36. Asst. ENG, Harvard & Radcliffe Col, 35-36; instr, Wells Col, 36-37; UNIV. RICHMOND, 37-38, asst. prof, 38-44, assoc. prof, 44-54, PROF, 54-, ASSOC. PROVOST, 74-, dean grad. sch, 65-73. Assoc. prof, Med. Col. Va, 47-56, prof, 56-62. MLA; Col. Eng. Asn. The life and works of Stephen Phillips. Add: University of Richmond, VA 23173.

PEPPER, ROBERT DAVID, b. Paterson, N.J, Aug. 24, 20; m. 41; c. 1. ENGLISH, HUMANITIES. B.A, Drew Univ, 41; M.A, Montclair State Col, 49; Ph.D.(Eng. lit), Stanford Univ, 63. Teacher private schs, Conn, Mich, South. Calif, 47-51; acting instr. Eng, Stanford Univ, 51-57; instr., South. Ore. Col, 57-58; Eng. & French, Col. San Mateo, 58-62; lectr. Eng. lang. & lit, Massey Univ, N.Z, 62 & 63; asst. prof. ENG. & HUMANITIES, CALIF. STATE UNIV, SAN JOSE, 63-68, assoc. prof, 68-73, PROF, 73- Asst. prof, World Campus Afloat, Chapman Col, 67; assoc. chmn. panel rhetoric & lit, NCTE. Nat. Convention, Tex, 66. MLA; Renaissance Text Soc. Shakespeare, Rabelais; Renaissance bibliography. Publ: Ed. & auth. introd, Four Tudor books on education, 66 & English writers on education, 1480-1603, 67, Scholars' Facsimiles; ed, Oscar Wilde: Irish poets and poetry of the nineteenth century, Bk. Club of Calif, 72; auth, Francis Clement's Petie schole at the Vautrollier Press, 1587, Library, 3/67; The importance of reading Alfred: Oscar Wilde's debt to Alfred de Musset, Bull. New York Pub. Libr, 71. Add: Dept. of English, San Jose State University, San Jose, CA 95114.

PEPPERDENE, MARGARET W, b. Vicksburg, Miss, Dec. 25, 19; div. ENGLISH. B.S, La. State Univ, 41; M.A, Vanderbilt Univ, 48, Ford fel, 51-52, Ph.D.(Eng), 53; Fulbright scholar, Queen's Univ, Ireland, 50-51. Asst. instr. Eng, Vanderbilt Univ, 51-52; instr, Miami Univ, 52-54; asst. prof, 55-56; fel, Dublin Inst. Adv. Stud, Ireland, 54-55; asst. prof. ENG, AGNES SCOTT COL, 56-59, assoc. prof, 59-67, PROF, 67-, CHMN. DEPT, 68- Am. Asn. Univ. Women fel, 54-55; Guggenheim fel, 56-57. U.S.N.R, 43-45, Lt. MLA; Mediaeval Acad. Am; S.Atlantic Mod. Lang. Asn. Old English literature, especially Beowulf; ecclesiastical history of Ireland and England; old Irish language and literature. Publ: Bede's Historia ecclesiastica: a new perspective, Celtica, 58; Beowulf and the coastguard, Eng. Stud, 66; plus others. Add: Agnes Scott College, Decatur, GA 30030.

PERIMAN, KENNETH IVOR, b. Potwin, Kans, May 6, 25; m. 49; c. 3. LITERATURE. B.A, Univ. Colo, 51, M.A, 53; summers, Colo. State Univ, 55, 56. Instr. Univ. Colo, 51-53; Eng. & speech, Colo. State Univ, 54-59, asst. prof, 59-62; lit, FT. LEWIS COL, 62-64, ASSOC. PROF. ENG, 64-, head dept. lit. & Eng, 62-71. Consult, Radio Sta. KLOV & KCOL, 55-62; lectr, Peace Corps Mission Pakistan, 61; Colo. State Univ. Seminars, 62; dir. Title III Prog. Intensive Eng. Bi-Lingual Stud. & assoc. dir, NDEA Inst. Adv. Stud-ESL, Ft. Lewis Col, 67-68; consult, Choice Bks. Col. Libr, 64-; KDGO Radio; Dictionary Am. Regional Eng; mem. ed. bd, West. Am. Lit. U.S.A.A.F, 43-46, Res, 46-53, 1st Lt. Nat. Thespian Soc; Am. Folklore Soc; Col. Eng. Asn; NCTE. Folklore; Bible studies, especially influence on arts; contemporary literature. Publ: Co-auth, Colorado Folk Song Quarterly, 61-; auth, Songs of Robert Burns, Colo. State Univ, 53; co-auth, Modern business communications, Pitman, 63; ed, Proceedings of NDEA institute, 68 & ESL for Navajo children, 68, Ft. Lewis Col. Add: 142-L, Ft. Lewis College, Durango, CO 81301.

PERKINS, DAVID DODD, b. Philadelphia, Pa, Oct. 25, 28. ENGLISH LITERATURE. A.B, Harvard, 51, A.M, 52, Ph.D, 55. Instr. ENG, HARVARD, 57-59, asst. prof, 59-60, assoc. prof, 60-64, PROF, 64- Guggenheim fel, Harvard, 62; Fulbright fel, Ger, 68-69; prof, Univ. Gottingen, 68-69; Guggenheim fel, 73. U.S.A, 55-57. MLA; Keats-Shelley Asn. Am. Eighteenth, 19th and 20th century literature. Publ: The quest for permanence: the symbolism of Wordsworth, Shelley and Keats, 59 & Wordsworth and the poetry of sincerity, 63, Harvard; ed, English romantic writers, Harcourt, 67. Add: Dept. of English, Harvard University, Cambridge, MA 02138.

PERKINS, GEORGE B, JR, b. Lowell, Mass, Aug. 16, 30. AMERICAN LITERATURE. A.B, Tufts Univ, 53; univ. fel, Duke Univ, 53-54, M.A, 54; univ. fel, Cornell Univ, 54-55, Ph.D, 60. Instr. Eng, Wash. Univ, 57-60; asst. prof, Baldwin-Wallace Col, 60-63; Fairleigh Dickinson Univ, 63-66; lectr. Am. lit, Univ. Edinburgh, 66-67; assoc. prof. ENG, EAST. MICH. UNIV, 67-70, PROF, 70-, dir. grad. stud, 69-73. Gen. ed, J. Narrative Tech, 71- MLA; Eng. Asn, Gt. Brit; AAUP. Middle English language and literature; folklore and folksong. Publ: Writing clear prose, 64, Varieties of prose, 66 & ed, Realistic American short fiction, 72, Scott; The theory of the American novel, 70 & American poetic theory, 72, Holt; The American tradition in literature, Grosset, 4th ed, 74; auth, Howells and Hawthorne, 19th-Century Fiction, 12/60; A medieval carol survival: the fox and the goose, J. Am. Folklore, 7/61; contrib, Contemporary novelists, St. James Press, London & St. Martin's Press, New York, 72; plus others. Add: 1316 King George Blvd, Ann Arbor, MI 48104.

PERKINS, HATTIE LOGAN, b. Joliet, Ill, June 27, 22; m. 48. ENGLISH, HUMANITIES. A.B, Samuel Houston Col, 43; Univ. Calif, Los Angeles, summer, 44; M.A, Prairie View Agr. & Mech. Col, 51; Columbia Univ, summer, 52; M.Ed, Univ. Denver, 59; John Hay fels, Bennington Col, summer, 64 & Northwestern Univ, 65-66; Ph.D.(humanities), West. Colo. Univ, 72. Teacher, Dallas Independent Sch. Dist, 44-59; asst. prof. Eng, lab. high sch, GRAMBLING COL, 59-65, ASSOC. PROF. ENG. & HUMANITIES, 66- NCTE; Conf. Col. Compos. & Commun. Humanities in colleges and universities; freshman composition and communication; language and linguistics. Publ: The teacher molds the future, La. Educ. J, 4/64; Dreams versus realities in higher education humanities programs: a critical moment, Humanities J, 9/72. Add: 106 Richmond Dr. Grambling, LA 71245.

PERKINS, LINDSEY SAUNDERS, b. Pine Castle, Fla, Oct. 31, 10; m. 36. SPEECH. B.A.E, Univ. Fla, 34; Duke Univ; scholar, Northwest. Univ, M.A, 39, Ph.D, 45. Prin, pub. sch, Fla, 28-29, teacher, schs, 29-31, 34-35, prin, 35-37; instr. SPEECH, N.Park Col, 38-40; substitute, BROOKLYN COL, 40-41, tutor, 41-45, instr, 45-49, asst. prof, 49-57, ASSOC. PROF, 57-, HEAD ORAL COMMUNS, DIV. VOC. STUD, 52-, dir. speakers bur, 45-49, supvr. div. community servs, 49-51. Training consult, Transportation Co, Inc, Orlando, Fla, 56-; assoc. ed, Jour. Commun, 49-63; Today's Speech, 53-61; assoc, Danforth Found, 57-59, sr. assoc, 59- Speech Commun Asn; Int. Commun. Asn; Speech Commun. Asn. East. St.(v.pres, 51). Rhetoric and perusasion; history of American public address. Publ: Co-auth, Antislavery and disunion, 1858-1861, Harper, 63; Oratory of Benjamin Ryan Tillman, Speech Monogr; The convention of 1787: a study in successful discussion, West. Speech. Add: Dept. of English, Brooklyn College, Bedford Ave. & Ave. H, Brooklyn, NY 11210.

PERKINS, MARJORIE WILLENE, b. Anniston, Ala, Mar. 17, 32. ENGLISH. B.A, Northeast La. Univ, 56; M.A, George Peabody Col, 60; assistantship, Univ. Ala, 69-71, Ph.D.(sec. educ), 72. Teacher Eng, John Jones Jr. High Sch, Gadsden, Ala, 56-58; Southside High Sch, 58-59; Eng. & jour, Gadsden High Sch, 59-65; Eng, GADSDEN STATE JR. COL, 65-69, chmn. div. Eng. & for. lang, 66-69, INSTR. ENG. & COORD. DEPT, 71-, RES. PROG. WRITING, 72- Consult. & hostess, Southeast. Regional Conf. Eng. in Two-Year Col, 74; consult, South. Asn. Cols. & Schs, 74- Am. Asn. Univ. Women (first v.pres, 73-74); NEA; NCTE; Southeast. Regional Conf. Eng. in Two-Year Col. Southern dialects; systems approach to composition. Add: 1109 Dwight Ave, Gadsden, AL 35904.

PERKUS, GERALD H, b. Brooklyn, N.Y, June 26, 38; m. 62; c. 3. VICTORIAN & AMERICAN LITERATURE. B.A, Brooklyn Col, 59; NDEA fel. &

Ph.D.(Eng), Univ. Rochester, 66. ASST. PROF. ENG, Babson Inst, 64-67; Wilkes Col, 67-72; HARTWICK COL, 72- Wilkes Col. res. fel, 68-72; asst. prof. humanities, grad. educ. prog. teachers, Temple Univ, 68-72. MLA; NCTE; Col. Eng. Asn. Victorian and Romantic poetry, 19th century American literature. Add: Dept. of English, Hartwick College, Oneonta, NY 13820.

PERLIS, ALAN DAVID, b. Boston, Mass, Sept. 29, 43; m. 71; c. 1. ENGLISH & AMERICAN LITERATURE. B.A, Univ. Vt, 65; M.A, Univ. Mich, 66, Ford Found. fel, 67-68, Ph.D.(Eng), 69. Instr. ENG, Univ. Mich, 69-70; ASST. PROF, BELOIT COL, 70-, DIR. PORTER SCHOLARS DIV, 73- Humanities improvement grants, 71-74. Victorian literature; modern novel; the poetry of Wallace Stevens. Publ: Wallace Stevens: A world of transforming shapes, Bucknell Univ, 75; As I lay dying: a study of time, S.Dak. Rev, winter 72; Wallace Stevens: the freedom to transform, Bucknell Rev, winter 74; plus numerous poems in various literary journals. Add: Dept. of English, Beloit College, Beloit, WI 53511.

PERLOFF, MARJORIE G, b. Vienna, Austria, Sept. 28, 31; U.S. citizen; m. 53; c. 2. ENGLISH LITERATURE. B.A, Barnard Col, Columbia Univ, 53; M.A, Cath. Univ. Am, 56, Ph.D.(Eng), 65. Asst. prof. ENG, Cath. Univ. Am, 65-71; assoc. prof, UNIV. MD, COLLEGE PARK, 71-73, PROF, 73- MLA; Col. Eng. Asn; Eng. Inst; AAUP. Modern British and American poetry; comparative literature; literary theory. Publ: Rhyme and meaning in the poetry of Yeats, Mouton, The Hague, 70; The poetic art of Robert Lowell, Cornell Univ, 73; Spatial form in Yeats's poetry, PMLA, 10/67; Angst and animism in the poetry of Sylvia Plath, J. Mod Lit, 1/70; The autobiographical mode of Goethe, Comp. Lit. Stud, 9/70; plus others. Add: 6905 Scotforth Rd, Philadelphia, PA 19119.

PERLUCK, HERBERT ALAN, b. Brooklyn, N.Y, June 12, 24; m. 44; c. 2. ENGLISH. B.S, Iowa State Univ, 48; M.A, Brown Univ, 50, Am. Counc. Learned Soc. fel. & Ph.D.(Eng), 55. Instr. ENG, Brown Univ, 50-55; asst. prof, R.I. Col, 55-57; instr, Conn. Col, 57-59; BROOKLYN COL, 60-66, asst. prof, 66-70, ASSOC. PROF, 70- Dir. educ, Progress for Providence proj, Off. Econ. Opportunity, 66-67. Med.Dept, A.U.S. Col. Eng. Asn. American Puritan history and expression; American romanticism and modern literature; English education. Publ: The heart's driving complexity: an unromantic reading of Faulkner's The bear, Accent, winter 60. Add: Dept. of English, Brooklyn College, Bedford Ave. & Ave. H, Brooklyn, NY 11210.

PERRILL, NORMAN KIETH, b. Hutchinson, Kans, Dec. 11, 31; m. 58. SPEECH COMMUNICATION. B.S, Northwest. Univ, 53, M.A, 54; Ph.D. (speech), Univ. South. Calif, 66. Instr. SPEECH, San Fernando Valley State Col, 65-66; asst. prof, ARIZ. STATE UNIV, 66-70, ASSOC. PROF, 70-, fac. res. grant, Shneidman tech. content anal, 68. U.S.A.F, 55-58, 1st Lt. Int. Commun. Asn; Speech Commun. Asn; West. Speech Commun. Asn; AAUP. Interpersonal and group communication; human communication theory. Add: Dept. of Speech & Theatre, Arizona State University, Tempe, AZ 85281.

PERRIN, (EDWIN) NOEL, b. New York, N.Y, Sept. 18, 27; m. 60; c. 2. ENGLISH LITERATURE. B.A, Williams Col, 49; M.A, Duke Univ, 50; M.Litt, Cambridge, 58. Instr. ENG, Univ. N.C, Greensboro, 56-59; asst. prof, DARTMOUTH COL, 59-66, assoc. prof, 66-72, PROF. & CHMN. DEPT, 72- Guggenheim fel, 70-71. U.S.A, 45-46, 51-52, Capt. American literature; history of expurgation. Publ: A passport secretly green, St. Martins, 61; Dr. Bowdler's legacy, Atheneum, 69; Amateur sugar maker, Univ. Press New Eng, 72; Vermont in all weathers, Viking, 73; plus others. Add: Dept. of English, Dartmouth College, Hanover, NH 03755.

PERRINE, LAURENCE, b. Toronto, Ont, Oct. 13, 15; m. 49; c. 2. ENGLISH & AMERICAN LITERATURE. B.A, Oberlin Col, 37, M.A, 39; Ph.D.(Eng) Yale, 48. Instr. ENG, SOUTH. METHODIST UNIV, 46-48, asst. prof, 48-55, assoc. prof, 55-60, PROF, 60- U.S.A, 42-46, M/Sgt. NCTE (dir, 62-65); MLA; Col. Eng. Asn; S.Cent. Mod. Lang. Asn.(pres, 70-71). Poetry explication; Victorian literature; Frost, Robinson and Dickinson. Publ: Sound and sense, an introduction to poetry, 56, Story and structure, 59, co-auth, Poetry: a closer look, 63, 100 American poems of the twentieth century, 66 & auth, Dimensions of drama, 73, Harcourt; The nature of proof in the interpretation of poetry, Eng, J, 9/62; The importance of tone in the interpretation of literature, 2/63 & Four forms of metaphor, 11/71, Col. Eng; plus others. Add: Dept. of English, Southern Methodist University, Dallas, TX 75275.

PERRY, DAVID SCOTT, b. Plainfield, N.J, Apr. 2, 30. English. B.A, Columbia Univ, 51; M.A, Columbia Univ, 52; Ph.D.(Eng), Princeton, 66. Instr. ENG, Hamilton Col, 55-58; from instr. to asst. prof, SIMMONS COL, 61-71, ASSOC. PROF, 71- U.S.A, 52-54; Bronze Star Medal. MLA. Nineteenth century in England, romantic movement; Bible; Greek mythology. Add: Dept. of English, Simmons College, Boston, MA 02115.

PERRY, EDWARD SAMUEL, b. New Orleans, La, June 4, 37; m. 61; c. 4. CINEMA STUDIES. B.A, Baylor Univ, 61; M.A, Univ. Iowa, 66, Ph.D.(dramatic art), 68. Asst. prof. dramatic art, Univ. Iowa, 68-69; assoc. prof. commun, Univ. Tex, Austin, 69-71; assoc. prof. CINEMA STUD, N.Y. UNIV, 71-72, PROF, 72-, CHMN. DEPT, 71- Vis. lectr, State Univ. N.Y. Purchase, 72-73; mem. film & media panel, N.Y. State Counc. Arts, 72-; assoc, Danforth Found, 73-; mem. steering comt, Am. Film Inst. Comt. Univ. Film Training & Stud, 73-; mem. bd, dir, Learning about Learning Found, 73-; Nat. Endowment for Humanities grant. Speech Commun. Asn.(mem. res. bd, 73-77); Soc. Cinema Stud; Univ. Film Asn.(mem. bd. dir, 69-70). Bibliography and research methodology; Italian cinema; pre-1915 cinema history. Publ: Co-auth, The new film index, Dutton, 74; ed, Performing arts resources, Theatre Libr. Asn, 74; auth, The seventh art as sixth sense, Educ. Theatre J, 69; A contextual analysis of M. Antonioni's L'eclisse, Speech Monogr, 70; Film meaning, Mill Mountain Rev, 74. Add: 110 Bleecker St, New York, NY 10012.

PERRY, JOHN DOUGLAS, JR, b. Bryn Mawr, Pa, Dec. 19, 39; m. 64; c. 2. AMERICAN LITERATURE. B.A, Yale, 61; M.A, Temple Univ, 63, Ph.D. (Eng), 68. Instr. ENG, Temple Univ, 65-68; SIMMONS COL, 68-69; ASST. PROF, 69- Asst. prof, Harvard Univ, Extension, 72- AAUP. Nineteenth century American fiction; 20th century American literature. Publ: Counterpoint in James Agee's A death in the family: the six extra scenes, Novel, 72; Gothic as vortex: the form of horror in Capote, Faulkner and Styron, Mod. Fiction Stud, 73. Add: Dept. of English, Simmons College, 300 The Fenway, Boston, MA 02115.

PERRY, JOHN OLIVER, b. Paris, France, Apr. 9, 29; U.S. citizen; div; c. 2. ENGLISH. A.B, Kenyon Col, 49; M.A, Univ. Fla, 51; Ph.D.(Eng), Univ. Calif, Berkeley, 58. Instr. ENG, Univ. Colo, 55-58; asst. prof, Harpur Col, State Univ. N.Y. Binghamton, 58-64; TUFTS UNIV, 64-66, ASSOC. PROF, 66- Fulbright lectr. Eng, Univ. Delhi, 71-72. MLA; AAUP. British novel; forms of personal writing; modern poetics and criticism. Publ: Ed. & compiler, Approaches to the poem, 65 & Backgrounds to modern literature, 68, Chandler; auth, The experience of poems, Macmillan, 72; Action, vision, or voice: moral dilemmas in Conrad, Mod. Fiction Stud, spring 64; Relationships of disparate voices in poems, Essays Criticism, 1/65; The temporal analysis of poems, Brit. J. Aesthet, 7/65. Add: Dept. of English, Tufts University, Medford, MA 02155.

PERRY, LOWELL G, b. Potomac, Ill, Mar. 6, 23; m. 47; c. 3. SPEECH, COMMUNICATION. B.A, Abilene Christian Col, 47; M.A, Ind. State Teachers Col, 48; Ph.D.(speech, radio & TV), Northwest. Univ, 56. PROF. COMMUN. & DIR. RADIO & TV, ABILENE CHRISTIAN COL, 48- Consult, Radio Piratininga Network, Sao Paulo, Brazil, 65-67. U.S.N.R, 43-46, Lt.(jg). Nat. Asn. FM Broadcasters; Int. Broadcasters Soc; Int. Christian Broadcasters. Study of audiences for religious broadcasting; study of audiences for all broadcasting; various phases of religious broadcasting. Publ: Religion on the air, Broadcasting, 11/15/54. Add: Dept. of Communication, Abilene Christian College, Abilene, TX 79601.

PERRY, MARGARET, b. Cincinnati, Ohio, Nov. 15, 33. AFRO-AMERICAN LITERATURE, LIBRARY SCIENCE. A.B, West. Mich. Univ, 54; certificat d'Etude Francaises, Univ. Paris, 56; City Col. N.Y, 57-58; M.S.L.S, Cath. Univ. Am. 59. Young adult & reference librn, N.Y. Pub. Libr, 54-55, 57-58; U.S. Army librn, Europe, 59-67; reference & circulation librn. Eng, U.S. Mil. Acad, 67-70; HEAD EDUC. LIBR, UNIV. ROCHESTER, 70-, ASST. PROF. AFRO-AM. LIT, 73- Am. Libr. Asn; Counc. Basic Educ; Col. Lang. Asn. Afro-American literature, especially Harlem Renaissance; academic librarianship. Publ: Ed, Criticism of American, British, European and classical authors: a selective bibliography, West Point, 68; auth, A bio-bibliography of Countee P. Cullen, Greenwood, 71; Race and education, Am. Libr, 11/71; Pinhead libraries and librarians, in praise of, In: What black librarians are saying, Scarecrow, 73; A dawn of a doom of a dream (short story), Phylon, 3/73; plus other articles and stories. Add: Education Library, University of Rochester, Rochester, NY 14627.

PERRY, MARVIN BANKS, JR, b. Powhatan, Va, Sept. 29, 18; m. 50; c. 2. ENGLISH. A.B, Univ. Va, 40; A.M, Harvard, 41, Ph.D.(Eng), 50; hon.LL.D, Wash. Col, 67. Instr. Eng, Univ. Va, 47-51; asst. prof, Washington & Lee Univ, 51-53, assoc. prof, 53-56, prof. & chmn. dept, 56-60; prof. & dean admis, Univ. Va, 60-67; PRES, Goucher Col, 67-73; AGNES SCOTT COL, 73- U.S.N.R, 42-67, Comdr.(Ret). MLA; Col. Eng. Asn; NCTE; Keats-Shelley Asn. Am. Keats: English literature of the 17th and 19th centuries. Publ: Modern minds; Nine short novels. Add: Office of the President, Agnes Scott College, Decatur, GA 30030.

PERRY, MERRILL IVAN, b. Hannibal, Mo, Aug. 26, 42. ENGLISH & AMERICAN LITERATURE. B.A, San Francisco State Col, 67; M.A, Northwest. Univ, 68, Ph.D.(Eng), 71. ASST. PROF. ENG, LEHMAN COL, 71- Modern British and American literature; contemporary American fiction; novel. Add: Dept. of English, Herbert H. Lehman College, Bedford Park Blvd. W, Bronx, NY 10468.

PERRY, MURVIN HENRY, b. Bruce, S.Dak, Apr. 28, 22; m. 51; c. 5. JOURNALISM. B.S, S.Dak. State Col, 50; M.A, State Univ. Iowa, 54, Ph.D.(mass commun), 59. Teacher Eng. & jour, Gregory High Sch, S.Dak, 47-48; publ. specialist, S.Dak. State Col, 49-51; intern info. serv, State Univ. Iowa, 51-52; spec. serv. technician, Vet. Admin, 52-56; asst. to dir. jour, State Univ. Iowa, 56-59, asst. prof. tech. jour, 59-63; DIR. SCH. JOUR, KENT STATE UNIV, 63- U.S.N, 42-46. Asn. Educ. Jour. Publ: Co-auth, Career guidance problems in Kansas high schools, Jour. Quart, 8/64; Educator-editor relations, spring 67 & Protect freedom of press, but enforce responsibility, summer 68, Jour. Educ. Add: School of Journalism, Kent State University, Kent, OH 44242.

PERRY, THOMAS AMHERST, b. Beaver City, Nebr, Apr. 26, 12; m. 37; c. 4. ENGLISH, COMPARATIVE LITERATURE. B.A, Park Col, 34; N.Mex. Highlands Univ, summer 34; M.A, State Univ. Iowa, 36, univ. fel, 42, Ph.D.(Eng), 43; Univ. Chicago, summer 41; Int. Grad. Sch, Oxford, summer 64. From instr. to asst. prof. Eng, Park Col, 36-42; instr, State Univ. Iowa, 43; from assoc. prof. to prof. Eng. & head div. lang. & lit, Cent. Methodist Col, 43-63; Fulbright lectr, Univ. Bucharest, 63-64; Herman Brown prof, Southwest. Univ.(Tex), 64-65; assoc. prof. Eng, E.TEX. STATE UNIV, 65-68, PROF, 68-72, LIT. & LANG, 72-, head dept Eng, 69-72. Vis. prof, Univ. Mo, 51-52; Smith-Mundt exchange prof, Univ. State of Mex, 59; vis. prof, Northeast Mo. State Col, summer 65; E.Tex. State Univ. fac. res. & travel grant to Romania from the Res. Assoc. Prog. of Soc. Sci. Found. & the Grad. Sch. Int. Stud. of Univ. Denver, summer, 68; mem. comt. variorum glossary, World Shakespeare Congr, Vancouver, B.C, 70-71; steering comt, Romanian Stud. Congr, Univ. Auckland, summer 73. MLA (mem. comt. int. bibliog, 70-74); S.Cent. Mod. Lang. Asn; Shakespeare Asn. Am; Am. Comp. Lit. Asn; Int. Comp. Lit. Asn. Shakespeare; literary theory and criticism; comparative literature, especially the Renaissance and Romanian-American literary relationships. Publ: Historical study of the two gentlemen of Verona; co-auth, Orientation English, Burgess, 39, rev. ed, 41, 46 & 49; auth, Emerson, the historical frame and Shakespeare, Mod. Lang. Quart, 12/48; Proteus, wry-transformed traveller, Shakespeare Quart, 1/54; contrib, World literature in English translation, Ungar, 69; plus others. Add: 214 Brookhaven Terr, Commerce, TX 75428.

PERRY, WILLIAM, b. Bradford, Mass, Sept. 9, 13; m. 45. ENGLISH. A.B, Harvard, 34, A.M, 46. Teacher, high sch, Mass, 35-42; instr. ENG, BOSTON UNIV, 46-48, asst. prof, 48-55, ASSOC. PROF, 55-, asst. dean, 58-59, assoc. dean, 59-69. U.S.N, 42-46, Lt. Comdr. Egypt Explor. Soc. Semantics, general education. Add: Dept. of English & Humanities, Div. of General Education, Boston University, 855 Commonwealth Ave, Boston, MA 02215.

PERSKY, PHILLIP, b. Independence, Kans, July 17, 23. ENGLISH. B.A, Univ. Kans, 48, M.A, 50; Ph.D.(Eng), Stanford Univ, 59. Asst. instr. ENG, SAN JOSE STATE UNIV, 52-53, instr, 53-56, asst. prof, 56-59, assoc. prof, 59-64, PROF, 64- Fulbright lectr. ling, Univ. Rome, Italy, 60-61; Counc. Am. Stud. dir, Eng. Lang. Sch, Rome, Italy, 61-62; Eng. lang. consult, Inst. Admin, Enugu, Nigeria, 64-66. U.S.A.A.F, 43-46. Nat. Asn. For. Stud. Affairs. Shakespeare; linguistics; teaching language. Publ: Co-auth, Bibliography of the works of Alfred Korzybski, Etc: Rev. Gen. Semantics, spring 50; auth, Review of the Alliance competition year and honors plays for 1953, Dramatists Alliance Bull, 53; contrib, The teaching of English in Nigerian schools, Ford Found, 66. Add: Dept. of English, San Jose State University, San Jose, CA 94114.

PETELLE, JOHN L, b. Fair Haven, Vt, Jan. 6, 38; m. 57; c. 1. SPEECH, DRAMATIC ART. B.S, Univ. Vt, 59; M.A, Univ. Nebr, 60; Ph.D.(speech, sociol), Univ. Minn, 62. Instr. SPEECH, Univ. Minn, 60-62; asst. prof, UNIV. NEBR, LINCOLN, 62-65, assoc. prof. & v.chmn. dept, 66-68, PROF. & CHMN. DEPT, 68- Speech Commun. Asn; Cent. States Speech Asn; Int. Commun. Asn. Communication theory and communication processing; small group interaction theory; persuasion. Publ: A schematic interpretation of two levels of persuasion, Speaker & Gavel, 5/65; A comparison of team quality ratings against strong versus weak opposition, Am. Forensic Asn. J, fall 67; The role of conflict in discussion, In: Small group communication: a reader, W.C. Brown, 70. Add: Dept. of Speech & Dramatic Art, 318 Burnett, University of Nebraska, Lincoln, NE 68508.

PETER, JOHN, b. Queenstown, S.Africa, Oct. 8, 21; m. 46; c. 5. ENGLISH. B.A, Univ. S.Africa, 41, LL.B, 44, D.Litt, 57; B.A, Cambridge, 47, M.A, 51; Webb scholar, 47-49; Reed scholar, 49-50; D.Litt.(Eng), Rhodes Univ, S.Africa, 73. Res. & supvr. Eng. stud, Gonville & Caius Col, Cambridge, 47-50; assoc. prof. ENG, Univ. Man, 50-56, PROF, 56-61; UNIV. VICTORIA, 61- Humanities Res. Counc. Can. fel, 57-58; Hugh LeMay fel, 57-58; vis. prof, Univ. Wis, 64-65; Commonwealth vis. prof, Oxford, 66-67. Doubleday Can. Novel Prize, 64. S.African Army, 43. Asn. Can. Univ. Teachers Eng. Renaissance; 19th and 20th century literature. Publ: Complaint and satire in early English literature, Clarendon Press, 56; Critique of Paradise lost, Columbia & Longmans, London, 60, reprint, 61; Along that coast, 64 & Runaway, 69, Doubleday; Take hands at winter, Doubleday & Longmans, London, 67; co-ed, Malahat Rev, 67-71. Add: 3950 Telegraph Bay Rd, Victoria, B.C, Can.

PETERS, ADA, b. Bangor, Maine, Aug. 23, 05; m. 30. ENGLISH. A.B, Univ. Maine, 27; A.M, Columbia Univ, 52. Instr. Eng. & French, Benedict Col, 27-28; ENG, TUSKEGEE INST, 28-36, 41-59, ASST. PROF, 59-, ACTING COORD. COMMUN, 62- NCTE; Col. Eng. Asn. Add: 1712 Patterson St, Tuskegee Institute, AL 36088.

PETERS, MARGOT MCCULLOUGH, b. Wausau, Wis. VICTORIAN LITERATURE, LINGUISTICS. B.A, Univ. Wis-Madison, 61, M.A, 65, Ph.D.(Eng), 69. ASST. PROF. ENG, Northland Col, 63-66; UNIV. WIS-WHITEWATER, 69- MLA; Midwest Mod. Lang. Asn; Bronte Soc; Women's Caucus Mod. Lang. Victorian literature; stylistics; English novel. Publ: Charlotte Bronte: style in the novel, Univ. Wis-Madison, 73; The phonological structure of James Joyce's Araby, Lang. & Style, spring 73; Charlotte Brontë: a critico-bibliographic survey 1945-1973, Brit. Stud. Monitor, 74. Add: Dept. of English, University of Wisconsin-Whitewater, Whitewater, WI 53190.

PETERS, PAUL STANLEY, JR, Theoretical Linguistics. See Volume III, Foreign Languages, Linguistics & Philology.

PETERS, ROBERT LOUIS, b. Eagle River, Wis, Oct. 20, 24; c. 3. ENGLISH. M.A. & scholar, Univ. Wis, 49, Ph.D.(Eng), 51. Instr, Univ. Idaho, 51-52; Eng. & humanities, Boston Univ, 52-54; asst. prof, Ohio Wesleyan Univ, 54-57; assoc. prof. Victorian lit, Wayne State Univ, 57-66; PROF. ENG, Univ. Calif, Riverside, 66-68; UNIV. CALIF, IRVINE, 68- Res. grants, Wayne State Univ, 58, 62-63; Am. Counc. Learned Socs. grant-in-aid, summer 63; vis. prof, Univ. Calif, Riverside, 63-64; Guggenheim fel, 67-68; asst. ed, J. Aesthet. & Art Criticism; MacDowell Colony fel, fall 73; YADDO fel, winter 73. U.S.A, 43-46. MLA; Poetry Soc. Am. Publ: Victorians on literature and art, Appleton, 60; Crowns of Apollo: Swinburne's theory of literature and art, 67, co-auth, The letters of John Addington Symonds, Vol. I, 67, Vol. II & III, 68 & auth, The Sow's head and other poems, 68, Wayne State Univ; Songs for a son: poems, Norton, 67; Byron exhumed (poems), Windless Orchard Press, 73; Connections: in the English Lake District (poems), Anvil, London, 73. Add: 433 Locust St, Laguna Beach, CA 92664.

PETERSON, ANNAMARIE W, b. New York, N.Y. ENGLISH, AMERICAN LITERATURE. B.A, Univ. Calif, Los Angeles, 55, M.A, 57, Ph.D.(Eng), 65. Asst. ENG, Univ. Calif, Los Angeles, 57-60, assoc, 60-65, lectr, 65-67; asst. prof, CALIF. STATE UNIV, NORTHRIDGE, 67-72, ASSOC. PROF, 72- MLA; Am. Stud. Asn; Philol. Asn. Pac. Coast. Hawthorne criticism; Israel Zangwill; the short story. Publ: Israel Zangwill (1864-1926): a selected bibliography, Bull. Bibliog, 9-12/61. Add: Dept. of English, California State University, Northridge, CA 91324.

PETERSON, BRENT DAN, b. American Fork, Utah, Jan. 29, 42; m. 66; c. 3. SPEECH & ORGANIZATIONAL COMMUNICATION. B.A, Brigham Young Univ, 67, M.A, 68; NDEA fel. & Ph.D.(orgn. commun), Ohio Univ, 70. Dir, Ctr. Commun. Res, Univ. Puget Sound, 70-71; assoc. dir, Ctr. Commun. Res. & Stud, Univ. Mont, 71-72; GRAD. COORD. SPEECH COMMUN, BRIGHAM YOUNG UNIV, 72- Exec. secy. & consult, Orgn. Assocs, 71- Int. Commun. Asn.(mem. comt. orgn. commun, 71-73); Speech Commun. Asn; West. Speech Commun. Asn.(chmn. orgn. & interpersonal commun, 71-73); Am. Bus. Commun. Asn. Auditing communicative effectiveness in large organizations; researching persuasive effects; values and their importance in cross cultural research. Publ: Co-ed, Communicating interpersonally: a reader, C.E, Merrill, 73, Communication probes, Sci. Res. Assocs, 74 & A scientific approach to speech communication, Wadsworth, 75; auth, Manager-subordinate perception of opinion leaders, J. Bus. Educ, fall,72. Add: F-526 Harris Fine Arts Center, Brigham Young University, Provo, UT 84602.

PETERSON, CARL ADRIAN, b. Warren, Pa, Dec. 21, 30; m. 56; c. 2. ENGLISH. B.A, Pa. State Univ, 52, M.A, 53; Ph.D, Univ. Wis, 61. Teaching asst, Univ. Wis, 53-57; instr. ENG, OBERLIN COL, 58-61, asst. prof, 61-68, ASSOC. PROF, 68- MLA. English novel and Victorian poetry; modern Greek literature; 19th century art and architecture. Add: Dept. of English, Oberlin College, Oberlin, OH 44074.

PETERSON, CARROLL V, b. North Branch, Minn, Dec. 30, 29; m. 54; c. 4. ENGLISH. B.S, Univ. Minn, 58; Woodrow Wilson fel. & M.A, Univ. Iowa, 59, Ph.D.(Eng), 63. Asst. ENG, Univ. Iowa, 62-63; asst. prof, Ill. State Univ, 63-65, assoc. prof, 65-68; FT. LEWIS COL, 68-70, PROF, 70- U.S.A, 51-54, Sgt. Writings of John Davidson; Byron's Don Juan. Publ: John Davidson, Twayne, 73. Add: Dept. of English, Ft. Lewis College, Durango, CO 81301.

PETERSON, CLELL T, b. Bemidji, Minn, Sept. 9, 18; m. 48; c. 1. ENGLISH. B.A, Univ. Minn, 49, M.A, 51, Ph.D, 62. Instr. ENG, Univ. Minn, 51-56; asst. prof, MURRAY STATE UNIV, 56-60, assoc. prof, 60-62, PROF, 62-, DIR. GRAD. STUD, 69- U.S.A, 42-45, Sgt. NCTE; S.Atlantic Mod. Lang. Asn; Wilson Ornith. Soc. English novel; romantic movement; natural history. Publ: Co-auth, Kentucky birds: a finding guide, Univ. Ky, 73; auth, The Jack London legend, 1/58, Jack London's Sonoma novels, 10/58 & Jack London's Alaskan stories, 4/59, Am. Bk. Collector. Add: Dept. of English, Murray State University, Murray, KY 42071.

PETERSON, DOUGLAS L, b. San Jose, Calif, Apr. 12, 24; m. 50; c. 3. ENGLISH LITERATURE. A.B, Stanford Univ, 49, M.A, 50, Ph.D.(Eng), 56. Instr. ENG, Univ. Tex, 55-56, asst. prof, 56-60; PROF, CALIF. STATE UNIV, HAYWARD, 60-, CHMN. DEPT, 71- Fulbright prof, Univ. Helsinki, 64-65; Huntington Libr. grant, 68, fel, 75; Am. Counc. Learned Soc. grant, 74-75. Calif. State Col. Hayward distinguished prof. award, 66. U.S.A.A.F, 43-46, S/Sgt. MLA; Renaissance Soc. Am. Lyric poetry of the English Renaissance; Medieval and Renaissance rhetoric; Shakespeare. Publ: The English lyric from Wyatt to Donne, Princeton, 67; Time, tide, and tempest, Huntington Libr, 73; The owl and the nightingale and Christian dialectic, J. Eng. & Ger. Philol, winter 56; Wisdom consum'd in confidence: an interpretation of Shakespeare's Julius Caesar, Shakespeare Quart, winter 65; Romeo and Juliet and the art of moral navigation, Pac. Coast Stud. Shakespeare, 66. Add: Dept. of English, California State University, Hayward, CA 94542.

PETERSON, ERLING WINSTON, b. Ray, N.Dak, Jan. 22, 21; m. 45; c. 4. ENGLISH EDUCATION. B.A, N.Cent. Col, 43; B.D, Evangel. Theol. Sem, 46; M.A, Univ. Wis-Madison, 50; Garrett Theol. Sem, 53; fel, North. Ill. Univ, 67-68, Ed.D, 69. Pastor, Wis. Counc. Churches, 46-51; Evangel. United Brethren, Kenosha, Wis, 51-56; United Church Christ, Windsor, 56-60; assoc. prof. ENG, N.Cent. Col, 60-70; PROF. & CHMN. DEPT, IND. CENT. COL, 70- Instnl. rep, Ill. Stud. Ctr. Prep. Eng. Teachers, 65-69. MLA; NCTE; Conf. Eng. Educ. Shakespeare. Publ: Effect upon teacher effectiveness of literature component of curriculum, U.S. Dept. of Health, Educ. & Welfare, 69; Current Christian education methods, Evangel. Theol. Sem, 69. Add: Dept. of English, Indiana Central College, 1400 E. Hannah Ave, Indianapolis, IN 46227.

PETERSON, GARY LEONARD, b. Ogden, Utah, May 20, 35; m. 58; c. 5. SPEECH & PUBLIC ADDRESS. B.S, Univ. Utah, 60; NDEA fel, Ohio Univ, 60-63, M.A, 61, Ph.D.(pub. address), 65. Instr. SPEECH, Univ. Wash, 63-66; asst. prof, Brigham Young Univ, 66-69; ASSOC. PROF, UNIV. PUGET SOUND, 69- U.S.A.R, 57-63. Speech Commun. Asn; West. Speech Commun. Asn. American public address, especially the Lincoln-Douglas debates and Mormon rhetoric; speech education. Publ: Whence cometh debate ethics, TKA Speaker, 5/62. Add: Dept. of Communication & Theatre Arts, University of Puget Sound, Tacoma, WA 98416.

PETERSON, JOYCE ELAINE, b. Baltimore, Md, Oct. 10, 34. ENGLISH LITERATURE. B.A, Univ. Calif, Irvine, 67, M.A, 68, NDEA fel, 69-70, Ph.D. (Eng), 73. Instr. ENG, Golden West Col, 70-71; assoc, Univ. Calif, Irvine, 71-72; ASST. PROF, UNIV. CALIF, LOS ANGELES, 72- MLA. Early English drama; Chaucer; teaching of English. Publ: The finished fragment: a reassessment of The squire's tale, Chaucer Rev, summer 70. Add: Dept. of English, University of California, Los Angeles, CA 90024.

PETERSON, LELAND D, b. Stanchfield, Minn, July 19, 26; m. 51; c. 4. ENGLISH. B.A, Univ. Minn, 54, M.A, 56, Ph.D, 62. Asst, Univ. Minn, 55-58; asst. prof. ENG, Southeast Mo. State Col, 58-61; OLD DOM. UNIV, 61-64, assoc. prof, 64-67, PROF, 67-, DIR. GRAD. STUD, 70- U.S.A.A.F, 45-46. MLA (mem. del. assembly, 71-). English literature of the 18th century; bibliography; Roman Augustan literature. Publ: Co-auth, Swift's Project: tract or travesty, 3/69 & On Peterson on Swift, 10/71, PMLA; auth, A variant of the 1742-1746 Swift-Pope Miscellanies, Bibliog. Soc. Am. Papers, 9/72; plus others. Add: Dept. of English, Old Dominion University, Norfolk, VA 23508.

PETERSON, LEVI S, b. Snowflake, Ariz, Dec. 13, 33; m. 58; c. 1. ENGLISH. B.A, Brigham Young Univ, 58, M.A, 60; univ. fel, Univ. Calif, Berkeley, 60-61; Ph.D.(Eng), Univ. Utah, 65. Asst. prof. ENG, WEBER STATE COL, 65-68, assoc. prof, 68-72, PROF, 72-, DIR. HONORS PROG, 73-, chmn. dept, 70-73. Rocky Mountain Mod. Lang. Asn; West. Lit. Asn. American frontier literature, especially Western fiction. Publ: Utah livestock law, 1848-1896, Utah Hist. Quart, summer 64; The primitive and civilized in Western literature, & Tragedy and western American literature, winter 72, West. Am. Lit. Add: Dept. of English, Weber State College, 3750 Harrison Blvd, Ogden, UT 84403.

PETERSON, OWEN M, b. Parker, S.Dak, Feb. 17, 24. SPEECH. B.A, Univ. Iowa, 46, M.A, 48, Ph.D.(speech), 52. Instr. SPEECH, DePauw Univ, 52-54; PROF, LA. STATE UNIV, BATON ROUGE, 54- Ed, South. Speech J, 61-66. Speech Commun. Asn.(exec. secy, 57-60, mem. admin. counc, 57-63); South.

Speech Commun. Asn.(mem. exec. counc, 61-). American and British public address. Publ: The role of public speaking in the early years of the British labor party, Quart. J. Speech, 10/62; Forum debating, Speech Teacher, 12/65; Yancey's speech education, South. Speech J, winter 67. Add: Dept. of Speech, Louisiana State University, Baton Rouge, LA 70803.

PETERSON, RICHARD GUSTAF, b. Chicago, Ill, Jan. 9, 36. ENGLISH. B.A, Univ. Minn, 56, Ph.D.(Eng. & Latin), 63; Woodrow Wilson fel, Northwest. Univ, 57-58, M.A, 58. Instr. Eng, Univ. Minn, 60-62; asst. prof. ENG. & LATIN, ST. OLAF COL, 63-68, ASSOC. PROF, 68- Am. Philos. Soc. grant, 69-70. Am. Soc. 18th Century Stud; Johnson Soc. Cent. Region; MLA; Class. Asn. Mid.W. & S. Poetry of the Restoration and early 18th century; Latin literature, especially poetry and history; poetry of T.S. Eliot. Publ: Larger manners and events: Sallust and Virgil in Absalom and Achitophel, PMLA, 5/67; The unity of Horace Epistle 1.7, Class. J, 4/68; The unavailing gift: Dryden's Roman farewell to Mr. Oldham, Mod. Philol, 2/69; plus others. Add: Dept. of English, St. Olaf College, Northfield, MN 55057.

PETERSON, RICHARD SCOT, b. Ayr, Scotland, July 14, 38; U.S. citizen; m. 65. ENGLISH LITERATURE & MUSIC. A.B, Princeton, 60; Fulbright scholar, Oxford, 60-61; M.A, Univ. Calif, Berkeley, 63, Ph.D.(Eng), 69. Instr. ENG, Princeton, 66-69, asst. prof, 69-72; LECTR, UNIV. VA, 72- Vis. prof, Lincoln Univ, 67-68. MLA; Northeast Mod. Lang. Asn; Renaissance Soc. Am. Renaissance literature; Ben Jonson; Renaissance music and art. Publ: Virtue reconciled to pleasure: Jonson's A celebration of Charis, Stud. Lit. Imagination, 4/73. Add: Dept. of English, 115 Wilson Hall, University of Virginia, Charlottesville, VA 22901.

PETERSON, SPIRO, b. New Haven, Conn, Dec. 25, 22; m. 51; c. 3. ENGLISH. A.B, Trinity Col(Conn), 47; Russell fel. from Trinity Col.(Conn), Harvard, 46-52, M.A, 47, Ph.D.(Eng), 53. Instr. ancient Greek, Trinity Col.(Conn), 42-43; teaching fel. ENG, Harvard, 49-52; instr. MIAMI UNIV, 52-54, asst. prof, 54-58, assoc. prof, 58-62, PROF, 62-, DEAN GRAD. SCH. & RES, 72-, chmn. dept. Eng, 64-72. Am. Counc. Learned Soc. grant-in-aid, Scotland, 60. U.S.A, 43-46. MLA; Am. Soc. 18th Century Stud; Johnson Soc. Great Lakes Region. Daniel Defoe's verses and fiction; 17th century literature, especially satire; 18th century literature, especially the novel. Publ: Counterfeit lady unveiled and other criminal fiction of seventeenth century England, Anchor Bks, 61; ed. & introd, John Tutchin: selected poems, Augustan Reprint Soc, William Andrews Clark Mem. Libr, 64; auth, Matrimonial theme of Defoe's Roxana, PMLA, 3/55; Defoe's Yorkshire quarrel, Huntington Libr. Quart, 11/55. Add: 115 N. University Ave, Oxford, OH 45056.

PETERSON, THEODORE B, b. Albert Lea, Minn, June 8, 18; m. 46; c. 4. MASS COMMUNICATIONS. B.A, Univ. Minn, Minneapolis, 41; M.S, Kans. State Univ, 48; Ph.D.(commun), Univ. Ill, Urbana, 55. From instr. to asst. prof, JOUR, Kans. State Univ, 45-48; instr, UNIV. ILL, URBANA, 48-55, assoc. prof, 55-57, PROF. & DEAN COL. OF COMMUN, 57- Pres, Am. Asn. Schs. & Depts. Jour, 64; judge, Nat. Mag. Awards, 67- Am. Counc. Educ. Jour; Asn. Educ. Jour.(pres, 63). Magazine publishing; history of press. Publ: Magazines in the twentieth century, 57, 64 & co-auth, Four theories of the press, 56, Univ. Ill; The mass media and modern society, Holt, 65, 71; contrib, Serial publications in large libraries, Univ. Ill, 70; The future of general adult books and reading in America, Am. Libr. Asn, 70. Add: 103 E. George Huff, Urbana, IL 61801.

PETERSON, VIRGIL A, b. Audubon, Iowa, Jan. 1, 25; m. 51; c. 2. ENGLISH. B.A, DePauw Univ, 49; M.A, Univ. Iowa, 50; Ph.D.(Eng), Univ. Calif, Los Angeles, 59. Instr. ENG, Miami Univ, 59-61, asst. prof, 61-63; lectr, Univ. Calif, Los Angeles, 63-65; asst. prof, Miami Univ, 65-66; ASSOC. PROF, W.VA. UNIV, 66-, DIR. HON. PROG, 69-72. Consult, Agency Int. Develop, 60-63; consult, Rand Corp, 63-64, ed. computer sci. dept. 64-65; consult, Action Agency, 72-; assoc, Danforth Found, 72- U.S.N, 43-46, 51-53, Lt. MLA; Asn. Vol. Action Scholars. Victorian literature; voluntary associations; experiential learning. Publ: Romola: a Victorian quest for values, Philol. Papers, 11/67; Trends in student voluntary associations, In: Voluntary action research, Lexington Bks, 72; co-auth, Voluntary associations in ancient Greece, J. Vol. Action Res, 73; plus others. Add: Dept. of English, West Virginia University, Morgantown, WV 26506.

PETERSON, WILLIAM MOORE, b. Pittsfield, Mass, July 18, 26; m. 59; c. 2. ENGLISH, DRAMA. A.B, Brown Univ, 47, A.M, 48; Univ. N.C, 50-52; Fulbright scholar, Oxford, 52-54, B.Litt, 54; Ph.D.(drama), Bristol Univ, 71. Instr. ENG, Ill. Col, 48-49; asst. prof, Jacksonville Univ, 55-56; Lake Erie Col, 56-62; lectr, Univ. Ibadan, 62-63; ASSOC. PROF, Lake Erie Col, 63-65; SOUTHAMPTON COL, LONG ISLAND UNIV, 67- MLA; AAUP. Restoration and eighteenth century drama; nineteenth century drama. Publ: Co-ed, Three hours after marriage, 61 & ed, The rival queans, 65, Lake Erie Col; auth, Pope and Cibber's The non-juror, 5/55 & The text of Cibber's She wou'd, and she wou'd not, 4/56, Mod. Lang. Notes; Cibber's She wou'd, and she wou'd not and Vanbrugh's Aesop, Philol. Quart, 10/56. Auth, libretto, The enchanted garden (children's opera), performed 3 & 12/72 & Punchinello, winter 74, Parrish Art Mus, Southampton, N.Y. Add: Div. of Humanities, Southampton College, Long Island University, Southampton, NY 11968.

PETERSON, WILLIAM SAMUEL, b. Black River Falls, Wis, June 14, 39; m. 61; c. 1. ENGLISH. B.A, Walla Walla Col, 61; M.A, Univ. Wis-Madison, 62; Ph.D.(Eng), Northwest. Univ, 68. Instr. ENG, Andrews Univ, 62-67, asst. prof, 67-70, ASSOC. PROF, 70-71; UNIV. MD, COLLEGE PARK, 71- Grants-in-aid, Am. Counc. Learned Soc, 69, Newberry Libr, 70 & Huntington Libr, 73; mem. bd. dirs. & chmn. publ. comt, Browning Inst, 72, ed, Browning Inst. Stud, 73- MLA; Res. Soc. Victorian Periodicals; Browning Inst. Victorian literature, especially Robert Browning and Elizabeth Barrett Browning. Publ: Interrogating the oracle: a history of the London Browning Society, Ohio Univ, 69; Gladstone's review of Robert Elsmere: some unpublished correspondence, Rev. Eng. Stud, 11/70; Henry James on Jane Eyre, Times Lit. Suppl, 7/30/71; co-auth, The J.S. Mill Marginalia in Robert Browning's Pauline: a history and transcription, Papers Bibliog. Soc. Am, 72; plus others. Add: Dept. of English, University of Maryland, College Park, MD 20742.

PETERSSON, ROBERT TORSTEN, b. Berkeley, Calif, June 14, 18; m. 46; c. 4. ENGLISH. A.B, Univ. Calif, 42; Ph.D, Princeton, 46. Instr. humanities, Univ. Chicago, 45-47; ENG, Yale, 47-52; asst. prof, SMITH COL, 52-57, assoc. prof, 57-64, PROF, 64-, chmn. dept, 63-66. Morse res. fel, Yale, 51-52; Guggenheim fel, 58-59. Nat. Cath. Bk. Award, 71. MLA; Milton Soc. Am; Renaissance Soc. Am. Seventeenth century art and literature. Publ: Sir Kenelm Digby, Harvard Univ, 56; ed, William Shakespeare, Richard II, Yale Univ, 57; auth, The art of ecstasy: Teresa, Bernini, and Crashaw, Routledge, 69, Atheneum, 70 & 74. Add: 63 Dryads Green, Northampton, MA 01060.

PETIT, HERBERT HANLEY, b. Lexington, Ky, Aug. 16, 11. ENGLISH PHILOLOGY. A.B, Transylvania Col, 32; A.M, Univ. Ky, 34; St. Louis Univ, 35-37; Ph.D, West. Reserve Univ, 52. Instr, Transylvania Col, 33-35; asst. to librn, St. Louis Univ, 35-37; secy, Eng. Teachers Inst. & instr. Eng, John Carroll Univ, 37-43, asst. prof, 43-47, registr, 43-46; asst. prof. Eng, Univ. Detroit, 47-52, assoc. prof, 52-57, prof, 57-58, acting asst. to dean arts & sci, 50-51; PROF. ENG. PHILOL, DUQUESNE UNIV, 58- provost, 68-70. Ed, Annuale Mediaevale. Ling. Soc. Am; MLA; Am. Dialect Soc; AAAS; Mod. Humanities Res. Asn, Gt. Brit; Renaissance Soc. Am; Milton Soc. Am. American dialects; historical syntax; current usage. Add: Dept. of English, Duquesne University, Pittsburgh, PA 15219.

PETITPAS, HAROLD M, b. St. John, N.B, Feb. 16, 24. ENGLISH, EDUCATION. B.A, Univ. West. Ont, 49; M.Ed, Univ. Montreal, 53; M.A, Univ. Ottawa, 54, Ph.D.(Eng), 58. Asst. prof. ENG, Marian Col.(Ind), 55-60; Dayton Univ, 60-65; SETON HALL UNIV, 65-66, ASSOC. PROF, 66- MLA. Philosophy of literature and criticism; interdisciplinary relationships; 19th century English literature. Publ: Newman's idea of literature, Renascence, winter 64; Newman's idea of science, Personalist, 7/67; Newman's universe of knowledge, Dalhousie Rev, winter 67. Add: Dept. of English, Seton Hall University, South Orange, NJ 07079.

PETRONELLA, VINCENT F, b. New York, N.Y, Jan. 10, 35; m. 65. ENGLISH. B.A, City Col. New York, 62; M.A, Univ. Ore, 64; Ph.D.(Eng), Univ. Mass, Amherst, 69. Vis. lectr. ENG, Univ. Mass, 64-66; asst. prof, BOSTON STATE COL, 66-69, assoc. prof, 69-74, PROF, 74- U.S.A, 57-59. MLA; NCTE; Shakespeare Asn. Am; Renaissance Soc. Am. Shakespeare and the English Renaissance; Italian Renaissance literature. Publ: Shakespeare's Henry V and the second tetralogy: meditation as drama, In: Costerus Essays IV, Holland, 72; Structure and theme through separation and union in Shakespeare's Comedy of errors, Mod. Lang. Rev, 7/74; Shakespeare's Phoenix and the turtle, and the defunctive music of ecstasy, In: Shakespeare studies, Univ. S.C, Vol. VIII, 74; plus others. Add: Dept. of English, Boston State College, 174 Ipswich St, Boston, MA 02215.

PETTEGROVE, JAMES PARKER, b. Machiasport, Maine, Jan. 14, 09; m. 34; c. 2. ENGLISH. B.A, Bowdoin Col, 30; M.A, Harvard, 31; Rhodes scholar, Oxford, 31-34, B.A, 33; Columbia Univ, 39-44. Instr. Eng. & philos, Bennington Col, 34-35; teaching fel, Bowdoin Col, 35-37; instr. ENG, MONTCLAIR STATE COL, 37-50, asst. prof, 50-63, PROF, 63- Ed. work, div. psychol. warfare, London, Supreme Hq. Allied Expeditionary Force, 44-45, head, U.S. Inform. Ctr, Linz & Vienna, Austria, 45-48; guest lectr. Am. poetry, Univ. Vienna, 46, & Fulbright lectr, sch. of theater, 63-64. MLA; Col. Eng. Asn.(regional. v.pres, 68-69). German influences on S.T. Coleridge; eighteenth century, especially Shaftesbury; American drama on the German stage, especially O'Neill. Publ: Co-transl, Ernst Cassirer, The philosophy of the enlightenment, Princeton Univ, 51, Beacon, 55 & 62; transl, Ernst Cassirer, Platonic Renaissance in England, Univ. Tex, 53; auth, Eugene O'Neill as thinker, 64 & Einiges über O'Neill-Ubersetzungen ins Deutsche, 71, Maske u. Kothurn. Add: Dept. of English, Montclair State College, Upper Montclair, NJ 07043.

PETTI, ANTHONY GAETANO, b. London, Eng, Feb. 12, 32; m. 57; c. 4. ENGLISH. B.A, Univ. London, 55, M.A, 57, D.Lit, 70. Asst. ENG, Univ. Col, Univ. London, 55-57, quain stud, 57-59, lectr, 60-69; PROF, UNIV. CALGARY, 69-, HEAD DEPT, 71- Dir, Univ. London Cath. Choir & Orchestra, 53-69; Harkness Commonwealth Fund fel, 59-60; dir. Calgary Renaissance Singers, 70-; Huntington Libr. fel, 70; mem. ed. bd, Ariel, 72-; grants from Univ. London, Univ. Calgary and Can. Counc. Brit. Army, 50-52, Res, 52-55. MLA; Cath. Rec. Soc. Eng; Asn. Can. Univ. Teachers Eng; Sacred Music & Drama Soc. Gt. Brit; Hopkins Soc. Renaissance literature, history and music. Publ: Ed, Letters of Richard Verstegan, 59 & Ellesmere manuscripts, 69, Cath. Rec. Soc, Eng; Anerio Missa pro defunctis, Chester, London, 66; co-ed, Glapthorne's Lady mother, Malone Soc, 67; New Catholic hymnal, Faber Music, 71 & St. Martin's, N.Y, 72; auth, Political satire in Pierce Penilesse, Nephilologus, 61; Beasts and politics in Elizabethan literature, Essays & Stud, 63; Unknown sonnets by Toby Mathew, Recusant Hist, 67. Add: Dept. of English, University of Calgary, Calgary, Alta. T2N 1N4, Can.

PETTIGREW, BESSIE JOYE, b. Columbia, S.C, Jan. 30, 35. BLACK LITERATURE & LANGUAGE. A.B, Converse Col, 57; M.A, Fla. State Univ, 64, Ph.D.(Eng. educ), 71. Teacher Eng. & jour, Dreher High Sch, S.C, 57-62; ENG. & ENG. EDUC, WINTHROP COL, 64-67, asst. prof, 68-72, ASSOC. PROF, 72- Proj. dir. teaching Eng. to slow learners, S.C. Comn. Higher Educ, 70-71; consult, Sec. Eng. Proj, U.S. Off. Educ, 71-73 & Ctr. Integrated stud, Univ. S.C, 71-72. S.Atlantic Mod. Lang. Asn; NCTE (Conf. Eng. Educ); Conf. Col. Compos. & Commun; AAUP. Black literature; teaching of English; linguistics. Publ: Contrib, The archetype of initiation in selected novels of Black adolescence, Wis. Eng. J, 3/72 & Eric, 72. Add: Dept. of English, Winthrop College, Kinard Bldg, Rock Hill, SC 29730.

PETTIT, HENRY (JEWETT, JR), b. Olean, N.Y, Dec. 8, 06; m. 27; c. 1. ENGLISH LITERATURE. A.B, Cornell Univ, 32, Ph.D, 38; A.M, Univ. Ore, 34. Teaching fel, Univ. Ore, 32-34; instr. Eng, Univ. Tulsa, 34-36; Cornell Univ, 36-38; Yale, 38-39; asst. prof, Beloit Col, 39-40; assoc. prof, UNIV. COLO, BOULDER, 40-48, prof, 48-72, hon. keeper rare books, Norlin Libr, 50-62, EMER. PROF. ENG, 72- Ed, Annual Bibliog. Eng. Lang. & Lit, 42-52; summer vis. prof. Eng, Univ. Vt, 58; mem, Nat. Adv. Counc, Ninth Triennial Congr. Int. Fed. Mod. Lang. & Lit, 58-63; Univ. Colo. fac. fels, 48, 54, 60, 66, 71-72; grants, Am. Philos. Soc, 60 & 66, Am. Counc. Learned Soc, 63; mem. ed. bds, West. Humanities Rev, Colo. Quart. & Eng. Lang.

Notes. U.S.N.R, 43-46, Lt. Comdr. Mod. Humanities Res. Asn, Gt. Brit. (Am. secy, 58-63, exec. comt, 64-72, adv. counc, 72-) MLA; Rocky Mt. Mod. Lang. Asn. (exec. secy. & ed. Bull, 66-69); AAAS. Bibliography; literary criticism; 18th century English literature. Publ: A bibliography of Young's Night-thoughts, Univ. Colo, 54; A collection of English prose, 1660-1800, Harper, 62; co-auth, The authentic Mother Goose, Swallow, 60; ed, The correspondence of Edward Young, 1683-1765, Oxford Univ, 72. Add: 907 Seventh St, Boulder, CO 80302.

PETTIT, NORMAN, b. Cambridge, Mass, Dec. 14, 29; m. 55; c. 3. ENGLISH, HISTORY. A.B, Harvard, 54; B.A, Oxford, 56, M.A, 59; Ph.D.(Am. stud), Yale, 63. Instr. ENG, Mass. Inst. Technol, 62-64, asst. prof, 64-67; ASSOC. PROF, BOSTON UNIV, 68- Egleston hist. prize, Yale, 62. MLA. Puritan studies. Publ: The heart prepared: grace and conversion in Puritan spiritual life, Yale Univ, 66; Lydia's conversion: an issue in Hooker's departure, Cambridge Hist. Soc. Proc, 64-66. Add: Dept. of English, Boston University, Boston, MA 02215.

PETTY, GEORGE RAYMOND, JR, b. Jersey City, N.J, Nov. 8, 28; m. 50; c. 5. OLD & MIDDLE ENGLISH. A.B, Princeton, 49; M.A, N.Y. Univ, 63, Ph.D.(Eng), 67. Pres, Flight Engrs. Int. Asn, Am. Fed. Labor-Congr. Indust. Orgn, 57-60; flight engr, Pan Am. World Airways, 60-63; asst. prof. Eng, Montclair State Col, 63-67, asst. to pres, 65-67; asst. prof. ENG, State Univ. N.Y. Stony Brook, 67-70; PROF. MONTCLAIR STATE COL, 70-, DIR. FRESHMAN ENG, 71- Am. Counc. Learned Soc. grant, 64-65; consult, fed. prospective teacher fel. prog, U.S. Off. Educ, 66-67; dir. proj. write, Instructional Resources Ctr, State Univ. N.Y. Stony Brook, 67-68; Nat. Endowment for Humanities & State Univ. N.Y. grants, 68; Nat. Endowment for Humanities younger humanist fel, summer 73. MLA; Mediaeval Acad. Am. Applied English linguistics; computer technology in the humanities and English studies. Publ: Co-auth, Project occult, N.Y. Univ, 71; TLE 6: options for the 70's, Holt, 72; Project occult: the ordered computer collation of unprepared literary text, In: Essays on editing modern literary texts, Ind. Univ, 69. Add: Dept. of English, Montclair State College, Upper Montclair, NJ 07043.

PEYTON, HENRY HALL, III, b. Mansfield, La, Feb. 6, 27; m. 56; c. 3. OLD & MIDDLE ENGLISH. B.A, Baylor Univ, 50, M.A, 53; Marston fel, Brown Univ, 62-63, Ph.D.(Eng), 68. Instr. Eng. & Latin, Valley Forge Mil. Acad, 54-59; ENG, Southeast. Mass. Univ, 64-67; ASSOC. PROF, MEMPHIS STATE UNIV, 67- MLA; Mediaeval Acad. Am; Eng. Inst. Middle English literature; Chaucer; Arthurian studies. Publ: An edition of ten poems from the Gawain cycle, Univ. Microfilms, 68. Add: Dept. of English, Memphis State University, Memphis, TN 38152.

PFAFF, DANIEL WAYNE, b. Nampa, Idaho, May 19, 40; m. 66; c. 2. JOURNALISM, MASS COMMUNICATIONS. B.S, Univ. Ore, 63; M.A, Pa. State Univ, University Park, 68; Ph.D.(mass commun), Univ. Minn, Minneapolis, 72. ASST. PROF. JOUR, PA. STATE UNIV, UNIVERSITY PARK, 71- Sig.C, U.S.A, 62-64, 1st Lt. Asn. Educ. Jour. Mass communication law; mass communication history. Publ: Race, libel and the Supreme Court, Columbia Jour. Rev, summer 69; The symbolic speech cases: an analysis, Jour. Quart, autumn 72. Add: Sch. of Journalism, Pennsylvania State University, 215 Carnegie Bldg, University Park, PA 16802.

PFEFFER, ARTHUR SAUL, b. Troy, N.Y, Feb. 18, 38; m. 58; c. 1. ENGLISH. B.A, Cornell Univ, 58; Gilman scholar. & jr. instructorship, Johns Hopkins Univ, 60-61, M.A, 61; NDEA fel, City Univ. New York, 65-67, Ph.D. (Eng), 67. Instr. Eng, Gannon Col, 61-63; asst. prof, Monroe Community Col, 63-64; Long Island Univ, 67-68; JOHN JAY COL. CRIMINAL JUSTICE, 68-72, ASSOC. PROF. ENG. & DIR. THEMATIC STUD. PROG, 72- MLA; Am. Stud. Asn. American literature of the 19th century and before, especially transcendentalism; Old English literature; multi-disciplinary curricula. Publ: Ed, Proceedings of the John Jay College faculty seminars, Vol. I, 70 & Vol. II, 71; The seafarer: form and theme, In: Studies in literature, City Univ. New York, 66; Wordsworth on imagination, PMLA, 1/69. Add: Dept. of English, John Jay College of Criminal Justice, 444 W. 56th St, New York, NY 10019.

PFEIFFER, JOHN RICHARD, b. Detroit, Mich, June 11, 38; m. 61; c. 7. BRITISH & AMERICAN LITERATURE. A.B, Univ. Detroit, 61, M.A, 63; Ph.D.(Eng), Univ. Ky, 69. Instr. ENG, U.S. Air Force Acad, 67-69, asst. prof, 69-71; CENT. MICH. UNIV, 71-73, ASSOC. PROF, 73- U.S.A.F, 67-71, Capt. MLA. Bibliography; 19th century British literature; popular modern literature. Publ: Fantasy and science fiction: a critical guide, Filter Press, 71; A continuing checklist of Shaviana, 71- & ed, Shaw and science fiction, 5/73, Shaw Rev; English 495, fantasy and science fiction at U.S. Air Force Acad, Extrapolation, 72; plus others. Add: Dept. of English, Central Michigan University, Mt. Pleasant, MI 48859.

PFISTER, EMIL R, b. Chicago, Ill, Jan. 3, 13; m. 40; c. 4. SPEECH. A.B, Cent. Mich. Col, 35; M.A, Univ. Mich, 39, fel, 40-43; Ed.D, Mich. State Univ, 55. Prin, high sch, Kingston, Mich, 35-40, Clare, 40-45; assoc. prof. SPEECH, Cent. Mich. Univ, 45-57, prof, 57-74, head dept, 59-68; PROF. & CHMN. DEPT, AMBASSADOR COL, 74- Vis. prof, Int. Christian Univ, Tokyo, 64-65; lectr, Austrian-Am. Inst, Bad Aussee, Austria, summer 67. Am. Inst. Parliamentarians; Speech Commun. Asn; NEA; Am. Acad. Arts & Sci; Nat. Soc. Stud. Commun. Speech rating scales; forensics; American speech for foreign students. Publ: Discussion guide book, 57 & co-auth, Fundamentals of forensics, 59, Cent. Mich. Univ; co-auth, Argumentation and debate, Dryden, 54 & Membership manual: encyclopedia of parliamentary law, Vantage, 70. Add: 105 San Miguel, Pasadena, CA 91105.

PFLAUM, MELANIE L, b. St. Louis, Mo, Apr. 12, 09; m. 30; c. 3. ENGLISH, CREATIVE WRITING. Ph.B, Univ. Chicago, 29; cert, Univ. Paris, 30; cert, Univ. Col, Univ. London, 30. Instr. creative writing, Northwest. Univ, 57-59; vis. lectr. Eng. lit, Inter-Am. Univ. P.R, 59-62, assoc. prof, 62-74; RES. & WRITING, 74- Vis. lectr, Silliman Univ, Philippines, 67-68; vis. prof, Mauna Olu Col, Hawaii, 68; vis. lectr, Univ. Canterbury, 70 & Covell Col, Univ. Pac, 73. Soc. Midland Auth; Soc. Women Geogr; AAUP. Publ: Bolero, Heinemann, 57; Windfall, 61 & The insiders, 63, Cassell; co-ed, Fourteen months with Fidel Castro, World, 67; Les bonnes familles, Bardon larks a desparee, un doux tyran (novel), Fleuve Noir, Paris, 70, 71 & 72; Ready by Wednesday, 70 & The gentle tyrants, Carlton; The second conquest, Univers Press, N.Z, 71; The Maine remembered, N.Z, 72 & Lili, 74, Pegasus; Costa Brava, Ed. San Juan, 72; Hemingway in Madrid, 72 & Teruel revisited, 73, Interam. Rev. Add: Chalet Windfall, El Tosalet, 323, Javea (Alicante), Spain.

PFLAUMER, ELIZABETH MAE, b. Cincinnati, Ohio, Feb. 23, 42. SPEECH COMMUNICATION, SPEECH & THEATRE EDUCATION. B.A, Asbury Col, 64; M.A, Ohio State Univ, 68, Ph.D.(speech commun. theory & res, psychol, speech educ), 70. Teacher speech & drama & dir. debate, Wayne Local High Sch, Waynesville, Ohio, 64-65; Lebanon High Sch, 65-67; teaching assoc. SPEECH COMMUN, Ohio State Univ, 67-69; ASST. PROF, NORTH. ILL. UNIV, 69- Consult, Toastmistress Am. Asn, Ohio Region, 68-69; Joliet Sch. Syst, Ill, 69-70; Environ. Designs Commun. Inst, North. Ill. Region, 70-72; Off. Supt. Pub. Instruct, Springfield, 71-72. Speech Commun. Asn; Cent. States Speech Commun. Asn; Int. Commun. Asn. Personality in listening and receptive communication in creativity; social and behavioral psychology of groups; instructional research and development in communication. Publ: A definition of listening, In: Vol. 2, Listening readings, Scarecrow, 71; Listening: a definition and application, Clearinghouse Reading & Commun. Skills, 10/72; Listening, In: Handbook on contemporary education, Bowker, 73. Add: 711 S. Main St, Apt. 205B, Sycamore, IL 60178.

PFLUG, RAYMOND J, b. Cincinnati, Ohio, Jan. 24, 19; m. 39; c. 3. AMERICAN LITERATURE. B.A, Stanford Univ, 47, M.A, 49; Univ. Calif, Berkeley, 49-51. Instr. Eng, Univ. Nev, 49-51; assoc. prof, Air Force Reserve Off. Training Corps, Univ. Ore, 51-52; INSTR. ENG, COL. SAN MATEO, 56-, CHMN. LEARNING CTR, 71- Fulbright vis. prof, Damascus Univ, Syria, 61-62; Bir-Zeit Col, Bir-Zeit, Jordan, 64-65. U.S.A.F, 42-46, 51-53, Capt. Am. Stud. Asn; NCTE; Conf. Col. Compos. & Commun; Nat. Asn. For. Stud. Affairs; Am. Asn. Teachers Eng. As Second Lang. American studies and English for foreign students; freshman composition. Publ: A basic course in modern English, Prentice-Hall, 63; The adventures of Huckleberry Finn: the evolution of a classic, Ginn, 65; The ways of language, Odyssey, 67. Add: Dept. of English, College of San Mateo, W. Hillsdale Blvd, San Mateo, CA 94402.

PFORDRESHER, JOHN CHARLES, b. Chicago, Ill, Oct. 15, 43; m. 68; c. 2. ENGLISH LITERATURE. B.A, Georgetown Univ, 65; Ph.D.(Eng), Univ. Minn, 70. Teaching asst. ENG, Univ. Minn, 69-70; ASST. PROF, Univ. N.H, 70-73; GEORGETOWN UNIV, 73- MLA; NCTE; New Eng. Mod. Lang. Asn; Tennyson Soc; Res. Soc. Victorian Periodicals. Tennyson; Arnold; Victorian novel. Publ: Ed, A variorum edition of Tennyson's Idylls of the king, Columbia Univ, 73; co-ed, Exploring life through literature, 73 & Science fiction/fact, 74, Scott; auth, A bibliographic history of Alfred Tennyson's Idylls of the king, Stud. Bibliog, 73. Add: Dept. of English, Georgetown University, Washington, DC 20007.

PHELPS, BERNARD FRED, b. Augusta, Ill, Sept. 8, 21; m. 44; c. 2. SPEECH. B.S. in Ed, Ind. State Univ, 46; M.A, Miami Univ, 48; Ph.D, Ohio State Univ, 57. Asst. SPEECH, Miami Univ, 46-47, instr, 47-52, asst. prof, 52-59; asst, Ohio State Univ, 53-54; assoc. prof, MIAMI UNIV, 54-64, PROF, 64-, DIR. HAMILTON CAMPUS. Public speaking consult, speakers bur, Armco Steel Corp, 59, exec. pub. speaking sem, 62. U.S.M.C.R, 42-45, Capt. Cent. State Speech Asn.(consult. ed, 60-64); Speech Commun. Asn. American historical and contemporary public address; speech education. Publ: Say it right with parliamentary procedure (rec. & script), Scott Publ: Dayton, 66. Add: Miami University, Hamilton Campus, 1601 Peck Blvd, Hamilton, OH 45011.

PHELPS, C. FRED, b. Lindsay, Okla, May 4, 25; m. 49; c. 2. RHETORIC & PUBLIC ADDRESS. B.A, Oklahoma City Univ, 50; M.A, Colo. State Col, 55; Ph.D.(rhetoric & pub. address), Univ. Mo, 66. Teacher high sch, Okla, 50-55; asst. prof. speech, St. Olaf Col, 55-57; assoc. prof, Kearney State Col, 58-65; PROF. PUB. ADDRESS, MORNINGSIDE COL, 65- Sig.C, U.S.A. Speech Commun. Asn; Cent. States Speech Commun. Asn. Public address and rhetoric; forensics; speech criticism. Add: Dept. of Speech & Drama, Morningside College, Sioux City, IA 51106.

PHELPS, WALDO WOODSON, b. San Francisco, Calif, June 15, 18. SPEECH EDUCATION. A.B, Santa Barbara State Col, 40; A.M, Univ. Denver, 41; Ph.D, Univ. South. Calif, 49. Lectr. SPEECH, Univ. South. Calif, 48; instr, UNIV. CALIF, LOS ANGELES, 49, 50, from asst. prof. to PROF. & CHMN. DEPT, 51- Speech Commun. Asn; West. Speech Commun. Asn. Speech education; importance of speech proficiency in public school teaching as related to the speech curricula of institutions offering teacher-training. Add: Dept. of Speech, 232 Royce Hall, University of California, Los Angeles, CA 90024.

PHELPS, WAYNE HOWE, b. Potsdam, N.Y, Sept. 2, 38. ENGLISH. B.A, St. Lawrence Univ, 59; Woodrow Wilson fel. & M.A, Princeton, 61, Ph.D.(Eng), 65. Instr. ENG, Univ. Pa, 62-65, ASST. PROF, 65-72, asst. stud. personnel off, col, 63-65, stud. personnel off, 65-66; VA. POLYTECH. INST. & STATE UNIV, 72- Manuscript Soc; MLA; Shakespeare Asn. Am; Malone Soc; Early Eng. Text Soc; Renaissance Eng. Text Soc; Renaissance Soc. Am. Shakespeare and Renaissance drama; English drama manuscripts to 1700. Add: Dept. of English, Virginia Polytechnic Institute & State University, Blacksburg, VA 24061.

PHIALAS, PETER GEORGE, b. Famagusta Cyprus, Feb. 22, 14; nat; m. 41; c. 2. ENGLISH LITERATURE. A.B, Mo. State Teachers Col, 38; A.M, Univ. Mo, 39; Ph.D, Yale, 48. Instr. ENG, Mo. State Teachers Col, Kirksville, 39-40; Univ. Mo, 40-43, 44-45; Yale, 47-51; from asst. prof. to assoc. prof, UNIV. N.C, CHAPEL HILL, 53-63, PROF, 63- MLA; Malone Soc; Renaissance Soc. Am; Mod. Humanities Res. Asn, Gt. Brit. Elizabethan drama. Publ: Shakespeare's romantic comedies, Univ. N.C, 66; Comic truth in Shakespeare and Jonson, S.Atlantic Quart, 63; Hamlet and the grave-maker, J. Eng. & Ger. Philol, 64; Shakespeare's Henry V and the second tetralogy, Stud. Philol, 65. Add: 1704 Curtis Rd, Chapel Hill, NC 27514.

PHIFER, (LYNDON) GREGG, b. Cincinnati, Ohio, May 17, 18; m. 56. SPEECH. A.B, Col. Pac, 40; A.M, State Univ. Iowa, 41, Ph.D, 49. Asst. prof. speech & Eng, Baldwin-Wallace Col, 46-48; instr. SPEECH, State Univ. Iowa, 48-49; asst. prof, FLA. STATE UNIV, 49-53, assoc. prof, 53-61, PROF, 61- Ed, South. Speech J, 66-69. Speech Commun. Asn.(parliamentarian legis. counc, 67-73, chmn. publ. bd, 73); Int. Commun. Asn; Am. Inst. Parliamentarians (dir, 66-71); AAUP. American public address in the Civil War and Reconstruction period; discussion participation and leadership; modern parliamentary procedure. Publ: Co-auth, An introduction to graduate study in speech and theatre, Mich. State Univ, 61, Argumentation and debate, Holt, 63 & Salesmanship: communication, persuasion, perception, Allyn & Bacon, 66; auth, Andrew Johnson at Cleveland and St. Louis, 1866: a study in textual authenticity, Quart. J. Speech; The new breed and our old tradition, South. Speech Commun. J, fall 71; Edith Bolling Wilson—gatekeeper extraordinary, Speech Monogr, 11/71; plus others. Add: 1584 Marion Ave, Tallahassee, FL 32303.

PHILBRICK, NORMAN (D), b. Ft. Wayne, Ind, Apr. 30, 13; m. 41; c. 4. DRAMATIC LITERATURE. A.B, Pomona Col, 35; A.M, Stanford Univ, 42; Ph.D, Cornell Univ, 49. Instr, Pomona Col, 37-41; drama, Stanford Univ, 43-47, asst. prof, 48-50, from assoc. prof. to prof, 50-68, acting exec. head dept. speech & drama, 50-51, exec. head, 54-62; DIR, PHILBRICK LIBR, 68- Instr, Pasadena Playhouse, 37-38; Scripps Col, 37-39; Fulbright fel, Australia, 62. Am. Theatre Asn.(exec. secy, 50-59, 2nd v.pres, 59, 1st v.pres, 60, pres, 61); Int. Fed. Theatre Res.(mem. bd. mgt, 61-); Int. Inst. Arts & Lett; Soc. Theatre Res, Eng; MLA; Am. Soc. Theatre Res. (mem. exec. bd, 70-73). Eighteenth-century English and American theatre and drama; late 19th century theatre history and production. Publ: Auth. introd. to History of American theatre by George O. Seilhamer, 68 & ed, Trumpets sounding: propaganda plays of the American Revolution, 72, Blom; auth, The spy as hero: an examination of Andre by William Dunlap, In: Studies in theatre and drama: essays in honor of Hubert C. Heffner, Mouton, The Hague, 72; Blanche Bates, In: Dictionary of American biography, Scribner, 73. Add: 25855 Westwind Way, Los Altos Hills, CA 94022.

PHILBRICK, THOMAS LESLIE, b. Providence, R.I, Mar. 7, 29; m. 53; c. 2. ENGLISH. B.A, Brown Univ, 50; M.A, Harvard, 54, Ph.D.(Eng), 59. Instr. ENG, Univ. Vt, 58-59, asst. prof, 59-62; assoc. prof, Univ. Pittsburgh, 62-66; Union Col, 66-67; PROF, UNIV. PITTSBURGH, 67- U.S.A, 50-52, Sgt. MLA. Fiction of James Fenimore Cooper; American fiction of the 18th and early 19th centuries; American romanticism. Publ: James Fenimore Cooper and the development of American sea fiction, 61 & ed, The crater, 62, Harvard Univ; auth, St. John de Crevecoeur, Twayne, 70; Cooper's The pioneers: origins and structure, PMLA, 12/64; The last of the Mohicans and the sounds of discord, Am. Lit, 3/71. Add: Dept. of English, University of Pittsburgh, Pittsburgh, PA 15213.

PHILIPS, DAVID EVAN, b. Wilkes-Barre, Pa, Aug. 30, 26; m. 50; c. 3. ENGLISH. B.A, Haverford Col, 50; M.A, Johns Hopkins Univ, 52; Univ. Pa, 53-56. Instr. ENG, Tufts Univ, 56-62; asst. prof, EAST. CONN. STATE COL, 62-68, ASSOC. PROF, 68-, chmn. dept, 67-69. Danforth Found. stud. grant, 60-61. U.S. Merchant Marine, 44-46; U.S.N.R, 50-, Lt. NCTE; MLA. Regional literature, especially Maineiana; American drama, especially Eugene O'Neill; popular literature of the late 19th and early 20th centuries. Add: Dept. of English, Eastern Connecticut State College, Willimantic, CT 06226.

PHILLABAUM, CORLISS E, b. Cortland, N.Y, Aug. 1, 33; m. 59; c. 2. DRAMA. A.B, Univ. Ill, 54; Rotary Found. fel, Univ. Munich, 54; M.A, Pa. State Univ, 61; Ph.D.(speech & theatre), Ohio State Univ, 62. Instr. speech, Mich. State Univ, 60-62; theatre, Lake Erie Col, 62-63; asst. prof. drama, Univ. Sask, 63-65; ASSOC. PROF. THEATRE ARTS, UNIV. WIS-MILWAUKEE, 65- Univ. Wis, Milwaukee res. grant, summers 67, 71. Sig.C, U.S.A, 56-58, 1st Lt. Speech Commun. Asn; Am. Theatre Asn. Contemporary European drama and theatre; 18th and 19th century Viennese theatre and drama; play direction. Publ: Panoramic scenery at Sadler's Wells, Ohio State Univ. Theatre Collection Bull, 59; Future prospects for tape exchange, TV Tech. Rev, 3/60; Faust, part one, Am. Rec. Guide, 8/61. Add: Dept. of Theatre Arts, University of Wisconsin-Milwaukee, Milwaukee, WI 53201.

PHILLIPPE, JAMES R, b. Dugger, Ind, Oct. 16, 19; m; c. 2. DRAMA. A.B, Ind. Univ, 41; fel. & M.A, Cornell Univ, 43; Ill. Univ, 49; Ohio State Univ, 49-50. Asst. prof. drama & radio, BUTLER UNIV, 46-49, from assoc. prof. to PROF. DRAMA, 49-, CHMN. DEPT. RADIO & TV, 65-, MGR. RADIO STA. WAJC, 73-, chmn. dept. drama, 46-61. American theatre. Add: 4723 Inwood Lane, Indianapolis, IN 46250.

PHILLIPS, BERNICE MAXINE, b. Birmingham, Ala, Nov. 13, 25. ENGLISH. A.B, Univ. Ala, 47, M.A, 57; Univ. Calif, Los Angeles, 49-50; Univ. N.C, 59-60, 61-63. Asst. to dean admin, Univ. Ala, 51-56, instr. ENG, 56-59, 60-61; Univ. N.C, Greensboro, 63-64; asst. prof, MARSHALL UNIV, 64-67, ASSOC. PROF, 67- Publ: How to visit a tombstone: a creative guide for freshman writing, Kendall/Hunt, 73. Add: Dept. of English, Marshall University, Huntington, WV 25701.

PHILLIPS, DAVID C, b. Monroe, Iowa, Dec. 1, 13; m. 38; c. 2. SPEECH. A.B, Grinnell Col, 35; summer, Columbia Univ, 37; M.A, State Univ. Iowa, 41; Ph.D.(speech), Univ. Wis, 46. Instr. speech, Grinnell Col, 40-42; Univ. Wis, 42-44; commun, Stephens Col, 44-46; asst. prof. SPEECH, Univ. Wis, Milwaukee, 46-47; assoc. prof, Univ. Tenn, 47-48; prof, UNIV. CONN, 49-69, head dept, 49-66, EMER. PROF, 69- Commun. consult, var. indust. & govt. agencies; ed, Today's Speech, 60-62. Speech Commun. Asn.(mem. admin counc, 39-73); Speech Asn. East. States (pres, 50-73). Publ: Oral communication in business, McGraw; co-auth, Introduction to radio and television, Ronald & Speech as communication, Allyn & Bacon, 66. Add: Dept. of Speech, University of Connecticut, Storrs, CT 06268.

PHILLIPS, ELIZABETH, b. Spruce Pine, N.C, Jan. 29, 19. AMERICAN LITERATURE. B.A, Univ. N.C, 39; M.A, State Univ. Iowa, 45; Ph.D.(Am. civilization), Univ. Pa, 57. Acting chmn. dept. ENG, Lees-McRae Jr. Col, 45-46; acting instr, Butler Univ, 46-48; from instr. to asst. prof, Milwaukee-Downer Col, 49-54; from asst. prof. to assoc. prof, WAKE FOREST UNIV, 57-68, PROF, 68-, chmn. dept, 71. Asst. coord. spec. prog. Am. civilization, Grad. Sch, Univ. Pa, 56; Smith-Mundt prof, Seoul Nat. Univ, 60-61, Fulbright lectr, 62-63; vis. lectr, Univ. Oslo, 60, 61; consult, Choice, 66-; R.J. Reynolds Tobacco Co. res. grant, 71. American poetry. Publ: Poe without Israfel: three essays on a human imagination, Univ. S.C, (in press): The hocus-pocus of Lolita, Lit. & Psychol, autumn 60; Song of myself: the numbers of the poem in relation to its form, Walt Whitman Rev, 9/70; plus poems in Am. Scholar, 44, 60, 61. Add: 2170 Royall Dr, Winston-Salem, NC 27106.

PHILLIPS, ELIZABETH C, b. Athens, Tenn, Nov. 11, 06; div. ENGLISH. B.A, Maryville Col, 28; Univ. N.C, summer, 44; M.A, Univ. Tenn, 49, Ph.D, 53. Asst. ENG, Univ. Tenn, 47-51; instr, MEMPHIS STATE UNIV, 53-56, asst. prof, 56-61, assoc. prof, 61-66, PROF, 66- Am. Stud. Asn; MLA. Development of the literary stage direction in British and American drama; 19th century American periodical writers; American novel, early and modern. Publ: Study guide to Faulkner's Absalom, Absalom!, 65, co-auth, Study guide to modern American drama, 66, auth, Critical guide to Ralph Ellison's Invisible man, 71, Critical guide to Richard Wright's Native son, 72 & Critical guide to The works of Lorraine Hansberry, 73, Monarch; auth, John Tomlin: the Literary postmaster of Jackson, Tennessee, W.Tenn. Hist. Soc, 54; Albee and the theatre of the absurd, Tenn. Stud. Lit, 65. Add: Dept. of English, Memphis State University, Memphis, TN 38152.

PHILLIPS, GENE DANIEL, S.J, b. Springfield, Ohio, Mar. 3, 35. MODERN FICTION, FILM. B.A, Loyola Univ. Chicago, 57, M.A, 59; Ph.L, West Baden Col, 59; Th.L, Bellarmine Sch. Theol, 66; Ph.D.(Eng), Fordham Univ, 70. Instr. ENG, St. Ignatius High Sch, Cleveland, Ohio, 59-62; ASST. PROF, LOYOLA UNIV. CHICAGO, 70- Am. Philos. Soc. grant, 71; trustee, Film Archive, Art Inst. Chicago, 72-; vis. prof. film, Northwest. Univ, summer 73; grad. res. comt. grant, Loyola Univ. Soc. Cinema Stud; MLA; Screen Educr. Soc. Modern fiction; film history. Publ: Graham Greene: the films of his fiction, Teachers Col, Columbia Univ, 74; The movie makers: artists in an industry, 73 & Evelyn Waugh and his officers, gentlemen, and rogues: the fact behind his fiction, 74, Nelson-Hall; Stanley Kubrick: a film odyssey, Curtis Publ, 74; Graham Greene: on the screen, In: Graham Greene: a collection of critical essays, Prentice-Hall, 73; Faulkner and the film: the two versions of Sanctuary, 1933 and 1961, Lit/Film Quart, summer 73. Add: Faculty Residence, Loyola University of Chicago, 6525 N. Sheridan Rd, Chicago, IL 60626.

PHILLIPS, GEORGE H, b. Plattesville, Wis, July 21, 07; m. 35; c. 2. JOURNALISM, PRINTING MANAGEMENT. B.S, S.Dak. State Univ, 29, M.S, 35; Ph.D.(commun), Univ. Iowa, 62. Sports ed, Daily Republic, Mitchell, S.Dak, 29-30; news ed, Daily News, Estherville, Iowa, 30-32; instr. Eng, Kans. State Teachers Col, 35-46; asst. prof. jour, Univ. Wichita, 47-49; prof. JOUR. & PRINTING, S.DAK. STATE UNIV, 49-73, EMER. PROF, 73- U.S.A.F, 43-46, Capt. Asn. Educ. Jour. Communications. Publ: Army-Navy Journal between two wars, Jour. Quart, fall 61; The Indian ring in Dakota Territory, 1870-1890, S.Dak Hist, fall 72. Add: 21 Grisham Circle, Bella Vista, AR 72712.

PHILLIPS, GEORGE LEWIS, b. Cambridge, Mass, Sept. 27, 09; m. 67. ENGLISH. A.B, Dartmouth Col, 31; A.M, Harvard, 32; Ph.D, Boston Univ, 37. Instr. Eng, W.Va. Univ, 37-40; asst. prof. comp. lit, Hofstra Col, 40-43; v.consul cult. relat, Bahia, Brazil, 43-44, Geneva, Switz, 44-47; asst. prof. ENG, SAN DIEGO STATE UNIV, 47-51, assoc. prof, 51-58, prof, 58-73, EMER. PROF, 73- Lectr, Asn. Cult. Brasil-Estados Unidos, 43-44. MLA; Am. Folklore Soc; Eng-Speaking Union; Philol. Asn. Pac. Coast; London Folklore Soc. Trade of chimney-sweeping; Edward Wortley Montagu, Jr. Publ: England's climbing boys, Harvard, 49; American chimney sweeps, Past Times Press, 58. Add: 4749 La Rueda Dr, La Mesa, CA 92041.

PHILLIPS, GERALD M, b. Cleveland, Ohio, Dec. 1, 28; m. 49; c. 4. DISTURBED COMMUNICATION. B.A, West. Reserve Univ, 49, fel, 49-56, M.A, 50, Ph.D, 56. Instr. SPEECH, N.Dak. State Univ, 56-58; asst. prof, Wash. State Univ, 58-64; PROF, PA. STATE UNIV, 64- Dir. oral commun. prog, Title IV, Elem. & Sec. Educ. Act, Area J, Pa, 66-; consult, Northwest Intermediate Unit Five, Erie, Pa, 70- & Pa. Med. Soc, 72-; marriage counr, 72-; dir. Equal Opportunity Prog, Pa. State Univ, 73- Teacher communication behavior; communication in race relations; communication pathologies. Publ: General semantics: home study course, Wash. State Univ, 62; co-auth, Speech: a course in fundamentals, Scott, 63; Communication and the small group, 66, 2nd ed, 73, co-auth, Communication in the classroom, 68 & Speech: science art, 70, Bobbs; Interpersonal dynamics of the small group, Random, 70; The reticent speaker, ERIC, 73; auth, Reticence: pathology of the normal speaker, Speech Monogr, 68; Oral communication revolution, Pa. Sch. J, 68; co-auth, The reticent speaker: etiology and treatment, J. Commun. Disorders, 73; plus others. Add: Dept. of Speech, 225 Sparks Bldg, Pennsylvania State University, University Park, PA 16802.

PHILLIPS, JAMES EMERSON, JR, b. Los Angeles, Calif, Nov. 11, 12; m. 55. ENGLISH. B.A, Univ. Calif, Los Angeles, 34, M.A, 36; Ph.D.(Eng), Columbia Univ, 40. Instr. ENG, UNIV. CALIF, LOS ANGELES, 39-42, asst. prof, 46-49, assoc. prof, 49-55, PROF, 55-, chmn. dept. Eng, 55-60, assoc. dean lett. & sci, 66-70. Guggenheim fel, 45-46; Fulbright res. scholar, Italy, 54-55; Am. Counc. Learned Soc. res. grant, 61-62. Distinguished Teaching Award, Univ. Calif, Los Angeles, 67. U.S.A, 42-46, T/Sgt. MLA; Renaissance Soc. Am; Int. Asn. Univ. Prof. Eng.(secy, 71-74). Spenser; Shakespeare; Renaissance comparative literature. Publ: The state in Shakespeare's Greek and Roman plays, Columbia Univ, 40; Images of a queen—Mary Stuart in sixteenth century literature, Univ. Calif, 64; Poetry and music in the seventeenth century, 53 & Daniel Rogers: a neo-Latin link between the Pleiade and Sidney's Areopagus, 65, Clark Libr, Univ. Calif, Los Angeles; ed, Twentieth century interpretations of Coriolanus, Prentice-Hall, 70; auth, The Tempest and the Renaissance idea of man, Shakespeare Quart, spring 64; Spenser's syncretistic religious imagery, ELH, 69, reprinted In: Critical essays on Spenser, Johns Hopkins, 70; Renaissance concepts of justice and the structure of The faerie queene, book V, Huntington Libr. Quart, 70, reprinted In: Essential articles for the study of Edmund Spenser, Anchor, 72. Add: Dept. of English, University of California, Los Angeles, 405 Hilgard Ave, Los Angeles, CA 90024.

PHILLIPS, JOHN R, b. Oxnard, Calif, Dec. 4, 18; m. 46; c. 3. ENGLISH LITERATURE. B.A, Pomona Col, 41; M.A, Univ. Calif, Berkeley, 58, Ph.D, 61. Sports asst, Post, Pasadena, Calif, 41-42; reporter & desk man, Star News, 45-49; dir. publicity, Roosevelt for Gov. Campaign, 49-50; ed. & pub, Chronicle, Calexico, Calif, 51-57; asst. jour, Univ. Calif, Berkeley, 58-59; asst. prof. ENG, WEST. MICH. UNIV, 61-65, ASSOC. PROF, 65- Mil. Intel, 42-45, T/Sgt; Bronze Star Medal. MLA; NCTE; Asn. Humanistic Psychol; AAUP. Nineteenth century English literature; literature and psychology; G.B. Shaw. Add: Dept. of English, Western Michigan University, Kalamazoo, MI 49007. (Deceased 74)

PHILLIPS, LOTTIE INEZ, b. Tuscaloosa, Ala. LINGUISTICS, ENGLISH & AMERICAN LITERATURE. B.A, Trevecca Nazarene Col, 51; M.A, Ball State Univ, 61, Ph.D, 73. Teacher ENG, Union High Sch, Modoc, Ind, 57-62; Muncie Pub. Sch. Corp, 62-65; asst. prof, OLIVET NAZARENE COL, 65-70, ASSOC. PROF, 70-, CHMN. DEPT, 71- Researcher, NCTE, 66-69; dir. workshop, Trevecca Nazarene Col, 70-73. NCTE; MLA; Col. Eng. Asn; Conf. Col. Compos. & Commun. Special education; English education; literary criticism. Publ: Preparation of secondary teachers for the teaching of slow learners, U.S. Off. Educ, 69. Add: Dept. of English, Olivet Nazarene College, Kankakee, IL 60901.

PHILLIPS, NORMA ANNE, b. Amsterdam, N.Y, Apr. 20, 31. ENGLISH. B.A, Univ. Rochester, 52; M.A, Northwest. Univ, 53; Fulbright fel, U.K, 54-55; Ph.D.(Eng), Yale, 58. Instr. ENG, Ind. Univ, 57-59; Conn. Col, 59-61, ASST. PROF, 62-64; QUEENS COL.(N.Y), 64- Am. Asn. Univ. Women Shirley Farr fel, 61-62. MLA; Mediaeval Acad. Am; Renaissance Soc. Am. Medieval and Renaissance literature; critical theory. Publ: The sacred fount: the narrator and the vampires, PMLA, 9/61; Observations on the derivative method of Skelton's realism, J. Eng. & Ger. Philol, 1/66; Milton's limbo of vanity and Dante's vestibule, Eng. Lang. Notes, 3/66. Add: Dept. of English, College of Liberal Arts & Science, Queens College, Flushing, NY 11367.

PHILLIPS, PHYLLIS (JOSEPHINE), b. Whitesboro, Tex, Nov. 20, 13. MODERN LANGUAGE. B.A, Southeast. State Col, 36; M.A, George Peabody Col, 37; Ed.D, Colo. State Col. Educ, 56. Teacher, high sch, Okla, 36-42; Tex, 42-45; N.Mex, 45-47; instr. Eng, PAN AM. UNIV, 47-52, assoc. prof. Eng, 52-60, TEACHER EDUC, 60-63, PROF, 63-, ADMIN. ASST. TO DEAN GRAD. SCH, 72- Improvement in the use of English mechanics and methods of teaching English; relationships between a knowledge of correct English usage and composition writing, as demonstrated by college freshmen; reading improvement in the secondary school. Publ: Three cornered classroom, Educ. Screen & Audiovisual Guide, 2/61. Add: 1800 W. Kuhn, Apt. A, Edinburg, TX 78539.

PHILLIPS, PHYLLIS PURNELL, b. Lebanon, Tenn, July 19, 27; m. 47; c. 3. SPEECH, ENGLISH. B.S, Auburn Univ, 61, M.Ed, 62, Ed.D.(speech path), 66. Teacher, Coopertown High Sch, Tenn, 47-49; typing, Army TI&E, Augsburg, Ger, 51-52; Eng, Lebanon Jr. High, Tenn, 57-59; elem, Morris Snower Sch, Ala, 61-63; ASST. PROF. SPEECH PATH, AUBURN UNIV, 63- Consult, Chambers County Health Dept, 67-; speech path. & audiol, Vet. Admin. Hosp, Tuskegee, Ala. Am. Speech & Hearing Asn; South. Speech Asn. Effect of speech improvement on speech of children in public schools; effect of speech training on classroom teachers' attitudes toward speech handicapped children. Publ: Speech and language problems in the classroom, 74, co-auth, Cleft palate and associated speech problems, 74, & ed, Clinical management of voice disorders, 74 & Stuttering, 74, Cliffs; auth, Teaching standard English as a second language, Ill. Speech & Hearing J, 69; Everybody's talking at me, Ala. Sch. J, 71. Add: Dept. of Speech Communication, 1191 Haley Center, Auburn University, Auburn, AL 36830.

PHILLIPS, RAYMOND CLARENCE, JR, b. Williamsport, Pa, Jan. 11, 32; m. 55; c. 3. AMERICAN LITERATURE, AMERICAN STUDIES. A.B, Dickinson Col, 53; M.A, Columbia Univ, 59; Ph.D.(Eng), Univ. Pa, 68. Instr. ENG, Colby Col, 59-61; assoc. prof, WESTERN MD. COL, 63-74, PROF, 74- U.S.A, 56-58. AAUP (v.pres, 66, pres, 67). American novel; literature of American West. Add: 131 Church St, New Windsor, MD 21776.

PHILLIPS, ROBERT LEE, b. Detroit, Mich, Nov. 5, 31; m. 52; c. 3. JOURNALISM. B.A, Miami Univ, 52; M.S, Univ. Ill, 54; Ph.D.(commun), Univ. Ore, 66. Instr. speech, ORE. STATE UNIV, 57-60, asst. prof. speech & asst. in inform, 60-64, assoc. prof. speech & dir. summer term, 64-71, PROF. JOUR, 71-, ASST. TO PRES, 71- Fel, acad. admin. internship prog, Am. Counc. Educ, 67-68. U.S.N, 54-57, Res, 57-, Lt. Comdr. Journalism; interpersonal communication; academic administration. Publ: Effects of emotional conflict on learning and persuasiveness in a broadcast discussion, Speech Monogr, 11/67; A typology of evasive responses, Educ. Broadcasting Rev, 8/68; Jam joint operation, TransAction, 9/71. Add: Summer Term Office, Administrative Services Bldg. A600, Oregon State University, Corvallis, OR 97331.

PHILLIPS, RON, b. Philippi, W.Va, Jan. 18, 24; m. 58. COMMUNICATIONS, JOURNALISM. B.A, Univ. Ore, 50; M.A, Brigham Young Univ, 57- ASSOC. PROF. JOUR, BLACK HILLS STATE COL, 53- U.S.A, 43-46, Sgt. Nat. Counc. Col. Pub. Adv. Add: Dept. of English, Black Hills State College, Spearfish, SD 57783.

PHILLIPS, STEVEN RAY, b. Cedar Falls, Iowa, Aug. 5, 39; m. 64; c. 2. ENGLISH LITERATURE. B.A, Union Col.(N.Y), 61; Ph.D.(Eng), Univ. Rochester, 69. Asst. prof. ENG, Rockford Col, 69-71; ASST. PROF. & ED. STUD. BURKE & HIS TIME, ALFRED UNIV, 71- U.S.N, 61-64, Lt.(jg). MLA; Am. Soc. 18th Century Stud. Eighteenth century literature; Ernest Hemingway; archetypal criticism. Publ: Johnson's Lives of the poets in the nineteenth century, Res. Stud, 71; Hemingway and the bullfight: the archetypes of tragedy, Ariz. Quart, 73; The double pattern of D.H. Lawrence's The horse dealer's daughter, Stud. Short Fiction, 73; plus one other. Add: Dept. of English, Alfred University, Alfred, NY 14802.

PHILLIPS, WILLIAM, b. N.Y. LITERARY CRITICISM & THEORY. B.S, City Col. New York, 28; M.A, N.Y. Univ, 30; Columbia Univ, 30-31. Instr, N.Y. Univ, 29-32, assoc. prof, 60, 61-63; Columbia Univ, 45; vis. lectr, Sarah Lawrence Col, 51-54, 56-57; New Sch. Soc. Res. & Univ. Minn, 53; PROF. ENG, RUTGERS UNIV, NEW BRUNSWICK, 63-; ED, PARTISAN REV, 34- Former consult. ed, Dial Press; Criterion Bks; Random House; consult, Chilmark Press; mem, N.J. Comt. Arts, 64-66; bd. dir, Am. Comt. Cult. Freedom, 58-68. Asn. Lit. Mag. Am; Coord. Counc. Lit. Mag.(chmn, 67-); PEN Club. Publ: Ed, Best American short novels, Dial, 46, Holt, 47; Short stories of Dostoevsky, Dial, 47 & Art and psychoanalysis, Meridian; co-ed, The partisan reader, Dial, The new partisan reader, Holt, Modern writing, 1, 2, 3, 4, & Stories in the modern manner, 1, 2; auth, A sense of the present, Chilmark, 68. Add: Dept. of English, Rutgers University, New Brunswick, NJ 08903.

PHILLIPS, WILLIAM JOHN, b. Philadelphia, Pa, Aug. 27, 95. ENGLISH LITERATURE. A.B, Univ. Pa, 20, A.M, 24, Ph.D, 30. Instr. Eng, Univ. Pa, 21-33, asst. prof, 33-46, asst. to dean admis. & field secy, 42-46, asst. to dir. exten. sch, 44-45; assoc. prof. Eng, URSINUS COL, 46-49, prof, 49-67, asst. registr, 46-48, registr, 48-52, dir. evening sch, 52-70, dir. summer sch, 67-70, LECTR. ENG, EVENING SCH, 70-, EMER. PROF, 67- Lectr, Univ. Pa, 46-66. U.S.A, 17-19; French Army, 18-19. MLA. Contemporary British literature; folklore; France on Byron. Add: 126 Upland Terr, Bala-Cynwyd, PA 19004.

PHILLIPS, WILLIAM LOUIS, b. Henry, Ill, Nov. 19, 21; m. 43, 72; c. 3. ENGLISH. B.A, Iowa State Teachers Col, 42; M.A, Univ. Chicago, 47, Ph.D. (Eng), 49. Instr. ENG, UNIV. WASH, 49-52, asst. prof, 52-61, ASSOC. PROF, 61-, ASSOC. DEAN, COL. ARTS & SCI, 63-, asst. dean, 59-63, acting dean, 70-71. Fulbright lectr, Univs. Toulouse & Nancy, 58-59, lectr, Sem. Am. Stud, Nice, France, 59; mem. visitation & appraisal comt, Nat. Comt. Accreditation Teacher Educ, 70-72; mem. nat. bd, Fed. Regional Accrediting Asns. Higher Educ, 72- U.S.A, 42-46, Capt. MLA; Am. Stud. Asn. American fiction; Sherwood Anderson. Publ: How Sherwood Anderson wrote Winesburg, Ohio, Am. Lit, 51; The imagery of Dreiser's novels, PMLA, 63. Add: Dept. of English, University of Washington, Seattle, WA 98105.

PHILLIPSON, JOHN SAMUEL, b. Rochester, N.Y, Jan. 23, 17. ENGLISH. B.A, Univ. Rochester, 47; M.A, Univ Wis, 49, Ph.D.(Eng), 52. Instr. ENG, Univ. Wis, 52-53; Villanova Univ, 53-54, asst. prof, 54-61; UNIV. AKRON, 61-65, ASSOC. PROF, 65- Bibliogr, Annual Bibliog. of Eng. Lang. & Lit, Mod. Humantities Res. Asn, 57-; ed, Abstr. Eng. Stud, 65- MLA; Mod. Humanities Res. Asn. Gt. Brit.(ed. Am. newslett, 72-); Col. Eng. Asn. Eighteenth century literature. Add: 2597 24th St, Cuyahoga Falls, OH 44223.

PHIPPS, CHARLES THOMAS, S.J, b. San Francisco, Calif, Mar. 7, 29. ENGLISH. A.B, Gonzaga Univ, 52, Ph.L, 53; M.S.T, Univ. Santa Clara, 60; Ph.D.(Eng), Univ. N.C, Chapel Hill, 65. Asst. prof. ENG, UNIV. SANTA CLARA, 65-70, ASSOC. PROF, 70- MLA. Nineteenth century English and American literature. Publ: Adaptation from the past, creation for the present: a study of Browning's The Pope, Stud. Philol, 7/68; Browning's Canon Guiseppe Caponsacchi, Eng. Lit. Hist, 12/69; The Bishop as bishop: clerical motif and meaning in The Bishop orders his tomb at St. Praxed's Church, Victorian Poetry, autumn 70. Add: Dept. of English, University of Santa Clara, Santa Clara, CA 95053.

PHIPPS, FRANK THOMAS, b. Dayton, Ohio, Dec. 20, 19; m. 43; c. 1. ENGLISH. B.A, Miami Univ, 46, M.A, 47; Univ. Calif, 48-49; Ph.D.(Eng), Ohio State Univ, 53. Asst. Eng, Miami Univ, 46-47, instr, 47-48; reader engineering, Univ. Calif, 49; asst. ENG, Ohio State Univ, 50-53; instr, UNIV. AKRON, 53-55, asst. prof, 55-57, assoc. prof, 57-65, PROF, 65-, head dept, 67-74. U.S.A.F, 41-46, 61-62, Res, 62-66, Col. NCTE; MLA; Am. Stud. Asn; Midwest Mod. Lang. Asn; Mod. Humanities Res. Asn; Asn. Depts. Eng. American literature, 1865 to present; American attitudes toward war, especially cultural history and history of ideas; the realists. Add: Dept. of English, University of Akron, Akron, OH 44301.

PHIPPS, PAUL, b. St. Louis, Mo, Feb. 18, 21; m. 49; c. 3. ENGLISH. A.B, Valparaiso Univ, 49; M.A, Univ. N.C, 50; summer, Northwest. Univ, 51; Fulton scholar, Johns Hopkins Univ, 52-56, Ph.D, 61. Instr. Eng, Valparaiso Univ, 50-52; dir. freshman writing, Johns Hopkins Univ, 53-56; asst. prof. ENG, VALPARAISO UNIV, 56-61, assoc. prof, 61-67, PROF, 67-, chmn. dept, 66-71, res. prof, 73-74. U.S.N, 42-46. MLA; Col. Eng. Asn. American literature of the South; English literature of the 19th century; modern English grammar. Add: Dept. of English, Valparaiso University, Valparaiso, IN 46383.

PHY, ALLENE STUART, b. Glasgow, Ky. ENGLISH, HUMANITIES. B.A, Univ. Ky, 59; M.A, George Peabody Col, 61, Ed.S, 65, Ph.D.(Eng), 69. Instr. Eng. as for. lang, Lycee Mohammad V, Morocco, 59-60; U.S. Naval Intel. Sch, 61-62; Eng. lang. & lit, Kansas City Jr. Col, 62-64; GEORGE PEABODY COL, 64-68, asst. prof. ENG. & COMP. LIT, 68-73, ASSOC. PROF, 73- Shakespeare Soc. Am; Popular Cult. Asn. The Jew in literature; the woman novelist in France and Italy; science fiction in literature. Add: Box 48, George Peabody College, Nashville, TN 37203.

PICCOLO, ANTHONY, b. Paterson, N.J, June 26, 39. ENGLISH & AMERICAN LITERATURE. B.A, Dartmouth Col, 61; M.A, N.Y. Univ, 62, Ph.D. (Eng), 69. Lectr. ENG, Hunter Col, 65-67; ASSOC. PROF, MANHATTANVILLE COL, 67- Add: Dept. of English, Manhattanville College, Purchase, NY 10577.

PICHASKE, DAVID RICHARD, b. Kenmore, N.Y, Sept. 2, 43; m. 69; c. 2. ENGLISH. B.A, Wittenberg Univ, 65; M.A, Ohio Univ, 67, Ph.D.(Eng), 69. ASSOC. PROF. ENG, BRADLEY UNIV, 69- Early English Text Soc; Soc. Stud. Mediaeval Lang. & Lit. Medieval English literature; Renaissance English literature; poetry of rock. Publ: Ed, Beowulf to Beatles: approaches to poetry, 72 & auth, Writing sense, 74, Free Press; Toward an aesthetics of rock, Ill. Eng. Bull, 72; Something is happening here, J. Popular Cult, 73; The Faerie Queene IV. ii and iii: Spenser on the genesis of friendship, Stud. Eng. Lit, 74. Add: Dept. of English, Bradley University, Peoria, IL 61606.

PICHÉ, PRISCILLA M, b. Apr. 5, 12; U.S. citizen. ENGLISH LITERATURE, LITERARY THEORY. B.A, Siena Heights Col, 37; M.A, Univ. Mich, 41; Ph.D.(Eng), Cath. Univ. Am, 52. Chmn. dept. ENG, Siena Heights Col, 52-60; Barry Col, 60-70; PROF, SIENA HEIGHTS COL, 70-, chmn. dept, 70-

71. Dir. Europ. stud, Univ. Neuchatel, 69-70. Am. Soc. Aesthet; Brit. Soc. Aesthet; MLA; Col. Eng. Asn. Metaphysical poetry; literary theory and criticism; curriculum and methodology. Publ: Syntactic analysis of songs and sonnets of John Donne, Cath. Univ. Am. Microcard, 51; Sophomore survey again, Col. Eng. Critic, 3/63; Hopkins' Spring and fall!, Explicator, 4/63; Shakespeare teaching: some suggestions, Council-Grams, 5/66. Add: 2719 Crooks Rd, Royal Oak, MI 48073.

PICK, JOHN, b. West Bend, Wis, Sept. 18, 11; m. 56. ENGLISH LITERATURE. A.B, Univ. Notre Dame, 33; A.M, Univ. Wis, 34, Ph.D, 38; Harvard, 34; Oxford, 38. Asst. Eng, Univ. Wis, 34-38, instr, 38-39; asst. prof, Boston Col, 39-41; master, Groton Sch, 43-45; assoc. prof. ENG, MARQUETTE UNIV, 45-48, PROF, 48- Fulbright lectr, Royal Univ. Malta, 55-56; cult. attaché, Embassy for Malta, Wash, D.C, 67- MLA. Victorian literature. Publ: Gerard Manley Hopkins, 42 & ed, A Hopkins reader, 53, Oxford Univ; Hopkins' Windhover, C.E. Merrill, 69; Renascence: a critical journal of letters, 48-69. Add: Dept. of English, Marquette University, Milwaukee, WI 53233.

PICKARD, JOHN BENEDICT, b. Newton, Mass, Oct. 4, 28; m. 56; c. 5. AMERICAN LITERATURE. A.B, Holy Cross Col, 50; Boston Col; Ph.D.(Eng), Univ. Wis, 54. Spec. instr. Eng, Far East exten, Univ. Calif, 56; asst. prof. AM. LIT, Rice Univ, 56-63; assoc. prof, UNIV. FLA, 63-68, PROF, 68- Am. Philos. Soc. grants, 62, 67. U.S.A, 54-56. MLA; S.Cent. Mod. Lang. Asn. Film; Bible as literature; nineteenth century American literature. Publ: John Greenleaf Whittier: an introduction and interpretation, 61 & Emily Dickinson: an introduction and interpretation, 67, Barnes & Noble; ed, Legends of New England, Scholars Facsimiles, 65 & Memorabilia of John Greenleaf Whittier, Emerson Soc, 68; ed, The letters of John Greenleaf Whittier (3 vols), Harvard, 74-75; plus others. Add: 406 N.E. Seventh Ave, Gainesville, FL 32601.

PICKENS, WILLIAM GARFIELD, b. Atlanta, Ga, Dec. 27, 27; m. 50; c. 3. AMERICAN LITERATURE, DIALECTOLOGY. B.A, Morehouse Col, 48; M.A, Atlanta Univ, 50; Trinity Col.(Conn), summers 54-58, 67; Univ. Hartford, 64-65; Ph.D.(Eng, ling), Univ. Conn, 69. Instr. Eng, Morehouse Col, 49-50; Eng. & jour, Hillside High Sch, Durham, N.C, 50; Eng. & social stud, Barnard-Brown Jr. High Sch, Hartford, Conn, 54-57; teacher Eng. & chmn. dept, Weaver High Sch, Hartford, 57-70; PROF. ENG. & LING. & CHMN. DEPT, MOREHOUSE COL, 70- AAUP; Col. Lang. Asn; MLA. Dialectology, field research; semantics. Publ: Ed, A guide to personal English, 68, General English, grades nine and ten, 69 & Program of English studies, grades nine through twelve, 70, Hartford Bd. of Educ; auth, Teaching negro culture in high schools—is it worthwhile?, J. Negro Educ, spring 65; Structure and meaning, In: Exercise exchange, Holt, 65. Add: Dept. of English & Linguistics, Division of Humanities, Morehouse College, Atlanta, GA 30314.

PICKERELL, ALBERT GEORGE, b. Cherryvale, Kans, May 7, 12; m. 54; c. 2. JOURNALISM. B.S, Kans. State Col, 34, M.S, 35; M.A, Stanford Univ, 48, Ph.D.(polit. sci), 51. Asst. prof, Stanford Univ, 47-50; staff asst. to Asst. Secy. State for Pub. Affairs, 50-51; assoc. prof. JOUR, UNIV. CALIF, BERKELEY, 51-61, PROF, 61-, statewide dir. inform, 61-65, chmn. dept. jour, 67-68. Fulbright lectr, Univ. Thammasat, 54-55; consult, U.S. Inform. Serv, Asia Found; Am. Specialist Prog, Asia, 65. U.S.A, 42-46, Maj. Asn. Educ. Jour; Pub. Relat. Soc. Am; Am. Col. Pub. Relat. Asn. Law of communications; public opinion and propaganda; Southeast Asia, especially Thailand. Publ: Co-auth, The University of California: a pictorial history, Univ. Calif, 68; auth, Journalism a happy game in Thailand, Int. Press Inst; California's newspaper retraction statute, Jour. Quart; California's Brown Act, Calif. Publ, 8-12/67; plus others. Add: 56 Gipsy Lane, Berkeley, CA 94705.

PICKERING, JAMES D, b. New York, N.Y, Dec. 24, 23; m. 46; c. 2. ENGLISH & COMPARATIVE LITERATURE. B.A, Wesleyan Univ, 47, M.A, 49; Yale, 43-44; Ph.D.(Eng. lit), Columbia Univ, 64. Teacher, Sch. Prof. Children, N.Y, 53-54; instr. ENG, GETTYSBURG COL, 54-57, asst. prof, 57-63, assoc. prof, 63-67, PROF, 67-, DEAN, 72- Vis. fel, Fiske Icelandic collection, Cornell Univ, 64-65. U.S.M.C.R, 43-44; U.S.N.R, 44-46, Lt.(jg). Medieval literature, especially Old English and Anglo-Latin; Old Icelandic and Scandinavian literature. Publ: The conversion of the Haugbúi, Tímarit fyrir thjothsraeknisfélags Islensk, winter 66. Add: Dept. of English, Gettysburg College, Gettysburg, PA 17325.

PICKERING, JAMES H, b. New York, N.Y, July 11, 37; m. 62; c. 2. ENGLISH, AMERICAN LITERATURE. B.A, Williams Col, 59; M.A, Northwest. Univ, 60, Ph.D.(Eng), 64. Instr. ENG, Northwest. Univ, 63-65; asst. prof, MICH. STATE UNIV, 65-68, assoc. prof, 68-72, PROF, 72-, GRAD. CHMN. & ASSOC. CHMN. DEPT, 68- MLA. American literature; American studies. Publ: Ed, James Fenimore Cooper's The spy, Col. & Univ, 71; co-ed, The Harper reader, Harper, 71; ed, Fiction 100, Macmillan, 74; auth, Satanstoe: Cooper's debt to William Dunlap, Am. Lit, 1/67. Add: Dept. of English, 201 Morrill Hall, Michigan State University, East Lansing, MI 48823.

PICKERING, SAMUEL FRANCIS, JR, b. Nashville, Tenn, Sept. 30, 41; m. 70. ENGLISH. B.A, Univ. of the South, 63; B.A, Cambridge, 65, M.A, 70; Ph.D.(Eng), Princeton, 70. ASST. PROF. ENG, DARTMOUTH COL, 70- Religion and literature; English novel. Publ: Dombey and son and Dickens' Unitarian period, Ga. Rev, 72; The reviews of Sydney Smith's sermons of 1800 and 1801 and the founding of the Edinburgh Review, Anglican Theol. Rev, 72; The sources of The author of Beltraffio, Ariz. Quart, 73. Add: Dept. of English, Dartmouth College, Hanover, NH 03755.

PICKETT, CALDER M, b. Providence, Utah, July 26, 21; m. 47; c. 2. JOURNALISM, AMERICAN STUDIES. B.S, Utah State Univ, 44; M.S.J, Northwest. Univ, 48; Ph.D.(Am. stud), Univ. Minn, 59. Instr. Eng. & jour, Utah State Univ, 46-48; JOUR, Univ. Denver, 49-51; asst. prof, UNIV. KANS, 51-59, assoc. prof, 59-61, prof, 61-73, OSCAR S. STAUFFER DISTINGUISHED PROF, 73-, acting dean jour, 60-61. Bk. Rev. Ed, Jour. Quart, 67- Standard Oil Found. distinguished teaching award, 67; Frank Luther Mott Res. Award, Kappa Tau Alpha, 69. Asn. Educ. in Jour. Journalism; history; American studies. Publ: Ed Howe; country town philosopher, Univ. Kans, 68; co-auth, An annotated journalism bibliography: 1958-1968, Univ. Minn, 69; John Steuart Curry and the Topeka murals controversy, Reg. Mus. Art, Univ. Kans, 12/59; Mark Twain as journalist and literary man: a contrast, Jour. Quart, winter 61; plus others. Add: School of Journalism, University of Kansas, Lawrence, KS 66044.

PICKETT, ROY, b. Waterloo, Iowa, June 14, 22; m. 47; c. 2. AMERICAN LITERATURE. B.A, State Univ. Iowa, 48, M.A, 51, Ph.D.(Am. civilization), 60. Instr. ENG, Agr. & Mech. Col. Tex, 51-52; State Univ. Iowa, 53-57; lectr, South. Ill. Univ, 57-60, asst. prof, 60-65; ASSOC. PROF, UNIV. N.MEX, 65- Planning mem, Comn. Eng. Insts, Col. Entrance Exam. Bd, 61, instr. ling. for Comn, South. Ill. Univ, 62; dir, Title XI NDEA Inst. Eng, Univ. N.Mex, summer 67. U.S.N.R, 42-46. MLA; NCTE; Conf. Col. Compos. & Commun; Ling. Soc. Am. Stylistics; H.L. Mencken; T.S. Eliot. Publ: Suggestions for using the Writer's resource book, Scott, 57; ed, The theme of the hero, W.C. Brown, 69. Add: Dept. of English, University of New Mexico, Albuquerque, NM 87106.

PICKREL, PAUL, b. Gilson, Ill, Feb. 2, 17. ENGLISH. A.B, Knox Col, 38; A.M, Yale, 42, Ph.D, 44. Instr. Eng, Lafayette Col, 41-42; Yale, 43-45, asst. prof, 45-50, lectr, 54-66, managing ed, Yale Rev, 49-66; chief bk. critic, Harper's Mag, 55-60; PROF. ENG, SMITH COL, 66-, CHMN. DEPT, 72- English fiction. Add: Wright Hall, Smith College, Northampton, MA 01060.

PICTOR, JAMES MATTHEW, b. Gary, Ind, Aug. 25, 41; m. 66; c. 3. ENGLISH & AMERICAN LITERATURE. B.A, St. Meinrad Col, 64; B.A, St. Joseph's Col.(Ind), 66; M.A, Purdue Univ, Lafayette, 70, NDEA fel, 71-72, Ph.D.(Eng), 72. Instr. ENG, Griffith High Sch, Ind, 66-69; ASST. PROF, ST. FRANCIS COL.(IND), 72- Col. Eng. Asn; MLA. Mass media and popular culture; English Renaissance literature; American novel. Publ: Mass media and popular culture (series of 15 articles), Ft. Wayne Jour-Gazette, 9-12/73. Add: Dept. of English, Saint Francis College, 2701 Spring St, Fort Wayne, IN 46808.

PIEHLER, PAUL, b. London, Eng, June 26, 29; nat; m. 54; c. 1. ENGLISH. B.A, Magdalen Col, 52, M.A, 56; Lawrence Chamberlain fel, Columbia Univ, 59-60, Ph.D, 61. Instr. Eng, Swedish Col. Econ. & Univ. Helsinki, Finland, 52-54; sr. master, Graham Eckes Sch, Palm Beach, Fla, 54-55; instr. med. & Renaissance lit, Columbia Univ, 55-60; ENG, Dartmouth Col, 60-61; asst. prof, Univ. Calif, Berkeley, 61-68; ASSOC. PROF, McGILL UNIV, 68- Brit. Army, 48-49, Lt. Medieval and Renaissance literature. Publ: The visionary landscape, Arnold, London, 71. Add: Dept. of English, McGill University, Montreal, P.Q, Can.

PIEPHO, EDWARD LEE, b. Detroit, Mich, Jan. 10, 42; m. 64. ENGLISH LITERATURE. A.B, Kenyon Col, 64; M.A, Columbia Univ, 66; DuPont fel, Univ. Va, 68-69, Ph.D.(Eng), 72. Instr. ENG. LIT, SWEET BRIAR COL, 69-72, ASST. PROF, 72- MLA; Renaissance Soc. Am; Shakespeare Asn. Am. Renaissance lyric poetry; Shakespeare; Chaucer. Add: Dept. of English, Sweet Briar College, Sweet Briar, VA 24595.

PIERCE, GLENN QUIMBY, b. Wichita, Kans, Nov. 20, 29; m. 56; c. 1. DRAMA. B.A, Univ. Kans, 57, M.A, 58; Ph.D.(theatre hist. & drama lit), Univ. Ill, 60. Asst. prof. speech & drama, San Fernando Valley State Col, 60-63; drama, CENT. MO. STATE UNIV, 63-70, PROF. THEATRE, 70- U.S.M.C.R, 47-49; U.S.A.F, 51-54, S/Sgt. Am. Theatre Asn; Speech Commun. Asn. Publ: Midwestern theatre: renaissance, Per/Se, fall 67. Add: Dept. of Theatre, Central Missouri State University, Warrensburg, MO 64093.

PIERCE, MERLE SCHEFFEL, b. Akron, Ohio, Feb. 27, 22; m. 51; c. 1. SPEECH. B.S.Ed, Kent State Univ, 43; M.S, Univ. Wis, Madison, 52, Ph.D.(speech), 58. Asst. prof. speech, Baldwin-Wallace Col, 50-55; Beloit Col, 55-56; sr. instr, Gen. Motors Inst, 56-58; mem. fac, Flint Jr. Col, 58-59; asst. prof, Cent. Mo. State Col, 59-62; speech, Univ. Nebr, Lincoln, 62-64, jour, 63-64, assoc. prof. & fac. coord. instr. TV, 64-68; dir. instr. resources, State Univ. N.Y. Col. Plattsburgh, 68-73; COORD. & MENTOR, EMPIRE STATE COL, 73- Exec. dir. instr. TV, Nebr. Educ. TV Counc. Higher Educ, Inc, 66-68; lectr, Instr. TV workshop, Gen. Beadle State Col, summer 67; participant, UNESCO Inst. Educ. Conf. Radio & TV in Teacher Educ, Hamburg, Ger, 68; exec. dir, Northeast N.Y. Educ. TV Asn, 68-74. U.S.A, 43-46. Nat. Asn. Educ. Broadcasters. Effectiveness of radio commercials; utilization of instructional television in higher education, especially closed-circuit television. Publ: Co-auth, Communication in industry, Gen. Motors Inst, 58; auth, Orientation to instructional television for faculties of higher education institutions by network ETV in Nebraska, Univ. Nebr, 69; Vocational guidance for the small high school, Ohio Schs, 4/48; Closed-circuit television: a teaching aid, J. Higher Educ, 11/60; co-auth, ITV helps achieve empathy in architectural design, Nat. Asn. Educ. Broadcasters J, 11-12/66. Add: 123 Hawkins Hall, Empire State College, Plattsburgh, NY 12901.

PIERCE, ROBERT BELL, b. Indiana, Pa, Nov. 19, 34; m. 66; c. 3. ENGLISH. A.B, Allegheny Col, 56; A.M, Harvard, 57, Ph.D.(Eng), 64. Instr. ENG, U.S. Air Force Acad, 57-59, asst. prof, 59-60; OBERLIN COL, 64-74, ASSOC. PROF, 74- U.S.A.F, 57-60, 1st Lt. MLA; Soc. Relig. Higher Educ; AAUP. Shakespeare, Renaissance; 18th century. Publ: Shakespeare's history plays: the family and the state, Ohio State Univ, 71; co-auth, The design of poetry, Pendulum, 73; auth, Moral education in the novel of the 1750's, Philol. Quart, 1/65; The generations in 2 Henry IV, In: 2 Henry IV, 68; The moral languages of Rosalynde and As you like it, Stud. Philol, 2/71. Add: Dept. of English, Oberlin College, Oberlin, OH 44074.

PIERCY, JOSEPHINE KETCHAM, b. Indianapolis, Ind. ENGLISH. A.B, Ind. Univ, 18, A.M, 19; A.M, Columbia Univ, 22; Ph.D, Yale, 37. Asst. ENG, Univ. Ill, 22-26; instr, IND. UNIV, BLOOMINGTON, 26-40, asst. prof, 40-50, assoc. prof, 50-64, prof, 64-66, EMER. PROF, 66- Ind. Univ. Grad. Sch. res. grants, 62-66. MLA; Col. Eng. Asn. Colonial period in American literary history; modern writers. Publ: Modern writers at work, Macmillan, 30; Studies in literary types in seventeenth century America, Yale Univ, 39, Shoestring, 69; Anne Bradstreet, Twayne, 65; introd, Anne Bradstreet's The tenth muse, 65, Cotton Mather's Bonifacius, 67 & Cotton Mather's Christian philosopher, 68, Scholars' Facsimiles; The Mather family, In: Encycl. Britannica, (in press). Add: 708 Ballantine Rd, Bloomington, IN 47401.

PIKE, BURTON E, Comparative Literature, German. See Volume III, Foreign Languages, Linguistics & Philology.

PILANT, ELIZABETH H, b. Musselshell Co, Mont, June 26, 05; m. 43. ENGLISH. B.A, Univ. Wash, 28; M.A, Univ. Hawaii, 31; Northwest. Univ, 31-32; Ed.D, Univ. Calif, 39. Head dept. Eng, Cashmere High Sch, Wash, 28-29; teacher, Mid-Pac. Inst, Honolulu, Hawaii, 29-31; instr, San Francisco Nat. Training Sch, 33-34; teacher, Univ. Utah, 34-35; teacher Eng. & supvr. counselors, Ventura Jr. Col, 36-39; dean women, West. Ill. State Univ, 40-43; asst. prof. Eng, Ball State Univ, 47-52, assoc. prof, 52-60, prof, 60-71; RETIRED. Am. Folklore Soc; NCTE; AAAS. Public school utilization of American folklore; children's preferences in illustrations; collection and collation of childrens' rhymes. Publ: Sky Bears: original poetry for children, Exposition, 52. Add: 5C Lewis Apts, 1100 N St, Sacramento, CA 95814.

PILECKI, GERARD ANTHONY, b. Rochester, N.Y, June 15, 25; m. 67; c. 1. ENGLISH. B.A, Univ. Toronto, 49, M.A, 51; Ph.D.(Eng), Cornell Univ, 61. Instr. Eng, St. John Fisher Col, 53-56; asst. prof, Univ. Sask, 59-61; assoc. prof, Univ. Toronto, 61-66; UNIV. HAWAII, 66-68, DEAN INSTR, HILO CAMPUS, 68- Assoc. ed, Conradiana, 68-; exchange prof. Eng. & Am. lit, Univ. Oslo, 72-73, sabbatical yr, 73-74. MLA. Nineteenth and twentieth century British literature; drama. Publ: Shaw's Geneva, Mouton, The Hague, 65; Conrad's Victory, Explicator, 1/65. Add: University of Hawaii, Hilo Campus, Hilo, HI 96720.

PILKINGTON, JOHN, b. Jacksonville, Fla, July 1, 18; m. 43; c. 1. ENGLISH. A.B, Centre Col, 40; Johns Hopkins Univ; M.A, Harvard, 47, Ph.D, 52. Asst. prof. ENG, UNIV. MISS, 52-56, assoc. prof, 56-60, PROF, 60-, ASSOC. DEAN GRAD. SCH, 70- Ed, Stud. in Eng. U.S.N.R, 42-46, Lt. Comdr. MLA; Am. Stud. Asn; S.Atlantic Mod. Lang. Asn; S.Cent. Mod. Lang. Asn. American literature, 1880-1914; Henry Blake Fuller and Stark Young. Publ: Francis Marion Crawford, 64 & Henry Blake Fuller, 71, Twayne; Bibliographical essay on Francis Marion Crawford, American Lit. Realism 1870-1910, spring 71; Fuller, Garland, Taft, and the art of the West, Papers Lang. & Lit, fall 72; Letters of a Southern drama critic, Yale/Theatre, spring 73; plus others. Add: P.O. Box 173, University, MS 38677.

PILKINGTON, WILLIAM THOMAS, b. Ft. Worth, Tex, June 29, 39; m. 68; c. 1. ENGLISH & AMERICAN LITERATURE. B.A, Univ. Tex, 61; M.A, Tex. Christian Univ, 63, Ph.D.(Eng), 69. Instr. ENG, Southwest Tex. State Univ, 65-68; Tex. Christian Univ, 68-69; asst. prof, TARLETON STATE UNIV, 69-71, ASSOC. PROF, 71- Mem. ed. adv. bd, West. Am. Lit, 73- MLA; West. Lit. Asn; Southwest. Am. Lit. Asn. Western American literature; American romantic literary period, 1830-1860; 20th century American fiction. Publ: William A. Owens, Steck, 68; My blood's country: studies in southwestern literature, Tex. Christian Univ, 73; Melville's Benito Cereno: source and technique, Stud. Short Fiction, spring 65; The southwestern novels of Harvey Fergusson, N.Mex. Quart, winter 66; Aspects of the western comic novel, West. Am. Lit, fall 66. Add: Dept. of English, Tarleton State University, Stephenville, TX 76401.

PILOTO, ALBERT EDWARD, b. Montreal, P.Q, Sept. 2, 19; m. 46; c. 2. ENGLISH. B.A, McGill Univ, 48, M.A, 50; Beaver scholar. & M.Litt, Cambridge, 54. Lectr. ENG, Univ. Malaya, 52-55; from instr. to ASSOC. PROF, UNIV. B.C, 55- Can. Army, 39-45. MLA; Humanities Asn. Can. Elizabethan period. Add: Dept. of English, University of British Columbia, Vancouver, B.C. V6T 1W5, Can.

PINCKERT, ROBERT C, b. St. Louis, Mo, Aug. 19, 30; m. 58; c. 1. ENGLISH. A.B, Columbia Univ, 52, Ph.D, 64; B.A, Cambridge, 54, M.A, 59. Instr. ENG, Columbia Univ, 57-61, asst. dean, 61-65; assoc. prof, JOHN JAY COL. CRIMINAL JUSTICE, 65-68, PROF, 68- U.S.A, 54-56. Sixteenth century humanism; Shakespeare. Add: Dept. of English, John Jay College of Criminal Justice, 315 Park Ave. S, New York, NY 10010.

PINEAS, RAINER, b. Berlin, Ger, July 26, 30; U.S. citizen; m. 55. ENGLISH LITERATURE. B.A, N.Y. Univ, 53; M.A, Columbia Univ, 54, Ph.D, 58. Instr. ENG, Pace Col, 58-61, asst. prof, 61-63; instr, Brooklyn Col, 63-66; asst. prof. ENG. & chmn. dept, Queensborough Community Col, 66-67; asst. prof, YORK COL.(N.Y), 67-68, assoc. prof, 69-73, PROF, 73-, chmn. dept, 67-72. Am. Philos. Soc. res. grant, 68. MLA; Renaissance Soc. Am; Am. Soc. Reformation Res; Conf. Brit. Stud; Amici Thomae Mori. Tudor religious polemics. Publ: Thomas More and Tudor polemics, Ind. Univ, 68; Tudor and early Stuart anti-Catholic drama, De Graaf, 72; Thomas More's use of the dialogue form as a weapon of religious controversy, Stud. Renaissance, 60; William Tyndale's use of history as a weapon of religious controversy, Harvard Theol. Rev, 4/62; plus one other. Add: Dept. of English, York College, 150-14 Jamaica Ave, Jamaica, NY 11432.

PINKA, PATRICIA GARLAND, b. Pittsburgh, Pa, Feb. 27, 35; m. 66; c. 1. SEVENTEENTH CENTURY ENGLISH LITERATURE. B.A, Univ. Pittsburgh, 56, Andrew Mellon fel, 67-68, Ph.D.(Eng), 69; M.A, San Francisco State Col, 64. Reporter, Valley Daily News, Tarentum, Pa, 56-57; Alameda Times Star, Calif, 59-60; teacher ENG, Alameda High Sch, 60-64, instr, Point Park Col, 66-67; ASST. PROF, AGNES SCOTT COL, 69- MLA; AAUP. John Donne; Ben Jonson; Henry James. Publ: The autobiographical narrator in the Songs and sonnets, In: That subtitle wreath, Agnes Scott Col, 73. Add: Dept. of English, Agnes Scott College, Decatur, GA 30030.

PINKERTON, JAN, b. Los Angeles, Calif, Apr. 14, 34; c. 4. AMERICAN LITERATURE. A.B, Univ. Calif, Berkeley, 55; Ph.D.(Eng), Harvard, 68. Lectr. ENG, Univ. Colo, 66-67; Ohio State Univ, 67-69; from asst. prof. to ASSOC. PROF, CHICAGO STATE UNIV, 70- MLA. Nineteenth century American literature; 20th century American and English literature. Publ: Ed, Love, capitalism, violence and other topics, Allyn & Bacon, 71; auth, The non-regionalism of Peter Taylor, Ga. Rev, winter 70; Wallace Stevens in the tropics: a conservative protest, Yale Rev, winter 71; Political realities and poetic release: prose statements by Wallace Stevens, New Eng. Quart, 12/71. Add: Dept. of English, Chicago State University, 95th and King Dr, Chicago, IL 60628.

PINKSTON, HAROLD EDWARD, Theology, English. See Volume IV, Philosophy, Religion & Law.

PINKUS, PHILIP, b. Toronto, Ont, Dec. 1, 22; m. 50. ENGLISH. B.A, Univ. Toronto, 49; M.A, Univ. Mich, 51, Ph.D.(Eng), 55. Instr. ENG, Northwest. Univ, 54-57; UNIV. B.C, 57-60, asst. prof, 60-64, assoc. prof, 64-72, PROF, 72- R.A.F, 39-46. MLA; Asn. Can. Univ. Teachers Eng. Satire; 18th century literature; Jonathan Swift. Publ: Grub Street stripped bare, Constable, 68; Satire and St. George, Queens Quart, spring 63; Jonathan Swift, In: Studies of major works in English, Oxford, 68. Add: Dept. of English, University of British Columbia, Vancouver, B.C, V6T 1W5, Can.

PINNEY, THOMAS, b. Ottawa, Kans, Apr. 23, 32; m. 56; c. 3. ENGLISH. B.A, Beloit Col, 54; Ph.D, Yale, 60. Instr. ENG, Hamilton Col, 57-61; Yale, 61-62; asst. prof, POMONA COL, 62-67, assoc. prof, 67-73, PROF, 73- Guggenheim fel, 67; Am. Counc. Learned Soc. grant, 74. Nineteenth century English literature. Publ: Essays of George Eliot, Columbia Univ, 63; co-ed, Selected writings of Macaulay, Univ. Chicago, 72; ed, Letters of Macaulay, Cambridge, 74- Add: Dept. of English, Pomona College, Claremont, CA 91711.

PINNEY, WILSON GIFFORD, b. Hartford, Conn, Oct. 12, 29; m. 54; c. 3. ENGLISH, EDUCATION. B.A, Trinity Col.(Conn), 54; Ed.M, Harvard, 55; Stanford,Univ, 57-58; Univ. Calif, Berkeley, 58-61. Assoc. subj. A, Univ. Calif, Berkeley, 58-61; INSTR. ENG, COL. SAN MATEO, 61- Instr. Eng, Exten, Univ. Calif, Santa Cruz, 69-70. NCTE. The short story; remedial college English; junior college English for non-transfer students. Publ: Co-auth, Reading and interpreting, Wadsworth, 68; auth, Two ways of seeing & Student guide to Two ways of seeing, Little, 71. Add: Dept. of English, 1700 W. Hillsdale Blvd, College of San Mateo, San Mateo, CA 94402.

PINSKER, SANFORD SIGMUND, b. Washington, Pa, Sept. 28, 41; m. 68; c. 2. MODERN LITERATURE. B.A, Washington & Jefferson Col, 63; M.A, Univ. Wash, 65, Ph.D.(Eng), 67. Teaching asst. ENG, Univ. Wash, 63-67; ASST. PROF, FRANKLIN & MARSHALL COL, 67- Fel, Grad. Inst. Mod. Lett, summer 70; Nat. Endowment for Humanities fel, 71. MLA. American-Jewish literature; modern literature, Conrad and Joyce. Publ: The schlemiel as metaphor, South. Ill. Univ, 71; contrib, Contemporary American-Jewish literature, Ind. Univ, 73; auth, Saul Bellow in the classroom, Col. Eng, spring 73; On David Wagoner, Salmagundi, winter 73. Add: Dept. of English, Franklin & Marshall College, College Ave, Lancaster, PA 17604.

PINSKY, ROBERT, b. Long Branch, N.J, Oct. 20, 40; m. 61. ENGLISH & AMERICAN LITERATURE. B.A, Rutgers Univ, 62; M.A. & Ph.D.(Eng), Stanford Univ, 67. Asst. prof. humanities, Univ. Chicago, 66-67; ENG, WELLESLEY COL, 67-73, ASSOC. PROF, 73- Modern and 19th century poetry; criticism of poetry. Publ: Landor's poetry, Univ. Chicago, 68. Add: Dept. of English, Wellesley College, Wellesley, MA 02181.

PIPER, HENRY DAN, b. Haskell, N.J, Feb. 20, 18; m. 53; c. 2. ENGLISH & AMERICAN LITERATURE. B.S, Princeton, 39; Harrison fel, Univ. Pa, 49-50, Ph.D.(Am. civilization), 50. Instr. ENG, Columbia Univ, 50-52; asst. prof, Calif. Inst. Technol, 52-56, assoc. prof, 56-62; PROF, SOUTH. ILL. UNIV, 62-, dean col. lib. arts & sci, 62-66. Vis. prof, Univs. Lille & Clermont, France, 53-54; Guggenheim fel, 57-58; commun. consult, Shell Oil Co. & Union Oil Co, 57-58, 61-62; sr. consult, Tech. Commun, Inc, Calif, 60-; Am. Counc. Learned Soc. grant, 61-62; vis. prof, Univ. Kent, 67-68. Am. Stud. Asn. American literature and civilization. Publ: Co-auth, Guide to technical reports, 58 & auth, F. Scott Fitzgerald: a critical portrait, 63, Holt; American literary manuscripts, Univ. Tex, 61; Dimensions in drama: six plays of crime and punishment, Scribner, 64; co-ed, Think back on us, a contemporary chronicle of the 1930's, 66, ed, A many windowed house, 70 & co-auth, Land between the rivers: the southern Illinois country, 73, South. Ill. Univ. Add: R.R. 1, Murphysboro, IL 62966.

PIPER, WILLIAM BOWMAN, b. Lexington, Ky, Dec. 7, 27; m. 56; c. 4. ENGLISH LITERATURE. B.A, Harvard, 51; M.A, Columbia Univ, 52; Ph.D.(Eng), Univ. Wis, 58. Instr. ENG, Cornell Univ, 58-61; asst. prof, Univ. Louisville, 61-64; assoc. prof, Case West. Reserve Univ, 64-69; PROF, RICE UNIV, 69- U.S.A, 46-48, S/Sgt. MLA. Eighteenth and seventeenth centuries; Shakespeare. Publ: Laurence Sterne, Twayne, 65; The heroic couplet, Case West. Reserve Univ, 69; co-ed, The writings of Jonathan Swift, Norton, 73; auth, Of Hamlet's transformation, South. Humanities Rev, 68; Moll Flanders as a structure of topics, Stud. Eng. Lit, 69; plus others. Add: 2132 Dryden Rd, Houston, TX 77025.

PIPES, WILLIAM HARRISON, b. Inverness, Miss, Jan. 3, 12; m. 38; c. 3. SPEECH, ENGLISH. B.S, Tuskegee Inst, 35; M.A, Atlanta Univ, 37; Ph.D.(speech), Univ. Mich, 43. Instr. Eng, Ft. Valley State Col, 37, 38-43; West. Ky. State Col, 37-38; prof. Eng. & speech, Langston Univ, summer 43; South. Univ, 43-45; pres, Alcorn Agr. & Mech. Col, 45-49; acad. dean ENG. & SPEECH, Philander Smith Col, 49-56; vis. prof, Wayne State Univ, 56-57; PROF, MICH. STATE UNIV, 57- Speech Commun. Asn; Col. Eng. Asn. Religion. Publ: Say amen, brother!, William-Frederick, 51; co-auth, The major in English, Ark. Exp. in Educ, 56; auth, Is God dead?, 66 & Death of an Uncle Tom, 67, Carlton; Old time negro preaching, Quart. J. Speech, 45; College students flunk teachers, Asn. Am. Cols. Bull, 51. Add: 519 West St, Lansing, MI 48915.

PIQUETTE, JULIA CAMILLA, b. Chicago, Ill, Jan. 24, 27. SPEECH, THEATRE. B.S, Northwest. Univ, 48, fel, 51-52, M.A, 52, Ph.D.(speech), 63. Chmn. dept. speech arts, high sch, Wis, 48-51; instr. speech & Eng, STATE UNIV. N.Y. COL. BUFFALO, 52-54, asst. prof, 54-60, assoc. prof, 61-63, PROF, SPEECH & THEATRE ARTS, 64-, CHMN. DEPT, 72- Dir. speech activities, Nat. Music Camp, Interlocken, Mich, summer 50; spec. consult. speech, State Educ. Dept, N.Y, summer 55; mem. adv. comt, elem. speech educ, Speech Asn. Am, 57-59, mem. comt. to evaluate & set speech proficiency standards for teachers, 61-62. Speech Commun. Asn. Creative dramatics. Publ: Creative dramatics for pre-adolescent, N.Y. State Educ, 5/56; Needed: adequate speech training for elementary education majors, Speech Teacher, 11/60. Add: Dept. of Speech, State University of New York College at Buffalo, Buffalo, NY 14222.

PISCATOR, MARIA LEY, b. Vienna, Austria; U.S. citizen. FRENCH & MODERN THEATER. B.A, Univ. Sorbonne, 31, Ph.D.(lit), 33. Dir. dramatic workshop, New Sch. Social Res, 39-56; guest prof. hist. mod. theater & play dir, South. Ill, Univ. Carbondale, 67-72, Univ. Windsor, 71; guest prof. hist. theater, acting & directing, Park Point Col. & Pittsburg Playhouse, 72-73; guest lectr, Univ. Mex, 73; PROF. ACTING & DIRECTING, NEW SCH. SOCIAL RES, 74- Eighteenth century theater; modern theater, theory and practice. Publ: The dance within me, Konegen, Vienna, 25; Le Gueux Chez Victor Hugo, 34, transl, Essay on Victor Hugo, 35, Droz, Paris; auth, Lot's wife, 45; The Piscator experiment, Heinemann, 68, South. Ill. Univ, 70. Add: Piscator Foundation, 17 E. 76th St, New York, NY 10021.

PITCHER, SEYMOUR MAITLAND, b. Watertown, N.Y, July 21, 06; wid; c. 1. ENGLISH & CLASSICAL PHILOLOGY. A.B, Hamilton Col, 28; A.M, Harvard, 29; Ph.D, Univ. Iowa, 37. Instr. Eng, Univ. Iowa, 31-38, asst. prof, 38-44, assoc. prof, 44-51; prof. Champlain Col, State Univ. N.Y, 51-53, prof. ENG. & COMP. LIT, STATE UNIV. N.Y. BINGHAMTON, 53-74, chmn. div. humanities, 54-60, dir. comp. lit. prog, 67-69, EMER. PROF, 74- The poetics of Aristotle; Shakespeare. Publ: The Anthus of Agathon; The case for Shakespeare's authorship of The famous victories, State Univ. N.Y, 61; transl, Aristotle: on poetic art, J. Gen. Educ. Add: 13602 Flying W Trail, San Antonio, TX 78228.

PITT, ARTHUR STUART, b. Bridgeport, Conn, May 26, 14; m. 42; c. 2. ENGLISH. B.A, Yale, 35, M.A, 37, Ph.D.(Eng), 39. Instr. Eng, Lafayette Col, 39-41; ENG, HIST. & GOVT, U.S. NAVAL ACAD, 41-45, asst. prof, 45-47, assoc. prof, 47-54, PROF, 54-, CHMN. DEPT. ENG, 70-, chmn. dept. lit, 67-70. U.S.N.R, 42-45, Lt. Comdr. MLA; Col. Eng. Asn. Modern novel and drama; American literature; modern literary criticism. Publ: Annapolis today, U.S. Naval Inst, rev; Franklin's An Arabian tale, PMLA, 3/42; The 53rd New York, N.Y. Hist, 10/56; Miriam Coffin as precursor of Moby Dick, Hist. Nantucket, 4/72; plus others. Add: Dept. of English, U.S. Naval Academy, Annapolis, MD 21402.

PITT, CARL ALLEN, b. Three Forks, Mont, Sept. 6, 11; m. 35. COMMUNICATION, PUBLIC ADDRESS. B.A, Intermountain Union Col, 33; M.A, Wash. State Col, 46; Ph.D.(speech), Purdue Univ, 52. Teacher adult educ, pvt. schs. & indust, 34-42; dir. forensics, high sch, Wash, 42-45; instr. speech, Univ. Wash, 46-48; part-time instr, Purdue Univ, 48-50; instr. Univ. Ill, Chicago Circle, 50-52, asst. prof, 52-59, assoc. prof, 59-67, prof, 67-73; LECTR. & WRITER, 73- Consult, Nat. Asn. Real Estate Bds, 51-53; Howard Dist. Chamber Commerce, 52-54. Asn. Higher Educ; Cent. States Speech Asn; Speech Commun. Asn; Int. Commun. Asn; South. Speech Commun. Asn; West. Speech Commun. Asn; Speech Asn. East. States; Am. Forensic Asn; Am. Inst. Parliamentarians; Int. Platform Asn. Contemporary public address: British contemporary oratory; parliamentary procedure. Publ: An analysis and criticism of the 1940 campaign speeches of Wendell L. Wilkie, Speech Monogr, 3/54; Walter Judd's keynote speech—a congruous configuration of communication, South. Speech J, summer 68; Improving the debater's research methods, Speaker & Gavel, 1/70; plus others. Add: 6326 37th S.W, Seattle, WA 98126.

PITT, DAVID GEORGE, b. Musgravetown, Nfld, Dec. 12, 21; m. 46; c. 2. ENGLISH. B.A, Mt. Allison Univ, 46; M.A, Univ. Toronto, 48, Humanities Res. Counc. Can. fel, 57, Ph.D, 58. Assoc. prof. ENG, MEM. UNIV. NFLD, 49-62, PROF, 62-, HEAD. DEPT, 70- Humanities Asn. Can; Asn. Can. Univ. Teacher Eng. Blake; poetry and the theory of language; Canadian literature: E.J. Pratt. Publ: Critical writings on E.J. Pratt, Ryerson-McGraw, 70. Add: Dept. of English, Memorial University of Newfoundland, St. John's, Nfld, Can.

PITTS, REBECCA E, b. Indianapolis, Ind, Dec. 6, 05. ENGLISH. B.A, Butler Univ, 26; M.A, Univ. Chicago, 30. Instr. ENG, Butler Univ, 46-48; Purdue Univ, 48-51; lectr, IND. UNIV-PURDUE UNIV, INDIANAPOLIS, 56-66, asst. prof, 66-71, ASSOC. PROF, 71-, summer fac. fels, 67, 68. MLA. Fielding and the 18th century novel; Shakespeare and Shakespeare criticism; T.S. Eliot's influence on Faulkner. Publ: Co-auth, A basic vocabulary, Littlefield, 65; auth, Prayer and the incarnation, Hibbert J, 4/53; This fell sergeant, death, Shakespeare Quart, autumn 69; The wall: Sartre's metaphysical trap, Hartford Stud. Lit, (in press). Add: 5625 Julian Ave, Indianapolis, IN 46219.

PITTS, WILLIS NORMAN, JR, b. Macon, Ga, Aug. 29, 07; m. 50. SPEECH, HISTORY. A.B, Talladega Col, 32; M.A, Univ. Mich, 41 & 42, univ. fel, 46-48, Rackham fel, 51-52, Ph.D.(speech), 52. Instr. Eng, Howard Univ, 48-49; asst. prof, Lincoln Univ.(Mo), 50-51; prof. speech, Tenn. State Univ, 52-54; instr. speech & acting dir. debate, Boston Univ, 54-55; teacher Eng. & dir. drama prog, pub. schs, Mass, 55-61, dir. speech ther, 61-65; asst. prof. speech & drama, BRIDGEWATER STATE COL, 65-68, assoc. prof, 68-72, PROF. SPEECH & THEATER, 72- Parshad fel, Boston Univ, 54-55. Cert clin. competence speech path, Am. Speech & Hearing Asn, 65. U.S.A, 42-45, S/Sgt. Speech Commun. Asn; Am. Speech & Hearning Asn. Negro history; speech pathology. Add: 165 Washington St, Sherborn, MA 01770.

PIXTON, WILLIAM HOOVER, b. Washington, D.C, Apr. 13, 37; m. 59; c. 1. ENGLISH ROMANTIC LITERATURE, COMPOSITION. B.A, George Washington Univ, 59, M.A, 64; Ph.D.(Eng. lit), Univ. N.C, Chapel Hill, 68. Asst. prof. Eng, E.Carolina Univ, 68-71; ASST. PROF. ENG. & DIR. FRESHMAN & SOPHOMORE ENG, TROY STATE UNIV, 71-, grant, 72-73. U.S.N.R, 59-64, Res, 64-71, Lt. MLA; S.Atlantic Mod. Lang. Asn; Keats-Shelley Asn. Am; NCTE; Conf. Col. Compos. & Commun. English romantic literature and freshman composition. Publ: Shelley's commands to the West Wind, S.Atlantic Bull, 11/72; The dangling gerund: a working definition, Col. Compos. & Commun, 5/73; The sensitive plant: Shelley's acquiescence to agnosticism, Ball State Univ. Forum, (in press). Add: Dept. of English, Troy State University, Troy, AL 36081.

PIZER, DONALD, b. New York, N.Y, Apr. 5, 29. ENGLISH. B.A, Univ. Calif, Los Angeles, 51, M.A, 52, Ph.D, 55. Asst. prof. Eng, NEWCOMB COL, TULANE UNIV, 57-61, assoc. prof, 61-64, prof, 64-72, PIERCE BUTLER PROF, 72- Guggenheim fel, 62-63; Fulbright lectr, Univ. Hamburg, 67-68; Rosenbach fel. bibliog, 71; Am. Counc. Learned Soc. fel, 71-72. U.S.A, 55-57. MLA; Am. Stud. Asn. Late 19th century American literature. Publ: Hamlin Garland's early work and career, Univ. Calif, 60; The literary criticism of Frank Norris, Univ. Tex, 64; The novels of Frank Norris, Ind. Univ, 66; Realism and naturalism in nineteenth century American literature,

South. Ill. Univ, 66; Hamlin Garland's diaries, Huntington Libr, 68; ed, American thought and writing: the 1890's, Houghton, 72. Add: Dept. of English, Newcomb College, Tulane University, New Orleans, LA 70118.

PLANTE, JULIAN GERARD, Classical Philology, Medieval Latin. See Volume III, Foreign Languages, Linguistics & Philology.

PLASBERG, ELAINE, b. San Francisco, Calif, Oct. 22, 30. ENGLISH LITERATURE. Ph.D, Boston Univ, 61. Instr. ENG, CALIF. STATE UNIV, NORTHRIDGE, 61-62, asst. prof, 62-67, assoc. prof, 67-73, PROF, 73- U.S.N, 53-56; Lt.(jg). English Romantic and Victorian ages; literary criticism. Publ: Covert drama in Wyatt, 67 & The schoolmaster, 72, Calif. Eng. J; Strindberg and the new poetics, Mod. Drama, 72. Add: Dept. of English, California State University, Northridge, 18111 Nordhoff St, Northridge, CA 91324.

PLASTERER, NICHOLAS NYLE, b. Mount Etna, Ind, Sept. 14, 09; m. 37. JOURNALISM. B.A, Albion Col, 33; M.S.J, Northwest. Univ, 40; J.D, Univ. Toledo, 51; Univ. Iowa, 63-64. Reporter, Sturgis Daily J, Mich, 28-30; Parma News, Mich, 33-35; Sturgis Daily News, 35-39; Fort Wayne J-Gazette, 40-42, copy reader, 52-53, city ed, 53-55; copy reader, Toledo Blade, 46-52; from asst. prof. to PROF. JOUR, LA. STATE UNIV, BATON ROUGE, 55- Copy ed, Birmingham News, summers 71, 73. U.S.A.A.F, 42-46, Capt. Asn. Educ. in Jour. Fair trial; free press; government and the press; reporting and editing. Publ: Assignment Jonesville, La. State Univ, 66; co-auth, Law guide for Louisiana newspapers, La. Press Asn, 67 & On the news desk, La. State Univ, 73; auth, Foreign news in two Iowa dailies, Iowa Publ, 9/66; The Croswell case: paradox of history?, Jour. Quart, spring 67. Add: 2404 Horace St, Baton Rouge, LA 70808.

PLASTRE, GUY, French & Italian Languages. See Volume III, Foreign Languages, Linguistics & Philology.

PLAYER, RALEIGH PRESTON, b. Shreveport, La, Nov. 17, 09; m. 38; c. 1. ENGLISH LANGUAGE & LITERATURE. B.A, Bishop Col, 29; M.A, Univ. Mich, 40, Ph.D.(Eng), 65. Teacher, pub. schs, La, 35-43; high sch, Tex, 43-44; asst. prof. Eng. & jour, Houston Col, 44-47; dir. pub. relat. jour, Tex. South. Univ, 47-48; asst. prof. ENG, ALA. STATE UNIV, 49-60, assoc. prof, 60-65, PROF, 65-, chmn. div. arts & sci, 69-71, dean col. arts & sci, 71-73. NCTE; MLA; Col. Eng. Asn. The fiction of William Faulkner; the criticism of Matthew Arnold; magazine journalism; the history of the English language. Publ: Review of Peavy's Go slow now, South. Humanities Rev, fall 73. Add: Dept. of English, Alabama State University, Montgomery, AL 36101.

PLOTINSKY, MELVIN LLOYD, b. New York, N.Y, May 21, 33; m. 73. ENGLISH. A.B, Kenyon Col, 54; Fulbright scholar, 54-55; Root-Tilden scholar, N.Y. Univ, 55-58, LL.B, 58; nat. fel, Harvard, 58-62, A.M, 60, Ph.D, 63. Instr. ENG, IND. UNIV. BLOOMINGTON, 62-64, asst. prof, 64-66, ASSOC. PROF, 66- MLA. Add: Dept. of English, Indiana University, Bloomington, IN 47401.

PLOTZ, JUDITH ANN ABRAMS, b. Brooklyn, N.Y, Dec. 29, 38; m. 63; c. 1. ENGLISH, ROMANTICISM. A.B, Radcliffe Col, 60; B.A, Cambridge, 62, M.A, 66; Ph.D.(Eng), Harvard, 65. ASST. PROF. ENG, GEORGE WASHINGTON UNIV, 65- Am. Asn. Univ. Women fel, England, 68-69. MLA. Theories of poetic decline. Add: Dept. of English, George Washington University, Washington, DC 20006.

PLUMLEY, WILLIAM C, b. Hamlin, W.Va. MODERN POETRY. A.B, Marshall Univ, 63, M.A, 71; M.Ed, Kent State Univ, 67. ASSOC. PROF. ENG, MORRIS HARVEY COL, 67- Nat. Teaching fel, 67-68; practicing poet, Arts in Classroom Series, W.Va. Dept. Educ, 73-74. Am. Poetry Soc. Appalachian poetry; Appalachian culture; contemporary culture. Publ: Many faces (poems), 69, ed, Poems from the hills, 70, Poems from the hills, 71 & co-ed, From the hills, 72, Morris Harvey Col; co-auth, Handbook of Appalachian materials, W.Va. Dept. Educ, 73; auth, Appalachia, W.Va. Sch. J, 70; Appalachian poetry, W.Va. Illustrated, 71; On Appalachia, Appalachia J, 72; plus many poems in nat. mags. Add: Dept. of English, Morris Harvey College, Charleston, WV 25304.

PLUMSTEAD, ARTHUR WILLIAM, b. Toronto, Ont, Mar. 27, 33; m. 55; c. 3. ENGLISH & AMERICAN LITERATURE. B.A, Univ. West. Ont, 55; M.A, Univ. Rochester, 57, Can. Stud. fel, 57-58, univ. fel, 58-59, Ph.D, 60. Asst. prof. ENG, Univ. Sask, 61-64; Univ. Minn, 64-66, assoc. prof, 67-68; UNIV. MASS, AMHERST, 68-70, PROF, 70- MLA. Nineteenth century American literature; Canadian literature of the North; Elizabethan drama. Publ: The wall and the garden, Minn. Univ, 68; co-ed, Emerson's journals, Harvard, Vol. VII, 69; Satirical parody in roister doister, Stud. Philol, 4/63; Melville's Bartleby, Melville Annual, 66. Add: Dept. of English, University of Massachusetts, Amherst, MA 01002.

POAG, THOMAS EDWARD, b. Gastonia, N.C, July 22, 09. SPEECH, DRAMA. A.B, Morgan State Col, 32; A.M, Ohio State Univ, 35; Ph.D, Cornell Univ, 43. Dir, Civic Theatre Guild, Columbus, Ohio, 34-38; instr. drama, Dillard Univ, 38-39; PROF. SPEECH & DRAMA & DIR. DIV. HUMANITIES, TENN. STATE UNIV, 39-, DEAN, SCH. ARTS & SCI, 63- Ed, Encore. Am. Theatre Asn; Speech Commun. Asn; Southeast. Theatre Conf; Nat. Asn. Dramatic & Speech Arts (pres, 42-51). The Negro in drama and the theatre from the Greeks to the present; dramatics in the Negro high school; better human relations through the medium of dramatic art. Publ: Co-auth, Desegregation in the educational theatre, Encore, 4/60. Add: School of Arts & Sciences, Tennessee State University, Nashville, TN 37203.

POE, HAROLD WELLER, b. Cincinnati, Ohio, May 21, 32; m. 54; c. 3. SPEECH, THEATRE. B.A, Beloit Col, 54; M.A, Fla. State Univ, 57, Ph.D. (speech & theatre), 67. Stage mgr, Westcott Auditorium, Fla. State Univ, 55-56; asst. prof. speech & theatre, UNIV. SOUTHWEST. LA, 56-64, assoc. prof, 64-69, PROF. SPEECH, 69-, designer-tech. dir, 56-66, dir. theatre area, 69-72. Theatre consult, Lafayette Munic. Auditorium, 58-59; designer, lighting & sound remodeling, Burke Theatre, 60, forestage & side stage, 66, complete rebldg. & reequip, 73; dir. & co-auth, Tea for 3 billion,

World Univ. Theatre Festival, Nancy, France, 67. Speech Commun. Asn; Am. Educ. Theatre Asn. Theatre architecture; playwriting. Add: 402 Auburn Dr, Lafayette, LA 70501.

POE, M. EVELYN, b. Chambersburg, Pa, Apr. 28, 19. ENGLISH. A.B, Houghton Col, 47; M.A, Cornell Univ, 48; Boston Univ, 51-53, 56-57, 70. Teacher High Sch, 47; prof. ENG. & head dept, Messiah Col, 48-61; ASSOC. PROF, Beirut Col. Women, 61-62; ELIZABETHTOWN COL, 62- Assoc. prof, Univ. Ctr, Harrisburg, 59-69; Houghton Col, summers 63, 64 & 66; mem. bd, Messiah Col, 73-76. AAUP; NCTE. Add: Dept. of English, Elizabethtown College, Elizabethtown, PA 17022.

POGER, SIDNEY BORIS, b. Everett, Mass, Apr. 24, 35; m. 59; c. 2. ENGLISH. B.A, Tufts Univ, 57; M.A, Columbia Univ, 59, Ph.D.(Eng), 65. Instr. ENG, UNIV. VT, 62-65, asst. prof, 65-69, assoc. prof, 69-74, PROF, 74-, summer res. grant, 68. MLA; Thoreau Soc; Emerson Soc; Can. Asn. Irish Stud. American literature; modern poetry; Milton. Publ: A note on Yeats' Two songs from a play, Eire-Ireland, 71; Thoreau as Yankee in Canada, Am. Transcendental Quart, 72; Yeats as Azad: a possible source in Thoreau, Thoreau J, 73; plus others. Add: Dept. of English, University of Vermont, Burlington, VT 05401.

POGUE, JIM C, b. Electra, Tex, Apr. 23, 30; m. 59. ENGLISH RENAISSANCE LITERATURE. B.S, Kans. State Teachers Col, 55, M.S, 56; Ph.D, Univ. Mo-Columbia, 64. Instr. Eng, Univ. Mo-Columbia, 56-63; asst. prof, Wayne State Col, 63-64; PROF. ENG. & CHMN. DEPT. HUMANITIES, UNIV. MO-ROLLA, 64-, ACTING DEAN FACULTIES, 73- U.S.A, 51-54, Sgt. MLA; Am. Soc. Engineering Educ. Add: Dept. of English, University of Missouri-Rolla, Rolla, MO 65401.

POINDEXTER, JAMES EDWARD, b. Richmond, Va, Feb. 15, 15; m. 40; c. 2. ENGLISH LITERATURE. A.B, Univ. N.C, 37, Ph.D.(Shakespearean criticism), 49; A.M, Emory Univ, 38; Oxford. Instr, Battle Ground Acad, Tenn, 38-39; Va. Episcopal Sch, Lynchburg, 39-40; part-time instr. ENG, Univ. N.C, 40-42, 46-48; assoc. prof, Miss. State Col. Women, 48-51; from assoc. prof. to prof, E.Carolina Col, 51-66; assoc. dean, MADISON COL. (VA), 66-67, PROF, 67-, head dept, 67-72. U.S.N, 42-45, Lt. Col. Eng. Asn; MLA; S.Atlantic Mod. Lang. Asn. Shakespeare; late Victorian literature; contemporary literature. Add: Dept. of English, Madison College, Harrisonburg, VA 22801.

POIRIER, (WILLIAM) RICHARD, b. Gloucester, Mass, Sept. 9, 25. AMERICAN & ENGLISH LITERATURE. B.A, Amherst Col, 49; M.A, Yale, 51; Fulbright fel, Cambridge, 52-53; Ph.D, Harvard, 59. Instr. Eng. & Am. lit, Williams Col.(Mass), 50-52; Harvard, 58-60, asst. prof, 60-63; PROF. ENG, RUTGERS UNIV, NEW BRUNSWICK, 63-, DIR. GRAD. STUD. ENG, 70-, chmn. dept, 63-72. Bollingen fel, 62-63; ed, Partisan Rev, 63- U.S.A, 43-46. Relations between English and American literature since 1800; contemporary literature and aesthetics; 17th century English literature. Publ: The comic sense of Henry James, 60 & The performing self, 71, Oxford Univ, N.Y. & Chatto & Windus, London; co-auth, In defense of reading, Dutton, 62; ed, The O. Henry awards: prize stories, Doubleday, annually 61-65; auth, A world elsewhere, Oxford Univ, 66; Norman Mailer, Viking, N.Y. & Collins, Eng, 73. Add: Dept. of English, Rutgers University, New Brunswick, NJ 08903.

POISSON, RODNEY, b. Victoria, B.C, June 16, 14; m. 42; c. 2. ENGLISH. M.A, Univ. B.C, 39; Can. Counc. fel, Univ. Wash, 58, Ph.D, 59. Instr. Eng. Univ. B.C, 46; asst. prof, Univ. Victoria, 46-53, assoc. prof, 53-65; vis. prof, Mt. Allison Univ, 65-66, prof, 66-67; prof. ENG. HURON COL.(ONT), 67-70, SR. PROF, 70-, head dept. & dean arts, 67-69. Can. Counc. grant, 64. R.C.N.V.R, 42-45, Lt. Comdr. Renaissance Soc. Am; Shakespeare Asn. Am; Humanities Asn. Can; Asn. Can. Univ. Teachers Eng; MLA. Milton and Shakespeare. Publ: Richard II: Tudor orthodoxy or political heresy, Humanities Asn. Bull, 63; Coriolanus as Aristotle's magnanimous man, Pac. Coast Stud. Shakespeare, 66; Othello: the base Indian yet again, Mod. Lang. Rev, 67. Add: Huron College, London, Ont. H6G 1H3, Can.

POLHEMUS, ROBERT M, b. San Francisco, Calif, Dec. 12, 35; m. 59; c. 3. ENGLISH. A.B, Univ. Calif, Berkeley, 57, M.A, 59, Ph.D.(Eng), 63. Asst. prof. ENG, STANFORD UNIV, 63-68, ASSOC. PROF, 68- MLA; Philol. Asn. Pac. Coast. Publ: The changing world of Anthony Trollope, Univ. Calif, 68; Trollope's note from underground, Nineteenth-Century Fiction, 3/66. Add: Dept. of English, Stanford University, Stanford, CA 94305.

POLISKY, JEROME B, b. Oshkosh, Wis, June 6, 33; m. 64. SPEECH. B.S, Univ. Wis, 56, M.S, 59, Ph.D.(speech), 65. Asst. prof. SPEECH ARTS, AM. UNIV, 61-66, ASSOC. PROF, 66-, CHMN. DEPT. SPEECH, 71- Am. Forensic Asn. Group discussion; political rhetoric. Publ: Co-auth, Rhetorical criticism: methods and models, W.C. Brown, 68; co-auth, The problem of textual accuracy, Great Debates, 62. Add: Dept. of Speech, American University, Washington, DC 20016.

POLITELLA, DARIO, b. Lawrence, Mass, Aug. 12, 21; m. 42; c. 3. ENGLISH, JOURNALISTIC STUDIES. A.B, Univ. Mass, 47; N.Y. State Publ. Asn. fel, Syracuse Univ, 47-49, M.A, 49, Ph.D.(mass commun), 65. Asst. prof. jour, Kent State Univ, 50-51, 53-55; instr, Syracuse Univ, 55-57; asst. prof. mass commun. Ball State Univ, 62-65; ASSOC. PROF. ENG. & JOURNALISTIC STUD, UNIV. MASS, AMHERST, 65- Ed. & founder, Col. Journalist, 63-; vis. assoc. prof. Eng, Univ. Mass, Amherst, summer 65; ed. mag, Alpha Phi Gamma, 65; coord. comn. on freedoms & responsibilities, Col. Stud. Press in Am, 66-; Assoc. Col. Press res. fel, fall 72; mem, Joint Comt. Educ. Jour, Asn. Educ. in Jour. & Am. Newspaper Publ. Asn, 70-73. U.S.A, 42-46, 51-52, 1st Lt; Bronze Star Medal, Air Medal. Nat. Counc. Col. Pub. Adv.(pres, 67-69); Asn. Educ. in Jour. Aviation history; school journalism; humor in the press. Publ: Standard operating procedures for student publications, Kent State Univ, 53; Operation grasshopper, Longo, Kans, 58; co-auth, My Sunderland, Sunderland, Mass, 68; auth, Directory of the college student press in America, Oxbridge Publ, biennially, 68-; The illustrated anatomy of campus humor, Newell, 71; The making of a journalist, Oxbridge, 73; Framework for freedom of the press, Scholastic Ed, 5/51; Freedom of the student press is a state of mind, Quill, 2/65. Add: Dept. of English, University of Massachusetts, Amherst, MA 01002.

POLK, NOEL EARL, b. Picayune, Miss. Feb. 23, 43; m. 67; c. 2. AMERICAN FICTION. B.A, Miss. Col, 65, M.A, 66; Ph.D.(Eng), Univ. S.C, 70. ASST. PROF. ENG, UNIV. TEX, ARLINGTON, 70- MLA. Southern literature; William Faulkner; textual criticism. Publ: Faulkner's The jail and the meaning of Cecilia Farmer, summer 72, Faulkner's Marionettes, summer 73 & A Eudora Welty checklist, fall 73, Miss. Quart; plus two others. Add: Dept. of English, University of Texas at Arlington, Arlington, TX 76019.

POLLAK, PAULINA S, b. San Francisco, Calif, June 17, 27; m. 69. ENGLISH. B.A, Univ. South. Calif, 49, M.A, 52, Bing Found. grant, 60, Ph.D, 61. Prod. asst. TV, Columbia Broadcasting Syst, 53-55; asst. producer TV commercials, J. Walter Thompson Co, 55-57; instr. ENG, San Fernando Valley State Col, 60-61; asst. prof, CALIF. STATE UNIV, FULLERTON, 61-64, assoc. prof, 64-68, PROF, 68- Discussion group leader world affairs, Univ. Calif, Los Angeles, 55-59; lectr, Univ. South. Calif, 58-61. Col. Eng. Asn; NCTE. Novels of Thomas Love Peacock, Joyce Cary and D.H. Lawrence. Publ: Peacock's use of music in his novels, J. Eng. & Ger. Philol, 7/55; The philosophical principles in Joyce Cary's work, West. Humanities Rev, spring 66; Letters of D.H. Lawrence to Sallie and Willie Hopkin, J. Mod. Lit, 6/73. Add: Dept. of English, California State University, Fullerton, 800 N. State College Blvd, Fullerton, CA 92634.

POLLAK, VIVIAN R, b. Washington, D.C, July 1, 38; m. 60; c. 2. ENGLISH & AMERICAN LITERATURE. A.B, Smith Col, 59; M.A, Brandeis Univ, 61, Ph.D.(Eng), 69. ASST. PROF. ENG, CHEYNEY STATE COL, 70- MLA. American poetry; 19th century American literature; women in American literature. Publ: That fine prosperity: economic metaphors in Emily Dickinson's poetry, Mod. Lang. Quart, 6/73; Emily Dickinson's valentines, Am. Quart, 3/73. Add: Dept. of English, Cheyney State College, Cheyney, PA 19319.

POLLARD, HAZEL M. (BATZER), b. Bay City, Mich, Apr. 29, 17; m. 72. ENGLISH, CRITICISM. B.A, Cent. Mich. Univ, 39; M.A, Univ. Mich, 47, Harry A. Parker fel, 48-49, univ. fel, 50-54, Ph.D.(Eng), 56. Res. asst. drama, Univ. Mich, 48-49; assoc. prof. Eng, Morningside Col, 54, prof. Eng. & dir. creative writing & compos, 55-58; assoc. prof. Eng, Tex. Woman's Univ, 59-60; East. Ill. Univ, 60-61; prof. & coord. humanities, Delta Col, 61-64; assoc. prof. Eng, East. Ill. Univ, 64-66; prof, Va. State Col, Norfolk, 66-67; ASSOC. PROF. GRAD. ENG, UNIV OTTAWA (ONT), 67- Res. honorarium, Univ. Mich, 58-59; consult. & lectr. educ. TV prog. lit. & art, Delta Col, 61-64; consult, Can. Counc. Res. Asn, 67- MLA; Shakespeare Asn. Am; Renaissance Soc. Am; Am. Soc. Aesthet; Am. Soc. Theatre Res. Renaissance drama, especially Shakespeare; metaphysical poetry; principles of approach to literature and other arts. Publ: Co-auth, From human sentience to drama: principles of critical analysis, tragic and comedic, Ohio Univ, 73; auth, Heroic and sentimental elements in Thomas Otway's tragedies, Univ. Salzburg, (in press); Shakespeare's influence in Thomas Otway's Caius Marius, Rev. Univ. Ottawa, 69. Add: Dept. of English, University of Ottawa, Ottawa, Ont. K1N 6N5, Can.

POLLARD, RICHARD N, b. S.Dak, Apr. 15, 22; m. 49, 72; c. 5. COMPARATIVE LITERATURE, ENGLISH RENAISSANCE, CRITICISM. A.B, Univ. S.Dak, 48, fel, 48-49, M.A, 49; fel, Univ. Strasbourg, France, 49-50; D. ès L, Univ. Paris, 60. Asst. prof. ENG, École Normale Inst, Strasbourg-Neudorf, France, 49-50; instr, Univ. S.Dak, 50-51; Black Hills Teachers Col, 51-52; asst. prof, Adams State Col, 52-61, assoc. prof, 61-64; East. Ill. Univ, 64-66; PROF, Norfolk State Col, 66-67; UNIV. OTTAWA, 67-, CO-DIR. Ph.D. PROG. ENG. RENAISSANCE, 67-, chmn. grad. Eng, 69-70. Fr. Govt. scholar, 49-50; res. grant appraiser, Can. Counc, 67- U.S.N, 42-43. MLA; Renaissance Soc. Am; Shakespeare Asn. Am; Renaissance Eng. Text Soc; Int. Platform Asn. Shakespeare; principles of literary and art criticism; various Renaissance areas. Publ: Humanities, Karamu, 66; co-auth, From human sentience to drama: principles of critical analysis, tragic and comedic, Ohio Univ, 74; auth, Authorship of the Spanish tragedy additions, Rev. Univ. Ottawa, 70; plus others. Add: Dept. of English, University of Ottawa, Ottawa, Ont. K1N 6N5, Can.

POLLIN, BURTON RALPH, b. Worcester, Mass, May 8, 16; m. 44; c. 2. ENGLISH. B.A, City Col. New York, 36, Tremaine fel, 37, John Hay Whitney fel, 52-53; Ph.D.(Eng), Columbia Univ, 62. Teacher & chmn. ENG, New York Bd. Educ, 36-63; assoc. prof, BRONX COMMUNITY COL, 63-64, PROF, 64- Lectr, City Col. New York, 47-63; Am. Philos. Soc. grants, 63, 64; Carl & Lily Pforzheimer Found. grant, 66; N.Y. State Univ. Res. Found. summer fels, 66, 67, 68, distinguished fel, 68; Am. Counc. Learned Soc. grant, 68; Guggenheim fel, 73-74. Qm.C, U.S.A, 43. MLA. English and American literature of early 19th century; English and French literary relations. Publ: Education and enlightenment in the works of William Godwin, Las Americas, 62; ed, introd. & notes, Godwin's Italian letters, Nebr. Univ, 65; co-ed. & introd, Political justice: a satirical poem of 1736, Augustan Reprint Soc, Univ. Calif, 65; ed. & introd, Four early pamphlets of William Godwin, 66 & co-ed. & introd, Godwin's uncollected writings: six pamphlets and material in periodicals, 68, Scholars' Facsimiles; auth, Godwin criticism, Toronto Univ, 67; Dictionary of names and titles in Poe's works, 68 & The music for Shelley's poetry: an annotated bibliography of 13000 musical compositions, 74, Da Capo; Discoveries in Poe, Notre Dame Univ, 70; ed, introd. & notes, De la justice politique: Benjamin Constant's translation of Godwin's major work, Laval Univ, 72; Godwin's Letters of Verax, J. Hist. Ideas, summer 64; Hamlet, a successful suicide, Shakespeare Stud. I, 66; Poe as possible author of Harper's Ferry, Am. Lit, 5/68. Add: 800 West End Ave, New York, NY 10025.

POLLOCK, JOHN JOSEPH, b. New York, N.Y, Jan. 14, 45; m. 69. SEVENTEENTH CENTURY LITERATURE. B.A, Univ. Calif, Davis, 67, M.A, 69, NDEA fel, 67-71, Ph.D.(Eng), 71. ASST. PROF. ENG, SAN JOSE STATE UNIV, 71- MLA; Am. Renaissance Soc; Philol. Asn; Pac. Coast. Late Renaissance poetry. Publ: Donne's Lamentation of Jeremy and the Geneva Bible, Eng. Stud, (in press); The divided consciousness of Henry Vaughan, Papers Lang. & Lit, (in press); George Herbert's enclosure imagery, Seventeenth Century News, (in press); plus one other. Add: Dept. of English, San Jose State University, 125 S. Seventh St, San Jose, CA 95114.

POLLOCK, THOMAS CLARK, b. Monmouth, Ill, Mar. 31, 02; m. 30. AMERICAN LITERATURE. A.B, Muskingum Col, 22, D.Litt, 48; A.M, Ohio State

Univ, 27; Ph.D.(Eng), Univ. Pa, 30; hon. Dr, Univ. Brazil, 59, Univ. Bahia, Brazil, 59. Prof. philos. Gordon Col, Univ. Panjab, Pakistan, 22-24; instr. pub. speaking, Muskingum Col, 24-25; asst. Eng, Ohio State Univ, 25-26, instr, 26-28, asst. prof, 33-36, assoc. prof, 36-38; assoc. prof. Eng. & chmn. div. humanities, Univ. Omaha, 32-33; prof. Eng. & head dept, N.J. State Teachers Col, Montclair, 38-41, dean instr, 43-44; prof. Eng, educ. & chmn. dept, N.Y. UNIV, 41-43, 44-47, prof. ENG, 47-69, dean, Wash. Sq. Col, 47-62, v.pres. & secy, 62-67, EMER. PROF. ENG, 70- Trustee, Col. Retirement Equities Fund, 62-70. MLA.(v.pres, 52); NCTE (pres, 48). American theatrical history; literary criticism and theory; English education. Publ: The Philadelphia Theatre in the eighteenth century, Univ. Pa; The nature of literature, Princeton; co-auth, Thomas Wolfe at Washington Square, N.Y. Univ. Add: 7 Washington Square, New York, NY 10003.

POLZIN, DONALD E, b. Chicago, Ill, Feb. 12, 30; m. 56; c. 2. DRAMA. A.B, Ill. Col, 51; A.M, Univ. Ill, 52; Northwest. Univ, 55; Ph.D, Univ. Iowa, 61. Instr. speech, Univ. Md, 55; speech & drama, Ill. Col, 55-57; asst. prof, Coe Col, 59-61; Wright Jr. Col, 61-62; North. ILL. UNIV, 62-66, assoc. prof, 66-71, PROF. THEATRE ARTS, 71- Chmn, res. resources proj, Am. Educ. Theatre Asn, 64-68; co-ed, Players Mag, 67-70; pres. Ill. conf, AAUP, 70-72; ed, Ill. Academe, 71-73. U.S.A, 53-55. Am. Theatre Asn; Speech Commun. Asn; Cent. States Speech Commun. Asn; Theatre Libr. Asn; Am. Soc. Theatre Res; Am. Nat. Theatre & Acad. Theatre aesthetics; dramatic theory and criticism; modern drama and theatre. Add: University Theatre, Northern Illinois University, De Kalb, IL 60115.

POMEROY, MARY JOSEPH, S.P, b. Chicago, Ill, Mar. 15, 00. ENGLISH LITERATURE. A.B, St. Mary-of-the-Woods Col, 21; A.M, Columbia Univ, 24; Ph.D, Cath. Univ. Am, 27. Assoc. prof. ENG, ST. MARY-OF-THE-WOODS COL, 24-25, 27-51, prof, 51-61, dir. develop, 56-67, coord. develop, 67-70, v.pres, 60-70, exec. secy-treas, Alumnae Asn, 34-61, EMER. PROF. ENG, 70- Dir. Missions, Sisters of Providence, 70- Add: Providence Convent, St. Mary-of-the-Woods, IN 47876.

POMEROY, RALPH STANLEY, b. Alameda, Calif, Aug, 31, 26; m. 53; c. 5. SPEECH. B.A, Univ. Calif, Berkeley, 49, M.A, 51; univ. fel, Stanford, 54-55, Field-Hotaling scholar, 55, Ph.D.(speech), 60. Teacher, high sch, Calif, 53-54; acting instr. speech, Stanford Univ, 54-55; instr. Eng. & philos, Menlo Jr. Col, 55-58; acting instr. SPEECH, UNIV. CALIF, DAVIS, 58-59, instr, 59-60, from asst. prof. to ASSOC. PROF, 60-, lectr. humanities, 59, acting dir. speech, 62-63. Vis. Scholar, Humanities Inst, Oriel Col, Oxford, summer 69; symp. contrib, Alfred Tarski Symp, Univ. Calif, Berkeley, 6/71. U.S.N, 44-46, 51-52. Ad Schuster Award in Poetry, Ina M. Coolbrith Circle, Calif, 57. Speech Commun. Asn; Rhet. Soc. Am; Am. Soc. 18th Century Stud; Eng-Speaking Union; Am. Philos. Asn. Rhetorical theory and criticism; American and British public address; ordinary-language philosophy. Publ: A prey of diverse colors, Cunningham, 62; Whately's Historic doubts: origin and argument, Quart. J. Speech, 2/63; Fitness of response in Bitzer's concept of rhetorical discourse, Ga. Speech Commun. J, fall 72; Ayer on probability and evidence, Philos. & Rhet, fall 73; plus one other. Add: Dept. of Rhetoric, University of California, Davis, CA 95616.

POMMER, HENRY FRANCIS, b. Philadelphia, Pa, Apr. 8, 18; m. 45. ENGLISH. A.B, Univ. Pa, 40; A.M, Yale, 42, Ph.D, 46. Instr. ENG, Swarthmore Col, 43-45; Cornell Univ, 45-49; asst. prof, Allegheny Col, 49-53, assoc. prof, 53-61, prof, 61-68, chmn. fac. counc, 56-57, dir, independent stud. prog, 64-68, summer sch, 66-68, grad. stud, 66-68; prof. Eng, Cedar Crest Col, 68-74, dean fac. & v.pres. acad. affairs, 68-73; DEAN, RIPON COL, 74- Fund. Advan. Educ. fel, Yale, 53-54; mem, comn. ethics, Unitarian Universalist Asn, 61-63, bd. trustees, 65-69. American literature; criticism. Publ: Milton and Melville, Univ. Pittsburgh, 50; Emerson's first marriage, South Ill. Univ, 67; Contents and basis of Emerson's belief in compensation, PMLA, 62; Mark Twain's Commissioner of the United States, Am. Lit, 62; The mysticism of Eugene O'Neill, Mod. Drama, 5/66. Add: Ripon College, Ripon, WI 54971.

PONDROM, CYRENA NORMAN, b. Ft. Worth, Tex, Aug. 8, 38; m. 61. COMPARATIVE LITERATURE. B.A, Univ. Tex, 59; Woodrow Wilson fel, Columbia Univ, 60-61, M.A, 61, Ph.D.(Eng. & comp. lit), 65. Instr. comp. lit, UNIV. WIS-MADISON, 63-66, asst. prof, 66-69, assoc. prof. Eng, 70-73, PROF. ENG. & ASST. CHANCELLOR, 73-, res. comt. summer award, 67, asst. to chancellor, 71-73. Bk. rev. ed, Contemporary Lit, 67-69, asst. ed, 69-71, assoc. ed, 71-73; Am. Counc. Learned Soc. stud. fel, 68-69; mem. nat. task force on equal employ. opportunity, Am. Counc. on Educ, 73- MLA; AAUP. Philosophical implications of modern literature; modern English literary magazines. Publ: Co-ed, The contemporary writer, Univ. Wis, 72; ed, The road from Paris, Cambridge Univ, 74; auth, Kafka and phenomenology: Josef K's search for information, Wis. Stud. Contemporary Lit, winter 67; Two demonic figures: Kierkegaard's Merman and Dostoevsky's Underground man, Orbis Litterarum, 68; Conjuring reality: I.B. Singer's The magician of Lublin, In: I.B. Singer, South. Ill. Univ, 68; plus others. Add: Office of the Chancellor, 175 Bascom Hall, University of Wisconsin-Madison, Madison, WI 53706.

POOL, JOHN PAUL, b. Birmingham, Ala, Nov. 15, 24; m. 48; c. 3. ENGLISH. B.A, Birmingham-South. Col, 50; Am. Counc. Learned Soc. fel, Harvard, 50-51, A.M, 53; Univ. Tenn, 52-53; fel, Univ. Ala, 60-62, Ph.D.(Eng), 64. Instr. ENG, Univ. Ala, Birmingham, 58-60, 62-64; assoc. prof, BIRMINGHAM-SOUTH. COL, 64-70, PROF, 70- U.S.N, 44-46. MLA; Renaissance Soc. Am; Mediaeval Acad. Am. Nineteenth century, Middle and Renaissance English literature; mysticism and imagination. Publ: Contrib, Essays in honor of Richebourg Gaillard McWilliams, Birmingham-South. Col. Bull, 70. Add: Dept. of English, Birmingham-Southern College, Birmingham, AL 35204.

POOLEY, ROBERT CECIL, b. Brooklyn, N.Y, Mar. 25, 98; m. 27; c. 2. ENGLISH. A.B, Colo. State Col. Educ, 26, fel, 26-27, A.M, 27; Ph.D, Univ. Wis, 32. Asst. prof. ENG, Colo. State Col. Educ, 27-31; UNIV. WIS-MADISON, 31-35, assoc. prof, 35-40, prof, 40-68, chmn. freshman Eng, 46-47, chmn. integrated lib. stud, 47-68, EMER. PROF, 68- Dir, Wis. Eng. Lang. Arts Curriculum Ctr, 63-68. Distinguished Serv. Award, Wis. Counc. Teachers Eng, 63. Consult, Army Serv. Forces, 42-43. NCTE (pres, 41); Conf. Res. Eng.(pres, 38); Am. Dialect Soc. English usage; English linguistics in education; teaching of literature. Publ: Teaching English usage, 46 & Teaching English grammar, 57, Appleton; co-ed, America reads series, Scott, 62-63, new ed, 68-69. Add: Apt. 402, 1580 Arcadia Dr, Jacksonville, FL 32207.

POPE, CURTIS L, b. Alba, Tex, Jan. 25, 19; m. 51. SPEECH, DRAMA. B.S, E.Tex. State Univ, 41; M.A, Univ. Iowa, 49, Ph.D.(drama), 57; Univ. Tex, 53; Univ. Mo, 55. Instr. radio, Univ. Iowa, 47-49; Univ. Va, summer 49; from instr. to PROF. SPEECH & DRAMA, E.TEX. STATE UNIV, 49-, HEAD DEPT, 65- Directing Award, Am. Col. Theatre Festival, Wash, D.C, 71. C.Eng, A.U.S, 41-46, Capt. Am. Theatre Asn. Scenic design; children's theatre; American theatre history. Add: Dept. of Speech & Drama, East Texas State University, Commerce, TX 75428.

POPE, ELIZABETH MARIE, b. Washington, D.C, May 1, 17. ENGLISH LITERATURE. A.B, Bryn Mawr Col, 40; Ph.D, Johns Hopkins Univ, 44. Instr. Eng, Mills Col, 44-47; Folger res. fel, Folger Shakespeare Libr, Wash, D.C, 47-48; from asst. prof. to assoc. prof. ENG, MILLS COL, 48-62, PROF PROF, 62- Am. Soc. Aesthetics; fel. Nat. Counc. Relig. Higher Educ. Seventeenth century theology and literature; Milton; Shakespeare. Add: Dept. of English, Mills College, Oakland, CA 94613.

POPE, JOHN COLLINS, b. Cleveland, Ohio, Dec. 4, 04; m. 32; c. 3. ENGLISH. A.B, Yale, 25, Ph.D, 31. Instr. ENG, YALE, 28-32, asst. prof, 32-42, assoc. prof, 42-45, prof, 45-71, EMER. PROF. ENG, 71- Guggenheim fel, 48-49. MLA; fel. Mediaeval Acad. Am; Am. Acad. Arts & Sci. Old English language and literature; history of Old English literature. Publ: The rhythm of Beowulf, Yale, 42, 2nd rev. ed, 66; ed, Seven Old English poems, Bobbs, 66 & Homilies of Aelfric: a supplementary collection, 2 vols, Early Eng. Text Soc, 67 & 68. Add: 596 Prospect St, New Haven, CT 06511.

POPE, KARL T, b. Vernal, Utah, May 7, 37; m. 60; c. 6. DRAMATIC ARTS & THEATRE. B.A, Brigham Young Univ, 62, M.A, 64; fel, Wayne State Univ, 63-66, Ph.D.(theatre), 66. Instr. educ, Brigham Young Univ, 60-63; speech, Wayne State Univ, 63-65; asst. prof, Kearney State Col, 65-66; DRAMATIC ARTS, BRIGHAM YOUNG UNIV, 66-73, ASSOC. PROF, 73- Theatre; interpretation; speech. Publ: A syllabus for students of voice, diction and interpretation, Brigham Young Univ, 71. Add: Dept. of Dramatic Arts, Brigham Young University, Provo, UT 84601.

POPE, WILLARD BISSELL, b. Detroit, Mich, May 29, 03; c. 2. ENGLISH LITERATURE. A.B, Hamilton Col, 25; Ph.D, Harvard, 32. Instr. ENG, Emory Univ, 26-29; N.C. State Col, 33-34; UNIV. VT, 34-36, asst. prof, 37-42, assoc. prof, 42-47, prof, 47-68, EMER. PROF, 68- Dir, Browning Inst, 72- MLA; Keats-Shelley Asn. Am.(dir, 49). Keats; Haydon. Publ: Ed, Diary of Benjamin Robert Haydon, (5 vols), 60-63 & Invisible friends: the correspondence of Elizabeth Barrett Barrett and Benjamin Robert Haydon 1842-1845, 72, Harvard; co-auth, What to read; co-ed, Life of Keats. Add: 100 Overlake Park, Burlington, VT 05401.

POPKIN, HENRY, b. Providence, R.I, Apr. 20, 24. ENGLISH. A.B, Brown Univ, 43; A.M, 44; A.M, Harvard, 46, Ph.D.(Eng), 51. Instr. ENG, Newark Col, Rutgers Univ, 46-49; tutor, Queens Col, 49-51, instr, 51; Brandeis Univ, 52-55, asst. prof, 55-59; asst. prof, N.Y. Univ, 60-61, assoc. prof, 61-67; PROF, STATE UNIV. N.Y. BUFFALO, 67- Fulbright prof. Am. lit, Univ. Lyons & Clermont-Ferrand, France, 59-60; New York dramatic critic, London Times, 60-, adv. drama, Col. Eng, 60-61. MLA. Elizabethan and modern drama; popular arts. Publ: Drama In: Contemporary Literary scholarship, Appleton, 58; The two theatres of Henry James, New Eng. Quart; The plays of Tennessee Williams, Tulane Drama Rev, 60. Add: Dept. of English, 6 Annex B, State University of New York at Buffalo, Buffalo, NY 14214.

POPOVICH, HELEN HOUSER, b. El Paso, Tex, Nov. 19, 35; m. 67. ENGLISH. B.A, Univ. Tex, El Paso, 55, M.A, 58; Ph.D.(Eng), Univ. Kans, 65. Asst. prof. ENG, UNIV. S.FLA, 65-73, ASSOC. PROF. & ASST. TO CHMN. DEPT, 73- MLA; NCTE; Shakespeare Asn. Am. Tragedy; Shakespeare; modern drama. Publ: Hamm: Beckett's God in Nagg's image, S.Atlantic Bull, 1/72. Add: Dept. of English, University of South Florida, Tampa, FL 33620.

PORTE, JOEL MILES, b. Brooklyn, N.Y, Nov. 13, 33; m. 62; c. 1. ENGLISH & AMERICAN LITERATURE. A.B, City Col. New York, 57; A.M, Harvard, 58, Ph.D, 62. Lectr. Eng, City Col. New York, summers 58 & 59; instr, HARVARD, 62-64, asst. prof, 64-68, assoc. prof, 68-69, PROF. ENG. & AM. LIT, 69- MLA; Am. Stud. Asn; Col. Eng. Asn. American literature; 19th century studies; modern literature. Publ: Emerson and Thoreau: transcendentalists in conflict, 66 & The romance in America: studies in Cooper, Poe, Hawthorne, Melville, and James, 69, Wesleyan Univ; Emerson, Thoreau, and the double consciousness, New Eng. Quart, 68; Henry Thoreau and the reverend poluphloisboios thalassa, In: The chief glory of every people, South. Ill. Univ, 73; The problem of Emerson, In: Harvard Eng. Stud. No. 4, Harvard, 73; plus others. Add: Dept. of English & American Literature & Language, Warren House, Harvard University, Cambridge, MA 02138.

PORTE, MICHAEL SHELDON, b. Chicago, Ill, Jan. 20, 32; m. 59; c. 3. COMMUNICATION, DRAMA. B.S. & M.S, Northwest. Univ, 53, Ph.D, 60; Columbia Univ, 53-54; Copenhagen Sch. Econ. & Bus. Admin, 65. Instr. bus. writing, Northwest. Univ, 56-60; asst. prof. Eng. & comp. lit, UNIV. CINCINNATI, 60-65, SPEECH, 65-66, assoc. prof, 66-69, PROF, 69-, DIR. COMMUN. FORUM & DIR. GRAD. STUD. SPEECH & THEATRE ARTS, 72- Fel, Weil Inst, Isak Dinesen's concept of God, summer 65; vis. prof. commun, Univ. South. Calif, 66; co-founder, Counc. Commun, Soc, 67; res. mod. theatre, Univ. Sussex, 68-69; consult, Procter & Gamble, 69-; mem. film adv. panel, Ohio Arts Counc, 72-74; consult, Nat. Safety Counc, Monsanto Res. Corp, Formica Res. & Develop, Alcoa, U.S. Steel & Instrument Soc. Am. Bus. Commun. Asn.(rev. ed, Bull, 62-65, pres, 68, chmn. grad. educ, 73); Int. Commun. Asn. Communication theory; drama and theatre; film. Publ: Co-auth, Effective reports and case analyses, Northwest. Univ. 59; auth, The servant in Restoration comedy, Xerox, 60; Technical writers manual, Mound Lab, 63; Report writing seminar for engineers, Badgett & Smith, 64; co-ed, Cinema now, Univ, Cincinnati, 68; co-auth, Television: escape or encounter; J. Univ. Film Producers Asn, 66; auth, Elements of a proposal, Writer's Dig, 67; co-auth, Building industrial communication courses, J. Commun, 67 & The surprising unconscious of Edward Albee, Drama Surv, winter 68-69; auth, Teaching communication in a business orientation program for Black students, Am. Bus. Commun. Asn. Bull, 6/72; Add: Communication Forum, Dept. of Speech & Theatre Arts, Box 379, University of Cincinnati, Cincinnati, OH 45221.

PORTER, AGNES LOUISE, b. Pittsburgh, Pa, Feb. 14, 32. SPEECH PSYCHOLOGY. B.A, Pa. State Univ, 54; M.A, Univ. Pittsburgh, 59; Ph.D.(commun), Ohio State Univ, 64. Asst. SPEECH, Univ. Pittsburgh, 56-57; instr, Marshall Univ, 59-61; asst, Ohio State Univ, 61-64; ASSOC. PROF, SOUTH. CONN. STATE COL, 65-, ed, Speech Jour, 66-73, dir. speech commun. prog, 68-73. Ed, W.Va. State Speech Jour, 60-61. Speech Commun. Asn; Int. Commun. Asn. Communications. Add: Dept. of Speech, Southern Connecticut State College, 501 Crescent St, New Haven, CT 06515.

PORTER, CAROLYN JANE, b. Houston, Tex, Jan. 2, 46. AMERICAN LITERATURE. B.A, Rice Univ, 67, M.A, 72, Ph.D.(Eng), 73. ASST. PROF. ENG, UNIV. CALIF, BERKELEY, 72- MLA. William Faulkner; novel; modern American literature. Add: Dept. of English, University of California, Berkeley, CA 94720.

PORTER, DAVID THOMAS, b. Buffalo, N.Y, Sept. 15, 28; m. 57; c. 3. ENGLISH & AMERICAN LITERATURE. A.B, Hamilton Col, 50; fel, Univ. Rochester, 61, Ph.D.(Eng), 63. Instr. ENG, UNIV. MASS, AMHERST, 62-64, asst. prof, 64-66, assoc. prof, 67-72, PROF, 72-, dir. grad. stud. Eng, 68-69. Fulbright-Hays lectr, Italy, 66-67; vis. prof, Univ. Keele, 69-70. U.S.A, 55-57. MLA; Col. Eng. Asn.(mem. comt. advan. degrees, 71-73). American poetry and poetics; literary criticism; contemporary British poetry. Publ: The art of Emily Dickinson's early poetry, Harvard, 66; Emily Dickinson: the formative years, Mass. Rev, spring 65; Emily Dickinson: poetics of doubt, Emerson Soc. Quart, 70. Add: Dept. of English, University of Massachusetts, Amherst, MA 01002.

PORTER, JACK, b. Clinton, Ky, Oct. 8, 25; m. 45; c. 3. COMMUNICATION ARTS. A.B, George Peabody Col, 49; M.A, Univ. N.C, 52; Ph.D.(commun. arts), Univ. Denver, 62. Instr. Eng. & speech, Maury High Sch, Norfolk, Va, 49-50; speech & drama, Armstrong Col. Savannah, 52-55; asst. prof, Furman Univ, 55-56; instr. Eng. & speech, N.C. STATE UNIV, 56-60, asst. prof, 60-65, DIR. TV & ASSOC. DIR. CONTINUING EDUC, 65- U.S.M.C, 42-45, Sgt. South. Speech Asn; Southeast. Theatre Conf.(v.pres); Nat. Asn. Educ. Broadcasters; Dept. Audiovisual Instr, NEA. Educational television; other instructional media. Publ: Teacher-speaker as speech-teacher, N.C. Educ, 4/65; Whence and whither: ETV in North Carolina, N.C. J. Speech, 11/67. Add: Box 5546, North Carolina State University, Raleigh, NC 27607.

PORTER, JENNY LIND, b. Ft. Worth, Tex, Sept. 3, 27. ENGLISH. B.A, Tex. Christian Univ, 48, M.A, 49; Ph.D, Univ. Tex, 55; hon. D.Litt, Univ. Free Asia, Pakistan, 70. Instr. ENG, Univ. Tenn, Knoxville, 58-59; asst. prof, W.Tex. State Col, 59-61; Southwest Tex. State Col, 61-64; assoc. prof. & chmn. dept, Tex. Lutheran Col, 64-68; PROF. & CHMN. DEPT, HUSTON-TILLOTSON COL, 68- Dallas Tex. Christian Univ. Woman's Club fel, 45-46; Jesse Jones fels, 51-56; Univ. Tex. fels, 51-53; Scarbrough fel, 54; lectr, various Tex. cities, 60-63; KLRN educ. TV, 63-64 mem, Ctr. Int. Stud. & Exchange, Rome, 71-; Consortium for Res. Training res. award, 74. Aleda Hall Int. lyric award, 57; Margie B. Boswell poetry prize, Tex. Christian Univ, 59; A.J. Armstrong-Browning Award, Poetry Soc. Tex, 60, awards, 65, 67; Tex. state poet laureate, 64, 65; Odessa Col. Writers' Workshop ms. award, 66; Gold Medal for poetry & humane endeavors, Poets Laureate Int. & Pres. Marcos of P.I, 70; Gold Medal, Leonardo da Vinci Acad, Rome, 72. Poetry Soc. Am.(Alice Fay di Castagnola Award, 70); Asn. Res. & Enlightenment; Poets Laureate Int; S.Cent. Mod. Lang. Asn. Middle English; romanticism; creative writing. Publ: The lantern of Diogenes, Naylor, 54; Azle and the attic room, Ward Ritchie, 57; The witch poesy, Steck, 60; co-auth, On the trellis of memory, Carlton, 71; co-auth, An ancient formula, In: The Edgar Cayce reader, Paperback Libr, 69; auth, The quiet window, In: The Diamond anthology of the Poetry Society of America, A.S. Barnes, 71; Travis' letters from the Alamo, In: Texas in color, Hastings, 71; plus many other transl, poems & arts. in var. jour. Add: Dept. of English, Huston-Tillotson College, 1820 E. Eighth St, Austin, TX 78752.

PORTER, MARVIN GILBERT, b. Dallas, Tex, Dec. 4, 37; m. 71; c. 1. AMERICAN & ENGLISH LITERATURE. B.A, N.Tex. State Univ, 61, fel, 61-62, M.A, 62; Ph.D.(Eng), Univ. Ore, 69. Instr. Eng, Univ. Ore, 62-64; Univ. Houston, 64-66; asst. prof, Lane Community Col, 66-67; instr, Univ. Ore, 67-70, asst. prof, 71; ASST. PROF. ENG. & DIR. UNDERGRAD. STUD, UNIV. MO-COLUMBIA, 71- Univ. Mo. Res. Counc. grant-in-aid, summer 73. U.S.M.C, 57-59. AAUP; MLA. Contemporary fiction; theory of literary criticism; American transcendentalism. Publ: Whence the power?: the artistry and humanity of Saul Bellow, Univ. Mo, 74; Herzog: a transcendental solution to an existential problem, Forum, spring 69; Narrative stance in Four Quartets: choregraphy and commentary, Univ. Rev, fall 69; Spiritual activism and radical sophistication in the contemporary American novel, Stud. in Novel, fall 71. Add: 700 Westmount, Columbia, MO 65201.

PORTER, RAYMOND JAMES, b. Mt. Vernon, N.Y, Jan. 3, 35; m. 60; c. 3. ENGLISH. B.A, Holy Cross Col, 57; M.A, Columbia Univ, 63, Ph.D,(Eng), 70. PROF. ENG, IONA COL, 61- MLA; Am. Comt. Irish Stud; James Joyce Soc. Irish literature; 19th century English novel; 20th century comparative novel. Publ: Co-ed. & contrib, Modern Irish literature: essays in honor of William York Tindall, Iona Col. & Twayne, 72; Brendan Behan, Columbia Univ, 73; P.H. Pearse, Twayne, 73; The Irish messianic tradition, Emory Univ. Quart, 66; co-auth, Jocelin and Oedipus, Cithara, 66; Leitmotiv in Iris Murdoch's Under the net, Mod. Fiction Stud, 69. Add: 46 Revere Rd, Larchmont, NY 10538.

PORTER, THOMAS EMMET, S.J, b. Cleveland, Ohio, Jan. 13, 28. ENGLISH. A.B, Loyola Univ. Chicago, 49, M.A, 54; Ph.L, W.Baden Col, 52, Th.L, 59; M.A, Cath. Univ. Am, 60; Ph.D.(Eng), Univ. N.C, 65. Grad. fel, Cath. Univ. Am, 59-60; asst. Univ. N.C, 63-64; asst. prof. ENG, UNIV. DETROIT, 64-69, assoc. prof, 69-72, PROF, 72-, ACTING DEAN ARTS & SCI, 73-, dean Colombiere Col, 64-68, chmn. dept. Eng, 69-70. Mem. bd. trustees, Marquette Univ, 73. MLA. Modern drama; dramatic criticism. Publ: Myth and modern American drama, Wayne State Univ, 69; Samuel Beckett: dramatic tradition and the Auslander, Eire-Ireland, 3/69. Add: Dept. of English, University of Detroit, 4001 W. McNichols, Detroit, MI 48221.

PORTNOFF, COLLICE HENRY, b. San Luis Obispo, Calif, Dec. 9, 98; m. 31; c. 1. ENGLISH. A.B, Univ. Calif, 21, A.M, 22; Ph.D, Stanford Univ, 27; fel, Am. Acad. Rome, 28, M.A, 28. Assoc. prof. Span, Ariz. State Col, 30-40; Cryptanalyst, U.S. Sig.C, Wash, D.C, 42; transl, Allied Mil. Govt, Wash, D.C, 42-43; prof. ENG, ARIZ. STATE UNIV, 45-70, chmn. dept, 54-59, EMER. PROF, 70- Carter Mem. fel, Am. Acad. Rome, 27-29; co-auth, Naked came I, produced, Ariz. State Univ, 57; bk. ed, Ariz. Repub. Phoenix. NCTE; Int. Soc. Gen. Semantics; Conf. Col. Compos. & Commun; Centro E Stud. Scamb. Int; Am. Transl. Asn; Am. Acad. Rome. Romance languages; the works of Maria Martinez Sierra. Add: Dept. of English, Arizona State University, Tempe, AZ 85281.

POSEY, HORACE GADSDEN, JR, b. Brooklyn, N.Y, Feb. 11, 28; m. 61; c. 2. ENGLISH LITERATURE. B.A, Univ. N.C, Chapel Hill, 56; B.A, Oxford, 59; Ph.D.(Eng), Univ. Wis-Madison, 64. Asst. ENG, Univ. Wis-Madison, 59-63; asst. prof, Univ. Toledo, 63-65; PURDUE UNIV, FT. WAYNE, 65-69, ASSOC. PROF, 69-, grant, 68. U.S.A.F, 50-54. MLA; Midwest Mod. Lang. Asn; AAUP. Nineteenth century British literature; British Romantic poetry; British Romantic poetic theory. Publ: Shelley and modern aesthetics, Bucknell Rev, spring 71; Muted satire in Anthem for doomed youth, Essays Criticism, 10/71. Add: 609 Springbrook Rd, Ft. Wayne, IN 46825.

POSS, STANLEY HORN, b. Pasadena, Calif, June 30, 27. ENGLISH. M.A, Claremont Grad. Sch, 52; fel, Univ. Wash, 52-54, Ph.D.(Eng), 59. Assoc. Eng, Univ. Wash, 54-56; from instr. to PROF, CALIF. STATE UNIV, FRESNO, 56- Fulbright prof. Am. lit, Ain Shams Univ, Cairo, 65-66; fel, Nat. Endowment for Humanities Summer Sem, Amherst, Mass, 73. Am. Comt. Irish Stud. James Joyce; modern novel; Irish history and literature. Publ: Ulysses and the comedy of the immobilized act, J. Eng. Lit. Hist; A portrait of the artist as beginner, Univ. Kans. City Rev; Interview with Christopher Isherwood, The London Mag. Add: Dept. of English, California State University, Fresno, Shaw & Cedar Ave, Fresno, CA 93710.

POST, MARY FRANCES, b. Whittier, Calif, Oct. 18, 30; m. 66. ENGLISH, LINGUISTICS. B.A, Whittier Col, 59; M.A, Calif. State Col. Los Angeles, 60; NDEA fel, Ind. Univ, 60-63, Ph.D.(ling), 64. Teacher, Artesia High Sch, 63-64; from asst. prof. to ASSOC. PROF. HUMANITIES & ENG, RIO HONDO COL, 64- Lectr, Calif. State Col. Los Angeles, 64-65, 66-68 & asst. prof. Eng. & ling, summer 67; lectr, Calif. State Col. Long Beach, 65-66. Ling. Soc. Am; MLA. Literature. Add: 5636 S. Norwalk Blvd, Whittier, CA 90601.

POST, ROBERT M, b. Buckhannon, W.Va, Dec. 2, 35. SPEECH. A.B, W.Va. Wesleyan Col, 56; M.A, Ohio Univ, 58, Ph.D.(speech), 61. Asst. SPEECH, Ohio Univ, 56-58, teaching fel, 58-60; instr, UNIV. WASH, 60-62, asst. prof, 62-68, ASSOC. PROF, 68- Speech Commun. Asn; West. Speech Commun. Asn. Plays of Edward Albee; oral interpretation of literature. Publ: The oral approach to the teaching of high school literature, 3/68 & An oral interpreter's approach to the teaching of elementary school literature, 9/71, Speech Teacher; Cognitive dissonance in the plays of Edward Albee, Quart. J. Speech, 2/69; plus others. Add: Dept. of Speech, University of Washington, Seattle, WA 98195.

POST, WINIFRED L, b. Worcester, Mass, Feb. 22, 11. ENGLISH. A.B, Radcliffe Col, 33, A.M, 34; M.A.T, Harvard, 41. Teacher Latin, Brantwood Hall, Bronxville, N.Y, 34-36; ENG, Hockaday Sch, Dallas, Tex, 36-39; head dept, Wykeham Rise, Wash, Conn, 40-42; TEACHER & DEPT. HEAD, DANA HALL SCH, WELLESLEY, MASS, 42- Winthrop Sargent Prize, Harvard, 32, 33, Phi Delta Kappa Prize, Harvard Sch. Educ, 41; mem. & chmn. Eng, exam. comt, Nat. Asn. Independent Schs, 46-53; exam. advan. placement in Eng, Col. Entrance Exam. Bd, 57-59, mem. Col. Bd. Comn. Eng, 59-, chmn. publ. comt, 12,000 Stud. & Their Eng. Teachers, 68; mem, Sch. & Col. Conf. Eng, 58- Williston Acad. citation, 65. Secondary school English. Publ: Five compositions from a college preparatory classroom, Mass. Counc. Pub. Schs, 62; End-of-year examinations in English for college-bound students, grades 9-12, Col. Bd. Comn. Eng, 63. Add: Dana Hall School, Wellesley, MA 02181.

POSTON, LAWRENCE S, III, b. Louisville, Ky, Oct. 29, 38; m. 66. ENGLISH. B.A, Univ. Okla, 60; M.A, Princeton, 62, Ph.D.(Eng), 63. Instr. ENG, UNIV. NEBR-LINCOLN, 63-64, asst. prof, 64-67, assoc. prof, 67-72, PROF, 72-, fac. summer fels, 65, 68. Mem. adv. comt, Am. Speech, 66-67. MLA; NCTE; AAUP (assoc. secy, Wash. Off, 69-71, ed, bull, 70-); Victorian Stud. Asn. West. Can. Victorian interest in the Italian Renaissance and Anglo-Italian literary relations; 19th century English literature; 19th century urban history. Publ: Setting and theme in Romola, Nineteenth-Century Fiction, 3/66; Thomas Adolphus Trollope: a Victorian Anglo-Florentine, Bull, John Rylands Libr, autumn 66; Browning's political skepticism, PMLA, 3/73. Add: Dept. of English, 201-C Andrews Hall, University of Nebraska-Lincoln, Lincoln, NE 68508.

POTEET, LEWIS JARRETTE, b. Watonga, Okla, June 21, 40; m. 63; c. 2. ENGLISH. A.B, Bethany Nazarene Col, 61; M.A, Univ. Okla, 63; fel, Univ. Minn, 66-67, Ph.D.(Eng), 68. Instr. Eng. & asst. dir. freshman Eng, Univ. Minn, 64-66; ASST. PROF. ENG. & DIR. FRESHMAN COMPOS, CONCORDIA UNIV, 67- MLA. Late Victorian English literature; American culture; art and architectural history. Publ: Co-auth, Themes and exercises, 64 & Expository writing: study and practice, 65, Univ. Minn. Add: Dept. of English, Concordia University, 1435 Drummond St, Montreal 25, P.Q, Can.

POTOKER, EDWARD M, b. Newark, N.J, June 13, 31; m. 58; c. 1. ENGLISH & COMPARATIVE LITERATURE. A.B, Dartmouth Col, 53; M.A, Columbia Univ, 55, pres. fel, 63-64, Ph.D.(comp. lit), 64; Fulbright scholar, Univ. Munich, 55-56. Collator ed. staff, New Yorker Mag, 57-58; instr. Eng, Univ. Rochester, 58-59; lectr, Hunter Col, 60; City Col. New York, 60-63, instr. ENG. & COMP. LIT, 64-65, asst. prof, 66-67; BARUCH COL, CITY UNIV. NEW YORK, 67-71, ASSOC. PROF. & CHMN. DEPT, 71- MLA; AAUP; Int. Platform Asn. Ronald Firbank; 20th century British fiction; modern German literature. Publ: Ronald Firbank, Columbia Univ, 69; Recent developments in German literature, In: Encycl. Int, Grolier, 68; Mostly mama, Dartmouth Alumni Mag, 72; ed, Ronald Firbank-Carl VanVechten correspondence, Bull. N.Y. Pub. Libr, 73-74; plus others. Add: Dept. of English, Baruch College, 17 Lexington Ave, New York, NY 10010.

POTTER, ADALINE PATES, b. Monongahela, Pa, Nov. 17, 09; m. 36. ENGLISH. A.B, Mt. Holyoke Col, 31; M.A, Smith Col, 35, grad. scholar, 38-40. Instr. ENG, Northfield Sch. Girls, 35-38; MT. HOLYOKE COL, 48-60, ASSOC. PROF. & FOR. STUDENT ADV, 60- Nat. Asn. For. Stud. Affairs; MLA. Linguistics; American literature; 18th century biography. Add: Dept. of English, Mt. Holyoke College, South Hadley, MA 01075.

POTTER, DAVID, b. New York, N.Y, May 12, 15; m. 50; c. 2. SPEECH. B.S, Rutgers Univ, 37, A.M, 39; summers, Northwest. Univ, 38-40; Ph.D, Columbia Univ, 43. Instr, Rutgers Univ, 37-40; instr, Teachers Col. & lectr, sch. dent. hyg, Columbia Univ, 40-43; asst. prof, Rutgers Univ, 46-49; prof. speech & head dept, Univ. Akron, 49-50; assoc. prof, Mich. State Univ, 50-60; PROF. SPEECH, SOUTH. ILL. UNIV, CARBONDALE, 60- Instr, Am. Inst. Banking, N.J, 38-39, 47-49; vis. prof, Col. Eng, N.Y. Univ, 48-49. Airways Commun. Syst, U.S.A, 44-46, Sgt. Speech Commun. Asn; Cent. States Speech Asn; Int. Commun. Asn. Adult Educ. Asn. U.S. Speech education; rhetoric and public address; behavioral sciences. Publ: Contrib, History of speech education of America; co-auth, Discussion, Wadsworth, 63; ed, Landmarks in rhetoric and public address, 63 & co-auth, The colonial idiom, 70, South. Ill. Univ; plus others. Add: 2704 Kent Dr, Carbondale, IL 62901.

POTTER, EDWARD EARLE, b. Rock Island, Ill, Mar. 22, 12; m. 38, 66; c. 1. ENGLISH. A.B, St. Ambrose Col, 36; A.M, Univ. Notre Dame, 38; Ph.D, Univ. Mich, 55. Instr. Eng. & polit. sci, Univ. Toledo, 38-41; sales promotion mgr, aviation div, B.F. Goodrich Co, Akron, Ohio, 43-47; assoc. prof. ENG, Evansville Col, 48-49; instr, EAST. MICH. UNIV, 50-54, asst. prof, 55-57, assoc. prof, 58-60, PROF, 61- Fel, Univ. Notre Dame, 36-38; Univ. Mich, 50. U.S.A, 42. NCTE; Conf. Col. Compos. & Commun; Ling. Circle N.Y; Am. Dialect Soc. Linguistics; Chaucer; English literature from 1660 to 1744. Publ: The dialect of Northwestern Ohio, Univ. Mich, 55. Add: Dept. of English, Eastern Michigan University, Ypsilanti, MI 48197.

POTTER, JAMES LAIN, b. Madison, Wis, July 30, 22; m. 44; c. 2. ENGLISH. A.B, Wesleyan Univ, 44, A.M, 47; Ph.D.(Eng), Harvard, 54. Instr. ENG, Boston Univ, 48-50; Tufts Col, 51-55; TRINITY COL.(CONN), 55-57, asst. prof, 57-70, ASSOC. PROF, 70- U.S.A, 43-45. Drama and film; poetry; criticism. Publ: Elements of literature, Odyssey, 67; Seminar on the creative process, CEA Critic, 1/61; The destined pattern of Spender's Express, Col. Eng, 66. Add: Dept. of English, Trinity College, Hartford, CT 06106.

POTTER, JOHN MATTHEW, b. Milwaukee, Wis, Sept. 22, 39; m. 66; c. 1. ENGLISH LITERATURE. B.A, Univ. Wis-Madison, 61; A.M, Harvard, 62; Ph.D.(Eng), Univ. Mich, Ann Arbor, 67. ASST. PROF. ENG, HUNTER COL, 67- City Univ. New York fac. res. grant, 71. Milton Soc. Am; Renaissance Soc. Am. Seventeenth century literature; Shakespeare classics. Publ: Co-ed, Andrew marvel the garden, C.E. Merrill, 70; auth, Old comedy in Bartholomew fair, Criticism, 68; Another porker in the garden of Epicurus Marvell's Hortus and The garden, Stud. Eng. Lit, 71. Add: Dept. of English, Hunter College, 695 Park Ave, New York, NY 10021.

POTTER, ROBERT A, b. New York, N.Y, Dec. 28, 34; m. 58; c. 4. ENGLISH, DRAMA. B.A, Pomona Col, 56; NDEA fel, Claremont Grad. Sch, 59-63, M.A, 63, Ph.D.(Eng), 65; Fulbright fel, Bristol Univ, 63-64. Instr. humanities, Harvey Mudd Col, 64-65; asst. prof. Eng, UNIV. CALIF, SANTA BARBARA, 65-72, LECTR. DRAMA, 72- Creative Arts Inst, Univ. Calif. grant, 68-69. U.S.A.R, 57-63. MLA; Am. Theatre Asn. Medieval drama; the Elizabethan stage; playwriting. Publ: Co-auth, Lawrence Durrell: a checklist, Univ. Calif. Libr, 63; auth, Where is Sicily? (play), Creative Arts Inst, Univ. Calif, 69; King Johan and the birth of Shakespeare, New Theatre, 4/64; Famous victories and lovely wars, Claremont Quart, summer 64; The idea of a morality play, In: Research opportunities in Renaissance drama, Reports MLA Conf, 71. Add: Dept. of Dramatic Art, University of California, Santa Barbara, CA 93106.

POTTER, ROBERT RUSSELL, b. New York, N.Y, July 31, 30; m. 65. ENGLISH. B.S, Columbia Univ, 56, M.A, 58, Ed.D, 66. Assoc. prof. Eng. & educ, State Univ. N.Y. Col. Oneonta, 65-68; ASST. PROF. ENG, UNIV. CONN, TORRINGTON, 68- U.S.A, 50-53. NCTE. Relationship of linguistic science and research to writing; folklore. Publ: Myths and folk tales around the world, 63 & Americans meet the challenge, 68, Globe Bk; Schoolroom grammar—what? or why?, 4/66 & Folklore—intercultural and intracommunity, 12/68, Eng. Rec; Sentence structure and prose quality, Res. Teaching Eng, 4/67. Add: Dept. of English, University of Connecticut, Torrington, CT 06790.

POTTLE, FREDERICK ALBERT, b. Lovell, Maine, Aug. 3, 97; m. 20; c. 2. ENGLISH LITERATURE & LANGUAGE. A.B, Colby Col, 17, D.Litt, 41; A.M, Yale, 21, Ph.D, 25; LL.D, Univ. Glasgow, Scotland, 36; D.Litt, Rutgers Univ, 51; L.H.D, Northwest. Univ, 67. Asst. prof, Univ. N.H, 21-23; instr. ENG, YALE, 25-26, asst. prof, 26-30, prof, 30-41, Sanford prof, 41-44, Sterling prof, 44-66, chmn. dept. English, 32-33, dir. grad. stud, 39-45, 49-50, pub. orator, 42, 46, EMER. STERLING PROF, 66- Messenger lectr, Cornell Univ, 41; Guggenheim fel, 45-46, 52-53; chmn. ed. comt, Yale Ed. Private Papers of James Boswell, 49-; trustee, Colby Col, 32-59, 67-; Gen. Theol. Sem, 47-68; Chancellor, Acad. Am. Poets, 50-72; pres, Conn. Acad. Arts & Sci, 67-68. Porter Prize, Yale, 25; Yale Grad. Sch. Asn. Wilbur Lucius Cross Medal, 67; William Clyde DeVane Medal, Phi Beta Kappa, Yale Col, 69. U.S.A, 17-19. MLA; Mediaeval Acad. Am; Am. Acad. Arts & Sci; Am. Philos. Soc; Utrechtsch Genoot.Kunsten Wetenschap. Wordsworth and Shelley; theory of poetry; James Boswell's private papers and bibliography of his publications. Publ: Stretchers, the story of a hospital on the Western Front, Yale, 29; The idiom of poetry, Cornell Univ, 41, rev. ed, 46, 63; James Boswell, the earlier years, 1740-1769, 66 & co-ed, Boswell in extremes, 1776-1778, 70, McGraw; auth, Boswell revalued, In: Literary views, Rice Univ. & Univ. Chicago, 64; Creed not annulled, In: Promise of greatness: the war of 1914-1918, Day, 68; Wordsworth in the present day, Proc. Am. Philos. Soc, 72; co-auth, Synchrony and diachrony, In: Literary theory and structure, Yale, 73; plus others. Add: 1504 A, Yale Sta, New Haven, CT 06520.

POTTS, NORMAN BLAINE, b. Nishnabotny, Iowa, June 16, 33; m. 56; c. 1. THEATRE ARTS, AMERICAN THEATRE HISTORY. B.A, Univ. North. Iowa, 53, M.A, Univ. Denver, 58; Ph.D.(theatre), Ind. Univ, 69. Teacher theatre, speech & Eng, Oakland Pub. High Sch, Iowa, 53-55; Humboldt Pub. High Sch, 55-57; asst. prof. theatre & speech, Huron Col, 58-60; theatre, speech & Eng, Ball State Univ, 60-65; lectr, theatre & Eng, Ind. Univ, Bloomington, 65-69; ASST. PROF. THEATRE, NORTH. ILL. UNIV, 69- Am. Theatre Asn; Speech Commun. Asn; Am. Soc. Theatre Res. American theatre history to 1830; theatre education, particularly in secondary schools; children's theatre. Publ: Children's theatre flowering in Minneapolis, fall 72 & Everyman players, summer 73, Players. Add: 423 Colonial Dr, De Kalb, IL 60115.

POULAKIDAS, ANDREAS K, b. Philiatra, Greece, May 21, 34; U.S. citizen; m. 66. ENGLISH, COMPARATIVE LITERATURE. M.Th, Nat. & Capodistrian Univ. Athens, Greece, 59; M.A, Ariz. State Univ, 62; Ph.D.(comp. lit), Ind. Univ, 67. Instr. Eng. & lit, Md. Inst, Col. Art, 64-67; From asst. prof. to ASSOC. PROF. ENG. & COMP. LIT, BALL STATE UNIV, 67- MLA; Am. Comp. Lit. Asn; AAUP; Int. Comp. Lit. Asn; Mod. Greek Stud. Asn. Modern Greek literature; Nikos Kazantzakis; history of ideas. Publ: Nikos Kazantzakis: Odysseus as phenomenon, Comp. Lit. Stud, 69; Kazantzakis' unacknowledged mentor: Dostoyevsky, Comp. Lit, 69; Kazantzakis' Zorba the Greek and Nietzsche's Thus spake Zarathustra, Philol. Quart, 70. Add: Dept. of English, Ball State University, Muncie, IN 47306.

POVEY, JOHN FREDERICK, b. London, Eng, Apr. 5, 29; U.S. citizen. ENGLISH. M.A, Univ. S.Africa, 57; Ph.D.(Eng), Mich. State Univ, 64. Assoc. prof. ENG, UNIV. CALIF, LOS ANGELES, 64-70, PROF, 70-, ASST. DIR. AFRICAN STUD. CTR, 64- Ed, African Arts. MLA; African Stud. Asn; NCTE; Teachers Eng. Speakers Other Lang. The use of English in both education and literature in Africa; English language usage and national economic policy in Africa. Publ: Introd, In: A bibliography of black literature, Johnson, 67; ed, African writing today, Manyland, 67; contrib, Protest and power in black Africa, Oxford Univ, 70, National identity, Heinemann, Melbourne, 70 & Introduction to Nigerian literature, Heinemann, London, 72; plus others. Add: African Studies Center, University of California, Los Angeles, CA 90024.

POWELL, ARNOLD FRANCIS, b. Montgomery, Ala, Feb. 18, 13; m. 36; c. 2. DRAMA. A.B, Birmingham-South. Col, 37; Ph.D, Vanderbilt Univ, 47. Instr. ENG, Univ. Ala, 40-42; Vanderbilt Univ, 46-47; asst. prof, BIRMINGHAM-SOUTH. COL, 47-48, assoc. prof, 48-54, PROF, 54-, CHMN. DEPT. DRAMA & SPEECH, 66- U.S.N, 42-46, Lt. Am. Theatre Asn; Illumin. Eng. Soc. Dramatic literature; playwriting; directing. Publ: The strangler, In: Playwrights for tomorrow, Vol. IV, Univ. Minn, 67; The death of Everymom, Per/se, winter 67 & In: Types of drama, Scott, 70. Add: Dept. of Drama & Speech, College Theatre, Birmingham-Southern College, Birmingham, AL 35204.

POWELL, GROSVENOR EDWARD, b. Corregidor, Philippines, June 24, 32; U.S. citizen; m. 70; c. 4. ENGLISH & AMERICAN LITERATURE. B.A, Univ. Md, 54; M.A, Stanford Univ, 56, Ph.D.(Eng), 65. Instr. ENG, Northwest. Univ, 60-63; asst. prof, UNIV. B.C, 63-69, ASSOC. PROF, 69- Fulbright-Hays lectr, Engelska Inst, Univ. Stockholm, 65-67. MLA; Can. Asn. Univ. Teachers; Asn. Can. Univ. Teachers Eng. American poetry; English romanticism; metaphysics and poetry. Publ: Co-auth, Private dealings: eight modern American writers, Almqust & Wiksell, 70; Of heroes and nobility: the personae of Wallace Stevens, summer 71 & Mythical and smoky soil: imagism and the aboriginal in the early poetry of Yvor Winters, (in prep), South. Rev; Coleridge's Imagination and the infinite regress of consciousness, ELH, 6/72. Add: Dept. of English, University of British Columbia, Vancouver 8, B.C, Can.

POWELL, JON TUDOR, b. London, Eng. Mar. 9, 34; U.S. citizen; m. 58; c. 3. BROADCASTING, EDUCATIONAL-TELEVISION. B.A, St. Martin's Col, 54; M.S, Univ. Ore, 56, Ph.D.(speech, radio, TV), 63. Asst. prof. speech, radio, TV. & dir. radio-TV, South. Ore. Col, 63-66; assoc. prof. & undergrad. coord. radio-TV, Ohio Univ, 66-69; ASSOC. PROF. RADIO-TV & COORD. RADIO-TV-FILM, NORTH. ILL UNIV, 69- Nat. Acad. TV Arts & Sci; Broadcast Educ. Asn; Speech Commun. Asn; Int. Broadcast Inst. International broadcasting; broadcasting law; mass communications. Publ: Broadcast advertising of medical products and services: its regulation by other nations, Fed. Commun. Bar J, Vol. XXV, No. 2; co-auth, The relationship between attractiveness and credibility of television commercials as perceived by children, Cent. States Speech J, summer 73; The broadcasting systems of Rhodesia and Zambia, In: Broadcasting in Africa: a continental survey of radio and television, Temple Univ, 74. Add: Dept. of Speech Communication, Northern Illinois University, De Kalb, IL 60115.

POWELL, VICTOR MORGAN, b. Moorhead, Minn, Nov. 25, 19; m. 47; c. 2. SPEECH. A.B, Univ. Minn, 41; A.M, Univ. Mo, 46, Ph.D, 54. Instr. SPEECH, Dartmouth Col, 46-47; from asst. prof. to assoc. prof, WABASH COL, 47-61, prof. & chmn. dept, 61-74, DEAN, 74- Dir. speech training, Eli Lilly & Co, 63-67; mem, Ind. State Comt. revision high sch. speech curriculum, 62-66; vis. prof, Univ. Hawaii, spring 67. U.S.A.A.F, 42-46. Speech Commun. Asn. Rhetoric; public address. Publ: Co-auth, New American speech, Lippincott, rev. ed, 63, 68, 73; contrib, Essays on teaching speech in the high school, Ind. Univ, 71. Add: Office of the Dean, Wabash College, Crawfordsville, IN 47933.

POWELL, WALTER ALLEN, b. Smithfield, Va, Dec. 28, 33; m. 56; c. 2. ENGLISH, AMERICAN LITERATURE. B.A, Miss. Col, 56; M.A, Univ. Miss, 59; Reed Smith fel, Univ. S.C, 66, Ph.D.(Eng), 67. Instr, high sch, Mont, 57-58; instr. ENG. & chmn. dept, Wingate Col, 59-65; PROF. & CHMN. DEPT, Ouachita Baptist Univ, 67-68; DALLAS BAPTIST COL, 68- NCTE; MLA; Col. Eng. Asn; S.Cent. Mod. Lang. Asn. British literature of the seventeenth century; twentieth century American literature before 1940; Victorian literature. Publ: A threefold approach to the novel, Eng. Teacher, fall 65;

Thomas Wolfe's Phoenix nest, Markham Rev, 5/70; George Herbert: doctor priest, Can. Counc. Teacher Eng. Bull, spring 71; plus others. Add: Dept. of English, Dallas Baptist College, Dallas, TX 75211.

POWELL, WOODROW WILSON, b. Bulloch Co, Ga, Feb. 20, 16. ENGLISH. B.S, Ga. State Teachers Col, 37; Univ. N.C; Am.M, Duke Univ, 41, Ph.D, 58. Prin, high sch, Ga, 40-41; part-time instr, Duke Univ, 46-48; prof. Eng, Salem Col, 48-49; asst. prof, Clemson Col, 49-53; Furman Univ, 53-55; asst. prof. ENG, Appalachian State Teachers Col, 55; PROF, GA. SOUTH. COL, 55- Southeast. Medieval & Renaissance Inst. fel, Univ. N.C, summer 69. U.S.N.R, 42-46. MLA; NCTE; Shakespeare Asn. Am. Jacobean drama; textual criticism in the dramatic writings of Thomas Heywood. Add: Box 2033, Georgia Southern College, Statesboro, GA 30458.

POWER, ALACOQUE, C.C.V.I, b. Waterford, Ireland, July 8, 12; U.S. citizen. ENGLISH. B.A, Incarnate Word Col, 45; M.A, Cath. Univ. Am, 53, Ph.D. (Eng, Am. lit), 60. Sch. supt, INCARNATE WORD COL, 60-66, PROF. ENG, 62-, head dept, 62-64, chmn. bd. dirs, 66-73. Consult, Jr. Great Bks. Prog, 60-66. NEA; Am. Asn. Sch. Adminr; Nat. Cath. Educ. Asn. Add: Dept. of English, Incarnate Word College, 4301 Broadway, San Antonio, TX 78209.

POWERS, DORIS COOPER, b. Englewood, N.J, Feb. 25, 18; m. 36. ENGLISH LITERATURE. B.A, Wellesley Col, 45; M.A, Occidental Col, 50; Ph.D.(Eng), Univ. Calif, Berkeley, 66. Instr. ENG, ARIZ. STATE UNIV, 60-62, asst. prof, 62-69, ASSOC. PROF, 69- MLA; Rocky Mountain Mod. Lang. Asn. Seventeenth century English literature; English utopian novel. Publ: English formal satire: Elizabethan to Augustan, Mouton, The Hague, 71; The American variants of Earl Brand, child no. 7, West. Folklore Quart, 4/58; Donne's compass, Rev. Eng. Stud, 5/58. Add: Dept. of English, Arizona State University, Tempe, AZ 85281.

POWERS, EDWARD CARROLL, U.S. citizen. ENGLISH, THEATRE HISTORY. A.B, Col. of the Holy Cross, 53; M.A, Boston Col, 61; Ph.D.(Eng), Tufts Univ, 73. Instr. Eng, Assumption Prep. Sch, 55-67, chmn. dept, 61-67, acad. dean, 67-68; ASST. PROF. ENG, WESTFIELD STATE COL, 68-, assoc. dean grad. stud, 72-73. MLA; Am. Soc. Theatre Res; Soc. Theatre Res, Eng. Shakespeare; 17th century English literature; 19th century British and American theatre history. Publ: The Othellos of Booth and Salvini: studies in 19th century dramatic method, Univ. Microfilms, 73. Add: Dept. of English, Westfield State College, Westfield, MA 01085.

POWERS, JAMES G, S.J, b. Spokane, Wash, Oct. 8, 31. ENGLISH. A.B, Gonzaga Univ, 55, Ph.L, 56, M.A, 60; S.T.L. & S.T.M, Univ. Santa Clara, 63; Ph.D.(Eng), Univ. Colo, 66. ASST. PROF. ENG, SEATTLE UNIV, 66-, DEAN ARTS & SCI, 73- MLA; Am. Conf. Acad. Deans; Nat. Cath. Educ. Asn. Neoclassical critical principles; 18th century pre-romanticism; philosophical and theological influences on the 18th century. Publ: The poetic posture of Joseph Warton at mid-eighteenth century, Univ. Microfilms, 68; The Catholic university, Seattle Times Mag, 5/68; A fact about Joseph Warton's Ode to fancy, Notes & Queries, 3/70; Mountain gloom and the modern church, Homiletic & Pastoral Rev, 8-9/72. Add: Dept. of English, Seattle University, Seattle, WA 98122.

POWERS, LYALL HARRIS, b. Winnipeg, Man, July 13, 24; m. 49; c. 2. ENGLISH. B.A, Univ. Man, 48, M.A, 51; Bourse du Govt. Français fel, Univ. Paris, France, 48-49; Royal Soc. Can. scholar, 53-54; Ph.D.(Eng), Ind. Univ, 55. Instr. ENG, Univ. Wis, 55; PROF. ENG. LANG. & LIT, UNIV. MICH, ANN ARBOR, 67- Vis. prof. Am. lit, Univ. Göttingen, 73. R.C.A.F. & Can. Army, 44-45. MLA. Henry James; English, French and American literature, 1850-1950; William Faulkner. Publ: Henry James: an introduction and interpretation, Holt, 70; ed, Studies in the Portrait of a lady, C.E. Merrill, 70; auth, Henry James and the naturalist movement, 71 & ed, Henry James' major novels: essays in criticism, 73, Mich. State Univ; auth, James' debt to Alphonse Daudet, Comp. Lit, 24: 150-162. Add: Dept. of English, 1635 Haven Hall, University of Michigan, Ann Arbor, MI 48104.

POWERS, WILLIAM JENNINGS, b. Davenport, Iowa, July 31, 30; m. 56; c. 3. AMERICAN LITERATURE. B.A, Univ. Ill, 56, M.A, 57, Ph.D.(Eng), 66. Asst. prof. Am. lit, Univ. N.C, Chapel Hill, 66-70, asst. dean arts & sci, 68-70; PROF. HUMANITIES & HEAD DEPT, MICH. TECHNOL. UNIV, 71- U.S.A.F, 50-54. MLA; S.Atlantic Mod. Lang. Asn; Midwest Mod. Lang. Asn; NCTE. The development of American narrative forms, colonial to the 19th century. Publ: Co-auth, The writer's mind, Prentice-Hall, 70; auth, Bulkington as Henry Chatillon, West. Am. Lit, summer 68. Add: Dept. of Humanities, Michigan Technological University, Houghton, MI 49931.

POWLES, MARIE ANTOINETTE, b. London, Eng, Sept. 11, 20; U.S. citizen; m. 47; c. 1. MEDIEVAL & RENAISSANCE LITERATURE. B.A, Wayne State Univ, 64, M.A, 67, Ph.D.(lib. arts), 71. Announcer news, Nippon TV, 53-54; teacher, Mod. Eng. Nursery Sch, 54-56; confidential secy. to mission comdr, Royal Air Force Mission, Wash, D.C, 58; exec. secy. to dir, Counseling Ctr, Mich. State Univ, 59-60; teaching asst. freshman lit, Wayne State Univ, 67-68; lectr. ENG, UNIV. N.C, WILMINGTON, 71-72, ASST. PROF, 72- Renaissance Soc. Am; S.Atlantic Mod. Lang. Asn; AAUP. Renaissance, especially George Sandys; translation of Ovid's Metamorphosis, 1632 and 1640 editions. Publ: Lion and the lamb (poem), Orphic Lute, winter 74; Chrysalis (poem), Archer, winter 74; Dramatic significance of the figures prefacing each book of Sandy's translation of Ovid's Metamorphosis, UD Rev, Vol. 10, No. 2; plus several others. Add: Dept. of English, University of North Carolina at Wilmington, P.O. Box 3725, Wilmington, NC 28401.

PRATOR, CLIFFORD HOLMES, JR, English as a Second Language. See Volume III, Foreign Languages, Linguistics & Philology.

PRATT, JOHN CLARK, b. St. Albans, Vt, Aug. 19, 32; m. 68; c. 6. ENGLISH, AMERICAN STUDIES. B.A, Univ. Calif, Berkeley, 54; M.A, Columbia Univ, 60; Ph.D.(Eng), Princeton, 65. Instr. Eng, U.S. Air Force Acad, 60-62, asst. prof, 65-67, assoc. prof, 67-73, chmn. comt. Am. stud, 70-73, prof, 73-74; CHMN. DEPT. ENG, COLO. STATE UNIV, 74- Consult. remedial Eng, U.S. Indust, Inc, 62-63; lectr, Univ. Colo, 67-68; consult, Hammond, Inc, 68; lectr, Far East div, Univ. Md, 69-70. U.S.A.F, 54-74, Lt. Col; Air medal, Bronze Star Medal. Rocky Mountain Am. Stud. Asn.(secy-treas, 67-68, v.pres, 68-69, pres, 70-72); Rocky Mountain Mod. Lang. Asn. American studies; American literature; George Eliot. Publ: The meaning of modern poetry, Doubleday, 62; John Steinbeck, Eerdmans, 70, ed, Ken Kesey's One flew over the cuckoo's nest, 73 & auth, The Laotians fragments, 73, Viking; contrib, Hemingway in our time, Ore. State Univ, 74. Add: Dept. of English, Colorado State University, Ft. Collins, CO 80521.

PRATT, ROBERT ARMSTRONG, b. Rockingham, Vt, July 22, 07; m. 36; c. 3. MEDIEVAL LITERATURE. A.B, Yale, 29, Ph.D.(Eng), 33; exchange fel, Univ. Florence, 31-32. Instr. ENG, Univ. Rochester, 33-36, asst. prof, 36-38; instr, Queens Col.(N.Y), 38-41, asst. prof, 41-48, assoc. prof, 48-51; PROF, Univ. N.C, 51-57; Univ. Ill, 58-61; UNIV. PA, 61- Guggenheim fel, 46, 54; mem. Inst. Advan. Stud, 55, 57-58. Am. Philol. Asn; MLA; fel. Mediaeval Acad. Am; Mod. Humanities Res. Asn; Am. Asn. Teachers Ital. Chaucer; medieval education. Publ: Co-auth, Sources and analogues of Chaucer's Canterbury tales, Univ. Chicago, 41; ed, Selections from the Tales of Canterbury and short poems by Geoffrey Chaucer, 66 & The tales of Canterbury by Geoffrey Chaucer, 74, Houghton; auth, The order of the Canterbury tales, PMLA, 51; Chaucer and Le Roman de Troyle et de Criseyde, Stud. Philol, 56; Three old French sources of the Nonnes preestes tale, Speculum, 72. Add: 537 New Gulph Rd, Haverford, PA 19041.

PRATT, SAMUEL MAXON, b. N.Adams, Mass, May 10, 19; m. 43; c. 1. ENGLISH, HUMANITIES. A.B, Dartmouth Col, 41; Ph.D, Cornell Univ, 51. Teacher, Greer Sch, N.Y, 41-42; asst. Eng, Cornell Univ, 46-49, instr, 49-52; asst. prof. ENG. & HUMANITIES, OHIO WESLEYAN UNIV, 52-55, assoc. prof, 55-62, PROF, 62- Reader, Testing Serv, Princeton, N.J, 56- U.S.A.A.F, 42-45. MLA; AAUP; NCTE. The English Renaissance; Shakespeare; English literary history. Publ: Antwerp and the Elizabethan mind, Mod. Lang. Quart, 3/63; Shakespeare and Humphrey Duke of Gloucester: a study in myth, Shakespeare Quart, spring 65; Jane Shore and the Elizabethans: some facts and speculations, Tex. Stud. Lit. & Lang, winter 70. Add: 34 Westgate Dr, Delaware, OH 43015.

PRATT, WILLIAM CROUCH, JR, b. Shawnee, Okla, Oct. 5, 27; m. 54; c. 3. ENGLISH LITERATURE. B.A, Univ. Okla, 49; M.A, Vanderbilt Univ, 51, Ph.D.(Eng), 57; Rotary Int. Found. fel, Univ. Glasgow, Scotland, 51-52. Teaching fel, Vanderbilt Univ, 52-53, instr. ENG, 55-57; MIAMI UNIV, 57-59, asst. prof, 59-64, assoc. prof, 64-68, PROF, 68-, dir. freshman Eng, 64-69. U.S.N.R, 45-56, 53-55, Lt. NCTE (state awards chmn, 68); Conf. Col. Compos. & Commun; Soc. Stud. South. Lit; Rhetoric Soc. Am; Eng. Inst. Modern poetry; Faulkner. Publ: The imagist poem, 63 & The fugitive poets: modern southern poetry in perspective, 65, Dutton; The college writer, Scribner, 69; transl, Ten poems of Rainer Marie Rilke, Sewanee Rev, fall 66 & Twelve poems of Rainer Marie Rilke, Colo. Quart, fall 72; contrib, Bibliographical guide to the study of Southern literature, La. State Univ, 69. Add: Dept. of English, Miami University, Oxford, OH 45056.

PRATT, WILLIS WINSLOW, b. Los Angeles, Calif, Aug. 20, 08; m. 31; c. 1. ENGLISH. A.B, Cornell Univ, 30, A.M, 31, Ph.D, 35. Instr. ENG, UNIV. TEX, AUSTIN, 36-39, asst. prof, 39-44, assoc. prof, 45-50, PROF, 50- U.S.A.A.F, 42-45. MLA; S.Cent. Mod. Lang. Asn; Mod. Humanities Res. Asn. Shelley in England from 1810 to 1900; Leigh Hunt; romantic literature. Publ: Variorum ed, Byron's Don Juan; co-auth, Modern drama; nine plays, Ginn, 66; auth, Byron at Southwell. Add: Dept. of English, University of Texas, Austin, TX 78712.

PRAUSNITZ, WALTHER GUNTHER, b. Cologne, Ger, Oct. 2, 24. ENGLISH. A.B, Univ. Chicago, 49, M.A, 50, Keim fel, 50-51, Ph.D.(Eng), 56. Instr. humanities, Wright Jr. Col, 51-52; asst. prof. ENG, CONCORDIA COL. (MOORHEAD, MINN), 52-54, assoc. prof, 54-56, PROF, 56-, DIR. LIB. ARTS STUD, 71- V.pres, N.Cent. Educ. TV Asn, 63-68; mem. gov. bd, Minn. State Arts Counc, 73- MLA; NCTE; Conf. Col. Compos. & Commun; Am. Asn. Higher Educ; AAUP. Literary criticism; 19th century English and Thomas Mann; theory of fiction. Publ: Craftsmanship of Henry James; Thomas Mann: artist in society, Discourse spring 67; ed, Capsules: a review of higher education news and research, Concordia Col, 70. Add: Liberal Arts Studies, Concordia College, Moorhead, MN 56560.

PREBLE, HARRY ELDON, b. Milton, Ill, Nov. 1, 25. ENGLISH. B.A, Univ. Ill, 51, M.A, 52, Ph.D, 60. Asst. prof. ENG, Ill. State Univ, 60-65; assoc. prof, Carthage Col, 65-68; PROF, MO. SOUTH. STATE COL, 68- George Gissing; Victorian fiction; William Faulkner. Add: Dept. of English, Missouri Southern State College, Joplin, MO 64801.

PRESAR, CHARLES IRVIN, b. Gary, Ind, Jan. 25, 32; m. 62; c. 4. DRAMATIC ARTS, SPEECH COMMUNICATION. B.A, Heidelberg Col, 53; Univ. Akron, summer 53; M.A, Northwest. Univ, 60; Bowling Green State Univ, summer 66; Harvard, summer 70; Univ. Colo, Boulder, 73-74. Instr. speech & drama, Harding High Sch, Marion, Ohio, 53; tech. coord, The Playhouse, Eagles Mere, Pa, summers 56-57; dir. bookmobile serv, Skokie Pub. Libr, Ill, 57-58; instr. speech, drama & Eng, Clay High Sch, Oregon, Ohio, 58-63; instr. Eng, Newfield High Sch, Seldon, L.I, N.Y, 63-64; oper. dir, Hall of Free Enterprise, N.Y. World's Fair, 64-65; instr. Eng, Steele High Sch, Amherst, Ohio, 66-67; asst. prof. SPEECH & DRAMATIC ARTS, W.VA. WESLEYAN COL, 67-72, ASSOC. PROF, 72-, CHMN. DEPT, 68- Summer fac. theatre, Huron Playhouse, Ohio, 62-63; mem, W.Va. Lang. Arts Col. Counc, 69- Ord.C, U.S.A, 54-56. Am. Theatre Asn; Speech Commun. Asn. Directing; dramatic literature; speech communication. Add: Dept. of Speech & Dramatic Arts, West Virginia Wesleyan College, Buckhannon, WV 26201.

PRESCOTT, ANNE LAKE, b. New York, N.Y, Jan. 19, 36; m. 57; c. 2. ENGLISH. B.A, Barnard Col, Columbia Univ, 59, Margaret Pickerel scholar, Columbia Univ, 59, M.A, 61, Ph.D.(16th century Eng), 67. Asst. prof. ENG, BARNARD COL, COLUMBIA UNIV, 67-73, ASSOC. PROF, 73- Renaissance Soc. Am; NCTE. The impact of the French Renaissance on England; fantasy and science fiction. Publ: An unknown translation of Du Bartas, Renaissance Quart, spring 66; The reception of Du Bartas in England, 68 & The reputation of Clement Marot in Renaissance England, 71, Stud. Renaissance. Add: Dept. of English, Barnard College, New York, NY 10027.

PRESCOTT, HERBERT, b. Northport, Maine, Apr. 22, 08; div; c. 2. ENGLISH, JOURNALISM. A.B, Bowdoin Col, 30; State Univ. Iowa, 40; A.M,

Univ. Maine, 41. Instr. high sch, Maine, 30-40; radio news ed, Jour. & Evening Bull, Providence, R.I, 41-44; instr. ENG. & JOUR, GRINNELL COL, 44-46, asst. prof, 46-48, assoc. prof, 48-57, PROF, 57-, FAC. DIR. BROADCASTING, 54-, dir. publicity, 44-50, pub. relat, 50-54. Ford Found. grant, 52-53. Communications; objective tests in English literature; radio players scriptbooks. Publ: English can be fun, 56 & co-auth, Getting the most out of literature, 60, J. Weston Walch; The man who wanted to play in Shakespeare, Today's Speech, 4/67; plus others. Add: Dept. of English, Grinnell College, Grinnell, IA 50112.

PRESCOTT, JOSEPH, b. Fall River, Mass, July 3, 13; m. 39; c. 1. ENGLISH LANGUAGE & LITERATURE. A.B, Harvard, 35, A.M, 37, Ph.D, 44. Asst. ENG, Harvard, 37-39; substitute lectr, Boston Univ, 39; instr, Univ. Ala, 39-44; Yale, 44; Univ. Conn, 44-46; asst. prof, WAYNE STATE UNIV, 46-53, assoc. prof, 53-59, PROF, 59- Campus rep, Am. Counc. Learned Soc, 52-56; Fund Advan. Educ. fel, Brit. Mus, 53-54; U.S. Inform. Serv. lectr, France, 57; William R. Brown lectr, West. Mich. Univ, 59; adv. ed, James Joyce Quart, 63-; vis. prof, Harvard, summer 66. MLA; Int. Asn. Univ. Prof. Eng; Mod. Humanities Res. Asn. Twentieth century literature and history of the novel. Publ: Ed, Configuration critique de James Joyce (2 vols), M.J. Minard, Paris, 59-60; auth, Exploring James Joyce, South. Ill. Univ, 64, 66 & James Joyce: the man and his works, Forum House Publ, Toronto, 69; Dorothy Miller Richardson, In: Encyclopaedia Britannica; Jane Eyre: a romantic exemplum with a difference, In: Twelve original essays on great English novels, Wayne State Univ, 60. Add: Dept. of English, Wayne State University, Detroit, MI 48202.

PRESLEY, DELMA EUGENE, b. Tallulah Lodge, Ga, May 16, 39; m. 61; c. 3. AMERICAN LITERATURE. A.B, Mercer Univ, 61; B.D, South. Baptist Sem, 64; Ph.D.(interdisciplinary humanities), Emory Univ, 69. Instr. ENG, Columbia Col.(S.C), 67-69; asst. prof, GA. SOUTH. COL, 69-72, ASSOC. PROF, 72- Proj. dir, Agraian Life Stud, Nat. Endowment for Humanities, 71-72 & Land & People of Liberty County, Ga, 72-73. MLA; Col. Eng. Asn. American literature; folklore; literature and religion. Publ: Moral function of southern grotesque, S.Atlantic Bull, 5/72; Approach to Fowles' Magus, J. Popular Cult, autumn 72; Tennessee Williams: 25 years of criticism, Bull. Bibliog, 2/73; plus others. Add: Dept. of English, Georgia Southern College, Box 8023, Statesboro, GA 30458.

PRESLEY, HORTON EDWARD, b. Akron, Ohio, May 24, 24; m. 46; c. 2. ENGLISH. B.A, South. Ill. Univ, 48; M.A, Univ. Ill, 52; Ph.D.(Eng), Kans. Univ, 66. Baptist pastor; asst. prof. ENG, OTTAWA UNIV, 56-66, assoc. prof, 66-74, PROF, 74-, CHMN. DIV. LANG. & LIT, 71- Renaissance Soc. Am. Influence of Renaissance stage design on text of plays written for a changed stage; science fiction criticism. Add: 1126 S. Hickory, Ottawa, KS 66067.

PRESS, DAVID ROBERT, b. Chicago, Ill, May 11, 35; m. 62; c. 3. SPEECH, DRAMA. B.S, Northwest. Univ, 57, M.A, 60; Univ. Chicago, 61-63; Andrew Mellon fel, Carnegie-Mellon Univ, 64-65, Ph.D.(drama), 71. Instr. speech & theater, Univ. Chicago High Sch, 60-64; resident guest artist acting & dir, E.Carolina Univ, 66-67; asst. prof. speech & theater, Simpson Col, 67-69; ASSOC. PROF. SPEECH & THEATRE & DIR. THEATRE, FROSTBURG STATE COL, 69-, managing dir, Allegheny Festival Theatre, 70-71. Am. Theatre Asn; Speech Commun. Asn; AAUP. Acting; directing; dramatic literature. Publ: Autocrat or collaborator: the Stanislavsky method of directing, Educ. Theatre J, 10/66; Gerhart Hauptmann: obscured by mislabelling, South. Speech J, summer 69. Add: Dept. of Speech & Theatre, Frostburg State College, E. College Ave, Frostburg, MD 21532.

PRESSON, ROBERT KING, b. Gloucester, Mass, Mar. 19, 17. ENGLISH. A.B, Harvard, 39, A.M, 41, Ph.D, 47. Instr. ENG, UNIV. WIS-MADISON, 47-50, asst. prof, 50-55, assoc. prof, 55-63, PROF, 63- MLA; Renaissance Soc. Am. Fourteenth century; sixteenth century dramatic literature. Publ: Shakespeare's Troilus and Cressida and the legends of Troy, Univ. Wis, 53; Boethius, King Lear, and Maystresse Philosophie, J. Eng. & Ger. Philol, 65; Some traditional instances of setting in Shakespeare's plays, Mod. Lang. Rev, 66; Two types of dreams in the Elizabethan drama, Stud. Eng. Lit, 67; plus others. Add: Dept. of English, Helen C. White Hall, University of Wisconsin-Madison, Madison, WI 53706.

PRESTON, DALLAS DWAIN, b. Barry, Ill, Feb. 21, 36; m. 62; c. 4. ENGLISH. B.S. in Ed, West. Ill. Univ, 57, M.S. in Ed, 67; fel, Univ. Ill, Urbana-Champaign, 67-68, cert. educ, 68, Ph.D.(Eng. educ), 72. Teacher Eng. & hist, Quincy Pub. Schs, Ill, 61-67; ASST. PROF. ENG, WEST. ILL. UNIV, 70-, DIR. FRESHMAN COMPOS, 72- U.S.A.F, 57-61. NCTE (judge, Nat. Achievement Awards, 72-73); Conf. Col. Compos. & Commun. Composition; English education. Publ: Zero (poem), Miss. Valley Rev, fall 72; The little red schoolhouse revisited, Ill. Quart, 2/73. Add: Dept. of English, Western Illinois University, Macomb, IL 61455.

PRESTON, IVAN L, b. Bryn Mawr, Pa, Dec. 18, 31; m. 61; c. 3. MASS COMMUNICATIONS. B.A, Col. Wooster, 53; M.A, Mich. State Univ, 61, Nat. Sci. Found. summer fel, 63, Ph.D.(commun. arts), 64. Advertising account asst, Ketchum, MacLeod & Grove, Inc, 56-57; ed. news serv, Carnegie Inst. Technol, 57-58; pub. relations account exec, Erwin Wasey, Ruthrauff & Ryan, 58-59; asst, Mich. State Univ, 59-63; asst. prof. JOUR, Pa. State Univ, 63-68; ASSOC. PROF, UNIV. WIS-MADISON, 68- Am. Asn. Advertising Agencies grant, 70-72; consult, Fed. Trade Comn, 73. Ord.C, U.S.A, 53-55. Asn. Educ. Jour.(head advertising div, 70-71); Am. Acad. Advertising. Mass communication theory; advertising; consumer affairs. Publ: Logic and illogic in the advertising process, 67 & co-auth, Puffery: a problem the Federal Trade Commission didn't want, 72, Jour. Quart; Advertising: more than meets the eye?, J. Advertising Res, 71. Add: School of Journalism, 5140 Vilas Hall, University of Wisconsin, Madison, Madison, WI 53706.

PRESTON, LILLIAN ELVIRA, b. Battle Creek, Iowa, Jan. 16, 18. SPEECH, TV & RADIO. A.B, Stetson Univ, 35, M.A, 40; Ph.D.(theatre), Univ. Fla, 57. Tech. dir, Stover Theatre, Stetson Univ, 49-51; assoc. prof. theatre, Adrian Col, 56-61; asst. prof. SPEECH, PA. STATE UNIV, 62-73, ASSOC. PROF, 73- Speech Commun. Asn; Nat. Asn. Educ. Broadcasters; Speech Asn. East. States; Am. Theatre Asn; Broadcast Educ. Asn. Radio and television. Publ: Cinderblossom (play), Eldridge, 60; Too many (play), Drama Shop, 63; Woodshed, 64, Women employees, 64 & My own dragon, 68,(plays), Baker Co; Ching's magic brush, Carolrhoda Bks, 73; Noble savage, fall 65 & Loutherbourg's letters, winter 66, Drama Critique; Call it theme, Dramatics, 4/68. Add: Dept. of Speech, Pennsylvania State University, University Park, PA 16802.

PRESTON, RAYMOND, b. London, Eng, Feb. 9, 19. ENGLISH LITERATURE. B.A, Cambridge, 41, M.A, 50. Assoc. prof. Eng, Trinity Col.(D.C), 60-68. The symbol in poetry and dream. Publ: Four quartets' rehearsed, 46 & Chaucer, 52, Sheed; Aristotle and the modern literary critic, J. Aesthet. & Art Criticism, fall 62; Dr. Johnson and Aristotle, Costerus, 73; plus others. Add: 1030 Bath St, Number 1, Santa Barbara, CA 93101.

PRESTON, THOMAS RONALD, b. Detroit, Mich, Oct. 31, 36; m. 60; c. 3. ENGLISH. B.A, Univ. Detroit, 58; univ. fel, Rice Univ, 58-62, M.A, 60, Ph.D, 62. Asst. prof. ENG, Duquesne Univ, 62-63; Univ. Fla, 63-67; assoc. prof, Loyola Univ.(La), 67-69; PROF. & HEAD DEPT, Univ. Tenn, Chattanooga, 69-73; UNIV. WYO, 73- Am. Soc. 18th Century Stud; MLA; Conf. Christianity & Lit. Late 18th century satire and sentiment; 18th century novel and lyric poetry. Publ: The biblical context of Johnson's Rasselas, PMLA, 69; Homeric allusion in A journey to the western islands of Scotland, Eighteenth Century Stud, 72; Disenchanting the man of feeling: Smollett's Ferdinand Count Fathom, Quick Springs of Sense, 73; plus two others. Add: Dept. of English, University of Wyoming, Laramie, WY 82071.

PREU, DANA McKINNON, b. Laurel, Miss, July 9, 32; m. 71. ENGLISH RENAISSANCE LITERATURE. B.S, Univ. South. Miss, 57, M.A, 59; Ph.D. (Eng), Univ. Ill, 65. Instr. ENG, Univ. South. Miss, 58-59; asst. prof, Fla. State Univ, 64-71; ASSOC. PROF, FLA. A&M UNIV, 71- Renaissance drama; Renaissance textual problems. Publ: Co-ed, The plays of George Chapman, Univ. Ill, 71, 74; auth, The marginal glosses in More's Utopia, Renaissance Papers, 71; A description of a Restoration prompt-book of Shirley's The ball, Restoration & 18th Century Theatre Res, 5/71. Add: Dept. of English, Florida A&M University, Box 272, Tallahassee, FL 32307.

PREU, JAMES ARTHUR, b. Hartford, Conn, Sept. 16, 08. ENGLISH. A.B, Boston Univ, 31; A.M, Harvard, 32, 32-34, summers, 33-39; Ph.D, Tulane Univ, 52. Instr. ENG, Sch. Organic Educ, Fairhope, Ala, 35-36; Hebron Acad, 36-38; prof. & head dept, Friends Univ, 38-45; from asst. prof. to PROF, FLA. STATE UNIV, 45-, DIR. UNIV. PRESS, 68- S.Atlantic Mod. Lang. Asn; NCTE. English literature of the 18th century. Publ: The dean and the anarchist, Fla. State Univ. Stud, 59, Haskell, 72; Swift's influence on Godwin's doctrine of anarchism, J. Hist. Ideas, 7/54; The tale of terror, Eng. J, 5/58. Add: Dept. of English, Florida State University, Tallahassee, FL 32306.

PREUS, OVE J. H, b. Madison, Wis, Apr. 30, 25; m. 52; c. 1. ENGLISH. B.A, Luther Col, 48; Univ. Montpellier, France, 49-50; Univ. Edinburgh, Scotland, 50-51; M.A, Univ. Minn, 54, Ph.D, 58. Instr. ENG, Luther Col. 52-53; Univ. Minn, 54-58; asst. prof, Augsburg Col, 58-60; assoc. prof, St. Olaf Col, 60-63; assoc. prof, CALIF. STATE UNIV, SACRAMENTO, 63-71, PROF, 71- U.S.A, 43-46. MLA; NCTE. Modern American drama. Add: Dept. of English, California State University, Sacramento, CA 95819.

PREYER, ROBERT OTTO, b. Greensboro, N.C, Nov. 11, 22; m. 47; c. 3. ENGLISH. A.B, Princeton, 47; M.A, Columbia Univ, 49, Ph.D, 52. Instr, Smith Col, 48-53; asst. prof. Eng. lit, BRANDEIS UNIV, 53-58, ASSOC. PROF. ENG, 58-, CHMN. DEPT. ENG. & AM. LIT, 62- Vis. instr, Amherst Col, 51-52; mem. adv. bd, Victorian Stud, 64-; adv. ed, Col. Eng, 66-; vis. prof, Eng. sem, Univ. Heidelberg, 73-74. U.S.N, 42-45, Ens. MLA; Nat. Asn. Advan. Colored People; Am. Civil Liberties Union; Tennyson Soc; AAUP; Browning Soc. Nineteenth century English literature; poetics and criticism. Publ: Bentham, Coleridge and the science of history, H. Poppinghaus, 58; auth. & ed, Victorian literature, Harper, 66; Victorian wisdom literature: fragments and maxims, 12/62 & Alfred Tennyson: the poetry & politics of conservative vision, 6/66, Victorian Stud; The fine delight that fathers thought: Gerard Manley Hopkins and the romantic survival, Victorian Poetry, 72. Add: Dept. of English & American Literature, Brandeis University, Waltham, MA 02154.

PRICE, CORA LEE BEERS, English, Latin. See Volume III, Foreign Languages, Linguistics & Philology.

PRICE, FRANK JAMES, b. Logansport, La, Mar. 1, 17; m. 40; c. 2. JOURNALISM. B.A, La. Polytech. Inst, 38; M.A, La. State Univ, 40; Ph.D.(mass commun), State Univ. Iowa, 56. Instr. jour, Univ. Ga, 40; asst, LA. STATE UNIV, BATON ROUGE, 40-42, instr, 42-47, asst. prof, 47-52, assoc. prof, 52-56, PROF. JOUR, 56-, dir, Sch. Jour, 56-69. Reporter, tel. ed. & ed. writer, La; copyreader, Fla; newsman, Assoc. Press; consult, La. Press Asn, 46-; consult, J. Forestry, 69-70. U.S.A, 45-46, Mil.Intel, Res, 46-53, Capt. Asn. Educ. in Jour. Foreign press; mass communications and society; international mass communications. Publ: Gossip: the grease in good soup, SE/Graphics Commun, 11/72; contrib, Pubs. Auxiliary, Quill, Jour. Quart, Progressive Farmer, Ford Times, Forests & People. Add: 545 Centenary Dr, Baton Rouge, LA 70808.

PRICE, GEORGE RENNIE, b. Langdon, N.Dak, Mar. 5, 09; m. 40; c. 3. ENGLISH. A.B, Univ. N.Dak, 31; A.M, Creighton Univ, 33; Ph.D, Univ. Wis, 41. Instr. ENG, Univ. N.Dak, 34-38; Okla. Agr. & Mech. Col, 40-42; from instr. to PROF. MICH. STATE UNIV, 42- Folger Shakespeare Libr. fel, 48; Huntington Libr. fel, 50-51. MLA; Bibliog. Soc. Eng; Bibliog. Soc. Univ. Va; Malone Soc. Jacobean drama; plays of Thomas Middleton; Shakespeare. Publ: Thomas Dekker, Twayne, 69. Add: Dept. of English, 201 Morrill Hall, Michigan State University, East Lansing, MI 48823.

PRICE, GRANVILLE, b. Dodge, Tex, May 25, 06; m. 38, 68. JOURNALISM. A.B, Univ. Tex, 26, A.M, 30; New Sch. Soc. Res, 35; Univ. Minn, 39-40; Ph.D, Univ. Mo, 54. Asst. prof. JOUR, Univ. Tex, 33-45, assoc. prof, 45-53; prof. & chmn. dept, Univ. Idaho, 54-62; PROF, NORTH. ILL. UNIV, 62- Ed. adv, Suburban Press Found, 66-73, dir, Suburban Press Res. Ctr, 73- Add: Dept. of Journalism, Northern Illinois University, De Kalb, IL 60115.

PRICE, HENRY THOMAS, b. Avon Park, Fla, Feb. 17, 37; m. 59; c. 2. JOURNALISM, COMMUNICATION. B.A, Univ. S.C, 59, M.A, 64; Ph.D. (commun), Mich. State Univ, 72. Asst. prof. JOUR, Univ. Mo, 65-69; UNIV. S.C, 69-72, ASSOC. PROF, 72- U.S.N, 59-62, Res, 62-65, Lt. Asn. Educ. in Jour. Newspaper design; newspaper readership and comprehension. Publ: The effect of newspaper design complexity on readership, comprehension, interestingness and pleasingness, Mich. State Univ, 72; What readers think about front page makeup, Mo. Press News, 6/69; Some possible effects of design on readership, 6/73 & Front-page design as evaluated by the newspaper reader, 6/73, ANPA News Res. Bull; plus others. Add: College of Journalism, University of South Carolina, Columbia, SC 29208.

PRICE, JOHN EDWARD, b. Detroit, Mich, Aug. 23, 41; m. 68; c. 1. ENGLISH LITERATURE. B.A, Marquette Univ, 63, M.A, 65; Ph.D.(Eng), Loyola Univ. Chicago, 70. Instr. ENG, DE PAUL UNIV, 68-70, asst. prof, 70-74, ASSOC. PROF, 74-, HEAD DIV, 73-, dir. col. writing prog, 71-72. Col. Eng. Asn; MLA; NCTE; Renaissance Soc. Am. Novelle and English Renaissance drama; comparative aesthetics. Publ: A secondary bibliography of George Gascoigne, with an introduction summarizing the trend of Gascoigne scholarship, Bull. Bibliog, 68. Add: Humanities Div, De Paul University, 2323 N. Seminary, Chicago, IL 60614.

PRICE, JOHN R, b. St. Louis, Mo, Mar. 27, 21. ENGLISH LITERATURE. A.B, St. Louis Univ, 43, Ph.L, 46, M.A, 48, Th.L, 53; Ph.D.(Eng), Univ. Wis, 59. Teacher, Rockhurst High Sch, 46-49; instr. ENG, Rockhurst Col, 59-61, asst. prof, 61-64, ASSOC. PROF, 64-69; KINGSBOROUGH COMMUNITY COL, CITY UNIV. NEW YORK, 69- MLA. Shakespeare; Renaissance rhetoric. Add: Dept. of English, Kingsborough Community College of City University of New York, Manhattan Beach, Brooklyn, NY 11235.

PRICE, JOSEPH E, JR, b. Charlotte, N.C, Oct. 27, 32; m. 71; c. 2. ENGLISH LANGUAGE & LITERATURE. B.A, Wake Forest Univ, 54; B.D, South. Baptist Theol. Sem, 57; M.A, Yale, 59; Ph.D.(Eng), Univ. Tenn, 67. Instr. Eng, Mars Hill Col, 59-61; asst. prof, Murray State Univ, 64-65, assoc. prof, 65-68; prof. Eng. & chmn. div. lang. & lit, Morehead State Univ, 68-71; ASSOC. DEAN, NORTH. KY. STATE COL, 71- Mem. bd. dirs, North. Ky. Chap, Am. Cancer Soc, 72- MLA; Mediaeval Acad. Am. Old English oral poetry; linguistics and teaching English; mythic interpretation of literature. Add: Box 207, Northern Kentucky State College, Highland Heights, KY 41076.

PRICE, JOSEPH GERARD, b. Philadelphia, Pa, May 25, 28. ENGLISH LITERATURE. A.B, St. Joseph's Col.(Pa), 51; M.A, Georgetown Univ, 58; Ph.D, Bryn Mawr Col, 61. Instr. Eng, Villanova Univ, 56-60, asst. prof, 60-62; Bowling Green State Univ, 62-66, assoc. prof. Eng. & dir. grad. stud, 66-68; PROF. ENG, PA. STATE UNIV, 68-, dir. eng. grad. stud, 71-72. Am. Counc. Learned Soc. grant, spring 72. U.S.A.F, 51-54, S/Sgt. MLA; Shakespeare Asn. Am; Renaissance Soc. Am. Shakespeare; Renaissance literature. Publ: The unfortunate comedy, Univs. Liverpool & Toronto, 68; From farce to romance, Shakespeare Jahrbuch, 63; All's well that ends well in the American theatre, Theatre Surv, 5/66; The interpretation of Shakespeare in the theatre, In: New directions in literary criticism, Pa. State Univ, 73. Add: Dept. of English, Pennsylvania State University, University Park, PA 16802.

PRICE, MARTIN, b. New York, N.Y, Jan. 29, 20; m. 41; c. 2. ENGLISH. B.A, City Col. New York, 38; M.A, Univ. Iowa, 40; Sterling fel, Yale, 47-48, Ph.D, 50. Teaching asst. ENG, Univ. Iowa, 39-41; instr, Drake Univ, 41-42; YALE, 48-51, Morse fel, 51-52, asst. prof, 52-58, assoc. prof, 58-64, PROF, 64-, chmn. dept, 68-71. Guggenheim fels, 57-58, 71-72. U.S.A, 44-45. Eighteenth century English literature; the English novel; critical theory. Publ: Swift's rhetorical art, Yale, 53; To the palace of wisdom, Doubleday, 64; co-ed, Oxford anthology of English literature, Oxford, 73. Add: 86 Everit St, New Haven, CT 06511.

PRICE, ROBERT, b. Radnorshire, Wales, Oct. 18, 00, nat; m. 38. ENGLISH. Ph.B, Denison Univ, 28; A.M, Ohio State Univ, 30, Ph.D.(Eng), 43; hon. L.H.D, Otterbein Col, 73. From asst. to instr. ENG, Ohio State Univ, 28-45; assoc. prof, OTTERBEIN COL, 45-46, prof, 47-70, chmn. dept, 55-65, EMER. PROF, 70- Libr. Cong. res. fel, 45. Ohioana Award, 55; Am. Asn. State & Local Hist. Award, 56. Soc. Stud. Mid. West. Lit. American middle western regional literature and folklore; W.D. Howells. Publ: English for engineers, McGraw; Johnny Appleseed: man and myth, Ind. Univ; The road to Boston: 1860 travel correspondence of William Dean Howels, Ohio Hist. Soc, 71; plus others. Add: 195 Hiawatha Ave, Westerville, OH 43081.

PRICE, ROBERT PAETZEL, b. Indianapolis, Ind, July 27, 19; m. 42; c. 3. ENGLISH. B.A, Southwest. at Memphis, 41; Memphis State Univ, summer, 41; M.A, Columbia Univ, 49; Ph.D.(col. & univ. govt), Univ. Mich. Ann Arbor, 69. Instr. ENG, OHIO NORTH. UNIV, 51-52, asst. prof, 52-54, assoc. prof, 54-70, PROF, 70-, acting chmn. dept. Eng, speech & theatre, 54-56, chmn. dept, 56-60, asst. to dean lib. arts, 60-63. Sig.C, U.S.A, 42-45. MLA; NCTE; AAUP. Higher education; dramatic literature; linguistics. Add: Dept. of English, Ohio Northern University, Ada, OH 45810.

PRICE, SHERWOOD ROY, b. Holland, Mich, Feb. 17, 14; m. 38, 56; c. 3. ENGLISH. A.B, Hope Col, 35; A.M, Univ. Mich, 36. Head dept. Eng, Lawrence Inst. Technol, 36-43; from instr. to PROF. ENG, MICH. TECHNOL. UNIV, 43- Teaching fel, Univ. Mich, 49-50, instr, 50-51; asst. ed, Wharve, publ. Mich. Technol. Univ. Grad. Sch, 66- NCTE; Conf. Col. Compos. & Commun; Col. Eng. Asn; AAUP. Teaching of English; American literature; photographic interpretation of literature. Publ: Opinion on the training of teachers in the humanities; The heart, the head, and Rappaccini's daughter. Add: Dept. of Humanities, Michigan Technological University, Houghton, MI 49931.

PRICHARD, NANCY SAWYER, b. Owosso, Mich, Mar. 9, 24; m. 54; c. 1. ENGLISH. B.A, Univ. Wash, 52, fel, 52-54, M.A, 54. Instr. Eng, Shoreline Community Col, 64-65, asst. prof, 65-66, assoc. prof, 66-67, prof, 68-72, asst. chmn. div. humanities & dir. col. exploratory prog, 66-69; asst. exec. secy, NCTE, 69-73, ASSOC. EXEC. SECY, 73- Mem, Nat. Jr. Col. Comt. Eng. in Two-Year Col, NCTE & Conf. Col. Compos. & Commun, 66-69, chmn. comt, 68-70; chmn, Pac. Northwest Regional Conf, Eng. in Two-Yr. Cols, 67-69; field reader, U.S. Off. Educ, 72- W.A.V.E.S, 44-45. NCTE; Conf. Col. Compos. & Commun; AAUP. The poetry of Michael Field; English literatures of the world, Africa, India, the Philippines, Australia; training of teachers for, and the teaching of, English at the junior college. Publ: Co-ed, Voices, Houghton, 70; Everybody's literature, Ky. Eng. Bull, winter 69-70; The training of junior college English teachers, Col. Compos. & Commun, 2/70; The chairman's professional responsibilities, Asn. Depts. Eng. Bull, 9/70; plus others. Add: National Council of Teachers of English, 1111 Kenyon Rd, Urbana, IL 61801.

PRIDE, ARMISTEAD SCOTT, b. Washington, D.C, May 27, 06; m. 51. JOURNALISM. A.B, Univ. Mich, 27; A.M, Univ. Chicago, 32; M.S.J, Northwest. Univ, 42, Am. Counc. Learned Soc. fel, 48-49, Ph.D.(Eng. & jour), 50. Instr. Eng. Tenn. State Col, 28-30; joint instr, Wiley Col. & Bishop Col, 32-33; instr, Bishop Col, 33-34; ed. dept. forms & reproduction, Mass. Geodetic Surv, 35-37; asst. prof. Eng. & dir. publicity, LINCOLN UNIV.(MO), 37-41, asst. prof. jour, 42-43, acting dir. sch. jour, 44-45, dir, 45-46, PROF. JOUR, 46-, CHMN. DEPT, 55-, dean, 46-55. City ed, Daily News, Lamar Colo. & correspondent, Assoc. Press, 43-44; res investr, Negro newspaper microfilming proj, comt. Negro stud, Am. Counc. Learned Soc, 46-47; Fulbright vis. prof, Univ. Cairo, Am. Univ.(Cairo) & Int. Univ. Rome, 56-57; col. group leader, Expt. Int. Living, Italy, summer 60; vis. prof, Chungang Univ, Korea, 63-64 & Temple Univ, 69-70. U.S.A, 44. Asn. Educ. in Jour; Am. Soc. Jour. Sch. Adminr.(v.pres, 56, pres, 58); Am. Counc. Educ. Jour. A register and history of Negro newspapers in the United States, 1827-1950. Publ: The Black press: a bibliography, Asn. Educ. in Jour, 68; Racial semantics, Jour. Educr, fall 68; Opening doors to minorities, Quill, 11/68; plus others. Add: 118 Douglas Dr, Jefferson City, MO 65101.

PRIEBE, RICHARD KARL, b. Philadelphia, Pa, Oct. 18, 42; m. 69. AFRICAN LITERATURE, ENGLISH. B.A, Franklin & Marshall Col, 64; Univ. Tübingen, 66-67; M.A, Univ. Mich, Ann Arbor, 68; Ph.D.(Eng), Univ. Tex, Austin, 73. Teacher Eng, Peace Corps, Nigeria, 64-66; Countee Cullen Elem. Sch, N.Y.C, 69-70; ASST. PROF. ENG, VA. COMMONWEALTH UNIV, 73- Contrib, African lit. sect, MLA Bibliog. Comt, 72- MLA; African Stud. Asn; Am. Folklore Soc; Asn. Commonwealth Lit. & Lang. Stud. African literature in English; Afro-American literature; Pidgins and Creoles. Publ: Co-ed, Palaver: interviews with five African writers in Texas, 72 & auth, Letters and manuscripts from southern Africa: a survey of the holdings of the Humanities Research Center, 72, Univ. Tex, Austin; The schizoid texture of Turbott Wolfe, Conch, 74; Demonic imagery and the apocalyptic vision in the novels of Ayi Kwei Armah, Yale Fr. Stud, 74; Escaping the nightmare of history: the development of a mythic consciousness in West African literature, Ariel, 73; plus numerous others. Add: Dept. of English, Virginia Commonwealth University, Richmond, VA 23284.

PRIEST, HAROLD MARTIN, b. Chicago, Ill, July 28, 02; m. 30, 49; c. 1. ENGLISH LITERATURE. A.B, Harvard, 25; A.M, Northwest. Univ, 26, Ph.D, 33; summers, Univ. Chicago, 28-29, Cornell Univ, 31. Asst. prof, Simpson Col, 26-29; Miami Univ, 30-31; prof, Kans. State Teachers Col, 33-46; assoc. prof. Eng. lit, UNIV. DENVER, 46-59, prof. ENG, 59-71, EMER. PROF, 71- MLA; Am. Comp. Lit. Asn; Renaissance Soc. Am. Comparative literature; influence of Dante on Chaucer; Tasso's influence in English literature, 1575-1675. Publ: Renaissance and Baroque lyrics, an anthology of translations, Northwest. Univ, 62; transl. & auth. introd, Adonis, selections from L'Adone of Giambattista Marino, Cornell Univ, 67; auth, Spenser's Faerie queene, a study guide, Dante's Purgatorio, a study guide, & Dante's Paradiso, a study guide, 69, Cliffs. Add: Dept. of English, University of Denver, Denver, CO 80210.

PRIESTLEY, FRANCIS ETHELBERT LOUIS, b. Banbury, Eng, Mar. 12, 05; m. 33; c. 1. ENGLISH. B.A, Univ. Alta, 30, M.A, 32; Open fel, Univ. Toronto, 37-38, 38-39, Ph.D.(Eng), 40; Royal Soc. Can. traveling fel. 39-40; hon. D.Litt, Mt. Allison Univ, 64, Univ. Alta. & Univ. West. Ont, 73. Instr. ENG, Univ. Alta, 31-32; Mt. Royal Col, 34-37; asst. prof, Univ. B.C, 40-44; UNIV. TORONTO, 44-49, assoc. prof, 49-54, prof, 54-72, EMER. PROF, 72- Nuffield Dom. fel, 49-50; vis. prof. Eng, Univ. West. Ont, 69-71, 73. Hist. Sci. Soc; fel. Royal Soc. Can; Int. Asn. Univ. Profs. Eng; Humanities Asn. Can. (pres, 62-64); fel. Royal Soc. Lit. U.K. History of ideas; 18th century and early Romantic period; Victorian poetry. Publ: Ed, Godwin's Political justice, 46, co-auth, Science and the creative spirit, 58, gen. ed, Collected works of J.S. Mill, 63 & auth, The humanities in Canada, 64, Univ. Toronto; Language and structure of Tennyson's poetry, Andre Deutsch, London, 73; Pope and the great chain of being, In: Essays. . .to A.S.P. Woodhouse, Univ. Toronto, 64; Browning's Paracelsus, UTQ, 64; Godwin and history, In: Essays. . .Felix Frankfurter, Bobbs, 66; plus others. Add: 269 Woburn Ave, Toronto, Ont. M5M 1L1, Can.

PRIESTLEY, MARY ELLEN, b. Ashland City, Tenn, Apr. 20, 17; m. 54; c. 2. ENGLISH. B.S, Mid. Tenn. State Univ, 38; M.A, George Peabody Col, 43; Univ. Mo, 46-47; Univ. London, 63-64; Ph.D.(Eng), Univ. Ala, 67. Overseas worker, Am. Red Cross, S.W. Pac, 43-45; writer & ed, Am. Nat. Red Cross, Midwest Area, 48-51; asst. ed, Pet Milk Mag, St. Louis, 51-53; assoc. ed, Du Pont Mag, Del. & ed, Ed. Notebk, Am. Asn. Indust. Ed, 53-55; assoc. prof. ENG, Union Col, 64-68; PROF, ELON COL, 68- MLA. English romantic period; contemporary drama; creative writing. Publ: English syntax in the early prose of Samuel Taylor Coleridge: a new reading of The watchman, 1796, Microfilm, Inc, 67. Add: Box 2224, Elon College, Elon College, NC 27244.

PRIMEAU, RONALD, b. Chicago, Ill, Feb. 6, 46; m. 70. ENGLISH & AMERICAN LITERATURE, RHETORIC. B.A, Univ. Ill, Chicago Circle, 68; M.A, Univ. Ill, Urbana, 69, Ph.D.(Eng), 71. ASST. PROF. ENG, CENT. MICH. UNIV, 71- MLA; NCTE; Col. Eng. Asn; Conf. Col. Compos. & Commun; Soc. Stud. Midwest. Lit. Romanticism and modernism; rhetoric; Afro-American literature. Publ: Literature is the stuffy art, New Orleans Rev, 2/73; Boswell's romantic imagination, Papers on Lang. & Lit, winter 73; Slave narrative turning midwestern: Deadwood Dick rides into difficulties, Mid. Am. I, 74; plus others. Add: Dept. of English, Central Michigan University, Mt. Pleasant, MI 48859.

PRIMER, IRWIN, b. Brooklyn, N.Y, Apr. 1, 29; m. 60; c. 2. ENGLISH. A.B, Brooklyn Col, 49; Columbia Univ, 49-51; scholar, Ind. Univ, summer 51; M.A, Yale, 54, Ph.D, 61. Mem. fac, Univ. Conn, 54-55; instr. ENG, Univ. Nebr, 55-56; New Haven State Teachers Col, 56-58; RUTGERS UNIV, NEWARK, 58-62, asst. prof, 62-67, assoc. prof, 67-71, PROF, 71-, chmn. dept, 69-74. MLA; Am. Soc. 18th Century Stud; Conf. Brit. Stud. The writings of Dr. Bernard Mandeville and his sources and influence; the theory of the passions, 16th-18th centuries; 18th-century fiction and satire. Publ: Ed, Bernard Mandeville, Fable of the bees, Capricorn, 62; auth, Godwin's Imogen: some implications of irony, N.Y. Pub. Libr, 63; Erasmus Darwin's Temple of nature: progress evolution and the Eleusinian mysteries, J. Hist. Ideas, 64. Add: Dept. of English, Rutgers University, Newark, NJ 07102.

PRINCE, GILBERT PARKER, JR, b. Los Angeles, Calif, May 11, 35; m. 58; c. 3. RESTORATION & EIGHTEENTH CENTURY LITERATURE. B.A, Calif. State Univ, Los Angeles, 61, M.A, 64; Ph.D.(Eng), Univ. Calif, Santa Barbara, 72. Assoc. ENG, Univ. Calif, Santa Barbara, 70-72; ASST. PROF, CALIF. STATE UNIV, CHICO, 72- U.S.A, 54-57. Col. Eng. Asn; NCTE; Conf. Eng. Educ. Eighteenth century verse satire; process of composition; English education. Publ: Unit on the Canterbury tales, NDEA Inst. in Eng, 66; Map writing, In: Language activities, NCTE, 73; Twain's A fable, Mark Twain J, 74. Add: Dept. of English, California State University, Chico, CA 95926.

PRINCE, WILLIAM STEVENS, b. Bend, Ore, Oct. 1, 22; m. 45; c. 3. ENGLISH. B.A, Univ. Calif, Santa Barbara, 50; Ph.D.(Am. stud), Yale, 54. Asst. prof. ENG, Univ. Conn, 55-62; PROF, PAC. UNIV, 62-, CHMN. DIV. HUMANITIES, 69- Reader, Educ. Testing Serv, 67- U.S.A.F, 43; Am. Field Serv, 44-45. Publ: On teaching modern poetry, autumn 64 & The art of being a teachman, fall 65, Improvement of Col. & Univ. Teaching. Add: Dept. of English, Pacific University, Forest Grove, OR 97116.

PRITCHARD, ALLAN, b. Comox, B.C, Aug. 8, 28. ENGLISH. B.A, Univ. B.C, 51; Humanities Res. Counc. Can. fel, 54-55; Ph.D.(Eng), Univ. Toronto, 58. Lectr. ENG, Univ. B.C, 55-58; from lectr. to assoc. prof, UNIV. TORONTO, 58-70, PROF, 70- Can. Counc. fel, 63-64, 69-70. Seventeenth century English literature. Publ: Ed, Abraham Cowley, the Civil War, Univ. Toronto, 73; auth, George Wither: the poet as prophet, Stud. Philol, 4/62; Abuses stript and whipt and Wither's imprisonment, Rev. Eng. Stud, 11/63. Add: Dept. of English, University College, University of Toronto, Toronto 5, Ont, Can.

PRITCHARD, JOHN PAUL, b. White Lake, N.Y, Feb. 8, 02; m. 26; c. 1. ENGLISH. B.A, Cornell Univ, 22, fel. & Ph.D.(Greek), 25. Prof. ancient lang, Catawba Col, 25-28; class. lang, Washington & Jefferson Col, 28-44; ENG, UNIV. OKLA, 44-56, res. prof, 56-72, EMER. RES. PROF, 72- Am. Philos. Soc. res. grants-in-aid, 51, 55, 58 & 59; Rockefeller res. grant-in-aid, 53. MLA. Classical and American literary criticism; Milton and Patristic literature; study of the New Testament on critical principles. Publ: Return to the fountains: some classical sources of American criticism, Duke Univ, 42 & Octagon, 66; Criticism in America, 1800-1950, 56, transl, August Boechkh, On interpretation and criticism, 68 & auth, A literary approach to the New Testament, 72, Univ. Okla; The literary wise men of Gotham, La. State Univ, 63. Add: 1119 W. Brooks, Norman, OK 73069.

PRITNER, CALVIN LEE, b. Kansas City, Kans, Aug. 23, 35; m. 53; c. 2. DRAMA. B.S, Kans. State Teachers Col, 57; M.A, Univ. Ill, 61, Ph.D.(theatre hist), 64. Asst. prof. THEATRE, South. Ill. Univ, Edwardsville Campus, 64-66; assoc. prof, ILL. STATE UNIV, 66-70, PROF. & CHMN. DEPT, 70- Drama consult, Ill. Mid-State Educ. Ctr, 66- U.S.N.R, 58-60. Am. Theatre Asn; Sec. Sch. Theatre Conf.(mem. governing bd, 65-68); Am. Soc. Theatre Res; Univ. & Col. Theatre Asn.(pres, 73-74). William Warren's management of the Chestnut Street Theatre; the acting of Charles Fechter and James Quin. Publ: Ed, Secondary school theatre bibliography, Am. Educ. Theatre Asn, 68, rev. ed, 70; auth, James Quin's acting, Cent. States Speech J, 5/65; William Warren's financial arrangements with traveling stars, Theatre Surv, 11/65; A theatre and its audience, Pa. Mag. Hist. & Biog, 1/67. Add: Dept. of Theatre, Illinois State University, Normal, IL 61761.

PROCTOR, JOHN WILLIAM, b. Boone Co, Mo, July 10, 22. ENGLISH. M.A, Univ. Mo-Columbia, 60, Ph.D.(Eng), 66. Instr. ENG, Univ. Mo-Columbia, 60-66; asst. prof, N.Mex. State Univ, 66-69; chmn. div. lang. & lit, NORTH. STATE COL, 69-73, CHMN. LETTERS, MOD. LANG. & SPEECH, 73- Instr, Univ. Mo Exten, 62-66, asst. prof, Univ. Mo-St. Louis, summer 67. U.S.N.R, 41-46. MLA; Rocky Mountain Mod. Lang. Asn; Int. Soc. Gen. Semantics; Conf. Col. Compos. & Commun. Add: Box 866, Northern State College, Aberdeen, SD 57401.

PROFFITT, EDWARD L. F, b. Minneapolis, Minn, July 1, 38; m. 67; c. 1. ENGLISH LITERATURE, HISTORY OF IDEAS. B.A, Cornell Univ, 61; M.A, Columbia Univ, 62, Ph.D.(Eng), 67. Instr. ENG, City Col. New York, 62-63; ASST. PROF, MANHATTAN COL, 67- MLA. Romanticism; 19th and 20th century literature. Publ: The structure of experience, Mouton, (in press); A clue to John Ray, Jr, Mod. Fiction Stud, (in press); plus poems in Commonweal and other poetry magazines. Add: Dept. of English, Manhattan College, Bronx, NY 10471.

PRONKO, LEONARD C, Romance Languages, Theatre. See Volume III, Foreign Languages, Linguistics & Philology.

PROPST, HATTIE CAREEN, b. Bristow, Okla, Sept. 5, 07. ENGLISH. B.S, Okla. State Univ, 36, M.S, 42, Ed.D, 61. Teacher, sec. schs, Okla, 36-45; PROF. ENG, NORTHEAST. STATE COL, 45- Teacher of the Year, Northeast. State Col, 64-65. NEA; NCTE. Principles and procedures for teaching written composition in college freshman English classes. Add: Dept. of English, Northeastern State College, Tahlequah, OK 74464.

PROSKY, MURRAY, b. Brooklyn, N.Y, Apr. 10, 36; m. 61; c. 2. ENGLISH. B.A, N.Y. Univ, 61; M.A, Univ. Wis, 62, Ph.D.(Eng), 66. Asst. prof. ENG, Seattle Univ, 65-68; Queens Col.(N.Y), 68-72; ASSOC. PROF, MONTCLAIR STATE COL, 72- U.S.A, 55-57. MLA. Yeats and the Irish revival; contemporary British novel; romantic poetry. Add: Dept. of English, Montclair State College, Upper Montclair, NJ 07043.

PROSSER, ELEANOR ALICE, b. Pasadena, Calif, Sept. 1, 22. DRAMATIC LITERATURE. A.B, Occidental Col, 50; M.A, Stanford, 57, Ph.D, 60. Asst. prof. Eng, San Jose State Col, 57-61, assoc. prof, 61-65, prof, 65-66; assoc. prof. DRAMATIC LIT, STANFORD UNIV, 66-68, PROF, 68- Vis. prof. Eng. lit, Stanford Univ, 63; Lilly fel, 64-65. Malone Soc; Shakespeare Asn. Am; Am. Theatre Asn; MLA. Medieval drama; Shakespeare; dramatic criticism. Publ: Drama and religion in the English mystery plays: a revaluation, 61 & Hamlet and revenge, 67, rev. ed, 71, Stanford Univ; Colley Cibber at San Diego, Shakespeare Quart, 63; Shakespeare, Montaigne, and the rarer action, Shakespeare Stud, 65. Add: Dept. of Drama, Stanford University, Stanford, CA 94305.

PROSSER, MICHAEL H, b. Indianapolis, Ind, Mar. 29, 36; m. 58; c. 3. SPEECH COMMUNICATION. B.A, Ball State Teachers Col, 58, M.A, 60; Ph.D. (speech, Eng), Univ. Ill, 64. Instr. speech & Latin, Urbana Jr. High Sch, Ill, 60-63; lectr. speech, State Univ. N.Y. Buffalo, 63-64, asst. prof. speech commun, 64-69; assoc. prof. speech, Ind. Univ. Bloomington, 69-72; PROF. SPEECH COMMUN. & CHMN. DEPT, UNIV. VA, 72- Vis. lectr, Queens Col.(N.Y), summers 66 & 67; consult. oral commun, President's Conf. East. R.R, 66; vis. assoc. prof. speech, Calif. State Col, Hayward, summer 71; chmn. int. commun. develop. counc, Midwest Univs. Consortium Int. Activities, 71-72; vis. prof. curriculum, develop. & educ. found, Mem. Univ. Nfld, spring 72. Speech Commun. Asn.(chmn. comn. for int. & intercult. commun, 71-73); Int. Commun. Asn; Soc. Cross-Cult. Res; Speech Asn. East. States (ed, Today's Speech, 68-70). Intercultural communication; public communication in the United Nations; classical rhetoric. Publ: Ed, An ethic for survival: Adlai E. Stevenson speaks on foreign affairs, 1936-1965, 69 & Sow the wind, reap the whirlwind: heads of state address the United Nations (2 vols), 70, William Morrow; co-ed, Reading in classical rhetoric, Allyn & Bacon, 69 & Readings in medieval rhetoric, Ind. Univ, 73; ed, Intercommunication among nations and peoples, Harper, 73; auth, Adlai E. Stevenson's United Nations audience, Cent. States Speech J, 11/65; A rhetoric of alienation as reflected in the works of Nathaniel Hawthorne, Quart. J. Speech, 2/68; The status of speech in New York, Today's Speech, 5/69; plus one other. Add: Dept. of Speech Communication, University of Virginia, 1 Dawson's Row, Charlottesville, VA 22903.

PROUDFIT, CHARLES LOUIS, b. Mishawaka, Ind, May 26, 37; m. 61; c. 2. ENGLISH. B.A, Univ. Mich, 59, M.A, 61, fel, 64-65, Ph.D.(Eng. lang. & lit), 66; Univ. Nebr, 61-62. Asst. prof. ENG, UNIV. COLO, BOULDER, 66-70, ASSOC. PROF, 70- Summer Res. Initiation fac. fel, 67, fac. fel, 73-74; mem. ed. bd, Eng. Lang. Notes, 67-70, ed, 70- MLA; Rocky Mountain Mod. Lang. Asn; Keats-Shelley Asn. Am. Romantic poetry and prose; Victorian prose; psychoanalysis and literature. Publ: Ed, Wordsworth: poet of the unconquerable mind: a collection of essays on Wordsworth's poetry, Wahr, 65 & Selected imaginary conversations of literary men and statesmen, Univ. Nebr, 69; Landor's hobbyhorse: a study in romantic orthography, Stud. Romanticism, summer 68; An unrecorded cancellans in the first edition of Walter Savage Landor's Imaginary conversations of literary men and statesmen, Notes & Queries, 9/68. Add: Dept. of English, University of Colorado, Boulder, CO 80302.

PROUDFIT, SHARON LOUISE WOOD, b. Adrian, Mich, Oct. 19, 38; m. 61; c. 2. ENGLISH. B.A, Univ. Mich, 60, M.A, 61, Ph.D.(Eng. lang. & lit), 67. ASST. PROF. ENG, COLO. WOMEN'S COL, 67- MLA; Rocky Mountain Mod. Lang. Asn; AAUP. Edwardian and Georgian novel; relationship between the literary and visual arts; impact of post-impressionism upon British fiction between 1910 and 1930, especially upon Virginia Woolf's novels. Publ: Rev. of Mitchell A. Leaska's Virginia Woolf's Lighthouse: a study in critical method, 9/71 & rev. of Harvena Richter's Virginia Woolf: the inward voyage, 9/72, Eng. Lang. Notes; Lily Briscoe's painting: a post-impressionist canvas of personal relationships in Virginia Woolf's To the lighthouse, Criticism, winter 71. Add: Dept. of English, Colorado Women's College, Denver, CO 80220.

PROVOST, GEORGE FOSTER, JR, b. Mansfield, La, Aug. 16, 25; m. 61; c. 3. ENGLISH. B.S, La. State Univ, 47, Ph.D, 55; M.A, Univ. Ore, 52. Instr. ENG, N.C. State Col, 55-57; asst. prof, Duquesne Univ, 57-60, assoc. prof, 60-63; Parsons Col, 63-64; DUQUESNE UNIV, 64-65, PROF, 65- Vis. prof. Eng, Univ. Ore, summer 70. U.S.N.R, 44-46. MLA. Shakespeare; Spenser; M.M. Boiardo. Publ: Co-auth, Annotated bibliography of Edmund Spenser, Duquesne Univ, 62; Pope's pastorals: an exercise in poetical technique, La. State Univ. Stud. Humanities Series No. 5, 54; On the music in Richard II and King Lear, Annuale Mediaevale, 62; The sorrows of Shakespeare's Richard II, La. State Univ. Stud. Humanities Series No. 12, 62. Add: Dept. of English, Duquesne University, Pittsburgh, PA 15219.

PRUITT, JAMES DONALD, b. Jacksonville, Ill, Nov. 20, 37; m. 60; c. 1. ENGLISH, EDUCATION. A.B, Ill. Col, 59; Ohio Univ, 59-60; fel, Univ. Denver, 67-68, Ph.D.(Eng. & educ), 68. Instr. Eng, Carthage Col, 61-63, asst. prof, 63-66; assoc. prof. Eng. & acting chmn. div. lang. & lit, North. State Col, 67-69; dept. chmn, State Community Col. E. St. Louis, Ill, 69-71; ASST. PROF, LEWIS & CLARK COMMUNITY COL, 71- Res. fel, Univ. Col. Oxford, summer 73. MLA; Renaissance Soc. Am. Shakespeare; public school law; higher education administration. Publ: Passive voice in research writing, J. Higher Educ, 11/68. Add: Division of Communications, Lewis & Clark Community College, Godfrey Rd, Godfrey, IL 62035.

PRYOR, WILLIAM LEE, b. Lakeland, Fla, Oct. 29, 26. ENGLISH & AMERICAN LITERATURE. A.B, Fla. South. Col, 49; M.A, Fla. State Univ, 50, teaching fel, 53-55, 57-58, Ph.D, 59; Univ. N.C, 52-53. Asst. prof. Eng. & dir. drama, Bridgewater Col, 50-52; instr. ENG, UNIV. HOUSTON, 55-59, asst. prof, 59-62, assoc. prof, 62-71, PROF, 71-, ED-IN-CHIEF, FORUM, 68-, assoc. ed, 67. Vis. instr, Fla. South. Col. & MacDill Army Air Base, summer, 51; vis. instr. Eng, Tex. South. Univ, 61-63; govt. & humanities, Dent. Br, Univ. Tex, 62-63; lectr. Eng, Women's Inst. Houston, 67- & humanities ser, Jewish Community Ctr, Houston, 72-; mem, Alliance Française. Conf. Col. Teacher Eng; S-Cent. Mod. Lang. Asn; Eng-Speaking Union; AAUP; S.Cent. Renaissance Conf. Early English biography; Renaissance and American drama. Publ: Contrib. auth, The literature of the United States, In: Panorama das literaturas, Vol. II, Ed. Municipio Nova Lisboa, Angola, 58. Originator, producer & moderator, The arts in Houston, ser. produced on KUHT-TV & KUHF-FM, 56-57, 58-63. Add: Dept. of English, University of Houston, 3801 Cullen Blvd, Houston, TX 77004.

PRZYBYLSKA, KRYSTYNA, b. Warsaw, Poland. MODERN THEATRE. M.A, Univ. Warsaw, 61, Ph.D.(Am. drama), 69; dipl. Am. stud, Smith Col, 65. Instr. Eng, Univ. Warsaw, 62-64, asst. prof, 67-69, assoc. prof, 69-70; lectr. Eng. & Slavic, Univ. Calif, Berkeley, 65-66; ASST. PROF. ENG, Univ. Brest, 70-71; IONA COL, 71- Continental and Anglo-Saxon theatre of the 20th century; forms of drama as related to the film; American novelists of the 20th century. Publ: Edward Albee's props, 6/66 & Eugene O'Neill: a rebellious naturalist, 5/70, Dialog; The modern Polish theatre, Queens Slavic Papers, 73; plus others. Add: Apt. 7D, 139 E. 94th St, New York, NY 10028.

PUCKETT, HARRY THOMAS, b. Jasonville, Ind, Jan. 19, 31; m. 71; c. 4. ENGLISH. B.S, Ind. Univ. Bloomington, 51, M.A, 69, Ph.D.(Eng), 71. ASST. PROF. ENG, LOYOLA UNIV. CHICAGO, 71- Twentieth century English and American poetry; Victorian poetry. Publ: T.S. Eliot on knowing: the word unheard, New Eng. Quart, 71. Add: Dept. of English, Loyola University of Chicago, 6525 N. Sheridan, Chicago, IL 60626.

PUCKETT, WALTER, S.M, b. Decatur, Ill, Feb. 2, 19. ENGLISH LITERATURE. B.S. Ed, Univ. Dayton, 40; M.Ed, St. Louis Univ, 47, Ph.D, 61. Assoc. prof. ENG, ST. MARY'S UNIV.(TEX), 63-68, PROF, 68-, CHMN. DEPT, 63-68, 70, 73-, grad. adv, 66-73. MLA; NCTE; Col. Conf. Compos. & Commun. Nineteenth century, especially Robert Browning; contemporary poetry and drama; history of dramatic monologue. Add: Dept. of English, St. Mary's University, 2700 Cincinnati, San Antonio, TX 78284.

PUGH, GRIFFITH T, b. Kingstree, S.C, Sept. 5, 08; m. 36; c. 3. ENGLISH. A.B, Univ. S.C, 30, M.A, 36; Ph.D, Vanderbilt Univ, 44. Prin. ENG, Brevard Inst, N.C, 32-33; instr, High Schs, Bishopville, S.C, 33-37; Greenville, 37-38; Winthrop Col, 38-43, asst. prof, 43-44, assoc. prof, 44-46, prof, 46-47; assoc. prof, FLA. STATE UNIV, 47-50, PROF, 50- MLA; S.Atlantic Mod. Lang. Asn; Am. Stud. Asn; NCTE. Literature of the American South. Publ: George Washington Cable: a biographical and critical study, Joint Univ. Libr, Nashville, 47; Guide to research writing, Houghton, 55, 2nd ed, 63, 3rd ed, 68. Add: Dept. of English, Florida State University, Tallahassee, FL 32306.

PUGLIESE, RUDOLPH E, b. Cleveland, Ohio, June 14, 18; m. 42; c. 1. DRAMATIC ARTS. B.A, Miami Univ, 47; M.F.A, Cath. Univ. Am, 49; Ph.D. (theatre), Ohio State Univ, 61. PROF. SPEECH & DRAMATIC ART, UNIV. MD, COLLEGE PARK, 48- U.S.A.A.F, 41-45, Capt. Am. Educ. Theatre Asn. Shakespearean production; American musical theatre; 19th century English theatre. Publ: Staging Julius Caesar, Players Mag, 12/62; Drama criticism by tape recording, Educ. Theatre J, 3/63; The beginning of modern stage directorial principles, Ohio State Univ. Theatre Collection Bull, 66. Add: Dept. of Speech & Dramatic Art, University of Maryland, College Park, MD 20742.

PUHVEL, MARTIN, b. Tallinn, Estonia, Dec. 9, 33; Can. citizen; m. 63. ENGLISH. B.A, McGill Univ, 53, Moyse traveling scholar. & M.A, 54; Humanities Res. Counc. Can. fel, 56; Ph.D.(Eng), Harvard, 58. Lectr. ENG, McGILL UNIV, 57-59, asst. prof, 59-64, ASSOC. PROF, 64- Can. Counc. summer res. grants, 58, 59, 61, 67, 69-71 & res. fel, 73-74. Mediaeval Acad. Am; PEN Club. Medieval studies; Old English; folklore. Publ: The swimming prowess of Beowulf, 71 & The deicidal otherworld weapon in Celtic and Germanic mythic tradition, 72, Folklore; The blithe-hearted morning raven in Beowulf, Eng. Lang. Notes, 73; plus others. Add: Dept. of English, McGill University, Montreal, P.Q, Can.

PULOS, CHRISTOS ERNEST, b. Council Bluffs, Iowa, Apr. 9, 09; m. 49; c. 2. ENGLISH. A.B, Univ. Nebr, 32; Ph.D, State Univ. Iowa, 47. Instr. ENG, UNIV. NEBR, LINCOLN, 47-49, asst. prof, 49-55, assoc. prof, 55-58, PROF, 58- A.U.S, 42-46, Capt. MLA. Shelley, Whitman and the new criticism. Publ: The deep truth: a study of Shelley's scepticism; Shelley and Malthus, PMLA; Whitman and Epictetus, J. Eng. & Ger. Philol. Add: Dept. of English, University of Nebraska, Lincoln, NE 68508.

PURAVS, OLGERTS, b. Riga, Latvia, Oct. 8, 34; U.S. citizen; m. 58; c. 2. ENGLISH. B.S, Univ. Mich, 57, Ph.D.(Eng), 67. Asst. prof. Eng, Univ. Ill, Urbana-Champaign, 67-72. MLA; Am. Soc. Aesthet. Aesthetics; environmental design; American literature & culture. Publ: Cultural values, environment, and the imagination, Arts in Soc, spring 72; Criticism and experience, J. Aesthet. Educ, 1/73. Add: 2310 Glenoak Dr, Champaign, IL 61820.

PURCELL, MARY-JOE, b. Rector, Ark, June 18, 29. ENGLISH LITERATURE. B.S.Ed, Univ. Ark, 50; M.A, Univ. Mo, 53, Ph.D, 59. Instr. ENG, Univ. Mo, 55-59; from assoc. prof. to PROF, CALIF. STATE UNIV, LONG BEACH, 59- MLA; NCTE. Publ: Co-ed, The narrative impluse, Odyssey, 63; co-auth, Beginning, middle, end: an introduction to the essay, Dickenson, 68. Add: Dept. of English, California State University, Long Beach, CA 90804.

PURDY, RICHARD LITTLE, b. Middletown, N.Y, Apr. 21, 04. ENGLISH. LITERATURE. A.B, Yale, 25, fel, 25-26, 27-28, Ph.D.(Eng), 30. Instr. ENG, YALE, 28-33, asst. prof, 33-46, assoc. prof, 46-70, EMER. ASSOC. PROF, 70-, FEL, BERKELEY COL, 33- MLA; Bibliog. Soc, Eng. Nineteenth century literature; Hardy and Browning. Publ: Larpent MS. of The rivals, Clarendon; Our exploits at West Poley & Thomas Hardy, a bibliographical study, Oxford Univ. Add: 245 Whitney Ave, New Haven, CT 06511.

PURDY, ROB ROY, b. Pensacola, Fla, Feb. 11, 14; m; c. 3. ENGLISH. A.B, Davidson Col, 37; M.A, Vanderbilt Univ, 38, Ph.D.(Eng), 46; Univ. Grenoble, summer 39; Am. Field Serv. fel, France, 39-40. Asst. prof. ENG, Florence State Col, 41-42; from asst. prof. to assoc. prof, VANDERBILT UNIV, 42-55, PROF, 55-, SR. V.CHANCELLOR, 66-, v.chancellor, 59-66. Chmn. comt. educ. inquiry, Carnegie Found, 52-57. U.S.N.R, 44-46, Lt.(jg). MLA. Medieval English. Publ: Ed, Fugitives' reunion, Vanderbilt Univ, 58. Add: Kirkland Hall, Vanderbilt University, Nashville, TN 37240.

PURIFOY, CECIL ERNEST, JR, b. Houston, Tex, Sept. 22, 27. ENGLISH, RELIGION. B.S. in Ed, Univ. Tex, Austin, 49; M.A, Mich. State Univ, 52, Ph.D.(Educ, relig), 70. Teacher, Hyattsville, Jr. High Sch, Md, 54-55; Houston Independent Sch, Dist, Tex, 55-64; teaching fel, Mich. State Univ, 64-66; asst. prof. educ, Univ. Tenn, Knoxville, 66-68; teacher, Balboa Sr. High Sch, C.Z, 68-69; ASST. PROF. educ, Univ. Tenn, Knoxville, 69-71; ENG, BALL STATE UNIV, 71- AAUP; Am. Libr. Asn; Asn. Childhood Educ. Int; Int. Reading Asn; NCTE; Children's Lit. Asn. Children's literature; the Bible as literature; religious education. Publ: How can health be maintained?, 7/64 & The college student and supply, 9/64, Christian Sci. Sentinel; O estudante universitario e o suprimento, O Arauto da Ciencia Crista, 4-6/70. Add: Dept. of English, Ball State University, Muncie, IN 47306.

PURNELL, ROSENTENE BENNETT, b. West Point, Miss, Dec. 24, 33; m. 59. ENGLISH. A.B, Tougaloo Col, 54; scholar. & M.A, Northwest. Univ, 58; South. Educ. Found. fel. & Ph.D.(Eng), Univ. Okla, 67. Teacher & head dept. high sch, Miss, 54-58; asst. prof. Eng. & speech, Alcorn A&M Col, 58-64; spec. instr. ENG, Univ. Okla, 66-67; ASSOC. PROF, FISK UNIV, 67-, CHMN. DEPT, 67-, DIR. INTERDISCIPLINARY PROG. HUMANITIES, 71- Spec. consult. Eng. for disadvantaged children, Mary Holmes Col, 68-; mem. bd. dirs, YWCA, 73-; mem, Nat. Counc. Negro Women; co-chairperson, Comn. on Status Women in Higher Educ. MLA; Asn. Depts. Eng; Int. Platform Asn; NCTE. Publ: In service training in teaching black literature, ADE Bull, 71; On teaching minorities fairly, 72 & Islands and exiles, 73, Col. Compos. & Commun; plus one other. Add: Dept. of English, Fisk University, Box 821, Nashville, TN 37203.

PURVES, ALAN CARROLL, b. Philadelphia, Pa, Dec. 14, 31; m. 60; c. 2. ENGLISH. A.B, Harvard Col, 53; M.A, Columbia Univ, 56, Ph.D, 60. Lectr, Hofstra Col, 56-58; instr. Eng, Columbia Col, Columbia Univ, 58-61, asst. prof, Barnard Col, 61-65; assoc. examr. humanities, Educ. Testing Serv, 65-67, examr, 67-68; assoc. prof. ENG. EDUC, UNIV. ILL, URBANA, 68-70, PROF, 70- Assoc. ed, Odyssey Rev, 61-63; mem. int. lit. comt, Int. Asn. Eval. Educ. Achievement, 65-, chmn. comt, 67-73; consult, Dartmouth Sem, 66; aesthet. educ. prog, Cent. Midwest Regional Educ. Lab, 67-68, staff assoc, 68-72; mem. fac, Int. Sem, Gränna, Sweden, 71. U.S.A, 53-55. MLA; Keats-Shelley Asn. Am; NCTE (mem. comt. res, 68, trustee, res. found, 69-72, ed, Res. in Teaching Eng, 73-). Literary response; education in literature; curriculum evaluation in English. Publ: Formal structure in Kubla Khan, Boston Univ, 62; ed, Theodore Spencer, collected essays, Rutgers Univ, 67; co-auth, The elements of writing about literature, 68 & Literature and the reader, 72, NCTE; co-auth, How porcupines make love, Xerox, 72; ed. & co-ed, Responding (18 vols), Ginn, 73; auth, Literature education in ten countries, Almqvist & Wiksell, 73; Literary criticism, testing and the English teacher, Col. Eng, 67; contrib, Formative and summative evaluation of student learning, Mcgraw, 70. Add: 310 W. Delaware, Urbana, IL 61801.

PUTNAM, ROBERT MORGAN, b. Elwood, Ill, June 22, 18; m. 44; c. 3. THEATRE, DRAMA. B.A, Cornell Col, 40; M.A, Univ. Wis, 53; Stanford Univ, 49-53, 61-62, summer, 63. Instr. speech, Knox Col, 46-49; asst. prof. THEATRE & DRAMA, WILLAMETTE UNIV, 53-57, ASSOC. PROF, 57- Acting asst. prof. speech, Stanford Univ, 61-62. U.S.A.A.F, 41-45, S/Sgt. Speech Commun. Asn; Am. Theatre Asn. Add: Dept. of Theatre, Willamette University, Salem, OR 97301.

PUTZEL, MAX, b. Denver, Colo, Apr. 5, 10; m. 40, 63; c. 9. ENGLISH & AMERICAN LITERATURE. A.B, Yale, 32, Ph.D.(Eng), 58; M.A, Wash. Univ, 53. Instr. ENG, Wash. Univ, 52-55; UNIV. CONN, 57-60, asst. 60-66, ASSOC. PROF, 66-, asst. dean grad. sch, 63-70. Am. Lit. Group, MLA. Eng. Inst; Col. Eng. Asn; Melville Soc. Am. William Faulkner's prose fiction, a genetic study. Publ: The man in the mirror: W.M. Reedy, Harvard, 63 & Greenwood, 73; ed, Sidney's Astrophil & Stella, Doubleday, 67; contrib, Dictung und Wirklichkeit, Ullstein, Munich, 72; auth, What is gothic about Absalom, Absolom?, fall 71 & Evolution of two characters in Faulkner's early and unpublished fiction, spring 73, South. Lit. J; plus others. Add: Dept. of English, University of Connecticut, Box U-25, Storrs, CT 06268.

PUTZEL, ROSAMOND, b. N.C, Apr. 16, 26. ENGLISH. A.B, Salem Col. (N.C), 47; teaching fel, Univ. N.C, 53, M.A, 51, Ph.D, 60; South. Fels. Fund fel, 58. Instr. math. & Eng, Stratford Col, 51-53; ENG, Univ. N.C, Greensboro, 56-60, asst. prof, 60-65; ASSOC. PROF, UNIV. DETROIT, 65- MLA; NCTE; AAUP. Drama and theatre; English Renaissance literature. Add: Dept. of English, University of Detroit, Detroit, MI 48221.

PUZON, BRIDGET, O.S.U, b. New York, N.Y, Aug. 4, 31. ENGLISH LITERATURE. B.A, Col. New Rochelle, 57; M.A, Boston Col, 63; Univ. Mich, Ann Arbor, 66; Ph.D.(Eng. lit), Harvard, 73. Instr. ENG, St. Joseph's Acad, Malone, N.Y, 57-58; Ursuline Acad, Dedham, Mass, 58-61; Ursuline Sch, New Rochelle, N.Y, 61-65; from instr. to ASST. PROF, Col. New Rochelle, 65-68; HOLLINS COL, 73- Researcher, Church Soc. Col. Work, Cambridge, Mass, 73. MLA; Am. Asn. Univ. Women. Modern British novel; Virginia Woolf; literature and society. Add: Dept. of English, Hollins College, VA 24020.

PYLE, EVERETT GUSTAV, b. Kewanee, Ill, Aug. 5, 13; m. 40; c. 2. ENGLISH. B.Ed, West. Ill. Univ, 35; M.A, State Univ. Iowa, 39, Ph.D.(Am. lit), 61. Teacher ENG, Mitchell Consol. Sch, Iowa, 36-38; pub. schs, Unionville, Mo, 38-41; instr, S.Dak. State Col, 45-46; mem. fac, UNIV. WIS-OSHKOSH, 46-55, assoc. prof, 55-61, PROF, 61-, DEAN GRAD. SCH, 62- NCTE. Romantic literature, especially Coleridge and Hazlitt; American literature, especially Brand Whitlock. Add: Office of Dean of the Graduate School, University of Wisconsin-Oshkosh, Oshkosh, WI 54901.

PYLES, THOMAS, b. Frederick, Md, June 5, 05; m. 29; c. 1. ENGLISH PHILOLOGY. A.B, Univ. Md, 26, A.M, 27; Ph.D, Johns Hopkins Univ, 38. Instr. Eng, Univ. Md, 27-40, asst. prof, 40-44; prof, Univ. Okla, 44-48; Univ. Fla, 48-66; prof. ENG. & LING, NORTHWEST. UNIV, 66-71, EMER. PROF, 71-; EMER. PROF. ENG, UNIV. FLA, 72- Instr. Eng, Johns Hopkins Univ, 38-44; Fulbright guest prof, Univ. Göttingen, 56-57; mem. ed. adv. bd, Funk & Wagnall Col. Standard Dictionary, N.Y, 63; int. ed. adv. comt, World Bk. Encycl. Dictionary, N.Y, 63; ed. comt, Dictionary Am. Regional Eng; ed. adv. comt, Thorndike-Barnhart Col. Dictionary; vis. prof, N.Y. Univ, summer 65; Northwest. Univ, 65; mem. adv. comt, Am. Speech, 66-67, 70-71. MLA; Ling. Soc. Am; Am. Dialect Soc.(secy-treas, 52-56, v.pres, 58-59, pres, 60-61, ed. comt, 60-71); NCTE (dir. col. sect, 67-70, comt. publ. of affiliates, 68-71); Mod. Humanities Res. Asn; Int. Asn. Univ. Prof. Eng; Am. Name Soc. Linguistics and mediaeval literature. Publ: Words and ways of American English, Random, 52; Origins and development of the English language, 64, 71 & co-auth, English: an introduction to language, 70, Harcourt; auth, The English language: a brief history, Holt, 68. Add: 629 N.E. Boulevard, Gainesville, FL 32601.

Q

QUAINTANCE, RICHARD EDGECOMBE, JR, b. New London, Conn, Mar. 16, 28; m. 51; c. 2. ENGLISH LITERATURE. B.A, Amherst Col, 50; M.A, Yale, 55, Ph.D. (Eng), 62. Instr. ENG, Robert Col, Turkey, 50-52; Duke Univ, 58-62; ASST. prof. Oakland Univ, 62-65; ASSOC. PROF, DOUGLASS COL, RUTGERS UNIV, 65- Am. Counc. Learned Soc. grant-in-aid, 63; mem, Eng. Inst. Mil.Intel, U.S.A, 52-54. MLA; Johnson Soc. Midwest (v.pres, 63, pres, 64-65). The conventions of love poetry and of satire; 18th century sentimentalism; French influence upon Restoration literature. Publ: French sources of the Restoration Imperfect enjoyment poem, Philol. Quart, 4/63. Add: Dept. of English, Douglass College, Rutgers University, New Brunswick, NJ 08903.

QUALLS, YOURA T, b. Clarksville, Tex. ENGLISH. B.A, Fisk Univ, 37; M.A, Radcliffe Col, 42, Ph.D.(hist. Am. civilization), 56. Instr. ENG, Fisk Univ, 37-39; assoc. prof, Langston Univ, 43-45, PROF, 46-49, 51-53; South. Univ, 56; Md. State Col, 57-64; TUSKEGEE INST, 64-, CHMN. DEPT, 67- Res. assoc, Ctr. Res. Lang. & Lang Behav. Univ. Mich, 67. NCTE; Conf. Col. Compos. & Commun; Col. Lang. Asn. American Quaker history; southern Negro dialect. Add: Dept. of English, Tuskegee Institute, AL 36088.

QUARNSTROM, I. BLAINE, b. Rupert, Idaho, Nov. 5, 35; m. 62; c. 3. THEATER, ORAL INTERPRETATION. B.S, Brigham Young Univ, 61, M.A, 63; Ph.D.(theater), Ohio State Univ, 67. Asst. speech, Brigham Young Univ, 61-63; theater, Ohio State Univ, 63-66; asst. prof. speech & drama, Cent. Mich. Univ, 66-72; ASSOC. PROF. THEATER ARTS & CHMN. DEPT, UNIV. SOUTH. MISS, 72- Speech Commun. Asn; Am. Theatre Asn; Southeast Theatre Conf. American theater history; experimentation with Readers Theater. Publ: Early twentieth century staging of Uncle Tom's cabin, Ohio State Univ. Theatre Collection Bull. No. 15, 68. Add: Dept. of Theater Arts, University of Southern Mississippi, Hattiesburg, MS 39401.

QUARTERMAIN, PETER ALLAN, b. Evesham, Eng, Apr. 6, 34; m. 63. ENGLISH. B.A, Nottingham Univ, Eng, 55, Gertrude Cropper scholar, 55-56, 57-59, Ph.D, 59; Fulbright-Rockefeller scholar, Yale & Univ. Chicago, 56. Eng-Speaking Union asst, Wash. Univ, 56-57; fel. Am. civilization, Univ. Pa, 59-60; asst. prof. ENG, Mills Col, 60-62; UNIV. B.C, 62-68, ASSOC. PROF, 68- Consult. ed, J. Creative Behav, 66-; mem, Nat. Coord. Counc. Educ. & Nat. Bd. Exam, Cert. Gen. Accountants Asn. Can, 66- Brit. Asn. Am. Stud; Am. Stud. Asn; Can. Asn. Am. Stud.(treas, 64-67). The American dream and the rejection of Europe; William Carlos Williams; psychology and teaching of creativity. Publ: Hawthorne and Puritanism, Micro-Rec, 64; co-auth, English, engineering, and creativity, J. Creative Behav, fall 67; auth, Louis Zukofsky, Open Lett, fall 73. Add: Dept. of English, University of British Columbia, Vancouver, B.C. V6T 1W5, Can.

QUATTROCKI, EDWARD A, b. Chicago, Ill, Dec. 13, 31; m. 58; c. 5. ENGLISH. B.A, De Paul Univ, 56; Fund Adult Educ. grant, Stanford Univ, 60, M.A, 64; NDEA fel, Loyola Univ.(Ill), 64-68, Schmitt Found. grant, 66-67, Ph.D.(Eng), 67. Asst. prof. ENG. LIT, OHIO UNIV, 67-71, ASSOC. PROF, 71- U.S.C.G, 52-54. MLA; Renaissance Soc. Am. Renaissance English literature; Utopian literature. Add: Dept. of English, Ohio University, Athens, OH 45701.

QUAYLE, CALVIN KING, b. Logan, Utah, July 22, 27; m. 49; c. 3. DRAMA. B.S, Utah State Univ, 50, M.S, 54; Univ. Wis, summer 50; Ph.D, Univ. Minn, 58. Instr. speech & Eng, Preston High Sch, Idaho, 51-53; Ford Found. teaching intern, Univ. Minn, 55-56; from instr. to assoc. prof. speech & drama, Chico State Col, 56-63; asst. prof, Univ. Mich, 63-65; PROF. SPEECH & CHMN. DEPT, UNIV. WIS-EAU CLAIRE, 65- U.S.A, 45-47, Res, 48-50, 2nd Lt. Am. Theatre Asn; Speech Commun. Asn. Dramatic literature and technical theatre, especially design. Add: Dept. of Speech, University of Wisconsin-Eau Claire, Eau Claire, WI 54701.

QUEENAN, JOHN THOMAS, b. New Brunswick, N.J, May 13, 21; m. 58; c. 1. ENGLISH. B.A, Rutgers Univ, 48, M.A, 49; Ph.D.(Eng), Univ. Pa, 55. Asst. prof. Eng. Villanova Univ, 49-55; Univ. North. Iowa, 55-56; mem. fac. dept. Eng, Wright Jr. Col, 56-65; chmn. Eng, ROCK VALLEY COL, 65-66, DEAN INSTR, 66- Lectr, Rutgers Univ, 51-55; Am. Philos. Soc. fel, 55-56; lectr. Ind. Univ, 56-62. U.S.A, 42-46, Sgt. Col. Eng. Asn; Conf. Col. Compos. & Commun. Development of nationalism in American literature; The Port-folio, 1801-1827, an early American magazine; John Gower. Publ: Television study guide for English 102, 63, Television study guide for American literature to 1865, 65 & Television study guide for American literature from 1865, 66, Chicago Bd. Educ; Literary criticism of Nathaniel Chapman, Yearbk, Am. Philos. Soc, 56; Suggestions for teaching literature on T.V, Col. Eng. Asn. Critic, 5/60. Add: Rock Valley College, Rockford, IL 61111.

QUEENER, LEA GIBBS, b. Tuckerman, Ark, July 16, 25; m. 46, 68; c. 1. SPEECH. B.S, Memphis State Univ, 56, M.A, 57; fel, Northwest. Univ, 60-61, Ph.D.(interpretation), 66. Instr. speech interpretation, MEMPHIS STATE UNIV, 57-61, asst. prof, 61-65, ASSOC. PROF. ORAL INTERPRETATION, 65- Vis. prof, Northwest. Univ, summer 63. Speech Commun. Asn.(chmn, interpretation div, 68-69); South. Speech Commun. Asn.(chmn, interpretation interest group, 68-69). Stylistics; prosody. Publ: The literary experience through oral interpretation, Memphis State Univ, 59; Language of poetry, Speech Asn. Am, 62; Contiguity figures: an index to the language-world relationships in Auden's poetry, In: Studies in interpretation, 72; co-ed, Bibliography of interpretation studies for 1969-71, N.C. Jour. Speech, 72-73. Add: Dept. of Speech & Drama, Memphis State University, Central Ave, Memphis, TN 38152,

QUICK, NICHOLAS WILSON, b. Carmel, Ind, June 30, 20; m. 41; c. 1. ENGLISH. A.B, Univ. Ill, 42, M.A, 47; Ph.D.(Eng), Univ. Tex, 54; J.D, John Marshall Law School, 73. From instr. to assoc. prof. Eng, Agr. & Mech. Col. Tex, 47-57, asst. to pres, 56-57; dean, Little Rock Univ, 57-60; dean of instr. & grad. stud, Midwest. Univ, 60-65, v.pres, 65-69; PROF. ENG, GA. SOUTH. UNIV, 69-, V.PRES, 72-, dean arts & sci, 69-72. U.S.A.A.F, 42-46, Capt. Conf. Col. Teachers Eng; Southwest Mod. Lang. Asn. Nineteenth century English literature. Publ: Thomas Hardy and Lord Byron; Byronism in the late nineteenth century; Matthew Arnold's Yellow gloves. Add: 19 Forest Pines Dr, Statesboro, GA 30458.

QUINBY, GEORGE HUNNEWELL, b. Newton, Mass, Mar, 26, 01; m. 39. ENGLISH. B.A, Bowdoin Col, 23; M.F.A, Yale, 46. Instr. ENG, Lafayette Col, 23-25; BOWDOIN COL, 34-36, asst. prof. & dir. dramatics, 36-46, assoc. prof, 46-49, prof, 49-69, EMER. PROF, 69- Theatre consult, Univ. Ohio, 46, Col. Wooster, 47; vis. lectr. drama, Queen's Univ, Can, 56; Smith-Mundt lectr. grant, Univ. Tehran, Iran, 56, Fulbright lectr. grant, 62; specialist, U.S. Dept. State, Kabul, Afghanistan, 58. Dramatists Guild; Am. Nat. Theatre & Acad; Am. Educ. Theatre Asn; U.S. Inst. Theatre Technol. Theatre architecture; playwrighting; production of Shakespeare. Publ: Theatre in Iran, In: A history of the theatre (rev. ed), Crown. Add: Dept. of English, Bowdoin College, Brunswick, ME 04011.

QUINLAN, MAURICE JAMES, b. East Hampton, Conn, Dec. 18, 04. ENGLISH. A.B, Yale, 26; A.M, Columbia Univ, 29, univ. fel, 37-38, Ph.D, 41. Instr. ENG, Dartmouth Col, 31-33; asst. prof, St. Joseph Col, 34-37, 38-42; assoc. prof. Lehigh Univ, 45-49; prof, Col. St. Thomas, 49-54; BOSTON COL, 54-70, EMER. PROF, 70- Ed. adv, Stud. In Burke & His Time, 70- MLA; Conf. Brit. Stud. Eighteenth century English literature and society. Publ: Victorian prelude, Columbia Univ, 41; William Cowper, Univ. Minn, 53; Samuel Johnson: a layman's religion, Univ. Wis, 64; Swift's use of literalization, PMLA, 12/67; Treason in Lilliput and in England, Tex. Stud. Lit. & Lang, spring 70; Balloons and the awareness of a new age, Stud. In Burke & his time, spring 73; plus others. Add: RFD, Enfield, NH 03748.

QUINLIVAN, FRANCES MARIE, b. Cleveland, Ohio. ENGLISH LITERATURE. A.B, West. Reserve Univ, 25, A.M, 28, Ph.D, 48. Instr. ENG, NOTRE DAME COL.(OHIO), 25-28, asst. prof, 28-48, PROF, 48- MLA; Col. Eng. Asn. Irish fiction, 1800-1880. Add: Dept. of English, Notre Dame College, South Euclid, OH 44121.

QUINN, DENNIS, b. New York, N.Y, Oct. 3, 28; m. 52; c. 3. ENGLISH. A.B, Univ. Wis, 51, M.A, 52, univ. fel, 53, Ph.D.(Eng), 58. Instr. ENG, UNIV. KANS, 56-60, from asst. prof. to assoc. prof, 60-71, PROF, 71- Fulbright Stud, Univ. Leyden, Neth, 55-56; Fulbright res. award, Univ. Salamanca, Spain, 62-63; Am. Philos. Soc. grant-in-aid, 62-63. U.S.A, 56-58. English literature of early 17th century; Mediaeval and Renaissance Biblical exegesis; English Bible. Publ: Donne's Christian eloquence, Eng. Lit. Hist, 12/60; John Donne's principles of Biblical exegesis, J. Eng. & Germanic Philol, 4/62. Add: Dept. of English, University of Kansas, Lawrence, KS 66045.

QUINN, EDWARD, b. Brooklyn, N.Y, Jan. 5, 32; m. 56; c. 4. ENGLISH. B.A, Brooklyn Col, 58; M.A, N.Y. Univ, 59, Ph.D.(Eng), 63. Instr. ENG, St. Francis Col, 62-65; asst. prof, CITY COL. NEW YORK, 65-70, ASSOC. PROF, 70- U.S.A, 53-54. Publ: Co-auth, Reader's encyclopedia of Shakespeare, 66 & Reader's encyclopedia of world drama, 69, Crowell; auth, Sense of the sixties, 68, co-ed, Interdiscipline, 72 & co-auth, The major Shakespearean tragedies, 73, Free Press; auth, Antedatings from Thomas Phaer, Notes & Queries, 64. Add: Dept. of English, City College of New York, Convent Ave. & 138th St, New York, NY 10031.

QUINN, ESTHER CASIER, b. Lyon Mountain, N.Y, May 3, 22; m. 51; c. 2. ENGLISH. B.A. & Hess Prize, Hunter Col, 46; univ. fel, Columbia Univ, 46-48, M.A, 48, Ph.D, 60. Lectr, Hunter Col, 48-61, instr. Eng, 61-64, asst. prof, 64-68; ASSOC. PROF. humanities, Fordham Univ, Lincoln Ctr, 68-70; ENG, HUNTER COL, 70- MLA; Int. Arthurian Soc; Mediaeval Acad. Am. Medieval literature; Arthurian romance; Chaucer. Publ: The quest of Seth, Univ. Chicago, 62; The quest of Seth, Solomon's ship and the Grail, Traditio, 65; contrib, In pursuit of perfection: studies in the paradoxes of courtly love, Kennikat, 74; plus others. Add: Dept. of English, Hunter College, 695 Park Ave, New York, NY 10021.

QUINN, JOHN JOSEPH, English Language, Medieval Literature. See Volume III, Foreign Languages, Linguistics & Philology.

QUINN, MARY BERNETTA, O.S.F, b. Lake Geneva, Wis, Sept. 19, 15. ENGLISH. B.A, Col. St. Teresa, 42; M.A, Cath. Univ. Am, 44; Ph.D, Univ. Wis, 52. MEM. FAC, DEPT. ENG, Col. St. Teresa, 45-69, chmn. dept, 51-52, 54-65; ALLEN UNIV, 69-73; NORFOLK STATE COL, 73- Mem. summer fac, Siena Col. Grad. Sch, 61, 63, 65; Nat. Found. Humanities & Arts fel, 67-68. S.Atlantic Mod. Lang. Asn; South. Humanities Conf; NCTE; Conf. Col. Compos. & Commun. American studies; modern literature, especially poetry; history of ideas; symbolic landscape in modern poetry. Publ: The metamorphic tradition in modern poetry, Rutgers Univ, 55, Gordian, 67; Give me souls: a life of Cardinal Raphael Merry del Val, 58 & To God alone the glory: a life of St. Bonaventure, 62, Newman; Ezra Pound: an introduction to his poetry, Columbia Univ, 72; plus others. Add: Dept. of English, Norfolk State College, Norfolk, VA 23504.

QUINN, ROBERT SAMUEL, b. Chicago, Ill, Apr. 19, 27; m. 64; c. 1. SPEECH, DRAMA. B.F.A, Art Inst. Chicago, 52, M.F.A, 53; Ph.D.(speech & TV), Univ. Wis-Madison, 66. Dir. community players, Recreation Dept, Bd. Educ, Sheboygan, Wis, 53-57; mem. staff, Goodman Sch, Art Inst. Chicago, 57-58; asst. prof. speech, TV & drama, Morningside Col, 59-61; SPEECH & DRAMA, UNIV. WIS, MARATHON CAMPUS, 63-, ASSOC. PROF, 70- U.S.N.R, 45-46. Am. Theatre Asn; Speech Commun. Asn. Creative drama for children; improvisational acting techniques; forensics. Publ: Co-auth, Educational films: theatre, Educ. Theatre J, 10/63. Add: Dept. of Speech, University of Wisconsin, Marathon Campus, 518 S. Seventh Ave, Wausau, WI 54401.

QUINN, VINCENT, b. New York, N.Y, Nov. 24, 26; m. 51; c. 2. ENGLISH. A.B, Columbia Univ, 48, M.A, 50, Ph.D, 59. Instr. ENG, Iona Col, 50-54, asst. prof, 54-59; instr, BROOKLYN COL, 59-63, asst. prof, 64-68, assoc. prof, 69-72, PROF, 73-, chmn. dept, 67-70. Assoc. ed, Rev. Nat. Literatures, 71- Intel.C, U.S.A, 45-47. MLA. Modern poetry; American literature. Publ: Hart Crane, 63 & Hilda Doolittle, 67, Twayne. Add: Dept. of English, Brooklyn College, Brooklyn, NY 11210.

QUINONES, RICARDO, b. Allentown, Pa, July 9, 35. RENAISSANCE, COMPARATIVE LITERATURE. B.A, Northwest. Univ, 57; Fulbright scholar, Univ. Clermont-Ferrand, 57-58; Univ. Munich, 58-59; Woodrow Wilson fel, Harvard, 59-60, Ph.D.(comp. lit), 63. Teaching asst. humanities, Harvard, 60-62, tutor hist. & lit, 62-63; asst. prof. COMP. LIT, CLAREMONT MEN'S COL, 63-69, ASSOC. PROF, 69-, summer res. grants, 66, 67 & 72. Milton fel, William Andrews Clark Mem. Libr, summer 68; Nat. Endowment for Humanities younger fel, 68-69; vis. prof, Harvard, summer 70; grad. ctr, City Univ. New York, 70-71; Richmond Col, summer 71. Renaissance Soc. Am; Dante Soc. Am; MLA (Comp. Lit. Group). Four phases of time and literary modernism; end of the Renaissance; themes of the Renaissance. Publ: The Renaissance discovery of time, Harvard, 72; Views of time in Shakespeare, JHI, 65; Four phases of time and literary modernism, Claremont Humanities Forum & Second World Conf. Time, Japan, 7/73; plus others. Add: Bauer Center, 900 Mills Ave, Claremont, CA 91711.

QUINTANA, RICARDO, b. Albany, N.Y, Oct. 6, 98; m. 28; c. 1. ENGLISH LITERATURE. A.B, Harvard, 20, A.M, 21, Ph.D, 27. Instr. ENG, Wash. Univ, 21-24; asst. prof, UNIV. WIS-MADISON, 27-30, assoc. prof, 30-36, prof, 36-69, EMER. PROF, 69- MLA. Seventeenth and eighteenth century literature; modern satire. Publ: Mind and art of Jonathan Swift, 36 & Swift: an introduction, 55; Oxford; ed, Two hundred poems, Longmans, Green, 47; co-ed, Seventeenth century verse and prose, 1600-1660, 51 & rev. ed, 71, Seventeenth century verse and prose, 1660-1700, 52 & auth, Oliver Goldsmith: a Georgian study, 67, Macmillan; ed, Eighteenth century plays, 52 & Jonathan Swift: Gulliver's travels and other writings, 58, Random; co-ed, English poetry of the mid and late eighteenth century, Knopf, 63; auth, Situational satire: a commentary on the method of Swift, 1/48 & Goldsmith's achievement as dramatist, 1/65, Univ. Toronto Quart; Samuel Butler: a restoration figure in a modern light, J. Eng. Lit. Hist, 3/51; plus others. Add: Dept. of English, University of Wisconsin-Madison, Madison, WI 53706.

QUIRK, EUGENE FRANCIS, b. Philadelphia, Pa, Sept. 29, 43; m. 66. ENGLISH & AMERICAN LITERATURE. B.A, La Salle Col, 65; M.A, Univ. Ark, 67; Fulbright fel, Univ. London, 71-72; Ph.D.(Eng), Univ. Ill, 72. Instr. ENG, Jefferson Col, 66-67; Univ. Ill, 69-71; ASST. PROF, UNIV. HARTFORD, 72- MLA; AAUP. The novel; Victorian literature; contemporary literature and film. Publ: Tulkinghorn's buried life: a study of character in Bleak house, J. Eng. & Ger. Philol, fall 73. Add: Dept. of English, University of Hartford, 200 Bloomfield Ave, West Hartford, CT 06117.

QUITSLUND, JON ALRIK, b. Washington, D.C, Mar. 27, 39; m. 62. ENGLISH. B.A, Reed Col, 61; Ph.D.(Eng), Princeton, 67. Asst. prof. ENG, GEORGE WASHINGTON UNIV, 64-73, ASSOC. PROF, 73- MLA; AAUP; Renaissance Soc. Am. The poetry of Edmund Spenser; philosophy and theology of the Renaissance; social history of Elizabethan England. Publ: Spenser's image of Sapience, Stud. In Renaissance, 69; Spenser's Amoretti VIII and Platonic commentaries on Petrarch, J. Warburg & Courtauld Insts, 73. Add: Dept. of English, George Washington University, Washington, DC 20006.

QURESHI, AHMAD HASAN, b. Raikot, India, Nov. 1, 26; Can. citizen; m. 62; c. 2. ENGLISH LITERATURE. B.A, Punjab Univ, India, 44, M.A, 49; B.S, Univ. Ill, 53, M.A, 55, Ph.D.(Eng), 58. Lectr. ENG, Dyal Singh Col, 49-50; Govt. Col, Mianwali, 50-51; asst. prof. Eureka Col, 59-60; UNIV. ALTA, 60-68, assoc. prof, 68-74, PROF, 74- Can. Coun. res. grant, 68. India's epic; Tennyson; Victorian poetry and poetics. Publ: Celestial labyrinth: India's epic poetry II, East West Rev, spring 71. Add: 11623 51st Ave, Edmonton, Alta. T6H 0M4, Can.

R

RABEN, JOSEPH, b. New York, N.Y, Sept. 3, 24; m. 52. ENGLISH. B.A, Univ. Wis, 44; M.A,Ind. Univ, 49, All-Univ. fel, 49-50, Ph.D.(Eng), 54. Teaching fel, ENG, Ind. Univ, 50-52; instr, Princeton, 52-54; QUEENS COL. (N.Y). 54-61, asst. prof, 62-67, assoc. prof, 67-70, PROF, 70- Consult. comput. applications in lit, Int. Bus. Machines Corp, 64; ed, Comput. & the Humanities, 66-; Am. Counc. Learned Soc. fel. for comput-oriented res. in humanities, 67; Philips lectr, Haverford Col, 68; mem. adv. comt. to Assoc. Univs. on nat. inst. for info. syst, 68-; chmn. working group on humanities, Int. Fed. Info. Processing, 71- U.S.A, 45-46. MLA; Am. Soc. Info. Sci. Romantic period of English literature; computer applications in the study of literature; computer-aided library research. Publ: Content analysis and the study of poetry, In: The analysis of communication content, Wiley, 69; co-auth, Information systems applications in the humanities, In: Annual review of information science, Am. Soc. Info. Sci, 72; plus others. Add: 46 Baker Hill Rd, Great Neck, NY 11023.

RABINOVITZ, RUBIN, b. New York, N.Y, July 18, 38. ENGLISH, COMPARATIVE LITERATURE. B.A, Rutgers Univ, New Brunswick, 59; Woodrow Wilson fel. & M.A, Columbia Univ, 61, univ. fel, N.Y. State col. fel. & Ph.D.(contemporary Eng. lit), 66; Inst. Int. Educ. fel, Univ. London, summer 62. Instr. Eng, Columbia Univ, 66-69, asst. prof. Eng. & comp. lit, 69-74; ASSOC. PROF. ENG, UNIV. COLO, BOULDER, 74- Nat. Endowment for Humanities fel, 73-74. MLA. Contemporary fiction; Samuel Beckett; mythology. Publ: The reaction against experiment in the English novel, 1950-1960, 67 & Iris Murdoch, 68, Columbia Univ; C.P. Snow versus the experimental novel, Columbia Univ. Forum, fall 67; Iris Murdoch's A fairly honourable defeat, N.Y. Times Bk. Rev, 2/70; Watt from Descartes to Schopenhauer, In: Modern Irish literature, Twayne, 72. Add: Dept. of English, University of Colorado, Boulder, CO 80302.

RABKIN, ERIC S, b. Queens, N.Y, Mar. 8, 46; m. 67; c. 1. ENGLISH & AMERICAN LITERATURE. A.B, Cornell Univ, 67; Ph.D.(Eng), Univ. Iowa, 70. Asst. prof. ENG, UNIV. MICH, ANN ARBOR, 70-74, ASSOC. PROF, 74- Grant, Horace H. Rackham Sch. Grad. Stud, summer 73; Am. Counc. Learned Soc. fel, 73. MLA; Midwest Mod. Lang. Asn; Popular Cult. Asn. Literary theory; modern fiction; aesthetics. Publ: Narrative suspense: When Slim turned sideways ..., Univ. Mich, 73; co-auth, Form in fiction, St, Martins, 74. Add: Dept. of English, University of Michigan, Ann Arbor, MI 48104.

RABKIN, GERALD EDWARD, b. Brooklyn, N.Y, Jan. 4, 30; m. 61. ENGLISH, DRAMATIC LITERATURE. B.A, Brooklyn Col, 51; M.A, Ohio State Univ, 52, Ph.D, 61. Asst. instr. Eng, Ohio State Univ, 61; instr, Ind. Univ, 61-63, asst. prof, 63-66, assoc. prof, 66-67; speech & drama, Univ. Kans, 67-70; PROF. ENG, LIVINGSTON COL, RUTGERS UNIV, 70- MLA; Am. Theatre Asn. Contemporary drama, especially English and American; film history and criticism. Publ: Drama and commitment, Ind. Univ, 64. Add: Dept. of English, Livingston College, Rutgers University, New Brunswick, NJ 08903.

RABKIN, NORMAN CLIFFORD, b. New York, N.Y, Mar. 14, 30; m. 54; c. 3. ENGLISH. A.B, Univ. Ill, 51; A.M, Harvard, 52, Ph.D, 59; Fulbright scholar, Italy, 54-55. Instr. ENG, UNIV. CALIF, BERKELEY, 59-60, asst. prof, 60-66, assoc. prof, 66-69, PROF, 69-, humanities res. prof, fall 65, asst. dean, Col. Lett. & Sci, 66-67, assoc. dean, 67-70, chmn. grad. stud, 72-73. Lectr, Eng. Inst, 65, sect. chmn, 68, mem. supvr. comt, 68-70, ed, Eng. Inst. Essays, 69; vis. asst. prof, Ind. Univ, summer 66; Guggenheim fel, 70-71; Nat. Endowment for Humanities sr. fel, 73-74. Bowdoin Prize, Harvard, 52. U.S.A, 55-57. MLA; Mod. Humanities Res. Asn; Shakespeare Asn. Am; Renaissance Soc. Am. Shakespeare; Elizabethan drama; Renaissance literature. Publ: Co-ed, Shakespeare's contemporaries: modern studies in English renaissance drama, 61, 2nd ed, 71 & auth, Twentieth century interpretations of The Duchess of Malfi, 68, Prentice-Hall; Approaches to Shakespeare, McGraw, 64; Shakespeare and the common understanding, Free Press, 67; Clarissa: a study in the nature of convention, J. Eng. Lit. Hist, 56; The double plot: notes on the history of a convention, Renaissance Drama, 64; Meaning and Shakespeare, In: Shakespeare 1971: proceedings of the World Shakespeare Congress, Univ. Toronto, 72. Add: 1020 Keith Ave, Berkeley, CA 94708.

RACIN, JOHN, b. Lakewood, Ohio, Aug. 26, 25; m. 47; c. 4. ENGLISH. A.B, Stanford Univ, 51; Ph.D, Ohio State Univ, 61. Instr. ENG, Ohio State Univ, 55-61; Miami Univ, 61-63, asst. prof, 63-64; assoc. prof, W.VA. UNIV, 64-74, PROF, 74-, COORD. GRAD. STUD, 72- Managing ed, Arch. Brit. Hist. & Cult, 67-; Southeast. Inst. Medieval & Renaissance Stud. fel, summer 69. MLA; Conf. Brit. Stud; Catch Soc. Am. English Renaissance; 17th century; Shakespeare. Publ: Sir Walter Raleigh as historian, Salzburg Stud. Eng. Lit, 74; The early editions of Sir Walter Raleigh's The history of the world, Stud. Bibliog, 64; Dover beach and the poetry of meditation, Victorian Poetry VII, 70. Add: Dept. of English, West Virginia University, Morgantown, WV 26506.

RACKHAM, ERIC N, b. Boylston, N.S, July 21, 11; U.S. citizen; m. 39; c. 1. ENGLISH LITERATURE. B.A, Mt. Allison Univ, 32; scholar & M.A, Univ. Mich, 37, Ph.D, 51. Prin. & teacher Eng, Whycocomagh Sch, N.S, 32-34, Bass River Sch, 34-36; instr, Univ. Colo, 37-42, asst. dean men & acting dir. admis. recs, 41-46, asst. dean col. arts & sci, 47-52; prof. Eng, Kent State Univ, 52-68, dean, col. arts & sci, 52-63, exec. dean educ. & stud. serv, 63-68; PRES, McKENDREE COL, 68- Am. Col. Personnel Asn; Am. Personnel & Guidance Asn; MLA. Biblical and Canadian literature. Add: 716 College St, Lebanon, IL 62254.

RACKIN, DONALD, b. Newark, N.J, Feb. 24, 33; m. 54; c. 2. ENGLISH. B.A, Rutgers Univ, 54; M.A, Columbia Univ, 55; Ph.D.(Eng), Univ. Ill, 64. Instr. Eng, Auburn Univ, 56-57; teaching asst, Univ. Ill, 57-62; instr, TEMPLE UNIV, 62-64, asst. prof, 64-68, ASSOC. PROF. ENG, 68-, chmn. freshman Eng, 68-70. AAUP; MLA(Annual Award, 67). Modern prose fiction; Victorian literature. Publ: Ed, Alice in Wonderland: text & context, Wadsworth, 69; auth, Alice's journey to the end of night, PMLA, 66; The moral rhetoric of Nabokov's Lolita, Four Quarters, 73; What you always wanted to know about Alice but were afraid to ask, Victorian Newslett, 73; plus one other. Add: Dept. of English, Temple University, Philadelphia, PA 19122.

RACKIN, PHYLLIS ROSALYN, b. Newark, N.J, Sept. 15, 33; m. 54; c. 2. ENGLISH. A.B, Rutgers Univ, 54; A.M, Auburn Univ, 57; fels, Univ. Ill, 57-58, 58-59, 59-60, Ph.D.(Eng), 62. Instr. ENG, UNIV. PA, 62-64, ASST. PROF, 64- Assoc. prof, Beaver Col, 70-71. MLA; Northeast Mod. Lang. Asn.(chmn, Shakespeare section, 71); Women's Caucus Mod. Lang. Literary criticism; Shakespeare. Publ: Hulme, Richards, and the development of textualist poetic theory, J. Aesthet. & Art Criticism, summer 67; Delusion as resolution in King Lear, Shakespeare Quart, winter 70; Shakespeare's boy Cleopatra, the decorum of nature and the golden world of poetry, PMLA, 3/72. Add: 405 W. Price St, Philadelphia, PA 19144.

RADER, KATHERINE, b. Norman, Okla, Feb. 25, 15. ENGLISH. A.B, Univ. Okla, 36, M.A, 40, Ph.D.(Eng), 51. From instr. to asst. prof. Eng, Northwest. State Col, 36-44; librn. & instr. Eng, Okla. Baptist Univ, 44-45; instr. Eng, Northeast. State Col, 45-46; from instr. to prof, Okla, Baptists Univ, 46-68, chmn. freshman Eng, 47-49; PROF. ENG, SCH. LIB. ARTS, CENT. STATE UNIV.(OKLA), 68- Delta Delta Delta Fiftieth Anniversary fel, 49-50. MLA; NCTE; S.Cent. Mod. Lang. Asn; AAUP; Am. Asn. Univ. Women. Milton; the Renaissance in England. Add: Dept. of English, School of Liberal Arts, Central State University, Edmond, OK 73034.

RADER, LOUIS, b. Stamford, Conn, June 2, 39; m. 66; c. 2. ENGLISH LITERATURE. B.A, Colby Col, 60; M.A, Cornell Univ, 61, Ph.D.(Eng), 64.

Asst. prof. ENG, KING'S COL.(PA), 64-67, ASSOC. PROF, 67- Gerard Manley Hopkins; 19th century literature; modern education. Publ: Hopkins' dark sonnets: another new expression, Victorian poetry, spring 67. Add: Dept. of English, King's College, River St, Wilkes-Barre, PA 18701.

RADER, RALPH WILSON, b. Muskegon, Mich, May 18, 30; m. 50; c. 5. ENGLISH LITERATURE. B.S, Purdue Univ, 52; Ph.D, Ind. Univ, 58. Instr. ENG, UNIV. CALIF, BERKELEY, 56-58, asst. prof, 58-63, assoc. prof, 63-67, PROF, 67- Am. Counc. Learned Soc. grant-in-aid, 59; Guggenheim fel, 73. MLA. Eighteenth and nineteenth century English literature; factual literature; theory of literary forms. Publ: Tennyson's Maud: the biographical genesis, Univ. Calif, 63; co-auth, Essays in eighteenth-century biography, Ind. Univ, 68 & Autobiography, biography, and the novel, Clark Libr, 73. Add: Dept. of English, University of California, Berkeley, CA 94720.

RADKE, MERLE LOUIS, b. Aurelia, Iowa, Feb. 25, 22; m. 44; c. 2. AMERICAN LITERATURE. B.S. Ed, Concordia Teachers Col.(Nebr), 46; M.A, Wayne State Univ, 54; Ph.D.(Eng), Northwest. Univ, 65. Prin, St. Peter Lutheran Sch, St. Johns, Mich, 43-47; E. Bethlehem Lutheran Sch, Detroit, 47-53; Mem. Lutheran Sch, Twin Falls, Idaho, 53-57; instr. ENG, CONCORDIA TEACHERS COL.(ILL), 57-58, asst. prof, 58-60, assoc. prof, 60-65, PROF, 65- Lectr, Concordia Teachers Col.(Nebr), 70-71. Lutheran Educ. Asn; NCTE; Asn. Supv. & Curriculum Develop; Am. Asn. Sch. Adminr; MLA; AAUP. Local color fiction in American magazines of the midwest, 1865-1900; Gothic novels and the plays derived therefrom; twentieth century American novels. Publ: Contrib, Lutheran Educ; Motif. Add: Dept. of English, Concordia Teachers College, 7400 Augusta St, River Forest, IL 60305.

RADLEY, VIRGINIA L, b. Marion, N.Y, Aug. 12, 27. ENGLISH LITERATURE. B.A, Russell Sage Col, 49; M.A, Univ. Rochester, 52; M.S, Syracuse Univ, 56, Ph.D, 58. Chmn. Eng, Emily Howland Cent. Sch, 49-51; sr. instr, Chatham Hall, Va, 52-55; asst. prof. Eng. & asst. dean stud, Goucher Col, 57-59; asst. prof. & dean freshmen, Russell Sage Col, 59-60, assoc. prof. Eng, 60-63, prof, 63-69, assoc. dean col, 60-61, chmn. dept. Eng. & speech, 61-68; acad. dean, Nazareth Col. Rochester, 69-73; PROVOST UNDERGRAD. EDUC, STATE UNIV. N.Y, 73- Eng. Inst; Nat. Asn. Women Deans & Coun; MLA. Romantic and Victorian periods; 19th century American literature; Elizabeth Barrett Browning. Publ: Samuel Taylor Coleridge, 66 & Elizabeth Barrett Browning, 72, Twayne; Elementary education and the liberal arts college, 60 & In praise of the resident poet in the Groves of Academe, 62, Lib. Educ; co-auth, New Look at Sonnet 110, Shakespeare Quart, 61. Add: Central Administration, State University of New York, 99 Washington Ave, Albany, NY 12210.

RADNER, JOHN BARNET, b. Oakland, Calif, Apr. 25, 39; m. 66. ENGLISH. B.A, Harvard, 60, Ph.D.(Eng), 66; B.A, Cambridge, 62. Instr. ENG, Harvard, 66-67, lectr, 67-68, ASST. PROF, 68-71, GEORGETOWN UNIV, 71- MLA; Am. Soc. 18th Century Stud; AAUP. Eighteenth century and romantic moral philosophy and criticism; utopian literature. Add: Dept. of English, Georgetown University, Washington, DC 20007.

RAE, WESLEY DENNIS, b. Minnewaukan, N.Dak, Aug. 12, 32; m. 58; c. 2. ENGLISH. B.S, N.Dak. State Univ, 54; M.A, Univ. Wis, 57, Ph.D, 61. Asst. prof. ENG, Utica Col, Syracuse Univ, 61-65, assoc. prof, 65-69, coord. div. lang, 64-69; assoc. prof. ENG, UNIV. MICH-FLINT, 69-72, PROF, 72-, CHMN. DEPT, 70- U.S.A, 54-56. MLA. Renaissance, mediaeval and classical literature. Publ: Thomas Lodge, Twayne, 67. Add: Dept. of English, University of Michigan-Flint, 1321 E. Court St, Flint, MI 48503.

RAEBURN, JOHN HAY, b. Indianapolis, Ind, July 18, 41; m. 63; c. 2. AMERICAN LITERATURE & STUDIES. A.B, Ind. Univ, Bloomington, 63; A.M, Univ. Pa, 64, Ph.D.(Am. civilization), 69. ASST. PROF. ENG, UNIV. MICH, ANN ARBOR, 67- Am. Stud. Asn; MLA; Pop. Cult. Asn; Midwest. Mod. Lang. Asn. American literature of 19th and 20th centuries, American film. Publ: Co-ed, Frank Capra: the man and his films, 74. Add: Dept. of English, University of Michigan, Ann Arbor, MI 48104.

RAETH, CLAIRE JOSEPH, b. Evanston, Ill, Nov. 16, 21. ENGLISH. A.B, Northwest. Univ, 42, A.M, 47, Ph.D.(Eng), 52. Instr. ENG, MIAMI UNIV, 50-53, asst. prof, 53-63, ASSOC. PROF, 63- MLA; NCTE. Eighteenth century literature; criticism; linguistics. Add: Dept. of English, Miami University, Oxford, OH 45056.

RAFFERTY, KEEN ALEXANDER, b. Robinson, Ill, Mar. 8, 02; m. 24; c. 2. JOURNALISM. A.B, Univ. N.Mex, 44; Univ. Ill; Univ. Denver. Reporter, Terre Haute Star, Ind, 24-25; tel. ed, Evansville Press, 25-27; head copy-desk, Baltimore Eve. Sun, Md, 27-38; mem. admin. staff, N.Mex. Highlands Univ. & East. N.Mex. Univ, 40-42; state inform. off, Office War Inform, N. Mex, 44; from assoc. prof. to prof. JOUR. & head dept, UNIV. N.MEX, 44-68, EMER. PROF. & EMER. CHMN. DEPT, 68- Pres, Am. Asn. Schs. & Depts. Jour, 61; vis. lectr, Col. Santa Fe, 67-68; Gov. appointee, West. Interstate Comn. Higher Educ, 68; lectr. jour, Univ. Ariz, 70-72. Am. Counc. Educ. Jour.(deleg, 55-60); Asn. Educ. Jour.(2nd v.pres, 53). Editing and editorial practices; the American newspaper. Publ: Co-auth, This is New Mexico, Horn & Wallace, 62, Modern journalism, Pitman, 62 & The American student and his college, Houghton, 67; auth, Editors unfettered, Saturday Rev, 11/44; co-auth, Educational backgrounds of American daily newspapermen, Jour. Quart, fall 54; auth, The Will Harrison Case, Quill, 6/64. Add: 2539 N. San Carlos Pl, Tucson, AZ 85712.

RAGSDALE, JAMES DONALD, b. Rome, Ga, July 30, 40; m. 73; c. 2. SPEECH. B.A, Howard Col, 61; fel, Univ. Ill, 61-64, M.A, 63, Ph.D. (speech), 64. Asst. SPEECH, Univ. Ill, 63-64; asst. prof, La. State Univ, 64-66; Ohio State Univ, 66-67; LA. STATE UNIV, BATON ROUGE, 67-72, ASSOC. PROF, 72-, Grad. Sch. Res. Counc. fac. fel, summer 65, subsistence grant, summer 68. Vis. asst. prof. Eng, Univ. Ky, summer 66. Speech Commun. Asn; Ling. Soc. Am; South. Speech Commun. Asn. Speech communication theory and research; psycholinguistics; English and American rhetorical theory. Publ: Brevity in classical rhetoric, South. Speech J, fall 65; Issues in phonological theory, Quart. J. Speech, 10/67; Effects of selected aspects of brevity on persuasiveness, Speech Monogr, 3/68. Add: Dept. of Speech, Louisiana State University, Baton Rouge, LA 70803.

RAGSDALE, WILMOTT, b. Aberdeen, Wash, Aug. 19, 15; m. 57; c. 3. JOURNALISM. B.A, Univ. Wash, 49; M.A, Johns Hopkins Univ, 50. Washington White House cor, Wall St. J, 39-42; war cor, Time & Life Mags, 42-47; assoc. ed, Newsweek Mag, 57-58; lectr. Eng, New Sch. Soc. Res, 51-53; assoc. prof. Eng, Grinnell Col, 53-57; Asia Found. vis. prof. JOUR, Thammasat Univ, Bangkok, 58-60; PROF, UNIV. WIS-MADISON, 60- UNESCO prof. commun, Univ. Philippines & consult, mass commun, UNESCO, Manila, 64-65; consult. prof. mass commun, Am. Univ. Cairo, 69-71; lectr. mass commun, U.S. Sept. State tour, Eng, Ger, Pakistan, 70. Overseas Press Club Am; Asn. Educ. in Jour. Add: School of Journalism & Mass Communication, University of Wisconsin-Madison, Madison, WI 53706.

RAHSKOPF, HORACE G, b. Olivia, Minn, Nov. 24, 97; m. 28; c. 1. SPEECH. A.B, Willamette Univ, 20; fel, State Univ. Iowa, 26-27, A.M, 27, fel, 31-32, Ph.D, 35; Curry Sch. Expression, 20-21; Univ. Mich, 30. Instr. speech, Wash. State Norm. Sch. Bellingham, 20-24; prof, Willamette Univ, 24-26; Ill. Wesleyan Univ, 27-28; asst. prof. SPEECH, UNIV. WASH, 28-35, assoc. prof, 36-43, prof, 43-68,; exec. off. dept, 47-62, EMER. PROF, 68- Educ. consult, Region XI Fed. Mediation & Conciliation Serv, 51-53; Boeing Co; U.S. Navy; Seattle Pub. Schs; Pac. Coast Savings & Loan Asn; vis. prof, Europ. div, Univ. Md, 57-58; Univ. Mich, summer 50; mem. adv. bd, Landmarks in Rhetoric & Pub. Address, South. Ill. Univ, 62-; vis. prof, Cent. Wash. State Col, 68-69; speech educ, Univ. B.C, summer 72. Speech Asn. Am.(1st v.pres, 49, pres, 50, assoc. ed, jour, 39-41); West. Speech Asn. (pres, 44); Nat. Soc. Stud. Commun; AAUP. Rhetoric and public address; theory of speech; voice science and phonetics. Publ: Basic speech improvement, Harper, 65; John Quincy Adams' theory and practice of public speaking, Arch. Speech, 9/36; The oratory of James Wilson of Pennsylvania, Speech Monogr, 38; The speaking of Clarence Darrow, In: American public address: studies in honor of Albert Craig Baird, Univ. Mo, 61. Add: 3925 51st NE, Seattle, WA 98105.

RAHTER, CHARLES AUGUSTUS, b. Harrisburg, Pa, May 24, 14; m. 52. ENGLISH. A.B, West. Md. Col, 49; M.A, Univ. Pa, 52, Ph.D.(Eng), 58. Instr. ENG, Douglass Col, Rutgers Univ, 55-58; assoc. prof, Elizabethtown Col, 58-60; from assoc. prof. to PROF, SUSQUEHANNA UNIV, 60- U.S.A.A.F, 42-45. MLA; NCTE. Linguistics. Publ: Some notes on the life and works of Thomas Churchyard, Notes & Queries, 62; Puck's headless bear—revisited, Susquehanna Univ. Stud, 65. Add: R.D. 3, Selinsgrove, PA 17870.

RAINBOW, RAYMOND SCOTT, JR, b. Fair Oaks, Pa, May 19, 19. ENGLISH LANGUAGE & LITERATURE. A.B, Westminster Col.(Pa), 42; A.M, Univ. Chicago, 47, Ph.D.(Eng. lang. & lit), 59. Instr. ENG, SOUTH. ILL. UNIV, CARBONDALE, 49-59, asst. prof, 59-68, ASSOC. PROF, 68- U.S.N.R, 42-46, Res, 46-60, Lt. Mod. Humanities Res. Asn; Soc. Advan. Scand. Stud. Middle English alliterative verse; Chaucer; Old English. Add: Dept. of English, Southern Illinois University, Carbondale, IL 62901.

RAINWATER, FRANK PALMER, b. Augusta, Ga, Aug. 3, 16. LITERATURE. B.A, Columbia Bible Col, 38; A.B, Univ. S.C, 43; M.A, Vanderbilt Univ, 48, Ph.D, 49. Prin, Hogue Jr. High Sch, Tignall, Ga, 38-39; asst. prin, Whigham High Sch, 39-42; supt. soc. sci, Mt. Croghan High Sch, S.C, 42-43; instr. Latin & Eng, Boys' High Sch, Anderson, 43-46; teaching fel, Vanderbilt Univ, 46-48; instr. Eng, Univ. Ky, 48-50, assoc. prof, Troy State Col, 50-58; humanities & Eng, Ferris Inst, 58-61; ENG, Jacksonville State Col, 61-67; PROF, GA. SOUTH. COL, 67- Lay-reader-in-charge, St. Philips Episcopal Church, Harrodsburg, Ky, 48-50; local coord, Nat. Teacher Educ. & Relig. Proj, Am. Asn. Cols. Teacher Educ, 56-59. S.Atlantic Mod. Lang. Asn. Milton's Comus: the dramas of Lord Byron; typical attitudes and values of American college students. Publ: Freshman English, Troy State Col, 52; The way to freedom, Comet Press, 56; An alert college in the sleepy South, In: Troy State University, Troy State Univ, 72. Add: Dept. of English, Georgia Southern College, Statesboro, GA 30458.

RAISOR, PHILIP DEAN, b. Muncie, Ind, Oct. 1, 38; m. 58; c. 3. ENGLISH & AMERICAN LITERATURE. A.B, La. State Univ, Baton Rouge, 62, M.A, 66; Satterfield fel, Kent State Univ, 68-69, Ph.D.(Eng), 73. Instr. ENG, Valparaiso Univ, 62-66; asst. prof, OLD DOMINION UNIV, 69-74, ASSOC. PROF, 74- S.Atlantic Mod. Lang. Asn; MLA; James Joyce Found. Modern English literature; 20th century American literature; James Joyce, Publ: The failure of Browning's Childe Roland, Tenn. Stud. Lit, 72; Up from adversity: William Faulkner's A fable, S.Dak. Rev, 73; Matthew Arnold's Balder dead: an exercise in objectivity, Stud. Eng. Lit, 73. Add: Dept. of English, Old Dominion University, Norfolk, VA 23508.

RAIZIS, MARIOS BYRON, b. Athens, Greece, Dec. 8, 31; U.S. citizen; m. 63; c. 2. ENGLISH & COMPARATIVE LITERATURE. B.Phil, Univ. Athens, 56; Fulbright grant, 57; M.S, Purdue Univ, 61; dipl, Inst. World Affairs, N.Y, 61; Danforth Found. grant, 62; Ph.D.(Eng), N.Y. Univ, 66. Instr. Eng, Corgialenios Col. Spetsai, 56-57; asst. librn, Athens Col, 58-59; asst. Eng, Purdue Univ, 59-61; libr. asst, Columbia Univ, 62; teacher developmental reading & head dept, St. Demetrios Sch. Astoria, 62-65; asst. prof. ENG, Wichita State Univ, 65-66; SOUTH. ILL. UNIV, CARBONDALE, 66-71, assoc. prof, 71-74, PROF, 74- Nat. Endowment Humanities fel, 72-73. Greek Army, 57-58. Fel. Byron Soc; Mod. Greek Stud. Asn; assoc. Ctr. Neo-Hellenic Stud; Rydal Mount Summer Sch. Asn. Myth in world literature; the poetry of Solomos; Kazantzakis's plays. Publ: Dionysios Solomos, Twayne, 72; co-auth, American poets and the Greek Revolution: a study in Byronic Philhellenism, 72 & ed, Greek Revolution and the American muse: a collection of Philhellenic poetry, 1821-28, 73, Inst. Balkan Stud, Thessaloniki, Greece; ed, The literary review: Greece, Fairleigh Dickinson Univ, 73; auth, Solonos and the Britannic muses, Neo-Hellenica, 70; Kazantzakis' Ur-Odysseus, Homer, and Gerhart Hauptmann, J. Mod. Lit, Vol. 2, No. 2; plus three others. Add: Dept. of English, Southern Illinois University, Carbondale, IL 62901.

RAJAN, BALACHANDRA, b. Toungoo, Burma, Mar. 24, 20; m. 46; c. 1. ENGLISH. B.A, Cambridge, 41, M.A, 44, Ph.D.(Eng), 46. Dir. stud. Eng, Trinity Col, Cambridge, 45-48; for. serv. off, Indian For. Serv, 48-61; prof. & head dept. ENG, Univ. Delhi, 61-64; vis. prof, Inst. Res. Humanities, Univ. Wis, 64-65; prof, Univ. Windsor, 65-66; SR. PROF, UNIV. WEST. ONT, 66- MLA; Renaissance Soc. Am; Milton Soc. Am. Seventeenth and twentieth century literature. Publ: Paradise lost and the seventeenth century reader, Chatto & Windus, 47; co-auth, T.S. Eliot: a study of his work by several hands, Dobson, 47; auth, The dark dancer, Simon & Schuster, 58; W.B. Yeats: a critical introduction, Hutchinson, 65; co-auth, Paradise lost: a tercentenary tribute, 69 & The prison and the pinnacle, 73, Univ. Toronto; auth, The lofty rhyme: a study of Milton's major poetry, Routledge & Kegan Paul, 70; The overwhelming question, Sewanee Rev, winter 66; Lycidas: the shattering of the leaves, Stud. Philol, 1/67; Comus: the inglorious likeness, Univ. Toronto Quart, 1/68. Add: Dept. of English, University of Western Ontario, London 72, Ont, Can.

RAKAUSKAS, WILLIAM VINCENT, b. Scranton, Pa, June 14, 34; m. 56; c. 3. ENGLISH. B.S, Univ. Scranton, 61, fel, 61-62, M.A, 63; Ed.D.(Eng), Temple Univ, 73. Teacher ENG, Scranton Tech. High Sch, 62-69; lectr, eve. col, UNIV. SCRANTON, 62-69, ASSOC. PROF, 69- Med.C, U.S.N, 53-57. NCTE; Conf. Col. Compos. & Commun. Laboratory approaches to teaching composition; special methods of teaching secondary English; secondary teacher preparation. Publ: Providing laboratory training for future teachers of composition, Eng. Educ, spring 72; A comparative study of a laboratory approach versus a conventional approach to teaching developmental composition at the University of Scranton, Diss. Abstr. Int, Vol. XXXIV, No. 4; Communications: a colloquium, Pa. Counc. Teachers Eng. Bull, (in press). Add: Dept. of English, University of Scranton, Linden St, Scranton, PA 18510.

RALEIGH, JOHN HENRY, b. Springfield, Mass, Aug. 30, 20. ENGLISH LITERATURE. A.B, Wesleyan Univ, 43; Ph.D, Princeton, 48. From asst. prof. to PROF. ENG, UNIV. CALIF, BERKELEY, 47-, humanities res. prof, spring 66, chmn. dept. Eng, summer 69, v.chancellor acad. affairs, 69-72. Guggenheim fel, 61-62. MLA. Literature and history; 19th and 20th century English and American literature. Publ: Matthew Arnold and American culture, Univ. Calif, 57 & 61; ed, History and the individual, Holt, 62; auth, The plays of Eugene O'Neill, 65 & Time, place, and idea: essays on the novel, 68, South. Ill, Univ; The city and the novel: England and American in the 19th century, Victorian Stud, spring 68; Tolstoy and the ways of history, fall 66 & Waverly as history, fall 70, Novel. Add: Dept. of English, University of California, Berkeley, CA 94720.

RALL, EILENE MUNCIE, b. Chicago, Ill, Jan. 2, 20; m. 42; c. 4. ENGLISH. A.B, Univ. Ill, 41; M.A, Tex. Christian Univ, 58. From instr. to ASSOC. PROF. ENG, TEX. CHRISTIAN UNIV, 61- NCTE; Conf. Col. Teachers Eng; Conf. Col. Compos. & Commun. Creative writing. Publ: Co-auth, Structures in composition, Scott, 70; auth, Supper (short story), Vision, 68; Posted (short story), Quartet, 68; My regards to Ustinov, Eng. J, 70; plus others. Add: Dept. of English, Texas Christian University, Ft. Worth, TX 76129.

RALPH, DAVID CLINTON, b. Muskogee, Okla, Jan. 12, 22; m. 47; c. 2. SPEECH. B.S, Northwest. Univ, 47, M.A, 48, Ph.D, 53. Instr. speech, Univ. Mo, 48-53; asst. prof, MICH. STATE UNIV, 53-57, assoc. prof, 57-62, prof, 62-68, PROF. COMMUN. & DIR. UNDERGRAD. PROG. COMMUN, 68-, CHMN. BASIC COURSE SPEECH, 61- U.S.N, 42-46, Lt. Speech Commun. Asn; Int. Commun. Asn; AAUP. Rhetoric and public address; communication; secondary education. Publ: Co-auth, A work book in group discussion, Edwards, 54 & 55 & Principles of speaking, Wadsworth, 62, 69 & 74. Add: Dept. of Communication, Michigan State University, East Lansing, MI 48823.

RAMBEAU, JAMES MORRIS, b. Philadelphia, Pa, Aug. 2, 38; m. 62; c. 1. ENGLISH. A.B, Kenyon Col, 60; Ph.D.(Eng), Rutgers Univ, New Brunswick, 71. Instr. ENG, Univ. Va, 66-70; ASST. PROF, PA. STATE UNIV, 70- Vis. lectr. Eng, Univ. Kent, 73-74. MLA; Am. Lit. Group, Mod. Lang. Asn. American literature. Add: Dept. of English, 117 Burrowes Bldg, Pennsylvania State University, University Park, PA 16802.

RAMSAY, ETHEL DAVIS, b. Salisbury, N.C, June 15, 05; m. 38; c. 5. ENGLISH, EUROPEAN HISTORY. A.B, Duke Univ, 26, M.A, 28; Univ. N.C, summers 31-33. Cadet teacher, E.K. Powe Sch, 27-29; teacher high sch, Miss, 29-31; Tenn, 31-34 & 58-62; Wash, 57-58; asst. prof. Eng, Tusculum Col, 62-63; instr, Columbia Basin Community Col, 63-70; RETIRED. Part-time instr, Eng. comp, Walters State Community Col, 73-; past amanuensis & res. asst. to Dr. Newman Ivey White; past mem. bk. rev. staff, Nashville Tennesean & Asheville Times. Conf. Col. Compos. & Commun; Am. Asn. Higher Educ; NCTE; NEA; Int. Soc. Gen. Semantics; AAUP. English poets of late 18th and early 19th centuries; all phases of college composition, including creative writing; American Negro folklore. Publ: Poetry in Poetry: Mag. Verse; Versecraft; The Archive; plus others. Add: 504 W. Sixth North St, Morristown, TN 37814.

RAMSAY, ORRINGTON C, b. Chicago, Ill, Aug. 1, 20; m. 43; c. 3. ENGLISH. B.S, Northwest. Univ, 43; M.A, Univ. Wis, 47, Ph.D, 50. Asst. prof. Eng, Carroll Col.(Wis), 48-49; assoc. prof, E.Cent. Col, 50-53; chmn. humanities div, Fullerton Col, 53-58; dir. res, Fullerton Union High Sch. Dist, Calif, 58-60; assoc. prof. ENG, CALIF. STATE UNIV. FULLERTON, 60-62, PROF, 63- Mem, Navy Japanese Lang. Intel. Sch, 43. U.S.N, 43-46, Lt. Col. Eng. Asn; MLA. Biological and psychological roots of language; deep structure grammar. Publ: English grammar: structure and processes 71 & co-auth, The Bible as living literature, 72, Anaheim. Add: 1324 N. Hollydale Dr, Fullerton, CA 92631.

RAMSEY, ALLEN RODELL, b. Missouri Valley, Iowa, May 1, 35; m. 67. LITERATURE OF THE ENGLISH RENAISSANCE. B.A, State Univ. Iowa, 57; M.A, John Carroll Univ, 66; Ph.D.(Renaissance lit), Tulane Univ, 72. Instr. ENG, Cleveland State Univ, 66-67; ASST. PROF, CENT. MO. STATE UNIV, 72- MLA; Renaissance Text Soc. Ovidian narrative poetry of the English Renaissance; Shakespeare. Add: Dept. of English, 236-N Martin, Central Missouri State University, Warrensburg, MO 64093.

RAMSEY, JAROLD WILLIAM, b. Bend, Ore, Sept. 1, 37; m. 59; c. 3. ENGLISH LITERATURE. B.A, Univ. Ore, 59; M.A, Univ. Wash, 63, Ph.D.(Eng), 66. Asst. prof. ENG, UNIV. ROCHESTER, 65-71, ASSOC. PROF, 71- Fairchild Award (poetry), 73; NEA Librettist grant, 74. Shakespeare; modern poetry; creative writing. Publ: Love in an earthquake, Univ. Wash, 73; contrib, Shaking the pumpkin, Doubleday, 72; plus poems & essays. Add: Dept. of English, University of Rochester, Rochester, NY 14627.

RAMSEY, LEE C, B. Ames, Iowa, July 21, 35. ENGLISH. B.A, Univ. Ore, 57, M.A, 58; Ph.D.(Eng), Ind. Univ, 65. Instr. ENG, Northwest. Univ, 63-66; ASST. PROF, UNIV. WIS-MADISON, 66- MLA; Mediaeval Acad. Am. Old and Middle English literature. Add: Dept. of English, University of Wisconsin-Madison, Madison, WI 53706.

RAMSEY, PAUL, b. Atlanta, Nov. 26, 24; m. 51; c. 4. ENGLISH. B.A, Univ. N.C, 47, M.A, 49; Ph.D.(Eng), Univ. Minn, 56. Instr. ENG, Univ. Ala, 48-50, 53-56, asst. prof, 56-57; Elmira Col, 57-62; assoc. prof, Raymond Col, Univ. of the Pac, 62-64; Univ. of the South, 64-66; vis. prof, UNIV. TENN, CHATTANOOGA, 66-67, prof, 67-69, ALUMNI DISTINGUISHED SERV. PROF, 69-, POET-IN-RESIDENCE, 66- Ed, Factotum, 48-49; mem, Acad. Am. Poets, 66-; res. grants, Univ. Chattanooga, 67 & 68; sr. Folger fel, Folger Shakespeare Libr, summer 67; dir. Tenn. Poetry Circuit, 67- Rochester Festival Relig. Arts First Prize for Poetry, 66; Beaudoin Gem Stone Award, 67; Roberts Mem. Prize Poetry, Lyric Mag, 72. U.S.N.R, 44-46, Lt.(jg). MLA; S.Atlantic Mod. Lang. Asn.(Bk. Award, 68; chmn. poetry readings, 72); Milton Soc; Poetry Soc. Am. Poet; Shakespeare; seventeenth-century. Publ: The lively and the just, Univ. Ala, 62; co-auth, Triptych, Raymond Col, 64; auth, In an ordinary place, N.C. State Univ, 65; A window for New York, Two Windows Press, 68; The doors, Tenn. Poetry Press, 68; The art of John Dryden, Univ. Ky, 69; The watch of judgment, In: Studies in criticism and aesthetics 1660-1800, Univ. Minn, 67; A question of judgment: Wimsatt on intent, In: Essays in criticism, 72; Absolutism and literary judgment, In: Yearbook of comparative criticism, 73; plus others. Add: Dept. of English, University of Tennessee, Chattanooga, TN 37401.

RAMSEY, ROY VANCE, b. Shawnee, Okla, July 20, 33; m. 57; c. 2. ENGLISH. B.A, Univ. Okla, 58, Ph.D.(Eng), 64. From instr. to asst. prof. ENG, Univ. Tex, 63-67; OHIO UNIV, 67-71, ASSOC. PROF, 71- U.S.M.C, 51-54. Mediaeval Acad. Am; MLA. Chaucer; late Medieval and early Renaissance literature. Add: Dept. of English, Ohio University, Athens, OH 45701.

RAMSEY, ROBERT W, b. Memphis, Tenn, Oct. 9, 12; m. 36; c. 2. CREATIVE WRITING. B.A, Univ. Ark, 35; Rosenwald fel, 42-43; M.A, Univ. Ariz, 49. Instr. ENG, UNIV. ARIZ, 47-52, asst. prof, 53-60, assoc. prof, 61-70, PROF, 70-, DIR. CREATIVE WRITING PROG, 67- U.S.N, 43-46, Res, 46-, Lt. Publ: Fire in summer, Viking, 42; The mockingbird, Dutton, 51; Fiesta, Day, 55. Add: Dept. of English, University of Arizona, Tucson, AZ 85721.

RAMSLAND, CLEMENT, b. Sacred Heart, Minn, Oct. 2, 03. HUMANITIES. B.A, Hamline Univ, 24; State Univ. Iowa, 27; M.A, Wash. State Univ, 29; Ph.D, Univ. Minn, 40. Asst. instr. speech & theater, Univ. Minn, 29-36; instr. theater, Northwest. Univ, 40-41; from instr. HUMANITIES to assoc. prof, UNIV. MINN, MINNEAPOLIS, 41-72, EMER. ASSOC. PROF, 72- U.S.N, 42-46, Lt. Comdr. Speech and theater; humanities in the modern world. Publ: Co-auth, Communicating through speech, Burgess, 50 & Voices of the industrial revolution, Univ. Mich, 57. Add: Dept. of Humanities, University of Minnesota, Minneapolis, MN 55455.

RANALD, MARGARET LOFTUS, b. Auckland, N.Z; nat; m. 55; c. 1. ENGLISH LITERATURE. B.A, Univ. N.Z, 49, M.A, 51; Fulbright travel grant & Smith-Mundt award, Univ. Calif, Los Angeles, 52, M.A, 54, Ph.D.(Eng), 58. Asst, Prime Minister's Dept, Wellington, N.Z, 49-55; Off. Secy, Princeton, 57; from instr. to asst. prof. ENG, Temple Univ, 57-61; asst. prof, QUEENS COL.(N.Y), 61-69, ASSOC. PROF, 69- Teaching asst, Univ. Calif, Los Angeles, 53-55; fac. res. award, Temple Univ, 60; consult, Educ. Testing Serv, Princeton, N.J, 60-; researcher, Harvard, 61-62; vis. assoc. prof. Eng, Univ. Calif, Los Angeles, summer 70; Folger Shakespeare Libr. fel, 70-71. MLA (assoc. bibliogr, 60-); Renaissance Soc. Am.(assoc. ed, Renaissance Quart, 63-). Shakespeare; English Renaissance drama and its backgrounds; opera. Publ: The betrothals of All's well that ends well, Huntington Libr. Quart, 2/63; The indiscretions of Desdemona, Shakespeare Quart, spring 63; Stephen Dedalus and the irony of religious ritual, James Joyce Quart, 1/64; plus others. Add: Dept. of English, Queens College, Flushing, NY 11367.

RANDALL, CHARLES HENRY, b. Wallace, Idaho, Sept. 28, 20; m. 45; c. 3. DRAMA. B.A, Cent. Wash. Col. Educ, 46; Colgate Univ; Univ. Wash; M.F.A, Yale, 50. Dir. dramatics, High Sch, Wash, 46-47; stage mgr, Brattle Theatre, Cambridge, Mass, 50-51; assoc. prof. DRAMA, Ithaca Col, 51-62, acting chmn, 56-62; from assoc. prof. to PROF, CALIF. STATE UNIV, FRESNO, 62- U.S.N.R, 42-46, Lt.(jg). Directing; academic theatre. Add: 479 E. San Ramon, Fresno, CA 93710.

RANDALL, DALE BERTRAND JONAS, b. Cleveland Heights, Ohio, Mar. 18, 29; m. 55; c. 2. ENGLISH. B.A, West. Reserve Univ, 51; M.A, Rutgers Univ, 53; Harrison fel, Univ. Pa, 55-56, Ph.D, 58. Asst. Eng, Rutgers Univ, 51-53; asst. instr, Univ. Pa, 53-55, 56-57; instr, DUKE UNIV, 57-60, asst. prof, 60-66, assoc. prof, 66-70, PROF. ENG. & ASSOC. DEAN GRAD SCH, 70-, asst. dean, 67-70. Bibliogr, Stud. Philol, 61-64; secy, Southeast. Inst. Medieval & Renaissance Stud, 65-68, co-chmn, 68-69, chmn, 71-; Guggenheim fel, 70-71. MLA; Renaissance Soc. Am; S.Atlantic Mod. Lang. Asn; Southeast. Renaissance Conf; Renaissance Eng. Text Soc. Seventeenth century English literature. Publ: The golden tapestry: a critical survey of non-chivalric Spanish fiction in English translation, 1543-1657, 63 & Joseph Conrad and Warrington Dawson: the record of a friendship, 68, Duke Univ; Jonson's gypsies unmasked: background and theme in The gypsies metamorphos'd, 74. Add: Dept. of English, 352 Allen Bldg, Duke University, Durham, NC 27706.

RANDALL, HELEN WHITCOMB, b. St. Johnsbury, Vt, June 7, 08. ENGLISH LITERATURE. A.B, Smith Col, 29, A.M, 31; Ph.D, Yale, 37. Teacher ENG, Black River Acad, Vt, 29-30; instr, SMITH COL, 31-38, asst. prof, 38-44, assoc. prof, 44-48, prof, 48-73, chmn. dept, 46-48, dean, 48-60, EMER. PROF, 73- Dean, Hartford Jr. Col, 39-40; Am. Asn. Univ. Women Sabin fel, 45-46. Porter Prize, Yale, 37. MLA. The critical theory of Lord Kames. Add: 39 Harrison Ave, Northampton, MA 01060.

RANDALL, JOHN HERMAN, III, b. New York, N.Y, Nov. 26, 23; m. 50. ENGLISH & AMERICAN LITERATURE. B.A, Columbia Univ, 43; M.A, Univ.

Calif, Berkeley, 50; Ford Found internship, 54-55; Ph.D, Univ. Minn, 57. Instr. Eng, Northwest. Univ, 55-58; asst. prof. Eng. & Am. lit, Wellesley Col, 58-60; lectr. Eng, BOSTON COL, 60-61, asst. prof. ENG. & AM. LIT, 61-62, 63-66, ASSOC. PROF, 66- Houghton Mifflin-New Eng. Quart. Lit. Award fel, 58; Am. Philos. Asn. summer grant, 61; Fulbright lectr. mod. Am. fiction, Univs. Liège, Ghent & Brussels, Belgium, 62-63. MLA; Am. Stud. Asn. Willa Cather; the Southern Renaissance; modern American fiction, 1920-1960. Publ: The landscape and the looking glass: Willa Cather's search for value, Houghton, 60; The genteel reader and Daisy Miller, Am. Quart, fall 65; Jay Gatsby's Hidden source of wealth, Mod. Fiction Stud, summer 67; Romeo and Juliet in the New World: a study of James, Wharton, and Fitzgerald, In: Costerus: essays in English and American language and literature, Amsterdam, 73. Add: Dept. of English, Boston College, Chestnut Hill, MA 02167.

RANDALL, JULIA SAWYER, b. Baltimore, Md, June 15, 23; div. ENGLISH, POETRY. A.B, Bennington Col, 45; M.A, Johns Hopkins Univ, 50. From instr. to asst. prof. ENG, Towson State Col, 58-62; asst. prof, HOLLINS COL, 62-66, ASSOC. PROF, 66- Sewanee Rev. fel. in poetry, 58; Nat. Found. Arts & Humanities grant, 66-67; Am. Acad. Arts & Lett. grant, 68-69. Writing poetry. Publ: The solstice tree, 52 & Mimic August, 60, Contemporary Poetry; The Puritan carpenter, Univ. N.C. Chapel Hill, 65; Adam's dream, Knopf, 70; plus several poems in various lit. mags. & journals. Add: Box 9642, Hollins College, VA 24020.

RANDALL, RANDOLPH C, b. Arcadia, Ind, June 10, 00; m. 32; c. 3. ENGLISH. A.B, Ind. Univ, 22; A.M, Columbia Univ, 26, Ph.D.(Eng. & comp. lit), 55. From instr. to assoc. prof. ENG, Centenary Col, 26-30; assoc. prof, Fenn Col, 31-36, prof, 36-65, chmn. dept, 31-65; prof. & chmn. dept, CLEVELAND STATE UNIV, 65-70, EMER. PROF, 70- MLA. American literature. Publ: James Hall: spokesman of the New West, Ohio State Univ, 64; authors of the Port Folio revealed by the Hall Files, Am. Lit, 1/40; Joseph Dennie's literary attitudes in the Port Folio, 1801-1812, In: Essays on periodical publishing in America, Duke Univ, 73. Add: 20231 S. Lake Shore Blvd, Cleveland, OH 44123.

RANDALL, VIRGINIA FRANCES, b. Brooklyn, N.Y, Nov. 8, 17. COMPARATIVE LITERATURE. B.A, Col. New Rochelle, 39; M.A, Ariz. State Univ, 60; Intercol. Prog. Grad. Stud. fel, Occidental Col, 60-62, Ph.D.(comp. lit), 66. Instr. ENG, ARIZ. STATE UNIV, 62-63, ASST. PROF, 63-, fac. res. fel, 63, 67. MLA; Cath. Renascence Soc. Meditative poetry in the 20th century; the poetry of Thomas Merton; T.S. Eliot. Add: Dept. of English, Arizona State University, Tempe, AZ 85281.

RANDEL, WILLIAM PEIRCE, b. New York, N.Y, Jan. 7, 09; m. 31; c. 2. ENGLISH. B.S, Columbia Univ, 32, Ph.D, 45; A.M, Univ. Mich, 33. Instr. Eng, Univ. Minn, 36-45; asst. prof, Mo. Sch. Mines, 45-47; from assoc. prof. to prof. Eng. & dir. Am. stud, Fla. State Univ, 47-65; prof. ENG, UNIV. MAINE, ORONO, 65-72, LLOYD H. ELLIOTT PROF, 72- Vis. prof, Univ. Helsinki, 50-51; Univ. Athens, 55-56; Jamaica, B.W.I, 57-58; Univ. Bologna, 65. MLA; Am. Dialect Soc; Am. Stud. Asn; Mod. Humanities Res. Asn; Int. Asn. Univ. Prof. Eng. American literature and civilization; American history. Publ: Edward Eggleston; The orphic sayings of Bronson Alcott; The Klu Klux Klan, 65 & Centennial: American life in 1876, 69, Chilton; ed, Edward Eggleston, the circuit rider, Col. & Univ, 66; auth, American Revolution: mirror of a people, Hammond, 73; Huxley's American visit, Am. Philos. Soc. Proc, 70; Koanga and its libretto, Music & Lett, 71; Delius in America, Va. Mag. Hist. & Biog, 71. Add: R.D. 1, Alfred, ME 04002.

RANDOLPH, ESTHER LAURSEN, b. Waterloo, Iowa, Aug. 31, 12; m. 35; c. 3. LITERATURE. B.A, Cent. Methodist Col, 33; M.A, Vanderbilt Univ, 36. Asst. speech, Cent. Methodist Col, 33-34; instr. ENG, WESTMINSTER COL. (MO), 44-61, ASST. PROF, 61- MLA. Contemporary poetry. Add: Dept. of English, Westminster College, Fulton, MO 65251.

RANDOLPH, JOHN WILSON, b. Corydon, Ky, Sept. 17, 11; m. 36; c. 3. ENGLISH & AMERICAN LITERATURE. A.B, Cent. Methodist Col, 32; M.A, Vanderbilt Univ, 34, fel, 34-36, Ph.D.(Eng. lit), 39; hon. LL.D, Drury Col, 60. Instr. Eng, Cent. Methodist Col, 36-43; WESTMINSTER COL.(MO), 43-44, prof. Eng. & chmn. dept, 46-63, DISTINGUISHED SERV. PROF. & A.P. GREEN PROF. ENG. LIT, 63-, CHMN. DIV. FINE ARTS, 67-, dean, 63-64. Distinguished alumnus award, Cent. Methodist Col, 58; ed, The Forensic, 59-63. U.S.N, 44-46, Res, 63-66, Lt. Comdr. MLA; Col. Eng. Asn. American popular music. Add: Westminster College, Fulton, MO 65251.

RANDOLPH, VANCE, b. Pittsburg, Kans, Feb. 23, 92; m. 30; wid. FOLKLORE. A.B, Kans. State Teachers Col, 14; M.A, Clark Univ, 15; Univ. Kans, 22-24; hon. Litt.D, Univ. Ark, 51. Writer staff, Appeal to Reason, 17; asst. instr. psychol, Univ. Kans, 24; scenario writer, Metro-Goldwyn-Mayer Studios, Culver City, Calif, 33-34; asst. state supvr, Fed. Writers Proj, 36-37; AUTHOR, 37- Am. Folklore Soc; Am. Dialect Soc. Folk speech. Publ: Ozark superstitions, Dover, 47; We always lie to strangers, 51, The talking turtle, 57 & Sticks in the knapsack, 58, Columbia Univ; co-auth, Down in the holler, Univ. Okla, 53; auth, Hot springs and hell, Folklore Assoc, 65; Ozark folklore: a bibliography, Ind. Univ, 72. Add: 900 N. Leverett St, Apt. 206, Fayetteville, AR 72701.

RANKIN, DAVID B, b. Inglewood, Calif, May 8, 31; m. 70. ENGLISH. B.A, Univ. South. Calif, 53, M.A, 60; Ph.D.(Eng), Univ. London, 65. Asst. prof. ENG, Calif. State Polytech. Col, 63-66; assoc. prof, CALIF. STATE COL, DOMINGUEZ HILLS, 66-71, PROF, 71- Vis. prof. Eng, Univ. Rouen, 72-73. MLA; NCTE. Rhetoric; stylistics; modern literature. Publ: Style and structure, Harcourt, 72; Ben Jonson: semanticist, ETC, 10/62; On O' Fleinn, on Orwell, Col. Eng, 10/70. Add: Dept. of English, California State College, Dominguez Hills, 1000 E. Victoria St, Dominguez Hills, CA 90747.

RANKIN, MARTHA FRAZER, b. Washington, Ga, Aug. 25, 17; m. 42; c. 2. ENGLISH, DRAMATIC ART. B.A, Huntingdon Col, 38; M.A, Univ. N.C, 40, M.A, 57. Assoc. prof. Eng, Huntingdon Col, 50-61, prof. drama & speech, 61-73; MEM. FAC, ST. JAMES SCH, 73- Southeast. Theatre Conf. Playwriting. Add: St. James School, N.Country Club Dr, Montgomery, AL 36106.

RANS, GEOFFREY, b. London, Eng, Mar. 12, 27; m. 58; c. 2. ENGLISH. B.A, Cambridge, 50, M.A, 53; Ph.D.(Eng), Univ. Leeds, 64. Lectr. ENG, UNIV. WEST. ONT, 60-63, asst. prof, 63-65, assoc. prof, 65-71, PROF, 71- Can. Counc. fel, 68-69. MLA; Asn. Can. Univ. Teachers Eng; Can. Asn. Am. Stud.(pres, 72-74). American literature; J.F. Cooper; Whitman. Publ: Edgar Allan Poe, Oliver & Boyd, 65; The novels of Saul Bellow, Rev. Eng. Lit, 64; E pluribus one loved folly, 71 & But the penalty of Adam: Cooper's sense of the subversive, 72, Can. Rev. Am. Stud; plus two others. Add: Dept. of English, University of Western Ontario, London, Ont. Can.

RANSOM, HARRY HUNTT, b. Galveston, Tex, Nov. 22, 08; m. 51. ENGLISH. B.A, Univ. of the South, 28, hon. Litt.D, 58; Harvard, 29-30; M.A, Yale, 30, Ph.D, 38; hon. LL.D, Baylor Univ, 58, Trinity Univ, 62, Tex. Christian Univ, 62; hon. L.H.D, Austin Col, 66, South. Methodist Univ, 72; hon. Litt.D, Univ. N.Dak, 70, Univ. Dallas, 71; hon. D.Eng, Colo. Sch. Mines, 72. Instr. Eng. & jour, N.Dak. State Teachers Col, 30-32; Eng. & hist, Colo. State Col, 34-35; Eng, Univ. Tex, Austin, 35-38, asst. prof, 38-42, assoc. prof, 46-47, prof. Eng. & dir. humanities res. ctr, 47-60, asst. dean grad. sch, 51-53, assoc. dean, 53-54, dean col. arts & sci, 54-57, v.pres. & provost univ, 57-60, pres, 60-61, chancellor, 61-71, EMER. CHANCELLOR, UNIV. TEX. SYST, 71- Consult. hist. of copyright law to legal firms & publ. co, 40-42; ed, Tex. Quart, 58-; mem, Counc. South. Univs, 61-71, pres, 62; trustee, Southwest Res. Inst, 61-; dir, Southwest Ctr. Advan. Stud, 62-66; trustee, Carnegie Found. Advan. Teaching, 62-71; mem. permanent comt, Oliver Wendell Holmes Devise, 64-72; mem. comt, Prof. Sch. & World Affairs, 65-67; mem, Int. Comn. Libr. Develop, 65-68, pres, 68; mem, Nat. Adv. Comn. Libr, 66-69; mem. nat. comt, Accrediting Bd. Comnr, 66-70; mem. comn. acad. affairs, Am. Counc. Educ, 66-70. U.S.A.A.F, 42-46, Maj. MLA; Grolier Club. Legal history; history of English and American copyright; Texas history. Publ: The first English copyright statute; sources of English copyright history; Notes of a Texas book collector. Add: Office of the Chancellor Emeritus, University of Texas System, P.O. Drawer 7878, Austin, TX 78712.

RANSON, HERBERT (ROBERT), b. Junction City, Kans, Nov. 28, 02; m. 32. ENGLISH LITERATURE. B.A, Univ. Kans, 24, M.A, 26; Denny fel. & Ph.D.(Eng), Univ. Wash, 36. Instr. Eng, Univ. Kans, 24-25; hist, Col. City Detroit, 26-29; teaching asst. & assoc. ENG, Univ. Wash, 30-40; prof. & chmn. dept, PAC. LUTHERAN UNIV, 40-68, EMER. PROF, 68- MLA. Shakespeare; 19th century English literature. Add: Dept. of English, Pacific Lutheran University, Tacoma, WA 98447.

RANTA, TAIMI MARIA, b. Marquette, Mich, Dec. 22, 19. ENGLISH. B.A, North. Mich. Univ, 39; M.Ed, Ohio Univ, 44; Jyväskylä Inst. Advan. Stud, Finland, 53; Ph.D, Univ. Minn, 64; Univ. Nebr, 68-69. Teacher, Elem. Schs, Hancock, Mich, 39-42; teaching fel, Ohio Univ, 42-44; instr. educ. & supvr. lab. schs. Eng. & soc. stud, Duluth State Teachers Col, 44-47; Univ. Minn, Duluth, 47-51; asst. prof. educ. & dir. elem. educ. prog, Hamline Univ, 51-53, 54-59; asst. prof. ENG, ILL. STATE UNIV, 59-64, assoc. prof, 64-68, PROF, 68- Fulbright res. grant, Finland, 53-54; Nat. Endowment for Humanities summer fel, 67; U.S. Off. Educ. grant, Tri-Univ. Proj, 68-69. Order of White Rose, Finland, First Class, 57; Distinguished Alumni Award, North. Mich. Univ, 67. MLA; NCTE (mem. adv. comt. elem. Eng, 72-); Am. Folklore Soc; Int. Reading Asn; Finnish Lit. Soc; AAUP; Am. Asn. Univ. Women; Conf. Eng. Educ.(mem. comt. prep. children's lit, 72-). Literacy, reading, folk and other literature in Finland; literature for children and adolescents. Publ: Kansakouluja Meillä ja Meren Takana, Valistus, 59; articles on education and school laws, Helsingin Sanomat, 54-56; Suomalainen Kansakoululapsi (the Finnish elem. sch. child), In: Finnish graded reader, For. Serv. Inst, U.S. Dept. State, 68; plus others. Add: Dept. of English, Illinois State University, Normal, IL 61761.

RAO, KOLAR S. NARAYANA, b. Chikkaballapur, India, July 1, 24; m. 67. ENGLISH, SPEECH. B.A, Univ. Mysore, 46, M.A, 47; M.A, Pa. State Univ, 62, Ph.D, 68. Lectr. Eng, Univ. Mysore, 46-57; instr. Eng. & speech, State Univ. N.Y. Albany, 59-61, asst. prof. ENG, 61-64; UNIV. WIS-OSHKOSH, 66-68, assoc. prof, 68-73, PROF, 73- Am. Counc. Learned Soc. ling. stud. grant, Univ. Mich, summer 59; Am. Stud. Asn. travel grant to attend Mod. Lang. Asn. meetings, 60; mem, Sahitya Akad, New Delhi; Am. Philos. Soc. res. grant, 70; Am. Counc. Learned Soc. travel grant, Cambridge, 72; Int. Congr. Comp. Lit. Asn. travel grant, Carleton Univ, 73. MLA (chmn. sem. Indian lit, 70 & mem. exec. comt, Eng. 12, 71-73); Ling. Soc. India. Indian studies; English and American literature. Publ: The novels of Kamala Markandaya, Lit. East & West, 6/71; The Indian novel in English: a search for identity, Stud. in Novel, summer 72; The untranslated translation and aesthetic consequences, Acta, 73; plus numerous others. Add: Dept. of English, University of Wisconsin-Oshkosh, Oshkosh, WI 54901.

RAPHAEL, LAWRENCE JOEL, Linguistics, Speech & Hearing Science. See Volume III, Foreign Languages, Linguistics, and Philology.

RARICK, GALEN RONALD, b. Muncie, Ind, Apr. 28, 23; m. 52; c. 2. JOURNALISM. B.A, Univ. Denver, 48; M.A, Stanford Univ, 51, Ph.D.(mass commun), 63; Univ. Mich, 58. Reporter & deskman, Ely Daily Times, Nev, 47-48; sports ed, Twin Falls Times-News, Idaho, 48-49; advert. mgr, Kermit Winkler County News, Tex, 49-50; staff writer, Congressional Quart. News Features, 51-54; ed-owner-publ, Booneville Independent, Miss, 54-57; asst. prof. JOUR, Hardin-Simmons Univ, 57-58; acting asst. prof, Univ. Calif, Berkeley, 59-62; assoc. prof, Univ. Ore, 62-67; PROF, OHIO STATE UNIV, 67- Mem. ed. bd, Jour. Monogr, 66-; mem. steering comt, News Res. Ctr, Am. Newspaper Publ. Asn, 69-72, dir, 73-; mem. ed. adv. bd, Jour. Quart, 72- AAUP; Asn. Educ. in Jour; Am. Asn. Pub. Opinion Res; AAAS. Newspaper audience analysis; attitude formation and change. Publ: Field experiments in newspaper item readership, Univ. Ore, 67; Television effects and socio-economic status, Educ. TV, 70; Political persuasion: the newspaper and the sexes, 70 & Differences between daily newspaper subscribers and nonsubscribers, summer 73, Jour. Quart; plus others. Add: School of Journalism, Ohio State University, Columbus, OH 43210.

RASOR, CHARLES LEWIS, b. Mountville, S.C, Sept. 1, 07; m. 34; c. 1. AMERICAN LITERATURE. A.B, Furman Univ, 29; A.M, Duke Univ, 40; summers, Univ. N.C, 31, 47. ASST. PROF. ENG, FURMAN UNIV, 46-,

REGISTR, 73-, dir. admis. & registration, 48-72. U.S.N.R, 43-46, Comdr. Possible sources of the Cask of Amontillado. Add: Office of the Registrar, Furman University, Greenville, SC 29613.

RASPA, RICHARD, b. Philadelphia, Pa, Sept. 13, 40; m. 72. RENAISSANCE LITERATURE. B.S, St. Joseph's Col.(Pa), 63; M.A, Univ. Notre Dame, 65, Ph.D.(Eng), 71. Instr. ENG, WAYNE STATE UNIV, 68-71, ASST. PROF, 71- Fulbright lectr. Am. lit, Italy, 74-75. Renaissance Soc. Am; MLA. Renaissance and modern drama; theory of comedy. Publ: Co-auth, Discovery in literature, Paulist Press, 70 & A skeleton key into the language of America, Harcourt, 74. Add: Dept. of English, Wayne State University, Detroit, MI 48202.

RATHBONE, ROBERT REYNOLDS, b. Exeter, N.H, Jan. 24, 16; m. 41; c. 1. ENGLISH, TECHNICAL WRITING. A.B, Middlebury Col, 39; A.M.T, Harvard, 47. Lectr. Eng, MASS. INST. TECHNOL, 50-52, asst. prof, 52-57, assoc. prof, 57-69, PROF. LIT, 69- Dir. spec. summer course, Mass. Inst. Technol, 57-68; writer, consult. & teacher, Nat. Cash Register Corp, 57; United Aircraft Corp, 57-60; co-dir. exten. course, Univ. Calif. Los Angeles, 61-68; dir. in-plant courses in writing, Mitre Corp, 65-68; dir. courses in tech. writing, Union Carbide Chem. Co, 57-68; U.S. Naval Electronics Lab. Ctr, 62-68; Reynolds Tobacco Co, 65-68. U.S.N.R, 42-46, Lt. Soc. Tech. Writers & Publ.(sr. mem. exec. comt, 58); Am. Soc. Eng. Educ. Communicative technical information to non-technical audiences; training courses in writing for engineers and scientists; information retrieval. Publ: Co-auth, A writers guide for engineers and scientists, 62 & Engineering communications, 64, Prentice-Hall; auth, Communicating technical information, Addison, 66; Co-operative teaching of technical writing in engineering courses, Am. Soc. Electrical Eng. J, 11/58; How to conquer words, Technol. Rev, 2/65; A new approach to effective writing, J. Tech. Writing & Commun, 7/72; plus one other. Add: 14N-416, Massachusetts Institute of Technology, Cambridge, MA 02139.

RATHBUN, JOHN W, b. Sioux City, Iowa, Oct. 24, 24; m. 47; c. 2. ENGLISH, AMERICAN STUDIES. Ph.B, Marquette Univ, 51, M.A, 52; Ph.D.(Am. cult), Univ. Wis, 56. Res. asst. ENG, Marquette Univ, 49-52; univ. Wis, 52-56; asst. prof, CALIF. STATE UNIV. LOS ANGELES, 56-61, assoc. prof, 61-65; PROF, 65- Am. Stud. Asn; MLA. American intellectual history and literature. Publ: Paul Tillich and the philosophy of Schelling, Int. Philos. Quart, 9/64; Billy Budd and the limits of perception, Nineteenth-Century Fiction, 6/65; Martin Luther King: the theology of social action, Am. Quart, 3/68. Add: 1406 Santa Teresa, South Pasadena, CA 91030.

RATHBURN, ROBERT CHARLES, b. Chicago, Ill, Dec. 17, 18; m. 48. ENGLISH. B.A, Northwest. Univ, 41, M.A, 42; Ph.D.(Eng), Univ. Minn, 56. Teaching asst. ENG, Northwest. Univ, 41-42; Univ. Pa, 45; instr, UNIV. MINN, MINNEAPOLIS, 46-59, asst. prof, 59-64, assoc. prof, 64-70, prof, 70- Vis. prof, Ariz. State Univ, summer 65; suprv. prof, Danforth Found. Summer Grad. Fel. Prog, 73. MLA; NCTE; Conf. Col. Compos. & Commun. Nineteenth and 20th century literature; the novel. Publ: From Jane Austen to Joseph Conrad, Univ. Minn, 58 & 75 prose pieces, Scribner, 61, rev. ed, 68. Add: 2360 Chilcombe Ave, St. Paul, MN 55108.

RATLIFFE, SHARON ANN, b. Dearborn, Mich, Sept. 23, 39. SPEECH COMMUNICATION. B.A, West. Mich. Univ, 63; M.A, Wayne State Univ, 65, Ph.D. (speech commun, educ. res), 72. Asst. prof. SPEECH COMMUN, WEST. MICH. UNIV, 65-74, ASSOC. PROF, 74- Speech Commun. Asn.(mem. legis. counc. & task force teacher prep. guidelines, 73-); Cent. States Speech Commun. Asn. (Outstanding Young Teacher Award, 70, chmn. adv. comt. & mem. exec. comt, 73-76). Teacher preparation in communication, kindergarten through college; communication theory; interpersonal communication. Publ: Co-auth, Speech in the junior high school, 68, auth, Dramatic arts in the secondary school, 68, co-ed, Michigan Speech Association curriculum guide ser.(8 in ser), 72 & co-auth, Adventures in the looking-glass: experiencing communication with yourself and others, 72, Nat. Textbk; co-auth, Discussion in the secondary school, In: Discussion and argumentation-debate in the secondary school, Nat. Textbk, 68 & Attitudinal differences between black and white college students, Speech Teacher, 9/70; plus others. Add: 1214 Eldridge, Kalamazoo, MI 49007.

RATNER, MARC LEONARD, b. New York, N.Y, Jan. 19, 26; m. 51; c. 3. ENGLISH & AMERICAN LITERATURE. B.S, Fordham Univ, 50; M.A, Univ. Pa, 51; fel, N.Y. Univ, 54-55, Ph.D, 59. Instr. Eng, Univ. Colo, 55-58, asst. dir. honors prog, 58-60; asst. prof. ENG, Univ. Mass, Amherst, 60-66, assoc. prof, 66-67; PROF, CALIF. STATE UNIV, HAYWARD, 67- Univ. Colo. res. grant, 59; lectr, Univ. Urbino, summer 63, 64, 65; Fulbright lectr, Univ. Frankfurt, 63-65; dir. Univ. Mass. Atlantic Stud. Ctr, Freiburg, Ger, 66-67; Fulbright lectr, Charles Univ, Prague, 71-73. U.S.A.A.F, 44-46, Sgt. MLA; Am. Stud. Asn. Critical study of novels of John Hawkes; 19th century American critical views on realism; surrealism in United States fiction of post World War II era. Publ: John Hawkes, Stud. Am, Vol. I, 65, Vol. II, 67; William Styron, Twayne, 73; The romantic Spenserian, Norweg. Am. Stud, 67; William Styron's Long march, Arlington Quart, winter 68. Add: Dept. of English, California State University at Hayward, 25800 Hillary St, Hayward, CA 94542.

RAUH, MIRIAM JOSEPH, C.S.C, b. Glandorf, Ohio, Dec. 17, 98. ENGLISH. Ph.B, St. Mary's Col.(Ind), 23; A.M, Univ. Notre Dame, 27; Ph.D, Columbia Univ, 45; hon. Litt.D, St. Mary's Col.(Ind), 69. Teacher, Col. St. Mary-of-the-Wasatch, 27-30; assoc. prof. ENG, ST. MARY'S COL.(IND), 31-45, prof, 45-69, head dept, 47-60, EMER. PROF, 69- Vis. scholar, Northwest. Univ, summer 61; vis. lectr, Cath. Univ. Am, summer 62. MLA; Renaissance Soc. Am; NCTE; Shakespeare Asn. Am; Conf. Col. Compos. & Commun; Ling. Circle N.Y. Ancient and Renaissance rhetoric and logic; Shakespeare; Milton. Publ: Shakespeare's use of the arts of language, Columbia, 47; Rhetoric in Shakespeare's time, Harcourt, 62; Orthodoxy in Paradise lost, Laval Theologique et Philosophique, 52; Discerning the ghost in Hamlet, PMLA, 12/61; Hamlet, a Christian tragedy, Stud. Philol, 4/62; plus others. Add: Dept. of English, St. Mary's College, Notre Dame, IN 46556.

RAVITZ, ABE CARL, b. New York, N.Y, May 20, 27; m. 47; c. 4. ENGLISH. B.A, City Col. N.Y, 49; M.A, N.Y. Univ, 50, Ph.D.(Eng), 55. Instr. ENG, Pa. State Univ, 53-56, asst. prof, 56-58; assoc. prof, Hiram Col, 58-60, PROF, 60-66; CALIF. STATE UNIV, DOMINGUEZ HILLS, 66-, CHMN. DEPT, 67- U.S.A, 46-47. MLA; Am. Stud. Asn. American literature and thought of the 17th to the 19th centuries; contemporary American fiction. Publ: Clarence Darrow and the American literary tradition, West. Res. Univ, 62; co-auth, The Haywood case, Chandler Publ, 63; auth, David Graham Phillips, Twayne, 66; The American disinherited, 70 & Disinherited drama, 73, Dickenson; ed, Complete works of David Graham Phillips, Garrett Press, 71; auth, Timothy Dwight: professor of rhetoric, New Eng. Quart; plus two others. Add: Dept. of English, California State College, Dominguez Hills, 1000 E. Victoria St, Dominguez Hills, CA 90747.

RAWLINS, JACK P, b. Chico, Calif, Dec. 25, 46; m. 68. BRITISH LITERATURE, HISTORY OF THE ENGLISH LANGUAGE. B.A, Univ. Calif, Berkeley, 68; M.Phil, Yale, 71, Ph.D.(Eng), 72. ASST. PROF. ENG, CALIF. STATE UNIV, CHICO, 72- Victorian novel; history of linguistics. Publ: Thackeray's novels: a fiction that is true, Univ. Calif, 74. Add: Dept. of English, California State University, Chico, CA 95926.

RAY, DAVID EUGENE, b. Sapulpa, Okla, May 20, 32; m. 70; c. 4. ENGLISH. B.A, Univ. Chicago, 52, M.A, 57. Instr. Eng, Cornell Univ, 60-64; asst. prof. lit. & humanities, Reed Col, 64-66; lectr. creative writing, Writers Workshop, Univ. Iowa, 69-70; ASSOC. PROF, Bowling Green State Univ, 70-71; ENG. & ED. NEW LETTERS, UNIV. MO-KANSAS CITY, 71- Woursell fel, Univ. Vienna, 66-71. MLA. English novel; American and English poetry; Black writers of America and the Third World. Publ: Ed, The Chicago Review Anthology, Univ. Chicago, 59; auth, X-Rays: a book of poems, 65, Dragging the main (poems), 68 & ed, From the Hungarian revolution, 66, Cornell, co-ed, A poetry reading against the Vietnam war, Sixties Press, 66; Richard Wright: impressions and perspectives, Univ. Mich, 73. Add: Dept. of English, University of Missouri-Kansas City, Kansas City, MO 64110.

RAY, DON ELDON, b. Moorcroft, Wyo, Oct. 26, 27; m. 52. ENGLISH LITERATURE. B.A, Tex. Christian Univ, 53; fel, Rice Univ, 55-57, Ph.D.(Eng. lit), 57. Instr. Eng. lit, Univ. Colo, 57-62; asst. prof. ENG, UNIV. CALGARY, 62-67, ASSOC. PROF, 67-, ASST. DEAN FAC. ARTS & SCI, 68-, admin. off. dept. Eng, 65-67. Univ. Colo. fac. fel. for. stud, 61. MLA; Milton Soc; Renaissance Soc. Am. Milton and the Elizabethan tradition of Christian learning; Milton's idea of freedom; Spenser's protestant and epic synthesis of the tradition of courtesy. Add: Dept. of English, University of Calgary, Calgary, Alta. T2N 1N4, Can.

RAY, GEORGE WASHINGTON III, b. Binghamton, N.Y, Dec. 4, 32; m. 56; c. 4. ENGLISH. A.B, Wesleyan Univ, 54; Colgate Univ, 57-59; Ph.D.(Eng), Univ. Rochester, 66. Instr. ENG, Univ. Rochester, 61-62; Univ. Va, 62-64; WASHINGTON & LEE UNIV, 64-66, asst. prof, 66-69, ASSOC. PROF, 69- Fel, coop. prog. humanities, Duke Univ, 67-68. U.S.M.C, 54-57, 1st Lt. MLA; AAUP; Renaissance Soc. Am. Renaissance drama. Add: Dept. of English, Washington & Lee University, Lexington, VA 24450.

RAY, GORDON N, b. New York, N.Y, Sept. 8, 15. ENGLISH. A.B. & A.M, Ind. Univ, 36, L.H.D, 64; A.M, Harvard, 38, Ph.D, 40; hon. Litt.D, Monmouth Col, 59, Syracuse Univ, 61, Duke Univ, 65, Univ. Ill, 68; hon. LL.D, N.Y. Univ, 61, Tulane Univ, 63, Univ. Calif, 68, Columbia Univ, 69, Univ. South. Calif, 74. Instr. Eng, Harvard, 40-42; prof, Univ. Ill, 46-60, head dept, 50-57, v.pres. & provost, 57-60; Berg prof. Eng. & Am. lit, N.Y. UNIV, 52-53, PROF. ENG, 62-; PRES. & MEM. BD. TRUSTEES, JOHN SIMON GUGGENHEIM MEM. FOUND 63-, assoc. secy. gen, 60-61, secy. gen, 61-63. Dexter fel, Harvard, 40-41; Guggenheim Mem. Found. fel, 41-42, 46, 56-57, mem. adv. bd, found, 59-60; vis. prof, Univ. Ore, 48; Rockefeller fel, 48-49; mem, U.S. Educ. Comn, U.K, 48-49; Lowell lectr, Boston Univ, 50; chmn. comt. inst. coop, Counc. Ten Univs. & Univ. Chicago, 58-60; mem, bd. trustees, Found. Libr. Ctr, 62-68, v.chmn, 63-65, chmn, 65-68; mem. bd. trustees, Ctr. Appl. Ling, 65-69; mem. counc, Smithsonian Inst, 68-, chmn, 70-; Beckman prof. Eng, Univ. Calif, Berkeley, 69; trustee, Pierpont Morgan Libr, 70-; Rosenbach Found, Phila, 72-; dir. & treas, Am. Counc. Learned Soc, 73-; ed. bd, Eng. Lang. Notes; Nineteenth Century Fiction; Manuscripts; adv. bd, Soho Bibliogs. U.S.N.R, 42-46, Lt. Fel. Am. Acad. Arts & Sci; Grolier Club (pres, 65-69); fel. Royal Soc. Lit. U.K; MLA (trustee, 66-). Publ: Ed, The letters and private papers of William Makepeace Thackeray, (4 vols), 45-46 & History of Mr. Polly, Houghton, 52; auth, The buried life, 52; Thackeray: the uses of adversity, 55; ed, Desert Daisy, Beta Phi Mu, 57; ed, Rose and the ring, History of Henry Esmond & Contributions to the Morning Chronicle, Univ. Ill; auth, Thackeray: the age of wisdom, McGraw, 58; co-ed, Henry James and H.G. Wells, Univ. Ill, 58. Add: 90 Park Ave, New York, NY 10016.

RAY, JAMES KENDALL, b. Minford, Ohio, Dec. 25, 05; m. 37. ENGLISH LITERATURE. A.B, Ohio Univ, 27; A.M, Univ. Mich, 33. Teacher high schs, Ohio, 27-31, 41-43, 45-48; instr. ENG, Clemson Col, 37-38; from asst. prof. to assoc. prof, OTTERBEIN COL, 48-71, EMER. PROF, 71- Instr, Portsmouth br, Ohio Univ, 46-48. U.S.A, 43-45. NCTE. Romantic period; English novel. Publ: Proverbs and proverbial allusions in the works of Christopher Marlowe, Mod. Lang. Notes, 6/35. Add: 653 Timberlake Dr, Westerville, OH 43081.

RAY, PAUL CHARLES, b. Antwerp, Belgium, May 15, 26; U.S. citizen; m. 55. ENGLISH, COMPARATIVE LITERATURE. B.S, Columbia Univ, 50, M.A, 51, Ph.D.(Eng), 62. Instr. ENG, Hofstra Univ, 59-62; Queens Col.(N.Y), 64-67; asst. prof, YORK COL.(N.Y), 67-71, ASSOC. PROF, 71- U.S.A, 44-46, Sgt. MLA; AAUP. English surrealism; contemporary fiction and poetry. Publ: The surrealist movement in England, Cornell Univ, 71; Sir Herbert Read and English surrealism, J. Aesthet. & Art Criticism, 66; The anti-surrealism of Christopher Caudwell, Comp. Lit. Stud, 69. Add: Dept. of English, York College, 150-14 Jamaica Ave, Jamaica, NY 11432.

RAY, ROBERT HENRY, b. San Saba, Tex. Apr. 29, 40; m. 62; c. 2. ENGLISH. B.A, Univ. Tex, 63, fel, summer 66, Ph.D.(Eng), 67. ASST. PROF. ENG, BAYLOR UNIV, 67- MLA; Renaissance Soc. Am; Shakespeare Asn. Am. Literature of the English Renaissance; poetry of George Herbert; plays of Shakespeare. Add: Dept. of English, Baylor University, Waco, TX 76703.

RAYMO, ROBERT ROWLAND, b. Pelham Manor, N.Y, Jan. 23, 25; m. 53; c. 1. ENGLISH. Fulbright scholar, Cambridge, 49-51, Ph.D.(mediaeval lit), 53. Asst. prof. ENG, Univ. Calif, Los Angeles, 53; PROF, Rutgers Univ, 57-64; N.Y. UNIV, 64-, CHMN. DEPT, 72- Presidential fel, Univ. Calif, Los Angeles, 56; Am. Philos. Soc. grant, 62. MLA; Mediaeval Acad. Am; Int. Asn. Univ. Prof. Eng. Mediaeval literature; history of satire. Publ: Ed, Speculum stultorum, Univ. Calif, 60 & Angles of vision, Houghton, 62; contrib, Cassell's Encycl. of Lit, London; auth, Medieval literature, In: Vol. I, The critical temper, Ungar, 69; A ME version of the Epistola Luciferi, In: Medieval literature and civilization, London, 69; plus numerous articles. Add: Dept. of English, New York University, New York, NY 10003.

RAYMOND, MEREDITH BRAGG, U.S. citizen. ENGLISH LITERATURE. B.S.Ed, Bridgewater State Col, 39; M.A, Middlebury Col, 43; fel, Boston Univ, 60-64, Ph.D.(Eng), 64. Lectr. ENG, Boston Univ, 60-64; UNIV. MASS, AMHERST, 64-65, asst. prof, 65-70, ASSOC. PROF, 70- MLA; AAUP. Victorian literature; poetry; criticism. Publ: Swinburne's poetics, Mouton, The Hague, 71; Swinburne among the nightingales, VI: 2 & The lake of Gaube: Swinburne's Dive in the dark and the Indeterminate moment, IX: 1-2, Victorian Poetry; The letters of Elizabeth Barrett Browning to Mary Russell Mitford, Browning Inst. J, 73; plus two others. Add: Dept. of English, University of Massachusetts, Amherst, MA 01002.

REA, MARY LOUISE, b. Macomb, Ill, June 10, 15; m. 43, 65; c. 1. ENGLISH. A.B, Knox Col, 36; M.A, Univ. Ill, 38, Ph.D.(Eng), 43; Oxford, summer, 48, Columbia Univ, summer, 52. Instr. Eng, Ill. Wesleyan Univ, 45-46; IND. UNIV-PURDUE UNIV, INDIANAPOLIS, 46-48, asst. prof, 48-62, assoc. prof, 62-67, PROF, 67-, chmn. dept, 46-64, acting chmn, 64-67. Dir. Dunes Arts Writers' Conf, 57-59. American Renaissance; American novel and drama; creative writing. Add: Dept. of English, Indiana University-Purdue University at Indianapolis, Indianapolis, IN 46205.

READ, ALLEN WALKER, ENGLISH LANGUAGE. See Volume III, Foreign Languages, Linguistics & Philology.

READ, BILL, b. Hutchinson, Kans, Sept. 6, 17. ENGLISH LITERATURE. A.B, Univ. Kans, 39; M.A, Harvard, 48; Ph.D, Boston Univ, 59; Nat. Univ. Mex. Instr. ENG, Univ. Kans, 39-41; acting chmn. dept, Suffolk Univ, 47-48; PROF, BOSTON UNIV, 48-, ACTING CHMN. DEPT. HUMANITIES, 74-, chmn. dept, 67-69. MLA; Col. Eng. Asn. Thomas Love Peacock; modern poetry; literary expressionism. Publ: The days of Dylan Thomas, 64, co-ed, The modern poets, 63 & Twentieth century poetry: American and British, 1900-1970, 70, McGraw. Add: Dept. of Humanities, Boston University, 855 Commonwealth Ave, Boston, MA 02215.

READ, (WILLIAM) CHARLES, Linguistics, Psycholinguistics. See Volume III, Foreign Languages, Linguistics & Philology.

READ, FORREST, b. Buffalo, N.Y, July 31, 26; m. 70; c. 4. ENGLISH. B.S.M.E, Princeton, 48; M.A, Univ. Buffalo, 51; Fels Found. fel, 59-60; Ph.D, Cornell Univ, 61. Instr. engineering, Univ. Buffalo, 49-51, 52-53; ENG, Union Col.(N.Y), 55-57; Cornell Univ, 57-61, asst. prof, 61-65; ASSOC. PROF, UNIV. N.C, CHAPEL HILL, 65- Robert D. Campbell vis. prof, Wells Col, 68-69. U.S.N.R, 44-46, Ens. Modern literature; English literature, 1500-1660. Publ: Pound-Joyce: letters and essays, New Direction, 67; co-auth, Translations: introduction and five poems, In: At the Hungarian Revolution, Cornell Univ, 65; auth, Ezra Pound et James Joyce; les odyssiens, L'Herne, Paris, 66; Herzog: a review, In: Saul Bellow and the critics, N.Y. Univ, 67. Add: Dept. of English, University of North Carolina at Chapel Hill, Chapel Hill, NC 27514.

READER, DENNIS JOEL, b. Santa Cruz, Calif, Sept. 4, 39; m. 64; c. 2. AMERICAN LITERATURE. B.A, Calif. State Univ, Fresno, 62; M.A, Calif. State Univ, San Francisco, 67; Ph.D.(lit), Univ. Calif, San Diego, 71. Instr. ENG, WEST. ILL. UNIV, 67-68, ASST. PROF, 71- Assoc. ed, Essays in Lit; dir, Ctr. for Regional Auth, West. Ill. Univ. MLA; AAUP. American Renaissance; 19th century American novel. Add: Dept. of English, Western Illinois University, Macomb, IL 61455.

REAMER, OWEN JORDAN, b. San Antonio, Tex, Oct. 10, 11. ENGLISH. A.B, Univ. Ill, 35, A.M, 36; Ph.D, Univ. Tex, 51. Asst, Univ. Ill, 35-41; asst. prof. ENG, Trinity Univ, Tex, 46-51, assoc. prof, 51-57, PROF, 57-66; UNIV. SOUTHWEST. LA, 66- Adj.Gen.C, U.S.A, 41-46, Res, 35-41, 46-61, Lt. Col.(Ret). MLA; S. Cent. Mod. Lang. Asn; S.Cent. Col. Eng. Asn.(pres, 71); S.Cent. Renaissance Conf. American literature; Hamlin Garland. Publ: Hamlin Garland and the Indians, N.Mex. Quart, fall 64; Spenser's debt to Marot—re-examined, Tex. Stud. Lit. & Lang, 69; Lanier's The marshes of Glynn—revisited, Miss. Quart, 70. Add: Dept. of English, University of Southwestern Louisiana, Lafayette, LA 70501.

REANEY, JAMES, b. Stratford, Ont, Sept. 1, 26; m. 51; c. 2. ENGLISH. B.A, Univ. Toronto, 48, M.A, 49, Ph.D.(Eng), 58. Asst. prof. ENG, Univ. Man, 55-60; assoc. prof, UNIV. WEST. ONT, 60-64, PROF, 64- Ed, Alphabet, 60- Can. Counc. Sr. Artist Award, 68. Asn. Can. Univ. Teachers Eng. (pres, 59-60). Literary symbolism; Canadian literature. Publ: The third eye, Can. Lit, 60; The condition of light: Henry James's The sacred fount, Univ. Toronto Quart, 1/62. Add: Dept. of English, University of Western Ontario, London, Ont. N6A 3K7, Can.

REARDON, JOHN D, b. New York, N.Y, Dec. 6, 27; m. 53; c. 4. ENGLISH & AMERICAN LITERATURE. B.A, N.Y. Univ, 49; M.A, Univ. Conn, 52; Ph.D, Univ. Kans, 57. Instr. Eng, Univ. Kans, 53-57; MIAMI UNIV, 57-59, asst. prof, 59-68, PROF. ENG. & AM. LIT, 68-; DIR. GRAD. STUD. ENG, 70- Consult, N.Y. Life Ins. Co, 58; Fulbright lectr, Univ. Baghdad, 65-66. MLA. Modern English and American fiction; nineteenth century literature; English and American drama. Publ: Poe's esthetic horror, Exercise Exchange, 57; Grave's Goodbye to a river, New Leader, 12/60; Hemingway's esthetic sportsmen, Univ. Rev, autumn 67; Biographies of early American dramatists, McGraw-Hill Encycle, (in press). Add: Dept. of English, Miami University, Oxford, OH 45056.

REARDON, WILLIAM ROBERT, b. Worcester, Mass, Dec. 27, 20; m. 43; c. 3. SPEECH, DRAMA. A.B, Clark Univ, 49; M.A, Stanford Univ, 50, Ph.D. (speech & drama), 53. Instr. speech & drama, State Univ. Iowa, 53-56, asst. prof, 56-57, assoc. prof, 57-60; vis. prof, La. State Univ, 60-61; PROF. DRAMA, Univ. Kans, 61-66; UNIV. CALIF, SANTA BARBARA, 66- Guest ed. theatre, Civil War Hist, Sept, 55; vis. prof, Univ. Calif, Santa Barbara, 65-66; dir. arts & humanities inst. in repertory theatre, U.S. Off. Educ. grant, summer 67 & dir. disadvantaged youth NDEA inst. in repertory theatre, summer 68. Margery Bailey Prize, 51; Samuel French Award, 56, 57, 58. U.S.M.C, 41-45. Am. Theatre Asn; Author's League Am. Dramatic literature;theatre history; creative writing. Publ: Day of discoveries, produced on CBS-TV, 58; The big smear, Crown, 60; co-auth, Satiric comedies, Ind. Univ, 70 & The Black teacher and the dramatic arts, Negro Univs, 70; The American theatre, 1864-1870: an economic portrait, Speech Monog, 11/66; auth, Theatre as art, In: The communicative arts and sciences of speech, C.E. Merrill, 67; O'Neill since world War II: critical reception in New York, Mod. Drama, 12/67; plus others. Add: Dept. of Dramatic Art, University of California, Santa Barbara, CA 93106.

REASKE, CHRISTOPHER RUSSELL, b. Montclair, N.J, Oct. 14, 41; m. 63; c. 2. ENGLISH. A.B, Yale, 63; A.M, Harvard, 64, Ph.D.(Eng), 68. ASST. PROF. ENG, UNIV. MICH, ANN ARBOR, 68- NCTE; Conf. Col. Compos. & Commun. English Renaissance literature; writing programs. Publ: How to analyze poetry, 65 & How to analyze drama, 65, Monarch; ed, Seven essayists, Scott, 68; auth, The college writer's guide to the study of literature, Random, 69. Add: Dept. of English, University of Michigan, Ann Arbor, MI 48104.

REAVER, JOSEPH RUSSELL, JR, b. Phoenixville, Pa, Aug. 4, 15; m. 46; c. 1. AMERICAN LITERATURE, FOLKLORE. A.B, Miami Univ, 37; scholar from Miami Univ, Ohio State Univ, 37-38, A.M, 38, scholar, 41-42, Ph.D.(Am. lit), 42. Asst. prof. ENG, The Citadel, 42-44; instr, Univ. Ill, 44-47; asst. prof, FLA. STATE UNIV, 47-50, assoc. prof, 50-63, PROF, 63- Fla. State Univ. Res. Counc. res. grants, summers 66 & 67, prof. Am. lit. & folklore, Fla. State Univ. Stud-Ctr, Florence, Italy, 68-69. NCTE; MLA; Am. Folklore Soc; Am. Dialect Soc; S.Atlantic Mod. Lang. Asn; Int. Soc. Ethnol. & Folklore; Am. Name Soc; Emerson Soc. Ralph Waldo Emerson; American folklore; contemporary American literature. Publ: Emerson as mythmaker, Univ. Fla, 54; co-auth, Humanities in contemporary life, 60 & The humanistic tradition, 64, Holt: Fundamentals of folk literature, Anthrop. Publ, 62; An O'Neill Concordance (3 vols), Gale Res. Co, 69; co-auth, Emerson's relevance today, Transcendental, 71; auth, Somewhere safe to sea, Vantage, 73; Thoreau's ways with proverbs, 69 & Emerson on the psychic potential, 71, Am. Transcendental Quart; From reality to fantasy: opening-closing formulas in the structures of American folk tales, South. Folklore Quart, 72; plus three others. Add: Dept. of English, Florida State University, Tallahassee, FL 32306.

REBHOLZ, RONALD ALEXANDER, b. St. Louis, Mo, May 28, 32. ENGLISH. A.B, St. Louis, Univ, 53; Stanford Univ, 53-54; B.A, Oxford, 58, Ph.D.(Eng), 65. Instr. ENG, STANFORD UNIV, 61-65, asst. prof, 65-69, ASSOC. PROF, 69- U.S.A, 54-56. MLA. The poems of Thomas Wyatt and Andrew Marvell; the plays of William Shakespeare. Publ: The life of Fulke Greville, First Lord Brooke, Clarendon, Oxford, 71. Add: Dept. of English, Stanford University, Stanford, CA 94305.

REBMANN, DAVID RAYMOND, b. Torrington, Conn, Dec. 14, 43; m. 66; c. 2. MODERN BRITISH & AMERICAN LITERATURE. B.A, Trinity Col.(Conn), 65; Ph.D.(Eng), Univ. Minn, Minneapolis, 71. ASST. PROF. ENG, UNIV. FLA, 70- Am. Philos. Soc. grant, summer 71. S.Atlantic Mod. Lang. Asn. Modern poetry; linguistics and literature; contemporary literature. Publ: Unpublished letters of William Cullen Bryant, Emerson Soc. Quart, fall 67. Add: Dept. of English, University of Florida, Gainesville, FL 32601.

REDD, TONY NEIL, b. Aiken, S.C, Feb. 23, 43. ENGLISH & AMERICAN LITERATURE. B.A, Furman Univ, 65; duPont fel. & M.A, Univ. Va, 66; NDEA fel. & Ph.D.(Eng), Univ. S.C, 72. Asst. prof. ENG, THE CITADEL, 66-68, 71-73, ASSOC. PROF, 73- S.Atlantic Mod. Lang. Asn; Soc. Stud. South. Lit. Twentieth century British and American literature; southern literature; Dame Rebecca West. Add: Dept. of English, The Citadel, Charleston, SC 29409.

REDDEN, DOROTHY S, b. Newark, N.J, Oct. 8, 20. ENGLISH & AMERICAN LITERATURE. A.B, Carleton Col, 42; M.A, Columbia Univ, 56; Ph.D.(Eng. & Am. lit), Stanford Univ, 65. Instr. ENG. & AM. LIT, Robert Col, Istanbul, 56-57; Univ. Ore, 59-61; Stanford Univ, 62-63; City Col. New York, 64-65; DOUGLASS COL, RUTGERS UNIV, 65-66, ASST. PROF, 66- MLA. Fiction; 19th century American literature; 20th century American and British literature. Publ: Flowering Judas: two voices, Stud. Short Fiction, winter 69. Add: Dept. of English, Douglass College, Rutgers University, New Brunswick, NJ 08903.

REDDEN, JAMES ERSKINE, Linguistics, African Studies. See Volume III, Foreign Languages, Linguistics & Philology.

REDDICK, DeWITT CARTER, b. Savannah, Ga, July 30, 04; m. 34; c. 2. JOURNALISM. B.J, Univ. Tex, 25, M.J, 27; Ph.D, Univ. Mo, 40. Reporter, Ft. Worth Star-Telegram, 25-27; instr. jour, UNIV. TEX, AUSTIN, 27-29, adj. prof, 30-35, asst. prof, 35-36, assoc. prof, 36-41, prof, 42-70, JESSE H. JONES PROF. JOUR. & EDUC, SCH. COMMUN, 70-, assoc. dean col. arts & sci, 56-59, dir. sch. jour, 59-63, dean sch. commun, 63-69. Consult. publs, Humble Oil & Refining Co, summers 53, 55 & 58-59; consult, Tex. Presby, 55-68; pres, Am. Asn. Schs. & Depts. Jour, 62; dean col. commun, Univ. Tenn, 69-70. Scarbrough Award, 55; Jour. Medal, Univ. Mo, 64; Citation for Meritorious Serv. to Jour. Educ, South. Ill. Univ, 68. Asn. Educ. in Jour.(2nd v.pres, 45, v.pres, 61, pres, 66); Am. Counc. Educ. Jour; Int. Counc. Indust. Ed; Jr. Col. Jour. Asn.(liaison off, 69-). Magazine writing and editing; industrial editing; religious journalism. Publ: Journalism and the school paper, 39, 5th ed, 63 & High school journalism workbook, 64, Heath; Modern feature writing, Harper & Bros, 49; Industrial editing, Bender, 62; Texas, In: Encycl. Britannica, 73. Add: Dept. of Journalism, School of Communication, University of Texas at Austin, Austin, TX 78712.

REDDICK, GLENN EUGENE, b. Rogers, Ark, July 17, 23; m. 47; c. 3. SPEECH. B.A, Colo. State Col. Educ; M.A, Univ. Fla, 49; Ph.D.(speech),

Univ. Ill, 54. Assoc. prof, SPEECH, N.CENT. COL, 52-57, PROF, 57-, HEAD DEPT, 52-, CHMN. DIV. CREATIVE ARTS, 61- Lectr, Evangel. Theol. Sem, 54- U.S.A.F, 42-46. Speech Asn. Am. American public address: speech correction; oral interpretation of literature. Publ: When the Southern senators said farewell, South. Speech J, 3/50; To eccentricity—and beyond, Vital Speeches, 3/65; Deception as a television comedy tool, Christian Century, 9/65. Add: 804 E. Chicago, Naperville, IL 60540.

REDDING, DAVID COLEMAN, b. Phila, Pa, Sept. 7, 28; m. 53; c. 4. ENGLISH. B.A, Swarthmore Col, 49; A.M, Univ. Pa, 55, Ph.D.(Eng), 60. Instr. ENG, Bates Col, 55-58; lectr, Univ. Pa, 58-59; instr, Russell Sage Col, 59-62; asst. prof, STATE UNIV. N.Y. ALBANY, 62-64, ASSOC. PROF, 64-, DIR. GRAD. STUD. ENG, 72- Consult, Choice: books for college libr, 64- Sig.C, U.S.A, 51-53. MLA; Renaissance Eng. Text Soc. Early 17th century poetry; Shakespeare. Publ: A note on a Jonson attribution, 2/60 & Some epigrams attributed to Sir John Davies, 11/61, Notes and Queries; co-auth, Shakespeare: Sonnet 110, a new look, Shakespeare Quart, autumn 61. Add: Dept. of English, State University of New York at Albany, Albany, NY 12203.

REDDING, JAY SAUNDERS, b. Wilmington, Del, Oct. 13, 06; m. 29; c. 2. ENGLISH. Ph.B, Brown Univ, 28; A.M, 32, D.Litt, 63; Columbia Univ, 33-34; Rockefeller fel, 39-40; Guggenheim fel, 45-46, 59-60; hon. D.Litt, Va. State Col, 63; L.H.D, Hobart Col, 64. Instr. Eng, Morehouse Col, 28-31; Louisville Munic. Col, 34-36; prof. & chmn. dept, South. Univ, 36-38; N.C. State Teachers Col, 38-43; prof, Hampton Inst, 43-53, Johnson Prof. creative lit, 53-66; dir. div. res. & publ, Nat. Endowment for Humanities, D.C, 66-70; PROF. ENG, CORNELL UNIV, 70- Vis. prof, Brown Univ, 49-50; U.S. State Dept. lectr, India, 52; participant, U.S. Comn. World Festival Negro Art, 64-66. Mayflower Award, 44; Distinguished Serv. Award, Nat. Urban League, 50. CLA; Am. Folklore Soc; Asn. Stud. Negro Life & Hist; Am. Soc. African Cult.(pres, 66-). Negro literature and history. Publ: On being Negro in America, Bobbs, 50; Stranger and alone, Harcourt, 51; The lonesome road, Doubleday, 58; co-auth, Soon one morning, Knopf, 63; auth, The Negro, Potomac, 67; The problems of the Negro writer, Mass. Rev, winter 64; Literature and the Negro, Contemporary Lit, winter 68. Add: Dept. of English, Goldwin Smith Hall, Cornell University, Ithaca, NY 14850.

REDFERN, RICHARD K, b. Dixon, Ill, Nov. 23, 16; m. 44; c. 4. ENGLISH. B.S, Univ. Ill, 37; M.A, Cornell Univ, 47, Ph.D.(Eng), 50. From asst. prof. to assoc. prof, ENG, State Univ. N.Y. Col. New Paltz, 50-65; prof, Parsons Col, 65-67; assoc. prof, Univ. North. Iowa, 67-68; PROF, CLARION STATE COL, 68- Exchange teacher, Geschwister-Scholl Gymnasium, Düsseldorf, 59-60; vis. prof, Pädagogische Hochschule, W.Ger, 70-71. U.S.A, 40-45, Capt. Counc. Basic Educ; MLA; NCTE. English usage; teaching of composition. Publ: Is jargon worse than error?, Eng. Record, 10/64; A brief lexicon of jargon, Col. Eng, 5/67; Is college English teaching sick?, Iowa Eng. Yearbook, 69; plus others. Add: Dept. of English, Clarion State College, Clarion, PA 16214.

REDINGER, RUBY V, b. Cleveland, Ohio, Apr. 3, 15. ENGLISH, LINGUISTICS. B.A, Cleveland State Univ, 36; West. Reserve Univ, 37, Ph.D.(Eng. & philos), 40. Lectr. Eng, Cleveland Col, West. Reserve Univ, 39-41; from instr. to assoc. prof. Eng. & philos. & chmn. dept, philos, Cleveland State Univ, 41-51; from lectr. to assoc. prof. ENG, BALDWIN-WALLACE COL, 57-69, PROF, 69- MLA. Eighteenth century literature; George Eliot. Publ: Co-auth, Explorations in living, Reynal & Hitchcock, 541; auth, The golden net, Crown, 48; Jonathan Swift: disenchanter, Am. Scholar, 46; The short story, In: Encyc. Am, Grolier, 46. Add: 138 Edgewood Dr, Berea, OH 44017.

REDMOND, EUGENE BENJIMAN, b. St. Louis, Mo, Dec. 1, 37. ENGLISH & BLACK AMERICAN LITERATURE. B.A, South. Ill. Univ, 64; M.A, Wash. Univ, 66. Teacher-counr. & poet-in-residence, South. Ill. Univ, 67-69; writer-in-residence Afro-Am. lit, Oberlin Col, 69-70; PROF. ENG. & POET-IN-RESIDENCE, CALIF. STATE UNIV, SACRAMENTO, 70- Vis. lectr. Afro-Am. lit, Webster Col, summer 67; consult, U.S. Dept. Educ. Stud. Arts in Am, 68; assoc. fel, Inst. of Black World, 69-; consult, Karamu House Theatre & Cult. Ctr, 69; Call & Response Writers Workshop, 69; Kent State Univ. African-Am. cosmology, spring 70; consult. & lectr, Black Am. mythology & lang. consortium, Univ. Pittsburgh, fall 70; contrib. mem, Black World Found, 71-; vis. lectr. writer-in-residence, South. Univ. Baton Rouge, summers 71 & 72. U.S.M.C, 58-61. Intercontinental World Poetry Soc; Int. Black Writers' Conf. Black American language and mythology; Black American music; American literature and poetry. Publ: Sentry of the four golden pillars (poetry), 70; River of bones and flesh and blood (poetry), 71; Songs from an Afro-phone (poetry), 72; Blood links and sacred places (record album), 73; & In a time of rain and desire, 73, Black River Writers; co-ed, Poetry for my people, South. Ill. Univ, 70; Ark of bones and other stories, 70, South. Ill. Univ; auth, Consider loneliness as these things (poetry), Centro Studi Scambi Int, 73; How many poets scrub the river's back, Confrontation, spring 71; The black American epic: its roots, its writers, Black Scholar, 1/71; contrib, Contemporary Black thought, Bobbs, 73; plus others. Add: Dept. of English, California State University, Sacramento, 6000 J St, Sacramento, CA 95819.

REDWINE, JAMES DANIEL, JR, b. Macon, Ga, Jan. 4, 32; m. 66; c. 1. ENGLISH. A.B, Duke Univ, 54; A.M, Columbia Univ, 56; Ph.D.(Eng), Princeton, 62. Instr. ENG, Univ. Cincinnati, 61-63; ASST. PROF, BOWDOIN COL, 64- MLA. Renaissance English literature. Publ: Ben Jonson's literary criticism, Univ. Nebr, 70; Beyond psychology: Jonson's theory of humour, ELH, 12/61. Add: 27 McKeen St, Brunswick, ME 04011.

REECE, JAMES BRADY, b. Carter Co, Tenn, m. 47. ENGLISH. A.B, Johns Hopkins Univ, 45; A.M, Duke Univ, 49, Ph.D.(Eng), 54. Asst. prof. ENG, OLD DOM. UNIV, 52-54, assoc. prof, 54-61, PROF, 61- MLA. American literature; Edgar Allan Poe. Publ: A Margaret Fuller satire on Longfellow, Boston Pub. Libr. Quart; New light on Poe's The masque of the red death, Mod. Lang. Notes. Add: Dept. of English, Old Dominion University, Norfolk, VA 23508.

REECE, SHELLEY C, b. Havensville, Kans, Apr. 19, 36; m. 58; c. 2. ENGLISH. B.A, Doane Col, 58; M.A, Univ. Nebr, 59, Ph.D.(Eng), 67. Instr.

Eng, Hastings Col, 59-60; Univ. Nebr, 64-66; asst. prof, San Jose State Col, 66-69, coord. freshman Eng, 67-69; ASST. PROF. ENG. & DIR. COMPOS, PORTLAND STATE UNIV, 69- Instr. descriptive rhetoric, NDEA Inst, N.Dak. State Univ, summer 68. Conf. Col. Compos. & Commun; MLA; NCTE. Basic research in rhetoric; exploiting inductive and descriptive methods; twentieth century British fiction. Add: Dept. of English, Portland State University, P.O. Box 751, Portland, OR 97207.

REED, BARBARA LORAINE, b. Newton, Mass, Feb. 27, 43. ENGLISH & AMERICAN LITERATURE. A.B, Hollins Col, 64; M.A, Ind. Univ, Bloomington, 67, Ph.D.(Eng), 70. Teaching asst. Eng, Ind. Univ, 64-69; ASST. PROF. ENG. & AM. LIT, UNIV. CALIF, IRVINE, 69-, asst. dean humanities, 73. AAUP. American prose fiction, especially 20th century; federal and early republic. Add: Dept. of English & Comparative Literature, University of California, Irvine, CA 92664.

REED, DAVID WOODERSON, English Language. See Volume III, Foreign Languages, Linguistics & Philology.

REED, GLENN ARMSTRONG, b. Fresno, Calif, July 23, 10; m. 40; c. 2. AMERICAN LITERATURE. A.B, Stanford, 34, A.M, 36, Ph.D, 50. Instr. Eng, Pasadena City Col, 37-44; asst. prof, SAN JOSE STATE UNIV, 44-46, assoc. prof, 46-50, PROF. ENG. & COORD. ENG. COMPOS, 50- Col. Eng. Asn; NCTE. Higher education in America. Publ: Another turn on James's The turn of the screw, Am. Lit; Fifty years of conflict in the graduate school, Ed. Rec. Add: Dept. of English, San Jose State University, San Jose, CA 95114.

REED, JOHN QUINCY, b. Slippery Rock, Pa, Dec. 30, 18; m. 49; c. 2. AMERICAN LITERATURE. B.A, Slippery Rock State Col, 40; M.A, Univ. Pittsburgh, 48; Ph.D, State Univ. Iowa, 55. Instr. ENG, Buena Vista Col, 48-50, asst. prof, 50-53, assoc. prof, 53-55; asst. prof, KANS. STATE COL. PITTSBURG, 55-58, assoc. prof, 58-60, PROF, 60-, CHMN. DEPT, 66- Am. Stud. Asn; NCTE; Mid-Continent Am. Stud. Asn; MLA. American humor and satire; American fiction. Publ: Benjamin Penhallow Shillaber, Twayne, 72. Artemus Ward, In: Encycl. Britannica, 60; Artemus Ward's first lecture, Am. Lit, 11/60; plus one other. Add: Dept. of English, Kansas State College of Pittsburg, Pittsburg, KS 66762.

REED, JOHN ROBERT, b. Duluth, Minn, Jan. 24, 38. ENGLISH. B.A,(music) & B.A.(Eng), Univ. Minn, Duluth, 59; Ph.D.(Eng), Univ. Rochester, 63. Instr. ENG, Univ. Cincinnati, 62-64; asst. prof, Univ. Conn, 64-65; WAYNE STATE UNIV, 65-68, assoc. prof, 68-71, PROF, 71-, res. fels, summers 66 & 68. Leverhulme Trust fel, Univ. Warwick, 66-67; Guggenheim fel, 70-71. MLA; Am. Soc. Aesthet; Tennyson Soc; Dickens Soc; AAUP. Modern British and Victorian literature; modern American literature. Publ: Old school ties: the public schools in British literature, Syracuse Univ, 65; Perception and design in Tennyson's Idylls of the king, Ohio Univ, 70; Swinburne's Tristram of Lyonese: the poet-lover's song of love, Victorian Poetry, spring 66; Bedlamite and Pierrot: Ernest Dowson's esthetic of futility, ELH, 3/68; Going back: the ironic progress of Lowell's poetry, Mod. Poetry Stud, 70; plus others. Add: Dept. of English, Wayne State University, Detroit, MI 48202.

REED, JOHN THOMAS, b. Terre Haute, Ind, May 3, 18. ENGLISH. B.A, Ind. Univ, 41; M.A, Northwest. Univ, 44, Ph.D, 56. Instr. ENG, Robert Col, Turkey, 45-46; Univ. San Francisco, 49-51; assoc. prof, IND. STATE UNIV, TERRE HAUTE, 56-71, PROF, 71- MLA. Add: Dept. of English, Indiana State University, Terre Haute, IN 47809.

REED, JOHN WILLIAM, b. North Fairfield, Ohio, Dec. 14, 27; m. 50, 70; c. 2. SPEECH, HOMILETICS. B.A, Bryan Col, 51; M.Div, Grace Theol. Sem, 54; M.A, Bowling Green State Univ, 61; Ph.D.(speech), Ohio State Univ, 66. Instr. speech & Eng, Stryker High Sch, Ohio, 55-61; prof. speech, Cedarville Col, 61-70, chmn. div. lang. & lit, 66-70; ASSOC. PROF. HOMILETICS, DALLAS THEOL. SEM, 70- Pastor, First Baptist Church, Stryker, Ohio, 54-61. Med.C, U.S.A, 46-47; Air Nat. Guard, 64-, Chaplain Lt. Col. Speech Commun. Asn. Oral interpretation of literature; homiletics; colonial history. Publ: The use of the Bible in the preaching of eight representative American preachers, Ohio Speech J, 63; contrib, Sermons in American history, Abingdon, 71 & America in controversy, W.C. Brown, 73. Add: Dept. of Practical Theology, Dallas Theological Seminary, 3909 Swiss Ave, Dallas, TX 75204.

REED, JOSEPH WAYNE, JR, b. St. Petersburg, Fla, May 31, 32; m. 55; c. 3. ENGLISH LITERATURE. B.A, Yale Univ, 54, M.A, 58, Ph.D, 61. Instr. ENG, WESLEYAN UNIV, 60-61, asst. prof, 61-67, assoc. prof, 67-71, PROF, 71-, chmn. dept, 71-73. U.S.N.R, 54-56, Lt.(jg). MLA. Eighteenth and 19th centuries; biography; film. Publ: Co-ed, Selected prose and poetry of the Romantic period, Holt, 63; auth, Faulkner's narrative, 73 & co-ed, Horace Walpole's family correspondence, 73, Yale; ed, Barbara Bodichon, American diary, 1857-8, Routledge & Kegan Paul, London, 72; auth, Browning and Macready: the final quarrel, PMLA, 60; Noah Webster's debt to Samuel Johnson, Am. Speech, 62; Boswell and the major, Kenyon Rev, 66. Add: Box S, Wesleyan Station, Middletown, CT 06457.

REED, KENNETH TERRENCE, b. Grand Rapids, Mich, Jan. 7, 37; m. 61; c. 3. AMERICAN & EUROPEAN LITERATURE. A.B, Miami Univ, 59; M.A, State Univ. Iowa, 61; Ph.D.(Eng), Univ. Ky, 68. Instr. Eng, St. Clair Community Col, 61-63; asst. prof, Transylvania Univ, 63-68; teaching fel, Univ. Ky, 66-67; asst. prof, MIAMI UNIV, 68-72; ASSOC. PROF. ENG. & COORD. HUMANITIES, 73- Miami Univ. summer res. grant, 72. MLA. Publ: S.N. Behrman, Twayne, 74; Oh these women! These women! Irving's shrews and coquettes, Am. Notes & Queries, 6/70; East egg, west egg, all around the tower: the geography of Fitzgerald's Gatsby, Fitzgerald-Hemingway Ann, 71; The pleasant circle broke: a reading of Whittier's Snowbound, Whittier Newslett, fall 71. Add: Dept. of English, Miami University, Oxford, OH 45056.

REED, LIBUSE LACINA, b. Cleveland, Ohio, June 27, 24; m. 45. ENGLISH. B.A, Heidelberg Col, 46; univ. scholar & M.A, Univ. Mich, 47; Ohio State Univ. Instr. ENG, Heidelberg Col, 47-52; asst. prof, OHIO WESLEYAN UNIV, 52-63, assoc. prof, 63-72, PROF, 72- Consult, Battelle Mem. Inst,

56-; Gen. Electric, 59-60; Am. Educ. Publ, 61-63; ed, Eng. Asn. Ohio Bull, 66-; consult. commun, Master Chem. Co, 70-73. Conf. Col. Compos. & Commun; MLA; Am. Bus. Writing Asn; NCTE. Report writing for business, industry and research; modern European fiction; American civilization. Add: 6 Westgate Dr, Delaware, OH 43015.

REED, MARK LAFAYETTE, b. Asheville, N.C, Sept. 26, 35; m. 58; c. 2. ENGLISH LITERATURE. B.A, Yale, 57; M.A, Harvard, 58, Ph.D.(Eng), 62; Fulbright scholar, Cambridge, 60-61. Instr. ENG, Harvard, 62-63; asst. prof, UNIV. N.C, CHAPEL HILL, 63-66, assoc. prof, 66-71, PROF, 71- Am. Philos. Soc. grant, 64, 68; Univ. N.C.-Duke Univ. Coop. Prog. grant, 65; Guggenheim fel, 65-66 & 70-71; vis. fel, Clare Hall, Cambridge, 65-66; assoc. ed, Cornell Wordsworth, 68- MLA; S.Atlantic Mod. Lang. Asn. English Romantic literature. Publ: Wordsworth: the chronology of the early years, Harvard, 67; Wordsworth, Coleridge, and the plan of the lyrical ballads, Univ. Toronto Quart, 65; The speaker of The prelude, In: Bicentenary Wordsworth Studies, Cornell Univ, 70; plus others. Add: Dept. of English, University of North Carolina at Chapel Hill, Chapel Hill, NC 27514.

REED, PETER J, b. London, Eng, May 14, 35; m. 61. ENGLISH. B.A, Univ, Idaho, 60; M.A, Univ. Wash, 63, Ph.D.(Eng), 65. Asst. prof. ENG, Univ, Minn, Minneapolis, 65-67; San Diego State Col, 67-68; UNIV. MINN, MINNEAPOLIS, 69-72, ASSOC. PROF, 72- R.A.F, 56-60. NCTE; MLA. Twentieth century British literature, especially the novel; 20th century American literature and novel. Publ: Writers for the 70's: Kurt Vonnegut, Warners, 72; Getting stuck: Joyce Cary's Gulley Vimson, Twentieth Century Lit, 10/70; The self-sparing usage of English, Eng. J, 11/71; The better the heart: Joyce Cary's Sara Monday, Tex. Stud. Lit. & Lang, spring 73; plus two others. Add: Dept. of English, University of Minnesota, Minneapolis, MN 55455.

REED, ROBERT RENTOUL, JR, b. New York, N.Y, Nov. 16, 11; m. 42; c. 2. ENGLISH. A.B, Pomona Col, 37; M.A, Columbia Univ, 46, Ph.D, 50. Headmaster, Hudson River Naval Acad, 45-46; teacher Latin & Eng, Halsted Sch, 46-47; instr. ENG, N.Y. Univ, 47-50; asst. prof, PA. STATE UNIV, 50-53, ASSOC. PROF, 53- U.S.C.G, 42-45. Shakespeare Asn. Am; Renaissance Soc. Am. Elizabethan and Stuart drama; modern European drama; Renaissance poetry. Publ: Young April, Elektra; Bedlam on the Jacobean stage, Harvard, 52 & 68; The occult on the Tudor and Stuart stage, Christopher, 65; Richard II: from mask to prophet, Pa. State Univ, 68; James Shirley and the sentimental comedy, Anglia, autumn 55; Hamlet: the pseudo-procrastinator, spring 58 & The origins of Ariel, winter 60, Shakespeare Quart. Add: 621 E. McCormick Ave, State College, PA 16801.

REED, VICTOR BRENNER, b. Birmingham, Ala, Feb. 1, 26; m. 55; c. 3. ENGLISH & COMPARATIVE LITERATURE. A.B, Harvard, 47, A.M, 48; Univ. Paris, 55; Ph.D.(comp. lit), Columbia Univ, 64. Lectr. ENG, City Col. New York, 50-55; lektor, Univ. Helsinki, 55-56; instr, Fairleigh Dickinson Univ, 58-60, asst. prof, 60-63; LEHMAN COL, 64-69, ASSOC. PROF, 70- Vis. asst. prof. ENG, Univ. Mass, 68. U.S.N, 43-46, Ens. MLA. Modernist English and American literature; Shakespeare. Publ: Co-auth, A casebook on Shakespeare's Sonnets, Crowell, 64; plus others. Add: Dept. of English, Herbert H. Lehman College, Bronx, NY 10468.

REEDS, JAMES A, Linguistics. See Volume III, Foreign Languages, Linguistics & Philology.

REEDY, GERARD CHARLES, S.J, b. New York, N.Y, Oct. 25, 39. ENGLISH LITERATURE. A.B, Fordham Univ, 63, M.A, 65; B.D, Woodstock Col, 70; Ph.D.(Eng), Univ. Pa, 73. ASST. PROF. ENG, FORDHAM UNIV, 73- MLA; AAUP; Am. Soc. 18th Century Stud. John Dryden; 17th century Anglican theology; intellectual history, English Restoration. Publ: The christology of Hans Urs von Balthasar, Thought, 70; The imagery of Charles II's coronation, In: Studies in change and revolution, Scolar Press, 72; Noumenal and phenomenal evidence in England, 1662-1682, Enlightenment Essays, 73. Add: Dept. of English, Fordham University, Bronx, NY 10458.

REEDY, JOHN EDWARD, b. Castleton, Md, Nov. 22, 26; m. 51; c. 2. ENGLISH, EDUCATION. A.B, Gordon Col, 50, B.D, 52; M.Ed, Univ. Maine, 56; D.Ed.(Eng), Boston Univ, 64; Summer Inst. Ling, 68; Univ. Edinburgh, 71-72. Teacher, High Sch, Mass, 56-62; asst. prof. ENG, Gordon Col, 62-65; assoc. prof, STATE UNIV. N.Y. COL. BUFFALO, 65-73, PROF, 73- NCTE (comt. compos. evaluation elem. Eng, 66-69); Conf. Eng. Educ.(comt. preparation elem. Eng. teachers, 68-71). Am. Asn. Oriental Res. Biblical concepts of life writing; teaching Bible as literature. Publ: Co-auth, The teaching of English in N.Y. State, 70 & The preparation of English teachers in N.Y, 72, N.Y. State Eng. Counc; co-auth, Teacher education programs: a model for curriculum revision, Eng. Educ, fall 72; plus others. Add: Dept. of English, State University of New York College at Buffalo, 1300 Elmwood Ave, Buffalo, NY 14222.

REES, COMPTON, JR, b. Paris, France, Sept. 6, 31; U.S. citizen; m. 55; c. 2. ENGLISH RENAISSANCE. B.A, Rice Univ, 53, M.A, 58, Ph.D, 62. Asst. & fel, Rice Univ, 57-61; instr. ENG, UNIV. CONN, 61-63, asst. prof, 63-67, ASSOC. PROF, 67- Consult, Choice, 64-; mem. ed. bd, Hartford Ser. in Lit, 69-; consult, Mich. Univ. Press, 70- U.S.A, 53-56. Renaissance Soc. Am; MLA; NCTE; Col. Eng. Asn. Renaissance history of ideas and aesthetics; mythology; Spenser and Shakespeare. Add: Dept. of English, University of Connecticut, Storrs, CT 06268.

REES, ENNIS, b. Newport News, Va, Mar. 17, 25; m. 46; c. 3. ENGLISH. A.B, Col. William & Mary, 46; M.A, Harvard, 48, Ph.D.(Eng), 51. Instr. ENG, Duke Univ, 49-52; Princeton, 52-54; asst. prof, UNIV. S.C, 54-56, assoc. prof, 56-63, prof, 63-65, CHAIR CLUB PROF, 65- U.S.A, 46-47. Sixteenth and 17th century English literature; verse translation; poetry. Publ: Tragedies of George Chapman: Renaissance ethics in action, Harvard, 54; Odyssey of Homer, a verse translation, 60 & Iliad of Homer, a verse translation, 63, Random; Riddles, riddles, everywhere, Abelard, 64; The song of Paul Bunyan and Tony Beaver, 64 & Potato talk, 69, Pantheon; Poems, 64 & Selected poems, 73, Univ. S.C; Fables from Aesop, Oxford, 66; Brer Rabbit and his tricks, W.R. Scott, 67. Transl. & reader, Selections from The Iliad and Odyssey of Homer (records), Vol. I, 62 & Vol. II, 67, auth. & reader, Selections from Fables from Aesop (record), 66, Selections from The song of Paul Bunyan and Tony Beaver (record), 66 & Brer Rabbit and his tricks & More of Brer Rabbit and his tricks, 71, Spoken Arts. Add: Dept. of English, University of South Carolina, Columbia, SC 29208.

REES, JOHN OWEN, JR, b. Cleveland, Ohio, Aug. 27, 23; m. 57; c. 1. ENGLISH, AMERICAN STUDIES. B.A, Amherst Col, 47; M.F.A, Univ. Iowa, 57, univ. fels, 60-61 & 62-63, Ph.D.(Eng. & Am. civilization), 65. Instr. ENG, Colgate Univ, 57-60; Univ. Colo, 63-65; asst. prof, KANS. STATE UNIV, 65-72, ASSOC. PROF, 72- Nat. Endowment Humanities younger scholar fel, 67-68; vis. assoc. prof. Eng, Univ. Iowa, summer 73. U.S.A.A.F, 43-46. MLA. American literature. Publ: Co-auth, Whitman and the foo-foos: an experiment in language, Walt Whitman Rev, 3/71; auth, Spenserian analogues in Moby-Dick, 8/72 & Shakespeare in the Blithedale Romance, 5/73, ESQ: A.J. Am. Renaissance; plus three others. Add: 114 Evergreen Ave, Manhattan, KS 66502.

REES, RALPH, b. Nanticoke, Pa, Aug. 8, 17. ENGLISH. A.B, Bucknell Univ, 39, M.A, 47; Ph.D.(Eng), Pa. State Univ, 56. Instr. ENG, BUCKNELL UNIV, 47-55, asst. prof, 55-60, ASSOC. PROF, 60- U.S.A.A.F, 42-45, S/Sgt. Modern American poetry; Melville; Hawthorne. Publ: The armor of Marianne Moore, Bucknell Rev, 5/67. Add: Dept. of English, Bucknell University, Lewisburg, PA 17837.

REES, ROBERT ALVIN, b. Los Angeles, Calif, Nov. 17, 35; m. 61; c. 4. AMERICAN LITERATURE. B.A, Brigham Young Univ, 60; Univ. Laval, summer 59; M.A, Univ. Wis, 62, Ph.D.(Eng), 66. Exec. secy. articulated instructional media prog, Univ. Wis, 64-66; ASST. PROF. ENG, UNIV. CALIF, LOS ANGELES, 66- Ed, Dialogue: A Journal of Mormon Thought, 70-; Ctr. Editions Am. Auth, 71; mem, Am. Lit. Group, MLA. U.S.A, 58. Mark Twain; the devil in American literature; literature and education. Publ: Co-auth, A checklist of Emerson criticism: 1951-1961, Transcendental, 64; co-ed, 15 American authors before 1900: bibliographic essays on research and criticism, 71 & Washington Irving's The adventures of Captain Bonneville (1837), (in press), Univ. Wis; The short story: an introductory anthology, Little, 74; auth, The imagination's new beginning: thought on esthetics and religion, 69 & Truth is the daughter of time: notes toward an imaginative Mormon history, 71, Dialogue, 71; James Russell Lowell, In: 15 American authors before 1900, Univ. Wis, 71; plus others. Add: Dept. of English, University of California, 2225 Humanities Bldg, Los Angeles, CA 90024.

REESE, MARTIN SYLVESTER, b. Gatesville, Tex, June 3, 17; m. 42. JOURNALISM. A.B, Tex. Tech. Col, 38, M.B.A, 40. Asst. prof. JOUR, SOUTH. METHODIST UNIV, 47-56, ASSOC. PROF, 56- U.S.N, 42-46, Capt. Nat. Counc. Col. Publ. Adv; Asn. Educ. in Jour; In-Plant Printing Mgt. Asn. Newspaper management; graphic arts; advertising. Add: Dept. of Journalism, Southern Methodist University, Dallas, TX 75275.

REESING, JOHN PALMER, JR, b. Gatesville, Tex, Sept. 15, 20. ENGLISH LITERATURE. A.B, Baylor Univ, 41; A.M, Tulane Univ, 42; Ph.D.(Eng), Harvard, 54. Instr. ENG, George Wash. Univ, 46-48, asst. prof, 48-49; instr, Oberlin Col, 53-54; asst. prof, GEORGE WASHINGTON UNIV, 54-57, assoc. prof, 57-62, PROF, 62-, chmn. dept, 63-70, acting chmn, 72-73. U.S.A.A.F, 42-46, Capt. MLA; Mod. Humanities Res. Asn; Int. Asn. Univ. Prof. Eng; Renaissance Soc. Am. Sixteenth and seventeenth century English literature, especially Milton; critical theory. Publ: The materiality of God in Milton's De doctrina Christiana, Harvard Theol. Rev, 57; Milton's poetic art, Harvard, 68. Add: Dept. of English, George Washington University, Washington, DC 20006.

REEVE, ALEXANDER, b. London, Eng, May 16, 00; m. 24; c. 1. SPEECH, DRAMA. Dir. prod, Royal Theatre & Opera House, Northampton Repertory Theatre, 43-56; vis. prof. speech & drama & dir. theatre, HOWARD PAYNE COL, 56-71, EMER. PROF. SPEECH & DRAMA, 71- Dir. winning play, Nat. Festival Brit. Drama, London, 35; dir, Barn Theatre, Eng; community playhouse, Brownwood, Tex; critic judge, Interscholastic One Act Play Contest, Tex; rep. Counc. Repertory Theatres, Int. Theatre Inst. World Congr, The Hague, 52; guest prof, Vanderbilt Univ, 53-54; dir, Howard Payne Col. Tour, Brit. Prof. Theatres, 59; substitute teacher speech-drama, Brownwood High Sch, Tex, 73-; guest lectr, stage dir. & theatre consult, var. cols, univs. & community orgns. Brit. Army, 18; sector warden, Air Raid Precautions, 38-45. AAUP. International theatre; theatre history and costume; repertory movement especially British and American. Add: 1201 Cottage St, Brownwood, TX 76801.

REEVE, FRANKLIN (DOLIER), b. Philadelphia, Pa, Sept. 18, 28; m. 55; c. 3. LITERATURE. A.B, Princeton, 50; M.A, Columbia Univ, 52, Ph.D, 58. Lectr. Russ, Columbia Univ, 52-55, instr, 55-58, asst. prof, 58-61; assoc. prof, WESLEYAN UNIV, 62-64, prof, 64-66, chmn. dept. Russ. lang. & lit, 62-66, vis. prof. humanities & tutor, col. lett, 67-68, ADJ. PROF. LETT, 68- Ford Found. fel, Paris, 55-56; Columbia Univ-Moscow Univ. fac. exchange fel, 61; Am. Counc. Learned Soc-U.S.S.R. Acad. Sci. prof. exchange fel, 61; vis. prof, Oxford, 64; vis. lectr. Eng. & fel, Saybrook Col, Yale, 72-; scholar-in-residence, Aspen Inst. Humanities, 73. Lit. Award, Nat. Inst. Arts & Lett, 70. PEN Club. Russian, American and English literature. Publ: Anthology of Russian plays (2 vols), Random, 61, 63; Aleksandr Blok: between image and idea, Columbia Univ, 62; ed, Great Soviet short stories, Dell, 63; auth, Robert Frost in Russia, Atlantic, Little, 64; The Russian novel, McGraw, 66; On some scientific concepts in Russian poetry at the turn of the century, Ctr. Advan. Stud, 66; Contemporary Russian drama, Pegasus, 68; The red machines, 68, In the silent stones, 68 & Just over the border, 69, Morrow; The brother, 71, The blue cat, 72 & White colors, 73, Farrar, Straus; plus others. Add: Higganum, CT 06441.

REEVES, GEORGE M, English & Comparative Literature. See Volume III, Foreign Languages, Linguistics & Philology.

REEVES, JOHN DRUMMOND, b. Troy, N.Y, Dec. 8, 14; m. 51. ENGLISH, CLASSICS. A.B, Williams Col, 37; A.M, Columbia Univ, 41. Instr, Irving Sch, N.Y, 37-40; Horace Mann Sch, 40-41, 46-47; classics & Eng, Whitman Col, 56-58, asst. prof, 58-62; assoc. prof. ENG, Millikin Univ, 62-65; LECTR, HOFSTRA UNIV, 65- Regional assoc, Am. Counc. Learned Soc,

57-59. U.S.N.R, 41-45, Lt. Archaeol. Inst. Am; Class. Asn; Col. Eng. Asn; MLA; AAUP. Classical mythology; literary forgeries; George Peele. Publ: Perseus and the flying horse in Peele and Heywood, Rev. Eng. Stud, 55; The cause of the Trojan War: a forgotten myth revived, Class. J, 2/66; Motivations in literary forgery, Hofstra Rev, winter 67; plus others. Add: Dept. of English, Hofstra University, Hempstead Turnpike, Hempstead, NY 11550.

REEVES, RUTH E, b. Mt. Zion, Ill, Dec. 20, 02; m. 28; c. 1. ENGLISH. B.A, Millikin Univ, 26; M.A, Univ. Houston, 48. Elem. teacher, Pub. Sch, Warrensburg, Ill, 20-22; Eng, High Sch, Decatur, Ill, 26-29; Kinkaid Sch, Houston, Tex, 30-48; San Jacinto High Sch, 48-55; supvr, Houston Independent Sch. Dist, 55-68, dir. Eng. instr, 69-71; RETIRED. Mem. fac, Univ. Houston, 43-48. NCTE (dir-at-large, 62-64). Teaching secondary schools. Publ: Lament for a lonesome corpse, Phoenix, 48; Understanding the novel, Doubleday, Vol. I & II, 62; Anthology of literature, Ginn, 64; The teaching of reading in our schools, Macmillan, 66; ed, Ideas for teaching English, grades 7, 8, 9, NCTE, 66; co-auth, Approaches to writing, 69 & Composition in action, Vols. I & II, 71, Sci. Res. Assocs; English I: a contemporary approach & English II, a contemporary approach, Hayden, 71. Add: 819 Jaquet Dr, Bellaire, TX 77401.

REEVES, TROY DALE, b. Gainesville, Tex, Sept. 28, 39; m. 70. ENGLISH LITERATURE, CREATIVE WRITING. B.A, N.Tex. State Univ; M.A, Univ. Kans, 64, M.Phil. 68, Ph.D.(Eng), 70. Minister, Church of Christ, Ethel, Tex, 59-62, asst. instr. Eng, Univ. Kans, 63-67; caseworker, N.Y.C. Dept. Social Serv, 67-68; ASST. PROF. ENG, ANGELO STATE UNIV, 69- Seventeenth century English literature; bibliography and literary research; Shakespeare. Publ: The preparation (poem), Christian Century, 4/68; Serving communion to old Sister Inez, Writer, 5/68; Prufrock at the Roxy, Ill. Quart, 3 2/71; plus other poems and stories. Add: Dept. of English, Angelo State University, San Angelo, TX 76901.

REEVES, WALTER PASCHAL, JR, b. Birmingham, Ala, Sept. 8, 17; m. 60; c. 2. ENGLISH. A.B, Univ. Ala, 39, M.S, 41; Th.M, South. Baptist Theol. Sem, 43; M.A, Duke Univ, 57, scholar, 58-59, Ph.D, 63. Instr. Eng. & biology, Warren Wilson Col, 53-56; ENG, Duke Univ, 56-58; asst. prof, Fla. South. Col, 59-61, assoc. prof, 61-64, chmn. dept, 60-64; asst. prof, UNIV. GA, 64-66, assoc. prof, 66-69, PROF. & ASSOC. TO PROVOST, 69- Summer res. award, Univ. Ga, 65-68. U.S.A, 44-46, Capt. MLA; Am. Stud. Asn; NCTE; Am. Name Soc; Soc. Stud. South. Lit.(chmn. bibliog. comt, 68-, bibliogr, 68-74); Melville Soc; S.Atlantic Mod. Lang. Asn. American literature; Southern literature; 20th century literature. Publ: Thomas Wolfe's Albatross: race and nationality in America, Univ. Ga, 68; Jones Very, Twayne, 69; co-ed, The notebooks of Thomas Wolfe, Univ. N.C, 69; ed, Studies in Look homeward, Angel, 70 & auth, A guide to Thomas Wolfe, 72, Merrill; ed, Thomas Wolfe and the Glass of time, Univ. Ga, 71; auth, The humor of Thomas Wolfe, South. Folklore Quart, 6/60; The silhouete of the state in Democratic vistas—Hegelian or Whitmanian?, Personalist, summer 62; Esther Jack as Muse, In: Thomas Wolfe: three decades of criticism, N.Y. Univ, 68. Add: Provost's Office, University of Georgia, Athens, GA 30602.

REGAN, ARTHUR E, b. Boston, Mass, Jan. 24, 36. ENGLISH. B.A, Harvard, 59, M.A, 61, fel, 62-65, Ph.D.(Eng), 65. Instr. ENG, N.Y. Univ, 65-67; ASST. PROF, SAN JOSE STATE UNIV, 67- Bernard Shaw; myth; comedy. Publ: The fantastic reality of Bernard Shaw, Shaw Rev, 1/68. Add: Dept. of English, San Jose State University, San Jose, CA 95192.

REGAN, CATHARINE ANN, b. Massena, N.Y, Jan. 15, 32. OLD ENGLISH & MEDIEVAL LITERATURE. A.B, Univ. Detroit, 54; M.A, Marquette Univ, 56; Ph.D.(Eng), Univ. Ill, Urbana, 66. Instr. ENG, Marquette Univ, 56-59; asst. prof, NORTHWEST. UNIV, 66-72, ASSOC. PROF, 72- MLA; Midwest Mod. Lang. Asn; Mediaeval Acad. Am. Old English literature; patrology. Publ: Evangelicalism as the informing principle of Cynewulf's Elene, Traditio, 73. Add: Dept. of English, Northwestern University, Evanston, IL 60201.

REGAN, CHARLES LIONEL, b. Natick, Mass, Sept. 18, 29; m. 53; c. 2. ENGLISH. A.B, Boston Col, 51; A.M, Harvard, 52, Ph.D.(Eng), 63. Instr. ENG, W.Va. Inst. Technol, 55-56; BOSTON COL, 57-63, asst. prof, 63-71, ASSOC. PROF, 71- MLA; Mediaeval Acad. Am. Medieval English language and literature. Publ: Chaucer's Parson's tale 1025: a probable source, Notes & Queries, 64; Melville's horned woman, 67 & John Gower and the fall of Babylon: Confessid Amantis, prologue 11, 670-686, 12/69, Eng. Lang. Notes. Add: Dept. of English, Boston College, Commonwealth Ave, Chestnut Hill, MA 02167.

REGAN, MARIANN SANDERS, English & Comparative Literature. See Volume III, Foreign Languages, Linguistics & Philology.

REGAN, ROBERT, b. Indianapolis, Ind, Mar. 13, 30; m. 60; c. 3. ENGLISH. B.A, Centenary Col, 51; M.A, Harvard, 52; Ph.D.(Eng), Univ. Calif, Berkeley, 65. Instr. ENG, Centenary Col, 55-56; asst. prof, Univ. Va, 63-67; ASSOC. PROF, UNIV. PA, 68- Fulbright-Hays lectr, Univ. Montpellier, 67-68; managing ed, Am. Quart, 68-70. U.S.N.R, 52-56, 60-61, Lt. Comdr. MLA; Am. Stud. Asn. Mark Twain's travel writings; Poe; American poetry. Publ: Unpromising heroes: Mark Twain and his characters, Univ. Calif, 66; ed, Poe: a collection of critical essays, Prentice-Hall, 67; auth, Hawthorne's plagiary: Poe's duplicity, Nineteenth-century Fiction, 12/70. Add: Dept. of English, University of Pennsylvania, Philadelphia, PA 19174.

REGUEIRO, HELEN, b. Montevideo, Uruguay, Sept. 18, 43; U.S. citizen. COMPARATIVE LITERATURE. B.A, Brandeis Univ, 64; Ph.D.(comp. lit), Brown Univ, 69. ASST. PROF. ENG. & COMP. LIT, COLUMBIA UNIV, 69- Chamberlain fel, Columbia Univ, 73; Soc. for Humanities jr. fel, Cornell Univ, 73-74. MLA; AAUP. Nineteenth and 20th century English, American, French, German and Greek poetry; 19th and 20th century novel; literary criticism and literary theory. Add: Dept. of English & Comparative Literature, Columbia University, New York, NY 10027.

REHDER, ROBERT M, b. Iowa. ENGLISH & COMPARATIVE LITERATURE. A.B, Princeton, 57, Near East. fel, 59-63, M.A, 62, U.S. Govt. res. fel, 63-64, Ph.D, 70; Rotary Int. fel. Ecole Lang. Orient, Paris, 57-58; Iranian Govt. fel, Univ. Tehran, 58-59. Teacher Am. lit, Iran-Am. Soc, Tehran, 58-59. Teacher Am. lit, Iran-Am. Soc, Tehran, 58-59; Eng, Princeton, 62-63; Univ. Md. in Europe, 65; Eng. & Europ. hist, Harcourt Tutors, London, 65-66; humanities, Drexel Inst. Technol, 67; ASST. PROF. COMP. LIT, UNIV. WIS-MADISON, 67-, grant, 71. Am. Philos. Soc. grant, 71; Nat. Endowment for Humanities fel, 71-72; vis. lectr. Eng, Univ. Stirling, 73-74. Am. Orient. Soc; MLA; Am. Comp. Lit. Asn. Modern English and French poetry; 19th century English and French literature; Islamic literature. Publ: New material for the text of Hafiz, Iran, 65; Une dentelle s'abolit, Nineteenth Century French Stud, 73; The unity of the Ghazals of Hafiz, Der Islam, 74; plus others. Add: Dept. of Comparative Literature, University of Wisconsin-Madison, Madison, WI 53706.

REHNER, MICHAEL JOHN, b. Erie, Pa, Mar. 17, 38; Can. citizen; m. 60; c. 2. AMERICAN LITERATURE, RHETORIC. B.S, Edinboro State Col, 60; Woodrow Wilson fel, Univ. Mich, 60-61, M.A, 61. Instr. ENG, Univ. Mich, 65-67; lectr, YORK UNIV, 67-70, asst. prof, 71-72, ASSOC. PROF, 72-, DIR. WRITING WORKSHOP, 69- Asn. Can. Univ. Teachers Eng; Conf. Col. Compos. & Commun; MLA; NCTE. Nineteenth century American fiction; rhetoric pedagogy; stylistics. Add: Writing Workshop, S713 Ross Bldg, York University, 4700 Keele St, Downsview, Ont. M3J 1P3, Can.

REHOR, CHARLES FRANK, b. Cleveland, Ohio, Sept. 5, 04. JOURNALISM. A.B, West. Reserve Univ, 26, A.M, 29, Ph.D, 41. Instr. Eng. & jour, CASE WEST. RESERVE UNIV, 29-36, asst. prof, 36-43, assoc. prof, 43-48, PROF. jour, 48-63, ENG, 63-, head dept. jour, 39-63. Shakespeare; the poems of John Milton. Add: Dept. of English, Case Western Reserve University, Cleveland, OH 44106.

REIBETANZ, JOHN, b. Queens, N.Y, July 28, 44; Can. citizen; m. 67; c. 1. ENGLISH LITERATURE. A.B, Brooklyn Col, 65; NDEA fel, Princeton, 65-68, M.A, 67, Procter fel, 67-68, Ph.D, 68. Asst. prof. ENG, VICTORIA COL, UNIV. TORONTO, 68-74, ASSOC. PROF, 74- Can. Counc. res. grant, 72-73, leave fel, 74-75. Can. Asn. Univ. Teachers; Asn. Can. Univ. Teachers Eng. Modern British and American poetry; Elizabethan and Jacobean drama; 17th century English poetry. Publ: Hieronimo in decimosexto: a private-theatre burlesque, Renaissance Drama, 72; Theatrical emblems in King Lear, In: Facets of King Lear, Univ. Toronto, 74. Add: Dept. of English, Victoria College, University of Toronto, Toronto, Ont. M5S 1K7, Can.

REICHARD, HUGO MANLEY, b. South Plainfield, N.J, Jan. 21, 18; m. 43; c. 3. ENGLISH. A.B, Univ. Mich, 39; Ph.D.(Eng), Harvard, 51. Instr. ENG, Duke Univ, 51-56; PURDUE UNIV, 56-58, asst. prof, 58-62, assoc. prof, 62-70, PROF, 70- U.S.A, 41-46, Capt. MLA. Eighteenth century English literature; literature and social sciences; theory of literature. Publ: Strange forms of life, J. Gen. Educ, 7/69; The elegist who sang for all he was worth, Dalhousie Rev, spring 71; The self-praise abounding in Swift's Verses, Tenn. Stud. Lit, 73; plus others. Add: Dept. of English, Heavilon Hall, Purdue University, West Lafayette, IN 47906.

REID, ALFRED SANDLIN, b. Orlando, Fla, Oct. 26, 24; m. 48; c. 2. ENGLISH. B.Ed, Univ. Miami, 48; M.A, Univ. Fla, 50, fel, 50-52, Ph.D.(Eng), 52. Instr. Eng, Univ. Fla, 49-50; Trinity Col.(Conn), 52-54; asst. prof, The Citadel, 54-55; FURMAN UNIV, 55-57, assoc. prof, 57-63, prof, 63-68, BENNETTE E. GEER PROF. LIT, 68-, chmn. dept. Eng, 72-73. Asst. prof, Teachers Col. Conn, 54; vis. prof, Univ. Fla, summer 58; ed, Furman Stud, 58-; South. Fels. Fund summer res. grant-in-aid, 60; fel, coop. prog. humanities, Univ. N.C, Chapel Hill & Duke Univ, 64-65; co-ed, S.C. Rev, 68-71, ed, 71-73. U.S.A, 44-46. Am. Stud. Asn; S.Atlantic Mod. Lang. Asn; Soc. Stud. South. Lit. Hawthorne; modern poetry; Southern literature. Publ: Yellow ruff and The scarlet letter, Univ. Fla, 55; ed, Sir Thomas Overbury's vision and other English sources of The scarlet letter, Scholar's Facsimiles & Reprints, 57; co-auth. & ed, The arts in Greenville, Furman Univ, 60; auth, Crumbling stones, poems, Robert Moore Allen, 63; Lady Godiva's lover, Drummer, 69; Hawthorne's Humanism: the birthmark and Sir Kenelm Digby, Am. Lit, 11/66; plus others. Add: Dept. of English, Furman University, Greenville, SC 29613.

REID, BENJAMIN LAWRENCE, b. Louisville, Ky, May 3, 18; m. 42; c. 2. ENGLISH. B.A, Univ. Louisville, 43, hon. D.H.L, 70; M.A, Columbia Univ, 50; J.S. Wilson fel, Univ. Va, 55-56, South. Found. fel, 56, Ph.D, 57. Instr. Eng, Iowa State Col, 46-48; Smith Col, 48-51; Sweet Briar Col, 51-56, asst. prof, 56-57; MT. HOLYOKE COL, 57-59, assoc. prof, 59-63, prof, 63-72, ANDREW W. MELLON PROF. HUMANITIES, 72- Fulbright res. grant, U.K, 63-64; mem. screening comt, Sr. Fulbright Grants in Eng, 64-67; Am. Counc. Learned Soc. fel, 66-67; Nat. Endowment for Humanities sr. fel, 71-72. MLA. Modern poetry; American literature; 18th century literature. Publ: Art by subtraction: a dissenting opinion of Gertrude Stein, 58 & William Butler Yeats: the lyric of tragedy, 62, Univ. Okla; The man from New York: John Quinn and his friends, Oxford, 68; The long boy and others, Univ. Ga, 69; Tragic occasions: essays on several forms, Kennikat, 71. Add: Dept. of English, Mt. Holyoke College, South Hadley, MA 01075.

REID, LOREN DUDLEY, b. Gilman City, Mo, Aug. 26, 05; m. 30; c. 4. SPEECH. A.B, Grinnell Col, 27; Univ. Chicago, 28; A.M, State Univ, Iowa, 30, Ph.D, 32. Instr, High Sch, S.Dak, 27-29; State Univ. Iowa, 31-33; High Sch, Mo, 33-35; Univ. Mo, 35-37, asst. prof, 37-39; speech & educ, Syracuse Univ, 39-41, assoc. prof, 41-44; PROF. SPEECH, UNIV. MO-COLUMBIA, 44-, chmn. dept, 47-52 & 66-67. Univ. Md. vis. prof, Ger. & Eng, 52-53, 60-61, Eng, 55; Carnegie vis. prof, Univ. Hawaii, 57; summers vis. prof, Univ. South. Calif, 47, 54, Univ. Utah, 52, San Diego State Col, 54, Univ. Mich, 57 & State Univ. Iowa, 58. James A. Winans Award, 69; Annual Distinguished Prof. Award, Univ. Mo, 70. Speech Commun Asn.(exec. secy, 45-51, 1st v.pres, 56, pres, 57, Golden Anniversary Award, 70); AAAS; NEA; Cent. States Speech Asn; Hansard Soc, London; fel. Royal Hist. Soc. Rhetoric and public address: fundamentals of speaking; teaching speech. Publ: Ed, American public address: Univ. Mo, 62; Charles James Fox, Longmans, 68; Teaching Speech, 69 & Speaking well, 2nd ed, 72, McGraw. Add: 115 Switzler Hall, University of Missouri-Columbia, Columbia, MO 65201.

REID, RANDALL C, b. Paso Robles, Calif, Oct. 4, 31; m. 54; c. 2. ENGLISH & AMERICAN LITERATURE. A.B, San Francisco State Col, 59; Woodrow

Wilson fel, Stanford Univ, 59-60, M.A, 61, NDEA fel, 65-66, Ph.D.(Eng. & Am. lit), 66. Instr. Eng, San Diego State Col, 61-63; instr. Eng. & acting fac. chmn, Deep Springs Col, 63-65; asst. prof. Eng. & humanities, Univ. Chicago, 66-69, assoc. prof, 69-71; DIR. & DEAN, DEEP SPRINGS COL, 69- Nat. Endowment for Humanities younger humanist fel, 72-73. U.S.N, 51-54. MLA. Publ: The fiction of Nathanael West: no redeemer, no promised land, Univ. Chicago, 68; Detritus, New Am. Rev, 4/72 & In: Prize stories 1973: the O. Henry awards, Doubleday, 73; A lecherous poet named Hench (fiction), Carolina Quart, fall 73. Add: Office of the Dean, Deep Springs College, Deep Springs, Calif, via Dyer, NV 89010.

REID, RONALD FORREST, b. Herrington, Kans, July 24, 28; m. 53; c. 2. SPEECH. Ph.D.(speech), Purdue Univ, 54. Instr. SPEECH, Wash. Univ, 54-56, asst. prof, 56-59; Purdue Univ, 59-61, assoc. prof, 61-66; PROF, UNIV. MASS, AMHERST, 66-, head dept, 66-70. Speech Commun. Asn; Speech Asn. East. States (pres, 68-69); Cent. States Speech Asn. American rhetoric and oratory; debate; speech education. Add: 63 Maplewood Dr, Amherst, MA 01002.

REIDENBAUGH, GERALD F, b. Lancaster, Pa, Feb. 8, 25; m. 56; c. 3. DRAMA. B.S, Syracuse Univ, 49, M.A, 51, Ph.D.(commun), 66. Instr. DRAMA, SYRACUSE UNIV, 51-56, asst. prof, 56-67, assoc. prof, CHMN. DEPT, 67-, ASST. DEAN ADMIN, COL. VISUAL & PERFORMING ARTS, 72-, acting chmn. dept, 57-58, 60-63, producing dir, New Playhouse, 60-63. Advisor, N.Y. State Commun. Theatre Asn, 64-; artistic dir, Syracuse Repertory Theatre, Syracuse Theatre Corp, 67-; mem. acad. comt, Am. Nat. Theatre Acad, 67- Am. Educ. Theatre Asn; Speech Commun. Asn; Nat. Theatre Conf. Theory of drama; theatre practice; community theatres. Add: Dept. of Drama, 213 Drama Center, Syracuse University, Syracuse, NY 13210.

REIFSNEIDER, ROBERT DANIEL, b. Pottstown, Pa, May 20, 12. THEATRE ARTS. A.B, Emerson Col, 38; A.M, Univ. Mich, 43. Instr. speech & drama, Bradford Jr. Col, 40-42; from asst. prof. dramatics to EMER. PROF. THEATRE ARTS, PA. STATE UNIV, UNIVERSITY PARK, 46- U.S.A, 42-46. Theatre; dance. Add: 243 Ridge Ave, State College, PA 16801.

REIFSNYDER, HENRY GILLAM, b. Philadelphia, Pa, July 3, 21; m. 47; c. 3. ENGLISH. A.B, Harvard Col, 42; A.M, Univ. Chicago, 47, Ph.D.(Eng. lang. & lit), 58. Instr. ENG, Univ. Idaho, 50-52; Pa. State Col, 52-55; Northwest. Univ, 55-59; asst. prof, IND. STATE UNIV, TERRE HAUTE, 59-62, assoc. prof, 62-70, PROF, 70- U.S.A, 42-46, 1st Lt. NCTE. English literature, 1660-1800; serious drama, 1660-1750. Add: Dept. of English, Indiana State University, Terre Haute, IN 47809.

REIGSTAD, PAUL MATTHEW, b. Minneapolis, Minn, Nov. 12, 21; m. 50; c. 2. ENGLISH & AMERICAN LITERATURE. B.A, St. Olaf Col, 43; M.A, Univ. N.Mex, 56, Ph.D.(Eng), 58. Instr. ENG, Pub. Schs, E.Grand Forks, Minn, 49-51; Fergus Falls, Minn, 51-54; asst. prof, PAC. LUTHERAN COL, 58-62, assoc. prof, 62-66, PROF, 66- Am-Scand. Found. fel, 65-66; Am. Philos. Soc. grant, 66. MLA; NCTE. Short story; Shakespeare; American pioneer novel. Publ: Rölvaag: his life and art, Univ. Nebr, 72. Add: Dept. of English, Pacific Lutheran University, Tacoma, WA 98447.

REILE, LOUIS, S.M, b. San Antonio, Tex, June 13, 25. ENGLISH, CINEMA. B.A, St. Mary's Univ, 49; Univ. Fribourg, 57-61; M.A, Johns Hopkins Univ, 65. Teacher Eng, Provencher Col, Man, 53-56; St. Mary's Sec, St. Louis, 56-57; ASSOC. PROF. ENG. & CINEMA, ST. MARY'S UNIV.(TEX), 65- Marianist Writers Guild. Cinema; fiction & poetry; journalism. Publ: Battle and Brother Louis, Newman, 59, 61; Pater Wilhelm Chaminade (German), Bergazi, Switz, 62; Running giant, Maryhurst, 67; Films in focus, Abbey, 70; Soundtrack, weekly cinema column in Alamo Messenger, 9/66; Cinescene, monthly column, Parent-Educator, Mag, 70-72; Give beauty back, S.A. Light, 5/72; plus others. Add: 2700 Cincinnati Ave, San Antonio, TX 78284.

REILLY, BARTHOLOMEW MICHAEL, b. Baltimore, Md, Aug. 12, 09; m. 51; c. 5. ENGLISH, THEOLOGY. A.B, Cath. Univ. Am, 31, M.A, 32, S.T.L, 45, S.T.D.(theol), 49; Stanford Univ, 41. Instr. classics, St. Joseph's Col. (Calif), 36-39; Eng, St. Patrick's Col.(Calif), 39-44; theol, St. Edward's Col.(Wash), 48-51; gen. mgr, Doc Newton, Inc, 51-57; chmn. dept. lang, Camp Lejeune Fed. Sch, 57-62; from assoc. prof. to PROF. ENG, E.CAROLINA UNIV, 62- Mediaeval Acad. Am. Arthurian romance; Shakespeare; Puritanism and literature. Publ: The Elizabethan Puritan's conception of the nature and destiny of man, Cath. Univ, 48. Add: Dept. of English, East Carolina University, Greenville, NC 27834.

REILLY, JOHN EDWARD, b. New Rochelle, N.Y, Mar. 5, 28; m. 55; c. 3. ENGLISH & AMERICAN LITERATURE. B.A, N.Y. Univ, 51; M.A, Rutgers Univ, 54; Ph.D.(Eng), Univ. Va, 65. Instr. Eng, Duquesne Univ, 57-62, asst. prof, 63-66, assoc. prof, 66-68; AM. LIT, COL. OF THE HOLY CROSS, 68-74, PROF, 74- U.S.A, 46-48. MLA; Poe Stud. Asn.(secy. & co-ed, Newslett, 73-). Edgar Allan Poe; nineteenth century American literature. Publ: The lesser death-watch and The tell-tale heart, Am. Transcendental Quart, 69; Ermina's gales: the poems Jane Locke devoted to Poe, In: Papers on Poe: essays in honor of John Ward Ostrom, 72; Poe in pillory, Poe Stud, 73; plus one other. Add: Dept. of English, College of the Holy Cross, Worcester, MA 01610.

REILLY, JOHN MARSDEN, b. Pittsburgh, Pa, Feb. 18, 33; m. 52; c. 3. AMERICAN & AFRO-AMERICAN LITERATURE. B.A, W.Va. Univ, 54; Woodrow Wilson fel, 54-55; M.A, Wash. Univ, 63, Danforth grant, 66-67, Ph.D.(Eng), 67. Instr. ENG, Wash. Univ, 60-61; asst. prof, Univ. P.R, 61-63; STATE UNIV. N.Y. ALBANY, 63-70, ASSOC. PROF, 70- Vis. asst. prof, Univ. Ore, 70; Nat. Endowment for Humanities fel, 70-71. MLA; NCTE; Col. Lang. Asn. Afro-American literature; popular culture; radical literature. Publ: Ed, Twentieth century interpretations of The invisible man, Prentice-Hall, 70; auth, Richard Wright: an essay in bibliography, Res. Am. Lit. Stud, 71; The dilemma in Chesnutt's The marrow of tradition, Phylon, 71; Two novels of working class consciousness, Midwest Quart, 73. Add: Dept. of English, State University of New York at Albany, 1400 Washington Ave, Albany, NY 12222.

REILLY, ROBERT JAMES, b. Detroit, Mich, Aug. 25, 25; m. 52; c. 2. ENGLISH. B.Ph, Univ. Detroit, 49, M.A, 51; Ph.D.(Eng), Mich. State Univ, 60. Instr. ENG, Univ. Detroit, 52-54; Mich. State Univ, 55-56; East. Mich. Univ, 56-57; UNIV. DETROIT, 57-58, asst. prof, 58-62, assoc. prof, 62-67, PROF, 68- Norman Foerster Award, 67. Eng.C, U.S.A, 43-46. MLA. American literature; religion, philosophy, and literature. Publ: Romantic religion: a study of Barfield, Lewis, Williams and Tolkien, Univ. Ga, 71; auth, Tolkien and the fairy story, spring 63 & God, man and literature, winter 67, Thought; Henry James and the morality of fiction, Am. Lit, 3/67. Add: Dept. of English, University of Detroit, College Park Station, Detroit, MI 48221.

REIMAN, DONALD HENRY, b. Erie, Pa, May 17, 34; m. 58; c. 1. ENGLISH LITERATURE. A.B, Col. Wooster, 56; fel, Univ. Ill, 56-58, 59, M.A, 57, Ph.D. (Eng), 60. Instr. Eng, Duke Univ, 60-62, asst. prof, 62-64; assoc. prof, Univ. Wis-Milwaukee, 64-65; ED, SHELLEY AND HIS CIRCLE, CARL H. PFORZHEIMER LIBR, 65- Spec. fel, Univ. Ill, 60, vis. lectr, summer 63; Am. Counc. Learned Soc. res. grant-in-aid, 61-62, stud. fel, 63-64; assoc. fel, Ctr. Advan. Stud. Wesleyan Univ, 63-64; adj. prof, Grad. Sch, City Univ. New York, 67-68; Grad. Col, Columbia Univ, 68-70, sr. res. assoc, univ, 70- Keats-Shelley Asn. Am.(mem. ed. bd, 68-73, treas, 73-); Eng. Inst; Grolier Club; Byron Soc.(mem. Am. comt, 73-); MLA (mem. ed. comt, 69-70); Mod. Humanities Res. Asn, Gt. Brit. P.B. Shelley's poetry and prose; romantic movement in England; theory of literature. Publ: Shelley's The triumph of life: a critical study, Univ. Ill, 65; Percy Bysshe Shelley, Twayne, 69; ed, The romantics reviewed (9 vols), Garland, 72; co-auth, The English romantic poets: a review of research, MLA, 72 & Editing texts of the romantic period, Hakkert, Toronto, 72; ed, Shelley and his circle, Harvard Univ, Vols V & VI, 73; auth, Appearance, reality, and moral order in Richard II, Mod. Lang. Quart, 3/64; Thematic unity in Lamb's familiar essays, J. Eng. & Ger. Philol, 7/65; Keats and the humanistic paradox, Stud. Eng. Lit, 71. Add: Carl H. Pforzheimer Library, Room 815, 41 E. 42nd St, New York, NY 10017.

REIMONDO, MARY SYLVIA, S.S.J, b. Buffalo, N.Y, May 9, 94. ENGLISH, DRAMA. B.S, Canisius Col, 29, M.A, 30; Ph.D.(Eng), Niagara Univ, 36. Head dept. Eng, Mt. St. Joseph Acad, 22-33; St. Mary's Acad, 33-35; Mt. St. Joseph Teachers Col, 36-65; Victory Acad, 65-70; PROF. CHILD PSYCHOL, GEN. PSYCHOL. & MED. ETHICS, SCH. OF NURSING, OUR LADY OF VICTORY INFANT HOME, 70- N.Y. State Eng. Counc. fel. award, 62; mem. adv. bd, Scholastic Mag, 67-; lectr. child & gen. psychol, prof. groups & parents. NCTE; Int. Reading Asn; Col. Reading Asn. Drama and the theater from the Greeks to contemporary theatre; English literature, from Anglo-Saxon to contemporary English authors. Publ: English arts and skills (4 vols), Macmillan, 63-, rev. ed, 65; Study guide Romeo and Juliet, Dell, 67; The paperback goes to college, Mass Media, 65; Should I—or should I not join teachers' associations?, N.Y.C. Teachers Asn. Rev, 65; The white plume, Sch. Paperback J, 67. Add: 790 Ridge Rd, Lackawanna, NY 14218.

REIN, IRVING JACOB, b. Chicago, Ill, Sept. 16, 37; m. 61; c. 2. SPEECH. B.A, Univ. Minn, 59, B.S, 60; M.A, Ariz. State Univ, 63; Ph.D.(rhetoric), Univ. Pittsburgh, 66. Instr. high sch, 60-62; lectr. pub. speaking, Harvard, 65-66, instr, 66-69; ASSOC. PROF. COMMUN. STUD, NORTHWEST. UNIV, 69- Participant, Nat. Conf. Develop. of Rhetoric, 70. Speech Commun. Asn. Consumer and cultural communication; persuasion. Publ: The relevant rhetoric, Free Press, 69; Rudy's red wagon: communication strategies in contemporary society, Scott, 72; The New England transcendentalists: philosophy and rhetoric, Philos. & Rhetoric, spring 68; Rhetoric and the arts: strategies of learning, Speech Teacher, fall 72. Add: 1822 Sheridan Rd, Evanston, IL 60202.

REINECKE, GEORGE F, b. New Orleans, La, Oct. 10, 24; m. 57; c. 6. ENGLISH LITERATURE. A.B, Loyola Univ.(La), 43; Sorbonne, 45; M.A, Tulane Univ, 51; Ph.D, Harvard, 60. Instr. ENG, Loyola Univ.(La), 48-54, asst. prof, 54-58; instr, UNIV. NEW ORLEANS, 58-61, asst. prof, 61-63, assoc. prof, 63-67, PROF, 67-, CHMN. DEPT, 72-, coord. Grad. Eng. Prog, 65-72. Vis. assoc. prof, Univ. Ore, 64-65; ed, La. Folklore Miscellany, 65-; assoc. ed, S.Cent. Mod. Lang. Asn. Bull, 73- U.S.A.A.F, 43-46. MLA; S.Cent. Mod. Lang. Asn.(pres, 69-70); Mod. Humanities Res. Asn; Mediaeval Acad. Am; Int. Arthurian Soc. Mediaeval English literature; Renaissance literature; American regional dialect and folklore. Add: Dept. of English, University of New Orleans, New Orleans, LA 70122.

REINER, KAROL STURM, b. New York, N.Y, Feb. 1, 31. SPEECH, ENGLISH AS A SECOND LANGUAGE. B.A, Brooklyn Col, 52; M.A, 56; Ph.D. (speech & ling), N.Y. Univ, 60. Speech therapist, Waterford Schs, 54-55; fel. speech, Brooklyn Col, 55-56, lectr, 56-60; prof. Eng. as second lang, Italo-Am. Associasione, Rome, 60-61; instr, N.Y. Univ, 61-62; asst. prof. SPEECH, C.W. POST COL, L.I. UNIV, 62-67, ASSOC. PROF, 67- Speech Commun. Asn; Am. Speech & Hearing Asn. Speech pathology; English as a second language. Add: Dept. of Speech, C.W. Post College, Long Island University, Greenvale, NY 11548.

REINERT, OTTO, b. Moss, Norway, Nov. 27, 23; m. 50; c. 5. ENGLISH. B.A, Lafayette Col, 47; M.A, Yale, 48, Ph.D.(Eng), 52; fel, Univ. Oslo, 51-52. Asst. Eng, N.Y. Univ, 49-50; instr, Wheaton Col.(Mass), 52-56; Univ. Wash, 56-58, asst. prof, 58-61; lectr, Univ. Oslo, 61-64; asst. prof, UNIV. WASH, 64-65, assoc. prof, 65-72, PROF. ENG. & COMP. LIT, 72- MLA; NCTE. Restoration and 18th century English literature; modern drama; Ibsen. Publ: Ed, Drama, 61, alternate ed, 64 & Modern drama, 62, alternate ed, 66 & Classic through modern drama, 70, Little; ed, Strindberg: a collection of critical essays, Prentice-Hall, 71; auth, Passion and pity in All for love, In: The hidden sense, Norway Univ, 63; Bartleby the inscrutable, In: Americana Norvegica, Univ. Pa, 66. Add: Dept. of English, University of Washington, Seattle, WA 98195.

REINITZ, NEALE ROBERT, b. New York, N.Y, Sept. 16, 23; m. 48; c. 1. ENGLISH. B.A, Univ. Wis, 47; M.A, Harvard, 49; Ph.D, Univ. Calif, Berkeley, 58. Instr. ENG, COLO. COL, 53-57, asst. prof, 57-60, assoc. prof, 60-66, PROF, 66- Fulbright lectr, Univ. Col, Jyväskylä, Finland, 60-61. U.S.A.A.F, 43-45, Sgt. MLA. The French revolution in the newspaper, verse and caricatures of the 1790's; the father and son theme in literature. Add: Dept. of English, Colorado College, Colorado Springs, CO 80903.

REIS, RICHARD H, b. Arlington, Mass, Sept. 21, 30; m. 56; c. 2. ENGLISH. A.B, St. Lawrence Univ, 52; A.M, Brown Univ, 57, Ph.D.(Eng), 62. Instr. ENG, Brown Univ, 59-61; Wash. Col, 61-62, asst. prof, 62-65; SOUTHEAST. MASS. UNIV, 65-68, assoc. prof, 68-73, PROF, 73- Vis. assoc. prof, Univ. Ky, summer 65; proj. dir. & consult, Upward Bound Prog, Off. Econ. Opportunity, 66-68. MLA. Modern novel; Romantic poets; linguistics and modern grammar. Publ: George MacDonald, Twayne, 73. Add: 429 Front St, Marion, MA 02738.

REISS, EDMUND, b. Brooklyn, N.Y, Oct. 12, 34; m. 55, 64; c. 2. ENGLISH & COMPARATIVE LITERATURE. A.B, Pa. State Univ, 55, M.A, 56; Dexter traveling fel, Harvard, 59, Ph.D, 60. Instr. Eng, Suffolk Univ, 57-60; asst. prof, West. Reserve Univ, 60-63, assoc. prof. Eng. & comp. lit, 63-64; ENG, Pa. State Univ, 64-67; PROF, DUKE UNIV, 67- Am. Philos. Soc. fel, 62; Am. Counc. Learned Soc. grant, 63, stud. fel, 66-67; Huntington Libr. fel, 65; contrib. ed, medieval rhet. sect, Biog. Dictionary Speech, 65-68; Pa. State Univ. Humanities Inst. fel, 66; co-ed, Chaucer Rev, 66-70; Duke Endowment grants, 68-69 & 70-71; vis. prof, Harvard, summers 69, 70 & 73; Am. Philos. Soc. grant, 70; assoc. ed, J. Medieval & Renaissance Stud, 70-; vis. prof, Columbia Univ, summer 73; Mem. ed. bd, Stud. Medieval Cult, 73 & Stud. Iconography, 73- MLA (bibliogr. & medieval Latin sect. head, Int. Bibliog, 66-); Int. Asn. Univ. Prof. Eng; Dante Soc. Am; Mediaeval Acad. Am; Int. Arthurian Soc; Early Eng. Text Soc. Medieval English and comparative literature; Arthurian literature; American literature. Publ: Mark Twain's Mysterious stranger and other stories, 62 & Mark Twain's A Connecticut Yankee in King Arthur's court, 63, New Am. Libr; Sir Thomas Malory, Twayne, 66; Elements of literary analysis, World, 67; The art of the Middle English lyric: essays in criticism, Univ. Ga, 72; Arthurian legend and romance: a select bibliography, Univ. Toronto, 74; Number symbolism and medieval literature, Medievalia et Humanistica, 70; The birth of the grail quest, In: Innovation in medieval literature, Univ. Pittsburgh, 71; Chaucer's Parodies of love, In: Chaucer the love poet, Univ. Ga, 73; plus several others. Add: Dept. of English, Duke University, Durham, NC 27706.

REITEN, PAULA, O.S.B, b. Grand Forks, N.Dak, Oct. 26, 24. ENGLISH & AMERICAN LITERATURE. B.A, Col. St. Benedict, 48; M.A, Univ. Minn, 57; summers, Marquette Univ. & Univ. Notre Dame; Ed. D.(Eng), Columbia Univ, 70. Teacher Eng, Cathedral High Sch, St. Cloud, Minn, 50-51, 57-58; from instr. to PROF. ENG. & AM. LIT, COL. ST. BENEDICT, 48-50, 58-, CHMN. DEPT. ENG, 61-68, 72-, registr, 51-56. NCTE; Col. Eng. Asn. Add: Dept. of English, College of St. Benedict, St. Joseph, MN 56374.

REITER, SEYMOUR, b. New York, N.Y, Nov. 29, 21; m. 49. ENGLISH LITERATURE, CREATIVE WRITING. A.B, Brooklyn Col, 43; M.A, N.Y. Univ, 47, Ph.D.(Eng), 54. Instr. Eng. & sci, Grace Church Sch, 44-46; Eng, Yale, 46-47; Athens Col, Greece, 47-48; ed, Am. Bk. Co, 49-51; instr. ENG, N.Y. Univ, 52-56; PROF, BROOKLYN COL, 56- MLA; Mod. Humanities Res. Asn. Drama; Romanticism. Publ: Co-auth, College writing and reading, Holt, 59, reprinted as A practical guide to rhetoric, Weybright & Talley, 69; Introduction to imaginative literature, Crowell, 60; auth, A study of Shelley's poetry, Univ. N.Mex, 67; World theatre, Horizon, 73. Add: Dept. of English, Brooklyn College, Brooklyn, NY 11210.

REMBERT, JAMES ALDRICH WYMAN, b. Columbia, S.C, May 22, 39; m. 63; c. 1. ENGLISH. B.A, The Citadel, 61; M.A, Univ. S.C, 64; Ph.D. (Eng), Univ. N.C, Chapel Hill, 69; M.Litt, Cambridge, 74. ASST. PROF. ENG, THE CITADEL, 68- Res. grants from The Citadel, Cambridge, 69-71 & 72-73. U.S.A, 63-65, Res, 66-68, Capt. MLA; S.Atlantic Mod. Lang. Asn. Eighteenth century English literature. Add: Dept. of English, The Citadel, Charleston, SC 29409.

REMLEY, DAVID A, b. Glendale, Calif, Aug. 30, 31; m. 63. ENGLISH, AMERICAN LITERATURE. A.B, Wabash Col, 53; A.M.T, Harvard, 54; Ph.D.(Am. lit. & hist), Ind. Univ, 67. Asst. prof. AM. LIT. & STUD, UNIV. N.MEX, 67-73, ASSOC. PROF, 73- U.S.A, 54-56. Am. Stud. Asn. Twentieth century American literature; Colonial and Federal American literature; history and literature of the American Southwest. Publ: Erna Fergusson, Steck, 68; William James: the meaning and function of art, Midcontinent Am. Stud. J, fall 63. Add: Dept. of English, University of New Mexico, Albuquerque, NM 87106.

REMLY, LYNN LOUISE, b. Minneapolis, Minn, Feb. 9, 43. ENGLISH, PHILOLOGY. B.A, Univ. Minn, 63, M.A, 67, Ph.D.(Eng), 68; Berlin fel, Free Univ. Berlin, 65-66. ASST. PROF. ENG, Augsburg Col, 68-70; KENT STATE UNIV, 70- MLA; Am. Inst. Archaeol. Medieval literature, principally English and German; history of religion; comparative religion and literature. Publ: Deus Caritas: the Christian meaning of the Secunda Pastorum, Neuphilol. Mitt, 71; Sacred poetry: the Anglo-Saxon gnomes, Folklore, 71; Salome in England: Vercelli Homily X, 165-174, Vetera Christianorum, 73. Add: Dept. of English, Kent State University, Kent, OH 44242.

RENDER, SYLVIA LYONS, b. Atlanta, Ga, June 8, 13; m. 35; c. 1. ENGLISH. B.S, Tenn. State Univ, 34; Univ. Chicago; M.A, Ohio State Univ, 52; Univ. Wis; Peabody scholar, George Peabody Col, 60-61, South. Educ. Found. fel, 61-62, Ph.D.(Eng), 62. Instr. ENG, Fla. Agr. & Mech. Univ, 52-56, asst. prof, 56-60, assoc. prof, 60-62, PROF, 62-64; N.C. CENT. UNIV, 64-, res. comt. writing grant, 64-65. Mary M. Sullivan Award, George Peabody Col, 60; Am. Philos. Soc. res. grant, 64; Coop. Prog. Humanities fel, Duke Univ, 67-68; consult, Ford Found. Div. Educ. & Res, 69-72; guest prof, George Peabody Col, summer 70; consult, Macmillan Co, 71; N.C. State Dept. Educ, 71; Ford Found. grant, 71; N.C. Cent. Univ. Fac. Res. Comt. grant, summer 72; consult, Durham County Bd. Educ, 73; manuscript historian, Libr. Congress, 73-75. MLA; Soc. Stud. South. Lit; Col. Lang. Asn; NCTE (mem. minorities lit. comt, 71-73); S.Atlantic Mod. Lang. Asn. American prose fiction; folklore; Afro-American literature and culture. Publ: Ed, Short fiction of Charles W. Chesnutt, Howard Univ, 73; Tar-heelia in Chesnutt, Col. Lang. Asn. J, 9/65; Charles W. Chesnutt, In: Encycl. Britannica, 69; plus others. Add: Manuscript Div, Library of Congress, Washington, DC 20540.

RENFROW, JACK N, b. Jena, La, Feb. 21, 31. RENAISSANCE ENGLISH. B.A, La. Polytech. Inst, 52, M.A, Univ. Denver, 53; Ph.D.(Eng), La. State Univ, 60. ASSOC. PROF. ENG, LAMAR UNIV, 59- U.S.A, 53-55. MLA; Shakespeare Asn. Am; Renaissance Soc. Am. Elizabethan drama, particularly Shakespeare; psychological studies of Shakesspeare. Publ: Hamlet and the psychologist, Shakespeare Newsletter, 4/63. Add: Dept. of English, Lamar University, Beaumont, TX 77705.

RENNER, DICK ARNOLD, b. La Crosse, Wis, Sept. 1, 29; m. 52; c. 2. ENGLISH LITERATURE. B.S, Univ. Wis, 51, M.A, 52; Ph.D.(Eng), Univ. Mo, 62. Asst. prof. ENG, Ariz. State Univ, 62-63; from asst. prof. to assoc. prof, Univ. Mo-Columbia, 63-69, dir. honors col, 66-69; PROF. ENG. & CHMN. DEPT, BALL STATE UNIV, 69- U.S.A, 52-54, Sgt. MLA. Seventeenth century English drama; modern drama. Add: Dept. of English, Ball State University, Muncie, IN 47306.

RENO, RAYMOND H, b. Detroit, Mich, Jan. 22, 24; m. 49; c. 5. ENGLISH. B.A, George Washington Univ, 50, M.A, 52, Ph.D, 58. Teaching fel, George Washington Univ, 50-51, instr. ENG, 51-56; assoc. prof, GEORGETOWN UNIV, 56-71, PROF, 71- U.S.A.A.F, 42-45, S/Sgt. Southeast. Renaissance Conf. Publ: The impact teacher, 3M Educ. Press, 67; Hamlet's quintessence of dust, Shakespeare Quart, spring 61; Hotspur: the integration of character and theme, Renaissance Papers, 62; plus others. Add: Dept. of English, Georgetown University, Washington, DC 20007.

RENOIR, ALAIN, b. France, Oct. 31, 21; U.S. citizen; m. 48; c. 2. ENGLISH, COMPARATIVE LITERATURE. A.B, Univ. Calif, Santa Barbara, 49; M.A, Harvard, 51, fel, 51-52, Ph.D.(comp. lit), 55. Instr. Eng, Ohio Univ, 52-53; Williams Col.(Mass), 53-55; asst. prof, UNIV. CALIF, BERKELEY, 55-61, assoc. prof, 61-66, PROF. ENG. & COMP. LIT, 66- Vis. lectr, Univ. Wash, summer 63; vis. prof. Eng. & mem. Humanities Inst, Univ. Wis, 63-64; NDEA Title IV consult, 64-65. Fr. Army, 39-40; U.S.A, 41-45. MLA; NCTE; Am. Comp. Lit. Asn.(secy, 64-67); Int. Comp. Lit. Asn.(secy, 64-67); Mediaeval Acad. Am; Mediaeval Asn. Pac. Medieval literature; literary criticism; comparative literature. Publ: The poetry of John Lydgate, Harvard, 67; Roland's lament: its meaning and function in the Chanson de Roland, Speculum, 60; The heroic oath in Beowulf, The Chanson de Roland and the Nibelungenlied, In: Studies in Old English literature in honor of Arthur G. Brodeur, Univ. Ore, 63; Wulf and Eadwacor: a noninterpretation, In: Franciplegius, N.Y. Univ, 65; plus others. Add: Dept. of Comparative Literature, University of California, Berkeley, CA 94720.

RENSHAW, EDYTH MAY, b. Okla, Nov. 10, 01. SPEECH, THEATER. B.A, South. Methodist Univ, 23, M.A, 28; N.Y. Univ, 27; State Univ. Iowa, 35; Carnegie grant & Ph.D.(speech educ), Columbia Univ, 50. Instr. speech, SOUTH. METHODIST UNIV, 24-28, asst. prof. speech & theater, 28-50, assoc. prof, 50-57, prof, 57-67, EMER. PROF. SPEECH, 67- Vis. prof. speech, Univ. Wash, 67-68; judge, George Freedley Bk. Award Comt, 69-73; vis. prof. speech & theater, S.Dak. State Univ, 71-72. Speech Commun. Asn; Theatre Libr. Asn. History of speech education; history of theater; children's theater. Publ: Co-auth, Workbook in fundamentals of speech; Lenora Corona: her life and art, Times Herald; Five private schools of speech, Hist. Speech Educ. in Am. Add: 3317 Rankin St, Dallas, TX 75205.

RENSKY, MIROSLAV, English, Linguistics. See Volume III, Foreign Languages, Linguistics & Philology.

REPLOGLE, JUSTIN M, b. Chicago, Ill, Sept. 18, 29; m. 51; c. 2. ENGLISH. B.A, Univ. Chicago, 48; B.S, Univ. Wis, 51, M.S, 52, Ph.D, 56. From instr. to PROF. ENG, UNIV. WIS-MILWAUKEE, 56- MLA. Recent literature; poetry. Publ: Auden's poetry, Univ, Wash, 68; Auden's homage to Thalia, Bucknell Rev, 63; Auden's Marxism, PMLA, 65; Auden's religious leap, Wis. Stud. Contemporary Lit, 65. Add: Dept. of English, University of Wisconsin, Milwaukee, WI 53211.

REPPERT, JAMES DONALD, b. Allentown, Pa, Mar. 7, 24; m. 52; c. 6. ENGLISH. A.B, Muhlenberg Col, 48; Univ. Wis, 48-49; M.A, Harvard, 49, Ph.D.(Eng), 53. Asst. ENG, Harvard, 49-53; instr, ALBRIGHT COL, 53-56, asst. prof, 56-59, assoc. prof, 60-63, PROF, 63-, CHMN. DEPT, 67- C.Eng, U.S.A, 43-46, S/Sgt. MLA; Col. Eng. Asn.(v.pres, 67-68, pres, 68-70); Am. Folklore Soc; Early Eng. Text Soc. English and Scottish traditional ballads; Chaucer. Publ: Wm. McMath and F.J. Child, PMLA, 6/56; F.J. Child and the ballad, Harvard Festschrift for J.B. Whiting, 73-74. Add: Dept. of English, Albright College, Reading, PA 19604.

RESNICK, NATHAN, b. Brooklyn, N.Y, June 13, 10; m. 43. ART, AMERICAN LITERATURE. B.S, L.I. Univ, 33; Art Stud. Lea, 33-45; B.S, Columbia Univ, 37; M.A, N.Y. Univ, 45. Instr. Eng, L.I. UNIV, 38-48, assoc. prof, 48-52, ART, 52-55, PROF, 55-, CHMN. DEPT, 61- Librn, L.I. Univ, 39-48, dir. libr, 48-, founder, Walt Whitman Colloquium, 64-, dir. planning, Brooklyn Ctr. Campus, 65-67; pres, Walt Whitman Birthplace Asn, 58-; consult, Photography in the Fine Arts, 66-; mem. int. adv. comt, Fund. Concerned Photography, 67-; trustee, Int. Cult. Ctr. Youth, Inc, 72- AAAS; Am. Libr. Asn; Col. Art Asn. Am. Modern art; Walt Whitman; photography. Publ: Walt Whitman and the authorship of the good gray poet & ed, Life, land and water in ancient Peru, 65, L.I. Univ; ed, Songbirds of America in color, sound and story, Cornell; co-auth, The third eye, Walker. Add: 72 Barrow St, New York, NY 10014.

RESNICK, ROBERT B, b. New York, N.Y, May 26, 22; m. 55; c. 2. ENGLISH LITERATURE & CRITICISM. A.B, Clark Univ, 47; M.A, Boston Univ, 48; Ph.D, N.Y. Univ, 61. Instr. ENG, Northeast. Univ, 53-54; SPRINGFIELD COL, 54-57, asst. prof, 57-62, assoc. prof, 62-68, PROF, 68-, chmn. dept, 63-67. Lectr, West. New Eng. Col, 56- N.Y. Univ. Founder's Day award, 61. U.S.A, 43-45. Col. Eng. Asn; MLA; NCTE. Seventeenth century English wit. Publ: Thomas Fuller, doctor of the sugar-coated pill, Loc Haven Rev, 64; Thomas Fuller's pulpit wit, Xavier Univ. Stud, 5/65; The function of Thomas Fuller's wit, Col. Lang. Asn. J, 12/67; plus others. Add: 94 Tiffany St, Springfield, MA 01108.

RESTAINO, KATHERINE MARIE, b. Brooklyn, N.Y, Nov. 14, 37; m. 65. ENGLISH. B.A, Good Counsel Col, 60; fels, Fordham Univ, 60-63, M.A, 62, Ph.D.(Eng), 66. Instr. Eng, Mercy Col.(N.Y), 63-66, asst. prof, 66-68, assoc. prof, 68-70, dir. honors prog, 67-70; ASSOC. PROF. ENG, COL.

WHITE PLAINS, 70-, PRES, 73-, acad. dean, 71-73, acting pres, 72-73. MLA; Am. Comp. Lit. Asn. English and Continental Renaissance literature; 18th century English literature; classical influence on English literature. Add: 989 Wilson Ave, Teaneck, NJ 07666.

REUBEN, ELAINE, Omaha, Nebr, June 26, 41; m. 73. ENGLISH & AMERICAN LITERATURE. B.A, Brandeis Univ, 63; M.A, Stanford Univ, 66, Ph.D. (Eng, drama), 70. Instr. Eng, Univ. Wis-Madison, 68-69, asst. prof, 69-73. MLA (chairwoman, Comn. Status of Women in the Prof, 73-74); Midwest Mod. Lang. Asn; NCTE; Pop. Cult. Asn. Dramatic literature; contemporary literature; feminist criticism and women's studies. Publ: Co-auth, Academic women, sex discrimination and the law, MLA Comn. Status of Women, 72; auth, Can a young girl from a small mining town find happiness writing criticism for the NYRB, 10/72 & Socialization in Mrs. Dalloway—a comment, 11/72, Col. Eng; Feminist criticism in the classroom, Substance, winter 72. Add: Apt. 3, 1530 Simpson St, Madison, WI 53713.

REUBEN, PAUL PURUSHOTTAM, b. Patna, India, July 2, 41; m. 68; c. 2. ENGLISH & AMERICAN LITERATURE. B.A, Patna Univ, 61, M.A, 63; Fulbright scholar, Bowling Green State Univ, 66-67, Ph.D.(Eng), 70. Lectr. ENG, Col. Commerce, Patna, India, 63-65; Patna Univ, 65-66; teaching fel, Bowling Green State Univ, 66-68 & 69-70; asst. prof, Defiance Col, 68-69; instr, Bowling Green State Univ, 70-71; ASSOC. PROF, CALIF. STATE COL, STANISLAUS, 70- Fulbright scholar & Smith-Mundt vis. scholar, U.S. Dept. State, 66-67; exec. comt. mem, Regional Counc. Int. Educ, 68-69. AAUP; MLA; Am. Stud. Asn; Thoreau Soc; Nat. Asn. For. Stud. Affairs. New England transcendentalism; new thought movement; late 19th century American literature. Publ: Thoreau in B.O. Flowers Arena, Thoreau Soc. Bull, fall 71; Walt Whitman in B.O. Flower's Arena, Walt Whitman Rev, 3/73. Add: Dept. of English, California State College, Stanislaus, 800 Monte Vista Ave, Turlock, CA 95380.

REUSS, CAROL, S.P, b. Cleveland, Ohio, Dec. 3, 32. MASS COMMUNICATION, JOURNALISM. B.A, St. Mary-of-the-Woods Col, 54; M.A, Univ. Iowa, 68, Ph.D, 71. From asst. ed. to managing ed, Tooling & Production Mag, 54-60; dir. pub. relations, St. Mary-of-the-Woods Col, 60-61, instr. JOUR, 64-67, asst. prof. & admin. asst. to pres, 70-71; asst. prof, LOYOLA UNIV.(LA), 71-73, ASSOC. PROF, 73- Participant, Int. Sem. Mass Communications, Sali, Yugoslavia, 72. Asn. Educ. Jour.(v.chmn. mag. div, 72-73, chmn, 73-74); Int. Commun. Asn; Women in Commun. Magazine practices; organization communication; history of journalism. Publ: The Ladie's Home Journal and Hoover's food program, Jour. Quart, winter 72; A judge speaks out, IABC News, 1/73; From and to and, new is et cetera, Cath. Sch. Ed, 6/73; plus others. Add: Dept. of Journalism, Loyola University, 6363 St. Charles Ave, New Orleans, LA 70118.

REUTER, JOHN EDWARD, b. South Dartmouth, Mass, Mar. 23, 33; m. 54; c. 4. ENGLISH LITERATURE. B.A, Univ. N.H, 58; M.A, Univ. Rochester, 63, Ph.D.(Eng. lit), 68. Instr. ENG, Fairleigh Dickinson Univ, 62-63; State Univ. N.Y. Binghamton, 63-67; asst. prof, State Univ. N.Y. Col. Oswego, 67-69; ASSOC. PROF, UNIV. MAINE, PORTLAND-GORHAM, 69- State Univ. N.Y. fel. & grant, 68. U.S.A, 54-56. Renaissance, Shakespeare, Milton; Restoration drama; development of the novel. Add: Dept. of English, University of Maine, Portland-Gorham, Gorham, ME 04038.

REVARD, CARTER CURTIS, b. Pawhuska, Okla, Mar. 25, 31; m. 56; c. 4. ENGLISH LITERATURE & LINGUISTICS. B.A, Univ. Tulsa, 52; Rhodes scholar, Oxford, 52, M.A, 59; Ph.D, Yale, 59. Instr. Eng, Amherst Col, 56-59, asst. prof, 59-61; WASH. UNIV, 61-66, ASSOC. PROF. ENG. LIT. & LANG, 66-, summer res. grant, 64. Vis. ling. scientist, Mo. Acad. Sci, 65-67; consult, lexicography proj, Syst. Develop. Corp, Calif, 66-67, assoc. res. scientist, 67-68. MLA; Ling. Soc. Am; Asn. Comput. Ling. History of English language; computational linguistics; Middle English language and literature. Publ: My right hand don't leave me no more (poems), Eedin, 70; Affixal derivation, zero derivation and semantic transformations, 2/68 & Notes on the conversion of nouns into verbs in English, 2/68, Syst. Develop. Corp. Doc; How to make a New Utopian dictionary of English, Proc, N.Y. Acad. Sci, 73; plus others. Add: Dept. of English, Washington University, St, Louis, MO 63130.

REVARD, STELLA PURCE, b. Queens, N.Y, June 9, 33; m. 56; c. 4. ENGLISH. B.A, Hunter Col, 55; M.A, Yale, 57, Ph.D.(Eng), 61. Instr. ENG, Univ. Buffalo, 58-59; asst. prof, SOUTH. ILL. UNIV. EDWARDSVILLE, 61-67, assoc. prof, 67-73, PROF, 73- MLA; Renaissance Soc. Am. Milton; 17th century; Renaissance. Publ: The dramatic function of the son in Paradise lost: a commentary on Milton's trinitarianism, J. Eng. & Ger. Philol, 1/67; Eve and the doctrine of responsibility in Paradise lost, PMLA, 1/73; Satan's envy of the kingship of the Son of God, Mod. Philol, 2/73; plus others. Add: Dept. of English, Southern Illinois University, Edwardsville, IL 62025.

REVERAND, CEDRIC DWIGHT, II, b. Brooklyn, N.Y, Dec. 3, 41; m. 65. ENGLISH LANGUAGE & LITERATURE. B.A, Yale, 63; M.A, Columbia Univ, 64; Ph.D.(Eng), Cornell Univ, 72. Exec. ed, Scott Meredith Lit. Agency, Inc, 64-66; lectr. ENG, St. John's Univ.(N.Y), 66-67; instr, UNIV. WYO, 71-72, ASST. PROF, 72- MLA. Restoration and 18th century English literature; 17th century English literature; the novel. Publ: Patterns of imagery and metaphor in Dryden's The medall, Yearbk. Eng. Stud, 72. Add: Dept. of English, University of Wyoming, Box 3353 University Sta, Laramie, WY 82071.

REVUTSKY, VALERIAN, b. Irzhavets, Ukraine, June 14, 11; Can. citizen; m. 52; c. 1. SOVIET LITERATURE & DRAMA. B.Sc, Polytech. Inst. Kiev, 34; scholar. & dipl. Russian drama, Moscow Drama Inst, 41; scholar. & M.A, Univ. Toronto, 57. Teaching fel. Russian drama, Moscow Theatrical Soc, 40-41; lectr. hist. theatre, Kiev Musico-Dramatical Conserv, 41-43; asst. prof, Lviv Drama Sch, 43-44; teaching fel. Russian lit, Univ. Toronto, 55-56; instr. SOVIET LIT. & POETRY, HIST. SOVIET & RUSSIAN DRAMA, UNIV. B.C, 60-63, asst. prof, 63-66, ASSOC. PROF, 66- Univ. B.C. Comt, Res. res. grants. Soviet Army. Can. Asn. Slavists; Far West. Slavic Conf; Shevchenko Sci. Soc. History of Ukrainian drama; Soviet drama and poetry. Publ: The five great Ukrainian actors, UNF, Paris, 55; co-ed, Section on drama, In: Vol. II, Ukraine: a concise encyclopedia, Univ. Toronto, 71; auth, M. Kulish in the modern Ukrainian theatre, Slavonic & E.Europ. Rev, London, 71; A survey of the post-war Ukranian drama, Can. Slavic Papers, 72; plus others. Add: Dept. of Slavonic Studies, University of British Columbia, Vancouver 8, B.C, Can.

REWA, MICHAEL PETER, JR, b. Northampton, Mass, Jan. 16, 38; m. 60; c. 3. ENGLISH. B.A, Trinity Col.(Conn), 59; M.A, Univ. Del, 61; univ. fel, Stanford Univ, 61-63, Fulbright fel, 63-64, Ph.D.(Eng. & humanities), 67. Instr. ENG, Dartmouth Col, 64-67, ASST. PROF, 67-70; UNIV. DEL, 70- MLA; S.Atlantic Mod. Lang. Asn. English literature of the 18th century; biography; Arthurian literature. Publ: Aspects of rhetoric in Johnson's professedly serious Rambler essays, Quart. J. Speech, 70; Biography as an imitative art, In: English symposium papers, State Univ. N.Y. Col. Fredonia, Vol. I, 70; Cudgels and catcalls: the failure of satire in Boswell's London journal, Satire, 73. Add: Dept. of English, University of Delaware, Newark, DE 19711.

REYNOLDS, BEATRICE KAY, b. Peoria, Ill, Feb. 10, 37. SPEECH. B.A, Univ. Maine, Orono, 59; M.A, Ohio Univ, 62; Ph.D.(speech), Pa. State Univ, 68. Chmn. dept. speech & drama, Stearns High Sch, Millinocket, Maine, 60-61; instr. SPEECH, Univ. Conn, Hartford, 62-65; asst. & instr, Pa. State Univ, 65-68; ASST. PROF, Rider Col, 68-71; BROOKLYN COL, 71- Speech Commun. Asn; Speech Commun. Asn. East. States. French rhetoric of the 18th century; French revolutionary history. Publ: Ed. & transl, Spokesmen of the French Revolution: historic issues, 1790-1794, Exposition, 74; auth, Context of Girondist rhetoric, West. Speech, fall 71; An interview with Ti-Grace Atkinson: her speeches and her speechmaking, Today's Speech, fall 73; The rhetorical methods of Pierre Vergniaud, 1791-1793, South. Speech Commun. J, winter 73; plus others. Add: Dept. of Speech, 4430 Boylan Hall, Brooklyn College, Brooklyn, NY 11210.

REYNOLDS, E. C. THEATRE. B.A, Idaho State Col, 50; M.S, Univ. Wis, 52, Ph.D, 61. Instr. SPEECH, Ohio State Univ, 56-62; assoc. prof, Mich. State Univ, 62-71; PROF, UNIV. WYO, 71- U.S.N, 44-46. Am. Theatre Asn; Speech Commun. Asn; Am. Community Theatre Asn. Theatre production; theatrical management; medieval and Renaissance history. Add: Dept. of Communication & Theatre, University of Wyoming, Laramie, WY 82071.

REYNOLDS, ELIZABETH ROGERS, b. Florence, S.C, June 27, 19; m. 48. ENGLISH. B.A, Winthrop Col, 40; Univ. N.C, 41; M.A, Columbia Univ, 45; Ph.D.(Eng), Univ. S.C, 69. Instr. Eng, Winthrop Col, 45-46; Temple Univ, 46-50; asst. prof. hist, Coker Col, 53-62; instr. ENG, Univ. S.C, 62-65; asst. prof, Univ. South. Miss, 65-67; VA. COMMONWEALTH UNIV, 67-71, ASSOC. PROF, 71- Col. Eng. Asn; MLA; S.Atlantic Mod. Lang. Asn; Southeast. Renaissance Conf. Old English poetry. Publ: A fire mist—a planet, Nelson, 56. Add: Dept. of English, Virginia Commonwealth University, 901 W. Franklin St, Richmond, VA 23220.

REYNOLDS, JACK ADOLPHE, b. New Orleans, La, Oct. 1, 09; m. 46; c. 1. ENGLISH. B.A, La. State Univ, 33, M.A, 34, fel. & Ph.D.(Eng), 42. Instr, La. State Univ; Warren Easton Sch, New Orleans, La; tech. dir, Cuban N.Am. Cult. Inst, Havana; asst. prof. ENG. UNIV. MIAMI, 47-49, assoc. prof, 49-52, PROF, 52-, GRAD. FAC, 58- Spec. lectr, Univ. Havana, 46; lectr, arts prog, Asn. Am. Cols, 57. U.S.N.R, 42-46, Lt. Comdr. MLA; NCTE; S.Atlantic Mod. Lang. Asn. English and Germanic philology; Romance philology; medieval and early Renaissance literature. Publ: Heraldry and you: modern heraldic usage in America, Nelson, 61; co-ed. & contrib, A Chaucerian puzzle and other medieval essays, 61 & Sweet smoke of rhetoric: Renaissance studies, 63, Univ. Miami. Add: Dept. of English, University of Miami, Coral Gables, FL 33124.

REYNOLDS, JERRY DEE, b. Grand Saline, Tex, Jan. 14, 34; m. 62; c. 3. SPEECH COMMUNICATION. B.A, Hardin-Simmons Univ, 55; M.A, Baylor Univ, 62; Ph.D.(speech commun), Ohio State Univ, 66. Teacher speech & drama, Brazosport Independent Schs, Freeport, Tex, 58-61; asst. prof. SPEECH, Ouachita Baptist Univ, 62-64; assoc. prof, Houston Baptist Univ, 66-67, 68-72; asst. prof, Ohio State Univ, 67-68; PROF. & HEAD DEPT, HARDIN-SIMMONS UNIV, 72- Consult, Southwest. Bell Telephone, Houston, Tex, summer 70; reader, Allyn & Bacon Publ, N.Y, 73- U.S.A, 56-58. Speech Commun. Asn.(bibliog. reader interpretation div, 68-); South. Speech Commun. Asn; AAUP. Oral performance of literature. Publ: Ed, Newslett. Ohio High Sch. Speech League, 67-68; auth, Experimental studies in oral interpretation: the audience response symposium, West. Speech J, 69. Add: Dept. of Speech, Hardin-Simmons University, Abilene, TX 79601.

REYNOLDS, NYDIA JOAN, b. Sanford, Colo, Dec. 16, 20. SPEECH. B.A, Adams State Col, 44; B.A, W.Tex. State Col, 45; M.A, Univ. Wash, 47; Ph.D. (speech), Univ. South. Calif, 60. Instr. SPEECH, Kansas State Univ, 47-52; Portland State Col, 54-57; assoc. prof, Dickinson State Col, 59-62, prof, 62-63; assoc. prof, BEMIDJI STATE COL, 63-67, PROF, 67- Speech Commun. Asn. Am; Cent. States Speech Asn; West. Speech Commun. Asn. History of oral interpretation in America; circuit chautauqua. Publ: Let them interpret freely, N.Dak. Teacher, 9/60; A lively art, Today's Speech, 4/61; It wasn't elocution; five professional oral interpreters, Quart. J. Speech, 10/61. Add: 1421 Minnesota Ave, Bemidji, MN 56601.

REYNOLDS, OTA THOMAS, b. Atkins, Iowa, Dec. 23, 14; m. 43; c. 3. RHETORIC & PUBLIC ADDRESS. B.A, State Univ. Iowa, 34, M.A, 36, Ph.D, 41. Teacher speech & hist, High Sch, Ill, 34-36; instr. SPEECH, Univ. Akron, 39-40; from instr. to asst. prof, South. Ill. Univ, 41-42; from instr. to assoc. prof, HUNTER COL, 43-66, PROF, 66-, chmn. dept. speech & theatre, 59-65. Speech Commun. Asn; Speech Asn. East. States; Int. Commun. Asn; AAUP; Cent. States Speech Asn.(v.pres, 42-43). Publ: Co-auth, History & criticism of American public address, Vol. I, McGraw, 43 & American public address, Univ. Mo, 61; auth, Antislavery and disunion, 1858-1861, Harper, 63. Add: Dept. of Communications, Hunter College, 695 Park Ave, New York, NY 10021.

REYNOLDS, TERENCE J, O.F.M, b. Lawrence, Mass, Aug. 19, 12. ENGLISH LANGUAGE & LITERATURE. B.A, St. Bonaventure Univ, 36, M.A, 42; M.A, Harvard, 46, Ph.D, 56; Oxford, 51-52. Prof. Eng, Siena Col, 46-51, 52-55; ed, St. Anthony Guild Press & The Anthonian, 56-60; prof. Eng,

St. Bonaventure Univ, 61-71, dean sch. grad. stud, 62-71; prof. Eng. lit, Univ. Scranton, 71-73. Bibliog. Soc, Eng; Cambridge Bibliog. Soc; Bibliog. Soc. Univ. Va; MLA; Renaissance Soc. Am. Elizabethan recusant literature; bibliography. Publ: Two men and Christ, 59 & Like no other teacher, 61, St. Anthony. Add: St. Anthony Friary, 63 Bartholdi Ave, Butler, NJ 07405.

REYNOLDS, WILLIAM D, b. Leavenworth, Kans, Sept. 9, 44; m. 71. ENGLISH & AMERICAN LITERATURE & LANGUAGE. A.B, Xavier Univ, 66; M.A, Columbia Univ, 67; Ph.D.(Eng), Univ. Ill, Urbana, 71. ASST. PROF. ENG, HOPE COL, 71- MLA; Midwest Mod. Lang. Asn. Science fiction; medieval allegory. Add: Dept. of English, Hope College, Holland, MI 49423.

RHINE, ROBLEY D, b. Winfield, Kans, Dec. 30, 30; m. 58. COMMUNICATION. B.A, Southwest. Col.(Kans), 53; M.A, Univ. Colo, 57; fel, Univ. Wis, 63-64, Ph.D.(speech), 67. Instr. speech, Southwest. Col.(Kans), 56-58; UNIV. COLO, DENVER CTR, 58-61, asst. prof, 64-71, ASSOC. PROF. COMMUN. & THEATER & ASSOC. DEAN DIV. ARTS & HUMANITIES, 71- Speech Commun. Asn; Asn. Dept. & Adminr. Speech Commun.(pres, 72-73); West. Commun. Asn. Intercultural communications; American public address; rhetorical theory. Publ: Co-auth, Speechmaking: a handbook, Pruett, 65; auth, introd, Symposium: influence of John Dewey upon speech, West. Speech, spring 68; co-auth, A bibliography of rhetoric and public address for the year 1967, Speech Mongr, 8/68. Add: Div. of Arts & Humanities, University of Colorado, 1100 14th St, Denver, CO 80202.

RHOADS, FORREST NEIL, SR, b. Drakesboro, Ky, June 28, 27; m. 48; c. 2. SPEECH. B.A, David Lipscomb Col, 51; Univ. Evansville, 56; Mich. State Univ, 62-64; M.A, Cent. Mich. Univ, 63; Ph.D.(speech), South. Ill. Univ, Carbondale, 70. Asst. prof. SPEECH, David Lipscomb Col, 64-73; LECTR, VANDERBILT UNIV, 74- Minister, Churches of Christ, 48-; registered rep, Investors Diversified Serv, 74- U.S.A, 46-47. Speech Commun. Asn; South. Speech Commun. Asn.(chmn. speech educ. interest group, 73-74); Int. Commun. Asn. Public speaking; preaching; business communication. Publ: A study of the effectiveness of Marshall Keeble as a preacher, privately publ, 70; ed. spec. issue on Communicating the gospel, 20th Century Christian, 71; contrib, Recent homiletical thought, Abingdon, 67. Add: 1101 Morrow Ave, Nashville, TN 37204.

RHODE, ROBERT BARTLETT, b. Ranchester, Wyo, Oct. 24, 16; m. 46; c. 2. JOURNALISM. A.B, Univ, Wyo, 38; A.M, Univ. Denver, 52. ASST. PROF. JOUR, Univ. Denver, 48-53; Univ. South. Calif, 53-55; UNIV. COLO, BOULDER, 55- Fulbright lectr. & res. grant mass media, Australia, 61. U.S.A, 41-46. Asn. Educ. in Jour; Nat. Press Photographers Asn. Publ: Coauth, Press photography: reporting with a camera, 61 & Introduction to photography, 65, 2nd ed, 71, Macmillan; auth, Australian journalism, Colo. Quart, spring 66. Add: School of Journalism, University of Colorado, Boulder, CO 80302.

RHODE, ROBERT DAVID, b. Jourdanton, Tex, May 30, 11; m. 41; c. 2. AMERICAN LITERATURE. A.B, Univ. Tex, 33, A.M, 35, Ph.D, 40. Tutor ENG, Univ. Tex, 36-38; instr, Okla. Col. Women, 38-39; asst. prof, TEX. A&I UNIV, 40-43, PROF, 46-, chmn. dept, 46-51, dir. grad stud, 51-62, dean, 62-72, v.pres, 67-72. U.S.N, 43-46, Lt. Comdr. S.Cent. Mod. Lang. Asn. Poetry; short story; intellectual history. Publ: Setting in the American short story of local color, Mouton, The Hague, 74. Add: Texas A&I University, Kingsville, TX 78363.

RHODES, BYNO RYVERS, b. Macon Co, Tenn, Jan. 25, 20. ENGLISH LITERATURE. A.B, Vanderbilt Univ, 40, A.M, 41, Ph.D, 51. Prof. ENG. & head dept, Lincoln Mem. Univ, 49-58; PROF, EAST. KY. UNIV, 58- Dir, NDEA Inst. Eng, 67 & 68. S.Atlantic Mod. Lang. Asn; NCTE. Swift and Mandeville; Chaucer; Milton. Add: Dept. of English, Eastern Kentucky University, Richmond, KY 40475.

RHODES, CAROLYN HODGSON, b. Birmingham, Ala, May 16, 25; m. 47, 69; c. 2. AMERICAN LITERATURE. A.B, Univ. Ala, 45; M.A, Columbia Univ, 47; Haggin fels, Univ. Ky, 57-59 & 63-64, M.A, 59, Ph.D.(Eng), 65. Instr. ENG, orientation prog. for. students, Univ. Ky, 64; asst. prof, OLD DOM. UNIV, 65-68, ASSOC. PROF, 68- MLA; S.Atlantic Mod. Lang. Asn; Sci. Fiction Res. Asn; AAUP; World Future Soc. American novel and poetry; utopian literature; psychology in literature. Publ: Intelligence testing in utopia, Extrapolation, 12/71. Add: Dept. of English, Old Dominion University, Norfolk, VA 23508.

RHODES, DENNIS HARRISON, b. Sweetwater, Tex, Feb. 7, 31; m. 53; c. 2. PUBLIC ADDRESS, FORENSICS. B.A, Univ. Tex, Austin, 57; M.Ed, Univ. Houston, 61; Ph.D.(pub. address & forensics), South. Ill. Univ, 64. Dir. of forensics, Stephen F. Austin High Sch, Houston, Tex, 58-61; S.Tex. Col, 61-62; asst. debate coach, South. Ill. Univ, Carbondale, 62-64; prof. SPEECH & chmn. div, Ark. State Univ, 64-70; PROF, MO. SOUTH. STATE COL, 70- U.S.A, 50-53. Am. Forensic Asn; Speech Commun. Asn. Publ: 1928 Presidential campaign, Cimmarron Valley Hist. 72; Joe T. Robinson's 1936 campaign in Craighead County, Craighead Hist. Quart, 73; Early political career of Joe T. Robinson, Pulaski Co. Hist. Soc, (in press); plus others. Add: Rt. 1, Joplin, MO 64801.

RHODES, ERNEST LLOYD, b. Mammoth, W.Va, Apr. 17, 15; m. 39; c. 2. ENGLISH. A.B, W.Va. Univ, 36; M.A, Univ. N.C, 49; Ph.D.(Eng), Univ. Ky, 59. Asst. prof. dramatics, Univ. Mass, Ft. Devens, 46-49; asst. prof. Eng. & dramatics, Morehead State Col, 49-50; instr. Eng, Univ. Ky, 50-58, tech. dir, Guignol Theater, 50-57, dir. exp. theater, 57-58; assoc. prof. ENG, Florence State Col, 58-59, prof, 59-60; assoc. prof, OLD DOM. UNIV, 60-66, PROF, 66- U.S.N.R, 42-46, Lt. Comdr. MLA; Malone Soc; Shakespeare Asn. Am; Renaissance Soc. Am; S.Atlantic Mod. Lang. Asn; Southeast. Renaissance Conf. College theater production; Renaissance literature; Elizabethan stage. Add: Dept. of English, Old Dominion University, Hampton Blvd, Norfolk, VA 23508.

RHYNSBURGER, DONOVAN, b. Pella, Iowa, Apr. 15, 03; m. 31; c. 1. SPEECH, DRAMATICS. B.S, State Univ. Iowa, 25; Chicago Art Theater, 26; M.F.A, Yale, 38. Instr. Eng, UNIV. MO-COLUMBIA, 25-28, asst. prof, 28-39, assoc. prof. SPEECH & DRAMATIC ART, 39-45, dir. dramatics, 40-68, chmn. dept, 55-59, prof, 45-73, EMER. PROF, 73- Speech Commun. Asn; Am. Educ. Theatre Asn; Am. Nat. Theatre & Acad. Add: Dept. of Speech & Dramatic Art, University of Missouri-Columbia, Columbia, MO 65201.

RHYS, BRINLEY JOHN, b. London, Eng, Apr. 3, 14; U.S. citizen; m. 59; c. 2. ENGLISH. B.A, George Peabody Col, 42; M.A, Vanderbilt Univ, 53; Ph.D.(Eng), Tulane Univ, 63. Instr. ENG, UNIV. OF THE SOUTH, 46-52, asst. prof, 52-63, assoc. prof, 63-65, PROF, 65-, CHMN. DEPT, 71- From ed. asst. to managing ed, Sewanee Rev, 46-53. Sig.C, U.S.A, 42-45, M/Sgt. Chaucer; Chekov. Publ: A preface to Chaucer, spring 64 & Minstrels and mystics, spring 67, Sewanee Rev. Add: Sewanee, TN 37375.

RIBMAN, RONALD BURT, b. New York, N.Y, May 28, 32; m. 67; c. 2. ENGLISH LITERATURE. B.B.A, Univ. Pittsburgh, 54, M.Litt, 58, Owens fel, 59-60, Ph.D, 62. Asst. prof. Eng. lit, Otterbein Col, 62-63; WRITER, 63- Rockefeller Found. grants, 66, 68; Guggenheim Found. fel, 70-71; Nat. Found. for Arts fel, 73-74. Obie Best Play Award, 66. U.S.A, 54-56. PEN Club. English romantic poets; modern British and American poets; John Keats. Publ: Harry, noon and night, Am. Place Theater, 65, Little, 67; The journey of the fifth horse, Am. Place Theater, 66, Nat. Educ. TV, 66, Little, 67, Can. Broadcasting Co, 69; The ceremony of innocence, 67 & Fingernails blue as flowers, 73, Am. Place Theatre; The final war of Olly Winter, CBS Playhouse, 67; Passing through from exotic places, Dramatists Play Serv, 70; co-auth, The poor man in the scales, Harper's Mag, 4/64; The burial of Esposito, In: The best short plays, 1971, Chilton, 71. Add: c/o Flora Roberts, 116 E. 59th St, New York, NY 10022.

RICE, ALVA WENONAH, b. Arlington, Va, Nov. 19, 14. COMMUNICATIONS. B.S, Madison Col, 35; fel, Ind. Univ, 45-46, M.A, 47; Univ. Oslo, summer 57; cert, Univ. London, 62. Teacher, Elem. Sch, Arlington, Va, 35-39; instr. Eng, Shenandoah Col, 40-42; Eng, social stud. & French, South. High Sch, Lothian, Md, 43-45; instr. freshman Eng, Ind. Univ, 45-46; from asst. to assoc. prof. ENG, Marshall Col, 46-55; ASSOC. PROF, Slippery Rock State Col, 55-60; BLOOMSBURG STATE COL, 60- Fulbright teaching lectr, Albay Norm, Legaspi, Philippines, 51-52. NCTE; Col. Eng. Asn; AAUP; Am. Asn. Higher Educ. Victorian literature, especially Browning; romantic literature, especially Wordsworth; modern poetry and criticism, especially T.S. Eliot. Add: 365 E. Second St, Bloomsburg, PA 17815.

RICE, FRANK MARTIN, b. Nebr, Apr. 10, 08. ENGLISH, EDUCATION. B.A, Grand Island Col, 29; M.A, Columbia Univ, 34; Univ. Wis, summers 36-41; John Hay fel, Yale, 52-53. Chmn. dept. Eng, Omaha Cent. High Sch, 34-62; prof. Eng. & co-dir. Nebr. Curriculum Develop. Ctr, UNIV. NEBR, LINCOLN, 62-73, asst. dir. Trainers of Teachers of Teachers, 69-72, EMER. PROF. ENG, 73- Coe fel, Univ. Wyo, 57. NCTE (dir, 57-60). Publ: Coauth, Literature of adventure, 56, Literature of achievement, 56 & English literature, 64, 67, Ginn; Social aspects of education, Prentice, 62; English and its teaching, Prof. Educr. Publ, 72. Add: Dept. of English, 338-A Andrews Hall, University of Nebraska, Lincoln, NE 68508.

RICE, GEORGE PHILIP, JR, b. Albany, N.Y, Sept. 8, 11. ENGLISH HISTORY, PUBLIC ADDRESS. B.S, State Univ. N.Y, 32, Wheelock scholar, 32, A.M, 36; Columbia Univ, 34; univ. scholar, Cornell Univ, 37-39; Ph.D, 44; J.D, Ind. Univ, 56. Instr. speech, Pa. State Col, 39-43, asst. prof, 44-45; tutor Eng, Cornell Univ, 43-44; lectr. Eng. & comp. lit, Columbia Univ, 45-48; PROF. SPEECH & CHMN. DEPT, BUTLER UNIV, 48-, fac. res. fel, 51. Educ. dir, Nat. Found. Educ. in Am. Citizenship, 50-, trustee; Ford fel, 53-54; partner, Tyler, Davis & Rice, Indianapolis; consult. ed, Scott, Foresman & Co, 70; Cent. States Speech J, 70-71; lectr, Purdue Univ, 70- Honor Medal, Freedoms Found, 56. Speech Commun. Asn.(mem. standing comn. on free speech, 65 & 68-, co-ed. 68 yearbk); East. Pub. Speaking Conf; Class. Asn. Atlantic States. Freedom of expression under law. Publ: Speakers and speeches in Tudor and Stuart England; The scholar and the twentieth century; Law for the public speaker, Christopher, 58; Speeches of Queen Elizabeth, Columbia Univ, rev. ed, 68. Add: 3470 N. Meridian St, Indianapolis, IN 46204.

RICE, HARRIET EPSTEIN, b. Rockland, Maine, Dec. 19, 42; m. 68. SPEECH COMMUNICATION. B.A, Univ. Maine, Orono, 64; M.A, Columbia Univ, 65; Ph.D.(oral interpretation), Purdue Univ, 71. Instr. SPEECH ARTS, Univ. Maine, Portland, 65-67; ASST. PROF, UNIV. MAINE, ORONO, 69- Speech Commun. Asn; Speech Commun. Asn. East. States. Relationship of the theories, methods and critical writings of Bertolt Brecht to oral interpretation. Add: Dept. of Speech, 335 Stevens Hall, University of Maine at Orono, Orono, ME 04473.

RICE, LEONARD WILLIAM, b. Garland, Utah, Dec. 9, 13. ENGLISH. A.B, Brigham Young Univ, 41; A.M, Univ. Wash, 43, Ph.D, 50. Asst. prof, Brigham Young Univ, 47-55, prof. Eng. & chmn. dept, 55-57, dean col. humanities & soc. sci, 57-60; prof. Eng, R.I. Col, 60-62, PRES, ORE. COL. EDUC, 62- Fel, Yale, 59-60. English language and literature; 18th century English novel. Add: Oregon College of Education, Monmouth, OR 97361.

RICE, SCOTT BRADLEY, b. Lewiston, Idaho, July 22, 41; m. 64; c. 2. ENGLISH LITERATURE. B.A, Gonzaga Univ, 64; NDEA fel, Univ. Ariz, 64-67, M.A, 66, Ph.D.(Eng), 68. Asst. prof. ENG, CALIF. STATE UNIV, SAN JOSE, 68-72, ASSOC. PROF, 72- Vis. prof, Univ. Lyon, 73-74. MLA; Rocky Mt. Mod. Lang. Asn; Philol. Asn. Pac. Coast; Am. Soc. 18th Century Stud; Southwest. Soc. 18th Century Stud. Eighteenth century English literature; Tobias Smollett; the novel. Publ: The satiric persona of Smollett's Travels, Stud. Scottish Lit, 7/72; Smollett's Travels through France and Italy and the genre of grand tour literature, Costerus: Essays Eng. & Am. Lang. & Lit, 72; Smollett's seventh travel letter and the design of formal verse satire, Stud. Eng. Lit, (in press). Add: Dept. of English, California State University, San Jose, CA 95192.

RICE, THOMAS JACKSON, b. Troy, N.Y, Aug. 13, 45; m. 67. ENGLISH LITERATURE. B.A, Univ. Del, 67; M.A, Princeton, 69, Ph.D.(Eng), 71. ASST. PROF. ENG, UNIV. S.C, 71- Mil.Intel, U.S.A, 72, 1st Lt. MLA; S.Atlantic Mod. Lang. Asn. Victorian fiction; modern British fiction; the historical novel. Publ: Oliver Twist and the genesis of Barnaby Rudge, Dickens Stud. Newslett, 73. Add: Dept. of English, University of South Carolina, Columbia, SC 29208.

RICE, WARNER GRENELLE, b. Aurora, Ill, July 25, 99; m. 29; c. 2. ENGLISH LITERATURE. A.B, Univ. Ill, 20, A.M, 22; A.M, Harvard, 23, Ph.D, 27; hon. L.H.D, Col. Wooster, 53 & Cent. Mich. Univ, 70. Asst. Eng, Univ. Ill, 20-22; Harvard, 23, tutor, 24, tutor & instr, 27-29; assoc. prof, UNIV. MICH, ANN ARBOR, 29-37, prof, 37-69, dir. gen. libr, 41-53, acting chmn. dept, ENG, 48-53, chmn. dept, 53-68, EMER. PROF, 69- Tutor & instr, Radcliffe Col, 27-29; mem. comn. Eng, Col. Entrance Exam. Bd; Eng. Inst; vis. Mellon prof. Eng, Univ. Pittsburgh, 70; consult, N.Y. State Educ. Dept, 70-71; Green Honors Prof. Eng, Tex. Christian Univ, 71-72; vis. prof, Pa. State Univ, University Park, 72-73. MLA; NCTE; Am. Libr. Asn; Asn. Chmn. Depts. Eng. Renaissance literature; English Hellenism; Milton. Add: Dept. of English, University of Michigan, 1609 Haven Hall, Ann Arbor, MI 48104.

RICH, MORTON DAVID, b. Newark, N.J, Sept. 11, 33; m. 55; c. 2. MODERN AMERICAN LITERATURE, ENGLISH EDUCATION. A.B, Cornell Univ, 54; M.Ed, Rutgers Univ, 62; N.Y. Univ, 62- Teacher ENG, Fair Lawn High Sch, N.J, 59-65; asst. prof, MONTCLAIR STATE COL, 65-72, ASSOC. PROF, 72- Consult, Rahway Jr. High Sch, N.J, 73-74. Ord.C, U.S.A, 55-56. MLA; NCTE; Col. Eng. Asn. Applied linguistics; poetry. Publ: Co-auth, A functioning study clinic, J. Nat. Asn. Sec. Sch. Prin, 4/65; auth, Methodical madness in a methods class, In: Through a glass darkly, NCTE, 72. Add: Dept. of English, Montclair State College, Valley Rd, Montclair, NJ 07043.

RICH, TOWNSEND, b. Buffalo, N.Y, Nov. 17, 09; m. 38; c. 2. ENGLISH. B.A, Yale, 31, M.A, 34, Ph.D.(Eng), 36. Teacher, Thacher Sch, Ojai, Calif, 31-33; from instr. to assoc. prof. ENG, Mich. State Univ, 36-48; PROF, STATE UNIV. N.Y. ALBANY, 48-, chmn. dept, 58-69. MLA; Shakespeare Asn. Am. Shakespeare; modern British novel; Bible. Publ: Harington and Ariosto; a study of Elizabethan verse translation, Yale; co-auth, A survey of the drama, Edwards Bros. Add: 166 Chestnut St, Albany, NY 12210.

RICHARD, JERRY, b. New York, N.Y, Mar. 13, 31; m. 61; c. 2. ENGLISH. B.A, Univ. Pa, 53; M.A, New Sch. Social Res, 55; M.A, San Francisco State Col, 61; Ford fel, Ind. Univ, 63-64. Instr. Eng, Univ. Mont, 61-63; asst. prof, Fresno State Col, 64-65; mem. fac, Goddard Col, 65-69; ASST. PROF. AM. LIT. & CULT, FAIRHAVEN COL, WEST. WASH. STATE COL, 69- NCTE. American literature; American culture; higher education. Publ: ed, The good life, New Am. Libr, 73; auth, Foggy Mountain, Antioch Rev, fall 68; Literature by theme, New Directions in Teaching, spring 70; The good man, Change, 10/71. Add: Fairhaven College, Western Washington State College, Bellingham, WA 98225.

RICHARD, MARGARET COSSÉ, b. New York, N.Y, Sept. 22, 05; m. 37. JOURNALISM, MASS COMMUNICATIONS. B.Litt, Columbia Univ, 27, M.S, 28; Univ. Minn, 58. Asst. ed, Bronxville Rev, N.Y, 26-29; from instr. to prof. jour. & dir. pub. inform, Col. New Rochelle, 29-42; lectr. Eng, Univ. Del, 47-48; feature writer, Journal-Every-Evening, Wilmington, Del, 48-49; woman's ed, Southwest Citizen, Lake Charles, La, 49-51; instr. Eng, McNeese State Col, 51-52, asst. prof. Eng. & jour, 52-53, assoc. prof, 53-55, prof. jour, 55-63, dir. publications, 53-63, coord. alumni affairs, 60-63; WRITER & RESEARCHER, 63- Sackett grad. scholar, Columbia Univ, 27; fel, Sarah Lawrence Col, 28-31; reporter, New York Herald-Tribune, N.Y, summers, 31-33; instr. Eng. & jour, Hunter Col, 33-37; serv. writer, Seventeen Mag, 45-47; mem, La. Comn. Educ. TV, 55-56. Dissenters who advanced the cause of freedom in the United States; laws of defamation in libel in Louisiana; a land grant which became subject of historic law suit when the area involved was incorporated into what is now Central Park in New York City. Publ: The suburban weekly, Columbia Univ, 28. Add: 83 Old Kings Highway, Wilton, CT 06897.

RICHARDS, BERTRAND FIELD, b. Newton, Ill, Apr. 18, 10; m. 66. ENGLISH. B.A, East. Ill. Univ, 59; M.A, Ind. State Univ, Terre Haute, 61; Ph.D.(Eng), Duke Univ, 71. Teacher Eng. & speech, Newton Community High Sch, 56-63; instr. ENG, IND. STATE UNIV, TERRE HAUTE, 63-66, asst. prof. 66-70, ASSOC. PROF, 70- Ill. Comn. Stud. Gifted Children res, 63-67. U.S.A, 42-43, Sgt. NCTE (mem. comt. semantics in sec. schs, 62-66); Conf. Eng. Educ; Conf. Col. Compos. & Commun. English language; Modern American poetry; semantics. Publ: Co-auth, Creative approaches to the teaching of English: secondary, Peacock 74; auth, The Effingham experiment, Teachers Col. J, 65; No there is not a dawn . . . an analysis of Luke Havergal by E.A. Robinson, Colby Libr. Quart, 72. Add: Room 241 Parsons Hall, Indiana State University, N. Sixth St, Terre Haute, IN 47809.

RICHARDS, EMMA S, b. Bridgeville, Pa, Apr. 14, 18; m. 39; c. 2. ENGLISH. B.A, Hunter Col, 48, N.Y. State Scholar & M.A, 49; Ph.D.(Eng), Lehigh Univ, 67. Teacher, Abington Twp. Schs, 51-54; Allentown Dist. Schs, 55-59; assoc. prof. ENG, KUTZTOWN STATE COL, 65-68, PROF, 68- English romanticism; Victorian prose; literary criticism and aesthetics. Publ: Art, death and futility in certain stories by Henry James, The New Century, spring, 67; On seeing The young fisherman by Franz Hals, Kutztown State Col. Bull, spring 68. Add: Dept. of English, Kutztown State College, Kutztown, PA 19530.

RICHARDS, GALE LEE, b. Salem, W.Va, July 31, 18; m. 44; c. 3. SPEECH. A.B, Univ. Akron, 40; A.M, Univ. Iowa, 42, Ph.D, 50. Instr. speech, Univ. Akron, 41-42; asst, Univ. Iowa, 42-43, 46-47; asst. prof. speech, Drake Univ, 47-48; Eng, Univ. Nev, 48-52; speech, Univ. Wash, 52-58; assoc. prof, Univ. South. Calif, 58-65; PROF. SPEECH & THEATRE, ARIZ. STATE UNIV, 65-, chmn. dept, 65-73. U.S.N.R, 42-45, Lt. Speech Commun. Asn; Int. Commun. Asn; West. Speech Commun. Asn.(2nd v.pres, 56). Rhetorical criticism; experimental studies in speech communication; speech pedagogy. Publ: A case study in deliberative persuasion, Speech Monogr; co-auth, Empirically-derived rating scale for intercollegiate discussion sequences, J. Commun. & Reporting in person, In: Municipal public relations, Int. City Mgr. Asn, 66; plus others. Add: Dept. of Speech & Theatre, Arizona State University, Tempe, AZ 85281.

RICHARDS, JANE GRILLS, b. Flint, Mich, Oct. 7, 19; m. 66. SPEECH, EDUCATION. B.A, Univ. Mich, 41, fel, 42-43, M.A, 43; Northwest. Univ, summers 45, 49; Ph.D.(educ. broadcasting), Mich. State Univ, 59. Teacher, High Sch, Mich, 41-42; instr. speech & radio, Sullins Col, 43-44; asst. prof, Alma Col, 44-45; assoc. prof. radio & dir. radio div, Commun. Ctr, Univ. N.C, Chapel Hill, 45-49; women's prog. & educ. off, CIE Radio Br, Supreme Comdr. Allied Powers, Tokyo, 50-51; teacher speech & group guid. counsel, High Sch, Mich, 53-55; assoc. prof. & coord. airborne TV, IND. STATE UNIV, TERRE HAUTE, 55-64, PROF. SPEECH & EDUC, 64-; EXEC. DIR, IND. HIGHER EDUC. TELECOMMUN. SYST, 72- Lectr, St. Mary-of-the-Woods Col, summers 63-65; consult, Nat. Prog. Improv. TV Instr, 66; mem, State Univs. Telecommun. Coord. Counc. Nat. Asn. Educ. Broadcasters; NEA; Asn. Educ. Commun. & Technol; Am. Asn. Higher Educ. Speech Commun. Asn. Communications technology; interinstitutional cooperation; curriculum and course design in broadcasting. Publ: The classroom teacher and ITV, Teachers Col. J, 5/63; Who needs enemies?, Ind. Sch. Bd. J, 8/64; Indiana, last again?, Hoosier Schoolmaster, 3/65. Add: Indiana Higher Education Telecommunication System, 1100 W. Michigan St, Indianapolis, IN 46202.

RICHARDS, LEWIS A, b. Calamata, Greece, Feb. 18, 25; U.S. citizen; m. 55; c. 3. ENGLISH. B.A, Univ. South. Calif, 55, M.A, 57, Ph.D.(comp. lit), 63. Asst. prof. Eng, Utah State Univ, 57-60; San Jose State Col, 60-63; assoc. prof. Eng. & chmn. div. lang. & lit, Gen. Beadle State Col, 63-64; assoc. prof. humanities, Rose Polytech. Inst, 64-67; ASSOC. PROF. LANG. & LIT. & CHMN. DEPT, WEST. N.MEX. UNIV, 67- Ed, West. Rev. MLA. English; humanities. Publ: An anthology of classical Greek literature, 66 & The real Zorbas and Nikos Kazantzakis, 68, Argonaut; Fact and fiction in Nikos Kazantzakis' Alexis Zorbas, fall 64 & Christianity in the novels of Nikos Kazantzakis, winter 67, West. Humanities Rev; English abroad: our language in Greece, Univ. Col. Quart, 1/65. Add: Dept. of Language & Literature, Western New Mexico University, Silver City, NM 88061.

RICHARDS, MARION KAZMANN, b. Philadelphia, Pa, Mar. 16, 25; wid; c. 1. ENGLISH, COMPARATIVE LITERATURE. B.A, Cornell Univ, 44; M.A, Columbia Univ, 45, Ph.D.(Eng), 61; Univ. Chicago, 49-50. Instr. Eng, Univ. Denver, 46-47; Wayne State Univ, 47-52; from asst. prof. to PROF. ENG. & COMP. LIT, SAN JOSE STATE UNIV, 57-, ASSOC. DEAN FAC, 73- Consult, Nat. Asn. For. Stud. Affairs, 62-65. MLA; AAUP. American and Russian comparative literature. Publ: Ellen Glasgow's development as a novelist, Mouton, The Hague, 71. Add: 63 Los Altos Square, Los Altos, CA 94022.

RICHARDS, MARY JULIET PROCTOR, b. El Paso, Tex, July 18, 44; m. 66. ENGLISH LITERATURE. B.A, South. Methodist Univ, 66; Woodrow Wilson fel, Univ. Wis-Madison, 66-67, M.A, 67, Henry Vilas fel, 70-71, Ph.D.(Eng), 71. ASST. PROF. ENG, UNIV. TENN, KNOXVILLE, 71- MLA; S.Atlantic Mod. Lang. Asn; Mediaeval Acad. Am. Old English literature and language; Middle English literature. Publ: On the date and provenance of MS Cotton Vespasian D. XIV ff.4-169, Manuscripta, 73; A reexamination of Beowulf ll. 3180-3182, Eng. Lang. Notes, 3/73. Add: Dept. of English, University of Tennessee, Knoxville, TN 37916.

RICHARDS, ROBERT F, b. Denver, Colo, Jan. 23, 14; m. 41. ENGLISH. B.A, Univ. Colo, 40; M.A, Univ. Denver, 49; Ph.D, Columbia Univ, 61. Mem. fac, Univ. Denver, 48-51; part-time instr, Hunter Col, 52-53; asst. prof. ENG, UNIV. DENVER, 55-65, ASSOC. PROF, 65-, dir, Lib. Stud. Bus. Leadership, 57-60, dir. grad. stud, Dept. Eng, 67-71. Consult, U.S. Air Force Acad, 55-62. U.S.A.F, 40-46, Res, 46-71, Col. AAUP; MLA; Rocky Mountain Mod. Lang. Asn; West. Lit. Asn. American literature; aesthetics; modern drama. Publ: Dictionary of American literature, Philos. Libr, 55, stud. outline ser, Littlefield-Owens, 59; ed, Concise dictionary of American literature (reprint), Greenwood, 69; co-auth, Feeling in The great Gatsby, West. Humanities Rev, summer 67; auth, Thomas Hornsby Ferril and the problems of the poet in the West, Kans. Quart, spring 70; Literature and politics, Colo. Quart, summer 70. Add: Dept. of English, University of Denver, Denver, CO 80210.

RICHARDSON, DON RAMON, b. Malta, Ohio, Aug. 7, 38; m. 57; c. 3. SPEECH. B.A, Auburn Univ, 61; M.A, Ohio Univ, 63, Ph.D.(speech), 64. Asst. prof. speech, Univ. Ga, 64-66; AUBURN UNIV, 66-68, assoc. prof, 68-72, ASSOC. PROF. SPEECH COMMUN. & ASST. DEAN GRAD. SCH, 72-, chmn. div. arts & sci, Auburn Univ, Montgomery, 69-72. Educ. & Indust. consult. commun; mem. ed. bd, South. Speech J; abstractor, Speech Monogr, Am. Bibliog. Ctr. Speech Commun Asn; South. Speech Commun Asn; Psychology of communication; experimental persuasion; behavior modification. Publ: A note on Gandhi's Ethos, Ohio Speech J, Vol. IV: 24-26; A comparative study of information retained from written, oral and combined written-oral communications, South. Speech J, Vol. 32: 41-48; co-auth, Increasing the reliability of judgments of acting performance, Quart. J. Speech, Vol. LII: 378-382. Add: Graduate School, Auburn University, Auburn, AL 36830.

RICHARDSON, GENEVIEVE, b. St. Joseph, Ill, Feb. 7, 09. THEATRE & SPEECH. B.A, Univ. Ill, 42, M.A, 48, Ph.D.(speech & theatre), 53. Teacher, Ill. pub. schs, 30-42; high sch, Ill, 42-45; speech & theatre, Geneva Col, 45-47; assoc. prof, UNIV. ILL, URBANA, 47-49, univ. theatre costumer, 47-69, EMER. ASSOC. PROF. THEATRE, 69- Am. Theatre Asn; Speech Commun. Asn; Children's Theatre Asn. Publ: A Christmas pageant, Instructor, 12/38; Lorado Taft and theatre, J. Ill. State Hist. Soc, winter 56; The Mermaid Theatre, Players Mag, 12/61. Add: 1721 W. Finland Dr, Deltona, FL 32763.

RICHARDSON, HAROLD EDWARD, b. Woodstock, Ky, July 13, 29; m. 53; c. 2. ENGLISH. A.B, East. Ky. Univ, 52, A.M, 54; A.M, Univ. South. Calif, 61, Ph.D. (Eng), 63. Instr. Fullerton Jr. Col, 56-63; assoc. prof, East. Ky. Univ, 63-65, prof, 65-68, chmn. dept, 65-67; PROF, UNIV. LOUISVILLE, 68- Asst. prof, Calif. State Col. Fullerton, 63; vis. prof, Calif. State Univ, Los Angeles, summers 67 & 71; Univ. South. Calif, summer 68. MLA; S.Atlantic Mod. Lang. Asn; Col. Conf. Compos. & Commun; NCTE; Am. Stud. Asn. American literature, beginnings to the present; English literature, 18th century. Publ: William Faulkner: the journey to self-discovery, Univ. Mo, 69; How to think and write, Scott, 70; co-auth, Muse of fire: approaches to poetry, Knopf, 70; auth, Cassius Marcellus Clay (1810-1903): sword of emancipation, Commonwealth, 74; Anderson and Faulkner, Am. Lit, 11/64; The ways that Faulkner walked: a pilgrimage, Ariz. Quart, summer 65; The decadence in Faulkner's Soldiers' pay: the faun, the worm, and the tower, Etudes Anglaises, fall 68; plus others. Add: Dept. of English, University of Louisville, Louisville, KY 40208.

RICHARDSON, JANETTE, b. Ontario, Ore, Aug. 18, 25. RHETORIC, COMPARATIVE LITERATURE. A.B, Univ. Ore, 46, M.A, 53; Ph.D.(Eng), Univ. Calif, Berkeley, 62. Asst. prof. RHETORIC & COMP. LIT, UNIV. CALIF, BERKELEY, 62-67, ASSOC. PROF, 67- MLA; Mediaeval Acad. Am; Am. Comp. Lit. Asn; Philol. Asn. Pac. Coast. Chaucer; mediaeval and renaissance rhetoric; renaissance drama. Publ: Blameth nat me, Mouton, 70; Hunter and prey: functional imagery in Chaucer's Friar's tale, Eng. Miscellany, 61; Virgil and Milton once again, Comp. Lit, 62; The facade of bawdry: Image patterns in Chaucer's Shipman's tale, ELH, 9/65. Add: Dept. of Rhetoric, University of California, Berkeley, CA 94720.

RICHARDSON, JOHN CURTIS, b. Milan, Italy, Oct. 12, 19; U.S. citizen; m. 42; c. 2. ENGLISH. B.A, Dartmouth Col, 41; M.A, Columbia Univ, 42; Ph.D. (Eng), Boston Univ, 59. From instr. to assoc. prof. ENG. & chmn. dept, UNIV. N.H, 46-71, PROF, 71- U.S.A, 42-46. MLA; Col. Eng. Asn. Modern British literature. Add: Dept. of English, University of New Hampshire, Durham, NH 03824.

RICHARDSON, L. JANETTE, b. Ontario, Ore. COMPARATIVE LITERATURE, RHETORIC. B.A, Univ. Ore, 46, M.A, 53; Ph.D.(Eng), Univ. Calif, Berkeley, 62. Teacher Eng, Gresham Union High Sch, Ore, 47-56; assoc, UNIV. CALIF, BERKELEY, 59-62, asst. prof. RHET. & COMP. LIT, 62-67, ASSOC. PROF, 67- MLA; Mediaeval Acad. Am; Am. Comp. Lit. Asn. Chaucer; mediaeval literature; rhetorical theory. Publ: Blameth me not, Mouton, 70; The function of formal imagery in Ovid's Metamorphoses, Class. J, 64; The facade of bawdry: image patterns in Chaucer's Shipman's tale, Eng. Lit. Hist, 65; contrib, Chaucer's mind and art, Oliver & Boyd, Edinburgh, 69; plus others. Add: Dept. of Comparative Literature, University of California, Berkeley, CA 94720.

RICHARDSON, LYON NORMAN, b. Andover, Ohio, July 20, 98; m. 23; c. 1. AMERICAN LITERATURE. A.B, West. Reserve Univ, 21, A.M, 25; Ph.D. (Eng. & Am. lit), Columbia Univ, 31. Prin, High Sch, Ohio, 22-23; instr. Eng, Adelbert Col, CASE WEST. RESERVE UNIV, 23-25, 27-35, asst. prof, 35-43, instr, Cleveland Col, 27-29, Sch. Educ, 28-33, asst. dean, 29-35, assoc. prof, Adelbert Col. & Grad. Sch, 43-46, dir. univ. litr, 46-67, prof. Eng. & chmn. grad. prog. Am. stud, 47-69, EMER. PROF. ENG. & AM. STUD, 69- Vis. prof. Eng, Duquesne Univ, 69-71. MLA; Am. Stud. Asn. Nineteenth and 20th century American literature. Publ: History of early American magazines, Nelson, 31, Octagon, 66; Henry James, Am. Bk. Co, 41, Univ. Ill, 66; Heritage of American literature, Ginn; plus others. Add: 3303 Ormond Rd, Cleveland Heights, OH 44118.

RICHARDSON, RALPH, b. Thayer, Kans, Aug. 8, 18; m. 39; c. 4. SPEECH. A.B, Univ. Kans, 40; A.M, Pa. State Col, 44; fel, Northwest. Univ, 46-48, Ph.D, 50. Teacher, High Sch, Kans, 40-41; instr. SPEECH, Pa. State Univ, 41-44 & 45-46; UNIV. CALIF, LOS ANGELES, 48-50, asst. prof, 51-57, ASSOC. PROF, 57-, dir. forensics, 63-65. Secy. to Gov, State of Calif, 58-59; pres, Los Angeles Bd. Educ, 61-62 & 65-67; trustee, Los Angeles Community Cols. Bd. Trustees, 73-77. U.S.N.R, 44-45. History and criticism of American public address; history and criticism of Southern public address, 1840-1900. Publ: Jefferson Davis, a study in sectional diplomacy, 1858; co-auth, Speech: idea and delivery. Add: Dept. of Speech, University of California, Los Angeles, CA 90024.

RICHARDSON, ROBERT DALE, JR, b. Milwaukee, Wis, June 14, 34; m. 59; c. 2. AMERICAN LITERATURE. B.A, Harvard, 56, Ph.D.(Eng), 61. Instr. ENG, Harvard, 61-63; asst. prof, UNIV. DENVER, 63-68, assoc. prof, 68-72, PROF, 72-, chmn. dept, 68-73. Assoc. ed, Denver Quart, 67; Huntington Libr. & Art Gallery fel, 73-74. MLA. American literature, 1760-1860; mythology; film and literature. Publ: Literature and film, 68 & co-auth, The rise of modern mythology, 72, Ind. Univ; auth, Miss Lonelyhearts, Univ. Rev, winter 66; The Puritan poetry of Anne Bradstreet, Tex. Stud. Lit. & Lang, autumn 67; Emerson, Adams and Marshall McLuhan, West. Humanities Rev, spring 68. Add: Dept. of English, University of Denver, Denver, CO 80210.

RICHETTI, JOHN J, b. New York, N.Y, Nov. 14, 38; m. 60; c. 2. ENGLISH. B.A, St. Francis Col.(N.Y), 60; M.A, Columbia Univ, 61, Ph.D.(Eng), 68. Instr. ENG, St. John's Univ.(N.Y), 61-65, asst. prof, 65; lectr, Columbia Univ, 67-68, asst. prof, 68-70; ASSOC. PROF, RUTGERS COL, RUTGERS UNIV, NEW BRUNSWICK, 70- Guggenheim Found. fel, 71-72. MLA. The English novel; 18th century English literature. Publ: Popular fiction before Richardson: narrative patterns 1700-1739, Oxford Univ, 69; Mrs. Elizabeth Rowe: the novel as polemic, PMLA, 12/67. Add: Dept. of English, Rutgers College, New Brunswick, NJ 08903.

RICHMOND, FARLEY P, b. Ardmore, Okla, Feb. 16, 38; m. 67. THEATRE. B.F.A, Univ. Okla, 60, M.F.A, 61; Fulbright-Hays fel, Mich. State Univ, 64-65, Ph.D.(speech, theatre), 66. Asst. instr. THEATRE, MICH. STATE UNIV, 63-64, asst. prof, 66-72, ASSOC. PROF, 72- Ford Found. fac. fel, Interrotating Prog. S.Asian Lang. & Area Stud, summer 67; J.D. Rockefeller III Fund fel, India, 69-70. Am. Theatre Asn.(chmn. Asian theatre prog, 73-75); Speech Commun. Asn; Asn. Asian Stud; Asia Soc.(mem. India counc). South Asian theatre and drama. Publ: Two Gujarati folk plays, Writers Workshop, 71; Bibliography of Asian theatre material, 71 & The religious ritual in Indian traditional theatre, 71, Drama Rev; The political role of theatre in India, 73 & The Vaisnavana drama of Assam, 74, Educ. Theatre J. Add: Dept. of Theatre, Michigan State University, East Lansing, MI 48823.

RICHMOND, HUGH MACRAE, b. Burton, Eng, Mar. 20, 32; m. 58. ENGLISH LITERATURE. B.A, Cambridge, 54; D.Phil, Oxford, 57. Asst. Lycée Jean Perrin, France, 54-55; instr. ENG. LIT, UNIV. CALIF, BERKELEY, 57-59, asst. prof, 59-63, assoc. prof, 63-68, PROF, 68-, summer fel, 61, res. prof, 68. Am. Counc. Learned Soc. fel, 64; fel, Humanities Inst, Univ. Calif, 73. Brit. Army, 50-51, 2nd Lt. MLA; Renaissance Soc. Am; Am. Comp. Lit. Asn. Renaissance English literature; comparative literature. Publ: The school of love, the evolution of the Stuart love lyric, Princeton, 63; Shakespeare's political plays, Random, 67; William Shakespeare, Henry IV, Part I, 67 & Shakespeare's sexual comedy, 71, Bobbs; ed, W. Shakespeare: Henry VIII, W.C. Brown, 71; auth, Renaissance landscapes, Mouton, The Hague, 73; The Christian revolutionary: John Milton, Univ. Calif, 74. Add: Dept. of English, University of California, Berkeley, CA 94720.

RICHMOND, LEE JOHN, b. Washington, Pa, Feb. 22, 36. ENGLISH & AMERICAN LITERATURE. A.B, Washington & Jefferson Col, 58; M.A, Syracuse Univ, 62, Ph.D.(Eng), 70. Instr. ENG, Syracuse Univ, 62-65; Cazenovia Col, 65-66; Hofstra Univ, 66-67; ST. JOHN'S UNIV, (N.Y), 67-70, ASST. PROF, 70- Am. lit. ed, Erasmus Rev: a Jour. of the Humanities, 71-72. William Holmes McGuffey Prize, 58. AAUP; MLA. Modern American and British poetry; 20th century American literature; the novel. Publ: Edgar Allan Poe's Morella: vampire of volition, Stud. Short Fiction, winter 72; The maladroit, the medico and the magician: Saul Bellows' Seize the day, Twentieth Century Lit, 1/73; Emily Dickinson's Death is a dialogue, Emily Dickinson Bull, spring 73. Add: Dept. of English, St. Johns' University, Jamaica, NY 11439.

RICHMOND, VELMA E. BOURGEOIS, b. New Orleans, La, Mar. 12, 31; m. 58; c. 2. ENGLISH. B.A, La. State Univ, 51, M.A, 52; pres. scholar, Johns Hopkins Univ, 52-53; Fulbright scholar & B.Litt, Oxford, 57; univ. fel. & Ph.D, Univ. N.C, 59. Instr. ENG, La. State Univ, 57-58; HOLY NAMES COL.(CALIF), 58-60, asst. prof, 60-65, assoc. prof, 65-68, PROF, 68-CHMN. DEPT. ENG, SPEECH & DRAMA, 70- MLA; Mediaeval Acad. Am; Col. Eng. Asn.(mem. comt. advan. degrees, 71-74); Renaissance Soc. Am. Mod. Humanities Res. Asn. Mediaeval and Renaissance literature; modern literature. Publ: Laments for the dead in medieval narrative, Duquesne Univ, 66; Lady Macbeth: feminine sensibility gone wrong, CEA Critic, 3/73; Guy of Warwick: a medieval thriller, S.Atlantic Quart. Add: Dept. of English, Speech & Drama, Holy Names College, 3500 Mountain Blvd, Oakland, CA 94619.

RICHMOND, WINTHROP EDSON, b. Nashua, N.H, Apr. 19, 16; m. 41; c. 2. ENGLISH LITERATURE, FOLKLORE. A.B, Miami Univ, 39; fel. from Miami Univ, Ohio State Univ, 39-40, A.M, 40, Ph.D, 47; Univ. Mich, 40. Asst. ENG, Ohio State Univ, 41-44; instr, 44-45; IND. UNIV, BLOOMINGTON, 45-48, asst. prof, 48-54, assoc. prof, 54-63, PROF, 63-, chmn. folklore prog, 55-57. Grant-in-aid, Am. Counc. Learned Soc, summer 40; lectr, Salzburg Sem. Am. Stud, Austria, 53; Fulbright res. prof, Norsk Folkeminnesamling, Oslo, Norway, 53-54; Fulbright vis. prof, Univ. Helsinki & Swed. Univ. Abo, 59-60; Ford grant int. stud, Nordisk Inst. Folkeminnevitskap, Univ. Oslo, 63, lectr. & res. prof, summer 68. MLA; fel. Am. Folklore Soc; Soc. Advan. Scand. Stud; Am. Dialect Soc. Folksongs; Scandinavian studies, literature. Publ: Studies in folklore, Ind. Univ, 57; Some effects of scribal and typographical error on oral transmission, In: The critics and the ballad, South. Ill. Univ, The study of folklore in Finland, J. Am. Folklore, 61; plus others. Add: Dept. of English, Indiana University, Bloomington, IN 47401.

RICHTMAN, JACK, French Language & Literature. See Volume III, Foreign Languages, Linguistics & Philology.

RICHWINE, KEITH NORTON, b. Harrisburg, Pa, Sept. 17, 30; m. 54. ENGLISH. B.S, Shippensburg State Col, 52; M.A, Pa. State Univ, 55; Ph.D, Univ. Pa, 68. Assoc. prof. ENG, W.Va. Wesleyan Col, 56-60; WEST. MD. COL, 62-72, PROF, 72-, CHMN. DEPT, 69- Lectr, Beaver Col, 60-62; vis. scholar, Harvard, 69. MLA; AAUP; Am. Stud. Asn. American literature and civilization; 20th century British literature and civilization. Publ: John Wain and The angry young men: an American reading list, 65 & Joseph Heller and Catch-22: a checklist, 72, Catoctin. Add: 10 Ridge Rd, Westminster, MD 21157.

RICKELS, MILTON HENRY, b. Porterville, Calif, Aug. 31, 20; m. 58; c. 1. ENGLISH. B.A, Fresno State Col, 45; M.A, Claremont Grad. Sch, 48; Ph.D. (Eng), La. State Univ, 53. Instr. ENG, La. State Univ, 51-53; asst. prof, George Pepperdine Col, 53-56, assoc. prof, 56-57; UNIV. SOUTHWEST. LA, 57-64, PROF, 64- Danforth Found. assoc, 72- S.Cent. Mod. Lang Asn; MLA; Am. Stud. Asn. Am. Folklore Soc; Soc. Stud. South. Lit.(mem. bibliog. comt, 69-). American literature and humor; modern literature. Publ: Thomas Bangs Thorpe, La. State Univ, 62; George Washington Harris, Twayne, 65; co-auth, Richard Wright, Steck-Vaughn, 70; auth, The imagery of George W. Harris, Am. Lit, 5/59; Existential themes in Beckett's Unnamable, Criticism, spring 62; Samuel Clemens and the conscience of comedy, South. Rev, 4/68. Add: Dept. of English, Box 1145, University of Southwestern Louisiana, Lafayette, LA 70501.

RICKELS, PATRICIA KENNEDY, b. Kemmerer, Wyo, Feb. 12, 27; m. 58; c. 1. ENGLISH. B.A, Univ. Wash, 48; M.A, La. State Univ, 51, Ph.D, 61. Instr. ENG, La. State Univ, 50-53; asst. prof, UNIV. SOUTHWEST. LA, 57-64, assoc. prof, 64-71, PROF, 71- Collector for La, Dictionary Am. Beliefs & Superstitions, Ctr. Comp. Stud. Folklore & Mythology, Univ. Calif, Los Angeles, 63-; Danforth assoc, 72- MLA; Am. Folklore Soc; Am. Stud. Asn. American literature; folklore, especially folk customs. Publ: Co-auth, Richard Wright, Steck, 70; auth, Some accounts of witch riding, 8/61 & Folklore of the sacraments and sacramentals in south Louisiana, 4/65, La. Folklore Miscellany; co-auth, Memories of Lead Belly, In: American Negro folklore, Quadrangle, 68. Add: Box 1145, University of Southwestern Louisiana, Lafayette, LA 70501.

RICKERT, ALFRED E, b. New York, N.Y, Nov. 1, 30; m. 57; c. 2. ENGLISH. DRAMA. B.S, N.Y. Univ, 52, M.A, 53; Ph.D.(theatre), Univ. Denver, 67. Teacher Eng, Pub. Schs, N.Y, 52-57; Colo, 57-59; asst. prof. theatre, Franklin Col, 59-62; from assoc. prof. to PROF. ENG, STATE UNIV. N.Y. COL. OSWEGO, 62-, asst. chmn. dept, 67-69. Ed, Theatre J. & Callboard, N.Y. State Community Theatre Asn, 71- U.S.A, 53-56. MLA; Am. Theatre Asn.(mem. nat. bibliog. comt, Res. Resources Proj, 63-68); Sec. Sch. Theatre Conf.(surv. chmn. status drama in Am. sec. schs. proj, 65-67). Modern and 19th century drama; theatre history. Publ: contrib, Bibliography of theatre arts publication in English, 1963, Am. Educ. Theatre Asn, 65; auth, Perceiving Pinter, Eng. Rev, 71; Two views of The Cenci: Shelley and Artaud, Forum, 73; plus three others. Add: Dept. of English, State University of New York College at Oswego, Oswego, NY 13126.

RICKETT, OLLA GOEWEY, b. Chazy, N.Y, Sept. 25, 04; div. THEATRE. A.B, State Univ. N.Y. Albany, 26; McGill Univ, 28; M.A, Syracuse Univ, 47; Univ. Montreal, 61; Ph.D.(drama & theatre), Cornell Univ, 64. Teacher high schs, N.Y, 26-28, 29-43; instr. drama, Syracuse Univ, 43-47; from instr. to assoc. prof. speech & theatre, State Univ. N.Y. Col. Cortland, 47-59; assoc. prof, State Univ. N.Y. Col. Oswego, 59-63, prof, 63-68, chmn. theatre staff; RETIRED. Lectr. dramatic lit, Univ. Tampa, 69-72; part-time lectr, dir. drama & librn, Interbay Boys' Club, Fla, 69- Speech Commun. Asn; Am. Theatre Asn; Children's Theatre Conf. French-speaking theatre of Montreal; children's theatre; history of American theatre. Publ: The French-speaking theatre of Montreal, Dissertation Abstracts, 64 & OP Microfilms, 65; Pi lights (poem), Delta Kappa Gamma Quart, 61; plus others. Add: 3814 Euclid Ave, Apt. 53, Tampa, FL 33609.

RICKEY, JOHN THOMAS, b. Cambridge, Ohio, Apr. 17, 20; m. 43; c. 3. SPEECH. B.S, Kent State Univ, 42, M.A, 51; Ph.D.(speech), Ohio State Univ, 55. Teacher speech & Eng, high schs, Ohio, 46-52; teaching fel. speech, Ohio State Univ, 52-55, asst. prof. speech educ, 55-56, SPEECH, 56-58; Purdue Univ, 58-61, assoc. prof, 61-67; PROF. BOWLING GREEN STATE UNIV, 67- Consult. ed, Speech Teacher, 61-64; Purdue Univ. Res. Found. grants, summers 62 & 63. U.S.N, 42-54, Lt. Speech Commun. Asn; Am. Forensic Asn.(ed, Register, 57-60); Cent. States Speech Asn.(assoc. ed, jour, 61-64); Nat. Soc. Stud. Commun. History of speech education; forensics, including debate, discussion and oratory; programmed learning. Publ: Co-auth, Interviewing principles and techniques, W.C. Brown, 68; auth, Persistent criticisms of debate, Gavel, 1/56; Some rhetorical aspects of the McGuffey readers, Speech Monogr, 6/56; Some of my best friends use debate texts, Cent. States Speech J, autumn 59. Add: Dept. of Speech, Bowling Green State University, Bowling Green, OH 43402.

RICKEY, MARY ELLEN, b. Baton Rouge, La, Jan. 11, 29. ENGLISH. B.A, La. State Univ, 49; M.A, Duke Univ, 50; Johns Hopkins Univ, 52-53; Ph.D, Univ. Fla, 55. Instr. ENG, La. State Univ, 50-52; from instr. to PROF, Univ. Ky, 55-68, UNIV. LOUISVILLE, 68- MLA; Renaissance Soc. Am; S.Atlantic Mod. Lang. Asn. English literature, especially Renaissance period and prosody. Publ: Rhyme and meaning in Richard Crashaw, 61 & Utmost art: complexity in the poetry of George Herbert, 66, Univ. Ky; co-ed, Certaine sermons or homilies, Scholars' Facsimiles, 69. Add: Dept. of English, University of Louisville, Louisville, KY 40208.

RICOU, LAURENCE RODGER, b. Brandon, Man, Oct. 17, 44; m. 66; c. 2. ENGLISH. B.A, Univ. Man, 65; M.A, Univ. Toronto, 67, fel, 68-70, Ph.D, 71. ASST. PROF. ENG, UNIV. LETHBRIDGE, 70- MLA; Asn. Can. Univ. Teachers Eng; Humanities Asn. Can; Asn. Can. & P.Q. Lit. Canadian literature. Publ: Vertical man/horizontal world: man and landscape in Canadian prairie fiction, Univ. B.C, 73; From king to interloper: man on the prairie in Canadian fiction, 1920-1929, In: The twenties in western Canada, Nat. Mus. Man, 72; Empty as nightmare: man and landscape in recent Canadian prairie fiction, Mosaic, winter 73. Add: Dept. of English, University of Lethbridge, 4401 University Dr, Lethbridge, Alta. T1K 3M4, Can.

RIDDEL, JOSEPH NEILL, b. Grantsville, W.Va, Sept. 11, 31; m. 57; c. 3. ENGLISH, AMERICAN LITERATURE. A.B, Glenville State Col, 53; M.S, Univ. Wis, 56, Ph.D.(Eng), 60. Asst, Univ. Wis, 55-60; instr. ENG, Duke Univ, 60-62, asst. prof, 62-64; vis. asst. prof, Univ. Calif, Riverside, 64-65; assoc. prof, State Univ. N.Y. Buffalo, 65-68, PROF, 68-73; UNIV. CALIF, LOS ANGELES, 73- Summers, Duke Univ. Res. Counc. fel, 63, State Univ. N.Y. Buffalo res. fels, 66, 67 & State Univ. N.Y. Res. Found. fels, 70 & 72. Explicator Prize, 65. U.S.A, 53-55. MLA. Modern American and modern British literature, especially poetry; poetic theory. Publ: The clairvoyant eye, the poetry and poetics of Wallace Stevens, 65 & The inverted bell: modernism and the counterpoetics of William Carlo Williams, 74, La. State Univ; C. Day Lewis, Twayne, 71; plus others. Add: Dept. of English, University of California, 405 Hilgard Ave, Los Angeles, CA 90024.

RIDDELL, JAMES ALLEN, b. Los Angeles, Calif, Nov. 7, 32; m. 64; c. 2. ENGLISH LITERATURE & LEXICOGRAPHY. B.A, Pomona Col, 54; M.A, Univ. South. Calif, 61, Ph.D.(Eng), 66. Lectr. ENG, Univ. South. Calif, 63-64; instr, Boston Univ, 64-66, asst. prof, 66-69; CALIF. STATE COL, DOMINGUEZ HILLS, 69-72, ASSOC. PROF, 72- U.S.C.G, 54-57, Res, 59-61, Lt. MLA; Bibliog. Soc; Shakespeare Asn. Am. Shakespeare; English Renaissance literature; early English dictionaries. Publ: Some actors in Ben Jonson's plays, Shakespeare Stud, 69; The reliability of early English dictionaries, In: Yearbk. Eng. Stud, 74; The begining: English dictionaries of the first half of the seventeenth century, Leeds Stud. Eng, 74. Add: Dept. of English, California State College Dominguez Hills, Dominguez Hills, CA 90747.

RIDENOUR, GEORGE MEYER, b. Findlay, Ohio, Sept. 30, 28. ENGLISH. B.A, Col. of Wooster, 50; Fulbright fel, Univ. Vienna, 51-52; M.A, Yale, 53, Ph.D.(Eng), 55. Instr. ENG, Yale, 55-60, asst. prof, 60-63; assoc. prof, Haverford Col, 63-65; PROF, Univ. N.Mex, 65-69; CITY UNIV. NEW YORK, 69- Nineteenth century. Publ: The style of Don Juan, Yale, 60; Browning's music poems, PMLA, 9/63. Add: 166 E. 35th, Apt. 16 E, New York, NY 10016.

RIDEOUT, JOHN GRANVILLE, b. Danville, Vt, Feb. 1, 15; m. 42; c. 2. ENGLISH LITERATURE. A.B, Colby Col, 36; Rhodes scholar, Oxford, 36, B.A, 38, M.A, 42; Ph.D, Brown Univ, 45. Instr. ENG, Beloit Col, 39-40; Brown Univ, 40-42; Wells Col, 42-46, asst. prof, 46; Univ. N.H, 46-49; assoc. prof, Idaho State Col, 49-53; prof. Eng. & chmn. div. humanities, Allen Univ, 54-59; Huston-Tillotson Col, 59-64; prof. Eng. & chmn. dept, LAKEHEAD UNIV, 64-70, PROF. ROMANTIC POETRY, 71- Asn. Am. Rhodes Scholars; Can. Asn. Rhodes Scholars; MLA; Asn. Can. Univ. Teachers Eng. The Romantic movement in English literature; Shelley. Add: Dept. of English, Lakehead University, Thunder Bay, Ont, Can.

RIDEOUT, WALTER BATES, b. Lee, Maine, Oct. 21, 17; m. 47; c. 3. AMERICAN LITERATURE. A.B, Colby Col, 38; A.M, Harvard, 39, fel, 46-49, Ph.D, 50. Instr. Eng, Northwest. Univ, 49-53, asst. prof. Am. lit, 53-57, assoc. prof, 57-63; prof, UNIV. WIS-MADISON, 63-72, HARRY HAYDEN CLARK PROF. ENG, 72-, vis. prof. Am. lit, 62-63, chmn. dept. Eng, 65-68, sr. vis. prof, Inst. Res. Humanities, 68-69. Guggenheim fel, 58-59. MLA; Am. Stud. Asn. Twentieth century American literature; critical biography of Sherwood Anderson; literary history of 1930's. Publ: Co-ed, Letters of Sherwood Anderson, Little, 53; auth, The radical novel in the United States, 1900-1954, 56 & ed, Caesar's column, 60, Harvard; co-ed, American poetry, Harper, 65. Add: Dept. of English, University of Wisconsin-Madison, 600 N. Park St, Madison, WI 53706.

RIDER, FREDERICK JOY, History of Consciousness, Humanities. See Volume I, History.

RIDER, JOHN R, b. Westfield, Ill, Apr. 19, 23; m. 48; c. 2. BROADCASTING, JOURNALISM. A.B, Ind. Cent. Col, 47; M.M.E, Chicago Musical Col, 54; Ph.D.(speech), Mich. State Univ, 63. Dir. pub. relat, Ind. Cent. Col, 47-49; teacher high sch, Ill. & Ind, 50-56; instr. speech & radio, MacMurray Col, 56-58, asst. to pres, 59-61; asst. prof. broadcasting, Univ. Tex, 62-63; assoc. prof. broadcasting & jour, Syracuse Univ, 63-68; PROF. MASS COMMUN, SOUTH. ILL. UNIV, EDWARDSVILLE, 68- Consult, Bell Tel. Labs, N.J, summer 66; trustee, Radio TV News Dir. Found, 67- U.S.N, 42-46, Lt.(jg). Radio-TV News Dirs. Asn; Asn. Educ. in Jour; Nat. Acad. TV Arts & Sci; Speech Commun. Asn; Documentary film. Publ: The student journalist and broadcasting, 68 & Your future in broadcasting, 71, Richards Rosen; A guide to the 1964 presidential elections, J. Broadcasting, fall 64; TV—it held the country together, N.Y. News Pub. Newslett, 11/64; Oh, the humanity, Quill, 8/65. Add: Communications Bldg, Southern Illinois University, Edwardsville, IL 62025.

RIDER, MAURICE LINCOLN, b. Grove City, Ohio, Oct. 26, 07; m. 33; c. 1. ENGLISH. B.Sc, Ohio State Univ, 30, M.A, 39, Ph.D, 50. Teacher Eng, West Mansfield High Sch, Ohio, 30-31; Dearborn High Sch, Mich, 31-36; Grove City High Sch, Ohio, 36-46; instr, Ohio State Univ, 46-50; PROF, UNIV. PA. 50- NCTE; MLA. Middle English; English for engineers; teaching of English. Publ: This blessed plot—this England, Pageant, 70; Engineers are writers too, Col. Eng, 2/54; In glorious titles he excels, Eng. J, 1/65; Of the titles of many books, Stud. in Humanities, 71; plus others. Add: Dept. of English, Indiana University of Pennsylvania, Indiana, PA 15701.

RIDGELY, JOSEPH V, b. Montgomery, Ala, June 23, 21; m. 56; c. 1. ENGLISH. B.A, Univ. Fla, 42, M.A, 46; M.A, Johns Hopkins Univ, 48, Ph.D, 56. Asst. prof. ENG, COLUMBIA UNIV, 58-63, assoc. prof, 63-70, PROF, 70- U.S.A.A.F, 42-45, Lt. MLA. American literature, 19th and 20th centuries. Publ: William Gilmore Simms, 62 & John Pendleton Kennedy, 66, Twayne. Add: 601-B Philosophy Hall, Columbia University, New York, NY 10027.

RIDLAND, JOHN MURRAY, b. London, Eng, July 4, 33; U.S. citizen; m. 57; c. 2. ENGLISH & AMERICAN LITERATURE. A.B, Swarthmore Col, 53; M.A, Univ. Calif, Berkeley, 58; Ph.D.(Eng), Claremont Grad. Sch, 64. From assoc. to ASSOC. PROF. ENG, UNIV. CALIF, SANTA BARBARA, 61- Ed, Little Sq. Rev, 66-72. Contemporary English and American literature. Publ: Fires of home, Scribners, 61; Ode on violence and other poems, Tenn. Poetry, 69. Add: Dept. of English, University of California, Santa Barbara, CA 93106.

RIDLEY, FLORENCE, b. Murfreesboro, Tenn, Nov. 13, 22. ENGLISH, MEDIEVAL LITERATURE. B.A, Randolph Macon Woman's Col, 44; M.A, Vanderbilt Univ, 52; fel, Harvard, 53-57, Ph.D.(Eng), 57. Instr. ENG, UNIV. CALIF, LOS ANGELES, 57-59, asst. prof, 59-66, assoc. prof, 66-69, PROF, 69- Renaissance Soc. Am; Mediaeval Acad. Am; MLA; Philol. Asn. Pac. Coast. Chaucer; the Scots Chaucerians; Conrad. Publ: Surrey's translation of Vergil's Aeneid, 63 & Chaucer's prioress and the critics, 65, Univ. Calif; A tale told too often, West. Folklore, 7/67; Middle Scots poetry: a checklist, 1956-1968, Stud. Scottish Lit, 7/70; The Middle Scots poets, In: Manual of writings in Middle English, Shoe String, Vol. IV, 73; plus three others. Add: Dept. of English, Humanities Bldg, 3331, University of California, 405 Hilgard Ave, Los Angeles, CA 90024.

RIED, PAUL EUGENE, b. Akron, Ohio, Oct. 11, 29; m. 52; c. 2. SPEECH. B.A, Baldwin-Wallace Col, 51; M.A, Ohio State Univ, 54, Ph.D, 59. Instr. speech, Hope Col, 55-57; asst. prof, Denison Univ, 57-60; Cent. Mo. State Col, 60-63; ASSOC. PROF. SPEECH & CHMN. DEPT. SPEECH EDUC, SYRACUSE UNIV, 63- U.S.N, 51. Speech Commun. Asn. Nineteenth century rhetoric in the United States; modern rhetorical theory. Publ: The Boylston Chair, West. Speech, 61; Joseph McKean: the second Boylston professor, Quart. J. Speech, 61. Add: Dept. of Speech Education, Syracuse University, Syracuse, NY 13210.

RIEGER, JAMES H, b. New York, N.Y, Sept. 5, 36. ENGLISH. A.B, Harvard, 58, Ph.D.(Eng), 63; M.A, Univ. Calif, Berkeley, 59. Instr. ENG, Harvard, 63-65; asst. prof, Univ. Calif, Berkeley, 65-69, summer fac. fel, 66; ASSOC. PROF, UNIV. ROCHESTER, 69- Am. Philos. Soc. grant, 68; Am. Counc. Learned Soc. grant-in-aid, 69. MLA; Keats-Shelley Asn. Am; Rydal Mount Summer Sch. Asn. English Romantic poetry and novel. Publ: The mutiny within: the heresies of Percy Bysshe Shelley, Braziller, 67; ed, Mary Shelley's Frankenstein, Bobbs, 74; contrib, Blake's sublime allegory, Univ. Wis, 73. Add: Dept. of English, University of Rochester, River Sta, Rochester, NY 14627.

RIEKE, RICHARD DAVIS, b. Alton, Ill, June 13, 35; m. 58; c. 3. RHETORICAL & COMMUNICATION THEORY. B.S, South. Ill. Univ, 57; M.A, Ohio State Univ, 58, Ph.D.(speech), 64. Asst. prof. speech, Ohio State Univ, 64-67, assoc. prof, 67-70; PROF. COMMUN. & CHMN. DEPT, UNIV. UTAH, 70- Vis. prof. speech, Univ. Minn, Minneapolis, summer 67; commun, Shaw Univ, fall 67 & spring 69; vis. lectr, McGill Univ. Debating Union, 69. Int. Commun. Asn; Speech Commun. Asn; Am. Forensic Asn.(secy, 68-69). Argumentation and decision-making; rhetorical criticism; communication and the law. Publ: Co-auth, Directing forensics, Intext, 68, Rhetoric of Black Americans, C.E. Merrill, 71 & Argumentation and decision-making, Wiley, (in press); contrib, The communicative arts and sciences of speech, C.E. Merrill, 67; co-auth, The dilemma of ethics and advocacy, West. Speech, 68; auth, The rhetoric of law, Today's Speech, 71. Add: Dept. of Communication, Speech-Communication Bldg, University of Utah, Salt Lake City, UT 84112.

RIFFE, NANCY LEE, b. Danville, Ky, Jan. 16, 33; div; c. 5. ENGLISH. B.A, Agnes Scott Col, 54; Woodrow Wilson fel, Radcliffe Col, 54-55, A.M, 55; Am. Asn. Univ. Women fel, Univ. Ky, 59-60, Ph.D, 63. Instr. Eng, Temple Univ, 60-64; prof. asst. test develop, Educ. Testing Serv, 64-65; asst. prof. ENG, Ursinus Col, 65-67; assoc. prof, LaSalle Col, 67-68; EAST. KY. UNIV, 68-71, PROF, 71- AAUP; S.Atlantic Mod. Lang. Asn. Renaissance English literature, especially Shakespeare, drama to 1642 and Milton; 18th century English periodicals and essayists. Publ: The Elizabethan stage: a bibliography, Shakespeare Newslett, 63; A finding list of some 18th century periodicals, Bull. N.Y. Pub. Libr, 63; A fragment of Milton, from the Italian, Mod. Philol, 66. Add: 109 Bridge Ave, Berea, KY 40403.

RIGA, FRANK P, b. Buffalo, N.Y, Jan. 1, 36; m. 60; c. 5. ENGLISH. B.A, State Univ. N.Y. Buffalo, 58, N.Y. State fel, 58-60, M.A, 62, Ph.D.(Eng), 67. Instr. ENG, D'Youville Col, 61-63; asst. prof, CANISIUS COL, 64-69, ASSOC. PROF, 69-, DIR. GRAD. STUD. ENG, 72-, fel, 68. MLA. English romanticism; tragedy. Add: Dept. of English, Canisius College, Buffalo, NY 14208.

RIGG, ARTHUR GEORGE, MEDIEVAL ENGLISH & LATIN. See Volume III, Foreign Languages, Linguistics & Philology..

RIGGS, JOSEPH H, b. Middlebourne, W.Va, Feb. 18, 28; m. 52; c. 4. SPEECH. B.A, Alderson-Broaddus Col, 52; M.A, W.Va. Univ, 53; Ph.D, Univ. Ill, 62. Instr. speech, Lehigh Univ, 53-54; Glenville State Col, 54-55; assoc. prof, Memphis State Univ, 55-66, prof. speech & dir. grad. stud, speech, 66-70; PROF. SPEECH & THEATRE, Ind. State Univ, 70-71; SLIPPERY ROCK STATE COL, 71-, COORD. ORAL HIST, 73- Instr, Am. Inst. Banking, 55-63; asst, Univ. Ill, 58-59; instr, Am. Savings & Loan Inst, 59-63; Am. Philos. Soc. summer grants, 62, 63; oral hist. consult, South. Col. Optometry, Memphis, 66-; dir. archives, Memphis Pub. Libr, 67- U.S.A.F, 46-48, Res, 48-66; U.S.N.R, 66-, Lt. Comdr. American public address: American history; political science. Publ: The papers of Senator Kenneth D. McKellar: a preliminary chronology, 60, A McKellar calendar of speeches, 62, ed, Gordon Browning: an oral memoir, 66 & co-ed, Everett R. Cook: a memoir, 71, Memphis Pub. Libr; ed, Southern College of Optometry institutional self-study, 66 & co-auth, Mr. Mac: a biography of William P. MacCracken, 70, South. Col. Optometry; Rhetorical events in the West Virginia statehood movement, W.Va. Hist, 56. Add: Dept. of Speech & Theatre, Slippery Rock State College, Slippery Rock, PA 16057.

RIGGS, WILLIAM GEORGE, b. Wellsville, N.Y, May 24, 38; m. 65; c. 3. ENGLISH LITERATURE. B.A, Univ. Rochester, 60; M.A, Univ. Calif, Berkeley, 62, Ph.D.(Eng), 68. Instr. ENG, BOSTON UNIV, 67-68, asst. prof, 68-73, ASSOC. PROF, 73- Am. Counc. Learned Soc. stud. fel, 73-74. MLA; Renaissance Soc. Am. Seventeenth century English literature; Milton. Publ: The Christian poet in Paradise lost, Univ. Calif, 72; The poet and satan in Paradise lost, 70 & The plant of fame in Lycidas, 73, Milton Stud. Add: Dept. of English, Boston University, 236 Bay State Rd, Boston, MA 02215.

RILEY, BRYAN M, b. Omaha, Nebr, Dec. 13, 24. ENGLISH. A.B, Creighton Univ, 48, A.M, 49; Oxford, 49-50; D.Univ, Univ. Sorbonne, 54; Louvain Univ, 59-60; Yeats Int. Summer Sch, Sligo, Ireland, 66. ASSOC. PROF. ENG, Black Hills Col, 62-63; East. N.Mex. Univ, 63-65; UNIV. WIS-OSHKOSH, 65- Add: Dept. of English, University of Wisconsin-Oshkosh, Oshkosh, WI 54901.

RILEY, DONALD W, b. Hamilton, Ohio, May 17, 01; m. 30. SPEECH. A.B, Miami Univ, 29; A.M, Ohio State Univ, 30, Ph.D, 44. From instr. to assoc. prof. speech & broadcasting, OHIO STATE UNIV, 30-70, EMER. PROF. COMMUN, 70- Guest lectr, Col. St. Mary Springs, 45-48; consult, Am. Legion Post, Columbus, Ohio, 46; vis. prof, Univ. of the Americas, 47-49, & 51-52; Margaret Shedd Writing Ctr, Mexico City, Mex, 50. Speech Commun. Asn; Eng-Speaking Union. Radio and television drama and program planning; radio and television production-direction; voice and diction. Publ: Handbook of radio drama techniques, Edwards Bros, 44; History of American radio drama, 1920-1948, Ohio State Univ. Add: 1666 Roxbury Rd, Columbus, OH 43212.

RILEY, JOBIE E, b. Springfield, Ohio, Oct. 9, 28; m. 55; c. 1. FORENSICS. A.B, Manchester Col, 54; B.D, Bethany Bibl. Sem, 58; M.A, Northwest. Univ, 59; Ph.D, Temple Univ, 74. Instr. speech, Chicago City Jr. Cols, 59-60; speech & Eng, Thornton Jr. Col, 60-61; asst. prof. Eng. & forensics, ELIZABETHTOWN COL, 61-68, ASSOC. PROF. COMMUN, 68- Speech Commun. Asn; Am. Forensic Asn. Add: Fairview Hall, Elizabethtown College, Elizabethtown, PA 17022.

RILEY, JOHN JAMES, b. Boston, Mass, Feb. 19, 22; m. 46; c. 2. ENGLISH & AMERICAN LITERATURE. A.B, Boston Univ, 49, A.M, 50; Ph.D.(Eng), Tufts Univ, 73. Instr. ENG. & AM. LIT, LOWELL TECHNOL. INST, 59-65, ASST. PROF, 65- Vis. assoc. prof. Eng. & Am. lit, Hellenic Col, 62-68; lectr, Univ. Trieste, 69. U.S.A, 43-45, Sgt; Bronze Star Medal. AAUP; MLA. Shakespeare's chronicle plays; Georgian poetry; modern British novel. Add: Dept. of English, Lowell Technological Institute, Lowell, MA 01854.

RILEY, MICHAEL HOWARD, b. Washington, D.C, Jan. 25, 40. ENGLISH LITERATURE. B.A, Wesleyan Univ, 62; M.A, Boston Univ, 65, fel, 66-69, Ph.D.(Eng), 70. ASST. PROF. ENG, UNIV. N.C, GREENSBORO, 69- South. Mod. Lang. Asn; Shakespeare Asn. Am. Renaissance drama; interdisciplinary research. Add: Dept. of English, University of North Carolina at Greensboro, Greensboro, NC 27412.

RINALDI, NICHOLAS M, b. Brooklyn, N.Y, Apr. 2, 34; m. 58; c. 4. ENGLISH. A.B, Fordham Univ, 57, M.A, 60, Ph.D.(Eng), 63. Adj. instr. Eng, Fordham Univ, 59-60; instr, St. John's Univ.(N.Y), 60-63, asst. prof, 63-66; assoc. prof, FAIRFIELD UNIV, 66-71, PROF. CONTEMPORARY LIT, 71- Adj. prof. Eng, City Col. New York, spring 66; Am. lit, Columbia Univ, summer 69; hist. of novel, Univ. Conn, summer 72. Creative writing; contemporary literature. Publ: Game imagery and game-consciousness in Faulkner's fiction, Twentieth Century Lit, 10/64; The TV savior image: a contemporary myth, Thought, 66; Game imagery in Faulkner's Absalom, Absalom!, Conn. Rev, 70; plus poems in several scholarly jour, 71-73. Add: Dept. of English, Fairfield University, Fairfield, CT 06433.

RINEAR, DAVID LESLIE, b. Matawan, N.J, Nov. 3, 44; m. 72. DRAMATIC ART, THEATRE HISTORY. B.A, Hiram Col, 66; Regent's fel. & M.A, Univ. Calif, Davis, 68; NDEA fel. & Ph.D.(theatre), Ind. Univ, 71. ASST. PROF. THEATRE, UNIV. PITTSBURGH, 71- Speech Commun. Asn; Am. Soc. Theatre Res. Nineteenth century British and American theatre history; performance aesthetics. Publ: Alfred Wigan: Victorian realist, Theatre Survey, 72; Kopit's debt to Chekhov, Today's Speech, 74. Add: Dept. of Speech and Theatre, 1117 CL, University of Pittsburgh, Pittsburgh, PA 15260.

RINEHART, HOLLIS, III, b. Jackson, Mich, June 6, 31. ENGLISH. B.A, Univ. Chicago, 50, Ph.D.(Eng), 65; M.A, Univ. Miami, 52. Instr. ENG, Northwest. Univ, 58-62; asst. prof, State Univ. N.Y. Binghamton, 64-67; YORK UNIV, 67-73, ASSOC. PROF, 73- MLA. Eighteenth century novel; literary criticism. Add: Dept. of English, York University, 4700 Keele St, Downsview, Ont. M3J 1P3, Can.

RINEHART, KEITH, b. Portland, Ore, Jan. 27, 18; m. 47; c. 2. ENGLISH. B.A, Univ. Ore, 40, M.A, 41; Ph.D.(Eng. lit), Univ. Wis, 51. Interpreter, Div. Mil. Govt, 44-46; instr. Eng, Mont. State Col, 46-47; teaching fel, Univ. Wis, 47-51; asst. prof. Eng, Stout State Col, 51-53; CENT. WASH. STATE COL, 53-57, assoc. prof, 57-63, PROF. ENG, 63-, chmn. div. lang. & lit, 63-66, chmn. dept. Eng, 66-68. MLA; NCTE. Literary criticism; history of ideas. Publ: The Victorian approach to autobiography, Mod. Philol, 2/54; The moral background of King Lear, Univ. Kans. City Rev, 54; The structure of Madame Bovary, French Rev, 2/58. Add: Dept. of English, Central Washington State College, Ellensburg, WA 98926.

RINGE, DONALD ARTHUR, b. New Orleans, La, Aug. 20, 23; m; c. 2. ENGLISH. B.A, Tulane Univ, 43, M.A, 48; Gen. Educ. Bd. fel, Harvard, 49-50, Ph.D.(Eng), 54. Instr. ENG, Tulane Univ, 48-49; col. eng, Univ. Mich, 53-55, asst. prof, 55-59, assoc. prof, 59-64, PROF, 64-65; UNIV. KY, 65- U.S.A, 43-45, 51-52. MLA; Am. Stud. Asn. Literature and art in early 19th century America; James Fenimore Cooper; early American fiction. Publ: James Fenimore Cooper, 62 & Charles Brockden Brown, 66, Twayne; The pictorial mode: space and time in the art of Bryant, Irving, and Cooper, Univ. Ky, 71. Add: 591 Springhurst Dr, Lexington, KY 40503.

RINGLER, RICHARD N, b. Milwaukee, Wis, Jan. 21, 34; m. 59; c. 2. ENGLISH. A.B, Harvard, 55, Ph.D, 61; M.A, Univ. Wis, 56. Instr. Eng. UNIV. WIS-MADISON, 61-62, asst. prof, 62-65, assoc. prof. ENG. & SCAND. STUD, 65-71, PROF, 71- Am. Counc. Learned Soc. fel, Reykjavik, Iceland, 65-66, London, 71-72. MLA; Mediaeval Acad. Am. Old English; old and modern Icelandic. Publ: Co-auth, Bright's Old English grammar and reader, 3rd ed, Holt, 71; auth, Him Seo Wen Geleah: the design for irony in Grendel's last visit to Heorot, Speculum, 66; introd. & bibliog, The black cliffs, Univ. Wis, 67. Add: 1240 Dartmouth Rd, Madison, WI 53705.

RINGLER, WILLIAM ANDREW, JR, b. Montclair, N.J, May 17, 12; m. 46; c. 3. ENGLISH LITERATURE. A.B, Princeton, 34, Class of 73 fel, 34-35, A.M, 35, Procter fel, 35-37, Ph.D.(Eng), 37. Instr. ENG, Princeton, 37-41, asst. prof, 41-42, 46-50; PROF, Wash. Univ, 50-62; UNIV. CHICAGO, 62- Guggenheim fel, 47-48, 57-58; Folger Shakespeare Libr. fel, 53; Charles K. Colver lectr, Brown Univ, 53; sr. res. assoc, Huntington Libr, 59-60; Australian-Am. Educ. Found. sr. scholar, Univ. Tasmania & vis. lectr, Australian univs, 72. U.S.A.A.F, 42-46, Maj. Shakespeare Asn. Am; Renaissance Soc. Am; Mod. Humanities Res. Asn. Gt. Brit; Renaissance Eng. Text Soc. Renaissance and Elizabethan literature; early Tudor poetry; textual criticism. Publ: Stephen Gosson, 42 & co-auth, John Rainolds' oratio in Laudem artis poeticae, 40, Princeton; auth, Poems of Sir Philip Sidney, Clarendon, 62; co-auth, An epilogue possibly by Shakespeare, Mod. Philol, 11/72; auth, Sir Philip Sidney, In: Encycl. Britannica, 73; Seven major Tudor poets, The Elizabethan sonnet & Minor Tudor poetry, In: New Cambridge bibliography of English literature, Cambridge, Vol. I, 73; plus others. Add: Dept. of English, University of Chicago, 1050 E. 59th St, Chicago, IL 60637.

RIPLEY, JOHN DANIEL, b. Londonderry, N.S, Jan. 27, 36; m. 72; c. 1. ENGLISH, SPEECH & DRAMA. B.A, Univ. N.B, 58, M.A, 59; Ph.D.(Eng), Univ. Birmingham, 63; Imp. Order Daughters Empire Overseas scholar; Can. Counc. fel. lectr. Eng, Dalhousie Univ, 61-62, asst. prof. & dir. drama workshop, 63-67; vis. assoc. prof. drama, Univ. Sask, 67-68; Can. Counc. Arts Bursary, 68-69; ASSOC. PROF. & DIR. DRAMA, McGILL UNIV, 69- Chmn, Can. Univs. Centennial Theatre Comt, 66-67. MLA; Can. Theatre Ctr; Can. Univ. Theatre Asn; Can. Child & Youth Drama Asn.(v.pres, 71-). Canadian theatre; drama in education; theatre history. Publ: Ed, Julius Caesar—J.P. Kemble 1814, Cornmarket, London, 70; auth, Imagination holds dominion—stage spectacle in Beerbohm Tree's productions, 1897-1900, Theatre Surv, spring 68. Add: Dept. of English, McGill University, Montreal, P.Q, Can.

RIPLEY, JOSEPH M, b. New York, N.Y, July 15, 27; m. 51; c. 2. SPEECH. B.A, Ohio State Univ, 52, M.A, 53, Ph.D.(speech, radio, TV), 61. Lectr. radio-TV, South. Ill. Univ, 55-56, instr, 56-57, assoc. dir, broadcasting serv, 57-61; assoc. prof. broadcasting, Univ. Wis, Madison, 64-67; PROF. Radio, TV & Films, UNIV. KY, 67-72, TELECOMMUN, 72-, chmn. dept. radio, TV & films, 67-72. Asst, Ohio State Univ, 53-55, asst. instr, 60-61. U.S.A, 45-48, 2nd Lt. Speech Commun. Asn; Cent. States Speech Asn; Asn. Prof. Broadcasting Educ. Radio-television; mass communications; social psychology. Publ: Co-auth, American broadcasting: workbook, Col. Printing, 65, Analysing broadcast programs; appeals, Col. Radio, 66 & Size and composition of station staffs, J. Broadcasting, 67; auth, An argument for television in the civil courtroom, J. Broadcasting, 67. Add: Dept. of Telecommunications, 322 Bowman Hall, University of Kentucky, Lexington, KY 40506.

RIPPY, FRANCES MAYHEW, b. Ft. Worth, Tex, Sept. 16, 29; m. 55; c. 3. ENGLISH. B.A, Tex. Christian Univ, 49; scholar, Vanderbilt Univ, 49-50, M.A, 51, fel, 51-52, Ph.D, 57; Fulbright scholar, Univ. London, Eng. & Brit. Mus, 52-53. Instr. ENG, Tex. Christian Univ, 53-55; Lamar State Col. Technol, 55, asst. prof, 57, 58 & 59; BALL STATE UNIV, 59-64, assoc. prof, 64-68, PROF, 68-, COORD. ENG. DOCTORAL STUD, 66-, CO-ED, FORUM, 61-, fac. res. grants, 60-61, 62-63, 69 & 73. Summers, vis. asst.

prof, Sam Houston State Teachers Col, 57; vis. lectr, Univ. P.R, 59 & 60, vis. prof, 61; Danforth fac. res. grant, 62, Danforth assoc, 66-; assoc. consult-evaluator, N.Cent. Asn. Col. & Sec. Schs, 73- Johnson Soc. Great Lakes Region (secy, 61-62); Johnson Soc. Midwest (secy, 61-62); Midwest Mod. Lang. Asn; MLA; Col. Eng. Asn; AAUP; Am. Soc. 18th Century Stud. Eighteenth century British novel; Restoration and 18th century British poetry; literary criticism. Publ: Imagery, John Dryden, and the poetry of statement, Forum, winter 60-61; Brevity, music, particularity, change: four premises of modern literature, Ball State Univ. Fac. Lecture Series, 65-66; Matthew Prior as the last Renaissance man, In: Studies in medieval, Renaissance, American literature: a Festschrift, Tex. Christian Univ, 71. Add: Dept. of English, Ball State University, Muncie, IN 47306.

RISSE, ROBERT GREGORY, b. St. Louis, Mo, Nov. 2, 29; m. 58; c. 3. ENGLISH. B.A, Grinnell Col, 51; M.A, Wash. Univ, 53, Ph.D.(Eng), 64. Instr. ENG, Boston Univ, 61-65; asst. prof, UNIV. MASS, BOSTON, 65-72, ASSOC. PROF, 72- Chaucer; Medieval literature; film history and criticism. Publ: The Augustinian paraphrase of Isaiah 14.13-14 in Piers Plowman and the commentary on the Fables of Avianus, Philol. Quart, 10/66. Add: Dept. of English, University of Massachusetts, Boston, MA 02116.

RISSO, RICHARD DAVID, b. San Francisco, Calif, Jan. 11, 32; m. 62; c. 2. DRAMA. B.A, San Jose State Col, 55; M.F.A, Carnegie Inst. Technol, 59; Conserv. d'Art Dramatique, Paris, 59-60; Ph.D.(drama), Stanford Univ, 64. Asst. prof. DRAMA, UNIV. CALIF, RIVERSIDE, 64-72, ASSOC. PROF, 72- Asst. producing dir, Ore. Shakespearean Festival, Ashland, 65- Play production on the Elizabethan stage. Publ: Co-auth, Digest of 500 plays, Collier Bks, 63. Add: Dept. of Drama, University of California, Riverside, CA 92502.

RITCH, KATHLEEN WALWORTH, b. New York, N.Y, Oct. 6, 30; m. 64; c. 2. ENGLISH. B.A, George Washington Univ, 52; M.A, Univ. Fla, 64. Res. psychologist, Cent. Intel. Agency, 52-56; ed. asst, G & C. Merriam Co, 56-57; INSTR. ENG, St. Johns River Jr. Col, 65-66; SANTA FE JR. COL, 67- NCTE. Linguistics. Publ: The comic aspects of The great Gatsby, Univ. Fla, 64. Add: 39D, 1800 N.W. Fourth St, Gainesville, FL 32601.

RITCHEY, R. DAVID, b. Shelbyville, Ky; m. 65; c. 1. THEATRE, SPEECH. B.A, Georgetown Col, 62; M.A, La. State Univ, Baton Rouge, 64, Ph.D.(theatre, speech), 71; Univ. Ky, 66. Instr. theatre, Ark. State Univ, 64-66; Georgetown Col, 66-68; ASST. PROF. SPEECH, AUBURN UNIV, 71- Am. Theatre Asn; South. Speech Asn; Speech Commun. Asn. Theatre history; theatre; public address. Publ: The Maryland Company of comedians, Educ. Theatre J, 72; Robert deLapouyade: the last of the Louisiana scene painters, La. Hist, 73; Columbia Garden: Baltimore's first pleasure garden, South. Speech J, 74; plus others. Add: Dept. of Speech, Auburn University, Auburn, AL 36830.

RITCHIE, HARRY M, b. Cleveland, Ohio, Jan. 9, 30; m. 53; c. 2. DRAMATIC ART. B.A, Oberlin Col, 52; M.F.A, Yale, 55, D.F.A, 60. Lectr. Eng, McGill Univ, 58-60; asst. prof. dramatic art, Univ. Calif, Berkeley, 60-64; ASSOC. PROF. DRAMA, TUFTS UNIV, 64- U.S.A, 55-57. Am. Theatre Asn; Speech Commun. Asn. Direction; teaching of acting; history of Irish drama. Publ: The influence of melodrama on the plays of Sean O'Casey, Mod. Drama, Fall 62; A suggested location for the Digby Mary Magdalene, Theatre Surv, Fall 63. Add: Dept. of Drama, Tufts University, Medford, MA 02155.

RITTER, CHARLES CLIFFORD, b. Fredericksburg, Va, Feb. 14, 28; m. 51; c. 2. THEATRE & SPEECH. B.A, Mary Washington Col, 51; Col. William & Mary, summer 51; M.A, Univ. Fla, 52; Ph.D.(speech & dramatic arts), Univ. Iowa, 56. Asst. prof. speech, Stetson Univ, 56-60; assoc. prof. THEATRE, OHIO STATE UNIV, 60-74, PROF, 74- U.S.N, 45-47. Speech Commun. Asn; Am. Theatre Asn. Directing; acting; theatre history and literature. Publ: Ed, The lively art of theatre: an anthology of plays, Allyn & Bacon, 70; auth, Introduction to theatre handbook, Col. Publ, 73; The educational theatre, In: The communicative arts and sciences of speech, C.E. Merrill, 67; plus one other. Add: Dept. of Theatre, Ohio State University, College of the Arts, Columbus, OH 43210.

RITTER, DARLENE MAE, b. Tilden, Nebr, May 15, 25. ENGLISH LITERATURE. B.S, Univ. Nebr-Lincoln, 49, 69; M.A, Colo. State Col, 58; Hellenic Inst, Athens, 65; Ind. Univ. Bloomington, 73. Teacher, North Bend Pub. Schs, Nebr, 43-46; Eng. & hist, Wisner, Nebr, 46-48; ENG, Fremont Sr. High Sch, 49-64; ASST. PROF, MIDLAND LUTHERAN COL, 64- John Hay fel, summer 62; Fulbright teacher, Italy, 62-63; Iceland, 66-67; U.S. Off. Educ. grantee, summer 71. NCTE; NEA. Icelandic sagas; Nebraska writer Willa Cather. Publ: Contrib, Corso D'Inglese, Soc. Ed. Dante Alighieri, 63. Add: Dept. of English, Midland Lutheran College, Fremont, NE 68025.

RITTER, JESSE PAUL, JR, b. Los Angeles, Calif, Oct. 16, 30; m. 49; c. 5. ENGLISH, COMPARATIVE LITERATURE. B.A, Kans. State Teachers Col, 55; M.A, Univ. Ark, 56, Ph.D.(Eng), 67. Asst. prof. Eng, East. Wash. State Col, 57-59; instr, N.Tex. State Univ, 60-62; North. Ill. Univ, 63-67; asst. prof. Eng. & dir. freshman Eng, 67-68; assoc. prof. ENG, SAN FRANCISCO STATE UNIV, 68-73, PROF, 73-, COORD. FRESHMAN ENG, 68- Secy-treas. Eng. Counc, Calif. State Univs. & Cols, 71-73. U.S.N, 51-54. NCTE. Railroad history; Southwestern blues music. Publ: Co-auth, Beyond survival, Heath, 72 & Focus/Media, Chandler, 73; auth, Teaching Kurt Vonnegut on the firing line, In: The Vonnegut Statement, 73; Fearful comedy: Catch-22 as avatar of the social surrealist novel, In: A Catch-22 casebook, Crowell, 73; plus others. Add: 222 Floribel Ave, San Anselmo, CA 94069.

RIVENBURGH, VIOLA K, b. Albert Lea, Minn, Mar. 15, 97; m. 26; c. 1. ENGLISH. A.B, Univ. Nebr, 19; M.A, Columbia Univ, 26. Instr. Eng, Univ. Hawaii, 24-26; ASST. PROF, UNIV. WASH, 42-68, ADVAN. WRITING COURSES, 68- Biography; English textbooks; Hawaii Foundation for History and the Humanities, especially research in history and related data for the Ethnic Research and Resources Center. Publ: Basic grammar: coordinated readings, Bobbs, 63; Princess Kaiulani of Hawaii, Tongg Publ. Co; Three aviation firsts, Light & Life, 73; Teaching outlining: a method, Col. Compos. & Commun. Bull; How to write that article, Nursing World, 58; From royalty to Rowdyism: but the high rise will win, Beacon Mag, 3/58; plus others. Add: 2307 33rd Ave. S, Seattle, WA 98144.

RIVERA, TOMAS, Romance Literatures, English. See Volume III, Foreign Languages, Linguistics & Philology.

RIVERS, CHARLES LEO, b. Aug. 8, 04; U.S. citizen. ENGLISH. A.B, Univ. Calif, Berkeley, 27, M.A, 28; Ph.D, Univ. South. Calif, 57. Instr. ENG, St. Mary's Col, 47-50; from assoc. prof. to PROF, NORTHWEST MO. STATE UNIV, 56- U.S.N, 42-45. Keats-Shelley Asn. Romantic movement; Victorian period; American literature. Publ: Three essays on Robert Browning's theory of the poet, 61, The twin revealment: subjective-objective polarity in the poetry of Robert Browning, 64, Robert Browning's Pauline: the dim orb of self, 65, Robert Browning's Sordello: an existential interpretation, 8/70 & Robert Browning's Paracelsus: a study in romantic irony, 2/72, Northwest Mo. State Col. Stud. Add: Dept. of English, Northwest Missouri State University, Maryville, MO 64468.

RIVERS, JAMES CLARK SEABROOK, b. Charleston, S.C, Oct. 13, 29; m. 60; c. 2. ENGLISH. B.S, Clemson Univ, 50; M.A, Univ. S.C, 60, Ph.D.(Eng), 67. Seismograph instrument engineer, Independent Exploration Co, 50-52; jr. physicist, field res. labs, Magnolia Petroleum Co, 52-54; asst. ENG, Univ. S.C, 61-62; asst. prof, Ga. Inst. Technol, 63-69, ASSOC. PROF, BAPTIST COL. CHARLESTON, 69- U.S.N, 54-57, Lt.(jg). MLA; S.Atlantic Mod. Lang. Asn; NCTE; Southeast Renaissance Conf. Relationship between science and literature; propaganda. Add: Dept. of English, Baptist College at Charleston, Charleston, SC 29411.

RIVES, RALPH HARDEE, b. Rocky Mount, N.C, Nov. 24, 30. DRAMATIC LITERATURE, ENGLISH. B.S, E.Carolina Univ, 52, M.A, 53; fel, Univ. Va, 55-58, Ed.D.(rhet), 60; cert, Oxford, 58. ASSOC. PROF. ENG, E.CAROLINA UNIV, 60- John Winant lectr. scholar, Brit-Am. Assocs, London, summer, 62. U.S.A, 53-55. Speech Commun. Asn; Orgn. Am. Hist. Southern United States history; North Carolina local history. Publ: The Jamestown celebration of 1857, Va. Mag. Hist. & Biog, 7/58; Public address in the Old Dominion, 1820-1840, South. Speech J, 61; Littleton Female College, N.C. Hist. Rev, 62. Add: Little Longwood, 309 Lewis St, Greenville, NC 27834.

RIVES, STANLEY GENE, b. Decatur, Ill, Sept, 27, 30; m. 57; c. 2. SPEECH. B.S, Ill. State Univ, 52, M.S, 55; Ph.D, Northwest. Univ, 63. Instr. SPEECH, W.Va. Univ, 55-56; asst. prof, ILL. STATE UNIV, 58-63, assoc. prof, 63-67, PROF, 67-, DEAN UNDERGRAD. INSTR, 72-, assoc. dean fac, 70-72. Vis. prof, Univ. Hawaii, 63-64; mem. bd. dirs, Nat. Debate Tournament, 68-; acad. admin. intern, Am. Counc. Educ, 69-70. U.S.A, 52-54. Speech Commun. Asn; Int. Commun. Asn; AAUP; Am. Forensic Asn; Midwest Forensic Asn.(gov, 61-63); Am. Asn. Higher Educ; Pac. Speech Asn. Rhetoric and public address; congressional debate; university administration. Publ: Co-auth, Individual speaking contests: preparation for participation, Burgess, 67 & Academic quicksand: some trends and issues in higher education, Prof. Educr. Publ, 73; auth, Fundamentals of oral interpretation of literature, Eichosha, Tokyo, 73; plus articles. Add: Office of Undergraduate Instruction, Illinois State University, Normal, IL 61761.

ROACH, HELEN PAULINE, b. St. Joseph, Mo, June 30, 03. SPEECH. A.B, Hunter Col, 24; A.M, Columbia Univ, 28, Ph.D, 48; summers, Acad. Speech Arts, 25, Inst. de Phonetique, Paris, 29. Teacher, pub. schs, N.Y, 24-29; instr, Hunter Col, 29-30; instr. SPEECH, BROOKLYN COL, 31-50, asst. prof, 51-63, ASSOC. PROF, 63- Spoken rec. comnr, White House Rec. Libr, 70-73. Speech Commun. Asn; Asn. Recorded Sound Collectors. Speech education; oral study of literature. Publ: History of speech education at Columbia College, 1754-1940, Columbia; Spoken records, Scarecrow, 63, 66, 70; Religion on the campus, Information. Add: Dept. of Speech, Brooklyn College, Brooklyn, NY 11210.

ROACH, JOSH PHILIP, b. Sault St. Marie, Mich, Oct. 3, 10; m. 32; c. 3. SPEECH. A.B, Hillsdale Col, 32; A.M, Univ. Mich, 36; Univ. South. Calif, 46; Ph.D, Univ. Denver, 54. Teacher pub. schs, Mich, 32-39, 42-43; dir. pub. relat, Hillsdale Col, 39-42; asst. prof. speech, Tex. Woman's Univ, 43-46, from assoc. prof. to prof, 46-72, dir. radio, 49-72, chmn. dept. speech, 63-68; RETIRED. Speech Commun. Asn; Am. Theatre Asn; Children's Theatre Conf. Educational theatre. Add: 409 Mimosa Dr, Denton, TX 76201.

ROACHE, JOEL HAYDEN, III, b. Louisville, Ky, Feb. 8, 41; m. 62; c. 1. ENGLISH. Woodrow Wilson fel. & B.A, Univ. Louisville, 62; M.A, Univ. Pa, 63, Ph.D.(Eng), 67. Instr. ENG, Col. Holy Cross, 66-67, asst. prof, 67-68; Univ. Wis-Madison, 68-72; ASSOC. PROF, UNIV. MD, EASTERN SHORE, 72- Mem. ed. bd, Forum in Marxist Criticism, 72-73. MLA; Am. Stud. Asn; NCTE; S.Atlantic Mod. Lang. Asn; Col. Lang. Asn; Am. Dialect Soc. American literature; Afro-American literature; radical criticism. Publ: Richard Eberhart: a poet in America 1904-1961, Oxford, 71; Treasure trove in the Pardoner's tale, J. Eng. & Ger. Philol, 1/65; Baudelarie and Symons: symbolism and decadence, Rev. Lit. Comp, 7-9/67; Review: radical perspectives in the arts, Col. Eng, 5/73. Add: Dept. of English & Languages, University of Maryland, Eastern Shore, Princess Anne, MD 21853.

ROBB, MARY MARGARET, b. Morning Sun, Iowa, Nov. 14, 00. SPEECH. A.B, Geneva Col, 21; A.M, State Univ. Iowa, 24; Ph.D, Columbia Univ, 41. Mem. staff Eng. & dramatic prod, Huron Col, 24-27; Eng, Am. Girls Col, Egypt, 27-28; SPEECH, Tex. Women's Col, 28-30; Chatham Col, 30-43; from asst. prof. to assoc. prof, UNIV. COLO, BOULDER, 46-59, prof, 59-69, EMER. PROF, 69- Prof, Metrop. State Col, 69-73. Speech Commun. Asn; West. Speech Commun. Asn. Bibliography of speech education; history of speech education; oral interpretation of literature. Add: Apt. 361, 2227 Canyon Blvd, Boulder, CO 80302.

ROBB, STEPHEN, b. Brooklyn, N.Y, Mar. 6, 39. SPEECH. A.B, Brooklyn Col, 60; A.M, Ind. Univ, 62, Ph.D.(speech), 67. ASST. PROF. SPEECH, PURDUE UNIV, WEST LAFAYETTE, 67- Speech Commun. Asn; Cent States Speech Commun. Asn; West. Speech Commun. Asn; South. Speech Commun. Asn. Contemporary American public address; rhetorical theory; dramatic criticism. Add: Dept. of Speech, Purdue University, West Lafayette, IN 47906.

ROBBINS, EDWIN W, b. Kansas City, Mo, June 7, 16; m. 40; c. 2. ENGLISH. B.A, Univ. Kansas City, 40; fel, Univ. Ill, 40-47, M.A, 41, Ph.D.(Eng), 48. Instr. ENG, Univ. Ill, summer 48; asst. prof, OHIO STATE UNIV, 48-54, assoc. prof, 54-58, PROF, 58-, v.chmn. dept, 53-66, dir. compos, 55-66. U.S.A, 43-45, M/Sgt. Renaissance Soc. Am; Milton Soc. Am; MLA. Tudor drama; 17th century English literature. Publ: Dramatic characterization in commentaries on Terence, Univ. Ill, 51; co-auth, Form and idea, Macmillan, 53, 61. Add: 164 W. 17th Ave, Columbus, OH 43210.

ROBBINS, GWEN, b. Conway Springs, Kans; c. 2. ENGLISH, SPEECH. B.S.Ed, Emporia State Col, 58; M.A, Wichita State Univ, 66. Lectr. Eng, Wichita State Univ, 65-66; asst. prof, Bethany Col.(Kans), 66-68; speech, Doane Col, 68-69; ASST. PROF. ENG. & DIR. CONT. EDUC, N.MEX. MIL. INST, 69- Add: 2703 Chrysler Dr, Roswell, NM 88201.

ROBBINS, JOHN ALBERT, b. Knoxville, Tenn, Dec. 5, 14; m. 50; c. 1. AMERICAN LITERATURE. A.B, Univ. Fla, 37, A.M, 38; Harrison fel, Univ. Pa, 39-41, Ph.D.(Am. civilization), 47. Asst. instr, Univ. Pa, 41-42, 45-46; instr, Duke Univ, 46-50; asst. prof. Eng, IND. UNIV, BLOOMINGTON, 50-55, assoc. prof. AM. LIT, 55-63, PROF, 63-, dir. freshman lit. course, 53-60, v.chmn. dept. Eng, 67-68. Fulbright lectr, France, 55-56; mem. ed. bd, Calendars of Am. Lit. Manuscripts, 65-; vis. prof, Univ. N.C, summer 67; mem. ed. bd, Emerson Soc. Quart, 72- U.S.N.R, 42-44, Lt. Comdr. Am. Stud. Asn; MLA (mem. comt. libr. manuscript holdings, Am. lit. sect, 51-, chmn, 61-, mem. bibliog. comt, 56-67); Am. Lit. Group, MLA (mem. bibliog. comt, 51-). Nineteenth century American literature; American poetry; Poe. Publ: Co-auth, American literary manuscripts, Univ. Tex, 61; ed, E.P. to L.U: nine letters written to Louis Untermeyer by Ezra Pound, Ind. Univ, 63 & American literary scholarship, Duke Univ, annually, 68-; auth, America and the poet; Merrill checklist of Edgar Allan Poe, C.E. Merrill, 69; Whitman, Hart Crane and Frost, In: American poetry, E. Arnold, London, 65; The narrative form of Song of myself, Am. Transcendental Quart, 71; Edgar Poe and the Philadelphians, Poe Stud, 72; plus others. Add: Dept. of English, Indiana University, Bloomington, IN 47401.

ROBBINS, ROSSELL HOPE, b. Wallasey, Eng, July 22, 12; nat; m. 39. MIDDLE ENGLISH LITERATURE. B.A, Univ. Liverpool, 33, dipl. educ, 34, Noble fel, 39-40; Ph.D.(Mid. Eng. relig. lyric), Cambridge, 37. Dir. stud, Cambridge, 35-37; Commonwealth fel. of Am, 37-39; instr, Brooklyn Col, 41-42; consult. educ. policies, Nat. Inst. Soc. Relat, Wash, D.C, 46; asst. prof. Eng, Polytech. Inst. Brooklyn, 46-49, assoc. prof, 49-54; MLA res. grant, 54; Guggenheim fel, 55-56; hon. assoc. univ. sem. Mediaeval stud, Columbia Univ, 56-59, 60-66; Can. Counc. prof. Eng, Mt. Allison Univ, 65; coop. prof. humanities prog, Duke Univ, 65-66; Mrs. William Beckman prof. Eng, Univ. Calif, Berkeley, 66; vis. prof, Eng. Summer Inst, Sir George Williams Univ, 68; Regents' prof, Univ. Calif, Riverside, 68-69; INT. PROF. ENG, STATE UNIV. N.Y. ALBANY, 69- Vis. prof, Univ. N.C, 58; Ford Found. vis. scholar, Dunster House, Harvard, 58, 59; official overseas guest, Brit. Univ. Teachers Eng, Hull, Eng, 62 & Brit. Asn. Advan. Sci, 63; Am. Counc. Learned Soc. grantee, 63; vis. scholar, Univ. Ctr, Va, 66; overseas guest, Humanities Asn. Can, 66 & 69; speaker, Int. Musicol. Congr, Ljubljana, Yugoslavia, 67; Fellows lectr, Huron Col.(Ont), 68; NDEA vis. prof, California State Col.(Pa), 69; speaker, Fed. Int. Langues et Lit. Mod, Pakistan, 69. Guest lectr, many cols. & univs, U.S, Can, Eng. & Europe. U.S.A, 43-45, Lt. MLA (chmn. bibliog. comt, 59-); Mediaeval Acad. Am; Mod. Humanities Res. Asn, Gt. Brit; Renaissance Soc. Am; fel. Royal Soc. Lit. U.K; Humanities Asn. Can; Int. Asn. Univ. Prof. Eng. Middle English literature and language; heretical witchcraft. Publ: Co-auth, The index of Middle English verse, 43, auth, Historical poems of the XIV and XV centuries, 59, & Early English Christmas carols, 61, Columbia Univ; Christopher Marlowe: Dr. Faustus, Barron's, 48, 67; The T.S. Eliot myth, Schuman, 51; Secular lyrics of the XIV and XV centuries, Clarendon, 52, 55, 61, 64, 68; Encyclopedia of witchcraft and demonology, 59, 60, 63, 65, 66, 68-73 & The hundred tales, 60, 62, Crown; Supplement to the index of Middle English verse, Univ, Ky, 65; Mirth in manuscripts, In: Essays and studies, Humanities, 68; Chaucer's lyrics, In: Companion to Chaucer studies, Oxford, 68; Chaucerian apocrypha, In: Manual of writings in Middle English, Vol. IV, Conn. Acad. Arts, 73; plus one other. Chaucer and Medieval studies in honor of Rossell Hope Robbins, Allen & Unwin, London, 74 & Kent State Univ, 74. Add: Katsbaan Onderheugel, Saugerties, NY 12477.

ROBBINS, WILLIAM, b. Cranbrook, B.C, Sept. 17, 09; m. 37; c. 1. ENGLISH. B.A, Univ. B.C, 30, M.A, 34; R.W. Leonard fel, Univ. Toronto, 38-39, Ph.D. (Eng), 42. Lectr. ENG, Wesley Col.(Man), 35-38; asst. prof, Victoria Col, 39-44; UNIV. B.C, 44-46, assoc. prof, 46-47, PROF, 47- Royal Soc. Can. fel, 54-55; Can. Counc. fel, 61-62. Fel. Royal Soc. Can. Nineteenth century literature. Publ: The ethical idealism of Matthew Arnold, Heinemann, London & Univ. Toronto, 59; Humanistic values in English literature, CBC Publ, 60; co-auth, As a man thinks, W.J. Gage, 3rd ed, 62; auth, The Newman brothers, Heinemann, London & Harvard, 66; Modern guides to faith, 7/45, Matthew Arnold and Ireland, 10/47 & Hamlet as allegory, 4/52, Univ. Toronto Quart. Add: Dept. of English, University of British Columbia, Vancouver, B.C. V6R 1H7, Can.

ROBERTS, EDGAR VERNE, JR, b. Minneapolis, Minn, Oct. 20, 28; m. 54; c. 3. ENGLISH. B.A, Univ. Minn, 51, M.A, 52, Ph.D.(Eng), 60; Univ. London, 55-56. Instr. ENG, Wayne State Univ, 57-61; Hunter Col, 61-64, asst. prof, 65-68; LEHMAN COL, 68-69, assoc. prof, 69-74, PROF, 74- Am. Counc. Learned Soc. grant-in-aid, 63; City Univ. New York fac. fel, 67. U.S.A, 46-47. MLA; NCTE; Soc. Theatre Res, Eng. The plays of Henry Fielding. Publ: Writing themes about literature, Prentice-Hall, 64, 3rd ed, 73; ed, Henry Fielding's The Grub-Street opera, 68 & John Gay's The beggar's opera, 69, Univ. Nebr; auth, Eighteenth-century ballad opera: the contribution of Henry Fielding, Drama Surv, spring 61; Henry Fielding's ballad opera The lottery and the English state lottery of 1731, Huntington Libr. Quart, 11/63; The songs and tunes in Henry Fielding's ballad operas, In: The eighteenth-century English stage, Methuen, 72; plus one other. Add: Dept. of English, Herbert H. Lehman College, Bronx, NY 10468.

ROBERTS, FRANCIS WARREN, b. Menard, Tex, Dec. 3, 16; m. 43; c. 2. ENGLISH. A.B, Southwest. Univ.(Tex), 38, hon. D.Litt, 71; M.A, Univ. Tex, 49, Ph.D, 56. Instr. Eng. & hist, Hebronville High Sch, Tex, 39-40; AV specialist, exten. div, UNIV. TEX, AUSTIN, 47-49, instr. ENG, 54-56, asst. prof, 58-59, ASSOC. PROF, 60-, DIR, HUMANITIES RES. CTR, 62-, assoc. dir, 60-61. Fulbright lectr. Am. stud, Univs. Pisa & Florence, 56-58; assoc. ed, Tex. Quart, 63- U.S.N. 40-45, Res, 50-54, Comdr.(Ret). MLA; S.Cent. Mod. Lang. Asn.(v.pres, 73-74, pres, 74-75); Mod. Humanities Res. Asn, Gt. Brit. Bibliography; D.H. Lawrence; 20th century American and English literature. Publ: Bibliography of D.H. Lawrence, Rupert Hart-Davis, London, 63; ed, Complete poems of D.H. Lawrence, 63, rev. ed, 73 & co-auth, Phoenix II, uncollected writings of D.H. Lawrence, 68, Heinemann, London; co-auth, The world of D.H. Lawrence, Thames & Hudson, London, 66. Add: Humanities Research Center, University of Texas at Austin, P.O. Box 7219, Austin, TX 78712.

ROBERTS, JAMES RUSSELL, b. Helena, Mont, Sept. 1, 03; m. 40; c. 1. AMERICAN LITERATURE. A.B, State Col. Wash, 30, A.M, 31; Ph.D, Univ. Wash, 40. Instr. Eng, Col. Puget Sound, 31-34; teaching fel, Univ. Wash, 34-39; assoc. prof. lang. & lit. & acting head div, East. Wash. Col, 39-46; asst. prof. ENG, Univ. Wash, 46-49; from assoc. prof. to prof, PAC. UNIV, 49-71, chmn. dept, 62-71, EMER. PROF, 71- Consult. Eng. curriculum, Portland Pub. Schs, Ore, 59; Eng, Ore. Counc. Advan. Placement, 60-61. MLA; NCTE; Philol. Asn. Pac. Coast. Dante studies in Florence, Italy; Emerson's debt to the 17th century. Publ: Listening to the wilderness with William Stafford, West. Am. Lit, (in press). Add: Dept. of English, Pacific University, Forest Grove, OR 97116.

ROBERTS, JEANNE A, b. Washington, D.C; m. 48, 66; c. 2. ENGLISH. Danforth grant, Univ. Va, 62-63, Ph.D, 64. Teacher, Am. Bi-Nat. Ctr, Bangkok, Thailand, 52-56; from instr. to asst. prof. & chmn. dept. ENG, Beirut Col. Women, 56-60; assoc. prof, AM. UNIV, 60-70, PROF, 70- Folger Libr, sr. fel, 69-70; lectr, Howard Univ, 71-72. MLA; Shakespeare Asn. Am; Renaissance Soc. Am. Shakespeare; Elizabethan drama, Milton. Publ: Language through literature, Khayat's Beirut, 59; The merry wives: suitably shallow but neither simple nor slender, Shakespeare Stud, 71; The merry wives as a Hallowe'en play, Shakespeare Surv, 72; The Windsor Falstaff, Papers Lit. & Lang, 73. Add: Dept. of Literature, American University, Massachusetts & Nebraska Aves, Washington, DC 20016.

ROBERTS, JOHN BUCKLEY, b. Poughkeepsie, N.Y, June 2, 18; m. 41. COMMUNICATIONS, RADIO & TELEVISION. A.B, N.Y. Univ, 40; A.M, State Univ. Iowa, 41; Univ. Pa, 47-50. Dir. radio, Univ. Maine, 41-44; from asst. prof. to prof. radio, TV & speech & dir. radio-TV film, TEMPLE UNIV, 46-67, PROF. COMMUN, 68- Moderator, Pub. Hearing Radio Prog, WFIL, 47-50, news commentator, WFIL & WFIL-TV, 50-70; founder WRTI-FM, 53 & WHYY-TV, 57, sponsor bd. mem, 57- Lindbach Found. Distinguished Teaching Award, 68. U.S.N.R, 44-46. Int. Commun. Asn; Radio-TV News Dirs. Asn; Broadcast Educ. Asn; AAUP; Speech Commun. Asn; Nat. Asn. Educ. Broadcasters; Asn. Educ. in Jour; Univ. Film Asn. Communication theory; mass communications; television news. Publ: Contrib, Handbook of group discussion, Houghton, 50. Add: Dept. of Radio-Television-Film, Temple University, Philadelphia, PA 19122.

ROBERTS, JOHN RICHARD, b. Brazil, Ind, Mar. 7, 34; m. 55; c. 6. ENGLISH. B.A, Ind. State Univ, 55; M.A, Univ. Ill, 57, Ph.D.(Eng), 62. Teaching asst. ENG, Univ. Ill, 57-62; instr, Univ. Wis, 62-64, asst. prof, 64-66; assoc. prof, Univ. Detroit, 66-68; UNIV. MO-COLUMBIA, 68-72, PROF, 72- Univ. Wis. summer res. grants, 63, 64 & 66; Univ. Mo. summer res. grants, 67, 68 & 71. MLA; Midwest Mod. Lang. Asn. Nondramatic English literature, 1600-1660; metaphysical poetry; English recusant literature. Publ: A critical anthology of English recusant devotional prose, 1558-1603, Duquesne Univ, 66; John Donne: an annotated bibliography of modern criticism, 1912-1967, Univ. Mo, 73; The influence of The spiritual exercises of St. Ignatius on the Nativity poems of Robert Southwell, J. Eng. & Ger. Philol, 62; Rosary in Elizabethan England, Month, 63; Donne's Satyre III reconsidered, CLA J, 12:105-115. Add: Dept. of English, University of Missouri-Columbia, Columbia, MO 65201.

ROBERTS, JOSEPH BOXLEY, JR, b. Yazoo City, Miss, Feb. 13, 18; m. 45; c. 2. ENGLISH. B.A, Univ. Ala, 50; Gen. Educ. Bd. Rockefeller Found. scholar, 50-51; M.A, Univ. N.C, 54; Ph.D.(Eng), Univ. Denver, 59. Asst. prof. ENG, U.S. Mil. Acad, 53-56; U.S. Air Force Acad, 56-57, assoc. prof. & dep. head dept, 59-63; PROF, TROY STATE UNIV, 68-, chmn. dept, 68-71, dean col. arts & sci, 71-72. U.S.A.F, 42-46, 51-68, Lt. Col; Bronze Star Medal. MLA; NCTE; S.Atlantic Mod. Lang. Asn. Shakespeare; Chaucer; modern literature. Publ: Faint voice calling (poetry), Hippogryph, 45; Web of our life (short stories), Humphries, 57; co-auth, The sound of wings (anthology), Henry Holt, 57; auth, On poetry and the poetic process (essays), Troy State Univ, 71; Literature as a catalytic agent, J. Eng. Educ, 10/62; On Allen Tate's The oath, Comment, Univ. Ala. Rev, spring 66; We have fallen on hard times, Phi Kappa Phi J, 73; plus one other. Add: Dept. of English, Troy State University, Troy, AL 36081.

ROBERTS, KATHRYN HEALY, Des Moines, Iowa, Jan. 27, 07; m. 27. ENGLISH, SPEECH. B.A, Univ. Idaho, 25; Mont. State Col, 46, 55; M.A, Univ. Wash, 49; San Diego State Col, summer 51. Head dept. Eng, Kellogg High Sch, Idaho, 25-27; teacher Eng. & drama, Gallatin County High Sch, 27-34; assoc. prof. SPEECH, MONT. STATE UNIV, 46-71, EMER. PROF, 71- Consult. post laryngectomy rehabil. for speech, Veterans Rehabil. Admin, Denver, Colo, 63. Remedial speech; creative writing. Publ: Who teaches whom—the teacher or the vet? Educ. Mag, 9/47; plus others. Add: Dept. of Speech, Montana State University, Bozeman, MT 59715.

ROBERTS, LEONARD WARD, b. Osborn, Ky, Jan. 28, 12; m; c. 4. ENGLISH. A.B, Berea Col, 39; M.A, State Univ, Iowa, 43; Ind. Univ, summer, 48; Ph.D, Univ, Ky, 54. Instr. health educ. & music, Brevard Col, 40-42; teaching fel, Univ. N.C, 43-45; instr. Eng, Berea Col. Found, 45-50; teaching fel, Univ. Ky; prof. Piedmont Col, 53-54; prof. & head dept. Eng. & chmn. div. langs, Union Col, 54-58; prof. Eng, Morehead State Col, 58-61; prof. Eng. & chmn. div. lang. & lit, W.Va. Wesleyan Col, 61-, res. grant, 62-63; PROF. ENG, PIKEVILLE COL, 68-, chmn. dept, 68-72. U.S.A, 30-33. Am. Folklore Soc; NCTE; Nat. Folk Festival Asn.(v.pres, 63-69, pres, 69-72); MLA. Publ: South from hell-fer-sartin, I bought me a dog, 54 & Nippy and the Yankee Doodle, 58, Counc. South. Mts; Up cutshin and down greasy, 59 & Tales and songs of Couch family, 59, Univ. Ky; Old Greasybeard: tales of the Cumberland Gap, Folklore Assoc, 69; Sang branch settlers: folksongs and tales of a Kentucky mountain family, Univ. Tex, 74; Magic folktales in America, In: Our living traditions: an introduction to American folklore, Basic Bks, 68. Add: Mare Creek, Stanville, KY 41659.

ROBERTS, MARGUERITE, b. Rockport, Ind. ENGLISH LITERATURE & PHILOLOGY. A.B, Evansville Col, 24; A.M, Radcliffe Col, 28, Ph.D, 43. Dean women, McMaster Univ, 37-46, lectr. ENG, 37-38, asst. prof, 38-46; lectr, Univ. Toronto, 46-47; PROF, WESTHAMPTON COL, 47-, dean, 47-65, chmn. dept. Eng, 65-71. Assoc. ed, Deans Jour, 42-50; app. by Secy. McNamara to Defense Adv. Comt. on Women in Serv, 65-68, chmn. sub-comt. educ. & mem. exec. comt, 67-68. MLA. Ellen Glasgow; theater and drama; Thomas Hardy and the Hardy circle. Publ: Tess in the theater, Univ. Toronto & Daiaka Sha, Tokyo; Farces and piracies of Mrs. Fiske's Tess, Colby; Hardy's poetic drama and the theatre, Pageant, 65; Dramatic element in Hardy's poetry, Queen's Quart. Add: Dept. of English, Westhampton College, Richmond, VA 23173.

ROBERTS, MARY MARGARET, b. Independence, Iowa, Mar. 30, 23. SPEECH. B.A, Luther Col, 44; M.A, Northwest. Univ, 49; Ph.D.(speech), La. State Univ, 59. Instr. speech & Eng, Red Wing High Sch, Minn, 44-46; speech & debate, Jefferson High Sch, Council Bluffs, Iowa, 46-49; asst. prof, Luther Col, 49-50; instr, Kans. State Teachers Col. Pittsburg, 50-54; ed. asst, Speech Asn. Am, 54-55; instr. speech, Appalachian State Teachers Col, summer 55; asst, La. State Univ, 56-57; instr. speech & debate, Univ. Pittsburgh, 57-60, asst. prof. speech & dir. debate, 60-61; assoc. prof. speech & adv. grad. stud. speech, KANS. STATE COL. PITTSBURG, 61-65, PROF. SPEECH & DIR. GRAD. STUD. SPEECH, 65- Speech Commun. Asn.(mem. ed. bd, Speech Teacher, 66-69, ed, 73-, mem. adv. comt. for speech commun. module of ERIC, 72-); Am. Forensic Asn.(mem. publ. comt, 61-63); Cent. States Speech Asn. American public address; history of speech education. Publ: Choosing the time and place for graduate work, Speech Teacher, 1/66; co-auth, Peter Marshall's sermon approach—innovative or traditional?, South. Speech J, summer 70. Add: Dept. of Speech & Theatre, Kansas State College of Pittsburg, Pittsburg, KS 66762.

ROBERTS, RUTH ELOISE, b. Poultney, Vt, Dec. 28, 14. ENGLISH, COMPARATIVE LITERATURE. A.B, Mt. Holyoke Col, 36; M.A, Columbia Univ, 39, Fisher fel, 55-56, Ph.D.(Arthurian Romance), 57; Fulbright grant, 54-55. Instr. ENG, Blackburn Col, 40-44; Bennett Col, 44-46; asst. prof, N.Y. State Col, Albany, 46-52; Wittenberg Univ, 57-60, assoc. prof, 60-63; STATE UNIV. N.Y. COL, FREDONIA, 63-69, PROF, 69- State Univ. N.Y. Res. Found. grants-in-aid, 66-70, fac. fel, 68. MLA; Int. Arthurian Soc; Mediaeval Acad. Am; Cambrian Archaeol. Asn; Mod. Humanities Res. Asn; Hon. Soc. Cymmrodorion. Celtic language and literature; Arthurian Romance; Chaucer. Publ: Tors fils Ares, Bibliog. Bull. Int. Arthurian Soc, 62. Add: Dept. of English, State University of New York College at Fredonia, Fredonia, NY 14063.

ROBERTS, THOMAS JOHN, b. Omaha, Nebr, June 10, 25; m. 51; c. 3. ENGLISH. B.A, Univ. Minn, Minneapolis, 48, M.A, 52, Ph.D.(Eng), 58; Univ. Kans, 52-55. Asst. prof. ENG, Am. Univ. Cairo, 58-60, assoc. prof, 61-63; Univ. Alaska, 60-61; asst. prof, UNIV. CONN, 63-67, ASSOC. PROF, 67- U.S.N, 43-46. MLA; NCTE. The theory of literature; applied English linguistics; popular culture. Publ: When is something fiction?, South. Ill. Univ, 72; Critics' recognition of an instance of literature, Lang. & Style, 68; Critics' conceptions of literature, Col. Eng, 69; plus others. Add: Dept. of English, University of Connecticut, Storrs, CT 06268.

ROBERTS, VERA MOWRY, b. Pittsburgh, Pa, Oct. 21, 18; m. 51; c. 1. ENGLISH, DRAMA. B.S, Frick Teachers Col, Univ. Pittsburgh, 36, M.A, univ, 40, Ph.D, 50. Dist. rep, Pa. State, 41-43; asst. prof. Eng, George Washington Univ, 46-54; instr. speech & drama, HUNTER COL, 55-61, asst. prof, 62-66, assoc. prof, 66-69, PROF. THEATRE, 69-, CHMN. DEPT. THEATRE & CINEMA, 70- Dir, Children's Theatre, Wash, D.C, 46-50; Arena Theatre, 50-54. Phi Delta Gamma Nat. Achievement Award, 66. U.S.N, 43-46, Lt. Fel. Am. Theatre Asn.(pres, 73); Am. Soc. Theatre Res; Speech Commun. Asn. Satire in American drama; theatre history; theatre criticism. Publ: On stage: a history of theatre, 62, 74 & The nature of theatre, 72, Harper. Add: Apt. W3D, 303 W. 66th St, New York, NY 10023.

ROBERTS, WARREN EVERETT, b. Norway, Maine, Feb. 20, 24; m. 50; c. 2. ENGLISH. B.A, Reed Col, 48, M.A, Ind. Univ, 50, Ph.D.(folklore), 53. Instr. Eng, IND. UNIV, 53-56, asst. prof, 56-61, assoc. prof, 61-66, PROF. FOLKLORE, 66- Fulbright res. scholar, Norway, 59-60; John Simon Guggenheim Mem. Found. fel, 66-67. U.S.A, 42-46, Lt. Fel. Am. Folklore Soc; Int. Soc. Folk Narrative Res. Folk architecture; the folktale; regional ethnology. Publ: Tale of the kind and unkind girls, 58 & co-auth, Volksmärchen aus dem Jeyporeland, 59, W. deGruyter, Berlin; auth, Norwegian folktale studies, Universitets Forlaget, Oslo, 64; Types of Indic oral tales, Folklore Fel. Commun, Helsinki, 60. Add: 1320 Pickwick Pl, Bloomington, IN 47401.

ROBERTSON, DAVID ALAN, b. Memphis, Tenn, May 10, 37; m. 58; c. 3. MODERN & BIBLICAL LITERATURE. B.A, Yale, 59, Ph.D.(relig), 66; B.D, South. Methodist Univ, 62; M.A, Univ. Toronto, 64; Ph.D.(Eng. lit), Univ. Calif, Irvine, 72. ASST. PROF. Old Testament, Perkins Sch. Theol, South. Methodist Univ, 66-70; ENG. LIT, UNIV. CALIF, DAVIS, 71- MLA; Soc. Biblical Lit. Contemporary poetry; biblical literature. Publ: Linguistic evidence in dating early Hebrew poetry, Soc. Biblical Lit, 72; The morphemes -y and -w in biblical Hebrew, Vetus Testamentum, 68; Job: a literary study, Soundings, 73. Add: Dept. of English, University of California, Davis, CA 95616.

ROBERTSON, DAVID ALLAN, JR, b. Chicago, Ill, July 30, 15; m. 40; wid; c. 3; m. 64; c. 3. ENGLISH LITERATURE. A.B, Princeton, 36, A.M, 39, Ph.D.(Eng), 40; Henry fel, Cambridge, 37-38. Instr. ENG, BARNARD COL, COLUMBIA UNIV, 40-47, asst. prof, 47-50, assoc. prof, 50-56, prof, 56-68, McINTOSH PROF, 68-, chmn. dept, 56-59, 64-67. Asst. secy, Eng. Inst, 46, secy, 47-48, ed, Essays, 46-48; Howard Found. fel, 53-54; mem. comn. Eng, Col. Entrance Exam. Bd, 59-64. U.S.N.R, 42-46, Lt. Comdr. MLA. Sir Charles Eastlake and the Victorian art-world. Publ: George Mallory, Faber & Faber, 69; The lady who reviewed Jane Eyre, Gazette Grolier Club, 2/70. Add: Dept. of English, Barnard College, Columbia University, New York, NY 10027.

ROBERTSON, DONALD JACKSON, b. Crookston, Minn, Aug. 6, 12; m. 36; c. 1. ENGLISH. A.B, Univ. N.Dak, 33, A.M, 36; Northwest. Univ, 33-34; Univ. Minn, 40-41. Teacher high sch, N.Dak, 34-35; Aggassiz Sch, Fargo, 35-36; N.Dak. State Teachers Col, Valley City, 36-40; Univ. Minn, 40-41; instr. ENG, UNIV. N.DAK, 41-42, ASST. PROF, 42-, ASST. TO PRES, 42-, DEAN UNIV. COL, 55- American literature; Nathaniel Hawthorne. Add: University College, University of North Dakota, Grand Forks, ND 58201.

ROBERTSON, DURANT WAITE, JR, b. Washington, D.C, Oct. 11, 14; m. 37; c. 3. ENGLISH. A.B, Univ. N.C, 35, M.A, 37, Am. Counc. Learned Soc. fel. & Ph.D, 45; D.Litt, Villanova Univ, 73. Asst, Univ. N.C, 36-38, instr, 42-45; Univ. Md, 38-42; Yale, 45-46; ENG, PRINCETON, 46-47, asst. prof, 47-55, assoc. prof, 55-60, PROF, 60- Mediaeval Acad. Am; Renaissance Soc. Am. Medieval literature. Publ: Co-auth, Piers Plowman and scriptural tradition, 51; transl, St. Augustine, On Christian doctrine, Lib. Arts, 58; auth, Preface to Chaucer, 62 & co-auth, Fruyt and Chaf, 63, Princeton; auth, Chaucer's London, Wiley, 68; ed, The literature of medieval England, McGraw, 70; auth, Abelard and Heloise, Dial, 72. Add: 93 Maclean Circle, Princeton, NJ 08540.

ROBERTSON, HENRY ALPHONSO, JR, b. Portsmouth, Va, Dec. 29, 19; m. 44. ENGLISH. B.S, Randolph-Macon Col, 40; M.A, Loyola Univ.(Ill), 58; ph.D.(Eng), Univ. Del, 66. Dir. univ. writing ctr, UNIV. DEL, 65-67, ASST. PROF. ENG, 67-, asst. dean col. arts & sci, 67-71. Consult. col. writing ctr, Del. Tech. & Community Col, 67-68. U.S.N, 41-63, Lt. Comdr. MLA; NCTE; Melville Soc. Am. Early American literature. Add: College of Arts & Sciences, University of Delaware, Newark, DE 19711.

ROBERTSON, JAMES HOLMAN, b. Brooklyn, N.Y, Mar. 6, 15; m. 41; c. 3. ENGLISH. B.S, N.Y. Univ, 37; A.M, Univ. Mich, 38, fels, 38-41 & 45-48, Ph.D, 50. Instr. ENG, UNIV. MICH, ANN ARBOR, 48-50, asst. prof, 50-57, assoc. prof, 57-69, PROF, 69-, resident dir. men's residence halls, 50, asst. dean Col. Lit, Sci. & Arts, 50-58, assoc. dean, 58-73, dir. Residential Col, 67-73. Adj.Gen.C, U.S.A, 41-45, Maj; Bronze Star Medal; Croix de Guerre, Belgium. Nat. Col. Honors Counc. American literature; James Kirke Paulding, a study in literary nationalism. Add: Residential College, University of Michigan, Ann Arbor, MI 48104.

ROBERTSON, ROBERT TELFER, b. Edendale, N.Z, Nov. 3, 24; m. 46; c. 7. ENGLISH, COMPARATIVE LITERATURE. B.A, Univ. Auckland, 46; M.A, Victoria Univ, N.Z, 50; Ph.D.(Eng), Queen's Univ.(Ont), 70. Sr. lectr. ENG, Univ. Otago, N.Z, 52-63; ASSOC. PROF, Va. Polytech. Inst, 63-73; UNIV. SASK, 73- Fulbright vis. prof, Univ. Tex, 59; Univ. Calif, Berkeley, 59-60; vis. prof, Va. Polytech. Inst, 63; nat. chmn. conf. Eng. lit. world, NCTE, 66-70; vis. prof, Queen's Univ.(Ont), 72-73; chmn. Can. Asn. Commonwealth Lang. & Lit. Stud, 73-76. Sporn Award, Va. Polytech. Inst, 67. N.Z. Infantry, 42-46. MLA (chmn. world lit. written in Eng, 72-75); Asn. Can. Univ. Teachers Eng; NCTE. World literature in English. Publ: Co-auth, Resources for the study of British Commonwealth literature, Univ. Tex, 59; auth, British Commonwealth literature as an academic discipline, Proc. AULLA Congr, 62; Canadian poetry and the regional anthology, Landfall, 62; Colonialism and regionalism . . . , Lit. Hist. & Lit. Criticism, 64. Add: Dept. of English, University of Saskatchewan, Saskatoon, Sask. S7N 0W0, Can.

ROBERTSON, THOMAS LUTHER, JR, b. Memphis, Tenn, Jan. 23, 19; m. 68; c. 2. ENGLISH. B.A, Millsaps Col, 41; M.A, Univ. Miss, 50; Peabody Col, summer, 52; Ph.D.(Eng), Vanderbilt Univ, 60. Telegraph ed, reporter & printer, newspapers, Miss, 41-49; teacher high sch, 52-53; instr. ENG, Exten. Sch, Univ. Miss, 53-54; ANDERSON COL, 56-62, asst. prof, 62-65, ASSOC. PROF, 65- U.S.A.A.F, 42-43. MLA; Midwest Mod. Lang. Asn. Linguistics; modern poetry; American folklore. Publ: The yellow canes; The leather greatcoat, Steck, 59; The Newman Kingsley controversy and the apologia, Mod. Lang. Notes. Add: 631 Maplewood Ave, Anderson, IN 46012.

ROBERTSON, WILLIAM JAMES, b. Chicago, Ill, Feb. 21, 24; m. 48; c. 1. SPEECH & DRAMA. B.F.A, Art Inst. Chicago, 49, M.F.A, 51; Lake Forest Col, 49; Ph.D.(speech), Univ. Wis, 63. Head dept. drama, Murray State Univ, 51-56; artist in residence, theatre arts, Antioch Col, 58-59; chmn. dept. SPEECH & DRAMA, Mt. Union Col, 59-63; ASSOC. PROF, Mankato State Col, 63-65; ORE. STATE UNIV, 65-, leave, Europe & Mid. East, 72. Teacher, Asn. Northwest Univs, London, 69. U.S.A, 42-44, 1st Lt. Am. Theatre Asn; Am. Nat. Theatre & Acad; Speech Commun. Asn. Theatre history; dramatic criticism; modern drama. Add: Dept. of Speech Communications, Oregon State University, Corvallis, OR 97331.

ROBERTZ, WILLIAM GEORGE, b. Duluth, Minn, Oct. 3, 29; m. 53; c. 2. SPEECH. B.A, Gustavus Adlophus Col, 51; M.A, Univ. Ill, 53, Ph.D, 60. Asst, Univ. Ill, 51-55; instr. commun. skills, Mich. State Univ, 55-57; asst. prof. SPEECH, GUSTAVUS ADOLPHUS COL, 57-62, assoc. prof, 63-66, PROF, 66-, acting head dept, 63-64, chmn. dept, 64-71. Speech Commun. Asn; Am. Forensic Asn; Cent. States Speech Commun. Asn. Rhetoric and public address. Add: Dept. of Speech, Gustavus Adolphus College, St. Peter, MN 56082.

ROBILLARD, DOUGLAS, b. Ponchatoula, La, Dec. 27, 28; m. 56; c. 2. ENGLISH. B.S, Columbia Univ, 55, A.M, 56; Ph.D.(Eng), Wayne State Univ, 65. Instr. ENG, Auburn Univ, 56-59; Wayne State Univ, 59-63; asst. prof, Ga. Inst. Technol, 63-66; assoc. prof, Ga. State Col, 66-67; assoc. prof, UNIV. NEW HAVEN, 67-69, PROF, 69-, DEAN ARTS & SCI, 73-, chmn. dept, 67-73. U.S.A.F, 48-52, S/Sgt. MLA. American literature; literary criticism. Publ: Ed, Poems of Herman Melville, Col. & Univ, 73; auth, Rossetti's Willowwood sonnets, Victorian Newslett, 62; Early fiction of John Cowper Powys, Stud. Lit. Imagination, 68; plus two others. Add: Dept. of English, University of New Haven, West Haven, CT 06505.

ROBINETT, BETTY W, Linguistics. See Volume III, Foreign Languages, Linguistics & Philology.

ROBINS, HARRY FRANKLIN, b. Milwaukee, Wis, Dec. 27, 15; m. 47; c. 3. ENGLISH. Strauss fel, Ind. Univ, 49-50, Ph.D, 50. From asst. prof. to assoc. prof. ENG, Univ. Ill, 50-64; PROF, UNIV. ARIZ, 64- A.U.S, 42-47, Lt. MLA. Seventeenth century English literature. Publ: If this be heresy: a study of Milton and Origen, Univ. of Ill, 63. Add: Dept. of English, University of Arizona, Tucson, AZ 85721.

ROBINSON, CECIL, b. Old Greenwich, Conn, July 19, 21; m. 54; c. 2. AMERICAN LITERATURE. B.A, Harvard, 43; M.A, Columbia Univ, 49, Ph.D, 60. Dir, Chilean-N.Am. Cult. Inst, Concepción, Chile, 51-52; from asst. prof. to PROF. ENG, UNIV. ARIZ, 53- For. stud. adv, Univ. Ariz, 54-58; vis. prof. Am. lit. from Columbia Univ. to Univ. Guanabara, Brazil, 63-64. Philol. Asn. Pac. Coast. Comparative study of American and Latin American literatures in terms of several major themes. Publ: A history of the Arizona-Sonora Project, 61 & With the ears of strangers, the Mexican in American literature, 63, Univ. Ariz; Legend of destiny: the American Southwest in the novels of Harvey Fergusson, Am. West, 11/67; The fall of 'the big house' in the literature of the Americas, Ariz. Quart, spring 68; A kaleidoscope of images, In: Bilingualism in the Southwest, Univ. Ariz, 73. Add: Dept. of English, University of Arizona, Tucson, AZ 85721.

ROBINSON, CHARLES EDWARD, b. Farmington, W.Va, Jan. 14, 41; m. 63; c. 2. ENGLISH. A.B, Mt. St. Mary's Col.(Md), 62; NDEA fel, Temple Univ, 62-65, Ph.D.(Eng), 67. Instr. ENG, UNIV. DEL, 65-67, asst. prof, 67-73, ASSOC. PROF, 73-, summer fac. fel, 68. Guest prof, Padagogische Hochscule, Essen, Ger, 72; Am. Counc. Learned Soc. grant-in-aid to study Shelley's manuscripts, Bodleian Libr, Oxford, 72. MLA; Keats-Shelley Asn. Am; Byron Soc. English romanticism; Byron and Shelley; literature of the doppelgänger. Publ: The Devil as doppelgänger in The deformed transformed: the sources and meaning of Byron's unfinished drama, Bull. N.Y. Pub. Libr, 70; The Shelley circle and Coleridge's The friend, Eng. Lang. Notes, 71; James T. Farrell's critical estimates of Hemingway, Fitzgerald/Hemingway Annual, 73. Add: Dept. of English, University of Delaware, Newark, DE 19711.

ROBINSON, CLAYTON, b. Niagara Falls, N.Y, Mar. 21, 31. ENGLISH. B.A, Trinity Univ, 59; M.A, Univ. South. Miss, 60; Ph.D.(Am. stud), Univ. Minn, 67. Instr. ENG, Massanutten Acad, Va, 60-61; ASST. PROF, MEMPHIS STATE UNIV, 61- Am. Stud. Asn. Impact of the city on rural immigrants to Memphis. Publ: Gilmore Millen's Sweet man: neglected classic of the Van Vechten vogue, Forum, fall-winter 70; Memphis in fiction: rural values in an urban setting, MVC Bull, 72; Faulkner and Welty and the Mississippi Baptists, Interpretations, 73. Add: Dept. of English, Memphis State University, Memphis, TN 38152.

ROBINSON, EDWARD RAY, b. Richmond, Ind, Jan. 14, 22; m. 47; c. 3. SPEECH. B.A, Earlham Col, 46; M.A, Ind. Univ, 51, Ph.D, 55. Teacher speech & Eng, Montverde Sch, 47-49; PROF. SPEECH, OHIO WESLEYAN UNIV, 51- U.S.M.C, 42-45. Speech Commun. Asn; Cent. States Speech Asn; Am. Forensic Asn. Debate and rhetoric. Add: Dept. of Speech, Ohio Wesleyan University, Delaware, OH 43015.

ROBINSON, ELEANOR M, b. Friedens, Pa, July 10, 20; m. 40; c. 3. ENGLISH. B.A, State Univ. N.Y. Buffalo, 63, M.A, 67. Teacher, Royalton-Hartland Cent. Sch, 63-64; instr. ENG, NIAGARA COUNTY COMMUNITY COL, 64-67, asst. prof, 67-73, ASSOC. PROF, 73- NCTE; Col. Eng. Asn; Conf. Col. Compos. & Commun. The Bible; Mark Twain; the teaching of technical writing skills. Publ: A study of Death in the woods, CEA Critic, 1/68; Cubism in three arts, Stud. Twentieth Century, fall 69; Gabriel Conroy's Cooked goose, Ball State Univ. Forum, spring 70. Add: 5829 Wynkoop Rd, Rte. 5, Lockport, NY 14094.

ROBINSON, ERWIN ARTHUR, b. Salisbury Center, N.Y, Dec. 22, 10; m. 33; c. 2. ENGLISH. B.A, Ohio Wesleyan Univ, 32; M.A, Ohio State Univ, 33, scholar, 34-36, Ph.D.(Eng), 36. Instr. ENG, Iowa State Teachers Col, 36-42, asst. prof, 42-44; Univ. Idaho, 45-46; UNIV. R.I, 46-51, assoc. prof, 51-57, PROF, 57- Am. Stud. Asn; MLA. Nineteenth century American literature; the American novel. Publ: Order and sentience in The fall of the House of Usher, 3/61 & Conservation in Cooper's The pioneers, 12/67, PMLA; The vision of Goodman Brown: a source and interpretation, Am. Lit, 5/63. Add: Dept. of English, University of Rhode Island, Kingston, RI 02881.

ROBINSON, FOREST ELMO, b. Portland, Ore, Oct. 22, 12; m. 46; c. 1. ENGLISH. B.A, Willamette Univ, 37; Univ. Wash, summer 38, 39 & 41-42; M.A, Columbia Univ, 47; Ph.D.(Eng), Univ. Colo, 65. Instr. ENG, Univ. Del, 46-48; Univ. Idaho, 49-52; asst. prof, Cent. Wash. State Col, 55-60; Col. of Guam, 60-62; PROF, BEMIDJI STATE COL, 63- Sig.C, U.S.A, 42-45. MLA. Sixteenth century literature; Romantic poets. Add: Dept. of English, Bemidji State College, Bemidji, MN 56601.

ROBINSON, FORREST DEAN, b. Berea, Ohio, Nov. 4, 31; m. 55; c. 3. AMERICAN LITERATURE, CREATIVE WRITING. B.A, Miami Univ, 53, M.A, 57; Univ. Iowa, 55-56; Breadloaf Sch. Eng, 63; Ph.D.(Eng), Ohio Univ, 66. Teacher ENG, Norton Sr. High Sch, 58-59; instr, Ohio Univ, 59-66; asst. prof, Heidelberg Col, 66-68; WEST. ILL. UNIV, 68-69, assoc. prof, 69-73, PROF, 73- Poetry ed, Miss. Valley Rev, 71- U.S.A, 53-55. MLA; Col. Eng. Asn. Creative writing, especially poetry; 20th century American literature. Publ: Frederick Henry: the Hemingway hero as storyteller, CEA Critic, 5/72; Poems, In: Prism Int, Kans. Quart, Christian Century & Denver Post. Add: Dept. of English, Western Illinois University, Macomb, IL 61455.

ROBINSON, FORREST GLEN, b. Milwaukee, Wis, Dec. 2, 40; m. 68. ENGLISH & AMERICAN LITERATURE. B.A, Northwest. Univ, Evanston, 63; M.A, Harvard, 64, Knox Mem. fel, 66-67; Cannady & Clark fel, 66, Ph.D. (Eng), 68. Instr. ENG. LIT, Harvard, 67-69, ASST. PROF, 69-70; UNIV. CALIF, SANTA CRUZ, 70- Guggenheim fel, 72-73. MLA. Biography of Henry A. Murray; history and literature of California. Publ: Ed, Sir Philip Sidney's An apology for poetry, Bobbs, 70; auth, The shape of things known: Sidney's apology in its philosophical tradition, Harvard, 72; co-auth, Wallace Stegner, Twayne, 74. Add: 621 Escalona Dr, Santa Cruz, CA 95060.

ROBINSON, FRANCIS CARLETON, b. Stronghurst, Ill, Feb. 21, 02; m. 39. ENGLISH. A.B, Hastings Col, 36; A.M, Univ. Nebr, 37; Ph.D, Stanford Univ, 52. Instr. ENG, Univ. Nebr, 38-41; Colo. Sch. Mines, 42-44; UNIV. COLO, BOULDER, 44-45, asst. prof, 47-57, assoc. prof, 57-66, prof, 66-70, EMER. PROF, 70- MLA. Western novels; novel in America. Add: Dept. of English, University of Colorado, Boulder, CO 80302.

ROBINSON, FRED COLSON, b. Birmingham, Ala, Sept. 23, 30; m. 60; c. 2. ENGLISH PHILOLOGY, MEDIEVAL LITERATURE. B.A, Birmingham-South. Col, 53; M.A, Univ. N.C, Chapel Hill, 54, Ph.D.(Eng), 61. Instr. Eng, Stanford Univ, 60-62, asst. prof, 62-65; Cornell Univ, 65-66, assoc. prof, 66-67; Stanford Univ, 67-72, PROF. Eng. Philol, 72-73; ENG, YALE, 73- Am. Counc. Learned Soc. fel, 68-69; Am. Philos. Soc. res. grant, summer 73. U.S.A, 54-56. MLA (chmn, res. & bibliog. comt, Old Eng. Group, 63-); Early Eng. Text Soc; Mediaeval Acad. Am; Ling. Soc. Am. English philology; Medieval literature. Publ: Old English literature: a select bibliography, Univ. Toronto, 69; The significance of names in Old English literature, Anglia, 68; Lexicography and literary criticism: a caveat, In: Philological essays in honor of Herbert Dean Meritt, Mouton, The Hague, 70; Syntactical glosses in Latin manuscripts of Anglo-Saxon provenance, Speculum, 73; plus others. Add: Dept. of English, Linsly-Chittenden Hall, Yale University, New Haven, CT 06520.

ROBINSON, HADDON W, b. New York, N.Y, Mar. 21, 31; m. 51; c. 2. PRACTICAL THEOLOGY, SPEECH. B.A, Bob Jones Univ, 51; Th.M, Dallas Theol. Sem, 55; M.A, South. Methodist Univ, 61; Ph.D.(speech), Univ. Ill, 64. Assoc. pastor, First Baptist Church, 56-58; assoc. prof. PRACTICAL THEOL, DALLAS THEOL. SEM, 58-74, PROF, 74- Speech Commun. Asn. Radio-TV; homiletics. Publ: Psalm 23, Moody, 68; co-auth, The speaking of Lyndon Johnson, Quart. J. Speech, 61; auth, The radio-TV audience and religion, Bibliotheca Sacra, 68. Add: Dept. of Practical Theology, Dallas Theological Seminary, Dallas, TX 75204.

ROBINSON, HORACE WILLIAM, b. Apache, Okla, Oct. 26, 09; m. 32; c. 3. DRAMA. A.B, Oklahoma City Univ, 31; A.M, State Univ. Iowa, 32; Stanford Univ, 48, 52. Instr, Oklahoma City Univ, 32-33; from instr. to PROF. SPEECH, UNIV. ORE, 33- Vis. assoc. prof, Univ. Calif, Los Angeles, 56-57; Fulbright lect. grant, Australia, summer 58; Fulbright res. grant, Finland, 63-64. Speech Commun. Asn; Am. Theatre Asn.(pres, 54); Nat. Theatre Conf; Am. Nat. Theatre & Acad. Theater architecture. Publ: Architecture for the educational theatre, Univ. Ore, 70. Add: University Theatre, University of Oregon, Eugene, OR 97403.

ROBINSON, JAMES E, b. Kansas City, Mo, Feb. 10, 28; m. 50; c. 4. ENGLISH. B.S, Rockhurst Col, 47; M.A, Creighton Univ, 49; Ph.D.(Eng), Univ. Ill, Urbana, 59. Teaching asst. ENG, St. Louis Univ, 49-50; Univ. Ill, 50-57; instr, UNIV. NOTRE DAME, 57-58, asst. prof, 58-63, assoc. prof, 63-69, PROF, 69-, humanities grant, 66-67, chmn. dept. Eng, 68-72. Huntington Libr. grant, summer 63; Am. Philos. Soc. grant, 67. MLA; AAUP; NCTE. Drama; rhetoric; literary theory. Publ: The scope of rhetoric, Scott, 70; Bartholomew Fair: comedy of vapors, Stud. Eng. Lit, spring 61; Time and The tempest, J. Eng. & Ger. Philol, 4/64; The ritual and rhetoric of A midsummer night's dream, PMLA, 5/68. Add: Dept. of English, University of Notre Dame, Notre Dame, IN 46556.

ROBINSON, JAMES KEITH, b. Waterman, Ill, July 24, 16; m. 45; c. 2. ENGLISH LITERATURE. A.B, Univ. Tenn, 38, univ. fel, 38-39; A.M, Harvard, 40, univ. fel, 46-48, Dexter traveling scholar, 47, Ph.D, 49. Tutor. ENG, Harvard, 46-48; Instr, Northwest. Univ, 48-52, asst. prof, 52-58; assoc. prof, UNIV. CINCINNATI, 58-62, PROF, 62-, head dept, 66-70. Vis. prof, Harvard, summer 63. U.S.N, 42-46, Lt. Comdr. MLA. Victorian and contemporary literature. Publ: Co-auth, A college book of modern verse, 58, A college book of modern fiction, 61 & American poetry, 65, Harper; A neglected phase of the aesthetic movement: English Parnassianism, PMLA, 53. Add: Dept. of English, University of Cincinnati, Clifton Ave, Cincinnati, OH 45221.

ROBINSON, JAY LUKE, b. Salt Lake City, Utah, Mar. 7, 32; m. 54; c. 4. ENGLISH. B.A, Univ. Calif, Berkeley, 54, M.A, 58, Ph.D, 62. Teaching asst. ENG, Univ. Calif, Berkeley, 57-60, assoc, 60-61; instr, Northwest. Univ, 61-63, asst. prof, 63-65; UNIV. MICH, ANN ARBOR, 65-68, assoc. prof, 68-74, PROF, 74- Fel, Inst. Advan. Stud. in Humanities, Univ. Edinburgh, 72; co-ed, Mich. Early Mod. Eng. Materials. U.S.M.C.R, 54-56, 1st Lt. Ling. Soc. Am; NCTE; Asn. Lit. & Linguistic Comput; Asn. Scottish Lit. Stud. Old and Middle English language and literature; English linguistics and lexicography; older Scottish literature and language. Publ: Co-auth, English linguistics: an introductory reader, Scott, 69; co-ed, Varieties of present-day English, Macmillan, 73; co-auth, Computers and dictionaries, In: Computers and Old English concordances, Univ. Toronto, 70 & Computer-produced microfilm in lexicography: toward a dictionary of early Modern English, In: The computer and literary studies, Univ. Edinburgh, 73; auth, The wall of Babel, or up against the language barrier, In: Varieties of present-day English, Macmillan, 73. Add: Dept. of English, University of Michigan, Ann Arbor, MI 48104.

ROBINSON, JOHN MEREDITH, b. Winnipeg, Man, Sept. 16, 26. ENGLISH. B.A, Univ. Man, 48, M.A, 50; Ph.D, Univ. Toronto, 60. Lectr. ENG, Univ. Man, 52-53; St. John's Col.(Man), 54-55; UNIV. MAN, 55-58, asst. prof, 58-64, ASSOC. PROF, 64-, awards off, 61-65, acting head dept. Eng, 71-72. Asn. Can. Univ. Teachers Eng; MLA; Humanities Asn. Can.(prairie region rep. & nat. exec, 72-74). Early 20th century literature. Publ: Introd. to Stephen Leacock's Last leaves, 70 & Rudy Wiebe's Peace shall destroy many, 72, McClelland & Stewart. Add: Dept. of English, University of Manitoba, Winnipeg, Man. R3T 2N2, Can.

ROBINSON, JOHN WILLIAM. b. London, Eng, June 18, 34; m. 59; c. 3. ENGLISH. B.A, Oxford, 57, M.A, 61; scholar, Glasgow Univ, 57-59, Ph.D. (Eng), 61. Asst. prof. ENG, UNIV. NEBR, LINCOLN, 61-67, PROF, 67-, CHMN. DEPT, 72-, assoc. dean col. arts & sci, 69-72. Res. grant, Huntington Libr, summer 72; mem. adv. comt, London Stage Inform. Bank, 72-; adv. bd, London stage 1800-1900, 73- Co-winner, Besterman Medal, Libr. Asn, Eng, 71. MLA; Soc. Theatre Res, Eng; Am. Soc. Theatre Res; Int. Fed. Theatre Res. English drama; bibliography; Shakespeare. Publ: Co-auth, English theatrical literature, 1554-1900: a bibliography, 70 & auth, Theatrical street ballads, 71, Soc. Theatre Res; Late medieval cult of Jesus and the mystery plays, PMLA, 65; A commentary on the York play of The birth of Jesus, J. Eng. & Ger. Philol, 71; contrib, The new Cambridge bibliography of English literature, Cambridge Univ, Vol. I, 74; plus others. Add: Dept. of English, University of Nebraska, Lincoln, NE 68508.

ROBINSON, LINDA JANE, b. Brisbane, Australia, Dec. 4, 14; U.S. citizen; m. 56. ENGLISH & AMERICAN LITERATURE. B.A, Univ. Tex, El Paso, 60, M.A, 62; tutor, Univ. Queensland, 64; Ph.D.(Eng), Tulane Univ, 68. Teacher Queensland Dept. of Educ, Australia, 35-38; St. Aidan's Church of Eng. Girls' Sch, Brisbane, 38-40; copywriter, WJIM Radio-TV, Lansing, Mich, 46-49; Johnston-Jones Advertising Agency, Brisbane, 50-52; ed, Crowsnest, Cunard Steamship Co, N.Y.C, 52-56; reporter, Farmington Daily Times, N.Mex, 56-57; instr. ENG, La. State Univ, New Orleans, 65-69; asst. prof. EAST. N.MEX. UNIV, 69-73, ASSOC. PROF, 73- Australian Women's Army Serv, 40-42, Capt. AAUP; MLA. Nineteenth century American literature; history of English language; Medieval literature. Publ: You must open your heart (short story), Women's World Mag, 3/52; contrib, Frontier College, Tex. West. Press, 64. Add: P.O. Box 635, Portales, NM 88130.

ROBINSON, LOLO, b. East Chicago, Ind, Dec. 3, 95. DRAMA, SPEECH. A.B, Univ. Ky, 30. Prog. supvr, radio studios, UNIV. KY, 40-49, ASST. PROF, radio arts, 46-49, ENG, 49-, ASSOC. DIR. THEATRE, Playwriting; drama production. Add: Fine Arts Bldg, University of Kentucky, Lexington, KY 40506.

ROBINSON, MARIE J, b. Monaca, Pa, Jan. 21, 15. SPEECH, DRAMA. B.L. I, Emerson Col, 35; M.A, Mich. State Univ, 44; Ph.D, Northwest. Univ, 60. Teacher high sch, 35-43; head dept. speech & drama, Bemidji State Teachers Col, 44-45; instr, Sch. Speech, Syracuse Univ, 45-49; assoc. prof. SPEECH, ILL. WESLEYAN UNIV, 50-61, PROF, 61-, head dept, 50-73. Vis. lectr, Carthage Col, 70; Dakota State Col, 70 & 71; Bowling Green State Univ, 71. Ill. Wesleyan Univ. Teacher of the Year, 66-67. AAUP; Am. Forensic Asn; Speech Commun. Asn.(chmn. interpretation standards, 72 & 73, high sch. & col. interpretation regulations, 72-73); Cent. States Speech Asn.(mem. adv. comt, 62-64); Am. Theatre Asn; Intercontinental Biog. Asn. Play revivals; choral speaking, verse choir; production of pre-modern drama. Publ: The theory and practice of nursing service administration, In: The influence of the arts, McGraw, 65; Speech: the future of . . . , Beacon Quart, winter 68; Speech—the multifaceted prism, Ill. J. Educ, 70; plus one other. Add: Dept. of Speech, Illinois Wesleyan University, Bloomington, IL 61701.

ROBINSON, MARION PARSONS, b. Cleveland, Ohio, June 24, 97. SPEECH. A.B, Oberlin Col, 19; A.M, Univ. Denver, 25; Ph.D, Univ. Wis, 45. From asst. to asst. prof, Univ. Denver, 23-42; instr, Univ. Md, 45-46; from asst. prof. to assoc. prof. SPEECH, GOUCHER COL, 46-63, EMER. PROF, 63- Danforth fel, Stratford-upon-Avon, summer 60; teacher, Baltimore Jr. Col, 62-63; prof, Tsuda Col. & Tokyo Joshi Daigaku, Japan, 63-64; part-time vis. lectr. speech & stage design, Goucher Col, 66-68; adv, Adventures in Learning, pvt. sch. for adults, 70-73. Theatre architecture; literary interpretation; phonetics. Publ: Poetry arranged for the speaking choir, 36, Poetry arranged for men to speak chorally, 39 & Poetry arranged for women to speak chorally, 40, Expression; Scenes for women from the plays of Shakespeare, Baker Co, 67. Add: 204 E. Jappa Rd, No. 309, Towson, MD 21204.

ROBINSON, PETER GORDON, Psycholinguistics, Sociolinguistics. See Volume III, Foreign Languages, Linguistics and Philology.

ROBINSON, WILLIAM H, JR, b. Newport, R.I, Oct. 24, 22; m. 48. ENGLISH & AMERICAN NEGRO LITERATURE. B.A, N.Y. Univ, 51; M.A, Boston Univ, 57; fel, Harvard, 62-64, Ph.D.(Eng), 64. Instr. Eng, Prairie View Col, 51-53, asst. prof, 54-55; prof, A&T State Univ, 56-61, 64-66; assoc. prof. Eng. & humanities, Boston Univ, 66-68; eng, Howard Univ, 69-72; PROF. ENG. & DIR. BLACK STUD. PROG, R.I. COL, 72- Assoc. prof. Am. Negro lit, Harvard Univ. Exten, 67-68; lectr, Univ. Mass, Boston, summer 68; R.I. Col, summers 68, delivered educ. TV lects, WNAC-TV, Boston, Mass, summer 68. Eng.C, U.S.A, 42-45. Col. Lang. Asn. American Negro literature; English literature—Shakespeare and Samuel Johnson. Publ: Black American poets of 18th and 19th century, W.C. Brown, 69; Phillis Wheatley: colonial quandary, Col. Lang. Arts, fall 65; Keeping the faith in Negro literature, Mosaic, fall 68. Add: Black Studies Program, Rhode Island College, Providence, RI 02908.

ROBINSON, WILLIAM RONALD, b. Steubenville, Ohio, Oct. 21, 27; m. 52; c. 4. AMERICAN & CONTEMPORARY LITERATURE. B.A, Ohio State Univ, 52, M.A, 56, Ph.D.(Eng), 62. Instr. ENG, Univ. Va, 62-64, asst. prof, 64-67; assoc. prof, UNIV. FLA, 67-71, PROF, 71- U.S.A, 46-47. Col. Eng. Asn; MLA; S.Atlantic Mod. Lang. Asn; AAUP; Soc. Cinema Stud. American literature; the theory of literature; movies. Publ: Edwin Arlington Robinson: a poetry of the act, West. Reserve Univ, 67; ed. & contrib, Man and the movies, La. State Univ, 67; auth, If you don't see, you're dead, Part I, 9-12/72 & Part II, 1-4/73, Contempora; The imagination of skin, Film J, Vol. II, No. 1; plus others. Add: Dept. of English, University of Florida, Gainesville, FL 32601.

ROBSON, JOHN M, b. Toronto, Ont, May 26, 27; m. 53; c. 3. ENGLISH. B.A, Univ. Toronto, 51, M.A, 53, Ph.D.(Eng), 56. Instr. ENG, Univ. B.C, 56-57; asst. prof, Univ. Alta, 57-58; VICTORIA COL, UNIV. TORONTO, 58-63, assoc. prof, 63-67, PROF, 67-, PRIN, 71- Gen. ed, Collected works of John Stuart Mill, Univ. Toronto, 63- MLA; Asn. Can. Univ. Teachers Eng; Conf. Brit. Stud. Rhetoric; 19th century British thought; the English novel. Publ: Ed, Edmund Burke, An appeal from the new to the old Whigs, Bobbs, 62 & J.S. Mill: a selection, Macmillan, Toronto, 66; auth, The improvement of mankind: the social and political thought of J.S. Mill, Univ. Toronto, 68; J.S. Mill and Jeremy Bentham, with some observations on James Mill, In: Essays in English literature from the Renissance to the Victorian age, Univ. Toronto, 64; Tragedy and society, Queen's Quart, 64; Principles and methods in the collected edition of J.S. Mill, In: Editing nineteenth-century texts, 67. Add: Principal's Office, Victoria College, University of Toronto, 73 Queen's Park Crescent, Toronto, Ont. M5S 1K7, Can.

ROBSON, ROY ANTHONY, Theoretical & Applied Linguistics. See Volume III, Foreign Languages, Linguistics & Philology.

ROBY, ROBERT CURTIS, b. New Albany, Ind, Dec. 2, 22; div; c. 1. ENGLISH. Fel, Northwest. Univ, 47-49, Ph.D.(Eng), 49. Instr. ENG, MARQUETTE UNIV, 49-55, from asst. prof. to ASSOC. PROF, 56- Ford fac. fel, 53-54. U.S.A.A.F, 43-45. MLA. Shakespeare; drama; contemporary English and American literature. Publ: Co-auth, Introduction to drama McGraw-Hill, 62; Two worlds: Maxwell Anderson's Winterset, Col. Eng. Add: Dept. of English, Marquette University, Milwaukee, WI 53233.

ROCH, JOHN HENRY, b. Albany, N.Y, Aug. 24, 16; m. 44; c. 5. AMERICAN LITERATURE. B.A, Univ. Mass, 43; M.A, Columbia Univ, 47, Ph.D.(Eng), 58. Instr. ENG, Univ. Md, 48-50; Clarkson Col. Technol, 52-54, asst. prof, 54-58, assoc. prof, 58-59; GLASSBORO STATE COL, 59-62, PROF, 62-, CHMN. DEPT, 63- Consult, res. planning div, Socony-Mobile Oil Co, 60. U.S.A, 43-46, Sgt. MLA; Col. Eng. Asn; AAUP; Am. Fed. Teachers. American literature; the short story. Publ: Color line, Writers' Forum, 42. Add: Dept. of English, Glassboro State College, Glassboro, NJ 08028.

ROCHAT, JOYCE HAMILTON, b. Hanover, N.H, m. 44; c. 2. AMERICAN LITERATURE, CREATIVE WRITING. B.A, Andrews Univ, 63, M.A, 65; Ph.D.(Eng), Mich. State Univ, 71. Dean of girls, Seminaire Adventiste Haiti, 53-58; instr. ENG, Lake Mich. Col, 64-68; asst. prof, ANDREWS UNIV, 70-71, ASSOC. PROF, 71- MLA. Twentieth century American literature; creative writing workshop methods and techniques; existential thought in literature. Publ: Dark sunrise, Rev. & Herald, 59; Curse of the voodoo gods (children's book), South. Publ, 60. Add: Dept. of English, Andrews University, Berrien Springs, MI 49104.

ROCHE, PAUL, b. India, Sept, 25, 28; m. 54; c. 2. ENGLISH. Ph.B, Gregorian Univ, 47, Ph.L, 49. Instr. Eng, Smith Col, 56-58; Bollingen Found. fel, 58-59; RESEARCHER, BRIT. MUS, 63- Poet-in-residence, King Col. (Tenn), 69-70, Emory & Henry Col, 70, Fontbonne Col, 71 & Calif. Inst. Arts, 72-73; consult, Four Winds Theatre, N.Y, 70-, Padworth Col, Berkshire, 72- & Avon Found, 72- Poetry Soc. Am.(di Castagnola award, 65); Poetry Soc, Eng.(Hunt Bartlett Award, 66). Creative writing; sound and form in modern poetry; The Iliad of Homer. Publ: The rat and the convent dove (fables), Hand & Flower, 52; O pale Galilean (novel), Harvill, London, 54; The Oedipus plays of Sophocles, 58, The Orestes plays of Aeschylus, 63, Prometheus bound (Aeschylus), 64, The love-songs of Sappho, 66 & Three plays of Plautus, 68, New Am. Libr; Vessel of dishonor (novel), 62 & The rank obstinacy of things, 63, Sheed; All things considered (poetry), 66 & To tell the truth, (poetry), 67, Duckworth, London; All things considered, Weybright & Talley, 68; Three plays of Euripides (Alcestis, Medea, The Bacchae), Norton, 74; T.S. Eliot: outline for a reassessment, Poetry Rev, 4/68; Pompeii revisited, New Yorker Mag. Add: The Stables, The Street, Aldermaston, Berkshire, England.

ROCHE, RUTH LAVARE, b. Salida, Colo, May 5, 17; m. ENGLISH, WORLD LITERATURE. B.A, Univ. Calif, 46, M.A, 48, Ph.D, 54. Instr. ENG, Bucknell Univ, 52-53; Chico State Col, 53-55, asst. prof, 55-58; SAN JOSE STATE UNIV, 58-62, ASSOC. PROF, 62- NCTE. General semantics; techniques of expository prose; English as a second language. Add: Dept. of English, San Jose State University, 125 E. Seventh St, San Jose, CA 95192.

ROCHE, THOMAS PATRICK, JR, b. New Haven, Conn, Apr. 19, 31. ENGLISH. B.A, Yale, 53; Henry fel, Pembroke Col, Cambridge, 54-55; M.A, Princeton, 57, Ph.D, 58. Teacher Latin, Hamden Hall Country Day Sch, Hamden, Conn, 53-54; instr. ENG, Williams Col, 58-60; PRINCETON, 60-62, asst. prof, 62-66, assoc. prof, 66-72, PROF, 72- Proctor & Gamble fac. fel, fall 61; bicentennial preceptorship, 63-65. MLA; Renaissance Soc. Am. Spenser's Faerie Queene; Renaissance poetry and allegory. Publ: The kindly flame: a study of the third and fourth books of Spenser's Faerie Queene, Princeton, 64. Add: Dept. of English, Princeton University, Princeton, NJ 08540.

ROCK, VIRGINIA J, b. Detroit, Mich, Sept. 23, 23. AMERICAN LITERATURE, AMERICAN STUDIES. A.B, Univ. Mich, 44, M.A, 47; fel, Duke Univ, 49-50; Am. Asn. Univ. Women fel, Univ. Minn, 53-54, Carnegie fel, 55-56, Ph.D, 61. Instr. compos, Univ. Mich, 46-47; from instr. to asst. prof. compos, drama & Am. & Eng. lit, Univ. Louisville, 47-49; asst. prof. Am. & Eng. lit, drama & teaching methods, Lake Erie Col, 50-53; instr. commun. & compos, Univ. Minn, 53-55, 57-58; asst. prof. Am. lit. & compos, Montclair State Col, 58-60; Am. thought & lang, Mich. State Univ, 60-65; AM. & MOD. LIT, YORK UNIV, 65-66, assoc. prof, 66-73, PROF, 73-, MASTER, STONG COL, 69-, v.chmn, Fac. Asn, 73-74. Fulbright-Hays lectr, Jagiellonian Univ, Poland, 62-64; chmn. Am. Lit. Group, MLA, 74-75. MLA; Col. Eng. Asn; Am. Stud. Asn; Can. Asn. Am. Stud.(secy, 66-70, pres, 70-72). Southern literature and culture; American literature of the 19th and 20th centuries; mass media. Publ: Biographical essays, In: I'll take my stand: the South and the agrarian tradition, Harper, 63; The fugitive agrarians in response to social change, South. Humanities Rev, summer 67; Checklist on agrarianism, Miss. Quart, summer 68 & In: Bibliographical guide to the study of Southern literature, La. State Univ, 69; plus others. Add: Dept. of English, York University, 4700 Keele St, Downsview, Ont. M3J 1P3, Can.

ROCKAS, LEO, b. Rochester, N.Y, Oct. 12, 28; m. 60; c. 2. ENGLISH. A.B, Univ. Rochester, 51, A.M, 52; Ph.D, Univ. Mich, 60. Instr. ENG, Wayne State Univ, 57-60; asst. prof, Rochester Inst. Technol, 61-62; State Univ. N.Y. Col. Geneseo, 62-67; ASSOC. PROF, Briarcliff Col, 67-71; UNIV. HARTFORD, 71- Instr, St. John Fisher Col, Inc, 62-63; mem, Eng. Inst. U.S.A, 46-48. MLA; NCTE; Conf. Col. Compos. & Commun. Shakespeare; rhetoric; eighteenth century English literature. Publ: Modes of rhetoric, St. Martins, 64; A program for literary theory, J. Gen. Educ, 1/63; The structure of Frye's Anatomy, Col. Eng, 4/67. Add: Dept. of English, University of Hartford, West Hartford, CT 06117.

ROCKLAND, MICHAEL AARON, American & Latin American Studies. See Volume I, History.

ROCKS, JAMES ENGEL, b. Cleveland, Ohio, May 26, 39; m. 73. ENGLISH. A.B, West. Reserve Univ, 61; M.A, Duke Univ, 62, Ph.D.(Eng), 66. ASST.

PROF. ENG, Tulane Univ, 65-72; LOYOLA UNIV. CHICAGO, 72- MLA. American, Southern and comparative literature. Publ: The mind and art of Caroline Gordon, Miss. Quart, winter 67-68; William Cullen Bryant, In: Fifteen American Authors before 1900, Univ. Wis, 71; Hamilton Basso and the worldview from Pompey's head, South Atlantic Quart, summer 72; plus others. Add: Dept. of English, Loyola University, Chicago, IL 60626.

ROCKWOOD, HORACE SEYMOUR, III, b. Stamford, Conn, Oct. 12, 33; m. 63; c. 2. ENGLISH. A.B, Boston Univ, 55; M.A, Univ. Mich, 56, Ph.D.(Eng), 66. Instr. ENG, Defiance Col, 61-62; East. Mich. Univ, 64-66, asst. prof, 66-69; PROF, CALIFORNIA STATE COL.(PA), 69- U.S.N.R, 57-61, Lt. MLA. English literature of the Renaissance and neo-classical period; the English novel. Add: Dept. of English, California State College, California, PA 15419.

ROCKWOOD, JEROME, b. New York, N.Y, Sept. 14, 27; m. 48; c. 2. THEATRE, SPEECH. B.A, Brooklyn Col, 48; M.A, West. Reserve Univ, 49; Ph.D.(speech arts), N.Y. Univ, 66. Lectr. speech, City Col. New York, 61-62; instr. SPEECH & THEATRE, St. John's Univ, 62-63, asst. prof, 63-65; Bronx Community Col, 65-67; ASSOC. PROF, MONTCLAIR STATE COL, 67- Barter Theatre Award, 49; N.Y. Univ. Founder's Day Award, 66. Armed Forces Radio Serv, 45-47, S/Sgt. Speech Asn. East. States. Theatre. Publ: The craftsmen of Dionysus: an approach to acting, Scott, 66. Add: 250 W. 94th St, New York, NY 10025.

RODABAUGH, DELMER, b. Norborne, Mo, Mar. 23, 11; m. 39. ENGLISH. A.B, Park Col, 32; M.A, State Univ. Iowa, 38; Columbia Univ, 46; Ph.D, Univ. Minn, 51. Instr. ENG. & supt, Cent. Consolidated High Sch, Hardin, Mo, 34-36; instr, Allerton High Sch, Iowa, 36-37; head dept, Monticello High Sch, 38-39; Faribault High Sch, Minn, 39-41; instr, Shorewood High Sch, Milwaukee, Wis, 41-43; Univ. Minn, 46-47; Purdue Univ, 47-49; Univ. Minn, 50-55, asst. prof, 52-55; assoc. prof, CALIF STATE UNIV, LONG BEACH, 55-61, PROF, 61- U.S.N, 43-45. MLA. Shakespeare; 19th century American romanticism. Publ: Co-auth, Prose and poetry of England & Prose and poetry of America, L.W. Singer Co. Inc, 63; auth, Assigning and commenting on themes, Col. Eng, 10/54. Add: Dept. of English, California State University, Long Beach, 6101 E. Seventh St, Long Beach, CA 90840.

RODAX, YVONNE, b. Minneapolis, Minn; m. 47; c. 1. ENGLISH, COMPARATIVE LITERATURE. A.B, Barnard Col, Columbia Univ, 44, A.M, univ, 51; Ph.D.(comp. lit), N.Y. Univ, 66. Free lance work in music & writing, Columbia Recording Corp; moving picture ed, Liberty Mag, 42-44; asst. Eng, Barnard Col, Columbia Univ, 50-51, admin. asst, univ, 51-53; dir. admis, Bradford Jr. Col, 53-59; instr. ENG, C.W. POST COL, L.I. UNIV, 59-65, asst. prof, 65-68, ASSOC. PROF, 68- MLA. Renaissance novella; Spenser and Sidney. Publ: The real and the ideal in the novella of Italy, France and England, Univ. N.C, 68. Add: Dept. of English, C.W. Post College, Long Island University, Greenvale, NY 11548.

RODDEN, DANIEL JOSEPH, b. Philadelphia, Pa, Feb. 15, 20. SPEECH, DRAMA. B.A, LaSalle Col, 41; M.F.A, Cath. Univ. Am, 49. Teacher, La Salle Col. High Sch, 40-42; instr. ENG, LaSALLE COL, 49-50, asst. prof, 50-58, assoc. prof, 58-70, PROF, 70-, managing dir. music theatre, 62-73. A.U.S, 42-46, Capt. MLA. Writing, editing and criticism for periodicals, television and radio. Publ: Lucky for me! (play), 47; Small beer in springtime (play), 49; The theatre in Philadelphia (8 articles in ser), 51-53; Ambassador (play), 72. Add: 5643 N. 20th St, Philadelphia, PA 19144.

RODEMAN, NORBERT R, b. Milwaukee, Wis, May 5, 14. SPEECH, ENGLISH. Ph.B, Marquette Univ, 37, scholar, 37-38, M.A, 38; fel, Northwest. Univ, 49-51, Ph.D, 51. Instr. pub. schs, Wis, 38-44; supvr. pub. relat. & training, Allis-Chalmers Mfg. Co, Milwaukee, 44-45; exec. secy, City of Milwaukee, 45-46; speech, Univ. Wis, Milwaukee & Racine, 46-49; bus. English & rhetoric, Marquette Univ, 47-49; asst. dir, Mus. Sci. & Indust, Chicago, 49-51; admin. asst. training & educ, Continental Casualty Co, Chicago, 51-55; asst. prof. speech, Queens Col.(N.Y), 55-58; instr. educ. broadcasting & dir. Eng, speech & drama, New York Pub. Schs, 58-64; prof. Eng. & speech & chmn. humanities, N.Y. Inst. Technol, 64-66; FREE LANCE ED, 66- Lectr, Wis. Inst. Mortuary Sci, 40-45; producer & dir. broadcasting workshop, Evanston, Ill. & dir, weekly drama, WGN & WISN, Chicago, 49-51; producer & dir. educ. broadcasts, WNYC, New York, N.Y, 55-58. U.S.A, 44-46. Nat. Asn. Educ. Broadcasters; Am. Soc. Training Dirs; Nat. Thespian Soc; AAUP; Speech Commun. Asn. Radio and television; drama and broadcasting; little theatre. Publ: The history of the little theatre movement in Wisconsin, 37 & An analysis of Beaumarchais and his play The barber of Seville, 38, Marquette; It is well, Steuben, 42; Spes mea in deo est, Wis. Consistory Publ, 43; The development of academic research in radio and television for the firsthalf of the twentieth century, a history and bibliography, (2 vols), Northwest. Univ, 51; New frontiers, Bd. Educ. Hicksville, N.Y, 61; The entered apprentice, Masonic Tidings, 42; Psalmody, The Villager, 12/59; plus others. Add: Apt. 16-W, 220-55 46th Ave, Bayside, NY 11361.

RODEWALD, FRED ARTHUR, b. Goliad, Tex, Apr. 17, 36; m. 59; c. 2. AMERICAN LITERATURE. B.A, Tex. A&M Univ, 58; M.A, N.Tex. State Univ, 59; Ph.D.(Eng), Univ. Okla, 68. Instr. ENG, Tex. A&M Univ, 59-66; asst. prof, STEPHEN F. AUSTIN STATE UNIV, 66-68, assoc. prof, 68-73, PROF, 73- AAUP; S.Cent. Mod. Lang. Asn. Modern American fiction; contemporary fiction. Publ: Co-auth, My kinsman Major Molineux: a reevaluation, Conf. Col. Teachers Eng, 69; auth, The needle (short story), Arlington Quart, 71; The comic eiron in novels of Peter DeVries, Quartet, 73. Add: Dept. of English, Box 3007, Stephen F. Austin Station, Nacogdoches, TX 75961.

RODGERS, MARY COLUMBRO, b. Aurora, Ohio, Apr. 17, 25; m. 65; c. 1. ENGLISH, EDUCATION. B.A, Notre Dame Col.(Ohio), 57; M.A, West. Reserve Univ, 62; fel, Ohio State Univ, 62-64, Ph.D.(Eng. & Eng. educ), 64. Teacher, Elem. & Sec. Schs, Ohio, 45-62; supvr. stud. teachers in Eng, Ohio State Univ, 62-64; asst. prof. Eng. & educ, Univ. Md, 65-67; assoc. prof, Trinity Col.(D.C), 67-68; ENG, D.C. TEACHERS COL, 68-73, PROF, 73- Fulbright fel, Univ. Rome, 64-65; consult. Eng. curriculum, Md. counties, 65-67; assoc. dir, NDEA Inst, Univ. Md, summer 66; vis. prof, NDEA Inst, Loyola Univ. & Mt. St. Agnes Col, summer 68; consult, Proj. Communicate of Northwest Mo, 68; pres, Md. Nat. Univ, 72-73; Nat. Open Univ, Wash, D.C, 73- Ling. Soc. Am; MLA; NCTE; Asn. Supv. & Curriculum Develop; Am. Asn. Higher Educ; Intercontinental Biog. Asn. Administration and academic supervision in open university systems models; verbal interaction analysis in the classroom; research in the teaching of English. Publ: State supervision of English and reading instruction, NCTE, 67; New design in the teaching of English, 68 & New design II, research in English education, 69, Int. Textbook: A clinical module as matrix of new design methodology, Trinity Col. Photographic Serv, 68; Maryland National University: design for personalized academic achievement, Rodgers Res/Teaching Assocs, 72; contrib, Supervision, emerging profession, Asn. Supv. & Curriculum Develop, 69; plus others. Add: 3916 Commander Dr, College Heights Estates, Hyattsville, MD 20782.

RODGERS, PAUL COCHRAN, JR, b. Belmont, Mass, June 20, 20; m. 45; c. 5. ENGLISH. A.B, Harvard, 42; Ph.D.(Eng), Columbia Univ, 55. Instr. ENG, Middlebury Col, 46-48; Hunter Col, 49-50; Bloomfield Col, 50-55; from asst. prof. to assoc. prof, Univ. Omaha, 55-63; ASSOC. PROF, Ind. State Univ, 63-66; WITTENBERG UNIV, 66- Am. Field Serv, 42-45. Prose criticism; 19th century American literature. Publ: A word to the wise, Prentice-Hall, 61; The stadium of discourse, Col. Compos. & Commun, 10/67. Add: Dept. of English, Wittenberg University, Springfield, OH 45501.

RODIN, DORIS G, b. Bucharest, Rumania, Mar. 10, 15; U.S. citizen; m. 36; c. 2. ENGLISH, CINEMA. B.S, Temple Univ, 36; M.A, Am. Univ, 49, 55, 59, 67; George Washington Univ, 59; Georgetown Univ, 62-63. TEACHER hist. & Eng, Sch. Dist, Phila, Pa, 37-48; McKinley High Sch, Wash, D.C, 53-54; Eng, Washington-Lee High Sch, Arlington, Va, 54-61, Yorktown High Sch, 61-66, Wakefield High Sch, 66-67; CREATIVE WRITING & CINEMA, GEORGE-MASON HIGH SCH, FALLS CHURCH, VA, 67- Consult. chmn. counc. instr, Arlington, Va, 60-61; teaching lit. & compos. & Arlington County compos. guide, 60-65; film educ, Arlington Teachers In-Serv. & Stud, 60-67, lectr, 61 & 62; consult, contemporary film, div. exten. & gen. stud, Univ. Va. & lectr, 64-65; consult, film instr. & lectr. north. Va. area, 66; lectr, Va. Polytech. Inst. NCTE; Am. Fed. Film Soc. Cinema as an art form; metonymy in film; idea of structure and form in literature; the transformational nature of human understanding. Add: 5032 Fulton St, N.W, Washington, DC 20016.

RODMAN, GEORGE BUSH, b. Frankfort, Ky, Sept. 11, 11; m. 39; c. 2. ENGLISH. A.B, Centre Col. Ky, 32; A.M, Univ. Va, 34; Ph.D, Univ. Wis, 40. Instr. ENG, Univ. Ark, 40-43; asst. prof, UNIV. WIS-MADISON, 46-47, assoc. prof, 47-54, PROF, 54-, CHMN. ENG, CTR. SYST, 64-, chmn. Eng, exten. div, 46-67. U.S.N.R, 43-46, Lt. MLA; AAUP. Seventeenth and 18th century English literature. Publ: Co-ed, Patterns in writing, Holt, 50, 56, 63; auth, Sentimentalism in Lillo's The London merchant, Eng. Lit. Hist. Add: Dept. of English, University of Wisconsin-Madison, 600 N. Park St, Madison, WI 53706.

RODNEY, ROBERT MORRIS, U.S. citizen; m. 38; c. 2. ENGLISH. B.S, Trinity Col.(Conn), 35; M.A, Univ. Mich, 36; Ph.D, Univ. Wis, 46. Instr. Eng. compos, Pa. State Col, 36-38, 40-42; asst, Univ. Wis, 38-40; instr. Eng, Ind. Univ, 42-44; asst. prof, Union Col, 46-48; prof. & head div, Northeast Mo. State Col, 48-56; assoc. prof, North. Ill. Univ, 56-60, prof, 60-67; PROF. ENG. & DEAN SCH. LIB. ARTS, EAST. MONT. COL, 67- Fulbright lectr, Univ. Sao Paulo, 64; mem, Counc. Cols. Arts & Sci. U.S.A.F.R, 50-71, Maj. MLA; Am. Asn. Higher Educ. Mark Twain's reputation abroad; American writers abroad; humanism in modern American writers. Publ: Co-auth, The art, humor and humanity of Mark Twain, 59 & The birds and beasts of Mark Twain, 66: Univ. Okla; Focus on spelling, Sernoll, 67; co-ed, A book of the sonnet: poems and criticism, Twayne, 73; co-auth, Julian Bryant: champion of the Negro soldier, Ill. State Hist. J, summer 63; auth, The human enterprise: an experimental program in adult liberal education at Northern Illinois University, Occasional Papers, Ctr. Stud. Lib. Educ. for Adults, 64; co-auth, Silvia Drake: self-portrait of a seamstress of Weybridge, Vt. Hist, 4/66; plus others. Add: 417 Silver Lane, Billings, MT 59102.

RODNON, STEWART, b. New York, N.Y, May 21, 27; div; c. 2. AMERICAN LITERATURE. B.S, L.I. Univ, 49; N.Y. State War Serv. scholar, 49-55; M.A, Brooklyn Col, 52; Ph.D.(Eng), N.Y. Univ, 61. Sr. publicity agent, State Dept. Labor, N.Y, 52-59; instr. eng, Monmouth Col, 59-62, asst. prof, 62-64; Ball State Univ, 64-66; RIDER COL, 66-72, ASSOC. PROF. ENG. & AM. STUD, 72- Asst, N.Y. Univ, 57-59. U.S.N, 45-46. MLA; NCTE. Modern American literature; European and American contemporary poetry and prose. Add: Dept. of English, Rider College, Trenton, NJ 08602.

ROELLINGER, FRANCIS XAVIER, b. Detroit, Mich, May 18, 07; m. 38; c. 2. ENGLISH. A.B, Univ. Mich, 29, A.M, 31, fel, 32-38, Ph.D, 38. Instr. ENG, Yale, 38-40; OBERLIN COL, 40-44, asst. prof, 46-50, assoc. prof, 50-58, prof, 58-73, EMER. PROF, 73- U.S.N.R, 44-46, Lt. MLA. Literary criticism; Henry James; E.S. Dallas. Publ: Psychical research and The turn of the screw, Am. Lit; Early development of Carlyle's style, PMLA; Winckelmann in Pater's Diaphaneite, Eng. Lang. Notes, 6/65. Add: 351 Elm St, Oberlin, OH 44074.

ROELOFS, GERRIT HUBBARD, b. Elma, N.Y, Aug. 6, 20; m. 49; c. 2. ENGLISH. B.A, Amherst Col, 42; Ph.D, Johns Hopkins Univ, 54. Instr. ENG, Univ. N.H, 51-55, asst. prof, 55-57; KENYON COL, 57-58, assoc. prof, 58-65, McILVAINE PROF, 65- Great Lakes Cols. Asn. res. grant medieval popular iconography, St. Augustine's Col.(Eng), 68. U.S.N.A.F, 42-46, Lt. MLA; NCTE. Mediaeval and Renaissance literature. Publ: Co-auth, The major poets, Harcourt, 69; auth, Henry Adams: pessimism and the intelligent use of doom, ELH, 50. Add: Milnor Lane, Box 309, Gambier, OH 43022.

ROEMER, KENNETH MORRISON, b. East Rockaway, N.Y, June 6, 45; m. 68; c. 2. AMERICAN CIVILIZATION. B.A, Harvard, 67; M.A, Univ. Pa, 68, univ. & Ford Found. fels, 69-71, Ph.D.(Am. civilization), 71. Asst. prof. ENG, UNIV. TEX, ARLINGTON, 71-74, ASSOC. PROF, 74- Managing ed, Am. Literary Realism, 1870-1910, 72- Am. Stud. Asn; MLA; AHA; Asn. Stud. Am. Indian Lit; Melville Soc. Am. Late 19th century American culture; American Indian literatures; American literature. Publ: American utopian literature (1888-1900), Am. Lit. Realism, summer 71; Sex roles, utopia and change, Am. Stud, fall 72; 1984 in 1894: Harben's Land of the changing sun, Miss. Quart, winter 72-73. Add: Dept. of English, University of Texas at Arlington, Arlington, TX 76019.

ROESLER, MIRIAM CLARE, O.S.F, b. Toledo, Ohio. ENGLISH & AMERICAN LITERATURE. A.B, Col. St. Francis, 38; M.A, DePaul Univ, 45; Ph.D.(Eng), Cath. Univ. Am, 62; Univ. London, 73; Yeats Int. Inst, Sligo, Ireland, 73. Instr. ENG, St. Francis Acad, Joliet, Ill, 38-45; St. Peter's High Sch, Mansfield, Ohio, 45-50; asst. prof, Col. St. Francis, 50-69; ASSOC. PROF, CARROLL COL.(MONT), 69-, dir. summer prog, London, summer 74. Asst. prof, St. Norbert Col, summer 53; Schmidt grant, Harvard, summer 65. NCTE; AAUP. Sea and death in Whitman's Leaves of Grass. Publ: Verse play, Cath. Sch. J, 51; Sea and death in Leaves of Grass, Walt Whitman Newsl. & Rev, Vol. X, No. 1; plus poems in Magnificat, Ave Maria & St. Anthony Messenger. Add: Dept. of English, Carroll College, Helena, MT 59601.

ROEVER, JAMES E, b. Reedsburg, Wis, June 27, 35; m. 66. SPEECH. B.A, Wartburg Col, 57; M.A, Univ. Kans, 58, Ph.D.(speech), Univ. Iowa, 62. Instr. speech & mass media, Hunter Col, 62-63, asst. prof, 63-64; pub. address & group commun, Northwest. Univ, 64-68; dir. res, Speech Asn. Am. 68-70; ASSOC. PROF. COMMUN. ARTS & SCI, QUEENS COL.(N.Y), 70- Cent. States Speech Asn; Speech Commun. Asn; Int. Commun. Asn; East States Speech Asn; AAAS. Communications research; research methodology. Add: Dept. of Communication Arts & Sciences, Queens College, Flushing, NY 11367.

ROGAL, SAMUEL J, b. Pittsburgh, Pa, Aug. 3, 34; m. 65; c. 2. ENGLISH. B.S.Ed, Clarion State Col, 56; Lehigh Univ, 56; M.A, Univ. Pittsburgh, 60. Instr. ENG, Waynesburg Col, 60-62; Iowa State Univ, 62-66; asst. prof, STATE UNIV. N.Y. COL. OSWEGO, 66-68, ASSOC. PROF, 68- Vis. lectr. pre-freshman prog, Tuskegee Inst, summer 66; vis. instr, Miss Hall's Sch, Pittsfield, Mass, 72. U.S.A, 57-59. MLA; Hymn Soc. Am; Augustan Reprint Soc; Am. Soc. 18th Century Stud. British literature of the 18th century; hymnology; composition and rhetoric. Publ: Teaching composition in the senior high school, Littlefield, 66; co-auth, Preparing the research paper, 67 & auth, The student-critic: an aid to writing, 70; Educators Publ. Serv; The paragraph, Dickenson, 68; Thomas Tickell's prospect of peace, Ill. Quart, 2/73; Bread to the hungry: John Wesley and the poor, Christian Advocate, 3/73; The Northfield and Mount Hermon Hymnal, Hymn, 4/73; plus others. Add: Dept. of English, State University of New York at Oswego, Oswego, NY 13126.

ROGERS, CARMEN, b. Creedmoor, N.C. ENGLISH LITERATURE. A.B, Meredith Col; scholar, Cornell Univ, 32-33, A.M. & Ph.D, 33. Instr. Eng, Meredith Col; assoc. prof, Coker Col. & Ga. State Col. Women; prof. & head dept, Miss. Woman's Col; dean stud, Beaver Col; from assoc. prof. to prof. ENG, FLA. STATE UNIV, 38-68, EMER. PROF, 68- Shakespeare Asn. Am; Renaissance Soc. Am; MLA; Southeast Renaissance Conf; S.Atlantic Mod. Lang. Asn. English and continental Renaissance literature; medical symbolism in the Faerie Queene; John Heminges and Henry Condell, editors Shakespeare First Folio. Publ: English Renaissance melanchology: A prologue: of men and moods, Fla. State Univ. Stud. in Eng. & Am. Lit, 52; Heavenly justice in the tragedies of Shakespeare, In: Studies in Shakespeare, Univ. Miami, 53; ed, Richard Carew's Examination of men's wits (1594 transl. of Juan Huarte, Examen de ingenios), Scholars' Facsimiles, 59. Add: Dept. of English, Florida State University, Tallahassee, FL 32306.

ROGERS, CAROLYN SHERRILL WHITE, b. Marion, Va, Jan. 29, 20; m. 61. MODERN AMERICAN & BRITISH LITERATURE. B.A, Emory & Henry Col, 64; M.A, Fla. State Univ, 68, Ph.D.(Eng), 72. Instr. Eng, Patrick Henry High Sch, 64-65; asst, Fla. State Univ, 68-72; ASST. PROF. ENG, MOUNTAIN EMPIRE COMMUNITY COL, 72- Mem, Southeast. Conf. Eng. Two-Yr. Col. Am. Stud. Asn; Shakespeare Asn. Am; S.Atlantic Mod. Lang. Asn; NCTE; Conf. Col. Compos. & Commun. Twentieth century drama, English and American; American short story, modern; Freshman composition. Add: Dept. of English, Humanities Div, Mountain Empire Community College, Big Stone Gap, VA 24219.

ROGERS, DANIEL JOHN, b. Calumet City, Ill, Feb. 8, 27. ENGLISH. B.A, Loras Col, 49; St. Meinrad Theol. Sem, 49-53; M.A, Univ. Wis, 57, Ph.D.(Eng), 64. Counsel, high sch, Iowa, 53-56; instr. ENG, LORAS COL, 57-65, asst. prof, 65-69, ASSOC. PROF, 69- Mem, exec. counc, Tri-State Consortium Insts. Higher Learning, 67- Conf. Col. Compos. & Commun; NCTE; MLA; AAUP. Poetry; the plays of T.S. Eliot; teaching of creative writing. Publ: Dramatic use of the liturgy in the plays of T.S. Eliot: a secular evolution, Univ. Microfilms, 64; Settling in at Nada Ranch (poem), Desert Call, 71; Three poems, Delta Epsilon Sigma Bull, 3/72; Motion (poem), Iowa Poetry Day Asn. Anthol, 73; plus others. Add: Dept. of English, Loras College, Dubuque, IA 52001.

ROGERS, DAVID M, b. Mt. Vernon, N.Y, Feb. 22, 32; m. 53; c. 3. ENGLISH. B.A, Syracuse Univ, 54, M.A, 56; Ph.D, Wayne State Univ, 62. Instr. ENG, Wayne State Univ, 57-62; asst. prof, St. Bonaventure Univ, 62-63; SETON HALL UNIV, 63-66, assoc. prof, 66-70, PROF, 70- MLA. Poetry of the romantic period; intellectual history. Publ: The function of form in poetry, Renascence, spring 67; Wordsworth's Roman antiquities, Durham Univ. J, 6/72; At St. Michael's Tor, Anglo-Welsh Rev, spring 73. Add: Dept. of English, Seton Hall University, South Orange, NJ 07079.

ROGERS, FRANKLIN ROBERT, b. July 25, 21; m. 46; c. 1. ENGLISH. B.A, Fresno State Col, 50, M.A, 52; Ph.D.(Eng), Univ. Calif, Berkeley, 58. Ref. librn, Fresno State Col, 51-52; teacher high sch, Calif, 52-54; instr. ENG, Univ. Wis-Milwaukee, 58-60, asst. prof, 60-63; vis. asst. prof, Univ. Calif, Davis, 63-64; assoc. prof, SAN JOSE STATE UNIV, 64-68, PROF, 68- Fulbright lectr, Fac. Lett, Lyon, France, 66-67, assoc. prof. Am. lit, 69-71. Sig.C, U.S.A, 43-46, S/Sgt. MLA. American literature. Publ: Mark Twain's burlesque patterns, South. Methodist Univ, 60; The pattern for Mark Twain's Roughing it, 61, Mark Twain's satires and burlesques, 67 & ed, Mark Twain's Roughing it, 72, Univ. Calif; Simon Wheeler, detective, N.Y. Pub. Libr, 63; auth, The tale of Gamelyn and the editing of the Canterbury tales, J. Eng. & Ger. Philol, 1/59; The road to reality: burlesque travel literature and Mark Twain's Roughing it, Bull. N.Y. Pub. Libr, 3/63; Mark Twain and Alphonse Daudet: tramp abroad and Tartarin sur les Alpes, Comp. Lit, summer 64. Add: Dept. of English, San Jose State University, 125 S. Seventh St, San Jose, CA 95114.

ROGERS, FREDERICK JOHN, b. Decatur, Mich, Jan. 26, 08; m. 47. ENGLISH. A.B, West. Mich. Univ, 30; A.M, Columbia Univ, 36; Ph.D.(Eng), Univ. Mich, 56. Teacher schs, Mich, 30-36; high sch, 36-42; asst. prof. ENG, WEST. MICH. UNIV, 46-53, assoc. prof, 53-66, prof, 66-71, head dept, 56-66, EMER. PROF, 71- U.S.A.A.F, 42-45. MLA; NCTE. Prose style; 18th century; humanities. Add: 2905 Memory Lane, Kalamazoo, MI 49007.

ROGERS, JAMES LLOYD, JR, b. Marceline, Mo, Feb. 26, 26; m. 46. JOURNALISM. B.A, Univ. Minn, 45; M.J, Univ. Tex, 49; Ph.D.(jour), Univ. Mo, 54. Instr. jour, Victoria Jr. Col, 46-48; teaching fel, Univ. Tex, 48-49; asst. prof, Tex. Col. Arts & Indust, 49-52; asst, Univ. Mo, 52-53; PROF. JOUR, N.TEX. STATE UNIV, 53-, DIR. INSTNL. ANALYSIS & PLANNING, 71-, news serv. dir, 53-71, asst. to pres, 64-65, admin. v.pres, 65-71. Participant, Inst. Educ. Mgt, Harvard Grad. Sch. Business, summer 71. U.S.A, 44-46. Asn. Instnl. Res; Soc. Col. & Univ. Planning; Am. Asn. Higher Educ. Attitude research applied to newspapers; general semantics in journalism; planning and management systems in higher education. Publ: The story of North Texas, N.Tex. State Univ, 65; How readership studies affect news features and advertising in newspapers, Am. Newspaper Publ. Asn; Prospective teachers, attitudes toward freedom of information, Jour. Quart. Add: Office of Analysis and Planning, North Texas State University, Denton, TX 76203.

ROGERS, JIMMIE NEAL, b. McNeil, Ark, May 9, 35; m. 57; c. 3. SPEECH COMMUNICATION. B.A, South. State Col.(Ark), 57; M.A, Univ. Ark, Fayetteville, 65; Ph.D.(commun), Fla. State Univ, 72. Teacher SPEECH, C.E. Byrd High Sch, Shreveport, La, 58-67; instr, UNIV. ARK, FAYETTEVILLE, 67-70, ASST. PROF, 70- Int. Commun. Asn; Speech Commun. Asn; South. Speech Commun. Asn. Southern political communication; attitude change. Publ: Co-auth, The selling of the Pentagon: was CBS the Fulbright propaganda machine?, Quart. J. Speech, 10/71; An experimental study of the effects of positive and negative feedback on the autonomic arousal of student speakers, spring 73 & auth, John Adams' summation speech in Rex. v. Wemms, et al: a delicate act of persuasion, (in press), South. Speech J. Add: Dept. of Speech, University of Arkansas, Fayetteville, AR 72701.

ROGERS, JOSEPH ALOYSIUS, b. St. Louis, Mo, Apr. 29, 12; m. 39; 68; c. 1. ENGLISH LITERATURE. A.B, St. Louis Univ, 35, M.A, 39, Ph.D, 57. Asst. prof. ENG, ST. LOUIS UNIV, 57-60, assoc. prof, 60-66, PROF, 66- U.S.N, 42-46, Res, 46-, Lt. Comdr. NCTE; Conf. Col. Compos. & Commun.(secy, 57-58). Dostoevsky; modern short story; modern novel. Publ: Integrated freshman English, 58, co-auth, Literary types and themes, 60 & co-ed, 2nd ed, 71, Holt. Add: Dept. of English, St. Louis University, St. Louis, MO 63103.

ROGERS, KATHARINE MUNZER, b. New York, N.Y, June 6, 32; m. 56; c. 3. ENGLISH. B.A, Barnard Col, Columbia Univ, 52; Fulbright scholar, Cambridge, 52-53; Ph.D.(Eng), Columbia Univ, 57. Instr. ENG, Skidmore Col, 54-55; Cornell Univ, 55-57; lectr, BROOKLYN COL, 58, instr, 58-65, asst. prof, 65-71, assoc. prof, 71-74, PROF, 74-, DOCTORAL FAC, CITY UNIV. N.Y, 72- Mod. Humanities Res. Asn; MLA; Women's Caucus Mod. Lang. Asn. Restoration and 18th century literature; 18th and 19th century novel; women in literature. Publ: The troublesome helpmate: a history of misogyny in literature, Univ. Wash, 66; William Wycherley, Twayne, 72; A defense of Thackeray's Amelia, Tex. Stud. Lit. & Lang, 70; The context of Arnold's plea for birth control in Culture & anarchy, Dalhousie Rev, 72; The pressure of convention on Thackeray's women, Mod. Lang. Rev, 72; plus others. Add: Dept. of English, Brooklyn College, Brooklyn, NY 11210.

ROGERS, PHILIP EDWARD, b. Mt. Vernon, N.Y, Sept. 3, 36; m. 58; c. 2. ENGLISH. B.A, Univ. Utah, 58; N.Y. Regents fel, Cornell Univ, 58-60, univ. fel, 59-60, M.A, 60; Ph.D.(Eng), Univ. Ill, 67. Lectr. Eng. & hist, Grammar Sch, Awo Omamma, Biafra, 60-61; ENG, Univ. Nigeria, 61-62; asst, Univ. Ill, 62-66, instr, 66-67; asst. prof, STATE UNIV. N.Y. BINGHAMTON, 67-73, ASSOC. PROF, 73- MLA. West African literature; Victorian novel; modern fiction. Publ: Mr. Pickwick's innocence, 6/72 & The Dynamics of time in the old curiosity shop, 9/73, NCF; Poems of regeneration: Chinua Achebe's Beware soul-brother, J. Commonwealth Lit, (in press). Add: Dept. of English, State University of New York at Binghamton, Binghamton, NY 13901.

ROGERS, PHILLIP W, b. Ennis, Tex, July 7, 38; m. 64; c. 2. ENGLISH. B.A, Univ. Tex, 60, M.A, 62; Ph.D.(Eng), Harvard, 67. Asst. prof. ENG, QUEEN'S UNIV.(ONT), 67-73, ASSOC. PROF, 73- Ed, Humanities Asn. Rev. Mediaeval Acad. Am; MLA; Asn. Can. Univ. Teachers Eng; Humanities Asn. Can. Medieval literature; history of English language; comparative linguistics. Add: Dept. of English, Queen's University, Kingston, Ont. K7L 3N6, Can.

ROGERS, POWELL BURWELL, b. Newport News, Va, July 11, 09. ENGLISH. A.B, Col. William & Mary, 30; A.M, Duke Univ, 32; Ph.D, Univ. Pa, 50. Teacher high schs, Va, Md. & N.C, 30-36; Va, 36-40; asst. instr. ENG, Univ. Pa, 46-48; instr, Bucknell Univ, 48-50, asst. prof, 50-56, assoc. prof, 56-63, prof, 63-73; RETIRED. Educ. adv. Civilian Conserv. Corps, 34. U.S.A, 41-46. Mediaeval Acad. Am; Am. Name Soc; Col. Eng. Asn; MLA; NCTE. Medieval courtesy literature; place and personal names; teaching of English. Publ: Inland ports, Am. Speech, 10/60; Naming Protestant churches in America, Names, 3/63; The first names of Virginia, Occasional Papers, Va. Place Names Soc, 2/67. Add: 16 White Oak Dr, Newport News, VA 23601.

ROGERS, ROBERT WENTWORTH, b. Boston, Mass, Dec. 1, 14; m. 46, 56; c. 5. ENGLISH LITERATURE. A.B, Univ. Mich, 36; A.M, Harvard, 37, Dexter scholar, 41, Ph.D, 42. Teaching fel. ENG, Harvard, 38-42, instr, 46-48, sr. tutor, Dunster House, 46-48; asst. prof, UNIV. ILL, URBANA, 48-51, assoc. prof, 51-55, PROF, 55-, DEAN COL. LIB. ARTS & SCI, 64-, exec. secy. dept. Eng, 53-57, acting head, 56-57, head dept, 57-64. Guggenheim fel, 57-58; vis. prof, Duke Univ, Summer 58; mem. bd. dirs, Ctr, Res. Librs, 65-67; mem, Counc. Cols. Arts & Sci, pres, 72; chmn. lib. arts deans, Comt. Inst. Coop, 69- U.S.N.R, 43-45, Lt. MLA; NCTE; Miss. Valley Deans. Alexander Pope; 18th century English literature; higher education. Publ: The major satires of Alexander Pope, Univ. Ill; The organization of departments of English, Col. Teaching Eng, 65; The Pilgrims and the Book, Pilgrim Soc, 72; co-auth, Opportunities and responsibilities for developing human resources, Lib. Educ, 69; auth, Notes on Alexander Pope's early education, S.Atlantic Quart, 71; co-auth, Recent studies in the Restoration and eighteenth century, Stud. Eng. Lit 1500-1900, 72. Add: College of Liberal Arts & Sciences, 294 Lincoln Hall, University of Illinois, Urbana, IL 61801.

ROGERS, THOMAS, b. Selbyville, Del, Dec. 26, 18; m. 41; c. 3. ENGLISH LITERATURE. A.B, Univ. Del, 40; A.M, Univ. Pa, 50, Ph.D.(Eng), 55. Instr. ENG, Univ. Del, 46-53; asst. prof, MacMurray Col, 53-57; State Univ. N.Y. L.I. Ctr, 57-59, ASSOC. PROF, 59-66; STATE UNIV. N.Y. STONY BROOK, 66- U.S.A, 41-45. MLA. The graveyard poets; 18th century English literature. Publ: Robert Blair and the grave; The testament dative of Robert Blair, Notes & Queries. Add: Dept. of English, State University of New York at Stony Brook, Stony Brook, NY 11790.

ROGERS, WILLIAM ELFORD, b. Greenville, S.C, Dec. 12, 44; m. 69. MEDIEVAL ENGLISH LITERATURE. B.A, Yale, 66; Ph.D.(Eng), Univ. N.C, Chapel Hill, 70. Instr. ENG, U.S. Mil. Acad, 70-72; ASST. PROF, GA. STATE UNIV, 72- Mil. Intel, U.S.A, 70-72, Res, 72-, Capt. MLA. Medieval literature; literary criticism. Publ: Image and abstraction: six Middle English religious lyrics, Anglistica, 72. Add: Dept. of English, Georgia State University, 33 Gilmer St. S.E, Atlanta, GA 30303.

ROGERS, WILLIAM NORRIS, II, b. San Francisco, Calif, Apr. 25, 40; m. 64; c. 1. ENGLISH LITERATURE. A.B, Stanford Univ, 62; M.A, Univ. Calif, Berkeley, 64, Ph.D.(Eng), 71. Asst. ENG, Univ. Calif, Berkeley, 67-68; ASST. PROF, SAN DIEGO STATE UNIV, 68- AAUP; MLA. Nineteenth century English critical prose and travel literature; English novel. Add: British Section, School of Literature, San Diego State University, San Diego, CA 92115.

ROGERS, WINSLOW SMITH, b. Boston, Mass, Jan. 4, 44; m. 69; c. 1. ENGLISH & AMERICAN LITERATURE. B.A, Amherst Col, 66; A.M, Harvard, 67, Ph.D.(Eng), 72. Teaching fel, Eng. & gen. educ, Harvard, 68-71; ASST. PROF, UNIV. MO-ST. LOUIS, 71- MLA. The English novel; Victorian and Edwardian literature. Add: Dept. of English, University of Missouri-St. Louis, MO 63121.

ROGERSON, BREWSTER, b. Charlotte, N.C, Jan. 16, 21. ENGLISH. A.B, Univ. N.C, 41; Ph.D, Princeton, 45. Instr. ENG, Univ. Calif, 45-47, asst. prof, 47-51; lectr, Princeton, 51; asst. prof, Conn. Col, 52; assoc. prof, KANS. STATE UNIV, 53-67, PROF, 67-, dir, honors prog, 58-61. Fund Advan. Educ. fel, 51. Fac. Lectr. Award, Kans. State Univ, 67. MLA; Royal Music Asn. History of criticism; 18th century; Publ: Co-ed, Eighteenth century English literature, Harcourt, 69; The art of painting the passions, J. Hist. Ideas, 1/53; Criticism: types, In: Encyclopedia of poetry and poetics, Princeton, 65. Add: Dept. of English, Kansas State University, Manhattan, KS 66506.

ROGGE, EDWARD, b. Superior, Wis, Oct. 1, 26; m. 48; c. 4. SPEECH. B.S, Univ. Wis, 49, M.S, 50; Ph.D, Univ. Mo, 58. Instr. SPEECH, Univ. Mo, 50-51, 53-57; asst. prof. TULANE UNIV, 57-61, ASSOC. PROF, 61-, DIR. ADMIS, 65-, ASST. PROVOST, 69-, asst. dean col. arts & sci, 62-65, Ellis L. Phillips Found. intern acad. admin, 64-65. Speech Commun. Asn; Am. Stud. Asn; South. Speech Commun. Asn; Asn. Col. Admis. Counsel. History of public address; rhetoric. Publ: Co-auth, Advanced public speaking, Holt, 66. Add: 7811 Green St, New Orleans, LA 70118.

ROHMAN, DAVID GORDON, b. Whitesboro, N.Y, Apr. 27, 28; m. 51; c. 7. ENGLISH. A.B, Syracuse Univ, 48, M.A, 55, Ph.D, 60. Instr. ENG, MICH. STATE UNIV, 58-60, asst. prof, 60-64, assoc. prof, 64-67, PROF, 67-, DEAN, JUSTIN MORRILL COL, 65-, asst. dean continuing educ, cols. arts & lett. & soc. sci, 63-65. U.S. Off. Educ. grant, 63. U.S.A, 51-53. MLA; NCTE. American transcendentalism: Henry Thoreau, Ralph Waldo Emerson; English composition; experimentalism in higher education. Add: Justin Morrill College, Michigan State University, East Lansing, MI 48823.

ROHRBERGER, MARY H, b. New Orleans, La, Jan. 22, 29. ENGLISH. B.A, Newcomb. Col, 50; M.A, Tulane Univ, 52, Ph.D, 61. Instr. Eng, Dillard Univ, 58-59; teaching fel, Tulane Univ, 59-61; asst. prof. ENG, OKLA. STATE UNIV, 61-65, assoc. prof, 65-73, PROF, 73- MLA; NCTE; AAUP. Criticism; genre study; short story and novel. Publ: Hawthorne and the modern short story, Mouton, 66; co-auth, An introduction to literature, 68 & Reading and writing about literature, 70, Random; auth, The man, the boy and the myth, Midcontinent Am. Stud. J, 62; Hawthorne's literary theory and the nature of his short stories, Stud. Short Fiction, 65; Point of view in Benito Cereno, Col. Eng, 66. Add: Dept. of English, Oklahoma State University, Stillwater, OK 74074.

ROHRIG, GLADYS M, b. Martinez, Ariz, Mar. 3, 03. SPEECH, THEATRE. A.B, DePauw Univ, 30; A.M, Northwest. Univ, 41; Ph.D.(theatre & pub. address), Ohio State Univ, 56. Teacher, Van Buren High Sch, 22-24; teacher & play dir, Brazil High Sch, 24-47; asst. prof. SPEECH & THEATRE & tech. dir. theatre, IND. STATE UNIV, TERRE HAUTE, 47-57, assoc. prof, 57-64, prof, 64-69, EMER. PROF, 69- Speech Commun. Asn. Theatre history; high school speech; directing practice. Publ: Analysis of certain acting editions and prompt books of plays by Dion Boucicault, Ohio State Univ, 56; Four courses of study for high school speech, Ind. Speech Asn, 61; To do's in directing plays, Ind. State Univ, 67; Characteristics of the effective teacher, 3/51 & Abstract of dissertation on analysis of Boucicault plays, 11/56, Teachers Col. J. Add: 474, R.R. 1, West Terre Haute, IN 47885.

ROHRLICH, BEULAH F, b. New York, N.Y, Mar. 1, 29; m. 51; c. 2. SPEECH. B.A, Queens Col, 50; M.A, Cornell Univ, 51; Ph.D.(speech educ), Syracuse Univ, 67. Instr, Sch. Gen. Stud. & Eng. Lang. Inst, Queens Col. (N.Y), 52-53, interviewer speech pathology, Hill Found. Stud, Univ. Iowa, 53-54, participant in res. wor, Ford Found. Stud, 56-57; instr. Eng, Essex Community Col, 58-59; rhetoric, Univ. Iowa, 61-63; Eng. & speech, Syracuse Univ, 63-64; developer & coordinator Speech Educ. Pilot Prog, Syracuse Pub. Sch, N.Y, 64-65; asst. prof. SPEECH, SYRACUSE UNIV, 67-73, ASSOC. PROF, 73-, COORD. INTERDISCIPLINARY PROG. DEVELOPMENT, COL. VISUAL & PERFORMING ARTS, 72-, chmn. dept, 69-72. Instr. sci. Eng, Syracuse Psychiat. Hospital, N.Y, 63-64. Nat. Women's Prof. Speech Asn; Speech Commun. Asn; Can. Speech Asn. Cross-cultural communication; undergraduate interdisciplinary program development; historical aspects of public address in United States and Canada. Publ: Rhetoric and the dragon, Cameo 11/71; Freedom in the press in Canada: how it happened, Can. Speech Commun. J, 11/72. Add: Dept. of Speech Communication, Syracuse University, Syracuse, NY 13210.

ROLFE, FRANKLIN PRESCOTT, b. Concord, N.H, Nov. 15, 02; m. 31. ENGLISH LITERATURE. B.S, Dartmouth Col, 24; A.M, Harvard, 25, Ph.D, 31. Instr. Eng, Stanford Univ, 25-27; Sheldon traveling fel, Harvard, 31-32; instr. Eng, UNIV. CALIF, LOS ANGELES, 32-35, asst. prof, 35-42, assoc. prof, 42-48, prof, 48-70, chmn. dept, 44-48, dean div. humanities, 47-61, dean, COL. LETT. & SCI, 61-70, EMER. DEAN, 70-, ACAD. ASST. TO EXEC. V.CHANCELLOR, 71- Mem. bd. dir. & chmn. accrediting comn. sr. cols. & univs, West. Asn. Schs. & Cols, 60-63; mem. nat. comt, Regional Accrediting Asn, 60-63; mem. exec. comt, West. Col. Asn, 60-63, v.pres, 64-66, pres, 66-68. MLA. History of prose fiction; Victorian literature. Add: College of Letters & Science, University of California, Los Angeles, CA 90024.

ROLLIN, ROGER BEST, b. McKeesport, Pa, Feb. 12, 30; m. 52; c. 2. ENGLISH LITERATURE. B.A, Washington & Jefferson Col, 52; M.A, Yale, 57, Ph.D, 60. Instr. ENG, FRANKLIN & MARSHALL COL, 59-60, asst. prof, 60-65, assoc. prof, 65-72, PROF, 72- U.S.A, 52-55. NCTE; MLA; Col. Eng. Asn; Popular Cult. Asn. Applications of psychology to literary theory and criticism; popular culture; 17th century English poetry and prose. Publ: Robert Herrick, Twayne, 66; Hero/anti-hero, McGraw, 73; Beowulf to Batman: the epic hero and pop culture, Col. Eng, 2/70; Paradise lost: tragical-comical-historical-pastoral, Milton Stud, 73; Milton and the metaphysical poets, Milton Encyclopedia, (in prep); plus three others. Add: Dept. of English, Franklin & Marshall College, Lancaster, PA 17604.

ROLLINS, RONALD G, b. Clendenin, W.Va, Oct. 16, 29; m. 53; c. 4. ENGLISH, MODERN IRISH & AMERICAN LITERATURE. A.B, Glenville State Col, 51; M.A, Marshall Univ, 53; Ph.D.(Eng), Univ. Cincinnati, 60. Teacher, Troy High Sch, 51; asst. Eng, Marshall Univ, 51-53; teaching fel, ENG, Univ. Cincinnati, 57-60; asst. prof, Marshall Univ, 60-66; ASSOC. PROF, OHIO WESLEYAN UNIV, 66- Fulbright grant, Pakistan, 64-65; Danforth assoc, 66-68. Intel.C, U.S.A, 53-56, Sgt. Am. Comt. Irish Stud; MLA; Col. Eng. Asn. Irish drama and fiction; American poetry. Publ: Form and content in Sean O'Casey's Dublin trilogy, Mod. Drama, 66; Shaw and O'Casey: John Bull and his other island, Shaw Rev, 67; Clerical blackness in the green garden: heroine as scapegoat in O'Casey's Cock-a-doodle dandy, James Joyce Quart, 71; plus one other. Add: Dept. of English, Ohio Wesleyan University, N. Sandusky St, Delaware, OH 43015.

ROLLINSON, PHILIP BRUCE, b. Chattanooga, Tenn, May 13, 39; m. 62; c. 3. RENAISSANCE LITERATURE. B.A, Univ. Chattanooga, 61; M.A, Univ. Va, 66, Ph.D.(Eng), 68. ASST. PROF. ENG, Univ. Chattanooga, summer 68; Vanderbilt Univ, 68-71; UNIV. S.C, 71- Fel, Folger Shakespeare Libr, 72. U.S.N.R, 61-65, Lt.(j.g). MLA; Renaissance Soc. Am; Mediaeval Acad. Am; Shakespeare Asn. Am. Milton; Spenser; Old English literature and culture. Publ: Some kinds of meaning in Old English poetry, Annuale Mediaevale, 70; The central debate in Comus, Philol. Quart, 70; A generic view of Spenser's Four hymns, Stud. Philol, 71. Add: Dept. of English, University of South Carolina, Columbia, SC 29208.

ROLLO, DUNCAN JAMES, b. Dundee, Scotland, July 13, 44; U.S. citizen; m. 69. AMERICAN LITERATURE & DRAMA. B.A, Glassboro State Col, 66; M.A, Kent State Univ, 68, Ph.D.(Eng), 74. INSTR. ENG, VA. POLYTECH. INST. & STATE UNIV, 69- Am. Soc. Theatre Res; MLA. Modern American drama; American theatre; modern American literature. Publ: Nine abstracts, Abstracts Eng. Stud, 4/69. Add: Dept. of English, Virginia Polytechnic Institute & State University, Blacksburg, VA 24061.

ROLOFF, LELAND H, b. San Diego, Calif, Aug. 15, 27; m. 66; c. 2. SPEECH. B.A, San Diego State Col, 50; M.A, Northwest. Univ, 51; Ph.D.(speech), Univ. South. Calif, 68. Instr. speech, Univ. Vt, 51-53; teacher Eng. high sch, Calif, 53-57; teacher-consult, Glendale pub. schs, 57-62; asst. prof. speech, Occidental Col, 62-66; South. Methodist Univ, 66-68; ASSOC. PROF. INTERPRETATION, NORTHWEST. UNIV, 68- Commun. consult. to indust. South. Methodist Univ. teaching award, 68. U.S.N, 45-46. Speech Commun. Asn. Interpretation; communications; poetry of Robinson Jeffers. Publ: Perception and evocation of literature, Scott, 73. Son of the sad fall (film), NBC, Los Angeles. Add: School of Speech, Northwestern University, Evanston, IL 60201.

ROMANO, JOHN RIGOLETTO, b. Chicago, Ill, May 23, 31; m. 61; c. 1. ENGLISH. A.B, Loyola Univ.(Ill.), 53; Fulbright fel, Univ. Florence, 53-54; M.A, Columbia Univ, 56; Pres. fel. & Ph.D.(Eng), 68. Instr. ENG, Hartwick Col, 59-60; St. Peter's Col.(N.J), 60-61; MIAMI UNIV, 62-67, asst. prof, 68-74, ASSOC. PROF, 74- Sig.C, U.S.A, 54-56. MLA; Renaissance Soc. Am. Renaissance English and Italian literature; Milton. Add: Dept. of English, Miami University, Oxford, OH 45056.

ROMMEL, GEORGE WILLIAM, b. New York, N.Y, Dec. 3, 21. ENGLISH. B.S.Ed, North. Ill. State Teachers Col, 46; M.A, Northwest. Univ, 51, Ph.D. (Eng), 53. Educ. adv, U.S. Army Educ. Prog, Germany, 49; instr. ENG, Beloit Col, 53; asst. prof, EAST. ILL. UNIV, 53-56, assoc. prof, 56-63, PROF, 63- U.S.A.A.F, 43-45, Lt. MLA; AAUP. Restoration period; 18th century; 19th century prose; Shakespeare. Add: Dept. of English, Eastern Illinois University, Charleston, IL 61920.

RONALD, MARGARET ANN, b. Seattle, Washington, Oct. 9, 39. ENGLISH LITERATURE. B.A, Whitman Col, 61; M.A, Univ. Colo, Boulder, 66; Ph.D. (Eng), Northwest. Univ, Evanston, 70. ASST. PROF. ENG, UNIV. NEV, RENO, 70-, summer res. grant, 73. MLA; Rocky Mountain Mod. Lang. Asn. The novel; Victorian literature; Western American literature. Add: Dept. of English, University of Nevada, Reno, NV 89507.

RONDEAU, MIRIAM BARBARA, S.N.J.M, Modern Languages. See Volume III, Foreign Languages, Linguistics & Philology.

RONSHEIM, SALLY B, b. New York, N.Y; m. 40; c. 3. ENGLISH. B.A, Brooklyn Col, 37; City Col. New York, 37-40; M.S, Long Island Univ, 62; Univ. London, 64; Ph.D.(higher educ), N.Y. Univ, 67. Librn. high sch, N.Y, 62-67; asst. dir. grad. libr. sci. prog, LONG ISLAND UNIV, 60-62, asst. prof. ENG, 64-73, ASSOC. PROF, 73- U.S. Dept. Health, Educ. & Welfare grant, West. Europe, 65-66; Mem. Conf. Eng. Educ. Comt. to Evaluate ERIC Doc, 68-, bd. dir, Nassau County Cent. Ref. Libr, 68- NCTE. Linguistics; teacher education in English; English literature and composition. Publ: Co-auth, New York portrait: a literary look at the empire state, Holt, 65; auth, Grammatical terminology: a combined traditional and modern linguistic glossary, C.W. Post Ctr, 72. Add: 39 Windsor Rd, Great Neck, NY 11021.

RONSLEY, JOSEPH, b. Chicago, Ill, June 3, 31; m. 56; c. 2. ENGLISH. B.S, Northwest. Univ, 53, M.A, 62, Ph.D.(Eng), 66. Lectr. ENG, McGill Univ, 65-67; asst. prof, Univ. Wis-Madison, 67-69; McGILL UNIV, 69-73, ASSOC. PROF, 73- Part-time consult, Can. Counc. & McGill-Queen's Univ. Press. U.S.A, 54-55. MLA; Can. Asn. Irish Stud.(chmn, 72-73); Int. Asn. Study Anglo-Irish Lit; Asn. Can. Univ. Teachers Eng. W.B. Yeats and the Irish literary revival. Publ: Yeats's autobiography: life as symbolic pattern, Harvard, 68. Add: Dept. of English, McGill University, Montreal, P.Q, Can.

ROOKE, BARBARA E, b. Toronto, Ont, Dec. 15, 17. ENGLISH LITERATURE. B.A, Queen's Univ.(Ont), 40, Leonard resident fel, 40-41, M.A, 41; Univ. Toronto, 45-47; Marty Mem. fel, 47-48; Royal Soc. Can. fel, 48-49; Ph.D. (Eng), Univ. London, 49. Lectr. ENG, Victoria Col, Univ. Toronto, 49-51; Univ. W.Indies, 51-57; Univ. Hong Kong, 58-65, reader, 65-67; assoc. prof, TRENT UNIV, 67-68, PROF, 68- R.C.A.F, 41-45. Early 19th century; S.T. Coleridge. Publ: Ed, S.T. Coleridge's The friend, In: Collected Coleridge, Routledge & Kegan Paul & Bollingen. Add: Dept. of English, Trent University, Peterborough, Ont. K9J 7B8, Can.

ROOT, VERNON METCALF, b. Baltimore, Md, Feb. 11, 23; m. 55; c. 2. PHILOSOPHY. B.S, Haverford Col, 44; Ph.D.(philos), Yale, 50. Instr. philos, Lehigh Univ, 50-52; tech. ed, APPLIED PHYSICS LAB, JOHNS HOPKINS UNIV, 52-58, supvr. educ. & training, 58-64, SUPVR. TECH. REPORT PUBL, 64- Pres, Counc. Commun. Soc, 69-73, exec. dir, 74- U.S.N.R, 44-46. Am. Philos. Asn; Soc. Tech. Commun.(v.pres, 58-59, pres, 59-61). Philosophy of Alfred North Whitehead; techniques of training specialists in linguistic and graphic communication. Publ: Co-auth, Your future in technical and science writing, Richards Rosen, 72; auth, Technical publications job patterns & knowledge requirements, Tech. Commun, 3rd quarter 68; Personnel management, In: Handbook of technical writing practices, Wiley, 71. Add: 5100 Saratoga Ave, Washington, DC 20016.

ROPER, ALAN HENRY, b. Bridgend, Wales, July 17, 33; m. 57; c. 1. ENGLISH. B.A, Cambridge, 57, M.A, 61; M.A, Dalhousie Univ, 59; Ph.D.(Eng), Johns Hopkins Univ, 61. Instr. ENG, Harvard, 61-62; tutor, Queens' Col, Cambridge, 62-65; asst. prof, UNIV. CALIF, LOS ANGELES, 65-68, assoc. prof, 68-71, PROF, 71-, summer fac. fel, 66, summer res. appointment, Humanities Inst, 67. Res. fel, Queens' Col, Cambridge, 62-65; Guggenheim fel, 69-70. R.A.O.C, Brit. Army, 52-54, 2nd Lt. MLA. Dryden and 17th century political poetry; Arnold and English landscape poetry; English comedy 1660-1780. Publ: Dryden's poetic kingdoms, Routledge & Kegan, 65; Arnold's poetic landscapes, Johns Hopkins Univ, 69; contrib, Seventeenth-century imagery, Univ. Calif, 71; auth, Dryden's The history of the league and the early editions of Maimbourg's Historie de la ligue, Papers Bibliog. Soc. Am, 72; Language and action in The way of the world, Love's last shift, and The relapse, ELH, 73; plus others. Add: Dept. of English, University of California, Los Angeles, CA 90024.

ROPER, GORDON HERBERT, b. Brantford, Ont, Apr. 22, 11; m. 36; c. 2. AMERICAN LITERATURE. A.M, Univ. Chicago, 39, Ph.D, 44. Asst. instr. Eng, Yale, 39-40; instr, Univ. Chicago, 41-44, 46; assoc. prof, Trinity Col, Univ. Toronto, 46-59, prof. & head dept, 59-66, Chancellors prof, 66-69, sr. fel, Massey Col, 61-69, prof, Grad. Sch, 59-69, assoc. prof, 46-59; PROF. ENG, TRENT UNIV, 69- Can. Army, 44-46, Lt. Melville Soc; Asn. Can. Univ. Teachers Eng; Bibliog. Soc. Can. Canadian and American literature; Melville; Hawthorne. Publ: Ed, Scarlett letter, Farrar, Straus, 49; co-ed, Omoo, Vol. II, In: Writing of Herman Melville, Northwest. Univ, 68; Introduction to Gabrielle Roy's Where nests the water hen, 61 & Introduction to Robertson Davies' Samuel Marchbank's almanac, 68, McClelland & Stewart; Mark Twain and his Canadian publishers: a second look, Papers Bibliog. Soc. Can, 66; plus others. Add: 78 Facendi Dr, Peterborough, Ont, K9J 6V1, Can.

ROPPOLO, JOSEPH PATRICK, b. Shreveport, La, Mar. 17, 13. ENGLISH. B.A, Centenary Col, 46; M.A, Tulane Univ, 48, Ph.D.(Eng), 50. Asst. prof. ENG, TULANE UNIV, 50-55, assoc. prof, 55-64, PROF, 64-, HEAD DEPT, ARTS & SCI, 69-, head dept, Univ. Col, 50-66. Eng. consult. to Col. Engineering, 52-63; vis. prof. Am. lit, Univ. Bombay, India, 66-67. MLA; Am. Stud. Asn; Soc. Stud. South. Lit. American literature; Chaucer; Edgar Allan Poe. Publ: Philip Barry, Twayne, 65; ed, Renaissance in the twenties, U.S. Info. Serv, Bombay, 66; The meaning of At Erst: prologue to Sir Thopas, B^2, 1884, Mod. Lang. Notes; Uncle Tom in New Orleans: three lost plays, New Eng. Quart; Meaning and The masque of the red death, Tulane Stud. Eng, 63; plus others. Add: 7447 Hampson St, New Orleans, LA 70118.

ROSA, ALFRED FELIX, b. Waterbury, Conn, Feb. 7, 42; m. 67; c. 1. ENGLISH. B.A, Univ. Conn, 64; Fairleigh Dickinson Univ, 64-65; M.A, Univ. Mass, Amherst, 66, Ph.D.(Am. lit), 71. Instr. ENG, UNIV. VT, 69-71, ASST. PROF, 71- Fulbright-Hays lectr, Univ. Sassari, 73-74. MLA (Early Am. Lit. Group); Pop. Cult. Asn; Conf. Col. Compos. & Commun. American literature; English language; popular culture. Publ: Co-ed, Language: introductory readings, 72 & Language awareness: essays for writing, 74, St. Martin's; co-ed, Contemporary fiction in America and England, 1950-1970, Gale Res, 74; ed, Essays on American literature in honor of Charles Angoff, Fairleigh Dickinson Univ, 75; Alcott and Montessori, Conn. Rev, 10/69; Charles Ives: music, transcendentalism and politics, New Eng. Quart, 9/71; Williams' Between walls, Explicator, 11/71. Add: Dept. of English, University of Vermont, 315 Old Mill, Burlington, VT 05401.

ROSA, JEAN, b. Toledo, Ohio, Oct. 6. 03. ENGLISH. A.B, Univ. Tulsa, 25; A.M, Columbia Univ, 28. Teacher, high sch, N.J, 28-37; instr. ENG, Okla. Agr. & Mech. Col, 42-44; from instr. to ASSOC. PROF, UNIV. HOUSTON, 44- NCTE; MLA. Eighteenth century English literature. Add: Dept. of English, University of Houston, 3801 Cullen Blvd, Houston, TX 77004.

ROSCELLI, WILLIAM JOHN, b. New York, N.Y, Mar. 26, 27; m. 50; c. 3. ENGLISH, CLASSICAL LANGUAGES. B.A, John Carroll Univ, 49; M.A, Marquette Univ, 52; Ph.D.(Eng); Ohio State Univ, 60. Asst. prof. ENG, Purdue Univ, West Lafayette, 60-66; assoc. prof, Univ. Fla, 66-71; PROF, NORTH. ILL. UNIV, 71-, acting chmn. dept, 73-74. U.S.A.F, 52-56. MLA; Renaissance Soc. Am; Milton Soc. Am; Southeast. Renaissance Conf; S.Atlantic Mod. Lang. Asn. English literature 1558-1660; Italian literature 1300-1600; Latin literature 100 B.C-100 A.D. Publ: Co-auth, The Celtic cross, Purdue Univ, 64; Isabella, sin, and civil law, Univ. Kansas City Rev, XXVIII: 215-227; A tale of a tub and the Cavils of the sour, J. Eng. & Germanic Philol, LXIV: 41-56; The metaphysical Milton (1625-1632), Tex. Stud. Lit. & Lang, VIII: 463-484. Add: Dept. of English, Northern Illinois University, De Kalb, IL 60115.

ROSE, CHARLES S, JR, b. Kokomo, Ind, Oct. 16, 30; m. 58; c. 2. ENGLISH. A.B, Vanderbilt Univ, 52; M.A, Univ. Fla, 54, Ph.D, 60. Asst. ENG, Univ. Fla, 57-60; asst. prof, AUBURN UNIV, 60-71, ASSOC. PROF, 71- U.S.A, 54-57. Modern novel; creative writing. Publ: Which corner of the heart, spring 59 & By the waters, winter 62, Sewanee Rev; As big as the world, Ga. Rev, winter 63. Add: Dept. of English, Auburn University, Auburn, AL 36830.

ROSE, CONSTANCE HUBBARD, Spanish & Comparative Literature. See Volume III, Foreign Languages, Linguistics and Philology.

ROSE, EDGAR SMITH, b. Refton, Pa, Dec. 20, 16; m. 47; c. 2. ENGLISH LITERATURE. A.B, Franklin & Marshall Col, 39; Scribner fel, Princeton, 44-45, M.A, 45, Ph.D.(Eng), 55. Instr. humanities, Univ. Chicago, 45-49, asst. prof, 49-56; ENG, HAVERFORD COL, 56-61, assoc. prof, 61-66, PROF, 66-; chmn. dept, 62-67. Am. Counc. Learned Soc. fel, 60-61. MLA; NCTE; Am. Soc. Aesthet. Eighteenth century English literature; literary theory and criticism; aesthetics. Publ: Co-auth, Learning to listen: a handbook for music, Univ. Chicago, 57, Phoenix ed, 61; auth, The anatomy of imagination, Col. Eng, 2/66. Add: Dept. of English, Haverford College, Haverford, PA 19041.

ROSE, EDWARD J, b. New York, N.Y, Sept. 28, 24; m. 47; c. 2. ENGLISH, INTERDISCIPLINARY CRITICISM. A.B, Brooklyn Col, 50, A.M, 52; Ph.D. (Eng), Univ. Toronto, 63. Ford Found. intern-instr. ENG, Colgate Univ, 54-55; prof, State Univ. N.Y. Col. Geneseo, 55-56; instr, Brooklyn Col, 56-57; asst. prof, UNIV. ALTA, 58-63, assoc. prof, 64-67, PROF, 67-, CHMN. DEPT, 71- Can. Counc. summer grant, 64, sr. res. grant, 70-71; Am. Counc. Learned Soc. grant-in-aid, 65-66; mem. adv. bd. ed, Blake Stud, 68-; mem. adv. acad. counc, Henry George Sch. Social Sci, N.Y.C, 69-; adv. dir, Blake Found, 70- U.S.A, 43-46. MLA; Asn. Can. Univ. Teachers Eng. Romanticism; American literature; interdisciplinary studies and comparative literature. Publ: Henry George, Twayne, 68; co-ed, Complete edition of Blake's designs for Young night thoughts (5 vols), Clarendon, (in press); Mental forms creating: fourfold vision and the poet as prophet in Blake's designs and verse, J. Aesthet. & Art Criticism, winter 64; Visionary forms dramatic: grammatical and iconographical movement in Blake's designs and verse, Criticism, spring 66; Annihilation and ambiguity: Moby-Dick and The town-ho's story, New Eng. Quart, 12/72; plus numerous others. Add: Dept. of English, University of Alberta, Edmonton, Alta. T6G 2E1, Can.

ROSE, ERNEST D, b. Pittsburgh, Pa, May 23, 26; m. 54; c. 3. MOTION PICTURES, COMMUNICATIONS ESTHETICS. A.B, Univ. Calif, Los Angeles, 49, M.S, 51; Ford Found fel, Stanford Univ, 59-60, Ph.D.(commun, int. relat), 64. Partner, Trans-lingual Int. Film Serv, 50-55; from asst. prof. to assoc. prof. motion pictures, Univ. Calif, Los Angeles, 54-61; film dir, Inst. Commun. Res, Stanford Univ, 61-63; head film & TV prod, Exten. Media Ctr, Univ. Calif, 63-68; PROF. COMMUN, TEMPLE UNIV, 68- Head motion picture unit, Tech. Coop. Admin, Iran, 51-53; film specialist, Hughes Aircraft Co, 53-54; vis. prof, Univ. P.R, Rio Piedras, summer 67; head U.S. del, mem. bur. & treas, Int. Ctr. Liaison Cols. Film & TV, Brussels, 70-75; vis. lectr, Univ. Ankara, Univ. Oslo, Univ. Zagreb and others. 72-73; Fulbright prof. film & TV, Acad. Music & Dramatic Art, Vienna, 72-73. U.S.N, 44-46. Univ. Film Asn.(pres, 68-70). Communication during crisis conditions; international propaganda; esthetics of combined sound patterns and moving images. Publ: International study resources: a reference guide to world film & TV schools, Gale, 74; Computer implications for the coding of moving images, Proc. UNESCO Conf. Cataloguing AV material, 73; contrib, American broadcasting: a history, Hastings House, 74 & The American cinema forum, Voice of Am, 74. Add: Dept. of Radio-Television-Film, School of Communications, Temple University, Philadelphia, PA 19122.

ROSE, HARRIET ANN, b. Orange, N.J, May 26, 40; m. 63. ENGLISH & AMERICAN LITERATURE. B.A, Rutgers Univ, Newark, 62; M.A, N.Y. Univ, 65; Ph.D.(Eng), Ind. Univ, Bloomington, 73. LECTR. ENG, UNIV. N.H, 69- MLA. Nineteenth and 20th century American fiction; literature and psychology. Publ: Towards the pleasure principle: character revelation in Benjamin Franklin's To the Royal Academy, Paunch, 2/72. Add: Dept. of English, University of New Hampshire, Durham, NH 03824.

ROSE MARGARET (DOSTAL), O.S.U, b. Bucyrus, Ohio, Sept. 9, 20. ENGLISH. A.B, Mary Manse Col, 46; A.M, Univ. Notre Dame, 56, Ph.D.(Eng),

64. Head dept. ENG, St. Ursula Acad, 51-58; instr, MARY MANSE COL, 61-63, chmn. dept, 64-68, PRES, 68- Judge, Court of Equity, Diocese of Toledo, 70-75; mem. bd. dir, Counc. Advan. Small Cols, 72-74. MLA; NCTE; Asn. Depts. Eng; Am. Asn. Higher Educ. Twentieth-century fiction; nineteenth-century American literature. Add: Mary Manse College, 2436 Parkwood Ave, Toledo, OH 43620.

ROSE, MARILYN GADDIS, Comparative Literature. See Volume III, Foreign Languages, Linguistics & Philology.

ROSE, PHYLLIS DAVIDOFF, b. New York, N.Y, Oct. 26, 42; m. 65; c. 1. ENGLISH LITERATURE. B.A, Radcliffe Col, 64; M.A, Yale, 65; NDEA fel. & Ph.D.(Eng), Harvard, 70. ASST. PROF. ENG, WESLEYAN UNIV, 69- Nat. Endowment for Humanities grantee, 73-74. MLA. Nineteenth and 20th century English literature. Publ: Huxley, Holmes and the scientist as aesthete, Victorian Newslett, fall 69; Mrs. Ramsay and Mrs. Woolf, Women's Stud, spring 73. Add: Dept. of English, Wesleyan University, Middletown, CT 06457.

ROSE, RUTH ORMSBY, b. West. Springs, Ill, Apr. 20, 05. ENGLISH. A.B, Smith Col, 26, alumnae fel, 26-27; M.A, Radcliffe Col, 27, Ph.D.(Germanic philol), 29. Assoc. prof. ENG, Coker Col, 29-30; asst. prof, South. Ill. Univ, 30-31; instr, Wheaton Col, 31-36; Mundelein Col, 36-37; Milwaukee-Downer Col, 41-44; asst. prof, West. Col, 44-47; assoc. prof, MAC-MURRAY COL, 47-51, prof, 51-73, head dept, 53-73, EMER. PROF, 73- Ford Found. grant, 52-53; fel, Radcliffe Col, 52-53. MLA; AAUP; Am. Stud. Asn; Midwest Mod. Lang. Asn. American literature; Shakespeare. Add: 50 Grove Hill Park, Newtonville, MA 02160.

ROSE, SHIRLEY, b. Brooklyn, N.Y, Feb. 21, 29; m. 47; c. 2. ENGLISH COMPARATIVE LITERATURE. A.B, Brooklyn Col, 50, A.M, 52; Ph.D. (Eng), Univ. London, 67. Instr. ENG, UNIV. ALTA, 61-65, asst. prof, 67-70, ASSOC. PROF, 70- Modern literature; comparative mythology; the novel. Publ: The unmoving center: consciousness in Dorothy Richardson's Pilgrimage, Contemporary Lit, 69; Dorothy Richardson's theory of literature: the writer as pilgrim, Criticism, 70; Dorothy Richardson recalls Yeats, Eire-Ireland, 72. Add: Dept. of English, University of Alberta, Edmonton, Alta. T6G 2G2, Can.

ROSE, STANLEY CHARLES, b. Welland, Ont, Oct. 17, 13; U.S. citizen; m. 67. ENGLISH & CHILDREN'S LITERATURE. B.A, Queen's Univ.(Ont), 48; M.A, Univ. Miami, 49; Univ. South. Calif, 49-58. Elem. teacher & acting prin, Bd. of Educ, Welland, Ont, 33-42; asst. master, Dellwood Sch, Hamilton, Bermuda, 42-43; prin, Springs Pub. Sch, E.Hampton, N.Y, 44-45; teacher, Brandon High Sch, Tampa, Fla, 45-48; Mirror Lake Jr. High Sch, St. Petersburg, 50-52; instr. Eng. & philos, Episcopal Sem, Montrouis, Haiti, 52-53; instr. Eng. & French, Modesto Jr. Col, 53-56; ASSOC. PROF. ENG, CALIF. STATE UNIV, LONG BEACH, 56- Instr, Castle AFB, Merced, Calif, 54-56; res, Dove Cottage Libr, Eng, 59, 73-74. Bermuda Vol. Rifle C, 43. Wordsworth; Byron; Shelley. Publ: The box Wordsworth, Kendall-Hunt, 73; Extra-curricular activities in English, School, 10/41. Add: Dept. of English, California State University, Long Beach, 6101 E. Seventh St, Long Beach, CA 90840.

ROSELIEP, RAYMOND, b. Farley, Iowa, Aug. 11, 17. ENGLISH. B.A, Loras Col, 39; M.A, Cath. Univ. Am, 48; Ph.D, Univ. Notre Dame, 54. Asst. pastor, Immaculate Conception Church, Gilbertville, Iowa, 43-45; managing ed, The Witness, 45-46; instr. Eng, Loras Col, 46-54; instr. relig. & chaplain, Mt. St. Francis Convent, 50-54; asst. prof. Eng, Loras Col, 54-60, assoc. prof, 60-66; RESIDENT CHAPLAIN, HOLY FAMILY HALL, MT. ST. FRANCIS CONVENT, 66- Soc. Midland Authors Kenneth F. Montgomery poetry Award, 68. MLA; Poetry Soc. Am; fel. Int. Poetry Soc. Catholic literary revival in England, especially Lionel Johnson; modern poetry, especially English and American. Publ: Some letters of Lionel Johnson, Univ. Notre Dame, 54; The linen bands (poems), 61 & The small rain (poems), 63, Newman; Love makes the air light (poems), Norton, 65; 9 poems, In: Heartland: poets of the Midwest, North. Ill. Univ, 67; poem, In: Out of the war shadow, War Resisters League, 67; Five poems, In: Inside outer space, Doubleday, 70. Add: Holy Family Hall, 3340 Windsor Extension, Dubuque, IA 52001.

ROSEN, AARON H, b. Utica, N.Y, Jan. 1, 26; m. 59. ENGLISH. A.B, N.Y. Univ, 47; M.A, Univ. Calif, Berkeley, 56, Ph.D.(Eng), 62. Instr. ENG, STATE UNIV. N.Y. BUFFALO, 60-62, asst. prof, 62-66, ASSOC. PROF, 66-, assoc. provost arts & lett, 67-70. Modern poetry; comparative literature. Publ: The sound of Auden, Kenyon Rev, 63; Criticism European style, Partisan Rev, 67; Taps for space, Choice, 70. Add: Dept. of English, State University of New York at Buffalo, Buffalo, NY 14214.

ROSEN, KENNETH FREDERIC, b. Boston, Mass, Aug. 30, 40; m. 64; c. 2. MODERN LITERATURE. B.A, Pa. State Univ, University Park, 62; M.F.A, Univ. Iowa, 64. Inst. ENG, UNIV. MAINE, PORTLAND-GORHAM, 65-67, asst. prof, 67-71, ASSOC. PROF, 71- Artist-in-the-schs, Maine Comn. for Arts & Humanities, spring 73. Publ: Whole Horse, Braziller, 73; plus poems and stories in other literary journals and magazines. Add: Dept. of English, University of Maine, Portland-Gorham, Gorham, ME 04038.

ROSEN, KENNETH MARK, b. New York, N.Y, Mar. 7, 38. AMERICAN LITERATURE. B.A, Cornell Univ, 59; M.A, Calif. State Univ, San Francisco, 64; fel, Univ. N.Mex, 68-69, Ph.D.(Eng), 69. Asst. prof. ENG, DICKINSON COL, 69-73, ASSOC. PROF, 73- Ford Found. humanities grants, 70-71, 72; ed, Hemingway Notes, 71- U.S.A, 59-62. Asn. Stud. Am. Indian Lit; MLA; Am. Stud. Asn; AAUP. The American novel; American Indian literature; Hemingway. Publ: The man to send rain clouds, Viking, 74; O'Neill's Brown and Wilde's Gray, Mod. Drama, 2/71; Kate Chopin's The awakening: ambiguity as art, J. Am. Stud, 8/71; Ten eulogies: Hemingway's Spanish death, Bull. N.Y. Pub. Libr, 74. Add: Dept. of English, Dickinson College, Carlisle, PA 17013.

ROSEN, ROBERT SAMUEL, German, Comparative Literature. See Volume III, Foreign Languages, Linguistics & Philology.

ROSEN, WILLIAM, b. Boston, Mass, July 1, 26; m. 60; c. 2. ENGLISH. A.B, Harvard Col, 48; M.A, Harvard, 49, Ph.D, 58. Teaching fel, Harvard, 51-53, 55-56; instr. ENG, Univ. Wis, 56-60; asst. prof, UNIV. CONN, 60-63, assoc. prof, 63-65, PROF, 65- Vis. Old Dominion prof. humanities, Hampton Inst, 69-70. Sig.C, U.S.A, 53-55. MLA; Renaissance Soc. Am. Shakespeare; Milton. Publ: Shakespeare and the craft of tragedy, Harvard, 60; co-ed, Shakespeare's Julius Caesar, New Am. Lib, 63. Add: Dept. of English, University of Connecticut, Storrs, CT 06268.

ROSENBAUM, MORTON, b. Pensacola, Fla, June 14, 22; m. 63; c. 3. ENGLISH. B.A, Wayne State Univ, 43, M.A, 46; Ph.D.(Eng), Univ. Wis, 52. Instr. ENG, Wayne State Univ, 52-54; asst. prof, Univ. Wichita, 54-57, assoc. prof, 57-60; CALIF. STATE UNIV, HAYWARD, 60-63, PROF, 63- Resident dir, Int. Progs. State Col. Syst. Calif. in Spain, 64-65, 67-69; mem, U.S. Fulbright Comn, 69-71. U.S.M.C, 42-46, Sgt. MLA; Milton; the 18th century. Add: Dept. of English, California State University, Hayward, 25800 Hilary St, Hayward, CA 94542.

ROSENBAUM, PETER S, Linguistics, Education. See Volume III, Foreign Languages, Linguistics & Philology.

ROSENBAUM, STANFORD PATRICK, b. Vancouver, B.C, Mar. 17, 29; m. 58; c. 2. ENGLISH & AMERICAN LITERATURE. B.A, Univ. Colo, 51; fel. & M.A, Rutgers Univ, 55; Fulbright scholar, Pembroke Col, Oxford, 56-57; fel. & Ph.D, Cornell Univ, 60. Instr. ENG, Cornell Univ, 58-60; Ind. Univ, 60-62, asst. prof, 62-65, assoc. prof. UNIV. TORONTO, 65-67, PROF, 67- Carnegie Found. interdisciplinary fel. philos. & lit, Brown Univ, 62-64; Guggenheim fel, 68-69. MLA. Nineteenth and 20th century British literature and philosophy; Henry James; the Bloomsbury group. Publ: Concordance to the poems of Emily Dickinson, Cornell Univ, 63; ed, Henry James' The ambassadors, Norton, 63; Anthology: English literature and British philosophers, Univ. Chicago, 72; The Bloomsbury group: a collection, Univ. Toronto, 74; Creativity and Jame's Spoils of Poynton, Criticism, 65; G.E. Moore's elements of ethics, 69 & Bertrand Russell: the logic of a literary symbol, 73, Univ. Toronto Quart; plus others. Add: Dept. of English, University of Toronto, Toronto, Ont, M5S 1A1, Can.

ROSENBERG, ALBERT, b. Philadelphia, Pa, Sept. 8, 17; m. 40; c. 3. ENGLISH. B.A, Univ. Calif, Los Angeles, 40, M.A, 47; Ph.D.(Eng), Univ. London, 50. Instr. ENG, Univ. Nebr, 50-53, fac. res. grant, 52-53; assoc. Eng. compos, dept. Eng, dramatic arts & speech, Univ. Calif, Davis, 54-57; assoc. prof, SAN JOSE STATE UNIV, 57-71, PROF, 71- Am. Philos. Soc. res. grant, 57. U.S.A, 44-47. MLA; Col. Eng. Asn; Philol. Asn. Pac. Coast; Am. Soc. Aesthet. Restoration and 18th century literature; history of medicine; contemporary fiction. Publ: Sir Richard Blackmore; a poet and physician of the Augustan Age, Univ. Nebr; Bishop Sprat on science and imagery, Isis; Prior's feud with the Duchess of Marlborough, J. Eng. & Germanic Philol. Add: Dept. of English, San Jose State University, 125 S. Seventh St, San Jose, CA 95114.

ROSENBERG, BRUCE, b. New York, N.Y, July 27, 34; m. 59; c. 2. ENGLISH, FOLKLORE. B.A Hofstra Univ, 55; M.A, Pa. State Univ, 62; Ph.D. (Eng), Ohio State Univ, 65. Instr. Eng, Univ. Wis, Milwaukee, 62; asst. prof, Univ. Calif, Santa Barbara, 65-67; Univ. Va, 67-69; PROF. ENG. & COMP. LIT. PA. STATE UNIV, 69- Am. Counc. Learned Soc. fel, 67-68; Newberry Libr. fel, summer 71; Nat. Endowment for Humanities fel, 72-73. Ord.C, U.S.A, 55-57, 1st Lt. MLA. Middle English literature; folklore; comparative literature. Publ: Ed, The folksongs of Virginia, Univ. Va, 69; auth, The art of the American folk preacher, Oxford, 70; co-ed, Medieval literature and folklore studies, Rutgers Univ, 71; auth, Annus Mirabilis distilled, PMLA, 6/64; Wandering Angus & Celtic renaissance, Philol. Quart, fall 67; Lord of the fire flies, Centennial Rev, winter 67. Add: Dept. of English, Pennsylvania State University, University Park, PA 16802.

ROSENBERG, DONALD MAURICE, b. Detroit, Mich, Feb. 27, 34; m. 66; c. 2. ENGLISH. B.A, Univ. Mich, 56; M.A, Wayne State Univ, 57, Ph.D.(Eng), 65. Asst. prof. ENG, N.Dak. State Col, 62-63; instr, Dartmouth Col, 63-65, asst. prof, 65-69; ASSOC. PROF, MICH. STATE UNIV, 69- Milton; seventeenth century prose; American Puritanism. Publ: Milton's Masque: a social occasion for philosophic laughter, Stud. Philol, 4/70; Satirical techniques in Milton's polemical prose, Satire Newslett, spring 71; Style and meaning in Milton's Anti-Episcopal tracts, Criticism, winter 73. Add: 215 Gunson, East Lansing, MI 48823.

ROSENBERG, EDGAR, b. Fuerth, Germany, Sept. 21, 25; U.S. citizen; m. 65. ENGLISH & COMPARATIVE LITERATURE. A.B, Cornell Univ, 49, A.M, 50; univ. fel, Stanford Univ, 51-52, Ph.D.(Eng), 58; Bread Loaf fel, 53. Teaching fel, Eng, Univ. Ill, 50-51; Stanford Univ, 51-53, 54-57; instr, San Jose State Col, 53-54; Harvard, 57-60, asst. prof, 60-65; assoc. prof, CORNELL UNIV, 65-69, PROF, 69-70, ENG. & COMP. LIT, 70-, res. grants 67-68 & summers 68 & 69. Vis. prof, Stanford Univ, 70; Guggenheim Mem. Found. fel, 73-74. MLA; Am. Comp. Lit. Asn; Dickens Soc. Dickens; English and continental fiction; Anglo-Judaic studies. Publ: From Shylock to Svengali, Stanford Univ, 60; Tabloid Jews and fungoid scribblers, Ktav, 73; ed, Charles Dickens' Great Expectations, Norton, 74; auth, The Jew in English drama, Bull. N.Y. Pub. Libr, fall 68; A preface to Great Expectations, Dickens Stud. Annual, Vol. II, 72; Small talk in Hammersmith: chapter 23 of Great expectations, Dickensian, 5/73; plus others. Add: Dept. of English, Cornell University, Ithaca, NY 14850.

ROSENBERG, ELEANOR, b. New York, N.Y, Apr. 9, 08. ENGLISH LITERATURE. A.B, Barnard Col, 29, A.M, Columbia Univ, 30, Ph.D, 49. Instr. eve. session, Brooklyn Col, 31-34; teacher high sch, New York, N.Y, 34-51; lectr. grad. sch, Columbia Univ, 49-52, vis. asst. prof. ENG, BARNARD COL, 51-52, asst. prof, 53-56, assoc. prof, 56-59, prof, 59-73, chmn. dept, 59-61, EMER. PROF. & PART-TIME TEACHER, 73- Guggenheim fel, 57-58. MLA; Renaissance Soc. Am; Mod. Humanities Res. Asn. Literature of the English Renaissance; patronage; Tudor Chronicles. Publ: Leicester, patron of letters, Columbia. Add: Dept. of English, Barnard College, Columbia University, New York, NY 10027.

ROSENBERG, JAMES LEROY, b. Sheridan, Wyo, May 19, 21; m. 49; c. 3. DRAMA & ENGLISH. A.B, Univ. Calif, Berkeley, 51; M.A, Univ. Denver, 52, Ph.D.(Eng), 54. Instr. Eng, Kans. State Univ, 53-57, asst. prof, 57-60, assoc. prof, 60-61; vis. assoc. prof. DRAMA, Tulane Univ, 61-62; PROF,

CARNEGIE-MELLON UNIV, 62- Fulbright prof, Univ. Birmingham, Eng, 68-69; lectr. U.S. Inform. Serv. Sem. in mod. theatre, Kassel, Ger, 72-73. U.S.A, 42-46. Modern theatre aesthetics; playwriting; Elizabethan drama. Publ: A primer of kinetics, Swallow, 61; co-auth, The context and craft of drama, 64 & The art of the theatre, 64, Chandler; transl, Three plays by Max Frisch, Hill & Wang, 67. Add: Dept. of Drama, Carnegie-Mellon University, 5000 Forbes Ave, Pittsburgh, PA 15213.

ROSENBERG, JEROME HOWARD, b. Brooklyn, N.Y, Jan. 22, 43; m. 66; c. 1. AMERICAN & BRITISH LITERATURE. A.B, Univ. Mich, Ann Arbor, 64; M.A, Univ. Conn, 65; Ph.D.(Eng), Univ. Tex, Austin, 71. Instr. ENG, MIAMI UNIV, 68-71, ASST. PROF, 71- Asst. ed, Abstracts of Eng. Stud, 68- MLA; Am. Stud. Asn. Nineteenth century American literature; Australian literature; autobiographical narrative. Publ: Narrative perspective and cultural history in Robbery under arms, Australian Lit. Stud, 5/73. Add: Dept. of English, Miami University, Oxford, OH 45056.

ROSENBERG, JOHN D, b. New York, N.Y, Apr. 17, 29; m. 72. ENGLISH LITERATURE. A.B, Columbia Col, 50, M.A, Columbia Univ, 51, Ph.D, 60; Kellett fel, Cambridge Univ, 51-53, A.B, 53, M.A, 58. Lectr. ENG, Columbia Univ, 53-54; instr, City Col. New York, 54-62; asst. prof, COLUMBIA UNIV, 62-65, assoc. prof, 66-67, PROF, 67-, CHMN. HUMANITIES PROG, COLUMBIA COL, 70- Coe grad. fel, 56-57; Fels fel, 59-60; Counc. Res. Humanities grant, 65; Lawrence H. Chamberlain fel, 65-66; Am. Counc. Learned Soc. fel, 65-66; Guggenheim fel, 68-69; pres, Urban Affairs Found, 68-; mem. adv. bd, Victorian Stud, 68-70, ed. bd, 70-; consult, Nat. Screening Comt, Fulbright Fel. Prog, 68-69; vis. fel, Clare Hall, Cambridge, 69. Ansley Award, 60. MLA(chmn. exec. comt, Victorian Group, 70-); Tennyson Soc. Victorian literature; general education; urban affairs. Publ: The darkening glass: a portrait of Ruskin's genius, Columbia Univ, 61; The genius of John Ruskin: selections, Braziller, 63; Swinburne: selected poetry and prose, Random, 68; The fall of Camelot: a study of Tennyson's Idylls of the King, Harvard, 73; King Lear and his comforters, Essays in criticism, 4/66; Introd. to Mayhew's London labour and the London poor, Dover, 68; Varieties of infernal experience: the city in nineteenth century English literature, Hudson Rev, autumn 70; plus others. Add: Dept. of English, Columbia University, New York, NY 10027.

ROSENBERG, MARVIN, b. Fresno, Calif, Nov. 6, 12; m. 37; c. 1. DRAMATIC ART. A.B, M.A. & Ph.D.(Eng), Univ. Calif. Ed, Off. War Inform, 43-45; chief Siam sect, int. broadcasting div, U.S. Dept. State, 45-47; PROF. DRAMATIC ART, UNIV. CALIF, BERKELEY, 48- Am. Theatre Asn; Am. Soc. Theatre Res; Philol. Asn. Pac. Coast; Shakespeare Asn. Am; Am. Soc. Aesthet. Literature and criticism of drama; Shakespeare; theatre history. Publ: The masks of Othello, 61 & The masks of King Lear, 72, Univ. Calif, Add: Dept. of Dramatic Art, University of California, Berkeley, CA 94720.

ROSENBERRY, EDWARD HOFFMAN, b. East Stroudsburg, Pa, Mar. 17, 16; m. 45. ENGLISH. B.S, Haverford Col, 37; M.A, Columbia Univ, 38; univ. fel. & Ph.D.(Eng), Univ. Pa, 53. Instr. ENG, Pa. State Teachers Col, Kutztown, 46-49; asst. prof, UNIV. DEL, 52-60, assoc. prof, 60-66, PROF, 66-, chmn. dept, 66-69. U.S.A, 42-46, Capt. NCTE; MLA; Am. Stud. Asn. Mid. Atlantic States (v.pres, 56); Melville and the comic spirit, Harvard, 55; Melville's Ship of fools, 12/60 & The problem of Billy Budd, 12/65; PMLA Hawthorne's Allegory of science, Am. Lit, 3/60. Add: 222 Hullihen Dr, Newark, DE 19711.

ROSENBLATT, JASON PHILIP, b. Baltimore, Md, July 3, 41; m. 64; c. 2. ENGLISH LITERATURE. B.A, Yeshiva Univ, 63; M.A, Brown Univ, 66, Ph.D.(Eng), 68. ASST. PROF. ENG, Univ. Pa, 68-74; GEORGETOWN UNIV, 74- Univ. Pa. summer res. fel, 69; vis. lectr. Swarthmore Col, 72-73. MLA; Milton Soc. Am; AAUP. The works of John Milton, 17th century English religious poetry. Publ: Structural unity and temporal concordance: the war in heaven in Paradise lost, PMLA, 1/72; Adam's Pisgah vision, J. Eng. Lit. Hist, 3/72; The mosaic voice in Paradise lost, In: Eyes Fast Fixt, Univ. Pittsburgh, 75; plus one other. Add: Dept. of English, Georgetown University, Washington, DC 20007.

ROSENBLATT, LOUISE MICHELLE (MRS. SIDNEY RATNER), b. Atlantic City, N.J, Aug, 23, 04; m. 32; c. 1. ENGLISH, COMPARATIVE LITERATURE. A.B, Barnard Col, Columbia Univ, 25, univ, 27-28; Univ. Grenoble, 25-26; Dr. Univ, Univ. Paris, 31. Asst. Eng, Barnard Col, Columbia Univ, 27-28, instr, 29-38; asst. prof, Brooklyn Col, 38-48; prof. sch. educ, N.Y. UNIV, 48-72, EMER. PROF. ENG. EDUC, 72- Guggenheim fel, 42-43; consult. advan. placement prog, Col. Entrance Exam. Bd, 55-57, mem. comn. Eng, 59-66; consult. Eng. curriculum, N.Y. State Dept. Educ, 62, 63; mem. exec. comt, Sch. & Col. Conf. Eng, 62-63; trustee, Res. Found, NCTE, 60-62, mem. comn. lit, 63-70; dir, res. develop. seminar, U.S. Off. Educ. grant, 63; consult, curriculum develop. ctr, Fla. State Univ, 63; Conn. State Dept. Educ, 66-67; Off. Educ, U.S. Dept. Health Educ. & Welfare, 66-68; distinguished lectr, NCTE, 70; vis. prof, Rutgers Univ, 72- Propaganda analyst, foreign broadcast intel. serv, Fed. Commun. Comn, 43-44; assoc. chief W.Europ. sect. & chief cent. reports sect, bur. overseas intel, Off. War Inform, 44-45. MLA; NCTE; Am. Soc. Aesthet; Conf. Res. Eng; Conf. Col. Compos. & Commun; Am. Comp. Lit. Soc; Conf. Eng. Educ. Theory of literature; 19th and 20th century Franco-English literary relations; education of teachers of English. Publ: L'Idée de l'art pour l'art dans la littérature anglaise, Champion, Paris, France, 31; Literature as exploration, Appleton, 38, Noble, 68 & Heinemann, London, 70; co-auth, The education of teachers of English, NCTE Curriculum Ser, Appleton, 63; The poem as event, Col. Eng, 11/64; Literature: the reader's role, In: The subjects in the curriculum, Odyssey, 68; auth, Literature and the invisible reader, In: The promise of English, NCTE, 70; plus others. Add: 11 Cleveland Lane, Princeton, NJ 08540.

ROSENDAHL, WILLIAM ARMOND, b. Montgomery, W.Va, Sept. 2, 13; m. 42; c. 2. ENGLISH. Ph.D.(Eng), Northwest. Univ, 49. Instr. Eng, Northwest. Univ, 46-49; asst. prof, Univ. Minn, Duluth, 49-53, assoc. prof, 53-56, prof, 56-66, chmn. dept, 50-66; PROF. ENG. & RHETORIC, UNIV. MINN, MINNEAPOLIS, 66-, ASST. CHMN. DEPT, 70- Chief of party, Univ. Minn-Concepcion Univ. Coop. Proj, 67. U.S.A, 42-46. Romantic period; eighteenth century English literature. Add: 1953 Summer St, St. Paul, MN 55113.

ROSENFELD, ALVIN HIRSCH, b. Phila, Pa, Apr. 28, 38; m. 66; c. 2. ENGLISH & AMERICAN LITERATURE. B.A, Temple Univ, 60; M.A, Brown Univ, 62, Ph.D.(Eng), 67. Lectr. Am. lit, Univ. Kiel, 64-65; instr. ENG, Brown Univ, 67-68; asst. prof, IND. UNIV, BLOOMINGTON, 68-72, ASSOC. PROF, 72- Contrib. ed, Am. Poetry Rev, 72- MLA; AAUP. American literature; modern poetry; Jewish literature. Publ: Co-auth, A birthday garland for S. Foster Damon, privately publ, 68; William Blake: essays for S. Foster Damon, Brown Univ, 69; ed, Collected poems of John Wheelwright, New Directions, 72; auth, John Wheelwright: New England's colloquy with the world, South. Rev, 72; The poetry of Paul Celan, Midstream, 72; Teaching modern poetry: the examples of T.S. Eliot and Hart Crane, Am. Poetry Rev, 73; plus others. Add: Dept. of English, Indiana University, Bloomington, IN 47401.

ROSENFELD, WILLIAM, b. Cleveland, Ohio, Jan. 2, 26; m. 55; c. 2. AMERICAN LITERATURE. B.A, Syracuse Univ, 51; M.A, Univ. Minn, 54, Ph.D, 61. Instr. Eng, Univ. Maine, 59-61; asst. prof, Wilmington Col.(Ohio), 61-62; Cent. Mich. Univ, 62-63; Baldwin-Wallace Col, 63-68, assoc. prof, 68-69; arts, KIRKLAND COL, 69-72, PROF. CREATIVE WRITING, 73-, CHMN. DIV. ARTS, 72- Fulbright lectr, Univ. Brazil, 67-68; mem, President's Adv. Counc, Ethan Allen Col, 73- Qm.C, U.S.N, 43-46. Am. Stud. Asn; MLA. Creative writing; classic and modern drama; 19th century and colonial American literature. Publ: Uncertain faith: Queequeg's Coffin and Melville's use of the Bible, Tex. Stud. Lit. & Lang, winter 66; Stanley, New Eng. Rev, 5-6/69; Astronaut, In: Gallery series II: poets, 70; plus two others. Add: Div. of the Arts, Kirkland College, Clinton, NY 13323.

ROSENFIELD, CLAIRE, b. Pittsfield, Mass, Feb. 15, 30. ENGLISH. B.A, Smith Col, 52; M.A, Radcliffe Col, 55, Ph.D.(Eng), 60. Instr. Eng, Univ. Tex, Austin, 60-61; Rutgers Univ, 61-63, asst. prof, 63-67; lectr. gen. educ, Harvard, 68-69; vis. assoc. prof, BROWN UNIV, 69-71, ASSOC. PROF, 71- Fel, Ctr. Advan. Stud. Behav. Sci, 63-64; scholar, Radcliffe Inst, Radcliffe Col, 67-69. MLA. The novel; the folk tale; oral tradition in primitive cultures. Publ: Co-auth, The personal voice: a contemporary prose reader, Lippincott, 64; auth, Paradise of snakes, Univ. Chicago, 67; The shadow within: the conscious and unconscious use of the double, Daedalus, spring 63; Despair and the lust for immortality, In: Nabokov: the man and his work, Univ. Wis, 67; New worlds, old myths, In: Twentieth-century interpretations of The old man and the sea, Prentice-Hall, 68. Add: Dept. of English, Brown University, Providence, RI 02912.

ROSENFIELD, LAWRENCE WILLIAM, b. Binghamton, N.Y. Aug. 11, 38; m. 59; c. 2. SPEECH, COMMUNICATIONS. B.A, Cornell Univ, 60, Ph.D. (speech), 63; M.A, Univ. Ill, 61. Asst. prof. speech, Univ. Wis, 63-67, assoc. prof, 67-69; PROF. speech, Univ. Wis, 69-71; COMMUN, HUNTER COL, 71- Consult, Inst. Govt. Affairs, Univ. Wis, 64-68. Speech Commun. Asn; Rhetoric Soc. Am; Acad. Polit. Sci. Criticism; rhetorical theory; multimedia instruction. Publ: Aristotle and information theory, Mouton, 68; An anatomy of critical discourse, 3/68 & Nixon-Truman analog: case study in criticism, 11/68, Speech Monogr; Politics and pornography, Quart. J. Speech, 73; plus others. Add: Dept. of Communications, Hunter College, 695 Park Ave, New York, NY 10021.

ROSENHEIM, EDWARD WEIL, JR, b. Chicago, Ill, May 15, 18; m. 47; c. 3. ENGLISH. B.A, Univ. Chicago, 39, M.A, 46, Ph.D.(Eng), 53. Instr. Eng, Gary Col, 46-47; humanities, UNIV. CHICAGO, 47-49, asst. prof, 49-55, assoc. prof, 55-62, PROF. ENG, 62-, dir. broadcasting, 54-57, Willett Fac. fel, 62. Ed, J. Gen. Educ, 54-56; distinguished vis. prof, Pa. State Univ, 61; consult. curriculum stud. ctr, Proj. Eng, Univ. Ore, 64-65; vis. prof, Univ. Wash, summer, 65; Guggenheim fel, 67-68; distinguished lectr, NCTE, 67-; co-ed, Mod. Philol, 68- Quantrell Award, Univ. Chicago, 53. Inf, U.S.A, 41-46, Capt. MLA; NCTE. English literature of late 17th and early 18th century, especially Jonathan Swift: satiric theory and practice in western literature; literature of controversy, especially 1700-1730 in England. Publ: Ed, Selected prose and poetry of Swift, Holt, 59; auth, What happens in literature, 60 & Swift and the satirist's art, 63, Univ. Chicago; The fifth voyage of Lemuel Gulliver, Mod. Philol, 3/62; The elegiac act, Col. Eng, 2/66; Swift and the Atterbury case, In: The Augustan milieu: essays presented to Louis Landa, Oxford, 70; plus others. Add: 5805 Dorchester Ave, Chicago, IL 60637.

ROSENMAN, JOHN BROWN, b. Cleveland, Ohio, Apr. 16, 41; m. 67; c. 1. AMERICAN LITERATURE. B.A, Hiram Col, 63; M.A, Kent State Univ, 66, fel, 66-70, Ph.D.(Eng), 70. Asst. prof. Eng, Lakehead Univ, 70-73. MLA. Works of William Faulkner and southern literature of the United States; 19th and 20th century American novel and short story. Publ: Co-ed, Art and literary review, Lakehead Univ. 72; auth, A note on William Faulkner's As I lay dying, Stud. Am. Fiction, spring 73. Add: Apt. 26, 1325 Yale Pl, Minneapolis, MN 55403.

ROSENTHAL, IRVING, B. New York, N.Y, July 31, 12; m. 43; c. 3. ENGLISH. B.S.S, City Col. New York, 33, fel, 33-34, M.S, 34; Columbia Univ. Tutor ENG, CITY COL. NEW YORK, 35-41, instr, 42-52, asst. prof, 52-59, assoc. prof, 59-70, PROF, 70-, asst. to pres. & dir. pub. relat, 33-43. Chmn. pub. comm, City Col. Alumni, 53-; adj. prof. C.W. Post Col, Long Island Univ, 67-70; coord. broadcast jour. internship prog, WCBS-TV, 69- U.S.A, 43-46, Lt. Am. Educ. Jour. Article writing; English composition; journalism education. Publ: Co-ed, Business English, 53 & co-auth, Creative writing made simple, 55, Doubleday; co-ed, Essays for today and tomorrow, Ronald, 61, co-auth, Modern journalism, Pitman, 62. Add: 62 Hampshire Rd, Great Neck, NY 11023.

ROSENTHAL, JUDITH ANN, b. Syracuse, N.Y, Aug. 22, 45; m. 73. ENGLISH & AMERICAN LITERATURE. B.A, State Univ. N.Y. Binghamton, 66; M.A, Univ. Pittsburgh, 67, Ph.D.(Eng), 70. Asst. instr. ENG, Univ. Pittsburgh, 70-71; ASST. PROF, CALIF. STATE UNIV, FRESNO, 71- MLA. Women in literature; modern drama; Renaissance literature. Publ: Co-auth, Norman Mailer: prisoner of sexism, Lilith, 4/71. Add: Dept. of English, California State University, Fresno, Shaw & Cedar Ave, Fresno, CA 93710.

ROSENTHAL, LEWIS, b. Schenectady, N.Y, May 8, 25; m. 62; c. 2. ENGLISH. B.A, Colgate Univ, 48; M.A, Auburn Univ, 54; Ph.D, La. State Univ, 68. Instr. ENG, Auburn Univ, 55-56; La. State Univ, 58-60; Mid. Tenn. State Col,

60-64; Butler Univ, 64-66, asst. prof, 66-68; YOUNGSTOWN STATE UNIV, 68-73, ASSOC. PROF, 73- U.S.A, 43-46. MLA; Midwest Mod. Lang. Asn; Renaissance Soc. Am. Renaissance and modern drama. Publ: Introd, In: Drug abuse: a course for educators, Butler Univ, 68. Add: Dept. of English, Youngstown State University, Youngstown, OH 44503.

ROSENTHAL, MACHA LOUIS, b. Washington, D.C, Mar. 14, 17; m. 39; c. 3. ENGLISH. A.B, Univ. Chicago, 37, scholar, 34-39, A.M, 38; Am. Counc. Learned Soc. fel, 42; Ph.D, N.Y. Univ, 49. Instr. ENG, Mich. State Univ, 39-45; asst, N.Y. UNIV, 45-46, instr, 46-50, asst. prof, 50-55, assoc. prof, 55-61, PROF, 61- Am. Counc. Learned Soc. faculty stud. fel, 51-52; Vis. prof, Univ. N.Mex, 56; poetry ed, The Nation, 56-61; judge, Nat. Book awards, 61, mem. comt, 62-66; Guggenheim fel, 60-61, 64-65, referee, 61- vis. expert Germany, 61; Pakistan, 65; Rumania, Poland & Bulgaria, 66; co-adjudicator, Denis Devlin Mem. Award, Ireland, 65-69; chmn, Delmore Schwartz Mem. Award Comt, 70-; poetry ed, The humanist, 71-; vis. prof. Eng, Univ. Pa, 74. MLA; AAUP; PEN Club. Modern poetry and criticism; American literature; problems of evaluation in criticism. Publ: Co-auth, Exploring poetry, 55, 73, auth, A primer of Ezra Pound, 60, ed, Selected poems and two plays of William Butler Yeats, 62, The new modern poetry: British and American poetry since World War II, 67, 100 postwar poems, British and American, 68, & co-ed, Chief modern poets of Britain and America, 70, Macmillan; The modern poets: a critical introduction, 60, Blue boy on skates: poems, 64, The new poets: American and British poetry since World War II, 67, auth, Beyond power: new poems, 69 & The view from the peacock's tail: poems, 72, Oxford; ed, The William Carlos Williams reader, New Directions, 66; auth, Randall Jarrell, Univ. Minn, 72; Dynamics of form and motive in some representative twentieth-century lyric poems, ELH, 3/70; The wasteland as an open structure, Mosaic, fall 72; Some thoughts on American poetry today, Salmagundi, spring-summer 73; plus others. Add: Dept. of English, Washington Square College, New York University, New York, NY 10003.

ROSENTHAL, PAUL IRWIN, b. San Diego, Calif, Jan. 21, 34; m. 65. SPEECH. B.A, Univ. Calif, Los Angeles, 56, M.A, 59, Ph.D.(speech), 63. Instr. SPEECH, San Fernando Valley State Col, 61-63, asst. prof, 63-64; UNIV. CALIF, LOS ANGELES, 64-71, ASSOC. PROF, 71- Speech Commun. Asn.(Golden Anniversary Award, 67); Am. Acad. Polit. & Soc. Sci; Int. Commun. Asn. Persuasive communication; argumentation. Publ: The Republican national convention, 12/64 & The concept of paramessage in persuasive communication, 2/72, Quart. J. Speech; The concept of ethos and the structure of persuasion, Speech Monogr, 6/66. Add: Communication Studies Program, 232 Royce Hall, University of California, Los Angeles, CA 90024.

ROSENTHAL, SIDNEY, b. Boston, Mass, Sept. 19, 21; m. 45; c. 3. ENGLISH, LITERATURE. A.B, Northeast. Univ, 43; A.M, Harvard, 49, fel, 64-65, Ph.D.(Eng), 68. Instr. Eng, Univ. Ill, 47-48; Colby Col, 48-51; teacher pub. schs, Mass, 51-67; asst. prof. Eng, R.I. Col, 67-68; humanities, Clarkson Col. Technol, 68-72; ASSOC. PROF. ENG, BOSTON STATE COL, 72- U.S.A, 43-45. English and American literature. Publ: Hamlet, Macbeth, Julius Caesar, King Lear & Dickens' Bleak house, In: Hymarx Col-Outline Ser, Stud. Outlines; Richard Aldington and the excitement of reason, In: 27 to 2, Clarkson, 70; plus poetry in Conn. Eng. J, fall & winter, 69. Add: Dept. of English, Boston State College, 625 Huntington Ave, Boston, MA 02115.

ROSENWALD, JOHN, b. Oak Park, Ill, June 25, 43; m. 66; c. 1. ENGLISH & AMERICAN LITERATURE. B.A, Univ. Ill, 64, M.A, 65; Fulbright scholar, Univ. Tübingen, 65-66; Ph.D.(Eng), Duke Univ, 69. ASST. PROF. ENG, ASSUMPTION COL, 69- Idealism and Utopian literature; prosody of modern verse; literature and society in Victorian England. Add: Assumption College, 500 Salisbury St, Worcester, MA 01609.

ROSIER, JAMES LOUIS, b. Chicago, Ill, Mar. 14, 32; m. 56; c. 3. ENGLISH LITERATURE & PHILOLOGY. B.A, Stanford Univ, 53, Baker fel, 56-57, Ph.D, 57; Free Univ. Berlin, 54-55. Instr. Eng, Cornell Univ, 57-60, asst. prof, 60-61; Univ. Mich, 61-63; assoc. prof. Eng. philol, UNIV. PA, 63-68, PROF. ENG, 68- Mem. sr. common room, Univ. Col, Oxford, 60-; grants-in-aid, Cornell Univ, 57-61, Am. Counc. Learned Soc, 60-61, Rackham Found, 61-63 & Am. Philos. Soc, 63-64; asst. ed, Mid. Eng. Dictionary, 61-63; Guggenheim fel, 63-64; vis. assoc. prof, Univ. Chicago, summer 66; Am. Philos. Soc. grant, 70-71; Am. Counc. Learned Soc. grant, 71-72. MLA (chmn. Old Eng, 63); Mediaeval Acad. Am; Renaissance Soc. Am. Old English literature and lexicography; Renaissance English language. Publ: The Vitellius Psalter, Cornell, 62; ed, Philological essays, Mouton, The Hague, 70; co-auth, Old English: language and literature, Norton, 72; auth, Design for treachery: the Unferth intrigue, 62 & Icge gold and incge lafe in Beowulf, 66, PMLA; Instructions for Christians, Anglia, 64. Add: 508 Cedar Lane, Swarthmore, PA 19081.

ROSS, ALBION, b. Ashland, Wis, Apr. 29, 06. JOURNALISM. B.A, Dartmouth Col, 29; Columbia Univ, 29-30, 45-46; Univ. Berlin, 32-33; Am. Univ. Beirut, 49. For. correspondent, New York Evening Post, New York Times, 31-38, 45-55; for. ed, San Francisco Chronicle, 38-41; commun. media consult, Int. Coop. Admin, U.S. Govt, 57-62; vis. lectr. JOUR, Univ. Ill, 62-63; Lucius W. Nieman prof, MARQUETTE UNIV, 63-72, ASSOC. PROF, 72- Assoc. ed. & phonetician, Missiongesellscaft Bethlehem, Immense, Switz, 74- A.U.S, 43-45, Capt. Asn. Educ. in Jour. Foreign and comparative journalism. Publ: Journey of an American, Bobbs, 57; English language bibliography on foreign press and comparative journalism, Marquette Univ, 66. Add: College of Journalism, Marquette University, 1135 W. Kilbourne Ave, Milwaukee, WI 53233.

ROSS, ALEXANDER M, b. Embro, Jan. 5, 16; nat; m. 50; c. 1. ENGLISH. B.A, Queen's Univ.(Can), 40, M.A, 48; Imp. Relat. Trust fel, Univ. London, 50-51. Master ENG, Lakehead Tech. Inst, Port Arthur, Ont, 48-50; prof, Ont. Agr. Col, 51-65; PROF. ENG. LANG. & LIT. & CHMN. DEPT, Wellington Col, UNIV. GUELPH, 65-70, COL. ARTS, 70- Can. Counc. award, 67 & 69. Can. Army, 42-46, Capt. MLA; Int. Asn. Univ. Prof. Eng; Asn. Can. Univ. Teachers Eng; Humanities Asn. Influence of the theories and representation of the picturesque; William Henry Bartlett, 1809-1854; history of the Ontario Agricultural College. Publ: William Henry Bartlett, Univ. Toronto, 73; History of the Ontario Agricultural College, Copp, 73; North to Ungava, & Britain's new universities, Queen's Quart; Some considerations of the antithesis between a liberal and a technical education, Voc. Aspect Sec. & Further Educ; plus one other. Add: Dept. of English Language and Literature, College of Arts, University of Guelph, Guelph, Ont. N1G 2W1, Can.

ROSS, DANFORTH RAYNOLDS, b. C.Z, Panama, Jan. 18, 11; m. 49; ENGLISH. B.A, Southwest. at Memphis, 33; M.A, Vanderbilt Univ, 37; Ph.D, Univ. Minn, 54. Lectr. ENG, Columbia Univ, 46-48; instr, Univ. Minn, 48-55; asst. prof, SOUTHWEST. AT MEMPHIS, 55-57, assoc. prof, 57-62, PROF, 62- Sewanee Rev. fel, 53-54. U.S.A.A.F, 42-45, M/Sgt. Am. Stud. Asn. Genteel tradition in American literature and philosophy; American short story; creative writing. Publ: The American short story, Univ. Minn, 61; The cloud, Sewanee Rev, spring 53. Add: Dept. of English, Southwestern at Memphis, Memphis, TN 38112.

ROSS, DONALD, JR, b. New York, N.Y, Oct. 18, 41; m. 63; c. 2. ENGLISH. B.A, Lehigh Univ, 63, M.A, 64; Ph.D.(Eng), Univ. Mich, 67. Instr. ENG, Univ. Pa, 67-68, ASST. PROF, 68-71; UNIV. MINN, MINNEAPOLIS, 71- MLA; Midwest Mod. Lang. Asn. American and British 19th century literature; stylistics; computer-aided research in humanities. Publ: Composition as a stylistic feature, Style, 70; Dreams and sexual repression in The Blithedale romance, PMLA, 71; co-auth, Eyeball: a computer program for description of style, Computers and Humanities, 72. Add: Dept. of English, University of Minnesota, Minneapolis, MN 55455.

ROSS, DONALD H, b. Jerome, Idaho, Aug. 30, 28; m. 55; c. 5. MODERN LITERATURE, CREATIVE WRITING. B.A, Univ. Ore, 52, M.A, 55; Ph.D.(Eng. lit), Univ. Colo, 63. Asst. prof. ENG, WASH STATE UNIV, 61-73, ASSOC. PROF, 73-, summer grant humanities, 68. Contrib. ed, Annual Bibliog. Eng. Lang. & Lit, Mod. Humanities Res. Asn, 65-69. Sig.C, U.S.A, 52-54. The novel, nineteenth century and modern. Publ: The writing performance, Lippincott, 73; The black bull, Sage, fall 67; Writer vs. reader, Writer's Digest, 2/72; plus two others. Add: Dept. of English, Washington State University, Pullman, WA 99163.

ROSS, DUNCAN, b. London, Eng, Aug. 25, 18; 49; c. 3. DRAMA. Prin, Old Vic Theatre Sch, Bristol, Eng, 53-61; assoc. prof. DRAMA, Univ. Wash, 62-65; artistic dir, Nat. Theatre Sch. Can, 66-67; PROF, UNIV. WASH, 67- Vis. lectr. drama, Bristol Univ, 53-60; external exam, Bretton Hall Col, Eng, 60-62; artistic dir, Seattle Repertory Theatre, 70-; mem. adv. panel, Nat. Endowment for Arts, 72- Acting. Add: 17019 12th Ave. N.W, Seattle, WA 98177.

ROSS, HEROLD TRUSLOW, b. Rochester, Ind, Oct. 27, 95; m. 21; c. 2. SPEECH. A.B, DePauw Univ, 18; Univ. Liverpool, Eng, 19; A.M, Columbia Univ, 24; Ph.D, State Univ. Iowa, 32. Head dept. high sch, Ind, 20-23; Eng. master, Cutler Sch, New York, N.Y, 23-24; instr, Iowa State Col, 24-27; mem. fac, DePAUW UNIV, 27-37, prof. SPEECH & head dept, 37-61, EMER. PROF, 61- Vis. prof, Wabash Col, 67; Cent. Mo. State Col, 68-69; historian, Delta Sigma Rho-Tau Kappa Alpha, 64-75; vis. prof. speech, Hanover Col, 70. Speech Commun. Asn. Am; Cent. St. Speech Asn. American oratory; Beveridge. Publ: Speech in a democracy; Basic principles of communication; Oratory, In: Encyc. Am, Grolier, 54; Delta Sigma Rho-Tau Kappa Alpha, Encycl. Educ, Macmillan, 71; History of Delta Sigma Rho-Tau Kappa Alpha, Speaker Gavel, Vol. II, no. 1. Add: 617 Ridge Ave, Greencastle, IN 46135.

ROSS, IAN SIMPSON, b. Dundee, Scotland, Aug. 9, 30; m. 73; c. 2. ENGLISH. M.A, St. Andrews Univ, Scotland, 54; Tyndall Bruce scholar. & B.Litt, Oxford, 56; univ. fel, Univ. Tex, 58-59, Ph.D.(Eng), 60. Teaching asst. ENG, Univ. Tex, 56-57, spec. instr, 57-58, 59-60; instr, UNIV. B.C, 60-62, asst. prof, 62-65, assoc. prof, 65-73, PROF, 73- R.A.F, 48-50. MLA; Am. Soc. 18th Century Stud; Stair Soc. Eighteenth century and Scottish literature; aesthetics; history of ideas. Publ: Mrs. Elizabeth Montagu in Scotland, 1766, Huntington Libr. Quart, XXVIII: 213-233; Scots law and Scots criticism: the case of Lord Kames, Philol. Quart, XLV: 614-623; Lord Kames and the Scotland of his day, OUP, 72. Add: Dept. of English, University of British Columbia, Vancouver 8, B.C, Can.

ROSS, JANET, b. Duluth, Minn, Apr. 19, 19. LINGUISTICS. B.A, Univ. Minn, 35, M.A, 41; Ph.D, Univ. Iowa, 60. Asst. Eng, Univ. Minn, 40-41, instr. & counsel, 46-47; instr. guid. & stud. pers, Univ. Wyo, 47-49; ENG, Fla. State Univ, 49-53; Univ. Iowa, 53-57; asst. prof, Macalester Col, 57-60; instr, Univ. B.C, 60-61; asst. prof, BALL STATE UNIV, 61-64, assoc. prof, 64-70, PROF, 70- Fulbright grant, sec. sch, Heerenveen, Netherlands, 53-54; Danforth grant, ling, Univ. Mich, summer, 63. MLA; Nat. Asn. For. Stud. Adv; NCTE; Teaching English as a foreign language. Publ: Co-auth, Language and life in the U.S.A, 60, rev. ed, 68, 3rd ed. (2 vols), 73, & Writing English, 65, Harper. Add: Dept. of English, Ball State University, Muncie, IN 47306.

ROSS, JOE CARL, b. Amory, Miss, Jan. 11, 32; m. 51; c. 3. BRITISH & AMERICAN LITERATURE. B.S, Tenn. Polytech. Inst, 55; M.A, George Peabody Col, 55; Ph.D.(Eng), Vanderbilt Univ, 67. Instr. Eng. & speech, Itawambo Jr. Col, 55-57; Tenn. Polytech. Inst, 57-64; asst. prof. ENG, Univ. Tenn, 63-66; assoc. prof, UNIV. ALA, BIRMINGHAM, 67-73, PROF, 73- Asst. prof. Eng, Tenn. Polytech. Inst, summers 65, 67. U.S.A, 51-53, M/Sgt. S.Atlantic Mod. Lang. Asn; MLA; Soc. Stud. South. Lit. Southern literature; black American literature; novel. Add: Dept. of English, University of Alabama in Birmingham, University Station, Birmingham, AL 35294.

ROSS, MALCOLM, b. Fredericton, N.B, Jan. 2, 11; m. 38; c. 1. ENGLISH LITERATURE. B.A, Univ. N.B, 33, D.Litt, 62; M.A, Univ. Toronto, 34; N.Y. Univ, 35-37; Ph.D, Cornell Univ, 41. Instr, Cornell Univ, 39-41; Ind. Univ, 41-42; dir. distribution, Nat. Film Bd, Can, 42-45; from asst. prof. to prof, Univ. Man, 45-49; prof. Eng, Queens Univ, Can, 50-63; prof. ENG, Trinity Col, Univ. Toronto, 63-73, dean arts, 65-73, acting provost, 68; THOMAS McCULLOCH PROF, DALHOUSIE UNIV, 73- Guggenheim fel, 49-50; ed, Queen's Quart, 52-56; mem. Humanities Res. Counc. Can; gen. ed, New Can. Libr; mem. acad. panel, Can. Counc, 65-68; chmn. comt. res, Asn. Univs.

& Cols. Can, 65-68; mem. Gaudry Comt. Res. Can, 67-68; vis. prof, Dalhousie Univ, 68-69; mem. nat. awards comt, Killaim Found, 73-76. MLA; Humanities Asn. Can.(pres, 56); fel. Royal Soc. Can. Victorian poetry and aesthetic theory. Publ: Milton's royalism, Cornell; Poetry and dogma, Rutgers & Univ. Toronto; Arts in Canada, Macmillan, Can, 59. Add: Dept. of English, Dalhousie University, Halifax, N.S, Can.

ROSS, MICHAEL LAWRENCE, b. Detroit, Mich, July 28, 36; m. 64; c. 2. VICTORIAN & MODERN ENGLISH LITERATURE. B.A, Harvard, 58, M.A, 59, Ph.D.(Eng), 66. Instr. ENG, Vassar Col, 64-67; asst. prof, McMASTER UNIV, 68-73, ASSOC. PROF, 73- Cornell Univ. Soc. for Humanities jr. fel, 67-68. Browning Inst. Victorian literature; English and American fiction. Publ: The mythology of friendship: D.H. Lawrence, Bertrand Russell, and The blind man, In: English literature and British philosophy, Univ. Chicago, 71; Mark Twain's Pudd'nhead Wilson: Dawson's Landing and the ladder of nobility, Novel: Forum on Fiction, spring 73. Add: Dept. of English, McMaster University, Hamilton, Ont, Can.

ROSS, MORTON LEE, b. Oelwein, Iowa, Sept. 3, 32; m. 55; c. 2. ENGLISH, AMERICAN STUDIES. B.A, Cornell Univ, 54; M.A, Univ. Iowa, 57, Ph.D. (Eng), 64. Instr. Eng, Northwest. Univ, 60-63; asst. prof. Eng. & Am. stud, Univ. Wyo, 63-67, ASSOC. PROF, 67-68; ENG, UNIV. ALTA, 68- Peace Corps lectr, 64. MLA; Am. Stud. Asn; West. Lit. Asn.(pres, 69). American literature and intellectual history. Publ: What happens in Rappaccini's daughter, Am. Lit, 71; Thoreau and Mailer: The mission of the rooster, West. Humanities Rev, 71; Bill Gorton, the preacher of The sun also rises, Mod. Fiction Stud, 72-73; plus others. Add: Dept. of English, University of Alberta, Edmonton, Alta, T6G 2G2, Can.

ROSS, RICHARD JOHN, b. Ludhiana, India, Nov. 6, 18; U.S. citizen; m. 45; c. 3. ENGLISH LITERATURE. A.B, Sterling Col, 41; M.A, Univ. Mich, 47, Ph.D, 58. Teacher ENG, Sch. Organic Educ, Fairhope, Ala, 41-42; teaching fel, COL. ENGINEERING, UNIV. MICH, ANN ARBOR, 46-51, instr, 52-58, asst. prof, 58-65, ASSOC. PROF, 65- U.S.A, 42-45. Renaissance poetry; criticism. Publ: Herrick's Julia in silks, Essays in Criticism, 4/65. Add: 3449 Craig Rd, Ann Arbor, MI 48103.

ROSS, ROBERT HENRY, JR, b. Germantown, Ohio, July 16, 16; m. 40; c. 3. ENGLISH. A.B, Dartmouth Col, 38; A.M, Columbia Univ, 40; Harvard, 40-42; Ph.D.(Eng), Ohio State Univ, 58. Asst. prof. Eng, Ohio Wesleyan Univ, 49-54, assoc. prof, 54-60, prof, 60-65, chmn. dept. humanities, 59-61; prof. Eng, Wash. State Univ, 66-70, dir. grad. stud. Eng, 69-70; prof, Bowling Green State Univ, 70-73, chmn. dept, 70-71. U.S.A.A.F, 42-46. MLA. Victorian literature; 20th century British literature; poetics. Publ: The Georgian revolt, 1910-1922, South. Ill. Univ, 65 & Faber, 67; co-ed, Poems and perspective, Scott, 71; ed, Tennyson's In memoriam, Norton, 73; auth, Samuel Sandford: villain from necessity, PMLA, 61; Sound and fury, In: Backgrounds to modern literature, Chandler, 68. Add: S. Main St, Haverhill, NH 03765.

ROSS, ROBERT N, b. New York, N.Y, Feb. 24, 41; m. 64; c. 3. SEMIOTICS, LITERARY THEORY. B.A, Williams Col, 63; M.A, Cornell Univ, 66, Ph.D. (Eng. lit), 69. Instr. lit, Univ. Pa, 67-69, asst. prof, 69-73; ANDREW MELLON FEL. ENG, UNIV. PITTSBURGH, 73- NCTE res. grant, 73-74. MLA; AAUP. Am. Arbit. Asn. Graph-theoretic methods applied to research in literary theory; literary semantics; empirical esthetics. Publ: To charm thy curious eye: Erasmus Darwin's poetry at the vestibule of knowledge, J. Hist. Ideas, 71; The coefficient of concordance: a mathematical tool for comparing literary texts, Style, 73; Conceptual network analysis, Semiotica, 73. Add: 3708 Spring Garden St, Philadelphia, PA 19104.

ROSS, RONALD PATRICK, American & Afro-American History. See Volume I, History.

ROSS, THEODORE JOHN, b. Boston, Mass, Oct. 3, 24; m. 56; c. 3. TWENTIETH CENTURY LITERATURE & FILM. B.A, Clark Univ, 48; M.A, Columbia Univ, 49. Instr. ENG, W.Va. Univ, 52-55; Wayne State Univ, 56-60; asst. prof, FAIRLEIGH DICKINSON UNIV, 60-68, assoc. prof, 68-72, PROF, 72- Lectr. film & cult. criticism, New Sch. Soc. Res, 65-70; consult. film, sub-comt. on educ, Gov. Comn. Arts, N.J, 66-70. Northeast Mod. Lang. Asn.(chmn. film & lit. sect, 72). Film; contemporary fiction; modern poetry. Publ: Ed, Film and the liberal arts, Holt, 70; co-ed, Focus on the horror film, Prentice Hall, 72; auth, On teaching poetry, Dissent, winter 64; contrib, Renaissance of the film, Collier Bks, 70; auth, Reading, writing and the movies, Chicago Rev, 73; plus others. Add: 2 Woodley Rd, Morristown, NJ 07960.

ROSS, THOMAS WYNNE, b. Colorado Springs, Colo, Apr. 16, 23; m. 43; c. 2. ENGLISH LITERATURE. A.B, Colo. Col, 46, A.M, 47; Ph.D, Univ. Mich, 51. Instr. Eng, Colo. Col, 51-53, asst. prof, 53-56; asst. dir Salzburg Sem, Austria, 56-58; assoc. prof. ENG, COLO. COL, 58-63, PROF, 63-, dir. admis, 58-61. Asst. prof. humanities, Mass. Inst. Technol, 55; res. fel, Oxford, Cambridge, Univ. Edinburgh, Scotland, summer 62; Am. Philos. Soc. res. grant, summer 67; NATO prof, Univ. Regensburg, 69. U.S.A, 43-46, T/Sgt. MLA; Mediaeval Acad. Am. Middle English poetry; Shakespeare. Publ: Edition of Thomas Kyd The Spanish tragedy, Oliver & Boyd, 68; Chaucer's bawdy, Dutton, 72; Five fifteenth century emblem verses, Speculum, 57; On the evil times of Edward II; a new version from MS Bodley 48, 58 & Claudius Plays at Shove-Groat, 66, Anglia. Add: Dept. of English, Colorado College, Colorado Springs, CO 80903.

ROSS, WILLIAM THOMAS, b. Clarksdale, Miss, July 13, 42; m. 64; c. 1. ENGLISH LITERATURE, POPULAR CULTURE. B.A, Memphis State Univ, 63; M.A, Univ. Va, 65, Ph.D.(Eng), 70. Jr. instr. ENG, Univ. Va, 67-68, instr, 68-69, Mary Washington Col, 69-70; ASST. PROF, UNIV. S.FLA, TAMPA, 70- Super. instr. basic courses, MLA, 70. S.Atlantic Mod. Lang. Asn; Popular Cult. Asn. British 19th century literature; George Orwell; cinema. Publ: Iris Murdoch, In: Counter currents, Kimball-Hunt, 73. Add: Dept. of English, University of South Florida, Tampa, FL 33620.

ROSS, WOODBURN OVERSTREET, b. Okla. City, Okla, Jan. 23, 05; m. 28; c. 2. ENGLISH LANGUAGE & LITERATURE. A.B, Univ. Mo, 25, A.M, 27; Ph.D, Yale, 35. Instr. ENG, Univ. Mo, 26-28; Dartmouth Col, 31-34; assoc. prof, Univ. N.Dak, 34-36; asst. prof, Wayne State Univ, 36-40, assoc. prof, 40-46, prof, 46-72, ombudsman, 71-72, dir. Monteith Col, 60-63, dean 63-72; RETIRED. MLA. Contemporary fiction; Middle English. Publ: Ed, Middle English sermons, Oxford; co-ed, Short stories in context, Am. Bk. Co. Add: 1022 Kensington Rd, Grosse Pointe Park, MI 48230.

ROSSER, PAUL F, b. Tahlequah, Okla, Nov. 9, 16; m. 43; c. 2. SPEECH. B.S, Seattle Pac. Col, 40; M.A, Univ. Wash, 51, Ph.C, 64. Instr. SPEECH, SEATTLE PAC. COL, 48-49, asst. prof, 49-53, assoc. prof, 53-68, PROF, 68-, CHMN. DEPT, 48- Lectr, Mgt. Develop. Prog, Boeing Airplane Co, 52-53. U.S.A, 42-45, T/Sgt. Speech Commun. Asn; West. Speech Asn; AAUP. Voice and laryngeal anatomy in voice production for speech; speech education for college students and teaching of speech at college or university level; curriculum development for speech education. Add: 2424 Lorentz Pl. N, Seattle, WA 98109.

ROSSI, ALFRED ANTHONY, b. Chicago, Ill, Aug. 18, 35; m. 61; c. 3. DRAMATIC ART. B.S, Loyola Univ.(Ill), 57; M.A, Univ. Kans, 60; Ph.D.(speech & theatre), Univ. Minn, 65. Teaching asst. speech & drama, Univ. Kans, 58-60; asst. instr, Univ. Minn, Minneapolis, 63-64; lectr, Hunter Col, 65; asst. prof. DRAMATIC ART, UNIV. CALIF, DAVIS, 65-72, ASSOC. PROF, 72- McKnight Found. grant, Minneapolis, 61-63; Rockefeller grant, New York, 64-65; Humanities Inst. grant, Europe, 68-69; dir. Mark Taper Forum, Los Angeles, 70; Colo. Shakespeare Festival, 72; Univ. Calif. regents creative arts grant, summer 73. U.S.A.F, 57-58. Am. Theatre Asn. Training of actors; directing on the open stage; repertory theatres. Publ: Minneapolis rehearsals: Tyrone Guthrie directs Hamlet, Drama Critique, winter 64 & Univ. Calif, 71; The university of California, Davis professional resident theatres, Drama Critique, fall 68; co-auth, The writings of Sir Tyrone Guthrie, Drama Surv, spring 63. Add: Dept. of Dramatic Art, University of California, Davis, CA 95616.

ROSSILLON, JOSEPH PIERRE, b. Olpe, Kans, Aug. 30, 33; m. 55; c. 5. SPEECH, DRAMA. B.S.Ed, Kans. State Teachers Col, 57, B.A, 57, M.S, 58; Ph.D.(speech & drama), South. Ill. Univ, 66. Tech. dir. theater, Marymount Col.(Kans), 58-59; tech. dir. theater & scene designer, Kans. State Teachers Col, 59-63; dir. instr. resources, SOUTHWEST MINN. STATE COL, MARSHALL, 65-67, ASST. TO PRES, 67- U.S.A, 53-55, Res, 55-61, Sgt. Nat. Col. Players; Speech Commun. Asn. Basic speech; oral communications. Add: Southwest Minnesota State College, Marshall, MN 56258.

ROSSKY, WILLIAM, b. Plainfield, N.J, July 11, 17; m. 43; c. 2. ENGLISH. A.B, Lafayette Col, 38; Blumenthal & Penfield fels. & Haydn scholar, N.Y. Univ, 38-41, M.A, 39, Ph.D.(Eng), 53. Instr. ENG, TEMPLE UNIV, 46-54, asst. prof, 54-57, assoc. prof, 57-64, PROF, 64-, chmn. dept, 64-67. Christian R. & Mary F. Lindback Distinguished Teaching Award, 61. U.S.A, 42-46, Capt. MLA; NCTE; Renaissance Soc. Am; AAUP; Shakespeare Asn. Am; Soc. Stud. South. Lit; Renaissance Eng. Text Soc. American literature, especially William Faulkner; English Renaissance, especially Shakespeare. Publ: Imagination in the English Renaissance: psychology and poetics, Stud. Renaissance, 58; As I lay dying; the insane world, Tex. Stud. Lit. & Lang, 62; The Reivers and Huckleberry Finn: Faulkner and Twain, Huntington Libr. Quart, 8/65. Add: 2369 Mt. Carmel Ave, Glenside, PA 19038.

ROSSMAN, CHARLES RAYMOND, b. Brookings, S.Dak, Feb. 13, 38; m. 63; c. 2. ENGLISH. B.A, Calif. State Col. Los Angeles, 62; M.A, Univ. South. Calif, 65, Ph.D.(Eng), 68. Teacher ENG, Colegio Abelardo Moncayo, Ecuador, 62-63; assoc, Univ. Calif, Los Angeles, 67-68; ASST. PROF, UNIV. TEX, AUSTIN, 68- Mem. ed. bd, D.H. Lawrence Rev, 71-; Tex. Stud, Lang. & Lit, 72-; Fulbright prof, Nat. Univ, Mex, 72-73. MLA. James Joyce; D.H. Lawrence; 20th century British literature. Publ: The gospel according to D.H. Lawrence, spring 70, Lawrence on the critic's couch, summer 70 & Four versions of Lawrence, spring 73, D.H. Lawrence Rev. Add: Dept. of English, University of Texas, Austin, TX 78712.

ROSSOW, FRANCIS C, b. Fowler, Mich, Mar. 4, 25; m. 50; c. 5. ENGLISH LITERATURE. B.A, Concordia Sem, 46, B.D, 48; M.A, Mich. State Univ, 59. Assoc. prof. ENG, CONCORDIA SR. COL, 59-73, PROF, 73- MLA. Publ: Broad is the way, Vantage, 71. Add: Dept. of English, Concordia Senior College, Ft. Wayne, IN 46805.

ROTEN, PAUL, b. Maryville, Tenn, Jan. 14, 20; m. 61; c. 1. SPEECH, LIBRARY SCIENCE. B.A, Ottawa Univ, 41; M.A, Univ. Mich, 48, fel, 48-50, 50-52, Ph.D, 63, M.A.L.S, 65. Instr. Eng, Levant High Sch, Kans, 41-42; Eng. & speech, Neodesha High Sch, 45-47; speech, Dartmouth Col, 50; asst. prof, Sioux Falls Col, 53-55, assoc. prof, 55-59; asst. prof, Manchester Col, 59-64; LIBRN, MENNONITE BIBL. SEM, 65- U.S.A, 42-45. Am. Libr. Asn; Am. Theol. Libr. Asn. Theatre history and criticism; forensics; interpretative reading. Add: 2800 Benham, Elkhart, IN 46514.

ROTH, AUDREY JOAN, b. Newark, N.J, Feb. 4, 27; m. 49; c. 2. ENGLISH. B.A, Ohio State Univ, 46, M.A, 47. Instr. humanities, Univ. Miami, 58-63; asst. prof. ENG, MIAMI-DADE COMMUNITY COL, 63-70, ASSOC. PROF, 70- Consult, Horizon Sch, 73- Conf. Col. Compos. & Commun.(mem. ed. bd, 72-75); MLA; Col. Eng. Asn.(dir, 72-75); NCTE (mem. col. sect, 74-76); Nat. Asn. Media Educ.(mem. bd. dir, 73-76). Teacher training; uses of media; freshman composition and literature. Publ: Co-auth, Prose as experience, 65 & Writing step by step, 69, Houghton; auth, The research paper: form and content, Wadsworth, 66, 2nd ed, 71; Success: a search for values, 69, co-ed, Alienation and belonging: a search for values, 70 & ed, Personal identity: a search for values, 71, Holt; co-auth, Words people use, Winthrop, 72; auth, An examination of setting as metaphor in the films of John Ford with particular reference to Fort Apache, CEA Critic, 5/72; Mother's chicken soup and the moving pictures, Fla. Eng. J, 9/72; E-Z off, E-Z on, and the super highway, Col. Compos. & Commun, 10/72; plus others. Add: Dept. of English, Miami-Dade Community College, North, 11380 N.W. 27th Ave, Miami, FL 33167.

ROTH, EMALOU, b. Ottumwa, Iowa, Apr. 1, 46. THEATRE HISTORY & CRITICISM. B.A, Clarke Col, 68; NDEA fel. & M.A, Univ. Kans, 69, Ph.D, 72. ASST. PROF. THEATRE, WINONA STATE COL, 72-, ASSOC. DIR. EXTERNAL STUD. PROG, 73- Am. Theatre Asn; AAUP. Dramatic literature; theatre history; theatre aesthetics. Publ: Immanent form; toward a dramatic-theatrical criticism, Univ. Kans, 72. Add: Dept. of Speech, Winona State College, Winona, MN 55987.

ROTH, FREDERIC HULL, JR, b. Cleveland, Ohio, July 27, 41; m. 63; c. 3. RENAISSANCE ENGLISH LITERATURE. B.A, Yale, 63; M.A, Columbia Univ, 67; Ph.D.(Eng), Univ. Va, 73. Instr. ENG, Robert Louis Stevenson Sch, Pebble Beach, Calif, 63-65; Landon Sch, Wash, D.C, 66-68; ASST. PROF, HAMILTON COL, 71- Nat. Endowment for Humanities summer stipend, 74. MLA; Shakespeare Asn. Am. Sixteenth and 17th century English literature; Milton. Publ: Marvell's Upon Appleton House: a study in perspective, Tex. Stud. Lit. & Lang, 72. Add: Dept. of English, Hamilton College, Clinton, NY 13323.

ROTH, GEORGE LEITH, JR, b. Somerset, Pa, Jan. 5, 25; m. 52; c. 2. ENGLISH. A.B, Franklin & Marshall Col, 44; A.M, Princeton, 46, Ph.D, 49. Instr. ENG, Univ. Va, 47-51; asst. prof, VA. MIL. INST, 51-56, assoc. prof, 56-61, PROF, 61-, HEAD DEPT, 68- MLA; NCTE. American literature. Publ: New England satire on religion, 1790-1820, New Eng. Quart, 55; American theory of satire, 1790-1820, Am. Lit, 58; Verse satire on faction, 1790-1815, William & Mary Quart, 60. Add: 108 McDowell St, Lexington, VA 24450.

ROTH, MARY AUGUSTINE, R.S.M, b. Minneapolis, Minn, Jan. 16, 26. ENGLISH. B.A, Univ. Minn, 47, M.A, 48; univ. fel, Cath. Univ. Am, 57-61, Ph.D, 61. Mem. fac. ENG, MT. MERCY COL.(IOWA), 48-56, PROF, 61-, CHMN. DEPT, 63- Exchange prof, Coe Col, 69; coord. educ, Sisters of Mercy, Cedar Rapids, Iowa, 71- Ling. Soc. Am. Prosody; literary theory; literary criticism. Publ: Coventry Patmore's essay on English metrical law: a critical education with commentary, Cath. Univ. Am, 61. Add: Dept. of English, Mt. Mercy College, 1330 Elmhurst Dr, Cedar Rapids, IA 52402.

ROTHMAN, JULIUS L, b. New York, N.Y, Sept. 22, 20; m. 48. AMERICAN LITERATURE. B.S.S, City Col. New York, 41; M.A, Columbia Univ, 47, Ph.D, 54. Lectr. ENG, Hunter Col, 47-50, 62-63; Rutgers Univ, 50-53; City Col. New York, 58-62; asst. prof, NASSAU COMMUNITY COL, 62-65, assoc. prof, 65-69, PROF, 69- U.S.A.A.F, 43-45, 2nd Lt. MLA; Col. Eng. Asn; James Branch Cabell Soc.(exec. v.pres, secy-treas. & ed, Cabellian, 68-72); NCTE. American literature; mythology and folklore; literary criticism. Publ: Jurgen: the Rabelaisian Babbitt, 11/68, & The Danish Jurgen, spring 71, Cabellian; A short history of The Cabellian, Nassau Rev, spring 73; plus five others. Add: Dept. of English, Nassau Community College, Stewart Ave, Garden City, NY 11530.

ROTHRAUFF, CONRAD, Classics, English. See Volume III, Foreign Languages, Linguistics & Philology.

ROTHSTEIN, ERIC, b. New York, N.Y, Mar. 12, 36; m. 65. ENGLISH. A.B, Harvard, 57; Ph.D.(Eng), Princeton, 62. Instr. ENG, UNIV. WIS-MADISON, 61-63, asst. prof, 63-66, assoc. prof, 66-70, PROF, 70-, grad. sch. grant, summer 64, 67-68. Am. Counc. Learned Soc. grant, 73-74. MLA; Augustan Reprint Soc; Am. Soc. 18th Century Stud; Johnson Soc. Cent. Region. Eighteenth century literature. Publ: Restoration tragedy: form and the process of change, 67 & co-ed, Literary monographs I-V, 67-73, Univ. Wis; auth, George Farquhar, Twayne, 67; ed, George Farquhar; the beaux' stratagem, Appleton, 67; co-ed, The Augustan milieu: essays presented to Louis A. Landa, Clarendon, 70; Structure as meaning in The Jew of Malta, J. Eng. & Ger. Philol, 4/66; The framework of Shamela, ELH, 8/68; Jonathan Swift as Jupiter: Baucis and Philemon, In: The Augustan Milieu, Clarendon, 70; plus others. Add: Dept. of English, University of Wisconsin-Madison, Madison, WI 53706.

ROTHWELL, HELEN FRANCIS, b. Nelsonville, Ohio, Aug. 7, 08; m. 43; c. 1. ENGLISH. B.S.Ed, Ohio Univ, 38, fel, 40, M.A, 41; Boston Univ, 45-47. Teacher pub. schs, Ohio, 26-32; Instr, Owosso Col, 32-45; assoc. prof. Eng. & Span, East. Nazarene Col, 45-58; Eng, Bethany Nazarene Col, 58-73; RETIRED. Publ: Co-auth, Catechism on the Christian religion, Pilgrim House, 44; auth, Fanny Crosby—blind poetess, 46 & Ira Sankey—gospel singer, 47, Boone Publ. Add: Dept. of English, Bethany Nazarene College, Bethany, OK 73008.

ROTHWELL, KENNETH SPRAGUE, b. Bay Shore, N.Y, May 26, 21; m. 54; c. 4. ENGLISH. B.A, Univ. N.C, 48; M.A, Columbia Univ, 49, Ph.D.(Eng), 56. Instr. Eng, Univ. Kans, 49-50, Univ. Rochester, 52-55; Univ. Cincinnati, 55-57; asst. prof, Univ. Kans, 57-62, from assoc. prof. to prof. ENG, 62-70; PROF. & CHMN. DEPT, UNIV. VT, 70- Am. Philos. Soc. grant-in-aid, 63, 68. U.S.A, 42-46, 1st Lt. Malone Soc; Renaissance Soc. Am; MLA; Cent. Renaissance Conf.(pres, 69); NCTE (mem. col. selection comt, 73-). Shakespeare and the Elizabethans; rhetoric and composition; American literature. Publ: Questions of rhetoric and usage, Little, 70; The meaning of structure in literature, Col. Eng, 5/63; Paradise lost but perhaps regained: on teaching Milton, Kans. Eng, 2/72; Some versions of Romeo, Lit/Film, 10/73; plus many others. Add: Dept. of English, University of Vermont, Burlington, VT 05401.

ROTHWELL, WILLIAM F, JR, b. Kans. City, Mo, Nov. 17, 20. DRAMA. B.A, Univ. Ariz, 42; Ph.D, Yale, 53. Asst. prof. Eng. & speech, Heidelberg Col, 53-54; instr. DRAMA, Univ. Calif, Berkeley, 54-57; asst. prof, VASSAR COL, 57-66, ASSOC. PROF, 66- U.S.A, 42-46, T/Sgt. Am. Theatre Asn. The Elizabethan stage; 18th century English theatre. Add: Dept. of Drama, Vassar College, Poughkeepsie, NY 12601.

ROTUNDO, BARBARA R, b. Swampscott, Mass, May 24, 21; m. 42; c. 3. ENGLISH & AMERICAN LITERATURE. B.A, Mt. Holyoke Col, 42; M.A, Cornell Univ, 58; Ph.D.(Eng), Syracuse, 68. Instr. ENG, Union Col, 55-57 & 58-59; STATE UNIV. N.Y. ALBANY, 62-63, asst. prof, 63-70, ASSOC. PROF, 70- MLA; Am. Stud. Asn; AAUP. Nineteenth century American literature; Mrs. James T. Fields and Boston 1840-1915; Nineteenth-century New England social and cultural history. Publ: Art. in Am. Heritage and other learned journals. Add: Dept. of English, Humanities Bldg 268, State University of New York at Albany, Albany, NY 12222.

ROUCH, JOHN SEARS, b. Cleveland, Ohio, Apr. 8, 29; m. 52; c. 5. ENGLISH. B.A, St. Bonaventure Univ, 51; M.A, Univ. Mich, 52; teaching fel, Univ. Cincinnati, 57-59, Ph.D, 61. Instr. ENG, Univ. Dayton, 54-57, asst. prof, 57-59; GANNON COL, 59-62, assoc. prof, 62-67, PROF. & CHMN. DEPT, 67- Ord.C, U.S.A, 52-54, Sgt. MLA; Johnson Soc. Cent. Region; NCTE; Conf. Col. Compos. & Commun. Restoration and 18th century; literary criticism; English novel. Add: Dept. of English, Gannon College, Erie, PA 16501.

ROUILLARD, ZELDA JEANNE, b. Kearney, Nebr, June 6, 29; m. 59; c. 1. ENGLISH COMPOSITION, AMERICAN FOLKLORE. A.B, Kearney State Col, 51; Fulbright scholar, Univ. Exeter, 51-52; M.A, Univ. Wyo, 53; Am. Asn. Univ. Women fel, Univ. Colo, Boulder, 58-59, Ph.D.(Eng), 59. Instr. Eng, Univ. Wyo, 52-54; Univ. Colo, Boulder, 54-60; teacher, N. High Sch, 60-65; E. High Sch, 67; Eng. & speech, Nederland Jr-Sr. High Sch, 67-69; ASSOC. PROF. ENG, WEST. STATE COL. COLO, 69- Reader, Col. Entrance Exam, 64. NCTE; MLA. American folklore, especially Rocky Mountain; medieval folklore, especially Arthurian romance. Add: Dept. of English, Western State College of Colorado, Gunnison, CO 81230.

ROULSTON, CHARLES ROBERT, b. Baltimore, Md, May 27, 30; m. 61. ENGLISH. B.A, Univ. Md, 54, Ph.D.(Eng), 65; M.A, Ind. Univ, 57. Instr. ENG, Univ. N.Dak, 57-60; Univ. Md, 61-64; asst. prof, MURRAY STATE UNIV, 64-65, assoc. prof, 65-66, PROF, 66- MLA. American literature. Add: Dept. of English, Murray State University, Murray, KY 42071.

ROUMM, PHYLLIS G, b. New Alexandria, Pa, Jan. 1, 27; m. 46; c. 4. ENGLISH & AMERICAN LITERATURE. B.S, Indiana Univ. Pa, 45, M.Ed, 63; Ohio Univ, summer 64, 65; Kent State Univ, 68-71. Teacher ENG, Elder's Ridge High Sch, 45-46; chmn. dept, Apollo High Sch, 46-47; teacher, Ind. Area Sr-Jr. High Sch, 59-67; ASSOC. PROF, INDIANA UNIV. PA, 67- MLA; NCTE; AAUP. American realism; women in American literature; contemporary British and American novel. Add: Dept. of English, Indiana University of Pennsylvania, Indiana, PA 15701.

ROUND, HAROLD LAPIDES, b. Baltimore, Md, Oct. 20, 11; m. 54; c. 2. ENGLISH, RELIGION. B.A, Johns Hopkins Univ, 32, Ph.D.(Semitic lang), 64. Asst. prof. Eng, UNIV. WIS-OSHKOSH, 66-70, ASSOC. PROF. ENG. & RELIGION, 70- Co-ed, Eng. Notes, 68-69. MLA. Eighteenth century British satire; literature of the Old Testament. Add: Dept. of English, University of Wisconsin-Oshkosh, Oshkosh, WI 54901.

ROUNDS, ROBERT W, b. Whitewater, Wis, Apr. 2, 05; m. 34; c. 3. ENGLISH. B.S, Harvard, 27; M.A, N.Y. Univ, 32, Ed.D.(educ), 42. Chmn. dept. ENG, jr. high sch, N.J, 30-44; prof, STATE UNIV. N.Y. COL. ONEONTA, 44-69, EMER. PROF, 69- Fulbright award, Dordrecht, Netherlands, 56-57; chmn. N.Y. comt, NCTE Achievement Awards Prog, 69-72. NCTE. Publ: Seventh grade book, In: Macmillan English series, Macmillan, 54-68; Using the New Yorker as a composition text, Col. Compos. & Commun, 10/68; The Dutch bicycle: a note for the record, Delta, fall 68; Discovery (poem), Calif. Eng. J, 4/73; plus one other. Add: 5 Davis Dr, Oneonta, NY 13820.

ROUNTREE, MARY MARTIN, b. Atlanta, Ga, Sept. 26, 31; m. 53; c. 2. ENGLISH. A.B, Univ. Ga, 52, M.A, 54; cert, Univ. Montreal, 53; certs, Univ. Grenoble, 55 & 56; M.A, Univ. Pittsburgh, 63, Ph.D.(Eng), 65. Instr. Eng, Univ. Ga, 54-55; French, Day Sch. Girls, 58-60; asst. prof. ENG, Mt. Mercy Col, 65-66; MT. HOLYOKE COL, 66-73, ASSOC. PROF, 73- Fulbright prof, Univ. Toulouse, 70-71. MLA. Modern American and 19th century French literature. Publ: Lettres inédites d'Audiberti à Jean de Boschère, Litterature, 4/73. Add: Dept. of English, Mt. Holyoke College, South Hadley, MA 01075.

ROUNTREE, THOMAS JEFFERSON, b. Dale Co, Ala, July 22, 27; m. 67. ENGLISH. B.A, Troy State Univ, 50; M.A, Univ. Ala, 52; Carnegie scholar, Tulane Univ, 53, Ph.D.(Eng), 62. Asst. prof. Eng, Southeast. La. Col, 58-60; E.Tex. State Univ, 60-61; instr, Univ. Ala, 61-62, asst. prof, 62-65, assoc. prof, 65-71, dir. creative writing, 63-71, univ. res. comt. res. grants, summers 65, 66, 68; PROF. ENG. & CHMN. DEPT, UNIV. S.ALA, 71- Lectr. creative writing, S.Dak. Fine Arts Conf, summers 62, 63. U.S.N.R, 45-46; U.S.A, 54-56. MLA; S.Atlantic Mod. Lang. Asn; Soc. Stud. South. Lit; Wordsworth Circle; Rydal Mt. Summer Sch. Asn. English romantic poets; American literature; creative writing. Publ: This mighty sum of things: Wordsworth's theme of benevolent necessity, Univ. Ala, 65; ed, Critics on Hawthorne, 72, Critics on Melville, 72 & Critics on Emerson, 73, Univ. Miami; auth, Whitman's indirect expression and its application to Song of myself, PMLA, 12/58; Wordsworth and Beattie's Minstrel, S.Atlantic Quart, spring 70; Poe's universe: The house of Usher and the narrator, Tulane Stud. Eng, 72; plus others. Add: Box U-342, University of South Alabama, Mobile, AL 36688.

ROUSE, HUBERT BLAIR, b. Orange, Va, Oct. 31, 12; m. 42; c. 2. ENGLISH. A.B, Randolph-Macon Col, 33; M.A, Univ. Va, 38; fel, Univ. Ill, 40-42, Ph.D. (Eng), 42. Teacher high schs, Va, 32-40; instr, Ohio State Univ, 46-49; asst. prof, Emory Univ, 49-55; assoc. prof. ENG. & head dept, Mt. Union Col, 55-57; assoc. prof, UNIV. ARK, FAYETTEVILLE, 57-61, PROF, 61- Am. Philos. Soc. res. grant, 62-; Univ. Ark. res. grant, Grad Sch, 62-, Alumni Distinguished Fac. Award. Res, 67; co-ed, Style, Univ. Ark, 67- U.S.N, 42-46, Lt. Comdr. MLA (secy, Eng, 12, 72, chmn, 73); Col. Eng. Asn; Am. Counc. Learned Soc; PEN Club; Am. Comp. Lit. Asn; Int. Comp. Lit. Asn. American, English, and comparative literature; nature writing; literary criticism. Publ: Letters of Ellen Glasgow, Harcourt, 58; Ellen Glasgow, Twayne, 62. Add: Dept. of English, University of Arkansas, Fayetteville, AR 72701.

ROUSE, JOHN L, b. York, Pa, July 2, 08; m. 40, 58; c. 3. ENGLISH. A.B, Harvard, 30; A.M, Columbia Univ, 33; Univ. N.C, 40-41. Teacher high sch, Pa, 35-40; asst. prof. Eng. & asst. dir. phys. educ, Randolph-Macon Col, 43-45; ASSOC. PROF. ENG, UNIV. MIAMI, 45- Romanticism; Pennsylvania Dutch; comparative arts. Add: Dept. of English, University of Miami, Coral Gables, FL 33146.

ROUSE, SARAH A, b. Columbia, Miss; m. 29. ENGLISH. B.A, William Carey Col, 55; M.A, Fla. State Univ, 57, Ph.D, 62. Dean women, William

Carey Col, 47-56; instr. ENG, Fla. State Univ, 57-59; assoc. prof, MISS. COL, 59-62, PROF, 62-, CHMN. HUMANITIES DIV, 67-, dean women, 59-67. MLA; Eudora Welty's fiction. Add: Dept. of English, Mississippi College, Clinton, MS 39058.

ROUSSEAU, GEORGE SEBASTIAN, b. Brooklyn, N.Y, Feb. 23, 41. ENGLISH LITERATURE. B.A, Amherst Col, 62; fel, Am. Sch. Class. Stud, 63-64; M.A, Princeton, 64; Woodrow Wilson fel, 65-66, Ph.D.(Eng), 66. Instr. ENG, Harvard, 66-68, asst. prof. UNIV. CALIF, LOS ANGELES, 68-69, ASSOC. PROF, 69- Gen. ed, Bicentennial Edition of the Works of Tobias Smollett, 67-; assoc. ed, Stud. in Burke & His Time, 70- Fel. Royal Soc. Med; fel. Royal Soc. Arts; MLA (del. assembly, 71-74). English literature 1660-1800; Alexander Pope and Tobias Smollett; literature and science in England. Publ: Co-auth, This long disease my life: Alexander Pope and science, Princeton, 68; ed, Twentieth century interpretations of The rape of the lock, Prentice-Hall, 69; co-ed, The Augustan Milieu: essays presented to Louis Landa, Clarendon, 70 & Tobias Smollett, Oxford, 71; ed, Organic form: the life of an idea, 72 & Goldsmith: the critical heritage, 74, Routledge, London; auth, Matt Bramble and the sulphur controversy in the eighteenth century: some medical background of Humphry Clinker, J. Hist. Ideas, 10/67; Pineapples, pregnancy, pica and peregrine pickle, In: Tobias Smollett, Oxford, 71; contrib, Studies in change and revolution: aspects of English intellectual history 1640-1800, Scolar, 72. Add: Dept. of English, University of California, Los Angeles, CA 90024.

ROVIT, EARL HERBERT, b. Boston, Mass, May 26, 27; m. 53; c. 3. ENGLISH. A.B, Univ. Mich, 50; M.A, Boston Univ, 51, Ph.D, 57. Instr. ENG, Bates Col, 53-55; Univ. Louisville, 55-57, asst. prof, 57-61, assoc. prof, 61-64; Wesleyan Univ, 64-65; CITY COL. NEW YORK, 65-74, PROF, 74- Fulbright prof. Am. stud, Univ. Freiburg, 60-61; Guggenheim fel, 65-66; Fulbright lectr, France, 68-69; assoc. prof, Univ. Paris, 69-70; fel, Sch. Lett, Ind, 69-72. U.S.A, 45-47. MLA; Am. Stud. Asn; PEN Club. American literature; American studies. Publ: Herald to chaos, Univ. Ky, 60; Ernest Hemingway, Twayne, 63; The player king, 65, A far cry, 67 & Crossings, 73, Harcourt; Saul Bellow, Univ. Minn, 67; American literature and the American experience, Am. Quart, 61. Add: Dept. of English, City College of New York, New York, NY 10031.

ROWAN, DONALD FREDERICK, b. Rochester, N.Y, Oct. 22, 25; m. 47; c. 2. ENGLISH. B.A, Univ. N.B, 50, Ph.D.(Eng), 67. B.A, Cambridge, 52, M.A, 60. Lectr. ENG, UNIV. N.B, 61-62, asst. prof, 62-67, assoc. prof, 67-69, PROF, 69- Asn. Can. Univ. Teachers Eng; MLA; Humanities Asn. Can; Malone Soc; Bibliog. Soc. Am; Renaissance Soc. Am; Shakespeare Asn. Am. Elizabethan stage directions and dramatic manuscripts; Elizabethan and Restoration theatre; continental Renaissance theatre. Publ: The swan revisited, RORD, 67; The cockpit-in-court, Elizabethan Theatre, 68; The English playhouse, Renaissance Drama IV, 72. Add: Dept. of English, University of New Brunswick, Fredericton, N.B, Can.

ROWE, HARRISON DAVIS, b. Lawrence Co, Ohio, Aug. 13, 26; m. 53; c. 4. ENGLISH, LINGUISTICS. B.A, Marshall Col, 52, M.A, 53; Dudley Beaumont fel, Univ. Fla, 55-56, South. Fel. Fund fel, 57, Ph.D.(Eng. & ling), 59. Instr. Eng, E.Carolina Col, 56-58, asst. prof, 58-61, assoc. prof, 61-63; asst. prof. ling, Wis. State Univ, Stevens Point, 63-64; West. Mich. Univ, 64-66, assoc. prof, 66-68; ENG, BALDWIN-WALLACE COL, 68-71, PROF, 71-, CHMN. DEPT, 72-, dir. summer prog. Finland, summer 72. Fulbright lectr, Finland, 61-62; summers, vis. lectr, U.S. Inform. Agency sem. Am. civlization, Helsinki, 62; vis. lectr, Asheville-Biltmore Col, 63; fac. res. fel, West. Mich. Univ, 66; vis. lectr, NDEA Inst, A&T State Univ. N.C, 68, assoc. dir, summer 69. U.S.A, 44-46, Ling. Soc. Am; MLA; Am. Dialect Soc; Int. Phonetic Asn; AAUP. American literature; 20th century American poetry; Robert Frost. Publ: Hart Crane: a bibliography, Swallow, 55; Basic elements in the criticism of Ezra Pound, Univ. Microfilms, 60; A primer of English phonology, West. Mich. Univ, 65; Materials in English for the study of the Finnish language, Baldwin-Wallace Col, 72; Emerson as quoter . . . , New Eng. Quart, 6/56; New England terms for bull . . . , Am. Speech, 5/57; plus one other. Add: Dept. of English, Baldwin-Wallace College, Berea, OH 44017.

ROWE, KAREN ELIZABETH, b. Philadelphia, Pa, July 26, 45. ENGLISH & AMERICAN LITERATURE. A.B, Mt. Holyoke, 67; M.A, Ind. Univ, 69, Woodrow Wilson fel, 70-71, Ph.D.(Eng), 71. ASST. PROF. ENG, UNIV. CALIF, LOS ANGELES, 71- Univ. Calif. Regents fac. fel, summer 72, fall 73. MLA; Renaissance Soc. Am. Sixteenth and 17th century English literature, poetry, prose and drama; Early American literature to 1800, poetry and prose; English poetry. Publ: A Biblical illumination of Taylorian art, Am. Lit, 11/68; Sacred or profane?: Edward Taylor's Meditations on Canticles, Mod. Philol, 11/74. Add: Dept. of English, University of California, 405 Hilgard Ave, Los Angeles, CA 90024.

ROWELL, CHARLES HENRY, b. Auburn, Ala, Oct. 19, 40. ENGLISH. B.S, Ala. A&M Univ, 61; M.A, Univ. Mo-Columbia, 62; Ford Found. fel, Ohio State Univ, 69-70, Ph.D.(Eng), 72. Instr. ENG, Tougaloo Col, 62-64; teaching asst, Ohio State Univ, 64-66; instr, Miss. Valley State Col, 66-67; ASSOC. PROF, SOUTH. UNIV, BATON ROUGE, 67- Lectr. Eng, Ohio State Univ, 70; Nat. Endowment for Humanities fel, 73-74; adv. ed, Obsidian Am. Folklore Soc; Col. Lang. Asn; S.Cent. Mod. Lang. Asn. Black American literature; modern English and American literature; medieval literature. Publ: A bibliography of bibliographies for the study of black American literature and folklore, Black Experience, 6/69; Checklist for building black collections, La. Libr. Asn. Bull, winter 73; The black poet in the afternoon: an interview with Alvin Aubert, Black World, 8/73; plus others. Add: Dept. of English, Southern University, Baton Rouge, LA 70813.

ROWLAND, BERYL, b. Tain, Scotland; Can. citizen; m. 48. ENGLISH LITERATURE. M.A, Univ. Alta, 58; Ph.D.(Eng), Univ. B.C, 62. Instr. ENG, Univ. B.C, 58-62, Univ. Toronto, 62-63; asst. prof, YORK UNIV, 63-67, assoc. prof, 67-71, PROF, 71- Vis. prof. Eng, Univ. Calif, Riverside, 70. Humanities Asn. Can; MLA; Mediaeval Acad. Am; Eng. Asn; Asn. Can. Univ. Teachers Eng; Melville Soc; Int. Asn. Univ. Prof. Eng. Middle English literature; women and Medieval gynecology; Herman Melville. Publ: Ed, Companion to Chaucer studies, Oxford Univ, 68; auth, Blind beasts: Chaucer's animal world, Kent State Univ, 71; Animals with human faces, Univ. Tenn, 73; ed, Chaucer and Middle English studies in honour of Rossell Hope Robbins, Allen & Unwin, 74 & Kent State Univ, 74; auth, The chess problem in The book of the Duchess, Anglia, 63; Melville's bachelors and maids: interpretation through metaphor and symbol, Am. Lit, 69; The physician's Historical thyng notable? and The man of law, Eng. Lit. Hist, 73. Add: 32 Valentine Dr, Don Mills, Ont, Can.

ROWLAND, J. CARTER, b. Lancaster, Ohio, Mar. 13, 26; m. 46; c. 4. ENGLISH. A.B, Gannon Col, 49; M.A, Pa. State Univ, 52; Ph.D.(Eng), West. Reserve Univ, 61. From instr. to prof. ENG, Gannon Col, 50-67, chmn. dept, 54-67; PROF, STATE UNIV. N.Y. COL. FREDONIA, 67-, V.PRES. ACAD. AFFAIRS, 72-, chmn. dept. Eng, 67-73. Fulbright-Hays lectr, Univ. Jordan, 65-66; dir, Am. Stud. Prog, Jordan, summer 66; Am. Philos. Soc. grant, summers 67, 68. U.S.A, 43-45, T/Sgt. MLA; NCTE (chmn, comt. bibliog, 64-69); Conf. Col. Compos. & Commun. Literary criticism; 18th century English literature; American literature after 1865. Publ: Bibliography college teaching of English, Nat. Counc. Teachers Eng, 65; Dr. Johnson's image before Hawkins, Rev. Eng. Stud, 68; The controversy over Dr. Samuel Johnson's burial, New Rambler, 1/70. Add: Dept. of English, State University of New York College at Fredonia, Fredonia, NY 14063.

ROWLAND, RICHARD (CRESWELL), b. Philadelphia, Pa, June 29, 17; m. 45; c. 4. ENGLISH. A.B, Columbia Col, 38; B.A, Oxford, 40, M.A, 43, D.Phil. (Eng), 57. Instr. ENG, Columbia Col, 40-41, 46-53; Sarah Lawrence Col, 47; asst. prof. Rollins Col, 55-57; assoc. prof. SWEET BRIAR COL, 57-62, PROF, 62- Fel. East Asian stud, Harvard, 59-60; mem. First Inst. in Chinese Civilization, Taiwan, 62. U.S.A, 41-46. MLA; Asn. Asian Stud. Drama, especially Jacobean; American literature; comparative literature, especially Chinese and Japanese. Add: Dept. of English, Sweet Briar College, Sweet Briar, VA 24595.

ROWLETTE, IRENE WILSON, b. Commerce, Tex, Jan. 10, 08; m. 28; c. 2. ENGLISH. B.S, South. State Col, 56; M.S, E.Tex. State Col, 57; Univ. Ark, 60; Ed.D.(educ. & Eng), N.Tex. State Univ, 64. Teacher, pub. schs, Ark, 51-59; Tex, 60-61; instr. ENG, HENDERSON STATE COL, 61-63, asst. prof, 63-66, assoc. prof, 66-71, PROF, 71- Selected factors associated with marks made by freshman college English students. Add: Dept. of English, Henderson State College, 1100 Henderson St, Arkadelphia, AR 71923.

ROWLETTE, ROBERT OREN, b. Maitland, Mo, July 11, 30; m. 55; c. 2. AMERICAN LITERATURE. B.A. & B.S, Northwest Mo. State Col, 52; M.A, Univ. Colo, 57; Ph.D.(Eng), Univ. Kans, 67. Teaching asst. Eng, Univ. Kans, 60-61; instr, Univ. Cincinnati, 61-64; asst. prof, BUTLER UNIV, 64-69, assoc. prof, 69-71; INDEPENDENT RES, 71- MLA; Am. Stud. Asn; AAUP. American Realism and Romanticism. Publ: Twain's Pudd'nhead Wilson: the development and design, Bowling Green Univ, 71; Twain, Sarah Grand, and The heavenly twins, winter 71-72 & Twain's barren tree in The mysterious stranger: two biblical parallels, summer 72, Mark Twain J; Mark Ward on Artemus Twain: Twain's literary debt to Ward, Am. Lit. Realism, winter 73. Add: 402 E. Sixth St, Maryville, MO 64468.

ROWLEY, T. LEONARD, b. Parowan, Utah, Feb. 22, 24; m. 49; c. 5. THEATRE ARTS, ENGLISH. A.B, Brigham Young Univ, 51, M.Ed, 55; Ph.D. (theatre), Univ. Minn, 67. Instr. Eng. & theatre, WEBER STATE COL, 55-62, assoc. prof. THEATRE, 62-67, PROF, 67-, CHMN. DEPT. THEATRE ARTS, 72- U.S.A.F, 42-45, S/Sgt. Am. Theatre Asn; Rocky Mount Theatre Conf.(pres, 66). Children's theatre; religious drama. Add: Dept. of Theatre Arts, Weber State College, 3750 Harrison Blvd, Ogden, UT 84403.

ROY, EMIL L, b. Fremont, Nebr, June 18, 33. ENGLISH. B.A, Univ. Redlands, 55; M.A, Univ. Calif, Berkeley, 56; Ph.D.(Eng), Univ. South. Calif, 61. Instr. ENG, Fullerton Jr. Col, 57-59; Cerritos Col, 60-61; Univ. South. Calif, 61-62, asst. prof, 62-64, 65-66; ASSOC. PROF, North. Ill. Univ, 66-68; Purdue Univ, West Lafayette, 68-73; Univ. P.R, Mayaguez, 73-74; PROF. & CHMN. DEPT, UNIV. TENN, MARTIN, 74- Fulbright prof, Univ. Kiel, Germany, 64-65. MLA. Publ: Co-auth, Studies in fiction, 65 & Studies in drama, 68, Harper; auth, Christopher Fry, 68 & British drama since Shaw, 72, South. Ill. Univ; Myth in Nietzsche, Windfall, 72; co-auth, Literary spectrum, Allyn & Bacon, 74; auth, World-view in Bernard Shaw, Drama Surv, winter 65; King Lear and Desire under the elms, Die Neueren Sprachen, 1/66; War and manliness in TrC, Comparative Drama, 72. Add: Dept. of English, University of Tennessee, Martin, TN 38237.

ROY, FLORA, b. Sask, Can. ENGLISH. B.A, Univ. Sask, 37, M.A, 39, Humanities Res. Counc. Can. fel, Univ. Toronto, 54-55, Ph.D.(Eng), Univ. Toronto, 60. Lectr. Eng, Univ. Toronto, 47-48; assoc. prof, Waterloo Col, Univ. West. Ont, 48-53, prof, 53-59, head dept, 48-59; PROF. ENG. & CHMN. DEPT, WILFRID LAURIER UNIV, 59- Can. Counc. grant, 62. Can. Philos. Asn; Asn. Can. Univ. Teachers Eng; Int. Asn. Univ. Prof. Eng. George Berkeley, Bishop of Cloyne; 18th century Irish and English philosophical and religious movements. Add: Dept. of English, Wilfrid Laurier University, Waterloo, Ont, Can.

ROY, GEORGE ROSS, b. Montreal, Can, Aug. 20, 24; m. 54; c. 1. ENGLISH, COMPARATIVE LITERATURE. B.A, Sir George Williams Univ, 50; M.A, Univ. Montreal, 51, Ph.D.(Eng), 59; French Govt. asst, 51-52; Dipl, Univ. Strasbourg, 54; Royal Soc. Can. fel, 56-58; D. Univ, Univ. Paris, 58. Lectr. Eng, Royal Mil. Col, St. John, 54-56; asst. prof, Univ. Ala, 58-61; Univ. Montreal, 61-62, assoc. prof, 62-63; prof, Tex. Technol. Col, 63-65; PROF. ENG. & COMP. LIT. & ED. STUD. SCOTTISH LIT, UNIV. S.C, 65- Huntington Libr. grant, 62; Can. Counc. & Am. Philos. Soc. grant, 63; mem. bd. gov. & chmn. libr. comt, Am-Scottish Found, N.Y. 66-; gen. ed, Scottish Poetry Reprints, Quarto Press, Feltham, Eng. & Dept. Eng. Bibliog. Ser, Univ. S.C. R.C.A.F, 42-46, Flying Off. MLA; Mod. Humanities Res. Asn; Int. Comp. Lit. Asn; Am. Comp. Lit. Asn; Edinburgh Bibliog. Soc; S.Atlantic Mod. Lang. Asn; Asn. Scottish Lit. Stud.(v.pres, 73-); fel. Soc. Antiq. Scotland. Comparative literature; Scottish literature; Robert Burns. Publ: Twelve modern French-Canadian poets, Ryerson, Toronto, 58; Le sentiment de la nature dans la poesie Canadienne anglaise 1867-1918, Nizet, Paris, 61; The letters of Robert Burns, Clarendon, Oxford; ed, Robert Sempill, the piper of Kilbarhan, Tragara, Edinburgh, 70; auth, French translations (and critics) of Robert Burns to 1893, 4, 7/63 & 4/64, Rev. Lit. Comp; Robert Burns,

Dept. Eng. Bibliog. Ser, Univ. S.C, 66; auth, Scottish literature section, In: New Cambridge bibliography of English literature, Cambridge, 71. Add: Dept. of English, University of South Carolina, Columbia, SC 29208.

ROYSTER, VERMONT (CONNECTICUT), b. Raleigh, N.C, Apr. 30, 14; m. 37; c. 2. JOURNALISM, POLITICAL SCIENCE. A.B, Univ. N.C, Chapel Hill, 35, hon. LL.D, 59; hon. Litt.D, Temple Univ, 64; hon. L.H.D, Elon Col, 68. Chief Washington correspondent polit. affairs, Wall Street Jour, 47-50, assoc. ed, 50-58, ed. in chief, 58-71; WILLIAM RAND KENAN PROF. JOUR. & POLIT. AFFAIRS & DIR, UNIV. PRESS, UNIV. N.C, CHAPEL HILL, 71- Mem. adv. bd, Pulitzer Prizes selection, Columbia Univ, 67-; contrib. ed. pub. affairs, Wall Street Jour, 71-; commentator radio & TV, CBS News, 72-; sr. fel, Inst. Policy Sci, Duke Univ, 73- Pulitzer Prize, 53. U.S.N, 41-46, Lt. Comdr. Am. Soc. Newspaper Ed.(pres, 65); Nat. Conf. Ed. Writers (pres, 57). American journalistic history; American political affairs since 1932. Publ: Journey through the Soviet Union, Dow Jones, 62; A pride of prejudices (essays), Knopf, 67; contrib, Main street and beyond, Doubleday, 59; plus numerous arts. in Am. Scholar, Columbia Jour. Quart, Quill, N.C. Law Rev, Reader's Dig. & Sat. Evening Post. Add: Howell Hall, School of Journalism, University of North Carolina at Chapel Hill, Chapel Hill, NC 27514.

RUANE, DARBY T, b. New York, N.Y, Mar. 31, 21. ENGLISH LITERATURE. B.S.Ed, Fordham Univ, 45, M.A, 54; Ph.D.(Eng. lit), St. John's Univ, 59. Teacher Eng. & hist, Cardinal Farley Mil. Acad, 45-50; Cardinal Hayes High Sch, 50-52; prin, St. Cecilia's Sch, 52-55; instr. ENG, IONA COL, 55-57, asst. prof, 57-59, assoc. prof, 59-71, PROF, 71- EXEC. DIR. INST. PERFORMING ARTS, 65- Cath. Renascence Soc; Col. Eng. Asn; NCTE; MLA. Walpole and 18th century drama; study of Byron's vision of judgment; romantic poets, especially Keats and Shelley. Publ: The Christian Brothers of Ireland, In: Encyclopaedia Britannica & Colliers encyclopedia, Collier-Macmillan. Add: Dept. of English, Iona College, New Rochelle, NY 10801.

RUBEL, WARREN G, b. Milwaukee, Wis, Sept. 26, 27; m. 50; c. 4. ENGLISH. B.A, Concordia Sem, 50, M.Div, 52; M.A, Wash. Univ, 61; Ph.D. (Am. lit), Univ. Ark, 64. Instr. Eng, St. Paul's Col.(Mo), 52-55; assoc. prof, Concordia Col.(Ind), 59-67, prof, 67-69; PROF. HUMANITIES, CHRIST COL, VALPARAISO UNIV, 69- Concordia Sem. grant & dir. cult. stud, 67-68. MLA; Conf. Christianity & Lit. Interpretation in the humanities; interdisciplinary concepts in the humanities; American literature. Publ: The gospel, the pastor, and culture, Concordia Theol. Monthly, 7-8/69; The American dream: antique at noon, The Cresset, 2/70; Voices of change: the arts and divine providence, In: The caring God, Concordia, 73. Add: Dept. of Humanities, Box 189, Valparaiso University, Valparaiso, IN 46383.

RUBEN, BRENT DAVID, b. Cedar Rapids, Iowa, Oct. 17, 44; m. 67; c. 1. COMMUNICATION. B.A, Univ. Iowa, 66, M.A, 68, Nat. Asn. Broadcasters grant, 69-70, Ph.D.(commun), 70. Assoc, Inst. Commun. Stud, Univ. Iowa, 68-69, instr. commun, Sch. Jour, 69-70, asst. prof, 70-71; ASST. PROF. COMMUN. & DIR. INST. COMMUN. STUD, RUTGERS UNIV, NEW BRUNSWICK, 71-, Grad. Col. res. grant, 73-74. Consult, Nat. Asn. TV & Radio Announcers, 69-; Agency Int. Develop, 69-; Iowa City Pub. Schs, 70-71; Franklin Twp. Pub. Schs, 71-; nat. planning comt, Nat. Gaming Counc, 71-, mem. counc; consult, New York Times; contrib. ed, Commun, 71-; assoc. ed, Newstatements, 71-; mem. bd. dirs, Newstatements, Commun. & Develop. Consult, 72- Soc. Gen. Systs. Res; Int. Commun. Asn; AAAS; Inst. Gen. Semantics. Publ: Co-auth, Intermedia, Univ. Assocs, 71; co-ed, Approaches to human communication, Spartan, 72; co-ed, Human communication and general system theory, 73 & co-auth, Human communication: games and simulations, 73, Hayden; auth, Interact, Mercer House, 73; plus others. Add: Institute for Communication Studies, Rutgers University, New Brunswick, NJ 08903.

RUBENSTEIN, JILL, b. Pittsburgh, Pa, May 14, 43. ENGLISH LITERATURE. A.B, Univ. Rochester, 65; M.A.T, Harvard, 66; M.A, Johns Hopkins Univ, 68, Ph.D.(Eng), 69. ASST. PROF. ENG, Ill. State Univ, 69-72; UNIV. CINCINNATI, 72- MLA. English Romantic literature; English novel; works of Sir Walter Scott. Publ: The defeat and triumph of bourgeois pacifism, Wordsworth Circle, autumn 71; Sound and silence in Coleridge's conversation poems, English, summer 72; The dilemma of history; a reading of Scott's Bridal of Triermain, Stud. Eng. Lit, autumn 72. Add: Dept. of English, University of Cincinnati, Cincinnati, OH 45221.

RUBIN, GARY NEIL, b. Baltimore, Md, Aug. 23, 47; m. 70. COMMUNICATION THEORY, CLASSICAL RHETORIC. B.S, Towson State Col, 69; M.A, Bowling Green State Univ, 70, Ph.D.(Eng), 72. ASST. PROF. SPEECH, OLD DOM. UNIV, 72- Speech Commun. Asn; Int. Commun. Asn. Proxemics; naturalistic experimentation; curriculum changes in basic speech courses. Publ: Projects for speech content analysis, Kendall/Hunt. Add: Apt. 203, 789 Hampshire Lane, Virginia Beach, VA 23462.

RUBIN, JOSEPH JAY, b. Philadelphia, Pa, July 20, 12. AMERICAN LITERATURE. A.B. & A.M, Pa. State Col, 33; Ph.D, Yale, 40. PROF. AM. LIT, PA. STATE UNIV, UNIVERSITY PARK, 51- Pub. & ed, Bald Eagle Press, State College, Pa. Am. Stud. Asn; MLA. Publ: Ed, Monument Edition of major novels of J.W. De Forest, Bald Eagle. Add: Dept. of English, Pennsylvania State University, University Park, PA 16802.

RUBIN, LARRY JEROME, b. Bayonne, N.J, Feb. 14, 30. LITERATURE. B.A, Emory Univ, 51, scholar, 51-52, M.A, 52, fels, 52-54, Ph.D, 56. Asst, Emory Univ, 54-55; instr. ENG, GA. INST. TECHNOL, 56-58, asst. prof, 58-65, assoc. prof, 65-73, PROF, 73- Smith-Mundt vis. prof. Am. lit, Jagiellonian Univ, 61-62; Fulbright lectr, Univ. Bergen, 66-67, Free Univ. W. Berlin, 69-70 & Univ. Innsbruck, 71-72. Lit. Achievement Award, Ga. Writers Asn, 63; Sidney Lanier Award, Oglethorpe Univ, 64; John Holmes Mem. Award, Poetry Soc. N.H, 65; Star Poetry Award, Kansas City Star, 69. S.Atlantic Mod. Lang. Asn; Poetry Soc. Am.(Reynolds Lyric Award, 61, Annual Award, 73). Modern American fiction. Publ: The world's old way, Univ. Nebr, 62; Lanced in light, Harcourt, 67; River imagery as a means of foreshadowing in The mill on the floss, Mod. Lang. Notes, 1/56; contrib, Thomas Wolfe and the Lost paradise, In: The Merrill studies in Look homeward, Angel, C.E. Merrill, 70 & Aspects of Naturalism in The house of mirth, In: The American novel, Free Press, 72; plus others. Add: Dept. of English, Georgia Institute of Technology, Atlanta, GA 30332.

RUBIN, LOUIS D, JR, b. Charleston, S.C, Nov. 19, 23; m. 51; c. 2. ENGLISH, AMERICAN LITERATURE. B.A, Univ. Richmond, 46, hon. Litt.D, 72; M.A, Johns Hopkins Univ, 49, Ph.D, 54. Instr. Eng. writing, Johns Hopkins Univ, 49-54; asst. prof. Am. civilization, Univ. Pa, 54-55; assoc. ed, Richmond News Leader, Va, 56-57; assoc. prof. ENG, Hollins Col, 57-60; prof, 60-67; UNIV. N.C, CHAPEL HILL, 67-73, UNIV. DISTINGUISHED PROF, 73- Sewanee Rev. fel, 53; Guggenheim fel, 57; vis. prof. hist, La. State Univ, summer 57; Fulbright lectr, Univ. Aix-Marseille & Am. Inst, Nice, France, 60; lectr, Bread Loaf Writers' Conf, 61; Am. Counc. Learned Soc. fel, 64-65; vis. prof, Univ. Calif, Santa Barbara, summer 66; gen. ed. South. Lit. Stud. Ser, La. State Univ, 64-72; vis. prof, Harvard, summer 69; Lamar lectr, Mercer Univ, 71. U.S.A, 43-46, Sgt. MLA (chmn. Am. Lit. Group, 74); South. Hist. Asn; S.Atlantic Mod. Lang. Asn; Am. Stud. Asn.(exec. secy, 54-55; v.pres, 60-61); Soc. Stud. South. Lit.(secy-treas, 68-72, v.pres, 72-73). Southern literature; American literature; the novel. Publ: Thomas Wolfe: the weather of his youth, 55, The curious death of the novel & other essays, 67 & ed, A bibliographical guide of the study of Southern literature, 69, La. State Univ; auth, The golden weather, Atheneum, 61; The faraway country: writers of the modern South, 63 & The teller in the tale, 67, Univ. Wash; George W. Cable; The life and times of a Southern Heretic, Pegasus, 69; The writer in the South, Univ. Ga, 72; ed, The comic imagination in American literature, Rutgers Univ, 73 & Thomas Wolfe: a collection of critical essays, Prentice-Hall, 73; plus others. Add: Dept. of English, University of North Carolina at Chapel Hill, Chapel Hill, NC 27514.

RUBIN, STEVEN H, b. New York, N.Y, July 16, 33; m. 56; c. 2. ENGLISH. B.A, Carleton Col, 55; M.A, N.Y. Univ, 60; Tulane Univ, 60-62. Instr. ENG, Univ. Del, 58-60; La. State Univ, New Orleans, 63-67, spec. lectr, 67-68; ASSOC. PROF, STATE UNIV. N.Y. COL. ONEONTA, 68- U.S.A, 55-57. MLA; NCTE; Radio-TV News Dir. Asn. American literature and civil rights; journalism. Publ: William Wycherley, the country wife, Chandler, 61. Add: Dept. of English, State University of New York College at Oneonta, Oneonta, NY 13820.

RUBIN, STEVEN JOEL, b. New York, N.Y, Feb. 2, 43. COMPARATIVE LITERATURE. B.A, Univ. R.I, 64; M.A, Univ. Mich, Ann Arbor, 65, fel, 65-69, Ph.D.(comp. lit), 69. From asst. prof. to ASSOC. PROF. ENG, UNIV. S.FLA, TAMPA, 69-, fac. develop. grant, 71-73. Vis. prof. comp. lit, Inst. Am. Univs. Aix-en-Provence, France, 72-73. MLA (chmn. Am. lit. abroad sect, 73-74); S.Atlantic Mod. Lang. Asn; Am. Comp. Lit. Asn. Twentieth century comparative literature; African literatures; Jewish literature. Publ: Camara Laye: commitment to timeless values, Africa Report, 5/72; Mali: new writing from an ancient civilization, Stud. Black Lit, autumn 73; contrib, Counter currents: an introduction to current literature, Kendall Hunt, 73. Add: Dept. of English, University of South Florida, Tampa, FL 33620.

RUBINSTEIN, ELLIOT L, b. Brooklyn, N.Y, Jan. 20, 36. ENGLISH. A.B, Rutgers Univ, 56; Woodrow Wilson fel, Columbia Univ, 56-57, M.A, 57, univ. fel, 60-61, Ph.D.(Eng), 64. Instr. ENG, Rutgers Univ, 61-64, asst. prof, 64-68; RICHMOND COL.(N.Y), 68-71, ASSOC. PROF, 71- MLA. English novel; Shakespeare; cinema studies. Publ: Ed, Twentieth century interpretations of Pride and prejudice, Prentice-Hall, 69; auth, Filmguide to The general, Ind. Univ, 73; Jane Austen's novels: the metaphor of rank, In: Literary monographs II, Univ. Wis, 68; Northanger Abbey: the Elder Morelands and John Homespun, Papers Lang. & Lit, fall 69; I Henry IV: the language of liability, Stud. Eng. Lit, spring 70; plus others. Add: Division of Humanities, Richmond College, 130 Stuyvesant Place, Staten Island, NY 10301.

RUBINSTEIN, SAMUEL LEONARD, b. Salem, N.J, May 20, 22; m. 51; c. 3. ENGLISH. Litt.B, Rutgers Univ, 49; M.F.A, State Univ, Iowa, 51. Asst. prof. Eng, humanities & fiction principles, PA. STATE UNIV, 52-60, assoc. prof, 60-66, PROF. ENG, 66- Edgar Allen Poe Special Award, Mystery Writers Am, 65; Christian R. & Mary F. Lindback Distinguished Teaching Award, Pa. State Univ, 66. U.S.A, 43-46. Fiction writing; contemporary American and European literature. Publ: The battle done, Morrow, 54, Arco, London, 56, Popular Libr, 56, 60; co-auth, The gravemaker's house, Harper, 64, Frameworks of exposition, Holt, 65, The brief essay (anthology), 66 & The plain rhetoric, 2nd ed, 68, Allyn & Bacon; auth, Writing; a habit of mind, Brown, 72; Deeply falls the word, New Directions, 2/53, 3/65; Composition: a collision with literature, Col. Eng, 1/66 & In: Teaching freshman composition, Oxford, 67; From need to desire, Col. Eng, 11/67. Add: 1861 N. Oak Lane, State College, PA 16801.

RUBINSTEIN, WILLIAM C, b. Brooklyn, N.Y, June 29, 20; m. 40; c. 3. ENGLISH. B.A, City Col. New York, 40; M.A, N.Y. Univ, 47; Ph.D.(Eng), Yale, 50. Instr. Eng, Brooklyn Col. & Brooklyn Polytech. Inst, 47-49; Univ. Wis, 49-53; from v.pres. to pres, Int. Telemeter Corp, 53-68; asst. prof. ENG, San Fernando Valley State Col, 58-59; assoc. prof, CALIF. STATE UNIV, FULLERTON, 66-70, PROF, 70- MLA. Shakespearean bibliography; modern fiction. Publ: Franz Kafka: a hunger artist, 1/52 & Kafka's Jackals and Arabs, spring 67, Monatshefte; Franz Kafka's A report to an academy, Mod. Lang. Quart, 12/52. Add: 1825 Avenida San Lorenzo, Fullerton, CA 92633.

RUBIO, GERALD JOHN, b. Brooklyn, N.Y, Mar. 6, 32; m. 63; c. 2. ENGLISH LITERATURE. B.A, Queens Col.(N.Y), 59; M.A, Univ. Wis-Madison, 63; Ph.D.(Eng), Univ. Ill, Urbana, 71. Instr. ENG, Univ. Wis-Madison, 62-63; Univ. Ill, Urbana, 63-67; ASST. PROF, UNIV. GUELPH, 67- U.S.N, 54-58, MLA; Northeast. Mod. Lang. Asn; Renaissance Soc. Am; Asn. Can. Univ. Teachers Eng; Renaissance & Reformation Soc. King Richard III of England; Renaissance literature; Shakespeare and Renaissance drama. Publ: Co-auth, How your teachers grade your themes, 66 & Illinois authors, 66, Ill. Asn. Teachers Eng. Add: Dept. of English, University of Guelph, Guelph, Ont. N1G 2W1, Can.

RUCH, VELMA NAOMI, b. Lamoni, Iowa, Feb. 28, 21. ENGLISH. B.A, Univ. Iowa, 43; M.A, Univ. Mich, 47; Torger Thompson fel, Univ. Wis, 55-56,

Ph.D.(Eng), 57. Teacher ENG, high sch, Iowa, 43-45; GRACELAND COL, 46-63, PROF, 63-, CHMN. DIV. LANG. & LIT, 65- Fulbright-Hays fel, Inst. Indian Stud, summer 65. MLA; NCTE. English and Norwegian literature; non-western studies. Add: Dept. of English, Graceland College, Lamoni, IA 50140.

RUCKER, BRYCE WILSON, b. Chelyan, W.Va, Oct. 16, 21; m. 44; c. 2. JOURNALISM. A.B, Univ. Ky, 47; M.S, Univ. Wis-Madison, 49; Ph.D.(jour), Univ. Mo-Columbia, 59. Asst. prof. JOUR, Univ. Tex, Austin, 49-50; Southwest Tex. State Col, 50-56; instr, Univ. Mo-Columbia, 58-59, asst. prof, 59-62, assoc. prof, 62-63; SOUTH. ILL. UNIV, CARBONDALE, 63-67, PROF, 67-, DIR. SCH. JOUR, 72-, res. dir, 63-69. U.S.A, 42-46. Asn. Educ. in Jour. Impact of consonance and dissonance on media imagery; monopoly, chain, cross-media, industrial and special interest ownership of mass media; attitudes toward the mass media. Publ: Co-auth, Modern journalism, Pitman, 62; auth, Twentieth century reporting at its best, Iowa State Univ, 64; The first freedom, South. Ill. Univ, 68; News services' crowd reporting in 1956 Presidential campaign, spring 60 & What solutions do people endorse in free press-fair trial dilemma? spring 67, Jour. Quart; Research, graduate study in journalism, Jour. Educ, summer 65. Add: 1009 Emerald Lane, Carbondale, IL 62901.

RUDE, LESLIE G, b. Montevideo, Minn, July 17, 31; m. 54; c. 2. SPEECH. B.A, Luther Col, 52; M.A, La. State Univ, 53; Ph.D, Univ. Ill, 62. Instr. speech & mgr, KWLC, Luther Col, 53-56; asst. prof. speech, Ind. State Col, 58-60, assoc. prof. speech & head dept, Luther Col, 60-65; assoc. prof. Eng, HARTWICK COL, 65-73, V.PRES. EDUC. AFFAIRS & DEAN COL, 71-, asst. dean fac, 65-67, acting dean, 67-68, dean, 68-71. Vis. prof, Appalachian State Teachers Col, 57 & 58. Speech Commun. Asn; Am. Conf. Acad. Deans; Am. Asn. Higher Educ; AAUP; East. Asn. Deans. Public address and rhetoric; political science. Publ: Hartwick College uses three-three-plus calendar, Col. & Univ. Bus, 10/69; The rhetoric of farmer-labor agitators, Cent. States Speech J, winter 69. Add: Office of the Dean, Hartwick College, Oneonta, NY 13820.

RUDENSTINE, NEIL LEON, b. Ossining, N.Y, Jan. 21, 35; m. 60; c. 3. ENGLISH. B.A, Princeton, 56; A.B, Oxford, 59, A.M, 63; Ph.D.(Eng), Harvard, 64. Instr. Eng, Harvard, 64-66, asst. prof, 66-68; assoc. prof. Eng, PRINCETON, 68-73, PROF. ENG. LIT, 73-, DEAN COL, 72-, dean stud, 68-72. U.S.A, 59-60, 1st Lt. MLA; Eng. Inst. Renaissance literature. Publ: Sidney's poetic development, Harvard, 67; co-ed, English poetic satire: Wyatt to Byron, Holt, 72; auth, Sidney's Energia, In: Elizabethan poetry, Oxford, 67. Add: Dept. of English, Princeton University, Princeton, NJ 08541.

RUDIN, SEYMOUR, b. New York, N.Y, June 10, 22. ENGLISH. B.A, City Col. New York, 41, M.S, 43; Ph.D.(Eng), Cornell Univ, 53. Instr. ENG, Assoc. Cols. Upper N.Y, 46-50; Cornell Univ, 51-54; UNIV. MASS, AMHERST, 54-56, asst. prof, 56-59, 60-65, assoc. prof, 65-72, PROF, 72- Lectr. speech, City Col. New York, 60; vis. asst. prof. Eng, Cornell Univ, 65. MLA. Dramatic literature and criticism; film and theatre; dance. Publ: Playwright to critic: O'Casey and Nathan, In: Irish Renaissance, Dolmen, Ireland, 65; Moliere and The misanthrope, In: Masterpieces of western literature, W.C. Brown, 66; Theatre chronicles, Mass. Rev, 69-72. Add: Dept. of English, University of Massachusetts, Amherst, MA 01002.

RUDINGER, JOEL DOUGLAS, b. Cleveland, Ohio, Dec. 12, 38; m. 64; c. 2. CREATIVE WRITING, AMERICAN LITERATURE. B.S, Bowling Green State Univ, 60, Ph.D.(Am. lit), 71; M.A, Univ. Alaska, 64; M.F.A, Univ. Iowa, 66. Teaching asst. ENG, Univ. Alaska, 60-61; instr, Univ. Ind, 66; teaching fel, Bowling Green State Univ, 66-67; instr. BOWLING GREEN STATE UNIV, FIRELANDS, 67-72, ASST. PROF, 72-, CHMN. DIV. COMMUN, 74- Ed, Jour. Ohio Folklore Soc, 67-68; Firelands Arts Rev, 72- Int. Popular Cult. Asn; Am. Folklore Soc. Folklore, local legend in oral tradition; 19th century American journals; transcendental meditation and the American Romantics. Publ: Martha Johnson: a study in the changing of traditions, J. Ohio Folklore Soc, 67; The Chinese Kite, Inkstone, 68; Union John, Mixer Mag, 72; plus one other. Add: Dept. of English, Bowling Green State University, Firelands Campus, Huron, OH 44839.

RUDISILL, AMANDA SUE, b. Hanover, Pa, June 26, 42. THEATRE. B.S, Millersville State Col, 64; M.A, Pa. State Univ, 66; Ph.D.(theatre), Northwest. Univ, 72. Asst. stage lighting, Northeast. Univ, 66-69; asst. prof. DRAMA, CALIF. STATE COL, SAN BERNARDINO, 69-73, ASSOC. PROF, 73- U.S. Inst. Theatre Technol; Soc. Theatre Res, Eng; Am. Theatre Asn; Children's Theatre Asn; Am. Nat. Theatre Asn. Creative dramatics, development for secondary school; oral interpretation, techniques for teaching; resident repertory theatre, possible national theatre forerunner. Publ: Co-auth, The enigma of the Master Betty mania, J. Popular Cult, (in press). Add: Dept. of Drama, School of Humanities, California State College, San Bernardino, 5500 State College Pkwy, San Bernardino, CA 92407.

RUDMAN, HARRY WILLIAM, b. New York, N.Y, July 22, 08; m. 47; c. 3. ENGLISH LITERATURE. A.B, City Col. New York, 28; A.M, Columbia Univ, 30, fel, 34-35, Ph.D, 40. Tutor ENG, City Col. New York, 30-34, instr, 35-47, asst. prof, 48-55, assoc. prof, 55-63, PROF, 63-68; BARUCH COL, CITY UNIV. NEW YORK, 68- U.S.A.A.F, 42-46, Maj. MLA;NEA. Romantic and Victorian literature; British history in the 19th century; the world of George Bernard Shaw. Publ: Italian nationalism and English letters, Allen & Unwin, London; co-ed, Business letter writing made simple, Doubleday; co-auth, A contemporary reader, Ronald, 61. Add: Dept. of English, Baruch College, City University of New York, 17 Lexington Ave, New York, NY 10010.

RUDNICK, HANS H, b. Belgard, Ger, Nov. 1, 35; m. 62; c. 3. CRITICISM, AESTHETICS. B.A, Kaiser-Karl-Schule, 57; Ph.D.(Am. lit. criticism), Univ. Freiburg, 66. Lectr. Ger, Univ. Pa, 62-63; instr. South. Methodist Univ, 63-64; asst. prof. Eng, SOUTH. ILL. UNIV, CARBONDALE, 66-73, ASSOC. PROF. ENG. & COMP. LIT, 73- MLA; Am. Comp. Lit. Asn. Sociology of literature; aesthetics; literary evaluation. Publ: Transl, Two Planets, South. Ill. Univ, 71; ed, Critical commentary of Hamlet, Reclam, Stuttgart, 72; auth, Zur Wertontologie des literarischen Kunstwerkes, Proc. XIVth Int. Philos. Congr, 68. Add: Dept. of English, Southern Illinois University, Carbondale, IL 62901.

RUDOLPH, CATHERINE, O.S.F, b. Cincinnati, Ohio, Aug. 3, 18. ENGLISH, CHILDREN'S LITERATURE. B.S, Marian Col.(Ind), 46; M.S, Butler Univ, 54. Critic teacher gen. elem, Marian Col.(Ind), 46-63, instr, 54-58; critic teacher, UNIV. DAYTON, 64-66, ASST. PROF. CHILDREN'S LIT, 66- Feature ed, Elem. Eng, NCTE, 72-; contrib. ed, Prim-Aid, 72- NCTE; Nat. Cath. Educ. Asn; Cath. Libr. Asn; Asn. Educ. Commun. & Technol; Cath. AV Educ. Asn. Publ: Illusr, Marilyn Brokamp's Tippy Toe and Taffy, McKnight, 66; auth, Trends in children's literature, Today's Cath. Teacher, 70; Creativity in the parochial schools, In: New issues and trends in education, Univ. Dayton; plus 56 arts. in, Sch. Arts, Progressive Teacher, Cath. Sch. J, Elem. Teacher's Ideas & Materials Workshop. Add: St. Anthony Convent, 830 Bowen St, Dayton, OH 45410.

RUDOLPH, EARLE LEIGHTON, b. Gurdon, Ark, Oct. 26, 17. ENGLISH. A.B, Univ. Ark, 38; A.M, Harvard, 40, Ph.D, 47. Asst, Rice Univ, 41-44; teaching fel, Harvard, 45-46; instr. Eng. & hist, Mass. Inst. Technol, 46-47; asst. prof. ENG, UNIV. ARK, FAYETTEVILLE, 47-48, assoc. prof, 48-55, PROF, 55- NCTE; MLA; S.Cent. Mod. Lang. Asn. American literature and humorists. Add: Dept. of English, University of Arkansas, Fayetteville, AR 72701.

RUDOLPH, ERWIN P, b. Keyesport, Ill, Apr. 30, 16; m. 38; c. 2. ENGLISH. A.B, Greenville Col, 38; M.A, Ohio State Univ, 44; Ph.D, Univ. Ill, 62. Instr. ENG, Greenville Col, 48-49; WHEATON COL.(ILL), 50-55, asst. prof, 55-60, assoc. prof, 60-66, PROF, 66-, chmn. div. lang. & lit, 66-73. Col. Eng. Asn; Conf. Christianity & Lit. Religious thought of William Law; Middle English literature and eighteenth century. Publ: Goodby, my son, Zondervan, 71; Masterworks of devotion, Eternity, 8/72-6/73. Add: 1963 Brentwood Lane E, Wheaton, IL 60187.

RUDOLPH, LEORA CALKINS, b. Shawano, Wis, Aug. 31, 08; m. 37, 58; c. 1. ENGLISH. A.B, Lawrence Col, 30; Univ. Wis; Yale, 30-31; A.M, Univ. Chicago, 35. Instr, Cornell Col, 33-35; teacher, sr. high sch, Wis, 35-37; teacher & head dept, 43-46; langs, Wayland Acad. & Jr. Col, 45-47; assoc. prof. Eng, Cent. Col.(Iowa), 47-58; instr. Eng. & comp. Am. lit, Univ. Wis-Green Bay, 58-66, asst. prof, 66-72; RETIRED. NCTE. English Renaissance literature; Spenser; Callidore. Publ: Hawthorne and American literary independence, Nat. Daughters of American Revolution Mag, 1/72; Courtesy: Elizabethan style, J. Wis. Counc. Teachers Eng, 73. Add: 703 Glenwood Ave, DePere, WI 54115.

RUDOLPH, ROBERT SAMUEL, b. Philadelphia, Pa, Oct. 5, 37; m. 60; c. 1. ENGLISH. B.A, Temple Univ, 59; M.A, Univ. Wis, 61, Ph.D.(Eng), 66. Asst. prof. Eng, UNIV. TOLEDO, 65-69, ASSOC. PROF. ENG. LANG. & LIT, 69- MLA; NCTE. Diachronic linguistics; Medieval English literature. Add: Dept. of English, University of Toledo, Toledo, OH 43606.

RUDOLPH, VALERIE CHRISTINE, b. St. Louis, Mo. ENGLISH LITERATURE, DRAMA. A.B, Wash. Univ. 62; M.A, Univ. Iowa, 63, Ph.D.(Eng), 71. Instr. ENG, PURDUE UNIV, W.LAFAYETTE, 68-71, ASST. PROF, 71- William Andrew Clark Libr. fel, summer 72. MLA; Am. Soc. 18th Century Stud. Eighteenth century British literature; drama; Fielding. Publ: Hurlothrumbo: sense and nonsense, Restoration & Eighteenth Century Theatre Res, 5/73; Whitman's mashed fireman revisited, J. Gen. Educ, 7/73. Add: Dept. of English, Purdue University, West Lafayette, IN 47907.

RUDRUM, ALAN WILLIAM, b. Great Yarmouth, Eng, Nov. 30, 32; div; c. 3. ENGLISH. B.A, Univ. London, 54; cert. educ, Cambridge, 55; Ph.D.(Eng), Univ. Nottingham, 61. Lectr. ENG, Univ. Adelaide, 58-64; Queen's Univ. (Belfast), 64-66; vis. asst. prof, Univ. Calif, Los Angeles, 66-67, asst. prof, Davis, 67-68; PROF, Kent State Univ, 68-69; SIMON FRASER UNIV, 69- Huntington Libr. grant, summer 68; Am. Philos. Soc. grant, 68; Can. Counc. res. grant, 71-72. Henry and Thomas Vaughan; Milton. Publ: Co-auth, Poems of Johnson & Goldsmith, E. Arnold, 65; auth, Critical commentary on Paradise lost, 66, Critical commentary on Comus . . . , 67, Modern judgements on Milton, 68 & A critical commentary on Samson Agonistes, 69, Macmillan, London; Henry Vaughan's The book, AUMLA, 61; Henry Vaughan and the theme of transfiguration, 63 & Coleridge's This lime-tree Bower my prison, 64, South. Rev, Adelaide; plus others. Add: Dept. of English, Simon Fraser University, Burnaby 2, B.C, Can.

RUDY, JOHN GEORGE, b. Kingston, N.Y, Sept. 21, 43; m. 69. ENGLISH & AMERICAN LITERATURE. B.A, State Univ. N.Y. Col. New Paltz, 66; M.A, Pa. State Univ, 68, Ph.D.(Eng), 71. ASST. PROF. ENG, IND. UNIV. KOKOMO, 71- MLA. Wordsworth studies; 19th century British and American literature. Add: Dept. of English, Indiana University at Kokomo, 2300 S. Washington St, Kokomo, IN 46901.

RUECHELLE, RANDALL C, b. Kalispell, Mont, Dec. 28, 20; m. 54; c. 2. SPEECH, RHETORIC. B.A, Univ. Chicago, 42, M.A, 44; Ph.D, Univ. South. Calif, 53. Assoc. prof. speech & chmn. dept, Colo. State Univ, 53-64; PROF. SPEECH & CHMN. DEPT. COMMUN. ARTS & SCI, CALIF. STATE COL, STANISLAUS, 64- Instr, Peace Corps Training Prog, summer 61. Speech Commun. Asn; Nat. Soc. Stud. Commun. Publ: Co-auth, Speaking and listening, W.C. Brown, 62 & Beginning speech, 64 & Workbook for beginning speech, 64, Allyn & Bacon. Add: Dept. of Communication Arts & Sciences, California State College, Stanislaus, Turlock, CA 95380.

RUECKERT, WILLIAM HOWE, b. Cleveland, Ohio, Nov. 4, 26; m. 54; c. 4. ENGLISH. B.A, Williams Col, 50; M.A, Univ. Mich, 51, Ph.D.(Eng), 56. Instr. ENG, Russell Sage Col, 54-56; Oberlin Col, 56-57; Univ. Ill, 57-60, asst. prof, 60-63, assoc. prof, 64-65; UNIV. ROCHESTER, 65-66, PROF, 67- U.S.N, 45-46. MLA. Literary criticism; modern British and American literature; literature and the self. Publ: Kenneth Burke and the drama of human relations, 63 & Critical responses to Kenneth Burke, 1924-1966, 69, Univ. Minn; Glenway Wescott, Twayne, 65. Add: Dept. of English, University of Rochester, Rochester, NY 14627.

RUFF, JAMES LYNN, b. Austin, Tex, Jan. 2, 39; m. 60; c. 1. ROMANTIC POETS, EIGHTEENTH CENTURY POETRY. B.A, Carleton Col, 60; M.A, Northwest. Univ, 61, Ph.D.(Eng), 68. Instr. ENG, Nat. Col. Educ, 64-66; asst. prof, Univ. N.Mex, 66-72; ASSOC. PROF, MADISON COL, 72- MLA. Critical study of Shelley's The revolt of Islam. Add: Dept. of English, Madison College, Harrisonburg, VA 22801.

RUFF, WILLIAM, b. Bluefield, W.Va, Mar. 30, 05. ENGLISH LITERATURE. A.B, Yale, 27, Ph.D, 30. Instr. ENG, Yale, 30-37, asst. prof, 37-42; assoc. prof, UNIV. FLA, 46-55, prof, 55-70, EMER. PROF, 70- U.S.A, 42-46. MLA. Literature of the 19th century; Scott, Dickens and Bernard Shaw. Publ: A bibliography of the poetical works of Sir Walter Scott, 1796-1832; co-auth, Humanities in contemporary life, Holt, 60; Scott bicentenary essays, Scottish Acad. Press, 73. Add: 903 N.E. Boulevard, Gainesville, FL 32601.

RUFFO-FIORE, SILVIA, b. Pittsburgh, Pa, Sept. 4, 39; m. 69. ENGLISH, COMPARATIVE LITERATURE. B.Ed, Duquesne Univ, 61, M.A, 63; Andrew Mellon fels, Univ. Pittsburgh, 65-66, 68-69, univ. fel, 67-68, Ph.D.(Eng), 70; Fulbright fel, Univ. Rome, 66-67. Asst. ENG, Duquesne Univ, 61-63; teacher, Fox Chapel High Sch, 63-65; Pittsburgh Acad, summers 65, 66; asst. prof, UNIV. S.FLA, 69-74, ASSOC. PROF, 74- MLA; S.Atlantic Mod. Lang. Asn; Dante Soc. Am; Renaissance Soc. Am; AAUP; Am. Asn. Univ. Women. John Donne; Petrarch and the Petrarchan tradition; Machiavelli. Publ: The unwanted heart in Petrarch and Donne, Comp. Lit, fall 72; Donne's Parody of the Petrarchan lady, Comp. Lit. Stud, 12/72; A new light on the suns and lovers in Petrarch and Donne, Forum Italicum, 74. Add: 506 Carriage Hills Dr, Tampa, FL 33617.

RUGGIERS, PAUL GEORGE, b. Paterson, N.J, Apr. 29, 18; m. 48; c. 1. ENGLISH. A.B, Washington & Jefferson Col, 40; Ph.D, Cornell Univ, 47. Asst. prof. ENG, UNIV. OKLA, 47-57, prof, 57-64, David Ross Boyd Prof, 64-72, GEORGE LYNN CROSS RES. PROF, 72-, dir. honors prog, 63-69. Ford fel, 53-54; Guggenheim fel, 56-57; Fulbright res. fel, Italy, 61-62; gen. ed, A variorum ed. of the works of Geoffrey Chaucer. Mil.Intel, U.S.A, 40-43. MLA; Mediaeval Acad. Am; S.Cent. Mod. Lang. Asn. Mediaeval literature; Middle English; mediaeval literature of the continent. Publ: Life of Dante, Univ. Calif, 54; Modern American reader, Am. Bk. Co, 58; Cultural leadership in the Great Plains, 56 & Florence in the time of Dante, 64, Univ. Okla. The art of the Canterbury tales, Univ. Wis, 65; co-auth, Bachelor of liberal studies: development of a curriculum at the University of Oklahoma, Ctr. Stud. Lib. Educ. Adults, 66; A theory of tragedy in Chaucer, Chaucer Rev, 73-74; Review of Sheila Delany, Chaucer's House of fame, Speculum, 73-74; plus others. Add: 760 Van Vleet Oval, Norman, OK 73069.

RUGOFF, MILTON, b. New York, N.Y, Mar. 6, 13; m. 37; c. 1. ENGLISH, HISTORY. B.A, Columbia Col, 33; M.A, Columbia Univ, 34, Ph.D, 40. ED, Alfred A. Knopf, Inc, 43-47; CHANTICLEER PRESS, INC, NEW YORK, 48- Am. Folklore Soc; Hakluyt Soc. Elizabethan literature; American biography; history of travel and exploration. Publ: A harvest of world folk tales, Viking, 49; The great travelers, S. and S, 61; Donne's imagery, Atheneum, rev. ed, 62; Prudery and passion: sexuality in Victorian America, Putnam, 71; ed, Britannica encyclopedia of American art, Simon, 73. Add: 18 Ox Ridge Rd, Elmsford, NY 10523.

RUHE, EDWARD LEHMAN, b. Allentown, Pa, Apr. 4, 23. ENGLISH. B.A, Swarthmore Col, 48; M.A, Columbia Univ, 51, Ph.D, 59; Fulbright fel, Univ. London, 52-53, Instr. ENG, W.Va. Univ, 51-52; Rutgers Univ, 53-54; Cornell Univ, 54-58; UNIV. KANS, 58-59, asst. prof, 59-62, assoc. prof, 62-68, PROF, 68- Elizabeth M. Watkins summer fac. scholar, Univ. Kans, 60; Fulbright vis. lectr, Univ. Adelaide, 65. U.S.N, 43-46. MLA; Milton Soc. Am; Johnson Soc. Midwest (pres, 61-62); AAUP. Milton tradition of the 18th century; London book trade, 1700-14; Australian Aboriginal art. Publ: Bark paintings from Arnhem Land, Univ. Kans. Art Mus, 66; ed, University of Kansas humanistic series, 71-; auth, Masterpieces of Australian bark painting, Univ. Art Gallery, State Univ. N.Y. Albany, 73. Add: Dept. of English, University of Kansas, Lawrence, KS 66045.

RUKEYSER, MURIEL, b. New York, N.Y, Dec. 15, 13; m; c. 1. LITERATURE, WRITING. Vassar Col, 30-32; Columbia Univ, summers, 31, 33; D.Litt, Rutgers Univ, 61. Mem. fac. lit, Sarah Lawrence Col, 46-66; RES. & WRITING, 66- Guggenheim fel, 42; Inst. Arts & Lett. grant, 43; lectr, Vassar Col, N.Y. Univ. & Columbia Univ; Am. Counc. Learned Soc. fel; mem. bd, Teachers & Writers Collaborative, 66-; Clark lectr, Scripps Col, 68. Harriet Monroe Poetry Award, 43. Nat. Inst. Arts & Lett; Soc. Am. Hist. Poetry; biography; relation of poetry and science. Publ: Willard Gibbs, Doubleday, 42; One life, Simon & Schuster, 58; Waterlily fire, Macmillan, 62; The speed of darkness, 68, The traces of Thomas Hariot, 69 & Breaking open, 73, Random; plus numerous others. Add: c/o Monica McCall, IFA, 1301 Sixth Ave, New York, NY 10019.

RULAND, RICHARD, b. Detroit, Mich, May 1, 32; m. 73. ENGLISH & AMERICAN LITERATURE. A.B, Univ. West. Ont, 53; M.A, Univ. Detroit, 55; Ph.D, Univ. Mich, 60. Instr. Eng. & Am. stud, Yale, 60-64, asst. prof, 64-67; assoc. prof. ENG. & AM. LIT, WASH. UNIV, 67-69, PROF, 69-, chmn. dept. 69-73. Vis. Bruern prof. Am. lit, Univ. Leeds, 64-65; Morse fel, Yale, 66-67; vis. prof, Univ. Mich, 67; mem. ed. bd, ESQ, 71-; vis. prof, Univ. Ore, 74; Fulbright-Hays prof, Netherlands, 75. MLA; Asn. Depts. Eng.(pres, 74). Nineteenth and twentieth century American literature; American-European cultural relations; the drama. Publ: The rediscovery of American literature: premises of critical taste, 1900-1940, Harvard, 67; ed, Walden: a collection of critical essays, Prenctice-Hall, 68 & The native muse: theories of American literature, Dutton, Vol. I, 72, Vol. II, 74; auth, Tocqueville's De la démocratie en Amérique and The education of Henry Adams, Comp. Lit. Stud, 65; Longfellow and the modern reader, Eng. J, 9/66; Melville and the fortunate fall: Typee as Eden, Nineteenth Century Fiction, 68; plus others. Add: Dept. of English, Washington University, St. Louis, MO 63130.

RULE, HENRY BURT, b. Houston, Tex, Mar. 15, 20; m. 48; c. 2. ENGLISH, AMERICAN LITERATURE. B.A, Univ. Tex, 44; M.A, Columbia Univ, 48; Ph.D.(Eng), Univ. Colo, 60. Instr, Am. Lit, N.Mex. Highlands Univ, 53-54; asst. prof. ENG, Ft. Wayne Ctr, Purdue Univ, 54-60; LAMAR UNIV, 60-61, assoc. prof, 61-64, PROF, 64- U.S.N.R, 44-46, Lt.(jg). MLA; Am. Stud. Asn. American realism; Mark Twain and Walt Whitman. Publ: Henry Adams' attack on two heroes of the old South, Am. Quart, summer 62; The role of satan in The man that corrupted Hadleyburg, Short Fiction Stud, fall 69; Walt Whitman and George Caleb Bingham, Walt Whitman Rev, 12/69. Add: Dept. of English, Lamar University, Beaumont, TX 77704.

RULE, PHILIP CHARLES, S.J, b. Cleveland, Ohio, Feb. 4, 31. NINETEENTH CENTURY BRITISH LITERATURE. A.B, Loyola Univ. Chicago, 54, Ph.L, 56, M.A, 57, S.T.L, 63; Ph.D.(Eng), Harvard, 68. Asst. prof. ENG, UNIV. DETROIT, 68-72, ASSOC. PROF, 72- Lit. ed, America, N.Y.C, 70-71. MLA; Midwest Mod. Lang. Asn; Conf. Christianity & Lit; Am. Film Inst; Brit. Film Inst. Romantic and Victorian literature; film criticism. Publ: Teaching film as literature, Soundings: An Interdisciplinary J, spring 70; The Old Testament vision in As I lay dying, In: Religious perspectives in Faulkner's fiction, Univ. Notre Dame, 72. Add: Lansing-Reilly Hall, University of Detroit, Detroit, MI 48221.

RULON, CURT MORRIS, b. Greeley, Iowa, Feb. 20, 37; m. 62; c. 2. ENGLISH, LINGUISTICS. A.B, Washburn Univ, 62; Ph.D.(Eng), Univ. Iowa, 67. ASST. PROF. ENG, N.TEX. STATE UNIV, 66- Vis. prof. Eng. & consult, tri-univ. proj. elem. educ. & Eng. lang. arts, Univ. Nebr, 68-69. U.S.N.R, 54-64. Ling. Soc. Am; Am. Dialect Soc. American dialectology; transformational-generative syntax and phonology. Publ: Co-auth, The English language: yesterday and today, Allyn & Bacon, 73; auth, Geographical delimitation of the dialect areas in Huckleberry Finn, Mark Twain J, 66; Distinctive feature phonology, rule ordering, and dialectal variation, Papers Ling, 70; plus others. Add: Dept. of English, North Texas State University, Denton, TX 76203.

RUMBLE, THOMAS CLARK, b. Deckerville, Mich, Jan. 1, 19; m. 46; c. 2. MEDIEVAL LITERATURE. B.A, Tulane Univ, 49, M.A, 50, Ph.D, 55. Instr. Eng, Univ. Miss, 50-52; Tulane Univ, 52-55; La. State Univ, 55-57; asst. prof, 57-59; Wayne State Univ, 59-62, assoc. prof, 62-65; prof, Univ. N.C, Greensboro, 65-66; PROF. ENG, WAYNE STATE UNIV, 66-, DEAN GRAD. STUD, 71-, asst. dean, 68-69, assoc. dean, 69-71, grad. chmn, 67-68. U.S.A.A.F, 41-45, S/Sgt. MLA; Mediaeval Acad. Am; Int. Arthurian Soc. Chaucer; medieval literature; Arthurian legend. Publ: The Breton lays in Middle English, Wayne State Univ, 65, 67; The tale of Tristram, In: Malory's originality, Johns Hopkins Univ, 64; Malory's Balin and the question of unity in the Morte Darthur, Speculum, 66; plus others. Add: Graduate Division, Wayne State University, Detroit, MI 48202.

RUNDEN, JOHN PAUL, b. Clinton, Ind, Mar. 22, 16; m. 44; c. 2. ENGLISH. B.S, Northwest. Univ, 38, M.A, 40; Ball State Univ, 40-42; Syracuse Univ, 43-44; Ph.D, Ind. Univ, 52. Teacher, high sch, Ind, 46; asst. prof. ENG, Franklin Col, 46-47; teaching fel, Ind. Univ, 47-51; instr. Univ. Ky, 52-54; assoc. prof, West. Ill. Univ, 54-59; PROF, WILLIAM PATERSON COL. N.J, 59- Admin. head, Purdue Univ. Exten. Ctr, Columbus, 46-47. U.S.A.A.F, 42-45. MLA; Melville Soc. Am; Int. Ling. Asn; Emerson Soc; NCTE. American Renaissance, especially Melville, Hawthorne, and Whitman; 20th century American poetry, especially Crane. Publ: Melville's Benito Cereno; a guided research text, Heath, 65; The poetry of Hart Crane; a guide, Simon & Schuster, 65; Rossetti and a Poe image, Notes & Queries, 6/58; The case for structural linguistics—grade school to college, N.J. Eng. Leaflet, 4/64; Whitman's The sleepers and the Indiana section of Crane's The bridge, Walt Whitman Rev, 12/69. Add: Glen Rock Rd, Little Falls, NJ 07424.

RUNDLE, JAMES URVIN, b. Galesburg, Ill, Apr. 29, 11; m. 46; c. 2. ENGLISH. B.A, Knox Col.(Ill), 33; M.A, Univ. N.Mex, 38; Ph.D.(Eng), Univ. Cincinnati, 47. Instr. Eng, Ind. Univ, 46-47; asst. prof, Park Col, 47-48; Ohio Univ, 48-50; head dept. lang. & lit, N.Mex. West. Col, 50-51; col. ed, Am. Bk. Co, 51-66, mgr. col. div, 57-66, v.pres, 61-66; lectr. Eng, Kingsborough Community Col, 66-67; North. Ariz. Univ, 67-68; prof, Franklin Pierce Col, 68-70, chmn. dept, 69-70; DEAN FAC, MIDDLESEX COMMUNITY COL, 70- Restoration comedy; current American written usage. Publ: The source of Dryden's comic plot in The assignation, Mod. Philol, 11/47; Wycherley and Calderon: a source for Love in a wood, PMLA, 9/49; The source of Shakespeare's Sonnet 30, Notes & Queries, 70. Add: Middlesex Community College, 100 Training Hill Rd, Middletown, CT 06437.

RUNKEL, HOWARD WILLIAM, b. Milwaukee, Wis, Apr. 9, 18; m. 49; c. 1. SPEECH. B.A, Univ. Wis, 41; M.A, Bucknell Univ, 42; Ph.D.(speech), Stanford Univ, 50. Orientation & educ. off, personnel ctr, U.S. War Dept, 43-46; chief training off. speech, Veterans Admin, San Francisco, Calif, 46-47; acting instr. speech & dir. stud. speakers' serv, Stanford Univ, 47-49; lectr. speech, Duke Univ, 49-50; PROF. RHETORIC & PUB. ADDRESS, WILLAMETTE UNIV, 50- Speech Commun. Asn. Hoover's speeches during his presidency; rhetorical style; semantics. Publ: A president prepares to speak, West. Speech; On stage fright, The Bull; A crusade shattered, Ore. J; plus articles on American eloquence and Presidential speaking. Add: Dept. of Rhetoric & Public Address, Willamette University, Salem, OR 97301.

RUNYAN, MICHAEL GRACEN, b. Covina, Calif, Jan. 5, 37; m. 70; c. 2. AMERICAN LITERATURE & HISTORY. A.B, Univ. Calif, Berkeley, 60, M A, 62; Ph.D.(Eng), Univ. Calif, Los Angeles, 70. Instr. jour. & Eng, Napa Jr. Col, 63-65; teaching asst, Univ. Calif, Los Angeles, 65-70; ASST. PROF. ENG, UNIV. ILL, URBANA, 70- Univ. Ill. summer fel, 71 & 73. U.S.N, 56-58. MLA. Early American literature. Publ: Ed, The poetry of William Bradford, John Colet, 74. Add: Dept. of English, University of Illinois, Urbana, IL 61801.

RUNZO, JAMES PHILIP, b. Oil City, Pa, Apr. 25, 43; c. 1. NINETEENTH CENTURY ENGLISH LITERATURE. B.A, Pa. State Univ, 65; M.A, Ind. Univ, Bloomington, 68, Ph.D.(Eng), 71. Instr. ENG, Canisius Col, 70-71; ASST. PROF, BEHREND COL, PA. STATE UNIV, 72- MLA. English romantic poetry; English Victorian novel and poetry. Publ: English criticism of the novel, 1830-1850, Mouton, (in press). Add: Behrend College, Pennsylvania State University, Station Rd, Erie, PA 16510.

RUOFF, A. LaVONNE, b. Charleston, Ill, Apr. 10, 30; m. 50, 67; c. 2. ENGLISH. B.S.Ed, Northwest Univ, 53, M.A, 54, Ph.D.(Eng), 66. Asst. instr. ENG, Univ. Ill, Chicago, 56-57; instr, Roosevelt Univ, 61-62, asst. prof, 62-66; UNIV. ILL, CHICAGO CIRCLE, 66-69, ASSOC. PROF, 69-, fac. summer fel, 67, summer instnl. award, 71. Am. Philos. Soc. grant-in-aid, 69; Huntington Libr. & Art Gallery fel, 73. MLA. English romantic literature; neo-Latin literature, native American literature. Publ: Ed, Landor's letters to his family: 1802-1825, 71 & 1826-1829, 72, Bull. John Rylands Libr; auth, The publication of the Imaginary conversations, J. Eng. & Germanic Philol. 72; Landor's letters to the Rev. Walter Birch, 69. Add: Dept. of English, University of Illinois at Chicago Circle, Box 4348, Chicago, IL 60680.

RUOFF, GENE WILLIAM, b. Paducah, Ky, July 23, 39; m. 67; c. 2. ENGLISH & AMERICAN LITERATURE. B.A, Centre Col. Ky, 61; Woodrow Wilson fels, 61-62, 64-65, Univ. Wis-Madison, M.S, 63, Ph.D.(Eng), 70. Instr. ENG, UNIV. ILL, CHICAGO CIRCLE, 66-70, asst. prof, 70-73, ASSOC. PROF, 73-, fac. fel, summer 71. MLA. Wordsworth; English Romanticism; modern fiction. Publ: Wordsworth on language: toward a radical poetics for English Romanticism, Wordsworth Circle, autumn 72; Wordsworth's Yew-trees and Romantic perception, Mod. Lang. Quart, 6/73; Religious implications of Wordsworth's imagination, Stud. Romanticism, summer 73. Add: Dept. of English, University of Illinois at Chicago Circle, Chicago, IL 60680.

RUOFF, JAMES E, b. Seattle, Wash, Apr. 12, 25; m. 48; c. 3. ENGLISH. B.A, Univ. Wash, 49; fel, Univ. Pa, 50-53, M.A, 51, Ph.D.(Eng), 54. Reader ENG, Univ. Wash, 48-49; asst. prof, Alfred Univ, 53-56; Wash. State Univ, 56-60; Wichita State Univ, 60-61, assoc. prof, 61-62, prof, 62-63; asst. prof, CITY COL. NEW YORK, 63-67, ASSOC. PROF, 67-, SUPVR. EVE. SESSION, 65- U.S.A, 43-46, 2nd Lt. NCTE; MLA. Renaissance literature; modern comparative literature; Elizabethan drama. Publ: Life and works of Lodowick Carlell, Univ. Pa, 54; Major Elizabethan poetry and prose, 68, Major Elizabethan drama, 69 & Handbook of Elizabethan & Stuart literature, 73, Crowell; co-auth, Shakespeare: the major tragedies, Free Press, 73; auth, Robert Penn Warren's teleology, Twentieth Century Lit, 60; Joyce's portrait of the would-be artist, Res. Stud, 60; Shakespeare and Kierkegaard, Comp. Lit, 68. Add: 2329 Hudson Terrace, Apt. D15, Ft. Lee, NJ 07024.

RUOTOLO, LUCIO PETER, b. New York, N.Y, Mar. 14, 27; m. 60; c. 3. ENGLISH. B.A, Colgate Univ, 51; M.A, Columbia Univ, 54, Ph.D.(Eng), 60. Acting instr. ENG, STANFORD UNIV, 57-60, instr, 60-61, asst. prof, 61-66, assoc. prof, 66-73, PROF, 73-, DIR. UNDERGRAD. STUD. DEPT. ENG, 72- Thomas J. Wilson Mem. Prize, Harvard Univ. Bd. Syndics, 72. U.S.A.A.F, 45-47. English romantics; 20th century British and American novel; the existential tradition in modern literature. Publ: Six existential heroes: the politics of faith, Harvard, 73; Keats and Kierkegaard, Renascence, summer 64; Three Prelude events, Col. Eng, 4/65; Donne's Holy sonnet XIV, J. Hist. Ideas, 7-8/66; plus others. Add: 951 Mears Ct, Stanford, CA 94305.

RUPP, RALPH RUSSELL, Speech Pathology, Audiology. See 12th Edition, American Men & Women of Science, Physical & Biological Sciences Section.

RUPP, RICHARD HENRY, b. Indianapolis, Ind, Nov. 16, 34; m. 63; c. 4. AMERICAN LITERATURE. B.A, Univ. Notre Dame, 56, M.A, 57; Ph.D. (Eng), Ind. Univ, Bloomington, 64. From instr. to asst. prof. ENG, Georgetown Univ, 61-68; asst. prof, Univ. Miami, 68-72; ASSOC. PROF, BROOKLYN COL, 72- MLA. Theory of American fiction; criticism of American literature. Publ: Celebration in post-war American fiction, 70, ed, Critics on Whitman, 72 & Critics on Emily Dickinson, 72, Univ. Miami; ed, Nathaniel Hawthorne's The Marble Faun, Bobbs, 71. Add: Dept. of English, Brooklyn College, Brooklyn, NY 11210.

RUS, LOUIS C, b. Rochester, N.Y, Mar. 3, 25; m. 42; c. 3. ENGLISH LANGUAGE. A.B, Univ. Mich, 46, M.A, 47, Ph.D.(Eng. ling), 55. Instr. ENG, Univ. Wyo, 48-50; asst. prof, Bowling Green State Univ, 55-59; assoc. prof, Calvin Col, 59-62; PROF, GRAND VALLEY STATE COL, 62- Fulbright res. fel, Mainz Univ, 57-58. Ling. Soc. Am. Modern American poetry; structural and transformational grammars. Publ: Teaching American poetry, Die Neueren Sprache, 57; co-auth, Success in English, Laidlaw Bros, 73; auth, Fries' function words of group A, 57 & Ambiguity in poetry, 58, Lang. Learning. Add: Dept. of English, Grand Valley State College, Allendale, MI 49401.

RUSCHE, HARRY GORDON, b. Dayton, Ohio, July 3, 36; m. 63; c. 2. ENGLISH. A.B, Univ. Cincinnati, 58, M.A, 60; Ph.D.(Eng), Univ. Rochester, 62. Asst. prof. ENG, EMORY UNIV, 62-71, ASSOC. PROF, 71- Fel, Southeast. Inst. Medieval & Renaissance Stud, Univ. N.C, Chapel Hill, summer 65; Folger Shakespeare Libr. fel, fall 66; Nat. Endowment for Humanities fel, 72-73. Astrology and literature; 16th century English literature; 17th century history. Publ: Merlini Anglici: astrology and propaganda from 1641 to 1651, 4/65 & Prophecies and propaganda, 10/69, Eng. Hist. Rev; Pride, humility and grace in book I of The faerie queene, Stud. Eng. Lit, winter 67. Add: Dept. of English, Emory University, Atlanta, GA 30322.

RUSH, MARY MINNIECE, b. Meridian, Miss, Nov. 8, 30. ENGLISH. A.B, Southwest. at Memphis, 52; A.M, Tulane Univ, 56. Instr. ENG, ST. MARY'S DOMINICAN COL, 56-59, asst. prof, 59-70, ASSOC. PROF, 70-, CHMN. DEPT, 72- Renaissance Soc. Am; S.Cent. Mod. Lang. Asn; AAUP. Add: 1509 Pine St, New Orleans, LA 70118.

RUSH, RICHARD RUSSELL, b. Orange, N.J, Aug. 12, 42; m. 68; c. 2. ENGLISH LITERATURE. A.B, Gonzaga Univ, 66; M.A, Univ. Calif, Los Angeles, 68, Woodrow Wilson fel. & Ph.D.(Eng), 70. ASST. PROF. ENG, SAN DIEGO STATE UNIV, 71- MLA; Philol. Asn. Pac. Coast. English Renaissance poetry; Milton; 20th century English novel. Publ: Thuanus and Theodoret, In: The Milton encyclopedia, Univ. Wis, 74. Add: School of Literature, San Diego State University, 5402 College Ave, San Diego, CA 92115.

RUSK, ELIZABETH HARTLEY, b. Champaign, Ill. ENGLISH, EDUCATION. A.B, Univ. Ill, 32, Ph.D, 53; B.J, Univ. Mo, 33; M.A, Columbia Univ, 35. Teacher Eng. & jour, Urbana High Sch, Ill, 35-39; Eng, high sch, N.C, 39-40; Univ. Minn. high sch, 40-41; Univ. Fla. lab. sch, 42-44; Univ. Chicago lab. sch, 44-49; asst. prof. educ, Univ. Tenn, 49-51; from asst. to assoc. prof. commun. skills, MICH. STATE UNIV, 53-58, prof. & dir. improvement serv, 58-61, PROF. ENG. & EDUC, 61-, dir. humanities teaching inst, 64-68. Grad. resid. scholar, Columbia Univ, 32-33; U.S. Off. Educ. grant, 63-66. NCTE. Teaching of English. Add: Dept. of English, Michigan State University, East Lansing, MI 48823.

RUSSELL, DOUGLAS A, b. Berkeley, Calif, Feb. 9, 27; m. 53; c. 2. SPEECH, DRAMA. B.A, Stanford Univ, 49, M.A, 50; Fulbright grant, Eng, 54-55; Danforth study grant, 59-60; M.F.A, Yale, 61. Instr. stage costume, Carnegie Inst. Technol, 50-51; Fla. State Univ, 51-54; costume & theatre hist, Univ. Kansas City, 55-58, asst. prof, 58-59; COSTUME DESIGN & ART HIST, STANFORD UNIV, 61-65, ASSOC. PROF, 65- Dir. costume design, Ore. Shakespearean Festival, Ashland, summers, 48-61; costume designer, Old Globe Theatre, summers, 64, 65 & 70-73; vis. prof, Univ. Victoria (B.C), summer 65; costume designer, Misalliance, Am. Conserv. Theatre, summer 66, costumes consult, Twelfth night, 67; assoc. prof, Stanford-in-Austria, 66-67, vis. prof, 70-71; spec. humanities & sci. grant, Stanford Univ, summer 73. Sig.C, U.S.A, 45-46. Am. Theatre Asn; AAUP. Costume; theatre and art history; anthology of Austrian drama including history of Austrian theatre. Publ: Stage costume design, Appleton, 73, Shakespearean costume, 59 & Mannerism in Shakespearean costume design, 12/64, Educ. Theatre J; Costume design for Prometheus bound, Theatre Crafts, 1-2/68; plus others. Add: Dept. of Drama, Stanford University, Stanford, CA 94305.

RUSSELL, HARRY KITSUN, b. Wilmington, N.C, Jan. 8, 02; m. 28; c. 2. ENGLISH & AMERICAN LITERATURE. A.B, Davidson Col, 23, D.Litt, 67; A.M, Univ. N.C, 28, Ph.D, 31. Prin, Oak Grove Sch, Va, 23-24; Instr, Am. Univ. Beirut, 24-27; ENG, UNIV. N.C, CHAPEL HILL, 28-30, 31-34, asst. prof, 34-39, assoc. prof, 39-45, prof, 45-69, EMER. PROF, 69- Am. Counc. Learned Soc. fac. stud. grant, 51-52; Kenan res. leave, 62. Tanner Award, 60; Nicolas Salgo Distinguished Teacher Award, 68. MLA; NCTE; S.Atlantic Mod. Lang. Asn. Technique of fiction; English novel. Publ: Co-ed, A state university surveys the humanities, Univ. N.C. & Literature in English, Henry Holt. Add: 712 Greenwood Rd, Chapel Hill, NC 27514.

RUSSELL, I. WILLIS, b. Baltimore, Md, May 10, 03; m. 29; c. 1. ENGLISH LANGUAGE & LITERATURE. A.B, John Hopkins Univ, 24, A.M, 29, Ph.D, 31. Asst, Johns Hopkins Univ, 25-28, 30-31; asst. prof, Birmingham-South. Col, 29-30; assoc. prof, Shorter Col, 31-35; asst. prof. ENG, UNIV. ALA, 35-44, assoc. prof, 44-47, prof, 47-72, EMER. PROF, 72- Ed, Among the New Words, 44-; Publ. Am. Dialect Soc, 65-72. MLA; NCTE; S.Atlantic Mod. Lang. Asn; Am. Dialect Soc.(secy-treas, 56-65, v.pres, 71-72, pres, 73); AAUP. Modern English; Elizabethan literature. Add: Rte. 3, Box 582, Cottondale, AL 35453.

RUSSELL, JOHN D, b. Chicago, Ill, Dec. 12, 28; m. 54; c. 2. ENGLISH, LITERATURES. A.B, Colgate Univ, 51; M.A, Univ. Wash, 56; Ph.D, Rutgers Univ, 59. Instr. ENG, Univ. S.C, 58-61, asst. prof, 61-65, assoc. prof, 65-68, PROF, 68-69; UNIV. MD, COLLEGE PARK, 69- Russell res. award, Univ. S.C, 62; Fulbright prof. Am. Lit, Univ. Brazil, 66-67. Allen Prize, Colgate Univ, 51; Explicator Award, 61. U.S.N, 52-55, Res, 55-, Lt. S.Atlantic Mod. Lang. Asn. Modern British literature; satire. Publ: Henry Green, Rutgers Univ, 60; co-auth, Satire: a critical anthology, World, 67; auth, Anthony Powell, Ind. Univ, 70; Salinger, from Daumier to Smith, Wis. Stud. Contemporary Lit, 63; There it is, 64 & Quintet from the '30's: Anthony Powell, 65, Kenyon Rev. Add: Dept. of English, University of Maryland, College Park, MD 20740.

RUSSELL, LESLIE A, b. Seattle, Wash, Aug. 17, 25; m. 52; c. 2. ENGLISH. B.A, Wash. State Univ, 51, M.A, 52; Univ. Mich, 54-57. ASST. PROF. ENG, North. Mich. Col, 57-61; N.Cent. Col.(Ill), 61-64; BEMIDJI STATE COL, 64- U.S.A, 43-46. NCTE; MLA; American literature of 19th century, especially frontier humor; American literary history; literary criticism. Add: Dept. of English, Bemidji State College, Bemidji, MN 56601.

RUSSELL, MARIANN B, b. New York, N.Y, May 23, 35. ENGLISH. B.A, St. John's Univ, 55; John Hay Whitney fel, Columbia Univ, 55, M.A, 57, Ph.D. (Eng), 65. Teacher ENG, New York City pub. schs, 55-57; instr, Morgan State Col, 61-62; Cheyney State Col, 64-65, asst. prof, 65-66, ASSOC. PROF, 66-69; SACRED HEART UNIV, 69- NCTE; AAUP; MLA. Contemporary British literature, especially work of Charles Williams, C.S. Lewis and J.R.R. Tolkien; Black literature, especially M.B. Tolson. Publ: White man's Black man: three views, CLA Jour, Vol. XVII, No. 1. Add: 334 S. Seventh Ave, Mt. Vernon, NY 10550.

RUSSELL, PATRICIA H, b. Washington, D.C, June 20, 38. ENGLISH, SHAKESPEARE. B.A, Sweet Briar Col, 60; M.A, Univ. Toronto, 62, Ph.D. (Eng), 65. Instr. ENG, Bryn Mawr Col, 64-66; ASST. PROF, UNIV. TORONTO, 66- Elizabethan drama. Publ: Romantic narrative plays: 1570-1590, Stratford-upon-Avon Stud, 67. Add: Dept. of English, New College, University of Toronto, Toronto, Ont, Can.

RUSSELL, ROBERT WILLIAM, b. Binghamton, N.Y, Dec. 30, 24; m. 51; c. 4. ENGLISH. B.A, Yale, 45, Garland fel, 45-46, M.A, 46; Int. Rotary Found. fel, 48-49; Fulbright scholar, 49-51; B.Litt, Oxford, 51; D.Litt, Hamilton Col, 63. Instr. Eng, Harpur Col, 46-48; prof. Eng. & humanities, shimer Col, 52-55; from asst. prof. to assoc. prof. ENG, FRANKLIN & MARSHALL COL, 55-68, PROF. & DANA PROF, 68- MLA. Nineteenth century English and American literature. Publ: To catch an angel, 62, An act of loving, 67 & The island, 73, Vanguard; co-auth, The disciplined imagination, Cummings, 69; auth, Poet in the classroom, Col. Eng, 5/67. Add: 1039 Wheatland Ave, Lancaster, PA 17603.

RUSSI, BERNARD A, JR, b. Zanesville, Ohio, Jan. 6, 33; m. 56; c. 3. SPEECH, MASS COMMUNICATIONS. B.S, Kent State Univ, 54; M.A, Ohio Univ, 55; fel, Wayne State Univ, 57-58; Ph.D.(mass commun), 63. Instr. SPEECH, MARIETTA COL, 55-60, asst. prof, 60-64, assoc. prof, 64-69, PROF, 69- Mass-commun. stud, Germany, 67-68. Propaganda in German broadcasting; effects of mass media on society. Publ: Teaching by radio, Nat. Asn. Educ. Broadcasters J, 7-8/66. Add: Dept. of Speech, Marietta College, Marietta, OH 45750.

RUST, JAMES DARIUS, b. Barth Co, Ind, May 3, 10; m. 35. ENGLISH. A.B, Ind. Univ, 34, A.M, 37; Ph.D, Yale, 45. Tutor ENG, Ind. Univ, 34-37, instr, 42-44; Univ. Mo, 37-41; Grinnell Col, 45-46, asst. prof, 46-47, MICH. STATE UNIV, 47-58, assoc. prof, 58-63, PROF, 63-, ASST. DEAN, COLL. ARTS & LETT, 62-, UNIV. OMBUDSMAN, 67- MLA; Col. Eng. Asn; Am. Col. Personnel Asn. Nineteenth century English literature; Victorian novel, research and publication field; comparative fiction. Add: 223 Northlawn Ave, East Lansing, MI 48823.

RUST, RICHARD DILWORTH, b. Provo, Utah, Sept. 4, 37; m. 60; c. 3. ENGLISH. B.S, Brigham Young Univ, 61; M.S, Univ. Wis, 62, Ph.D.(Eng), 66. Asst. prof, ENG, UNIV. N.C, CHAPEL HILL, 66-71, ASSOC. PROF, 71- Fulbright lectr, Univ. Heidelberg, 71-72. Am. Lit. Group, MLA; MLA; S.Atlantic Mod. Lang. Asn; Am. Stud. Asn. Nineteenth century American literature, especially writers of the American renaissance period: literature and art of the American frontier. Publ: Ed, Glory and pathos: responses of nineteenth century American authors to the Civil War, Holbrook, 70; & Astoria by Washington Irving, Univ. Wis, (in press); co-auth, Mark Twain's The turning point of my life, Am. Lit, 1/69; auth, Henry Wadsworth Longfellow, In: Fifteen American authors before 1900, Univ. Wis, 71; Washington Irving rediscovers the frontier, Am. Transcendental Quart, spring 73. Add: Dept. of English, University of North Carolina, Chapel Hill, NC 27514.

RUTENBERG, DANIEL, b. Chicago, Ill, Sept. 1, 29; m. 54; c. 3. HUMANITIES, ENGLISH. A.B, Univ. Chicago, 47, M.A, 62; Ph.D.(Eng), Univ. Fla, 67. Instr. Eng, Odessa Col, 62-63; logic, St. Petersburg Jr. Col, 63-64; HUMANITIES, UNIV. S.FLA. TAMPA, 64-66, asst. prof, 66-70, ASSOC. PROF, 70-, CHMN. DEPT, 71- U.S.A, 51-53. MLA. Late Victorian poetry. Publ: A new date for the Rhymers' Club, Eng. Lit. in Transition, 9/69; Crisscrossing the bar: Tennyson and Lionel Johnson on death, Victorian Poetry, summer 72. Add: Dept. of Humanities, University of South Florida, Box LAN 122, Tampa, FL 33620.

RUTH, JOHN L, b. Harleysville, Pa, Jan. 8, 30; m. 51; c. 3. ENGLISH. B.A, East. Baptist Col, 56; M.A, Harvard, 60, Ph.D.(Eng), 68. Asst. prof. ENG, EAST. BAPTIST COL, 62-68, assoc. prof, 68-72, PROF, 72- Vis. prof. Am. lit, Univ. Hamburg, 68-69. MLA; Am. Stud. Asn; Melville Soc. Am; Hymn Soc. Am. American hymnody; Melville; religion in 19th century American literature. Add: Dept. of English, Eastern Baptist College, St. Davids, PA 19087.

RUTHERFORD, CHARLES SHEPARD, b. Chicago, Ill, Sept. 10, 40; m. 62; c. 2. MEDIEVAL LITERATURE. B.A, Carleton Col, 62; M.A, Ind. Univ, Bloomington, 66, Ph.D.(Eng), 70. Lectr. ENG, UNIV. MD, COLLEGE PARK, 68-70, ASST. PROF, 70- MLA; S.Atlantic Mod. Lang. Asn; Medieval Acad. Am. Chaucer; Middle English poetry; Old English poetry. Publ: Pandarus as lover: a joly wo or loves shotes keene, Annuale Mediaevale, 72; A new dog with an old trick: archetypal patterns in Sounder, J. Popular Film, spring, 73. Add: Dept. of English, University of Maryland, Taliaferro Hall, College Park, MD 20742.

RUTLEDGE, DONALD G, b. St. Catharines, Ont, June 6, 27; m. 47; c. 3. ENGLISH, EDUCATION. B.A, McMaster Univ, 49; Univ. London, 64-65; M.A, Univ. Toronto, 69. Instr. Eng, St. Catharines Col. Inst. & Voc. Sch, 52-57; head dept, Niagara Falls Col. Voc. Inst, 57-59; dir. publ, TORONTO BD. EDUC, 60-73, DIR. CURRICULUM DEVELOP, 73-, dir. lang. stud. ctr, 63-73. Instr. Univ. Toronto Schs, 59-60; lectr. teaching Eng, Ont. Col. Educ, summer 60 & 61; Can. Counc. award, 62-63; Can. co-chmn. comn. on Eng. in secondary schs, Int. Conf. Teaching of Eng, York Univ, 71. Can. Counc. Teachers Eng; NCTE (nat. comn. on Eng. curriculum, 73-76). Teaching of English; psycholinguistics; contemporary poetry. Publ: Co-auth, Writing with a purpose, Books I and II, 54, 55, The apprentice writer, 56, Form and content, 57, Prose, mostly modern, 59 & The blue guitar, 68, McClelland & Stewart; ed, Encounter series of Canadian novels, Learning Concepts, Toronto, 71; auth, Responding: two, Ginn, 73; Poetry and precision, summer 65 & Teaching literature: some honest doubts, spring 68, Toronto Educ. Quart. Add: Education Centre, Toronto Board of Education, 155 College St, Toronto, Ont. M5T 1P6, Can.

RUYS, CONSTANCE, b. Maassluis, The Netherlands, Jan. 30, 22; U.S. citizen. THEATRE. B.A, Univ. Calif, Berkeley, 47; M.S, Univ. Calif, Los Angeles, 51; Univ. Leiden, 52-53; Columbia Univ, 53-54; Ph.D.(drama), Stanford Univ, 56. Instr. speech & drama, San Jose State Col, 57; from asst. prof. to assoc. prof, Cedar Crest Col, 57-62; PROF. THEATRE & CHMN. DEPT, WESLEYAN COL.(GA), 62- Shell spec. res. grants, Eng, summer 69. Am. Soc. Theatre Res; Soc. Theatre Res, Eng; Am. Theatre Asn. Medieval and Renaissance drama, especially the Chambers of rhetoric of the low countries. Publ: John Pickeryng, merchant adventurer and playwrite, In: Costerus essays in English and American language and philology, Amsterdam, 73. Add: Dept. of Theatre, Wesleyan College, Macon, GA 31201.

RYALS, CLYDE de L, b. Atlanta, Ga, Dec. 19, 28; m. 71. ENGLISH. A.B, Emory Univ, 47, M.A, 49; Ph.D, Univ. Pa, 57. Instr. ENG, Univ. Md, 56-57; Univ. Pa, 57-60, asst. prof, 60-64, assoc. prof, 64-69, prof, 69-73, grad. chmn, 69-72; PROF, DUKE UNIV, 73- Mem. ed. bd, Victorian Poetry, 64-; Guggenheim fel, 72-73. MLA; Am. Soc. Aesthet; NCTE. Nineteenth century literature. Publ: Theme and symbol in Tennyson's poetry to 1850, & ed, Tennyson's Poems, chiefly lyrical, 66, Univ. Pa; ed, Mrs. Humphry Ward's Robert Elsmere, Univ. Nebr, 67; auth, From the great deep, Ohio Univ, 67. Add: 1620 University Dr, Durham, NC 27707.

RYAN, ALVAN SHERMAN, b. Needham Heights, Mass, May 2, 12; m. 37; c. 2. ENGLISH. B.S, Univ. Mass, 34; A.M, Harvard, 38; Ph.D.(Eng), State Univ. Iowa, 40. Asst. & lectr. Eng, State Univ. Iowa, 37-39, instr, 39-42; asst. prof. Eng, Univ. Notre Dame, 43-46; assoc. prof, Univ. Mass, 46-47, prof, 47-49; assoc. prof. gen. prog. lib. educ, Univ. Notre Dame, 51-54; assoc. prof. Eng, 54-62, prof. & head dept, 62-65; prof. Eng. & chmn. div. humanities, UNIV. MASS, BOSTON, 65-67, PROF. ENG, 67- Lectr, Wellesley Col, 49; Fund Advan. Educ. fac. fel. & vis. fel, Princeton, 55-56; Fulbright prof. Am. lit, Univ. Saarland, 61-62; mem. bd. acad. adv, Marlboro Col, Vt, 72- Gold Medal Award professional serv, Assoc. Alumni Univ. Massachusetts, Amherst, 72. Col. Eng. Asn.(chmn. nat. comt. doctoral stud. & preparation for teaching, 55-57); MLA; AAUP. Romantic poetry; Victorian literature; literary criticism. Publ: Ed, The Brownson reader, Kenedy, 55; auth, Newman's conception of literature, Univ. Iowa Humanistic Stud, 42; Frost and Emerson: voice and vision, Mass. Rev, 10/59 & In: Profile of Robert Frost, Merrill, 71; R.P. Warren's Night rider: the nihilism of the isolated temperament, In: Robert Penn Warren: a collection of critical essays, N.Y. Univ, 65. Add: 224 Marlborough St, Boston, MA 02116.

RYAN, AYLMER ARTHER, b. Can, Aug. 5, 12; m. 45; c. 3. ENGLISH. B.A, Univ. Alta, 39, M.A, 40; hon.LL.D, Sir George Williams Univ, 72. From lectr. to PROF. ENG, UNIV. ALTA, 46-, PROVOST, 53-, EXEC. ASST. TO PRES, 60- Can. Army, 42-46, Res, 52-63, Lt. Col. Asn. Can. Univ. Teachers Eng. English literature; Chaucer. Add: President's Office, University of Alberta, Edmonton, Alta. T6G 2U9, Can.

RYAN, HALFORD ROSS, b. Anderson, Ind, Dec. 29, 43; m. 70. SPEECH, PUBLIC SPEAKING. B.A, Wabash Col, 66; Rockefeller theol. fel, Princeton Theol. Sem, 66-67; M.A. Univ. Ill, Urbana, 68, Ph.D.(speech), 72. Asst. SPEECH, Univ. Ill, Urbana, 67-70; instr, WASH. & LEE UNIV, 70-72, ASST. PROF, 72- Speech Commun. Asn; AAUP. Publ: Free speech in ancient Athens, Free Speech J, 72. Add: Div. of Speech, Dept. of English, Washington & Lee University, Lexington, VA 24450.

RYAN, HAROLD FRANCIS, S.J, b. Sunnyside, Utah, Mar. 9, 08. ENGLISH & AMERICAN LITERATURE. A.B, Gonazga Univ, 32, A.M, 33; S.T.L, Alma Col, 40; Ph.D, St. Louis Univ, 44. Instr. Eng, LOYOLA MARYMOUNT UNIV, 33-35, asst. prof, 44-49, assoc. prof, 49-52, PROF. ENG, 52-, COMMUN. ARTS, 64-, dean grad. div, 50-71. Lectr, Cath. Univ. Rio de Janeiro & Cath. Univ. São Paulo, 49; mem. exec. comt, Asn. Grad. Schs. Cath. Univs, 67. MLA; Col. Eng. Asn; Ling. Soc. Am. Shakespearean drama; structural linguistics; mass media and creative literature. Publ: Reflections of a humanist on the university as a medium, In: Graduate education—today and tomorrow, Univ. N.Mex, 72. Add: Dept. of Communication Arts, Loyola Marymount University, 7101 W. 80th St, Los Angeles, CA 90045.

RYAN, LAWRENCE VINCENT, b. St. Paul, Minn, June 22, 23; m. 45; c. 4. ENGLISH. B.A, Col. St. Thomas, 44; M.A, Northwest. Univ, 46, Ph.D.(Eng), 52. Instr. ENG, Col. St. Thomas, 46-52; STANFORD UNIV, 52-55, asst. prof, 55-59, assoc. prof, 59-63, PROF, 63-, assoc. dean sch. humanities & sci, 67-70, CHMN. HUMANITIES SPEC. PROG, 73-, dir. grad. prog. humanities, 58-67, acting dean, 74. Huntington Libr. grants-in-aid, 53, 56 & 72; Am. Philos. Soc. grant-in-aid, 57; co-ed, Neo-Latin News, 57-; Guggenheim fel, 58; assoc, Harvard Renaissance Ctr, Florence, 64; Am. Counc. Learned Soc. grant-in-aid, 71. U.S.M.C.R, 43-46, 1st Lt. MLA; Renaissance Soc. Am; Conf. Brit. Stud. Literature of the English Renaissance; modern Latin literature; literature of the Italian Renaissance. Publ: Ed, A science reader, Holt, 59; auth, Roger Ascham, Stanford Univ, 63; ed, The schoolmaster (1570), Folger-Cornell, 67; Shakespeare's 1 Henry VI, New Am. Libr, 67; co-auth, Hope for T.S. Eliot's Empty men, PMLA, 9/58; auth, Book four of Castiglione's Courtier: climax or afterthought, Stud. Renaissance, 72; plus others. Add: Dept. of English, Stanford University, Stanford, CA 94305.

RYAN, MARYBRIDE, O.P, b. Waterford, Ireland, Apr. 13, 13; U.S. citizen. ENGLISH LITERATURE. B.A, Univ. Ottawa, 42; M.A, Marquette Univ, 52; trustee scholar, Cath. Univ. Am, 53-57, Ph.D, 58. Teacher, St. Henry Separate High Sch, Sask, 34-47, prin, 47-50; teacher Eng, hist. & relig, St. Joseph Sch, Muskegon, Mich, 50-53; PROF. ENG, AQUINAS COL, 58-, chmn. dept, 59-68. Vis. prof. Eng. & medieval lit, World Campus Afloat, Chapman Col, fall 70. NCTE; Conf. Col. Compos. & Commun. Medieval language and literary theory; methods of teaching language. Publ: John of Salisbury on the arts of language in the Trivium, Cath. Univ. Am, 58; contrib, New Cath. Encycl, McGraw, 67. Add: Dept. of English, Aquinas College, 1607 Robinson Rd, Grand Rapids, MI 49506.

RYAN, PAT M, b. Lexington, Ky, Feb. 13, 28; m. 55; c. 3. ENGLISH, THEATRE HISTORY. B.A, Univ. Calif, Berkeley, 49; M.A, Stanford Univ, 50; Ph.D.(hist. theatre), Yale, 59. Instr. Eng. & speech, Colo. Sch. Mines, 55-56; assoc. prof. drama & theatre hist, Univ. Ariz, 59-62; asst. prof. ENG, Calif. State Polytech. Col, 62-63; prof. & chmn. div, Wayne State Col, 63-64; East. Mont. Col, 64-65; assoc. prof, Ind. Univ, Ft. Wayne, 65-67; PROF, STATE UNIV. N.Y. COL. BROCKPORT, 67-, dir. sponsored res, 70-72. Consult, Anglo-Am. lit, U.S. Peace Corps Training Prog, Calif. State Polytech. Col, 55; Ind. Univ. Found. grant-in-aid for travel & research in United Kingdom & Ireland, 66; sr. Fulbright-Hays scholar Am. lit, Turku Univ. & Abo Acad, Finland & in France, Belgium, Eng, Norway, Sweden & Denmark, 72-73; vis. lectr. Eng, Univ. N.C, Greensboro & N.C. Cent. Univ, 73-74. Med.C, U.S.A, 51-53. Am. Soc. Theatre Res; MLA; Orgn. Am. Hist. Anglo-American drama; literature of the American frontier; theatre history. Publ: Ed, Aristotle, Rhetoric: an abstract of principles of public speaking, Colo. Sch. Mines, 56; auth, Thomas Lodge, gentleman, Shoe String Press, 58; compiler, History of the modern theatre: a selected bibliography Univ. Ariz, 60; ed, Wolfe, The mountains, Univ. N.C, 70 & Oxford Univ, 71; compiler, American drama bibliography: a checklist of publications in English, Pub. Libr. Ft. Wayne, Ind, 68; auth, Tombstone theatre tonight! a chronicle of entertainment on the Southwestern mining frontier, Westerners, 66; compiler, Black writing in the U.S.A: a bibliographic guide, Drake Mem. Libr, 69; contrib, Encycl. dello Spettacolo, Rome & Notable American women, 1607-1950, 71; Viola Allen, Brock Pemberton & Antoinette Perry, Dictionary Am. Biog, (in press); plus numerous others. Add: P.O. Box 662, Clarkson, NY 14430.

RYAN, ROBERT EDMUND, b. Chicago, Ill, Mar. 11, 32; m. 58; c. 3. ENGLISH & AMERICAN LITERATURE. B.A, Loyola Univ.(Calif), 54, M.A, 56; Ph.D.(Eng), Univ. South. Calif, 67. Instr. ENG, U.S. Armed Forces Inst, 55-57; Univ. Md, N.Atlantic Div, 59-60; U.S. Air Force Acad, 60-62, asst. prof, 64-67, ASSOC. PROF, 67-68; PURDUE UNIV, Westville, 68-72; PURDUE UNIV, WEST LAFAYETTE, 72- Lectr, Univ. Colo, 67-68. U.S.A.F, 55-68, Capt. MLA; Mod. Humanities Res. Asn.(contrib. ed, Annual Bibliog, 68-). Literature and the history of ideas; literary naturalism; Stephen Crane. Add: Dept. of English, Purdue University, West Lafayette, IN 47907.

RYAN, STEPHEN P, b. Philadelphia, Pa, Dec. 8, 10; m. 38. ENGLISH. A.B, St. Joseph's Col.(Pa), 32; M.A, Univ. Pa, 34; Ph.D, Univ. Col. Dublin, Nat. Univ. Ireland, 56. From instr. to prof. ENG, Xavier Univ.(La), 37-57, 58-60; vis. lectr, Loyola Univ.(Ill), 57-58; PROF, UNIV. SCRANTON, 60-, chmn. dept, 64-72. Vis. prof. Eng, Univ. Col, Dublin, Nat. Univ. Ireland, 58; Univ. Scranton fac. res. grant, summer 68. MLA. Publ: Edward Martyn's last play, Studies, summer 58; W.B. Yeats and Thomas Mac-

Donagh, Mod. Lang. Notes, 12/61; James Joyce and Edward Martyn, Xavier Univ. Stud, summer 62. Add: Dept. of English, University of Scranton, Scranton, PA 18510.

RYAN, WILLIAM MARTIN, b. Clinton, Iowa, June 22, 18; m. 44. MEDIEVAL LITERATURE & LINGUISTICS. A.B, St. Ambrose Col, 40; A.M, Univ. Mich, 50; Ph.D.(Anglo-Saxon), Univ. Tex, 55. Instr. ENG, St. Ambrose Col, 46-50, asst. prof, 50-52; instr, UNIV. MO-KANSAS CITY, 55-57, asst. prof, 57-61, assoc. prof, 61-65, PROF, 65- U.S.N.R, 43-46, Lt.(jg). MLA; Mediaeval Acad. Am. Anglo-Saxon homilies; Middle English; modern American grammar. Publ: William Langland, Twayne, 68; Pseudosubjunctive Were, Am. Speech, 2/61; The classifications of Browning's Difficult vocabulary, Stud. Philol, 7/63. Add: Dept. of English, University of Missouri-Kansas City, Kansas City, MO 64110.

RYDAHL, EUGENE E, b. Grand Rapids, Mich, Dec. 11, 28; m. 49; c. 3. THEATRE. B.S, Cent. Mich. Univ, 51; M.A, State Univ. Iowa, 55, Ph.D, 58. Assoc. prof. theatre & dir. drama, Nebr. State Teachers Col, Chadron, 58-61; asst. prof. speech & drama, CENT. MICH. UNIV, 61-63, ASSOC. PROF. SPEECH & DRAMATIC ARTS & DIR. UNIV. THEATRE, 63- Speech Commun. Asn; Am. Theatre Asn; Nat. Soc. Stud. Commun; Children's Theatre Conf. European theatre history; American theatre history; playwriting. Publ: The benefit performance in London to 1737, Cent. States Speech J, 11/65. Add: Dept. of Drama, Central Michigan University, Mt. Pleasant, MI 48858.

RYF, ROBERT STANLEY, b. Berne, Ind, Aug. 12, 18; m. 43; c. 2. ENGLISH. A.B, Occidental Col, 39, M.A, 53; Ph.D, Columbia Univ, 56. Instr. Eng, OCCIDENTAL COL, 55-56, asst. prof. ENG. & COMP. LIT, 56-59, assoc. prof, 59-63, prof, 63-72, ARTHUR G. COONS PROF, 72-, dean students, 61-65, chmn. dept. Eng, 65-67, dean fac. & acad. v.pres, 67-72. Fac. award lectr. & Haynes summer fel, 59; Mosher res. grant, 60. U.S.N.R, 40-45, Lt. MLA; AAUP. Twentieth century English and American literature. Publ: New approach to Joyce, Univ. Calif, 62; Henry Green, 67 & Joseph Conrad, 70, Columbia Univ; Joyce's visual imagination, Tex. Stud. Lang. & Lit, 59; Conrad's stage victory, 64 & The secret agent on stage, 72, Mod. Drama. Add: Dept. of English & Comparative Literature, Occidental College, Los Angeles, CA 90041.

RYSKAMP, CHARLES ANDREW, b. East Grand Rapids, Mich, Oct. 21, 28. ENGLISH. A.B, Calvin Col, 50; M.A, Yale, 51, Hale fel, 54-55, Ph.D.(Eng), 56; Lang. fel. & Yale fel, Pembroke Col, Cambridge, 53-54. Instr. Eng, Princeton, 55-59, asst. prof, 59-63, assoc. prof, 63-69; DIR, PIERPONT MORGAN LIBR, NEW YORK, 69- John E. Annan bicentennial preceptor, 61-64, cur. Eng. & Am. lit, Univ. Libr, 67-69. Procter & Gamble fel, 58-59; Counc. Humanities jr. fel, 60-61; publs. chmn, Princeton Libr. Chronicle, 62-70; Bollingen Found. fel, 65-67; Guggenheim Found. fel, 66-67; prof, Princeton, 69- Keats-Shelley Asn. Am; Am. Soc. 18th Century Stud; Asn. Int. Bibliophilie; Asn. Art Mus. Dirs; Master Drawings Asn; Conf. Brit. Stud; MLA; Cowper Soc; Grolier Club. Eighteenth century English literature; William Cowper. Publ: William Cowper of the inner temple, esquire, Cambridge, 59; co-auth, Boswell: the ominous years, McGraw, 63; ed, The cast-away, 63 & Wilde and the nineties, 66, Princeton; William Blake, Engraver, 69. Add: 29 E. 36th St, New York, NY 10016.

RYTHER, DWIGHT WARREN, b. Ft. Leavenworth, Kans, July 27, 03. ENGLISH. B.S.C, Univ. Ga, 25, A.M, 30. Instr, Univ. Ga, 29-30; prof. Eng, dean & exec. v.pres, William Jennings Bryan Univ, 30-56; ASSOC. PROF. ENG, REGISTR. & DIR. ADMIS, KING'S COL.(N.Y), 56-, v.pres, 62-64. U.S.A, 42-45, Lt. Col. Add: King's College, Briarcliff Manor, NY 10510.

RYTHER, MARY RUTH, b. Marlow, Okla, Aug. 11, 25; m. 49; c. 2. ENGLISH LITERATURE. B.A, Univ. Okla, 47, M.T, Cent. State Univ.(Okla), 62. Teacher Eng. & speech, Walters, Sterling & Okarche, Okla, 54-64; instr. ENG, PANHANDLE STATE COL, 64-67, asst. prof, 67-70, ASSOC. PROF, 70- MLA. Modern British novel; romantic period; American novel. Add: Dept. of English, Panhandle State College, Goodwell, OK 73939.

S

SAAD, YOUSSEF S, b. Alexandria, Egypt, Aug. 22, 37; U.S. citizen. ENGLISH, COMPARATIVE LITERATURE. B.A, Univ. Alexandria, 59; M.A, Univ. N.C, Chapel Hill, 64; Ph.D.(comp. lit), Univ. Utah, 70. Cataloguer, Arabic, Libr. Congr, 63-65; teaching asst. Arabic, Eng. & world lit, Univ. Utah, 66-70; asst. prof. ENG, WINSTON-SALEM STATE UNIV, 70-71, ASSOC. PROF, 71- Vis. prof. Arabic, Monterey Inst. Foreign Stud, Calif, summer 70; Eng, Univ, Alexandria, 72-73. MLA; Mid.E. Stud. Asn. Arabic. Publ: The impact of Middle Eastern thought on western tradition, Univ. Utah Chronicle, 2/68. Add: Apt. 112, 1525 Woods Rd, Winston-Salem, NC 27106.

SAAGPAKK, PAUL FRIIDRIH, b. Saaremaa, Estonia, Sept. 2, 10; U.S. citizen. ENGLISH PHILOLOGY, CONTEMPORARY BRITISH LITERATURE. Dipl, Tartu Univ, 35; Brit. Counc. scholar, Southampton Univ, 36; Phil.lic, Univ. Uppsala, 47; Ph.D.(Eng), Columbia Univ, 66. Lectr. philos. & educ, Tartu Univ. Exten, 33-35; instr. Eng, Gustavus-Adolphus Gymnasium, Estonia, 35-40; Tallinn Col, Estonia, 36-40; prin, Tallinn Sch. Lang, 40-41; lectr. Eng, Univ. Uppsala Exten, 45-46; asst. prof. psychol, Upsala Col, 47, ENG, 48-58; lectr, UNIV. MASS, AMHERST, 64-70, ASSOC. PROF, 70- Instr. Ger, Rutgers Univ, 47; asst. prof. psychol. & Eng, N.J. State Teachers Col, Newark, 47; Am. Counc. Learned Soc. grant, 59-62; Fulbright res. scholar, Univ. Helsinki, 70-71. MLA; AAUP; Finnish Lit. Soc; Am. Comp. Lit. Asn; PEN Club; Estonian Learned Soc. Am. Modern novel; literature and psychology; Estonian lexicography. Publ: An Estonian-English dictionary, Nordic Press, 55; Estonian literature, In: Colliers's Encycl, 51; A survey of psychopathology in British literature from Shakespeare to Hardy, Lit. & Psychol, 68; The Yale lectures on Estonian poetry, 1968-1969, Tulimuld, 69; plus others. Add: Dept. of English, University of Massachusetts, Amherst, MA 01002.

SAALBACH, ROBERT P, b. Pittsburgh, Pa, July 13, 13; m. 35; c. 2. AMERICAN LITERATURE. B.A, Univ. Pittsburgh, 34; M.A, Univ. Chicago, 39; Ph.D, Univ. Wash, 51. Instr. ENG, Pa. State Col, 40-41; Carnegie Inst. Technol, 42-44; Univ. Idaho, 47-49; fel, Univ. Wash, 49-51, acting instr, 51-52; asst. prof, S.Dak. Sch. Mines & Technol, 52-55; prof. & head dept, Scottsbluff Col, 55-58; asst. prof, Ark. State Col, 58-59; IND. STATE UNIV, 59-64, assoc. prof, 64-71, PROF, 71- Vis. lectr, Augustana Col.(S.Dak), summer 53. U.S.Maritime Serv, 44-47. MLA; NCTE; Col. Eng. Asn; Conf. Col. Compos. & Commun; Am. Stud. Asn. Theodore Dreiser; American literature; women's liberation. Publ: Teaching students to organize, Eng. J, 58 & In: Teaching English in today's high schools, Holt, 65; Literature and morality, PMLA, 71; Thoreau and civil disobedience, Ball State Forum, 72; plus others. Add: 1301 Royce Ave, Terre Haute, IN 47802.

SABATELLI, PHILIP JOSEPH, b. Philadelphia, Pa. GENERAL SEMANTICS, INTERPERSONAL COMMUNICATION. B.A, Temple Univ, 64, M.A, 66, Ph.D.(speech commun), 70; Univ. Denver, summer 68. ASST. PROF. SPEECH, UNIV. N.H, 69- Speech Commun. Asn; Int. Soc. Gen. Semantics; Inst. Gen. Semantics; Biofeedback Res. Soc; AAUP. Language and behavior; personality theory; individual and group therapy programs. Publ: General semantics, rhetoric and social psychology: an integrative conceptual framework, Univ. Denver, 72; General semantics and biofeedback: synergy for self-awareness, McGill Univ, 73. Add: Dept. of Speech & Drama, Paul Arts Ctr, University of New Hampshire, Durham, NH 03824.

SACCIO, PETER CHURCHILL, b. Brooklyn, N.Y, May 28, 41. ENGLISH LITERATURE. B.A, Yale, 62; Ph.D.(Eng), Princeton, 68. Instr. ENG, Princeton Univ, 65-66; DARTMOUTH COL, 66-68, asst. prof, 68-73, ASSOC. PROF. PROF, 73-, fac. fel, 69-70. MLA; Renaissance Soc. Am. Elizabethan drama. Publ: The court comedies of John Lyly: a study in allegorical dramaturgy, Princeton, 69; The oddity of Lyly's Endimion, Elizabethan Theatre V, 73. Add: Dept. of English, Dartmouth College, Hanover, NH 03755.

SACHS, HARLEY LUTHER, b. Chicago, Ill, Jan. 1, 31; m. 60; c. 3. TECHNICAL COMMUNICATIONS, CREATIVE WRITING. A.B, Ind. Univ, Bloomington, 53, M.A.T, 55; Univ. Stockholm, 56-59; Copenhagen Univ, 62. Lectr. adult educ. exten, Univ. Stockholm, 57-60; instr. ENG, South. Ill. Univ, Alton campus, 63-65; asst. prof, MICH. TECH. UNIV, 65-73, ASSOC. PROF, 73- Pres, Idea Develop. Co, Inc, 69- U.S.A, 53-55. AAUP; NCTE; Soc. Tech. Commun. Publ: Hur Mannen forlorade Hornen (play), Univ. Stockholm, 59; Cave 48 (short story), Sou'wester, winter 64; The thrill in business writing, J. Tech. Writing, 7/71; Toward greater efficiency of information transfer, J. Irreproducible Results, 3/72; plus others. Add: Dept. of Humanities, Michigan Technological University, Houghton, MI 49931.

SACKETT, SAMUEL JOHN, b. Redlands, Calif, Jan. 23, 28; m. 50; c. 2. ENGLISH. A.B, Univ. Redlands, 48, M.A, 49; fel. & Ph.D.(Eng), Univ. Calif, Los Angeles, 56. Instr. Eng. & jour, Hastings Col, 49-51; teaching asst, Univ. Calif, Los Angeles, 52-53; asst. prof. ENG, FT. HAYS KANS. STATE COL, 54-57, assoc. prof, 57-65, PROF, 65- MLA; NCTE; Am. Folklore Soc; NEA; AAUP; Am. Asn. Higher Educ; Johnson Soc. Midwest (pres, 62-63). Neoclassical English literature; Kansas regional literature; American folklore. Publ: Ed, Voyages of Mr. Job Vinegar, Augustan Reprint Soc, 58; co-auth, Kansas folklore, Univ. Nebr, 61; auth, English literary criticism, 1726-1750, Ft. Hays Kans. State Col, 62; transl, The man who had his hair cut short, Horizon, 65; auth, Cowboys and the songs they sang, W.R. Scott, 67; E.W. Howe, Twayne, 72; plus others. Add: Box 386, Hays, KS 67601.

SACKS, SHELDON, b. New York, N.Y, Feb. 20, 30; m. 52; c. 2. ENGLISH. B.S, Northwest. Univ, 52, M.A, 53; univ. fel, Univ. Chicago, 53-54, vis. comt. fel, 54-55, Ph.D, 59; Fulbright grant, Univ. London, 55-56. Instr. ENG, Univ. Tex, 56-58; asst. prof, Univ. Calif, Berkeley, 58-64, assoc. prof, 65-66; UNIV. CHICAGO, 66-67, PROF. ENG. & LING, 67-, ED, CRITICAL INQUIRY, 74- Vis. prof, Univ. Rome, 61-62. E. Harris Harbison Award Gifted Teaching, Danforth Found, 70. MLA; Ling. Soc. Am. Henry Fielding; history of English prose fiction; linguistic theory. Publ: Fiction and the shape of belief, Univ. Calif, 64; co-auth, An analytic reader, Little, 64; ed, R.S. Crane's The critical and historical principles of literary history, Univ. Chicago, 71; auth, Golden birds and dying generations, Comp. Lit. Stud, 9/69; Clarissa and the tragic traditions, Stud. 18th Century Cult, 72; Story, plot, and lyric narration, Critical Inquiry, 12/74; plus others. Add: Dept. of English, University of Chicago, Chicago, IL 60637.

SACKTON, ALEXANDER HART, b. Galveston, Tex, Jan. 30, 11. ENGLISH LITERATURE. B.S, Univ. Pa, 31; B.A, Cambridge, 34, M.A, 38; Ph.D, Harvard, 41. Instr. ENG, Agr. & Mech. Col. Tex, 36-38, 41-42; asst. prof, Univ. Del, 45-46; UNIV. TEX, AUSTIN, 46-50, assoc. prof, 50-68, PROF, 68- U.S.A.A.F, 42-45. MLA; Mod. Humanities Res. Asn, Gt. Brit; S.Cent. Mod. Lang. Asn; Renaissance Soc. Am. English Renaissance; poetry; drama. Publ: Rhetoric as a dramatic language in Ben Jonson; The paradoxical encomium in Elizabethan drama, 49 & Architectonic structure in Paradise regained, 54, Univ. Tex. Stud. Eng; Donne and the privacy of verse, Stud. Eng. Lit, 1500-1900, winter 67. Add: Dept. of English, Parlin Hall, University of Texas at Austin, Austin, TX 78712.

SADDLEMYER, ANN, b. Prince Albert, Sask, Nov. 28, 32. ENGLISH. B.A, Univ. Sask, 53, honours cert. Eng, 55; McLaughlin fel, Queen's Univ.(Ont), 55-56, M.A, 56; Imp. Order, Daughters of Empire War Mem. Overseas fel, Univ. London, 58-59, Can. Counc. fels, 58-60, Ph.D.(Eng), 61. Instr. Eng, Univ. Victoria, 56-57 & 60-61, asst. prof, 61-63, assoc. prof, 63-68, PROF, 68-71; ENG, VICTORIA COL. & DRAMA, GRAD. DRAMA CTR, UNIV. TORONTO, 71-, DIR. CTR, 72- Lectr, Univ. Sask, summer 57; Can. Counc. res. grants, summers 62 & 63, leave fel, 68-69; mem. scholar. comt, Can. Fed. Univ. Women, 64-; spec. lectr, Yeats Centenary Festival, Ireland, summer 65, lectr, Yeats Int. Summer Sch, 66 & 67; Guggenheim fel, 65-66. Soc. Auth, Eng; Shaw Soc, Eng; Soc. Theatre Res, Eng; Asn. Can. Univ. Teachers Eng; Humanities Asn. Can; Can. Asn. Irish Stud.(secy, 71-72); Int. Asn. Stud. Anglo-Irish Lit. Anglo-Irish literature, chiefly J.M. Synge, W.B. Yeats and Lady Gregory; modern poetry and drama; Canadian theatre and drama. Publ: Co-auth, The world of W.B. Yeats: essays in perspective, Univ. Victoria, Wash. Univ. & Dolmen, Dublin, 65; auth, In defence of Lady Gregory, playwright, 66 & Synge and modern comedy, 68, Dolmen, Dublin; The plays of J.M. Synge (2 vols), Oxford, 68; ed, The plays of Lady Gregory, Books 1-4, Vols. V-VIII of Code Edition, Colin Smythe, 70, A selection of letters from John M. Synge to W.B. Yeats and Lady Gregory, Cuala, 71 & Letters to Molly: J.M. Synge to Maire O'Neill, Belknap, Harvard, 71; auth, Stars of the Abbey's ascendency, In: Theatre and nationalism in 20th century Ireland, Univ. Toronto, 71; A reading of the Aran Islands and related writings, In: Sunshine and the moon's delight, Colin Smythe, 72; Deirdie of the sorrows: literature first. . . drama afterwards, In: Synge centenary essays, Dolmen, Dublin, 72; plus others. Add: Dept. of English, Victoria College, University of Toronto, Toronto, Ont. M5S 1K7, Can.

SADLER, DAVID FRANCIS, b. Iva, S.C, Feb. 11, 23; m. 44; c. 4. AMERICAN STUDIES. A.B, Antioch Col, 47; A.M, Univ. Minn, 48, Ph.D, 54. Asst. prof. ENG, Hamline Univ, 48-52; instr, Univ. Minn, 53-54; Gen. Motors Inst, 54-55; asst. prof, WEST. MICH. UNIV, 55-60, assoc. prof, 60-64, PROF, 64-, chmn. dept, 66-70. U.S.A.A.F, 43-46. Am. Stud. Asn; NCTE; AAUP. American literature; the 1920's and 1930's; children's literature. Publ: The second Mrs. Bundren, Am. Lit, 3/65; From Where the wild things are to Wild in the world, Children's Lit. in Educ, 1/74. Add: Dept. of English, Western Michigan University, Kalamazoo, MI 49001.

SADLER, GLENN EDWARD, b. Long Beach, Calif, Dec. 8, 35. ENGLISH. A.B, Wheaton Col, 58; M.A, Univ. Calif, Los Angeles, 60; Ph.D.(Eng), Univ. Aberdeen, 67. Asst. prof. ENG, Westmont Col, 68-71; vis. prof, Schiller Col, London Stud. Ctr, 72; ASSOC. PROF, POINT LOMA COL, 73- Fel, Univ. Edinburgh, 68-69; Am. Philos. Soc. grant stud. Charles Williams, 69-70. U.S.A.F, 61-63. MLA; AAUP; Sci. Fiction Res. Asn. Nineteenth century English literature; English novel; Oxford Christians, C.S. Lewis, Charles Williams and J.R.R. Tolkien. Publ: Ed, The gifts of the Child Christ: fairytales and stories for all ages (2 vols), Eerdmans, 73; co-auth, It must have been McNutt, Regal, 74; auth, The fantastic imagination in George MacDonald, In: Imagination and the spirit, Eerdmans, 71; An unpublished story by George MacDonald, J. Children's Lit, 73. Add: Sea View House, 4368 Bermuda Circle, San Diego, CA 92107.

SADLER, MARY LYNN VEACH, b. Duplin County, N.C, May 9, 40; m. 66. ENGLISH LITERATURE, PHILOLOGY. B.A, Duke Univ, 62; M.A, Univ. Ill, Urbana, 63, Ph.D.(Eng), 67; Univ. Calif, Los Angeles, summer 67. Instr. ENG, Agnes Scott Col, 66-67; from asst. prof. to assoc. prof, Drake Univ, 67-73; ASSOC. PROF, N.C. A&T STATE UNIV, 73- Teaching Award, Iowa Realty & Drake Univ, 71. MLA. Seventeenth century English literature. Publ: Typological imagery in Samson Agonistes, J. Eng. Lit. Hist, 70; Chaucer's The book of the Duchess and the Law of kinde, Annuale Mediaevale, 70; Regeneration and typology: Samson Agonistes and its relation to De doctrina, Paradise lost, and Paradise regained, Stud. Eng. Lit, 72. Add: 1601 Red Forest Rd, Greensboro, NC 27410.

SAFER, ELAINE BERKMAN, b. Brooklyn, N.Y, Sept. 18, 37; m. 60; c. 3. ENGLISH. B.A, Brooklyn Col, 58; M.S, Univ. Wis, 59; M.A, West. Reserve Univ, 61, Ph.D.(Eng), 67. Teaching fel. ENG, West. Reserve Univ, 61-63; instr, Northwest. Univ, 63-66; asst. prof, UNIV. DEL, 67-73, ASSOC. PROF, 73- MLA; Milton Soc. Am; Renaissance Soc. Am; AAUP. Milton; 17th century literature; modern novel. Publ: Co-auth, John Milton: L'Allegro and Il Penseroso, C.E. Merrill, 70; auth, Sufficient to have stood: Eve's responsibility in Book IX, Milton Quart, 10/72; The Socratic dialogue & Knowledge in the making in Paradise regained, Milton Stud, 74; Nativity ode and the Ode as genre, In: Milton Encycl, Univ. Wis, 74; plus others. Add: Dept. of English, University of Delaware, Newark, DE 19711.

SAFFELL, HELEN WEAVER, b. Alliance, Ohio, Dec. 20, 22; m. 55. ENGLISH. B.A, Mt. Union Col, 44; M.A, Univ. Mich, 45. Instr. ENG, Mt. Union Col, 46-50; West. Col, 54-55; asst. prof, MT. UNION COL, 55-66, ASSOC. PROF, 67- NCTE; Conf. Col. Compos. & Commun; Int. Reading Asn. Beowulf syntax. Add: Homeworth, OH 44634.

SAFRANEK, WILLIAM P, b. Winona, Minn, June 9, 29; m. 53; c. 6. ENGLISH & AMERICAN LITERATURE. A.B, Marquette Univ, 51; M.A, Univ. Wis, 55, Ph.D, 61. Asst. prof. ENG, Wis. State Col, Oshkosh, 58-61; from asst. prof. to ASSOC. PROF, GONZAGA UNIV, 61- U.S.N, 51-54, Res, 54-, Lt. NCTE. Nineteenth century American literature. Add: Dept. of English, Gonzaga University, Spokane, WA 99202.

SAGER, ALLAN HENRY, Theology, Speech Communication. See Volume IV, Philosophy, Religion & Law.

SAHA, PROSANTA KUMAR, English, Linguistics. See Volume III, Foreign Languages, Linguistics & Philology.

SAID, EDWARD WILLIAM, b. Jerusalem, Palestine, Nov. 1, 35; U.S. citizen; m. 70; c. 1. ENGLISH. A.B, Princeton, 57; fel, Harvard, 59-61, A.M, 60, Ph.D. (Eng), 64. Tutor hist. & lit, Harvard, 61-63; instr. Eng, COLUMBIA UNIV, 63-65, asst. prof, 65-68, assoc. prof, 68-70, PROF. ENG. & COMP. LIT, 70- Fel, Ctr. Advan. Stud, Univ. Ill, 67-68; vis. asst. prof. Eng, Harvard, summer 68 & vis. prof. comp. lit, 73-74; fel, Guggenheim Found, 73. MLA; fel. Acad. Lit. Stud. Eighteenth century English literature; modern comparative literature; theory and philosophy of criticism. Publ: Joseph Conrad and the fiction of autobiography, 66 & Swift's Tory anarchy, Harvard Univ; ed, The Arabs today: alternatives for the future, Follett, 73; auth, Beginnings: intention and method, Basic Bks, 74; Abecedarium cultural: structuralism (essay), In: Modern French criticism, Univ. Chicago, 69; On originality, Harvard Stud. Eng, 73; U.S. policy and the conflict of powers in the Middle East, J. Palestine Stud, 73; plus two others. Add: Dept. of English, Columbia University, New York, NY 10027.

ST. ARMAND, BARTON LEVI, b. Providence, R.I, May 8, 43. AMERICAN LITERATURE. A.B, Brown Univ, 65, NDEA fel, 65-68, A.M, 66, Ph.D. (Am. stud), 68. ASST. PROF. ENG, BROWN UNIV, 68- Bronson fel, 73; ed, Emerson Soc. Quart, 72-; Novel, 73- MLA; Col. Eng. Asn. Nineteenth century American literature; occult and alchemical studies; 19th century American painting. Publ: The roots of horror in the fiction of H.P. Lovecraft, Mirage, 74; Poe's sober mystification: the uses of alchemy in The gold-bug, Poe Stud, 6/71; Hawthorne's Haunted mind: a subterranean drama of the self, Criticism, winter 71; Jewett and Marin: the inner vision, In: Appreciation of Sarah Orne Jewett, Colby Press, 73. Add: Dept. of English, Brown University, Providence, RI 02912.

ST. CLAIR, FOSTER YORK, b. Rockland, Maine, Mar. 2, 05; m. 36; c. 3. ENGLISH LITERATURE. A.B, Harvard, 26, A.M, 27, Ph.D, 31. Instr. ENG, Univ. Wis, 27-29; prof. & head dept, Jamestown Col, 31-47; prof, UNIV. N.DAK, 47-73, head dept, 47-67, EMER. PROF, 73- MLA. Marie de France, her poetical works; Shakespeare; English literature 1500-1900. Publ: Drayton's first revision of his sonnets; Emerson among the Siphars. Add: 8801 Shenandoah Pl, Tucson, AZ 85710.

ST. JACQUES, RAYMOND CLAUDE, b. Ottawa, Ont, Mar. 19, 38; m. 64; c. 3. ENGLISH LITERATURE. B.A, Univ. Ottawa, 62, M.A, 64, Ph.D.(Eng), 67; fel, Cornell Univ, 64-65. Lectr. ENG, Bruyere Col, 63-64; D'Youville Col, 66-67; asst. prof, UNIV. OTTAWA, 67-71, ASSOC. PROF, 71- MLA (Can. del, 73-75); Mediaeval Acad. Am; Asn. Can. Univ. Teachers Eng. Piers Plowman; Old and Middle English; Anglo-Norman literature. Publ: The liturgical associations of Langland's Samaritan, Traditio, 69; Concience's final pilgrimage in Piers Plowman and the cyclical structure of the liturgy, Rev. Univ. Ottawa, 70. Add: Dept. of English, University of Ottawa, Ottawa, Ont. K1N 6N5, Can.

SAINTONGE, CONSTANCE, b. New London, Conn, Feb. 8, 05; m. ENGLISH. A.B, Mt. Holyoke Col, 28, A.M, 31; Col. of France, 33-34, 38; Oxford, 38. Asst. ENG, MT. HOLYOKE COL, 28-30, instr, 31-43, asst. prof, 43-56, assoc. prof, 56-70, EMER. ASSOC. PROF, 70- Europ. observer, Save Children Fed, 46, 47; regional judge, Book-of-the-Month Club Writing Fel. Prog, 68-69; bd. dirs, Mt. Holyoke Quart, 70-, ed, Common Wages, Mt. Holyoke Col, 71- Henry James' revisions of Roderick Hudson. Publ: An 18th century racketteer, Mod. Hist, 35; In defense of Criseyde, Mod. Lang. Quart, 12/54; plus others. Add: P.O. Box 82, South Hadley, MA 01075.

SALAMON, LINDA BRADLEY, b. Elmira, N.Y, Nov. 20, 41; m. 64; c. 2. ENGLISH LITERATURE, RENAISSANCE INTELLECTUAL HISTORY. B.A, Radcliffe Col, 63; A.M, Bryn Mawr Col, 64, Ph.D.(Eng), 71. Lectr. Eng, Duke Univ, 66-67; Dartmouth Col, 67-72; Smith Col, 72-73; resident fel, Radcliffe Col, 73-74, fel, Radcliffe Inst, 73-75. Renaissance Soc. Am. Sixteenth century poetry; art and literary relations; women in literature. Publ: The courtier and The scholemaster, Comp. Lit, 73; A face in The glasse: Gascoigne's Glasse of government, Stud. Philol, 74; A gloss on Daunsinge: Sir Thomas Elyot and T.S. Eliot's Four quartets, ELH, 74. Add: Radcliffe Institute, 3 James St, Cambridge, MA 02138.

SALE, RICHARD BARKSDALE, JR, b. Holdenville, Okla, Nov. 10, 30; m. 51; c. 3. ENGLISH. B.A, Univ. Tex, 52, M.A, 54, Ph.D.(Eng), 63. Teacher, High Sch, Tex, 53-55; dir. pub. inform, Del Mar Col, 55-57, asst. prof. ENG, 57-65; N.TEX. STATE UNIV, 65-68, assoc. prof, 68-73, PROF, 73-, fac. res. grants, 66 & 67. Fulbright lectr. Am. civilization & lit, Univ. Mohammed V, Morocco, 63-64. MLA. Victorian period; contemporary novel and poetry. Publ: Ed, Hog killin time and other poems, Trilobite Press, 73; Exchange teacher (poem), Midwest Quart. summer 67; Total recall, Nation, 6/68; I was a smuggler's aide in Algeciras, Prism Int. summer 68; plus numerous poems. Add: Dept. of English, North Texas State University, Denton, TX 76203.

SALE, ROGER H, b. New Haven, Conn, Aug. 19, 32; m. 55; c. 2. ENGLISH LITERATURE. B.A, Swarthmore Col, 53; M.A, Cornell Univ, 54, Ph.D, 57. Instr. ENG, Amherst Col, 57-60, asst. prof, 60-62; UNIV. WASH, 62-66, assoc. prof, 66-69, PROF, 69- Nat. Endowment for Humanities fel, 69-70. English Renaissance literature; the novel. Publ: Discussions of the novel, Heath, 60; Reading Spenser, 68 & On writing, 70, Random; Modern heroism, Univ. Calif, 73; England's Parnassus, 64, Achievement of William Empson, 66 & Rene Wellek's history, 67, Hudson Rev. Add: Dept. of English, University of Washington, Seattle, WA 98105.

SALE, WILLIAM MERRITT, JR, b. Louisville, Ky, Feb. 16, 99; m. 29; c. 3. ENGLISH LITERATURE. A.B, Univ. Wis, 22; A.M, Harvard, 23; Ph.D, Yale, 30. Instr. Yale, 25-35; asst. prof. Eng, CORNELL UNIV, 36-39, assoc. prof, 40-47, prof, 47-69, chmn. dept. lit, 50-56, chmn. dept. Eng, 62-69, EMER. PROF. ENG, 69- MLA. Literary criticism; 18th century literature; prose fiction. Publ: Samuel Richardson; Samuel Richardson, master printer; co-auth, The use of language. Add: 309 Parkway, Ithaca, NY 14850.

SALEM, JAMES MORRIS, b. Portage, Wis, Nov. 15, 37; m. 58; c. 4. ENGLISH, MODERN DRAMA. B.S, Wis. State Univ, La Crosse, 61; Kent State Univ, 61-62; NDEA fel, La. State Univ, 62-65, Ph.D.(Eng), 65. Asst. prof. Eng, Kent State Univ, 65-67; UNIV. ALA, 67-68, ASSOC. PROF. ENG. & DIR. AM. STUD, 68- Consult. Am. lit, Scarecrow Press, N.J, 67- U.S.A, 56-64. Am. Stud. Asn. American popular culture; American literature; American drama. Publ: Drury's guide to best plays (2nd ed), 69, ed, The teacher as writer, 70, auth, Part IV: the screenplay from the Jazz singer to Dr. Strangelove (2 vols), 71 & Part I: American drama, 1909-1969 (2nd ed), 73, Scarecrow; ed, A new generation of essays, W.C. Brown, 72; auth, Eugene O'Neill and the sacrament of marriage, Serif, 6/66; Philip Barry and the spirituality of love, Renascence, winter 67; Shaw on Broadway, 1894-1965, Shaw Rev, 1/68; plus three others. Add: 50 Southmont Dr, Tuscaloosa, AL 35401.

SALENIUS, ELMER WILLIAM, b. Maynard, Mass, Oct. 6, 17. ENGLISH. A.B, Boston Univ, 39, Ph.D.(Eng), 51; A.M, Harvard, 41. Instr. ENG, Col. Lib. Arts, Boston Univ, 46-52; FRAMINGHAM STATE COL, 52-53, asst. prof, 53-57, assoc. prof, 57-58, PROF, 58-, CHMN. DEPT, 61- U.S.A, 41-46, Capt. MLA; Col. Eng. Asn; NCTE. Modern drama; Shakespeare. Add: 13 Woodleigh Rd, Framingham, MA 01701.

SALERNO, HENRY FRANK, b. New Rochelle, N.Y, July 30, 19; m. 48; c. 2. ENGLISH. B.A, Univ. Colo, 49, M.A, 50; univ. fel, Univ. Ill, 50-55, Ph.D. (Eng. lit), 56. Instr. ENG, Univ. Colo, 55-57; Purdue Univ, 57-58, asst. prof, 58-64, assoc. prof, 64-68; PROF, STATE UNIV. N.Y. COL. FREDONIA, 68- Ed, First Stage, 61-68; Drama & Theatre, 68- MLA; Renaissance Soc. Am; Shakespeare Soc. Renaissance drama; Italian popular comedy and the Elizabethan drama; modern drama. Publ: Scenarios of the

Commedia dell'Arte, N.Y. Univ, 67; English drama in transition, Pegasus, 68; co-auth, Drama and tradition, Am. Bk. Co, 68; auth, Probable source of Dead man's fortune, Renaissance News, 60; The problem play, Eng. Lit. in Transition, 11/68; plus others. Add: Dept. of English, State University of New York College at Fredonia, Fredonia, NY 14063.

SALERNO, NICHOLAS ANDREW, b. Chicago, Ill, June 21, 36. ENGLISH LITERATURE. B.A, Ariz. State Univ, 57, M.A, 59; fel, Stanford Univ, 59-60, Ph.D, 62. Instr. ENG, Ariz. State Univ, 58-59; teaching asst, Stanford Univ, 59-61; instr, ARIZ. STATE UNIV, 61-62, asst. prof, 62-66, assoc. prof, 66-70, PROF, 70- Ariz. State Univ. fac. res. fels, 62-73; Nat. Found. Arts & Humanities jr. fel, 67-68. Med.Serv.C, U.S.A, 57-58, Res, 58-, Capt. NCTE; Philol. Asn. Pac. Coast; MLA; Am. Film Inst. Nineteenth century English literature; film history. Publ: Co-ed, Strategies in prose, Holt, 68, 70 & 73, The experience of literature, Prentice-Hall, 70 & Composition and literary form, Winthrop Publ, 72; auth, The game of love, Arion, fall 63; Algernon C. Swinburne, Victorian Poetry, winter 66; Marvell and the Foror Hortensis, Stud. Eng. Lit, winter 68. Add: Dept. of English, Arizona State University, Tempe, AZ 85281.

SALISBURY, LEE HARVEY, b. New York, N.Y, June 6, 27; m. 54; c. 4. DRAMA, CROSS CULTURAL COMMUNICATION. B.S, N.Y. Univ, 49; M.A, Columbia Univ, 50. Teacher, High Sch, Conn, 50-54; speech therapist, San Lorenzo Valley Sch, Calif, 54-55; asst. prof. speech & drama, UNIV. ALASKA, FAIRBANKS, 55-60, assoc. prof, 60-67, PROF. SPEECH & THEATER ARTS, 67-, DIR. DRAMA WORKSHOP, 55- Actor, Thirteen Players, N.Y, 47; Knickerbocker Repertory Co, N.J, 48; Straight Wharf Theatre, Mass, 49-50; tech. dir, Kennebunkport Playhouse, Maine, 52; dir, Milford Playhouse, Conn, 53; drama dir, YWCA, Bridgeport, Conn, 54; lang. arts consult, Bur. Indian Affairs, 62; speech pathologist, Alaska Crippled Children's Asn, summer 63; dir. & prin. investigator, Col. Orientation Prog. Alaskan Natives, Bur. Res, U.S. Off. Educ, summers 64-67; native commun. consult, U.S. Pub. Health Serv. Rehabil. Unit, 66; Ford Found. Alaska Rural Sch. Proj, 66-67; VISTA training prog, 66-67; vis. prof, Univ. Hawaii, 67-68; native commun. consult, NDEA Workshop Indian educ, Univ. Kans, 68; prof, NDEA workshop teachers Eng. speakers other lang. & dialects, Univ. South. Calif, 68; mem, Alaska Educ. Broadcast Comn, 69- U.S.N, 45-46. Speech Commun. Asn.(mem. legis. counc, 68); Int. Soc. Commun; Teachers Eng. to Speakers Other Lang; Am. Theatre Asn; Int. Soc. Gen. Semantics. Drama; speech; cross cultural communication. Publ: Co-auth, Cross-cultural communication and dramatic ritual, In: Communication: concepts and perspectives, Spartan-Macmillan, 67; auth, Teaching English to Alaska natives, Teachers Eng. Speakers Other Lang. Proc, 66 & J. Am. Indian Educ, 2/67; Role conflict in native communication, J. Eng. as Second Lang, spring 69. Add: Dept. of Speech, Drama & Radio, University of Alaska, Fairbanks, AK 99701.

SALISBURY, RALPH J, b. Arlington, Iowa, Jan. 24, 26; m; c. 3. CREATIVE WRITING, MODERN LITERATURE. M.F.A, Univ. Iowa, 51. Mem. fac. Eng. lit, Tex. A&M Univ, 51-54; creative writing & lit, Drake Univ, 54-60; PROF. ENG, UNIV. ORE, 60- Writing poetry and fiction. Publ: Ghost grapefruit and other poems, Ithaca, 72; stories in Perspective & other rev; poems in Poetry & New Yorker & other jours. Add: Dept. of English, University of Oregon, Eugene, OR 97403.

SALOMON, BROWNELL, b. New York, N.Y, Nov. 4, 33; m. 63; c. 1. ENGLISH. B.A, Univ. Fla, 55, M.A, 62; Ph.D.(Eng), Tulane Univ, 67. Asst. prof. ENG, BOWLING GREEN STATE UNIV, 66-72, ASSOC. PROF, 73- U.S.N.R, 56-60, Lt. Comdr. MLA; Renaissance Soc. Am. English Renaissance drama; Shakespeare; medieval drama. Publ: Early English drama, 975-1585: a select, annotated bibliography of full-length studies, Res. Opportunities in Renaissance Drama, 70; The theological basis of imagery and structure in The malcontent, Stud. Eng. Lit, 74; Visual and aural signs in the performed English Renaissance play, Renaissance Drama, 72; plus others. Add: Dept. of English, Bowling Green State University, Bowling Green, OH 43403.

SALOMON, LOUIS BERNARD, b. Louisville, Ky, April 28, 08; m. ENGLISH. B.A, Univ. Louisville, 28; M.A, Univ. Pa, 29, Ph.D.(Eng), 31. Asst. prof. ENG, West. Ky. Teachers Col, 31-38; PROF, BROOKLYN COL, 38- Fulbright lectr, Turku, Finland, 58-59 & Amsterdam, Netherlands, 67-68. U.S.A.A.F, 42-46, Lt. Col. NCTE; MLA; Am. Name Soc. American literature; 19th century English literature; semantics. Publ: The devil take her, Univ. Pa, 31 & A.S. Barnes, 61; Semantics and common sense, Holt, 66. Add: Dept. of English, Brooklyn College, Brooklyn, NY 11210.

SALOMON, ROGER BLAINE, b. Providence, R.I, Feb. 26, 28; m. 50; c. 2. ENGLISH. A.B, Harvard, 50; M.A, Univ. Calif, 51, Ph.D, 57. Instr. ENG, Mills Col, 55-57; Yale, 57-62, asst. prof, 62-66; assoc. prof, CASE WEST. RESERVE UNIV, 66-69, PROF, 69- Morse fel, 60-61; Guggenheim fel, 72-73; mem. adv. screening comt. Am. lit, Comt. Int. Exchange Persons. U.S.A.F, 52-53, 1st Lt. MLA; Am. Stud. Asn; AAUP. American literature; 19th and 20th century English literature. Publ: Twain and the image of history, Yale, 61; Escape from history; Mark Twain's Joan of Arc, Philol. Quart, 1/61; Realism as disinheritance: Twain, Howells & James, Am. Quart, winter 64; Mark Twain & Victorian nostalgia, In: Patterns of commitment in American literature, Univ. Toronto, 67. Add: 2830 Coventry Rd, Shaker Heights, OH 44120.

SALPER, ROBERTA LINDA, b. Boston, Mass, Sept. 16, 40. LATIN AMERICAN & SPANISH LITERATURE. B.A, Boston Univ, 59; fel, Inst. Int. Madrid, 61-62; univ. fel, Harvard, 59-61, M.A, 61, Ph.D.(Romance lang), 67. Teaching asst. Span, Harvard, 60; instr. Span. lit, Milton Col, 65-66; asst. prof. Hispanic lit, Univ. Pittsburgh, 68-70, fac. res. grant, summer 69, asst. dean, Col. Arts & Sci, 69-70, dir. comp. lit. prog, 70; vis. assoc. prof. Span. & planning consult, STATE UNIV. N.Y. COL. OLD WESTBURY, 70-71, ASSOC. PROF. HUMANITIES, 71-, CHAIRWOMAN DEPT. COMMUN. & CREATIVE ARTS, 73- Harvard fel, Madrid, Spain, 66-68; Ctr. Int. Stud. Univ. Pittsburgh travel grant, Cuba, summer 69; guest lectr. women's educ, Sorbonne, 70; vis. distinguished prof. women's stud, San Diego State Col, 70-71; State Univ. N.Y. fac. res. grant, summer 72; Nat. Endowment for Humanities younger humanist fel, 72-73; lectr, Harvard Divinity Sch, 72; mem. ed. bd, J. Women's Stud. MLA (comn. status women, 69-71). Caribbean literature; women in history. Publ: Female liberation: history and current politics, Random, 72; contrib, Female studies I, II, V, Know, Ind, 70-72; auth, Literature and revolution in Cuba, Monthly Rev, 70; Women's studies, Ramparts, 12/71; Women in Cuba, Ms Mag, 12/73; plus others. Add: Dept. of Communicative & Creative Arts, State University of New York College at Old Westbury, Old Westbury, NY 11568.

SALZ, PAULINA J, English. See POLLAK, PAULINA S.

SALZBERG, ALBERT C, b. New York, N.Y, June 27, 35. ENGLISH LITERATURE. B.A, Brooklyn Col, 57, M.A, 59; Ph.D, N.Y. Univ, 63. Asst. ENG, Brooklyn Col, 58, lectr, 59; Hunter Col, 59-60; instr, R.I. COL, 62-63, asst. prof, 63-68, ASSOC. PROF, 68- Donald E. Whiteside Sr. Eng. Award, Brooklyn Col, 57; Founder's Day Distinguished Scholar Award, N.Y. Univ, 63. MLA; NCTE; AAUP; Col. Eng. Asn; Am. Fed. Teachers. Neoclassical and mediaeval literature. Add: Dept. of English, Rhode Island College, Providence, RI 02908.

SALZBERG, JOEL, b. Brooklyn, N.Y, May 31, 34. AMERICAN LITERATURE. B.A, City Col. New York, 56; M.A, Ind. Univ, 60; Ph.D.(Eng), Univ. Okla, 67. Asst. prof. ENG, Univ. North. Iowa, 65-68; UNIV. COLO, DENVER CENTER, 68-72, ASSOC. PROF, 72- MLA. American Romanticism; psychology and literary criticism; 19th century realism. Add: Dept. of English, University of Colorado, Denver Center, Denver, CO 80202.

SALZMAN, ERIC, b. New York, N.Y, Sept. 8, 33; m. 60; c. 2. MUSIC THEATRE. B.A, Columbia Univ, 54; M.F.A, Princeton, 56; Fulbright grant, Acad. St. Cecilia, Rome, 56-58 & Darmstadt, Ger, summer 57. Music critic, New York Times, 58-62; New York Herald-Tribune, 62-66; asst. prof. music, Queens Col.(N.Y), 66-68; music dir, WBAI-FM, 62-63, 68-71; ARTISTIC DIR, QUOG MUSIC-THEATER, N.Y.C, 70- Ford fel, Europe, 64-65; vis. lectr, Inst. Torquato di Tella, Buenos Aires, 69. Sang Prize, Knox Col. Am. Soc. Composers, Auth. & Publ. Twentieth century music. Publ: Twentieth century music: an introduction, Prentice-Hall, 67, rev. ed, 73; contrib, The new American arts, Horizon 65; plus many large scale works for multi-media, music theatre, audio & video recording. Add: 29 Middagh St, Brooklyn, NY 11201.

SALZMAN, JACK, b. Cologne, Ger, Dec. 8, 37; U.S. citizen; m. 59; c. 2. ENGLISH. B.A, Brooklyn Col, 58; M.A, N.Y. Univ, 60, Ph.D.(Eng), 65. Lectr. ENG, Brooklyn Col, 59-64; instr, Mich. State Univ, 64-65; asst. prof, LONG ISLAND UNIV, 65-71, ASSOC. PROF, 71- Fulbright lectr. Am. lit, Turku Univ, Finland, 67-68 & Japan, 72. MLA; Am. Stud. Asn. American literature, 1900 to present. Publ: Ed, Years of protest: collection of American writings of the 1930's, Pegasus, 67, Sister Carrie, Bobbs, 69, Equality, Greenwood, 70, Merrill studies in an American tragedy, C.E. Merrill, 71 & Theodore Dreiser: the critical reception, David Lewis, 73; auth, Critical recognition of Sister Carrie, J. Am. Stud, 69; Robert Cantwell, Contemporary Novelists, 72; ed, I find the real American tragedy, Resources Am. Lit. Stud, 72; plus others. Add: Dept. of English, Brooklyn Center, Long Island University, Brooklyn, NY 11201.

SAMPLEY, ARTHUR McCULLOUGH, b. Leander, Tex, Jan. 9, 03; m. 30, 61; c. 2. ENGLISH LITERATURE. A.B, Univ. Tex, 23, A.M, 25, Ph.D, 30; B.L.S, Columbia Univ, 47. Tutor Eng, Univ. Tex, 23-25, instr, 25-28; assoc. prof, La. State Norm. Col, 30-31; head dept, Sul Ross State Teachers Col, 31-35; prof, N.Tex. State Univ, 35-53, distinguished prof, 53-72, dir. libr, 44-53, dean arts & sci, 53, v.pres, 53-59; RETIRED. Vis. prof, Univ. Tex, 40-41; state poet laureate, Tex, 51-53. Anderson Award, Stanford Univ, 39; Award, Tex. Inst. Lett, 47, 51 & 71. U.S.A.A.F, 43-44, 1st Lt. Poetry Soc. Am.(Edwin Markham Award, 64, 65); MLA. Elizabethan drama; Peele; poetry. Publ: This is our time, 43, Of the strong and the fleet, 47 & Furrow with blackbirds, 51, Kaleidograph; Selected poems 1937-1971, N.Tex. State Univ, 71; The text of Peele's David and Bethsabe, PMLA, 9/31; Maxwell Anderson's poetic tragedies, Col. Eng, 5/44; The tensions of Robert Frost, S.Atlantic Quart, autumn 66. Add: 2011 W. Oak, Denton, TX 76201.

SAMPSON, EDWARD C, b. Ithaca, N.Y, Dec. 20, 20; m. 68; c. 2. ENGLISH. B.A, Cornell Univ, 42, Ph.D, 57; M.A, Columbia Univ, 48. Instr. Eng, Hofstra Univ, 46-49; fel, Cornell Univ, 49-52; instr. lib. stud, Clarkson Col. Technol, 52-53, asst. prof, 53-57, assoc. prof, 57-61, PROF, 61-66, humanities, 66-69; ENG, STATE UNIV. N.Y. COL. ONEONTA, 69- Fulbright lectr, Univ. Panjab, Pakistan, 59-60; fac. res. fel, State Univ. N.Y, summer 73. U.S.A.A.F, 42-46, Capt. MLA. Hawthorne; E.B. White. Publ: Critical study of E.B. White, Vol. 233, In: Twayne United States authors series, Twayne, (in press); Motivation in The scarlet letter, 1/57 & Three unpublished letters by Hawthorne to Epes Sargeant, 3/62, Am. Lit; afterword, The house of the seven gables, Signet, 61. Add: Dept. of English, State University of New York College at Oneonta, Oneonta, NY 13820.

SAMPSON, HAROLD P, b. Jefferson, Ohio, June 15, 25; m. 51; c. 2. SPEECH. B.S, Sioux Falls Col, 50; M.A, Univ. S.Dak, 53; Woods fel, 63; Ph.D.(speech), South. Ill. Univ, 66. Instr. speech & bus. admin, Parkston High Sch, S.Dak, 50-52; speech, Watertown High Sch, S.Dak, 52-58; asst. prof, Nebr. Wesleyan Univ, 58-66; assoc. prof, CENT. MO. STATE UNIV, 66-68, prof. speech & chmn. div. lang. & lit, 68-73, DEAN GRAD. SCH, 73-, chmn. dept. speech, 67-73. U.S.A, 43-46, T/Sgt. Speech Asn. Am; Am. Forensic Asn; Cent. States Speech Asn. Speech education. Add: Graduate School, Central Missouri State University, Warrensburg, MO 64093.

SAMPSON, HERBERT GRANT, b. Bishopton, Que, May 7, 32. ENGLISH. B.A, Bishop's Univ, 52, M.A, 54; B.Mus, McGill Univ, 50; Ph.D.(Eng), Mich. State Univ, 64. Lectr. music, Univ. Alta, 53-54; Eng, Queen's Univ. (Ont), 58-62, asst. prof, 62-64; vis. assoc. prof, Col. William & Mary, 64-65; dir. concerts, QUEEN'S UNIV.(ONT), 65-71, ASSOC. PROF. ENG, 68-, summer res. grant, 59. Can. Counc. grant, 60; res. award humanities, 73, 74. Hon. mem. Asn. Col. & Univ. Concert Masters; Asn. Can. Univ. Teachers Eng; Humanities Asn. Can. Structure of 18th century drama. Publ: The Anglican tradition in eighteenth-century verse, Mouton, 71; Structure in the poetry of Thoreau, Costerus, 72. Add: Dept. of English, Queen's University, Kingston, Ont. K7L 3N6, Can.

SAMPSON, WILLIAM ROBERT, b. Detroit, Mich, Apr. 23, 42; m. 70; c. 1. SPEECH COMMUNICATION. B.A, West. Mich. Univ, 64; M.A, Wayne State Univ, 67, Ph.D.(speech), 73. Teacher speech & Eng, Utica Community Schs, Mich, 64-66; instr. SPEECH, Macomb County Community Col, 65-66, 66-68; asst. prof, FERRIS STATE COL, 68-72, ASSOC. PROF, 72- Speech Commun. Asn; Int. Commun. Asn; Int. Soc. Gen. Semantics; NEA. Communication theory; small group behavior; instructional development. Add: Dept. of Speech, Ferris State College, Big Rapids, MI 49307.

SAMS, HENRY WHITTINGTON, b. Clarksville, Va, Feb. 26, 12; m. 35; c. 4. ENGLISH LITERATURE. A.B, Oberlin Col, 33, A.M, 35; Ph.D, Univ. N.C, 40. Instr, Oberlin Col, 36-37, 38-40; Univ. N.C, 37-38, 39-40; asst. prof, The Citadel, 40-42; instr, Queen's Col.(N.Y), 42-43; ENG. LIT, Univ. Chicago, 46-49, assoc. prof, 49-59; PROF. & HEAD DEPT, PA. STATE UNIV, UNIVERSITY PARK, 59-, ASSOC. DEAN GRAD. SCH, 73- Ed, J. Gen. Educ, 69- U.S.N.R, 43-45, Lt. Col. Eng. Asn; MLA; NCTE. Jonathan Swift; rhetoric; literary criticism. Publ: Self-love and the doctrine of work; Anti-Stoicism in the seventeenth and early eighteenth century England; new problems in reading and writing. Add: Dept. of English, Pennsylvania State University, University Park, PA 16801.

SAMUEL, DOROTHY IONE JOHNSON, b. Atlantic City, N.J, Jan. 16, 17; m. 39. ENGLISH, FRENCH. B.S, Va. Union Univ, 36; M.A, Atlanta univ, 42; Ohio State Univ, 48-49; scholar, Univ. Pa, summer 57; Univ. Leiden, summer 61; Ford Found grant, Vanderbilt Univ, 68-69. Teacher, High Sch, N.C, 37-41; Ga, 42-43; Ala, summer 45; asst. prof. & chmn. dept. French, Tex. Col, 47-48; head dept. Eng, Mary Allen Col, 50-52; assoc. prof. French & Eng. & chmn. dept. French, Tex. Col, 52-58, acting head div. humanities & fine arts, 57-58; ASSOC. PROF. French & Eng, TENN. STATE UNIV, 58-66, ENG, 66- MLA; Int. Comp. Lit. Asn; Col. Eng. Asn; Int. Platform Asn. Anglo-French and Franco-American comparative literature; 19th and 20th century poetry. Publ: Geoffrey Chaucer and Chretien de Troyes: parallels in the Clerk's tale & the Romance of Erec and Enide, 11/59 & Yeats and his antithetical hypothesis in Ego dominus tuus and in The second coming, 11/71, Fac. J; Poe and Baudelaire: parallels in form and symbol, CLA J, 12/59; plus one other. Add: Dept. of English, Box 432, Tennessee State University, Nashville, TN 37203.

SAMUEL, IRENE, b. New York, N.Y, May 14, 15. ENGLISH LITERATURE. A.B, Cornell Univ, 35, A.M, 36, Ph.D, 40. Instr, Bath Jr. Col, N.Y, 36-37; instr. Eng. & asst. drama, Rockford Col, 37-38; asst. ENG, Cornell Univ, 41; instr, Queens Col.(N.Y), 42-44; HUNTER COL, 44-48, asst. prof, 49-61, assoc. prof, 62-65, prof, 65-71, EMER. PROF, 71- Vis. assoc. prof, Wash. Univ, 58; N.Y. Univ, 60; Guggenheim fel, 66-67; Huntington Libr. grant, 71; vis. prof. Eng, Univ. West. Ont, summer 71; Andrew Mellon vis. prof, Univ. Pittsburgh, 72; vis. prof, Emory Univ, 74. Milton Soc. Am. (v.pres, 68, pres, 69, hon. scholar, 72); MLA; Int. Asn. Univ. Prof. Eng; Acad. Lit. Stud. Milton; Swift; literary criticism of the Renaissance. Publ: Plato and Milton, 47, 65 & Dante and Milton, 66, Cornell Univ; transl. & co-auth, Introd. & notes, Tasso, Discourses on the heroic poem, Clarendon, 73; auth, Samson agonistes as tragedy, In: Calm of mind, Case West. Reserve, 72; Milton on comedy and satire, Huntington Libr. Quart, 72; The regaining of paradise, In: The prison and the pinnacle, Univ. Toronto, 73; plus others. Add: 17 W 67th St, New York, NY 10023.

SAMUELS, ERNEST, b. Chicago, Ill, May 18, 03; m. 38; c. 3. AMERICAN LITERATURE. Ph.B, Univ. Chicago, 23, J.D, 26, A.M, 31, Ph.D, 42. Instr. ENG, State Col. Wash, 37-39; NORTHWEST. UNIV, EVANSTON, 42-46, asst. prof, 46-49, assoc. prof, 49-54, PROF, 54-71, EMER. PROF, 71- Vis. assoc. prof, Univ. Chicago, 50; Guggenheim fel, 55-56 & 71-72; Fulbright lectr. to Belgium, 58-59; ed. adv. comt, Adams papers; mem. ed. bd, Am. Lit, 65-71; Leo S. Bing vis. prof, Univ. South. Calif, 66-67; mem, Ill. State Comn. Scholars, 66-71. Francis Parkman Prize, 59; Bancroft Prize, 59; Pulitzer Prize in Biog, 65. MLA; Am. Stud. Asn. Post Civil War; Henry Adams; Bernard Berenson. Publ: The young Henry Adams, 48, Henry Adams: the middle years, 58 & Henry Adams: the major phase, 64, Harvard Univ; ed, History of the U.S.A, Univ. Chicago, 67 & The education of Henry Adams, Houghton, 73; contrib, Major American writers, Harcourt, 62; auth, Henry Adams and the gossip mills, In: Essays in literature in honor of B. McElderry, Ohio Univ, 67; plus others. Add: Dept. of English, Northwestern University, Evanston, IL 60201.

SANCETTA, JOYCE KELLOGG, b. Carlisle, Pa, Dec. 18, 12; m. 48; c. 2. ENGLISH. B.A, Col. Wooster, 34; scholar. & fel, Yale, 34-38, Ph.D.(Eng), 38. Asst. ENG, Conn. Col. Women, 37-38; instr, Ala. Col, 38-42; N.J. Col. Women, Rutgers, 42-43; Braircliff Jr. Col, 43-44; Brooklyn Col, summer 44; Bard Col, 44-45; West. Reserve Univ, 45-47; asst. prof, Goucher Col, 47-48; COL. WILLIAM & MARY, 57-59, assoc. prof, CHRISTOPHER NEWPORT COL, 66-69, PROF, 69- MLA; South. Mod. Lang. Asn; Asn. Depts. Eng. Romantic English literature. Add: Dept. of English, Christopher Newport College, Newport News, VA 23606.

SANDEEN, ERNEST E, b. Warren Co, Ill, Dec. 15, 08; m. 36; c. 2. AMERICAN LITERATURE. B.A, Knox Col, 31, Honnold fel, 31-33; B.Litt, Oxford, 33; Ph.D, State Univ. Iowa, 40. Instr. ENG, Knox Col, 35-37; State Univ. Iowa, 37-43; asst. prof, UNIV. NOTRE DAME, 46-47, assoc. prof, 47-60, PROF, 60-, chmn. dept, 65-68. Fulbright fel, Denmark, 57-58; summer instr, Univ. Minn, 61. U.S.N.R, 43-46, Lt. MLA; Col. Eng. Asn. Creative writing; poetry. Publ: Co-auth, Fifty years of the American novel, 51 & American classics reconsidered, 58, Scribner; auth, Children and older strangers, Univ. Notre Dame, 61. Add: Dept. of English, University of Notre Dame, Notre Dame, IN 46556.

SANDEFUR, RAY HAROLD, b. Nowata, Okla, Jan. 4, 15; m. 36; c. 2. SPEECH. A.B. & B.S, Emporia State Teachers Col, 36; M.A, Univ. Colo, 41; Ph.D, State Univ. Iowa, 50. Instr, High Sch, Kans, 36-43; asst. prof. PROF. SPEECH, UNIV. AKRON, 50-, DEAN COL. FINE & APPLIED ARTS, 67-, head dept. speech, 50-68, chmn. div. humanities, 57-67. U.S.N.R, 43-46, Lt.(jg). Speech Commun. Asn; Cent. States Speech Asn. Public address; rhetorical theory. Publ: Co-auth, Guidelines for effective speaking, W.C. Brown, 67; auth, Logan's oration—how authentic?, Quart. J. Speech, 60; co-auth, Parliamentary idiom in a municipal university, West. Speech, 65. Add: 1333 Shanabrook Dr, Akron, OH 44313.

SANDELIN, CLARENCE KENNETH, b. Des Moines, Iowa, Oct. 16, 15; m. 41; c. 3. ENGLISH. B.A, State Univ. Iowa, 39, M.A, 42; Ph.D.(Eng), Univ. Wis, 56. Mem. staff & fac. logistics mgt, U.S. Army Command & Gen. Staff Sch, 44-45; instr. ENG, U.S. Armed Forces Inst, Gen. Hq, Allied Forces Pac. Area Command, 45-46; Drake Univ, 46; Univ. South. Calif, 47-49; asst. prof. & head dept, CALIF. STATE UNIV, LOS ANGELES, 49-50, assoc. prof, 50-63, PROF, 63-, chmn. div. lang. arts, 50-57. Exec. dir, Mgt. Co. Am, 56-58; pub. speaker, U.S. & Can, 56-58; mgt. consult. & dir. var. corps, 56-60; consult, TV Eng. Course, 60-61; bk. consult, Scott, Foresman & Co, 61; staff contrib, Abstr. Eng. Stud, 62-63, asst. ed, 63-65; pres, Wilderness Found, 63-; consult & host, The absurd arts: mass media in critical perspective, NBC TV Ser, 67-68. U.S.A, 42-46, Res, 57-69, Col. MLA; Col. Eng. Asn; Philol. Asn. Pac. Coast; NCTE. American studies in literature and popular culture of the 20th century; literary achievement of Henry Adams and his contemporaries. Publ: Robert Nathan, In: Twayne's U.S. Auth. Ser, 64 & Muriel Spark, In: Twayne's Europ. Auth. Ser,(in press), Twayne. Add: 817 Irving Dr, Burbank, CA 91504.

SANDERLIN, GEORGE WILLIAM, b. Baltimore, Md, Feb. 5, 15; m. 36; c. 4. ENGLISH. A.B, Am. Univ.(D.C), 35; scholar, Johns Hopkins Univ, 35-38, Ph.D, 38. From instr. to assoc. prof. ENG, Univ. Maine, 38-55; PROF, SAN DIEGO STATE UNIV, 55- AAUP. Mediaeval literature; Renaissance history. Publ: College reading, rev. ed, 58, co-auth, Effective writing and reading, 62 & auth, Effective writing, 66, Heath; St. Jerome and the Bible, 61 & St. Gregory The Great, 64, Farrar, Straus; First around the world, 64, Eastward to India, 65, Across the ocean sea, 66, 1776: journals of American independence, 68 & The sea-dragon: journals of Francis Drake's voyage around the world, 69, Harper; Benjamin Franklin: as others saw him, 71 & The settlement of California, 72, Coward, McCann & Geoghegan; Bartolomé de Las Casas: a selection of his writings, Knopf, 71. Add: Dept. of English, San Diego State University, San Diego, CA 92115.

SANDERLIN, ROBERT REED, b. Memphis, Tenn, Sept. 19, 37; m. 60; c. 2. ENGLISH. B.S, Memphis State Univ, 60, M.A, 61; Ph.D.(Eng), Univ. N.C, 68. Instr. Eng, N.C. State Univ, 62-65; Univ. N.C, 65-67; asst. prof, Univ. South. Miss, 67-69; exec. asst. to chancellor, UNIV. TENN, CHATTANOOGA, 69-71, assoc. dir. office urban affairs, 71-72, ASST. PROF. ENG, 72- Coord, Bur. Indian Affairs prog. & disadvantaged youth prog, Univ. South. Miss, summer 67; invitee, 1st Annual Jefferson Lectures, Nat. Humanities Found, D.C, 72. MLA; Southeast. Mod. Lang. Asn; NCTE. Add: Dept. of English, University of Tennessee at Chattanooga, Chattanooga, TN 37401.

SANDERS, CHARLES, b. Brooklyn, N.Y, Feb. 4, 35; m. 61; c. 2. ENGLISH. A.B, Univ. N.C, 57, M.A, 58; Ph.D.(Eng), Univ. Mich, 65. Lectr. ENG, Univ. Mich, 64-65; asst. prof, UNIV. ILL, URBANA-CHAMPAIGN, 65-68, assoc. prof, 68-71, PROF, 71- MLA; NCTE. Twentieth century British and American poetry; satire; history of the essay. Publ: Co-auth, At length: twenty essays for composition, 68 & auth, The scope of satire, 71, Scott; auth, W. Somerset Maugham, North. Ill. Press, 70; plus three others. Add: Dept. of English, 127 English Bldg, University of Illinois at Urbana-Champaign, Urbana, IL 61801.

SANDERS, CHARLES RICHARD, b. Murfreesboro, Tenn, Aug. 14, 04. ENGLISH LITERATURE. Ph.B, Emory Univ, 26, A.M, 27; Ph.D, Univ. Chicago, 34. Asst. prof. ENG, Emory Jr. Col, 28-37; instr, DUKE UNIV, 37-38, asst. prof, 38-43, assoc. prof, 43-52, PROF, 52- Instr, Univ. Chicago, 32-33. English literary biography; 19th century English literature. Publ: Coleridge and the broad church movement, 42; The Strachey family, 1588-1932, Duke Univ, 53; Lytton Strachey, 57; Carlyle letters, 70-; The correspondence and friendship of Thomas Carlyle and Leigh Hunt, Bull. John Rylands Libr, 63. Add: 103 Pinecrest Rd, Durham, NC 27705.

SANDERS, DAVID SCOTT, b. Kellogg, Idaho, June 14, 26; m. 48; c. 3. AMERICAN LITERATURE. A.B, Univ. Calif, Los Angeles, 49, M.A, 53, Ph.D, 56. Instr. Eng, Univ. Md, 56-59; asst. prof, Harvey Mudd Col, 59-63, assoc. prof, 63-69, prof, 69-70; prof. humanities & chmn. dept, Clarkson Col, 70-73; PROF. HUMANITIES & SOC. SCI. & CHMN. DEPT. HUMANITIES, HARVEY MUDD COL, 73- Prof, Claremont Grad. Sch, 73-; Fulbright lectr, Univ. Salamanca, 66-67. U.S.N, 44-46. Am. Stud. Asn; MLA; Am. Soc. Engineering Educ. Modern American novel; John Dos Passos; literature and politics. Publ: John Hersey, Twayne, 67; ed, Studies in U.S.A, Merrill, 72; auth, The anarchism of John Dos Passos, 61 & Dos Passos early novels: lies and the system, 66, S.Atlantic Quart; The art of fiction: John Dos Passos, Paris Rev, 69; plus others. Add: Dept. of Humanities, Harvey Mudd College, Claremont, CA 91711.

SANDERS, FRANKLIN DAVID, b. Baltimore, Md, Oct. 25, 34. ENGLISH. B.A, Bob Jones Univ, 56; M.A, Univ. N.C, 58, Ph.D.(Eng), 63. Instr. ENG, Univ. N.C, 57-60, teaching fel, 60-61; instr, Univ. Richmond, 61-63, asst. prof, 63-66, assoc. prof, 66-68, acting chmn. dept, 68; ASSOC. PROF, E.CAROLINA UNIV, 68- Vis. asst. prof, Col. William & Mary, 64; asst. dir, Bread Loaf Sch. Eng, Middlebury Col, 65-; pres, Regional Col. Eng. Asn, 67-68; Nat. Defense fel, 68. MLA; Col. Eng. Asn; S.Atlantic Mod. Lang. Asn. Literary criticism; Shakespeare; 17th century English literature. Publ: Co-auth, The loser, Funk, 68. Add: Dept. of English, East Carolina University, Greenville, NC 27834.

SANDERS, FREDERICK KIRKLAND, b. Charleston, S.C, Dec. 30, 36; m. 65; c. 2. ENGLISH & AMERICAN LITERATURE. B.A, Wofford Col, 58; Bread Loaf Sch. English, summer 61; M.A, Emory Univ, 63; Ph.D.(Eng), Univ. Ga, 71. Teacher, Murray High Sch, Charleston, S.C, 58-59, Spartanburg Day Sch, 59-61; instr. ENG, Converse Col, 62-65; Univ. Ga, 68-69; ASST. PROF. GA. SOUTH. COL, 69- Eighteenth century English literature; early American literature; modern literature. Publ: Theme and structure in The fathers, Arlington Quart, winter 67-68; Mr. Thoreau's time bomb, Nat. Rev, 6/68; The view beyond the dinghey, Sewanee Rev, summer 71. Add: Dept. of English, Georgia Southern College, Statesboro, GA 30458.

SANDERS, GERALD ALBERT, Linguistics. See Volume III, Foreign Languages, Linguistics & Philology.

SANDERS, NORMAN JOSEPH, b. Birkenhead, Eng, Apr. 22, 29; m. 51. ENGLISH. B.A, Univ. Birmingham, 50, dipl, 51; Ph.D.(Eng), Shakespeare Inst, Eng, 57. Fulbright scholar & asst. prof. ENG, Univ. Ala, 57-58; fel, Shakespeare Inst, Univ. Birmingham, 58-62; assoc. prof, UNIV. TENN, 62-65, PROF, 65- Fulbright travel award, 57; secy, Shakespeare Conf, 59 & 61; mem. adv. bd, World Ctr. Shakespeare Stud, 72. Brit. Army, 51-53, Sgt. Malone Soc; Shakespeare Asn. Am; MLA; S.Atlantic Mod. Lang. Asn; Renaissance Soc. Am; Mod. Humanities Res. Asn; Int. Asn. Univ. Prof. Eng. Literature of Elizabethan and Jacobean periods; drama; 18th century literature. Publ: Shakespearean essays, Univ. Tenn, 64; auth, Analysis of The taming of the shrew, A.R.D.M. Corp, 67; ed, Julius Caesar, 67 & The two gentlemen of Verona, 68, Penguin; auth, Robert Greene's James the Fourth, Methuen, London, 70; ed, Richard the Second, W.C. Brown, 70 & A midsummers night's dream, Macmillan, London, 72; auth, The shift of power in Julius Caesar, Rev. Eng. Lit, 64; Shakespeare critical studies, In: Shakespeare survey 20, 24, 25 & 26, Cambridge, 67, 71, 72 & 73; contrib, Shakespeare's text, In: Shakespeare: a bibliographical guide, Oxford, 73; plus others. Add: 7113 Deane Hill Dr, Knoxville, TN 37919.

SANDERSON, DAVID ROLAND, b. St. Louis, Mo, June 23, 41; m. 63; c. 3. ENGLISH & AMERICAN LITERATURE. B.A, Gordon Col, 62; M.A, Johns Hopkins Univ, 64; Ph.D.(Eng), Univ. Calif, Davis, 69. Instr. ENG, Millikin Univ, 64-66; ASST. PROF, BELOIT COL, 69- Ed. assoc. Beloit Poetry J, 71- MLA. English romantic poetry and prose; nonfictional prose. Publ: Wordsworth's world, 1809: a stylistic study of the Cintra pamphlet, Wordsworth Circle, 70; Robert Southey and the standard Georgian style, Midwest Quart, 71; Coleridge's political sermons: discursive language and the voice of God, Mod. Philol, 73; plus one other. Add: Dept. of English, Beloit College, Beloit, WI 53511.

SANDERSON, JAMES LEE, b. Hiseville, Ky, Aug. 22, 26; m. 49; c. 1. ENGLISH. A.B, Univ. Mich, 47, M.A, 49; Ph.D.(Eng), Univ. Pa, 60. Asst. instr, Univ. Pa, 54-55; asst. prof. ENG, Grove City Col, 55-56, assoc. prof, 56; asst. prof, COL. S. JERSEY, RUTGERS UNIV, 60-63, assoc. prof, 63-67, PROF. & CHMN. DEPT, 67-, acting chmn. dept, 64-67. U.S.N, 44-46, 52-53, Lt.(jg). MLA; NCTE. English Renaissance literature; Shakespeare. Publ: Shakespeare's Henry IV, part 1, Norton, 62; co-auth, Exposition and the English language, Appleton, 63 & Phaedra and Hippolytus: myth and dramatic form, Houghton, 66; auth, Eipgrames per Benjamin Rudyerd, Rev. Eng. Stud, XVII: 241-255; Bérenger de la Tour and Sir John Davies, Libr. Chronicle, 33: 116-125; The theme of patience in The comedy of errors, Tex. Stud. Lang. & Lit, (in press). Add: 49 Grove St, Haddonfield, NJ 08033.

SANDERSON, RICHARD ARLO, b. Oskaloosa, Iowa, May 9, 30; m. 56; c. 2. COMMUNICATION. B.A, Cornell Col, 52; State Univ. Iowa, 52-53 & summer 55; M.A, Univ. South. Calif, 58, Ph.D.(commun), 61. Instr. drama, Cornell Col, summer 52; film supvr, Univ. Ky, 56-57; asst. prof. media & pub. admin. & audio visual adv, Sch. Pub. Admin. Proj. Pakistan, Univ. South. Calif, 61-62; asst. prof. educ. commun. & assoc. dir, Commun. Ctr, Univ. Hawaii, 62-67, assoc. prof. educ. commun. & dir. Commun. Ctr, 67-68; Fulbright lectr. mass commun, Univ. Chiengmai, 68-69; assoc. prof. cinema & dir, Dept. Photography & Cinema, Ohio State Univ, 69-70; PROF. EDUC. COMMUN. & MEDIA SPECIALIST, INST. RESOURCES CTR, UNIV. HAWAII, HONOLULU, 70- Dir, NDEA Title XI Media Specialist Workshops, summer 65; Title VI-A Fac. Develop. Media Workshops, 67-68. U.S.A, 53-55. Univ. Film Asn; Asn. Educ. Commun. & Technol. Inter-cultural and international communication through mass media; Educational and documentary film research and production. Publ: The motion picture: communication channel for information skills, concepts, attitudes, In: Instructional process and media integration, Rand McNally, 68; producer, Life in China, Dept. Photography & Cinema, Ohio State Univ, 72; co-auth, China-watching with film, J. Univ. Film Asn, 73; plus others. Add: Instructional Resources Center, University of Hawaii, 1733 Donaghho Rd, Honolulu, HI 96822.

SANDERSON, SARAH E, b. Fairmont, W.Va, Jan. 17, 32; m. 56; c. 2. SPEECH, COMMUNICATION. A.B, Fairmont State Col, 53; M.A, Bowling Green State Univ, 55; Ph.D.(speech), Univ. South. Calif, 65. Teacher high sch, Ohio, 53-54; asst. prof. speech & radio, Georgetown Col, 56-57; instr. speech & coordinator women's activities, Harbor Col, Calif, 59-61; prin, Lahor Am. Sch, W.Pakistan, 61-62; asst. prof. speech & commun, UNIV. HAWAII, MANOA, 67-72, ASSOC. PROF, 72- Consult, U.S. Weather Bur, 66, Pac. Region, Weather Bur. Airport Sta, 67; ed, Pac. Speech Quart, Hawaii, 66-68; Univ. Hawaii curriculum develop. geant, summer 67, merit award, 67-68; vis. prof, Chiang Mai Univ, Thailand, 68-69; vis. fel. psychol, Ohio State Univ, 69-70; res. & scriptwriter, Life in China (films), produced by Ohio State Univ, 71-; proj. dir. weather commun, Nat. Weather Serv. Pac. Region, 72; prof. coord. commun. & jour. teachers sem, East-West Ctr. Commun. Inst, Univ. Hawaii, summer 72, dir. commun. in Asia, Summer Study Tour Abroad, summer 73, mem, Asian Mass Commun. Res. & Inform. Ctr. Speech Commun. Asn; Int. Soc. Gen. Semantics. Rhetorical theory and criticism; weather communications; intercultural communications. Publ: Co-auth, Weather communication: a programmed introduction, Environmental Sci. Serv, Pac. Region, Hawaii, 67; auth, Recipe for a course in weather communications—Hawaiian style, Bull-Am. Meteorological Soc, 10/66; An introduction to Kenneth Burke, Pac. Speech Quart, 3/67; plus others. Add: Program in Communication, University of Hawaii at Manoa, Honolulu, HI 96816.

SANDFORD, WILLIAM PHILLIPS, b. Champaign, Ill, Oct. 27, 96. SPEECH. A.B, Univ. Mich, 20, A.M, 23; Ph.D, Ohio State Univ, 29. Instr, Univ. Minn, 20-21; Ohio State Univ, 21-25, asst. prof, 25-26; asst. prof. in charge courses in speech, Univ. Ill, 26-29, assoc. prof, 29-35; in business, 35-41; dir. sales serv, Ill. Agr. Asn, 41-46; prof. SPEECH, ST. LOUIS UNIV, 46-65, EMER. PROF, 65- History of rhetorical theory; early Jesuit rhetoric. Publ: Co-auth, Principles of effective speaking, 6 eds, Ronald, 28-63; auth, Effective business speech, 4 eds, 29-60 & co-auth, Business speeches by business men, 30, McGraw; auth, English theories of public address, 1530-1828, Hedrick, Columbus, Ohio, 30, 39, 65; auth, Speak well and win, McGraw, 44; Real estate salesman's complete ideas handbook, Prentice-Hall, 58. Add: Dept. of Speech, St. Louis University, St. Louis, MO 63103.

SANDIFER, CHARLEY LAFAYETTE, b. Star, Miss, Apr. 14, 19; m. 44; c. 6. ENGLISH COMPOSITION & LITERATURE. A.B, Miss. Col, 43; Th.M, New Orleans Baptist Theol. Sem, 47; M.A, Univ. Miss, 56. Instr. ENG, Clarke Mem. Col, 47-51, chmn. dept. 50-51; instr, Tift Col, 56-58; prof. Chowan Col, 59-66, chmn. dept, 60-66; ASSOC. PROF, Gaston Col, 66-67; GARDNER-WEBB COL, 67- Inglis Fletcher, especially her Colonial North Carolina; Thomas Dixon, Jr. theme study. Add: P.O. Box 902, Boiling Springs, NC 28017.

SANDKE, THOMAS JOHN, b. Chicago, Ill, Aug. 11, 19; m. 42; c. 2. ENGLISH. B.A, Cent. YMCA Col, 40; M.A, Pa. State Col, 41; Ph.D.(Eng), Univ. Chicago, 67. Asst. prof. ENG, ROOSEVELT UNIV, 49-61, assoc. prof, 61-68, PROF, 68- U.S.N, 42-45, Lt. MLA; Am. Soc. Theatre Res; Int. Fed. Theatre Res. Nineteenth century American literature and drama; history of drama and theater. Publ: Teaching the reading of plays, Proc. Int. Reading Asn, 5/68. Add: 755 W. Buena, Chicago, IL 60613.

SANDLE, FLOYD LESLIE, b. Magnolia, Miss, July 4, 13; m. 41; c. 5. SPEECH, DRAMA. A.B, Dillard Univ, 37; M.A, Univ. Chicago, 47; N.Y. Univ, 51-52; Ph.D.(speech), La. State Univ, 59. Instr. high sch, 37-38; Grambling Col, 38-43; instr. & dir. gen. educ, U.S. Air Force Inst, New Guinea, 43-45; asst. prof. soc. sci. & Eng, GRAMBLING COL, 45-47, head dept. speech & drama, 47-49 & 50-68, acting dean col, 49-50; ACAD. DEAN DIV. GEN. STUD, 63- Vis. prof. speech, La. State Univ, Baton Rouge, 72-73. U.S.N, 43-45. Am. Theatre Asn; Nat. Asn. Dramatics & Speech Arts (treas, 49-51, v.pres, 53-55, pres, 55-57); South. Speech Commun. Asn. Theatre history; general education; English; playwriting. Publ: The Negro in the American educational theatre, Edwards Brothers, 64; Orientation: an image of the college, W.C. Brown, 67; Administering the high school drama program, Encore, spring 56; Community relations and community recreation through community drama, Speech Teacher, 9/57; Black theatre: ideas that matter in the pursuit of human dignity, Develop. in Speech, 5/73. Add: 102 Richmond Dr, Grambling, LA 71245.

SANDLER, FLORENCE ROSEMARY, b. Greymouth, N.Z, Oct. 24, 38; m. 67. ENGLISH LITERATURE. B.A, Univ. Canterbury, 59, M.A, 61; Ph.D.(Eng), Univ. Calif, Berkeley, 68. Jr. lectr. ENG, Victoria Univ. Wellington, 61-63; asst. prof, Univ. Ill, Chicago Circle, 66-70; ASSOC. PROF, UNIV. PUGET SOUND, 70- MLA; Renaissance Soc. Am; Milton Soc. Am; AAUP. Biblical tradition in English literature and politics, especially Milton; comparative mythology. Publ: The iconoclastic enterprise: Blake's critique of Milton's religion, Blake Stud, 72; Icon and iconoclast, In: Achievements of the left hand, Univ.Mass, 74; The poet and the ploughman: an essay on Langland and Milton, In: A poet amongst poets, Univ. Wis, 74. Add: Dept. of English, University of Puget Sound, Tacoma, WA 98416.

SANDMAN, JOSEPH THOMAS, b. Buffalo, N.Y, Mar. 30, 23. ENGLISH. B.S, Canisius Col, 43, A.M, 48; Columbia Univ. Instr. ENG, CANISIUS COL, 47-52, asst. prof, 52-72, ASSOC. PROF, 72- Mem. Am. lit. comt, N.Y. State Col. Proficiency Exam. Prog, 64- NCTE; MLA. American literature; drama; history of English language. Add: Dept. of English, Canisius College, Buffalo, NY 14208.

SANDO, EPHRIAM GERALD, b. Chicago, Ill, Mar. 1, 34. ENGLISH. B.A, Univ. Calif, Los Angeles, 56, M.A, 58, fel, 59-60, Ph.D, 62. From instr. to asst. prof. ENG, Univ. Iowa, 62-67; ASSOC. PROF, CALIF. STATE COL, DOMINGUEZ HILLS, 67- Teaching fel. & asst, Univ. Calif, Los Angeles, 58-59, 60-62. MLA. Victorian literature; T.S. Eliot's literary criticism; creative writing. Publ: Co-transl, F.P. Bargebuhr's The Alhambra: a cycle of studies on the eleventh century in Moorish Spain, W. de Gruyter, Berlin, 68; transl. of Judah Halevi, In: High wedlock then be honoured, Viking, 70; auth, And faces are but a gallery of pictures & Circe bewitched, Phoenix, 2/74; plus others. Add: Dept. of English, California State College, Dominguez Hills, 1000 E. Victoria St, Dominguez Hills, CA 90747.

SANDS, DONALD B, b. Waterbury, Conn, Aug. 12, 20; wid; c. 2. ENGLISH. B.A, Lehigh Univ, 42; M.A, Harvard, 48, Ph.D.(Eng), 53. Instr. Eng, Univ. Ark, 45-46; Eng. & Ger, Univ. Maine, 46-47; asst. Ger, Harvard, 47-48; instr. Eng. & Ger, Bowdoin Col, 48-50; asst, Harvard, 50-53; asst. ed, G. & C. Merriam Co, 53-57; asst. prof. ENG, Boston Col, 57-59, assoc. prof, 59-64, UNIV. MICH, ANN ARBOR, 64-67, PROF, 67- Definer, Mid. Eng. Dictionary, 64-65; co-chmn. Mich. Place Name Survey of U.S, 71- Sig.C, U.S.A, 42-45, Sgt. MLA; Am. Name Soc; Am. Dialect Soc. Middle English narrative; lexicography; German expressionistic poetry. Publ: William Caxton's Reynard the fox, Harvard, 61; A concise bibliography for students of English, Stanford Univ, 61; Middle English verse romances, Holt, 63. Add: Dept. of English, 1618 Haven Hall, University of Michigan, Ann Arbor, MI 48104.

SANDSTROEM, YVONNE LUTTROPP, b. Västerås, Sweden, Aug. 10, 33; U.S. citizen; m. 54; c. 2. ENGLISH & SCANDINAVIAN LITERATURE. A.M, Brown Univ, 66, Ph.D.(Eng), 70. ASST. PROF. ENG, SOUTHEAST. MASS. UNIV, 69- MLA; Soc. Advan. Scand. Stud; Renaissance Soc. Am. Seventeenth century English literature; modern Scandinavian literature; translations of Swedish literature. Publ: The machine theme in some poems by Lars Gustafsson, Scand. Stud, 2/72; Three poems from the New World; a commentary, Am-Swed. Yearbk, 72; Some notes on contemporary Swedish poetry, Mundus Artium, 1/73. Add: Dept. of English, Southeastern Massachusetts University, North Dartmouth, MA 02747.

SANDSTROM, GLENN A, b. Spokane, Wash, Dec. 22, 25; m. 48; c. 4. ENGLISH. B.A, Wash. State Univ, 48, M.A, 50; Ph.D.(Eng), Univ. Ill, 56. Asst. prof. ENG, SAN DIEGO STATE UNIV, 56-61, assoc. prof, 61-66, PROF, 66- U.S.N, 44-46, Res, 46-66, Lt. Comdr. Philol. Asn. Pac. Coast; Am. Stud. Asn. American, British Victorian and continental fiction. Publ: The outsiders of Stendhal and Camus, Mod. Fiction Stud, fall 64; James Lee's wife, and Browning's, Victorian Poetry, autumn 66; Identity diffusion in Joe Christmas and Quentin Compson, Am. Quart, summer 67. Add: Dept. of English, San Diego State University, 5402 College Ave, San Diego, CA 92115.

SANDY, ALAN FRANCIS, JR, b. Minneapolis, Minn, Mar. 4, 32; m. 56. ENGLISH & AMERICAN LITERATURE. B.A, Amherst Col, 54; M.A, Univ. Calif, Berkeley, 61, Ph.D.(Eng), 65. Instr. ENG, Princeton, 63-66; asst.

prof, Univ. Calif, Los Angeles, 66-71; ASSOC. PROF, CALIF. STATE COL, SONOMA, 71-, grant, 73-74. U.S.A.F, 55-57, Capt. MLA; Am. Stud. Asn; Philol. Asn. Pac. Coast. American and English literature; comparative literature; literature and psychology. Publ: Co-ed, The adventures of Captain Bonneville, Univ. Wis, (in press). Add: Dept. of English, California State College, Sonoma, Rohnert Park, CA 94928.

SANDY, STEPHEN MERRILL, U.S. citizen; m. 69. AMERICAN LITERATURE. M.A, Harvard, 60. MEM. LIT. FAC, BENNINGTON COL, 69- Fulbright lectr. Am. lit, Univ. Tokyo, 67-68; vis. asst. prof. Eng, Brown Univ, 68-69; Vt. Counc. on Arts grant, 73-74. MLA; Asn. Asian Stud. Readership of romantic fiction in Federal America. Publ: Caroms, Croton Press, 60; Mary Baldwin, Dolmen, Dublin, 62; The destruction of Bulfinch's house, Identity, 64; Stresses in the peaceable kingdom, 67 & Roofs, 71, Houghton; Japanese room, Hellcoal Press, 69. Add: Dept. of Literature, Bennington College, Bennington, VT 05201.

SANER, REGINALD ANTHONY, b. Jacksonville, Ill, Dec. 30, 30; m. 58; c. 2. ENGLISH, ITALIAN. B.A, St. Norbert Col, 50; M.A, Univ. Ill, Urbana, 54, Ph.D.(Eng), 61; Fulbright grant, Florence, Italy, 60. Asst. instr. ENG, Univ. Ill, 56-60, instr, 61-62; asst. prof, UNIV. COLO, BOULDER, 62-67, ASSOC. PROF, 67-, fac. fel, spring 67. U.S.A, 51-53, 1st Lt. Shakespeare Asn. Am; Renaissance Soc. Am; Dante Soc. Am. Renaissance drama; modern drama. Add: Dept. of English, University of Colorado, Boulder, CO 80302.

SANFORD, CHARLES LeROY, b. Salem, N.J, Feb. 29, 20; m. 43; c. 2. AMERICAN CIVILIZATION. B.A, Middlebury Col, 42; M.A, Brown, 46; M.A, Harvard, 49, Ph.D.(Am. civilization), 52. Instr. Am. lit, Middlebury Col, 50-51; Eng. & Am. lit, Amherst Col, 52-54; asst. prof. lang. & lit, RENSSELAER POLYTECH. INST, 55-58, assoc. prof, 58-64, prof, 64-73, WILLIAM ELLSWORTH LASLIN PROF. TECHNOL. & CULT, 73-, ASSOC. DIR, CTR. HUMAN DIMENSIONS SCI. & TECHNOL, 74- Vis. Lectr, Middlebury Col, 54-55; reader advan. placement exams. in Eng, Educ. Testing Serv, Princeton, N.J, 60-; Fulbright lectr. Am. stud, Univs. Clermont-Ferrand & Strasbourg, France, 61-62; mem. ed. bd, Am. Quart, 65-; vis. prof. Eng, Union Col, 69; consult. Am. stud. & lit, Nat. Endowment for Humanities, 72-73. U.S.N.A.F, 43-45, Lt. Am. Stud. Asn. Communications; automobile culture. Publ: The quest for paradise, Univ. Ill, 61; ed, Benjamin Franklin and American character, Heath, 55 & Quest for America, 1810-1824, Anchor Bks, Doubleday, 64; Manifest destiny, Wiley, 74; auth, The hereditary duality, Weidenfeld & Nicolson, 74; Modernity and the human condition, South. Rev, winter 68; Technology and culture at the end of the nineteenth century: the will to power, In: Vol. I, Technology in western civilization, Oxford, 67. Add: 393 Hamilton, Albany, NY 12210.

SANTANGELO, GENNARO, b. New York, N.Y, May 5, 29; m. 57; c. 1. LITERATURE. B.S, Fordham Col, 51; M.A, Univ. N.C, 53, Ph.D, 62; Int. Educ. Exchange Serv. fel, Univ. Pisa, Italy, 53-54. Asst. Eng, Univ. N.C, 55-57; instr, George Wash. Univ, 57-59; asst. prof, 59-61; lit, State Univ. N.Y. BINGHAMTON, 61-66, univ. res. grant, summer 62; Eng, SAN DIEGO STATE UNIV, 67-73, PROF, COMP. LIT, 73- Am. Philos. Soc. grant-in-aid, 65; Sr. Fulbright lectr, Turku Univ, 66-67. MLA. Nineteenth century novel; English and American literature. Publ: Towards a definition of American Victorianism, Dalhousie Rev, autumn 65; The absurdity of The minister's black veil, Pac. Coast Philol, 4/70; Villari's Life and time of Savanorola and Romola, Anglia, 72. Add: Dept. of English, San Diego State University, 5402 College Ave, San Diego, CA 92115.

SANTAS, JOAN, b. Chicago, Ill, July 4, 30; m. 53; c. 2. AMERICAN LITERATURE. B.A, Knox Col, 52; M.A, Cornell Univ, 54, Ph.D.(Eng), 63. Lectr, Univ. Calif, Berkeley, 61-62; Boston Univ, 62-64; Radcliffe Inst. Independent Stud, 64-66; instr, Boston Univ, 65-67; asst. prof. ENG, Northeast. Univ, 67-68; lectr, Towson State Col, 68-71; ASST. PROF, CALIF. STATE COL, DOMINGUEZ HILLS, 71- Americana; Southern literature; poetry. Publ: Ellen Glasgow's American dream, Univ. Va, 65. Add: Dept. of English, California State College, Dominguez Hills, 1000 E. Victoria St, Dominguez Hills, CA 90247.

SAPPENFIELD, JAMES A, b. Indianapolis, Ind, Nov. 1, 40; m. 62; c. 1. ENGLISH. B.A, South. Ill. Univ, 62; NDEA fel, Stanford Univ, 62-65, M.A. & Ph.D.(Eng), 66. Asst. prof. ENG, UNIV. WIS-MILWAUKEE, 66-71, ASSOC. PROF, 71- MLA. American literature before 1860; Benjamin Franklin. Publ: Benjamin Franklin: controversialist, Grassroots Ed, 9-10/67; introd. to A history of American literature, Johnson, (in press). Add: Dept. of English, University of Wisconsin-Milwaukee, Milwaukee, WI 53211.

SARASON, BERTRAM DANIEL, b. New York, N.Y, Oct. 21, 10; m. 72; c. 2. ENGLISH. Ph.D.(Eng), N.Y. Univ, 51. Teacher ENG, Woodstock Sch, Vt, 45-46; assoc. prof, SOUTH. CONN. STATE COL, 46-57, PROF, 57- Instr, N.Y. Univ, 48; Mod. Lang. Asn. Am. grant, 53; vis. fel, Princeton, 54; Fund Advan. Educ. fel, 54-55; ed, Teacher Educ. Quart, 63; Conn. Rev, 67. Int. Hemingway Soc.(exec. secy). Edmund Burke; Age of Johnson; Hemingway. Publ: Edmund Burke and the two Annual registers, PMLA; Editorial mannerisms in the early Annual registers, Pub. Bibliog. Soc. Am; Hemingway and the sun set, Wash, D.C, 72; plus one other. Add: Dept. of English, Southern Connecticut State College, 501 Crescent St, New Haven, CT 06515.

SARGENT, RALPH MILLARD, b. Austin, Minn, May 10, 04; m. 29; c. 2. ENGLISH & AMERICAN LITERATURE. A.B, Carleton Col, 25; Ph.D, Yale, 31. Instr. high sch, Minn, 25-26; from instr. to asst. prof, Carleton Col, 31-34; prof. ENG, Knox Col, 37-41; from assoc. to Gummere prof, HAVERFORD COL, 41-70, chmn. dept, 49-62, PROF. EMER, 70- Trustee, Highlands Biol. Sta, N.C. MLA; Renaissance Soc. Am; Botanical Soc. Am. Elizabethan literature; Shakespeare; modern American literature. Publ: At the court of Queen Elizabeth, Oxford; Books of the Renaissance, Haverford Col; Shakespeare's As you like it, Penguin; ed, Peter Kalm's Travels into North America, Imprint Soc, 72. Add: 520 Panmure Rd, Haverford, PA 19041.

SARGENT, SEYMOUR HERBERT, b. Concord, N.H, Apr. 23, 32; m. 62; c. 2. CONTEMPORARY LITERATURE. B.A, Univ. N.H, 54; M.A, Univ. Minn, 60, Ph.D.(Eng), 70. Instr. Eng, Univ. N.Dak, 61-63; Univ. Vt, 63-67; teaching asst, Univ. Minn, 67-69; instr, UNIV. WIS-OSHKOSH, 69-70, ASST. PROF, 70-74, LIBR. SCI, 74- U.S.A, 55-57. MLA; NEA. Shakespeare; contemporary literature. Publ: Julius Caesar and the historical film, Eng. J, 2/72. Add: Dept. of Library Science, University of Wisconsin-Oshkosh, Oshkosh, WI 54901.

SARLOS, ROBERT KAROLY, b. Budapest, Hungary, June 6, 31; U.S. citizen; m. 62; c. 2. THEATRE HISTORY. B.A, Occidental Col, 59; Ph.D.(hist. of theatre), Yale, 65. Instr. Eng, Mitchell Col, 62-63; lectr. DRAMATIC ART, UNIV. CALIF, DAVIS, 63-64, acting asst. prof, 64-65, asst. prof, 66-70, ASSOC. PROF, 70- Consult. hist. & restoration, Woodland Opera House proj, Yolo County Historical Soc, 70- Int. Fed. Theatre Res; Am. Soc. Theatre Res; AAUP. Elizabethan, Baroque and American theatre. Publ: Two outdoor productions of Giuseppe Galli Bibiena, Theatre Serv, 5/64; co-auth, The Woodland Opera House: the end of an era in California theatre, Calif. Hist. Soc. Quart, 12/69; auth, Wharf and dome: materials for the history of the Provincetown players, Theatre Res, 70; plus two others. Add: Dept. of Dramatic Art, University of California, Davis, CA 95616.

SARTON, MAY, b. Wondelgem, Belg, May 3, 12; U.S. citizen. ENGLISH. L.H.D, Russell Sage Col, 59. Script writer documentary film, Off. War Inform, 44-45; Briggs-Copeland instr. compos, Harvard, 50-53, vis. scholar creative writing, 59-60; vis. lectr, col. arts prog, Danforth Found, 60-61; lectr, Wellesley Col, 60-63; poet-in-residence, Lindenwood Col, 64; WRITER. Lucy Martin Donnelly fel, Bryn Mawr Col, 53-54; Guggenheim fel, 54-55; Nat. Found. Arts & Humanities grant, 67. Golden Rose Award, 45; Edward Bland Mem. Prize, Poetry Mag, 45. Poetry Soc. Am. (Reynolds lyric award, 53); fel. Am. Acad. Arts & Sci. Publ: Encounter in April (poetry), 37, The single hound (novel), 38 & Inner landscape (poetry), 39, Houghton; The bridge of years (novel), Doubleday, 46; The lion and the rose (poetry), 48, Shadow of a man (novel), 50, A shower of summer days (novel), 52, The land of silence (poetry), 53, Faithful are the wounds (novel), 55, The fur person, the story of a cat, 56, The birth of a grandfather (novel), 57, In time like air (poetry), 57 & I knew a Phoenix (autobiography), 59, Rinehart; The leaves of the tree (poetry), Cornell Col. Chapbook, 50; The small room (novel), 61, Cloud, stone, sun, vine (poetry), 61, Joanna and Ulysses (novel), 63, Mrs. Stevens hears the mermaids singing (novel), 65, Miss Pickthorn and Mr. Hare (novel), 66, A private mythology (poetry), 66, Plant dreaming deep (autobiography), 68 & As we are now, 73, Norton; As does New Hampshire (poetry), Richard Smith, 67; The writing of a poem, Scripps Col. Bull, 2/57; The school of Babylon, In: The moment of poetry, Johns Hopkins, 62; plus others. Add: Box 99, York, ME 03909.

SASEK, LAWRENCE ANTON, b. Glen Carbon, Ill, Mar. 22, 23; m. 60. ENGLISH. B.A, Univ. Ill, 47, M.A, 48; Ph.D, Harvard, 53. Teaching fel, ENG, Harvard, 51-53; instr, LA. STATE UNIV, BATON ROUGE, 53-56, asst. prof, 56-61, assoc. prof, 61-69, PROF, 69- U.S.A, 43-46. MLA; Renaissance Soc. Am; NCTE. John Milton; 16th and 17th century English literature. Publ: Literary temper of the English Puritans, 61 & ed, The poems of William Smith, 70, La. State Univ; auth, The drama of Paradise lost, XI-XII, La. State Univ. Stud. in the Humanities, 62. Add: Dept. of English, Louisiana State University, Baton Rouge, LA 70803.

SATIN, JOSEPH, b. Philadelphia, Pa, Dec. 16, 22; m. 46; c. 2. COMPARATIVE LITERATURE. B.S, Temple Univ, 46; A.M, Columbia Univ, 48, Ph.D, 52. Instr. integrated stud, W.Va. Univ, 52-54; asst. prof. lang. & lit, Moorhead State Col, 54-56, assoc. prof, 56-58, prof, 58-63; prof. Eng. & chmn. dept, Midwest. Univ, 63-73; PROF. ENG. & DEAN SCH. HUMANITIES, CALIF. STATE UNIV, FRESNO, 73- Hardin prof, 66; Piper prof, 67. U.S.A, 42-46. MLA; NCTE; Conf. Col. Compos. & Commun. Shakespearean sources; Dantesque traditions in Shakespeare; plays of Ugo Betti. Publ: Ideas in context, 58, The 1950's: America's placid decade, 60, Reading literature (4 vols), 64, Shakespeare and his sources, 66 & Reading stories, poems, plays, 68, Houghton; Humanities handbook (2 vols), 69 & The visual rhetoric, 69; Holt, The cultural heritage of Africa, Dodd, (in press). Add: School of Humanities, California State University, Shaw & Cedar Aves, Fresno, CA 93710.

SATO, TOSHIHIKO, b. Hiroshima, Japan, Mar. 28, 29. COMPARATIVE LITERATURE. B.A, Seinan Gakuin Col, Japan, 52; M.A, Waseda Univ, Japan, 54; fel, Univ. Wis, 54-55; fel, Univ. Wash, 61-62, Ph.D.(comp. lit), 66. Instr. Eng, Nihon Univ, Tokyo, 58-60; asst. prof. Japanese & comp. lit, Univ. Kans, 63-66; Univ. Iowa, 66-68; PROF. comp. lit, Alcorn Col, 68-69; LIT, VA. STATE COL, 69- Am. Philos. Soc. fel, 69. Am. Comp. Lit. Asn; MLA; Asn. Asian Stud; Soc. Advan. Scand. Stud. Literary criticism; Japanese-Western literary relations. Publ: Abraham Lincoln, Iwasaki-Shoten, 58; contrib, Ibsen parallels in modern Japanese drama, Yearbk. Gen. & Comp. Lit, 62, H.C. Andersen's The improvisator in Japan, Anderseniana, 63 & Ibsen in Japanese feminist movement, Ibsen-Aarbok, 68. Add: Dept. of English, Virginia State College, Petersburg, VA 23803.

SATTERTHWAITE, ALFRED WANNER, b. Reading, Pa, Dec. 31, 14; m. 43; c. 2. COMPARATIVE LITERATURE. A.B, Harvard, 36, A.M, 40, Ph.D, 56. Tutor, St. John's Col, 48-51; teaching fel. gen. educ, Harvard, 53-56; from asst. prof. to assoc. prof. ENG, HAVERFORD COL, 56-68, PROF, 68-, CHMN. DEPT, 67- U.S.A, 42-46, Capt. Renaissance Soc. Am. Publ: Spenser, Ronsard, and DuBellay, Princeton, 60. Add: Dept. of English, Haverford College, Haverford, PA 19041.

SATTLER, JOHN WILLIAM, b. Tyndall, S.Dak, Oct. 1, 03; m. 31; c. 1. SPEECH. B.A, Yankton Col, 26; M.A, Univ. Mich, 31; fel, Northwest. Univ, 40-41, Ph.D.(speech), 43. Assoc. prof. SPEECH, Berea Col, 31-40, PROF, 41-47; EAST. MICH. UNIV, 47-, HEAD. DEPT, 63-, head. dept. speech & Eng, 52-63. Consult. conf. tech, bus. & indust, 48-; Chmn. workshop in Eng, comt. on teacher educ, comn. res. & serv, N. Cent. Asn. Cols. & Sec. Schs, 59-62; visitation consult, Nat. Counc. for Accreditation Teacher Educ. Insts, 64-65. Speech Commun. Asn; Cent. States Speech Asn. Communications; conference techniques; public address. Publ: Pilot workshop in English, N. Cent. Asn. Quart, fall 62. Add: 1440 Collegewood Dr, Ypsilanti, MI 48197.

SAUER, FRANK, b. New York, N.Y, July 9, 36; m. 60; c. 2. ENGLISH. B.A, St. John's Col, 58; M.A, St. John's Univ.(N.Y), 60; N.Y. Univ, 60-68. Teaching fel. speech, St. John's Univ.(N.Y), 58-59, ENG, 59-60, instr, 60-

62, ASST. PROF, 62-66; Dutchess Community Col, 66-72; ROCKLAND COMMUNITY COL, 72- Lectr, City Col. New York, 66-; Mary Rogers Col, summer 67. MLA. Neo-classical; American literature; modern British. Publ: A critical commentary on J.D. Salinger's The catcher in the rye, Thor, 65. Add: Dept. of English, Rockland Community College, 145 College Rd, Suffern, NY 10901.

SAUER, PHILIP R, b. Winona, Minn, Aug. 10, 07; m. 36; c. 3. ENGLISH LITERATURE. B.A, Northwest. Col.(Wis), 29; M.A, Univ. Wis, 32; Ph.D, Univ. Freiburg, 37; Oxford, 67. Chmn. dept. Eng, Winona High Sch, 33-36; PROF. ENG, BEMIDJI STATE COL, 37-, chmn. div. lang. & lit, 37-69. Assoc. prof. Eng, Ariz. State Col, 47-48. NCTE. Publ: English metrical psalms from 1600-1660, Univ. Freiburg Press, 38; Heinrich von Rohr and the Lutheran immigration to New York and Wisconsin, Wis. Mag. Hist, 3/35; One hundred root words for vocabulary building, Eng, J, 36. Add: Dept. of English, Bemidji State College, Bemidji, MN 56601.

SAUL, GEORGE BRANDON, b. Shoemakersville, Pa, Nov. 1, 01; m. 25, 37; c. 3. ENGLISH. A.B, Univ. Pa, 23, A.M, 30, Harrison scholar, 30-31, Ph.D, 32. Asst. ENG, Univ. Pa, 22-23; instr, UNIV. CONN, 24-29, asst. prof, 29-32, assoc. prof, 32-42, prof, 42-72, EMER. PROF, 72- Contrib. ed, J. Irish Lit, 71. MLA; Poetry Soc. Am; Am. Comt. Irish Stud. Yeats; general Irish literature; post-Victorian literature. Publ: Stephens, Yeats and other Irish concerns, N.Y. Pub. Libr, 54; Prolegomena to the study of Yeats's poems, 57 & Prolegomena to the study of Yeats's plays, 58, Univ. Pa; Quintet: essays on five American women poets, 67 & Withdrawn in gold, 70, Mouton, The Hague; Concise introduction to types of literature in English, 69, & Rushlight heritage, 69, Walton; A brief introduction to traditional Irish literature and its background, 70, Seumas O'Kelly, 71 & Daniel Corkery, 73, Bucknell Univ; In...luminous wind, In: No. VII, Yeats Centenary papers, Dolmen, Dublin, 66. Add: 136 Moulton Rd, Storrs, CT 06268.

SAULS, RICHARD LYNN, b. Shellman, Ga, Jan. 11, 33; m. 52; c. 1. ENGLISH & AMERICAN LITERATURE. B.A, South. Missionary Col, 56; M.A, George Peabody Col, 62; Ph.D.(Eng), Univ. Iowa, 72. Supvry. instr. sec. educ, South. Missionary Col, 61-64, instr. ENG, 64-67, asst. prof, 67-68, assoc. prof, 68-69; ATLANTIC UNION COL, 69-73, PROF, 73- MLA; NCTE; Milton Soc. Am; Conf. Col. Compos. & Commun; Conf. Christianity & Lit. Thomas Traherne; devotional literature; poetry. Publ: Traherne's hand in the Credenhill records, Library, 69; The careless compositor for Christian ethicks, Papers Bibliog. Soc. Am, 69; Traherne's debt to Puente's Meditations, Philol. Quart, 71. Add: Dept. of English, Atlantic Union College, South Lancaster, MA 01561.

SAUNDERS, CARLETON EARL, b. Couer d'Alene, Idaho, Aug. 2, 04; m. 33. SPEECH, LITERATURE. A.B, West. Mich. Univ. 28; M.A. Columbia Univ, 33; D.A.(speech), Staley Col, 57. Master Eng. & French, Midwest Jr. Sch, Ill, 28-30; teacher High Sch, N.J. 30-48; asst. prof. speech & chmn. dept, State Univ. N.Y. Col. Cortland, 48-52; asst. prof, WORCESTER STATE COL, 52-55, assoc. prof, 55-69, prof, 69-73, chmn. speech & drama dept, 55-73, EMER. PROF. SPEECH, 73- Speech. Commun. Asn. Add: 11 Sun Valley Dr, Worcester, MA 01609.

SAUNDERS, DORIS BOYCE, b. Winnipeg, Man, Nov. 16, 01. ENGLISH LITERATURE. B.A, Univ. Man, 21, M.A, 25; Can. Fedn. Univ. Women traveling scholar, 25; dipl. educ, Oxford, 23, B.Litt, 36; LL.D, Univ. B.C, 57. Prof. ENG. LIT, UNIV. MAN, 28-68, dean jr. women, 33-45, registr, Univ. Col, 63-68, EMER. PROF, 68- Pres, Can. Fedn. Univ. Women, 55-58; Winifred Cullis Lectr. fel, sponsored by Brit-Am. Assoc, 66; mem. Nat. Exec. of Humanities Asn. Can, 67-68. Asn. Can. Univ. Teachers Eng; Int. Fed. Univ. Women. Dr. Samuel Johnson's knowledge and use of the English writers before 1600; Canadian literature. Publ: The Grove collection in the University of Manitoba, Papers Bibliog. Soc. Can, 63; Two novelists—Patricia Blondal, and Margaret Laurence, Alumni J, spring 66; Foreward, In: Frederick Philip Grove, Twayne, 73. Add: Apt. 200 Crescent Villa, Wellington Crescent, Winnipeg, Man. R3M 0A1, Can.

SAVAGE, EDWARD BERNHARD, b. Bonesteel, S.Dak, June 28, 23. COMPARATIVE LITERATURE. B.A, Hamline Univ, 48; M.A, Univ. Minnesota, 53, Ph.D, 59. Instr. Eng, Tarsus Am. Col, Turkey, 48-51; asst. prof. Am. Univ. Cairo, 53-57, assoc. prof, 59-61; instr, Univ. Minn, 57-59; assoc. prof, Hastings Col, 61; Hope Col, 61-66; from assoc. prof. to PROF. RHET, UNIV. MINN, ST. PAUL, 66- Vis. prof. opera, Inst. Europ. Stud, Vienna, 65 & comp. lit, 72-73; vis. assoc. prof, Columbia Univ, 66-68. U.S.N.R, 43-46, Lt.(jg). MLA; AAUP. Comparative drama; mediaeval studies; musical drama. Publ: The rose and the vine: a study of the evolution of the Tristan and Isolt tale in drama, Am. Univ. Cairo, 61; Technical English for agricultural students, Off. Int. Prog, Univ. Minn, 71; Masks and mummeries in Caligula & Enrico IV, Mod. Drama, 64; The Bacchae as theatre of spectacle, Drama Surv, 64; Love & infamy: the paradox in Monteverdi's L'incoronazione de Poppea, Comp. Drama, 70; plus one other. Add: Dept. of Rhetoric, University of Minnesota, St. Paul, MN 55101.

SAVAGE, GEORGE, b. Tacoma, Wash, Apr. 25, 04; m. 29; c. 2. DRAMA, THEATER ARTS. A.B. & M.A, Univ. Wash, 28, Denny fel, 31, Ph.D, 35. From teaching fel. to assoc. prof. creative writing, Univ. Wash, 30-51; THEATRE ARTS, UNIV. CALIF, LOS ANGELES, 51-56, prof, 56-71, fel, Inst. Creative Arts, EMER. PROF, 71- Dramatist Guild fel, 40; Nat. Theatre Conf. fels, 44-51; mem, Nat. Lexicographical Bd, 45-58; mem. adv. bd, Calif. Jr. Prog, 53-; vis. prof. drama, Univ. Iowa, summer 55; Fulbright sr. lectr. & vis. prof, Bristol Univ, 58-59; mem. bd, Inner City Repertory Co, 66-; mem. bd, Argo Theatre, 69-; collab, Prog. Continuing Educ, Educ. Testing Serv, 73; judge, New York Univ. Playwrighting Competition, spring 73. Margot Jones Award, 64; Medallion of Honor, Theta Alpha Phi, 67. Nat. Theatre Conf; Am. Nat. Theatre & Acad; Theatre Libr. Asn; Am. Theatre Asn; Int. Fed. Theatre Res; Soc. Theatre Res, Eng; fel. Int. Inst. Arts & Lett; Dramatists Guild. Development of new plays through production; 18th century; regional American drama. Publ: Ed, In the heart of Maryland and other Belasco plays, Princeton, 41; co-auth, Phoenix and the dwarfs, 44 & ed. & foreword, On being an author, 48, Macmillan; El motocidista, Apuntes, 7/64. Co-auth, The garbage hustlers, produced by Las Palmas Theatre,

64 & Theatre L'Homme Dieux, 65; Dash point, produced by Theatre L'Homme Dieux, 66; The bereavement of Babs Bursette, produced by Va. City Players, 66; Bear McCready, produced by Evergreen Theatre, 69; Farley's return 72 & Above the timberline, 72, produced by Hungry Mule Players; The days of Wakefield's bar, produced by Evergreen Stage Co, 73. Add: 1818 Overland Ave, Los Angeles, CA 90025.

SAVAGE, THOMAS GERARD, S.J, b. Oak Park, Ill, July 27, 26. ENGLISH LANGUAGE & LITERATURE. A.B, Loyola Univ.(Ill), 49, A.M, 53; M.A, Oxford, 62. Instr. Eng. & speech, St. Xavier High Sch, Cincinnati, Ohio, 51-54; ASSOC. PROF. ENG, XAVIER UNIV, 62-, CHMN. DEPT, 65- NCTE; MLA; Conf. Col. Compos. & Commun; Christian Preaching Conf. Theology and contemporary cultural patterns; theology and contemporary literature. Publ: And now a word from our creator, Loyola Univ, 72. Add: Dept. of English, Xavier University, Cincinnati, OH 45207.

SAVEREID, SEVERT J, b. Boone, Iowa, Dec. 9, 19; m. 45; c. 3. RHETORIC, PUBLIC ADDRESS. B.S, Northwest. Univ, 41, M.A, 43; Cornell Univ, 49-54. Instr. pub. speaking, Wesleyan Univ, 47-49; rhetoric & pub. address, Cornell Univ, 49-54; asst. prof, Smith Col, 54-56; UNIV. MASS, AMHERST, 56-68, ASSOC. PROF. SPEECH, 68-, asst. dean, col. arts & sci, 68-71. New Eng. Forensic Conf.(pres, 60); New Eng. Speech Asn.(secy, treas, 63-). House of commons debate 1603-1642; ethics of persuasion. Add: Dept. of Speech, University of Massachusetts, Amherst, MA 01003.

SAVESON, JOHN EDWARD, b. Chicago, Ill, Aug. 20, 23; m. 51; c. 2. ENGLISH. B.A, Denison Univ, 47; M.A, Univ. Chicago, 48; Ph.D.(Eng), Cambridge, 56. Instr. ENG, Valparaiso Univ, 48-49; Univ. Md, 54-56; asst. prof, Valparaiso Univ, 56-59, assoc. prof, 59-64, prof, 64-66; PROF. & CHMN. DEPT, MANSFIELD STATE COL, 66- U.S.N.R, 43-46, Lt.(jg). MLA; Renaissance Soc. Am. Seventeenth century theology and rhetoric; John Smith; moral psychology of Joseph Conrad. Publ: Joseph Conrad: the making of a moralist, Rodopi, Amsterdam, 72; Descartes' influence on John Smith: Cambridge platonist, 4/59 & Differing reactions to Descartes among the Cambridge platonists, 10-12/60, J. Hist. Ideas; Shelley's Julian and Maddalo, Keats-Shelley J, winter 61. Add: Dept. of English, Mansfield State College, Mansfield, PA 16933.

SAVESON, MARILYN BUEHRER, b. Englewood, N.J, Aug. 6, 27; m. 51; c. 3. ENGLISH, FRENCH. Ph.B, Univ. Chicago, 46, M.A, 49; Ph.D.(mod. langs), Cambridge, 56. Instr. Eng, Valparaiso Univ, 49-51; Univ. Md. Overseas Prog, Eng, 54-55; ENG, George Washington Univ, 56; asst. prof, Valparaiso Univ, 56-59, assoc. prof, 59-66; PROF, MANSFIELD STATE COL, 67- MLA. English novel; Zola and naturalism. Add: Box 22, Mainesburg, PA 16932.

SAVVAS, MINAS, b. Athens, Greece, Apr. 2, 39; U.S. citizen. COMPARATIVE LITERATURE, CREATIVE WRITING. B.A, Univ. Ill, 64, M.A, 65; Ph.D.(Eng), Univ. Calif, Santa Barbara, 71. Asst. prof. ENG, Univ. Calif, Santa Barbara, 65-68; ASSOC. PROF, SAN DIEGO STATE UNIV, 68- U.S.A, 57. MLA; Mod. Greek Stud. Asn. Modern Greek literature; continental novel; translation. Publ: Chekov's tragicomedy, Lang. Quart, fall 70; Kazantzakis and Marxism, J. Mod. Lit, winter 72; Greece today, Colo. Quart, summer 73; plus others. Add: School of Literature, San Diego State University, San Diego, CA 92115.

SAWEY, ORLAN, b. Grit, Tex, May 8, 20; m. 42; c. 3. AMERICAN LITERATURE. B.A, Tex. Col. Arts & Indust, 42; teaching fel, Univ. Tex, 50-52, M.A, 47, Ph.D, 53. Tutor, Univ. Tex, 46-47; from instr. to asst. prof, Eng, Tex. Col. Arts & Indust, 47-55; from assoc. prof. to prof, Harding Col, 55-58; prof. & head dept, Lincoln Mem. Univ, 58-60; prof. & chmn. dept, Clinch Valley Col, Univ. Va, 60-62; prof, Appalachian State Teachers Col, 62-65; prof. Eng. & head dept, Pan Am Col, 65-69; PROF. ENG, TEX. A&I UNIV, 69-, CHMN. DEPT, 71- Med. Dept, U.S.A, 42-46, T/Sgt. MLA; West. Hist. Asn; West. Lit. Asn; Am. Folklore Soc. Regional American literature; Western and Southwestern literature; folklore. Publ: Bernard DeVoto, Twayne, 69. Add: Dept. of English, Texas A&I University, Kingsville, TX 78363.

SAWIN, HORACE LEWIS; b. Lexington, Ky, Feb. 18, 23; m. 55; c. 2. ENGLISH LITERATURE. A.B, Univ. Ky, 47, M.A, 48; Ph.D, Duke Univ, 55. Instr. ENG, La. State Univ, 55-56; UNIV. COLO. BOULDER, 56-57, asst. prof, 57-62, assoc. prof, 62-66, PROF. & ASSOC. DEAN COL. ARTS & SCI, 66- U.S.A, 43-45. MLA; Mod. Humanities Res. Asn, Gt. Brit; NCTE (ed, Jour, 58-62). Victorian literature; bibliography. Publ: Co-auth, Annual bibliography of English language and literature, Cambridge, 59; Written words, Random, 62. Add: College of Arts & Sciences, University of Colorado, Boulder, CO 80302.

SAWYER, CORINNE HOLT, b. Chisholm, Minn, Mar. 4, 24; m. 65. ENGLISH, DRAMA. B.A, Univ. Minn, 45, M.A, 47; Univ. Fla, 50-51; Ph.D.(Eng), Birmingham Univ, 53. Instr. radio & TV, Univ. Miami, 47-50; Eng. & speech, Univ. Md, overseas div, 53-58; asst. prof. TV, E.Carolina Col, 58-62, assoc. prof, 62-66; asst. prof. ENG, CLEMSON UNIV, 66-71, ASSOC. PROF, 71-, CHMN. HONORS PROG, 73-, pres. fac. senate, 71-72. MLA; S.Atlantic Mod. Lang. Asn; Southeast Renaissance Conf; NCTE; Renaissance Soc; Malone Soc. Shakespearean studies; Elizabethan literature. Publ: Co-auth, Huckleberry Finn—adapted for children's theatre, Children's Theatre, 45; auth, John Darrell: minister and exorcist, Univ. Fla, 62; An addition to the canon of Bacon's writings, Mod. Lang. Rev, 54. Add: Dept. of English, Clemson University, Clemson, SC 29631.

SAWYER, DAVID ELYOT, b. Ottawa, Ill, Jan. 17, 41; m. 62; c. 3. ENGLISH LITERATURE. B.A, St. Olaf Col, 63; M.A, Univ. Nebr-Lincoln, 64, Ph.D. (Eng), 70. Instr. ENG, Univ. Nebr-Lincoln, 65-70; ASST. PROF, LYCOMING COL, 70- NCTE; Conf. Col. Compos. & Commun. Seventeenth century British literature; Shakespeare. Add: Dept. of English, Lycoming College, Williamsport, PA 17701.

SAWYER, PAUL SIMON, b. New York, N.Y, Sept. 10, 20; m. 63; c. 2. LITERATURE, THEATRE HISTORY. A.B, Brooklyn Col, 41; A.M, Columbia Univ, 46, Ph.D.(Eng). & comp. lit), 54; A.M, State Univ. Iowa, 48; diplome superieur, Univ. Paris, 50. Instr. Eng, Univ. Miami, 46-47; asst. jour,

State Univ. Iowa, 47-48; instr. Eng, BRADLEY UNIV, 54-55, asst. prof. Eng. & jour, 55-57, assoc. prof, 58-63, PROF. ENG, 63-, dir. compos, 59-62, interim head dept, 68-69. Folger Shakespeare Libr. fel, summer 70; Am. Philos. Soc. grants, summers 72 & 73; Henry E. Huntington Libr. fel, summer 73. U.S.A.F, 43-45, Res, 46-60, Capt; Distinguished Flying Cross, Air Medal. MLA; Col. Eng. Asn; Soc. Theatre Res. Eighteenth century English drama; 18th century English literature. Publ: Musset's translation of Confessions of an English opium eater, French Rev, 2/69; The popularity of various types of entertainment at Lincoln's Inn Fields and Covent Garden Theatres 1720-1733, Theatre Notebook, summer 70; John Rich's contribution to the eighteenth century London stage, In: The eighteenth century English stage, Methuen, 72. Add: Dept. of English, Bradley University, Peoria, IL 61606.

SAWYER, THOMAS MITCHELL, b. Hillsdale, Mich, Nov. 11, 17; m. 47; c. 4. ENGLISH, SPEECH. A.B, Kenyon Col, 39; M.A, Univ. Mich, 47, Ph.D, 53. Instr. Eng, Iolani Sch, Honolulu, Hawaii, 40-41; speech, Kenyon Col, 42-43; teaching fel. ENG, COL. ENGINEERING, UNIV. MICH, ANN ARBOR, 45-48, instr, 48-54, asst. prof, 54-58, assoc. prof, 58-63, PROF, 63-, chmn. dept, 66-71. Assoc. ed, Inst. of Sci. & Tech, Univ. Mich, 56-58, ed. assoc, 60, res. asst, human factors group, Proj. Mich, 58-59; Fulbright lectr. Eng, W.Pakistan, 63-64; vis. prof, Univ. Wales, spring 72. Vol, Am. Field Serv, 43-45. Am. Soc. Engineering Educ; NCTE; Rhetoric Soc. Am; Int. Commun. Asn. Communication sciences; English; literature of science. Publ: How to do an experiment involving electronic equipment, Phi Kappa Phi J, fall 71; Rhetoric in an age of science and technology, Col. Compos. & Commun, 12/72; Humanities department administration in British universities, Bull. Asn. Dept. Eng, 5/73; plus three others. Add: Dept. of Humanities, College of Engineering, University of Michigan, Ann Arbor, MI 48105.

SAXON, ARTHUR HARTLEY, b. Pittsburgh, Pa, Mar. 24, 35; m. 57; c. 2. HISTORY OF THE THEATRE, DRAMATIC LITERATURE. B.A, Univ. Pittsburgh, 56; Woodrow Wilson fel, Columbia Univ, 60-61, M.A, 61; Jr. Sterling & univ. fels, Yale, 63-66, Ph.D.(hist. of the theatre), 66. Asst. prof. speech, theatre & Eng, Univ. Pittsburgh, 66-69; ASSOC. PROF. THEATRE, Univ. Conn, 69-71; CITY COL. NEW YORK & GRAD. SCH, CITY UNIV. NEW YORK, 71- Am. ed, Theatre Res/Recherches Thêâtrales, 70-73; Guggenheim fel, 71-72; mem. adv. bd, London Stage, 1800-1900, 73- Am. Soc. Theatre Res; Soc. Theatre Res, Eng; Soc. Hist. Theatre; Am. Theatre Asn; Theatre Libr. Asn. History of 19th century British theatre; history of the circus and popular entertainments. Publ: Enter foot and horse: a history of hippodrama in England and France, Yale Univ, 68; A brief history of the Claque, Theatre Surv, 64; Giuseppe Galli-Bibiena's Architetture e Prospettive, Maske & Kothurn, 69; La Carrière Française d'Andrew Ducrow, Cirque dans Univers, 73. Add: Dept. of Speech & Theatre, City College of New York, 138th St. at Convent Ave, New York, NY 10031.

SAXTON, (OLIVER) KENNETH, b. Burgettstown, Pa, Sept. 1, 05. ENGLISH. B.S, Geneva Col, 30; M.Ed, Univ. Pittsburgh, 37; summers, Harvard, Claremont Col. Teacher high sch, Pa, 39-44; head dept. Eng, Williams Mem. Inst. Counc, 44-47; asst. prof. Eng, Geneva Col, 47-70, dean men, 49-70; RETIRED. Add: 3770 37th St. Extension, Beaver Falls, PA 15010.

SAYRE, ROBERT FREEMAN, b. Columbus, Ohio, Nov. 6, 33; m. 61. ENGLISH. B.A, Wesleyan Univ, 55; M.A, Yale 58, Ph.D.(Eng), 62. Vis. instr. ENG, Wesleyan Univ, 60; instr, Univ. Ill, 61-63, asst. prof, 63-65; UNIV. IOWA, 65-66, assoc. prof, 66-72, PROF, 72-, Old Gold summer fel, 67. Univ. Ill. res. grant, Grad. Col, 62, summer fel, 63; lectr. Am. lit, Lund Univ, Sweden, 63-64, res. fel, 64-65; dir, Iowa Conf. Mod. Lett, 10/67; res. prof, Univ. Iowa, 69-70, 73-74; Guggenheim fel, 73-74. U.S.N, 55-57. Midwest Mod. Lang. Asn.(chmn. Am. lit. sect, 73); NCTE; Am. Stud. Asn. American autobiography; self and social vision; American Indian literature. Publ: The examined self: Benjamin Franklin, Henry Adams, and Henry James, Princeton, 64; introd, Vachel Lindsay: Adventures, rhymes, and designs, Eakins, 68; Vision and experience in Black Elk speaks, Col. Eng, 71; Autobiographies and Utopias, Salmagundi, 72; plus others. Add: Dept. of English, University of Iowa, Iowa City, IA 52242.

SCALES, LUTHER LEE, JR, b. Shawmut, Ala, Nov. 2, 31; m. 58; c. 2. ENGLISH. A.B, Davidson Col, 53; Princeton Theol. Sem, 53-54; M.A, Tulane Univ, 60; Ph.D.(Eng), Drew Univ, 69. Instr. Eng, Am. hist. & civics, E. Jefferson Consol. High Sch, La, 59-60; Eng, St. Martin's Protestant Episcopal High Sch, 60-62; instr. Eng. & chmn. div. fine arts & lang, Lees-McRae Col, 62-65; res. fel. Eng, lit, Drew Univ, 68-69; ASST. PROF. ENG, GA. SOUTH. COL, 69- U.S.A, 55-57. NCTE; MLA; Col. Eng. Asn; Keats-Shelley Asn. Am; AAUP; S.Atlantic Mod. Lang. Asn; Milton Soc. Am; Byron Soc. Romantic period; Milton and the English Romantic writers. Publ: The poet as Miltonic Adam in Alastor, Keats-Shelley J, 73. Add: Dept. of English, Journalism & Philosophy, Georgia Southern College, Statesboro, GA 30458.

SCAMMON, RICHARD LEWIS, b. Detroit, Mich, Mar. 29, 14; m. 46; c. 1. THEATRE ARTS. B.A, Univ. Richmond, 39; M.A, State Univ. Iowa, 46. Instr. speech, Univ. Richmond, 39-41; from instr. to PROF. DRAMA & THEATRE, IND. UNIV, BLOOMINGTON, 46- Guest prof. & theatre dir, Univ. Wyo, summers 60 & 66; dir. Stephen Foster story, Bardstown, Ky, summer 63; dir-designer plays & musicals, Univ. Theatre, Ind. Univ; theatre archit. consult, De Pauw Univ, spring 72; guest dir, Evansville Civic Theatre, summer 72; theatre consult, Rochester Shakespeare Theatre, N.Y, 12/72. Med. Admin.C, U.S.A, 42-44, 1st Lt. Am. Theatre Asn; U.S. Inst. Theatre Technol. Stage direction and design, especially in the legitimate theatre. Add: Dept. of Theatre & Drama, Indiana University, Bloomington, IN 47401.

SCANLAN, MARY HONORA, b. Portland, Maine, Aug. 18, 12. ENGLISH. B.A, Marygrove Col, 34; M.A, Northwest. Univ, 40; scholar, Cath. Univ. Am; scholar. & Ph.D.(Eng), Columbia Univ, 50. Teacher, sec. schs; instr. ENG, Rosary Col, 38-40; Douglass Col, 42-47; prof, Col. Steubenville, 50-57; ASSOC. PROF, SETON HALL UNIV, 57- MLAA; NCTE. Medieval period; 19th century. Add: Dept. of English, Seton Hall University, South Orange, NJ 07079.

SCANLON, LAWRENCE EUGENE, b. Montclair, N.J, Sept. 12, 27; m. 52; c. 3. ENGLISH LITERATURE. B.A, Wesleyan Univ, 51; M.A, Rutgers Univ, 52; Fulbright grant, Univ. Vienna, 52-53; Ph.D, Syracuse Univ, 58. Asst. prof. ENG, Mt. Holyoke Col, 58-63; HARTFORD COL. WOMEN, 63-67, ASSOC. PROF, 67- Fulbright vis. lectr, Japan, 64-65. U.S.A, 45-46. Am. Stud. Asn. Hawthorne; Mark Twain; short story. Publ: First Came Commodore Perry, Eicho-sha, Tokyo, 69; The heart of The Scarlet Letter, Forum, 62; Harry James' compositional resource and value intrinsic, Tex. Stud. Lit. & Lang, 63; Unheroic Huck, East-West Rev, winter 66; plus others. Add: 101 Holcomb, East Granby, CT 06026.

SCARGILL, MATTHEW HARRY, b. Barnsley, Eng, Sept. 19, 16; m. 48. ENGLISH, LINGUISTICS. B.A, Univ. Leeds, 38, Parkinson scholar, 38-40, Ph.D.(Eng), 40. Asst. dir. exam, Civil Serv. Comn. Eng, 46-48; from asst. prof. to assoc. prof. Eng, Univ. Alta, Calgary, 48-62, prof. Eng. & dean fac. arts & sci, 62-64; PROF. LING, UNIV. VICTORIA, 64-, dean fac. grad. stud, 63-70. Ling. Soc. Am; Can. Ling. Asn.(pres, 62-64). English language. Publ: Co-auth, Three Icelandic sagas, Am-Scand. Found, 50; auth, English handbook, Longmans, 52; co-auth, Looking at language, 65 & Dictionaries of Canadian English, 67, Gage. Add: Dept. of Linguistics, University of Victoria, Victoria, B.C, Can.

SCARRITT, CHARLES WESLEY, b. Kansas City, Mo, Sept. 22, 01; m. 47; c. 2. JOURNALISM. B.J, Univ. Mo, 39; A.M, 50; summers, Univ. N.Dak, 39, Univ. Ark, 45. Teaching asst, Univ. Ga, 40-42; instr. JOUR, Auburn Univ, 42-44; Stephens Col, 44-45; Tex. West. Col, 45-48; asst. prof, Univ. Ala, 48-59, assoc. prof, 59-72; RETIRED. Consult. ed, Am. Asn. Cost Engineers Bull, 63- Asn. Educ. Jour. History of journalism; interpretive reporting; press law. Add: 24 Fairmont Dr, Tuscaloosa, AL 35401.

SCHAAL, DAVID GEORGE, b. Beaver Falls, Pa, July 28, 20; m. 43; c. 1. THEATER, DRAMA. B.A, Geneva Col, 42; summer fel. & M.A, West. Reserve Univ, 46; summer fel, Univ. Ill, 55, Ph.D.(Am. theater hist), 56. Instr. speech & drama, State Univ. N.Y. Col. Potsdam, 46-49; asst. prof. & dir. speech & drama, Cent. Conn. State Col, 51-53; instr. theater & drama, Cornell Univ, 53-56; asst. prof, UNIV. IOWA, 56-62, assoc. prof, 62-69, PROF. SPEECH & DRAMA, 69-, res. prof, 65. Assoc. ed, Educ. Theatre J, 66-68, ed, 69-71. Distinguished Serv. Award, Geneva Col, 67. Am. Theatre Asn.(chmn, rare bks. proj, 62-68); Am. Soc. Theatre Res; Speech Commun. Asn; AAUP. American theater history; contemporary theory and production; directing. Publ: The English background of American rehearsal direction practices in the eighteenth century, 12/60 & The rehearsal situation at Daly's Theatre, 3/62, Educ. Theatre J; The creative thesis in directing, designing and acting, In: An introduction to graduate study in speech and theatre, Mich. State Univ, 61. Add: Dept. of Speech & Dramatic Art, University of Iowa, Iowa City, IA 52242.

SCHAEFER, WILLIAM DAVID, b. Dighton, Mass, May 11, 28; m. 58. ENGLISH. B.A, N.Y. Univ, 57; M.S, Univ. Wis, 58, Ph.D, 62. Asst. prof. ENG, UNIV. CALIF, LOS ANGELES, 62-67, assoc. prof, 67-71, PROF, 71- Fulbright grant, Bedford Col, Univ. London, 61; exec. secy, MLA, 71-; ed, PMLA, 71- Univ. Wis. distinguished teaching award, 60. U.S.A, 54-62, Sgt. MLA. Victorian poetry. Publ: James Thomson (B.V): beyond The city, 65 & The speedy extinction of evil and misery: selected prose of James Thomson (B.V), 67, Univ. Calif; The two cities of dreadful night, PMLA, 12/62; Henley and The hound of heaven, Victorian poetry, autumn 67. Add: Modern Language Association, 62 Fifth Ave, New York, NY 10011.

SCHAEFFER, SUSAN FROMBERG, b. Brooklyn, N.Y, Mar. 25, 41; c. 1. ENGLISH & AMERICAN LITERATURE. B.A, Univ. Chicago, 61, M.A, 63, Ph.D.(Eng), 66. Asst. ENG, Wright Jr. Col, 63-64; asst. prof, Ill. Inst. Technol, 64-66; BROOKLYN COL, 66-72, ASSOC. PROF, 72- Fiction, poetry and scholarship; Vladimir Nabokov. Publ: Falling (novel), 73, Anya (novel), 74 & Granite lady (poetry), 74, Macmillan; The witch and the weather report (poetry), Seven Woods, 72; The unwritten chapters in The real life of Sebastian Knight, Mod. Fiction Stud, 68; The editing blinks of Vladimir Nabokov's The eye, Univ. Windsor Rev, 73; Bend sinister and the novelist as anthropomorphic deity, Centennial Rev, 73. Add: Dept. of English, Brooklyn College, Bedford Ave. & Ave. H, Brooklyn, NY 11229.

SCHAFER, WILLIAM JOHN, b. Richmond, Ind, Sept. 18, 37; m. 58; c. 2. ENGLISH. A.B, Earlham Col, 59; M.A, Univ. Minn, 64, Ph.D.(Eng. & art hist), 67. Instr, ENG. & HUMANITIES, BEREA COL, 64-73, assoc. prof, 73-74, PROF, 74- Nat. Endowment for Humanities younger humanist fel, 71-72. AAUP. Black music and its influence on American popular culture; contemporary American and British fiction; history of ideas in American culture. Publ: Rock music, Augsburg Publ, 72; co-auth, The art of ragtime, La. State Univ, 73; contrib, Contemporary novelists, St. Martin's, 73; co-auth, Play it one more time, chief! J. Am. Folklore, 9/73. Add: Dept. of English, Berea College, Berea, KY 40403.

SCHAFFER, BYRON S, JR, b. Lake Forest, Ill, Aug. 10, 32; m. 56; c. 2. THEATRE. B.A, Beloit Col, 54; M.A, Northwest. Univ, 59; Ph.D.(theatre), Ohio State Univ, 67. Asst. theatre, Northwest. Univ, 58-59; asst. prof. Eng, W.Va. Inst. Technol, 59-62; asst. theatre, Ohio State Univ, 62-64; PROF. THEATRE ARTS, NORTH. ILL. UNIV, 64- Ed, Players Mag, 67-; mem. exec. comt, Gov. Adv. Comn. Financing Arts in Ill, 70-72; dir, Dinglefest Theatre Co, 70- U.S.N, 54-57, Lt. Nat. Col. Players; Am. Theatre Asn. (publ. comt, 68-); Am. Nat. Theatre & Acad; Speech Commun. Asn.(chmn. theatre div, 70-72). Nineteenth century theatre history. Add: Players Magazine, Theatre, Northern Illinois University, DeKalb, IL 60115.

SCHAFFER, PAULINE W, Speech, Drama. See NELSON, PAULINE W.

SCHAMBERGER, JOHN EDWARD, b. Sterling, Colo, July 6, 32; m. 60. AMERICAN & ENGLISH LITERATURE. B.S, Colo. State Univ, 54; M.A, Univ. Colo, Boulder, 60; Ph.D.(Eng), Univ. Pa, 69. Instr. AM. LIT, Marietta Col, 62-65; ASSOC. PROF, COLO. STATE UNIV, 65- Intel.C, U.S.A, 54-57. Publ: The influence of Dugald Stewart and Richard Price on Emerson's concept of the Reason: a reassessment, Emerson Soc. Quart, 72; Grapes of gladness: a misconception of Walden, Am. Transcendental Quart, 72. Add: Dept. of English, Colorado State University, Ft. Collins, CO 80521.

SCHARBACH, J. ALEXANDER, b. Gervais, Ore, June 13, 09; m. 48; c. 1. ENGLISH. B.A, Univ. Notre Dame, 32; M.A, Univ. Wash, 41. From instr.

ENG. to prof. & head dept, Mt. Angel Col, 32-44; asst. prof, Univ. Portland, 45-51; PORTLAND STATE UNIV, 52-61; assoc. prof, 61-68, PROF, 68- MLA; NCTE; AAUP. Rhetoric and literary criticism; teaching of composition. Publ: Matthew Calbraith Perry: boy sailor, Bobbs, 55; The gold race, Dodd, 56; co-auth, Research writing craft, Portland State Col, Coop, 57; auth, Critical reading and writing, McGraw, 65, co-auth, The lively rhetoric, 68 & 72 & The new lively rhetoric, 70, Holt; Rhetoric and literary criticism: why their separation, Col. Compos. & Commun, 5/72. Add: Dept. of English, Portland State University, P.O. Box 751, Portland, OR 97207.

SCHARFENBERG, JEAN, b. Davenport, Iowa, Aug. 19, 22. THEATRE. B.S.Ed, Cent. Mo. State Col, 47; M.A, Univ. Wash, 56; Ph.D.(theatre), Univ. Wis, 62. Instr. theatre, Marylhurst Col, 51-54; Olympic Col, 56-58; speech & acting, Univ. Wis, 61-63; asst. prof. acting & directing, Univ. Iowa, 63-66; assoc. prof, ILL. STATE UNIV, 66-72, PROF. THEATRE, 72- ADV. FAC. WOMEN'S PLAY READERS, 67- Univ. Wis. res. grant, Actors Studio, New York, 62; adv, Iowa City Community Theatre, 64-66. Speech Commun. Asn; Am. Theatre Asn. Actor training; unification of production and directing. Publ: Directing—a selected and annotated bibliography for the secondary school theatre teacher and student, Am. Educ. Theatre Asn, 9/68. Add: Dept. of Theatre, Illinois State University, Normal, IL 61761.

SCHAUT, QUENTIN LEMAR, Religion, English Literature. See Volume IV, Philosophy, Religion & Law.

SCHECHNER, RICHARD, b. Newark, N.J, Aug. 23, 34. THEATRE. B.A, Cornell Univ, 56; M.A, State Univ. Iowa, 58; Ph.D, Tulane Univ, 62. Asst. prof. theatre, Tulane Univ, 62-67; PROF. DRAMA, N.Y. UNIV, 67- Ed, Tulane Drama Rev, 62-67; The Drama Rev, 67-69; dir, New Orleans Group, 65-67; The Performance Group, New York, 67- U.S.A, 58-60. AAAS. Literature; relationship of theatre to ritual, social anthropology; performance theory. Publ: Public domain, Bobbs, 69; Environmental theater, Hawthorn, 73; Negotiations with environment, Tri-Quart, spring 68; Actuals: a look into performance theory, Theatre Quart, 71; Drama, script, theatre performance theory, Theatre Quart, 71; Drama, script, theatre performance, Drama Rev, 73. Add: 29 Washington Sq. W, New York, NY 10011.

SCHEELE, HENRY ZAEGEL, b. Sheboygan, Wis, Aug. 27, 33; m. 56; c. 2. SPEECH, COMMUNICATION. B.A, Lake Forest Col, 56; M.S, Purdue Univ, 58, Ph.D.(speech), 62. Asst. prof. SPEECH, PURDUE UNIV, WEST LAFAYETTE, 62-72, ASSOC. PROF, 72-, res. grant, 64. Speech Commun. Asn; Cent. States Speech Commun. Asn. Political communication. Publ: Charlie Halleck: a political biography, Exposition, 66; Some reactions by congressmen to speaking in the United States House of Representatives, Today's Speech, 2/66; The rhetorical training of congressman Charles A. Halleck of Indiana, Ind. Speech, 4/68; Evaluations by experts and laymen of selected political speakers, South. Speech J, summer 68. Add: Dept. of Communication, Heavilon Hall, Purdue University, West Lafayette, IN 47907.

SCHEFF, EDWARD AARON, b. Brooklyn, N.Y, Feb. 14, 37; m. 58; c. 3. SPEECH COMMUNICATION. B.A, Brooklyn Col, 59; M.A, Univ. Kans, 60, Ph.D.(content anal), 65. Instr. speech & theater, Wright Jr. Col, 60-61; asst. prof. SPEECH, Univ. Mass, Amherst, 65-72; ASSOC. PROF. & CHMN. DEPT. SPEECH & THEATRE, RHODE ISLAND COL, 72- Nat. Soc. Stud. Commun; Speech Commun. Asn. East. States. Behavior prediction by semantic differential; content analysis of spoken communication; political demagoguery. Add: Dept. of Speech & Theatre, Rhode Island College, Providence, RI 02908.

SCHEIB, MARLIN EDWIN, b. Keystone, Iowa, Oct. 11, 31; m. 65. SPEECH SCIENCE. A.B, Luther Col, 58; M.A, La. State Univ, 62; Ph.D.(speech), Univ. Kans, 65. Instr. speech, Univ. S.Fla, 64-65, asst. prof, 65-67, assoc. prof, 67-69; speech sci, Univ. Mo-Kansas City, 69-71; PROF. SPEECH COMMUN, UNIV. S.FLA, 71- U.S.N, 50-54. Speech Commun. Asn; AAUP. Experimental phonetics; computer based instruction. Add: Box 17552, Tampa, FL 33612.

SCHEICK, WILLIAM JOSEPH, b. Newark, N.J, July 15, 41; m. 63. AMERICAN LITERATURE. B.A, Montclair State Col, 63; M.A, Univ. Ill, Urbana, 65, fel, 68-69, Ph.D.(Am. lit), 69. ASST. PROF. ENG, UNIV. TEX, AUSTIN, 69- Mem. ed, bd, Tex. Stud. Lit. & Lang, 71-; Eng. Lit. in Transition, 71-; Univ. Tex, Austin Res. Inst. grant, 73-74. American literature; theology and art; 17th century thought and art. Publ: The will and the word: the poetry of Edward Taylor, Univ. Ga, 74; Anonymity and art in The life and death of that reverend man of God, Mr. Richard Mather, Am. Lit, 1/71; The widower narrator in Nathaniel Ward's The simple cobbler of aggawam in America, New Eng. Quart, 3/74; New England Puritanism and the new left, Thought Quart. Rev, spring 71 & In: New theology, No. 9, Macmillan, 72. Add: Dept. of English, Parlin Hall, University of Texas, Austin, TX 78712.

SCHEIDEL, THOMAS MAYNARD, b. Columbus, Nebr, July 24, 31; m. 53; c. 2. SPEECH. B.A, Willamette Univ, 53; M.A, Univ. Wash, 55, Ph.D.(speech), 58. Asst. prof. SPEECH, Univ. Wash, 58-60; Cornell Univ, 60-63; assoc. prof, Univ. Ill, Urbana, 63-69; PROF, UNIV. WIS-MADISON, 69- Res. assoc, Educ. TV Proj, Univ. Ore, summer 61. Speech Commun. Asn; Nat. Soc. Stud. Commun. Oral persuasion; communication in small groups. Publ: Persuasive speaking, 67 & Speech Communication and human interaction, 72, Scott; Sex and persuasibility, 11/63 & co-auth, Speech as process: a case study, 3/68, Speech Monogr; Feedback in small group communication, Quart. J. Speech, 10/66. Add: Dept. of Communication Arts, University of Wisconsin-Madison, Madison, WI 53706.

SCHEIDENHELM, RICHARD JOY, American History, Literature. See Volume I, History.

SCHEJBAL, JAROSLAV, b. Prague, Czech, July 13, 22; m. 58; c. 1. AMERICAN RENAISSANCE LITERATURE. B.A, Charles Univ, Prague, 47, M.A, 48, Ph.D.(Am. lit), 52; Salzburg Sem. Am. Stud, summers 47, 48. Lectr. Eng, Inst. Mod. Lang, Prague, 49-53, sr. lectr, 54-62; ASSOC. PROF. AM. LIT, Palacky Univ, Czech, 63-68; UNIV. ILL, CHICAGO CIRCLE, 68- Sr. fel, Salzburg Sem. Am. Stud, summer 66. Czech. Infantry, 48. American and European picaresque novel; grotesque in American and European novel; feeling of loneliness in literature of the American Renaissance. Publ: Ed, American literature, I-II, an anthology, Nat. Publ, 59, 62 & Days and nights of America, a critical anthology of short stories, Slovenský Spisovatel, 64; auth, Sense of duty in the work of Graham Greene, 2/57 & The dilemma of Sherwood Anderson, 2/57, Světová Lit; Nathanael West's surrealist grotesques, a critical introduction, Mladá Fronta, 68. Add: Dept. of English, College of Liberal Arts & Sciences, University of Illinois at Chicago Circle, Box 4348, Chicago, IL 60680.

SCHELL, EDGAR THOMAS, b. Phila, Pa, Dec. 5, 31; m. 57; c. 2. ENGLISH. A.B, Temple Univ, 59; M.A, Univ. Calif, Berkeley, 61, Ph.D.(Eng), 65. Assoc. speech, Univ. Calif, Berkeley, 63-64; asst. prof. ENG, UNIV. CALIF, IRVINE, 65-71, ASSOC. PROF, 71- U.S.A.F, 51-54. MLA. Medieval and Renaissance drama; dramatic literature; critical theory. Publ: Co-ed, Morality plays and moral interludes, Holt, 69; auth, Prince Hal's second conversion, winter 70 & Who said that Hamlet or Hamlet?, winter 73, Shakespeare Quart; The structure of Wit and science, Stud. Eng. Lit, (in press). Add: Dept. of English, University of California, Irvine, CA 92664.

SCHELL, GEORGE AARON, b. Waco, Tex, May 11, 39; m. 60; c. 1. SPEECH COMMUNICATION. B.A, Baylor Univ, 61, M.A, 63. ASSOC. PROF. SPEECH COMMUN. & CHMN. DEPT. & DIR. FORENSICS, LOYOLA MARYMOUNT UNIV, 63- Chmn. & mem. bd. trustees, Nat. Debate Tournament, 67-72, mem. comt, 73-75; lectr, Georgetown Univ, summers 67-72; Baylor Univ, summer 73. Am. Forensic Asn. Debate. Publ: The negative: topicality, significance, practicality and disadvantage, Persuador, fall 68; Study guide on controlling air and water pollution, 11/70 & Study guide on unilateral United States military intervention, 11/69, Rostrum. Add: Dept. of Speech Communication, Loyola Marymount University, 7101 W. 80th St, Los Angeles, CA 90045.

SCHEMM, MILDRED WALKER, b. Philadelphia, Pa, May 2, 05; m. 27; c. 3. ENGLISH LITERATURE. B.A, Wells Col, 26; M.A, Univ. Mich, 34. Asst. prof. ENG. LIT. & WRITING, WELLS COL, 55-56, from assoc. prof. to prof, 56-68, EMER. PROF, 68- Fulbright lectr. Am. lit, Doshisha Women's Col. & Nara Women's Univ, Japan, 59-60. Writing novels. Publ: Fireweed, 34, Light from Arcturus, 35, Dr. Norton's wife, 38, The Brewers' big horses, 40, Winter wheat, 44, The quarry, 47, Medical meeting, 49, The southwest corner, 51, Unless the wind turns, 53, The curlew's cry, 55, & The body of a young man, 60, Harcourt; If a lion could talk, Harcourt Brace & Jovanovich, 70; A piece of the world, Atheneum, 72. Add: Grafton, VT 05146.

SCHENDLER, SYLVAN, b. New York, N.Y, May 28, 25. ENGLISH. M.A, Univ. Chicago, 48; Ph.D.(Eng), Northwest. Univ, 56. Instr. Eng, N.Mex. Col, 48-50; Wayne Univ, 50-54; Tex. West. Col, 55-56; Smith Col, 56-57, asst. prof, 57-62, vis. prof. Am. lit, Univ. Hong Kong, 66-67; prof. Eng. & chmn. dept, Point Park Col, 67-71; DIR, AM. STUD. RES. CTR, HYDERABAD, INDIA, 71- Dir. Am. Stud, Univ. Mass, 57; vis. prof, Univ. Helsinki, Finland, 60; ed, Indian Jour. Am. Stud, 71- U.S.A, 43-46. MLA; Asn. Depts. Eng; Col. Eng. Asn. American civilization. Publ: Living language, Harcourt, 53; co-auth, American pantheon, Delacorte, 66; auth, Eakins, Little, 67; Point Park College, Point Park Col, 68; plus others. Add: Apt. 15 E, 186 Riverside Dr, New York, NY 10024.

SCHENKKAN, ROBERT, b. Mar. 4, 17, N.Y, N.Y; m. 44; c. 4. DRAMA. A.B, Univ. Va, 41; Rockefeller fel, Univ. N.C, 41-42, A.M, 46; Nat. Theatre Conf. fel. in playwriting, 47; Fund Adult Educ. stud. fel. in TV, 52. Spec. lectr, Univ. N.C, 46-47, instr. radio, 47-48, asst. prof, 48-52, assoc. prof, 52-55, dir. TV, consolidated UNC, WUNC-TV, 53-55; PROF. RADIO, TV & FILM & DIR. COMMUN. CTR, UNIV. TEX, AUSTIN, 55- Pres. & gen. mgr, KLRN-TV & KUT-FM, 61-; dir, Tex. Educ. Media Prog, 62- & Tex. Educ. & Knowledge Network, 69-; consult, Agency Int. Develop, 67-; World Bank, 68; Fulbright lectr, Chile, 69 & 72; chmn, Nat. Educ. TV Affil. Counc, 69; mem. adv. screening comt. commun, Comt. Internat. Exchange Persons, 70-; stud. grant, Ford Found, 70; chmn. bd. mgrs. & bd. dir, Pub. Broadcasting Serv, 73-74; mem. exec. comt, Counc. State Educ. Telecommun. Authorities. Raven Award, 41; Jabberwock Award, 41. U.S.N.R, 42-46, Comdr.(Ret). Nat. Asn. Educ. Broadcasters (v.chmn, 68, chmn. educ. TV stations, 69-72); South. Educ. Commun. Asn. Production and teaching; international radio and television; educational technology and systems. Publ: Fourteen plays for the church; co-auth, The knowledge network, Univ. Tex, 66; transl, Lady from the sea, Peer Gynt, The wild duck: plays of Henrik Ibsen, 66. Add: KLRN-TV, P.O. Box 7158, University of Texas at Austin, Austin, TX 78712.

SCHEPS, WALTER, b. New York, N.Y, June 19, 39; m. 63; c. 2. ENGLISH. B.A, City Col. New York, 63; Woodrow Wilson fel, NDEA fel. & Ph.D.(Eng), Univ. Ore, 66. Asst. prof. ENG, Case West. Reserve Univ, 66-69; OHIO STATE UNIV, 69-71, ASSOC. PROF, 71- Reader, Thomas Y. Crowell Co, 71-; Chaucer Rev. & Stud. in Scottish Lit, 72- MLA; Mediaeval Acad. Am; Soc. Advan. Scand. Stud. Chaucer; 15th-century literature; popular literature in the Middle Ages. Publ: Chaucer's anti-fable: reductio ad absurdum in the Nun's priest's tale, Leeds Stud. Eng, 70; Middle English poetic usage in Blind Harry's Wallace, Chaucer Rev, 70; Chaucerian synthesis: the art of The Kingis Quair, Stud. Scottish Lit, 71; plus one other. Add: Dept. of English, Ohio State University, Columbus, OH 43210.

SCHER, SAUL N, b. New York, N.Y, Oct. 21, 32; m. 59; c. 1. BROADCASTING, FILM. B.A, Queens Col.(N.Y), 54; M.F.A, Columbia Univ, 60; Ph.D. (mass commun), N.Y. Univ, 65. Asst. prof. educ. TV, Univ. Mass, Amherst, 65-67; RADIO-TV-FILM, Univ. Md, College Park, 67-69; ASSOC. PROF, UNIV. MAINE, ORONO, 69- Coord, U.S. Off. Educ. TV Workshop for teachers of the deaf, summer 66; Coe res. grantee, 70-71. Broadcast Educ. Asn; Nat. Asn. Educ. Broadcasters; Am. Film Inst; Speech Commun. Asn. History and criticism of broadcasting and motion pictures. Publ: The critics look at television, Wadsworth, 75; An old city hall tradition: New York's mayors and WNYC, J. Broadcasting, spring 66; The deaf: new audience for TV?, Audiovisual Instr, 1/67; The role of the television critic: four approaches, Today's Speech, summer 74. Add: Dept. of Speech, University of Maine at Orono, Orono, ME 04473.

SCHERTING, JOHN ANDREW, b. Auburn, Wash, Dec. 2, 34; m. 59; c. 3. AMERICAN STUDIES & LITERATURE. B.A, Cent. Wash. State Col, 60; Ph.D.(Am. stud), Wash. State Univ, 70. ASST. PROF. AM. LIT. & DIR. AM. STUD, UTAH STATE UNIV, 69- Transp.C, U.S.A, 54-56. Am. Stud. Asn. American values. Publ: Roderick Hudson: a reevaluation, Ariz. Quart, 8/69; Echoes of Thomas Wolfe in Dylan Thomas, Stud. Short Fiction, 8/72; An approach to the western poetry of Thomas Hornsby Ferril, West. Am. Lit, 11/72. Add: Dept. of English, Utah State University, Logan, UT 84322.

SCHERZER, EDWIN J, b. Louisville, Ky, Nov. 7, 25. ENGLISH. B.A, St. Meinrad Col, 50; M.A, Fordham Univ, 54. Asst. prof. ENG, BELLARMINE COL, 55-71, ASSOC. PROF, 71- NCTE; Speech Commun. Asn; South. Speech Commun. Asn. Mediaeval and Renaissance literature; drama; music. Add: Dept. of English, Bellarmine College, Louisville, KY 40205.

SCHEUERLE, WILLIAM HOWARD, b. Irwin, Pa, Mar. 12, 30; m. 58; c. 2. ENGLISH. B.A, Muskingum Col, 52; M.A, Univ. Pa, 54; cert, Int. Grad. Summer Sch, Oxford, 61; Ph.D.(Eng), Syracuse Univ. 64. Instr. ENG, Westminster Col.(Pa), 56-58; asst. prof, UNIV. S.FLA, TAMPA, 64-67, assoc. prof, 67-72, PROF. & ASST. V.PRES. ACAD. AFFAIRS, 72- Vis. instr, Muskingum Col, summer 56; Am. Philos. Soc. grant, 66; Nat. Endowment for Humanities summer stipend, 67; Univ. S.Fla. fac. award, 67, res. grant, 68-69; coord. humanities & fine arts, State Univ. System, Fla, 69-71. U.S.A, 54-56 Milton Soc. Am; MLA; NCTE; Res. Soc. Victorian Periodicals. Seventeenth and nineteenth century British literature; Henry Kingsley; Victorian novels. Publ: Ed, Introduction to Henry Kingsley's Ravenshoe, Univ. Nebr, 67; auth, The neglected brother: a study of Henry Kingsley, Fla. State. Univ. 71; Gabriel Hounds and Joyce's The dead, Stud. Short Fiction, summer 65; Romantic attitudes in Geoffry Hamlyn, Australian Lit. Stud, 12/55; Magdalene at Michael's gate: a neglected lyric, Victorian Poetry, summer 67. Add: Dept. of English, University of South Florida, Tampa, FL 33620.

SCHICK, GEORGE BALDWIN POWELL, b. Aurora, Ill, July 20, 03; m. 36; c. 1. ENGLISH LITERATURE. Ph.B, Univ. Chicago, 26, A.M, 28, Ph.D, 53. Instr, Univ. Ark, 28-30; Beloit Col, 30-33; mem. fac. ENG. & READING, PURDUE UNIV, W. LAFAYETTE, 35-59, asst. prof, 39-40, prof, 50-70, EMER. PROF, 70- Ed, J. Developmental Reading, 59-63, J. Reading, 63-67; prof. lectr, Calif. State Univ, Fullerton, 70- Outstanding Contribution to Reading Improvement, Int. Reading Asn, 67; Oscar S. Causey Award, Nat. Reading Conf, 71. U.S.N, 43-46, Comdr. MLA; Nat. Reading Conf. (mem. bd. dir, 66-70, ed. yearbook, 66-70); Col. Reading Asn; West. Col. Reading Asn. Criticism; 18th century literature; reading improvement. Publ: Co-auth, Design for good reading Harcourt, 62 & 69; Guidebook for teachers of reading, 66 & Guide to the teaching of reading, 73, Psychotechnics; Reading at efficient rates, McGraw, 70; Developing reading proficiency, Merrill, 71; auth, Better reading programs show lasting benefits, Personnel J, 56; Joseph Warton's conception of a true poet, Boston Univ. Stud. Eng, 59; Diversity & college reading programs, Perspective in Reading, 64. Add: Institute of Reading, California State University, Fullerton, 800 N. State College, Fullerton, CA 92634.

SCHICK, JOSEPH SCHLUETER, b. Davenport, Iowa, Mar. 23, 10. ENGLISH. B.A, State Univ. Iowa, 31; M.A, Univ. Chicago, 32, Ph.D.(Eng. & Am. hist), 37. Instr. ENG, State Univ. Iowa, 35-36; prof, Minn. State Teachers Col, Duluth, 38-42, 45-46; PROF, IND. STATE UNIV, TERRE HAUTE, 46- Lectr, Caserta Tech. Inst, Italy, 45. U.S.A, 42-45. MLA. History of the theater on the frontier; early 19th century American literature. Publ: Early theater in eastern Iowa, Univ. Chicago, 39; Origin of The cask of Amontillado, Am. Lit. J, 34; Poe and Jefferson, Va. Mag. of Hist. & Biog, 46. Add: Dept. of English, Indiana State University, Terre Haute, IN 47809.

SCHIEDER, RUPERT MOHL, b. Ft. Frances, Ont, Sept. 8, 15. ENGLISH. M.A. & Ph.D.(Eng), Univ. Toronto, 54. Teaching fel, Trinity Col, 49-51; prof. Eng. & head dept, Can. Servs. Col, 51-58; asst. prof. ENG, TRINITY COL.(ONT), 58-65, assoc. prof, 65-73, PROF, 73- R.C.A.F, 42-46. MLA; Humanities Asn. Can. Victorian literature and fiction. Publ: Introd. & ed, Prester John, Nelson, 64; introd, Woodsman of the West, McClelland & Stewart, 65; Loss and gain? the theme of conversion in late Victorian fiction, Victorian Stud, 9/65; chap, In: Literary history of Canada, Univ. Toronto, 65. Add: Dept. of English, Trinity College, University of Toronto, Toronto, Ont. H5S 1H8, Can.

SCHIEFELBUSCH, RICHARD LOUIS, Speech Pathology. See 12th Edition, American Men & Women of Science, Social & Behavioral Sciences Section.

SCHIFFMAN, JOSEPH, b. New York, N.Y. June 13, 14; m. 41; c. 2. ENGLISH. B.A, L.I. Univ, 37; M.A, Columbia Univ, 47; Ph.D, N.Y. Univ, 51. Instr. Eng, L.I. Univ, 45-49, asst. prof, 49-51, assoc. prof, 51-58, coord. grad. prog. Am. Stud, 56-58; PROF. ENG, DICKINSON COL, 58-, JAMES HOPE CALDWELL PROF. AM. STUD, 68-, chmn. dept. eng, 59-68. Vis. prof, Univ. Pa, summers, 60, 67; acting ed, Am. Quart, 60; head Am. lit, Int. Bibliog. Comt, 61-; founding dir, Am. Stud. Res. Ctr, India, 64; vis. Fulbright prof, Univ. Bordeaux, France, 65-66. Lindback Found. Award Distinguished Teaching, 62. U.S.A, 42-45. MLA; NCTE; Am. Stud. Asn. (acting exec. secy, 60-61). American literature and civilization. Publ: Introduction to Lindsay Swift's Brook Farm, Corinth, 61; ed, Three shorter novels of Herman Melville, Harper, 62 & Duke of Stockbridge, Harvard, 62; co-auth, A critical history of American literature: from its beginnings to the present, Cassell's Encyclopedia of World Literature, 73. Add: Dept. of English, Dickinson College, Carlisle, PA 17013.

SCHILLER, ANDREW, Linguistics. See Volume III, Foreign Languages, Linguistics & Philology.

SCHILLER, PHILOMENE CLARA, b. Denver, Colo, Nov. 10, 15. EDUCATION, ENGLISH. A.B, Univ. Denver, 37; M.A, St. Louis Univ, 56; Ph.D.(educ), Fordham Univ, 60; summer, Georgetown Univ, 64. Asst. prof. educ, Webster Col, 52-56, assoc. prof, 60-63; PROF. EDUC. & LECTR. LING, LORETTO HEIGHTS COL, 64- Assoc. dir, Rocky Mount Educ. Lab, 66-67. NCTE. Linguistics; reading. Publ: The effects of the functional use of certain reading skills in seventh-grade social studies, J. Educ. Res, 12/63; The revolution in grammar, Statement, 12/66; Linguistics in junior high school, Eng. J, 5/68. Add: Depts. of Education & English, Loretto Heights College, 3001 S. Federal Blvd, Denver, CO 80236.

SCHILLING, LESTER LORENZO, JR, b. Kalamazoo, Mich, June 11, 20; m. 44; c. 2. SPEECH, DRAMA. B.S, West. Mich. Col, 42; A.M, Columbia Univ, 46; Ph.D, Univ. Wis, 60. Teacher speech & drama, High Sch, Mich, 42-46; chmn. dept, Ind. Cent. Col, 46-48; asst. prof, Linfield Col, 48-57, assoc. prof. drama, 57-63, PROF, 63-67; SPEECH, SOUTHWEST TEX. STATE UNIV, 67- Vis. prof, Univ. Ore, summers 63, 64. Speech Commun. Asn; Am. Theatre Asn. Voice science; oral interpretation. Add: Dept. of Speech, Southwest Texas State University, San Marcos, TX 78660.

SCHLEGEL, DOROTHY BADDERS, b. Harford Co, Md, July 18, 10; m. 41. COMPARATIVE LITERATURE. B.A, Dickinson Col, 32; M.A, Col. William & Mary, 48; Ph.D.(comp. lit), Univ. N.C, 54; Columbia Univ, West. Reserve Univ, Middlebury Col, Univ. Va. & Univ. Vienna, 54; Univ. Frankfurt, 54-55; Univ. Paris, 55. Teacher, Jr. High Sch, Pa, 32-34, Sr. High Sch, 34-37; instr. St. Helena Exten, Col. William & Mary, 48; asst. prof, COMP. LIT. & ENG, Longwood Col, 53-57, assoc. prof, 57-63, PROF, 63-66; NORFOLK STATE COL, 66- Col. Eng. Asn; NCTE; MLA; Int. Comp. Lit. Asn; James Branch Cabell Soc. The third Earl of Shaftesbury; secret societies in the 18th century; James Branch Cabell. Publ: Shaftesbury and the French deists, Univ. N.C, 56; James Branch Cabell and Southern romanticism, Longwood Col, 59; Writing from research, McCutchan, 64; Shaftsbury's Hermetic symbolism, Proc. 4th Congr. Int. Comp. Lit. Asn, 66; Cabell's translation of Virginia, Cabellian, 69; Freemasonry and the Encyclopédie reconsidered, Stud. Voltaire & 18th Century, 72; plus others. Add: 476 Linkhorn Dr, Virginia Beach, VA 23451.

SCHLEINER, WINFRIED, b. Mannheim, Ger, Oct. 19, 38; m. 68; c. 2. ENGLISH LITERATURE. Staatsexamen (Eng. & Fr), Univ. Kiel, 64; A.M, Brown Univ, 65, Ph.D.(Eng), 68. Asst. master & schoolmaster Eng. & Fr, Max-Planck Schule, Kiel, Ger, 68-70; ASST. PROF. ENG, R.I. Col, 70-73; UNIV. CALIF, DAVIS, 73- Folger Shakespeare Libr. fel, 73. English Renaissance literature; comparative literature. Publ: The imagery of John Donne's sermons, Brown Univ, 70; Rank and marriage: a study of the motif of Women willfully tested, Comp. Lit. Stud, 72; The Erona episode in the Old and New Arcadia, Stud. Philol, 73; Aeneas' flight from Troy, Comp. Lit, 74. Add: Dept. of English, University of California, Davis, CA 95616.

SCHLESINGER, LORRAINE ANNE, English, American Literature. See Brown, Lorraine Anne.

SCHLESS, HOWARD HUGH, b. Philadelphia, Pa, Oct. 6, 24; m. 51; c. 3. ENGLISH. B.A, Harvard, 49; M.A, Yale, 51; Ph.D.(Eng), Univ. Pa, 56. Teacher, William Penn Charter Sch, 52-54; asst. instr. Eng, Univ. Pa, 54-55; instr. ENG. & COMP. LIT, COLUMBIA UNIV, 56-58, asst. prof, 58-63, assoc. prof, 63-71, PROF, 71- Nat. Dante Prize, 49. U.S.A, 43-46. MLA; Mediaeval Acad. Am; AAUP. Comparative mediaeval literature; 17th century political verse; a revaluation of Chaucer and Dante. Publ: Poems on affairs of state, vol. 3, Yale, 68; Chaucer and Dante, In: Critical approaches to mediaevel literature, Columbia Univ, 60; Comic element in Wakefield Noah, In: Studies in medieval literature, Univ. Pa, 61; Transformations: Chaucer and Italian, In: Writers and their backgrounds, Bell, London, 74. Add: Dept. of English, Columbia University, New York, NY 10027.

SCHLISSEL, LILLIAN FISCHER, b. Brooklyn, N.Y, Feb. 22, 30; m. 63. ENGLISH, AMERICAN STUDIES. B.A, Brooklyn Col, 51; univ. fels, Yale, 52-53, 54-55, Coe fel, 53-54, Ph.D, 57. Instr. ENG, BROOKLYN COL, 57-65, asst. prof, 65-72, PROF, 72-, DIR, PROG. AM. STUD, 72- MLA; Am. Stud. Asn. Nineteenth century American literature, especially Washington Irving. Publ: Ed, The world of Randolph Bourne, 65 & Conscience in America: a documentary history of conscientious objection in America, 1757-1967, 68, Dutton; auth, John Quidor in New York, Am. Quart, winter 65. Add: Dept. of English, Brooklyn College, Brooklyn, NY 11210.

SCHLOBIN, ROGER CLARK, b. Brooklyn, N.Y, June 22, 44; m. 70. MEDIEVAL LANGUAGE & LITERATURE. B.A, C.W. Post Col, 66; M.A, Univ. Wis-Madison, 68; Ph.D.(Eng), Ohio State Univ, 71. Teaching asst. Eng. & asst. dir, Ctr. Medieval & Renaissance Stud, Ohio State Univ, 69-71; ASST. PROF. ENG, PURDUE UNIV, N.CENT. CAMPUS, 71-, Res. Found. grant, summer 71. Dormitory suprv, Univ. Wis, 66-70; instr. Eng, Upward Bound Prog, Ohio Dominican Col, 68-71; consult, Michigan City Pub. Libr, 72- Int. Arthurian Soc; Early Eng. Text Soc; Midwest Mod. Lang. Asn; MLA; Mediaeval Acad. Am. Arthurian literature; medieval romance; Chaucer. Publ: Ed, Three Gawain romances: The Grene Knight, The Turke and Gowin, and The marriage of Gawaine, Ohio State Univ, 71. Add: Dept. of English, Purdue University, North Central Campus, Westville, IN 46391.

SCHLOSSER, RALPH WIEST, b. Schoeneck, Pa, July 21, 86; m. 09; c. 5. ENGLISH. A.B, Elizabethtown Col, 11; A.B, Ursinus Col, 11, A.M, 12, D.Litt, 32; A.M, Columbia Univ, 22; Union Theol. Sem.(N.Y), 29-30. Prof. ENG, ELIZABETHTOWN COL, 12-70, dean instr, 22-27, pres, 27-70, EMER. PROF, 70- Prof, Harrisburg Area Col, 46-48 & Juniata Col, summers 43-49. Court scene of Merchant of Venice translated into Pennsylvania German dialect; studies in Shakespeare; history of Elizabethtown College 1899-1970. Publ: History of Elizabethtown College 1899-1970, Elizabethtown Col, 71. Add: Brethren Village, Lancaster, PA 17601.

SCHLOSSER, WILLIAM EDWIN, b. Chicago, Ill, June 22, 20; m. 47; c. 3. THEATRE. B.Ed, Chicago Teachers Col, 46; M.A, Northwest. Univ, Evanston, 48; Ed.D.(theater educ), Univ. Ore, 56. Instr. theater, Univ. Ore, 48-51; teacher drama, McMinville High Sch, 54-56; asst. prof. THEATER, Los Angeles State Col, 56-59; PROF, CALIF. STATE UNIV, NORTHRIDGE, 59- A.U.S, 42-46. AAUP; Am. Theatre Asn. Musical theater; contemporary drama; theater education. Add: Dept. of Theatre, California State University, Northridge, 18111 Nordhoff St, Northridge, CA 91324.

SCHLUETER, PAUL, b. Chicago, Ill, May 10, 33; div; c. 3. MODERN BRITISH & AMERICAN LITERATURE. B.A, Univ. Minn, Minneapolis, 58;

M.A, Univ. Denver, 63; Ph.D.(Eng), South. Ill. Univ, Carbondale, 68. Instr. Eng, Col. St. Thomas, 59-60; Eng. & jour, Moorhead State Col, 60-62; ENG, South. Ill. Univ, Carbondale, 63-66; asst. prof, Adrian Col, 66-68; Univ. Evansville, 69-72; guest prof, Univ. Hamburg, 73; ASST. PROF, KEAN COL. N.J, 73- Guest prof, Eng, Midwest. Univ, summer 64; assoc. secy. & ed, Lamda Iota Tay Newslett, 67-68. MLA; Conf. Christianity & Lit.(ed. jour, 71-72, secy, 71-73); Col. Eng. Asn. Modern fiction; women writers; religion and the arts. Publ: The novels of Doris Lessing, South. Ill. Univ, 73; ed, The small personal voice: essays. . . by Doris Lessing, Knopf, 74; contrib, Richard Aldington: an intimate portrait, South. Ill. Univ, 65, Encycl. World Lit. in 20th Century, Ungar, 67 & Encycl. Britannica, 3rd ed, 74; plus others. Add: Dept. of English, Kean College of New Jersey, Union, NJ 07083.

SCHMIDT, CARL PETER, b. New York, N.Y, Sept. 30, 33; m. 63; c. 3. MODERN JAPANESE LITERATURE, ENGLISH EDUCATION. B.S, State Univ. N.Y. Col. Cortland, 54; M.A, Hofstra Univ, 58; fel, N.Y. Univ, 60-61, Ph.D.(Eng. educ), 64. ASSOC. PROF. ENG. EDUC. & HUMANITIES, N.Y. UNIV, 65- Fulbright lectr, Osaka Univ, 63-64. U.S.A, 54-56. Asn. Asian Stud; NCTE; Col. Eng. Asn; MLA. Modern Japanese fiction; literary criticism; the readers response. Publ: Non-western literature and the reader's response, Res. in Educ, 1/71; The modern Japanese novel: form and feeling, Asia, summer 71; Enhancing reader response to Asian literature, N.Y. Univ. Educ. Quart, winter 72; plus others. Add: Division of English Education, Theatre & Speech, 829 Shimkin Hall, New York University, New York, NY 10003.

SCHMIDT, DOLORES BARRACANO, b. New York, N.Y, May 16, 31; m. 59; c. 3. ENGLISH, AMERICAN STUDIES. A.B, Hunter Col, 53; M.A, Univ. Pa, 56. Instr. Eng, Univ. Nev, 57-59; co-adj, Rutgers Univ, 59-60; asst. prof, East. Ill. Univ, 60-61; Mayville State Col, 61-62; Slippery Rock State Col, 68-73; EQUAL EMPLOYMENT OPPORTUNITY COORD, STATE UNIV. N.Y. ALBANY, 73- Univ. Pa. Libr. scholar, 55-57; Am. Stud. grant, Univ. Pa, 55-56; res. ed, Whitman Variorum Ed, N.Y. Univ. Press, 56-57; panelist, Col. Conf. Compos. & Commun, Calif, 59; ed, Res. in Progress: Women and Lit, 71-73; mem. bibliog. comt, Am. Quart, 72- Am. Asn. Univ. Women Creative Writing Award, 62. Am. Stud. Asn.(mem. comt. on status of women, 72-); MLA (mem. prog. comt, 71-76); Northeast Mod. Lang. Asn; Women's Caucus Mod. Lang.(pres, 71-73); AAUP. Twentieth century American novel; American literary and intellectual history; women in American society. Publ: Co-auth, The deputy reader, Scott, 65; co-ed, Pittsburgh regional ecology, Vulcan, 71; auth, Sexism in education, In: Female studies V: women and education, a feminist perspective, Know, 70; The missing women: American history textbooks, In: Women and American studies, Am. Stud. Asn, 71; The great American bitch, Col. Eng, 5/71. Add: Equal Employment Opportunity Office, State University of New York at Albany, Albany, NY 12222.

SCHMIDT, EMILE O, b. New York, N.Y, July 28, 27; m. 58; c. 3. DRAMA. A.B, Ursinus Col, 51; A.M, Columbia Univ, 53. Stage mgr. theatre, The Barnstormers, Tamworth, N.H, 51-52; pub. dir, Empress Playhouse, St. Louis, Mo, 53-54; Hilltop Theatre, Baltimore, Md, 54; asst. prof. ENG. & DRAMA & dir. drama, Springfield Col, 55-62; asst. prof, GETTYSBURG COL, 62-73, ASSOC. PROF, 73-, DIR. DRAMA, 62- Pub. dir, Lakes Region Playhouse, Laconia, N.H, 53-57; founder, producer & dir, Ivy Players, Springfield, Mass, 59-62; Gettysburg Summer Theatre, 63-67; managing dir, CPC Summer Theatre, Gettysburg, Pa, 73. U.S.N. Am. Theatre Asn. Shakespearean productions in New York, 1924-52; avant-garde theatre in Europe today; summer theatre repertory. Publ: The pack away proscenium, Theatre Crafts, 3/69; The Bowery! the Bowery!, Players Mag, 7/70. Add: Dept. of English, Gettysburg College, Gettysburg, PA 17325.

SCHMIDT, JAMES NORMAN, b. Chicago, Ill, Jan. 10, 12. CONTINENTAL & AMERICAN LITERATURE, CREATIVE WRITING. Cert, Ecole des Beaux Arts, Paris, 33; A.B, Univ. of the Americas, 57; M.A, Univ. Guanajuato, 67. Reporter, Chicago Tribune, Ill. & Paris Tribune, France, 34-36; ed, Compton's Pictured Encycl, 39-40; mil. corresp, U.S. Army, 44-46; writer, 47-55; dir. creative writing, Inst. Allende, Mex, 58-61; PROF. LIT, OHIO UNIV, 66- U.S.A, 44-46, 1st Lt; Bronze Star Medal. American history 1846-1848; American literature to Civil War. Publ: Fr. Juniper and the General, Morrow, 57; In Mexico, Morrow, 59 & Penguin, 65, 73; The fell of dark, Lippincott, 60; Terry's guide to Mexico, Doubleday, 62; The Valley of Lotus House, Michael Joseph, London, 63; Navy that crossed mountains, 64, Maya—the forgotten empire, 65, Strange world of reptiles, 66, The young generals, 67 & Charro—the Mexican horseman, 69, Putnam; plus six others. Add: Dept. of English, Ohio University, Athens, OH 45701.

SCHMIDT, MARY THECLA, S.C, b. Pittsburgh, Pa, June 26, 11. ENGLISH. A.B, Seton Hill Col, 32; A.M, Univ. Pittsburgh, 34; Seton Hill Col. Alumnae fel, Yale, 42-43, Ph.D, 43. Instr. ENG, SETON HILL COL, 36-39, asst. prof, 43-49, assoc. prof, 49-60, PROF, 60-, PRES, 70-, v.pres, 57-70. MLA. Early Tudor English prose and humanism; Thomas More. Publ: Ed, The supplication of souls, Newman, 50. Add: Office of the President, Seton Hill College, Greensburg, PA 15601.

SCHMIDT, RALPH NORMAN, (SR), b. Milwaukee, Wis, Nov. 25, 10; m. 33; c. 2. SPEECH, EDUCATION. B.A, Carroll Col.(Wis), 32; M.A, Northwest. Univ, 41; Ph.D.(speech & educ), Syracuse Univ, 50. Teacher, high sch, Wis, 32-42; prof. speech & econ, Jamestown Col, 42-43; instr. speech, Lafayette Col, 43-44; teacher high sch, Pa, 44-45; instr. SPEECH, Sch. Speech & Drama, SYRACUSE UNIV, 45-46, UTICA COL, 46-50, asst. prof, 50-56, assoc. prof, 56-69, PROF, 69- Speech consult. & dir. speech prog, N.Y. State Bankers' Sch. Pub. Relat, 45-56; speech consult, W.Can. Valley Cent. Sch, N.Y, 56-66; Found. Econ. Educ. fel, summer 59; parliamentarian, N.Y. State Convention of Universalists, 69-; N.Y. State Nurses Asn, 71- Speech Commun. Asn; Am. Arbit. Asn; Am. Inst. Parliamentarians. Comparative effectiveness of audience vs instructor criticism in developing effectiveness in public speaking; preaching of Olympia Brown, America's first woman preacher to be ordained by a recognized national religious denomination. Publ: How to speak with confidence, Fell, 65; Some current problems in contest speech, Quart. J. Speech, 2/43; A philosophy to guide us in teaching public speaking, Speech Teacher, 1/56; Olympia Brown: two sermons, Annual J. Universalist Hist. Soc, 64. Add: Dept. of Speech, Utica College of Syracuse University, Utica, NY 13502.

SCHMIDTBERGER, LOREN F, b. Victoria, Kans, Oct. 10, 28; m. 58; c. 6. ENGLISH LITERATURE. A.B, Ft. Hays Kans. State Col, 51; M.A, Fordham Univ, 57, Ph.D.(Am. lit), 65. Instr. Eng. lit, ST. PETER'S COL.(N.J), 55-58, asst. prof, 58-65, ASSOC. PROF, 65- U.S.A, 51-53, 1st Lt. MLA; Col. Eng. Asn. Medieval and American literature. Publ: Dreiser's An American tragedy, 66 & Faulkner's Absalom, Absalom!, 66, Simon & Schuster, Add: R.D. 1 Box 209-F, Hackettstown, NJ 07840.

SCHMITT, ALBERT RICHARD, German Language & Literature. See Volume III, Foreign Languages, Linguistics & Philology.

SCHMITTER, DEAN MORGAN, b. Richland, Iowa, June 14, 17; m. 62; c. 1. ENGLISH. B.A, La. State Univ, 38; M.A, Columbia Univ, 48, Ph.D.(Eng), 55. Lectr. ENG, COLUMBIA UNIV, 47-50, instr, 50-55, asst. prof, 55-60, assoc. prof, 60-74, PROF, 74- Counc. Res. Humanities grant, 59. U.S.N.R, 41-46, Lt. MLA; Renaissance Soc. Am. Seventeenth century literature; American literature. Publ: English 100, Inst. Univ. Stud, 63; ed, William Faulkner, 73 & auth, Mark Twain, 74, McGraw; auth, The occasion for Marvell's Growth of popery, J. Hist. Ideas, 60. Add: 66 Taillon Terr, Closter, NJ 07624.

SCHMITTLEIN, ALBERT EDWARD, b. Pittsburgh, Pa, Mar. 25, 26; m. 55; c. 4. AMERICAN LITERATURE. A.B, Univ. Pittsburgh, 50, Ph.D, 62; A.M, Columbia Univ, 53. Teacher, Jr. & Sr. High Schs, Pa, 50-51, 53-57; assoc. prof. ENG. SLIPPERY ROCK STATE COL, 57-63, PROF, 63-, dir. pub. relat, 57-60, dir. lib. arts, 64-65, dean col. arts & sci, 65-71, sch. humanities & fine arts, 71-73. Acad. colleague, Univ. Hawaii, 68; coord. current issues, Indust. Sem. Ser, Armco Steel, Pa, 70-74. Gold Key Award, Columbia Univ, 71. U.S.N, 44-46; for. correspondent, U.S.N. & U.S.M.C, 51-52. MLA; NCTE; Am. Conf. Acad. Deans; Am. Asn. Higher Educ; AAUP; Am. Counc. Educ. Higher education. Publ: Real information on Europe, Typographic, 52; Aesthetics of the organic novel, Slippery Rock Fac. Publ, 63; co-auth, Autobody repair: workbook I, Chilton, (in press); auth, I.T.A. and creative writing, Instructor, 66; Liberal education: the Phoenix, Slippery Rock State Col. Honors Convocation, 71; Convocation: American education—the progress, Educ. Rec, fall 72. Add: R.D. 2, Slippery Rock, PA 16057.

SCHMITZ, ROBERT MORELL, b. St. Louis, Mo, Dec. 22, 00; m. 34; c. 2. ENGLISH LITERATURE. A.B, Wash. Univ, 25, A.M, 29; Ph.D, Columbia Univ, 47. Asst, Univ. Ill, 29; instr, Wash. Univ, 30-36; Columbia Univ, 37-40; asst. prof. ENG, WASH. UNIV, 40-47, assoc. prof, 47-53, prof, 53-69, chmn. dept, 64-66, EMER. PROF, 69- MLA. Eighteenth century literature and bibliography. Publ: Pope's Windsor forest 1712, 52 & Pope's essay on criticism 1709, 62, Wash. Univ; The Arsenal proof sheets of Pope's Iliad, Mod. Lang. Notes, 59 & In: Essential articles for the study of Alexander Pope, 68, plus one other. Add: Dept. of English, Washington University, St. Louis, MO 63130.

SCHMUTZLER, KARL E, b. Barberton, Ohio, Feb. 11, 22. ENGLISH. B.A, Wheaton Col.(Ill), 43; M.A, Ohio State Univ, 48, Ph.D.(Eng), 56. Instr. ENG, King's Col.(Del), 49-50; from grad. asst. to instr, Ohio State Univ, 51-57; asst. prof, CENT. CONN. STATE COL, 57-61, assoc. prof, 61-66, PROF, 66-, chmn. dept, 66-69. Summers, Folger fel, Folger Shakespeare Libr, 60; Danforth Found. grant, 62. U.S.N, 43-46, Lt.(jg). NCTE; New Eng. Asn. Teachers Eng; MLA; Renaissance Soc. Am; Bibliog. Soc. Am. Renaissance bibliography; English metrical psalmody, 1500-1700; George Sandys, especially his paraphrases on the Psalms. Publ: Another manuscript version of Sandys' Song of Solomon & Harington's metrical paraphrases of the seven penitential Psalms: three manuscript versions, 59, Papers Bibliog. Soc. Am. Add: Dept. of English, Central Connecticut State College, New Britain, CT 06050.

SCHNEEMAN, PETER HENRY, b. St. Paul, Minn. ENGLISH & AMERICAN LITERATURE, CREATIVE WRITING. B.A, Univ. Minn, Minneapolis, 59, M.A, 67, Ph.D.(Eng. lit), 72. Instr. ENG. LIT, Kent State Univ, 64-65; teaching assoc, Univ. Minn, 65-71; ASST. PROF, PA. STATE UNIV, UNIVERSITY PARK, 71- U.S.A, 62-64. Twentieth century British and American literature. Publ: American autumn, New Am. Rev, 1/70; God of many names, Am. Rev, 2/73; 3 fingers of Figures for Gass, Minn. Rev, spring 73. Add: Dept. of English, Pennsylvania State University, University Park, PA 16802.

SCHNEEWIND, JEROME B, Philosophy. See Volume IV, Philosophy, Religion & Law.

SCHNEIDAU, HERBERT N, b. New Orleans, La, Aug. 26, 35; m. 61; c. 2. ENGLISH. B.A, Dartmouth Col, 57; M.A, Princeton, 60, Ph.D.(Eng), 63. Instr. ENG, Duke Univ, 61-63; asst. prof, State Univ. N.Y. Buffalo, 63-68, ASSOC. PROF, 68-70; UNIV. CALIF, SANTA BARBARA, 70- Modern literature; Chaucer; Bible and literature. Publ: Ezra Pound; the image and the real, La. State Univ, 69; Pound and Yeats: the question of symbolism, summer 65 & The Age of interpretation and the moment of immediacy, summer 70, ELH; Vorticism and the career of Ezra Pound, Mod. Philol, 2/68; plus others. Add: Dept. of English, University of California, Santa Barbara, CA 93106.

SCHNEIDEMAN, ROBERT IVAN, b. Bay City, Mich, June 23, 26; m. 67. THEATRE. B.S, Northwest. Univ, 48, M.A, 49, Ph.D, 56. Instr. DRAMATIC PROD. NORTHWEST. UNIV, 53-59, asst. prof, 59-63, assoc. prof, 63-68, PROF, 68-, coord, annual festival arts, 67, chmn. dept. theatre, 68-70. Mem. Adv. Bd, World Ctr. Shakespeare Stud, 72- Am. Theatre Asn.(exec. secy-treas, 62-64). Elizabethan and contemporary drama in production; contemporary acting and methods of training. Add: Dept. of Theatre, Northwestern University, Evanston, IL 60201.

SCHNEIDER, BEN ROSS, JR, b. Cincinnati, Ohio, July 7, 20; m. 49; c. 4. ENGLISH. B.A, Williams Col.(Mass), 42; M.A, Columbia Univ, 47, Ph.D, 55. Instr. ENG, Univ. Cincinnati, 47-48; Univ. Colo, 50-54; Ore. State Col, 54-55; from instr. to PROF, LAWRENCE UNIV, 55- Dir, London Stage Info. Bank Proj, 70- U.S.A, 42-46. MLA; Soc. Theatre Res, Eng; Asn. Comput. Mach; fel. Royal Soc. Arts. Romantics; 18th century; computer applications in literary research. Publ: Wordsworth's Cambridge education, Cambridge, 57; co-auth, Themes and research papers, Macmillan, 61; auth, The ethos of Restoration comedy, Ill. Univ, 71; The coquette-prude as an actress's line in Restoration comedy during the time of Mrs. Oldfield, Theatre Notebk, summer 68; The production of machine-readable text, Comput. & Humanities, 9/71; Analysis of a data base for information retrieval, In: Computers in literary research, Edinburg, 73; plus one other. Add: Dept. of English, Lawrence University, Appleton, WI 54911.

SCHNEIDER, DUANE BERNARD, b. South Bend, Ind, Nov. 15, 37; m. 59; c. 4. ENGLISH. B.A, Miami Univ, 58; M.A, Kent State Univ, 60; Ph.D.(Eng. lit), Univ. Colo, 65. Instr. Eng. in engineering, Univ. Colo, 60-65; asst. prof. ENG, OHIO UNIV, 65-70, ASSOC. PROF, 70- MLA. Romantic movement in English literature. Publ: Sydney Smith in America to 1900: two check lists, Bull. N.Y. Pub. Libr, 10/66; Thomas Wolfe and the quest for language, Ohio Univ. Rev, 69; The art of Anaïs Nin, South. Rev, spring 70; plus two others. Add: Dept. of English, Ohio University, Athens, OH 45701.

SCHNEIDER, ELISABETH (WINTERSTEEN), b. Salt Lake City, Utah, Sept. 7, 97. ENGLISH LITERATURE, AESTHETICS. A.B, Smith Col, 20; A.M, Univ. Pa, 26, Ph.D, 33; Oxford, 30-31. From instr. to prof. ENG. LIT, TEMPLE UNIV, 26-64, EMER. PROF, 65- Vis. prof. & lectr, Univ. Calif, Santa Barbara, 65-71. Col. Eng. Asn.(v.pres, 61-63, pres, 63-64); MLA (Distinguished Article Award, 66, 73; Mod. Humanities Res. Asn, Gt. Brit; NCTE. Romanticism; modern poetry; T.S. Eliot. Publ: Aesthetics of William Hazlitt, Univ. Pa, 33, 2nd ed, 52; Aesthetic motive, Macmillan, 39; Samuel Taylor Coleridge: selected poetry & prose, Holt, 51, 2nd ed, Rinehart, 71; Coleridge, opium, and Kubla Khan, Univ. Chicago, 53 & Octagon, 66; co-ed, The range of literature, Am. Bk. Co, 60 & 67 & Van Nostrand, 73; ed, Poems and poetry, Van Nostrand, 64; auth, The dragon in the gate: studies in the poetry of G.M. Hopkins, Univ. Calif, 68; William Hazlitt, In: English Romantic poets and essayists, N.Y. Univ, 66; The wreck of the Deutschland, PMLA 3/66 & Mod. Lang. Asn, 67; Prufrock and after: the theme of change, PMLA, 9-10/72; plus one other. Add: 924 Jimeno Rd, Santa Barbara, CA 93103.

SCHNEIDER, FRANZ, b. Wiesbaden, Ger, Mar. 17, 28; U.S. citizen; m. 51; c. 6. ENGLISH & COMPARATIVE LITERATURE. B.A, Wash. State Univ, 52; M.A, Univ. Wash, 54, Ph.D.(comp. lit), 59. Instr. Eng. & comp. lit, GONZAGA UNIV, 57-59, asst. prof, 60-62, assoc. prof. ENG. & COMP. LIT, 63-67, PROF, 67-, acting dir. honors prog, 63-72. Part-time instr. Ger, Univ. Wash, 53-54, fel. Eng, 55-56, assoc, 57; mem. & consult, Wash. Comn. for Humanities, 72- Philol. Asn. Pac. Coast; MLA. Realism and naturalism; symbolism; translations of German poetry. Publ: World poetry, Washington Square, 62; co-auth, Last letters from Stalingrad, Murrow Co, 62; Naturalism, In: Encycl. World Lit, Ungar, 64. Add: Dept. of English, Gonzaga University, Spokane, WA 99202.

SCHNEIDER, GILBERT DONALD, Linguistics, Anthropology. See Volume III, Foreign Languages, Linguistics & Philology.

SCHNEIDER, LUCY, C.S.J, b. Salina, Kans, Jan. 15, 27. ENGLISH, AMERICAN LITERATURE. B.A, Marymount Col.(Kans), 48; M.A, Marquette Univ, 55; Ph.D.(Eng), Univ. Notre Dame, 67. ASSOC. PROF. ENG, MARYMOUNT COL.(KANS), 67- Midwest Mod. Lang. Asn. Works of Jane Austen, Willa Cather and Henry James. Publ: The little white attic and the east room: their function in Mansfield Park, Mod. Philol, 2/66; Osculation and integration: Isabel Archer in the one-kiss novel, Col. Lang. Asn. J, 12/66; Of light and land: Willa Cather's Lucy Gayheart, Kans. Quart, fall 73. Add: Marymount College, Salina, KS 67401.

SCHNEIDER, ROBERT L, b. Westcliffe, Colo, Oct. 13, 27; m. 59. ENGLISH LITERATURE. A.B, Univ. Colo, 50; M.A, Cornell Univ, 52, Ph.D, 54. Instr. ENG, UNIV. ILL, URBANA, 54-58, asst. prof, 58-65, ASSOC. PROF, 65- U.S.A, 46-47. MLA. Victorian literature; prose fiction. Add: Dept. of English, University of Illinois, Urbana, IL 61801.

SCHNEIDER, VALERIE LOIS, b. Chicago, Ill, Feb. 12, 41. SPEECH & COMMUNICATION. B.A, Carroll Col, 63; M.A, Univ. Wis-Madison, 66; Ph.D. (speech), Univ. Fla, 69. Interim asst. prof. SPEECH, Univ. Fla, 69-70; asst. prof, Edinboro State Col, 70-71; ASSOC. PROF, E.TENN. STATE UNIV, 71- Speech Commun. Asn; South. Speech Commun. Asn. Persuasion; rhetorical criticism; speech education. Publ: Informal persuasion analysis, 1/71 & Role-playing and your local newspaper, 9/72, Speech Teacher; Parker's assessment of Webster: argumentative synthesis through the tragic metaphor, Quart. J. Speech, 10/73. Add: C-5 Greenwood Apts, Johnson City, TN 37601.

SCHNITZER, ROBERT C, b. New York, N.Y, Sept. 8, 06; m. 53. THEATRE. A.B, Columbia Univ. 27. Stage mgr. & actor, Theatre Guild, 27-36; state dir. Del. & dep. nat. dir, Fed. Theatre Proj, 36-39; exec. dir, Civic Theatre, Kalamazoo, Mich, 39-40; mem. fac, Vassar Col, 41-42; Smith Col, 42-43; Sch. Dramatic Arts, Columbia Univ, 48-54; gen. mgr. Am. Nat. Theatre & Acad. & prof. agent. State Dept, Int. Cult. Exchange Serv, 54-60; gen. mgr, Theatre Guild Am. Repertory Co, 60-61; prof. speech & exec. dir. prof. theatre prog, Univ. Mich, Ann Arbor, 61-73. Owner & dir, Robin Hood Summer Theatre, Del, 33-40; consult, Martha Graham Sch. Dance, Rollins Sch. Theatre, Randall Sch. Theatre, Dramatic Workshop of New Sch, Denver Red Rocks Theatre & Utah Centennial, 45-49; gen. mgr, Am. Nat. Theatre & Acad. Exp. Theatre, 46-47, Album, 51; Rockefeller Found. grant, 48; gen. mgr, U.S. participation Denmark Hamlet Festival, 49; first Am. ballet theatre tour, Europe, 50; U.S. official participation, Congr. Cult. Freedom Festival, 52; Cheryl Crawford Prod, 52-53; Gilbert Miller Prod, 53-54; deleg, U.S. nat. conf. on UNESCO, 53-57; First Inter-Am. Conf. Exchange of Persons, 58; gen. mgr, U.S. salute to France, 55; mem, Fulbright Selection Comt. Theatre Arts, 55-59; vis. theatre expert, German For. Off. Cult. Exchange Prof, 65; mem, Nat. Counc. Arts & Govt; Mich. State Counc. Arts, 66-72; exec. dir, Univ. Resident Theatre Asn, 69- Sidney Howard Award, 47; Arts Mgt. Career Award, 71; Univ. Mich. Pres. Citation, 71. Am. Red Cross, China, 42-45. Fel. Am. Theatre Asn; Am. Nat. Theatre & Acad; Nat. Theatre Conf; Theatre Libr. Asn; U.S. Inst. Theatre Technol; Univ. Resident Theatre Asn.(exec. dir, 69-). Publ: Numerous articles in professional journals. Add: 6 Woods End Lane, Westport, CT 06880.

SCHOECK, RICHARD J, b. New York, N.Y, Oct. 10, 20; m. 45; c. 3. ENGLISH. McGill Univ, 37-38; fel, M.A. & Ph.D.(Eng. lang. & lit), Princeton Univ, 49. Instr. Eng, Cornell Univ, 49-55; asst. prof, Univ. Notre Dame, 55-58, assoc. prof, 58-61; prof. Eng, St. Michael's Col, Univ. Toronto, 61-71, head dept, 65-71; prof. vernacular lit, Pontif. Inst. Mediaeval Stud, 63-71; dir. res. activities, Folger Shakespeare Libr. & dir. Folger Inst. Renaissance & 18th Century Stud, 71-74; PROF. ENG. & MEDIEVAL & RENAISSANCE STUD, UNIV. MD, COLLEGE PARK, 74-, adj. prof. Eng, 72-74. Asn. Advan. Educ. fel, 51-52; assoc. ed, Neo-Latin News, 55-63; asst. ed, Nat. Law Forum, 58-60; res. fel, St. Thomas More proj, Yale, 59-60, ed, 60-, St. Thomas More lectr, 67; Vincent J. Flynn lectr, Col. St. Thomas, 60; gen. ed, Patterns & Lit. Criticism ser, Univs. Toronto & Chicago, 62-; contrib, New Cath. Encycl, 66; vis. prof. Eng, Princeton, 64; Can. Counc. grant, 64; co-chmn, Conf. Medieval Bibliog, 65-68; UNESCO & Am. Counc. Learned Soc. grants; Guggenheim fel, 67-68; Can. Counc. fel, 69; mem. exec. comt, Complete Works of Erasmus, Toronto, 69-; mem. ed. bd, Am. J. Jurisp, 69-; acting dir. res. activities, Folger Shakespeare Libr, 70-71; mem. ed. bd, Folger Ed. Works of Richard Hooker, 70-; mem. int. steering comt, Neo-Latin Congr, 71-73; mem. adv. bd, Yale Ed. of Works of St. Thomas More, 71-; mem. bd. trustees, Natural Law Inst. Notre Dame, 71-; ed, Shakespeare Quart, 72-; consult, Nat. Endowment for Humanities, 72-; gen. ed, The confutation of Tyndale's answer (3 vols), Yale, 73. Sig.C, U.S.A, 40-46, Lt. MLA; Mediaeval Acad. Am; Renaissance Soc. Am.(rep. hist. of law to counc, 67-69); Renaissance Eng. Text Soc.(mem. counc, 67-69); Eng. Asn, Gt. Brit; Selden Soc; Malone Soc; Anglo-Norman Text Soc; Bibliog. Soc, Eng; Am. Cath. Hist. Asn; Asn. Can. Univ. Teachers Eng; fel. Royal Hist. Soc; fel. Royal Soc. Can; Cath. Comn. Intellectual & Cult. Affairs; Can. Hist. Asn; Mod. Humanities Res. Asn; Am. Soc. Legal Hist; Int. Asn. Neo-Latin Stud.(1st v.pres, 73-). Legal history, including Anglo-Norman and Inns of Court; Lord Acton; literature and humanism, 1300-1600. Publ: Co-auth, Chaucer criticism, Vol. I, 60 & Vol. II, 61 & ed, Legends of saints, 61, Univ. Notre Dame; co-ed, Voices of literature, Holt, Toronto, Vol. I, 62 & Vol. II, 64; ed, Editing sixteenth century texts, Univ. Toronto, 66; co-ed, Style, rhetoric and rhythm: essays by M.W. Croll, Princeton, 66; auth, Rhetoric and law in sixteenth century England, Stud. Philol, 53; Canon law in England on eve of the Reformation, 63 & On rhetoric in fourteenth-century Oxford, 68, Mediaeval Stud. Add: Dept. of English, University of Maryland, College Park, MD 20742.

SCHOELL, EDWIN ROBERT, b. Buffalo, N.Y, Dec. 17, 17; m. 47 SPEECH. A.B, La. State Univ, 39; Mich. State Univ; fel, Univ. Denver, 46-47, M.A, 47, fel, 50-51, Ph.D.(speech & theatre), 51; Col. Pac. Instr. commun, Mich. State Univ, 47-48; asst. prof. SPEECH, Col. Pac, 48-50; from asst. prof. to PROF, UNIV. CALIF, SANTA BARBARA, 51-, chmn. dept, 66-72. Consult, Hillside Inst. for Cerebral Palsied, 53-57; Santa Barbara Soc. for Crippled Children & Adults, 55-57. U.S.A.A.F, 42-45, Maj. Speech Commun. Asn; West. Speech Asn. Speech communication; non-professional theatre influences on American drama; creative writing. Publ: The changing community theatre, West. Speech J; The drama in the community theatre & College and university productions, a five-year study, Educ. Theatre J. Add: Dept. of Speech, University of California, Santa Barbara, CA 93106.

SCHOEN, CAROL BRONSTON, b. Plainfield, N.J, May 14, 26; m. 49; c. 2. AMERICAN LITERATURE. B.A, Radcliffe Col, 48; M.A, Columbia Univ, 63, Ph.D.(Eng. & comp. lit), 68. Lectr. Eng, Brooklyn Col, 67-68; LEHMAN COL, 68-73, ASST. PROF. ACAD. SKILLS, 73- MLA; Col. Eng. Asn; NCTE. American Jewish writers; remediation. Publ: The house of the seven deadly sins, Am. Transcendental Quart, 73; co-auth, Affective strategies for cognitive learning, City Univ. New York Conf, 74. Add: Dept. of Academic Skills, Herbert H. Lehman College, Bedford Park Blvd, Bronx, NY 10468.

SCHOEN, KATHRYN T, b. Owensboro, Ky, Nov. 5, 22; m. 43; c. 2. SPEECH EDUCATION. B.S, Capital Univ, 57; M.A, Ohio State Univ, 62, Ph.D.(speech educ), 65. Teacher pub. schs, Ohio & Utah, 45-62; instr. educ, OHIO STATE UNIV, COLUMBUS, 62-65, asst. prof. speech, 65-67, asst. prof. speech & educ. & allied med. professions, 67-69, assoc. prof. ALLIED MED. PROFESSIONS & SPEECH COMMUN, 69-72, PROF, 72-, ASSOC. PROF. EDUC, 69-, ASSOC. PROVOST FAC, 72-, dir. med. commun, 69-71, asst. dir, Sch. Allied Med. Professions, 69-71, assoc. dir, 71-72. Consult. div. allied health manpower, U.S. Pub. Health Serv, 72, mem. Nat. Adv. Counc. on health profession educ, 72-; mem. bd. vis, Sch. Health Related Professions, Univ. Pittsburgh, 73- Speech Commun. Asn; Int. Commun. Asn; AAUP; Asn. Schs. Allied Health Professions (mem. adv. comt. core curriculum proj, 71-72); Am. Asn. Univ. Women. Communications; medical and allied health education. Publ: Co-auth, Teaching speech, Merrill, 69; auth, Planning the curriculum, In: Educating personnel for the allied health professions and services, Mosby, 72; Medical communications, In: Introduction to health professions, Mosby, 72; The climate of expectation, Am. J. Occupational Therapy, 4/72; plus others. Add: Box 5690, Columbus, OH 43221.

SCHOENBAUM, SAMUEL, b. New York, N.Y, Mar. 6, 27; m. 46. ENGLISH. A.B, Brooklyn Col, 47; A.M, Columbia Univ, 49, Ph.D.(Eng), 53. From lectr. to instr. Eng, Brooklyn Col, 48-53; instr, NORTHWEST. UNIV, EVANSTON, 53-56, asst. prof, 56-59, assoc. prof, 59-63, prof, 63-71, SNYDER PROF. ENG. LIT, 71- Guggenheim fels, 53-56 & 69-70; vis. prof, King's Col, Univ. London, 61; Newberry fel, summer 62; vis. prof. Shakespeare & Elizabethan drama, Univ. Chicago, summer 64 & fall 65; Columbia Univ, summer 66; Shakespeare, Univ. Wash, summer 68; Nat. Endowment for Humanities sr. fel, 73-74; mem. adv. comt, Int. Shakespeare Conf, exec. bd, Shakespeare Quart. & Variorum Shakespeare Comt. MLA; AAUP. Elizabethan drama; Shakespeare. Publ: Middleton's tragedies: a critical study, Columbia Univ, 55; ed, The bloody banquet, Malone Soc, 61; reviser, Annals of English drama, Methuen, 64; ed, Renaissance drama, 64 & auth, Internal evidence and Elizabethan dramatic authorship, 66, Northwest. Univ; ed, Henry VIII, Signet Shakespeare, 67; auth, Shakespeare's lives, Clarendon, 70; co-ed, A new companion to Shakespeare studies, Cambridge, 71; auth, The widow's tears and the other Chapman, Huntington Libr. Quart, 60; Shakespeare and Johnson: fact and myth, In: The Elizabethan theatre II, Macmillan, Toronto, 70; plus others. Add: Dept. of English, Northwestern University, Evanston, IL 60201.

SCHOENEWOLF, CARROLL ROBERT, b. Fredericksburg, Tex, Oct. 9, 35; m. 63, 72; c. 1. AMERICAN LITERATURE. B.A, Sul Ross State Univ, 57, M.A, 63; Ph.D.(Eng), Univ. Okla, 73. Instr. ENG, Tex. A&M Univ, 63-65; ASST. PROF, STEPHEN F. AUSTIN STATE UNIV, 68- Moody Found. grant, summer 72. MLA. American fiction; modern American poetry; composition. Publ: Jarrell's use of metaphor in The death of the ball turrett gunner, Eng. Tex, summer 72; co-auth, A marriage of English and music, Mus. Educators J, 3/73. Add: Dept. of English, Stephen F. Austin State University, Nacogdoches, TX 75961.

SCHOFF, FRANCIS GORDON, b. London, Eng, Oct. 22, 06; U.S. citizen; m. 37. ENGLISH LITERATURE. Ph.D, Univ. Minn, 62. From instr. to PROF. ENG, N.DAK. STATE UNIV, 37- U.S.A.A.F, 42-46, 1st Lt. MLA; NCTE; Shakespeare Asn. Am; Renaissance Soc. Am. Shakespeare; 18th century literature; English drama. Add: Dept. of English, North Dakota State University, Fargo, ND 58102.

SCHOLES, ROBERT, b. Brooklyn, N.Y, May 19, 29; m. 51; c. 2. ENGLISH. A.B, Yale, 50; M.A, Cornell Univ, 56, fel, 58-59, Ph.D, 59. Instr. ENG, Univ. Va, 59-61, asst. prof, 61-63; assoc. prof, Univ. Iowa, 64-66, PROF, 66-70; BROWN UNIV, 70- Summers, res. grants-in-aid, Am. Philos. Soc, 61; Am. Counc. Learned Soc, 62, 67; jr. fel, Inst. Res. Humanities, Univ. Wis, 63-64. U.S.N.R, 51-55, Lt. MLA; N.East Mod. Lang. Asn; James Joyce Found; William Morris Soc. & Kelmscott Fel. Literary theory; narrative literature; James Joyce. Publ: Approaches to the novel, Chandler, 61; Cornell Joyce collection: a catalogue, Cornell, 61, rev, 66; co-auth, The workshop of Daedalus, Northwest. Univ, 65; co-auth, The nature of narrative, 66, auth, The fabulators, 67, Elements of fiction, 68, Elements of poetry, 69, co-auth, Elements of the essay, 69, Elements of drama, 70, Elements of writing, 72, ed, Some modern writers, 71 & auth, Structuralism in literature, 74, Oxford; co-ed, Joyce's Dubliners, Viking, 69; ed, Poetic theory—poetic practice, Midwest Mod. Lang. Asn, 69; The philosopher critic, Tulsa Univ, 70. Add: Dept. of English, Brown University, Providence, RI 02912.

SCHOLNICK, ROBERT JAMES, b. Boston, Mass, June 22, 41; m. 64; c. 1. AMERICAN LITERATURE. A.B, Univ. Pa, 62; M.A, Brandeis Univ, 64, Ph.D.(Eng. & Am. lit), 69. Asst. prof. ENG, COL. WILLIAM & MARY, 67-72, ASSOC. PROF, 73- MLA. American poetry; Walt Whitman; genteel tradition. Publ: Walt Whitman and the magazines, Am. Lit, 5/72; The shadowed years, Colby Libr. Quart, 6/72. Add: Dept. of English, College of William & Mary, Williamsburg, VA 23185.

SCHOLTEN, MARTIN EDWIN, b. Muscatine, Iowa, Apr. 1, 11. ENGLISH. A.B, State Univ. Iowa, 33; A.M, Univ. Mich, 35; Ed.D, 58. Chmn. Eng. dept, high sch, 35-41; asst. prof. ENG, UNIV. TOLEDO, 45-62, prof, 62-71, EMER. PROF, 71- U.S.A.A.F, 41-45. NCTE; Poetry Soc. Am. Modern poetry and aesthetics; modern critical theory; book of verse. Publ: The labyrinth, Outposts, London, 59; Poetry as experience, 3/52 & Poetry of Edwin Muir, 3/60, Col. Eng. Add: Dept. of English, University of Toledo, Toledo, OH 43606.

SCHONHORN, MANUEL, b. Brooklyn, N.Y, Jan. 29, 30; m. 58; c. 2. ENGLISH. B.A, Brooklyn Col, 55; M.A, Univ. Pa, 59, Ph.D.(Eng), 63. Instr. ENG, Univ. Kans, 62-64, asst. prof, 64-66; State Univ. N.Y. Binghamton, 66-68; assoc. prof, SOUTH. ILL. UNIV, 68-73, PROF, 73- Am. Philos. Soc. res. grant, summer 66; State Univ. N.Y. fac. fels, summers 67 & 68. Sig.C, U.S.A, 52-54. MLA. Daniel Defoe; Alexander Pope; 18th century history of ideas. Publ: Daniel Defoe and the accounts of the apparition of Mrs. Veal, Augustan Reprint Soc, 65; Defoe's History of the Pyrates, Dent, London & Everyman's Libr, 72; Fielding's digressive-parodic artistry, Tex. Stud. Lit. & Lang, 7/68; The audacious contemporaneity of Alexander Pope, Stud. Eng. Lit, summer 68; Defoe's Journal of the plague year: topography and intention, Rev. Eng. Stud, 11/68. Add: Dept. of English, Southern Illinois University, Carbondale, IL 62901.

SCHOOLEY, FRANK ELLSWORTH, b. Effingham, Ill, Mar. 1, 06. JOURNALISM. B.S, Univ. Ill, 29. From asst. prof. to PROF. RADIO-TV, UNIV. ILL, URBANA, 29- News internee, Nat. Asn. Broadcasters, Syracuse, N.Y, 45; dir. broadcasting, Station WILL, AM-FM & TV, 55-73. Add: 227 Gregory Hall, University of Illinois, Urbana, IL 61801.

SCHORER, MARK, b. Sauk City, Wis, May 17, 08; m. 36; c. 2. ENGLISH LITERATURE. A.B, Univ. Wis, 29, Ph.D, 36, Litt.D, 62; A.M, Harvard, 30. Instr, Dartmouth Col, 36-37; ENG, Harvard, 37-40, Briggs-Copeland instr, 41-45; assoc. prof, UNIV. CALIF, BERKELEY, 45-47, prof, 47-73, chmn. dept. 60-65, EMER. PROF, 73- Guggenheim fel, 41-42, 47-48, 73-74; fel, Sch. Lett, Ind. Univ, 48-; Fulbright lectr, Univ. Pisa, 52-53 & Rome, 64; lectr, seminars in Am. stud, Univ. Tokyo, 56; fel, Ctr. Advan. Stud. Behavioral Sci, Stanford Univ, 58-59; Bollingen fel, 60; bd. dir, Am. Counc. Learned Soc, 65-72; appointment Inst. Creative Arts, Univ. Calif, Berkeley, 66-67; Nat. Endowment for Humanities sr. fel, 74-75. Nat. Inst. Arts & Lett; Am. Acad. Arts & Lett; MLA (exec. counc, 61-65); Col. Eng. Asn.(bd. dir, 67-). Eighteenth to 20th century literature. Publ: William Blake, Henry Holt, Vintage; The wars of love, McGraw, Avon, 54; Sinclair Lewis: an American life, McGraw, 61; The world we imagine; selected essays, Farrar, Straus, 68; D.H. Lawrence, Delta, 69. Add: 68 Tamalpais Rd, Berkeley, CA 94708.

SCHRADER, ALLEN, b. Watertown, S.Dak, Nov. 12, 18. LITERARY CRITICISM. B.A, Los Angeles State Col, 56, M.A, 58; Univ. South. Calif, summers, 58- Instr. ENG, Tex. A&M Univ, 57-61, asst. prof, 61-67; ASSOC. PROF, UNIV. CALIF, LOS ANGELES, 67- U.S.A, 41-45, Sgt. NCTE; MLA. Music; literary criticism; biography. Publ: From Emerson to Salinger to Parker, Sat. Rev, 4/58; The man with twenty fingers, Southwest Rev, summer 64. Add: 2920 Griffith Park Blvd, Los Angeles, CA 90027.

SCHRADER, RICHARD JAMES, b. Canton, Ohio, Aug. 24, 41. MEDIEVAL ENGLISH LITERATURE. B.A, Univ. Notre Dame, 63; M.A, Ohio State Univ, 65, Ph.D.(Eng), 68. Instr. ENG, PRINCETON, 68-69, ASST. PROF, 69-, JOHN WITHERSPOON BICENTENNIAL PRECEPTOR, 72- AAUP; Early Eng. Text Soc; Asn. Scottish Lit. Stud; MLA; Mediaeval Acad. Am. Old English literature; late Middle English poetry; medieval Scottish literature. Publ: The reminiscences of Alexander Dyce, Ohio State Univ, 72; Fitzgerald and Charles G. Norris, Fitzgerald Newslett, 64; Chauntecleer, the Mermaid, and Daun Burnel, Chaucer Rev, 70; Beowulf's obsequies and the Roman epic, Comp. Lit, 72. Add: Dept. of English, Princeton University, Princeton, NJ 08540.

SCHRAER, MIMOSA (SUMMERS), b. Huntsburg, Ohio, Nov. 18, 39; m. 68. ENGLISH. B.A, Pan Am. Col, 61; NDEA fel, Tex. Technol. Col, 61-64, M.A, 63, Ph.D.(Eng), 65. Lectr. ENG, Hong Kong Baptist Col, 65-67; from asst. prof. to ASSOC. PROF, William Jewell Col, 67-73; PAN AM. UNIV, 73- Reviewer, Choice. MLA. American literature. Publ: Rappaccini walks in Eden, Perspectives, fall 72. Add: Dept. of English, Pan American University, Brownsville Ctr, Brownsville, TX 78520.

SCHRAMM, ALLAN N, b. Marietta, Ohio, Mar. 24, 37; m. 60; c. 3. COMMUNICATIONS. B.A, Ohio State Univ, 58, M.A, 60, Ph.D.(speech), 67. Instr. SPEECH, Univ. Md, 60-63; assoc. prof, STATE UNIV. N.Y. COL. ONEONTA, 65-73; PROF, 73-, DIR. HONORS PROG, 72- East. Commun. Asn; Speech Commun. Asn; Int. Commun. Asn. Oral communication of literature; semantic differential and the measurement of meaning; meaning in media. Add: Dept. of Speech & Theater, State University of New York at Oneonta, Oneonta, NY 13820.

SCHRAMM, DAVID EUGENE, b. Klickitat, Wash, May 13, 36; m. 61; c. 3. ENGLISH LITERATURE. B.A, Concordia Sem, 58, M.Div, 61; M.A, Wash. Univ, 63, Ph.D.(Eng), 71. ASSOC. PROF. ENG, CONCORDIA SR. COL, 64- MLA; NCTE. The novel; 19th century English literature; theory and pedagogy in the humanities. Add: Dept. of English, Concordia Senior College, Ft. Wayne, IN 46825.

SCHRAMM, HAROLD BERTRAM, b. Rockville Centre, N.Y, Feb. 14, 43; m. 69; c. 2. ENGLISH LITERATURE, LITERARY CRITICISM. A.B, Col. of the Holy Cross, 65; M.A, Univ. Del, 67, Ph.D.(Eng), 69; J.D, Univ. Conn, 73. ASST. PROF. ENG, Cent. Conn. State Col, 68-69; WEST. CONN. STATE COL, 69- Fel, Shakespeare Inst, Univ. Bridgeport, summer 69; lectr. law, Univ. Conn, 72-74; asst. reporter judicial decisions, State of Conn, 73- Nathan Burkan Mem. Award, Am. Soc. Composers, Auth. & Publ, 72. Renaissance drama; literary criticism; jurisprudence. Publ: Contrib, A guide to freshman English, Univ. Del, 68. Add: Canfield Dr, Bridgewater, CT 06752.

SCHREIBER, FLORA RHETA, b. New York, N.Y, Apr. 24, 16. SPEECH. B.S, Columbia Univ, 38, M.A, 39; cert. speech, Univ. London, 37; cert, Mus. Mod. Art Film Libr, 40; cert. radio, N.Y. Univ, 41. Fac. drama, Exeter Col, Univ. Southwest Eng, summer 37; speech & drama, Brooklyn Col, 44-46; from instr. to asst. prof, Adelphi Col, 47-52; FAC. COMMUN, NEW SCH. SOC. RES, 52-; ASSOC. PROF. SPEECH & DRAMA, JOHN JAY COL. CRIMINAL JUSTICE, 64- Adj. lectr. speech, Baruch Col, 53-64; Hunter Col, 60-61; consult, Nat. Broadcasting Corp, 61-62; Ruder & Finn, 62-66; Batten, Barten, Durstine & Osborn, 63-64; columnist-correspondent, Bell-McClure Syndicate, 69-70; United Features Syndicate, 71-72; contract writer, New York Times Spec. Features, 73- Award, Family Serv. Asn, 60. Soc. Mag. Writers (v.pres, 72-74); Auth. League Am; AAUP; Speech Commun. Asn; Speech Commun. Asn. East. States; Am. Asn. Univ. Women. Publ: William Schuman: a biography, Schirmer, 54; Your child's speech, Putnam, 56; A job with a future in law enforcement and related fields, Grosset, 70; Sybil, Regnery, 73; Your child's speech, Ballantine, 73; contrib, Encycl. Americana year book, Grolier, 59, Psychological and psychiatric aspects of speech and hearing, C.C. Thomas, 60 & Prose by professionals, Doubleday, 68; plus numerous others. Add: 32 Gramercy Park South, New York, NY 10003.

SCHREIBER, MORRIS, b. New York, N.Y, June 1, 12; m. 38; c. 1. ENGLISH, EDUCATION. A.B, City Col. New York, 33, M.S.Ed, 39. Instr. Eng. jr. & sr. high sch, N.Y. City Bd. Educ, 36-52, asst. prin. jr. high sch, 52-58, prin. elem. schs, 59-67; ASSOC. PROF. ENG. & EDUC, N.Y. INST. TECHNOL, 67- Educ. Award, Univ. Ill, 51. Poetry Soc. Am; NCTE (ed. & recordings consult, 63-64). Speech and drama. Publ: The anatomy of language (record series), Folkways Records, 59; Famous myths and legends of the world, 60 & ed, Favorite tales from Shakespeare, 59, Grosset; ed, Annotated list of recordings in language arts, NCTE, 64; auth, Great themes in literature (cassette series), Viewlex, Inc; auth, Junior talks about the war, 41 & To catch the conscience, spring 58, High Points; Adventures in audio, In: Studies in the mass media, NCTE, 60. Add: 3871 Bedford Ave, Brooklyn, NY 11229.

SCHREIBER, RONALD P, b. Chicago, Ill, Jan. 25, 34. VISIONARY LITERATURE, MODERN POETRY. B.A, Wesleyan Univ, 55; M.A, Columbia Univ, 59, Ph.D.(Eng), 67. Lectr. & preceptor, ENG, Sch. Gen. Stud, Columbia Univ, 59-67; asst. prof, UNIV. MASS, BOSTON, 67-74; ASSOC. PROF, 74- Part-time instr. Eng, Rutgers Univ. Newark Campus, 60-61; co-ed, Hanging Loose (poetry mag), 66- U.S.A, 55-57. Modern nonmetrical poetry; general poetics; gay studies. Publ: Asst. ed, Granger's index to poetry, Columbia Univ, 5th ed, 62; ed, 31 new American poets, Hill & Wang, 69; auth, Living space (poems), Red Dot Bks, 72; plus others. Add: 15 Westwood Rd, Somerville, MA 02143.

SCHREINER, PHILIP J, b. Crookston, Minn, Feb. 5, 25; m. 53; c. 2. ORGANIZATIONAL COMMUNICATION, BUSINESS ADMINISTRATION. B.A, Calif. State Univ, 55; M.A, Univ. Iowa, 59; Ph.D.(speech), Univ. Calif, Los Angeles, 66. Asst. prof. Grad. Sch. Mgt, Univ. Calif, Los Angeles, 66-70; ASSOC. PROF. SPEECH COMMUN, CALIF. STATE UNIV, FULLERTON, 70- Small group business administration. Publ: A manual of style for the preparation of papers and reports, South-West. Publ, 71; co-auth, Adjusting managerial acts to behavioral concepts, Calif. Mgt. Rev, winter 67; auth, Manecutive behavior: a problem, evaluation and proposal, J. Mgt. Educ, 1/69; Borrowing behavior and its implications for management: a case study, Credit Union Exec, spring 71. Add: Dept. of Speech Communication, California State University, Fullerton, 800 N. State College Blvd, Fullerton, CA 92637.

SCHRERO, ELLIOT MITCHELL, b. Chicago, Ill, June 21, 22; m. 50; c. 2. ENGLISH LANGUAGE & LITERATURE. A.B, Univ. Chicago, 44, A.M, 45,

Ph.D.(Eng), 54. Instr. Eng, Roosevelt Univ, 48-54; publ, mkt. & advert, 54-67; assoc. creative dir, Commun. Affiliates, Inc, 67-68; ASSOC. PROF. ENG, RIDER COL, 68- Lectr. world lit, Fairleigh Dickinson Univ, 60-66; consult, TAW Int. Leasing, Inc, 69-; Setauket Ctr. Corp, 70-; Phoenix Commun, Inc, 72- MLA; Northeast Mod. Lang. Asn.(chmn. sect. oral stud. lit, 74); NCTE; AAUP. Nineteenth century fiction; oral aspects of literature; social relations of literature. Publ: The narrator's palace of thought in The sacred fount, Mod. Philol, 2/71; Intonation and moral insight: reading Henry James aloud, Oral Eng, summer 72; Intonation in nineteenth century fiction, Quart. J. Speech, 10/74; plus others. Add: 377 Rutland Ave, Teaneck, NJ 07666.

SCHRIBER, MARY SUZANNE, b. Muskegon, Mich. Sept. 22, 38. COMPARATIVE LITERATURE. B.A, Mich. State Univ, 60, NDEA fel, 62-65, M.A, 63, grad. off. fel, 66-67, Ph.D.(comp. lit), 67; Fulbright fel, Sorbonne, 65-66. Asst. prof. ENG, NORTH. ILL. UNIV, 67-72, ASSOC. PROF, 72- MLA; Midwest Mod. Lang. Asn; AAUP. Edith Wharton and France; the French and American novel; 19th century French and American literature. Publ: A dream deferred: the literature of Black Americans, In: Racism in America: an interdisciplinary analysis, North. Ill. Univ, 71; You've come a long way, Babbitt, Twentieth Century Lit, 4/71; Emerson, Hawthorne, and the Artist of the beautiful, Stud. Short Fiction, 10/71. Add: Dept. of English, Northern Illinois University, DeKalb, IL 60115.

SCHRODER, CHARLES FREDERICK, b. Walhalla, S.C, Oct. 21, 33. MUSIC, COMPARATIVE LITERATURE. B.A, Furman Univ, 55; M.A, Univ. N.C, 58; Elsa A. Sawyer fel, Univ. Wis, 57-58; Danforth study grant, summer 61; Ph.D.(music, comp. lit), Univ. Iowa, 65. Instr. piano & theory, Bethany Col, 60-63, ASST. PROF, 63-64; humanities, Chadron State Col, 64-66; MUSIC & COMP. LIT, WEST. CAROLINA UNIV, 66- Arch. consult, Consortium Appalachian Stud, 72- Am. Folklore Soc; Am. Soc. Aesthet; Am. Musicol. Soc. Origins of the musical prelude; literary-musical relations; aesthetics of the folk arts. Publ: A word for musicology, Music J, 9/60; Music theory enhances musicianship, 1/61 & The value of piano study, 4/62, Instrumentalist. Add: Div. of Humanities, Western Carolina University, Cullowhee, NC 28723.

SCHRODER, WILLIAM T, b. Duluth, Minn, July 29, 17; m. 44; c. 2. ENGLISH LITERATURE. A.B, Marquette Univ, 38; A.M, Harvard, 46; Ph.D. (Eng. lit), Northwest. Univ, 59. Asst, Univ. Mich, 46; instr. ENG, Marquette Univ, 46-48; Loyola Univ.(Ill), 48-50; asst. prof, Georgetown Univ, 54-61; assoc. prof, St. Michael's Col.(N.Mex), 62-68, dir. summer sessions, 63-72; PROF, COL. SANTA FE, 68- U.S.N, 40-46, 50-54, Res, 54-70, Comdr. MLA. Renaissance literature. Add: Dept. of English, College of Santa Fe, Santa Fe, NM 87501.

SCHROEDER, ELVER AUGUST, b. Breese, Ill, June 9, 10; m. 37; c. 3. ENGLISH LITERATURE. A.B, Elmhurst Col, 34; A.M, Univ. Ill, 37; Ph.D, Univ. Mich, 50. Teaching fel, Univ. Mich, 38-43, 46; PROF. ENG, OREGON STATE UNIV, 46- U.S.N.R, 43-45. Swinburne. Add: Dept. of English, Oregon State University, Corvallis, OR 97330.

SCHROEDER, FRED ERICH HARALD, b. Manitowoc, Wis, June 3, 32; m. 54; c. 1. AMERICAN STUDIES, ENGLISH. B.S, Univ. Wis-Milwaukee, 60, Woodrow Wilson fel, 60-61; M.A, Univ. Minn, 63, Ph.D.(Am. stud), 68. Teacher, Elem. Schs, Wis, 52-57; Sec. Sch, 57-60; teaching asst, ENG, Univ. Minn, 61-63; instr, UNIV. MINN, DULUTH, 63-68: asst. prof, 68-71, ASSOC. PROF, 71- Nat. Endowment for Humanities younger fel, 69-70; lectr, team leader, Nat. Humanities Ser, 70-71; Montgomery lectr, Univ. Nebr, 71; consult. bd. mem, Nat. Am. Stud. Fac. Community Mus. Prog, 72-; consult, Nat. Humanities Fac, 73- Am. Stud. Asn; Popular Cult. Asn; Oral Hist. Asn; Nat. Asn. Humanities Educ; AAUP; NCTE. American aesthetics; teacher training in humanities and composition; popular culture. Publ: Joining the human race; how to teach the humanities, Everett/Edwards, 72; And now a word from the silent generation, In: Finding a voice, Scott, 73; plus others. Add: Dept. of English, University of Minnesota, Duluth, MN 55812.

SCHROEDER, HENRY ALFRED, JR, b. New York, N.Y, Apr. 2, 34; m. 67; c. 3. ENGLISH, COMPARATIVE LITERATURE. B.A, Yale, 59, Carnegie fel, 59-60, Woodrow Wilson fel, 62-63, Ph.D.(Eng), 64; Woodrow Wilson fel, Harvard, 60-61, A.M, 61. Instr. Eng, Yale, ASST. PROF, 66-68; COMP. LIT, UNIV. MASS, AMHERST, 68- Morse fel, Yale, 67-68. U.S.M.C, 53-56, Sgt. Medieval literature. Add: Dept. of Comparative Literature, University of Massachusetts, Amherst, MA 01002.

SCHROEDER, MARY CARRUTHERS, English Literature & Language. See Carruthers, Mary.

SCHROEDER, NEIL ROLF, b. Cleveland, Ohio, Nov. 12, 30; m. 56; c. 3. HISTORY OF THE THEATRE. A.B, Brown Univ, 52; Ph.D, Yale, 62. Asst. Eng, Brown Univ, 52-56; instr, Cent. Conn. State Col, 58-60; CLARKE UNIV, 60-62, asst. prof, 62-66, ASSOC. PROF. ENG. & THEATRE ART, 66-, ASSOC. CHMN. THEATRE ART, 72- Soc. Theatre Res, Eng; Am. Soc. Theatre Res; Am. Theatre Asn. Theatre history; history of Shakespearean production. Add: Dept. of Visual and Performing Arts, Clark University, Worcester, MA 01610.

SCHROEDER, ROSE MARY, O.S.F, b. Greensburg, Ind, Apr. 12, 22. ENGLISH. B.A, Marian Col.(Ind), 45; M.A, Fordham Univ, 48; Ph.D.(Eng), Univ. Cincinnati, 60. Instr. ENG, MARIAN COL.(IND), 50-55, 56-57, asst. prof, 57-60, assoc. prof, 60-66, PROF, 66- MLA; NCTE; Col. Eng. Asn; Cath. Renascence Soc. Medieval English literature; American literature. Add: Dept. of English, Marian College, Indianapolis, IN 46222.

SCHROETER, JAMES MARVIN, b. Hammond, Ind, June 29, 27; m. 50; c. 2. ENGLISH. B.A, Sorbonne, 49; B.A, Univ. Chicago, 50, M.A, 52, Ph.D, 59. Instr. Eng, Univ. Nebr, 52-53; lectr. Eng. & humanities, Univ. Col, Univ. Chicago & Chicago City Jr. Col, 53-61; asst. prof. Eng, Temple Univ, 61-62; assoc. prof, Ill. Inst. Technol, 62-68, PROF, 68-74; AM. LIT, UNIV. LAUSANNE, 74- Vis. prof, Univ. Nebr, summer 62; Fulbright lectr, Univ. Nantes, France, 68-69. Olga Menn Fiction Award, 50. U.S.A.A.F, 45-46. MLA; NCTE; Melville Soc. Am. Modern American fiction; literary criticism; comparative drama. Publ: Willa Cather and her critics, Cornell Univ. & Oxford, 67; Poe's Ligeia, PMLA, 61; Yeats and the tragic tradition, South. Rev, 65; Willa Cather and the professors house, Yale Rev, 65; plus others. Add: Faculty of Letters, University of Lausanne, 1005 Lausanne, Switz.

SCHROTH, RAYMOND A, S.J, b. Trenton, N.J, Nov. 8, 33. JOURNALISM, AMERICAN STUDIES. A.B, Fordham Univ, 55, M.A, 64; lic. philos, Loyola Sem, 60; B.D, Woodstock Col, 67; M.Phil, George Washington Univ, 70, Ph.D.(Am. stud), 71. Teacher lit, hist. & relig, McQuaid Jesuit High Sch, Rochester, N.Y, 61-64; managing ed, Woodstock Lett, 64-67; instr. Am. civilization, George Washington Univ, 67-68; ASSOC. PROF. COMMUN, FORDHAM UNIV, 69- Assoc. ed, Commonweal, 72- U.S.A, 55-57. Am. Stud. Asn; Asn. Educ. in Jour; AAUP. Journalism history; contemporary American literature. Publ: Jesuit spirit in a time of change, Newman, 67; The eagle and Brooklyn, Greenwood, 74; James Baldwin's search, Cath. World, 64; Mailer and his gods, Commonweal, 5/69; College as Camelot, Saturday Rev. Educ, 12/72; plus others. Add: Dept. of Communications, Fordham University, Bronx, NY 10458.

SCHUCHARD, W. RONALD, b. Abilene, Tex, Nov. 7, 39; m. 62; c. 2. MODERN BRITISH LITERATURE. B.A, Univ. Tex, Austin, 61, M.A, 67, Ph.D.(Eng), 70; Dip. Ed, Makerere Univ, Uganda, 63. Educ. off. ENG, Govt. of Kenya, 63-65; ASST. PROF, EMORY UNIV, 69- MLA; S.Atlantic Mod. Lang. Asn. Modern British poetry and poetics: T.S. Eliot. Publ: Eliot and Hulme in 1916: toward a revaluation of Eliot's critical and spiritual development, PMLA, 10/73. Add: Dept. of English, Emory University, Atlanta, GA 30322.

SCHUELER, DONALD G, b. New York, N.Y, Aug. 6, 29. ENGLISH. B.A, Univ. Ga, 51; M.A, La. State Univ, 60, Ph.D.(Eng), 62. Instr. Eng, UNIV. NEW ORLEANS, 60-63, asst. prof, 63-66, assoc. prof, 66-69, PROF, 69-, chmn. freshman Eng, 66-69. U.S.M.C, 46-48. MLA; S.Cent. Mod. Lang. Asn. Medieval literature. Publ: Problems in English grammar, C.E. Merrill, 65; Age of the lover in Gower's Confessio Amantis, Medium Aevum, fall 67; Tristram section of Malorys Morte d'Arthur, Stud. Philol, 1/68; Gower's characterization of Genius in the Confessio Amantis, Mod. Lang. Quart, 9/72; plus one other. Add: Dept. of English, University New Orleans, New Orleans, LA 70122.

SCHUELLER, HERBERT MATTHEW, b. Vesta, Minn, Oct. 20, 09; m. 34; c. 2. ENGLISH. B.A, Univ. Minn, 31, M.A, 32; Ph.D, Univ. Mich, 42. Instr. high sch, Minn, 34-36; Tracy Jr. Col, 36-37; Crosby-Ironton Jr. Col, 37-40; teaching fel, Univ. Mich, 40-41; instr. ENG, WAYNE STATE UNIV, 41-45, asst. prof, 45-50, assoc. prof, 50-56, PROF, 56-, DIR. UNIV. PRESS, 70-, acting chmn. dept, 55-56, chmn. dept, 56-68, acting assoc. dean, Col. Lib. Arts, 62-63. Am. Counc. Learned Soc. fac. stud. fel, 52, travel grants, Eng. & Switz, 62; ed, Criticism, 59-63; J. Aesthet. & Art Criticism, 63- Am. Soc. Aesthet.(trustee, 62-64, ed. jour, 63-); Am. Philos. Asn; Asn. Am. Univ. Presses; AAAS; fel. Royal Soc. Arts. The letters of John Addington Symonds; 18th century British aesthetic theory; aesthetics as related to literature and music. Publ: John Addington Symonds as a theoretical and as a practical critic, Univ. Microfilms, 64; transl, Aesthetics—the science, 62, Max Rieser's An analysis of poetic thinking, 69 & ed, The letters of John Addington Symonds (3 vols), 67-69, Wayne State Univ; auth, Freidrich Kainz, the aesthetician, 10/61 & Romanticism reconsidered, 62, J. Aesthet. & Art Criticism; An American in Rome: the experiments of W.W. Story, In: Frontiers of American culture, Purdue, 68; plus others. Add: Dept. of English, Wayne State University, Detroit, MI 48202.

SCHUG, CLAYTON HORN, b. Monroeville, Ohio, Jan. 6, 09; m. 39; c. 1. SPEECH. B.A, Ohio State Univ, 30, M.A, 31; summers, Northwest. Univ, 30, Univ. Wis, 32-35. Instr. SPEECH, PA. STATE UNIV, UNIVERSITY PARK, 31-38, asst. prof, 38-44, assoc. prof, 44-54, prof, 54-71, EMER. PROF, 71- Assoc. ed, The Gavel, 53-63; past ed, Bull. Debating Asn. Pa. Cols. Citations, Am. Forensic Asn, 64 & Pa. Cols. Debating Asn, 65. East. Forensic Asn.(v.pres, 54-56, pres, 56-58); Speech Commun. Asn.(legis. assembly, 66-68); Am. Forensic Asn; East. States Speech Asn.(mem, exec. counc, 66-68). Standards and objectives in the field of forensics; avoiding abuses in speech activities; attitude change among high school and college debaters. Publ: A study of attitude toward debate, 11/52 & A study of attitude change toward debate propositions among high school and college debaters, 1/54, Speech Teacher; A study of the status of intramural forensics on the American college campus, Speaker & Gavel, 3/68. Add: 333 S. Patterson St, State College, PA 16801.

SCHULER, ROBERT MICHAEL, b. Louisville, Ky, May 30, 43; m. 68. ENGLISH LITERATURE. B.A, Bellarmine Col, 65; M.A, Univ. Colo, Boulder, 66, Ph.D.(Eng), 71. ASST. PROF. ENG, UNIV. VICTORIA (B.C), 71- Renaissance Soc. Am. Renaissance literature; alchemy; history of science and its relation to literature. Publ: W.B. Yeats: artist of alchemist?, Rev. Eng. Stud, 2/71; William Blomfild, Elizabethan alchemist, Ambix, 9/73. Add: Dept. of English, University Victoria, Victoria, B.C. V8W 2Y2, Can.

SCHULMAN, GRACE, b. New York, N.Y. MODERN POETRY. B.S, Am. Univ, 54; M.A, New York Univ, 60, Ph.D.(Eng. lit), 71. Grad. asst. ENG, New York Univ, 64-70; adj. asst. prof, BARUCH COL, 71-72, ASST. PROF, 72- Poetry ed, The Nation, 72-; fels, Yaddo, summer 73; MacDowell Colony, 73; Karolyi Found, France, 73; dir, Poetry Ctr, Young Men's & Young Women's Hebrew Asn, 74-; contrib, Am. Poetry Rev. Andiron Award for Best Dissertation, New York Univ, 71. Publ: Ed, Ezra Pound: a collection of criticism, McGraw, 74; auth, Women the inventors, 12/72, Political poetry: dual vision, 4/73 & Mark Van Doren as an American, 10/73, The Nation; plus many others. Add: 14F, One University Pl, New York, NY 10003.

SCHULTE, EMERITA SCHROER, b. Coldwater, Ohio, June 23, 24; m. 47. ENGLISH. B.S.Ed, Bowling Green State Univ, 52; M.Ed, Miami Univ, 58; Ph.D.(elem. educ), Ohio State Univ, Columbus, 67. Teacher elem. educ, Mercer County Schs, Ohio, 45-53; Coldwater Schs, 53-60, supvr, 60-62; asst. prof. res, Miami Univ, 62-63; teaching assoc, Ohio State Univ, Columbus, 63-66; asst. prof. ENG, BALL STATE UNIV, 66-70, ASSOC. PROF, 70- NCTE; Int. Reading Asn; Nat. Soc. Stud. Educ; Asn. Supv. & Curriculum Develop. Literature for children and adolescents; American literature. Publ: Contrib, Development of lifetime reading habits, Int. Reading Asn, 68; auth, Today's literature for today's children, Elem. Eng, 3/72. Add: Dept. of English, Ball State University, Muncie, IN 47306.

SCHULTE, HENRY F, b. Lincoln, Nebr, Sept. 24, 24; m. 51; c. 2. JOURNALISM. B.A, McGill Univ, 51; M.Sc, Columbia Univ, 52; Ph.D.(commun), Univ. Ill, 66. Reporter, Ann Arbor News, Mich, 52-53; ed. & correspondent, United Press, London, Eng, 54-56, news ed, Madrid, Spain, 56-57; mgr, United Press Int, Spain, 57-62, ed, N.Y, 64-65; Instr. JOUR, Univ. Ill, 62-64; assoc. prof, Pa. State Univ, 65-69; PROF, SYRACUSE UNIV, 69-, DEAN SCH. PUB. COMMUN, 72-, chmn. dept, 69-72. Overseas Press Club Am; Int. Asn. Mass Commun. Res; Int. Press Inst; Inter-Am. Press Asn. International communications; communications history. Publ: The Spanish press, 1470-1966: print, power and politics, Univ. Ill, 68. Add: Office of the Dean, S.I. Newhouse School of Public Communications, Syracuse University, Syracuse, NY 13210.

SCHULTZ, ELIZABETH AVERY, b. Athens, Tenn, Mar. 3, 36. AMERICAN LITERATURE. B.A, Wellesley Col, 58; M.A, Univ. Mich, 62, fel, 63-66, Ph.D.(Eng), 67. Instr. ENG, Baika Jr. Col, 58-61; Univ. Mich, 63-66; ASST. PROF, UNIV. KANS, 67- Instr, Tuskegee Inst, summer 65. Nineteenth century American novel; the American short story. Add: Dept. of English, University of Kansas, Lawrence, KS 66044.

SCHULTZ, HOWARD, b. Hobart, Okla, Dec. 13, 07; m. 29, 67; c. 3. ENGLISH. A.B, Univ. Tex, 33, A.M, 34; A.M, Harvard, 39, Ph.D, 40. Instr. Eng, Univ. Tex, 34-38; Northwest Univ, 40-42; ed. tech. copy, Gen. Motors, Inc, 42-46; asst. prof. ENG, Univ. N.H, 46-50, assoc. prof, 50-60, PROF. 60-67; SOUTH. ILL. UNIV, CARBONDALE, 67- MLA. Milton and the Renaissance in literature; folklore, especially music and dance. Publ: Milton and forbidden knowledge, Mod. Lang. Asn, 55; co-auth, Technical report writing, McKay, 62; auth, Christ and Antichrist in Paradise regained, PMLA, 52; Some recent studies in Paradise regained, ELH, 66; Recent studies in the English Renaissance, Stud. Eng. Lit, 67. Add: Dept. of English, Southern Illinois University, Carbondale, IL 62901.

SCHULTZ, MARTIN C, Speech Pathology, Audiology. See 12th Edition, American Men & Women of Science, Physical & Biological Sciences Section.

SCHULTZ, WERNER WILLIAM, b. Ottawa, Ont, Dec. 19, 13; U.S. citizen; m. 42; c. 2. ENGLISH. B.A, Hiram Col, 41; M.A, Oberlin Col, 50; Cambridge, 67; N.Y. Univ, 69; Ohio Univ, 71. Instr. ENG, Hiram Col, 46; ASST. PROF, YOUNGSTOWN STATE UNIV, 46- U.S.A, 42-46, Sgt. Col. Eng. Asn; MLA; Ling. Soc. Am. English literature especially 19th century; English language; linguistics. Add: Dept. of English, Youngstown State University, 410 Wick Ave, Youngstown, OH 44503.

SCHULTZ, WILLIAM J, b. Dodge City, Kans, Oct. 5, 36; m. 60; c. 4. AMERICAN LITERATURE. B.A, Hastings Col, 58; M.A, Univ. Ark, Fayetteville, 64; Ph.D.(Eng), Kans. State Univ, 68. Instr. ENG, Sterling Col, 61-64; ASST. PROF, MUSKINGUM COL, 68- AAUP; MLA. William Faulkner; American literature before 1860. Add: Dept. of English, Muskingum College, New Concord, OH 43762.

SCHULZ, JOAN E, b. Chicago, Ill, Aug. 12, 30. ENGLISH. B.S, North. Ill. Univ, 52, M.S, 54; M.A, Univ. Ill, 58, Ph.D.(Eng), 63. Instr. ENG. LIT, North Ill. Univ, 58-61; asst. prof, STATE UNIV. N.Y. ALBANY, 62-68, ASSOC. PROF, 68- MLA. Twentieth century Southern literature; women in literature. Publ: Nineteenth-century British fiction, In: Good reading, New Am. Libr, 68. Add: Dept. of English, State University of New York at Albany, 1400 Western Ave, Albany, NY 12203.

SCHULZ, MAX FREDERICK, b. Cleveland, Ohio, Sept. 15, 23; m. 52; c. 3. ENGLISH LITERATURE. A.B, Univ. Pittsburgh, 49, M.A, 50; Univ. Minn, 50-51; Ph.D.(Eng. lit), Wayne State Univ, 59. Instr. Eng, Youngstown Univ, 53-54; teaching fel, Wayne State Univ, 54-57; instr. ENG, Tulane Univ, 57-60, asst. prof, 60-61; Ohio Univ, 61-63; assoc. prof, UNIV. SOUTH. CALIF, 63-67, PROF, 67-, CHMN. DEPT, 68- Ed. adv. Eng. romanticism, Col. Eng, 64-66; vis. prof, Univ. Del, 65; vis. Fulbright prof, Graz Univ, Austria, 65-66; vis. prof, State Univ. N.Y. Stony Brook, 70-71; assoc. ed, Critique, 71- U.S. Merchant Marine, 42-46. MLA; Mod. Humanities Res. Asn, Gt. Brit; Keats-Shelley Asn. Am; NCTE; Col. Eng. Asn; Int. Asn. Univ. Prof. Eng. English Romantic literature; Samuel Taylor Coleridge; contemporary fiction. Publ: The poetic voices of Coleridge, Wayne, 63; Radical sophistication: studies in contemporary Jewish-American novelists, 69 & Black humor fiction of the sixties: pluralistic definition of man and his world, 73, Ohio Univ; Coleridge, Wordsworth, and the 1800 preface to Lyrical ballads, Stud. Eng. Lit, autumn 65; Coleridge, In: The English Romantic poets: a review of research, Mod. Lang. Asn, 72; Towards a definition of black humor, South. Rev, winter 73; plus others. Add: Dept. of English, University of Southern California, Los Angeles, CA 90007.

SCHULZ, RONALD EDWARD, b. Montevideo, Minn, May 22, 19; m. 48; c. 1. DRAMA. B.S, Northwest. Univ, 47, M.A, 48, fel, 48-52. Staff mem. theatre, Northwest. Univ, 48-50, teaching fel. dramatic prod, 50-52, lectr, summers 51, 52; asst. prof. SPEECH & THEATRE ARTS, TEX. TECH UNIV, 52-59, assoc. prof, 59-67, PROF, 67-, dir. theatre, 56-72, acting head dept. speech, 57-58. U.S.A, 41-45, Capt. Univ. & Col. Theatre Asn; AAUP. Dramatic literature and criticism; theatre history; acting and directing. Add: University Theatre, P.O. Box 4298, Texas Tech University, Lubbock, TX 79409.

SCHULZE, EARL JOHN, b. Chicago, Ill, Mar. 9, 33; m. 56; c. 1. ENGLISH, ROMANTICS. A.B, Princeton, 54; Ph.D.(Eng), Northwest. Univ, 62. Instr. ENG, Northwest. Univ, 58-59; North Park Col, 59-63; UNIV. MICH, ANN ARBOR, 63-64, asst. prof, 64-68, ASSOC. PROF, 68- MLA. Romantics; literary criticism. Publ: Shelley's theory of poetry, Mouton, 66; Andrew Marvell, the reach of wit, Publ. Mich. Acad. Sci, Art & Lett, 64. Add: Dept. of English, University of Michigan, Ann Arbor, MI 48104.

SCHULZE, IVAN LEONARD, b. Baltimore, Md, Aug. 21, 99; m. 26; c. 1. ENGLISH LITERATURE. A.B, Johns Hopkins Univ, 22, A.M, 27, Ph.D. (Eng), 30. Asst, Eng, Johns Hopkins Univ, 25-26, instr, 29-30; head master, Garey's Sch, Md, 26-29; assoc. prof. Eng, Tex. Woman's Univ, 30-38, PROF, 38-69, librn, 46-69; RETIRED. MLA; Am. Libr. Asn; S.Cent. Mod. Lang. Asn. English Renaissance; Shakespeare; Spenser. Add: 610 Woodland, Denton, TX 76201.

SCHUMAN, SAMUEL, b. Chicago, Ill, Sept. 26, 42; m. 62; c. 2. ENGLISH LITERATURE. B.A, Grinnell Col, 64; M.A, San Francisco State Col, 66; Ph.D.(Eng), Northwest. Univ, 69. Instr. Eng. & world classics, St. Mary's Col, 66-67; ASST. PROF. ENG, CORNELL COL, 70- AAUP; MLA; NCTE. Renaissance drama. Publ: Co-ed, Renaissance drama 1968, Northwest. Univ, 68; auth, Cyril Tourneur, Twayne, 74; The ring and the jewel in Webster's tragedies, Tex. Stud. Lit. & Lang, 72; Occasion's bald behind, Mod. Philol, 73; Vladimir Nabokov's Invitation to a beheading and Robert Heinlein's They, Twentieth Century Lit, 73. Add: Dept. of English, Cornell College, Mt. Vernon, IA 52314.

SCHUSTER, EDGAR HOWARD, b. Minneapolis, Minn, Apr. 7, 30; m. 55; c. 2. MODERN GRAMMAR, MODERN LITERATURE. B.A, Columbia Col, 52; M.Ed, Temple Univ, 62; Ph.D.(Eng. educ), Univ. Pa, 73. Teacher Eng, Cheltenham High Sch, 58-62; Springfield High Sch, 62-63; textbk. auth, McGraw-Hill Bk. Co, 63-65; ASST. PROF. ENG, BEAVER COL, 65- NCTE. Modern literature; literary criticism; modern grammatical theory. Publ: Grammar, usage, and style, 65, ed, American literature: themes and writers, 67, rev. ed, 73 & co-auth, American English today, 70, rev. ed, 74; auth, How good is the new grammar?, 9/61 & Discovering theme and structure in the novel, 10/63, Eng. J. Add: 7301 Granite Rd, Melrose Park, PA 19126.

SCHUSTER, LOUIS ANTHONY, S.M, b. Chicago, Ill, Dec. 4, 16. ENGLISH LITERATURE. B.A, St. Mary's Univ. San Antonio, 37; M.A, St, Louis Univ, 45; B.A, Oxford, 54, M.A, 57; Folger Shakespeare Libr. fel, summer 57; South. Fel. Fund fel, Belgium, 60-61; Ph.D.(Eng), Univ. Tex, 61. Teacher Eng. & Latin, McBride High Sch, St. Louis, Mo, 37-38, chmn. dept. Eng, 39-45; teacher Eng, Latin & Spanish, Cent. High Sch, San Antonio, Tex, 38-39; instr. ENG, ST. MARY'S UNIV. SAN ANTONIO, 45-49, asst. prof, 54-57, assoc. prof, 58-61, PROF, 61-, chmn. dept, 60-63, 65-66, 68-71. Yale Univ. res. fel, summers 65-67, spring 68; summers, Huntington fel, 64, Duke Univ. fel, 66; lectr. Annual St. Thomas More Lect, Yale Univ, 70. Minnie Stevens Piper Prof, 71. Malone Soc; Renaissance Soc. Am; S.Cent. Renaissance Conf.(pres); MLA; Conf. Col. Teachers Eng.(pres, 62-63). Shakespeare; neo-Latin drama; modern American fiction. Publ: Ed. & transl, Henry VIII: a neo-Latin drama by Nicolaus Vernulaeus, Univ. Tex, 64; co-ed, The confutation of Tyndale's answer, Vol. 8, Parts I, II & III, In: Complete works of St. Thomas More, Yale, 73; The Anglo-Saxon workshop of Ezra Pound, S.Cent. Bull, Vol. 32, No. 3; The inner self of St. Thomas More as polemicist, Moreana, 35: 77-82; Six ways of looking at a convention, Counc-Grams NCTE, Vol. 34, No. 2; plus five others. Add: Dept. of English, St. Mary's University of San Antonio, San Antonio, TX 78284.

SCHUSTER, MARY FAITH, O.S.B, b. Pilot Grove, Mo, July 10, 14. ENGLISH. A.B, Mt. St. Scholastica Col, 41; Ed.M, St. Louis Univ, 50, Ph.D.(Eng), 53. Instr. high sch, Mo, 41-46; Kans, 46-50, 52-53; ENG, Donnelly Col, 53-58, 60-62, 63-67; PROF, Marillac Col, 58-60; BENEDICTINE COL, 62-63, 67- Secy, Am. Benedictine Acad, 55-57, chmn, 73- MLA. Renaissance literature. Publ: Meaning of the mountain, Helicon, 63; contrib, Catholic adult education, Bruce, 59; Prose style of Thomas More and Francis Bacon, PMLA; Poem at night, America, 8/69; plus others. Add: Dept. of English, Benedictine College, South Campus, Atchison, KS 66002.

SCHUSTER, RICHARD, b. New York, N.Y, Aug. 31, 27; m. 48; c. 1. ENGLISH. B.A, Yale, 47; M.A, Columbia Univ, 48, Ph.D.(Eng. & comp. lit), 61. Instr. ENG, Butler Univ, 48-50; PROF, NEW ENG. COL, 64- MLA; Mediaeval Acad. Am; NCTE; Ling. Soc. Am. American fiction of later 19th century; American humor of 19th century; linguistics. Publ: The selfish and the strong, Random, 58. Add: New England College, Henniker, NH 03242.

SCHUTTE, WILLIAM METCALF, b. New Haven, Conn, May 9, 19; m. 43, 67; c. 3. ENGLISH LITERATURE. A.B, Yale, 41, A.M, 47, Ph.D, 54. Instr. ENG, Carnegie Inst. Tech, 47-49, asst. prof, 49-55, assoc. prof, 55-60; PROF, LAWRENCE UNIV, 60- Consult, Commun. to Indust; Carnegie award, 54; fac. fel, Newberry Libr, 69-71. Renaissance Soc. Am; MLA; NCTE; Shakespeare Asn. Am. Shakespeare; Renaissance drama; modern novel. Publ: Joyce and Shakespeare, Yale, 57; co-auth, Communication in business and industry, Holt, 60; auth, Personal integrity, Norton, 61; Twentieth century interpretations: James Joyce, a portrait of the artist as a young man, Prentice-Hall, 68. Add: Dept. of English, Lawrence University, Appleton, WI 54911.

SCHUTZ, WALTER STANLEY, b. Freetown, W.Africa, June 25, 24; U.S. citizen; m. 48; c. 4. THEATER, SPEECH. B.A, Otterbein Col, 49; B.S, Ohio State Univ, 51, M.A, 54; Ph.D.(speech), Mich. State Univ, 67. Orgn. dir, Licking County Farm Bur, Ohio, 49-50; teacher, high schs, Ohio, 51-56, dir. dramatics, 53-56; instr. speech & theater & asst. dir. theater, Col. Wooster, 56-59, 60-61; asst. prof. speech & dir. broadcasting, Muskingum Col, 61-68; assoc. prof. SPEECH & THEATER, COL. WOOSTER, 68-71, PROF, 71-, ASSOC. DIR. THEATER, 68- U.S.N, 43-46; Res, 47-52. Speech Commun. Asn; Am. Theatre Asn; Cent. States Speech Commun. Asn. The nature of farce: definition and devices; American writers of farce; history of farce. Add: Dept. of Speech, College of Wooster, Wooster, OH 44691.

SCHWAB, ARNOLD T, b. Los Angeles, Calif, Jan. 5, 22. ENGLISH. A.B, Univ. Calif, Los Angeles, 43; A.M, Harvard, 47, Ph.D.(Eng), 51. Sheldon fel, Harvard, 51-52; instr. Eng, Univ. Calif, Los Angeles, 52-54; Univ. Mich, 54-55; res. dir, Wisdom Mag, 56-57; asst. prof. ENG, CALIF. STATE UNIV, LONG BEACH, 61-64, assoc. prof, 64-69, PROF, 69- Am. Counc. Learned Soc. grant, 66. Commonwealth Club Calif. silver medal, 64. U.S.N.R, 43-46, Lt.(jg). MLA. American and English literature; literary criticism; biography. Publ: James Gibbons Huneker: critic of the seven arts, Stanford Univ, 63; Conrad's American speeches and his reading from Victory, Mod. Philol, 5/65; James Huneker on Whitman: a newly discovered essay, Am. Lit, 5/66; Joseph Conrad and Warrington Dawson, Mod. Philol, 5/71; plus others. Add: Dept. of English, California State University, Long Beach, 6101 E. Seventh St, Long Beach, CA 90840.

SCHWAB, WILLIAM, b. Bad Kreuznach, Ger, Nov. 8, 23; nat. ENGLISH. B.A, Bethany Col, 45; M.A, Univ. Wis, 47, Ph.D.(Eng), 51. Instr. Eng, Purdue Univ, 50-53; commun. skills, Mich. State Univ, 53-57, asst. prof, 57-59; Eng, OAKLAND UNIV, 59-60, assoc. prof, 60-65, prof, 65-70, PROF. LING. & ENG. & CHMN. DEPT. LING, 70- Fulbright lectr, Univ. Philippines, 54-55; Fulbright lectr. ling. & methods teaching Eng. as a second lang, Univ. Philippines & Ateneo de Manila Univ, 63-64; mem. Philippine long-range planning team, Fulbright-Hays Prog, 67; Fulbright lectr, 5th Am. Stud. Sem, Manila, 68; lectr, Ateneo de Manila Univ, winter 70. MLA; Ling. Soc. Am. English grammar; linguistics; English as a foreign language. Publ: Guide to modern grammar and exposition, Harper, 67; Is freshman English obsolete?, J. Higher Educ; Some structural problems for tagalong students in English, Lang. Learning; Language and related problems of foreign students, Asn. Am. Cols. Bull. Add: Dept. of Linguistics, Oakland University, Rochester, MI 48063.

SCHWABER, PAUL, b. New York, N.Y, Apr. 17, 36. ENGLISH. A.B, Wesleyan Univ, 57; M.A, Univ. Calif, Berkeley, 59; Ph.D.(Eng. & comp. lit), Columbia Univ, 66. Instr. Eng, Wellesley Col, 65-66; asst. prof. lett. & Eng, WESLEYAN UNIV, 66-72, ASSOC. PROF. LETT, 72-, co-dir, Col. Lett, 73-76. Jr. fel, Soc. Humanities, Cornell Univ, 70-71. MLA; New Eng. Col. Eng. Asn.(dir, 71-74). English romanticism; modern poetry; relations of Freudian psychoanalysis to literary studies. Publ: Co-ed, Of poetry and power: poems occasioned by the presidency & by the death of John F. Kennedy, Basic Bks, 64; On reading Poe, Lit. & Psychol, 71; Robert Lowell in mid-career, West. Humanities Rev, 71; Women and Freud's imagination, Am. Scholar; plus three others. Add: College of Letters, Wesleyan University, Middletown, CT 06457.

SCHWALBE, DORIS J, b. London, Eng, Dec. 3, 22; U.S. citizen. ENGLISH. B.A, Univ. Toledo, 44, B.E, 48, M.A, 52; summer, Univ. Hawaii, 51; Ph.D. (Eng), Univ. Colo, 62. Teacher high sch, Ohio, 50-52; trade sch, 52-53; instr. ENG, Univ. Colo, Boulder, 53-58; UNIV. COLO, DENVER CTR, 58-66, asst. prof, 66-71, ASSOC. PROF, 71- W.A.V.E.S, 45-46. MLA; Rocky Mountain Mod. Lang. Asn. Add: Dept. of English, University of Colorado, Denver Center, Denver, CO 80202.

SCHWARTZ, ELIAS, b. New York, N.Y, March 29, 23; m; c. 5. ENGLISH A.B, New York Univ, 47; M.A, Univ. Chicago, 49; Ph.D, Stanford Univ, 54. Instr. ENG, Univ. Nebr, 49-50; Univ. Notre Dame, 54-57, asst. prof, 57-62; assoc. prof, Harpur Col, 62-69; PROF, STATE UNIV. N.Y. BINGHAMTON, 69- U.S.A.A.F, 43-45. Shakespeare; literary theory and criticism. Publ: The forms of feeling, Kennikat, 72; Stylistic impurity and the meaning of Othello, Stud. Eng. Lit, spring 70; Tonal equivocation and the meaning of Troilus and Cressida, Stud. Philol, 7/72; plus two others. Add: Dept. of English, State University of New York at Binghamton, Binghamton, NY 13901.

SCHWARTZ, JAMES WALDEMAR, b. Fenton, Iowa, Apr. 18, 16; m. 41; c. 2. JOURNALISM. B.S, Iowa State Univ, 41, M.S, 60. PROF. & HEAD DEPT. JOUR, IOWA STATE UNIV, 45- U.S.A, 42. Asn. Educ. Jour.(pres, 68). Publ: Ed, The publicity process, Iowa State Univ, 66. Add: Dept. of Journalism, Iowa State University, Ames, IA 50010.

SCHWARTZ, JOSEPH MICHAEL, b. Apr. 9, 25; m. 54. ENGLISH. Ph.B, Marquette Univ, 46, M.A, 47; Ph.D.(Eng), Univ. Wis, 52. Teaching fel, Eng, Marquette Univ, 46-47; Univ. Wis, 48-50; instr. speech & Eng, MARQUETTE UNIV, 47-48, ENG, 50-54, asst. prof, 54-58, assoc. prof, 58-64, PROF, 64-, CHMN. DEPT, 63- Ford Found. Grant, 56-58; chmn, region X, Woodrow Wilson Nat. Fel. Found, 67-72. MLA; NCTE (bd. dir, 65-68); Cath. Renascence Soc.(mem. ed. bd, Renascence, 71-). Hawthorne; American prose and poetry, 1900 to the present; rhetoric. Publ: Contrib, American classics reconsidered, Scribner, 58; co-auth, A reader for writers, 62, 66, 71 & Exposition, 66, 71 & Poetry; meaning and form, 69, McGraw; co-auth, Perspectives on language, 63 & The province of rhetoric, 65 Ronald; Hart Crane, an annotated critical bibliography, David Lewis, 70; Hart Crane: a descriptive bibliography, Univ. Pittsburgh, 72; plus three others. Add: Dept. of English, Marquette University, Milwaukee, WI 53233.

SCHWARTZ, RICHARD BRENTON, b. Cincinnati, Ohio, Oct. 5, 41; m. 63; c. 1. ENGLISH LITERATURE. A.B, Univ. Notre Dame, 63; fel, Univ. Ill, Urbana, 63-64, A.M, 64, dissertation fel, 66-67, Ph.D.(Eng), 67. Instr. ENG, U.S. Mil. Acad, 67-69; asst. prof, UNIV. WIS-MADISON, 69-72, ASSOC. PROF, 72- Nat. Endowment for Humanities summer stipend, 70. U.S.A, 67-69, Capt. MLA; Am. Soc. 18th Century Stud; Johnson Soc. Cent. Region. Samuel Johnson; 18th century English prose and intellectual history. Publ: Samuel Johnson and the new science, Univ. Wis, 71; Dr. Johnson and the satiric reaction to science, Stud. Burke & His Time, 69; Johnson's Journey, J. Eng. & Ger. Philol, 70; Johnson's Mr. Rambler and the periodical tradition, Genre, 74. Add: Dept. of English, University of Wisconsin-Madison, Madison, WI 53706.

SCHWARTZ, ROBERT GEORGE, JR, b. Colorado Springs, Colo, May 2, 36; m. 59; c. 3. EIGHTEENTH CENTURY ENGLISH LITERATURE. B.A, Univ. Colo, 58; M.A, Univ. Mo, 63, Ph.D.(Eng), 70. Instr. Eng, Kemper Mil. Sch. & Col, 58-63; develop. assoc. pub. relat. & fund raising, Rockford Col, 63-65; instr. ENG, Univ. Mo, 65-69; asst. prof, CENT. MO. STATE UNIV, 69-72, ASSOC. PROF, 73- Consult, Sheed & Ward Publ. Co, 72- MLA; Am. Soc. 18th Century Stud. Eighteenth century aesthetics; 18th century novel; satire. Add: Dept. of English, Central Missouri State University, Warrensburg, MO 64093.

SCHWARTZ, SHEILA RUTH, b. New York, N.Y, m. 49; c. 3. LANGUAGE ARTS, ENGLISH. B.A, Adelphi Col, 46; M.A, Columbia Univ, 48; Ed.D, N.Y. Univ, 64. Instr, Hofstra Univ, 58-60; teaching fel, N.Y. Univ, 60-61; instr, City Col. New York, 62-63; from assoc. prof. to PROF, ENG. EDUC, STATE UNIV. N.Y. NEW PALTZ, 63- Consult. desegregation insts, U.S. Off. Educ, summer 65; sec. Eng. curriculum, Kingston Schs, 65-66; cult, understanding & enrichment humanities proj, N.Y. State Dept. Educ, 65-66; revision of sec. sch. lit. curriculum, Cleveland Heights Sch. Syst, 66; humanities inst, Gadsden Schs, Ala, 66; Bds. of Coop. Educ. Servs, Yorktown Heights, N.Y, 67; SCOPE, Suffolk County, N.Y, 68-69; chmn. comt. innovation, Nat. Conf. Eng. Educ; consult. Eng. curriculum revision, Hyde Park Schs, 73; pres, N.Y. State Eng. Counc, 74. NCTE (dir, sec. sect, 70-73); Nat. Asn. Humanities Educ. (pres, 71-72). Secondary school humanities; K-12 literature curriculum. Publ: Co-auth, How people lived in ancient Greece and Rome, Benefic, 67; ed, Professional book review column, Elem. Eng, 69-72; auth, Teaching the humanities, Macmillan, 70; Science fiction in the secondary school, Dell, 74; Old and new humanities, Eng. Educ, fall 73; History of humor, In: Humor and the English teacher, Ariz. Eng. Publ, 74; Jewish literature, Eng. Rec, winter 74; plus others. Add: Division of Education, State University of New York College at New Paltz, New Paltz, NY 12561.

SCHWARZ, ALFRED, b. Vienna, Austria, Mar. 3, 25; nat; m. 50; c. 2. ENGLISH. B.A, Univ. Minn, 45; A.M, Harvard, 47, Dexter fel, summer 50, Ph.D.(Eng), 51. Teaching fel. ENG, Harvard, 49-50; instr, Princeton, 50-54, asst. prof, 54-61; WAYNE STATE UNIV, 61-63, assoc. prof, 63-66, PROF, 66- Jr. fel, Counc. Humanities, Princeton, 55-56; vis. prof, Univ. Rochester, 60-61; fac. res. fel, Wayne State Univ, summers 62 & 67. U.S.A, 43-46. MLA. Literary criticism and poetics; drama, especially forms of tragic drama; comparative literature. Publ: Hugo von Hofmannsthal: three plays, Wayne State Univ, 66; Otto Ludwig's Shakespearean criticism, In: Perspectives of criticism, Harvard, 50; An example of eighteenth-century pathetic tragedy: Rowe's Jane Shore, Mod. Lang. Quart, 9/61; Toward a poetic of modern realistic tragedy, Mod. Drama, 9/66. Add: Dept. of English, Wayne State University, Detroit, MI 48202.

SCHWARZ, DANIEL ROGER, b. Rockville Centre, N.Y, May 12, 41; m. 63; c. 2. ENGLISH. B.A, Union Col.(N.Y), 63; M.A, Brown Univ, 65, Wilbour fel, 65-66, Ph.D.(Eng), 68. ASST. PROF. ENG, CORNELL UNIV, 68- MLA. The British novel, especially Hardy, Conrad, Lawrence and Joyce; theory of the novel; 20th century British poetry. Publ: The unity of Eliot's Gerontion: the failure of meditation, Bucknell Rev, spring 71 & In: T.S. Eliot: a collection of criticism, McGraw, 74; The narrator as character in Hardy's major fiction, Mod. Fiction Stud, summer 72; The journey to Patusan: the education of Jim and Marlow in Lord Jim, Stud. Novel, fall 72; plus eight others. Add: Dept. of English, Cornell University, Ithaca, NY 14850.

SCHWEDA, DONALD NORMAN, b. Chicago, Ill, Apr. 18, 37; m. 57; c. 1. AMERICAN & ENGLISH LITERATURE. B.S, Ill. Inst. Technol, 62; A.M, Univ. Fla, 63; Univ. Ill, Urbana, 63; Ph.D.(Eng), Loyola Univ. Chicago, 73. Teacher ENG, Kelvyn Park High Sch, Chicago, Ill, 62; Mount Prospect High Sch, 64; instr, QUINCY COL, 64-66, ASSOC. PROF. & CHMN. DEPT, 68- Evaluator, Clearing House Reading & Commun. Skills, Educ. Resources Inform. Ctr, 74- U.S.N, 54-58. MLA; AAUP; NCTE; Asn. Depts. Eng. American poetry; 19th century American literature; Shakespeare. Publ: Emersonian ideas and Whitman's Song of myself, J. Loyola Hist. Soc, fall 67. Add: Dept. of English, Quincy College, Quincy, IL 62301.

SCHWEIK, ROBERT CHARLES, b. Chicago, Ill, Aug. 5, 27; m. 54; c. 2. ENGLISH. B.A, Loyola Univ.(Ill), 51; Ph.D, Univ. Notre Dame, 58. Instr. ENG, Marquette Univ, 53-58, asst. prof, 59-64, assoc. prof, 64-69; PROF, STATE UNIV. N.Y. COL. FREDONIA, 69- Vis. prof, Univ. Wis-Superior, summer 68; mem. ed. bd, Eng. Lit. in Transition, 70-; vis. prof, Univ. Trier (W.Ger), 72-73. U.S.N, 44-45. MLA (mem. Victorian bibliog. comt, 68-72). Victorian novel; bibliography. Publ: Ed, Emily Bronte's Wuthering heights, Cambridge, 69; co-auth, Hart Crane: a descriptive bibliography, Univ. Pittsburg, 72; auth, The early development of Hardy's Far from the madding crowd, Tex. Stud. Lit. & Lang, autumn 67; Current problems in textual scholarship on Thomas Hardy, Eng. Lit. in Transition, 71; A first draft chapter of Hardy's Far from the madding crowd, Eng. Stud, 72; plus others. Add: Dept. of English, State University of New York College at Fredonia, Fredonia, NY 14063.

SCHWERMAN, ESTHER LOUISE, b. Mundelein, Ill. ENGLISH. M.Mus, Am. Conservatory Music, 34; Ph.D.(Eng-Ger. lit. interpretation), Univ. Chicago & Northwest. Univ, 51. Instr. ENG. & LIT. INTERPRETATION, Joliet Jr. Col, 34-41; ASST. PROF, Lake Forest Col, 41-45; Univ. Denver, 45-47; DUKE UNIV, 47- Speech Commun. Asn. English and German literature, especially influence and importance of Rainer Maria Rilke upon English and American literature. Add: 909 Lambeth Circle, Durham, NC 27705.

SCHWIENHER, WILLIAM KAYE, b. St. Louis, Mo, Aug. 8, 16; m. 71. SPEECH. B.A, St. Louis Univ, 40, S.T.B, 50, M.A, 65; Ph.D.(radio, TV & film), Northwest. Univ, 70. Instr. sci. & math, Campion High Sch, Prairie du Chien, Wis, 42-47; prod. dir, Sacred Heart Radio & TV Prog, 50-68; assoc. prof. RADIO, TV & FILM & EDUC. TV PRODUCER, PURDUE UNIV, WEST LAFAYETTE, 70-, HEAD, BROADCAST DIV. DEPT. COMMUN, 72- Sociological effects of the mass media; commercialization in American broadcasting; psychological factors of successful television. Add: Telecommunication Center, Purdue University, West Lafayette, IN 47907.

SCOFIELD, ALICE G, b. Newman, Calif, Sept. 25, 20; wid; c. 1. ENGLISH EDUCATION. B.A, Mills Col, 39; M.A, Stanford Univ, 42, M.A, 55. PROF. ENG. & EDUC. & DIR. SEC. INTERN PROG, SAN JOSE STATE UNIV, 55-, hon. teacher of year award. NCTE; Nat. Soc. Stud. Educ; Int. Reading Asn. Add: Dept. of English, San Jose State University, San Jose, CA 95114.

SCOGGINS, JAMES LAWRENCE, b. Chattanooga, Tenn, Jan. 1, 34; m. 57; c. 3. ENGLISH. A.B, Univ. Chattanooga, 58; M.A, Johns Hopkins Univ, 59; Ph.D.(Eng), Univ. Ill, 63. Instr. ENG, Univ. Ill, 63; asst. prof, UNIV. MINN, MINNEAPOLIS, 63-66, assoc. prof, 66-71, PROF, 71- Fulbright lectr, Charles Univ, Prague, Czechoslovakia, 70-71; lectr, Rydal Mt. Summer Sch, summer 71. U.S.A.F, 52-56. MLA; Charles Lamb Soc; Keats-Shelley Asn; Rydal Mt. Summer Sch. Asn. English Romantic period; modern poetry. Publ: Imagination and fancy, Univ. Nebr, 67; chap, In: Studies in criticism and aesthetics, 1660-1800, Univ. Minn, 67; Images of Eden in the essays of Elia, J. Eng. & Ger. Philol, 72; plus others. Add: Dept. of English, University of Minnesota, Minneapolis, MN 55455.

SCOTT, A. C, b. Eng, Dec. 3, 09; m. 36; c. 1. THEATRE, DRAMA. A.R.C.A, Royal Col. Art, London, Eng, 34. Field off, Brit. Counc. Cult. Relat, 46-54; sr. res. fel, Inst. Orient. Stud, Hong Kong Univ, 54-60; ed. mem. theatre & fine arts, Mod. China Res. Proj, Columbia Univ, 60-62; PROF. THEATRE &

DIR, ASIAN THEATRE PROG, UNIV. WIS-MADISON, 63- Guggenheim fel, Indonesia, 70. R.A.F, 42-46, Flight Lt. Am. Theatre Asn; Asn. Asian Stud; Soc. Auth, Eng. The theatre in Asia; intercultural relationships in theatre. Publ: Auth. & transl, Traditional Chinese plays, Vols. I, II & III, Univ. Wis, 67-73; auth, The theatre in Asia, Macmillan, 73. Add: Dept. of Theatre & Drama, University of Wisconsin-Madison, University Ave, Madison, WI 53706.

SCOTT, ARTHUR LINCOLN, b. Kew Gardens, N.Y, May 31, 14; m. 40; c. 3. ENGLISH. B.A, Princeton, 37; M.A, Univ. Mich, 40, Ph.D.(Eng), 48. Instr. ENG, Alborz Col, Iran, 37-39; UNIV. ILL, URBANA-CHAMPAIGN, 47-54, asst. prof, 54-62, assoc. prof, 62-70, EMER. ASSOC. PROF, 70- U.S.N.R. 43-46. MLA. Mark Twain and the rise of realism in American fiction; the short story; modern American literature. Publ: Ed, Mark Twain: selected criticism; South. Methodist Univ, 55; auth, On the poetry of Mark Twain, Univ. Ill, 66; Mark Twain at large, Regnery, 69; plus others. Add: 4433 Carmelo St, San Diego, CA 92107.

SCOTT, AURELIA GRETHER, b. Decatur, Ind; m. 26; c. 2. ENGLISH & COMPARATIVE LITERATURE. A.B, Univ. Wis, 26; Univ. Berlin, 26-27; Yale, 27-29; A.M, West. Reserve Univ, 37; Ph.D, Columbia Univ, 54. Instr. Ger, Laurel Sch, 35-37; Eng. and mod. langs, High Mowing Sch, 42-47; ENG, St. Margaret's Sch, 47-48; Masters Sch, 48-49; asst. prof, Wagner Col, 49-54, assoc. prof, 54-59, prof, 59-61; assoc. prof, QUEENSBOROUGH COMMUNITY COL, 61-66, PROF, 66- Consult, State of N.Y, 62. MLA. Modern English and continental literature; modern Russian literature; Goethe. Publ: Emily Dickinson's three gems; Elizabeth of Hungary; Goethe's Zuleika. Add: Dept. of English, Queensborough Community College, City University of New York, Bayside, NY 11364.

SCOTT, CHARLES THOMAS, Linguistics. See Volume III, Foreign Languages, Linguistics & Philology.

SCOTT, EVAN JAMES, b. Avalon, Wis, Dec. 25, 07. COMPARATIVE LITERATURE. B.A, Univ. Wis, 29, M.A, 37, Ph.D.(comp. lit), 47. Asst. prof. Eng, Colo. Col, 47-53; lectr, UNIV. COLO, COLORADO SPRINGS CTR, 54-62, asst. prof, 62-68, assoc. prof. & assoc. chmn. dept, 68-71, prof. & chmn. fac. eng, 71-73, EMER. PROF. ENG, 73- U.S.A.A.F, 43-45. Literary criticism, 1918-1939. Add: Dept. of English, University of Colorado, Colorado Springs Center, Colorado Springs, CO 80907.

SCOTT, JAMES BURTON, b. Niagara Falls, N.Y, Nov. 24, 26; m. 50; c. 8. MODERN AMERICAN FICTION & DRAMA. B.A, Univ. Buffalo, 51, M.A, 57; Ph.D.(Am. lit), Syracuse Univ, 64. Instr. ENG, Univ. Buffalo, 53-58; Syracuse Univ, 58-64; asst. prof, UNIV. BRIDGEPORT, 64-72, ASSOC. PROF, 72- C.Eng, U.S.A, 44-46. MLA. Melville; modern American novel; modern American drama. Publ: Golding's Lord of the flies, Barrister, 67; Sister Carrie, 6/59 & The theme of betrayal in Robert Penn Warren's stories, 6/64, Thoth. Add: Dept. of English, University of Bridgeport, Bridgeport, CT 06602.

SCOTT, JAMES FRAZIER, b. Atchison, Kans, July 9, 34; m. 61; c. 1. ENGLISH, CINEMA. B.S, Rockhurst Col, 55; M.A, Univ. Kans, 57, Ph.D. (Eng), 60. Instr. ENG, Univ. Ky, 60-62; asst. prof, ST. LOUIS UNIV, 62-65, assoc. prof, 65-72, PROF, 72- MLA. Nineteenth century fiction; the aesthetics of cinema. Publ: The Gothic element in Thomas Hardy's fiction, Nineteenth-Century Fiction, 63; The achievement of Ingmar Bergman, J. Aesthet, 65; George Eliot, positivism, and the social vision of Middlemarch, Victorian Stud, 72. Add: Dept. of English, St. Louis University, St. Louis, MO 63103.

SCOTT, JOSEPH WRIGHT, b. Champaign, Ill, Oct. 17, 13. THEATRE. A.B, Univ. Ill, 35; M.A, State Univ. Iowa, 36; summers, Columbia Univ, 38, 39; Ph.D.(theatre), Ohio State Univ, 49. Instr. speech, UNIV. ILL, URBANA, 36-42, 46-47, asst. prof, 47-50, assoc. prof. & supvr. dramatic prod, 50-62, prof. & exec. dir. univ. theatre, 62-71, EMER. PROF. SPEECH & THEATRE, 71- Instr. & tech. dir. theatre, Ohio State Univ, 46-47. A.U.S, 42-46, Capt. Speech Commun. Asn; Am. Theatre Asn. Oriental theatre. Add: 211 W. Clark St, Champaign, IL 61820.

SCOTT, KENNETH W, b. Perth Amboy, N.J, Aug. 23, 23; m. 49; c. 3. LITERATURE. B.A, Queens Col, 44; M.A, Columbia Univ, 47. Instr. ENG, L.I. UNIV, 47-60, asst. prof, 60-65, ASSOC. PROF, 65-70, PROF, 70- MLA. Victorian literature, especially popular fiction; American literature, especially frontier literature and the dime novel; relationship between motion pictures and literature. Publ: Blunt's sonnets and another poem to Skittles, Victorian Poetry, spring 65; G.P.R. James's Ticonderoga and a Mohawk Valley legend, N.Y. Folklore Quart, 12/67; The heritage of the desert: Zane Grey discovers the West, Markham Rev, 2/70; plus others. Add: Dept. of English, Long Island University, Brooklyn. NY 11201.

SCOTT, NATHAN ALEXANDER, JR, Theology, Literary Criticism. See Volume IV, Philosophy, Religion & Law.

SCOTT, PETER DALE, b. Montreal, Que, Jan. 11, 29; m. 56; c. 3. ENGLISH, POLITICAL SCIENCE. B.A, McGill Univ, 49, Ph.D.(polit. sci), 55; Inst. Polit. Stud, Paris, 50; Oxford, 50-52. Lectr. polit. sci, McGill Univ, 55-56; for. serv. off, Can. For. Serv, 56-61; lectr. speech, UNIV. CALIF, BERKELEY, 61-62, acting asst. prof, 62-63, asst. prof, 63-66, ENG, 66-68, ASSOC. PROF, 68-, humanities res. fel, 68. Guggenheim fel, 69-70. Vietnam war; medieval Latin poetry; literature and politics. Publ: Poems, Fantasy, Oxford, 52; co-auth, Politics of escalation, Beacon, 66 & Education at Berkeley, Univ. Calif, 68; co-transl, Zbigniew Herbert: selected poems, Penguin, 68; auth, The war conspiracy, Bobbs, 72; Alcuin as poet: rhetoric and belief in his Latin verse, Univ. Toronto Quart, 4/64; Alcuin's Versus de Cuculo: the vision of pastoral friendship, Stud. Philol, 7/65; chap. In: Pentagon Papers: critical essays, Beacon, 72; plus others. Add: 2823 Ashby Ave, Berkeley, CA 94705.

SCOTT, ROBERT IAN, b. Berkeley, Calif, Apr. 23, 31; m. 53; c. 3. ENGLISH LITERATURE, LINGUISTICS. B.A, Reed Col, 53; M.A, Claremont Grad. Sch, 55; Fulbright scholarship, Australian Nat. Univ, 54-56; Ph.D. (Eng), State Univ. N.Y. Buffalo, 64. Lectr. ENG, Univ. West. Australia,

56; instr, State Univ. N.Y. Buffalo, 57-63; asst. prof, South. Ore. Col, 63-66; ASSOC. PROF, UNIV. SASK, 66- Can. Counc. res. grants, summers 69, 71; Am. Philos. Soc. res. grant, summer 73. Can. Ling. Asn; Can. Asn. Am. Stud; Can. Counc. Teachers Eng. Modern American literature; transformational grammars and rhetorics; semantics. Publ: Co-auth, A new curriculum for division III English (grades 7, 8, and 9), Sask. Dept. Educ, 68; auth, The writer's self-starter, Collier-Macmillan, 72; A permutational test of grammaticality, Lingua, 69; Zen bones, Queen's Quart, 72; Two field-kernels for courses in English, Linguistics, 73. Add: Dept. of English, University of Saskatchewan, Saskatoon, Sask. S7N 0W0, Can.

SCOTT, ROBERT LEE, b. Fairbury, Nebr, Apr. 19, 28; m. 47; c. 3. SPEECH. B.A, Colo. State Col. Educ, 50; M.A, Univ. Nebr, 51; Ph.D. (speech), Univ. Ill, 55. Asst. prof. SPEECH, Univ. Houston, 53-57; UNIV. MINN, MINNEAPOLIS, 57-61, assoc. prof, 61-64, PROF, 64- U.S.M.C, 45-46. Speech Commun. Asn.(ed, Quart. J. Speech, 72-74); NCTE. Criticism of contemporary public address; contemporary rhetorical theory. Publ: Co-auth, Thinking and speaking: a guide to intelligent oral communication, Macmillan, 62, 68 & 73; co-auth, The rhetoric of black power, Harper, 69; Moments in the rhetoric of the Cold War, Random, 72; auth, On viewing rhetoric as epistemic, Cent. States Speech J, 2/67; auth, On not defining rhetoric, Philos. & Rhetoric, spring 73; The conservative voice in radical rhetoric, Speech Monog, 6/73; plus 12 others. Add: Dept. of Speech Communication, University of Minnesota, Minneapolis, MN 55455.

SCOTT, VIRGIL JOSEPH, b. Vancouver, Wash, Aug. 1, 14; m. 35; c. 4. ENGLISH. A.B, Ohio State Univ, 36, A.M, 37, Ph.D, 45. Instr. Ohio State Univ, 41-45; Univ. Minn, 45-47; PROF. ENG, MICH. STATE UNIV, 47- Ohioanna Award, 48. MLA. Fiction; contemporary literature. Publ: The dead tree gives no shelter; The hickory stick; Savage affair, 58 & I, John Mordaunt, 64, Harcourt; Studies in the short story, Holt, 68. Add: Dept. of English, Michigan State University, East Lansing, MI 48823.

SCOTT, WILBUR S, b. Philadelphia, Pa, Nov. 14, 14; m. 36; c. 3. ENGLISH & AMERICAN LITERATURE. B.A, Columbia Univ, 39; Ph.D, Princeton, 43. Instr. ENG, Univ. Rochester, 43-46; from instr. to PROF, HOFSTRA UNIV, 46-, FEL, NEW COL, 63- Fulbright fel. & lectr. Turku Univ, Finland, 59-60, Lyon Univ, 68-69. American literature; modern poetry; modern literary criticism. Publ: Five approaches to modern literary criticism, Macmillan, 62; co-auth, The main lines of American literature, Henry Holt, 51. Add: The New College, Hofstra University, Hempstead, NY 11550.

SCOTT, WILLIAM CLYDE, Classics. See Volume III, Foreign Languages, Linguistics & Philology.

SCOTT, WILLIAM OSBORNE, b. Berlin Twp, Mich, Feb. 19, 32; m. 61. ENGLISH. B.A, Univ. Chicago, 52; B.A, Univ. Mich, 54; M.A, Duke Univ, 55; Ph.D.(Eng), Princeton, 59. Instr. ENG, UNIV. KANS, 58-61, asst. prof, 61-65, ASSOC. PROF, 65- MLA; Renaissance Soc. Am; Shakespeare Asn. Am. Renaissance literature; literary criticism. Publ: Ramism and Milton's concept of poetic fancy, Philol. Quart, 4/63; Seasons and flowers in The winter's tale, Shakespeare Quart, autumn 63; Proteus in Spenser and Shakespeare: the lover's identity, Shakespeare Stud, 65; plus others. Add: Dept. of English, University of Kansas, Lawrence, KS 66044.

SCOTTO, ROBERT MICHAEL, b. New York, N.Y, June 17, 42; m. 66. MODERN FICTION. B.A, Manhattan Col, 64; M.A, Brooklyn Col, 65; Ph.D.(Eng), City Univ. New York, 70. Instr. ENG, St. John's Univ, 66-69, asst. prof, 69-71, assoc. prof, 71-72; ASST. PROF, BARUCH COL, 72- MLA. Modern British novel; contemporary American novel. Publ: Ed, A critical edition of Catch-22, Delta-Dell, 73; ed. & contrib, The contemporary American novel: essays in criticism, Everett/Edwards, 74; auth, Visions and epiphanies, James Joyce Quart, 10/73. Add: Dept. of English, Baruch College, 17 Lexington Ave, New York, NY 10010.

SCOUTEN, ARTHUR HAWLEY, b. Feb. 15, 10. ENGLISH LITERATURE. A.B, La. State Univ, 35, A.M, 38, Ph.D, 42; D.Litt, Thiel Col, 66. Instr. La. State Univ, 40-42; Agr. & Mech. Col. Tex, 42-43; Univ. Tex, 43-46; asst. prof, Ala. Polytech. Inst, 46-47; ENG. LIT, UNIV. PA, 47-50, assoc. prof, 50-60, PROF, 60- Vis. prof. Eng. lit, Univ. S.Fla, 72; Univ. Warwick, Eng, 73-74. Soc. Theatre Res; Mod. Humanities Res. Asn; Acad. Lit. Stud. British drama, 1660-1800. Publ: Ed, A bibliography of the writings of Jonathan Swift, Univ. Pa, rev. ed, 63; auth, Ten English farces, Univ. Tex; London stage, part III, 63 & London stage, part I, 65, South. Ill. Univ; Warren, Huey Long and All the king's men, Four Quarters, 72; Dr. Johnson and Imlac, Eighteenth Century Stud, 73. Add: Dept. of English, University of Pennsylvania, Philadelphia, PA 19104.

SCOWCROFT, RICHARD, b. Ogden, Utah, June 26, 16; m. 48; c. 3. ENGLISH LITERATURE. A.B, Univ. Utah, 37; A.M, Harvard, 41, Ph.D, 46. Teaching fel, Harvard, 42-46, Briggs-Copeland instr, 46-47; asst. prof. ENG. LIT, STANFORD UNIV, 47-50, assoc. prof, 50-57, PROF, 57- The writers art. Publ: Children of the covenant, 45; First family, 50 & A view of the bay, 55, Houghton; Wherever she goes, 67 & The ordeal of Dudley Dean, 69, Lippincott; Back to Fire Mountain, Atlantic Monthly Press, 73. Add: Dept. of English, Stanford University, Stanford, CA 94305.

SCRIBNER, SIMON, C.S.C, b. Buffalo, N.Y, Feb. 10, 13. ENGLISH. A.B, Univ. Notre Dame, 36; A.M, Cath. Univ. Am, 41, Ph.D, 48. Instr. high sch, Ind, 36-37; Sacred Heart Col, 37-38; Cath. Univ. Am, 45-46; PROF. ENG, ST. EDWARD'S UNIV, 46-, trustee, 46-64, dir. stud. activities, 53-58, alumni dir, 60-64. Minnie Stevens Piper Found. award, 68. Literature; literary criticism; science fiction. Publ: Figures of word repetition in the first book of Sir Philip Sidney's Arcadia. Add: Dept. of English, St. Edward's University, Austin, TX 78704.

SCRIMGEOUR, GARY JAMES, b. Auckland, N.Z, Jan. 15, 34; m. 65; c. 1. ENGLISH, DRAMA. B.A, Univ. Sydney, 55; M.A, Wash. Univ, 59; Charles G. Osgood fel, Princeton, 62, Jane E. Proctor fel, 63; Ph.D.(Eng), 68. Asst. Eng, Wash. Univ, 57-59; instr, Univ. Fla, 59-61; compos, Eve. Col, Rutgers Univ, 62-64; lectr. eng, Ind. Univ, 64-65; sr. lectr, Univ. N.S.W, 66; asst. prof, Ind. Univ, Bloomington, 67-69; drama ed, Benjamin Bloom Inc, 69-70; RES. SCIENTIST HWY. SAFETY, INST. RES. PUB. SAFETY, SCH. PUB. &

ENVIRON. AFFAIRS, IND. UNIV, BLOOMINGTON, 70- Consult, Law Enforcement Assistance Admin, 71; Alcohol Safety Action Prog, 71- Am. Soc. Theatre Res; Law & Soc. Asn; Int. Platform Asn. Highway safety; 19th-century English drama; American novel. Publ: Co-auth, Judicial seminar in alcohol safety, 71, Prosecutors' seminar in alcohol safety, 72 & Probation seminar in alcohol safety, 73, Ind. Univ; auth, Naturalist drama and Galsworthy, Mod. Drama, 11/63; Against the Great Gatsby, Criticism, winter 66; Nineteenth century drama, Victorian Stud, 9/68. Add: Institute for Research in Public Safety, School of Public & Environmental Affairs, Indiana University, Bloomington, IN 47401.

SCULLY, DANIEL WILLIAM, b. London, Ohio, Mar. 25, 27; m. 54; c. 3. SPEECH. B.A, Ohio State Univ, 48, Ph.D, 60; M.A, La. State Univ, 51. Asst. instr. Eng, Ohio State Univ, 55-56; asst. prof. speech & dir. radio, East. Ill. Univ, 56-59; lectr. Eng, Univ. Minn, Duluth, 59-60; assoc. prof. SPEECH & THEATRE, ADRIAN COL, 60-65, PROF, 65-, CHMN. DEPT, 62-, CHMN. DIV. HUMANITIES, 73- U.S.N.R, 45-46. Speech Commun. Asn; MLA; Am. Theatre Asn; Cent. States Speech Asn; NEA; Am. Asn. Higher Educ. Phonetics; history of speech education; theatre history. Publ: Alfred Ayres, drama critic, as compiler of a pronouncing dictionary, Quart. J. Speech, 2/65; The London merchant of 1731 can die as a salesman today: modern production for the period play, Speech Teacher, 3/66; To be or not to be: Sir Henry Irving vs. Constant Coquelin, Cue, spring 67; plus others. Add: Dept. of Speech & Theatre, Adrian College, Adrian, MI 49221.

SEABURY, HUGH FRANCIS, b. Bloomfield, Iowa, Mar. 12, 06; m. 28. SPEECH EDUCATION. A.B, Univ. North. Iowa, 28; A.M, Univ. Iowa, 33; Roberts fel, Columbia Univ, 34-36, D.Ed, 38. Teacher, High Schs, Iowa, 28-34, 36-37; asst. secy, Teachers Col, Columbia Univ, 34-36; prof. SPEECH EDUC. & head dept, Southwest Tex. State Teachers Col, 37-47; assoc. prof. UNIV. IOWA, 48-55, PROF, 55- Adv. pers. bur, City Col. New York, 35; instr, Sch. Commerce, N.Y. Univ, 35; San Antonio Aviation Cadet Ctr, Tex, 43-44; chief instr. training, U.S. Army Air Force Sch. Applied Tactics, Orlando, Fla, 44-46; mem. educ. adv. staff, Air Univ, 46-48. Speech Commun. Asn; (ed, Speech Teacher, 64-66, adv. ed, 66-); NEA. Speech eduction in 20th century public schools; objectives and scope of speech education. Publ: Co-auth, Our speech, Steck, 40 & Teaching speech in today's secondary schools, Holt, 65; auth, Objectives of speech fundamentals, Speech Teacher, 3/54; Speech education, In: Encycl. Educ. Res, Macmillan, 69; plus numerous others. Add: 616 Holt Ave, Iowa City, IA 52240.

SEALTS, MERTON MILLER, JR, b. Lima, Ohio, Dec. 8,15; m. 42. ENGLISH. A.B, Col. Wooster, 37; Ph.D.(Eng), Yale, 42. Instr. ENG, Univ. Mo, 41-42; Wellesley Col, 46-48; asst. prof, Lawrence Univ, 48-51, assoc. prof, 51-58; prof, 58-65, chmn. dept, 57-59; PROF, UNIV. WIS-MADISON, 65- Fund Advan. Educ. fel, 53-54; Guggenheim fel, 62-63; mem. ed. bd, Am. Quart, 65-68; Nat. Endowment for Humanities sr. fel, 75. Edward & Rosa Uhrig Mem. teaching award, Lawrence Univ, 65. U.S.A.A.F, 42-46, Maj. MLA; NCTE; Am. Stud. Asn; Melville Soc.(pres, 53). English and American literature; Herman Melville, 1819-1891; Ralph Waldo Emerson, 1803-1882. Publ: Melville as lecturer, Harvard, 57; co-ed, Billy Budd, sailor, by Herman Melville, Univ. Chicago, 62; ed, The journals and miscellaneous notebooks of Ralph Waldo Emerson, Vol. V, 65 & Vol. X, 73, Belknap; auth, Melville's reading: a check-list of books owned and borrowed, 66 & The early lives of Melville: nineteenth century biographical sketches and their authors, 74, Univ. Wis; co-ed, Emerson's Nature: origin, growth, meaning, Dodd, 69. Add: Dept. of English, University of Wisconsin-Madison, Madison, WI 53706.

SEAMAN, JOHN EUGENE, b. Denver, Colo, Mar. 23, 32; m. 53; c. 4. ENGLISH. B.A, Princeton, 54; M.A, Stanford Univ, 59, Ph.D.(Eng), 62. Instr. ENG, Univ. Wis, 60-63; asst. prof, Colo. State Univ, 63-68, assoc. prof, 68-69; PROF. & CHMN. DEPT, UNIV. OF THE PAC, 69- U.S.A, 54-56. Rocky Mountain Mod. Lang. Asn; MLA; Milton Soc. Am. English Renaissance, Shakespeare, Milton; stylistics. Publ: The moral paradox of Paradise lost, Mouton, 71; The blind curtain and Hamlet's guilt, West. Humanities Rev, 69; The rose of May in Claudius's Garden, Etudes Anglaises, 12/69; A doctor of arts with a topical focus, ADE Bull, 5/70. Add: Dept. of English, University of the Pacific, Stockton, CA 95204.

SEAMON, ROGER, b. Perth Amboy, N.J, May 29, 37; m. 58; c. 2. ENGLISH. B.A, Univ. Calif, Berkeley, 59; NDEA fel. & M.A, Claremont Grad. Sch, 61, Ph.D.(Eng), 66. Instr. ENG, Whitman Col, 62-64; UNIV. B.C, 64-66, ASST. PROF, 66- Can. Counc. res. grant, 69-70. Philol. Asn. Pac. Coast; MLA; Can. Asn. Am. Stud. Eighteenth century satire; psychoanalytic criticism; 19th century novel. Publ: The bottle in the fire: resistance as creation in William Carlos William's Paterson, 20th Century Lit, 4/65; The rhetorical pattern of mock-heroic satire, Humanities Asn. Bull, autumn 66; Sinners in the hands of a happy god: hierarchical values in Song of myself, Can. Asn. Am. Stud. Bull, winter 67. Add: Dept. of English, University of British Columbia, Vancouver 8, B.C, Can.

SEARLE, WILLIAM MINER, b. Denver, Colo, July 21, 37; m. 64; c. 1. AMERICAN & MODERN COMPARATIVE LITERATURE. B.A, Harvard, 60; M.A, Univ. Calif, Berkeley, 62, Ph.D.(Eng), 68. Asst. prof. ENG, UNIV. PITTSBURGH, 68-73, ASSOC. PROF, 73- Publ: The saint and the skeptics: Joan of Arc in the work of Mark Twain, Anatole France and Bernard Shaw, Wayne State Univ, (in press); Shaw's Saint Joan as protestant, Shaw Rev, 9/72. Add: Dept. of English, University of Pittsburgh, Pittsburgh, PA 15213.

SEARLES, JO C, b. Arkansas City, Kans, Nov. 16, 26; m. 48; c. 4. AMERICAN LITERATURE, POETRY. B.A, Univ. Calif, Berkeley, 49; M.A, Pa. State Univ, 65, Ph.D.(Eng), 71. Instr. Am. lit, Brazil-U.S. Cult. Inst, Minas Gerais, 60-61; ASST. PROF. ENG, PA. STATE UNIV, BEAVER CAMPUS, 72-, chmn. commun. skills intensive prog, 72, Lib. Arts Fund for Res. grant, 72. MLA; NCTE; Am. Stud. Asn; Col. Eng. Asn. Early American literature. Publ: Having a ripping good time, Eng. Rec, 72; Art of Dickinson's household thought, Concerning Poetry, 73. Add: Dept. of English, Pennsylvania State University, Beaver Campus, Monaca, PA 15061.

SEARLES, JOHN REXFORD, b. Elroy, Wis, Jan. 21, 10; m. 35; c. 1. ENGLISH LITERATURE. A.B. & A.M, Univ. Wis, 33, Ph.D, 42. Mem. fac, Wis. State Teachers Col, Platteville, 42-43, 46-47; asst. prof. Eng, exten. ctr, UNIV. WIS-MADISON, 47-52, lectr. educ. & Eng, 52-53, assoc. prof, 53-59, PROF. ENG, CURRICULUM & INSTR, 59- U.S.N, 44-46. Teaching of language and literature. Publ: Co-auth, English: language, grammar, and composition, In: Encyclopedia educational research, Macmillan, 60; plus high sch. lit. bks. Add: 17 Harrison St, Madison, WI 53705.

SEARS, CATHERINE MARY, R.S.M, English. See Volume III, Foreign Language, Linguistics and Philology.

SEARS, DONALD ALBERT, b. Portland, Maine, May 25, 23; m. 45, 64; c. 4. LITERATURE, LANGUAGE. B.A, Bowdoin Col, 44; M.A, Harvard, 47, Ph.D. (Eng), 52. Instr. Eng, Dartmouth Col, 48-52; asst. prof, Upsala Col, 52-54, assoc. prof, 54-58, prof, 58-62, dir. freshman Eng, 53-58; prof. Eng. & chmn. dept, Skidmore Col, 62-64; staff assoc. comn. plans & objectives higher educ, Am. Counc. Educ, 64-65; PROF. Eng, Howard Univ, 65-66; lang, Ahmadu Bello Univ, Nigeria, 66-67; ENG, CALIF. STATE UNIV, FULLERTON, 67- Ed, CEA Critic, 60-70; dir, Book-of-the-Month Club Writing Fel. Prog, 66-70. Lindback Found. Award, 61. U.S.A.A.F, 43-46, 50. Col. Eng. Asn.(exec. dir, 62-70); Ling. Soc. Am; Milton Soc. Am; MLA; Philol. Asn. Pac. Coast; Malone Soc. American studies; history of the English language; linguistics. Publ: The Harbrace guide to the library and the research paper, 56, 60, 73, The discipline of English, 63, 74 & co-auth, The sentence in context, 60, Harcourt. Add: Dept. of English, California State University, Fullerton, CA 92634.

SEARS, JOHN FRANKLIN, b. Salem, Mass, Dec. 15, 41; m. 66; c. 1. ENGLISH, AMERICAN CIVILIZATION. B.A, Harvard, 65, Ph.D.(Am. civilization), 72. Instr. Eng, Tufts Univ, 70-71, ASST. PROF, 71-72; HUMANITIES, BOSTON UNIV, 72- MLA. The American wilderness, literature and art; American poetry and philosophy; American religious history. Publ: Philip Freneau, In: The American biographical encyclopedia, 74. Add: College of Basic Studies, Boston University, 871 Commonwealth Ave, Boston, MA 02215.

SEARS, LLOYD CLINE, b. Odon, Ind, May 13, 95; m. 17; c. 2. ENGLISH LITERATURE. A.B, Cordell Christian Col, 17; A.B, Univ. Okla, 19; fel, Univ. Kans, 20-21, A.M, 21; Ph.D, Univ. Chicago, 35. Instr. Eng, Cordell Christian Col, 16-18; prof, Harper Col, 18-20, 21-24; head dept. Eng, & dean, HARDING COL, 24-27, 28-33, 34-60, EMER. PROF. ENG. & EMER. DEAN, 60- Instr, Univ. Chicago, 27-28. MLA; NEA; NCTE. The Renaissance and Elizabethan period in English literature; the problem of evil in Shakespeare. Publ: For freedom: the biography of John Nelson Armstrong, Sweet, 69; The eyes of Jehovah: the life and faith of James A. Harding, Gospel Advocate, 70; Shakespeare's philosophy of evil, Christopher, 74. Add: Harding College, Box 941, Searcy, AR 72143.

SEARS, RICHARD DUANE, b. Morris Co, Kans, Jan. 26, 40; m. 66; c. 1. ENGLISH. B.A, Univ. Mo, Kansas City, 61, M.A, 64; Ph.D.(Eng), Ohio Univ, 66. Asst. prof. ENG, Ohio Univ, 66-67, BEREA COL, 67-74, ASSOC. PROF, 74- Publ: Pioneer families of Sullivan County, Missouri. Add: Dept. of English, Berea College, Berea, KY 40403.

SEARY, EDGAR RONALD, b. Sheffield, Eng, Jan. 17, 08; m. 35; c. 3. ENGLISH. B.A, Univ. Sheffield, Eng, 29, M.A, 30, Town Trustees fel. & Ph.D. (Eng), 33, Litt.D, 71; hon. D.Litt, Mem. Univ. Nfld, 73. Lectr. Eng, Dolmetscher Inst, Ger, 33; sr. lectr, Rhodes Univ. S.Africa, 35-51; prof, Col. Arts & Sci, Iraq, 51-53; PROF. & HEAD DEPT, MEM. UNIV. NFLD, 53-, HENRIETTA HARVEY PROF. ENG, 70- Can. Centennial Medal, 67. S.African Army, 40-45, Capt. Can. Humanities Asn; Can. Ling. Asn.(pres, 60-62); Asn. Can. Univ. Teachers Eng.(pres, 63-66); fel. Royal Hist. Soc; fel, Soc. Antiq. London. Colonial and dominion literatures; place-names; history of criticism. Publ: South African short stories, Oxford, 47; Reading English, Macmillan, 58; co-auth, The Avalon Peninsula: an ethno-linguistic study, Nat. Mus. Can, 68; Place names of the Avalon Peninsula of the Island of Newfoundland, Univ. Toronto, 71. Add: Dept. of English Language & Literature, Memorial University of Newfoundland, St. John's, Nfld, Can.

SEAT, WILLIAM ROBERT, III, b. Lexington, Miss, Nov. 9, 20. ENGLISH LANGUAGE & LITERATURE. B.A, DePauw Univ, 43; M.A, Univ. Chicago, 48; Ph.D, Ind. Univ, 57. Instr. ENG, Glendale High Sch, Ind, 46-48; Eng, DePauw Univ, 48-50; asst. prof, NORTH. ILL. UNIV, 54-57, assoc. prof, 57-61, PROF, 61-, DIR. FRESHMAN ENG, 72- U.S.A.A.F, 43-46, 1st Lt. MLA; NCTE. Anglo-American travel literature; 19th century English prose; structural linguistics. Publ: The enigma of Poe, 60 & co-auth, Young Coleridge, 63, Heath; auth, Close reading of factual prose, Harper, 62; co-auth, The new University reader, Am. Bk. Co, 66, Focus on spelling, Sernoll, 67 & The strategy of prose, Van Nostrand, 70; auth, Miss Martineau in Cincinnati, Ohio Hist. Quart, 7/59; Harriet Martineau in America, Notes & Queries, 6/59; Chappie, Crusader, 1/60. Add: Dept. of English, Northern Illinois University, De Kalb, IL 60115.

SEBOUHIAN, GEORGE, b. New York, N.Y, Nov. 29, 31; m. 65; c. 2. LITERATURE. B.A, Murray State Univ, 59; M.A, Vanderbilt Univ, 60; Ph.D. (Eng), Ohio State Univ, 73. Teacher ENG, Pub. Schs, Fla. & Ohio, 60-65; instr, Miami Univ, 65-68; ASST. PROF, STATE UNIV. N.Y. COL. FREDONIA, 72- U.S.A.F, 51-55. MLA; AAUP. American Puritans; American transcendentalists; mysticism. Publ: Emerson's Experience: an approach to content and method, Emerson Soc. Quart, 67. Add: Dept. of English, Fenton Hall, State University of New York College at Fredonia, Fredonia, NY 14063.

SECORD, ARTHUR, b. Deward, Mich, Dec. 8, 04. SPEECH. A.B, West. Mich. Univ, 27; A.M, Univ. Mich, 31, Ph.D, 41. Instr. West. Mich. Univ, 28-35, 36-37; instr. & dir. debate, Univ. Mich, 35-36, 37-43; asst. prof. speech & dir. speech clinic, Univ. Mo, 43-44; instr, BROOKLYN COL, 44-46, asst. prof. & supvr. adult educ, 47-50, assoc. prof. speech, 51-55, prof. speech & dir. community serv, 55-70, EMER. PROF. SPEECH, 70- Pitch regulating mechanism of human larynx. Add: 4 Garden St, Great Neck, NY 11021.

SECRIST, ROBERT HEROLD, English Linguistics. See Volume III, Foreign Languages, Linguistics & Philology.

SEDELOW, SALLY YEATES, b. Greenfield, Iowa, Aug. 10, 31; m. 58. LINGUISTICS, INFORMATION SCIENCE. B.A, Univ. Iowa, 53; M.A, Mt. Holyoke Col, 56; nonresident scholar, Bryn Mawr Col, 56-57, fel, 57-58, Ph.D. (Anglo-Saxon & Eng. lit), 60; Harvard, summer 57. Asst. pub. relat, Sweet Briar Col, 53-54; instr. Eng. lang. & lit, Smith Col, 59-60; asst. prof. Eng, Parsons Col, 60-61; Rockford Col, 61-62; human factors scientist artificial intel. & nat. lang, res. directorate, Syst. Develop. Corp, 62-64; asst. prof. Eng, St. Louis Univ, 64-66; assoc. prof. Eng. & computer & inform. sci, Univ. N.C, Chapel Hill, 66-70; PROF. LING. & COMPUT. SCI, UNIV. KANS, 70- Columnist, feature writer & reporter-photographer, Adair County Free Press, Iowa, 48-51; Mt. Holyoke Col. News Bur. intern, Springfield Republican, Mass, 54-56; consult, Syst. Develop. Corp, 64-67; prin. investr. stylistic anal. proj, U.S. Off. Naval Res, 64-; consult, T.Y. Crowell Co, 66-67; field reader, U.S. Off. Educ, 67-; ed, Comput. Stud. in Humanities & Verbal Behav, 67-; chmn. spec. interest comt. lang. anal. & stud. in humanities, Asn. Comput. Machinery, 67-71; mem. instnl. comput. serv. adv. panel, Nat. Sci. Found, 68-72, prin. investr, Network Computational Res. Lang, 71-73, comput. adv. panel, 72-; mem, Comt. Inform. Technol, Am. Counc. Learned Soc, 69; res. adv. panel, Nat. Endowment for Humanities, 73-; comput. sci. eval. panel, Fulbright-Hays Sr. Prog, 73- MLA; Asn. Comput. Mach; Am. Soc. Inform. Sci; Mediaeval Acad. Am; Renaissance Soc. Am; Asn. Comput. Ling; Midwest Mod. Lang. Asn.(secy, comput. appl. sect, 71-72, chmn, 72-73). Computational stylistics; mediaeval and Renaissance prose and poetry; Milton. Publ: The narrative method of Paradise lost, Edwards Bros, 60; co-auth, Language research and the computer, Univ. Kans, 72; auth, Shakespeare studies & the computer, Proc. World Shakespeare Congr, 72; Language analysis in the humanities, Commun. Asn. Comput. Mach, 72; co-auth, Models, computing & stylistics, In: Current trends in stylistics, Ling. Res, Inc, 72; plus several others. Add: Dept. of Linguistics, Blake Hall, University of Kansas, Lawrence, KS 66045.

SEELIG, SHARON CADMAN, b. Mountain Lake, Minn, Jan. 8, 41; m. 67. ENGLISH LITERATURE. B.A, Carleton Col, 62; Fulbright fel, Free Univ. Berlin, 63-64; Woodrow Wilson fel. & M.A, Columbia Univ, 64, Newberry Libr. fel, 66-67, Ph.D.(Eng.& comp. lit), 69. Instr. ENG, Wellesley Col, 67-69; Northfield Sch, 69-70; lectr, MT. HOLYOKE COL, 70-71, ASST. PROF, 71- Regional assoc, Am. Lit. Manuscripts Census, 70- MLA; AAUP. Seventeenth-century English literature; Shakespeare. Add: Dept. of English, Mt. Holyoke College, South Hadley, MA 01075.

SEELY, FREDERICK FRANKLIN, b. Cedar Rapids, Iowa, Sept. 13, 02. ENGLISH LITERARY HISTORY. A.B, Dartmouth Col, 26; A.M, Harvard, 31; Ph.D, State Univ. Iowa, 41. Journalist, Miami, Fla, 26-28; publicist, Wash, D.C, 28-30; instr. ENG, ALLEGHENY COL, 31-38, asst. prof, 38-46, assoc. prof, 46-49, prof, 49-69, EMER. PROF, 69- Adj. prof. Eng, Barry Col, 69- MLA. Seventeenth century drama. Add: 225 Meadow St, Meadville, PA 16335.

SEELYE, JOHN DOUGLAS, b. Hartford, Conn, Jan. 1, 31; m. 68. ENGLISH & AMERICAN LITERATURE. B.A, Wesleyan Univ, 53; M.A, Claremont Grad. Sch, 56, Ph.D.(Am. lit), 61. Asst. prof. ENG, Univ. Calif, Berkeley, 60-65; assoc. prof, Univ. Conn, 66-71, PROF, 71-74, UNIV. N.C, CHAPEL HILL, 74- Mem. ed. bd, Am. Lit, 71-; contrib. ed, New Republic, 72-; Nat. Endowment for Humanities sr. fel, 72; Guggenheim fel, 73. U.S.N.R, 53-55, Lt.(jg). MLA; Am. Stud. Asn; Pop. Cult. Asn; PEN Club; Am. Antiq. Soc. American studies, technology, progress and nature in literature; American maritime literature; frontier literature. Publ: Melville: the ironic diagram, 70 & The true adventures of Huckleberry Finn, 70, Northwest. Univ; The kid (novel), Viking, 72; Dirty Tricks (novel), Liveright, 74; contrib, Literature in Revolution, Holt, 72. Add: Dept. of English, University of North Carolina at Chapel Hill, Chapel Hill, NC 27514.

SEGURA, ANDREW RICHARD (CYRIL), F.S.C, b. New Iberia, La, Nov. 25, 17. ENGLISH. B.A, St. Mary's Univ. San Antonio, 38, M.A, 43; fel, Univ. N.Mex, 59-60, Ph.D.(Eng), 61. PROF. ENG, CHMN. DEPT, COL. SANTA FE, 58-, chmn. div. humanities, 58-71. NCTE; MLA; Conf. Col. Compos. & Commun; Christian Bros. Educ. Asn. English literary Renaissance period; Edmund Spenser; primitivism in The Faerie Queene. Add: Dept. of English, College of Santa Fe, Santa Fe, NM 87501.

SEIB, KENNETH ALLEN, b. Shelby, Ohio, Mar. 27, 38; m. 66. ENGLISH & AMERICAN LITERATURE. A.B, Ashland Col, 60; Woodrow Wilson fel, Columbia Univ, 60-61, M.A, 61; Andrew Mellon fel, Univ. Pittsburgh, 62-63, Ph.D.(Eng), 66. Teaching fel. ENG, Univ. Pittsburgh, 61-62; asst. prof, Ill. State Univ, 63-66; lectr, Europ. Div, Univ. Md, 66-68; ASSOC. PROF, CALIF. STATE UNIV, FRESNO, 68- Fresno State Col. Found. res. grant, 68-72; Fulbright-Hays teaching grant, 70-71; vis. prof. Am. lit. & Eng. stud, Ruhr Univ, 70-71; Univ. Bergen, 71. MLA. Twentieth century American and English literature. Publ: James Agee's A death in the family: a critical commentary, 65 & Albert Camus' The plague: a critical commentary, 66, Stud. Master; James Agee: promise and fulfillment, Univ. Pittsburgh, 68; A note on Hawthorne's Pearl, Emerson Soc. Quart, 65; Shakespeare's well: a note on Sonnet 73, Shakespeare Newslett, 67; Trout fishing in America: Brautigan's funky fishing yarn, Critique, 71. Add: Dept. of English, California State University, Fresno, Fresno, CA 93710.

SEIBEL, ROY WILLIAM, b. Fairview, Okla, Sept. 27, 17; m. 38; c. 2. SPEECH. A.B, Tabor Col, 43; M.A, Baylor Univ, 47; B.D, N.Am. Baptist Sem, S.Dak, 55; Ph.D.(speech), Univ. Minn, 66. PROF. PASTORAL MINISTRIES, N.AM. BAPTIST SEM, S.DAK, 55- Speech Commun. Asn; Cent. States Speech Asn. Add: North American Baptist Seminary, Sioux Falls, SD 57105.

SEIBERT, THOMAS L, b. Cincinnati, Ohio, Jan. 19, 32; m. 62; c. 4. ENGLISH. B.A, Loyola Univ.(Ill), 55, M.A, 59; Ph.L, West Baden Col, 57; Univ. Cincinnati, 62-65. Instr. ENG, Villa Madonna Col, 61-62; COL. MT. ST. JOSEPH, 62-63, asst. prof, 63-64, assoc. prof, 64-65, PROF, 65-, chmn. dept, 63-72. NCTE; MLA; Midwest Mod. Lang. Asn. Restoration literature; American literature; classical Greek and Roman literature. Add: Dept. of English, College of Mt. St. Joseph-on-the-Ohio, Mt. St. Joseph, OH 45051.

SEIDEL, MICHAEL ALAN, b. New York, N.Y, Aug. 24, 43. ENGLISH LITERATURE. B.A, Univ. Calif, Los Angeles, 66, Ph.D.(Eng), 70. ASST. PROF. ENG, YALE, 70- Clark Mem. Libr. fel, summer 71. MLA; Augustan Reprint Soc. Satire; 17th and 18th century English literature. Publ: Patterns of oppression and anarchy in Samuel Butler's Hudibras, Eighteenth Century Stud, winter 71-72; Restoration mob: drones and dregs, Stud. Eng. Lit, summer 72. Add: Dept. of English, Yale University, New Haven, CT 06520.

SEIDEN, MORTON IRVING, b. New York, N.Y, July 29, 21. ENGLISH, COMPARATIVE LITERATURE. B.S, N.Y. Univ, 43; M.A, Columbia Univ, 44, fel, 44-45, Ph.D.(Eng. & comp. lit), 52. Instr. ENG, City Col. New York, 45-46; N.Y. Univ, 46-49; Smith Col, 49-52; Queens Col.(N.Y), 52-53; BROOKLYN COL, 53-63, asst. prof, 63-67, assoc. prof, 67-70, PROF, 70- Lectr, Columbia Univ, grad. sch, 48-49, summer sch, 49. Brooklyn Col. award excellence in teaching, 67. MLA; Mod. Humanities Res. Asn; Eng. Inst. Nineteenth and twentieth century English literature; English, Irish Renaissance; comparative literature. Publ: William Butler Yeats: the poet as a mythmaker—1865-1939, Mich. State Univ, 62; The paradox of hate: a study in ritual murder, Yoseloff, 68; Myth in the poetry of William Butler Yeats, Am. Imago, 12/48; W.B. Yeats as a playwright, West. Humanities Rev, winter 49; co-auth, Ivan Goncharov's Oblomov: a study of the anti-Faust as a Christian saint, Can. Slavic Stud, spring 69; plus others. Add: Dept. of English, Brooklyn College, Bedford Ave. & Ave. H, Brooklyn, NY 11210.

SEIGEL, JULES PAUL, b. Liberty, N.Y, Oct. 10, 31; m. 59; c. 3. ENGLISH. B.S, State Univ. N.Y. Col. Cortland, 59; M.A, Univ. Md, 62, Ph.D, 65. Teaching asst. ENG, Univ. Md, 60-64, instr, 64-65; ASST. PROF, UNIV. R.I, 65- Fac. res. fel, summer 68. U.S.A.F, 50-54. MLA. Romantic and Victorian literature; 19th century English and American literature. Publ: Carlyle: the critical heritage, Routledge & Kegan Paul, 71; Puritan light reading, New Eng. Quart, 6/64; The enlightenment and language of signs, J. Hist. Ideas, 1/69; plus others. Add: Saugatucket Rd, Peace Dale, RI 02879.

SEIGER, MARVIN, b. New York, N.Y, Apr. 14, 24; m. 54; c. 1. SPEECH & DRAMA. B.A, Univ. Calif, 48, M.A, 50; Ph.D, Ind. Univ, 60. Instr. speech & theatre, Ind. Univ, 54-55; PROF. THEATRE & CINEMA & CHMN. DEPT, HUNTER COL, 55-, ASSOC. PROVOST, 71- George Shuster fac. fel, Hunter Col, 62; consult, theatre, N.Y. Comn. on the Arts, 63; consult, Julliard Sch. Drama, 69-70. U.S.A, 43-45. Dramatists Guild; Speech Commun. Asn; Am. Theatre Asn.(managing ed, Educ. Theatre J, 62-65); U.S. Inst. Theatre Technol. Modern theatre history; dramatic theory; playwriting. Publ: Blue concerto, In: Best short plays, 55-56, Beacon, 56. Add: Dept. of Theatre & Cinema, Hunter College, 695 Park Ave, New York, NY 10021.

SEIGLER, MILLEDGE BROADUS, b. Aiken, S.C, Dec. 10, 09. AMERICAN LITERATURE. A.B, Furman Univ, 30; A.M, Duke Univ, 36, Ph.D, 41. Instr, Winthrop Col, 37-38; asst. ENG, Duke Univ, 38-39; asst. prof, Catawba Col, 39-41; UNIV. S.C, 41-46, assoc. prof, 46-49, PROF, 49- State chmn, Fulbright selection comt, S.C, 51-; Fulbright prof, Auslands Inst. & Univ. Mainz, 55-56; mem. staff, Nat. War Col, summers 64, 65. U.S.N.R, 42-70, Capt. MLA; Col. Eng. Asn; NCTE; S.Atlantic Mod. Lang. Asn; Southeast Renaissance Conf.(pres, 53). Milton. Add: Dept. of English, University of South Carolina, Columbia, SC 29208.

SEILER, WILLIAM JOHN, b. Milwaukee, Wis, Oct. 17, 42; m. 66; c. 1. SPEECH COMMUNICATION. B.Ed, Univ. Wis-Whitewater, 65; M.A, Kans. State Univ, 67; Ph.D.(speech), Purdue Univ, West Lafayette, 71. ASST. PROF. SPEECH, Purdue Univ, Calumet Campus, 70-72; UNIV. NEBR-LINCOLN, 72- Prof. instr. commun, Nebr. Law Enforcement Training Ctr, 73. Speech Commun. Asn; Int. Commun. Asn; Cent. States Speech Commun. Asn. Speech education; organization communication. Publ: Communication is personal: a course syllabus for fundamentals of human communication, Prog. Develop. Assocs, 73; co-auth, College student exposure to mass media news, Col. Stud. Surv, 69; auth, The effect of visual materials on attitudes, credibility, and retention, Speech Monogr, 71; Audiovisual materials in classroom instruction: a theoretical approach, Speech Teacher, 72. Add: Dept. of Speech & Dramatic Art, University of Nebraska-Lincoln, Lincoln, NE 68505.

SEINFELT, FREDERICK WILLIAM, b. Munson, Pa, Aug. 22, 32; m. 60; c. 2. ENGLISH. B.A, Pa. State Univ, 53, M.A, 56, George Moore fel. & Ph.D. (Eng), 67. Asst. prof. ENG, IND. UNIV. PA, 60-65, assoc. prof, 65-68, PROF, 68- U.S.A, 56-59. NEA. Victorian, Edwardian and modern British and American literature. Add: 210 Courtland Rd, Indiana, PA 15701.

SELDEN, SAMUEL, b. Canton, China, Jan. 2, 99; m. 51; c. 2. THEATER ARTS. A.B, Yale, 22; Guggenheim scholar, 38-39; Litt.D, Ill. Col, 52. Asst. tech. dir, co. actor & stage mgr, Provincetown Playhouse, Intimate Opera Co, New York, Cape Playhouse, Dennis, Mass, & Gladys Klark Players, 22-27; instr. Eng. Univ. N.C, 27-36; asst. prof. dramatic art, 36-44, prof, chmn. dept, & dir. Carolina Playmakers, 44-59; prof. & chmn. dept. THEATER ARTS, UNIV. CALIF, LOS ANGELES, 59-66, EMER. PROF, 66-; distinguished vis. prof. theater, South. Ill. Univ, 66-67; VIS. PROF. DRAMATIC ART, UNIV. N.C, CHAPEL HILL, 67- Nat. Theatre Conf. (exec. secy, 67-); Am. Theatre Asn; Am. Nat. Theatre & Acad. Relationship of dancing, music and painting to the art of stage directing. Publ: Ed, Organizing a community theater, Theatre Arts; co-auth, Stage scenery and lighting, 59, auth, First steps in acting, rev. ed, 64, Introduction to playwriting, 66, co-auth, Essentials of stage scenery, 73 & Modern theatre practice, rev. ed, 73, Appleton; The stage in action, South. Ill. Univ, 67; What do theatrical agents think of university graduates?, Speech Teacher, 9/67; Notes on the American theatre audience, Players Mag, 12-1/68-69. Add: Dept. of Dramatic Art, University of North Carolina at Chapel Hill, Chapel Hill, NC 27514.

SELIG, KARL-LUDWIG, Romance Languages & Literatures. See Volume III, Foreign Languages, Linguistics & Philology.

SELIG, ROBERT L, b. New York, N.Y, June 24, 32. ENGLISH. B.A, Univ. N.C, 54; Woodrow Wilson Nat. fel, Columbia Univ, 56-57, M.A, 58, Ph.D. (Eng), 65. Instr. ENG, Queens Col.(N.Y), 61-67; asst. prof, PURDUE UNIV, CALUMET CAMPUS, 67-71, ASSOC. PROF, 71- MLA. Publ: The red haired lady orator: parallel passages in The Bostonians and Adam Bede, 9/61 & The valley of the shadow of books: alienation in Gissing's New Grub

Street, 9/70, Nineteenth-Century Fiction; A sad heart at the late-Victorian culture market: George Gissing's In the year of Jubilee, Stud. Eng. Lit, autumn 69. Add: Dept. of English, Purdue University, Calumet Campus, Hammond, IN 46323.

SELLER, HOWARD JAY, b. Los Angeles, Calif, Apr. 7, 38. ENGLISH. B.A, Univ. Calif, Los Angeles, 60; M.A, Univ. South. Calif, 62, Ph.D.(Eng), 65. Instr. ENG, Portland State Col, 64-65; asst. prof, CALIF. STATE UNIV, FULLERTON, 65-70, ASSOC. PROF, 70-, CHMN. DEPT, 73- MLA; Philol. Asn. Pac. Coast; AAUP. Victorian literature in England; history and development of the English novel; the teaching of composition. Publ: Some effects of dramatic irony in King Lear and Othello, Calif. Eng. J, 2/70. Add: Dept. of English, California State University, Fullerton, CA 92634.

SELLERY, J'NAN MORSE, b. Oakland, Calif; m. 47; c. 4. MODERN BRITISH & AMERICAN LITERATURE. B.A, Univ. Calif, Riverside, 65, M.A, 67, NDEA fel, 67-70, Ph.D.(Eng), 70. Asst. prof. LIT, HARVEY MUDD COL, 70-74, ASSOC. PROF, 74- MLA; AAUP; Am. Asn. Univ. Women. Modern British and American poetry; literature, mythology and psychology of C.G. Jung; modern comparative fiction. Publ: Co-auth, Goethe's Faust Part I: essays in Criticism, Wadsworth, 69; The scapegoat, some literary permutations, Houghton, 72; Fictive modes in Charles Williams' All hallows eve, Genre, 10/68; Language and moral intelligence in the Enlightenment: Fielding's plays and Pope's Dunciad, Enlightenment Essays, spring & summer 70; Checklist of Elizabeth Bowen, Bull. N.Y. Pub. Libr, 4/70. Add: Dept. of Humanities, Harvey Mudd College, Claremont, CA 91711.

SELLIN, PAUL R, b. Everett, Wash, Nov. 14, 30; m. 57; c. 3. ENGLISH. B.A, Wash. State Univ, 52; M.A, Univ. Chicago, 55, fel, 55-56, Ph.D, 63; Van Loon fel, Netherlands Ministry Educ, Univ. Leyden, 59-60. Lectr. Eng. lang. & lit, Roosevelt Univ, 58-59, instr, 60-62, asst. prof, 62-66, univ. res. fel, 63-64; ENG, UNIV. CALIF, LOS ANGELES, 66-69, ASSOC. PROF, 69- Am. Counc. Learned Soc. grant-in-aid & Am. Philos. Soc. grant, summer 73; co-investr, Nat. Endowment for Humanities grant, 73-75. U.S.A, 52-54. MLA; Renaissance Soc. Am. Anglo-Dutch relations in the seventeenth century; Renaissance literary criticism; Milton. Publ: Daniel Heinsius and Stuart England, Oxford & Leiden Univ, 68; transl, Daniel Heinsius, On plot in tragedy, Calif. State Univ, Northridge, 71; auth, Puritan and Anglican: a Dutch perspective, Stud. Philol, 68; The first collection of Dutch love emblems: the identity of Theocritus á Ganda, Mod. Lang. Rev, 71; Le pathétique retrouvé: Racine's Catharsis reconsidered, Mod. Philol, 73. Add: Dept. of English, University of California, Los Angeles, CA 90024.

SELLMAN, HUNTON DADE, b. Md, May 20, 00; m. 33; c. 2. DRAMATIC ART. B.S, Purdue Univ, 22; M.S, Univ. Ariz, 25; Univ. Calif, 26; Univ. N.C, 28; Yale, 29-30. Instr, Sacramento Jr. Col, 26-29; from assoc. to assoc. prof. dramatic art, State Univ. Iowa, 30-46; prof. DRAMA, SAN DIEGO STATE UNIV, 46-71, chmn. dept, 54-59, EMER. PROF, 71- Consult, Sea World, winter 66. Am. Theatre Asn; Am. Nat. Theatre & Acad; Illuminating Engineering Soc; Nat. Theatre Conf. Publ: Stage scenery and lighting, 59, Modern theater practice, 5th ed, 73 & Essentials of stage lighting, 72, Appleton. Add: Dept. of Drama, San Diego State University, San Diego, CA 92115.

SELLS, LARRY FRANCIS, b. Anderson, Ind, Feb. 4, 42; m. 68; c. 2. ENGLISH LITERATURE. B.A, Franklin Col, 63; Woodrow Wilson fel, Yale, 63-64; M.A, Pa. State Univ, University Park, 66, Ph.D.(Eng), 70. Instr. ENG, WESTMINSTER COL.(PA), 68-71, ASST. PROF, 71- Am. Soc. 18th Century Stud; Augustan Reprint Soc; NCTE. Henry Fielding; 18th century English literature; the novel. Add: Dept. of English, Westminster College, New Wilmington, PA 16142.

SELTZ, HERBERT ARNOLD, b. Louisville, Ky, June 2, 27; m. 54; c. 2. RADIO, TELEVISION. B.S, Miami Univ, 50; M.S, Ind. Univ, 58. Instr. RADIO & TV, IND. UNIV, BLOOMINGTON, 53-57, asst. prof, 58-61, assoc. prof, 62-67, PROF, 68-, DIR. PROG, WFIU/WTIU, 74- Nat. Endowment for Arts grants, 68; Corp. Pub. Broadcasting TV opera-prod. grant, 70; mem. prog. selection comt, Pub. TV Libr, 70; dir, Myshkin (TV opera), Pub. Broadcasting System, 73. Broadcast Media Award, San Francisco State Col, 67; Nat. Educ. TV Award for Excellence in Cult. Prog, 69; Peabody Award for TV Opera Myshkin, 73; Ohio State Award for Myshkin, 74. U.S.A.A.F, 45-46. Nat. Asn. Educ. Broadcasters; Int. Music Ctr; Royal TV Soc; Brit. Film Inst; AAUP. Serious music on television; cable television and public access; international television. Publ: Co-auth, Production diary of the debates, In: The great debates, Ind. Univ, 62; auth, Stage to television: the advocate, spring 64 & co-auth, The unknown great debates, summer 69, TV Quart; plus others. Add: Radio & Television Services, Radio-TV Bldg, Indiana University, Bloomington, IN 47401.

SELTZER, ALVIN JAY, b. Philadelphia, Pa, Apr. 10, 39; m. 68; c. 1. ENGLISH & AMERICAN LITERATURE. B.S, Temple Univ, 60; A.M, Univ. Mich, Ann Arbor, 61; Univ. Calif, Berkeley, 63-64; Boston Univ, 64-65; Ph.D.(Eng), Pa. State Univ, State College, 70. Acting instr. ENG, Univ. Wis-Milwaukee, 61-63; instr, TEMPLE UNIV, 68-70, ASST. PROF, 70- Continental fiction. Publ: Chaos in the novel—the novel in chaos, Schocken, 74. Add: 315 Ashbourne Rd, Elkins Park, PA 19117.

SELTZER, DANIEL, b. Passaic, N.J, Feb. 13, 33. ENGLISH LITERATURE. B.A, Princeton, 54; Fulbright grant, New Col, Oxford & Woodrow Wilson fel, 54-55; Ph.D, Harvard Univ, 59. Teaching fel, Harvard, 56-59, instr. Eng, 59-61, from asst. prof. to prof. Eng. & assoc. dir. Loeb Drama Ctr, 61-70, acting dir, Loeb Drama Ctr, 63-64; PROF. ENG, PRINCETON, 70-, CHMN. COMT. THEATRE, 70- Dexter res. fel, Harvard, 59. MLA; Shakespeare Asn. Am; Renaissance Soc. Am. Shakespeare and Elizabethan drama; Elizabethan theatre and techniques of Elizabethan acting; modern drama. Publ: Ed, Pickeryng, Horestes 1567, Clarendon Press, 63; Shakespeare, Troilus and Cressida, New Am. Libr, 63; The staging of Shakespeare's last plays, Stratford-on-Avon Stud, 66; Shakespeare's texts and modern productions, In: English Institute essays, AMS Press, 69; The actors and staging, In: A new companion to Shakespeare studies, Cambridge Univ, 71; plus others. Add: Dept. of English, McCosh Hall 22, Princeton University, Princeton, NJ 08540.

SELTZER, LEON FRANCIS, b. Philadelphia, Pa, Aug. 9, 40. ENGLISH. B.A, Temple Univ, 62; M.A, Univ. Ill, 64; Ph.D.(English), State Univ. N.Y. Buffalo, 68. Asst. prof. ENG, Queens Col.(N.Y), 67-70; ASSOC. PROF, CLEVELAND STATE UNIV, 70- Cleveland State Univ. res. initiation grant, summer 72. MLA; NCTE; Midwest Mod. Lang. Asn. Contemporary American fiction; 19th and 20th century American novel; modern British fiction. Publ: The vision of Melville and Conrad: a comparative study, Ohio Univ, 70; Camus's Absurd and the world of Melville's Confidence man, PMLA, 3/67; Like repels like: the case of Conrad's antipathy for Melville, Conradiana, 69. Add: Dept. of English, Cleveland State University, 22nd & Euclid Ave, Cleveland, OH 44115.

SELZ, WILLIAM AARON, b. Dayton, Ohio, Nov. 16, 16; m. 51. ENGLISH. B.A, Harvard, 38, M.A, 40, Ph.D.(Eng), 43. Instr. freshman compos, Harvard, 43-45; Eng. Univ. Chicago, 45-46; Cornell Univ, 46-50; chmn. div. lang, Wayne State Col, 50-59; assoc. prof. ENG, UNIV. S.DAK, 59-60, PROF, 60- MLA; NCTE. Renaissance; 19th century novel; contemporary literature. Add: 614 Poplar Ave, Vermillion, SD 57069.

SEMEL, ANN, b. Jan. 19, 32; U.S. citizen. AMERICAN LITERATURE. B.A, Notre Dame Col.(Mo), 60; M.A, Univ. Notre Dame, 63, Ph.D.(Eng), 72. Instr. ENG, ST. MARY'S UNIV.(TEX), 67-70, asst. prof, 70-73, ASSOC. PROF, 73-, GRAD. ADV, 74- S.Cent. Mod. Lang. Asn; NCTE; Conf. Col. Teachers Eng. American literature of the 19th and 20th centuries; literature of American minorities. Publ: Introduction to literature of American minorities, Simon & Schuster, 74; The Bible in American literature, Cath. Libr.World, 12/73; contrib, Literary encyclopedia of the Bible, Harper, (in press). Add: Dept. of English, St. Mary's University, 2700 Cincinnati, San Antonio, TX 78284.

SEMON, KENNETH JEFFREY, b. Milwaukee, Wis, Sept. 18, 45. ENGLISH LITERATURE. B.A, Univ. Wis-Madison, 68; Woodrow Wilson fel, Univ. Wash, Seattle, 70-71, Ph.D.(Shakespeare), 71. ASST. PROF. ENG, UNIV. KY, 71- Mem, Delphi Proj. Undergrad. Educ, Univ. Tex, Dallas, 73. MLA; Renaissance Soc. Am; Shakespeare Asn. Am; Southeast. Renaissance Conf; Milton Soc. Am. Renaissance drama; theory of fiction; Renaissance prose. Publ: Shakespeare's Tempest: beyond a common joy, ELH, 73; Fantasy and wonder in Shakespeare's last plays, Shakespeare Quart, 74; Pericles: an order beyond reason, Essays in Lit, 74. Add: Dept. of English, University of Kentucky, Lexington, KY 40506.

SENA, JOHN F, b. Summit, N.J, June 26, 40; m. 66; c. 2. ENGLISH LITERATURE. B.A, Seton Hall Univ, 62; Fulbright fel, 62-63, M.A, Princeton, 65, Ph.D.(Eng), 67. Asst. prof. ENG, OHIO STATE UNIV, 67-71, ASSOC. PROF, 71- Am. Philos. Soc. grant, 68; Ohio State Univ. grant, 69. MLA; Am. Soc. 18th Century Stud; Am. Soc. Hist. Med. Eighteenth century English literature; history of medicine; satiric theory. Publ: A bibliography of melancholy: 1660-1800, Nether, London, 70; Smollett's Persona and the melancholic traveler, 18th Century Stud, 6/68; Melancholy in Anne Finch and Elizabeth Carter: the ambivalence of an idea, Mod. Lang. Rev. Yearbk, 71; Melancholic madness and the puritans, Harvard Theol. Rev, 7/73. Add: Dept. of English, Ohio State University, Columbus, OH 43210.

SENATORE, JOHN J, b. Rockvale, Colo, Jan. 19, 26; m. 66. ENGLISH, INTERPERSONAL COMMUNICATIONS. B.A, Univ. North. Colo, 51, M.A, 55; Harvard, summer 64; grants, Univ. Denver, summer 67. Teacher, high sch, Nebr, 51-53; jr. high sch. & high sch, Colo, 53-58; instr. ENG, Pueblo Jr. Col, 58-60, asst. prof, 58-60; ASSOC. PROF, SOUTH. COLO. STATE COL, 60- Mem, Creative Educ. Found; Inst. Gen. Semantics. U.S.A, 44-46. NEA; Int. Soc. Gen. Semantics. Social-psychology of communications; creativity; effective and innovative teaching. Publ: Showing relationships, S&O, 66, 67; co-auth, Nothing never happens, Glencoe-Benziger, 74; auth, Rolfe Humphries: poet as teacher, Creative Writing, 10/56; SVO: key to clearer language teaching, Eng. J, 10/56; The ready-made student, Clearing House, 2/57. Add: 85 Scotland Rd, B-3, Pueblo, CO 81001.

SENCER, ROBERT ABNER, b. New York, N.Y, Jan. 17, 21; m. 44; c. 3. COMMUNICATION THEORY. B.F.A, Univ. Ariz, 41; Knights of Columbus fel. & M.A, Cath. Univ. Am, 43; Ph.D, Mich. State Univ, 65. Instr. dramatic arts, Univ. Ariz, 45-47; Eng, N.Y. Univ, 48-49; from instr. to assoc. prof, Rensselaer Polytech. Inst, 49-70; PROF. COMMUN, MONT. STATE UNIV, 70- United Serv. Orgn. dir, 43-45; asst. dir, Tech. Writers Inst, 52-; consult, N.Y. Tel. Co, 58-59; Watervliet Arsenal, 59-61; Sterling-Winthrop Res. Inst, 62; NASA summer fac. fel, 68. Int. Commun. Asn; Am. Bus. Commun. Asn; Soc. Tech. Commun.(chmn, comt. on res. & assoc. ed, Jour, 53-). Human verbal communication; linguistic variables in human communication; technical and professional communication. Publ: Creativity in a communicative atmosphere, 5/71 & To research or not to research, 5/73, Proc. Int. Tech. Commun. Conf; The university as an information system, Proc. Am. Soc. Info. Sci, 10/73; plus three others. Add: Dept. of Speech Communication, Montana State University, Bozeman, MT 59715.

SENDRY, JOSEPH M, b. Cleveland, Ohio, Oct. 22, 35. ENGLISH. B.A, Cath. Univ. Am, 57; Woodrow Wilson fel, Univ. Mich, 57, M.A, 58; Ph.D.(Eng), Harvard, 63. Asst. prof. ENG, CATH. UNIV. AM, 63-66, ASSOC. PROF, 66- Nat. Endowment for Humanities summer grant, 71; vis. fel, St. Edmund's House, Cambridge, 71. MLA; Tennyson Soc. Keats; Victorian poetry; 19th century novel. Publ: Co-ed, John Keats: a thematic reader, Scott, 71; auth, In memoriam and Lycidas, PMLA, 10/67; The In memoriam manuscripts: some solutions to the problems, Harvard Libr. Bull, 4/73; plus others. Add: Dept. of English, Catholic University of America, Washington, DC 20017.

SENG, PETER J, b. Milwaukee, Wis, Mar. 30, 22. ENGLISH LITERATURE. A.B, Marquette Univ, 48; M.A, Harvard, 49, Dexter traveling fel, 52, Ph.D.(Eng), 55. Instr. ENG, Northwest. Univ, 52-55, asst. prof, 56-59, CONN. COL, 59-65, assoc. prof, 65-70, PROF, 70- U.S.A.A.F, 42-46. Renaissance Soc; Malone Soc. Literature of the English Renaissance; 16th and 17th century songs and ballads; Shakespeare. Publ: Co-auth, Poems: Wadsworth handbook and anthology, 61 & Plays: Wadsworth handbook and anthology, 70, Wadsworth; auth, The vocal songs in the plays of Shakespeare, Harvard, 67. Add: Dept. of English, Box 1527, Connecticut College, New London, CT 06320.

SENSABAUGH, GEORGE FRANK, b. Dublin, Tex, July 15, 06; m. 38; c. 2. ENGLISH LITERATURE. A.B, Vanderbilt Univ, 28; A.M, Univ. N.C, 30, Ph.D, 34. Teaching fel, Univ. N.C, 28-31; instr. ENG, 31-35; STANFORD UNIV, 35-37, asst. prof, 37-43, assoc. prof, 43-47, prof, 47-71, dir, Army Specialized Training Prog, 43-44, EMER. PROF. ENG, 71- Guggenheim fel, 44-45; fel, Henry E. Huntington Libr, 50-51; Am. Counc. Learned Soc. grant, 48; Am. Philos. Soc. grant, 56; Folger Shakespeare Libr. grant, 63; mem. ed. bd, Stud. Eng. Lit, 63-; vis. fel, Newberry Libr. sem, 71. MLA; Renaissance Soc. Am; Milton Soc. Am.(pres, 66-67); Philol. Asn. Pac. Coast (pres, 67). Publ: The tragic muse of John Ford, 44 & That grand Whig, Milton, 52, Stanford Univ; Milton in early America, Princeton, 64. Add: 1350 Byron St, Palo Alto, CA 94301.

SERAPHIM, M, O.S.F, b. Philadelphia, Pa. ENGLISH, JOURNALISM. A.B, Col. St. Francis, 37; A.M, Univ. Mich, 44. Instr, high sch, Ohio, 37-40; asst. prof. Eng. & jour, COL. ST. FRANCIS, 40-62, prof, 62-66, PROF. ENG, 66- Vis. lectr, St. John Col.(Ohio), 63-66. AAUP; MLA. Obligation of art to morality; poems. Add: Dept. of English, College of St. Francis, 500 Wilcox St, Joliet, IL 60435.

SERENO, KENNETH KEALA, b. Dec. 16, 34; U.S. citizen; m; c. 5. SPEECH COMMUNICATION, PSYCHOLOGY. B.A, Univ. Hawaii, 56, M.A, 59; Ph.D. (speech), Univ. Wash, 64. Asst. SPEECH COMMUN, Univ. Hawaii, 56-58; instr, 58-60; asst, Univ. Wash, 60-61, assoc, 61-64, asst. prof, 64-68; ASSOC. PROF, UNIV. SOUTH. CALIF, 68- Assoc. ed, Speech Monogr, 68-; consult. ed, West. Speech J, 70-; adv. ed, Pac. Speech J, 70-; consult, Am. Asn. Pub. Adminr; Parent-Teachers Asn, State of Hawaii; Credit Union League & Community Develop. Bur, State Wash; Boeing Aircraft Corp; Mayor's Off. & Model Cities Prog, City & County Honolulu; U.S. Air Force; Welton-Becket Architects; Govt. Affairs Inst, Agency Int. Develop. Int. Commun. Asn; Speech Commun. Asn.(publ, chmn. rhet. & commun. theory div, 70-); West. Speech Commun. Asn.(chmn. behav. sci. interest group, 71-). Factor analytic study of the three components of attitudes; cost-effectiveness of mass media in affecting traffic safety, work safety, and health practices. Publ: Co-auth, Foundations of communication theory, 70 & Advances in communication research, 73, Harper & Group processes and communication, Sci. Res. Assocs, (in press); co-auth, Attitudes toward Black Muslims, Encore, 70; auth, Ego-involvement: a neglected variable in speech communication research, Quart. J. Speech, 69; co-auth, Ego-involvement and attitude change: toward a reconceptualization of persuasive effect, Speech Monogr, 72; plus many others. Add: Dept. of Speech Communications, University of Southern California, Los Angeles, CA 90007.

SERIGHT, ORIN DALE, English, Linguistics. See Volume III, Foreign Languages, Linguistics & Philology.

SERONSY, CECIL COWDEN, b. Lowellville, Ohio, Apr. 28, 08; m. 47. ENGLISH LANGUAGE & LITERATURE. B.A, Univ. Va, 30; M.A, Harvard, 39, Ph.D.(Eng), 52. Instr. high sch, Ohio, 30-38; Eng, Purdue Univ, 46-48; teaching fel. gen. educ, Harvard, 51-52; prof. ENG, BLOOMSBURG STATE COL, 53-73, chmn. dept, 59-64, EMER. PROF, 73- Huntington Libr. grant, 63-64. MLA; Renaissance Soc. Am. English Renaissance poetry and drama; English romanticism; Shakespeare and Daniel. Publ: Samuel Daniel, Twayne, 67; Well-languaged Daniel: a reconsideration, Mod. Lang. Rev; supposes as the unifying theme in The taming of the shrew, Shakespeare Quart; Daniel and Wordsworth, Stud. Philol; plus many others. Add: 14 Central Ave, Bloomsburg, PA 17815.

SESHACHARI, CANDADAI, b. Secunderabad, India, Jan. 10, 28; c. 2. AMERICAN LITERATURE, ETHICS. B.A, Osmania Univ, India, 51, M.A, 53; Smith-Mundt Fulbright fel, Univ. Utah, 59-60, univ. fel, 60-63, cert. Am. stud, 63, Ph.D.(Eng. lit), 64. Lectr. ENG, Osmania Univ, India, 59, reader, 64-69; asst. prof, WEBER STATE COL, 69-71, ASSOC. PROF, 71- Mem. & treas. bd. dirs, Am. Stud. Res. Ctr, India, 64-69. Rocky Mt. Mod. Lang. Asn; West. Lit. Asn. Civil rights movement in America; Mahatma Gandhi. Publ: Gandhi and the American scene: an intellectual history and inquiry, Nachiketa Publ, 69; Gandhian nonviolence and the American negro, West. Humanities Rev, winter 64; Reinhold Niebuhr: the case against Gandhi, Indian J. Am. Stud., 7/69; Gandhi and pacifism: a dream and its distortions, In: Gandhi and the West, Univ. Mysore, 70. Add: Dept. of English, Weber State College, 3750 Harrison Blvd, Ogden, UT 84403.

SESSIONS, WILLIAM ALFRED, b. Conway, S.C, Aug. 4, 28; m. 61; c. 2. ENGLISH. A.B, Univ. N.C, 48; M.A, Columbia Univ, 53, Ph.D.(Eng), 66; Fulbright fel, Univ. Freiburg, Ger, 57-58. Asst. prof. ENG, W.Ga. Col, 54-60; Spring Hill Col, 60-62; St. John's Univ, 62-66; assoc. prof, GA. STATE UNIV, 66-72, PROF, 72- MLA; Renaissance Soc. Am. Francis Bacon; John Milton; 17th century English poetry. Publ: Romeo and Juliet: a critical analysis, Simon & Schuster, 66; Flannery O'Connor: a memoir, Natural Cath. Reporter, 9/64; A correspondence, In: The added dimension: the art and mind of Flannery O'Connor, Fordham Univ, 67; Giovanni Papini, In: Modern Catholic authors, Fordham Univ, 68; plus others. Add: Dept. of English, Georgia State University, Atlanta, GA 30303.

SETZLER, EDWIN (LAKE), b. Newberry, S.C, Feb. 14, 03. ENGLISH LANGUAGE. A.B, Newberry Col, 22, A.M, 23, hon. Litt.D, 55; A.M, Univ. Va, 24; Univ. N.C, 27-28; hon. D.Ed, Lenoir-Rhyne Col, 72. Instr. chem, Newberry Col, 22-23; Eng. & hist, Clemson Col, 24-25; assoc. prof. Eng, LENOIR-RHYNE COL, 25-30, prof, 30-72, acad. dean & registr, 36-66, consult. to admin, 66-67, EMER. PROF. ENG, 72- NCTE; S.Atlantic Mod. Lang. Asn. Publ: Co-auth, The Jefferson Anglo-Saxon grammar and reader, Macmillan, 38, 2nd ed, 39. Add: 718 Fourth Ave. N.W, Hickory, NC 28601.

SEVERNS, JAMES (GEORGE), b. Bourbon, Ind, Feb. 18, 29; m. 59; c. 3. DRAMA. B.S, Purdue Univ, 51; M.A, Ind. Univ, 56; Univ. Bristol, 56-57; Ph.D.(drama), Univ. Iowa, 71. Asst. prof. DRAMA, NORTHEAST MO. STATE UNIV, 59-62, ASSOC. PROF, 63- Researcher, Brit. Mus. Libr, London, 71-72. U.S.M.C, 51-53, 1st Lt. Am. Theatre Asn; Speech Commun. Asn. G.B. Shaw. Add: Dept. of Drama, Northeast Missouri State University, Kirksville, MO 63501.

SEVERS, JONATHAN BURKE, b. Trenton, N.J, Nov. 9, 03. ENGLISH LITERATURE. A.B, Rutgers Univ, 25; A.M, Princeton, 27; univ. fel, Yale, 30-31, Mitchell fel, 34-35, Ph.D, 35. Teacher high sch, N.J, 25-26; instr. ENG, LEHIGH UNIV, 27-33, asst. prof, 33-36, assoc. prof, 36-41, prof, 41-59, distinguished prof, 59-69, EMER. PROF, 69- MLA; fel. Royal Soc. Arts; Mediaeval Acad. Am.(Haskins Medal, 46). Chaucer; medieval, romantic literature. Publ: Literary relationships of Chaucer's Clerkes tale, Yale, 41; co-auth, Sources and analogues of Chaucer's Canterbury tales, Univ. Chicago, 41. Add: Dept. of English, Lehigh University, Bethlehem, PA 18015.

SEVIER, ANNE, b. Landrum, S.C, Mar. 16, 07. ENGLISH. A.B, Winthrop Col, 28; A.M, Univ. S.C, 39; summers, Univ. N.C, 42, 43, 47, 49, Univ. London, 56. Teacher, high sch, S.C. & N.C, 28-45; instr. Eng, Winthrop Col, 45-47, asst. prof, 47-72; RETIRED. Col. Eng. Asn; S.Atlantic Mod. Lang. Asn; NCTE; Am. Stud. Asn. Sonnet criticism of the Victorian era. Add: Park Hills, Landrum, SC 29356.

SEWALL, RICHARD BENSON, b. Albany, N.Y, Feb. 11, 08. ENGLISH LITERATURE. A.B, Williams Col, 29; Ph.D, Yale, 33. Instr. ENG, Clark Univ, 33-34; YALE, 34-40, asst. prof, 40-50, assoc. prof, 50-59, PROF, 59-, assoc. dean freshman year, 47-51, master, Ezra Stiles Col, 59-70. MLA; Philos. Educ. Soc; Col. Eng. Asn. The influence of Rousseau in England in the 18th century; literary criticism; theory of tragedy. Publ: The vision of tragedy, Yale, 59; The Lyman letters: new light on Emily Dickinson and her family, Univ. Mass, 66; Emily Dickinson: twentieth century views, & co-auth, Tragedy: modern essays in criticism, Prentice-Hall. Add: Dept. of English, 410 Sterling Library, Yale University, New Haven, CT 06520.

SEWARD, WILLIAM WARD, JR, b. Surry, Va, Feb. 2, 13; m. 41; c. 2. ENGLISH LANGUAGE & LITERATURE. A.B, Univ. Richmond, 34, M.A, 35; fel, Duke Univ, 38-39, 40-41. Teacher, sec. schs, Va. & N.C, 35-38; instr. ENG, Univ. Richmond, 39-40; head dept, Greenbrier Mil. Sch, 41-42; prof. & head dept, Tift Col, 42-45; instr, OLD DOM. UNIV, 45-47, asst. prof, 47-51, assoc. prof, 51-57, PROF 57-, head dept, 47-61. Exten. lectr, Univ. Va, 52-54. Norman Medal, Univ. Richmond, 34. MLA; Poetry Soc. Am; NCTE; Int. Mark Twain Soc. Hemingway; contemporary American and British literature; English neo-classicism. Publ: Literature and war, Baylor Univ, 43; Skirts of the dead night, Bookman Assocs, 50; Contrasts in modern writers, Frederick Fell, Inc, 63; My friend Ernest Hemingway, A.S. Barnes, 69. Add: Dept. of English, Old Dominion University, Norfolk, VA 23508.

SEWELL, ERNESTINE PORCHER, b. Texarkana, Tex. ENGLISH LITERATURE, LINGUISTICS. B.A, Henderson State Col, 37; Univ. Tex, Austin, 38; M.A, E.Tex. State Univ, 55, Ph.D.(Eng), 68; Univ. Houston, 61-63. Instr. ENG, San Jacinto Jr. Col, 61-64; UNIV. TEX, ARLINGTON, 64-68, asst. prof, 68-71, ASSOC. PROF, 71- MLA; Col. Eng. Asn; Am. Stud. Asn. British writers in transition, 1870-1910; southwest literature; linguistic explication of literature. Publ: Loula Grace Erdman, Steck, 70; contrib, Guide to critical reviews of United States fiction, 1870-1910, Scarecrow, 71; auth, The real Anabasis of Captain Robson, Yearbook W.Tex. State Hist. Asn, 72; Name-calling as a convention in English literature, In: Love, wrestling, butch and O.K, Names Inst. Press, 73; plus others. Add: Dept. of English, University of Texas at Arlington, Arlington, TX 76019.

SEXTON, ANNE, b. Newton, Mass, Nov. 9, 28; m. 48; c. 2. POETRY. Hon. Litt.D, Tufts Univ, 70, Regis Col, 71, Fairfield Univ, 71. Assoc. prof. Eng, Boston Univ, 70-71; Crawshaw prof. lit, Colgate Univ, 72; PROF. ENG, BOSTON UNIV, 72- Am. Acad. Arts & Lett. fel, 63-64; Congr. for Cult. Freedom travel grant, 65; Guggenheim grant, 69-70. Pulitzer Prize for Poetry, 67. Fel. Royal Soc. Lit. U.K. Publ: To bedlam and part way back, 60, All my pretty ones, 62 & The death notebooks, 74, Houghton; Selected poems, Oxford, 64; Live or die, Oxford, 64, Houghton, 66; Love poems, Houghton, 69, Oxford, 69; Transformations, Houghton, 71, Oxford, 72; Book of folly, Chatto & Windus, 74. Add: 14 Black Oak Rd, Weston, MA 02193.

SEXTON, RICHARD J, b. New York, N.Y, Mar. 11, 12; m. 36, 61; c. 4. ENGLISH. A.B, Fordham Univ, 32, M.A, 35, Ph.D.(Eng), 65; Oxford, 38; Cambridge, 38. ASSOC. PROF. ENG, FORDHAM UNIV, 35- Bene Merenti Medal, Fordham Univ, 55. MLA; NCTE; Col. Eng. Asn; Melville Soc. Am; Eng. Inst; AAUP. Literary criticism. Publ: The complex of Yvor Winters' criticism, Mouton, The Hague, 73. Add: Dept. of English, Fordham University, Bronx, NY 10458.

SEYBOLD, ETHEL LOUISE, b. Baylis, Ill, May 6, 10. ENGLISH, LINGUISTICS. A.B, Ill. Col, 29; scholar. & A.M, Univ. Mo, 32; univ. fel. & M.A, Yale, 45, Ph.D.(Eng), 47. Teacher high sch, 29-31, 32-43; instr. ENG, ILL. COL, 43-44, assoc. prof, 46-51, prof. & co-chmn. dept, 51-72, EMER. PROF, 72- Mem. ed. bd, Thoreau Ed, Ctr. Ed. Am. Auth, MLA, 66- MLA. Nineteenth century American literature. Publ: Thoreau, the quest and the classics, Yale, 51. Add: Dept. of English, Illinois College, Jacksonville, IL 62650.

SEYDOW, JOHN JOSEPH, b. Philadelphia, Pa, July 19, 41; m. 65; c. 2. ENGLISH. B.A, La Salle Col, 65; M.A, Ohio Univ, 66, Ph.D.(Eng), 68. Asst. prof. ENG, LA SALLE COL, 68-73, ASSOC. PROF, 73- Eighteenth to twentieth century American literature. Publ: The sound of passing music: John Neal's battle for American literary independence, Costerus, spring 73. Add: Dept. of English, La Salle College, Philadelphia, PA 19141.

SEYMOUR, THADDEUS, b. New York, N.Y, June 29, 28; m. 48; c. 5. ENGLISH. A.B, Univ. Calif, 50; M.A, Univ. N.C, 51, Ph.D, 55. Instr. Eng, Dartmouth Col, 54-57, asst. prof, 57-59, assoc. prof, 59-67, prof, 67-69, dean, 59-69; PRES, WABASH COL, 69- Eighteenth century English literature; periodicals; South Sea company. Add: 400 E. Pike St, Crawfordsville, IN 47933.

SEYMOUR, VICTOR, b. Brooklyn, N.Y, May 17, 29; m. 65; c. 1. SPEECH, THEATRE. B.S, Univ. Utah, 54; M.A, Columbia Univ, 58; Ph.D.(theatre), Univ. Wis, 65. Instr. speech, Bates Col, 58-60; lectr, Hunter Col. in the Bronx, 62-65; asst. prof. SPEECH, THEATRE, N.Y. Inst. Technol, 65-68; QUEENSBOROUGH COMMUNITY COL.(N.Y), 68-71, ASSOC. PROF, 71-

Off. observer, Actors Studio Dir. Unit, New York, N.Y, 60-; dir. theatre, N.Y. Inst. Technol, 65-68. U.S.A, 51-53. Speech Commun. Asn. Publ: Director's workshop: six years' activity of the Actors Studio Directors Unit, 3/66 & Theatre keeps pace in secondary education, 10/68, Educ. Theatre J. Add: Dept. of Speech & Drama, Queensborough Community College, 56th Ave, New York, NY 11364.

SHAABER, MATTHIAS ADAM, b. Reading, Pa, Dec. 13, 97; m. 33. ENGLISH LITERATURE. A.B, Univ. Pa, 18, A.M, 24, Ph.D, 28. Instr. ENG, UNIV. PA, 19-20, 22-33, asst. prof, 33-39, assoc. prof, 39-42, PROF, 42- Vis. lectr, Univ. South. Calif, 39; Columbia Univ, 48; Duke Univ, 50. Elizabethan literature; Shakespeare; English journalism of the 16th and 17th centuries. Add: Dept. of English, University of Pennsylvania, Philadelphia, PA 19104.

SHAARA, MICHAEL JOSEPH, JR, b. Jersey City, N.J, June 23, 28; m. 50; c. 2. ENGLISH LITERATURE, CREATIVE WRITING. B.A, Rutgers Univ, 51; Columbia Univ, 52-53; Univ. Vt, 53-54. Instr. Eng, FLA. STATE UNIV, 61-64, asst. prof. creative writing, 64-68, ASSOC. PROF. CREATIVE WRITING & WRITER-IN-RESIDENCE, 68-, instr, Freshman Eng. TV Prog, 61-65. Asolo Theatre, Sarasota, Fla. grant drama anal, summer 70. Am. Med. Asn. award med. jour, 66. U.S.A, 46-47, Res, 47-51, Sgt. AAUP; Conf. Col. Compos. & Commun. Civil War literature; modern American literature; drama. Publ: The broken place, New. Am. Libr, 68; The killer angels, McKay, 74; plus numerous short stories & arts. Add: 3019 Thomasville Rd, Tallahassee, FL 32303.

SHACKFORD, JOHN BRANNER, b. Waynesville, N.C, May 18, 08; m. 42; c. 3. ENGLISH LITERATURE. B.S, Northwest. Univ, 30, A.M, 31; Univ. N.C, 35-37; Ph.D, State Univ. Iowa, 46. Instr. ENG, Lingnan Univ, China, 31-34; S.Dak. State Col, 35, asst. prof, 37-42; Ball State Teachers Col, 46-47; prof, Jamestown Col, 47-48; CORNELL COL, 48-73, EMER. PROF, 73- Ford fel, 53-54. U.S.N, 42-45, Lt. MLA. Romantic doctrine of poetic imagination; rational structure of Shakespeare's plays. Publ: Ed, David Crockett, the man and the legend; The bond of kindness: Shylock's humanity, Univ. Kans. City Rev. Add: Dept. of English, Cornell College, Mt. Vernon, IA 52314.

SHADOIAN, JACK, b. New York, N.Y, Aug. 7, 40; m. 64; c. 1. ENGLISH & AMERICAN LITERATURE. B.A, City Col. New York, 63; M.A, Univ. Conn, 65, fel, 66-67, Ph.D.(Eng. & John Suckling), 67. ASST. PROF. ENG, Pa. State Univ, 67-70; UNIV. MASS, AMHERST, 70-, fac. growth grant, summer 72. Consult, Nat. Proj. Ctr. Film & Humanities, 73. Popular Cult. Asn; Film-Eng. Humanities Asn. Renaissance and modern literature; American film; popular music. Publ: The achievement of Comment C'est, Critique, 70; Titus Andronicus, Discourse, 70; Michael Curtiz' 20,000 years in Sing Sing, J. Popular Film, 73. Add: Dept. of English, University of Massachusetts, Amherst, MA 01002.

SHAFER, ROBERT EUGENE, b. Beloit, Wis, Mar. 30, 25; m. 53. ENGLISH. B.A, Univ. Wis, 50, M.A, 53; Ed.D, Teachers Col, Columbia Univ, 58. Asst. prof. Eng. & Educ, San Francisco State Col, 55-58; ASSOC. PROF, Wayne State Univ, 58-62; Teachers Col, Columbia Univ, 62-66; PROF. ENG, ARIZ. STATE UNIV, 66- Consult. Eng. curriculum, pub. schs, Okla. City, 59; Detroit, 60; Dayton, 61; Paterson, 62-63; Phoenix, 69; lectr, Fremdsprachenschule, Hamburg, summer 63; consult, State of Hawaii, 65 & 68; curriculum develop. ed, Eng. J, 66-69; consult, San Diego City Schs, 67 & 68; lectr. Eng. & educ, Univ. South. Calif, 68, 69 & 70; Fla. State Univ, 69, 70; consult, Curriculum Ctr. Eng, Northwestern Univ, 69-70; Univ. Ill, Champaign, 70; lectr. Eng. & educ, Univ. Maine, summers, 70-72; sr. res. assoc, W.Ger. Inst. Res. Int. Educ, Frankfurt, Max-Planck Inst. Educ. Res, W.Berlin & lectr, Oxford Univ, 72-73. U.S.M.C, 43-46, 50-51, Sgt. NCTE (v.pres, 67-68, chmn. liaison comt. soc. & cult. prob. of professions & schs, 70-73); MLA; Int. Reading Asn. (mem. comt. gifted, 71-74); Am. Stud. Asn; Ling. Soc. Am. Teaching of English; reading; teaching English as a second language. Publ: Co-auth, Personal code: a scholastic literature unit, 61 & Success: a scholastic literature unit, 63, Scholastic Bd. Serv; co-auth, High school—college articulation, 63 & Ends and issues in English, 64, NCTE; co-auth, Success in reading, Silver-Burdett, Vols. I-VI, 67-68, Vols. VII-VIII, 73 & Language change and communication, Sci. Res. Assocs, 66; auth, On reading and the mother tongue, In: English in education, Oxford Univ, 73. Add: Dept. of English, Arizona State University, Tempe, AZ 85281.

SHAFTEL, OSCAR HAMILTON, b. Brooklyn, N.Y, May 5, 12; m. 45; c. 3. ENGLISH LITERATURE, ORIENTAL CULTURE. A.B, City Col. New York, 31; M.A, Harvard, 32, Ph.D.(Eng, philos), 36. Instr. Eng, Queens Col. (N.Y), 37-48, asst. prof, 48-53; PRATT INST, 65-67, assoc. prof. Eng. & humanities, 67-73, PROF. HUMANITIES, 73- Ed, Schocken Bks, 64-; adj. assoc. prof. orient. relig, Queens Col. (N.Y), 73- U.S.A.A.F, 42-46, Capt. Oriental religions and literature. Publ: An understanding of the Buddha, Schocken, 74. Add: 3915 45th St, Long Island City, NY 11104.

SHAHEEN, NASEEB, b. Chicago, Ill, June 24, 31. RENAISSANCE ENGLISH LITERATURE. B.A, Am. Univ. Beirut, 62; M.A, Univ. Calif, Los Angeles, 66, Woodrow Wilson fel, 68-69, Ph.D.(Eng), 69. ASST. PROF. ENG. LIT, MEMPHIS STATE UNIV, 69-, fac. res. grants, summers 70, 73. MLA. Artistic use of the Bible in English literature. Publ: Deriving adjectives from nouns, Costerus, 72; Milton's muse and the De Doctrina, Milton Quart, 74; auth, Introduction, The Faerie Queene, Scolar Press, Eng, 74; plus others. Add: Dept. of English, Memphis State University, Memphis, TN 38152.

SHAIN, CHARLES EDWARD, b. Tamaqua, Pa, June 3, 15; m. 43; c. 1. AMERICAN & BRITISH LITERATURE. A.B, Princeton, 36, A.M, 47, Ph.D, 49, hon. LL.D, 69; hon. L.H.D, Wesleyan Univ, 68; hon. Litt.D, Emerson Col, 69. Instr, Princeton, 48-49; from asst. prof. to prof. Eng, Carleton Col, 49-62; PRES, CONN. COL, 62- Fulbright res. scholar, Univ. London, 52-53; lectr, Salzburg Sem. in Am. stud, Austria, 60. U.S.A.A.F, 42-46. MLA. America in 19th century British literature. Publ: F. Scott Fitzgerald, Univ. Minn, 61. Add: Connecticut College, New London, CT 06320.

SHAMO, GEORGE WAYNE, b. Hurricane, Utah, June 24, 38; m. 61; c. 3. SPEECH. B.S, Brigham Young Univ, 62; M.S, South. Ill. Univ, 63, Ph.D. (speech), 67. Asst. SPEECH, South. Ill. Univ, 62-65; ASST. PROF, Memphis State Univ, 65-71; PURDUE UNIV, WEST LAFAYETTE, 71- Speech Commun. Asn; South. Speech Commun. Asn. Cognitive dissonance; structural linguistics; listening behavior. Add: Dept. of Communication, Purdue University, West Lafayette, IN 47907.

SHANK, THEODORE, b. Brawley, Calif, Feb. 1, 29; m. 67; c. 2. THEATRE, DRAMA. B.A, Univ. Calif, Santa Barbara, 50, M.A, Los Angeles, 52; Ph.D. (theatre & drama), Stanford Univ, 56. From instr. to PROF. DRAMATIC ART, UNIV. CALIF, DAVIS, 56-, chmn. dept, 61-69. Lectr, Univs. London, Exeter, Paris & TV, London, spring 70; Calif. Inst. Arts, spring 71 & 72; fel, Humanities Inst, Univ. Calif, summer 73. U.S.A, 53-55. Am. Soc. Theatre Res. Directing; contemporary theatre history; playwriting-collective theatre. Publ: The art of dramatic art, Dickenson, 68 & Dell, 72; The theatre of the cultural revolution, Yale Fr. Stud, 71; Collective creation, Drama Rev, 6/72; Theatre collectives, In: Contemporary dramatists, St. James Press, 73; plus others. Add: Dept. of Dramatic Art, University of California, Davis, CA 95616.

SHANKMAN, FLORENCE V, b. Norwalk, Conn; m. 37; c. 3. READING, LANGUAGE ARTS. B.S, Columbia Univ, 34, M.A, 36; M.A, N.Y. Univ, 55, Ed.D. (psychol. & reading), 59. Elem. teacher, Norwalk, Conn, 30-37, 53-59; teacher for. born, 39-47; instr. remedial reading, N.Y. Univ. Reading Inst, 55-59; supvr. instr, 59-62; asst. prof. educ, Univ. Bridgeport, 62-65; assoc. prof, Keene State Col, 65-67; TEMPLE UNIV, 67-72, PROF. CURRICULUM & INSTR, 72- Mem, Acad. Reading Experts aid N.Y.C. Schs, 60-67; guest prof. reading, Univ. South. Calif, summer 62; reading consult, Roosevelt Sch, Stamford, Conn, 63-65; guest prof, N.Y. Univ, summer 65; mem, Educ. Policies Comn, N.H, 66-67; guest prof, Colo. State Col, summer 67; Col. Holy Names (Calif), summer 69. Int. Reading Asn; World Cong. Reading; Am. Psychol. Asn; Nat. Soc. Stud. Educ; NCTE; Asn. Childhood Educ. Int; Asn. Supv. & Curriculum Develop; NEA; Am. Educ. Res. Asn; Col. Reading Asn; Am. Asn. Elem/Kindergarten/Nursery Educ; Nat. Educ. Asn. Young Children; AAUP; World Educ. Fel; Jean Piaget Soc; Nat. Reading Conf. Games, puzzles and activities for reading; study skills in reading; motivating children to read. Publ: Successful practices in remedial reading, Atherton, 63; ed, Readings in the language arts (3 vols), 69, Research studies in reading (2 vols), 69 & auth, Activities and games to reinforce phonics and linguistics, 73, Simon & Schuster; ed, Methods of teaching reading, 70 & auth, Games and activities to reinforce reading skills, 72, MSS Inform. Corp; auth, We discover the encyclopedia (film), Coronet, 71; Crossword puzzle (8 bks), Continental Press, 72, 73; plus others. Add: Dept. of Curriculum & Instruction, Temple University College of Education, Montgomery & Park, Philadelphia, PA 19122.

SHANLEY, JAMES LYNDON, b. Allenhurst, N.J, July 3, 10; m. 38; c. 2. ENGLISH LITERATURE. A.B, Princeton, 32, Scribner fel, 35-36, Ph.D, 37. Instr. ENG, NORTHWEST. UNIV, 36-40, asst. prof, 40-46, assoc. prof, 46-51, PROF, 51-, ASSOC. DEAN COL. ARTS & SCI, 52-, educ. coord. Navy V-12 prog, 45-46, asst. dean, 46-52. MLA; NCTE; Thoreau Soc. Spenser; Chaucer; Thoreau. Add: College of Arts & Sciences, Northwestern University, Evanston, IL 60201.

SHANNON, EDGAR FINLEY, JR, b. Lexington, Va, June 4, 18; m. 56. ENGLISH. A.B, Washington & Lee Univ, 39, hon. Litt.D, 59; A.M, Duke Univ, 41, hon. LL.D, 64; A.M, Harvard, 47; Rhodes scholar from Va, Oxford, 47-50, Ph.D.(Eng), 49; hon. LL.D, Southwest. at Memphis, 60 & Hamden-Sydney Col, 71; hon. L.H.D, Wake Forest Univ, 64, Jefferson Med. Col, 67 & Bridgewater Col, 70; hon. Litt.D, Centre Col, 68. Assoc. prof. naval sci. & tactics, Harvard, 46, instr. Eng, 50-52, asst. prof. & head tutor, 52-56; assoc. prof, UNIV. VA, 56-59, PROF. ENG, 59-, pres, 59-74. Guggenheim fel. & Fulbright res. fel, Oxford, 53-54; chmn, Va. selection comt. Fulbright scholars, 59-; mem. comt. on standards, South. Asn. Cols. & Schs, 60-67; Nat. Comn. on Accrediting, 61-67; adv. panel on Reserve Off. Training Corps Affairs, Armed Forces Policy Bd, U.S. Dept. Defense, 61-69; Rhodes Scholar. Selection Comt, 61-64; South. Regional Educ. Bd, 62-71; bd. admin, Va. Inst. Marine Sci, 62-71; chmn. gov. comt, Va. Assoc. Res. Ctr, 62-67; pres, Counc. South. Univs, 62-64, 71-72; mem. bd. visitors, U.S. Naval Acad, 62-64 & U.S. Air Force Acad, 65-67; mem. bd. trustees, Darlington Sch, 65-; mem. counc, Harvard Grad. Soc. Advan. Stud. & Res, 65-71; mem. U.S. Nat. Comn. for UNESCO, 66-67; mem. bd. dir. Am. Counc. Educ, 67-70; mem. adv. comt. instnl. relat, Nat. Sci. Found, 68-72, chmn, 70-72; mem. bd. consult, Nat. War Col, 69-71; pres, Asn. Va. Cols, 69-71; v.chmn, Am. Counc. Educ, 71-72. U.S.N, 41-46, Lt. Comdr; U.S.N.R, Res, Capt. (Ret); Bronze Star Medal. Nat. Asn. State Univs. & Land Grant Cols.(pres, 65-66, chmn, exec. comt, 66-67); MLA; Newcomen Soc. English literature of the 19th century. Publ: Tennyson and the reviewers, 1827-1851, Harvard Univ; Emma: character and construction, PMLA; Lockwood's dreams and the exegesis of Wuthering Heights, Nineteenth Century Fiction, 9/59. Add: Pavilion VIII, East Lawn, University of Virginia, Charlottesville, VA 22903.

SHANOWER, DONALD, b. Canton, Ohio, Dec. 15, 21; m. 51; c. 5. SPEECH & DRAMA. A.B, Kent State Univ, 47, M.A, 49; West. Reserve Univ, summers, 50-51; Ph.D.(speech & theatre), 60. Asst. instr. speech, Kent State Univ, 48-49; instr, Col. Wooster, 49-53; asst. prof, N.CENT. COL.(ILL), 55-60, assoc. prof. speech & theatre, 60-64, PROF. SPEECH, 64-, CHMN. DEPT, 65- U.S.A, 42-46, Sgt. Speech Commun. Asn; Am. Theatre Asn. American theatre history; British theatre. Add: Dept. of Speech, North Central College, Naperville, IL 60540.

SHAPIRO, ARNOLD, b. Paterson, N.J, Oct. 7, 34; m. 62; c. 2. ENGLISH. B.A, Rutgers Univ, 55; M.A, Johns Hopkins Univ, 56; Ph.D.(Eng), Ind. Univ, 65. Instr. ENG, OHIO STATE UNIV, 64-65, asst. prof, 65-70, ASSOC. PROF, 70- Fulbright prof. Am. lit, Univ. Helsinki, 71-72. U.S.A, 60-62. MLA. Publ: Wuthering Heights as a Victorian novel, Stud. Novel, 69; Browning's psalm of hate: Caliban upon Setebos, Psalm 50, and The tempest, Papers Lang. & Lit, 72; A new (old) reading of Bishop Blougram's apology, Victorian Poetry, 72; plus others. Add: Dept. of English, Ohio State University, 164 W. 17th Ave, Columbus, OH 43210.

SHAPIRO, GLORIA KAUFMAN, English & American Literature. See KAUFMAN, GLORIA (SHAPIRO).

SHAPIRO, HAROLD ISRAEL, b. Brooklyn, N.Y, Mar. 13, 31; m. 53; c. 2. ENGLISH. A.B, Cornell Univ, 52; A.M, Yale, 55, Ph.D.(Eng), 62. Instr. ENG, Bucknell Univ, 57-59; Hofstra Univ, 60-62, asst. prof, 62-69, assoc. prof, 69-72, prof, 72-73; assoc. prof, Univ. Hawaii, 73; PROF, UNIV. N.C, CHAPEL HILL, 74- Nat. Found. Arts & Humanities fel, 67-68. John Ruskin; Victorian literature; literary criticism. Publ: Ed, Ruskin in Italy: letters to his parents, 1845, Clarendon, 72; auth, The poetry of architecture: Ruskin's preparation for MP, Renaissance & Mod. Stud, 71. Add: Dept. of English, University of North Carolina, Chapel Hill, NC 27514.

SHAPIRO, KARL JAY, b. Baltimore, Md, Nov. 10, 13; m. 45; c. 3. ENGLISH. Johns Hopkins Univ, 37-39; D.H.L, Wayne State Univ, 72; D.Litt, Bucknell Univ, 73. Consult. poetry, Libr. Congr, 46-47; assoc. prof. Eng, Johns Hopkins Univ, 47-50; ed, Poetry, 50-55; vis. prof. ENG, Univ. Calif, 55-56; from assoc. prof. to prof, Univ. Nebr, 56-66, Montgomery lectr, 53; PROF, Univ. Ill, Chicago, 66-67; UNIV. CALIF, DAVIS, 67- Guggenheim fel, 45, 54; ed, Prairie Schooner, 53-66. Pulitzer Prize, 45; Bollingen Prize, 68. U.S.M.C, 40-45. Am. Acad. Arts & Lett. Poetry; literary criticism. Publ: Poems, 35; Person, place and things, 42; The place of love, 42; V-Letter and other poems, 44; Essay on Rime, 45, Poems 42-53, 53, Poems of a Jew, 58, In defense of ignorance, 60, co-auth, The bougeois poet, 64, auth, White-haired lover (poems), 68 & Selected poems, 68, Random; Trial of a poet, 47; Bibliography of modern prosody, 48; Beyond criticism, 53; Prose keys to modern poetry, 62 & A prosody handbook, 64, Harper; co-auth, Start with the sun, 60 & auth, Primer for poets, 65, Univ. Nebr; ed, American poetry, Crowell, 60; auth, To abolish children (essays), Quadrangle, 68; Edsel (novel), 71. Add: Dept. of English, University of California, Davis, CA 95616.

SHAPIRO, MICHAEL, b. Rochester, N.Y, Mar. 31, 38; m. 61; c. 3. ENGLISH. B.A, Univ. Rochester, 59; M.A, Columbia Univ, 60, Ph.D.(Eng), 67; Univ. Birmingham, 60. Lectr. ENG, Pace Col, 61-62; City Col. New York, 61-65; instr, N.Y. Inst. Technol, 66-67; asst. prof, UNIV. ILL, URBANA, 67-73, ASSOC. PROF, 73- MLA; Renaissance Soc. Am; Malone Soc; Shakespeare Asn. Am. Elizabethan drama; Renaissance literature. Publ: Children's troupes: dramatic illusion and acting style, Comp. Drama, 69; Toward a reappraisal of the children's troupes, Theatre Surv, 72; Audience vs. dramatist: Jonson's Epicoene and other plays of the children's troupes, Eng. Lit. Renaissance, 73; plus one other. Add: Dept. of English, University of Illinois at Urbana, Urbana, IL 61801.

SHARF, DONALD J, b. Detroit, Mich, Aug. 4, 27; m. 52; c. 2. SPEECH. B.A, Wayne State Univ, 51, M.A, 52; Ph.D.(speech), Univ. Mich, 58. Asst. ed, G. & C. Merriam Co, 57-61; asst. prof, State Univ. N.Y. Buffalo, 61-64; SPEECH, UNIV. MICH, ANN ARBOR, 64-67, assoc. prof, 67-73, PROF, 73- Res. Found. State Univ. N.Y. res. fel, 62; traineeship commun. sci. sem, Voc. Rehabil. Admin, 63. U.S.A, 45-46. Am. Speech & Hearing Asn; Acoust. Soc. Am; Int. Soc. Phonetic Sci; Am. Asn. Phonetic Sci. Speech intelligibility and analysis; perceptual phonetics. Publ: Co-auth, Perceptual parameters of consonant sounds, 71 & Response latency in speech shadowing as an indicator of distinctive features of consonants, 72, Lang. & Speech; co-auth, Identification of place of consonant articulation from vowel formant transitions, J. Acoust. Soc. Am, 72; plus others. Add: Speech & Hearing Science Lab, University of Michigan, 1111 E. Catherine, Ann Arbor, MI 48104.

SHARMA, GOVIND NARAIN, b. Jaipur, India, Mar. 11, 27; m. 47; c. 3. ENGLISH. B.A, Agra Univ, 46; M.A, Rajasthan Univ, 49; Ph.D.(Eng), Univ. Toronto, 63. Lectr. ENG, Delhi Col, Univ. Delhi, 49-54; Maharaja's Col, Jaipur, 54-56; Hindu Col, Univ. Delhi, 56-64, sr. lect, Hastinapur Col, 64-66, reader, Dept. Eng, 66-68; assoc. prof, ACADIA UNIV, 68-73, PROF, 73- Asn. Can. Univ. Teachers Eng; Humanities Asn. Can; MLA. Victorian literature; Romantic literature; history of ideas. Publ: Dryden: an essay of dramatic poesy, Rama Brothers & Co, 67; The way of all flesh—a consideration, Lit. Criterion, summer 67; Samuel Butler and Edmund Burke: a comparative study in British conservatism, Dalhousie Rev, spring 73. Add: Dept. of English, Box 257, Acadia University, Wolfville, N.S, Can.

SHARMA, MOHAN LAL, b. Bilga, India, Feb. 5, 19; m. 47; c. 2. ENGLISH & AMERICAN LITERATURE. Punjab Univ, India, 39, M.A, 41; Ph.D.(Eng), Ohio State Univ, 65. Lectr. Eng, Lyallpur, Rohtak, D'sala & Ludhiana State Cols, India, 42-56; sr. lectr, Ludhiana State Col, India, 56-59; asst. Ohio State Univ, 60-65; assoc. prof, SLIPPERY ROCK STATE COL, 65-68, PROF. ENG. & AM. EAST. LIT, 68- MLA; Am. Name Soc. English, American and comparative literatures. Publ: Afro-American music and dance, 70 & The black American's prowess on the playing field, 70, Philos. Libr; The functional English preface, Forum, summer 67; Mark Twain's passage to India, Mark Twain J, summer 68; Martin Luther King: modern America's greatest theologian of social action, J. Negro Hist, 8/68. Add: Dept. of English, Slippery Rock State College, Slippery Rock, PA 16057.

SHARP, CORONA, b. Pasadena, Calif, May 14, 22. ENGLISH, FOREIGN LANGUAGES. B.A, Univ. West. Ont, 47; M.A, Univ. Notre Dame, 56, Can. Counc. fel, 60-62, Ph.D.(Eng), 62. Lectr. ENG, BRESCIA COL.(ONT), 57-59, asst. prof, 62-65, assoc. prof, 65-66, PROF. & HEAD DEPT, 66- Summers, Can. Counc. res. grant, 66; Huron Col. res. grant, 68. MLA; Asn. Can. Univ. Teachers Eng; Shakespeare Asn. Am; Humanities Asn. Can. American literature; modern Swiss drama; Shakespeare. Publ: The confidante in Henry James, Univ. Notre Dame, 63; Fatherhood in Henry James, 4/66 & Dürrenmatt and the spirit of play, 10/69, Univ. Toronto Quart; Dürrenmatt's play Strindberg, Mod. Drama, 12/70; plus others. Add: Dept. of English, Brescia College, 1285 Western Rd, London, Ont. N6G 1H2, Can.

SHARP, HARRY W, JR, b. Leavenworth, Kans, Aug. 1, 37; m. 60; c. 2. RHETORIC, COMMUNICATION. A.B, Univ. of the Pac, 59; M.S, Purdue Univ, 61, fel, 62-63, Ph.D.(speech), 67. Instr. speech, Purdue Univ, 61-62; Col. Wooster, 63-65, ASST. PROF, 65-67; RHETORIC, UNIV. CALIF, DAVIS, 67- Vis. lectr, Humboldt State Col, spring 67. Speech Commun. Asn; Am. Forensic Asn. Government—press relations; contemporary persuasion theory and public address. Publ: Co-auth, Reflective thinking and performance in problem-solving discussions, J. Commun, 3/63 & Effects of organization on the speaker's ethos, Speech Monogr, 6/66; auth, The telecasting of John Kennedy's news conference, J. Broadcasting, 68. Add: Dept. of Rhetoric, University of California, Davis, CA 95616.

SHARP, LIONEL RICHARD, b. New York, N.Y, Sept. 8, 27; m. 59; c. 2. ENGLISH. B.A, Syracuse Univ, 50, 54-58; Occidental Col, 50-51; M.A, State Univ. N.Y. Albany, 54. Instr. Eng, Syracuse Univ, 54-60; tech. writer, Gen. Electric Co, 60-62; ASSOC. PROF. ENG, CAZENOVIA COL, 62- Commun. analyst, 61-; dir. summer inst, Nat. Endowment for Humanities, 68, 71, consult-panelist, Div. Educ. Prog, 70-; mem. comn. on compos, NCTE, 68-70, consult, 68-; dir. summer inst, Nat. Endowment for Humanities & Ford Found, 69; affil. speaker, Conf. Col. Compos. & Commun, 72; consult, Miami-Dade Jr. Col. South, 72; Queensborough Community Col, 72; vis. eval. team mem, Comn. Higher Educ, Mid. States Asn. Cols. & Sec. Schs, 72- NCTE (dir-at-large, 70-73); Conf. Col. Compos. & Commun.(asst. chmn, nat. jr. col. comt, 68-69, chmn, 69-70; secy. Conf, 71-72, asst. chmn, 72-73, assoc. chmn, 73-74). American literature; composition; curriculum development. Publ: Co-auth, Composition and grammar (grade 10) & Composition and language (grades 11 & 12), Ginn, 68. Add: Dept. of Languages & Literature, Cazenovia College, Cazenovia, NY 13035.

SHARP, NICHOLAS ANDREW, b. Kansas City, Mo, Jan. 24, 44; m. 69; c. 3. ENGLISH RENAISSANCE LITERATURE. B.A, Univ. Kans, 66; M.A, Ohio State Univ, Columbus, 68, Ph.D.(Eng), 71. ASST. PROF. ENG, VA. COMMONWEALTH UNIV, 71- MLA; S.Atlantic Mod. Lang. Asn. English education; children's literature; Renaissance literature. Add: Dept. of English, Virginia Commonwealth University, 901 W. Franklin, Richmond, VA 23284.

SHARP, WILLIAM LESLIE, b. Sept. 3, 24; m. 49; c. 3. DRAMA, ENGLISH. B.A. & M.A, Univ. Chicago, 49; Ph.D, Stanford Univ, 54. Instr. Eng, Rice Inst, 49-51; asst. prof. drama & Eng, Univ. Calif, Riverside, 54-60, assoc. prof. drama, 60-64; vis. assoc. prof. speech & drama, Stanford Univ, 64-66, assoc. prof, 66-70; PROF. DRAMATIC ARTS & CHMN. DEPT, EMERSON COL, 70- Vis. assoc. prof, Breadloaf Sch. Eng, 66-72; vis. prof, Middlebury Col, 69-70. U.S.A, 43-46. Am. Theatre Asn. Publ: Language and drama: meanings for the director and the actor, Chandler Publ, 70; introduction, In: School for scandal, Chandler Editions in Drama, 61; An unfashionable view of Tennessee Williams, Tulane Drama Rev, spring 62; Restoration comedy: an approach to modern production, Drama Surv, winter 68-69; plus two others. Add: Dept. of Dramatic Arts, Emerson College, Boston, MA 02116.

SHARPHAM, JOHN RAYMOND, b. Sydney, Australia, Nov. 29, 40; m. 68. THEATRE EDUCATION. B.A, Univ. Sydney, 62, dipl. educ, 63; Australian-Am. Educ. Found. travelling fel, 69; M.A, Univ. Colo, 70, univ. fel, 70-71, George F. Reynolds fel, 71-72, Ph.D.(commun, theatre), 72. Teacher Eng. lit, Ft. Street Boys' High Sch, Sydney, Australia, 64-66; lectr. Eng. & drama, Alexander Mackie Col, Sydney, 66-69; ASST. PROF. CREATIVE DRAMA, ILL. STATE UNIV, 72- Vis. prof. drama, Mem. Univ. Nfld, 72-73. Australian Col. Educ; Speech Commun. Asn; Int. Commun. Asn; Brit. Children's Theatre Asn; Can. Speech Commun. Asn. Creative drama; aesthetic education; theatre in education. Publ: Co-auth, The interpretative experience as a rhetorical transaction, Cent. States Speech J, fall 71; auth, Creative drama in four countries, Can. Speech Commun. J, 12/72; co-auth, Professional actors in the university classroom, Phi Delta Kappan, 12/73. Add: Dept. of Theatre, Illinois State University, Normal, IL 61761.

SHARPLES, EDWARD, JR, b. Westport, Mass, Apr. 9, 33; m. 56; c. 2. ENGLISH. A.B, Univ. Mass, 55; Ph.D.(Eng), Univ. Rochester, 64. Instr. ENG, WAYNE STATE UNIV, 61-64, asst. prof, 64-71, ASSOC. PROF, 71-, V.CHMN. DEPT, 69-, fac. res. fel, 68-69. U.S.A.R, 57-65, Sgt. MLA; Col. Eng. Asn; AAUP. Nineteenth century; Thomas Carlyle. Add: Dept. of English, Wayne State University, Detroit, MI 48202.

SHARPLESS, FRANCIS PARVIN, b. Lancaster, Pa, Nov. 21, 29; m. 51; c. 4. ENGLISH. B.A, Haverford Col, 51; M.A, Princeton, 57, Ph.D.(Eng), 62. Instr. humanities, Drexel Inst. Technol, 57-61; ENG, Univ. Pa, 61-64, asst. prof, 64-66; Goucher Col, 66-67; CHMN. DEPT, GERMANTOWN FRIENDS SCH, 67-, DIR. STUD, 73- Ed, Hayden Humanities Texts, Hayden Bk. Co, 71- U.S.N, 51-54, Lt. MLA; NCTE. Theory and practice of teaching the humanities; 19th century British literature and critical theory. Publ: The literary criticism of John Stuart Mill, Mouton, 67; Irony in Joyce's Portrait: the stasis of pity, James Joyce Quart, summer 67; Reflections on The college teaching of English, Col. Eng, 10/67; The intermediate college, Col. Bd. Rev, spring 71; plus others. Add: Germantown Friends School, Philadelphia, PA 19144.

SHATTUCK, CHARLES HARLEN, b. Belvidere, Ill, Nov. 23, 10; m. 36; c. 2. ENGLISH LITERATURE. A.B, Univ. Ill, 32, A.M, 34, Ph.D, 38. Asst. ENG, UNIV. ILL, 34-38, instr, 38-40, assoc, 40-44, asst. prof, 44-48, assoc. prof, 48-57, PROF, 57-, dir. univ. theatre, 43-63, assoc. mem, Ctr. Advan. Stud, 61-62, 65. MacCracken prof. & dir. exp. theater, Vassar Col, 48-49; ed, Accent, 40-60; Accent Anthol, 48; Folger fel, summers 59, 61 & 74; John Simon Guggenheim fel, 61-62, 68-69. George Freedley Award, Theatre Libr. Asn, 69. Shakespeare Asn. Am; Am. Soc. Theatre Res; MLA; Soc. Theatre Res, Eng. Dramatic literature; theater history. Publ: Bulwer and Macready, a chronicle of the early Victorian theatre, 58, William Charles Macready's King John, 62, The Shakespeare prompt books: a descriptive catalogue, 65 & The Hamlet of Edwin Booth, 69, Univ. Ill; Mr. Macready produces As you like it, Beta Phi Mu, 63; co-auth, The laurel Shakespeare: The merry wives of Windsor, Dell, 66; ed, John Philip Kemble's Prompt books (11 vols), Folger Shakespeare Libr, 74; auth, A Victorian stage manager: George Cressall Ellis, Theatre Notebook, spring 68; The theatrical management of Edwin Booth, In: The theatrical manager in England and America, Princeton Univ, 71; Shakespeare's plays on stage and screen, In: The riverside Shakespeare, Houghton, 74; plus others. Add: Dept. of English, 212 English Bldg, University of Illinois, Urbana, IL 61801.

SHATTUCK, ROGER WHITNEY, French Literature. See Volume III, Foreign Languages, Linguistics & Philology.

SHATZKY, JOEL LAWRENCE, b. Vancouver, Wash, Nov. 30, 43; m. 67; c. 1. MODERN DRAMA. B.A, Queens Col.(N.Y), 64; M.A, Univ. Chicago, 65; Ph.D.(Eng), N.Y. Univ, 70. ASST. PROF. ENG, STATE UNIV. N.Y. COL. CORTLAND, 68-, Res. Found. fel, summer 70. Modern American and European drama. Publ: The reactive image in Death of a salesman, Players, 2-3/73; Ibsen and naturalism, Edda, 74. Add: Dept. of English, State University of New York College at Cortland, Cortland, NY 13045.

SHAVER, CHESTER LINN, b. Somerset, Pa, Nov. 23, 07; m. 37; c. 2. ENGLISH LITERATURE. A.B, Oberlin Col, 28; A.M, Harvard, 29, Dexter traveling fel, 37, Ph.D, 37. Instr. ENG, L.I. Univ. 29-30, OBERLIN COL, 30-40, asst. prof, 40-46, assoc. prof, 46-49, PROF, 50-, chmn. dept, 52-55, 64-70, acting chmn, 61. Haskell traveling scholar, 56-57; Am. Counc. Learned Soc. traveling scholar, 59; hon. ed, The Wordsworth Circle, 70-; assoc, Trustees Dove Cottage, Grasmere, Westmoreland, Eng, 70-; v.pres, Rydal Mount Summer Sch. Asn, 72-73, pres, 73-74. AAUP; MLA. Poetry of the Romantic movement; Wordsworth. Publ: Ed, The letters of William and Dorothy Wordsworth: the early years, 1787-1805, Oxford, 67; articles on Byron, DeQuincey, Keats, Shelley, & Wordsworth, In: Encyclopedia international, Grolier, 63; Three unpublished Wordsworth letters, Notes & Queries, 1/67. Add: 265 E. College St, Oberlin, OH 44074.

SHAVER, CLAUDE L, b. Kirksville, Mo, May 16, 05; m. 28; c. 1. LINGUISTICS, THEATRE. B.S, Northeast Mo. State Teachers Col, 26; M.A, State Univ. Iowa, 29; Ph.D, Univ. Wis, 37; Univ. Calif, Berkeley, 55; Univ. Mich. Ling. Inst, summer, 57. Instr. speech, Northeast Mo. State Teachers Col, 26-28; LA. STATE UNIV, BATON ROUGE, 28-37, assoc. prof, 37-48, prof. SPEECH, LING. & THEATRE, 48-72, ALUMNI PROF, 72-, CHMN. INTERDEPT. LING. PROG, 61-, mem. univ. Caribbean Prog, C.Z, 51-52, P.R, summer, 53. Vis. prof, Univ. Denver, summer, 43; South. Ill. Univ, 63; Smith-Mundt grant, Chinese Refugee Cols, Hong Kong, 60-61; vis. prof, Univ. Hawaii, 65-66; NDEA Inst. Eng, Univ. Alaska, summer 67; NDEA Inst. Eng. for Speakers of Other Lang, Dialects, Univ. South. Calif, summer 68. Speech Commun. Asn; Am. Theatre Asn; Am. Nat. Theatre & Acad; Nat. Theatre Conf; South. Speech Commun. Asn.(pres, 50-51, ed, South. Speech J, 44-48); Southwest Theatre Conf; Ling. Soc. Am; Am. Dialect Soc; Am. Soc. Theatre Res; Teachers of Eng. to Speakers of Other Lang. Theatre history; teaching English as a foreign language; linguistics. Publ: Co-auth, Speech methods and resources, Harper, 61, Minstrel show, In: Encyclopaedia Britannica, 61 & Steele MacKaye and the American Delsartians, In: History of speech education in America, Appleton, 54. Add: Dept. of Speech, Louisiana State University, Baton Rouge, LA 70803.

SHAW, JOHN BURNHAM, b. Chicago, Ill, Sept. 24, 22; m. 48; c. 3. ENGLISH. B.A, Oberlin Col, 47; Ph.D.(Eng), Johns Hopkins Univ, 52. Instr. ENG, Williams Col, 52-55; from asst. prof. to PROF, HIRAM COL, 55- Vis. lectr, Bristol Univ, 64-65. U.S.A, 43-45. MLA; Shakespeare Asn. Am. Shakespearean drama. Publ: Co-auth, Working with poetry, Educators Publ. Serv, 68; What is the matter? in Othello, Shakespeare Quart, spring 66; King Lear: the final lines, Essays in Criticism, 7/66; The staging of parody and parallels in I Henry IV, Shakespeare Surv, 67. Add: Dept. of English, Hiram College, Hiram, OH 44234.

SHAW, LEROY ROBERT, German. See Volume III, Foreign Languages, Linguistics & Philology.

SHAW, MYRON B, b. Canton, Ohio, June 30, 30; m. 56; c. 2. SPEECH, BROADCASTING. B.S, Kent State Univ, 53; A.M, Univ. Mich, 58, Ph.D. (speech), 62. Instr. SPEECH, Univ. Mich, 61-64; ASSOC. PROF, STATE UNIV. N.Y. COL. GENESEO, 64- U.S.A.F, 54-58, S/Sgt. Speech Commun. Asn. Broadcast programming. Publ: College station extends beyond the campus, Broadcast Mgt/E, 2/68; Station of the year award, Col. Radio, 10/66; Inside WGSU-FM, Col. Scene, 12/66. Add: 24 Stuyvesant Manor, Geneseo, NY 14454.

SHAW, PETER, b. New York, N.Y, Nov. 25, 36; m. 58; c. 2. ENGLISH & AMERICAN LITERATURE. A.B, Bard Col, 58; M.A, Columbia Univ, 62, Ph.D.(comp. lit), 65. Lectr. Eng, Fairleigh Dickinson Univ, 61; gen. stud, Columbia Univ, 61-62, preceptor Eng, 62-65; asst. prof, State Univ. N.Y. Stony Brook, 65-68; assoc. ed, Commentary Mag, 68-69; ASSOC. PROF. ENG, STATE UNIV. N.Y. STONY BROOK, 71- Vis. lectr, New Sch, 67; Am. Counc. Learned Soc. grant, summer 72; Nat. Endowment for Humanities fel, 73. MLA. Contemporary and American literature. Publ: Blood is thicker than irony: Henry Adams' history, New Eng. Quart, spring 67; auth, numerous articles in var. periodicals. Add: 106 W. 69th St, New York, NY 10023.

SHAW, PRISCILLA WASHBURN, b. Boston, Mass, Sept. 25, 30; div. ENGLISH. B.A, Swarthmore Col, 52; Ph.D.(comp. lit), Yale, 60. Teacher French & Eng, Shipley Sch. Girls, 56-58; instr. French, Haverford Col, 58; Douglass Col, Rutgers Univ, 59-61; Eng, Yale, 61-63, asst. prof, 63-66; ASSOC. PROF. LIT, UNIV. CALIF, SANTA CRUZ, 66- MLA. Modern poetry. Publ: Rilke, Valery & Yeats: domain of the self, Rutgers Univ, 64. Add: 150 Sunnyside, Santa Cruz, CA 95062.

SHAW, W. DAVID, b. Ottawa, Ont, July 2, 37. ENGLISH. B.A, Univ. Toronto, 59; A.M, Harvard, 60, Ph.D.(Eng), 63. Tutor ENG, Harvard, 62-63; asst. prof, Cornell Univ, 63-69; ASSOC. PROF, VICTORIA COL, UNIV. TORONTO, 69- Vis. assoc. prof, Univ. Calif, Riverside, 68-69. MLA. Publ: The dialectical temper: the rhetorical art of Robert Browning, Cornell Univ, 68; In memoriam and the rhetoric of confession, Eng. Lit. Hist, 71; Imagination and intellect in Tennyson's Lucretius, Mod. Lang. Quart, 72; Tennyson's Tithonus and the problem of mortality, Philol. Quart, 73; plus others. Add: 18 McNairn Ave, Toronto, Ont. M5M 2H5, Can.

SHAW, WILLIAM HARLAN, b. Tulia, Tex, Apr. 3, 22; m. 45; c. 2. THEATER, FINE ARTS. B.A, Hardin-Simmons Univ, 43, M.A, 49; Ph.D.(theater), La. State Univ, 55. Instr. THEATER, Hardin-Simmons Univ, 49-50, asst. prof, 55-56; instr, Ill. State Normal Univ, 50-53; asst. prof, Wash. Univ, 56-61; Fla. State Univ, 61-67, assoc. prof, 67-68; UNIV. NEW ORLEANS, 68-72, PROF, 72- Mem. Fla. State Univ, Res. Counc, 66-67. U.S.N.R, 43-46, Lt. (jg). Am. Theatre Asn; Speech Commun. Asn; Southwest Theatre Conf. German expressionism; men's wear since 1860; theater costume. Publ: Co-auth, Introduction to theatrical arts, Kendall/Hunt, 71; auth, Basic pattern drafting for the theatrical costumer, Drama Bk. Specialists, 74. Add: Dept. of Drama & Communications, University of New Orleans, Lakefront, New Orleans, LA 70122.

SHAWCROSS, JOHN THOMAS, b. Hillside, N.J, Feb. 10, 24. ENGLISH. A.B, N.J. State Col, Montclair, 48; A.M, N.Y. Univ, 50, Ph.D, 58. From instr. to prof. Eng, Newark Col. Engineering, 48-63; PROF. ENG, Douglass Col,

Rutgers Univ, 63-67; Univ. Wis-Madison, 67-70; STATEN ISLAND COMMUNITY COL. & GRAD. CTR, CITY UNIV. NEW YORK, 70- Lectr, City Col. New York, 58-63; vis. prof, N.Y. Univ, 62 & 65; C.W. Post Col, L.I. Univ, 63; Univ. Del, 65-66; State Univ. N.Y. Stony Brook, 74. U.S.N.R, 42-46, Lt.(jg). Milton Soc.(treas, 62-72, v.pres, 73, pres, 74-); Col. Eng. Asn; Renaissance Soc. Am; Bibliog. Soc. Am; NCTE; MLA. Milton; 17th century; modern poetry. Publ: Complete English poetry of John Milton, N.Y. Univ. & Anchor, 63, Complete poetry of John Donne, Anchor, 67 & N.Y. Univ. & Univ. London, 68; co-auth, Language and style in Milton, Ungar, 67; auth, Paradise lost: a guide, 67 & Hamlet; a guide, 68, Educ. Res. Assoc; Milton; the critical heritage, 68 & ed, Milton: the critical heritage, 1732-1801, 72, Routledge & Kegan Publ; ed, The complete poetry of John Milton, Doubleday, 71; co-ed. & contrib, Achievements of the left hand: essays on Milton's prose, Univ. Mass, 74; Balanced structure of Paradise lost, Stud. Philol, 65; Tenure of kings and magistrates, familiar letters, In: The prose of John Milton, Doubleday, 67; Metaphor of inspiration, In: Th' upright heart and pure, Duquesne Univ, 67. Add: Dept. of English, Graduate Center, City University of New York, W. 42nd St, New York, NY 10036.

SHEA, DANIEL BARTHOLOMEW, JR, b. Minneapolis, Minn, Oct. 29, 36; m. 58; c. 5. AMERICAN LITERATURE. B.A, Col. St. Thomas, 58; M.A, Stanford Univ, 62, Ph.D.(Eng), 66. Instr. ENG, WASH. UNIV, 62-66, asst. prof, 66-70, ASSOC. PROF, 70- Fulbright-Hays lectr. Am. lit, Univ. Caen, 68-69; vis. lectr, Claremont Grad. Sch, summer 70; Nat. Endowment for Humanities fel, summer, 72; mem. ed. bd, Early Am. Lit, 72- MLA. Early American literature; American autobiography. Publ: Spiritual autobiography in early America, Princeton, 68; The art and instruction of Jonathan Edwards' Personal narrative, Am. Lit, 3/65; Jonathan Edwards, historian of consciousness, In: Major writers of Early American literature, 72. Add: Dept. of English, Washington University, St. Louis, MO 63130.

SHEA, FRANCIS XAVIER, S.J, b. Dorchester, Mass, Apr. 22, 26. ENGLISH, THEOLOGY. B.A, Boston Col, 49, M.A, 50; Ph.L, Weston Col, 50, S.T.L, 57; Ph.D.(Eng), Univ. Minn, 61. Asst. prof. mod. lit, Boston Col, 63-68, assoc. prof, 68-71, asst. dir. honors prog, 64-67, exec. v.pres, 69-71; PRES, COL. ST. SCHOLASTICA, 71-, PROF. ENG, 72- Mem. const: comt, Boston Theol. Inst, 65; nat. selection comt, Danforth Teachers Grant, 64-67. MLA. Our mutual friend, Charles Dickens; the poetry of John Clare; theological perspectives on modern literature. Publ: Theology as an academic discipline, In: The role of theology in the university, Bruce, 67; Religion and romanticism, Stud. Romanticism, 70; Reason and the religion of the counter-culture, Harvard Theol. Rev, 1/73; plus others. Add: College of St. Scholastica, Duluth, MN 55811.

SHEA, JOHN STEPHEN, b. New York, N.Y, July 18, 33; m. 62; c. 3. ENGLISH. A.B, Iona Col, 54; A.M, Marquette Univ, 56; scholar, Ind. Univ, summer 58; Danforth grant, Univ. Minn, 62-64, Ph.D.(Eng), 67. Instr. Eng, Wash. Univ, 64-67, asst. prof, 67-69, chmn. freshman Eng, 65-68; asst. prof. ENG, LOYOLA UNIV. CHICAGO, 69-72, ASSOC. PROF, 72-, ASST. CHMN. DEPT, 73- Reader advan. placement exam, Col. Entrance Exam. Bd, 68-73; ed, Restoration & 18th-Century Theatre Res, 72- MLA; Am. Soc. 18th Century Stud. Restoration and 18th century English literature; literary criticism. Publ: Co-auth, Themes and exercises, Dept. Eng, Univ. Minn, 60, 61 & 62; ed, Mandeville's Aesop dress'd, Augustan Reprint Soc, 66; co-ed, Studies in Criticism and aesthetics, 1660-1800, Univ. Minn, 67. Add: Dept. of English, Loyola University of Chicago, 6525 N. Sheridan Rd, Chicago, IL 60626.

SHEAFFER, MARY PATRICIA A, b. Chambersburg, Pa, June 2, 39. ENGLISH. B.S, Shippensburg State Col, 61; M.A, Tulane Univ, 62, Ph.D.(Eng. lit), 65; summer, Oxford, 68. Asst. prof. ENG, Miss. State Univ, 65-67; ASSOC. PROF, MILLERSVILLE STATE COL, 67- Miss. State Univ. Develop. Fund grant Victorian lit, Univ. London, summer 66, Univ. Edinburgh, summer 67. MLA. British nineteenth century and Renaissance literature. Publ: Speak for yourself, J. Col. Compos. & Commun, 12/67. Add: Dept. of English, Millersville State College, Millersville, PA 17551.

SHEAR, WALTER L, b. Hillsboro, Wis, Sept. 24, 32; m. 64; c. 1. ENGLISH. B.A, Univ. Wis, 54, Ph.D.(Eng), 61; M.A, State Univ. Iowa, 57. Assoc. prof. ENG, KANS. STATE COL. PITTSBURG, 60-70, PROF, 70- U.S.A, 54-56. MLA; Am. Stud. Asn. American literature; modern literature. Publ: Culture conflict in The assistant, 66 & Characterization in The scarlet letter, summer 71, Midwest Quart; Flannery O'Connor, Renascence, spring 68; plus one other. Add: Dept. of English, Kansas State College of Pittsburg, Pittsburg, KS 66762.

SHEARER, NED ALAN, b. Akron, Ohio, Mar. 6, 38; m. 61; c. 2. SPEECH. A.B, Oberlin Col, 59; M.S, Univ. Wis, 61, Ph.D.(speech), 67. Asst. prof. speech, Univ. Calif, Los Angeles, 65-73; ASSOC. PROF. COMMUN. ARTS & SCI. & CHMN. DEPT, WEST. ILL. UNIV, 73- Speech Commun. Asn. Communication, rhetoric and public address; parliamentary procedure. Publ: Co-auth, Rhetoric and public address: a bibliography, 1947-1961, Univ. Wis, 64; ed, Bibliographic annual in speech communication, Speech Commun. Asn, 70, 71, 72; ed, A bibliography of communication, rhetoric and public address, In: Bibliographic annual in speech communication, Speech Commun. Asn, 70, 71, 72; auth, Psychology as foundation to rhetoric: Alexander Bain and association psychology's relation to rhetorical theory, West. Speech, summer 71; Alexander Bain and the genesis of paragraph theory, Quart. J. Speech, 12/72. Add: Dept. of Communication Arts & Sciences, Western Illinois University, Macomb, IL 61455.

SHEARER, WILLIAM M, b. Zanesville, Ohio, June 24, 26; m. 54; c. 2. SPEECH. B.A, Ind. Univ, 51; M.A, West. Mich. Univ, 54; Ph.D.(speech), Univ. Denver, 58. Asst. prof. SPEECH, Minot State Col, 54-56; assoc. prof, NORTH. ILL. UNIV, 58-66, PROF, 67- Nat. Insts. Health fel, Stanford Univ, 63-64; vis. prof. exp. phonetics, Univ. Fla, 68-69. U.S.N, 44-46. Am. Speech & Hearing Asn. Stuttering; hearing. Publ: Illustrated speech anatomy, C.C. Thomas, 63; co-auth, Self-recovery from stuttering, J. Speech & Hearing Disorders, 8/65; auth, Behavior of middle ear muscle during stuttering, 5/66 & co-auth, Prenatal auditory imprinting in chickens, 3/67, Science. Add: Dept. of Communication Disorders, Northern Illinois University, De Kalb, IL 60115.

SHEARON, FORREST BEDFORD, b. Bolivar, Tenn, Sept. 7, 34; div; c. 2. BRITISH LITERATURE, HUMANITIES. A.B, Union Univ.(Tenn), 56; John Hay fel, Northwest. Univ, 62-63; M.A, Univ. Louisville, 65, Ph.D.(Eng), 73. Teacher Eng, Halls High Sch, Tenn, 56-58; Pleasure Ridge Park High Sch, Louisville, Ky, 58-65; instr, Ky. South. Col, 65-67, ASST. PROF, 67-69; Univ. Louisville, 69-73; HUMANITIES, EAST. KY. UNIV, 73- MLA. Eighteenth century British literature; George Crabbe. Publ: The South from a distance, Northwest. Tri-Quart, spring 63; The prince introduces Imlac to general semantics, ETC, 3/73. Add: General Studies Humanities Program, Eastern Kentucky University, Richmond, KY 40475.

SHEATS, PAUL DOUGLAS, b. Albany, N.Y, June 17, 32; m. 64; c. 2. ENGLISH. B.A, Harvard, 54, M.A, 63, Ph.D.(Eng), 66; A.B, Oxford, 57. Instr. ENG, Haverford Col, 58-60; teaching fel, Harvard, 63-66; asst. prof, UNIV. CALIF, LOS ANGELES, 66-72, ASSOC. PROF, 72- Mem, Univ. Calif. Humanities Inst, summer 68. U.S.A.F.R, 57-63. MLA. Wordsworth; Romantic poetry. Publ: The making of Wordsworth's poetry, 1785-1798, Harvard, 73; Stylistic discipline in The fall of Hyperion, Keats-Shelley J, 68; Excursion and return in The prelude, In: The Wordsworth circle, 70. Add: 2225 Humanities Bldg, University of California, Los Angeles, CA 90024.

SHECHNER, MARK EPHRAIM, b. Newark, N.J, June 22, 40; m. 67. MODERN FICTION. B.A, Univ. Calif, Los Angeles, 62, M.A, 64; Ph.D.(Eng), Univ. Calif, Berkeley, 70. ASST. PROF. ENG, STATE UNIV. N.Y, BUFFALO, 70- Literature and psychology; psychoanalytic psychology. Publ: Joyce in Nighttown, Univ. Calif, 74. Add: Dept. of English, State University of New York at Buffalo, Buffalo, NY 14214.

SHECHTER, STANLEY JACOB, Classical Philology. See Volume III, Foreign Languages, Linguistics & Philology.

SHEDD, GORDON MICHAEL, b. Rochester, N.Y, Nov. 1, 33; m. 54; c. 4. ENGLISH. A.B, Juniata Col, 58; M.A, Pa. State Univ, 61, fel, 63, Ph.D. (Eng), 65. Instr. ENG, PA. STATE UNIV, UNIVERSITY PARK, 63-65, ASST. PROF, 65- Pa. State Univ. Class of 1933 award for distinguished contrib. in humanities, 68. Mediaeval Acad. Am. Medieval literature; contemporary American literature. Publ: Knight in tarnished armour: the meaning of Sir Gawain and the Green Knight, Mod. Lang. Rev, 1/67; Flamenca: a medieval satire on courtly love, Chaucer Rev, summer 67. Add: Dept. of English, Pennsylvania State University, University Park, PA 16802.

SHEDD, ROBERT GORDON, b. Detroit, Mich, Mar. 30, 21; m. 43; c. 3. ENGLISH. A.B, Univ. Mich, 42, M.A, 47, Ph.D.(Eng), 53. Teaching fel, Univ. Mich, 46-50, instr, 50-52; Eng, Ohio State Univ, 52-55, asst. prof, 55-62, assoc. prof, chmn. dept. & dir. Lakewood Acad. Ctr, 62-66; PROF. ENG. & HUMANITIES, UNIV. MD, BALTIMORE COUNTY CAMPUS, 66- Assoc. ed, Mod. Drama, 60-; judge, Hopwood awards, Univ. Mich, 66 & 68; mem, NDEA Inst. Advan. Placement, Mt. Mary Col, 67; chief reader, Advan. Placement Eng. Exam, 68- Jule & Avery Hopwood awards, Univ. Mich, 48. U.S.N.R, 42-46, Lt. MLA; NCTE; Col. Eng. Asn. Shakespearean studies; modern drama; problems in dramatic structure. Publ: Co-ed, Masters of modern drama, 62 & co-auth, From Sophocles to Sartre, 69, Random; auth, Annual bibliography on modern drama, Mod. Drama, 60- Add: Dept. of English, University of Maryland, Baltimore County Campus, Baltimore, MD 21228.

SHEEHAN, JAMES CLEMENT, b. Fitchburg, Mass, May 9, 42. ENGLISH LITERATURE. B.A, Tufts Univ, 63; M.A, Univ. Mich, 68, Ph.D.(Eng), 71. ASST. PROF. ENG, UNIV. AKRON, 71- U.S.N, 64-67, Lt. MLA; AAUP. Renaissance and 17th century English literature. Add: Dept. of English, University of Akron, Akron, OH 44325.

SHEEHAN, PAUL V, b. Everett, Wash, Aug. 7, 04; m. 32; c. 1. JOURNALISM. A.B, Univ. Wash, 26, A.M, 30; Ph.D, Univ. South. Calif, 42. Instr. JOUR, Fresno State Col, 30-36; vis. lectr, Syracuse Univ, 36-37; asst. prof, CALIF. STATE UNIV, FRESNO, 38-43, assoc. prof, 43-46, prof, 46-69, chmn. dept, 51-69, EMER. PROF, 69- Chmn. curriculum comt. on jour, Calif. State Dept. Educ, 51; spec. asst. to state dir. educ. & coord. statewide inform. prog. on Calif. state building needs, 58. Asn. Educ. in Jour. Journalism. Publ: Better business letters, Benjamin H. Sanborn & Co, 39; Reportorial writing, Chilton, 72. Add: Suite 207, 311 N. Fulton St, Fresno, CA 93701.

SHEEN, EDWIN DRUMMOND, b. Decatur, Ill, Jan. 22, 02; m. 43. ENGLISH. A.B, Millikin Univ, 25; M.A, Univ. Ill, 27, Ph.D, 57; Univ. Chicago, 29, 36-37, 41-42, 46-47; summers, 38 & 42; Northwest. Univ, summers, 30 & 31. Instr. Eng. & jour, Howard Univ, 29-33; prof. & head dept, Eng. & speech, Samuel Huston Col, 33-35; instr. Eng, Lincoln Univ, 35-36; assoc. prof. Eng. & French, Livingstone Col, 37-38; prof. & head dept, ENG, Fayetteville St. Teachers Col, 38-43; assoc. prof, Prairie View Agr. & Mech. Col, 43-52, prof, 52-56; asst. prof, Lincoln Univ, 56-57, assoc. prof, 57-58; W.Va. State Col, 58-62, prof, 62-68, chmn. div. humanities, 67-68; RETIRED. Vis. prof, N.C. Cent. Univ, 68-69. Shakespeare Asn. Am; Col. Lang. Asn. Leslie Stephen as man of letters and critic of literature. Publ: Leslie Stephen and modern criticism, CLA J, 9/58. Add: P.O. Box 375, Institute, WV 25112.

SHEFFEY, RUTHE GARNETTA, U.S. citizen; m. 50; c. 2. ENGLISH. A.B, Morgan State Col, 47; M.A, Howard Univ, 49; Ph.D.(Eng), Univ. Pa, 59. Instr. ENG, Claflin Col, 48-49; MORGAN STATE COL, 49-54, asst. prof, 54-62, assoc. prof, 62-68, PROF, 68-, CHMN. DEPT, 70-, fac. res. grants, summer 62, 63-64, fall 67. Pres. mid. Atlantic region, Col. Eng. Asn, 65-66; Eng. consult, Wash. Integrated Sec. Educ. Proj, 67-68. Creative Scholarship award, Col. Lang. Asn. MLA; NCTE; Col. Eng. Asn; Col. Lang. Asn. Eighteenth century English literature; multi-ethnic textbooks; black poetry. Publ: Impressions in asphalt: a multi-ethnic literary anthology for senior high and junior colleges, Scribner, 69; Color symbolism in costumes at three Shakespearean festivals, Drama Critique, winter 64; From delight to wisdom: thematic progression in the poetry of Robert Frost, CLA J, 9/64; Wit and irony in contemporary black poetry, Black World, 6/73; plus others. Add: Dept. of English, Morgan State College, Baltimore, MD 21212.

SHEIDLEY, WILLIAM EDWARDS, b. Kansas City, Mo, May 29, 40; m. 62; c. 2. ENGLISH, RENAISSANCE LITERATURE. A.B, Stanford Univ, 62, A.M, 66, Ph.D.(Eng), 68. Asst. prof. ENG, UNIV. CONN, 66-72, ASSOC. PROF, 72-, fac. summer fel, 69, res. found grants, 69 & 73. MLA. Sixteenth century poetry. Publ: The seduction of the reader in Marlowe's Hero and Leander, Concerning Poetry, 70; George Turbervile and the problem of passion, J. Eng. & Ger. Philol, 70; A timely anachronism: tradition and theme in Barnabe Googe's Cupio conquered, Stud. in Philol, 72. Add: Dept. of English, U-25, University of Connecticut, Storrs, CT 06268.

SHELBY, MAURICE EARL, b. Knoxville, Tenn, May 14, 32; m. 54; c. 2. SPEECH. B.A, Univ. Wash, 61; Ph.D.(speech), Ohio State Univ, 63. Asst. prof. speech & jour, Baylor Univ, 63-64; ASSOC. PROF. SPEECH, Univ. Mo-Columbia, 64-71; UNIV. MASS, AMHERST, 71- Mem. comt. hist. broadcasting, Asn. Prof. Broadcasting, 67- U.S.N, 52-56. Speech Commun. Asn; Broadcast Educ. Asn. Broadcast criticism; children's programming; impact of mass media. Publ: Children's programming trends on network television, summer 64 & Patterns in thirty years of broadcast criticism, winter 66-67, J. Broadcasting; Derived values and children's attitudes toward a children's television program, Speech Monogr, 6/65. Add: Dept. of Speech, University of Massachusetts, Amherst, MA 01002.

SHELLEY, ALFRED BERNARD ROWLAND, b. Apr. 5, 02; m. 40; c. 2. ENGLISH LITERATURE. B.S, Tufts Univ, 25; A.M, Harvard, 26. Teacher high sch, Fairhaven, Mass, 26-37, Haverhill, 27-28; instr. Va. Mil. Inst, 28-31; from instr. to assoc. prof. ENG, N.C. STATE UNIV, 35-71, EMER. ASSOC. PROF, 71- Writing consult, Nationwide Insurance Co, 55-60; Bell Telephone Laboratories, Burling, N.C, 57; Russell Hosiery Mills, 59; N.C. Employment Security Comn, 65, 66; Home Security Co, 66-67; Aeroglyde Corp, 68. NCTE; Col. Eng. Asn; Conf. Col. Compos. & Commun; Am. Bus. Writing Asn. Restoration, 19th century drama; business communications. Publ: Co-auth, Handbook of English, Ginn; auth, Business writing, N.C. State Univ, 68; Accreditation of business writing for English, Col. Eng, 3/62. Add: 1206 Canterbury Rd, Raleigh, NC 27608.

SHELTON, LEWIS EDWARD, b. Hartford City, Ind, Oct. 12, 41; m. 68. DRAMA. B.A. & B.S, Taylor Univ, 63; M.A, Ind. Univ, 65; M.A, Univ. Wis-Madison, 68, univ. fel. & Ph.D.(theatre), 71. Teacher soc. sci. & Eng, Garrett High Sch, Ind, 64-66; ASST. PROF. THEATRE, Calif. State Univ, Hayward, 71-73; KANS. STATE UNIV, 73- Am. Theatre Asn; Speech Commun. Asn. Dramatic criticism; stage directing theory and history; theatre history. Add: Dept. of Speech, Kansas State University, Manhattan, KS 66502.

SHEPARD, BERNARD A, b. Syracuse, N.Y, Jan. 29, 18; m; c. 2. JOURNALISM. A.B, Union Col, 39; B.S, Columbia Univ, 40; M.S, Syracuse Univ, 49, Ph.D, 59. Writer, newspapers, N.Y, 40-47; pub. relat. dir, State Citizens' Counc, 47-48; instr. JOUR. & ENG, CALIF. STATE UNIV, FRESNO, 48-51, asst. prof, 51-56, assoc. prof, 56-59, PROF, 59- News writer & broadcaster, Sta. KFRE, Columbia Broadcasting Syst; Calif. State Cols. grant jour, Israel, 66. Distinguished Teaching Award, Calif. State Univ, 69; Award Jour. Educ, Calif. Newspaper Publ. Asn, 70. U.S.A, 42-46, Capt. Add: Dept. of Journalism, California State University, Fresno, Shaw & Cedar Ave, Fresno, CA 93710.

SHEPARD, DAVID W, b. River Falls, Wis, Jan. 10, 22; m. 48; c. 2. SPEECH & ENGLISH. B.S, Univ. Minn, 47, M.A, 49, Ph.D.(speech & Eng), 53. Instr. rhet, Univ. Minn, St. Paul, 48-51; SPEECH, Hamline Univ, 51-54; PROF, BALL STATE UNIV, 54- Eli Lilly grant, 57; ed, Ind. Speech Notes, 70- U.S.M.C, 41-45, T/Sgt. Speech Commun. Asn; Cent. States Speech Asn; Am. Forensic Asn. Content analysis of public address; rhetorical theory. Publ: Co-auth, A handbook for beginning debaters, 3rd ed, Burgess, 66; auth, Rhetoric and formal argument, West. Speech, autumn 66; The role of logic?, Quart J. Speech, 10/69; Burden of what?, J. Am. Forensic Asn, winter 73; plus others. Add: 3500 W. Gilbert, Muncie, IN 47304.

SHEPARD, DOUGLAS H, b. New York, N.Y, Dec. 6, 27; m. 50; c. 2. ENGLISH. B.A, Brooklyn Col, 51; M.A, Univ. Iowa, 53, Ph.D.(Eng), 57. Instr. ENG, Univ. Minn, Duluth, 55-59, asst. prof, 59-62; STATE UNIV. N.Y. COL. FREDONIA, 62-64, from assoc. prof. to PROF, 64-, res. found. grant-in-aid, 63-64, summer res. fel. found. fels, 65 & 66. Grant-in-aid, Univ. Minn, 61-62, summer res. fel, 62. U.S.N, 46-47. Bibliog. Soc. Univ. Va. Elizabethan shorthand; 18th century publishing; bibliography. Publ: Some bookseller-publishers, 1659-1800, Notes & Queries, 5/69; The creative researcher, Ref. Quart, 70; contrib, A guide to critical reviews of U.S. fiction, 1870-1910, Scarecrow, 71; plus two others. Add: Dept. of English, State University of New York College at Fredonia, Fredonia, NY 14063.

SHEPHARD, ESTHER, b. Minneapolis, Minn, July 29, 91; m. 14, 21; c. 1. ENGLISH. A.B, Univ. Wash, 20, Loretta Denny fel, 20, M.A, 21, Ph.D, 38. Instr. Eng, Reed Col, 21-22; Eng. & drama, Univ. Wash, 28-30, summer 31; prof. ENG, Lower Columbia Jr. Col, 34-35; from instr. to prof, SAN JOSE STATE UNIV, 39-59, EMER. PROF, 59- MLA; Am. Orient. Soc. American humor and folklore; Walt Whitman; the Chinese legend of Chih Nu and Niu Lang. Publ: Walt Whitman's prose, Harcourt, 38; Paul Bunyan (illustrated by Rockwell Kent), McNeil Press, 2nd ed, Harcourt, 24; The inside front and back covers of Whitman's earliest known notebook: some observations on photocopy and verbal descriptions, PMLA, 10/72; plus others. Add: 55 S. Sixth St, San Jose, CA 95112.

SHEPHERD, ALLEN GLASS, III, b. Boston, Mass, July 11, 36; m. 61; c. 2. ENGLISH & AMERICAN LITERATURE. A.B, Harvard, 58; A.M, Brown Univ, 60; Ph.D.(Eng), Univ. Pa, 65. Instr. ENG, UNIV. VT, 65-66, asst. prof, 66-70, ASSOC. PROF, 70- U.S.A, 60-61, Res, 61-67, Capt. MLA; Col. Eng. Asn; Soc. Stud. South. Lit. Twentieth century Southern writers, especially Faulkner, Warren and Welty; politics and literary criticism. Publ: Robert Penn Warren as a philosophical novelist, West. Humanities Rev, spring 70; The poles of fiction, Warren's At heaven's gate, Tex. Stud. Lit. & Lang, winter 71; The literary radicalism of John Macy, Res. Stud, spring 71. Add: Dept. of English, 315 Old Mill, University of Vermont, Burlington, VT 05401.

SHEPHERD, LOUIS P, b. St. Louis, Mo, Aug. 21, 18; m. 41; c. 1. ENGLISH. B.S, Ed, Kans. State Teachers Col, 41; A.M, Columbia Univ, 45; Stanford Univ, 45; Boston Univ, 57-58. Teacher, high sch, Kans, 41-42; Grace Church Sch, 42-43; McBurney Sch, 43-45; instr. Eng, Ore. State Col, 45-46; acting instr, Stanford Univ, 46-47; asst. prof. Eng. & speech, Calif. State Polytech. Col, 47-51; ASSOC. PROF. ENG, FITCHBURG STATE COL, 52- Film productions. Publ: Cape House (novel), Dell, 73; Norman Douglas' lesser known novels, Boston Univ. Grad. J, 10/58; Creating exciting films with still photos, Better Home Movie Making, 5-6/63; plus others. Add: Dept. of English, Fitchburg State College, Fitchburg, MA 01420.

SHERBO, ARTHUR, b. Haverhill, Mass, May 27, 18; m. 47; c. 3. ENGLISH. B.A, Bowdoin Col, 47; M.A, Columbia Univ, 48, Ph.D.(Eng), 50. Instr. ENG, Univ. Ill, 50-53, asst. prof, 53-56; MICH. STATE UNIV, 56-57, assoc. prof, 57-62, PROF, 62- Guggenheim fel, 57-58. U.S.A, 42-46. MLA. Samuel Johnson; Christopher Smart; 18th century English literature. Publ: Samuel Johnson, editor of Shakespeare, Univ. Ill, 56; English sentimental drama, 57, New essays by Arthur Murphy, 63 & Christopher Smart, scholar of the university, 67, Mich. State Univ; ed, Johnson on Shakespeare, Vols. VII & VIII, Yale, 68. Add: Dept. of English, Michigan State University, East Lansing, MI 48823.

SHERBOURNE, JULIA FLORENCE, b. Sunbury, Ohio, Jan. 27, 00. ENGLISH. A.B, Taylor Univ, 26; M.A, Univ. Mich, 31. Teacher schs, Ohio, 19-20, 21-24; high schs, Mich, 27-30; mem. fac. Eng, John Brown Univ, 33-47; instr, Univ. Ark, 47-60; asst. prof. Eng. & reading, Fla. Presby. Col, 60-66, assoc. prof, 66-68; Eng. Orange County Community Col, 68-72; RETIRED. Nat. Reading Conf; Int. Reading Asn. Teaching of reading to college students; applying reading rate techniques to foreign languages. Publ: Toward reading comprehension, Heath, 58, form 2, 66; That all may learn to read, J. Develop. Reading, 60; Handle with care, Col. Eng; Raising foreign language reading rates, Reading Horizons, summer 67; plus others. Add: 1382 Watergate Dr, Aldersgate LL3, Kissimmee, FL 32741.

SHERIDAN, EDWARD PHILIP, b. Merced, Calif, July 9, 16. ENGLISH LITERATURE. A.B, Stanford Univ, 39, A.M, 40; Ph.D, Yale, 49. Instr. Calif. Inst. Technol, 45-46; ENG, Yale, 48-52; asst. prof, CARLETON COL, 52-57, assoc. prof, 57-66, PROF, 66-, chmn. dept, 67-70. A.U.S, 42-45. MLA; Early Eng. Text Soc. Renaissance literature. Add: Dept. of English, Carleton College, Northfield, MN 55057.

SHERIDAN, HARRIET W, b. New York, N.Y, July 21, 25; m. 50; c. 2. ENGLISH, EDUCATION. A.B, Hunter Col, 44; Nicholson fel. & M.A, Smith Col, 45; univ. fel. & Ph.D.(Eng), Yale, 50. Tutor Eng, Hunter Col, 47-49; asst. prof. CARLETON COL, 53-63, assoc. prof. ENG. & EDUC, 63-67, PROF, 67-, CHMN. DEPT, 73-, chmn. fac, 71-73. Hill Family Found. res. grant Eng. Educ, 60-; field reader, U.S. Off. Educ, 64-; dir, NDEA Inst. Advan. Stud, summer 66; ed, Minn. Eng. J, 67-, chmn. ed. bd, Minn. Counc. Teachers Eng, 73-; mem. Gov. adv. counc, Minn. Right-to-Read Prog, 72-NCTE; Int. Reading Asn; AAUP. Medieval literature; rhetoric; English education. Publ: Structure and style, Harcourt, 66. Add: Dept. of English, Carleton College, Northfield, MN 55057.

SHERIDAN, MARGARET GERTRUDE, Buffalo, N.Y, Oct. 3, 08; m. 37; c. 1. ENGLISH, MUSIC. B.A, Univ. Buffalo, 29, M.A, 32; B.S, Juilliard Sch. Music, 41; B.S.L.S, Col. St. Catherine, 56. Teacher, high sch, N.Y, 29-38; instr. singing, Juilliard Inst. Musical Art, 41-42; commun, American Univ, 43-44; music: appreciation, hist. & singing, Chevy Chase Jr. Col, 44-46; asst. prof. singing, Col. St. Catherine, 46-55; teacher & librn, jr. high sch, Pa, 56-60; instr. Eng. & libr. sci, Pa. State Univ. Altoona, 60-62, Eng, 62-64, asst. prof, 64-73, assoc. prof, 73-74; RES. & WRITING, 74- Lectr. & part-time instr. singing, Univ. Minn, 47-51; lectr. class voice, Univ. Buffalo, summers 50 & 51; Inst. Arts & Humanistic Stud. of Pa. State Univ, grant, 66; ed-in-chief, Rambler Cent. Pa. Writers Guild, 72, co-ed, 73-, chmn. guild, 74-75. Civilian volunteer, exp. in music therapy, U.S. Army, Walter Reed Hospitals, Wash, D.C. & Md, 43-45. NEA; Am. Libr. Asn; Nat. Asn. Teachers Singing; Am. Asn. Univ. Women; NCTE (judge, Achievement Awards in Writing, 62-73). The American art song; the teaching of writing; Blair County cultural history. Publ: Vincent Novello and his circle of literary and musical acquaintances, Univ. Buffalo, 32; Blair County culture: a pilot study—1916-1926 and 1956-1966, Pa. State Univ, 67; co-auth, Interim syllabus in English 800 privately publ, 72; co-ed. & contrib, The little book, Blair, 72. Add: R.D. 4, Box 843, Altoona, PA 16601.

SHERLOCK, WARREN CURTIS, b. New York, N.Y, Aug. 5, 29; m. 55; c. 3. SPEECH. B.A, Univ. Calif, Santa Barbara, 55; M.A, Cath. Univ. Am, 57. From asst. prof. to ASSOC. PROF. SPEECH & COMMUN. ARTS, LOYOLA MARYMOUNT UNIV, 60-, chmn. dept. speech, 60-71. U.S.A, 52-54, Sgt. Am. Theatre Asn; Speech Commun. Asn; Nat. Asn. Educ. Broadcasters. Theatre; communication arts. Add: Dept. of Communication Arts, Loyola Marymount University, Los Angeles, CA 90045.

SHERMAN, CHARLES EDWIN, b. Philadelphia, Pa, Mar. 20, 34; m. 60; c. 3. COMMUNICATION ARTS. B.S, Temple Univ, 60, M.A, 62; Ph.D.(mass commun), Wayne State Univ, 67. Grad. asst. TV & radio prod, Temple Univ, 60-62; TV producer & dir, Wayne State Univ, 62-63, TV prod. supvr, 63-64, instr. speech, 64-66, asst. to dir. mass commun, 66-67; asst. prof. speech, UNIV. WIS-MADISON, 67-70, ASSOC. PROF. SPEECH & ASSOC. CHMN. DEPT. COMMUN. ARTS, 70- Chmn. comt. citizens rights & access, Gov. Cable Comn, Wis, 71-72. U.S.A, 55-57. Speech Commun. Asn; Broadcast Educ. Asn.(chmn. int. interest group, 71-73); Nat. Asn. Educ. Broadcasters. International broadcasting; broadcast regulation. Publ: The Asian Broadcasting Union, fall 69 & Turmoil and transition in international broadcasting, summer 71, J. Broadcasting; International broadcasting cooperation in Africa, Broadcasting in Africa (in press); plus two others. Add: Dept. of Communication Arts, University of Wisconsin-Madison, 821 University Ave, Madison, WI 53706.

SHERMAN, FRANK E, b. Lakeview, Mich, Oct. 4, 27; m. 54; c. 2. AMERICAN LITERATURE. A.B, Univ. Calif, Berkeley, 51, M.A, 54, Ph.D.(Eng), 62. Instr. ENG, Univ. Wis, Milwaukee, 61-65; asst. prof, Roosevelt Univ, 67; DePAUL UNIV, 67-71, ASSOC. PROF, 71- Res. grant, Univ. Wis, summer 63. Med.C, U.S.A, 46-47. Colonial American literature. Add: Dept. of English, DePaul University, Lincoln Park Campus, Chicago, IL 60614.

SHERMAN, ROGER, b. Waterbury, Conn, Oct. 5, 30; m. 52; c. 2. SPEECH. B.A, Univ. Conn, 56; M.A, Univ. Minn, 58; William C. Trueblood scholar, Univ. Mich, summer 59, Ph.D.(speech), 65. Instr. speech, Univ. Conn, 58-60; Univ. Mich, 61-62; East. Mich. Univ, 62-63; ASST. PROF. Eng. & speech, Wesleyan Univ, 63-66; SPEECH, Boston Univ, 66-71; UNIV. HARTFORD, 71- U.S.A, 52-54, Sgt. Speech Commun. Asn. Rhetoric and public address: persuasion; psycholinguistics. Add: Dept. of Communications & Theatre, University of Hartford, Hartford, CT 06117.

SHERR, PAUL CLINTON, b. Allentown, Pa, Mar. 22, 20; m. 57; c. 3. ENGLISH. Cert. Ger, Univ. Strassburg, 53; cert. Ger, Univ. Munich, 54; B.A, Muhlenberg Col, 57; M.A, Lehigh Univ, 60; Ph.D.(Eng), Univ. Pa, 65. PROF. ENG, RIDER COL, 64- MLA; NCTE. American studies; drama. Publ: The short story and the oral tradition, Boyd & Fraser, 70; The threatened teacher syndrome, ADE Bull, 70; Richard Wright: The expatriate pattern, Black Acad. Rev, 71; Change your luck: a Negro satirizes white America, Phylon, 71; plus three others. Add: Dept. of English, Rider College, Trenton, NJ 08602.

SHERRER, CHARLES DAVID, b. Marion, Ohio, Sept. 21, 35. ENGLISH LITERATURE. A.B, Univ. Notre Dame, 58, M.A, 65; S.T.B, Pontif. Gregorian Univ, 60, S.T.L, 62; Ph.D.(Eng), Univ. N.C, Chapel Hill, 69. Instr. Eng, Univ. Portland, 63-64, asst. prof, 69-74, chmn. dept, 70-74; PRES, KING'S COL.(PA), 74- MLA; AAUP. Shakespeare. Add: King's College, Wilkes-Barre, PA 18711.

SHERRIFFS, RONALD EVERETT. BROADCAST COMMUNICATION. B.A, San Jose State Col, 55, M.A, 57; Ph.D.(commun), Univ. South. Calif, 64. Instr. SPEECH, Mich. State Univ, 60-61; ASST. PROF, Tex. Technol. Col, 64-65; UNIV. ORE, 65- U.S.N.R, 57-60, Lt. Comdr. West. Speech Commun. Asn; Broadcast Educ. Asn. Government support programs—cultural activities; educational broadcasting. Publ: Co-auth, Speech communication via radio and television, W.C. Brown, 71; auth, Governmental support to the theatre in Great Britain, Theatre Surv, 11/65; Old ways to solve new problems, Audiovisual Instr, 9/68. Add: Dept. of Speech, University of Oregon, Eugene, OR 97403.

SHERWIN, JOSEPH STEPHEN, b. New York, N.Y, Aug. 20, 23; m. 53; c. 2. ENGLISH. B.S, Univ. Wis, 45; M.A, Columbia Univ, 47; Ed.D.(Eng. & Eng. educ), N.Y. Univ, 54. Instr. ENG, Sampson Col, 47-48; N.Y. Univ, 52-54; asst. prof, State Univ. Col. Geneseo, 54-56; assoc. prof, STATE UNIV. COL. BUFFALO, 56-59, PROF, 59-, chmn. dept, 63-69. Teacher Eng, high schs, New York, N.Y, 45-47; bk. rev. column, St. Louis Post-Dispatch, 47-61; lectr. Eng, City Col. New York, 50; State Univ. Res. Found. grant, 55-57; curriculum consult, Clarence Cent. Schs, 59-61; State Univ. Res. Found. fel, summer 60. NCTE (mem. comt. res, 67-, exec. comt. conf. Eng. educ, 72); AAUP; Conf. Col. Compos. & Commun; MLA; Thoreau Soc. Theory of literature; English usage; American transcendentalism. Publ: A word index to Walden with textual notes, Univ. Va, 60; Four problems in teaching English: a critique of research, NCTE, 69; Literature and communication: a search for a unifying principle, J. Commun, summer 57; Religious celebrations in school, In: Religion, government and education, Soc. Advan. Educ, 61; co-auth, Variant punctuation in two editions of Walden, Thoreau Soc. Bull, winter 61. Add: 214 Roycroft Blvd, Snyder, NY 14226.

SHERWIN, OSCAR, b. New York, N.Y, July 6, 02; m; c. 2. ENGLISH LITERATURE. A.B, Columbia Univ, 22, M.A, 28; Ph.D.(lit), N.Y. Univ, 40. Instr. ENG, L.I. Univ, 30-32; from instr. to asst. prof, CITY COL. NEW YORK, 33-51, assoc. prof, 51-59, prof, 59-67, EMER. PROF, 67- MLA; AHA; Asn. Stud. Afro-Am. Life & Hist. Social backgrounds of 18th century English literature; American slavery and abolition. Publ: Prophet of liberty: Wendell Phillips, 58, John Wesley: friend of the people, 61, Uncorking old sherry: Richard Brinsley Sheridan, 60 & George Selwyn: a gentleman of wit and fashion, 63, Twayne; The life and times of Oliver Goldsmith, Crowell-Collier, 62; Art's spring-birth: The ballad of Jacob and Josep, Stud. Philol, 45; A man with a tail: Lord Monboddo, J. Hist. Med. & Allied Sci, 58; Madan's cure-all, Am. J. Econ. & Sociol, 63. Add: 207 W. 106th St, New York, NY 10025.

SHERWIN, WILMA, b. Winchester, Ill, July 26, 22. LITERATURE. B.S.Ed, West. Ill. Univ, 47, M.S.Ed, 49; Ph.D.(Eng), Univ. Ill, 58. Teacher, Oakland Sch, Greenfield, Ill, 42-43; Winchester Elem. Sch, 43-45; speech, Eng. & jour, Mt. Morris High Sch, 47-48; asst. prof. ENG, Anderson Col, 58-60; assoc. prof. Clarion State Col, 61-64; asst. prof, Wesleyan Col.(N.Y), 64-68; PROF, Greenville Col, 68-70; ROBERTS WESLEYAN COL, 70- Add: Dept. of English, Roberts Wesleyan College, Rochester, NY 14514.

SHERWOOD, IRMA Z, b. New York, N.Y, Oct. 6, 18; m. 44; c. 3. ENGLISH. B.A, Barnard Col, Columbia Univ, 40; M.A, Yale, 42, Ph.D.(Eng), 45. Instr. ENG, Newcomb Col, Tulane Univ, 44-45; Cornell Univ, 45-46; UNIV. ORE, 46-48, asst. prof, 62-72, ASSOC. PROF, 72- MLA; Am. Soc. 18th Century Stud; Johnson Soc. Northwest. Eighteenth century English literature. Publ: Co-auth, A writer's reader, Harcourt, 50; auth, The novelists as commentators, In: The age of Johnson, Yale, 49; Johnson's achievement in allegory, Trans. Johnson Soc. Northwest, 68; Vanbrugh's Romeo and Juliet: a note on The relapse, Restoration & 18th Century Theatre Res, 11/73. Add: Dept. of English, University of Oregon, Eugene, OR 97403.

SHERWOOD, JOHN COLLINGWOOD, b. Hempstead, N.Y, Dec. 30, 18; m. 44; c. 3. ENGLISH LITERATURE. A.B, Lafayette Col, 41; M.A, Yale, 42, Ph.D, 45. Instr. ENG, Cornell Univ, 44-46; asst. prof, UNIV. ORE, 46-55; assoc. prof, 55-61, PROF, 61- Am. Counc. Learned Socs. fac. stud. fel, 52-53. MLA. History of criticism; 18th century; Anglo-Irish. Publ: Co-auth, A writer's reader, Harcourt, 50; co-auth, Reading and rhetoric from Harper's, 63 & auth, Discourse of reason, 2nd ed, 64, Harper; Dr. Kinsey and Professor Fries, Col. Eng, 2/60; Dryden and the critical theories of Tasso, Comp. Lit, fall 66; Joyce and the empire: some thoughts on Finnegans wake, Stud. Novel, 69. Add: Dept. of English, University of Oregon, Eugene, OR 97403.

SHERWOOD, WILLIAM ROBERT, b. York Harbor, Maine, July 23, 29; m. 67. ENGLISH. A.B, Harvard, 51, A.M, 56; Ph.D.(Eng), Columbia Univ, 64. Lectr. ENG, City Col. New York, 59-60; instr, Vassar Col, 60-65, asst.

prof, 65-67; Lehman Col, 67-70, assoc. prof, 70-73, chmn. dept, 70-72; ASSOC. PROF, VASSAR COL, 73- U.S.A, 54-56. AAUP; MLA. History of the novel; American poetry; American literature of the nineteenth century. Publ: Co-auth, The English novel: background readings, Lippincott, 67; auth, Circumference and circumstance: stages in the mind and art of Emily Dickinson, Columbia Univ, 68. Add: Dept. of English, Vassar College, Poughkeepsie, NY 12601.

SHIELDS, BRUCE PHILBROOK, b. Tacoma Park, Md, July 13, 39; m. 62; c. 2. ENGLISH & MEDIEVAL LITERATURE. A.B, Harvard Col, 61; Edinburgh Univ, 61-62; M.A, Rutgers Univ, 64, Ph.D.(Eng), 70. Teaching asst. ENG, Rutgers Univ, New Brunswick, 63-68; instr, Russell Sage Col, 68-70, asst. prof, 70-74. MLA; Mediaeval Acad. Am; Int. Ctr. Medieval Art. Medieval Biblical exegesis. Add: 3 Lewis St, Troy, NY 12180.

SHIELDS, DONALD J, b. Paris, Ill, Oct. 28, 37; m. 62; c. 1. SPEECH, POLITICAL SCIENCE. B.S, East. Ill. Univ, 59; M.S, Purdue Univ, 61, Ph.D. (speech), 64. Staff asst. SPEECH, Ind. State Democratic Comt, 62; asst. prof, Cornell Univ, 64-65; IND. STATE UNIV, TERRE HAUTE, 65-71, ASSOC. PROF, 71- Speech Commun. Asn; Nat. Soc. Stud. Commun; Am. Forensic Asn. Political persuasion and communications networks. Add: Dept. of Speech, Indiana State University, Terre Haute, IN 47809.

SHIELDS, ELLEN FRANCES, b. Philadelphia, Pa, Dec. 15, 37. ENGLISH. A.B, Chestnut Hill Col, 59; M.A, Villanova Univ, 62; Ph.D.(Eng), Univ. Ill, 66. Instr. ENG, Univ. Ill, 65-66; asst. prof, UNIV. WATERLOO, 66-72, ASSOC. PROF, 72- MLA; Asn. Can. Univ. Teachers Eng. Modern British literature. Add: Dept. of English, University of Waterloo, Waterloo, Ont. W2L 3G1, Can.

SHIELDS, ELLIS GALE, b. Winfield, Kans, Feb. 11, 19; m. 43; c. 1. ENGLISH & COMPARATIVE LITERATURE. A.B, Southwest. Col.(Kans), 41; Ph.D, Univ. South. Calif, 56. Asst. prof. Eng. & Latin, Northwest. State Col.(La), 46-53; instr. Eng, Tex. West. Col, 53-54; asst. prof. Eng. & comp. lit, Kans. State Col. Pittsburg, 55-58, assoc. prof, 58-61, prof, comp. lit, 61-66; PROF. ENG. & CHMN. DEPT, DAVIS & ELKINS COL, 66- Deacon, Episcopal Church, 71-, priest, 72- U.S.N, 42-45, Res, 45-, Lt. Comdr. MLA. Mediaeval rhetorical and poetic theory; 19th century literary and historical criticism. Publ: Francis Jeffrey, critic of the romantics, 7/56, Poetic theory in the Middle Ages, 7/58 & The flowers of rhetoric, 7/59, Educ. Leader. Add: Dept. of English, Speech & Drama, Davis & Elkins College, Elkins, WV 26241.

SHIELDS, KENNETH DALE, b. Wichita, Kans, Mar. 10, 31; m. 68; c. 1. ENGLISH. Scholar & B.A, Greenville Col, 52; scholar & M.A, Univ. Kans, 54; Ph.D.(Eng), Univ. Edinburgh, 64; Fulbright scholar, U.K. Asst. prof. ENG, SOUTH. METHODIST UNIV, 61-68, ASSOC. PROF, 68-, counc. humanities fel, 63-64, coord. discourse & lit, 67-71. MLA; NCTE. British poetry of the 18th century; British novel from its beginnings to the present; the Bloomsbury group. Add: Dept. of English, Southern Methodist University, Dallas, TX 75275.

SHIFFLER, HARROLD C, b. Muskogee, Okla, Jan. 6, 18; m. 48; c. 3. DRAMATIC ARTS. B.A, Drake Univ, 39; M.F.A, Univ. Iowa, 51, Ph.D.(dramatic art), 53. Instr. commun. skills, Univ. Iowa, 51-53, dramatic art, 53-55, asst. prof, 55-59; PROF. SPEECH & DRAMATIC ARTS & HEAD DEPT, HASTINGS COL, 59- Sig.C, U.S.A, 42-45. Speech Commun. Asn; Am. Theatre Asn. Acting, directing; colonial America theatre history. Publ: Theatre philatelic: a handbook, Am. Topical Asn, 69; The Chicago church-theatre controversy of 1881-1882, J. Ill. Hist. Soc, winter 60; Religious opposition to the eighteenth century Philadelphia stage, Educ. Theatre J, 10-/62; Theatre on postage stamps, Players, 10-11/70. Add: Dept. of Speech, Hastings College, Hastings, NE 68901.

SHILKETT, CAROL LEE, b. San Bernardino, Calif, Jan. 4, 47. MEDIEVAL LITERATURE. A.B, Univ. Redlands, 68; M.A, Mich. State Univ, 69, Ph.D. (Eng), 72. ASST. PROF. ENG, ALFRED UNIV, 72- MLA; Mediaeval Acad. Am; Int. Arthurian Soc. Chaucer; medieval romance. Add: Dept. of English, Alfred University, Alfred, NY 14802.

SHIMER, DOROTHY BLAIR, b. Hackensack, N.J, Apr. 24, 11; m. 47. ENGLISH, ASIAN LITERATURE. A.B, Skidmore Col, 32; A.M, Middlebury Col, 45; Syracuse Univ, summer 46; Oxford, summer 61. Ed. & asst. exec. secy, United Chapters Phi Beta Kappa, 32-44; dir. pub. relat, Colby Jr. Col, 44-45; Marietta Col, 45-47, dean women, 46-47; co-dir, Hawaii Chapter & Asia-Pac. Div, World Brotherhood, 50-60; asst. prof. Eng. & speech, Maunaolu Col, 60-63, assoc. prof. Eng, 63-68; ASST. PROF, UNIV. HAWAII, 69- Mem, Hawaii State Comn. Status of Women, 70- MLA; NCTE; Conf. Col. Compos. & Commun; Conf. Eng. Lit. World; Am. Asn. Univ. Women (v.pres from S.Pac. Region, 71-75). Modern Asian literature. Publ: Chinese/Japanese literature unit, teacher's manual on world literature, Harcourt, 68; Mentor book of Modern Asian literature, 69 & ed, Voices of Modern Asia, 73, New Am. Libr; Bhabani Bhattacharya, a biography, Twayne, 74; Notes on Sophomores favor old masters, Yearbook Comp. & Gen. Lit, 66; Asian drama via Aristotle, West. Humanities Rev, winter 67; Asian thought in T.S. Eliot's Four quartets, Asian Pac. Quart, summer 73. Add: 45-090 L Namoku St, Kaneohe, HI 96744.

SHINAGEL, MICHAEL, b. Vienna, Austria, Apr. 21, 34; U.S. citizen; m. 56, 73; c. 2. ENGLISH LITERATURE. A.B, Oberlin Col, 57; fel, Harvard, 57-64; M.A, 59, Ph.D.(Eng), 64. Tutor ENG, Harvard, 58-64; from instr. to asst. prof, Cornell Univ, 64-67; assoc. prof, UNION COL.(N.Y), 67-72, PROF, 72-, chmn. dept, 67-73. Dir, Harvard Summer Inst. Eng, 62; comn. Eng, Col. Bd, 62; reader, Eng. compos. & advan. placement exam in Eng, 66-73; mem. regional selection comt, Woodrow Wilson Nat. Fel. Found, 66-68; Nat. Endowment for Humanities grant, 66-67. U.S.A, 52-54. MLA; Asn. Dept. Eng; NCTE; Am. Soc. 18th Century Stud. English literature of the 18th century; satire; novel. Publ: Co-auth, Handbook on summer institutes in English, Col. Bd, 65; auth, Daniel Defoe and middle-class gentility, Harvard, 68; Concordance to poems of Jonathan Swift, Cornell Univ, 72; The maternal theme in Moll Flanders: craft and character, Cornell Libr. J, winter 68; Memoirs of a woman of pleasure; pornography and the mid-18th century English novel; In: Studies in change and revolution, Scolar, 72. Add: Humanities Bldg, Union College, Schenectady, NY 12308.

SHINE, MURIEL GRUBER, b. Philadelphia, Pa, Oct. 24, 17; m. 46; c. 1. ENGLISH. B.A, N.Y. Univ, 56, M.A, 57, Ph.D.(Eng), 67. ASSOC. PROF. ENG, PACE UNIV, 60- MLA; AAUP. Nineteenth century English and American literature; drama—Shakespeare to contemporary. Publ: The fictional children of Henry James, Univ. N.C, 69. Add: Dept. of English, Pace University, 1 Pace Plaza, New York, NY 10038.

SHIPLEY, JOHN B, b. New York, N.Y, July 6, 23; m. 53; c. 3. ENGLISH LITERATURE. B.A, Univ. N.C, 47; M.A, Columbia Univ, 48, Ph.D, 63. Instr. ENG, Univ. Kans, 48-49; Alfred Univ, 52-54; Univ. Colo, 55-60; Ohio Univ, 60-63, asst. prof, 63-65, assoc. prof, UNIV. ILL, CHICAGO CIRCLE, 65-71, PROF, 71- U.S.A.A.F, 43-46, Sgt. MLA; Conf. Brit. Stud; NCTE (ed-in-chief, Abstracts Eng. Stud, 62-). Eighteenth century English literature; the novel. Publ: A new Fielding essay from the Champion, 63 & The authorship of The cornish squire, 68, Philol. Quart; Daniel Defoe and Henry Baker: some of their correspondence again and its provenance, Bodleian Libr. Rec, 67; plus others. Add: Dept. of English, Box 4348, University of Illinois at Chicago Circle, Chicago, IL 60680.

SHIPPS, ANTHONY WIMBERLY, b. Tryon, N.C, Aug. 26, 26; m. 49; c. 1. ENGLISH, LIBRARY SCIENCE. A.B, Mercer Univ, 49; M.A, Northwest. Univ, 51, Ph.D.(Eng), 59; A.M.L.S, Univ. Mich, 60. Instr. Eng, Wayne State Univ, 54-59; asst. librarian, Utah State Univ, 60-61; circulation librarian, Univ. Colo. Libr, 61-62, humanities librarian, 62-64, head ref. dept, 64-67; LIBRARIAN FOR ENG, IND. UNIV. LIBR, BLOOMINGTON, 67- U.S.N, 44-46. MLA; Am. Libr. Asn. Literary quotations; English Renaissance. Add: 2500 E. Eighth St, Bloomington, IN 47401.

SHIRLEY, FRANCES ANN, b. Altoona, Pa, June 11, 31. ENGLISH. A.B, Bryn Mawr Col, 53, M.A, 54, Ph.D.(Eng), 60; Johns Hopkins Univ, 54-56; Univ. Birmingham, 59. Instr. ENG, WHEATON COL.(MASS), 60-63, asst. prof, 63-67, assoc. prof, 67-73, PROF, 73-, asst. dean, 63-64. Soc. Theatre Res, Eng; Am. Soc. Theatre Res; MLA; AAUP. Elizabethan drama; Shakespeare; romantic literature. Publ: Shakespeare's use of off-stage sounds, Univ. Nebr, 63; ed, John Webster's The devil's law-case, In: Regent Renaissance Drama Series, Univ. Nebr, 72. Add: Dept. of English, Wheaton College, Norton, MA 02766.

SHIRLEY, FRANKLIN RAY, b. Glencoe, Ky, June 17, 14; m. 45; c. 3. SPEECH. A.B, Georgetown Col, 38; Univ. Cincinnati, 40-41; M.A, Columbia Univ, 48; Ph.D, Univ. Fla, 59. Teacher, pub. schs, Ky. & Ohio, 34-43; instr. Eng. & speech, Baylor Sch. for Boys, 43-46; assoc. prof. speech, Carson-Newman Col, 46-48; instr. speech & drama, WAKE FOREST UNIV, 48-56, asst. prof, 56-60, assoc. prof. SPEECH, 60-64, PROF, 64-, CHMN. DEPT, 61-, speech & drama div, Eng. dept, 48-60. Teaching fel, Univ. Fla, 53-54; vis. prof, Univ. South. Calif, summer 60; teacher communicating ideas & applied speaking, grad. training ctr, West. Elec. Co, 60-; alderman, City of Winston-Salem, N.C, 63-72, mayor, 72- Am. Forensic Asn.(v.pres, 61-63); Speech Commun. Asn.(legis. counc, 62-65); South. Speech Commun. Asn.(1st v.pres, 65-66, pres, 66-67); South. Humanities Conf. Southern public address: especially the rhetoric of Zebulan B. Vance; pronuntiatio or delivery, one of the five canons of classical rhetoric. Publ: Zebulon B. Vance: Tarheel spokesman, McNally, 63; Why not meet the issues?, Speech Activities Mag, spring 51; Teachers, mend your speech, N.C. Educ. J, 12/52; In unity there is strength, South. Speech J, fall 67. Add: Dept. of Speech Communication & Theater Arts, Wake Forest University, Winston Salem, NC 27103.

SHIVERS, ALFRED SAMUEL, b. Lakeland, Fla, Jan. 16, 29; m. 59; c. 3. ENGLISH. B.A, Univ. Fla, 55, M.A, 59; Ph.D, Fla. State Univ, 62. Asst. prof. Eng, Wis. State Col, Superior, 62-63; Colo. State Univ, 63-64; AM. LIT, North. Ill, Univ, 64-66; assoc. prof, STEPHEN F. AUSTIN STATE UNIV, 66-67, PROF, 67- U.S.N, 57-59, Lt.(jg). NCTE; MLA. Jack London biography and criticism; biography and criticism on Jessamyn West; Maxwell Anderson, Publ: Jessamyn West, Twayne, 72. Add: Dept. of English, Stephen F. Austin State University, Nacogdoches, TX 75961.

SHOCKLEY, MARTIN STAPLES, b. Stuart, Va, Mar. 24, 08; m. 36; c. 2. ENGLISH. A.B, Univ. Richmond, 28; fel, Duke Univ, 31-32, A.M, 32; Ph.D, Univ. N.C, 38. Head dept, high sch, Va, 29-31; teaching fel, Univ. N.C, 34-35; asst. prof, The Citadel, 35-38; ENG, Univ. Okla, 38-40, assoc. prof, 40-44; Carleton Col, 44-46; PROF, Evansville Col, 46-50; N.TEX. STATE UNIV, 50- Fulbright prof. Am. lit, Univ. Cape Town, 63. MLA; NCTE; Col. Eng. Asn; Poetry Soc. Am; Am. Stud. Asn; S.Cent. Mod. Lang. Asn. American literature; the Antebellum Theatre in Richmond, Virginia. Publ: Co-auth, Reading and writing, Holt, 62; auth, Southwest writers anthology, Steck, 67; American plays in the Richmond theatre, Stud. Philol, 1/40; The reception of The grapes of wrath in Oklahoma, Am. Lit, 1/44; American literature in American education, Col. Eng, 10/46. Add: Box 5651, North Texas Station, Denton, TX 76203.

SHOEMAKER, FRANCIS, b. Conshohocken, Pa, Dec. 19, 09; m. 37. ENGLISH, HUMANITIES. A.B, Lehigh Univ, 31; Harvard; A.M, Colo. State Col. Educ, 37; Ph.D, Columbia Univ, 42. Teacher high schs, Pa, 32-36; instr, Colo. State Col. Educ, 36-37, asst. prof, 37-38, assoc. prof, 38-46; asst. prof. educ, Univ. Wis, 46-50, assoc. prof, 50-52; ENG, TEACHERS COL, COLUMBIA UNIV, 52-55, PROF, 55-, DIR. INT. PROG. & SERV, 65-, coord. proj. for Nat. Prof. Educ. in India, 63-65. Advan. Sch. fel, 39-40; dir. commun, Am. Nat. Red Cross, 42-45, res. assoc, State Dept. Educ, N.Y, 45-46; consult, humanities, Comn. Teacher Educ. & Prof. Standards, 49; consult. textbook develop, Ministry of Educ, India, 61-63. NCTE; Conf. Col. Compos. & Commun; NEA; MLA; Col. Eng. Asn; Nat. Soc. Stud. Educ; Nat. Soc. Stud. Commun; African Stud. Asn; Asn. Asian Stud; Soc. Int. Develop. Humanities; communication arts; teacher preparation. Publ: Aesthetic experience and the humanities, Columbia Univ, 43; ed, Communication and the communication arts, Teachers Col, 56; co-ed, Communication in general education, W.C. Brown, 61; ed, New ways in English, Prentice-Hall, 68; New dimensions for world cultures, Teachers Col. Rec, 4/68. Add: Office of International Programs & Services, Teachers College, Columbia University, New York, NY 10027.

SHOENBERG, ROBERT EDWARD, b. Philadelphia, Pa, Aug. 6, 35; m. 62; c. 2. ENGLISH. B.A, Amherst Col, 57, M.A, Univ. Mich, 58, Ph.D.(Eng),

62. Teaching fel, Univ. Mich, 58-61, instr, 61-62; Williams Col, 62-65, asst. prof, 65-68; asst. v.pres. acad. affairs, State Univ. N.Y. Col. Buffalo, 68-69, assoc. v.pres. acad. affairs, 69-72; DEAN UNDERGRAD. STUD, UNIV. MD, COLLEGE PARK, 72- Am. Counc. Educ. fel. admin. Univ. South. Calif, 67-68. MLA. Victorian novel; English Renaissance drama. Publ: The literal-mindedness of Samuel Butler (1835-1902), Stud. Eng. Lit, fall 64. Add: 1115 Undergraduate Library, University of Maryland, College Park, MD 20742.

SHOKOFF, JAMES, b. Teaneck, N.J, Aug. 18, 35; m. 62; c. 2. ENGLISH LITERATURE, FILM. B.A, Rutgers Univ, 60; Woodrow Wilson fel, Columbia Univ, 60-61, M.A, 65; Ph.D.(Eng), Univ. Ill, Urbana, 70. Teacher ENG, Benjamin Franklin High Sch, N.Y.C, 62-66; teaching asst, Univ. Ill, Urbana, 66-68, instr, 68-70; asst. prof, STATE UNIV. N.Y. COL. FREDONIA, 70-73, ASSOC. PROF, 73- Managing ed, Drama & Theatre, 71- U.S.A, 54-56. English Romantic literature; film study; dramatic literature. Publ: Ed, The voices of war, Wiley, 72; auth, Charles Lamb and the Elizabethan dramatists, Wordsworth Circle, 73; Soul-making in Ode on a Grecian urn, Keats-Shelley J, (in press). Add: Dept. of English, State University of New York College at Fredonia, Fredonia, NY 14063.

SHOOK, ANDREW WOODSON, b. Plevna, Kans, Dec. 10, 13; m. 47; c. 3. SPEECH. B.A, Univ. of the Pac, 37, M.A, 40; Ph.D.(speech), N.Y. Univ, 55. Teacher, high sch, Calif, 40-42; instr. speech, Univ. of the Pac, 45-46; N.Y. Univ, 46-52; assoc. prof. & dir. speech clinic, Northeast Mo. State Teachers Col, 52-57; asst. prof. UNIV. GUAM, 57-58, prof. & chmn. div, 58-67, ACAD. V.PRES, 67- Vis. lectr, Univ. S.Fla, 63-64. U.S.A.A.F, 43-45, S/Sgt, cryptographer. Speech pathology and therapy; English as a second language, especially speech aspects. Publ: Co-auth, American English pronunciation for Micronesian speakers (instructional manual), Col. Guam, 66. Add: Box EK, University of Guam, Agana, Guam 96910.

SHOOK, LAURENCE KENNEDY, b. Toronto, Ont, Nov. 6, 09. ENGLISH, VERNACULAR LITERATURE. B.A, Univ. Toronto, 32, M.A, 33; Ph.D.(Eng) Harvard, 40; hon. D.Litt, West. Mich. Univ, 72. PROF. ENG, ST. MICHAEL'S COL, UNIV. TORONTO, 40-; VERNACULAR LIT, PONTIFICAL INST. MEDIAEVAL STUD, 46-, pres, 61-73. Pres, St. Michael's Col, Univ. Toronto, 52-58. R.C.A.F, 43-45, Flight Lt. Asn. Can. Univ. Teachers Eng; Medieval Acad. Am.(v.pres, 67). Anglo-Saxon; Chaucer; higher education. Publ: Transl, Heloise and Abelard, Regnery, 51 & The Christian philosophy of Saint Thomas Aquinas, Random, 56; ed, The theology of renewal, Herder, 68; auth, Catholic post-secondary education in English-speaking Canada: a history, Univ. Toronto, 71; The burial mound in Guthlac A, Mod. Philol, 8/60; Old English riddle no. 20, In: Studies in honour of F.P. Magoun, Jr, N.Y. Univ, 65; University centres and institutes of medieval studies, J. Higher Educ, 12/67. Add: 59 Queen's Park Crescent E, Toronto, Ont. M5S 2C4, Can.

SHORES, DAVID LEE, b. Tangier, Va, Jan. 28, 33; m. 56; c. 2. ENGLISH, LINGUISTICS. B.A, Randolph-Macon Col, 55; M.A, George Peabody Col, 56, Ed.S, 64, Ph.D.(Eng), 66; Vanderbilt Univ, 63-66. Instr. Eng. & Ger, Richard Bland Col, Col. William & Mary, 61-62; asst. prof. ENG, OLD DOM. UNIV, 66-68, assoc. prof, 68-70, PROF, 70-, GRAD. PROG. DIR. ENG, 73-, dir. freshman Eng, 70-73. Instr. & assoc. dir, U.S. Off. Educ. Inst. Col. Eng. Instr. Black Cols, 70-73; consult, Nat. Teachers Exam, Educ. Testing Serv, 72-73. U.S.A, 57-59. MLA; Ling. Soc. Am; NCTE; S.Atlantic Mod. Lang. Asn-A.D.S.(chmn, 71); Am. Dialect Soc.(regional secy, 73-76); Southeast Conf. Ling. Old and Middle English language and literature; Chaucer; English linguistics. Publ: A descriptive syntax of the Petersborough Chronicle from 1122 to 1154, Mouton, The Hague, 71; ed, Contemporary English: change and variation, Lippincott, 72; auth, The merchant's tale: some lay observations, Neuphilogische Mitteilunben, 70; The Petersborough Chronicle: continuity and change in the English language, S.Atlantic Bull, 11/70; Morspho-syntactic relations in the Peterborough Chronicle, 1122-1154, Eng. Stud, 2/71; plus others. Add: Dept. of English, Old Dominion University, Norfolk, VA 23508.

SHORT, CLARICE EVELYN, b. Kans, Mar. 30, 10. ENGLISH. A.B, Univ. Kans, 32, M.A, 33; Ph.D.(Eng. & German), Cornell Univ, 41; Oxford, 50; Harvard, 55. From asst. prof. to assoc. prof. ENG, Ft. Hays Kans. State Col, 41-46; from instr. to assoc. prof, UNIV. UTAH, 46-62, PROF, 62- MLA; Rocky Mount Mod. Lang. Asn.(pres, 65-66). English literature of the 19th century. Publ: William Morris and Keats, PMLA; Thomas Hardy and the military man, Nineteenth Century Fiction; Tennyson and The lover's tale, PMLA, 3/67. Add: Dept. of English, University of Utah, Salt Lake City, UT 84112.

SHORTER, ROBERT NEWLAND, b. Canton, Ohio, May 11, 31; m. 57; c. 1. ENGLISH. A.B, Union Col.(N.Y), M.A, Duke Univ, 58, Ph.D.(Eng), 64. Instr. ENG, WAKE FOREST UNIV, 58-64, asst. prof, 64-68, ASSOC. PROF, 68- Qm.C, U.S.A, 52-54. MLA. Chaucer; medieval drama. Publ: Becket as Job: T.S. Eliot's Murder in the cathedral, S.Atlantic Quart, fall 68. Add: Dept. of English, Wake Forest University, Winston-Salem, NC 27109.

SHOTT, HUGH I, II, b. Bluefield, W.Va, June 23, 26; m. 57; c. 2. ENGLISH. A.B, W.Va. Univ. 49; M.A, Univ. Va, 51; Ind. Univ, 51; B.S, Concord Col, 53; Ph.D.(Eng), Univ. Denver, 56. Instr. ENG, Concord Col, 53-57; asst. prof, 57-58; instr. E.Tex. State Univ, 58-59, asst. prof, 59-61, assoc. prof, 61-66; PROF, N.GA. COL, 66- U.S.N, 44-46. Col. Eng. Asn. English syntax. Add: Dept. of English, North Georgia College, Dahlonega, GA 30533.

SHOUP-HUMMEL, JUNE ELEANOR, b. Sturgis, Mich, Feb. 1, 29; m. 70. SPEECH COMMUNICATION. B.A, Univ. Mich, 50, M.A, 58, Ph.D.(ling), 64. Res. asst, Speech Res. Lab, Univ. Mich, 57-58, admin. asst, Eng. Lang. Inst, 58-60, lectr, 58-64, asst. dir. & assoc. res. linguist, Commun. Sci. Lab, 61-66, asst. prof. commun. sci, 64-66; assoc. dir, SPEECH COMMUN. RES. LAB, CALIF, 66-67, DIR, 67- Acoust. Soc. Am; Int. Phonetic Asn; Ling. Soc. Am; Asn. Machine Transl. & Comput. Ling. Publ: Co-auth, A physiological theory of phonetics, The elements of an acoustic phonetic theory & Glossary of terms from the physiological and acoustic phonetic theories, J. Speech & Hearing Res, 3/66. Add: Speech Communications Research Laboratory, Inc, 800 A Miramonte Dr, Santa Barbara, CA 93109.

SHOUSE, CLAUDE F, b. Marksberry, Ky, Mar. 11, 07; m. 32; c. 2. ENGLISH. A.B, Georgetown Col, 28; M.A, Univ. Ky, 41; Ph.D.(educ), Univ. South. Calif, 53. Instr. Eng. & Latin, Millersburg Mil. Inst, Ky, 28-32; Eng. & lang, Linsly Inst, Wheeling, W.Va, 32-45; for. lang, Brown Mil. Acad, San Diego, Calif, 45-46; prof. ENG, SAN DIEGO STATE UNIV, 46-72, chmn. dept, 66-68, EMER. PROF, 72- Consult. in reading, Grossmont Union High Sch. Dist, 61-64; Sweetwater Union High Sch. Dist, 67-; establisher, dir. & developer, Study Skills Ctr, Georgetown Col, spring, 73. Int. Reading Asn; MLA. The writing laboratories in universities and colleges; the improvement of reading; English for international students. Add: Dept. of English, San Diego State University, 5402 College Ave, San Diego, CA 92115.

SHOWALTER, DAN MCGREGOR, b. Olathe, Colo, Sept. 29, 13. ENGLISH LITERATURE. B.A, West. State Col. Colo, 52, M.A, 65. Teacher, elem. sch, Colo, 39-40; asst. prin, Jr. High Sch, 40-44; prin, Elem. Sch, 44-47; county supt. schs, Montrose County, Colo, 47-48; supt. schs, Olathe, Colo, 50-53; teacher, High Sch, Colo, 53-56, v.prin, 56-57; instr. Eng, Mesa Col, 57-59; dean of boys, High Sch, Colo, 59-61; INSTR. ENG. & LIT, MESA COL, 61-, CHMN. DIV. HUMANITIES, 64-, HEAD DEPT. ENG, 63-64 & 73-, actor summer stock, 71. Lectr, Univ. Colo, 67-68. NEA. Christinia Rosetti; John Donne; the stage, modern day, London. Add: Dept. of English, Div. of Humanities, Mesa College, North Ave, Grand Junction, CO 81501.

SHOWALTER, ELAINE C, b. Cambridge, Mass, Jan. 21, 41; m. 63; c. 2. ENGLISH LITERATURE. B.A, Bryn Mawr Col, 62; M.A, Brandeis Univ, 64; Ph.D.(Eng), Univ. Calif, Davis, 70. Teaching asst. ENG, Univ. Calif, Davis, 64-66; instr, DOUGLASS COL, RUTGERS UNIV, 67-70, ASST. PROF, 70-, Fac. Res. Counc. fel, 72-73. MLA (comn. status of women, 71-72). Victorian literature; English novel; women writers. Publ: Ed, Women's liberation and literature, Harcourt, 71; contrib, Women in sexist society, Basic Bks, 71; co-ed, Female studies in teaching about women, Know, Inc, 71; co-auth, Victorian women and menstruation, Victorian Stud, 70; auth, Killing the angel in the house, Antioch Rev, 73. Add: Dept. of English, Douglass College of Rutgers University, New Brunswick, NJ 08903.

SHRIVE, FRANK NORMAN, b. Hamilton, Ont, Sept. 27, 21; m. 43; c. 2. ENGLISH. B.A, McMaster Univ, 50; M.A, Univ. Toronto, 54; grant-in-aid, Humanities Asn. Can, Harvard, 55; Ph.D, Queen's Univ, Can, 61. Lectr. ENG, Royal Mil. Col. Can, 53-57; asst. prof, McMASTER UNIV, 57-62, assoc. prof, 62-66, PROF, 66-, CHMN. DEPT, 67- Can. Council grants-in-aid, 61, 63, 67; cor. mem. Humanities Res. Counc. Can, 64; attorney-gen, Ont. Panel Obscene Lit, 64- R.C.A.F, 41-45, Res, 46-63, Squadron Leader. Humanities Asn. Can; Asn. Can. Univ. Teachers Eng. Canadian literature; American literature, 1870-1960. Publ: Charles Mair: literary nationalist, Univ. Toronto, 65; plus others. Add: Dept. of English, McMaster University, Hamilton, Ont, Can.

SHRODES, CAROLINE, b. Madison, Minn, July 19, 08. ENGLISH. Ph.B, Univ. Chicago, 28, A.M, 34; Ph.D, Univ. Calif, 49. Teaching asst. Eng, Univ. Wis, 37-39; asst. prof. Eng. & psychol, Stockton Jr. Col, 39-46; PROF. ENG, SAN FRANCISCO STATE UNIV, 46-, MEM. FAC, UNION GRAD. SCH, 73-, chmn. dept. Eng, 63-73. Ed, Studies in Lang. & Lit, Harper & Row, 73- MLA; Am. Psychol. Asn; NCTE; Asn. Depts. Eng.(pres, 69-70, mem. exec. comt, 69-71). Bibliotherapy; the inter-relationships of literature and psychology; application of depth psychology to aesthetic theory. Publ: Co-ed, Psychology through literature, Oxford, 43; co-auth, Reading for rhetoric, 62, 67, Reading for understanding, 68 & The conscious reader, 74, Macmillan; auth, Bibliotherapy: an application of psychoanalytic theory, Am. Imago, 60; The scholars and the anti-self, 70 & How to change the English department, 71, Bull. Asn. Depts. Eng. Add: 590 Sausalito Blvd, Sausalito, CA 94965.

SHROEDER, JOHN WILLIAM, b. Kansas City, Mo, June 25, 25; m. 52; c. 1. ENGLISH, RENAISSANCE & AMERICAN LITERATURE. B.A, Univ. Kansas City, 49; M.A, Yale, 53, Ph.D.(Eng), 54; hon. M.A, Brown Univ, 62. Instr. ENG, Northwest. Univ, 54-57, asst. prof, 57-60; assoc. prof, BROWN UNIV, 60-70, PROF, 70-, ASSOC. DEAN GRAD. SCH, 69-, asst. dean, 68-69. Med. Dept, A.U.S, 43-46. Bibliography; Shakespeare; 19th century American novel. Publ: The great folio of 1623, Shoe String, 56; Spenser's erotic drama, ELH, 6/62; Miles Coverdale's calendar, EIHC, 10/67; Some unfortunate idyllic love affair, BBr, 3/68. Add: Dept. of English, Brown University, Providence, RI 02912.

SHROYER, FREDERICK BENJAMIN, b. Decatur, Ind, Oct. 28, 16; m. 49; c. 1. ENGLISH. Ph.D.(Eng), Univ. South. Calif, 54. Asst. prof. ENG, CALIF. STATE UNIV, LOS ANGELES, 50-54, assoc. prof, 55-59, PROF, 59-, chmn. dept. lang arts, 51-53, founder & dir, Pac. Coast writers conf, 53-56. Founder & dir, Idyllwild writers conf, Idyllwild Found, 56; Huntington-Hartford Found. fels, 58 & 65; lectr, mod. Am. novel & Am. novel, 1930-1960, KCOP-TV, KNXT-TV & CBS-TV, 59-60; panelist-lectr, Cavalcade of Books, KNXT, 59-62; consult, CBS Network lit. serv, 60; lit. ed, Los Angeles Sunday Herald-Examiner, 62-; Bingham Prof. humanities, Univ. Louisville, 69-70. Outstanding Professor Award, Calif. State Univ, Los Angeles, 67. U.S.A.A.F, 42-45, Capt. Nat. Acad. TV Arts & Sci. Joseph Sheridan Le-Fanu; minor Victorian fiction and periodical literature. Publ: Co-auth, A college treasury, 56, 2nd ed, 67 & Short story, 65, Scribner; auth, Wall against the night, Appleton, 57; It happened in Wayland, Reynal, 63; There none embrace, Ward, Lock, London, 66; co-auth, Muse of fire, Knopf, 70 & Types of drama, Scott, 70; co-auth, introd, Uncle Silas, Dover, 66 & The castles of Athlin and Dunbayne, Arno, 72; plus others. Add: 362 Coral View, Monterey Park, CA 91754.

SHTOGREN, JOHN ALEXANDER, JR, b. Detroit, Mich, May 13, 44; m. 70. MODERN LITERATURE, EDUCATIONAL TECHNOLOGY. A.B, Univ. Mich, Ann Arbor, 66, M.A, 67, Ph.D.(Eng), 71. Vis. prof. Eng, Dartmouth Col, summer 72; asst. prof, Albion Col, 72-73; PROG. COORD. ADULT EDUC, UNIV. CTR. ADULT EDUC, 73- Consult, Univ. Mich. Ctr. Prog. Learning, 68-73; U.S. Army Command & Gen. Staff Col, 70 & 72; Asn. Independent Cols. & Univs. Mich, 72-73. MLA; Nat. Soc. Prog. Instr. Modern American literature; educational technology; creativity. Publ: Co-auth. & co-ed, Quest: an academic skills program, Harcourt, 73. Add: University Center for Adult Education, 60 Farnsworth, Detroit, MI 48202.

SHUCARD, ALAN ROBERT, b. Brooklyn, N.Y, Dec. 2, 35; m. 62; c. 1. AMERICAN & ENGLISH LITERATURE. A.B, Union Col.(N.Y), 57; M.A, Univ. Conn, 63; Can. Coun. fel, Univ. B.C, 69; Ph.D.(Am. lit), Univ. Ariz, 71. Instr. II ENG, Univ. B.C, 65-70; asst. prof, UNIV. WIS-PARKSIDE, 70-73, ASSOC. PROF, 73- Wis. Alumni Res. Found. grant, 72. U.S.A, 59-62. MLA. Modern poetry; Afro-American literature; American literature. Publ: The gorgon bag, 70 & The louse on the head of a yawning lord, 72, Ladysmith, Quebec, Mari Evans, Kenneth Leslie & Stanley Moss, In: Contemporary poets, 2nd ed, St. James Press, London, 74; plus others. Add: Div. of Humanitistic Studies, University of Wisconsin-Parkside, Kenosha, WI 53140.

SHUCK, EMERSON CLAYTON, b. Findlay, Ohio, Apr. 15, 16; m. 36; c. 4. AMERICAN LITERATURE. B.S, Otterbein Col, 38, hon. D.Litt, 63; A.M, Ohio State Univ. 39; Ph.D.(Eng), Univ. Wis, 43. Asst, Ohio State Univ. & Univ. Wis, 39-43; asst. prof. Eng, Bowling Green State Univ, 43-46, assoc. prof, 46-48, prof, 48-63, dir. grad. sch, 45-50, dean, 50-55, col. lib. arts, 55-63; v.pres. acad. affairs, Ohio Wesleyan Univ, 63-67; PRES, EAST. WASH. STATE COL, 67-, PROF. ENG, 68- Mem. bd. dir, Am. Asn. State Cols. & Univs, 71-74; mem. comn. acad. affairs, Am. Counc. Educ, 72-75. Attitudes of American novelists toward religion, 1830-1930; Poe and science. Add: Eastern Washington State College, Cheney, WA 99004.

SHUFFELTON, FRANK CHARLES, b. St. Marys, Ohio, Mar. 10, 40; m. 63; c. 1. ENGLISH & AMERICAN LITERATURE. B.A, Harvard, 62; M.A, Stanford Univ, 68, Ph.D.(Eng), 72. Instr. ENG, Stanford Univ, 66-68; UNIV. ROCHESTER, 69-72, ASST. PROF, 72- U.S.C.G.R, 63-66, Lt. MLA. Early American literature; 19th century American literature; poetry. Publ: Thomas Prince and his edition of Thomas Hooker's Poor doubting Christian, Early Am. Lit, winter 71. Add: Dept. of English, University of Rochester, Rochester, NY 14627.

SHUFORD, CECIL EUGENE, b. Fayetteville, Ark, Feb. 21, 07; m. 37; c. 3. JOURNALISM. B.A, Univ. Ark, 28; scholar, Northwest. Univ, 28-29, M.S.J, 29; summers, scholars, MacDowell Writers Colony, Peterboro, N.H, 29, 30; Univ. Wis, 41. Instr. jour, Ala. Polytech. Inst, 29-30; Eng, Univ. Ark, 34-37; JOUR, N.TEX. STATE UNIV, 37-41, asst. prof, 41-47, assoc. prof, 47-59, PROF, 59-, DIR. JOUR, 46- Asst. prof. jour. & Eng. & dir. pub, Trinity Univ, 37-38. Voertman Award, Tex. Inst. Lett, 73. U.S.A.A.F, 42-45, 1st Lt. Am. Soc. Jour. Sch. Adminr.(v.pres, 56); Poetry Soc. Am.(Michael Sloane Fel. Award, 63, William Marion Reedy Mem. Award, 66). Freelance writing, especially in fields of poetry. Publ: The red bull and other poems, South & West, 65; Selected poems 1933-1971, N.Tex. State Univ, 72; Ours was the best generation, Scribner's Mag, 8/37; Do newspapers pay?, Quill, 5/55; Journalism as a liberal arts subject, Am. Soc. Jour. Sch. Adminr. Bull, winter-spring 55-56. Add: 2910 E. McKinney, Denton, TX 76201.

SHUGG, WALLACE, b. Boston, Mass, Apr. 28, 29. ENGLISH. A.B, Williams Col, 49; A.M, Columbia Univ, 58, Ph.D.(Eng), 66. Asst. prof. ENG, Manhattan Community Col, 66-67; UNIV. MD, BALTIMORE COUNTY, 67-72, ASSOC. PROF, 72- U.S.N, 50-54. English literature of the 17th century. Publ: The Cartesian beast-machine in English literature, 1663-1750, J. Hist. Ideas, 4-6/68; Humanitarian attitudes in the early animal experiments of the Royal Society, Ann. of Sci, 9/68; Henry More's Circulatio sanguinis: an unexamined poem in praise of Harvey, Bull. Hist. Med, 3-4/72; plus one other. Add: 301-E N. Chapelgate, Baltimore, MD 21229.

SHUGRUE, MICHAEL FRANCIS, b. Chicago, Ill, July 28, 34. ENGLISH LITERATURE. A.B, Univ. Nebr, 56; M.A, Duke Univ, 57, Ph.D, 60. Instr. Eng, Univ. Ill, 60-62; asst. prof. Eng. & asst. to chancellor, Univ. Nebr, 62-63; asst. prof. Eng, Univ. Ill, Urbana, 63-65; secy. for Eng. & coord. Asn. Dept. Eng. MLA, 65-73; PROF. ENG. & DIR. ACAD. PROGS, CITY COL. NEW YORK, 73- Assoc. dir, Eng. Teacher Prep. Study Stud, 65-67; dir. Eng. Inst. Materials Ctr, 66-67; adj. prof, N.Y. Univ, 65-73; chmn. basic studies task force, U.S. Off. Educ, 72- MLA; NCTE. Daniel Defoe; 18th century English literature and novel. Publ: Ed, Marivaux's The virtuous orphan, South. Ill. Univ, 65 & Farquhar's The recruiting officer, Univ. Nebr, 66; auth, How the new English will help your child, Asn. Press; ed, Selected poetry and prose of Defoe, Holt, 68; auth, English in a decade of change, Pegasus, 68; co-ed, Foundation of the novel: representative early 18th century fiction, Garland, 72-73 & Prospects for the 70's, MLA, 73. Add: Office of the President, City College of New York, 138th St. & Convent Ave, New York, NY 10031.

SHUMAKER, ARTHUR WESLEY, b. Indianapolis, Ind, Oct. 15, 13; m. 47; c. 1. ENGLISH & AMERICAN LITERATURE. A.B, DePauw Univ, 34; A.M, Ind. Univ, 42; Ph.D.(Eng), State Univ. Iowa, 58. Instr. French, Fed. Adult Educ, Indianapolis, Ind, 34-35; teacher high sch, 35-42; instr. ENG, DePAUW UNIV, 42-43, 46-47, asst. prof, 47-53, assoc. prof, 53-59, PROF, 59-, COORD. GEN. STUD, 61-, DIR. CONVOCATIONS, 67-, secy. fac, 61-73. Consult, Alaska Methodist Univ, 61-62, vis. prof, summer 62; Ind. Cent. Col, summer 63. Ind. Auth. Special Award, 63. U.S.A, 43-46. MLA; NCTE; Conf. Col. Compos. & Commun; Asn. Gen. & Lib. Stud; Soc. Stud. Midwest. Lit; Asn. Col. & Univ. Concert Mgr. Literature of Indiana. Publ: Co-auth, Literary map of Indiana, Ind. Col. Eng. Asn. & Ind. Counc. Teachers Eng, 56; auth, History of Indiana literature, Ind. Hist. Soc, 62; Indiana literature and suggestions for teaching it, Ind. Soc. Stud. Quart, spring 66; Bolton, Sarah Tittle Barrett & Johnston, Annie Fellows, In: Notable American women, 1607-1950: a biographical dictionary, Belknap, 71. Add: Dept. of English, DePauw University, Greencastle, IN 46135.

SHUMAKER, RONALD CLAIR, b. Punxsutawney, Pa, July 30, 40; m. 68. ENGLISH LANGUAGE & LITERATURE. B.S, Clarion State Col, 62; M.A, Purdue Univ, W.Lafayette, 65; Ph.D, Univ. Pittsburgh, 74. Teacher Eng. & French, Fox Chapel Area Schs, Pa, 62-63; asst. ENG, Purdue Univ, W.Lafayette, 63-64; instr, Clarion State Col, 64-67; grad. fel, Univ. Pittsburgh, 67-68; ASSOC. PROF, CLARION STATE COL, 68- MLA; NEA. Victorian literature: fiction; structuralism. Add: Dept. of English, Clarion State College, Clarion, PA 16214.

SHUMAKER, WAYNE, b. Indianapolis, Ind, Feb. 8, 10; m. 40; c. 2. ENGLISH LITERATURE. A.B, DePauw Univ, 31; A.M, Harvard, 32; Ph.D, Univ. Calif, 43. Acting prof, Cent. Norm. Col, 34-35, 37-39; asst. prof, Hokkaido Univ, Japan, 35-37; instr, Univ. Denver, 41-42; asst. prof. ENG, UNIV. CALIF, BERKELEY, 46-53, assoc. prof, 53-59, PROF, 59- Vis. prof, Int. Christian Univ, Tokyo, 64-65; dir, Univ. Calif. Stud. Ctr, Tokyo, 64-65. U.S.N.R, 42-46, Lt. MLA; Renaissance Soc. Am; Milton Soc. Am. Milton and Chaucer; critical theory; occult thought in the Renaissance. Publ: Elements of critical theory, 52, English autobiography, 54 & The occult sciences in the Renaissance, 72, Univ. Calif; Literature and the irrational, 60 & An approach to poetry, 65, Prentice-Hall; Unpremeditated verse: feeling and perception in Paradise lost, Princeton, 67. Add: Dept. of English, University of California, Berkeley, CA 94720.

SHUMAN, R. BAIRD, b. Paterson, N.J, June 20, 34. ENGLISH, EDUCATION. A.B, Lehigh Univ, 52; Ed.M, Temple Univ, 53; cert, Univ. Vienna, 54; Ph.D, Univ. Pa, 61. Asst. instr. Eng, Univ. Pa, 55-57; instr. humanities, Drexel Inst. Technol, 57-59; asst. prof. Eng, San Jose State Col, 59-62; EDUC, DUKE UNIV, 62-63, assoc. prof, 63-67, PROF, 67- Lectr. Am. lit, Linz Sem. Austrian Teachers, Austria, 53; scholar, Univ. Pa, 56; vis. lectr. Eng, Moore Inst. Art, 58; vis. prof. humanities, Phila. Conserv. Music, 58-59. MLA; NCTE (state chmn. achievement awards prog, 65-68); Int. Asn. Univ. Prof. Eng. Renaissance education; American drama; archaeology. Publ: Clifford Odets, 61, Robert E. Sherwood, 64 & William Inge, 65, Twayne; Nine black poets, 68, ed, An eye for an eye, 69 & ed, A galaxy of black writing, 70, Moore; auth, Creative approaches to the teaching of English: secondary, Peacock, 74; Hearn's gift from the sea: Chita, Eng. J, 67. Add: Dept. of Education, Box 6696, Duke University, Durham, NC 27708.

SHUMWAY, ERIC BRANDON, b. Holbrook, Ariz, Nov. 8, 39; m. 63; c. 5. ENGLISH LITERATURE, POLYNESIAN LANGUAGES. B.A, Brigham Young Univ, 64, M.A, 66; Ph.D.(Eng), Univ. Va, 73. Instr. ENG, CHURCH COL. HAWAII, 66-69, asst. prof, 69-74, ASSOC. PROF, 74- Browning's love poetry; love in 19th century literature; the Tongan oral tradition. Publ: Intensive course in Tongan, Univ. Hawaii, 71. Add: 55629 Iosepa, Laie, HI 96762.

SHURR, WILLIAM HOWARD, b. Evanston, Ill, Aug. 29, 32; m. 68; c. 1. AMERICAN LITERATURE. A.B, Loyola Univ. Chicago, 55, Ph.L, 58, M.A, 59, S.T.L, 64; Ph.D.(Eng), Univ. N.C, Chapel Hill, 68. Asst. prof. ENG, Univ. Tenn, 68-72; ASSOC. PROF, WASH. STATE UNIV, 72- Reader, PMLA, 71-; mem. ed. bd, Poe Stud. & ESQ: A J. Am. Renaissance, 72- MLA; Melville Soc; Hopkins Soc. General world literature; history of theology. Publ: Ed, Prose and poetry of England, Random & Singer, 58; auth, The mystery of iniquity, Melville as poet, 1857-1891, Univ. Ky, 72; Typology and historical criticism of the American Renaissance, ESQ: A J. of Am. Renaissance, 73; Sylvester Judd and Gerard Manley Hopkins' Margaret, Victorian Poetry, 73; Once more to the Woods: a new point of entry into Frost's most famous poem, New Eng. Quart, 74. Add: Dept. of English, Washington State University, Pullman, WA 99163.

SHURTER, ROBERT LeFEVRE, b. Ellenville, N.Y, Oct. 22, 07; m. 28; c. 2. AMERICAN LITERATURE. A.B, Amherst Col, 28; A.M, Columbia Univ, 29; Ph.D, West. Reserve Univ, 36. Instr. Eng, CASE WEST. RESERVE UNIV, 30-37, asst. prof, 37-40, assoc. prof, 40-47, prof, 46-71, head dept. lang. & lit, 46-71, dir, eng. sci, & mgt. war training & evening div, 44-46, publicity rep, 45-47, dir, div. humanities & soc. stud, 49-59, EMER. PROF. ENG, 71- Lectr, John Huntington Polytech. Inst, 35-; commun. consult, 49-; chmn. adv. comt, Martha Holden Jennings Found, 63- NCTE; Am. Soc. Engineering Educ; MLA. General education in engineering institutions; the Utopian novel in America; Shakespearean performances in pre-Revolutionary America. Publ: Effective letters in business, 2nd ed, 54, Written communication in business, 57 & A concise grammar reference, 59, McGraw; co-auth, Business research and report writing, 65 & Critical thinking, 66, McGraw; A program for effective writing, Appleton, 67; The utopian novel in America, 1865-1900, A M S Publ, 73. Add: 5424 Azure Way, Sarasota, FL 33581.

SHUSTER, GEORGE N, b. Lancaster, Wis, Aug. 27; 94; m; c. 1. GERMAN HISTORY. A.B, Univ. Notre Dame, 15, M.A, 20; cert, Univ. Poitiers, 19; Carl Schurz Mem. Found. fel, Ger, 30-31; Ph.D, Columbia Univ, 39; Dr. Phil, Univ. Freiburg, 58; hon. LL.D, Ind. Univ, 68. Prof. Eng, Univ. Notre Dame, 21-24; pres, Hunter Col, 39-60; ASST. TO PRES, UNIV. NOTRE DAME, 61- Soc. Sci. Res. Counc. fel, Ger, 39-40; mem, U.S. Nat. Comn, UNESCO, 46-, U.S. rep. on exec. bd, 58-63; land comnr, State Dept, Bavaria, 50-51; trustee, Carnegie Endowment Int. Peace, 54-64, hon. trustee, 64-; mem, Am. Counc. Educ, 60. Butler Medal, Columbia Univ; Laetare Medal, Univ. Notre Dame. U.S.A, 17-19, 42-45. MLA; Am. Acad. Arts & Sci; Counc. For. Relat. Comparative literature; poetry of the Renaissance; philosophy of American higher education. Publ: The Germans, Dial, 30; Strong man rules: rise to power of Hitler, Appleton, 34; UNESCO: assessment and promise, Counc. For. Relat, 61; The ground I walked on, Ger. ed, Carolus, Ger, 63; Catholic education in a changing world, Holt, 68. Add: Office of the President, University of Notre Dame, Notre Dame, IN 46556.

SHUSTERMAN, DAVID, b. Altoona, Pa, Apr. 4, 12; m. 36; c. 1. ENGLISH. B.A, N.Y. Univ, 49, M.A, 50, Ph.D, 53. Instr. ENG, Univ. Kans, 53-56; IND. UNIV. SOUTHEAST, 56-58, asst. prof, 58-62, assoc. prof, 62-67, PROF, 67- Univ. Kans. summer fac. res. fel, 55; Ind. Univ. summer fac. res. fels, 57, 62 & 68. A.U.S, 43-46, S/Sgt. MLA. Victorian novel; 20th century English novel; American novel. Publ: The quest for certitude in E.M. Forster's fiction, Ind. Univ, 65; Peter Cunningham: friend of Dickens, Dickensian, 1/57; The curious case of Professor Godbole: a passage to India re-examined, PMLA, 9/61; The Reader fallacy and Bartleby the Scrivener, New Eng. Quart, 3/72. Add: Dept. of English, Indiana University Southeast, 4201 Grantline Rd, New Albany, IN 47150.

SHUTTLEWORTH, JACK M, b. Covington, Ohio, Oct. 24, 35; m. 56; c. 3. ENGLISH & AMERICAN LITERATURE. B.A, Ohio Wesleyan Univ, 57; M.A, Stanford Univ, 64; Ph.D.(Eng. lit), Univ. Denver, 68. U.S. AIR FORCE, 57-, instr. ENG, Prep. Sch, U.S. AIR FORCE ACAD, 64-65, from asst. prof. to ASSOC. PROF, 67- Lectr. Eng, Univ. Colo, Colorado Springs, 68-71. U.S.A.F, 57-, Lt. Col; Bronze Star Medal. Mod. Humanities Res. Asn. (contrib. ed, Annual bibliography of English language & literature, 68-); Bibliog. Soc. Univ. Va; Conf. Col. Compos. & Commun. Seventeenth century drama; Herbert of Cherbury; 20th century novel. Publ: Co-ed, Satire:

Aesop to Buchwald, Odyssey, 71; ed, The life of Lord Herbert of Cherbury, Oxford, 74. Add: Dept. of English & Fine Arts, U.S. Air Force Academy, CO 80840.

SIBLEY, AGNES, b. Marston, Mo, Oct. 24, 14. ENGLISH LITERATURE. A.B & A.M, Univ. Okla, 36; residence scholar, Columbia Univ, 36-38, Fisher fel, 46-47, Ph.D, 47. Instr. ENG, Cottey Col, 41-43; from assoc. prof. to PROF, LINDENWOOD COL, 43- Exchange teacher, Bishop Otter Col, Eng, 51-53. AAUP. Publ: Alexander Pope's prestige in America, 1725-1835, King's Crown Press, 49; Exchange teacher, Caxton Printers, Ltd, 61; May Sarton, Twayne, 73. Add: Dept. of English, Lindenwood College, St. Charles, MO 63301.

SIBLEY, FRANCIS MARTIN, b. Baton Rouge, La, Feb. 20, 30; m. 56; c. 3. ENGLISH. B.A, N.Ga. Col, 53; B.A, Auburn Univ, 57; M.A; Ph.D.(Eng), La. State Univ, 69. Asst. prof. Eng, Fresno State Col, 63-67; Univ. Puget Sound, 67-69; ASSOC. PROF. LIT, PARK COL, 69- Curriculum improvement grant to Harvard & Oberlin Univ, 67. U.S.A, 53-55, Res, 55-58, 1st Lt. Am. Stud. Asn; MLA. American literature; literary criticism: aesthetics and criticism, particularly I.A. Richards. Publ: How to read I.A. Richards, Am. Scholar, spring 73. Add: Dept. of Literature, Park College, Parkville, MO 64152.

SICHERMAN, CAROL MARKS, b. Boston, Mass, May 8, 37; m. 69; c. 1. ENGLISH LITERATURE. B.A, Barnard Col, 58; M.A, Univ. Wis, 59, Ph.D. (Eng), 64; Fulbright scholar, Oxford, 60-62, B.Litt, 62. Instr. ENG, Cornell Univ, 63-65, ASST. PROF, 65-69; LEHMAN COL, 69- Shakespeare; 17th century poetry. Publ: Co-ed, Christian ethicks, Cornell Univ, 68; auth, Thomas Traherne and Christian platonism, PMLA, 66; Donne's discoveries, Stud. Eng. Lit, 71; Coriolanus: the failure of words, ELH, 72. Add: Dept. of English, Herbert H. Lehman College, Bedford Park Blvd. W, Bronx, NY 10468.

SIDNELL, MICHAEL JOHN, b. London, Eng, Sept. 29, 35; m. 58; c. 4. ENGLISH LITERATURE. B.A, Univ. London, 56, univ. studentship, 60-61, M.A, 61, Ph.D, 67. Lectr. Eng, Mt. Allison Univ, 58-62, asst. prof, 62-64; Eng. lit, Trent Univ, 64-67, ASSOC. PROF, 67-69; ENG, TRINITY COL, UNIV. TORONTO, 69- Brit. Counc. travel grant, 60; Marjorie Young Bell fel, 63; Can. Counc. res. grants, 67, 68 & sr. fel, 71-72; vis. prof, Grad. Sch, York Univ, 68-69; secy, Grad. Ctr. Study Drama, Univ. Toronto, 70- Brit. Army, 56-58, Res, 58-, Lt. Am. Comt. Irish Stud. Anglo-Irish literature; theatre; modern poetry and drama. Publ: Co-auth, Druid Craft: the writing of The shadowy waters: manuscripts of W. B. Yeats, Vol. I, Univ. Mass, 71; auth, Manuscript versions of Yeats's The Countess Cathleen, Papers Bibliog. Soc. Am, 68; Yeats's first work for the stage, In: W. B. Yeats 1865-1965, Ibadan Univ, 65; Towards bureau politocracy, J. Can. Stud, 5/72. Add: Dept. of English, Trinity College, University of Toronto, Hoskin St, Toronto, Ont. M5S 1H8, Can.

SIEBERT, DONALD TATE, JR, b. Muskogee, Okla, Oct. 26, 40; m. 68. ENGLISH LITERATURE. B.A, Univ. Okla, 62, M.A, 64; Ph.D.(Eng. lit), Univ. Va, 72. Instr. ENG, U.S. Naval Acad, 67-69; ASST. PROF, UNIV. S.C, 72- U.S.N, 64-69, Res, 69-, Lt. Comdr. MLA; Am. Soc. 18th Century Stud. Eighteenth century; satire; history of ideas. Publ: Laokoon and Polymetis: Lessing's treatment of Joseph Spence, Lessing Yearbk, III, 71. Add: Dept. of English, University of South Carolina, Columbia, SC 29208.

SIEBERT, FREDRICK SEATON, b. Tower, Minn, Dec. 13, 02; m. 32; c. 2. JOURNALISM. A.B, Univ. Wis, 23; J.D, Univ. Ill, 29. From instr. to asst. prof, Univ. Ill, 30-39; prof, Northwest. Univ, 40-41; prof. jour. & dir. sch. jour. & commun, Univ. Ill, 41-57; dean col. commun. arts, MICH. STATE UNIV, 57-67, PROF. JOUR, 67- Government and mass communications; freedom of the press; history of freedom of the press. Publ: Rights and privileges of the press; Freedom of the press in England; Four theories of the press. Add: 539 S. Kedzie Hall, Michigan State University, East Lansing, MI 48823.

SIEGCHRIST, MARK, b. June 30, 44; U.S. citizen. VICTORIAN LITERATURE. B.A, Yale, 66; M.A. & Ph.D.(Eng), Univ. Pa, 70. ASST. PROF. ENG, Agnes Scott Col, 70-74; MARQUETTE UNIV, 74- MLA. Victorian poetry; modern British fiction. Publ: Browning's Red cotton night-cap country: the process of imagination, Victorian Poetry, (in press); The puritan St. Jerome in Browning's Fra Lippo Lippi, Stud. in Browning, fall 73; The role of Vivian in Arnold's Tristram and Iseult, Criticism, (in press). Add: Dept. of English, Marquette University, Milwaukee, WI 53233.

SIEGEL, BEN, b. Cleveland, Ohio, July 6, 25; m. 56; c. 2. LITERARY CRITICISM. A.B, San Diego State Col, 48; M.A, Univ. Calif, Los Angeles, 50; Ph.D, Univ. South. Calif, 56. Lectr. Eng, Univ. South. Calif, 53-57; asst. prof. ENG, CALIF. STATE POLYTECH. UNIV, POMONA, 57-62, assoc. prof, 62-66, PROF, 66-, chmn. dept, 58-62, head dept. lang. arts, 62-65. Asst. Eng, Univ. Calif, Los Angeles, 50-51; instr. Eng. & hist, Los Angeles Eve. Adult Sch, 54-56; world lit, Chouinard Art Inst, 56-57; Danforth fel, Divinity Sch, Univ. Chicago, summer 59. U.S.A, 43-46, S/Sgt. Am. Stud. Asn; Col. Eng. Asn; MLA (chmn. conf. biog, 67, chmn. conf. Am. novel, 69-73); Pop. Cult. Asn.(chmn. conf. Am. novel, 73). Contemporary American fiction; literature and religion; biography. Publ: Co-auth, The Puritan heritage: America's roots in the Bible, New Am. Libr, 63; Biography past and present, Scribner, 65; auth, Isaac Bashevis Singer, Univ. Minn, 69; Sholem Asch, Twayne, (in prep); Literary criticism past and present, Dickenson, (in prep); Saints and sinners: Israel Joshua Singer's Little heroes, South. Ill. Univ, (in prep); Bernard Malamud's Sad and bitter clowns, In: Bernard Malamud and the critics, N.Y. Univ, 70; Daniel Fuchs, In: Encycl. Contemporary Am. Novelist, St. James, 72. Add: 239 Monterrey Dr, Claremont, CA 91711.

SIEGEL, MICHAEL ALAN, b. Brooklyn, N.Y, Mar. 16, 45; m. 70. SPEECH COMMUNICATION, MASS COMMUNICATION. B.A, William Paterson Col, 66, M.A, 70; fel, Univ. Utah, 70-72, Ph.D.(speech commun), 72. Teacher, Madison Sch, Newark, N.J, 66-70; ASST. PROF. SPEECH, FITCHBURG STATE COL, 72- TV moderator, Montachusett Cable TV, Mass, 73-; consult, Lunenburg Pub. Schs, 73-; consult. pub. relat, Fitchburg Pub. Schs, 74- Speech Commun. Asn. Role of negro radio stations in their communities; Arab and Israeli propaganda in America; merger of conservative and reform Jewish synagogues in Salt Lake City. Add: Dept. of English, Fitchburg State College, 160 Pearl St, Fitchburg, MA 01420.

SIEGEL, PAUL N, b. Paterson, N.J, June 24, 16; m. 48; c. 1. ENGLISH LITERATURE. B.S, City Col. New York, 36; A.M, Harvard, 39, Ph.D, 41. Instr, Univ. Conn, 46; City Col. New York, 46-49; assoc. prof. ENG, Ripon Col, 49-52, PROF, 52-56; L.I. UNIV, 56-, chmn. dept, 56-71. Ford Found. Fund Advan. Educ. fel, 52-53; ed. consult, PMLA, 63-; consult. mem, World Ctr. Shakespeare Stud, London, 72; mem. adv. bd, World Ctr. Shakespeare Stud, U.S, 72- Columbia Univ. sem. in the Renaissance. Med.Admin.C, 41-46, Capt. MLA; Shakespeare Asn. Am. Shakespeare; Marxist literary criticism; 20th century novel. Publ: Shakespearean tragedy and the Elizabethan compromise, N.Y. Univ, 57; His infinite variety, Lippincott, 63; Shakespeare in his time and ours, Univ. Notre Dame, 68; ed, Leon Trotsky on literature and art, Pathfinder, 70; contrib, Reader's Encycl. of Shakespeare, Crowell, 66 & The achievement of Isaac Bashevis Singer, South. Ill. Univ, 69; auth, The conclusion of Richard Wright's Native son, PMLA, 74. Add: Dept. of English, Long Island University, Zeckendorf Campus, Brooklyn, NY 11201.

SIEGEL, ROBERT HAROLD, b. Oak Park, Ill, Aug. 18, 39; m. 61; c. 3. ENGLISH ROMANTIC PERIOD. B.A, Wheaton Col.(Ill), 61; M.A, Johns Hopkins Univ, 62; Ph.D.(Eng), Harvard, 68. Acting chmn. dept. Eng, Trinity Col.(Ill), 62-63; from instr. to ASST. PROF. ENG, DARTMOUTH COL, 67-, fac. fel, 71-72. MLA; Conf. Christianity & Lit.(dir, 69-72). Coleridge; modern poetry; American poetry. Publ: The beasts and the elders (poetry), Univ. Press New Eng, 73; contrib, Imagination and the spirit, Eerdmans, 71. Add: Dept. of English, Dartmouth College, Hanover, NH 03755.

SIEMENS, LLOYD GEORGE, b. Winnipeg, Man, Jan. 17, 35; m. 57; c. 2. ENGLISH. B.A, Univ. Man, 56, B.Paed, 59; M.A, Univ. Wis, 60, univ. fel, Can. Counc. fel. & Ph.D.(Thomas Hardy), 67. Instr. ENG, United Col, Winnipeg, 60-63; asst. prof, Univ. B.C, 66-68; UNIV. WINNIPEG, 68-70, ASSOC. PROF, 70- Can. Asn. Univ. Teachers; Asn. Can. Univ. Teachers Eng. Late Victorian and Edwardian literature; Shakespeare. Publ: Parody in the poems of Thomas Hardy, Dalhousie Rev, 72. Add: Dept. of English, University of Winnipeg, Winnipeg 2, Man, Can.

SIEMENS, REYNOLD GERRARD, b. Winnipeg, Man, Apr. 6, 32; m. 63; c. 2. ENGLISH, MUSIC. B.A, Univ. Man, 63; M.A, Univ. Wis, Madison, 64, Ph.D.(Eng), 66. Asst. prof. ENG, UNIV. ALTA, 66-71, ASSOC. PROF, 71- Lectr. lang. & lit, Hawkwood Col, Eng, summer 66; lectr. Eng, Univ. B.C, summer 67; Univ. Alta. res. grant, 66-67; pres. humanities res. award, 67-68. Dipl, Curtis Inst. Music, 56. MLA; Philol. Asn. Pac. Coast; Asn. Can. Univ. Teachers Eng. Romanticism; English novel. Publ: The Wordsworth collection, Univ. Alta, 71; If music and sweet poetry agree: Thomas Ford's Since first I saw your face, Renaissance Quart, summer 68; Dorothy Wordsworth papers, Wordsworth Circle, 72; The Juxth position of composed renderings in Ford's The good soldier, Humanities Asn. Bull, 72. Reynold Siemens, cellist, with the Boyd Neel orchestra (recording), Cello Classics, 62; Stravinsky conducts, I-IV (recordings), 61-63 & The music of Arnold Schoenberg, I-IV (recordings), 61-63, Columbia; Recollections of the last days of Bruno Schmidt (recording), Menno Classics, 72. Add: Dept. of English, University of Alberta, Edmonton, Alta, Can.

SIEMON, JAMES EDWARD, b. Wenatchee, Wash, Oct. 3, 36; ENGLISH. A.B, Stanford Univ, 58, Ph.D.(Eng), 66. Acting instr. Eng, Stanford Univ, 62-63; instr. Univ. Wash, 64-66, asst. prof, 66-72; res. comt. fac. fel. & vis. lectr, Univ. Wis-Madison, 72-73. MLA; Philol. Asn. Pac. Coast; Archaeol. Inst. Am; Shakespeare Asn. Am. Seventeenth century lyric; Renaissance drama. Publ: The Merchant of Venice: act V as ritual reiteration, Stud. Philol, 4/70; Generic limits in Marvell's Garden, Papers Lang. & Lit, summer 72; The canker within: some observations on the role of the villain in three Shakespearean comedies, Shakespeare Quart, fall 72. Add: 132 N. Franklin Ave, Wenatchee, WA 98801.

SIES, LUTHER FRANK, b. Westminster, Md, July 29, 27; m. 67. SPEECH PATHOLOGY, SEMANTICS. A.B, West. Md. Col, 48, Ed.M, 54; B.S, Towson State Col, 50; Ed.D.(speech path), George Washington Univ, 62. Teacher, Elem. Sch, Carroll Co, Md, 52-54; asst. dir. off campus div, Col. Gen. Stud, George Washington Univ, 54-56; supvr. sect. speech path, Walter Reed Army Hosp, 56-61; coord. speech path. & audiol. serv, State Univ. Iowa, 61-63; prof. speech & drama & chmn. dept, Towson State Col, 63-66; assoc. prof. speech, Nassau Community Col, 66-67; DIR. SPEECH & HEARING CTR, LEHMAN COL, 67- Esophageal speech consult, George Washington Univ. Hospital, 59-61; speech path. consult, Veterans Admin. Hosp, Iowa City, 61-63; mem. ed. bd, Inst. Gen. Semantics, 68; dir. speech & hearing serv, Prospect Hosp, Pediat. Screening Prog, 71- Linguistic characteristics of dyphasic speech; clinical applications of general semantics; dysphonia plica ventricularis. Publ: Fundamentals of speech, W.C. Brown, 66; ed, Aphasia theory and therapy, Univ. Park, 74; co-auth, The communication contract, C.C. Thomas, 74; co-auth, Personal account of dysphasia, 8/63 & auth, Acronymic elements in aphasic speech, 5/64, J. Speech & Hearing Disorders; Wendell Johnson—an appreciation, ETC: Rev. Gen. Semantics, 10/68. Add: Speech & Hearing Center, Herbert H. Lehman College, Bedford Park Blvd. W, Bronx, NY 10468.

SIGER, LEONARD P, b. Baltimore, Md, Aug. 3, 29; m. 63. ENGLISH. M.A, Univ. Chicago, 51; Ph.D, Johns Hopkins Univ, 60. Asst. prof. Eng, Gallaudet Col, 56-60, from assoc. prof. to prof, 60-68; MEM. STAFF SPEC. EDUC, BALTIMORE CITY PUB. SCHS, 70- Mem, Counc. Orgn. Serving the Deaf, Baltimore Metrop. Area. Am. Instr. Deaf; Nat. Asn. Deaf. Communication; education of the deaf; transportation. Publ: Numerous arts. on commun. systs. of the deaf & nonverbal commun. of the hearing. Add: 3606 Marmon Ave, Baltimore, MD 21207.

SIGGINS, CLARA M, b. Sept. 16, 08; m. 32. ENGLISH. B.S, Columbia Univ, 35, M.A, 36; Ph.D.(Eng), St. John's Univ.(N.Y), 41. Instr. Eng, Mt. St. Mary's Col.(N.H), 45-50; assoc. prof. Eng, BOSTON COL, 55-68, PROF.

CONTEMPORARY POETRY & MOD. DRAMA, 68- Reviewer, Best Sellers, Univ. Scranton, 56- AAUP; MLA; Col. Eng. Asn; NCTE. Literary criticism; mediaeval literature. Add: Dept. of English, Boston College, Chestnut Hill, MA 02167.

SIGMAN, JOSEPH THOMAS, b. Duryea, Pa, Nov. 30, 34; Can. citizen. ENGLISH LITERATURE. B.A, Kings Col.(Pa), 60; M.A, Univ. Pa, 62, fel, 64-65, Ph.D.(Eng), 67. Asst. prof. ENG, McMASTER UNIV, 65-74, ASSOC. PROF, 74- U.S.C.G, 54-58. Thomas Carlyle and George MacDonald. Publ: Diabolico-angelical indifference: the imagery of polarity in Sartor Resartus, South. Rev, 9/72; Nifl, Muspel, Adam Kadman, and the biblical imagery of Sartor Resartus, ELH, (in press). Add: Dept. of English, McMaster University, Hamilton, Ont, Can.

SIGWORTH, OLIVER FREDERIC, b. Glendale, Ariz, July 31, 21; m; c. 2. ENGLISH. A.B, Univ. Calif, 47, M.A, 48, Ph.D, 51. Teaching asst, Univ. Calif, 48-51; instr. ENG, Univ. Nev, 51-52; San Francisco State Col, 52-53; UNIV. ARIZ, 53-57, asst. prof, 57-62, assoc. prof, 62-66, PROF, 66- Fund Advan. Educ. fel, 55-56; vis. lectr, Univ. B.C, summer 64. A.U.S, 43-46, S/Sgt. MLA; Philol. Asn. Pac. Coast; Rocky Mountain Mod. Lang. Asn; Am. Soc. 18th Century Stud; Southwest Soc. 18th Century Stud. Eighteenth century English literature; interrelationships of literature and other arts in 18th century England; early Romantic period. Publ: Four styles of a decade, 1740-1750, N.Y. Pub. Libr, 61; William Collins, Twayne, 65; Nature's sternest painter: essays on the poetry of George Crabbe, Univ. Ariz, 65; ed, Criticism and aesthetics, 1660-1800, Rinehart, 71; auth, Johnson's Lycidas: the end of Renaissance criticism, Eighteenth Century Stud, 67; A way of looking at some Baroque poems, Stud. 18th Century Cult, 74. Add: Dept. of English, University of Arizona, Tucson, AZ 85721.

SIKES, JAMES DAVIS, b. Midland, Tex, Dec. 1, 31. DRAMA. B.A, Baylor Univ, 53, M.A, 56; fel, Univ. Denver, 59-60, Ph.D.(theatre), 63. Instr. speech & drama & acting chmn. dept, Univ. Corpus Christi, 56-57; asst. prof. drama, Colo. State Col, 57-59; instr. speech & theatre, Foothill Jr. Col. Dist, 63-69; assoc. prof. speech, Ore. Col. Educ, 69-70; PROF. THEATRE ARTS & CHMN. DIV. ART, THEATRE & DANCE, JACKSONVILLE UNIV, 70- U.S.A.F, 53-55, 61-62, Capt. Am. Theatre Asn; Speech Commun. Asn; U.S. Inst. Theatre Technol. Add: College of Fine Arts, Jacksonville University, Jacksonville, FL 32211.

SIKKINK, DONALD ELWYN, b. Cresco, Iowa, Apr. 27, 28; m. 52; c. 4. SPEECH. B.A, Univ. Minn, 49, M.A, 51, Ph.D.(speech), 54. Mem. staff, Off. Naval Res. Proj, Univ. Minn, 52-53, Ford Found. teaching internship, 53-54; dir. forensics, Stanford Univ, 54-56; asst. prof. speech, S.Dak. State Col. Agr. & Mech. Art, 56-59, assoc. prof, 59-62, prof, 62-63; head dept, 59-63; assoc. prof, ST. CLOUD STATE COL, 63-65, dean sch. arts & sci, 65-70, CHMN. DEPT. SPEECH COMMUN. & DIR. SELF-SELECTION PROJ, 70- Speech Commun. Asn. Experimental study of communication. Publ: Modern parliamentary practices, Burgess; Conditions affecting the communication of controversial statements in connected discourse, Speech Monogr. Add: 1016 Kilian Blvd, St. Cloud, MN 56301.

SIKS, GERALDINE BRAIN, b. Thorp, Wash, Feb. 11, 12; m. 41; c. 2. DRAMA. B.A, Ellensburg Norm. Sch, Wash, 35; M.A, Northwest. Univ, 41. Teacher, pub. schs, Wash, 32-37, Ill, 38-42; theatre asst, UNIV. WASH, 49-50, assoc. asst. DRAMA, 50-51, instr, 51-56, asst. prof, 56-61, assoc. prof, 61-65, PROF, 65- Assoc. dir, Children's Theatre, Evanston, Ill, 37-41; summer vis. prof, Univ. Toledo, 61; San Jose State Col, 63; U.S. Off. Educ. Res. contract, Europe, 65-66; lectr, Univ. Hawaii, summer 66; consult, Am. Educ. Theatre Asn, Int. Theatre Conf, Wash, D.C, 67; field reader, Bur. Res, U.S. Off. Educ, 70-73. Blue Book Award, 55; co-recipient, Nat. Playwright Contest 1st Award, 55; Jr. Eaves Award, 62. Children's Theatre Asn; NCTE; Am. Theatre Asn; Am. Asn. Childhood Educ. Elementary education and drama, especially children's drama; arts education in early childhood education. Publ: Creative dramatics: an art for children, 58, Japanese transl, 74, co-auth, Creative dramatics in home, school and community, 52 & auth, Children's literature for dramatization, 64, Harper; co-ed, Children's theatre and creative dramatics, Univ. Wash, 61; auth, Theatre arts materials research, U.S. Off. Educ. Bur. Res, 66; A view of current European theatres for children, Educ. Theatre J, 5/67; On teaching drama, In: On teaching speech in the elementary and junior high schools, Ind. Univ, 71; The elementary program, In: Drama education guidelines, Wash. State Pub. Instr. Off, 72. Add: 1754 N.E. 90th St, Seattle, WA 98115.

SILBERG, JACK, Philosophy, English. See Volume IV, Philosophy, Religion & Law.

SILLARS, MALCOLM O, b. Union City, N.J, Feb. 12, 28; m. 48; c. 3. SPEECH. B.A, Univ. Redlands, 48, M.A, 49; Ph.D, State Univ. Iowa, 55. Instr. speech, Iowa State Univ, 49-54; Los Angeles State Col, 54-56; from asst. prof. to assoc. prof. speech, San Fernando Valley State Col, 56-61, prof, 62-71, chmn. dept, 56-63, 66-68, assoc. dean sch. lett. & sci, 63-66, acting dean, 69-70, acting pres, 69; PROF. COMMUN, UNIV. MASS, AMHERST, 71- Res. assoc, Univ. Ill, 61-62; vis. prof, Univ. Utah, 71. Speech Commun. Asn.(assoc. ed, Quart. J. Speech, 63-66, dir. summer conf, 70, chmn. educ. policies bd, 70-71, chmn. awards comt, 72, mem. Am. bicentennial comt, 72-); Am. Forensic Asn.(secy-treas, 55-57); Am. Stud. Asn; East. Commun. Asn. American public address; contemporary rhetorical theory. Publ: Co-auth, Speech: content and communication, Chandler, 62; Robert Penn Warren's All the kings men, a study in populism, Am. Quart, 56; The 1960 Democratic Convention, Quart. J. Speech, 60; The rhetoric of the petition in Boots, Speech Monogr, 6/72. Add: Dept. of Communication Studies, University of Massachusetts, Amherst, MA 01002.

SILVEIRA, GERALD E, b. Gloucester, Mass, June 25, 26. ENGLISH. B.A, Boston Univ, 50; M.A, Rutgers Univ, 52; South. Fel. Fund grant, N.Y. Univ, 56-58. Instr. ENG, Ala. Col, 52-56; asst. prof, L.I. UNIV, 58-70, ASSOC. PROF, 70- Fulbright teaching asst, Ger, 54-55. U.S.A, 44-46. MLA; NCTE; Teachers Eng. to Speakers Other Lang. English as a second language. Add: 81 Columbia Heights, Brooklyn, NY 11201.

SILVERMAN, ALBERT H, b. Chicago, Ill, Jan. 15, 19; m. 45; c. 2. ENGLISH, DRAMA. B.A, Chicago Teachers Col, 42; M.A, Univ. Chicago, 48; Ph.D. (Eng), Tulane Univ, 54. Instr. Eng. & humanities, Univ. Ark, 48-50; ENG, Tulane Univ, 50-54; asst. prof, Xavier Univ.(La), 54-56; assoc. prof, CHICAGO CITY COL, 56-70, PROF, 70- U.S.A.A.F, 43-46. Shaw Soc, Eng. Bernard Shaw, Ibsen and Strindberg. Publ: Sex and money in Chaucer's Shipman's tale, Philol. Quart, 7/53; Bernard Shaw's Shakespeare criticism, Pul. MLA, 9/57; Bernard Shaw's political extravaganzas, Drama Surv, winter 67. Add: 1919 Main St, Evanston, IL 60202.

SILVERMAN, KENNETH EUGENE, b. New York, N.Y, Feb. 5, 36; m. 57; c. 2. ENGLISH, AMERICAN STUDIES. B.A, Columbia Univ, 56, M.A, 58, Ph.D. (Eng), 64. Instr. Eng, Univ. Wyo, 58-59; preceptor, Columbia Col, 62-64; ASSOC. PROF. ENG. & GRAD. ADV. AM. STUDIES, N.Y. UNIV, 64- Consult, CEEP Prog. Am. Lit, State Univ. N.Y, 67-69; assoc, Danforth Found, 68-; ed. bd, Early Am. Lit, 69-72; Nat. Endowment Humanities Bicentennial grant, 72-74. MLA. American culture, 1600-1800; American romantic literature. Publ: Ed, Colonial American poetry, Hafner, 68; auth, Timothy Dwight, Twayne, 69; ed, Literature in America I: the founding of a nation, Free Press, 71; ed, Selected letters of Cotton Mather, La. State Univ, 71; Cotton Mather's foreign correspondence, Early Am. Lit, winter 69; Forward to Vernon L. Parrington's The Connecticut wits, Crowell, 69. Add: Dept. of English, New York University, 19 University Pl, New York, NY 10003.

SILVERMAN, OSCAR ANSELL, b. Uniontown, Pa, Feb. 13, 03; div; c. 2. ENGLISH. A.B, Yale, 25, Ph.D.(Eng), 41; M.A, Univ. Wis, Madison, 26. Asst. eng, Univ. Wis, Madison, 25-26; instr, STATE UNIV. N.Y. BUFFALO, 26-28, 30-33, asst. prof, 33-40, assoc. prof, 40-43, prof, 43-68, chmn. Eng, 56-63, dir. libr, 60-68, EMER. DIR. LIBR, 68- Instr. Eng, U.S. Army Univ.(France), 45-46; Carnegie fel, Harvard Col, 53-54. MLA; AAUP; Grolier Club. Contemporary literature; Joyce. Publ: Ed, The management of universities by S.P. Capen, Foster & Stewart, 53 & James Joyce's Epiphanies, Lockwood Libr, Buffalo, 56. Add: 786 W. Ferry St, Buffalo, NY 14222.

SILVERSTEIN, NORMAN, b. Bronx, N.Y, Mar. 15, 22. ENGLISH. B.A, City Col. New York, 43; M.A, Columbia Univ, 47, Ph.D.(Eng), 60. Instr. ENG, Syracuse Univ, 48-51; from asst. prof. to assoc. prof, QUEENS COL. (N.Y), 53-73, PROF, 73- Fulbright lectr, Univ. Lodz, 65-66; adv. ed, Lit/Film Quart; contrib. film ed, Salmagundi; trustee, James Joyce Found. Sig.C, U.S.A, 43-46, Sgt. MLA; Eng. Inst; Soc. Auth, Eng. James Joyce; 17th century; film. Publ: Co-auth, The film experience, Harper, 68 & Delta, 69; auth, Godard and revolution, Film & Filming, (London), 6/71; Two R.D. Laing films: Wednesday's child and Asylum, Film Quart, summer 73; guest ed, Film as literature and language, J. Mod. Lit, 4/73; plus others. Add: Dept. of English, Queens College, Flushing, NY 11367.

SILVERSTEIN, THEODORE, b. Liverpool, Eng, Oct. 11, 04; nat; m. ENGLISH. A.B, Harvard, 26, A.M, 27, Ph.D, 30. Instr. Eng, Harvard, 30-37; assoc. prof, Univ. Kans. City, 37-42; Guggenheim fel, 46-47; asst. prof. Eng, UNIV. CHICAGO, 47-51, assoc. prof, 51-55, prof, 55-73, chmn. comt. ideas & methods, 65-73, EMER. PROF. ENG, 73- Inst. Advan. Stud. fel, 55-56. U.S.A.A.F, 42-46. MLA. Other world literature; mediaeval poetry and philosophy; Dante. Publ: Visio sancti Pauli; Ed, Medieval English lyrics, Edward Arnold, 72; auth, Dante and the legend of the Miraj, J. Near East. Stud. Add: Dept. of English, University of Chicago, Chicago, IL 60637.

SILVIA, DANIEL (SHIVER, JR), b. Wilmington, N.C, July 14, 34. MEDIAEVAL & RENAISSANCE ENGLISH LITERATURE. A.B, Univ. N.C, 56, M.A, 58; univ. fel, Univ. Ill, 58-60, Ph.D, 62. Asst. ENG, Univ. Ill, 60-62; asst. prof, UNIV. CALIF, DAVIS, 62-70, ASSOC. PROF, 70-, GRAD. ADV. ENG, 72- Fel. humanities inst, Univ. Calif, 68. MLA; Mediaeval Acad. Am. Chaucer; early English literature; paleography and bibliography. Add: Dept. of English, University of California, Davis, CA 95616.

SIMEONE, WILLIAM E, b. Redgranite, Wis, Dec. 31, 22; m. 46; c. 2. ENGLISH LITERATURE. B.A, Univ. Wis, 43, M.A, 47; Ph.D, Univ. Pa, 50. Asst. prof. Eng, SOUTH. ILL. UNIV, CARBONDALE, 50-57, assoc. prof, 57-65, PROF. ENG, 65-, CHMN. DEPT, 72-, dean grad. sch, 65-69. Guggenheim fel, 59; Am. Counc. Learned Soc. grant-in-aid, 60. U.S.A, 43-46. MLA; Am. Folklore Soc; Renaissance Soc. Am. Seventeenth century literature; British and Italian folklore. Publ: Co-auth, Fanshawe's Pastor Fido, Clarendon Press, 64; May games and Robin Hood legend, 51 & Italian folklore scholars, 60, J. Am. Folklore. Add: Dept. of English, Southern Illinois University, Carbondale, IL 62902.

SIMLEY, ANNE, b. Black Earth, Wis, Jan. 16, 91. HUMANITIES. A.B, Carleton Col, 17; A.M, Univ. Wis, 28, summers, 31-38; summer, Garrett Biblical Inst, 55. Teacher, high sch, Minn, 17-22; mem. fac, Northwest Sch. Agr, Crookston, 22-30; assoc. prof. speech, HAMLINE UNIV, 30-58, chmn. dept. speech & dramatics, 50-58, EMER. PROF. SPEECH, 58- Consult. in speech, Minn. State High Sch. League, 58-65; instr, Col. St. Catherine, 62-66; cert. volunteer reader, Taping for Blind, Libr. of Congress, 68- Publ: Oral interpretation handbook, 60, Stories to tell or read aloud, 62 & Folk tales to tell or read aloud, 63, Burgess. Add: Apt. 2, 2350 Chalet Gardens Rd, Madison, WI 53711.

SIMMONDS, JAMES DUDLEY, b. Mt. Magnet, Australia, Dec. 15, 33; m. 55; c. 1. ENGLISH. B.A, Univ. West. Australia, 55; M.A, Melbourne Univ, 58; Ph.D.(Eng), La. State Univ, 61. Instr. ENG, Univ. Ky, 60-61; lectr, Univ. Sydney, 61-63; Preston Tech. Col, 64-65; asst. prof, UNIV. PITTSBURGH, 65-66, ASSOC. PROF, 66-, Charles E. Merrill res. fel, summer 67. Ed, Milton Stud, 69- Milton Soc. Am; MLA; Renaissance Soc. Am; Renaissance Eng. Text Soc. Henry Vaughan; Milton; 17th century literature. Publ: Co-auth, Henry Vaughan: a bibliographical supplement, 1946-1960, Univ. Ala, 63; auth, Masques of God: form and theme in the poetry of Henry Vaughan, Univ. Pittsburgh, 72; The identity of Henry Vaughan's suppressed poems, Mod. Lang. Quart, 12/61; Vaughan's masterpiece and its critics: The world revaluated, Stud. Eng. Lit, winter 62. Add: Dept. of English, University of Pittsburgh, Pittsburgh, PA 15260.

SIMMONS, (JOSEPH) EDGAR, b. Natchez, Miss, May 28, 21; m. 54; c. 2. ENGLISH. B.S, Columbia Univ, 47, M.A, 48; Sorbonne, France, 53-54.

Instr. ENG, DePauw Univ, 48-50; asst. prof, Col. William & Mary, 55-63; Miss. Col, 63-66; Univ. Tex. El Paso, 66-69. Shellenger Found. grants, 66-68. U.S.A.A.F, 42-45. Am. Soc. Aesthet. Meaning of symbol; new approach to college freshman English; poetry. Publ: Co-auth, The honey and the gall, poems about marriage, Macmillan, 67; Southern writing of the sixties/poetry, La. State Univ, 67 & New Directions 20 (poetry), New Directions, 68; auth, Driving to Biloxi (poems), La. State Univ, 68; City lovers (poem), Harper's Mag, 4/68; Faulkner (poem), Yale Rev, summer 68; Music from a sloven town (poem), Antioch Rev, summer 68; plus others. Add: 633 Lexington Ave, Jackson, MS 39209.

SIMMONS, JAMES C, b. Cincinnati, Ohio, Mar. 18, 39. ENGLISH LITERATURE. B.A, Miami Univ, 61; M.A, Univ. Calif, Berkeley, 63, Ph.D.(Eng), 66. ASST. PROF. ENG, BOSTON UNIV, CHARLES RIVER CAMPUS, 66- MLA. Victorian novel; utopian literature; Southern regionalism in American literature. Add: Dept. of English, Boston University, Charles River Campus, 236 Bay State Rd, Boston, MA 02215.

SIMMONS, JOSEPH LARRY, b. Tylertown, Miss, Dec. 9, 35; m. 64; c. 3. ENGLISH. B.Mus, Fla. State Univ, 56; B.A, N.Y. Univ, 62; Ph.D.(Eng), Univ. Va, 67. Instr. ENG, N.Tex. State Univ, 62-64; asst. prof, TULANE UNIV, 67-69, ASSOC. PROF, 69- Huntington Libr. res. fel, summer 69; Folger Libr. res. fel, summers 70 & 72; Nat. Endowment for Humanities Younger Humanists fel, 73-74. MLA; Shakespeare Asn. Am. Shakespearean and Renaissance drama; 17th century poetry. Publ: Shakespeare's pagan world: the Roman tragedies, Univ. Va, 73; Elizabethan stage practice and Marlowe's The Jew of Malta, Renaissance Drama, 71; A source for Shakespeare's Malvolio: the Elizabethan controversy with the Puritans, Huntington Libr. Quart, 73. Add: Dept. of English, Tulane University, New Orleans, LA 70118.

SIMMONS, WALTER (LEE), b. Tarboro, N.C, July 30, 03; m. 29; c. 1. ENGLISH LITERATURE. A.B, Washington & Lee Univ, 24; A.M, Harvard, 28; Ph.D, Ohio State Univ, 38. Instr, Ga. Sch. Tech, 24-26; Ohio Wesleyan Univ, 28-31, asst. prof, 31-38, assoc. prof, 38-39; vis. prof, Kent State Univ, 39-40, asst. prof. ENG, 40-45, assoc. prof, 45-46; prof, UNIV. R.I, 46-72, chmn. dept, 46-66, EMER. PROF, 72- Vis. assoc. prof, Westminster Col.(Mo), 35-36. Col. Eng. Asn; MLA. Late 18th century English literature; American literature. Add: Dept. of English, University of Rhode Island, Kingston, RI 02881.

SIMMS, THEODORE F, b. Flushing, N.Y, July 31, 36; m. 60; c. 2. ENGLISH. B.A, N.Y. Univ, 57, M.A, 64, Ph.D.(Eng), 66; Fulbright scholar, Australia, 57-58. Asst. Eng, Wash. Sq. Col, N.Y. Univ, 58-60; instr, STATEN ISLAND COMMUNITY COL, 60-64, asst. prof, 64-67, assoc. prof, 67-72, PROF. ENG. & SPEECH, 72- City Univ. N.Y. summer res. grant, 67. MLA; NCTE. Modern English poetry; Australian literature. Publ: Improving college study skills, Glencoe, 70; Revising the theme, Harper, 74. Add: Dept. of English, Staten Island Community College, 715 Ocean Terrace, Staten Island, NY 10301.

SIMON, JOHN KENNETH, English, French. See Volume III, Foreign Languages, Linguistics & Philology.

SIMON, MARC, b. Philadelphia, Pa, Jan. 20, 38; m. 60; c. 3. BRITISH & AMERICAN LITERATURE. B.S, Temple Univ, 60; Univ. Pa, 60; M.A, Johns Hopkins Univ, 61; Ph.D.(Eng), N.Y. Univ, 68. Sr. lectr. ENG, McGILL UNIV, 69-70, ASST. PROF, 70- Adj.Gen.C, U.S.A, 60-69, Capt. Nineteenth and twentieth century British and American poetry; dramatic monologue; genesis of literary composition. Publ: Samuel Greenberg and Hart Crane: a study of the lost manuscripts, Mouton; Hart Crane and Samuel Greenberg: an emblematic interlude, Contemporary Lit, spring 71; Hart Crane's Greenberg Mss. and the launching of Voyages II, J. Mod. Lit, 74. Add: Dept. of English, McGill University, Montreal, P.Q, Can.

SIMONS, HERBERT W, b. Brooklyn, N.Y. Aug. 15, 35; m. 60. SPEECH. B.A, Univ. Vt, 56; M.S, Purdue Univ, 58, res. fel, 59-60, Ph.D, 61. From asst. prof. to PROF. SPEECH, TEMPLE UNIV, 60- Instr. oral commun, Philadelphia Electric Co, 60-; U.S. Navy Regional Accounting Off, Philadelphia, 61-62; mem. workshop, Del. Right-of-way Authority, 63; U.S. Army Northeast Regional Training Command, 63. Speech Commun. Asn; Int. Commun. Asn. Communication theory; organizational communications; experimental research in persuasion. Publ: Global vs. fractionated judgements of communication behavior, Cent. States Speech J, 5/63; co-auth, Preliminary validation report on the Purdue Oral Communications Rating Form, Pers. J, 4/63. Add: Dept. of Speech, Temple University, Philadelphia, PA 19122.

SIMONS, KATHERINE GAUSS, b. Shenandoah, Iowa, Aug. 23, 07. ENGLISH. A.B, Grinnell Col, 29; M.A, Columbia Univ, 31, Roberts fel, 30-31, 34-35. Head dept. high sch, Iowa, 31-34; asst. prin. & head dept. Eng, Radford Sch. Girls, 35-39; instr. ENG, UNIV. NEW MEXICO, 39-43, asst. prof, 43-51, assoc. prof, 51-68, prof, 68-73, admin. asst, grad. sch, 48-61, EMER. PROF, 73- Renaissance Soc. Am; Malone Soc. Shakespeare; English Renaissance. Add: 615 Vassar Dr, N.E, Albuquerque, NM 87106.

SIMONSON, HAROLD PETER, b. Tacoma, Wash, Dec. 27, 26; m. 51; c. 3. ENGLISH & AMERICAN LITERATURE. B.A, Univ. Puget Sound, 50, B.Ed, 51; M.A, Northwest. Univ, 51, Ph.D, 58; Univ. Edinburgh, 54; Princeton Theol. Sem, 64; B.Phil, Univ. St. Andrews, 72. Instr. Eng, Thessalonika Agr. & Indust. Inst, Greece, 53-54; from instr. to prof. AM. LIT, Univ. Puget Sound, 55-68; PROF, UNIV. WASH, 68- Fulbright grant, 53. U.S.A, 46-48. MLA; Am. Stud. Asn; NCTE; Melville Soc. Am. American Middle West realism; Frederick Jackson Turner's frontier thesis; literature and theology. Publ: Zona Gale, Twayne, 62; Trio, Harper, 62; co-auth, Salinger: clamor and criticism, Heath, 63; Writing essays, Harper, 66; Francis Grierson, Twayne, 66; American perspectives, McGraw, 68; auth, The closed frontier, 70 & Strategies in criticism, 71, Holt; co-ed, Dimensions of man, Harper, 73; auth, Jonathan Edwards: theologian of the heart, 74; Frederick Jackson Turner: frontier history as art, Antioch Rev, summer 64; The closed frontier and American tragedy, Tex. Quart, spring 68; auth, Huckleberry Finn as tragedy, Yale Rev, summer 70; plus one other. Add: Dept. of English, University of Washington, Seattle, WA 98105.

SIMONSON, SOLOMON S, b. Brooklyn, N.Y, Apr. 19, 14; m. 57; c. 3. RHETORIC, PROPAGANDA. B.A, Brooklyn Col, 35, M.A, 39; LL.B, St. Lawrence Univ, 38; Ph.D.(logic & rhetoric), Northwest. Univ, 43. Instr. speech, Brooklyn Col, 35-41; teaching fel, Northwest. Univ, 41-43, res. fel, 43-45; asst. prof. Eng. & speech, Iowa State Teachers Col, 45-46; assoc. prof. speech & law, Univ. Denver, 46-49; prof. speech & chmn. dept, State Univ. N.Y. Col, Fredonia & dir. commun, univ. ctr, 49-59; prof. educ. & chmn. dept. lang, speech & commun, grad. sch. educ, YESHIVA UNIV, 59-65, HEAD DOCTORAL RES. ENG, SPEECH & COMMUN, FERKAUF GRAD. SCH. HUMANITIES & SOC. SCI, 65- Lectr, Adult Educ. Counc, Am. Asn. UN, Anti Defamation League, 46-49; contrib. ed, Colliers Encycl, 49-; Ford Found. award, 53; consult, col. orgn. & acad. design, Verrazano Col, Woodridge & New York City, 66- NCTE; Int. Commun. Asn. Rhetorical theory; communications and mass media. Publ: Crisis in television: a study of the private judgment and the public interest, Living Bks, 66; A new curriculum for teenagers, Clearing House, 9/65; A new curriculum in English, speech and communications, Sch. & Soc, 10/65; A graduate curriculum in the humanities, Improving Col. & Univ. Teaching, summer 66. Add: Ferkauf Graduate School of Humanities and Social Science, Yeshiva University, 55 Fifth Ave, New York, NY 10019.

SIMPSON, ARTHUR LEE, JR, b. Houston, Tex, Dec. 12, 31. ENGLISH & AMERICAN LITERATURE. B.A, Rice Univ, 53, M.A, 57, Ph.D.(Eng), 68. Asst. prof. ENG, UNIV. WYO, 68-72, ASSOC. PROF, 72-, DIR. FRESHMAN ENG, 69- MLA; NCTE; Col. Conf. Compos. & Commun. Victorian poetry; Edwardian literature; American novel. Publ: Meredith's pessimistic humanism: a new reading of Modern love, Mod. Philol, 5/70; Aurora as artist: a reinterpretation of Tennyson's Tithonus, Philol. Quart, 10/72; contrib, Guide to Steinbeck: a handbook to the major works, Scarecrow, (in press). Add: Dept. of English, University of Wyoming, Laramie, WY 82071.

SIMPSON, CLARENCE J, b. Ludlow, Ky, Apr. 24, 15; m. 40; c. 2. RENAISSANCE LITERATURE. A.B, Asbury Col, 36; A.M, Univ. Cincinnati, 39; Stanford fel, Henry E. Huntington Libr, San Marino, Calif, 48; Ph.D, Stanford Univ, 51. Asst. Eng, Univ. Cincinnati, 37-40, instr, 40-44; asst. prof, Wheaton Col, 44-48, assoc. prof. & chmn. dept, 48-51; prof, Southwest. Col. (Kans), 51-53; prof. & chmn. dept, WHITWORTH COL, 53-63, dean fac, 63-69, acting pres, 69-70, exec. v.pres, 70-71, PROF. ENG, 71- Mem. exec. comt, Wash. Comn. Humanities, 71- Medieval precedents for Renaissance thought. Add: Dept. of English, Whitworth College, Spokane, WA 99251.

SIMPSON, CLAUDE MITCHELL, JR, b. Kans. City, Mo, July 29, 10; m. 33. AMERICAN LITERATURE. A.B. & Mus.B, South. Methodist Univ, 30, A.M, 31, Litt.D, 66; A.M, Harvard, 34, Ph.D, 36. Instr. Eng, E.Carolina Col, 35-36; Univ. Wis. 36-39; Harvard, 39-42, fac. instr, 42-46, asst. prof, 46-47; prof, Ohio State Univ, 47-64; Coe prof. Am. lit, STANFORD UNIV, 64-73, assoc. dean humanities & sci, 72-73, EMER. COE PROF. AM. LIT, 73-; SR. RES. ASSOC, HUNTINGTON LIBR, 73- Vis. lectr, Boston Univ, 40; Rockefeller fel, 46-47; Fulbright res. grant, 50-51; vis. prof, Stanford Univ, 60, 62-63; Chicago Folklore prize, 67; Guggenheim fel, 67-68; Huntington Libr. res. grant, 71-72. U.S.N.R, 42-45, Lt. Comdr. MLA; Am. Folklore Soc; fel. Am. Acad. Arts & Sci. American fiction; English and American balladry; American linguistics. Publ: Local colorists, Harper, 59; gen. ed, Centenary edition of the works of Nathaniel Hawthorne, Ohio State Univ, 62-; The British broadside ballad and its music, Rutgers Univ, 66; co-auth, A treasury of the world's finest folk song, Crown, rev. ed, 67; plus others. Add: Huntington Library, San Marino, CA 91108.

SIMPSON, GRELLET COLLINS, b. Norfolk, Va, Apr. 20, 09; m. 39. ENGLISH. B.A, Randolph-Macon Col, 30, LL.D, 59; M.A, Univ. Va, 36, Ph.D, 49. Instr. Eng, Randolph-Macon Acad, 30-31; Randolph-Macon Col, 31-36, assoc. prof, 38-42, prof, 46-56, dir. counselling, 46-52, dean fac, 52-56; PROF. ENG, MARY WASHINGTON COL, UNIV. VA, 56-, PRES, 72-, chancellor, 56-72. DuPont fel, Univ. Va, 36-38; Bradshaw fel, 48-49; mem, Ashland Town Counc, Va, 54-56. With Am. Red Cross, 42-46. Chaucerian studies; modern continental drama and poetry; modern American fiction. Add: Mary Washington College, Fredericksburg, VA 22401.

SIMPSON, HAROLD BURTON, b. Lansing, Mich, Mar. 6, 16; m. 46; c. 2. ENGLISH. A.B, Kalamazoo Col, 37; A.M, Univ. Mich, 42, Ph.D.(Eng), 65. From instr. to asst. prof. Eng, Carroll Col, 46-48; teaching fel, Univ. Mich, 48-51; coord. grad. training, U.S. Naval Lab, 51-54; sr. engineering writer, Westinghouse Air Arm Div, 54-57; sr. sci. writer, Gen. Motors Res. Labs, 58-61; coordinator res. reports, Lockheed Electronics Co, 62-66; assoc. prof. ENG, ADRIAN COL, 66-68, PROF, 69-, CHMN. DEPT, 66- Consult, tech. writing, 52-57. U.S.N.R, 42-46, Lt. MLA; NCTE; AAAS; Soc. Tech. Writers & Publ. Scientific and technical writing; English usage; Shakespeare. Publ: Scientific writing: its characteristics and its effectiveness, Am. Press, 68; A harmless connective?, Col. Eng, 5/52; Form and style in technical reports, Soc. Tech. Writers & Ed. J, 7/59; A descriptive analysis of scientific writing, Dissertation Abstracts, 66. Add: Dept. of English Language & Literature, Adrian College, Adrian, MI 49221.

SIMPSON, HASSELL ALGERNON, b. Barksdale, S.C, May 8, 30; m. 53; c. 3. ENGLISH & AMERICAN LITERATURE. B.S, Clemson Univ, 52; M.A, Fla. State Univ, 57, Ph.D.(Eng), 62. Instr. ENG, Fla. State Univ, 58-59; Auburn Univ, 59-62; assoc. prof, HAMPDEN-SYDNEY COL, 62-65, PROF, 65-, CHMN. DEPT, 68-, chmn. div. humanities, 70-73. A.U.S, 52-54, 1st Lt. MLA; S.Atlantic Mod. Lang. Asn. Modern fiction; American literature; Southern literature. Publ: Rumer Godden, Twayne, 73. Add: Dept. of English, Hampden-Sydney College, Hampden-Sydney, VA 23943.

SIMPSON, HERBERT M, b. Baltimore, Md, Aug. 2, 34. ENGLISH, DRAMATIC LITERATURE. A.B, Univ. Md, 57, M.A, 63, Ph.D.(Eng), 65. Instr. ENG, Univ. Md, 63-65, lectr, 65-66; asst. prof, STATE UNIV. N.Y. COL. GENESEO, 66-71, ASSOC. PROF, 71- State Univ. N.Y. res. grants, summer 68. U.S.A, 57-59. MLA; Col. Eng. Asn. Modern American literature; contemporary drama, especially American; American drama criticism. Publ: Dating a Mencken letter, Menckeniana, summer 67; Why not theatre of the absurd in the public schools?, Md. Eng. J, summer 67; Tiny Alice: limited affirmation in a conflict between theatre and drama, Forum, 68; plus one other. Add: Dept. of English, State University of New York College at Geneseo, Geneseo, NY 14454.

SIMPSON, LEWIS PEARSON, b. Jacksboro, Tex, July 18, 16. AMERICAN HISTORY & LITERATURE. A.B, Univ. Tex, 38, A.M, 39, Ph.D, 48. Tutor Eng, Univ. Tex, 41-42, 44-45, instr, 46-48; asst. prof, LA. STATE UNIV, BATON ROUGE, 48-53, assoc. prof, 53-60, prof, 60-71, WILLIAM A. READ PROF. ENG. LIT, 71- Guggenheim fel, 54-55; co-ed, South. Rev, 63-; mem. bd. ed, Am. Lit, Duke Univ. & Am. Lit. Section, MLA, 69-72; consult, Comt. Sr. Fel. Am. Lit, Nat. Endowment for Humanities, 70-73; Lamar Mem. lectr, Mercer Univ, 73. MLA; Am. Stud. Asn; South. Hist. Asn; Orgn. Am. Hist. Literary and cultural history of the early American republic, with special attention to its 18th century background; Southern literature; history of the literary vocation in America. Publ: Ed, Federalist literary mind, 62 & auth, The man of letters in New England and the South; essays on the history of the literary vocation in America, 73, La. State Univ; ed, Profile of Robert Frost, Merrill, 71 & The poetry of community: essays on the Southern sensibility of history and literature (Spectrum Ser), Ga. State Univ, 72; auth, The Southern writer and the great literary secession, Ga. Rev, winter 70; Literary ecumenicalism of the American enlightenment, In: The Ibero-American American enlightenment, Univ. Ill, 71; Southern spiritual nationalism: notes on the background of modern Southern fiction, In: Cry of home: cultural nationalism and the modern writer, Univ. Tenn, 72; plus others. Add: Dept. of English, Louisiana State University, Baton Rouge, LA 70803.

SIMPSON, LOUIS A. M. ENGLISH. B.S, Columbia Univ, 48, A.M, 50, Ph.D, 59. Ed, Bobbs-Merrill Pub. Co, 50-55; instr. ENG, Columbia Univ, 55-59; asst. prof, Univ. Calif, Berkeley, 59-61, assoc. prof, 61-65, PROF, 65-68; STATE UNIV. N.Y. STONY BROOK, 68- Prix de Rome fel, Am. Acad. Arts & Let, 57; Hudson Rev. fel. in poetry, 57; Guggenheim fel, 62. Distinguished Alumni Award, Columbia Univ, 60, Medal for Excellence, 65; Pulitzer Prize for Poetry, 64. U.S.A, 43-45, Sgt. Am. Acad. Rome. American poetry; Scottish literature; English and comparative literature. Publ: The arrivistes (poems), Fine Ed, 49; Good news of death and other poems, Scribner, 55; A dream of governors (poems), 59 & At the end of the open road, 63, Wesleyan Univ; Riverside drive, Atheneum, 62; James Hogg, a critical study, 63 & An introduction to poetry, 67, St. Martin's; Selected poems, Harcourt, 65; Adventures of the letter I, 71 & North of Jamaica, 72, Harper. Add: Dept. of English, State University of New York at Stony Brook, Stony Brook, NY 11790.

SIMS, DWIGHT JOHNSTON, b. Evansville, Ind, Dec. 22, 38; m. 62; c. 2. ENGLISH LITERATURE. B.A, Univ. Calif, Berkeley, 61; M.A, San Francisco State Col, 63; Ph.D.(Eng), Univ. Calif, Los Angeles, 71. Teaching asst. ENG, Univ. Calif, Los Angeles, 64-68; instr, TEMPLE UNIV, 68-71, ASST. PROF, 71- Renaissance Soc. Am. English and continental Renaissance. Publ: The syncretic myth of Venus in Spenser's legend of chastity, Stud. Philol, 74. Add: Dept. of English, Temple University, Philadelphia, PA 19122.

SIMS, EDWARD JAMES, b. New Britain, Conn, Mar. 13, 27. ENGLISH. B.S, Springfield Col, 51; M.S, State Univ. N.Y. Col. Albany, 53, Danforth fel, Boston Univ, summer, 56; Ed.D, Columbia Univ, 63. Instr. Eng. & dir. pub. inform, SPRINGFIELD COL, 52-56, asst. prof, Eng. & chmn. dept, 56-61, assoc. prof. Eng. & coordinator arts & sci, 61-62, PROF. ENG, 68- Lectr. commun, Springfield Hosp. Sch. Nursing, 58-60; compos, West. New Eng. Col, 62-64. U.S. Merchant Marine 45-47. Col. Eng. Asn; NCTE; MLA. American literature; composition. Publ: Co-auth, Modern journalism, Pitman, 62; The challenge of advanced placement, Improving Col. & Univ. Instr, Vol. XIV, No. 3. Add: Dept. of English, Springfield College, Springfield, MA 01109.

SIMS, JAMES HYLBERT, b. Orlando, Fla, Oct. 29, 24; m. 44; c. 5. ENGLISH LITERATURE. B.A, Univ. Fla, 49, M.A, 50, South. Fel. Fund fel, grant, 57-58, Ph.D, 59. Asst. ENG, Univ. Fla, 49-50; instr, Tenn. Temple Col, 50-51; Tri-State Baptist Col, 51-54; Univ. Fla, 55-59; prof. & chmn. dept, Tift Col, 59-61; Austin Peay State Univ, 61-66; PROF, UNIV. OKLA, 66- Consult, Choice, 64-; fel, Southeast. Inst. Medieval & Renaissance Stud, 65, 66; assoc. ed, 17th Century News, 68-; Huntington Libr. fel, 73; Nat. Endowment for Humanities summer stipend, 74. U.S.N, 43-46. S.Cent. Renaissance Conf; Milton Soc. Am; MLA; Southeast. Renaissance Conf. Biblical literature; Renaissance literature, especially Milton. Publ: The Bible in Milton's epics, 62 & Dramatic use of Biblical allusions in Marlowe and Shakespeare, 66, Univ. Fla; Paradise lost: Arian document or Christian poem?, Etudes Anglaises, 10-12/67; Christened classicism in Paradise lost and the Lusiads, Comp. Lit, fall 72; Delicious paradise in OS Lusiadas and in Paradise lost, Ocidente, 11/72. Add: Dept. of English, University of Oklahoma, 760 Van Vleet, Norman, OK 73069.

SIMSON, GEORGE K, b. Port Angeles, Wash, Apr. 18, 31; m. 53; c. 3. ENGLISH, BIOGRAPHY. A.B, Whitman Col, 52; U.S. Army Lang. Sch, 53-54; M.A, Wash. State Univ, 57; spec. grant, Univ. Minn, 62, Ph.D.(Eng), 63. Teaching asst. ENG, Wash. State Univ, 55-57; Univ. Minn, 57-59, instr, 59-62; South. Colo. State Col, 62-63; ASST. PROF, UNIV. HAWAII, MANOA, 63- Founder, annual MLA conf. on biog, 64; Univ. Hawaii Res. Counc. travel grant, summer 65. U.S.A, 52-55, Russian transl. MLA; Conf. Brit. Stud. Biography; literary criticism; modern British literature. Publ: Legal sources of Franklin's Edict, Am. Lit, 60. Add: Dept. of English, University of Hawaii at Manoa, Honolulu, HI 96822.

SINANOGLOU, LEAH, b. Valparaiso, Ind, Sept. 12, 45. ENGLISH LITERATURE. B.A, Carleton Col, 67; fac. fel, Columbia Univ, 67-71, M.A, 68, Woodbridge distinguished fel, 69-70, Woodrow Wilson fel. & Ph.D.(Eng), 71. ASST. PROF. ENG, UNIV. ILL, CHICAGO CIRCLE, 72-; fac. summer res. grant, 74. Nat. Endowment for Humanities younger humanist fel, summer 73. MLA; Milton Soc. Am. Seventeenth century English literature; medieval literature; literature and social organization. Publ: The Christ child as sacrifice: medieval tradition and the Corpus Christi plays, Speculum, 7/73. Add: Dept. of English, University of Illinois at Chicago Circle, Chicago, IL 60680.

SINCLAIR, ARTHUR HAYFORD, b. Trenton, N.J, Oct. 31, 26; m. 58; c. 3. THEATRE, SPEECH. B.S, Trenton State Col, 53; M.S, Northwest. Univ, 57; State Univ. Iowa, 59-62. Asst. prof. SPEECH & THEATRE, Cent. Col. (Mo), 57-58; Muskingum Col, 58-59; asst, State Univ. Iowa, 59-62; ASSOC.

PROF, KUTZTOWN STATE COL, 62- Instr. speech & theatre, Northwest. Univ, summers, 56-58; artist acting-mime, Reading Sch. Dist, Berks County, Pa, 72- U.S.A, 53-56. Am. Theatre Asn. Publ: Media's mettle, 72 & The other passion plays, 73, Compass; contrib, Production slides, Theatre, U.S.A, 73. Add: Dept. of Speech & Theatre, Kutztown State College, Kutztown, PA 19530.

SINCLAIR, GILES MERTON, b. Kent Co, Mich, Apr. 24, 16; m. 44; c. 2. AMERICAN LITERATURE & LINGUISTICS. A.B, West. Mich. Univ, 38; A.M, Duke Univ, 45; Ph.D, Univ. Mich, 53. Instr. Eng, Wayne Univ, 45-47; Kans. State Col, 48-52; asst. prof, West. Mich. Univ, 52-53; PROF. ENG. & CHMN. LANG. ARTS DIV, HUMBOLDT STATE UNIV, 53- Fulbright lectr. Am. lit, Monash Univ, Australia, 67-68. U.S.N.R, 41-45, Lt. NCTE; MLA. Seventeenth century phonology; English pedagogy. Publ: Chaucer—translated or obliterated, 54 & An ounce and a pound, 61, Col. Eng. Add: Language Arts Division, Humboldt State University, Arcata, CA 95521.

SINCLAIR, MARJORIE PUTNAM, b. Sioux Falls, S.Dak, Nov. 27, 13; m. 39. ENGLISH. B.A, Mills Col, 35, M.A, 37; Univ. Hawaii, 55-60. Instr. ENG, UNIV. HAWAII, MANOA, 55-62, asst. prof, 62-71, ASSOC. PROF, 71- MLA; Asn. Asian Stud; NCTE. Chinese and Japanese poetry; modern poetry; Hawaiian legends and history. Publ: Kona, 47, & The wild wind, 50, Day; co-auth, The poems of T'ao Ch'ien, 53 & A grass path, 55, Univ. Hawaii. Add: Dept. of English, University of Hawaii at Manoa, Honolulu, HI 96822.

SINCLAIR, REID B, b. Hot Springs, Va, Aug. 24, 32; m. 67; c. 4. ENGLISH. A.B, Randolph-Macon Col, 53; M.A, Vanderbilt Univ, 54; Ph.D.(Eng), 65. Instr. ENG, Univ. Richmond, 56-58; Wake Forest Col, 61-65; asst. prof, Ohio Univ, 65-70; assoc. prof, CAMPBELL COL, 71-73, PROF, 73-, CHMN. DEPT, 71- Lectr, Univ. Maine, Orono, 70-71. Intel.C, U.S.A, 54-56. MLA; AAUP. Satire; Swift's verse; North Carolina literature. Add: Dept. of English, Campbell College, Buies Creek, NC 27506.

SINGER, MARY W, Latin, English. See Volume III, Foreign Languages, Linguistics & Philology.

SINGH, RAMAN KUMAR, b. Manaswal, India, Mar. 20, 38; m. 60; c. 2. ENGLISH & AMERICAN LITERATURE. B.A, St. Stephen's Col, India, 58; dipl. jour, London Polytech, 59; Free Univ. Berlin, 63-64; M.A, West. Mich. Univ, 65; M.A, Purdue Univ, 67, Ph.D.(Eng), 71. Instr. ENG, MARY WASHINGTON COL, 67-70, asst. prof, 70-73, ASSOC. PROF, 73- Ed, Stud. Black Lit, 70- American fiction; black-American literature; the novel. Publ: Co-ed, Black literature in America: a casebook, Crowell, 70; ed, Aspects of the black novel, Aurora, (in press); auth, Richard Wright's tragic vision in The outsider, Stud. Black Lit, fall 70; The traditions of the black novel, Colo. Quart, summer 71; Christian heroes and anti-heroes in Richard Wright's fiction, Negro Am. Lit. Forum, winter 72; plus others. Add: Dept. of English, Mary Washington College, Fredericksburg, VA 22401.

SINGLETARY, CRAIG EVERETT, b. Portland, Ore, Apr. 14, 31; m. 55; c. 4. SPEECH. B.A, Lewis & Clark Col, 54; M.A, Univ. Ore, 63, NDEA fel. & Ph.D.(speech), 68. Asst. prof. SPEECH, LINFIELD COL, 60-72, ASSOC. PROF, 72- U.S.A.F, 51-52. Speech Asn. Am. American oratory; forensics; radio and television history. Add: Dept. of Speech, Linfield College, McMinnville, OR 97128.

SINGLETON, RALPH HERBERT, b. Cleveland, Ohio, May 25, 00; m. 24; c. 3. ENGLISH. A.B, Oberlin Col, 23, M.A, 30; Ph.D.(Eng), West. Reserve Univ, 39. Instr. Eng, Iowa State Col, 23-26, from instr. to assoc. prof, Oberlin Col, 26-58, prof, 58-66; VIS. PROF, PORTLAND STATE UNIV, 66- U.S.A, 18. NCTE; MLA; Conf. Col. Compos. & Commun. English novel; 17th century; writing of prose fiction. Publ: Ed, Two and twenty: a collection of short stories, St. Martin's 62; Barchester towers, 63 & Tom Jones, 63, Wash. Square; ed, Reviewing the years, Crown, 63; co-auth, Introduction to literature, World Publ, 66; auth, Style, Chandler Publ, 66; The art of prose fiction, World Publ, 67; co-auth, The lively rhetoric, 68, 2nd ed, 72 & co-auth, The new lively rhetoric, 70, Holt; Milton's Comus and the comus of Erycius Puteanus, PMLA; plus others. Add: 2280 S.W.Seymour Dr, Portland, OR 97201.

SINNOTT, BETHANY STRONG, b. Rockwood, Tenn, Apr. 6, 41; m. 69. ENGLISH LITERATURE. A.B, Duke Univ, 62; M.A, Northwest. Univ, 63; Ph.D. (Eng), Univ. N.C, Chapel Hill, 72. Instr. ENG, Univ. Bridgeport, 64-65; asst. prof, CATAWBA COL, 69-74, ASSOC. PROF, 74- MLA; AAUP; Renaissance Soc. Am. Shakespeare; Renaissance literature. Add: Dept. of English, Catawba College, Salisbury, NC 28144.

SIPAHIGIL, TEOMAN, b. Istanbul, Turkey, Feb. 13, 39; U.S. citizen. ENGLISH & AMERICAN LITERATURE. B.A, Earlham Col, 61; M.A, Miami Univ, 63; Ph.D.(Eng), Univ. Calif, Los Angeles, 70. ASST. PROF. ENG, UNIV. IDAHO, 70- Renaissance Soc. Am. Tudor and Elizabethan drama; Shakespeare. Publ: Othello's name, once again, Notes & Queries, 4/71; Othello, IV.2.29-36: a note, Eng. Lang. Notes, 12/71. Add: Dept. of English, University of Idaho, Moscow, ID 83843.

SIPORIN, RAE LEE, b. Detroit, Mich, Apr. 12, 40. MEDIEVAL ENGLISH LITERATURE, HISTORY & STRUCTURE OF THE ENGLISH LANGUAGE. B.A, Wayne State Univ, 62; M.A, Univ. Calif, Los Angeles, 64, Mabel Wilson Richards fel, 67, Ph.D.(Eng), 68. Ed. asst, Survey Eng. Dialects, Leeds Univ, 64-65; ASST. PROF. ENG, UNIV. PITTSBURGH, 68-, LIASON ACAD. AFFAIRS & EXEC. ASST. TO V.CHANCELLOR PLANNING & BUDGET, 73-; asst. dean col. arts & sci, 70-72. Am. Counc. Educ. admin. intern, Univ. Pittsburgh-Ohio State Univ, 72-73. Am. Dialect Soc; Ling. Soc. Am; Am. Asn. Higher Educ; Ctr. Appl. Ling; MLA. Sociolinguistics, language usage; history of English language; syntax of English. Publ: Ed, Female studies V: women and education, Know, Inc, 72; contrib, Negation, In: Integration of transformational theories of syntax, 68; contrib, Survey of English dialects: East Midland counties and East Anglia, Arnold, 70; auth, Women and education: the conference as catalyst, In: Female Studies V: women and education, Know, Inc, 72. Add: Office of Planning & Budget, University of Pittsburgh, Fifth Ave, Pittsburgh, PA 15260.

SIRE, JAMES WALTER, b. Inman, Nebr, Oct. 17, 33; m. 55; c. 4. ENGLISH. B.A, Univ. Nebr, 55; M.A, Wash. State Univ, 58; Ph.D.(Eng), Univ. Mo, 64. Instr. Eng, Univ. Mo, 58-64; asst. prof, Nebr. Wesleyan Univ, 64-66, assoc. prof, 66-68; ED, INTER-VARSITY PRESS, DOWNERS GROVE, 68-, ASSOC. PROF. ENG. & PHILOS, TRINITY COL.(ILL), 71-, assoc. prof, Eng, North. Ill. Univ, 69-70. Vis. prof, Univ. Nebr, summer 66; vis. asst. prof, Univ. Mo, summer 67. Ord.C, U.S.A, 55-57, 1st Lt. MLA; Conf. Christianity & Lit; Am. Sci. Affiliation. Milton; literary criticism; Plotinus. Publ: Co-auth, Papers on literature: models and methods, Holt, 70; auth, A program for a new man, Inter-Varsity, 73; The problem of truth in the teaching of myth, Nebr, Eng. Counsel, 3/65; Life in a world where God is dead, 4/66 & Mr. Sammler and the God of our fathers, 6/71, Christianity Today. Add: Box F, Downers Grove, IL 60515.

SIRLUCK, ERNEST, b. Winkler, Man, Apr. 25, 18; m. 42; c. 2. ENGLISH LITERATURE. B.A, Univ. Man, 40; Kemp fel, Univ. Toronto, 41, M.A, 41, Open fel, 42, Ph.D, 48; LL.D, Queen's Univ.(Ont), 68. Teaching fel, Univ. Toronto, 45, lectr, 46-47; asst. prof. Eng, Univ. Chicago, 47-53, assoc. prof, 53-58, prof, 58-62; prof, Univ. Toronto, 62-70, assoc. dean, 62-64, dean sch. grad. stud, 64-70, v.pres, 68-70; PRES. & V.CHANCELLOR, UNIV. MAN, 70- Guggenheim fel, 53-54; Am. Counc. Learned Soc. fel, 58-59; chmn, Ont. Counc. Grad. Stud, 63-70; overseas fel, Churchill Col. Cambridge, 66; chmn, Inter-Provincial Comt. Univ. Rationalization, 71-73; dir, Asn. Univ. & Col. Can, 71- Order of Brit. Empire. Can. Army, 42-45, Maj. MLA; Renaissance Eng. Text Soc.(pres, 59-66); Asn. Can. Univ. Teachers Eng; fel, Royal Soc. Can. Milton; Puritan revolution; university administration. Publ: Complete works of John Milton, Vol. II, Yale, 59; co-ed, Pattern of literary criticism (10 vols), Univ. Chicago & Univ. Toronto, 65-; co-auth, Graduate studies in the University of Toronto, 65; auth, Paradise lost: a deliberate epic, Heffer, 67; The role of research in Canadian universities, Queen's Printer, Ottawa; Faerie Queene, Book II and the Nicomachean ethics, 50 & Milton's political thought: the first cycle, 64, Mod. Philol; Milton's idle right hand, J. Eng. & Ger. Philol, 61; plus others. Add: Office of the President, University of Manitoba, Winnipeg, Man. R3T 2N2, Can.

SISCO, JOHN ISODORE, b. Jamestown, N.Dak, June 27, 31; m. 57; c. 3. SPEECH. B.S, Valley City State Col, 54; M.A, Northwest. Univ, 59; Ph.D. (speech), Univ. Minn, Minneapolis, 66. Teacher, high sch, Minn, 54-56, jr. high sch, 56-62; instr. speech, Univ. Minn, 62-65; asst. prof, Univ. Houston, 65-68; ASSOC. PROF. SPEECH EDUC. & STATE COORD. FLA. FORENSICS, UNIV. S.FLA, 68-, CHMN. DEPT. SPEECH COMMUN, 72- Consult, Broward Co. Commun. Skills Assessment Proj, Fla, 71; Ky. Asn. Commun. Arts Conf, 72; vis. prof. Kans State Col. Pittsburgh, 73. U.S.A, 50-52, Sgt. Speech Commun. Asn; South. Speech Commun. Asn.(chmn. speech educ, 67-68, pres. asn, 72-73); Asn. Dept. & Adminr. Speech Commun. Rhetoric of American social movements; performance objectives in speech communication education; speech education in secondary schools. Publ: Ed, Florida speech and drama curriculum guide, Fla. State Dept. Educ, 72; co-auth, Practical experiences in extemp and debate, Mediatronics, 73; auth, Interpersonal small group communication, Bull. Nat. Asn. Sec. Sch. Prins, 12/70; co-auth, Speech, English and drama certification policies in the South, summer 71 & auth, Action proposals in research and service, fall 73, South. Speech Commun. J. Add: Dept. of Speech Communication, University of South Florida, Tampa, FL 33620.

SISK, JOHN PAUL, b. Spokane, Wash, Mar. 25, 14. ENGLISH. A.B, Gonzaga Univ, 36, A.M, 39; LL.D, 61; Univ. Wash, 50. Teaching fel. ENG, GONZAGA UNIV, 38-39, instr, 39-42, asst. prof, 46-52, assoc. prof, 52-63, PROF, 63-, chmn. dept, 63-67. Nat. Endowment for Humanities sr. fel, 72-73. Carl Foreman Award, Harcourt, Brace & Highroads Prod, 61. U.S.A.A.F, 42-46, Capt. Philol. Asn. Pac. Coast. Shakespeare; English romanticism; contemporary American literature and culture. Publ: Person and institution, Fides, 70; Bondage and release in The merchant of Venice, Shakespeare Quart, spring 69; On intoxication, Commentary, 2/72; Honesty as a policy, Am. Scholar, spring 72. Add: Dept. of English, Gonzaga University, E. 502 Boone Ave, Spokane, WA 99202.

SITTER, JOHN EDWARD, b. Cumberland, Md, Jan. 4, 44; m. 71; c. 1. ENGLISH. B.A, Harvard, 66; Ph.D.(Eng), Univ. Minn, 69. ASST. PROF. ENG, UNIV. MASS, AMHERST, 69- William Andrews Clark Libr. fel, Univ. Calif, Los Angeles, 72. MLA; Am. Soc. 18th Century Stud. English poetry, 1600 to 1900; 18th century thought; satire. Publ: The poetry of Pope's Dunciad, Univ. Minn, 71. Add: Dept. of English, University of Massachusetts, Amherst, MA 01002.

SITTON, FRED, b. Pyote, Tex, Mar. 27, 24; m. 47. THEATRE. B.A, Tex. Col. Mines, 43; M.A, Tex. West. Col, 51; M.F.A, Univ. Tex, Austin, 54; L.D.A, Univ. N.C, Chapel Hill, 59; Ph.D.(theatre), Northwest. Univ, 62. Teacher speech & Eng, Pecos High Sch, Tex, 47-51; THEATRE, Myers Park High Sch, Charlotte, N.C, 54-58; PROF, VALPARAISO UNIV, 61-, dir, Bridge-VU Repertory Theatre, 68-71. U.S. Maritime Serv, 43-46, Lt.(jg). Am. Theatre Asn. Epic theatre: Bertolt Brecht; early American theatre; contemporary drama and dramatists. Add: Dept. of Theatre, Valparaiso University, Valparaiso, IN 46383.

SIVIER, EVELYN M, b. Milwaukee, Wis, May 15, 16; m. 59; c. 1. SPEECH, DRAMA. B.A, San Jose State Col, 51; Field-Hotaling fel, Stanford Univ, 51-52, M.A, 52; univ. fel, Wayne State Univ, 55-56, Ph.D.(oral interpretation & humanities), 61. Teaching asst. voice & diction, Stanford Univ, 51-52; instr. oral interpretation & voice & diction, Wayne State Univ, 52-55, 56-57; asst. prof. oral interpretation & theatre, Humboldt State Col, 57-59; ASSOC. PROF. ORAL INTERPRETATION & ACTING HEAD AREA INTERPRETATIVE READING, WAYNE STATE UNIV, 66- Speech Commun. Asn; Am. Theatre Asn. Theory and criticism of oral interpretation; history of oral interpretation; voice and articulation pedagogy. Publ: The Adelphi Theatre, San Francisco, 1850-1858, In: Abstracts of masters theses in speech and dramatic art, Speech Asn. Am, 53. Add: 31205 Ramble Rd, Franklin, MI 48025.

SIXBEY, GEORGE LAWTON, b. Mayville, N.Y, Dec. 31, 07. ENGLISH. A.B, Am. Univ.(D.C), 30; A.M, George Wash. Univ, 33; Univ. Md, 33-38; univ. scholar, Yale, 39-40, Ph.D, 41. Instr. Eng, Am. Univ.(D.C), 31-35; Univ. Md, 35-40; asst. prof, Marietta Col, 40-46; prof, Centenary Col, 46-48; prof. & head dept, Ark. State Teachers Col, Conway, 48-60; prof. Eng. & chmn. dept. lang, Northeast La. State Col, 60-63; prof. Eng. & chmn. div. humanities, SOUTH. STATE COL.(ARK), 63-72, distinguished prof, ENG, 72-73, EMER. PROF, 73- Prof, Fairmont Sch, 31-32; Bratton Mem. lectr, All Saints' Jr. Col, Miss, 60. S.Cent. Mod. Lang. Asn; S.Cent. Col. Eng. Asn; South. Humanities Conf; Church Hist. Soc. American literature; English education; religion. Publ: Contrib. & ed, The English major, Ark. Exp. Teacher Educ; Chanting the square deific—a study in Whitman's theology, Am. Lit, 38; Campus revolt in historical perspective, South. Humanities Rev, spring 71. Add: P.O. Box 306, St. Michaels, MD 21663.

SIZEMORE, CHRISTINE WICK, b. Washington, D.C, Nov. 17, 45; m. 68. ENGLISH RENAISSANCE & 20TH CENTURY LITERATURE. B.A, Carnegie Inst. Technol, 67; M.A. & univ. fel, Univ. Pa, 68, Ph.D.(Eng), 72. ASST. PROF. ENG, GA. STATE UNIV, 72- Renaissance Soc. Am; Mod. Lang. Asn; S.Atlantic Mod. Lang. Asn. Seventeenth century English prose; modern British novel; English Puritans. Add: 860 Peachtree Battle Circle N.W, Atlanta, GA 30327.

SKAGGS, CALVIN LEE, b. Perryville, Mo, June 29, 37; m. 60; c. 2. ENGLISH, CINEMA. B.A, Henderson State Teachers Col, 57; M.A, Duke Univ, 59, Ph.D.(Eng), 66. Instr. ENG, DREW UNIV, 62-66, asst. prof, 66-71, ASSOC. PROF, 71- MLA; Eng. Inst; AAUP. Contemporary poetry; critical theory of fiction; film history and criticism. Add: Dept. of English, Drew University, Madison, NJ 07940.

SKAGGS, PEGGY LaNELL DECHERT, b. Menard, Tex; m; c. 2. AMERICAN LITERATURE. B.A, South. Methodist Univ, 50; M.A, Tex. A&M Univ, 65, Ph.D.(Eng), 72; Univ. Ariz, 67. Instr. ENG, Iraan-Sheffield Independent Sch. Dist, Tex, 64-66; ANGELO STATE UNIV, 66-70, ASST. PROF, 70- MLA. Kate Chopin; folklore; regional literature. Add: Dept. of English, Angelo State University, San Angelo, TX 76901.

SKARDA, PATRICIA LYN, b. Clovis, N.Mex, Mar. 31, 46. 19TH CENTURY BRITISH LITERATURE. B.A, Tex. Tech Univ, 69; Sweet Briar Col, 64-68; NDEA fel, Univ. Tex, Austin, 70-72, Ph.D.(Eng), 73. Teaching asst. ENG, Univ. Tex, Austin, 69-70, 72-73; ASST. PROF, SMITH COL, 73- Dir, N.Mex. Girls State, 73; govt. suprv, Girls Nation, 73. MLA; AAUP. Romantic and Victorian literature; Gerard Manley Hopkins; poetic theory. Add: Dept. of English, Smith College, Northampton, MA 01060.

SKEELS, DELL R, b. Moscow, Idaho, June 16, 15. LITERATURE, ANTHROPOLOGY. A.B, Univ. Idaho, 41, fel, 41-42, A.M, 42; fel, Univ. Wash, 48-49, Ph.D, 49. Assoc, UNIV. WASH, 46-49, instr. HUMANISTIC & SOC. STUD, 49-53, asst. prof, 53-57, assoc. prof, 57-63, PROF, 63- Am. Counc. Learned Soc. grant-in-aid, Univ. Wash, 48. Mediaeval Acad. Am; Soc. Stud. Mediaeval Lang. & Lit; MLA; Int. Arthurian Soc; Am. Folklore Soc. Style in the primitive literature of the Nez Perce Indians; mediaeval studies; folklore. Publ: Romance of Perceval in prose—a translation of the E manuscript of the Didot Perceval, Univ. Wash, 61. Add: 362 Loew Hall, University of Washington, Seattle, WA 98105.

SKELLY, MADGE, b. Pittsburgh, Pa, May 9, 03; m. 28. SPEECH PATHOLOGY & AUDIOLOGY, THEATRE. B.A, Seton Hill Col, 24; M.A, Duquesne Univ, 28; Upjohn fel, Eng, 51; Univ. Ariz, 57-58; Ph.D.(educ, speech path), St. Louis Univ, 62. Dir. col. theatre, Seton Hill Col, 27-34; actor-dir, Prof. Theatre, 34-36, 40-46, dir, 48-57; dean sch. drama, Duquesne Univ, 36-40; dir. theatre, Temple Univ, 46-48; prof. speech, Univ. Ariz, 57-58; assoc. prof, Maryville Col.(Mo), 58-63, dir. col. theatre, 58-62; prof. speech path, St. Louis Univ, 62-63; CHIEF, AUDIOL. & SPEECH PATH. SERV, CONSOL. VET. ADMIN. HOSP, ST. LOUIS, 64-; ADJ. PROF. COMMUN. DISORDERS, ST. LOUIS UNIV, 70-; SOUTH. ILL. UNIV, 73- Prof. speech path, Fontbonne Col, 63-70; Dept. Health, Educ. & Welfare summer fels, Jersig Clin, 64, Columbia Univ. Med. Sch, 64, Univ. Kans. Med. Sch, 65-66 & Univ. Miami Med. Sch, 67; dir. speech & hearing serv, Shriner's Hosp. Children, St. Louis, 64-70; externship, Univ. Kans. Med. Ctr, 65-66; Hines Res. Ctr, 67-68; consult, Christian Welfare Hosp, Cardinal Ritter Geriat. Inst, St. Mary's Hosp, St. Joseph's Hosp. & Mo. Baptist Hosp, 67-70; consult. dir, Speech & Hearing Clin, Mt. St. Rose Hosp. & Rehab. Ctr, 70-; abstractor, DSH Abstr, 71- Yale Univ. Citation, 67; Fed. Employee of Year, 69; Founders Day Award, St. Louis Univ, 70; Fed. Woman's Award, 74. Am. Speech & Hearing Asn.(mem. manpower comn, 71-); Asn. Mil. Surg. U.S; Int. Asn. Logopedics & Phoniatrics. Communication problems consequent to cancer and cancer surgery, cerebral insult and gestural communication for the speechless. Publ: Glossectomy speech rehabilitation, C.C. Thomas, 73; Compensatory physiologic phonetics for the glossectomee, 2/71 & Dysphonias associated with spinal bracing in scoliosis, 5/71, J. Speech & Hearing; co-auth, Visor flap reconstruction for a massive oropharyngeal defect, Plastic & Reconstruct. Surg, 4/73; plus 12 others. Add: Audiology & Speech Pathology Service, Consolidated Veterans Administration Hospital, 915 N. Grand, St. Louis, MO 63125.

SKELTON, ROBIN, b. East Yorkshire, Eng, Oct. 12, 25; m. 57; c. 3. ENGLISH. B.A, Univ. Leeds, 50, M.A, 51. Asst. lectr. ENG, Univ. Manchester, 51-62; lectr, Workers Educ. Asn. & Manchester Extra Mural Dept, 52-61; vis. prof, Univ. Mass, 62-63; assoc. prof, UNIV. VICTORIA (B.C), 63-67, PROF, 67-, HEAD DEPT. CREATIVE WRITING, 73- R.A.F, 44-47, Sgt. Int. PEN Club; Soc. Auth, Eng; League Can. Poets; fel. Royal Soc. Lit. U.K. Twentieth century poetry and Irish literature; contemporary art. Publ: John Ruskin: the final years, Univ. Manchester, 55; Patmos and other poems, Routledge & Kegan Paul, 55; The poetic pattern, Routledge & Kegan Paul & Univ, Calif, 56, 2nd ed, 60; Third day lucky, (poems), 58, Begging the dialect, (poems), 60, The dark window, (poems), 62, Six Irish poets, 62 & ed, David Gascoyne: collected poems, 65, Oxford; auth, Cavalier poets, Longmans Green, 60; Two ballads of the muse, (poems), privately publ, 60; Viewpoint: an anthology, 62, ed, Edward Thomas: selected poems, 62, Hutchinson Educ; An Irish gathering, (poems), Dolmen, Oxford & Dufor, 64; ed, Five poets of the Pacific Northwest, Univ. Wash, 64; auth, Poetry of the thirties, 64 & Poetry of the forties, 68, Penquin; co-auth, The world of W.B. Yeats, 65 & Irish Renaissance, 65, Dolmen & Oxford; ed, Philip O'Connor: selected poems, Cape, 67; Selected poems, McClelland & Stewart, 68; The writings of J.M. Synge, 71 & J.M. Synge and his world, 71,

Thames & Hudson; The practice of poetry, Heinemann Educ, 71; ed, The collected plays of Jack B. Yeats, Secker & Warburg & Bobbs, 71; auth, J.M. Synge, Bucknell Univ, 72; J.M. Synge: four plays and the Aran Islands, In: Worlds classics, 62 & J.M. Synge: collected poems, Vol. I, In: Collected works of J.M. Synge, 62, Oxford; auth Poetry, In: Teach yourself, Eng. Univ, 63; ed, Selected poems of Byron, In: Poetry bookshelf, Heinemann, 63. Add: Dept. of Creative Writing, University of Victoria, Victoria, B.C, Can.

SKELTON, SUSAN, b. Montgomery, Ala, June 18, 45. COMPARATIVE LITERATURE. B.A, Auburn Univ, 68; Fulbright grant, Univ. Strasbourg, 68-69; M.A, Univ. South. Calif, 70, Ph.D.(comp. lit), 73. LECTR. COMP. LIT, UNIV. WIS-MILWAUKEE, 73- MLA; Midwest Mod. Lang. Asn; Soc. Relig. Higher Educ; Am. Comp. Lit. Asn. Romanticism; symbolism; literary translation. Add: 2623 N. Wahl Ave, Milwaukee, WI 53211.

SKINNER, JAMES LISTER, III, b. Emory, Ga, Sept. 24, 38; m. 61; ENGLISH. A.B, N.Ga. Col, 60; NDEA fels, Univ. Ark, 62 & 65, M.A, 62, Ph.D.(Eng), 65. Asst. ENG, Univ. Ark, 61-63; assoc. prof, PRESBY. COL.(S.C), 65-69, PROF, 69-, dir. freshman Eng, 70-73. U.S.A, 63-65, Capt. NCTE; MLA. William Cowper; A.E. Housman; 18th and 19th century English literature. Add: Dept. of English, Presbyterian College, Clinton, SC 29325.

SKINNER, KNUTE R, b. St. Louis, Mo, Apr. 25, 29; m. 61; c. 2. ENGLISH. A.B, Colo. State Col, 51; M.A, Middlebury Col, 54; Ph.D, State Univ. Iowa, 58. Teacher ENG, Boise Sr. High Sch, 51-54; instr, State Univ. Iowa, 54-55, 56-57, 60-61; asst. prof, Okla. Col. Women, 61-62; WEST. WASH. STATE COL, 62-73, PROF, 73- Poetry Soc. Am. Poetry; creative writing. Publ: Stranger with a watch, Golden Quill, 65; A close sky over Killaspuglonane, Dolmen, 68; In dinosaur country, Pierian, 69; The sorcerers: a Laotian tale, Goliards, 72; Six poems, In: New generation: poetry anthology, Ann Arbor Rev. Bks, 71; Two poems, Counter/Measures, 72; Some hand, handsome, Confrontation, spring 73. Add: Dept. of English, Western Washington State College, Bellingham, WA 98225.

SKIPP, FRANCIS E, b. New York, N.Y, June 15, 19; m. 42; c. 3. ENGLISH. A.B, Colgate Univ, 40; A.M, Univ. Miami, 58; South. fel, Duke Univ, 60-61, Ph.D.(Am. lit), 62. Instr. humanities, UNIV. MIAMI, 61-63, asst. prof, 63-65, ENG, 65-67, ASSOC. PROF, 67- U.S.A.F, 41-53, Lt. Col. MLA. Modern and Early American novel and novelists. Publ: The editing of Look homeward, angel, Papers. Bibliog. Soc. Am. 63; Walt Whitman and Shelley: a possible source for the sleepers, Walt Whitman Rev, 65; Thomas Wolfe, Max Perkins and politics, Mod. Fiction Stud, 68. Add: Dept. of English, University of Miami, Coral Gables, FL 33124.

SKITTER, HANS GUNTER, German & American Literature. See Volume III, Foreign Languages, Linguistics & Philology.

SKLARE, ARNOLD BERYL, b. Chicago, Ill, June 30, 24. ENGLISH. B.A, Univ. Ill, 46, M.A, 47; D.Univ, Univ. Paris, 49. Instr. ENG, Ind. Univ, 49-50; Univ. Bridgeport, 55-57; asst. prof, Pace Col, 57-61; SOUTHAMPTON COL, L.I. UNIV, 61-63, assoc. prof, 63-71, PROF, 71-, CHMN. DEPT, 72- U.S.M.C, 43-45. MLA. Nineteenth and twentieth century Anglo-American and European literature. Publ: Creative report writing, 63 & co-auth, Stories from six authors, second series, 66, McGraw; auth, Art of the novella, 64 & co-auth, Essentials of rhetoric, 65, Macmillan; auth, The technician writes, Boyd & Fraser, 71. Add: Dept. of English, Southampton College, Long Island University, Southampton, NY 11968.

SKLOOT, ROBERT, b. Brooklyn, N.Y, July 27, 42. THEATRE, DRAMA. A.B, Union Col.(N.Y), 63; M.A, Cornell Univ, 65; Ph.D.(theatre & drama), Univ. Minn, Minneapolis, 68. ASSOC. PROF. THEATRE & DRAMA, UNIV. WIS-MADISON, 68- Vis. asst. prof. theatre, Queen's Univ.(Ont), summer 71. Am. Theatre Asn; Am. Nat. Theatre & Acad; Speech Commun. Asn; AAUP. British, classical and American drama. Publ: The time plays of J.B. Priestley, Quart. J. Speech, 12/70; The theatre and the crisis of language, J. Aesthet. Educ, 10/72; Submitting self to flame: the artist's quest in Tennessee Williams, 1935-1954, Educ. Theatre J, 5/73. Add: Dept. of Theatre & Drama, 6004 Vilas Hall, University of Wisconsin-Madison, Madison, WI 53706.

SKLUTE, LARRY MARTIN, b. Brooklyn, N.Y, Mar. 14, 40; m. 62; c. 1. ENGLISH, COMPARATIVE LITERATURE. B.A, Brooklyn Col, 61; M.A, Ind. Univ, 64, Ph.D.(comp. lit), 67. Instr. ENG, Colby Col, 64-66; ASST. PROF, Univ. Calif, Berkeley, 67-72; LA. STATE UNIV, BATON ROUGE, 72- MLA; Mediaeval Acad. Am; Am. Comp. Lit. Asn. Medieval romance; Chaucer; Old English. Add: Dept. of English, Louisiana State University, Baton Rouge, LA 70803.

SKRILETZ, DOROTHY JUNE, b. Elyria, Ohio, June 12, 27. SPEECH. B.A. & B.S, Bowling Green State Univ, 49, M.A, 51; Jenny McGraw Fiske fel, Cornell Univ, 55-56; Ph.D.(pub. address), Mich. State Univ, 66. Secy. to pres, Bowling Green State Univ, 49-51; teacher, high schs, Ohio, 51-53; residence counsel, Stephens Col, 53-55; instr. speech, Mich. State Univ, 56-59; from credential coord. & instr. to asst. prof. SPEECH, CALIF. STATE UNIV, LONG BEACH, 59-66, assoc. prof, 66-71, PROF, 71-, chmn. pub. address area, 67-68, acting chmn. dept. speech, 68, chmn, 68-71. Speech Commun. Asn; West. Speech Commun. Asn. Public speaking; Bernard Shaw; speech education. Publ: The rhetoric: an aid in the study of drama, South. Speech J, spring 60. Add: Dept. of Speech, California State University, Long Beach, 6101 E. Seventh St, Long Beach, CA 90801.

SKULSKY, HAROLD LAWRENCE, b. Brooklyn, N.Y, Apr. 12, 35; m. 64; c. 1. ENGLISH. B.A, Columbia Univ, 56; M.A, Harvard, 57, Ph.D.(Eng), 61. Instr. ENG, Johns Hopkins Univ, 62-64; ASST. PROF, Univ. Wis-Madison, 64-66; SMITH COL, 66-71, ASSOC. PROF, 71- Renaissance Soc. Am; MLA. Classical and Renaissance literature; Renaissance philosophy. Publ: Paduan epistemology, J. Hist. Philos, 10/68; Literature and philosophy, J. Aesthetics & Art Criticism, winter 68; contrib, Acta conventus neolatini lovaniensis, Wilhelm Fink, 73. Add: Dept. of English, Smith College, Northampton, MA 01060.

SKVORECKY, JOSEF VACLAV, b. Nachod, Czech, Sept. 27, 24; m. 58. ENGLISH, FILM. Ph.Dr.(Am. philos), Charles Univ, Prague, 51. Spec. lectr. Eng. & Slavic drama, UNIV. TORONTO, 69-71, writer-in-residence, 70-71, ASSOC. PROF. ENG. & FILM, 71- Auth. League Am; PEN Club. Fiction; detective fiction; film. Publ: Ed, Selected works of Sinclair Lewis, 61-68, Selected works of Ernest Hemingway, 62-68 & co-ed, The jazz inspiration: an anthology of jazz inspired poetry, 66, Odeon, Prague; auth, Reading detective stories, Ceskoslovensky Spisovatel, Prague, 65; co-ed, The face of jazz: an anthology of jazz autobiographies, St. Hudebni Vydavatelstvi, Prague, 66; ed, News from Czechoslovakia: documents about the Writers Union weekly Listy in 1968, Suhrkamp, Frankfurt/Main, 68; auth, About them—which is about us: essays on modern American literature, Kruh, Hradec Kralove, Czech, 68; All the bright young men and women: a history of the Czech cinema, Martin, Toronto, 71. Add: Dept. of English, Erindale College University of Toronto, Mississauga Rd, Mississauga, Ont, Can.

SLABEY, ROBERT M, b. Hamden, Conn, Aug. 21, 31. AMERICAN LITERATURE. B.S.S, Fairfield Univ, 53; M.A, Univ. Notre Dame, 55, Ph.D.(Eng), 61. Teaching fel, Univ. Notre Dame, 54-57, instr. ENG, 57-58; Pa. State Univ, 58-60; asst. prof, Villanova Univ, 60-63; Andrew Mellon fel, Univ. Pittsburgh, 63-64; asst. prof, UNIV. NOTRE DAME, 64-67, ASSOC. PROF, 67- Fulbright prof, Univ. Oslo, 68-69. MLA; Am. Stud. Asn. Modern American fiction; Southern literary tradition; ecological sensibility in American literature. Publ: Henry James and The most impressive convention in all history, Am. Lit, 58; Myth and ritual in Light in August, Tex. Stud. Lit. & Lang, 60; The structure of Hemingway's In our time, Moderna Sprak, 66. Add: Dept. of English, University of Notre Dame, Notre Dame, IN 46556.

SLACK, ROBERT CHARLES, b. Pittsburgh, Pa, Jan. 12, 14; m. 42; c. 3. ENGLISH. A.B, Univ. Pittsburgh, 35, A.M, 41, Ph.D.(Eng), 53. From instr. to PROF. ENG, CARNEGIE-MELLON UNIV, 46-, dir. grad. stud, 71-73, co-chmn. Eng, 73-74. Carnegie Corp. vis. assoc. prof, Yale, 55-56. U.S.A, 41-46, Capt. MLA; NCTE. Victorian literature; modern fiction; poetry. Publ: Ed, Bibliographies of studies in Victorian literature for the ten years 1955-1964, Univ. Ill, 67; Jude the obscure, Mod. Libr. Col. Ed, Random, 67; ed, English literature, Noble, 68; co-auth, Write on! A preparation for college composition, Glencoe, 71; auth, Thomas Wolfe: the second cycle, In: Thomas Wolfe: three decades of criticism, N.Y. Univ, 68; plus others. Add: Dept. of English, Carnegie-Mellon University, Pittsburgh, PA 15213.

SLAGER, WILLIAM R, Applied Linguistics. See Volume III, Foreign Languages, Linguistics & Philology.

SLATE, JOSEPH EVANS, b. Lubbock, Tex, Dec. 31, 27; m. 50, 72; c. 2. ENGLISH. B.A, Univ. Okla, 49, M.A, 52; Ph.D, Univ. Wis, 57. Instr. ENG, McMicken Col, Univ. Cincinnati, 54-57; assoc. prof, Austin Col, 57-59; instr, UNIV. TEX, AUSTIN, 59-62, asst. prof, 62-66, ASSOC. PROF, 66- Dir, Insts. Advan. Stud. Eng, 66-68; guest prof. Am. film & lit, Univ. Vienna, 72-73. U.S.A, 45-47. Am. Stud. Asn; MLA. American culture; modern poetry; film and literature. Publ: W.C. Williams and the modern short story, South. Rev, summer 68; Dahlberg's moral book of erotic beasts, In: Edward Dahlberg, American Ishmael, privately publ, 68; Kora in opacity: Williams' improvisations, J. Mod. Lit, 5/71; plus others. Add: Dept. of English, University of Texas at Austin, Austin, TX 78712.

SLATER, JOSEPH, b. Elyria, Ohio, July 17, 16; m. 39; c. 2. ENGLISH. B.A, Colgate Univ, 37; M.A, Columbia Univ, 39, Ph.D, 56. Instr. ENG, Lafayette Col, 38-41; Rutgers Univ, 47-51, lectr, 51-54, asst. prof, 54-57, assoc. prof, 57-61; PROF, COLGATE UNIV, 61-, chmn. dept, 61-66. Fulbright guest prof, Univ. Würzburg, Ger, 57-58; guest prof, Univ. Konstanz, 71. U.S.N.R, 44-46, Lt.(jg). MLA. American literature; 19th century British literature. Publ: Ed, Correspondence of Carlyle and Emerson, Columbia Univ, 64; auth, Byron's Hebrew melodies, Stud. Philol; George Ripley and Thomas Carlyle, PMLA; Goethe, Carlyle, and the open secret, Anglia, 58. Add: Dept. of English, Colgate University, Hamilton, NY 13346.

SLATIN, MYLES, b. Brooklyn, N.Y, Mar. 3, 24; m. 45; c. 2. ENGLISH. B.A, Queens Coll.(N.Y), 47; M.A, Yale, 49, Ph.D.(Eng), 57. Instr. ENG, STATE UNIV. N.Y. BUFFALO, 52-58, asst. prof, 58-62, assoc. prof, 62-65, PROF, 65-, asst. dean col. arts & sci, 58-63, assoc. dean, 63-67, acting dean, 65-67, coord, inform. & lit. resources & dir. univ. libr, 68-72. AAUP; MLA. Nineteenth and 20th century British and American literature; Ezra Pound; Norman Mailer. Publ: More by Ezra Pound, Yale Libr. Gazette, 55; A history of Cantos I-XVI by Ezra Pound, Am. Lit, 63. Add: Dept. of English, State University of New York at Buffalo, Buffalo, NY 14214.

SLATOFF, WALTER JACOB, b. New York, N.Y, Mar. 1, 22; m. 46; c. 2. ENGLISH. A.B, Columbia Univ, 43; M.A, Univ. Mich, 50, Rackham fel, 54-55, Ph.D.(Eng), 55. Instr. ENG, Univ. Mich, 53-54; CORNELL UNIV, 55-58, asst. prof, 58-61, assoc. prof, 61-66, PROF, 66- U.S.A, 43-46. NCTE. American literature; prose fiction. Publ: Quest for failure: a study of William Faulkner, 61 & With respect to readers: dimensions of literary response, 70, Cornell Univ; Against detachment, Col. Eng, fall 70. Add: Dept. of English, Cornell University, Ithaca, NY 14850.

SLATTERY, KENNETH MARTIN, b. Youngstown, Ohio, Nov. 14, 38; m. 65; c. 2. DRAMA, SPEECH. B.S, Ball State Univ, 63, M.A, 65; Ph.D.(speech), Kent State Univ, 73. Teacher elem. lang. arts, Randolph County Schs, Ind, 63-64; theatre foremen, Ball State Univ, 64-65; instr. SPEECH, Black Hills State Col, 65-66; Univ. Portland, 66-67; West. Ill. Univ, 67-69; ASSOC. PROF. & HEAD DEPT, MORRIS HARVEY COL, 71- AAUP; Speech Commun. Asn; Am. Asn. Higher Educ. American theatre; speech communication and education. Publ: Negro theatre in America prior to the Civil War, Ft. Wayne Pub. Libr, 69 & Playbill, 72. Add: 2512 Cherokee, Charleston, WV 25304.

SLATTERY, MARGARET PATRICE, C.C.V.I, b. St. Louis, Mo, June 19, 26. ENGLISH. B.A, Incarnate Word Col, 52; M.A, Marquette Univ, 55; Ph.D. (Eng), Cath. Univ. Am, 66; Univ. Edinburg, summer 66. Instr. ENG, INCARNATE WORD COL, 52-54, 55-56, asst. prof, 56-61, assoc. prof, 68-73, PROF, 73-, PRES, 72-, acad. dean, 69-72. Hon. adv, Brit. Univ. Summer Schs, 68- MLA; NCTE. English novel of nineteenth and twentieth centuries; American literature of twentieth century. Publ: The function of time in The great Gatsby and Babylon revisited, Fitzgerald Newletter, fall

67; Structural unity in T.S. Eliot's Ash Wednesday, Renascence, spring 68; Hemingway's A farewell to arms, Explicator, 10/68. Add: Incarnate Word College, 4301 Broadway, San Antonio, TX 78209.

SLATTERY, MARY FRANCIS, S.C, b. Wilkes-Barre, Pa, Mar. 8, 09. ENGLISH. B.A, Col. Mt. St. Vincent, 31; M.A, Cath. Univ. Am, 42, Ph.D.(Eng), 51. Teacher, St. Peter's High Sch, N.Y, 33-46; assoc. prof. Eng, Col. Mt. St. Vincent (N.Y), 50-62, style ed, New Cath. Encycl, 62-66; DIR. EDUC, SISTERS OF CHARITY, MT. ST. VINCENT, N.Y, 66- Lectr. as mem, IV Int. Cong. on Aesthet, Athens, 60; mem. counc, Sisters of Charity, N.Y, 66-; adj. asst. prof. lit. theory, George Washington Univ, 69-73. Am. Soc. Aesthet; MLA. Literary theory; history of literary theory; aesthetics. Publ: Hazard, form and value, Wayne State Univ, 72; Formal specification, J. Aesthet. & Art Criticism, fall 66; What is literary realism?, JAAC, 72. Add: 142 Audubon Ave, New York, NY 10032.

SLAUGHTER, EUGENE EDWARD, b. Pontotoc, Okla, June 9, 09; m. 33; c. 3. ENGLISH. A.B, Southeast. Okla. State Col, 29; A.M, Vanderbilt Univ, 30, fel, 30-32, Ph.D.(Eng), 46. Assoc. prof. ENG, SOUTHEAST. STATE COL, 32-45, PROF, 46-, HEAD DEPT. ENG. & SPEECH, 60- Consult, U.S. Off. Educ, 64-, chief mod. lang. br, div. educ. personnel training, 65-67; mem, Nat. Naval Res. Policy Bd, U.S. Dept. Navy, 65-67. U.S.N, 42-45, 50-52, Capt. MLA; Mod. Humanities Res. Asn, Gt. Brit; NCTE. Chaucer and the Middle Ages; Milton and the Renaissance; English teaching as a profession. Publ: Virtue according to love in Chaucer, Bookman Assoc, 57; co-auth, The national interest and the teaching of English, NCTE, 61; auth, Chaucer's Pandarus: Virtuous uncle and friend, J. Eng. & Ger. Philol, 49; Love and grace in Chaucer's Pandarus, In: Essays in honor of Walter Clyde Curry, Vanderbilt Univ, 55; 1967 certification to teach English in the elementary or the secondary school, Eng. J, 4/68. Add: Dept. of English & Speech, Southeastern State College, Durant, OK 74701.

SLAUGHTER, HOWARD K, b. New Orleans, La, Feb. 23, 27; m. 56; c. 3. SPEECH & DRAMA. B.A, Univ. Calif, Berkeley, 48; M.A, Univ. Hawaii, 51; Ph.D.(humanities), Univ. Pittsburgh, 66. Rep. indust. relat, U.S. Steel Corp, 51-57; instr. speech & Eng, New Castle Ctr, Pa. State Univ, 57-60, asst. prof. speech & theatre, Altoona Campus, 60-67; asst. prof. SPEECH & THEATRE ARTS, UNIV. AKRON, 67-69, ASSOC. PROF, 70-, DIR. THEATRE, 70-, assoc. dir, 67-69. Univ. Pittsburgh grants for Irish Room Comt, 64, 65; mem, Brit. Nat. Bibliog, 72- Am. Theatre Asn; Speech Commun. Asn. Irish theatre. Publ: Ed, The plays of George Fitzmaurice, Vol. II, 69, Vol. III, 70 & George Fitzmaurice and his enchanted land, 72, Dolmen, Dublin; auth, How free is labor's speech, Today's speech, 3/58; Portable lighting bars, Pittsburgh J. Theatre Res, 3/63. Add: Dept. of Speech, University of Akron, Akron, OH 44302.

SLAVICK, WILLIAM HENRY, b. Memphis, Tenn, July 7, 27; m. 55; c. 6. ENGLISH. B.A, Univ. Notre Dame, 49, M.A, 51, South. fel, 60-61, Ph.D, 71. Univ. Munich, Ger, 57-58; Fulbright grant, 57-58. Instr. Eng, Notre Dame Col.(Sask), 51-52; La. State Univ, 58-60; asst. prof, St. Mary's Col. (Ind), 61-63; State Univ. N.Y. Col. Geneseo, 63-67, Marquette Univ, 67-68, assoc. prof. Eng. & chmn. div. humanities, Mt. St. Paul Col, 68-70; ASSOC. PROF. ENG, UNIV. MAINE, PORTLAND-GORHAM, 70- Mem. bd, Citizens for Educ. Freedom, 61-69. U.S.A, 53-55. MLA; Soc. Stud. South. Lit; AAUP. Elizabeth Madox Roberts; William Faulkner; Du Bose Heyward. Add: 242 Ludlow St, Portland, ME 04102.

SLEDD, HASSELL BRANTLEY, b. Spring Hope, N.C, May 9, 26; m. 59; c. 4. ENGLISH. A.B, Univ. N.C, 48, A.M, 49; Ph.D.(Eng), Boston Univ, 65. Instr. Eng, N.Tex. State Col, 49-51; intern commun, Col. Basic Stud, Boston Univ, 60-62; instr. ENG, Northeast. Univ, 62-65, asst. prof, 65-69; assoc. prof, SLIPPERY ROCK STATE COL, 69-72, PROF, 72- Lectr, evening div, Boston Univ, 59-60; evening col, Northeast. Univ, 59-60. U.S.A, 44-46. MLA; Col. Eng. Asn; Renaissance Soc. Am. Renaissance; twentieth century; Victorian literatures. Publ: Ed, Poets at Northeast Series, Northeast. Univ, 68; The 1584 publication of Henry Constable's Diana augmented, Stud. Bibliog, 70; contrib, Encycl. World Biog, McGraw, 72. Add: Dept. of English, Slippery Rock State College, Slippery Rock, PA 16057.

SLEDD, JAMES HINTON, b. Atlanta, Ga, Dec. 5, 14; m. 39; c. 5. ENGLISH PHILOLOGY. A.B, Emory Univ, 36; Rhodes scholar, Oxford, 36-39; B.A, 39; Ph.D, Univ. Tex, 47. Instr. Eng, Univ. Tex, 39-45; Univ. Chicago, 45-46; asst. prof, Duke Univ, 46-48; Univ. Chicago, 48-53, assoc. prof, 53-57; Univ. Calif, 57-59; PROF, Northwest. Univ, 59-64; ling, UNIV. TEX, AUSTIN, 64-72, ENG, 64- Am. Counc. Learned Soc. fel, Ling. Inst, 48, fac. study grant-in-aid, 50-51; Guggenheim fel, 53-54; vis. prof, Univ. Calif, 56-57; Univ. Ceylon, 59-60; Univ. Col, Univ. London, 63. MLA; Ling. Soc. Am. Chaucer; history and structure of the English language; English lexicography. Publ: Co-auth, Dr. Johnson's dictionary, Univ. Chicago; A short introduction to English grammar, 59, co-auth, Dictionaries and THAT dictionary, 62 & co-ed, English linguistics, 70, Scott; auth, Bi-dialectalism: the linguistics of white supremacy, Eng. J, 12/69. Add: 3704 Gilbert St, Austin, TX 78703.

SLEETH, CHARLES ROBERT, b. Barrackville, W.Va, Aug. 10, 14; m. 40; c. 3. ENGLISH. A.B, W.Va. Univ, 33, A.M, 34; Rhodes scholar, Oxford, 34-37; B.A, 36, dipl. comp. philol, 37; univ. fel, Princeton, 37-38, Proctor fel, 38-39, M.A, 39, Ph.D.(Indo-Europ. ling), 41. Instr. Eng, Princeton, 39-41; prof, Greensboro Col, 41-42; asst. prof, Univ. Okla, 42-43; instr. Ger, Princeton, 46-51; asst. ed, G. & C. Merriam Co, 51-53, assoc. ed. in charge etymology, 53-62; asst. prof. ENG, BROOKLYN COL, 62-68, ASSOC. PROF, 68- U.S.A, 43-46, T/Sgt. Ling. Soc. Am; MLA. Old and Middle English; linguistics; lexicography. Publ: Ed. in charge etymologies, Webster's third new international dictionary, 61 & co-ed. in charge etymologies, Webster's seventh new collegiate dictionary, 63, Merriam. Add: Dept. of English, Brooklyn College, Brooklyn, NY 11210.

SLEPIAN, BARRY, b. Boston, Mass, Feb. 4, 35; m. 71; c. 1. ENGLISH. A.B, Univ. Pa, 56, A.M, 58, Ph.D.(Eng), 62. Instr. ENG, Drexel Inst. Technol, 60-61; Univ. Pa, 61-64, asst. prof, 64-68; TEACHER, W.PHILA. HIGH SCH, 68- Dir, NDEA Inst. Eng. for Teachers of Disadvantaged Youth, 67 & 68. NCTE. Eighteenth century British literature; English education. Publ: Co-ed, Afro-American literature (4 vols), Houghton, 71; auth, The ironic intention of Swift's verses on his own death, Rev. Eng. Stud, 8/63; co-auth, What is Fanny Hill?, Essays in Criticism, 1/64. Add: 2401 Pennsylvania Ave, Philadelphia, PA 19130.

SLETHAUG, GORDON EMMETT, b. Kalispell, Mont, Sept. 22, 40; m. 64; c. 3. ENGLISH. B.A, Pac. Lutheran Univ. 62; M.A, Univ. Nebr, 64, Ph.D.(Eng), 68. Instr. ENG, Univ. Nebr, 65-68; asst. prof, UNIV. WATERLOO, 68-74, ASSOC. PROF. & DIR. GRAD. AFFAIRS, 74- Can. Asn. Univ. Teachers; Can. Asn. Am. Stud; MLA. Puritanism; transcendentalism; existential fiction. Publ: Form in Salinger's shorter fiction, Can. Rev. Am. Stud, spring 72; Barth's refutation of the idea of progress, Critique, spring 72; Edward Taylor's copy of Thomas Taylor's Types: a new Taylor document, Early Am. Lit, fall 73. Add: Dept. of English, University of Waterloo, University Ave. W, Waterloo, Ont. N2L 3G1, Can.

SLIGHTS, CAMILLE, b. Omaha, Nebr; m. 63; c. 1. ENGLISH. B.A, Univ. Omaha, 57; M.A, Univ. Nebr, 61, Ph.D.(Eng. lit), 67. Instr. ENG, Univ. Nebr, 58-61; Univ. Ill, 64-66; N.Y. Univ, 66-68, asst. prof, 68-69; Carroll Col, 69-73; SESSIONAL LECTR, UNIV. SASK, 73- MLA. Publ: Ingenious piety: Anglican casuistry of the seventeenth century, Harvard Theol. Rev, 70; To stand inquiring right: the casuistry of Donne's Satyre III, Stud. Eng. Lit, 72; The parallel structure of Troilus and Cressida, Shakespeare Quart, 74; plus others. Add: Dept. of English, University of Saskatchewan, Saskatoon, Sask, Can.

SLOAN, JOHN HERBERT, b. Beckley, W.Va, May 6, 33; m. 56; c. 4. SPEECH. B.A, Marietta Col, 54; M.A, Univ. Ala, 56; univ. fel, Univ. Ill, 59-61, Ph.D.(speech), 61. Instr. Eng, Bowdoin Col, 56-57; speech, Marietta Col, 57-59; asst. prof, Univ. Hawaii, 61-64; Univ. Ala, 64-65, assoc. prof, 65-69, prof, 69-70; PROF. SPEECH & DRAMA & CHMN. DEPT, MEMPHIS STATE UNIV, 70- Speech Commun. Asn. American public address; contemporary rhetorical theory; rhetorical theory and criticism. Publ: I have kept the faith: William Jennings Bryan and the Democratic nominating convention of 1904, South. Speech J, winter 65; The miraculous uplifting: Emerson's relationship with his audience, Quart, J. Speech, 2/66; Understanding McLuhan: some implications for the teacher and critic of speech, Speech Teacher, 3/68. Add: Dept. of Speech & Drama, Memphis State University, Memphis, TN 38111.

SLOAN, THOMAS O, b. West Frankfort, Ill, July 12, 29; m. 52; c. 3. RHETORIC. B.A, South. Ill. Univ, 51, M.A, 52; Ph.D, Northwest. Univ, 60. Lectr. speech, South. Ill. Univ, 56; asst. interpretation, Northwest. Univ, 57-58; instr. Eng, Washington & Lee Univ, 58-60; asst. prof. speech, Univ. Ill, Urbana, 60-65, assoc. prof, 65-70, fac. fel, 64, instr. develop. award, 65, asst. dean lib. arts & sci, 66-67, assoc. head dept. speech, 67-68; PROF. RHET, UNIV. CALIF, BERKELEY, 70-, CHMN. DEPT, 72-, vis. assoc. prof, 68-69. Huntington Libr. res. award, 67. U.S.N.R, 52-55, Lt. Speech Commun. Asn; MLA; Renaissance Soc. Am. Rhetoric and poetry in the English Renaissance; interpretation of literature. Publ: Co-auth, The oral study of literature, 66 & Interpretation: an approach to the study of literature, 72, Random; ed, The passions of the mind in general, Univ. Ill, 71; auth, A rhetorical analysis of John Donne's The prohibition, Quart. J. Speech, 62; The rhetoric in the poetry of John Donne, Stud. Eng. Lit, 63; Rhetoric and meditation: three case studies, J. Medieval & Renaissance Stud, 71. Add: Dept. of Rhetoric, University of California, Berkeley, CA 94720.

SLOANE, DAVID EDWARD EDISON, b. West Orange, N.J, Jan. 19, 43. AMERICAN LITERATURE. B.A, Wesleyan Univ, 64; M.A, Duke Univ, 66, Ph.D.(Eng), 70. Tutor Eng, Duke Univ, 66-68; instr, Lafayette Col, 68-70, asst. prof, 70-74; dir, Writing Ctr, Livingston Col, Rutgers Univ, 73-74. Am. Lit. Group, Mod. Lang. Asn; MLA; Col. Eng. Asn. American literature, 1600-1970, 1860-1910, remedial writing. Publ: Contrib, Thomas Hardy, North. Ill. Univ, 73; auth, Rational empiricism and romanticism in Poe's Berenice, Am. Transcendental Quart, 73; In search of a realist poetic tradition, Am. Lit. Realism 1870-1910, 73; plus others. Add: New Brunswick, NJ.

SLOANE, WILLIAM, b. Glasgow, Scotland, Mar. 13, 10; nat; m. 47; c. 1. ENGLISH LITERATURE. A.B, Hamilton Col, 32; A.M, Columbia Univ, 33, fel, 35-36, Ph.D.(Eng), 47. Instr. ENG, St. Francis Col, 34-35; Hamilton Col, 36-40; Russell Sage Col, 40-42; assoc. prof, DICKINSON COL, 46-51, prof, 51-53, MARTHA PORTER SELLERS PROF, 52-, chmn. dept, 51-56. Folger Libr. fel, 58; vis. prof, Bowling Green State Univ, 61. U.S.A, 42-46, Capt. Friends Hist. Asn; MLA; Col. Eng. Asn; NCTE. Seventeenth century English literature; Chaucer; the English novel. Publ: The British Isles, Holiday; Children's books in England and America in the seventeenth century, Columbia Univ. Add: Dept. of English, Dickinson College, Carlisle, PA 17013.

SLOAT, CLARENCE, Linguistics, English. See Volume III, Foreign Languages, Linguistics & Philology.

SLOCA, CHARLES, b. Rahway, N.J, Dec. 22, 21; m; c. 4. ENGLISH. B.S, Rutgers Univ, 43; A.M, Cornell Univ, 46, Ph.D, 50. Asst. & teaching fel, Cornell Univ, 46-50; asst. prof. Eng, Lebanon Valley Col, 50-54; assoc. prof, Bethany Col.(W.Va), 54-55; prof, Waynesburg Col, 55-57; prof. ENG, PARSONS COL, 57-73, DIR, ENG. INST, 65-, dean fac, 57-65. Pastor, New Sweden United Methodist Church, 64-, Glasgow United Methodist Church, 67-; dir, weekly radio scripture study prog, Church of Jesus Christ, 68-, New Found. Peace, 71- Speech Commun. Asn. The nature of dramatic conflict; use of English language: problems and solutions; allegory or parable study of scripture. Publ: A proposal to improve the results of reading instruction, 71 & The Tree of life study of holy scripture, 72, Labarum. Add: 401 E. Burlington Ave, Fairfield, IA 52556.

SLOCUM, SALLY KENNEDY, b. Spartanburg, S.C, July 28, 40; m. 71. MEDIEVAL ENGLISH, POETRY. B.A, Columbia Col, 62; M.A, Univ. Tenn, 64, Ph.D.(Eng), 68. Teaching asst. ENG, Univ. Tenn, 65-66; instr, UNIV. AKRON, 66-68, ASST. PROF, 68-, DIR. ENG. COMPOS, 73- MLA; Medieval Acad. Am; AAUP; Int. Arthurian Soc. Geoffrey Chaucer; Arthurian literature; 14th century Medieval literature. Publ: Contrib, Contemporary novelists, St. James, 72. Add: Dept. of English, University of Akron, E. Buchtel Ave, Akron, OH 44325.

SLONIM, RUTH, b. Chicago, Ill, Jan. 30, 18. ENGLISH. M.A, Univ. Minn, 42. Instr. Eng. & dir. pub. relat, Minn. State Teachers Col, Duluth, 38-44; asst. prof. Eng, Cent. Wash. Col. Educ, 44-46; vis. prof. humanities, Univ. P.R, 46-47; from instr. to assoc. prof. ENG, WASH. STATE UNIV, 47-64, PROF, 64- Vis. prof. Eng, Sch. Irish Stud, Dublin, fall 70; humanities rep. adv. panel, Oceanic Educ. Found, 71- Am. Comt. Irish Stud; Int. Comt. Anglo-Irish Stud; fel, Int. Poetry Soc. Publ: London: an appreciation, Humphries, 54; San Francisco: The city in verse, Wash. State Univ, 65; Quarry, Botteghe Oscure, spring 58; Proems and poems, Wash. State Rev, spring 68; Yeats post facto (poem), In: Int. Who's Who in Poetry Anthology, 72; plus others. Add: Dept. of English, Avery Hall, Washington State University, Pullman, WA 99163.

SLOTKIN, ALAN ROBERT, English Linguistics, American Literature. See Volume III, Foreign Languages, Linguistics & Philology.

SLOTKIN, RICHARD S, b. New York, N.Y, Nov. 8, 42; m. 63; c. 1. ENGLISH, HISTORY. B.A, Brooklyn Col, 63; fel, Brown Univ, 63-66, Ph.D.(Am. civilization), 67. Asst. prof. ENG, WESLEYAN UNIV, 66-73, ASSOC. PROF, 73- Wesleyan Ctr. Humanities fel, 69-70; Nat. Endowment for Humanities younger humanist fel, 73-74. AHA (A.J. Beveridge Award, 73); MLA; Am. Stud. Asn; Popular Cult. Asn; West. Hist. Asn. American popular culture; mythology; literature. Publ: Regeneration through violence, Wesleyan Univ, 73; Dreams and genocide, J. Popular Cult, 5/71; Literature and cultural history, Col. Eng, 8/72; Narratives of Negro crime, Am. Quart, 4/73; plus others. Add: Dept. of English, Wesleyan University, Middletown, CT 06457.

SLOW, JOHN RALPH, b. Eldorado, Ill, July 20, 02; m. 25; c. 2. ENGLISH. A.B, Univ. Ill, 25, A.M, 28; M.S, South. Ill. Univ, 57, Ph.D.(Eng. educ), 61. Teacher high sch, Ill, 25-27; instr. Eng, Univ. Ill, 28-32; supt. schs, Eldorado, Ill, 33-58; chmn. dept. ENG, Tex. Mil. Inst, 58-59; PROF, MURRAY STATE UNIV, 59- NCTE. Seventeenth century English literature; improvement of writing by college students. Publ: Improvement of student writing, Sch. & Soc, 4/63; Influence of high school writing experience on college English composition, J. Educ. Res, 7-8/64; Parental education of English composition students, Col. Compos. & Commun, 2/68. Add: Dept. of English, Murray State University, Murray, KY 42071.

SMALL, EDWARD STUART, b. New York, N.Y, Oct. 15, 39; m. 68. FILM COMMUNICATION THEORY. A.B, Hope Col, 62; M.A, Univ. Ark, Fayetteville, 66; Ph.D.(film), Univ. Iowa, 72. Instr. Eng, California State Col.(Pa), 65-66; Aquinas Col, 66-67; prof. & int. dir, Sophia Univ, Japan, 70-71; ASST. PROF. FILM, UNIV. MO-COLUMBIA, 72- Univ. Film Asn. Japanese animated film; cinevideo bionics; semiotics. Publ: House (film), privately produced, 68; co-auth, Alpha Mandala (film), Univ. Iowa, 72; co-auth, In progress (film), Filmmaker's Coop. N.Y, 72. Add: Radio, Television & Film Div, 200 Swallow Hall, University of Missouri-Columbia, Columbia, MO 65201.

SMALL, GEORGE A, b. Butler, Pa, Dec. 19, 23. LITERATURE, PHILOLOGY. B.A. & M.A, Univ. N.Mex, 52; Ph.D, Univ. Pa, 56. Prof. Eng, L.I. UNIV, 56-73, PROVOST, 73- U.S.M.C, 42-46. MLA. American literature and drama; English philology. Add: University Center, Long Island University, Greenvale, NY 11548.

SMALL, RAY, b. Winters, Tex, Aug. 2, 15; m. 38; c. 2. ENGLISH. B.A, West Tex. State Univ, 37; M.A, Univ. Tex, Austin, 41, Ph.D.(Eng), 58. Instr. ENG, Amarillo Col, 46-56, assoc. prof, 56-59, PROF, 59-61; UNIV. TEX, EL PASO, 61-, DEAN, COL. LIB. ARTS, 67-, asst. to pres, 61-63, dean arts & sci, 63-67. MLA. William Butler Yeats; Cardinal Newman and the Oxford movement. Add: Dept. of English, University of Texas at El Paso, El Paso, TX 79902.

SMALL, SAMUEL ASA, b. Arkansas City, Kans, Mar. 27, 93. ENGLISH. A.B, Univ. Tenn, 18; A.M, Johns Hopkins Univ, 24, Ph.D, 25; Oxford, 37. Training off, U.S. Veterans Bur, Wash, D.C, 19-22; asst. prof. ENG, Univ. Fla, 25-28; assoc. prof, Birmingham-South. Col, 28-30; prof. Limestone Col, 30-32; prof. & chmn. dept, Houghton Col, 32-43; W.VA. WESLEYAN COL, 43-59, EMER. PROF, 59- U.S.A, 17-18, Lt. MLA; NCTE; Mediaeval Acad. Am; NEA; Shakespeare Asn. Am. Senecan conscience motif in Shakespearian tragedy; Shakespeare character interpretation; Shakespearian and mediaeval studies. Publ: Higher education in the age of science, Christopher, 70; Structure of Falstaff's humor and Shakespeare's ghosts, S.Atlantic Bull; The inventus stage of life, Malone Anniversary Stud. Add: 842 Park Ave, Baltimore, MD 21201.

SMALLENBURG, HARRY RUSSELL, b. Burbank, Calif, July 17, 42. ENGLISH LITERATURE. B.A, Univ. Calif, Santa Barbara, 65; M.A, Univ. Calif, Berkeley, 66, Ph.D.(Eng), 70. ASST. PROF. ENG, WAYNE STATE UNIV, 70- MLA; Milton Soc. Am. Milton; English Renaissance literature; creative writing. Publ: Milton's cosmic sentences, Lang. & Style, 72; Government of the spirit: style, structure and theme in Treatise of civil power, In: Achievements of the left hand: essays on the prose of John Milton, Univ. Mass, 74. Add: Dept. of English, Wayne State University, Detroit, MI 48202.

SMALLEY, BARBARA MARTIN, b. Everton, Ind; m. 52. MODERN NOVEL. B.S, Ind. Univ, Bloomington, 54; M.A, Univ. Ill, Urbana, 65, Ph.D.(comp. lit), 68. Teaching asst. French, UNIV. ILL, URBANA, 63-65, ASST. PROF. ENG. & COMP. LIT, 68- MLA; AAUP; Am. Comp. Lit. Asn; Int. Comp. Lit. Asn. Psychological narrative; 19th century novel; George Eliot. Publ: George Eliot and Flaubert: pioneers of the modern novel, 73 & ed, G.H. Lewes, Ranthorpe, 74, Ohio Univ; The compulsive patterns of Dostoevsky's Underground man, Stud. Short Fiction, 10/73. Add: 1006 S. Busey, Urbana, IL 61801.

SMALLEY, DONALD ARTHUR, b. N.Manchester, Ind, Apr. 2, 07; m. 37, 52. ENGLISH LITERATURE. A.B, Ind. Univ, 29, A.M, 31; Austin scholar, Harvard, 34-35, univ. fel, 35-36, Ph.D, 39. Instr. ENG, Ind. Univ, 30-41, asst. prof, 41-47, assoc. prof, 47-51, prof, 51-59; PROF, UNIV. ILL, URBANA, 59- MLA. Life and writings of Robert Browning; Anglo-American travel literature. Publ: Browning's essay on Chatterton, Harvard, 48; ed, Domestic manners of the Americans, Vintage, Knopf, 49 & Poems of Robert Browning, Houghton, 56; auth, Trollope; the critical heritage, 68 & co-ed, Browning: the critical heritage, 69, Routledge & Kegan Paul; auth, Anthony Trollope, In: Victorian fiction, a guide to research, Harvard, 64. Add: 1006 S. Busey, Urbana, IL 61801.

SMALLEY, WEBSTER LEROY C, b. Walla Walla, Wash, Feb. 23, 21; m. 46; c. 3. THEATRE. B.A, Univ. Wash, 46; M.A, Columbia Univ, 48; Ph.D. (speech & drama), Stanford Univ, 60. Head script dept, Am. Nat. Theatre & Acad. & Exp. Theatre, Inc, N.Y.C, 49-50; instr. playwriting, Univ. Ill, 50-51; Univ. Mo, 52-53; assoc. prof. theatre, Univ. Ill, Urbana, 55-69; PROF. PLAYWRITING, DEPT. DRAMA, UNIV. TEX, AUSTIN, 69-, CHMN. DEPT, 72- Dir, E.P. Conkle Workshop for Playwrights, Univ. Tex, 70-; chmn. playwrights proj, Univ. Resident Theatre Asn, 72- New Play of the Year Award, Southeast Theatre Conf, 63. U.S.A, 43-46, Sgt. Am. Theatre Asn; Speech Commun. Asn; Nat. Theatre Conf. Theatre; playwriting. Publ: Co-auth, Five plays by Langston Hughes, Univ. Ind, 63; auth, The man with the oboe (play) Players Mag, 4/63. Add: Dept. of Drama, Drama Bldg, University of Texas at Austin, Austin, TX 78712.

SMALLWOOD, CLYDE GEORGE, b. Nida, Okla, Nov. 5, 17; m. 56; c. 6. PHILOSOPHY, DRAMA. B.A, Abilene Christian Col, 54; Kingfisher fel, Univ. Okla, 55-56, M.A, 56; M.A, Univ. Ark, 61; fel, Univ. Denver, 61-62, Ph.D.(theatre), 62. Instr. philos, Univ. Okla, 56-58; asst. prof, Phillips Univ, 58-59; instr. speech & philos, Northeast. State Col, 59-60; asst. theatre, Univ. Ark, 60-61; asst. prof. speech & drama, NORTH. ARIZ. UNIV, 62-63, philos, 63-66, ASSOC. PROF. HUMANITIES, 66- Priest, Protestant Episcopal Church, 67- U.S.A.A.F, 42-45, 1st Lt. Southwest. Philos. Soc; Am. Theatre Asn; Speech Commun. Asn. Existentialist philosophy; theatre of the absurd. Add: Dept. of Humanities, University Box 6031, Northern Arizona University, Flagstaff, AZ 86001.

SMALLWOOD, OSBORN TUCKER, b. Hillhouse, Miss, Aug. 12, 11; m. 39; c. 4. SPEECH COMMUNICATION, ENGLISH. B.S, N.C. A&T Col, 37; M.A, Howard Univ, 39; Ph.D.(Eng), N.Y. Univ, 48. Chmn. dept. Eng, Samuel Huston Col, 39-42; specialist hist. res, Off. Price Admin, Wash, D.C, 42-44; pastor, St. Matthew's Lutheran Church, Baltimore, Md, 44-46; instr. Eng, Howard Univ, 47-48, asst. prof, 48-52, assoc. prof, 52-61; for. serv. off, U.S. Inform. Agency, Wash, D.C, 61-70; PROF. SPEECH COMMUN. & DIR. INT. EDUC, OHIO STATE UNIV, 70- Fulbright prof, Anatolia Col, Greece, 55-57; dir, Ger. Am. Inst, Regensburg, W.Ger, 61-66; dir, Am. House, Frankfurt, 66-70; consul, Am. Consulate Gen, Frankfurt, 69-70. Meritorious Honor Award, U.S. Inform. Agency, 67. Speech Commun. Asn; Int. Stud. Asn; Nat. Asn. For. Stud. Affairs. Afro-American rhetoric; intercultural communications; English. Publ: Das Minderheitenproblem in den U.S.A, Verlag Dr. Max Gehlen, Berlin, 63; ed, Universities and transnational approaches to the solution of world problems, Ohio State Univ, 73; The historical significance of Whittier's anti-slavery poems, J. Negro Hist, 4/50; John Ruskin and the Oxford movement, Col. Lang. Asn. J, 59; The Negro in American society today, Am. Scene, 68; plus others. Add: Office of International Programs, Ohio State University, 190 N. Oval Dr, Columbus, OH 43210.

SMART, GEORGE K, b. Hartford, Conn, Nov. 29, 10. AMERICAN CULTURAL HISTORY. A.B, Univ. Ala, 33; A.M, Harvard, 34, Shattuck scholar. & Austin fel, 36-37. Asst. ENG, Harvard, 36-37; instr, Northwest. Univ, 37-39; asst. prof, Univ. Ala, 39-46; assoc. prof, UNIV. MIAMI, 46-68, PROF, 68-, chmn. comt. Am. civilization, 58-72. Lectr, De Paul Univ, 38-39. MLA; S.Atlantic Mod. Lang. Asn; Southeast. Am. Stud. Asn.(pres, 57-58); Am. Stud. Asn. Cultural history of colonial Virginia; American radicalism from 1825 to 1860; religious elements in Faulkner. Publ: Co-auth, Literature and society, 1956-1960, 62, auth, Religious elements in Faulkner's early novels, 65 & co-auth, Literature and society, 1960-1965, 67, Univ. Miami. Add: Dept. of English, University of Miami, Coral Gables, FL 33146.

SMEATON, B. HUNTER, Linguistics. See Volume III, Foreign Languages, Linguistics & Philology.

SMEDICK, LOIS KATHERINE, b. Middletown, Conn, Mar. 19, 33. MEDIEVAL STUDIES. B.A, Wilson Col, 55; Howard Lehman Goodhart fel, 61-63; Ph.D.(medieval stud), Bryn Mawr Col, 67; M.S.L, Pontif. Inst. Mediaeval Stud, 68. Asst. prof. ENG, UNIV. WINDSOR, 63-68, ASSOC. PROF, 68- Mediaeval Acad. Am. Old English poetry; middle English Rhythmical prose. Add: Dept. of English, University of Windsor, Windsor, Ont, N9B 3P4, Can.

SMETANA, CYRIL L, O.S.A, b. Racine, Wis, May 5, 20. ENGLISH. B.A, Manhattan Col, 43; M.A, Fordham Univ, 48, Ph.D.(Old Eng), 52. Instr. ENG, Fordham Univ, 52-53; assoc. prof, St. Francis Xavier Univ, 60-65; asst. prof, YORK UNIV, 66-73, ASSOC. PROF, 73- Summer lectr, Chestnut Hill Col, 48, Mt. St. Vincent Univ, 61, 65 & lector in philos, Augustinian Order, 62. MLA; Mediaeval Acad. Am. Old English literature; prose and poetry; the Latin homiliary of Paul the deacon. Publ: Aelfric and Haymo of Halberstadt, 61, Traditio; Second thoughts on soul and body I, 67 & Capgrave's Life of St. Norbert: diction dialect and spelling. 34: 422-434, Mediaeval Stud. Add: P.O. Box 550, King City, Ont, Can.

SMILEY, SAM MAX, b. Columbus, Ind, Feb. 15, 31; m. 52; c. 3. DRAMA. B.F.A, Ill. Wesleyan Univ, 52; M.F.A, Univ. Iowa, 52-55; Eli Lilly Found. fels, Ind. Univ, 61-62, Ph.D.(dramatic lit), 67. Asst. drama, Univ. Iowa, 54-55; instr. Ga. State Col. Women, 56-57; from asst. prof. to PROF, Univ. Evansville, 57-69; Univ. Mo-Columbia, 69-73; THEATRE & DRAMA, IND. UNIV, BLOOMINGTON, 73- Vis. instr, Univ. Idaho, summer 59; mem, Ind. Governor's Comn. on Arts, 62 & 63; assoc. ed, Quart. J. Speech, 70-71; chmn. playwriting awards, Am. Col. Theatre Festival, 73. Am. Theatre Asn; Speech Commun. Asn. Dramatic theory; playwriting; directing. Publ: Playwriting: the structure of action, Prentice-Hall, 71; The drama of attack, Univ. Mo, 72; New playwrights in action, Players, 69; Friends of the party: American Writers' Congresses, Southwest Rev, 69; contrib, Studies in theatre and drama, Mouton Publ, Netherlands, 72; plus two others. Add: Dept. of Theatre & Drama, Theatre Bldg, Indiana University, Bloomington, IN 47401.

SMITH, ALBERT SCOTT, b. Middletown, Conn, Dec. 19, 04; m. 34; c. 2. ENGLISH, SPEECH. B.A, Wesleyan Univ, 26; M.A, Princeton, 30; Univ. Conn, 57-59. Instr. speech, Chestnut Hill Acad, Pa, 26-29; ENG, Hoffman Sch. for Individual Develop, N.Y.C, 31-32; teacher, pub. sch, Conn, 32-62; head dept. Eng, Mitchell Col.(Conn), 62-66; asst. prof, MANCHESTER COMMUNITY COL, 66-73, ASSOC. PROF, 73-, chmn. dept, 66-68. Fulbright consult. teaching Eng, El Shams Univ. & Giza & Kubbab Model Schs, Cairo, 51-52; instr, Univ. Hartford, 43-62. NCTE. Publ: Co-auth, Modern verse, Bk. II, Henry Holt, 39 & What about censorship?, Conn. Eng. News, spring 68. Add: Dept. of English, Manchester Community College, Box 1046, Manchester, CT 06040.

SMITH, ALFRED WINN, b. Decherd, Tenn, Feb. 5, 12; m. 38; c. 1. LINGUISTICS. B.A, Vanderbilt Univ, 33, univ. scholar, 33-34, M.A, 34; Ph.D, Peabody Col, 54. Instr. Ger & Fr, Univ. Miss, 38-40; Emory Univ. Jr. Col, 40-43; Ger, Vanderbilt Univ, 46-53; assoc. prof. ENG, Southwest. State Col, 53-54; asst. prof, MEMPHIS STATE UNIV, 54-59, from assoc. prof. to PROF, 59-, dir, NCTE Ling. Inst, summer, 63. U.S.N.R, 43-45, Lt. Comparative semantics; modern grammar. Publ: Semantic shift of Teutonic noun cognates in English and German, George Peabody Col, 54. Add: Dept. of English, Memphis State University, Memphis, TN 38111.

SMITH, ALICE GUSTAVA, C.S.J, b. Alton, Iowa, Dec. 21, 99. ENGLISH. B.A, Col. St. Catherine, 24; B.A, Oxford, 29; M.A, 33. Instr. ENG, Col. St. Catherine, 24-30, asst. prof, 30-40, prof, 40-71; RETIRED. Vis. prof, Loretto Heights Col, summers 54, 56; vis. prof. Eng, Mt. St. Mary's Col. (Calif), summer 59. Col. Eng. Asn. Publ: Frost for Saint Brigid, Sheed, 49; Cause of our joy, N.Cent. Publ, 56; plus others. Add: Dept. of English, College of St. Catherine, St. Paul, MN 55105.

SMITH, ARTHUR JAMES MARSHALL, b. Montreal, Que, Nov. 8, 02. ENGLISH. B.Sc, McGill Univ, 25, M.A, 26, hon. D.Litt, 58; Ph.D, Univ. Edinburgh, 31; hon. LL.D, Queen's Univ.(Ont), 66, Dalhousie Univ, 69; hon. D.C.L, Bishop's Univ, 67. Asst. prof, Ball State Teachers Col, 29-30; prof, Doane Col, 33-34; from instr. to prof. ENG, MICH. STATE UNIV, 36-72, EMER. PROF, 72- Guggenheim fel, 40-41; Rockefeller Found. fel, 44-46; lectr, Univ. Wash, summer 49; Am. asst. ed, Essays in criticism, 51-53; teaching, summers, Queen's Univ, 52-60; Univ. B.C, 56; Can. Counc. vis. prof, Dalhousie Univ, 66-67; vis. prof, State Univ. N.Y. Stony Brook, 69; McGill Univ, 69-70. Can. Gov-Gen. Medal Poetry, 43; Can. Counc. Medal Serv. Can. Lett, 68. MLA; Royal Soc. Can.(Lorne Pierce Medal Serv. Can. Lett, 66). Canadian literature; modern poetry and criticism. Publ: Ed, Oxford book of Canadian verse, 60, Poems new and collected, 67 & Modern Canadian verse, 67, Oxford Univ; auth, The colonial century, Vol. I & The Canadian century, Vol. II, In: The book of Candian prose, Gage, Toronto, 73; ed, Seven centuries of verse, Scribners, 3rd ed, 67; auth, Towards a view of Canadian letters: selected essays, 1928-1972, Univ. B.C, 73; co-auth, Exploring poetry, Macmillan, 2nd ed, 73; auth, Canadian poetry & Light verse, In: Encycl. of Poetry & Poetics, Princeton, 65; plus others. Add: 640 Bailey St, East Lansing, MI 48823.

SMITH, ARTHUR L (ASANTE), b. Valdosta, Ga, Aug. 14, 42; m. 66; c. 1. COMMUNICATION. B.A, Okla. Christian Col, 64; M.A, Pepperdine Univ, 65; Ph.D.(commun), Univ. Calif, Los Angeles, 68. Asst. prof. COMMUN, Purdue Univ, 68-69; assoc. prof, Univ. Calif, 69-73; PROF, STATE UNIV. N.Y, BUFFALO, 73- Ed, J. Black Stud, 69- Int. Commun. Asn; Speech Commun. Asn; African Stud. Asn. Interracial communication; ethnorhetorics; language strategies. Publ: Rhetoric of black revolution, 69 & The voice of black rhetoric, 71, Allyn & Bacon; Rhetoric of revolution, Moore, 70; Language, communication and rhetoric in black America, Harper & Row, 72; Transracial communication, Prentice-Hall, 73. Add: Dept. of Speech Communication, State University of New York at Buffalo, Buffalo, NY 14226.

SMITH, BARBARA HERRNSTEIN, b. New York, N.Y, Aug. 6, 32. ENGLISH LITERATURE. B.A, Brandeis Univ, 54, M.A, 55, Ph.D.(Eng, Am. lit), 65. Instr. Eng. & Am. lit, Brandeis Univ, 61-62; mem. fac. lit, Bennington Col, 62-74; PROF. ENG. & COMMUN, UNIV. PA, 74- Nat. Endowment for Humanities fel, 70-71; vis. lectr, Annenberg Sch. Commun, Univ. Pa, 73-74; mem. ed. bd, Critical Inquiry. Christian Gauss Award, 68; Explicator Award, 68. MLA. Literary theory; aesthetics; linguistic theory. Publ: Ed, Discussions of Shakespeare's sonnets, Heath, 64; auth, Poetic closure: a study of how poems end, Univ. Chicago, 68; ed, Shakespeare's sonnets, Avon Bks. & N.Y. Univ, 69; The new imagism, Midway, winter 69; Literature as performance, fiction and art, J. Philos, 8/70; Poetry as fiction, New Literary Hist, winter 71 & In: New directions in literary history, Johns Hopkins Univ, 74. Add: 606 N. Chester Rd, Swarthmore, PA 19081.

SMITH, BEN H, JR, b. Richmond, Va, Feb. 5, 32; m. 55; c. 3. ENGLISH LITERATURE. B.A, Randolph-Macon Col, 53; dipl, Univ. Edinburgh, Scotland, 56; Ph.D, Univ. N.C, 62. From asst. prof. to assoc. prof. ENG, MARY BALDWIN COL, 60-72, PROF, 72- U.S.C.G, 53-55, Lt.(jg). MLA. Middle Ages; Renaissance; modern literature. Publ: Patience's riddle, Piers Plowman B, XIII, Mod. Lang. Notes, 12/61. Add: Dept. of English, Mary Baldwin College, Staunton, VA 24401.

SMITH, BEVERLEE ANN, b. Chicago, Ill, Dec. 18, 30; m. 50; c. 2. ENGLISH. B.A, St. Xavier Col.(Ill), 62; fel, Loyola Univ. Chicago, 62-66, M.A, 64, Ph.D.(Eng), 71. ASST. PROF. ENG, PURDUE UNIV, CALUMET CAMPUS, 66- NCTE; AAUP. John Dryden and The medal; social criticism of Defoe relating to the poor; modern English fiction and poetry. Add: 4608 W. 175th Pl, Country Club Hills, IL 60477.

SMITH, BOBBY LEE, b. Mountain View, Okla, Nov. 1, 30; m. 50; c. 4. ENGLISH. B.A, Univ. Okla, 53, M.A, 58, Ph.D.(Eng), 65. Instr. ENG, Northwest. State Col, 60-62; Univ. Okla, 64-65; asst. prof, KENT STATE UNIV, 65-69, ASSOC. PROF, 69-, ASST. CHMN. DEPT, 73-, chmn. undergrad. stud, 67-70, summer res. fels, 68 & 70, acting chmn. dept. Eng, summer 73. MLA; Am. Comt. Irish Stud. Modern British fiction and drama; modern Irish literature, especially drama. Publ: The English research paper, C.E. Merrill, 69; Satire in The plough and the stars, Ball State Univ. Forum, summer 69; O'Casey's satiric vision, James Joyce Quart, fall 70; From athlete to statue: satire in Sean O'Casey's The silver tassie, Ariz. Quart, winter 71; plus four others. Add: Dept. of English, Kent State University, Kent, OH 44242.

SMITH, CALVIN CLIFTON, b. Alleghany, Va, June 21, 26; m. 57; c. 1. ENGLISH. B.A, Capital Univ, 50; Middlebury Col, summer 50; M.A, Duke Univ, 52, Ph.D.(Eng), 57; Univ. Sorbonne, 53-54. Instr. Eng, South. Methodist Univ, 56-57, asst. prof, 57-62, assoc. prof, 62-63, dir. freshman Eng, 59-61, asst. dean col. arts & sci, 61-63; assoc. prof. ENG, STATE UNIV. N.Y. COL. FREDONIA, 63-73, PROF, 73- Qm.C, A.U.S, 44-46, M/Sgt. MLA. Milton; Elizabethan drama; rhetoric. Publ: Auth, Apocalypse as drama, spring 70 & transl, José Maria Bellido's The scorpion, spring 73, Drama & Theatre; auth, Bartholomew fair: cold decorum, S.Atlantic Quart, 72. Add: Dept. of English, State University of New York College at Fredonia, Fredonia, NY 14063.

SMITH, CAROL HERTZIG, b. Pittsburgh, Pa, Aug. 17, 29; m. 53; c. 1. ENGLISH. B.A, Ohio Wesleyan Univ, 52; Univ. Vienna, Austria, 53-54; M.A, Univ. Mich, 55, teaching fel, 55-57, Mary Maquire Walker scholar, 57-59, Ph.D, 62. Instr. ENG, DOUGLASS COL, RUTGERS UNIV, 59-62, asst. prof, 62-67, assoc. prof, 67-70, PROF, 70-, Rutgers Res. Counc. scholar, 68-69, Rutgers fac. fel, spring 73. NCTE; MLA. Modern literature, especially drama, novel and poetry. Publ: T.S. Eliot's dramatic theory and practice: from Sweeney agonistes to The elder statesman, Princeton, 63; T.S. Eliot: the poet as playwright, Nation, 10/66; co-auth, Woman and success, New Soc, 10/70. Add: Dept. of English, Douglass College, Rutgers University, New Brunswick, NJ 08903.

SMITH, CHARLES ALLEN, b. Paw Paw, Mich, Sept. 29, 09; m. 50; c. 4. ENGLISH. A.M, Univ. Mich, 37, fel, 45-47; West. Mich. Univ; Northwest. Univ. Teacher high sch, Mich, 34; dir. freshman col, Sturgis, Mich, 34-35; ASSOC. PROF. ENG, WEST. MICH. UNIV, 35- Res. analyst, instrumentation and control div, Pneumo Dynamics Corp, 59- Detective novel; midwest history; metropolitan transportation problems. Publ: Co-auth, Transportation dilemma of greater metropolitan areas, Soc. Automotive Engineers, 62; Metropolitan transportation problems, & Airport transportation in the Chicago metropolitan area, Human Sci. Res, Inc, 61. Add: Dept. of English, Western Michigan University, Kalamazoo, MI 49001.

SMITH, CHARLES DANIEL, b. Akron, Ind, Oct. 16, 14; m. 38; c. 3. RHETORIC, PUBLIC ADDRESS. A.B, Ind. Univ, 36; M.A, Wash. Univ, 49, Ph.D. (rhet. & pub. address), 54. Instr. pub. address & Eng, Wash. Univ, 46-53; asst. prof. PUB. ADDRESS, SYRACUSE UNIV, 54-64, ASSOC. PROF, 64-, CHMN. DEPT, 65-69. U.S.A, 40-45, Maj. Speech Commun. Asn.(assoc. ed. hist. Brit. pub. address, Quart. J. Speech, 67-68); Royal Hist. Soc. Textual critism of debates in the British House of Commons; Lord North, prime minister, 1770-82. Publ: Lord North's posture of defense, 2/59 & Lord North, a reluctant debater: the making of a cabinet minister, 1754-1767, 2/67, Quart. J. Speech; Tracing the correspondence of George III and Lord North, Manuscripts, fall 62. Add: 416 Hall of Languages, Syracuse University, Syracuse, NY 13210.

SMITH, CHARLES ROGER, b. Omaha, Nebr, Sept. 8, 41; m. 68. ENGLISH & MEDIEVAL LITERATURE. B.A, Univ. Nebr, 65, M.A, 66; Ph.D.(Eng. lit), Princeton, 72. Instr. ENG, COLO. STATE UNIV, 69-72, ASST. PROF, 72- Medieval Acad. Am; AAUP. English Medieval literature. Publ: The lesson of the master: an interpretive note, Stud. Short Fiction, 69. Add: Dept. of English, Colorado State University, Ft. Collins, CO 80521,

SMITH, CHARLES WILLARD, b. Pottstown, Pa, Jan. 24, 99; m. 25; c. 2. ENGLISH. A.B, Princeton, 22, A.M, 25; Ph.D.(Eng), 37. Instr. Eng, biol. & Latin, Pingry Sch, N.J, 22-24; Eng, BUCKNELL UNIV, 25-28, asst. prof, 28-37, assoc. prof, 37-46, prof. Eng. lit, 46-54, John P. Crozer prof, 54-69, chmn. dept. Eng, 54-64, secy. fac, 52-68, EMER. JOHN P. CROZER PROF. ENG. LIT, 69- Dir, Inst. For. Stud, Bucknell Univ, 44-54, chmn. bd. dirs, univ. players, 48-52, consult, Inst. Int. Educ, 50, fac. rep, Bd. Trustees, 53-55; chmn, Comt. Acad. Freedom & Tenure, 62-68; vis. prof. Eng, Susquehanna Univ, 69-74. Lindback Award, 63; Bucknell Class of 56 Lect. Award, 67. U.S.A.R, 22-32, 2nd Lt. MLA; Nat. Asn. For. Stud. Affairs; Shakespeare Asn. Am. Shakespeare; history of the English language; 19th century and recent poetry. Publ: Browning's star imagery. Add: Brown Lane, College Park, Lewisburg, PA 17837.

SMITH, CHARLES WILLIAM, b. Baltimore, Md, Mar. 18, 34; m. 69; c. 3. ENGLISH & AMERICAN LITERATURE. B.S, Frostburg State Teachers Col, 57; M.A, Univ. Md, College Park, 65, Ph.D.(Eng), 71. Teacher Jr. High Sch, Baltimore County, Md, 58-59; comput. programmer, Baltimore & Ohio Railroad, 59-62; grad. asst. ENG, Univ. Md, College Park, 62-64, instr, 64-69; ASST. PROF, U.S. NAVAL ACAD, 69- Instr. report writing, Prince George's County Fire Dept, Md, 68-69. U.S.N.R, 52-60. MLA; Col. Eng. Asn; AAUP. Classical literature; Victorian literature; principles of composition. Add: Dept. of English, United States Naval Academy, Annapolis, MD 21402.

SMITH, DAVID QUINTIN, b. Tiffin, Ohio, Nov. 30, 38; m. 60; c. 2. ENGLISH LITERATURE. A.B, Columbia Univ, 60; M.A, N.Y. Univ, 63; Ph.D.(Eng), Univ. Ill, Urbana, 68. Asst. prof. ENG, UNIV. TOLEDO, 67-73, ASSOC. PROF, 73- MLA; AAUP. English Romanticism; Wordsworth; Blake. Add: Dept. of English, University of Toledo, Toledo, OH 43606.

SMITH, DAVID RODMAN, b. Langdon, N.Dak, May 21, 23; m. 51; c. 3. ENGLISH & AMERICAN LITERATURE. B.A, Pomona Col, 44; M.A, Claremont Grad. Sch, 50, Ph.D, 60. Teacher, High Sch, Calif, 54-55; instr. ENG, Fullerton Jr. Col, 55-57; Pomona Col, 57-58; CALIF. INST. TECHNOL, 58-60, asst. prof, 60-66, ASSOC. PROF, 66-, MASTER STUD. HOUSES, 69-, DIR. BAXTER ART GALLERY, 70- Fulbright fel, France, 61-62; Am. Philos. Soc. grant, 63. U.S.M.C.R, 42-46, Capt. Rise of the international novel; nationalism in American and commonwealth literature; Joseph Conrad. Publ: Conrad's Manifesto: preface to a career, Rosenbach Found, 66; Nostromo and the three sisters, Stud. in Eng. Lit, 62; Plus ça change, Claremont Quart, 63; One word more about the nigger of the Narcissus,

Nineteenth Century Fiction, 68. Add: Division of Humanities & Social Sciences, California Institute of Technology, 1201 E. California Blvd, Pasadena, CA 91109.

SMITH, DENZELL STEWART, b. New Richmond, Wis, Mar. 30, 29; m. 52; c. 2. ENGLISH. B.A, Univ. Minn, 50, M.A, 54; M.A, 58, Ph.D.(Eng), 65; Univ. Oslo, 54-55. Asst. prof. ENG, Univ. Md, College Park, 64-68, ASSOC. PROF, 68-72; IDAHO STATE UNIV, 72- Danforth assoc, 66- Excellence in Teaching Award, Univ. Md, 66. U.S.M.C, 51-52, Sgt. MLA (mem. Eng. sect, Int. Bibliog. Comt, 64-70, sect. head, 67-70). English Renaissance drama; bibliography and Scandinavian literature. Publ: Co-ed, The predecessors of Shakespeare: a survey and bibliography of recent studies in English Renaissance drama, Univ. Nebr, 73; auth, The credibility of the wooing of Anne in Richard III, Papers on Lang. & Lit, 71; Prospero as a Shaman, Rendezvous, 72; co-auth, Other dramatists, In: The predecessors of Shakespeare: a survey and bibliography of recent studies in English Renaissance drama, Univ. Nebr, 73; plus others. Add: Dept. of English, Idaho State University, Pocatello, ID 83201.

SMITH, DON NOEL, b. Big Rock, Va, Aug. 12, 37; m. 67; c. 2. ENGLISH. B.A, Berea Col, 62; M.A, Ohio Univ, 63; Ph.D.(Eng), Univ. Mich, Ann Arbor, 70. Instr. ENG, Ohio Univ, 63-64; lectr, Univ. Md, Abroad, 64-67; asst. prof, Univ. Wis-Madison, 70-71; PROF. & HEAD DEPT, FROSTBURG STATE COL, 71- MLA; AAUP. American literature, modern. Publ: The structural scheme of Gulliver's travels, Marab, 65; Musical form and principles in the scheme of Ulysses, Twentieth-Century Lit, 72; The artistry of John Donne's Devotions, Univ. Dayton Rev, 73. Add: Dept. of English, Frostburg State College, Frostburg, MD 21532.

SMITH, DONAL IAN BRICE, b. Auckland, N.Z, Feb. 4, 34; m. 59. ENGLISH. B.A, Univ. Auckland, 55, M.A, 56; D.Phil, Oxford, 63. Jr. lectr. ENG, Univ. Auckland, 56; lectr, UNIV. TORONTO, 60-63, asst. prof, 63-68, assoc. prof, 68-72, PROF, 72- Can. Counc. fel, 65-66; Nuffield Found. travel award, 72. Seventeenth century English literature; editing. Publ: Ed, Editing eighteenth century texts, Univ. Toronto, 68, The rhearsal transpos'd and the rehearsal transpos'd the second part, Clarendon, 71 & Editing seventeenth century prose, Hakkert, Toronto, 72; auth, Marvell's political beliefs, Univ. Toronto Quart, 66; Andrew Marvell, In: English poetry, select bibliographical guides, Oxford Univ, 71. Add: Dept. of English, University College, University of Toronto, Toronto, Ont, Can.

SMITH, DONALD GEORGE, b. Ottawa, Can, Mar. 20, 20. ENGLISH. B.A, McGill Univ, 50; Angier Duke Mem. fel, Duke Univ, 51-52, Ph.D.(Eng), 56. Instr. ENG, W.Va. Univ, 53-55; Univ. Calif, Santa Barbara, 55; asst. prof, Upsala Col, 60-62, assoc. prof, 62-65, prof. & chmn. dept, 65-69; prof, Willamette Univ, 69-73. R.C.N, 40-45. MLA; Asn. Depts. Eng; Col. Eng. Asn; Am. Theatre Asn. Italian Renaissance; 17th century English literature. Add: 831 St. Philip St, New Orleans, LA 70116.

SMITH, DONALD KLIESE, b. Belgrade, Nebr, Nov. 29, 15; m. 41; c. 3. SPEECH. B.A, Kearney State Teachers Col, 36; Ph.M, Univ. Wis, 41, Ph.D.(speech), 51. Teacher high sch, Nebr, 36-38, prin, 38-39; teacher, Wis, 39-42; instr. educ, Univ. Wis, 46-49; lectr. speech, Univ. Minn, 49-50, asst. prof, 50-53, assoc. prof, 53-58, PROF, 58-72, chmn. dept. speech & theatre arts, 59-63, asst. v.pres. acad. admin, 63-66, assoc. v.pres, 66-68, v.pres. admin, 68-72; resident dir. Indonesian Higher Educ. Proj, Mid-west. Univ. Consortium Int. Activities, 72-73; PROF. COMMUN. ARTS, UNIV. WIS-MADISON, 73-; V.PRES. ACAD. AFFAIRS, UNIV. WIS. SYST, 73- A.U.S, 43-46, Capt. Speech Commun. Asn; NCTE; Cent. States Speech Asn.(pres, 60-61). American public address; rhetorical theory; speech pedagogy. Publ: Co-auth, Teaching of speech, 52, Speaking and listening, 56, Prentice Hall & Discussion, Macmillan, 56; auth, Man speaking: a rhetoric of public speech, Dodd, 69. Add: 1600 Van Hise Hall, University of Wisconsin-Madison, Madison, WI 53706.

SMITH, DOROTHY ANITA, O.P, b. Providence, R.I, Apr. 2, 27. WORLD & ENGLISH LITERATURE. B.S, Fordham Univ, 57; M.A, St. John's Univ. (N.Y), 61, Ph.D.(Eng), 70. ASSOC. PROF. ENG, DOM. COL, BLAUVELT, 61-, CHMN. DIV. HUMANITIES, 72-, chmn. dept. Eng, 69-71. MLA; NCTE; Col. Eng. Asn. Greek and Roman classics; British poetry. Publ: R.S. Thomas: the poet as querulous, Univ. Microfilms, 70. Add: Div. of Humanities, Dominican College, Western Highway, Blauvelt, NY 10913.

SMITH, DOROTHY ANN, R.S.M, b. Burt, N.Y, Feb. 7, 34. ENGLISH. B.A, Nazareth Col. Rochester, 57; M.A, Canisius Col, 65. Teacher Eng, Mt. Mercy Acad, Buffalo, N.Y, 58-67; chmn. dept, Trocaire Col, 67-70; ASST. PRIN, MT. MERCY ACAD, 70- Chmn. relig. life, Sisters Assembly of Buffalo, 70-73. Nat. Asn. Sec. Sch. Prin. Organizational development; communications. Publ: Something solid as a spirit (poetry), Pageant, 69. Add: 373 Perry St, Buffalo, NY 14204.

SMITH, E. DEBS, b. Jester, Okla, Dec. 16, 14; m. 38; c. 1. ENGLISH. B.S, Abilene Christian Col, 41; M.A, Univ. Denver, 43, Ph.D, 52. Dir. & chmn. relig, EAST. N.MEX. UNIV, 47-51, PROF. ENG, 52-, CHMN. DEPT. ENG. & JOUR, 61- West. Writers Am; NCTE.(dir, 62-). Southwest literature; general semantics. Add: Dept. of English, Eastern New Mexico University, Portales, NM 88130.

SMITH, E. MARCEL, b. Mobile, Ala, Oct. 1, 34; m. 57; c. 2. ENGLISH. B.A, Univ. Ala, 55, M.A, 56, Ph.D.(Eng), 66. Instr. ENG, Va. Polytech. Inst, 56-57; Pensacola Jr. Col, 57-61; ASST. PROF, UNIV. ALA, 66- Consult. written commun, Commun. Skills Co, Huntsville, Ala, 67- MLA; Ling. Soc. Am. Nineteenth century English literature; contemporary British and American verse; linguistics. Publ: Three poems, Arlington Quart, winter 67. Add: Dept. of English, University of Alabama, University, AL 35486.

SMITH, ELDEN T, b. Elyria, Ohio, Nov. 7, 10; m, 37; c. 2. SPEECH, DRAMA. A.B, Ohio Wesleyan Univ, 32; A.M, West. Reserve Univ, 33, scholar, 45-47, Nat. Theatre Conf. fel, 46-47, Ph.D, 48; hon. L.H.D, Ohio Univ, 67, Findlay Col, 70, Chapman Col, 72; hon. LL.D, Ohio North. Univ, 72. Instr. speech & drama, Bowling Green State Univ, 40-42, asst. prof, 42-45, assoc. prof, 45-48, prof, 48-61, chmn. dept, 47-55; provost, Ohio Wesleyan Univ, 61-62, pres, 62-68; EXEC. ASSOC, ASN. AM. COLS, 69- Exec. secy, Nat. Counc. Independent Cols. & Univs, 69- Theater history; George Pierce Baker and the Harvard forty-seven work shop; a handbook of verbs. Add: Association of American Colleges, 1818 R St. N.W, Washington, DC 20009.

SMITH, ELSDON COLES, b. Virginia, Ill, Jan. 25, 03; m. 33; c. 1. ONOMASTICS. B.S, Univ. Ill, 25; LL.B, Harvard, 30. Pvt. law pract, 30-; instr, Chicago Law Sch, 33-35; mem, Int. Comt. Onomastic Sci, 51- Am. Name Soc.(pres, 51-54); Am. Dialect Soc; Am. Folklore Soc; MLA; Eng. Place-Name Soc; Am. Bar Asn. Personal names. Publ: Bibliography of personal names, N.Y. Pub. Libr, 50; The story of our names, 50 & Dictionary of American family names, 56, Harper & Bros; Treasury of name lore, 67 & New dictionary of American family names, 72, Harper; American surnames, Chilton, 69. Add: 8001 Lockwood Ave, Skokie, IL 60076.

SMITH, ELTON E, b. New York, N.Y, Nov. 9, 15; m. 42; c. 3. ENGLISH, BIBLE. B.S, N.Y. Univ, 37; Harvard Divinity Sch, 38-39; B.D, Andover Newton Theol. Sch, 40; M.A, Syracuse Univ, 59, fel, 60-61, Ph.D, 61; hon. D.D, Linfield Col, 56. Pastor, Mass, Ore. & N.Y, 40-61; asst. prof. Eng. & Bible, UNIV. S.FLA, TAMPA, 61-64, assoc. prof. ENG, BIBLE & HUMANITIES, 64-66, PROF, 67- Fulbright-Hays lectr, Univ. Algiers, 70-71. MLA; S.Atlantic Mod. Lang. Asn; Conf. Christianity & Lit.(v.pres, 73-). The Biblical doctrine of the Kingdom of God; 18th and 19th century British literature; critical study of the novels and plays of Charles Reade. Publ: The two voices: a Tennyson study, Univ. Nebr, 64; co-auth, William Godwin: a critical study of his works, 65 & auth, Louis MacNeice: a critical study, 70, Brit. Auth. Ser, Twayne; The inescapable themes, 3/66 & A generation of existential men?, 3/67, Watchman Exam; Tennyson criticism, Victorian Newslett, spring 67. Add: Div. of Language Literature, University of South Florida, Tampa, FL 33620.

SMITH, ESTHER MARIAN GREENWELL, b. Portland, Ore, Oct. 22, 14; m. 42; c. 3. VICTORIAN ENGLISH, EDUCATION. B.A, Linfield Col, 37, M.Ed, 55; Andover-Newton Theol. Sch, 40-42; summers, Univ. Syracuse, 60, 61; Ph.D.(Eng), Univ. Fla, 72. Teacher, Dallas High Sch, Ore, 37-40; instr. Eng, Portland State Col, 54-57; teacher, North High Sch, Syracuse, N.Y, 57-58; W.Genessee High Sch, Camillus, N.Y, 58-61; instr. Eng. educ, Fla. South. Col, 61-66; PROF. ENG, POLK COMMUNITY COL, 66- Kipling Soc; MLA. Rudyard Kipling; science fiction. Publ: Co-auth, William Godwin, Twayne, 65; auth, Polk Junior College style manual for research and term papers, Polk Community Col, 70; From despair to dedication (youth fiction), 12/57 & Curriculum material for intermediates-seniors, 1/58, 2/58, 4/58, 11/58, Baptist Leader; Fog (children's fiction), Junior, 65. Add: 402 W. Oak Dr, Lakeland, FL 33803.

SMITH, F. LESLIE, b. Orlando, Fla, Jan. 19, 39; m. 61; c. 1. MASS COMMUNICATION. B.S, Univ. Fla, 61; M.A, Ohio Univ, 64; Ph.D.(commun), Fla. State Univ, 72. Instr. radio-TV, St. Petersburg Jr. Col, 64-67; ASST. PROF. commun. arts, Univ. W. Fla, 67-70; RADIO-TV-FILM, N. TEX. STATE UNIV, 72- Sig.C, U.S.A, 61-63, Res, 63-72, Capt. AAUP; Broadcast Educ. Asn. Normative behavior in broadcast news; history of radio and TV; education for broadcasting. Publ: Education for broadcasting: 1929-1963, J. Broadcasting, 11/64; The selling of the Pentagon: case study of a controversy, In: Mass news, Prentice-Hall, 73; co-auth, Perceived ethicality of some TV news production techniques by a sample of Florida legislators, Speech Monogr, 11/73. Add: Div. of Radio-TV-Film, North Texas State University, Denton, TX 76203.

SMITH, FRANCIS J, S.J, b. Lorain, Ohio, May 22, 20. LITERARY CRITICISM. Litt.B, Xavier Univ.(Ohio), 42; M.A, Loyola Univ.(Ill), 46; S.T.L, W.Baden Col, 53; A.M, Oxford, 60. Instr. Eng. & Latin, High Sch, Univ. Detroit, 46-49, instr. ENG, univ, 58-60, asst. prof, Colombiere Col, 60-63; JOHN CARROLL UNIV, 63-67, assoc. prof, 67-72, PROF, 72- MLA. T.S. Eliot; Chaucer; modern fiction. Publ: O'Connor's religious viewpoint in The violent bear it away, Renascence, winter 70; Mirth and marriage in The parlement of foules, Forum, winter 73. Add: Dept. of English, Rodman Hall, John Carroll University, Cleveland, OH 44118.

SMITH, FREDERIK NORTHROP, b. Baltimore, Md, Jan. 26, 40. ENGLISH & AMERICAN LITERATURE. B.A, Loyola Col.(Md), 62; M.A, Univ. Va, 64, Ph.D.(Eng), 70. ASST. PROF. ENG, CASE WEST. RESERVE UNIV, 67- MLA; Am. Soc. 18th Century Stud. Jonathan Swift; stylistics; contemporary fiction and drama. Publ: Dramatic elements in Swift's Journal to Stella, 18th Century Stud, summer 68; Uncertainty in Pinter: The dwarfs, Theatre Annual, 70; The epistemology of fictional failure: Swift's Tale of a tub and Beckett's Watt, Tex. Stud. in Lit. & Lang, winter 74. Add: Dept. of English, Case Western Reserve University, Cleveland, OH 44106.

SMITH, FRELLSEN FLETCHER, b. Winn Parish, La, Jan. 27, 08; m. 34; c. 5. ENGLISH. A.B, La. Polytech. Inst, 28; A.M, Univ. Tex, 30; Harvard, 30-31; Univ. Okla, 41; Univ. Denver, 48, 53; Univ. Minn, 57. Instr, High Sch, La, 27-28, Ouachita Jr. Col, 31-36; head dept. Eng, Northeast Ctr, La. State Univ, 36-38; assoc. prof, La. Tech Univ, 38-48, prof, 48-72; RETIRED. Col. Eng. Asn; S.Cent. Mod. Lang. Asn. Add: 1007 Nelson St, Ruston, LA 71270.

SMITH, GARLAND GARVEY, b. Wilmore, Ky, Aug. 29, 01; m. 40; c. 2. OLD & MIDDLE ENGLISH. B.M, South. Col.(Fla), 20; A.B, Centenary Col. La, 21; fel, South. Methodist Univ, 22-23, A.M, 23; A.M, Harvard, 25, Ph.D, 31. Asst. Latin & Greek, Centenary Col. La, 20-21; instr. Eng. South. Methodist Univ, 23-24, asst. prof, 25-28; Emory Univ, 30-37, assoc. prof, 37-42, prof, 42-69, dir. grad. stud, 45-53; PROF. ENG, MERCER UNIV, ATLANTA, 69- MLA; S.Atlantic Mod. Lang. Asn; AAUP. Philology; Anglo-Saxon nominal compounds. Publ: Ed, Thomas Holcroft's plain and succinct narrative of the Gordon riots. Add: 516 Durand Dr. N.E, Atlanta, GA 30307.

SMITH, GAYLE S, b. Chicago, Ill, Jan. 12, 23; m. 44, 71; c. 2. ENGLISH. Ph.B, Univ. Chicago, 46; B.S, Iowa State Col, 48; M.A, Cornell Univ, 51, Ph.D, 57. Instr. ENG, UNIV. MD, COLLEGE PARK, 53-57, asst. prof, 57-63, ASSOC. PROF, 63-, dir. gen. educ. prog, 65-68. Am. Field Serv, 42-43; U.S.A, 43-45. MLA. English romantic literature; English lyric poetry, 18th to 19th century. Add: Dept. of English, University of Maryland, College Park, MD 20742.

SMITH, GEORGE WILLIAM, JR, b. Hanover, N.H, Aug. 19, 24. ENGLISH. A.B, Williams Col, 48; A.M, Harvard, 50, fel, 53-54, Ph.D, 58. Asst. Eng, Middlebury Col, 52-53; instr, Vanderbilt Univ, 56-57; Univ. Ky, 58-60; asst. prof, Boston Col, 60-66; res. & writing, 66-70; asst. prof, Bridgewater State Col, 70-73; RETIRED. U.S.A, 42-46. Charles Dickens; English novel; ballads. Add: Highland Park Terrace, White River Junction, VT 05001.

SMITH, GERALD ALFRED, b. Canandaigua, N.Y, Mar. 16, 21; m. 45; c. 7. ENGLISH LITERATURE. A.B, Univ. Notre Dame, 43; M.A, Univ. Rochester, 47; Pres. scholar, Johns Hopkins Univ, 49-51, Ph.D, 57. Instr. ENG, Univ. Rochester, 47-48, asst. prof, 57-58; jr. instr, Johns Hopkins Univ, 48-51; instr, Univ. Md, 51-55; asst. prof, Canisius Col, 55-57; assoc. prof, STATE UNIV. N.Y. COL. GENESEO, 58-60, PROF, 60-, chmn. div. humanities, 66-69. Summer res. fels, Res. Found. State Univ. N.Y, 60-61, 63, spec. consult, 72-73, mem, univ. awards comt, State Univ. N.Y, 72-75. U.S.N, 42-46, Lt. MLA; Malone Soc; Shakespeare Asn. Am; AAUP. Renaissance drama; Shakespeare. Publ: Ed, John Marston's The fawn, Univ. Nebr, 65; auth, T.S. Eliot's love song..., Explicator, 10/62; Death of King Lear, Mod. Lang. Notes, 6/55. Add: Dept. of English, State University of New York College at Geneseo, Geneseo, NY 14454.

SMITH, GORDON CALDECOTT, b. Toronto, Ont, Sept. 15, 10; nat; m. 46. SPEECH. B.A, Univ. West. Ont, 37; B.A, Roosevelt Univ, 49; M.A, Univ. Kans, 50; Ph.D.(rhetoric), Univ. Utah, 59. Instr. Eng, Ore. State Col, 46; teacher, High Sch, Wash, 46-47; asst. speech, Univ. Utah, 52; instr. speech & radio, N.Mex. Highlands Univ, 54-55; commun. skills, Mich. State Univ, 55-59, asst. prof. Am. thought & lang, 59-68, assoc. prof, 68-71, prof, 71-73; RETIRED. Med.C, U.S.A, 42-45. History of oratory; rhetorical theory; 19th century prose. Add: 1668 Linden St, East Lansing, MI 48823.

SMITH, GORDON ROSS, b. N.J, May 23, 17; m. 48; c. 2. ENGLISH. B.S, Columbia Univ, 48, M.A, 49; Ph.D, Pa. State Univ, 56. Instr, Waynesburg Col, 49-50; from instr. to prof. ENG, Pa. State Univ, 50-66; PROF, TEMPLE UNIV, 66-, chmn. grad. Eng, 67-70. Folger Shakespeare Libr. fel, 58; Fulbright lectr, Royal Univ. Malta, 62-63. U.S.A, 43-46. MLA (assoc. bibliogr, 59-, head gen. sect. annual bibliog, 66-69). Publ: A classified Shakespeare bibliography, 1936-1958, 63 & ed, Essays on Shakespeare, 65, Pa. State Univ; auth, Brutus, virtue, and will, Shakespeare Quart, 59; Authoritarian patterns in Shakespeare's Coriolanus, Lit. & Psychol, 59; Isabella and Elbow in varying contexts of interpretation, J. Gen. Educ, 65. Add: Dept. of English, Temple University, Philadelphia, PA 19122.

SMITH, GROVER C, b. Atlanta, Ga, Sept. 6, 23. ENGLISH. A.B, Columbia Univ, 44, M.A, 45, Proudfit fel, 45-46, Ph.D, 50. Instr. ENG, Rutgers Univ, 46-48; Yale, 48-52; DUKE UNIV, 52-55, asst. prof, 55-61, assoc. prof, 61-66, PROF, 66- Guggenheim fel, 58; Am. Counc. Learned Soc. & Am. Philos. Soc. grant, 65-66. Poetry Chap-Book Award, Poetry Soc. Am, 57. A.U.S, 43. Twentieth century literature. Publ: T.S. Eliot's poetry and plays: a study in sources and meaning, Univ. Chicago, 56, rev. ed, 74; ed, Josiah Royce's seminar, 1913-1914, Rutgers Univ, 63; ed, Letters of Aldous Huxley, Chatto and Windus, London, 69 & Harper, 70; auth, Archibald MacLeish, Univ. Minn, 71; Ford Madox Ford, Columbia Univ, 72; The naked new-born babe in Macbeth: some iconographical evidence, Renaissance Papers 1964, 65; Yeats, Gogarty and the Leap Castle ghost, In: Modern Irish literature: essays in honor of William York Tindall, Iona Col, 72; plus one other. Add: Box 4052, Duke Sta, Durham, NC 27706.

SMITH, HALLETT DARIUS, b. Chattanooga, Tenn, Aug. 15, 07; m. 31; c. 2. ENGLISH LITERATURE. A.B, Univ. Colo, Boulder, 28, hon. L.H.D, 68; Ph.D, Yale, 34. Instr. ENG, Williams Col.(Mass), 31-36, asst. prof, 36-39; assoc. prof, 39-45, PROF, 45-49; CALIF. INST. TECHNOL, 49-; SR. RES. ASSOC. ENG. LIT, HENRY E. HUNTINGTON LIBR, SAN MARINO, 70- Guggenheim fel, 47-48; chmn. div. humanities. Calif. Inst. Technol, 49-70. MLA; Malone Soc; Shakespeare Asn. Am; Renaissance Eng. Text Soc. Elizabethan poetry, Harvard, ed, Twentieth century interpretations of The tempest, Prentice-Hall, 70; auth, Shakespeare's romances, Huntington, 72. Add: 1455 S. Marengo Ave, Pasadena, CA 91106.

SMITH, HARRIS GORDON, b. Mt. Pulaski, Ill, Oct. 26, 21; m. 52; c. 1. JOURNALISM. B.S, Univ. Ill, Urbana, 50, M.S, 52. Instr. JOUR, Univ. Kans, 52-53; asst. prof, BOSTON UNIV, 57-65, ASSOC. PROF, 65- U.S.M.C, 41-46, Maj. Photo-journalism. Add: Division of Journalism, School of Public Communication, Boston University, 640 Commonwealth Ave, Boston, MA 02215.

SMITH, HARRY WILLARD, JR, b. Alexandria, La, July 10, 32; m. 61; c. 2. THEATRE. B.A, La. Col, 59; M.A, Tulane Univ, 60, Ph.D.(theatre), 65. Instr. speech, Univ. Wyo, 60-61; dramatic art, Univ. Calif, Berkeley, 61-63; assoc. prof. Eng. & speech, Southeast. La. Col, 65-69; ASSOC. PROF. THEATRE, FLA. TECHNOL. UNIV, 69-, ASST. DEAN COL. HUMANITIES & FINE ARTS, 73- Am. Theatre Asn. Film; film history; film aesthetics. Publ: Dir, Mine: a film about property, 72 & Sewer line inspection (indust. film), 73; auth, Synge's playboy and the proximity of violence, Quart. J. Speech, 12/69. Add: College of Humanities & Fine Arts, Florida Technological University, Alafaya Trail, Orlando, FL 32816.

SMITH, HELEN KATHERINE, b. Riverside, Calif, Apr. 28, 14. READING. B.Ed, Ill. State Univ, 35; M.A, Univ. Colo, 40; scholar. & Ph.D.(educ, reading), Univ. Chicago, 65. Teacher, reading consult. high schs, Ill, 36-57; reading consult, Bloom Twp. High Sch, 58-59; diagnostician reading clinic, Univ. Chicago, 57-58, res. asst, 58-59, instr. reading, 59-61, asst. prof. & dir. reading clinic, 61-68; assoc. prof. EDUC. & READING, Univ. Ill, Chicago, 68-69; PROF, UNIV. MIAMI, 69- Consult, Atlanta Univ. Reading Prog, 62-; mem. adv. bd, J. Reading & Optometric Forum, 67-69. Nat. Conf. Res. Eng; Int. Reading Asn.(dissertation reading award, 65; chmn. outstanding dissertation awards comt, 67-68); Am. Educ. Res. Asn; NCTE. Reading especially high school and remedial; English. Publ: Ed, Perception and reading, 68 & Meeting individual needs in reading, 71, Int. Reading Asn; co-ed, Clinical studies in reading, III, Univ. Chicago, 68; auth, The development of effective, flexible readers, In: New developments in reading, Univ. Chicago, 65; Responses of good and poor readers when asked to read for different purposes, Reading Res. Quart, fall 67. Add: School of Education, University of Miami, Coral Gables, FL 33124.

SMITH, HELENA M, b. Livermore, Pa, Apr. 25, 24. ENGLISH. B.S. in Ed, Ind. State Col, 47; M.Ed, Pa. State Univ, 51, Ph.D, 59. Teacher ENG, high sch, Pa, 47-53; supvr. stud. teachers, Mansfield State Col, 53-54, asst. prof, 54-57; assoc. prof, INDIANA UNIV. PA, 58-60, PROF, 60- NCTE; MLA. Negro characterization in the American novel. Add: Dept. of English, Indiana University of Pennsylvania, Indiana, PA 15701.

SMITH, HENRY NASH, b. Dallas, Tex, Sept. 29, 06; m. 36; c. 3. AMERICAN LITERATURE. A.B, South. Methodist Univ, 25, D.Litt, 66; A.M. Harvard, 29, Ph.D, 40; LL.D, Colo. State Univ, 70. From instr. to assoc. prof. Eng, South. Methodist Univ, 27-41; PROF. Eng. & hist, Univ. Tex, 41-47; ENG, Univ. Minn, 47-53; UNIV. CALIF, BERKELEY, 53-, chmn. dept. Eng, 57-61, prof. arts & sci, 68-69. Vis. lectr, Harvard, 45-46; Huntington Libr. fel, 46-47; lit. ed, Mark Twain Estate, 53-64; fel, Ctr. Advan. Stud. Behav. Sci, Stanford Univ, 60-61; mem. bd. dir, Am. Counc. Learned Soc, 62-67. MLA (v.pres, 66-68, pres, 69). Publ: Virgin land: the American West as symbol and myth, Harvard, 50 & Vintage, 57; ed, Mark Twain of the enterprise, Univ. Calif, 57; auth, Mark Twain: the development of a writer, Harvard, 62 & Atheneum, 67; co-ed, Mark Twain-Howells letters, Harvard, 2 vols, 62; auth, Mark Twain's Fable of progress, Rutgers Univ, 64; ed, Popular culture and industrialism, 1865-1890, Anchor, 67. Add: Dept. of English, University of California, Berkeley, CA 94720.

SMITH, HERBERT F, b. Elmira, N.Y, June 18, 33; m. 56; c. 2. LITERATURE. A.B, Boston Univ, 55, A.M, 56; Ph.D.(Eng), Rutgers Univ, 61. From instr. to asst. prof. ENG, Univ. Wis, Madison, 61-65, ASSOC. PROF, 65-69; UNIV. VICTORIA (B.C), 69- Nat. Trust Hist. Preserv. fel, summer 59; Fulbright lectr. Am. lit, Univ. Aix-Marseilles, 63-64. MLA. American literature of the 19th century; French literature of the 18th century. Publ: John Muir, 65 & Richard Watson Gilder, 69, Twayne; Literary criticism of James Russell Lowell, Nebraska, 69; Therese the philosopher, Grove, 70; Barth's endless road, Critique, 63; Melville's master in chancery, Am. Quart, winter 65; Usher's madness and Poe's organicism, Am. Lit, 11/67. Add: Dept. of English, University of Victoria, Victoria, B.C, Can.

SMITH, HUBERT WAYNE, b. Manning, Kans, Sept. 22, 06; m. 30; c. 1. AMERICAN LITERATURE. A.B, Park Col, 28; State Univ. Iowa, 29; M.S, Northwest. Univ, 33; Ph.D, Univ. Pa, 49. Ed, W.F. Hall Printing Co, Chicago, Ill, 29-32; instr. high sch, Ind, 33-35; Ill, 35-36; asst. prof. ENG, Ind. State Teachers Col, 36-43; Univ. Denver, 46-47; from assoc. prof. to prof, UTAH STATE UNIV, 47-71, EMER. PROF, 71- U.S.N, 43-45, Lt. Comdr. MLA; NCTE; Col. Eng. Asn. Criticism of American fiction; Samuel Croxall; agricultural journalism. Publ: Co-auth, Communication skills: the basic course, Stacey, 58. Add: Dept. of English, Utah State University, Logan, UT 84321.

SMITH, J. HAROLD, b. West Liberty, Ohio, Mar. 24, 08. ENGLISH. A.B, Goshen Col, 32; State Univ. Iowa, 34; A.M, Univ. Kans, 41; Ph.D, Univ. Wis, 55. From teacher to prof. & dean men, Hesston Col, 34-44; asst, Univ. Wis, 46-49; assoc. prof. ENG, Goshen Col, 49-54; exten, Univ. Wis, 54-56; from asst. prof. to assoc. prof, CENT. MICH. UNIV, 56-65, PROF, 65- NCTE; Col. Eng. Asn. American literature. Publ: Heredity and environment in Mark Twain; Mark Twain: rebel pilgrim, Heath Cote, 73; Women in Mark Twain's world, Carlton, 73. Add: Box 74, Anspach Hall, Central Michigan University, Mt. Pleasant, MI 48858.

SMITH, JACK ALAN, b. Headland, Ala, May 18, 32; m. 57; c. 2. OLD ENGLISH LITERATURE & LINGUISTICS. B.S, Troy State Col, 53; M.A, Auburn Univ, 62, fel, 63-64, Ph.D.(Eng), 69. Teacher art & Eng, Bellingrath Jr. High Sch, Montgomery, Ala, 55-58; Key West High Sch, Fla, 58-63; instr. Eng, Auburn Univ, 64-66; asst. prof, UNIV. SOUTH. MISS, 66-69, assoc. prof, 69-71, PROF. ENG. & ADMIN. ASST. TO DEAN UNIV, 71- Ed, Miss. Folklore Register, 68- U.S.A.F, 53-55. Ling. Soc. Am; Am. Dialect Soc; Mediaeval Acad. Am; Am. Name Soc. Add: Dept. of English, University of Southern Mississippi, Southern Sta. Box 418, Hattiesburg, MS 39401.

SMITH, JAMES FREDERICK, JR, b. Richmond, Va, June 19, 46; m. 70; c. 1. AMERICAN LITERATURE. A.B, Boston Col, 68; M.A, Pa. State Univ, 69, Ph.D.(Eng), 72. ASST. PROF. ENG, PA. STATE UNIV, 71- MLA; Northeast. Mod. Lang. Asn. Twentieth century American fiction; American studies. Publ: A stereotyped archetype: E.E. Cummings' Jean Le Nègre, Stud. Am. Fiction, 73. Add: 2816 Carnation Ave, Willow Grove, PA 19090.

SMITH, JAMES PENNY, b. Memphis, Tenn, May 10, 35. MODERN ENGLISH & AMERICAN LITERATURE. B.A, Southwest. at Memphis, 57; M.A, Univ. N.C, 59, Ph.D.(Eng), 68. Instr. ENG, GA. INST. TECHNOL, 60-65, asst. prof, 65-69, ASSOC. PROF, 69- Res, Ga. Tech Found, summer 72; mem. summer sem. col. teachers, Nat. Endowment for Humanities, 73. MLA; S.Atlantic Mod. Lang. Asn; Soc. Stud. South. Lit. James Joyce; Frances Newman; Peter Taylor. Publ: Narration and theme in Taylor's A woman of means, 68 & A Peter Taylor checklist, 68, Critique. Add: Dept. of English, Georgia Institute of Technology, Atlanta, GA 30332.

SMITH, JAMES STEEL, b. St. Johns, P.Q, Jan. 30, 13; m. 42; c. 1. ENGLISH, POPULAR CULTURE. B.A, Univ. Calif, Berkeley, 34, M.A, 35, Ph.D.(Eng), 52. Asst. prof. ENG, Calif. State Polytech. Col, 46-54; Los Angeles State Col, 54-57; assoc. prof, CALIF. STATE UNIV, NORTHRIDGE, 57-60, PROF, 60-, fac. res. grant, summer, 64. Mem. ed. bd, Conf. Col. Compos. & Commun, 61-64. U.S.A, 42-46, S/Sgt. MLA; Col. Eng. Asn. Esthetic problems in museum display; children's literature. Publ: Co-ed, Think before you write, 51 & Thought and statement, 55, 60, Harcourt; auth, A critical approach to children's literature, McGraw, 67; Life looks at literature, Am. Scholar, winter 57-58; Visual criticism: a new medium for critical comment, Criticism, summer 62; The beauty of collected things: the museum as critic, Antioch Rev, winter 66-67; plus others. Add: Dept. of English, California State University, Northridge, 18111 Nordhoff St, Northridge, CA 91324.

SMITH, JOHN BRISTOW, b. Columbia, S.C, Mar. 29, 40; m. 63; c. 1. MODERN BRITISH & AMERICAN LITERATURE, COMPUTER STUDIES OF LANGUAGE. B.A, Univ. of the South, 62; M.A, Univ. S.C, 64; Ph.D.(Eng), Univ. N.C, 70. ASST. PROF. ENG, PA. STATE UNIV, UNIVERSITY PARK, 70-, RES.

CONSULT, COMPUT. CTR, 70- Nat. Sci. Found. Inst. grant, 71-72; Am. Counc. Learned Soc. grant, 73. MLA (chmn. sem. comput. stud. lang. & lit, 73); Midwest Mod. Lang. Asn; Asn. Comput. Mach; Asn. Lit. & Ling. Comput. Computer studies of language and literature; James Joyce. Publ: Contrib, a design for a general statistical analyzer for natural language texts, In: Automated language analysis, Univ. N.C, 70; auth, RATS: a middle level text utility system, Comput. & Humanities, 72; Image and imagery in Joyce's Portrait, In: Directions in literary criticism, Pa. State Univ, 73; plus seven others. Add: Dept. of English, Pennsylvania State University, University Park, PA 16802.

SMITH, JOHN HAZEL, b. Harrisburg, Ill, Jan. 9, 28; m. 51; c. 3. ENGLISH. A.B, Univ. Ill, 49, M.A, 51, Ph.D, 58; Univ. Ill. fel. to Brit. Mus, 56-57. Asst, Univ. Ill, 49-56; instr. ENG, Wayne State Univ, 57-61; asst. prof, Marquette Univ, 61-64. ASSOC. PROF, 64-66; BRANDEIS UNIV, 66- Huntington Libr. fel, summer 64; vis. assoc. prof, Brandeis Univ, 65-66; Guggenheim Found. fel, 66-67; vis. prof, Clark Univ, summer 68; Univ. Ill, 68-69. Renaissance Soc. Am; Malone Soc; Renaissance Eng. Text Soc. Renaissance drama: textual and critical studies; neo-Latin literature. Publ: A humanist's Trew imitation: a critical edition and translation of Thomas Watson's Absalom, Univ. Ill, 63; George Chapman: The gentlemen usher, Univ. Nebr, 69; Two Latin comedies by John Foxe the martyrologist, Cornell Univ, 73; Shylock: devil incarnation or poor man wronged?, J. Eng. & Ger. Philol, 61; The composition of the quarto of Much ado about nothing, Stud. Bibliog, 63; The genesis of the Strozza subplot in George Chapman's The gentleman usher, PMLA, 10/68. Add: Dept. of English, Brandeis University, Waltham, MA 02154.

SMITH, JOHN WARREN, b. Navasota, Tex, Feb. 28, 28; m. 59; c. 2. ENGLISH & AMERICAN LITERATURE. B.A, Sam Houston State Col, 48; M.A, Columbia Univ, 49; Univ. Mich, 50-51; summer, Univ. Houston, 53; Ph.D.(Eng), Univ. Tex, 57. Instr, Sul Ross State Col, summer 49; ENG, Univ. Tex, 56-57; asst. prof, Tex. Christian Univ, 57-69, acting assoc. dean, AddRan Col. Arts & Sci, 57-58, 69; ASSOC. PROF, W.TEX. STATE UNIV, 69- U.S.A, 50-52. S.Cent. Mod. Lang. Asn; Thoreau Soc; Am. Stud. Asn. Christian science; transcendentalism; English Romanticism. Publ: Coauth, Patterns for prose writing, Scott, 69. Add: Dept. of English, West Texas State University, Canyon, TX 79016.

SMITH, JOSEPH PERCY, b. Canora, Sask, Mar. 22, 14; m. 42; c. 4. ENGLISH. B.A, Univ. Sask, 40, M.A, 45; fel, Univ. Calif, Berkeley, 47-48, Ph.D.(Eng), 49; hon. D.Lit, Carleton Univ, 70. Instr. Eng, Univ. Sask, 45-46; teaching asst, Univ. Calif, Berkeley, 46-47; asst. prof, Univ. Sask, 48-51, assoc. prof, 51-58, prof, 58-64; exec. secy, Can. Asn. Univ. Teachers, 64-69; Nuffield Found. traveling fel, 69-70; PROF. ENG. & ACAD. V.PRES, UNIV. GUELPH, 70- Can. Counc. sr. fel, 60-61. R.C.A.F, 42-45. Can. Soc. Stud. Higher Educ.(mem. ed. bd, 70-); Asn. Can. Univ. Teachers Eng; Humanities Asn. Can; Can. Asn. Univ. Teachers (secy, 55-57, Milner Mem. Award, 73, mem. ed. bd). Shakespeare; George Bernard Shaw; higher education in Canada. Publ: The unrepentant pilgrim: a study of the development of Bernard Shaw, Houghton, 65; Bernard Shaw's first critic, Univ. Toronto Quart, summer 71; What matters academic freedom?, Stoa, fall 71; George Bernard Shaw, In: Encycl. Am, Grolier, 73; plus others. Add: Room 357, McLaughlin Library, University of Guelph, Guelph, Ont. N1G 2W1, Can.

SMITH, JOYCE CAROL OATES, b. Lockport, N.Y, June 16, 38; m. 61. ENGLISH. B.A, Syracuse Univ, 60; M.A, Univ. Wis, 61. Instr. ENG, Univ. Detroit, 62-64; asst. prof, 64-67; ASSOC. PROF, UNIV. WINDSOR, 67- Guggenheim fel, 67-68. MLA. Tragedy and comedy. Publ: The edge of impossibility: tragic forms in literature, Vanguard, 72; Ionesco's dances of death, Thought, autumn 65; The ambiguity of Troilus and Cressida, Shakespeare Quart, spring 66; Essence and existence in Shakespeare's Troilus and Cressida, Philol. Quart, 4/67. Add: Dept. of English, University of Windsor, Windsor, Ont. N9B 3P4, Can.

SMITH, JULIAN, b. New Orleans, La, Dec. 14, 37; m. 64; c. 3. AMERICAN LITERATURE, FILM. B.A, Tulane Univ, 59, M.A, 62; Woodrow Wilson fel, Columbia Univ, 59-60. Instr. ENG, Spring Hill Col, 62-63; Georgetown Univ, 63-65; Univ. N.H, 65-69; asst. prof, Ithaca Col, 69-73; HON. FEL, UNIV. N.H, 73- Nat. Endowment for Humanities res. grant, 70. MLA; Am. Film Inst. Literature and film; American film. Publ: Nevil Shute, In: Twayne English authors series, 75; Looking away: Hollywood and Vietnam, Scribners, 74; Coming of age in America: young Ben Franklin and Robin Molineux, Am. Quart, 65; Hawthorne's Legends of the Province House, 19th Century Fiction, 69; Hemingway and the thing left out, J. Mod. Lit, 70; plus others. Add: Woodman Barn, Packers Falls Rd, Durham, NH 03824.

SMITH, LABAN C, b. Mar. 8, 11; m. 62; c. 3. ENGLISH, EDUCATION. B.A, Univ, Wis, 32, M.A, 33, Ph.D.(educ), 36; Univ. Chicago, 44-45. Prof. educ. psychol, Stout Inst, 37-39; assoc. prof. educ, Ala. Polytech. Inst, 39-42; prof. Eng, Ind. State Teachers Col, 46-51; dir. rural educ, Repub. Panama, 51-54; PROF. ENG, IND. STATE UNIV, TERRE HAUTE, 54- Am. Counc. Teacher Educ. fel, 39-40. U.S.N.R, 42-44, Lt. Shakespeare. Publ: No better land (novel), Macmillan, 46. Add: 201 Potomac Ave, Terre Haute, IN 47803.

SMITH, LeROY WALTER, b. Mt. Rainier, Md, Dec. 5, 26; m. 46; c. 2. ENGLISH. B.A, Am. Univ, 47; M.A, George Washington Univ, 49; Ph.D.(Eng), Duke Univ, 56. Instr. Eng, Gettysburg Col, 51-54; asst. ed, Air Univ. Quart. Rev, 55-56; asst. prof. ENG, COL. WILLIAM & MARY, 56-62, assoc. prof, 62-67, PROF, 67-, dir, NDEA Insts. Eng. summers 66, 67. MLA; NCTE. Henry Fielding; influence of 17th century theories of the passions on 18th century literature; the English and American novel. Publ: Fielding and Mandeville: the war against virtue, Criticism, 61; Science and the novel, In: Science and society, Col. William & Mary, 65; C.P. Snow as novelist: a delimitation, S.Atlantic Quart, 65. Add: Dept. of English, College of William & Mary, Williamsburg, VA 23185.

SMITH, LEWIS, b. White Plains, N.Y, Aug. 14, 16; m. 59. ENGLISH. B.A, Harvard, 40, M.A, 48; Ph.D, State Univ. Iowa, 53. Instr. ENG, State Univ. Iowa, 47-49; Univ. Chicago, 49-51; prof, Knoxville Col, 53-55; Benedict Col, 56-58; assoc. prof, Tex. South. Univ, 58-65; prof, Lakehead Univ, 65-69;

vis. prof. Eng, Doshisha Woman's Col, 69-71; ASSOC. PROF, FISK UNIV, 71- U.S.N, 40-46, Lt. Comdr. NCTE; Col. Eng. Asn. Add: Dept. of English, Fisk University, Nashville, TN 37203.

SMITH, LORETTA WAGNER, b. Alvord, Iowa; wid; c. 2. SPEECH. A.B, Univ. S.Dak, 29, A.M, 32; Ph.D, State Univ. Iowa, 37. Supvr. speech, univ. high sch, Univ. S.Dak, 34-36; instr. speech & supvr. teacher training work in speech, State Univ. Iowa, 37-39; asst. prof. SPEECH & THEATER, BROOKLYN COL, 39-52, assoc. prof, 52-63, prof, 63-70, dep. chmn. dept, 59-66, EMER. PROF, 70- Am. Speech & Hear. Asn; Speech Commun. Asn. East. States. Placement tests in speech at college level; diagnosis of speech of prospective teachers; articulatory tests. Publ: Speech needs and abilities of prospective teachers, State Univ. Iowa, 37; Practical guide for student teachers of the speech arts and speech correction, Brooklyn Col, 62; co-auth, Speech fundamentals, Prentice-Hall, 53. Add: Rockledge House, 177 E. Hartsdale Ave, Hartsdale, NY 10530.

SMITH, M. B, b. Aberdeen, S.Dak, Sept. 8, 20; m. 43. SPEECH. B.S, North. State Col, 42; M.A, Univ. Minn, 47, Ph.D.(speech psychology), 54. Assoc. prof. SPEECH, Jamestown Col, 46-47; instr, UNIV. NORTH. IOWA, 47-50, asst. prof, 50-54, assoc. prof, 54-63, PROF, 63- U.S.A, 41-43, S/Sgt. Speech Commun. Asn. Speech as behavior; speech criticism. Add: Dept. of Speech, University of Northern Iowa, Cedar Falls, IA 50613.

SMITH, M. DOROTHY, S.S.J, b. Grand Rapids, Mich, June 9, 08. RENAISSANCE. A.B, Nazareth Col.(Mich), 36; M.A, Univ. Notre Dame, 40; Ph.D.(Eng), Fordham Univ, 48. Instr. ENG, NAZARETH COL.(MICH), 44-49, asst. prof, 49-53, assoc. prof, 53-58, PROF, 58-, ALUMNI DIR, 73-, chmn. dept, 52-69, acting chairperson, 72. NCTE; Col. Eng. Asn. Early Tudor drama; history and structure of the English language; Shakespeare. Add: Dept. of English, Nazareth College, Nazareth, MI 49074.

SMITH, MARION B, b. Toronto, Ont, Sept. 9, 12; m. 37; c. 2. ENGLISH, DRAMA. B.A, Univ. Toronto, 33, M.A, 34; Ph.D.(Eng), Univ. Pa, 39. Instr. ENG, Univ. Toronto, 45-46; Univ. B.C, 47-53, asst. prof, 53-57, assoc. prof, 57-63; Univ. Man, 63-64, PROF, 64-67; BROCK UNIV, 67-, DIR. DRAMA, 67-, chmn. depts. Eng. & drama, 69-71, drama, 71-72. Can. Counc. sr. fel, 62-63, res. grant, 68, res. fels 69-70 & 69-73. Asn. Can. Univ. Teachers Eng.(pres, 61-62); Int. Asn. Univ. Prof. Eng. Elizabethan and modern drama; humanities in higher education; Renaissance literature. Publ: Marlowe's imagery and the Marlowe canon, Univ. Pa, 40, Octagon, 69; Dualities in Shakespeare, Univ. Toronto, 66; ed, Hamlet, Macmillan Col. Classics Shakespeare Ser, Vol. II, 69; auth, Shakespeare and the polarity of love, Humanities Asn. Bull, 6/65; Three dirty woods-some thoughts on semantics & higher education, 4/69 & co-auth, The natural sciences, criticism and the humanities, 69, J. Aesthetic Educ; plus others. Add: Dept. of Drama, Brock University, St. Catherines, Ont, Can.

SMITH, MARJORIE MARIE, b. Huntington, Ind, Apr. 2, 18. THEATRE, SPEECH. B.A, Univ. Ill, 49, M.A, 50; Stanford Univ, 50-51; Ph.D.(theatre), Univ. Mich, 59. Instr. commun. skill, Air Univ, 53; costume design, Univ. Mich, 55-59; instr. & designer THEATRE, CALIF. STATE UNIV, LOS ANGELES, 59-71, ASSOC. PROF, 71-, DIR. DRAMA, 61- Costume designer &/or dir. various theatre prod. U.S.A.F, 42-46, 51-53, Res, 55-68, Lt. Col. Am. Theatre Asn; Am. Nat. Theatre & Acad. Theatre of Bertolt Brecht—techniques and theories; 20th century inter-movement in theatre and art; processes in advanced theatrical makeup. Add: Dept. of Speech & Drama, California State University, Los Angeles, 5151 State College Dr, Los Angeles, CA 90032.

SMITH, MARK RICHARD, b. Charlevoix, Mich, Nov. 19, 35; m. 63; c. 4. FICTION. B.A, Northwest. Univ, Evanston, 60; Rockefeller Found. grant, 65-66; Guggenheim Found. fel, 68-69. Instr. ENG. UNIV. N.H, 66-68, asst. prof, 68-71, ASSOC. PROF, 71- Adv, Rockefeller Found, 67-69. Fiction writing; the novel; American fiction. Publ: Toyland, 65 & The middleman, 67, Little; The death of the detective, Knopf, 74; Beer, Audience, 73. Add: Dept. of English, Hamilton-Smith, University of New Hampshire, Durham, NH 03824.

SMITH, MARY DAEHLER, b. Colorado Springs, Colo, Sept. 19, 30; m. 57. LINGUISTICS, LITERATURE. B.A, Colo. Col, 50; Am. Counc. Learned Soc. fel, Radcliffe Col, 50-51, M.A, 51; Ph.D(19th century novel), Harvard, 66. Instr. ENG, Univ. Colo, 57-61; asst. prof, NEBR. WESLEYAN UNIV, 61-66, ASSOC. PROF, 66- MLA. Transformational grammar; 19th century English novel; structural linguistics. Publ: All her perfections tarnished: the thematic function of Esther Summerson, Victorian Newslett, spring 70. Add: Dept. of English, Nebraska Wesleyan University, Lincoln, NE 68504.

SMITH, MILO LE ROY, b. Spokane, Wash, Feb. 13, 25; m. 49; c. 3. THEATRE, DRAMA. B.A, North. Idaho Col. Educ, 50; M.A, Univ. Ore, 56, Ph.D.(theatre, drama), 69; Stanford Univ, 50-51. Teacher, Dallas High Sch, Ore, 52-55; asst. theatre, Univ. Ore, 55-56; ASSOC. PROF. THEATRE & DRAMA, CENT. WASH. STATE COL, 56- U.S.M.C, 43-46, 51-52, 1st Lt. Am. Theatre Asn. Theatre history, directing and management. Publ: The Klaw-Erlanger Bogeyman myth, Players Mag, 12-1/69. Add: Dept. of Theatre & Drama, Central Washington State College, Ellensburg, WA 98926.

SMITH, MILTON SHUMWAY, b. Cranston, R.I, Sept. 2, 12; m. 50. ENGLISH & AMERICAN LITERATURE. B.A, Wesleyan Univ, 33; M.A, Harvard, 34; Yale, 34 37; Ph.D.(Eng), Fordham Univ, 55. Res. asst, Yale, 38-41; instr, Hillyer Col, Univ. Hartford, 46-47, asst. prof, 47-51; res. assoc, The Correspondence of Edmund Burke, Sheffield, Eng, 54-55; assoc. prof. Am. & Eng. Lit, Southeast. La. Col, 56-61; prof. Eng. & chmn. dept, Yankton Col, 61-63; prof. lit, Houston Baptist Col, 63-67; PROF. LIT. & COORD. HUMANITIES, VA. WEST. COMMUNITY COL, 67- Part-time asst. prof, Trinity Col.(Conn), 47-51; prof. Eng, summer sch, Mitchell Col.(Conn), 61-65; mem. adv. counc. S.E. Conf. Eng. Two-Year Col, 72- Instr. navigation & commun, U.S. Navy Flight Prep. Sch, Wesleyan Univ, 43-44; U.S.N.R, 44-45; instr. navigation, U.S. Naval Amphibious Base, Little Creek, Va, 45. MLA; Col. Eng. Asn; NCTE; Renaissance Soc. Am; Mod. Humanities Res. Asn; Am. Stud. Asn; NEA; Col. Conf. Teachers Eng; Conf. Col. Compos. & Commun. Edmund Burke, statesman; 18th century literature; Tudor prose. Publ: Co-auth, A checklist of the correspondence of Edmund Burke, Cambridge, 55; auth, Ancient and modern sea charts, Motor Boating Mag, 43; Emerson's idealism in the hot war of ideologies, Proc. La. Acad. Sci, 4/58; Hayward's historiography in the tacitean tradition, Miss. Quart, 9/61; plus others. Add: 1929 Greenwood Rd. S.W, Roanoke, VA 24015.

SMITH, NELSON CHARLES, b. New York, N.Y, July 24, 40; m. 62; c. 2. ENGLISH. A.B, Princeton, 62; M.A.T, Oberlin Col, 63; Ph.D.(Eng), Univ. Wash, 67. Teacher, Oberlin Pub. Schs, 62-63; acting instr. ENG, Univ. Wash, 65-67; instr, UNIV. VICTORIA (B.C), 67, ASST. PROF, 67- Can. Counc. fel, 73-74. Melville Soc. Am; Asn. Can. Univ. Teachers Eng; Victorian Stud. Asn. West. Can. Nineteenth century; English and American novel. Publ: The art of Gothic: Ann Radcliff's major novels, Univ. Microfilms, 67. Add: Dept. of English, University of Victoria, Victoria, B.C, Can.

SMITH, PATRICK D, b. Galena, Kans, Mar. 17, 24; m. 46; c. 2. ENGLISH. B.A, Ozark Bible Col, 53; B.S, & M.S, Kans. State Col, 57; Ed.D, Colo. State Col, 68. Supt. schs, Stoutland Sch. Dist, Mo, 57-60; asst. prof. ENG, Cent. Mo. State Col, 61-67; chmn. dept. Eng, SCH. OF THE OZARKS, 67-72, ASSOC. PROF. ENG. & CHMN. DEPT. CRIMINAL JUSTICE ADMIN, 72- U.S.N, 41-49. NCTE; MLA; Col. Conf. Compos. & Commun; Col. Eng. Asn. Walt Whitman; Thomas Traherne. Publ: The lost years, Pageant, 60; A manual of police report writing, 67 & English for law enforcement officers, 68, C.C. Thomas. Add: Dept. of English, School of the Ozarks, Point Lookout, MO 65726.

SMITH, PATRICK J, b. Menominee, Mich, Sept. 7, 31; m. 54; c. 7. ENGLISH, FILM. B.S, Marquette Univ, 53, M.A, 59; Ph.D.(Eng), Univ. Calif, Davis, 66. Assoc, Univ. Calif, Davis, 62-64, ENG, 64-66; ASST. PROF, UNIV. SAN FRANCISCO, 66- U.S.A.F, 53-57, Res, 1st Lt. Modern English and American literature; film study and filmmaking; theology. Publ: Prelude for a Titan (film), released by AC Spark Plug Div, Gen. Motors, 61; auth. poem, In: Mark in time, 71; ed, Smells like dead fish (film), Ichan Prod, 73. Add: Dept. of English, University of San Francisco, San Francisco, CA 94117.

SMITH, PAUL, b. Bangor, Maine, Sept. 14, 21; m. 56. ENGLISH. A.B, Univ. Maine, 43; A.M, Columbia Univ, 47, Ph.D.(Eng), 51. Mem. fac. Eng. Wis. State Univ, 50-52; Albright Col, 52-53; Univ. Ky, 53-54; Chicago Teachers Col. & Univ. Chicago, 54-65; mem. staff, Harvard, 65- Mil.Intel, U.S.A, 43-46. MLA; NCTE; Teachers Eng. to Speakers Other Lang; Nat. Asn. For. Stud. Affairs. Nineteenth century literature; English as a foreign language; drama. Publ: On teaching a language, 56 & Litteratura gratia litteraturae, 68, Mod. Lang. J; Visual interference, AFLT, 71. Add: Box 303, Cambridge, MA 02138.

SMITH, PAUL, b. Rochester, N.Y, Dec. 23, 25; m. 52; c. 3. ENGLISH. B.A, Univ. Rochester, 50, M.A, 51; Ph.D.(Eng), Harvard, 67. Instr. ENG, TRINITY COL.(CONN), 59-62, asst. prof, 62-66, assoc. prof, 66-71, PROF, 71-, CHMN. DEPT, 72- Consult. curriculum, Ga. State Dept. Educ, 68- U.S.A, 42-46. MLA; NCTE. Stylistics; English curriculum. Publ: Co-auth, An anatomy of literature, Harcourt, Brace, Jovanovich, 72; auth, The confidence man and the literary world of New York, Nineteenth Century Fiction, 3/62; Criticism and the curriculum, Col. Eng, 10/64; Restless casuistry: Shelley's composition of The Cenci, Keats-Shelley J, winter 64. Add: Dept. of English, Trinity College, Hartford, CT 06106.

SMITH, PHILIP EDWARD, II, b. Atlanta, Ga, Aug. 9, 43; m. 67. ENGLISH & AMERICAN LITERATURE. B.A, Occidental Col, 65; M.A, Northwest. Univ, 66, Ph.D.(Eng), 69; D.E.S, Cambridge, 70. ASST. PROF. ENG, UNIV. PITTSBURGH, 70- AAUP. Nineteenth and 20th century English and European drama; modern poetry; Oscar Wilde. Publ: Ethan Frome notes, Cliff's Notes, 68. Add: Dept. of English, University of Pittsburgh, Pittsburgh, PA 15260.

SMITH, RALPH RUGGLES, b. Modesto, Calif, Jan. 3, 44. SPEECH, AMERICAN HISTORY. B.A, Univ. Calif, Los Angeles, 65; M.A, Columbia Univ, 69; Ph.D.(hist), Univ. South. Calif, 73. Lectr. SPEECH, Queens Col. (N.Y), 66-69; LEHMAN COL, 70-73, ASST. PROF, 73- Speech Commun. Asn. American religious history; public address; nonverbal communication. Publ: Co-auth, Nonverbal communication, Bobbs, 71. Add: Dept. of Speech, Herbert H. Lehman College, Bedford Park Blvd. W, New York, NY 10468.

SMITH, RAYMOND ALFRED, b. Cleveland, Ohio, Apr. 6, 23. DRAMA, THEATRE ARTS. A.B, West. Reserve Univ, 51, M.A, 53, M.F.A, 55. Lectr. dramatic arts, West. Reserve Univ, 57-58; instr. drama & speech, Women's Col. N.C, 58-61; asst. prof. THEATRE ARTS, UNIV. KY, 61-65, ASSOC. PROF, 65- U.S.A, 45-46, T/Sgt. Am. Nat. Theatre & Acad; Am. Theatre Asn. Theatre direction and design. Publ: Theatre at the crossroads, Univ. Ky. Alumni Asn, spring 70. Add: Dept. of Theatre Arts, Room 109, Fine Arts Bldg, University of Kentucky, Lexington, KY 40506.

SMITH, RAYMOND GEORGE, b. Colfax, Wis, May 15, 17; m. 38. SPEECH. A.B, Earlham Col, 38; M.A, Ind. Univ, 39; univ. fel, Univ. Wis, 48-49, Ph.D, 50. Instr. speech, Valley City State Teachers Col, N.Dak, 40-42; radio operating, U.S. Army Air Force, Truax Field, Wis, 42-44; Scott Field, Ill, 44-46; SPEECH, IND. UNIV, BLOOMINGTON, 46-48, asst. prof, 49-57, assoc. prof, 57-64, PROF, 64- Assoc. ed, Speech Monogr, 63; dir, U.S. Off. Educ. Doctoral Res. Training Grant, 66-73. Cent. States Speech Asn; AAAS; Speech Commun. Asn; Int. Commun. Asn; Am. Educ. Res. Asn. Experimental public address; behavioral sciences; perceptual response communication inventory. Publ: Principles of public speaking, Ronald, 58; co-auth, Speaking effectively, Holt, 57; Speech-communication: theory and models, Harper, 70; plus one other. Add: Dept. of Speech, Speech & Hearing Bldg, Indiana University, Bloomington, IN 47401.

SMITH, RICHARD EMMANUEL, b. New Amsterdam, Guyana, Jan. 1, 36; m. 63; c. 3. ENGLISH LITERATURE, FOLKLORE. B.A, Inter-Am. Univ, P.R, 59; B.D, Univ. Waterloo, 62; M.A, Ohio State Univ, 67, Ph.D.(Eng), 70. Clergyman, Lutheran Church in Guyana, 62-65; ASST. PROF. ENG, BUCKNELL UNIV, 71- MLA; Medieval Acad. Am. Medieval English literature. Publ: A study of the correspondences between the Roman de Renard, West African folk tales, and Jamaica Anansi tales, Univ. Mich, 71. Add: Dept. of English, Bucknell University, Lewisburg, PA 17837.

SMITH, RICHARD GORDON, b. Chicago, Ill, Feb. 23, 28; m. 50; c. 1. DRAMA. B.S, Purdue Univ, 51; M.A, Univ. Ill, Urbana, 54, Ph.D.(theatre), 71. Asst. oral interpretation, Univ. Ill, 53-54; instr. theater arts, Denison Univ, 55-59, asst. prof, 59-66; speech & theater, Univ. Ill, Urbana, 67-69; lectr. THEATRE, STATE UNIV. N.Y. BINGHAMTON, 69-71, asst. prof, 71-73, ASSOC. PROF, 73- U.S.N, 46-47. Speech Asn. Am; Am. Theatre Asn. Theatre architecture and planning; stage lighting; Kabuki theater of Japan. Add: Dept. of Theatre, State University of New York,at Binghamton, Vestal Pkwy. E, Binghamton, NY 13901.

SMITH, ROBERT ALSTON, b. Hickory, N.C, Oct. 22, 09; m. 64. ENGLISH. B.S, J. C. Smith Univ, 36; A.M, N.Y. Univ. Instr. ENG, Paul Quinn Col, 37-40; Prairie View Col, 40-42; MORGAN STATE COL, 46-47, asst. prof, 47-68, ASSOC. PROF, 68-, DIR, MORGAN STATE COL-UNIV. PA. COOP. PROJ, 72-, dir. spec. proj, 70-72. Vis. scholar, N.C. Cent. Univ, 70-71; consult. humanities, Triangle Asn. Cols, 71-72. U.S.C.G, 43-46. NCTE; Conf. Col. Compos. & Commun; Col. Lang. Asn. History of the English language; Negro literature; humanities. Publ: Claude McKay: an essay in criticism & Poetry of Countee Cullen, Phylon; Measuring English proficiency beyond the freshman year, Col. Compos. & Commun. Add: Dept. of English, Morgan State College, Cold Spring Lane & Hillen Rd, Baltimore, MD 21239.

SMITH, ROBERT WAYNE, b. Kokomo, Ind, Jan. 3, 26; m. 56; c. 3. SPEECH. A.B, Univ. South. Calif, 50, M.A, 51; Ph.D.(speech), Univ. Wis, 57. Asst. prof. SPEECH, Shepherd Col, 55-57; instr, Univ. Mich, 58; asst. prof, Mid-west. Univ, 58-59; Univ. Va, 59-62; ALMA COL, 62-67, ASSOC. PROF, 67-, CHMN. DEPT, 65- Guest linguistics, Univ. Mich, 57. U.S.N, 44-46, 51-52. Speech Commun. Asn; Cent. States Speech Asn. American public address: rhetorical theory; Greco-Roman oratory. Publ: Ed, Christ and the modern mind, Intervarsity, 72; James Ussher: biblical chronicler, Anglican Theol. Rev, 4/59; Refutation and rebuttal, Am. Speech, 5/64; Textual critic: hung-up on trivia?, South. Speech Commun. J, summer 72; plus others. Add: Dept. of Speech & Theatre, Alma College, Alma, MI 48801.

SMITH, ROBERT WAYNE, b. Ellwood City, Pa, May 15, 28. THEATER ARTS. B.S. in Ed, Pa. State Univ, University Park, 56; M.A, Columbia Univ, 59; Ph.D.(theater arts), Bowling Green State Univ, 70. Teacher Eng, speech & drama, Ellwood City Sch. Dist, Pa, 56-65; instr. speech & theater, Wilbur Wright Col, 65-67; asst. prof. theater arts, Calif. State Univ, Fresno, 71-73. Sig.C, U.S.A, 48-52. Am. Theatre Asn; Speech Commun. Asn; NEA. Theater history; empirical researcher in theater. Publ: An investigation of actor-character relationships in a theatrical production, Empirical Res. in Theatre, 71; Actor-character personality identification, 71, co-auth, The relationship of semantic compatability to performance ratings in the theatre, 72 & auth, Approaching the teaching of the secondary school theatre course, 73, Am. Theatre Asn. Conv. Add: Apt. 4, 959 Cross St, California, PA 15419.

SMITH, ROWLAND JAMES, b. Johannesburg, S.Africa, Aug. 19, 38; Can. citizen; m. 62; c. 2. ENGLISH LITERATURE. B.A, Univ. Natal, 59, Ph.D. (Eng), 67; Transvaal Rhodes scholar, Oxford, 60, M.A, 67. Jr. lectr. Latin, Univ. Natal, 60; lectr. ENG, Univ. Witwatersrand, 63-67; asst. prof, DALHOUSIE UNIV, 67-70, ASSOC. PROF, 70-, ASST. DEAN ARTS & SCI, 72- Vis. fel, Dalhousie Univ, 65-66. Asn. Can. Univ. Teachers of Eng.(secy-treas, 68-70); Can. Asn. African Stud; Eng. Inst; MLA. Literature and politics in the twentieth century; African literature written in English. Publ: Lyric and polemic: the literary personality of Roy Campbell, McGill-Queen's Univ, 72. Add: Dept. of English, Dalhousie University, Halifax, N.S, Can.

SMITH, THOMAS FRANCIS, b. Waterbury, Conn, June 10, 29; m. 56; c. 4. ENGLISH. B.A, Univ. Conn, 51, M.A, 53; fel, Univ. Mich, 53-54; Ph.D, Univ. Pittsburgh, 62. Instr, Univ. Conn, 51-53; ENG, DUQUESNE UNIV, 55-60, asst. prof, 60-64, assoc. prof, 64-69, PROF, 69- MLA; AAUP. The novel; literary criticism. Publ: Balance in James' Portrait of a lady, Four Quart, 64; Color and light in The dead, James Joyce Quart, 65. Add: 122 Harvest Dr, Verona, PA 15147.

SMITH, THOMAS NORRIS, b. Hartford, Conn, Feb. 19, 37; m. 62; c. 2. ENGLISH LITERATURE. B.S, Univ. Conn, 59, Ph.D.(Eng), 68; M.A, Univ. Ill, Urbana, 60. Asst. prof. ENG, Univ. Alaska, 64-66; UNIV. HARTFORD, 67-71, ASSOC. PROF, 71- Reading consult, Advan. Placement Prog, Educ. Testing Serv, 65-66; res. fel, Univ. Conn, 66-67; consult, Bilingual Educ. Prog, Teachers Corps, 73- Medieval Inst; MLA; Renaissance Soc. Am; AAUP. Medieval narrative literature; English Renaissance literature. Add: Dept. of English, University of Hartford, 200 Bloomfield Ave, West Hartford, CT 06117.

SMITH, VONCILE MARSHALL, b. Ft. Myers, Fla, Mar. 17, 31; m. 51; c. 5. SPEECH COMMUNICATION, COMMUNICATION THEORY. B.A.E, Univ. Fla, 60, M.A, 64, Ph.D.(speech), 66. Asst. prof. SPEECH, FLA. ATLANTIC UNIV, 66-70, ASSOC. PROF, 70-, CHMN. DEPT. COMMUN, 73- Speech Commun. Asn; Asn. Depts. & Adminr. Speech Commun; AAUP; South. Speech Commun. Asn; Am. Speech & Hearing Asn. Special studies in communication on and by women; interpersonal communication; language development. Add: Dept. of Communication, College of Humanities, Florida Atlantic University, Boca Raton, FL 33432.

SMITH, WALTER RHEA, b. Jackson, Tenn, Feb. 2, 18. BRITISH LITERATURE. B.A, Lambuth Col, 39; M.A, South. Methodist Univ, 40; Ford Found. fel, Europe, 51; Ph.D, Univ. Calif, Berkeley, 51. Lectr. ENG, South. Methodist Univ, 46-48; from asst. prof. to PROF, MEMPHIS STATE UNIV, 51-, DEAN, COL. ARTS & SCI, 60- Med.Serv.C, 41-46, Maj. NCTE. Chaucer; British drama; Victorian prose. Add: College of Arts & Sciences, Memphis State University, Memphis, TN 38111.

SMITH, WARREN HUNTING, b. Geneva, N.Y, Oct. 25, 05. ENGLISH. B.A, Yale, 27, Ph.D.(Eng), 31; hon. Litt.D, Hobart & William Smith Cols, 58. ASSOC. ED, YALE ED. HORACE WALPOLE'S CORRESPONDENCE & RES. ASSOC, YALE, 34- Off. Strategic Serv, 42-45. Soc. Archit. Hist. Horace Walpole's correspondence; architectural history; history of Hobart College. Publ: An elegant but salubrious village, W.F. Humphrey, Geneva, 31; Architecture in English fiction, 34 & Originals abroad, 52, Yale; The Misses Elliot of Geneva, Farrar & Rinehart, 40; Hobart and William Smith, Hobart & William Smith Cols, 72; Architectural design on English title-pages, Library, 33; Horace Walpole and 2 Frenchwomen, In: The age of Johnson, Yale, 49; Horatius Italicus, In: Horace Walpole, Yale, 67. Add: 165 Bishop St, New Haven, CT 06511.

SMITH, WARREN S, b. Bangor, Pa, Mar. 11, 12; m. 43; c. 3. THEATRE, THE ARTS. B.A, Muhlenberg Col, 33; M.A, State Univ. Iowa, 37. Instr. Eng. & drama, High Sch, Pa, 33-42; prof. theatre arts, PA. STATE UNIV, 46-47, DIR. GEN. EDUC. IN ARTS, 67-, asst. dir. inst. arts & humanities, 67-70. Am. Counc. Learned Soc. grant-in-aid to Eng, 65; consult. fine arts, Dept. Pub. Instr, Commonwealth Pa, 65-68, lectr, Nat. Humanities Ser, 73- U.S.A, 42-46. Am. Nat. Theatre & Acad; Asn. Gen. & Lib. Stud. General education in the arts; contemporary art forms. Publ: The religious speeches of Bernard Shaw, Pa. State Univ, 63; Shaw on religion, 67 & The London heretics, 67, Constable, London, Dodd, New York; ed. & contrib, Bernard Shaw's plays, Norton, 70; The artist in the community of scholars, Am. Asn. Univ. Prof. Bull, 59; London Quakers at the turn of the century, Quaker Hist, 64; The new arts in Europe, Christian Century, 73; plus others. Add: 127 Arts Bldg, Pennsylvania State University, University Park, PA 16802.

SMITH, WILLIAM DAVID, b. Clarksville, Ark, Nov. 26, 33; m. 56. SPEECH, COMMUNICATION. B.A, David Lipscomb Col, 56; M.A, South. Ill. Univ, 60, Ph.D.(speech), 64. Instr. SPEECH, SOUTH. ILL. UNIV, CARBONDALE, 61-64, asst. prof, 64-71, ASSOC. PROF, 71- Cent. States Speech Asn. Award, 66; Pi Kappa Delta faculty award, 66. Speech Commun. Asn; Nat. Soc. Stud. Commun. Theories of rhetorical criticism: interpersonal communication; speech education. Publ: Co-auth, Oral communication of ideas, Stipes, 65, 2nd ed, 66 & 3rd ed, 67. Add: Dept. of English, Southern Illinois University, Carbondale, IL 62901.

SMITH, WILLIAM JAY, b. Winnfield, La, Apr. 22, 18; m. 47, 66; c. 2. ENGLISH. B.A, Wash. Univ, 39, M.A, 41; dipl, Univ. Poiters, France, 38; Columbia Univ, 46-47; Rhodes scholar, Oxford, 47-48; Univ. Florence, Italy, 48-50; hon. Litt.D, New Eng. Col, 73. Asst. French, Wash. Univ, 39-41; instr. Eng. & French, Columbia Univ, 46-47; lectr. Eng, Williams Col, 51, poet in residence & lectr. Eng, 59-65, 66-67; writer-in-residence, HOLLINS COL, 65-66, PROF. ENG, 67- Ed. consult, Grove Press, 52-53; mem. staff, writers conf, Univ. Conn, 57 & Ind. Univ, 61; mem, Vt. House of Rep, 60-62; mem. jury, Lamont poetry selection, Acad. Am. Poets, 61-63; Nat. Bk. Award poetry, 62, children's lit, 70; Brandeis Univ. Creative Arts Award, 63; Ford Found. fel, 64-65; jury, Bollingen Award, Yale, 65; consult. poetry, Libr. Congr, 68-70; mem. vis. comt, Dept. of Eng, Harvard, 70-; Nat. Endowment for Arts grant, summer 72; vis. prof. writing & acting chmn. div, Sch. Arts, Columbia Univ, 73. Poetry Mag. Prize, 45 & 64; Henry Bellamann Major Award for Poetic Achievement, 70; Russell Loines Award for Poetry, Nat. Inst. Arts & Lett, 72. U.S.N.R, 41/45, Lt. Asn. Am. Rhodes Scholars; Auth. Guild; Auth. League Am; PEN Club; British and American poetry of the 19th and 20th centuries; children's literature; European poetry. Publ: Laughing time, 55 & Poems 1947-1957, 57, Little; The spectra hoax, Wesleyan Univ, 61; co-auth, The golden journey: poems for young people, Reilly & Lee, 65; auth, The tin can and other poems, 66, Mr. Smith and other nonsense, 68 & New and selected poems, 70 & The streaks of the tulip—selected criticism, 72, Delacorte; Poems from France, 67 & ed, Poems from Italy, 72, Crowell. Add: Dept. of English, Hollins College, VA 24020.

SMITH, WILLIAM RAYMOND, History, English. See Volume I, History.

SMITH, WILLIAM STEPHEN, b. Devil's Lake, N.Dak, Mar. 18, 17; m. 47; c. 2. SPEECH. B.Ed, North. Ill. Univ, 41; M.A, Stanford Univ, 49, Ph.D, 53. Asst. prof. SPEECH, Northwest. State Col.(La), 50-52; PROF, AUBURN UNIV, 52- U.S.A.F.R, 41-47, Res, 47-, Lt. Col. South. Speech Commun. Asn.(pres, 61-62); Speech Commun. Asn. Public address; group problem solving; leadership. Publ: Co-auth, Method and means of public speaking, 62 & auth, Group problem solving through discussion, 65, Bobbs; co-auth, Building better speech, Noble, 62. Add: Dept. of Speech Communication, Auburn University, Auburn, AL 36830.

SMITH, WINSTON, b. Demopolis, Ala, June 2, 37. ENGLISH. B.A, Birmingham-South. Col, 59; M.A, Vanderbilt Univ, 62, Ph.D.(Eng), 65. Instr. Eng, Vanderbilt Univ, 64-66; asst. prof, UNIV. ALA, 66-70, ASSOC. PROF. ENG. & DIR. GRAD. STUD, 70- MLA; S.Atlantic Mod. Lang. Asn; Soc. Stud. South. Lit. American poetry; colonial and 19th century American literature. Publ: Johnson Jones Hooper: a critical study, In: Modern language microcard series A, 62; Days of exile, Drake, 67; Early history of Demopolis, Ala. Rev, 4/65; Simon Suggs and the satiric tradition, In: Essays in honor of Richebourg Gaillard McWilliams, Birmingham-South. Col, 70. Add: Dept. of English, College of Arts & Sciences, University of Alabama, Drawer AL, University, AL 35486.

SMITHBERGER, ANDREW THOMAS, b. Harriettsville, Ohio, Mar. 14, 05; m. 30; c. 4. ENGLISH LITERATURE. A.B, Ohio Univ, 25; A.M, Univ. Notre Dame, 27. Instr. ENG, UNIV. NOTRE DAME, 27-30, asst. prof, 30-33, assoc. prof, 33-38, prof, 38-71, asst. chmn. dept, 64-71, EMER. PROF, 71- Managing ed, Natural Law Forum, 56-70. Col. Eng. Asn; AAUP. English literature from 1780 to 1830. Publ: Essays: British and American, Houghton; co-auth, On poetry, Odyssey. Add: 53085 Oakmont Park, East Dr, South Bend, IN 46637.

SMITHER, NELLE, b. Memphis, Tenn, June 13, 09. AMERICAN & ENGLISH LITERATURE. B.A, Goucher Col, 31; M.A, Columbia Univ, 36; Bloomfield Moore fel, Univ. Pa, 36-38, Ph.D.(Eng), 42. Instr. ENG, Queens Col, 42-46; asst. prof, DOUGLASS COL, RUTGERS UNIV, NEW BRUNSWICK, 46-52, assoc. prof, 52-66, PROF, 66- MLA; Am. Soc. Theatre Res. American literature; drama; stage history. Publ: A history of the English theatre in New Orleans, 1806-1842, Blom, 67; Charlotte Cushman's apprenticeship in New Orleans, La. Hist. Quart, 10/48; The sovereign in the ascendant: Charlotte Cushman's first New York engagement, Bull. New York Pub. Libr, 9/66. Add: Dept. of English, Douglass College, Rutgers University, New Brunswick, NJ 08903.

SMITHERMAN, GENEVA, Brownsville, Tenn, Dec. 10, 40; div; c. 1. ENGLISH LINGUISTICS, AFRO-AMERICAN LANGUAGE & LITERATURE. B.A, Wayne State Univ, 60, M.A, 62; fel, Univ. Mich, 68, Ph.D.(Eng, educ), 69. Teacher Eng. & Latin, Detroit Pub. Schs, 60-65; instr. Eng, East. Mich. Univ, 65-66; Wayne State Univ, 66-69, asst. prof. Eng. & Eng. educ, 69-71; lectr. AFRO-AM. STUD, Harvard, 71-73; ASST. PROF. & PROG. COORD, CTR. BLACK STUD, WAYNE STATE UNIV, 73- Consult, Detroit Dialect Stud, 68; mem, Comn. Eng. Curriculum, NCTE, 71-73. NCTE; Conf. Col. Compos. & Commun; Col. Lang. Asn. Black cognitive and communication styles; black English and language arts education for black students; Afro-American poetry. Publ: Black language and culture: sounds of soul, Harper, 74; White English in blackface, or Who do I be?, Black Scholar, 5-6/73; God don't never change: black English from a black perspective, Col. Eng, 3/73; The power of the rap: the black idiom and the new black poetry, Twentieth Century,Lit, 10/73; plus others. Add: Center for Black Studies, Wayne State University, Detroit, MI 48202.

SMITHLINE, ARNOLD, b. New York, N.Y, Apr. 4, 25; m. 50; c. 2. ENGLISH. B.A, Brooklyn Col, 50, M.A, 52; Ph.D.(Eng), N.Y. Univ, 62. Teacher ENG, Charles Evans Hughes High Sch, 56-62; instr, Hunter Col, 62-66; asst. prof, QUEENSBOROUGH COMMUNITY COL, 66-68, assoc. prof. & chmn. dept, 68-70, PROF, 70- Lectr, Queens Col.(N.Y), 59-69; State Univ. N.Y. Res. Found. fac. fel, 67, res. grant-in-aid, 67-68. U.S.A.F, 43-46. Am. Stud. Asn; Emerson Soc; MLA; Northeast Mod. Lang. Asn; NCTE. American literature; 17th century English literature; comparative religion. Publ: Natural religion in American literature, Col. & Univ, 66; Eureka: Poe as transcendentalist, 65 & Henry Miller and the transcendental spirit, 66, Emerson Soc. Quart; plus others. Add: 2520 Eileen Rd, Oceanside, NY 11572.

SMOCK, GEORGE EDWARD, b. Delphi, Ind, May 16, 05; m. 35; c. 4. ENGLISH. A.B, DePauw Univ, 27; A.M, Univ. Chicago, 28; Ph.D, Cornell Univ, 34. Instr. Eng. & speech, Ill. Col, 28-29; Eng, DePauw Univ, 29-33; Eng. & speech, Purdue Univ, 34-35; prof. ENG. & HEAD DEPT, S.Dak. State Univ, 35-46; IND. STATE UNIV, TERRE HAUTE, 46-71, EMER. PROF, 71- NCTE; MLA; Midwest. Eng. Conf.(Chmn, 56). Sir. Walter Scott; English novel. Publ: John Locke and the Augustan age of literature, Philos. Rev. Add: 7215 Wabash Ave, Terre Haute, IN 47803.

SMOOT, JEAN JOHANNESSEN, b. Spartanburg, S.C, June 10, 43; m. 65; c. 2. ENGLISH, COMPARATIVE LITERATURE. B.A, Eckerd Col, 64; Fulbright spec. stud, Nat. Univ. Mex, 65; Woodrow Wilson fels. & Ph.D.(comp. lit), Univ. N.C, 68. Instr. ENG, N.C. STATE UNIV, 68, ASST. PROF, 68-, asst. prof. Span, summer sch, 68. Nat. Endowment for Humanities younger humanist summer stipend, 72. S.Atlantic Mod. Lang. Asn; MLA; Am. Comp. Lit. Asn; Int. Comp. Lit. Asn; Am. Asn. Univ. Women. Fifth-century Greek literature; comparative relationships among English, French and Spanish literatures during the Renaissance; the rise of the American novel. Publ: Variations in water imagery in James Joyce and Bossuet, spring 68 & Alceste: the incomplete Don Quijote, fall 70, Romance Notes. Add: 5301 Thayer Dr, Raleigh, NC 27609.

SMYSER, HAMILTON MARTIN, b. Delaware, Ohio, July 28, 01; m. 49. ENGLISH PHILOLOGY. A.B, Ohio Wesleyan Univ, 23; A.M, Ohio State Univ, 24; Ph.D, Harvard, 32. Asst. ENG, Ohio State Univ, 23-25; asst. prof, Ohio Univ, 25-26; asst, Harvard, 26-29, instr, 29-34; asst. prof, CONN. COL, 34-38, assoc. prof, 38-45, prof, 45-68, chmn. dept, 50-52, 54-55, 61-66, EMER. PROF, 68- Asst. ed, Speculum, 47-69. MLA; fel. Mediaeval Acad. Am.(pres, 69-71); Am. Scand. Found. Medieval Latin; Middle English; Old Norse. Publ: Co-auth, Survivals in Old Norwegian, Waverley Press; Chronicle of the pseudo-turpin, Mediaeval; Domestic background of Troilus and Criseyde, Speculum. Add: Connecticut College, 5 N. Ridge Rd, New London, CT 06320.

SMYSER, JANE WORTHINGTON, b. Johnstown, Pa, Aug. 1, 14; m. 49. ENGLISH LITERATURE. A.B, Wells Col, 36; A.M, Yale, 41, Ph.D, 44. Instr. ENG, CONN. COL, 42-43, 44-47, asst. prof, 47-55, assoc. prof, 55-62, PROF, 62- Ford fel, 52-53. MLA. Wordsworth and Coleridge; 19th and 20th century English literature. Publ: Wordsworth's reading of Roman prose, Yale, 46; co-ed, The prose works of William Wordsworth, Clarendon, 74; auth, The epigraphs to the poetry of T.S. Eliot, Am. Lit, 3/49; Coleridge's use of Wordsworth's Juvenilia, 6/50 & Wordsworth's dream of poetry and science, 3/56, PMLA. Add: Dept. of English, Connecticut College, New London, CT 06320.

SMYTHE, JAMES ERWIN, b. Birmingham, Ala, Aug. 6, 23; m. 48; c. 2. ENGLISH. B.A, George Pepperdine Col, 45; M.A, Univ. Ill, 50, Ph.D.(Eng), 55. Teacher ENG, Athens Bible Sch, 46-48; asst. instr, Univ. Ill, 48-52; PROF, PEPPERDINE UNIV, MALIBU, 52-, CHMN. HUMANITIES DIV, 71-, chmn. dept. Eng, 68-71. AAUP. English novel, especially Sir Walter Scott; the Bible as literature; philology. Publ: The religious and moral philosophy of Sir Walter Scott. Add: Div. of Humanities, Pepperdine University, Malibu, 24255 Pacific Coast Hwy, Malibu, CA 90265.

SMYTHE, TED CURTIS, b. Tacoma, Wash, May 6, 32; m. 56; c. 3. MASS COMMUNICATION, HISTORY. B.S, Sterling Col, 54; M.A, Univ. Ore, 62; Ph.D.(mass commun), Univ. Minn, 67. Dir. pub. relat, Sterling Col, 56-60; asst. prof. COMMUN, CALIF. STATE UNIV, FULLERTON, 63-67, assoc. prof, 67-73, PROF, 73- Vis. lectr, Dept. Commun, Hong Kong Baptist Col, 70-71. U.S.A, 54-56. Asn. Educ. in Jour. International communications. Publ: Co-ed, Readings in mass communication: concepts and issues in the mass media, W.C. Brown, 72, rev. ed, 74; auth, The birth of Twin Cities' commercial radio, Minn. Hist, fall 69; Pulitzer's World and the Venezuela incident, Jour. Quart, winter 69; plus others. Add: 519 Swanson, Placentia, CA 92670.

SNAPP, ROBERT EDWIN, b. Hinton, Okla, May 10, 10; m. 40; c. 1. DRAMATIC ART. B.A, Univ. N.Mex, 32, M.A, 34; M.F.A, Yale, 40. Instr. Eng, UNIV. N.MEX, 34-40, asst. prof. DRAMA, 40-46, assoc. prof, 46-49, PROF,

49-, chmn. dept, 40-71. U.S.A.A.F, 42-45. Am. Theatre Asn; Am. Nat. Theatre & Acad; Nat. Theatre Conf; Southwest. Theatre Conf. Educational theatre; the place of the director in theatre production. Publ: New Mexico speech, N.Mex. Sch. Rev; Can I make a living in the theatre, Dramatic Mag. Add: Dept. of Dramatic Art, University of New Mexico, Albuquerque, NM 87106.

SNARE, GERALD HOWARD, b. Los Angeles, Calif, Dec. 4, 41. ENGLISH LITERATURE. A.B, Univ. Calif, Santa Barbara, 63; M.A, Univ. Calif, Los Angeles, 65, Ph.D.(Eng), 68. ASST. PROF. ENG, NEWCOMB COL, TULANE UNIV, 68- MLA; Renaissance Soc. Am. Spenser; Renaissance literature; Renaissance philosophy. Publ: Ed, The third part of the Countesse of Pembrokes Yuychurch, Calif. State Univ, Northridge, 73; contrib, Milton encyclopeida, Univ. Wis, 74; auth, Milton's Siloa's brook again, Milton Quart, 70; Satire, logic, and rhetoric in Harvey's earthquake letter to Spenser, Tulane Stud. Eng, 70; Spenser's fourth grace, J. Warburg & Courtauld Insts, 71; plus one other. Add: Dept. of English, Newcomb College of Tulane University, New Orleans, LA 70118.

SNIDERMAN, STEPHEN LEE, b. Detroit, Mich, Feb. 25, 43; m. 66; c. 1. CREATIVE WRITING. B.A, Mich. State Univ, 64; M.A, Univ. Mich, 65; Ph.D.(Eng), Univ. Wis, 70. ASST. PROF. ENG, YOUNGSTOWN STATE UNIV, 69- MLA. Twentieth century American literature. Publ: It was all Yossarian's fault: power and responsibility in Catch-22, Twentieth Century Lit, 74. Add: Dept. of English, Youngstown State University, 410 Wick, Youngstown, OH 44503.

SNIPES, HELEN JOANN, b. Warrensburg, Mo, Oct. 13, 35; c. 1. AMERICAN LITERATURE. B.S.E, Cent. Mo. State Univ, 65, M.A, 67; fel, Kans. State Univ, 67-70, Ph.D.(Am. lit), 72. Teaching asst. ENG, Cent. Mo. State Univ, 65-67; ASST. PROF, CAMERON COL, 70- AAUP; Am. Asn. Univ. Women; MLA. Modern poetry, drama and novel. Add: Dept. of Language Arts, Cameron College, Gore Blvd, Lawton, OK 73501.

SNIPES, WILSON CURRIN, b. Rocky Mount, N.C, Mar. 15, 24; m. 50; c. 2. ENGLISH. B.A, Univ. of the South, 48; M.A, Fla. State Univ, 50; Stanford Univ; Ph.D, Vanderbilt Univ, 57. Instr. Eng, Adm. Farragut Acad, 48-49; Delta State Col, 50-51; Univ. Fla, 54-57; prof, Converse Col, 57-59, dean col, 59-61; prof. Eng, Mercer Univ, 61-66, Am. Heritage lectr, 63; PROF. ENG. & HEAD DEPT, VA. POLYTECH. INST. & STATE UNIV, 66- Consult. sec. schs, Curriculum in Ky. & W.Va, 67- U.S.N.R, 42-, Capt. MLA; Conf. Col. Compos. & Commun; NCTE; South. Humanities Conf.(chmn, 72-73); Col. Eng. Asn.(chmn. comt. advan. degrees, 72-73). Samuel Taylor Coleridge's Shakespearean criticism; Shakespeare's chronicle plays; the humor of Augustus Baldwin Longstreet. Publ: Essays on language, Mercer Univ, 62; Writer and audience: forms of non-fiction prose, Holt, 70; Nine haiku, Folio, 6/67; An inquiry: peer group teaching in freshman English, 5/71 & Oral composing as an approach to writing, 5/73, Col. Compos. & Commun; plus two others. Add: Dept. of English, 204 Williams Hall, Virginia Polytechnic Institute & State University, Blacksburg, VA 24061.

SNODGRASS, WILLIAM D, b. Beaver Falls, Pa, Jan. 5, 26; m. 67; c. 3. ENGLISH, SPEECH. B.A, State Univ. Iowa, 49, M.A, 51, M.F.A, 53, 53-55. Instr. Eng, Cornell Univ, 55-57; Univ. Rochester, 57-58; PROF, Wayne State Univ, 59-67; ENG. & SPEECH, SYRACUSE UNIV, 68- Participant, Morehead Writer's Conf, Morehead, Ky, summer 55, Antioch Writer's Conf, Yellow Springs, Ohio, summers 58 & 59; Hudson Rev. fel. poetry, 58-59; resident, YADDO, Saratoga, N.Y, 59, 60, 61 & 65; Nat. Inst. Arts & Lett. grant, 60; Ford Found. grant theater, 63-64; Nat. Counc. Arts sabbatical grant, 66-67; Guggenheim fel, 72-73; mem, Acad. Am. Poets, 73; lectr, U.S. & Can. univs; State Dept. lectr, Bulgaria, Romania, Hungary, Ger, Portugal, Belgium & Scotland. Ingram-Merrill Award, 58; Longview Lit. Award, 59; Spec. Citation, Poetry Soc. Am, 60; Pulitzer Prize Poetry, 60; Guiness Poetry Award (Gt. Brit), 61; Miles Mod. Poetry Award, 66. U.S.N, 44-46. Nat. Inst. Arts & Lett. Publ: Heart's needle, Knopf, 59; After experience, Harper, 67; transl, Gallows' songs, Univ. Mich, 67; plus others. Add: Dept. of English, Syracuse University, Syracuse, NY 13210.

SNOW, DOROTHY, b. Logan, Utah, Oct. 6, 01. ENGLISH LITERATURE. A.B, Univ. Utah, 23; A.M, Radcliffe Col, 25; Ph.D, Univ. Calif, 36. Instr. ENG, UNIV. UTAH, 24-29, 32-35, asst. prof, 36-47, assoc. prof, 47-52, prof, 52-70, EMER. PROF, 70- MLA. Eighteenth century—1750 on; Romantic movement—1798-1830; American literature, especially Henry James. Add: 1107 E. South Temple St, Apt. 9, Salt Lake City, UT 84102.

SNOW, ROYALL HENDERSON, b. Chicago, Ill, Jan. 21, 98; m. 35. ENGLISH. B.S, Harvard, 20; Rhodes scholar, Oxford, 22-25, B.A, 24, B.Litt, 25. Lectr, Queen's Univ.(Can), 20-21; asst. prof. ENG, Dalhousie Univ, 21-22; Washington & Jefferson Col, 25-28; OHIO STATE UNIV, 28-34, assoc. prof, 34-62, EMER. ASSOC. PROF, 62- Nineteenth century poetry; honors programs. Publ: Thomas Lovell Beddoes, Covici-Friede; English romantic poets & Victorian and later English poets, Am. Bk. Co. Add: Dept. of English, Ohio State University, Columbus, OH 43210.

SNOW, (CHARLES) WILBERT, b. White Head Island, St. George, Maine, Apr. 6, 84. ENGLISH. A.B, Bowdoin Col, 07, hon. A.M, 25, hon. Litt.D, 73; A.M, Columbia Univ, 10; hon. LL.D, Wesleyan Univ, 45; hon. D.Litt, Marietta Col, 46; hon. D.F.A, Nasson Col, 63; hon. D.H, Univ. Maine, Orono, 69. Instr. Eng. & debating, N.Y. Univ. 07-08; Bowdoin Col, 08-09; Williams Col, 09-10; Eskimo teacher & reindeer agent, Bur. Educ, Alaska, 11-12; instr. ENG, Univ. Utah, 13-15; Ind. Univ, 16-18, asst. prof, 19-21; acting prof, Reed Col, 18-19; asst. prof, WESLEYAN UNIV, 21-26, assoc. prof, 26-29, prof, 29-72, EMER. BENJAMIN D. WAITE PROF, 72- Lt. gov, Conn, 45-47, gov, 46-47; spec. lectr, U.S. Dept. State, 51-52; mem, Conn. Constitutional Convention, 65; chmn, Conn. Bd. Educ. U.S.A, 17-18, Res, Capt. MLA. Creative writing; books of verse; poetry. Publ: Collected poems, Wesleyan Univ, 63, rev. ed, 73; Colline's child (autobiog), 74. Add: 473 Newfield St, Middletown, CT 06457.

SNYDER, CAROLINE GROTE, German Literature, English. See Volume III, Foreign Languages, Linguistics & Philology.

SNYDER, EDWINA HUNTER, b. Coushatta, La, Apr. 4, 32; m. 60; c. 1. SPEECH, ORAL INTERPRETATION. B.A, La. Col, 52; M.R.E, Southwest. Baptist Theol. Sem, 55; M.A, Northwest. Univ, 58, Ph.D, 65. Youth dir, Univ. Baptist Church, 54-55; educ. dir, First Baptist Church, Va, 55-57; Instr. speech & Eng, Baptist Missionary Training Sch, Chicago, 57-58; SPEECH, GEORGETOWN COL, 58-61, asst. prof, 61-67, assoc. prof, 67-72, PROF. & ACTING CHMN. DEPT, 72-, chmn, 65-68. Speech Commun. Asn. Chorus speaking in Germany 1918-1964; development of chorus speaking groups in United States; program planning and performance tours. Add: Dept. of Speech, Georgetown College, Georgetown, KY 40324.

SNYDER, JOHN RUDOLPH, b. Canton, Ill, Dec. 31, 42; m. 68; c. 1. ENGLISH, AMERICAN STUDIES. B.A, Univ. Ill, Urbana, 65; Woodrow Wilson fel, Claremont Grad. Sch, 65-67, M.A, 66, Ph.D.(Eng. & Am. lit), 71. Asst. prof. Eng. & Am. lit, Franklin & Marshall Col, 69-71, Eng. & Am. stud, Southampton Col, L.I. Univ, 71-74; ASSOC. PROF. ENG, UNIV. HOUSTON, CLEAR LAKE CITY CTR, 74- MLA. Nineteenth century American literature; 19th century intellectual history, American, British, European; political theory. Publ: The dear love of man: tragic and lyric communion in Walt Whitman, Mouton, 74; The irony of national union: violence and compassion in Walt Whitman's Drum-taps, Can. Rev. Am. Stud, fall 73. Add: School of Human Sciences & Humanities, University of Houston at Clear Lake City, Clear Lake City, TX 77058.

SNYDER, LEE LAMAR, b. Drums, Pa, July 21, 21; m. 56. ENGLISH. A.B, Muhlenberg Col, 42; M.A, Univ. Chicago, 47; Ph.D, Univ. Pa, 69. Asst. prof. Eng, PHILA. COL. TEXTILES & SCI, 57-60, assoc. prof, 60-63, PROF. ENG. & CHMN. DEPT. HUMANITIES & SOC. SCI, 63-, acting chmn. dept. Eng, 62-63. Mem. comt. compiling quart. bibliog. on present-day Eng. for Am. Speech, 51-66. U.S.A, 42-46, Res, 46-, Lt. Col. MLA; Am. Name Soc; NCTE; Col. Eng. Asn. Old English place-names. Add: Dept. of Humanities & Social Sciences, Philadelphia College of Textiles & Science, Philadelphia, PA 19144.

SNYDER, RICHARD CLEMENT, b. Wilkinsburg, Pa, Apr. 24, 20. ENGLISH LITERATURE, COMPOSITION. B.Ed, Duquesne Univ, 41; M.A, Univ. Pittsburgh, 42, Ph.D.(Eng), 55; Univ. Chicago, 51. Teacher ENG, Redstone Twp. High Sch, Republic, Pa, 42-43; Findlay Twp. High Sch, Imperial, 43-45; N.Cath. High Sch, Pittsburgh, 45-46; from lectr. to ASSOC. PROF. ENG, UNIV. PITTSBURGH, 46-, col. adv, 52-58. Ford Found. fac. fel, 51-52. MLA; AAUP; NCTE; Conf. Col. Compos. & Commun; Col. Eng. Asn. English romanticism; English Victorianism; poetry of William Shenstone. Publ: The humanities in general education, Col. Eng, 11/53. Add: Dept. of English, University of Pittsburgh, Pittsburgh, PA 15260.

SNYDER, RICHARD LAURENCE, b. Findlay, Ohio, Feb. 8, 25; m. 48; c. 2. ENGLISH. A.B. & B.S, Ind. Univ, 50, M.A, 51; Ph.D, Trinity Col, Univ. Dublin, 61. Asst. prof. ENG, ASHLAND COL, 52-54, assoc. prof, 54-58, PROF, 58-, CHMN. DEPT, 72- Fulbright fel, Repub. of Ireland, 59-60. U.S.A.A.F, 43-45; Distinguished Flying Cross. MLA; Col. Eng. Asn. Creative writing; modern British and American and continental literature. Publ: Last day of the queen, Liverpolitan, London, 63. Add: Dept. of English, Ashland College, Ashland, OH 44805.

SNYDER, ROBERT L, b. Hastings-on-Hudson, N.Y, June 8, 28; m. 52; c. 4. SPEECH. A.B, Wartburg Col, 53; M.A, Univ. Iowa, 54, Ph.D.(speech), 65. Instr. SPEECH, Kans. State Univ, 54-59, asst. prof, 59-64; assoc. prof. UNIV. WIS-OSHKOSH, 64-68, PROF, 68- U.S.A, 46-48, Res, 50-51. Broadcast Educ. Asn; Nat. Asn. Educ. Broadcasters; Univ. Film Asn; Am. Film Inst. Motion picture history. Publ: Pare Lorentz and documentary film, Univ. Okla, 68; Pare Lorentz, an appreciation, Focus!, autumn 72. Add: Dept. of Radio-TV-Film, Arts & Communication Center, University of Wisconsin-Oshkosh, Oshkosh, WI 54901.

SNYDER, SHERWOOD, III, b. Benton Harbor, Mich, June 29, 33; m. 52; c. 1. THEATRE, SPEECH. B.A, West. Mich. Univ, 57; M.S, Univ. Ore, 58; Ph.D. (theatre, film), Univ. Minn, 66. Instr. speech & theatre, Macalester Col, 59-61; theatre exten, Univ. Minn, 62-66; ASSOC. PROF. SPEECH & THEATRE, CHICAGO STATE UNIV, 67- U.S.N, 50-54. Am. Nat. Theatre & Acad; Am. Theatre Asn; Children's Theatre Conf. Early American drama; folk drama; direction. Publ: Minneapolis theatre in the round, Theatre-U.S.A, 1-2/67. Add: Dept. of Speech, Chicago State University, 95th at M.L. King Dr, Chicago, IL 60628.

SNYDER, SUSAN BROOKE, b. Yonkers, N.Y, July 12, 34. ENGLISH. A.B, Hunter Col, 55; M.A, Columbia Univ, 58, Fels Found. fel, 60, Ph.D.(Eng), 63. Lectr. ENG, Queens Col.(N.Y), 61-63; instr, SWARTHMORE COL, 63-66, asst. prof, 66-70, ASSOC. PROF, 70- Grants, Huntington Libr, summers 66 & 71; Folger Shakespeare Libr, summer 70. Nat. Endowment Humanities fel, 67-68 & res. grant, summer 69; Folger Shakespeare Libr. sr. fel, 72-73; mem. ed. bd, Shakespeare Quart, 73- Renaissance Soc. Am; Shakespeare Asn. Am; AAUP. Shakespeare; Spenser; Renaissance translation. Publ: King Lear and the prodigal son, Shakespeare Quart, 66; Romeo and Juliet: comedy into tragedy, Essays Criticism, 70; Donne and DuBartas: The progress of the soul as parody, Stud. Philol, 73; plus three others. Add: Dept. of English, Swarthmore College, Swarthmore, PA 19081.

SNYDER, WILLIAM WALTER, b. Cleveland, Ohio, Oct. 27, 22; m. 51. ENGLISH. A.B, Baldwin-Wallace Col, 46; fel. & M.A, West. Reserve Univ, 48; Ph.D.(speech & Eng), Univ. Denver, 53. Instr. Eng, West. Reserve Univ, 47-48; Eng. & speech, Allegheny Col, 48-51; assoc. prof. speech & drama & head dept, Queens Col, 52-55; asst. prof. humanities, Sacramento State Col, 55-58; head div. communs, Univ. Idaho, 58-62; prof. Eng. & head div. commun, Calif. West. Univ, 62-64; PROF. ENG. & CHMN. DEPT, SOUTHWEST. COL.(CALIF), 64- Consult. bus. commun. & human relat, evening col, Queens Col; State Dept. Pub. Works, Calif; speech, Carmichael Sch. Dist, Calif; Better Teaching Conf, North. Calif, 56-58; consult, UNESCO, 61; evaluator, Dept. Audio-Visual Instr, Nat. Educ. Asn, 63; consult. mgt, E.L. Shaner & Assoc, 63- U.S.A.A.F, 42-45. Speech Commun. Asn; Col. Eng. Asn; Am. Theatre Asn; Am. Asn. Teachers Ger. Literature and language; theories of learning; educational psychology. Publ: Three plays by Max Frisch, a translation and criticism, Denver Press. Add: Dept. of Language Arts, Southwestern College, Chula Vista, CA 92010.

SOBCHACK, THOMAS J, b. Allentown, Pa, May 20, 37; m. 61. ENGLISH, CINEMA. A.B, Columbia Col, 59; M.A, Hunter Col, 61; Ph.D.(Eng), City Univ. New York, 68. Instr. ENG, UNIV. UTAH, 66-67, asst. prof, 67-72, ASSOC. PROF, 72- MLA; Col. Eng. Asn. Modern British literature; theory and criticism of the film. Add: Dept. of English, University of Utah, Salt Lake City, UT 84112.

SOCHATOFF, ALBERT FRED, b. Pittsburgh, Pa, Aug. 3, 08; m. 31; c. 2. CLASSICAL PALEOGRAPHY. A.B, Univ. Pa, 29; Ph.D, Univ. Pittsburgh, 33. Instr, Arnold Sch, Pittsburgh, Pa, 30-32, head dept. Latin, 33-40; asst, Univ. Pittsburgh, 31-33; hist, Shady Side Acad, 40-43, 45-48; asst. prof. ENG, CARNEGIE-MELLON UNIV, 48-51, assoc. prof, 51-65, prof, 65-73, THOMAS S. BAKER PROF, 73-, assoc. head dept, 66-70. Consult. commun, indust. orgn, Pittsburgh. Am. Philol. Asn. Commentaries in the manuscripts d, k and m of Petronius. Publ: Reading of plays, Improving Col. & Univ. Teaching; Articles on text of Petronius, Satiricon, Trans. Am. Philol. Asn, 63, 65, 67 & Class. J, 70; plus others. Add: Dept. of English, Carnegie-Mellon University, Pittsburgh, PA 15213.

SOELLNER, ROLF, b. Nurnberg, Ger, Feb. 10, 22; m. 53. ENGLISH. Studienreferendar, Univ. Erlangen, 50; M.A, Univ. Ill, 51, fel, 51-53, Ph.D.(Eng), 53. Fel, Univ. Ill, 53-54; asst. prof. humanities, Ill. Wesleyan Univ, 54-55, assoc. prof, 55-60, head dept. Eng, 58-60, chmn. div. humanities, 59-60; assoc. prof. ENG, Kans. State Univ, 61-67, acting head dept, 62-63; PROF, OHIO STATE UNIV, 67- Guggenheim fel, 60-61. MLA; Renaissance Soc. Am. Renaissance literature; Shakespeare. Publ: Co-ed, Measure for measure: text, source and criticism, Houghton, 66; auth, Shakespeare's patterns of self-knowledge, Ohio State Univ, 72; Madness of Hercules and the Elizabethans, Comp. Lit, 58; Hang up philosophy, Mod. Lang. Quart, 62; Prudence and the price of Helen: the debate of the Trojans in Troilus and Cressida, Shakespeare Quart, 69. Add: Dept. of English, Ohio State University, 164 W. 17th Ave, Columbus, OH 43210.

SOENS, ADOLPH LEWIS, JR, b. Durango, Colo, Mar. 13, 31; m. 49; c. 3. ENGLISH. B.A, Harvard, 52; M.A, Princeton, 54, Ph.D.(Eng), 57. Instr. ENG, Smith Col, 55-56; from instr. to asst. prof, Univ. Colo, 56-64; Drake Univ, 64-65; asst. prof, UNIV. NOTRE DAME, 65-71, ASSOC. PROF, 72-; fac. fel, summer 65. Fulbright fel, Magdalen Col, Oxford, 57-58; ed, Abstr. Eng. Stud, 64. Publ: Fencing in Elizabethan and Jacobean drama; Sidney's defence of poetry, Univ. Nebr; Donne and Casaubon, Times Lit. Suppl, 5/58; Benedick as Signior Montanto, Eng. Lang. Notes, 3/64; American bind; Chinese box; a cold look at a hot war, Chicago, Rev. Vol. XIX, No. 2. Add: Dept. of English, University of Notre Dame, Notre Dame, IN 46556.

SOFIELD, DAVID ROBINSON, b. Chicago, Ill, Mar. 15, 35; m. 58; c. 2. ENGLISH LITERATURE. A.B, Princeton, 57; Ph.D.(Eng), Stanford Univ, 71. Instr. ENG, AMHERST COL, 65-67, asst. prof, 67-72, ASSOC. PROF, 72- Med.C, U.S.A, 57-59. MLA. Seventeenth century English literature; modern poetry. Add: Dept. of English, Amherst College, Amherst, MA 01002.

SOGLIUZZO, A. RICHARD, b. New York, N.Y, Jan. 30, 34; m. 62; c. 2. CONTEMPORARY AMERICAN & ITALIAN THEATRE. A.B, Hunter Col, 56; M.A, Columbia Univ, 60; Ph.D.(theatre, comp. lit), Ind. Univ, Bloomington, 67. Lectr. speech-theatre, Brooklyn Col, 64-67; instr. THEATRE, City Col. New York, 67-68; ASST. PROF, State Univ. N.Y. Col. Brockport, 68-70; STATE UNIV. N.Y. ALBANY, 70-, fels, 71 & 73. Fulbright-Hays sr. res. fel, Italy, 74-75. Sig.C, U.S.A, 57-59, Res, 59-63. Pirandello Soc; Am. Theatre Asn; Theatre Libr. Asn; MLA. Modern American Italian theatre and drama; Luigi Pirandello. Publ: Post World War II Italian drama, In: Crowell's handbook of modern drama, 71; Luigi Pirandello, regista, Quad. Ist. Studi Pirandelliani, Rome, 3/73; Notes for a history of the early Italian American theatre of New York, Theatre Surv, 11/73; plus others. Add: Dept. of Theatre, State University of New York at Albany, 1400 Washington Ave, Albany, NY 12222.

SOKOLNICKI, ALFRED JOHN, b. Milwaukee, Wis, May 21, 18; m. 51. SPEECH PATHOLOGY, PHONETICS. Ph.B, Marquette Univ, 42, M.A, 47; hon. L.H.D, Alliance Col, 61. Instr. speech, MARQUETTE UNIV, 45-53, asst. prof, 53-58, assoc. prof, 58-62, prof, 62-69, DEAN, COL. SPEECH, 69-, dir. speech ther. prog, 45-69. Chmn. scholarship selection comt, var. nat. orgn, 66- A.U.S, 42-52, M/Sgt. Am. Speech & Hearing Asn; Nat. Rehab. Asn; Polish Inst. Arts & Sci. Am. Aphasia; cerebral palsy; phonetics. Publ: The aphasic child, In: Catholic special education, Herder, 71. Add: College of Speech, Marquette University, Milwaukee, WI 53233.

SOLDATI, JOSEPH ARTHUR, b. Rochester, N.H, Sept. 27, 39; m. 67. ENGLISH & AMERICAN LITERATURE. B.A, Oglethorpe Col, 61; M.A, Univ. Calif, Santa Barbara, 68; Ph.D.(Eng), Wash. State Univ, 72. Teaching asst. ENG, Wash. State Univ, 68-71, ASST. PROF, 71-72; ORE. COL. EDUC, 72- Intel.C, U.S.A, 62-64. Rocky Mountain Mod. Lang. Asn. English and American gothic literature; late 19th century poetry; ethnic literature. Publ: Notes on the American wasteland: a white man's way toward understanding, In: Man and the land convocation,II, Ore. Col. Educ, 73; The Americanization of Faust: a study of Brockden Brown's Wieland, Emerson Soc. Quart, 1/74. Add: Dept. of Humanities, Oregon College of Education, Monmouth, OR 97361.

SOLEM, DELMAR EVERETT, b. Volin, S.Dak, Jan. 13, 15; m. 48; c. 3. DRAMA. B.A, Yankton Col, 37; M.A, Northwest. Univ, 47, fel, 49-52, Ph.D, 52. Instr. speech & drama, Purdue Univ, 47-48; drama, Johns Hopkins Univ, 48-49; asst. prof. drama & chmn. dept, Knox Col, 52-56; prof. drama & chmn. dept, Univ. Miami, 56-68; prof. speech & drama & coord. grad. stud, Univ. Ga, 68-72; PROF. DRAMA, UNIV. MIAMI, 72- Vis. prof, Univ. Colo, summers 52 & 53; Northwest. Univ, summer 56; exec. dir. & founder, South. Shakespeare Repertory Theatre, 60-; Univ. Miami res. grant to Univ. Oslo, 67; U.S. Dept. State specialist grant to Brit. Honduras, 67-68 & theatre specialist, 71; consult. & adjudicator, Ministry Educ, Nassau, Bahama Islands, 68-70 & 71. U.S.N.R, 43-46, Ens. Am. Theatre Asn.(admin. v.pres, 56-60); Southeast. Theatre Conf.(v.pres, 59, pres, 60); Speech Commun. Asn; Am. Nat. Theatre & Acad. Production of Elizabethan drama; dramatic literature; Ibsen's use of legend, myth and folklore in Peer Gynt. Publ: Some Elizabethan game scenes, Educ. Theater J, 3/54; An experimental Twelfth night, 59 & Symbolic expression: coordinating the arts, 62, South. Speech J. Add: Dept. of Drama, University of Miami, P.O. Box 8273, Coral Gables, FL 33124.

SOLENSTEN, JOHN MARTIN, b. Madelia, Minn, Sept. 16, 29; m. 58; c. 2. ENGLISH, AMERICAN STUDIES. B.A, Gustavus Adolphus Col, 51; B.S, Mankato State Col, 56, M.A, 61; Ph.D.(Eng. & Am. stud), Bowling Green State Univ, 68. Teacher Eng, Hopkins Sr. High Sch, Minn, 56-72; instr, Wartburg Col, 62-64; Wittenberg Univ, 64-68; ASSOC. PROF. ENG. & AM. STUD, MANKATO STATE COL, 68-, stud. grant, 72. Lang. arts consult, South. Minn. High Schs, 68-73. U.S.A, 51-53, Sgt; Bronze Star Medal. Am. Stud. Asn; Popular Cult. Asn; Norweg-Am. Hist. Asn; NCTE; Soc. Stud. Midwest Lit. The American 1890's; Richard Harding Davis; 19th century Scandinavian literature. Publ: Wister, Davis, and the Virginian, Am. Lit. Realism, spring 72; Davis, Wister, and the mild, mild West, West. Am. Lit, spring 74; Hawthorne's Mrs. Bullfrog and the folktale, J. Popular Cult, spring 74; plus three others. Add: Dept. of English, Mankato State College, Mankato, MN 56001.

SOLER, WILLIAM GORDAN, b. Philadelphia, Pa, Mar. 15, 09; m. 30; c. 1. ENGLISH, ENGLISH EDUCATION. B.S.Ed, Temple Univ, 36, Ed.M, 47, Ed.D.(Eng), 53. Teacher Eng, Phila. Bd. Educ, 29-53; Akiba Acad, 59-61; chmn. dept. Eng, HARCUM JR. COL, 64-68, PROF. ENG. & CHMN. DIV. HUMANITIES, 68- Col. Eng. Asn; NCTE. Literature of the 18th and 19th centuries; American and British essay; English education in junior college. Publ: A reattribution; John Dickinson's authorship of the pamphlet A caution 1798, Pa. Mag. Hist. & Biog, 1/53; John Dickinson's Ode on the French Revolution, Am. Lit, 11/53; John Dickinson's attitude toward the French, 1797-1801, Del. Hist, 9/55. Add: Pelham Park Apt. 405, 229 W. Upsal St, Philadelphia, PA 19119.

SOLETA, CHESTER ANTHONY, C.S.C, b. South Bend, Ind, May 15, 15. ENGLISH LITERATURE. A.B, Univ. Notre Dame, 38; Holy Cross Col, 38-42; Ph.D, Yale, 46. From instr. ENG. to assoc. prof, UNIV. NOTRE DAME, 46-60, PROF, 60-, v.pres. acad, affairs, 58-65. MLA. Romantic poetry. Add: Dept. of English, University of Notre Dame, Notre Dame, IN 46556.

SOLIMINE, JOSEPH, JR, b. Newark, N.J, Oct. 8, 34; m. 58; c. 2. ENGLISH. B.A, Brown Univ, 56; M.A, Univ. R.I, 59; Ph.D.(Eng), Univ. Pa, 64. Instr. Eng, Ohio Univ, 61-64; asst. prof, Wayne State Univ, 64-67; YOUNGSTOWN STATE UNIV, 67-68, ASSOC. PROF. ENG. LIT, 68- MLA; Tennyson Soc. Victorian literature; 19th century culture. Publ: The Burkean idea of the state in Tennyson's poetry: the vision in crisis, Huntington Libr. Quart, 2/67; Browning's My last duchess, Explicator, 9/67; The Idylls of the king, Personalist, winter 69; plus others. Add: 204 Ewing Rd, Youngstown, OH 44512.

SOLLERS, JOHN F, b. Baltimore, Md, Aug. 24, 04; m. 37; c. 2. DRAMA. A.B, Carnegie Inst. Technol, 32, M.A, 33; Ph.D.(drama), Stanford Univ, 62. Instr. drama & speech, Univ. Idaho, 36-43; asst. tech. dir. drama, Stanford Univ, 43-46; asst. prof, Lawrence Col, 46-53; prof, COL. OF IDAHO, 55-69, EMER. PROF. ENG. & DRAMA, 69- Assoc. prof. drama, Univ. Wis-Superior, 70-71, lectr, spring 73. Add: 1502 Ellis Ave, Caldwell, ID 83605.

SOLOMON, ARTHUR LEWIS, b. New York, N.Y, Oct. 1, 18; m. 43; c. 4. SPEECH PATHOLOGY, HUMAN RELATIONS. B.A, Antioch Col, 46; M.A, Univ. N.C, 47; Ph.D.(speech path. & audiol-psychol), Stanford Univ, 60. Teaching & clin. asst, Stanford Univ, 51-53; speech consult, Stanislaus County Schs, Calif, 53-56; mem. fac. & dir. speech & hearing clinic, Chico State Col, 56-62; assoc. prof. speech, dir. commun. prog. & asst. dean stud, Antioch Col, 62-69; PROF. SPEECH & CHMN. DEPT, WEST. WASH. STATE COL, 69- Advan. speech cert, Am. Speech & Hearing Asn, 55, cert. clin. competence, 60; speech clin. supv, Easter Seal Soc, summers 57-62; mem. counseling staff, Chico State Col, 59-62; participant, Shakespeare workshops, Siskyou County & South. Ore. State Col, summers 59-62; vis. fel. counseling psychol, Ohio State Univ, summer 64; mem, NDEA Inst. in Counseling & Guid, Stanford Univ, summer 66; participant, Nat. Training Lab. in Human Relat, Col. South. Utah, summer 66; vis. prof, Univ. Kans. summer 67; mem, Nat. Training Lab. Inst. for Appl. Behav. Sci; mem. prof. adv. bd, Ohio Soc. for Crippled Children & Adults. U.S. Maritime Serv, 42-45. Am. Speech & Hearing Asn; Nat. Soc. Stud. Commun. Language disability and parent-child relations; communication barriers among normative groups; human relations. Publ: Co-auth, The student as speaker and listener—a report of the Antioch Conference on communication skills and interpersonal relationships, 66 & Interpersonal communication, C.C. Thomas, 70; auth, Emotional and behavioral problems of children with functional defects of articulation, Child Develop, 12/61; A comprehensive summer program for speech habilitation in a rural setting, J. Calif. Speech & Hearing Asn, 5/63. Add: Dept. of Speech, Western Washington State College, High St, Bellingham, WA 98225.

SOLOMON, H. ERIC, b. Boston, Mass, Oct. 8, 28; m. 54; c. 2. ENGLISH. B.A, Harvard, 50, M.A, 52, Ph.D.(Eng), 58. Teaching fel. ENG, Harvard, 51-53, 55-58; instr, Ohio State Univ, 58-61, asst. prof, 61-64; assoc. prof, SAN FRANCISCO STATE UNIV, 64-68, PROF, 68- Am. Philos. Soc. travel grant, 61-62. U.S.A, 53-55. MLA; Am. Stud. Asn. American literature; 19th century fiction. Publ: The faded banners: an anthology of 19th century Civil War fiction, Yoseloff, 58; Stephen Crane in England, Ohio State Univ, 64; Stephen Crane: from parody to realism, Harvard, 66; The incest theme in Wuthering Heights, Nineteenth-Century Fiction, 6/59; Huckleberry Finn once more, 12/60 & Jane Eyre: fire and water, 12/63, Col. Eng. Add: Dept. of English, San Francisco State University, San Francisco, CA 94132.

SOLOMON, JAN, English & American Literature, American Studies. See COHN, JAN KADETSKY.

SOLOMON, MARGARET CLAIRE, b. Enid, Okla, Nov. 27, 18; div; c. 2. ENGLISH. B.A, Univ. Hawaii, Manoa, 60; M.A, Univ. Calif, Berkeley, 61; Ph.D.(Eng), Claremont Grad. Sch, 67. Instr. ENG, Univ. Hawaii, Manoa, 60-64; La Verne Col, 65; assoc. prof, UNIV. HAWAII, MANOA, 66-74, PROF, 74- MLA; James Joyce Found; AAUP. James Joyce. Publ: Eternal geomater, the sexual universe of Finnegans wake, South. Ill. Univ, 69; Character as linguistic mode: a new look at streams of consciousness in Ulysses,

In: Ulysses: cinquante ans après, Ed. Didiers, Paris, 74; Striking the lost chord: the motif of waiting in the sirens episode of Ulysses, In: Yeats, Joyce, Beckett, Bucknell Univ, 74; The Porters: a square drama of three tiers in the round, In: A conceptual guide to Finnegans wake, Pa. State Univ, 74. Add: Dept. of English, University of Hawaii at Manoa, Honolulu, HI 96822.

SOLOMON, STANLEY J, b. New York, N.Y, Jan. 3, 37; m. 58; c. 1. ENGLISH. B.A, Brooklyn Col, 57; M.A, Univ. Kans, 60; Ph.D.(Eng), Temple Univ, 68. Instr. ENG, Doane Col, 60-62; Chatham Col, 62-64; asst. prof, Temple Univ, 67-68; IONA COL, 68-69, ASSOC. PROF, 69-, DIR. FILM STUD, 70-, CHMN. DEPT. ENG, 71- MLA; Am. Film Inst; AAUP; Col. Eng. Asn. Film studies; 18th-century literature. Publ: Armageddon; Stopover (two one-act plays), Lutheran Church Press, 69; The film idea, 72 & ed, The classic cinema, 73, Harcourt; auth, Film as an urban art, Carnegie Rev, 4/70; Conflicting sensibility in death poetry: 1740 to the Romantic Age, Enlightenment Essays, summer 71; Ironic perspective in Edgeworth's Castle Rackrent, J. Narrative Tech, 1/72; plus others. Add: Dept. of English, Iona College, New Rochelle, NY 10801.

SOLSTAD, KENNETH deFOREST, b. Orange, N.J, Oct. 9, 42. MODERN ENGLISH. B.A, Yale, 64; M.A, Univ. Calif, Berkeley, 66, Ph.D.(Eng), 71. Vis. asst. prof. ENG, Ill. Col, 72; ASST. PROF, CAMERON COL, 72- AAUP. The fiction of Kingsley Amis; contemporary British fiction. Add: Dept. of Language Arts, Cameron College, Lawton, OK 73501.

SOLVE, MELVIN THEODOR, b. Rosedale Twp, Minn, Apr. 15, 90; m. 21. ENGLISH LITERATURE. A.B, Univ. Ore, 18; fel, Nat. Univ. Norway, 20-21; Ph.D, Univ. Mich, 26. Instr, Univ. Ore, 19-20, 21-23; Univ. Mich, 23-26, asst. prof, 26-28; assoc. prof, UNIV. ARIZ, 28-33, prof. ENG, 33-56, head dept, 38-51, chmn. fac, 46-53, EMER. PROF, 56- Assoc. ed, Ariz. Quart, 45- MLA. Romantic movement in English literature; college composition; the humanities. Publ: Shelley: his theory of poetry, Russell, 64. Add: 190 Del Monte Blvd, Pacific Grove, CA 93950.

SOMMER, GEORGE J, b. New York, N.Y, July 15, 27; m. 51; c. 4. MEDIEVAL LITERATURE. A.B, Manhattan Col, 48; A.M, N.Y. Univ, 53; Ph.D, Fordham Univ, 63. Instr. ENG, Manhattan Col, 52-57; PROF, MARIST COL, 57- U.S.N.R, 45-46. MLA; NCTE. Chaucer; metaphysical poets. Publ: The attitudes of the narrator in Chaucer's Troilus and Criseyde, N.Y-Pa. MLA Newslett, 10/68. Add: Dept. of English, Marist College, Poughkeepsie, NY 12601.

SOMMER, RICHARD J, b. St. Paul, Minn, Aug. 27, 34; m. 61. ENGLISH. B.A, Univ. Minn, 56; A.M, Harvard, 57, Ph.D.(Eng), 62. Asst. prof. ENG, Sir George Williams Univ, 62-67, ASSOC. PROF, CONCORDIA UNIV, 67- Asn. Can. Univ. Teachers Eng. Eighteenth-century novel; modern poetry; critical theory. Publ: The odyssey and primitive religion, 62 & co-auth, Strangers and pilgrims: an essay on the metaphor of journey, 64, Norweg. Univs; Homage to Mr. MacMullin, Delta, Can, 68. Add: Dept. of English, Concordia University, Montreal 107, P.Q, Can.

SONNENFELD, ALBERT, French & Comparative Literatures. See Volume III, Foreign Languages, Linguistics & Philology.

SONNICHSEN, CHARLES LELAND, b. Fonda, Iowa, Sept. 20, 01; m. 33, 56; c. 3. ENGLISH. A.B, Univ. Minn, 24; A.M, Harvard, 27, Ph.D, 31. Asst. master, St. James Sch, Minn, 24-26; instr. ENG, Carnegie Inst. Technol, 27-29; assoc. prof, UNIV. TEX, EL PASO, 31-33, prof, 33-68, H.Y. Benedict prof, 68-72, Minnie Stevens Piper prof, 72, chmn. dept, 33-72, dean grad. sch, 60-68, EMER. PROF. ENG, 72-; ED. & DIR. PUBL, ARIZ. HIST. SOC, 72- Vis. prof, Univ. Tex, 37-38 & 47; Rockefeller fel, Univ. Okla, 49. Standard Oil Co. Teaching Award, 72. West. Writers Am; Rocky Mountain Mod. Lang. Asn; West. Lit. Asn.(pres, 66); West. Hist. Asn. History and literature of the Southwest. Publ: I'll die before I'll run, Harper, 51 & Devin, 62; Tularosa, 61 & Southwest in life and literature, 62, Devin; Outlaw, Swallow, 66; El Paso, 1571-1917, 68 & co-auth, The State National Bank of El Paso, 71, Tex. West. Col; ed, Morris Parker's White oaks, 71 & auth, Colonel Green and the copper skyrocket, 74, Univ. Ariz; The grassroots historian, Southwest. Hist. Quart, 1/70; The Wyatt Earp syndrome, 5/70 & Instant millionaire, 11/71, Am. West. Add: Arizona Historical Society, 949 E. Second St, Tucson, AZ 85719.

SOONS, C. ALAN, Spanish & Comparative Literature. See Volume III, Foreign Languages, Linguistics & Philology.

SOPER, PAUL LEON, b. Bemidji, Minn, Feb. 6, 06; m. 33; c. 2. SPEECH, THEATRE. B.S, Univ. Wash, 30, fel, 30-31, M.A, 32; Ph.D, Cornell Univ, 41; H.L.D, Findlay Col, 62. Instr. speech & theatre, West. State Col. Colo, 31-36; ENG. & SPEECH, UNIV. TENN, KNOXVILLE, 36-38, 39-41, asst. prof, 41-44, assoc. prof, 44-47, PROF, 47-, head dept. speech & theatre, 68-72. Speech Commun. Asn; Am. Theatre Asn; South. Speech Asn.(pres, 43-44). Public speaking; dramatic criticism; theatre production. Publ: Basic public speaking, Oxford, 49, 56 & 63; Representationalism versus form in the theatre, 10/41 & Backgrounds of naturalism in the theatre, 2/47, Quart. J. Speech; GBS as play director, Tenn. Stud. Lit, 61. Add: Dept. of Speech & Theatre, University of Tennessee, Knoxville, TN 37916.

SORBER, EDNA C, b. Philadelphia, Pa, Mar. 19, 19. SPEECH. B.A, Beaver Col, 40; M.S, Univ. Pa, 47; Univ. Colo, summer 48; Ph.D.(speech), Univ. Wis, 59. Teacher high schs, Pa. & Colo, 43-51; asst. prof. SPEECH, Southwest. Col.(Kans), 51-56; Stephen F. Austin State Col, 56-59; assoc. prof, UNIV. WIS-WHITEWATER, 59-61, PROF, 61- Speech Commun. Asn; Am. Forensic Asn. American Indian oratory. Publ: Tournaments: for better and better, Speech Teacher, 1/59; Indian eloquence as American public address, Indian Hist, fall 72; The noble eloquent savage, Ethnohistory, Vol. 9, No. 3; plus two others. Add: Dept. of Speech Communication, University of Wisconsin-Whitewater, Whitewater, WI 53190.

SoRELLE, ZELL RODGERS, b. Clarendon, Tex; m. 35; c. 1. SPEECH. B.S, W.Tex. State Univ, 54, M.A, 55; Ph.D.(ling, speech), Univ. Denver, 65; Edinboro Col, 69; Purdue Univ, 71. ASSOC. PROF. SPEECH & PHONETICS, W.TEX. STATE UNIV, 61- Int. Soc. Phonetic Sci; Phonetic Soc. Japan; Ling. Soc. Am; Am. Dialect Soc; Speech Commun. Asn. Phonetics; dialectology; oral interpretation. Publ: Phonology of Texas Panhandle speech, In: Language behavior, Mouton, The Hague, 70; co-auth, Phonetics: relevancy to prosthodontia, Stud. of Sounds, 71; Texas Panhandle speech, Amarillo, 71; plus others. Add: Dept. of Speech, West Texas State University, Canyon, TX 79105.

SORENSEN, FREDERICK (CHESTER), b. Mendon, Utah, Apr. 8, 08; m. 33; c. 2. ENGLISH. B.S, Utah State Agr. Col, 29; M.A, Stanford Univ, 34, Briggs scholar, 34-35, univ. fel, 35-36, Ph.D, 38. Instr, Ind. State Teachers Col, Terre Haute, 38-44; Mich. State Col, 44-45; asst. prof. Eng. & commun, Univ. Denver, 45-48; assoc. prof. ENG, Ala. Polytech. Inst, 48-52; prof. & head dept, Pa. State Teachers Col, Edinboro, 52; ASSOC. PROF, E.CAROLINA UNIV, 52- NCTE; MLA; Int. Soc. Gen. Semantics. Elizabethan literature; communications; general semantics. Publ: Sir Walter Raleigh's marriage, Stud. Philol; A functional core for the basic communications course, Quart. J.Speech; The basic communications course, Col. Eng. Add: Dept. of English, East Carolina University, Greenville, NC 27834.

SORENSEN, GEORGE WENDELL, b. Dallas, Tex, Oct. 11, 36; m. 58; c. 1. AMERICAN THEATRE HISTORY. B.A, Baylor Univ, 57; M.A, Univ. Colo, Boulder, 66; Univ. Mo-Columbia, 70-74. Teacher drama, Cooper High Sch, Abilene, Tex, 60-67; instr. drama. & dir. theatre, Hardin-Simmons Univ, 67-70; teaching asst. speech, Univ. Mo-Columbia, 70-71; ASSOC. PROF. THEATRE ARTS & CHMN. DEPT, TEX. CHRISTIAN UNIV, 71- Chmn. regional playwriting awards, Am. Col. Theatre Festival, 73-74. U.S.A, 58-60, Res, 61-63. Am. Theatre Asn; Southwest Theatre Conf; Speech Commun. Asn. Nineteenth century American actors; rhetorical criticism; dramatic theory and criticism. Add: Dept. of Theatre Arts, Texas Christian University, Ft. Worth, TX 76129.

SORENSEN, GERALD C, b. Rochester, Minn, Nov. 13, 36; m. 59; c. 2. ENGLISH. B.A, Grinnell Col, 58; M.A, Univ. Minn, 60, Ph.D, 66. Instr. ENG, UNIV. ILL, CHICAGO CIRCLE, 65-66, ASST. PROF, 66- Midwest Mod. Lang. Asn. Victorian fiction; bibliography; textual criticism. Publ: Co-ed, The Victorian mind, Putnam, 69, Cassell's, 70 & Nineteenth-century English verse drama, Fairleigh Dickinson Univ, 73; contrib, Secondary annotated bibliography of Thomas Hardy, North. Ill. Univ, 73. Add: Dept. of English, University of Illinois at Chicago Circle, Chicago, IL 60680.

SORLIEN, ROBERT PARKER, b. Minneapolis, Minn, Nov. 3, 16; m. 41; 58; c. 5. ENGLISH & AMERICAN LITERATURE. A.B, Harvard Col, 38; A.M.T. Harvard Univ, 42; cert, Univ. Birmingham, Eng, 47; Charlotte Beebe Wilbour fel, Brown Univ, 50-51, Ph.D, 55. Librn, William Penn Charter Sch, Germantown, Pa, 38-39; instr. ENG, Englewood Sch. Boys, N.J, 39-42; R.I. State Col, 46-47; asst. prof, UNIV. R.I, 47-55, assoc. prof, 55-68, PROF, 68-, faculty fel, 62-63. Guest lectr. oral Eng. comprehension, U.S. Naval War Col, 59-65; trustee, Conf. Theol. Col. & Univ. Fac, Inc, 59-62, 63-66, 68-, v.pres. & prog. chmn, 62-63; Am. Philos. Soc. Philadelphia, grant-in-aid, 66-68. U.S.M.C.R, 42-46, Maj. New Eng. Col. Eng. Asn.(2nd v.pres, 68, pres, 69-70); MLA; AAUP; New Eng. Renaissance Soc. Seventeenth century English literature; Renaissance newsletters, commonplace books and sermons; metaphysical poetry. Publ: Thomas More anecdotes in an Elizabethan diary, Moreana, 5/72. Add: Dept. of English, University of Rhode Island, Kingston, RI 02881.

SOSNOSKI, JAMES JOSEPH, b. Dickson City, Pa, June 18, 38; m. 65; c. 1. ENGLISH. A.B, Loyola Univ.(Ill), 60, M.A, 65; Ph.D.(Eng), Pa. State Univ, 67. Asst. prof. ENG, MIAMI UNIV, 67-72, ASSOC. PROF, 72- MLA; Col. Eng. Asn; Mediaeval Acad. Am; Early Eng. Text Soc. Literary criticism; Medieval literature. Publ: Craft and intention in James Agee's A death in the family, J. Gen. Educ, 68. Add: Dept. of English, Miami University, Oxford, OH 45056.

SOUDEK, LEV I, English & Applied Linguistics. See Volume III, Foreign Languages, Linguistics & Philology.

SOUDERS, ROBERT LIVINGSTON, b. Preston, Minn, June 18, 20; m. 46. AMERICAN STUDIES. A.B, St. Olaf Col, 44; M.A, Univ. Chicago, 46; Univ. Minn, 50-53; Ph.D, Univ. Iowa, 58. Chmn. dept. Eng, High Sch, Tracy, Minn, 44-45; instr, St. Olaf Col, 46-47, asst. prof, 47-49; instr. commun, Univ. Minn, 50-53; State Univ. Iowa, 54-56; asst. prof. ENG, CALIF. STATE UNIV, CHICO, 56-60, assoc. prof, 60-66, PROF, 66-, COORD. AM. STUD, 62-, DEAN SCH. HUMANITIES & FINE ARTS, 69-, asst. v.pres. acad. affairs, 67-69. U.S.A, 41-42. Am. Stud. Asn; NCTE. The American businessman, 1865-1900; American studies programs in Europe. Publ: Coauth, Writing a term paper, State Univ. Iowa, 56; auth, Essays and fairy tales, Eng. Bull, 56. Add: School of Humanities & Fine Arts, California State University, Chico, First & Normal St, Chico, CA 95926.

SOULE, DONALD E, b. Norwalk, Conn, June 19, 27; m. 55. THEATRE. B.A, Yale, 47; M.A, Univ. Wis, 51; Fulbright scholar, Univ. London, 57-58; Ph.D, Stanford Univ, 59. Instr. speech & drama, Stanford Univ, 56-57; asst. prof. THEATRE, UNIV. B.C, 58-62, assoc. prof, 62-67, PROF, 67-, ASST. DEAN ARTS, 70- U.S.N.R, 44-46. Am. Theatre Asn; Int. Theatre Inst; Can. Theatre Ctr. Dramatic theory; history of the theatre; performance theory. Publ: Comedy, irony and a sense of comprehension, In: Of several branches, Univ. Toronto, 68; Research for a theatre of the future, Stage Can. Suppl, 71. Add: Office of the Dean of Arts, University of British Columbia, Vancouver 8, B.C, Can.

SOULE, GEORGE, b. Fargo, N.Dak, Mar. 3, 30; m. 61; c. 1. ENGLISH LITERATURE. B.A, Carleton Col, 51; Rotary Int. fel, Cambridge, 52-53; M.A, Yale, 56, Sterling fel, 57-58, Ph.D, 60. Instr. ENG, Oberlin Col, 58-60; asst. prof, Univ. Wis, 60-62; CARLETON COL, 62-66, assoc. prof, 66-71, PROF, 71-, dir. centennial celebration, 65-67, NDEA Summer Eng. Inst, 65. Consult, U.S. Dept. Health, Educ. & Welfare, 65-66. U.S.A, 54-55. MLA; Shakespeare Asn. Am. Shakespeare; Boswell and Johnson; British studies. Publ: Ed, The theatre of the mind, Prentice-Hall, 75; auth, Hamlet's quietus, Col. Eng, 12/64; The open heart, Setting the Stage, 66. Add: Dept. of English, Carleton College, Northfield, MN 55057.

SOULES, EUGENE H, b. San Francisco, Calif, Dec. 17, 32; m. 57; c. 1. ENGLISH. B.A, San Francisco State Col, 57, M.A, 58; Ph.D.(Eng), Univ. of the Pac, 65. Instr. ENG, Shasta Col, 58-62, chmn. dept, 60-62; asst, Univ. of the Pac, 62-65; asst. prof, CALIF. STATE COL, SONOMA, 65-68, assoc. prof, 68-72, PROF, 72-, chmn. dept, 67-70. U.S.A, 53-55. MLA; NCTE (mem. comt. affiliate relations, 73-). Mediaeval English literature, especially Chaucer; linguistics. Add: Dept. of English, California State College, Sonoma, 1810 E. Cotati Ave, Rohnert Park, CA 94928.

SOUTH, MALCOLM HUDSON, b. Gloucester, Va, Apr. 12, 37; m. 64; c. 2. ENGLISH LITERATURE. Merit scholar, Col. William & Mary, 58, A.B, 59; NDEA fel, Duke Univ, 59-61, M.A, 61; Ph.D.(Eng), Univ. Ga, 68. Asst. prof. ENG, Campbell Col, 61-62; instr, Clemson Univ, 62-64; asst. prof, E.CAROLINA UNIV, 66-74, ASSOC. PROF, 74- S.Atlantic Mod. Lang. Asn; Victorians Inst. Sixteenth and 17th century English literature; the novel. Publ: A note on Spenser and Sir Thomas Browne, Mod. Lang. Rev, 67; 'The Vncleane birds, in Seuenty-Seuen': The alchemist, Stud. Eng. Lit, 73. Add: Dept. of English, East Carolina University, Greenville, NC 27834.

SOUTHER, JAMES WALTER, b. San Bernardino, Calif, Dec. 3, 19; m. 45; c. 2. ENGLISH. B.S, Univ. Wash, 47, M.A, 48. PROF. TECH. & SCI. WRITING, UNIV. WASH, 48-, DIR. PLACEMENT CTR, 62- Consult. & teacher, Civil Serv. Comn, Seattle & Denver Regions, 65-74. U.S.A.A.F, 42-45, S/Sgt. Am. Soc. Eng. Educ; AAAS; assoc. fel. Soc. Tech. Commun. Industrial communications and technical and scientific writing; managing industrial communications. Publ: Guide to technical writing, Univ. Wash, 54; co-auth, Technical report writing, Wiley, 57 & 74; auth, Career planning and placement manual, Col. Placement Counc, 74; Writing better reports, Am. Med. Asn, 11/66; Better staff communications, Am. Soc. Training Develop. J, 6/67; The technical supervisor and the writing process, Tech. Writing & Commun, 7/71. Add: 301 Loew Hall, University of Washington, Seattle, WA 98105.

SOUTHWELL, SAMUEL BEALL, b. Lockhart, Tex, Jan. 15, 22; m. 45; c. 2. ENGLISH, VICTORIAN LITERATURE. B.J, Univ. Tex, 46, M.A, 49, Ph.D. (Eng. lit), 56; hon. Dr, Autonomous Univ. Guadalajara, 65. Asst. prof. Eng, Tex. A&M Univ, 47-55; assoc. prof, Panamerican Univ, 55-56; Tex. A&M Univ, 56-59; educ. exchange off, U.S. Embassy, Mex, 59-61; U.S. consul cult. affairs, Guadalajara, Mex, 62-65; assoc. prof. Eng, UNIV. HOUSTON; 65-70, PROF. ENG. LIT, 70-, ASST. TO V.PRES. & DEAN FAC, 67-, chmn. dept, 69-73. MLA; Col. Eng. Asn. Victorian prose and poetry. Publ: If all the rebels die, Doubleday, 66. Add: Dept. of English, University of Houston, Houston, TX 77004.

SOUTHWORTH, JAMES GRANVILLE, b. Monroe, Mich, Oct. 18, 96. ENGLISH LITERATURE. A.B, Univ. Mich, 18; B.A, Oxford, 27, M.A, 33; Ph.D, Harvard, 31. Prof. ENG, Col. Puget Sound, 28-29; Heidelberg Col, 31-33; from assoc. prof. to prof, UNIV. TOLEDO, 34-66, EMER. PROF, 66- U.S.A, 17-19. MLA; Col. Eng. Asn. Criticism of the romantic poets, 1798 to 1885. Publ: Some modern American poets, 50; More modern American poets, 54, Verses of cadence, 54 & Prosody of Chaucer, 63, Vauxhall Gardens; Chaucer's prosody: a plea for a reliable text, In: Chaucer's mind and art, Oliver & Boyd, 68. Auth, Mid-century American Poetry (lectr. tape), Eichosa, Tokyo, 73. Add: 625 Virginia St, Toledo, OH 43620.

SPACKS, PATRICIA MEYER, b. San Francisco, Calif, Nov. 17, 29; m. 55; c. 1. ENGLISH LITERATURE. B.A, Rollins Col, 49; univ. scholar, Yale, 49, M.A, 50; McEnerney fel, Univ. Calif, 53, Ph.D, 55. Instr. Eng, Ind. Univ, 54-56; humanities, Univ. Fla, 58-59; ENG, WELLESLEY COL, 59-61, asst. prof, 61-65, assoc. prof, 65-68, PROF, 68- Am. Asn. Univ. Women Farr fel. & Wellesley Col. jr. leave grant, 62-63; John Simon Guggenheim Found. fel, 69-70; Nat. Endowment for Humanities sr. fel, 74. MLA. Women's writing; 18th-century novel and autobiography; 18th-century poetry. Publ: The varied God: a critical study of The seasons, Univ. Calif, 59; The insistence of horror: aspects of the supernatural in 18th-century poetry, 62, The poetry of vision, 67 & An argument of images: the poetry of Alexander Pope, 71, Harvard; ed, Eighteenth-century poetry, 64, Late Augustan prose, 71 & Late Augustan poetry, 73, Prentice-Hall; auth, John Gay, Twayne, 65; The world of Hedda Gabler, Tulane Drama Rev, 62; In search of sincerity, Col. Eng, 68; Free women, Hudson Rev, 71. Add: Dept. of English, Wellesley College, Wellesley, MA 02181.

SPANGEHL, STEPHEN DOUGLAS, b. Brooklyn, N.Y, July 11, 43; m. 65. MEDIAEVAL LITERATURE, LINGUISTICS. B.A, N.Y. Univ, 65, N.Y. State Regents fel, 65-67, M.A, 66; Ph.D.(Eng), Univ. Pa, 72. ASST. PROF. ENG, UNIV. AKRON, 69- Mediaeval Acad. Am; MLA; Ling. Soc. Am. Middle English literature; syntax and semantics in modern English; prosody. Add: Dept. of English, University of Akron, Akron, OH 44325.

SPANGLER, GEORGE MERVIN, b. New Oxford, Pa, Mar. 7, 37; m. 60; c. 2. AMERICAN LITERATURE. A.B, Haverford Col, 59; Woodrow Wilson fel, Univ. Calif, Berkeley, 60, M.A, 62, Ph.D.(Eng), 65. ASSOC. PROF. ENG, CALIF. STATE UNIV, FULLERTON, 66- MLA; Am. Stud. Asn. American fiction 1870-1920; theory of fiction. Publ: Pudd'nhead Wilson: a parable of property, Am. Lit, 3/70; The shadow of a dream: Howell's homosexual tragedy, Am. Quart, spring 71; Moral anxiety in A modern instance, New Eng. Quart, summer 73; plus ten others. Add: Dept. of English, California State University, Fullerton, 800 N. State College Blvd, Fullerton, CA 92631.

SPANOS, WILLIAM V, b. Newport, N.H, Jan. 1, 25; m. 54; c. 3. ENGLISH, EXISTENTIAL PHILOSOPHY. B.A, Wesleyan Univ, 50; Wesleyan Univ. Winchester fel. & M.A, Columbia Univ, 54; Ph.D.(Eng), Univ. Wis, 64. Master Eng, Mt. Hermon Sch, 51-53; asst. ed, Encycl. Americana, Grolier, 54-56; instr. ENG, Univ. Ky, 60-62; ASST. PROF, Knox Col, 62-66; STATE UNIV. N.Y. BINGHAMTON, 66- State Univ. N.Y. fac. fel, spring 67; Fulbright prof. Am. lit, Nat. Univ. Athens, 69-70; founder & co-ed, boundary 2, 72- U.S.A, 43-45. MLA; Col. Eng. Asn; Mod. Greek Stud. Asn. Modern British and American poetry; modern drama; redefining modernism in literature. Publ: Ed, A casebook on existentialism, Crowell, 66; auth, The Christian tradition in modern British verse drama: the poetics of sacramental time, Rutgers Univ, 67; Modern drama and the Aristotelian tradition: the formal imperatives of absurd time, Contemporary Lit, summer 71; The detective and the boundary: some notes on the postmodern literary imagination, fall 72 & co-ed, Contemporary Greek writing, winter 73, boundary 2; plus several others. Add: Dept. of English, Harpur College, State University of New York at Binghamton, Binghamton, NY 13901.

SPARKS, GEORGE FRAY, b. Emporia, Kans, June 29, 12; m. 43. SPEECH, RHETORIC. B.S, Kans. State Teachers Col, 36; M.A, Northwest. Univ, 41; Ph.D.(speech), Univ. Utah, 52. From instr. to PROF. SPEECH, UNIV. ARIZ, 46- Dir. Eng. Lang. Inst. For. Stud, Inst. Int. Educ, Univ. Ariz, 61-69. Speech Commun. Asn. Classical and historical rhetoric; public speaking; English for foreign students. Publ: Ed, A many colored toga: the diary of Henry Fountain Ashurst, Univ. Ariz, '62. Add: Dept. of Speech, University of Arizona, Tucson, AZ 85721.

SPARLING, RUSSELL PAUL, b. St. Louis, Mo, Mar. 5, 39; m; c. 2. AMERICAN & ENGLISH LITERATURE. B.A, Univ. Tex, Arlington, 62; Woodrow Wilson fel, Duke Univ, 62-63, M.A, 63, NDEA fel, 68-69, univ. fel, 69-70, Ph.D.(Eng), 72. Instr. ENG, Col. William & Mary, 64-68; ASST. PROF. W.TEX. STATE UNIV, 70- Conf. Col. Teachers Eng; Southeast. Am. Stud. Asn; MLA. Modern drama; American studies. Add: Dept. of English, West Texas State University, Canyon, TX 79015.

SPATZ, JONAS, b. Brooklyn, N.Y, Sept. 2, 35; m. 62. ENGLISH. B.A, Brooklyn Col, 58; M.A, N.Y. Univ, 60; Ph.D.(Eng), Ind. Univ, 64. Instr. ENG, Brooklyn Col, 64-66; asst. prof, UNIV. MO-KANSAS CITY, 66-69, ASSOC. PROF, 69-, asst. prof. res. grant, summer 68. U.S.A.F, 59, Res, 59-65. MLA. American literature; nineteenth century English literature. Publ: Hollywood in fiction: some versions of the American myth, Mouton, The Hague, 68; Dreiser's Bulwark: an archaic masterpiece, In: The forties, Everett Edwards, 69; Love and death in Tennyson's Maud, Tex. Stud. Lit. & Lang, 74; The mystery of Eros: sexual initiation in Coleridge's Christabel, PMLA, 75. Add: Dept. of English, University of Missouri-Kansas City, Kansas City, MO 64110.

SPATZ, LOIS S, b. Baltimore, Md, Mar. 28, 40; m. 62. ENGLISH, CLASSICS. B.A, Goucher Col, 60; M.A.T, Johns Hopkins Univ, 61; M.A, Ind. Univ, 64, Ph.D.(classics), 68. Teaching asst. Greek, Ind. Univ, 61-62; lectr. classics in transl. Latin, Brooklyn Col, 65-66; assoc. prof. West heritage, Park Col, 68-73; ASST. PROF. ENG, UNIV. MO-KANSAS CITY, 73- Am. Philol. Asn. Greek drama; mythology; Bible as literature. Publ: Metrical motivs in Aristophanes' Clouds, Quad. Urbinati, 72. Add: Dept. of English, University of Missouri-Kansas City, 5315 Holmes, Kansas City, MO 64110.

SPAULDING, KENNETH ANSEL, b. Choteau, Mont, Apr. 26, 13; m. 37; c. 1. ENGLISH. B.A, Univ. Mont, 36, M.A, 37; Ph.D.(Eng), State Univ. Iowa, 51. From instr. to asst. prof. ENG, Agr. & Mech. Col, Tex, 40-46; from asst. prof. to assoc. prof, Univ. Conn, 46-64; vis. lectr, Univ. Mass, 64-65, dir. grad. stud, 65-68; CHMN. DEPT, WIS. STATE UNIV, EAU CLAIRE, 68- Fulbright lectr, Iran, 59-61; dir, Eng. Lang. Serv, Inc, Guinea, 62- U.S.N, 44-45. MLA; Col. Eng. Asn. Edgar Allan Poe; Melville, Hawthorne and James; Western American exploration. Publ: Ed, On the Oregon Trail: Robert Stuart's journey of discovery, 53 & Fur hunters of the Far West, 56, Univ. Okla; auth, Anne Bradstreet, James Brown, William Hill Brown & Charles Brockden Brown, In: Encyclopedia Americana, Grolier, 68. Add: Dept. of English, Wisconsin State University, Eau Claire, WI 54701.

SPEARMAN, WALTER SMITH, b. Newberry, S.C, Jan. 9, 08; m. 37; c. 2. JOURNALISM. A.B, Univ. N.C, 29, A.M, 37; cert, Univ. Lyon, 30. PROF. JOUR, UNIV. N.C, CHAPEL HILL, 35-, managing ed, Alumni Rev, 38-42. Reporter, book ed. & drama critic, The Charlotte News, N.C, 30-35; ed. writer, Greensboro Daily News, 56; Fund Adult Educ. fel, Harvard, 57-58. Qm.C, U.S.A, 42-45, 2nd Lt. Asn. Educ. in Jour. Editorial writing; book, movie and play reviewing. Publ: Death of the swan; Transient; Country Sunday; The Carolina playmakers: the first fifty years, Univ. N.C, 70. Add: School of Journalism, University of North Carolina at Chapel Hill, Chapel Hill, NC 27514.

SPEARS, GEORGE J, b. Olean, N.Y, Mar. 7, 09; m. 54. ENGLISH LITERATURE. A.B, Univ. Buffalo, 42, Ed.M, 45; Ph.D, Univ. Ottawa, 52. Lectr. Eng. & asst. dean, Univ. Buffalo, 45-51; assoc. prof. Eng, Russell Sage Col, 51-62, prof, 62-69, dean eve. col, 51-63, dir. summer session, 51-69; CHMN. LANG, LIT. & PHILOS, DIR. LIBR. SERV. & AUDIO-VISUAL SERV, MANATEE JR. COL, BRADENTON, 69- Lectr, summers, Univ. South. Calif, 52, N.Y. Univ, 53, Univ. Ottawa, 54; acting dean, Jr. Col. Albany, 62-69. MLA; Asn. Univ. Eve. Cols. Publ: The satire of Saki, Exposition, 63; History of Russell Sage College, Artcrafter, 65. Add: 1025 Whitfield Ave, Sarasota, FL 33580.

SPEARS, IRENE OSMOND, b. Provo, Utah, Sept. 15, 07; m. 45; c. 6. ENGLISH, FRENCH. B.A, Brigham Young Univ, 29; M.A, Stanford Univ, 34, Ph.D, 42; Univ. Paris, summer 62. Instr. high sch, 29-33; lang, BRIGHAM YOUNG UNIV, 29-36, asst. prof, 36-45, assoc. prof. ENG, 45-64, prof, 64-73, res. grant, 63; EMER. PROF, 73- Rocky Mountain Lang. Asn; MLA; NCTE; AAUP. Translations or adaptations of French, Spanish, German and Italian. Publ: Selected poems of Victor Hugo (adaptations), 64 & Continental verse (adaptations), 67, Brigham Young Univ. Add: 3224 N. Mojave Lane, Provo, UT 84601.

SPEARS, MONROE KIRK, b. Darlington, S.C, Apr. 28, 16; m. 41; c. 1. ENGLISH LITERATURE. A.B. & A.M, Univ. S.C, 37; Scribner & Procter fel, Princeton, 38-40, Ph.D, 40. Instr. ENG, Univ. Wis, 40-42; asst. prof, Vanderbilt Univ, 46-48, assoc. prof, 48-52; prof, Univ. of the South, 52-64; MOODY PROF, RICE UNIV, 64- Ed, Sewanee Rev, 52-61; Rockefeller Found. fel. to India & Eng, 56; vis. prof, Univ. Wash, summer 60; Univ. Mich, summer 61; Swarthmore Col, 61-62; Guggenheim fel. to Eng. & Austria, 65-66 & 72-73. Sig.C, U.S.A.A.F, 42-46, Capt. Contemporary literature; 18th century literature. Publ: Co-auth, Literary works of Matthew Prior, Clarendon & Oxford, 59; auth, Poetry of W.H. Auden, 63 & Dionysus and the city: modernism in twentieth century poetry, 70 & 71, Oxford Univ; ed, W.H. Auden: a collection of critical essays, Prentice-Hall, 64; auth, Hart Crane, Univ. Minn, 65; ed, Shakespeare, narrative poems, Dell, 68; auth, Space against time in modern American poetry, Tex. Christian Univ, 72. Add: Dept. of English, Rayzor Hall, Rice University, Houston, TX 77001.

SPEARS, WOODRIDGE, b. East Point, Ky, Jan. 22, 13; m. 35; c. 3. ENGLISH. A.B, Morehead State Univ, 35; A.M, Univ. Ky, 47, Ph.D, 53. Teacher, Pub. Sch, Ky, 35-45; instr. ENG, Univ. Ky, 45-46, 48-51, 52-53; assoc. prof, GEORGETOWN COL, 53-63, PROF, 63- S.Atlantic Mod. Lang. Asn; Poetry Soc. Am; NCTE. Milton; the American novel; Southern history. Publ: The feudalist, 46; Elizabeth Madox Roberts, a biographical and critical study, 53; River island, 63; Willow near water in word of a metal, In: Kentucky Harvest, Brandenburg, 69; Today at April, In: Diamond Anthology, A.S. Barnes, 70; plus others. Add: 905 Shoshone, Georgetown, KY 40324.

SPECK, PAUL SURGI, b. New Orleans, La, Sept. 13, 46; m. 67; c. 3. ENGLISH & AMERICAN LITERATURE. B.A, Univ. St. Thomas, (Tex), 68; NDEA fel, Auburn Univ, 68-71, M.A, 70, Ph.D.(Eng), 73. ASST. PROF. ENG, SOUTHEAST. LA. UNIV, 72- MLA. Eighteenth century British literature; the novel; drama. Publ: A structural analysis of Henry James's Roderick Hudson, Stud. in the Novel, fall 70. Add: Dept. of English, Southeastern Louisiana University, P.O. Box 802, University Station, Hammond, LA 70401.

SPECKMAN, WILLIAM HENRY, b. Mishawaka, Ind, May 26, 40; m. 66; c. 2. LITERATURE. B.A, West. Mich. Univ, 62; Woodrow Wilson fel, Brandeis Univ, 62-63; Entrance fel, Univ. Chicago, 63; M.A, Claremont Grad. Sch, 68, Danforth Found. Kent fel, 69-70, Ph.D.(Eng), Am. lit), 71. Instr. Eng, Grand Valley State Col, 65-67; humanities, Harvey Mudd Col, 68-70; ASST. PROF. ENG, STATE UNIV. N.Y. BINGHAMTON, 70- MLA; Soc. Relig. Higher Educ. American Indian mythology; satire; theory of value. Add: Dept. of English, State University of New York at Binghamton, Binghamton, NY 13901.

SPECTOR, ROBERT DONALD, b. New York, N.Y, Sept. 21, 22; m. 45; c. 2. ENGLISH. B.A, L.I. Univ, 48; M.A, N.Y. Univ, 49; Ph.D, Columbia Univ, 62. Instr. ENG, L.I. UNIV, 48-59, asst. prof, 59-61, assoc. prof, 61-64, PROF, 64-, CHMN. DEPT, 70-, trustee, 68-69. Co-ed, Belles Lettres in Eng. Ser, Johnson Reprint Corp, 66- U.S.C.G, 42-45. MLA; Soc. Advan. Scand. Stud; Am-Scand. Found. Contemporary literature; 18th century English literature and linguistics. Publ: Seven masterpieces of Gothic horror, 63, ed, Dicken's Hard times, 64 & Goldsmith's Vicar of Wakefield, 64, Bantam; ed, Essays on the 18th century novel, Ind. Univ, 65; auth, English literary periodicals, Mouton, The Hague, 66; Tobias George Smollett, 69 & Pär Lagerkvist, 73, Twayne; Lagerkvist's dialogue of the soul, Scand. Stud, 65; Smollett's traveler, In: Tobias Smollett, Oxford, 71; The connoisseur, In: English writers of the eighteenth century, Columbia, 71; plus two others. Add: Dept. of English, Long Island University, 385 Flatbush Ave. Extension, Brooklyn, NY 11201.

SPEHAR, ELIZABETH MARIE, b. Crested Butte, Colo, Jan. 2, 24. ENGLISH, SLAVISTICS. B.A, Rosary Col, 45; cert, Laval Univ, 44; M.A, Univ. Colo, 46, Ph.D, 62. Instr. Eng, Univ. Colo, 46-50; teacher, Leadville High Sch, 51-52; teacher, librn. & asst. prin, Crested Butte High Sch, 52-56; instr, ENG, WEST. STATE COL. COLO, 56-60, asst. prof, 60-62, ASSOC. PROF, 62- Colo. chmn, NCTE Achievement Awards, 65-68. NCTE; AAUP; NEA; Am. Asn. Advan. Slavic Stud. Hopkins and Chaucer; contemporary Yugoslav literature; methods of teaching English. Publ: Chaucer's Anelida and Arcite: a new edition, Diss. Abstr, 62; co-auth, Teaching composition, Colo. State Dept. Educ, 64; auth, Barron's simplified edition of Jane Austen's Pride and prejudice, Barron's Educ. Ser, 71; From university to junior high: the adaptation of a system, Colo. Sch. J, 2/59; Bulatiovic's The red cock flies to heaven, Slavic Rev, 12/63; Literary Ljubljana today, Prosveta, 5/64. Add: Dept. of English, Western State College of Colorado, Gunnison, CO 81230.

SPEIRS, LOGAN HASTIE, b. Riga, Latvia, Mar. 9, 38; British citizen; m. 70. ENGLISH. B.A, Cambridge, 60, M.A, 65. Lectr. ENG, Univ. Amsterdam, 61-68; asst. prof. UNIV. CALIF, SANTA BARBARA, 69-72, ASSOC. PROF, 72- Lectr. Eng, Univ. Nijmegen, 63-67; Univ. Calif. humanities grantee, 73. Eighteenth and 19th century British novel; Richardson and Jane Austen. Publ: Tolstoy and Chekhov, Cambridge, 71; Anna Karenina, a study in structure, 1/66 & Tolstoy's thinking in War and peace, 11/69, Neophilologus; Essay on Chekhov's The cherry orchard, 6/68, Oxford Rev; plus two others. Add: Dept. of English, University of California, Santa Barbara, CA 93106.

SPEIRS, RUSSELL FREEMAN, b. Buffalo, N.Y, Feb. 19, 01. ENGLISH. B.O.E, Syracuse Univ, 23; M.A, Univ. South. Calif, 35. Instr. Eng. & dir dramatics, COLGATE UNIV, 23-60, prof. ENG, 66-71, EMER. PROF, 71- U.S.A.F, 42-45, S/Sgt. Play-writing. Publ: Shouts from the bottom of a deep well, Needleshop, 71; Andy Kerr: a man who served, Salina, 71; Professor of Victorian literature, Eng. J, 32; Lost with frost, Yankee Mag, 1/72; One third of an island, Down East, 6/72; plus others. Add: Kingston Rd, Elbridge, NY 13060.

SPENCER, BENJAMIN TOWNLEY, b. Winchester, Ky, Apr. 23, 04; m. 24; c. 1. ENGLISH & AMERICAN LITERATURE. A.B, Ky. Wesleyan Col, 25, hon. D.Litt, 49; Johns Hopkins Univ, 25-26; Univ. Chicago, 25, 27; Taft fel, Univ. Cincinnati, 27-28, A.M, 27, Ph.D, 30. Assoc. & assoc. prof. Eng, Ky. Wesleyan Col, 26-30; asst. prof, OHIO WESLEYAN UNIV, 30-34, assoc. prof, 34-37, prof, 37-69, dir. libr, 38-40, EMER. PROF. ENG, 69- Libr. Congr. res. grant, 45-46; vis. prof, Uppsala Univ, Sweden, 52-53; Fulbright lectr. Am. lit, Univs. London & Manchester, 59-60; vis. prof. grad. summer sch. for teachers, Wesleyan Univ, 58, 63, 65, 67 & 72; vis. prof, Mich. State Univ, spring 70; Bowling Green State Univ, spring 71. MLA. English Renaissance; literary nationalism in America; 19th century American literature. Publ: Quest for nationality, Syracuse; ed, The Bondman, 32 & co-auth, Seventeenth century studies, 33, Princeton; Pound: the American strain, PMLA, 12/66; auth, Sherwood Anderson: American mythopoeist, Am. Lit, 3/69; Shakespeare and the hazards of nobility, Centennial Rev, winter 73. Add: Dept. of English, Ohio Wesleyan University, Delaware, OH 43015.

SPENCER, CHRISTOPHER, b. Cleveland, Ohio, Apr. 14, 30; m. 52; c. 3. ENGLISH. A.B, Princeton, 52; M.A, Yale, 53, Ph.D.(Eng), 55. Instr. Eng, Duke Univ, 55-58; asst. prof, Little Rock Univ, 58-59, assoc. prof. & head dept, 59-62, chmn. div. humanities, 60-62, assoc. prof. ENG, Ill. State Univ, 62-65, PROF, 65-70; UNIV. N.C, GREENSBORO, 70-, acting head dept, 73. Guggenheim fel, 67. MLA; Shakespeare Asn. Am; S.Atlantic Mod. Lang. Asn; Southeast Renaissance Conf; AAUP. Shakespeare; Elizabethan and Restoration drama. Publ: Davenant's Macbeth from the Yale manuscript, Yale, 61; Five Restoration adaptations of Shakespeare, Univ. Ill, 65; Nahum Tate, Twayne, 72; Macbeth and Davenant's The rivals, Shakespeare Quart, 69; co-auth, Styan Thirlby: a forgotten editor of Shakespeare, Shakespeare Stud, 70; auth, Shakespeare's Merchant of Venice in sixty-three editions, Stud. Bibliog, 72. Add: Dept. of English, University of North Carolina at Greensboro, Greensboro, NC 27412.

SPENCER, DAVID GELVIN, b. Maitland, Mo, July 13, 24; m. 48; c. 3. ENGLISH. A.B, Univ. Calif, 48, M.A, 49, Ph.D.(Eng), 52; Johns Hopkins Univ, 49-50. Instr. ENG, Ore. State Univ, 52-55, asst. prof, 55-59; Loyola Univ. (Ill), 59-61, assoc. prof, 61-66, prof, 66-69; PROF. & CHMN. DEPT, CALIF. STATE COL, BAKERSFIELD, 69- Co-ed, Restoration & 18th Century Theatre Res, Loyola Univ.(Ill), 62-69. U.S.A, 43-46. Int. Asn. Univ. Prof. Eng; Am. Soc. 18th Century Stud; Int. Soc. 18th Century Stud; MLA; Johnson Soc. Great Lakes Region (v.pres, 60-61, secy, 62-63). Political poetry and satire; 18th century English literature; 18th century drama. Publ: Co-ed, Exposition and persuasion, 57 & co-auth, Contexts for composition, 65, 69 & 72, Appleton; co-ed, Contemporary drama: thirteen plays, Scribner, 62, 2nd ed, 70 & Restoration and eighteenth century theatre research: a bibliographical guide 1900-1968, South. Ill. Univ, 71; auth, Henry Mackenzie: a practical sentimentalist, PLL, 67. Add: Dept. of English, California State College, Bakersfield, 9001 Stockdale, Bakersfield, CA 93309.

SPENCER, JEFFRY BURRESS, b. San Francisco, Calif, Jan. 2, 27; m. 48; c. 3. ENGLISH LITERATURE. A.B, Univ. Calif, Berkeley, 48; M.A, De-Paul Univ, 60; Ph.D.(Eng), Northwest. Univ, 71. Instr. ENG, Mundelein Col, 60-65, asst. prof, 66-69; ASSOC. PROF, CALIF. STATE COL, BAKERSFIELD, 73- Summer fel, Henry E. Huntington Libr. & Art Gallery, 73; Am. Philos. Soc. grant, 74; Nat. Endowment for Humanities summer stipend, 74. MLA; Am. Soc. 18th Century Stud. Literature and the visual arts; Restoration and 18th century literature. Publ: Heroic nature: ideal landscape in English poetry from Marvell to Thomson, Northwest. Univ, 73. Add: Dept. of English, California State College, Bakersfield, CA 93309.

SPENGEMANN, WILLIAM CHARLES, b. San Jose, Calif, Aug. 11, 32; m. 62. ENGLISH. A.B, San Jose State Col, 57; Ph.D, Stanford Univ, 61. Asst. instr. Eng, Stanford Univ, 58-60; asst. prof, Univ. Hawaii, 61-62; Univ. Conn, 62-66, assoc. prof, 66-67; ENG. & AM. LIT, CLAREMONT GRAD. SCH, 67-70, PROF, 70- Teaching fel, Stanford Univ, 58-60, Stanford-Wilson fel, 60-61; asst. provost, Univ. Conn, 65-67; Nat. Endowment for Humanities fel, 69. Best Essay Prize, Am. Quart, 65. U.S.M.C, 54-56, 1st Lt. MLA; Philol. Asn. Pac. Coast. American literature; autobiography; romanticism. Publ: Mark Twain and the backwoods angel, Kent State Univ, 67; co-auth, Autobiograph and the American myth, Am. Quart, fall 65. Add: Dept. of English & American Literature, Claremont Graduate School, Claremont, CA 91711.

SPERRY, STUART M, b. New York, N.Y, Feb. 22, 29. ENGLISH. A.B, Princeton, 51; A.M, Harvard, 55, Ph.D, 59. Lectr. ENG, IND. UNIV, BLOOMINGTON, 58-59, instr, 59-62, asst. prof, 62-65, assoc. prof, 65-70, PROF, 70- Vis. assoc. prof, Univ. Calif, Riverside, 68-69. U.S.A, 51-53, 1st Lt. MLA. Romantic period. Publ: Keats the poet, Princeton, 73; Keats's Skepticism and Voltaire, Keats-Shelley J, winter 63; Richard Woodhouse's interleaved and annotated copy of Keats's Poems (1817), Lit. Monogr, 67. Add: Dept. of English, Indiana University, Bloomington, IN 47401.

SPEVACK, MARVIN, b. New York, N.Y, Dec. 17, 27. ENGLISH. A.B, City Col. New York, 48; A.M, Harvard, 50, Ph.D.(Eng), 53. Teaching fel. gen. educ, Harvard, 51-53; instr. ENG, City Col. New York, 55-60, asst. prof, 61-63; PROF, UNIV. MÜNSTER, 63- Instr, Psychol. Warfare Sch, U.S. Army, 54-55; vis. prof, Univ. Münster, 61-62; Univ. Munich, 62-63; Folger Shakespeare Libr. sr. fel, 70-; Guggenheim fel, 73-74. Shakespeare; Elizabethan literature; drama. Publ: A complete and systematic concordance to the works of Shakespeare, (6 vols), Georg Olms Hildesheim, Germany, 68-70; ed, Shakespeare's Romeo and Juliet, W.C. Brown, 70; ed, Lord Byron's Werner in the acting version of William Charles Macready, Fink, Munich, 70; The Harvard concordance to Shakespeare, Harvard Univ, 73; auth, Shakespeare's early use of wordplay: Love's labour's lost, In: Festschrift für Edgar Mertner, Fink, Munich, 69; Shakespeare's English: the core vocabulary, Rev. Nat. Lit, fall 72. Add: Englisches Seminar, Universitaet Münster, Münster, Germany.

SPICER, HAROLD, b. Gosport, Ind, Dec. 10, 21; m. 46; c. 3. ENGLISH. B.A, DePauw Univ, 47, M.A, 49; fel, Ind. Univ, 54-55, Danforth grant, 59-60, univ. fel, 60, Ph.D.(Eng), 62. Instr. Eng, West. Ill. State Col, 49-55, asst. prof, 55-57; DePauw Univ, 57-62, assoc. prof. 63; ENG. & JOUR, IND. STATE UNIV, TERRE HAUTE, 63-72, PROF, 73- Lectr, Ind. Univ. Exten. Ctr, Indianapolis, 60-63, vis. prof, summer 62; Eli Lilly res. grant, summer 63; Ind. State Univ. Found. res. grant, summer 63; nat. coord. of dist. chmn, Nat. Counc. Col. Publ. Adv, 64-65, chmn. publ. & ed, Col. Press Rev, 65-67; consult, Little, Brown & Co, Boston, 69-70. U.S.N.R, 42-46. MLA; Mod. Humanities Res. Asn. English romanticism; American romanticism; journalism. Publ: An introduction to news writing, Ind. State Univ, 65; Biblical imagery in William Blake's America, Abstr. Eng. Stud, 11/71; To burst joy's grape: negative capability in Keats odes, Ind. Eng. J, summer 73; Hawthorne's credo of the beautiful, Mod. Lang. Rev, 74; plus others. Add: 706 Highwood Ave, Greencastle, IN 46135.

SPIEGLER, MARLENE, b. Moscow, U.S.S.R, Feb. 17, 34; Australian citizen; div. ENGLISH & COMPARATIVE LITERATURE. B.A, Australian Nat. Univ, 66; M.A, Univ. Calif, Los Angeles, 68, Ph.D.(Eng), 70. ASST. PROF. ENG. & COMP. LIT, COLUMBIA UNIV, 70-, summer grant, 71. MLA; Renaissance Soc. Am. English Renaissance 1500-1600 and continental Renaissance epic and lyric poetry; lyric as genre. Add: Dept. of English & Comparative Literature, Columbia University, New York, NY 10027.

SPIELBERG, PETER, b. Vienna, Austria, July 2, 29; U.S. citizen; m. 56; c. 2. ENGLISH, LITERATURE. A.B, City Col. New York, 52; M.A, N.Y. Univ,

57; Ph.D.(Eng), State Univ. N.Y. Buffalo, 61. Instr. ENG, State Univ. N.Y. Buffalo, 58-61; ASSOC. PROF, BROOKLYN COL, 61- Twentieth century literature; James Joyce. Publ: James Joyce's manuscripts and letters at the University of Buffalo: a catalogue, State Univ. N.Y. Buffalo, 62; co-auth, Reference books: a practical guide for college students, Random, 69; auth, Bedrock, Crossing, 73; Joyce's errata for American editions of A portrait, In: Joyce's Portrait: criticisms and critiques, Appleton, 62; The sisters: no Christ at Bethany, James Joyce Quart, spring 66; The albatross in Albee's Zoo, Col. Eng, 4/66. Add: Dept. of English, Brooklyn College, Brooklyn, NY 11210.

SPILKA, MARK, b. Cleveland, Ohio, Aug. 6, 25; div; c. 3. ENGLISH. B.A, Brown Univ, 49; M.A, Ind. Univ, 53, Ph.D.(comp. lit), 56. Ed. asst, Am. Mercury, 49-51; instr. Eng. lit, Univ. Mich, 54-58, asst. prof. Eng, 58-63; assoc. prof, BROWN UNIV, 63-67, PROF. ENG. LIT, 67-, chmn. dept. Eng, 68-73. Fel, Ind. Sch. Lett, 61, summer 63; managing ed, Novel: a forum on fiction, Brown Univ, 67-; Guggenheim fel, 67-68; vis. prof. Eng, Hebrew Univ, Jerusalem, spring 72; dir. summer sem, Nat. Endowment for Humanities, 74. U.S.A.A.F, 44-46. MLA. English and American novel, especially 19th and 20th centuries; comparative literature; modern literary criticism. Publ: Love ethic of D.H. Lawrence, 55 & Dickens and Kafka: a mutual interpretation, 63, Ind. Univ; ed, D.H. Lawrence: a collection of critical essays, Prentice-Hall, 63. Add: Dept. of English, Brown University, Providence, RI 02912.

SPILLER, ROBERT ERNEST, b. Phila, Pa, Nov. 13, 96; m. 22; c. 3. AMERICAN LITERATURE. A.B, Univ, Pa, 17, Harrison fel, 19-20, A.M, 21, Ph.D, 24; Litt.D, Thiel Col, 63, Col. Wooster, 68; hon. D. Phil, Kiel, 65; L.H.D, Univ. Pa, 67. Instr. Eng, Univ. Pa, 20-21; Swarthmore Col, 21-25, asst. prof, 25-30, assoc. prof, 30-34, prof, 34-45, chmn. div. humanities, 35-40; prof. ENG, UNIV. PA, 46-60, Schelling prof, 60-67, chmn. dept. Am. civilization, 47-49, 51-53, 55-58, FELIX E. SCHELLING EMER. PROF, 67- Guggenheim fel, 28-29; ed, Am. Lit, 32-39; chmn. ed. bd, Am. Quart, 51-; vis. prof, Univ. Oslo, 50; Kings Col, Univ. London, 58-59; Univ. N.C, 67-68; chmn, comt. Am. stud, Am. Counc. Learned Soc, 62, 63; mem. Comt. Int. Exchange of Persons, Conf. Bd, Assoc. Res. Counc, 60-63; hon. consult, Am. cult. hist, Libr. Congr, 67-70. U.S.A, 17-18. MLA (1st v.pres, 57); NCTE; Am. Stud. Asn.(pres, 54, 55). American literary history; James Fenimore Cooper; Ralph Waldo Emerson. Publ: The cycle of American literature, Free Press, Macmillan, 55; co-ed, Emerson: early lectures (3 vols), 59-72 & Emerson: collected works, Vol I, 71, Harvard; Fenimore Cooper, critic of his times, Russell, 63; chmn. ed. bd. & contrib, Literary history of the United States, 4th ed, 74, auth, The third dimension, 65 & The oblique light, 68, Macmillan; ed, The American literary revolution, 1783-1837, Anchor, Doubleday, 67; plus others. Add: 740 Wolcott Dr, Philadelphia, PA 19118.

SPILLMAN, RALPH R, b. Pinnacle, N.C, June 1, 09; m. 42; c. 2. ENGLISH. A.B, Guilford Col, 38; M.A, Univ. N.C, 46. Instr. ENG, GA. INST. TECHNOL, 45-47, asst. prof, 47-62, assoc. prof, 62-70, PROF, 70- Consult. tech. writing, Pratt & Whitney Aircraft, summer 68; liaison off, NCTE & Ga. Counc. Teachers Eng, 71-; consult. tech. writing, Bell Labs, fall 72; Coca Cola Co, Atlanta, 73. Am. Bus. Commun. Asn; S.Atlantic Mod. Lang. Asn; NCTE. Early American literature; technical writing. Publ: Co-auth, Modern technical and industrial reports, Putnam, 62. Add: Dept. of English, Georgia Institute of Technology, Atlanta, GA 30332.

SPINGARN, EDWARD, b. New York, N.Y, Feb. 6, 24; div. ENGLISH. A.B, Brooklyn Col, 46; A.M, Columbia Univ, 48, Ph.D, 59. Instr. Eng, Brooklyn Col, 60-65, asst. prof, 65-70; ENG. & SPEECH, JOHN JAY COL. CRIMINAL JUSTICE, 70-72, ASSOC. PROF, 72-, ASSOC. DEAN FAC, 73-, acting chief librn, 72, exec. asst. to dean fac, 72-73. Coord. pub. rel, Sch. Gen. Stud, Brooklyn Col, 60-66, dir. pub. relat, 63-66, coord. res, 66-67; vis. asst. prof. Eng, Chapman Col. World Campus Afloat, 67. Restoration drama; American musical comedy. Publ: Perfect 36, Pyramid Bk, 57, 60. Add: Office of Associate Dean of Faculty, John Jay College of Criminal Justice, 444 W. 56th St, New York, NY 10019.

SPINGARN, LAWRENCE PERRY, b. Jersey City, N.J, July 11, 17; m. 49. ENGLISH LITERATURE. B.S, Bowdoin Col, 40; M.A, Univ. Mich, 48; Univ. Calif, Los Angeles, 49-51. Spec. asst. Latin Am. Lit. Libr. Congr. 41-43; ed, Funk & Wagnalls Encycl, 43-44; instr. Eng, Pomona Col, 48-49; writer fiction & poetry, 49-59; asst. prof. ENG, LOS ANGELES VALLEY COL, 59-66, assoc. prof, 66-70, PROF, 70- Free-lance ed, various publs, 43-48; MacDowell Colony resid. fel, summer 46; Huntington Hartford Found. resid. fel, summers, 55, 56; YADDO Found. resid. fel, 58. Huntington Hartford Found. Award, 50. Poetry Soc. Am; fel. Int. Inst. Arts & Lett; Auth. League Am; Poetry Soc, Eng. Translation: modern Portuguese poetry since 1915. Publ: Rococo summer and other poems, Dutton, 47; The lost river, William Heinemann, London, 51; Letters from exile, Longmans, London & New York, 61; Madame Bidet & other fixtures (poems), 68, Freeway problems—and others (poems), 70 & ed, Poets West; an anthology from the 11 Western states, 73, Perivale; auth, The ambassador, In: Best American short stories, Houghton, 68. Add: 13830 Erwin St, Van Nuys, CA 91401.

SPIVACK, BERNARD, b. New York, N.Y, Dec. 12, 11; m. 56; c. 1. ENGLISH. A.B, Univ. Ala, 31; M.A, Harvard, 32; Cutting fel, Columbia Univ, 46, Ph.D, 50. Instr. Eng, Columbia Univ, 42-50; assoc. prof. humanities, Fisk Univ, 51-54, prof. Eng. & chmn. dept, 56-64; PROF. ENG, UNIV. MASS, AMHERST, 64- Fulbright teaching fel, 54; Ford Found. fel, 54-56; vis. prof, Univ. Freiburg, 70-71. Clarke F. Ansley Award, 52. MLA. Romantic literature; history of the drama; Shakespeare and Elizabethan literature. Publ: Co-auth, Story of art, Halcyon House, 40; Shakespeare and the allegory of evil, Columbia Univ, 58. Add: Dept. of English, University of Massachusetts, Amherst, MA 01002.

SPIVACK, CHARLOTTE KESLER, b. July 23, 26; m. 56. ENGLISH. Fel. Cornell Univ, 47-48; M.A, 48; Gregory fel, Univ. Mo, 50-52, Ph.D, 54. Instr. ENG, Univ. Mo, 52-54; asst. prof, Col. William & Mary, 54-56, assoc. prof, Fisk Univ, 56-64; lectr, UNIV. MASS, AMHERST, 64-66, assoc. prof, 66-72, PROF, 72- Am. Asn. Univ. Women fel, 59-60. MLA; Renaissance Soc. Am; Dante Soc; Col. Eng. Asn. Medieval and Elizabethan drama; Shakespeare. Publ: Co-auth, Early English drama, Am. R.D.M. Corp, 66; auth, George Chapman, Twayne, 67; Elizabethan theatre: circle and center, fall 69 & Job and Faust: the eternal wager, winter 71, Centennial Rev; Bedlam and Bridewell: ironic design in Dekker, Komos, winter 72; plus many others. Add: Dept. of English, University of Massachusetts, Amherst, MA 01002.

SPIVAK, GAYATRI C, b. Calcutta, India, Feb. 24, 42; m. 64. ENGLISH, COMPARATIVE LITERATURE. B.A, Univ. Calcutta, 59; M.A, Cornell Univ, 62, Ph.D.(comp. lit), 67; Cambridge, 63-64. Inst. ENG. & COMP. LIT, UNIV. IOWA, 65-66, asst. prof, 66-70, ASSOC. PROF, 70-, Old Gold fac. summer res. fel, 68. Northeast. Mod. Lang. Asn.(secy. comp. lit, 73-74); AAUP; Am. Comp. Lit. Asn.(mem. comt. grad. prog, 72-); MLA(chmn. pedag. publ. comt, 73-75); Midwest Mod. Lang. Asn. Modernism in English, French, and German poetry with special references to Yeats and Mallarme; theory of language with special reference to contemporary French thought; Sanskrit and Indian aesthetics. Publ: Myself must I remake: the life and poetry of W.B. Yeats, 74; Principles of the mind: continuity in Yeats' poetry, Mod. Lang. Notes, 12/68; Allégorie et historie de la poésie, Poétique, 71; Stylistic contrast between Yeats and Mallarme, Lang. & Style, spring 72; plus one other. Add: Dept. of Comparative Literature, University of Iowa, Iowa City, IA 52242.

SPIVEY, HERMAN EVERETTE, b. Hemingway, S.C, Aug. 10, 07; m. 28; c. 4. AMERICAN LITERATURE. A.B, Univ. N.C, 28, A.M, 29, Ph.D, 36, hon. LL.D, 69; hon. Litt.D, Maryville Col.(Tenn), 68. Instr. Eng, Univ. N.C, 29-30, 33-36; Univ. Fla, 30-33, asst. prof, 36-39, assoc. prof, 39-42, prof, 42-48; prof. & head dept, Univ. Ky, 48-50; dean grad. sch, 50-61; acad. v.pres, Univ. Tenn, 60-68; PROF. ENG, UNIV. FLA, 68- Fulbright lectr, Italy, 55; India, 56; mem, Nat. Assembly Soc. Policy & Develop, 68-; nat. lectr, Phi Betta Kappa, 70-71. U.S.N, 42-46, Capt. MLA; Bibliog. Soc. Am; S.Atlantic Mod. Lang. Asn. Current American literature. Publ: American literary manuscripts, Univ. Tex, 60; Edgar Allan Poe and Lewis Gaylord Clark, PMLA, 12/39; Manuscript resources for the study of W.C. Bryant, Papers Bibliog. Soc. Am, 3rd. quart/50; The mind and creative habits of Elizabeth M. Roberts, In: Essays in honor of C.A. Robertson, Univ. Fla, 65; plus others. Add: Dept. of English, University of Florida, Gainesville, FL 32601.

SPIVEY, TED RAY, b. Ft. Pierce, Fla, July 1, 27; m. 62. ENGLISH LITERATURE. A.B, Emory Univ, 49; M.A, Univ. Minn, 51, Ph.D.(Eng), 54. Instr. ENG, Emory Univ, 54-56; asst. prof, GA. STATE UNIV, 56-59, assoc. prof, 59-63, PROF, 63- U.S.N, 45-46. S.Atlantic Mod. Lang. Asn. Nineteenth century English novel; modern American fiction and British poetry. Publ: Co-auth, A manual of style, Foote & Davies, 61, rev. ed, 64; auth, Thomas Hardy's tragic hero, Nineteenth Century Fiction, 54; Hemingway's pursuit of happiness on the open road, Emory Univ. Quart, 55; Damnation and salvation in The picture of Dorian Gray, Boston Univ. Stud. Eng, 60. Add: Dept. of English, Georgia State University, Atlanta, GA 30303.

SPOLSKY, ELLEN, b. New York, N.Y, Apr. 7, 43; m. 62; c. 2. ENGLISH LITERATURE. A.B, McGill Univ, 64; A.M, Ind. Univ, Bloomington, 68, Ph.D.(Eng), 69. ASST. PROF. ENG, UNIV. N.MEX, 68- MLA; Mediaeval Acad. Am; Asn. Comput. Mach. Old and Middle English literature; semantics; stylistics. Publ: Computer-assisted semantic analysis of poetry, Comput. Stud. Humanities & Verbal Behavior, 10/70; The semantic structure of the Wanderer, J. Lit. Semantics, (in press); Old English kinship terms and Beowulf, Neuphilol. Mitt, (in press). Add: Dept. of English, University of New Mexico, Albuquerque, NM 87106.

SPORRE, ROBERT A, b. Minneapolis, Minn, June 25, 22. DRAMA, SPEECH. B.A, State Univ. Iowa, 49; M.F.A, Tex. Christian Univ, 57; Ph.D.(drama), Ohio State Univ, 64. Asst. to dean col. fine arts & instr. drama, Univ. Tex, Austin, 57-60; asst, Ohio State Univ, 60-63; PROF. speech & theatre, Univ. Wis-Platteville, 63-72; DRAMA, EAST. KY. UNIV, 72- Mem, Wis. Gov. Comt. of Fine Arts, 65; Wis. State Univ. Syst. res. grant, 68-69; guest lectr. dramatic lit, Cent. Wash. State Col, 70-72; dir, Pioneer Summer Festival. U.S.A, 42-46. Am. Theatre Asn; Speech Commun. Asn. Acting as a test to determine an individual's response; Greek chorus, to find and explore the use of the voice and movement as employed by the Greeks and to modify it for today's use. Publ: Dance in opera: 1600 to 1850, Players Mag, 2/62. Add: Dept. of Drama & Speech, Eastern Kentucky University, Richmond, KY 40475.

SPOVE, STEEN HOLST, b. Copenhagen, Denmark, Mar. 12, 37; m. 60; c. 3. ENGLISH. A.B, Guilford Col, 63; M.A, Harvard, 65; Ph.D.(Eng), Univ. N.C, Chapel Hill, 73. ASST. PROF. ENG, NEWBERRY COL, 64-68, 72- Asst. ed, Stud. Short Fiction, 65- Danish Air Force, 56-58, Sgt. MLA; NCTE; Col. Eng. Asn; Mediaeval Acad. Am; Conf. Col. Compos. & Commun. Renaissance drama; Chaucer. Add: Dept. of English, Newberry College, Newberry, SC 29108.

SPRADLEY, JOHN O, b. Denver, Colo, July 17, 27; m. 60; c. 3. ENGLISH. B.S, Regis Col.(Colo), 51; M.A. & Ph.L, St. Louis Univ, 58; U.S. Steel fel, Univ. Colo, 62-63, Ph.D.(Eng), 63. Asst. prof. ENG, Seattle Univ, 63-67; assoc. prof, METROP. STATE COL, 67-71, PROF, 71-, chmn. dept, 71-73. Contrib. ed, Annual Bibliog. Eng. Lang. & Lit, Mod. Humanities Res. Asn. U.S.N, 45-46. MLA; NCTE; Conf. Col. Compos. & Commun. Add: Dept. of English, Metropolitan State College of Colorado, Denver, CO 80204.

SPRAGUE, ARTHUR COLBY, b. Boston, Mass, April 6, 95; m. 46. ENGLISH LITERATURE. A.B, Harvard, 19, A.M, 20, Ph.D, 25. Instr. Eng, Harvard, 25-30, asst. prof, 30-36; assoc. prof. ENG. LIT, BRYN MAWR COL, 36-50, prof, 50-63, EMER. PROF, 63- Vis. fel, Shakespeare Inst, 63-65; vis. prof. Eng, Univ. Basel, 66. Shakespeare; theatrical history. Publ: Shakespeare and the actors & Shakespearian players and performances, Harvard; Shakespeare's histories, Soc. Theatre Res, Eng, 64; co-auth, Shakespeare's plays today, Sidgwick & Jackson, London, 71; auth, Shakespeare's unnecessary characters, Shakespeare Surv. 20, 67. Add: 829 Barnwell St, Columbia, SC 29201.

SPRAGUE, CLAIRE SACKS, b. New York, N.Y, Aug. 22, 26. MODERN AMERICAN & ENGLISH LITERATURE. B.A, Univ. Wis, 46, M.A, 47, Ph.D. (Eng), 55; Inst. Int. Educ. fel, Univ. London, summer 48; Cooper Union, 51-53. Asst, Univ. Wis, 46-50, 55; instr. Eng, 54; humanities, Reed Col, 55-

56; Eng, Brooklyn Col, 56-62, asst. prof, 62-68, assoc. prof, 68-70; prof. Eng. & assoc. dean grad. stud, John Jay Col. Criminal Justice, 70-73; PROF. ENG, BROOKLYN COL, 73- Instr, Queens Col.(N.Y), summer 58; Fulbright lectr. Am. lit, Univ. Zaragoza, 61-62; Am. Philos. Soc. grant, summer 63; co-chmn. fac. sem. Am. civilization, Columbia Univ, 63-64. Am. Asn. Univ. Women fel, fall 64; Am. Counc. Learned Soc. grant-in-aid, spring 65. MLA; Am. Stud. Asn. Publ: Co-auth, Hamlet: enter critic, Appleton, 60; auth, Van Wyck Brooks: the early years, Harper, 68; Edgar Saltus, Twayne, 68; ed, Virginia Woolf, Prentice-Hall, 71; auth, The Edgar Saltus collection, Yale Univ. Libr. Gazette, 10/67; Possible or necessary, New Theatre Mag, autumn 68; plus others. Add: 61 W. Ninth St, New York, NY 10011.

SPRAGUE, ROSEMARY, b. New York, N.Y. ENGLISH LITERATURE, CREATIVE WRITING. A.B, Bryn Mawr Col; M.A, West. Reserve Univ, fel. & Ph.D, 59. Dir. dramatics, Notre Dame Col.(Ohio), 47-50; lectr. ENG, Fenn Col, 51-53, 56-57, 60-62; West. Reserve Univ, 53-54, 57-59; Cleveland Inst. Art, 61-62; assoc. prof, LONGWOOD COL, 62-65, prof, 65-67, BD. OF VISITORS DISTINGUISHED PROF, 67- Scholar, First Sch. Lett, Kenyon Col; lectr, St. Thomas More Inst, Univ. Montreal & Shakespeare Seminar, Stratford, Ont; fel. Southeast. Inst. Medieval & Renaissance Stud, Univ. N.C, Chapel Hill, summer 67. MLA; Am. Libr. Asn; NCTE; Soc. Theatre Res, Gt. Brit; Victorian Soc; Medieval Acad. Am. Victorian poetry and drama; Renaissance; Medieval studies. Publ: Heir of Kiloran, 56; Fife and fandango, 61; ed, The poems of Robert Browning, Crowell, 64; auth, Forever in joy: a biography of Robert Browning, 65, Red lion and gold dragon, 67 & George Eliot: a biography, 68, Chilton; The prize comedy: London, 1843, Theatre Annual, 56; plus others. Add: Dept. of English, Longwood College, Farmville, VA 23901.

SPRICH, CHARLES ROBERT, b. St. Louis, Mo. ENGLISH LITERATURE. B.S, Mass. Inst. Technol, 61; M.A, Brandeis Univ, 63; Ph.D.(Eng. lit), Tufts Univ, 71. Asst. prof. ENG, BENTLEY COL, 66-73, ASSOC. PROF, 73- Instr. Eng, Northeast. Univ, summers 62-66, lectr, Grad. Div, 66-68; mem. bd. dirs, Boston Ctr. Adult Educ, 63-64; lectr. Eng, Exp. Col, Tufts Univ, 69-71. MLA; Col. Eng. Asn. Late Victorian literature; the modern novel; applications of psychoanalysis to literary criticism. Publ: Co-auth, Hell, Encycl. Britannica, 64; auth, Theme and structure in T.S. Eliot's The hippopotamus, 4/69 & co-auth, A biographical sketch of James MacPherson, 3/72, CEA Critic. Add: Dept. of English, Bentley College, Waltham, MA 02154.

SPRINCHORN, EVERT MANFRED, b. Jamestown, N.Y, Oct. 7, 23. DRAMA, SCANDINAVIAN LITERATURE. B.Sc, Drexel Inst, 48; M.A, Columbia Univ, 50, Ph.D.(comp. lit), 60; Gustav V fel, Am-Scand. Found, 53-54. Instr. DRAMA, VASSAR COL, 56-60, asst. prof, 60-63, assoc. prof, 63-67, PROF, 67-, CHMN. DEPT. DRAMA & DIR. EXP. THEATRE, 69- Vis. prof. drama, Columbia Univ, 61-62; prof. theatre hist, Yale Sch. Drama, 67; vis. prof. theatre, City Univ. New York, 70-71. Eng.C, U.S.A, 43-46, Sgt. Soc. Theatre Res, Eng; Am. Soc. Theatre Res; Int. Fed. Theatre Res; Shaw Soc; Strindberg Soc; Soc. Advan. Scand. Stud. Theatre history; Scandinavian drama. Publ: Co-ed, Wagner on music and drama, Dutton, 64; ed, Ibsen: letters and speeches, Hill & Wang, 64 & Strindberg's autobiographical writings, Doubleday, 66-68; auth, Logic of a dream play, Mod. Drama, 12/62; Odds on Hamlet, Columbia Forum, fall 64; Portrait of artist as Achilles, In: Approaches to 20th century novel, Crowell, 65. Add: Dept. of Drama, Vassar College, Poughkeepsie, NY 12601.

SPRINGER, ANGUS, b. Beatrice, Nebr, Oct. 22, 07; m. 33; c. 2. DRAMA, SPEECH. A.B, Ozark Wesleyan Col, 29; A.B, State Univ. Iowa, 30; M.A, Northwest. Univ, 40; Ph.D.(drama), N.Y. Univ, 56. Teacher, high sch, Mo, 32-42, Kans, 43; from assoc. prof. to PROF. DRAMA & SPEECH & HEAD DEPT, SCH. FINE ARTS, SOUTHWEST. UNIV.(TEX), 44- Am. Theatre Asn; Southwest Theatre Conf.(pres, 63). Interpretation of education in the American drama; aesthetic analysis of poetry; lecture-recitals in poetry and drama. Publ: Problems of higher education in the Broadway drama; Producing Antigone, & Lighting the stage, Players Mag. Add: Box 249, Southwestern University, Georgetown, TX 78626.

SPRINGER, HASKELL SAUL, b. New York, N.Y, Nov. 18, 39; m. 64; c. 2. ENGLISH. B.A, Queens Col.(N.Y), 61; M.A, Ind. Univ, Bloomington, 65, Ph.D.(Eng), 68. Instr. ENG, Univ. Va, 66-68; asst. prof, UNIV. KANS, 68-72, ASSOC. PROF, 72- MLA; Midwest Mod. Lang. Asn; AAUP. Classic American literature; American sea narrative; textual scholarship. Publ: Ed, Studies in Billy Budd, C.E. Merrill, 70; auth, The Leatherwood God: from narrative to novel, Ohio Hist, 65; The poetics of E.E. Cummings, S.Atlantic Bull, 67; Creative contradictions in Irving, Am. Transcendental Quart, 70. Add: Dept. of English, University of Kansas, Lawrence, KS 66045.

SPRINGER, MARLENE ANN, b. Murfreesboro, Tenn, Nov. 16, 37; m. 65; c. 2. NINETEENTH CENTURY BRITISH & AMERICAN LITERATURE. B.A, Centre Col. Ky, 59; Rotary Found. fel, Univ. Calcutta, 60; M.A, Ind. Univ, Bloomington, 63, Ph.D.(Eng), 69. Instr. ENG, Univ. Southwest. La, 63-64; lectr, Univ. Kans, 68-69; ASST. PROF, UNIV. MO-KANSAS CITY, 70- MLA; Midwest Mod. Lang. Asn; Women's Caucus Mod. Lang. Women in literature; Thomas Hardy; Kate Chopin. Publ: Emily Dickinson's humorous road to heaven, Renascence, 71; Invention and tradition: allusion in Thomas Hardy's Desperate remedies, Colby Libr. Quart. Add: 1517 Rhode Island St, Lawrence, KS 66044.

SPRINGER, MARY DOYLE, b. Chicago, Ill, Dec. 18, 18; m. 46; c. 2. ENGLISH. B.A, Holy Names Col.(Calif), 63; M.A, Univ. Calif, Berkeley, 65, Ph.D.(Eng), 73. ASST. PROF. ENG. & CHAIRPERSON DEPT, ST. MARY'S COL. CALIF, 65- Vis. prof. humanities, New Sch. Col, 69-70. Am. Fed. Teachers; MLA; AAUP. Novella theory; literary criticism; women's studies. Add: Dept. of English, St. Mary's College of California, Moraga, CA 94575.

SPRINGER, NORMAN, b. New York, N.Y, Sept. 25, 22; m. 46; c. 2. ENGLISH. M.A, Univ. Chicago, 50; teaching fel, State Univ. Iowa, 50-52, Ph.D, 58; Danforth teaching fel, 57-58. Instr. ENG, State Univ. Iowa, 52-54; Grinnell Col, 54-58, asst. prof, 58-60; assoc. prof, ST. MARY'S COL. CALIF, 60-68, PROF, 68- Vis. prof, New Sch. Col, New Sch. Social Res, 69-70. U.S.A.A.F, 43-46, Sgt, Distinguished Flying Cross; Air Medal & Oak Leaf. MLA; Philol. Asn. Pac. Coast; AAUP. Literary criticism; drama and modern novel; humanities. Publ: Bartleby and the terror of limitation, PMLA, 9/65; A teacher in an alien field, In: The changing college classroom, Jossey-Bass, 69. Add: Dept. of English, St. Mary's College of California, Moraga, CA 94556.

SPROUL, HAROLD ATLEE, b. Halifax, N.S, Apr. 25, 27. DRAMA. A.B, Acadia Univ, 47; M.F.A, Yale, 51. Instr. drama, Stevens Inst. Technol, 51-52; Eng, Univ. Del, 56-60; ASSOC. PROF. DRAMA & ENG. & DIR. UNIV. THEATRE, COLGATE UNIV, 60-, PROD. DIR, SUMMER THEATRE, 66-, univ. res. counc. grant, 63. Writing consult. & lectr, Continental Diamond Fibre Corp, 58; Danforth Found. study. grant, summer 61; consult. directing, Rome Community Theatre. U.S.A, 52-55, 1st Lt. Am. Theatre Asn. Modern drama; contemporary British drama; theatre aesthetics. Publ: Othello: the dynamics of stasis in tragedy, Costerus Essays, Vol. X. Add: Dana Arts Center, Colgate University, Hamilton, NY 13346.

SPROULE, HUGH DOUGLAS, b. Napanee, Ont, May 6, 18; m. 62. ENGLISH. B.A, Dalhousie Univ, 52; M.A, McGill Univ, 58. ASST. PROF. ENG, McGill Univ, 53-66; DALHOUSIE UNIV, 66- McGill Univ-Can. Counc. travel & res. grants, 58-62. R.C.N, 40-46. MLA; Mediaeval Acad. Am; Charles Lamb Soc; Navy Rec. Soc, Eng. Admiral James Burney of the Royal Navy. Add: Dept. of English, Dalhousie University, Halifax, N.S, Can.

SPROULE, JAMES MICHAEL, b. Dayton, Ohio, Feb. 8, 49; m. 73. SPEECH COMMUNICATION. B.A. & M.A, Ohio State Univ, 71, Ph.D.(speech), 73. ASST. PROF. SPEECH COMMUN, UNIV. TEX. OF THE PERMIAN BASIN, 73- Speech Commun. Asn; Int. Commun. Asn; South. Speech Commun. Asn; Am. Forensic Asn; Cent. States Speech Asn. Argumentation; persuasion; rhetorical theory. Publ: Access to the broadcast forum: a rhetorical problem, Speaker & Gavel, 3/73; Newspapers as political persuaders: the campaign against James G. Blaine, Cent. States Speech J, 4/74. Add: Dept. of Speech Communication, University of Texas of the Permian Basin, Odessa, TX 79762.

SQUIER, CHARLES LA BARGE, b. Milwaukee, Wis, Apr. 28, 31; m. 57; c. 2. ENGLISH. A.B, Harvard, 53, M.A.T, 57; Ph.D.(Eng), Univ. Mich, 63. Instr. ENG, Univ. Mich, 61-63; UNIV. COLO, BOULDER, 63-64, asst. prof, 64-70, ASSOC. PROF, 70- U.S.A, 53-55. Shakespeare Asn. Am. Renaissance poetry and drama; modern American poetry. Publ: Co-auth, The sonnet, Wash. Square, 65. Add: Dept. of English, University of Colorado, Boulder, CO 80302.

SQUIRE, DONALD HOVMAND, b. Grand Island, Nebr, Dec. 13, 37; m. 63; c. 1. MODERN LANGUAGES & LITERATURES, RENAISSANCE STUDIES. B.A, Univ. Nebr-Lincoln, 62; Ph.D.(romance lang), Univ. Fla, 72. Asst. prof. romance lang, Col. William & Mary, 66-69; ASSOC. PROF. ENG, UNIV. P.R, MAYAGUEZ, 70-, CHMN. DEPT, 73- Mem. & chmn. comt. examr. in Eng, Col. Entrance Exam. Bd, P.R, 71- U.S.A, 55-58, Res, 58-60. MLA; Renaissance Soc. Am; AAUP; Am. Asn. Teachers Span. & Port; Teachers Eng. to Speakers Other Lang. Renaissance prose fiction; Cervantes; the lost generation. Publ: La novela de Ignacio Aldecoa, Isla Lit, 12-1/70-71; Cervantes y Hoffmann ante un tema similar, Atenea, 70. Add: 56 Calle Zafiro, Mayagüez, PR 00708.

SQUIRE, JAMES R, b. Oakland, Calif, Oct. 14, 22; m. 45; c. 3. ENGLISH, EDUCATION. B.A, Pomona Col, 47, D.Litt, 66; M.A, Univ. Calif, Berkeley, 49, Ph.D.(Eng. educ), 56. Teacher, Pub. Schs, Calif, 48-54; supvr. Eng, Univ. Calif, Berkeley, 50-59, prin. univ. demonstration sec. sch, 54, assoc. dir. supervised teaching, 54-59; asst. prof. Eng, Univ. Ill, 59-60, assoc. prof, 61-64, prof, 64-68; SR. V.PRES. & ED-IN-CHIEF, GINN & CO, 68- Mem. comn. Eng, Col. Entrance Exam. Bd, 60-65; U.S. Off. Educ. res. grant stud. high sch. Eng. progs, 63; Brit. Eng. progs, 67. U.S.A, 43-45, Sgt. NCTE (exec. secy, 59-67; exec. comt. award, 67); Col. Lang. Asn.(creative scholar. award, 62); Conf. Col. Compos. & Commun.(treas, 59-68); MLA; Int. Reading Asn; Conf. Res. Eng; Am. Supv. & Curriculum Develop; Am. Educ. Res. Asn; Asn. Am. Publ.(mem. sch. div. exec. comt, 71-74). Teaching of English; response to literature. Publ: Co-auth, Teaching of language and literature, Harcourt, 61 & 69, National interest and the teaching of English, 61 & auth, Responses of adolescents to four short stories, 63, NCTE; co-auth, Greek myths and legends, Macmillan, 67 & High school English instruction today, Appleton-Century-Crofts, 68; auth, Response to literature, NCTE, 68; ed, A new look at progressive education, Asn. Supv. & Curriculum Develop, 72. Add: Ginn & Co, 191 Spring St, Lexington, MA 02173.

SQUIRES, EDGAR LARRY, b. Salt Lake City, Utah, June 10, 25; m. 53; c. 4. ENGLISH. B.A, San Francisco State Col, 52; M.A, Univ. Calif, Los Angeles, 63; Ph.D.(Eng), Univ. Calif, Davis, 66. Assoc. ENG, Univ. Calif, Davis, 63-65; asst. prof, HUMBOLDT STATE UNIV, 65-71, ASSOC. PROF, 71- U.S. Maritime Serv, 43-46. MLA. Phenomenological studies of a certain aspect of fiction. Add: Dept. of English, Humboldt State University, Arcata, CA 95521.

SQUIRES, MICHAEL GEORGE, b. Arlington, Va, July 18, 41; m. 64; c. 2. ENGLISH LITERATURE. B.A, Bucknell Univ, 63; M.A, Univ. Va, 64; fel, Univ. Md, 66-67, Ph.D.(Eng), 69. Instr. ENG, Va. Commonwealth Univ, 64-65; Univ. Md, 67-69; ASST. PROF, VA. POLYTECH. INST. & STATE UNIV, 69- MLA; Col. Eng. Asn; Conf. Col. Compos. & Commun. Nineteenth and 20th century English literature; the novel; rhetoric. Publ: The pastoral novel: studies in George Eliot, Thomas Hardy and D.H. Lawrence, Univ. Va, 74; Far from the madding crowd as modified pastoral, Nineteenth Century Fiction, 12/70; Pastoral patterns and pastoral variants in Lady Chatterley's lover, Eng. Lit. Hist, 3/72; Adam Bede and the locus amoenus, Stud. Eng. Lit, autumn 73. Add: Dept. of English, Virginia Polytechnic Institute & State University, Blacksburg, VA 24061.

SQUIRES, RADCLIFFE, b. Salt Lake City, Utah, May 23, 17; m. 46. ENGLISH. B.A, Univ. Utah, 40; A.M, Univ. Chicago, 46; Ph.D, Harvard, 52. Instr. ENG, Dartmouth Col, 46-48; from teaching fel. to instr, Harvard, 48-52; from instr. to assoc. prof, UNIV. MICH, 52-64, PROF, 64- Fulbright prof, Univ. Salonika, Greece, 59-60; leader poetry workshop, Utah Writers Conf, 63; adv. ed, Col. Eng, 65-; Mich. Quart. Rev, 67-71, ed, 71- U.S.N.R, 41-45, Lt. Auth. League Am. Poetic theory; Karl Shapiro; Allen Tate. Publ: Where the compass spins, 51 & Frederic Prokosch, 64, Twayne; The loyalties of Robinson Jeffers, 56, The major themes of Robert Frost, 63, Fingers of Hermes, 65 & The light under islands, 67, Univ. Mich; Allen Tate: a literary biography, Bobbs, 71; ed, Allen Tate and his work, Univ. Minn, 72; auth, Waiting in the bone, Cummington, 73; Mr. Tate whose wreath should be a moral, In: Aspects of American poetry, Ohio State Univ, 62; Tilbury town today, In: Robinson centenary essays, Univ. Ga, 70. Add: 7270 Warren Rd, Ann Arbor, MI 48105.

SRAIL, GEORGE WILLIAM, b. Cleveland, Ohio, Apr. 29, 13; m. 38; c. 1. SPEECH, DRAMATICS. A.B, West. Reserve Univ, 34, A.M, 36; Univ. Chicago, 37-38. Instr, Adelbert Col, West. Reserve Univ, 34-36, asst. dean, 35-38, acting dean, 38-39, asst. dean, 39-42; employment mgr, Fisher Body Co, 42-46; from asst. prof. to assoc. prof. SPEECH & DRAMATIC ARTS, Fenn Col, 46-62, prof, 62-65, chmn. dept. 50-65, PROF, CLEVELAND STATE UNIV, 65-, chmn. dept, 65-72. Speech Commun. Asn. Parliamentary procedure and law; writing of plays. Publ: Parliamentary law wheel, Johnsen, 50; Key to effective speech, 59, Pandectic approach to effective speech, 65 & Sample speeches—effective speech, 67, Braun; Looking toward college, Ohio Col. Asn, 37; Problems in building vocabulary, Ohio J. Speech, 62. Add: Dept. of Speech & Dramatic Arts, Cleveland State University, Cleveland, OH 44115.

STACKPOOLE, EDWARD VINCENT, S.J, b. San Francisco, Calif, Sept. 21, 25. ENGLISH LITERATURE. A.B, Gonzaga Univ, 49, M.A, 51; S.T.L, Maison St-Augustin, Belgium, 57; B.A, Oxford, 61, M.A, 65. Instr. ENG, Bellarmine Col. Prep, 50-53; asst. prof. UNIV. SAN FRANCISCO, 61-69, ASSOC. PROF, 69-, CHMN. DEPT, 68- MLA; NCTE; Conf. Col. Compos. & Commun; Mediaeval Acad. Am. Chaucer; rhetorical theory. Publ: Co-auth, The relevance of rhetoric, Allyn & Bacon, 66. Add: Dept. of English, University of San Francisco, San Francisco, CA 94117.

STACY, BILL WAYNE, b. Bristol, Va, July 26, 38; m. 59; c. 2. SPEECH. B.S.Ed, Southeast Mo. State Col, 60; M.S, South. Ill. Univ, 65, Ph.D.(commun), 68. Instr. SPEECH, South. Ill. Univ, 65-67; asst. prof, SOUTHEAST MO. STATE UNIV, 67-72, ASSOC. PROF, 72- South. Speech Commun. Asn; Cent. States Speech Commun. Asn. Contemporary political public address; communication theory and interpersonal communication. Add: Dept. of Speech, Southeast Missouri State University, Cape Girardeau, MO 63701.

STADE, GEORGE, b. New York, N.Y, Nov. 25, 33; m. 56; c. 4. ENGLISH. B.A, St. Lawrence Univ, 55; M.A, Columbia Univ, 58; Ph.D, 65. Instr. ENG, Rutgers Univ, 60-61; asst. prof, COLUMBIA UNIV, 62-69, PROF, 69- Counc. Res. Humanities grant, 67, 68. MLA; Conf. Col. Compos. & Commun. Modern literature; popular fiction; theory of literature. Publ: Robert Graves, Columbia Univ, 67; co-auth, Selected letters of E.E. Cummings, Harcourt, 68; contrib, A closer look at Ariel, Harper's Mag. Press, 72; plus numerous articles. Add: 711 Amsterdam Ave, New York, NY 10025.

STAEBLER, WARREN, b. Cincinnati, Ohio, Nov. 16, 12; m. 37; c. 3. ENGLISH. A.B, Princeton, 33; A.M, Univ. Cincinnati, 38, Ph.D, 41. Head dept. ENG, Perkiomen Sch, Pa, 34-36; instr, Univ. Kans. City, 36-39; Taft teaching fel, Univ. Cincinnati, 39-41; instr, Miami Univ, 41-43, asst. prof, 43-46; assoc. prof, EARLHAM COL, 46-53, PROF, 53- Head mission, Am. Friends Serv. Comt, Italy, 51-53. Am. Stud. Asn; MLA; AAUP. Music criticism; influence of the figure of Socrates in Europe in the 18th century; the self, sex, and war in fifteen Shakespeare plays. Publ: The liberal mind of John Morley, Princeton; Silence is where words come from (monogr), Earlham Col, 70; Ralph Waldo Emerson, Twayne, 73. Add: Dept. of English, Earlham College, Richmond, IN 47374.

STAFFORD, ARNOLD JOHN, b. Windermere, Fla, Aug. 30, 17; m. 40; c. 1. AMERICAN LITERATURE & HISTORY. A.B, Maryville Col, 38; A.M, Vanderbilt Univ, 39; Ph.D, Univ. Tex, 48. Instr. ENG, Univ. Miss, 39-41; assoc. prof, Trinity Univ, 44-45; instr, Univ. Tex, 46-47; Univ. Calif, Los Angeles, 47-49, asst. prof, 49-52; Brooklyn Col, 53-58; from assoc. prof. to PROF, CALIF. STATE UNIV, NORTHRIDGE, 58- Am. Counc. Learned Soc. res. grant, 52-53; Fulbright prof, France, 56-57, Japan, 62-63; Smith-Mundt vis. prof, Iran, 57-58; chmn. acad. senate, Calif. State Univs. & Cols, 68-69. MLA; Am. Stud. Asn; NCTE; Philol. Asn. Pac. Coast. Nineteenth century American literary criticism; literature and society; concept of sympathy. Publ: The literary criticism of young America, Univ. Calif; The power of sympathy, Am. Stud, spring 68; Sympathy comes to America, In: Themes and directions in American literature, Purdue Univ, 69; plus two others. Add: Dept. of English, California State University, Northridge, 18111 Nordhoff St, Northridge, CA 91324.

STAFFORD, OTTILIE FRANK, b. Middletown, N.Y, Feb. 12, 21; m. 48; c. 2. ENGLISH LITERATURE. B.A, Atlantic Union Col, 41; A.M, Boston Univ, 48, Ph.D, 60. Teacher, Elem. Sch, Elmira, N.Y, 41-42; music, Phila. Acad, 42-43; Ariz. Acad, 43-45; ENG, Greater Boston Acad, 45-47; instr, South. Missionary Col, 47-49; ATLANTIC UNION COL, 49-53, asst. prof, 53-55, assoc. prof, 55-62, PROF. & CHMN. DEPT, 62- NCTE. Contemporary English and American poetry; literary criticism. Add: Dept. of English, Atlantic Union College, South Lancaster, MA 01561.

STAFFORD, TONY JASON, b. Belmont, N.C, Oct. 9, 35; m. 59, 74; c. 3. ENGLISH LITERATURE. B.A, Wake Forest Univ, 57; M.A, Univ. Tex, El Paso, 61; Ph.D.(Eng), La. State Univ, 66. Instr. ENG, La. State Univ, 63-64; ASST. PROF, UNIV. TEX, EL PASO, 64-, CHMN. DEPT, 72-, res. grant, 67-68. U.S.A, 57-59. Shakespeare; modern drama. Publ: Shakespeare in the Southwest, Tex. West. Col; Hamlet's house of death, Papers Lang. & Lit; Satiric intent in Much ado, Arlington Quart. Add: Apt. 50, 125 Vaquero, El Paso, TX 79912.

STAFFORD, WILLIAM EDGAR, b. Hutchinson, Kans, Jan. 17, 14; m. 44; c. 4. LITERATURE & COMPOSITION. B.A, Univ. Kans, 37, M.A, 45; Ph.D, State Univ, Iowa, 53; hon. Litt.D, Ripon Col, 66; Linfield Col, 70; Oberlin Col, 71; hon. D.F.A, Sterling Col, 73. Asst. Eng. compos, Univ. Kans, 40-41; instr. Eng, Lewis & Clark Col, 48-50; asst. Eng. lit, State Univ. Iowa, 50-52; from instr. to asst. prof, ENG. LIT. & COMPOS, Lewis & Clark Col, 52-55; assoc. prof, Manchester Col, 55-56; asst. prof, San Jose State Col, 56-57; PROF, LEWIS & CLARK COL, 57- Scholar, YADDO, N.Y, 56; mem. comn. lit, NCTE, 66- Nat. Bk. Award, 62. Alternative serv. relig. objectors, 41-44. MLA; NCTE; Philol. Asn. Pac. Coast. Writing, especially poetry. Publ: Down in my heart, Brethren Publ. House, 47; West of your city, Talisman, 60; Traveling through the dark, 62, The rescued year, 66, Allegiances, 70 & Someday, maybe, 73, Harper; The achievement of Brother Antoninus, Scott, 67; Friends to this ground, Nat. Counc. Teachers Eng, 67. Add: Dept. of English, Lewis & Clark College, Portland, OR 97219.

STAFFORD, WILLIAM TALMADGE, b. Marianna, Fla, Oct. 31, 24; m; c. 3. ENGLISH. B.A, Univ. Fla, 48; M.A, Columbia Univ, 50; Ph.D.(Eng), Univ. Ky, 56. Asst, ENG, Univ. Ky, 50-53; instr, PURDUE UNIV, WEST LAFAYETTE, 53-56, asst. prof, 56-59, assoc. prof, 59-64, PROF, 65- Founder & managing ed, Mod. Fiction Stud, 55-68, ed, 68-72, co-ed, 72-; Fulbright lectr, Turku Univ, Finland & Swed. Univ. Abo, 63-64; mem. comt. lit, Col. Entrance Exam Bd, 64-70; vis. prof, Univ. Ky, summer 66; Columbia Univ, summer 67; Fulbright lectr, Univ. Zagreb, 70-71; vis. prof, Grad. Inst. Mod. Lett, Univ. Tulsa, summer 73; mem. adv. bd, Essays in Lit, 73- U.S.A, 43-46, Sgt. MLA; Midwest Mod. Lang. Asn; AAUP; Int. Asn. Univ. Prof. Eng; Popular Cult. Asn.(mem. fac. adv. counc, 72-); Conf. Ed. Learned Journals. American literature; western movies; modern fiction. Publ: Ed, Melville's Billy Budd and the critics, Wadsworth, 61, 2nd ed, 68, James Daisy Miller: the story, the play, the critics, Scribner, 63, Twentieth century American writing, Odyssey, 65 & Perspectives on James's The portrait of a lady, N.Y. Univ, 67; co-ed, Frontiers of American culture, Purdue Univ, 68; ed, Studies in the American, C.E. Merrill, 71; auth, Emerson and the James family, Am. Lit, 1/53; Henry James, In: American literary scholarship, Duke Univ, 66, 67, 68, 69, 70 & 72; A whale, an heiress, and a southern demigod, Col. Lit, 5/74. Add: Dept. of English, Purdue University, West Lafayette, IN 47907.

STAGEBERG, NORMAN CLIFFORD, English. See Volume III, Foreign Languages, Linguistics & Philology.

STAGG, LOUIS CHARLES, b. New Orleans, La, Jan. 3, 33; m. 59; c. 2. ENGLISH. B.A, La. Col, 55; M.A, Univ. Ark, 57, Ph.D, 63. Asst. Eng, Univ. Ark, 55-59; asst. prof, William Jewell Col, 59-60; instr, Stephen F. Austin State Col, 60-62; asst. prof, MEMPHIS STATE UNIV, 62-69, DIR. ENG. DRAMA PLAYERS, 68-, ASSOC. PROF. ENG, 69., fac. res. seed grants 69-71 & spring 73, fac. res. grant, summer 71. Nat. Endowment for Humanities summer stipend, 67. MLA; South. Humanities Conf; S.Cent. Mod. Lang. Asn.(secy, Eng. I, 70 & chmn, 71); S.Cent. Renaissance Conf; Shakespeare Asn. Am; Renaissance Soc. Am; AAUP. Renaissance drama; development of English drama from the medieval beginnings through the Renaissance and on to existentialism and modern rock opera; world drama, tragedy. Publ: Co-auth, An index to Poe's critical vocabulary, Transcendental Bks, 66; auth, An index to the figurative language of John Webster's tragedies, Index to the figurative language of Ben Johnson's tragedies & An index to the figurative language of Ben Johnson's tragedies & An index to the figurative language of Thomas Heywood's tragedies, 67, An index to the figurative language of George Chapman's tragedies, An index to the figurative language of Thomas Middleton's tragedies, An index to the figurative language of Cyril Tourneur's tragedies & An index to the figurative language of John Marston's tragedies, 70, Bibliog. Soc, Univ. Va; Figurative imagery in revenge tragedies by three seventeenth century contemporaries of Shakespeare, S.Cent. Bull, winter 66; co-auth, Special collections on Southern culture in college and university libraries, Humanities in the South, spring 67; auth, Characterization through nature imagery in the tragedies of George Chapman, Ball State Univ. Forum, winter 68. Add: 5219 Mason Rd, Memphis, TN 38117.

STAGGS, KENNETH WALTON, b. Gould, Okla, May 4, 31; m. 53; c. 3. AMERICAN LITERATURE, CREATIVE WRITING. B.A, Baylor Univ, 53; M.A, Univ. Tex, Austin, 56, Ph.D.(Eng), 68. Instr. ENG, San Antonio Col, 62-66; ASST. PROF, TRINITY UNIV, 66- Prof, Eng. for Speakers Other Lang. Inst, summer 68; Nat. Endowment for Humanities young humanist grant, summer 71. AAUP; MLA. Nineteenth century American literature; textual criticism; poetics. Publ: Co-ed, J.F. Cooper's Gleanings in Europe. England, (in press) & Sketches of Switzerland, (in press), State Univ. N.Y; auth, Cooper's Gleanings in Europe. England: a problem in copy-text, CEAA Newslett, 6/70. Add: Dept. of English, Trinity University, 715 Stadium Dr, San Antonio, TX 78284.

STAHLKE, HERBERT FREDERIC WALTER, Linguistics, African Studies. See Volume III, Foreign Languages, Linguistics & Philology.

STAHR, WILLIAM E, b. Portsmouth, Va, June 3, 29; m. 51; c. 1. AMERICAN LITERATURE. A.B, Univ. Md, 51, A.M, 53; Ph.D.(Am. lit), George Washington Univ, 65. Instr. ENG, Univ. Md, 59-63; AM. UNIV, 63-66, ASST. PROF, 66- AAUP. The movement for a native American literature; Hemingway-Fitzgerald era. Add: Dept. of Literature, American University, Washington, DC 20016.

STAINTON, WALTER HUTCHINSON, b. Orange, N.J, Apr. 19, 97; m. 32; c. 3. DRAMA, THEATRE. A.B, Cornell Univ, 20, Ph.D, 27. Instr, Cornell Univ, 21-27; Dartmouth Col, 27-28; asst. prof. pub. speaking, CORNELL UNIV, 28-40, assoc. prof. speech & drama, 40-52, prof, 52-65, exec. dir, univ. theatre, 47-52, EMER. PROF. SPEECH & DRAMA, 65- Mem. bd. dir, Nat. Bd. Rev. Motion Pictures, 53-73. Chem. Warfare Serv, 42-46, Maj. Speech Commun. Asn; Am. Theatre Asn; Theatre Libr. Asn; Soc. Motion Picture & TV Engineers; Brit. Film Inst; Soc. Cinema Stud. Theater and cinema; history of the cinema. Add: Headwaters, Ellis Hollow Rd, Ithaca, NY 14850.

STALEY, HARRY C, b. Gloversville, N.Y, June 26, 24; m. 53; c. 1. ENGLISH. B.A, St. John's Univ.(N.Y), 48; M.A, Univ. Pa, 53, Ph.D.(Eng), 67. Instr. Eng. & drama, Loyola Col.(Md), 54-56; asst. prof. ENG, STATE UNIV. N.Y. ALBANY, 56-61, assoc. prof, 61-70, prof, 70- Lectr, Am. Col. Paris, 65-66; Inst. Sci. & Man, N.Y, summer 67. Ariz. Quart. Award, 56. U.S.A, 42-46. Modern drama; modern American and British literature. Add: Dept. of English, State University of New York at Albany, Albany, NY 12203.

STALEY, THOMAS F, b. Pittsburgh, Pa, Aug. 13, 35; m. 60; c. 4. ENGLISH & COMPARATIVE LITERATURE. A.B. & B.S, Regis Col, 57; M.A, Univ. Tulsa, 58; fel. & Ph.D, Univ. Pittsburgh, 62. Asst. prof. ENG, Rollins Col, 61-62; UNIV. TULSA, 62-68, assoc. prof. & assoc. dean grad. sch, 68-69, PROF. & DEAN GRAD. SCH, 69- Vis. lectr, Univ. Pittsburgh, 63, vis. prof, 67; ed, James Joyce Quart; Danforth assoc, 64-; Fulbright res. prof, Trieste, Italy, 66-67; assoc. ed, Univ. Tulsa Monograph Ser, 66-; chmn. James Joyce Symposium, Dublin, 67-; adv. ed, Twentieth Century Lit, 68-; pres. Undercroft Montessori Sch. Bd, 68-, Am. Counc. Learned Soc. grant, 69; Fulbright lectr, Italy, 71; guest ed, Mod. Fiction Stud, Italo Svevo number, spring 72; adv. ed, Virginia Woolf Quart; bd. mem, Cascia Hall Prep Sch. MLA; Private Libr. Asn; Am. Comt. Irish Stud; AAUP; James Joyce Found.(pres, 68-70); S.Cent. Mod. Lang. Asn.(assoc. ed). Modern British and European fiction; theory of the novel; modern Irish literature. Publ: James Joyce today, Ind. Univ, 66; co-auth, Dubliners: a critical handbook, Wadsworth, 68; The shapless god: essays on the modern novel, 68 & co-ed, Approaches to Ulysses: ten essays, 71, Univ. Pittsburgh; auth, Essays on Italo Svevo, Univ. Tulsa, 68; Italo Svevo and the ambience of Trieste, Mod. Fiction Stud, spring 72; Ulysses: fifty years in the Joycean conundrum, Mosaic, fall 72; The artist as autobiographer, J. Mod. Lit, winter 73; plus others. Add: Office of the Dean of the Graduate School, University of Tulsa, Tulsa, OK 74104.

STALKER, JAMES CURTIS, b. Louisville, Ky, June 23, 40; m. 64; c. 1. APPLIED ENGLISH LINGUISTICS, MODERN LITERATURE. B.A, Univ. N.C, Chapel Hill, 62; M.A, Univ. Louisville, 64; Ph.D.(appl. Eng. ling), Univ. Wis-Madison, 70. Instr. ENG. LING, Univ. Wis-Exten, 67-69; ASST. PROF, MICH. STATE UNIV, 69- Ling. Soc. Am; NCTE; Teachers Eng. to Speakers Other Lang. Linguistics and literature, stylistics; application of linguistic theory and data to education. Publ: Co-auth, Miscue analysis and the training of junior and senior high English teachers, NCTE/ERIC, 73; auth, Syntactic and semantic pattern matches in James Dickey's False youth: Autumn: clothes of the age, Conf. Semantics & Lit, Univ. North. Iowa, 73. Add: Dept. of English, Michigan State University, East Lansing, MI 48824.

STALLARD, OWEN M, b. Lafayette, Ind, Nov. 14, 09; m. 38. SPEECH. B.S, Purdue Univ, 38, M.S, 43; Ed.D, Ind. Univ, 54. Instr. Eng, speech & hist, Klondike High Sch, 38-42; Shadeland High Sch, 42-43; SPEECH, PURDUE UNIV, WEST LAFAYETTE, 45-54, asst. prof, 55-61, ASSOC. PROF, 62- Med.Dept, U.S.A, 43-45. Cent. States Speech Asn; Speech Commun. Asn. Undergraduate speech instruction; speech education. Publ: An experimental study of the use of the magnetic tape recorder in the extemporaneous speaking situation, Speech Monogr, 6/55. Add: Dept. of Speech, Purdue University, West Lafayette, IN 47907.

STALLBAUMER, VIRGIL R, b. Seneca, Kans, Feb. 9, 98. ENGLISH LITERATURE. A.B, St. Benedict's Col.(Kans), 20; A.M, Univ. Notre Dame, 28; Ph.D, Johns Hopkins Univ, 34. Prof. ENG. & head dept, St. Benedict's Col. (Kans), 25-28, 29-31, 34-35; instr. & chmn. dept, St. Benedict's Prep. Sch, N.J, 35-37; prof, Urban Div, Seton Hall Univ, Newark, 37-51, head dept, 37-51, prof. Eng, SETON HALL UNIV, SOUTH ORANGE, 51-67, RES. PROF. ENG. LIT, 67- Asst. ed, China Monthly, 44-50. MLA. Early Anglo-Saxon schools. Add: 528 High St, Newark, NJ 07102.

STALLINGS, FRANK LOYD, JR, b. Clarendon, Tex, Mar. 13, 28; m. 69. ENGLISH. B.A, W.Tex. State Univ, 50, M.A, 55; Ph.D, Univ. Tex, 61. Instr. ENG, Univ. Tex, Austin, 57-60; asst. prof, Univ. Tex, Arlington, 60-65, ASSOC. PROF, 65-70; Thomas More Col, 70-72; NORTH. KY. STATE COL, 72-, CHMN. DEPT. HUMANITIES, 74- Ed, Stud. & Critiques, Univ. Tex, Arlington, 66; assoc. ed, Am. Lit. Realism, 1870-1910, 67-71; ed, Border States, Ky-Tenn. Am. Stud. Asn, 73- MLA; S.Atlantic Mod. Lang. Asn; Am. Stud. Asn. American literature, especially Thoreau; American realism, 1870-1910. Publ: Compiler, Bibliography of secondary comments about David Graham Phillips, Am. Lit. Realism, 70; auth, The West as mirage in literature, Bull. Miss. Valley Collection, 72. Add: Dept. of Humanities, Northern Kentucky State College, Highland Heights, KY 41076.

STALLKNECHT, NEWTON PHELPS, Comparative Literature, Philosophy. See Volume III, Foreign Languages, Linguistics & Philology.

STALLMAN, ROBERT LESTER, b. Kankakee, Ill, Jan. 6, 30; m. 71; c. 2. ENGLISH. B.A, Univ. N.Mex, 57, M.A, 61; Ph.D.(Eng), Univ. Ore, 66. Asst. prof. ENG, WEST. MICH. UNIV, 66-72, ASSOC. PROF, 72- U.S.A, 52-54, Sgt. Victorian poetry; poetics; criticism. Publ: Unravelling Rapunzel, Victorian poetry, 69. Add: Dept. of English, Western Michigan University, Kalamazoo, MI 49001.

STALLMAN, ROBERT WOOSTER, b. Milwaukee, Wis, Sept. 27, 11; m. 39; c. 2. ENGLISH. A.B, Univ. Wis, 33, A.M, 39, Ph.D, 42. Part-time instr. ENG, Univ. Wis, 39-42; instr, R.I. State Col, 42-43; Yale, 43-44; lectr, Katherine Gibbs Sch, Mass, 44-46; asst. prof, Univ. Kans, 46-49; assoc. prof, UNIV. CONN, 49-53, PROF, 53- Assoc. ed, West. Rev, 46-49; lectr, Univ. Minn, summer 47; dir, Univ. Conn. Writers' Conf, 50-53; Ford Found. fel. stud. art, Europe, 53-54; lectr. critic's prog, Univ. Tex, 57; Fulbright lectr. Am. lit, Univ. Strasbourg, 58-59; U.S. Inform. Serv. vis. lectr, Third Blerancourt Sem. Am. Lit, Chateau de Blerancourt, France, Ctr. Cult. Am, Paris & Univs. Rome, Naples, Bari, Milan, Bologna, Zurich, Lausanne, Bern, Geneva, Mannheim, Freiburg, Frankfort, Ljubljana & Zagreb, 58-59; lectr, Trinity Col, summer 59; First Bingham Distinguished prof. humanities, Univ. Louisville, spring 66; mem. adv. bd, Am. Lit. Abstr, 68-; Stud. in Novel, 69-; Citizen chair Eng, Univ. Hawaii, spring, 70; adv. ed, Stud. in Short Fiction; vis. lectr, Univ. of the South, Bowdoin Col; Univ. Mo; Conn. Col. Grants, Univ. Conn. Res. Found, 67-, 68 & 69; Am. Counc. Learned Soc; Mod. Lang. Asn; Am. Philos. Soc. Distinguished Fac. Award, 64 & 67. MLA. Contemporary literature, poetry and fiction; critical studies of novels; bibliographies and poems. Publ: Stephen Crane: an omnibus, Knopf, 52 & Heinemann, London, 54; co-ed, Stephen Crane: letters, 60, The war dispatches of Stephen Crane, 64 & The New York City sketches of Stephen Crane, 66, N.Y. Univ; ed, The art of Joseph Conrad: a critical symposium, 60 & auth, The houses that James built and other literary studies, 61, Mich. State Univ; Stephen Crane: a biography, Braziller, 68 & rev. ed, 73; ed, Stephen Crane: Sullivan County tales and sketches, 68 & auth, Stephen Crane: a critical bibliography, 72, Iowa State Univ; auth, Stephen Crane, In: Encycl. Britannica, 74; plus others. Add: 1 Westwood Rd, Storrs, CT 06268.

STAMBUSKY, ALAN ANTHONY, b. Niagara Falls, N.Y, Jan. 17, 29; m. 55; c. 3. DRAMATIC ART. B.A, Niagara Univ, 51; univ. scholar, Cath. Univ. Am, 53-55, M.A, 55; univ. scholar & Ph.D.(theater & drama), Univ. Wis, 60. Instr. drama & speech, Nazareth Col.(N.Y), 55-57; teaching asst, Univ. Wis, 57-60; asst. prof. speech, Ill. State Univ, 60-61; DRAMATIC ART, UNIV. CALIF, DAVIS, 61-66, assoc. prof, 66-71, PROF, 71-, acting chmn. dept. dramatic art & speech, 63-64, chmn, 69-72. Univ. Calif. Regents fac. res. fel, 63; Univ. Calif, Humanities Inst. grant, 67-68. Cent. States Speech Asn. Award, 61. Sig.C, U.S.A, 51-53. Am. Theatre Asn.(liaison rep, 67-69, mem. bd. dirs. & comt. publ. & res, 67-72, admin. v.pres, 69-70); Speech Commun. Asn.(liaison rep, 67-69); Mediaeval Acad. Am; Univ. & Col. Theatre Asn. Origin and development of political and ecclesiastical censorship of drama; psychology of directing for the stage; artistic and psychological interrelationship of acting and directing. Publ: Bernard Shaw's farcical vision: comic perspective in the traditional mode, Drama Critique, 5/60; Chaucer and Molière: kindred patterns of the dramatic impulse in human comedy, Lock Haven Rev, fall 63; Arthur Miller: Aristotelian canons in the twentieth century drama, In: Modern American drama: essays in criticism, Everett Edwards, spring 69; plus others. Add: Dept. of Dramatic Art, University of California, Davis, CA 95616.

STAMM, JANET, b. Vandergrift, Pa, Oct. 28, 13. ENGLISH. A.B, Mt. Holyoke Col, 35; A.M, Univ. Pa, 51, Senatorial scholar, 55-56, Ph.D, 59. Instr. ENG, Susquehanna Univ, 47-48; Bradford Jr. Col, 49-50; instr. & dean women, Cedar Crest Col, 51-55; asst. prof, Muhlenberg Col, 58-65; PROF, BLOOMSBURG STATE COL, 65- MLA. Structure and theory of drama; Shakespearean drama, especially comedies; structure of English as language. Publ: Women in men's education, Basic Col. Quart, summer 57; poems in Friends J, 57-; introd, Alpha...perhaps, Vantage, 66. Add: Dept. of English, Bloomsburg State College, Bloomsburg, PA 17815.

STAMPFER, JUDAH L, b. Jerusalem, Israel, Nov. 11, 23; U.S. citizen; div; c. 1. ENGLISH. B.A, Univ. Chicago, 43, M.A, 44; D.D, Yeshiva Univ, 47; M.A, Columbia Univ, 47; Ph.D, Harvard, 59. Asst. prof. ENG, Univ. Man, 52-55; fel, Harvard, 55-59; asst. prof, STATE UNIV. N.Y. STONY BROOK, 59-63, assoc. prof, 63-71, PROF, 71- Judge, Jewish Bk. Counc. Am, 62-66; fel, Macdowell Colony Creative Writing, summer 64. Jewish Bk. Counc. Am. Poetry Award, 60. Elizabethan and Shakespearean studies; fiction; modern poetry. Publ: Jerusalem has many faces (poetry), Farrar, 50; Sol Myers, Macmillan, 62; The tragic engagement, Funk, 69; The cantos of mutability: Spenser's last testament of faith, Univ. Toronto Quart, 52; The catharsis of King Lear, Shakespeare Survey, 60 & In: King Lear Casebook & Shakespeare's Tragedies; On translating Biblical poetry, Judaism, fall 65. Add: Dept. of English, State University of New York at Stony Brook, Stony Brook, NY 11790.

STANBROUGH, JANE, b. Kansas City, Mo, June 9, 29. AMERICAN LITERATURE. B.S, Okla. Baptist Univ, 51; M.A, Univ. Mo-Kansas City, 55; M.A, Univ. Denver, 68, Ph.D.(Eng), 71. Instr. ENG, Univ. Denver, 69-71; ASST. PROF, UNIV. COLO, COLORADO SPRINGS CTR, 71- MLA. Nineteenth century American literature; novel; women and literature. Publ: Zelda and the Fitzgerald legend, Univ. Denver Quart, fall 70. Add: Dept. of English, University of Colorado, Cragmor Rd, Colorado Springs, CO 80907.

STANDIFORD, LESTER ALAN, b. Cambridge, Ohio, Oct. 30, 45; m. 70. ENGLISH & AMERICAN LITERATURE, CREATIVE WRITING. B.A, Muskingum Col, 67; Columbia Univ, 67; NDEA fel, Ohio State Univ, 68; univ. fel, Univ. Utah, 68-73, M.A, 70, Ph.D.(Eng), 73. ASST. PROF. LIT. & CREATIVE WRITING, UNIV. TEX, EL PASO, 73- U.S.A.F.R, 63-69. Assoc. Writing Prog. Film studies; minorities literature; contemporary fiction and poetry. Publ: Novels into film: Catch-22 as watershed, South. Humanities Rev, winter 73; Circle of the deer, Beloit Poetry J, summer 73; Charting the darker mountains: the poetry of Howard McCord, Nova, spring 74; plus others. Add: Dept. of English, University of Texas at El Paso, El Paso, TX 79968.

STANDLEY, ARLINE ELIZABETH REILEIN, b. Buffalo, N.Y, Feb. 14, 18. ENGLISH, COMPARATIVE LITERATURE. B.A, Univ. Iowa, 62, Ph.D. (comp. lit), 67. ASST. PROF. ENG, IND. UNIV. FT. WAYNE, 67-, CHMN. DEPT. ENG. & LING, 72- MLA; Am. Comp. Lit. Asn. Denis Diderot; Locke; 18th century English fiction. Add: Dept. of English & Linguistics, Indiana University at Ft. Wayne, 2101 Coliseum Blvd. E, Ft. Wayne, IN 46805.

STANDLEY, FRED LLOYD, b. Huntington, W.Va, Dec. 3, 32; m. 56. ENGLISH. B.A, W.Va. Wesleyan Col, 54; M.Div, Garrett Theol. Sem, 58; M.A, Northwest. Univ, 59, Ph.D.(Eng), 64. Instr. ENG, MacMurray Col, 59-60; asst. prof, FLA. STATE UNIV, 63-68, assoc. prof, 68-72, PROF, 72-, CHMN. DEPT, 73-, dir. grad. stud, 70-73. Grad. res. counc. award, Fla. State Univ, summer 64, counc. instr. award, summer 67, fac. res. counc. grant, summer 70, fac. develop. grant, 71; Nat. Endowment for Humanities grant, summer 69; Southeast. Conf. Eng. in Two-Year Cols. MLA; S.Atlantic Mod. Lang. Asn; NCTE; Conf. Col. Compos. & Commun; Col. Eng. Asn. Victorian literature; contemporary fiction; literary criticism. Publ: Stopford Brooke, Twayne Eng. Auth. Ser, 72; Jamed Baldwin: the crucial situation, S.Atlantic Quart, summer 66; Bernard Malamud: the novel of redemption, South. Humanities Rev, 71; John Stuart Mill Marginalia in Robert Browning's Pauline: a history and transcription, Papers Bibliog. Soc. Am, 72; plus others. Add: 2412 Perez Ave, Tallahassee, FL 32304.

STANFORD, ANN, b. La Habra, Calif; m. 42; c. 4. ENGLISH. B.A, Stanford Univ, 38; Radcliffe Col, 39; Univ. Chicago, 41; M.A, Univ. Calif, Los Angeles, '58 & 61, Ph.D.(Eng), 62. Asst. prof. ENG, CALIF. STATE UNIV, NORTHRIDGE, 62-66, assoc. prof, 66-68, PROF, 68- Ed. consult, Los Angeles County Counc. In-Serv. Educ, 58-59; consult, jour. dept, Univ. Calif, Los Angeles, 62-64; Calif. State Univ, Northridge summer fel, 66; Nat. Endowments Arts stud. grant, 67. Silver Medal Poetry, Commonwealth Club Calif, 59; Shelley Mem. Award, Poetry Soc. Am, 69; Nat. Inst. Award in Lit, Am. Acad. Arts & Lett, 72. MLA; NCTE; Poetry Soc. Am; PEN

Club; AAUP. American colonial literature; Renaissance literature; contemporary English and American poetry. Publ: In narrow bound, 43 & The white bird, 49, Swallow; Magellan: a poem to be read by several voices, Talisman, 58; The weathercock, 66 & The descent: poems, 70, Viking; The Bhagavad Gita: a new verse translation, Herder, 70; ed, The women poets in English: an anthology, McGraw, 73; auth, Anne Bradstreet: dogmatist and rebel, New Eng. Quart, 9/66; Poetry: 1900 to the 1930's, In: American literary scholarship: 1965, Duke Univ, 67; May Swenson: the art of perceiving, South. Rev, winter 69. Add: Dept. of English, California State University, Northridge, 18111 Nordhoff St, Northridge, CA 91324.

STANFORD, DONALD ELWIN, b. Amherst, Mass, Feb. 7, 13; m. 53. ENGLISH. B.A, Stanford Univ, 33, Ph.D, 53; M.A, Harvard, 34. Instr. ENG, Colo. State Col, 35-37; Dartmouth Col, 37-41; Univ. Nebr, 41-42; from instr. to PROF, LA. STATE UNIV, BATON ROUGE, 49, ED, SOUTH. REV, 63-, ed, Humanities Ser, Univ. Press, 62-68. Guggenheim fel, 59-60; vis. assoc. prof, Duke Univ, 61-62; Nat. Endowment for Humanities res. grant, summer 72; La. State Univ. Found. distinguished fac. fel, 73-74. MLA; S.Cent. Mod. Lang. Asn; PEN Club; S.Atlantic Mod. Lang. Asn. The poetry of Edward Taylor; 17th century New England theology and literature; contemporary British and American poetry. Publ: New England earth, Colt; The traveler, Cummington; Poems of Edward Taylor, Yale, 60; The earliest poems of Edward Taylor, Am. Lit, 5/60; Robert Bridges and the free verse rebellion, J. Mod. Lit, 9/71; Edward Taylor, In: Major writers of early American literature, Univ. Wis, 72. Add: Dept. of English, Louisiana State University, Baton Rouge, LA 70803.

STANFORD, RANEY, b. Durham, N.C, Sept. 30, 24; m. 51; c. 4. MODERN LITERATURE, HISTORY OF THE NOVEL. A.B, Univ. N.C, Chapel Hill, 48; M.A, Columbia Univ, 51, Ph.D.(Eng. & comp. lit), 64. Instr. COMP. LIT, Univ. Colo, Boulder, 55-59; from instr. to asst. prof, Purdue Univ, West Lafayette, 60-70; ASSOC. PROF, CALIF. STATE UNIV, HAYWARD, 70- U.S.A.A.F, 43-46, 2nd Lt. MLA. Esthetics of the novel. Publ: The hero and his alien world: the tradition of heroism in the modern novel, 74; the romantic hero and that fatal selfhood, Centennial Rev, 68; Novels of E.L. Wallant, Colo. Quart, 69; The subversive hero and beginning fiction, Discourse; plus three others. Add: Dept. of English, California State University, Hayward, 25800 Hillary St, Hayward, CA 94542.

STANGE, GEORGE ROBERT, b. Chicago, Ill, Sept. 28, 19; m; c. 3. ENGLISH LITERATURE. B.S, Harvard, 41, Am. Counc. Learned Soc. fel, 42, fel, 47-49, Ph.D.(Eng), 51. Asst. ed, Little Brown & Co, 46-47; tutor hist. & lit, Harvard, 47-49; mem. fac. lit, Bennington Col, 49-51; Eng, Univ. Minn, 51-55, assoc. prof, 55-60, prof, 60-67, chmn. comp. lit. prog, 65-67; FAY PROF. ENG. LIT, TUFTS UNIV, 67-, chmn. dept, 67-72. Fund Advan. Educ. fac. fel, 55-56; assoc. mem. fac, Cambridge, 55-56; vis. prof, Univ. Chicago, 60-61; Guggenheim fel, 61-62; chmn, Fulbright screening comt. Eng, 66-68. U.S.N, 43-46, Lt. Nineteenth century literature. Publ: Ed, Poetry of Coleridge, Dell, 59; ed, Thackeray's Henry Esmond, Holt, 62; auth, Matthew Arnold: the poet as humanist, Princeton, 67; co-auth, Victorian poetry and poetics, Houghton, 2nd ed, 68; Art criticism as a prose genre, In: The art of Victorian prose, Oxford, 68. Add: Dept. of English, Tufts University, Medford, MA 02155.

STANGER, ALLEN BORDEN, Religion. See Volume IV, Philosophy, Religion and Law.

STANIFORTH, GWENDOLYN E, b. Chicago, Ill, Oct. 8, 33. ENGLISH. B.A, Ill. Col, 54; M.A, Univ. Calif, Los Angeles, 59, Ph.D.(Eng), 66. Asst. ref. librn, Huntington Libr, 54-59, asst. to head ref. dept, 60-61; asst. prof. ENG, CALIF. STATE UNIV, HAYWARD, 64-70, ASSOC. PROF, 70- MLA; Renaissance Soc. Am. John Donne; Ben Jonson; William Shakespeare. Add: Dept. of English, California State University, Hayward, 25800 Hillary St, Hayward, CA 94542.

STANKIEWICZ, MARKETA GOETZ, German & Comparative Literature. See Volume III, Foreign Languages, Linguistics & Philology.

STANLEY, GEORGE EDWARD, Linguistics, German. See Volume III, Foreign Languages, Linguistics and Philology.

STANLEY, JULIA PENELOPE, English Linguistics. See Volume III, Foreign Languages, Linguistics & Philology.

STANLIS, PETER J, b. Newark, N.J, Aug. 12, 20; m. 45. ENGLISH LITERATURE, HISTORY OF IDEAS. B.A, Middlebury Col, 42, M.A, Bread Loaf Sch, 44; Rackham fel, Univ. Mich, 44, Ph.D, 51. Asst. prof. ENG, Ithaca Col, 45-46; instr, Univ. Mich, 46-48; Wayne State Univ, 48-52; Univ. Detroit, 52-53, asst. prof, 53-56, assoc. prof, 56-60, prof, 60-68; PROF. & CHMN. DEPT, ROCKFORD COL, 69-, DISTINGUISHED PROF. HUMANITIES, 73- Newberry Libr. fel, 55; ed, The Burke Newslett, 59-67; guest prof, Bread Loaf Grad. Sch, summers 61, 62; secy, Edmund Burke Mem. Found, 63-; co-ed, Stud. Burke & His Times, 67-68, ed, 68-72, exec. ed, 72- U.S.A.A.F 42-43. MLA; Col. Eng. Asn; Burke Soc. Am; Burke Soc, Austria; Johnson Soc. Great Lakes Region; Conf. Brit. Stud; Am. Soc. 18th Century Stud. Eighteenth century English literature, especially Dr. Johnson and Edmund Burke; the natural law; political philosophy. Publ: Edmund Burke and the natural law, Univ. Mich, 58, 2nd ed, 65; co-auth, A methodology for studying the services of local government, Southeast. Mich. Metropolitan Community Res. Corp, 61; auth, Edmund Burke: selected writings and speeches, Doubleday, 63; The relevance of Edmund Burke, Kenedy, 64; Edmund Burke, the Enlightenment and the modern world, Univ. Detroit, 67; Robert Frost: the individual and society, Rockford Col, 73. Add: Dept. of English, Rockford College, Rockford, IL 61101.

STANNARD, UNA, b. Boston, Mass, Dec. 31, 27. ENGLISH & AMERICAN LITERATURE. B.A, Boston Univ, 50; M.A, Radcliffe Col, 55, Ph.D, 59. Instr. Eng, Wheaton Col.(Mass), 57-58; Univ. Calif, Berkeley, 59-60, asst. prof, 60-65; RES. & WRITING, 65- Am. Asn. Univ. Women nat. fel, 56-57. MLA. Ideas of childhood from 1750-1925 in England and America. Publ: The new Pamela, Ballantine Bks, 69, 71; Married women v. husbands' names, Germainbooks, 73; The male maternal instinct, Trans-action, 11-12/70; The mask of beauty, In: Woman in sexist society, Basic Bks, 71; Clothing and sexuality, Sexual Behavior, 5/71; plus others. Add: 91 St. Germain Ave, San Francisco, CA 94114.

STANTON, FRED E, b. Ore, Mar. 9, 16; m. 49; c. 3. SPEECH. Ph.D, Wash. State Univ, 62. ASSOC. PROF. SPEECH, GONZAGA UNIV, 49- Am. Speech & Hearing Asn. Programmed instruction; disorders of speech and hearing. Add: Dept. of Speech, Gonzaga University, Spokane, WA 99202.

STANTON, ROBERT BRUCE, b. Craig, Colo, Dec. 4, 25; m. 48; c. 2. ENGLISH. B.A, Univ. Kansas City, 49, M.A, 50; Ph.D.(Eng), Ind. Univ, 53. Instr. ENG, Northwest. Univ, 53-56; UNIV. WASH, 56-58, asst. prof, 58-67, ASSOC. PROF, 67- Fulbright lectr, Kumamoto Univ, Japan, 61-62 & Inst. Am. Stud, Taipei, Taiwan, summer 62; vis. prof. & adv, Am. Stud. Prog, Univ. Philippines, 64. U.S.A, 44-46. MLA; NCTE. Nathaniel Hawthorne; 19th century American literature; symbolism in the novel. Publ: The short story and the reader, 60 & An introduction to fiction, 65, Holt; Hawthorne, Bunyon and the American romances & The trial of nature: an analysis of The Blithedale romance, 61, PMLA; The Scarlet letter as dialectic of temperament and ideas, Stud. Novel, 70; plus others. Add: Dept. of English, University of Washington, Seattle, WA 98105.

STANTON, STEPHEN SADLER, b. Ann Arbor, Mich, June 24, 15. ENGLISH. B.S, Harvard, 38; M.A, Univ. Mich, 42; Ph.D.(Eng. & comp. lit), Columbia Univ, 55. Teacher, St. Paul's Sch, Concord, N.H, 38-41; instr. Eng, Univ. Mich, 46; Williams Col.(Mass), 49-51; lectr, Barnard Col, Columbia Univ, 54-55; from asst. prof. to PROF. ENG, UNIV. MICH, ANN ARBOR, 55- U.S.N.R, 43-46, Lt. MLA; NCTE. Modern European and American drama; Shakespeare and English drama; modern English and American literature. Publ: A casebook on Candida, Crowell, 62; ed, Camille and other plays, Hill & Wang, 57; Shaw's debt to Scribe, PMLA, 12/61; Ibsen, Gilbert and Scribe's Bataille de dames, Educ. Theatre J, 3/65; Walter Hasenclever's Humanity, Mod. Drama, 2/71. Add: Dept. of Humanities, 1521 E. Engineering, University of Michigan, Ann Arbor, MI 48104.

STANTON-MICHAELS, ELIZABETH, b. Syracuse, N.Y, Sept. 12, 10; m. 72. ENGLISH. A.B, Denison Univ, 31; A.M, Radcliff Col, 33; Ph.D, Ohio State Univ, 42. Tutor Eng, Am. Col, Bulgaria, 32-35; asst, Ohio State Univ, 36-39; instr. Eng. & humanities, Stephens Col, 39-45; asst. prof. Eng, Denison Univ, 45-47, vis. prof, 56-57; assoc. prof. & dean women, Beloit Col, 47-50; dean & v.pres, Am. Col. Girls, Turkey, 50-56; asst. prof. Eng, Ohio Univ, 57-65, assoc. prof, 65-72, dir. exten. div, 62-69, independent stud, 69-72. Am. Asn. Univ. Women (mem. fels. awards comt, 66-73, chmn. Am. fels. awards comt, 66-73). Administration. Add: 68 Curve St, Wellesley, MA 02181.

STANWOOD, PAUL GRANT, b. Iowa, Apr. 25, 33; m. 64; c. 2. ENGLISH LITERATURE. B.A, Iowa State Teachers Col, 54; M.A, Univ. Mich, 56, Ph.D, 61; Fulbright grant, Univ. Mainz, Ger, 58-59; M.A, Cambridge, 68. Teaching fel, Univ. Mich, 56-58, 59-61; instr. ENG, Tufts Univ, 61-63, asst. prof, 63-65; UNIV. B.C, 65-67, ASSOC. PROF, 67- Frank L. Weil Inst, Peterhouse, Cambridge, summer 63; Can. Counc. fel, 68-69 & 73-74; vis. prof, Peterhouse, Cambridge, 68-69; Folger Shakespeare Libr. sr. fel, 72. Renaissance Soc. Am; MLA; Milton Soc. Am; Can. Asn. Univ. Teachers. Textual bibliography; 17th century English literature; Tudor and Stuart history. Publ: Ed, John Cosin, A collection of private devotions, Oxford, 67; Henry More's Democritus Platonissans, Univ. Calif, Los Angeles, 68; auth, St. Teresa and Joseph Beaumont's Psyche, J. Eng. & Ger. Philol. 7/63; A Donne discovery, Times Lit. Suppl, 10/19/67; Contemporary and patristic borrowing in the Caroline divines, Renaissance Quart, winter 70; plus others. Add: Dept. of English, University of British Columbia, Vancouver 8, B.C, Can.

STAPLES, HUGH B, b. Malden, Mass, Oct. 7, 22; m. 49; c. 2. ENGLISH. A.B, Harvard, 47; Ph.D, Univ. Calif, 54. From instr. to asst. prof. Eng, Northwest. Univ, 54-61; assoc. prof, Univ. Calif, Davis, 61-66; prof, UNIV. CINCINNATI, 66-70, ROPES PROF. COMP. LIT, 70-, dir. grad. stud. Eng, 66-72. Consult. ed, James Joyce Quart. Sig.C, 42-46, 1st Lt. MLA. Modern American literature; Irish literature. Publ: Robert Lowell: the first twenty years, Farrar, Straus, 62 & Faber, London, 62; ed, The Ireland of Sir Jonah Barrington, Univ. Wash, 67; plus numerous articles. Add: Dept. of English, University of Cincinnati, College of Arts & Science, Cincinnati, OH 45221.

STAPLETON, K. LAURENCE, b. Holyoke, Mass, Nov. 20, 11. ENGLISH, POLITICAL THEORY. A.B, Smith Col, 32, alumnae fel, London Sch. Econ. & Polit. Sci. & Bedford Col, Univ. London, 32-33; Guggenheim fel, 47-48. Examiner, State Pub. Employ. Serv, Mass, 33-34; instr. Eng, BRYN MAWR COL, 34-38, asst. prof, 38-42, assoc. prof, 42-48, prof. Eng. & polit. theory, 48-64, MARY E. GARRETT PROF. ENG, 64-, chmn. dept, 54-65. Nat. Endowment for Arts fel, 72-73. Renaissance Soc. Am; MLA; Eng. Asn, Gt. Brit. Literary criticism; modern poetry; 17th century English literature. Publ: Justice and world society, Univ. N.C, 44; Design of democracy, Oxford, 49; ed, H.D. Thoreau: a writer's journal, Dover, 60 & Heinemann, London, 61; auth, Yushin's log and other poems, A.S. Barnes, N.Y, Rutherford, N.J. & Yoselof, London, 69; The elected circle: studies in the art of prose, Princeton, 73, The theme of virtue in Donne's verse epistles, Stud. Philol, 4/58; Milton's concept of time in the Christian doctrine, Harvard Theol. Rev, 1/64; Perspectives of time in Paradise lost, Philol. Quart, 10/66. Add: Dept. of English, Bryn Mawr College, Bryn Mawr, PA 19010.

STAPPENBECK, HERBERT LOUIS, b. San Antonio, Tex, Feb. 5, 35; m. 58; c. 3. AMERICAN LITERATURE, BIBLIOGRAPHY. B.A, St. Mary's Univ, 56; M.A, Univ. Tex, Austin, 58, Ph.D.(Eng), 68. Instr. ENG, San Antonio Col, 58-63, asst. prof, 63-65; teaching assoc, Univ. Tex, Austin, 68-69; ASST. PROF, UNIV. MO-COLUMBIA, 69- Regional assoc, MLA proj. revise Am. Lit. Manuscripts, 70-; Am. Philos. Soc. res. grant, summer 73. MLA; AAUP. Joseph Hergesheimer; American literature between Civil War and World War I. Publ: A catalogue of the Joseph Hergesheimer collection at the University of Texas, 74. Add: Dept. of English, University of Missouri-Columbia, Columbia, MO 65201.

STARBUCK, GEORGE EDWIN, b. Columbus, Ohio, June 15, 31; m. 55, 62, 68; c. 5. POETRY, ENGLISH. Calif. Inst. Technol, 47-49; Univ. Calif. Berkeley, 50-51; Univ. Chicago, 54-57; Harvard, 57-58. Ed, fiction, nonfiction & poetry, Houghton Mifflin Co, 58-61; Am. Acad. Arts & Lett. Prix de Rome fel, Am. Acad. Rome, 61-63; librn. & lectr. Eng, State Univ. N.Y. Buffalo, 63-64; from lectr. to assoc. prof. creative writing & dir. grad. prog, Univ. Iowa, 64-70; PROF. CREATIVE WRITING & DIR. GRAD. PROG, BOSTON UNIV, 71- Yale Series Younger Poets Award, 60; Guggenheim fel, 61-62. U.S.A, 52-54. PEN Club; MLA; New Univ. Conf; New Eng. Col. Eng. Asn. History of poetic style. Publ: Poems, Bone thoughts, Yale, 60; Elegy in a country church yard, Pym-Randall, 73; White paper, Atlantic Monthly, 66. Add: 236 Bay State Rd, Boston, MA 02215.

STARCK, KENNETH, b. Loveland, Colo, Sept. 5, 34; c. 3. COMMUNICATION THEORY, JOURNALISM. A.B, Wartburg Col, 56; M.A, Univ. Mo-Columbia, 60; Ph.D.(jour), South. Ill. Univ, Carbondale, 68. Dir. news bur, Wartburg Col, 56-58; instr. jour, Univ. Mo, 60-61; reporter, Herald & Rev, Decatur, Ill, 61-62; educ. ed, Commercial Appeal, Memphis, Tenn, 62-64; instr. JOUR, South. Ill. Univ, Carbondale, 65-66, 67-68, asst. prof, 68-71; lectr, Univ. Tampere, Finland, 66-67; ASSOC. PROF, UNIV. S.C, 71- Panelist-speaker, numerous press groups, 69-71. Asn. Educ. in Jour.(mem. ad hoc comt. cable commun-CATV, 71-72); Soc. Advan. Scand. Stud. Press responsibility, ethics; public attitudes toward mass media. Publ: Co-auth, Backtalk: press councils in America, Canfield, 72 & Red China's external propaganda during Sino-U.S. rapprochement, Jour. Quart, winter 72; auth, Values and information source preferences, J. Commun, 3/73; Defining perceptions of the function of the media, Gazette, 73. Add: College of Journalism, University of South Carolina, Columbia, SC 29208.

STARK, BRUCE RODERICK, English, Linguistics. See Volume III, Foreign Languages, Linguistics & Philology.

STARK, IRWIN, b. Passaic, N.J, Nov. 17, 12; m. 36; c. 2. ENGLISH. B.A, City Col. New York, 35, M.S, 40. Lectr. ENG, CITY COL. NEW YORK, 53-57, instr, 57-62, asst. prof, 62-68, assoc. prof, 68-71, PROF, 71- Vis. lectr, Hebrew Univ, Israel, 66-67. Writing and teaching of fiction. Publ: The invisible island, Viking, 48; co-auth, Breakthrough: a treasury of American-Jewish literature, McGraw, 64; auth, Subpoena, New Am. Libr, 66. Add: Dept. of English, City College of New York, New York, NY 10031.

STARK, JOHN OLSEN, b. Superior, Wis, Sept. 13, 39; m. 68; c. 1. AMERICAN LITERATURE. B.A, Northland Col, 61; M.A, Claremont Grad. Sch, 63; Ph.D.(Eng), Univ. Wis, 70. Instr. Eng, Univ. Wis-Eau Claire, 64-67; asst. prof, Kent State Univ, 69-73. MLA. Contemporary American fiction; 20th century American literature; stylistics. Publ: The literature of exhaustion: Borges, Nabokov and Barth, Duke Univ, 74; Barbary Shore: the basis of Mailer's best work, Mod. Fiction Stud, autumn 71; Borge's Tlön, Uqbar, Orbis Tertius and Nabokov's Pale fire, Tex. Stud, spring 72; The style of Tender is the night, Fitzgerald/Hemingway Annual, 72. Add: Apt. 4, 3631 Napoli Lane, Middleton, WI 53562.

STARKE, CATHERINE JUANITA, b. Charlotte, N.C, Apr. 5, 13; m. 39. ENGLISH. B.A, Hunter Col, 36; M.A, Columbia Univ, 37, Ed.D.(Eng), 63. Teacher, High Sch, Va, 38-46; instr. ENG, Morgan State Col, 47-50, asst. prof, 50-56; JERSEY CITY STATE COL, 57-63; assoc. prof, 63-68; PROF, 68- MLA; NCTE. Negro fictional portraits in American literature. Publ: Negro stock characters, archetypes, and individuals in American literature, Univ. Microfilms, 63; Symbolism of the Negro college in three recent novels, Phylon, 17: 4. Add: Dept. of English, Jersey City State College, Jersey City, NJ 07305.

STARKEY, PENELOPE SCHOTT, b, Washington, D.C, Apr. 20, 42. ENGLISH LITERATURE. B.A, Univ. Mich, Ann Arbor, 63; Sir George Williams Univ, 65-66; M.A, Queens Col.(N.Y), 68; Ph.D.(Eng), City Univ. New York, 71. Lectr. ENG, DOUGLASS COL, RUTGERS UNIV, 71-72, ASST. PROF, 72- Mem. adv. comt, New Writer, 72- MLA; Scottish Text Soc; Col. Eng. Asn; Poetry Soc. Am.(John Masefield Mem. Award, 74). Medieval and Renaissance English literature; modern prosody. Publ: Gavin Douglas's Eneados: dilemmas in the nature prologues, Stud. Scottish Lit, 73; What the counseling office doesn't tell you, New Directions Women in N.J, fall 73; poems in CEA Critic, Counter/Measures, Lyric, Mich. Quart. Rev, Northwest Rev, Proteus, and others. Add: Dept. of English, Douglass College, Rutgers University, New Brunswick, NJ 08903.

STARKMAN, MIRIAM KOSH, b. Poland, May 31, 16; m. 41; c. 1. ENGLISH LITERATURE. A.B, Brooklyn Col, 35; A.M, Columbia Univ, 39, fel, 43-44, Ph.D, 48. From instr. to assoc. prof. Eng. LIT, QUEENS COL.(N.Y), 44-64, PROF, 64- Lectr, Columbia Univ, 48-49; Ford Found. fel, 54-55; Fulbright prof, Israel, 62-63; Guggenheim fels, 62-63; vis. prof, Wis. Univ, summer 64; adv. screening comt, Eng. lang. & lit, Comt. Int. Exchange Persons, 64-67; vis. prof, Tel-Aviv Univ, 72. Seventeenth century; Milton; Swift. Publ: Swift's satire on learning in Tale of a tub, Princeton, 50; ed, Swift, Gulliver's travels and other writings, Bantam, 62 & Seventeenth century English poetry (2 vols), Knopf, 67; auth, Quakers, phrenologists, and Jonathan Swift, J. Hist. Ideas, 6/59; Noble numbers and the poetry of devotion, In, Reason and imagination, Columbia Univ, 62; Swift's rhetoric: the overfraught pinnace, S. Atlantic Quart, spring 69. Add: Dept. of English, Queens College, Flushing, NY 11367.

STARLIN, GLENN, b. Spokane, Wash, Dec. 13, 13; m. 39; c. 2. SPEECH. B.A, Univ. Idaho, 38; M.A, Univ. Iowa, 39, Ph.D.(speech & drama), 51. Instr. SPEECH & DRAMA, Univ. Akron, 40-43; asst. prof, UNIV. ORE, 47-52, assoc. prof, 52-59, PROF, 59-, V.PROVOST, 73-, asst. to pres, 53-54, head dept. speech, 55-64, assoc. dean col. lib. arts, 65-68, acting dean, 68-70. Instr, Univ. Iowa, 49-50; prog. assoc, Nat. Educ, TV & Radio Ctr, Ann Arbor, Mich, 54-55; dir. inter-instnl. TV teaching proj, Ore. State Syst. Higher Educ, 57-63; consult. TV in higher educ, State Univ. N.Y, 61-62; Fulbright lectr. & consult. educ. TV, Univ. London, 64-65. Civilian in Mil. Intel. Div, U.S. Dept. War, 43-47. Asn. Prof. Broadcasting Educ.(pres, 58-60); West. Radio & TV Asn; Speech Commun. Asn; West. Speech Asn; Nat. Asn. Educ. Broadcasters; Int. Commun. Asn. Television; radio; theater. Publ; Co-auth, Inter-institutional teaching by television in Oregon, Ore. State Syst. Higher Educ, 57-64; auth, Television and higher education, N.Y. State Educ. Dept, 62; co-auth, Speech communication via radio and television, W.C. Brown, 71. Add: Office of Academic Affairs, University of Oregon, Eugene, OR 97403.

STARLING, JEREMIAH PELLETIER, b. Wilmington, N.C, Aug. 17, 38; m. 65; c. 2. ENGLISH LANGUAGE & LITERATURE. A.B, Davidson Col, 60; M.A, Univ. N.C, Chapel Hill, 61, Ph.D.(Eng), 68; Rotary fel, Edinburgh Univ, 62-63. Instr. ENG, UNIV. LOUISVILLE, 66-68, asst. prof, 68-72, ASSOC. PROF, 72-, ASSOC. DEAN GRAD. SCH, 72-, CHMN. DEPT. ENG, 74-, acting chmn, 71, asst. dean grad. sch, 71-72. MLA; Mod. Humanities Res. Asn; Keats-Shelley Asn. Am; Browning Inst; Browning Soc; Byron Soc. English romantic poetry; 18th century and 19th century Romantic philosophy, especially theory of mind and imagination; 19th century fiction. Add: Dept. of English, University of Louisville, S. Third St, Louisville, KY 40208.

STARMER, GARRETT LUDLOW, b. San Francisco, Calif, Oct. 23, 15; m. 46; c. 4. SPEECH PATHOLOGY. A.B, Stanford Univ, 40, M.A. & Calif. admin. credential, 43; Northwest. Univ, 40; Ph.D.(speech), Univ. Utah, 52. Asst. instr. speech reeduc, Stanford Univ, 40-41; instr. & boys counsel, War Relocation Authority High Sch, Calif, 42-43; asst. prof. speech, Mont. State Col, 43-45; assoc. prof. & head dept, Hendrix Col, 45-46; PROF. SPEECH & SPEECH PATHOL, CALIF, STATE UNIV, CHICO, 46-, head TV serv. Ctr, 53-68. Bd. dir, Educ. TV station KVIE, Sacramento, Calif, 53-61, v.pres, 58-61; instr, Stanford Univ, 55, spec. lectr, 56; dir. summer speech & reading clin, Chico, Calif, 58-62; chmn. comt. for TV in teacher educ, Calif. Counc. Teacher Educ, 58-63; mem. bd. dir, Educ. TV station KIXE, Redding, Calif, 61-69, chmn. bd, 64-69; participant, Behav. Modification, 68; trainee, Int. Inst. Laryngetomees, 68; private practice speech pathol. & counselling. Am. Speech & Hearing Asn; Am. Soc. Clin. Hypnosis; Int. Transactional Anal. Asn. Add: 795 Stilson Canyon Rd, Chico, CA 95926.

STAROBA, FRANK JOSEPH, b. Chicago, Ill, Mar. 9, 34; m. 57; c. 1. DRAMA. B.A, DePauw Univ, 56; fel. & M.A, Northwest. Univ, 57; D.F.A.(directing), Yale, 64. Asst. prof. theatre, speech & drama, Col. William & Mary, 61-66; co-producer, Wedgewood Theatre, Va, 66-67; assoc. prof. FED. CITY COL, 68-71, PROF. COMMUNICATIVE ARTS, 71-, DIR. DIV. FINE ARTS, 72- Am. Theatre Asn. Playwriting; directing; acting. Add: Federal City College, Second & D St. N.W, Washington, DC 20001.

STARR, GEORGE A, b. New York, N.Y, Dec. 13, 34. ENGLISH. B.A, Yale, 56; B.A, Cambridge, 58; Ph.D.(Eng), Princeton, 63. From instr. to PROF. ENG, UNIV. CALIF, BERKELEY, 62- Am. Counc. Learned Soc. fel, 66-67. English literature 1660-1800; the English novel. Publ: Defoe and spiritual autobiography, 65 & Defoe and casuistry, 71, Princeton Univ, ed, Moll Flanders, Oxford Univ, 71. Add: Dept. of English, University of California, Berkeley, CA 94720.

STARR, HERBERT WILLMARTH, b. New York, N.Y, Apr. 6, 16; m. 47. ENGLISH LITERATURE. A.B, Temple Univ, 38, A.M, 39; Ph.D, Univ. Pa, 41. Instr, W.Va. Univ, 41-42; Princeton, 44; Lafayette Col, 44-46; assoc. prof. ENG, TEMPLE UNIV, 46-72, EMER. PROF, 72- U.S.A, 42-43. MLA; Mod. Humanities Res. Asn, Gt. Brit. 18th century English literature, especially Thomas Gray; Conan Doyle. Publ: Gray as a literary critic; A bibliography of Thomas Gray; co-ed. & illusr, Leaves from the copper beeches, 59; co-ed, The complete poems of Thomas Gray, English, Latin and Greek, 66, rev. ed, 72 & ed, The correspondence of Thomas Gray with corrections and additions (3 vols), 72, Oxford; ed, Twentieth century interpretations of Gray's Elegy, Prentice-Hall, 68 & Elegy written in a country churchyard (essays), Merrill, 68; plus articles in scholarly journals. Add: 300 Hathaway Lane, Wynnewood, PA 19096.

STARR, LOUIS MORRIS, History, Journalism. See Volume I, History.

STARR, NATHAN COMFORT, b. Eau Claire, Wis, Mar. 29, 96; m. 26; c. 4. ENGLISH LITERATURE. A.B, Harvard, 17, A.M, 24, Ph.D, 28; B.A, Oxford, 22, M.A, 25; hon. D.Litt, Rollins Col, 49. Asst. Eng, Harvard & Radcliffe Cols, 21-24, instr. & tutor, 25-29; assoc. prof, Colgate Univ, 29-30; St. John's Col.(Md), 30-34, asst. to pres, 32-34; instr. Eng, Williams Col. (Mass), 34-36, asst. prof, 36-40, asst. dean & acting dean, 36-38; assoc. prof. Eng, Rollins Col, 41-44, prof, 44-52; Fulbright vis. lectr, Kansai Univ, Japan, 52-53; vis. prof. & prof. ENG. & HUMANITIES, UNIV. FLA, 53-63, EMER. PROF, 63- Mem. staff, div. world trade intel, U.S. Dept. State, 43-44; fel, Newberry Libr, 51; mem. fac, New Sch. Soc. Res, 64- U.S.A, 17-19, Lt. MLA; Col. Eng. Asn; Int. Arthurian Soc; NCTE. English and American romanticism; Arthurian legend, especially 20th century; early printing, 1455-1550. Publ: Dynamics of literature, Columbia Univ, 45; King Arthur today, Univ. Fla, 54; ed, The pursuit of learning, Harcourt, 56 & The humanistic tradition, Holt, 64; auth, introd, C.S. Lewis' Till we have faces, Seabury, 68; Long yesterday and other poems, Bauhan, 72; Smollett's sailors, Am. Neptune, 72. Add: 333 E. 68th St, New York, NY 10021.

STARR, WENDELL REASON, b. Lewiston, Nebr, Oct. 13, 14; m. 54. ENGLISH, EDUCATION. B.A, Ottawa Univ.(Kans), 36; M.A, Univ. Colo, 47; Ph.D.(educ), Univ. Minn, 58. Teacher, high sch, Colo. & Wyo, 36-42 & 46; Instr. ENG, Univ. Colo, 46-49; from asst. prof. to assoc. prof, UNIV. NORTH. COLO, 58-68, PROF, 68- U.S.A, 42-46, S/Sgt. NCTE; Conf. Eng. Educ; Conf. Col. Compos. & Commun. Methods of teaching language, composition and literature. Add: Dept. of English, University of Northern Colorado, Greeley, CO 80639.

STASHEFF, EDWARD, b. New York, N.Y, Feb. 18, 09; m. 34; c. 4. SPEECH. A.B, Columbia Univ, 29, M.A, 34; hon. LL.D, East. Mich. Univ, 68. Teacher Eng. & speech, high schs, New York, N.Y, 30-44; writer-dir, bd. of educ, FM Radio Sta, WNYE, New York, 44-48; dir. educ, TV Sta. WPIX, New York, 48-50; TX supvr, bd. of educ, New York, 50-52; assoc. prof. SPEECH, UNIV. MICH, ANN ARBOR, 52-58, PROF, 58- Educ. consult, CBS TV, 45-47; lectr, Teachers Col, Columbia Univ, 46-48; consult, Ford Found. Overseas Develop, 55; Midwest Prog. Airborne TV Instr, 61-62; Ford Found, 60-63; consult. & prog. assoc, Nat. Educ. TV-Radio Ctr, 57-59; assoc. ed, Quart. J. Speech, 60-63; dir. prod, Instruct. TV Trust Israel, 65-66. Asn. Educ. Radio-TV(v.pres, 54); Nat. Asn. Educ. Broadcasters; Speech Commun. Asn. Educational television; television production; international broadcasting. Publ: Co-auth, Shakespearean night's entertainment, Bass Publ, 35, Teaching through radio and television, Rinehart, 52, Your speech, Harcourt, 2nd ed, 60 & The television program, Hill & Wang, 4th ed, 68; auth, What will the satellites say, In: On speech and speakers, Holt, 68. Add: 307 Westwood, Ann Arbor, MI 48103.

STASNY, JOHN F, b. St. Paul, Minn, May 2, 25; m. 51; c. 5. ENGLISH, HUMANITIES. A.B, Col. St. Thomas, 49; M.A, Marquette Univ, 50; Columbia Univ, 53-55. Instr. ENG, Marquette Univ, 50-53; W.VA. UNIV, 55-66, asst. prof, 66-70, ASSOC. PROF, 70- Ed, Victorian Poetry: A Critical Jour. Victorian Lit. U.S.A.F, 43-46. MLA (chmn. Victorian sect, 72-73). Publ: Co-auth, Anthology of readings: humanities, W.Va. Univ, 67; auth, W. Winwood Reade's The martyrdom of man: a Darwinian history, 61 & Doctor Johnson and Walter Pater on stoicism: a comparison of views, 63, W.Va. Univ. Philol. Papers. Add: Dept. of English, West Virginia University, Morgantown, WV 26506.

STATES, BERT O, b. Punxsutawney, Pa, Aug. 8, 29; m. 51; c. 2. THEATRE ARTS, ENGLISH. B.A, Pa. State Univ, 50, M.A, 55; D.F.A.(theatre arts), Yale, 60. Asst. prof. Eng, Rensselaer Polytech. Inst, 59-60; Skidmore Col, 60-64; theatre arts, Univ. Pittsburgh, 64-67; assoc. prof. THEATRE ARTS & ENG, CORNELL UNIV, 67-73, PROF, 73- Sig.C, U.S.A, 51-53. Theory of drama; dramatic literature. Publ: Irony and drama: a poetics, Cornell Univ, 71; Chekhov's dramatic strategy, Yale Rev, winter 67; Pinter's Homecoming: the shock of non-recognition, autumn 68 & The word pictures in Hamlet, autumn 73, Hudson Rev; plus others. Add: 925 Cayuga Heights Rd, R.D. 1, Ithaca, NY 14850.

STATHIS, JAMES JOHN, b. New York, N.Y, Jan. 31, 37. ENGLISH. B.A, Univ. Ala, 60; M.S, Univ. Wis, 61, Ph.D.(Eng), 64. ASSOC. PROF. ENG, VANDERBILT UNIV, 64-, DIR. GRAD. STUD, 74- Nat. Endowment Arts & Humanities fel, 68. U.S.A, 57-59. MLA; NCTE. Restoration of 18th century literature, especially Swift, Restoration comedy and tragedy. Publ: A bibliography of Swift studies, 1945-1965, Vanderbilt Univ, 67; Diminution in the pulpit: Swift's sermon upon the martyrdom of King Charles I, Tenn. Stud. Lit, 67; Swift and the rhetoric of the Anglican Via media, In: Rhetoric: theories for application, NCTE, 67. Add: Dept. of English, Vanderbilt University, Box 1682, Sta. B, Nashville, TN 37203.

STATON, WALTER F, JR, b. Philadelphia, Pa, June 2, 24; m. 47; c. 5. ENGLISH. A.B, Univ. Pa, 48, M.A, 49, Ph.D, 55. Instr. ENG, Albright Col, 50-51; asst. prof, Erskine Col, 51-53; W.Va. Univ, 54-55; asst. prof, South. Ill. Univ, 55-67; assoc. prof, PURDUE UNIV, WEST LAFAYETTE, 67-71, PROF, 71- Harrison fel, 53-54, Huntington Libr. grant-in-aid, 59; Folger Libr. grant, 60; Newberry Libr. grant, 63. C.Eng, U.S.A, 43-46. MLA; Renaissance Soc. Am; Am. Asn. Teachers Italian; Malone Soc. Renaissance literature. Publ: Co-ed, Guarini's Il Pastor Fido, Oxford, 63; Spenser's April lay, Stud. Philol, 62; Ovidian elements in MND, Huntington Libr. Quart, 63. Add: Dept. of English, Graduate School, Purdue University, West Lafayette, IN 47907.

STAUB, AUGUST W, b. New Orleans, La, Oct. 9, 31; m. 52; c. 1. DRAMA, ENGLISH. B.A, La. State Univ, 52, M.A, 54, Ph.D.(theatre), 60. Instr. speech, La. State Univ, 55-56; Eng. & speech, East. Mich. Univ, 56-58; asst. prof. speech, Univ. Fla, 60-64; assoc. prof. DRAMA, UNIV. NEW ORLEANS, 64-68, PROF, 68-, CHMN. DEPT. DRAMA & COMMUN, 66- Assoc. dir, Dunes Summer Theatre, 56-59; La. State Univ. Found. distinguished fac. fel, 70-71. U.S.A, 52-54, 1st Lt. Am. Theatre Asn; Speech Commun. Asn.(assoc. ed, Speech Teacher, 65-67); South. Speech Asn; Southwest Theatre Conf.(v.pres, 71-72, pres, 72-73); Univ. & Col. Theatre Asn.(v.pres, 71-73, exec. v.pres, 73-74). Theatre history; mass media; modern theatre. Publ: Co-auth, Explorations of literature, La. State Univ, 66; ed, Introduction to theatrical arts, Kendall Hunt, 71; auth, Creating Theatre, Harper, 73; contrib, Contemporary rhetoric, Scott, 71; plus others. Add: Dept. of Drama & Communications, University of New Orleans, New Orleans, LA 70122.

STAUDACHER, JOSEPH M, b. Milwaukee, Wis, May 4, 14; m. 43; c. 6. SPEECH EDUCATION. B.A, Marquette Univ, 39, M.A, 42; M.A, Northwest. Univ, 48. Instr. SPEECH, Univ. Detroit, 40-42; Marquette Univ, 45-47; asst, Northwest. Univ, 47-48; instr, MARQUETTE UNIV, 48-49, asst. prof, 49-58, assoc. prof, 58-67, PROF, 67- Audience measurement on broadcast research; closed-circuit television in teaching basic speech course. Publ: Co-auth, The speech arts, Lyons & Carnahan, 66; Fundamentals of speech, Random, 69; Laymen, proclaim the word, Franciscan Herald, 73. Add: Dept. of Speech, Marquette University, Milwaukee, WI 53233.

STAUFFER, DONALD B, b. East Orange, N.J, Sept. 22, 30; m. 57; c. 3. ENGLISH. B.A, Wesleyan Univ, 52; M.A, Ind. Univ, 56, Ph.D.(Eng), 63. Instr. ENG, Williams Col, 61-64; asst. prof, STATE UNIV. N.Y. ALBANY, 64-68, ASSOC. PROF, 68- U.S.A, 53-55. MLA (bibliog. comt, 64-71); AAUP. Prose style; Edgar Allan Poe; American poetry. Publ: A short history of American poetry, Dutton, 74; Style and meaning in Ligeia and William Wilson, Stud. Short Fiction, summer 65; co-auth, MLA Int. Bibliog, PMLA, 65-71; auth, Poe as phrenologist: the example of Monsieur Dupin, In: Papers on Poe, Chantry Music Press, 72; plus others. Add: Dept. of English, State University of New York at Albany, Albany, NY 12222.

STAUFFER, JAMES PAUL, b. Ithan, Pa, Sept. 9, 15; m. 38; c. 3. ENGLISH LITERATURE. A.B, Pac. Union Col, 41, A.M, 44; Ph.D, Harvard, 52. Prin. elem. sch, Calif, 38-40, instr, 40-42; Eng, Pac. Union Col, 42-45, asst. prof, 45-50, assoc. prof, 50-56, prof, 56-64, registr, 44-46, chmn. dept. Eng, 56-64, div. lang. & lit, 58-64; PROF. ENG. & DEAN GRAD. SCH, LOMA LINDA UNIV, 64- MLA; NCTE; Asn. Higher Educ. General education in the humanities; Browning; contemporary English and American poetry. Add: Graduate School, Loma Linda University, Loma Linda, CA 92354.

STAUFFER, RUTH M, b. Denver, Colo, Oct. 15, 12. ENGLISH & COMPARATIVE LITERATURE. A.B, Univ. Colo, 33; Ph.D, Radcliffe Col, 42. Instr, Univ. Rochester, 41-46; mem. fac. Eng, Sarah Lawrence Col, 46-48; from asst. prof. to assoc. prof, Hofstra Univ, 48-71; RETIRED. Mem, Eng. Inst. MLA. Role of women in Renaissance in England. Add: Crane Neck Rd, Setauket, NY 11733.

STAVIG, MARK LUTHER, b. Northfield, Minn, Jan. 20, 35; m. 57; c. 3. ENGLISH. B.A, Augustana Col.(S.Dak), 56; Fulbright fel. & B.A, Oxford, 58, M.A, 62; Danforth fels, Princeton, 60 & 61, M.A, 60, Ph.D.(Eng), 61. Instr. ENG, Univ. Wis-Madison, 61-63, asst. prof, 63-68; ASSOC. PROF, COLO. COL, 68- Danforth fel, Harvard, 63-64. MLA. Elizabethan drama; 17th century poetry. Publ: Ed, 'Tis pity she's a whore, Crofts Classics, 66; auth, John Ford and the traditional moral order, Univ. Wis, 68. Add: Dept. of English, Colorado College, Colorado Springs, CO 80902.

STAVIG, RICHARD THORSON, b. Tacoma, Wash, May 14, 27; m. 50; c. 2. ENGLISH. B.A, Augustana Col, 50; M.A, Princeton, 53, Ph.D.(Eng), 54. Instr. ENG, Washington & Jefferson Col, 53-55; asst. prof, KALAMAZOO COL, 55-59, assoc. prof, 59-63, PROF, 63- Fulbright prof, Heidelberg, 58-59. U.S.N, 45-46. MLA; Melville Soc. Am. American literature. Add: 2623 Lomond Dr, Kalamazoo, MI 49008.

STAVROU, CONSTANTINE NICHOLAS, b. Buffalo, N.Y, Mar. 6, 23. ENGLISH & AMERICAN LITERATURE. B.A, Univ. Buffalo, 46, M.A, 47, Ph.D.(Eng), 52. Instr. Eng. & Am. stud, Univ. Buffalo, 46; prof. ENG, Lamar State Col. Technol, 60-62; State Univ. N.Y. Col. Potsdam, 62-67; PROF, CANISIUS COL, 68- Nineteenth century, especially Byron and Blake; contemporary literature, especially D.H. Lawrence; American literature, especially William Faulkner and Tennessee Williams. Publ: Whitman and Nietzsche, Univ. N.C, 64; The pursuit of death in Herman Hesse, 73; Albee in wonderland, 73; Lawrence Ferlinghetti, 74; Nada, religion, and Hemingway, J. Lib. Arts, fall 66; plus others. Add: Dept. of English, Canisius College, Buffalo, NY 14208.

STEADMAN, JOHN MARCELLUS, III, b. Spartanburg, S.C, Nov. 25, 18. ENGLISH LITERATURE. A.B, Emory Univ, 40, scholar. & M.A, 41; T.W. Hunt scholar, Princeton, 47-48, M.A, 48, Proctor fel, 48-49, Ph.D.(Eng), 49. Instr. Eng, Ga. Sch. Technol, 41-42; asst. prof, Univ. N.C, 49-51; res, London & Oxford, 53-61; res. assoc, HUNTINGTON LIBR, 62-66, SR. RES. ASSOC, 66-, ED, HUNTINGTON LIBR. QUART, 62-; PROF. ENG, UNIV. CALIF, RIVERSIDE, 67-, vis. prof, 66-67. Huntington Libr. grant-in-aid, 61-62; mem. ed. bd, Milton Stud, A variorum commentary on poems of John Milton, Complete prose works of John Milton & Milton Encycl. U.S.A.A.F, 42-46; U.S.A, 51-52, Capt. MLA (chmn. Spenser group, 66, Milton group, 68, Renaissance drama & iconographical stud, 70 & Lit. & other arts, 73); Dante Soc. Am; Renaissance Soc. Am; Milton Soc. Am.(pres, 73). Milton; epic theory; iconography and emblem books. Publ: Milton and the Renaissance hero, Clarendon, 67; Milton's epic characters: image and idol, Univ. N.C, 68; The myth of Asia, Simon & Schuster, 69, & Macmillan, London, 70; Disembodied laughter: Troilus and the apotheosis tradition, Univ. Calif, 72; Passions well imitated, In: Calm of mind, Case West. Reserve Univ, 71; Iconography and Renaissance drama, In: Research opportunities in Renaissance drama, Northwest. Univ, 72; Renaissance dictionaries and manuals, In: New aspects of lexicography, South. Ill. Univ, 72; plus others. Add: Henry E. Huntington Library, San Marino, CA 91108.

STEADMAN, MARK SIDNEY, JR, b. Statesboro, Ga, July 2, 30; m. 52; c. 3. ENGLISH. A.B, Emory Univ, 51; M.A, Fla. State Univ, 56, Ph.D.(Eng), 63. Instr. ENG, CLEMSON UNIV, 57-60, asst. prof, 60-64, ASSOC. PROF, 64- Danforth Assoc, 67. U.S.N, 51-53. S.Atlantic Mod. Lang. Asn. American humor; modern fiction. Add: Dept. of English, Clemson University, Clemson, SC 29631.

STEAHLY, VIVIAN EUGENIA EMRICK, b. Wapakoneta, Ohio, July 10, 15; m. 36; c. 1. FOREIGN LANGUAGES, ENGLISH. B.A, Ohio State Univ, 36, B.Sc. in Ed, 36; M.A, Univ. Cincinnati, 41. Instr. French, Latin, Eng, Georgetown High Sch, Ohio, 36-39; Eng. Seaford High Sch, Del, 42-43; Univ. Tenn, 47-48; French, Latin, Eng, Winfield High Sch, W.Va, 55-58; asst. prof. Eng. & French, Morris Harvey Col, 58-66, educ, 64-65, head dept. mod. lang, 62-64; ASST. PROF. ENG, OHIO STATE UNIV, 67- Writing & ed. consult, W.Va, Univ. Bd. Gov. & W.Va. State Dept. Educ, 66. MLA; AAAS; Asn. Higher Educ. Freelance writing; 18th century literature; technical writing and editing. Publ: Contrib. auth, The Mott basic language skills program workbook series 600B, Allied Educ. Counc, 66; Seven steps to sensible structure and style, 70, I always wanted to live in the chicken yard and other bits of assorted wisdom and nostalgia, 73 & The gift and other tales, 74; Whitehall; Stimulating the student writer, Nat. Educ. Asn. J, 11/67; plus others. Add: 206 Stinebaugh Dr, Wapakoneta, OH 45895.

STECK, JAMES SPEROW, b. Franklin Co, Pa, Feb. 21, 11; m. 46; c. 2. ENGLISH. B.A, Fairmont State Col, 41; DuPont jr. fel, Univ. Va, 47-48, M.A, 48, DuPont sr. fel, 48-50; D.Ed.(Eng), Pa. State Univ, 68. Teacher, sr. high sch, Md, 41-42; Antietam St. Sch, 46; asst. prof. ENG, Union Col, 50-51, assoc. prof. & head dept, 51-54; teacher, sr. high sch, Md, 54-56; assoc. prof, SHIPPENSBURG STATE COL, 56-68, PROF, 68-, asst. chmn. dept, 72. Consult. Eng, U.S. Armed Forces Inst, Univ. Md, 72. Qm.C, U.S.A, 42-45, 45-46, 1st Lt. MLA. Bibliographical study of Dryden's plays; eighteenth century novel; the fiction of W.H. Hudson. Publ: The intellectual pleasures of the Puritans, Shippensburg Col, 67; Center rule lines in printing: a new kind of bibliographical evidence, In: Papers of the bibliographical society, Univ. Va, 48-49; Dryden's Indian emperour: the early editions and their relation to the text, Stud. in Bibliog, 49. Add: Dept. of English, DHC-115 Shippensburg State College, Shippensburg, PA 17257.

STEDMAN, JANE WINIFRED (MRS. GEORGE C. McELROY), b. Detroit, Mich, June 8, 20; m. 50. ENGLISH. B.A, Wayne Univ, 42, M.A, 43; Edinburgh Univ. Carnegie fel. & Ph.D.(Eng), Univ. Chicago, 55. Instr. ENG, Wayne Univ, 46-50; lectr, ROOSEVELT UNIV, 52-55, asst. prof, 55-61, assoc. prof, 61-66, PROF, 66- Lectr. Eng. & humanities, Univ. Chicago, 54-61; Ind. Univ, Gary, 59-65; Roosevelt Univ. fac. res. grant, 68; fels, Am. Counc. Learned Soc, 70-71 & John Simon Guggenheim Mem. Fund, 73-74; res. award, Fulbright-Hayes Prog, res. in U.K, 73-74. AAUP; Dickens Fel; Soc. Theatre Res; Brontë Soc.(prize, 65). W.S. Gilbert; 19th century fiction; 19th century drama. Publ: Gilbert before Sullivan, Univ. Chicago, 67; The genesis of Patience, Mod. Philol, 8/68; Gilbert's stagecraft: little blocks of wood, In: Gilbert and Sullivan papers, Univ. Kans, 71; From dame to woman: W.S. Gilbert and theatrical transvestism, In: Suffer and be still: women in theVictorian age, Ind. Univ, 72; plus others. Add: 1411 E. 54th Pl, Chicago, IL 60615.

STEDMAN, RAYMOND W, b. Rochester, Pa, June 8, 30; m. 59; c. 3. COMMUNICATION. A.B, Westminster Col.(Pa), 52; M.A, Univ. South. Calif, 53, Ph.D.(commun), 59. Asst. to pres, adminr. educ. broadcasting, dir. spec.

pub. relat. campaigns & lectr, Dept. Telecommun, Univ. South. Calif, 53-62; asst. prof. jour. & commun. & dir. TV, Univ. Fla, 62; admin. dean, Seminole Col. & mem. exec. comt, Orlando Jr. Col, Univ. Orlando, Fla, 62-63; assoc. prof. & head dept. commun, Rollins Col, 63-64; assoc. prof. speech, Nassau Commun. Col, N.Y, 64-65; PROF. ENG. & ASSOC. DEAN FOR COMMUN, BUCKS COUNTY COMMUNITY COL, 65- Chief announcer & news dir, KTHE-TV, Los Angeles, 53-54; producer-host, CBS Radio's Trojan digest, 56-62; producer TV series, KNXT-CBS, 60-61; consult, TV workshop, Counc. Nat. Orgns, 53; spec. writer Armed Forces Radio & TV Serv. Speech Commun. Asn; Nat. Acad. TV Arts & Sci. Speech, mass communication history. Publ: The serials, Univ. Okla, 71; A guide to public speaking, Prentice-Hall, 71. Add: 444 Merion Dr, Newtown, PA 18940.

STEDMOND, JOHN MITCHELL, b. Leicester, Eng, May 14, 16; m. 40. ENGLISH. B.A, Univ. Sask, 50, M.A, 51; Imp. Order Daughters of Empire scholar, 51-52, 52-53; Ph.D.(Eng), Aberdeen Univ, 53. Asst. lectr. ENG, Aberdeen Univ, 51-52; instr, Univ. Sask, 53-56, spec. lectr, 56-57, asst. prof, 57-58; QUEEN'S UNIV.(ONT), 58-60, assoc. prof, 60-63, PROF, 63-, CHMN. DEPT, 68-, ed, Queen's Quart, 59-63; R. Samuel McLaughlin res. chair, 64-65. Assoc. dir, McGill-Queen's Univ. Press, 71-; chmn, Humanities Res. Counc. Can, 72-74. Royal Can. Ord. Corps, 42-45. MLA; Humanities Asn. Can.(secy-treas, 56, v.pres, 58-60, pres, 72-73); Asn. Can. Univ. Teachers Eng; fel. Royal Soc. Can. Prose fiction; Laurence Sterne; modern literary criticism. Publ: The comic art of Laurence Sterne, Univ. Toronto, 67; co-ed, The winged skull: essays on Laurence Sterne, Kent State Univ, Ohio & Methuen, Eng, 71; Genre and Tristram Shandy, Philol. Quart; Style and Tristram Shandy, Mod. Lang. Quart, 59; Satire and Tristram Shandy, Stud. Eng. Lit, 61. Add: Dept. of English, Queen's University, Kingston, Ont, Can.

STEELE, ELIZABETH, b. Indianapolis, Ind, May 27, 21; m. 47. ENGLISH. A.B, Butler Univ, 44; Nat. Univ. Mexico, summers 45, 48; M.A, Univ. N.Mex, 50; Ph.D.(Eng), Bowling Green State Univ, 67. Teacher, High Sch, Ind, 44-47; Ohio, 57-62; asst. prof. ENG, UNIV. TOLEDO, 68-73, ASSOC. PROF, 73- NCTE; MLA. Sir Hugh Walpole; English lectures in the United States between World War I & II; English fictionists 1910-1940. Publ: Hugh Walpole, Twayne, 72. Add: Dept. of English, University of Toledo, Toledo, OH 43606.

STEELE, HAROLD GLENDON, b. Jackson, Ohio, June 13, 10. ENGLISH. A.B, Northwest. Univ, 32; A.M, Ohio State Univ, 33; South. Methodist Univ, 40. Assoc. prof. Eng, W.Va. Wesleyan Col, 35-45; ASSOC. PROF. ENG, BOWLING GREEN STATE UNIV, 46-, DIR. ENG, ADVISING, 66-, asst. dean lib. arts, 51-64. English and American novel; The Bible as literature; world literature. Add: Dept. of English, Bowling Green State University, Bowling Green, OH 43403.

STEELE, JAMES A, b. London, Ont, May 31, 34; m. 59; c. 3. ENGLISH. B.A, Univ. Toronto, 55, M.A, 59; Can. Counc. fel, Univ. London, 60, Ph.D.(Eng), 65. Lectr. ENG, McGill Univ, 61-63; asst. prof, CARLETON UNIV, RIDEAU RIVER CAMPUS, 64-66, ASSOC. PROF, 67- Seventeenth century English poetry; Edmund Waller; Canadian literature. Publ: Co-ed, The struggle for Canadian universities: a dossier, New Press, 69; auth, The universities: takeover of the mind, In: Close the forty-ninth parallel, Univ. Toronto, 70; Thomas Gray and the season for triumph, In: Fearful joy: papers from the Thomas Gray Bicentenary Conference at Carleton University, McGill-Queen's, 73. Add: Dept. of English, Carleton University, Rideau River Campus, Ottawa 1, Ont, Can.

STEELE, (HENRY) MAXWELL, b. Greenville, S.C, Mar. 30, 22; m. 60; c. 1. ENGLISH. B.A, Univ. N.C, Chapel Hill, 46; Acad. Julienne, Paris, 51-52; Brit. Inst, Univ. Sorbonne, 52-55; Litt.D, Belmont Abbey Col, 70. Lectr. creative writing, Univ. N.C, 56-58; Univ. Calif. exten. div, 63-64; writer-in-residence, UNIV. N.C, CHAPEL HILL, 66-67, lectr. ENG, 67-68, assoc. prof, 68-72, PROF, 72-, DIR. CREATIVE WRITING, 68- Saxton Lit. fel, 47-48; Nat. Endowment to Arts grant, 67; lectr. writing, Univ. Calif. Community of Writers, Squaw Valley, 70-, mem. bd. dirs, 72- Mayflower Award, 50; Harper Prize, 50. U.S.A.A.F, 43-46. Fiction writing. Publ: Debby, Harper Bros, 50; The goblins must go barefoot, 66, Where she brushed her hair, 68 & The cat and the coffee drinkers, 69, Harper; co-ed, American literary anthology three, Viking, 70; auth, The ragged halo, In: A tricentennial anthology of South Carolina literature, Univ. S.C, 72. Add: Dept. of English, University of North Carolina at Chapel Hill, Chapel Hill, NC 27514.

STEELE, ROBERT SCOTT, b. Butler, Pa, Nov. 7, 17. CINEMA, COMMUNICATION. B.A, Ohio Wesleyan Univ, 40; B.D, Hartford Sem. Found, 44; Univ. London, 56-58; Ph.D.(commun), Ohio State Univ, 59. Radio writer-producer, WKPT, Tenn, 44-45; managing ed, Motive, 45-49; res. assoc. commun, educ. & cinema, Ohio State Univ, 50-52; writer & dir. cinema, India, 53-56; radio writer, Far East. Div. BBC, London, 56-58; ASSOC. PROF. CINEMA & COMMUN, BOSTON UNIV, 58- Mem, ed. bd, Univ. Film Asn, 60-66; sponsor, Int. Film Sem, 62-; Lilly Found. res. grant, 63-64; mem, film adv. bd, U.S. Nat. Stud. Asn, 64-68; Louis E. Taubman Found. grant, 65; assoc. ed, Film Heritage, 65-; Glide Found. grant, 66; contrib. ed, Film World, 66-; Boston Univ. grant, 67-68; mem, Am. Film Inst. Univ. Adv. Bd, 73-; consult, United Int. Films, 73-; film critic, Friends J. Soc. Cinematologists (treas, 61-64; pres, 64-66); Univ. Film Asn; John Dewey Soc; Am. Fed. Film Soc; Asia Soc; Soc. Film & TV Educ, Eng; Cinema Critics Guild; Soc. Hist. & Res, Eng. Indian art and religion; world cinema; film criticism. Publ: An experimental approach to the production of a motion picture surveying the Sarvodaya Movement in India, Univ. Mich, 59; The classification of cinema literature, Scarecrow, 67; contrib, Humanities, religion and the arts tomorrow, Holt, 71, Mass culture revisited, Van Nostrand, 71 & Focus on Bonnie and Clyde, Prentice-Hall, 73. Add: School of Public Communication, Boston University, 640 Commonwealth Ave, Boston, MA 02215.

STEELE, THEODORE MANNING, b. Springfield, Mass, Aug. 6, 14; m. 41; c. c. 1. ENGLISH LANGUAGE & LITERATURE, PHILOSOPHY. B.A, Dartmouth Col, 35, Campbell fel, 35-37; A.B, Oxford, 37, M.A, 39; Rockefeller fel, Columbia Univ, 46-47, Ph.D.(Eng. lit), 49. Instr. Eng. & speech, Bryn Mawr Col, 38-40; Eng, Columbia Univ, 40-41, lectr, 41-46, asst. prof, 49-55; chmn. dept. speech, Sch. Gen. Stud, 46-55; dir. commun, Midtown Mgt. Ctr, N.Y.C, 55-57; v.pres. commun, Richardson, Bellows, Henry & Co, N.Y.C, 57-62; pres. commun, St. Thomas Assocs, Inc, N.Y.C, 62-63; sr. v.pres. commun, Golightly & Co, Int, N.Y.C, 63-66; assoc. prof. ENG, CASTLETON STATE COL, 66-69, PROF, 69-, dean col, 66-70. U.S.N.R, 42-46, Res, 46-68, Comdr.(Ret); Distinguished Flying Cross, Bronze Star Medal, four Air Medals. Elizabethan drama; speech. Publ: History of VB-109, 44, History of VPB-109, 46 & Hegel's influence on Shakespearean criticism, 49, Fenellosa; co-auth, I took the sky road, Dodd, 45. Add: Dept. of English, Castleton State College, Castleton, VT 05735.

STEENE, BIRGITTA, b. Uddevalla, Sweden, Oct. 7, 28; m. 61; c. 1. COMPARATIVE LITERATURE. B.A, Univ. Uppsala, Sweden, 51; Univ. Kans, 51-52; M.A, Univ. Wash, 55, Ph.D.(comp. lit), 60. Instr. Eng, La. State Univ, 59-60; asst. prof, Univ. Alta, 60-62; Scand. & gen. lit, Univ. Pa, 62-65; ASSOC. PROF. ENG, TEMPLE UNIV, 67- Sweden-Am. Found. scholar, 52; asst, Univ. Wash, 53-55, assoc, 55-57; Am. Asn. Univ. Women scholar, 55; Swedish Inst. grant, 65-67. Soc. Advan. Scand. Stud; Am. Asn. Comp. Lit; MLA. Modern drama; comparative literature; American and Scandinavian literature. Publ: Ingmar Bergman, 68 & August Strindberg, 69, Twayne; Shakespearean elements in Strindberg's history plays, Comp. Lit, summer 59; Faulkner and the American South, Mod. Sprak, 9/60; Critical reception of American drama in Sweden, Mod. Drama, spring 62. Add: Dept. of English, Temple University, Philadelphia, PA 19122.

STEENSMA, ROBERT CHARLES, b. Sioux Falls, S.Dak, Nov. 24, 30. ENGLISH LANGUAGE & LITERATURE. B.A, Augustana Col.(S.Dak), 52; M.A, Univ. S.Dak, 55; Haggin fel, Univ. Ky, 57-58, res. fel, 58-59, Ph.D, 61. Instr. ENG, Augustana Col.(S.Dak), 55-57; asst. prof, Univ. S.Dak, 59-62; Utah State Univ, 62-66, res. grant, 63-64; assoc. prof. & asst. chmn, UNIV. UTAH, 66-70, PROF, 70-, DIR. ADVAN. PLACEMENT, 68-, assoc. dir. NDEA Inst. Eng, summer 66. Fulbright lectr, Finland, 72-73. U.S.N.R, 48-, Capt. MLA; Naval Hist. Found. Jonathan Swift; 18th century English literature; western American literature. Publ: Ed, Sir William Temple's Essay upon the origin and nature of government, Augustan Reprint Soc, 64; auth, Articulation and communication in the teaching of English, Utah Dept. Pub. Instr, 65; The shearsman and the blue guitar, Utah Counc. Teachers Eng, 65; Sir William Temple, Twayne, 70; Influence of Sir William Temple on Jonathan Swift, Proc. Utah Acad, 64; Swift and Epicurus, Bull. Rocky Mountain Mod. Lang. Asn, 64; Ben Jonson: a checklist, 1947-1964, Res. Opportunities Renaissance Drama, 66; plus others. Add: Dept. of English, University of Utah, Salt Lake City, UT 84112.

STEER, HELEN VANE, b. Manchester, Eng, May 20, 26. DRAMA, SPEECH. B.A, La. State Univ, 54, M.A, 58, Ph.D.(speech), 67. Instr. speech & drama & drama dir, Samford Univ, 56-59; asst. prof. SPEECH & DRAMA, E.CAROLINA UNIV, 63-71, ASSOC. PROF, 71- Drama ed, South. Speech J, 66-69; coord. N.C. Sect, Oral Interpretation Dir, Speech Commun. Asn, 73- Speech Commun. Asn; Am. Theatre Asn; AAUP. Stage dialects; voice and articulation. Publ: Contrib, The East Carolina University summer theatre: four seasons of professional theatre on campus, N.C. J. Speech, 11/67. Add: Dept. of Drama & Speech, Box 2712, East Carolina University, Greenville, NC 27834.

STEESE, PETER B, b. Fillmore, N.Y, Dec. 16, 33; m. 56; c. 2. ENGLISH. B.A, Houghton Col, 54; M.A, Case West. Reserve Univ, 58, Ph.D.(Eng), 63. Instr. Eng, Pa. State Univ, 61-64, asst. prof, 64-66, asst. dir, McKeesport campus, 66-67; ASSOC. PROF. ENG, STATE UNIV. N.Y. COL. FREDONIA, 67- Danforth Found. assoc, 71- U.S.A, 54-56. MLA; Am. Soc. 18th Century Stud. Eighteenth century English literature; James Boswell; the English Bible as literature. Publ: Ed, Ecclesiastes, a casebook, Allyn & Bacon, 66; auth, Dennis's influence on Watts's preface to Horae lyricae, Philol. Quart, 4/63; Herbert and Crashaw: two paraphrases of the Twenty-Third Psalm, J. Bible & Relig, 4/65; Boswell, Walking upon ashes, In: English Symposium Papers, I, State Univ. N.Y. Col. Fredonia, 70. Add: Dept. of English, State University of New York College at Fredonia, Fredonia, NY 14063.

STEEVES, EDNA L, b. Los Angeles, Calif, 1909; m. 47. ENGLISH & COMPARATIVE LITERATURE. A.B, Univ. Calif, Los Angeles, 32; M.A, Univ. Chicago, 36; Ph.D.(Eng. & comp. lit), Columbia Univ, 48. Instr. Eng, Columbia Univ, 43-47; Eng. Clin, Dartmouth, 53-55; asst. prof, Castleton State Col, 62-64; prof. Eng. & educ, Shippensburg State Col, 64-65; assoc. prof. ENG, Newberry Col, 65-66; Univ. Richmond, 66-67; UNIV. R.I, 67-74, PROF, 74-, fac. fel, 72. Lit. consult, ed. & mem. ed. bd, Abstracts of Eng. Stud, 67-; lit. consult, Stud. in Burke; Folklore Stud. MLA; Northeast Mod. Lang. Asn; Col. Eng. Asn.(nat. comn. feminist concerns, 73-); AAUP; Milton Soc. Am. Eighteenth century English-French literature; history of feminism; Milton studies. Publ: Art of sinking in poetry, Russell & Russell, 68; co-auth, Wild sports in the Far West, Duke Univ, 68; auth, Négritude and the noble savage, J. Mod. African Stud, 3/73; Pre-feminism in 18th century novel, Tex. Quart, winter 73. Add: Dept. of English, University of Rhode Island, Kingston, RI 02881.

STEFANILE, FELIX N, b. U.S, Apr. 13, 20; m. 53. MODERN POETRY. B.A, City Col. New York, 44. Vis. poet & lectr. mod. poetry, PURDUE UNIV, WEST LAFAYETTE, 61-62, asst. prof. ENG, 62-64, assoc. prof, 64-69, PROF, 69- Ed. & publ, Sparrow Mag, 54- Nat. Endowment Arts & Humanities Award, 67; Emily Clark Balch Prize, 72. U.S.A, 42-46. MLA. Contemporary American and European poetry. Publ: A fig tree in America (poems), Elizabeth Press, 70; The imagination of the amateur, Trace, 66 & In: American literary anthology, Farrar, Strauss, 68; American legend, Riding the storm, The weather didn't do us any good (poems), Va. Quart. Rev, summer 72; plus others. Add: 103 Waldron St, West Lafayette, IN 47906.

STEFANSON, DONALD HAL, b. Bottineau, N.Dak, Aug. 24, 36; m. 70. EIGHTEENTH CENTURY ENGLISH LITERATURE. B.S, N.Dak. State Univ, 60; M.A, Univ. Nebr, 63; Ph.D.(Eng), Univ. Iowa, 71. Instr. Eng, Cent. Mo. State Col, 63-65; admin. asst, Ctr. Textual Stud, Univ. Iowa, 69-70; ASST. PROF. ENG, Morningside Col, 70-73; RUST COL, 73- MLA; AAUP; Am. Soc. 18th Century Stud. Analytical bibliography and textual editing; history, development and technique of prose narrative fiction. Publ: Co-ed, Eidolons, Ragnarok, 72; co-auth, The Leigh Hunt Manuscripts, Univ. Iowa Libr, 73; auth, Limits of setting in realism, Morningside Rev, 71. Add: Div. of Humanities, Rust College, Rust Ave, Holly Springs, MS 38635.

STEFFAN, (TRUMAN) GUY, b. Bellwood, Pa, Feb. 20, 10; m. 38. ENGLISH LITERATURE. A.B, Dickinson Col, 31; M.A, Univ. Wis, 33, fel, 36-37, Ph.D, 37. From asst. to instr, Univ. Wis. & univ. exten. div, 31-38; instr. ENG, UNIV. TEX, AUSTIN, 38-42, 44-46, asst. prof, 46-49, assoc. prof, 49-61, PROF, 61-, instr. navigation, naval flight prep sch, 42-44. Univ. res. grant-in-aid, Univ. Tex, 47, 65; mem. adv. bd, Stud. Romanticism, 61-MLA; S.Cent. Mod. Lang. Asn; Byron Soc. Romantic period of English literature; Byron; modern drama. Publ: Byron's Don Juan: auth, Vol. I, The making of a masterpiece, 57 & co-auth, Vols. II & III, A variorum edition, 57, 2nd ed, 71, Byron's Cain: twelve essays and text with variants and annotations, 69 & auth, From Cambridge to Missolonghi: Byron letters at the University of Texas, 72, Univ. Tex; co-auth, Lord Byron: Don Juan, Penguin, 73; The token-web, the Sea-Sodom and Canto I of Don Juan, Tex. Stud. Eng, 47; The devil a bit of our Beppo, Philol. Quart, 4/53; Seven accounts of the Cenci and Shelley's drama, Stud. Eng. Lit. 1500-1900, fall 69. Add: Dept. of English, University of Texas, Austin, TX 78712.

STEGNER, STUART PAGE, b. Salt Lake City, Utah, Jan. 31, 37; m. 59; c. 2. AMERICAN LITERATURE. A.B, Stanford Univ, 59, M.A. & Ph.D.(Eng), 65. Asst. prof. Eng, Ohio State Univ, 65-67; AM. LIT, CROWN COL, UNIV. CALIF, SANTA CRUZ, 68-71, ASSOC. PROF, 71-, FEL, 68- American literature; folklore. Publ: Escape into aesthetics, 66 & The edge (novel), 68, Dial; Nabokov's congeries, Viking, 68; The immortality of art, South. Rev, 4/66; Protest songs from the Butte mines, West. Folklore, 7/67; Hawks and harriers, Mademoiselle, 9/68. Add: Dept. of English, University of California, Santa Cruz, CA 95060.

STEGNER, WALLACE EARLE, b. Lake Mills, Iowa, Feb. 18, 09; m. 34; c. 1. ENGLISH. A.B, Univ. Utah, 30, hon. Litt.D, 68; A.M, State Univ. Iowa, 32, Ph.D, 35; Univ. Calif, 32-33; hon. D.F.A, Univ. Calif, Davis, 69, hon. Litt.D, Utah State Univ, 72; hon. LL.D, Univ. Sask, Regina, 73. Instr, Augustana Col, 33-34; Univ. Utah, 34-37; Univ. Wis, 37-39; Eng, Harvard, 39-45; prof. Eng. & dir. writing ctr, STANFORD UNIV, 45-70, EMER. PROF. ENG, 70- Guggenheim fels, 49, 59; Rockefeller Found. grant, Asia, 50-51; fel, Ctr. Advan. Stud. Behav. Sci, 55-56; asst. to Secy. Interior, 61-62; mem. adv. bd, Nat. Parks, Hist. Sites, Bldg. & Monuments, 62-; Nat. Endowment for Humanities sr. fel, 72-73. Little-Brown Novelette Prize, 37; O. Henry 2nd Prize, 42, 48, 1st Prize, 50; Pulitzer Prize in Fiction, 72. MLA; fel. Am. Acad. Arts & Lett; Nat. Inst. Arts & Lett. The writing of fiction; contemporary American writing; western American history. Publ: Big rock candy mountain, Duell; Beyond the hundredth meridian, Houghton, 54; Wolf willow, 62 & All the little live things, 67, Viking; The gathering of Zion, McGraw, 64; Angle of repose, Doubleday, 71; plus others. Add: 13456 S. Fork Lane, Los Altos Hills, CA 94022.

STEIBLE, DANIEL JOSEPH, b. Cincinnati, Ohio, June 3, 12; m. 39; c. 4. ENGLISH LANGUAGE & LITERATURE. A.B, Xavier Univ, 35; A.M, Univ. Cincinnati, 36, Ph.D, 39. Instr. ENG, sch. commerce, St. John's Univ.(N.Y), 39-42; CHMN. DEPT, EDGECLIFF COL, 42-, HEAD DIV. HUMANITIES, 54-Co-ord. comt. on lib. arts educ, N.Cent. Asn. Cols. & Sec. Schs, 58-62. NCTE; Asn. Higher Educ. Modern drama; 18th century; American novel; linguistics. Publ: Concise handbook of linguistics, Philos. Libr, 67; A college reviews its policy on comprehensives, Cath. Educ. Rev, 4/55; co-auth, A college examines its use of test results, J. Educ. Res, 4/57. Add: Dept. of English, Edgecliff College, Cincinnati, OH 45206.

STEIG, MICHAEL, b. New York, N.Y, Feb. 19, 36; m. 56; c. 2. ENGLISH LITERATURE. B.A, Reed Col, 58; fel, Univ. Wash, 59-62, M.A, 60, Ph.D. (Eng), 63. Acting instr. ENG, Univ. Wash, 62-63; asst. prof, Mich. State Univ, 63-66; SIMON FRASER UNIV, 66-69, assoc. prof, 69-71, PROF, 71-Can. Counc. leave fel, 68-69; Am. Counc. Learned Soc. fel, 71-72. MLA (secy. lit. & psychol. group, 71, chmn, 72 & secy. lit. & other arts group, 73). The English novel; 19th century English literature; literature and psychology. Publ: Dickens' excremental vision, Victorian Stud, 70; Anality in The mill on the floss, Novel, 71; Mr. Turveydrop from Gillray to Bleak house, Huntington Libr. Quart, 72. Add: Dept. of English, Simon Fraser University, Burnaby, B.C, Can.

STEIN, ARNOLD, b. Brockton, Mass, Apr. 27, 15; m. 42; c. 2. ENGLISH LITERATURE. A.B, Yale, 36; A.M, Harvard, 38, Ph.D, 42. Instr, Univ. Minn, 40-46; asst. prof, Ohio State Univ, 46-48; assoc. prof. Eng. lit, Univ. Wash, 48-53, prof, 53-71; ENG, JOHNS HOPKINS UNIV, 71-74, SIR WILLIAM OSLER PROF, 74- Ford Found. Advan. Educ. fel, 53-54; Guggenheim fel, 59-60. Renaissance Soc. Am; MLA; Milton Soc. Am; Acad. Lit. Stud. Criticism; 17th century and contemporary literature. Publ: Answerable style, 53, Heroic knowledge, 57 & John Donne's lyrics: the eloquence of action, 62, Univ. Minn; ed, Theodore Roethke: essays on the poetry, Univ. Wash, 65; auth, George Herbert's lyrics, Johns Hopkins Univ, 68; ed, On Milton's poetry, Fawcett, 69. Add: Dept. of English, Johns Hopkins University, Baltimore, MD 21218.

STEIN, CHARLES HAPPY, b. St. Louis, Mo, Mar. 16, 40; m. 63; c. 3. ENGLISH. B.S, St. Louis Univ, 61, fel, 62-63, 64-65, asst, 63-64, Ph.D.(Eng), 68. Instr. ENG, Univ. Mo, St. Louis, 65-66; St. Louis Col. Pharmacy, 66-67; from asst. prof. to ASSOC. PROF, CREIGHTON UNIV, 67- Air Nat. Guard, 61-67. NCTE; Conf. Col. Compos. & Commun. Elizabethan literature, including drama; composition-rhetoric literature. Add: Dept. of English, Creighton University, 2500 California St, Omaha, NE 68178.

STEIN, FRANK, b. Chester, Pa, Dec. 24, 08; m. 58. SPEECH, DRAMA. A.B, Pa. State Col, 32; M.F.A, Fordham Univ, 48; Ph.D, Univ. Denver, 54. Instr. Eng. & speech, CONCORD COL, 48-52, asst. prof, 52-53, assoc. prof, 53-54, prof, 54-62, speech & theatre, 62-65, SPEECH, 65-71, EMER. PROF, 71- U.S.A.A.F, 42-46, 1st Lt. Philosophy of theatre and education; teaching of oral and written communication. Add: Division of Language & Literature, Concord College, Athens, WV 24712.

STEIN, JESS, b. New York, N.Y, June 23, 14; m. 43; c. 2. ENGLISH, LINGUISTICS. A.B, Wayne State Univ, 33; M.A, Univ. Chicago, 34. Ed, Scott Foresman & Co, Chicago, Ill, 34-42; chief, ref. & rev. units, Off. Censorship, Washington, D.C, 42-45; ed. ref, RANDOM HOUSE, INC, 45-50, head col. & ref. depts, 50-59, V.PRES, 60-, MEM. BD. DIRS, 66- Chmn. Col. Publ. Group, 60-61; v.chmn. col. sect, Am. Textbk. Publ. Inst, 61-62, mem. bd. dirs, 62-66, treas, 64-65, chmn. statist. comn, 68; mem. bd. dirs. L.W. Singer Co, 61-68; Random House Can. Ltd, 65-68; mem, Govt. Adv. Comt. Int. Bk. Prog, 64-66; v.pres, Alfred A. Knopf, Inc, 69-; pres, Jess Stein Assocs, 73- MLA; Ling. Soc. Am; Am. Dialect Soc; Col. Eng. Asn; Am. Hist. Asn; AAAS; NCTE; Am. Geog. Soc; Am. Polit. Sci. Asn; Speech Commun. Asn. Lexicography; educational publishing. Publ: Ed, American college dictionary, 47-, American everyday dictionary, 49-, American vest pocket dictionary, 51, Basic everyday encyclopedia, 54-, Vest pocket dictionary of rhymes, 60, Random House dictionary of the English language, 66 & Great Russian stories & ed. & transl, Tolstoy's Kreutzer sonata, Random. Add: Random House, Inc, 201 E. 50th St, New York, NY 10022.

STEIN, MEYER LEWIS, b. Escanaba, Mich, July 30, 20; m. 49; c. 2. JOURNALISM, MASS COMMUNICATIONS. B.J, Univ. Mo, 42; M.A, Stanford Univ, 61. Reporter-ed, Daily Tribune, Royal Oak, Mich, 46-51; reporter-rewrite, San Francisco Examiner, Calif, 51-61; PROF. JOUR. & CHMN. DEPT, N.Y. Univ, 61-74; CALIF. STATE UNIV, LONG BEACH, 74- Mem. adv. bd, Freedom of Inform. Ctr, Univ. Mo, 68- U.S.A, 42-45. Asn. Educ. in Jour.(mem. jour. counc, 70-); Soc. Prof. Jour. Freedom of Inform. Ctr, Univ. Mo, 68- U.S.A, 42-45. Asn. Educ. in Jour.(mem. jour. counc, 70-); Soc. Prof. Jour. Freedom of information; press performance. Publ: Your career in journalism, 65, Freedom of the press, 66, Under fire: the story of American war correspondents, 68 & When Presidents meet the press, 69, Messner; Write clearly . . . speak effectively, 67, How to write high school and college papers, 69 & Reporting today, 71, Cornerstone Libr; Blacks in communications, 72; The news media and society, 74; plus others. Add: Dept. of Journalism, California State University, Long Beach, CA 90840.

STEIN, ROBERT DAVID, b. Chicago, Ill, Oct. 9, 37; m. 60. ENGLISH. A.B, Brown Univ, 59; M.A, Northwest. Univ, 61, Ph.D.(Eng), 68. Lectr. ENG, Northwest. Univ, 64-65; instr, Univ. Chicago, 65-67, asst. prof, 67-73; PROF. & CHMN. DEPT, WASHBURN UNIV, TOPEKA, 73- MLA. Literature, science and religion in the 19th century; critical theory; the arts of Victorian prose. Add: Dept. of English, Washburn University of Topeka, Topeka, KS 66621.

STEIN, ROGER BREED, b. Orange, N.J, Mar. 29, 32; m. 54; c. 2. AMERICAN LITERATURE & INTELLECTUAL HISTORY. A.B, Harvard, 54, Sheldon traveling fel, 57-58, A.M, 58, Samuel S. Fels fel, 59-60, Ph.D.(hist. Am. civilization), 60. Teaching fels, Harvard, 55-57, 58-59; instr. ENG, Univ. Wash, 60-61, asst. prof, 61-67, ASSOC. PROF, 67-70; STATE UNIV. N.Y. BINGHAMTON, 70- Guggenheim Found. fel, 68-69. Am. Acad. Arts & Sci. Monogr. Prize, 60. MLA; Am. Stud. Asn; Am. Stud. Asn. Pac. Northwest (pres, 63-64); Orgn. Am. Hist. American studies; 19th century American literature, art, and aesthetic thought. Publ: John Ruskin and aesthetic thought in America, 1840-1900, Harvard, 67; The view and the vision: landscape painting in nineteenth century America, Henry Gallery, Univ. Wash, 68; The glass menagerie revisited: catastrophe without violence, West. Humanities Rev, spring 64; Royall Tyler and the question of our speech, New Eng. Quart, 12/65; Seascape and the American imagination: the Puritan seventeenth century, Early Am. Lit, spring 72. Add: Dept. of English, State University of New York at Binghamton, Binghamton, NY 13901.

STEIN, WILLIAM BYSSHE, b. Congo, Ohio, May 25, 15; m. 46. ENGLISH. B.A, Rutgers Univ, 48; M.A, Univ. Fla, 49, Ph.D.(Eng), 51. Lectr. ENG, Rutgers Univ, 47-48; fel, Univ. Fla, 48-50; instr, Princeton, 50-51; asst. prof, Washington & Jefferson Col, 51-53, assoc. prof, 53-61, PROF, 61-66; HARPUR COL, STATE UNIV. N.Y. BINGHAMTON, 66- Bollingen fel, 53-55; Fulbright lectr, Univ. Mainz, 59-60. U.S.A.A.F, 40-45. MLA. American and modern literature; 18th century English literature and the novel. Publ: Hawthorne's Faust: a study of the devil archetype, Univ. Fla; Two Brahman sources of Thoreau and Emerson, Scholar's Facsimiles, 67; Walden: the wisdom of the centaur, ELH, 58; Stephen Crane's homo absurdus, Bucknell Rev, 59. Add: Dept. of English, State University of New York at Binghamton, Binghamton, NY 13901.

STEINBERG, ABRAHAM H, b. College Point, N.Y, Sept. 18, 17; m. 51. ENGLISH. B.A, Brooklyn Col, 37; M.A, Columbia Univ, 39; Ph.D, N.Y. Univ, 56. PROF. ENG, NEWARK COL. ENGINEERING, 55- Instr, City Col. New York, summer 56; lectr, Baruch Sch, eve. session, 56. U.S.A, 43-46. Am. Soc. Engineering Educ; Yivo Inst. Jewish Res.(Essay Award, 54). Jewish characters in American novel; literature and psychology. Publ: Fitzgerald's portrait of a psychiatrist, Univ. Kansas City Rev, spring 55; Francis Hopkinson, Lit. & Psychol, summer 58. Add: 175 W. 93rd St, Apt. 15-C, New York, NY 10025.

STEINBERG, CLARENCE B, Medieval English. See Volume III, Foreign Languages, Linguistics & Philology.

STEINBERG, DANNY D, b. Toronto, Ont, Aug. 10, 31; m. 64; c. 1. PSYCHOLINGUISTICS. B.A, Univ. B.C, 60; M.A, Univ. Hawaii, 64, Ph.D.(psychol), 66. Res. assoc. psycholing, Educ. Res. & Develop. Ctr, Univ. Hawaii, 66-67; asst. prof. speech commun, UNIV. HAWAII, MANOA, 69-70, ASSOC. PROF. ENG. AS SECOND LANG, 70- Nat. Inst. Ment. Health res. fel, Inst. Commun. Res, Univ. Ill, Urbana, 67-69. Am. Psychol. Asn; Ling. Soc. Am. Psycholinguistic processes; semantic theory; infant reading. Publ: Co-auth. & ed, Semantics: an interdisciplinary reader in philosophy, linguistics and psychology, Cambridge, 71; auth, Analyticity, amphigory and the semantic interpretation of sentences, J. Verbal Learning & Verbal Behav, 70; Negation, analyticity, amphigory, and the semantic interpretation of sentences, J. Exp. Psychol, 70; Phonology, reading and Chomsky and Halle's optimal orthography, J. Psycholing. Res, 73. Add: Dept. of English as a Second Language, University of Hawaii at Manoa, Honolulu, HI 96822.

STEINBERG, ERWIN RAY, b. New Rochelle, N.Y, Nov. 15, 20; m. 54; c. 1. ENGLISH. B.S, State Univ. N.Y. Albany, 41, M.S, 42; summers, Columbia Univ, 46-47, Oxford, 48; Ph.D, N.Y. Univ, 56. Instr. ENG, CARNEGIE-MELLON UNIV, 46-49, asst. prof, 49-55, assoc. prof, 55-61, PROF, 61-, DEAN, MARGARET MORRISON CARNEGIE COL, 60-, DEAN COL. HU-

MANITIES & SOC. SCI, UNIV, 68-, head dept. gen. stud, col, 56-61, dean div. humanities & soc. sci, univ, 65-68. Commun. consult; coord, Proj. Eng, U.S. Off. Educ, 63-64; vis. scholar, Ctr. Advan. Stud. Behav. Sci, 70-71. Carnegie Teaching Award, 56. U.S.A.A.F, 43-46. NCTE; MLA. The teaching of English; the modern novel; the relation of language to thought. Publ: Needed research in the teaching of English, U.S. Govt. Printing Off, 63; co-auth, Communication in business and industry, Holt, 60; Personal integrity, 61 & ed, The rule of force, 62, Norton; gen. ed, Insight series (14 vol), 68-73 & co-ed, English education today, 70, Noble; English then and now, Random, 70; auth, The stream of consciousness and beyond in Joyce's Ulysses, Univ. Pittsburgh, 73; The judgement in Kafka's The judgement, Mod. Fiction Stud, 62; The Proteus episode: signature of Stephan Dedalus, James Joyce Quart, 68; A model for dismantling: proposed guidelines for the Doctor of Arts, Proc. Wingspread Conf. Doctor Arts Degree, Counc. Grad. Schs, 70. Add: College of Humanities & Social Sciences, Carnegie-Mellon University, Schenley Park, Pittsburgh, PA 15213.

STEINBERG, MOSES WOLFE, b. Ottawa, Ont, Feb. 16, 18; m. 45; c. 5. ENGLISH. B.A, Queen's Univ, Can, 43, McCullough scholar & Leonard fel, 43, Leonard traveling fel, 44, M.A, 44; Sir Joseph Flavelle fel, Univ. Toronto, 44-46, Ph.D, 52. Tutor, Queen's Univ, Can, 41-42, 43-44; asst. prof. ENG, UNIV. B.C, 46-54, assoc. prof, 54-62, PROF, 62- Can. Counc. sr. res. fel, 62-63. MLA; Humanities Asn. Can; Asn. Can. Univ. Teachers Eng; Int. Asn. Univ. Prof. Eng. Early modern period, especially H.G. Wells. Publ: Shaw festival papers, Univ. B.C, 56; Aspects of modern drama, Holt-Dryden, 60; Arthur Miller and the idea of modern tragedy, Dalhousie Rev, 60. Add: Dept. of English, University of British Columbia, Vancouver, B.C. V6T 1W5, Can.

STEINBERG, THEODORE LOUIS, b. Baltimore, Md, Jan. 8, 47; m. 69. RENAISSANCE ENGLISH, MODERN JEWISH LITERATURE. B.A, Johns Hopkins Univ, 68; A.M, Univ. Ill, 69, Ph.D.(Eng), 71. Teaching asst. ENG, Univ. Ill, 68-70; ASST. PROF, STATE UNIV. N.Y. COL. FREDONIA, 71-, summer grants, 72 & 73. MLA; Northeast Mod. Lang. Asn; Medieval Acad. Am; Early Eng. Text Soc. Spenser; Medieval and Renaissance mythography. Publ: Spenser's Shepherdes calender and E.K.'s, Mod. Lang. Stud, winter 73; The anatomy of Euphues, Stud. Eng. Lit, winter 74. Add: Dept. of English, State University of New York College at Fredonia, Fredonia, NY 14063.

STEINBRECHER, GEORGE, JR, b. Chicago, Ill, July 10, 15. ENGLISH LANGUAGE & LITERATURE. B.A, Univ. Chicago, 41, M.A, 43, Ph.D, 53. Instr. ENG, Wilson Br, CITY COLS. CHICAGO, 49-55, WRIGHT COL, 55-62, assoc. prof, 62-64, PROF, 64- Lectr, Downtown Ctr, Univ. Chicago, 47-52. U.S.A.A.F, 42-45, Sgt. NCTE; Am. Civil Liberties Union. Theodore Dreiser; Joyce Cary; teaching literature through the arts. Publ: Inaccurate accounts of Dreiser's Sister Carrie, Am. Lit, 1/52; Teaching literature through art, 2/53 & Joyce Cary: master novelist, 5/57, Col. Eng. Add: 3716 N. Lakewood Ave, Chicago, IL 60613.

STEINER, HENRY-YORK, b. Chicago, Ill, Mar. 12, 32; m; c. 2. ENGLISH. B.A, Grinnell Col, 56; M.A, Yale, 57; Ph.D.(Eng), Univ. Ore, 63. Instr. Eng, Grinnell Col, 57-59; asst. prof, Yankton Col, 62-63, assoc. prof, 63-64; asst. prof, Grinnell Col, 64-68, assoc. to dean col, 67-68; ASSOC. PROF. ENG. & DEAN UNDERGRAD. COL, EAST. WASH. STATE COL, 68-. Ed. Consult, Holt, Rinehart, & Winston, Inc, 66-; vis. prof, Univ. Ore, 66. U.S.A, 51-53. MLA. Romantic literature; poetic theory; dramatic theory. Publ: St. Peter and I, Grinnell Col, 57; co-auth, Twelve poets, alternate ed, Holt, 67. Add: Eastern Washington State College, Cheney, WA 99004.

STEINER, JOAN ELIZABETH, b. Oberlin, Ohio, Feb. 16, 33. ENGLISH & AMERICAN LITERATURE. A.B, Oberlin Col, 55; M.A, Univ. Mich, Ann Arbor, 56, fel, 62-63, Ph.D.(Eng), 71. Teacher Eng, Grosse Pointe Pub. Schs, Mich, 56-59; staff mem Second Congr. Dist. Off, U.S. House Rep, 65-67; instr. ENG, DREW UNIV, 68-71, ASST. PROF, 71- MLA. Twentieth century British and American fiction; history of the novel; Afro-American literature. Add: Dept. of English, Drew University, Madison, NJ 07940.

STEINER, ROGER JACOB, Romance Languages, Linguistics. See Volume III, Foreign Languages, Linguistics & Philology.

STEINER, THOMAS ROBERT, b. Budapest, Hungary, Aug. 18, 34; U.S. citizen; m. 66; c. 2. ENGLISH, COMPARATIVE LITERATURE. B.A, Cornell Univ, 55; M.A, Columbia Univ, 60, Ph.D.(Eng), 67. Lectr. ENG, Hunter Col, 62-64; Brooklyn Col, 64-66; asst. prof, UNIV. CALIF, SANTA BARBARA, 66-74, ASSOC. PROF, 74- Fel, Calif. Humanities Inst, 69-70; consult-reader, PMLA, 71; consult, Harcourt Brace Jovanovich, Inc, 72. Prize, Nathanael West essay contest, South. Rev, 70. U.S.N, 56-59, Res, Lt. Comdr. MLA; Am. Soc. 18th Century Stud. Eighteenth century English literature; classical relations of English literature; literature and society. Publ: Critical contexts of eighteenth century translation, Mouton, (in press), Precursors to Dryden, Comp. Lit. Stud, 3/70; West's Lemuel and the American dream, South. Rev, 10/71. Add: Dept. of English, University of California, Santa Barbara, CA 93106.

STEINHOFF, WILLIAM RICHARD, b. Chicago, Ill, Feb. 13, 14; m. 40. ENGLISH. Ph.D, Univ. Calif, 48. Instr. ENG, UNIV. MICH, ANN ARBOR, 48-52, asst. prof, 52-57, assoc. prof, 57-63, PROF, 63-, chmn. jr-sr. counr, 56-59. Ford Found. fac. fel, 54-55; vis. prof, Univ. Aix-Marseille, 64-65. U.S.A, 43-46. MLA; NCTE; Col. Eng. Asn. Nineteenth century literature; modern rhetoric; English and American novel. Publ: Points of departure, Harper, 60; The metaphorical texture of Daniel Deronda, Bks. Abroad, 61; George Orwell and the origins of 1984, Univ. Mich, 74; plus others. Add: 519 Onondaga, Ann Arbor, MI 48104.

STEINMANN, MARTIN, JR, b. Minneapolis, Minn, Mar. 3, 15. ENGLISH. B.A, Univ. Minn, 37, M.A, 46, Ph.D.(Eng), 54. Teaching asst. Eng. lit. & compos, UNIV. MINN, MINNEAPOLIS, 38-40, instr, 46-54, asst. prof, 54-56, assoc. prof, 56-60, PROF. ENG, 60-, asst. dir. freshman Eng, 48-50, dir, 50-64. U.S.N.R, 43-45, Lt.(jg). Am. Soc. Aesthet; MLA; Ling. Soc. Am; Lectological Asn. Linguistic, literary and rhetorical theory. Publ: Co-ed, The permanence of Yeats, Macmillan, 50; Collier, 61, From Jane Austen to Joseph Conrad, Univ. Minn, 58, 67 & Literature for writing, Wadsworth, 62, 67; ed, New rhetorics, Scribner, 67; auth, Tragedy or tragedy?, Essays in Criticism, 1/56; Rhetorical research, 1/66 & Literature, knowledge and the language of literature, 4/73, Col. Eng. Add: Dept. of English, University of Minnesota, Minneapolis, MN 55455.

STEINMETZ, MARION LEE, b. Hutchinson, Kans, Mar. 6, 27; m. 50; c. 2. ENGLISH. B.A, Sterling Col, 50; univ. scholar, Brown Univ, 50-51, M.A, 51, univ. fel, 51-52, Ph.D, 57. Instr. ENG, Brown Univ, 52-54; Univ. Kans, 54-55; asst. prof, Kans. State Teachers Col, 55-59; EAST. ILL. UNIV, 50-63, assoc. prof, 63-68, PROF, 68- MLA; NCTE. American literature; 19th century American poetry. Publ: Poetry of the American Civil War, Mich. State Univ, 60; Analyzing literary works: a guide for college students, Harper, 62; Shadows have darkly fallen: the poetic aftermath of the American Civil War, Centennial Rev, 61. Add: Dept. of English, Eastern Illinois University, Charleston, IL 61920.

STEKERT, ELLEN JANE, b. New York, N.Y, May 26, 35. FOLKLORE. B.A, Cornell Univ, 57; M.A, Ind. Univ, 61; Ph.D.(folklore), Univ. Pa, 65. Asst. prof. Eng. & folklore, Wayne State Univ, 63-68, assoc. prof, 68-72, Prof, 72-, dir. univ. folklore arch, 67-73; PROF. ENG, UNIV. MINN, MINNEAPOLIS, 73- Teaching asst. Eng, Cornell Univ, 54-57; mem. staff, seminars Am. cult, N.Y. State Hist. Soc, 55; teaching assoc. Ind. Univ, 57-58, asst. to chmn. folklore comt, 58-59, grant, Univ. res. div, 59; asst. ed, J. Am. Folklore, 58-59, assoc. ed, 68-; res. asst, Univ. Pa, 61-63; vis. prof. anthrop, Univ. Calif, Berkeley, 72-73. Am. Folklore Soc. Publ: Co-ed, The urban experience and folk tradition, Univ. Tex, 71; Tylor's theory of survivals and national romanticism: their influence on early American folksong collectors, South. Folklore Quart, 9/68; Cents and nonsense in the urban folksong movement: 1930-1966, In: Folklore and society, Folklore Assocs, 66; Focus for conflict: southern mountain medical beliefs in Detroit, J. Am. Folklore, 6/70; plus others. Add: Dept. of English, University of Minnesota, Minneapolis, MN 55455.

STELZIG, EUGENE LOUIS, b. Bischofshofen, Austria, Aug. 18, 43; U.S. citizen; m. 68. ENGLISH & AMERICAN LITERATURE. B.A, Univ. Pa, 66; Woodrow Wilson fel, 66-67; Thouron-Univ. Pa. Brit-Am. exchange fel, Cambridge, 66-68, B.A, 68, M.A, 72; univ. fel, Harvard, 68-72, M.A, 69, Ph.D.(Eng), 72. ASST. PROF. ENG, STATE UNIV. N.Y. COL. GENESEO, 72-, Res. Found. res. fel, summer 74. MLA. British romantic literature, especially William Wordsworth; American and European romanticism. Publ: All shades of consciousness: Wordsworth's poetry and the self in time, Mouton, 74; co-ed, An interview with William Styron, Handle, spring 64. Add: Dept. of English, State University of New York College at Geneseo, Geneseo, NY 14454.

STEMPEL, DANIEL, b. Brooklyn, N.Y, Aug. 20, 20; m. 51; c. 2. ENGLISH. A.B, City Col. New York, 41; A.M, Harvard, 42, fel, 47-49, Ph.D, 49. Asst. prof. ENG, UNIV. HAWAII, MANOA, 49-56, assoc. prof, 56-63, PROF, 63- Instr. gen. educ, Harvard, 51-52; Fulbright lectr, Univ. Bergen, 62-63 & Univ. Turku, Finland, 69-70. U.S.N.R, 43-46, Lt. MLA. English and comparative literature; philosophy and literature; romanticism. Publ: The silence of Iago, PMLA, 1/69; Revelation on Mount Snowdon: Wordsworth, Coleridge and the Fichtean imagination, J. Aesthetics & Art Criticism, spring 71; Angels of reason: science and myth in the Enlightenment, J. Hist. Ideas, (in press); plus 11 others. Add: Dept. of English, University of Hawaii at Manoa, Honolulu, HI 96822.

STEMPEL, GUIDO HERMANN, III, b. Bloomington, Ind, Aug. 13, 28; m. 52; c. 3. MASS COMMUNICATION. A.B, Ind. Univ, 49, A.M, 51; Ph.D.(mass commun), Univ. Wis, 54. From instr. to asst. prof. JOUR, Pa. State Univ, 55-57; from assoc. prof. to prof, Cent. Mich. Univ, 57-65; from assoc. prof. to PROF. & DIR. SCH, OHIO UNIV, 65- Ed, Jour. Quart, 73. U.S.A, 54-55. Asn. Educ. in Jour.(chmn. comt. res. & mem. exec. comt, 68-71). Content analysis; survey research; political communication. Publ: Effects on performance of a cross-media monopoly, Jour. Monogr, No. 29, 73; The Prestige Press in two Presidential elections, winter 65, The Prestige Press meets the third party challenge, winter 69 & Visibility of Blacks in news and news-picture magazines, summer 71, Jour. Quart; plus others. Add: School of Journalism, Ohio University, Athens, OH 45701.

STEN, CHRISTOPHER WILLIE, b. Minneapolis, Minn, Jan. 3, 44; m. 69. AMERICAN LITERATURE. B.A, Carleton Col, 66; M.A, Ind. Univ, Bloomington, 68, Ph.D.(Am. lit), 71. ASST. PROF. AM. LIT, GEORGE WASHINGTON UNIV, 70- Regional assoc, Am. Lit. Manuscripts, 72-74. MLA. Herman Melville; 19th century American literature; American novel. Publ: The dialogue of crisis in The confidence-man: Melville's new novel, Stud. Novel, 9/74; Bartleby the transcendentalist: Melville's dead letter to Emerson, Mod. Lang. Quart, 3/74. Add: Dept. of English, George Washington University, Washington, DC 20006.

STENERSON, DOUGLAS C, b. Barron, Wis, Aug. 29, 20; m. 57. AMERICAN STUDIES, ENGLISH. A.B, Harvard Col, 42, I.A, Harvard Grad. Sch. Bus. Admin, 43; M.A, Univ. Minn, 47, South. Fel. Fund grant, 57-58, Ph.D.(Am. stud), 61. Asst. Eng, Macalester Col, 46-47, asst. prof, 58-59; instr, Univ. Minn, 47-55; asst. prof, Univ. Miami, 55-57; Winona State Col, 59-63, assoc. prof, 63-67, head dept, 66-67; assoc. prof. ENG. & AM. STUD, ROOSEVELT UNIV, 67-68, PROF. & GRAD. ADV. ENG, 68- Fulbright lectr, Univ. Helsinki, 65-66; vis. prof, Univ. Minn, summer 67; consult. examr, N.Cent. Asn. Cols. & Sec. Schs, 69-; Roosevelt Univ. fac. res. grant, 70; consult. panelist, Nat. Endowment for Humanities. McKnight Found. Humanities Award, 61. Qm.C, A.U.S, 43-46. Am. Stud. Asn; MLA; AAUP. Trends and continuities in American literature and thought between the 1890's and the 1930's; American literature of the early 19th century and its intellectual background; colonial literature. Publ: Introd. to William Allen White's A certain rich man, Johnson Reprint, 70; auth, H.L. Mencken: iconoclast from Baltimore, Univ. Chicago, 71; Emerson and the agrarian tradition, J. Hist. Ideas, 1/53; The forgotten man of H.L. Mencken, Am. Quart, winter 66; An Anglican critique of the early phase of the great awakening in New England: a letter by Timothy Cutler, William & Mary Quart, 7/73; plus others. Add: Dept. of English, Roosevelt University, 430 S. Michigan Ave, Chicago, IL 60605.

STENGER, HAROLD LeROY, JR, b. Philadelphia, Pa, Aug. 17, 14; m. 43. ENGLISH. A.B, Univ. Pa, 36, A.M, 40, Harrison fel, 40-41, Ph.D.(Eng), 54. Asst. instr. ENG, Univ. Pa, 37-40; from instr. to PROF. & CHMN. DEPT, MUHLENBERG COL, 56-, CHMN. DIV. HUMANITIES, 67-, JOHN & FANNIE SAEGER PROF. COMP. LIT, 69- U.S.N, 42-46, Res, 51-69, Capt. MLA. Elizabethan drama, especially Thomas Middleton; romantic poetry, especially Wordsworth and Shelley. Publ: Second maiden's tragedy; Middleton's tragic vision, Muhlenberg Essays, 68. Add: Dept. of English, Muhlenberg College, Allentown, PA 18104.

STENSLAND, ANNA LEE, b. Ashland, Wis, July 25, 22. ENGLISH, ENGLISH EDUCATION. B.A, Northland Col, 44; M.A, Univ. Wis, 47, Ph.D.(Eng. & educ), 58. Teacher Eng, Boyd High Sch, Wis, 44-46; Merrill High Sch, Wis, 47-49; asst. prof. Eng. educ, Peru State Teachers Col, 49-51; ENG, Dakota Wesleyan Univ, 51-57; Stout State Col, 58-60; UNIV. MINN, DULUTH, 60-62, assoc. prof, 62-68, PROF, 68- NCTE (dir, 61-71, ed, Jr. Mem. Newslett, 68-71); Int. Reading Asn; AAUP. Teaching poetry in junior and senior high schools; Indian literature; teaching reading in secondary schools. Publ: An annotated bibliography of literature by and about the American Indian, NCTE, 73; Whither literature teaching of the seventies?, Minn. Eng. J, 67; American Indian culture; promises, problems and possibilities, Eng. J, 71; American Indian culture and the reading program, J. Reading, 71. Add: Dept. of English, Humanities Div, 413 Humanities Bldg, University of Minnesota, Duluth, MN 55812.

STEPANCHEV, STEPHEN, b. Mokrin, Yugoslavia, Jan. 30, 15. AMERICAN LITERATURE. A.B, Univ. Chicago, 37, A.M, 38; Ph.D, N.Y. Univ, 50. Instr. ENG, Purdue Univ, 38-41; N.Y. Univ, 46-47, 48-49; from instr. to PROF, QUEENS COL.(N.Y), 49- Fulbright grant, 56-57. U.S.A, 41-46. MLA. American poetry. Publ: American poetry since 1945: a critical survey, Harper, 65; Spring in the harbor, Amity, 67; A man running in the rain (poems), 69 & The mad bomber (poems), 72, Black Sparrow; Geese at the window, Sewanee Rev, spring 64; Death by accident, Mass. Rev, summer 66; The key, Art & Lit, winter 67. Add: Dept. of English, Queens College, Flushing, NY 11367.

STEPHENS, DONALD, b. Yorkton, Sask, Oct. 25, 31; m. 59; c. 2. CANADIAN, MODERN BRITISH. B.A, Univ. N.B, 54, Sherwood scholar, Bichell fel, Can. Counc. fels. & M.A, 55; War Mem. & Can. Counc. fels. & Ph.D, Univ. Edinburgh, 58. Instr. ENG, UNIV. B.C, 55-56, 58-59, asst. prof, 59-64, ASSOC. PROF, 64- Assoc. ed, Canadian Literature, Univ. B.C. Humanities Asn. Can; MLA; Asn. Can. Univ. Teachers Eng. Canadian literature; the short story. Publ: Bliss Carman, Twayne, 66; Contemporary voices, Prentice-Hall, 72; Writers of the prairie, Univ. B.C, 73. Add: Dept. of English, University of British Columbia, Vancouver, B.C, V6T 1W5, Can.

STEPHENS, EDNA BUELL, b. Spiro, Okla, June 15, 03. ENGLISH. B.A, Univ. Ark, 27, M.A, 33, Ph.D, 60. Instr. Span, John Brown Univ, 33-37; pub. schs, Ark, 38-39; high schs, Tex, 39-42, 45-49; dep. asst. censor Span, U.S. Off. Censorship, 42-45; instr. Eng, Frank Phillips Col, 49-61; assoc. prof, E.TEX. STATE UNIV, 61-68, prof, 68-73, fac. res. grant, 70, EMER. PROF. LANG. & LIT, 73- MLA; NCTE. Haiku; modern poetry; Romantic poetry. Publ: John Gould Fletcher, Twayne, 67; Plum petals and other poems, Cantrell, 71; John Gould Fletcher, In: Dictionary of American biography, 73; plus two others. Add: 2616 Tanglewood, Commerce, TX 75428.

STEPHENS, FRAN CARLOCK, b. Albuquerque, N.Mex, June 3, 35. LITERATURE OF THE ENGLISH ROMANTIC PERIOD. B.A, Tex. A&I Univ, 56; M.A, Univ. Tex, Austin, 67, Ph.D.(Eng. lit), 70. Teacher Eng, Briscoll Independent Sch. Dist, 56-59; Brooks County Independent Sch. Dist, 60-64; Mineral Wells Independent Sch. Dist, 65-66; instr. compos, Weatherford Jr. Col, 65-66; ASST. PROF. ENG, WICHITA STATE UNIV, 70-, grant, summer 72. Nat. Endowment for Humanities younger humanist stipend, summer 72. AAUP; MLA. Samuel Taylor Coleridge family; textual criticism; 19th century English bibliography. Publ: The Hartley Coleridge letters: a calendar and index, Univ. Tex, (in press); The Coleridge collection: a sample, Libr. Chronicle, 3/70; Hartley Coleridge and the Brontes, London Times Lit. Suppl, 5/70; Cottle, Wise and the MS Ashley 408, Papers Bibliog. Soc. Am. (in press). Add: Dept. of English, Wichita State University, Wichita, KS 67208.

STEPHENS, GEORGE DARWIN, b. Cooper, Tex, June 14, 10; m. 62. ENGLISH. A.B, Trinity Univ, 31; M.A, Univ. Tex, 33; Ph.D, Univ. South. Calif, 53. Instr. Eng, Polytech. Inst. P.R, 33-35; Tex. Agr. & Mech. Col, 37-41; Univ. Nebr, 41-42; George Pepperdine Col, 46-47; El Camino Col, 48-51; from instr. to assoc. prof, Calif. State Univ, Long Beach, 51-59, prof, 59-74; RETIRED. Fulbright lectr. Am. lit, Univ. Chile, 58. U.S.N, 42-46, Lt. American literature; world drama; satire. Publ: Scientific handicapping, Prentice-Hall, 63; co-auth, Satire: theory and practice, Wadsworth, 62; Our town: great American tragedy?, Mod. Drama, 2/59; Huckleberry Finn as a journey, Mark Twain J, summer 66. Add: Dept. of English, California State University, Long Beach, 6101 E. Seventh St, Long Beach, CA 90801.

STEPHENS, JAMES WILLIS, b. Frankfort, Ky, Aug. 11, 41; m. 64; c. 2. ENGLISH RENAISSANCE LITERATURE. B.A, Univ. Ky, 63, M.A, 64; Ph.D. (Eng), Univ. Wis-Madison, 68. ASST. PROF. ENG, Univ. Wis-Oshkosh, 67-69; MARQUETTE UNIV, 69- Nat. Endowment for Humanities summer stipend, 72; fel, Inst. Res. Humanities, Univ. Wis, 74-75. MLA. Publ: Francis Bacon and the philosophical style, Univ. Wis, (in press); Bacon's theory of the philosophical style, 8/70 & Bacon's new English rhetoric and the debt to Aristotle, 11/72, Speech Monogr; Bacon's fable-making, Stud. Eng. Lit, winter 74. Add: Dept. of English, Marquette University, 635 N. 13th St, Milwaukee, WI 53233.

STEPHENS, JOHN CALHOUN, JR, b. Augusta, Ga, July 23, 16; m. 47; c. 1. ENGLISH LITERATURE. A.B, Emory Univ, 37, A.M, 38; Ph.D, Harvard, 50. Teacher high sch, Ga, 38-39; instr, Clemson Col, 39-40; Eng, Emory Univ, 46-47, asst. prof, 50-56, assoc. prof, 56-60, chmn. dept. Eng, 59-61, dean, 61-73, prof, 60-73; PROF. ENG. & DEAN, FRANKLIN COL. ARTS & SCI, UNIV. GA, 73- Guggenheim fel, 57-58. U.S.A.A.F, 41-46, Lt. Col. MLA; S.Atlantic Mod. Lang. Asn. English literature of the neo-classic period; periodical essay. Publ: Ed, Georgia, a poem, 1736 & Longsword: Steele and the Bishop of St. Asaph's preface. Add: Office of the Dean, Franklin College of Arts & Sciences, University of Georgia, Athens, GA 30602.

STEPHENS, MARTHA THOMAS, b. Mar. 19, 37; m. 62; c. 2. ENGLISH. A.B, Woman's Col. Ga, 58; M.A, Univ. Ga, 61; Ph.D.(Eng), Ind. Univ, 68. ASST. PROF. ENG, UNIV. CINCINNATI, 67- Consult. South. lit, Time-Life, winter 68. Southern literature; American Negro literature; English language studies. Publ: The question of Flannery O'Connor, La. State Univ, 73; The Bobbs-Merrill archives: three best sellers, Ind. Bookman, winter 67; Flannery O'Connor and the sanctified-sinner tradition, Ariz. Quart, autumn 68; Richard Wright's fiction: a reassessment, Ga. Rev, winter 71. Add: Dept. of English, University of Cincinnati, Cincinnati, OH 45221.

STEPHENS, ROBERT OREN, b. Corpus Christi, Tex, Oct. 2, 28; m. 56; c. 3. ENGLISH. B.A, Tex. Col. Arts & Indust, 49; M.A, Univ. Tex, 51, Ph.D. (Eng), 58. Teacher, high sch, Tex, 49-50; spec. instr. ENG, Univ. Tex, 57-58; instr, 58-61; asst. prof, UNIV. N.C, GREENSBORO, 61-66, assoc. prof, 66-68, PROF. & DIR. GRAD. STUD. ENG, 68- Vis. asst. prof, Appalachian State Univ, summer 62, vis. assoc. prof, summer 67; Duke Univ-Univ. N.C. coop. prog. in humanities fel, 65-66; Danforth assoc, 67. U.S.N.R, 51-55, Res, 55-64, Lt. MLA; Am. Stud. Asn. Contemporary American literature; southern American literature; American Renaissance. Publ: Hemingway's nonfiction: the public voice, Univ. N.C, 68; Ernest Hemingway: the critical reception, David Lewis, 74; Hemingway's riddle of Kilimanjaro: idea and image, Am. Lit, 3/60; Language magic and reality in For whom the bell tolls, Criticism, 72; Hemingway and Stendhal: the matrix of A farewell to arms, PMLA, 73; plus two others. Add: Dept. of English, University of North Carolina at Greensboro, Greensboro, NC 27412.

STEPHENSON, EDWARD A, b. Social Circle, Ga, Dec. 13, 17; m. 43; c. 2. ENGLISH. B.A, Univ. Fla, 39, M.A, 41; Ph.D, Univ. N.C, 58. Jr. instr. ENG, Johns Hopkins Univ, 41-43; instr, Univ. Fla, 46-47; part-time instr, Univ. N.C, 47-51, instr, 53-54; Univ. Va, 54-58; asst. prof, Hunter Col, 58-61; prof, Old Dom. Col, 61-65; assoc. prof, UNIV. GA, 65-69, PROF, 69-, dir. comp. ling, 71-73. Ed, miscellany sect, Am. Speech, 63-; vis. prof, Univ. Va, summer 65. U.S.N.R, 43-46, 51-53, Lt. Comdr. MLA; Mediaeval Acad. Am; Am. Dialect Soc; S.Atlantic Mod. Lang. Asn. English linguistics; mediaeval literature. Publ: Linguistic resources of the Southern Historical Collection, Am. Speech, 12/56; On the interpretation of occasional spellings, Publ. Am. Dialect Soc, 11/67; The beginnings of the loss of postvocalic /r/ in North Carolina, J. Eng. Ling, 3/68. Add: Dept. of English, University of Georgia, Athens, GA 30601.

STEPHENSON, MURIEL LOIS, b. St. Paul, Minn, Jan. 15, 23; m. 48; c. 2. ENGLISH LITERATURE, HUMANITIES. B.S.Ed, Moorhead State Col, 44; M.A, Univ. N.Dak, 68, Ph.D.(Eng. lit), 72. Instr. ENG. & HUMANITIES, UNIV. ALBUQUERQUE, 69-72, ASST. PROF, 72-, chairperson, fac. senate, 73-74. AAUP; MLA. Nineteenth century English literature; 20th century European literature; 20th century British and American literature. Add: 12441 Chelwood Pl. N.E, Albuquerque, NM 87112.

STEPHENSON, WILLIAM CURTIS, b. Minneapolis, Minn, Sept. 30, 39; m. 61; c. 2. ENGLISH ROMANTIC POETRY. B.A, Pomona Col, 61; M.A, Univ. Calif, Berkeley, 63; Ph.D.(Eng. lit), Univ. Minn, Minneapolis, 69. Instr. ENG, Univ. Minn, Minneapolis, 63-69; ASST. PROF, UNIV. TEX, AUSTIN, 69- MLA. Nineteenth and 20th century literature. Publ: Co-auth, The inward journey, Harcourt, 73; auth, Romanticism and modern science, In: Studies in relevance: romantic and Victorian writers in 1972, Univ. Salzburg, 73; The fall from innocence in Keats's Lamia, Papers Lang. & Lit, winter 74. Add: Dept. of English, University of Texas at Austin, Austin, TX 78712.

STEPHENSON, WILLIAM EATON, b. Plymouth, Ind, Oct. 31, 30; m. 67. ENGLISH. A.B, Ind. Univ, 51; M.A, Univ. Calif, Berkeley, 59, Woodrow Wilson fels, 60-62, Ph.D.(Eng), 63. Asst. prof. ENG, Univ. Calif, Los Angeles, 63-70; ASSOC. PROF, E.CAROLINA UNIV, 70- Univ. Calif. fel, 64; Clark Libr. summer fel, Univ. Calif, 65; Am. Counc. Learned Soc. study fel, 66-67; Humanities Inst. grant, Univ. Calif, 68-69; Res. Counc. grant, E.Carolina Univ, 71. MLA; S.Atlantic Mod. Lang. Asn; Univ. Film Asn; Am. Film Inst. Drama of the Restoration and the 18th century; literature of the 18th century; film literature since 1930. Publ: The comedy of evil in Apuleios, Arion, autumn 64; Religious drama in the Restoration, Philol. Quart, autumn 71; Kes and the press, Cinema J, spring 73. Add: Dept. of English, East Carolina University, Greenville, NC 27834.

STEPSIS, ROBERT PETER, b.Brooklyn, N.Y, Apr. 26, 42; m. 65; c. 1. ENGLISH, MEDIEVAL LITERATURE. B.A, Univ. Notre Dame; Woodrow Wilson fel. & Ph.D, Harvard, 67. Asst. prof. ENG, Lake Forest Col, 67-72; ASSOC. PROF, ST. LOUIS UNIV, 72- Nat. Endowment for Humanities summer stipend, 73. Mediaeval Acad. Am. Medieval chronicles; Chaucer; medieval history of ideas. Publ: Co-auth, Contrast and conversion in Cynewulf's Elene, Neuphilologische Mitt, 69; auth, Pierre de Langtoft's Chronicle: an essay in medieval historiography, Medievalia & Humanistica, 72; Fulfillment of self and union with God in the writings of Bernard of Clairvaux, Am. Benedictine Rev, 73. Add: Dept. of English, St. Louis University, St. Louis, MO 63103.

STERLING, WALLACE STINE, b. Jacksonville, Fla, Dec. 14, 35. DRAMA, SPEECH. B.A.E, Univ. Fla, 57, M.A, 59; summer, Univ. Ill, 60; Ph.D. (theater), South Ill. Univ, 66. Instr. speech & drama, Ark. Polytech. Col, 59-62; spec. teacher, pub. schs, Ark, 62-63; from asst. prof. to ASSOC. PROF. SPEECH & DRAMA, UNIV. AKRON, 66- Artistic dir, Peninsula Summer Theatre, 73-74. Am. Theatre Asn; Speech Commun. Asn; Am. Nat. Theatre & Acad; Am. Soc. Theatre Res; Int. Fed. Theatre Res; Nat. Col. Players (exec. secy-treas, 72-76). The American theater; contemporary resident professional theater; the teaching of acting. Publ: Carros, corrales and court theatres: the Spanish stage in the XVI and XVII centuries, Quart, J. Speech, 2/63; What do you want: good grammar or good drama?, Acta Symbolica, 71. Add: Dept. of Speech and Theatre Arts, University of Akron, Akron, OH 44325.

STERN, BERNARD HERBERT, b. New York, N.Y, Dec. 18, 11. ENGLISH LITERATURE. A.B, Brooklyn Col, 32; A.M, Columbia Univ, 34; dipl, Univ. Colo, 43; Ph.D, N.Y. Univ, 40. Tutor Eng, Brooklyn Col, 33-39, from instr. to assoc. prof, 39-58, prof, 58-71, assoc. dir, sch. gen. stud, dean summer session & spec. baccalaureate degree prog. adults, 68-71, asst. dir. sch. gen. stud; PROF. ENG, EMPIRE STATE COL, 71-, dean learning ctr, 71-72. Grant, Ctr. Stud. Lib. Educ. for Adults, 53-56. U.S.N.R, 42-46, Lt. MLA; Asn. Univ. Eve. Cols. Hellenism in English literature; rise of Romantic Hellenism in English literature; adult education. Publ: Rise of Romantic Hellenism in English literature, 1732-1784, Banta Publ. Co, 40; Reading for pleasure, Brooklyn Col. Press, 50 & 52; Never too late for college, Ctr. Stud. Lib. Educ. for Adults, 63. Add: Dept. of English, Empire State College, 56 Lexington Ave, New York, NY 10010.

STERN, FREDERICK CURTIS, b. Vienna, Austria, Apr. 28, 29; U.S. citizen; m. 50; c. 4. MODERN EUOPEAN & AMERICAN LITERATURE. M.A, Univ. Chicago, 63; Ph.D.(Am. lit), Purdue Univ, 70. Instr. ENG, Purdue Univ, Calumet Campus, 64-65; ASST. PROF, UNIV. ILL, CHICAGO CIRCLE, 66-MLA; Midwest Mod. Lang. Asn; NCTE; Am. Stud. Asn. Modern American and British literature; critical theory. Publ: The lost cause: F.O. Matthiessen, Christian socialist as critic, Purdue Univ, 70; The other Parnell, Eire-Ireland, 7/72; Parnell is dead: Ivy Day in the committee room, James Joyce Quart, 10/73; Black lit, white crit?, Col. Eng, 74. Add: Dept. of English, University of Illinois at Chicago Circle, Box 4348, Chicago, IL 60680.

STERN, HERBERT J, b. Buffalo, N.Y, May 24, 30; m. 56; c. 2. ENGLISH. B.A, Univ. Buffalo, 52; M.A, Columbia Univ, 53; Ph.D.(Eng), Ind. Univ. 65. From instr. to asst. prof. ENG, WABASH COL, 58-67, ASSOC. PROF, 67-Fulbright lectr. Eng. lit, Univ. Thessaloniki, 65-66, Fulbright prof. Am. lit, 66-67; mem. selection comt, Greek Fulbright applicants, 65-67; panelist, Nat. Endowment for Humanities selection & evaluation proj. grant applicants, 68-; reader, Univ. Tex. Press, 69-; travel grant to India, Nat. Counc. Assoc. Int. Stud, summer 71. Publ: Wallace Stevens: art of uncertainty, Univ. Mich, 66; Wallace Stevens: the businessman as poet, Fulbright Rev, fall 66; plus others. Add: Dept. of English, Wabash College, Crawfordsville, IN 47933.

STERN, MILTON R, b. Boston, Mass, Aug. 22, 28; m. 49; c. 2. ENGLISH. A.B, Northeast. Univ, 49; M.A, Univ. Conn, 51; Ph.D.(Eng), Mich. State Univ, 55. Part time instr. ENG, Univ. Conn, 49-51; instr, Univ. Ill, 54-57, asst. prof, 57-58; UNIV. CONN, 58-60, assoc. prof, 60-63, PROF, 63- Am. Counc. Learned Soc. grant, 61; vis. prof, Coe Inst. Am. Stud, Univ. Wyo, 64; Fulbright prof. Am. lit, Univ. Warsaw, 64-65; fel, John Simon Guggenheim Mem. Found, 71-72; secy-treas, Conn. Humanities Counc, Nat. Endowment for Humanities, 72- MLA; NCTE; Col. Eng. Asn. American literature; the politics of American literature. Publ: The fine hammered steel of Herman Melville, 57 & 68 & The golden moment: novels of F.S. Fitzgerald, 70, Univ. Ill; Melville's Typee and Billy Budd, Dutton, 58; Discussions of Moby Dick, Heath, 60; co-auth, The Viking portable American literature survey (4 vols), Viking, 62 & 68; auth, Melville's Typee, 71, Melville's Moby Dick, I & II, 71, The poetry of Herman Melville, 71, Melville's Benito Cereno, 71, Melville's Billy Budd, 71 & Melville's Bartleby the scrivener, 71, Everett Edwards; Some techniques of Melville's perception, PMLA, 6/58; Herman Melville, In: Patterns of commitment in American literature, Univ. Toronto, 67; Millennium, Moby Dick and politics, Emerson Soc. Quart, fall 68; plus others. Add: Dept. of English, U-25, University of Connecticut, Storrs, CT 06268.

STERN, PHILIP VAN DOREN, Civil War History. See Volume I, History.

STERN, RICHARD G, b. New York, N.Y, Feb. 25, 28; m. 50; c. 4. ENGLISH. B.A, Univ. N.C, 47; M.A, Harvard, 49; Ph.D, State Univ. Iowa, 54. Fulbright asst, Jules Ferry Col, Versailles, France, 49-50; asst, Heidelberg, 50-51; part-time instr. ENG, Coe Col, 52-53; State Univ. Iowa, 53-54; instr, Conn. Col, 54-55; UNIV. CHICAGO, 55-56, asst. prof, 56-62, assoc. prof, 62-65, PROF, 65- Vis. lectr, Univ. Venice, 62-63; vis. prof, Univ. Calif, Santa Barbara, summers 64, 68; State Univ. N.Y. Buffalo, 67; vis. prof. Eng. & comp. lit, Harvard, summer 69 & Amer. lit, Univ. Nice, summer 70; Guggenheim fel, 73-74. Longwood Award, 61; Friends of Lit. Award, 63; Rockefeller Award, 65; Nat. Found. Arts & Sci. Award, 67-68; Nat. Inst. Arts & Lett. Award, 68. Prose fiction. Publ: Golk, Criterion, 60; Europe, 61 & In any case, 62, McGraw; Teeth, dying and other matters, 64 & Stitch, 65, Harper; ed, Honey and wax, Univ. Chicago, 66; auth, 1968; a short novel, an urban idyll, 5 stories and 2 trade notes, Holt, 70; The books in Fred Hampton's apartment, 73 & Other men's daughters, 73, Dutton; plus three others. Add: 1050 E. 59th St, Chicago, IL 60637.

STERNE, RICHARD CLARK, b. Brooklyn, N.Y, June 6, 27; m. 53; c. 2. ENGLISH, AMERICAN STUDIES. A.B, Columbia Univ, 47; A.M, Harvard, 51, Ph.D.(Eng), 57. Instr. contemporary civilization, N.C. State Col, 48-49; ENG, SIMMONS COL, 52-55, asst. prof, 55-63, assoc. prof, 63-68, PROF, 68-, CHMN. AM. STUD. COMT, 67- Fulbright lectr, Univs. Lille & Rennes, France, summer sch. Univs. Bordeaux & Toulouse, France, 58-59 & Univ. Lisbon, 62-63. U.S.N.R, 45-46. Am. Stud. Asn; AAUP. Nineteenth century American literature; comparative study of American and European literature and thought in the 20th century. Publ: The nation and its century, Nation, 9/65; Puritans at Merry Mount: variations on a theme, Am. Quart, winter 70; A Mexican flower in Rappaccini's garden, Nathaniel Hawthorne J, 74. Add: Dept. of English, Simmons College, 300 The Fenway, Boston, MA 02115.

STERNER, ALICE, b. Bloomsburg, Pa, Feb. 22, 02. ENGLISH. B.S, Univ. Pa, 24; M.A, Columbia Univ, 29, Ph.D, 46. Teacher ENG, High Sch, Burlington, N.J, 24-26; Nutley, N.J, 27-32; chmn. dept, Barringer-Newark, N.J, 33-46; asst. prof, Calif. West. Univ, 61-64; dir. reading, The Bishop's Sch, La Jolla, Calif, 65-69; RETIRED. NCTE. Motion picture appreciation; listening; television appreciation. Publ: Radio, motion picture and reading interests, T.C, 47. Add: 730 Amiford Dr, San Diego, CA 92107.

STERNLICHT, SANFORD, b. New York, N.Y, Sept. 20, 31; m. 56; c. 2. ENGLISH. B.S, State Univ. N.Y. Col. Oswego, 53; M.A, Colgate Univ, 55; Ph.D.(Eng), Syracuse Univ, 62. Instr. Eng, STATE UNIV. N.Y. COL. OSWEGO, 59-60, asst. prof, 60-62, PROF, 62-72, THEATRE, 72-, CHMN. DEPT, 73- State Univ. N.Y. res. fels, 63, 65, 69 & 70, grant-in-aid, 64; Poetry Soc. Am. writing fel, 65; Leverhulme vis. fel, Univ. York, Eng, 65-66; mem, World Ctr. Shakespeare Stud, 72- U.S.N, 55-59, Res, 59-, Comdr. MLA; Poetry Soc. Am; Shakespeare Asn. Am; Naval Hist. Found. Drama; Shakespeare; American history. Publ: Gull's way, Richard Smith, 61; The Blue Star Commodore, Bloch Publ, 61; Love in Pompeii, South & West, 67; co-auth, The black devil of the bayous, Gregg, 68; auth, John Webster's imagery and the Webster canon, Univ. Salzburg, Austria, 72; The sin of pride in Golding's The spire, Minn. Rev, 1/65; Hamlet: six characters in search of a play, Col. Eng, 4/66; Songs of innocence and experience, Midwest Quart, 7/68. Add: 87 Sheldon Ave, Oswego, NY 13126.

STETLER, CHARLES E, b. Pittsburgh, Pa, Sept. 12, 27; m. 55; c. 3. MODERN AMERICAN LITERATURE. B.A, Duquesne Univ, 50, M.A, 61; Ph.D.(Eng), Tulane Univ, 66. Instr. ENG, Rollins Col, 61-62; asst. prof, Loyola Univ. (La), 62-67; ASSOC. PROF, CALIF. STATE UNIV, LONG BEACH, 67-U.S.N, 45-46 & 50-52. Contemporary American literature; the novel. Publ: Roger, Karl, Rick, and Shane are friends of mine (poetry), Ma, 73; E.E. Cummings' 73 poems: with life's eye, Xavier Univ. Stud, spring 68; co-auth, Edward Field: stand-up poet, Minn. Rev, spring 69; auth, James Purdy's Malcolm: allegory of no man, Critique, fall 73. Add: Dept. of English, California State University, Long Beach, 6101 E. Seventh St, Long Beach, CA 90840.

STETNER, S.C.V, U.S. citizen; m. 56; c. 2. ENGLISH & COMPARATIVE LITERATURE. M.A, Columbia Univ, 48, Ph.D.(comp. lit), 59. Instr. ENG, Brooklyn Col, 55-59; PROF, C.W. POST COL, L. I. UNIV, 59- Fulbright prof, Univ. Delhi, 63-64; prof. hist. west. cult, Juilliard Sch, Lincoln Ctr, N.Y, 71- U.S.A.F, 41-45, Capt.(Ret); Air Medal & 6 Oak Leaf Clusters. History of drama; Renaissance studies. Publ: Co-auth, Regan's profession, Eng. Stud, 70 & Lear's darker purpose, Lit. & Psychol, 71; auth, Baptista and his daughters, Psychoanal. Rev, 73. Add: Dept. of English, C.W. Post College, Long Island University, Greenvale, NY 11548.

STEVENS, A. WILBER, b. Brooklyn, N.Y, Aug. 16, 21; m. 55; c. 2. ENGLISH. A.B, Brown Univ, 42; fel, Univ. Wash, 44-46, M.A, 56, Ph.D, 57; cert, Univ. London, 49. Assoc. Eng, Univ. Wash, 47-48, instr, 48-54; vis. lectr, Idaho State Univ, 54-56, asst. prof, 56-60, assoc. prof. & chmn. dept, 61-64; prof. & chmn. dept, Park Col, 64-66; prof. Eng. & chmn. ctr. lang. & lit. stud, Prescott Col, 66-73, provost, 68-72; PROF. ENG. & DEAN COL. ARTS & LETT, UNIV. NEV, LAS VEGAS, 73- Ed. & pub, Interim, 44-58; deleg, Int. Theatre Inst, Bombay, India, 56; Fulbright prof. Eng. lang. & lit, Mandalay, Burma, 56-57; vis. prof. Am. lit, Chulalongkorn Univ, Bangkok, 57; deleg, UNESCO Conf, San Francisco, 57; Fulbright prof. Am. lit, Univ. Brazil, 59-60; vis. prof, Ariz. State Univ, summer 68, State Univ. N.Y. Buffalo, summer 71 & Utah Shakespeare Festival, summer 72. MLA; Philol. Asn. Pac. Coast; Asia Soc; Rocky Mountain Mod. Lang. Asn.(pres, 72-73); Am. Soc. Aesthet; Col. Eng. Asn; Mod. Humanities Res. Asn; Am. Soc. Theatre Res; Eng-Speaking Union; Conf. Christianity & Lit; S.Cent. Mod. Lang. Asn; Renaissance Soc. Am; Int. Comp. Lit. Asn. English Renaissance, especially Shakespeare; contemporary British poetry, fiction and drama; religion and literature. Publ: Pocatello, 65; ed, Interim, 2 vols, Kraus Reprint Corp, 66; ed. & auth. introd, Poems southwest, 68 & Stories southwest, 73, Prescott Col; auth, Concept of prose tragedy in America, Educ. Theatre, 12/52; George Orwell and Southeast Asia, Yearbk. Comp. Lit, 63; Contemporary Indian fiction in English: concept and development, Proc. Int. Comp. Lit. Asn, Bordeaux, 72; plus poetry. Add: Office of the Dean, College of Arts and Letters, University of Nevada, Las Vegas, NV 89154.

STEVENS, ARETTA JANE, English. See McCLURE, ARETTA STEVENS.

STEVENS, DAVID RANALD, b. Beeville, Tex, Mar. 26, 17; m. 51; c. 4. ENGLISH. B.A, Univ. Tex, Austin, 48, M.A, 49, Ph.D.(Eng. & philos), 54. Instr. ENG, Del Mar Col, 54-66; assoc. prof, SOUTHWEST TEX. STATE UNIV, 66-70, PROF, 70- U.S.A, 43-46. S.Cent. Mod. Lang. Asn; MLA. Biography; literature. Publ: Concerning generative rhetoric, Col. Compos. & Commun, 10/67; Presidential remarks, Texas College English, 70; ed, A boyhood on the south Texas range: Prague Ranch, 1907-1913, Texana, 72. Add: Dept. of English, Southwest Texas State University, San Marcos, TX 78666.

STEVENS, EARL EUGENE, b. Chicago, Ill, Apr. 6, 25; m. 52. ENGLISH. A.B, Ind. Univ, 49; Princeton, 49-50; M.A, Univ. Mich, 51; Southern fel. & Ph.D, Univ. N.C, 63. Instr, Univ. N.C, 52-55, 57-58; assoc. prof. Eng, W.Tex. State Col, 56-57; asst. prof, Pfeiffer Col, 58-63, chmn. div. fine arts, 61-62; assoc. prof. ENG, Trinity Univ, 63-64; assoc. prof, Wis. State Univ, Stevens Point, 64-67, PROF, 67-68; R.I. COL, 68- U.S.A, 45-46. MLA. Victorian literature; the novel; criticism. Publ: The Tyrian trader in Mathew Arnold's The scholar gypsy, Victorian Newslett, 63; contrib, Joseph Conrad: an annotated secondary bibliography, North. Ill. Univ, 71; auth, John Galsworthy, In: British winners of the Nobel Literary Prize, Univ. Okla, (in press). Add: Dept. of English, Rhode Island College, Providence, RI 02908.

STEVENS, EDWIN LOCKWOOD, b. Delhi, N.Y, Nov. 21, 13; m. 61; c. 4. SPEECH. A.B, Rutgers Univ, 36; M.A, Columbia Univ, 42. Asst. purchasing agent, Rutgers Univ, 36-40, instr. SPEECH, 40-42; Columbia Univ, 42-43; asst. prof, GEORGE WASHINGTON UNIV, 47-50, assoc. prof, 50-61, PROF, 61- Consult. & mem. fac, For. Serv. Inst, U.S. Dept. State, 48-; Indust. Col. Armed Forces, 48-; Walter Reed Army Grad. Sch. Dentistry, 54-; consult, Nat. War Col, 47-57; lectr, Naval War Col, 63-; consult, U.S. Civil Serv. Comn, 63-; U.S. Dept. Agr, 66-; U.S. Dept. Treas, 67-; chmn. senate exec. comt, George Washington Univ, 65-66, chmn. fac. senate exec. comt, 72-75. Patriotic Civilian Serv. Award, Dept. Army, 64; Distinguished Serv. Award, Indust. Col. Armed Forces, 73. U.S.A, 43-46, Res, 46-50, 1st Lt. Speech Commun. Asn. Group discussion; conference leadership, Publ: Co-auth, Speech is easy, rev. mil. ed, 42 & auth, You can talk well, 46, co-auth, rev. ed, 60, Rutgers Univ. Add: Dept. of Speech & Drama, George Washington University, Washington, DC 20006.

STEVENS, HAROLD RAY, b. Macon, Ga, May 20, 36; m. 59; c. 2. ENGLISH. B.A, West. Md. Col, 58; Ph.D.(Eng), Univ. Pa, 64. Instr. ENG, Butler Univ,

63-65, asst. prof, 65-66; WEST. MD. COL, 66-70, ASSOC. PROF, 70- MLA; Byron Soc; Int. Joseph Conrad Soc. Publ: Co-auth, Joseph Conrad and the Falconhurst, J. Mod. Lit, 70; contrib, Joseph Conrad, North. Ill. Univ, 71; auth, Theme and structure in Manfred: the Biblical basis, UNISA Eng. Stud, 73; plus others. Add: Dept. of English, Western Maryland College, Westminster, MD 21157.

STEVENS, JOHN DEAN, Mass Communication History & Law. See Volume I, History.

STEVENS, MARTIN, b. Hamburg, Ger, Jan. 11, 27; U.S. citizen; m. 47; c. 3. ENGLISH LANGUAGE & LITERATURE. B.A, West. Reserve Univ, 49, M.A, 50; Ph.D, Mich. State, 56. Instr. commun. skills, Mich. State Univ, 50-56; assoc. prof. ENG, Univ. Louisville, 56-64, PROF, Ohio State Univ, 64-69; STATE UNIV. N.Y. STONY BROOK, 69-, CHMN. DEPT, 73- Consult. pub. schs, Louisville, 62-63; Guggenheim fel, 66-67; Fulbright Res. award, U.K, 66-67. U.S.N, 45-46. MLA; NCTE; Mediaeval Acad. Am. Old and Middle English language and literature; linguistics; teaching of English. Publ: Co-auth, Communication: principles and practice, Wadsworth, 59, Glossary for college English, McGraw, 66, Masterworks of English prose, Holt, 68 & Old English literature: 22 analytical essays, Univ. Nebr, 69; auth, The reshaping of Everyman, Germanic Rev, 72; A source for Frou-Frou in Anna Karenina, Comp. Lit, 72; The medieval theatre of the world, Chaucer Rev, 73; plus numerous others. Add: Dept. of English, State University of New York at Stony Brook, Stony Brook, NY 11785.

STEVENS, PETER STANLEY, b. Manchester, Eng, Nov. 17, 27; Can. citizen; m. 57; c. 3. CANADIAN LITERATURE. B.A, Univ. Nottingham, 50, educ. cert, 51; M.A, McMaster Univ, 63; Ph.D.(Eng), Univ. Saskatchewan, 68. Teacher, Manchester City Pub. Schs, 52-57; ENG, Hillfield Col, 57-61, head dept, Hillfield-Strathallan Col, 61-64; from lectr. to asst. prof, Univ. Saskatchewan, 64-69; ASSOC. PROF, UNIV. WINDSOR, 69- Lectr. Eng, McMaster Univ, 61-64. League Can. Poets. Modern American literature; literature of the transition, 1880-1920. Publ: Ed, The McGill movement, McGraw, 69; auth, Nothing but spoons, Delta Can, 69; A few myths, Talonbooks, 71; Breadcrusts and glass, Fiddlehead, 72; co-ed, Forum, 72 & ed, Raymond Knister, Univ. Toronto, 74; auth, And the dying sky like blood, Borealis, 73; contrib, The love poetry in Canadian literature, 71; Canadian literature, In: Literatures in English, Routledge & Kegan Paul, 74; English poetry in Canada 1967-72, In: Oxford companion to Canadian history and literature, 74. Add: Dept. of English, University of Windsor, Windsor, Ont. N8Y 1L3, Can.

STEVENS, ROBERT LOWELL, b. Albion, Ill, May 7, 21; m. 46; c. 2. ENGLISH. B.A. in Ed, Ariz. State Univ, 43; M.A, Univ. Ill, 50, Ph.D, 55. Teacher high sch, Ill, 46-48; vis. instr. ENG, Mont. State Univ, summer 54; asst. prof, Chico State Col, 55-56; assoc. prof, NORTH. ARIZ. UNIV, 56-62, PROF, 62-, ASST. PROVOST, 72-, CHMN. DEPT. SPEECH & THEATRE, 74-, chmn. dept. Eng, 69-70, assoc. dean Col. Sci. & Humanistic Stud, 70-72. U.S.N.R, 43-46, Lt.(jg). NCTE; NEA. American literature; teaching of English, secondary level and college freshman level. Publ: Co-auth, Better English, 53 & English skills, 59, Ginn; co-auth, Harbrace guide to sentence building, 61 & Competence in English, 67, Harcourt. Add: Box 15096, Northern Arizona University, Flagstaff, AZ 86001.

STEVENS, WILLIAM JOHN, English. See Volume III, Foreign Languages, Linguistics & Philology.

STEVENSON, DAVID LLOYD, b. Escondido, Calif, June 10, 10. ENGLISH. A.B, Univ. Calif, 33, A.M, 35; Ph.D, Columbia Univ, 41. Instr. Eng, Calif. Inst. Technol, 37-39, Univ. Wis, 39-40; Wayne Univ, 40-41; Univ. Calif, 41-43; chief regional analyst, compliance div, War Prod. Bd, 43-47; assoc. prof. Eng, West. Reserve Univ, 47-57, prof. & coord. grad. stud, 57-63; PROF. ENG, GRAD. DIV, HUNTER COL. & CITY UNIV. NEW YORK, 63-, chmn. dept, Hunter Col, 67-70. MLA; Malone Soc; Renaissance Soc. Am; Shakespeare Soc. Am; Eng. Inst. Shakespeare; English Renaissance; modern American literature. Publ: The love-game comedy, Columbia Univ, 46, AMS Press, 66; co-auth, Stories of modern America, St. Martins, 61; auth, The achievement of Shakespeare's Measure for Measure, Cornell Univ, 67; The Elizabethan Age, Fawcett, 67; The activists, Daedalus, Spring 63; James Jones and Jack Kerouac, novelists of disjunction, In: Creative present, Doubleday, 63; L'individu, le Milieu at la Liberte dan les Romans de William Styron, Lett. Mod, 67. Add: Dept. of English, Hunter College, 695 Park Ave, New York, NY 10021.

STEVENSON, DWIGHT WARD, b. Uniontown, Pa, Oct. 7, 33; m. 55; c. 2. AMERICAN LITERATURE, RHETORIC. A.B, Univ. Ky, 55; M.A, Univ. Mich, 57, Ph.D.(Eng. lang, lit), 65. Instr. ENG, COL. ENGINEERING, UNIV. MICH, ANN ARBOR, 60-65, asst. prof, 65-69, ASSOC. PROF. HUMANITIES, 69- U.S.A.R, 55-56, Capt. Am. Stud. Asn; Am. Soc. Engineering Educ. Technical communication; theatre; theatrical scene design. Publ: Co-auth, Problems in exposition, Crowell, 72. Add: Dept. of Humanities, College of Engineering, University of Michigan, Ann Arbor, MI 48104.

STEVENSON, JOHN WEAMER, b. Pittsburgh, Pa, July 24, 18; m. 41; c. 1. ENGLISH. A.B, Wofford Col, 48; M.A, Vanderbilt Univ, 49, fels, 49-50, 53-54, Ph.D.(Eng), 54. Instr. ENG, Presby. Col.(S.C), 50-51, asst. prof, 51-54, assoc. prof, 54-57, prof. & chmn. dept, 58-62; assoc. prof, Millsaps Col, 57-58; PROF. & CHMN. DEPT, CONVERSE COL, 62-, HEAD DIV. LANG. & LIT, 71- Coop. Prog. in Humanities fel, Duke Univ. & Univ. N.C, 66-67; assoc. ed, Humanities in South, 71- U.S.A, 41-45. MLA; S.Atlantic Mod. Lang. Asn; S.Atlantic Asn. Depts. Eng.(pres, 73-74). Nineteenth century; modern poetry. Publ: The pastoral setting in the poetry of A.E. Housman, S.Atlantic Quart; Arcadia re-settled: pastoral poetry and romantic theory, Stud. Eng. Lit, fall 67; The ceremony of Housman's style, Victorian Poetry, spring 72; plus others. Add: 736 Maple St, Spartanburg, SC 29302.

STEVENSON, KAY GILLILAND, b. Roanoke, Ala, Sept. 26, 40; m. 66. ENGLISH LITERATURE. B.A, Agnes Scott Col, 62; M.A, Univ. Calif, Los Angeles, 64; M.Phil, Yale, 67, Ph.D.(Eng), 71; summers, Univ. Paris, 69, 71; Geothe Inst, Ger, 73. Instr. hist, Marlborough Sch, Los Angeles, 64-65; Eng, Am. Col. Switz. & Leysin Am. Sch, 67-69; UNIV. NEW HAVEN, 70-72, asst. prof, 72-73, DIR. FRESHMAN ENG, 73- MLA; Medieval Acad. Am; NCTE. Chaucer; 17th century English literature; Medieval French and English literature. Add: Dept. of English, University of New Haven, West Haven, CT 06516.

STEVENSON, RICHARD COLTON, b. Boise, Idaho, Feb. 19, 39; m. 67; c. 2. ENGLISH NOVEL, VICTORIAN LITERATURE. A.B, Harvard Univ, 61, A.M, 63, Frank Knox traveling fel, 65-66, Ph.D.(Eng), 69. Asst. prof. ENG, UNIV. ORE, 68-73, ASSOC. PROF, 73- Nat. Endowment Humanities Younger Humanist fel, 73-74. Novel; the heroine in English fiction; narrative technique. Publ: Laetitia Dale and the comic spirit in The egoist, Nineteenth Century Fiction, 3/72; Innovations of comic method in George Meredith's Evan Harrington, Tex. Stud. Lit. & Lang, summer 73; Stein's prescription for "how to be" and the problem of assessing Lord Jim's career, Conradiana, forthcoming. Add: Dept. of English, University of Oregon, Eugene, OR 97403.

STEVENSON, STANLEY WARREN, b. Hamilton, Ont, Sept. 20, 33; m. 54; c. 4. ENGLISH. B.A, Bishop's Univ, 52; fel, McGill Univ, 53-54, M.A, 54; Ph.D, Northwest. Univ, 58. Instr. ENG, Frontier Col, 54; asst, Northwest. Univ, 54-56; instr, Univ. Sask, 56-59; lectr, Univ. Man, 59-60; instr, UNIV. B.C, 61-63, asst. prof, 63-67, ASSOC. PROF, 67- Can. Counc. sr. fel, 67-68. Asn. Can. Univ. Teachers Eng. Romantic literature; Renaissance literature. Publ: Divine analogy: a study of the creation motif in Blake and Coleridge, Inst. Eng. Sprache & Lit, 72; Shakespeare's hand in The Spanish tragedy 1602, Stud. Eng. Lit, spring 68; Lamia: a stab at the Gordian knot, Stud. Romanticism, 72; Kubla Khan as symbol, Tex. Stud. Lit. & Lang, 73; plus one other. Add: Dept. of English, University of British Columbia, Vancouver 8, B.C, Can.

STEVENSON, WILLIAM HANDFORTH, b. Bradford, Eng, Oct. 17, 28. ENGLISH. B.Litt, Oxford, 51; M.A, Edinburgh Univ, 53. Lectr. Eng, Kumasi Col. Technol, Ghana, 57-59; Univ. Ibadan, 59-65, sr. lectr, 65-68, PROF. Eng. lit, 68-69 & 70-71; ENG, BOSTON UNIV, 71-, ed, Stud. in Romanticism, 71-74. William Blake; English poetry, especially metrics. Publ: Ed, The poems of William Blake, Longman/Norton, 71. Add: Dept. of English, Boston University, 236 Bay State Rd, Boston, MA 02215.

STEVICK, PHILIP T, b. Elyria, Ohio, Oct. 17, 30; m. 53; c. 3. ENGLISH. B.A, Kent State Univ, 55, M.A, 56; Ph.D.(Eng) Ohio State Univ, 63. Instr. ENG, Mt. Union Col, 56-59; asst. instr, Ohio State Univ, 61-63; asst. prof, Univ. Conn, 63-65; assoc. prof, TEMPLE UNIV, 65-67, PROF, 67- Vis. prof. Eng, Ind. Univ, 71. U.S.A, 51-53. MLA. The theory of fiction; 18th century English literature; Contemporary fiction. Publ: The theory of the novel, 67 & ed, Anti-story: an anthology of experimental fiction, 71, Free Press; auth, The chapter in fiction, Syracuse Univ, 70; ed, Samuel Richardson's Clarissa, Rinehart, 71; auth, Fielding and the meaning of history, PMLA, 12/64; The Augustan nose, Univ. Toronto Quart, 1/65; Novel and anatomy: notes toward an amplification of Frye, Criticism, spring 68. Add: Dept. of English, Temple University, Philadelphia, PA 19122.

STEVICK, ROBERT DAVID, b. Iowa City, Iowa, Jan. 17, 28; m. 52; c. 2. ENGLISH. B.A, Univ. Tulsa, 49, M.A, 51; Ph.D, Univ. Wis, 56. Instr. ENG, Fresno State Col, 56-58, asst. prof, 58-60; lectr, Univ. Col. W.Indies, 60-62; asst. prof, UNIV. WASH, 62-65, assoc. prof, 65-69, PROF, 69-, CHMN. DEPT, 71- Fulbright Australian-Am. Educ. Found. res. grant, 68-69. U.S.A, 50-52. MLA; Mediaeval Acad. Am; Ling. Soc. Am. Medieval English literature; English language history. Publ: One hundred Middle English lyrics, Bobbs, 63; English and its history: the evolution of a language, Allyn & Bacon, 68; Suprasegmentals, meter, and the manuscript of Beowulf, Mouton, The Hague, 68; The oralformulaic analyses of Old English verse, Speculum, 62; The biological model and historical linguistics, Language, 63; The text and composition of The seafarer, PMLA, 65. Add: Dept. of English, University of Washington, Seattle, WA 98195.

STEWART, ALLEGRA, b. Indianapolis, Ind, July 26, 99. ENGLISH. A.B, Butler Univ, 21; A.M, Columbia Univ, 23; Ph.D, Univ. London, 33. Instr. ENG, BUTLER UNIV, 23-26, asst. prof, 26-33, assoc. prof, 33-40, Demia Butler prof, 40-69, EMER. PROF, 69- MLA; Col. Eng. Asn; Mod. Humanities Res. Asn; Milton Soc. Chaucer; Milton; Gertrude Stein. Publ: Gertrude Stein and the present, Harvard, 67; The quality of Gertrude Stein's creativity, Am. Lit, 1/57. Add: Dept. of English, Butler University, Indianapolis, IN 46208.

STEWART, BAIN TATE, b. Shelbyville, Tenn, Apr. 24, 15; m. 42. ENGLISH LITERATURE & COMPOSITION. A.B, Vanderbilt Univ, 36, A.M, 37; Ph.D, Northwest. Univ, 42. Instr. ENG, UNIV. TENN, KNOXVILLE, 40-42, 46-47, asst. prof, 47-54, assoc. prof, 54-61, PROF, 61- U.S.A, 42-46. MLA; NCTE; S.Atlantic Mod. Lang. Asn; Shakespeare Asn. Am; Conf. Col. Compos. & Commun. Renaissance English poetry and drama; freshman English. Publ: Readings and assignments: a practical approach to college writing, Holt, 61; The misunderstood dreams in the plays of Shakespeare and his contemporaries, Vanderbilt Stud. Humanities; Characterization through dreams in the drama of Shakespeare's day, Tenn. Stud. Lit. Add: Dept. of English, University of Tennessee, Knoxville, TN 37916.

STEWART, CHARLES JOSEPH, b. Terre Haute, Ind, July 3, 36; m. 58; c. 2. SPEECH. B.S, Ind. State Univ, 58; M.A, Univ. Ill, 60, Ph.D.(speech), 63. Instr. speech, PURDUE UNIV, 61-63, asst. prof, 63-67, assoc. prof, 67-73, PROF. COMMUN, 73-, fac. res. grants, summers 64 & 65. Air Nat. Guard, 54-61, 62; U.S.A.F, 61-62, S/Sgt. Speech Commun. Asn; Cent. States Speech Asn. Rhetoric of social movements; rhetoric of the Civil War; labor agitation in America. Publ: Co-auth, A man named John F. Kennedy, 64; Paulist Press, On speech and speakers, 68 & ed, On speech communication, 72, Holt; co-ed. & contrib, Explorations in rhetorical criticism, Pa. State Univ, 73 & America in controversy, Brown, 73; contrib, Preaching in American history, 69 & Sermons in American history, 71, Abingdon; co-auth, The congressional case for a school prayer amendment, Cent. States Speech J, 70; plus others. Add: Dept. of Communication, Purdue University, West Lafayette, IN 47906.

STEWART, DAVID H, b. Ft. Wayne, Ind, Aug. 12, 26; m. 49; c. 2. ENGLISH, RUSSIAN. A.B, Univ. Mich, 47, M.A, 49, fel, 54-55, Ph.D.(Eng, comp. lit), 59; Cert. Russ. & M.A, Columbia Univ, 54. Instr. Eng, Valparaiso Univ,

49-50; Univ. Ore, 50-52; Russ, Univ. Mich, 55-56; ENG, East. Mich. Univ, 56-57, asst. prof, 57-59; Univ. Alta, 59-60; Univ. Mich, 60-63, assoc. prof, 63-68; prof. & chmn. dept, Idaho State Univ, 68-71; PROF. & HEAD DEPT, PA. STATE UNIV, UNIVERSITY PARK, 71- Fac. res. grant, East. Mich. Univ, spring 59; Horace H. Rackham res. grant, Univ. Mich, summer 66. U.S.N, 44-46. Pac. Northwest Col. Eng. Asn.(pres, 68-70); Rocky Mountain Mod. Lang. Asn.(pres, 69-70); Am. Comp. Lit. Asn; MLA; Col. Eng. Asn; NCTE; Am. Stud. Asn. Modern American literature; Russian literature. Publ: Mikhail Sholokhov: a critical introduction, Univ. Mich, 67; Anna Karenina: the dialectic of prophecy, PMLA, 6/64; Cather's mortal comedy, Queen's Quart, summer 66; Science and humanism once more, West. Humanities Rev, spring 70; plus others. Add: Dept. of English, Pennsylvania State University, University Park, PA 16802.

STEWART, DONALD CHARLES, b. Kansas City, Mo, June 24, 30; m. 55; c. 2. ENGLISH LITERATURE. B.A, Univ. Kans, 52, M.A, 55; Ph.D, Univ. Wis, 62. Instr. ENG, Univ. Ill, Urbana, 62-63, asst. prof, 63-68; ASST. PROF, KANS. STATE UNIV, 68- NCTE Res. Found. grant-in-aid, 67-68; ed, Kans. Eng, 71- NCTE; Conf. Col. Compos. & Commun.(affil. speaker, 73-74). Research in the teaching of college English; prose fiction of George Meredith. Publ: The authentic voice, W.C. Brown, 72; Prose with integrity: a primary objective, Col. Compos. & Commun, 10/69; The bear and the mountain, Kans. Quart, 6/71; plus three others. Add: Dept. of English, Kansas State University, Manhattan,KS 66502.

STEWART, DOROTHEA LOU, b. Buies Creek, N.C, Apr. 10, 27. LINGUISTICS, AMERICAN LITERATURE. B.A, Woman's Col. Univ. N.C, 48; M.A, E.Carolina Col, 62. Teacher Eng. & French, high schs, N.C, 48-60; asst. prof. ENG, CAMPBELL COL.(N.C), 60-71, ASSOC. PROF, 71- Am. Stud. Asn; S.Atlantic Mod. Lang. Asn; N.C-Va. Col. Eng. Asn. Add: Box 274, Campbell College, Buies Creek, NC 27506.

STEWART, GARRETT FITZGERALD, b. Detroit, Mich, Jan. 5, 45. ENGLISH LITERATURE. B.A, Univ. South. Calif, 67; Ph.M, Yale, 70, Ph.D.(Eng), 71. ASST. PROF. ENG, BOSTON UNIV, 71- The novel; prose style. Publ: Co-auth, Grammar as style: exercises in creativity, Holt, 71; auth, Dickens and the trials of imagination, Harvard, 74; The golden bower of Our mutual friend, ELH, spring 73. Add: Dept. of English, Boston University, 236 Bay State Rd, Boston, MA 02215.

STEWART, GARY L, b. Salt Lake City, Utah, Mar. 5, 37; m. 61; c. 2. SPEECH, DRAMA. B.S, Brigham Young Univ, 61, M.S, 62; Ph.D.(dramatic art), Univ. Iowa, 68. Instr. SPEECH, Univ. Tex, Austin, 66-67; ASST. PROF, UNIV. MASS, AMHERST, 67- Speech Commun. Asn; Am. Theatre Asn. Dramatic theory and criticism; American theatre and drama. Add: Dept. of Speech, University of Massachusetts, Amherst, MA 01002.

STEWART, GUY HARRY, b. Keyser, W.Va, Feb. 12, 24; m. 48; c. 3. JOURNALISM. B.S.J, W.Va. Univ, 48; M.A, 49; Ph.D.(hist), Univ. Ill, 57. Asst. exten. ed, W.Va. Univ, 48-49, asst. univ, ed, 49-50; assoc. prof, JOUR, Tenn. Polytech. Inst, 50-60; W.VA. UNIV, 60-65, PROF, 65- Univ. senate grants, W.Va. Univ, 61, 62; Benedum Found. grants, 63, 67. U.S.N, 43-46, Lt.(jg). Asn. Educ. in Jour. British journalism education. Publ: A touch of charisma, W.Va. 4-H All Stars, 69; Journalism education in Britain enters a period of change, Jour. Quart, spring 68; contrib, Education for newspaper work, South. Newspaper Publ. Assoc. Found, 73. Add: School of Journalism, West Virginia University, Morgantown, WV 26506.

STEWART, JACK F, b. Aberdeen, Scotland, Apr. 13, 35; m. 62; c. 2. ENGLISH. M.A, Univ. Edinburgh, 57, dipl. educ, 58; Ph.D.(Eng), Univ. South. Calif, 67. Instr. Eng. commun, Univ. South. Calif, 63-67; asst. prof. ENG, UNIV. B.C, 67-71, ASSOC. PROF, 71- Philol. Asn. Pac. Coast(chmn, gen. lit, 71-72); Johnson Soc. Northwest (treas, 68-69); MLA. Techniques and philosophy of modern fiction, especially Woolf and Lawrence; theories of fiction; theory of humor, wit, comic satire and irony in literature. Publ: Apotheosis and apocalypse in Faulkner's Wash, Stud. Short Fiction, fall 69; Sterne's Absurd comedy, Univ. Windsor Rev, spring 70; Existence and symbol in The waves, Mod. Fiction Stud, fall 72; plus five others. Add: Dept. of English, University of British Columbia, Vancouver 8, B.C, Can.

STEWART, JAMES TATE, b. Shelbyville, Tenn, Apr. 20, 23; m. 49; c. 5. ENGLISH. B.A, Vanderbilt Univ, 43, fel, 47-49, Ph.D, 54; M.A, Harvard, 47; Univ. Paris, 45; Middlebury Col, 46. Instr. ENG, Vanderbilt Univ, 49-51; teacher, Baylor Sch, 51-52; asst. prof, Wofford Col, 52-55; assoc. prof, FURMAN UNIV, 55-61, PROF, 61-, chmn. dept, 61-72. U.S.A, 43-46. MLA; S.Atlantic Mod. Lang. Asn. English Renaissance; Spenser. Add: Dept. of English, Furman University, Greenville, SC 29613.

STEWART, JOHN CRAIG, b. Selma, Ala, Jan. 20, 15; m. 60; c. 1. CREATIVE WRITING, AMERICAN LITERATURE. B.A, Univ. Ala, 48, M.A, 50. Instr. LIT. & CREATIVE WRITING, Univ. Ala, 50-55, asst. prof, 55-60, Univ. Ala. Exten-Mobile, 60-64; asst. prof. & chmn. dept, UNIV. S.ALA, 64-66, assoc. prof, 67-72, PROF, 72-, DIR. CREATIVE WRITING PROG, 67- U.S.A.A.F, 41-46, Maj. S.Atlantic Mod. Lang. Asn; Auth. Guild. Am. Historical and literary research for original work with novel, short story and some history. Publ: Through the first gate (novel), Dodd, 50; Alabama's Baldwin County, Ala. State Planning Bd, 53; co-auth, Know Alabama—a history of Alabama, Colonial Press, 56, Viewpoint Publ, 69; auth, Muscogee twilight (novel), Am. South. Publ, 65; Governors of Alabama, Pelican Publ (in press); A tale of the southern coast (short story), Comment, fall 64; The last day (short story), Atlantic Monthly, 2/48 & In: Alabama Prize stories, Strode Publ, 70; Fiction as communication, New Writers, fall 73; plus several others. Add: Dept. of English, University of South Alabama, Gaillard Dr, Mobile, AL 36688.

STEWART, JOHN LINCOLN, b. Alton, Ill, Jan. 24, 17; m. 39, 64; c. 4. ENGLISH. A.B, Denison Univ, 38; A.M, Ohio State Univ, 39, Ph.D, 47; M.A, Dartmouth Col, 57; hon. D.A, Denison Univ, 64. Instr. Eng, Ohio State Univ, 45-46; Univ. Calif, Los Angeles, 47-49; asst. prof, Dartmouth Col, 49-57, prof, 57-64, assoc. dir, Hopkins Ctr, 62-64; PROF. LIT, UNIV. CALIF, SAN DIEGO, 64-, PROVOST, JOHN MUIR COL, 65- Howard Found. fel, 53-54; trustee, Kinhaven Music Sch, 61-65; Dartmouth Col. fac. fel, 62-63. U.S.A, 42-45. MLA; Col. Art Asn. Am. Music; literature of contemporary South; aesthetics. Publ: Exposition for science and technical students, Dryden, 50; The essay: a critical anthology, Prentice-Hall, 52; John Crowe Ransom, Univ. Minn, 62; The burden of time: the fugitives and agrarians, Princeton, 65. Add: John Muir College, University of California at San Diego, La Jolla, CA 92037.

STEWART, KEITH, b. Mt. Vernon, Wash, May 26, 21; m. 49; c. 3. ENGLISH. B.A, Stanford Univ, 44; Scribner fel, Princeton, 45-47, Ph.D.(Eng), 53. Instr. ENG, Univ. Va, 48-52; UNIV. CINCINNATI, 52-56, asst. prof. 56-62, ASSOC. PROF, 62- MLA. Eighteenth century English literature; American literature; English novel. Add: McMicken College of Arts & Sciences, University of Cincinnati, Cincinnati, OH 45221.

STEWART, LARRY LeROY, b. Shenandoah, Iowa, Apr. 18, 41; m. 66; c. 2. ENGLISH & AMERICAN LITERATURE. B.A, Simpson Col, 63; M.A, West. Reserve Univ, 64; Ph.D.(Eng), Case West. Reserve Univ, 71. Instr. ENG, COL. WOOSTER, 67-71, ASST. PROF, 71- MLA. Eighteenth century English literature; literature of childhood and adolescence. Add: Dept. of English, College of Wooster, Wooster, OH 44691.

STEWART, LAWRENCE DELBERT, b. Champaign, Ill, Nov. 7, 26. ENGLISH ROMANTIC LITERATURE, 20TH CENTURY AMERICAN LITERATURE. B.Sc, Northwest. Univ, 48, M.A, 49, Ph.D.(Eng), 52. Instr. ENG, Univ. Calif, Los Angeles, 52-54, asst. prof, 54-55; archivist, Ira Gershwin, Beverly Hills, Calif, 55-69; asst. prof. ENG, CALIF. STATE UNIV, NORTHRIDGE, 69-72, ASSOC. PROF, 72- Sig.C, U.S.A, 44-46. MLA; Auth. League Am. Gertrude Stein circle; American musical theatre; Joseph Johnson circle, 1760-1809. Publ: John Scott of Amwell, Univ. Calif, 56; co-auth, The Gershwin years, Doubleday, 73; auth, Paul Bowles: the illumination of North Africa, South. Ill. Univ, 74; Fitzgerald's film scripts for Babylon revisited, Fitzgerald/Hemingway Annual, 71; Gertrude Stein and the vital dead, Mystery & Detection Annual, 72; co-auth, Preface to The Gershwin years in song, Quadrangle, 73. Add: Dept. of English, California State University, Northridge, 18111 Nordhoff, Northridge, CA 91324.

STEWART, MAAJA AGUR, b. Estonia, June 27, 38; U.S. citizen; m. 59; c. 1. ENGLISH. A.B, Oberlin Col, 60; M.A, Univ. Mich, 61, Ph.D.(Eng), 66. ASST. PROF. ENG, NEWCOMB COL, TULANE UNIV, 65- MLA. Eighteenth century English literature; theory of comedy; English novel. Add: Dept. of English, Newcomb College of Tulane University, New Orleans, LA 70118.

STEWART, MARY E, b. Millington, Tenn. ENGLISH. B.A, Knoxville Col, 43; M.A, Atlanta Univ, 49; Hill Family Found. grant, Univ. Minn, Minneapolis, 65-66. ASSOC. PROF. ENG, KNOXVILLE COL, 49- Vis. prof, Macalester Col, 65-66; mem, Southeast. Conf. Eng. in Two Yr. Cols. NCTE; Conf. Col. Compos. & Commun; AAUP; Col. Eng. Asn. Add: 8739 Armour Rd, Millington, TN 38053.

STEWART, MARY MARGARET, b. Santa Monica, Calif, Aug. 4, 31. LITERATURE. A.B, Monmouth Col, 53; Strauss fel. & Ph.D.(Eng), Ind. Univ, 59. Asst. ENG, Ind. Univ, 57-59; instr, GETTYSBURG COL, 59-61, asst. prof, 61-65, assoc. prof, 65-68, PROF, 68- Vis. prof, Ind. Univ, summer 67. MLA. Eighteenth century, especially James Boswell; mid-18th century poets, particularly William Collins. Publ: Boswell's denominational dilemma, PMLA, 12/61; Boswell and the infidels, Stud. Eng. Lit, 64; James Boswell and the national church of Scotland, Huntington Libr. Quart, 67. Add: Dept. of English, Gettysburg College, Gettysburg, PA 17325.

STEWART, PAUL ROBERT, b. Franklin, Nebr, Sept. 8, 22; m. 46; c. 2. ENGLISH. A.B, Univ. Nebr, 47, M.A, 49; Ph.D.(Eng), Univ. Ill, 54. From asst. instr. to instr. ENG, Univ. Nebr, 47-49, 51-54; asst. prof, BUTLER UNIV, 54-58, assoc. prof, 58-65, PROF, 65-, DIR. UNIV. HONORS PROG, 68-, DEAN UNIV. COL, 71-, dir, 64-71. U.S.N, 42-46, Lt.(jg). MLA. American literature; the little magazine. Publ: The Prairie Schooner story: a little magazine's first 25 years; co-auth, Keys to good English, 67 & Keys to English mastery, 68, Econ. Co. Add: 5130 N. Pennsylvania, Indianapolis, IN 46205.

STEWART, POWELL, b. Norwood, Ohio, Apr. 16, 07; m. 40; c. 1. ENGLISH. B.S, Bowdoin Col, 28; A.M, Harvard, 29; Ph.D, Univ. Tex, 39. Instr. ENG, UNIV. TEX, AUSTIN, 29-42, asst. prof, 42-50, assoc. prof, 51-59, prof, 59-70, EMER. PROF, 70- U.S.A.A.F, 42-45, Capt. English drama and poetry of the 18th century. Publ: British newspapers and periodicals, 1632-1800; The loyal London mercuries, Stud. Eng. Auth, Teaching English (16 half-hour films), Univ. Tex, 60; plus others. Add: 5411 Shoal Creek Blvd, Austin, TX 78756.

STEWART, STANLEY N, b. Minneapolis, Minn, June 5, 31; m. 56; c. 1. ENGLISH. B.S, Univ. Calif, Los Angeles, 56, M.A, 58, Ph.D, 61. Asst, Univ. Calif, Los Angeles, 56-59; instr. ENG, UNIV. CALIF, RIVERSIDE, 61-62, asst. prof, 62-66, ASSOC. PROF, 66- Asst. prof, Univ. Calif, Los Angeles, summer 62; assoc. prof, Columbia Univ, summer 68; sr. fel, John Simon Guggenheim Mem. Found, 71-72. MLA; Renaissance Soc. Am; Augustan Reprint Soc. Seventeenth century literature; literary criticism. Publ: The enclosed garden: the tradition and the image in seventeenth-century poetry, Univ. Wis, 66; The unity of prose: from description to allegory, Harper, 67; Anne Collins: divine songs and meditations, Augustan Reprint Soc, 62; The expanded voice: the art of Thomas Traherne, Huntington Libr, 70; Marvell and the Ars moriendi, In: Seventeenth-century imagery, Univ. Calif, 71; Thomas Wilson's Christian dictionary and the idea of Marvell's Garden, In: New aspects of lexicography, South. Ill. Univ, 72; plus others. Add: Dept. of English, University of California, Riverside, Riverside, CA 92502.

STEWART, VINCENT (ASTOR, JR), b. San Augustine, Tex, May 13, 39; m. 65; c. 1. ENGLISH, LINGUISTICS. B.A, Stephen F. Austin State Col, 61, M.A, 62; Univ. Iowa, 62-64. Asst. prof. creative writing, Northeast Mo. State Col, 64-66; instr. ENG, Va. Polytech. Inst, 66-68; ASSOC. PROF, LOCK HAVEN STATE COL, 68- Vis. lectr, Stephen F. Austin State Col, summer 64; curriculum consult, creative writing, Hawaii Curriculum Ctr, Honolulu, Hawaii, summer 68. MLA; NCTE; Conf. Col. Compos. & Commun. Poetry prosody; creative writing; American literature. Publ: Words for the builder (poems), Brush Mountain, 67; auth, Three dimensions of poetry: an introduction, Scribner, 69; Out of the looking glass: illusion and reality in Mark Twain's Tom Sawyer, 1/65 & Writing English, not writing, 1/66, Mo. Eng. Bull; Five poems, Hudson Rev, winter 66-67. Add: 401 S. Main St, Jersey Shore, PA 17740.

STEWART, WILLIAM DONALD, b. Tacoma, Wash, Sept. 26, 20; m. 48, 60; c. 2. ENGLISH. B.A, Univ. Puget Sound, 42, M.A, 50, B.Ed, 51; Ph.D, Univ. Mainz, Ger, 53. Press off, Off. Mil. Govt. for Hesse, Ger, 45-48; instr. Eng. compos, Univ. Puget Sound, 50, asst. prof. Eng. compos. & lit, 56-59; lectr. Am. Stud, Univ. Mainz, 51-53; chmn. dept. Eng, Lambuth Col, 53-55; press off, Radio Liberation, Munich, Ger, 55-56; asst. prof. Eng, Cent. Mo. State Univ, 59-61; prof. & chmn. dept, Col. Emporia, 61-64; PROF. ENG, UNIV. TAMPA, 64-, chmn. dept, 64-71. U.S.A, 42-46. MLA; Int. Shakespeare Asn. Old English; Middle English; 16th century. Add: 5006 Longfellow, Tampa, FL 33609.

STIBBS, JOHN HENRY, b. Chicago, Ill, Feb. 10, 09; m. 41; c. 3. ENGLISH LITERATURE. A.B, Univ. Wis, 31; A.M, Univ. Mich, 37, fel, 37-42, Ph.D, 42. Instr, U.S. Naval Acad, 46; asst. prof, Newcomb Col, TULANE UNIV, 46-47, asst. prof. Eng. & asst. dean col. arts & sci, 47-48, PROF. ENG. & DEAN STUD, 49- Ford Found. consult, Univs. Pakistan, 57; U.S. State Dept. consult, Free Univ. Berlin, 64. U.S.N, 42-46, Comdr. MLA; Nat. Asn. Stud. Personnel Adminr; Am. Col. Personnel Asn; Renaissance Soc. Am; S.Cent. Mod. Lang. Asn. Shorter prose works of Sir Walter Raleigh. Publ: The student and mental health: an international view, Rive-Side Press, 59; Children can have manners, Look Mag, 6/58; Barriers and aids to communication in international academic exchange, Ger. Develop. Inst, 67; plus others. Add: Dept. of English, Tulane University, New Orleans, LA 70118.

STICKNEY, RUTH, b. Eldorado, Ark, Nov. 26, 23. ENGLISH LITERATURE. B.S, Univ. Houston, 45, M.A, 47; Ph.D.(Eng), Univ. Minn, 57. Instr. Eng, Univ. Houston, 45-49, 50-51; lectr. Eng. lang. & lit, Training Col, Swansea, S.Wales, 49-50; asst. ENG, Univ. Minn, 51-54, instr, 54-55; asst. prof, Univ. Houston, 57-65; assoc. prof, Tex. South. Univ, 65-69; KUTZTOWN STATE COL, 69-73, PROF, 73- MLA; AAUP; Malone Soc. Renaissance aesthetic theory; influence of Roman satirists on the course of formal verse satire in England in the 17th century; theory of imitation in poetry, its classical origins and its development in English poetic and critical theory. Add: Dept. of English, Kutztown State College, Kutztown, PA 19530.

STIEHL, HARRY CHARLES, b. Tampico, Mex, Jan. 29, 27; U.S. citizen. MODERN LITERATURE & HISTORY. B.A, Univ. Tex, Austin, 47; Ph.D. (Eng), 69; M.A, Univ. Calif, Berkeley, 49. Translator, U.S. Air Force Intel, 50-51; ed, San Francisco Bay Window, 57-59; ed, Ramparts, 61-67; asst. prof. ENG, SAN DIEGO STATE UNIV, 69-72, ASSOC. PROF, 73- Vis. prof. Eng, La. State Univ, Baton Rouge, spring 67. U.S.M.C, 51-56, Capt. Modern languages. Publ: The Marine graveyard on Point Loma, 71, Achievement in American Catholic Poetry, 72 & Soliloquy art, 72, Sea Vineyard Eds; Lytton Strachey, Twayne, 73; contrib, Best poems of 1964, Pac. Bks, 65; plus numerous articles. Add: School of Literature, San Diego State University, 5402 College Ave, San Diego, CA 92115.

STIKER, JEFF M, b. New York, N.Y, Apr. 29, 27; m. 57; c. 3. ENGLISH LITERATURE. B.A, Drake Univ, 51, M.A, 56; Columbia Univ; Northwest. Univ. Instr. ENG, LEWIS UNIV, 56-58, asst. prof, 58-68, ASSOC. PROF, 68- U.S.A, 45-46. NCTE; AAUP; Eighteenth century English literature; Renaissance English literature. Publ: The logical structure of Shakespeare's Sonnet 64, Exercise Exchange, 3/66; Bladen and Hays: Pope's Dunciad, IV, 560, Notes & Queries, 12/66. Add: Dept. of English, Lewis University, Lockport, IL 60441.

STILL, JAMES A, b. LaFayette, Ala, July 16, 06. ENGLISH. A.B, Lincoln Mem. Univ, 29, hon. L.H.D, 74; M.A, Vanderbilt Univ, 30; B.S, Univ. Ill, 31; hon. Litt.D, Berea Col, 73. Librn, Hindman Settlement Sch, 32-39, 52-62; assoc. prof. ENG, Morehead State Univ, 62-70; MEM. STAFF, HINDMAN SETTLEMENT SCH, 72- MacDowell Colony fel, 38; Guggenheim Found. fels, 41-42 & 46-47; contrib. ed, Appalachian Heritage, 73-; participant, Cent. Appalachian Folk-speech Workshop, Alice Lloyd Col, 74. O'Henry Mem. Prize, 39; South. Auth. Award, 40; Am. Acad. Arts & Lett. Award, 47. U.S.A.A.F, 41-45, T/Sgt. Creative writing, poetry, novel, short story. Publ: Hounds on the mountain, 37, River of earth, 40 & On troublesome creek, 41, Viking; Way down yonder on Troublesome Creek, Putnam, 74; contrib, From the mountain, Memphis State Univ, 72; Lamp (poem), Appalachian Heritage, winter 73; plus others. Add: Hindman Settlement School, Hindman, KY 41822.

STILLIANS, BRUCE MOORE, b. Villisca, Iowa, Nov. 22, 30; m. 55. ENGLISH. B.A, Univ. Iowa, 52, M.A, 57, Ph.D.(Eng. lit), 62. Asst. prof. ENG, UNIV. HAWAII, MANOA, 62-68, ASSOC. PROF, 68- Univ. Iowa fel, 61-62, Am. Counc. Learned Soc. assoc, 64-66. U.S.A, 53-54. MLA; Am. Name Soc. American and English literature of the 19th century; criticism; the rural community. Add: Dept. of English, University of Hawaii at Manoa, Honolulu, HI 96822.

STILLINGER, JACK, b. Chicago, Ill, Feb. 16, 31; m. 52, 71; c. 4. ENGLISH. B.A, Univ. Tex, 53; Woodrow Wilson fel, Northwest. Univ, 53-54, M.A, 54; Ph.D, Harvard, 58. Asst. prof. ENG, UNIV. ILL, URBANA, 58-61, assoc. prof, 61-64, PROF, 64- Ed, J. Eng. & Ger. Philol, 61-73; fel, John Simon Guggenheim Mem. Found, 64-65. MLA; Keats-Shelley Asn. Am. English romantic movement. Publ: Ed, The early draft of John Stuart Mill's Autobiography, 61 & auth, The hoodwinking of Madeline and other essays on Keats's poems, 71, Univ. Ill; ed, Anthony Munday's Zelauto: the fountaine of fame, South. Ill. Univ, 63; ed, Wordsworth: selected poems and prefaces, 65 & John Stuart Mill: Autobiography and other writings, 69, Houghton; ed, The letters of Charles Armitage Brown, 66 & auth, The texts of Keats's poems, 74, Harvard Univ; auth, Twentieth century interpretations of Keats's odes, Prentice-Hall, 68. Add: 100 English Bldg, University of Illinois, Urbana, IL 61801.

STILLMAN, DONALD GALE, b. Cortland, N.Y, Sept. 28, 04; m. 34; c. 2. ENGLISH. A.B, Lafayette Col, 26; A.M, Univ. Mich, 32, Ph.D, 42; hon. L.H.D, Clarkson Col. Technol, 73. Master Eng, Peddie Sch, N.J, 26-31; from instr. to assoc. prof, Bucknell Univ, 34-49; prof. lib. stud. & head dept, CLARKSON COL. TECHNOL, 49-65, prof. HUMANITIES & chmn. dept, 65-70, EMER. PROF, 70- MLA; NCTE; Am. Soc. Eng. Educ. Renaissance literature and textual criticism; Milton as proofreader. Publ: Clarkson at 75: a portrait of the college, Clarkson Col. Technol, 72. Add: 7 College Park Rd, Potsdam, NY 13676.

STIMPSON, CATHARINE R, b. Bellingham, Wash, June 4, 36. CONTEMPORARY LITERATURE, CRITICAL THEORY. A.B, Bryn Mawr Col, 58; B.A, Cambridge, 60, M.A, 65; Ph.D.(Eng), Columbia Univ, 67. Instr. ENG, BARNARD COL, COLUMBIA UNIV, 63-68, ASST. PROF, 68- Nat. Emergency Civil Liberties Comt. MLA (mem. comn. status of women, 73-). Post-modern literature; women and literature; relationship of revolution to literature. Publ: J.R.R. Tolkien, Columbia Univ, 69; ed, Women and the Equal Rights Amendment, 72 & Discrimination against women, 73, Bowker. Add: Dept. of English, 423 Barnard Hall, Barnard College, Columbia University, New York, NY 10027.

STINE, LAWRENCE, b. Shelby Co, Ind. SPEECH, DRAMA. A.B, Butler Univ, 47; M.A, State Univ. Iowa, 51, Ph.D.(speech, dramatic art), 62. Instr. SPEECH, Butler Univ, 47-50; S.DAK. STATE UNIV, 52-53, asst. prof, 53-61, assoc. prof, 61-63, PROF, 63-, DIR. THEATRE, 53-, ASSOC. DEAN COL. ARTS & SCI, 69-, head dept. speech, 63-69. Outstanding Teaching Award, S.Dak. State Univ, 59. U.S.A, 42-43. Speech Commun. Asn; Am. Theatre Asn. Oral communications; interpretation; dramatic literature. Add: College of Arts & Science, South Dakota State University, Brookings, SD 57006.

STINEBACK, DAVID CEBURN, b. Toronto, Ont, Mar. 30, 43; U.S. citizen; m. 67; c. 1. AMERICAN LITERATURE & INTELLECTUAL HISTORY. A.B, Stanford Univ, 65; M.A, Yale Univ, 67; Ph.D.(Am. stud), Yale, 69. ASST. PROF. ENG, UNION COL.(N.Y), 69- MLA; Am. Stud. Asn. American fiction; novel; American Indian history and culture. Publ: Ed, Edgar Huntly, Col. & Univ, 73; auth, On history and its consequences: A.B, Guthrie's These thousand hills, West. Am. Lit, 71; On the limits of fiction, Midwest Quart, 7/73. Add: Dept. of English, Humanities Bldg, Union College, Schenectady, NY 12308.

STINSON, JOHN JEROME, b. Brooklyn, N.Y, Sept. 30, 40; m. 69; c. 2. MODERN BRITISH LITERATURE. B.A, St. John's Univ.(N.Y), 62, M.A, 63; N.Y. State Regents fel, New York Univ, 62-64, Ph.D.(Eng), 71. Instr. ENG, STATE UNIV. N.Y. COL. FREDONIA, 65-71, ASST. PROF, 71-, res. award, 73. MLA. Modern American literature; popular culture. Publ: The Christian symbolism in After the fall, Mod. Drama, 12/67; Trying to exorcise the beast: the grotesque in the fiction of William Golding, Cithara, 11/71; Anthony Burgess: novelist on the margin, J. Pop. Cult, summer 73. Add: Dept. of English, Fenton Hall, State University of New York College at Fredonia, Fredonia, NY 14063.

STIRLING, THOMAS BRENTS, b. Walla Walla, Wash, Mar. 30, 04. ENGLISH. LL.B, Univ. Wash, 26, Ph.D, 34. Assoc. Eng, UNIV. WASH, 32-34, instr, 34-37, asst. prof, 37-43, assoc. prof, 43-49, prof, 49-70, EMER. PROF. ENG. LIT, 70- MLA (chmn. Shakespeare group, 55-56); Shakespeare Asn. Am. Sixteenth century literature; Shakespeare. Publ: The populace in Shakespeare, 49 & Unity in Shakespearian tragedy, 56, Columbia Univ; The Shakespeare sonnet order: poems and groups, Univ. Calif, 68. Add: Box 65, Arch Cape, OR 97102.

STITES, WILLIAM HARRISON, b. Tyrone, Okla, Aug. 4, 22; m. 48; c. 3. SPEECH. B.A, La. Polytech. Inst, 44; M.A, Univ. Denver, 48, fel, 52-54, Ph.D.(rhet), 54. Asst. prof. SPEECH, ARIZ. STATE UNIV, 54-59, assoc. prof, 59-65, PROF, 65- Consult, 56- U.S.M.C, 42-46, Res, 46-, Capt. Speech Commun. Asn. Rhetoric; public address; study of forensic development in listening comprehension and symbol composition. Add: Dept. of Speech, Arizona State University, Tempe, AZ 85281.

STITZEL, JUDITH GOLD, b. New York, N.Y, Mar. 23, 41; m. 61; c. 1. ENGLISH. B.A, Columbia Univ, 61; M.A, Univ. Wis, 62; Ph.D.(Eng), Univ. Minn, 68. Asst. prof. ENG, W.VA. UNIV, 68-72, ASSOC. PROF, 72- MLA (mem. women's caucus, 70-); NCTE (mem. comt. learning skills ctr, 73-); Conf. Col. Compos. & Commun. Literary criticism; pedagogy; women's studies. Publ: Blifil and Henry Fielding's conception of evil, Philol. Papers, 6/70; Learning from our mistakes, J. Eng. Teaching Tech, spring 73. Add: Dept. of English, Armstrong Hall, West Virginia University, Morgantown, WV 26506.

STIVER, HARRY E, JR, b. Kansas City, Mo, Mar. 25, 28; m. 54; c. 3. THEATRE ARTS, SPEECH. A.B, Hastings Col, 50-; M.A, Univ. Nebr, Lincoln, 52; Newhouse Found. scholar, Stanford Univ, 54, Fulbright award, Athens, 55; univ. scholar. & Ph.D.(theatre arts), Univ. Ill, Urbana, 60. Instr. & dir. theatre, high sch, Nebr, 49-51; asst. speech & supv. exp. theatre, Univ. Nebr, Lincoln, 51-52; instr. theatre arts & speech, chmn. dept. speech & drama & dir. theatre, Hastings Col, 52-54; asst. theatre arts, Stanford Univ, 54-55; Fulbright prof. Eng. lang. progs. & mem. bd. rev. & interviews for Fulbright grants to Am, Univ. Athens, 55-56; instr. hist. theatre, theatre architecture, scene design & speech & tech. dir. univ. theatre, Univ. Nebr, Lincoln, 56-57, instr. hist. theatre, directing, adv. directing & speech & assoc. dir. univ. theatre, 57-58; teaching asst. acting, oral interpretation & speech, Univ. Ill, Urbana, 58-60; asst. prof. mod. drama, hist. theatre & adv. directing & dir. theatre, West. Wash. State Col, 60-61; assoc. prof. theatre arts, Ill. State Univ, 61-64, prof, 64-66, dir. univ. theatre, 61-66; vis. prof. DRAMA, CALIF. STATE UNIV, LONG BEACH, 64-65, PROF. & CHMN. DEPT, 65- Mem. regular acting co, Hayloft Theatre, Lincoln, Nebr, summer 52 & Paul Bunyan Theatre, Bemidji, Minn, summer 53; int. theatre chmn, Nebr, 56-58; nat. playwriting contest, West. Wash. State Col, 60; regional chmn, Nat. Univ. Theatre Festival, Wash, D.C, 63-64. U.S.N. 45-46. Am. Nat. Theatre Asn; Speech Commun Asn; Am. Theatre Asn. Publ: Co-auth, Directing for the theatre, 74 & co-auth, A director's workbook, 74, Brown. Add: Dept. of Theatre Arts, California State University, Long Beach, 6101 E. Seventh, Long Beach, CA 90801.

STOCK, ELY, b. Philadelphia, Pa, Apr. 7, 37; m. 58; c. 3. ENGLISH, AMERICAN STUDIES. A.B, Brooklyn Col, 58; fel, Brown Univ, 59-60, Ph.D.(Am. civilization), 66. Asst. prof. ENG, Sam Houston State Teachers Col, 61-63; instr, Boston Univ, 64-66, asst. prof, 66-68; asst. prof. & asst. chmn. Am civilization prog, Brown Univ, 68-71; ASSOC. PROF, STATEN ISLAND COMMUNITY COL, 71- MLA; Am. Stud. Asn; NCTE; New Eng. Am. Stud. Asn.(secy-treas, 69-71); Col. Eng. Asn.(mem. Eng. in two-year cols. comt, 72-73). American literature and history. Publ: History and the Bible in Hawthorne's Roger Malvin's burial, Essex Inst. Hist. Collections, 10/64; The Biblical context of Ethan Brand, Am. Lit, 5/65; Witchcraft in The hollow of the three hills, Am. Transcendental Quart, spring 72; plus others. Add: 543 Hillcrest Ave, Westfield, NJ 07090.

STOCK, IRVIN, b. New York, N.Y, Apr. 16, 20; m. 42; c. 2. ENGLISH. B.A, N.Y. Univ, 40; M.A, Columbia Univ, 41, Ford Found. fel, 51-52, Ph.D, 53; Fulbright fel, France, 50-51. Instr. ENG, Bergen Jr. Col, 47-48; asst. prof, Rollins Col, 52, assoc. prof, 53-57, prof, 57-66; assoc. prof, UNIV. MASS, BOSTON, 66-68, PROF, 68-, chmn. dept, 67-69. Fulbright prof. Am. lit, Univ. Montpellier, 65-66. U.S.A.A.F, 43-46. MLA. The novel; 19th century English literature; the drama. Publ: William Hale White (Mark Rutherford): a critical study, Columbia Univ, 56; A view of Wilhelm Meister's apprenticeship, PMLA, 3/57; The novels of Saul Bellow, South. Rev, 1/67; Mary McCarthy, In: American writers series pamphlet, Univ. Minn, 68; plus others. Add: Dept. of English, University of Massachusetts, Boston, MA 02116.

STOCK, ROBERT DOUGLAS, b. Akron, Ohio, Dec. 2, 41. ENGLISH. B.A, Kent State Univ, 63; M.A, Princeton, 65, Ph.D.(Eng), 67. Asst. prof. ENG, UNIV. NEBR, LINCOLN, 67-72, ASSOC. PROF, 72- MLA; Am. Soc. 18th Century Stud. Literary criticism, religion and politics in 18th century thought; Samuel Johnson; Edmund Burke. Publ: Samuel Johnson and neoclassical dramatic theory, 73 & ed, Samuel Johnson's literary criticism, 74, Univ. Nebr. Add: Dept. of English, 304 Andrews Hall, University of Nebraska, Lincoln, NE 68508.

STOCKHOLDER, KATHERINE S, b. New York, N.Y, July 19, 28; m. 58; c. 3. RENAISSANCE LITERATURE, SHAKESPEARE. B.A, Hunter Col, 50; M.A, Columbia Univ, 52; Ph.D.(Eng), Univ. Wash, 62. Instr. ENG, Univ. Ill, 59-60; lectr, Univ. Ghana, 64-66; ASSOC. PROF, UNIV. B.C, 66- MLA; Philol. Asn. Pac. Coast; Asn. Can. Univ. Teachers. Neoplatonism in the Renaissance; psychological approaches to literary criticism. Publ: The other coriolanos, PMLA, 3/70; Hamlet. Between night and day, Lit. & Psychol, spring 71; Egregiously an ass: chance & accident in Othello, Stud. Eng. Lit, spring 73. Add: Dept. of English, University of British Columbia, Vancouver, B.C, Can.

STOCKING, DAVID MACKENZIE, b. Detroit, Mich, Mar. 9, 19; m. 55; c. 1. ENGLISH. A.B, Univ. Mich, 39, Ph.D, 49; A.M, Harvard, 40. From asst. prof. to PROF. ENG, BELOIT COL, 48-, CHMN. DEPT, 72- Ed, Beloit Poetry J; Fund. Advan. Educ. fel, 54-55. U.S.N.R, 42-46, Lt.(jg). MLA; NCTE. Ideas of John Jay Chapman. Publ: Asst. ed, The journals of Claire Clairmont, Harvard Univ, 69. Add: Dept. of English, Beloit College, Beloit, WI 53511.

STOCKING, FRED HOLLY, b. Detroit, Mich, Mar. 5, 15; m. 39; c. 3. ENGLISH. B.A, Williams Col.(Mass), 36; M.A, Univ. Mich, 37, Ph.D, 46. From instr. to prof. Eng, WILLIAMS COL, 40-72, MORRIS PROF. RHETORIC, 72-, dir. sch. banking, 61-74, chmn. dept. Eng, 63-66. Chmn. Advan. Placement Exam. Comt. in Eng, 56-61; dir. summer insts. humanities, Williams Col, 59 & 67, Bennington Col, 60 & 62-65, Colo. Col, 61; vis. prof, Portland State Col, 61-62; scholar in residence, Fairfax County Pub. Schs, spring 68; vis. prof, Univ. Hawaii, Hilo campus, summer 68; distinguished NCTE lectr, 69; mem, Nat. Humanities Fac, 73-74. NCTE; MLA. Add: Dept. of English, Williams College, Williamstown, MA 01267.

STOCKING, MARION KINGSTON, b. June 4, 22; U.S. citizen; m. 55. ENGLISH & AMERICAN LITERATURE. A.B, Mt. Holyoke Col, 43, Class of 05 fel, 45; Pa-Del. Am. Asn. Univ. Women fel, 48; Ph.D.(Eng), Duke Univ, 52. Instr. ENG, Univ. Maine, 46-48; Univ. Colo, 50-54; asst. prof, BELOIT COL, 54-59, assoc. prof, 59-65, PROF, 65-, dir. underclass common course, 67-70. Ed, Beloit Poetry J, 56- MLA; Keats-Shelley Asn. Am. Romantic period of English literature, specifically Claire Clairmont; creative writing. Publ: Journals of Claire Clairmont, Harvard, 68; I got the idear, Colo. Quart; Notes on three Shelley letters, Keats-Shelley Mem. Bull; A folk song chapbook, Beloit Poetry J. Add: Dept. of English, Beloit College, Beloit, WI 53511.

STOCKTON, EDWIN L, JR, b. Winston-Salem, N.C, June 27, 33; m. 57. AMERICAN LITERATURE. B.A, Univ. N.C, 55, M.A, 58; fel, Fla. State Univ, 58-60, Ph.D, 60. Asst. prof. Am. Lit, Northeast La. State Col, 60-63; assoc. prof, RADFORD COL, 63-65, PROF. AM. LIT. & LING, 65-, chmn. dept. Eng, 66-67 & 69-70. MLA; Thoreau Soc; S.Atlantic Mod. Lang. Asn; Col. Eng. Asn; NCTE; South. Humanities Conf. American literature; history of the English language; linguistics. Publ: The influence of the Moravians upon The leather-stocking tales, Moravian Hist. Soc, 64. Add: Box 674, Radford College, Radford, VA 24141.

STOCKWELL, JOHN CHARLES, b. Philadelphia, Pa, Dec. 13, 44; m. 71; c. 2. DRAMA. B.A, Cedarville Col, 66; M.A, Bowling Green Univ, 67, fel, 67-69, Ph.D.(drama), 70. Teaching asst. drama, Bowling Green Univ, 66-67; asst. prof. & acting chmn. dept. drama & speech, Cedarville Col, 69-70; asst. prof. drama, Wis. State Univ-Whitewater, 71; ASST. PROF. DRAMA, DIR. THEATRE & ASST. TO DEAN, CALIF. STATE UNIV, NORTHRIDGE, 71- Am. Theatre Asn; Speech Commun. Asn; U.S. Inst. Theatre Technol. Behavioral research in theatre; theatre administration and management; arts pedagogy. Publ: Co-auth, The effects of body image satisfaction and boundary on pantomimic movement, spring 72, The effects of the nature and degree of body cathexis on pantomimic movement, spring 72 & Body buffer zone and proxemics in blocking, fall 73, Empirical Res. in Theatre; plus one other. Add: Dept. of Drama, California State University, Northridge, 18111 Nordhoff St, Northridge, CA 91324.

STOCKWELL, ROBERT PAUL, English Language & Linguistics. See Volume III, Foreign Languages, Linguistics & Philology.

STODDARD, DONALD RICHARD, b. Wakefield, Mass, Sept. 22, 36; m. 66; c. 2. AMERICAN & ENGLISH LITERATURE. B.S, Northeast. Univ, 59, M.A, 61; Ph.D.(Eng), Univ. Pa, 70. Eve. instr. ENG, Augusta Col, 61-62; instr, Northeast. Univ, 62-63; eve. instr, Univ. Pa, 63-66; ASSOC. PROF, SKIDMORE COL, 66- Fulbright lectr. Am. lang. & lit, Univ. Cluj, Romania, 72-73. Sig.C, U.S.A, 61-62, 1st Lt. MLA; Melville Soc. Am; Thoreau Soc. American literature; the novel; modern British literature. Publ: The relevance of Walden, Skidmore Alumnae Quart, spring 69; Proza ironica a lui John Barth, 4/73 & Magia verbala a lui James Merrill, 5/73, Steaua; plus others. Add: Dept. of English, Skidmore College, Saratoga Springs, NY 12866.

STODDARD, FLOYD GRADY, b. Bonham, Tex, Jan. 11, 38. ENGLISH. B.A, Univ. Tex, Austin, 56, M.A, 58; summer fel, Cornell Univ, 64, Ph.D.(Eng), 65; dipl. film, Orson Welles Cinema, Boston, 70. Instr. ENG, La. State Univ, 60-62; Univ. Tex, Austin, 65-67, asst. prof, 67-70; ASSOC. PROF, Hawthorne Col, 70-71; EAST STROUDSBURG STATE COL, 71- Univ. Tex. Res. Inst. grants, 65, 66, 67 & 68; Nat. Found. Arts & Humanities summer stipend, 68. MLA; Am. Comt. Irish Stud. Nineteenth and 20th century poetry; 20th century bibliography; media studies. Publ: The Lord Dunsany collection, spring 67 & The Louis MacNeice collection, spring 68, Libr. Chronicle Univ. Tex; Two autograph letters of William Wordsworth, Mod. Philol, 11/71. Add: R.D. 2, Box 302, Stroudsburg, PA 18360.

STODDARD, RICHARD FOSTER, b. Salem, Mass, Sept. 28, 42. HISTORY OF THEATRE. B.A, Tufts Univ, 67; Ph.D.(hist. of theatre), Yale, 71. ASST. PROF. DRAMA & THEATRE, UNIV. GA, 71- Am. Soc. Theatre Res; Am. Theatre Asn; Soc. Theatre Res, Eng; Theatre Libr. Asn. History of theatre architecture and scene design; theatre bibliography. Publ: Thomas Joyce, Edwin Booth's costumer, Educ. Theatre J, 70; A reconstruction of Charles Bulfinch's First Federal Street Theatre, Boston, Winterthur Portfolio, 70; Notes on John Joseph Holland, with a design for the Baltimore Theatre, 1802, Theatre Surv, 71. Add: Dept. of Drama & Theatre, University of Georgia, Athens, GA 30602.

STODDER, JOSEPH HENRY, Blue Island, Ill, Mar. 6, 29; m. 57; c. 4. ENGLISH & COMPARATIVE LITERATURE. A.B, Spring Hill Col, 50; M.A, Loyola Univ. Los Angeles, 59; Ph.D.(Eng), Univ. South. Calif, 64. Instr. ENG, Loyola Univ. Los Angeles, 59-62; asst. prof, Mt. St. Mary's Col. (Calif), 62-68; ASSOC. PROF, CALIF. STATE POLYTECH. UNIV, POMONA, 68- U.S.A.F, 50-55, Res, 55-, Lt. Col. MLA; Col. Eng. Asn. Renaissance drama; modern drama; theatre of the absurd. Publ: Satire in Jacobean tragedy, Salzburg, 74; Influences of Othello on Büchner's Woyzeck, Mod. Lang. Rev, 1/74. Add: Dept. of English, California State Polytechnic University, 3801 W. Temple Ave, Pomona, CA 91768.

STOERKER, LEWIS WALDO, b. Jefferson City, Mo, Apr. 8, 21; m. 45; c. 2. SPEECH, DRAMATIC ART. A.B, Elmhurst Col, 45; M.F.A, Yale, 47. Ed, Lawson News, Chicago, 40; tech. asst. drama, Yale, 46-47; instr. Eng. & tech. dir. univ. theatre, Mont. State Univ, 47-48; asst. prof. drama, chmn. dept. & dir. col. theatre, Ripon Col, 48-53; asst. dir, WBBM-TV, Chicago, Ill, 53-55; asst. prof. speech & dramatic arts, chmn. dept. & dir. col. theatre, Lakeland Col, 55-58; asst. prof. DRAMA, UNIV. MO-COLUMBIA, 58-62, ASSOC. PROF, 62-, DESIGNER & TECH. DIR, UNIV. THEATRE, 58-, DIR. PUB. RELAT, THEATRE, 73- Founder & pres, Rock Bridge Mem. State Park, 65-; lt. gov, Optimist Int, 72. Am. Theatre Asn; Am. Nat. Theatre & Acad; Children's Theatre Asn; Speech Commun. Asn. Theatre production, children's theatre and theatre planning. Add: 117 Fine Arts Centre, University of Missouri-Columbia, Columbia, MO 65201.

STOKES, ELMORE EWING, JR, b. Houston, Tex, Sept. 14, 22. ENGLISH. B.A, Univ. Tex, 43, M.A, 48, fel, 50-51, Ph.D.(Eng), 51. Instr. ENG, Tex. A&M Univ, 51-53, asst. prof, 53-58, assoc. prof, 58-60; vis. lectr, Univ. Tex, 60-61; assoc. prof, TEX. A&M UNIV, 61-63, PROF, 63- Bibliogr, Shaw Rev, 65-69. U.S.N, 43-46. S.Cent. Mod. Lang. Asn; S.Cent. Col. Eng. Asn; Col. Eng. Asn; NCTE; Shaw Soc, Eng; William Morris Soc. & Kelmscott Fel; AAUP. George Bernard Shaw; William Morris; 19th century English literature. Publ: Bernard Shaw and 19th century thought, 1/59 & Sydney Carlyle Cockerell: 1867-1962, 9/62, Shaw Rev; Morris and Bernard Shaw, J. William Morris Soc, Eng, 61. Add: 1203 Goode Dr, College Station, TX 77840.

STOKES, FRANK CHRISTOPHER, b. Johnstown, Pa, Jan. 23, 31; m. 54; c. 4. ENGLISH LITERATURE. B.A, Univ. Ill, Urbana, 57, M.A, 59, Ph.D.(Eng), 72. Instr. ENG, East. Ky. State Col, 59-60; asst. prof, Wisconsin State Col, Platteville, 60-64; State Univ. N.Y, Plattsburgh, 64-67; assoc. prof, East. N.Mex. Univ, 68-69; ASST. PROF, EAST. ILL, UNIV, 69- U.S.A.F, 50-54. Victorian fiction and nonsense. Add: Dept. of English, Eastern Illinois University, Charleston, IL 61920.

STOKES, GEORGE MITCHEL, b. Paducah, Tex, Apr. 12, 18; m. 46; c. 2. SPEECH. B.S, West Tex. State Col, 40; M.A, Baylor Univ, 47; Ph.D, Northwest. Univ, 54. Head dept. speech, Wayland Baptist Col, 47-50; prin. high sch, Mabank, Tex, 51-52; PROF. SPEECH, BAYLOR UNIV, 52- Mem. orgn. comt, Nat. Red. Cross, 67. U.S.A, 41-45, Capt. Speech Commun. Asn; South. Speech Asn. Texas place names. Add: Dept. of Speech, Baylor University, Waco, TX 76703.

STOKES, GEORGE STEWART, b. Philadelphia, Pa, Nov. 2, 10. LITERATURE. A.B, Univ. Pa, 32, A.M, 38, Ph.D, 46. Instr. ENG, Washington & Jefferson Col, 41; Cedar Crest Col, 41-46; TEMPLE UNIV, 46-49, asst. prof, 49-57, assoc. prof, 57-66, PROF, 66- MLA; Am. Stud. Asn. Colonial New England. Publ: Agnes Repplier: lady of letters, Univ. Pa, 49. Add: Dept. of English, Temple University, Philadelphia, PA 19122.

STOKES, JOHN LEMACKS, III, b. Greensboro, N.C, Feb. 25, 39; m. 63; c. 3. ENGLISH, HUMANITIES. A.B, Pfeiffer Col, 61; B.D, Emory Univ, 64; Ph.D. (humanities), Drew Univ, 69. Asst. prof. Eng, Oklahoma City Univ, 68-70; assoc. prof. & chmn. dept, Campbell Col, 70-71; assoc. prof. Eng. & coord. univ. stud, Oklahoma City Univ, 71-73; ASSOC. PROF. ENG. & DIR. MULTIPLE ABILITIES PROG, UNIV. N.C, WILMINGTON, 73- Nat. Asn. Humanities Educ. New humanities; contemporary world literature; creativity and innovation in higher education. Publ: Turn me loose . . . , let me go, Humanities J, 12/73; A time for change, Improving Col. & Univ. Teaching, (in press). Add: Dept. of English, University of North Carolina, Wilmington, Wilmington, NC 28401.

STOKES, THOMAS JOSEPH, S.J, b. Philadelphia, Pa, Feb. 3, 04. ENGLISH LITERATURE. A.B, Boston Col, 27, A.M, 28; Woodstock Col.(Md), 31-35; Johns Hopkins Univ, 36-38. Instr. ENG, Georgetown Univ, 28-31; assoc. prof, ST. JOSEPH'S COL.(PA), 38-47, PROF, 47- Speech; drama. Add: Dept. of English, St. Joseph's College, Philadelphia, PA 19131.

STOKOE, WILLIAM CLARENCE, JR, Linguistics, English. See Volume III, Foreign Languages, Linguistics & Philology.

STOLL, JOHN EDWARD, b. Chicago, Ill, Mar. 3, 33; m. 55; c. 2. VICTORIAN & MODERN ENGLISH. B.A, Northwest. Univ, 54, M.A, 56; Ph.D.(Eng), Wayne State Univ, 66. Teaching asst. ENG, Ind. Univ, 56-57; instr, Chicago City Cols, Wright Campus, 57-58; Univ. Notre Dame, 58-60; Mich. State Univ. Exten, 60-61; asst. prof, Southeast Mo. State Col, 61-63; teaching asst, Wayne State Univ, 63-64; asst. prof, Grove City Col, 64-65; instr, Wayne State Univ, 65-66, asst. prof, Ball State Univ, 66-70; prof, Belmont Col, 70-71; asst. prof, Univ. Ga, 71-73; HEAD DEPT. ENG. & HUMANITIES, MISS. INDUST. COL, 73- MLA. Psychology and literature; literature and religion; literary criticism. Publ: D.H. Lawrence's Sons and lovers: self-encounter and the unknown self, 68 & W.H. Auden: a reading, 70, Ball State Univ; The great deluge: a Yeats bibliography, 71 & D.H. Lawrence, 1911-1972; an international bibliography, 73, Whitston; The novels of D.H. Lawrence: a search for integration, Univ. Mo, 71; Common imagery in Joyce and Lawrence, 70 & Wordsworth for modern students, fall 70, Forum; Psychological dissociation in the Victorian novel, Lit. & Psychol, spring 70. Add: Dept. of English, Mississippi Industrial College, Holly Springs, MS 38635.

STOLP, DOROTHY E, b. Sprague, Wash, Aug. 24, 14. THEATRE. B.A, East. Wash. State Col, 40; M.A, Northwest. Univ, 48; Ph.D.(speech, theatre), La. State Univ, 52. Instr. SPEECH & DRAMA, Hutchinson Jr. Col, 49; Pa. State Teachers Col, Bloomsburg, 52; asst. prof, Ore. Col. Educ, 53-54; SOUTH. ORE. COL, 54-57, assoc. prof, 57-62, PROF, 62- U.S.C.G, 44-46. Am. Nat. Theatre & Acad; Am. Theatre Asn; Children's Theatre Asn; Univ. & Col. Theatre Asn. American theatre. Add: P.O. Box 73, Ashland, OR 97520.

STOLZENBACH, NORMA FRIZZELLE, b. Tex, Feb. 6, 04; m. 29; c. 1. ENGLISH, THEATER. B.A, Univ. Toledo, 48, M.A, 49; Ph.D.(speech & theater), Univ. Mich, 54. Dir. univ. theater, UNIV. TOLEDO, 43-47, lectr, Eng, speech & radio, 47-49, asst. prof. Eng, 49-55, assoc. prof, 55-69, prof. speech communication, 69-72, dir. theater activities, 55-65, EMER. PROF, 73- Vis. dir. & prof, Huron Playhouse, summer 57; lectr, Univ. Philippines, Far East. Univ. & Philippine Normal Col, summer 65. English speech in foreign countries. Publ: Fundamentals of oral interpretation, Univ. Publ, 69; The Wheeler Opera House, Quart. J. Hist. Soc. Northwest Ohio; contrib, Toledo Theater, In: History of Lucas County; auth, The teaching of voice & diction, Educ. Horizons, summer 64. Add: 2119 Evergreen Rd, Toledo, OH 43606.

STONE, ALBERT, JR, b. Brenham, Tex, Aug. 18, 16; m. 66. ENGLISH. B.A, Univ. Tex, 37, LL.B, 40; M.A, Univ. Houston, 56; Ph.D.(Eng), Harvard, 63. Assoc. prof. ENG, Lowell Technol. Inst, 62-67; PROF. & CHMN. DEPT, HELLENIC COL, 67- A.U.S, 42-46, Maj. MLA. Victorian novel. Add: Dept. of English, Hellenic College, Brookline, MA 02146.

STONE, ALBERT EDWARD, b. New London, Conn, Jan. 1, 24; m. 54; c. 2. ENGLISH, AMERICAN STUDIES. B.A, Yale, 49, Ph.D.(Am. stud), 57; M.A, Columbia Univ, 55. Instr. Eng. & hist, Casady Sch, 49-52; Eng, Yale, 55-59, asst. prof. ENG. & AM. STUD, 59-62; PROF, EMORY UNIV, 62-, chmn. dept. Eng, 62-68. Morse fel, Yale, 60-61; E.Harris Harbison award, 65-66; Fulbright lectr. Am. lit, Charles Univ, Prague, 68-69; mem. adv. counc. Am. stud, Comt. for Int. Exchange of Persons, Fulbright Prog, 70-74, chmn, 72-74. U.S.A, 42-46. Am. Stud. Asn; Col. Eng. Asn; MLA. Mark Twain; Henry James; American autobiography. Publ: The innocent eye: childhood in Mark Twain's imagination, Yale, 61; ed, Letters from an American farmer, New Am. Libr, 63, XX-century interpretations of The ambassadors, Prentice-Hall, 69 & Mark Twain, Personal recollections of Joan of Arc, Univ. Calif, (in press). Add: Dept. of English, Emory University, Atlanta, GA 30322.

STONE, DONALD DAVID, b. Los Angeles, Calif, Jan. 17, 42. ENGLISH LITERATURE. B.A, Univ. Calif, Berkeley, 63; Woodrow Wilson fel, Harvard, 63-64, M.A, 64, univ. fel, 65-68, Ph.D.(Eng), 68. Dexter traveling fel, 68; asst. prof, ENG, QUEENS COL.(N.Y), 68-72, ASSOC. PROF, 72- Howard Mumford Jones Prize, 68. MLA. Victorian literature; history of the novel. Publ: Novelists in a changing world, Harvard Univ, 72; Sense and semantics in Jane Austen, Nineteenth Century Fiction, 6/70; Victorian feminism and the 19th century novel, Women's Stud, winter 72. Add: Dept. of English, Queens College, Flushing, NY 11367.

STONE, EDITH O, b. Fresno, Calif, Dec. 17, 16. ENGLISH, LINGUISTICS. B.A, Pac. Union Col, 38, M.A, 48; Ph.D.(Eng), Univ. Mich, 60. Teacher ENG, Fresno Union Acad, 39-47; Lynwood Acad, 47-48; instr, Andrews Univ, 48-50, asst. prof, 50-54, assoc. prof, 54-56; prof. & chmn. dept, Columbia Union Col, 56-71; PROF, ANDREWS UNIV, 71- NCTE; MLA; Ling. Soc. Am; Ling. Asn. Gt. Brit; Teachers Eng. to Speakers Other Lang. Applied linguistics. Add: Dept. of English, Andrews University, Berrien Springs, MI 49104.

STONE, EDWARD, b. N.J, Aug. 29, 13; m. 51; c. 3. ENGLISH. B.A, Univ. Tex, 34, M.A, 37; fel, Duke Univ, 46-49, Ph.D.(Eng), 50. Tutor Eng, Univ. Tex, 38-39; instr, Newcomb Col, 39-42; Duke Univ, 49-52; asst. prof, Ga. Inst. Technol, 52-53; asst. prof. Eng. & dir. freshman compos, Univ. Va, 53-56; assoc. prof. ENG, OHIO UNIV, 56-61, PROF, 61-, chmn. dept, 58-63. Fulbright lectr, Nat. Univ. Mex, 66; Univ. Buenos Aires, 68. U.S.C.G, 42-46. MLA; NCTE. Henry James; Stephen Crane; William Faulkner. Publ: Incident at Harper's Ferry, Prentice-Hall, 56; What was naturalism?, 59 & Henry James: seven stories and studies, 61, Appleton; co-auth, Casebook of Ezra Pound, Crowell, 59; auth, The battle and the books: some aspects of Henry James, 64 & Voices of despair, 66, Ohio Univ; A certain morbidness, South. Ill. Univ, 69. Add: Dept. of English, Ellis Hall, Ohio University, Athens, OH 45701.

STONE, GEORGE WINCHESTER, JR, b. Washington, D.C, Dec. 18, 07; m. 36; c. 3. ENGLISH LITERATURE. A.B, Dartmouth Col, 30; Ph.D, Harvard, 40; hon. Litt.D, Middlebury Col, 60; hon. D.L.H, Hofstra Col, 63; hon. LL.D, George Washington Univ, 68. Instr. ENG, George Washington Univ, 33-35, asst. prof, 35-39, assoc. prof, 39-48, PROF, 48-55; N.Y. UNIV, 55-, dean grad. sch. arts & sci, 64-71, dean libr, 71-73. Folger fel, 47; Guggenheim fel, 50-52, 63-64; Fulbright res. fel, Eng, 63-64; v.pres, Int. Fed. Mod. Lang. & Lit, 66-69; mem. exec. comt, U.S. Nat. Comn. for UNESCO, 67-70. U.S.N, 43-46, Lt. Comdr. MLA (exec. secy, 56-63, pres, 67). Garrick and Shakespeare; 14th century literature; 18th century drama. Publ: The London stage, 1747-1776, South. Ill. Univ, 62. Add: 9 Washington Mews, New York, NY 10003.

STONE, HARRY, b. New York, N.Y, Feb. 1, 26; m. 51. ENGLISH. B.A, Univ. Calif, Los Angeles, 47, fel, 49-52, M.A, 50, Ph.D, 55. Asst, Univ. Calif, Los Angeles, 52-54; instr. ENG, Northwest. Univ, 55-57, asst. prof. 57-60; CALIF. STATE UNIV, NORTHRIDGE, 60-63, assoc. prof, 63-66, PROF, 66- Calif. State Univ, Northridge res. grants, 64-68, All-Col. res. fel, 68; Trustees of Calif. State Univ. creative res. fel, 66; Guggenheim fel, 68-69. U.S.N.R, 44-46, Lt.(jg). MLA(chmn. Dickens Sem, 70-72); NCTE; Philol Asn. Pac Coast; Dickens Soc; Dickens Fel; Int. Asn. Prof. Eng. Charles Dickens; 19th century English and American literature; the novel. Publ: Charles Dickens' uncollected writings from Household words, 1850-1859, 2 vols, Ind. Univ, 68; Dickens' use of his American experiences in Martin Chuzzlewit, PMLA; 57; Dickens and interior monologue, Philol. Quart, 59; Fire, hand, and gate: Dickens' Great expectations, Kenyon Rev, 62. Add: Dept. of English, California State University, Northridge, 18111 Nordhoff St, Northridge, CA 91324.

STONE, IRVING, b. San Francisco, Calif, July 14, 03; m. 34; c. 2. BIOGRAPHY. A.B, Univ. Calif, Berkeley, 23, fel, 24-26, hon. LL.D, 68; fel, Univ. South. Calif, 23-24, M.A, 24, hon. Litt.D, 65; hon. Litt.D, Coe Col, 67, Calif. State Cols, 71. BIOGRAPHER, AUTH. & ART CRITIC, 26- Prof. creative writing, Ind. Univ, 48; Univ. Wash, 61; mem, Calif. Civil War Centennial Comn, 61-65; specialist cult. exchange, U.S. Dept. of State, Soviet Union, Poland, Yugoslavia, 62; Calif. chmn, Nat. Libr. Week, 62; founder, Acad. Am. Poets, 62-66; mem, Eleanor Roosevelt Mem. Found, 63; mem. Am. Assembly, Columbia Univ, 63-67; v.pres, Eugene V. Debs Found, 63-; mem. adv. bd, Univ. Calif. Inst. Creative Arts, 63-; prof. writing biog. & biog. novel, Univ. South. Calif, 66; founder, Calif. State Cols. Comt. Arts, 67; trustee, Douglass House Found, Watts, Calif, 67-73; contrib. mem, Am. Sch. Class. Stud, Athens, 67-; participant, Arden House Conf. on U.S. & E.Europ, 67 & 69; charter mem. Berkeley fels, Univ. Calif, Berkeley, 68-; founder, Irving & Jean Stone Awards for Best Biog. Novel & Hist. Novel of Year, 68-; chmn. Allan Nevins Mem. Fund, Huntington Libr, 72-73; mem. ed. rev. comt, Forum Contemporary Hist, 72- Knight Commander, Order of Merit, Italy; Golden Lily of Florence, Italy; Christopher Award; Rupert Hughes Award; Gold Medal, Counc. Am. Artist Soc; Am. Revolution Round Table Award, 66; Hon. Citizen, Athens, Greece, 72. Soc. Am. Hist; Renaissance Soc. Am; Acad. Motion Picture Arts & Sci; Auth. League Am; PEN Club; Fels. for Schweitzer (founder & pres); West. Writers Am.(Golden Spur Award, 57); Acad. Polit. Sci. American political history; art, painting and sculpture. Publ: Pageant of youth, 33; Lust for life, 34; co-auth, Dear Theo, 37; auth, Sailor on horseback, 38; False witness, 40; Clarence Darrow for the defense, 41; They also ran, 43; Immortal wife, 44; Adversary in the house, 47; Earl Warren, 48, The passionate journey, 49; ed, We speak for ourselves, 50; auth, The President's lady, 51; Love is eternal, 54; Men to match my mountains, 56; The biographical novel: three views of the novel, 57; The agony and the ecstacy, 61; co-ed, Lincoln: a contemporary portrait, 62; co-auth, I, Michelangelo, sculptor, 62; auth, The Irving Stone reader, 63; The story of Michelangelo's Pieta, 64; The great adventure of Michelangelo, 65; Those who love, 65; ed, There was light: autobiography of a university, Berkeley, 70 & auth, The passions of the mind, 71, Doubleday; The trip that Abraham Lincoln promised Mary, In: Good Housekeeping treasury, Simon & Schuster, 60; California, In: American panorama, Doubleday, 69; Mary Todd Lincoln: a final judgment? Saturday Rev/World, 2/74; plus others. Add: Doubleday & Co, Inc, 277 Park Ave, New York, NY 10017.

STONE, MARLENE CAROLE, b. Clinton, Mo, Sept. 27, 38. SPEECH, MASS COMMUNICATIONS. A.B, Univ. Mo-Columbia, 60, A.M, 61; Temple Univ, 72-74. Costumier, Stephens Col, 61-62; instr. speech, drama & Eng, Ky. Wesleyan Col, 62-64; ASSOC. PROF. SPEECH & MASS COMMUN, TOWSON STATE COL, 64- Speech Commun. Asn; Speech Commun. Asn. East. States; Cent. States Speech Commun. Asn. Oral interpretation; readers theatre. Publ: Co-auth, Fundamentals of speech, Brown, 66. Add: Dept. of Communications Arts & Science, Towson State College, York Rd, Towson, MD 21204.

STONE, MARTHA CALLICOTT, b. St. Louis, Mo, Oct. 19, 04; m. 21, 35. ENGLISH. B.S, Southeast Mo. State Teachers Col, 27; A.M, Univ. Mo, 29; Cornell Univ, 33-35; Univ. Md, 48-54. Teacher, High Sch, Mo, 27-28; instr. Eng, Jefferson City Jr. Col, Mo, 31-32; Syracuse Univ, 36-37; teacher, High Sch, Md, 44-48; instr. Eng, Univ. Md, 48-70; RETIRED. Lectr, Army Exten. Prog, 57-67. MLA; Shakespeare Asn. Am; Renaissance Soc. Am; Mid. Atlantic Col. Eng. Asn.(secy-treas, 58-69). English Renaissance; literary and rhetorical criticism. Add: Rte. 8, Box 464, 28 Queens Rd, Salisbury, NC 28144.

STONE, ROBERT K, b. Chicago, Ill, Mar. 9, 26; m. 48; c. 2. ENGLISH. Ph.B, Univ. Chicago, 47, M.A, 50; Ph.D.(Eng), Univ. Ill, 63. Asst. ENG, Univ. Ill, Urbana, 53-61, instr, 61-63, asst. prof, 63-65; assoc. prof, UNIV. WIS-MILWAUKEE, 65-67, PROF, 67-, DIR. LOWER DIV. COURSES, 65- U.S.A. & U.S.A.A.F, 44-46. MLA; NCTE; Conf. Col. Compos. & Commun. Chaucer; medieval literature; rhetoric and composition. Publ: Middle English prose style, Mouton, The Hague, 70. Add: Dept. of English, University of Wisconsin-Milwaukee, Milwaukee, WI 53201.

STONE, VERNON A, b. Bowling Green, Ky, Oct. 21, 29; m. 66; c. 2. BROADCAST JOURNALISM, MASS COMMUNICATION. B.A, West. Ky. Univ, 51; M.A, Univ. Iowa, 53; Ph.D.(mass. commun), Univ. Wis, 66. Reporter & TV news coord, WHAS Inc, 53-62; from asst. prof. to PROF. JOUR. & MASS COMMUN, UNIV. WIS-MADISON, 65- Asn. Educ. Jour.(secy. radio-TV div,

68-70, v.head, 70-72, head, 72-74, secy. adv. bd, 73-74); Broadcast Educ. Asn; Int. Commun. Asn; Radio-TV News Dir. Asn.(dir, 72-74). Minorities and women in mass media; communication process and effects. Publ: Careers in broadcast news, Radio-TV News Dir. Asn, 72; A primacy effect in decision-making by jurors, J. Commun, 9/69; co-auth, Television and family communication, J. Broadcasting, fall 71; co-auth, Source-message orientation and components of source credibility, J. Quart, winter 72. Add: School of Journalism & Mass Communication, 5136 Vilas Hall, University of Wisconsin-Madison, Madison, WI 53706.

STONE, WILFRED HEALEY, b. Springfield, Mass, Aug. 18, 17; m. 54; c. 2. ENGLISH LITERATURE. A.B, Univ. Minn, 41, A.M, 46; Rockefeller Found. fel, Harvard, 46, univ. fel, 47-49, Fulbright grant-in-aid, 49-50, Ph.D, 50. Instr, Univ. Minn, 46; from instr. to asst. prof. ENG, STANFORD UNIV, 50-57, assoc. prof, 57-63, PROF, 63- Ford grant, Harvard, Yale & Columbia Univ, 53-54; Guggenheim grant, Cambridge, 57-58; Am. Counc. Learned Soc. award, 67; Guggenheim Mem. award, 68; Nat. Endowment for Humanities fel, 72-73. Lloyd W. Dinkelspiel Award, Stanford Univ, 62; Christian Gauss Prize, 66. U.S.N.R, 42-45, Lt. MLA; AAUP. Nineteenth century and modern English literature; novel and poetry; religion and art of Mark Rutherford. Publ: Religion and art of William Hale White, 54 & The cave and the mountain: a study of E.M. Forster, 66, Stanford Univ; co-auth, Form and thought in prose, Ronald, 54, 60 & 68; Prose style: a handbook for writers, McGraw, 68; auth, The confessional fiction of Mark Rutherford, Univ. Toronto Quart, 10/53; E.M. Forster and Matthew Arnold, Lang. Mod, 1-2/68; E.M. Forster on love and money, In: Aspects of E.M. Forster, Arnold, London, 68. Add: Dept. of English, Stanford University, Stanford, CA 94305.

STONE, WILLIAM B, b. Milwaukee, Wis, May 31, 29; m. 53; c. 3. ENGLISH. B.A, Univ. Chicago, 48, M.A, 57. Instr. ENG, Univ. Ky, 58-61; Wis. State Col. La Crosse, 61-62; lectr, Ind. Univ. Northwest, 62-71; RES. & WRITING, 71- U.S.A, 52-54. MLA; NCTE; Col. Conf. Commun. & Compos; Midwest Mod. Lang. Asn. American prose fiction; literary realism and naturalism; rhetoric. Publ: Literature and class ideology: Henry IV, part one, Col. Eng, 5/72; Ike McCaslin and the Grecian urn, Stud. Short Fiction, 1/73; Towards a definition of literary realism, Centrum: Working Papers Minn. Ctr. Advan. Stud. Lang, Style & Lit. Theory, spring 73; plus others. Add: 5704 S. Kenwood Ave, Chicago, IL 60637.

STONEBURNER, CHARLES JOSEPH (TONY), b. Brooklyn, N.Y. Dec. 14, 26; m. 62; c. 2. ENGLISH, RELIGION. A.B, DePauw Univ, 46; B.D, Drew Univ, 50; Drew Univ. Tipple fel, Yale, 53-54; M.A, Univ. Mich, 62, Ph.D, 66. Minister, Northeast Ohio Conf, Methodist Church, 50-56; dir. relig. life & instr. Eng, Kans. Wesleyan Univ, 56-59; asst. dir, Wesley Found, Univ. Mich, 62-63; asst. prof. ENG. LIT. & COMPOS, DENISON UNIV, 66-69, ASSOC. PROF, 69- Assoc. ed, East-West Rev, 64-71; mem. bd. dir, Church Soc. Col. Work, 67-; ed, Good Work, 68-69; examr, N.Cent. Asn. Cols. & Sec. Schs, 71- Fel. Soc. Arts, Relig. & Contemporary Cult; Church Soc. Col. Work. The sermon as literature, particularly the 17th century Angelican sermon; frontier Methodism in Ohio and elsewhere; David Jones and other 20th century poets. Publ: Co-auth, The recognition of Austin Warren, Ann Arbor, 66; ed, Parable, myth & language, Church Soc. Col. Work, 68; auth, Denise Levertov, Angelican Theol. Rev, 7/68; Listen to the wind: an introduction to Gary Snyder, Nat. Stud. Mag, 5/72; Images of the life of man in a sample of poems, In: Humanities, religion, and the arts tomorrow, Holt, 72. Add: 203 N. Plum St, Granville, OH 43023.

STONESIFER, RICHARD JAMES, b. Lancaster, Pa, June 21, 22; m. 47; c. 1. ENGLISH. A.B, Franklin & Marshall Col, 46; M.A, Northwest. Univ, 47; Ph.D, Univ. Pa, 53. Mem. fac, Franklin & Marshall Col, 47-63; assoc. prof. commun. & asst. to provost, Annenberg Sch. of Commun, Univ. Pa. 63-; prof. eng. & dean col. lib. arts, Drew Univ, 65-71; PRES, MONMOUTH COL.(N.J), 71- Moderator & producer, WGAL-TV New Books of Significance, Col. of the Air, 54-61. U.S.A.A.F, 43-46. Contemporary British and American literature; Georgian poetry; Faulkner. Publ: W.H. Davies: a critical biography, Jonathan Cape, London, 63; co-auth, TV as art, NCTE, 66. Add: 95 Buttonwood Dr, Fair Haven, NJ 07701.

STOPPE, RICHARD LEON, b. Reading, Pa, Apr. 18, 37; m. 56; c. 3. SPEECH, PHILOSOPHY OF RELIGION. A.B, Upsala Col, 57; M.A, Wheaton Col, 63; Ph.D.(speech), Wayne State Univ, 66. Pastor, Church of God, 57-62; chmn. dept. speech, Oral Roberts Univ, 65-68; ASSOC. PROF. SPEECH & DIR. GRAD. STUD. PUB. ADDRESS, SOUTH. ILL. UNIV, EDWARDSVILLE, 68- Consult, develop. dept. speech, theatre & telecommunications, Oral Roberts Univ, 64-65; consult, mgt. & programming, radio station KORU-FM stereo, 67-68. Speech Commun. Asn; Cent. States Speech Commun. Asn; South. States Speech Commun. Asn; Nat. Asn. Broadcasters. History of American public address; speech psychology; philosophy of religion. Publ: Communicating the gospel; The age of communications; Communicative climate. Add: Dept. of Speech-Theater, Southern Illinois University, Edwardsville, IL 62025.

STOREY, GEORGE GILBERT, b. Scottdale, Pa, June 15, 16; m. 42; c. 3. ENGLISH PHILOLOGY. A.B, Geneva Col, 36; A.M, Duke Univ, 37; A.M, Harvard, 40, Ph.D, 49. Instr. ENG, Geneva Col, 38-40, asst. prof, 41-44, 46-48; Butler Univ, 48-55, assoc. prof, 55-58; URSINUS COL, 58-67, PROF, 67-, CHMN. DEPT, 71- U.S.N, 44-46, 51-52, Lt. MLA; NCTE; AAUP; Col. Eng. Asn. Life and works of Robert Buchanan. Add: Dept. of English, Ursinus College, Collegeville, PA 19426.

STORRER, WILLIAM ALLIN, b. Highland Park, Mich, Mar. 22, 36; m. 64, 69; c. 1. COMMUNICATIONS, COMPARATIVE ARTS. A.B, Harvard, 59; M.F.A, Boston Univ, 63; Ph.D.(comp. arts), Ohio Univ, 68. Electronics engineer, Raytheon Co, Mass, 58-60; tech. dir. small stage, Boston Arts Festival, 61 & 62; dir. dramatics, Melrose High Sch, Mass, 62-63; instr. drama & speech & dir. playhouse & repertory theatre, Hofstra Univ, 63-66; asst. prof. theatre & dir. univ. theatre, Univ. Toledo, 68-69; asst. prof. theatre & speech & chmn. dept, Southampton Col, Long Island Univ, 69-70; assoc. prof. theatre & film & chmn. dept, 70-73; ASST. PROF. COMMUN, ITHACA COL, 73- Dir. musical, operetta, opera & several plays, 61-; lectr, Exten. Prog, Hofstra Univ, 65; vis. assoc. prof, World Campus Afloat, 72; stage dir. & vis. assoc. prof, Tex. Tech Univ, 71; Soc. Integrated Arts (pres, 72-); Am. Theatre Asn; Soc. Archit. Hist; Univ. Film Asn; Speech Commun. Asn; Col. Art. Asn. Am. Origins and development of world theatrical forms; architectural history; inter-relations of the arts. Publ: The architecture of Frank Lloyd Wright: a complete catalog, MIT, 74; arts, in Opera & Opera News, 60-66, Jewish Advocate, 62-73 & Good Times Gazette, 73- Add: Div. of Communications, Ithaca College, Ithaca, NY 14850.

STORY, GEORGE MORLEY, b. Nfld, Oct. 13, 27. ENGLISH. B.A, McGill Univ, 50; Rhodes scholar, Oxford, 51-53, D.Phil.(Eng), 54. Asst. prof. ENG, MEM. UNIV. NFLD, 54-58, assoc. prof, 59-62, PROF, 63- Can. Ling. Asn; Class. Asn. Can; Bibliog. Soc, Eng; Am. Dialect Soc. Mediaeval and Renaissance literature; textual criticism and bibliography; philology and dialect lexicography. Publ: Co-auth, The sonnets of William Alabaster, 59 & auth, Sermons of Lancelot Andrewes, 67, Oxford; co-auth, The study of English, St. Martins, 62 & The Avalon Peninsula of Newfoundland, Nat. Mus. Can, 68; co-ed, Christmas mumming in Newfoundland, Univ. Toronto, 69. Add: Dept. of English, Memorial University of Newfoundland, St. John's, Nfld, Can.

STORY, PATRICK LEE, b. St. Louis, Mo, May 9, 40; m. 61; c. 2. ENGLISH & AMERICAN LITERATURE. B.A, Univ. Mo-Columbia, 62; M.A, Northwest. Univ, 63, Ph.D.(Eng), 68. Instr. ENG, Univ. Mo-St. Louis, summer 65; acting asst. prof, UNIV. CALIF, LOS ANGELES, 66-68, ASST. PROF, 68-, fac. fel, summer 69. MLA. British romanticism; literary criticism; modern poetry. Publ: Byron's death and Hazlitt's Spirit of the age, Eng. Lang. Notes, 9/69; A contemporary commentary on Hazlitt's Spirit of the age, Wordsworth Circle, spring 70; Pope, pageantry, and Shelley's Triumph of life, Keats-Shelley J, 72/73. Add: Dept. of English, University of California, Los Angeles, Los Angeles, CA 90024.

STOTT, WILLIAM MERRELL, b. New York, N.Y, June 2, 40; m. 62; c. 2. AMERICAN STUDIES, ENGLISH. A.B, Yale, 62, Carnegie fel, 62-63, NDEA fel, 68-71, M.Ph, 70, Ph.D.(Am. stud), 72; Woodrow Wilson fel, Stanford Univ, 63-64. For. serv. off, U.S. Inform. Agency, 64-68; ASST. PROF. AM. STUD. & ENG, UNIV. TEX, AUSTIN, 71- Am. Stud. Asn. Literature; mass culture; American cultural history. Publ: Documentary expression and thirties America, Oxford Univ, 73. Add: 1213 Red Bud Trail, Austin, TX 78746.

STOUT, DOUGLAS A, b. Raymond, Calif, Sept. 24, 23; m; c. 2. ENGLISH. B.A, Fresno State Col, 49; M.A, San Francisco State Col, 55, Ed.D, Univ. Calif, Berkeley, 64. Teacher, Edison High Sch, 50-52; pub. sch, Calif, 52-55; instr. ENG, SAN FRANCISCO STATE UNIV, 55-59, asst. prof, 59-64, assoc. prof, 64-70, PROF, 70- Fulbright lectr, Thailand, 61-62; Sabbatical leave, Japan, 66-67, leave of absence, 67-68. U.S.N, 43-45. NCTE. Writing. Publ: Profiles of American college students, Seibido, 69; Voices and views of Americans in conflict, 70; American Folktales and legends, 71; Spoken English today, Japan, 74. Add: Dept. of English, San Francisco State University, San Francisco, CA 94132.

STOUT, GARDNER DOMINICK, JR, b. New York, N.Y, June 30, 31; m. 55; c. 3. ENGLISH. A.B, Princeton, 54; Yale, 54-55; M.A, Stanford Univ, 58, Ph.D, 62. Acting instr. ENG. LIT, UNIV. CALIF, BERKELEY, 60-61, acting asst. prof, 61-62, asst. prof, 62-67, ASSOC. PROF, 67- U.S.A, 55-57, Res, 57-61. MLA. English literature of the 18th century. Publ: Ed, Laurence Sterne: a sentimental journey through France and Italy, Univ. Calif, 67; auth, Yorick's Sentimental journey: a comic Pilgrim's progress for the man of feeling, ELH, 63; Some borrowings in Sterne from Rabelais and Cervantes, 65 & Sterne's borrowings from Bishop Joseph Hall's Quo vadis? 65, Eng. Lang. Notes. Add: Dept. of English, University of California, Berkeley, CA 94720.

STOVALL, FLOYD, b. Temple, Tex, July 7, 96. LITERATURE. A.B, Univ. Tex, 23, A.M, 24, Ph.D, 27. Tutor Eng, Univ. Tex, 23-24, instr, 24-25, asst. prof, 27-35, chmn. dept, 33-35; prof. & dir, N.Tex. State Univ, 35-49, dean col. arts & sci, 46-49; prof. Eng, Univ. N.C, 49-55; Poe prof, Univ. Va, 55-67, chmn. dept, 56-61; RETIRED. MLA; NCTE. English romantic literature; American literature; Shelley, Whitman and Poe. Publ: Desire and restraint in Shelley, Duke Univ, 31; American idealism, Univ. Okla, 43, ed, Whitman's prose works (2 vols), N.Y. Univ, 63; The poems of Edgar Allan Poe, 65, Edgar Poe the poet, 69 & The foreground of Leaves of grass, 74, Univ. Va. Add: 1631 Bruce Ave, Charlottesville, VA 22903.

STRANAHAN, BRAINERD PAYNE, b. Middletown, Conn, Nov. 27, 32; m. 62; c. 2. ENGLISH. B.A, Williams Col, 55; M.A, Univ. Mich, 56; Union Theol. Sem, summer 56; Ph.D.(Eng), Harvard, 65. Asst. prof. ENG, Case West. Reserve Univ, 65-68; HIRAM COL, 68-73, ASSOC. PROF, 73- U.S.N.R, 56-60, Res, 60-68, Lt. Comdr. MLA. Seventeenth and 18th century English. Add: Dept. of English, Hiram College, Box 404, Hiram, OH 44234.

STRANDBERG, VICTOR HUGO, b. Deerfield, N.H, May 16, 35; m. 61; c. 2. ENGLISH. A.B, Clark Univ, 57; M.A, Brown Univ, 59, Ph.D.(Eng. & Am. lit), 62. Instr. ENG, Univ. Vt, 62-63, asst. prof, 63-66; DUKE UNIV, 66-69, ASSOC. PROF, 69- Fulbright prof. & lectr. Am. lit, Univ. Uppsala, 73. MLA; S.Atlantic Mod. Lang. Asn. Modern American literature; Robert Penn Warren. Publ: A colder fire: the poetry of Robert Penn Warren, Univ. Ky, 65; Theme and metaphor in Brother to dragons, PMLA, 9/64; Faulkner's inversion, Sewanee Rev, spring 65; Poe's hollow men, Univ. Rev, spring 69. Add: Dept. of English, Duke University, Durham, NC 27706.

STRANDNESS, THEODORE BENSON, b. St. Paul, Minn, Mar. 23, 15; m. 43; c. 3. AMERICAN LITERATURE. B.A, Jamestown Col, 37; M.A, Univ. Minn, 42; Ph.D, Mich. State Univ, 51. From assoc. prof. commun. skills to PROF. AM. THOUGHT & LANG, MICH. STATE UNIV, 55-, ED, UNIV. COL. QUART, 55-61, 67-, chmn. dept. Am. thought & lang, 62-67. U.S.N, 42-46. Col. Eng. Asn; MLA; NCTE; Conf. Col. Compos. & Commun. American studies; communication theory; English language arts. Publ: Co-auth, The experience of writing, Prentice-Hall, 58 & American identity, Heath, 62; auth, Samuel Sewall: a Puritan portrait, Mich. State Univ, 68; plus others. Add: Dept. of American Thought & Languages, Michigan State University, East Lansing, MI 48823.

STRATFORD, PHILIP C, b. Chatham, Ont, Oct. 13, 27; m. 52; c. 6. ENGLISH, COMPARATIVE LITERATURE. B.A, Univ. West. Ont, 50; Dr.Univ, Paris, 54. Lectr. ENG, Univ. Windsor, 54-56; asst. prof, Univ. West. Ont, 57-63, assoc. prof, 63-64; UNIV. MONTREAL, 64-67, PROF, 67-, CHMN. DEPT, 69- Nuffield Found. travel grant, 60; Brit. Counc. scholar, 61; Can. Counc. fel, 70-71. Univ. West. Ont. Pres. Medal, 64. Can. Comp. Lit. Asn. (pres, 73-); Humanities Asn. Can. Graham Greene; comparative Canadian literature; contemporary drama. Publ: Faith and fiction: creative process in Greene and Mauriac, Univ. Notre Dame, 64; Chalk and cheese: Greene and Mauriac, Univ. Toronto, 64; transl, Jean le Moyne, Convergence, 66 & Claire Martin, In an iron glove, 68, Ryerson; auth, Marie-Claire Blais, Forum House, 71; ed, The portable Graham Greene, Viking & Andre Laurendeau: witness for Quebec, Macmillan, Toronto, 73; auth, One meeting with Mauriac, fall 59 & Unlocking the potting shed, winter 61, Kenyon Rev. Add: Dept. of English, University of Montreal, Montreal, P.Q, Can.

STRATHMANN, ERNEST ALBERT, b. Baltimore, Md, Jan. 24, 06; m. 34; c. 2. ENGLISH LITERATURE. A.B, Johns Hopkins Univ, 26, A.M, 28, Ph.D.(Eng. lit), 30; hon. D.Litt, Pomona Col, 70. Jr. instr. ENG, Johns Hopkins Univ, 27-30, res. assoc, 30-32; asst. prof, POMONA COL, 32-39, assoc. prof, 39-44, prof, 44-71, chmn. dept, 41-43, 47-49 & 50-59, dean fac, 59-70, EMER. PROF. ENG, 71- Fel, Folger Shakespeare Libr, 39-40, summers 56, 63; Henry F. Huntington Libr, summer 44; Guggenheim fel, 46-47, 54-55; vis. prof, Univ. Rochester, 51-52; chmn, Am. Conf. Acad. Deans, 68-69; mem. comn. lib. learning, Asn. Am. Cols, 68-71. MLA; Renaissance Soc. Am. English Renaissance literature; Sir Walter Raleigh. Publ: Asst. ed, Variorum edition of Spenser's works, Johns Hopkins Univ, Vol. II, 32; auth, Sir Walter Raleigh: a study in Elizabethan skepticism, Columbia Univ, 51; co-auth, gen. introd. to William Shakespeare: the complete works, Penguin, 69. Add: 760 W. Tenth St, Claremont, CA 91711.

STRATTON, JOHN DAVID, b. Alhambra, Calif, Apr. 9, 44; m. 66; c. 1. ENGLISH, DRAMA. B.A, Calif. West. Univ, 66; M.A, Univ. Nebr, 68, Ph.D. (Eng), 71. Instr. ENG, Univ. Nebr, 69-70; ASST. PROF, UNIV. ARK, LITTLE ROCK, 70- AAUP. Experimental fiction. Add: 400 Springwood Dr, Little Rock, AR 72205.

STRAUCH, CARL FERDINAND, b. Lehighton, Pa, Sept. 25, 08; m. 37; c. 1. ENGLISH. A.B, Muhlenberg Col, 30, hon. D.H.L, 73; Univ. Pa, 31; A.M, Lehigh Univ, 34; fel, Yale, 38-39, Ph.D, 46. Instr. ENG, LEHIGH UNIV, 34-37, 39-41, asst. prof, 41-46, assoc. prof, 46-52, prof, 52-70, DISTINGUISHED PROF, 70- Lehigh Inst. res. grant-in-aid, 49-50; Am. Philos. Soc. grant-in-aid, 50-55. MLA; Emerson Soc; Am. Stud. Asn; Bibliog. Soc. Am. Romanticism; 20th century. Publ: Co-auth, American literary masters, Holt, 65; ed, S. Reed's Observations on the growth of the human mind, Scholars' Facsimiles, 69 & Style in the American Renaissance, Transcendental, 70; auth, Kings in the back row . . . a reading of The catcher in the rye, Wis. Stud. Contemporary Lit, 61; Hatred's swift repulsions: Emerson . . . and others, Stud. Romanticism, winter 68; Ishmael: time and personality in Moby Dick, Stud. Novel, 69; plus others. Add: Dept. of English, Lehigh University, Bethlehem, PA 18015.

STRAUSS, ALBRECHT BENNO, b. Berlin, Ger, May 17, 21; nat. ENGLISH. B.A, Oberlin Col, 42; fel, Tulane Univ, 46-48, M.A, 48; fel, Harvard, 52-55, Ph.D.(Eng), 56. Instr. ENG, Tulane Univ, 48-49; Brandeis Univ, 51-52; Yale, 55-59; asst. prof, Univ. Okla, 59-60; UNIV. N.C, CHAPEL HILL, 60-64, assoc. prof, 64-70, PROF, 70-, dir. grad. stud, 67-68. Mem. adv. bd, Fla. Sterne Ed, 69-; ed. comt, Yale Ed. of Works of Samuel Johnson, 72-; ed. bd, Stud. Philol, 73-74, ed, 74- U.S.A, 42-46. MLA; S.Atlantic Mod. Lang. Asn; AAUP; Am. Soc. 18th Century Stud; Col. Eng. Asn. Eighteenth century English literature; English novel; stylistics. Publ: Co-ed, Essays in English literature of the classical period presented to Dougald MacMillan, Univ. N.C, 67 & The Rambler, Vols. III, IV & V In: The Yale edition of the works of Samuel Johnson, Yale Univ, 69; auth, On Smollett's Language, In: English Institute essays, 1958, Columbia Univ, 59; Poetic theory of Cleanth Brooks, Centenary Rev; The dull duty of an editor: on editing the text of Johnson's Rambler, Bookmark, 6/65. Add: 2 Dogwood Acres, Chapel Hill, NC 27514.

STRAUSS, MARY THERESE, b. Pittsburgh, Pa. AMERICAN LITERATURE. B.A, Carlow Col, 57; M.A, Univ. Pittsburgh, 61, fel, 66-70, Ph.D.(Eng), 70. Dir, Alumnae Asn, Carlow Col, 59-62; instr. ENG, Long Beach City Col, 62-63; Kent State Univ, 63-66; ASST. PROF, ROBERT MORRIS COL, 70- MLA; Col. Eng. Asn; AAUP. William Faulkner; 19th century American literature; James Joyce. Add: 612 Broadhead Rd, Pittsburgh, PA 15205.

STRAWN, ROBERTSON IRVING, b. Columbus, Kans, Mar. 30, 09; m. 31; c. 5. SPEECH, ENGLISH. A.B, Kans. State Teachers Col, Pittsburg, 31; M.A, Univ. Kans, 34; Ph.D, Univ. Mich, 41. Teacher Eng. & speech, pub. schs, Kans. & Okla, 32-39; chmn. dept. fine arts, Nebr. State Teachers Col, Kearney, 41-46; from prof. lang. & lit. & chmn. dept. to PROF. SPEECH & DRAMATIC ART, KANS. STATE COL. PITTSBURG, 46- Ed-in-chief, Kans. Speech J, 70- U.S.N, 45-46, Lt. Speech Commun. Asn; Am. Dialect Soc. Teaching of phonetics; discussion. Add: Dept. of Speech, Kansas State College of Pittsburg, Pittsburg, KS 66764.

STREETER, DONALD CLINT, b. Huron, S.Dak, Apr. 24, 11; m. 41; c. 2. SPEECH. B.S, Univ. Minn, 33; M.A, State Univ. Iowa, 38, Ph.D, 48. Instr. SPEECH, State Univ. Iowa, 38-41, 46-48; Southwest Tex. State Col, 41-42, 45-46; assoc. prof. & chmn. dept, Memphis State Univ, 48-57; PROF, UNIV. HOUSTON, 57-, chmn. dept, 57-69. Consult, Nat. Inst. Banking, 53-56; Tex. East. Gas Transmission, 58-59; U.S. Chamber Commerce, 58-60; Houston Counc. Engrs, 60-62; U.S. Steel, 61; Esso Prod. Res, 64-66; Ranger Ins, 66. Speech Commun. Asn. Rhetoric; theatre history. Publ: Co-auth, Speech handbook, 59, auth, Speech handbook for teachers, 64 & Speech communication handbook, 72, Prentice-Hall; co-auth, History & criticism of American public address, Vol. III, McGraw, 60; auth, Phonetics, physiology, voice & pronunciation, workbook, privately publ, 68; Major public addresses of L.Q.C. Lamar, Speech Monogr, 50. Add: Dept. of Speech, University of Houston, Houston, TX 77004.

STREETER, ROBERT EUGENE, b. Williamsport, Pa, Dec. 7, 16; m. 41; c. 2. ENGLISH. A.B, Bucknell Univ, 38, hon. L.H.D, 60; M.A, Northwest. Univ, 40, Ph.D.(Eng), 43. Instr. ENG, Bucknell Univ, 42-46, asst. prof, 46-47; UNIV. CHICAGO, 47-53, assoc. prof, 53-58, PROF, 58-, dean col, 54-59, dean div. humanities, 63-73. Prof. & Am. adv. to chmn. dept. Eng, Seoul Nat. Univ, 46-47. MLA; Am. Stud. Asn. Seventeenth and 18th century American literature; the novel; rhetorical theory. Add: Dept. of English, University of Chicago, Chicago, IL 60637.

STRICKLAND, RUTH G, b. Duluth, Minn, Oct. 1, 98. ENGLISH EDUCATION. M.A, Columbia Univ, 35, Ph.D, 38. Teacher, Pub. Sch, Minn, 18-23; critic teacher, Winona State Col, 23-24; N.Y. State Teachers Col, Geneseo, 25-27; Wash. State Teachers Col, Bellingham, 27-31; instr. elem. educ, Temple Univ, 32-37; dir, Kans. State Teachers Col, Emporia, 37-39; prof, Eng. educ, IND. UNIV, BLOOMINGTON, 39-63, res. prof, 63-72, EMER. RES. PROF. EDUC, 72- Consult, Japanese Ministry Educ, 48; pub. schs. of five counties, Calif, 56-63; curriculum consult, Pub. Schs, Columbus, Ind, 57-58; U.S. Off. Educ, Proj. Eng. grants, 59-63. NCTE (2nd v.pres, 53, 1st v.pres, 59, pres, 60); Conf. Res. Eng.(pres, 54); Int. Asn. Childhood Educ. Study of the structure of children's language; research in linguistics as applied to elementary English. Publ: Language arts in the elementary school (3rd ed), Heath, 69; Language in the schools, In: The learning of language, Appleton, 71; On teaching oral language in elementary schools, In: On teaching speech in elementary and junior high schools, Ind. Univ, 71; plus one other. Add: School of Education, Indiana University, Bloomington, IN 47401.

STRIDER, ROBERT EDWARD LEE, II, b. Wheeling, W.Va, Apr. 8, 17; m. 41; c. 4. ENGLISH. A.B, Harvard, 39, A.M, 40, Ph.D, 50; hon. LL.D, Concord Col, 61, Bowdoin Col, 67; hon. L.H.D, Univ. Maine, 62, Bates Col, 68; hon. HH.D, Nasson Col, 62; hon. D.S.B.A, Bryant Col, 67; D.Ed, Suffolk Univ, 68. Instr. ENG, Conn. Col, 46-51, asst. prof, 51-57; PROF, COLBY COL, 57-, PRES. COL, 60-, dean fac, 57-60. U.S.N.R, 42-46, Lt. MLA; Asn. Am. Cols.(chmn, 73-74). Seventeenth century English literature. Publ: Robert Greville, Lord Brooke. Add: Office of the President, Colby College, Waterville, ME 04901.

STROHM, PAUL HOLZWORTH, JR, b. Chicago, Ill, July 30, 38; m. 60; c. 2. ENGLISH. B.A, Amherst Col, 60; M.A, Univ. Calif, Berkeley, 62. Ph.D, 65. Asst. prof. ENG, IND. UNIV, BLOOMINGTON, 65-68, assoc. prof, 68-73, PROF, 73- Mediaeval Acad. Am; MLA; AAUP. Middle English literature; medieval literary genres. Publ: The allegory of The tale of Melibee, Chaucer Rev, 67; The Malmesbury medallions and twelfth century typology, Mediaeval Stud, 71; Generic distinctions in the Middle English Troy narratives, Speculum, 71; plus others. Add: Dept. of English, Indiana University, Bloomington, IN 47401.

STRONG, LEAH AUDREY, b. Buffalo, N.Y, Mar. 14, 22. AMERICAN STUDIES, UNITED STATES LITERATURE. A.B, Allegheny Col, 43; A.M, Cornell Univ, 44; Ph.D.(Eng), Syracuse Univ, 53. Instr. Eng, Syracuse Univ, 47-52; asst. prof, Cedar Crest Col, 53-61; PROF. U.S. LIT, WESLEYAN COL.(GA), 61- Southeast. Am. Stud. Asn; Am. Stud. Asn; MLA; S.Atlantic Mod. Lang. Asn. Mark Twain; American novel, 1870-1920; American folklore. Publ: Joseph Hopkins Twichell: Mark Twain's friend and pastor, Univ. Ga, 66; Mark Twain and frontier folklore, Pac. Northwest Quart, 7/67; The daughter of the Confederacy, Miss. Quart, fall 67; American folklore for the undergraduate, N.C. Folklore, 11/71. Add: Dept. of American Studies, Wesleyan College, Macon, GA 31201.

STROTHER, DAVID B, b. New Albany, Ind, June 17, 28; m. 50; c. 4. SPEECH. A.B, Georgetown Col, 50; M.A, Northwest. Univ, 51; Sara H. Moss fel, Univ. Ga, 55, 56; Ph.D, Univ. Ill, 58. Asst. prof. SPEECH, Univ. Ga, 51-58; Univ. Wash, 58-67; assoc. prof, WASH. STATE UNIV, 67-72, PROF, 72- Univ. Wash. Grad. Sch. res. grant, summer 62; prin. investr, U.S. Off. Educ. grant, 71; assoc. ed, Quart. J. Speech, 72-74. Speech Commun. Asn; West. Speech Asn. Persuasion in the court of law; British public address; Renaissance rhetoric. Publ: Modern British eloquence, Funk, 69; contrib, Quart. J. Speech; Speech Teacher; South. Speech J. Add: Dept. of Speech, Washington State University, Pullman, WA 99163.

STROTHER, EDWARD SPENCER, b. New Albany, Ind, Oct. 20, 21; m. 42; c. 3. SPEECH, THEATER. A.B, Ind. Univ, 43; M.A, Northwest Univ, 46, Ph.D. (speech), 51. Instr. SPEECH, BALL STATE UNIV, 46-49, asst. prof, 51-55, assoc. prof, 55-59, PROF, 59-, ADMIN. ASST. TO HEAD DEPT, 73- U.S.M.C, 43-46, 1st Lt. Speech Commun. Asn; Am. Theatre Asn. Public address. Publ: Co-auth, Speech education for the elementary teacher, Allyn & Bacon, 66 & The effective speaker, Houghton, 68. Add: Dept. of Speech, Ball State University, Muncie, IN 47306.

STROUD, THEODORE ALBERT, b. Marcella, Ark, Jan. 25, 14; m. 39. ENGLISH. A.B, Ark. Col, 32; A.M, Univ. Ark, 37; fel, Univ. Chicago, 39-40, Ph.D, 47. Instr, Univ. Ark, 37-38; Univ. Chicago, 43-46; asst. prof, Univ. Fla, 46-47; assoc. prof. ENG, DRAKE UNIV, 47-51, PROF, 51-, interim chmn. dept, 72-73. Ford fel, 54-55. MLA. Middle English; the Fi manuscript of Chaucer's Canterbury tales. Publ: Co-ed, The literature of comedy, Ginn, 68. Add: Dept. of English, Drake University, Des Moines, IA 50311.

STROUP, THOMAS BRADLEY, b. Fletcher, N.C, Dec. 21, 03; m. 28; c. 1. ENGLISH LITERATURE. A.B, Univ. N.C, 26, A.M, 27, Ph.D, 33. Asst. ENG, Univ. N.C, 26-27, instr, 29-33; Ga. Inst. Tech, 27-28; asst. prof, Wofford Col, 28-29; instr, Univ. Fla, 33-35, assoc. prof, 38-44, prof, 44-48; Ga. Teachers Col, 35-38; UNIV. KY, 48-73, distinguished prof, Col. Arts & Sci, 61-62, EMER. PROF, 73- Spec. lectr, Damascus Univ, 55-56; Folger Shakespeare Libr. fels, summers 50, 57 & 67. U.S.N.R, 43-45, Lt. MLA; S.Atlantic Mod. Lang. Asn.(pres, 53); Shakespeare Asn. Am; Milton Soc; Int. Asn. Univ. Prof. Eng. Publ: Co-ed, The works of Nathaniel Lee, Scarecrow, Vols. I & II, 54 & 55; ed, Selected poems of George Daniel, 59, auth, Microscosmos: the shape of the Elizabethan play, 65 & Religious rite and ceremony in Milton's poetry, 68, Univ. Ky, ed, The cestus: a mask, Univ. Fla, 61; The structure of Anthony and Cleopatra, Shakespeare 400, 64; Doctor Faustus and Hamlet: contrasting kinds of Christian tragedy, Comp. Drama, 71; When I consider: Milton's sonnet XIX, Stud. Philol, 72; plus others. Add: 417 Kingsway Dr, Lexington, KY 40502.

STROUT, ALAN LANG, b. Cohoes, N.Y, Mar. 3, 95. ENGLISH. A.B, Dartmouth Col, 18; A.M, Univ. Chicago, 20; Univ. Wis, 25; Ph.D, Yale, 28. Instr. ENG, Dartmouth Col, 18-19; Univ. Mo, 19-20; Univ. Wis, 21-25; prof, Acadia Col, 26-27; TEX. TECH UNIV, 28-61, EMER. PROF, 61-; PROF, EAST. MONT. COL, 68- Am. Counc. Learned Soc. grant, 32; Am. Philos. Soc. grant, 50. The age of Wordsworth, especially the Blackwood group; John Wilson; James Hogg. Publ: Ed, John Bull's letter to Lord Byron: auth, A bibliography of articles in Blackwood's Magazine, 1817-1826, Libr, Tex. Technol. Col, 59. Add: 2512 21st St, Lubbock, TX 79410.

STROVEN, CARL GERHARDT, b. East Highlands, Calif, Apr. 12, 01; m. 24; c. 1. AMERICAN LITERATURE. A.B, Stanford Univ, 26, A.M, 28; Ph.D, Duke Univ, 39. Instr. ENG, Univ. Hawaii, 27-37; Duke Univ, 38-39; asst. prof, UNIV. HAWAII, MANOA, 39-43, assoc. prof, 43-46, prof, 46-66, EMER. PROF, 66- Pacific voyages; literature of the Pacific Islands; literature of Hawaii. Publ: Co-ed, The spell of the Pacific: an anthology of its literature, Macmillan, 49; A Hawaiian reader, 59, Best South sea stories, 64 & True tales of the South seas, 66, Appleton; The spell of Hawaii, Meredith, 68. Add: 2240 Cummings Dr, Santa Rosa, CA 95404.

STROZIER, ROBERT MANNING, II, b. Rock Hill, S.C, Dec. 30, 34; m. 66; c. 2. RENAISSANCE LITERATURE. B.M.E, Ga. Inst. Technol, 58; Woodrow Wilson fel, Univ. Chicago, 59-60, M.A, 61, Ph.D.(Eng. lit), 70. Instr. ENG, WAYNE STATE UNIV, 67-69, ASST. PROF, 69- Asst. to ed, Mod. Philol, Univ. Chicago, 62-63. U.S.M.C, 58-59. Renaissance Soc. Am. Renaissance intellectual history; Renaissance criticism. Publ: Poetic conception in Sir Philip Sidney's An apology for poetry, Yearbk. Eng. Stud, 3/72; Roger Ascham and Cleanth Brooks: Renaissance and modern critical thought, Essays in Criticism, 10/72; Theory and structure in Roger Ascham's The schoolmaster, Neuphilol. Mitt, 3/73. Add: Dept. of English, Wayne State University, Detroit, MI 48202.

STRUBLE, GEORGE GOODELL, b. Inwood, Iowa, Jan. 26, 00. LITERATURE. B.S, Univ. Kans, 22, M.S, 25; Univ. Chicago, 27; Ph.D, Univ. Wis, 31; Cornell Univ, 37; Laval Univ, 49. Teacher & prin, High Schs, P.I, 23-25; asst. prof. Eng, Baker Univ, 25-26; instr, Univ. N.Dak, 26-28; fel. & asst, Univ. Wis, 28-31; assoc. prof. ENG, LEBANON VALLEY COL, 31-48, PROF, 48-, dir. div. humanities, 51-60. Spec. lectr, Temple Univ, 55- American English; 17th century literature; English of the Pennsylvania Germans. Add: Dept. of English, Lebanon Valley College, Annville, PA 17003.

STRYKER, DAVID, b. Deerfield, Ill, July 24, 16; m. 40; c. 3. ENGLISH. A.B, Lake Forest Col, 38; A.M, Northwest. Univ, 39, Ph.D, 47. Teacher high sch, Ill, 39-45; instr. ENG, Northwest. Univ, 45-47; asst. prof, UNIV. FLA, 47-56, assoc. prof, 56-64, PROF, 64-, ASST. DEAN COL. ARTS & SCI, 73- Fulbright lectr. Am. lit, Chulalongkorn Univ, Bangkok, 67-68 & Univ. Algiers, 71-72. MLA; NCTE; S.Atlantic Mod. Lang. Asn. Victorian literature; Anthony Trollope in the United States; contemporary literature. Publ: Ed, Educating the teacher of English, 65, New trends in English education, 66 & Method in the teaching of English, 67, NCTE, co-ed, Approaches to literature, Singer/Random, 69. Add: Dept. of English, University of Florida, Gainesville, FL 32611.

STUART, DABNEY, b. Richmond, Va, Nov. 4, 37; m. 65; c. 2. MODERN FICTION, POETRY. A.B, Davidson Col, 60; A.M. & Woodrow Wilson scholar, Harvard, 62. Instr. ENG, Col. William & Mary, 61-65; WASHINGTON & LEE UNIV, 65-66, asst. prof, 66-68, ASSOC. PROF, 69- Poetry ed, Shenandoah, 66-; vis. asst. prof. Eng, Middlebury Col, 68-69; poet-in-schs, Richmond Intercult Ctr. for Humanities, Va, 71-72; Albemarle County Dept. Educ, Va, 72-73. Auth. Guild; AAUP. Fiction of Vladimir Nabokov; modern poetry. Publ: The diving bell, 66 & A particular place, 69, Knopf; The other hand, La. State Univ, 74; Angles of perception, Mod. Lang. Quart, 9/68; All the mind's a stage, Univ. Windsor Rev, spring 69; Laughter in the dark: the dimensions of parody, Tri-Quarterly, winter 70. Add: Dept. of English, Washington & Lee University, Lexington, VA 24450.

STUART, GABY E, b. Singapore, Malaya, Feb. 10, 26; nat; m. 65; BRITISH LITERATURE, CRITICISM. Ph.D.(Eng), Univ. Calif, Berkeley, 56. Assoc, Univ. Calif, Berkeley, 52-54; asst. prof. ENG, Univ. Calif, Los Angeles, 54-56; Univ. Calif, Berkeley, 56-57; lectr, Ohio State Univ, Columbus, 57-58; asst. prof, Calif. State Univ, San Francisco, 60-64; ASSOC. PROF, CALIF. STATE UNIV, LOS ANGELES, 64-, ASST. DEAN GRAD. STUD. LETT. & SCI, 70- Dutch E.Indies W.A.C, 44-46. Philol. Asn. Pac. Coast. Poetics; 17th century literary criticism. Publ: Sarah Scott's Agreeable ugliness: a translation, Mod. Lang. Notes, 70: 577-579; William Herbert, Third Earl of Pembroke, Poems (1660), Augustan Reprint Soc, 55. Add: Graduate Studies Office, School of Letters and Science, California State University, Los Angeles, CA 90032.

STUART, ROBERT LEE, b. Berkeley, Calif, Apr. 22, 37. AMERICAN LITERATURE. A.B, Stanford Univ, 59, A.M, 67, Ph.D.(Eng), 70; Th.M, Sch. Theol. Claremont, 62. ASST. PROF. ENG, UNIV. REDLANDS, 69- AAUP; MLA; Soc. Relig. Higher Educ. Colonial American literature; religion and literature; American studies. Publ: The writer-in-waiting, Christian Century, 4/65; Mr. Stoddard's Way: church and sacraments in Northampton, Am. Quart, 5/72. Add: Dept. of English, University of Redlands, Redlands, CA 92373.

STUBBLEFIELD, CHARLES, b. Dallas, Tex, Sept. 27, 22. ENGLISH. B.A. & M.A, E.Tex. State Univ, 49; M.A, Univ. Denver, 63, Ph.D.(Eng), 67. Instr. ENG, Univ. Denver, 65-67; asst. prof, UNIV. NEBR, LINCOLN, 67-71, ASSOC. PROF, 71- U.S.A.A.F, 42-45, 1st Lt. MLA; Col. Eng. Asn. Publ: The child that went forth, Eng. J, 2/65; Lula (short story), Prairie Schooner, winter 71-72; Some thoughts about King John, CEA Critic, 3/73. Add: Dept. of English, University of Nebraska, Lincoln, NE 68508.

STUBBS, DAVID C, b. Savannah, Ga, July 31, 07; m. 31; c. 1. ENGLISH. B.A, Emory Univ, 29, B.D, 35; S.T.M, Union Theol. Sem.(N.Y), 41; Ed.D.(relig. educ), Columbia Univ, 51; M.A, Fla. State Univ, 56, Ph.D.(Eng), 68. Prof. educ, Kwansei Gakuin Univ, Japan, 38-40 & 51-66; missions, Scarritt Col. Christian Workers, 46-50; part time instr. ENG, Fla. State Univ, 66-68; assoc. prof, VALDOSTA STATE COL, 68-73, PROF, 73- U.S. Merchant Marine, 45. MLA; AAUP. Indigenization in Christian missions; writings of Clive Staples Lewis. Publ: Co-transl, Saikaku Ihara's This scheming world, Charles Tuttle, 65. Add: Dept. of English, Valdosta State College, Valdosta, GA 31601.

STUBBS, JOHN C, b. Phila, Pa, Aug. 5, 36; m. 59; c. 1. ENGLISH. A.B, Yale, 58; Univ. Paris, 56-57; Ph.D.(Eng), Princeton, 63. Instr. ENG, Univ. Wis, 62-64; asst. prof, UNIV. ILL, URBANA-CHAMPAIGN, 64-69, ASSOC. PROF, 70- MLA; Am. Stud. Asn. Film as literature; literature and psychology. Publ: John Barth as novelist of ideas, 66 & The search for perfection in Rabbit, run, 68, Critique; The pursuit of form: a study of Hawthorne and the romance, Univ. Ill, 70; Hawthorne and the New England romance, PMLA, 68. Add: 1609 Chevy Chase Dr, Champaign, IL 61820.

STUCKEY, JOHANNA HEATHER, b. Gananoque, Ont, Sept. 5, 33. ENGLISH, COMPARATIVE LITERATURE. B.A, Univ. Toronto, 56, M.A, 60; Can. Fed. Univ. Women fel, Univ. London, 56-57, univ. fels, 58-60, Can. Counc. fel, 60-61; Ph.D.(Eng), Yale, 65. Lectr. Eng, Univ. Md, Europ. Div, 61-64; humanities, YORK UNIV, 64-65, asst. prof. HUMANITIES & ENG, 65-71, ASSOC. PROF, 71-, CHMN. DIV. HUMANITIES, 74- MLA; Asn. Can. Univ. Teachers Eng; Am. Philol. Asn; Humanities Asn. Can; Can. Counc. Teachers Eng. Restoration and 18th century English literature particularly Restoration drama; influence of Petronius on English and American literature; woman studies. Publ: Petronius in Restoration England, Class. News & Views, 1/71; Petronius the ancient: his reputation and influence in seventeenth century England, Rivista de Studi Classici, summer 72. Add: Dept. of English & Humanities, Founders College, York University, 4700 Keele St, Downsview, Ont. M3J 1P3, Can.

STUCKEY, WILLIAM JOSEPH, b. St. Louis, Mo, Jan. 15, 23; m. 57; c. 3. ENGLISH. A.B, Wash. Univ, 49, Henrietta Heerman fel, 56-57, Ph.D, 59; M.F.A, State Univ. Iowa, 52. Instr. ENG, Iowa State Col, 51-53; asst, Wash. Univ, 53-56, instr, 57-58; Hamline Univ, 58-59, asst. prof, 59-61; PURDUE UNIV, WEST LAFAYETTE, 61-67, from assoc. prof. to PROF, 67- U.S.A, 43-46, Sgt. MLA; NCTE. Modern literature; American literature; creative writing. Publ: Pulitzer prize novels, Univ. Okla, 66; Caroline Gordon, Twayne, 72; My Antonia: a rose for Miss Cather, Stud. Novel, 72; plus others. Add: Dept. of English, Purdue University, West Lafayette, IN 47906.

STUEBER, STEPHANIE, C.S.J, b. St. Louis, Mo, June 15, 15. ENGLISH. A.B, Fontbonne Col, 36; M.A, St. Louis Univ, 45, Ph.D.(Eng), 54. Acad. dean, FONTBONNE COL, 55-66, PROF. ENG, 66-, DIR. DIV. HUMANITIES & SCI, 73- English Renaissance prose; relationship between theology and literature. Publ: Diction in Hooker's polity, PMLA, 55. Add: Dept. of English, Fontbonne College, 6800 Wydown Blvd, St. Louis, MO 63105.

STUMP, HARLEY H, b. Perryton, Tex, Apr. 11, 15; m. 37; c. 2. ENGLISH, EDUCATION. A.B, Southwest. State Col.(Okla), 44; M.Ed, Univ. Okla, 52, Ph.D.(educ), 64; B.D, Bethany Theol. Sem, 54. Pastor, Church of the Brethren, Tex, 37-40; Okla, 40-52; Calif, 54-57; teacher ENG, Bethany Theol. Sem, 52-54; PROF. & HEAD DEPT, McPHERSON COL, 57- Lecturing prof, East. N.Mex. State Col, summer 64. Philosophy of education. Publ: The sacred church (poem), Church Mgt, 45; Phoenix (poem), Am. Asn. Poetry, 58. Add: Dept. of English, McPherson College, McPherson, KS 67460.

STUNZ, ARTHUR NESBITT, b. St. Joseph, Mo, Aug. 6, 04; m. 29. ENGLISH. A.B. & B.S, Univ. Mo, 26; A.M, Univ. Chicago, 28; Ph.D, State Univ. Iowa, 39. Teacher social sci, Hutchins Intermediate Sch, Detroit, Mich, 26-27; instr. ENG, Elmira Col, 28-29; State Univ. Iowa, 29-39; asst. prof, ASHLAND COL, 39-42, assoc. prof, 42-45, PROF, 45-, chmn. dept, 49-72, dir. div. humanities, 68-72. MLA; NCTE; Col. Eng. Asn. George Herbert; Macbeth; Johnny Appleseed. Publ: Letter reporting 1650 adjectival use of romantic, Times Lit. Suppl; The date of Macbeth, J. Eng. Lit. Hist; co-auth, John Chapman—Johnny Appleseed, 1774-1845, In: Yearbook Men's Garden Clubs of America. Add: Dept. of English, Ashland College, Ashland, OH 44805.

STUPPLE, ALEXANDER JAMES, b. Highland Park, Ill, Apr. 6, 38. AMERICAN LITERATURE. B.A, Northwest. Univ, 63, M.A, 66, Ph.D.(Eng), 71. Instr. ENG, East. Ill. Univ, 66-67; ASST. PROF, CALIF. STATE UNIV, FULLERTON, 70- Nineteenth and 20th century American literature; utopianism and science fiction; ontology. Publ: Co-ed, Science fiction for teachers, Col. Eng. Asn, 74; auth, Anti-utopian science fiction, In: Science fiction for teachers, Col. Eng. Asn, 74. Add: Dept. of English, California State University, Fullerton, CA 92634.

STURCKEN, JOHNYE CANNON, b. Kenedy, Tex, Dec. 7, 23. ENGLISH. B.B.A, Baylor Univ, 45; M.A, Univ. Tex, 56, Ph.D.(Eng), 63. Asst. prof. Eng, Cent. Mo. State Col, 63-66, assoc. prof, 66-68; E.TEX. STATE UNIV, 68-73, PROF. ENG. & DEAN COL. LIB. & FINE ARTS, 73-, dean grad. sch, 72-73. MLA; Renaissance Soc. Am. English Renaissance period. Add: College of Liberal & Fine Arts, East Texas State University, Commerce, TX 75428.

STURGES, CHRISTINE ANNE, b. Danbury, Conn, Jan. 29, 45. THEATRE. A.B, Col. William & Mary, 67; M.A, Northwest. Univ, 69, Ph.D.(theatre), 71. ASST. PROF. THEATRE ARTS, UNIV. NORTH. COLO, 71- Am. Theatre Asn; Children's Theatre Asn. Child drama research. Add: Dept. of Theatre, University of Northern Colorado, Greeley, CO 80639.

STURGES, IRENE M, b. Provo, Utah, Apr. 15, m. 44; c. 1. ENGLISH. A.B, Univ. Utah, 44, M.A, 52, Ph.D.(Eng), 60. Lectr. ENG, UNIV. UTAH, 56-64, asst. prof, 64-69, ASSOC. PROF, 69- MLA; NCTE (mem. comt. scholarly appraisals lit. works taught high sch, 67-). Victorian novel; English education; Henry James. Add: Dept. of English, 327 Orson Spencer Hall, University of Utah, Salt Lake City, UT 84112.

STURM, ALBERT, b. Schwanenstadt, Austria, Jan. 22, 37; m. 62; c. 1. THEATRE ARTS, GERMAN. Dr.Phil.(theatrical sci, Ger), Univ. Vienna, 64. Lectr. theatre arts, Horak-Konservatorium, 64-65; Ger. lang. & lit, Hotelfachschule Bad Hofgastein, 65-67; BALDWIN-WALLACE COL, 68-71, asst. prof. THEATRE ARTS, 71-73, ASSOC. PROF, 73- Promotion of Sci.

Award, Govt. of Upper Austria, 64. MLA; AAUP. European theatre history; B. Brecht. Publ: History of the Upper Austrian theatre in the 16th and 17th century, Austrian Acad. Sci, 64; contrib, The world of the stage as the stage of the world, Schroeder, 67. Add: Dept. of Speech & Theatre Arts, Art & Drama Center, Baldwin-Wallace College, Berea, OH 44017.

STURM, RALPH D, b. Maryville, Mo, Jan. 23, 27. ENGLISH LITERATURE. A.B, Immaculate Conception Col, 48; M.A, Univ. Ottawa, 54, Ph.D.(Eng), 64. Instr. Eng. lit, Immaculate Conception Sem.(Mo), 54-64; Webster Col, 64-65; asst. prof, Univ. Notre Dame, 65-67; Univ. Mass, Boston, 67-70; ASSOC. PROF. ENG, EDINBORO STATE COL, 70- Univ. Mass. res. grant, 68-69. MLA; NCTE. Critical theory; myth in literature; Wallace Stevens. Publ: D.H. Lawrence and Christianity, Cath. World, 11/68; Thomas Merton: poet, Am. Benedictine Rev, 3/71. Add: Dept. of English, Edinboro State College, Edinboro, PA 16412.

STYAN, JOHN LOUIS, b. London, Eng, July 6, 23; m. 45; c. 4. ENGLISH, DRAMA. M.A, Cambridge, 47. Asst. master grammar sch, Eng, 48-50; staff tutor lit. & drama, Dept. Adult Educ, Univ. Hull, 50-62, sr. staff tutor, 62-65; PROF. ENG, UNIV. MICH, ANN ARBOR, 65-, CHMN. DEPT, 73- Mem, Univs. Counc. Adult Educ. Broadcasting Subcomt, Gt. Brit, 62-65; adult educ. liaison comt, Brit. Broadcasting Corp, 62-65; adult educ. adv. comt, Independent TV Authority, 62-65; adv. bd, World Ctr. Shakespeare Stud, 72- Brit. Army, 42-46, Lt. MLA; Guild Drama Adjudicators, Gt. Brit; Brit. Drama League; Shakespeare Asn. Am. Contemporary drama; Shakespeare; dramatic theory. Publ: The elements of drama, 60, The dark comedy, 62, The dramatic experience, 65, Shakespeare's stagecraft, 67 & Chekhov in performance, 71, Cambridge Univ; ed, The challenge of the theatre, Dickenson, 72; auth, The actor at the foot of Shakespeare's platform, Shakespeare Surv, 12/59; Television drama, Stratford-upon-Avon Stud, 4/62; The play as a complex event, Genre, 1/68; plus others. Add: Dept. of English, University of Michigan, Ann Arbor, MI 48104.

STYZA, CLARENCE J, b. Merrill, Wis, Sept. 9, 08; m. 49; c. 1. GERMAN & RUSSIAN LITERATURE. B.Ed, Wis. State Univ, Stevens Point, 33, B.Ed, 34; M.A, Northwest. Univ, 37; Sorbonne, 44; Ph.D.(Eng), George Peabody Col, 49. Teacher, elem. & sec. schs, Wis, 28-30, 33-40; instr. ENG, Col. St. Teresa (Minn), 40-42; PROF, STATE UNIV. N.Y. COL. BROCKPORT, 48- Prof, Univ. Alaska, summer 63. U.S.A, 42-47, Capt. Publ: One act plays: Memories of 1918, 38, Washington the farmer, 39, One happy family, 40, Life with Willie, 40, It's a date, 42, Spring formal, 44, Loulabelle, 56 & Christmas in review, 58, Heuer; Air mail to G.K. Chesterton, America, 12/13/41; You can go home again, N.Y. State Alumni Bull, 1/64; The specialist, Phi Delta Kappan, 6/68. Add: Dept. of English, State University of New York College at Brockport, Brockport, NY 14420.

SUBERMAN, JACK, b. New York, N.Y, June 18, 20; m. 42; c. 1. ENGLISH. B.A, Univ. Fla, 46, M.A, 47; Ph.D, Univ. N.C, 54. Instr. Eng, Univ. N.C, 52-53; N.C. State Univ, 53-55, asst. prof, 55-57, assoc. prof, 57-61, prof, 61-67, dir. freshman Eng, 57-63, summer sessions, 59-67; PROF. ENG. & DEAN COL. HUMANITIES, FLA. ATLANTIC UNIV, 67- Deleg, South. Asn. Cols. & Schs, 62-67. U.S.A.A.F, 42-45, Capt. S.Atlantic Mod. Lang. Asn; South. Humanities Conf. Shakespearian literature; linguistics; rhetoric. Publ: Co-auth, Basic composition, 56 & 68 & Languages reader for writers, 66, Prentice-Hall. Add: College of Humanities, Florida Atlantic University, Boca Raton, FL 33432.

SUDERMAN, ELMER FRANCIS, b. Isabella, Okla, Sept. 19, 20; m. 46; c. 2. AMERICAN LITERATURE. A.B, Tabor Col, 44; M.A, Univ. Kans, 49, fel, 51-54, Ph.D.(Eng), 61. Prin. elem. sch, Kans, 44-46; asst. instr. ENG, Univ. Kans, 46-49, 58-59; instr, Bethel Col, 49-51; asst. prof. & acting head dept, Baker Univ, 55-58; asst. prof, Kans. State Teachers Col, 59-60; GUSTAVUS ADOLPHUS COL, 60-63, assoc. prof, 63-66, PROF, 66-, chmn. dept, 67-70. Summers, vis. prof, Tabor Col, 50, Bluffton Col, 62 & 66, vis. lectr, Univ. S.Dak, 63 & 65; vis. assoc. prof, Earlham Col, 64-65; Gustavus Adolphus Col. res. grant, 65-68; vis. prof, Univ. Kans, summer 68; Kans. State Teachers Col, summers 69-73; ed, Minn. Eng, 73- MLA; Am. Stud. Asn; NCTE; Mid-Continent Am. Stud. Asn; Midwest Mod. Lang. Asn. American fiction; religion in fiction. Publ: The social gospel novelists's criticism of American society, Mid-Continent Am. Stud. J, spring 66; The damnation of Theron Ware as a criticism of American religious thought, Huntington Libr. Quart, 11/69; Main Street today, S.Dak. Rev, winter 69-70; plus others. Add: Dept. of English, Gustavus Adolphus College, St. Peter, MN 56082.

SUDRANN, JEAN, b. Brooklyn, N.Y, June 24, 19. ENGLISH. B.A, Mt. Holyoke Col, 39; M.A, Columbia Univ, 40, Woolley fel, 49-50, Ph.D.(Eng), 50. Instr. ENG, Wheaton Col, 41-45; from instr. to assoc. prof, MT. HOLYOKE COL, 47-49, 50-64, PROF, 64-, chmn. dept, 63-65, 66-67, 71-72. Am. Asn. Univ. Women Nat. fel, 57-58; mem. selection comt, Region I, Woodrow Wilson Nat. Fels, 66-67. MLA. Theory of literary criticism; 19th century poetry; fiction of 19th and 20th centuries. Publ: The philosopher's property: Thackeray and the use of time, Victorian Stud, 6/67; Daniel Deronda and the landscape of exile, ELH, 9/70; Hearth and horizon: changing concepts of the domestic life of the heroine, Mass. Rev, spring 73; plus five others. Add: Dept. of English, Mt. Holyoke College, South Hadley, MA 01075.

SUGARMAN, ALFRED, b. Portland, Ore, Dec. 28, 18; m. 64; c. 1. SPEECH. B.A, Univ. Wash, 49, M.A, 51; Ph.D.(speech), State Univ. Iowa, 64. Asst. prof. SPEECH, Univ. Omaha, 53-56; instr, Univ. Wash, 57-63; asst. prof, PORTLAND STATE UNIV, 63-71, ASSOC. PROF, 71- Chmn, City-County Comn. Aging, Portland & Multnomah County, Ore, 72- U.S.N, 42-45. Speech Commun. Asn. History and criticism of public address; urban communication. Add: Dept. of Speech, Portland State University, Portland, OR 97207.

SUGG, RICHARD PETER, b. St. Louis, Mo. AMERICAN LITERATURE, FILM. B.A, Univ. Notre Dame, 63; M.A, Univ. Fla, 67, Ph.D.(Am. lit), 69. ASST. PROF. humanities, Univ. Fla, 69-70; ENG, Ark. State Univ, 71-73; UNIV. KY, 73- MLA; Am. Film Inst. Modern American literature; film. Publ: The bridge: a description of its life, Univ. Ala, 74; Appreciating poetry, Houghton, 75; The imagination's white buildings and Quaker Hill, Erasmus Rev, 71; Hemingway, money and The sun also rises, Fitzgerald/Hemingway Annual, 72; The triadic structure of Heart of darkness, Conradiana, 74; plus others. Add: Dept. of English, University of Kentucky, Lexington, KY 40506.

SUITS, CONRAD B, b. Detroit, Mich, Mar. 16, 22; m. 55; c. 2. ENGLISH LITERATURE. A.B, Wayne State Univ, 43; A.M, Johns Hopkins Univ, 47; Ph.D, Univ. Chicago, 61. Instr. Eng, Wilson Jr. Col, Ill, 57-59; head dept. lang. & arts, Asheville-Biltmore Col, 61-62; assoc. prof. ENG, Ill. State Univ, 62-70; PROF, CENT. WASH. STATE COL, 70- U.S.A, 43-46. Eighteenth century English literature; American literature. Publ: Ed, Stories for writing, Harper, 71; auth, Who wrote The history of Francis Wills?, Philol. Quart, 4/64; The role of the horses in A voyage to the Houyhnhnms, Univ. Toronto Quart, 1/65. Add: Dept. of English, Central Washington State College, Ellensburg, WA 98926.

SUKKARY, SHAWKY EL, b. Cairo, Egypt, July 8, 22; m. 66; c. 2. ENGLISH, ARABIC. B.A, Cairo Univ, 43, dipl. educ, 45, dipl. transl. & jour, 45; M.A, Univ. Manchester, 51, Ph.D.(Eng), 53. Assoc. prof. Eng, Univ. Khartoum, 57,68; contrib, B.B.C, London, Eng, 69-70; asst. prof. ENG, SACRAMENTO STATE UNIV, 70-71, ASSOC. PROF, 71- Assoc. prof. Eng, Cairo Univ, 54-62; vis. prof, Univ. Libya, summers 55-56; contrib, Radio & TV, Cairo, 58-68; consult, Ministry Educ, Cairo, 60-68; dir. transl, Supreme Counc. Islamic Affairs, 62-63; vis. prof, Hiram Col, 63-64; Sacramento State Col, 64-65; prof. transl. & Eng, Al-Azhar Univ, Cairo, 65-68; prof. drama, Cairo Inst. Dramatic Arts, 65-68; expert, Defense Lang. Inst, Monterey, Calif, 73- MLA; Philol. Asn. Pac. Coast; Mid.E. Asn; Am. Stud. Asn. Translation from and into Arabic, English and French; English and American literature; Arabic and Islamic culture and comparative literature. Publ: Plays of Shaw with introduction and notes, Dar Al-Nahda, Cairo, 57-63; co-auth, Political diplomatic English-Arabic dictionary, Auth. Publ, 59; auth, Dictionary of English-French-Arabic political terms, Anglo-Egyptian Bkshop, Cairo, 60; Studies on Islam (in English), Supreme Counc. Islamic Affairs, Cairo, 62-63; co-auth, Bertrand Russell's Autobiography, Dar-Al-Maaref Egypt, 71; auth, W. Morris's prose romances, Cairo Bull Eng. Stud, 59; plus many others. Add: Dept. of English, Sacramento State University, 6000 Jay St, Sacramento, CA 95819.

SULLENS, IDELLE, b. Prairie City, Ore, June 28, 21. ENGLISH, HUMANITIES. A.B, Stanford Univ, 43, Ph.D.(Eng), 59; M.A, Univ. Wash, 54. INSTR. ENG. & HUMANITIES, MONTEREY PENINSULA COL, 58-, chmn. dept, 68-69. U.S.N.R, 44-48, 50-54, Comdr.(Ret). Early Eng. Text Soc; MLA; NCTE. Medieval literature; the works of Robert Mannyng of Brunne, 1303-1338. Publ: Principles of grammar, Prentice-Hall, 66; co-auth, The inquiring reader, Heath, 67 & 74; auth, The whole idea catalog, Random, 71; plus two others. Add: Box 4418, Carmel, CA 93921.

SULLIVAN, ALVIN D, b. Pasagoula, Miss, Oct. 24, 42. MODERN LITERATURE. B.A, Tulane Univ, 64; M.A, South. Ill, Univ, Edwardsville, 68; Ph.D. (Eng. lit), St. Louis Univ, 72. Instr. ENG, SOUTH. ILL. UNIV, EDWARDSVILLE, 68-72, ASST. PROF, 72- Ed, Papers on Lang. & Lit, 73- MLA. Modern British and American literature. Publ: Co-auth, D.H. Lawrence and The dial, South. Ill. Univ. Press, 70; co-ed, The dial—two author indexes, South. Ill. Univ. Libr, 71; co-ed, Toward the modern, Papers on Lang. & Lit. Suppl, 72; auth, Eberhart's Seals, terns, time, Explicator, 9-12/71; Days of the Phoenix, J. Mod. Lit, 71; The Phoenix riddle, Papers on Lang. & Lit, fall 71. Add: Papers on Language & Literature, Southern Illinois University, Edwardsville, IL 62025.

SULLIVAN, BARBARA W, b. New York, N.Y, Apr. 29, 35; m. 60. ENGLISH, JOURNALISM. B.S, Univ. Fla, 56; M.A, Univ. Ga, 65, Ph.D.(Eng), 68. Prof. Eng, Tift Col, 67-69, head dept, 67-72; pub. relat. dir, Wilmington Col, 72-73; CHMN. MOD. LANG, TIFT COL, 73- S.Atlantic Mod. Lang. Asn; Am. Col. Pub. Relat. Asn. Alienation theme in works of Hawthorne, Twain, Sherwood Anderson, Faulkner and Wolfe; journalism for non-professionals. Add: Dept. of Modern Languages, Tift College, Forsyth, GA 31029.

SULLIVAN, DANIEL JOSEPH, C.M, b. New York, N.Y, Mar. 31, 27. ENGLISH. B.A, Mary Immaculate Sem, 53; B.A, Oxford Univ, 59, M.A, 64; D.Phil.(Anglo-Irish lit), Nat. Univ. Ireland, 70. Instr. Eng. & Theol, Niagara Univ, 53-55, assoc. prof. ENG, 59-65; ST. JOHN'S UNIV.(N.Y), 65-71, PROF, 71- MLA; NCTE; Am. Comt. Irish Stud. Anglo-Irish literature. Add: Dept. of Humanities, St. Johns University, Howard Ave, Staten Island, NY 10301.

SULLIVAN, EMILY BRADSHER, b. Roxboro, N.C, Jan. 14, 18; m. 45; c. 2. ENGLISH. A.B, Meredith Col, 38; M.A, Univ. Pa, 40. Instr. ENG, HIGH POINT COL, 61-64, asst. prof, 64-67, ASSOC. PROF, 67- NCTE; MLA. Medieval literature, especially Chaucer; 20th century Southern fiction, especially Faulkner and Thomas Wolfe. Add: Dept. of English, High Point College, Montlieu Ave, High Point, NC 27262.

SULLIVAN, ERNEST WALTER, II, b. Madison, Wis, June 30, 44; m. 69. SEVENTEENTH CENTURY LITERATURE. B.A, Univ. Calif, Los Angeles, 66, Ph.D.(Eng), 73. ASST. PROF. ENG, TEX. TECH UNIV, 72- Huntington Libr. fel, summer 74. MLA. Bibliography; John Donne. Publ: Authoritative manuscript corrections in Donne's Biathanatos, Stud. Bibliog, 74; Post seventeenth century texts of John Donne's Biathanatos, Publ. Bibliog, Soc. Am, 74. Add: Dept. of English, Texas Tech University, Lubbock, TX 79409.

SULLIVAN, FRANK, b. Denver, Colo, June 6, 12; m. 36; c. 1. ENGLISH. A.B, Regis Col.(Colo), 34; fel, St. Louis Univ, 34-36, A.M, 36; Ph.D, Yale, 40. Instr. ENG, St. Louis Univ, 36-41, asst. prof, 41-44, assoc. prof, 44-46; LOYOLA MARYMOUNT UNIV, 46-48, PROF, 48- MLA; Mediaeval Acad. Am; Am. folklore Soc; Bibliog. Soc. Am; NCTE; Col. Eng. Asn; Early Eng. Text. Soc. English philology; Chaucer. Publ: Moreana: a check-list of material by and about St. Thomas More, Rockhurst Col, 46; Syr Thomas More: a first bibliographical notebook, 56 & co-auth, Moreana: materials summarized and criticized concerning Sir Thomas More Knight, 5 Vols, 64-70, Loyola Univ. Los Angeles. Add: Dept. English, Loyola Marymount University, Los Angeles, CA 90045.

SULLIVAN, HARRY RICHARDS, b. New York, N.Y, Mar. 5, 16; m. 50. ENGLISH. B.A, La. State Univ, 49; M.A, Stanford Univ, 50; Univ. Toronto; Ph.D, Univ. Ga, 60. Instr. ENG, Northeast La. State Col, 52-53; Univ. Ga, 53-55; ASST. PROF, N.Ga. Col, 56-61; UNIV. S.C, 61- S.Atlantic Mod. Lang. Asn; MLA. Nineteenth century English literature. Publ: Review of Lucifer by J.C. Powys, West. Humanities Rev, summer 57; The South and emancipation in the British West Indies, Ga. Rev, 9/63; MacLeish's Ars poetica, Eng. J, 12/67; plus others. Add: Dept. of English, University of South Carolina, Columbia, SC 29208.

SULLIVAN, JOHN FRANCIS, b. Detroit, Mich, Jan. 6, 18; m. 52; c. 6. ENGLISH. B.S, Univ. Detroit, 40, M.A, 47; Ph.D, Univ. Mich, 59. Instr. ENG, Univ. Detroit, 46-54, asst. prof, 54-58; UNIV. WINDSOR, 58-61, assoc. prof, 61-67, PROF, 67-, HEAD DEPT, 69-74 & 75- Can. Counc. sr. fel, 67-68. U.S.A, 42-45. MLA; Shakespeare Soc. Am; Renaissance Soc. Am; NCTE; Cath. Rec. Soc, Eng. Shakespeare; political thought of the 16th century; Robert Persons, S.J, and recusant history. Publ: Collab, The college research paper; auth, Poetry in English, 1900-1930, Edward Arnold, 65; ed, Henry IV, part I, In: Vol. II, Shakespeare Series, College Classics in English, Macmillan Toronto, 69. Add: Dept. of English, University of Windsor, Windsor, Ont. N9B 3P4, Can.

SULLIVAN, KEVIN, b. New York, N.Y, Oct. 22, 18. ENGLISH. B.A, Georgetown Univ, 41; Ph.L, Woodstock Col, 42; fel, Princeton, 45-46; Ph.D, Columbia Univ, 57. Asst. prof. Eng, St. Joseph Col, 46-50; instr, Columbia Univ, 52-57, from asst. dean to assoc. dean grad. fac, 58-70; prof. Eng, Baruch Col, 72-73; PROF. ENG. & DIR, INST. IRISH STUD, QUEENS COL. (N.Y), 73- Int. Asn. Stud. Anglo-Irish Lit; Am. Comt. Irish Stud; MLA. Anglo-Irish literature. Publ: Joyce among the Jesuits; The world of Brendan Behan, New Eng. Libr, 65; Conor Cruise O'Brien introduces Ireland, Andre Deutsch, 69; Oscar Wilde, Columbia Univ, 72; contrib, Modern Irish literature, Iona Univ, 72. Add: 10 Gramercy Park, New York, NY 10003.

SULLIVAN, M. ROSENDA, O.S.F, U.S. citizen. LITERARY CRITICISM. B.A, Marquette Univ, 28, M.A, 30; Ph.D, Cath. Univ. Am, 42. Prof. ENG. & chmn. dept, ALVERNO COL, 42-70, EMER. PROF, 70- Cath. Renascence Soc.(treas, 51-63). Modern fiction; teaching of secondary English. Publ: Structure in language and literature, Sadlier, 69. Add: Dept. of English, Alverno College, 3401 S. 39th St, Milwaukee, WI 53215.

SULLIVAN, MAJIE PADBERG, b. St. Louis, Mo, July 30, 11; m. 36; c. 1. ENGLISH. A.B, Maryville Col. Sacred Heart (Mo), 33; fel, St. Louis Univ, 33-35, M.A, 35. BIBLIOGR, 46- Bibliography and critical evaluation of all printed scholarship of St. Thomas More. Publ: Moreana: preliminary checklist, Rockhurst Col, 46; Standard editions of major authors, 50 & Moreana: material for the study of St. Thomas More, Vol. A-F, 64, Vol. G-N, 65, Vol. N-R, 66 & Vol. S-Z, 68, Loyola Univ; Moreana, index, 71. Add: 8010 Campion Dr, Los Angeles, CA 90045.

SULLIVAN, MARIE DENISE, S.P, b. Indianapolis, Ind, Jan. 14, 12. ENGLISH LITERATURE. B.A, St. Mary-of-the-Woods Col, 40; M.A, Ind. Univ, 48; M.A, Ind. State Teachers Col, 57; Ph.D.(Eng), Univ. Notre Dame, 61. Assoc. prof. ENG, ST. MARY-OF-THE-WOODS COL, 61-73, PROF, 73- NCTE; MLA. Tudor prose, especially the Tudor sermon. Add: Dept. of English, St. Mary-of-the-Woods College, St. Mary-of-the-Woods, IN 47876.

SULLIVAN, MARY C, R.S.M, b. Rochester, N.Y, June 15, 31. LITERATURE, RELIGION. B.A, Nazareth Col. Rochester, 54; M.A, Univ. Notre Dame, 61, Ph.D.(Eng), 64. Asst. prof. Eng, Catherine McAuley Col, 63-65, pres, 65-68; asst. prof. Eng, Marymount Col.(N.Y), 67-69; ASSOC. PROF. LANG. & LIT, ROCHESTER INST. TECHNOL, 69- Consult. & Evaluator, Comn. Higher Educ, Mid. States Asn, 68- MLA; Col. Eng. Asn; Am. Acad. Relig; Joseph Conrad Soc; AAUP. Nineteenth and 20th century English and American literature; religion and literature. Publ: Catherine of Dublin, Pageant, 65; The function of setting in Howells' The landlord at Lion's Head, Am. Lit, 63; Moby Dick, CXXIX: the cabin, Nineteenth Century Fiction, 65; plus others. Add: Dept. of Language & Literature, College of General Studies, Rochester Institute of Technology, One Lomb Memorial Dr, Rochester, NY 14623.

SULLIVAN, MARY ROSE, b. Boston, Mass, May 13, 31. ENGLISH & COMPARATIVE LITERATURE. A.B, Emmanuel Col, 52; M.A, Cath. Univ. Am, 58; Ph.D.(Eng), Boston Univ, 64. Instr. ENG, Emmanuel Col, 60-64, asst. prof, 64-66; UNIV. COLO, DENVER, 66-67, assoc. prof, 67-70, PROF, 70- Am. Counc. Learned Soc. fel, 73. U.S.N, 52-56, Res, 57-, Capt. MLA; Am. Asn. Univ. Women (fel. comt, 74-); AAUP; Browning Inst. Victorian poetry; 19th and 20th century English novel; 20th century comparative literature. Publ: Browning's voices in The ring and the book, Univ. Toronto, 69; Synge, Sophocles, and the unmaking of myth, Mod. Drama, 12/69; Easy rider: critique of the new hedonism?, West. Humanities Rev, spring 70; Black and white characters in Hard times, Victorian Newsletter, fall 70. Add: Div. of Arts & Humanities, College of Undergraduate Studies, University of Colorado at Denver, 1100 14th St, Denver, CO 80202.

SULLIVAN, MAUREEN, b. Hartford, Conn, July 4, 35. ENGLISH. A.B, Albertus Magnus Col, 57; M.A, Yale, 58, M.A, 63, Ph.D.(Eng), 67. Teacher ENG, High Schs, Conn, 58-62; ASST. PROF, Univ. Pa, 68-74; MARQUETTE UNIV, 74- Folger Shakespeare Libr. sr. fel, 74-75. Eng. Inst; MLA; AAUP; Am. Soc. 18th Century Stud. Restoration and 18th century drama; comedy; the novel, 18th-20th centuries. Publ: Ed, Colley Cibber: three sentimental comedies, a critical edition, Yale Univ, 73. Add: Dept. of English, Marquette University, Milwaukee, WI 53233.

SULLIVAN, NANCY, b. Newport, R.I, July 3, 29. ENGLISH. B.A, Hunter Col, 51; M.A, Univ. R.I, 53; Brown Univ, 53-55; Ph.D.(Eng), Univ. Conn, 63. Asst. ENG, Univ. R.I, 51-53; Brown Univ, 53-54, instr, 55-60, asst. prof, 61-63; R.I. COL, 63-65, assoc. prof, 65-68, PROF, 68- Corp. of YADDO fels, summers 67 & 68. Devins Award, 65. MLA; Poetry Soc. Am. American and British contemporary poetry; aesthetics. Publ: The history of the world as pictures and other poems, Univ. Mo, 65; Perspective and the poetic process, Mouton, 68; Body English (poems), Hellcoal Press, Brown Univ, 72; Poems, Quart. Rev. Lit, Vol. 12; Lawrence Durrell's epitaph for the novel, Personalist, winter 63. Add: Hillsdale Rd, West Kingston, RI 02892.

SULLIVAN, WALTER L, b. Nashville, Tenn, Jan. 4, 24; m. 47; c. 3. ENGLISH. B.A, Vanderbilt Univ, 47; M.F.A, State Univ. Iowa, 49; hon. Litt.D, Episcopal Theol. Sem. (Ky), 73. Instr. ENG, VANDERBILT UNIV, 49-52, asst. prof, 52-57, assoc. prof, 57-63, PROF, 63- Ford Found. fel, 51-52; Sewanee Rev. fel, 55; lectr, WDCN-TV, Nashville, Tenn, 72-73. U.S.M.C, 43-46, 1st Lt. S.Atlantic Mod. Lang. Asn; MLA. Fiction writing; contemporary British and American fiction; theological themes in modern literature. Publ: Sojourn of a stranger, 57 & The long, long love, 59, Henry Holt; Death by melancholy, La. State Univ, 72; plus others. Add: Dept. of English, Box 1623, Station B, Vanderbilt University, Nashville, TN 37203.

SULLIVAN, WILLIAM HOWARD, b. Castleberry, Ala, Jan. 24, 35. ENGLISH LITERATURE. B.A, Univ. Ala, 61; M.A, Northwest. Univ, 63; Ph.D.(Eng), Univ. Wis, 69. Instr. ENG, Millikin Univ, 63-64; asst. prof, Univ. Wis-Waukesha, 69; vis. lectr, Univ. Stirling, 70; ASST. PROF, UNIV. ILL, CHICAGO CIRCLE, 72- Am. Philos. Soc. grant-in-aid, 70. U.S.N, 53-57. Nineteenth century aestheticism; writings of Walter Pater; physical theories of time. Publ: Four early essays from Pater's The Renaissance: the aesthetics for a humanist myth, Victorian Newslett, fall 71; Report on research at Oxford University: Walter Pater's unpublished mss. of Gaston de Latour, Am. Philos. Soc. Yr. Bk, 72. Add: Dept. of English, University of Illinois at Chicago Circle, Box 4348, Chicago, IL 60680.

SULLIVAN, WILLIAM JOHN, b. Providence, R.I, Dec. 16, 37; m. 59; c. 4. ENGLISH, AMERICAN STUDIES. B.Ed, Keene State Col, 64; M.A, Univ. Utah, 66, NDEA fel, 66-69, Ph.D.(Eng. & Am. stud), 69. ASST. PROF. ENG. & AM. STUD, KEENE STATE COL, 69- American cultural and social history; contemporary American literature; Colonial American literature and thought. Publ: Dreiser's tropistic theory of morality, Bull. Rocky Mountain Lang. Asn, winter 67; In search of Bartram, Univ. Utah Papers in Lang. & Lit, 69; Review of Arts in the young republic, West. Humanities Rev. Add: Dept. of English, Keene State College, Main St, Keene, NH 03431.

SULLIVAN, WILLIAM P, b. Malden, Mass, Jan. 17, 23; m. 52; c. 7. ENGLISH. A.B, Tufts Col, 47; M.A, Columbia Univ, 48, Ph.D, 61. Instr. ENG, Rockhurst Col, 49-50; Fordham Col, 50-52; Stephens Col, 53-58; asst. prof, McNeese State Col, 58-63; assoc. prof, Col. St. Rose, 63-68; PROF, MARSHALL UNIV, 68- U.S.N.R, 43-46, Lt.(jg). MLA; Soc. Stud. South. Lit; AAUP. American literature; Renaissance; literary criticism. Add: Dept. of English, Marshall University, Huntington, WV 25701.

SULLOWAY, ALISON G, b. New York, N.Y, July 31, 17; wid; c. 3. ENGLISH. M.A, Columbia Univ, 58, univ. fel, 62-63, Am. Asn. Univ. Women fel, 63-64, pres. fel, 64-65, Ph.D.(Eng. lit), 68. Lectr. ENG, Columbia Univ, 58-59; Barnard Col, Columbia Univ, 61-62; instr, Beloit Col, 65-68; asst. prof, CEDAR CREST COL, 68-72, ASSOC. PROF, 72- Ansley Publ. Award, Columbia Univ, 68. MLA. Victorian literature; the novel; Shakespeare. Publ: Gerald Manley Hopkins and the Victorian temper, Columbia Univ, 68 & Routledge & Kegan Paul, 72; St. Ignatius Loyola and the Victorian temper: Hopkins Windhover as diabolic gravity, Hopkins Quart, 74. Add: Dept. of English, Cedar Crest College, Allentown, PA 18104.

SULLWOLD, GEORGE JOHN, JR, b. St. Paul, Minn, Oct. 12, 12. COMPARATIVE LITERATURE. B.A, Univ. Calif, Los Angeles, 30, M.A, 36; Ph.D, Univ. Wash, 58. Assoc. prof. Eng, St. John's Univ.(Shanghai), 40-49; assoc, Univ. Wash, 51-54; instr. classics & humanities, Stanford Univ, 55-62; asst. prof. ENG, UNIV. SANTA CLARA, 62-68, ASSOC. PROF, 68-, CHMN. DEPT. CLASSICS, 72- MLA. Renaissance; 18th century. Add: Dept. of English, University of Santa Clara, Santa Clara, CA 95053.

SULOWAY, IRWIN J, b. Chicago, Ill, Aug. 11, 21; m. 46; c. 2. ENGLISH. B.Ed, Chicago Teachers Col, 43; M.A, Northwest. Univ, 48, Ph.D.(Eng), 51. Lectr. Eng, Northwest. Univ, 48-50; instr, CHICAGO STATE UNIV, 51-59, assoc. prof, 59-61, prof. Eng. & asst. dean, 61-65, dean arts & sci, 65-68, dean faculty, 68-71, PROF. ENG, 71- Managing ed, Chicago Schs. J, 55-63; mem. teacher training team, U.S. Dept. State, S.Vietnam, 63-65. U.S.A.F, 43-46, Res, 46-49, T/Sgt. NCTE (asst. secy. & asst. ed, 51-52, dir, 52-60); Conf. Col. Compos & Commun. Victorian literature; the nature of language; teaching language. Publ: Co-auth, Developing permanent interest in reading, Univ. Chicago, 56, The education of teachers in English, Appleton, 63 & Promising practices in the teaching of English, Nat. Counc. Teachers Eng, 63; co-auth, Language and teaching: essays in honor of W. Wilbur Hatfield, Chicago State Col, 69. Add: Dept. of English, Chicago State University, 95th St. & King Dr, Chicago, IL 60628.

SULTAN, STANLEY, b. Brooklyn, N.Y, July 17, 28; m. 48; c. 2. ENGLISH. A.B, Cornell Univ, 49; M.A, Boston Univ, 50; Woodward fel. & univ. fel, Yale, Ph.D, 55. Instr. ENG, Smith Col, 55-59; asst. prof, CLARK UNIV, 59-62, assoc. prof, 62-68, PROF, 68- Fel, YADDO-Saratoga Springs, N.Y, 57; Shell asst. for res, 60-62. Int. Asn. Stud. Anglo-Irish Lit; Malone Soc. Twentieth century literature; literary theory; English drama. Publ: The argument of Ulysses, Ohio State Univ, 65; ed, The playboy of the Western world, Imprint Soc, 71; auth, Son of the Cantos?, Chelsea, 71; Call me Ishmael: the hagiography of Isaac McCaslin, Tex. Stud. Lit. & Lang, 61; plus one other. Add: Dept. of English, Clark University, Worcester, MA 01610.

SUMERLIN, CLAUDE WINDELL, b. Corpus Christi, Tex, Mar. 11, 23; m. 47; c. 1. JOURNALISM. B.A, Tex. Col. Arts & Indust, 47; M.A, Baylor Univ, 49; Univ. Tex, summer 56; Newspaper Fund fel, Univ. Mo, summer 60, Ph.D.(jour), 68. Sports writer, San Antonio Express, Tex, 47-48; asst. sports ed, San Antonio Eve. News, 48; teacher Eng, Allen Mil. Acad, Bryan, Tex, 49-50; Van High Sch, 50-59; assoc. prof. jour, Ouachita Baptist Univ, 59-65, prof, 65-68, dir. news bur, 59-68; PROF. JOUR. & CHMN. DEPT, HENDERSON STATE COL, 68- Chief judge contest entries, La. Press Women, 67; wire desk ed, T.B. Butler Publ. Co, Tex, summer 72. Wall St. J. Newspaper Fund Spec. Awards, summers 61 & 62. U.S.A.A.F, 43-45, T/Sgt; Air Medal with 4 Oak Leaf Clusters. Assoc. Col. Press; Int. Newspaper Advert. Exec. Asn; Hist. Comn, South. Baptist Convention; Nat. Counc. Col. Publ. Adv; Columbia Scholastic Press Adv. Asn. Theology of Robert Browning; history of Southern Baptist state newspapers. Publ: Polio victim overcomes obstacles, Ark. Baptist Newsmag, 69; Christopher Smart's A song to

David: its influence on Robert Browning, In: Costerus essays in English and American language and literature, Amsterdam, 72; J.J. Taylor: seed sower in Brazil, Quart. Rev. & Ark. Baptist Newsmag, 72; plus others. Add: Dept. of Journalism, Box 2650 Henderson State College, Arkadelphia, AR 71923.

SUMMERS, CLAUDE JOSEPH, b. Galvez, La, Dec. 6, 44. ENGLISH LITERATURE. B.A, La. State Univ, 66; Woodrow Wilson fel, Univ. Chicago, 66-67, M.A, 67, univ. fel, 67-68, Danforth fel, 68-69, Ford Found. fel, 69-70, Ph.D.(Eng), 70. Asst. prof. ENG, UNIV. MICH-DEARBORN, 70-73, ASSOC. PROF, 73- Assoc. ed, Seventeenth Century News, 73- MLA; Milton Soc. Am; Renaissance Soc. Am. Seventeenth century poetry; Renaissance drama; modern poetry. Publ: Co-ed, The poems of Owen Felltham, Seventeenth Century News, 73; auth, Christopher Marlowe and the politics of power, Univ. Salzburg, 74; The frightened architects of Marvell's Horatian ode, Seventeenth Century News, 70; Isabella's plea for Gaveston in Marlowe's Edward II, Philol. Quart, 73; Tamburlaine's opponents and Machiavelli's Prince, Eng. Lang. Notes, 74. Add: Dept. of Humanities, University of Michigan-Dearborn, 4901 Evergreen Rd, Dearborn, MI 48128.

SUMMERS, HARRISON BOYD, b. Stanford, Ill, Mar. 19, 94; m. 17; c. 2. TELEVISION, RADIO. A.B, Fairmount Col, 17; A.M, Univ. Okla, 21; Ph.D, Univ. Mo, 31. Prof. speech, Park Col, 22-23; Kans. State Col. Agr. & Appl. Sci, 23-29; dir. pub. serv, East. Div, Nat. Broadcasting Co, 39-42; mgr. pub. serv. div, Am. Broadcasting Co, 42-46; prof. SPEECH, OHIO STATE UNIV, 46-64, EMER. PROF, 64-; RES. & WRITING, 64- Vis. prof. TV & radio, Mich. State Univ, 64-65; telecommun, Univ. South. Calif, summer 65; radio & TV, Bowling Green State Univ, fall 66. Speech Commun. Asn. Radio and television programming; audience research. Publ: Radio censorship; co-auth, How to debate, Wilson; Broadcasting and the public, Wadsworth, 66; Comparative earning rates of large scale and small-scale industry, 1910-1929. Add: 1504 Guilford Rd, Columbus, OH 43221.

SUMMERS, HOLLIS SPURGEON, b. Eminence, Ky, June 21, 16; m. 43; c. 2. ENGLISH. A.B, Georgetown Col, 37, hon. D.Litt, 65; M.A, Bread Loaf Sch. Eng, 43; Ph.D, State Univ, Iowa, 49. From asst. prof. to prof. ENG, Georgetown Col, 44-49; Univ. Ky, 49-59; PROF, OHIO UNIV, 59- Fund Advan. Educ. grant, 51-52; vis. McGuffey prof. creative writing, Ohio Univ, 57-58; distinguished prof. Eng, 64; spec. lectr. contemporary lit, Univ. Auckland, 72; mem, Ohio Arts Counc, 73; Am. Acad. Poets. Poetry Soc. Am; MLA. Publ: City limit, Houghton, 48; Brighten the corner, Doubleday, 52; The weather of February, 57, The walks near Athens, 59, The day after Sunday, 68 & The garden (novel), 72, Harper; Someone else (poems for children), Lippincott, 62; Seven occasions, 64, The peddler and other domestic matters, 67, Sit opposite each other (poetry), 70 & Start from home (poetry), 72, Rutgers Univ; ed, Discussions of the short story, Heath, 65; How they chose the dead, La. State Univ, 73. Add: 181 N. Congress, Athens, OH 45701.

SUMMERS, JOSEPH HOLMES, b. Louisville, Ky, Feb. 9, 20; m. 43; c. 3. ENGLISH. A.B, Harvard, 41, fel, 45-48, M.A, 48, Ph.D.(Eng), 50. Tutor hist. & lit, Harvard & Radcliffe Cols, 45-48; instr. ENG, Bard Col, 48-50; asst. prof, Univ. Conn, 50-55, assoc. prof, 55-59; prof, Wash. Univ, 59-66, chmn. dept, 63-64; PROF, Mich. State Univ, 66-69; UNIV. ROCHESTER, 69- Fund Advan. Learning fel, Italy, 52-53; Guggenheim fel, Eng, 57-58; vis. prof, Amherst Col, 62-63; Fulbright lectr, univ. & vis. fel, All Souls Col, Oxford, 66-67; sr. fel, William Andrews Clark Mem. Libr, Univ. Calif, Los Angeles, summer 68; vis. prof. Eng, Univ. Kent, 72. Eng. Inst; MLA; fel. Soc. Relig. Higher Educ. Seventeenth century literature; Shakespeare. Publ: George Herbert: his religion and art, 54 & The muse's method; an introduction to Paradise lost, 62, Harvard Univ; ed, Marvell, selected poems, Del, 61, The lyric and dramatic Milton, Columbia Univ, 64 & The selected poetry of George Herbert, New Am. Libr, 67; auth, The heirs of Donne and Jonson, Oxford Univ, 70; The masks of Twelfth night, Univ. Kansas City Rev, 55; The embarrassments of Paradise lost, York Tercentenary Essays, 68; The anger of Prospero, Mich. Quart. Rev, 73. Add: Dept. of English, University of Rochester, Rochester, NY 14627.

SUMMERSGILL, TRAVIS L, b. New York, N.Y, June 28, 17; m. 56; c. 1. ENGLISH LITERATURE. B.A, Bucknell Univ, 39; M.A, Harvard, 40, Ph.D, 48. Assoc. prof. ENG, Col. William & Mary, 48-56; prof. & chmn. dept, Park Col, 56-58; from assoc. prof. to PROF, UNIV. HAWAII, MANOA, 58-, chmn. dept, 61-64. Fulbright grant, Japan, 54-55. U.S.A, 42-45, Capt. MLA. Elizabethan drama; Chaucer. Add: Dept. of English, University of Hawaii at Manoa, Honolulu, HI 96822.

SUNDELL, MICHAEL GORDON, b. New York, N.Y, Apr. 1, 34; m. 59; c. 3. ENGLISH LITERATURE, ART HISTORY. A.B, Hamilton Col, 56; Univ. Montpellier, 56-57; A.M, Yale, 58, Ph.D.(Eng), 62. Instr. ENG, Hamilton Col, 61-62; from instr. to asst. prof, Queens Col.(N.Y), 62-68; from asst. prof. to assoc. prof, Case West. Reserve Univ, 68-73; PROF. & CHMN. DEPT, GEORGE MASON UNIV, 73- Vis. assoc. prof. mod. lang, Univ. Orleans, France, 71; vis. lectr, U.S. Inform. Agency, Ger, 72-73; consult. ed. & art critic, Cleveland Mag, 72-73. MLA. Victorian literature; contemporary American art; Victorian art. Publ: Ed, Twentieth century interpretations of Vanity fair, Prentice-Hall, 69; auth, The intellectual background and structure of Arnold's Tristram and Iseult, 63 & Story and context in The strayed reveller, 65, Victorian Poetry; Spiritual confusion and artistic form in Victorian poetry, Victorian Newslett, 71. Add: Dept. of English, George Mason University, Fairfax, VA 22030.

SUNDELL, ROGER HENRY, b. Jamestown, N.Y, May 1, 36; m. 64. ENGLISH LITERATURE. B.A, Yale, 59; M.A, Wash. Univ, 63, Ph.D.(Eng), 65. Instr. ENG, Univ. Del, 64-68, asst. prof, 66-68; UNIV. WIS-MILWAUKEE, 68-70, ASSOC. PROF, 71-, assoc. chmn. dept, 70-73. Assoc. ed, Seventeenth Century News, 73- MLA; Milton Soc. Am. English Renaissance literature; John Milton; short fiction. Publ: Co-ed, The art of fiction: a handbook and anthology, Holt, 67, 73; The narrator as interpreter in Paradise regained, Milton Stud, 70. Add: Dept. of English, University of Wisconsin-Milwaukee, Milwaukee, WI 53201.

SUNDSTROM, AILEEN L, b. Detroit, Mich, Mar. 2, 25; m. 54. SPEECH, ENGLISH. A.B, Wayne State Univ, 46, M.A, 47, Ph.D.(speech), 64. Teacher & dir. radio & speech, Detroit Bd. Educ, 47-65; asst. prof. Eng. & speech, Mercy Col.(Mich), 65-67; ASSOC. PROF. SPEECH, HENRY FORD COMMUNITY COL, 67- Teacher, part-time, Wayne State Univ, 57-68; Ford Found. scholar, 61. Speech Commun. Asn; Nat. Col. Honors Counc; Am. Forensic Asn.(Key excellence, 65). Academically gifted and talented students; interpretative reading. Publ: The influence of the traditional schools of interpretation on the contemporary eclectic philosophy of reading aloud, Speech Monogr, 4/65. Add: Henry Ford Community College, 5101 Evergreen Rd, Dearborn, MI 48128.

SUNDWALL, McKAY, b. Provo, Utah, Apr. 4, 40; m. 63; c. 2. ENGLISH & COMPARATIVE LITERATURE. A.B, Mich. State Univ, 62; A.M, Harvard, 65, univ. fel, 67-70, Dexter traveling fel, 69, Ph.D.(Eng), 72. ASST. PROF. ENG, COLUMBIA UNIV, 70- Vis. asst. prof. lit, State Univ. N.Y. Col. Purchase, 72-73; Columbia Univ Chamberlain fel, Counc. Res. in Humanities fel, summer 74. MLA; Mod. Humanities Res. Asn; Mediaeval Acad. Am; Dante Soc. Am; Int. Arthurian Asn; Viking Soc. North. Res. Old and Middle English language and literature; Old Germanic language and literature; medieval Romance. Add: Dept. of English, Columbia University, New York, NY 10027.

SUPER, ROBERT HENRY, b. Wilkes-Barre, Pa, June 13, 14; m. 53; c. 2. ENGLISH LITERATURE. A.B, Princeton, 35, Procter fel, 37-38, Ph.D, 41; Henry fel, Oxford, 35-36, B.Litt, 37. Instr. ENG, Princeton, 38-42; asst. prof, Mich. State Norm. Col, 42-47; lectr, UNIV. MICH, ANN ARBOR, 47, asst. prof, 47-54, assoc. prof, 54-60, PROF, 60- Fulbright res. grant, U.K, 49-50; F.I. Carpenter vis. prof, Univ. Chicago, summer 54; Am. Counc. Learned Soc. fel, 59-60; Guggenheim fel, 62-63 & 70-71; vis. prof, Rice Univ, 65-66; Univ. Calif, Los Angeles, summer 67; Harris Found. lectr, Northwest. Univ, spring 68; vis. prof, Univ. Calif, Berkeley, summer 73. Field intel. off, For. Econ. Admin, 45. MLA. English literature of the 19th century; Matthew Arnold. Publ: Publication of Landor's works, Bibliog. Soc, London, 54; Walter Savage Landor: a biography, N.Y. Univ, 54; ed, Matthew Arnold's complete prose works, 60- & auth, The time-spirit of Matthew Arnold, 70, Univ. Mich. Add: 1221 Baldwin Ave, Ann Arbor, MI 48104.

SUSSMAN, HARVEY MARTIN, Speech Science, Neurolinguistics. See Volume III, Foreign Languages, Linguistics & Philology.

SUSSMAN, HERBERT L, b. New York, N.Y, Jan. 20, 37; m. 60; c. 2. ENGLISH. B.A, Princeton, 58; M.A, Harvard, 59, Ph.D, 63. Asst. prof. ENG, Univ. Calif, Berkeley, 63-71; ASSOC. PROF, NORTHEASTERN UNIV, 71- Victorian literature. Publ: Victorians and the machine, Harvard, 68. Publ: Hunt, Ruskin and the scapegoat, Victorian Stud, 68; Form in Wilde's critical writings, Stud. Philol, 73. Add: Dept. of English, Northeastern University, Boston, MA 02115.

SUTHER, MARSHALL E, JR, b. Norfolk, Va, Jan. 21, 18. ENGLISH & COMPARATIVE LITERATURE. A.B, Univ. N.C, 39; M.A, Tulane Univ, 41; Ph.D, Columbia Univ, 56. Instr. Eng. & humanities, Columbia Col, 46-48; Eng. & French, State Univ. N.Y. Maritime Col, 56-58; asst. prof. Eng, Columbia Univ, 58-63, assoc. prof. COMP. LIT, 63-68; PROF, RICHMOND COL.(N.Y), 68- U.S.M.C.R, 43-46, T/Sgt. AAUP. English romantic literature, especially Coleridge; aesthetic theory. Publ: The dark night of Samuel Taylor Coleridge, 60 & Visions of Xanadu, 65, Columbia Univ. Add: Div. of Humanities, Richmond College, 130 Stuyvesant Pl, Staten Island, NY 10301.

SUTHERLAND, EDWIN VAN VALKENBURG, b. Philadelphia, Pa, Sept. 16, 13; m. 37; c. 2. ENGLISH & COMPARATIVE LITERATURE. B.S, U.S. Mil. Acad, 36; M.A, Columbia Univ, 51; Ph.D, Univ. Pa, 64. U.S. ARMY, 36-, assoc. prof. ENG, U.S. MIL. ACAD, 48-52, PROF, 61-, HEAD DEPT, 65- U.S.A, 36-, Col. Int. Arthurian Soc; Int. Soc. Ethnol. & Folklore. International folklore. Add: Dept. of English, U.S. Military Academy, West Point, NY 10996.

SUTHERLAND, JOHN HALE, b. Boston, Mass, May 10, 23; m. 48; c. 3. ENGLISH. A.B, Swarthmore Col, 48; M.A, Univ. Pa, 50, Ph.D, 51. Instr. ENG, COLBY COL, 51-54, asst. prof, 54-59, assoc. prof, 59-70, PROF, 70-, acting chmn. dept, 70-72. MLA; AAUP. Eighteenth century English literature; William Blake. Publ: Mr. Spectator's London, Heath, 59; Blake and Urizen, In: Blake's visionary forms dramatic, twenty new essays, Princeton Univ, 70; Blake: a crisis of love and jealousy, PMLA, 72; plus two others. Add: Box 76, East Vassalboro, ME 04935.

SUTHERLAND, RAYMOND CARTER, b. Horse Cave, Ky, Nov. 5, 17. ENGLISH. B.A, Transylvania Col, 39; lic, Gen. Theol. Sem, 42; M.A, Univ. Ky, 50, Ph.D.(Eng), 53. Instr. ENG, Univ. Tenn, 53-56, asst. prof, 56-57; GA. STATE UNIV, 57-61, assoc. prof, 61-63, PROF, 63- Regents Ga. Univ. Syst. res. grant, Oxford, 59-60. U.S.A, 44-48, Capt. MLA; Mediaeval Acad. Am; Archaeol. Inst. Am; S.Atlantic Mod. Lang. Asn; Bibliog. Soc. Am. Sub-Roman culture and Beowulf; Chaucer and medieval religion. Publ: Principles and rules of versification, Foote & Davies, 64; Bellum and post-bellum papers, Ky. Hist. Soc. Register, 69; Mediaeval elements in The spire, 10/69 & co-ed, Papers by medievalists, 10/71, Stud. Lit. Imagination; plus others. Add: Dept. of English, Georgia State University, 33 Gilmer St. S.E, Atlanta, GA 30303.

SUTHERLAND, ROBERT SHERMAN, b. Obion County, Tenn, July 2, 13. ENGLISH LITERATURE. B.A, Union Univ.(Tenn), 35; M.A, Murray State Col, 50; Univ. Miss, 50, 55; Ed.D.(higher educ, Eng), Ariz. State Univ, 64. Teacher Eng, Troy High Sch, Tenn, 35-37; Obion Sch, 50-51; asst. mgr. promotion & res, Memphis Publ. Co, 50-56; assoc. prof. Eng, Grand Canyon Col, 56-61; asst. col. admin. & admin. asst. to dean, col. educ, Ariz. State Univ, 61-62; assoc. prof. Eng, GRAND CANYON COL, 62-64, PROF. ENG. & DEAN COL, 64-, asst. dean, 59-64. C.Eng, U.S.A, 41-45, 51-53, Res, 53-, Maj. NCTE. Characteristics of effective college instruction; psychoanalysis of Chaucer's Canterbury Pilgrims. Add: Office of the Dean, Grand Canyon College, 3300 W. Camelback Rd, P.O. Box 11097, Phoenix, AZ 85017.

SUTHERLAND, RONALD, b. Montreal, P.Q, Nov. 10, 33; m. 58; c. 5. ENGLISH, COMPARATIVE LITERATURE. B.A, McGill Univ, 54, M.A, 55;

McGill-Glasgow exchange fel, Univ. Glasgow, 55-56; Ph.D.(comp. lit), Wayne State Univ, 60. Lectr. ENG, Wayne State Univ, 58-59; UNIV. SHERBROOKE, 59-62, CHMN. DEPT, 62- MLA; Asn. Can. Univ. Teachers Eng. (exec, 66-68). Linguistics; medieval literature; comparative Canadian literature. Publ: Co-auth, L'Esprit de la langue anglaise, W.J. Gage, Toronto, 65; auth, The romaunt of the rose & Le roman de la Rose, Blackwell & Mott, 67, Univ. Calif, 68; Frederick Philip Grove, McClelland & Stewart, 69; Second image: comparative studies in Quebec/Canadian literature, 71 & Lark des neiges (novel), 71, New Press, Toronto; Structural linguistics and English prosody, Col. Eng, 10/58, In: Readings in applied English linguistics, Appleton, 2nd ed, 64 & In: The structure of verse: modern essays in prosody, Fawcett, 66; The romaunt of the rose and source manuscripts, PMLA, 6/59; plus others. Add: Dept. of English, University of Sherbrooke, P.Q. J1K 2G3, Can.

SUTHERLAND, STELLA (HELEN), History, English. See Volume I, History.

SUTHERLAND, WILLIAM OWEN SHEPPARD, b. Wilmington, N.C, Jan. 19, 21; m. 47; c. 4. ENGLISH LITERATURE. A.B, Univ. N.C, 42, A.M, 47, Ph.D, 50. Part-time instr. ENG, Univ. N.C, 46-50, instr, 50-51; Northwest. Univ, 51-54; asst. prof, UNIV. TEX, AUSTIN, 54-58, assoc. prof. 58-65, PROF, 65- C.Eng, U.S.A, 42-45, Capt. MLA; S. Cent. Mod. Lang. Asn. (exec. comt, 68-70); NCTE; Conf. Col. Compos. & Commun.(exec. comt, 68-70). Elizabethan drama; 18th century English literature, especially periodicals and drama. Publ: Art of the satirist, Univ. Tex, 65; Essay forms in Aaron Hill's Prompter, In: Studies in the early English periodical, Univ. N.C, 57; Techniques for a subject index of eighteenth century journals, Univ. Tex. Libr. Chronicles; Popular imagery in The medal, Univ. Tex. Stud. Eng, 56. Add: Dept. of English, University of Texas at Austin, Austin, TX 78712.

SUTTLES, WILLIAM MAURRELLE, b. Ben Hill, Ga, July 25, 20; m. 50. SPEECH, RELIGION. B.C.S, Ga. State Univ, 42; M.Div, Yale, 46; Th.M, Emory Univ, 47, M.R.E, 53; Ed.D, Auburn Univ, 58; D.D, Mercer Univ, 72. Asst. registr. & instr. Eng. & speech, GA. STATE UNIV, 42-44, asst. prof. Eng. & speech, 46-55, assoc. prof. SPEECH & chmn. dept, 55-58, PROF, 57-, EDUC. ADMIN. & HIGHER EDUC, 70-, EXEC. V.PRES. & PROVOST, 70-, dean stud, 56-62, v.pres. acad. affairs, 64-69. Pastor, Haralson Baptist Church, Ga, 50-; Luthersville Baptist Church, 51-62; v.pres, Rich's Inc, Atlanta, 62-64; mem. southeast. regional manpower adv. comt, U.S. Dept. Labor, 72- Rural minister of the yr, Emory Univ. & Progressive Farmer Mag, 59; clergyman of the yr, Ga. Region, Nat. Conf. Christians & Jews, 71. U.S.N, 44-46. Speech Commun. Asn; South. Speech Commun. Asn. Higher education. Publ: Next steps, Manpower Resources South, 61; Your community needs you and you need your community, Proc. South. Indust. Rels. Conf, 63; The growth of Georgia State Col, Atlanta Econ. Rev, 68. Add: Office of Executive Vice President & Provost, Georgia State University, 33 Gilmer St. S.E, Atlanta, GA 30303.

SUTTON, BETTY SMITH, b. Indianapolis, Ind, July 9, 22; m. 44, 71; c. 2. EIGHTEENTH CENTURY ENGLISH LITERATURE. B.S, Ohio State Univ, 59, M.A, 62; Ph.D.(Eng), Mich. State Univ, 70. Asst. instr. Eng. compos, Ohio State Univ, 59-62, instr. ENG, 62-69; ASST. PROF, INDIANA UNIV. PA, 69-70; OHIO STATE UNIV, 70- Am. Soc. 18th Century Stud; MLA. Restoration literature; Counter-Enlightenment literature. Add: Dept. of English, Ohio State University, 164 W. 17th Ave, Columbus, OH 43210.

SUTTON, CARL, b. Ft. Worth, Tex, Jan. 25, 20; m. 45. AMERICAN & ENGLISH LITERATURE. B.A, Tex, Christian Univ, 38, M.A, 40; fel, Univ. Tex, 42-43. Instr. ENG, Ga. Inst. Technol, 45-46; ASST. PROF. N.TEX. STATE UNIV, 46- Guest bk. reviewer, Ft. Worth Star-Telegram, 64-66. Ctr. Stud. Democratic Insts; S.Cent. Mod. Lang. Asn; S.Cent. Renaissance Conf. American periodicals of the first half of the 19th century; influence of current periodicals on American politics; symbolism in the poetry of Gerard Manley Hopkins. Publ: Time is ruthless; Benjamin Franklin, rational opportunist. Add: 1411 Greenwood Dr, Denton, TX 76201.

SUTTON, GEORGE W, b. London, Ky, Sept. 16, 36; m. 61; c. 2. ENGLISH. B.A, Georgetown Col, 58; M.A, Univ. Miss, 60, Ph.D.(Eng), 67. Instr. ENG, U.S. Naval Acad, 64-67; assoc. prof, EAST. KY. UNIV, 67-74, PROF, 74- U.S.N, 63-67, Lt.(jg). MLA. William Faulkner; 20th century American novel. Add: Dept. of English, Eastern Kentucky University, Richmond, KY 40475.

SUTTON, MAX KEITH, b. Huntsville, Ark, June 3, 37; m. 60; c. 3. ENGLISH. B.A, Univ. Ark, 59; M.A, Duke Univ, 60, Ph.D.(Eng), 64. Asst. prof. ENG, UNIV. KANS, 64-68, ASSOC. PROF, 68- MLA. Victorian literature. Publ: Smart's Compleat cat, Col. Eng, 1/63; Inverse sublimity in Victorian humor, Victorian Stud, 12/66. Add: Dept. of English, University of Kansas, Lawrence, KS 66044.

SUTTON, VIVIAN R, b. Clarence, N.Y; m. 41; c. 1. ENGLISH & AMERICAN LITERATURE, WRITING. A.B, Oberlin Col, 34; M.A, Bryn Mawr Col, 37, Ph.D.(Eng), 42; Ohio State Univ, 37-39 & 40-41. Instr. ENG, Conn. Col, 42-44; Ohio State Univ, 46; asst. prof, Trenton State Col, 60-61; STATE UNIV. N.Y. COL. ENVIRON. SCI. & FORESTRY, 62-67, ASSOC. PROF, 67- MLA. Contemporary American and English literature and the environment; American writers and the natural world. Publ: Co-auth, Plato to Alexander Pope: backgrounds of modern criticism, Odyssey, 66. Add: Dept. of English, State University of New York College of Environmental Science & Forestry, Syracuse, NY 13210.

SUTTON, WALTER, b. Milwaukee, Wis, Jan. 25, 16; m. 41; c. 1. AMERICAN LITERATURE, LITERARY CRITICISM. B.A, Heidelberg Col, 37; M.A, Ohio State Univ, 38, Howald scholar, 47-48, Ph.D, 46. Asst. prof. Eng, SYRACUSE UNIV, 48-52, assoc. prof, 52-59, prof, 59-71, DISTINGUISHED PROF. HUMANITIES, 71-, chmn. dept. Eng, 71-74. Counc. Humanities vis. fel, Princeton, 60-61; vis. prof, Univ. Minn, 60; Univ. Wash, summer 66; Colgate Univ, 67; Univ. Hawaii, summer 68; consult. Am. lit, Col. Entrance Exam. Bd, 68-70; mem. ed. bd, Am. Lit, 73- U.S.C.G, 42-45. Am. Soc. Aesthet; MLA. American fiction; modern criticism; modern poetry. Publ: The western book trade, Ohio State Univ, 61; Ezra Pound (20th century views), 63 & Modern American criticism, 63, Prentice-Hall; co-auth, Plato to Alexander Pope: backgrounds of modern criticism, Odyssey, 66; co-ed, American literature: tradition and innovation, Heath, 69; auth, American free verse, New Directions, 73; Criticism and poetry, In: American poetry, Arnold, London, 65; Mauberley, The waste land, and the problem of unified form, Contemporary Lit, 68. Add: Dept. of English, Syracuse University, Syracuse, NY 13210.

SUTTON, WILLIAM ALFRED, b. Cleveland, Ohio, Dec. 2, 15; m. 39; c. 1. ENGLISH, AMERICAN LITERATURE. A.B, West. Reserve Univ, 36; M.A, Ohio State Univ, 37, Ph.D.(Eng), 43. Instr. ENG, Muskingum Col, 39-41; asst. prof, Univ. Tenn, 46-47; BALL STATE UNIV, 47-51, assoc. prof, 51-56, PROF, 56-, coord. M.A. prog. Eng, 67-71. A.U.S, 43-46, Res, 46-51, Capt. NCTE (mem. nominating comt, 54); Col. Eng. Asn. Erskine Caldwell; Robert Frost; Carl Sandburg. Publ: Co-auth, The education of teachers of English, Appleton, 63; auth, Exit to Elsinore, Ball State Monogr, 67; The road to Winesburg, Scarecrow, 72; Sexual fairness in language, Delaware Press, 73; On caring less, CEA Forum, 2/72; The Swedishness of Carl Sandburg, Am. Scand. Rev, summer 72; Margaret Bourke-White and Erskine Caldwell, Courier, spring 73; plus many others. Add: Dept. of English, Ball State University, Muncie, IN 47306.

SVANOE, HAROLD C, b. Oslo, Norway, May 15, 10; m. 35; c. 3. SPEECH. B.A, Augustana Col.(S.Dak), 32; M.A, Univ. Denver, 39; Ph.D, Northwest. Univ, 53. Teacher hist. & speech, Centerville High Sch, S.Dak, 33-36; Milbank High Sch, 36-39; asst. prof. SPEECH, Cent. Mo. State Col, 39-42, assoc. prof. & head dept, 42-49; assoc. prof, Cent. Methodist Col, 49-57; LUTHER COL.(IOWA), 57-72, PROF, 72- Speech Commun. Asn; Norweg-Am. Hist. Asn; Am. Forensic Asn. Argumentation and debate; phonetics; public address. Add: Dept. of Speech, Luther College, Decorah, IA 52101.

SWAIM, KATHLEEN MACKENZIE, b. Carlisle, Pa, Jan. 23, 36. ENGLISH. B.A, Gettysburg Col, 57; M.A, Pa. State Univ, 58; Fulbright fel, Trinity Col. (Dublin), 62-63; M.A, Middlebury Col, 63; Ph.D.(Eng), Univ. Pa, 66. Instr. ENG, Dickinson Col, 58-60; Univ. Pa, 64-66, asst. prof, 66-67; UNIV. MASS, AMHERST, 67-72, ASSOC. PROF, 72-, fac. growth grant, summer 68, acting assoc. head dept. Eng, 73. Mem. ed. bd, Eng. Lit. Renaissance, 68-; Milton Stud, 71- MLA; NCTE; Milton Soc. Am; Renaissance Soc. Am. Milton; Swift; allegory. Publ: Co-auth, A concordance to Milton's English poetry, Clarendon, Oxford, 72; auth, A reading of Gulliver's travels, Mouton, The Hague, 72; contrib, Milton Studies, Univ. Pittsburgh, Vols. II & V, 71 & 73. Add: Dept. of English, University of Massachusetts, Amherst, MA 01002.

SWAIN, VICTOR CROWELL, b. New Brunswick, N.J, Aug. 31, 12. ENGLISH. Mus.B, Yale, 38; B.A, Univ. Bridgeport, 48; M.A, Columbia Univ, 51, Ph.D, 61. Instr. ENG, UNIV. BRIDGEPORT, 48-57, asst. prof, 57-67, ASSOC. PROF, 67- U.S.N.R, 43-46. Col. Eng. Asn; Milton Soc. Am; MLA. Milton and 17th century English literature. Publ: On the meaning of wit in seventeenth century England, Univ. Microfilms, 62. Add: Dept. of English, University of Bridgeport, Bridgeport, CT 06602.

SWAN, JESSE R, JR, b. Great Falls, Mont, Apr. 12, 16; m. 44; c. 4. DRAMA, SPEECH. A.B, Univ. Calif, Berkeley, 39; Pasadena Playhouse Col. Theatre, 39-41, 46-47; M.A, Univ. South. Calif, 55. From assoc. prof. to PROF. DRAMA & SPEECH, SCRIPPS COL, 56-, supv. dir, Shakespeare Summer Festival, 61-67. From assoc. prof. to prof. drama & speech, Claremont Men's Col. & Harvey Mudd Col, 56-; prof, Pitzer Col, 56- U.S.A.F, 41-44, Capt. Am. Theatre Asn. Add: Dept. of Drama & Speech, Scripps College, Claremont, CA 91711.

SWAN, WALLACE JOHN, b. Brooklyn, N.Y, June 7, 38; m. 63; c. 1. ENGLISH. A.B, Univ. Fla, 63, Ph.D.(Eng), 67. Asst. prof. ENG, MURRAY STATE UNIV, 67-68, ASSOC. PROF, 68- U.S.A.F, 56-60, Res, 60-62. MLA; S.Atlantic Mod. Lang. Asn. Old English; Middle English literature; historical linguistics. Add: P.O. Box 996, University Station, Murray, KY 42071.

SWANK, EARLE ROBERT, b. Tamaqua, Pa, Oct. 6, 21. ENGLISH. A.B, Muhlenberg Col, 43; A.M, Harvard, 48. Instr. ENG, CARNEGIE-MELLON UNIV, 48-50, asst. prof, 50-62, LECTR, 62-, DEAN DIV. STUD. AFFAIRS, 68-, dean men, 59-67, dean stud, 67-68. Add: Div. of Student Affairs, Carnegie-Mellon University, 5000 Forbes Ave, Pittsburgh, PA 15213.

SWANN, BRIAN S.F, b. Wallsend, Northumberland, Eng, Aug. 13, 40. ENGLISH. B.A, Queens' Col, 62; M.A, Cambridge, 64; Ph.D.(Eng), Princeton, 70. Instr. ENG, Princeton Univ, 65-66; Rutgers Univ, 66-67; ASST. PROF, Princeton Univ, 70-72; COOPER UNION, 72- MLA; Poetry Soc. Am. Nineteenth century English novel; modern-contemporary, British-American poetry; 20th century Italian poetry. Publ: Co-ed & transl, The collected poems of Lucio Piccolo, Princeton Univ, 73; Theodore Roethke and The shift of things, Literary Rev, winter 73; The mill on the floss and tragedy, Eng. Miscellany, spring 74; Daniel Deronda: Jewishness, Ecumenicism, and the novel, Novel, spring 74; plus others. Add: Dept. of Humanities, Cooper Union, Cooper Square, New York, NY 10003.

SWANSON, DONALD ROLAND, b. Pittsburgh, Pa, Nov. 20, 27; m. 55. ENGLISH. B.A, Wash. & Jefferson Col, 53, M.A, Univ. Conn. 55; Ph.D.(Eng), Rutgers Univ, 65. Instr. ENG, Upsala Col, 55-58, asst. prof, 58-66, assoc. prof, 66-71; PROF, WRIGHT STATE UNIV, 71- Coord, Orange Opportunity Corp, 66; fac. fel, Upsala Col, summer 66, fac. res. fel, 69. U.S.N, 45-46. MLA; Eng. Inst; Col. Eng. Asn.(treas, 71-73). Modern British literature. Publ: Three conquerers, Mouton, 69; Richard Hughes, Twayne, 74; Far and fair within: a walk to Wachusett, E.S.Q, 3rd quarter 69; The exercise of irony in Benito Cereno, Am. Transcendental Quart, summer 70; The growth of a poem: Coleridge's Dejection, BSU Forum, fall 71; plus many others. Add: Dept. of English, Wright State University, Dayton, OH 45431.

SWANSON, JOHN WESLEY, b. Chesterton, Ind, July 5, 04. THEATRE. B.L, Northwest. Univ, 26, A.M, 27. From asst. prof. to EMER. PROF. SPEECH & THEATRE, UNIV. ILL, URBANA, 27-, STAFF ASSOC, OFF. PRES, 65-, vis. lectr. theatre, 70-71. Vis. prof, Ill. State Univ, 67-68. Am. Theatre Asn; Am. Soc. Theatre Res; Am. Nat. Theatre & Acad; Nat. Col. Players (pres, 40-45); Soc. Theatre Res, Gt. Brit. The new movement in the theater; Edward Gordon Craig. Add: Dept. of Speech, Lincoln Hall, University of Illinois, Urbana, IL 61801.

SWANSON, ROY ARTHUR, Comparative Literature. See Volume III, Foreign Languages, Linguistics & Philology.

SWANSON, WILLIAM JOSEPH, b. Philadelphia, Pa, Mar. 4, 31. AMERICAN LITERATURE, SPANISH. A.B, San Diego State Col, 58; M.A, Fla. State Univ, 59; Ed.D.(Eng), Univ. North. Colo, 72; hon. Litt.M, Inst. Estud. Iberoam, Mexico, 73. Instr. Eng, Jacksonville Univ, 59-61; asst. prof. Eng. & Span, Abraham Baldwin Agr. Col, 62-65; instr, W.Ga. Col, 65-67; asst. prof. ENG, SOUTHWEST. STATE COL, 68-73, ASSOC. PROF, 73- Prof. Mexican idioms & acting dean stud, Inst. Estud. Iberoam, Coahuila, Mexico, summer 66. Med.Serv.C, U.S.A, 49-52, Sgt. AAUP; Am. Asn. Teachers Span. & Port; S.Cent. Mod. Lang. Asn. Twentieth century American literature; Mexican folklore. Publ: Religious implications in The confessions of Nat Turner, 7/70 & Ernest Cudlipp and the law of love, 4/71, Cimarron Rev; Les deux morts de Felix Faure, James Joyce Quart, fall 71. Add: Division of Language Arts, Southwestern State College, Weatherford, OK 73096.

SWARD, ROBERT S, b. Chicago, Ill, June 23, 33; m. 60; c. 4. ENGLISH. B.A, Univ. Ill, 56; Bread Loaf Sch. Eng, summers, 56-58; M.A, State Univ. Iowa, 58; poetry fel, Bread Loaf Writers' Conf, 58; Fulbright grant, Univ. Bristol, Eng, 60-61. Instr. Eng, Conn. Col, 58-59; Cornell Univ, 62-66; writer-in-residence creative writing, Univ. Iowa, 66-67; Poetry Workshop, Aspen Writers' Conf, 67-69; ED. & PUBL, SOFT PRESS, 70- Fel. poetry workshop, State Univ. Iowa, 56-58, teaching grant, 58; writing fel, MacDowell Colony, Peterbourough, N.H, 59, 61-62; fel, Yaddo, 60-61, 63; Huntington-Hartford Found. & Guggenheim fels, creative writing, 64-65; Wurlitzer Found. fel, Taos, N.Mex, 65; D.H. Lawrence fel, Univ. N.Mex, summer 66; poetry reader, Northwest Poetry Circuit, 69; Poet-in-residence, Univ. of Victoria, 69-73; reader, Univ. Pittsburgh Poetry Series, 71; mem, Comt. Small Mag. Ed. & Publ, 70- Dylan Thomas Poetry Award, 58. U.S.N, 51-53. Mod. Poetry Asn. Literature of the 20th century, especially poetry; recent Canadian literature; Vancouver Island poetry. Publ: Advertisements, Odyssey Chapbook Publ, 58; Uncle dog, and other poems, Putnam, London, 62; Kissing the dancer, and other poems, 64 & Thousand-year-old fiancée and other poems, 65, Cornell Univ; In Mexico, Ambit, London, 66; Hannah's cartoon 70 & ed, Vancouver Island poems, 73, Soft Press; Horgbortom stringbottom, I am yours, you are history, 70 & Poems: new & selected (1957-1973), 73, Swallow; The Jurassic Shales (novel), Coach House, Toronto, 74; chap, In: New: American & Canadian poetry, Crossing Press, 73; plus others. Add: 1050 St. David St, Victoria, B.C, Can.

SWARDSON, HAROLD ROLAND, b. Chicago, Ill, Sept. 16, 25; m. 49; c. 3. ENGLISH. B.A, Tulane Univ, 47, M.A, 48; Ph.D, Univ. Minn, 56. Instr. ENG, Univ. Cincinnati, 48-49; OHIO UNIV, 54-57, asst. prof, 57-62, assoc. prof, 62-69, PROF, 69- U.S.N, 44-46, 52-54, Comdr. Literary criticism; seventeenth century literature. Publ: Poetry and the fountain of light, Allen & Unwin, London, 62. Add: 50 Sunnyside Dr, Athens, OH 45701.

SWAYZE, WALTER EUGENE, b. Toronto, Can, Nov. 20, 22; m. 47; c. 3. ENGLISH. B.A, Univ. Toronto, 44; fel. & M.A, Yale, 48, Sterling fel. & Ph.D. (Eng), 51. Teaching fel. ENG, Univ. Toronto, 45-46; instr, Col. William & Mary, 49-51, asst. prof, 51-53; PROF. & CHMN. DEPT, United Col, Winnipeg, 53-67; UNIV. WINNIPEG, 67- Can. Counc. sr. fel, 58-59. R.C.N.V.R, 44-45. MLA; Asn. Can. Univ. Teachers Eng; Humanities Asn. Can.(nat. v.pres, 73-); Can. Counc. Teachers Eng; Can. Asn. Irish Stud. Milton; Anglo-Irish; Canadian literature. Publ: The Sir William Watson Collection, Yale Univ. Libr. Gazette, 10/52; Early Wordsworthian biography, Bull. N.Y. Pub. Libr, 60; The odyssey of Margaret Laurence, Eng. Quart, fall 70. Add: Dept. of English, University of Winnipeg, 515 Portage Ave, Winnipeg, Man. R3B 2E9, Can.

SWEDENBERG, HUGH THOMAS, JR, b. Milledgeville, Ga, Aug. 2, 06; m. 36; c. 1. ENGLISH LITERATURE. A.B, Presby. Col.(S.C), 28, hon. Litt.D, 72; A.M, Columbia Univ, 29; Ph.D, Univ. N.C, 37. Asst. prof. ENG, Presby. Col.(S.C), 29-31, prof, 33-36; from instr. to PROF. UNIV. CALIF, LOS ANGELES, 37-, Clark Libr. prof, William Andrews Clark Mem. Libr, 69-71. Guggenheim fel, 50; Folger Shakespeare Libr. fel, 62; vis. Rushton prof, Birmingham-South. Col, spring 66. MLA; Int. Asn. Univ. Prof. Eng. English literature of the 17th and 18th centuries. Publ: The theory of the epic in England, 1650-1800, co-ed, The works of John Dryden: poems, 1681-1684, Vol. II, 72 & ed, England in the Restoration and early eighteenth century: essays on culture and society, 72, Univ. Calif; ed, Essential articles for the study of John Dryden, Archon Bks, 66; Restoration and early eighteenth century poetry, Knopf, 68. Add: Dept. of English, University of California, Los Angeles, CA 90024.

SWEENEY, FRANCIS, S.J, b. Milford, Mass, Feb. 19, 16. ENGLISH. B.A, Col. Holy Cross, 39; Weston Col, 42-44, 45-49; M.A, Boston Col, 44. Instr. Eng. & Latin, Cranwell Sch, 44-45; ASST. PROF. ENG, BOSTON COL, 51- Founder & dir, Boston Col. Humanities Ser; Younger Poets Ser; reviewer, N.Y. Times Book Rev. MLA. Modern Rome; Jesuitica. Publ: Baroque moment, McMullen Bks, 51; Bernardine Realino, Macmillan, 51; ed, Vatican impressions, Sheed, 62; co-auth, The crowned hilltop, Hawthorne, 62; ed, The knowledge explosion, Farrar, Straus 66 & The Vatican and world peace, Colin Smythe, Eng, 70. Add: Dept. of English, Boston College, Chestnut Hill, MA 02167.

SWEENEY, GERARD MICHAEL, b. New York, N.Y, Sept. 17, 42; m. 68; c. 1. ENGLISH & AMERICAN LITERATURE. B.S, Manhattan Col, 64; M.A, New York Univ, 66; Ph.D.(Eng), Univ. Wis-Madison, 72. Teacher ENG, Stepinac High Sch, White Plains, N.Y, 66-67; res. asst, Univ. Wis, 68-69, teaching asst, 69-71; ASST. PROF, UNIV. AKRON, 71- MLA; AAUP. American fiction; Herman Melville. Publ: The Medea Howells saw, 3/70 & Melville's Hawthornian bell-tower: a fairy-tale source, 5/73, Am. Lit; Beauty and truth: Poe's A descent into the maelström, Poe Stud, 6/73. Add: Dept. of English, University of Akron, Akron, OH 44325.

SWEENEY, MARY ROSE, U.S. citizen. ENGLISH, EDUCATIONAL PSYCHOLOGY. B.S. Ed, Southwest Mo. State Col, 43; M.A, Univ. Mo, Columbia, 48; Ed.D.(Eng. educ), Univ. Kans, 60. Teacher pub. schs, Mo. & Wash, 42-44 & 49-50; instr. Eng, Drury Col, 44-46; Southwest Mo. State Col, 46-48; receptionist & secy. law firm, Eisenhower, Hunter & Ramsdell, Wash, 48-49; instr. ENG, SOUTHWEST MO. STATE UNIV, 50-53, asst. prof, 53-58, assoc. prof, 58-60, PROF, 60-, asst. dean fac, 65-72. MLA; Am. Personnel & Guidance Asn; Nat. Asn. Gen. & Lib. Stud. American literature particularly Emily Dickinson; novel as genre; reading problems. Publ: Co-auth, High school English—quantity or quality?, Bull. Nat. Asn. Sec. Sch. Prin, 12/62 & Reading in High Sch, fall 63. Add: Dept. of English, Southwest Missouri State University, Springfield, MO 65802.

SWEENEY, PATRICIA RUNK, b. Buffalo, N.Y, Oct. 4, 38; m. 67; c. 1. ENGLISH. B.A, Univ. Rochester, 60; Woodrow Wilson fel, Univ. Calif, Berkeley, 60-61, univ. fels, 61-63, M.A, 62, Ph.D.(Eng), 67. Lectr. ENG, City Col. New York, 63-65; instr. Univ. Mass, Amherst, 65-67, asst. prof, 67-69; Tougaloo Col, 69-71; mem. summer sch. fac, Millsaps Col, 70-72; adj. asst. prof, Franklin & Marshall Col, spring 73. O'Connor stud. award, Univ. Rochester, 60; Carnegie Col. Teaching internship, City Col. New York, summer 63. MLA. Nineteenth-century fiction; children's literature. Publ: The question of snobbery in Great expectations, Dickensian, 1/68. Add: 112 E. Ridge St, Carlisle, PA 17013.

SWEETKIND, MORRIS, b. Odessa, Russia, Dec. 8, 98; U.S. citizen; m. 27; c. 2. ENGLISH. Ph.B, Yale, 20, M.A, 23. Teacher Eng. & chmn. dept, Cheshire Acad, 20-71; RETIRED. Lectr, Univ. Conn, 39-50; South. Conn. State Col, 50-55; instr. lit. criticism, Eng. inst, Univ. Calif, Los Angeles, summer 66. U.S.A, 18. NCTE. English and American poetry; drama; literary criticism. Publ: Teaching poetry in high school, 63 & ed, Hardy's The Mayor of Casterbridge, 65, Macmillan; co-auth, Introducing the drama, 63 & Tragedy, history, and romance, 68, Holt; Wonderful world (poems for children), Mack, 67; ed, Ten great one act plays, Bantam, 68; auth, Getting into poetry, Holbrook, 72; Poetry in a scientific world, Eng. J, 3/70. Add: 4 Birch Dr, New Haven, CT 06515.

SWEETSER, WESLEY DUAINE, b. National City, Calif, May 25, 19; m. 42; c. 4. ENGLISH. B.A, Univ. Colo, 38, M.A, 46, Ph.D.(Eng. lit), 58. Instr. Eng, Univ. Colo, 45-48; asst. prof, Peru State Teachers Col, 48-50; assoc. prof, U.S. Air Force Acad, 58-63; asst. prof. air sci, Univ. Nebr, 63-66; vis. prof. ENG, Nebr. Wesleyan Univ, 66-67; assoc. prof, STATE UNIV. N.Y. COL. OSWEGO, 67-69, PROF, 69- C.Eng, U.S.A, 40-41; U.S.A.F, 42-45, 51-65, Maj. MLA; Arthur Machen Soc. Arthur Machen; Ralph Hodgson; colonial backgrounds in 19th century British literature. Publ: Arthur Machen, Twayne, 64; co-auth, A bibliography of Arthur Machen, Univ. Tex, 65; Arthur Machen: surface realities or essence of spirit, 64; contrib, Thomas Hardy: an annotated bibliography of writings about him, North. Ill. Univ, 73; plus one other. Add: R.D. 5, Ridgeway Sites, Oswego, NY 13126.

SWENEY, JOHN ROBERT, b. Shenandoah, Iowa, Nov. 25, 37; m. 61; c. 3. ENGLISH & AMERICAN LITERATURE. B.A, Colo. Col, 60; M.A, Claremont Grad. Sch, 62; Ph.D.(Eng), Univ. Wis-Madison, 68. Instr. ENG, Whitman Col, 62-64; COLBY COL, 67-68, asst. prof, 68-73, ASSOC. PROF, 73- NDEA Inst. Ling. fel, summer 68. AAUP. Restoration literature. Publ: The dedication of Thomas Southerne's The wives excuse, Library, 70; Dryden's Lines to Mrs. Creed, Philol. Quart, 72; The religion of Lady Elizabeth Howard Dryden, Notes & Queries, 72. Add: Dept. of English, Colby College, Waterville, ME 04901.

SWETMAN, GLENN ROBERT, b. Biloxi, Miss, May 20, 36; m. 64; c. 2. ENGLISH, LANGUAGES. B.S, Univ. South. Miss, 57, fel, 57-58, M.A, 59; fel, Tulane Univ, 61-64, Ph.D.(Eng), 66. Instr. Eng, Ark. State Univ, 58-59; McNeese State Col, 59-61; Univ. Col, Tulane Univ, 61-64; asst. prof, Univ. South. Miss, 64-66; assoc. prof, La. Polytech. Inst, 66-67; PROF. ENG, NICHOLLS STATE UNIV, 67-, head dept, 67-70. Fel, Boswell Inst, 64; mem. exec. bd, Int. Boswellian Inst, 72-; mem. exec. bed, South. Lit. Festival Asn, 72- KQUE Haiku Poetry Award, 64; Green World brief forms award, 65; Col. Arts Poetry Award, 66; Yokosuka Black Ship Festival Poetry Award, Japan, 67; Order of Gracian, Int. Boswellian Inst, 70. U.S.A.R, 57-63, Sgt. Fel. Int. Poetry Soc; Soc. Stud. South. Lit; Nat. Fed. State Poetry Soc.(nat. del. & 3rd v.pres, 72-); Inst. Elec. & Electronics Engrs; MLA; NCTE; Am. Soc. Engineering Educ. Modern poetry, especially Wallace Stevens; creative writing; foreign language studies. Publ: Deka #1 (poems), Argus, 73; Tunnel of love, Pterodactyl Press, 73 & Tunel de amor, Xavier Univ, Bolivia, 73; Franz Kafka and the psychological aberration, McNeese Rev, winter 60-61; The haiku, the sonnet, and the English language, summer 64 & co-auth, Quechua poetry, winter 68, Quartet. Add: Dept. of English, Nicholls State University, Thibodaux, LA 70301.

SWETNAM, FORD T, JR, b. Alexandria, Va, Aug. 30, 41. LITERATURE. A.B, Hamilton Col, 63; Woodrow Wilson fels, Cornell Univ, 63-64, 66-67, M.A, 64, Ph.D.(Eng), 67. ASST. PROF. ENG, OHIO STATE UNIV, 67-, res. grant, 68. Nat. Endowment for Humanities summer stipend, 68. MLA. Romanticism; life in general. Publ: The satiric voices of The prelude, In: Bicentenary Wordsworth studies, Cornell Univ, 70; The controversial use of Wordsworth's comedy, Wordsworth Circle, 72; Wordsworth, In: The English romantic poets, MLA, 72. Add: Dept. of English, Ohio State University, Columbus, OH 43210.

SWIFT, MARVIN HENRY, b. Detroit, Mich, Apr. 22, 23; m. 47; c. 3. WRITTEN COMMUNICATION, ORGANIZATIONAL BEHAVIOR. B.A, Univ. Mich, 47, M.A, 49; Wayne State Univ, 48-49. Sect. head coord. reports, GEN. MOTORS INST, 54-62, sr. tech. instr. tech. writing, 54-64, ASSOC. PROF. humanities, 64-68, COMMUN, 68- U.S.A.A.F, 43-45, 2nd Lt. Conf. Col. Compos. & Commun; NCTE; AAAS; Am. Bus. Commun. Asn; Int. Commun. Asn. Humanities; social and behavioral sciences; linguistics and technical writing. Publ: Co-auth, Industrial report writing, Gen. Motors Inst, 55; auth, College composition for communication on the job, ABCA Bull, 9/71; Clear writing means clear thinking means..., Harvard Bus. Rev, 1-2/73. Add: General Motors Institute, 1700 W. Third Ave, Flint, MI 48502.

SWIGART, FORD HARRIS, JR, b. Barberton, Ohio, Jan. 30, 29; m. 57; c. 3. ENGLISH. B.A, Otterbein Col, 51; M.A, Univ. Pittsburgh, 59, Ph.D.(Eng.

novel), 66. Asst. prof. ENG, Univ. Pittsburgh, Johnstown, 56-66; assoc. prof, IND. UNIV. PA, 66-69, PROF, 69- Danforth Assoc, 70- NCTE; AAUP. Shakespeare; 18th century; interdisciplinary studies. Publ: Ann Radcliffe's veil imagery, Stud. Humanities, 3/69. Add: Dept. of English, Indiana University of Pennsylvania, Indiana, PA 15701.

SWIGGART, PETER, b. Nashville, Tenn, Nov. 17, 27; m. 52; c. 2. AMERICAN LITERATURE. B.A, Princeton, 50; Sterling fel, Yale, 53-54, Ph.D, 54. Instr. Eng, Amherst Col, 54-56; Sewanee Rev. fel, 56-57; asst. prof. Eng, Univ. Tex, 57-58; Fulbright lectr. Am. lit, Austria, 59-60; asst. prof. ENG, Univ. Tex, 62-63; BRANDEIS UNIV, 63-65, ASSOC. PROF, 65- U.S.A, 46-47. Modern American fiction; 19th century American literature; aesthetics and theory of literature. Publ: The art of Faulkner's novels, Univ. Tex, 62; Anatomy of writing, Prentice-Hall, 66. Add: Dept. of English, Brandeis University, Waltham, MA 02154.

SWIGGER, RONALD T, b. Oklahoma City, Okla. COMPARATIVE LITERATURE. B.A, Univ. N.Mex, 63; Ph.D.(comp. lit), Ind. Univ, 67. Lectr. COMP. LIT, Brooklyn Col, 67-69; ASST. PROF, UNIV. MD, COLLEGE PARK, 69- MLA; Am. Comp. Lit. Asn; Int. Comp. Lit. Asn; AAUP; S.Atlantic Mod. Lang. Asn. Modern literature; romanticism. Publ: Reflections on language in Queneau's novels, Contemporary Lit, fall, 72. Add: Dept. of Comparative Literature, University of Maryland, College Park, MD 20740.

SWINGLE, LARRY J, b. Columbus, Ohio, Aug. 24, 40; m. 62. ENGLISH. B.A, Ohio State Univ, 62; M.A, Univ. Wis, 63, Ph.D.(Eng), 67. ASST. PROF. ENG, Univ. Wash, 66-73; UNIV. KY, 73- MLA. Nineteenth century English literature. Add: Dept. of English, University of Kentucky, Lexington, KY 40506.

SWINNEY, DONALD HENRY, b. Muskogee, Okla, Feb. 1, 19; m; c. 3. SPEECH, DRAMA. M.A, Univ. Idaho, 47; Ph.D.(theatre), Ind. Univ, 62. PROF. theatre, Univ. Denver, 48-49; SPEECH & DRAMA, HOFSTRA UNIV, 50-, DIR. PLAYHOUSE, 66- Theatre consult, E-W Ctr. Theatre Auditorium, Univ. Hawaii, 61-63; Munic. Theatre-Concert Hall, Honolulu, Hawaii, 62-; Ruben Dario Teatro Nac, Managua, Nicaragua, 66-; State Univ. N.Y. Stony Brook, 67-; consult, Nat. Theatre Guatamala, 72. Med.Dept, U.S.A, 42-45. Am. Theatre Asn; U.S. Inst. Theatre Technol.(tech. secy, 63-65, pres, 65-68). Drama, especially design, technical aspects and history and theory; theatre consultation, especially planning and equipping. Publ: The Globe Playhouse at Hofstra, Educ. Theatre J. Add: Dept. of Drama, Hofstra University, Hempstead, NY 11550.

SWITZER, LESTER ERNEST, b. Berkeley, Calif; m. 58; c. 4. COMMUNICATIONS, AFRICAN HISTORY. B.A, Univ. Calif, Berkeley, 57, M.A, 59; grant, Berkeley Baptist Div. Sch, 61-63; Human Sci. Res. Counc. grant, 66-67; Ph.D.(hist), Univ. Natal, 72. Mem. staff newspapers, Africa, Gt. Brit. & U.S, 63-71; asst. prof. JOUR, Calif. State Univ, Los Angeles, 71-73, chmn. dept, 72-73; LECTR, RHODES UNIV, S.AFRICA, 73- African Stud. Asn. South African history; African ethnic journalism. Add: Dept. of Journalism, Rhodes University, P.O. Box 94, Grahamstown, C.P, Republic of South Africa.

SWORTZELL, LOWELL STANLEY, b. Washington, D.C, Aug. 5, 30; m. 59. EDUCATIONAL THEATRE, SPEECH & DRAMA. B.A, George Washington Univ, 53, M.A, 54; fel, Yale, 56-59; Ph.D.(educ. theatre), N.Y. Univ, 63. Asst. playwriting & theatre hist, Yale Sch. Drama, 58-59; asst. prof. speech & drama, Hofstra Univ, 59-60; dramatic art, N.Y. Univ, 60-65; speech & educ, Univ. Wis, 65-66; assoc. prof. EDUC. THEATRE, N.Y. UNIV, 66-70, PROF, 70- Mem, bd. trustees, Children's Mus. Washington D.C, 60-; co-dir, Children's Summer Theatre, Rutgers Univ, 61-62; Children's Theatre Inst, Univ. Wis, 65. U.S.A, 54-56. Am. Theatre Asn; Children's Theatre Asn; Speech Commun. Asn.(assoc. ed, Speech Teacher, 65-); Am. Soc. Theatre Res. Children's theatre; playwriting; education. Publ: Our American cousin, Dramatic Publ, 61; A partridge in a pear tree, French, 67; All the world's a stage: an anthology of plays for children, Delacorte, 72; The art of children's theatre, Houghton, (in press); Plays for children, 2/62 & 5/66, Why the peacock is proud, 10/71, Play's Mag; co-auth, Right on, Toady! relevancy in children's theatre, Children's Theatre Rev, 5/73. Add: Program in Educational Theatre, School of Education, New York University, New York, NY 10003.

SYKES, ROBERT HOWARD, b. Wheeling, W.Va, Dec. 1, 27; m. 52; c. 2. ENGLISH, AMERICAN STUDIES. A.B, W.Liberty State Col, 54; M.A, Univ. Pa, 55; Danforth fel, Univ. Pittsburgh, 60-61, Ph.D.(Eng), 61. Assoc. prof. Eng, Bethany Col, 55-68, dir. Am. stud. & W.Va. regional stud, 66-68; PROF. ENG. & CHMN. DEPT. & CHMN. DIV. LANG. & LIT, W.LIBERTY STATE COL, 68-, DIR. SCH. HUMANITIES, 71- Fulbright exchange prof, Univ. Tokyo, 64-65; lectr, Nat. Defense Inst, Washington & Jefferson Col, 67. U.S.A, 47-51, S/Sgt. MLA; Counc. Int. Educ.(mem. ed. bd, 66-). American literature; Asian studies; West Virginia regional studies. Publ: Proud heritage of West Virginia, Benedum Found, 67; Literary history of West Virginia, Educ. Found. Inc, 68; Japan's first bookmobile, Libr. J, 2/48; The horrid, obscure hurt of Henry James, Libr. Harbinger, spring 62; A source for Mark Twain's feud, W.Va. Hist. Quart, 4/68. Add: Dept. of English, School of Humanities, West Liberty State College, West Liberty, WV 26078.

SYLVESTER, BICKFORD, b. Washington, D.C, Dec. 31, 25; m. 60; c. 1. ENGLISH & AMERICAN LITERATURE. B.A, Univ. Conn, 53, M.A, 58; Ph.D.(Eng), Univ. Wash, 66. Instr. ENG, Kent State Univ, 57-60; asst. prof, Calif. State Col. Hayward, 64-66; UNIV. B.C, 66-68, ASSOC. PROF, 68- Can. Counc. summer grant, 67 & res. fel. in England, 68-69. U.S.A, 44-46. NCTE; MLA; Philol. Asn. Pac. Coast; Can. Asn. Am. Stud. American literature; romanticism. Publ: Natural mutability and human responsibility: form in Shakespeare's Lucrece, Col. Eng, 4/65; Hemingway's extended vision: The old man and the sea, PMLA, 3/66; Informed illusion in The old man and the sea, Mod. Fiction Stud, winter 66-67. Add: Dept. of English, University of British Columbia, Vancouver, B.C. V6T 1W5, Can.

SYLVESTER, RICHARD STANDISH, b. St. Louis, Mo, Nov. 30, 26; m. 56. ENGLISH. B.A, St. Louis Univ, 49; Rhodes scholar. & B.A, Oxford, 52, M.A, 56; fel. & Ph.D, Yale, 56. Instr. ENG, St. Louis Univ, 52-53; YALE, 55-65, PROF, 65-, EXEC. ED, YALE ED. COMPLETE WORKS OF ST. THOMAS MORE, 58- Secy, Yale Stud. Eng, 65-; co-ed, Archives, 66-; mem. ed. comt, Folger Ed. Works of Richard Hooker, 68-; adv. comt, Toronto Ed. of Erasmus in Eng, 69-; ed. comt, Folger Shakespeare Libr, 71-, consult, 73-74. U.S. Merchant Marine, 44-46. MLA; Asn. Am. Rhodes Scholars; Renaissance Soc. Am; Renaissance Eng. Text Soc.(v.pres, 71-). Thomas More and his circle; English Renaissance literature, 1475-1700; neo-Latin literature. Publ: Cavendish's Life of Wolsey, Oxford, 59; co-auth, Two early Tudor lives, 62, auth, Thomas More's History of Richard III, 63 & ed, St. Thomas More: action and contemplation, 72, Yale Univ; co-auth, Pace's De fructu, Renaissance Soc. Am, 67; co-ed, Thomas More's prayer book, 69; ed, Seventeenth century verse, 69 & Sixteenth century verse, 74, Anchor Bks. Add: 479 Ridge Rd, Hamden, CT 06517.

SYLVESTER, WILLIAM ARTHUR, b. Washington, D.C, July 1, 18; m. 47; c. 4. ENGLISH. A.B, Columbia Univ, 40; M.A, Univ. Chicago, 47; Ph.D, Univ. Minn, 51. Instr. Eng, Univ. Minn, 48-51; Univ. Ore, 51-52; asst. prof, Kans. State Col, 52-57; ed. tech. publ, Standard Oil Co.(Ohio), 57-60; asst. prof. Eng, Case Inst. Technol, 60-65; assoc. prof, STATE UNIV. N.Y. BUFFALO, 65-69, PROF. ENG. & COMP. LIT, 69-, dir. teaching fels, 65-66, chmn. summer session, 66, dir. electronic poetry workshop, summer 66. Ford fel, 54-55; lectr. Spanish, Colombia, 73. U.S.N.R, 41-46, Lt. MLA. Latin-Greek English; French-German drama; poetry readings. Publ: Transl, Agamemnon, Bobbs, 72; auth, Sestina, Poetry, 58; Essay upon a disjunctive principle in poetry, Col. Eng, 1/67; contrib, Commonweal; West. Humanities Rev; Poems in English and French, et Maintenant, 73; plus other poems. Add: Dept. of English, State University of New York at Buffalo, Buffalo, NY 14214.

SYLVIA, MARY, S.S.J, English, Drama. See REIMONDO, MARY SYLVIA, S.S.J.

SYMONIK, EMIL F, b. Fifield, Wis, Oct. 8, 16; m. 50; c. 3. ENGLISH. B.Ed, Milwaukee State Teacher's Col, 44; M.Ed, Wis. State Col, Milwaukee, 56. Teacher, Fifield Sch. Syst, 35-41; prin, Neopit Grade Sch, 45-47; PROF. ENG. & CHMN. DEPT, MILWAUKEE SCH. ENG, 47- Am. Soc. Eng. Educ; NCTE. Reading improvement; word use; drop out problems. Publ: Co-auth, Practical English, 58, McGraw, auth, rev. ed, 71; co-auth, Basic composition (manual), Milwaukee Sch. Eng, 60. Add: 7040 N. 40th St, Milwaukee, WI 53209.

SYMONS, JAMES MARTIN, b. Jacksonville, Ill, May 7, 37; m. 59; c. 3. SPEECH & DRAMA. B.A, Ill. Col, 59; M.A, South. Ill. Univ, Carbondale, 64; Ph.D.(theatre), Cornell Univ, 70. Asst. prof. speech & drama, Yankton Col, 64-67; Moorhead State Col, 70-71; asst. prof. & chmn. dept, Cols. St. Catherine & St. Thomas, 71-74; ASSOC. PROF. THEATRE & CHMN. DEPT, STATE UNIV. N.Y. ALBANY, 74- George Freedley Award, Theatre Libr. Asn, 71. U.S.N, 59-63, Lt.(jg). Speech Commun. Asn; Am. Theatre Asn. Russian theatre; Shakespearean production methods. Publ: Meyerhold's theatre of the grotesque, Univ. Miami, 71. Add: Dept. of Theatre, State University of New York at Albany, Albany NY 12203.

SYMULA, JAMES FRANCIS, b. Canandaigua, N.Y, June 8, 35; m. 58; c. 3. ENGLISH EDUCATION. B.S, State Univ. N.Y. Col. Cortland, 57, M.S, 63; D.Ed.(Eng. educ), State Univ. N.Y. Buffalo, 69. Teacher ENG, Marion Cent. Sch, N.Y, 57-64; Cent. High Sch, Auburn, 64-66; ASSOC. PROF, STATE UNIV. N.Y. COL. FREDONIA, 69- Proj. dir. develop. grant, Comput. Based Resource Unit, 71-72; chmn. proj. comt. on censorship, N.Y. State Eng. Counc, 72-; proj. dir. educ. prog. migrant youth, Workshop Teachers Migrant Children, 73; dir, Fredonia Migrant Tutorial Prog, 73- NCTE; Nat. Asn. Visual Literacy. Censorship of high school literature; media in the English classroom; visual response to literature. Publ: Ed, Trees to toads: a child's world CBRU, 72 & On the road CBRU, 73, Res. & Develop. Complex, State Univ. N.Y; auth, Are teachers responsible for censorship, Eng. J, 1/71; Search and destroy, Utah Counc. Eng. J, fall 72; Push it around and think about it, Eng. Rec, summer 73. Add: 3 Middlesex Dr, Fredonia, NY 14063.

SYNDERGAARD, LARRY EDWARD, b. Des Moines, Iowa, July 30, 36; m. 58; c. 2. ENGLISH LITERATURE, SCANDINAVIAN STUDIES. B.S.(forestry) & B.S.(gen. sci), Iowa State Univ, 59; Royal Col. Vet. & Agr, Denmark, 59-60; M.S, Univ. Wis-Madison, 63, Ph.D.(Eng), 70. ASST. PROF. ENG, WEST. MICH. UNIV, 68- Mem, Medieval Inst, West. Mich. Univ, 70- MLA; Mediaeval Acad. Am; Soc. Advan. Scand. Stud; Am. Folklore Soc; Am-Scand. Found. Folk literature; Scandinavian and medieval literature. Publ: Co-ed, Studies in medieval culture IV, West. Mich. Univ, 73; auth, The Skogsra of folklore and Strindberg's The crown bride, Comp. Drama, winter 72-73. Add: Dept. of English, Western Michigan University, Kalamazoo, MI 49001.

SYPHER, FRANCIS JACQUES, JR, b. Hackensack, N.J, Nov. 4, 41; m. 70. ENGLISH LITERATURE. A.B, Columbia Univ, 63, M.A, 64, Ph.D.(Eng. & comp. lit), 68. Preceptor ENG, Columbia Univ, 65-68; ASST. PROF, STATE UNIV. N.Y. ALBANY, 68- Res. Found. State Univ. N.Y. fac. res. fel, summer 73. MLA; AAUP; Tennyson Soc. Writings of Algernon Charles Swinburne; Victorian poetry; the novel. Publ: Swinburne and Wagner, Victorian Poetry, 6/71; A history of Harpers' Latin dictionary, 10/72 & Victoria's lapse from virtue: a lost leaf from Swinburne's La Soeur de la Reine, 10/73, Harvard Libr. Bull. Add: Dept. of English, 373 Humanities Bldg, State University of New York at Albany, Albany, NY 12222.

SYPHER, WYLIE, b. Mt. Kisco, N.Y, Dec. 12, 05; m. 29; c. 2. ENGLISH LITERATURE. A.B, Amherst Col, 27; fel, Tufts Col, 27-29, A.M, 29; A.M, Harvard, 32, Ph.D, 37; hon. Litt.D, Middlebury Col, 69; hon. L.H.D, Simmons Col, 73. Instr. Eng, SIMMONS COL, 29-36, asst. prof, 36-41, assoc. prof, 41-45, prof. Eng. & chmn. div. lang, lit. & arts, 45-66, alumnae prof. Eng. & chmn. dept, 66-72, dean grad. div, 50-67, LECTR. ENG, COORD. GRAD. PROG. & EMER. PROF, 73- Guggenheim fels, 50 & 59; lectr, Breadloaf Sch. Eng, 57-, Robert Frost prof. lit, Grad. Sch, 68. Dante Soc. Am; PEN Club. Theory of the fine arts; 18th century English literature; criticism of the fine arts and contemporary literature. Publ: Guinea's captive kings, 42 & 69; ed, Enlightened England, 47 & 62; auth, Four stages of Renaissance style, 55; Rococo to cubism in art and literature, 60, Loss of the self, 62 & Literature and technology, 68, Random; ed, Art history, 63 & Comedy, 65. Add: Dept. of English, Simmons College, 300 The Fenway, Boston, MA 02115.

SYRKIN, MARIE, b. Berne, Switz, Mar. 22, 99; nat; m. 30; c. 1. ENGLISH. B.A, Cornell Univ, 20, M.A, 22. Assoc. prof. Eng, BRANDEIS UNIV, 50-66, EMER. PROF. HUMANITIES, 66-; ED-IN-CHIEF, HERZL PRESS, 70- English; education; Anglo-Jewish literature. Publ: Your school, your children, Wyn; Blessed is the match; Way of valor; ed, Hayim Greenberg anthology, Wayne State Univ, 68; auth, Golda Meir: Israel's leader, Putnam, 69; ed, Golda Meir speaks out, Weidenfeld & Nicolson, Jerusalem, 73; auth, Don't flunk the middle-class teacher, N.Y. Times Mag, 12/68; contrib, The Israel/Arab reader, Citadel, 69 & Israel, the Arabs and the Middle East, Quadrangle, 72; plus one other. Add: Herzl Press, 515 Park Ave, New York, NY 10022.

SZANTO, GEORGE H, b. Londonderry, North. Ireland, June 4, 40; U.S. citizen; m. 63; c. 2. COMPARATIVE LITERATURE, THEATRE. B.A, Dartmouth Col, 62; Fulbright fel, Univ. Frankfurt, 62-63; Wilson & univ. fels, Harvard, 63-65, 66-67, Ph.D.(comp. lit), 67; Harvard traveling fel, Univ. Aix Marseille, 65-66. ASST. PROF. Ger. & comp. lit, UNIV. CALIF, SAN DIEGO, 67-70, DRAMATIC & COMP. LIT, 70-, HEAD SECT. COMP. LIT, 72-, summer fac. fel, 68. Southeast Theatre Conf. Annual New Play Proj. Award, 73. MLA; Am. Fed. Teachers. Dramatic theory; propaganda theory; popular culture. Publ: Narrative consciousness, Univ. Tex, 72; The phenomenological novel, Tex. Quart, fall 68; The dramatic process, Bucknell Rev, 72. Add: Dept. of Literature, University of California San Diego, P.O. Box 109, La Jolla, CA 92037.

SZARMACH, PAUL EDWARD, b. Buffalo, N.Y, June 22, 41; m. 63. OLD & MIDDLE ENGLISH LANGUAGE & LITERATURE. A.B, Canisius Col, 63; A.M, Harvard, 64, Ph.D.(Eng), 68. Instr. ENG, U.S. Mil. Acad, 68-70; ASST. PROF, STATE UNIV. N.Y. BINGHAMTON, 70-, Res. Found. summer fels, 71, 72. Soc. Relig. Higher Educ. res. assoc. fel, Pontif. Inst. Mediaeval Stud, Toronto, 72-73. Mil.Intel, U.S.A, 68-70, Capt. MLA; Mediaeval Acad. Am; Int. Arthurian Soc; Early Eng. Text Soc; Soc. Relig. Higher Educ. Old English prose and poetry; 14th century English literature; English language. Publ: Caesarius of Arles and the Vercelli Homilies, Traditio, 70; Three versions of the Jonah story, In: Anglo-Saxon England, Cambridge Univ, 72; Vercelli Homily XX, Mediaeval Stud, 73. Add: Dept. of English, State University of New York at Binghamton, Binghamton, NY 13901.

SZITTYA, PENN RODION, b. Chester, Pa, Apr. 17, 45; m. 69. ENGLISH LANGUAGE & LITERATURE, MEDIEVAL STUDIES. Woodrow Wilson fel, Ind. Univ, Bloomington, 66-67; Ph.D.(Eng), Cornell Univ, 71. ASST. PROF. ENG, BOSTON UNIV, 71- MLA; Medieval Acad. Am. Old and Middle English language and literature. Publ: The angels and the theme of Fortitudo in the Chanson de Roland, Neuphilol. Mitt, 71; The living stone and the patriarchs: typological imagery in Andreas, J. Eng. & Germanic Philol, 73; The friar as false apostle: antifraternal exegesis and the Summoner's tale, Stud. Philol, 74. Add: Dept. of English, Boston University, 236 Bay State Rd, Boston, MA 02215.

T

TAAFFE, JAMES G, b. Cincinnati, Ohio, Sept. 15, 32; m. 55; c. 2. ENGLISH. A.B, Columbia Col, 54; A.M, Ind. Univ, 56, Ph.D, 60. Instr. ENG, Williams Col, 59-62; asst. prof, Vassar Col, 63-64; CASE WEST. RESERVE UNIV, 64-65, assoc. prof, 66-69, PROF, 69-, DEAN GRAD. STUD, 72-, chmn. dept. Eng, 69-72, asst. to pres, 71-72. Newberry Libr. fel, summer 63; Am. Philos. Soc. fel, summers 67 & 69; mem. comt. exam, Advan. Placement Eng, Col. Entrance Exam. Bd, 67-68, chmn, 68-73; Nat. Endowment for Humanities fel, summer 71. MLA; Milton Soc. Am; Dante Soc. Milton studies; romantic and Victorian poetry; 17th century English literature. Publ: Co-auth, Poems on poetry, Dutton, 65; auth, A student's guide to literary terms, World, 67; co-auth, The Milton handbook, 5th ed, 69 & ed, Abraham Cowley: selected poetry and prose, 70, Appleton; co-ed, Reading English poetry, Macmillan, 71; auth, Abraham Cowley, Twayne, 72; Poet and lover in Wordsworth's Lucy poems, Mod. Lang. Rev, 66; Michaelmas, the lawless hour and the occasion of Milton's Comus, Eng. Lang. Notes, 69; Lycidas and the prophetic mantle, Milton Quart, 72; plus others. Add: 103 Pardee Hall, Case Western Reserve University, Cleveland, OH 44106.

TABBERT, RUSSELL DEAN, English Linguistics. See Volume III, Foreign Languages, Linguistics & Philology.

TACEY, WILLIAM SANFORD, b. Sullivan Co, N.Y, Apr. 29, 04; m. 33; c. 1. SPEECH. B.A, Geneva Col, 28; M.A, Columbia Univ, 32; Ed.D, Pa. State Univ, 60. Teacher, rural schs, Sullivan County, N.Y, 22-24; social stud. & speech, high sch, McKeesport, Pa, 28-46; instr. SPEECH, Pa. State Univ, 46-47; from instr. to prof, UNIV. PITTSBURGH, 47-74, EMER. PROF, 74- Corp. consult. commun, 49-; ed, Parliamentary J, 72- Speech Commun. Asn; Am. Inst. Parliamentarians; Speech Commun. Asn. East. States; Am. Soc. 18th Century Stud.(chmn. comn. on publ, 71-73); AAUP. Public address; business communications; speech education. Publ: Business and professional speaking, W.C. Brown, 70, 74; Humor booklet, Toastmasters Int, 67; Tools of the parliamentarian, Parliamentary J, 1/66; Put humor in your speeches, Today's Speech, 10/67; plus others. Add: Dept. of Speech, University of Pittsburgh, Pittsburgh, PA 15260.

TADE, GEORGE THOMAS, b. Casey, Ill, Dec. 17, 23; m. 46; c. 2. SPEECH. B.S, Ind. State Col, 45, M.S, 46; Ind. Univ, 48-50; Wash. Univ, 49-50; Ph.D, Univ. Ill, 55. Asst. to dir. radio, Ind. State Col, 45-46; head dept. speech, Greenville Col, 46-53, prof. & dean, 53-59; Chapman Col, 59-62; PROF. SPEECH, TEX. CHRISTIAN UNIV, 62-, DEAN, SCH. FINE ARTS, 73-, chmn. humanities div, 71-73. Pastor, Sandoval Christian Church, 46-48; interim pastor, Ill. Christian Churches, 48-59. Speech Commun. Asn; South. Speech Commun. Asn; Int. Commun. Asn. Mediaeval rhetoric; works of St. Ignatius Loyola. Publ: Spiritual exercises: a method of self-persuasion, 57 & Rhetorical aspects of the Spiritual exercises in the medieval tradition of preaching, 65, Quart. J. Speech; The anti-Texas address: John Q. Adams' personal filibuster, South. Speech J, 65; plus others. Add: School of Fine Arts, Texas Christian University, Ft. Worth, TX 76129.

TAFT, FREDERICK L, b. Cleveland, Ohio, Aug. 5, 06; m. 31; c. 2. ENGLISH. A.B, Amherst Col, 28; Ph.D, West. Reserve Univ, 42. Teaching fel. Eng, West. Reserve Univ, 36-37, instr, 37-38, lectr, grad. sch, 46-53; instr, Case Inst. Technol, 38-43, asst. prof, 46-49, assoc. prof, 50-56, prof, 56-67, dir, Sears Libr, 59-67; prof. ENG, CASE WEST. RESERVE UNIV, 67-71, acting dir. libr, 67-68, assoc. dir, 68-71, EMER. PROF. ENG, 71- Secy, Int. Asn. Technol. Univ. Libr, 68-70. MLA. English literature, 17th and early 18th century; John Milton. Publ: Ed, Apology for Smectymnus, In: Complete prose works of John Milton. Add: 20849 Byron Rd, Shaker Heights, OH 44122.

TAFT, WILLIAM HOWARD, b. Mexico, Mo, Oct. 24, 15; m. 41; c. 3. JOURNALISM. A.B, Westminster Col.(Mo), 37; B.J, Univ. Mo, 38, M.A, 39; Ph.D.(Am. cult), West. Reserve Univ, 51. Asst. prof. bus. admin. & jour, Youngstown Col, 46-48; prof. Eng. & jour, Defiance Col, 48-50; assoc. prof. JOUR. & head dept, Memphis State Col, 50-56; assoc. prof, UNIV. MO-COLUMBIA, 56-65, PROF, 65-, DIR. GRAD. STUD, 70- Wash. Jour. Ctr. fel, 67. U.S.A.A.F, 41-45, Capt. Asn. Educ. in Jour; Am. Hist. Asn; Orgn. Am. Hist; Am. Acad. Polit. & Soc. Sci. Journalism history; history of Toledo, Ohio, Blade, 1835-1935; journalism historical research problems. Publ: Let's publish that top rated yearbook, 61, Outline of American journalism, 68 & 72 & Newspapers as tools for historians, 70, Lucas; co-auth, Modern journalism, Pitman, 62; Missouri newspapers, Univ. Mo, 64; Missouri newspapers: when and where, 1808-1963, State Hist. Soc. Mo, 64; co-auth, Mass media and the national experience, Harper, 71; compiler, Mass media and society: a documentary history, Random, 74; Magazines, newspapers, In: American family encyclopedia yearbook, annually, 60-; plus others. Add: School of Journalism, University of Missouri-Columbia, Columbia, MO 65201.

TAGLIABUE, JOHN, b. Cantu, Italy, July 1, 23; U.S. citizen; m. 46; c. 2. ENGLISH. B.A, Columbia Col, 44, scholar. & M.A, Columbia Univ, 45, scholar, 47-48; Fulbright grant, Univ. Florence, Italy, 50-52. Instr. Eng. & Am. lit, Am. Univ.(Beirut), 45-46; State Col. Wash, 46-47; asst. prof, Alfred Univ, 48-50; assoc. prof. ENG, BATES COL, 50-58, 60-72, PROF, 72- Fulbright lectr. Am. lit, Univ. Pisa, 50-52; Tokyo & Jôchi Univs. & Tsuda Col, 58-60; lectr, Int. Inst, Madrid, summers 66, 67; Univ. Natal, summer 68. American and English literature; Shakespeare; modern comparative literature. Publ: Poems, Harper & Bros, 59, 60; contrib, Japan: theme and variation, Tuttle, 58; auth, A Japanese journal, 66 & The Buddha uproar, 67, Kayak; The doorless door (poems), Grossman, 70; plus others. Add: 59 Webster St, Lewiston, ME 04240.

TAGUE, WILMA LONG, b. Rockford, Ill, Mar. 2, 08; m. 35; c. 2. ENGLISH LITERATURE, CREATIVE WRITING. B.A, Rockford Col, 29; M.A, Univ. Wis-Madison, 60, Ph.D, 72. Instr. Eng. lit, Edgewood Col, 60-61; ENG, CARTHAGE COL, 61-62, asst. prof, 62-73, ASSOC. PROF, 73- Col. Eng. Asn; MLA; Midwest Mod. Lang. Asn; Milton Soc. Am; AAUP; Int. Arthurian Soc; Int. Fed. Mod. Lang. & Lit. John Gower; Arthurian studies in 20th century literature. Add: 809 17th Pl, Kenosha, WI 53140.

TAJUDDIN, MOHAMMAD, b. Nirmal, A.P, India, Aug. 17, 26; m. 53; c. 3. ENGLISH, COMPARATIVE LITERATURE. B.A, Osmania Univ, India, 46, M.A, 48; M.A, Univ. Chicago, 63; Ph.D.(comp. lit), Ind. Univ, Bloomington, 67. Lectr. ENG, Osmania Univ, India, 49-61; assoc. prof, Richmond Prof. Inst, 66-68; asst. prof, ROYAL MIL. COL.(QUE), 68-70, ASSOC. PROF, 70- Mem. adv. bd, Sayeedia Res. Inst, Hyderabad, A.P, India, 72- Asn. Can. Univ. Teachers Eng; MLA. Tragicomic mode in contemporary fiction; East-West literary relations; John Hawkes. Add: Dept. of English, Royal Military College, St. Jean, Que, Can.

TALBERT, ERNEST WILLIAM, b. San Jose, Calif, Apr. 3, 09; m. 34; c. 2. ENGLISH LITERATURE. A.B, San Jose State Col, 29; A.M, Stanford Univ, 31, scholar, 31-32, Victor fel, 32-33, univ. fel, 33-34, Ph.D, 36. Instr. ENG, Compton Dist. Jr. Col, 34-36; Univ. Idaho, 36-38; Univ. Tex, 38-42; asst. prof, Duke Univ, 42-46, assoc. prof, 46-49; prof, UNIV. N.C, CHAPEL HILL, 49-63, ALUMNI DISTINGUISHED PROF, 63- Carnegie grant-in-aid, 47, 49; Folger fel, 50; gen. ed, Recent lit. of Renaissance: a bibliog. & index, Stud. in Philol, 50-53; sr. fel, Southeast. Inst. Medieval & Renaissance Stud, summer 65; Kenan res. leave, 68; ed, Stud. in Philol, 69- Acad. Lit. Stud; MLA; Renaissance Soc. Am. Literature of the late Middle Ages and the Renaissance. Publ: Co-auth, Classical myth and legend in Renaissance dictionaries, Univ. N.C, 55, Greenwood, 73; Problem of order, Univ. N.C, 62; Elizabethan drama and Shakespeare's early plays, Univ. N.C, 63, rev. ed, Gordian, 73; co-auth, Critical approaches to six major English works: Beowulf through Paradise lost, Univ. Pa, 68 & 71; auth, The interpretation of Jonson's Courtly spectacles, PMLA, 46; The political import and the first two audiences of Gorboduc, In: Studies in honor of D.T. Starnes, Univ. Tex, 67; co-ed, Wyclyf and his followers, In: A manual of writings in Middle English, 1050-1500, II, Conn. Acad. Arts & Sci, 70. Add: Dept. of English, University of North Carolina, Chapel Hill, NC 27514.

TALBOT, CARL, b. New York, N.Y, July 14, 28; m. 54; c. 1. SPEECH, DRAMA. B.A, Univ. Ill, 51; M.S, Univ. South. Calif, 54; M.A, Occidental Col, 63; Ph.D.(speech), Univ. Calif, Los Angeles, 66. Instr. speech, Calif. Lutheran Col, 64-65; asst. prof, Univ. of the Pac, 66-70, assoc. prof. drama, 70-71; DIR. LIBR. SERV, MODESTO JR. COL, 71- West. Speech Commun. Asn; Speech Commun. Asn. Readers theatre; screenplay writing; oral interpretation. Add: 1137 Benjamin Holt Dr, Stockton, CA 95207.

TALENTINO, ARNOLD V, b. Oneida, N.Y, Apr. 25, 36; m. 65; c. 2. ENGLISH LITERATURE. A.B, Hamilton Col, 58; M.A, Cornell Univ, 60; M.S, Syracuse Univ, 66; Ph.D.(Eng. lit), State Univ. N.Y. Binghamton, 70. ASST. PROF. ENG. LIT, STATE UNIV. N.Y. COL. CORTLAND, 70-, summer res. fel, 71. Med.C, U.S.A, 61-63. MLA. Medieval literature; mythology; Re-

TATE / 619

naissance literature. Publ: Making city walls resound: Elene, 151 v, Papers Lang. & Lit, spring 73. Add: Dept. of English, State University of New York College at Cortland, Cortland, NY 13045.

TALLEY, CHARLES HORTON, b. Tingley, Iowa, May 14, 06; m. 28; c. 2. SPEECH. B.A, Simpson Col, 27; M.A, Northwest. Univ, 31; Ph.D, State Univ. Iowa, 36. Instr. & later prof. speech, Nebr. Wesleyan Univ, 31-36, dean, Col. Lib. Arts, 36-38; from assoc. prof. to prof. speech, Tex. State Col. Women, 38-48; South. Ill. Univ, 48-72, dean, Sch. Commun, 54-70, dean, Col. Commun. & Fine Arts, 70-72; RETIRED. Sr. res. assoc, Nat. Defense Res. Comt, 43-44. Speech Commun. Asn. Comparison of public speaking and conversation; intelligibility factors of speech in noise. Publ: Comparison of conversation and audience speech, Arch. Speech; Hi fidelity sound systems for theatres, Players Mag. Add: 2122 N. Towner, Santa Ana, CA 92706.

TANNACITO, DAN JOHN, b. Brooklyn, N.Y, Oct. 30, 43; m. 69; c. 1. VICTORIAN LITERATURE, CRITICAL THEORY. A.B, Boston Col, 64; D.A, Univ. Ore, 70, Ph.D.(Eng), 72. Instr. compos. & lit, Univ. Ore, 65-70; VICTORIAN LIT. & CRITICISM, UNIV. PITTSBURGH, 70-72, ASST. PROF, 72- MLA. Language, style and structure of Victorian poetry and fiction; psychoanalytic, sociological and linguistic criticism; narrative theory. Publ: A critical review of Tennyson studies: 1967-1972, Victorian Poetry, winter 74. Add: Dept. of English, University of Pittsburgh, Pittsburgh, PA 15260.

TANNER, JAMES THOMAS FONTENOT, b. Woodsboro, Tex, Oct. 27, 37. ENGLISH. B.A, Tex. Wesleyan Col, 61; Nat. Defense fel, Tex. Technol. Col, 61-64, M.A, 63, Ph.D.(Eng), 65. Instr. ENG, Wayne State Univ, 64-65; asst. prof, N.TEX. STATE UNIV, 65-69, ASSOC. PROF, 69- U.S.A, 56-59. MLA; NCTE. Walt Whitman; New England transcendentalism; influence of the evolution theory. Publ: Walt Whitman: a supplemental bibliography, Kent State Univ, 68; The Lamarckian theory of progress in Leaves of grass, 3/63 & The superman in Leaves of grass, 12/65, Walt Whitman Rev; Walt Whitman—curious eclectic, Long-Islander, 5/64. Add: Dept. of English, North Texas State University, Denton, TX 76203.

TANNER, JIMMIE EUGENE, b. Hartford, Ark, Sept. 27, 33; m. 58; c. 2. AMERICAN LITERATURE. B.A, Okla. Baptist Univ, 55; M.A, Univ. Okla, 57, South. Fel. Fund fel, 60-61, Danforth Found. fel, 62-63, Ph.D.(Eng), 64. Asst. Eng, Univ. Okla, 55-57, 59-60; instr, Lamar State Col. Tech, 58; Okla. Baptist Univ, 58-61, asst. prof, 61-64; assoc. prof, Franklin Col, 64-65; Okla. Baptist Univ, 65-68, prof, 68-72; PROF. ENG. & DEAN FAC, HARDIN-SIMMONS UNIV, 72- Mem. ed. staff, D.H. Lawrence Rev, 68- U.S.A.R, 57-67, Capt. MLA; AAUP. Modern novel in English; Shakespeare. Publ: Contrib, Annotated bibliography of D.H. Lawrence, North. Ill. Univ, 74; The messianic image in Mac Flecknoe, Mod. Lang. Notes, 3/61; The chronology and the enigmatic end of Lord Jim, Nineteenth Century Fiction, 3/67. Add: Hardin-Simmons University, Abilene, TX 79601.

TANSELLE, GEORGE THOMAS, b. Lebanon, Ind, Jan. 29, 34. ENGLISH. B.A, Yale, 55; M.A, Northwest. Univ, 56, Ph.D.(Eng), 59. Instr. ENG, Chicago City Jr. Col, Wright Br, 58-60; UNIV. WIS-MADISON, 60-61, asst. prof, 61-63, assoc. prof, 63-68, PROF, 68- Mem, Planning Inst. Comn. Eng, Col. Entrance Exam. Bd, 61; Guggenheim fel, 69-70; mem. adv. comt, Ctr. Eds. Am. Authors, 70-73; Am. Counc. Learned Soc. fel, 73-74. MLA; NCTE; Bibliog. Soc, London; Bibliog. Soc. Am.(mem. counc, 70-); Bibliog. Soc. Univ. Va; Cambridge Bibliog. Soc; Edinburgh Bibliog. Soc; Manuscript Soc; Am. Antiq. Soc.(mem. publ. comt, 72-); Bibliog. Soc. Can; Bibliog. Soc. Australia & N.Z; Printing Hist. Soc; Grolier Club. Jenkins Award in Bibliog, 73. American literature; analytical bibliography; publishing history. Publ: Royall Tyler, 67 & Guide to the study of United States imprints, 71, Harvard; co-ed, The writings of Herman Melville, Northwest. Univ. & Newberry Libr, 68- Add: Dept. of English, University of Wisconsin-Madison, Madison, WI 53706.

TANZY, CONRAD EUGENE, b. Akron, Ohio, Feb. 10, 24; m. 48; c. 5. ENGLISH. B.A, Ohio State Univ, 49, M.A, 52, Ph.D, 61. Instr. ENG, FLA. STATE UNIV, 58-61, asst. prof, 61-68, ASSOC. PROF, 68-, DIR. UNDERGRAD. STUD. ENG, 68-, DIR. FRESHMAN COMPOS, 74-, asst. dean arts & sci. & dir. div. basic stud, 62-64, dir. univ. stud. ctr, Florence, Italy, 66-67. U.S.A, 43-46, S/Sgt. MLA. Victorian publishing; Browning; Victorian novel. Publ: Browning, Emerson and Bishop Blougram, Victorian Stud, 58. Add: Dept. of English, Florida State University, Tallahassee, FL 32306.

TAPLIN, GARDNER B, b. Newton, Mass, June 13, 12. ENGLISH LITERATURE. A.B, Amherst Col, 34; A.M, Harvard, 35, Ph.D, 42. Instr. ENG, Pomfret Sch, Conn, 42-43; Loomis Sch, 43-46; Ind. Univ, 46-50, asst. prof, 50-53; lectr, Boston Univ, 54-56; assoc. prof, Longwood Col, 56-60; NEWCOMB COL, TULANE UNIV, 60-65, PROF, 65- Guggenheim fel, 58-59; mem. ed. bd, Victorian Poetry, 63-; Stud. in Browning & His Circle, 73- MLA. Victorian and American literature; 19th century American-Italian relationships. Publ: Life of Elizabeth Barrett Browning, Yale, 57. Add: Dept. of English, Newcomb College, Tulane University, New Orleans, LA 70118.

TARANOW, GERDA, b. New York, N.Y. THEATRE HISTORY. B.A, N.Y. Univ, 52, M.A, 55; Ph.D, Yale, 61. Instr. ENG, Quinnipiac Col, 61-62; Univ. Ky, 63-65, asst. prof, 65-66; Syracuse Univ, 66-67; CONN. COL, 67-70, ASSOC. PROF, 70- Fel, Yale, 62-63; summer res. fel, Univ. Ky, 65. MLA; Am. Soc. Theatre Res; Int. Fed. Theatre Res; Soc. Theatre Hist, France; Theatre Libr. Asn; Asn. Recorded Sound Collections; AAUP. Shakespeare; drama. Publ: Sarah Bernhardt: the art within the legend, Princeton, 72. Add: Dept. of English, Connecticut College, New London, CT 06320.

TARBET, DAVID WILLIAM, b. Port Arthur, Ont, Sept. 27, 41; m. 65; c. 2. ENGLISH LITERATURE. B.A, Univ. Toronto, 65; M.A, Univ. Rochester, 68, Ph.D.(Eng), 70. Instr. ENG, Univ. Rochester, 68-69; ASST. PROF, STATE UNIV. N.Y. BUFFALO, 69-, DIR. M.A. IN HUMANITIES, 72- Am. Counc. Learned Soc. stud. fel, 74. MLA; Am. Soc. 18th Century Stud. Restoration and 18th century English literature; history of philosophy. Publ: The fabric of metaphor in Kant's Critique of pure reason, J. Hist. Philos, 7/68; Lockean intuition and Johnson's characterization of aesthetic response, Eighteenth Century Stud, fall 71; Contemporary American pastoral: a poetic faith, Eng. Rec, winter 72. Add: Dept. of English, Annex B-7, State University of New York at Buffalo, Buffalo, NY 14214.

TARCAY, EILEEN SCHULTZ, b. Hiawatha, Utah, Aug. 26, 14; m. 57; c. 1. ENGLISH, AMERICAN STUDIES. A.B, Univ. Utah, 35, M.A, 53, fel, 53-54; cert, Johns Hopkins Univ, 74. Instr. ENG, Gazi Eğitim Enstitusu, Ankara, Turkey, 63-64; Univ. Md, Baltimore County Campus, 66-67; COPPIN STATE COL, 67-68, asst. prof, 68-74, ASSOC. PROF, 74- Am. Stud. Asn; Col. Eng. Asn; NCTE; Conf. Col. Compos. & Commun. American women writers; American cultural history, 1915-1925; creative writing. Publ: Margaret Fuller D'Ossoli, West. Humanities Rev, winter 52; Among the Lamanites: the Indians and the Mormons, West. Folklore, 5/59; Here and there in the humanities, column in West. Humanities Rev, summer 55-autumn 59, winter 69-, co-auth, autumn 67-69. Add: Dept. of English, Coppin State College, Baltimore, MD 21216.

TARONE, ELAINE E, Applied Linguistics, Phonetics. See Volume III, Foreign Languages, Linguistics & Philology.

TARPLEY, FRED ANDERSON, Linguistics, English. See Volume III, Foreign Languages, Linguistics & Philology.

TARR, RODGER LeROY, b. Mercer, Pa, Sept. 11, 41; m. 62; c. 2. NINETEENTH CENTURY ENGLISH LITERATURE. B.A, Fla. South. Col, 63; M.A, Kent State Univ, 65; Ph.D.(Eng), Univ. S.C, 68. Asst. prof. ENG, ILL. STATE UNIV, 68-71, ASSOC. PROF, 71-, res. grant, summer 71. Res. fel, Univ. Edinburgh, 68-69; Am. Philos. Soc. res. grant, 68-69. MLA (Victorian bibliog. comt, 72-); Dickens Soc. Victorian novel and prose; bibliography. Publ: A bibliography of English language articles on Thomas Carlyle, S.C. Bibliog. Ser, 72; Foreign philanthropy in Bleak house: a Carlylean influence, Stud. in Novel, 71; Dickens' debt to Carlyle in The chimes, 19th Century Fiction, 72; A bibliography of Carlyle's libraries, Stud. in Bibliog, 73. Add: Dept. of English, Illinois State University, Normal, IL 61761.

TARVER, JERRY L, b. Sicily Island, La, Nov. 7, 34; m. 57; c. 2. SPEECH. B.A, La. State Univ, 57, M.A, 60, Ph.D.(speech), 64. Instr. SPEECH, Southeast. La. Col, 60-62; UNIV. RICHMOND, 63-64, asst. prof, 64-66, assoc. prof, 66-73, PROF, 73-, CHMN. DEPT. SPEECH & DRAMATIC ARTS, 67- U.S.A, 58-60, Lt. Speech Commun. Asn; South. Speech Commun. Asn.(3rd v.pres, 66-67, exec. secy, 72-75). Public address; rhetorical criticism; forensics. Publ: Reflections on a new debate handbook, J. Am. Forensic Asn, 1/65; A lost form of pulpit address, South. Speech J, spring 66; co-auth, John C. Calhoun's rhetorical method in defense of slavery, In: Oratory in the Old South, 1828-1860, La. State Univ, 70; plus others. Add: Box 444, University of Richmond, Richmond, VA 23173.

TASCH, PETER ANTHONY, b. Brooklyn, N.Y, Nov. 28, 33; m. 61; c. 3. ENGLISH. A.B, Bucknell Univ, 54; M.A, Columbia Univ, 59; dipl. Eng. stud, Univ. Edinburgh, 60; jr. fel, Harvard, 61-64. Instr. ENG, West. Md. Col, 58-59; Brooklyn Col, 60-61; TEMPLE UNIV, 64-70, asst. prof, 70-72, ASSOC. PROF, 72- Ed, Scriblerian & Kit-Cats, 68- Adj.Gen.C, U.S.A, 54-57. MLA; Am. Soc. 18th Century Stud. Restoration and 18th century drama; Kit-Cat and Scriblerus Club members; 18th century novel. Publ: Ed, Fables of John Gay, Imprint Soc, 70; auth, The dramatic cobbler, life of Isaac Bickerstaff, Bucknell Univ, 71. Add: Dept. of English, Temple University, Philadelphia, PA 19122.

TASHJIAN, DICKRAN LEVON, b. Medford, Mass, Jan. 25, 40; m. 64; c. 1. AMERICAN LITERATURE. B.A, Brown Univ, 62, Ph.D.(Am. civilization), 69; M.A, Univ. Minn, Minneapolis, 64. Lectr. Am. lit, Providence Col, 67-68; asst. prof. COMP. CULT, UNIV. CALIF, IRVINE, 69-73, ASSOC. PROF, 73-, Humanities Inst. summer fel, 72. Modern American literature; American art; material culture. Publ: Co-auth, Memorials for children of change: the art of early New England stonecarving, Wesleyan Univ, 74; auth, The counterfeiters by Andre Gide: the esthetic ontology of dada, Minn. Rev, 66; co-auth, Gravestones of Rhode Island, R.I. Hist, 68. Add: Program in Comparative Culture, University of California, Irvine, CA 92664.

TASSIN, RAYMOND JEAN, b. Holdenville, Okla, Apr. 20, 26; m. 48; c. 1. JOURNALISM, AMERICAN LITERATURE. B.A, Univ. Okla, 50, M.A, 57; Ph.D.(jour, Am. Lit), Univ. Mo-Columbia, 64. Reporter & asst. news ed, Chickasha Daily Express, 50-51; managing ed, Clinton Daily News, 51-53; ed. & publ, Konawa Leader, 53-56; rewrite deskman, Daily Oklahoman, 56-57; asst. prof. JOUR, Baylor Univ, 57-60; CHMN. DEPT, CENT. STATE UNIV.(OKLA), 61- Mem. comn, Okla. Dept. Educ, 68 & 69. U.S.N, 44-46, Res, 47-, Lt. Comdr. Asn. Educ. in Jour; West. Writers Am. Medal of honor winners; famous and unknown journalists; ethics of U.S. journalists. Publ: Daily newspaper semi-merger, privately publ, 57; Red men in blue, 60 & Steel trails of vengeance, 71, Avalon; Stanley Vestal: champion of the old west, Arthur Clark, 73; Discount homebuilding, Drake, 74; plus others. Add: 600 Park Pl, Edmond, OK 73034.

TATE, ALLEN, b. Winchester, Ky, Nov. 19, 99; m. 24. POETRY. A.B, Vanderbilt Univ, 22; Guggenheim fel, 28-30; Litt.D, Colgate Univ, 56, Univ. Ky, 60, Carleton Col, 63, Univ. of the South, 70. South. ed, Hound & Horn, 31-35; lectr. Eng. lit, Southwest. Col, 34-36; prof. Eng, Woman's Col, Univ. N.C, 38-39; resident fel. creative writing, Princeton, 39-42; fel. Am. let, Libr. Congr, 43-44; ed, Sewanee Rev, 44-46; lectr, N.Y. Univ, 47-51; prof. ENG, UNIV. MINN, 51-68, REGENTS' EMER. PROF, 68- Free lance writer, 24-; Fulbright prof, Oxford & Univ. Leeds, Eng, 58-59. Sinkler Prize, 28, 32; Bollingen poetry prize, 56; Brandeis Univ. Medal Award for poetry, 61; Gold Medal, Dante Alighieri Soc, Florence, 62. Soc. Am. Hist; Nat. Inst. Arts & Lett.(pres, 68-); Am. Acad. Arts & Lett. Literary criticism; novels; poems. Publ: On the limits of poetry, Swallow-Morrow; Collected essays, 59 & Essays of four decades, 69, Swallow; Poems, Scribner, 60. Add: Running Knob Hollow Rd, Sewanee, TN 37375.

TATE, CECIL FOSTER, b. Atlanta, Ga, June 12, 31; m. 67; c. 2. ENGLISH & AMERICAN LITERATURE. B.A, Univ. Md, College Park, 57; Ohio State Univ, 57-60; M.A, Emory Univ, 67, Ph.D.(Am. stud), 70. Instr. Eng, Morris

Brown Col, 68-69; BOSTON COL, 69-70, asst. prof. ENG, 70-74, ASSOC. PROF, 74-, CHMN. AM. STUD. PROG, 70- Am. Stud. Asn; MLA. Cultural history; literary criticism. Publ: The search for a method in American studies, Univ. Minn, 73. Add: American Studies Program, Boston College, Beacon St, Chestnut Hill, MA 02167.

TATE, GARY LEE, b. Hiawatha, Kans, Aug. 2, 30; m. 52; c. 2. ENGLISH, LINGUISTICS. B.A, Baker Univ, 52; M.A, Univ. N.Mex, 56, Ph.D.(Eng), 58. Instr. Eng, Univ. Wyo, 57-58; asst. prof, Ohio Wesleyan Univ, 58-60; Univ. Tulsa, 60-64, assoc. prof, 64-70; prof, North. Ariz. Univ, 70-71; LEVY PROF. LIT, TEX. CHRISTIAN UNIV, 71- Danforth assoc, 67-70. U.S.A, 52-54. NCTE; MLA; Col. Eng. Asn; Conf. Col. Compos. & Commun. Rhetoric; English linguistics; teaching composition. Publ: Reflections on high school English, Univ. Tulsa, 66; co-auth, Teaching freshman composition, 67 & co-ed, Teaching high school composition, 70, Oxford Univ; co-auth, Classics in linguistics, Philos. Libr, 67; ed, From discovery to style, Winthrop, 73; plus others. Add: Dept. of English, Texas Christian University, Ft. Worth, TX 76129.

TATE, WILLIAM, b. Calhoun, Ga, Sept. 21, 03; m. 32; c. 2. ENGLISH. A.B, Univ. Ga, 24, A.M, 27; hon. LL.D, LaGrange Col, 71. Instr. Eng. & debating, Univ. Ga, 24-29; master dept. Eng, McCallie Sch, Chattanooga, Tenn, 29-36; asst. prof. Eng. & dean freshmen, UNIV. GA, 36-37, dean men, 37-39, dean stud. & asst. to pres, 39-46, assoc. prof. Eng, 42-71, dean men, 46-71, EMER. PROF. ENG. & EMER. DEAN MEN, 71- Georgia literature; social changes in the South. Add: 436 Dearing St, Athens, GA 30601.

TATHAM, CAMPBELL, b. New York, N.Y, July 5, 40; div; c. 4. CONTEMPORARY LITERATURE. B.A, Amherst Col, 62; M.A, N.Y. Univ, 64; Ph.D. (Eng), Univ. Wis-Madison, 68. Asst. prof. ENG, UNIV. WIS-MILWAUKEE, 68-72, ASSOC. PROF, 72- Nat. Endowment for Humanities summer stipend, 72. MLA. Contemporary fiction; existential phenomenology; modes of experimental criticism. Publ: Vision and value in Uncle Tom's children, Stud. in Black Lit, 72; High-altitude hermeneutics, Diacritics, 73; Message (concerning the fictions of one John Barth), Boundary 2, 74; plus others. Add: Dept. of English, University of Wisconsin-Milwaukee, Milwaukee, WI 53201.

TATHAM, LEWIS CHARLES, JR, b. Trenton, N.J, Jan. 11, 25; m. 63; c. 5. ENGLISH. A.B, Clark Univ, 48; M.A, Univ. Fla, 52, Ph.D.(Eng), 65. Instr. ENG, Va. Polytech. Inst, 54-57, asst. prof, 57-60; instr, Univ. Fla, 62-65, asst. prof, 65-66; PROF, AUSTIN PEAY STATE UNIV, 66- U.S.A, 42-46. MLA. Literature of the Romantic period; contemporary poetry. Add: Dept. of English, Austin Peay State University, Clarksville, TN 37040.

TATUM, NANCY R, b. Pittsburg, Kans, Aug. 14, 30. ENGLISH LITERATURE & HISTORY. B.A, Univ. Ark, 52; M.A, Bryn Mawr Col, 54, Ph.D, 60. Instr. ENG. & asst. to dean, Lake Erie Col, 58-59; instr, WASHINGTON COL, 60-61, asst. prof, 61-65, assoc. prof, 65-69, PROF, 69- MLA; Shakespeare Asn. Am; Renaissance Soc. Am. Restoration drama; Shakespearean stage technique; 17th century English social and economic history. Add: Dept. of English, Washington College, Chestertown, MD 21620.

TAUBE, MYRON, b. New York, N.Y, May 14, 29; m. 53; c. 4. CREATIVE WRITING. B.A, N.Y. Univ, 51, M.A, 54, Ph.D, 59. Instr. ENG, N.Y. Univ, 55-59; Hunter Col, 59-60; adj. prof, Staten Island Community Col, 60-61; asst. prof, Long Island Univ, 61-64; prof, Kutztown State Col, 64-66; vis. assoc. prof, UNIV. PITTSBURGH, 66-67, ASSOC. PROF, 67- Ord.C, U.S.A, 51-53, Sgt. MLA; Col. Eng. Asn; AAUP. Victorian novel; contemporary short fiction; 18th century English literature. Publ: Contrast as a principle of structure in Vanity fair, Nineteenth-Century Fiction, 9/63; The atmosphere . . . from Cyprus: Hardy's development of theme in Jude the obscure, Victorian Newslett, fall 67; Moll Flanders and Fanny Hill: a comparison, Ball State Forum, spring 68; plus others. Add: Dept. of English, University of Pittsburgh, Pittsburgh, PA 15213.

TAUBER, ABRAHAM, b. New York, N.Y, Nov. 8, 12; m. 36; c. 3. SPEECH. B.S.S, City Col. New York, 31; A.M, Columbia Univ, 32, Ph.D, 58. Instr. speech, City Col. New York, 32-33, sch. educ, 34-39, eve. session, 34-39, 46-58; teacher speech & Eng, High Sch. of Sci, Bronx, N.Y, 39-58; dean, Bronx Community Col, City Univ. New York, 58-66, dean-in-charge, 66; PROF. SPEECH & CHMN. DEPT, YESHIVA UNIV, 66-; ADJ. PROF. SPEECH & DRAMA, JOHN JAY COL. CRIMINAL JUSTICE, 72- Dir. speech ctr, YMHA & YWHA, 40-48; vis. prof. speech, Yeshiva Univ, 38-66; consult. Ford Found. Operation Second Chance, 60-63; U.S. Off. Educ. Operation Giant Step, 65-66; prof. speech, Hunter Col, 67-68; head teacher & lectr. Eng. lit. & compos, Westchester Coop. Col. Ctr, State Univ. N.Y. Col. Purchase, 71-73; Westchester Community Col, 73-; adj. prof. educ, Lehman Col, 73; trustee, Grand St. Boys Found. Overseas Am. Red Cross, 43-44. Speech Commun. Asn; Phoemic Spelling Counc; Am. Soc. Geoling. (pres, 68-69); Simpler Spelling Asn.(exec. bd). Linguistics; speech. Publ: George Bernard Shaw on language, 63 & Better English thru simplified spelling: a history of spelling reform, 75, Philos. Libr; Innovation for excellence in higher education for the many, Ford Found. Subsidized Report, 69. Add: 441 16 N. Broadway, Yonkers, NY 10701.

TAVE, STUART MALCOLM, b. New York, N.Y, Apr. 10, 23; m. 48; c. 4. ENGLISH. B.A, Columbia Univ, 43; M.A, Harvard, 47; Kellett fel. Columbia Univ, Oxford, 47-49, Fulbright fel, 49-50, D.Phil.(Eng), 50. Lectr. ENG, Columbia Univ, 50-51; instr, UNIV. CHICAGO, 51-55, asst. prof, 55-60, assoc. prof, 60-64, prof, 64-71, WILLIAM RAINEY HARPER PROF, 71-, CHMN. DEPT. ENG, 72-, master col. div. humanities & assoc. dean col, 66-70. Guggenheim fel, 59-60; vis. assoc. prof, Univ. Wis, 62; Stanford Univ, 63; vis. prof, Univ. Wash, 66; Am. Counc. Learned Soc. fel, 70-71. U.S.N, 43-46, Lt. MLA. Eighteenth and 19th century English literature. Publ: Amiable humorist, 60 & Some words of Jane Austen, 73, Univ. Chicago; New essays by De Quincey, Princeton, 66. Add: Dept. of English, University of Chicago, Chicago, IL 60637.

TAYLER, EDWARD WILLIAM, b. Berlin, Ger, Mar. 13, 31; U.S. citizen; m. 61; c. 5. ENGLISH LITERATURE. B.A, Amherst Col, 54; fel, Stanford Univ, 56-58; Ph.D, 60. Acting instr. & asst, Stanford Univ, 54-56, 58-60; instr. ENG. LIT, COLUMBIA UNIV, 60-62, asst. prof, 62-65, assoc. prof, 65-67, PROF, 67- Counc. Res. Humanities fel, 62, 64 & 66; Henry E. Huntington grant, Huntington Libr, 62; Guggenheim Mem. Found. fel, 68-69. Renaissance Soc. Am. Renaissance English literature. Publ: Nature and art in Renaissance England, Columbia Univ, 64; Literary criticism of seventeenth century England, Knopf, 67. Add: 608 Philosophy Hall, Columbia University, New York, NY 10027.

TAYLER, IRENE, U.S. citizen. LITERATURE, ART HISTORY. B.A, Stanford Univ, 56, M.A, 61, Ph.D.(Eng. lit), 67. Teaching asst. ENG, Stanford Univ, 58-60; lectr, Columbia Univ, 61-71; ASST. PROF, CITY COL. NEW YORK, 71-, fac. res. grant, 72-73. Am. Counc. Learned Soc. stud. grant, 68-69. MLA. Eighteenth and 19th century English literature and art. Publ: Blake's illustrations to the poems of Gray, Princeton Univ, 71; Metamorphoses of a favorite cat, In: Visionary forms dramatic, Princeton Univ, 70; Say first! what mov'd Blake, In: Blake's sublime allegory, Univ. Wis, 73; The woman scaly, Midwest Mod. Lang. Asn. Bull, spring 73. Add: Apt. 92, 464 Riverside Dr, New York, NY 10027.

TAYLOR, ALEXANDER DOUGLAS, b. Rumford, Maine, July 8, 31; m. 50; c. 3. MODERN POETRY, CONTEMPORARY DANISH LITERATURE. B.A, Skidmore Col, 53; John Hay fel, Williams Col, summer 63; Coe fel, Yale, summer 64; M.A, Univ. Conn, 64, Ph.D.(Eng), 70; Fulbright fel, Denmark, 65-66. ASST. PROF. ENG, EAST. CONN. STATE COL, 69- Am. Philos. Soc. res. grant, Denmark, summer 71; Am. Counc. Learned Soc. res. grant, Denmark, 72-73; lectr. Am. stud, Magleas Folkehøjskole, Birkerød, Denmark, 72. Contemporary Danish poetry; translation, theory and practice. Publ: Co-ed, American literature: 4 themes, Gyldendal, Copenhagen, 66; ed. & transl, Selected poems of Benny Andersen, Princeton Univ, 74; auth, Kafka's Metamorphosis: the waking, Stud. Short Fiction, summer 65. Add: 321 Jackson St, Willimantic, CT 06226.

TAYLOR, ALFRED HEBER, b. Friendship, Tenn, Aug. 1, 24; m. 50; c. 2. JOURNALISM, ENGLISH. B.A, Univ. Ark, 48; M.A, Vanderbilt Univ, 49; Gen. Educ. Bd. fel, Univ. Mo, 52-53, Fulbright grant, 53-54, Ph.D.(jour), 55. Instr. Eng. & jour, Abilene Christian Col, 49-54, asst. prof, 54-56, assoc. prof. Eng. & chmn. jour. dept, 57-64; assoc. prof. Eng, Univ. Tenn, Martin, 56-57; Eng. & jour, Wis. State Univ, Superior, 64-67, 69-71; PROF. JOUR. & CHMN. DEPT, Univ. Ark, Little Rock, 71-73; SOUTHWEST TEX. STATE UNIV, 73- U.S.A, 43-46. Asn. Educ. in Jour. Norwegian press history; American press history; current press or communications problems. Publ: Campus to squad room, Pub. Relat. J, 6/68; The Sunday Times: a Memphis paper that failed, W.Tenn. Hist. Soc. Papers, 70. Add: Dept. of Journalism, Southwest Texas State University, San Marcos, TX 78666.

TAYLOR, ALINE MACKENZIE, b. Sept. 18, 11; m. 49. ENGLISH LITERARY HISTORY. A.B, Newcomb Col, 31; Ph.D.(Eng. & philos), Bryn Mawr Col, 43. Instr. ENG, TULANE UNIV, 38-40, asst. prof, 43-49, assoc. prof, 49-56, PROF, 56- Guggenheim fel, 52-53; Am. Counc. Learned Soc. grant, summer 61; Folger Shakespeare Libr. fel, summer 63. MLA; Soc. Theatre Res, Gt. Brit; Amici Thomae Mori (U.S. secy, 63-). Dramatic literature and stage history; 17th century theatre music and musicians; John Dryden. history of the English recusants of the 17th century. Publ: Next to Shakespeare: Otway's Venice preserv'd and The orphan and their history on the London stage, Duke, 50; Gulliver's voyage to Brobdingnag, 2 parts, 55, 57, Tulane Stud. Eng; Dryden's Enchanted isle and Shadwell's Dominion, Stud. in Philol, 67. Add: Dept. of English, Tulane University, New Orleans, LA 70118.

TAYLOR, ANNE ROBB, b. Shanghai, China, Dec. 23, 18; U.S. citizen. ENGLISH. A.B, Mt. Holyoke Col, 39, A.M, 41; Folger Shakespeare Libr. fel, summer 65; Ph.D, Brown Univ, 68. Teacher, 41-43; secy, St. John's Church, Wash, D.C, 48-54; admin. asst, Hazen Found, 54-56; Conn. Col, 56-60; asst. prof. ENG, Skidmore Col, 66-68; ASSOC. PROF. UNIV. WIS, SUPERIOR, 68- W.A.V.E.S, 43-46, Lt.(jg). Eng. Inst; Bibliog. Soc. Eng. Lord Berners and his translations; Shakespeare. Add: Dept. of English, University of Wisconsin, Superior, WI 54880.

TAYLOR, ARVILLA KERNS, b. San Antonio, Tex, Feb. 6, 31. RENAISSANCE & ENGLISH LITERATURE. B.A, Univ. Tex, Austin, 51, M.A, 53, Ph.D. (Eng. lit), 69. Instr. hist, San Antonio Jr. Col, 57; asst. prof. ENG, Colo. State Univ, 65-66; Wichita State Univ, 67-69; ASSOC. PROF, MIDWEST. UNIV, 69- S.Cent. Mod. Lang. Asn; AAUP. Medieval and Renaissance as the same world order, comparative French, German, Spanish and English literature; man's limitations and potentials; Shakespeare and Conrad, existential heroes in action. Add: Dept. of English, Midwestern University, Taft Ave, Wichita Falls, TX 76308.

TAYLOR, CHARLES BRUCE, JR, b. Aug. 14, 43; U.S. citizen; m. 64; c. 2. RENAISSANCE LITERATURE. B.A, Northwest. Univ, 65; M.A, Univ. Iowa, 66; Ph.D.(Eng), North. Ill. Univ, 71. Asst. prof. ENG, Angelo State Univ, 69-73; LECTR, UNIV. TEX, AUSTIN, 73- English Renaissance poetry; black African literature; bibliography. Publ: A freshman views the heart of darkness, Conradiana, winter 71; Studyman praises loneliness, La. Rev, winter 72; McMurty's thalia, myth or reality, J. Am. Stud. Asn. Tex, spring 74. Add: 5303 Ravensdale, Austin, TX 78723.

TAYLOR, CHARLES HENRY, JR, b. Boston, Mass, Oct. 2, 28; m. 50; c. 4. ENGLISH. B.A, Yale, 50, Kent fel, 51-54, M.A, 52, Ph.D.(Eng), 55; Wilson fel, Trinity Col, Eng, 50-51. Instr. Eng, Ind. Univ, 55; assoc. prof. ENG, YALE, 61-65, PROF, 65-, PRESIDENT'S REP, 72-, asst. dean, 61-63, assoc. dean, 63, provost, 64-72. MLA; Soc. Relig. Higher Educ. Romantic poetry. Publ: Early collected editions of Shelley's poems, Yale, 58; ed, Essays on the Odyssey: selected modern criticism, Ind. Univ, 63; auth, The obstacles to Odysseus' return, Yale Rev, spring 61. Add: Box 30, Sterling Memorial Library, Yale University, New Haven, CT 06520.

TAYLOR, DONALD STEWART, b. Portland, Ore, Aug. 8, 24; m. 52; c. 3. ENGLISH. A.B, Univ. Calif, 47, M.A, 48, Ph.D, 50. Instr. ENG, Northwest. Univ, 50-54; Univ. Wash, 54-55, asst. prof, 55-62, assoc. prof, 62-68; PROF, UNIV. ORE, 68- Vis. instr, Univ. Calif, 51; Guggenheim fel, 72-73. A.U.S, 43-45. Philol. Asn. Pac. Coast; MLA; Modern fiction; 18th century English literature; theory of literary history. Publ: Co-ed, Complete works of Chatterton, Clarendon, 71; Catalytic rhetoric: Henry Green's theory of the modern novel, Criticism, 65; R.G. Collingwood: art, craft and history, Clio, 6/73. Add: Dept. of English, University of Oregon, Eugene, OR 97403.

TAYLOR, DOUGLAS HANSON, b. Faribault, Minn, Dec. 8, 38; m. 66; c. 2. AMERICAN LITERATURE & ECCLESIASTICAL HISTORY. B.A, Whitman Col, 60; M.A, Univ. Wash, 63; Ph.D.(Eng), Univ. Calif, Davis, 67. Assoc. ENG, Univ. Calif, Davis, 66-67; asst. prof, State Univ. N.Y. Col. Buffalo, 67-69; ASSOC. PROF. & CHMN. DEPT, CALIF. STATE COL, STANISLAUS, 69- Nat. Endowment for Humanities grant, summer 73. MLA; NCTE. John Wise; 17th and 18th century American Congregational Church; the development of American prose style. Add: Dept. of English, California State College, Stanislaus, 800 Monte Vista Ave, Turlock, CA 95380.

TAYLOR, EDMUND DENNIS, b. Baltimore, Md, Feb. 26, 40; m. 66; c. 1. ENGLISH. B.A, Holy Cross Col, 60; Ph.D.(Eng), Yale, 66. Instr. ENG, Bowdoin Col, 62-63; ASST. PROF, Univ. Calif, Santa Barbara, 65-71; BOSTON COL, 71- Humanities summer grant, Univ. Calif, Santa Barbara, 66. MLA. Hardy and modern poetic traditions; The confidence man: Chaucer's Pardoner to the present; Kierkegaard's Fear and trembling as a model for literary criticism. Publ: The riddle of Hardy's poetry, Victorian Poetry, 74. Add: Dept. of English, Boston College, Chestnut Hill, MA 01742.

TAYLOR, ESTELLE WORMLEY, b. Washington, D.C, Jan. 12, 24; m. 53. ENGLISH & AMERICAN LITERATURE. B.S, Miner Teachers Col, 45; M.A, Howard Univ, 47; South. fel, Cath. Univ. Am, 68-69, Ph.D.(Eng), 69. Instr. humanities, & Eng, Howard Univ, 47-52; teacher ENG, Langley Jr. High Sch, 52-55; East. High Sch, 55-63; instr, D.C. TEACHERS COL, 63-66, asst. prof, 66-69, assoc. prof, 69-71, PROF, 71- Col. Lang. Asn; MLA; NCTE; Shakespeare Asn. Am. Renaissance literature, especially Shakespeare; the works of Walt Whitman and American literature; Chaucer. Publ: Analysis and comparison of the 1855 and 1891 versions of Whitman's To think of time, Walt Whitman Rev, 12/67; Chaucer's Monk's tale: an apology, 12/69 & Shakespeare's use of s endings of the verbs to do and to have in the first folio, 12/72, Col. Lang. Asn. J. Add: Dept. of English, District of Columbia Teachers College, 1100 Harvard St, Washington, DC 20009.

TAYLOR, GARLAND FORBES, b. Shelbyville, Tenn, Nov. 19, 09; m. 35; c. 2. ENGLISH. A.B, Tulane Univ, 32, A.M, 34; Ph.D.(Eng), Yale, 40. Sharp teaching fel, Tulane Univ, 32-34, from instr. to asst. prof. Eng, 37-42, assoc. prof, 44-47, prof, 47-59, chmn. freshman & sophomore Eng, 39-42, acting librn, 44-45, librn, 45-48, dir. libr, 48-59; acad. dean, William Jewell Col, 59-64; PROF. ENG. & DEAN LIB. ARTS, MERCER UNIV, 64- Mem. comt. on findings, South. Baptist Educ. Study Task, 65-67; mem. comn. fac. & stud, Asn. Am. Cols, 68-70. Red Cross Mil. Welfare Serv, N.Africa & Italy, 42-44. Eighteenth century English dramatic literature and theatrical history; R.B. Sheridan; academic administration. Publ: Co-auth, Louisiana purchase, La. State Mus. & La. Landmarks Soc; contrib, A study of administration in church-related liberal arts colleges, U.S. Off. Educ, 62. Add: Dean's Office, College of Liberal Arts, Mercer University, Macon, GA 31207.

TAYLOR, GORDON OVERTON, b. Los Angeles, Calif, Oct. 1, 38; m. 64. ENGLISH, AMERICAN LITERATURE. Woodrow Wilson Nat. fel. & A.B, Harvard, 60; M.A, Univ. Calif, Berkeley, 62, Ph.D.(Am. lit), 67. Instr, ENG, Harvard, 66-68, ASST. PROF, 68-69; UNIV. CALIF, BERKELEY, 69- MLA; AAUP. Nineteenth and 20th century American fiction; imaginative artistry in recent American non-fiction; American cultural history. Publ: The passages of thought: psychological representation in the American novel, 1870-1900, Oxford, 69; Astigmatic images: the American novels of Henry Adams, Harvard Eng. Stud. I, 70; Joyce Carol Oates, artist in wonderland, South. Rev, spring 74; Of Adams and Aquarius, Am. Lit, spring 74. Add: Dept. of English, University of California, Berkeley, Berkeley, CA 94720.

TAYLOR, HARRY WERBAYNE, b. Van Buren, Ark, May 5, 13; m. 33; c. 1. ENGLISH. A.B, Emmanuel Missionary Col, 34; A.M, Univ. Mich, 44; Boston Univ, summers 47-52. Instr. Eng. & French, Bethel Acad, Wis, 34-37; head dept. Eng, Oshawa Missionary Col, 37-45, asst. prin, 42-45; assoc. prof. ENG, Atlantic Union Col, 45-53; ANDREWS UNIV, 53-59, PROF, 59-, acting head dept, 53-54 & 70, chmn. div. lang. lit. & speech, 58-60. NCTE. British romantic poetry; Biblical literature. Publ: Quiz fun, Rev. & Herald Pub. Asn, 44; Orange-and-black miscellany, 47, Adventures in Bible literature, 62, Adventures in literature and life, 63 & Adventures in creative writing, 66, Andrews Univ. Bookstore. Add: Dept. of English, Andrews University, Berrien Springs, MI 49104.

TAYLOR, HENRY SPLAWN, b. Loudoun Co, Va, June 21, 42; m. 68; c. 1. CREATIVE WRITING, CONTEMPORARY AMERICAN LITERATURE. B.A, Univ. Va, 65; M.A, Hollins Col, 66. Instr. Eng, Roanoke Col, 66-68; asst. prof, Univ. Utah, 68-71; ASSOC. PROF. LIT, AM. UNIV, 71- Dir, Univ. Utah Summer Writers Conf, 69-72. MLA. Southern American fiction; contemporary American poetry. Publ: The horse show at midnight (poems), La. State Univ, 66; Breakings (poems), Solo, 71; Points of departure: an introduction to poetry, Winthrop, 74; transl, Euripides' The children of Herakles, Oxford, (in press); ed, The water of light: a miscellany in honor of Brewster Ghiselin, (in press) & auth, An afternoon of pocket billiards (poem), (in press), Univ. Utah. Add: 6931 Hector Rd, McLean, VA 22101.

TAYLOR, HUBERT V, b. Ash Grove, Mo, Oct. 23, 13; m. 41; c. 2. SPEECH, MUSIC. A.B, Lafayette Col, 35; B.Mus, Westminster Choir Col, 38; B.D, Columbia Theol. Sem, 47; Ph.D.(speech), Northwest. Univ, 64. PROF. SPEECH & MUSIC, COLUMBIA THEOL. SEM, 47- Mem. content comt, The Hymnbook, 55; ed. comt. for revision Bk. Common Worship & Hymnal, 68-72. Speech Commun. Asn.(mem. ed. comt, Preaching in Am. Hist). Slavery and the deliberations of the Presbyterian Assembly, 1833-1838; rhetorical theory and homiletics. Publ: Preaching on slavery, In: Preaching in American history, 69 & contrib, Sermons in American history, 71, Abingdon. Add: Dept. of Speech, Columbia Theological Seminary, Decatur, GA 30031.

TAYLOR, IRMA STOCKWELL, b. Paterson, N.J. SPEECH. A.B, Fla. South. Col, 38; M.A, Univ. Wis-Madison, 43. Teacher speech & Eng, Andrew Jackson High Sch, Jacksonville, Fla, 39-43, 44-45; speech clinician, Duval Co. Pub. Schs, 43-44; acting chmn. dept. speech, Ga. State Col. Women, 45-46; chmn. dept. speech, Mary Baldwin Col, 46-47; dir, Speech & Hearing Clin, NORTHWEST. STATE UNIV, 48-69, assoc. prof. SPEECH, 67-73, PROF, 73- Am. Speech & Hearing Asn. Add: Dept. of Speech, Box 4133, Northwestern State University, Natchitoches, LA 71457.

TAYLOR, IVAN EARLE, b. Jamaica, B.W.I, Apr. 29, 04; nat; m. 53. ENGLISH. B.A, Howard Univ, 31, M.A, 32; Ph.D, Univ. Pa, 42. Instr. Eng, Va. Union Univ, 32-33; Lincoln Univ.(Pa), 33-37; prof. Eng. & dean, Samuel Huston Col, 37-39; prof. Eng, Shaw & St. Augustine's Col, 39-43; dean, Bennett Col, 43-45; prof. ENG, HOWARD UNIV, 45-72, 73-74, EMER. PROF, 72- MLA; Col. Eng. Asn; Col. Lang. Asn. Medieval literature; 17th century literature. Publ: Co-auth, Reading for writing; Samuel Pepys, Twayne 68; John Milton as a linguist, Mod. Lang. J; George Herbert's sophistication, Anglican Theol. Rev. Add: 67 Ward Ave, Mandeville, Jamaica, B.W.I.

TAYLOR, JAMES SHEPPARD, b. Montgomery, Ala, Dec. 15, 43; m. 72; c. 2. SPEECH. B.A, Auburn Univ, 65, M.A, 66; Ph.D.(speech), Fla. State Univ, 66. Asst. prof. SPEECH, N.C. State Univ, 68-69; Auburn Univ, 69-73; ASSOC. PROF. & CHMN. DEPT, HOUSTON BAPTIST UNIV, 73- AAUP; Speech Commun. Asn. Experimental persuasion; American public address; group dynamics. Publ: Co-auth, William Huskisson and free trade, N.C. J. Speech, 72, Loyalist propaganda in the sermons of Charles Inglis, 1770-1780, West. Speech, 73 & Charles T. Walker: the black spurgeon, Ga. Speech J, 73; plus others. Add: Dept. of Speech & Drama, Houston Baptist University, 7502 Fondren Rd, Houston, TX 77036.

TAYLOR, JEROME, b. Chicago, Ill, Nov. 21, 18; m. 46; c. 9. ENGLISH LANGUAGE & LITERATURE. A.B, Cath. Univ. Am, 43; M.A, Univ. Chicago, 45, univ. fel, 45-46, Danforth grant, 58-59, Ph.D, 59; Am. Counc. Learned Soc. fel, Pontifical Inst. Medieval Stud, 52-53. Instr. Eng. & gen. lang, Univ. Chicago, 46-48; ENG, Dartmouth Col, 48-53; asst. prof, Univ. Notre Dame, 53-59, assoc. prof, 59-62; Univ. Chicago, 62-67, PROF, 67-70, assoc. chmn. dept. Eng, 63-65, chmn. comt. Medieval stud, 66-70; UNIV. WIS-MADISON, 70- Danforth Found. spec. res. grant, 60-61; mem. adv. counc, Inst. Europ. Stud, 63-; Guggenheim fel, 64-65; Am. Counc. Learned Soc. grant, 73; Am. Philos. Soc. grant, 73; dir. summer sem. col. teachers Eng. & hist, Nat. Endowment for Humanities, 73, 74; sr. fel, Inst. Res. in Humanities, Univ. Wis-Madison, 73-74; Nat. Endowment for Humanities sr. fel, 74-75. Harbison Award for Distinguished Teaching, 64-65. MLA; Midwest Mod. Lang. Asn; Mediaeval Acad. Am. Middle English literature, especially Chaucer; history of the liberal, especially the verbal, arts during the Middle Ages; medieval drama. Publ: Hugh of St. Victor's Didascalicon: a medieval guide to the arts, Columbia Univ, 61; co-ed, Chaucer criticism: the Canterbury tales, 61 & Chaucer criticism: the Troilus and minor poems, 62, Univ. Notre Dame; co-ed. & transl, M.-D. Chenu, Nature man, and society in the twelfth century, 68 & contrib. & co-ed, Medieval English drama: essays critical and contextual, 72, Univ. Chicago. Add: Dept. of English, Helen C. White Hall, University of Wisconsin-Madison, 600 N. Park St, Madison, WI 53706.

TAYLOR, JOHN ALFRED, b. Springfield, Mo, Sept. 12, 31; m. 73. ENGLISH. B.A, Univ. Mo, 53; M.A, Univ. Iowa, 57, Ph.D.(Eng), 59. Instr. ENG, Univ. N.H, 59-61, asst. prof, 61-62; Rice Univ, 62-64; State Univ. N.Y. Col. Buffalo, 64-66; ASSOC. PROF, WASHINGTON & JEFFERSON COL, 66- Rockefeller Found. grant, 70. U.S.A, 53-55. MLA; AAUP. Writing poetry and plays; teaching creative writing. Publ: The soap duckets, Verb Publ, 65; Portfolio 3:12, poems by John Taylor, Portfolio, 71; The censor (poem), Colo. State Rev, 67; Six poems, Poetry Northwest, winter 68-69; Snail poem, N.Y. Quart, fall 70. Add: Dept. of English, Washington & Jefferson College, Washington, PA 15301.

TAYLOR, JOHN ALFRED, b. St. Louis, Mo, July 23, 36; div; c. 2. ENGLISH. A.B, Princeton, 58; B.A, Oxford, 60; Ph.D.(Eng), Univ. Calif, Berkeley, 68. ASST. PROF. ENG, UNIV. CHICAGO, CHICAGO CIRCLE, 67- MLA. Add: Dept. of English, University of Chicago, 5801 S. Ellis, Chicago, IL 60637.

TAYLOR, JOHN CHESLEY, b. Edinburg, Tex, Apr. 22, 35; m. 58; c. 3. ENGLISH. A.B, Univ. Tex, 57; Woodrow Wilson Found. fel, Tulane Univ, 57, South. Found. fel, 57-59; M.A, 59, Ph.D.(Eng), 66. Instr. ENG, Loyola Univ.(La), 61-62, 64-66; ASST. PROF, WASH. STATE UNIV, 66- U.S.A, 62-64, 1st Lt. Seventeenth century English literature; modern fiction. Publ: The short story: fiction in transition, 69 & Ritual, realism and revolt: major traditions in the drama, 72, Scribners; Metaphors of the moral world: structure in The changeling, Tulane Stud. Eng, 72. Add: Dept. of English, Washington State University, Pullman, WA 99163.

TAYLOR, JOHN RAYMOND, b. Akron, Ohio, Aug. 29, 23. ENGLISH LITERATURE. B.A, Bethany Col.(W.Va), 44; M.A, Princeton, 50; Univ. Kans, 51-53; Shakespeare Inst, Univ. Birmingham, 59; Univ. Edinburgh, 63; Oxford, 67. Instr. ENG, Univ. Nebr, 46-48; Univ. Kans, 51-53; Ohio North. Univ, 53-54, asst. prof, 54-55; instr. BETHANY COL.(W.VA), 55-56, asst. prof, 56-58, ASSOC. PROF, 58-, DIR, BETHANY-AT-OXFORD PROG, 72-, acting chmn. dept, Eng, 58-59, 67-68. MLA. Shakespeare; Renaissance; 18th century English literature. Add: Box T, Bethany, WV 26032.

TAYLOR, LOUIS, b. Columbus, Ohio, May 4, 00; m; c. 1. ENGLISH. M.A, Ohio State Univ, 27. ASST. PROF. ENG, ARIZ. STATE UNIV, 49- Study of the horse; semantics. Publ: The horse America made, 61, Ride American, 63, Bits: their history, use and misuse, 66 & Ride Western, 68, Harper; Out of the West, A.S. Barnes, 65; The story of America's horses, World Publ, 68; Harper's encyclopedia for horsemen, Harper, 73; plus others. Add: 6714 Indian Bend Rd, Scottsdale, AZ 85251.

TAYLOR, MARION ANSEL, b. Chicago, Ill, Feb. 23, 04; div; c. 1. ENGLISH, FICTION. Ph.D.(Shakespeare), Univ. Iowa, 31. Instr. Eng, Ill. State Norm. Univ, 32-34, asst. prof, 34-42; SOUTH. ILL. UNIV, EDWARDSVILLE, 58-60, assoc. prof. Shakespeare, 60-63, prof, 63-73, EMER. PROF. ENG, 73- Fulbright lectr, Univ. Saugar & Univ. Jammu & Kashmir, India, 60-61; Istanbul Univ, 65-66. Renaissance Soc. Am; Shakespeare Asn. Am. Shakespeare; creative writing, especially novels, short stories and plays. Publ: Whiz, 54 & American geisha, 56, Geoffrey Bles, London; A new look at the old sources of Hamlet, Mouton, The Hague, 68; Bottom, thou art translated: political allegory in A midsummer night's dream and related literature, Ed. Rodopi, Netherlands, 73; He that did the tiger board, Shakespeare Quart, 64; Albee and Strindberg, Papers Eng. Lang. & Lett, 65; Lady Arabella Stuart and Beaumont and Fletcher, Papers Lang. & Lit, fall 72; plus others. Add: 549 Nevada St, East Alton, IL 62024.

TAYLOR, MARK, b. White Plains, N.Y, Mar. 13, 39; m. 63; c. 2. ENGLISH LITERATURE. A.B, Yale, 61; M.A, City Univ. New York, 65, Ph.D.(Eng), 69. ASST. PROF. ENG, MANHATTAN COL, 69- Poetry ed, Commonweal Mag, 72. MLA. Shakespeare; the Renaissance; modern fiction. Publ: The soul in paraphrase: George Herbert's poetics, Mouton, 74; Baseball as myth, 5/72, History, humanism and Simone Weil, 8/73 & W.H. Auden's vision of eros, 10/73, Commonweal. Add: Dept. of English, Manhattan College, Bronx, NY 10471.

TAYLOR, MICHAEL J. H, b. London, Eng, Apr. 13, 35; m. 59; c. 2. ENGLISH. B.A, Univ. Col. S.Wales, 59, Dipl.Ed, 60; Ph.D.(Eng), Univ. Birmingham, 63. Asst. prof. ENG, Univ. Calgary, 63-67; ASSOC. PROF. UNIV. N.B, FREDERICTON, 67- Shakespeare; Elizabethan and Jacobean drama; Marlowe and Jonson. Add: Dept. of English, University of New Brunswick, Fredericton, N.B, Can.

TAYLOR, MYRON WILFRED, b. Marion, Ohio, Feb. 9, 30. ENGLISH. B.A, N.Cent. Col.(Ill), 51; M.A, Ohio State Univ, 52; Ph.D.(Eng), Wash. Univ, 61. Lectr. ENG, South. Ill. Univ, 60-61, asst. prof, 61-65; ASSOC. PROF, Millikin Univ, 65-69; STATE UNIV. N.Y. ALBANY, 69- U.S.A, 53-56. MLA; Milton Soc. Am. Seventeenth century literature; Shakespeare; 17th century English theology. Publ: The passion of Antonio, Christian Scholar, 67; Tragedy and the house of Polonius, Stud. Eng. Lit, 68; Julius Caesar and the irony of history, Shakespeare Quart, summer 73. Add: Dept. of English, State University of New York at Albany, Albany, NY 12203.

TAYLOR, ORLANDO LeROY, Linguistics, Speech. See Volume III, Foreign Languages, Linguistics & Philology.

TAYLOR, RICHARD DEAN, b. Cambridge, N.Y, Dec. 24, 35; m. 63; c. 2. ENGLISH. A.B, Brown Univ, 57; M.A, Univ. Manchester, 64; Ph.D.(Eng), Univ. Durham, 66. Lectr. ENG, Univ. Sierra Leone, 63-65; Univ. Reading, 65-66; asst. prof, Dartmouth Col, 66-71; READER & CHMN. DEPT. ENG, UNIV. IFE, NIGERIA, 72- U.S.N, 57-60, Lt.(jg). MLA; AAUP. Modern poetry in English; African literature and Negro writing in the new world. Publ: Frank Pearce Sturm: his life, letters and collected work, Univ. Ill, 68; the resurrected Christ, a modern Nō drama, Ariel, 71; The notebooks of Ernest Fenollosa: translation from the Japanese Nō, Lit. East. & West, 12/72; Assimilation from the Japanese No, In: Yeats and the theatre, Macmillan, 74. Add: Dept. of English, University of Ife, Ile-Ife, Nigeria.

TAYLOR, STANLEY H, b. Chicago, Ill, Mar. 25, 29. SPEECH. B.A, Mich. State Univ, 51, M.A, 57, Ph.D.(Speech), 67; Yale, 53. Assoc. prof. speech & chmn. dept, East. N.Mex. Univ, 64-69; ASST. PROF. COMMUN. ARTS & ASST. CHMN. DEPT, 70- Res. analyst, Foote Cone & Belding Advert. Speech Commun. Asn. Small groups; cross-national communication; advertising research. Add: 1657 Maywood Ave, Upland, CA 91786.

TAYLOR, VELMA LOTUS (ADAMS), b. Ongo, Mo, Jan. 22, 10; m. 47. ENGLISH, EDUCATION. B.S, Kans. State Teachers Col, 34, M.S, 35; scholar, George Peabody Col, 43, M.Ed, 44; Ph.D.(educ), Ind. Univ, 53. Teacher, high schs, Okla, Kans, S.C, Fla. & Calif, 36-48; prof. Eng, head dept. Eng. & div. lang. & lit, Col. Emporia, 53-54; assoc. prof. ENG, CENT. MO. STATE UNIV, 54-63, PROF, 63- NCTE. English; education. Publ: Analysis of current magazine fiction with reference to American social classes, Ind. Univ. Bull, 1/54. Add: 209 Grover, Warrensburg, MO 64093.

TAYLOR, VI MARIE, b. Dallas, Tex, Dec. 19, 22; wid. ENGLISH. B.A, N.Tex. State Univ, 43; M.A, Tex. Woman's Univ, 51; Ph.D.(Curriculum & Eng), Mich. State Univ, 65. Teacher Eng, Seymour Pub. Schs, Tex, 44; & Eng. & speech, Wharton County Jr. Col, 47-48; Eng, Wharton Pub. Schs, 48-49; secy. to pres, Tex. Woman's Univ, 51-56; teacher Eng, Austin Pub. Schs, 56-59; Okemos Pub. Schs, Mich, 59-73; INT. COORD. PROG. SERV, DELTA KAPPA GAMMA SOC, 73- Consult, Am. Schs. Cent. Am. Countries, winter 64; vis. prof, Univ. Alaska & consult, Alaska Dept. Educ, summer 66; consult, D.C. Pub. Schs, spring 69; NEA Overseas Teacher Prog, Nepal, summer 73. NCTE; NEA. Creativity in writing of junior high school students; imagery; Browning. Publ: Status of the legal profession in Texas, State Bar Tex, 56. Add: 7703 Longpoint, Austin, TX 78731.

TAYLOR, WALTER F, JR, b. Jackson, Miss, June 11, 27; m. 64; c. 5. MODERN FICTION, AMERICAN LITERATURE. B.A, Univ. Miss, 51, fel, 51-52; Ph.D.(Eng), Emory Univ, 64. Instr. ENG, Ga. Inst. Technol, 57-59; La. State Univ, 59-64; ASSOC. PROF, Univ. Southwest. La, 64-68; UNIV. TEX, EL PASO, 68- U.S.A, 46-48. The literary impact of white southern culture and Negro culture on each other; American literature; recent fiction. Publ: Faulkner: social commitment and the artistic temperament, South. Res, 10/70; Faulkner's Pantaloon: the Negro anomaly at the heart of Go down, Moses, Am. Lit, 11/72; Faulkner's curse, Ariz. Quart, winter 72. Add: Dept. of English, University of Texas at El Paso, El Paso, TX 79968.

TAYLOR, WARREN, b. Bedford Co, Tenn, July 2, 03; m. 33; c. 4. ENGLISH LITERATURE. A.B, Vanderbilt Univ, 24, A.M, 26; Ph.D, Univ. Chicago, 37. Mem. fac, Univ. Tenn, 26-29; Univ. Chicago, 34-37; prof. ENG, OBERLIN COL, 30-35, 37-70, chmn. humanities prog, 47-70, chmn. dept. Eng, 55-58, EMER. PROF, 70-; DISTINGUISHED PROF. HUMANITIES, HIRAM COL, 70- Fund Adv. Educ. fac. fel, 51-52; consult, Univ. Ark, 53; summers, vis. prof, Portland State Col, 50 & 56; State Univ. N.Y. Col. Albany, 51 & 58; Univ. N.Mex, 55; Col. Pac, 59; N.Mex. Highlands Univ, 60, 61, 62, 63 & 64; grants, comt. prod. works, Oberlin Col, summers 65 & 66. MLA; Renaissance Soc. Am. Interdisciplinary courses and programs in humanities; Elizabethan rhetoric; American studies. Publ: Tudor figures of rhetoric, Univ. Chicago, 37 & 72; The humanities at Oberlin, 58; co-auth, Poetry in English, Macmillan, 63; auth, Models for writing and thinking, World, 66; Tudor figures of rhetoric, Lang. Press, 72. Add: 227 S. Professor St, Oberlin, OH 44074.

TAYLOR, WELFORD DUNAWAY, b. Caroline Co, Va, Jan. 3, 38; m. 60. ENGLISH. B.A, Univ. Richmond, 59, M.A, 61; Ph.D.(Eng), Univ. Md, 66. Instr. ENG, Richmond Prof. Inst, 61-63; UNIV. RICHMOND, 64-66, asst. prof, 66-69, assoc. prof, 69-73, PROF, 73- MLA. Amelie Rives; Sherwood Anderson; American literature 1890 to the present. Publ: Ed, The buck fever papers, Univ. Va, 71 & Virginia authors past and present, Va. Asn. Teachers Eng, 72; auth, Amélie Rives (Princess Troubetzkoy), Twayne, 73; Amélie Rives: a Virginia Princess, Va. Cavalcade, spring 63; The Virginia corner, monthly column in Richmond Times-Dispatch. Add: 5 Calycanthus Rd, Richmond, VA 23221.

TEBBEL, JOHN WILLIAM, b. Boyne City, Mich, Nov. 16, 12. JOURNALISM. A.B, Cent. Mich. Col. Educ, 35, D.Litt, 48; M.S, Columbia Univ, 37. City ed, Isabella County Times-News, Mich, 36-37; reporter, Detroit Free Press, 37-39; feature writer & ed, Providence Jour, R.I, 39-41; managing ed, Am. Mercury, 41-43; assoc. ed, E.P. Dutton & Co, 43-46; asst. prof. JOUR, N.Y. UNIV, 46-54, PROF, 54-, chmn. dept, 54-65. Asst. Columbia Univ, 42-46; Sunday staff writer, N.Y. Times, 43; consult, Ford Found, 66-; Nat. Endowment for Humanities grant, 67-69. Bibliog. Soc. Am. Journalism history. Publ: An American dynasty & George Horace Lorimer and the Saturday Evening Post, Doubleday; Life and good times of William Randolph Hearst, Dutton; Makers of modern journalism, Prentice-Hall; Compact history of the American newspaper & The American magazine: a compact history, Hawthorn; A history of book publishing in the U.S, Vol. I, Bowker, 72. Add: Washington Square College, New York University, Washington Square, New York, NY 10003.

TEDFORD, BARBARA WILKIE, b. Marshall, N.C, Jan. 21, 36; m. 58. ENGLISH. B.A, Maryville Col, 57; M.A, Univ. Tenn, 60; Andrew Mellon fel, Univ. Pittsburgh, 69-70, Ph.D.(Eng), 70. Instr. Eng, Davis & Elkins Col, 60-62, asst. prof, 62-69; humanities, Robert Morris Col, 70-74. S.Atlantic Mod. Lang. Asn; AAUP; Am. Asn. Univ. Women. Nineteenth century; Henry James; Ivan Turgenev. Publ: A recipe for satire and civilization, Costerus Essays in Eng. & Am. Lang. & Lit, 72. Add: c/o Mrs. Jessie H. Wilkie, Skyland, NC 28776.

TEDFORD, THOMAS LEE, b. Little Rock, Ark, Oct. 8, 30; m. 51; c. 2. SPEECH. B.A, Ouachita Baptist Univ, 51; M.A, La. State Univ, 53, Ph.D. (speech), 58. Asst. prof. speech, Georgetown Col, 55-57; chmn. dept, Ouachita Baptist Univ, 58-60; assoc. prof. speech, Delta State Col, 60-63; chmn. dept, Appalachian State Univ, 63-67; PROF. DRAMA & SPEECH, UNIV. N.C, GREENSBORO, 67- Speech Commun. Asn.(ed, Free Speech Newslett, 67-70, ed, Free Speech Yearbk, 70-72, chmn. comn. on freedom of speech, 73-); South. Speech Commun. Asn; AAUP. Rhetoric and public address; ethics of persuasion; freedom of speech. Publ: Teaching freedom of speech through the use of common materials, Speech Teacher, 11/67. Add: Dept. of Drama & Speech, University of North Carolina at Greensboro, Greensboro, NC 27412.

TEDLOCK, ERNEST WARNOCK, JR, b. St. Joseph, Mo, Dec. 20, 10; m. 38; c. 3. ENGLISH. A.B, Univ. Mo, 32, M.A, 33; Univ. Chicago, 32; Rockefeller Found. fel, 44-45; Ph.D.(Eng), Univ. South. Calif, 50. Instr. Eng, Univ. N. Mex, 43-47, asst. prof, 47-52, assoc. prof, 52-59, prof, 59-73; RETIRED. MLA (chmn, Eng. II, 67-68); Rocky Mountain Mod. Lang. Asn.(ed, News Bull, 52-54). Modern fiction; modern poetry; D.H. Lawrence. Publ: Ed, Dylan Thomas: the legend and the poet, William Heinemann, 60, Frieda Lawrence Collection of D.H. Lawrence manuscripts, 48, co-ed, Steinbeck and his critics, 57 & auth, D.H. Lawrence: artist and rebel, 63, Univ. N. Mex; ed, Frieda Lawrence: the memoirs and correspondence, Knopf, 61 & D.H. Lawrence and Sons and lovers: sources and criticism, N.Y. Univ, 65. Add: P.O. Box 53, Cerrillos, NM 87010.

TEELE, ROY EARL, Comparative Literature. See Volume III, Foreign Languages, Linguistics & Philology.

TEELING, JOHN PAUL, b. Denver, Colo, Dec. 11, 23. ENGLISH. A.B, St. Louis Univ, 46; M.A, Marquette Univ, 52; Ph.D.(Eng), Univ. N.C, 64. Instr, ENG, REGIS COL.(COLO), 56-57, 62-63, asst. prof, 64-69, ASSOC. PROF, 69- Vis. prof, Univ. Baghdad, 66-68; rector, Regis Jesuit Community, 71- MLA. Works of Joyce Cary; Jesuits in the Renaissance; The Arabs of Baghdad. Add: Dept. of English, Regis College, Denver, CO 80221.

TEES, ARTHUR THOMAS, b. Bismarck, N.Dak, Jan. 16, 30; m. 51. THEATRE. B.A, Univ. N.Dak, 50; B.D, Garrett Sem, 54; M.S, N.Dak. State Univ, 62; Ph.D.(theatre, drama), Univ. Kans, 67. Instr. speech, N.Dak. State Univ, 62-63; THEATRE, Southwest. Col, 63-65; ASSOC. PROF, CENT. MO. STATE UNIV, 67- Am. Theatre Asn; Speech Commun. Asn; AAUP. American drama, especially Maxwell Anderson; Medieval theatre and drama. Publ: Introd. & index to Theatrical management, Blom, 68; auth, The place of the common man: Robert Bolt: A man for all seasons, Univ. Rev, 10/69; Legal and poetic justice in Maxwell Anderson's plays, N.Dak. Quart, winter 70; Winterset: four influences on Mio, Mod. Drama, 2/72. Add: Dept. of Theatre, Central Missouri State University, Warrensburg, MO 64093.

TEETER, DWIGHT LELAND, JR, b. Los Angeles, Calif, Jan. 6, 35; m. 56; c. 3. COMMUNICATIONS LAW & HISTORY. A.B, Univ. Calif, Berkeley, 56, M.J, 59; Ph.D.(mass commun), Univ. Wis-Madison, 66. Reporter, Waterloo Daily Courier, Iowa, 57-60; Madison State Jour, Wis, 60-61; pub. relat. rep, State Hwy. Comn, Wis, 61-62; proj, res. & teaching asst. jour, Univ. Wis-Madison, 62-64, asst. prof, 66-68, assoc. prof, 68-72; asst. prof, Iowa State Univ, 64-66; ASSOC. PROF. JOUR. & DIR. GRAD. STUD, SCH. COMMUN, UNIV. KY, 72- Treas, Jour. Counc, Inc, 71-74. Asn. Educ. in Jour.(chmn. prof. freedom & responsibility comt, 71-73, mem, 73-76, head law div, 73-74); Orgn. Am. Hist. Publ: Co-auth, Law of mass communications, Found. Press, 69, 73; co-auth, Retreat from obscenity: Redrup v. New York, Hastings Law J, 69 & Obscenity, 1971: rejuvenation of state power and the return to Roth, Villanova Law Rev, 71; contrib, Mass media and the national experience, Harper, 71; plus others. Add: Office of Director of Graduate Studies, School of Communication, University of Kentucky, Lexington, KY 40506.

TEETS, BRUCE EARLE, b. Terra Alta, W.Va, May 13, 14; m. 39; c. 1. ENGLISH. A.B, Fairmont State Col, 38; A.M, W.Va. Univ, 41; Ph.D.(Eng), Duke Univ, 55. Teacher, high sch, W.Va, 33-49; Md, 51-52; instr. ENG, Duke Univ, 52-53, 54-55, res. asst, 53-54; asst. prof, Univ. Miami, 55-59, assoc. prof, 59-65; Purdue Univ, Indianapolis, 65-68; CENT. WASH. STATE COL, 68-74, PROF, 74- MLA; NCTE. Joseph Conrad; English novel; literary criticism. Publ: Ed, Castle Rackrent, Univ. Miami, 64; co-ed, Joseph Conrad: an annotated bibliography of writings about him, North. Ill. Univ, 71; auth, Conrad and guides to art as Psychagogia, Conradiana, 70. Add: Dept. of English, Central Washington State College, Ellensburg, WA 98926.

TEEVAN, THOMAS FOSTER, b. Tacoma, Wash, Oct. 16, 14. ENGLISH LITERATURE. B.A, Univ. Puget Sound, 36; M.A, Univ. Wash, 49, Ph.D, 57. Master ENG, Iolani Sch, Honolulu, Hawaii, 37-39; instr, St. John's Univ, China, 39-43; UNIV. HAWAII, MANOA, 54-58, ASST. PROF, 58- Japanese prisoner of war, 43-45. MLA; Philol. Asn. Pac. Coast; Am. Comt. Irish Stud. English literature of the 18th century; Anglo-Irish literature. Add: Dept. of English, University of Hawaii at Manoa, Honolulu, HI 96822.

TEICH, NATHANIEL, b. Boston, Mass, Feb. 10, 39; m. 65; c. 1. ENGLISH & COMPARATIVE LITERATURE. B.S, Carnegie Inst. Technol, 60; M.A, Columbia Univ, 62; Ph.D.(Eng), Univ. Calif, Riverside, 70. Ed. law, Calif. State Bar Asn-Univ. Calif, Berkeley Exten, 64-65; ASST. PROF. ENG, UNIV. ORE, 69- Eng.C, U.S.A, 62-64, Res, 64-65, 1st Lt. MLA. Romanticism; literary history; film. Publ: Criticism and Keats's Grecian urn, Philol. Quart, 65; Coleridge's Biographia and the contemporary controversy about style, Wordsworth Circle, 72; Pasolini's Medea and its dramatic heritage, In: Literature and film, Univ. South. Calif, (in press). Add: Dept. of English, University of Oregon, Eugene, OR 97403.

TEICHGRAEBER, STEPHEN E, b. Kansas City, Mo, July 28, 40. ENGLISH. A.B, Rockhurst Col, 62; M.A, Rice Univ, 64, Ph.D.(Eng), 67. ASST. PROF. ENG, COL. OF THE HOLY CROSS, 67- MLA. Edith Wharton; Henry James. Add: Dept. of English, College of the Holy Cross, Worcester, MA 01610.

TEICHMAN, MILTON, b. Brooklyn, N.Y, July 21, 30; m. 55; c. 2. ENGLISH. B.A, Brooklyn Col, 52; M.A, Duke Univ, 53; Syracuse Univ, 53-54; Ph.D. (Eng), Univ. Chicago, 66. Lectr. ENG, Ind. Univ, Calumet Ctr, 57-62; asst. prof, MARIST COL, 62-66, assoc. prof, 66-71, PROF, 71- MLA; NCTE. English Romantic movement; Victorian poetry; Augustan satire. Publ: Marist College experiment in interdepartmental freshmen composition, Col. Comp. & Commun, 12/67; The marriage metaphor in The rime of the ancient mariner, Bull. N.Y. Pub. Libr. Add: Dept. of English, Marist College, Poughkeepsie, NY 12601.

TELLER, STEPHEN JAMES, b. Chicago, Ill, Feb. 15, 40. ENGLISH. A.B, Roosevelt Univ, 62; M.A, Univ. Ill, 63, Ph.D.(Eng), 67. Asst. prof. ENG, KANS. STATE COL. PITTSBURG, 67-72, ASSOC. PROF, 72- Shakespeare; Elizabethan and Jacobean drama. Add: Dept. of English, Kansas State College of Pittsburg, Pittsburg, KS 66762.

TEMBECK, ROBERT EDWARD, b. Cairo, Egypt, June 23, 40; Can. citizen; m. 69. THEATRE, COMMUNICATION. B.A, Am. Univ. Cairo, 61; M.S, S.Dak. State Univ, 63; Ph.D.(theatre), Univ. Minn, 68. Instr. Eng, Col. Gen. & Voc. Educ. P.Q, Bois de Boulogne, 68-69, Edouard Montpetit, 69-70; ASST. PROF. DRAMA & COMMUN, McGILL UNIV, 70- Mem. bd. dir, Quebec Drama Festival, 71-73. Best Dir. Trophies, Dominion Drama Festival, 69 & 70. Nonverbal communication in theatre. Publ: Time and dialectic in Altona, Mod. Drama, summer 69. Add: Dept. of English, McGill University, P.O. Box 6070, Montreal 101, P.Q, Can.

TEMPLE, RUTH ZABRISKIE, b. Passaic, N.J, Dec. 26, 08. COMPARATIVE LITERATURE. A.B, Mt. Holyoke Col, 29; A.M, Radcliffe Col, 30; Bryn Mawr Col, 32-33; Ph.D, Columbia Univ, 47. Instr. Eng. lit, Mt. Holyoke Col, 31-32; grad. sch, Columbia Univ, 35-36, Barnard Col, 38-39; Queens Col.(N.Y), 39-42; Wells Col, 42-43; asst. prof, Russell Sage Col, 43-48; Eng. Brooklyn Col, 48-58, assoc. prof, 58-66, prof, 66-73; ADJ. PROF. COMP. LIT, GRAD. CTR, CITY UNIV. NEW YORK, 73- Mem. bibliog. comt, Eng. Lit. in Transition; Am. Asn. Univ. Women state fel, N.J, 51; Fulbright prof. Am. lit, Univ. Strasbourg, 63-64. Eng. Inst; NCTE; Mod. Humanities Res. Asn, Gt. Brit; MLA; Am. Comp. Lit. Asn; Int. Asn. Univ. Prof. Eng. French and English poetry, novel and criticism. Publ: The critic's alchemy, Twayne, 53 & Col. & Univ, 62; co-ed, A library of literary criticism: modern British literature (3 vols), 66, auth, Twentieth century British literature: a reference guide and bibliography, 68, co-ed, The literatures of the world in English translation: a bibliography, Vol. I, The literatures of Greece and Rome, 68 & Vol. III, The Romance literatures, 70, Ungar; auth, Nathalie Sarraute, Columbia Univ, 68; The ivory tower as lighthouse in Edwardians and late Victorians, Eng. Inst. Essays, 60; Never say I: To the lighthouse as vision and confession, In: Virginia Woolf, a collection of critical essays, Prentice, 71. Add: Chesterfield, MA 01012.

TEMPLEMAN, WILLIAM DARBY, b. Princeton, Ky, Apr. 2, 03; m. 37. ENGLISH LANGUAGE & LITERATURE. A.B, West. Reserve Univ, 24; univ. scholar, Harvard, 24-25, A.M, 25, Shattuck scholar, 28-29, Townsend scholar, 29-30, Ph.D, 30. Instr. Eng, Adelbert Col, West. Reserve Univ, 25-28, asst. dean, 27-28, instr. ENG, Cleveland Col, 25-27; asst. prof, Univ. Ill, 30-45; assoc. prof, UNIV. SOUTH. CALIF, 45-47, prof, 47-72, chmn. univ. senate, 55-57, head dept. Eng, 57-64, EMER. PROF, 72- Summer vis. prof, Univ. Colo, 54; N.Y. Univ, 55; Fulbright vis. prof, Univ. Ankara, 66-67. MLA. English and American literature of the 18th and 19th centuries; studies in Matthew Arnold, Tennyson, Carlyle, Whitman, G.M. Hopkins, Ruskin and Thoreau. Publ: Co-auth, Freshman guide to writing, Doubleday, 35; co-ed, English prose of the Victorian era, Oxford, 38; auth, Life and work of William Gilpin (1724-1804), 39 & ed, Bibliographies of studies in Victorian literature for 1932-1944, 45, Univ. Ill; co-ed, Models and motivations for writing, Nelson, 41; auth, Analysis of prose, 64 & On writing well: selected readings from two centuries, 65, Odyssey; The four freedoms and two more, Univ. Rev, 3/70. Add: 6336 W. 84th St, Los Angeles, CA 90045.

TEMPLETON, JOAN, b. New Orleans, La, Jan. 30, 40; m. 68. ENGLISH. B.A, Centenary Col, 60; NDEA fel, Univ. Ore, 60-63, M.A, 62, Ph.D.(Eng), 66. Asst. prof. ENG, L.I. UNIV, 66-72, ASSOC. PROF, 72- MLA. Modern drama. Add: Dept. of English, Long Island University, Brooklyn, NY 11201.

TEMPLIN, LAWRENCE HOWARD, b. East. Weymouth, Mass, Apr. 4, 22; m. 47; c. 3. ENGLISH. A.B, Bethel Col.(Kans), 48; M.A, Ind. Univ, 60, Ph.D.(Eng), 64. Asst. prof. ENG, BLUFFTON COL, 61-64, assoc. prof. 64-67, PROF. & CHMN. DEPT, 67- MLA; NCTE. George Eliot; literary social science. Publ: The pathology of youth, J. Human Relat, spring 68; The Quaker influence on Walt Whitman, Am. Lit, 5/70. Add: Dept. of English, Bluffton College, Bluffton, OH 45817.

TENENBAUM, ELIZABETH BRODY, b. Bronx, N.Y, May 29, 44; m. 67. ENGLISH & AMERICAN LITERATURE. B.A, Radcliffe Col, 66; M.A, Univ. Calif, Berkeley, 68; Ph.D.(Eng), Stanford Univ, 72. ASST. PROF. ENG, VASSAR COL, 71- MLA; Eng. Inst. The novel; modern literature; literary criticism. Add: Dept. of English, Vassar College, Poughkeepsie, NY 12601.

TENER, ROBERT LAWRENCE, b. Barberton, Ohio, May 1, 24; m. 71. AMERICAN & BRITISH DRAMA. B.A, Univ. Akron, 46; Ohio State Univ, 46-48; M.A, West. Reserve Univ, 49, Ph.D.(Eng), 65; B.S.Ed, Kent State Univ, 64. Instr. humanities, Univ. Akron, 46; grad. asst. Eng. & math, Ohio State Univ, 46-47; asst. prof. speech & Eng, Wilkes Col, 55-59; teacher speech, drama & Eng, Milan High Sch, Ohio, 59-60; ASSOC. PROF. ENG. & LING, KENT STATE UNIV, 60- MLA. Use of space in drama; Black drama in America; continental drama, especially theatre of the absurd. Publ: Role playing as a Dutchman, Stud. Black Lit, 72; A portfolio for Nausikaa, Class. Bull, 73; Uncertainty as a dramatic formula, Can. Humanities Asn. Rev, 73. Add: Dept. of English, Kent State University, Kent, OH 44240.

TEN HARMSEL, HENRIETTA, b. Hull, Iowa, June 21, 21. ENGLISH LITERATURE. A.B, Calvin Col, 49; M.A, Univ. Mich, 58, univ. fel, 60-61, Ph.D, 62. Instr. ENG, CALVIN COL, 58-60, asst. prof, 62-63, assoc. prof, 63-65, PROF, 65- Am. Asn. Univ. Women fel, 65-66. MLA; Conf. Christianity & Lit. Jane Austen; 17th century Dutch poetry. Publ: Transl, Revius: Dutch metaphysical poet, Wayne State Univ, 68; auth, From animal to Christ in Adam Bede, spring 71 & Tragedy and the Christian faith, winter 73, Christianity & Lit; Young Goodman Brown and The enormous radio, Stud. in Short Fiction, fall 72. Add: Apt. F-10, 2880 Marshall S.E, Grand Rapids, MI 49508.

TENNYSON, GEORG BERNHARD, b. Washington, D.C, July 13, 30; m. 53; c. 2. ENGLISH. A.B, George Washington Univ, 53, M.A, 59; Fulbright fel, Univ. Freiburg, 53-54; M.A, Princeton, 61, Ph.D.(Eng), 63. Instr. ENG, Univ. N.C, Chapel Hill, 62-64; asst. prof, UNIV. CALIF, LOS ANGELES, 64-67, assoc. prof, 67-71, PROF, 71-, summer fac. fel, 65. Mem. adv. bd, Victorian Stud, 70-; John Simon Guggenheim Mem. Found. fel, 70-71; ed, Nineteenth-century Fiction, 71- Sig.C, U.S.A, 54-56. MLA; Philol. Asn. Pac. Coast; Victorian Soc; Carlyle Soc; Res. Soc. Victorian Periodicals. Victorian literature; drama; German literature, romantic to modern. Publ: Sartor called Resartus, Princeton, 66; An introduction to drama, Holt, 67; ed, A Carlyle Reader, Random, 68; auth, Carlyle and the modern world, Carlyle Soc, 72; The Bildungsroman in nineteenth century English literature, In: Medieval epic to epic theater of Brecht, Univ. South. Calif, 68; Owen Barfield and the rebirth of meaning, South. Rev, 69; Thomas Carlyle and Jane Welsh Carlyle, In: Victorian prose: a guide to research, MLA, 73. Add: Dept. of English, University of California, Los Angeles, CA 90024.

TENOEVER, DONALD ALOYSIUS, b. Cincinnati, Ohio, Sept. 4, 26. ENGLISH, HISTORY OF FINE ARTS. A.B, Athenaeum of Ohio, 47, S.T.L, 51, M.Ed, 53; M.A, Univ. Cincinnati, 56. ASSOC. PROF. Eng, ATHENAEUM OF OHIO, 58-68, HIST. FINE ARTS, 64- Thomas Jefferson and Federal period authors; classic revival architecture in the Middle West. Add: St. Gregory Seminary, 6616 Beechmont Ave, Cincinnati, OH 45230.

TERFLOTH, JOHN HELLMUTH, b. Essen, Ger, May 25, 23; U.S. citizen; m. 50; c. 2. DRAMA. Cand.phil, Univ. Mainz, 49; B.A, Univ. Alta, 56; M.F.A, Carnegie-Mellon Univ, 59; Ph.D.(drama), Univ. Iowa, 62. Ed, Sued West Funk, Ger, 50-54; instr. DRAMA, Univ. Iowa, 61-62, asst. prof, 62-66; assoc. prof, UNIV. ALTA, 66-72, PROF. & CHMN. GRAD. PROG, 72- Old Gold summer res. fel, Univ. Iowa, 65; Can. Counc. res. grant, 70-71. Am. Theatre Asn; Am. Soc. Theatre Res; Can. Univ. Theatre Asn.(chmn. prog. comt. jour. commun, 70-72). Eighteenth and nineteenth century theatre history; dramatic theory, romanticism; contiental drama 1700-1870. Publ: Das Theater als Mittel zur persönlichkeitsentwicklung, 73 & Politisches Theater in Amerika, Wunschtraum oder Wirklichkeit, 73, Maske & Kothurn; contrib, School teacher and student Schauspielführer, Hiersemann, Stuttgart, 74; plus others. Add: Dept. of Drama, University of Alberta, Edmonton, Alta. T6G 2G2, Can.

TERMINE, BENJAMIN, b. Norristown, Pa, Nov. 22, 24. SPEECH, DRAMA. B.A, Temple Univ, 49; M.F.A, Cath. Univ. Am, 51. Instr. acting, Am. Theatre Wing, N.Y, 53-58; speech, Baruch Sch. Bus, 58-65; PROF. SPEECH & DRAMA, JOHN JAY COL. CRIMINAL JUSTICE, 65-, chmn. dept, 73. Mem, Am. Theatre Wing Toni Award Comt, 60-61. Hosp.C, U.S.N, 43-46. Am. Acad. Polit. & Soc. Sci; Speech Commun. Asn; Am. Theatre Asn; Am. Nat. Theatre & Acad; Am. Theatre Asn.(chmn. inform. comt, 67). Publ: Euripides revisited, Athene, summer 57; The three-in-one technique (training for professional actors in New York), Showbusiness, 9/58; Observations on the drama of the theatre for the forgotten in Riker's Island, Correction Sidelight, Vol. XI, No. 3, Plays, Eh, Paisan! (produced in Norristown, Pa, 49); Oops, I'm a gentleman (produced in Norwalk, Conn); Lily (produced in Monticello, N.Y, 59). Add: 970 Ohayo Mountain Rd, Woodstock, NY 12498.

TERRELL, CARROLL FRANKLIN, b. Richmond, Maine, Feb. 21, 17. ENGLISH, COMPARATIVE LITERATURE. B.A, Bowdoin Col, 45; M.A, Univ. Maine, 50; Duke Univ, summer 53; Ph.D.(Eng), N.Y. Univ, 56; Alliance Francaise, summer 57. Instr. ENG, UNIV. MAINE, ORONO, 48-52, asst. prof, 52-57, assoc. prof, 57-66, PROF, 66- Managing ed, Paideuma. A.U.S, 41-45, Capt. MLA; Col. Eng. Asn. Contemporary poetry; poetry of Ezra Pound; life and thought of T.S. Eliot. Publ: The Pound era, 72 & An introduction to poetry of Ezra Pound, 73, Boston Herald Traveller; The sacred edict of K'ang-Hsi, Paideuma, spring 73. Add: Dept. of English, University of Maine, Orono, ME 04473.

TERRELL, DAHLIA JEWEL, b. Ladonia, Tex, Dec. 4, 19; m. 41; c. 2. ENGLISH. B.A, Tex. Technol. Col, 40, M.Ed, 48; Delta Kappa Gamma Soc. scholars, Univ. Tex, 65-66, Ph.D.(Eng), 66. Teacher, jr. & sr. high schs, Tex, 40-43, 45-49; dean of girls, High Sch, 49-53; instr. ENG, TEX. TECH UNIV, 56-63, asst. prof, 66-71, ASSOC. PROF, 71- MLA; Am. Asn. Univ. Women; Col. Eng. Asn; AAUP. Bibliography; editing for editions of American authors; 19th century American literature. Publ: Co-auth, Bold land, Tex. Tech Univ, 70; auth, A textual study of Washington Irving's A tour on the prairies, Diss. Abstr, 67; Textual errors in A tour on the prairies, Am. Transcendental Quart, 1/70; co-auth, Sunny land in the Southwest: a look at place names, S.Cent. Names Inst. Publ. 2, 73. Add: Dept. of English, Texas Tech University, Lubbock, TX 79409.

TERRIE, HENRY LARKIN, JR, b. Charleston, W.Va, Jan. 10, 21; m. 48; c. 2. ENGLISH. A.B, Yale, 43; A.M, Princeton, 52, Ph.D.(Eng), 55. Instr. ENG, Phillips Acad, 48; Univ. Minn, 48-49; DARTMOUTH COL, 52-55, asst. prof, 55-59, assoc. prof, 59-63, PROF, 63-, ASSOC. DEAN FAC. HUMANITIES, 72-, chmn. dept. Eng, 67-72. Mem. alumni bd, Yale, 65-71. U.S.N, 43-46, Lt. MLA; AAUP. American literature; the novel; Henry James. Publ: Co-auth, American literature, Ginn, 64; auth, Henry James and the explosive principle, 19th-Century Fiction, 61; The image of Chester in The ambassadors, Eng. Stud, 65. Add: 4 Parkway, Hanover, NH 03755.

TERRIS, VIRGINIA RINALDY, b. Brooklyn, N.Y, Aug. 26, 17; m. 42; c. 4. AMERICAN LITERATURE. B.A, N.J. Col. Women, Rutgers Univ, 38; N.Y. Univ, 41-42, Ph.D.(Eng), 73; M.A, Adelphi Univ, 64. Instr. Eng. & art, Morris Jr. Col, 40-42, ed, Random, McGraw, Holt, Harpers, Longmans, Pitman, Harcourt and others, 44-62; instr. ENG, ADELPHI UNIV, 62-71, ASST. PROF, 71- MLA; Am. Stud. Asn; AAUP. Emily Dickinson; women in American literature; history of American poetry. Publ: Co-auth, The many worlds of poetry, Knopf, 69; auth, Women in America: a bibliography, Gale, 75. Add: Dept. of English, Adelphi University, Garden City, NY 11520.

TERRY, REGINALD CHARLES, b. Buckinghamshire, Eng, Nov. 2, 32; m. 60; c. 2. ENGLISH LITERATURE. B.A, Univ. Leicester, 59; M.A, Bristol Univ, 64; Ph.D.(Eng), Univ. London, 70. Prin, Folk House Adult Educ. Ctr, Bristol, 60-65; ASST. PROF. ENG, UNIV. VICTORIA (B.C), 65- Novels of Anthony Trollope. Publ: Edward Dahlberg & Herbert Read an exchange of letters, In: Herbert Read: a memorial symposium, Methuen, 70; Three lost chapters of Anthony Trollope's first novel, Nineteenth Century Fiction, 6/72. Add: Dept. of English, University of Victoria, Victoria, B.C, Can.

TERWILLIGER, ERNEST WILLIAM, b. Utica, N.Y, June 12, 19; m. 43; c. 1. ENGLISH. A.B, Hope Col, 40; M.A, State Univ. N.Y. Col. Teachers, Albany, 42; Ph.D.(Eng), Cornell Univ, 53. Instr, State Univ. N.Y. Col. Teachers, Cortland, 47-48; asst. prof. ENG, ITHACA COL, 49-55, from assoc. prof. to PROF, 55-, chmn. dept, 53-71. U.S.A.A.F, 42-46. Modern English literature; American literature. Add: Dept. of English, College of Arts & Sciences, Ithaca College, Ithaca, NY 14850.

TESKE, CHARLES BAHN, b. Easton, Pa, Sept. 24, 32; m. 59; c. 2. ENGLISH LITERATURE. B.A, Lafayette Col, 54; M.A, Yale, 55, univ. fel, Selden fel, Mitchell-Univ. fel, Danforth teaching grant, Yale, Ph.D, 62. Instr. Eng, Oberlin Col, 58-63, asst. prof, 63-67, assoc. prof, 67-70, assoc. dean arts & sci, 68-70; DEAN HUMANITIES & ARTS, EVERGREEN STATE COL, 70- Coord, collaborative prog. in humanities, Great Lakes Cols. Asn, 67- Eighteenth century literary ballads; English and Scottish popular ballads; relationships between England and Germany in the pre-romantic period. Publ: Gay's Twas when the seas were roaring and the rise of pathetic balladry, Anglia, 65. Add: Evergreen State College, Olympia, WA 98505.

TEST, GEORGE AUSTIN, b. York, Pa, Mar. 14, 21; m. 46; c. 2. LITERATURE. A.B, Swarthmore Col, 49; M.A, Univ. Pa, 51, Ph.D, 61. Instr. ENG, Allegheny Col, 53-60; assoc. prof, STATE UNIV. N.Y. COL. ONEONTA, 60-63, PROF, 63-, CHMN. DEPT, 70- State Univ. N.Y. res. grants, 61-63; ed, Satire Newslett, 63-; Fulbright lectr, Univ. Chile, 66-67. U.S.A, 42-45. MLA; NCTE. American literature; satire. Add: Dept. of English, State University of New York College at Oneonta, Oneonta, NY 13820.

TEUNISSEN, JOHN JAMES, b. Calgary, Alta, Oct. 5, 33; m. 56; c. 2. ENGLISH. B.A, Univ. Sask, 60, univ. fel, 61, M.A, 62; univ. fel, Univ. Rochester, 62, Can. Counc. fel, 63, Ph.D, 67. Instr. Eng, Univ. Sask, 64-65, lectr, 65-66, asst. prof, 66-68, Univ. Mass, Amherst, 68-71, assoc. prof, 71-72; PROF. ENG. & HEAD DEPT, UNIV. MAN, 72- Univ. Sask. summer grant, 67; Can. Counc. short-term res. grants, 67 & 68. Asn. Can. Univ. Teachers Eng; MLA. Milton; 17th century literature; American literature. Publ: Co-ed, A key into the language of America, Wayne State Univ, 73; co-auth, Poe's Journal of Julius Rodman as parody, 19th Century Fiction, 72; auth, Blockheadism in the propaganda plays of the American Revolution, Early Am. Lit, 72. Add: Dept. of English, University of Manitoba, Winnipeg, Man. R3T 2N2, Can.

TEW, ARNOLD GERARD, b. Brooklyn, N.Y, Mar. 10, 38; m. 59; c. 3. AMERICAN LITERATURE. B.B.A, City Col. New York, 58; M.A, Columbia Univ, 61; Ph.D.(Eng), Case. West. Reserve Univ, 69. Lectr. Eng, City Col. New York, 59-61; ed, Prentice-Hall, 61; instr, ENG, CLEVELAND STATE UNIV, 61-64, asst. prof, 64-73, ASSOC. PROF, 74-, V.PRES. STUD. SERV, 72-, asst. to dean arts & sci, 65-66, asst. dean, 67-69, assoc. dean, 69-70, dean stud. life, 71-72. Danforth Teacher's grant, 66-67; Am. Counc. Educ. fel. acad. admin. prog, Colo. Comn. Higher Educ, 70-71. MLA; Am. Asn. Higher Educ; Nat. Asn. Stud. Personnel Adminr. Nineteenth century American novel and magazine. Add: 3000 Berkshire, Cleveland Heights, OH 44118.

TEZLA, ALBERT, b. South Bend, Ind, Dec. 13, 15; m. 41; c. 2. ENGLISH & HUNGARIAN LITERATURE. B.A, Univ. Chicago, 41, M.A, 47, Ph.D.(Eng. romance), 52. Instr. ENG. ROMANCE, UNIV. MINN, DULUTH, 49-53, asst. prof, 53-56, assoc. prof, 56-61, PROF, 61- Fulbright res. fel, Vienna, Austria, 59-60; Am. Counc. Learned Soc. res. grants, 61-62, 68; Inter-Univ. Comt. on Travel Grants res. fel, Hungary, 63-64; Off. Int. Prog, Univ. Minn. & Cultural Relat. Inst. Hungary res. grants, summers 65, 72; vis. prof, Columbia Univ, 66, adv. Ph.D. cand. in Hungarian lit, 67, vis. scholar, 75; summer res. appointment, Univ. Minn, 67. Outstanding Teacher Award, Univ. Minn, Duluth, 65; Commemorative Medallion, Hungarian Inst. Cult. Relat, 70. U.S.N, 42-46, Lt. History of Hungarian literature. Publ: An introductory bibliography to the study of Hungarian literature, 64 & Hungarian authors: a bibliographical handbook, 70, Harvard; six sections, In: East Central Europe: a guide to basic publications, Univ. Chicago, 69; transl, Ferenc Santa's God in the wagon, New Hungarian Quart, 71. Add: Dept. of English, University of Minnesota, Duluth, MN 55812.

THACKABERRY, ROBERT EUGENE, b. Sloan, Iowa, June 5, 11; m. ENGLISH. A.B, State Univ. Iowa, 33, A.M, 34, Ph.D, 37. Instr, Grinnell Col, 37-38; ENG, UNIV. AKRON, 38-41, asst. prof, 41-43, assoc. prof, 47-56, PROF, 56- U.S.A, 43-46. MLA; Mediaeval Acad. Am. Middle English literature; Chaucer. Add: Dept. of English, University of Akron, Akron, OH 44304.

THACKREY, DONALD EUGENE, b. Lyons, Kans, Nov. 14, 28; m. 50; c. 2. ENGLISH LITERATURE, RESEARCH ADMINISTRATION. B.A, Univ. Nebr-Lincoln, 53, M.A, 54; Ph.D.(Eng), Univ. Mich, Ann Arbor, 69. Teaching fel. Eng, UNIV. MICH, ANN ARBOR, 54-57, asst. ed, Willow Run Labs, 57-58, ed, 58-62, ed. publ, Off. Res. Admin, 62-60, DIR. PUBL. & PROG. DEVELOP, DIV. RES. DEVELOP. & ADMIN, 70- U.S.A.F, 46-49. Eighteenth century English literature; Samuel Johnson; chess. Publ: Emily Dickinson's approach to poetry, Univ. Nebr, 54; ed, Research: definitions and reflections, Univ. Mich, 67; contrib, The communication of the word, In: Emily Dickinson, Prentice-Hall, 63 & 14 by Emily Dickinson, Scott, 64. Add: 204 Research Administration Bldg, University of Michigan, Ann Arbor, MI 48104.

THADDEUS, JANICE FARRAR, b. New York, N.Y, July 20, 33; m. 63; c. 2. ENGLISH. A.B, Barnard Col, Columbia Univ, 55; A.M, Columbia Univ, 59, Ph.D.(Eng), 65. Instr. ENG, BARNARD COL, COLUMBIA UNIV, 59-63, lectr, 64-72, ASST. PROF, 72- Insanity and poetry in the 18th century; modern poetry. Publ: When women look at men, Harper, 63. Add: Dept. of English, Barnard College, Columbia University, New York, NY 10027.

THALE, JEROME, b. Evanston, Ill, June 6, 27; m. 50; c. 5. ENGLISH. B.A, Loyola Univ.(Ill), 49; M.A, Northwest. Univ, 50, Ph.D.(Eng), 53. Instr. ENG, Univ. Notre Dame, 52-56; asst. prof, MARQUETTE UNIV, 56-59, assoc. prof, 59-65, PROF, 65- U.S.N, 45-46. MLA; NCTE. Modern British literature; Victorian literature. Publ: Novels of George Eliot, Columbia Univ, 59; C.P. Snow, Scribner, 65; C.P. Snow: the art of worldliness, Kenyon Rev, 60; War and peace: the art of incoherence, Essays in Criticism, 10/66; History and anti-history; style and anti-style, Col. Eng, 1/68. Add: 4525 N. Bartlett, Shorewood, WI 53211.

THALER, ALWIN, b. Hamburg, Ger, Jan. 10, 91; m. 20; c. 2. ENGLISH LITERATURE. A.B, Adelphi Col, 12; Litt.D, 67; A.M, Columbia Univ, 14; Ph.D, Harvard, 18. Instr. Eng, Adelphi Col, 12-13; Northwest. Univ, 13-16; Sheldon traveling fel, Harvard, 19-20; asst. prof. ENG, Univ. Calif, 20-23; prof, UNIV. TENN, KNOXVILLE, 23-61, EMER. PROF, 61- Vis. prof, Stanford Univ, 25; Guggenheim fel, 29-30; Keenan vis. prof, Univ. N.C, 52; Emory Univ, 61-63; Tenn. Wesleyan Col, 64; ed, Tenn. Stud. Lit, 56-63, mem. adv. bd, 63-; ed. consult, PMLA, 60- U.S.N, 18-19. MLA; Shakespeare Asn. Am. Shakespeare; Elizabethan and restoration drama; Milton and Spenser. Publ: Shakespeare to Sheridan, Shakespeare's silences, 29 & Shakespeare and Sir Philip Sidney, Harvard; co-ed, Representative English comedies, Macmillan, Vol. IV, 36; auth, Shakespeare and democracy, 41, co-ed, Shakespearean essays, 64 & auth, Shakespeare and our world, 66, Univ. Tenn. Add: 2115 Terrace Ave, Knoxville, TN 37916.

THARPE, JAC LYNDON, b. Maynardville, Tenn, Jan. 7, 28; m. 56; c. 2. COMPARATIVE LITERATURE. B.A, Univ. Tenn, 57, M.A, 58; Ph.D.(comp. lit), Harvard, 65. Instr. ENG, Univ. Tenn, 58-61, asst. prof, Univ. Alaska, 64-65; assoc. prof, Tex. Technol. Col, 65-67; PROF, Hiram Scott Col, 67-70; UNIV. SOUTH. MISS, 70- Nathaniel Hawthorne; 20th century American studies; John Barth. Publ: Nathaniel Hawthorne: identity and knowledge, 67 & John Barth: the comic sublimity of paradox, 74, South. Ill. Univ; ed, Frost: centennial essays, Col. & Univ. Press Miss, 74. Add: Dept. of English, University of Southern Mississippi, Hattiesburg, MS 39401.

THATCHER, DAVID S, b. Bexhill, Eng, Feb. 16, 37; m. 63; c. 2. ENGLISH. B.A, Cambridge, 61, M.A, 64; Univ. Copenhagen, 61-62; M.A, McMaster Univ, 64; Ph.D.(Eng), Univ. Alta, 67. Asst. prof. ENG, UNIV. VICTORIA (B.C), 67-72, ASSOC. PROF, 72- Can. Counc. leave fel, 73-74. Friedrich Nietzsche; Thomas Hardy; W.B. Yeats. Publ: Nietzsche in England, 1890-1914, Univ. Toronto, 70; ed. & contrib, Friedrich Nietzsche: a symposium to mark the centenary of the publication of The birth of tragedy, Malahat Rev, 10/72. Add: Dept. of English, University of Victoria, Victoria, B.C, Can.

THAYER, CALVIN G, b. San Francisco, Calif, June 19, 22; m. 44; c. 5. ENGLISH RENAISSANCE. B.A, Stanford Univ, 43, M.A, Univ. Calif, Berkeley, 47, Ph.D.(Eng), 51. Instr. ENG, La. State Univ, 50-51; Univ. Okla, 51-53, asst. prof, 53-56, assoc. prof, 56-63, prof, 63-66; vis. prof, OHIO UNIV, 66-67, PROF, 67- Assoc. ed, Bucknell Rev, 67-; ed. consult, The Milton Quart, 67-; ed, Ohio Rev, 72; vis. lectr. Shakespeare, Univ. Calif, Berkeley, summer 72. Medieval and Renaissance drama; 16th century non-dramatic literature. Publ: Ben Jonson: studies in the plays, Okla. Univ, 63; Hamlet: drama as discovery and as metaphor, Stud. Neophilologica, 56; Shakespeare's second tetralogy: an underground report, Ohio Univ. Rev, 67; Murry's Shakespeare, D.H. Lawrence Rev, 69. Add: Dept. of English, Ohio University, Athens, OH 45701.

THAYER, DAVID LEWIS, b. Monterey, Calif, Apr. 30, 30; m. 56. DRAMATIC ART, COMMUNICATIONS RESEARCH. B.S, Lewis & Clark Col, 52; M.A, Univ. Iowa, 55, Ph.D.(dramatic art), 60. Instr. speech & dramatic art, UNIV. IOWA, 55-60, asst. prof, 60-65, assoc. prof, 65-68, PROF. SPEECH & DRAMATIC ART, 68-, prof. in charge of theatre, 68-73. Chmn. stage design & tech. develop, Am. Educ. Asn, 65-67. Am. Theatre Asn; Illuminating Engineering Soc; U.S. Inst. Theatre Technol.(bd. dir, 63-72, ed. bd, 65-). Theatrical production; experimental research in theatre; theatre history. Publ: Techniques of television lighting, Soc. Motion Picture & TV Engineers J, 4/57; Use of Smith's semantic differential for theatrical performance concepts, Speech Monogr, 6/64; Planning for lighting control systems, Theatre Design & Technol, 5/65. Add: Theatre, University of Iowa, Iowa City, IA 52242.

THEALL, DONALD F, b. Mt. Vernon, N.Y, Oct. 13, 28; m. 50; c. 6. ENGLISH, COMMUNICATIONS. B.A, Yale, 50; M.A, Univ. Toronto, 51, Ph.D.(Eng), 54. Asst. instr. Eng, Univ. Toronto, 52-53, lectr, 53-56, asst. prof, 56-60, assoc. prof, 60-64, prof. Eng. & chmn. joint depts, 64-65; prof. & chmn. dept. Eng. & commun, York Univ.(Ont), 65-66; prof. ENG, McGILL UNIV, 66-72, MOLSON PROF, 72-, CHMN. DEPT, 66- Secy, Ford Found. cult. & commun. sem, Univ. Toronto, 53-54; Dept. of Citizenship & Immigration res. grant, 56-59; mem. Eng. sub-comt, Univ. Toronto-Toronto Bd. Educ. Curriculum Stud. & Publ. Design for Learning, 60-61; Can. govt. & indust. res. grant, stud. audiovisual effects of Expo 67, 67-; chmn, Can. Asn. Chmn. Eng, 71-74. Int. Commun. Asn; MLA; Philol. Soc, Eng; Ling. Soc. Am; Can. Ling. Asn; Asn. Can. Univ. Teachers Eng. English; communications; linguistics. Publ: Co-auth, Let's speak English (4 vols, 15 transl), Gage, 60-62; auth, Here comes everybody, Explorations II, 54; The medium is the rear view mirror: understanding McLuhan, McGill-Queens Univ, 71; Appendix on rhetoric, In: Design for learning, Univ. Toronto, 62; The rape of the lock; In: Studies of major works in English, Oxford, 68. Add: Dept. of English, McGill University, Montreal, P.Q, Can.

THEARLE, BEATRICE JUNE (MRS. JONAS WHALEY), b. Baltimore, Md, Oct. 3, 22; m. 58. ENGLISH LITERATURE. A.B, Univ. Md, 44, M.A, 45, Ph.D, 58. Teacher, Hyattsville High Sch, 45-46; asst, Univ. Md, 46-51; teacher math, Westminster High Sch, 51-52; dist. dir. & training adv, Girl Scout Counc, Baltimore Area, 52-53; instr. Eng, Latin & Span, Baltimore Inst, 53-55; mem. fac. ENG, TOWSON STATE COL, 55-61, PROF, 61- MLA. Malory in the 19th century; Thomas Hardy, Spenser. Publ: Co-auth, Anyone can learn to spell, 55. Add: Dept. of English, Towson State College, Baltimore, MD 21204.

THEINER, PAUL FRANK, b. New Britain, Conn, Jan. 13, 37; m. 59; c. 4. ENGLISH. B.A, Univ. Conn, 58; A.M, Harvard, 59, fel, 61-62, Ph.D.(Eng), 62. Instr. ENG, Univ. Calif, Berkeley, 62-63, asst. prof, 63-69; assoc. prof, SYRACUSE UNIV, 69-74, PROF, 74- Fel, Inst. Res. in Humanities, Univ. Wis, 65-66. MLA; Mediaeval Acad. Am; Am. Comp. Lit. Asn; Northeast Mod. Lang. Asn. Chaucer; medieval Latin literature; literary theory. Publ: The man of law tells his tale, Stud. in Medieval Cult, 74; Some literary aspects of the peasant's revolt of 1381, Proc. 6th Congr. Int. Asn. Comp. Lit, 74; The Medieval Terence, Harvard Stud. Eng, 74. Add: Dept. of English, Syracuse University, Syracuse, NY 13210.

THEOBALD, JOHN R, b. Nina Tal, India, Sept. 5, 03; U.S. citizen; m. 43; c. 3. ENGLISH, THEOLOGY. B.A, Oxford, 25, M.A, 28; S.T.M, Union Theol. Sem, 29; Ph.D.(Eng), Univ. Iowa, 45. Lectr. Eng, Queen's Univ.(Ont), 29-30; instr, Amherst Col, 31-39; Trinity Col.(Conn), 40-41; Grinnell Col, 41-43, asst. prof, 43-44; res. assoc, naval warfare, Div. War Res, Univ. Calif, 44-46; from assoc. prof. to prof. ENG, SAN DIEGO STATE UNIV, 46-69, EMER. PROF, 69- Writing poetry. Publ: The earthquake and other poems, Bruce Humphries, 48; An Oxford odyssey, Janus, 55; co-auth, Introducing poetry, Holt, 64; contrib. poems, Atlantic Monthly, Kenyon Rev, Sat. Rev, Poetry & other mag. Add: 1390 Merritt Dr, El Cajon, CA 92020.

THIBEAULT, MARY LOU, b. Casco, Maine, Jan. 17, 36; wid. ENGLISH. B.A, Mt. Holyoke Col, 59; M.A, Trinity Col.(Conn), 63; Ph.D.(Eng, higher educ. admin), Antioch Col, 73. Teacher Eng, Manchester High Sch, Conn, 59-65; asst. prof, Manchester Community Col, 66-68; dean col, William Smith Col, 68-70; assoc. prof. Eng. & dean stud, Kingsborough Community Col, N.Y, 70-73; ASST. TO PRES, HARTFORD COL. WOMEN, 73- Hartford Col. Counseling Ctr. consult. estab. new ctrs, 73- Basic communications skills for educationally disadvantaged women; higher education administration. Publ: Drugs and discipline, Col. Mgt, 72; Composition without tears, Improv. Col. & Univ. Teaching, 74. Add: Hartford College for Women, 1265 Asylum Ave, Hartford, CT 06105.

THIEBAUX, MARCELLE, b. Jersey City, N.J, Oct. 31, 31; c. 2. ENGLISH, COMPARATIVE LITERATURE. B.A, Smith Col, 53; M.A, Univ. Conn, 55; Ph.D.(Eng. & comp. lit), Columbia Univ, 62. Asst. prof. ENG, Seton Hall Univ, 63-68, ASSOC. PROF, 68-70; ST. JOHN'S UNIV.(N.Y), 70- MLA; Mediaeval Acad. Am. Medieval English; middle English literature. Publ: The stag of love: the chase in medieval literature, Cornell Univ, 74; The mediaeval chase, Speculum, 67; The mouth of the boar as a symbol in medieval literature, Romance Philol, 69; Sir Gawain, the Fox and Henry of Lancaster, Neuphilol. Mitt, 70. Add: 305 W. 86th St, New York, NY 10024.

THIESSEN, VALOR EUGENE, b. Douglas, Okla, Oct. 30, 17; m. 40. ENGLISH, JOURNALISM. B.S, Okla. Agr. & Mech. Col, 40; M.A, Univ. Okla, 50, fel, 52-55; hon. L.H.D, Southwest. State Col, 72. Instr. Eng, OKLAHOMA CITY UNIV, 47-48, ENG. & JOUR, 52-58, ASSOC. PROF, 58- Eng.C, 42-46, 50-52, Col. Novel; short story; essay. Publ: My brother Cain; The fifth chrysanthemum, Esquire; The lie, This Week; plus others. Add: Dept. of English, Oklahoma City University, Oklahoma City, OK 73106.

THIMMESH, HILARY, O.S.B, b. Osakis, Minn, Mar. 2, 28. ENGLISH. B.A, St. John's Univ.(Minn), 50; M.A, Cornell Univ, 56, Ph.D, 63. Instr. ENG, ST. JOHN'S UNIV.(MINN), 56-59, asst. prof, 59-61, 63-71, ASSOC. PROF, 71-, dir. honors prog, 59-61, dean, 67-71. Influence of Islam on mediaeval Christianity; Mediaeval English verse; Piers Plowman. Add: Dept. of English, St. John's University, Collegeville, MN 56321.

THISTLE, MELVILLE WILLIAM, b. St. John's, Nfld, Apr. 22, 14; m. 41; c. 2. GENERAL SEMANTICS, HISTORY OF SCIENCE. B.Sc, Mt. Allison Univ, 36, M.A, 38. Biochemist food res, Nat. Res. Counc. Can, 38-46, head food eng, 46-51, inform. officer pub. relat, 51-54, mgr. pub. relat, 54-69; PROF. JOUR, CARLETON UNIV, 69- Statistician, Royal Comn. Dominion-Prov. Relat, N.B, 37; ed. sci. proj, Royal Comn. Govt. Orgn, 61-62. Award, Can. Centennial Comn, 67. Inst. Gen. Semantics; Int. Soc. Gen. Semantics; Can. Asn. Sci. Writers; AAAS; Int. Commun. Asn. Theory of human communication; history of Canadian science. Publ: Peter the sea trout, Ryerson, Toronto & Bouregy, 54; ed, Happy journey, 58 & auth, Time touch me gently, 70, Ryerson, Toronto; The inner ring, Toronto Univ, 66, Oxford Univ, 68; ed, Wartime letters of C.J. Mackenzie and General A.G.L. McNaughton, Toronto Univ, (in press). Add: 1476 Farnsworth Ave, Ottawa, Ont. K1H 7C3, Can.

THOMAS, ALAN CEDRIC, b. U.K; Can. citizen. VICTORIAN LITERATURE. B.A, Carleton Univ, 63; M.A, Univ. Toronto, 64, Ph.D.(Eng), 70. ASST. PROF. ENG, UNIV. TORONTO, 67-, consult, Instruct. Media Ctr, 72-73. Victorian literature, social history, and journalism. Publ: Victorians (videotapes ser), Univ. Toronto, 73-74. Add: Div. of Humanities, Scarborough College, University of Toronto, 1265 Military Trail, Scarborough, Ont, Can.

THOMAS, (FREDERICK) BRYCE, b. Orleans, Vt, Jan. 8, 16; m. 50; c. 5. ENGLISH. B.S, Bowdoin Col, 38; M.A, Johns Hopkins Univ, 48; Ph.D.(Eng), Fordham Univ, 67. Teaching fel, Bowdoin Col, 39-41; jr. instr, Johns Hopkins Univ, 46-48; assoc. prof. ENG, PACE UNIV, 48-67, PROF, 67- U.S.A, 42-46. NCTE; MLA. Byron; Shakespeare; Chaucer. Add: Dept. of English, Pace University, 41 Park Row, New York, NY 10038.

THOMAS, CLARA, b. Strathroy, Ont, May 22, 19; m. 42; c. 2. ENGLISH. B.A, Univ. West. Ont, 41, M.A, 44; Ph.D, Univ. Toronto, 62. Asst. prof. ENG, YORK UNIV, 61-67, assoc. prof, 67-69, PROF, 69- Part-time instr, Univ. West. Ont, 47-61; Univ. Toronto, 58-61; Can. Counc. res. grant, 63, spec. award, 67-68 & 73-74. Asn. Commonwealth Lit. & Lang. Stud; Humanities Asn. Can; Asn. Can. Univ. Teachers Eng.(pres, 71-72); Can. Asn. Am. Stud. Canadian and Commonwealth literature; 19th century English literature. Publ: Canadian novelists, 1920-45, Longmans, 46; Love and work enough: the life of Anna Jameson, Univ. Toronto, 67; Ryerson of upper Canada, Ryerson, 69; Margaret Laurence, McClelland & Stewart, 69; Our nature—our voices, New Press, 72; contrib, Read Canadian, James, Lewis & Samuel, 72; auth, Canadian women in fiction and fact, Can. Lit, 68; Crusoe and the precious kingdom, J. Can. Fiction, 72; The town—our tribe, Lit. Half-Yearly, 72. Add: Dept. of English, York University, 4700 Keele St, Downsview 463, Ont, Can.

THOMAS, DEBORAH ALLEN, b. Biddeford, Maine, Sept. 1, 43; m. 66. ENGLISH & AMERICAN LITERATURE. A.B, Brown Univ, 65; M.A, Duke Univ, 66; Ph.D.(Eng), Univ. Rochester, 72. ASST. PROF. ENG, FAIRLEIGH DICKINSON UNIV, FLORHAM-MADISON, 73- MLA; Northeast Mod. Lang. Asn; NCTE; Dickens Soc; Dickens Fel. Nineteenth century British literature; the novel; the short story. Publ: Contributors to the Christmas numbers of Household words and All the year round, 1850-1867 (2 parts), Dickensian, 9/73 & 1/74; The equivocal explanation of Dickens' George Silverman, In: Vol. III, Dickens studies annual, South. Ill. Univ, 74. Add: Dept. of English, Fairleigh Dickinson University, Florham-Madison Campus, Madison, NJ 07940.

THOMAS, GLYN N, b. Wales, Mar. 30, 20; nat; m. 42; c. 2. ENGLISH LITERATURE. B.A, Univ. Ill, 42, M.A, 46, fel, 48-49, Ph.D.(Eng), 49. Instr. ENG, Univ. Ill, 49-50; asst. prof, UNIV. WYO, 50-62, PROF, 62-, DIR. HONORS PROG, 65- U.S.A, 42-46. MLA; NCTE; Nat. Intercol. Honors Counc. Nineteenth century English literature. Add: Dept. of English, University of Wyoming, Laramie, WY 82071.

THOMAS, GORDON KENT, b. Takoma Park, Md, Jan. 14, 35. ENGLISH. B.A, Brigham Young Univ, 59, Phi Kappa Phi fel, 59-60, M.A, 60; summer, Univ. Oviedo, 62; Ph.D.(Eng), Tulane Univ, 68. Instr. lang. arts, CHURCH COL. HAWAII, 60-62, Eng. & Spanish, 62-63, asst. prof. ENG, 63-68, assoc. prof, 68-71, PROF, 71-, chmn. dept, 68-72. Fulbright lectr. Am. & comp. lit, Inst. Caro y Cuervo, Colombia, 70, Nat. Univs. La Plata & Buenos Aires, Arg, 71. MLA; NCTE; AAUP; Philol. Asn. Pac. Coast. English Romantics; Shakespeare; 18th century English literature. Publ: Wordsworth's Dirge and promise, Univ. Nebr, 71; Equivoques in Wordsworth: Oh, wondrous power of words, Wordsworth Circle, spring 74; The doctrine of the devil in literature, New Era, (in press); The knight amid the dunces, Restoration & 18th Century Theatre Res, (in press). Add: Dept. of English, Church College of Hawaii, Laie, HI 96762.

THOMAS, GORDON L, b. Kent, Eng, Dec. 4, 14; U.S. citizen; m. 41; c. 2. SPEECH. A.B, Albion Col, 36; M.A, Mich. State Univ, 41; Ph.D, Northwest. Univ, 52. Teacher Eng. & speech, Fenton High Sch, Mich, 36-39; asst. speech, Mich. State Univ, 39-41; instr. Eng. & speech, Univ. Miami, 41-42; from instr. to PROF. COMMUN. & SECY. FAC, MICH. STATE UNIV, 45- Mem. staff, Mich. State Univ/Agency Int. Develop. Sem. Commun, 58- U.S.A.A.F, 42-45. Speech Commun. Asn; Cent. States Speech Asn. History of public speaking; comparison of written and spoken style; bibliography of quantitative studies in speech. Publ: Auth, A survey of college and university holdings of significant recordings in public address, Mich. State Univ. Speech Commun. Lab, 68; co-auth, The colonial idiom, South. Ill. Univ, Carbondale, 70; auth, Address, 10/66 & The city of man, 1/67, Mich. Munic. Rev; Graduate degree practices in speech, Speech Teacher, 11/68; plus numerous others. Add: Dept. of Communication, Michigan State University, East Lansing, MI 48824.

THOMAS, J. JAMES, b. Greenfield, Ind, Nov. 13, 33; m. 54; c. 3. LITERATURE, HUMANITIES. B.A, Taylor Univ, 55; B.D, Garrett Theol. Sem, 59; Ph.D.(relig. & lit), Northwest. Univ, 67. Asst. prof. ENG. & HUMANITIES, SAGINAW VALLEY COL, 67-72, ASSOC. PROF, 72- MLA. Contemporary literature; existentialism and literature. Publ: The revolutionary hero, Univ. Ctr. Monog. Series, 71. Add: Dept. of English, Saginaw Valley College, University Center, MI 48710.

THOMAS, JOE DAVID, b. Carrollton, Mo, Jan. 1, 08; m. 39; c. 2. ENGLISH. Ph.B, Univ. Chicago, 29, A.M, 30. Instr. ENG, RICE UNIV, 30-45, asst. prof, 45-52, assoc. prof, 52-69, PROF, 69-, asst. registr, 46-53, acting registr, 53-54. MLA; Col. Eng. Asn. Bibliography; Victorian literature; modern drama and fiction. Publ: Composition for technical students, Scribner, 49, rev. ed, 57, 65; Poetic truth and pathetic fallacy, Tex. Stud. Lit. &

Lang, autumn 61; The soul of man under socialism, Rice Univ. Stud, winter 65; The dark at the end of the tunnel, Stud. Short Fiction, fall 66. Add: Dept. of English, Rice University, Houston, TX 77001.

THOMAS, JOHN DAVID, b. Akron, Ohio, Sept. 15, 35; m. 61; c. 2. SPEECH. B.A, David Lipscomb Col, 57; M.A, Univ. Fla, 60; Ph.D.(speech), Univ. Ill, 65. Chmn. dept. speech, FREED-HARDEMAN COL, 59-69, asst. to dean, 64-69, dir. res, 67-69, ACAD. DEAN, 69- Minister, Churches of Christ, 51- Speech Communication Asn; Am. Asn. Higher Educ. Classical rhetorical theory; learning theory and programmed instruction; institutional research. Publ: Organizing speeches, Bk. I & II, Univ. Ill, 64. Add: Freed-Hardeman College, Henderson, TN 38340.

THOMAS, JONATHAN, b. Flushing, N.Y, June 17, 22; m. 46; c. 1. ENGLISH. A.B, Colgate Univ, 48; A.M, Columbia Univ, 57; Louis Bevier fel, Rutgers Univ, 58-59, Ph.D.(Eng), 66. Preceptor, Colgate Univ, 48-49; adminr. & exec. asst, Port N.Y. Authority, 49-55; teaching asst. ENG, Rutgers Univ, 59-61, instr, Douglass Col, 62-65; asst. prof, TRENTON STATE COL, 65-68, assoc. prof, 68-71, PROF, 71- U.S.A, 42-45. NCTE; MLA; Asn. Humanistic Psychol. Work of Mark Twain and Nathaniel Hawthorne; affective education. Publ: Co-ed, A chance acquaintance, Ind. Univ, 71; auth, Jubilee days, Howells Sentinel, 11/64. Add: Dept. of English, Trenton State College, Trenton, NJ 08625.

THOMAS, JUDITH (ANN) WAUGH, b. New Kensington, Pa, Nov. 9, 40; m. 69; c. 3. SPEECH EDUCATION. B.S, Edinboro State Col, 62; Kalamazoo Col, summer 63; Univ. Puget Sound, summer 65; M.Ed, Duquesne Univ, 67; Ed.D.(speech educ), W.Va. Univ, 71. Teacher Eng. & Span, Highlands Sch. Dist, Natrona Heights, Pa, 62-67; instr. educ. psychol. & for. lang, W.Va. Univ, 67-70; asst. prof. speech, Pa. State Univ, 70-71; ASSOC. PROF. SPEECH & SOCIOL, WEST LIBERTY STATE COL, 71-, DIR. INTERETHNIC SENSITIVITY WORKSHOP, 72- Lectr, Nat. Clergymen's Conf, summers 72, 73; consult, Interethnic Educ. for Hancock Co, W.Va, 72-74; Danforth assoc, 73- NEA; Speech Asn. Am; Afro-Am. Hist. Found; For. Lang. Asn; Am. Educ. Stud. Asn. The need for interethnic education; verbal problems of culturally different children; John Rockefeller's inauguration as president of West Virginia Wesleyan College. Publ: The effects of choral responding, inductive reasoning, selective positive reinforcement on verbally indigent students, W.Va. Univ, 71; co-auth, The role of teacher education in promoting ethnic awareness, fall 73 & auth, What educators need to know about interethnicity, spring 74, W.Va. Rev. Educ. Res. Add: Dept. of Fine Arts, Office 102, West Liberty State College, West Liberty, WV 26074.

THOMAS, LEROY, b. Mangum, Okla, Apr. 2, 34; m. 55; c. 2. ENGLISH. B.A, Southwest. State Col, 56; M.A, Okla. State Univ, 59, Ph.D.(Eng), 71; Okla. Univ, 63-64, summers 60, 61, 64. Instr, high sch, Okla, 56; ENG, SOUTHWEST. STATE COL, 56-57, from instr. to assoc. prof, 59-71, PROF, 71- NCTE. Analysis of the theme of alienation in contemporary Southern fiction. Add: 806 Cedar Ave, Weatherford, OK 73096.

THOMAS, MALAYILMELATHETHIL KORUTHU, b. Vanmazhi, Kerala, India, Jan. 26, 32. ENGLISH, EDUCATION. B.A, Travancore Univ, India, 52; B.D, Serampore Col, India, 56; Th.M, Princeton Theol. Sem, 60; M.A, Morehead State Univ, 61; M.A. & Ed.D, Univ. Tulsa, 64. Asst. prof. ENG, MOREHEAD STATE UNIV, 64-65, assoc. prof, 65-67, PROF, 67- MLA; NCTE; AAUP. Religion; education. Add: Dept. of English, Morehead State University, Morehead, KY 40351.

THOMAS, MARY JEAN, b. Pawhuska, Okla, Apr. 11, 30. SPEECH, PHILOSOPHY. B.S, Ft. Hays Kans. State Col, 55; M.A, Kans. State Univ, 58; State Univ. Iowa, 59-60; Ph.D.(speech), Pa. State Univ, 67. Instr. broadcasting, Univ. S.Dak, 60-62; speech & broadcasting, Pa. State Univ, 62-66; asst. prof. speech, Univ. Mass, 66-68; CASE WEST. RESERVE UNIV, 68-72, ASSOC. PROF. SPEECH COMMUN, 72- Vis. lectr. educ. TV, Univ. Mont, summer 63. Speech Commun. Asn; Speech Asn. East. States; Nat. Asn. Broadcasters; Nat. Acad. TV Arts & Sci. Political communication; mass media; history of rhetorical theory and philosophy of rhetoric. Publ: Contrib, Recent homiletical theories, Abingdon, 67; co-auth, Survey history of rhetorical theory, Wadsworth, 70; co-auth, Checkmate in Cleveland: the rhetoric of controversy during the Stokes years, Case West. Univ. Press, 72. Add: Dept. of Speech Communication, Case Western Reserve University, Cleveland, OH 44106.

THOMAS, MARY OLIVE, b. Opelika, Ala, Jan. 27, 21. ENGLISH. A.B, Agnes Scott Col, 42; M.A, Univ. N.C, 44; scholar, Duke Univ, 45-49, 52-53, Ph.D.(Eng), 56; summer, Inst. Int. Educ. traveling scholar, Univ. Birmingham, Eng, 48; Fulbright grant, Italy, 49-50. Instr. ENG, Auburn Univ, 55-57; from instr. to asst. prof, Milwaukee-Downer Col, 57-61; GA. STATE UNIV, 61-64, ASSOC. PROF, 64- Res. analyst, signal corps, U.S. Dept. Army, 44-45. MLA; Renaissance Soc. Am; S.Atlantic Mod. Lang. Asn; Mod. Humanities Res. Asn; Southeast Renaissance Conf; Renaissance Eng. Text Soc; Col. Eng. Asn. Shakespeare; Renaissance literature; aesthetics. Publ: The repetitions in Antony's death scene, Shakespeare Quart, 58; Cleopatra and the Mortal wretch, Shakespeare-Jahrbuch, 63; ed, Ben Jonson: quadricentennial essays, Stud. in Lit. Imagination, 4/73. Add: Dept. of English, Georgia State University, 33 Gilmer St, Atlanta, GA 30303.

THOMAS, OWEN PAUL, b. Norfolk, Va, May 10, 29; m. 52, 73; c. 3. ENGLISH. A.B, Oberlin Col, 56; Woodrow Wilson fel, Univ. Calif, Los Angeles, 56-57, A.M, 57, Ph.D, 60. Sr. ed, RAND Corp, 57-58; asst. Eng, Univ. Calif, Los Angeles, 58-59; sr. writer, Space Tech. Lab, 59-60; instr. ENG, IND. UNIV. BLOOMINGTON, 60-63, asst. prof, 63-66, assoc. prof, 66-69, PROF, 69- Vis. prof, Univs. Zagreb & Sarajevo, 62-63; sr. Fulbright fel, Zagreb, Yugoslavia, 66-67. U.S.N, 50-54. American literature; English linguistics; stylistics. Publ: Transformational grammar and the teacher of English, 65 & Arts & skills of English, 72, 2nd ed, 74, Holt; Metaphor, Random, 69. Add: Dept. of English, Indiana University, Bloomington, IN 47401.

THOMAS, PETER D, b. Gloucester, Eng, May 11, 28; m. 66. ENGLISH & AFRICAN STUDIES. B.A, Oxford, 50, M.A, 54; L.G.S.M, Hampshire Sch. Drama, Eng, 56. Dept. headmaster & sr. Eng. master, grammar sch, Eng, 54-56; headmaster, Painswick Sch. Maladjusted Children, Eng, 57; sr. Eng. master, Opoku Ware Sch. Boys, Ghana, 58-60; lectr. & sr. lectr. ENG, Univ. Nigeria, 60-65; vis. lectr, Univ. Utah, 65-68; jr. fel, Mackinac Col, 68-69; PROF. HUMANITIES, LAKE SUPERIOR STATE COL, 69- Vis. lectr, Poetry Mich, Mich. State Counc. Arts, 69-; ed, Woods-Runner, 70- NCTE; Poetry Soc, Eng. Life and works of Edward Thomas; African folklore and modern African writing in English and French; world mythology. Publ: Sun Bells (poems), Denim Press, 74; co-ed, Revealer of secrets, Ginn, London, 74; auth, African, American—or human?, Presence Africaine, fall 71; John Bull speaks, West. Humanities Rev, summer 73; Shadows of prophecy, J. Mod. African Stud, 7/73; plus others. Add: Dept. of Humanities, Lake Superior State College, Easterday Ave, Sault Ste. Marie, MI 49783.

THOMAS, RAYMOND LAWRENCE, b. Indiana, Pa, Jan. 21, 36; m. 64; c. 4. ENGLISH. B.S, Ind. Univ. Pa, 57; Woodrow Wilson fel, Columbia Univ, 58-59, M.A, 59; Danforth Found. grant, Pa. State Univ, 64-65, Ph.D.(Eng), 68. Consult. Spanish, Sch. Dist. Bristol Twp, Bucks County, Pa, 57-58; instr. ENG, W.Va. Univ, 59-61; assoc. prof, INDIANA UNIV. PA, 62-69, PROF, 69- Scholar, Cambridge, 72. Milton Soc. Am; MLA. Milton studies; 17th century English literature. Add: 514 School St, Indiana, PA 15701.

THOMAS, SIDNEY, b. New York, N.Y, Dec. 21, 15; m. 40; c. 2. ENGLISH LITERATURE, ART HISTORY. B.A, City Col. New York, 35; M.A, Columbia Univ, 38, Ph.D, 43. Tutor Eng, City Col. New York, 39-43; instr, Queens Col.(N.Y), 46-54; asst. ed, Webster's 3rd Int. Dictionary, 58-61; assoc. prof. FINE ARTS, SYRACUSE UNIV, 61-66, PROF, 66- Res. fel, Folger Shakespeare Libr, 47-48. U.S.A, 43-45, S/Sgt. MLA; Shakespeare Asn. Am.(bibliogr, 49-54). Shakespeare; Elizabethan drama; art criticism. Publ: The antic Hamlet, King's Crown, 43; co-auth, The nature of art, Crown, 64; auth, The date of The comedy of errors, Shakespeare Quart, 56; The printing of Greenes Groatsworth of Witte and Kind-harts dreame, Stud. Bibliog, 66; The Queen Mab speech in Romeo and Juliet, Shakespeare Surv, 72; plus others. Add: Dept. of Fine Arts, Syracuse University, Syracuse, NY 13210.

THOMAS, STAFFORD H, b. Lynchburg, Va, Aug. 9, 29; m. 64; c. 2. SPEECH. B.A, Univ. Colo, 51; M.A, Univ. Wyo, 57; Ph.D.(speech), Univ. Wash, 64. ASST. PROF. SPEECH COMMUN, UNIV. ILL, URBANA, 64-, assoc. head dept, 68-71. Chancellor's Summer Instr. Develop. Award, 65. Speech Commun. Asn; Cent. States Speech Commun. Asn. Voice science; rhetoric and communication theory; speech and drama history. Publ: Effects of monotonous delivery on intelligibility, 6/69 & A terrorist's rhetoric: Citizen Lequinio's De l'eloquence, 3/72, Speech Monogr; Teaching segmental audience structure, Speech Teacher, 11/73; plus others. Add: Dept. of Speech Communication, University of Illinois, Urbana, IL 61801.

THOMAS, WALTER KEITH, b. Brockville, Ont, Dec. 9, 27; m. 52; c. 3. ENGLISH. B.A, Univ. Toronto, 50, M.A, 51, fel, 52-53, Ph.D.(Eng), 56. Instr. ENG, Univ. Toronto, 53-56; assoc. prof. & acting head dept, Acadia Univ, 56-57, prof. & head dept, 57-60; PROF, UNIV. WATERLOO, 60-, acting dean arts, 60-61, chmn. dept. Eng, 60-65. Can. Counc. grant-in-aid, 67. MLA; Asn. Can. Univ. Teachers Eng. Eighteenth century English poetry; romantic English poetry; satire. Publ: Form and substance: a guide to the research paper, W.J. Gage, Toronto, 64; Crabbe's borough: the process of montage, Univ. Toronto Quart, 1/67; The matrix of Absalom and Achitophel, Philol. Quart, 70; The mythic dimension of Catch-22, Tex. Stud. in Lit. & Lang, 73; plus others. Add: Dept. of English, University of Waterloo, Waterloo, Ont. N2L 3G1, Can.

THOMAS, WANDA CLAYTON, b. Salt Lake City, Utah, Dec. 6, 12; div; c. 2. SPEECH, THEATRE. B.A, Univ. Utah, 34, Rockefeller fel. & M.A, 46; cert, Univ. Calif, 38, Ph.D, 57. Instr. stagecraft, lighting, voice & acting & dir. theatre, Sacramento Col, 46-47; instr. SPEECH, UNIV. UTAH, 47-56, asst. prof, 56-61, assoc. prof, 61-69, PROF, 69-, assoc. dir. univ. theatre, 47-56, honors adv. speech & theatre stud, Honors Prog. Prof. speech, Univ. Guam, 70-72. Acad. Polit. Sci. Regional historical dramatic material; comparative dramatic literature; children's theater. Publ: Three dramas from Mormon country; Hansclodhopper and the princess; Peterle; auth, An American poet, American poet series, produced by Utah Network Instruct. TV in coop. with KUED, 68-70. Add: Dept. of Speech, University of Utah, Salt Lake City, UT 84112.

THOMPSON, CLAUD ADELBERT, b. Milwaukee, Wis, Sept. 15, 33; m. 68; c. 1. ENGLISH LITERATURE. A.B, Ripon Col, 55; A.M, Columbia Univ, 60; B.D, Seabury-West. Theol. Sem, 64; Episcopal Church Found. fel, 68-70; Ph.D.(Eng), Univ. Wis-Madison, 71. Instr. Eng, Carnegie-Mellon Univ, 59-61; Episcopal chaplain, Lawrence Univ, 64-66, lectr. Eng, 65-66; asst. Episcopal chaplain, Univ. Wis-Madison, 66-68; ASST. PROF. ENG, UNIV. SASK, 70- Asn. Can. Univ. Teachers Eng; Milton Soc. Am. Seventeenth century English literature; Milton; religion and literature. Publ: That two handed engine will smite: time will have a stop, Stud. Philol, 4/62; Rhetorical madness: an ideal in the Phaedrus, Quart. J. Speech, 12/69; Spenser's Many faire pourtraicts, and many a faire feate, Stud. Eng. Lit, winter 72. Add: Dept. of English, University of Saskatchewan, Saskatoon, Sask. S7N 0W0, Can.

THOMPSON, CRAIG RINGWALT, b. Carlisle, Pa, June 25, 11; m. 38; c. 2. ENGLISH LITERATURE & HISTORY. A.B, Dickinson Col, 33, hon. Litt.D, 66; A.M, Princeton, 35, Ph.D, 37; hon. M.A, Univ. Pa, 71. Instr. Eng, Cornell Univ, 37-42; Yale, 43-45; assoc. prof, Elmira Col, 45-46; Lawrence Col, 46-50, prof, 50-60; PROF. Eng. & hist, Haverford Col, 60-68; ENG, UNIV. PA, 68- Guggenheim fel, 42-43, 54-55, 68-69; Am. Counc. Learned Soc. fel, 53; consult, Folger Libr, 57-58, fel, 53-56, 57, 59, 74; librn, Haverford Col, 60-69. MLA; Am. Soc. Church Hist; Am. Soc. Reformation Res. Literary, ecclesiastical and intellectual history. Publ: Erasmus: Inquisitio de Fide, 50 & ed, More's translations of Lucian, 74, Yale; co-ed, Thought and experience in prose, Oxford, 51, 56; auth, Ten colloquies of Erasmus, Lib. Arts, 57; The colloquies of Erasmus, Univ. Chicago, 65. Add: Dept. of English, University of Pennsylvania, Philadelphia, PA 19104.

THOMPSON, ERNEST CLIFFORD, JR, b. Scarville, Iowa, May 2, 31; m. 58. SPEECH. B.A, State Univ. Iowa, 53; M.A, State Univ. Wash, 55; Ph.D, Univ. Minn, 60. Instr. speech, Purdue Univ, 58-60; asst. prof, Boston Univ, 60-62; asst. prof. speech & head dept, Parsons Col, 62-63; asst. prof. speech, STATE UNIV. N.Y. BUFFALO, 63-66, ASSOC. PROF. SPEECH COMMUN,

66- Speech Commun. Asn; Cent. States Speech Asn. Persuasion theory. Publ: An experimental investigation of relative effectiveness of organizational structure in oral communication, South. Speech J, 60; A case study in demagoguery: Henry Harmon Spaulding, West. Speech J, fall 66; Some effects of message structure on listener comprehension, Speech Monogr, spring 67. Add: Dept. of Speech Communication, State University of New York at Buffalo, Buffalo, NY 14214.

THOMPSON, FRANCIS JOHN, b. New York, N.Y, Sept. 3, 07; m. 41; c. 4. CONTEMPORARY & AMERICAN LITERATURE. A.B, Columbia Univ, 29, A.M, 30; Ph.D, N.Y. Univ, 40; Instr, City Col. New York, 30-41; asst. prof. Eng. writing, speech & drama, Johns Hopkins Univ, 46-53; prof. ENG, Rollins Col, 53-55; assoc. prof, UNIV. TAMPA, 55-64, PROF, 64-, CHMN. DIV. HUMANITIES, 72- Bk. reviewer, Tampa Tribune, 62- U.S.A, 42-46, 1st Lt. Am. Stud. Asn; S.Atlantic Mod. Lang. Asn; Col. Eng. Asn. Comparative literature; 19th century Irish literature; medieval English literature. Publ: Abraham's wife, Vanguard, 53; contrib, Alaska: one man says yes, Fla. Accent, 71; contrib, Beyond the square, Linden, 72; plus others. Add: Div. of Humanities, University of Tampa, Tampa, FL 33606.

THOMPSON, GARY RICHARD, b. Los Angeles, Calif, Dec. 11, 37; m. 59; c. 3. ENGLISH & AMERICAN LITERATURE. B.A, San Fernando Valley State Col, 59; NDEA fel, Univ. South. Calif, 59-62, M.A, 60, Ph.D.(Eng), 67- Teaching asst. ENG, Univ. South. Calif, 62; instr, Ohio State Univ, 62-63; Univ. Calif, Los Angeles, 64-66; instr, WASH. STATE UNIV, 66-67, asst. prof, 67-70, ASSOC. PROF, 71- Ed, Poe Stud, 68-; Wash. State Univ. res. grants, 68-71, chmn. prog. lit. stud, 70-72; ed, ESQ: J. Am. Renaissance, 71-; Nathaniel H. Seefurth Found. grant, 73; Nat. Endowment Humanities summer fel, 73. MLA (Am. Lit. Group, Conf. Ed. Learned J); Melville Soc. Am; Soc. Stud. South. Lit. American romantic movement; Gothic tradition in literature; 19th century literature. Publ: Ed, Great short works of Edgar Allan Poe, Harper & Row, 70; co-ed, Ritual, realism & revolt: major traditions in the drama, Scribners, 72; auth, Poe's fiction: romantic irony in the Gothic tales, Univ. Wis, 73; ed, The Gothic imagination: essays in dark romanticism, Wash. State Univ, 74; auth, Poe's readings of Pelham, Am. Lit, 5/69; Unity, death & nothingness—Poe's romantic skepticism, PMLA, 3/70; Themes, topics criticism, In: American literary scholarship: an annual, Duke Univ, 71-73. Add: Dept. of English, Washington State University, Pullman, WA 99163.

THOMPSON, GORDON W, b. Denver, Colo, July 8, 39; m. 62; c. 3. ENGLISH. B.A, Dartmouth Col, 61; M.A, Univ. Wis, 62, Ph.D.(Eng), 66. Asst. prof. ENG, EARLHAM COL, 66-72, ASSOC. PROF, 72- MLA; Midwest Mod. Lang. Asn. Poetry of Robert Browning; Victorian and Edwardian novel. Publ: Technique in The ring and the book, Stud. Eng. Lit, fall 70; A spirit birth conceived of flesh: Browning's theory of art, Tenn. Stud. Lit, 69. Add: Dept. of English, Earlham College, Richmond, IN 47374.

THOMPSON, IRENE S, b. New York, N.Y, Mar. 30, 19; m. 55; c. 1. ENGLISH. B.A, Adelphi Col, 39; M.A, N.Y. Univ, 55; Univ. Fla, 55-58. Teacher, Erasmus Hall High Sch, 54; Montauk Jr. High Sch, 54-55; teaching asst, Univ. Fla, 55-58; vis. lectr. lit, Gakshuin Univ, Tokyo, 58-59; teacher, Gainesville High Sch, 62-66; ASST. PROF. ENG, UNIV. FLA, 66- Chairperson, Comn. on Status of Women, Univ. Fla, 71-, spec. asst. to v.pres. acad. affairs, 73- South. Mod. Lang. Asn; MLA; AAUP; NCTE. Publ: Co-auth, A guide to principal sources for American civilization, 1800-1900, Columbia Univ, Vols. I & II, 60 & 62. Add: 207 N.W. 32nd St, Gainesville, FL 32607.

THOMPSON, JAMES ROY, b. Put-in-Bay, Ohio, Feb. 2, 33; m. 58; c. 2. ENGLISH LITERATURE. B.A, Bowling Green State Univ, 58, M.A, 59; Taft mem. fel, Univ. Cincinnati, 60, Ph.D.(Eng), 64. From instr. to ASSOC. PROF. ENG, OHIO UNIV, 62- Byron Soc; Keats-Shelley Asn. Am; MLA. Byron; Leigh Hunt; English romantic poetry; 19th century English literature. Publ: Leigh Hunt, Twayne, 74; Byron's plays and Don Juan: genre and myth, Bucknel Rev, 12/67. Add: Windhover Farm, R.R. 3, Athens, OH 45701.

THOMPSON, JESSE JACKSON, b. Sanger, Calif, July 26, 19; m. 45; c. 4. SPEECH PATHOLOGY, PSYCHOLINGUISTICS. B.A, Santa Barbara State Col, 41; M.Sc, Univ. South. Calif, 47, Ph.D.(speech path), 57. Speech & hearing therapist pub. schs, Calif, 47-51; coord, spec. educ, Riverside County Supt. Schs. Off, Calif, 51-53, asst. supt. schs, 53-56; dir. speech & hearing clinic, CALIF. STATE UNIV, LONG BEACH, 56-65, PROF. COMMUN. DISORDERS, 65-, DIR, CTR. HEALTH MANPOWER EDUC, 72-, chmn. dept. speech, 65-68, coord, Univ. Clinics & Allied Health Prog, 70-72. Consult, Speech & Lang. Develop. Ctr, Calif, 62-; Providence Speech & Hearing Clinic, Calif, 67-; proj. dir. speech & hearing serv, Childrens Hosp. Orange County, Calif, 67-68; mem, Nat. Counc. YMCA's, 70-; consult, Head Start Prog, Compton-Willowbrook-Enterprise, 70- Ord.C, 41-46, Capt. Am. Speech & Hearing Asn; Int. Platform Asn; Asn. Schs. Allied Health Prof; AAUP; Am. Congr. Rehab. Med; Nat. Alliance Family Life. Learning disabilities in pre-school minority children. Publ: Co-auth, Speech ways, 55, Phonics, 61 & Talking time, 2nd ed, 66, Webster Div, McGraw; plus others. Add: 13282 Cedar St, Westminister, CA 92683.

THOMPSON, JOHN ANDERSON, b. Grand Rapids, Mich, June 14, 18; m. 43, 62; c. 3. ENGLISH. A.B, Kenyon Col, 40; M.A, Columbia Univ, 47, Ph.D. (Eng), 57. Instr. Eng, Sarah Lawrence Col, 47-48; Columbia Col, 48-56; exec. dir, Farfield Found, 56-65; assoc. prof. ENG, STATE UNIV. N.Y. STONY BROOK, 65-68, PROF, 68- Judge, contest for little mag, 67-68. U.S.A.F, 40-45, S/Sgt. Prosody; Elizabethan literature; contemporary poetry and fiction. Publ: The founding of English metre, Columbia Univ, 61; The talking girl Pym-Randall, 68; Blank verse, In: Encyclopedia of poetry and poetics, Princeton, 65; Vacancies of August, Commentary, 11/66; An alphabet of poets, N.Y. Rev. Books, 8/68. Add: Dept. of English, State University of New York at Stony Brook, Stony Brook, NY 11790.

THOMPSON, KARL FREDERICK, b. York, Pa, Dec. 31, 17; m. 42; c. 3. ENGLISH LITERATURE. A.B, Yale, 41, A.M, 42, univ. fel. & Ph.D.(Eng), 50. Asst. in instr, Yale, 46-47; instr. Eng, Oberlin Col, 48-53; asst. prof. HUMANITIES, MICH. STATE UNIV, 53-59, assoc. prof, 59-64, PROF, 64-, CHMN. DEPT, 68- Folger Libr. res. fel, 58; Guggenheim fel, 59-60. U.S.A.A.F, 42-46. MLA; Renaissance Soc. Am. Shakespeare; 18th century English literature; general education. Publ: Ed, Classics of western thought: Middle Ages, Renaissance and Reformation, Harcourt, 64; auth, Modesty and cunning: Shakespeare's use of literary tradition, Univ. Mich, 71; Shakespeare's romantic comedies, PMLA; Richard II, martyr, 57 & The unknown Ulysses, 68, Shakespeare Quart. Add: 550 Collingwood Dr, East Lansing, MI 48823.

THOMPSON, KENT ELGIN, b. Waukegan, Ill, Feb. 3, 36; Can. citizen; m. 60; c. 2. ENGLISH LITERATURE, CREATIVE WRITING. B.A, Hanover Col, 57; M.A, State Univ. Iowa, 62; Ph.D.(Eng), Univ. Wales, 65. Instr. ENG, Ripon Col, 61-63; asst. prof, Colo. Woman's Col, 65-66; ASSOC. PROF, UNIV. N.B, 66- Publ: Ed, Stories from Atlantic Canada, Macmillan, Can, 73. Add: Dept. of English, University of New Brunswick, Fredericton, N.B, Can.

THOMPSON, LOUIS F, b. New York, N.Y, Sept. 14, 23; m. 48; c. 2. ENGLISH. A.B, Columbia Univ, 48; M.A, Lehigh Univ, 52, Ph.D, 59. Instr. Eng. & math, Carson Long Inst, New Bloomfield, Pa, 48-50; ENG, Lehigh Univ, 50-58; asst. prof, Col. William & Mary, 58-63; PROF, BLOOMSBURG STATE COL, 63-, CHMN. DEPT, 64-, acting chmn. dept, 63-64. Ed, PCTE Newslett, 72- U.S.A.F, 42-45, Res, 45-71, Lt. Col. MLA; NCTE. Middle English, especially artistry in Chaucer's writings. Add: Dept. of English, Bloomsburg State College, Bloomsburg, PA 17815.

THOMPSON, M. GERALDINE, C.S.J, b. Toronto, Ont, June 1, 08. ENGLISH. B.A, Univ. Toronto, 28, M.A, 48, Ph.D.(Eng), 55. Lectr. ENG, ST. MICHAEL'S COL, UNIV. TORONTO, 50-58, asst. prof, 58-62, assoc. prof, 62-68, PROF, 68- Can. Counc. sr. fel, 67-68. Asn. Can. Univ. Teachers Eng. Renaissance prose, centering on Erasmus; seventeenth century satire, especially that of Donne; sixteenth century paradox. Publ: Under pretext of praise: a study of Erasmus's satirical work, Univ. Toronto, 73; Erasmus and the tradition of paradox, Stud. Philol, 1/64; Donne's Notitia: the evidence of the satires, Univ. Toronto Quart, 10/66. Add: Dept. of English, St. Michael's College, 50 St. Joseph St, Toronto, Ont. M5S 1J4, Can.

THOMPSON, PAUL VERN, b. Chicago, Ill, July 10, 09; m. 34; c. 3. ENGLISH LITERATURE. A.B, Dartmouth Col, 30; A.M, Univ. Colo, 32; Ph.D, Northwest. Univ, 37. Asst. Eng, UNIV. COLO, BOULDER, 30-32, instr, 34-37, asst. prof, 37-41, assoc. prof, 41-48, prof, 48-70, prof. humanities & chmn. integrated stud, 70-72, EMER. PROF, 72- Jonathan Swift; English novel; opera. Publ: An unpublished letter of Swift, Libr. J, 67. Add: 325 16th St, Boulder, CO 80302.

THOMPSON, PHYLLIS HOGE, b. Elizabeth, N.J, Nov. 15, 26; m. 51, 64; c. 4. ENGLISH. B.A, Conn. Col, 48; M.A, Duke Univ, 49; Ph.D.(Eng), Univ. Wis, 57. Prof. ENG, Milton Col, 62-64; PROF, UNIV. HAWAII, 64- Danforth assoc, 66-; Nat. Endowment Humanities proj. grant poetry workshops, 68-69; dir, Hawaii Poets in Schs. Prog, 71-73; vis. prof. creative writing & Eng, San Francisco State Univ, 73. MLA; NCTE. W.B. Yeats poetry, teaching and writing. Publ: Artichoke and other poems, Univ. Hawaii, 69; ed, Any direction—anthology, Hawaii State Found. Cult. & Arts, 72; auth, The creation frame (poems), Univ. Ill, 73. Add: Dept. of English, University of Hawaii, 1733 Donaghho Rd, Honolulu, HI 96822.

THOMPSON, RICHARD J, b. Buffalo, N.Y, Apr. 7, 31; m. 59; c. 3. ENGLISH LITERATURE. B.S, Canisius Col, 53; A.M, Univ. Buffalo, 58; Ph.D.(Eng), State Univ. N.Y. Buffalo, 64. Instr. ENG, CANISIUS COL, 58-61, asst. prof, 62-68, assoc. prof, 68-72, PROF, 72- U.S.A, 53-55. MLA. Modern Irish literature; American literature; modern American novel. Publ: British and American fiction of the sixties, 10/67 & Dublin bookscene, 7-8/71, Choice; If ever you go to Dublin town, Ireland of the Jour, 9-10/72. Add: 34 Summit Ave, Buffalo, NY 14214.

THOMPSON, ROGER MARK, Linguistics, Sociolinguistics. See Volume III, Foreign Languages, Linguistics & Philology.

THOMPSON, SHARON POWERS, b. San Diego, Calif, Apr. 25, 38. ENGLISH LITERATURE & LANGUAGE. B.A, Univ. Minn, 64, M.A, 69, Samuel Holt Monk fel, 69-70, Ph.D.(Eng), 73; dipl. Eng. stud, Cambridge, 68. Asst. prof. Eng, Montclair State Col, 73-74. MLA; AAUP. Semantic analysis of imgery; Renaissance English literature; romantic poetry. Publ: Co-ed, Shelley's poetry and prose: a Norton critical edition, Norton, 74. Add: 44 Mt. Hebron Rd, Upper Montclair, NJ 07043.

THOMPSON, WAYNE NOEL, b. Chicago, Ill, Dec. 22, 14; m. 56. SPEECH, RHETORIC. B.Ed, West. Ill. Univ, 36; M.A, Northwest. Univ, 39, Ph.D. (speech), 43; George Washington Univ, 42-43; N.Y. Univ, summer 45. Teacher, high schs, Ill, 36-40; Ky, 41-42; instr. SPEECH, Univ. Mo, 42; Am. Univ, 42-43; asst. prof, Bowling Green State Univ, 43-45; Univ. Ill, Chicago, 47-51, assoc. prof, 51-57, prof, 57-63; Univ. Tex, Austin, 63-68, res. leave, spring, 65; PROF, UNIV. HOUSTON, 68- Instr, West. Ill. Univ, summer 42; asst. prof, Univ. Mo, 45-47; asst. to exec. secy, Speech Asn. Am, 45-47, ed, Speech Monogr, 63-65, mem. comt. publ, 63-65, 68-70; lectr, Univ. Denver, summer 50; ed, J. Commun, Nat. Soc. Stud. Commun, 59-61; Univ. Ill. sabbatical leave, spring 61. Speech Commun. Asn; Am. Forensic Asn; South. Speech Commun. Asn.(pres, 73-74). Experimental rhetoric; classical rhetoric; persuasion. Publ: Co-auth, Basic experiences in speech, Prentice-Hall, 51, 2nd ed, 58; auth, Fundamentals of communication, McGraw, 57; Quantitative research in public address and communication, Random, 67; Modern argumentation and debate, Harper, 71; Contemporary public address as a research area, 47 & A conservative view of a progressive rhetoric, 63, Quart. J. Speech; The symposium: a neglected source for Plato's ideas on rhetoric, South. Speech Commun. J, 72. Add: 5643 Meadow Lake Lane, Houston, TX 77027.

THOMPSON, WENDEL LAWRENCE, b. Le Mars, Iowa, Apr. 15, 36; m. 62; c. 3. SPEECH, PSYCHOLOGY. B.A, Westmar Col, 58; M.A, Univ. Iowa, 63, Ph.D.(speech), 65. Asst. prof. speech, Univ. Conn, 65-66; SOC. SCI. ANALYST, U.S. INFORM. AGENCY, 66- Speech Commun. Asn; Broadcast Educ. Asn. Radio audience research; mass media; methodology. Publ: Co-auth, Increasing returns in international mail surveys, Pub. Opinion

Quart, spring 74. Add: Office of Research, Media Research Div, U.S. Information Agency, 1750 Pennsylvania Ave. N.W, Washington, DC 20547

THOMPSON, WILLIAM DAVID, Homiletics, Speech. See Volume IV, Philosophy, Religion & Law.

THOMPSON, WILLIAM IRWIN, b. Chicago, Ill, July 16, 38; m. 60; c. 2. ENGLISH, LITERARY ANTHROPOLOGY. B.A, Pomona Col, 62, Woodrow Wilson fels, Cornell Univ, 62 & 64, M.A, 64, Ph.D.(Eng), 66. Teaching asst. Eng, Cornell Univ, 62-64; instr. HUMANITIES, Mass. Inst. Technol, 65-66, asst. prof, 66-68; assoc. prof, YORK UNIV, 68-72, PROF, 72-, FOUNDER & DIR, LINDISFARNE ASN, 73- Caspar Whiting Fund Boston grant, 67; Old Dominion fel, 67-68. Comparative cultural history. Publ: The imagination of an insurrection: Dublin, Easter 1916, a study of an ideological movement, Oxford, 67; At the edge of history, 71 & Passages about earth, 74, Harper; Collapsed universe and structured poem: an essay in Whiteheadian criticism, Col. Eng, 66; Los Angeles: reflections at the edge of history, Antioch Rev, 68; The individual as institution, Harpers, 9/72. Add: Lindisfarne Association, P.O. Box 1395, Southampton, NY 11968.

THOMPSON, WILLIAM ROSS, b. Steubenville, Ohio, Nov. 16, 18; m. 45; c. 2. AMERICAN LITERATURE. B.A, Tex. Christian Univ, 48, fel, 48, M.A, 50; fel, Tex. Technol. Col, 50, grant, 56, Ph.D, 57. Instr. Eng, Howard County Jr. Col, 52-54; Tex. Technol. Col, 54-56; assoc. prof, Arlington State Col, 57-59; Tex. Wesleyan Col, 59-63; Univ. Alaska, 63-65; PROF. ENG. & CHMN. DIV. LANG, LIT. & SPEECH, FT. HAYS KANS. STATE COL, 65-, DEAN, FAC. LIB. ARTS, 72- U.S.A, 41-45. MLA; S.Cent. Mod. Lang. Asn; Rocky Mountain Mod. Lang. Asn; NCTE; Am. Asn. Higher Educ. Hawthorne source studies; Melville interpretive studies. Publ: The paradise of bachelors and the Tartarus of maids: a reinterpretation, Am. Quart, 57; The Biblical sources of Hawthorne's Roger Malvin's burial, PMLA, 3/62; Broceliande: E.A. Robinson's Palace of art, New Eng. Quart, 6/70. Add: 2401 Lincoln Dr, Hays, KS 67601.

THOMSON, (SARAH) ELIZABETH, b. Quincy, Fla, Feb. 20, 06. SPEECH. A.B, Fla. State Univ, 27; A.M, Univ. Mich, 45; Curry Col, 28-29; Elizabeth Grimbal Sch. Theater, 32; West. Reserve Univ, 47. From instr. to assoc. prof. SPEECH, FLA. STATE UNIV, 29-71, EMER. PROF, 71- Consult. speech, State Dept. Educ, Fla, 48. Speech Commun. Asn; Am. Speech & Hearing Asn; South. Speech. Commun. Asn. Physiological research in oral interpretation. Publ: Making dramatics functional for holidays, Fla. Educ. Bull. Add: 530 Williams St, Tallahassee, FL 32303.

THOMSON, GEORGE HENRY, b. Bluevale, Ont, July 22, 24; m. 56. ENGLISH. B.A, Univ. West. Ont, 47; Ph.D.(Eng), Univ. Toronto, 52. Teaching fel, Univ. Toronto, 48-51; lectr. Eng, Mt. Allison Univ, 53-55, asst. prof, 55-59, assoc. prof, 59-66; vis. prof, Wayne State Univ, 66-67; Can. Counc. sr. fel, 67-68; PROF. ENG, UNIV. OTTAWA, 69- MLA; Asn. Can. Univ. Teachers Eng; Eng. Asn, Gt. Brit; Am. Soc. Aesthet. Narrative theory; modern British fiction. Publ: The fiction of E.M. Forster, Wayne State Univ, 67; ed, Albergo Empedocle and other writings by E.M. Forster, Liveright, 71; auth, Trumpet-major chronicle, Nineteenth Century Fiction, 6/62; The Lord of the Rings: the novel as traditional romance, Wis. Stud. Contemporary Lit, winter 67; A Forster miscellany, In: Aspects of E.M. Forster, Arnold, London & Harcourt, N.Y, 69; plus others. Add: 655 Echo Dr, Ottawa, Ont, Can.

THOMSON, PAUL VAN KUYKENDALL, b. Weehawken, N.J, Dec. 14, 16; m. 45; c. 7. ENGLISH. A.B, Columbia Univ, 37; S.T.B, Berkeley Divinity Sch, 40; S.T.M, Gen. Theol. Sem, 43; M.A, Brown Univ, 52, univ. fel, 53-54, Ph.D, 56; hon. M.A, Providence Col, 59; hon. D.H.L, Salve Regina Col, 66. Instr. ENG, PROVIDENCE COL, 49-51, asst. prof, 51-55, assoc. prof, 55-58, PROF, 58-, ACAD. V.PRES, 65- Mem, Am. Counc. Educ, 65- U.S.N.R, 43-46, Lt. MLA; AAUP; Francis Thompson Soc. Relation between religion and literature in the 19th century in England: notebooks of Francis Thompson. Publ: Francis Thompson: a critical biography, Nelson, 61; The tragedy of the Spanish Inquisition, the bridge IV, Pantheon, 62; Should Catholic colleges by abolished, Columbia Col. Today, fall 66; Francis Thompson and the surrogate theory of poetry, In: Hound of heaven: a commemorative volume, Francis Thompson Soc, 67. Add: Office of the Academic Vice President, Providence College, River Ave. & Eaton St, Providence, RI 02918.

THONSSEN, LESTER, b. Sutherland, Iowa, Nov. 26, 04; m. 27. SPEECH. A.B, Huron Col, 26, D.Litt, 58; M.A, Univ. Iowa, 29, Ph.D.(speech), 31. Instr. SPEECH, Pac. Univ, 26-28; from instr. to prof, City Col. New York, 31-65; PROF, METROP. STATE COL. COLO, 65- Vis. prof, Calif. State Univ, Los Angeles, 65; summer vis. prof, Mont. State Univ, State Univ. N.Y. Col. Fredonia, Univ. Iowa, Univ. Colo, Adams State Col. Colo, Univ. South. Calif, Univ. Hawaii & Teachers Col, Columbia Univ. Speech Commun. Asn.(ed, Speech Monographs, 48-50, pres, Speech Asn. Am, 56, co-recipient Golden Anniversary Book Award, 71); NEA; West. Speech. Commun. Asn. Rhetorical theory; public address; speech criticism. Publ: Co-ed, Bibliography of speech education, 39, ed, Selected readings in rhetoric, 42, co-ed, Bibliography of speech education: supplement, 1939-1948, 50 & ed, Representative American speeches, annual, 59-70, Wilson; co-auth, Speech preparation and delivery, Lippincott, 42 & Basic training in speech, D.C. Heath, 47, 53; co-auth, Speech criticism, 48, 70 & Ideas that matter, 61, Ronald; co-ed, Chironomia by Gilbert Austin, South. Ill. Univ, 66; contrib, History and criticism of American Public address, (2 vols), McGraw, 43 & American public address, Univ. Mo, 61. Add: 955 Eudora St, Denver, CO 80220.

THORN, ARLINE ROUSH, b. New Haven, W.Va, Nov. 22, 46; m. 68. COMPARATIVE & ENGLISH LITERATURE. A.B, Marshall Univ, 67; univ. fel, Univ. Ill, Urbana, 67-69, M.A, 68, Woodrow Wilson fel, 70, Ph.D.(comp. lit), 71. Instr. ENG, W.VA. STATE COL, 71, ASST. PROF, 71- AAUP; Am. Comp. Lit. Asn. Charles Dickens; history and theory of the novel; literary criticism. Publ: Co-auth, The velluminous word: McLuhan-D.H. Lawrence, Midwest Monogr, 71; The pivotal character in Dickens' novels, Papers W.Va. Asn. Col. Eng. Teachers, spring 72; Shelley's Cenci as tragedy, Costerus: Essays Eng. Lit. & Lang, 12/73. Add: 1593 Campbell Dr, Huntington, WV 25705.

THORN, ERIC P, b. Vienna, Austria, Nov. 30, 29; U.S. citizen; m. 68; c. 1. ENGLISH, COMPARATIVE LITERATURE. A.B, Brooklyn Col, 50, M.A, 56; N.Y. Univ, summers, 57- Instr. ENG, MARSHALL UNIV, 56-60, asst. prof, 60-64, ASSOC. PROF, 64-, ed. proc. Eng. insts, 60-, dir. interdisciplinary stud. & univ. honors, 70-72. Benedum res. grants, summers, 66-68. Qm.C, U.S.A, 52-54. MLA; Teachers of Eng. to Speakers Other Lang; AAUP. Naturalistic movement; realistic orientation in literature; contemporary drama. Publ: Convenient reference to literary terms, Marshall Univ, 62; Has anyone seen Studs Lonigan?, PRJM, spring 71; James Joyce: early intimations of structural unity, Costerus J: Essays in Eng. & Am. lang. & lit, 12/73. Add: Dept. of English, Marshall University, Huntington, WV 25705.

THORNBERRY, RICHARD THAYER, b. East Cleveland, Ohio, Oct. 8, 25; m. 51; c. 2. ENGLISH. B. Naval Sci, Marquette Univ, 45, Ph.B, 48; M.A, Univ. Mich, 51; Ph.D.(Shakespeare), Ohio State Univ, 64. Asst, Ohio State Univ, 55-57, 59-61, instr. ENG, 58-59; asst. prof, WEST. ILL. UNIV, 61-66, assoc. prof, 66-70, PROF, 70- U.S.N, 43-47, 52-53, Res, 53-66, Lt. Comdr. MLA; Shakespeare Asn. Am. Shakespeare; Elizabethan drama. Add: Dept. of English, Western Illinois University, Macomb, IL 61455.

THORNBURG, FRANK B, b. Huntington, W.Va, Mar. 17, 23; m. 44; c. 7. JOURNALISM. B.S, Univ. Tenn, 48, 66-67; M.A, Univ. Fla, 51. Chmn. dept. jour, Richmond Prof. Inst, 51-55, dir. summer session, 52, pub. relat, 53; asst. prof, Univ. Tenn, 55-62; assoc. prof. JOUR. & dir. pub. relat, Oklahoma City Univ, 62-63, chmn. dept, 62-63; ASSOC. PROF, UNIV. TENN, 66- Pub. relat. consult, Richmond Area Community Chest, 55; Knoxville Chamber Commerce, 57; South. Highland Handicraft Guild, Asheville, N.C, 60; consult, Col. Manpower, N.Y.C, 68-71; consult. mkt, Gabriel Sedlmyer Franzsikaner, Ger, 70-71; Albers Drug Co, Knoxville, Tenn, 71-73; consult. advert, Krystal Restaurants, Chattanooga, 70-; mem, Graphic Arts Tech. Found, 73-; consult, Oak Ridge Assoc. Univs, 73-74. U.S.A.A.F, 43-45, 1st Lt. Int. Graphic Arts Educ. Asn; Asn. Educ. in Jour. Graphic communications; visual communications; photography. Publ: Advertising at Tennessee, South. Advert. & Publ, 2/67. Add: 9400 Briarwood Blvd, Knoxville, TN 37919.

THORNBURG, ROBERT BRENNER, b. Hagerstown, Md, Nov. 1, 20; m. 50; c. 2. ENGLISH. A.B, Gettysburg Col, 42; A.M, Univ. Pa, 50, Ph.D, 56. Instr. Eng, Gettysburg Col, 46-47; Muhlenberg Col, 51-53; Eng. compos, Pa. State Univ, 54-56; asst. prof. ENG, Juniata Col, 56; assoc. prof, MUHLENBERG COL, 62-66, PROF, 66- Sig.C, U.S.A, 42-46. MLA; NCTE; Asn. Lutheran Col. Fac. Literature of the English Renaissance; the sonnet; interdisciplinary studies in the humanities. Add: Dept. of English, Muhlenberg College, Allentown, PA 18104.

THORNE, DOROTHY GILBERT, b. Rich Square, Ind, July 4, 02; m. 54. ENGLISH. A.M, Columbia Univ, 29; Univ. Wis, summer 33; Univ. N.C, 34-35. Instr. ENG, GUILFORD COL, 26-28, assoc. prof, 29-52, prof. & acting librn, 52-54, prof, 65-71, chmn. dept, 65-68, cur. Quaker Collection, 68-71, EMER. PROF, 71- Aspects of Quaker thought and history; Guilford College, past and present. Publ: Guilford: a Quaker college, Guilford Col, 37; co-auth, The Cowper translation of Madame Guyon's poems, PMLA, 39; auth, Joe Cannon's Carolina background, 46 & North Carolina Friends and the Revolution, 61, N.C. Hist. Rev. Add: Dept. of English, Guilford College, Greensboro, NC 27410.

THORNE, WILLIAM BARRY, b. Vancouver, B.C, Aug. 17, 35; m. 63; c. 4. RENAISSANCE DRAMA, MODERN AMERICAN & BRITISH LITERATURE. B.A, Univ. B.C, 57, M.A, 60; Ph.D.(Eng), Univ. Wis, 64. Lectr. Eng, Royal Roads Mil. Col, 62-63, spec. lectr, 63-64, asst. prof, 64-65, acting head dept, 63-65; ASSOC. PROF. ENG, QUEEN'S UNIV.(ONT), 65- Can. Counc. grant, 66. MLA; Asn. Can. Univ. Teachers Eng; Humanities Asn. Can. Shakespeare; drama; modern Canadian literature. Publ: Things newborn: a study of the rebirth motif in The winter's tale, Humanities Bull, winter 68; Cymbeline: lopped branches and the concept of regeneration, spring 69 & Pericles and the incest-fertility opposition, winter 71, Shakespeare Quart; plus others. Add: Dept. of English Language & Literature, Queen's University, Kingston, Ont, Can.

THORNTON, HORTENSE ELOISE, b. Miami, Fla, July 6, 41; m. 67. AFRO-AMERICAN LITERATURE. B.A, Howard Univ, 63, Ph.D.(Eng), 70. Instr. Eng, Tex. South. Univ, summers 65, 66; lectr, Ohio State Univ, 66-69, vis. asst. prof, 69-70, asst. prof, 70-72, ASSOC. PROF, 72-73; ENG. & ETHNIC STUD, CALIF. STATE UNIV, SACRAMENTO, 73- Nat. Endowment for Humanities res. grant, 71-73. MLA (mem. comn. minority groups & stud. lang. & lit, 72-); Col. Lang. Asn; AAUP. Publ: Sexism as quagmire—Nella Larsen's Quicksand, Col. Lang. Asn, spring 73. Add: Dept. of English, California State University, Sacramento, 6000 J. St, Sacramento, CA 95819.

THORNTON, ROBERT DONALD, b. West Somerville, Mass, Aug. 10, 17; m. 43; c. 2. ENGLISH LITERATURE. A.B, Wesleyan Univ, 39, Dennison fel, 39-40; A.M, West. Reserve Univ, 40; A.M, Harvard, 43, Dexter fel. & Ph.D, 49. Instr. ENG, Fenn Col, 39-40; Worcester Acad, 40-41; teaching fel, Harvard, 41-42, 46-48, asst, 48-49; asst. prof, Univ. Colo, 49-56; head dept, St. Stephen's Episcopal Sch, 56-57; assoc. prof, Univ. S.C, 57-60; PROF, Kans. State Univ, 60-68; STATE UNIV. N.Y. COL. NEW PALTZ, 72-, chmn. dept, 68-72, fac. res. fel. & grant-in-aid, 73, exchange scholar, 74. Am. Philos. Soc. grant, 55-56; Guggenheim fel, 58-59; Am. Counc. Learned Soc. grant-in-aid, 63; fac. res. grant, Kans. State Univ, 64; guest lectr, Univ. Mo, Kansas City, 67-68. U.S.N.R, 42-46, Lt.(jg). MLA; Mod. Humanities Res. Asn. Robert Burns; cultural history of Scotland; the Enlightenment. Publ: Tuneful flame, Univ. Kans, 57; James Currie and Robert Burns, Oliver & Boyd, 63; Robert Burns: selected poetry and prose, Houghton, 66; The influence of the Enlightenment upon eighteenth-century British antiquaries, 63 & Robert Burns and the Scottish Enlightenment, 68, Stud. Voltaire; The trip to Liverpool, Burns Chronicle, 73; plus one other. Add: Dept. of English, State University of New York College at New Paltz, New Paltz, NY 12561.

THORNTON, WELDON E, b. Mitchell Co, Ga, Dec. 27, 34; m. 55; c. 3. ENGLISH. A.B, Mercer Univ, 55; M.A, Emory Univ, 57; Ph.D.(Eng), Univ. Tex, Austin, 61. Instr. ENG, UNIV. N.C, CHAPEL HILL, 61-63, asst. prof, 63-66, ASSOC. PROF, 66- Am. Philos. Soc. grant, summer 65; panelist,

Res. Div, Nat. Endowment for Humanities, 72-; Am. Counc. Learned Soc. grant-in-aid, 73. Int. Asn. Stud. Anglo-Irish Lit.(U.S. bibliographer, 70-); Am. Comt. Irish Stud; Can. Asn. Irish Stud; MLA. Modern British and American fiction; Irish literary Renaissance. Publ: Allusions in Ulysses: an annotated list, Univ. N.C, 68. Add: Dept. of English, University of North Carolina, Chapel Hill, NC 27514.

THORPE, JAMES, b. Aiken, S.C, Aug. 17, 15; m. 41; c. 3. ENGLISH LITERATURE. A.B, The Citadel, 36, hon. Litt.D, 71; A.M, Univ. N.C, 37; Ph.D, Harvard, 41; Litt.D, Occidental Col, 68; L.H.D, Claremont Univ, 68. Instr. Eng, Univ. Miss, 37-38; asst. prof, Princeton, 46-51, assoc. prof, 51-64, prof, 64-66, master grad. col, 48-54, asst. dean grad. sch, 48-58, mem. grad. rec. exam. comt, 63-66; DIR. HUNTINGTON LIBR, ART GALLERY & BOT. GARDENS, 66- Guggenheim fel, 49-50, 65-66; trustee, Kent Sch, 52-59; mem, Fulbright Selection Adv. Comt, 64-66. U.S.A.A.F, 41-45, Col. MLA (comt. res. activities, 50-73); fel. Am. Antiq. Soc. Textual criticism; 17th century literature; literary theory. Publ: Rochester's poems on several occasions, 50 & Poems of Sir George Etherege, 63, Princeton; ed, Aims and methods of scholarship, 63, 70, ed, Relations of literary study, 67 & Use of manuscripts in literary research, 74, MLA; auth, Literary scholarship, 64 & ed, Bunyan's Pilgrim's progress, 69, Houghton; auth, Principles of textual criticism, Huntington Libr, 72. Add: Huntington Library, Art Gallery & Botanical Gardens, San Marino, CA 91108.

THORPE, MICHAEL, b. Great Yarmouth, Norfolk, Eng, Sept. 18, 32. ENGLISH LITERATURE. B.A, Univ. London, 54; dipl. educ, Univ. Leicester, 55; M.A, Univ. Singapore, 64. Lectr. ENG, Nanyang Univ, 62-64; sr. lectr, Univ. Leiden, 65-70; assoc. prof, UNIV. CALGARY, 70-73, PROF, 73- Victorian, Modern British and Commonwealth fiction and poetry. Publ: Siegfried Sassoon: a critical study, Oxford, London 66 & N.Y, 67; Matthew Arnold, Evans, 69; By the Niger and other poems, Fortune, 69; The poetry of Edmund Blunden, Bridge Bks, 71; ed, Clough: the critical heritage, Routledge & Kegan, 72; auth, Doris Lessing, Longmans, 73. Add: Dept. of English, University of Calgary, Calgary, Alta. T2N 1N4, Can.

THORSEN, TOR HENRY, b. Brooklyn, N.Y, Jan. 10, 26. ENGLISH. B.A, Columbia Univ, 50, M.A, 52. Instr. ENG, Russell Sage Col, 61-62; ASST. PROF, Towson State Col, 62-63; Alliance Col, 63-68; ALLEGHENY COUNTY COMMUNITY COL, BOYCE CAMPUS, 68- U.S.A.A.F, 44-46. Movements and trends in contemporary writing, especially post-absurdist novel, drama and film; careers and business opportunities in publishing, editing, writing and education; international business and trade. Publ: Contrib, West. Pa. Phoenix, 72-; Mensa College, 7-8/73 & Mensa action, 9/73, Int. J; plus others. Add: Apt. 508, 800 Penn Center Blvd, Pittsburgh, PA 15235.

THORSLEV, PETER L, JR, b. Harlan, Iowa, Oct. 17, 29. ENGLISH. B.A, Dana Col, 50; Shevlin fel, Univ. Minn, 56-57, M.A, 57, univ. fel, 57-59, Ph.D, 59. Instr. ENG, Northwest. Univ, 59-60; asst. prof. UNIV. CALIF, LOS ANGELES, 60-66, assoc. prof, 66-71, PROF, 71-, CHMN. DEPT, 73- Guggenheim fel, 66-67. Sig.C, U.S.A, 50-53. MLA; Keats-Shelley Asn. English romantic literature; Anglo-German literary relations. Publ: The Byronic hero, Univ. Minn, 62; contrib, Romantic and Victorian, Fairleigh Dickinson Univ, 71; auth, Incest as romantic symbol, Comp. Lit. Stud, 1/65; plus others. Add: Dept. of English, University of California, Los Angeles, CA 90024.

THORSON, GERALD HOWARD, b. Menomonie, Wis, June 8, 21; m. 53; c. 6. ENGLISH & COMPARATIVE LITERATURE. B.A, Augsburg Col, 43; M.A, Univ. Minn, 48; Thompson fel, Univ. Wis, 48-49, summer 53; Sverdrup fel, 49, 50, 51; Ph.D, Columbia Univ, 57. Instr. Eng, Augsburg Col, 46-52, asst. prof, 52-55, assoc. prof, 55-59, prof, 59-64, chmn. dept, 52-64, chmn. div. humanities, 58-64; PROF. ENG. & CHMN. DEPT, ST. OLAF COL, 64-, CHMN. DIV. LANG. & LIT, 73- Lectr, Wagner Col, 51-52; Danforth sem. fel, Univ. Chicago, summer 59; Fulbright prof. Am. lit, Univ. Iceland, 61-62; Univ. Minn. rep, 50th Anniversary, Univ. Iceland, 61; mem. hymn text comt, Inter-Lutheran Comn. on Worship, 67-; guest prof. Am. lit, Univ. Konstanz, 70-71. U.S.A, 43-46. NCTE; Norweg-Am. Hist. Asn; Lutheran Soc. Worship, Music & the Arts (assoc. ed, Response). Mediaeval literature; contemporary American and Norwegian-American novel. Add: Old Dutch Rd, Rte. 1, Northfield, MN 55057.

THORSON, JAMES LLEWELLYN, b. Yankton, S.Dak, Jan. 7, 34; m. 70. ENGLISH & AMERICAN LITERATURE. B.S, Univ. Nebr, 56, M.A, 61; Ph.D. (Eng), Cornell Univ, 66. Instr. ENG, Univ. Nebr, 61-62; asst. prof, UNIV. N.MEX, 65-70, ASSOC. PROF, 70-, dir. grad. stud. Eng, 69-71. Greater univ. fund grant, Univ. N.Mex, 67; sr. Fulbright lectr. Eng, Univ. Macedonia, Yugoslavia, 71-72; vis. tutor Eng, Jesus Col, Oxford, 73. U.S.N, 56-59, Lt. AAUP; MLA; Bibliog. Soc. Am. Restoration and 18th century English literature; bibliography; American literature. Publ: The publication of Hudibras, Papers Bibliog. Soc. Am, 66; Samuel Butler, 1612-1680: a bibliography, Bull. Bibliog, 1/73; A broadside by Samuel Butler, Bodleian Libr. Rec, 2/74. Add: Dept. of English, University of New Mexico, Albuquerque, NM 87131.

THRANE, JAMES R, b. Los Angeles, Calif, May 24, 27; m. 50; c. 1. ENGLISH. A.B, Univ. Calif, Los Angeles, 49, M.A, 50; Ph.D, Columbia Univ, 56. Instr. ENG, Northwest. Univ, 56-60; ASST. PROF, Univ. Wis, Milwaukee, 60-66; SAN DIEGO STATE UNIV, 66- Adj. Gen. Dept, A.U.S, 45-46. MLA. Victorian and Edwardian literary history. Publ: Joyce's sermon on hell: its source and its backgrounds, Mod. Philol, 2/60. Add: Dept. of English, San Diego State University, 5402 College Ave, San Diego, CA 92115.

THROCKMORTON, HELEN JEAN, b. Wichita, Kans, Sept. 7, 23. ENGLISH. A.B, Friends Univ, 45; M.Ed, Univ. Colo, 56, Ed.D.(Eng. educ), 72. Teacher Eng, Kingsdown, Kans, 45-47; Eng. & U.S. hist, Dodge City, Kans, 47-49; ENG, Wichita High School East, 50-54; instr. & freshman coord, WICHITA STATE UNIV, 54-57, asst. prof, 57-67, ASSOC. PROF, 67-, IN CHARGE ENG. EDUC, 62- NCTE; Conf. Eng. Educ. English education; composition. Publ: Co-auth, New dimensions in English, McCormick-Mathers, 66; co-auth, How to read a poem, 66 & How to read a short story, 69, Ginn; A way of speaking and embracing, Educ. in Mid-Am, 72. Add: Dept. of English, Wichita State University, 1845 Fairmount, Wichita, KS 67208.

THUNDYIL, ZACHARIAS PONTIAN, b. Changanacherry, Kerala, India, Sept. 28, 36. ENGLISH, LINGUISTICS. B.Ph, Pontif. Athenaeum, India, 58, L.Ph, 59, B.Th, 61, S.T.L, 63; M.A, DePaul Univ, 66; Ph.D.(Eng), Univ. Notre Dame, 69. Instr. philos, Dharmaram Col, Bangalore, India, 63-64; asst. prof. ENG, NORTH. MICH. UNIV, 68-72, ASSOC. PROF, 72- MLA; Int. Arthurian Soc; Midwest Mod. Lang. Asn; Ling. Soc. Am; Am. Dialect Soc; Mediaeval Acad. Am; Conf. Christianity & Lit; AAUP. Anthropological linguistics; American dialect survey; feminism in the Middle Ages. Publ: Covenant in Anglo-Saxon thought, Macmillan, 72; co-ed, Language and culture, North. Mich. Univ, 73; auth, Circumstance, circumference, and center, Hartford Stud. Lit, 71; Oaths in Germanic folklore, Folklore, 71; Beowulf and Jus diaboli, Christian Scholar's Rev, 73; plus others. Add: Dept. of English, Northern Michigan University, Marquette, MI 49855.

THUNE, ENSAF, b. Cairo, Egypt, Aug. 3, 28; U.S. citizen; m. 56; c. 2. ENGLISH LITERATURE, DRAMA. B.A, Univ. Cairo, Egypt, 49; M.A, Univ. Wash, 55, Ph.D.(Eng), 62. Instr. ENG. LIT, Univ. Cairo, 52-54; East. Wash. Col, 56-57; Univ. Wash, 60-62; lectr, Highline Col, 62-65; asst. prof, HOFSTRA UNIV, 65-70, ASSOC. PROF, 70-, DIR. INST. ARTS, 73- Shakespeare lectr, Adult Educ. Prog, 68. MLA. History of American Repertory theatre beginning with Eva Le Gallienne's Civic Repertory Theatre in the early twenties and tracing the movement down to the present day. Publ: Co-auth, The short story: a critical anthology, Macmillan, 73; Tragedy and myth in Rosmersholm, Scand. Stud, (in press). Add: Institute of the Arts, Hofstra University, Hempstead, NY 11550.

THURMAN, AURELIUS LA GRANT, JR, b. Decatur, Ala, July 20, 20; m. 42; c. 4. SPEECH. A.B, Cent. Col.(Mo), 42; A.M, Univ. Mo, 50, Ph.D.(speech), 53. Instr. speech, Univ. Mo, 48-53; asst. prof. commun, MICH. STATE UNIV, 53-63, assoc. prof. AM. THOUGHT & LANG, 63-65, PROF. & ASSOC. CHMN. DEPT, 65- U.S.A.A.F, 42-46. Speech Commun. Asn; Cent. States Speech Commun. Asn; Nat. Soc. Stud. Commun; Adult Educ. Asn; Am. Stud. Asn; Asn. Gen. & Lib. Stud. Rhetoric and public address general education; adult education. Add: 1809 Linden St, East Lansing, MI 48823.

THURMAN, KELLY, b. Lebanon Junction, Ky, May 11, 14; m. 43; c. 2. ENGLISH. A.B, West. Ky. Col; M.A, Univ. Ky, Ph.D.(Eng), State Univ. Iowa. Teacher, pub. schs, Ky, 36-45; instr. ENG, Denison Univ, 45-46; State Univ. Iowa, 46-48; asst. prof, Auburn Univ, 48-50; prof. & head dept, Union Univ. (Tenn), 50-58; prof. Eng, Stephen F. Austin State Col, 58-62; prof. & chmn. dept, Oklahoma City Univ, 62-66; PROF. ENG, EAST. KY. UNIV, 66-, CHMN. DEPT, 67- MLA; NCTE. American fiction; literary theory. Publ: Semantics, Houghton, 60; Pulitzer prizewinning fiction, ser, Oklahoma City Mag, 63-64. Add: 444 Breck Ave, Richmond, KY 40475.

THURMAN, WAYNE LAVERNE, b. Detroit, Mich, June 11, 23. SPEECH. B.S, Southeast Mo. State Col, 47, A.B, 47; M.A, State Univ. Iowa, 49; fel, Purdue Univ, 51-53, Ph.D.(speech path). Asst. prof. speech, Southeast Mo. State Col, 49-51; PROF. SPEECH & DIR. SPEECH & HEARING CLIN, EAST. ILL. UNIV, 53-, HEAD DEPT, 62- U.S.A, 43-46, Sgt. Am. Speech & Hearing Asn. Natural pitch level of voice and scaling techniques for voice quality deviations from normal. Publ: Developing vocal skills, Holt, 62 & 70. Add: 877 First St, Charleston, IL 61920.

THURSTON, JARVIS (AYDELOTTE), b. Huntsville, Utah, Apr. 20, 14; m. 43. ENGLISH. B.A, Univ. Utah, 36; M.A, State Univ. Iowa, 44, Ph.D.(Eng), 46. Asst. prof. ENG, Univ. Louisville, 46-50; WASH. UNIV, 50-55, assoc. prof, 55-61, PROF, 61-, chmn. dept, 66-69. Ed, Perspective, 47- MLA. Contemporary American and British literature; poetics; theory of the novel. Publ: Short fiction criticism, Swallow, 60; Anderson and Winesburg, mysticism and craft, Accent; The cross, In: Great western short stories, Am. West, 67; plus others. Add: Dept. of English, Washington University, St. Louis, MO 63130.

THURSTON, PAUL THAYER, b. Brewer, Maine, Feb. 6, 26; m. 48; c. 5. ENGLISH, LINGUISTICS. B.S, Univ. Fla, 54, fel, 55-57, Ph.D.(Eng. & ling), 61. Correspondence dir. & documents off, Austria Nat. Tracing Bur, UN Relief & Rehabil. Admin, 46-47; asst. chief secy, Allied Secretariat, Allied Comn. Austria, 47-49; instr. Eng, UNIV. FLA, 57-62, asst. prof. ENG. & LOGIC, 62-65, assoc. prof, 65-68, PROF, 68- U.S.A, 43-46, M/Sgt. S.Atlantic Mod. Lang. Asn. The love relationships in Chaucer's poetry; post World War II displaced persons problems; concentration camps: genesis and operation. Publ: Co-auth, An analysis of the records of Mauthausen, UN Relief & Rehabil. Admin, Vienna, 48; auth, Artistic ambivalence in Chaucer's Knight's tale, Univ. Fla, 68. Add: Dept. of English, University of Florida, Gainesville, FL 32603.

TIBBETTS, ARNOLD M, b. San Antonio, Tex, Oct. 20, 27; m. 51; c. 4. ENGLISH. B.A, Univ. Colo, 49; M.A, Univ. Iowa, 57; Ph.D.(Eng), Vanderbilt Univ, 64. Geophysicist, United Geophys. Co, Pure Oil Co, 49-54; instr. Eng, Univ. Iowa, 54-57; asst. prof, West. Ill. Univ, 57-59; commun. skills, Air Univ, 59-61; instr. ENG, Vanderbilt Univ, 61-64, asst. prof. UNIV. ILL, URBANA, 64-70, ASSOC. PROF, 70-, fac. fel, 66. Superior Performance Award, Air Univ, 61; Fac. Instr. Award, Univ. Ill, 67. U.S.N.R, 45-46. NCTE; Conf. Col. Compos. & Commun. Rhetoric; grammar; usage. Publ: Co-auth, Strategies of rhetoric, 69, 2nd ed, 74 & The critical man, 72, Scott; auth, Were 19th century textbooks prescriptive, 1/66 & Practical uses of a grammatical system, 5/70, Col. Eng; The real issues in the language controversy, Eng. J, 1/66. Add: 100 English Bldg, University of Illinois, Urbana, IL 61801.

TICHY, HENRIETTA, b. Mar. 24, 12. ENGLISH LITERATURE. A.B, Hunter Col, 32; A.M, Columbia Univ, 34; grad. fac. res. fel, N.Y. Univ, 39-40, Ph.D, 42. Instr. & tutor ENG, Hunter Col, 34-39, 40-41, instr, 41-44, asst. prof, 44-59, assoc. prof, 59-68; LEHMAN COL, 68-70, PROF, 70- MLA; Soc. Tech. Commun.(chmn. educ. & res, 73-); AAAS. Technical writing; 18th century literature; literature of the Bible. Publ: Biblical influences in English literature; Effective writing for engineers, managers, scientists, Wiley, 66; The Bible in English literature; Engineers can write better, Chem. Prog. Add: Dept. of English, Lehman College, Bedford Park Blvd. W, Bronx, NY 10468.

TIDWELL, JAMES NATHAN, b. Miles, Tex, Feb. 24, 11; m. 46; c. 1. ENGLISH. A.B, Hardin-Simmons Univ, 29; A.M, Univ. Okla, 33; Am. Counc. Learned Soc. fel, Ling. Inst, 40; univ. fel, Ohio State Univ, 41-42, Ph.D, 47. Asst. prof, Westminster Col.(Mo), 36-42; instr, Ohio State Univ, 46-47; from assoc. prof. to PROF. ENG, SAN DIEGO STATE UNIV, 47-, acting dean, Col. Arts & Lett, 72-73. Fel, Ohio State Univ, 49; Fulbright lectr, Univ. Athens, 56-57. U.S.N, 42-46, Res, 48-71, Comdr.(Ret). MLA; Am. Dialect Soc; Ling. Soc. Am; Philol. Soc. Pac. Coast; Am. Folklore Soc. Lexicography; American language and folklore. Publ: Ed, The lion of the West, Stanford Univ, 54 & A treasury of American folk humor, Crown, 56. Add: Dept. of Linguistics, San Diego State University, San Diego, CA 92115.

TIEDT, IRIS McCLELLAN, b. Dayton, Ohio, Feb. 3, 28; m. 49; c. 2. ENGLISH EDUCATION. B.S, Northwest. Univ, 50; univ. fels, Univ. Ore, 59-60, M.A, 61; Am. Asn. Univ. Women fel, Stanford Univ, 66-67, Ph.D. (teacher educ), 72. Teacher, pub. schs, Ill, 50-51; Anchorage Sch. Dist, Alaska, 51-59; teacher & librn, pub. schs, Ore, 59-61; asst. prof. Eng. educ, San Jose State Col, 61-68; from asst. prof. to PROF. ENG. EDUC. & DIR. GRAD. READING PROG, UNIV. SANTA CLARA, 68- Ed, Elem. Teacher's Ideas & Materials Workshop, Parker; instr. NDEA Inst, San Jose State Col, co-dir. workshops in creativity in teaching, 63-68. NCTE (comt. reading ladders for human relat, 68-70, ed. Elem. Eng, 72-); Int. Reading Asn; MLA. Roles of women; modern linguistic theory related to curriculum theory; English education. Publ: Creative writing ideas, Contemporary Press, 65; co-auth, The elementary teachers' ideas handbook, 65, Contemporary English in the elementary school, 67, 75 & co-ed, Readings on contemporary English in the elementary school, 67, Prentice-Hall & Unrequired reading: an annotated bibliography, Ore. State Univ, 67; auth, Sexism in education, Gen. Learning Corp, 74; co-ed, Books/literature/children, Houghton, 75; auth, Literature learnings, In: Teaching the disadvantaged child, Oxford, 68; Realistic counseling for high school girls, Sch. Councr, 72; Rhyming phenomena in the English language, Recreational Ling, 73; plus others. Add: Dept. of Education, University of Santa Clara, Santa Clara, CA 95053.

TIEDT, SIDNEY WILLIS, b. Chicago, Ill, Aug. 15, 27; m. 49; c. 2. ENGLISH EDUCATION. B.S, Northwest. Univ, 50, M.A, 53; fels, Univ. Ore, 59 & 60, Ed.D, 61. Teacher, sch. adminr. & prin. pub. schs, 50-59; PROF. EDUC, SAN JOSE STATE UNIV, 61-, dir, NDEA Contemporary Eng. Inst, 65. Consult, Eval. Eng. Progs, Fresno Sch. Dist, Calif, 68, Oakland, 68; mem, Creative Educ. Found; co-ed, The Elem. Teacher's Ideas & Materials Workshop, monthly periodical, 68- U.S.N, 45-46. NCTE (comt. compos. eval, 65-68); Am. Educ. Res. Asn. Creativity; composition especially English language; the role of the federal government in education. Publ: The elementary teacher's complete ideas handbook, 65 & co-auth, Contemporary English in the elementary school and readings on contemporary English in the elementary schools, (2 vols), 67 & 74, Prentice Hall; auth, The role of the federal government in education, 66 & ed, Teaching the disadvantaged child, 68, Oxford; co-auth, The elementary school curriculum, Harper, 68; & Unrequired reading: an annotated bibliography for teachers and administrators, Ore. State Univ, 2nd ed, 67; co-ed, Contemporary foundations series (6 bks), Gen. Learnings Corp, 74; auth, Self-involvement in writing, Elem. Eng, 5/67; co-auth, The secret world of children, Childhood Educ, 2/68; Historical development of federal aid programs, In: Status and impact of educational finance programs, Nat. Educ. Finance Proj, 71. Add: San Jose State University, San Jose, CA 95114.

TIEMENS, ROBERT KENT, b. Archer, Iowa, Sept. 4, 35; m. 56; c. 2. SPEECH. B.A, Morningside Col, 57; M.A, Univ. Iowa, 58, Ph.D. (speech, drama), 62. Asst. prof. speech, North. Ill. Univ, 61-63; Wayne State Univ, 63-68, assoc. prof, 68-72; PROF. COMMUN, UNIV. UTAH, 72- Speech Commun. Asn; Broadcast Educ. Asn; Asn. Educ. Jour; Univ. Film Asn; West. Speech Commun. Asn. Behavioral studies in visual communication. Publ: Validation of speech ratings by retention tests, Speech Teacher, 65; Relationships of camera angle to communicator credibility, J. Broadcasting, 70. Add: Dept. of Communication, University of Utah, Salt Lake City, UT 84112.

TIEMERSMA, RICHARD ROBERT, b. Chicago, Ill, Feb. 9, 19; m. 49; c. 2. ENGLISH LANGUAGE & LITERATURE. A.B, Calvin Col, 49; M.A, Northwest. Univ, 50, Ph.D.(Eng), 62. Instr. humanities, Chicago City Jr. Col, 52-55; ENG, CALVIN COL, 55-57, asst. prof, 57-62, assoc. prof, 62-63, PROF, 63- Vis. lectr, Hope Col, summer 54; Danforth teaching fel, 60. Qm.C, 42-46, Capt. MLA. Victorian literature. Publ: Education in a period of world crisis, 7-8/58 & In the style of old documents, 11/59, Reformed J; Into the charmed circle, Young Calvinist, 9/63. Add: Dept. of English, Calvin College, Grand Rapids, MI 49506.

TIERNEY, JAMES EDWARD, b. Newark, N.J, Jan. 23, 35. ENGLISH LITERATURE. B.A, Seton Hall Univ, 56; M.A, Fordham Univ, 64; Ph.D.(Eng. lit), New York Univ, 69. Instr. ENG. LIT, UNIV. MO-ST. LOUIS, 68-69, ASST. PROF, 69-, summer grants, 69 & 70. Nat. Endowment for Humanities fel, 73-74. MLA. Eighteenth century British periodical, novel and drama. Publ: Florio—an analogue of Tom Jones?, Yearbk. Eng. Stud, spring 73; The Museum—the super-excellent magazine, Stud. Eng. Lit, summer 73; Museum attributions in John Cooper's unpublished letters, Stud. in Bibliog, summer 74. Add: Dept. of English, University of Missouri-St. Louis, 8001 Natural Bridge Rd, St. Louis, MO 63121.

TIETZE, FREDERICK I, b. Chicago, Ill, Mar. 22, 16; m. 41; c. 3. ENGLISH. Ph.B. & M.S, Univ. Wis, 47; Ph.D, 52. Asst. prof. ENG, Drury Col, 49-50; instr, exten. div, Univ. Wis, 51-53, asst. prof, 53-57, univ. res. comt. grant, 56; asst. prof, South. Ill. Univ, 57-58; DE PAUL UNIV, 58-61, ASSOC. PROF, 61- U.S.A.A.F, 42-45, 2nd Lt. MLA; NCTE; Conf. Col. Compos. & Commun. Victorian literature; Alfred Tennyson; the American city. Publ: Ed, The changing metropolis, Houghton, 64; auth, College study guide: freshman English 102, Am. Sch, 68; Tennyson at Cambridge, Trans. Wis. Acad, 57. Add: Dept. of English, De Paul University, Chicago, IL 60614.

TILDEN, LORRAINE F, b. Peoria, Ill, May 16, 12; m. 48. HISPANIC AMERICAN LITERATURE. B.A, Univ. Calif, Los Angeles, 48, fel, 56-57; M.A, Claremont Grad. Sch, 54; Univ. Redlands, 60-61; summers, Whittier Col, 54; Univ. Madrid, 55, Univ. Guanajuato, 64; Univ. Calif, Riverside, 67. Teacher, Eng. Sch, Havana, Cuba, 37-41; asst. Spanish, Scripps Col, 50-52; asst. prof. Span. & Eng. & lectr. Speakers' Bur, Chaffey Col, 54-56; instr, Mt. San Antonio Col, 54-56, 58-60; lectr. Spanish, Claremont Men's Col, 59-61; assoc. prof. humanities, Upland Col, 62-65; TEACHER WORLD MYTHOLOGY, GLENDORA HIGH SCH, 67- Debate coach, La Verne Col, 62-64; mem, int. civic comt, People-To-People, 65-66; field stud, Italy & Greece, 71. Am. Asn. Teachers Span. & Port; NCTE. English, Colombian, Mexican, Spanish and world literature; mythology, Greek, Roman, comparative and medieval. Publ: Modernism in the poetry of José Asunción Silva, Col. Press, 54; ed, Spanish dialogues, 61; Comments on the review ¿Cómo se dice?, Hispania, 3/65; plus others. Add: 351 Oakdale Dr, Claremont, CA 91711.

TILFORD, JOHN EMIL, JR, b. Atlanta, Ga, June 21, 12; m. 34; c. 1. VICTORIAN LITERATURE. A.B, Emory Univ, 34, M.A, 36; Ph.D, Univ. Mich, 42. Asst. Eng, Emory Univ, 36-37, instr, 37-39, asst. prof, 42-48, assoc. prof, 48-57; asst. to pres, Louisville & Nashville R.R. Co, 57-61; prof. Eng, JACKSONVILLE UNIV, 61-63, J. RICHARD GRETHER PROF. ENG, 63-, acting dean fac, 62-63, chmn. div. humanities, 62-67, dean, Col. Arts & Sci, 67-72. Ford fel, 52-53. Prof. of the Year, Jacksonville Univ, 64. U.S.N.R, 43-46, Lt. MLA; S.Atlantic Mod. Lang. Asn; South. Humanities Conf.(v.chmn, 63-64, chmn, 64-65). English novel; George Borrow; Thackeray; Henry James. Add: Jacksonville University, Jacksonville, FL 32211.

TILLEY, WESLEY H, b. Austin, Tex, July 4, 21; m. 44; c. 3. ENGLISH LITERATURE. B.A, Univ. Tex, 42; M.A, Univ. Chicago, 46, Ph.D, 63. Instr. Eng. & humanities, Univ. Chicago, 47-49; asst. prof, Univ. Fla, 49-62; assoc. prof. Eng. lit, Davidson Col, 62-64; prof. Eng. & chmn. dept, Millikin Univ, 64-68, chmn. div. humanities, 65-68; prof. Eng. & chmn. div. humanities, Notre Dame Col.(N.Y), 68-70; v.pres. acad. affairs, STOCKTON STATE COL, 70-72, PROF. ENG, 72- Danforth grant, 58-59. Am. Asn. Higher Educ; Am. Asn. Univ. Adminr; AAUP; MLA; Mind Asn; NCTE. Nineteenth century British literature; history and theory of English fiction. British philosophy. Publ: The background of the Princess Casamassima, Univ. Fla, 60; Literature, method, and contemporary education, Col. Eng, 10/67. Add: 306 Cynwyd Dr, Absecon, NJ 08201.

TILLINGHAST, JOHN KIETH, b. Elmira, N.Y, Dec. 28, 26. SPEECH, THEATRE. B.S, Ithaca Col, 51; M.F.A, Yale, 54; Ph.D.(critical analysis), Ind. Univ, 64. Instr. theatre, Allegheny Col, 55-59; dir, Pittsburgh Playhouse, 60-61; asst. prof. theatre, Ind. Univ, Bloomington, 64-70, asst. dir, Theatre, 68-70; PROF. SPEECH COMMUN. & THEATRE & CHMN. DEPT, MANSFIELD STATE COL, 70- Founder & dir, Mansfield Festival Theatre, 72- U.S.A, 45-47, S/Sgt. Am. Theatre Asn. The director and the actor in the American theatre. Add: Dept. of Speech Communication & Theatre, Mansfield State College, Mansfield, PA 16933.

TILLINGHAST, RICHARD WILLIFORD, b. Memphis, Tenn, Nov. 25, 40. ENGLISH. B.A, Univ. of the South, 62; A.M, Harvard, 63, Ph.D.(Eng), 70. Asst. prof. Eng, Univ. Calif, Berkeley, 68-73; WRITING, 73- Modern poetry; mysticism; music. Publ: Sleep watch, Wesleyan Univ, 69. Add: 112 Edison Ave, Corte Madera, CA 94925.

TILLMAN, JAMES SHANNON, JR, b. Oxford, Miss, Sept. 30, 44; m. 67; c. 1. SEVENTEENTH CENTURY ENGLISH LITERATURE. B.A, Tulane Univ, 66; NDEA fel, Univ. Rochester, 66-70, Ph.D.(Eng), 70. Instr. ENG, Univ. Rochester, 69-70; ASST. PROF, GA. STATE UNIV, 71- MLA; NCTE. Seventeenth century prose; history of science. Add: Dept. of English, Georgia State University, 33 Gilmer St. S.E, Atlanta, GA 30303.

TILLSON, MERL WILLIAM, b. Richmond, Ind, Feb. 28, 20; m. 43; c. 1. ENGLISH. A.B, Earlham Col, 46; M.A, Univ. Denver, 47, Ph.D.(lit), 51. Instr. drama, Ohio Univ, 46-48; ENG, Purdue Univ, 50-52, asst. prof, 53-59, assoc. prof, 59-63; prof, Wilmington Col, 64-65; St. Mary's Col.(Ind), 65-66; assoc. prof, Ind. Univ, 66-68, West. State Col. Colo, 68-69; PROF, METROPOLITAN STATE COL, 69- Writing grant, Purdue Univ, summer, 57; fel. folklore, Purdue Univ. & Ind. Univ, summer, 59; sabbatical leave & Purdue res. grant, 61-62; consult, Nat. Counc. Alcoholism, 73- U.S.N.A.F, 42-45; U.S.N.R, Lt. MLA. Publ: Ed, Play-party in Indiana, Ind. Hist. Soc, 59, Today's poets, Am. Poets Free Press, 64 & Quotations in context, Salem, 65 & Harper, 66; auth, Walden invaded, Windfall, 66; Unknown soldier (poem), Poet & Critic, Vol. I, No. 1; The mushroom hunters (poem), Trace Mag, spring 66; Mountain interval (poem), Creste Butte Chronicle, 3/69; plus others. Add: Dept. of English, Metropolitan State College, 14th & Cherokee, Denver, CO 80204.

TILTON, ELEANOR M, b. Boston, Mass, Aug. 20, 13. AMERICAN LITERATURE. B.A, Mt. Holyoke Col, 34; univ. scholar. & M.A, Boston Univ, 35; univ. fel, Columbia Univ, 38-39, Am. Asn. Univ. Women fel, 42-43, Ph.D. (Am. lit), 47. Instr. Eng. lit, Mt. Holyoke Col, spring 37; ENG, Vassar Col, 39-42; MacMurray Col, 43-46; Temple Univ, 47-48, asst. prof, 48-50; from asst. prof. to PROF, BARNARD COL, COLUMBIA UNIV, 50-, chmn. dept, 61-63. Bibliog. Soc. Am. res. grant, 48-52; Barnard Col. fac. res. grant, 58, 65, 66-67; Am. Counc. Learned Soc. grant-in-aid, 60; Guggenheim fel, 64-65. MLA; AAUP. Colonial period and early 19th century American literature; letters of Ralph Waldo Emerson; romanticism. Publ: Amiable autocrat, a biography of Oliver Wendell Holmes, Henry Schuman, 47; co-auth, A bibliography of Oliver Wendell Holmes, N.Y. Univ, 53; Melville's Rammon: a text and commentary, Harvard Libr. Bull, 59; Holmes and his critic Motley, Am. Lit, 65; Mr. Emerson of Boston, In: The chief glory of every people, South. Ill. Univ, 73. Add: Dept. of English, Barnard College, Columbia University, New York, NY 10027.

TILTON, JOHN WIGHTMAN, b. Mannington, W.Va, Apr. 1, 28; m. 50; c. 4. ENGLISH. A.B, Bucknell Univ, 52, M.A, 54; Ph.D.(Eng), Pa. State Univ, 62. From asst. prof. ENG. to PROF, BUCKNELL UNIV, 54- U.S.A.F, 45-47. MLA; NCTE. Neoclassical literature; satire; modern satirical fiction. Publ: The two modest proposals: a dual approach to Swift's irony, 12/66 & Giles goat-boy: an interpretation, spring 70, Bucknell Rev; Kafka's America as a novel of salvation, Criticism, fall 61. Add: 40 S. Front St, Lewisburg, PA 17837.

TIMKO, MICHAEL, b. Garfield, N.J, Aug. 16, 25; m. 47; c. 3. ENGLISH LITERATURE. A.B. & B.J, Univ. Mo, 49, Gregory fel. & M.A, 50; univ. fel, Univ. Wis, 54, Ph.D, 56. Instr. Eng. compos. & lit, Univ. Mo, 50-52; Eng. lit, Univ. Ill, 56-59, asst. prof, 59-61; ENG, QUEENS COL.(N.Y), 61-66, assoc. prof, 66-71, PROF, 71-, CHMN, 72- Mem. Eng. Inst; mem. bibliog. comt. & contrib. ed, Victorian Stud, 63-66; mem. ed. bd, Victorian Poetry, 66- U.S.N, 43-46. MLA; Am. Soc. Theatre Res. Victorian literature; British and American drama; fiction. Publ: Innocent Victorian: the satiric poetry of A.H. Clough, Ohio Univ, 66; co-auth, Arthur Hugh Clough: a descriptive catalogue, N.Y. Pub. Libr, 66 & Thirty-eight short stories: an introductory anthology, Knopf, 68; auth, Ah, did you once see Browning plain?, Stud. Eng. Lit, autumn 66; Wordsworth's Ode and Arnold's Dover Beach: celestial light and confused alarms, Cithara, 11/73; auth, Arnold, Tennyson and the English idyl: ancient criticism and modern poetry, Tex. Stud. in Lit. & Lang, spring 74. Add: Dept. of English, Queens College, Flushing, NY 11367.

TIMMERMAN, JOHN JOHNSON, b. Iowa City, Iowa, Nov. 2, 08; m. 38; c. 4. ENGLISH. A.B, Calvin Col, 31; A.M, Univ. Mich, 32; Ph.D, Northwest. Univ, 48. Instr, Grundy Jr. Col, 32-34; Calvin Col, 34-35; East. Acad, 37-38; high sch, Mich, 38-45; assoc. prof. ENG, CALVIN COL, 45-51, PROF, 51-, chmn. dept, 56-72. Fulbright sr. lectr, Univ. Amsterdam, 63-64. Victorian biography; American realism. Add: Dept. of English, Calvin College, Grand Rapids, MI 49506.

TIMMIS, JOHN HENRY, III, b. Warren, Pa, Jan. 1, 34; m. 70; c. 3. COMMUNICATION, HISTORY. B.A, Pa. State Univ, 59, M.A, 62, Ph.D.(commun, hist), 66; Univ. Munich, 60, 66. Instr. COMMUN, Pa. State Univ, 60-66; from asst. prof. to ASSOC. PROF, OHIO UNIV, 66- Systs. anal. consult, Naval Command & Control Systs, 61-66; res. engr, HRB-Singer, Inc, Pa, 62-67; historiographic methods consult, Arms Control & Disarmament Agency, Dept. of State, 63-67; methodology consult, Off. Naval. Intel, 63- U.S.M.C, 53-56, Sgt. Speech Commun. Asn; Am. Hist. Soc; Operations Res. Soc. Am; Speech Asn. East. States; Eng. Hist. Soc. Jurisprudence. Publ: Develop a methodology to detect. . . violations of disarmament treaties, 64 & Historical analysis of arms control treaties, 65, Dept. of State; Systematic naval intelligence using the HORIZON system, HRB-Singer, 66; Thine is the kingdom: the trial of Thomas Wentworth, Earl of Strafford, Univ. Ala, 74; Karosserie Glaeser: builders of the classic era, J. Transportation Hist, 65. Add: College of Communication, Ohio University, Athens, OH 45701.

TINDALL, SAMUEL JONES, JR, b. Columbia, S.C, May 22, 37; m. 60; c. 3. ENGLISH. A.B, Columbia Col, 59; M.A, Univ. S.C, 66, Woodrow Wilson fel. & Ph.D.(Eng), 69. ASST. PROF. ENG, DUQUESNE UNIV, 69- U.S.N, 59-64, Lt. S.Atlantic Mod. Lang. Asn. Victorian literature. Add: Dept. of English, Duquesne University, Pittsburgh, PA 15219.

TINDALL, WILLIAM YORK, b. Williamstown, Vt, Mar. 7, 03; m. 37; c. 1. ENGLISH LITERATURE. A.B, Columbia Univ, 25, A.M, 26, Cutting traveling fel, 32-33, Ph.D, 34; LL.D, Iona Col, 68. Instr, N.Y. Univ, 26-31; ENG, COLUMBIA UNIV, 31-37, asst. prof, 37-45, assoc. prof, 45-50, prof, 50-71, EMER. PROF, 71- Guggenheim fel, 54. Eng. Inst; MLA. Publ: The literary symbol, Columbia, 55; Forces in modern British literature, Vintage, 56; Reader's guide to James Joyce, Noonday, 59. Add: 25 Claremont Ave, New York, NY 10027.

TING, NAI-TUNG, b. Hangchow, China, Apr. 22, 15; U.S. citizen; m. 48. ENGLISH. B.A, Nat. Tsing Hua Univ, China, 36; M.A, Harvard, 38, Ph.D, 41. Prof. Eng, Hangchow Christian Col, China, 41-42; Nat. Honan Univ, 42-43; Nat. Cent. Univ, 43-50; Lingnam Univ, 51-52; U.S. Dept. State res. fel, Yale, 54-55; prof. ENG. & head dept, New Asia Col, Hong Kong, 55-56; asst. prof, Pan Am. Col, 57-59; assoc. prof, 59-66; WEST ILL. UNIV, 66-69, PROF, 69- Sr. lectr, Chinese Univ. Hong Kong, 64; Am. Counc. Learned Soc. grant-in-aid, 64; assoc. prof, Wis. State Univ, Eau Claire, 65. Int. Soc. Folk Narrative Res; Am. Folklore Soc. Comparative folk narrative research; English Renaissance and English Romantic poetry. Publ: AT type 301 in China and some countries adjacent to China: a study of a regional group and its significance in world tradition, Fabula, 70; Laotzu, semanticist and poet, Lit. East & West, 6/70; Chinese weather proverbs, Proverbium, 72; plus others. Add: 10 Woodland Lane, Macomb, IL 61455.

TINKLER, JOHN DOUGLAS, b. Brighton, Tenn, Sept. 26, 33; m. 56; c. 2. ENGLISH, PHILOLOGY. B.A, Vanderbilt Univ, 55; M.A, Univ. Fla, 57; Univ. Mich, summer 59; Ph.D.(Eng. & philol), Stanford Univ, 64. Instr. ENG, Univ. Tenn, 61-64, asst. prof, 64-67; assoc. prof, UNIV. TENN, CHATTANOOGA, 67-72, PROF, 72- Southeast. Mod. Lang. Asn; Southeast. Renaissance Conf. Old English vocabulary; Elizabethan English; modern English grammar and vocabulary. Publ: Old English words in Rohan, Tolkien and the critics, 68; Vocabulary and syntax of the Old English version in the Paris Psalter, Mouton, 71. Add: Dept. of English, University of Tennessee, Chattanooga, TN 37401.

TINSLEY, JAMES R, b. Nanticoke, Pa, Nov. 19, 29; m. 51. ENGLISH. A.B, Wilkes Col, 51, M.A, Univ. Pa, 56, Ph.D.(Eng), 62. Instr. ENG, Fenn Col, 58-59; asst. prof, State Univ. N.Y. Col. New Paltz, 60-63; St. John's Univ.(N.Y), 63-65; State Univ. N.Y. Col. Cortland, 65-67; ASSOC. PROF, NORTHEAST. ILL. STATE COL, 67- Sig.C, U.S.A, 51-54, Sgt. MLA. Modern American drama and poetry. Publ: A middle class comedy of manners, Satire Newsletter, fall 67. Add: Dept. of English, Northeastern Illinois State College, Bryn Mawr at St. Louis, Chicago, IL 60625.

TINTERA, JAMES, b. Cicero, Ill, Jan. 24, 24; m. 47; c. 2. SPEECH, MASS COMMUNICATIONS. B.S, Northwest. Univ, 47, M.A, 48; Ed.D, Mich. State Univ, 55. Instr. speech, Mich. State Univ, 49-51, prog. mgr. WKAR-TV, 51-53, instr. educ. admin, 53-56, asst. prof, 56-59, assoc. prof. educ, 59-62; PROF. SPEECH, WAYNE STATE UNIV, 62- Ford Found. Fund adult educ. stud. grant, 53; consult. educ. TV, Asn. Col. Teacher Educ, 55; workshops, Kans. State Teachers Col. & Fla. Agr. & Mech. Univ, 55-56; Nat. Asn. Educ. Broadcasters res. grant, 58-59, prog. award, 59-60; chief invest, NDEA Title VII grant, 59-63; dir, State of Mich. Educ. TV Stud, 60-61. U.S.A, 43-46, 1st Lt. Speech Commun. Asn; Am. Educ. Res. Asn; Asn. Prof. Broadcasting Educ. Programmed learning; evaluation and use of learning resources in colleges and universities. Publ: Instructor in Michigan, Off. Pub. Instr, Lansing, Mich, 61; Use of mass media in teacher training, U.S. Off. Educ, Wash, D.C, 63; Studies in mass communication education, Wayne State Univ, 63. Add: Center for Instructional Technology, Wayne State University, 5035 Woodward, Detroit, MI 48202.

TISCHLER, NANCY MARIE, b. DeQueen, Ark, Mar. 20, 31; m. 58. LITERATURE. B.S, Wilson Teachers Col, 52; Fulbright scholar, Univ. Col. South West, Exeter, Eng, 52-53; M.A, Univ. Ark, 54, Ph.D, 57. Asst, Univ. Ark, 53-56; asst. prof. Eng, George Washington Univ, 56-62, assoc. prof, Susquehanna Univ, 62-66, PROF. HUMANITIES & CHMN. PROG, PA. STATE UNIV, CAPITOL CAMPUS, 66- MLA; Conf. Christianity & Lit.(pres, 70-72). Drama; modern novel; Southern literature. Publ: Tennessee Williams: rebellious puritan, Citadel, 61; Black masks: Negro characters in modern Southern fiction, Pa. State Univ, 68; Negro literature and classic form, Contemporary Lit, summer 69; William Faulkner and the Southern Negro, In: Bear, man and God, 2nd ed, 71; The distorted mirror, Tennesee Williams' self-portraits, Miss. Quart, fall 72. Add: Humanities Program, Pennsylvania State University, Capitol Campus, Middletown, PA 17057.

TISDALE, ROBERT GEORGE, b. Caldwell, N.J, Oct. 4, 34; m. 57; c. 3. ENGLISH. A.B, Princeton, 56, M.A.T, Wesleyan Univ, 58; M.A, Yale, 63, Ph.D.(Eng), 68. Instr. ENG, Dartmouth Col, 63-66; asst. prof, CARLETON COL, 66-70, ASSOC. PROF, 70-, ASSOC. DEAN COL, 73- Eng. Inst. American literature; modern poetry, especially Wallace Stevens. Add: Dept. of English, Carleton College, Northfield, MN 55057.

TISON, JOHN LAURENS, JR, b. Cedartown, Ga, Aug. 24, 14; m. 45; c. 1. ENGLISH. A.B, Univ. of the South, 34; M.A, Syracuse Univ, 36; Ph.D, Univ. N.C, 53. Instr. ENG, UNIV. GA, 37-43, asst. prof, 46-59, ASSOC. PROF, 59- U.S.N, 43-46, Lt.(jg). Renaissance; Shakespeare. Publ: Shakespeare's Consolatio for exile, Mod. Lang. Quart, 60. Add: Dept. of English, University of Georgia, Athens, GA 30601.

TITUS, CATHERINE FONTELLE, b. Lexington, Mo, Dec. 13, 09. ENGLISH. A.B, Cent. Methodist Col, 31; Univ. Wis, summer 37, 38; Univ. Kansas City, 46-47; M.A, Univ. Mo, 50, Ph.D.(Eng), 55. Teacher, High Sch, Mo, 31-43, 46-47; ENG, Trenton Jr. Col, 47-52; asst, Univ. Mo, 52-55; asst. prof, CENT. MO. STATE UNIV, 55-58, assoc. prof, 58-63; PROF, 63-, HEAD DEPT, 72-, dir. honors prog, 58-69. W.A.C, 43-46, 1st Lt. NEA; NCTE; Nat. Col. Honor Counc. Realism in Howells; Margaret Fuller and American criticism. Publ: Co-auth, Readings 10-20, Wadsworth, 67. Add: Dept. of English, Central Missouri State University, Warrensburg, MO 64093.

TITUS, WARREN IRVING, b. Deposit, N.Y, July 17, 21; m. 53; c. 3. ENGLISH, AMERICAN STUDIES. B.M, Rollins Col, 43; M.A, Columbia Univ, 47; Penfield fel, N.Y. Univ, 53-55, Ph.D.(Am. civilization), 57. Instr. music, Cranford High Sch, N.J, 48-49; instr. ENG, GEORGE PEABODY COL, 49-53, 54-56, asst. prof, 56-59, assoc. prof, 59-64, PROF, 64- Adv. folklore, annual bibliog. articles in Am. stud, Am. Quart, 62-; Am. Philos. Soc. grant, 64; Fulbright grant, 66. U.S.A, 43-46. Am. Stud. Asn; S.Atlantic Mod. Lang. Asn; Col. Eng. Asn. The American political novel; biographies of Charles Dudley Warner and Edgar Lee Masters; American literary realism, 1870-1910. Publ: Winston Churchill, 63 & John Fox, Jr, 71, Twayne; The progressivism of the muckrakers: a myth re-examined through fiction, J. Cent. Miss. Valley Am. Stud. Asn, spring 60. Add: Dept. of English, George Peabody College, Nashville, TN 37203.

TJOSSEM, HERBERT KARL, b. Marshalltown, Iowa, Mar. 14, 23; m. 50; c. 5. ENGLISH. B.A, Univ. Minn, 42; M.A, Univ. Chicago, 45; Fulbright fel, Univ. Heidelberg, 53-54; Ph.D, Yale, 56. Instr. ENG, Yale, 46-47; Iowa State Teachers Col, 48-51; LAWRENCE UNIV, 55-60, asst. prof, 60-63, assoc. prof, 63-71, PROF, 71- Am. Counc. Learned Soc. grant, 62. MLA; Midwest Mod. Lang. Asn; NCTE. Middle English language and literature; history of the English language. Publ: Co-auth, Themes and research papers, Macmillan, 62. Add: Dept. of English, Lawrence University, Appleton, WI 54910.

TOBIAS, RICHARD CLARK, b. Xenia, Ohio, Oct. 10, 25; m. 49; c. 3. ENGLISH. B.Sc, Ohio State Univ, 48, M.A, 51, Ph.D, 57. Instr. ENG, Univ. Colo, 51-55; asst, Ohio State Univ, 55-57; instr, UNIV. PITTSBURGH, 57-59, asst. prof, 59-65, assoc. prof, 65-69, PROF, 69- Regional assoc, Am. Counc. Learned Soc, 61-63; C.E. Merrill fel. humanities, summer 62. U.S.A, 44-46. MLA; AAUP. Victorian and Romantic literature; theory of comedy. Publ: The art of James Thurber, Ohio Univ, 69; Tennyson's Painted shell, Victorian Newslett, 71; Year's work in Victorian poetry, Victorian Poetry, 72; contrib, Victorian bibliography for 1972, Victorian Stud, 73; plus others. Add: 5846 Darlington Rd, Pittsburgh, PA 15217.

TOBIN, TERENCE A, b. Chicago, Ill, Sept. 24, 38. ENGLISH, DRAMA. B.A, Pine Hills Col, 61; M.A, Loyola Univ.(Ill), 64, Ph.D.(Eng), 67. Asst. prof. ENG, Purdue Univ, Calumet Campus, 66-71, XL grant, 68; ASSOC. PROF, CITY COLS. CHICAGO, 71- Music & drama critic, Gary Post Tribune, 67-; Am. Philos. Soc. grants, 69 & 73. MLA. Scottish theater and drama; restoration and 18th century British literature; American humor 1880-1920. Publ: Ed, The assembly, 72 & ed, George Ade's letters, 73, Purdue Univ; auth, Plays by Scots, 1660-1800, Univ. Iowa, 74; The beginning of theater in Scotland, Theatre Surv, 5/66; Popular entertainment in 17th century Scotland, Theatre Notebook, 12/68; School plays in 17th century Scotland, Seventeenth Century News, 1/69. Add: 508 Napoleon St, Valparaiso, IN 46383.

TODD, CARL E, b. Fairfax, S.C, Oct. 17, 20; m. 46; c. 3. ENGLISH EDUCATION, EDUCATIONAL ADMINISTRATION. B.S, Clemson Univ, 42; M.A, George Peabody Col, 47, M.Ed, 51; Ed.D.(educ. admin. & Eng. educ), Univ. Ala, 65. Asst. prof. Eng, Cumberland Univ, 47-50; registr, Howard Col, 51-56; asst. prof. commun, Air Univ, 56-57; acad. dean, Va. Intermont Col, 57-65; head dept. Eng. & dean grad. sch, Ouachita Baptist Univ, 65-67; PROF. EDUC. ADMIN. & ENG. EDUC. & ASST. DEAN, UNIV. S.ALA, 67- U.S.A, 42-46; U.S.A.F.R, 46-72, Col.(Ret). NCTE; Nat. Educ. Asn; MLA. American literature; educational administration. Publ: Ed, Southwestern University, 73; auth, The English programs and staffs of thirty-one Baptist colleges, South. Baptist Educator, 3/52; Why students leave college, Ala. Sch. J, 4/56. Add: 2304 Burma Hills Dr, Mobile, AL 36609.

TODD, DONALD, b. Denver, Colo, Nov. 18, 28. DRAMA. B.A, Univ. Denver, 48, M.A, 51, summers, 52, 59 & 60, 68-69; summer, La. State Univ, 64. Instr. speech & drama, Spelman Col, 48-50; instr, Lincoln Univ.(Mo); 51-52; asst. prof. Eng, speech & drama, Wiley Col, 52-53; instr. drama, Emily Griffith Opportunity Sch, Denver, Colo, 53-54; asst. prof. Eng, speech & drama & dramatic dir, Wiley Col, 54-58; asst. prof. Eng, speech & drama, South. Univ, 58-64; DIR, OPEN DOOR THEATRE, 68-; INSTR. DRAMA, UNIV. COLO, DENVER, 69- Summer instr, Atlanta Univ, 49-50; dir, Lowry AFB Playhouse, 53-54; dir. community theatres, Points East Theatre, Denver, 66-67; summer drama dir, Model City Resident Cult. Ctr, 70; Fort Carson Army Base, 71; instr, Community Col. Denver, Auraria Campus, 70; Univ. Colo, Boulder, 71; Metrop. State Col, 72; consult, Colo. Counc. Arts & Humanities, 72- Larry Tajiri Mem. Award, Denver Post, 69. Asn. Stud. Afro-Am. Life & Hist; Am. Theatre Asn; Nat. Asn. Speech & Dramatic Arts; Speech Commun. Asn. Speech; drama. Add: 2534 Humboldt, Denver, CO 80205.

TODD, EDGELEY WOODMAN, b. Deerfield, Ill, Jan. 26, 14; div; c. 2. ENGLISH. B.A, Lake Forest Col, 37; M.A, Northwest. Univ, 39, Ph.D.(Eng), 52. Instr. ENG, Ill. Inst. Technol, 41-43; Northwest. Univ, 43-46; Univ. Colo, 46-51; asst. prof, Cent. Wash. Col. Educ, 52-54; assoc. prof, COLO. STATE UNIV, 54-60, PROF, 60- Huntington Libr. res. fel, summers 53, 54 & 55. American literature; American West in literature; Western history. Publ: Listeners guide to musical form, W.C. Brown, 49; ed, Adventures of Captain Bonneville, 61 & Astoria, 64, Univ. Okla. & A doctor on the California trail: the diary of Dr. John H. Wayman, Old West Publ, 71; auth, Benjamin L.E. Bonneville, In: The mountain men and the fur trade of the far West, Vol. 5, Arthur Clark, 68; plus others. Add: Dept. of English, Colorado State University, Ft. Collins, CO 80521.

TODD, HAL J, b. Denver, Colo, Jan. 18, 23; m. 54. DRAMA. B.S, Univ. Colo, 45; M.A, Stanford Univ, 50; Hotelling fel. & Ph.D.(theatre), Univ. Denver, 55. From teacher to asst. prof, San Francisco State Col, 52-53; dir, Idaho State Univ, 54-60; vis. prof, Carnegie Inst. Technol, 60-61; asst. prof, Northwest. Univ, 61-62; dir, actor & writer TV, Universal Studios, Hollywood, 62-64; PROF. DRAMA & CHMN. DEPT, SAN JOSE STATE UNIV, 64- Designer theatre, Univ. Mont, summer 50; dir. & actor, Porterville Barn Theatre, 50-52; var. Shakespeare festivals & theatres in the U.S; dir. theatre tour, U.S. Dept. State, New Zealand, 59; Ford Found-New Dramatists dir-observer grant, 59; dir. plays, United Serv. Orgn. tours, 59 & 68; dir, writer & actor, It's a man's world, My three sons, Fugitive, Sundays in New York, Revue Studios, 62-63; v.pres, Regional Theatre Conf, 66-; founding mem. San Francisco Actor's Workshop; prof. dir, Pittsburgh Playhouse, 67-68, Seattle Repertory Theatre, 67-68. Civil Eng.C, U.S.N, 42-46, Lt.(jg). Rocky Mountain Theatre Conf.(pres, 58-59); Am. Theatre Asn.(dir, 59-61); Northwest Drama Conf.(dir, 65). Children's Theatre Conf. Publ: Profile staging, Players, 57. Add: Dept. of Drama, San Jose State University, San Jose, CA 95030.

TODD, HOLLIS BAILEY, b. Amory, Miss, Aug. 28, 17. SPEECH, BIBLE. A.B, Miss. Col, 40; B.D, New Orleans Baptist Theol. Sem, 45; A.M, La. State Univ, 49, Ph.D, 65; Univ. South. Calif, 50. Pastor, First Baptist Church, Golden Meadow, La, 42-45; assoc. pastor, Istrouma Baptist Church, Baton Rouge, 45-47; assoc. prof, Ouachita Col, 47-49; from assoc. prof. to PROF. SPEECH, MISS. COL, 49-, HEAD DEPT, 65- Acting pastor, Immanuel Baptist Church, Vicksburg, Miss, 50- South. Speech Commun. Asn. Theory and practice of John A. Broadus. Add: Dept. of Speech, Mississippi College, Clinton, MS 39058.

TODD, JANET M, b. Llandrindod-Wells, Wales, Sept. 10, 42; m. 66; c. 2. ENGLISH LITERATURE, WOMEN'S STUDIES. B.A, Cambridge, 64, M.A, 68; dipl. Eng. second lang, Univ. Leeds, 68; Ph.D.(Eng), Univ. Fla, 71. Teacher ENG, Mfantsipim Sch, Ghana, 64-65; asst. lectr, Univ. Cape Coast, 65-66; ASST. PROF, UNIV. P.R, MAYAGÜEZ, 72- Ed. & founder, Mary Wollstonecraft Newslett, 72- MLA; Women's Caucus Mod. Lang. Romantic poetry; women writers of the late 18th century. Publ: In Adam's garden: a study of John Clare's pre-asylum poetry, Univ. Fla, 73; Parallelism in structure and lexis in Little Dorrit, Atenea, 9-12/72; Language of sex in A vindication of the rights of woman, Mary Wollstonecraft Newslett, 4/73; Very copys of nature: John Clare's descriptive poetry, Philol. Quart, 1/74. Add: Dept. of English, University of Puerto Rico, Mayagüez, PR 00708.

TODD, JOHN EMERSON, b. Wilkes-Barre, Pa, Nov. 24, 30. ENGLISH. B.A, Oberlin Col, 53; M.A, Columbia Univ, 54; Alumni Res. Found. fel, Univ. Wis, 64-65, Ph.D.(Eng), 65. ASST. PROF. ENG, Univ. Mich, Ann Arbor, 65-72; BARUCH COL, 72- MLA (bibliographer, 67-); NCTE. American literature; Shakespeare. Publ: Emily Dickinson's use of the persona, Mouton, 73; Emily Dickinson's use of the persona in her love poetry, Mich. Acad. Papers, 68. Add: Dept. of English, Baruch College, 17 Lexington Ave, New York, NY 10010.

TODD, JULIA McAMIS, b. Port Gibson, Miss, Aug. 5, 18. SPEECH. A.B, Miss. Col, 40; New Orleans Baptist Theol. Sem, 43-45; A.M, La. State Univ, 49; Univ. South. Calif, 50. Assoc. prof, Ouachita Col, 47-49; SPEECH & ART, MISS. COL, 49-72, PROF, 72- South. Speech Commun. Asn. Costuming for the New Testament period. Add: Dept. of Speech, Mississippi College, Clinton, MS 39056.

TODD, WALDEMAR DWIGHT, b. Chelsea, Okla, May 25, 05. COMPARATIVE LITERATURE. B.S. & M.S, Univ. Va, 31; Ph.D, Columbia Univ, 51. Tutor Eng, École Normale, Rouen, France, 31-32; chmn. dept, North. Okla. Jr. Col, 35-40; asst. prof. COMP. LIT, Wash. & Lee Univ, 46-49; PROF, STATE UNIV. N.Y. MARITIME COL, 51-, CHMN. DEPT. HUMANITIES, 73- U.S.N.R, Lt. Comdr. Art; music. Add: Dept. of Humanities, State University of New York Maritime College at Ft. Schuyler, New York, NY 10465.

TODD, WILLIAM BURTON, b. Chester, Pa, Apr. 11, 19; m. 42; c. 4. ENGLISH LITERATURE. B.A, Lehigh Univ, 40, fels, 40-41, 45-47, M.A, 47; Ph.D, Univ. Chicago, 49. Prof. Eng. & Am. lit. & chmn. dept. Salem Col. (N.C), 49-54; asst. librn. bibliog, Houghton Libr, Harvard, 55-58; assoc. prof. ENG. LIT. & BIBLIOG, UNIV. TEX, 58-59, PROF, 60- Fulbright res. fel, U K, 52-53; lectr. bks. & bibliog, Univ. Kans, 55; Harvard Found. grant, 57-58; Am. Counc. Learned Soc. fel, 61-62; Guggenheim fel, 65-66; J.P.R. Lyell reader in bibliog, Oxford, 69-70; vis. fel, All Souls Col, Oxford, 70; consult, Nat. Libr. Australia, Canberra, 73; D. Nichol Smith lectr, Australian Nat. Univ, 73. U.S.A, 41-45, Maj. MLA; Bibliog. Soc, London; Bibliog. Soc. Am.(ed, Papers, 67-); Int. Asn. Univ. Prof. Eng; Grolier Club; Eng. Inst. English literature and bibliography of the 18th and 19th centuries. Publ: New adventures among old books, Univ. Kans, 58; Burke's reflections on the Revolution, Rinehart, 59; Thomas J. Wise centenary studies, 59, Guy of Warwick, 68 & Suppressed commentaries on the Wiseian forgeries, 69, Univ. Tex; Bibliography of Burke, R. Hart-Davis, London, 64; Directory of printers, London & vicinity, 1800-1840, Printing Hist. Soc, London, 72. Add: Dept. of English, University of Texas, Austin, TX 78712.

TOELKEN, JOHN BARRE, b. Ware, Mass, June 15, 35; m. 57; c. 5. MEDIEVAL LITERATURE. B.S, Utah State Univ, 58; fel, Wash. State Univ, 57-59, M.A, 59; Ph.D.(medieval lit), Univ. Ore, 64. Instr. ENG, Wash. State Univ, 59-60; Univ. Ore, 60-64; Univ. Utah, 64-65, asst. prof. & asst. chmn. dept, 65-66; asst. prof, UNIV. ORE, 66-69, assoc. prof, 69-73, PROF, 73- Ed, Ore. Folklore Bull, 60-; Northwest Folklore, 63-; summer lectr, Portland State Col, 62; Reed Col, 63; assoc. dir. NDEA summer Eng. Inst. Univ. Utah, 65; vis. asst. prof, Univ. Calif, Los Angeles, summer 66; Univ. Mass, summer 68; cur, Randall V. Mills Mem. Arch. Northwest Folklore, 70- Ersted Award for Distinguished Teaching, Univ. Ore, 70; E. Harris Harbison Award for Gifted Teaching, Danforth Found, 71; Danforth Assoc. Award, 73. Am. Folklore Soc.(ed, J. Am. Folklore, 73-78); Int. Soc. Ethnol. & Folklore; Philol. Asn. Pac. Coast. Folklore, especially traditional ballad; native American literature and religion, especially Navaho. Publ: Riddles wisely expounded, West. Folklore, 66; Toward an oral canon for the child ballads, J. Folklore Inst, 67; The folklore of academe, In: The study of American folklore, Norton, 68; plus others. Add: Dept. of English, University of Oregon, Eugene, OR 97403.

TOEPFER, RAYMOND GRANT, b. Hays, Kans, Feb. 26, 23; m. 46; c. 2. ENGLISH. B.A, Univ. Wis, 42, M.A, 43; Ph.D.(Eng. lit), City Univ. New York, 71. Copy ed, Grolier Encycl, 46-47; asst. mgr, Defi Manufacturing Co, New York, 47-63; LECTR. ENG, BROOKLYN COL, 64-72, ASST. PROF, 72-; FREE LANCE WRITER & NOVELIST, 46- A.U.S, 43-46. Victorian era in English literature; Civil War period in American history; 20th century American fiction. Publ: The scarlet guidon, Coward, 58; The witness, F. Muller, 66; The white cockade, 66, The second face of valor, 66, Liberty and Corporal Kincaid, 68 & The beat of a distant drum, 69, Chilton. Add: Dept. of English, Brooklyn College, Bedford Ave, & Ave. H, Brooklyn, NY 11210.

TOLER, COLETTE, S.C, b. Pittsburgh, Pa. ENGLISH. B.Mus, Seton Hill Col, 57; M.A, Univ. Notre Dame, 62, Schmidt fel, 64, Ph.D.(Eng), 65. From asst. prof. to PROF. ENG, SETON HILL COL, 65-, ACAD. DEAN, 72- Vis. prof, Col. Mt. St. Vincent, 68-69. MLA. Art and civilization in the fiction of Willa Cather; existential fiction; the art film as an art form. Publ: Willa Cather's vision of the artist, Personalist, autumn 64; Look on-make no sound, Notre Dame Eng. J, fall 64; A matter of optics, Ave Maria, 9/65. Add: Dept. of English, Seton Hill College, Greensburg, PA 15601.

TOLIVER, HAROLD EARL, b. McMinnville, Ore, Feb. 16, 32; m. 54; c. 2. ENGLISH & AMERICAN LITERATURE. B.A, Univ. Ore, 54; M.A, Johns Hopkins Univ, 58; Ph.D.(lit), Univ. Wash, 61. Asst. prof. LIT, Ohio State Univ, 61-64; Univ. Calif, Los Angeles, 65-66; from assoc. prof. to PROF, UNIV. CALIF, IRVINE, 66- Guggenheim fel, 64-65. U.S.A, 54-56. MLA; AAUP. Renaissance; pastoral literature; fiction. Publ: Marvell's ironic vision, Yale, 65; co-ed, Forms of poetry, 68-72 & Essays in Shakespearean criticism, 70, Prentice-Hall; co-ed, Perspectives on poetry, Perspectives on fiction, Perspectives on drama, Oxford, 68; auth, Pastoral forms and attitudes, Calif. Univ, 71; Animate illusions, Nebr. Univ, 73. Add: Dept. of English & Comparative Literature, University of California, Irvine, CA 92664.

TOLLESON, FLOYD CLYDE, JR, b. Stroud, Okla, Mar. 14, 15; m; c. 1. ENGLISH. B.A, Univ. Wash, 36, M.A, 48, Ph.D.(Eng), 55. Teacher, high sch, Wash, 39-48, 51-52; instr. Eng, Wash. State Col, 48-51; assoc. Eng, Univ. Wash, 52-55; assoc. prof. ENG, Univ. Idaho, 55-69, head dept. humanities, 65-68; PROF. & CHMN. DEPT, CARTHAGE COL, 69- Consult. curriculum guide, Idaho State Dept. Educ, 67; humanities, Boise Pub. Schs, 67; vis. prof, Lewis-Clark Normal Sch, 68-69. U.S.A, 44-46. MLA; Midwest. Mod. Lang. Asn; NCTE. Victorian literature; Browning. Add: Dept. of English, Carthage College, Kenosha, WI 53140.

TOMAN, GEORGE EDWARD, b. Virginia, Minn, Feb. 22, 12; m. 43; c. 1. ENGLISH, PHILOSOPHY. B.A, St. John's Univ, 36; M.A, Univ. Minn, 49; Harvard, summer 53. Instr. ENG, COL. ST. THOMAS, 46-49, asst. prof, 50-57, ASSOC. PROF, 57- Mem, Comt. Analysis Prose Style, NCTE, 46-65. U.S.N, 42-46, Lt.(jg). MLA; Col. Conf. Compos. & Commun; NCTE. Eighteenth century; rhetorical theory; modern philosophy. Add: Dept. of English, College of St. Thomas, St. Paul, MN 55101.

TOMARKEN, EDWARD LEE, b. Olean, N.Y, Dec. 26, 38; m. 66; c. 1. ENGLISH. B.A, Univ. Calif, Los Angeles, 60; Can. Counc. fel, Univ. Toronto, 65-66, Ph.D.(Eng), 69. Instr. ENG, Princeton, 66-68; lectr, CITY COL. NEW YORK, 68-70, ASST. PROF, 70- MLA. Eighteenth century English and comparative literature; literary criticism. Add: Dept. of English, City College of New York, Convent Ave. & 138th St, New York, NY 10031.

TOMPKINS, KENNETH D, b. Corning, N.Y, Oct. 14, 34; m. 56; c. 4. ENGLISH. B.A, Univ. Rochester, 60; M.A, Ind. Univ, 66, Ph.D.(Eng), 67. Asst. prof. ENG, Millikin Univ, 65-68; chmn. dept, Cent. Col.(Iowa), 68-70; dean exp. stud, STOCKTON STATE COL, 70-73, PROF. LIT, 74- MLA. Chaucerian studies; Tudor drama. Add: Dept. of English, Stockton State College, Pomona, NJ 08204.

TONKIN, HUMPHREY RICHARD, b. Truro, Eng, Dec. 2, 39; m. 68. ENGLISH, INTERLINGUISTICS. B.A, Cambridge, 62, M.A, 66; A.M. & Ph.D.(Eng), Harvard, 66. Asst. prof. Eng, UNIV. PA, 66-71, ASSOC. PROF. ENG. & V.PROVOST UNDERGRAD. STUD, 71- Am. Comp. Lit. Asn; MLA; Milton Soc. Am; Renaissance Soc. Am; Am. Counc. Teaching For. Lang. Spenser and Renaissance literature; Esperanto and international language problems; English local history, especially the history of Cornwall. Publ: A Research bibliography on Esperanto and international language problems, JEN, New York, 67; Spenser's courteous pastoral, Clarendon, 72; ed, Elizabethan bibliographies supplements: Sir Walter Ralegh, Nether, London, 72; Spenser's Garden of Adonis and Britomart's Quest, PMLA, 73; Some notes on myth and allegory in the Faerie queene, Mod. Philol, 73; Theme and emblem in Spenser's Faerie queene, Eng. Lit. Hist, 73. Add: Office of Vice Provost for Undergraduate Studies, University of Pennsylvania, Philadelphia, PA 19174.

TOOKEY, MARY D. WEBBER, b. Lincoln, Nebr, July 15, 29; m. 50; c. 4. ENGLISH. B.A, Univ. Nebr-Lincoln, 50; M.A, Bradley Univ, 65. ASST. PROF. ENG, EUREKA COL, 65- NCTE; AAUP. Publ: Apology (poem), World Call, 11/67; Father's occupations as related to GRE aptitude test scores of Eureka College students, Ill. Sch. Res, 5/68; To a newborn child (poem), Maj. Poets, fall 72; plus others. Add: Humanities Div, Eureka College, Eureka, IL 61530.

TOOLE, WILLIAM BELL, III, b. Augusta, Ga, Sept. 23, 30; m. 55; c. 2. ENGLISH. B.A, Presby. Col, 54; Carnegie Found. scholar. & M.A, Vanderbilt Univ, 55, South. Fel, 58-60, Ph.D.(Eng), 63. Instr. ENG, Presby. Col, 55-56, asst. prof, 56-58; instr, Vanderbilt Univ, 60-63; asst. prof, N.C. STATE UNIV, 63-66; assoc. prof, 66-71, PROF, 71-, ASSOC. DEAN, SCH. LIB. ARTS, 72-, asst. dean, 71-72. U.S.A, 48-49. Shakespeare Asn. Am; MLA; Southeast Renaissance Conf; S.Atlantic Mod. Lang. Asn. Mediaeval, Renaissance and modern English. Publ: Shakespeare's problem plays: studies in form and meaning, Mouton, 66; The attractions of the journey: a comment on the structure of Paradise lost, Arlington Quart, 6/68; Chaucer's Christian irony: the relationship of character and action in The pardoner's tale, Chaucer Rev, summer 68; The collision of action and character in Titus Andronicus: a failure in dramatic strategy, In: Renaissance papers 1971, Southeast. Renaissance Conf, 72. Add: Dept. of English, North Carolina State University, Raleigh, NC 27607.

TOOR, DAVID, b. Brooklyn, N.Y, June 18, 34; m. 58; c. 2. ENGLISH. B.A, Brooklyn Col, 56; M.A, N.Y. Univ, 57; Ph.D.(Eng), Univ. Ore, 65. Lectr. ENG, Brooklyn Col, 57-59; instr, Pa. State Univ, 59-62; Univ. Ore, 63-65; ASSOC. PROF, STATE UNIV. N.Y. COL. CORTLAND, 65- Tech. consult, N.Y. State Counc. Arts, 68- MLA. English prose stylistics; Elizabethan and Jacobean literature; contemporary English and American literature. Publ: Narrative irony in Henry James'..., Univ. Rev, 12/67; Shakespeare's Richard II, Explicator, 11/72; Guilt and retribution in Fitzgerald's Babylon revisited, Fitzgerald-Hemingway Annual, 73. Add: Dept. of English, State University of New York College at Cortland, Cortland, NY 13045.

TORCHIANA, DONALD T, b. Philadelphia, Pa, Oct. 22, 23; div; c. 3. ENGLISH. B.A, DePauw Univ, 47; M.A, State Univ, Iowa, 49, Ph.D.(Eng), 53. Instr. ENG, State Univ. Iowa, 52-53; NORTHWEST. UNIV, 53-58, asst. prof, 58-63, assoc. prof, 63-67, PROF, 67- Fulbright lectr, Univ. Col, Galway, Ireland, 60-62 & 69-70; consult, Royal Irish Acad, 70-; chmn, Screening Bd. Int. Exchange of Persons, 72. U.S.A.A.F, 43-45. Irish Georgian Soc; MLA; Am. Soc. 18th Century Stud; Am. Comt. Irish Stud. Eighteenth century and modern literature. Publ: W.B. Yeats and Georgian Ireland, Northwest. Univ. & Oxford, 66; plus others. Add: 1220 Hinman Ave, Evanston, IL 60202.

TORCZON, VERNON JAMES, b. Columbus, Nebr, July 1, 32; m. 55; c. 5. ENGLISH. A.B, Creighton Univ, 54; M.A, Univ. Nebr, 58, Ph.D.(Eng), 60. Instr. ENG, Ohio State Univ, 60-63, asst. prof, UNIV. NEW ORLEANS, 63-66, ASSOC. PROF, 66- Fel, Southeast. Inst. Medieval & Renaissance Stud, summer 66. Mil.Intel, U.S.A, 54-56, 1st Lt. MLA; Renaissance Soc. Am; Mod. Humanities Res. Asn. Spenser; Shakespeare; Elizabethan poetics. Publ: Spenser's orgoglio and despaire, Tex. Stud. Lit. & Lang, spring 61; Paperback editions of Hamlet: the limits of editorial eclecticism, Col. Eng, 4/67. Add: Dept. of English, University of New Orleans, New Orleans, LA 70122.

TORRENCE, DONALD L, b. Sparta, Ill, Oct. 19, 26; m. 51; c. 2. SPEECH. B.A, Univ. Ill, 48, M.A, 51, Ph.D, 57. Instr. speech & Eng, Wesleyan Univ, 55-58; ASSOC. PROF, SPEECH, KNOX COL, 58- U.S.N, 44-46, 52-53, Lt. (jg). Speech Commun Asn. Rhetorical theory; communication. Publ: A philosophy for rhetoric from Bertrand Russell, Quart. J. Speech, 4/59. Add: Dept. of Speech, Knox College, Galesburg, IL 61401.

TORSEY, KATHLEEN E, b. Lewiston, Maine, Oct. 15, 14. SPEECH. A.B, Bates Col, 36; M.S.O, Curry Col, 40; Ed.M, Boston Univ, 56; Ph.D.(speech), Univ. Fla, 64. Teacher, high schs, Maine, 36-42; high schs, R.I, 42-46; chmn. dept. speech & theatre, Colby Jr. Col, 46-66; ASSOC. PROF. SPEECH COMMUN, UNIV. GA, 66- Speech Commun. Asn; South. Speech Commun. Asn. Voice science; education. Add: Dept. of Speech Communication, G.G.S. Bldg, University of Georgia, Athens, GA 30601.

TORTORIELLO, THOMAS ROSS, b. Springfield, Mass, July 25, 41; m. 73. RHETORIC, PUBLIC ADDRESS. B.A, Curry Col, 65; M.S, Emerson Col, 67; Ph.D.(commun. theory), Ohio State Univ, Columbus, 70; Boston Univ, 70-71. Asst. prof. speech commun, Emerson Col, 70-71; ASST. PROF. SPEECH COMMUN. & DIR. PERSUASION LAB, UNIV, DAYTON, 71- Consult, Columbus & Dayton Police Depts, Ohio, 72; Dayton Montgomery County Criminal Justice Ctr, 72-; Pub. Serv. Careers, Dept. Labor, 73; adv, Youth in Govt, 73- Speech Commun. Asn; Int. Commun. Asn. Program evaluation; business and organizational communication; judicial rhetoric. Publ: Co-auth, Community centered team policing, Dayton-Montgomery County Criminal Justice Ctr, 4/73 & Evaluating instructional films, J. Law Enforcement Educ. & Training, 4/73. Add: 2410 Verdi Ct, Dayton, OH 45449.

TOSCAN, RICHARD ERIC, b. New York, N.Y, July 1, 41. THEATRE HISTORY, CONTEMPORARY DRAMATIC LITERATURE. A.B, Purdue Univ, Lafayette, 63; Woodrow Wilson fel, Univ. Ill, Urbana, 63-64, univ. fel, 64, A.M, 65, Nat. Endowment for Humanities grant, 67-69, Ph.D.(theatre), 70. Asst. prof. theatre, Calif. State Univ, Fresno, 67-69, Eng, 69-70, dir. exp. col, 68-70; ASST. PROF. DRAMA & ASST. CHMN. DIV, UNIV. SOUTH. CALIF, 70- Am. Soc. Theatre Res; Am. Theatre Asn. American theatre history; 20th century dramatic literature and European theatre history. Publ: Low time (on the aisle), Drama & Theatre, spring 62; MacGowran on Beckett, Theatre Quart, 7-9/73; Contemporary theatre: running out of the sixties, Educ. Theatre News, 6/73. Add: Division of Drama, University of Southern California, Los Angeles, CA 90007.

TOSH, L. WAYNE, Computational Linguistics, Germanic Languages. See Volume III, Foreign Languages, Linguistics & Philology.

TOTH, SUSAN ERICKSON ALLEN, b. Ames, Iowa, June 24, 40; c. 1. ENGLISH & AMERICAN LITERATURE. B.A, Smith Col, 61; M.A, Univ. Calif, Berkeley, 63; Ph.D.(Eng), Univ. Minn, 69. Instr. ENG, San Francisco State Col, 63-64; ASST. PROF, MACALESTER COL, 69- Am. Stud. Asn; MLA. Local color and 1890s; women's studies; cross-disciplinary studies in geography and literature. Publ: Geography as art: local color American literature, Minn. Geogr, XXIII, 20-27; Mary Wilkins Freeman's parable of wasted life, Am. Lit, 1/71; The value of age in the fiction of Sarah Orne Jewett, Stud. Short Fiction, summer 71; plus others. Add: Dept. of English, Macalester College, St. Paul, MN 55105.

TOUSTER, EVA BEACH, b. Winston-Salem, N.C, Dec. 28, 14; m. 44; c. 1. ENGLISH. A.B, Murray State Col, 35; M.A, Univ. N.C, 44; Ph.D.(Eng), Vanderbilt Univ, 51. Spec. lectr. ENG, Vanderbilt Univ, 51; assoc. prof, GEORGE PEABODY COL, 64-70, PROF, 70-, CHMN. DEPT, 73- MLA. Anglo-Saxon poetry; literary theory and criticism. Publ: Metrical variations as a poetic device in Beowulf, Anglia; Thematic patterns in Lorca's Blood wedding, Mod. Drama, 64; Tradition and the academic talent, CEA Critic, 5/71; plus others. Add: Dept. of English, George Peabody College for Teachers, Nashville, TN 37203.

TOWERS, AUGUSTUS ROBERT, JR, b. Richmond, Va, Jan. 21, 23; m. 67; c. 1. ENGLISH. A.B, Princeton, 45, Proctor fel, 50-51, Ph.D.(Eng), 52. Instr. ENG, Princeton, 51-54; QUEENS COL.(N.Y), 54-61, asst. prof, 61-63, assoc. prof, 63-67, PROF, 68-, chmn. dept, 69-72, chmn. Pres. Comn. on Orgn. Queens Col, 72. U.S.A, 42-43. MLA; Eng. Inst. History and criticism of the novel; 18th century fiction; creative writing. Publ: The necklace of Kali, 60 & The monkey watcher, 64, Harcourt; Amelia and the state of matrimony, Rev. Eng. Stud; Stern's cock and bull story, ELH. Add: Dept. of English, Queens College, Flushing, NY 11367.

TOWERS, TOM HAMILTON, b. Eau Claire, Wis, Apr. 30, 32; m. 58; c. 3. AMERICAN LITERATURE. B.A, Univ. Chicago, 51; Idaho State Univ, 52-53; B.A, Univ. N.Mex, 58, M.A, 59; Ph.D.(Eng), Tulane Univ, 71. Instr. ENG, Purdue Univ, 61-68; asst. prof, Wis. State Univ-Whitewater, 68-71; ASSOC. PROF, UNIV. R.I, 71- U.S.A, 53-56. MLA; Popular Cult. Asn; AAUP; Am. Lit. Group, Mod. Lang. Asn. American literature, 1865-1914; American popular culture. Publ: The problem of determinism in Fredericks's first novel, Col. Eng, 65; Savagery and civilization: the moral dimensions of Howells's A boy's town, Am. Lit, 69; Twain's Connecticut yankee: the trouble in Camelot, In: Challenges in American culture, Bowling Green Univ, 70. Add: Dept. of English, University of Rhode Island, Providence, RI 02908.

TOWNE, FRANK McCONNELL, b. Fullerton, Calif, Jan. 8, 13; m. 39; c. 2. ENGLISH, HUMANITIES. A.B, Univ. Calif, 35; A.M, Univ. Calif, Los Angeles, 41, Ph.D.(Eng), 49. Instr. ENG, Athens Col, 36-40; teaching asst, Univ. Calif, Los Angeles, 40-41, instr, exten. div, 46-47; instr, WASH. STATE UNIV, 47-49, asst. prof, 49-52, assoc. prof, 52-59, PROF, 59-, CHMN. LIT. STUD, 73-, chmn. dept. Eng, 68-70. Vis. assoc. prof, Columbia Univ, 53-54; Fulbright lectr, Univs. Salonika, Greece, 57-58 & Athens, Greece, 58-59. U.S.A, 43-45. MLA. Literary criticism; comparative literature. Publ: Wyclif and Chaucer on the contemplative life, In: Essays critical and historical dedicated to Lily B. Campbell, Univ. Calif, 50; Logic, lyric and drama, Mod. Philol; The new criticism in France, Res. Stud, 3/67. Add: Dept. of English, Washington State University, Pullman, WA 99163.

TOWNE, RALPH L, JR, b. New York, N.Y, Aug. 18, 30. RHETORIC, PUBLIC ADDRESS. B.A, Lehigh Univ, 53; M.A, Northwest. Univ, 54; Ph.D.(rhetoric & pub. address), Mich. State Univ, 61. Instr. SPEECH, Univ. Dubuque, 54-55; asst. prof, Iowa State Univ, 55-62; from asst. prof. to ASSOC. PROF, TEMPLE UNIV, 62- Speech Commun. Asn. History of public address; rhetoric. Publ: Co-auth, Robert G. Ingersoll: a case study in free speech, Today's Speech, 11/62. Add: Dept. of Speech & Dramatic Arts, Temple University, Philadelphia, PA 19122.

TOWNS, JAMES EDWARD, b. Clovis, N.Mex. SPEECH EDUCATION, PUBLIC ADDRESS. B.A, Hardin-Simmons Univ, 65; M.A, South. Ill. Univ, Carbondale, 66, NDEA fel, 68-70, Ph.D.(speech), 70. Instr. speech, STEPHEN F. AUSTIN STATE UNIV, 66-68, ASST. PROF. COMMUN, 70- Speech Commun. Asn; South. Speech Commun. Asn. The basic speech course; public speaking and leadership; communication in the grief process. Publ: Co-ed, Principles of speech-communication handbook, privately publ, 72; auth, A collection of W.A. Criswell's most famous and significant speeches, 74 & contrib, The scholarly minister as a public speaker, 74, Crescendo. Add: Dept. of Communication, Stephen F. Austin State University, Box 6174 SFA Sta, Nacogdoches, TX 75961.

TOWNSEND, DABNEY WINSTON, JR, Philosophy, Literature. See Volume IV, Philosophy, Religion & Law.

TOWNSEND, FRANCIS GUIBOR, b. Maplewood, Mo, Aug. 21, 15; m. 42. ENGLISH. A.B, St. Louis Univ, 37, fel, 40-42, M.A, 42; Ph.D, Ohio State Univ, 49. Asst. ENG, Ohio State Univ, 46-48; instr, Univ. Ill, 48-51, asst. prof, 51-53; Ohio State Univ, 53-56; PROF, FLA. STATE UNIV, 56-, head dept, 56-70. U.S.M.C.R, 42-45. NCTE; MLA. Victorian non-fiction prose; bibliography. Publ: Ruskin and the landscape feeling. Add: 2116 W. Randolph Circle, Tallahassee, FL 32303.

TOWNSEND, JAMES BENJAMIN, b. Stillwater, N.Y, Feb. 17, 18; m. 45; c. 4. ENGLISH LITERATURE, HUMANITIES. A.B, Princeton, 40; M.A, Harvard, 42; Ph.D.(Eng), Yale, 51. Instr. ENG, Northeast. Univ, 42; Yale, 47-48, 49-53; asst. prof, Univ. N.C, Greensboro, 53-57; STATE UNIV. N.Y. BUFFALO, 57-62, assoc. prof, 62-64, PROF, 64-, dir. M.A. in humanities, 60-

66, chmn. dept. art, 69-71. Fund Advan. Educ. fac. fel. & vis. fel, dept. art & archit, Princeton, 54-55; Comt. Allocation Res. Funds grant, State Univ. N.Y. Buffalo, 59 & travel grant, 63-64; Fund Young Scholars grant, Yale, 61; State Univ. N.Y. summer fac. fels, 64, 67; asst. dir, Nat. Portrait Gallery, Smithsonian Inst, 67-68. U.S.A, 42-45, Sgt. MLA; Col. Art Asn. Am; AAUP. Late Victorian and early modern English literature; 19th and 20th century art history and criticism; correlation of the fine arts and literature. Publ: John Davidson, poet of Armageddon, Yale, 61: 100, Albright-Knox Art Gallery, 62; ed, This new man: a discourse in portraits, 68 & Presidential portraits, 68, Smithsonian Inst; auth, Martha Visser 't Hooft, paintings and drawings 1952-1973, Charles Burchfield Ctr, 73; The quest for John Davidson, Princeton Univ. Libr. Chronicle; Buffalo: Athens on Niagara, 2/62 & Albright-Knox-Buffalo—toward a phenomenology of the urban arts, 1/67, Art News; plus others. Add: Dept. of English, State University of New York at Buffalo, Buffalo, NY 14214.

TOWNSEND, PATRICIA ANN, b. Lufkin, Tex, May 25, 33. PUBLIC ADDRESS. B.S, Stephen F. Austin State Col, 53, M.A, 56; univ. fel, Univ. Wis, 57-58, Ph.D, 59. Teaching asst, Stephen F. Austin State Col, 53-54; teacher speech & Eng, Blocker Jr. High Sch, Texas City, Tex, 54-56; res. asst, Univ. Wis, 56-57, teaching asst, 58-59; asst. prof. SPEECH, State Col. Iowa, 59-66; assoc. prof, UNIV. WIS-WHITEWATER, 66-68, PROF, 68-, DIR. GRAD. PROG. SPEECH, 66- Speech Commun. Asn; Cent. States Speech Commun. Asn. Graduate speech instruction; rhetoric. Add: Dept. of Speech Communication, University of Wisconsin-Whitewater, Whitewater, WI 53190.

TOWNSEND, ROBERT CAMPBELL, b. New Rochelle, N.Y, June 5, 35; m. 57; c. 3. ENGLISH LITERATURE. B.A, Princeton, 57; Fulbright fel. & M.A, Cambridge, 59; Woodrow Wilson fel. & Ph.D, Harvard, 62. Teaching fel. gen. educ, Harvard, 60-62; instr. ENG, AMHERST COL, 62-64, asst. prof, 64-68, ASSOC. PROF, 68- MLA. Romantic and literary criticism. Publ: John Wordsworth and his brothers poetic development, PMLA, 3/66; W.K. Wimsatt's criticism, Mass. Rev, winter 66; Cambridge English, Critical Surv, winter 67. Add: Dept. of English, Amherst College, Amherst, MA 01002.

TRACE, ARTHER STORREY, JR, b. Denver, Colo, Jan. 6, 22; m. 49; c. 2. ENGLISH. A.B, Univ. Denver, 48; M.A, Columbia Univ, 48; Ph.D, Stanford Univ, 54. Instr. ENG, Univ. Nebr, 48-50; acting instr, Stanford Univ, 50-54; instr, Purdue Univ, 54-56; asst. prof, JOHN CARROLL UNIV, 56-61, assoc. prof, 61-67, PROF, 67- Mem, Reading Reform Found, 64. U.S.A, 43-46. MLA. English literary criticism; Russian literature. Publ: What Ivan knows that Johnny doesn't, Random, 61; co-auth, The Open Court basic readers, Open Court, 63 & Preparatory reading for writing, Houghton; auth, Reading without Dick and Jane, Regnery, 64; The American moral crisis, Exposition Press, 69; The future of literature, Phaedra, 72. Add: Dept. of English, John Carroll University, Cleveland, OH 44118.

TRACHTENBERG, ALAN, b. Philadelphia, Pa, Mar. 22, 32; m. 52; c. 3. ENGLISH, AMERICAN STUDIES. A.B, Temple Univ, 54; Univ. Conn, 56; Ph.D. (Am. stud), Univ. Minn, 62. Instr. Eng, Gen. Col, Univ. Minn, Minneapolis, 56-61; Pa. State Univ, University Park, 61-63, asst. prof, 63-66, assoc. prof, 66-69; AM. STUD. & ENG, YALE UNIV, 69-72, PROF, 72- Am. Counc. Learned Soc. grant-in-aid, 64-65, study fel, 68-69; fel, Ctr. Adv. Stud. Behav. Sci, 68-69; mem. ed. bd, Am. Quart, 68-72. MLA; Am. Stud. Asn. American literature; American cultural history. Publ: Brooklyn Bridge: fact and symbol, 65 & co-ed, The city: American experience, 71, Oxford; ed, Democratic vistas, 1860-1880, Braziller, 70; ed, Memoirs of Waldo Frank, Univ. Mass, 73; auth, The American scene: versions of the city, Mass. Rev, spring 67; The journey back: myth and history in Tender is the night, Eng. Inst. Essays, 68; The form of freedom in Huck Finn, South. Rev, 71. Add: American Studies Program, Yale University, New Haven, CT 06520.

TRACHTMAN, LEON EMANUEL, b. New York, N.Y, Sept. 26, 25; m. 52; c. 4. SCIENCE COMMUNICATION. A.B, Hamilton Col, 48; A.M, Johns Hopkins Univ, 51. Asst. prof. Eng. & speech, Hood Col, 51-56; sci. writer, Nat. Insts. Health, 56-58; Purdue Res. Found, Lafayette, Ind, 58-61, exec. secy, 61-65; asst. prof. indust. mgt, PURDUE UNIV, WEST LAFAYETTE, 63-64, assoc. prof. Eng, 65-73, ASSOC. PROF. COMMUN. & HEAD DEPT. POLIT. SCI, 73-, ASSOC. DEAN, DIV. HUMANITIES, SOC. SCI. & EDUC, 71-, asst. dean, 67-71. U.S.A, 43-45. AAAS; Nat. Asn. Sci. Writers. Problems of science communication; science-society interactions; science and public policy. Publ: Co-ed, Growth in living systems, Basic Bks, 61; contrib, Our working world (6 vols), Sci. Res. Assocs, 64-73; co-auth, Science in the press, Sci. Res, 3/69 & Jogging the imagination, Psychol. Today, 3/73; plus one other. Add: School of Humanities, Social Science & Education, Purdue University, West Lafayette, IN 47907.

TRACI, PHILIP J, b. East Cleveland, Ohio, June 27, 34. SHAKESPEARE, ENGLISH RENAISSANCE DRAMA. B.A, West. Reserve Univ, 56; M.A, Duke Univ, 58, Ph.D.(Eng), 65; Harvard, 58-59. Instr. ENG, Tufts Univ, 59-60, 61-63, 64-65; asst. prof, Sir George Williams Univ, 65-66; Drew Univ, 66-70; ASSOC. PROF, WAYNE STATE UNIV, 70- Renaissance Soc. Am; MLA; NCTE. Shakespeare; English Renaissance Drama; world drama. Publ: The love play of Antony and Cleopatra, Mouton, 69; Joseph Papp's happening and the teaching of Hamlet, Eng. J, 1/69; Suggestions about implications of Bawdry in Romeo and Juliet, 73 & ed, A Festschrift in honor of Allan Gilbert, 73, S.Atlantic Quart. Add: Dept. of English, Wayne State University, Detroit, MI 48202.

TRACY, CLARENCE (RUPERT), b. Can, May 9, 08; m. 40; c. 3. ENGLISH LITERATURE. B.A, Univ. Toronto, 30; Ph.D, Yale, 35; hon. D.C.L, Bishop's Univ, 71. Lectr, Queen's Univ.(Can), 30-31; instr, Cornell Univ, 34-36; from lectr. to asst. prof, Univ. Alta, 36-47; assoc. prof, Univ. N.B, 47-50; prof. Eng. lit, Univ. Sask, 50-64, prof. Eng, & head dept. & dean residences, 64-66; prof, Univ. B.C, 66-68, prof. & head dept. Acadia Univ, 68-73; RETIRED. Mem, Humanities Res. Counc. Can, 62-66; acad. panel, Can. Counc, 65-67; vis. prof. Eng, Univ. Toronto, 73-74. Can. Army, 40-41, Lt. Fel. Royal Soc. Can; Am. Soc. 18th Century Stud; MLA; Humanities Asn. Can.(secy-treas, 52-54, pres, 54-56); Int. Asn. Univ. Prof. Eng; Asn. Can. Univ. Teachers Eng; Johnson Soc. Northwest (pres, 66-68). Samuel Johnson; Pope, Swift. Publ: Artificial bastard: biography of Richard Savage, Univ. Toronto, 53; ed, Poetical works of Richard Savage, Cambridge, 62; ed, The spiritual quixote, 67 & ed, Samuel Johnson: life of Savage, 71, Oxford; co-auth, Browning's mind and art, Oliver & Boyd, 68; auth, The unity of Gulliver's travels, Queen's Quart, 61-62; Melanchola marked him for her own: Thomas Gray two hundred years afterwards, Trans. Royal Soc. Can, 71; Boswell: the cautious empiricist, In. The Triumph of Culture, 72. Add: Port Maitland, N.S, Can.

TRACY, JAMES ALBERT, b. Sioux Rapids, Iowa, Mar. 2, 01; m. 34; c. 2. SPEECH. B.A, Univ. Iowa, 29; M.A, Univ. Denver, 33. Teacher, high sch, Iowa, 30-31; Colo, 34-41; mem. faculty SPEECH, South. Idaho Col. Educ, 41-45; asst. prof, Stetson Univ, 45-46; Bowling Green State Univ, 46-47; assoc. prof, MURRAY STATE UNIV, 47-66, prof, 66-71, EMER. PROF, 71- Nat. Guard, 21-24; U.S.M.C.R, 28-32. Speech Commun. Asn. Forensics; speech correction. Publ: A study of personality traits of mature actors and mature public speakers, Speech Monogr, 10/35. Add: P.O. Box 2305, Campus Station, Murray, KY 42071.

TRACY, ROBERT E, b. Woburn, Mass, Nov. 23, 28; m. 56; c. 3. ENGLISH. A.M, Harvard, 54, fel, 54-58, Ph.D, 60. Instr. ENG, Carleton Col, 58-60; asst. prof. UNIV. CALIF, BERKELEY, 60-66, ASSOC. PROF, 66- Bruern fel. Am. stud, Univ. Leeds, 65-66; humanities res. fel, Univ. Calif, Berkeley, 69; Leverhulme res. fel, Trinity Col.(Dublin), 71-72. MLA; Philol. Asn. Pac. Coast; Am. Soc. Theatre Res. Victorian literature; absurdism; Anglo-Irish literature. Publ: Ed, The Aran Islands and other writings, Random, 62; ed, The way we live now, Bobbs, 74; contrib, Oxford companion to the theatre, 3rd ed, 67; Myth and reality in The adventures of Tom Sawyer, South. Rev, spring 68; Ireland: the patriot game, In: The cry of home: cultural nationalism and the modern writer, Univ. Tenn, 72; plus others. Add: 2611 Derby St, Berkeley, CA 94705.

TRAFTON, DAIN ATWOOD, b. Lewiston, Maine, Sept. 22, 38; m. 60; c. 2. ENGLISH, COMPARATIVE LITERATURE. B.A, Harvard, 61; M.A, Univ. Calif, Berkeley, 63, Ph.D.(Eng), 68; Univ. Florence, 64-65. Acting instr. ENG, Univ. Calif, Berkeley, 67-68; asst. prof, Dartmouth Col, 68-74; ASSOC. PROF. & CHMN. DEPT, ROCKFORD COL, 74- Nat. Endowment for Humanities younger humanist fel, 72-73. MLA; Renaissance Soc. Am. Shakespeare; 16th century European literature; Renaissance in Europe. Publ: Tasso's Dialogue on the court, Dartmouth Col. & Eng. Lit. Renaissance, 73; On Corneille's Horace, Interpretation, 72; Structure and meaning in The courtier, Eng. Lit. Renaissance, 72; Ancients and Indians in Montaigne's Des coches, Symposium, 73. Add: Dept. of English, Rockford College, Rockford, IL 61101.

TRAHAN, ELIZABETH WELT, Slavic & Comparative Literature. See Volume III, Foreign Languages, Linguistics & Philology.

TRAHERN, JOSEPH BAXTER, JR, b. Clarksville, Tenn, Feb. 20, 37; m. 58; c. 2. ENGLISH. B.A, Vanderbilt Univ, 58, M.A, 59; M.A, Princeton, 62, Ph.D.(Eng), 63; Fulbright fel, Oxford, 62-63. Asst. prof. ENG, UNIV. ILL URBANA-CHAMPAIGN, 63-71, ASSOC. PROF, 71- U.S.A, 59-60, Res, 60-66, Capt. MLA; Medieval Acad. Am. Old and Middle English language and literature. Publ: The Ioca monachorum and the Old English Pharaoh, Eng. Lang. Notes, 69; Joshua and Tobias in the Old English Andreas, Stud. Neophilol, 70; Amalarius Be Becnum: a fragment of the Liber officialis in Old English, Anglia, 73. Add: Dept. of English, University of Illinois at Urbana-Champaign, Urbana, IL 61801.

TRAMEL, AGNES CATHERINE, b. Sulphur Springs, Tex, Jan. 5, 03. ENGLISH. A.B, South. Methodist Univ, 24; A.M, Radcliffe Col, 28; summers, Univ. Calif, 35, Univ. Tex, 36-41, 48-50. Teacher, jr. high sch, Tex, 24-26; asst. prof. Eng, Tex. Woman's Univ, 29-73; RETIRED. Conf. Col. Teacher Eng; S.Cent. Mod. Lang. Asn; S.Cent. Col. Eng. Asn. English literature of the 16th century; a wedding in the chapel. Add: 718 Schmitz St, Denton, TX 76201.

TRASCHEN, ISADORE, b. Newark, N.J, Dec. 24, 15; m. 44; c. 5. ENGLISH. A.B, N.Y. Univ, 39; M.A, Columbia Univ, 48, Ph.D, 52. Instr. ENG, Seton Hall Univ, 51-52; from asst. prof. to PROF, RENSSELAER POLYTECH. INST, 52- Fulbright lectr. mod. Am. lit, Univ. Poitiers, 63-64. U.S.A.A.F, 42-45. MLA. Modern drama; comparative modern literature; modern American and English poetry. Publ: Co-auth, The drama: traditional and modern, Allyn & Bacon, 68 & Short fiction: a critical anthology, Prentice-Hall, 2nd ed, 68; auth, Modern literature and science, Col. Eng, 64; Use of myth in Death in Venice, Mod. Fiction Stud, 65; Robert Frost: some divisions in a whole man, Yale Rev, autumn 65; plus others. Add: Dept. of English, Rensselaer Polytechnic Institute, Troy, NY 12181.

TRAUGER, WILMER KOHL, b. Revere, Pa, Sept. 12, 98; m. 30; c. 1. ENGLISH. A.B, Gettysburg Col, 22; A.M, Harvard, 26, Ph.D, 40. Prin, Nockamixon High Sch, Revere, Pa, 17-18, 19-20; instr. ENG, STATE UNIV. N.Y. COL. POTSDAM, 27-35, prof, 36-64, EMER. PROF, 64- Mem, N.Y. State Curriculum Comt, 33-36; Nat. Counc. Eng. Articulation Comt, 34-37; Nat. Proj. Eng. grant, 62-64; mem, N.Y. State Eng. Counc. Comt. Ling, 63; instr. ling, Appalachia Educ. Lab, W.Va, summer 67; vis. prof. ling. & dialect, Union Col.(Ky), 65-; consult. writing, South. Railway Syst, 70- U.S.A, 18. Teachers Eng. to Speakers Other Lang; Conf. Col. Compos. & Commun; NCTE; AAUP. Applied linguistics; Appalachian dialect. Publ: Language arts in elementary schools, McGraw, 63. Add: Box 244, R.D. 3, Reading, PA 19606.

TRAUGOTT, ELIZABETH CLOSS, Linguistics. See Volume III, Foreign Languages, Linguistics & Philology.

TRAUGOTT, JOHN LEWIS, b. Indianapolis, Ind, Nov. 20, 21; m. 67; c. 2. ENGLISH LITERATURE. B.S, Purdue Univ, 42; M.A, Univ. Calif, 48, Wall scholar. & Ph.D.(Eng), 51. Asst. prof. ENG, Univ. Conn, 51-55; from asst. prof. to PROF, UNIV. CALIF, BERKELEY, 56- Ford fel, 55-56; Fulbright lectr, Univ. Aix Marseille, 63-64. U.S.N, 44-45. MLA. English literature and philosophy of the 17th and 18th centuries; Shakespeare; aesthetics of comic literature. Publ: Tristram Shandy's world, Univ. Calif, 54; Voyage to nowhere: Swift and More, Sewanee Rev, autumn 61; Rake's progress from court to comedy, Stud. Eng. Lit, winter 66; Swift our contemporary, Univ. Rev, Dublin, spring 67. Add: Dept. of English, University of California, Berkeley, CA 94720.

TRAUTMANN, FREDRICK, b. Plymouth, Ohio, Aug. 25, 36; div. SPEECH. B.S, Wis. State Univ, River Falls, 62; M.S, Purdue Univ, 64; Ph.D.(speech), 66. ASST. PROF. SPEECH, TEMPLE UNIV, 66- U.S.A, 56-59. Speech Commun. Asn. Rhetorical theory; American public address; history of public discourse in Pennsylvania. Publ: Kossuth in Indiana, Ind. Mag. Hist, 12/67; Instant speech criticism: the distance of nearness, Today's Speech, 4/68; Harriet Beecher Stowe; public reader, Cent. States Speech J, 5/73. Add: Dept. of Speech, Temple University, Philadelphia, PA 19122.

TRAVERS, LINUS, b. Boston, Mass, Apr. 12, 36; m. 64; c. 1. ENGLISH LITERATURE. B.A, Yale, 58, M.A.T, 59; Ph.D.(Eng. lit), Boston Univ, 72. Instr. ENG, Old Dom. Univ, 63-64; teaching fel, Boston Univ, 64-67, spec. lectr, 67-69; instr, Pine Manor Jr. Col, 69-71; ASST. PROF, BOSTON STATE COL, 71- U.S.N.R, 59-63, Lt.(jg). AAUP; MLA; NCTE. Eighteenth century English drama; sentimental and comic literature. Add: 94 Warren St, Needham, MA 02192.

TRAVIS, MILDRED KLEIN, b. Cleveland, Ohio, June 18, 26. ENGLISH, AMERICAN LITERATURE. B.A, West. Reserve Univ, 48; M.A.Ed, Ariz. State Univ, 54, Ph.D.(Eng), 71; M.A, Miss. State Univ, 62; Univ. Miss, 62; Univ. Ky, 62-64. High sch. teacher Eng, St. Johns High Sch, Ariz, 48-49; soc. worker, Dept. Welfare, City of Cleveland, 49-50; recreational dir. & spec. proj, U.S. Dept. Army & U.S. Dept. State, Frankfurt, Ger, 50-52; elem. sch. teacher, Stockton Unified Sch. Dist, Calif, 53-58; Osborn Sch. Dist, Phoenix, Ariz, 58-60; teaching asst. Eng, Miss. State Univ, 60-62; teaching fel, Univ. Ky, 62-63; pub. sch. teacher, Calexico, Calif, 67-69; Stockton, Calif, 69-70; & Scottsdale, Ariz, 70-72; MEM. STAFF, ARIZ. STATE UNIV, 72- Part-time registr. worker, Ariz. State Univ, 62- MLA; Emerson Soc; Melville Soc. Am; Soc. Stud. South. Lit. American literature or studies, especially of the 19th century; contemporary literature or studies; studies in the Renaissance, particularly literature. Publ: Toward the explication of Pierre: new perspectives in technique and meaning, Univ. Microfilms, 71; Woman as nature: major women in Faulkner's novels, Miss. State Univ. Abstr. Theses, 64; Mardi: Melville's Allegory of love, Emerson Soc. Quart, 66; A note on The bell-tower, Melville's Blackwood article, Poe Stud, 73; plus others. Add: Apt. 10B, 615 E. Apache Blvd, Tempe, AZ 85281.

TRAWICK, BUCKNER BEASLEY, b. Opelika, Ala, Oct. 13, 14; m. 43; c. 2. ENGLISH LITERATURE. A.B, Emory Univ, 35; A.M, Harvard, 36, Ph.D, 42. Instr, Clemson Agr. Col, 37-38; Univ. Miss, 38-40; Temple Univ, 46; asst. prof. ENG, UNIV. ALA, 46-51, assoc. prof, 51-62, PROF, 62- Ford fac. fel, Harvard, 52-53; consult. Orient. lit, Crowell-Collier Publ. Co, 62-67. U.S.A.A.F, 42-45. MLA. Shakespeare: the Bible as literature; Victorian poetry. Publ: World literature (2 vols), 53, 55 & The Bible as literature, Vol. I, The Old Testament and the Apocrypha, Vol. II, The New Testament, 68, 70, Barnes & Noble; ed, Selected prose works of Arthur Hugh Clough, Univ. Ala, 64; auth, Shakespeare's Othello: analysis and criticism, Randall, 69; The sea of faith and the battle by night in Dover Beach, PMLA, 12/50; The moon metaphor in One word more, Notes & Queries, 59. Add: University of Alabama, Box 1606, University, AL 35486.

TRAWICK, LEONARD MOSES, b. Decatur, Ala, July 4, 33; m. 60. ENGLISH. B.A, Univ. of the South, 55; M.A, Univ. Chicago, 56; Fulbright fel, Univ. Dijon, France, 56-57; teaching fel, Harvard, 60-61, Ph.D, 61. Instr. ENG, Columbia Univ, 61-66, asst. prof, 66-69; assoc. prof, CLEVELAND STATE UNIV, 69-73, PROF, 73- Dir, NDEA Summer Inst. Eng, Columbia Univ, 66. U.S.A, 56-57, Res, 57-64. MLA. English romantic literature; American literature; poetics. Publ: Backgrounds of romanticism, Ind. Univ, 67; Beast forms (poems), Cleveland State Univ, 71; Sources of Hazlitt's metaphysical discovery, Philol. Quart, 4/63; Hazlitt, Reynolds and the ideal, Stud. Romanticism, summer 65; The present state of Blake studies, Stud. Burke & His Time, winter, 70-71. Add: Dept. of English, Cleveland State University, Cleveland, OH 44115.

TREICHLER, PAUL FELIX, b. Springfield, Mass, May 14, 05. DRAMA. A.B, Mont. State Univ, 31, A.M, 32; Yale, 32-34. Prof. DRAMATICS & dir. dept, ANTIOCH COL, 34-71, EMER. PROF, 71- Dir, Antioch Area Theatre, 47-71. Style and reaction in the theatre; psychic stimulation of prostatic secretion. Add: Dept. of Dramatics, Antioch College, Yellow Springs, OH 45387.

TREJO, ARNULFO DUENES, b. Durango, Mex, Aug. 15, 22; U.S. citizen; m. 67; c. 3. LIBRARY SCIENCE, LATIN AMERICAN BIBLIOGRAPHY. B.A, Univ. Ariz, 49; M.A, Univ. of the Americas, Mex, 51; M.A, Kent State Univ, 53; Litt.D.(Span. lang. & lit), Nat. Univ. Mex, 59. Ref. librn, Univ. of the Americas, Mex, 53-54; asst. to dir, reorgn. of Cent. Libr, Nat. Univ. Mex, 54-55; librn, ref. dept, Univ. Calif, Los Angeles, 55-59, asst. prof. libr. sci, 65-66; asst. librn, Calif. State Univ, Long Beach, 59-63; dir. libr, Stanford Univ. Sch. Grad. Bus. Admin, Lima, Peru, 63-65; assoc. prof. libr. sci. & bibliog. Latin Am. Cols, Univ. Ariz, 66-68; Am. Libr. Asn. & U.S. Agency Int. Develop. consult, Inst. Advan. Admin. Stud. & Simon Bolivar Univ, Venezuela, 68-70; ASSOC. PROF. LIBR. SCI. & ENG, UNIV. ARIZ, 70- Mem, Sem. Acquisition of Latin Am. Libr. Materials, 58. Simon Bolivar Award, Col. Librn. & Archivists, Venezuela, 70. U.S.A, 43-45, Sgt; Bronze Star Medal. AAUP; Am. Libr. Asn; Nat. Asn. Span-Speaking Librn. U.S. (pres, 71-). Mexican American literature. Publ: Bibliografía comentada sobre administración de negocios y disciplinas conexas, Addison-Wesley, 67; Diccionario etimológico del léxico de la delincuencia, Union Tipográfica Ed. Hispano Am, Mexico City, 69; Introducción a las jergas delictivas de la América Latina, Folklore Am, 6/66; Electronic information services to advance Latin American research, In: Vol. I, 68, Final report and working papers, Seminar on the acquisition of Latin American library materials, Pan Am. Union; Bicultural Americans with a Hispanic tradition, Wilson Libr. Bull, 3/70. Add: Graduate School of Library Science, College of Education, University of Arizona, Tucson, AZ 85721.

TREMAINE, HADLEY PHILLIP, b. Dover, N.J, Apr. 21, 39; m. 73. ENGLISH. B.A, Montclair State Col, 61; M.A, Univ. Mich, Ann Arbor, 62, Ph.D.(comp. lit), 65. ASSOC. PROF. ENG, HOOD COL, 65- Comparative literature of the Middle Ages. Publ: Beowulf's Ecg Brun and other rusty relics, Philol. Quart, 4/69; The three Saxon princes at the Destruction of Da Derga's hospital, Eire-Ireland, autumn 69. Add: Dept. of English, Hood College, Frederick, MD 21701.

TRENT, JIMMIE DOUGLAS, b. Lima, Okla, Nov. 17, 33; m. 69; c. 2. SPEECH. B.S.Ed, Kans. State Teachers Col, 55, M.S, 59; Univ. Ill, 64; Ph.D.(speech), Purdue Univ, 66. Dir. forensics, High Schs, Kans, 55-57; instr. speech & dir. forensics, Kans. State Teachers Col, 57-60; instr. speech, Purdue Univ, 60-62; asst. prof, East. Ill. Univ, 62-64; asst. prof. & dir. masters degree prog, Wayne State Univ, 64-68, grad. off. & asst. to dean col. liberal arts, 68-69, assoc. prof. & chmn. grad. prog. speech commun. & theatre, 69-71; CHMN. DEPT. COMMUN. & THEATRE, MIAMI UNIV, 71- Guest prof. speech, Univ. Mass, summer 67. Speech Commun. Asn; Int. Commun. Asn; Interstate Oratorical Asn.(exec. secy, 64). Argumentation; leadership behavior; organizational communication. Publ: Ed, Winning orations: 65-70, Interstate Oratorical Asn, 65-71; co-auth, Concepts in communication, Allyn & Bacon, 73; auth, Small group discussions, In: Introduction to the field of speech, Scott, 65; Value premises: an important part of argument, Issues, 67; Toulmon's model of an argument: an examination and extention, Quart. J. Speech, 68. Add: 101 Country Club, Oxford, OH 45056.

TRENT, JUDITH SWANLUND, b. Grand Rapids, Mich, Aug. 29, 40; m. 69. SPEECH COMMUNICATION. B.S, West. Mich. Univ, 62; M.A, Univ. Mich, Ann Arbor, 68, Ph.D.(speech), 70. Teacher speech, Belleville High Sch, 62-67; asst. prof. speech & res. grant, Youngstown State Univ, 70-71; ASST. PROF. SPEECH, UNIV. DAYTON, 71-, summer res. grant, 73. Speech Commun. Asn; Cent. States Speech Asn; Int. Commun. Asn; Am. Forensic Asn; Pub. Relat. Soc. Am. Political communication; rhetoric of women's rights; communication theory. Publ: Co-auth, Discussion and argumentation—debate in the secondary school, Nat. Textbk, 68; co-auth, Concepts in communication, 73 & Instructor's guide to accompany concepts in communication, 73, Allyn & Bacon; auth, The National Rifle Association: credibility in a propaganda compaign, J. Am. Forensic Asn, 71; Richard Nixon's methods of identification in the Presidential campaigns of 1960 and 1968: a content analysis, Today's Speech, 71. Add: Dept. of Communication Arts, University of Dayton, Dayton, OH 45469.

TRESER, ROBERT MORRIS, b. New Castle, Pa, Oct. 22, 26; m. 52. c. 2. DRAMA, SPEECH. B.S, Lehigh Univ, 45; M.F.A, Univ. Okla, 53; Ph.D.(theatre), Tulane Univ, 67. Dir. theatre, Univ. South. Miss, 56-65; PROF. SPEECH & DRAMA & CHMN. DEPT, WHITTIER COL, 65- Sig.C, U.S.A, 45-48, 51-52, Sgt. Am. Theatre Asn; Am. Nat. Theatre & Acad. History of theatre; acting; directing. Add: Dept. of Speech & Drama, Whittier College, Whittier, CA 90608.

TRICOMI, ALBERT HENRY, b. New York, N.Y, Dec. 30, 42; m. 68; c. 1. ENGLISH, DRAMA. A.B, Columbia Col, 64; Woodrow Wilson fel, Northwest. Univ, 64-65, M.A, 65, Ph.D.(Eng), 69. ASST. PROF. ENG, N.C. Cent. Univ, 68-69; STATE UNIV. N.Y. BINGHAMTON, 69-, univ. fel, 69-70. MLA. Shakespeare; Elizabethan-Jacobean drama; Renaissance literature. Publ: The rhetoric of aspiring circularity in Emerson's Circles, Emerson Soc. Quart, winter 72; Bussy D'Ambois and The revenge of Bussy D'Ambois: joint performance . . ., Eng. Lang. Notes, 6/72; The revised version of Chapman's Bussy D'Ambois: a shift in point of view, Stud. in Philol, 7/73. Add: Dept. of English, State University of New York at Binghamton, Vestal Pkwy. E, Binghamton, NY 13901.

TRIEBER, JACOB MARSHALL, b. Little Rock, Ark, Nov. 27, 27; m. 56; c. 2. ENGLISH, HUMANITIES. B.S, Purdue Univ, 50; M.A, Univ. Ark, 54; Ed.D. (col. teaching Eng), N.Tex. State Univ, 61. Asst. dir, Kyoto Am. Sch. Japan, 47; instr. Eng, Tex. Christian Univ, 56-58; assoc. prof, Buena Vista Col, 60-61; Eng. & gen. humanities, Sterling Col, 61-62, head dept, 62-63; dir. exp. prog. humanistic stud, Wis. State Univ, Eau Claire, 63-64; prof. ENG, Mansfield State Col, 64-67; PROF. & head dept, Pembroke State Col, 67-71; S.C. STATE COL, 71- Mil.Intel, U.S.A, 46-48. Nat. Asn. Gen. & Lib. Stud; Col. Eng. Asn; MLA. Interdisciplinary humanities; American literature. Publ: The development of a program in humanities for the junior college curriculum, N.Tex. State Univ, 61. Add: Dept. of English, South Carolina State College, Orangeburg, SC 29115.

TRILLING, LIONEL, b. New York, N.Y, July 4, 05; m. 29; c. 1. ENGLISH LITERATURE. A.B, Columbia Univ, 25, A.M, 26, Ph.D, 38; Litt.D, Trinity Col, 55, Harvard, 63, Case West. Reserve Univ, 68, Univ. Durham, 73, Univ. Leicester, 73; L.H.D, Northwest. Univ, 64. Instr, Univ. Wis, 26-27; eve. session, Hunter Col, 27-32; Eng, COLUMBIA UNIV, 32-39, asst. prof, 39-45, assoc. prof, 45-48, prof, 48-65, George Edward Woodberry prof. LIT. & CRITICISM, 65-70, UNIV. PROF, 70- George Eastman vis. prof, Oxford, 63-64; Charles Eliot Norton prof. poetry, Harvard, 69-70; vis. fel, All Souls Col, Oxford, 72-73. Am. Acad. Arts & Sci; Nat. Inst. Arts & Lett. Nineteenth century English literature; American literature. Publ: Matthew Arnold, Norton, 39, Columbia Univ, 49; The liberal imagination, 50, The opposing self, 55 & Beyond culture, 65, Viking; Sincerity and authenticity, Harvard, 73; plus others. Add: 35 Claremont Ave, New York, NY 10027.

TRIMBLE, JOHN CLIFTON, b. Carters Creek, Tenn, Dec. 8, 28; m. 49; c. 1. SPEECH. B.A, David Lipscomb Col, 50; M.A, Northwest. Univ, 52, Ph.D. (speech), 66. Instr. SPEECH, Purdue Univ, 56-59; asst. prof, Mid. Tenn. State Col, 59-62, Miss. State Col. Women, 62-67; UNIV. S.ALA, 67-69, ASSOC. PROF, 69- Speech Commun. Asn; South. Speech Commun. Asn. American public address; rhetorical and homiletical theory. Add: 5521 Vanderbilt Dr. N, Mobile, AL 36608.

TRIMBLE, MARTHA SCOTT, b. Ft. Collins, Colo, May 27, 14. ENGLISH & AMERICAN LITERATURE. B.S, Colo. State Col. A&M, 36; M.A, Univ. Colo, Boulder, 40; summers, Bread Loaf Sch. English, 41, State Univ. Iowa, 42, Harvard, 63. Teacher Eng, Washington County High Sch, Akron, Colo, 36-39; instr, Colo. State Univ, Ft. Lewis, 39-40; Colo. State Univ, 40-43; mem. part-time staff, Larimer County Court & Radio Sta. KCOL, Ft. Collins, Colo, 46-61; instr. ENG, COLO. STATE UNIV, 61-65, asst. prof, 65-71, ASSOC. PROF, 71- U.S. Off. Educ. grant, 64-65. W.A.V.E.S, U.S.N.R, 43-46, Lt. Rocky Mountain Mod. Lang. Asn.(v.pres, 74-); MLA; West. Lit. Asn.(treas, 66-73); AAUP; NCTE; Conf. Col. Compos. & Commun. Development and demonstration of the effectiveness of using programed material for teaching fundamental tools and techniques required for English composition at the university level. Publ: Programed review of English. Unit I, Spelling, Unit. II, Diction & Unit III, Writing, Harper, 69; N. Scott Momaday, Boise State Col, 73. Add: 1909 Stover St, Ft. Collins, CO 80521.

TRIMPI, WILLIAM WESLEY, JR, b. New York, N.Y, Sept. 3, 28; m. 51; c. 2. ENGLISH. A.B, Stanford Univ, 50; M.A, Harvard, 53, Ph.D.(Eng), 57. Instr. ENG, STANFORD UNIV, 57-60, asst. prof, 60-63, assoc. prof, 63-68, PROF, 68- Am. Counc. Learned Soc. grant, 63-64. MLA; Renaissance Soc. Am. Late classical literature and literary theory; medieval and Renaissance literature and literary theory. Publ: The glass of Perseus, Swallow, 53; Ben Jonson's poems, Stanford Univ, 63; The ancient hypothesis of fiction: an essay on the origins of literary theory, 71 & The quality of fiction: the rhetorical transmission of literary theory, 74, Traditio; The meaning of Horace's Ut pictura poesis, J. Warburg & Courtauld Insts, 73; plus others. Add: 375 Old La Honda Rd, Woodside, CA 94062.

TRITSCHLER, DONALD, b. Cincinnati, Ohio, Aug. 5, 30; m. 52; c. 2. ENGLISH. B.S, Northwest. Univ, 51, fel, 52-55, Ph.D, 56; M.A, Univ. Chicago, 52. Instr. Eng, La. State Univ, 55-56; asst. prof, Univ. Pittsburgh, 56-63; assoc. prof, Skidmore Col, 63-69; assoc. higher educ, BUR. COL. EVAL, N.Y. STATE DEPT. EDUC, 69-70, CHIEF, 70- Secy, N.Y. State Adv. Counc. Grad. Educ, 70- MLA; Am. Lit. Asn; Milton Soc. Am. Twentieth century American and British literature; literary criticism; educational evaluation and administration. Publ: Co-auth, Master's degrees in the state of New York, 1969-1970, N.Y, State Dept. Educ, 72; auth, The unity of Faulkner's shaping vision, Mod. Fiction Stud, winter 60; The metamorphic stop of time in A winter's tale, PMLA, 9/63; The stories in Dylan Thomas' Red notebook, J. Mod. Lit, 9/71. Add: Bureau of College Evaluation, Div. of Academic Program Review, New York State Dept. of Education, Albany, NY 12210.

TROENDLE, DOROTHY, b. Montreal, P.Q, Jan. 21, 18; U.S. citizen; m. 40; c. 3. ENGLISH, LINGUISTICS. Ed.B, R.I. Col. Educ, 50; M.A, Brown Univ, 52, Ph.D.(Eng); 60; Harvard, 63-65. Instr. Eng, Wheaton Col.(Mass), 60-62; asst. prof, R.I. Sch. Design, 63-65; PROF. ENG. & LING, SALVE REGINA COL, 65- Consult. elem. educ, Tri-Univ. Proj, Nebr, 67-68. MLA; NCTE. Education. Add: 24 Doro Pl, Rumford, RI 02916.

TROMBLY, THELMA WOODHOUSE, Speech Pathology. See 12th Edition, American Men & Women of Science, Physical & Biological Sciences Section.

TROTTER, MARGRET GUTHRIE, b. Staunton, Va, Oct. 27, 07. COMPARATIVE LITERATURE, MODERN POETRY. A.B, Wellesley Col, 30, Horton-Hallowell fel, 41-42; A.M, Columbia Univ, 38; Ph.D, Ohio State Univ, 43. Off. secy, Conf. South. Mt. Workers, 30-37; asst. ENG, Ohio State Univ, 38-41; asst. prof, Tusculum Col, 42-44; AGNES SCOTT COL, 44-54, assoc. prof, 54-67, PROF, 67- MLA; S.Atlantic Mod. Lang. Asn; Eng. Inst; AAUP. West Virginia state history; Harington's sources; modern poetry and drama. Publ: White sands of Carrabelle, Ga. Rev, 54; The time sheet, Perspective, 57-58. Add: Dept. of English, Agnes Scott College, Decatur, GA 30030.

TROWBRIDGE, CLINTON W, b. Jan. 14, 28; U.S. citizen; m; c. 4. ENGLISH. A.B, Princeton, 50; M.A, Univ. Fla, 52, Ph.D.(Eng), 57. Asst. humanities, philos. & Eng, Univ. Fla, 50-55, instr. ENG, 55-57; asst. prof, Rollins Col, 57-61; assoc. prof, Col. Charleston, 61-65; DOWLING COL, 65-68, PROF, 68- Contemporary American fiction; interdisciplinary courses; creative writing. Publ: The Crow Island Journal, Harper, 70; The symbolic structure of The catcher in the rye, 67 & The symbolic vision of Flannery O'Connor: patterns of imagery in The violent bear it away, spring 68, Sewanee Rev; plus others. Add: Rte. 25A, East Setauket, NY 11733.

TROWBRIDGE, HOYT, b. Chicago, Ill, Apr. 6, 09; m. 32; c. 2. ENGLISH LITERATURE. A.B, Univ. Wis, 31; A.M, 33, Ph.D, 35. Instr. Eng, Univ. Wis, 35-39; asst. prof, 39-40; assoc. prof, Univ. Ore, 40-45; vis. assoc. prof. humanities, col, Univ. Chicago, 45-46; prof. Eng. Univ.Oregon, 46-57; prof. & chmn. dept, UNIV. N.MEX, 57-61, PROF, 69-, dean, Col. Arts & Sci, 61-69, acting acad. v.pres, 63-64. Consult, higher educ, Ark. Exp. in Teacher Educ, 54-56. MLA; Rocky Mountain Mod. Lang. Asn; Am. Soc. 18th Century Stud.(chmn. comn. on publ, 71-73). Eighteenth century literature, history of literary criticism; literary theory. Publ: General education in the colleges of Arkansas, 58; ed, Letters on chivalry and romance, Augustan Reprint Soc, 63; Scattered atoms of probability, 18th Century Stud, 71. Add: Dept. of English, University of New Mexico, Albuquerque, NM 87131.

TROWBRIDGE, RONALD LEE, b. Ft. Wayne, Ind, Dec. 4, 37; m. 62; c. 2. ENGLISH LANGUAGE & LITERATURE. B.A, Univ. Mich, 60, fel, 61-65, M.A, 62, Ph.D.(Eng), 67. Instr. ENG, EAST. MICH. UNIV, 65-67, asst. prof, 67-72, ASSOC. PROF, 72- Ed-in-chief, Mich. Academician, 73- Neoclassic period, 1660-1798; Victorian literature; Thomas Carlyle's humor. Publ: Carlyle's Illudo chartis as a prophetic exercise in the manner of Swift and Sterne, Stud. Scottish Lit, 10/68; Thomas Carlyle's Masks of humor, Mich. Academician, fall 70. Add: Dept. of English, Eastern Michigan University, Ypsilanti, MI 48197.

TROYER, HOWARD WILLIAM, b. La Grange Co, Ind, Sept. 4, 01; m. 33; c. 3. ENGLISH LITERATURE. A.B, Earlham Col, 25, L.H.D, 65; A.M, Univ. Wis, 28, fel, 28-29, Ph.D.(Eng. lit), 38; Columbia Univ, 30-31. Chmn. dept, pub. schs, Ind, 24-26; asst, Univ. Wis, 26-28, instr, 29-30; prof. Eng, Lawrence Col, 31-57; dean, CORNELL COL, 57-69, EMER. DEAN, 69- Consult, Off. Sci. Res. & Develop, Wash, D.C, 45-46; Ford fel, 51-52; Fulbright lectr, Ger, 54-55. MLA; Col. Eng. Asn. Renaissance and 18th century English literature; life and writings of Edward Ward. Publ: Ned Ward of Grub Street; The salt and the savor; The four wheel drive story. Add: 578 Spanish Dr. S, Sarasota, FL 33577.

TRUBY, JOHN DAVID, b. Bellefonte, Pa, Apr. 17, 38; m. 61; c. 1. MASS COMMUNICATION. B.A, Pa. State Univ, 60, M.A, 62, Ph.D.(speech), 70. News-prod, WMAJ Radio, 61-62; pub. relat. dir, Clarion State Col, 62-65; sr. copywriter, Barash Advert, 65-67; freelance writer, 67-69; PROF. MASS COMMUN, IND. UNIV. PA, 69- Prof. criminol. sem, Ind. Univ. Pa, summers 71- First place award, 4th Estate Nat. Jour. Awards, 72. U.S.A, 60-66, Sgt. Journalism; investigation; history. Publ: Co-auth, Speech: science/art, Bobbs, 69; auth, The quiet killers, 72 & Silencers, snipers and assassins, 72, Paladin Press; Lewis, Gun heard 'round the world, Normount Publ, 74; contrib, The Civil War, Mankind Press, 71; plus numerous arts. Add: Dept. of Journalism, Indiana University of Pennsylvania, Indiana, PA 15701.

TRUE, MICHAEL D, b. Oklahoma City, Okla, Nov. 8, 33; m. 58; c. 6. ENGLISH & AMERICAN LITERATURE. B.A, Univ. Okla, 55; M.A, Univ. Minn, 57; Ph.D.(Am. lit), Duke Univ, 64; Harvard, 67. Lectr. ENG, Duke Univ, 60-61; N.C. Col. Durham, 61; from instr. to asst. prof, Ind. State Univ, 61-65; from asst. prof. to ASSOC. PROF, ASSUMPTION COL.(MASS), 65- Vis. lectr. Eng. & educ, Clark Univ, 68-73; vis. lectr. Eng, Quinsigamond Community Col, 71-72. U.S.A, 57-58. New Eng. Col. Eng. Asn.(dir, 66-69); MLA; NCTE. American literature of World War I; American literary radicals; contemporary poetry. Publ: Worcester poets: with notes toward a literary history, Worcester Poetry Asn, 72; The achievement of a literary radical, Bull. N.Y. Pub. Libr, 10/65; Flannery O'Connor: backwoods prophet in the secular city, Papers Lang. & Lit, spring 69; Death of a literary radical: Paul Goodman, 1911-1972, Commonweal, 9/72. Add: Dept. of English, Assumption College, Worcester, MA 01609.

TRUEBLOOD, PAUL GRAHAM, b. Macksburg, Iowa, Oct. 21, 05; m. 31; c. 2. ENGLISH LITERATURE. A.B, Willamette Univ, 28; A.M, Duke Univ, 30, Ph.D, 35; fel, Pendle Hill, 34-35. Instr, Friends Univ, 31-34; head Eng. stud, Mohonk Sch, 35-37; instr, Univ. Idaho, 37-40; assoc. prof, Stockton Col, 40-46; asst. prof, Rollins Col, 46-47; ENG, Univ. Wash, 47-52; vis. prof, Univ. Ore, 54-55; prof. & head dept, WILLAMETTE UNIV, 55-71, EMER. PROF, 71- Byron consult, univ. press, Univ. Chicago, 50-; Am. Counc. Learned Soc. scholar, 52-53; contrib, Bread Loaf Writers Conf, 58; vis. prof, Univ. B.C, 63; guest lectr, Pierce Col, Athens, 65; travel, res. & writing, Europe, 71-72; participant, Int. Byron Sem, Cambridge, 74. AAUP; Byron Soc; MLA; Keats-Shelley Asn. Am; Philol. Asn. Pac. Coast. English romantic poetry, especially Byron and Wordsworth. Publ: Flowering of Byron's genius, Russell, 62; Lord Byron, Twayne, 69 & 70; The last attachment, Keats-Shelley J, 1/52; The noble revolutionary, Saturday Rev, 12/54; Lord Byron's political realism, Byron J, 4/73. Add: 2635 Bolton Terr. S, Salem, OR 97302.

TRUESCHLER, JOSEPHINE, b. Baltimore, Md, July 28, 27. ENGLISH & AMERICAN LITERATURE, GREAT BOOKS. B.A, Col. Notre Dame, 49; M.Ed, Johns Hopkins Univ, 54, cert. advan. stud. educ, 58, M.A, 60. Elem. teacher, Pub. Sch, Md, 51-59; instr. educ, COL. NOTRE DAME (MD), 59-62, asst. prof. ENG, 62-67, ASSOC. PROF, 67- Distinguished Teacher Award, Col. Notre Dame, 67. MLA. Studies of modern American fiction; the notion of the existential hero. Publ: What color is Tuesday?, 12/52 & God rest ye when winter comes, 12/53, 1/54, Cath. Educr; plus poems. Add: Dept. of English, College of Notre Dame of Maryland, Baltimore, MD 21210.

TRUNK, CECILIA MAZUROWSKI, b. Bay City, Mich, July 26, 08; m. 70. ENGLISH. A.B, Nazareth Col, 38; M.A, Univ. Detroit, 45; summers, Univ. Notre Dame; scholar, Univ. Mich, 63, M.A.L.S, 66; fel, Univ. Ill, 67-68, advan. cert, 68. Teacher St. Benedict High Sch, 39-45; instr. Eng, Nazareth Col, 45-47; teacher high schs, Mich, 47-61; mem. fac. Eng, Nazareth Col, 61-63; chmn. dept, St. David High Sch, 63-65; St. Rita High Sch, 65-67; prof. libr. sci, Clarion State Col, 68-71; RETIRED. Ed. adv, Crusader, 56; mem. sem, Oxford & Univ. London, 62. NCTE; Am. Libr. Asn; Nat. Cath. Libr. Asn; Nat. Cath. Drama Asn; Conf. Eng. Educ. Chekhov's art; Akira Kurosawa's film art; the mythic concept in William Golding's novels. Publ: Harry Behn: wizard of song and lore, 10/67 & Implications in William Golding's Pincher Martin, 1/68, Cath. Educr; The qualitative aspect of library service, Cath. Libr. World, 2/68; plus others. Add: 4333 Rush Blvd, Youngstown, OH 44512.

TRUSS, TOM JAMES, JR, b. Birmingham, Ala, May 5, 27; m. 52; c. 4. ENGLISH. B.A, Vanderbilt Univ, 48, M.A, 50; Ph.D, Univ. Wis, 57. Instr. ENG, Univ. S.Dak, 52-57; asst. prof, Univ. Miss, 57-61, assoc. prof, 61-64, prof, 64-66; staff assoc, AM. ASN. UNIV. PROF, 66-69, ASSOC. SECY, 70- Victorian literature. Add: American Association of University Professors, Suite 500, Dupont Circle, N.W, Washington, DC 20036.

TSUBAKI, ANDREW TAKAHISA, b. Tokyo, Japan, Nov. 29, 31; U.S. citizen; m. 63; c. 2. SPEECH & DRAMA. B.A, Tokyo Gakugei Univ, 54; Univ. Sask, 58-59; M.F.A, Tex. Christian Univ, 61; Ph.D.(speech, drama), Univ. Ill, Urbana, 67. Designer-tech. dir. & instr. speech & drama, Bowling Green State Univ, 64-68; ASSOC. PROF. SPEECH & DRAMA & ORIENT. LANG. & LIT. & DIR, INT. THEATRE STUD. CTR, UNIV. KANS, 68- Am. Theatre Asn.(v.chmn, Asian theatre prog, 73-); Asn. Asian Stud. Japanese theatre and drama; Asian theatre and aesthetics. Publ: The sound of night (Japanese play), Players Mag, 10/64; Kaoru Osanai: Gordon Craig's production of Hamlet at the Moscow Art Theatre, Educ. Theatre J, 12/68; Zeami and the transition of the concept of Yugen: a note on Japanese aesthetics, J. Aesthetics & Art Criticism, fall 71. Add: International Theatre Studies Ctr, University of Kansas, Lawrence, KS 66045.

TSUZAKI, STANLEY MAMORU, Linguistics, Applied Linguistics. See Volume III, Foreign Languages, Linguistics & Philology.

TUBBS, STEWART LEROY, b. Cleveland, Ohio, Sept. 6, 43; m. 65; c. 1. SPEECH COMMUNICATION, SOCIAL PSYCHOLOGY. B.S.Ed, Bowling Green State Univ, 65, M.A, 66; Ph.D.(speech commun, psychol), Univ. Kans, 69. Asst. dir. commun. develop, Univ. Kans, Exten, 68-69; asst. prof. COMMUN, GEN. MOTORS INST, 69-70, ASSOC. PROF, 70- Consult, Gen. Motors Corp, 69-; vis. scholar, Univ. Mich, 73. Am. Psychol. Asn; Int. Commun. Asn; Speech Commun. Asn. Interpersonal communication; group dynamics; organizational development. Publ: Ed. & contrib, New directions in communication, Int. Commun. Asn, 72; co-auth, Human communication: an interpersonal perspective, Random, 74; auth, Explicit versus implicit conclusions and degree of audience commitment, Speech Monogr, 3/68; Game-playing behavior, conformity-inducing messages and interpersonal trust, J. Commun, 12/71; co-auth, The effect of Machiavellianism and justification on attitude change following counter-attitudinal advocacy, J.

Personality & Soc. Psychol, 6/72. Add: Dept. of Communication & Organizational Behavior, General Motors Institute, 1200 W. Third Ave, Flint, MI 48502.

TUCKER, CYNTHIA GRANT, b. New York, N.Y, June 17, 41; m. 66. COMPARATIVE LITERATURE, ENGLISH. B.A, Denison Univ, 63; NDEA fel. & Ph.D.(comp. lit), Univ. Iowa, 67. ASST. PROF. ENG, MEMPHIS STATE UNIV, 67- MLA. Renaissance European literature; developments in the sonnet tradition. Add: Dept. of Foreign Language, Memphis State University, Memphis, TN 38111.

TUCKER, DUANE EMERY, b. Syracuse, Kans, Sept. 28, 23; m. 45; c. 2. SPEECH. B.A, Kans. State Teachers Col, 47; M.A, Univ. Wis, 49, Annie Gorham fel. & Ph.D, 59. Sch. specialist radio-TV educ, Ore. State Univ, 51-57, dir. debate & asst. prof. speech, 57-59; assoc. prof. SPEECH, BOWLING GREEN STATE UNIV, 63-67, PROF, 67-, DIR. BROADCASTING, 68-, head radio-TV area, 59-72. Asn. Prof. Broadcasting Educ. Radio and television broadcasting. Publ: Radio for children, Gen. Exten. Div, Ore. State Syst. Higher Educ, 53; co-auth, Anti-slavery and disunion, Harper, 62; Bowling Green thinks big in planning a television studio, Am. Sch. & Univ, 5/67. Add: WBGU-TV, Bowling Green State University, Bowling Green, OH 43403.

TUCKER, EDWARD FREDERICK JOHN, b. Buckfastleigh, Eng, Jan. 2, 33; U.S. citizen; m. 62; c. 2. ENGLISH LITERATURE. B.A, West Liberty State Col, 65; M.A. & Woodrow Wilson fel, Univ. Ill, Urbana, 66; univ. fel. & Ph.D.(Eng), Harvard, 70. Teaching fel. ENG, Harvard, 67-70; ASST. PROF, SOUTH. METHODIST UNIV, 70- Nat. Endowment for Humanities summer stipend, 71, proj. dir, 72-73. Brit. Army, 50-55. MLA; Medieval Acad. Am; S.Cent. Mod. Lang. Asn; Col. Eng. Asn; Conf. Col. Teachers Eng. Medieval literature; law and lawyers in English literature; pedagogy. Publ: The Harvard manuscript of Parkhurst's Ignoramus, 71 & Ignoramus and 17th-century satire of the law, 71, Harvard Libr. Bull. Add: Dept. of English, Southern Methodist University, Dallas, TX 75275.

TUCKER, EDWARD LLEWELLYN, b. Crewe, Va, Nov. 19, 21. ENGLISH. B.A, Roanoke Col, 46; M.A, Columbia Univ, 47; Ph.D, Univ. Ga, 57. Asst. prof. ENG, VA. POLYTECH. INST, 60-66, ASSOC. PROF, 66- Southern literature. Publ: Richard Henry Wilde: life and selected poems, Univ. Ga, 66. Add: Dept. of English, Virginia Polytechnic Institute, Blacksburg, VA 24061.

TUCKER, KENNETH PAUL, b. Louisville, Ky, Dec. 2, 40. ENGLISH. B.A, Univ. Louisville, 63, M.A, 65; Ph.D.(Eng), Univ. Ky, 70. ASST. PROF. ENG, MURRAY STATE UNIV, 70- MLA; Renaissance Soc. Am; NCTE. Shakespeare; Elizabethan drama; nondramatic Elizabethan literature. Add: Dept. of English, Murray State University, Murray, KY 42071.

TUCKER, MARTIN, b. Philadelphia, Pa, Feb. 8, 28. ENGLISH. Scholar. & B.A, Wash. Sq. Col, N.Y. Univ, 49; fel, Univ. Ariz, 53, M.A, 54; Ph.D, N.Y. Univ, 63. Asst. prof. ENG, LONG ISLAND UNIV, 58-66, assoc. prof, 66-69, PROF, 69- Helene Wurlitzer Found. grant, Taos, N.Mex, 56-57; grant, Long Island Univ, 64, ed, Confrontation Mag, 70-; mem. admis. & scholar. comt, British Univ. summer sch. prog, 65-; consult, col. comprehensive test, Educ. Testing Serv, 65-; co-moderator, Writers Alive, Brooklyn Acad. Arts & Sci, 67-68; co-ed. & consult, Belles-Lett. Eng, Johnson Reprint Corp, 67-; fel. creative writing, Ossabaw Island Proj, Ga, 68. Scholar Award, Bread Loaf Writing Ctr, 59. MLA; African Stud. Asn; PEN Club (ed, PEN Newslett, 73-). Contemporary British and American fiction: English and African literature; African prose fiction. Publ: Co-auth, A modern library of criticism on modern British literature, 64, Moulton's library of literary criticism, 67, Africa in modern literature, 68 & The critical temper, 70, Ungar; ed, Introd. to Olive Schreiner's Undine, Johnson Reprint Corp, 72; auth, Wole Soyinka, Columbia Univ. Forum, summer 73. Add: Dept. of English, Long Island University, Brooklyn, NY 11201.

TUCKER, MELVIN JAY, History. See Volume I, History.

TUCKER, RAYMOND KENNETH, b. Providence, R.I, June 22, 27; m. 52; c. 3. SPEECH, COMMUNICATIONS. B.A, Denver Univ, 51; M.A, Northwest. Univ, 54, Ph.D.(speech), 56; Harvard, 65-66. Asst. dir. training, U.S. Steel Corp, 55-57; asst. prof. SPEECH, Purdue Univ, 58-60; assoc. prof, West. Ill. Univ, 60-68; PROF, BOWLING GREEN STATE UNIV, 68- U.S.A.A.F, 45-47. Speech Commun. Asn; Nat. Soc. Stud. Commun; Data Processing Mgt. Asn. Publ: Speech teacher in industry, 60 & Computer simulations, 68, Speech Teacher; co-auth, Image of college debater, J. Am. Forensic Asn, 67. Add: 941 Melrose St, Bowling Green, OH 43402.

TUCKER, ROBERT GARLAND, b. Portsmouth, N.H, Apr. 3, 21; div. c. 3. ENGLISH. A.B, Amherst Col, 49; M.A, Harvard, 51; Ph.D, Univ. Iowa, 61. Instr. ENG, UNIV. MASS, AMHERST, 52-62, asst. prof, 62-67, ASSOC. PROF, 67- Danforth Found. fac. grant, 59-60; co-ed, Mass. Rev, 72- Mosely Prize, 49. U.S.M.C, 43-45. MLA; Col. Eng. Asn. Creative writing; 20th century English and American literature; Anglo-Irish studies. Publ: Co-auth, Curious quire, Univ. Mass, 62; co-auth, Freedom, joy and indignation: letters from E.E. Cummings, 63 & auth, The wearing of the green, 72, Mass. Rev; plus others. Add: Bartlett Hall, University of Massachusetts, Amherst, MA 01002.

TUCKEY, JOHN SUTTON, b. Washington, D.C, July 27, 21; m. 45; c. 2. ENGLISH. A.B, Univ. Notre Dame, 43, M.A, 49, Ph.D.(Eng), 53. Instr. ENG, PURDUE UNIV, 53-55, asst. prof, 56-59, assoc. prof, 60-65, PROF. CALUMET CAMPUS, 65-, SECT. CHMN, 63-, Purdue Res. Found. grants, Mark Twain Papers, Univ. Calif, Berkeley, 61, unpub. Mark Twain manuscripts, 62, Mark Twain manuscripts, summer, 64. Am. Philos. Soc. grant & ed. Mark Twain papers, summer 65; Nat. Endowment for Humanities sr. fel, 73. U.S.N.R, 44-46, Lt.(jg). MLA; Col. Eng. Asn; NCTE; Am. Stud. Asn; Midwest Mod. Lang. Asn. Mark Twain studies; textual criticism. Publ: Mark Twain and little satan: the writing of The mysterious stranger, Purdue Univ, 63; Mark Twain's Which was the dream? and other symbolic writings of the later years, 67 & Mark Twain's Fables of man, 72, Univ. Calif; Mark Twain's The mysterious stranger and the critics, Wadsworth, 68, Table of green fields explained, Essays in Criticism, 10/56; The me and the machine, Mark Twain's later dialogue, 1/70 & Hannibal, Weggis and Mark Twain's Eseldorf, 5/70, Am. Lit. Add: Dept. of English, Purdue University, Calumet Campus, 2233 171st St, Hammond, IN 46323.

TUERK, RICHARD CARL, b. Baltimore, Md, July 10, 41; m. 63; c. 2. AMERICAN LITERATURE & ENGLISH. A.B, Columbia Univ, 63; M.A, Johns Hopkins Univ, 64, Ph.D.(Eng), 67. Asst. prof. Eng, Univ. Calif, Riverside, 67-72; ASSOC. PROF. LIT. & LANG, E.TEX. STATE UNIV, 72- Chief ed, Sadakichi Hartmann Newslett, 73- MLA; Thoreau Soc; AAUP; Emerson Soc. American Renaissance; transcendentalism in America; 19th century American literature. Publ: Central still: circle and sphere in Thoreau's prose, Mouton, 74; Thoreau's early version of a myth, Am. Transcendental Quart, 71; Los Angeles' reaction to Emerson's visit to San Francisco, New Eng. Quart, 71; Sadakichi Hartmann's How Poe wrote The raven: a biochemical explanation, Markham Rev, 73. Add: Dept. of Literature & Languages, East Texas State University, Commerce, TX 75428.

TUFTE, VIRGINIA J, b. Meadow Grove, Nebr, Aug. 19, 18; m. 40; c. 1. ENGLISH. A.B, Univ. Nebr, 44; M.A, Ariz. State Univ, 50; M.A, Univ. Calif, Los Angeles, 62, Ph.D.(Eng), 64. Asst. prof. ENG, UNIV. SOUTH. CALIF, 64-69, ASSOC. PROF, 69- Fel, William Andrews Clark Mem. Libr, 63-64. MLA; Ling. Soc. Am; Renaissance Soc. Am. Renaissance poetry; English grammar and style. Publ: Co-auth, Transformational grammar: a guide for teachers, Eng. Lang. Serv, 68; auth, The poetry of marriage—a critical history of Epithalamia, Univ. South. Calif. Stud. Comp. Lit, Vol. 2, Hennessey & Ingalls, 70; High wedlock then be honored, an anthology of Epithalamia, Viking, 70; Grammar as style & co-auth, Grammar as style: exercises in creativity, Holt, 71; Rhetoric and the Epithalamium, Pac. Coast Philol, 4/66; Gertrude Stein's Prothalamium—a unique poem in a classical mode, Yale Univ. Libr. Gazette, 7/68; England's first Epithalamium and the vesper adest tradition, Eng. Miscellany, 69. Add: Dept. of English, University of Southern California, Los Angeles, CA 90007.

TUFTS, JOHN MARSHALL, b. Columbus Twp, N.Y, Sept. 1, 14; m. 42, 67; c. 2. ENGLISH. B.S, Hamilton Col, 38; M.A, Columbia Univ, 48, Ed.D, 56. Teacher, High Sch, N.Y, 38-41; Tex, 46-48; grad. asst, Columbia Univ, 48-51; instr. ENG, WEST. CONN. STATE COL, 51-53, asst. prof, 53-56, assoc. prof, 56-60, PROF, 60-, CHMN. DEPT, 72- Ed, Teacher Educ. Quart, 54-56. U.S.N.R, 41-45, Lt. NEA; AAUP. Improvement of reading; linguistics; contemporary literature. Add: Dept. of English, Western Connecticut State College, Danbury, CT 06810.

TUNBERG, JACQUELINE DUFFIÉ, b. Los Angeles, Calif; m; c. 2. ENGLISH, DRAMA. B.A, Univ. South. Calif, 57, M.A, 60, Ph.D.(Eng), 65. Instr. ENG, Mt. St. Mary's Col, 61-63; lectr, SAN DIEGO STATE UNIV, 65-66, ASST. PROF, 66- Am. Soc. Composers, Auth. & Publ; MLA. British and American drama; European drama; playwriting. Publ: Co-auth, On Christmas Day (anthem), Lorenz, 54; auth, British and American verse drama from 1900 to 1965, Mouton, 68; Preface to Justine by D.A.F. de Sade, 68 & Preface to Juliette by D.A.F. de Sade, 68, Greenleaf Classics. Add: Dept. of English, San Diego State University, 5402 College Ave, San Diego, CA 92115.

TUNG, MASON, b. Shanghai, China, Feb. 1, 28; U.S. citizen; m. 61; c. 2. ENGLISH. A.B, Univ. Taiwan, 51; M.A, Baylor Univ, 57; Ph.D.(Eng), Stanford Univ, 62. Asst. prof. ENG, UNIV. IDAHO, 62-66, assoc. prof, 66-70, PROF, 70-, summer res. grants, 67, 70. Renaissance Soc. Am; Milton Soc. Am; MLA. John Milton; Edmund Spenser; Renaissance emblem literature. Publ: Samson impatiens: a reinterpretation of Milton's Samson Agonistes, Tex. Stud. Lit. & Lang, winter 68; Spenser's Graces and Costalius' Pegma, Eng. Miscellany, 72; Whitney's A choice of emblemes revisited, Stud. in Bibliog, 75. Add: Dept. of English, University of Idaho, Moscow, ID 83843.

TURCO, LEWIS, b. Buffalo, N.Y, May 2, 34; m. 56; c. 2. ENGLISH. B.A, Univ. Conn, 59; grad. fel, Univ. Iowa, 59-60, M.A, 62; fel, Yaddo Found, 59; Bread Loaf poetry fel, Middlebury Col, summer 61. Instr. ENG, Univ. Conn, 59; Cleveland State Univ, 60-64; asst. prof, Hillsdale Col, 64-65; STATE UNIV. N.Y. COL. OSWEGO, 65-67, assoc. prof, 67-69, PROF. ENG. & WRITING ARTS & DIR. PROG. WRITING ARTS, 70- Founder & dir, Cleveland State Univ. Poetry Ctr, 61-64; State Univ. N.Y. Res. Found. fac. fels, 65-67, 68-69, 70-71; 73-74; hon. trustee, Theodore Roethke Mem. Found, 68; vis. prof, State Univ. N.Y. Col. Potsdam, 68-69. Acad. Am. Poets Prize, Univ. Iowa, 60; Helen Bullis Prize, Poetry Northwest, 71. U.S.N, 52-56. Writing arts; American and British poetry & poetics. Publ: First poems, Golden Quill, 60; The book of forms: a handbook of poetics, Dutton, 68; Awaken, bells falling: poems 1959-1967, Univ. Mo, 68; The literature of New York, N.Y. State Eng. Counc, 70; The inhabitant (poems), 70 & Pocoangelini: a fantography (poems), 71, Despa; Poetry: an introduction through writing, Reston, 73; The weed garden (poems), Peaceweed, 73. Add: 54 W. 8th St, Oswego, NY 13126.

TUREEN, JACK, b. Paterson, N.J, Aug. 3, 26; m. 54. SPEECH. B.A, Brooklyn Col, 49, fel, 50-52, M.A, 52; United Cerebral Palsy Asn. fel, 51; N.Y. War Serv. scholar, 58; Ph.D, N.Y. Univ, 59. Instr. speech path, LONG ISLAND Univ, 50-54; speech educ, Brooklyn Col, 54-57; asst. prof. speech, HOFSTRA UNIV, 57-65, assoc. prof. & dept. rep, 65-69, PROF. SPEECH & CHMN. DEPT. SPEECH ARTS & SCI, 69- Lectr, div. gen. stud, Brooklyn Col, 52-63; mem. rehabil. codes comt, Fed. Div. Voc. Rehabil, 62; auth. & recipient, Off. Educ. prog. develop. grants, 67, 68; speech consult, Asn. Advan. Multiply Handicapped Blind Children, 67- Founder's Day Award, N.Y. Univ, 59. U.S.N.R, 44-46. Am. Speech & Hearing Asn; Speech Commun. Asn; East. States Speech Commun. Asn; Am. Asn. Mental Deficiency. Mental retardation; stuttering. Publ: Co-auth, Parental attitudes towards standards of fluency, Am. Speech & Hearing Asn. J, 52; auth, The relationship of speech defects and reading achievement, Diss. Abstr, 59. Add: Dept. of Speech Arts & Sciences, 108 Roosevelt Hall, Hofstra University, Hempstead, NY 11550.

TURLISH, LEWIS AFTON, b. Philadelphia, Pa, Mar. 8, 42; m. 66; c. 2. AMERICAN LITERATURE & STUDIES. B.A, Geneva Col, 64; M.A, Univ. Mich, 66, Ph.D.(Eng), 69. Instr. ENG, Bates Col, 69-70; Univ. Natal, 70; ASST. PROF, BATES COL, 70- Nat. Endowment Humanities res. grant, 72. MLA; Eng. Inst. American fiction; novel; literature and political ideology. Publ: Ed, Jeremy Belknap, The foresters, Scholars' Facsimiles & Reprints, 69; The rising tide of color: a note on the historicism of The Great Gatsby, Am. Lit, 11/71. Add: Dept. of English, Bates College, Lewiston, ME 04240.

TURNER, ALBERTA TUCKER, b. New York, N.Y, Oct. 22, 19; m. 43; c. 2. SEVENTEENTH CENTURY & CONTEMPORARY POETRY. B.A, Hunter Col, 40; M.A, Wellesley Col, 41, Ph.D.(Eng), Ohio State Univ, 46. Instr. ENG, Ohio State Univ, 46-47; lectr, Oberlin Col, 47-69; lectr, CLEVELAND STATE UNIV, 68-69, asst. prof, 69-73, ASSOC. PROF, 73- Mem, Acad. Am. Poets; assoc. ed, Field: Contemporary Poetry & Poetics, 70- Milton Soc. Am; Midwest Mod. Lang. Asn. Milton; contemporary poetics. Publ: Co-ed, Milton's familiar letters, for Yale edition of Milton's complete prose, Yale, 50-; auth, Need (poems), Ashland Poetry, 71; Learning to count (poems), Pittsburgh Univ, 74; Another 17th century Anglo-Saxon poem, 48 & French verse in the Oxford and Cambridge University miscellanies, 1600-1660, 49, Mod. Lang. Quart; Returner re-turned, Midwest Quart, 71. Add: Dept. of English, Cleveland State University, Euclid at 24th St, Cleveland, OH 44115.

TURNER, AMY LEE, b. Gainesville, Tex, Aug. 23, 09. ENGLISH, ARCHITECTURE. B.A, Rice Univ, 31, Ph.D.(Eng. lit), 55; M.A, Univ. Colo, 37. Educator, pub. schs, Tex, 31-41; cartographer, Army Map Serv, San Antonio, Tex, 41-42; Hydrographic Off, Wash, D.C, 42-46; instr. archit, UNIV. HOUSTON, 46-57, ASSOC. PROF. ENG, 57-, fac. support prog. grant, 67. U.S.N, 42-46, Lt. MLA; Milton Soc. Am; AAUP. The visual arts in Milton's poetry; John Milton's use of maps in his prose and poetry. Publ: Milton and Jansson's sea atlas, Milton Quart, 70; Milton and Millet, S.Cent. Bull, 70; contrib, Milton encyclopedia, Univ. Wis, 74. Add: Dept. of English, University of Houston, 3801 Cullen Blvd, Houston, TX 77004.

TURNER, (HENRY) ARLIN, b. Abilene, Tex, Nov. 25, 09; m. 37; c. 3. AMERICAN LITERATURE. B.A, W.Tex. State Col, 27; M.A, Univ. Tex, 30, Ph.D, 34. Instr. ENG, Univ. Tex, 33-36; La. State Univ, 36-37, asst. prof, 37-46, assoc. prof, 46-49, prof, 49-53; DUKE UNIV, 53-74, JAMES B. DUKE PROF, 74-, chmn. dept, 58-64. Guggenheim fel, 47-48, 59-60; vis. prof, Univ. Montreal, 51; Fulbright lectr, Univ. West. Australia, 52; managing ed, Am. Lit, 54-63, ed, 69-, assoc. Am. Counc. Learned Soc, 56-67; vis. prof, Univ. Bombay, 64; Fulbright lectr, Univ. Hull, Eng, 66-67; Nat. Endowment for Humanities sr. fel, 73-74. South. Hist. Asn. Sydnor Prize, 56-57. U.S.N.R, 42-46, Lt. Comdr. MLA (secy, Am. Lit. Group, 49-53, chmn, 66-67); NCTE; Am. Stud. Asn.(v.pres, 69-70); Col. Eng. Asn; Soc. Am. Hist; Southeast. Am. Stud. Asn.(v.pres, 55-56 & 68-70, pres, 56-57 & 70-72); Soc. Stud. South. Lit.(v.pres, 71-73, pres, 73-). American and Southern literature; Nathaniel Hawthorne. Publ: Hawthorne as editor, La. State Univ, 41, Kennikat, 72; George W. Cable: a biography, Duke Univ, 56, 2nd ed, La. State Univ, 66; ed, The Blithedale romance, Norton, 58 & Creoles and Cajuns, Doubleday, 58; auth, Mark Twain and George W. Cable: the record of a literary friendship, Mich. State Univ, 60; Nathaniel Hawthorne: an introduction and interpretation, Barnes & Noble, 61, 2nd ed, Holt, 67; George W. Cable, Steck-Vaughn, 69; ed, Chita, Univ. N.C, 69; ed, Miss Ravenel's conversion, 69 & Studies in the Scarlet letter, 70, C.E. Merrill; ed, The silent South, Patterson Smith, 69 & The Negro question, W.W. Norton, 68; auth, The comic imagination in American literature, Rutgers Univ, 73; contrib, The chief glory of every people, Univ. South. Ill, 73. Add: Dept. of English, Duke University, Durham, NC 27706.

TURNER, DARWIN THEODORE TROY, b. Cincinnati, Ohio, May 7, 31; div; m. 68; c. 3. ENGLISH. B.A, Univ. Cincinnati, 47, M.A, 49; Ph.D.(Eng), Univ. Chicago, 56. Asst. prof. Eng, Clark Col, 49-51; Morgan State Col, 52-57; prof. & head dept, Fla. Agr. & Mech. Univ, 57-59; Agr. & Tech. Col. N.C, 59-70, dean grad. sch, 66-70; PROF. ENG, Univ. Mich, 70-71; UNIV, IOWA, 71-, DIR, AFRO-AM. STUD, 72- Am. Counc. Learned Soc. grant-in-aid, 65; fel. coop. humanities prog, Duke Univ-Univ. N.C, 65-66; consult, NDEA Insts. Eng, 66-; Dept. Health, Educ. & Welfare, 66-; vis. prof, Univ. Wis, 69; Univ. Hawaii, summer 71; dir, Grad. Rec. Exam. Bd, 70-73; Rockefeller Found. grant, 72; consult, Nat. Endowment for Humanities, 72- Col. Lang. Asn.(secy, 58-63, pres, 63-65, Creative Scholar. Award, 71); NCTE (trustee, Res. Found, 70-); MLA; Col. Conf. Compos. & Commun; Col. Eng. Asn. American literature; literature by American Negroes; British and American drama. Publ: Katharsis, Wellesley, 64; co-ed, Images of the Negro in America, Heath, 65; auth, Nathaniel Hawthorne's The scarlet letter, Dell, 67; ed, Black American literature: essays, 69, Black American literature: fiction, 69, Black American literature: poetry, 69 & Black American literature: essays, poetry, fiction, drama, 70, C.E. Merrill; compiler, Afro-American writers: a bibliography, Appleton, 70; auth, In a minor chord, South. Ill. Univ, 71; co-auth, The teaching of literature by Afro-Americans, NCTE, 71; ed, Black drama in America, Fawcett, 71; co-ed, Voices from the black experience: literature, 72 & Responding: five, 73, Ginn; auth. of many articles & poems. Add: Dept. of English, University of Iowa, Iowa City, IA 52242.

TURNER, FREDERICK HODSON, JR, b. Philadelphia, Pa, Feb. 7, 43; m. 71; c. 1. SPEECH COMMUNICATION. B.S, Millersville State Col, 65; M.A, Temple Univ, 68, Ph.D.(speech), 71. ASST. PROF. SPEECH, RIDER COL, 71- Rhetoric Soc. Am; AAUP; Speech Commun. Asn. Rhetorical theory; persuasive communication; group processes. Publ: The effects of speech summaries on audience comprehension, Cent. States Speech J, spring 70; The New Jersey Indians were exploited too, Trenton Mag, 8/73. Add: Dept. of Communications, Rider College, Rte 206, Trenton, NJ 08602.

TURNER, FREDERICK WILLIAM III, b. Chicago, Ill, June 8, 37; m. 59; c. 3. ENGLISH. A.B, Denison Univ, 59; A.M, Ohio State Univ, 61; Ph.D.(folklore), Univ. Pa, 65. Instr. ENG, Haverford Col, 62-63; from instr. to asst. prof, Univ. R.I, 63-67, asst. prof, UNIV. MASS, AMHERST, 67-70, ASSOC. PROF, 70- Consult, Asn. Am. Indian Affairs, 71. American history; cultural anthropology; folklore. Publ: Ed, Geronimo: his own story, Dutton, 70; auth, Introduction to V.I. Armstrong's I have spoken, Swallow, 71 & to Charles Eastman's Indian boyhood, Fawcett, 72; ed, An American Indian reader, Viking, 73; auth, The dark side of Horatio Alger: Black jazz artists, Mass. Rev, 69; Melville's post-meridian fiction, Mid-Continent Am. Stud, 69; Red man, white man, man on the moon, Evergreen Rev, 70; plus others. Add: Dept. of English, University of Massachusetts, Amherst, MA 01002.

TURNER, JOHN MILLS, JR, b. Richmond, Va, Dec. 19, 08; m. 34; c. 2. AMERICAN LITERATURE. A.B, Lynchburg Col, 29; A.M, Univ. Mich, 33; A.M, Harvard, 39, Dexter traveling fel, 40, Ph.D, 56. Teacher ENG, high sch, Va, 29-32; assoc. prof, LYNCHBURG COL, 33-41, PROF. & CHMN. DIV. LANG. & LIT, 41- V.PRES. COL, 72-, dean, 52-72. Avery Hopwood Major Award, Univ. Mich, 33. MLA; Col. Eng. Asn. Influence of Darwinism upon major American writers from 1859 to 1910. Add: 118 Langhorne Lane, Lynchburg, VA 24501.

TURNER, KATHARINE CHARLOTTE, b. Normal, Ill, Mar. 11, 10. ENGLISH. B.Ed, Ill. State Norm. Univ, 30; M.A, Univ. Mich, 31, Ph.D.(Eng), 39. Asst. prof. Eng, Cent. Mich. Col, 39-43; res. cryptanalyst, U.S. War Dept, 43-46; asst. prof. ENG, ARIZ. STATE UNIV, 46-49, assoc. prof, 49-55, PROF, 55- Smith-Mundt lectr, Tamkang Eng. Col, Formosa, 55-56. American literature; creative writing. Publ: Red men calling on the great white father, Univ. Okla, 51; Writing: the shapes of experience, Pruett, 67. Add: 1216 Maple, Tempe, AZ 85281.

TURNER, MAXINE THOMPSON, b. Butler, Ga, Mar. 27, 35. EIGHTEENTH CENTURY STUDIES B.A, Huntingdon Col, 57; M.A, Auburn Univ, 61, Ph.D. (Eng), 70; cert. 18th century stud, Univ. Edinburgh, summer 67. Lectr. ENG, Montgomery Col, 61-62; instr, Upper Iowa Univ, 62-63; Auburn Univ, 67-68; ASST. PROF, GA. INST. TECHNOL, 70- MLA; Am. Soc. 18th Century Stud; Hymn Soc. Am; Am. Asn. Univ. Women; AAUP. Literature and theology; history of science; 18th century studies. Publ: Three eighteenth century revisions of the Bay Psalm Book, New Eng. Quart, 72; Samuel Johnson, churchman, St. Luke's J. Theol, 72; Joseph Addison's five hymns, The Hymn, 72; plus three others. Add: Dept. of English, Georgia Institute of Technology, 225 North Ave. N.W, Atlanta, GA 30332.

TURNER, MURIEL, English, Journalism. See ABELSETH, MURIEL.

TURNER, RICHARD CHARLES, b. Boston, Mass, Aug. 1, 44; m. 66; c. 2. RESTORATION & EIGHTEENTH CENTURY ENGLISH LITERATURE. A.B, Boston Col, 66; M.A, Emory Univ, 68, Ph.D.(Eng), 72. ASST. PROF. ENG, IND. UNIV-PURDUE UNIV, INDIANAPOLIS, 70- MLA; Am. Soc. 18th Century Stud. Restoration and 18th century poetry and drama; literary criticism; contemporary American poetry. Publ: Burbank and grub-street: a note on T.S. Eliot and Swift, Eng. Stud, 8/71. Add: Dept. of English, Indiana University-Purdue University at Indianapolis, 925 W. Michigan, Indianapolis, IN 46202.

TURNER, RICHARD M, b. Algona, Iowa, Dec. 15, 32; m. 55; c. 2. ENGLISH. B.A, Grinnell Col, 55; M.A, Univ. Colo, 61, Ph.D.(Eng), 67. From instr. to asst. prof. ENG, SOUTHWEST MO. STATE UNIV, 61-71, ASSOC. PROF, 71- U.S.A, 55-57. NCTE; Midwest Mod. Lang. Asn. Victorian literature; prosody; satire. Add: Dept. of English, Southwest Missouri State University, Springfield, MO 65802.

TURNER, ROBERT KEAN, JR, b. Richmond, Va, Nov. 30, 26; m. 48; c. 3. ENGLISH. B.A, Va. Mil. Inst, 47; M.A, Univ. Va, 49; Ph.D.(Eng), 58. Instr. ENG, Va. Mil. Inst, 57-58; asst. prof, 58-62; assoc. prof, UNIV. WIS-MILWAUKEE, 62-65, PROF, 65-, chmn. dept, 67-70. U.S.N, 44-46, Res, 46-68, Lt. Comdr. Bibliog. Soc. London; MLA (chmn. New Variorum Shakespeare Comt, 72-); Malone Soc; Renaissance Eng. Text Soc. Analytical bibliography and textual criticism of Elizabethan and Jacobean drama. Publ: Ed, a king and no king, 63 & The fair maid of the west, 67, Univ. Nebr; co-ed, Henry VI, Parts II & III, Penguin Bks, 67; contrib. ed, Dramatic works of F. Beaumont & J. Fletcher, Cambridge, 66- Add: Dept. of English, University of Wisconsin-Milwaukee, Milwaukee, WI 53201.

TURNER, ROBERT Y, b. Marshalltown, Iowa, Feb. 19, 27; ENGLISH. A.B, Princeton, 49; A.M, Univ. Chicago, 51, William Rainey Harper fel, 53-54; Carnegie teaching fel, 54-55, Ph.D, 58. Instr. ENG, Dartmouth Col, 55-58; UNIV. PA, 58-61, asst. prof, 61-64, ASSOC. PROF, 64- U.S.N.R, 45-46. MLA. Elizabethan drama and Shakespeare. Publ: Dramatic conventions in All's well that ends well, PMLA, 60; Shakespeare's apprenticeship, Univ. Chicago, 74; The causal induction in some Elizabethan plays, Stud. in Philol, 63; Characterization in Shakespeare's early history plays, ELH, 64; Shakespeare and the public confrontation scene in early history plays, Mod. Philol, 64. Add: Dept. of English, University of Pennsylvania, Philadelphia, PA 19104.

TURNER, RUFUS P, b. Houston, Tex, Dec. 25, 07; m. 28. ENGLISH. B.A, Los Angeles State Col, 58; M.A, Univ. South. Calif, 60, Ph.D.(Eng), 66. Assoc. prof. Eng, Calif. State Univ, Los Angeles, 65-73; RETIRED. AAAS; Soc. Tech. Writers & Publ; MLA; NCTE. Eighteenth century British literature; linguistics; semantics. Publ: Technical writer's & editor's stylebook, Sams, 64; Grammar review for technical writers, 64 & Technical report writing, 65, Holt; plus 3 others. Add: 122 E. Mariposa St, Altadena, CA 91001.

TURNER, SUSAN JANE, b. Kansas City, Mo, Sept. 7, 13. ENGLISH, AMERICAN LITERATURE. A.B, Univ. Ky, 34, M.A, 36; Ph.D, Columbia Univ, 56. Teacher ENG, Margaret Hall Sch. Girls, Versailles, Ky, 36-41; instr, Univ. Tenn, 42-44; VASSAR COL, 44-49, 51-55, asst. prof, 55-57, assoc. prof, 57-63, prof, 63-73, EMER. PROF, 74- Ingram-Merrill Found. stud. grant avant-garde writing & Am. Lit. criticism of 1920's, 66-67. MLA. Eighteenth century English literature; American literature, after 1870, especially literature and literary criticism 1915-1930. Publ: A history of The Freeman, literary landmark of the early twenties, Columbia Univ, 63; plus others. Add: Dept. of English, Vassar College, Poughkeepsie, NY 12601.

TURNER, WILLIAM HENRY, b. Borger, Tex, Apr. 24, 39; m. 60; c. 2. ENGLISH. B.A, Tex. A&M Univ, 61; M.A, Univ. Toronto, 63, Prov. Ont. & univ. fels, 64-66, Ph.D.(Eng), 69. Instr. ENG, Northview Heights Col, 63-64; Northwest. Univ, 66-67; ASST. PROF, TEX. A&M UNIV, 68- MLA. Eighteenth and 19th century British novel. Add: Dept. of English, Texas A&M University, College Station, TX 77843.

TURNEY, CHARLES, b. Philadelphia, Pa, Dec. 1, 30; m. 59; c. 2. ENGLISH. B.A, Univ. Richmond, 58, M.A, 59; Ph.D.(Eng), Rutgers Univ, 65. Instr. Eng, Douglass Col, Rutgers Univ, 61-64, asst. prof, 65-66; assoc. prof,

Univ. Richmond, 66-69, PROF. ENG, V.PRES. ACAD. AFFAIRS & DEAN COL, CATAWBA COL, 69- Sig.C, U.S.A, 54-56. MLA; S.Atlantic Mod. Lang. Asn. Elizabethan non-dramatic literature; modern British and American literature. Add: Catawba College, Salisbury, NC 28144.

TURPIE, MARY CHRISTINE, b. Columbus, Ohio, Sept. 24, 09. AMERICAN LITERATURE & CIVILIZATION. B.S, Univ. Minn, 30, A.M, 41, Am. Asn. Univ. Women fel, 42-43, Ph.D, 43. Instr, high sch, Elk River, Minn, 30-40; Eng, UNIV. MINN, MINNEAPOLIS, 43-45, asst. prof, 45-56, assoc. prof, 56-67, PROF. ENG. & CHMN. PROG. AM. STUD, 67- Am. Counc. Learned Soc. grant-in-aid, 43-44. NCTE; Am. Stud. Asn. The arts as documents for American studies; 19th century American literature. Publ: Growth of Emerson's thought; Paintings, music and architecture for the study of American civilization; Studies in American culture, Univ. Minn, 60. Add: Dept. of English, University of Minnesota, Minneapolis, MN 55455.

TUSO, JOSEPH FREDERICK, b. Oak Park, Ill, Nov. 2, 33; m. 58; c. 5. ENGLISH LITERATURE, HISTORY OF ENGLISH LANGUAGE. A.B, Don Bosco Col, N.J, 55; M.A, Univ. Ariz, 64, Ph.D.(Eng), 66. U.S. AIR FORCE, 55-, instr. ENG, U.S. AIR FORCE ACAD, 64-65, asst. prof, 66-68, ASSOC. PROF, 69- U.S.A.F, 55-, Lt. Col; Distinguished Flying Cross; Bronze Star Medal; Air Medal & Oak Leaf. MLA. Old and Medieval English language and literature; 20th century American literature. Publ: Dialectal variations in vocabulary in three late tenth century Old English gospels, Linguistics, 9/68; Beowulf 461b and Thorpe's Wara, Mod. Lang. Quart, 9/68; Faulkner's Wash, Explicator, 9/68. Add: Dept. of English, U.S. Air Force Academy, CO 80840.

TUTTLE, DONALD REUEL, b. Waucoma, Iowa, Sept. 23, 08; m. 31; c. 1. ENGLISH & AMERICAN LITERATURE. A.B, Oberlin Col, 30; A.M, West. Reserve Univ, 33, Ph.D, 39. Head dept. Eng, Nash Jr. Col, 30-33; instr. Eng, Fenn Col, 33-34, asst. prof, 34-37, assoc. prof, 37-42, 45-48, prof, 48-62, acting dir, dept. testing & guid, 42-44, voc. counsel, 44-46; EDUC. PROG. SPECIALIST, OFF. EDUC, U.S. DEPT, HEALTH, EDUC. & WELFARE, 62- War prod. trainer, War Manpower Comn, 42-44; evaluator, Comn. Eng. Insts, State Univ, Iowa, 62. U.S.N.R, 44-45, Lt. MLA; NCTE (2nd v.pres, 60-61); Col. Eng. Asn. Samuel T. Coleridge; Henry D. Thoreau; Percy's reliques and the Gothic romance as sources of Coleridge's Christabel. Publ: Education of teachers: curriculum programs, NEA, 59; The case of basic education, Little, 59; Basic considerations in preparing, certifying, and assigning teachers of English, Col. Eng, 63; plus others. Add: Office of Education, Dept. of Health, Education and Welfare, Washington, DC 20201.

TUTTLE, PRESTON HEATH, b. Wooster, Ohio, Feb. 14, 14; m. 41, 61; c. 2. THEATRE, DRAMA. B.A, Univ. Ill, 34, M.A, 56, Ph.D.(speech, drama), 63. Instr. speech & theatre, Univ. Ore, 58-62; Eng. & speech, Univ. Ill, 64-67; guest prof. speech & dramatic art, Univ. Ark, 67-68; WRITER & RESEARCHER DRAMATIC THEORY, 68- Am. Theatre Asn; Speech Commun. Asn; AAUP; AAAS; West. Speech Commun. Asn. Dramatic theory, especially the relationship between emotional content and dramatic form; theatre history; directing. Add: 75 S. Stanworth Dr, Princeton, NJ 08540.

TUTTLE, ROBERT C, b. Portland, Ore, Nov. 12, 23; m. 71; c. 3. ENGLISH, AMERICAN LITERATURE. B.A, Univ. Wash, 49, Ph.D.(Eng), 65. Instr. ENG, Cent. Wash. State Col, 51-53; Cent. Ore. Col, 53-55; from instr. to PROF, PORTLAND STATE UNIV, 55- U.S.N, 42-45. MLA; NCTE. American poetry, especially 19th century; romantic literary criticism. Add: Dept. of English, Portland State University, Box 751, Portland, OR 97207.

TUTTLE, ROBERT EUGENE, b. Waucoma, Iowa, May 30, 10. ENGLISH. A.B, Oberlin Col, 32, M.A, 34; Cornell Univ, 34-35; Ohio State Univ, 35-40. Instr. Eng, Gen. Motors Inst, 40-42, 45-49, asst. chmn. Eng. & psychol. dept, 49-56, acting chmn. Eng. & cult. stud. dept, 56-57, chmn. humanities dept, 57-68, asst. to dean engineering & prof. humanities, 68-70; RETIRED. U.S.A.A.F, 42-45, 2nd Lt. NCTE; Conf. Col. Compos. & Commun.(chmn, 57-58). English composition and language; technical writing. Publ: Co-auth, Writing useful reports, Appleton, 56 & The years 1919-1969—a history of G.M.I, Gen. Motors Inst, 69; auth, Trends in technical reporting, Am. Bus. Writing Asn. Bull, 3/56; Composition vs. communication—the wrong debate, Col. Compos. & Commun, 12/56; The freshman course at General Motors Institute, In: Communication in general education, W.C. Brown, 60. Add: Apt. 1007, 200 S. Birch Rd, Ft. Lauderdale, FL 33316.

TUTTLETON, JAMES WESLEY, b. St. Louis, Mo, Aug. 19, 34; m. 70. ENGLISH. B.A, Harding Col, 55; M.A, Univ. N.C, 57, Smith Fund grant, 62, Ph.D.(Eng), 63. Instr. ENG, Clemson Univ, 56-59; Univ. N.C, 62-63; Univ. Wis, Madison, 63-64, asst. prof, 64-68; ASSOC. PROF, N.Y. UNIV, 68- Univ. Wis. res. counc. grant, 64 & 65; Am. Philos. Soc. res. grant, 66; Nat. Endowment for Humanities fel, 67-68. U.S.A.F.R, 57-63. MLA; Am. Stud. Asn. American literature; English literature; American history. Publ: The novel of manners in America, Univ. N.C, 72; Aiken's Mr. Arcularis, Am. Imago, 63; Steinbeck in Russia, Mod. Fiction Stud, 65. Add: Dept. of English, New York University, New York, NY 10003.

TUVESON, ERNEST LEE, b. La Grande, Ore, Sept. 5, 15. ENGLISH LITERATURE. A.B, Reed Col, 34; univ. fel, Univ. Wash, 38-42, A.M, 41; Cutting traveling fel, Columbia Univ, 47-48, Ph.D, 49. Exam, U.S.Civil Serv. Comn, 42-43; instr. ENG, Brown Univ, 46-48; from lectr. to asst. prof, UNIV. CALIF, BERKELEY, 48-55, assoc. prof, 55-60, PROF, 60- Guggenheim fel, 51-52; fel, Folger Shakespeare Libr, 56. With War Dept, 43-45; vis. distinguished prof. humanities, Univ. Colo, 70. MLA; AHA; Am. Soc. Church Hist. Influence of millennialist ideas on culture; American romanticism; conception of the United States as a chosen nation. Publ: Millennium and Utopia; The imagination as a means of grace: Locke & the aesthetics of romanticism, Univ. Calif, 60; ed, Swift: a volume of critical essays, Prentice-Hall, 64; auth, Redeemer nation: the idea of America's millennial role, Univ. Chicago, 68; Swift: view from within the satire, In: The satirist's art, Ind. Univ, 72; The turn of the screw: a palimpsest, Stud. Eng. Lit, fall 72; The jolly corner, Stud. Short Fiction (in press). Add: Dept. of English, University of California, Berkeley, CA 94720.

TWOMBLY, ROBERT GRAY, b. New York, N.Y, May 16, 35; m. 60; c. 4. ENGLISH. B.A, Amherst Col, 57; Ph.D.(Eng), Yale, 65. Instr. ENG, City Col. New York, summer 57; Univ. Conn, 60-62; UNIV. TEX, AUSTIN, 63-65, asst. prof, 65-69, ASSOC. PROF, 69- Univ. Tex. Humanities Res. Counc. grant, Eng, summer 65. MLA(chmn. symbolism & allegory conf, 66-67); Soc. Higher Educ.(fel, 69-70). John Donne; 16th century religious literature; Shakespeare. Publ: Hubris, health, and holiness: the despair of J.F. Powers, In: Seven contemporary authors, Univ. Tex, 66; Wyatt's They flee from me, 68 & Thomas Wyatt's translation of the penitential psalms, 69, Tex. Stud. Lit. & Lang. Add: Dept. of English, University of Texas at Austin, Austin, TX 78712.

TYLER, PRISCILLA, b. Cleveland, Ohio, Oct. 23, 08. ENGLISH, LINGUISTICS. B.A, Radcliffe Col, 32; M.A, Case West. Reserve Univ, 34, Ph.D, 53. Teacher Eng, Latin & French, Cleveland Heights Bd. of Educ, Ohio, 35-45; lectr. Eng, Case West. Reserve Univ, 45-46, asst. prof, 46-59; educ, grad. sch. educ, Harvard, 59-63; assoc. prof. Eng, Univ. Ill, Urbana, 63-67; PROF. EDUC. & ENG, UNIV. MO-KANSAS CITY, 67- Mem. Eng. comt, Col. Entrance Exam. Bd, 49-54; African lang. comt, Educ. Serv, Inc, 62-; comt. developing materials teaching Eng. as second lang, Counc. Pub. Educ, 63- NCTE (2nd v.pres, 62-63; chmn. comt. ling. & reading, 63-67, mem. comn. compos, 68-71); Conf. Col. Compos. & Commun.(chmn, 63); Conf. Eng. Lit. of World (secy, 65-). Bibliography of texts in English used in the United States from 1600 to the present; English literatures of the world; history of the study of language. Publ: Ed, Writers the other side of the horizon, 64 & Linguistics and reading, 66, NCTE; auth, Linguistic criticism and literature in four centuries, In: The English language in the school program, 66; A poet's art of grammar, In: New directions in elementary English, 67; ed, Writers in the world tradition of English, Univ. Rev, winter 70. Add: Dept. of English & School of Education, University of Missouri-Kansas City, Kansas City, MO 64110.

TYNAN, DANIEL JOSEPH, b. Yonkers, N.Y, May 27, 44; M. 66; c. 2. AMERICAN & ENGLISH LITERATURE. B.A, Fordham Univ, 66; M.A, Univ. Wis, 67, Ph.D.(Eng), 72. Instr. ENG, COLO. COL, 70-71, ASST. PROF, 71- AAUP. Science and literature in 19th century American literature; tragedy in American literature, 1870-1914; the contemporary novel, relationship between fiction and life. Publ: J.N. Reynolds' Voyage of the Potomac: another source for The narrative of Arthur Gordon Pym, Poe Stud, 12/71. Add: Dept. of English, Colorado College, Colorado Springs, CO 80903.

TYNE, JAMES LAWRENCE, S.J, b. New York, N.Y, Jan. 22, 21. LITERATURE. A.B, Loyola Univ.(Ill), 44; M.A, Fordham Univ, 49; M.A, Yale, 55, Ph.D, 62. Instr. ENG, Fordham Univ, 60-62; Canisius Col, 62-63, asst. prof, 63-69; ASSOC. PROF, FORDHAM UNIV, 70- MLA; Am. Soc. 18th Century Stud. Eighteenth century English literature. Publ: The assumption in tradition, Thought, spring 52; Gulliver's maker and gullibility, Criticism, spring 65; Vanessa and the Houyhnhnms, Stud. in Eng. Lit, summer 71. Add: Dept. of English, Fordham University, Bronx, NY 10458.

TYNER, RAYMOND E, b. Athens, Ga, Feb. 27, 24. ENGLISH LITERATURE. A.B, Berry Col, 45; M.A, Univ. Ga, 48; Univ. N.C, 52-53; Ph.D, Univ. London, 55, 63-64. Instr. ENG, Clemson Col, 48-50, asst. prof, 50-52; prof. & chmn. dept, Berry Col, 56-58; prof, Erskine Col, 58-64, chmn. dept, 60-64; asst. prof, C.W. Post Col, L.I. Univ, 64-65; prof, Ky. Wesleyan Col, 65-68; ASSOC. PROF, SAGINAW VALLEY COL, 68-, ED, UNIV. MONOGR SERIES, 72- Ed, Green River Rev. & Int. Poetry Rev. U.S.M.C, 43-45, 2nd Lt. MLA; Renaissance Soc. Am; Milton Soc. Am. Seventeenth century English literature; Milton's garden imagery. Add: Dept. of English, Saginaw Valley College, University Center, MI 48710.

TYSON, ARCHIE MERVIN, b. Red Lion, Pa, Apr. 24, 11; m. 45; c. 1. ENGLISH LITERATURE. A.B, Gettysburg Col, 31; A.M, Univ. Mich, 34; Harvard, 40; Ph.D, Univ. Pa, 52. Teacher, high sch, Pa, 31-46; instr. Eng, Rider Col, 46-47, asst. prof, 47-52; prof, Pa. State Teachers Col, Kutztown, 52-59, head dept, 57-59; prof. & chmn. dept, MARSHALL UNIV, 59-67, dean, Col. Arts & Sci, 67-68, v.pres. acad. affairs, 68-71, dir, Inst. Self Stud. & honors prog, 71-73, DIR, WRITING PROG, 73- U.S.A.A.F, 43-45, S/Sgt. MLA; Am. Conf. Acad. Deans; NCTE; NEA; Conf. Col. Compos. & Commun; Asn. Higher Educ. Nineteenth century literature; English linguistics; Elizabethan minor drama. Publ: Co-auth, Communication: a basic teaching skill. Add: Dept. of English, Marshall University, Huntington, WV 25701.

TYSON, J. PATRICK, b. Ft. Worth, Tex, June 19, 36; m. 63; c. 2. ENGLISH. B.A, Tex. Tech. Col, 58; M.A, Tex. Christian Univ, 61; Ph.D.(Eng), Tulane Univ, 67. Instr. ENG, La. State Univ, New Orleans, 64-65; WHITMAN COL, 65-66, asst. prof, 66-70, ASSOC. PROF. & GARRETT FEL, 70- MLA. Add: Dept. of English, Whitman College, Walla Walla, WA 99362.

U

UBANS, MARIS ULDIS, b. Riga, Latvia, Dec. 4, 29; U.S. citizen. THEATRE ARTS, DRAMA. B.S, Syracuse Univ, 54; M.A, Northwest. Univ, 55. Admin. off, Int. Refugee Orgn, UN, Bad Kissingen, Ger, 48-50; lectr. dramatic prod, Northwest. Univ, 55-56; instr. speech & drama, Occidental Col, 56-57; asst. circulation mgr, Standard Rate & Data, Inc, Skokie, Ill, 57-58; instr. DRAMA, N.C. Cent. Univ, 58-59; from asst. prof. to ASSOC. PROF, CALIF. STATE UNIV, LOS ANGELES, 59- Vis. dir, Pomona Col, fall 62; staff critic, Educ. Theatre J, 69-; consult. box off. mgt, Lost Colony Theatre, Manteo, N.C, 72- Am. Theatre Asn; Asn. Advan. Baltic Stud. Musical theatre; translation of European dramatic works; stage directing and production. Publ: Theatre in review, irregular column in Educ. Theatre J, 69-; Latvian comedy: development of various types of style and form, 1890-1950, J. Baltic Stud, fall-winter 72. Add: 2955 Hollyridge Dr, Hollywood, CA 90068.

UDELL, GERALD R, b. Akron, Ohio, Feb. 16, 22; m. 48. ENGLISH, LINGUISTICS. B.A, Univ. Akron, 55; M.A, West. Reserve Univ, 56; Univ. Mich, summer 61; Ph.D.(Eng), Univ. Chicago, 66. Instr. ENG, S.Dak. State Univ, 59-60; asst. prof, Youngstown Univ, 61-63; Okla. State Univ, 63-65; Univ. Mo, Columbia, 65-67; ASSOC. PROF, OHIO UNIV, 67- U.S. Maritime Serv, 42-45, Lt.(jg). MLA; Ling. Soc. Am; Am. Dialect Soc; Am. Name Soc; AAUP. Dialect study; linguistic theory; Old English Literature. Publ: Contrib, Studies in linguistics in honor of Raven I. McDavid, Jr, Univ. Ala, 72; auth, Concerning black McGuffey readers, Acta Symbolica, spring 72; On first looking into Chomsky's Halle, Am. Speech, 73. Add: 7072 Strausser St, North Canton, OH 44720.

UEDA, MAKOTO, Literature, Aesthetics. See Volume III, Foreign Languages, Linguistics & Philology.

UHLMAN, THOMPSON POTTER, b. St. Joseph, Mo, Mar. 18, 26; m. 52; c. 1. ENGLISH. B.A, Univ. South. Calif, 48, M.A, 52, M.A, 64, Ph.D. (Eng), 68. TEACHER ENG. LATIN & FRENCH, HUNTINGTON PARK HIGH SCH, 53-, CHMN. DEPT. FOR. LANG, 69- U.S.N.R, 44-46. NCTE; MLA. Eighteenth century English literary criticism; contemporary American literature; the biographical and critical writings of Samuel Johnson. Publ: On A brief lexicon of jargon, Col. Eng, 1/68; Tate's Death of little boys, Explicator, 3/70. Add: 4365 Birchwood Ave, Seal Beach, CA 90740.

ULANOV, BARRY, b. New York, N.Y, Apr. 10, 18; m. 39; c. 3. ENGLISH. A.B, Columbia Univ, 39, Ph.D.(comp. lit), 55; D.Litt, Villanova Univ, 65. Instr. ENG, Princeton, 50-51; BARNARD COL, COLUMBIA UNIV, 51-56, asst. prof, 56-59, assoc. prof, 59-66, PROF. & ADJ. PROF, UNIV, 66-, chmn. dept, 67-72. Guggenheim fel, 62-63; Am. Counc. Learned Soc. grant, 62-63. Spiritual Life Award, 63; O'Brien Award for Distinguished Teaching, Newman Soc, 65. MLA; Mediaeval Acad. Am; Cath. Renascence Soc. (pres, 60-66). Relationship between literature and the arts; literature, theology and the drama; psychology and religion. Publ: Sources and resources: the literary traditions of Christian humanism, Newman, 60; Makers of the modern theater, 61 & co-auth, Modern culture and the arts, 67, McGraw; auth, Seeds of hope in the modern world, Kenedy, 62; Contemporary Catholic thought, Sheed, 63; Two worlds of American art, Macmillan, 65; The making of a modern saint, Doubleday, 66; The song of songs: the rhetoric of love, In: The bridge, Pantheon, 62; The relevance of rhetoric, NCTE, 66; Music in the church: a declaration of independence, In: Crisis in church music, Liturgical Conf, 67. Add: Barnard College, Columbia University, New York, NY 10027.

ULIN, RICHARD O, b. Boston, Mass, Aug. 3, 17; m. 60; c. 2. ENGLISH, EDUCATION. A.B, Harvard, 38, M.A, 42, fel, 46-49; M.Ed, 49, D.Ed, 60. Teacher, Pembroke Country Day Sch, Kansas City, 39-41; dir. freshman activities, Harvard, 41-42; teacher high sch, Mass, 49-65; ASSOC. PROF. ENG. EDUC. & ASST. DEAN SCH. EDUC, UNIV. MASS, AMHERST, 65- U.S. Dept. Health, Educ. & Welfare grant, 56-61; lectr, Eng. & educ, Tufts Univ, 58-65; consult, Oxford Univ. Press, 65-, Upward Bound, Off. Econ. Opportunity, 65-; dir, Inst. Advan. Stud. Eng, U.S. Off. Educ, 66-68; consult, Choice, 67-, Holt, Rinehart & Winston, Publ, 68-; prof. educ. & chmn. dept, Univ. Botswana, Lesotho & Swaziland, 72-74. U.S.N, 42-46, Lt. NCTE; New Eng. Asn. Teachers Eng; NEA. English education—literature and composition; education of the disadvantaged; effect of ethnicity on the educational process. Publ: Italo-American and Yankee boys, J. Exp. Educ, fall 65; Are English teachers teachable, Sch. & Society, 10/67; Sequence in the English curriculum: mirage or miracle?, High Sch. J, 1/73. Add: 96 Alpine Dr, Amherst, MA 01002.

ULLMANN, SAMSON OETTINGER ALTMAYER, b. Brooklyn, N.Y, June 18, 22. ENGLISH. A.B, Harvard, 43, A.M, 49, Ph.D.(Eng), 54; M.A, Stanford Univ, 47. Teaching fel. Eng, Harvard, 49-52; instr. Eng. & humanities, Univ. Minn, 52-57; asst. prof. ENG, UNION COL. (N.Y), 57-62, ASSOC. PROF, 62- U.S.A.A.F, 42-46, Lt. MLA; NCTE. Victorian literature; Matthew Arnold; Leslie Stephen. Publ: Ed, Men, books, and mountains; auth, Dating through calligraphy: the example of Dover Beach, Stud. Bibliog, 73. Add: Humanities Bldg, Union College, Schenectady, NY 12308.

ULLOTH, DANA ROYAL, b. Orlando, Fla, Oct. 19, 41; m. 65; c. 2. BROADCASTING, FILM. B.A, South. Missionary Col, 63; M.A, Univ. Mo-Columbia, 69, Ph.D.(speech), 71. Aerospace engr, U.S. Army Missile Command, Redstone Arsenal, Ala, 66-67; asst. ed, Univ. Mo-Columbia, 70-71; ASST. PROF. speech & broadcasting, Andrews Univ, 71-73; BROADCASTING, ITHACA COL, 73- Consult, Cent. Mo. State Univ, Warrensburg, 70; Farm Credit Banks, St. Louis, 70-71. U.S.A, 64-66. Am. Film Inst; Broadcast Educ. Asn; Speech Commun. Asn. Broadcast regulation and responsibility; broadcast effects on audiences. Add: Dept. of Television-Radio, School of Communication, Ithaca College, Ithaca, NY 14850.

ULREICH, JOHN CHARLES, JR, b. New York, N.Y, Sept. 16, 41; m. 66. SIXTEENTH & SEVENTEENTH CENTURY ENGLISH LITERATURE. B.A, & Woodrow Wilson fel, Hamilton Col, 63; M.A, Harvard, 64, fel, 65-67, Ph.D.(Eng), 69. Instr. ENG, Hamilton Col, 67-69, asst. prof, 69-71; UNIV. ARIZ, 71-74, ASSOC. PROF, 74- Nat. Humanities Found. summer res. grant, 73. MLA; Milton Soc. Am; Philol. Asn. Pac. Coast. Milton; 17th century poetry; Coleridge and romantic poetry. Publ: The typological structure of Milton's imagery, Milton Stud. V, 74; The typological structure of Sonnet 23, Milton Quart, 74; Milton's Haemony, Stud. Eng. Lit, 75; plus two others. Add: Dept. of English, University of Arizona, Tucson, AZ 85721.

ULREY, EVAN, b. Martinsville, Ill, Aug. 25, 22; m. 51; c. 3. SPEECH. B.A, Harding Col, 46; M.A, La. State Univ, 48, fel, 52-55, Ph.D.(speech), 55. Minister, Church of Christ, La, 46-50; PROF. SPEECH & CHMN. DEPT, HARDING COL, 50-, chmn. div. humanities, 54-56, lectr, 67. Minister, Church of Christ, Kans. & Ark; lectr, Abilene Christian Col, 51, 62; David Lipscomb Col, 60; lectr, Denmark, Ger, summer 69; dir, Ark. Consortium for Humanities, 72-73. Speech Commun. Asn; Am. Forensic Asn. Public address; phonetics; speech training and early speaking of Barton Warren Stone. Add: Dept. of Speech, Harding College, Searcy, AR 72143.

UMBACH, HERBERT HERMAN, b. St. Louis, Mo, Apr. 6, 08; m. 34; c. 1. ENGLISH & AMERICAN LITERATURE. Concordia Col, 20-26; M.Div, Concordia Sem, 29; univ. scholar, Wash. Univ, 29-30; A.M, 30, univ. fel, 30-31; Ph.D, Cornell Univ, 34; American Univ.(D.C), 49-50. Instr. ENG, Univ. Kans, 31-32; VALPARAISO UNIV, 34-38, asst. prof, 38-43, assoc. prof, 43-47, PROF, 47-, res. prof. Eng. lit, 66-68. Exchange prof. Eng. lang. & lit, Calif. Lutheran Col, 69-70. MLA; Am. Folklore Soc; Am. Stud. Asn. The faith of John Milton; John Donne's religious beliefs and writings; literary criticism. Publ: Ed, The prayers of John Donne, Bookman Assoc, 51 & Col. & Univ, 51; auth, The rhetoric of Donne's sermons, PMLA, 6/37; The merit of metaphysical style in Donne's Easter sermons, ELH, 6/45. Add: Dept. of English, Valparaiso University, Valparaiso, IN 46383.

UMBERGER, WALLACE RANDOLPH, JR, b. Christiansburg, Va, Jan. 19, 42. DRAMATIC LITERATURE & CRITICISM. A.B, Univ. N.C, Chapel Hill, 64, M.A, 66; Schubert Found. fel, 65, 66; univ. fac. grant, N.C. Cent. Univ, 68; grad. fel, Tulane Univ, 67, Ph.D.(theatre), 70. Prod. mgr, Lost Colony, Manteo, N.C, 65-68; assoc. prof. DRAMATIC ART, N.C. CENT. UNIV, 68-69, CHMN DEPT, 70- Dir, Jenney Wiley Summer Music Theatre, Prestonsburg, Ky, 71-72; guest lectr. playwrighting, N.C. Sch, Arts, 72; dir. over 50 plays, univ. & summer stock. Am. Theatre Asn; Southeast. Theatre Conf. Greek theatre history; 20th century European theatre; playwrighting. Publ: Amen to a mantis (play), South. Theatre, 68; Poetry, S.Carolinian Rev, 70; Strike at the wind (outdoor drama), Robeson Hist. Asn, 73; plus others. Add: Quarry Roost, 8 Gray Bluff Trail West, Rte. 7, Chapel Hill, NC 27514.

UMBLE, ROY HERMAN, b. Akron, Ohio, May 11, 13; m. 38; c. 2. SPEECH. A.B, Goshen Col, 35; A.M, Northwest. Univ, 38, grad. fel, 42, Ph.D, 49. Instr. high sch, Ill, 35-36; Ind, 36-38; speech, Univ. Pittsburgh, 38-44, asst. dean men, 41-44; assoc. prof. SPEECH, GOSHEN COL, 46-49, PROF, 49-, dir. Barbados Sem, summer 67. Fulbright grant, Pierce Col, Greece, 56-58; lectr, Mennonite Bibl. Sem, 65-; vis. scholar, Union Theol. Sem, 66-67. Speech Commun. Asn; Am. Speech & Hearing Asn; Cent. States Speech Commun. Asn; Nat. Asn. For. Stud. Affairs; Christian Soc. Drama; Am. Theatre Asn. Mennonite preaching, 1864-1944. Add: Dept. of Communication, Goshen College, Goshen, IN 46526.

UNDERHILL, WILLIAM R, b. Van Buren, Ind, June 10, 20; m. 45; c. 2. ENGLISH, SPEECH. B.A, Manchester Col, 46; M.A, Northwest. Univ, 47, Ph.D. (speech), 55; Georgetown Univ, 52; Ind. Univ, Bloomington, 53. Grad. instr. speech & debate coach, Northwest. Univ, 46-47; instr. ENG. & SPEECH, IOWA STATE UNIV, 47-48, asst. prof, 48-51, assoc. prof, 51-55, PROF, 55-, CHMN. DEPT. SPEECH ADMIN, 69-, dir. debate, 53-55, asst. dean stud. affairs, 56-57, prof. in charge speech, 60-69. U.S.A.A.F, 42-45 & 51-53, Capt; Air Medal & Oak Leaf; Distinguished Flying Cross. Speech Commun. Asn. Public address; American history; language and thought. Publ: Public address and psychological warfare, Today's Speech, 9/61; Harry S. Truman: spokesman for containment, 10/61 & Fulton's finest hour, 4/66, Quart. J. Speech. Add: 404 25th St, Ames, IA 50010.

UNDERWOOD, GARY NEAL, English Linguistics. See Volume III, Foreign Languages, Linguistics & Philology.

UNDERWOOD, SAM JESSE, b. Middlesex, N.C, May 17, 22; m. 54; c. 2. ENGLISH. A.B, Univ. N.C, 47, M.Ed, 53; Ph.D, Mich. State Univ, 57. Teacher Eng, Pub. Schs, N.C, 48-52; asst, Univ. N.C, 52-53; asst. prof. Eng. & dir. publicity, Alma Col, 53-55; assoc. prof. & dir. reading clinic, Furman Univ, 57-59; prof. Eng, Md. State Teachers Col, Frostburg, 59-62; PROF. ENG. & CHMN. DEPT, HIGH POINT COL, 62- Eng. consult, Greenville Pub. Schs, 56; lectr, Columbia Scholastic Press Asn; distinguished vis. prof, Pa. State Univ, 62. U.S.A, 41-46, Sgt. NCTE; Southeast Renaissance Conf; Columbia Scholastic Press Asn; Columbia Scholastic Press Adv. Asn; NEA. American literature; philosophy of literature; higher education. Publ: Role of yearbook advisor, 61 & Responsibilities of yearbook publishers to their patrons, 62, Columbia Scholastic Press; co-auth, Modern English grammer: readings, 72 & The art and poetry of Geneva D. and Pearl Highfill, 74, Delmar; plus numerous articles. Add: 503 E. Farriss Ave, High Point, NC 27262.

UNDERWOOD, WILLARD ALVA, b. Fairmount, Ill, Aug. 14, 43. SPEECH, DRAMA. B.S, Ill. State Univ, 65, M.S, 67; LaSalle Exten. Univ, 65-69; Ohio State Univ, 68; fel, Bowling Green State Univ, 70-72, Ph.D.(speech), 72. Teacher speech & music, Spalding Inst, Peoria, Ill, 65-67; instr. SPEECH & DRAMA, West. Ill. Univ, 67-70; ASST. PROF, TEX. A&I UNIV, 72- Speech Commun. Asn; NEA; AAUP; Music Educ. Nat. Conf. Oral communication; cross-cultural communication; third-world. Publ: A survey of lawyers' training in and attitudes toward speech in Illinois, J. Am. Forensic Asn, spring 69; Conceptualization of an utilitarian model for mass persuasion, TAIUS J, 73. Add: Dept. of Speech & Drama, Texas A&I University, Kingsville, TX 78363.

UNGER, LEONARD HOWARD, b. New York, N.Y, July 26, 16; m. 46; c. 3. ENGLISH. A.B, Vanderbilt Univ, 37; A.M, La. State Univ, 38; Ph.D, State Univ, Iowa, 41. Asst. prof, Bard Col, 46-47; from asst. prof. to PROF. ENG, UNIV. MINN, MINNEAPOLIS, 47- U.S.A.A.F, 42-45. Seventeenth century literature; modern literature; literary criticism. Publ: Donne's poetry and modern criticism, Regnery, 50; The man in the name, 56 & ed, T.S. Eliot: moments and patterns, 67, Univ. Minn. Add: Dept. of English, University of Minnesota, Minneapolis, MN 55455.

UNGER, RICHARD L, b. Springfield, Ill, Mar. 11, 39. COMPARATIVE LITERATURE, ENGLISH. A.B, St. Louis Univ, 61; M.A, Cornell Univ, 62, Ph.D.(comp. lit), 67. ASST. PROF. Ger, Univ. Mo-St. Louis, 66-68; comp. lit, Emory Univ, 68-71; ENG. & COMP. LIT, MISS. STATE UNIV, 71- MLA; AAUP. Hölderlin; English and German romanticism; Shelley. Publ: Contrib, (12 articles on Ger. writers) Encyclopedia of world biography, McGraw, 73. Add: Dept. of English, Mississippi State University, Mississippi State, MS 39762.

UNTERECKER, JOHN E, b. Buffalo, N.Y, Dec. 14, 22; div. ENGLISH LITERATURE. A.B, Middlebury Col, 44; M.A, Columbia Univ, 48, Ellis fel, 55, Ph.D, 56. Tutor ENG, City Col. New York, 46-48, instr, 48-58; asst. prof, Columbia Univ, 58-61, assoc. prof, 61-66, PROF, 66-73; UNIV. HAWAII, MANOA, 74- Am. Counc. Learned Soc. grant-in-aid, 61 & 73; Counc. Res. Humanities grant-in-aid, 61; Am. Philos. Soc. grant, 62; Guggenheim fel,

64-65; vis. prof. Eng, Univ. Hawaii, Manoa, autumn 69; poetry fel, YADDO, summers 69, 70 & 72; lectr. Yeats Int. Summer Sch, Sligo, Ireland, summers 73 & 74; vis. prof. Eng, Univ. Tex, Austin, 74. Van Amoringe Award Best Book of Year, 70; Ohioana Award for Best Book on Ohio Personality, 71. PEN Club; Auth. Guild; Am. Comt. Irish Stud. Aesthetics; children's literature; contemporary literature, particularly poetry and drama. Publ: A reader's guide to William Butler Yeats, Noonday, 59; Yeats, a collection of critical essays, Prentice-Hall, 63; Lawrence Durrell, Columbia Univ, 64; The dreaming zoo, Walck, 65; ed, Approaches to the twentieth-century novel, Crowell, 65; auth, Yeats and Patrick McCartan, A Fenian friendship, 67 & Stone, 74, Dolmen, Dublin; Voyager: a life of Hart Crane, Farrar, Strauss, 69 & Blond, 70; co-ed, Yeats, Joyce, Beckett, Bucknell Univ, 74; auth, Shifting patterns in American literature, Int. Lit. Annual I, 58; The architecture of The bridge, Wis. Stud. Contemporary Lit, 62; Lawrence Durrell, In: On contemporary literature, Avon, 64. Add: Dept. of English, University of Hawaii at Manoa, 1733 Donaghho Rd, Honolulu, HI 96822.

UNTHANK, LUISA-TERESA BROWN, b. Wakefield, Eng. ENGLISH LITERATURE. B.A, London; Am. Asn. Univ. Women fel, Univ. N.C, 64-65, M.A, 65; Ph.D.(Eng. lit), Univ. Liverpool, 73. Instr. ENG. LIT, N.Mex. State Univ, 60-63; ASST. PROF, CUMBERLAND COL.(KY), 64-Tutor Eng. lit, Univ. Liverpool, 71-72. Soc. Auth, Eng; Soc. Women Writers & Journalists; Brontë Soc; AAUP. Eighteenth century English literature; Victorian novels; Medieval literature. Publ: Contrib, Little but good—Maria Edgeworth, Mich. Quart. Rev, spring 72, Barbara Hofland—Yorkshire writer, Dalesman, 8/72 & Reporting from America, Brit. Vegetarian, 10/73; plus others. Add: Dept. of English, Cumberland College, Williamsburg, KY 40769.

UPHAUS, ROBERT WALTER, b. East Orange, N.J, June 15, 42; m. 65; c. 2. ENGLISH & AMERICAN LITERATURE. B.A, Calif. State Col, Los Angeles, 64; M.A, Univ. Wash, 66, Ph.D.(Eng), 69. Instr. ENG, Bellevue Community Col, 66-68; asst. prof, MICH. STATE UNIV, 68-72, ASSOC. PROF, 72- Vis. lectr. Eng, Univ. Leeds, 71-72. MLA; Am. Soc. 18th Century Stud; Irish Am. Cult. Inst. Shakespeare; 18th century English literature; contemporary American literature. Publ: Ed, American protest in perspective, Harper, 71; auth, Shaftesbury on art: the rhapsodic aesthetic, J. Aesthet. & Art Criticism, spring 69; Sentiment and spleen: travels with Sterne and Smollett, Centennial Rev, fall 71; Swift's poetry: the making of meaning, 18th Century Stud, summer 72. Add: Dept. of English, Michigan State University, East Lansing, MI 48824.

UPHOLD, WILLIAM B, JR, Humanities. See Volume IV, Philosophy, Religion & Law.

UPTON, ALBERT, b. Denver, Colo, Nov. 13, 97; m. 33, 55; c. 2. ENGLISH. A.B, Univ. Denver, 21; Ph.D, Univ. Calif, 29. Prof. Eng. & head dept, WHITTIER COL, 29-70, dir. gen. stud. lower div. & dir. col. press, 60-70, EMER. PROF. ENG, 70- Mem. adv. bd, J. Creative Behav, 67-; mem. staff, Inst. Creative Behav. U.S.N, 17-18. Conf. Col. Compos. & Commun; NCTE; Nat. Soc. Stud. Commun. Language psychology. Publ: Design for thinking, Stanford Univ, 61, Pac. Bks, 73; co-auth, Creative analysis, Dutton, 62; auth, Communication and the problem-solving process, In: Communication, Macmillan, 67; chaps, In: Communication, Spartan, 70 & Language behavior, Mouton, 70; plus others. Add: 1431 La Habra Dr, Lake San Marcos, CA 92069.

URAY, RICHARD MARTIN, b. Cleveland, Ohio, Oct. 29, 24; m. 50. BROADCASTING, EDUCATION. B.S, Kent State Univ, 49, M.A, 50; Ed.D, Univ. Houston, 63. Staff announcer, Radio Sta. WAKR, Akron, Ohio, 46-49; prod. mgr, Radio Sta. WBBW, Youngstown, 49-50; asst. prof. broadcasting, Univ. Houston, 50-58; dir. acad. affairs broadcasting, South. Ill. Univ, Carbondale, 58-66; CHMN. BROADCASTING SEQUENCE, UNIV. S.C, 66- Ed, Monitor, Alpha Epsilon Rho, 72- U.S.N, 43-46, Res, 46-70, Lt. Broadcast Educ. Asn; Nat. Acad. TV Arts & Sci; Nat. Asn. Educ. Broadcasters; AAUP; Speech Commun. Asn. Educational broadcasting; commercial television programming; broadcast journalism. Publ: An evaluation of scores on certain psychological examination by radio announcers, Univ. Houston, 63. Add: Broadcasting Sequence, College of Journalism, University of South Carolina, Columbia, SC 29208.

USREY, MALCOLM ORTHELL, b. Shamrock, Tex, Aug. 25, 29; m. 60; c. 1. ENGLISH. B.A, Abilene Christian Col, 51; Univ. Colo, summer 53; M.A, Tex. Technol. Col, 56, Ph.D.(Eng), 63. Teacher pub. schs, Tex, 51-57; instr, ENG, Abilene Christian Col, 57-59, asst. prof, 59-61; CLEMSON UNIV, 63-71, ASSOC. PROF, 71- S.Atlantic Mod. Lang. Asn. Romantic and Victorian literature; children's literature. Add: 122 Ft. Rudledge Rd, Clemson, SC 29631.

USSERY, HULING EAKIN, JR, b. Carlsbad, N.Mex, June 4, 25; m. 58; c. 1. ENGLISH, MEDIEVAL STUDIES. B.A, Univ. Nev, Reno, 48; A.M, Univ. Mich, Ann Arbor, 49, Ph.D.(Eng. lang. & lit), 63. Instr. ENG, Wayne State Univ, 54-58; Mich. State Univ, 58-60, asst. prof, 63-66; TULANE UNIV, 66-72, ASSOC. PROF, 72- U.S.N, 43-46. Medieval Acad. Am; MLA; Ling. Soc. Am; Am. Hist. Asn. Medieval studies; Old and Middle English; Chaucer. Publ: Chaucer's physician: medicine and literature in fourteenth-century England, Tulane Univ, 71. Add: Dept. of English, Tulane University, New Orleans, LA 70118.

UTTERBACK, RAYMOND VICTOR, b. Salem, Ore, Nov. 17, 36; m. 62. ENGLISH. B.S, Northwest Christian Col, 59; B.A, Univ. Ore, 59; M.A, 60; Rockefeller Bros. fel, Yale, 60-61; Ph.D.(Eng), Boston Univ, 67; cert, Shakespeare Inst, Univ. Birmingham, 69. Asst. prof. ENG, Baldwin-Wallace Col, 64-68; GA. STATE UNIV, 68-71, ASSOC. PROF, 71- Shakespeare Asn. Am; S.Atlantic Mod. Lang. Asn; Renaissance Soc. Am; Southeast. Renaissance Conf. Shakespeare; Renaissance literature; English drama. Publ: Dramatic perspectives on Shakespeare's history plays: a review article, & ed, Vol. 5, No. 1, Stud. Lit, Imagination, 72; auth, The death of Mercutio, Shakespeare Quart, 73. Add: Dept. of English, Georgia State University, 33 Gilmer St. S.E, Atlanta, GA 30303.

UTZ, KATHRYN E, B. Attica, Ohio, Sept. 1, 10. ENGLISH. A.B & B.Sc. in Ed, Capital Univ, 41; M.A, Ohio State Univ, 47, Ph.D.(Am. lit), 52. Asst. Eng, Ohio State Univ, 47-51, instr, 51-52; teacher high sch, Ohio, 41-43, 52-53; mem. fac. ENG, UNIV. WIS-WHITEWATER, 53-55, assoc. prof, 55-59, PROF, 59- Smith-Mundt vis. prof. Eng, Univ. Recife & Educ. Inst, Belo Horizonte, Brazil, 57-58; hon. mem, Eng. Teachers Asn. State of Minas Gerais, Brazil. Sig.C, W.A.C, 43-46, T/Sgt. MLA; Col. Eng. Asn; NCTE; Conf. Col. Compos. & Commun; Am. Stud. Asn; AAUP. American literature; drama; Chaucer. Add: 968 W. Conger St, Whitewater, WI 53190.

UZZELL, MINTER, b. Baird, Tex, Aug. 6, 09; m. 36; c. 2. ENGLISH, HUMANITIES. A.B, Hardin-Simmons Univ, 30; Th.M, Southwest. Baptist Theol. Sem, 33; M.Th, Berkeley Baptist Divinity Sch, 37; M.A. & Ed.D, Univ. Tulsa, 54. Instr. Eng, speech & jour, Bacone Col, 48-50; PROF. ENG. & HUMANITIES, NORTHEAST. STATE COL, 59-, dean stud, 61-69. Chaplains C, U.S.A, 41-63, Lt. Col. NEA; Asn. Higher Educ. English; American Indian education at the college level. Add: Dept. of English, Northeastern State College, Tahlequah, OK 74464.

V

VAGENAS, PETER THOMAS, b. Davenport, Iowa, Sept. 8, 32; m. 60; c. 2. THEATRE. A.B, Augustana Col.(Ill), 57; M.A, State Univ. Iowa, 59; fel, Univ. Denver, 63-65, Ph.D.(design), 66. Designer & instr. theatre. Univ. Toledo, 60-62; Mankato State Col, 62-63; designer & asst. prof. theatre, Univ. Denver, 65-66; East. Ill. Univ, 66-67; Univ. Mass, Amherst, 67-70; ASSOC. PROF. THEATRE & DESIGNER, CENT. WASH. STATE COL, 70- U.S.A, 53-55. Am. Theater Asn; Speech Commun. Asn; U.S. Inst. Theatre Technol. Constructivism in scenic design. Add: Dept. of Theatre & Drama, Central Washington State College, Ellensburg, WA 98926.

VAID, KRISHNA BALDEV, b. Dinga, India, July 27, 27; m. 52; c. 3. ENGLISH & AMERICAN LITERATURE. B.A, Univ. Panjab, Lahore, India, 46; M.A, Panjab Univ, Chandigarh, 49; Smith-Mundt fel, Harvard, 58-59, Rockefeller Found. fel, 59-61, Ph.D.(Eng), 61. Lectr. ENG, Univ. Delhi, 50-62; reader, Panjab Univ, India, 62-66; PROF, STATE UNIV. N.Y. COL. POTSDAM, 66-, dir, Star Lake Writing Workshop, summers 67, 68. Vis. prof. Eng, Case West. Reserve Univ, summer 68; Brandeis Univ, 68-69. Modern English, American and Indian novel; translation. Publ: Steps in darkness, Orion, 62; Technique in the tales of Henry James, Harvard Univ, 64; Silence, 72 & Bimal in Bog (2 vols), 72, Writers Workshop, Calcutta; Quest for quality, Bks. Abroad, autumn, 59; contrib, A death in Delhi, Univ. Calif, 73. Add: Dept. of English, State University of New York College at Potsdam, Potsdam, NY 13676.

VALDES, HELEN JOYCE MERRILL, b. Houston, Tex, June 16, 19; div; c. 2. ENGLISH LITERATURE. B.A, Univ. Tex, 40, M.A, 48, Ph.D, 61; E.D. Farmer fel. from Univ. Tex, Nat. Univ. Mex, 49; Rice Univ, 55-58. Asst. prof. ENG, UNIV. HOUSTON, 58-66, ASSOC. PROF, 66-, DIR. ENG. AS FOR. LANG, 58- Consult. Eng. as a second lang, Nat. Asn. For. Stud. Affairs, 66- W.A.V.E.S, 42-46, Res, 46-51, Lt. MLA; Conf. Col. Teachers Eng; Nat. Asn. For. Stud. Affairs (mem. bd, 68-69); Am. Counc. Teaching For. Lang; NCTE; Asn. Teachers Eng. As Second Lang.(secy, 67-68, exec. counc, 68-69); Teachers Eng. to Speakers Other Lang. English as a foreign language; the English novel; English and American satire. Publ: Co-auth, Writer's workbook, Form D, Prentice-Hall, 67. Add: Dept. of English, University of Houston, Houston, TX 77004.

VALENCIA, WILLA FERREE, b. Palatka, Fla, June 2, 28; div; c. 1. ENGLISH. B.A, Bob Jones Univ, 50; M.Ed, Univ. Chattanooga, 57; M.A, Univ. Tenn, 62; Ph.D.(Eng), Univ. Ill, 68. Instr. ENG, Tenn. Temple Col, 55-60; Knoxville Col, 60-62; asst, Univ. Ill, 62-67; asst. prof, VALDOSTA STATE COL, 67-70, assoc. prof, 70-73, PROF, 73-, CHMN. DEPT, 70- MLA; Col. Eng. Asn; Soc. Stud. South. Lit. The post-World War II English and American novel. Add: Dept. of English, Valdosta State College, Valdosta, GA 31601.

VALENCY, MAURICE, b. New York, N.Y, Mar. 22, 03; m. 36. ENGLISH & COMPARATIVE LITERATURE. A.B, City Col. New York, 23; A.M, Columbia Univ, 24, LL.B, 27, Ph.D.(Eng), 39. Instr. philos, City Col. New York, 30-32; Eng, Brooklyn Col, 32-44, asst. prof, 44; lectr. comp. lit, COLUMBIA UNIV, 42-46, assoc. prof. Eng, 46-54, prof. comp. lit, 54-69, Brander Matthews prof. DRAMATIC LIT, 69-71, EMER. PROF, 71-; DIR. ACAD. STUD, JUILLIARD SCH, 71- Ford Found. fel, 58; Guggenheim fels, 60 & 66; mem. bd. dirs, Dramatists Play Serv, 60-66; gen. adv. humanities, text-film div, McGraw-Hill Publ. Co, 67-72; adv. ed, Encycl. Am, 68- Dante Soc; Am. Comp. Lit. Asn; Dramatists Guild Fund (v.pres, 62-); MLA; Renaissance Soc. Am; Am. Soc. Composers, Auth. & Publ.(awards, 64-); Asia Soc; Int. Asn. Univ. Prof. Eng; Auth. League Am.(v.pres, 67-68, secy, 68-); Authors League Fund; Acad. Lit. Stud. Renaissance literature; drama; modern poetry. Publ: The tragedies of Herod, Columbia Univ, 39; co-auth, The madwoman of Chaillot, 49, The enchanted, 50, Ondine, 55, & The visit, 56, Random; co-auth, La perichole, Schirmer, 56; auth, In praise of love, 58 & The flower and the castle, 63, Macmillan; Feathertop, 59 & The Thracian horses, 63, Dramatists Play Serv; co-auth, Palace of pleasure, Capricorn, 60; auth, The breaking string, 66 & The cart and the trumpet, 73, Oxford Univ; plus others. Add: 404 Riverside Dr, New York, NY 10025.

VALENTINE, MARY HESTER, S.S.N.D, b. Pueblo, Colo, Sept. 5, 09. ENGLISH. B.A, Mt. Mary Col, 37; M.A, Loyola Univ.(Ill), 42; Univ. Notre Dame, 51, 53; Fordham Univ, 54; Columbia Univ, 62. Instr. ENG, MT. MARY COL, 51-54, assoc. prof, 54-70, PROF. & CHMN. DEPT, 71- Vis. prof. writing, St. Mary Col.(Kans), 58; Savage Consolini Univ. Lect. Bur. lectr, 60-64; compos. consult. curriculum comt, Wis. Lang-Arts, 63; ed, Sister Formation Conf, 65-; lectr, U.S. Inform. Serv, 70-71; vis. prof. Eng, Sogang Univ. & Song Sim Col, Korea, 70-71; Nat. Inst. Humanities. NCTE (chmn. nat. convention, 58, mem. curriculum comn, 70-73); MLA; Asn. Dept. Eng. Work in editing the letters of Mary Theresa Gerhardinger; contemporary literature, especially novelists and poets; contemporary religious life. Publ: Mother Stanislaus Kostka, Notre Dame Univ, 50; Canticle for the harvest, Kenedy, 51; ed, Program for progress, Fordham Univ, 66; auth, The post-conciliar nun, Hawthorn, 68; Restitution, In: Wide, wide world, Scott, 60; Greek tragedy and the novels of Alan Paton, Wis. Stud. Lit, 64; Teaching Initiate the heart and The juggler, NCTE, 66. Add: Dept. of English, Mt. Mary College, 2900 Menomonee River Pkwy, Milwaukee, WI 53222.

VALENTINE, MILTON ALBERT, b. Lodi, Calif, Feb. 14, 24; m. 50; c. 5. SPEECH, COMMUNICATION. A.B, Stanford Univ, 45, M.A, 50, Ph.D. (speech path. & audiol), 58. Sr. clinician speech path, Stanford Univ, 46-47; instr. speech reeducation, Ore. State Sch. Deaf, summer 47; speech & drama, Univ. Del, 48-51; acting instr. speech path, Stanford Univ, 51-52; acting asst. prof, 57; asst. prof. Eng. & speech & dir. speech & hearing clin, Univ. Colo. 52-57, assoc. prof. SPEECH, 58-64; PROF, ORE. STATE UNIV, 64- Mem. staff, Psychol. Serv. Ctr, Univ. Del, 49-51; spec. lectr, Univ. Colo. Sch. Med, 58-64; audiologist in asn. with V. Hildyard M.D, Denver, 58-64; mem. staff, Bur. Commun. Res, Inst. Behavioral Sci, Univ. Colo, 60-64; consult, bus. & indust. commun, Consul. Assoc, 64- ; consult, div. crippled children, Ore. Med. Sch, 66-67. U.S.A.A.F, 42-44, Sgt. Am. Speech & Hearing Asn; Nat. Soc. Stud. Commun. Psychoacoustics; human communitcation theory; organizational communication. Publ: Information theory, In: Psychology of communication, Appleton, 63; co-auth, Some persistent problems in interpersonal communitcation, Personnel J, 64 & A method of obtaining employee commitment, Northwest Bus. Mgt, 68. Add: Dept. of Speech Communication, Oregon State University, Corvallis, OR 97331.

VALES, ROBERT L, b. Cleveland, Ohio, June 23, 33. ENGLISH. B.A, West. Reserve Univ, 60, M.A, 61, Ph.D.(Eng), 64. Instr. ENG, Ohio State Univ, Lakewood, 63-65; asst. prof, Univ. Ill, Chicago Circle, 65-70; ASSOC. PROF, GANNON COL, 70- Co-ed, Genre, 68-; Nat. Endowment for Humanities summer stipend, 73. Transp.C, U.S.A, 53-55. MLA; NCTE; Am. Soc. 18th Century Stud. English literature of the 18th century. Publ: Peter Pindar (John Wolcot), G.K. Hall, 74; Thief and theft in Huckleberry Finn, Am. Lit, 66. Add: Dept. of English, Gannon College, Erie, PA 16501.

VALGEMAE, MARDI, b. Viljandi, Estonia, Nov. 10, 35; U.S. citizen; m. 57; c. 2. ENGLISH. B.A, Rutgers Univ, 57; Woodrow Wilson fel, Univ. Calif, Los Angeles, 60-61, M.A, 62, Ph.D.(Eng), 64. Asst. prof. ENG, Univ. Calif, Los Angeles, 64-68; ASSOC. PROF, LEHMAN COL, 68- Drama ed, Mana, 64-; Univ. Calif. fac. summer fel, 66; artistic consult, Theatre NOW Troupe, Century City Playhouse, Los Angeles, 67-68; vis. asst. prof. lectr, George Washington Univ, summer 68; City Univ. New York fac. res. grant, 69-70; Am. Counc. Learned Soc. Europ. travel grant, summer 70. U.S.A, 58-60, 1st Lt. MLA; Am. Comp. Lit. Asn; Asn. Advan. Baltic Stud.(v.pres. res. & conf, 71-72). Modern drama; Baltic studies. Publ: Accelerated grimace: expressionism in the American drama of the 1920s, South. Ill. Univ, 72; co-ed, Baltic literature and linguistics, Asn. Advan. Baltic Stud, 73; auth, Albee's Great god Alice, Mod. Drama, winter 67; Socialist allegory of the absurd, Comp. Drama, spring 71; Expressionism and the new American drama, Twentieth Century Lit, 10/71; plus 22 others. Add: Dept. of English, Herbert H. Lehman College, Bedford Park Blvd. W, Bronx, NY 10468.

VALLETTA, CLEMENT LAWRENCE, b. Easton, Pa, July 31, 38. AMERICAN CIVILIZATION. B.A, Univ. Scranton, 61; M.A, Univ. Pa, 62, Ph.D. (Am. civilization), 68. Instr. ENG, KING'S COL.(PA), 64-66, asst. prof, 66-70, ASSOC. PROF, 70-, CHMN. DEPT, 71- MLA; NCTE; Asn. Depts. Eng; Am. Stud. Asn. Americanization of ethnic groups; influence of relativity physics in non-scientific aspects; American civilization, folk, ecological, literary aspects. Publ: Putting on the American dream, Dialogist, 69; Friendship and games in Italian American life, Keystone Folklore Quart, 70; Einstein, Edison and the conquest of irony, Cithara, 72; plus others. Add: Dept. of English, King's College, 133 N. River, Wilkes-Barre, PA 18711.

VAN, THOMAS A, b. New York, N.Y, May 22, 38; m. 63. ENGLISH, LINGUISTICS. B.A, City Col. New York, 60; NDEA fel. & M.A, Duke Univ, 63, NDEA fel. & Ph.D.(Eng), 66. Instr. ENG, Univ. N.C, Chapel Hill, 65-66; asst. prof, Univ. Ky, 66-70; ASSOC. PROF, UNIV. LOUISVILLE, 70- MLA; NCTE; Mediaeval Acad. Am. Chaucer; the pearl poet; semantics. Publ: Second meanings in Chaucer's Knight's tale, Chaucer Rev, fall 68; Imprisoning and ensnarement in Troilus and the Knight's tale, Papers on Lang. & Lit, VIII: 3-12; Theseus and the Righte way of the Knight's tale, Stud. in Lit. Imagination, IV: 83-100. Add: Dept. of English, University of Louisville, Louisville, KY 40208.

VAN ARSDEL, ROSEMARY, b. Seattle, Wash, Sept. 1, 26; m. 50; c. 2. ENGLISH. B.A, Univ. Wash, 47, M.A, 48; Ph.D.(Eng), Columbia Univ, 61. Acting instr. Eng, Univ. Wash, 61, lit, 63; lectr. ENG, UNIV. PUGET SOUND, 66-67, asst. prof, 67-70, ASSOC. PROF, 70-, ADJ. PROF, SCH. LAW, 73-, CHMN. DEPT, UNIV, 70- Mem. study group, Victorian Periodicals Newslett, 68- MLA; Conf. Brit. Stud; NCTE; Tennyson Soc; Dickens Fel; Browning Inst; Ruskin Asn; Kipling Soc; Res. Soc. Victorian Periodicals. Victorian periodicals, especially the Westminster Review; Victorian prose and poetry; 19th century radical thought. Publ: Co-auth. & assoc. ed, The Wellesley index to Victorian periodicals, Univ. Toronto, 66-; auth, Victorian periodical research, Albion, 70; The Westminster Review: a change of editorship, 1840, Stud. Bibliog, 72; contrib, Dictionary of British radicals, Univ. Ga, (in press); plus four others. Add: 4702 N.E. 39th, Seattle, WA 98105.

VANCE, THOMAS HUME, b. Washington, D.C, Oct. 22, 08; m. 50; c. 2. ENGLISH & AMERICAN LITERATURE. A.B, Yale, 29, A.M, 32, Ph.D, 35; Sorbonne, Paris, 29-30. Instr. Princeton, 35-39; Univ. Va, 39-40; asst. prof. ENG, DARTMOUTH COL, 40-42, 46-50, PROF, 50- Vis. prof, Am. Inst, Munich, 51-52. U.S.N.R, 42-46, Lt. MLA. Dante, Shelley, Eliot; poems. Publ: Skeleton of light, Univ. N.C, 61. Add: Dept. of English, Dartmouth College, Hanover, NH 03755.

VANCE, WILLIAM LYNN, b. Dupree, S.Dak, Apr. 19, 34. ENGLISH. A.B, Oberlin Col, 56; M.A, Univ. Mich, 57, Ph.D, 62. Instr. ENG, Univ. Mich, 61-62; BOSTON UNIV, 62-64, asst. prof, 64-69, assoc. prof, 69-73, PROF. & ASSOC. CHMN. DEPT, 73- MLA; AAUP. American literature; the novel;

Walt Whitman. Publ: Co-ed, American literature, Little, 70; auth, Tragedy and the tragic power of laughter: The scarlet letter and The house of the seven gables, Nathaniel Hawthorne J, 71; Dreiserian tragedy, Stud. Novel, spring 72; Man or beast: the meaning of Cooper's The prairie, PMLA, 3/74; plus several others. Add: Dept. of English, Boston University, 236 Bay State Rd, Boston, MA 02215.

VAN CROMPHOUT, GUSTAAF VICTOR, b. Erembodegem, Belgium, Mar. 22, 38; U.S. citizen; m. 63; c. 2. ENGLISH & AMERICAN LITERATURE. Licenciaat, State Univ. Ghent, 59; Fulbright travel grant, Univ. Minn, 61, 66. Smith-Mundt award, 61-62, Ph.D.(Eng), 66. Instr. AM. LIT, State Univ. Ghent, 66-68; asst. prof, NORTH. ILL. UNIV, 68-71, ASSOC. PROF, 71- Belg. Army, 59-60. MLA; Midwest Mod. Lang. Asn. Colonial American literature; 19th century American literature; comparative literature. Publ: Artist and society in Henry James, Eng. Stud, 68; Emerson, Hawthorne, and The Blithedale romance, Ga. Rev, 71; Blithedale and the Androgyne myth, ESQ, 72; plus others. Add: Dept. of English, Northern Illinois University, De Kalb, IL 60115.

VANDE GUCHTE, MARTEN, b. Detroit, Mich, Feb. 9, 31; m. 53; c. 3. SPEECH, SPEECH & HEARING SCIENCE. A.B, Calvin Col, 53; M.Ed, Wayne State Univ, 54; Ph.D.(speech path), Mich. State Univ, 69. Asst. speech, Calvin Col, 54-55, instr, 57-63; asst. instr. speech & hearing sci, Mich. State Univ, 63-65; asst. prof. SPEECH, CALVIN COL, 65-66, assoc. prof, 66-70, PROF. & CHMN. DEPT, 70- Qm.C, U.S.A, 55-57. Am. Speech & Hearing Asn. Speech for the foreign student. Add: Dept. of Speech, Calvin College, Grand Rapids, MI 49506.

VANDE KIEFT, RUTH MARGUERITE, b. Holland, Mich, Sept. 12, 25. ENGLISH & AMERICAN LITERATURE. A.B, Meredith Col, 46; M.A, Univ. Mich, 47, univ. fels, 50-52, 54-56, Anna Olcott Smith fel, 55-56, Ph.D, 57; Oxford, 53-54. Instr. ENG, Calvin Col, 47-50; Wellesley Col, 56-59; asst. prof, Fairleigh Dickinson Univ, 59-60; instr, QUEENS COL.(N.Y), 61-62, asst. prof, 63-69, ASSOC. PROF, 70- Am. Asn. Univ. Women fel, 60-61; Yaddo fel, 61. MLA; Soc. Stud. South. Lit; Soc. Bibl. Lit. Modern Southern fiction; American literature; the Bible. Publ: Eudora Welty, Twayne, 62; ed, Thirteen stories by Eudora Welty, Harcourt, 65; auth, Patterns of communication in Great expectations, Nineteenth-Century Fiction, 3/61; Judgment in the fiction of Flannery O'Connor, Sewanee Rev, spring 68; Faulkner's defeat of time in Absalom, absalom!, South. Rev, fall 70. Add: Dept. of English, Queens College, Flushing, NY 11367.

VAN DEN BERG, SARA STREICH, b. St. Paul, Minn, May 19, 42; m. 66. ENGLISH LITERATURE. B.A, Univ. Minn, 64; Woodrow Wilson fel, Yale, 64-65, M.A, 65, univ. fels, 65-68, M.Phil, 67, Ph.D.(Eng), 69. Instr. ENG, Fordham Univ, 68-69; ASST. PROF, 69-70; FAIRFIELD UNIV, 70- Vis. asst. prof. Eng, Occidental Col, 73-74. Northeast Mod. Lang. Asn.(chmn. Milton sect, 73-74); MLA; Eng. Inst; Shakespeare Asn. Am; Philol. Asn. Pac. Coast. Renaissance English literature; Ben Jonson; Milton. Publ: Ed, Poems of Anne Killigrew, Scolar, 74; auth, The play of wit and love: Demetrius On style and Jonson's A celebration of Charis, ELH, 74. Add: Dept. of English, Fairfield University, North Benson Rd, Fairfield, CT 06430.

VANDERBEETS, RICHARD, b. Los Angeles, Calif, Dec. 6, 32; m. 59; c. 4. ENGLISH. B.A, San Jose State Col, 59; M.A, Univ. Idaho. 63; Ph.D.(Eng), Univ. of the Pac, 73. Instr. ENG, Univ. Idaho, 63-64; Menlo Col, 64-65; Robert Col, Istanbul, 65-66; ASST. PROF, SAN JOSE STATE UNIV, 66- Co-ed, Am. Lit. Abstracts, 67- U.S.N, 52-56. MLA; AAUP; Philol. Asn. Pac. Coast. Colonial American literature; American Indian; American history and culture. Publ: Co-auth, American short fiction, 69 & co-ed, Classic short fiction, 72, Bobbs; Drama: a critical collection, Harper, 71; A critical guide to Herman Melville, Scott, 71; auth, Held captive by Indians, selected narratives, 1642-1836, Univ. Tenn, 73; Harold Frederic and comic realism: the drama proper of Seth's brother's wife, 1/68 & The Indian captivity narrative as ritual, 1/72, Am. Lit; Milton in early America: the example of Benjamin Franklin, Milton Quart, 5/72; plus others. Add: Dept. of English, San Jose State University, 125 S. Seventh St, San Jose, CA 95192.

VANDERBURG, RAY HERSCHEL, b. Dec. 14, 15; U.S. citizen; m. 40; c. 3. JOURNALISM HISTORY. B.A, Southeast. State Col, 36; M.Ed, Univ. Okla, 45; Ed.D.(jour, higher educ), Okla. State Univ, 59. Teacher elem. Eng, Sumner Schs, Tex, 36-37; Eng, Forest Chapel Schs, 37-38; Washita High Sch, Okla, 38-39; Purcell Schs, 39-41; prin. hist, Plainview Schs, Tex, 41-42; Beggs Schs, Okla, 42-44; supt. schs, Crandall Schs, 44-46; instr. ENG. & JOUR. & chmn. dept, Northeast. Okla. A&M Col, 46-56; asst. prof, Kans. State Col. Pittsburg, 56-60; assoc. prof, WEST. ILL. UNIV, 60-70, PROF, 70- Asn. Educ. in Jour; AAUP. Publ: The paradox that was Arthur Brisbane, Jour. Quart, summer 70. Add: Dept. of English, Western Illinois University, W. Adams St, Macomb, IL 61455.

VANDERHAAR, MARGARET M, English & American Literature. See ALLEN, MARGARET VANDERHAAR.

VANDERLIP, ELDAD C, b. Heerlen, Netherlands, Feb. 3, 23; U.S. citizen; m. 56. COMPARATIVE LITERATURE, ENGLISH. A.B, Sir George Williams Univ, 48; M.A, Pasadena Col, 50; B.D, Calif. Baptist Theol. Sem, 51; Ph.D, Univ. South. Calif, 59. Instr. ENGLISH, WESTMONT COL, 56-59, asst. prof, 59-62, assoc. prof, 62-67, PROF, 67-, CHMN. DIV. MOD. LANG. & LIT, 59- MLA; NCTE. Renaissance period in Europe; relationship of aesthetics and values; contemporary novel. Add: 654 Circle Dr, Montecito, CA 93108.

VAN DER POLL, JAN, b. The Hague, Netherlands, Oct. 2, 38; m. 65; c. 1. THEATRE, AESTHETICS. B.A, Phillips Univ, 62; M.A, Univ. Okla, 65; Ph.D.(drama, philos), Univ. Mo-Columbia, 71. Instr. drama & speech, South. Ill. Univ, Edwardsville, 65-67; asst. instr. speech, Univ. Mo-Columbia, 67-69; instr. drama & speech, LA. STATE UNIV, BATON ROUGE, 69-71, ASST. PROF. DRAMA, 71- Lectr, Law Enforcement Inst, La. State Univ, 70-, coord-dir, Summer Dinner Theatre, 71-; state coord, La. Col. & Univ. Theatre Festival, 73-74. Am. Theatre Asn; Speech Commun. Asn. Dramatic theory and criticism; tragedy. Add: Dept. of Speech, Louisiana State University, Baton Rouge, LA 70803.

VANDERPOOL, WILLIAM S, JR, b. El Paso, Tex, Feb. 1, 22; m. 48; c. 3. SPEECH. A.B, Duke Univ, 43, LL.B, 48, J.D, 70; fel. & M.A, La. State Univ, 52, fel. & Ph.D.(speech), 53. Trial attorney, antitrust div, U.S. Dept. Justice, 48-50; instr. polit. sci, Ill. Inst. Tech, 50; asst. teacher speech, La. State Univ, 50-53; assoc. prof, chmn. dept. & chmn. div. fine arts, GRINNELL COL, 53-57, PROF. SPEECH, 57-, DIR. FORENSICS, 53- Vis. prof, Appalachian State Univ, 73-74. U.S.N, 43-46. Am. Bar Asn; Speech Commun. Asn. Semantics; argumentation and its legal history; communication in industry. Publ: U.S. Supreme Court decisions on free speech, Speech Monogr; contrib, Logical thinking, In: English can be fun. Add: Dept. of Communication, Grinnell College, Grinnell, IA 50112.

VANDERSEE, CHARLES ANDREW, b. Gary, Ind, Mar. 25, 38. AMERICAN LITERATURE. B.A, Valparaiso Univ, 60; Danforth & Woodrow Wilson fels. & M.A, Univ. Calif, Los Angeles, 61, Ph.D.(Eng), 64. Asst. prof. Eng, UNIV. VA, 64-70, ASSOC. PROF. ENG. & ASST. DEAN COL. ARTS & SCI, 70- Bruern fel, Univ. Leeds, 68-69; Am. Counc. Learned Soc. fel, 72-73. MLA; Am. Stud. Asn; Soc. Relig. Higher Educ. American literature—19th century; Henry Adams; American identity. Publ: Ed, John Hay's The bread-winners, Col. & Univ, 73; auth, Henry Adams and the invisible Negro, S.Atlantic Quart, winter 67; Henry Adams and 1905: prolegomena to The education, J. Am. Stud, 10/68; The Hamlet in Henry Adams, Shakespeare Surv, 71; plus others. Add: Dept. of English, Wilson Hall, University of Virginia, Charlottesville, VA 22903.

VANDER VEN, TOM ROBERT, b. Durand, Mich, Nov. 18, 37; m. 58, 72; c. 2. ENGLISH. A.B, Univ. Mich, 61, A.M, 63; fel, Univ. Colo, 67; Ph.D.(Eng), 68. Teacher high sch, Wyo, 61-64; asst. prof. ENG, IND. UNIV, SOUTH BEND, 67-72, ASSOC. PROF, 72-, chmn. dept, 69-73, summer fac. fel, 72. MLA. Robert Frost; Alfred Kreymborg. Publ: Co-ed, Bibliography: American studies dissertations, Am. Quart, 66-72, ed, 73-; auth, Robert Frost's dramatic principle of oversound, Am. Lit, 5/73. Add: Dept. of English, Indiana University at South Bend, South Bend, IN 46615.

VAN DER WEELE, STEVE JOHN, b. Sheboygan, Wis, Oct. 13, 20; m. 50; c. 2. ENGLISH LANGUAGE & LITERATURE. A.B, Calvin Col, 49; M.S, Univ. Wis, 50, Ph.D.(Eng), 55. Asst. ENG. LANG. & LIT, CALVIN COL, 50-52, instr, 53-54, 55-57, asst. prof, 57-59, assoc. prof, 59-61, PROF, 61-, DIR. WRITTEN RHET. PROG, 67- U.S.A.A.F, 42-44; Mil. Govt, 44-45. Renaissance Soc. Am; Conf. Christianity & Lit.(treas, 60-61, ed. newslett. & secy, 70-71); MLA. Literature of the 18th century; Shakespeare; world literature. Publ: Co-compiler, Garlands for Christmas, Macmillan, 65; Those religious novels, 1/60 & William Butler Yeats: in and beyond the classroom, 12/64, Reformed J; Shakespeare and the Christian faith, Christianity Today, 9-25/61; plus others. Add: 1915 Orville St. S.E, Grand Rapids, MI 49506.

VAN DEUSEN, (L) MARSHALL, b. Hudson, N.Y, June 14, 22; m. 46; c. 3. ENGLISH. A.B, Williams Col.(Mass), 45; Univ. Birmingham, Eng, 45-46; M.A, Univ. Pa, 48, Ph.D.(Am. civilization), 52. Lectr. Eng, Univ. Calif, Los Angeles, 50-53; instr, Stanford Univ, 53-54; asst. prof. Am. civilization, UNIV. CALIF, RIVERSIDE, 54-60, assoc. prof. ENG, 60-67, PROF, 67- Fulbright lectr. Am. lit, Univ. Oslo, Norway, 58-59; sr. lectr. Eng. & chmn. div. humanities, Univ. W.Indies, Barbados, 64-65. U.S.A, 42-46. MLA. American literature and literary criticism. Publ: A metaphor for the history of American criticism, Lundequistska Bokhandeln, Sweden & Ejnar Munksgarrd, Denmark, 61; J.E. Spingarn, Twayne, 69; In defense of Yvor Winters, Thought, autumn 57; Narrative tone in The custom house and The scarlet letter, Nineteenth Century Fiction, 6/66. Add: Dept. of English, University of California, Riverside, CA 92502.

VANDIVER, EDWARD PINCKNEY, JR, b. Anderson, S.C, Oct. 16, 02. ENGLISH LITERATURE. A.B, Furman Univ, 22; A.M, Univ. N.C, 28, Ph.D, 31. Teacher high sch, S.C, 22-26; teaching asst. Eng, Univ. N.C, 27-29; assoc. prof, Miss. Col, 29-30; prof. & head dept, Mary Baldwin Col, 31-46; Mercer Univ, 47-48; Erskine Col, 48-49; prof. Eng, Furman Univ, 49-66; RES. & WRITING, 68- Vis. prof, Anderson Col.(S.C), 66-68. MLA. The parasite in the Elizabethan drama; the influence of Shakespeare on authors of the 19th century. Publ: Highlights of Shakespeare's plays, Barron's, 65. Add: 703 E. Calhoun St, Anderson, SC 29621.

VAN DOMELEN, JOHN EMORY, b. Macon, Ga, Dec. 5, 35; m. 62; c. 3. RENAISSANCE LITERATURE. B.A, Calvin Col, 57; M.A, Univ. Mich, 60; Ph.D.(Eng), Mich. State Univ, 64. Asst. instr. ENG, Mich. State Univ, 60-63; assoc. prof, Wis. State Univ, Platteville, 63-67; assoc. prof, Univ. North. Iowa, 67-70; from assoc. prof to PROF, TEX. A&M UNIV, 70- Am. Philos. Soc. grant, 65; Wis. State Univ. res. grant, 65. U.S.A, 57-59, 61-62. MLA; S.Cent. Mod. Lang. Asn; Shakespeare Asn. Am. Shakespeare; English literature 1880-1920; literary criticism. Publ: The published writings of George Wilson Knight, In: The morality of art, Routledge, 69; Awful eloquence and right expression in Conrad, Stud. S.Cent. Mod. Lang. Asn, 70; Conrad and journalism, Jour. Quart, 70; plus others. Add: Dept. of English, Texas A&M University, College Station, TX 77840.

VAN DOREN, CHARLES LINCOLN, b. New York, N.Y, Feb. 12, 26; m. 57; c. 2. ENGLISH, PHILOSOPHY. B.A, St. John's Col.(Md), 47; M.A, Columbia Univ, 49, Cutting fel, 51-52, Ph.D.(Eng), 59. Instr. Eng, Columbia Univ, 55-59, asst. prof, 59; ed. consult, Ctr. Stud. Democratic Insts, 60-61; INST. PHILOS. RES, 61-67, ASSOC. DIR, 67- Gen. consult, San Francisco Prod, Inc, Chicago, 60-65, v.pres, 65-; consult, Encycl. Britannica, Inc, 60-73, v.pres. ed, 73-; consult. Encycl. Britannica Educ. Corp, 65-; Libr. Resources, Inc, 69- English literature; American history. Publ: Co-ed, The American treasury: 1455-1955, 55 & co-auth, Lincoln's commando, 57, Harper; auth, Growing up series (4 vols), Hill & Wang, 61-64; The idea of progress, 67, co-ed, A documentary history of the Mexican Americans, 71 & Great documents in American Indian history, 72, Praeger; exec. ed, The annals of America (20 vols), Encycl. Britannica, 69; co-auth, How to read a book, Simon & Schuster, 72; ed, Webster's American biography, Merriam, 73-74; plus others. Add: Institute for Philosophical Research, 201 E. Erie St, Chicago, IL 60611.

VAN DOREN, JOHN, b. New York, N.Y, Apr. 18, 28. ENGLISH, HISTORY. B.A, St. John's Col.(Md), 47; Ph.D.(hist), Columbia Univ, 52. Instr. hist, Brandeis Univ, 56-58, asst. prof. Eng, 58-62; lectr, Smith Col, 63-64; asst. prof, Boston Univ, 64-68; ED, THE GREAT IDEAS TODAY, ENCYCL. BRITANNICA, 71- Consult, Inst. Philos. Res, Chicago, 70- Add: The Great Ideas Today, 201 East Erie St, Chicago, IL 60611.

VANE, GEORGE THOMAS, b. Princeton, Ill, Oct. 25, 22. ENGLISH LITERATURE. A.M, Univ. Chicago, 48; Ph.D, Univ. Minn, 58. From asst. prof. to PROF. ENG, HAMLINE UNIV, 48- U.S.A, 42-46, Sgt. MLA; NCTE; AAUP. Eighteenth century English drama. Add: Dept. of English, Hamline University, St. Paul, MN 55104.

VAN EGMOND, PETER, b. Montgomery, Ala, Oct. 25, 37; m. 58; c. 2. AMERICAN LITERATURE. B.A, Miss. Col, 59; M.A, Univ. Miss, 61; Ph.D.(Eng), Univ. N.C, 66. Instr, ENG, Davidson Col, 64-66; ASST. PROF, UNIV. MD, COLLEGE PARK, 66- Vis. asst. prof. Eng, Vanderbilt Univ, summer 66; Fulbright-Hays lectr. Am. stud, Graz Univ, 68-69. MLA (Am. Lit. Group; mem. int. bibliog. comt, 67-). American and modern poetry. Publ: Ed, Memoirs of Thomas B. Harned: Whitman's friend and literary executor, Transcendental, 72; auth, Walt Whitman on the platform, South. Speech J, 6/67; Naming techniques in John Galsworthy's The Forsyte saga, Names, 12/68. Add: 3106 Old Largo Rd, Upper Marlboro, MD 20870.

VAN FOSSEN, RICHARD WAIGHT, b. Washington, D.C, July 17, 27; m. 55; c. 2. ENGLISH. A.B, Duke Univ, 49, A.M, 51; fel, Harvard, 54-56, Ph.D, 58. Instr. ENG, Clemson Col, 50-52; Duke Univ, 56-59; asst. prof, Cornell Col, 59-62, assoc. prof, 62-69, prof, 69-70; vis. prof, UNIV. TORONTO, 70-71, PROF, 71- Folger Shakespeare Libr. fel, 62; Newberry Libr. grant-in-aid, 63, 66; Assoc. Cols. Midwest-Newberry Libr. fel, 65-66; vis. assoc. prof, Univ. Chicago, summer 67. U.S.N, 45-46. MLA; Renaissance Soc. Am; Asn. Can. Univ. Teachers Eng. Renaissance dramatic and nondramatic literature; Canadian literature. Publ: Ed, A woman killed with kindness, Harvard & Methuen & Co, 61 & The Jew of Malta, Univ. Nebr, 64. Add: 81 Metcalfe St, Toronto, Ont. M4X 1S1, Can.

VAN GELDER, LIZETTE O, b. Arnheim, Holland, Apr. 10, 18. ENGLISH. A.B, Syracuse Univ, 40, A.M, 44; Columbia Univ, 50. Teacher, pub. schs, N.Y, 40-43; asst. prof. Eng, Howard Col, 44-48, assoc. prof, 48-62, dir. freshman compos, 48-57; asst. prof. ENG, Univ. Ky, 62-65, ASSOC. PROF, 65-70; PURDUE UNIV, WEST LAFAYETTE, 70- Vis. assoc. prof. & dir. Eng. teachers workshop, State Univ. Iowa, summer 62; dir, NDEA Eng. Insts, Univ. Ky, 65-68; consult, U.S. Off. Educ, 65 & 67; vis. assoc. prof, Univ. Hawaii, summer 69. NCTE; Conf. Col. Compos. & Commun; Conf. Eng. Educ; AAUP. Add: Dept. of English, Purdue University, West Lafayette, IN 47907.

VAN HAITSMA, GLENN A, b. Zeeland, Mich, Sept. 3, 27; m. 56; c. 4. ENGLISH LANGUAGE & LITERATURE. A.B, Hope Col, 49; M.A, Syracuse Univ, 50, fel, 50-52, Ph.D, 61. Asst, Syracuse Univ, 52-53 & 57-58; investr, U.S. State Dept, 55-56; asst. prof. ENG, CARROLL COL.(WIS), 58-63, assoc. prof, 63-68, PROF, 68- Intel.C, U.S.A, 53-55, Res, 55-61. NCTE; MLA; Midwest Eng. Conf. Milton, 17th century literature and contemporary theology; English romanticism, especially S.T. Coleridge; Third World literature. Publ: Coleridge's idea of culture, 64 & Notes toward a definition of a romantic cosmology, 66, Wis. Stud. Lit. Add: 519 Grove St, Waukesha, WI 53186.

VANN, JERRY DON, b. Weatherford, Tex, Jan. 17, 38; m. 58; c. 2. ENGLISH. B.A, Tex. Christian Univ, 59, M.A, 60; Ph.D.(Eng), Tex. Technol. Col, 67. Instr. ENG, N.TEX. STATE UNIV, 64-67, asst. prof, 67-71, ASSOC. PROF, 71- Bibliogr, Stud. in Novel, 68-; contrib. ed, MHRA Annual Bibliog, 68-; N.Tex. State Univ. fac. develop. leave fel, 70-71; Am. Philos. Soc. fel, 72. Res. Soc. Victorian Periodicals (bibliogr, 69-); Dickens Fel. Serialization of Dickens' novels; Victorian poetry; the English novel. Publ: Co-auth, Samuel Beckett, 69 & auth, Graham Greene, 70, Kent State Univ; ed, Critics on Henry James, Univ. Miami, 72; auth, The death of Dora Spenlow in David Copperfield, Victorian Newslett, fall 62; An unpublished DeQuincey letter, Philol. Quart, 71; Pickwick in the London newspapers, Dickensian, 73; plus two others. Add: 811 W. Oak, Denton, TX 76201.

VAN NOPPEN, JOHN JAMES, III, b. Spray, N.C, Sept. 3, 06; m. 39; c. 3. ENGLISH. A.B, Univ. N.C, 28; M.A, Teachers Col, Columbia Univ, 38, Ed.D, 40; Univ. London, summer 65. Teacher Eng. & Latin, high schs. & prep. schs, N.C, N.Y, Pa. & Italy, 28-40; acad. dean, Penn Hall Jr. Col, 40-41; teacher Eng, Scarsdale, N.Y, 41-42; indust. engineer, Gen. Motors Corp. & Firestone Tire & Rubber Co, 42-45; head dept. educ, Hiram Col, 45-46; asst. prof. ENG, Youngstown Col, 46-47; prof, APPALACHIAN STATE UNIV, 47-72, EMER. PROF, 72- Asst, Teachers Col, Columbia Univ, 39-40; mem. staff, Pittsburgh Sch. Surv, 39-40. NEA; S.Atlantic Mod. Lang. Asn; Eng-Speaking Union. Writing of biographies and historical novels. Publ: Co-auth, Daniel Boone backwoodsman: the green woods were his portion, Appalachian Press, 66 & Western North Carolina since the Civil War, 73. Add: Appalachian State University, Boone, NC 28607.

VAN NOSTRAND, ALBERT DOUGLASS, b. Babylon, N.Y, May 25, 22; m. 43; c. 5. ENGLISH. A.B, Amherst Col, 43; A.M, Harvard, 48, Ph.D.(Eng), 51. Asst. prof. ENG, BROWN UNIV, 51-57, assoc. prof, 57-68, PROF, 68-, CHMN. DEPT, 73- Guggenheim fel, 57-58; Fulbright lectr, Brazil & U.S. Inform. Agency grant, S.Am, 61-62; consult, Dept. State, 67; Agency Int. Develop, 68-69; mem. Latin Am. rev. comn, Fulbright-Hays prog, 71-74; Nat. Humanities Fac, 72-74. U.S.N.R, 43-46. MLA; Am. Stud. Asn; AAUP. Rhetoric; American fiction; Pan-American literature. Publ: Literary criticism in America: an anthology, 57, co-ed, Conscious voice: American poetry, Bobbs, 59; auth, Denatured novel, Bobbs, 60, 62, Greenwood, 73; Everyman his own poet, McGraw, 68. Add: 57 Appian Way, West Barrington, RI 02890.

VAN PELT, ELIZABETH STANFIELD, b. Kenvir, Ky, Sept. 8, 21; m. 58; c. 2. ENGLISH. A.B, Univ. Ill, 43, M.A, 52, Ph.D.(Eng), 62. Teacher high schs, Ill, 43-56; asst. ENG, Univ. Ill, 56-62; asst. prof, ST. CLOUD STATE COL, 63-66, assoc. prof, 66-67, PROF, 67- American literature, especially Hawthorne. Add: Dept. of English, St. Cloud State College, St. Cloud, MN 56301.

VAN SCYOC, LEO L, b. Gravity, Iowa, Aug. 18, 26; m. 48; c. 4. ENGLISH. A.B, Ft. Hays Kans. State Col, 50, M.S, 50; Ph.D.(Eng), Univ. Kans, 58. Teacher high sch, Kans, 50-53; instr. ENG, UNIV. ARK, FAYETTEVILLE, 57-59, asst. prof, 59-62, assoc. prof, 62-67, PROF, 67- U.S.N.R, 44-46. MLA; NCTE; Conf. Eng. Educ; Conf. Col. Compos. & Commun. American literature; English Renaissance; English language. Add: Dept. of English, University of Arkansas, Fayetteville, AR 72701.

VAN SLOOTEN, HENRY, b. Bancroft, Idaho, Dec. 31, 16; m. 41; c. 6. ENGLISH. Ph.D, Univ. South.Calif, 57. Instr. ENG, Los Angeles Harbor Jr. Col, 49-54; asst. prof, Los Angeles State Col, 54-58; assoc. prof, CALIF. STATE UNIV, NORTHRIDGE, 58-61, PROF, 61-, chmn. dept, 66-67. Lectr. libr. sci, Univ. Tex, Austin, summers 70, 71. U.S.N.R, 42-45, Lt. Col. Eng. Asn; Philol. Asn. Pac. Coast; NCTE; MLA. Hardy and Conrad; Victorian literature. Publ: Co-auth, Read and write: studies in current English, Harper, 61, 66, 72. Add: Dept. of English, California State University, Northridge, CA 91326.

VAN TASSEL, DANIEL ELLSWORTH, b. Minneapolis, Minn, Apr. 28, 40; m. 62; c. 2. ENGLISH LITERATURE. B.A, St. Olaf Col, 62; M.A, Univ. Iowa, 64, Ph.D.(Eng), 70. Instr. ENG, Concordia Col.(Moorhead, Minn), 64-66; Chapman Col, 66-67; ASST. PROF, PAC. LUTHERAN UNIV, 70- MLA. Victorian literature; 20th century British literature; Shakespeare. Publ: The search for manhood in D.H. Lawrence's Sons and lovers, Costerus: Essays Eng. & Am. Lang. & Lit, 72. Add: Dept. of English, Pacific Lutheran University, Tacoma, WA 98447.

VANTUONO, WILLIAM JOHN, b. Newark, N.J, Jan. 2, 27; m. 57; c. 2. MIDDLE ENGLISH LITERATURE. B.S, Seton Hall Univ, 50, M.A, 54 & 62; Ph.D.(Eng), New York Univ, 69. Teacher ENG, Newark Bd. Educ, N.J, 50-69; ASSOC. PROF, ESSEX COUNTY COL, 69- U.S.A, 45-46. MLA. The Pearl-poet in Middle English literature. Publ: Patience, Cleanness, Pearl, and Gawain: the case for common authorship, Annuale Mediaevale, 71; The structure and sources of Patience, Mediaeval Stud, 72; The question of quatrains in Patience, Manuscripta, 72. Add: 754 Clifton Ave, Newark, NJ 07104.

VAN VORIS, WILLIAM H, b. San Francisco, Calif, Sept. 6, 23; m. 49; c. 2. ENGLISH. B.A, Univ. Calif, 49; Ph.D.(Eng), Trinity Col.(Dublin), 56. Instr. ENG, Univ. Ore, 53-57; from asst. prof. to ASSOC. PROF, SMITH COL, 57- Vis. lectr, Trinity Col.(Dublin), 63-64. U.S.N.R, 42-45. Restoration and 18th century drama and poetry; modern Irish and Anglo-Irish drama. Publ: The cultivated stance: the designs of Congreve's plays, Dolmen, 65. Add: Dept. of English, Smith College, Northampton, MA 01060.

VAN WART, JAMES, b. Springfield, Mass, Dec. 6, 25. DRAMA. A.B, Middlebury Col, 48; Columbia Univ, 49-50. Asst. drama, Williams Col, 48-49; instr. drama & speech, Middlebury Col, 50-56; HOFSTRA UNIV, 57-60, asst. prof, 60-65, assoc. prof, 65-69, PROF. DRAMA, 69-, dir. playhouse, 59-66, chmn. dept. speech & drama, 65-71. Prof. dir. & actor, summer theatres, 49-62. U.S.N.R, 43-45. Am. Theatre Asn; Archaeol. Inst. Am. Theatre archaeology; play directing; conservation of natural resources. Add: Dept. of Drama, Hofstra University, Hempstead, NY 11550.

VARDAMAN, GEORGE T, b. San Antonio, Tex, Aug. 6, 20. SPEECH, COMMUNICATIONS. Ph.D, Northwest. Univ, 52. From assoc. prof. to PROF. COMMUN, UNIV. DENVER, 51-, ASST. DEAN GRAD. STUD, COL. BUS. ADMIN, 67-, ASSOC. DEAN, BUS. & PUB. ADMIN, 69-, chmn. dept. admin. commun, 62-67. Commun. consult; v.pres. & mem. exec. comt, Nat. Ctr. Commun. Arts & Scis, 65- Counc, 69-73; chmn. stud. minorities for grad. bus, Grad. Bus. Admis; ed, Mgt. & Commun. Ser, Auerback Publ, Inc, 70- U.S.A.A.F, 40-45. Fel. Acad. Mkt. Sci; Nat. Soc. Stud. Commun.(mem. nat. counc, 65-); West. Speech Asn. Speech; industrial communications; management. Publ: Co-auth, Managerial control through communication, 68 & Communication in modern organizations, 73, Wiley; Effective communication of ideas, Van Nostrand-Reinhold, 70; auth, Dynamics of managerial leadership, Auerbach, 73; How to develop a communication system, Int. Counc. Indust. Eds. Reporting, 1/64; A college level program in writing proficiency, Col. News & Views, 5/66. Add: P.O. Box 691, Indian Hills, CO 80454.

VARDY, AGNES MARIA, Comparative Literature, German. See Volume III, Foreign Languages, Linguistics & Philology.

VARGISH, THOMAS, b. Poultney, Vt, Feb. 13, 39; m. 63. ENGLISH. B.A, Columbia Col, 60; B.A, Oxford, 62, Rhodes scholar, M.A, 67; Osgood fel, Princeton, Ph.D.(Eng), 66. Instr. ENG, DARTMOUTH COL, 65-66, asst. prof, 66-70, ASSOC. PROF, 70-, fac. fel, 67-68. Humanities Found. summer grant, 67; Guggenheim fel, 72-73. Nineteenth century English literature; 19th century novel, English and continental; modern American literature. Publ: Newman: the contemplation of mind, Clarendon, 70; Gnostic Mythos in Moby Dick, PMLA, 6/66; Revenge and Wuthering Heights, Stud. Novel, spring 71. Add: Dept. of English, Dartmouth College, Hanover, NH 03755.

VARLEY, HENRY LELAND, b. Melrose, Mass, Sept. 28, 10; m. 36; c. 3. ENGLISH & AMERICAN LITERATURE. A.B, Wesleyan Univ, 34, A.M, 35; fel, Univ. Wis, 35-36, Ph.D, 52. Teaching fel, Wesleyan Univ, 36-38; instr. ENG, UNIV. MASS, AMHERST, 38-46, asst. prof, 46-50, assoc. prof, 50-56, prof, 56-74, EMER. PROF, 74- Vis. instr, Wesleyan Univ, 45; Amherst Col, 46; Fulbright prof, Japan, 58-59, Malaya, 68-69; vis. lectr, Am. Stud. Sem, Kyoto, 61; vis. prof, Doshisha Univ, Japan, 74. Kipling; English and American literature, 1890-1940. Add: Dept. of English, University of Massachusetts, Amherst, MA 01002.

VARMA, DEVENDRA P, b. Darbhanga, India, Oct. 17, 23; Can. citizen; m. 47; c. 1. ENGLISH. B.A, Patna Univ, 42, M.A, 44; Ph.D.(Eng), Univ. Leeds, 55; Univ. London, 55-56. Asst. prof. ENG, Patna Univ, 44-56; prof, Ranchi Univ, 56-57; Tribhuvan Univ, Nepal, 57-58; Damascus Univ, 58-61; Univ. Delhi, 61-62; Ain Shams Univ, Cairo, 62-63; PROF, DALHOUSIE UNIV, 63- MLA. Gothicism and Gothic movement in eighteenth century English literature. Publ: Gulliver in the Kingdom of Coins, Patna Univ, 42; The Gothic flame, Barker, London, 57, Russell, 66; Palmyra: caravan city of Queen Zenobia, 60 & Literature and aesthetics, 61, Damascus Univ; Seven horrid novels, Folio Soc, London, 68; Radcliffe's Italian, Russell, 68; ed, Forty rare Gothic romances, Arno & McGrath, 70-73; auth, The evergreen tree of diabolical knowledge, Consortium, 72. Add: Dept. of English, Dalhousie University, Halifax, N.S, Can.

VARNADO, ALBAN F, b. Baton Rouge, La, Dec. 24, 20. SPEECH, DRAMA. A.B, La. State Univ, 41, M.A, 47, Ph.D.(speech, drama), 54. Instr. speech, St. Louis Univ, 48-49; SPEECH & DRAMA, Univ. Kansas City, 54-56, asst. prof, 56-59; UNIV. NEW ORLEANS, 59-61, assoc. prof, 61-68, PROF, 68-, DIR. DIV. CONTINUING EDUC, 73-, eve. div, 64-73. U.S.A.F, 42-45, 49-52, 1st Lt. Speech Commun. Asn; Am. Theatre Asn; Asn. Continuing Higher Educ.(pres-elect, 73-74). A history of theatrical activity in Baton Rouge, Louisiana from 1819-1900; Reverend Gilbert Austin's Chironomia. Publ: Problems of the director in central staging, South. Speech J, 9/47. Add: Division of Continuing Education, University of New Orleans, New Orleans, LA 70122.

VARNER, JOHN GRIER, b. Mt. Pleasant, Tex, Mar. 30, 05; m. 39. ENGLISH. A.B, Austin Col, 26; fel, Univ. Va, 30-38, A.M, 32, Ph.D, 40. Asst. prof, Washington & Lee Univ, 38-43; dir, Centro-Venezolano Am, Caracas, Venezuela, 43-47; asst. cult. attaché, Am. Embassy, Mexico City, Mex, 47; assoc. prof. ENG, UNIV. TEX, AUSTIN, 47-70, prof, 70-72, EMER. PROF, 72- U.S. Dept. State lectr, S.Am. & Cent. Am, 51; Am. Philos. Soc. & Univ. Tex. Res. Counc. res. grants, Spain, 54. Cor. mem. Royal Acad. Cordoba; Latin Am. Stud. Asn. Latin American literature; history of colonial Latin America; North American literature. Publ: Auth. introd. & compiler, Edgar Allan Poe and the Philadelphia Saturday Courier, Univ. Va, 33; auth, English grammar for Venezuelans, 44; co-ed, Florida of the Inca, 51 & auth, El Inca, the life and times of Garcilaso de la Vega, 68, Univ. Tex. Add: 2510 Jarratt Ave, Austin, TX 78703.

VASILEW, EUGENE, b. New York, N.Y, Oct. 13, 20; m. 49; c. 3. SPEECH. B.A, N.Y. Univ, 42; M.A, Univ. Iowa, 47; Ph.D, Ohio State Univ, 55. Instr. SPEECH, Univ. Buffalo, 47-49; Hofstra Col, 52-56; asst. prof, Lehigh Univ. 56-60; HARPUR COL, STATE UNIV. N.Y. BINGHAMTON, 60-62, assoc. prof, 61-62, PROF, 62-, ombudsman, 69-73. Ed, Today's Speech, 70-72. Am. Field Serv, 42-44; U.S.A, 45. Speech Commun. Asn; AAUP; Asn. Comput. Mach. Rhetoric; public address; mass communication. Publ: Norman Thomas at the Townsend Convention 1936, Speech Monogr, 11/57; The new style in political campaigns, Lodge in New Hampshire 1964, Rev. Polit, 4/68. Add: R.D. 1, Binghamton, NY 13903.

VASTA, EDWARD, b. Forest Park, Ill, Jan. 18, 28; m. 53; c. 6. ENGLISH. B.A, Univ. Notre Dame, 52; Fulbright Scholar. grant, Univ. Florence, 52-53; M.A, Univ. Mich, 54; univ. fels, Stanford Univ, 54 & 55, Danforth grant, 61, Ph.D.(Eng. & humanities), 63. Instr. ENG, UNIV. NOTRE DAME, 58-61, asst. prof, 61-66, assoc. prof, 66-69, PROF, 69-, CHMN. DEPT, 72- U.S.N, 46-48. MLA; Mediaeval Acad. Am; AAUP; Midwest Mod. Lang. Asn. Medieval literature; general humanities. Publ: The spiritual basis of Piers plowman, Mouton, The Hague, 65; ed, Middle English survey; critical essays, 65 & Interpretations of Piers plowman, 68, Univ. Notre Dame; auth, Great expectations and The great Gatsby, Dickensian, 64; Truth, the best treasure, in Piers plowman, Philol. Quart, 65; Pearl: immortal flowers and the pearl's decay, J. Eng. & Ger. Philol, 67. Add: 52140 Harvest Dr, South Bend, IN 46637.

VAUGHAN, JOSEPH LEE, b. Lynchburg, Va, Jan. 26, 05; m. 38; c. 2. ENGLISH. A.B, Univ. Va, 26, A.M, 27, Ph.D, 40. Instr. Eng. UNIV. VA, 30-35, asst. prof, 35-40, assoc. prof, 40-45, prof, 45-60, provost, 56-60, lectr. undergrad. sch. commerce, 45-60, chancellor community cols, 60, prof. HUMANITIES, SCH. ENGINEERING & APPLIED SCI, 60-70, JOSEPH L. VAUGHAN PROF, 70- Assoc. dir. spec. sch. teachers Eng. & speech in engineering cols, Univ. Mich, 41; consult. & vis. lectr, Inst. Textile Tech, 47-51, pres, 51-53; consult, Chesapeake & Potomac Telephone Co; Fieldcrest Mills; Sperry Rand Corp, 60-; chmn. sci. inform. counc, Nat. Sci. Found, 63- Ed. Eng. notes sect, J. Eng. Educ, 36-40; assoc. ed, Good Reading. MLA; Ling. Soc. Am. Communication techniques in scientific work; basic principles of writing. Publ: Oral communications for the layman, Univ. Va, 62. Add: Dept. of Humanities, School of Engineering & Applied Science, University of Virginia, Charlottesville, VA 22903.

VAUGHN, BILL EDWARD, b. Brownwood, Tex, May 28, 33; m. 55; c. 2. SPEECH COMMUNICATION. B.A, Bethany Nazarene Col, 61; M.A, Univ. Kans, 67, Ph.D.(speech commun), 71; M.Div, Nazarene Theol. Sem, 65. PROF. SPEECH COMMUN. & CHMN. DEPT, BETHANY NAZARENE COL, 68-, CHMN. DIV. LANG, LIT. & SPEECH, 69- Speech Commun. Asn. Analysis of public address with a concentration in pulpit address. Publ: A Burkeian analysis of the 1957 Billy Graham New York Crusade, 67 & Billy Graham: a rhetorical study in adaptation, 71, Univ. Kans; ed, Readings in preaching, 68, Modern rhetorical theory, 69 & Preaching with persuasion, 70, Bethany Press; auth, Visual discrimination of certain consonant sounds, Quart. J. Speech, 70. Add: 2805 Windsor Blvd, Oklahoma City, OK 73127.

VAUGHN, JACK ALFRED, b. Snohomish, Wash, Dec. 26, 35. THEATER ARTS. B.A, Univ. Wash, 57; M.F.A, Univ. Hawaii, 60; Ph.D.(theatre), Univ. Denver, 64. Assoc. prof. Eng, Jamestown Col, 64-67, theatre & speech, 67-68; asst. prof. ENG, CALIF. STATE COL. DOMINGUEZ HILLS 68-71, ASSOC. PROF, 71- Am. Theatre Asn; Speech Commun. Asn. Seventeenth century drama; restoration comedy. Publ: Two comedies by Thomas D'Urfey, Fairleigh Dickinson Univ, 74; A D'Urfey play dated, Mod. Philol, 5/67; Persevering, unexhausted bard: Tom D'Urfey, Quart. J. Speech, 12/67. Add: Dept. of English, California State College, 1000 E. Victoria, Dominguez Hills, CA 90747.

VAWTER, MARVIN L, b. Covington, Ky, Apr. 5, 40; m. 60. ENGLISH. B.A, Univ. Cincinnati, 62, M.A, 66; Ph.D.(Eng), Univ. Wis, 70. Teaching fel. Eng, Univ. Cincinnati, 64-66, lectr. theatre, 64-66, dir. dramatic inst. & summer theatre prog, summer 66; teaching asst. ENG, Univ. Wis, 66-68, master teaching asst, 69; ASST. PROF, UNIV. ILL, URBANA, 69- Exec. dir, Ill. Humanities Counc, 73-; consult, Ky. Bicentennial Comn; mem. midwest adv. comt, Nat. Endowment for Humanities. MLA; Cent. Renaissance Conf; Renaissance Soc. Am. Shakespeare and the politics of the

Renaissance; Renaissance neostoicism and political drama. Publ: Julius Caesar: rupture in the bond, J. Eng. & Ger. Philol, 73; Division 'tween our souls: Shakespeare Stud, 73; Political imperatives in Ben Jonson's Sejanus, Stud. Lit. Imagination, 4/73. Add: Illinois Humanities Council, 411 Gregory Hall, University of Illinois, Urbana, IL 61801.

VEILLEUX, JULIETTE, b. Sherbrooke, P.Q, Sept. 15, 14. ENGLISH. B.A, Univ. Montreal, 48, M.A, 56; Ph.D, Fordham Univ, 63. Prof. Greek & Eng, Col. Sacré-Coeur, 48-66; Asst. prof. ENG, UNIV. SHERBROOKE, 66-72, ASSOC. PROF, 72- Delivered fifteen lect. on Eng, CBC-TV, 66-67; vis. prof, Cath. Univ, Angers, 67-68. Publ: Dynamisme de la vie communautaire, (transl, Marie Beha, Dynamics of community), 71, La jeunesse s'interroge, (transl, Andrew Greeley, Youth asks: does God still speak?), 73 & Au seuil de la promesse divine, (transl, Threshold of God's promise), 73, Ed. Paulines, Sherbrooke. Add: Faculte des Arts, University of Sherbrooke, Sherbrooke, P.Q. J1K 2R1, Can.

VELER, RICHARD PAUL, b. Lorain, Ohio, Oct. 29, 36. ENGLISH, AMERICAN LITERATURE. B.A, Wittenberg Univ, 58; Woodrow Wilson fel. & M.A, Harvard, 59; Ph.D.(Am. lit), Ohio State Univ, 64. Asst. prof. ENG, WITTENBERG UNIV, 65-69, ASSOC. PROF, 69-, CHMN. DEPT, 71-, assoc. dean col. & dir. summer sch, 69-71. MLA; Col. Eng. Asn; NCTE. Mark Twain; Nelson Algren; Walter Tittle. Publ: Ed, Papers on Poe: essays in honor of John Ward Ostrom, Chantry, 72. Add: Dept. of English, Wittenberg University, Springfield, OH 45501.

VELZ, JOHN WILLIAM, b. Englewood, N.J, Aug. 5, 30; m. 67. ENGLISH. B.A, Univ. Mich, 53, M.A, 54; Ph.D, Univ. Minn, 63. Asst, Univ. Minn, 54-56, instr, 56-58; ENG, Col. St. Thomas, 58-60; asst. prof, Rice Univ, 63-69; PROF, UNIV. TEX, AUSTIN, 69- Nat. Endowment for Humanities fel, 67-68; Folger Shakespeare Libr. fel, 68. MLA (ed, Julius Caesar, New Variorum Shakespeare, 66-, ed, Coriolanus, 72-); Shakespeare Asn. Am; Renaissance Soc. Am; Malone Soc; Renaissance Eng. Text Soc. Shakespeare; Tudor drama; medieval drama. Publ: Shakespeare and the classical tradition: a critical guide to commentary, 1660-1960, Univ. Minn, 68; co-ed, James G. McManaway, Studies in Shakespeare, bibliography, and theater, Shakespeare Asn. Am, 69; auth, Sovereignty in the Digby Mary Magdalene, Comp. Drama, 3/68; Pirate Hills and the Quartos of Julius Caesar, Papers of Bibliog. Soc. Am, 69; Undular Structure in Julius Caesar, Mod. Lang. Rev, 71; plus others. Add: Dept. of English, University of Texas at Austin, Austin, TX 78712.

VENDERBUSH, KENNETH RAY, b. Detroit, Mich, May 31, 30. SPEECH. B.A, Kalamazoo Col, 52; M.A, Wayne State Univ, 57; Ph.D. (speech), Ohio State Univ, 68. Instr. speech, St. Lawrence Univ, 56-57, dean men, 57-61; Lawrence Univ, 61-69; v.pres. stud. affairs & dean, GRAND VALLEY STATE COL, 69-73, MEM. FAC, WILLIAM JAMES COL, 73- Asst. to exec. dean stud. relat, Ohio State Univ, 60-61. U.S.C.G.R, 54-56. Speech Commun. Asn; Nat. Asn. Stud. Personnel Adminr. Counseling; general communications; behavioral science. Add: 1441 Mackinaw Rd. S.E, Grand Rapids, MI 49506.

VENDLER, HELEN HENNESSY, b. Boston, Mass, Apr. 30, 33; div; c. 1. ENGLISH. A.B, Emmanuel Col, 54; Fulbright fel, Univ. Louvain, 54-55; Boston Univ, 55-56; univ. fels. & Ph.D.(Eng), Radcliffe Col, 60. Instr. ENG, Cornell Univ, 60-63; lectr, Swarthmore & Haverford Cols, 63-64; asst. prof, Smith Col, 64-66; assoc. prof, BOSTON UNIV, 66-68, PROF, 68- Am. Counc. Learned Soc. grant-in-aid, summer 64; Fulbright lectr, Univ. Bordeaux, 68-69; Am. Counc. Learned Soc. & Guggenheim Found. fels, 71-72; judge, Nat. Bk. Awards in Poetry, 72; poetry consult, N.Y. Times Bk. Rev, 72-; dir, Nat. Endowment for Humanities Summer Sem, 73. Explicator Award, 69. MLA (Lowell Prize, 69); Am. Acad. Arts & Sci. Modern American and English poetry; 17th century English poetry; romantic and lyric poetry. Publ: Yeats's Vision and the later plays, 63 & On extended wings: Wallace Stevens' longer poems, 69, Harvard Univ; co-ed, I.A. Richards: essays in his honor, Oxford Univ, 73; auth, George Herbert's Vertue, Ariel, 4/70; The re-invented poem: George Herbert's Alternatives, In: Forms of lyric, Columbia Univ, 70; plus three others. Add: Dept. of English, Boston University, 236 Bay State Rd, Boston, MA 02215.

VENETTOZZI, VICTOR A, b. Herkimer, N.Y, Jan. 29, 17; m. 49; c. 3. ENGLISH. B.A, East. Ky. State Col, 53, M.A, 54; Univ. Ky, 55-56; State Univ. Iowa, 60; fel, Cornell Col, 60, M.A, 65. Asst. prof. ENG, East. Ky. State Col, 54-59; from asst. prof. to ASSOC. PROF, MOREHEAD STATE UNIV, 60- U.S.A, 41-46, S/Sgt. NEA. Creative writing. Add: Dept. of English, Morehead State University, Morehead, KY 40351.

VENEZKY, RICHARD L, Computer Sciences, Linguistics. See Volume III, Foreign Languages, Linguistics & Philology.

VERBILLION, JUNE, b. Chicago, Ill, Nov. 23, 26. ENGLISH LANGUAGE & LITERATURE. B.A, De Paul Univ, 47; M.A, Loyola Univ.(Ill), 50, Ed.D, 60. Teacher Eng. & French, Siena High Sch, Chicago, Ill, 47-50, ENG, Harrison High Sch, 50-52, Foreman High Sch, 52-60; from asst. prof. to PROF, NORTHEAST. ILL. UNIV, 60- Mem. Chicago Teachers Rev. Sch, 62, 63. NCTE; Int. Reading Asn. Children's literature; teaching the language arts; biography. Publ: A new look at Fr. Faber, Herder, 61; Linguistics, the key to language instruction? Educ. Digest, 5/63. Add: Dept. of English, Northeastern Illinois University, Chicago, IL 60625.

VERDERBER, RUDOLPH FRANCIS, b. Cleveland, Ohio, Aug. 7, 33; m. 73; c. 2. SPEECH. B.S, Bowling Green State Univ, 55, M.A, 56; Ph.D.(speech), Univ. Mo, Columbia, 62. Instr. SPEECH, UNIV. CINCINNATI, 59-63, asst. prof, 63-66, assoc. prof, 66-71, PROF, 71- Speech Commun. Asn; Am. Forensic Asn; Cent. States Speech Asn. Rhetoric and public address; argumentation and debate; interpersonal communication. Publ: An invitation to debate, privately pub, 65; 66, 67; Krieg Press, 68, 69, 70, 71; The challenge of effective speaking, Wadsworth, 70, 73; The one-point debate, Speech Teacher, 3/63; Teaching reasoning in the beginning high school and college speech course, Ohio Speech J, 67; Judges' criteria and debater adaptation: empirical evidence, J. Am. Forensic Asn, winter 68. Add: Dept. of Speech, University of Cincinnati, Cincinnati, OH 45221.

VERGARA, ALLYS DWYER, b. New York, N.Y, Aug. 10, m. 29. ENGLISH. A.B, Col. New Rochelle, 24; A.M, Columbia Univ, 36, Ph.D, 44. Actress, theatres, 24-34; from assoc. prof. to PROF. SPEECH & ENG, COL. NEW ROCHELLE, 34- Consult, UN; Cath. Int. Union Sociol. Serv, 48- Comprehension of poetry. Add: Dept. of Education, College of New Rochelle, New Rochelle, NY 10805.

VERNON, JOHN EDWARD, b. Cambridge, Mass, June 3, 43; m. 68. MODERN LITERATURE. B.A, Boston Col, 65; NDEA, Univ. Calif, Davis, 65-68, M.A, 67, Ph.D.(Eng), 69. ASST. PROF. ENG, Univ. Utah, 69-71; STATE UNIV. N.Y. BINGHAMTON, 71- State Univ. N.Y. Res. Found. grant, 73; N.Y. State Counc. Arts grant, 73-74. MLA. Modern poetry; modern culture; phenomenology. Publ: The garden and the map: schizophrenia in twentieth century literature and culture, Univ. Ill, 73; Theodore Roethke's Praise to the end!, 71 & Naked criticism, 1/74, Iowa Rev; Poetry and the body, Am. Rev, 2/73. Add: Dept. of English, University of New York at Binghamton, Binghamton, NY 13901.

VEST, EUGENE BARTLETT, b. Cuba, Ill, Oct. 12, 06. ENGLISH. B.A, Northwest. Univ, 28, fel. & M.A, 29; scholar. & M.A, Harvard, 31, scholar. & Ph.D, 32. Prof. ENG. & head dept, Dak. Wesleyan Univ, 32-37; asst. prof, Monmouth Col, 38-42, 46-47; Galesburg Div, UNIV. ILL, CHICAGO CIRCLE, 47-48, assoc. prof, 48-49, Chicago Undergrad. Div, 49-53, PROF, UNIV, 53-, head. div. humanities, 50-64. U.S.A, 42-46, Capt. MLA; NCTE; Col. Eng. Asn; Conf. Col. Compos. & Commun; Am. Dialect Soc; Am. Name Soc. Shakespeare; Chicago literary history; American dialects. Publ: The psychomachia of Prudentius in the Middle Ages; co-auth, Romeo and Juliet: a scene-by-scene analysis with critical commentary, 65, auth, Volpone: an act-by-act analysis with notes, 65 & Rivals and school for scandal: analytic notes and review, 66, Stud. Master, Am. R.D.M; Whence that word?, Ill. Libr, 6/58; Cockeram had a word for it, Word Stud, 2/61; Names on the ocean bottom, Names, 12/68; plus one other. Add: Dept. of English, Box 4348, University of Illinois at Chicago Circle, Chicago, IL 60680.

VETTER, DALE BENJAMIN, b. Henry Co, Ill, Aug. 11, 08; m. 32; c. 4. LITERARY HISTORY. A.B, N.Cent. Col, 30; A.M, Northwest. Univ, 35, Ph.D, 46; Univ. Chicago, 37, 39. Teacher high sch, Ill, 30-32, supt. schs, 32-35, teacher pub. schs, 36-37, teacher & librn. high sch, 37-41; asst. prof. LIT. HIST, ILL. STATE UNIV, 41-46, assoc. prof, 46-53, PROF, 53- Newberry Libr. fel, 54. MLA. Augustan Reprint Soc; AAUP; Am. Civil Liberties Union. Life and literary criticism of William Walsh; English literary history, 1660-1745; English literature and politics, 1688-1714. Publ: William Walsh's In defence of painting, Mod. Lang. Notes, 12/51. Add: 214 W. Willow, Normal, IL 61761.

VIA, JOHN ALBERT, b. Gorman, Tex, Oct. 13, 37; m. 60; c. 1. ENGLISH LITERATURE. B.A, Baylor Univ, 59; M.A, Miss. State Univ, 61; fel, Univ. Ill, 66-67, Ph.D.(Eng), 68. ASST. PROF. ENG, Univ. Ky, 67-74, summer res. fels, 68, 69, & 71; MERCER UNIV. ATLANTA, 74- U.S.A.R, 63-69, Sgt. MLA; Milton Soc. Am; Southeast Renaissance Conf; S.Atlantic Mod. Lang. Asn. John Milton; 17th-century English nondramatic literature; Sir Thomas Elyot. Publ: The rhythm of regenerate experience: L'Allegro and Il penseroso, Renaissance Papers 1969, 70; Milton's The passion: a successful failure, Milton Quart, 71; Milton's antiprelatical tracts: the poet speaks in prose, Milton Stud, 73. Add: Dept. of English, Mercer University in Atlanta, 3000 Flowers Rd. N.E, Atlanta, GA 30341.

VICHERT, GORDON STEWART, b. Ipin, China, July 10, 34; Can. citizen; m. 58; c. 3. ENGLISH. B.A, McMaster Univ, 57, M.A, Univ. Toronto, 58; Ph.D.(Eng), Univ. London, 64. Lectr. ENG, Col. Technol, Nigeria, 58-60; lectr, McMASTER UNIV, 60-62, asst. prof, 64-68, ASSOC. PROF, 68- MLA; Asn. Can. Univ. Teachers Eng. Shakespeare; 18th century prose; African literature. Publ: Bernard Mandeville and A dissertation upon drunkenness, Notes & Queries, 8/64; Some recent Mandeville attributions, Philol. Quart, 4/66. Add: Dept. of English, McMaster University, Hamilton, Ont. L8S 4M4, Can.

VICKERY, JOHN B, b. Toronto, Ont, Aug. 20, 25; m. 50; c. 1. ENGLISH. B.A, Univ. Toronto, 47; M.A, Colgate Univ, 49; Am. Counc. Learned Soc. fel, Harvard, 51-52; Ph.D, Univ. Wis, 55. Instr. ENG, Univ. Tenn, 54-56; Northwest. Univ, 56-59; asst. prof, Purdue Univ, 59-64, assoc. prof, 64-65; vis. prof, Calif. State Col, Los Angeles, 65-66; assoc. prof, UNIV. CALIF, RIVERSIDE, 66-72, PROF, 72- MLA. Modern literature. Publ: Ed, Myth and literature, 66 & auth, Robert Graves and the white goddess, 72, Univ. Nebr; ed, Goethe's Faust: essays in criticism, 68 & co-ed, Light in August and the criticial spectrum, 71, Wadsworth; co-ed, The shaken realist, La. State Univ, 70; co-auth, The scapegoat: ritual and literature, Houghton, 71; auth, The literary impact of The golden bough, Princeton Univ, 73; Finnegans wake and sexual metamorphosis, Contemporary Lit, 72; plus two others. Add: Dept. of English, University of California, Riverside, CA 92502.

VICKREY, JOHN FREDERICK, b. Chicago, Ill, Aug. 24, 24; m. 66. ENGLISH LINGUISTICS & PHILOLOGY. Ph.B, Univ. Chicago, 49, M.A, 52; Ph.D.(Eng), Ind. Univ, 60. Instr. Eng, Rutgers Univ, 57-61; asst. prof, LEHIGH UNIV, 61-69, ASSOC. PROF. ENG. LIT, 69- U.S.A, 43-46. MLA; Mediaeval Acad. Am. Old English, Old Saxon and Middle English language and literature. Publ: Selfsceaft in Genesis B, Anglia, 65; The vision of Eve in Genesis B, Speculum, 69; Exodus and the battle in the sea, Traditio, 72; plus others. Add: Dept. of English, Lehigh University, Bethlehem, PA 18015.

VIERECK, PETER, b. New York, N.Y, Aug. 5, 16; m. 72; c. 2. POETRY, HISTORY. B.S, Harvard, 37, A.M, 39, Ph.D, 42; Henry fel. from Harvard, Christ Church, Oxford, 37-38; hon. D.H.L, Olivet Col, 59. Instr. hist. & lit, Harvard, 46-47; asst. prof. hist, Smith Col, 47-48; assoc. prof, MT. HOLYOKE COL, 48-49, EUROP. & RUSSIAN HIST, 49-55, ALUMNAE FOUND. PROF, 55- Vis. lectr, Smith Col, 48-49; Guggenheim fels, poetry, 49, hist, 55; vis. lectr, Poet's Conf, Harvard, 53; Am. Poetry Conf, Oxford, summer, 53; Whittal lectr. poetry, Libr. Congr, 54 & 63; Fulbright prof. Am. poetry, Univ. Florence, 55; Elliston poetry lectr, Univ. Cincinnati, 56; vis. lectr, Univ. Calif, Berkeley, 57 & 64; Rockefeller Found. summer researcher hist. & Ger, 58; U.S. Dept. State cult. exchange poet, U.S.S.R, 61; Twentieth Century Fund travel & poetry res. grant, Russia, 62; lectr. poetry, City Col. New York & New Sch. Social Res, 64; dir. poetry workshop, N.Y. Writer's Conf, 65-67; Four-col. Asian-African stud. prog. comt. summer stud. grant, 66; lectr. var. Europ. univs. Garrison Prize for Poetry, Phi Beta Kappa, 36; Harvard Bowdoin Medal for Prose, 39; Tietjens Prize for Poetry, 48; Pulitzer Prize for Poetry, 49. U.S.A, 43-45. AHA. Modern European and Russian history; Anglo-American poetry; modern Russian culture. Publ: Metapolitics: from the Romantics to Hitler, Knopf, 41; Terror and decorum, Scribner, 48 & rev. ed, Greenwood, 73; Conservatism revisited: the revolt against revolt, Scribner, 49 & Lehmann, London, 50; Strike through the mask, Scribner, 50 & rev. ed, Greenwood, 73; Dream & responsibility: essays on the tension between poetry & society, Univ. Press, Washington, 53; Shame & glory of the intellectuals: Gaylord Babbit versus the rediscovery of values, Beacon, 53 & rev. ed, Capricorn, 65; The persimmon tree: pastoral poems, Scribner, 56; Conservatism: from John Adams to Churchill, Van Nostrand, 56 & 67; The unadjusted man: a new hero for Americans, Beacon, 56, Capricorn, 62 & rev. ed, Greenwood, 73; The tree witch: a verse drama, Scribner, 61 & rev. ed, Greenwood, 73; Metapolitics: the roots of the Nazi mind, Capricorn, 61 & 65; co-auth, The radical right, Doubleday, 63 & rev. ed, Anchor, 64; auth, Conservatism revisited and the new conservatism: what went wrong? Free Press, 65; New and selected poems, 1932-1967, Bobbs, 67; The mob within the heart: Soviet Russia's rebel writers, a first-hand account, Tri-Quart. Mag, spring 65; Burkean conservatism versus the radical right, In: Outside looking in: critiques of American institutions, Harper, 72; Conservatism, In: Encycl. Britannica, 74. Add: Dept. of History, Mt. Holyoke College, South Hadley, MA 01075.

VIETH, DAVID MUENCH, b. New Haven, Conn, Feb. 10, 25; m. 51; c. 1. ENGLISH. B.A, Yale, 45, univ. fel. & M.A, 48, Selden & Sterling fels. & Ph.D. (Eng), 53; cert. Japanese, U.S. Navy Orient. Lang. Schs, Univ. Colo. & Okla. State Univ, 46. Instr. ENG, Univ. Del, 48-49; Yale, 52-56; asst. prof, Mont. State Univ, 56-58; assoc. prof, Univ. Kans, 58-63; Hunter Col, 63-65; PROF, SOUTH. ILL. UNIV, 65- Am. Philos. Soc. grant-in-aid, 59-60; res. grants, Mont. State Univ, 57-58; Univ. Kans, 60-63; Hunter Col, 63-65; South. Ill. Univ, 65-72; mem. adv. bd, Yale Ed. of Poems on Affairs of State, 63-; Papers on Lang. & Lit, 65- U.S.N.R, 43-46, Lt.(jg). Am. Soc. 18th Century Stud. John Wilmot, second Earl of Rochester; English literature of the Restoration and 18th century; textual criticism. Publ: Attribution in Restoration poetry: a study of Rochester's Poems of 1680, 63 & The complete poems of John Wilmot, Earl of Rochester, 68, Yale; co-auth, Gyldenstolpe manuscript miscellany of poems by John Wilmot, Earl of Rochester, and other Restoration authors, Almqvist & Wiksell, Stockholm, 67; ed, John Dryden's All for love, Univ. Nebr, 72; auth, Irony in Dryden's Ode to Anne Killigrew, Stud. Philol, 65; Wycherley's The country wife: an anatomy of masculinity, Papers on Lang. & Lit, 66; The art of the prologue and epilogue: a new approach based on Dryden's practice, Genre, 9/72; plus others. Add: Dept. of English, Southern Illinois University, Carbondale, IL 62901.

VIITANEN, WAYNE JOHN, b. St. Paul, Minn, May 22, 40; m. 67. AMERICAN LITERATURE. B.S, Wis. State Univ-River Falls, 62; M.S, S.Dak. State Univ, 64; Ph.D.(Am. lit), South. Ill. Univ, Carbondale, 72. Instr. ENG, S.Dak. State Univ, 64-66; Wis. State Univ-Eau Claire, 66-67; ASST. PROF, UNIV. ARK, MONTICELLO, 72- AAUP; MLA. Folklore of the mid-South; modern American literature. Publ: The winter the Mississippi ran backwards: early Kentuckians report the New Madrid, Missouri, earthquake of 1811-1812, Register Ky. Hist. Soc, 1/73; Folklore and fakelore of an earthquake, Ky. Folklore Record, (in press). Add: Dept. of Language & Literature, University of Arkansas, Monticello, AR 71655.

VILLAREJO, OSCAR MILTON, b. Milwaukee, Wis, May 3, 09; m. 45. COMPARATIVE LITERATURE. B.A, George Washington Univ, 47, M.A, 49; cert, Shakespeare Inst, Univ. Birmingham, 48; Ph.D, Columbia Univ, 53. Instr. Eng, George Washington Univ, 47-49; instr. Span, Eng. & French, New Lincoln Sch, N.Y.C, 49-53; asst. prof. Eng. lit. & chmn. dept. Eng, Nasson Col, 54-55; Eng. & Span, Tex. Lutheran Col, 55-56; assoc. prof. Eng. & chmn. dept, South. State Col, 56-57; asst. prof. Eng, Memphis State Univ, 57-59; assoc. prof, Wis. State Col, Stevens Point, 59-60; prof, Glassboro State Col, 60-64; ASSOC. PROF. Spanish, C.W. Post Col, L.I. Univ, 64-66; Georgetown Univ, 66-70; comp. lit, Univ. Md, College Park, 70-71; ENG, GEORGE WASHINGTON UNIV, 72- Vis. scholar, Duke Univ, summers 57 & 59; chmn, Nat. Acad. Counc, Nat. Confederation Am. Ethnic Groups, 72- U.S.M.C, 43-46, T/Sgt. MLA; Malone Soc; Renaissance Soc. Am; Naval Hist. Found. Spanish and English literary relations during the Renaissance; Shakespeare and the English Renaissance; Arctic and Antarctic explorations. Publ: Dr. Kane's voyage to the polar lands, Oxford, 65; Listas del Peregrino de Lope de Vega, Rev. Filol. Española, Madrid, 63; Lista II de El Peregrino: la lista maestra del año 1604 de los 448 tiulos de las comedias de Lope de Vega, Segismundo, Rev. Hisp. Teatro, 66; Shakespeare's Romeo and Juliet: its Spanish source, In: Shakespeare Survey 20, Cambridge, 67; plus others. Add: 4213 Jenifer St. N.W, Washington, DC 20015.

VILLARREAL, JESSE JAMES, b. San Antonio, Tex, Oct. 22, 13; m. 35; c. 2. SPEECH. A.B, Univ. Tex, 35, A.M, 37; Ph.D, Northwest. Univ, 47. From assoc. prof. to PROF. SPEECH, UNIV. TEX, AUSTIN, 47-, CHMN. CTR. COMMUN. RES, 68-, chmn. dept. speech, 61-68. Ed, DSH Abstr. Am. Speech & Hearing Asn; Speech Commun. Asn. Speech and hearing disorders; English as a second language; English phonetics and American dialects. Publ: Co-auth, Psychotherapy of stuttering, C.C. Thomas, 62; First course in speech; Aural comprehension of English for native speakers of Spanish. Add: Dept. of Speech, University of Texas at Austin, Austin, TX 78712.

VINCE, RONALD WINSTON, b. Simcoe, Ont, Sept. 19, 37; m. 67. ENGLISH LITERATURE, DRAMA. B.A, McMaster Univ, 60; M.A, Rice Univ, 62; Ph.D.(Eng), Northwest. Univ, 68. Lectr. ENG, McMASTER UNIV, 66-68, asst. prof, 68-72, ASSOC. PROF, 72-, ASST. DEAN HUMANITIES STUD, 71- Can. Asn. Univ. Teachers; Asn. Can. Univ. Teachers Eng. Elizabethan drama; literary criticism; comparative drama. Publ: Thomas Nabbes's Hannibal and Scipio: sources and theme, Stud. Eng. Lit, 71; Morality and masque: the context for Thomas Nabbes's Microcosmus, Eng. Stud, 72; A reading of The sleepers, Walt Whitman Rev, 72. Add: Dept. of English, McMaster University, Hamilton, Ont. L8S 4L9, Can.

VINCENT, HOWARD P, b. Galesburg, Ill, Oct. 9, 04; m. 31; c. 2. ENGLISH. B.A, Oberlin Col, 26; M.A, Harvard, 27, Dexter traveling fel, summer 30, Ph.D, 33; hon. D.Litt, Hillsdale Col, 58. Instr. Eng, W.Va. Univ, 27-28; teacher, Park Sch. of Cleveland Heights, 31-32; PROF. ENG, Hillsdale Col, 35-42; Ill. Inst. Technol, 42-61; KENT STATE UNIV, 61- Fulbright lectr, Univs. Lyons & Bordeaux, 54-55; dir. libr. serv, U.S. Inform. Serv, France, 55-57; Fulbright lectr, Univ. Liège & State Univ. Ghent, 61-62; Rome, spring 67. Eng. Inst; Col. Eng. Asn; MLA; Melville Soc. Am. Eighteenth century English literary history, especially theatre; 19th century American literature; 19th century French art. Publ: Collected poems of Herman Melville, Packard, 47; The trying-out of Moby-Dick, Houghton, 49; co-ed, Moby-Dick, Hendricks, 52; ed, Bartleby the scrivener: a symposium, 66 & Melville and Hawthorne in the Berkshires, 68, Kent State Univ; Daumier and his world, Northwest. Univ, 68; Guide to Herman Melville, 69 & The Merrill checklist of Herman Melville, 69, C.E. Merrill; Twentieth century interpretations of Billy Budd, Prentice-Hall, 71. Add: Dept. of English, Kent State University, Kent, OH 44240.

VINCENT, JAMES EDWIN, b. Johnstown, Pa, Oct. 14, 29. SPEECH, DRAMA. B.S, Ind. State Col, 51; M.F.A, Ohio Univ, 53; Ph.D.(speech & drama), Univ. Wis, Madison, 62. Instr. speech & drama, North. Ill. Univ, 57-59; assoc. prof. Eng. & speech, Edinboro State Col, 62-63; SPEECH & DRAMA, MT. UNION COL, 63-71, PROF, 71- Bk. rev. ed, Speech Teacher, 62-65. Speech Commun. Asn; Am. Theatre Asn. Dramatic literature; dramatic production; oral interpretation of modern poetry. Add: Dept. of Drama & Speech, Mt. Union College, Alliance, OH 44601.

VINCENT, MARY LOUISE, b. St. Paul, Minn, Feb. 19, 16. ENGLISH. B.S, Univ. Minn, 38, Marston fel, 38, M.A, 43, Ph.D.(Eng), 67. Teacher high sch, 38-39; instr. ENG, HIRAM COL, 39-47, asst. prof, 47-51, assoc. prof, 51-55, PROF, 55- Vis. lectr, gen. educ. div, Cleveland Col. & West. Reserve Univ, 45-61. MLA; Midwest Mod. Lang. Asn. Poetry of Herbert Read and Robert Graves; Kay Boyle; Lafcadio Hearn. Publ: Two painters of the tropics: Lafcadio Hearn and Paul Gauguin in Martinique, Caribbean Stud, 10/70. Add: 6781 Brown St, Hiram, OH 44234.

VINOCUR, JACOB, b. Lansing, Mich, Oct. 6, 20; m. 47; c. 2. ENGLISH. B.A, Mich. State Univ, 47, M.A, 49; Ph.D.(Eng), Univ. Wis, 58. Instr. lib. stud, Univ. Wis, 53-54; from instr. to prof. Eng, Univ. Mont, 54-65; Phillips fel, Duke Univ, 65-66; assoc. dean grad. sch, Mich. State Univ, 66-68; V.PRES. ACAD. AFFAIRS, NORTH. MICH. UNIV, 68- Reader's Digest prof. Am. stud, Univ. Dijon, 58-59; consult. exam, N.Cent. Asn. Col. & Univ, 67. U.S.N, 42-46. MLA. Modern British literature; problems of university administration. Publ: Teacher in France, Univ. Bookman, 61; Edmund Wilson's Patriotic gore, West. Humanities, 63; co-auth, The continuing debate: essays on education, St. Martin's Press Rev, 64. Add: Office of the Vice President, Northern Michigan University, Marquette, MI 49855.

VINSON, JAMES, b. Henderson, N.C, Jan. 22, 21; m. 48; c. 1. ENGLISH. B.A, St. Augustine's Col, 48; M.A, Univ. Pittsburgh, 49. Asst. prof. ENG, Tex. South. Univ, 50-51; ASSOC. PROF, ALA. A&M UNIV, 51-, acting head dept, 62-71. U.S.A, 41-45. MLA; Renaissance Soc. Am; AAUP; Col. Lang. Asn; Am. Guild Organists. Renaissance rhetoric; continuity of English prose; Christian mysticism in literature of England and America; aesthetic qualities in lyricism. Add: Dept. of English, Alabama A&M University, Normal, AL 35762.

VIOLI, UNICIO JACK, b. Chicago, Ill, Oct. 6, 16; m. 42; c. 1. ENGLISH, COMPARATIVE LITERATURE. B.S, Univ. Wis, 43; cert, Durham Univ, Eng, 45; M.A, Columbia Univ, 47, Ph.D, 55. Instr. ENG, Fordham Univ, 47-48; Wagner Col, 50-55; instr, Brooklyn Col. & City Col. New York, 55-58; asst. prof, FAIRLEIGH DICKINSON UNIV, 59-68, PROF, 68- Periodicals ed, Shakespeare Newsletter; ed. consult, Monarch Press, New York, 63- Contrib. to Italica. U.S.A, 43-46. Am. Soc. Geoling; Am. Asn. Teachers Ital. Shakespeare; National Audubon Society. Publ: Shakespeare's sonnets: a critical commentary, 63, The New Testament: a commentary and guide, 63, Shakespeare's Measure for measure: a guide, 64 & Greek and Roman classics, 65, Simon & Schuster; Shylock, anti-Semitism & historical truth, Issues, 63; Shakespeare & Americans today, 67 & Shakespeare emasculated, 68, Lit. Half-Yearly. Add: Dept. of English, Fairleigh Dickinson University, Rutherford, NJ 07070.

VIRTUE, JOHN BERNARD, b. Winona, Minn, Sept. 25, 01; m. 35; c. 2. ENGLISH. A.B, Univ. Nebr, 24; Ph.D, Yale, 35. From asst. instr. to instr. ENG, Univ. Wis, 24-27; Northwest. Univ, 30-34; Univ. Kans, 35-37, asst. prof, 37-46; assoc. prof, EAST. MICH. UNIV, 46-52, prof, 52-72, EMER. PROF, 72- MLA. English literature of the Victorian era; Shakespeare. Add: 926 Sheridan St, Ypsilanti, MI 48197.

VITALE, GEOFFREY EDWARDS, b. London, Eng, July 9, 33. EIGHTEENTH CENTURY ENGLISH LITERATURE. Lic. ès Lett, Univ. Bordeaux, 62; dipl. etudes super, Univ. Paris, 63, Dr. Univ, 69. Teacher Eng, Lycée Moulay Hassan & Lycée Moulay Abdallch Casablanca, 57-62; asst, Ecole Motelière de Paris, 62-63; lectr. transl, Univ. Paris, 63-65; asst. prof. Eng. lit. & transl, Laval Univ, 66-70; DIR. ENG. LIT. & MEM. FAC. LIT, UNIV. QUEBEC, TROIS-RIVIERES, 70- R.A.F, 54-56, Res, 56-58. Asn. Univ. Partiellement ou Entièrement Lang. Française. Eighteenth century literature; English vocabulary; translation. Publ: Co-auth, Revision of translation and up-dating of guide bleu: Liban, Hachette, 65 & Words in context, Bordas, 73; auth, Cordelia's death and the problem of succession, Notes & Queries. Add: Dept. of Literature, University of Quebec, P.O. Box 500, Trois-Rivières, P.Q, Can.

VITALE, PHILIP HAROLD, b. Chicago, Feb. 13, 13; m. 48; c. 2. ENGLISH. Ph.D.(Eng), Loyola Univ.(Ill), 41. Asst. prof. ENG, DePAUL UNIV, 46-48, assoc. prof, 48-50, PROF, 50-, chmn. dept, 50-60. U.S.A, 42-45. Mod. Humanities Res. Asn; MLA. Nineteenth century; literary criticism; Catholic literature. Publ: Catholic literary opinion in the nineteenth century, Acad. Libr. Guild, 55; An outline guide for English majors, 58 & Questions and problems in bibliography and research, 66, Auxiliary Univ. Press; Basic tools of research, 63, Tom Jones: a handbook, 67 & Henry James: the

Portrait of a lady, 73, Barron's; Bibliography: historical and bibliothecal, Loyola Univ, 71; plus others. Add: Rte. 3, 150 Hawthorne Rd, Barrington, IL 60010.

VITELLI, JAMES ROBERT, b. Trenton, N.J, Nov. 15, 20; m. 43; c. 5. AMERICAN STUDIES. A.B, Col. Wooster, 42; M.A, Univ. Pa, 48, Ph.D. (Am. civilization), 55. Instr. Eng, LAFAYETTE COL, 50-55, asst. prof, 55-60, assoc. prof, 60-68, PROF. ENG. & AM. CIVILIZATION, 68-, CHMN. PROG. AM. CIVILIZATION, 60-, acting chmn. dept. Eng, 70-71, Humanities Enrichment leave, 71-72. Fulbright lectr, Univ. Trieste, 56-58; vis. lectr. Am. lit, Univ. Bombay, 64-65. U.S.N.R, 43-46, Lt.(jg). Am. Stud. Asn; MLA; AAUP. Randolph Bourne: youth and politics and literature; American literary traditions and the public man of letters. Publ: Ed. & introd, An amazing sense: selected poems and letters of Emily Dickinson, Popular Prakashan, Bombay, 66; auth, Van Wyck Brooks, Twayne, 69; ed, and introd. to Van Wyck Brooks' The ordeal of Mark Twain, 70 & Van Wyck Brooks' Three essays on America, 70, Dutton. Add: 100 Pennsylvania Ave, Easton, PA 18042.

VITTUM, HENRY EARL, b. Laconia, N.H, Aug. 2, 22; m. 46. ENGLISH, EDUCATION. B.Ed, Plymouth State Col, 48; Ed.M, Tufts Univ, 52; Rutgers Univ, 53-56; Danforth fel, N.Y. Univ, 59-60, Ph.D.(higher educ), 62. Instr. Eng, Newark Col. Eng, 52-55, asst. prof, 55-56; educ, Rutgers Univ, 56-62, assoc. prof, 62-65; ENG, PLYMOUTH STATE COL, 65-68, PROF, 68- U.S.A.A.F, 42-45. NCTE; AAUP; MLA; Victorian Soc; Res. Soc. Victorian Periodicals; Dickens Fel. Victorian literature; 17th century British literature; American colonial intellectual history. Publ: Ed, A Christmas carol, Bantam, 66; auth, Review of the national interest and the teaching of English, J. Teacher Educ, 9/61. Add: Dept. of English, Plymouth State College, Plymouth, NH 03264.

VITZTHUM, RICHARD C, b. Minneapolis, Minn, June 11, 36, m. 60; c. 2. ENGLISH. B.A, Amherst Col, 57; M.A.T, Harvard, 58; Stanford Wilson fel, Stanford Univ, 61-62, Ph.D.(Eng), 63. Teaching asst. ENG, Stanford Univ, 58-61; instr, Univ. Rochester, 62-64; asst. prof, U.S. Naval Acad, 64-66; UNIV. MD, COLLEGE PARK, 66-69, ASSOC. PROF, 69- Md. Res. Bd. summer grant, 68, publ. grant, 72; Fulbright prof, Ruhr Univ, 69-70. MLA; Am. Stud. Asn. Philip Freneau's poetry; American literature of the Neoclassic era, 1765-1815. Publ: The American compromise: theme and method in the histories of Bancroft, Parkman, and Adams, Univ. Okla, 73; The historian as editor: Parkman's reconstruction of sources . . . , J. Am. Hist, 12/66; Theme and method in Bancroft's History of the United States, New Eng. Quart, 68; contrib, History and fiction: American prose in the 19th century, Sammlung Vandenhoeck, 72. Add: R.R. 1, Box 214A, Davidsonville, MD 21035.

VIVIAN, CHARLES HORTON, b. Elizabeth, N.J, Mar. 15, 20; m. 48; c. 2. ENGLISH LITERATURE. A.B, Brown Univ, 40; A.M, Harvard, 41, fel, 46-48, Ph.D, 49. Asst. ENG, Brown Univ, 45-46; tutor, Harvard, 46-48; asst. prof, South. Methodist Univ, 48-54; lectr, Tufts Univ, 54-58; assoc. prof, BENTLEY COL, 63-72, PROF, 72- U.S.A, 41-45, Capt. MLA; NCTE; AAUP. English literature of the 19th century; Dickens. Publ: An outline of English composition, Barnes & Noble; Radical journalism in the 1830's, Mod. Lang. Quart; The one Mont Blanc, Keats-Shelley J. Add: Dept. of English, Bentley College, Beaver & Forest St, Waltham, MA 02154.

VLIET, RODNEY MERYL, b. Alma, Mich, Apr. 22, 40; m. 62; c. 2. LITERATURE. B.S.L, Minn. Bible Col, 62; M.A, Ft. Hays Kans. State Col, 65; Ph.D.(arts & lett), Mich. State Univ, 74. Prof. Eng, Great Lakes Bible Col, 65-73; PRESIDING PROF. ENCOUNTER STUD, JOHN WESLEY COL, 73- Instnl. rep, Mich. Acad. Sci, Arts & Lett, 73- Value theory; religion and literature; methods of instruction in the humanities in higher education. Add: Dept. of Encounter Studies, John Wesley College, 1020 S. Washington, Owosso, MI 48867.

VOGEL, DAN, b. Brooklyn, N.Y, Feb. 12, 27; m. 50; c. 3. ENGLISH. B.A, Brooklyn Col, 48; M.A, Rutgers Univ, 49; Ph.D.(Am. lit), N.Y. Univ, 56. Instr. ENG, YESHIVA UNIV, 49-55, asst. prof, 56-62, PROF, 62-, asst. registr, 51-55, acting registr, Stern Col. Women, 55-58, dean, 58-67. MLA. Herman Melville; Ralph Waldo Emerson; Nathanial Hawthorne. Publ: The dramatic chapters in Moby-Dick, Nineteenth Century Fiction; Steinbeck's Flight: the myth of manhood, Col. Eng; Roger Chillingworth: the satanic paradox in The scarlet letter, Criticism. Add: Dept. of English, Yeshiva University, 253 Lexington Ave, New York, NY 10016.

VOGEL, NANCY, b. Lawrence, Kans. ENGLISH & AMERICAN LITERATURE. B.A. & B.S, Univ. Kans, 63, M.A, 65, Ph.D, 71. ASST. PROF. ENG, FT. HAYS KANS. STATE COL, 71- NCTE. American poetry and prose; the pastoral tradition. Publ: Set theory: a paradigm pertinent to English education, Eng. Educ, winter 73; Robert Frost, teacher, Phi Delta Kappa, 74; A post mortem on The death of the hired man, In: Frost centennial volume, Univ. & Col. Press Miss, 74. Add: Dept. of English, Fort Hays Kansas State College, Hays, KS 67601.

VOGEL, ROBERT MAIER, b. Columbus, Ind, July 26, 14; m. 43; c. 1. ENGLISH. A.B, Wabash Col, 35; Univ. Wis, 36; A.M, Univ. Mich, 40; Ed.D, Columbia Univ, 53. Prof. speech, Adrian Col, 35-40; instr. Eng. & dir. dramatics, Univ. Rochester, 40-42; asst. prof. Eng, Trinity Col.(Conn), 47-55, dir. exten. div. & summer sch, 50-55, dean grad. stud, 55-64, dean col, 64-67; pres, Bradford Jr. Col, 67-72; EXEC. DIR, GREATER HARTFORD CONSORTIUM FOR HIGHER EDUC, 72- Trustee, Kingswood Sch, 63-67. U.S.N.R, 42-45, Lt. New Eng. Conf. Grad. Educ.(secy-treas, 60-63, v.pres, 63-64, pres, 64-65). Relation of language to individual and group problem solving. Add: Greater Hartford Consortium for Higher Education, 201 Bloomfield Ave, West Hartford, CT 06117.

VOGEL, STANLEY MORTON, b. Norwalk, Conn, Jan. 21, 21. AMERICAN LITERATURE. A.B, N.Y. Univ, 42; fel, Yale, A.M, 45, Ph.D, 49; Oxford, 50; Harvard, 58. Instr. Princeton, 47-48; from asst. prof. to assoc. prof. Am. lit, SUFFOLK UNIV, 48-57, PROF. ENG, 57-, CHMN. DEPT, 61- Lectr, Emerson Col, 55-63. MLA. Publ: German literary influences on the American transcendentalists, Yale, 55; co-auth, American literature, Vols. I & II, 61 & The English novel in the 19th century, 67, Stud. Outline Co. Add: Dept. of English, Suffolk University, 41 Temple St, Boston, MA 02114.

VOGELBACK, ARTHUR LAWRENCE, b. New York, N.Y, Mar. 24, 07; m. 43; c. 1. ENGLISH. Ph.B, Wesleyan Univ, 30; M.A, Columbia Univ, 32; Ph.D. (Eng), Univ. Chicago, 38. Asst. prof. Eng, Mary Washington Col, 38-46, prof, 47-53; assoc. prof, Ripon Col, 46-47; dean fac, 53-55, acting pres, 55; prof. ENG, Sweet Briar Col, 55-67, chmn. dept, 59-60; prof, SALISBURY STATE COL, 67-74, EMER. PROF, 74- Vis. prof, Univ. Tenn, 49; U.S. Dept. State Smith-Mundt vis. prof, Aarhus Univ, Denmark, 50-51; Am. Philos. Soc. res. grants, 55, 59; fel, Newberry Libr, Chicago, 58; South. Fel. Fund res. grant, 59; res. grant, Res. Counc, Univ. Ctr, Richmond, Va, 60; Fulbright prof. Am. lit. & chmn. dept. Eng, Univ. São Paulo, 65-66. U.S.N.R, 42-46, Comdr. MLA; Am. Stud. Asn. American literature; primitivism. Publ: Shakespeare and Melville's Benito Cereno, Mod. Lang. Notes; Mark Twain and the fight for control of the Tribune, Am. Lit; Mark Twain and the Tammany ring, PMLA. Add: Dept. of English, Salisbury State College, Salisbury, MD 21801.

VOGELER, MARTHA SALMON, b. New York, N.Y, July, 24; m. 62. ENGLISH LITERATURE. B.A, N.J. State Col, 46; M.A, Columbia Univ, 52, Ph.D.(Eng), 59. Lectr. ENG, Columbia Univ, 55-60; New York Univ, 56-59; instr, Vassar Col, 59-62; asst. prof, Long Island Univ, 62-66; assoc. prof, CALIF. STATE COL, FULLERTON, 69-73, PROF, 73- Am. Counc. Learned Soc. grant, 67; Am. Philos. Soc. grants, 67 & 70. MLA; AAUP; Tennyson Soc; Res. Soc. Victorian Periodicals; Philol. Soc. Pac. Coast. Victorian biography, aesthetics and religious thought. Publ: Ed, Order and progress, Harvester, 74; auth, Matthew Arnold & Frederic Harrison, Stud. Eng. Lit, fall 72; The religious meaning of Marius the Epicurean, 19th Century Fiction, 12/64; The Victorians and the hundred best, Tex. Quart, spring 68. Add: Dept. of English, California State University, Fullerton, 800 N. State College Blvd, Fullerton, CA 92634.

VOGLER, RICHARD ALLEN, b. Los Angeles, Calif, Nov. 4, 32; m. 63. ENGLISH LITERATURE & ART. B.A, Washington & Lee Univ, 54; M.A, Univ. Calif, Berkeley, 60; Ph.D.(Eng), Univ. Calif, Los Angeles, 70. Fulbright exchange teacher Eng, Hamburg, Ger, 54-55; teacher, Bakersfield High Sch, Calif, 60-62; teaching asst. Eng. & asst. to cur, Grunwald Graphic Art Ctr, Univ. Calif, Los Angeles, 62-66; ASST. PROF. ENG, CALIF. STATE UNIV, NORTHRIDGE, 70- MLA. Victorian novel; Victorian illustration and art; George Cruikshank. Publ: An Oliver Twist exhibition: a memento for the Dickens centennial, Univ. Calif, Los Angeles, 70; auth, Introd, Max Beckmann graphics; Tucson Art Ctr, 73; contrib, The inimitable George Cruikshank: an exhibition of books, Univ. Louisville, 68; auth, Oliver Twist: Cruikshank's pictorial prototypes, In: Vol. 2, Dickens Studies Annual, South. Ill. Univ, 72; Cruikshank and Dickens: a reassessment of the role of the artist and the author, Princeton Univ. Libr. Chronicle, fall-winter 73. Add: Dept. of English, California State University, Northridge, 18111 Nordhoff St, Northridge, CA 91324.

VOIGT, FREDERICK, b. Mattoon, Ill, June 19, 31. RHETORIC, COMMUNICATIONS. B.S. Ed, East. Ill. Univ, 53; M.S, South. Ill. Univ, 60, Ph.D. (rhetoric), 64. Teacher, high sch, Ill, 53-56; Pa, 57-58; lectr. speech, Univ. Md, Europe, 60-61; asst. prof, West. Ill. Univ, 63-66; assoc. prof. COMMUN, MOREHEAD STATE UNIV, 66-68, PROF, 68-, chmn. div, 66-73. Speech Commun. Asn; NEA. German rhetoric. Add: Route 5, Pine Hills, Morehead, KY 40351.

VOIGT, MILTON, b. Milwaukee, Wis, Mar. 19, 24; div; c. 3. ENGLISH. Ph.B, Univ. Wis, 48; M.A, Univ. Calif, 50; Ph.D, Univ. Minn, 60. Instr. ENG, Univ. Idaho, 52-55; Univ. Ky, 56-60; asst. prof, UNIV. UTAH, 60-64; assoc. prof, 64-68, PROF, 68-, CHMN. DEPT, 71-, assoc. dean col. lett. & sci, 65-66, acting dean, 66-67, dean, 67-70. U.S.A.A.F, 43-45. MLA; NCTE; AAUP; Am. Soc. 18th Century Stud. Restoration and 18th century; literary criticism. Publ: Swift and the twentieth century, Wayne State Univ, 64. Add: 1376 Princeton Ave, Salt Lake City, UT 84105.

VOITLE, ROBERT (BROWN), b. San Francisco, Calif, July 20, 19; m. 46; c. 2. ENGLISH. A.B, Harvard, 48, A.M, 50, Ph.D, 53. Teaching fel, Harvard, 51-52; instr. ENG, UNIV. N.C, CHAPEL HILL, 52-54, asst. prof, 54-59, assoc. prof, 59-64, PROF, 64- MLA; Milton Soc. Am; Johnson Soc. London; Conf. Brit. Stud. English literature and intellectual history 1600-1800. Publ: Samuel Johnson the moralist, Harvard, 61. Add: Dept. of English, University of North Carolina at Chapel Hill, Chapel Hill, NC 27514.

VOLBACH, WALTHER RICHARD, b. Mainz, Ger, Dec. 24, 97; nat; m. 24. DRAMA. Ph.D, Univ. Münster, 20. Stage dir, State Theatres, Berlin, Stuttgart & Vienna, 28-35; dir. dramatics, Marquette Univ, 39-41; dir. opera, Cleveland Inst. Music, 42-43; prof. drama & dir. theatre & opera, Tex. Christian Univ, 46-58, prof. theatre & chmn. dept. theatre arts, 58-65; vis. prof. theatre hist, Univ. Mass, Amherst, 65-71; Univ. Calif, Santa Barbara, spring 71; RETIRED. Theatre Libr. Asn. Award, 69. Am. Nat. Theatre & Acad; Nat. Theatre Conf; Am. Theatre Asn; Am. Soc. Theatre Res. History of drama and theatre; problems of play and opera productions. Publ: Problems of opera production, Archon Bks, 67; Adolphe Appia, prophet of the modern theatre, Wesleyan Univ, 68; Memoirs of Max Reinhardt's theatres, 1920-1922, Theatre Surv, 72; Adolphe Appia und Houston Stewart Chamberlain, Musikforsch, 10/65; Time and space on the stage, Educ. Theatre J, 5/67; plus others. Add: 378D Northampton Rd, Amherst, MA 01002.

VOLPE, EDMOND LORIS, b. New Haven, Conn, Nov. 16, 22; m. 50; c. 2. ENGLISH. A.B, Univ. Mich, 43; A.M, Columbia Univ, 47, Ph.D.(Am. lit), 54. Instr. Eng, N.Y. Univ, 49-54; City Col. New York, 54-74, chmn. dept, 64-70; PRES, RICHMOND COL.(N.Y), 74- Fulbright prof, France, 60-61; vis. prof. Am. lit, Columbia Univ, 70-71. U.S.A, 43-46. Col. Eng. Asn; Asn. Dept. Eng; MLA; NCTE; Am. Stud. Asn. Henry James; modern American literature. Publ: A reader's guide to William Faulkner, Farrar, Straus, 64; co-ed, Eleven modern short novels, Putnam, 72; auth, Putting the docere back into doctor, Bull. Asn. Dept. Eng, 2/71. Add: Richmond College, 130 Stuyvesant Pl, Staten Island, NY 10301.

VON ABELE, RUDOLPH, b. Englewood, N.J, Oct. 15, 22; m. 61. EUROPEAN LITERATURE, LITERARY CRITICISM. Ph.D, Columbia Univ, 46. PROF. ENG, AM. UNIV, 47- Fund Advan. Educ. fel, 53-54; Fulbright lectr. Am. lit, Univ. Graz, 56-57. Am. Soc. Aesthet. Comparative literature; aesthetics; literary theory. Publ: Alexander H. Stephens, Knopf, 46; The death of the artist, Nijhoff, The Hague, 55; The vigil of Emmeline Gore, 62 & The party, 63, Houghton; Ulysses: the myth of myth, 6/54 & Only to grow: change in the poetry of E.E. Cummings, 12/55, PMLA. Add: 3040 Idaho Ave. N.W, Washington, DC 20016.

VON ENDE, FREDERICK ALBERT, b. Pittsburgh, Pa, June 12, 42; m. 64; c. 1. MEDIEVAL & 17TH CENTURY ENGLISH LITERATURE. B.A, McMurry Col, 64; NDEA fel, Tex. Christian Univ, 64-67, M.A, 66, Ph.D.(Eng), 72. Instr. ENG, Tex. Christian Univ, 67-68; asst. prof, PAN AM. UNIV, 68-72, ASSOC. PROF, 72- NCTE; Conf. Col. Teachers Eng; Col. Eng. Asn. Medieval English literature; Arthurian legend and lore; Milton. Publ: The Corrida pattern in For whom the bell tolls, re: arts & lett, 70; George Herbert's The sonne: in defense of the English language, Stud. Eng. Lit, 72; Child's play, you say?, CEA Critic, 73. Add: Dept. of English, Pan American University, Edinburg, TX 78539.

VON KLEMPERER, ELIZABETH GALLAHER, b. Claremont, N.H, July 9, 23; m. 53; c. 2. ENGLISH. A.B, Smith Col, 44; Fulbright scholar, Paris, 50-51; Ph.D.(Eng), Harvard, 58. Teaching asst, Harvard, 47-48, 51-52; instr. ENG, SMITH COL, 52-60, asst. prof, 61-66, ASSOC. PROF, 67- U.S.N.R, 44-46, Lt.(jg). Victorian prose and poetry; English and French fiction of late 19th and 20th centuries. Add: Wright Hall 105, Smith College, Northampton, MA 01060.

von MOLTKE, HENRY, b. Chicago, Ill, July 12, 30; m. 56; c. 2. SPEECH. B.A, Wayne State Univ, 56; M.A, Univ. Wis, 57; Ph.D.(speech), Mich. State Univ, 61. Asst. speech, Univ. Wis, Madison, 56-57; instr, Flint Community Jr. Col, 57-58, 60-62; Mich. State Univ, 58-60; asst. prof. & chmn. dept, Rockford Col, 62-64; asst. prof, Kent State Univ, 64-65; secy. fac. affairs, Bd. Col. Educ, Lutheran Church Am, N.Y, 65-67; dir. univ. planning & v.pres. educ. serv, Waterloo Lutheran Univ, 67-68; acad. dean & dean col, Lenoir-Rhyne Col, 68-70; DEAN ARTS & SCI, GLASSBORO STATE COL, 70- Dir. forensics & sponsor forum, Rockford Col, 62-64; mem. policy comt, Dept. Higher Educ. Nat. Counc. Churches, 65-67; coord. comt, Harcap Col. Prog, N.Y, 65-67. U.S.M.C, 51-53. Speech Commun. Asn. Public address; propaganda and persuasion; communication theory and practices. Add: Arts & Sciences, Glassboro State College, Glassboro, NJ 08028.

von SZELISKI, JOHN JEROME, b. Washington D.C, Nov. 13, 34; m. 56; c. 2. DRAMA. B.S, Purdue Univ, 56, M.S, 58; Ph.D.(theatre), Univ. Minn, 62. Writer & producer educ. broadcasting, WBAA, Purdue Univ, 56-58; asst. prof. drama & radio & head dept, Univ. Tampa, 58-61; ASSOC. PROF. DRAMA & DIR. ADAMS MEM. THEATRE, WILLIAMS COL, 62-, chmn. dept, 62-72. Am. Theatre Asn. Dramatic theory and criticism; theatre aesthetics. Publ: Pessimism and modern tragedy, Educ. Theatre J, 3/64; Dreiser's experiment with tragic drama, Twentieth Century Lit, 4/66; The sound of today's theatre, Antioch Rev, summer 66. The language of music, produced by Nat. Asn. Educ. Broadcasters radio network, 57. Add: Dept. of Drama, Williams College, Williamstown, MA 01267.

VOORHEES, RICHARD JOSEPH, b. Toluca, Ill, Sept. 30, 16; m. 42. ENGLISH. M.A, Univ. Ill, 41; Ph.D, Ind. Univ, 58. Instr. ENG, PURDUE UNIV, WEST LAFAYETTE, 46-54, asst. prof, 54-60, assoc. prof, 60-64, PROF, 64- U.S.A, 42-46. NCTE. Twentieth century British fiction. Publ: Paradox of George Orwell, Purdue Res. Found, 61; P.G. Wodehouse, Twayne, 67; The novels of E.M. Forster, 1/54 & Recent Greene, spring 63, S.Atlantic Quart; Kingsley Amis: three hurrahs and a reservation, Queen's Quart, spring 72; plus others. Add: 2304 Happy Hollow Rd, West Lafayette, IN 47907.

VOPAT, CAROLE GOTTLIEB, b. New York, N.Y, May 8, 44; m. 70. MODERN LITERATURE. B.A, Rutgers Univ, Newark, 64; M.A, Univ. Conn, 66; Ph.D.(Eng), Univ. Wash, 70. Teaching asst. ENG, Univ. Conn, 64-66; Univ. Wash, 66-69, instr, 69-70; ASST. PROF, UNIV. WIS-PARKSIDE, 70- Kiekhofer-Steiger Distinguished Teaching Award, 73. MLA; Midwest Mod. Lang. Asn. Women's studies; black studies. Publ: Reaching the other: teaching prose fiction, Col. Compos. & Commun, 2/73; Jack Kerouac's On the road: a re-evaluation, Midwest Quart, 7/73; Aesthetic purity vs. mind-rape, Arts in Soc, spring 74; plus others. Add: Division of Humanities, University of Wisconsin-Parkside, Kenosha, WI 53140.

VORPAHL, BEN MERCHANT, b. Cedar City, Utah, June 17, 37; m. 61. ENGLISH. B.A, Univ. Wyo, 59; M.A, Univ. Wash, 60; Ph.D.(Eng), Univ. Wis, 64. Asst. prof. ENG, Univ. Calif, Los Angeles, 64-72; ASSOC. PROF, UNIV. GA, 73- Nat. Endowment for Humanities res. fel, 72-73. MLA; Philol. Asn. Pac. Coast. Literature and history of the American frontier; literature and the graphic arts. Publ: My dear Wister: the Frederic Remington-Owen Wister Letters, Am. West, 72; The Eden theme and three novels by Timothy Flint, Stud. Romanticism, spring 71; Henry James and Owen Wister, Pa. Mag. Hist. & Biog, 7/71; Murder by the minute: old and new in The bride comes to Yellow Sky, Nineteenth Century Fiction, 9/71. Add: Dept. of English, University of Georgia, Athens, GA 30601.

VOS, ALVIN PAUL, b. Pella, Iowa, Aug. 13, 43; m. 67. ENGLISH LITERATURE. B.A, Calvin Col, 65; Ford Found fel, Univ. Chicago, 65, M.A, 66, Ph.D.(Eng), 71. ASST. PROF. ENG, STATE UNIV. N.Y. BINGHAMTON, 70- MLA; Renaissance Soc. Am. Renaissance poetry and prose. Publ: The formation of Roger Ascham's prose, Stud. in Philol, 7/74. Add: Dept. of English, State University of New York at Binghamton, Binghamton, NY 13901.

VOS, NELVIN LeROY, b. Edgerton, Minn, July 11, 32; m. 58; c. 3. ENGLISH, THEOLOGY. A.B, Calvin Col, 54; A.M, Univ. Chicago, 55, Ph.D.(theol. & lit), 64. Instr. ENG, Unity Christian High Sch, 55-57; Calvin Col, 57-59; asst. prof, Trinity Christian Col, 63-65; assoc. prof, MUHLENBERG COL, 65-70, PROF, 70- MLA; Conf. Christianity & Lit.(secy. & ed. newslett, 65-67, pres, 68-70). Comic theory; contemporary drama; theology and culture. Publ: The drama of comedy: victim and victor, 66 & For God's sake laugh, 67, John Knox; Versions of the absurd theater: Ionesco and Albee, Eerdmans, 68; The process of dying in the plays of Edward Albee, Educ. Theatre J, 3/73. Add: Dept. of English, Muhlenberg College, Allentown, PA 18104.

VOSS, THOMAS GORMAN, b. Racine, Wis, Aug. 25, 38; m. 64; c. 3. AMERICAN & ENGLISH LITERATURE. B.A, St. Francis Col, 61; M.A, Marquette Univ, 62; Ph.D.(Am. lit), Univ. Wis-Madison, 66. Asst. prof. Am. lit, Cath. Univ. Am, 65-70; dean & chief exec. off, TUSCULUM COL, 70-73, PRES, 73- Cath. Univ. Am. & Wash. Eve. Star res. grants, 67-68; Fulbright prof, Univ. Trondheim, 68-69. MLA. Rhetoric; W.C. Bryant. Add: Tusculum College, Greenville, TN 37743.

VOTAW, MAURICE ELDRED, b. Eureka, Mo, Apr. 29, 99. JOURNALISM. A.M, Univ. Mo, 21. Instr. jour, Univ. Ark, 19-20; from instr. to prof, St. John's Univ, China, 22-39; 48-49; lectr. Eng, Cent. Polit. Univ, China, 39-48; asst. prof. jour, Univ. Mo-Columbia, 50-70; res. assoc, Chinese Univ. Hong Kong, 71-72; RETIRED. Adv, Ministry Inform, Repub. China, Chungking, 39-46, Nanking, 46-48. Victory Medal, 46. The Far East; South Pacific; Middle East. Add: 114 S. Garth Ave, Columbia, MO 65201.

VOTORAS, TAKI PANAJOTIS, b. Athens, Greece, Feb. 20, 32; U.S. citizen. ENGLISH LITERATURE. A.B, Wayne State Univ, 58, M.A, 60; fel, Univ. Conn, 67-68, Ph.D.(Eng), 72. Instr. Eng, Defiance Col, 61-62; instr. Eng. as for. lang, Int. Sch, Genoa, Italy, 62-63; instr. ENG, R.I. COL, 63-67, asst. prof, 68-74, ASSOC. PROF, 74- Lectr. lit. & art, Swain Sch. Design, Mass, 68-70. MLA. Eighteenth century English poetry; literary criticism; translations from Greek to English. Add: Dept. of English, Rhode Island College, Mt. Pleasant Ave, Providence, RI 02908.

VOWLES, RICHARD BECKMAN, b. Fargo, N.Dak, Oct. 5, 17; m. 42; c. 2. COMPARATIVE, ENGLISH & SCANDINAVIAN LITERATURE. B.S, Davidson Col, 38; Am-Scand. Found. fel, Univ. Stockholm, 39-40; Vick Found. fel, Yale, 40-41, A.M, 42, Ph.D, 50. Chem. eng, Hercules Powder Co, 41-42; econ. consult, U.S. Dept. War, 43-44; Am. v.consul, U.S. For. Serv, 44-46; asst. prof. Eng, Southwest. at Memphis, 48-50; Queens Col.(N.Y), 50-51; Univ. Fla, 51-56, assoc. prof, 56-61; PROF. COMP. LIT. & SCAND. STUD, UNIV. WIS-MADISON, 61-, chmn. dept. comp. lit, 63-67 & 71-72. Res. fel, Yale, 55; Fulbright fel, 55-56; gen. ed, Nordic Transl. Ser, 62-; U.S. Dept. State lectr, Finland, Denmark & Sweden & Swedish Govt. grant, summer 63; vis. res. prof, Univ. Helsinki, 68; Fulbright lectr, Eng, 68; Strindberg fel, Swedish Inst, Stockholm, summer 73. Am-Scand. Found; Soc. Advan. Scand. Stud.(mem. adv. comt, 64-); Strindberg Soc; MLA. Modern Scandinavian literature; comparative drama; dramatic theory. Publ: Ed, Paer Lagerkvist's collected fiction, Dramatic theory: a bibliography & August Strindberg: a survey and a fragment; ed. & transl, Peder Sjögren, Bread of love, Univ. Wis, 65; ed, Two novels by August Strindberg, Bantam, 68; co-ed, Comparatists at work, Blaisdell, 68; plus others. Add: 1115 Oak Way, Madison, WI 53705.

VOYLES, JIMMY PONDER, b. Cairo, Ga, Nov. 21, 38; m. 60; c. 2. ENGLISH & AMERICAN LITERATURE. B.A, Miss. Col, 60; M.A, Fla. State Univ, 64; Ph.D.(Eng), Univ. Ga, 71. Teacher Am. hist, Central High Sch, Thomasville, Ga, 60-62; instr. ENG, Norman Col, 62-67; ASST. PROF, Ga. South. Col, 69-70; MISS. COL, 70- MLA. Southern American literature; 18th century English literature. Publ: Richard Malcolm Johnston's literary career: an estimate, Markham Rev, 73-74. Add: Dept. of English, Mississippi College, Clinton, MS 39056.

VRIEZE, JACK W, b. Quincy, Fla, Apr. 3, 24; m. 49; c. 5. THEATRE, SPEECH. A.B, Kenyon Col, 47; Ph.D.(speech, dramatic art), State Univ. Iowa, 53. Dir. theatre, Wis. State Univ, Whitewater, 52-66; PROF. SPEECH & HEAD DEPT. SPEECH & THEATRE, FROSTBURG STATE COL, 66- Comptroller, Nat. Children's Theatre Conf, 66-70. U.S.N, 43-46, Ens. Am. Theatre Asn; Speech Commun. Asn. Theatre production; promotion of educational theatre; audience response in the theatre. Publ: Problems, gains and goals in developing a strong region, Sec. Sch. Theatre Conf. Newslett, 67. Add: Dept. of Speech, Frostburg State College, Frostburg, MD 21532.

VUCINICH, MARY COCHNOWER, b. Cincinnati, Ohio, Jan. 3, 07; m. 60. ENGLISH. B.S, Univ. Cincinnati, 28, Wesleyan fel, 30-32, M.A, 31; univ. scholar, State Univ. Iowa, 36-38, Ph.D.(Eng), 38. Chmn. dept. Eng. & dean women, Kanawha Jr. Col, 38-39; asst. prof. Eng, Morris Harvey Col, 39-42; asst. prof. Eng. & librn, Cincinnati Col. Pharmacy, 42-43, assoc. prof. Eng. & psychol, 45-47; chmn. art dept, Lincoln Jr. High Sch, Charleston, W.Va, 43-44; asst. prof. ENG, STATE UNIV. N.Y. COL. BUFFALO, 47-51, prof, 51-73, EMER. PROF, 73- Poetry award, N.Y. State div, Am. Asn. Univ. Women, 68. Art; poetry; religion; history. Publ: Co-auth, God and the villagers, State Univ. N.Y. Col. Buffalo, (in press); John Ford, In: Seventeenth-century studies, Princeton, 33. Add: 382 Wendel Ave, Kenmore, NY 14223.

VUKOV, EILEEN HELENANNE, English, Philosophy. See KRUEGEL, EILEEN HELENANNE.

W

WAAL, CARLA RAE, b. Milwaukee, Wis, June 15, 33; m. 74. DRAMA, THEATER. B.S, Univ. Richmond, 53; M.A, Univ. Va, 57; Univ. Oslo, 59, 62-63; Ph.D. (speech & theater), Ind. Univ, 64. Teacher, Jr. High Sch, Va, 53-55; instr. Eng. & speech, Heidelberg Col, 58-60; asst. prof. DRAMA & THEATER, Univ. Ga, 64-69, assoc. prof, 69-73; PROF, UNIV. MO-COLUMBIA, 73- Participant, Scand. Stud. Sem, Swed, summer 68; Ibsen Sem, Cambridge, summer 70. Speech Commun. Asn.(assoc. ed, 65-71); Am. Theatre Asn; S.Atlantic Mod. Lang. Asn.(Scand. chmn, 72-73); Soc. Advan. Scand. Stud. Modern drama; Scandinavian theater history and literature. Publ: Johanne

Dybwad: Norwegian actress, Univ. Oslo, 67; Hamsun's Ved rigets port on the Norwegian stage, Scand. Stud, 5/69; The plays of Knut Hamsun, Quart. J. Speech, 2/71; Rhetoric in action: orators in the plays of Henrik Ibsen, South. Speech Commun. J, spring 72. Add: Dept. of Speech and Dramatic Art, University of Missouri-Columbia, 129 Fine Arts Ctr, Columbia, MO 65201.

WACHTEL, ALBERT, b. Queens, N.Y, Dec. 20, 39; m. 58; c. 7. MODERN BRITISH & AMERICAN LITERATURE. B.A, Queens Col.(N.Y), 60; NDEA fel, State Univ, N.Y. Buffalo, 60-63, Ph.D.(Eng. lit), 68. Instr. Eng, State Univ. N.Y. Buffalo, 63-66, asst. to dean, 66-68; ASST. PROF. ENG. LIT, UNIV. CALIF, SANTA BARBARA, 68- Creative Arts Inst. fel, 70. James Joyce Soc. Modern fiction; literary theory; psychology and literature. Publ: On analogical action, J. Aesthet. & Art Criticism, 63; The boundaries of narrative, J. Aesthet. Educ, 68; The burden, Spectrum, 71. Add: Dept. of English, University of California, Santa Barbara, CA 93106.

WADDEN, ANTHONY THOMAS, b. Sioux City, Iowa, July 13, 39; m. 64; c. 3. BRITISH & AMERICAN LITERATURE. B.A, Univ. Iowa, 61, M.A, 63, Slone fel, 69-70, Ph.D.(Eng), 70. Lectr. ENG, Calif. State Polytech. Col, 64-66; teaching asst, Univ. Iowa, 68-69; ASST. PROF, GONZAGA UNIV, 70- MLA; West. Am. Lit. Asn; Philol. Asn. Pac. Coast. Psychology and narrative literature; 19th century British and American novel. Publ: J. Hyatt Downing: chronicler of an era, Books at Iowa, 4/68; Late to the harvest: the fiction of J. Hyatt Downing, West. Am. Lit, fall 71. Add: Dept. of English, Gonzaga University, Spokane, WA 99202.

WADDINGTON, MIRIAM (DWORKIN), b. Winnipeg, Man; m. 39; c. 2. LITERATURE. B.A, Univ. Toronto, 39, dipl. social work, 42, M.A, 68; M.S.W, Univ. Pa, 45. Ed. asst, Mag. Digest, Toronto, 39-40; caseworker, Jewish Family Serv, Toronto, 42-45; asst. dir, Jewish Child Welfare Agency, Montreal, 45-46; lectr, McGill Sch. Social Work, 46-49; caseworker, Montreal Children's Hosp, 53-55; John Howard Soc, Montreal, 55-57; Jewish Family Serv, Montreal, 57-60; supvr. North York Family Serv. Toronto, 60-62; PROF. ENG, YORK UNIV, 64- Can. Counc. sr. fel, 62-63, leave fel, 68-69, sr. fel. poetry, 70-71; vis. prof. Can. lit, Carleton Univ, 69-70. PEN Club; MLA. Poetry; modern fiction; creative process. Publ: Green world, First Statement, Montreal, 45; The second silence, 55 & The season's lovers, 58, Ryerson; The glass trumpet, 66, Say yes, 69 & Driving home: poems new and selected, 72, Oxford, Toronto; Call them Canadians, Queen's Printer, 68; A.M. Klein, Copp Clark, 70; The dream telescope, Anvil & Routledge Kegan Paul, 73; ed, John Sutherland: essays, controversies, poems; auth, Form in poetry, J. Otto Rank Asn, 6/68; Canadian tradition in Canadian literature, J. Commonwealth Lit, 12/69; All nature into motion: the poetry of John Sutherland, Can. Lit, summer 69. Add: 32 Yewfield Crescent, Don Mills, Ont. M3B 2Y6, Can.

WADDINGTON, RAYMOND BRUCE, b. Santa Barbara, Calif, Sept. 27, 35; m. 57; c. 2. ENGLISH. B.A, Stanford Univ, 57; fel, Rice Univ, 58-61, Ph.D. (Eng), 63. Instr. ENG, Univ. Houston, 61-62; Univ. Kans, 62-64, asst. prof, 64-65; UNIV. WIS-MADISON, 66-68, assoc. prof, 68-74, PROF, 74- Am. Philos. Soc. grant, 65; fel, Johns Hopkins Univ, 65-66; Henry E. Huntington Libr. fel, summer 67; Inst. for Res. in Humanities, Univ. Wis, 71-72; Guggenheim fel, 72-73. MLA; Milton Soc. Am. Renaissance; 17th century English poetry; Milton. Publ: The mind's empire: myth and form in George Chapman's narrative poems, Johns Hopkins, 74; co-ed, The rhetoric of Renaissance poetry, Univ. Calif, 74; auth, Antony and Cleopatra, Shakespeare Stud. II, 66; The iconography of silence and Chapman's Hercules, J. Warburg & Courtauld Insts, 70; The death of Adam: vision and voice in books XI and XII of Paradise lost, Mod. Philol, 72. Add: Dept. of English, University of Wisconsin-Madison, 600 N. Park St, Madison, WI 53706.

WADE, LUTHER IRWIN, III, b. Elkin, N.C, Sept. 29, 37; m. 60; c. 2. DRAMA, SPEECH. B.A, La. State Univ, 60, B.M, 65, M.A, 66, univ. fel, 68-69, Ph.D.(drama, speech), 69; Woodrow Wilson fel, Univ. Minn, 62-63. Suprv. listening rooms, La. State Univ. Libr, 67-68; ASST. PROF. SPEECH, ENG. & DRAMA, SOUTHEAST. LA. UNIV, 69-, HEAD DEPT. SPEECH, 71- U.S.A, 60-62, 1st Lt. Speech Commun. Asn; South. Speech Commun. Asn; Am. Theatre Asn; Southwest Theatre Conf. Musical theatre; theatre history; voice training and phonetics, linguistics. Add: Dept. of Speech, Southeastern Louisiana University, Hammond, LA 70401.

WADE, PHILIP TYREE, b. Covington, Va, Feb. 17, 31; m. 55; c. 2. ENGLISH. A.B, Guilford Col, 57; M.A, Univ. Ark, 59; Ph.D.(Eng), Univ. N.C, 66. Asst. prof. ENG, Univ. Fla, 67-69; PROF, WEST. CAROLINA UNIV, 69- U.S.N, 51-54. MLA; English Romantic literature, especially Shelley. Add: Central Dr, Cullowhee, NC 28723.

WADE, SETH, b. Decatur, Ky, Nov. 12, 28; m. 62; c. 3. ENGLISH. A.B, Univ. Ky, 52; M.A, La. State Univ, 54; Univ. Fla, 54-54; Ohio State Univ, 57-59. Asst. ENG, La. State Univ, 52-53; Univ. Fla, 53-54; instr, Univ. Ky, North. Ctr, 54-55; teaching asst, Ohio State Univ, 57-59, asst. instr, 59-60; mem. fac, West. Ky. State Col, 61-62; ASST; PROF, PAN AM. UNIV, 62- U.S.A, 55-57. NCTE. Creative writing and modern poetry. Publ: Mr. many, (poems and drawings), Funch, 69; The broken eye, (poems), Mitchell, 74; Henry's Wdpile, (poems), Ganglia, Toronto, 74; contrib. poems, Beloit Poetry J, summer 66, sinter 66-67, South. Humanities Rev, summer 67 & Wis. Rev, spring 68. Add: 1100 West Samano, Edinburg, TX 78539.

WADLEIGH, PAUL C, b. Indianapolis, Ind, Dec. 6, 25; m. 46; c. 3. DRAMA. A.B, Ind. Univ, 49, M.S, 50, Ph.D, 62. Asst. prof. speech, West. Wash. State Col, 61-65; ASSOC. PROF. SPEECH & THEATRE, WASH. STATE UNIV, 65- U.S.N.R, 44-46, 52-54, Res, 54-, Lt. Am. Theatre Asn; Speech Commun. Asn. Theatre arts; dramatic literature. Add: Dept. of Speech & Drama, Washington State University, Pullman, WA 99163.

WADSWORTH, FRANK WHITTEMORE, b. New York, N.Y, June 14, 19; m. 43; c. 2. ENGLISH. Wilson fel, Jr. fel, Scribner fel. & Ph.D.(Eng), Princeton, 51. Instr. Eng, Princeton, 49-50; Univ. Calif, Los Angeles, 50-53, asst. prof, 53-58, assoc. prof, 58-61; prof. Eng. & dean div. humanities, Univ. Pittsburgh, 62-67; PROF. ENG. & ACAD. V.PRES, STATE UNIV. COL. N.Y. PURCHASE, 67- Nat. rep. & consult, Woodrow Wilson Nat. Fel. Found, 58-61, trustee, 73-; Folger Shakespeare Libr. fel, 61; Guggenheim fel, 61-62; dir, Wenner-Gren Found. Anthrop. Res, 70- U.S.N.R, 42-46. MLA; Malone Soc; Am. Soc. Theatre Res; Int. Fed. Theatre Res; Renaissance Soc. Am. Drama, especially 16th and 17th century English; stage history. Publ: The poacher from Stratford, Univ. Calif, 58; The relationship of Lust's Dominion and John Mason's The Turke, J. Eng. Lit. Hist; Webster's Duchess of Malfi in the light of contemporary ideas on marriage and remarriage, Philol. Quart. Add: Office of the Academic Vice President, State University of New York College at Purchase, Purchase, NY 10577.

WADSWORTH, RANDOLPH LINCOLN, JR, b. Cincinnati, Ohio, July 26, 35; m. 57. ENGLISH, COMPARATIVE LITERATURE. A.B, Princeton, 57; M.A, Stanford Univ, 64, Ph.D.(Eng), 67; Leverhulme fel, London, 64-65. Instr. Eng. & French, Mt. Hermon Sch, Mass, 59-61; instr. ENG, Univ. Wis-Madison, 65-66, ASST. PROF, 66-70; MIAMI UNIV, 70- MLA. Seventeenth century literature. Publ: On The snayl by Richard Lovelace, Mod. Lang. Rev, 9/70; On the role and characterization of the Tortores in Arnoul Greban's Mystere de la passion, Rev. Litt. Comp, 11/70; art. on Lovelace, In: Readers' encyclopedia of literature, Crowell; plus others. Add: Dept. of English, Miami University, Oxford, OH 45056.

WAGENKNECHT, EDWARD, b. Chicago, Ill, Mar. 28, 00; m. 32; c. 3. ENGLISH & AMERICAN LITERATURE. Ph.B, Univ. Chicago, 23, A.M, 24; Ph.D, Univ. Wash, 32. Teacher ENG, Univ. Chicago, 23-25, Univ. Wash, 25-43; Ill. Inst. Technol, 43-47; prof, BOSTON UNIV, 47-65, EMER. PROF, 65- English and American novel; Charles Dickens; Mark Twain. Publ: Ed, Introduction to Dickens, Scott, 52; auth, Cavalcade of the American novel, 52 & Cavalcade of the English novel, rev. ed, 54, Holt; Unknown Longfellow, Boston Univ, 54; Seven worlds of Theodore Roosevelt, 58 & ed, Stories of Christ and Christmas, 63, McKay; ed, Chaucer: modern essays in criticism, 59, auth, Nathaniel Hawthorne, man and writer, 61, Washington Irving: moderation displayed, 62, Edgar Allan Poe: the man behind the legend, 63, Harriet Beecher Stowe: the known and the unknown, 65, Henry Wadsworth Longfellow: portrait of an American humanist, 66 & John Greenleaf Whittier: a portrait in paradox, 67, William Dean Howells: The friendly eye, 69, James Russell Lowell: portrait of a many-sided man, 71, Ambassadors for Christ, 72 & Ralph Waldo Emerson: portrait of a balanced soul, 74, Oxford; ed, Fireside book of Christmas stories, Grosset; auth, Mark Twain, the man and his work, rev. ed, 61, Movies in the age of innocence, 62, Chicago, 64, Seven daughters of the theater, 64, Dickens and the scandalmongers: essays in criticism, 65, The man Charles Dickens: a Victorian portrait, rev. ed, 66, Merely players, 66, The personality of Chaucer, 68, As far as yesterday, 68, ed, John Greenleaf Whittier's The supernaturalism of New England, 69, auth, The personality of Milton, 70, The personality of Shakespeare, 72 & ed, The letters of James Branch Cabell, 74, Univ. Okla; auth, Nine before Fotheringhay, (under name of Jullian Forrest), 66 & The glory of the lilies: a novel about Joan of Arc, (under name of Jullian Forrest), 69, G. Bles, London; ed, Marilyn Monroe: a composite view, Chilton, 69. Add: 233 Otis St, West Newton, MA 02165.

WAGER, WILLIS JOSEPH, b. Pittsburg, Kans, July 24, 11; m. 47; c. 3. ENGLISH LITERATURE, MUSIC. A.B, Wash. Univ, 31, A.M, 32; Ph.D, Inst. Int. Educ. exchange fel, Univ. Frankfort, 33-34; Penfield fel, N.Y. Univ, 34-35, Ph.D, 43. Asst. Eng. & jour, Wash. Univ, 32-33; Eng, N.Y. Univ, 35-36, instr, 36-38; lit. ed, G. Schirmer, Inc, 38-44; assoc. prof, Berea Col, 44-46; PROF. ENG. & CHMN. DEPT. GEN. STUD, SCH. FINE & APPLIED ARTS, BOSTON UNIV, 46- Fulbright prof. humanities, Pädagogische Hochschule, Berlin, 63-64; consult. music, Stud. Higher Educ, Phila, 63-; Fulbright prof. Am. lit, Istanbul Univ, 66-68 & Teheran Univ, 68-70. Chaucer; Mark Twain; medieval and Renaissance music; American literature. Publ: From the hand of man, Boston Univ, 62; co-auth, Liberal education and music, Teachers Col, Columbia Univ, 62; auth, American literature: a world view, N.Y. Univ. & Univ. London, 68; co-auth, History of music, Free Press, 73. Add: 319 St. Paul St, Brookline, MA 02146.

WAGES, JACK DOUGLAS, b. Lubbock, Tex, Apr. 5, 38; m. 59. AMERICAN LITERATURE. B.A, N.Tex. State Univ, 60; M.A, Univ. Tex, Austin, 63; Ph.D.(Eng), Univ. Tenn, Knoxville, 68. Asst. prof. ENG, TEX. TECH UNIV, 68-72, ASSOC. PROF, 72- State coord. achievement awards in writing, NCTE, 71-74. AAUP; MLA; NCTE; Col. Eng. Asn; Am. Name Soc. Early American literature; satire; short fiction. Publ: Mock Wills: parody in the colonial South, Satire Newslett, spring 72; Isaac Asimov's debt to Edgar Allan Poe, Poe Stud, 6/73; Father Benjamin and the ladies: chauvinist or champion?, Proc. Conf. Col. Teachers Eng, 9/73; plus three others. Add: Dept. of English, Texas Tech University, Lubbock, TX 79409.

WAGGONER, GEORGE RUBLE, b. Wagoner, Okla, Feb. 4, 16. ELIZABETHAN DRAMA, COMPARATIVE EDUCATION. A.B, Univ. Kans, 36, A.M, 39; Ph.D, Univ. Wis, 47; Ph.D.(humanities & educ), Univ. Oriente, Venezuela, 69. Instr. Eng, Univ. Kans, 38-41; asst. prof. Eng. lit, Pa. State Univ, 47-48; asst. prof. Eng, Ind, Univ, 48-53, assoc. prof, 53-54; asst. dean col. arts & sci, 48-52, assoc. dean, 52-54; PROF. ENG. & DEAN COL. LIB. ARTS & SCI, UNIV. KANS, 54- Consult, Counc. Cent. Am. Univ; mem. Comn. on Cols. & Univs, N.Cent. Asn. Cols. & Sec. Schs, 62-63; mem. exec. comt, Inter-Univ. Comt. on Superior Stud; cor. ed, J. Higher Educ; consult, Inst. for Support Higher Educ, Bogota, Colombia, summer 70 & planning off, univ. sector, Nat. Counc. Univs. Venezuela, 73-74. NCTE; MLA; Renaissance Soc. Am; Comp. & Int. Educ. Soc; Latin Am. Stud. Asn; Midwest Latin Am. Stud. Asn. Latin American universities; university administration. Publ: Co-ed, Metodología de la educación universitaria, 69, co-auth, Education in Central America, 71 & co-ed, Autonomia, planificación, coordinación, innovaciones: perspectivas latinoamericanas, 72, Univ. Kans. Add: College of Liberal Arts & Sciences, University of Kansas, Lawrence, KS 66045.

WAGGONER, HYATT HOWE, b. Pleasant Valley, N.Y, Nov. 19, 13; m. 37; c. 2. AMERICAN LITERATURE. A.B, Middlebury Col, 35; M.A, Univ. Chicago, 36; Ph.D, Ohio State Univ, 42; hon. M.A, Brown Univ, 57. Instr. Eng, Univ. Omaha, 39-42, Eng. & Am. lit, Univ. Kans. City, 42-44, asst. prof, 44-47, assoc. prof, 47-50, prof, 50-56, chmn. dept, 52-56; PROF. ENG, BROWN UNIV, 56-, chmn. Am. civilization prog, 60-70. Chmn, Am. lit. group, MLA, 62- MLA; Am. Stud. Asn. Science and American literature; Hawthorne; American poetry. Publ: The heel of Elohim: science and values in modern American poetry, Univ. Okla, 50; Hawthorne, a critical study, Harvard, 55, rev. ed, 63; William Faulkner: from Jefferson to the world, Univ. Ky, 59; American poets: from the Puritans to the present, Houghton, 68; plus others. Add: Dept. of English, Brown University, Providence, RI 02912.

WAGNER, ARTHUR, b. New York, N.Y, May 11, 23; m. 56; c. 2. THEATRE. B.A, Earlham Col, 46; M.A, Smith Col, 48; Danforth Found. grant, Stanford Univ, 61-62, Ph.D.(drama), 62. Dir, Springfield Jewish Community Ctr, Mass, 48-49; Springfield Civic Theatre, 49-50; instr. theatre, Rollins Col, 56-57, asst. prof, 57-62, assoc. prof, 62-64; prof, 64-65, head theatre arts dept, 57-65; prof. theatre, Tulane Univ, 65-67; Ohio Univ, 67-69; Temple Univ, 69-72; PROF. DRAMA & CHMN. DEPT, UNIV. CALIF, SAN DIEGO, 72-. U.S.A, 43-46. Am. Theatre Asn; Univ. & Col. Theatre Asn.(v.pres, 72-). Applications of theories of transactional analysis to the training and work of the actor, especially the work of Dr. Eric Berne. Publ: A playwright triumphs, Harpers, 9/66; Transactional analysis and acting, Tulane Drama Rev, summer 67; Permission and protection in actor training, Drama Rev, spring 69. Add: Dept. of Drama, University of California, San Diego, La Jolla, CA 92037.

WAGNER, BERNARD MATHIAS, b. Sidney, Ohio, Jan. 12, 02. ENGLISH LITERATURE. Ph.B, Georgetown Univ, 24; A.M, Princeton, 25; A.M, Harvard, 27, univ. scholar, 29-30, Dexter scholar, 30, Austin fel, 30-31. Asst. prof. ENG, GEORGETOWN UNIV, 31-35, assoc. prof, 35-38, prof, 35-72, chmn. dept, 38-51, EMER. PROF, 72- MLA; Malone Soc; Bibliog. Soc, Eng. Elizabethan drama and poetry; eight prose writers; appreciation of Shakespeare. Add: 3900 Cathedral Ave. N.W, Washington, DC 20016.

WAGNER, C. ROLAND, b. New York, N.Y, May 10, 24; m. 55; c. 3. ENGLISH, PHILOSOPHY. A.B, Bucknell Univ, 47; Ph.D.(philos), Yale, 52; M.A, Columbia Univ, 52. Instr. Eng. & humanities, Univ. N.H, 52-53; asst. prof. philos, Univ. Del, 53-60; assoc. prof, NEW COL. HOFSTRA, 60-63, HUMANITIES, 63-70, PROF, 70- Fulbright teaching award, Univs. Caen & Poitiers, 58-59. U.S.A.A.F, 43-46. Am. Philos. Soc. Psychoanalysis; Wallace Stevens and Italo Svevo. Publ: The silence of The stranger, Mod. Fiction Stud, spring 70; The excremental and the spiritual in A passage to India, Mod. Lang. Quart, 9/70; Italo Svevo: the vocation of old age, Hartford Stud. Lit, 70; plus others. Add: Div. of Humanities, New College of Hofstra, Hempstead, NY 11550.

WAGNER, FREDERICK JOHN, b. Tyvan, Sask, Oct. 15, 08; m. 47; c. 2. ENGLISH LITERATURE. B.A, Capital Univ, 29; M.A, Univ. Minn, Minneapolis, 37; Univ. London, 52, 53. Instr. Eng, St. Paul-Luther Col, 31-33; Luther Col.(Sask), 35-40, asst. prof, 40-45, assoc. prof, 45-50, prof, 50-65, dean of men, 35-50; asst. prof. ENG, UNIV. SASK, REGINA, 65-68, ASSOC. PROF, 68- R.C.A.F, 42-46. Asn. Can. Univ. Teachers Eng. J.H. Shorthouse; 19th century English religious novel. Publ: J.H. Shorthouse (1834-1903): a bibliography, Bull. Bibliog. & Mag. Notes, 71. Add: Dept. of English, University of Saskatchewan, Regina, Sask. S4S 0A2, Can.

WAGNER, LILLIAN ROSE, b. Alton, Iowa, Aug. 30, 09. SPEECH. B.A, Univ. S.Dak, 32; M.A, Univ. Iowa, 40; Ph.D.(speech), Univ. Wis-Madison, 52. Teacher, rural schs, Iowa & S.Dak, 32-36; speech & Eng, Marcus High Sch, Iowa, 36-39; dir. SPEECH, Kewanee High Sch, Ill, 39-43; instr, Col. St. Teresa (Mo), 43-44; Duluth State Teachers Col, 44-46; Univ. Wis-Milwaukee, 46-48; PROF, UNIV. NORTH. IOWA, 50- Speech Commun. Asn. History of rhetorical theory; oratory of colonial period; oratory of civil rights movement. Publ: Contrib, A history of speech education in America, Appleton, 54. Add: Dept. of Speech, University of Northern Iowa, Cedar Falls, IA 50613.

WAGNER, LINDA WELSHIMER, b. St. Marys, Ohio, Aug. 18, 36; m. 57; c. 3. ENGLISH, WRITING. B.A. & B.S, Bowling Green State Univ, 57, M.A, 59, Licentiate, 61, Ph.D.(Eng) 63; Univ. B.C, summer 63. Teacher, high sch, Mich, 57-59; Ohio, 59-60; instr. ENG, Bowling Green State Univ, 60-62; asst. prof, Wayne State Univ, 67-68; from asst. prof. to PROF, MICH. STATE UNIV, 68- MLA; NCTE. Modern American poetry and fiction. Publ: The poems of William Carlos Williams: a critical study, 64 & The prose of William Carlos Williams, 70, Wesleyan Univ; Intaglios: poems, South-West, 67; Denise Levertov, 67 & Phyllis McGinley, 71, Twayne; ed, William Faulkner: four decades of criticism, 73 & Ernest Hemingway, Five decades of criticism, 74, Mich. State Univ; T.S. Eliot, McGraw, 74; Hemingway and Faulkner: inventors/masters, (in press); Ophelia, Shakespeare's pathetic plot device, Shakespeare Quart, winter 63; A bunch of marigolds, Kenyon Rev, 1/67; The latest Creeley, Am. Poetry Rev, fall 74; plus many others. Add: 1620 Anderson Way, East Lansing, MI 48823.

WAGNER, M. JOHN, b. Chicago, Ill, Aug. 27, 17; m. 54; c. 2. ENGLISH. B.A, Univ. Chicago, 39, M.A, 40; Ph.D.(Eng), Northwest. Univ, 56. Instr. ENG, Northwest. Univ, 45-47; Ill. Inst. Technol, 51-52 & 55-56; Lake Forest Col, 52-55; asst. prof, Humboldt State Col, 56-59; Univ. Puget Sound, 59-62; Calif. State Polytech. Col. Pomona, 62-64; CALIF. STATE UNIV, FULLERTON, 64-65, assoc. prof, 65-67, PROF. & CHMN. DEPT, 67- U.S.A.A.F, 41-45. MLA. Eighteenth century English; fiction writing. Publ: Co-auth, The gift of Rome, Atlantic Monthly Press, Little, 61. Add: Dept. of English, California State University, Fullerton, 800 N. State College Blvd, Fullerton, CA 92631.

WAGNER, VERN, b. Broadview, Mont, July 23, 19; m. 41; c. 3. ENGLISH, AMERICAN LITERATURE. B.A, Univ. Wash, 46, M.A, 48, Ph.D.(Eng), 50. Instr. Eng, Univ. Wash, 50; prof. Eng. & chmn. dept. lang, Nebr. State Teachers Col, Chadron, 50-52; from asst. prof. to assoc. prof. ENG, WAYNE STATE UNIV, 52-71, PROF, 71- Mem. comt. teacher training & qualifications, NCTE, 57-; Fulbright prof, Univ. Helsinki, 59-60. U.S.A, 43-46, Staff Sgt. NCTE; Col. Eng. Asn.(dir, 67-). Nineteenth and twentieth century American literature. Publ: The suspension of Henry Adams; a study in manner and matter, Wayne State Univ, 69; The lecture lyceum and the problem of controversy, J. Hist. Ideas, 1/54; The maligned style of Theodore Dreiser, West. Humanities Rev, spring, 65; Hawthorne's smile, Tex. Quart, winter 73. Add: Dept. of English, Wayne State University, Detroit, MI 48202.

WAGONER, DAVID R, b. Massillon, Ohio, June 5, 26; m. 61. ENGLISH. B.A, Pa. State Univ, 47; M.A, Ind. Univ, 49. Instr. ENG, DePauw Univ, 49-50; Pa. State Univ, 50-53; UNIV. WASH, 54-55, asst. prof, 55-61, assoc. prof, 61-66, PROF, 66-, summer res. grant, grad. sch, 63. Guggenheim fel, 56; vis. prof, Univ. Ore, 59; Ford Found. fel. theatre, 64-65; lit. adv, Seattle Repertory Theatre, 64-; vis. prof, sch. lett, Ind. Univ, 65; ed, Poetry Northwest, 66-; Elliston lectr. mod poetry, Univ. Cincinnati, 68. Nat. Inst. Arts & Lett. Award, 67. Novels; poetry. Publ: Rock, Viking, 58; A place to stand, 58, The nesting ground, 63, Staying alive (poems), 66, Riverbed (poems), 72 & Sleeping in the woods (poems), 74, Ind. Univ; The escape artist, 65, Baby, come on inside, 68, Where is my wandering boy tonight?, 70 & The road to many a wonder, 74, Farrar, Straus; ed, The notebooks of Theodore Roethke, Univ. Wash, 69; auth, Working against time (poems), Rapp & Whiting, London, 70; Straw for the fire: from the notebooks of Theodore Roethke, 1943-1946, Doubleday, 72. Add: Dept. of English, University of Washington, Seattle, WA 98105.

WAHL, WILLIAM BUDD, b. Oshkosh, Wis, Oct. 11, 20; m. 64; c. 3. ENGLISH & AMERICAN LITERATURE. B.A, San Francisco State Col, 53, M.A, 54, Ph.D.(Eng), Univ. Salzburg, 73. Instr. Eng, Sequoia High Sch, 54-56; stage prod, Eng. & speech, Col. San Mateo, 56-60; ENG, City Col. San Jose, 64-66; ASST. PROF, CALIF. POLYTECH. STATE UNIV, SAN LUIS OBISPO, 66- Lectr, Salzburger Volkshochschule, Austria, 71-73; Am. ed, Salzburg Stud. Eng. Lit, 73- U.S.N, 40-45. Poetic drama; communication. Publ: A lone wolf howling: the thematic content of Ronald Duncan's plays, 73 & Ronald Duncan, verse dramatist and poet (interview), 73, Salzburg Stud. Eng. Lit. Add: Dept. of English, California Polytechnic State University, San Luis Obispo, CA 93407.

WAIDELICH, RICHARD LONG, b. Allentown, Pa, May 30, 24; m. 50; c. 2. ENGLISH. A.B, Muhlenberg Col, 45; M.A, Harvard, 46, Ph.D, 53. Teaching fel, Harvard, 47-51; instr. Eng, Amherst Col, 51-54; asst. prof, Goucher Col, 54-60; ENG. & COMP. LIT, SAN FRANCISCO STATE UNIV, 60-65, assoc. prof, 65-69, PROF, 69- Am. Comp. Lit. Asn. European Romantic literature; modern American and European poetry; Bible as literature. Publ: The theme of change in Matthew Arnold's poetry. Add: Dept. of English, San Francisco State Univ, 1600 Holloway Ave, San Francisco, CA 94132.

WAINGROW, MARSHALL, b. Bridgeport, Conn, Mar. 26, 23; m. 50, 67; c. 3. ENGLISH. B.S, Harvard, 44; M.A, Univ. Rochester, 46, Ph.D, Yale, 51. Instr. Eng, Pa. State Univ, 48-49; Yale, 52-56, asst. prof, 57-59; PROF. ENG, CLAREMONT GRAD. SCH, 59- Morse fel, Yale, 56-57; Am. Counc. Learned Soc. grant-in-aid, 63; Guggenheim fel, 70-71; Am. Philos. Soc. grant, 72-73. MLA. Eighteenth century literature; Boswell and Johnson. Publ: Co-ed, R.L.S, Stevenson's letters to Charles Baxter, Yale, 56; 18th century English literature, Harcourt, 69; ed, The correspondence and other papers of James Boswell relating to the making of the life of Johnson, Heinemann & McGraw, 69. Add: Dept. of English & American Literature, Claremont Graduate School, Claremont, CA 91711.

WAITE, JOHN ALLAN, b. Denver, Colo, Apr. 15, 15. ENGLISH. A.B, Univ. Colo, 36, M.A, 37; Ph.D, Univ. Md, 51; Univ. Denver; Northwest. Univ; Univ. Calif. Instr. Eng. & speech & asst. to dean admin, Stephens Col, 37-42; asst. prof. speech, radio & drama, Kalamazoo Col, 44-45; from asst. prof. to assoc. prof. ENG, MICH. STATE UNIV, 46-71, PROF, 71-, asst. dean col. arts & lett, 67-72. Am. Stud. Asn. Dramatic literature; American civilization; masses: 1911-1917, a study in American rebellion. Add: Dept. of English, Michigan State University, East Lansing, MI 48823.

WAITH, EUGENE MERSEREAU, b. Buffalo, N.Y, Dec. 29, 12; m. 39; ENGLISH LITERATURE. A.B, Yale, 35, Ph.D.(Eng), 39. Instr. ENG, YALE, 39-43, asst. prof, 46-52, assoc. prof, 52-63, PROF, 63- Secy, Eng. Inst, 53-58, chmn, 62-63. U.S.A, 43-46, 1st Lt. MLA. Shakespeare; 17th century drama; modern drama. Publ: The pattern of tragicomedy in Beaumont and Fletcher; ed, Macbeth, rev. ed, 54, ed, Bartholomew fair, 63 & co-ed, Shakespeare's poems, 64, Yale Univ; auth, Herculean hero, Columbia Univ, 62; ed, Shakespeare: the histories, a collection of critical essays, 65 & auth, The dramatic moment, 67, Prentice-Hall; Ideas of greatness, Routledge & Kegan Paul, 71; Dryden and the tradition of serious drama, In: John Dryden, G. Bell, 72. Add: Dept. of English, Yale University, New Haven, CT 06520.

WALCOTT, FRED GEORGE, b. Sparta, Mich, Sept. 8, 94; m. 19; c. 2. ENGLISH. A.B, Univ. Mich, 28, M.A, 30, D.Ed, 45. Prin, high sch, Mich, 25-27, teacher, 28-35; instr. educ, univ. high sch, Univ. Mich, 35-45, asst. prof. EDUC. & ENG, 46-50, assoc. prof, UNIV. MICH, ANN ARBOR, 50-54; PROF, 54-, head dept. Eng, univ. high sch, 35-50. MLA; NCTE; Soc. Advan. Educ; Philos. Educ. Soc; Nat. Soc. Stud. Educ; John Dewey Soc. Matthew Arnold; teaching of English; philosophy of education. Publ: Co-auth, Facts about current English usage; auth, The origins of culture and anarchy; Matthew Arnold and popular education in England, Univ. Toronto, 70; John Dryden's answer to Thomas Rymer's The tragedies of the last age, Philol. Quart. Add: 2401 Vinewood Blvd, Ann Arbor, MI 48104.

WALCUTT, CHARLES CHILD, b. Montclair, N.J, Dec. 22, 08; m. 34, 62; c. 2. AMERICAN FICTION, ENGLISH. A.B, Univ. Ariz, 30; A.M, Univ. Mich, 32, Ph.D, 37; Northwest. Univ, 33-35. Teaching asst, Northwest. Univ, 33-35; teaching fel, Univ. Mich, 35-37, instr, 37-38; asst. prof. ENG, Univ. Okla, 38-40, assoc. prof, 40-44; prof, Mich. State Norm. Col, 44-47; Washington & Jefferson Col, 47-48, Wallace prof. rhetoric, 48-51; assoc. prof, QUEENS COL.(N.Y), 51-58, PROF, 58- GRAD. FAC, 62- Mem. nat. adv. counc, NCTE, 40-44; secy. adv. counc. & chmn. lit. & social sect, MLA, 45-55, mem. adv. counc, Am. lit. group, 57-60; chmn. best critical volume of the year award, Explicator & Univ. S.C, 55-; Fulbright dir, Am. inst, Univ. Oslo, 57-58; lectr, Am. sem, France, 58; Am. Counc. Learned Soc. grant-in-aid, 59; Counc. Basic Educ. res. fel, 60-61; Fulbright prof, 65-66; lectr, Am. Sem, Rome, 66. Eng. Inst; MLA; NCTE; S.Cent. Mod. Lang. Asn. Modern and American literature; naturalism in American fiction; reading. Publ: Co-auth, The mind in the making, Harper, 39 & A report on the college study of American literature, NCTE, 48; auth, The romantic compromise in the novels of Winston Churchill, Univ. Mich, 51; American literary naturalism, a divided stream, 56, Man's changing mask: modes and methods of characterization in fiction, 66, Jack London, 66 & John O'Hara, 69, Univ. Minn; ed. & co-auth, Tomorrow's illiterates, Little, 61; An anatomy of prose, 62 & co-auth, Teaching reading: a phonic-linguistic approach to developmental reading, 74, Macmillan; Basic reading, Text ser, 63-65, 66, Reading goals: the blue book, 66, Reading goals: the red book, 66 & Reading goals: the orange book, 67, Lippincott; Your child's reading: a guide for parents who want to help, Cornerstone Libr, 64 & Reading: chaos and cure, McGraw, 56; co-ed. & contrib, The explicator cyclopedia (3 vols), Quadrangle, 66-68; auth, Joyce's Ulysses, Explicator, 3/56; Myth in action, Ariz. Quart, winter 58; Hamlet: the plot's the thing, Mich. Quart. Rev, 1/66. Add: Dept. of English, Queens College, Flushing, NY 11367.

WALDEN, DANIEL, b. Philadelphia, Pa, Aug. 1, 22; m. 57; c. 2. AMERICAN STUDIES. B.A, City Col. N.Y, 59; M.A, Columbia Univ, 60; Ph.D.(Am. civilization), N.Y. Univ, 64. Instr. hist, Queens Col.(N.Y), 60-63; asst. prof, New Sch. Soc. Res, 60-63; Mich. State Univ, 63-66; ASSOC. PROF. AM. STUD, PA. STATE UNIV, 66-, res. grant, 67-68. Univ. Col. grant, Mich. State Univ, 65-66; Truman Libr. grant, 67-68; consult, U.S. Inform. Agency, 73- Sig.C, U.S.A, 41-45, T/Sgt. MLA; Am. Stud. Asn; Asn. Jewish Stud. American ethnic literature; American culture. Publ: The problem of color in the 20th century, complete issue of J. Human Relat, 66; ed, American reform: the ambiguous legacy, Ampersand, 67; auth, W.E.B. DuBois, Twayne, 68-69; co-ed, Readings in American nationalism, Van Nostrand, 70; co-ed, On being black, 70, ed, W.E.B. DuBois: the crisis writings, 72 & On being Jewish, 74, Fawcett; auth, W.E.B. DuBois: from negro to black, Forum Press, 73; co-ed, The contemporary new communities movement in the United States, Univ. Ill, 74; auth, The contemporary opposition to the ideas of Booker T. Washington, J. Negro Hist, 4/60; Race and imperialism: the Achilles Heel of the progressives, Sci. & Soc, spring 67; The intellectual and the American dream, J. Human Relat, fall 67. Add: Dept. of English, Pennsylvania State University, University Park, PA 16802.

WALDHORN, ARTHUR, b. Brooklyn, N.Y, Sept. 30, 18; m. 42; c. 2. ENGLISH. B.A, N.Y. Univ, 38, M.A, 40, Ph.D.(Eng), 50. Instr. ENG, Colby Acad, 39-41; Sewanhaka high sch, 41-42; Brooklyn Col, 49-50; assoc. prof, CITY COL. NEW YORK, 46-68, PROF, 68-, supvr. Eng, Sch. Gen. Stud, 61-68; asst. chmn. dept, 70-72, assoc. dir, Leonard Davis Ctr. for Performing Arts, 72- Vis. lectr, Pace Col, 49-55; ed. adv, Cadillac Publ. Co, 54-; Fulbright lectr. Am. lit, Italy, 58-59, Univ. Hull, Eng, 65-66; Univ. Tokyo, Keio Univ. & Kyoto Summer Sem, summer 73. U.S.A.A.F, 42-45. Col. Eng. Asn; MLA; NCTE. American literature; contemporary comparative literature. Publ: Co-ed, A bible for the humanities, Harper, 54; auth, Concise dictionary of Americanisms, Philos. Libr, 55; co-auth, From Homer to Joyce, Holt, 59; co-ed, American literature: readings and critiques, Putnam, 61; co-ed, Good reading, New Am. Libr, 65; co-ed, The rite of becoming, World, 66; auth, Ernest Hemingway, Farrar, 72; ed, Hemingway: a collection of criticism, McGraw, 73; auth, Whitman's Leaves of grass, Critical Quart, winter 66. Add: Dept. of English, City College of New York, New York, NY 10031.

WALDMEIR, JOSEPH J, b. Detroit, Mich, Dec. 12, 23; m. 47; c. 1. ENGLISH. B.A, Wayne State Univ, 48; M.A, Univ. Mich, 49; Ph.D, Mich. State Univ, 59. Instr. Eng, Univ. Detroit, 50-54; MICH. STATE UNIV, 56-57, from instr. to asst. prof. Am. thought & lang, 58-65, ASSOC. PROF. ENG, 65- Fulbright lectr, Univ. Helsinki, 63-64 & prof, Copenhagen Univ, 67-68. Col. Bk. Award, Mich. State Univ, 61. U.S.A, 43-45, Sgt. Am. Stud. Asn; Can. Asn. Am. Stud; Popular Cult. Asn. Contemporary American and European literature. Publ: Confiteor Hominem: Ernest Hemingway's religion of man, Prentice-Hall, 56, Scribner, 62; Recent American fiction, Houghton, 63, American novels of the Second World War, Mouton, 68; Quest without faith, Nation, 11/61; Only an occasional rutabaga: American fiction since 1945, Mod. Fiction Stud, winter 69-70. Add: Dept. of English, Michigan State University, East Lansing, MI 48823.

WALDO, TOMMY RUTH, b. Dallas, Tex, Jan. 14, 16; wid; c. 2. ENGLISH, MUSIC. A.B, Agnes Scott Col, 38; fel, Univ. Fla, summer 53, M.A, 55, fels, summer 57 & fall 59, Ph.D, 61. Asst. music, UNIV. FLA, 53-55, instr, 55-60, ENG, 60-61, asst. prof, 61-68, ASSOC. PROF, 68- Organist, Holy Trinity Episcopal Church, Gainesville, Fla, 41-42; assoc. organist, First Baptist Church, 45-58, organist, 58-; fac. res. grad. sch, Univ. Fla, summer 65 & humanities counc. res. grant, summer 68. MLA; S.Atlantic Mod. Lang. Asn; Southeast. Renaissance Conf. English Renaissance; organ and piano; humanities. Publ: Co-auth, Musical terms in The taming of the shrew: evidence of single authorship, Shakespeare Quart, spring 59; auth, Mimesis: usages antedating OED, Notes & Queries, 4/65; Music and musical terms in Richard Edward's Damon and Pithias, Music & Lett, 1/68. Add: Dept. of English, Anderson 200, University of Florida, Gainesville, FL 32601.

WALDOFF, LEON, b. Hattiesburg, Miss, Feb. 16, 35; m. 60; c. 1. ENGLISH. B.A, Northwest. Univ, 57; M.A, Univ. Mich, 63, fel, 64-66, Ph.D.(Eng), 67. Instr. ENG, Univ. Mich, 66-67; asst. prof, UNIV. ILL, URBANA, 67-73, ASSOC. PROF, 73-, dir. introd. courses Eng, 71-73. Summer fac. fels, Univ. Ill, 69, 71. U.S.A, 58, 61-62. MLA. Romantic poetry; psychoanalytic criticism. Publ: Prufroch's defenses and our responses, Am. Imago, 69; From abandonment to skepticism in Keats, Essays Criticism, 71; Wordsworth's healing power, Hartford Stud. Lit, 72. Add: 100 English Bldg, University of Illinois, Urbana, IL 61801.

WALDREP, REEF V, JR, b. Red Bay, Ala, Sept. 16, 15; m. 49; c. 1. JOURNALISM. A.B, Birmingham South. Col, 39; M.A, Univ. Ala, 42; Ed.D, Univ. Tenn, 55. From assoc. prof. to PROF. JOUR, WEST. ILL. UNIV, 59- Sig.Intel, U.S.A, 42-46. Asn. Educ. in Jour. Content analysis; reporting education; college newspapers. Add: Dept. of English, Western Illinois University, Macomb, IL 61455.

WALDRIP, LOUISE BAKER, b. Ft. Worth, Tex; m. 35; c. 2. ENGLISH. B.S, Mary Hardin-Baylor Col, 37; M.A, Baylor Univ, 61; Baptist Gen. Convention fel. & Ph.D.(Eng), Univ. Tex, 67. Teacher high schs, Tex, 42-45, 48-53; instr. Eng, Baylor Univ, 60-62, 65-66, asst. prof, 66-73; PROF. ENG. & CHMN. DIV. COMMUN, LYNCHBURG BAPTIST COL, 73- Am. Stud. Asn. Publ: Collab, A bibliography of the works of Katherine Anne Porter, Scarecrow, 69. Add: Rte. 1, Box 125, Fincastle, VA 24090.

WALEN, HARRY LEONARD, b. Winchester, Mass, June 26, 15; m. 39; c. 3. ENGLISH. A.B, Harvard, 37, A.M, 42. Teacher, Los Alamos Ranch Sch, N.Mex, 37-42, head dept. Eng, 39-42; Groton Sch, Mass, 42-46; instr. Eng, Newton Jr, Col, 46-51; teacher, Newton High Sch, Mass, 46-51, mem. admin, 51-54; directing ed, sec. sch. Eng. textbks, Ginn & Co, Mass, 54-61; prin, NEEDHAM HIGH SCH, MASS, 61-72, CAREER DEVELOP. ADV, 72- Ed, Eng. Leaflet, New Eng. Asn. Teachers Eng, 47-54, pres, 61-63, 64-65; chmn. comt. Eng. curriculum, Mass. Educ. Stud, 64-65; John Hay fel, summer 65; assoc. chmn, Boston convention, NCTE, 65, local chmn, Nat. Conf. on Humanities, 71; chmn. adv. comt, sec. sch. testing, Educ. Testing Serv, 66-68; commonwealth fel, State Dept. Educ, Mass, 72. Citation, Comn. Md, 70. NCTE; Nat. Asn. Sec. Sch. Prin.(mem, curriculum comt, 68-71); Headmasters Asn; Am. Asn. Sch. Admin. English learning environments; evaluation of alternative programs. Publ: Co-auth, Types of literatures, 64, 67, 70, American literature & English literature, Ginn; auth, A man named Robert Frost, 10/66 & English teaching: past, present and future, 11/71, Eng. J; The dilemma of the American high school, Nat. Asn. Sec. Sch. Prin. Bull, 11/72; plus others. Add: 6 Floral St, Newton Highlands, MA 02161.

WALHOUT, CLARENCE P, b. Muskegon, Mich. Jan. 22, 34; m. 58; c. 3. ENGLISH. A.B, Calvin Col, 55; M.A, Univ. Mich, 56; Ph.D.(Eng), Northwest. Univ, 64. Teacher, high sch, Mich, 58-59; vis. lectr. ENG, Calvin Col, 63-64; asst. prof, Wake Forest Univ, 64-71; assoc. prof, CALVIN COL, 71-74, PROF, 74- Fel, Coop. Prog. in Humanities, 67-68. U.S.A.R, 57-63. MLA; Soc. Stud. South. Lit. Southern literature; Robert Penn Warren. Publ: John Pendleton Kennedy: late disciple of the enlightenment, J. South. Hist, 66; The earth is the Lord's: religion in Faulkner, Christian Scholar's Rev, 74. Add: Dept. of English, Calvin College, Grand Rapids, MI 49506.

WALKER, ALBERT LYELL, b. Okla. City, Okla, Jan. 20, 07. ENGLISH LITERATURE. A.B, Park Col, 29; A.M, State Univ. Iowa, 30, Ph.D, 36. Instr. Eng, Univ. Ark, 30-32; instr. IOWA STATE UNIV, 35-36, asst. prof, 36-40, assoc. prof, 40-42, PROF. ENG, 42-, dir. freshman Eng. & chmn. curriculum comt. div. sci. & humanities, 42-59, chmn. dept. speech, 59-69, chmn. dept. Eng, 59-72. Gen. Educ. Bd. & Rockefeller fel, Univ. Chicago, 40-41. NCTE; MLA. Shakespeare, conventions of writing as modified and changed as plays increased and developments in his language and metaphor; modern American fiction, especially work and techniques of William Faulkner; theory of literature. Publ: Essentials of good writing, Heath, 52, 59; The range of literature, Am. Bk. Co, 60, 67, Van Nostrand, 73; Convention in Shakespeare's description of emotion, Philol. Quart, 1/38. Add: 3620 Story St, Ames, IA 50010.

WALKER, BIRON HELTON, b. Mountain View, Mo, Aug. 31, 15; div; c. 1. ENGLISH. M.A, Univ. Fla, 41. Instr. ENG, UNIV. FLA, 42-47, asst. prof, 47-61, assoc. prof, 61-70, PROF, 70-, fac. develop. fel, 68-69. Modern poetry. Publ: Co-auth, The modern essay, 68, Imaginative literature, 72 & College English: the first year, 73, Harcourt; The pollen storm (poems), Poet & Critic, 67; How now (poem), Ga. Rev, 68; Love (poem), New Orleans Rev, 68; plus others. Add: 1818 N.W. Eighth Ave, Gainesville, FL 32601.

WALKER, DAVID ELLIS, JR, b. Richmond, Va, Oct. 5, 38; m. 64; c. 2. SPEECH COMMUNICATION. B.A, David Lipscomb Col, 60; M.A, Univ. Fla, 61, Ph.D.(speech), 69. Instr. SPEECH, Jacksonville Univ, 63-65; MID. TENN. STATE UNIV, 65-67, asst. prof, 67-70, ASSOC. PROF, 70-, DIR. DIV. SPEECH COMMUN, 69-, dir. forensics, 65-70. Lectr, Forensic Workshop, David Lipscomb Col, 67; Ala. Christian Col, 67; Educ. Conf. & Forensic Workshop, Mid. Tenn. State Univ, 72; state coord, Interchange, 71-73. Speech Commun. Asn; South. Speech Commun. Asn. Rhetoric of Restoration movement; homiletics; forensics. Publ: Is contemporary debate educational?, Forensic, 71; contrib, The key issue: financing education, Springboards, Inc, 72; auth, Should our students major in speech?, Speech Teacher, 9/72. Add: Dept. of Speech & Theatre, Middle Tennessee State University, Murfreesboro, TN 37130.

WALKER, FRANKLIN TRENABY, b. Rocky Mount, Va, Apr. 20, 93; m. 25; c. 4. ENGLISH. A.B, Roanoke Col, 17; Th.M, South. Baptist Theol. Sem, 22; A.M, Columbia Univ, 26, summer, 28; Univ. Va, 29-30, 36, summers, 27, 30, 34; Ph.D, George Peabody Col, 43. Head dept. Eng. & pub. speaking, Greenbrier Mil. Sch, W.Va, 17-19; head dept. Eng. & dir. publicity, Bluefield Col, 22-26; prof. Eng. lit, Carson-Newman Col, 26-34; acting head dept. ENG, Miss. Col, 35-36; head dept, Piedmont Col, 37; assoc. prof, Ouachita Col, 37-38; prof, William Jewell Col, 38-48, acting head dept, 43-48; prof, MISS. COL, 48-60, head dept, 48-56, EMER. PROF, 60- Teacher, Cross Sch, Louisville, Ky, 22 & Civilian & Conserv. Corps Camp, Va, 35; prof. Eng, Peabody Col, summer 40; prof. humanities & head dept, Milligan Col, 60-62. MLA; Balzac Soc. Am. American literature. Publ: Life of John Francis Herget, William Jewell Col, 42; Abstract of William Peterfield Trent, a critical biography, George Peabody Col, 43; Biographical sketches of ten William Jewell professors, In: Church and College, William Jewell Col, 47-48. Add: 399 Urban Rd, Reno, NV 89502.

WALKER, FRED BYNUM, b. Huntsville, Ala, May 31, 14; m. 40; c. 3. SPEECH, BIBLE. A.B, Wabash Col, 37; M.A, Univ. Fla, 47; Ph.D.(Eng), George Peabody Col, 68. Instr. & asst. speech, Univ. Fla, 45-46; instr. SPEECH & BIBLE, DAVID LIPSCOMB COL, 59-62, asst. prof, 62-72, ASSOC. PROF, 72- Co-ed, Personal Evangelism, Christian Lighthouse Publ. Co, 63-74. Speech Commun. Asn. Publ: Following through for Christ, Gospel Advocate, 62. Add: Dept. of Speech, David Lipscomb College, Granny White Pike, Nashville, TN 37203.

WALKER, GEORGE WILLIAM, b. Ont, July 18, 14; U.S. citizen; m. 44. ENGLISH. A.B, Alma Col, 38; M.A, Wayne State Univ, 46; Ph.D.(Eng), Univ. N.C, 50. Instr. Eng, Wayne State Univ, 45-46; prof. & chmn. div. humanities, Lander Col, 50-56; W.Ga. Col, 57-60, dean, 60-68, v.pres, 68-72; PRES, EMANUEL COUNTY JR. COL, 72- Vis. prof. Eng, Appalachian State Col, summer 53. U.S.A.F, 41-45, Res, Maj. S.Atlantic Mod. Lang. Asn. American and 19th century British literature; administration in higher education. Add: Emanuel County Junior College, Swainsboro, GA 30401.

WALKER, IMOGENE BISHOP, b. Elgin, Ill, Sept. 5, 06; m. 33; c. 1. ENGLISH. Ph.D.(Eng), Univ. Calif, 37. Lectr. ENG, Univ. Calif, 46-49, 50-52; assoc. prof, MILLS COL, 52-66, prof, 66-72, chmn. div. lett, 64-68, dir. grad. study, 69-72, EMER. PROF, 72- Lectr, Uppsala Univ, 50. Victorian literature; Jane Austen. Publ: James Thomson (B.V): a critical study. Add: Dept. of English, Mills College, Box 9920, Oakland, CA 94613.

WALKER, JACK HARRISON, b. Collingsworth Co, Tex, Aug. 3, 15; m. 41; c. 1. RADIO, TELEVISION. B.S, W. Tex. State Col, 47, M.A, 48; dipl, NBC Inst, Univ. Calif, Los Angeles, 48; Ph.D, Univ. Denver, 51. PROF. SPEECH, W. TEX STATE UNIV, 48-, HEAD DEPT, 70- Tex. Educ. Asn. TV res. grant, summer, 61. U.S.A.A.F, 42-46. NEA; Speech Commun. Asn. Televiewing habits of school children and teachers. Add: Dept. of Speech, West Texas State University, Canyon, TX 79016.

WALKER, JOHN, Hispanic & English Literature. See Volume III, Foreign Languages, Linguistics & Philology.

WALKER, JOHN DAVID, b. Mineral Wells, Tex, July 19, 31; m. 52; c. 5. ENGLISH, EIGHTEENTH CENTURY LITERATURE. B.A, Abilene Christian Col, 52; M.A, Univ. Tex, 56; Rice Univ, 60-61; Danforth teacher grant & Ph.D.(Eng), 67. Instr. ENG, Ctr. Col, Ky, 56-60; asst. prof, STATE UNIV. N.Y. BINGHAMTON, 64-70, ASSOC. PROF, 70- Restoration drama; John Dryden; Alexander Pope. Publ: Architectonics of George Herbert's The temple, ELH, 62. Add: Dept. of English, Harpur College, State University of New York at Binghamton, Binghamton, NY 13901.

WALKER, JONES MORTON, b. Amarillo, Tex, Jan. 27, 20; m. 54; c. 1. THEATRE, HISTORY. B.F.A, Tex. Christian Univ, 48; M.A, Univ. Minn, 54. Instr. speech & theater, Univ. Minn, 49-52; theater, UNIV. MO-KANSAS CITY, 52-56, asst. prof, 56-63, ASSOC. PROF. SPEECH & THEATRE, 63-, ASST. DIR. PLAYHOUSE, 72- Co-founder & stage dir-designer, Kans. City Lyric Theatre, 58-63; assoc. dir, Mo. Repertory Theatre, 63- U.S.A, 42-45. Musical theatre; history of American drama; theatrical production—technical methods and effects. Add: Dept. of Speech & Theatre, University of Missouri-Kansas City, Kansas City, MO 64110.

WALKER, KENNETH ERVIN, b. Old Fort, N.C, June 13, 36; m. 55; c. 2. ENGLISH & AMERICAN LITERATURE. A.B, Mercer Univ, 61; M.Div, Crozer Theol. Sem, 61-62; M.A, Wake Forest Univ, 65; NDEA fel, Univ. Ga, 69-71, Ph.D.(Eng), 73. Instr. ENG, Mercer Univ, 65-67; VA. POLYTECH. INST. & STATE UNIV, 67-72, ASST. PROF, 72- U.S.A, 55-57. MLA; S.Atlantic Mod. Lang. Asn; Col. Eng. Asn; NEA. Nineteenth and 20th century American literature; 19th century English literature. Publ: Co-auth, Eliot: Silas Marner, 67 & auth, Hawthorne: The house of the seven gables, Barron; auth, Solzhenitsyn's First circle, In: Magill's literary annual, Salem Press, 70; Stevens' Idea of order at Key West, Explicator, 6/74; Wallace Stevens as disaffected flagellant, Markham Rev, 2/74. Add: Dept. of English, Virginia Polytechnic Institute & State University, Blacksburg, VA 24061.

WALKER, LOUISE JEAN, b. Jackson, Mich, Feb. 10, 91. ENGLISH. A.B, Albion Col, 17; M.A, Columbia Univ, 24; Univ. Colo, 31; Univ. Mich, 39. Teacher, High Schs, Mich, 17-19, 21-23; Ind, 19-21; assoc. prof. ENG, WEST. MICH. UNIV, 23-65, EMER. PROF, 65- Vis. prof, N.Mex. Highlands Univ, summer 32 & 35. NCTE; NEA; Am. Folklore Soc. Writing for children; Indian folklore; writing for professional magazines. Publ: The legends of Greensky Hill, 59 & Daisy strikes on Saturday night, Eerdmans, 68; Red Indian legends, Odhams, 61; Woodland wigwams, 64 & Beneath the singing pines, 67, Hillsdale. Add: 1546 Sherman St. S.E, Grand Rapids, MI 49506.

WALKER, PHILLIP N, b. Ellensburg, Wash, June 24, 21; m. 42; c. 1. SPEECH, DRAMA. B.A, Univ. Wash, 46, M.A, 47; Univ. Calif, Los Angeles, 51; Ph.D.(commun), Univ. South. Calif, 72. Instr. speech, North. Mich. Col, 47-48; assoc. prof. speech & drama, Univ. Southwest. La, 48-50; CALIF. STATE UNIV, FRESNO, 50-67, PROF. speech, 67-72, THEATRE ARTS, 72-, chmn. dept. speech arts, 66-69, acting dean sch. arts & sci, 69-70; head div. speech & music, 70-71, asst. dean sch. prof. stud, 71-72. U.S.A.A.F, 43-45, 1st Lt. Speech Commun. Asn; Am. Theatre Asn. Publ: Mark Twain, playwright, Quart. J. Speech, 56; Arthur Miller's The crucible: tragedy or allegory, 56 & American acting and the new critics, 58, West. Speech. Add: Dept. of Theatre Arts, California State University, Fresno, CA 93726.

WALKER, RALPH SPENCE, b. Aberdeen, Scotland, May 25, 04; m. 38; c. 2. ENGLISH. M.A, Univ. Aberdeen, 28, Murray scholar, 30, Dey scholar, 31; hon. scholar. & B.A, Cambridge, 31, M.A, 34. Lectr. Eng. lang. & lit, Univ. Aberdeen, 35-42, Eng. lit, 42-48, sr. lectr, 48-55; Molson prof. ENG, McGILL UNIV, 55-70, chmn. dept, 55-66, EMER. PROF, 70- Ed, Aberdeen Univ. Rev, 43-47; Fulbright traveling fel. & res. assoc, Yale, 52; Nuffield traveling fel, 62-63; Can. Counc. sr. res. fel, 66-67; lectr, Univ. Victoria (B.C), summer 70; supvr, St. Catharine's Col, Cambridge, 70-73; lectr. Shakespeare, London semester, Beaver Col, 73- Int. Asn. Univ. Prof. Eng. The letters of Thomas Twining; 18th century correspondence. Publ: James Beattie's diary 1773 & James Beattie's daybook, Aberdeen Univ; Ben Jonson's timber, Syracuse Univ; ed, James Boswell's correspondence with John Johnston of Grange, McGraw, Heinemann, 66; auth, Charles Burney's theft, 1777, Trans. Cambridge Bibliog. Soc, 62; ed, Charles Burney's tour, 1780, Aberdeen Univ. Rev, spring 73. Add: Peaveley House, Haslingfield, Cambridge CB3 7JE, England.

WALKER, RICHARD WALLER, b. Memphis, Tenn, Feb. 8, 25; m. 54; c. 2. SPEECH PATHOLOGY. B.A, Harding Col, 50; M.A, La. State Univ, 51, Ph.D, 61. Asst. prof. SPEECH, HARDING COL, 53-61, assoc. prof, 61-68, PROF, 68- U.S.A, 43-46, Sgt. Am. Speech & Hearing Asn. Psychoacoustics and improvement of the normal voice. Add: Dept. of Speech, Harding College, Searcy, AR 72143.

WALKER, ROBERT HARRIS, b. Cincinnati, Ohio, Mar. 15, 24; m. 53; c. 3. AMERICAN CIVILIZATION. B.S, Northwest. Univ, 45; M.A, Columbia Univ, 50; Univ. Montpellier, 50; Harrison fel, Univ. Pa, 52-53, 54-55, Ph.D.(Am. civilization), 55. Educ. spec, U.S. War Dept, Shizuoka, Japan, 46-47; instr. Eng, Carnegie Inst. Technol, 50-51; Am. civilization & ed. Am. Quart, Univ. Pa, 53-54; asst. prof, Univ. Wyo, 55-59, acting dir. Am. stud, 56-59; assoc. prof. Am. lit, GEORGE WASHINGTON UNIV, 59-63, PROF. AM. CIVILIZATION, 63-, dir. Am. Stud. Prog, 59-65, 68-70. Instr, Haverford Col, 54-55; consult, U.S. Inform. Agency & U.S. For. Serv. Inst, 59-, Peace Corps, 61-62; vis. prof. Am. stud, Kyoto & Doshisha Univs, Japan, summer 64; Stetson Univ, summer 65; consult, U.S. State Dept, Ger. & Sweden, 5/65; Esso lectr, Europe, 6-12/66; dir, Nat. Endowment Humanities, div. educ. & pub. prog, 66-68; vis. prof. Eng, Univ, Hawaii, summer 67; Woodrow Wilson fel, 72-73. U.S.N.R, 43-46. Am. Stud. Asn.(pres, 70-71); Orgn. Am. Hist. Social themes in American literature; the Gilded Age; American reform movements. Publ: Ed, American studies in the U.S, La. State Univ, 58; auth, Poet and the Gilded Age, Univ. Pa, 63; Everyday life in the age of enterprise, Putnam, 67; Patterns in recent American literature, Stetson Univ, 68; ed, Contributions in American studies series, Greenwood, 70-; contrib, History of the scientific and cultural development of mankind, UNESCO. Add: 3915 Huntington St. N.W, Washington, DC 20015.

WALKER, ROBERT JEFFERSON, b. Gooding, Idaho, Apr. 22, 22; m. 46; c. 2. SPEECH COMMUNICATION. B.S.Ed, Univ. Ill, 46; M.A, Northwest. Univ, 48; Ph.D.(mass commun), Wayne State Univ, 66. Instr. Eng. & speech, Kennedy-King Col, 46-48; asst. prof. speech & theatre, Chicago Teachers Col, 50-61; PROF. SPEECH, NORTHEAST. ILL. UNIV, 61- U.S.N, 43-46, Lt.(jg). Int. Commun. Asn; Speech Commun. Asn. Interpersonal communication; mass media; organizational communication. Add: Dept. of Speech & Performing Arts, Northeastern Illinois University, Bryn Mawr & St. Louis, Chicago, IL 60625.

WALKER, SAMUEL JAY, JR, b. New York, N.Y, July 30, 29; div. VICTORIAN & AFRO-AMERICAN LITERATURE. B.S.S, City Col. New York, 51; M.A, Columbia Univ, 52; Ph.D.(Victorian biog), Univ. Nottingham, 59. Instr. Eng, Tuskegee Inst, 54-56; lectr, Tottenemham Tech. Col, London, 59-60; PROF. ENG. & BLACK STUD, State Univ. N.Y. Col. Geneseo, 60-72; DARTMOUTH COL, 72- Vis. prof. Eng. & black stud, Univ. Rochester, 71-72. U.S.A, 52-54. Asn. Stud. Afro-Am. Life & Hist; MLA; African Stud. Asn; African Stud. Asn. Early black American literature, 18th and 19th century; 20th century black novel; American biography. Publ: Co-ed, Perspectives in 20th century black separatism, N.Eng. Univ, 74; auth, Frederick Douglass and woman suffrage, Black Scholar, 3-4/73; Black studies: phase two, Am. Scholar, autumn 73; Zora Neale Hurston's Their eyes were watching God: black novel of sexism, Mod. Fiction Stud, (in press). Add: Hinman Box 6032, Dartmouth College, Hanover, NH 03755.

WALKER, SAUNDERS E, b. Birmingham, Ala; m. 45; c. 1. ENGLISH, SPEECH & DRAMA. A.B, Talladega Col, 29; M.A, Univ. Mich, 34, M.A, 52; Harvard, 36; Ph.D.(Eng), West. Reserve Univ, 56. Teacher, high sch, Ala, 31-35; Prof. Eng, chmn. dept. lit. & founder & dir. Little Theater, Tuskegee Inst, 35-67; PROF. ENG. & CHMN. DIV. HUMANITIES, FT. VALLEY STATE COL, 67- Instr, Prairie View State Col, summer 35; lit. therapist, Cent. State Hosp, Milledgeville, Ga, 71; mem. eval. comt, South. Asn. Schs. & Cols, 72; consult, Talladega Col, 73. MLA; NCTE; Shakespeare Asn. Am. Folk speech of eastern Alabama; humanities in southern Negro colleges; literary heritage of college freshman. Publ: Why the humanities, Ft. Valley State Col. Bull, 5/67; column, Lexicographer's corner, Leader-Tribune, Ft. Valley, Ga, 70- & Tuskegee News, Tuskegee, Ala, 71-; Putting the humanities to work, Ft. Valley State Col. Bull, 5/73. Add: P.O. Box 1633, Ft. Valley State College, Ft. Valley, GA 31030.

WALKER, WARREN STANLEY, b. Brooklyn, N.Y, Mar. 19, 21; m. 43; c. 2. ENGLISH. B.A, State Univ. N.Y. Albany, 47, M.A, 48; Ph.D.(Eng), Cornell Univ, 51. Instr. Eng, State Univ. N.Y. Albany, 48; teaching fel. Am. lit, Cornell Univ, 50-51; prof. Eng, Blackburn Col, 51-59, chmn. humanities div. & Eng. dept; prof. Eng, Parsons Col, 59-64, chmn. div. humanities, 59-60, dean arts & sci, 60-64; prof. ENG, TEX. TECH UNIV, 64-71, HORN PROF, 71- Fulbright lectr, Am. lit, Univ. Ankara, 61-62; Res. Inst. Lang. & Lit. travel grants, summers 63 & 64; State of Tex. res. grants, summers 66-67, 69-70 & 71; archivist, Arch. Turkish Oral Narrative, 69-; mem. ed. bd, Definitive edition of the works of James Fenimore Cooper, Ctr. Ed. Am. Authors, MLA, 70-; Tex. Tech Univ. fac. develop. leave, spring 71; Am. Counc. Learned Soc. travel grant, fall 73; U.S. rep, First Int. Conf. Turkish Folklore, Ankara, 10/73; bibliogr, Stud. in Short Fiction, 73- Citation, Ministry Educ, Turkey. U.S.A.A.F, 42-45. MLA; Am. Folklore Soc; fel. Mid.E. Stud. Asn. N.Am; NCTE; S.Cent. Mod. Lang. Asn; Col. Eng. Asn; AAUP. American literature; folklore; prose fiction. Publ: Co-auth, Nigerian folk tales, Rutgers Univ, 61; auth, James Fenimore Cooper: an introduction and interpretation, Barnes & Noble, 62; Twentieth century short story explications, Shoe String, 62 & 67, suppl. I & II, 70 & 73; ed, James Fenimore Cooper, The red rover, 63 & James Fenimore Cooper, The sea lions, 65, Univ. Nebr; co-ed, The Erie Canal: gateway to empire, Heath, 63; ed, Prose lyrics: a collection of familiar essays, Odyssey, 64; Leatherstocking and the critics, Scott, 65; co-auth, Tales alive in Turkey, Harvard, 66; co-ed, The book of Dede Korkut, a Turkish epic, Univ. Tex, 72; auth, Burne's influence on Sohrab and Rustum: a closer look, Victorian Poetry, 72; Recent interpretations of short fiction, Stud. in Short Fiction, summer 73; co-auth, An ancient god in modern Turkey: some aspects of the cult of Hizir, J. Am. Folklore, 7-9/73. Co-auth, Turkish folktales (rec. album), Folkways, 65. Add: Dept. of English, Texas Tech University, Lubbock, TX 79409.

WALKER, WILLIAM EDWARD, b. Meridian, Miss, May 20, 25. ENGLISH. B.A, Univ. S.C, 47; M.A, Columbia Univ, 48; univ. fel, Vanderbilt Univ, 52-53, Ph.D, 57; South. Fels. grant, 56-57. Instr. Eng, Darlington Sch. Boys, Rome, Ga, 48-52; Col. William & Mary, 53-55; asst, Vanderbilt Univ, 55-56, instr, 57-58; assoc. prof. Eng, dean admis. & registr, Converse Col, 58-60; asst. prof. & coord. freshman Eng, Memphis State Univ, 60-63; assoc. prof. Eng. & humanities & chmn. dept, New Haven Col, 63-64; instr. Eng, UNIV. BRIDGEPORT, 64-65, assoc. prof. Eng. & asst. dean undergrad. stud, Col. Arts & Sci, 65-73, PROF. ENG, 73- U.S.N.R, 43-46. MLA; NCTE; AAUP; Conf. Col. Compos. & Commun. American and English literature; William Blake. Publ: Ed, Myth and reality: essays in memory of R.C. Beatty, Vanderbilt Univ, 64; auth, Restoration, New Repub, 5/55; co-auth, A time for cod, Saltwater Sportsman, 12/70. Add: 202 Iranistan Ave, Bridgeport, CT 06604.

WALKING BULL, MONTANA HOPKINS RICKARDS, b. Butte, Mont, Jan. 22, 13; m. 43; c. 2. ENGLISH EDUCATION. B.F.A, Univ. Okla, 35, Ed.M, 42; Univ. Ore, 50-58; Mus. Art Sch.(Ore), 60-63; Ore. Col. Educ, 63-69; D.Ed, Univ. Ore, 67. Teacher pub. schs, Okla, 35-38; Tex, 42-43; instr. Eng. composition, San Diego Jr. Col, 46-47; teacher pub. schs, Ore, 47-63; asst. prof. HUMANITIES & EDUC, ORE. COL. EDUC, 63-67, PROF, 67- Lectr. Eng. & jour, East. Mont. Col, summer 55; consult. Eng. ability grouping, Sunset High Sch, Ore, 62-63; ed, Cherokee News, 67-69; ed. & writer, Literature about the American Indian & Art and culture of the American Indian, U.S. Off. Educ, 70-71; book reviewer, Sunday Oklahoman. AAUP; Nat. Indian Educ. Asn; NEA; NCTE. Joaquin Miller, Oregon poet; history of Eugene, Oregon public schools; Southern American literature. Publ: Co-auth, Duo & Two by two; ed, Why schools tick; co-ed, Anthology of poetry, 70, Singing birds, 71 & OCE Calapooya collage of poetry, 72 & 73, Ore. Col. Educ; auth, Lay support means school growth, Am. Sch. Bd. J, July, 56; Selling the community on school needs and purposes, High Sch. J, 2/59; co-auth, A high school building and the future, Am. Sch. Bd. J, 6/59. Add: Dept. of Humanities, Oregon College of Education, Monmouth, OR 97361.

WALL, CAREY GAIL, b. Detroit, Mich, June 28, 36. ENGLISH & AMERICAN LITERATURE. B.A, Univ. Mich, 58; Woodrow Wilson fel, 58-59; Ph.D.(Eng), Stanford Univ, 64. Instr. ENG, Queens Col.(N.Y), 63-66; ASST. PROF, Univ. Calif, Los Angeles, 66-71; SAN DIEGO STATE UNIV, 71- MLA. Faulkner; 20th century American and British fiction. Publ: Drama and technique in Faulkner's The hamlet, Twentieth Century Lit, 4/68; The sound and the fury: the emotional center, Midwest Quart, 70; art. on Hawkes's Second skin, Bucknell Rev, (in press). Add: School of Literature, San Diego State University, 5402 College Ave, San Diego, CA 92115.

WALL, CAROLYN J, b. San Francisco, Calif, Apr. 5, 22. ENGLISH. B.A, Col. Holy Names, 45; M.A, Cath. Univ. Am, 60, Ph.D.(Eng), 65. Teaching asst. ENG, Cath. Univ. Am, 62-63, mem. summer session fac, 64, 65, asst. prof, summer 67; instr. Col. Holy Names (Calif), 65-68, ASST. PROF, 68-72; Univ. Nev, Las Vegas, 72-73; COL. OF THE HOLY CROSS, 73- MLA. Medieval literature, symbolism; English stylistics, relationship between language and literature. Publ: Language and aesthetic value in Winter is another country, J. Eng. Teaching Techniques, 69; The apocryphal and historical backgrounds of Play XLVI of the York cycle, Mediaeval Stud, 70; York Pageant XLVI and its music, Speculum, 71; plus others. Add: Dept. of English, College of the Holy Cross, Worcester, MA 01610.

WALL, DONALD CLARK, b. Rochester, N.Y, Mar. 30, 35; m. 60; c. 3. ENGLISH LITERATURE. B.A, Syracuse Univ, 57; M.A, Fla. State Univ, 60, Ph.D.(Eng), 63. Asst. prof. Eng, Lycoming Col, 63-68, ASSOC. PROF, 68-70; ENG. & HUMANITIES, EAST. WASH. STATE COL, 70- English literature of the 17th and 18th centuries; popular fiction, mystery-detective novel. Add: 1102 Gary St, Cheney, WA 99004.

WALLACE, ALVA DAYLE, b. Mt. Calm, Tex, May 10, 08; m. 33; c. 3. ENGLISH LITERATURE. A.B, Tex. Tech. Col, 28, A.M, 29; Columbia Univ, 28; Ph.D, Yale, 33. Asst. Eng, Yale, 32-33, res. asst, 33-34, instr, 34-35; asst. prof, Univ. Omaha, 35-37, assoc. prof, 37-44; WAYNE STATE UNIV, 44-50, prof, 50-73, hon. Sterling fel, 39-40, EMER. PROF. ENG, 73- Res. assoc. libr, Yale, 50- MLA; Col. Eng. Asn. William Godwin. Publ: Short stories in context; co-ed, Horace Walpole's correspondence. Add: Dept. of English, Wayne State University, Detroit, MI 48202.

WALLACE, EMILY MITCHELL (MRS. GREGORY M. HARVEY), b. Springfield, Mo, Nov. 17, 33; m. 69. ENGLISH & AMERICAN LITERATURE. A.B, Southwest Mo. State Col, 58; M.A, Bryn Mawr Col, 59, Workman travelling fel, 61-62, Ph.D.(Eng), 65. Teacher, Shipley Sch, 59-60; instr. Eng, Univ. Pa. 62-66, asst. prof, 66-67; Swarthmore Col, 67-68, 69-70, fac. res. grants, 68 & 70; RES. & WRITING, 70- Univ. Pa. fac. summer res. fel, 66; Am. Asn. Univ. Women fel, 68-69. MLA; Eng. Inst; Am. Stud. Asn; Renaissance Soc. Am. Contemporary poetry; American literature; Renaissance poetry and drama. Publ: A bibliography of William Carlos Williams, Wesleyan Univ, 68; ed, Selected letters of William Carlos Williams (4 vols), New Directions, (in prep); auth, Penn's poet friends (Williams and Ezra Pound), Pa. Gazette, 2/73; ed. & auth, Introd, An interview with William Carlos Williams, Mass. Rev, winter 73; auth, The forms of the emotions . . . , In: William Carlos Williams, the Leverton lecture series, Vol. I, Fairleigh Dickinson Univ, 74. Add: 1939 Panama St, Philadelphia, PA 19103.

WALLACE, EUNICE EWER, b. Logan, Utah, May 25, 14; m. 39; c. 3. ENGLISH EDUCATION. B.A, Col. Idaho, 34; summer, Univ. Calif, Berkeley, 38; Idaho State Univ, 56-58; Ed.M, Ore. State Univ, 60, Ph.D.(Eng. educ), 64; Am. Univ, 67-68. Teacher, pub. schs, Idaho, 34-37, supvr. vocal music, 37-38; instr. Eng, Ore. State Univ, 59-61, asst. Eng. educ, 61-64; asst. prof. ENG, Paterson State Col, 64-67; D.C. Teachers Col, 67-68; ASSOC. PROF, BOISE STATE COL, 68- Ore. State Univ. grant, 60-62; consult. workshop col. & univ. teaching, Ore. State Univ, 63-73; in-serv. training Eng. & lang. arts, N.J, Idaho, Utah, Wash, Mont. & Ore, 66-73. NCTE. Reading problems among college students; spelling problems among high school and college students of Oregon; team-teaching. Publ: Principles of spelling, 67 & co-auth, Word book (grades 1-8), 74, Lyons & Carnahan; auth, They made Wyoming their own, Joslyn & Rentschler, 71; co-auth, English, spoken and written, In: Classroom practices in teaching English, 68-69, NCTE, 68; plus others. Add: Dept. of English, Boise State College, Boise, ID 83725.

WALLACE, JOHN MALCOLM, b. London, Eng, Feb. 28, 28. ENGLISH LITERATURE. B.A, Cambridge, 50; M.A, 55; cert, London, Eng, 52; Ph.D, Johns Hopkins Univ, 60. Instr, high sch, London, Eng, 52-54; ENG, Cornell Univ, 60-63; asst. prof, Johns Hopkins Univ, 63-66, assoc. prof, 66-67; PROF, UNIV. CHICAGO, 67- Folger Libr. summer fel, 61; Newberry Libr. summer fel, 64; fel, Guggenheim Found, 69-70; overseas fel, Churchill Col, Cambridge, 69-70; grant, Am. Counc. Learned Soc, summer 73. Seventeenth century English literature and history. Publ: Co-ed, Style, rhetoric & rhythm: essays by Morris Croll, Princeton Univ, 66; auth, Destiny his choice: the loyalism of Andrew Marvell, Cambridge Univ, 68. Add: Dept. of English, University of Chicago, 1050 E. 59th St, Chicago, IL 60637.

WALLACE, KARL RICHARDS, b. Hubbardsville, N.Y, Nov. 10, 05; m. 29; c. 3. RHETORIC. A.B, Cornell Univ, 27, A.M, 31, Ph.D.(rhetoric & pub. address), 33. Instr. pub. speaking, Iowa State Col, 27-30, asst. prof, 33-36; instr, Cornell Univ, 32-33; Eng, Wash. Univ, 36-37; assoc. prof. pub. speaking & chmn. sch, Univ. Va, 37-45, prof. speech & chmn. sch. speech & drama, 45-47; prof. SPEECH & head dept, Univ. Ill, Urbana, 47-68; PROF, UNIV. MASS, AMHERST, 68- Ed, Quart. J. Speech, 45-47; vis. lectr, Thirty-Third Annual Conf. Speech Educ, 67. Speech Commun. Asn.(pres, 54); Conf. Col. Compos. & Commun; NCTE. History of rhetoric and public address; oral communication. Publ: Francis Bacon on communication and rhetoric, Univ. N.C, 43; co-auth, Fundamentals of public speaking, 47, 4th ed, 68 & ed, History of speech education in America, 54, Appleton; auth, Francis Bacon on the nature of man: the faculties of man's soul, Univ. Ill, 67; co-ed, An historical anthology of select British speeches, Ronald, 67; auth, Understanding discourse: the speech act and rhetorical action, La. State Univ, 70; Goals, concepts, and the teacher of speech, Speech Teacher, 3/68; Francis Bacon on understanding, reason and rhetoric, Speech Monogr, 6/71; Topoi and the problem of invention, Quart. J. Speech, 12/72. Add: Dept. of Speech, University of Massachusetts, Amherst, MA 01002.

WALLACE, ROBERT, b. Springfield, Mo, Jan. 10, 32; m. 65. ENGLISH. A.B, Harvard, 53; M.A, Cambridge, 59. Instr. ENG, Bryn Mawr Col, 57-61; asst. prof, Sweet Briar Col, 61-63; Vassar Col, 63-65; ASSOC. PROF, CASE WEST. RESERVE UNIV, 65- U.S.A, 55-57. Publ: This various world and other poems, Scribner, 57; Views from a ferris wheel, (poems), 65, co-auth, Poems on poetry, 65 & auth, Ungainly things (poems), 68, Dutton. Add: Dept. of English, Case Western Reserve University, Cleveland, OH 44106.

WALLACE, ROBERT K, b. Seattle, Wash, Aug. 2, 44; m. 68. ENGLISH & AMERICAN LITERATURE. B.A, Whitman Col, 66; Woodrow Wilson fel, Columbia Univ, 66-67, M.A, 67, E.J. Noble fel, 67-70, N.Y. State Regents fel, 70-71, Ph.D.(Eng. & Am. lit), 72. ASST. PROF. HUMANITIES, NORTH. KY. STATE COL, 72- MLA. Nineteenth century fiction; music and literature; British novel. Add: Dept. of Humanities, Northern Kentucky State College, Highland Heights, KY 41076.

WALLACE, ROBERT MARSDEN, b. Spartanburg, S.C, May 7, 07; m. 48; c. 3. EIGHTEENTH CENTURY ENGLISH LITERATURE. A.B, Wofford Col, 28; A.M, Univ. N.C, 30, Ph.D, 45. Instr. ENG, Ga. Sch. Tech, 30-32; Judson Col, 33-35; Univ. Ala, 35-44; Woman's Col. Univ. N.C, 44-45; from asst. prof. to assoc. prof, Univ. Ala, 45-59, prof, 59-63; Univ. N.C, Charlotte, 63-73, chmn. dept, 63-71; RETIRED. Columnist, The Nation, 58-63. S.Atlantic Mod. Lang. Asn. Augustan literature, novel and biography; Henry Fielding. Publ: Henry Fielding's knowledge of history and biography, Stud. in Philol; contrib, Henry Fielding, Collier's Encycl. Add: Rte. 1, Box 82E, Holly Ridge, NC 28445.

WALLACE, WESLEY HERNDON, b. Denver, Colo, Apr. 18, 12; m. 56; c. 1. RADIO, TELEVISION & MOTION PICTURES. B.S, N.C. State Col, 32; M.A, Univ. N.C, Chapel Hill, 54; Asian scholar, Duke Univ, 59, Ph.D.(hist. & polit. sci), 62. Announcer-writer, WPTF Radio Co, N.C, 34-42; dir. radio, U.S. Army Forces, West. Pac, Philippines, 46-47; gen. mgr, Manila Broadcasting Co, Philippines, 47-50; lectr. RADIO, TV & MOTION PICTURES, UNIV. N.C, CHAPEL HILL, 52-54, asst. prof, 54-57, assoc. prof, 57-66, PROF, 66-, CHMN. DEPT, 63-, acting chmn, 62-63. Consult. develop. televised course mass commun, South. Regional Educ. Bd, Ga, 64-66. U.S.A, 42-46, Res, 47-64, Lt. Col. AHA; South. Hist. Asn; Broadcast Educ. Asn; Nat. Asn. Educ. Broadcasters. Social and economic development of advertising and of American broadcasting; comparative analysis of international broadcasting systems. Publ: Cultural and social advertising in early North Carolina newspapers, 7/56 & North Carolina's agricultural journals, 1838-1861: a crusading press, 7/59, N.C. Hist. Rev; Growth, organization, and impact, In: Understanding television: an introduction to broadcasting, Hastings, 64. Add: Dept. of Radio, Television, and Motion Pictures, University of North Carolina at Chapel Hill, Chapel Hill, NC 27514.

WALLACKER, BENJAMIN E, East Asian Philology. See Volume III, Foreign Languages, Linguistics & Philology.

WALLER, CHARLES THOMAS, b. Dublin, Ga, Jan. 18, 34. FOLKLORE, EIGHTEENTH CENTURY ENGLISH LITERATURE. A.B, Wake Forest Univ, 56; Rockefeller fel, Yale Div. Sch, 57-58; M.A, Univ. Ga, 60; Mellon fel. & Ph.D.(Eng), Univ. Pittsburgh, 65. Instr. ENG, UNIV. GA, 58-60 & 64-65, ASST. PROF, 66- U.S.A, 60-62. MLA; Am. Folklore Soc; S.Atlantic Mod. Lang. Asn; South. Folklore Soc. Folklore of Georgia; history and development of Georgia. Publ: Co-auth, A treasury of Georgia folklore, Cherokee, 72 & Slavery times when I wuz chillun down on Marster's plantation, Beehive, 73; Swift's poems on woods halfpence, S.Atlantic Bull, 3/69; Swift's apologia pro satura sua, Satire Newsletter, fall 72. Add: Dept. of English, University of Georgia, Athens, GA 30601.

WALLER, FREDERICK O, b. Eugene, Ore, May 13, 19; m. 46; c. 5. ENGLISH LITERATURE. B.A, Univ. Ore, 41, M.A, 48; Ph.D, Univ. Chicago, 57. Instr. Eng, Chicago undergrad. div, Univ. Ill, 50-57; asst. prof, PORTLAND STATE UNIV, 57-61, from assoc. prof. to PROF. ENG, 61-, HEAD. DEPT, 68-, ACTING DEAN, COL. ARTS & LETT, 73-, dean undergrad. stud. & assoc. dean fac, 61-68. U.S.A, 41-46, Res, 46-73, Lt. Col. MLA; AAUP; NCTE; Bibliog. Soc. Univ. Va. Textual criticism in the Elizabethan drama; Shakespeare. Publ: None for the road, New Republic, 57; Printer's copy for The two noble kinsmen, Stud. Bibliog, 58; The use of linguistic criteria in determining the copy and dates for Shakespeare's plays, In: Pacific Coast studies in Shakespeare, Univ. Ore, 66. Add: College of Arts & Letters, Portland State University, P.O. Box 751, Portland, OR 97207.

WALLER, GARY FREDRIC, b. Auckland, N.Z, Jan. 3, 45; m. 66; c. 2. ENGLISH LITERATURE. B.A, Univ. Auckland, 65, M.A, 66; fel, Cambridge, 68-69, Ph.D.(Eng), 69. Jr. lectr. ENG, Univ. Auckland, 66, lectr, 69-72, sr. lectr, 72; ASST. PROF, DALHOUSIE UNIV, 72- MLA; Renaissance Soc. Am. Elizabethan poetry; Shakespeare; Renaissance philosophy. Publ: Forward with caution, N.Z. Church Union, 66; The strong necessity of time: time in Shakespeare and the Elizabethans, Mouton, The Hague, 74; Bruno, Calvin, and the Sidney circle, Neophilologus, 72; Time, providence, and tragedy in King Lear and The atheist's tragedy, Eng. Miscellany, 72; The popularization of Calvinism: Thomas Beard's The theatre of Gods judgements, Theology, 72. Add: Dept. of English, Dalhousie University, Halifax, N.S, Can.

WALLER, JOHN OSCAR, b. Los Angeles, Calif, Oct. 29, 16; m. 46. ENGLISH. B.A, San Diego State Col, 41; M.A, Univ. South. Calif, 49, Ph.D.(Eng), 54. Instr. Eng, San Diego State Col, 46-48; dir. pubs, Oxnard High Sch. Dist, Calif, 51-52; asst. prof. ENG, Walla Walla Col, 52-55, assoc. prof, 55-60; PROF, ANDREWS UNIV, 60-, CHMN. DEPT, 62- Asst. ed, Abstr. of Eng. Stud, 64-66, ed, 67- U.S.N.R, 41-45, Lt.(jg). MLA; NCTE; Eng. Asn, Gt. Brit; Tennyson Soc. English men of letters and American Civil War; Victorian literature; theories of literary criticism. Publ: Charles Dickens and the American Civil War, Stud. in Philol, 7/60; Christ's second coming—Christina Rossetti and the pre-millennialist William Dodsworth, Bull. N.Y. Pub. Libr, 9/69; Matthew Arnold's Rugby chapel and Thomas Arnold's Sermons, Stud. Eng. Lit, fall 69; plus several others. Add: 310 Grove St, Berrien Springs, MI 49103.

WALLER, MARTHA STIFLER, b. Peking, China, June 27, 20; U.S. citizen; m. 43; c. 5. ENGLISH. B.A, Mt. Holyoke Col, 41; M.A, Columbia Univ, 42; Mary E. Woolley fel, Ind. Univ, 71-72, Ph.D.(Eng), 73. Instr. ENG, Ind. Cent. Col, 60-61, asst. prof, 62-71, ASSOC. PROF, 71-74; BUTLER UNIV, 74- MLA; NCTE; Col. Eng. Asn; AAUP. Chaucer and the history of Rome. Publ: Co-auth, Cloak and cipher, Bobbs, 62. Add: 1701 W. 51st St, Indianapolis, IN 46208.

WALLINS, ROGER PEYTON, b. New York, N.Y, Oct. 24, 41; m. 67; c. 2. ENGLISH & AMERICAN LITERATURE. A.B, City Col. New York, 62; M.A, Ohio State Univ, 64, Ph.D.(Eng), 72. ASST. PROF. ENG, UNIV. IDAHO, 70-, dir. compos, 70-73. NCTE; Conf. Col. Compos. & Commun; Dickens Soc. Victorian literature; composition. Publ: Dickens and decomposition, Dickens Stud. Newslett, 74. Add: Dept. of English, University of Idaho, Moscow, ID 83843.

WALLIS, CHARLES LANGWORTHY, b. Hamilton, N.Y, May 1, 21; m. 47; ENGLISH. B.A, Univ. Redlands, 43; M.A, Univ. Rochester, 45; M.Div, Colgate-Rochester Divinity Sch, 45. Instr. ENG, KEUKA COL, 45-59, PROF, 59-, minister, col. church, 46-65, chmn. dept. Eng, 59-70. Chaplain, Veterans Admin. Hosp, Canandaigua, N.Y, 44-46; ed, Pulpit Preaching, 48-72; mem. ed. staff, Interpreter's Bible, 53-57; consult. ed, Harper & Row Publ, 54; ed, N.Y. Folklore Quart, 55-62; asst. ed, Ministers Manual, 55-67, ed, 67-; ed. fel, Ministers Res. Found, Inc, 56-59; gen. ed, Harpers New Anvil Libr, 62-; managing ed, Harpers Church Life Ser, 63-; ed, Harpers Album Ser, 64-; minister, Keuka Park Church, 65-; daily radio prog, For Heaven's sake, 67-; ed, New pulpit digest, 72- Civil War Centennial Medallion, 62. Am. Baptist Hist. Soc; Col. Eng. Asn; Am. Folklore Soc; AAUP; Am. Acad. Religion; NCTE; Poetry Soc. Am. Religious folklore; epitaphic literature. Publ: Ed, Selected poems of John Oxenham, Poems of Edwin Markham, Treasury of sermon illustrations, The funeral encyclopedia, Stories on stone: a book of American epitaphs, Worship resources for the Christian year, A treasury of story-sermons for children, Autobiography of Peter Cartwright, Riverside sermons, The greatest sermons of George H. Morrison, Speaker's illustrations for special days, Table of the Lord, Notable sermons from Protestant pulpits, Treasury of poems for worship and devotion, Lenten-Easter sourcebook, 1010 sermon illustrations from the Bible, Eighty-eight evangelistic sermons, The treasure chest, Speaker's resources from contemporary literature, Flapdoodle, trust and obey, Words of life, The eternal light & 365 table graces for the Christian home; co-auth, Twentieth century Bible commentary, Christmas in our hearts, Candle, star, and Christmas tree & When Christmas came to Bethlehem; co-ed, Prayers for public worship; ed, Holy, holy land, 68, Close your eyes when praying, 68 & Our American heritage, 70, Harper; The Charles L. Allen treasury, Revell, 70; American epitaphs: grave and humorous, Dover, 73; contrib, World Book Encycl, Field. Add: Dept. of English, Keuka College, Keuka Park, NY 14478.

WALSER, RICHARD, b. Lexington, N.C, Oct. 23, 08. AMERICAN LITERATURE. A.B, Univ. N.C, 29, A.M, 33. Teacher, high schs, 30-42; instr. ENG, Univ. N.C, 46; N.C. STATE UNIV, 46-47, asst. prof, 47-53, assoc. prof, 53-57, prof, 57-70, EMER. PROF, 70- Guggenheim fel, 57-58. U.S.N.R, 42-46; Bronze Star Medal. MLA; S.Atlantic Mod. Lang. Asn; Am. Folklore Soc. Folklore; American humor. Publ: Thomas Wolfe; an introduction and interpretation, Holt, 61; The Black poet: biography of George Moses Horton, Philos. Libr, 66; Literary North Carolina, N.C. Dept. Arch. & Hist, 70; Tar heel laughter, Univ. N.C, 74; Ham Jones: Southern folk humorist, J. Am. Folklore, 10-12/65; Alexander Martin, poet, Early Am. Lit, spring 71; The angel and the ghost, In: Thomas Wolfe and the glass of time, Univ. Ga, 71; plus two others. Add: Dept. of English, North Carolina State University, Raleigh, NC 27607.

WALSH, CHAD, b. South Boston, Va, May 10, 14; m. 38; c. 4. ENGLISH. A.B, Univ. Va, 38; A.M, Univ. Mich, 39, Ph.D, 43; hon. D.Litt, Rockford Col, 63 & St. Norbert Col, 72. Res. analyst, U.S. War Dept, 43-45; asst. prof. ENG, BELOIT COL, 45-48, assoc. prof, 48-52, PROF, 52-, WRITER-IN-RESIDENCE, 71-, chmn. dept. Eng, 62-70. Asst. priest, St. Paul's Episcopal Church, Beloit, Wis, 48- MLA; AAUP; fel. Soc. Arts, Relig. & Contemporary Cult. The preposition at the end of a clause in early Middle English: utopian and dystopian literature; relation between religion and the arts; modern poetry. Publ: Stop looking and listen, 47; The factual dark, 49; Early Christians of the 21st century, 50; Knock and enter, 53 & co-auth, The rough years, 60, Morehouse; auth, C.S. Lewis: apostle to the skeptics, co-auth, Campus Gods on trial, 53, ed, Garland for Christmas, 65 & Honey and the gall, 67, Macmillan; auth, Faith and behavior, 54; Eden two-way, 54, Nellie and her flying crocodile, 56 & From Utopia to nightmare, 62, Harper; co-auth, Why go to church, Reflection Bks, 62; auth, Doors into poetry, Prentice-Hall, 62; The psalm of Christ, Westminster, 63; The unknowing dance, Abelard, 64; Today's poets, Scribner, 64; The end of nature, Swallow, 69; God at large, Seabury, 71. Add: Dept. of English, Beloit College, Beloit, WI 53511.

WALSH, EDWARD JOHN, b. Pittsburgh, Pa, Mar. 1, 32; m. 54; c. 2. ENGLISH. B.S.Ed, Clarion State Col, 54; M.Litt, Univ. Pittsburgh, 59. Instr. pub. schs, 56-61; asst. prof. ENG, SLIPPERY ROCK STATE COL, 61-63, ASSOC. PROF, 63-, ASST. CHMN. DEPT, 73- U.S.A, 54-56. MLA; NCTE. Nineteenth century American literature; journalism; poetry. Publ: Co-auth, Time out for in-service education, Sch. Bds, 11/65, Susie learns to read i/t/a, 4/67 & A common sense approach to the teaching of grammar, 2/68, Progressive Teacher. Add: 339 Library Dr, Slippery Rock, PA 16057.

WALSH, FREDERICK GEORGE, b. New Bedford, Mass, May 31, 15; m. 45; c. 2. DRAMATIC ARTS, SPEECH. B.S, N.C. State Col, 36, M.S, 39; Rockefeller Found. fel, 38-40; M.A, Univ. N.C, 40; M.F.A, West. Reserve Univ, 51, Ph.D.(drama), 52; summer, Stanford Univ, 51. Teacher pub. schs, S.C, 36-37; teaching fel. indust. arts, N.C. State Col, 37-38; vis. lectr. drama & speech, Ohio Univ, 40-41; designer, Baltimore Mus. Art, Md, 41-42; instr. DRAMA & SPEECH, Bowling Green State Univ, 45-46, asst. prof, 46-48, assoc. prof, 48-50; PROF. & CHMN. DEPT, N.DAK. STATE UNIV, 52- Designer, Burning Hills Amphitheatre, Medora, N.Dak; Custer Mem. Theatre, Mandon, N.Dak; dir. & auth, outdoor dramas, Medora & Mandon, 58-61; fac. representative, N.Dak. State Univ, 67-; lectr, U.S. Dept. of State Bureau of Educ. & Cult. Affairs, 71; dir, Prairie Stage, 72- Speech Commun. Asn; Am. Theatre Asn; N.Cent. Theatre Asn. (pres, 56). Outdoor community commemorative drama; drama in its relationship to religion; auditorium and theatre design. Publ: The trial of Louis Riel, Inst. Regional Stud, 65. Add: Dept. of Speech, North Dakota State University, Fargo, ND 58102.

WALSH, GRACE, b. St. Paul, Minn, June 18, 10. SPEECH. B.E, Wis. State Col, 32; Northwest. Univ; Ph.M, Univ. Wis, 39, summers, 42-43, 51-54. Teacher, high sch, Wis, 32-42, 43-44, Iowa, 42-43; PROF. SPEECH & DIR. FORENSICS, UNIV. WIS-EAU CLAIRE, 45- Vis. prof, Univ. South. Calif, summer 59 & Calif. State Col, Fullerton, summer 69. Gold Award, 100th Anniversary Interstate Oratorical Asn. Speech Commun. Asn.(secy, forensic div, 73-75); Cent. States Speech Asn; NEA; Am. Forensic Asn. Intercollegiate discussion, debate and oratory. Publ: Tournaments for better or worse?, Speech Teacher; The Irish national debate championship, J. Am. Forensic Asn, spring 70; The case for Eau Claire, Forensic, 1/72; plus two others. Add: Dept. of Speech, University of Wisconsin-Eau Claire, Eau Claire, WI 54701.

WALSH, MARY MARGARET, O.S.B, b. Concordia, Kans, Nov. 20, 27. ENGLISH LANGUAGE & LITERATURE. B.A, Mt. St. Scholastica Col, 48; M.A, Creighton Univ, 60; Col. St. Thomas, summers 61-62; NDEA fel, Syracuse Univ, 64, Ph.D.(Eng. lang. & lit), 68. Instr. Eng, Donnelly Col, summer 64; asst. prof. Eng. lang. & lit, BENEDICTINE COL, 67-72, ASSOC. PROF. ENG, 72- Asst. prof, Emmanuel Col.(Mass), summer 68. MLA. Eighteenth century English literature; grammatical theory, especially transformational grammar; literary criticism. Publ: Swift eyesight like a flame, Thoth, spring 66. Add: Dept. of English, Benedictine College, Atchison, KS 66002.

WALSH, WILLIAM PATRICK, b. Portland, Ore, Feb. 11, 40; m. 64; c. 1. SHAKESPEARE, ELIZABETHAN DRAMA. B.A, Univ. Calif, Riverside, 62, M.A, 64, Ph.D.(Eng), 71. Lectr. ENG, Calif. State Col, Los Angeles, 69-71; ASST. PROF, BUTLER UNIV, 71- MLA; Renaissance Soc. Am; Shakespeare Soc. Am. Robert Greene. Publ: Sexual discovery and Renaissance morality in Marlowe's Hero and Leander, Stud. Eng. Lit, winter 72. Add: Dept. of English, Butler University, Indianapolis, IN 46208.

WALTER, JOHN ARNOLD, b. Lacy, Okla, Mar. 7, 14; m. 36; c. 4. TECHNICAL WRITING & EDITING. A.B, Tex. Tech. Col, 35, A.M, 37; summers, Duke Univ, 39, Univ. Tex, 40-41, 48-50. Instr. Eng, Tex. Tech. Col, 37-42; report writing, Gen. Motors Inst, 42; from asst. prof. to assoc. prof. tech. writing & Am. lit, UNIV. TEX, AUSTIN, 46-49, PROF. ENG, 69-, ASSOC. CHMN. DEPT, 64-, SCI. REPORTS ED, MIL. PHYSICS RES. LAB, acting chmn. dept, spring 73. Summers, consult. tech. commun, Tex. Instruments, Inc, Dallas, Tex, 58-61; Int. Data Syst, 63; consult, Tex. Water Develop. Bd, 67 & Guef Publ. Co, 70. U.S.N.R, 44-46, Lt. Fel. Soc. Tech. Commun; NCTE. Engineering and science writing and editing. Publ: Co-auth, Theory of technical writing, Univ. Tex; Technical writing, Holt, 3rd ed, 70; auth, Style manuals, & Basic recommended reference shelf, In: Handbook of technical writing practices, Wiley-Interscience, 71; Some shibboleths in teaching technical writing, J. Tech. Writing & Commun, 71; plus others. Add: Dept. of English, University of Texas, Austin, TX 78712.

WALTER, OTIS MONROE, b. Chicago, Ill, Apr. 20, 21. SPEECH. A.B, Northwest. Univ, 42, A.M, 43, Ph.D, 48. PROF. speech, UNIV. PITTSBURGH, 57-71, RHET. THEORY, 71- Rhet. area chmn, Univ. Ala, 70-71. Speech Commun. Asn. Philosophy; psychology; rhetoric. Publ: Co-auth, Thinking and speaking, 62, 3rd ed, 73 & auth, Speaking to inform and persuade, 66, Macmillan; Descartes on reasoning, Speech Monogr, 51; Improvement of attitude research, J. Soc. Psychol, 51. Add: Dept. of Speech, University of Pittsburgh, Pittsburgh, PA 15213.

WALTERS, DOROTHY JEANNE, b. Edmond, Okla, Mar. 17, 28. ENGLISH. B.A, Univ. Okla, 48 & 51, Ph.D.(Eng), 60. Instr. ENG, Univ. Colo, 60-62, asst. prof, 62-67; ASSOC. PROF, WICHITA STATE UNIV, 67- Univ. Colo. Counc. creative res. fel, 66. MLA. Writing by women; women's studies; 20th century literature. Publ: Flannery O'Connor, Twayne, 73; Solipsism in Emily Dickinson, Univ. Colo. Stud, 8/63. Add: Dept. of English, Wichita State University, Wichita, KS 67208.

WALTERS, THEODORE WILLIAM, S.J, Linguistics. See Volume III, Foreign Languages, Linguistics & Philology.

WALTERS, WALTER H, b. Troy, Ala, Dec. 19, 17; m. 47; c. 3. THEATRE ARTS. B.S, Troy State Univ, 39; La. State Univ, 41; Ph.M, Univ. Wis-Madison, 47; M.F.A, West. Reserve Univ, 49, Ph.D.(lit. & drama), 50. Teacher, high schs, Ala, 39-42; asst. Eng. lit, Univ. Wis-Madison, 46-48; instr. THEATRE ARTS, PA. STATE UNIV. UNIVERSITY PARK, 50-51, asst. prof, 51-55, assoc. prof, 55-58, PROF, 58-, from acting dean to DEAN ARTS & ARCHIT, 68-, DIR. UNIV. ARTS SERV, 73-, head dept. theatre arts, 54-66, assoc. dean col. arts & archit, 66-68. Bk. rev. ed, Educ. Theatre J, 56-58; chmn. theatre admin. proj, Am. Theatre Asn, 62-65; theatre consult, Pa. State Univ. Arts Complex, 62-65; mem. adv. counc, Am. Acad. Rome, 68-; mem. ed. adv. bd, Arts in Society, 69- U.S.N.R, Lt; Meritorious serv. citation. Am. Theatre Asn; U.S. Inst. Theatre Technol. (ed, Newslett, 66-68, 1st v.pres, 70-71, pres, 71-72); Children's Theatre Conf; Int. Counc. Fine Arts Deans (v.chmn, 73, chmn, 74); Univ. & Col. Theatre Asn.(dir, 70-71); fel. Am. Theatre Asn. Theatre management and administration; dramatic literature; theatre criticism. Publ: Co-auth, Attending the theatre, Pa. State Univ, 57. Add: College of Arts & Architecture, Pennsylvania State University, 111 Arts Bldg, University Park, PA 16802.

WALTHER, JOHN DANIEL, b. Elizabeth, N.J, June 26, 27. MODERN ENGLISH & AMERICAN LITERATURE. B.A, Univ. S.C, 59, M.A, 61; fel, Vanderbilt Univ, 62-64, Ph.D.(Eng), 71. Teacher ENG, Univ. S.C, 60-62; instr, Vanderbilt Univ, 64-65; UNIV. S.FLA, TAMPA, 65-69, ASST. PROF, 69- AAUP; Am. Fed. Teachers; MLA; S.Atlantic Mod. Lang. Asn. American drama; American fiction; modern American poetry and creative writing. Publ: Calque de figure humaine, S.Fla. Rev, fall 73; Flower child, Ellipsis, fall 73; Luke looks homeward: an interview with Fred W. Wolfe, Miss. Quart, spring 74. Add: Dept. of English, University of South Florida, Tampa, FL 33620.

WALTON, GERALD WAYNE, b. Neshoba, Miss, Sept. 11, 34; m. 60; c. 3. ENGLISH. B.S, Univ. South. Miss, 56; M.A, Univ. Miss, 59, Ph.D.(Eng), 67. Instr, UNIV. MISS, 56-62, asst. prof. Eng, 62-67, dir. freshman Eng. prog, 63-69, assoc. prof, 67-70, PROF. ENG. & ASSOC. DEAN COL. LIBERAL ARTS, 70- Univ. Nebr. fel, 69-70. U.S.A.F.R, 59-65. MLA; Am. Dialect Soc; Am. Asn. Cols. Teacher Educ; NCTE. Quakerism in the American novel; Southern speech and folklore; William Faulkner and the South. Publ: Tennie's Jim and Lucas Beauchamp, Am. Notes & Queries, 10/69; A study of lower class and middle class students' sentence conjoining and embedding, Stud. Eng, 6/70; A word list of Southern farm terms from Faulkner's The hamlet, Miss. Folklore Register, summer 72; plus several others. Add: Dept. of English, University of Mississippi, University, MI 38677.

WALTON, JAMES HACKETT, b. Blue Island, Ill, Sept. 23, 37; m. 63; c. 1. ENGLISH. A.B, Univ. Notre Dame, 59; Woodrow Wilson fel, Northwest. Univ, 59, M.A, 60, univ. fels, 60-62, Ph.D.(Eng), 66. Instr. ENG. UNIV. NOTRE DAME, 63-66, asst. prof, 66-71, ASSOC. PROF, 71- Joseph Conrad; 18th century novel; Victorian poetry. Publ: Conrad and naturalism: The secret agent, Tex. Stud. Lit. & Lang, summer 67; Mr. X's little joke: the design of Conrad's The informer, Stud. Short Fiction, summer 67; Conrad and The secret agent: the genealogy of Mr. Vladimir, Polish Rev, summer 67. Add: Dept. of English, University of Notre Dame, Notre Dame, IN 46556.

WALTS, ROBERT WARREN, b. New Albany, Ind, Apr. 1, 21; m. 44; c. 3. ENGLISH. B.A, Rutgers Univ, 50, M.A, 51, fel, 51-52, Ph.D.(Eng), 53. Instr. ENG, Univ. Mo, 52-53; asst. prof, Univ. Ga, 53-56; assoc. prof, Ga. State Col, 56-59; SOUTHWEST TEX. STATE UNIV, 59-61, PROF, 61-, chmn. dept, 65-72. U.S.N.R, 42-45. MLA; Bibliog. Soc. Am. Shakespeare; William Dean Howells. Publ: The rise of Silas Lapham: a study guide, Shelley Publ. Co, 63; William Dean Howells and his Library edition, Papers Bibliog. Soc. Am, 58; The felicity of the marine imagery in Romeo and Juliet, S.Cent. Mod. Lang. Asn. Bull, 62. Add: Dept. of English, Southwest Texas State University, San Marcos, TX 78666.

WALZ, VINCENT (PHYLLIS MARIE), D.C, b. St. Louis, Mo, July 25, 28. ENGLISH. A.B, Fontbonne Col, 51; Ph.D.(Eng), St. Louis Univ, 68. Instr. Eng, Marillac Col, 60-61, 65-66, asst. prof, 66-68, assoc. prof. Eng. & chmn. dept. humanities, 68-72, PROF. ENG, 72-73; ST. MARY'S SEM. COL, 73- Lectr, Seton Hill Col, summers 70 & 71. MLA; NCTE; Midwest Mod. Lang. Asn; Conf. Col. Compos. & Commun; Conf. Eng. Educ. Robert Frost; creativity; modern literature. Publ: Doubleness in Robert Frost's Poetry of paradox, Univ. Microfilms, 69; Heard from down under (poem), Poetry Ctr. Speaking, 6/73. Add: Div. of Communications and Humanities, St. Mary's Seminary College, Perryville, MO 63775.

WALZL, FLORENCE LITCHFIELD, b. Minneapolis, Minn, Nov. 19, 09; m. 40. ENGLISH. B.A, Univ. Minn, 30, M.A, 31, Ph.D.(Eng), 35. Asst. prof. ENG, Bowling Green State Univ, 34-40; vis. scholar, Johns Hopkins Univ, 40-41; Columbia Univ, 50-51; asst. prof, Col. Notre Dame, 51-54; assoc. prof, UNIV. WIS-MILWAUKEE, 54-65, PROF, 65-, Univ. Wis. res. summer res. grants, 57, 67, 69, 74. Instr, East. Ill. State Teachers Col, 34-36. MLA; NCTE; Milton Soc. Am; James Joyce Found; Am. Comt. Irish Stud; AAUP; Am. Asn. Univ. Women. Renaissance literature; 20th century literature; James Joyce studies. Publ: The liturgy of the Epiphany season and the epiphanies of Joyce, PMLA, 9/65; Gabriel and Michael: the conclusion of The dead, fall 66 & Joyce's The sisters: a development, summer 73, James Joyce Quart; plus others. Add: Dept. of English, University of Wisconsin-Milwaukee, Milwaukee, WI 53201.

WANAMAKER, MURRAY GORHAM, b. St. John, N.B, Aug. 17, 20; m. 51; c. 2. ENGLISH, LINGUISTICS. B.A, Acadia Univ, 41, B.Ed, 42; fel, Queen's Univ.(Ont), 47-49, M.A, 49; fel, Univ. Mich, 61-62, Ed.D.(Eng), 65. Lectr. ENG, Acadia Univ, 52-54, asst. prof, 54-58, assoc. prof, 58-64, prof, 64-66; assoc. prof, UNITED COL, UNIV. WINNIPEG, 66-73, PROF, 73- Intel.C, Can. Army, 42-47, Capt. Can. Counc. Teachers Eng; Asn. Can. Univ. Teachers Eng; Can. Ling. Asn; NCTE; Can. Asn. Univ. Teachers; Am. Dialect Soc.(mem, ed. adv. bd, 72-). History of English; dialectology; American literature. Publ: Canadian English: whence? whither?, J. Educ, 11/59; Your dialect is showing, In: Looking at language, W.J. Gage, Toronto, 66; Dialectology, In: Introductory essays in linguistics, Univ. Victoria, 67. Add: Dept. of English, University of Winnipeg, Winnipeg, Man. R3B 2E9, Can.

WANG, ALFRED SHIH-PU, b. Shanghai, China, Mar. 16, 33; U.S. citizen; m. 61; c. 2. ENGLISH. A.B, Davidson Col, 58; M.A, Tulane Univ, 64, Ph.D. (Eng), 67. Asst. prof. ENG, South. Univ, New Orleans, 64-67; E.CAROLINA UNIV, 67-73, ASSOC. PROF, 73- MLA; S.Atlantic Mod. Lang. Asn; AAUP. Publ: Tar River poets, In: East Carolina poetry forum, 70; When today's toil surrendered, In: National poetry anthology, 70; auth, Walt Whitman and Lao-chuang, Walt Whitman Rev, 71. Add: 203 King George Rd, Greenville, NC 27834.

WANG, JOAN PARSONS, b. Cincinnati, Ohio, Oct. 21, 25; wid; c. 2. ENGLISH, COMPARATIVE LITERATURE. A.B, Radcliffe Col, 47; M.A, Brown Univ, 49; fels, Ind. Univ, 61-62 & 63-64, Ph.D.(comp. lit), 64. ASST. PROF. ENG, INDEPENDENT STUD. DIV, DIV. CONTINUING EDUC, IND. UNIV, BLOOMINGTON, 66- Cert. Merit, Nat. Univ. Exten. Asn, 71. MLA; Writing syllabi for independent study courses in English and world literature; modern European drama; women's studies. Add: Dept. of English, Indiana University, Bloomington, IN 47401.

WANG, JOHN CHING-YU, Chinese & English Literature. See Volume III, Foreign Languages, Linguistics & Philology.

WANG, VERONICA CHOW, b. Peking, China, Oct. 11, 36; U.S. citizen; m. 61; c. 2. ENGLISH. A.B, Queens Col.(N.C), 59; M.A, Tulane Univ, 64, Ph.D. (Eng), 67. Asst. prof. ENG, South. Univ, New Orleans, 65-67; E. CAROLINA UNIV, 67-73, ASSOC. PROF, 73- MLA. Add: Dept. of English, East Carolina University, Greenville, NC 27834.

WANG, WILLIAM S. Y, Linguistics. See Volume III, Foreign Languages, Linguistics & Philology.

WANT, ELMER CLEVELAND, JR, b. Pine Bluff, Ark, Jan. 26, 34; m. 66; c. 3. ENGLISH LITERATURE. B.A, Hendrix Col, 56; Carnegie fel. & M.A, George Peabody Col, 57; Horlock scholarship & M.Div, Episcopal Theol. Sem. Southwest, 66; South. Fel. Fund grant & Ph.D.(Eng), Vanderbilt Univ, 68. Asst. prof. ENG, Hendrix Col, 58-60, 61-63; instr, TEX. A&M UNIV, 66-68, asst. prof, 68-74, ASSOC. PROF, 74- Nat. Endowment for Humanities summer stipend, 72. MLA; Church Hist. Soc. Victorian English literature; religion and literature. Publ: Frederick Denison Maurice and Eustace Conway, Anglican Theol. Rev, 10/72; co-auth, The Cambridge Apostle as student journalists: a key to authorship in the Metropolitan Quarterly Magazine, Victorian Periodicals Newsletter, 12/73. Add: Dept. of English, Texas A&M University, College Station, TX 77843.

WARD, AILEEN, b. Newark, N.J. ENGLISH. B.A, Smith Col, 40; M.A, Radcliffe Col, 42, Ph.D, 53; Fulbright fel, Cambridge, 49-50; Litt.D, Skidmore Col, 73. Instr. Eng, Dalton Sch, New York, N.Y, 40-43; teaching fel. & tutor, Radcliffe Col, 43-45; instr. Eng, Wellesley Col, 46-47; Barnard Col, 47-49; assoc, Inst. Int. Educ, 52-53; Fund. Advan. Educ, 53; asst. prof. Eng, Vassar Col, 54-58; Am. Asn. Univ. Women Shirley Farr fel, 58-59; mem. fac, Sarah Lawrence Col, 60-64; PROF. ENG, BRANDEIS UNIV, 64-, CHMN. DEPT, 73- Writing fel, YADDO, 54-55, 66-67, 71; Guggenheim fel, 66-67; mem. jury, Nat. Bk. Award Arts & Lett, 67; Radcliffe Inst. fel, Cambridge, 70-71. MLA; Eng. Inst. New Eng. Col. Eng. Asn. Duff Cooper Mem. Prize, 63; Nat. Bk. Award Arts & Lett, 64; Rose Mary Crawshay Prize, 64. The life of William Blake. Publ: John Keats: the making of a poet, Viking, 63; ed, The poems of William Blake, Limited Ed. Club, 71; auth, The forging of Orc: Blake and the idea of revolution, In: Literature in revolution, 72; plus articles in Stud. in Philol, Philol. Quart and others. Add: Dept. of English, Brandeis University, Waltham, MA 02145.

WARD, DOROTHY HACKETT, b. Chattanooga, Tenn, Nov. 29, 05; wid; c. 1. DRAMA, SPEECH. A.B, Univ. Chattanooga, 28; M.F.A, Yale, 46. GUERRY PROF. DRAMATICS & SPEECH, UNIV. TENN, CHATTANOOGA, 40-, CHMN. DEPT, 72-, dir. univ. players, 40-72. Carnegie-Univ. Chattanooga study grant, summer 51; dir. Apprentice Players, Univ. Chattanooga; dramatic dir, Chattanooga Opera Asn, 55-; adapter, The juggler of our lady, Channel 12-TV, Chattanooga, 56; Univ. Chattanooga study grant, Gt. Brit, summer 63; lectr, Westham House Residential Col, Eng, 63; auth. & producer, The nutcracker and the queen of the mice, Tivoli Theatre, 66. Add: Dept. of Dramatics & Speech, University of Tennessee, Chattanooga, TN 37403.

WARD, DOYLE GLYNN, b. Clinton, Ark, Jan. 21, 35; m. 56; c. 2. SPEECH. B.A, Harding Col, 56; M.A, Univ. Ill, 58; Ph.D.(speech), Univ. Mo, 66. Speech correctionist, schs, Champaign, Ill, 57-58; asst. prof. speech, Harding Col, 58-64, assoc. prof, 66-68; SPEC. EDUC, SOUTHWEST TEX. STATE UNIV, 68-73, PROF, 73- Am. Speech & Hearing Asn. Add: Dept. of Special Education, Southwest Texas State University, San Marcos, TX 78666.

WARD, FERDINAND J, C.M, b. Chicago, Ill, Oct. 2, 93. ENGLISH. A.B, DePaul Univ, 15; B.Th, St. Mary's Sem.(Mo), 20; summers, Univ. Chicago, 21 & 22 & Northwest. Univ, 23, M.A, Cath. Univ. Am, 37; St. Louis Univ, 51. Dean men, Dallas Univ, 22-23; asst. prof. Eng, DePaul Univ, 23-43; 46-48, alumni dir, 48-49; dean, St. Louis Prep. Col, 49-52; ASST. PROF. ENG, DePAUL UNIV, 52- Nat. Guard, 12-15; U.S.A, 43-46, Res, 46-54, Capt. Conf. Col. Compos. & Commun; NCTE; Col. Eng. Asn. Literary criticism; remedial writing. Publ: Contrib, Conf. Col. Compos. & Commun. Add: Dept. of English, DePaul University, 2233 N. Kenmore, Chicago, IL 60614.

WARD, HERMAN M, b. Jersey City, N.J, Mar. 11, 14; m. 43; c. 4. ENGLISH. A.B, Montclair State Col, 35; A.M, Princeton, 37, Ph.D, 40. Asst. prof. ENG, Jersey City State Col, 46-47; PROF, TRENTON STATE COL, 47- Fulbright fel, Anatolia Col, Greece, 52-53, Univ. Iceland, 62-63; consult. Eng, Princeton High Sch, 61-62; exchange prof, Univ. Frankfurt, 66-67. Intel.C, U.S.A, 42-45, S/Sgt. NCTE. Teaching of high school English; Irish and Greek literature; creative writing. Publ: Co-auth, Prose and poetry high school literature series, L.W. Singer, 50; auth, Poems for pleasure, Hill & Wang, 63; co-auth, Three voices, Univ. Graphics, 67; auth, Byron and the magazines, Univ. Salzburg, 73. Add: Dept. of English, Trenton State College, Trenton, NJ 08625.

WARD, JEAN M, b. Eugene, Ore, Jan. 14, 38; m. 60; c. 2. SPEECH. B.S, Univ. Ore, 60, M.S, 64. High sch. teacher, Fern Ridge Sch. Dist, Ore, 62-64; instr. SPEECH COMMUN, LEWIS & CLARK COL, 64-67, asst. prof, 67-72, ASSOC. PROF, 72-, CHAIRPERSON DEPT. COMMUN, 74- Int. Commun. Asn; Speech Commun. Asn; Am. Forensic Asn; West. Speech Asn. Women in American public address; nonverbal communication; intercultural communication. Publ: Ed, Dollars for education, 72 & co-ed, Democratic alternatives, 74, Nat. Textbk. Add: Dept. of Communication, Lewis & Clark College, Portland, OR 97219.

WARD, JOSEPH ANTHONY, JR, b. Baltimore, Md, Feb. 26, 31. ENGLISH. A.B, Univ. Notre Dame, 52; M.A, Tulane Univ, 54, Ph.D, 57. Instr. ENG, Tulane Univ, 56-57; asst. prof, Univ. Southwest. La, 57-61; assoc. prof, 61-64; RICE UNIV, 64-67, PROF, 67-, chmn. dept, 68-73. Guggenheim fel, 60-61; vis. assoc. prof, La. State Univ, summer 63; vis. prof. Eng, Columbia Univ, summer 68 & George Washington Univ, summer 72. MLA. American literature; the novel. Publ: The imagination of disaster: evil in the fiction of Henry James, Univ. Nebr, 61; The search for form: studies in the structure of James's fiction, Univ. N.C, 67; The function of the cetological chapters in Moby Dick, Am. Lit, 56; John Updike's fiction, Critique, spring 62; Emerson and The educated will: notes on the process of conversion, ELH, 12/67; plus others. Add: Dept. of English, Rice University, Houston, TX 77001.

WARD, JOSEPH THOMAS, b. Melrose, Iowa, Jan. 23, 25; m. 53; c. 9. ENGLISH. A.B, Univ. Notre Dame, 48, Ph.D.(Eng), 59; Cath. Univ. Am, 48-50; M.A, Univ. Mont, 53. Asst. ENG, Univ. Mont, 53; instr, Carroll Col. (Mont), 53-55, asst. prof, 58; asst, Notre Dame Univ, 59; assoc. prof, CARROLL COL.(MONT), 60-67, PROF, 67-, CHMN. DEPT, 58-, CHMN. DIV. FINE ART & COMMUN, 61- American literature, especially Herman Melville; aesthetics. Publ: James Kittleson, poet-priest of the plains, Rocky Mountain Rev, 67. Add: Dept. of English, Carroll College, Helena, MT 59601.

WARD, KATHRYN PAINTER, b. Philadelphia, Pa. ENGLISH. B.A, George Washington Univ, 35, M.A, 36, Ph.D.(Eng), 46; Dr.l'Inst, Sorbonne, 36. Instr. ENG, UNIV. MD, COLLEGE PARK, 38-43, asst. prof, 45-49, ASSOC. PROF, 52- Assoc. dir. Eng, Soviet Purchasing Comn, 43-45; lectr, U.S. Dept. Agr. Grad. Sch, 45-49; cult. attaché & chmn. Am. educ. comn, Am. Embassy, Greece, 49-51; consult, U.S. State Dept, 51-52; lectr, Army Exten. Prog, 52-; mem. nat. screening comt, Inst. Int. Educ, 72. AAUP; MLA; Col. Eng. Asn. Eighteenth century novel; Restoration and 18th century drama; biography. Publ: George Powell, playwright-actor; Greek art, past and present; The isles of Greece, Greek Am. Cult. J; The first professional theatre in Maryland, Md. Eng. J, 71. Add: 3622 Prospect Ave. N.W, Washington, DC 20007.

WARD, LOUIS RANDOLPH, b. Big Four, W.Va, Dec. 13, 15; m. 38; c. 5. ENGLISH. B.A, Univ. Colo, 39, M.A, 40; Ph.D.(educ. psychol), Purdue Univ, 59. Prin, Delcarbon Grade Sch, Colo, 40-41; instr. Eng. compos. & phys. educ, Pa. State Col, 42-44; master Eng, Howe Mil. Sch, Ind, 44-46; instr, Purdue Univ, 45-56; commun. skills, Mich. State Univ, 56-59; prof. lang. & soc. sci. & head dept, S.Dak. Sch. Mines & Technol, 59-61; PROF. ENG, LAKE SUPERIOR STATE COL, MICH. TECHNOL. UNIV, 67- Univ. fel, Univ. Colo, 39-40; All-Univ. res. grant, Mich. State Univ, 58. NCTE. Composition; developmental reading. Publ: Measuring comprehension in reading, Col. Eng, 5/56; To the Macbeths, in sorrow, Basic Col. Quart, fall 58. Add: 616 Dillon Ave, Sault Ste. Marie, MI 49783.

WARD, ROBERT ERNEST, b. Utica, N.Y, Apr. 17, 27; m. 69. EIGHTEENTH CENTURY ENGLISH LITERATURE. A.B, Syracuse Univ, 53; M.A, State Univ. N.Y. Albany, 54; Ph.D.(Eng), Univ. Iowa, 69. Teacher ENG, Bainbridge Cent. Sch, N.Y, 54-55; Utica Free Acad, 55-65; asst. prof, WEST. KY. UNIV, 69-73, ASSOC. PROF, 73-, res. grant, 72. U.S.A, 46-47, 50-51. Am. Soc. 18th Century Stud; MLA; S.Atlantic Mod. Lang. Asn; Mod. Humanities Res. Asn; Am. Comt. Irish Stud. Anglo-Irish culture and literature of the 18th century. Publ: Prince of Dublin printers: the letters of George Faulkner, Univ. Ky, 72; co-auth, Checklist and census of 400 imprints of G.Faulkner, 1725-1775, Ragnarok Press, 73; auth, Five minor Irish dramatists of the eighteenth century, Twayne, (in prep); Friendship and A history of Ireland, Eire-Ireland, fall 72. Add: Dept. of English, Western Kentucky University, Bowling Green, KY 42101.

WARD, ROBERT JACKSON, b. Cuyahoga Falls, Ohio, July 17, 26; m. 51; c. 2. ENGLISH. B.A, Univ. Akron, 51; M.A, Ohio State Univ, 52; Ph.D, Univ. Mo, 67. Instr. Eng, Univ. Mo, 52-59; asst. prof, North. Ill. Univ, 59-63; UNIV. NORTH. IOWA, 63-67, assoc. prof, AM. LIT, 67-74, PROF, 74- Abstractor, Abstr. Eng. Stud; prof. Eng. & head dept, East. Mont. Col, 71-72; instr. judo, Univ. North. Iowa, 73- U.S.N, 44-46. MLA; NCTE; Am. Stud. Asn; Midwest Mod. Lang. Asn. American and popular fiction; poetry. Publ: Still life, Midwest Rev, 1/64; Europe in American historical fiction, Midcontinent Am. Stud. J, spring 67; Relation of source to meaning and form in Melville's Benito Cereno, Midwest Mod. Lang. Asn, 11/67; plus others. Add: Dept. of American Literature, University of Northern Iowa, Cedar Falls, IA 50613.

WARD, ROBERT STAFFORD, b. Waltham, Mass, Dec. 20, 06; m. 44; c. 3. ENGLISH. B.A, Yale, 29; M.A, Boston Univ, 33, Ph.D.(Eng), 50; LL.B, Harvard, 37. Prof. ENG, UNIV. MIAMI, 46-72, chmn. div. humanities, 62-66, chmn. grad. Am. stud, 68-72, EMER. PROF, 72- South. Fel. Fund. summer fel, 58; Univ. Miami humanities res. award, summer 67, dir, Naval Reserve Off. Sch. U.S.N.R, 42-, Comdr. Thoreau Soc; MLA; Am. Stud. Asn. Henry W. Longfellow; Nathaniel Hawthorne; American studies. Publ: Longfellow and Melville: the ship and the whale, Emerson Soc. Quart, 61; The American system in literature, 9/65 & Longfellow's roots in Yankee soil, 68, New Eng. Quart. Add: 4620 S.W. 62nd Ave, Miami, FL 33155.

WARD, STANLEY SIDNEY, b. Bristol, Va, Dec. 19, 42; ENGLISH LITERATURE. B.A, Duke Univ, 65; Woodrow Wilson fel, Harvard, 65-66, M.A, 66, Ph.D.(Eng), 73. Instr. ENG, N.C. STATE UNIV, 70-71, ASST. PROF, 71- AAUP. Romantic and Victorian poetry; 19th century novel. Add: Dept. of English, North Carolina State University, Hillsborough St, Raleigh, NC 27607.

WARD, WILBER HENRY, III, b. Tuscaloosa, Ala, July 26, 43; m. 62; c. 1. AMERICAN LITERATURE. B.A, Univ. Ala, 66; M.A, Univ. Tenn, Knoxville, 68, univ. fel, 70-71, Ph.D.(Eng), 71. ASST. PROF. ENG, APPALACHIAN STATE UNIV, 71- Cert. Excellence in Teaching, Asn. Depts. Eng-MLA, 70. Med.C, U.S.A, 62-63, Res, 63-68. S.Atlantic Mod. Lang. Asn. Literary treatments of Bacon's Rebellion in Virginia; 19th century American fiction; Faulkner. Add: Dept. of English, Appalachian State University, Boone, NC 28607.

WARD, WILLIAM SMITH, b. Cynthiana, Ky, Feb. 3, 07; m. 39; c. 2. ENGLISH. A.B, Georgetown Col, 28, Litt.D, 57; M.A, Harvard Univ, 30; Ph.D, Duke Univ 43. Instr. ENG, UNIV. KY, 30-35, asst. prof, 38-46, assoc. prof, 46-51, PROF, 51-, head dept, 51-64, Distinguished Prof. Arts & Sci, 72-73. NCTE; MLA; S.Atlantic Mod. Lang. Asn. Poetry of the English Romantic period; periodical literature of the early 19th century. Publ: Index and finding list of serials published in the British Isles, 1789-1832, 53, Criticism of poetry in British periodicals in the early 19th century, 55 & British periodicals and newspapers, 1789-1832: a bibliography of secondary sources, 72, Univ. Ky; Literary reviews in British periodicals, 1798-1820: a bibliography, (2 vols), Garland, 72. Add: Dept. of English, University of Kentucky, Lexington, KY 40506.

WARD, WINIFRED, b. Eldora, Iowa, Oct. 29, 84. SPEECH, DRAMA. Ph.B, Univ. Chicago, 18; hon. L.H.D, Adelphi Col, 53, West. Col. Women, 57, East. Mich. Univ, 70. Teacher dramatics, pub. schs, Adrian, Mich, 08-16; asst. prof. speech & drama, Northwest. Univ, 18-50; LECTR. & WRITER, 50- Supvr. dramatics, pub. schs, Evanston, Ill, 24-50; Alumni Medal, Northwest. Univ, 50; summers, Univ. Minn, 50, San Jose State Col, 51, Natl. Col. Educ, 53, Mich. State Univ, 54, Union Theol. Sem, 57, Boston Univ, 59, San Francisco State Col, 62, Univ. Wash, 63. Am. Theatre & Asn.(Eaves award, 60, merit award, 71, hon. dir. children's theatre div); Am. Nat. Theatre & Acad. Publ: Theatre for children, 39, rev. ed, 52 & Stories to dramatize, 52, Children's Theatre Press; Playmaking with children, Appleton, 47, rev. ed, 57; Drama with and for children, Dept. Health, Educ. & Welfare, 60. Co-auth, Creative drama: the first steps (film). Add: 1600 Hinman Ave, Evanston, IL 60201.

WARDE, WILLIAM BOOTH, JR, b. Minneapolis, Minn, Feb. 13, 33; m. 61; c. 2. ENGLISH LITERATURE. B.S, Bemidji State Col, 58; M.A, Univ. Ark, Fayetteville, 60, Ph.D.(Eng), 70. From instr. to ASST. PROF. ENG, N.TEX. STATE UNIV, 65- Manuscript ed, Southwest J. Social Educ, 70- U.S.A, 53-55. MLA; AAUP. Eighteenth century English novel and literature; short story. Publ: Revisions in the published texts of Samuel Richardson's preface to Clarissa, S.Cent. Bull, winter 71; Survival into oblivion; a political commentary, Southwest. Am. Lit, spring 72. Add: Dept. of English, North Texas State University, Denton, TX 76203.

WARDHAUGH, RONALD, Applied English Linguistics. See Volume III, Foreign Languages, Linguistics & Philology.

WARDLE, RALPH MARTIN, b. Woonsocket, R.I, May 10, 09; m. 36; c. 4. ENGLISH. A.B, Dartmouth Col, 31; A.M, Harvard, 34, Ph.D, 40. Instr, Palo Verde Ranch Sch, Ariz, 31-33; asst. Eng, Harvard, 34-38; instr, Univ. Omaha, 38-40; Cornell Univ, 40-44; assoc. prof, UNIV. NEBR. AT OMAHA, 44-46, prof, 46-62, Jefferis prof. Eng. lit, 62-71, FOUND. PROF. ENG, 71-, head dept, 46-69. Brooks fel. lit, Univ. Queensland, summer 66. MLA; NCTE. English literature, 1750-1830. Publ: A primer for readers, F.S. Crofts; Mary Wollstonecraft: a critical biography, Univ. Kans. & Richards, London; Oliver Goldsmith & ed, Godwin and Mary: the letters of William Godwin and Mary Wollstonecraft, 66, Univ. Kans. & Constable, London; auth, Hazlitt, Univ. Nebr, 71. Add: 1227 S. 52nd St, Omaha, NE 68106.

WAREN, STANLEY A, b. New York, N.Y, Mar. 23, 19; m. 49; c. 1. SPEECH, THEATRE. B.S.S, City Col. New York, 38; M.A, Columbia Univ, 39, Ph.D, 53. PROF. SPEECH & THEATRE, City Col. New York, 40-72, chmn. dept, 67-72; MEM. DOCTORAL FAC, CITY UNIV. NEW YORK, 68-, EXEC. OFF. PH.D. PROG. THEATRE, 72- Dir. & treas, Counc. Stock Theatres, 59-61; invitational dir, Cape Town Performing Arts Bd, S.Africa, 66; vis. dir, Union Artists African Music & Drama Asn, 66; mem, Soc. Stage Directors & Choreographers. U.S.A.F, 42-46, Capt. Am. Theatre Asn; Speech Commun. Asn. Oral interpretation of literature. Publ: Theatre in South Africa, Educ. Theater J, 10/68; Creative dramatics with Bantu children, Pac. Speech, spring 69; Diploma in drama, Uganda, Working Papers in Commun, 4/72; plus two others. Add: Ph.D. Program in Theatre, City University of New York, 33 W. 42nd St, New York, NY 10036.

WARFIELD, JACK W, b. Milwaukee, Wis, Jan. 23, 15; m. 40; c. 3. MASS COMMUNICATIONS. A.B, Univ. Wis, 37; M.A, Univ. Minn, 38; Ph.D, Univ. Utah, 53. Instr. drama, Ala. Col, 39-40; speech, drama & radio, Univ. Ark, 40-42; radio, W.Va. Univ, 46-47; asst. prof. drama, Mary Washington Col, 47-51; dean, col. theatre arts, Pasadena Playhouse, 52-55; staff dir. TV, KTLA, Hollywood, Calif, 55-57; production asst. film, Roland Reed Prod, Inc, Hollywood, 57; asst. prof. telecommun, Univ. South. Calif, 57-59; ASSOC. PROF. RADIO-TV-FILM, WAYNE STATE UNIV, 59- Summer guest prof, Nev. South. Univ, 64 & 65; Fulbright lectr, Univ. Chiengmai, 66-67; guest prof, Univ. N.B, summer 68; dir. TV training course, Macomb Community Col, winter 69; guest prof, Inst. Technol, Col. Educ, Wayne State Univ, summer 71. A.U.S, 42-46, Res, 46-53, Capt. Speech Commun. Asn; Broadcast Pioneers; Nat. Asn. Educ. Broadcasters; AAUP; Nat. Acad. TV Arts & Sci. Educational theatre and television. Publ: A case for operational training, 68, Teaching at Chiengmai University, fall 70 & A need for communication arts studies on the university level in Canada, 72, Improving Col. & Univ. Teaching; plus others. Add: Dept. of Speech Communication-Theatre, Wayne State University, Detroit, MI 48202.

WARHAFT, SIDNEY, b. Winnipeg, Man, Dec. 8, 21; m. 53; c. 1. ENGLISH. B.A, Univ. Man, 49; Fr. Govt. bursary, Univ. Paris, 49-50; M.A, Northwest. Univ, 52, Ph.D, 54; Folger Shakespeare Libr. summer grant, 52; Royal Soc. Can. overseas scholar, 52-53. Lectr. ENG, Univ. Man, 54-55; asst. prof, Col. Engineering, Univ. Mich, 55-57; Univ. South. Calif, 57-58; UNIV. MAN, 58-62, assoc. prof, 62-66, PROF, 66-, head dept, 66-71. Univ. Mich. fac. res. grant, 56; Can. Counc. fels, 64-65 & 71-72, mem. acad. panel, 69-71. R.C.A.F, 42-45. MLA; Asn. Can. Univ. Teachers Eng; Int. Asn. Prof. Eng; Shakespeare Asn. Am. Seventeenth century English literature; Shakespeare; the modern novel. Publ: Ed, Francis Bacon: a selection of his works, 65 & co-ed, English poems, 1250-1800, 66, Macmillan, Can; auth, The mystery of Hamlet, ELH, 9/63; Threne and theme in Watt, Wis. Stud. Contemporary Lit, 9/63; The providential order in Bacon's new philosophy, Stud. Lit. Imagination, 4/71. Add: Dept. of English, University of Manitoba, Winnipeg, Man, Can.

WARING, WALTER WEYLER, b. Kans, May 13, 17; m. 46; c. 3. ENGLISH LITERATURE. A.B, Kans. Wesleyan Univ, 39; A.M, Univ. Colo, 46; Ph.D, Cornell Univ, 49. Instr, Univ. Colo, 46-47; from asst. prof. to PROF. ENG. & CHMN. DEPT, KALAMAZOO COL, 49- U.S.A, 42-45. MLA. English literature of the 19th century; recent American and British poetry. Add: Dept. of English, Kalamazoo College, Kalamazoo, MI 49001.

WARLOW, FRANCIS WAYLAND, b. Philadelphia, Pa, June 29, 09. ENGLISH. A.B, Johns Hopkins Univ, 31; A.M, Univ. Pa, 46, Ph.D.(Eng), 58; Middlebury Col, 48. Instr. ENG, Carson Long Inst, 33-40; Muhlenberg Col, 46-47; asst. prof, DICKINSON COL, 47-53, assoc. prof, 53-61, PROF, 62- Fulbright lectr, Univs. Rennes & Grenoble, 61-62; staff assoc, Am. Asn. Univ. Prof, 67-69. Sig.C, U.S.A.F, 41-46, Lt. Col. MLA; NCTE. American literature; modern British-American poetry, novel and drama; creative writing. Publ: Bayani, Saturday Evening Post, 5/46; Richard Wilbur, Bucknell Rev; Marianne Moore's To a snail, Explicator, 68. Add: Dept. of English, Dickinson College, Carlisle, PA 17013.

WARNCKE, WAYNE WARREN, b. Union City, N.J, Apr. 25, 27; m. 50; c. 2. ENGLISH LITERATURE. B.A, Syracuse Univ, 53; M.A, Univ. Mich, 54, Ph.D.(Eng), 65; Danforth grant, 62-63 & summer 64. Instr. ENG, Marshall Univ, 54-58, asst. prof, 58-62, assoc. prof, 62; asst. prof, Wittenberg Univ, 63-66; assoc. prof, HARTWICK COL, 66-71, PROF, 71- Consult. reader, PMLA, 68-73. U.S.M.C, 45-49. MLA; Col. Eng. Asn. Modern British literature; English Renaissance literature; American literature. Publ: Samuel Johnson on Swift, J. Brit. Stud, 5/68; George Orwell's Dickens, S.Atlantic Quart, summer 70; George Orwell on T.S. Eliot, West. Humanities Rev, Summer 72; plus two others. Add: Dept. of English, Hartwick College, Oneonta, NY 13820.

WARNER, EDWARD FRANCIS, b. Wilkes-Barre, Pa, Sept. 5, 39; m. 61; c. 3. ENGLISH, COMMUNICATION. A.B, King's Col.(Pa), 61; Newark State Col, 63; M.S, Univ. Scranton, 67; Marywood Col, 71. Teacher Eng, Asbury Park High Sch, 61-64; chmn. dept, Scranton Prep. Sch, 64-67; ASSOC. PROF. ENG. & COMMUN, DIR. FORENSICS & DIR. COMMUN, UNIV. SCRANTON, 67- Chmn. dist. 7, Nat. Debate Comt, 72-73. Am. Forensic Asn; AAUP; NCTE. Development of debate theory; nature of communication. Publ: Co-auth, Fundamental oral communication, 72 & auth, Fundamental debate, (in press), Univ. Scranton. Add: Poplar Lane, R.D. 3, Wyoming, PA 18644.

WARNER, FRANK LAWRENCE, b. Rocky Mount, N.C, May 2, 39. THEATRE ARTS, DRAMA. B.A, Duke Univ, 61; M.A, Univ. N.C, Chapel Hill, 63, 64; Ph.D.(theatre), Tulane Univ, 68. ASST. PROF. THEATRE, TULANE UNIV, 67- Actor & costume asst, Lost Colony, Manteo, N.C, summers 62 & 63; actor, Triangle Repertory Co, Durham, N.C, summers 64 & 65; dir, Town & Gown Players, Hammond, La, 69; Tulane Summer Lyric Theatre, New Orleans, summers 71 & 72; actor, Tulane Ctr. Stage, summer 73. Am. Theatre Asn; AAUP; Southwest Theatre Conf; Speech Commun. Asn. American theater history; musical theatre. Publ: Songs my uncle taught me, N.C. Folklore J, 7/63; Recorded original performances from the American theatre prior to 1943, Educ. Theatre J, 3/74. Add: 1508 Constantinople, 8, New Orleans, LA 70115.

WARNER, JOHN M, b. Haydenville, Mass, Apr. 30, 35. ENGLISH LITERATURE. B.A, Univ. Mass, 56; M.A, Harvard, 60, Ph.D.(Eng. lit), 64. Instr. ENG. LIT, DREW UNIV, 62-64, asst. prof, 64-71, ASSOC. PROF, 71- MLA. Add: Dept. of English, Drew University, Madison, NJ 07940.

WARNER, JOHN RILEY, b. Terre Haute, Ind. Mar. 28, 13. ENGLISH LITERATURE. B.A, Ind. State Univ, Terre Haute, 38, M.A, 40; Ph.D.(Eng), Univ. Colo, Boulder, 55. Instr. ENG, PURDUE UNIV, WEST LAFAYETTE, 46-50 & 51-52, ASST. PROF, 55- Intel.C, U.S.A, 42-45, T/Sgt; Bronze Star Medal. British humor. Publ: Co-auth, Words in context, Appleton, 61, rev. ed, 66; auth, Dickens looks at Homer, Dickensian, 1/64; A test of meaning, CEA Critic, 4/64; The dichotomy of Ibsen's Mrs. Linde, Discourse, winter 70. Add: Dept. of English, Heavilon Hall, Purdue University, West Lafayette, IN 47907.

WARNER, STEPHEN DOUGLAS, b. Far Rockaway, N.Y, Oct. 10, 39; m. 65; c. 3. AMERICAN LITERATURE, NOVEL. A.B, Dickinson Col, 62; M.A, Ind. Univ, Bloomington, 69, Ph.D.(Am. lit), 71. ASST. PROF. ENG, STATE UNIV. N.Y. COL. FREDONIA, 70- Intel.C, U.S.A, 62-67, Capt. MLA; NCTE. American Picaresque; 19th century American fiction; contemporary American fiction. Publ: Robert Frost in the clearing: the risk of spirit in substantiation, In: Robert Frost centennial essays, Univ. South. Miss, 74. Add: Dept. of English, State University of New York College at Fredonia, Fredonia, NY 14063.

WARNKE, FRANK JOSEPH, b. Marlboro, Mass, Nov. 3, 25; m. 50. ENGLISH. A.B, Yale, 48; Univ. Calif, 48-49; M.A, Columbia Univ, 51, Am. Counc. Learned Soc. fel, 52-53, Ph.D.(Eng. & comp. lit), 54. Lectr. ENG, Columbia Univ, 50-52; instr, City Col. New York, 53-54; Yale, 54-59, asst. prof, 59-61; assoc. prof, UNIV. WASH, 61-63, PROF, 63-, CHMN. DEPT. COMP. LIT, 67- Morse fel, 57-58; Fulbright lectr, Ger, 63-64 & 68-69. Cristo-Loveanu Prize, 51. MLA; Am. Comp. Lit. Asn; Philol. Asn. Pac. Coast. Renaissance and Romantic periods, English and continental; 17th century, especially poetry, English and continental. Publ: European metaphysical poetry, 61 & Versions of Baroque, 72, Yale; co-auth, Seventeenth century prose and poetry, Harcourt, 63, Culture and crisis: a college reader, Holt, 64 & Encyclopedia of poetry and poetics, Princeton, 65; auth. & ed, John Donne: poetry and prose, Random, 67; auth, Marino and the English metaphysicals' Stud. Renaissance; The poet as librettist, Hugo von Hofmannsthal and der Rosenkavalier, Opera News: Sacred play: Baroque poetic style, J. Aesthet. & Art Criticism, summer 64. Add: Dept. of Comparative Literature, University of Washington, Seattle, WA 98195.

WARREN, BERNICE S, b. Ozark, Mo, June 5, 34. ENGLISH. B.S, Southwest Mo. State Col, 55; M.A, Univ. Ark, 59; Ph.D.(Eng), Univ. Mo, Columbia, 67. Teacher, pub. schs, Mo, 55-56; Cent. High Sch, 56-57; supvr. ENG, Southeast Mo. State Col, 58-60; instr, Univ. Mo, Columbia, 60-66; asst. prof, South. Ill. Univ, 66-69; ASSOC. PROF, SOUTHWEST MO. STATE UNIV, 69- MLA; NCTE; AAUP; Conf. Col. Compos. & Commun. Restoration and 18th century British literature; freshman composition. Add: Dept. of English, Southwest Missouri State University, Springfield, MO 65802.

WARREN, CLIFTON LANIER, b. Portsmouth, Va, Mar. 31, 32; m. 59; c. 2. COMPARATIVE LITERATURE. B.A, Richmond Col, 52; M.A, Univ. Richmond, 54; Ph.D, Ind. Univ, 62. Assoc. world lit, Ind. Univ, 57-58; head dept. Eng. & comp. lit, Okla. City Univ, 58-62; from assoc. prof. to PROF. ENG. & HUMANITIES, CENT. STATE UNIV.(OKLA), 62-, CHMN. DEPT. CREATIVE STUD, 72- Book & film critic, WKY-TV, 61- U.S.M.C, 54-56. MLA; S.Cent. Mod. Lang. Asn; NCTE. Literature and films; contemporary novel. Publ: Tennessee Williams as a cinematic writer, Diss. Abstr, 62. Add: Dept. of Creative Studies, Central State University, Edmond, OK 73034.

WARREN, JOHN W, b. Clarksville, Ark, June 27, 27; m. 48; c. 2. ENGLISH LITERATURE. B.A, Abilene Christian Col, 48; M.A, Univ. Ark, 51; fel, Univ. Tenn, 54-57, Ph.D, 61. Instr. ENG, Univ. Tenn, 57-61; assoc. prof, David Lipscomb Col, 61-62; PROF. & CHMN. DEPT, TENN. TECHNOL. UNIV, 62- S.Atlantic Mod. Lang. Asn; MLA; Conf. Col. Compos. & Commun. Nineteenth century English literature; Landor's views on English life and literature. Add: P.O. Box 94A, Dept. of English, Tennessee Technological University, Cookeville, TN 38501.

WARYE, RICHARD JONATHAN, b. Columbus, Ohio, Mar. 4, 29; m. 64; c. 1. SPEECH, DRAMA. B.Sc.Ed, Ohio State Univ, 51, M.A, 52, Ph.D.(theatre), 66. Teacher pub. schs, Ohio, 53-60; instr. speech, Bates Col, 60-67, asst. prof, 67-68; SPEECH & THEATRE, BRIDGEWATER STATE COL, 68-71, ASSOC. PROF, 71- U.S.N.R, 53-56, Lt. Speech Commun. Asn; Am. Theatre Asn; AAUP; New Eng. Theatre Conf. Children's theatre; community theatre; technical theatre. Add: Dept. of Speech and Theatre, Bridgewater State College, Bridgewater, MA 02324.

WASHBURN, DONALD EDWARD, b. Neptune, N.J, June 14, 32; m. 58; c. 2. SPEECH, ENGLISH. B.A, Yale, 54, M.A.T, 55; Ph.D.(speech), Univ. Denver 62. Teacher Eng, Valley Regional High Sch, 55-56; master, Mt. Hermon Sch, 56-58; teaching fel. speech, Univ. Denver, 59-60, instr. commun, 60-62; asst. prof. SPEECH & ENG, Edinboro State Col, 62-64, assoc. prof, 64-68, prof, 68-69; East Stroudsburg State Col, 69-70; CHMN. DEPT, NORTH ADAMS STATE COL, 70- Creative Educ. Found. Int. Soc. Gen. Semantics; Col. Eng. Asn; Int. Commun. Asn; Soc. Gen. Systs. Res; World Future Soc. Semantics; general systems; creativity. Publ: Co-auth, Guidelines to world literature: the ancient world, Letter, 65 & 66; Coping with increasing complexity, Gordon & Breach, 74; auth, Psyche as fact territory: epistemological implications of a Jungian psychology, Gen. Semantics Bull, 63; Intrapersonal communication in a Jungian perspective, J. Commun, 65; The extensional world of Francois Rabelais, In: Communication: general semantics perspectives, Spartan, 70. Add: Dept. of English & Speech, North Adams State College, Church St, North Adams, MA 01247.

WASHINGTON, MARY ALDRIDGE, b. Lubbock, Tex, Sept. 21, 33; m. 64. ENGLISH LITERATURE. B.A, Univ. Tex, 56; M.A, Univ. Mo, 62, Ph.D. (Eng. lit), 69. Instr. Eng, Univ. Mo, 62-69; ED, UTAH STATE UNIV. PRESS, 69- MLA; Renaissance Soc. Am. Printing; Renaissance. Publ: Bibliography of Sir Philip Sidney, Univ. Mo, 71; Bibliography of western manuscripts in Merrill Library, Utah State Univ, 72. Add: Utah State University Press, UMC 05, Logan, UT 84322.

WASILIFSKY, ADOLPH M, b. Baltimore, Md, July 8, 06; m. 33; c. 3. ENGLISH. A.B, Loyola Col, 28; fel, Georgetown Univ, 28-29, M.A, 29; Ph.D, Cornell Univ, 35; summers, Laval Univ, 54-55. Instr. Eng, St. Norbert Col, 29-31; speech, Cath. Univ. Am, 31-35; asst. prof. ENG, Univ. Detroit, 35-36; prof, St. Joseph Col.(Md), 36-71, chmn. dept, 36-68; lectr, Univ. Md, 71-73; RETIRED. Lectr. Eng. & speech, Mt. St. Mary's Col.(Md), 36-68; Ford Found. grant. stud. Chinese lit. in transl. & Chinese cult, summers, 62, 63, 66-67. MLA; Col. Eng. Asn. Comparative literature, especially 16th, 17th and 19th centuries. Publ: The talking voice. Add: Rte. 1, Box 31, Emmitsburg, MD 21727.

WASSER, HENRY, b. Pittsburgh, Pa, Apr. 13, 19; m. 42; c. 2. ENGLISH. B.A. & M.A, Ohio State Univ, 40; Ph.D.(Eng. & comp. lit), Columbia Univ, 51. Teaching fel. Eng, George Washington Univ, 40-43; instr, Univ. Akron, 43-44; N.Y. Univ, 45-46; tutor, City Col. New York, 46-52, instr, 52-55, asst. prof, 55-61, assoc. prof, 61-66; prof. Eng. & dean fac, Richmond Col. (N.Y), 66-73; PROF. ENG. & ACAD. V.PRES, CALIF. STATE UNIV, SACRAMENTO, 73- Fulbright prof, Univ. Salonika, 55-56 & Univ. Oslo, 62-64; dir, Am. Inst. Univ. Oslo, 63-64; sem. assoc, univ. sem. in Am. stud, Columbia Univ, 61-69, sem. higher educ, 69-; Am-Scand. Found. Thord-Gray award, 71 & 72; 2nd v.pres, Asn. Upper Level Cols. & Univs, 71-72; vis. prof. Am. stud, Univ. Sussex, spring 72; Ger. Acad. Exchange Serv. award, 73. Melville Soc. Am.(historian, 69-); MLA; Am. Stud. Asn.(mem. exec. count, 68-). Henry Adams and the Adams family; post-Civil War American literature and thought; higher education. Publ: The scientific thought of Henry Adams, Nicolaides, Greece, 56; co-ed, Americana Norvegica: Norwegian contributions to American studies, Univ. Pa, 66; Power centers in Swedish universities, Educ. Forum, 1/73; Higher education planning in Sweden and Denmark, Univ. Quart, 4/73; An American university and universal higher education, Higher Educ, 5/73; plus others. Add: Office of the Academic Vice-President, California State University, Sacramento, 6000 J St, Sacramento, CA 95819.

WASSERMAN, GEORGE RUSSELL, b. Pittsburgh, Pa, June 30, 27; m. 53; c. 1. ENGLISH LITERATURE. B.A, Univ. Pittsburgh, 51, M.A, 53; Ph.D, Univ. Mich, 58. Assoc. prof. ENG. LIT, RUSSELL SAGE COL, 58-71, PROF, 71- MLA. Dryden; restoration English literature; literary criticism. Publ: John Dryden, Twayne, 64; The domestic metaphor in Astraea Redux, Eng. Lang. Notes, III: 106-111; The irony of John Crowe Ransom, In: John Crowe Ransom: critical essays, La. State Univ, 68; The argument and imagery of Hudibras, Part I, SEL, XIII: 405-421; plus others. Add: Dept. of English, Russell Sage College, Troy, NY 12180.

WASSERMAN, JERRY STEVEN, b. Cincinnati, Ohio, Nov. 2, 45. ENGLISH & COMPARATIVE LITERATURE. B.A, Adelphi Univ, 67; M.A, Univ. Chicago, 68; NDEA fel, Cornell Univ, 69-72, Ph.D.(Eng), 72. Instr. ENG, Ill. State

Univ, 68-69; ASST. PROF, UNIV. B.C, 72- Can. Asn. Univ. Teachers; Philol. Asn. Pac. Coast; Am. Lit. Asn. Twentieth century literature; the novel; dramatic literature. Publ: Ed, The grand inquisitor, C.E. Merrill, 70; auth, St. Mawr and the search for community, Mosaic, winter 72; The word as object: the Rabelaisian novel, Novel, (in press). Add: Dept. of English, University of British Columbia, Vancouver 8, B.C, Can.

WASSERMAN, RACHAEL CHAIT, b. Montreal, P.Q, June 25, 09; m. 33; c. 1. ENGLISH LANGUAGE & LITERATURE. B.A, McGill Univ, 29, M.A, 30; A.M, Radcliffe Col, 31; Ph.D.(Eng), Cornell Univ, 43. From asst. prof. to prof. Eng, SIR GEORGE WILLIAMS UNIV, 43-48, PROF. ENG. & HUMANITIES, 48- Fel. World Acad. Art & Sci; Humanities Asn. Can. Anglo-Saxon; Middle English; Chaucer. Add: Dept. of English Language & Literature, Sir George Williams University, 1455 de Maisonneuve Blvd. W, Montreal, P.Q, 107, Can.

WASSERSTROM, WILLIAM, b. Brooklyn, N.Y, Oct. 14, 22; m. 44; c. 3. ENGLISH. A.B, Bucknell Univ, 46; A.M, Columbia Univ, 47, Ph.D, 51. Instr. Eng, Adelphi Col, 51-52; asst. prof. Eng. lit, Swarthmore Col, 52-54; ENG, Univ. Rochester, 54-60; PROF, SYRACUSE UNIV, 60- Am. Philos. Soc. grant, 58; vis. prof, Cornell Univ, summer 65; Fulbright prof. Am. lit, Univs. Bologna & Pisa, 65-66; NATO vis. prof. Am. lit, Univ. Venice, 71; mem. ed, bd, Lit. & Psychol, 60-; Hartford Stud. Lit, 68- U.S.A.A.F, 43-46. MLA; Am. Stud. Asn. Modern American literature; modern European literature; literature and psychology. Publ: Heiress of all the ages: sex and sentiment in the genteel tradition, 59 & Van Wyck Brooks, 68, Univ. Minn; A dial miscellany, 63, The time of the dial, 63 & Civil liberties and the arts: selections from Twice a year 1938-1948, 64, Syracuse Univ; The modern short novel, Holt, 65; The genius of American fiction, Allyn & Bacon, 71; The legacy of Van Wyck Brooks, South. Ill. Univ, 71; Fitzgerald, Columbia Univ. Forum, 65; Hemingway, the dial and Ernest Walsh, S.Atlantic Quart, spring 66; Cagey John Berryman, Centennial Rev, 7/68; The Hemingway problem, Va. Quart. Rev, 69; plus others. Add: 308 Hall of Languages, Syracuse University, Syracuse, NY 13210.

WASSON, JOHN M, b. Thayer, Mo, Feb. 23, 28; m. 49; c. 4. ENGLISH LITERATURE. A.B, Cent. Methodist Col, 50; M.A, Univ. Mo, 52; univ. honors fel, Stanford Univ, 53, Ph.D, 59. Asst. prof. Eng. lit, Wash. State Univ, 57-62; assoc. prof. Eng. & humanities, Parsons Col, 62-63; asst. prof. ENG. LIT, WASH. STATE UNIV, 63-64, assoc. prof, 64-68, PROF, 68- Fel, Inst. Renaissance Stud, 63. U.S.A, 46-48, 50-51. MLA; Malone Soc; Renaissance Soc. Am; Int. Shakespeare Asn. Medieval drama; Renaissance drama; Shakespeare. Publ: Subject and structure, Little, 63, 66, 70, rev. ed, 72; In defense of King Henry VIII, Res. Stud, 64; Measure for measure: a text for court performance, Shakespeare Quart, 70; Interpolations in Everyman, Theatre Notebook, 72; plus others. Add: Dept. of English, Washington State University, Pullman, WA 99163.

WASSON, RICHARD HOWARD, b. Chicago, Ill, Oct. 7, 30; m. 54; c. 1. ENGLISH. B.A, Cornell Col, 52; M.A, Univ. Iowa, 55; Knapp fel. & Ph.D.(Eng), Univ. Wis, 61. Instr. ENG, Univ. Ill, Urbana, 61-64, asst. prof, 64-68, assoc. prof, 68-70; LIVINGSTON COL, RUTGERS UNIV, 70-71, PROF, 71- Am. Counc. Learned Soc. fel, summer 63; Univ. Ill. summer fels, 63 & 66. MLA; AAUP. Modern literature; novel; rhetoric of class in literature. Publ: Co-auth, Marshall McLuhan and D.H. Lawrence, Depot Press, 71; auth, Hesse's Steppenwoolf, J. Pop. Cult, summer 70; Marshall McLuhamn, Mass. Rev, 71; co-ed, New Marxist criticism, J. Col. Eng, 11/73; plus five others. Add: Dept. of English, Livingston College, Rutgers University, New Brunswick, NJ 08904.

WASWO, RICHARD ARTHUR, b. Washington, D.C, Oct. 26, 39; m. 64. ENGLISH, RENAISSANCE STUDIES. A.B, Stanford Univ, 61; A.M, Harvard, 62, Ph.D.(Eng), 70. Instr. Eng. & humanities, San Francisco State Col, 64-65; ASST. PROF. ENG, San Jose State Col, 67-70; UNIV. VA, 70- MLA; S.Atlantic Mod. Lang. Asn; Renaissance Soc. Am; Southeast. Renaissance Conf. Renaissance literature and theology; aesthetic and literary theory. Publ: The fatal mirror: themes and techniques in the poetry of Fulke Greville, Univ. Va, 72; Damnation, Protestant style: Macbeth, Faustus, and Christian tragedy, J. Medieval & Renaissance Stud, spring 74. Add: Dept. of English, University of Virginia, Charlottesville, VA 22901.

WATERMAN, ARTHUR E, b. Niagara Falls, N.Y, Mar. 18, 26; m. 48; c. 5. AMERICAN LITERATURE. A.B, Allegheny Col, 49; M.A, Univ. Wis, 50, Ph.D, 56. Instr. ENG, Univ. Wis, Manitowoc, 55-56; asst. prof, Cent. Mich. Univ, 56-60; assoc. prof, 60-62; GA. STATE UNIV, 62-66, PROF, 66- V.pres, Mich. Counc. Teachers Eng, 61-62. U.S.N.R, 43-46. MLA; Col. Eng. Asn; NCTE. American drama; modern American fiction since World War II, Susan Glaspell. Publ: Susan Glaspell, Twayne, 66; A chronology of American literary history, C.E. Merrill, 70; From Iowa to Greece: George Cram Cook, Quart. J. Speech, 2/59; The plays of D.H. Lawrence, Mod. Drama, 2/60; The novels of Wright Morris, Critique, winter 61. Add: Dept. of English, Georgia State University, Atlanta, GA 30303.

WATERMAN, MARGARET, b. Athol, Mass, Oct. 6, 09. ENGLISH. A.B, Mt. Holyoke Col, 31; A.M, Univ. Wis, 33, Ph.D, 42. Asst. Eng, Univ. Wis, 31-38, 39, 40-41; acting instr, Wis. State Teachers Col, Platteville, 38-39; Univ. Colo, 39-40; instr, Hiram Col, 41-42; asst. prof, Lake Forest Col, 42-44; editorial asst, Dictionary of Americanisms, Univ. Chicago Press, 44-46; asst. prof. ENG, Case West. Reserve Univ, 46-65, ASSOC. PROF, 65-73; UNIV. WIS-MADISON, 73- Mem. staff, Dictionary Am. Regional Eng, 68-73; assoc. ed, 73- American language. Publ: Themecraft, Howard Allen, 59, 62; co-auth, Papa Gorski, Harcourt, 69. Add: Dept. of English, University of Wisconsin-Madison, Madison, WI 53706.

WATERS, CHARLES McMANUS, b. Clarksville, Tenn, May 11, 20; m. 49; c. 2. ENGLISH. B.S, Austin Peay State Col, 49; M.A, Univ. Tenn, 52. Instr. jour, AUSTIN PEAY STATE UNIV, 49-54, asst. prof. ENG, 54-62, ASSOC. PROF, 62-, dir. pub. relat, 49-60. U.S.A, 42-45, Tech. Sgt. American literature; Edgar Allan Poe. Add: Route 7, Clarksville, TN 37040.

WATERS, D. DOUGLAS, b. Ida, La, May 1, 29; m. 49. ENGLISH. B.A, David Lipscomb Col, 54; M.A, Vanderbilt Univ, 55, teaching fel, 58-59, Ph.D, 60. Asst. prof. ENG, George Pepperdine Col, 59-60; assoc. prof,

Northeast Mo. State Col, 60-62, PROF, 62-68; UNIV. WIS-EAU CLAIRE, 68- Vis. asst. prof, Univ. South. Calif, summer 60. Edmund Spenser; Robert Browning; Shakespeare. Publ: Duessa as theological satire, Univ. Mo, 70; Errour's den and Archimago's hermitage: symbolic lust and symbolic witchcraft, ELH, 9/66; Duessa and Orgoglio: Red Crosse's spiritual fornication, Renaissance Quart, summer 67. Add: Dept. of English, University of Wisconsin-Eau Claire, Eau Claire, WI 54701.

WATERS, LEONARD A, S.J, b. Jackson, Nebr, Feb. 24, 08. ENGLISH LITERATURE. A.B, St. Louis Univ, 34, M.A, 35; Ph.D.(Eng), Univ. Mich, 48. Asst. prof. Eng. lit, St. Louis Univ, 48-52, assoc. prof, 52-56; Marquette Univ, 56-58; Creighton Univ, 58-60; Eng, Jesuit Col, Marquette Univ, 60-73; SPEC. ASST. TO PRES, CREIGHTON UNIV, 73- Res. fel, Yale, 67; mem. bd. gov, Creighton Univ, 68. MLA; NCTE. Aesthetics; literary criticism; Romanticism. Add: Creighton University, 2500 California, Omaha, NE 68178.

WATERS, LOUIS ADDISON, JR, b. Syracuse, N.Y, Sept. 3, 18; m. 62; c. 2. COMPARATIVE LITERATURE. A.B, Harvard, 40; cert, Univ. Colo, 45; A.M, Lehigh Univ, 46; Ph.D, Columbia Univ, 61. Instr. Eng, Lehigh Univ, 40-41; asst. prof. Eng. & Russ, Univ. Fla, 49-50; Bradley Univ, 54-55; Eng, Ore. State Univ, 55-58; from asst. prof. to PROF. ENG. & HUMANITIES, SAN JOSE STATE UNIV, 58- Coord. lang. training, Nat. Security Agency, 51-52. U.S.N.R, 41-46, Comdr. MLA; Keats-Shelley Asn. History of ideas; classical and oriental literature; aesthetics. Publ: The idea of nature in poetry of William Blake, Univ. Microfilms, 61; plus others. Add: Dept. of English, San Jose State University, 125 S. Seventh St, San Jose, CA 95192.

WATERS, WALTER KENNETH, JR, b. Kansas City, Mo, Apr. 27, 27; m. 56; c. 2. THEATRE, SPEECH. A.B, Park Col, 50; M.A, Stanford Univ, 51, Ph.D.(theatre), 64; Ind. Univ, summer 56. Instr. Eng, Doane Col, 52-53; speech & drama, Dillard Univ, 54-57; asst. prof. theatre, Portland State Col, 58-61; dir. theatre & cult. affairs, Monticello Col, 62-65; assoc. prof. & dir. THEATRE, STEPHEN F. AUSTIN STATE UNIV, 65-72, PROF, 72- Stage dir, New Savoy Opera Co, 59-62; Field Hotaling fel, Stanford Univ, 54; chmn. comt. on ethics, Nat. Asn. Schs. Theatre, 71- Portland Ore. Arts Comn. Citation for Contribution to the Arts, 61. U.S.N. Am. Educ. Theatre Asn; Speech Commun. Asn. History of stage lighting; American theatre, especially the stock company; interrelationship of the fine arts. Add: Dept. of Theatre, Stephen F. Austin State University, Nacogdoches, TX 75961.

WATERSTON, ELIZABETH, b. Montreal, P.Q, Apr. 18, 22; m. 49; c. 5. ENGLISH & CANADIAN LITERATURE. B.A, Univ. Toronto, 44, Ph.D.(Eng), 50; M.A, Bryn Mawr Col, 45. Lectr. ENG, Sir George Williams Univ, 45-48; teaching asst, Univ. Toronto, 48-50; asst. prof, Sir George Williams Univ, 50-56, acting chmn, 56-58; asst. prof, Univ. West. Ont, 58-66; assoc. prof, UNIV. GUELPH, 66-71, PROF, 71-, CHMN. DEPT, 74- Mem. ed. bd, Can. Stud. in Eng. Humanities Asn. Can; Asn. Can. Univ. Teachers Eng; Asn. Can. Stud. U.S; Can. Asn. Am. Stud; Can. Asn. Commonwealth Lang. & Lit. Stud; Asn. Stud. Can. & Que. Lit. Nineteenth century Canadian literature; travel books; Scottish studies. Publ: Pioneers in agriculture, Clark, Irwin, 54; co-auth, Composition for Canadian universities, Macmillan, 64; auth, Survey: a short history of Canadian literature, Methuen, 73; Irving Layton: apocalypse in Montreal, Can. Lit, 70; seven biographies, In: Dictionary of Canadian biography, Univ. Toronto, 71-73; Galt, Scott, Cooper: frontiers of Canadian realism, J. Can. Fiction, 72; plus others. Add: Dept. of English, University of Guelph, Guelph, Ont, Can.

WATKINS, CHARLOTTE CRAWFORD, b. New Haven, Conn, Apr. 21, 13; m. 51. ENGLISH. A.B, Wellesley Col, 33; Ph.D.(Eng), Yale, 37. Instr. ENG, Dillard Univ, 37-40, assoc. prof, 40-43; assoc. prof, Morgan State Col, 43-45, prof, 45-48, head dept, 43-48; PROF, HOWARD UNIV, 48- MLA; Ling. Soc. Am; Col. Eng. Asn; NCTE; AAUP; Res. Soc. Victorian Periodicals; Browning Inst. Victorian literature; 18th century literature; contemporary English literature. Publ: What was Pope's debt to Edward Young?, J. Eng. Lit. Hist; The Abstruser themes of Browning's Fifine at the fair, PMLA, 59; Browning's Red cotton night-cap country and Carlyle, Victorian Stud, 6/64. Add: 1311 Delaware Ave. S.W, Washington, DC 20024.

WATKINS, EVAN PAUL, b. Wichita, Kans, Oct. 25, 46; m. 68; c. 1. ENGLISH. B.A, Univ. Kans, 68; Ph.D.(Eng), Univ. Iowa, 72. ASST. PROF. ENG, MICH. STATE UNIV, 72- MLA. Literary criticism; contemporary British and American literature; 20th century American literature. Add: Dept. of English, Morrill Hall, Michigan State University, East Lansing, MI 48824.

WATKINS, FLOYD C, b. Cherokee Co, Ga, Apr. 19, 20; m. 42; c. 3. ENGLISH. B.S, Ga. South. Col, 46; A.M, Emory Univ, 47; Ph.D, Vanderbilt Univ, 52. Teaching fel, Vanderbilt Univ, 47-49; instr. ENG, EMORY UNIV, 49-52, asst. prof, 52-57, assoc. prof, 57-61, PROF, 61- Guggenheim fel, 62-63. U.S.A.A.F, 42-45. MLA; S.Atlantic Mod. Lang. Asn; Soc. Stud. South. Lit. Southern and modern literature. Publ: Thomas Wolfe's characters, Univ. Okla; co-auth, Old times in the Faulkner country, Univ. N.C; co-ed, The literature of the South, Scott; co-auth, Yesterday in the hills, Quadrangle, 63; co-ed, Writer to writer, Houghton, 66; auth, The death of art, Univ. Ga, 70; The flesh and the word, Vanderbilt Univ, 71. Add: 519 Durand Dr. N.E, Atlanta, GA 30307.

WATKINS, JOHN PIERCE, b. Brownsville, Pa, Mar. 19, 31; m. 57; c. 2. ENGLISH. B.A, Calif. State Col.(Pa), 53; M.A, W.Va. Univ, 53; Danforth fel, Univ. Pittsburgh, Ph.D.(Eng), 64. Assoc. prof. ENG, CALIFORNIA STATE COL.(PA), 57-64, PROF, 64-, CHMN. DEPT, 66- Danforth teaching fel, 61. MLA; Mediaeval Acad. Am; Int. Arthurian Soc. Old and Middle English literature. Add: Dept. of English, California State College, California, PA 15419.

WATKINS, LLOYD I, b. Cape Girardeau, Mo, Aug. 29, 28; m. 49; c. 3. SPEECH. B.S, Southeast Mo. State Col, 49; M.S, Univ. Wis, 51, fel, 53-54, Ph.D.(speech), 54. Instr. high sch, Mo, 48-50; asst. prof. Eng. & speech, Moorhead State Col, 54-56; assoc. prof. speech, Ohio Univ, 56-64, asst. to acad. v.pres, 64-66; exec. v.pres, Idaho State Univ, 66-69; pres, Iowa Asn. Private Cols. & Univs, 69-73; PRES, W.TEX. STATE UNIV, 73- Baker

Fund res. grant, Ohio Univ, summer 63. Nat. Asn. Col. & Univ. Summer Sessions (pres, 65-66); Speech Commun. Asn. Asn. Higher Educ. American political rhetoric; French revolutionary oratory; higher education administration. Publ: Affiliating the advanced public speaking course with a charitable organization, Speech Teacher, 1/63; Lord Brougham's comments on the education of an orator, West. Speech, 5/65; co-auth, Rhetoric as the logic of the behavioral sciences, Quart. J. Speech, 12/65. Add: Office of the President, West Texas State University, Canyon, TX 79016.

WATSON, ALAN M, b. Santa Fe, N.Mex, Oct. 6, 40; m. 64; c. 1. ENGLISH LITERATURE & ART HISTORY. A.B, Dartmouth Col, 62; Ecole Practique des Hautes Etudes, Paris, 64; M.A, Univ. N.Mex, 65, Ph.D.(Eng), 69; Univ. London, 66-68. ASST. PROF. ENG, MONT. STATE UNIV, 68- MLA; Rocky Mt. Mod. Lang. Asn; Johnson Soc. Northwest. William Blake; art and literature in the late 18th century; Shakespeare. Publ: William Blake's illustrated verse, Blake Stud, 69; Blake's illustrations to the poems of Gray, Art Bull, 73; Blake's frontispiece to the Visions of the daughters of Albion, Trans. Samuel Johnson Soc, 74. Add: Dept. of English, Montana State University, Bozeman, MT 59715.

WATSON, BARBARA BELLOW, b. Philadelphia, Pa; m. 46; c. 3. ENGLISH. A.B, Univ. Wis, 42; M.A, Columbia Univ, 44, Ph.D.(Eng), 63. Instr. ENG, South. Conn. State Col, 60-61; Adelphi Univ, 61-63; asst. prof, CITY COL. NEW YORK, 63-69, assoc. prof, 70-73, PROF, 74-, DIR, WOMEN'S STUDIES PROG, 72- MLA; Shaw Soc. Am; Col. Eng. Asn. Bernard Shaw; modern British and American poetry; women studies. Publ: A Shavian guide to the intelligent woman, Chatto & Windus, 64, Norton 64 & 72; The dangers of security: E.E. Cummings' revolt against the future, Kenyon Rev, autumn 56; Socialism for millionaires: Major Barbara, Mod. Drama, 12/68; The new woman and the new comedy, Shaw Rev, winter 73. Add: Dept. of English, City College of New York, 138th St. & Convent Ave, New York, NY 10031.

WATSON, CHARLES NELLES, JR, b. Brooklyn, N.Y, Sept. 14, 39; m. 65; c. 2. AMERICAN LITERATURE. A.B, Princeton, 61; M.A, Duke Univ, 64, Ph.D.(Eng), 69. ASST. PROF. ENG, Wash. State Univ, 68-70; SYRACUSE UNIV, 70- MLA (Am. Lit. Group). Nineteenth century American fiction. Publ: Melville and the theme of Timonism, Am. Lit, 11/72; The estrangement of Hawthorne and Melville, New Eng. Quart, 9/73. Add: Dept. of English, Syracuse University, Syracuse, NY 13210.

WATSON, CHARLES SULLIVAN, b. Anderson, S.C, May 18, 31; m. 67. ENGLISH. A.B, Duke Univ, 53; M.A, Columbia Univ, 58; Ph.D.(Eng), Vanderbilt Univ, 66. Instr. ENG, Ga. Inst. Technol, 58-61; asst. prof, UNIV. ALA, 66-70, ASSOC. PROF, 70- U.S.A, 53-56. MLA. American drama and fiction; William Gilmore Simms. Publ: Jeffersonian republicanism in William Ioor's Independence, the first play of South Carolina, S.C, Hist. Mag, 7/68; Eighteenth and nineteenth century drama, In: Bibliographical checklist of southern literature, La. State Univ, 69; A new approach to Simms: imagery and meaning in The Yemassee, Miss. Quart, spring 73; plus others. Add: Dept. of English, University of Alabama, Box 3697, University, AL 35486.

WATSON, CRESAP SHAW, b. Ft. Worth, Tex, Oct. 28, 28; m. 48; c. 3. ENGLISH. B.A, Brown Univ, 49; Ph.D.(Eng), Univ. Dublin, Ireland, 53. Instr, Eng, La. State Univ, Baton Rouge, 52-55, asst. prof, 55-60; assoc. prof. & chmn. dept. ENG. & SPEECH, UNIV. NEW ORLEANS, 60-72, PROF, 72- Ed, La. Eng. J, 60- NCTE; Col. Eng. Asn; S.Cent. Mod. Lang. Asn. Anglo-Irish literature; modern fiction and drama; the novel. Publ: Realism, determinism and symmetry in The real Charlotte, Hermathena, Dublin; What do you teach them in high school? Eng. J; plus others. Add: Dept. of English, University of New Orleans, New Orleans, LA 70122.

WATSON, EDWARD ANTHONY, b. Jamaica, West Indies, Oct. 29, 36; m. 63; c. 2. ENGLISH LITERATURE. B.A, Howard Univ, 61; M.A, Univ. Chicago, 62; Ph.D.(Eng), Univ. Toronto, 67. Lectr. Eng, Univ. Ill, Chicago, 62-63; Atkinson Col, York Univ, 65-66; asst. prof, UNIV. WINDSOR, 66-70, ASSOC. PROF. ENG. LIT, 70- Can. Counc. res. grant, 68 & 71; vis. prof, Atkinson Col, York Univ, summer 69; Wayne State Univ, 69-70. Can. Asn. Univ. Teachers; Asn. Can. Univ. Teachers Eng. Contemporary critical theory; 18th century criticism; theories of the imagination. Publ: Incongruity without laugher: Kenneth Burke's theory of the grotesque, Univ. Windsor Rev, spring 69; The university and the destructive element in the liberal spirit, Dalhousie Rev, autumn 70; Bessie's blues, New Lett, winter 71. Add: Dept. of English, University of Windsor, Windsor, Ont. N9B 3P4, Can.

WATSON, HAROLD FRANCIS, b. Milford, Pa, Apr. 2, 95; m. 24, 69; c. 2. ENGLISH LITERATURE. A.B, N.Y. Univ, 18, A.M, 20; Ph.D, Columbia Univ, 31; hon. Litt.D, Simpson Col, 73. Instr. Eng, N.Y. Univ, 18-19; Hedding Col, 19-21; asst. prof, Univ. Maine, 22-24; prof. & head dept, SIMPSON COL, 24-60, chmn. div. humanities, 37-60, acting dean col, 58-59, EMER. PROF. ENG, 60- MLA. Elizabethan literature; poetry of the romantic period; sea novels of the 19th century. Publ: Co-auth, Writing for freshman, 30 & Adventures in contemporary reading, 32; The sailor in English fiction and drama, 1550-1800, 31; Coasts of treasure island, Naylor, 69; A note on Watsonian heraldry, 9/67 & An old sea dog in Baker St, 3/68, Baker St. J. Add: 518 E. Ash St, Fayetteville, AR 72701.

WATSON, MELVIN RAY, b. Lynchburg, Va, May 31, 14. ENGLISH. A.B, Univ. Va, 35; A.M, La. State Univ, 38; Ph.D, John Hopkins Univ, 44. Asst. prof. Eng. lit, Queens Col.(N.C), 41-42; Mary Wash. Col, 45-46; prof. ENG, La. State Univ, 46-64; PROF, CHAPMAN COL, 64-, CHMN. DIV. HUMANITIES, 69-, chmn. dept. Eng, 64-69. MLA; Philol. Asn. Pac. Coast; Mod. Humanities Res. Asn, Gt. Brit. Literature of the neo-classical period; Keats and Shelley; Brontes. Publ: Magazine serials and the essay tradition; Critical essays on Keats and Shelley; Contribution to fiction of the Brontes. Add: Div. of Humanities, Chapman College, Orange, CA 92666.

WATSON, RICHARD ALAN, b. Hollywood, Calif, Feb. 2, 36; Can. citizen; m. 59. ENGLISH, COMMUNICATIONS. B.A, Univ. B.C, 58; Ph.D.(Eng), Univ. Wash, 68. Instr. ENG, Calif. State Col. Los Angeles, 63-65, asst. prof, 65-66; CHAPMAN COL, 66-72, ASSOC. PROF, 72- Publ: Models of the future, 74 & In: Prisms, 74, Harper; Inside-out ceremonies: a trope from Quantities and The damages, Minn. Rev, 10/68; co-auth, Experimental analysis of physiques as social stimuli, Perceptual & Motor Skills, 10/68 & Facilitative effects of shock and sensory deprivation on bar-pressing, Psychonomic Sci, 12/68. Add: Dept. of English, Chapman College, 333 N. Glassel St, Orange, CA 92666.

WATSON, ROBERT WINTHROP, b. Passaic, N.J, Dec. 26, 25; m. 52; c. 2. ENGLISH. B.A, Williams Col, 46; Swiss-Am. Exchange fel, Univ. Zurich, 46-47; M.A, Johns Hopkins Univ, 50, Ph.D.(Eng), 55. Instr. ENG, Williams Col, 46, 47-48, 52-53; Johns Hopkins Univ, 50-52; UNIV. N.C, GREENSBORO, 53-55, asst. prof, 55-59, assoc. prof, 59-63, PROF, 63- Dir, Assoc. Writing Prog, 67-72; vis. prof, Calif. State Univ, Northridge, 68-69. U.S.N, 43-45. MLA. Modern poetry and literature; poetics; the novel. Publ: A paper horse and other poems, 62, Advantages of dark (poems), 66, Christmas at Las Vegas (poems), 71 & Selected poems, 74, Atheneum; Three sides of the mirror (novel), Putnam, 66. Add: 527 Highland Ave, Greensboro, NC 27403.

WATSON, SARA RUTH, b. East Cleveland, Ohio, Jan. 7, 07. ENGLISH. A.B, West. Reserve Univ, 28, A.M, 29, Ph.D, 32. Res. assoc. West. Reserve Univ, 32-39; assoc. prof. ENG, CLEVELAND STATE UNIV, 39-40, prof, 40-70, EMER. PROF, 70- Spec. lectr, Cleveland Mus. Art, 32. Hist. & Heritage Award, Am. Soc. Civil Engineers, 73. Soc. Technol. & Cult; MLA; Mod. Humanities Res. Asn, Gr. Brit; Milton Soc. Am; Renaissance Soc. Am; Viola da Gamba Soc. Am. English Renaissance; history of civil engineering; bridges in history and legend. Publ: Co-auth, Bridges in history and legend, Jansen, 36, Bridges and their builders, Putnam, 41, Dover, 57 & Famous engineers, Dodd, 50; auth, V.Sackville-West, Twayne, 72; The engineer and the climate of opinion, J. Engineering Educ, 57; George Moore and the Dolmetsches, 63 & Robert Louis Stevenson and his family of engineers, 67, Eng. Lit. in Transition; plus others. Add: 3570 Glen Allen Dr, Cleveland Heights, OH 44121.

WATSON, THOMAS L, b. Dallas, Tex, May 24, 25. ENGLISH. B.A, Univ. Tex, 45, M.A, 49, Ph.D.(Eng), 58. Instr. ENG, Texas A&M Col, 46-48; Univ. Tex, 55-58; asst. prof, LA. STATE UNIV, 60-65, ASSOC. PROF, 65- Fulbright fel, Univ. Paris, 57-58; Fulbright lectr. Am. Lit, Univ. Aix Marseilles, 58-59. U.S.A.F, 51-53, 1st Lt. S.Cent. Mod. Lang. Asn; MLA. Twentieth century English poetry and fiction; 19th century French poetry. Publ: The French reputation of W.B. Yeats, Comp. Lit, summer 60; The detractor-backbiter: Iago and the tradition, Tex. Stud, winter 64; The ethics of feasting: Dickens' use of Agape, In: Essays in honor of E.L. Marilla, La. State Univ, 70; plus others. Add: Dept. of English, Louisiana State University, Baton Rouge, LA 70803.

WATSON, THOMAS STONEMAN, b. Cleveland, Ohio, May 2, 24; m. 50; c. 2. THEATRE. B.A, West. Reserve Univ, 48, M.A, 55, M.F.A, 61, res. grant, 62-63, Ph.D.(dramatic arts), 64. Scenic designer, Kalamazoo Civic Theatre, 50-54; instr. dramatic arts, Univ. Del, 55-60; lectr, West. Reserve Univ, 61-63; drama & speech, State Univ. N.Y. Buffalo, 63-64, asst. prof, 64-66; assoc. prof. dramatic arts & speech & chmn. dept, UNIV. DEL, 66-73, ASSOC. PROF. DRAMATIC ARTS, 73-, fac. fel, 68. Prod. mgr. & instr. dance educ, Conn. Col. Women, summers 52-63; theatre consult, Fine Arts Ctr, South. Methodist Univ, Sept. 64; Studio Arena Theatre, Buffalo, N.Y, Aug. 65; Park Sch, Baltimore, Md, 67-; chmn, Del. State Arts Counc, 68-69, chmn. performing arts comt, 70-; ed, Theatre Design & Technol, 72- Eng.C, U.S.A, 43-45, T/Sgt. Am. Theatre Asn; Speech Commun. Asn; Am. Soc. Theatre Res; U.S. Inst. Theatre Technol.(dir, 67-68). Theatre direction, design, and dance production; theatre architecture and architectural history; theatre history, especially 17th to 19th century English stage. Publ: Three theatres of Arch Lauterer, J. Am. Inst. Architects, 2/62; An ideal dance theatre, Dance Scope, winter 65; The dancer's space, Impulse, 67. Add: Dept. of Dramatic Arts, University of Delaware, Newark, DE 19711.

WATSON, WALLACE STEADMAN, b. Florence, S.C, July 8, 36; m. 58; c. 2. ENGLISH, HUMANITIES. B.A, Wofford Col, 58; M.A, Duke Univ, 60; Ph.D. (Eng), Ind. Univ, 66. Instr. Eng, Woman's Col, Univ. N.C, 60-62; teaching assoc, Ind. Univ, 62-66; ASST. PROF. Eng. & basic stud, Austin Col, 66-67; ENG, South. Methodist Univ, 67-70; PARK COL. (MO), 70-, CHMN. DEPT. COMMUN. & LIT, 73- Nat. Endowment for Humanities younger humanist stipend, summer 72. Conrad; Pound; Eliot. Add: Dept. of Literature, Park College, Kansas City, MO 64152.

WATT, DONALD J, b. Malden, Mass, Oct. 21, 38; m. 64; c. 1. ENGLISH. A.B, Boston Col, 60, M.A, 61; Harvard, 61-62; Ph.D.(Eng), Univ. Conn, 68. Asst. prof. ENG, STATE UNIV. N.Y. COL. GENESEO, 67-72, ASSOC. PROF, 72- State Univ. N.Y. Fac. summer fel, 68. U.S.A, 63-65, 1st Lt. MLA. Modern British literature; Aldous Huxley. Publ: Ed, The collected poetry of Aldous Huxley, Harper, 71; auth, Vision and symbol in Aldous Huxley's Island, Twentieth Century Lit, 10/68; G.E. Moore and the Bloomsbury Group, Eng. Lit. in Transition, 10/69; The criminal-victim pattern in Huxley's Point counter point, Stud. Novel, 3/71. Add: Dept. of English, Blake D, State University of New York College at Geneseo, Geneseo, NY 14454.

WATT, IAN PIERRE, b. Windermere, Eng, Mar. 9, 17; m. 47; c. 2. ENGLISH. B.A, St. John's Col, 38, M.A, 46, fel, 48-52; Commonwealth fel, Univ. Calif, Los Angeles & Harvard, 46-48. From asst. prof. to prof. Eng, Univ. Calif, Berkeley, 52-62; dean Eng. stud, Univ. E.Anglia, Eng, 62-64; PROF. ENG, STANFORD UNIV, 64-, chmn. dept, 68-71. Consult. ed. col. div, Bobbs-Merrill Co, 61-73; v.chancellor's distinguished visitor, Australian Nat. Univ, 66; fel, Am. Counc. Learned Soc, 66-67; fel, Ctr. Advan. Stud. Behav. Sci, 66-67; citizen's chair of lit, Univ. Hawaii, 68; vis. prof. Eng, Williams Col, 70-71; Guggenheim fel, 72-73; vis. lectr, Univ. Tours, Univ. Canterbury & Sorbonne. Brit. Army, 39-46, Lt. MLA; fel. Am. Acad. Arts & Sci. Modern myths; 18th century literature; Joseph Conrad. Publ: Rise of the novel, Univ. Calif. & Chatto & Windus, 57; ed, Jane Austen: a collection of critical essays, Prentice-Hall, 63 & Tristram Shandy, Houghton, 65; auth, The English novel: Scott to Hardy, Goldentree Bibliographies, Appleton, 68; The Augustan background, Fawcett, 68; ed, The Victorian novel: modern essays in criticism, Oxford Univ, 71 & Conrad's The secret agent: a casebook, Macmillan, 73; Joseph Conrad: alienation and commitment, In: The English mind, Cambridge, 64; Conrad, James and Chance, In: Imagined worlds, London, 68, The Bridge over the River Kwai as myth, Berkshire Rev, 71; plus others. Add: Dept. of English, Stanford University, Stanford, CA 94305.

WATT, WILLIAM WHYTE, b. Watertown, Wis, Nov. 18, 12; m. 37; c. 4. ENGLISH. A.B, Harvard, 32, A.M, 33; Ph.D, Yale, 35. Instr. ENG, LAFAYETTE COL, 35-38, asst. prof, 38-43, assoc. prof, 43-47, PROF. & HEAD DEPT, 47- U.S.N.R, 44-46, Lt. Col. Eng. Asn; MLA. English literature, especially Victorian; composition. Publ: Shilling shockers of the Gothic school, Harvard, 32; co-ed, Biography: varieties and parallels, 41 & English literature and its backgrounds, 49, ed, Dickens' Hard times, 58, auth, One Man's meter, 59, ed, A comparative reader, 61 & auth, An American rhetoric, 4th ed, 70, Holt; co-auth, A dictionary of English literature, Barnes & Noble, 45; ed, E.B. White's Second tree from the corner, 62 & co-ed, An E.B. White reader, 66, Harper; auth, A short guide to English usage, World Publ, 67. Add: Dept. of English, Lafayette College, Easton, PA 18042.

WATTERS, REGINALD EYRE, b. Toronto, Ont, Apr. 15, 12; m. 44; c. 3. AMERICAN & CANADIAN LITERATURES. B.A, Univ. Toronto, 35, M.A, 37; Univ. Calif, 37-38; Ph.D, Univ. Wis, 41. Instr, Univ. Wash, 41-44; Ind. Univ, 44-46; assoc. prof, Eng, Univ. B.C, 46-54; prof, 54-61; PROF. ENG. & HEAD DEPT, ROYAL MIL. COL. (ONT), 61-, acting dean of arts, 72-73. Vis. prof, Univ. Toronto, 49-50; mem, Humanities Res. Counc. Can; Can. Counc. sr. fel, Australia, 58-59; Australian Humanities Res. Counc. traveling lectr, 59; Can. Counc. sr. fel. for res. in Can. lit, 67-68. Can. Asn. Commonwealth Lit. & Lang. Stud; Asn. Can. Stud; Melville Soc. Am; Asn. Can. Univ. Teachers Eng; Humanities Asn. Can. Bibliography; humor; Australian literature. Publ: British Columbia, a centennial anthology, McClelland & Stewart, Toronto, 58; Check list of Canadian literature and background materials, 1628-1950, 59, rev. ed. (1628-1960), 72 & co-auth, On Canadian literature: 1806-1960, a check list, 66, Univ. Toronto; co-auth, The creative reader. Ronald. 2nd ed. 62 & Canadian anthology, Gage, Toronto, rev. ed, 66, 3rd ed, 74; auth, The meanings of the white whale, Univ. Toronto Quart, 1/51; A special tang: Stephen Leacock's Canadian humour, Can. Lit, summer 60; A quest for national identity: Canadian literature vis-a-vis the literatures of Great Britain and the United States, Proc. Third Cong. Int. Comp. Lit. Asn, Mouton, The Hague, 62. Add: Dept. of English, Royal Military College of Canada, Kingston, Ont. K7L 2W3, Can.

WATTS, ANN CHALMERS, b. Evanston, Ill, Apr. 14, 38; m. 62; c. 2. ENGLISH. B.A, Radcliffe Col, 59; Ph.D(Eng), Yale, 65. Asst. prof. ENG, Tufts Univ, 64-71; ASSOC. PROF, RUTGERS UNIV, NEWARK, 71- MLA; Mediaeval Acad. Am. Old English literature; Middle English literature; 19th century English and American literature. Publ: The lyre and the harp, Yale Univ, 69; Chaucerian selves, Chaucer Rev, 70; Amor Gloriae in Chaucer's House of fame, J. Medieval & Renaissance Stud, 73. Add: Dept. of English, Hill Hall, Rutgers University, 360 High St, Newark, NJ 07102.

WATTS, BILLIE DEAN, b. Winfield, Kans, June 27, 30; m. 65; c. 2. THEATRE. B.S, Kans State Teachers Col, 53, M.S, 56; Ph.D(theatre), Univ. Ore, 70. Instr. drama & speech, Argentine High Sch, 56-57; DRAMA, Black Hills Teachers Col, 57-59; S.Eugene High Sch, Ore, 61-62; asst. prof, Morehead State Univ, 64-67; Ore. State Univ, 67-69; ASSOC. PROF, ANGELO STATE UNIV, 69- U.S.N, 48-49 & 53-54. Am. Theatre Asn; Southwest Theatre Conf; U.S. Inst. Theatre Technol; Speech Commun. Asn. Theatre architecture and lighting. Publ: Staging the high school play, S.Dak. J. Speech, 5/59. Add: Dept. of Fine Arts, Angelo State University, San Angelo, TX 76901.

WATTS, CHARLES HENRY, II, b. New York, N.Y, Oct. 17, 26; m. 51; c. 3. AMERICAN LITERATURE. A.B, Brown Univ, 47, Ph.D.(Eng), 53; M.A, Columbia Univ, 48; Litt.D, Franklin Col, 65; LL.D, Dickinson Sch. Law, 68; hon. H.H.D, Alderson-Broaddus Col, 69. Instr. Eng, Brown Univ, 50-54, asst. prof, 54-57, assoc. prof, 57-62, prof, 62, dean col, 58-62; dir, Am. Counc. Educ, 62-64; PRES, BUCKNELL UNIV, 64- Mem. bd. examining chaplains, Episcopal Church, 70-; chmn, Pub. Comt. for Humanities, Pa, 72-; mem. bd. comnrs, Nat. Comn. on Accrediting, 72-; mem. adv. comt, Inst. Educ. Leadership, 73-; trustee, Riverdale Country Sch; inc. trustee, Episcopal Diocese of Harrisburg, Pa; dir, Peddie Sch, Hightstown, N.J, 71-; Pa. Power & Light Co, 71-; Beneficial Corp, Morristown, N.J; Pa. Comn. Independent Cols. & Univs. Educational administration. Publ: Thomas Holley Chivers: his literary career and his poetry, Univ. Ga; co-auth, The conscious voice, an anthology of American poetry, Lib. Arts; Complete works of Thomas Holley Chivers, Brown Univ, Vol. I, 57. Add: President's Office, Bucknell University, Lewisburg, PA 17837.

WATTS, JOHN RANSFORD, b. Boston, Mass, Feb. 9, 30; m. 51; c. 1. THEATRE ARTS. A.B, Boston Col, 50, M.Ed, 65; M.F.A, Yale, 53; Harvard, 57-58; Oxford, 73. Instr. speech & drama, Boston Col, 55-58; asst. prof. THEATRE ARTS, SCH. FINE & APPLIED ARTS, BOSTON UNIV, 58-68, PROF, 68-, CHMN. DEPT. THEATRE EDUC, 59-67, 72-, assoc. dir. univ. arts ctr, 63-64, asst. dean sch. fine & appl. arts, 67-72. Lectr. drama, Boston Ctr. Adult Educ, 55-58; managing dir, Poets' Theatre, Cambridge, Mass, 55-56; gen. mgr, Theatre-on-the-Green, Wellesley, 58; Metrop. Boston Arts Ctr, summers 59-61; Boston Arts Festival, 62, assoc. dir, 63; consult. & designer, Brandeis Univ. Festivals Creative Arts, Cambridge Drama Festival, South Shore Music Circus; summer adminr, Boston Univ. Tanglewood Inst; chmn, Mass. Counc. Arts & Humanities, 68-72; mem. adv. comt. educ. arts, Mass. Bd. Higher Educ; Mass. rep, Assoc. Counc. Arts & N.Am. Assembly State & Provincial Art Agencies; mem. bd. dirs, Ctr. Creative Cinematography, Corp. Pub. Broadcasting, 71-; lectr, Sem. Urban & Human Renewal, Europe, summer 72; dir. drama, Walnut Hill Sch, 72-73; mem. bd. dirs, Metrop. Cult. Alliance, 72-; producing dir, Theatre Co. Boston, 73- U.S.A, 53-55. Am. Theatre Asn; New Eng. Theatre Conf; Am. Nat. Theatre & Acad. Theatre in education; arts in contemporary society; creative process. Add: School of Fine & Applied Arts, Boston University, Boston, MA 02215.

WAUGH, BUTLER HUGGINS, b. Pittsburgh, Pa, May 9, 34; m. 53; c. 6. FOLKLORE. A.B, Washington & Jefferson Col, 55; Danforth Found. fel, 55-59; Johns Hopkins Univ, 55-56; Ph.D, Ind, Univ, 59. Instr. ENG, Univ. Kans, 59-61; asst. prof, Univ. Fla, 61-67, assoc. prof, 67-70; PROF. FLA, INT. UNIV, 70-, DEAN COL. ARTS & SCI, 70-, exec. asst. to pres, 69-70. Coord. humanities & fine arts, State Univ. Syst. Fla, 68-69. Am. Folklore Soc; MLA; S.Atlantic Mod. Lang. Asn. Modern British and American poetry; comparative folktale study; structural analysis of traditional literature. Publ: Negro tales of John Kendry, Midwest Folklore, 58; The child and the snake in North America, Norveg, 60; Deep and surface structure, S.Atlantic Bull, 68; plus others. Add: College of Arts & Science, Florida International University, Tamiami Trail, Miami, FL 33144.

WAXMAN, RUTH, b. Jaffa, Israel, Feb. 22, 16; U.S. citizen; m. 42; c. 3. ENGLISH & COMPARATIVE LITERATURE. B.A, Univ. Chicago, 37, Ph.D. (Am. theatre), 41. Instr. ENG, Woodrow Wilson Col, 46-47; Adelphi Univ, 47-58; asst. prof, C.W. Post Col, Long Island Univ, 58-69; MANAGING ED, JUDAISM (MAG), 70- Lectr, Univ. Judaism, 70; State Univ. N.Y. Stony Brook, 73. Publ: Co-ed, Faith and reason, KTAV, 73. Add: 85 Bayview Ave, Great Neck, NY 11023.

WEALES, GERALD CLIFFORD, b. Connersville, Ind, June 12, 25. ENGLISH LITERATURE. A.B, Columbia Col, 49, Columbia Univ, A.M, 50, Ph.D, 58. Instr. ENG, Ga. Inst. Technol, 51-53; Newark Col. Engineering, 53-55; Wayne State Univ, 55-56; asst. prof, Brown Univ, 57-58; UNIV. PA, 58-63, assoc. prof, 63-67, PROF, 67- Lectr, Eng. Inst, 59, 63. U.S.A, 42-46, Sgt. Modern American and English drama. Publ: Religion in modern English drama, Univ. Pa, 61; American drama since World War II, Harcourt, 62; ed, Edwardian plays, Hill & Wang, 62; A play and its parts, Basic Bks, 64; ed, The complete plays of William Wycherley, Doubleday Anchor, 66 & N.Y. Univ, 67; auth, The jumping-off place; American drama in the 1960's, Macmillan, 69; Clifford Odets, playwright, Bobbs, 71. Add: Dept. of English, University of Pennsylvania, Philadelphia, PA 19174.

WEATHERBY, HAROLD L, JR, b. Montgomery, Ala, Apr. 6, 34. ENGLISH LITERATURE. B.A, Vanderbilt Univ, 56; Woodrow Wilson fel, 56-57; M.A, Yale, 57, Ph.D, 62; Southern fel, 60-61. Instr. ENG, VANDERBILT UNIV, 62-63, asst. prof, 63-67, ASSOC. PROF, 67-, univ. summer grant, 63. U.S.A, 57-59, Res, 59-, 1st Lt. Thomas Hardy; the influence of the Oxford movement in Victorian literature. Publ: Cardinal Newman in his age, Vanderbilt Univ, 73. Add: Box 1580, Vanderbilt University, Nashville, TN 37235.

WEATHERFORD, RICHARD MORRIS, b. Seattle, Wash, May 14, 39; m. 67; c. 2. AMERICAN LITERATURE. B.A, Pac. Univ, 61; M.A, Univ. Wash, 62; NDEA fel, Univ. Calif, Los Angeles, 67-70; Ph.D.(Am. lit), 70. Instr. ENG, Centralia Col, 62-64; ASST. PROF, Linfield Col, 64-67; OHIO STATE UNIV, COLUMBUS, 70- Am. Philos. Soc. grant, 71-72. MLA (Am. Lit. Group). Late 19th century American literature; 20th century American novel; Northwest Coast of North America Indians. Publ: Ed, Stephen Crane: the critical heritage, Routledge & Kegan Paul, 73; auth, Stephen Crane in The lotus and Chips, spring 70 & A manuscript of Black riders came from the sea, summer 70, Stephen Crane Newslett; Stephen Crane and O. Henry: a correction, Am. Lit, 1/73. Add: Dept. of English, Ohio State University, 164 W. 17th Ave, Columbus, OH 43210.

WEATHERHEAD, ANDREW KINGSLEY, b. Manchester, Eng, Oct. 8, 23; U.S. citizen; m. 52; c. 3. ENGLISH. M.A, Cambridge, 49; M.A, Univ. Edinburgh, 49; Ph.D.(Eng), Univ. Wash, 58. Instr. ENG, Col. Puget Sound, 51-53, asst. prof, 53-58; assoc. prof, La. State Univ, New Orleans, 58-60; asst. prof, UNIV. ORE, 60-62, assoc. prof, 62-65, PROF, 66- Nat. Endowment for Humanities sr. fel, 74-75. Modern literature. Publ: A reading of Henry Green, 61 & The edge of the image, 67, Univ. Wash; contrib, American literary scholarship, Duke Univ, 69, 70, 71, 72; auth, Stephen Spender and the thirties, Bucknell Univ, 74; Philip Larkin of England, J. Eng. Lit. Hist, 71; Stephen Spender: lyric impulse and will, Contemporary Lit, 71. Add: 2698 Fairmount Blvd, Eugene, OR 97403.

WEATHERLY, EDWARD HOWELL, b. Hannibal, Mo, July 27, 05; m. 32; c. 2. ENGLISH LITERATURE. A.B. & B.J, Univ. Mo, 26, A.M, 29; Univ. Colo, 26; Ph.D, Yale, 32. Instr. ENG, Univ. Mo, 27-30; prof, McKendree Col, 32-33; instr, Northwest. Univ, 33-37; asst. prof, UNIV. MO-COLUMBIA, 37-40, assoc. prof, 40-44, prof, 44-72, chmn. dept, 45-51, EMER. PROF, 72- MLA; Early Eng. Text Soc; Johnson Soc. Midwest (pres, 63-64); Midwest Mod. Lang. Asn. Middle English literature; 18th century English literature; world literature. Publ: Co-auth, English heritage, & Heritage of European literature, Ginn; ed, Correspondence of John Wilkes and Charles Churchill, Columbia Univ. Add: 501 S. Glenwood Ave, Columbia, MO 65201.

WEATHERS, WINSTON, b. Pawhuska, Okla, Dec. 25, 26. ENGLISH, RHETORIC. B.A, Univ. Okla, 50, M.A, 51, Danforth fel. & Ph.D.(Eng), 64; Middlebury Col, summer 52. Asst. prof. ENG, Cottey Col, 51-54; instr, UNIV. TULSA, 58-62, asst. prof, 62-65, assoc. prof, 65-69, PROF, 69- Vis. prof, NDEA Eng. Inst, Ohio State Univ, summer 67. Rhetoric and style; literary theory; William Blake. Publ: Co-auth, The strategy of style, McGraw, 67; The prevalent forms of prose, Houghton, 68; auth, The archetype and the psyche, Univ. Tulsa, 68; Par Lagerkvist: a critical essay, Eerdmans, 68; co-auth, Copy and compose, 69 & The attitudes of rhetoric, 70, Prentice; auth, Messages from the asylum, Joseph Nichols, 70; Indian and white: sixteen eclogues, Univ. Nebr, 70; The lonesome game, David Lewis, 70; Eugene O'Neill and the tragedy of communication, Etc: Rev. Gen. Semantics, 62; The rhetoric of the series, Col. Compos. & Commun, 66; The writer & his region, Southwest. Am. Lit, 72. Add: Dept. of English, University of Tulsa, Tulsa, OK 74104.

WEAVER, CARL HAROLD, b. Lima, Ohio, Oct. 15, 10; m. 34; c. 3. INTERPERSONAL COMMUNICATION. B.A, Bluffton Col, 36; M.A, Ohio State Univ, 50, Ph.D.(commun. in bus. & indust), 57. Teacher Eng. & speech, high schs, Ohio, 36-56; asst. prof. speech, Cent. Mich. Univ, 57-61; assoc. prof, Univ. Md, 61-66; PROF. COMMUN, OHIO UNIV, 66- Vis. prof. speech educ, Univ. Alta, summer 60; psychol. speech, Queens Col, summers 65 & 66. Am. Psychol. Asn; Int. Commun. Asn.(exec. secy, 58-61); Speech Commun. Asn. Listening; psychology of speech. Publ: Co-auth, Fundamentals of speech communication, 64 & auth, Speaking in public, 66, Am. Bk. Co; Human listening: processes and behavior, Bobbs, 72; History of the ICA, Int. Commun. Asn, 74; co-auth, Listener comprehension of compressed speech when the difficulty, rate of presentation, and sex of the listener are varied, Speech Monogr, 35: 20-25; auth, The range of the communicative act, Conn. State Speech J, 5: 21-28; co-auth, A listening test for the intermediate grades, Cent. States Speech J, spring 73; plus five others. Add: 64 Eden Pl, Athens, OH 45701.

WEAVER, GORDON ALLISON, b. Moline, Ill, Feb. 2, 37; m. 61; c. 2. ENGLISH. B.A, Univ. Wis-Milwaukee, 61; Woodrow Wilson Found. fel, Univ. Ill, Urbana, 61-62, M.A, 62; Ph.D.(Eng), Univ. Denver, 70. Instr. ENG, Siena Col.(N.Y), 63-65; asst. prof, Marietta Col, 65-68; Univ. South. Miss, 70-72, ASSOC. PROF, 72-, DIR, CTR. FOR WRITERS, 71- Woodrow Wilson Nat. Found. fel, 61-62; coord. & participant, Poetry in the Schs, Nat. Endowment for Arts, Miss, 72-74, La, 74. St. Lawrence Award for Fiction, 73. U.S.A, 55-58. Creative writing; genre studies; prosody. Publ: Count a lonely cadence, Regnery, 68; The entombed man of Thule, La. State Univ, 72; ed, Selected poems of Father Ryan, Univ. & Col. Press Miss, 73; auth, Such waltzing was not easy, Univ. Ill, 74; plus over 50 articles. Add: Dept. of English, Southern Station, Box 37, University of Southern Mississippi, Hattiesburg, MS 39401.

WEAVER, JACK WAYNE, b. Damascus, Va, Apr. 7, 32; m. 57; c. 3. ENGLISH LITERATURE. B.A, Berea Col, 54; M.A, Univ. N.C, Chapel Hill, 59, Ph.D.(Eng), 66. Asst. prof. ENG, Greensboro Col, 59-66, assoc. prof, 66-67; WINTHROP COL, 67-72, PROF, 72-, coord. freshman Eng, 68-73. Piedmont Univ. Ctr. res. grant, 65-66; Greensboro Col. res. grant, 66-67; Winthrop Col. res. grant, 68, 73; Nat. Counc. Humanities summer stipend, 73. U.S.A, 54-56. MLA; South. Mod. Lang. Asn; AAUP. Modern Irish literature; Romantic English poetry and criticism; English novel. Publ: Stage-management in the Irish theatre, Eng. Lit. in Transition, 66; An exile's return, Eire, 68. Add: 144 Brookwood Lane, Rock Hill, SC 29730.

WEAVER, JENNINGS CLARK, b. Elgin, Ore, Nov. 2, 02; m. 31; c. 1. BROADCAST COMMUNICATION. B.S, Wash. State Univ, 29; Ph.M, Univ. Wis, 31; N.Y. Univ, summer 44. Instr. speech & theater, Kearney State Col, 31-37; asst. prof. theater & broadcasting, Baylor Univ, 37-39; assoc. prof, Tex. Woman's Univ, 39-49; asst. prof. speech & broadcasting, Univ. Fla, 49-56, assoc. prof. commun, 56-64; ASSOC. PROF. & DIR. BROADCAST COMMUN, FLA. STATE UNIV, 64-, res. counc. grants, 67-69. Ed, Players Mag, Nat. Theater Publ, 45-61; chmn. curriculum comt. radio, TV & film, Speech Asn. Am, 60-67; lectr, Queens Col.(N.Y), summers 66, 67. Nat. Soc. Stud. Commun; Speech Commun Asn; South. Speech Asn; Asn. Prof. Broadcasting Educ; Nat. Asn. Educ. Broadcasters; hon. life mem. Am. Theatre Asn. Audible speech symbols as indicators in broadcast communication; visible and audible speech characteristics as indicators of personality dominance; visible-audible speech symbols and pulse rate as indicators of personality. Publ: Evaluating equipment for a low cost ETV studio, 63 & Voice and personality interrelationships, 73, South. Speech Commun. J, Broadcasting curricula in higher education, Bull. Nat. Asn. Sec. Sch. Prin, 10/66; plus one other. Add: 1708 Myrick Rd, Tallahassee, FL 32302.

WEAVER, ROBERT BULLARD, b. Alliance, Ohio, Sept. 19, 26; m. 58; c. 3. ENGLISH. B.S, U.S. Naval Acad, 49; M.A, Univ. Tex, 57. Instr. Eng, U.S. Air Force Acad, U.S. Air Force, 56-59, asst. prof, 59-60, 64-66, ASSOC. PROF, 66-72; LANG. & LIT, RENSSELAER POLYTECH. INST, 72- Consult, Kaman Nuclear Div, Kaman Corp, 67-68; exchange prof. Eng, Philippine Mil. Acad, 70-72. U.S.A, 45; U.S.N, 45-49; U.S.A.F, 49-72, Lt. Col. (Ret). Soc. Tech. Commun; NCTE. Technical writing; communication and rhetoric. Publ: Co-auth, Good books, NCTE, 60. Add: 1 North Ridge, Ballston Lake, NY 12019.

WEAVER, ROBERT GLENN, b. Lancaster Co, Pa, Sept. 13, 20; m. 41, 65; c. 3. ENGLISH COMPOSITION. B.A, Duke Univ, 43; M.A, Univ. Del, 51. Dir. develop. & mgt, New Holland Mach, Div. Sperry Rand, 54-55; training coord. personnel & mgt, PA. STATE UNIV, UNIVERSITY PARK, 55-58, ASSOC. PROF. ENG, 58- Prof. professional writing, U.S. Army War Col, 68- Management communications; fiction and nonfiction writing. Publ: Co-auth, Writing for business and industry, 62, The plain rhetoric, 64, The brief essay, 65 & Writing the research paper, 66, Allyn & Bacon; co-auth, Gravemaker's house (novel), 64 & auth, Nice guy, go home (novel), 68, Harper; co-auth, Frameworks of exposition, Holt, 65; auth, Meet General Bafflegot, Army Mag, 7/73; plus many others. Add: 36 Burrowes S, Pennsylvania State University, University Park, PA 16801.

WEBB, BENJIMAN DANIEL, German Literature & Expressionistic Drama. See Volume III, Foreign Languages, Linguistics & Philology.

WEBB, BERNICE LARSON, b. Ludell, Kans; m. 61; c. 2. ENGLISH. A.B, Univ. Kans, 56, Whitcomb fel, 56-57, M.A, 57, univ. fels, 57-59, Ph.D.(Eng), 61; exchange scholar, Univ. Aberdeen, Scotland, 59-60. Asst. instr, ENG, Univ. Kans, 57-58; teaching fel, 60-61; asst. prof. UNIV. SOUTHWEST. LA, 61-67, ASSOC. PROF, 67-, dir. sem, NDEA Inst, summer 66. William Herbert Carruth Mem. poetry prizes, 54-61; Edna Osborne Whitcomb prizes, 55-56; awards in poetry, drama & short stories, 62-73; ed, The Magnolia, 67-71; ed, Louisiana Poets, 70-; vis. prof. creative writing & world lit, World Campus Afloat, 72; coord. & consult, Poetry in the Schs, Lafayette Parish, La, 74. Col. Eng. Asn; S.Cent. Mod. Lang. Asn; MLA; S.Cent. Col. Eng. Asn. Contribution of William Poel to the presentation of verse drama; examination of the plays of Christopher Fry; Gertrude Atherton as novelist; history of colonies in Kansas. Publ: The basketball man: James Naismith, Univ. Kans, 73; James Bond as literary descendant of Beowulf, S.Atlantic Quart, winter 68; Lost and found, Kans. Mag, 68; Animal imagery and juvenile delinquents in Joyce Cary's Charley is my darling, S.Cent. Bull, winter 72; plus others. Add: Box 861, University of Southwestern Louisiana, Lafayette, LA 70501.

WEBB, CARL CURTIS, b. Hazelton, Kans, Dec. 22, 04; m. 28; c. 1. JOURNALISM. B.S, Univ. Ore, 32, M.A, 50. ASSOC. PROF. JOUR, UNIV. ORE, 43- Newspaper management. Add: School of Journalism, University of Oregon, Eugene, OR 97403.

WEBB, CHESTER JAMES, b. Whitewater, Wis, Feb. 9, 07. DRAMATIC ART, SPEECH. A.B, Cornell Col, 38; A.M, Univ. Mich, 47. Teacher high sch, Iowa, 38-42, 46-47; assoc. prof. dramatic art & dir. theatre, Cornell Col, 47-72; RETIRED. Teacher speech, Univ. Md, Eng, Morocco & Ger, 53-54. U.S.A, 42-45. Add: 5402 E. Shorelane Dr, Michigan City, IN 46361.

WEBB, EUGENE, b. Santa Monica, Calif, Nov. 10, 38; m. 64. ENGLISH, COMPARATIVE LITERATURE. B.A, Univ. Calif, Los Angeles, 60; M.A, Columbia Univ, 26, Ph.D.(comp. lit), 65. ASST. PROF. ENG, Simon Fraser Univ, 65-66; UNIV. WASH, 66- MLA. Twentieth century English, German and French literature; 18th century English. Publ: Samuel Beckett: a study of his novels, 70 & The plays of Samuel Beckett, 72, Univ. Wash. & Peter Owen, London; Criticism & the creative process, W. Coast Rev, fall 67. Add: Dept. of English, University of Washington, Seattle, WA 98195.

WEBB, HENRY JAMESON, b. Indianapolis, Ind, Mar. 12, 15; m. 40; c. 4. ENGLISH LITERATURE. B.S, N.Y. Univ. 37; A.M, State Univ. Iowa, 38, Ph.D, 41. Instr. ENG, Univ. Utah, 40-41; asst. prof, The Citadel, 41-42; instr, Ill. Inst. Technol, 42-43; from asst. prof. to assoc. prof, UNIV. UTAH UTAH, 46-57, PROF, 57-, DIR. GRAD. STUD. ENG, 67- U.S.A, 43-46. MLA; Am. Mil. Inst; Rocky Mountain Mod. Lang. Asn. Renaissance military literature; Shakespeare; military history. Publ: Elizabethan military science, Univ. Wis, 65; The military background in Othello, Philol. Quart; Elizabethan science of gunnery, Isis; Military newsbooks during the age of Elizabeth, Eng. Stud. Add: Dept. of English, University of Utah, Salt Lake City, UT 84112.

WEBB, HOWARD WILLIAM, JR, b. Dayton, Ohio, June 23, 25; m. 47; c. 3. ENGLISH. B.A, Denison Univ, 47; M.A, State Univ. Iowa, 50, fel. & Ph.D. (Am. stud), 53. Asst. prof. ENG, Cent. Mo. State Col, 53-56, assoc. prof, 56; lectr, SOUTH. ILL. UNIV, CARBONDALE, 56-57, asst. prof, 57-62, assoc. prof, 62-67, PROF, 67-, chmn. dept, 68-72. Mem. Am. Lit. Group, MLA. MLA; Am. Stud. Asn; Melville Soc. Am; NCTE. American fiction; Melville; Twain. Publ: Co-ed, Illinois prose writers, South. Ill. Univ, 68; auth, Meaning of Ring Lardner's fiction: a re-evaluation, Am. Lit, 60; The singular worlds of Jack Kerouac, In: Contemporary American novelists, South. Ill. Univ, 64; Recent scholarship on Mark Twain and Henry James, In: The teacher and American literature, NCTE, 65; plus others. Add: Dept. of English, Southern Illinois University, Carbondale, IL 62901.

WEBB, JAMES WILSON, b. Noxapater, Miss, May 17, 10; m. 36; c. 1. ENGLISH. B.S, Miss. State Univ, 33; M.A, Univ. N.C, 46, Ph.D, 58. Teacher Eng. & sci, Bond High Sch, 33-34; asst, Miss. State Univ, 34-35; teacher Eng, hist. & mil. sci, Chamberlain-Hunt Acad, 35-41; asst. prof. Eng, UNIV. MISS, 47-55, dir. pers. admin, 55-60, PROF. ENG. & CHMN. DEPT, 60- Curator, Rowan Oak, Miss. U.S.A, 41-46, Res, 46-, Lt. Col. MLA; S-Cent. Mod. Lang. Asn; Am. Stud. Asn; Am. Stud. Asn. Lower Miss. Mark Twain; Mississippi writers; American literature. Publ: Co-ed, William Faulkner of Oxford, La. State Univ, 65; Rowan Oak—the home of William Faulkner, S.Cent. Bull, 2/64; Rowan Oak, Faulkner's golden bough, VI: 39-50 & Faulkner writes A fable, VII: 1-13, Stud. Eng, Univ. Miss; plus others. Add: Dept. of English, Room 309 Bishop Hall, University of Mississippi, Oxford Campus, University, MI 38677.

WEBB, MARGARET JOSEPHINE, b. Hamilton, Ohio, Oct. 5, 32. ENGLISH. B.A, Wellesley Col, 54; M.A, Miami Univ, 63; Ph.D.(Eng), Univ. Ill, 67. Copywriter, Standard Publ, Ohio, 54-55; Macmillan Co, N.Y, 55-58; teacher, high sch, Ohio, 59-63; ASST. PROF. ENG, EAST. MICH. UNIV, 67- NCTE; Col. Eng. Asn. Victorian fiction; 18th century fiction. Add: Dept. of English, Eastern Michigan University, Ypsilanti, MI 48197.

WEBB, RALPH, JR, b. Denver, Colo, Dec. 14, 34; m. 56; c. 2. SPEECH. B.A, Colo. State Col, 56, M.A, 59; Ph.D.(speech), Univ. Wis, 65. Instr. speech, Univ. Colo, 57-60; teaching asst, Univ. Wis, 60-61, asst. to assoc. dean lett. & sci. col, 61-64; asst. prof. SPEECH, PURDUE UNIV, WEST LAFAYETTE, 65-71, ASSOC. PROF, 71- Speech Commun. Asn; Cent. State Speech Commun. Asn. Verbal behavior; language in communication. Publ: Co-auth, Effects of verbal decision behavior upon respiration during speech production, J. Speech & Hearing Res, 3/67. Add: Dept. of Communication, Purdue University, West Lafayette, IN 47906.

WEBBER, EDWIN JACK, Romance Language & Literature. See Volume III, Foreign Languages, Linguistics & Philology.

WEBBER, EVERETT, b. Charleston, Miss, Aug. 30, 09; m. 30; c. 2. ENGLISH. A.B, Col. Ozarks, 31; A.M, Univ. Mo, 33. WRITER & ASST. PROF. ENG. & JOUR, NORTHWEST. STATE UNIV, 56- Authors Guild. American frontier history; early Louisiana history; history of French and Spanish Bourbon dynasties. Publ: Backwoods teacher; Escape to Utopia, Hastings, 59. Add: Dept. of English, Northwestern State University, Natchitoches, LA 71457.

WEBBER, JOAN, b. Buffalo, N.Y, Sept. 9, 30; m. 63; c. 1. ENGLISH. B.A, Barnard Col, Columbia Univ, 51; M.A, Univ. Rochester, 52; Ph.D.(Eng), Univ. Wis, 60. Instr. ENG, Univ. Colo, 55-56; teaching asst, Univ. Wis, 56-58; instr, Ohio State Univ, 60-62, asst. prof, 62-65, assoc. prof, 65-68, PROF, 68-73; UNIV. WASH, 73- Guggenheim fel, 65-66; vis. prof, Univ. Wash, summer 67; Univ. N.Mex, summer 68; mem. adv. bd, Dictionary of Tudor & Stuart biography, 73-; mem. ed. bd, Mod. Lang. Quart, 73- MLA; AAUP. Renaissance literature, especially 17th century English; literary epic. Publ: Contrary music: the prose style of John Donne, 63 & The eloquent I: style and self in seventeenth century prose, 68, Univ. Wis; plus numerous articles on Milton and other Renaissance writers. Add: Dept. of English, University of Washington, Seattle, WA 98195.

WEBER, BROM, b. New York, N.Y, May 14, 17; m. 39; c. 2. ENGLISH. B.S.S, City Col. New York, 38; Coe fel. & M.A, Univ. Wyo, 55; Carnegie fel, Univ; Minn, Ph.D.(Am. studies), 57. Writer & ed, Hist. Records Surv, 38-39; U.S. Govt, 40-45; instr. Eng, City Col. New York, 45-50; lectr. lit. & writing, New Sch. Soc. Res, 48-54; asst. prof. Eng, Purdue Univ, 57-58; Univ. Minn, 58-60, secy, Prog. Am. Stud, 58-63, assoc. prof. ENG, 60-63; PROF, UNIV. CALIF, DAVIS, 63- Vis. prof, DePauw Univ, summer 58; Can. Counc. Sr. Non-Resident fel, 63; vis. prof, U.S. Educ. Found. Conf. Am. Lit. & Hist, India, 63; guest lectr, Far East & Europe; summer vis. prof, Univ. Wash, 65, Univ. Wyo, 66, Univ. Colo, 68; Fulbright vis. prof, France, 66-67; Fulbright vis. prof, Korean-Am. Educ. Comn. & U.S. Educ. Found. in China, 73. McKnight Found. Humanities Award, 62. Am. Stud. Asn; MLA. American literature and culture; modern fiction and poetry. Publ: Hart Crane: a biographical and critical study, Bodley Press, 48, Univ. Microfilms, 65, rev. ed, Russell, 70; ed, The letters of Hart Crane, 1916-1932, Hermitage, 52 & Univ. Calif, 65; ed, Sut Lovingood, Grove, 54;

auth, An anthology of American humor, Crowell, 62; ed, The story of a country town, Holt, 64; auth, Sherwood Anderson, Univ. Minn, 64; ed, The complete poems and selected letters and prose of Hart Crane, Doubleday Anchor, 66, Liveright, 66 & Oxford Univ, 68; co-ed, American literature: tradition and innovation (3 vols), D.C. Heath, 69; ed, Sense and sensibility in twentieth-century writing, South. Ill. Univ, 70; plus others. Add: 23 Almond Lane, Davis, CA 95616.

WEBER, BURTON JASPER, b. St. Louis, Mo, Jan. 30, 34; m. 59; c. 2. ENGLISH LITERATURE. A.B, Washington Univ, 55; M.A, Univ. Minn, 58, Ph.D, 65. Asst. prof. ENG, UNIV. SASK, 65-70, ASSOC. PROF, 70- Milton; Shakespeare; 17th century English poetry. Publ: Construction of Paradise lost, 71 & Wedges and wings, 74, South. Ill. Univ. Add: 2030 McTavish, Regina, Sask, Can.

WEBER, DANIEL BARR, b. Kalamazoo, Mich, Feb. 4, 28; m. 50; c. 2. AMERICAN LITERATURE & STUDIES. A.B, West. Mich. Col, 51, M.A, 56; Ph.D.(Am. stud), Univ. Minn, 64. Instr. ENG, CENT. MICH. UNIV, 60-65, asst. prof, 65-69, ASSOC. PROF, 69-, DIR. PROG. AM. STUD, 72- Lectr, Fulbright-Hays Overseas lectr, Univ. Philippines, 66-67. U.S.N, 45-46; U.S.M.C, 51-54, Res, 54-60, Capt. Am. Stud. Asn. American nature writings; 20th century American fiction; American romanticism. Publ: Ed, From Michigan to Murfreesboro, Cent. Mich. Univ, 65; Nature and man, Am. Embassy Philippines, 67; Society and the American novel, 1920-1960, Diliman Rev, 67. Add: American Studies Program, Central Michigan University, Mt. Pleasant, MI 48858.

WEBER, FRANCESCA CABRINI, S.N.J.M, b. Los Angeles, Calif, Sept. 21, 20. ENGLISH LITERATURE. A.B, Col. Holy Names (Calif), 43; M.A, Univ. Calif, Los Angeles, 45; Ph.D.(Eng), Univ. Calif, Berkeley, 60. From instr. to assoc. prof. ENG, HOLY NAMES COL.(CALIF), 52-72, PROF, 72-, DEAN GRAD. SCH, 70- Augustan Reprint Soc. Eighteenth century English literature; satire. Add: Dept. of English, Holy Names College, 3500 Mountain Blvd, Oakland, CA 94619.

WEBER, JOHN SHERWOOD, b. Reading, Pa, Sept. 21, 18; m. 59; c. 2. ENGLISH, COMPARATIVE LITERATURE. A.B, Temple Univ, 39, M.A, 40; Ph.D.(Eng. & comp. lit), Univ. Wis, 47. Instr. ENG, Univ. Wis, 41-45; George Washington Univ, 45-46; N.Y. Univ, 46-47; Queens Col.(N.Y), 47-50; asst. prof, PRATT INST, 51-55, assoc. prof, 55-59, PROF, 59-, CHMN. DEPT, 63-, dir. dramatics, 52-58, chmn. Eng, eve. sch, 54-59. Educ. consult, New Am. Libr, 60-67. MLA; NCTE; Conf. Col. Compos. & Commun; Col. Eng. Asn.(columnist, CEA Critic, 60-63). Comparative literature; drama; humanities. Publ: Co-auth, From Homer to Joyce, Holt, 59; ed, Good reading, New Am. Libr, 52, 56, 60, 64, 69; auth, The relevance of the past, McGraw, 74. Add: Box 116, Cragsmoor, NY 12420.

WEBER, RICHARD BAKER, b. Summit, N.J, Aug. 15, 29; m. 55; c. 3. AMERICAN STUDIES & LITERATURE. B.A, Bates Col, 54; M.A, State Univ. Iowa, 58; N.Y. Univ, 58-66; Ph.D.(Am. cult. & poetry), Union Grad. Sch, 71. Master Eng, Brooklyn Polytech. Prep. Country Day Sch, 57-60; instr, Skidmore Col, 60-64; Univ. Louisville, 64-68; from asst. prof. to ASSOC. PROF. HIST. & AM. STUD, SOUTHAMPTON COL, L.I. UNIV, 68- U.S.A, 47-49, 50-51, S/Sgt. Poetry. Publ: Hurricane watch (poem), Colo. Quart, summer 70; Sweet baskers and hammerheads (poem), In: Muse of fire, Knopf, 71; Tuning in to late afternoon on Channel 7 (poem), J. Popular Film, fall 72; plus others. Add: Dept. of History, Southampton College, Long Island University, Southampton, NY 11968.

WEBER, SARAH APPLETON, b. New York, N.Y, Apr. 14, 30; m. 65; c. 2. ENGLISH, MEDIEVAL LITERATURE. B.A, Vassar Col, 52; M.A, Ohio State Univ, 57, Ph.D.(medieval Eng. lit), 61. Instr. Eng, Smith Col, 62-65; RES. & WRITING, 65- Poetry ed, Lit. East & West, 67-; scholar, Radcliffe Inst, 70-72. Mediaeval Acad. Am; MLA. Poetry and poetics; Middle English language and literature. Publ: Theology and poetry in the Middle English lyric: a study of sacred history and aesthetic form, Ohio State Univ, 68; The plenitude we cry for (poem), Doubleday, 72; Exercises in resemblances, Exercise Exchange, 10/58; Avatara in the West, Lit. East & West, 6/66; plus poetry. Add: 124 Dorset Rd, Syracuse, NY 13210.

WEBSTER, DAVID HUME, b. Cambridge, Mass, June 12, 04; m. 29; c. 3. ENGLISH. A.B, Univ. Nebr, 26; A.M, Univ. Wis, 27, Ph.D, 36. Instr, Univ. Wis, 29-36; prof, Wis. State Teachers Col, Whitewater, 36-42; from instr. to assoc. prof. Eng, TEMPLE UNIV, 46-62, prof, 62-72, acting dean men, 54-56, asst. dean col. lib. arts, 63-64, assoc. dean, 64-66, EMER. PROF. ENG, 72- U.S.A.A.F, 42-46. Elizabethan drama. Publ: Co-auth, Writer's adviser & Guide and handbook for writing, 64, Am. Bk. Co. Add: Dept. of English, Temple University, Philadelphia, PA 19122.

WEBSTER, GRANT T, b. Fargo, N.Dak, Mar. 15, 33; m. 63; c. 2. ENGLISH & AMERICAN LITERATURE. A.B, Carleton Col, 54; A.M, Columbia Univ, 58; Ph.D.(Eng. lit), Ohio State Univ, Columbus, 63. Asst. prof. ENG, Univ. South. Calif, 63-67; from asst. prof. to ASSOC. PROF, STATE UNIV. N.Y. BINGHAMTON, 67- U.S.A, 54-56. MLA; AAUP. Modern American literary criticism; 18th century English literature. Publ: T.S. Eliot as critic: the man behind the masks, Criticism, 66; Leslie Fiedler: adolescent and Jew as critic, Denver Quart, 67; Allen Tate: the conservative critic, S.Atlantic Quart, 67. Add: Dept. of English, State University of New York at Binghamton, Binghamton, NY 13901.

WEBSTER, HARVEY CURTIS, b. Chicago, Ill, Nov. 6, 06; m. 32. LITERATURE. A.B, Oberlin Col, 27, A.M, 29; Ph.D, Univ. Mich, 35. Instr, Colo. State Col, 35-36; asst. prof, Univ. Louisville, 36-45; acting head dept. Eng, Fisk Univ, 45-46; vis. lectr, Ill. Inst. Technol, 46-47; asst. prof, Univ. Chicago, 47-48; assoc. prof. Eng, UNIV. LOUISVILLE, 48-53, prof, 53-73, dir. radio educ, 48-53, head dept. ENG, 67-68, EMER. PROF, 73- Fulbright vis. prof, Univ. Durham, 50-51. Univ. Leeds, 62-63; vis. prof, Univ. Mont, 65-66; consult. Eng, Int. Hardy Festival, 69. MLA; Mod. Humanities Res. Asn; AAUP. Nineteenth century British literature; contemporary American and British literature. Publ: On a darkling plain: the life and thought of Thomas Hardy; ed, The Mayor of Casterbridge; auth, After the trauma: representative British novelists since 1920, Univ. Ky, 70; Allan Seager as social novelist, Critique, winter 63; Without a peer, Kenyon Rev, summer 64; introd, Walden, Harper, 9/65; The world of Graham Greene, In: Graham Greene, Univ. Ky, 67; plus others. Add: Dept. of English, University of Louisville, Louisville, KY 40208.

WEBSTER, MILDRED E, b. Webster, N.Dak, Oct. 16, 08. ENGLISH. A.B, Jamestown Col, 29; M.A, Univ. N.Dak, 36; Univ. Chicago, 41; Breadloaf Sch. Eng, 47; Mich. State Univ, 47-68. Teacher, sec. Eng, Webster, Tolna & Clyde, N.Dak, 29-31, 33-35, 36-38; Ironwood, Mich, 38-43; St. Joseph, Mich, 43-73; RETIRED. Instr, Mich. State Univ, summer 62; chmn, Conf. Dept. Chmn. Eng, 67-68, co-chmn, 66-69; instr, evening sch, Lake Mich. Col, 67-69; chmn. sec. comt, NCTE, 68-69; participant, York Int. Conf. on Teaching Eng, York Univ, summer 71. NCTE. Middle English; curriculum studies; literary criticism. Publ: Vocabulary of An holy medytacion, Philol. Quart, 37; co-auth, Literature of the Americas: twentieth century, Ginn, 57; auth, Preventing plagiaristic patchwork, Mich. Eng. Teacher, 64. Add: 3105 Kevin St, St. Joseph, MI 49085.

WEBSTER, ROBERT GORDON, b. Newburyport, Mass, Nov. 16, 02. AMERICAN LITERATURE. A.B, Univ. N.H, 26; Oxford & Cambridge, 35; Harvard, 42, 48-49. Instr. ENGLISH, UNIV. N.H, 27-37, asst. prof, 37-48, assoc. prof, 48-55, prof, 55-70, acting chmn. dept, 49-50, EMER. PROF, 70- Publ: Co-auth, College developmental reading manual, Houghton; Technical report writing, MacKay Pub, 62. Add: Box 576, 28 Woodman Rd, Durham, NH 03824.

WEDGE, GEORGE FRANCIS, b. Rochester, N.Y, Sept. 13, 27; m. 53; c. 3. ENGLISH, LINGUISTICS. B.A, Middlebury Col, 52; M.A, Univ. Minn, Minneapolis, 55, Ph.D.(Eng), 67; Am. Counc. Learned Soc. grant-in-aid, Univ. Wash, summer 62. Instr. Eng, UNIV. KANS, 58-68, asst. prof. ENG. & LING, 68-69, ASSOC. PROF, 69- Assoc. ed, Critique, 56-58; vis. acting asst. prof, Inst. in Eng, Kans. State Univ, summers 65-67; adv. ed, Kans. Quart, 70- U.S.N, 45-50. Ling. Soc. Am; Mediaeval Acad. Am. Old and Middle English; English syntax. Publ: Two bibliographies: J.F. Powers; Flannery O'Connor, Critique, fall 58; co-auth, Tag questions syntactic variables, and grammaticality, In: Papers from the Fifth Kansas linguistics conference, Univ. Kans, 71; auth, A model for generative metrics, In: Soundstream to discourse, Univ. Mo, 71. Add: Dept. of English, University of Kansas, Lawrence, KS 66045.

WEE, DAVID LUTHER, b. Madison, Wis, Jan. 20, 39; m. 61; c. 3. ENGLISH. B.A, St. Olaf Col, 61; Am. Lutheran Church fel, Stanford Univ, 62-63, M.A, 65, Ph.D.(Eng), 67; Leverhulme fel, Univ. Col, Univ. London, 64-65; Luther Theol. Sem, Minn, 66-67. From asst. prof. to ASSOC. PROF. ENG, ST. OLAF COL, 65-, sr. fel, Paracollege, 71-72. Danforth assoc, St. Olaf Col, 69-; vis. prof. Eng, Univ. North. Iowa, summer 72; sr. commons room visitor, Mansfield Col, Eng, 73. AAUP. Victorian literature. Publ: Studying the humanities: heaven on earth?, Minn. Eng. J, 4/68; Athletics as a human experience, Event, 10/71. Add: Dept. of English, St. Olaf College, Northfield, MN 55057.

WEEG, MARY, b. La Salle, Ill, Apr. 26, 30. ENGLISH. B.A, Univ. Ill, 53, M.A, 56; Ph.D.(Eng), Ind. Univ, 64. Teacher, High Schs, Ill, 53-67, dept. chmn, 64-67; La Salle Jr. Col, 56-67; INSTR. ENG. & CHMN. DEPT. HUMANITIES, ILL. VALLEY COMMUNITY COL, 67- MLA; NCTE. American literature—late 19th and 20th century; Dreiser, Hemingway, Faulkner & E.L. Masters, Add: 601 Fourth St, La Salle, IL 61301.

WEEKS, GRACE EZELL, Romance Languages. See Volume III, Foreign Languages, Linguistics & Philology.

WEEKS, ROBERT LEWIS, b. Huntington, W.Va, July 9, 24; m. 50; c. 2. ENGLISH LITERATURE. A.B, W.Va. Univ, 48, M.A, 49; Ph.D, Ind. Univ, 56. Instr. ENG, W.Va. Univ, 49-51; Wis. State Col, Eau Claire, 54-55, asst. prof, 55-56, assoc. prof, 56-61, prof, 61-63; assoc. prof, Stephen F. Austin State Col, 63-66; PROF, COLO. WOMEN'S COL, 66- Danforth Found. assoc, 71- Sig.C, U.S.A, 44-46. MLA; Am. Civil Liberties Union. Eighteenth century English literature; modern literature, especially poetry; criticism. Publ: To the maker of globes and other poems, 64 & For those who waked me and other poems, 69, South & West; To the master of clouds, Juniper Bks, 70; plus many poems & articles in mags. & journals. Add: Dept. of English, Colorado Women's College, Denver, CO 80220.

WEES, WILLIAM CHARLES, b. Joplin, Mo, June 20, 35; m. 58; c. 3. ENGLISH. B.A, Northwest. Univ, 57; M.A, Univ. Rochester, 58; Ph.D.(Eng), Northwest. Univ, 64. Asst. prof. ENG, Colby Col, 61-69; ASSOC. PROF, McGILL UNIV, 69- MLA; Asn. Can. Univ. Teachers Eng. Literature and film. Publ: Vorticism and the English avant-garde, Univ. Toronto, 72; Ezra Pound as a vorticist, Wis. Stud. Contemporary Lit, 65; England's avant-garde: the vorticist-futurist phase, West. Humanities Rev, 68. Add: Dept. of English, P.O. Box 6070, McGill University, Montreal 101, P.Q, Can.

WEGELIN, CHRISTOF, b. St. Gall, Switz, Nov. 20, 11; nat, 49; m. 46; c. 2. AMERICAN & ENGLISH LITERATURE. Univ. Zurich, 38-40; A.M, Univ. N.C, 42; Ph.D, Johns Hopkins Univ, 47. Jr. instr. ENG, Johns Hopkins Univ, 45-46; instr, Princeton, 46-49, asst. prof, 49-52; UNIV. ORE, 52-57, assoc. prof, 57-63, PROF, 63- Bissing fel, Johns Hopkins Univ, 50-51; Fulbright lectr, Ger, 55-56; Am. Counc. Learned Soc. res. grant-in-aid, 62 & 67; ed. consult, PMLA, 63-; guest prof, Univ. Zurich, 64; Guggenheim fel, 64-65; Nat. Endowment for Humanities res. grant, 71-72. MLA; Int. Asn. Univ. Prof. Eng; Philol. Asn. Pac. Coast (pres, 72-73); Am. Comp. Lit. Asn; Int. Comp. Lit. Asn. American literature; comparative literature; fiction. Publ: The image of Europe in Henry James, South. Methodist Univ, 58; ed, The American novel: background readings and criticism, Free Press, 72; auth, Hemingway and the decline of international fiction, Sewanee Rev, spring 65; Robert Penn Warren, Contemporary Novelists, 72; The American schlemiel abroad: Malamud's Italian stories and the end of American innocence, Twentieth-Century Lit, 4/73. Add: Dept. of English, University of Oregon, Eugene, OR 97403.

WEGNER, ROBERT E, b. Cleveland, Ohio, Mar. 1, 29; m. 50; c. 3. ENGLISH, CREATIVE WRITING. B.A, Mich. State Univ, 50; M.A, West. Reserve Univ, 52, Ph.D.(Eng), 59; State Univ. Iowa, 52-53. Asst. prof. ENG,

Wilmington Col, 55-57; ALMA COL.(MICH), 57-63, assoc. prof, 63-69, PROF, 69- Cent. States Col. Asn, vis. lectr, Augustana Col, 67. MLA. Modern poetry. Publ: The prose and poetry of E.E. Cummings, Harcourt, 65; I'm going down to watch the horses come alive (short story), In: The age of anxiety, Allyn & Bacon, 72; plus poems, articles & short stories. Add: Dept. of English, Alma College, Alma, MI 48801.

WEHMEYER, WILLIAM ANTHONY, b. Yonkers, N.Y, Nov. 24, 30; m. 65. ENGLISH. A.B, Hamilton Col, 52; M.A, Cath. Univ. Am, 54; Ph.D.(Eng), Univ. Notre Dame, 62. Asst. prof. ENG, ST. BONAVENTURE UNIV, 62-64, assoc. prof, 64-70, PROF, 70-, CHMN. DEPT, 68- U.S.A, 54-56. MLA; NCTE. Nineteenth century American literature; Middle English literature. Add: Box 26, St. Bonaventure University, St. Bonaventure, NY 14778.

WEHNER, RALPH S, b. Lima, Ohio, June 18, 07; m. 37; c. 2. ENGLISH. B.S, Mt. Union Col, 31; scholar, West. Reserve Univ, 38-39, A.M, 39, res. fel, 45, Ph.D.(Eng), 68. Asst. ENG, Mt. Union Col, 37-38; instr, West. Reserve Univ, 40-45; asst. prof, Westminster Col, 46-47; assoc. prof, THIEL COL, 47-68, PROF, 68- U.S.A, 43-44. MLA; NCTE; Col. Eng. Asn; Emerson Soc. English and American literature; American culture; Albert Gallatin Riddle. Publ: Minerva, Ohio, 1944: a portrait of a community, West. Reserve Univ, 44. Add: 112 Shenango St, Greenville, PA 16125.

WEHTJE, VERNE VIRGIL, b. Walla Walla, Wash, Nov. 26, 32; m. 51; c. 2. ENGLISH. B.A, Walla Walla Col, 56; M.A, Univ. Wash, 62; Ph.D, Univ. Nebr, 67. Instr. ENG, Auburn Acad, 56-58; Can. Union Col, Alta, 58-60; Union Col.(Nebr), 60-63, asst. prof, 63-66, assoc. prof, 66-68, prof, 68-69, chmn. dept, 64-69; PROF. & CHMN. DEPT, PAC. UNION COL, 69- MLA; NCTE. English literature, 19th century; Thomas Carlyle. Add: Dept. of English, Pacific Union College, Angwin, CA 94508.

WEIDHORN, MANFRED, b. Vienna, Austria, Oct. 10, 31; U.S. citizen. ENGLISH. B.A, Columbia Univ, 54, Ph.D.(Eng), 63; M.A, Univ. Wis, 57. Instr. ENG, Univ. Ala, 57-58; Brooklyn Col, 60-63; asst. prof, YESHIVA COL, 63-68, assoc. prof, 68-73, PROF, 73- Danforth Assoc, 69. U.S.A, 54-56. Sir Winston Churchill; Shakespeare; politics and literature. Publ: Dreams in 17th century English literature, Mouton, The Hague, 70; Richard Lovelace, Twayne, 70; Sword and pen: a survey of the writings of Sir Winston Churchill, Univ. N.Mex, 74; Lear's schoolmasters, Shakespeare Quart, summer 62; Dreams and guilt, Harvard Theol. Rev, 1/65; The anxiety dream in literature from Homer to Milton, Stud. Philol, 1/67. Add: Dept. of English, Yeshiva College, 500 W. 185th St, New York, NY 10033.

WEIGEL, JOHN ARTHUR, b. Cleveland, Ohio, Aug. 17, 12. ENGLISH. B.A, Case West. Reserve Univ, 33, M.A, 37, fel. & Ph.D.(Eng), 39; M.A, Columbia Univ, 51. Teacher, High Sch, Ohio, 33-37; lectr. ENG, Cleveland Col, West. Reserve Univ, 37-39; instr, MIAMI UNIV, 39-45, from asst. prof. to assoc. prof, 45-55, PROF, 56- Ford Found. fel, 52-53; lectr. psychol, Columbia Univ, 53-54. NCTE; MLA. Modern British novel; verbal behavior. Publ: Lawrence Durrell, Twayne, 65 & Dutton, 66; Lawrence Durrell's first novel, 7/68 & The entropy is the message, 7/69, Twentieth Century Lit; Confession of a verbal behaviorist, Col. Compos. & Commun, 10/68. Add: Dept. of English, Upham Hall, Miami University, Oxford, OH 45056.

WEIGLE, CLIFFORD FRANCIS, b. San Francisco, Calif, Sept. 17, 06; m. 30; c. 1. COMMUNICATION, JOURNALISM. A.B, Stanford Univ, 29, A.M, 36; Univ. Calif, 41; Univ. Minn, 47-48. Mem. ed. dept, San Francisco News, 29-34; instr. jour, Stanford Univ, 34-36, asst. prof, 37-42, assoc. prof, 43-48; prof. & dean, sch. jour, Univ. Ore, 48-50; prof. jour. & assoc. exec. head dept. commun. & jour, STANFORD UNIV, 50-61, prof. commun. & exec. head dept, 61-68, Paul C. Edwards prof. commun, 68-72, EMER. PROF, 72- Mem. fac, U.S. Army Univ, Shrivenham, Eng, 45-46. Asn. Educ. Jour. History of journalism; professional training and standards. Add: 760 Santa Ynez, Stanford, CA 94305.

WEIL, HERBERT S, JR, b. New Orleans, La, Jan. 3, 33; m. 61; c. 2. ENGLISH, COMPARATIVE LITERATURE. B.A, Tulane Univ, 54; Fulbright fel, Univ. Paris & Univ. Lille, 54-55; Woodrow Wilson fel, M.A. & Ph.D. (Eng), Stanford Univ, 64. Instr. ENG, UNIV. CONN, 62-64, asst. prof, 64-68, ASSOC. PROF, 68- Supply C, U.S.N, 55-58, Lt.(jg). MLA; Am. Comp. Lit. Asn; Shakespeare Asn. Am. Literature and film; characterization; audience and reader response. Publ: Co-ed, Reading, writing and re-writing, Lippincott, 63; ed, Discussions of Shakespeare's romantic comedy, Heath, 66; auth, Oedipus Rex: the oracles and the action, Tex. Stud, 68; Comic structure and tonal manipulation in Shakespeare and some modern plays, Shakespeare Surv, 69; Form and context in Measure for measure, Critical Quart, 70. Add: Dept. of English, University of Connecticut, Storrs, CT 06268.

WEIMER, DAVID RHOADS, b. New London, Ohio, Feb. 19, 27; m. 47; c. 3. AMERICAN LITERATURE. A.B, Oberlin Col, 49; A.M, Johns Hopkins Univ, 50; Shevlin fel, Univ. Minn, 52, Ford Found. internship, 53, Ph.D.(Am. stud), 54. Instr. Eng, Univ. Mich, 53-57; asst. prof. AM. STUD. & ENG, RUTGERS UNIV, 57-63, assoc. prof, 63-72, PROF, 72-, res. fels, 60, 61-62, 63, 67. Res. fel, Univ. Mich, 56; vis. lectr. Am. stud. & Eng, Univ. Minn, summer 61 & Ein Shams Univ, Cairo, 73; Fulbright lectr, Univ. Brazil, 63-64. U.S.N.R, 45-46. Intellectual history; American fiction and poetry; 20th century architectural and city planning thought. Publ: Ed, City and country in America, Appleton, 62; auth, The city as metaphor, 66 & ed, Modern American classics, 69, Random; co-ed, America (7 Vols), 73 & Literature of America, 74, McDougal-Littell. Add: Dept. of English, Scott Hall, Rutgers University, New Brunswick, NJ 08903.

WEIMER, JOAN MYERS, b. Cambridge, Mass, Mar. 12, 36; m. 71; c. 3. AMERICAN LITERATURE, WOMEN'S STUDIES. A.B, Tufts Univ, 57; M.A, Rutgers Univ, New Brunswick, 64, Ph.D.(Eng), 70. Instr. ENG, DREW UNIV, 68-70, ASST. PROF, 70- Feminist criticism of literature; images of women in the popular imagination in Egypt and Brazil. Publ: Co-ed, Vol. I, 19th century fiction, Vol. II, 19th century poetry, Vol. III, 18th and 19th century exposition, Vol. IV, 20th century fiction, Vol. V, 20th century poetry, Vol. VI, 20th century exposition, Vol. VII, 20th century drama, In: America, McDougall Littell, 73. Add: Dept. of English, Drew University, Madison, NJ 07940.

WEIMER, MARY E, b. Rockwood, Pa, Oct. 24, 10. ENGLISH. A.B, Wittenberg Univ, 32; M.A, Univ. Pittsburgh, 48; Univ. Colo, summer, 58; scholar. Harvard, summer, 62. Chmn. dept. ENG, high sch, Pa, 32-48; instr, Pa. State Univ. Somerset exten, 45-46; IND. INST. TECHNOL, 48-50, PROF, 50-, chmn. dept, 50-70. Reviewer & consult. techn. writing, Holt, Rinehart & Winston, Inc, 67- Am. Soc. Engineering Educ; Conf. Col. Compos. & Commun; NCTE; Soc. Tech. Writers & Pub; AAUP. Nineteenth century drama; modern drama. Add: Apt. 407, 2301 Fairfield Ave, Ft. Wayne, IN 46807.

WEIMER, RAE O, b. Mason City, Nebr, Nov. 2, 03; m. 42; c. 2. JOURNALISM. Kearney State Col, 22-25; Ohio State Univ, summer 50; Syracuse Univ, summer 53. Reporter, Moline Dispatch, Ill, 25; reporter & state ed, Marion Star, Ohio, 25-26; sports ed. & tel. ed, Olean Herald, N.Y, 26-27; state ed, Ft. Wayne Journal-Gazette, Ind, 27-28; Akron Beacon Journal, Ohio, 28-30, asst. city ed, 31-33; Akron Times Press, 34-35, news ed, 36-38; city ed, Buffalo Times, N.Y, 38-39; copy desk, Cleveland Press, 39-40; asst. managing ed, PM, N.Y, 40-46, managing ed, 46-48; v.pres, Weimer Orgn, Ohio, 48-49, pres, 56-57; dir. sch. jour, UNIV. FLA, 49-54, sch. jour. & commun, 54-67, PROF. JOUR, 67-, EMER. DEAN COL. JOUR. & COMMUN, 68-, dean, 67-68, spec. asst. to pres, 68-73. Consult, Legis. Comt. Educ. TV in Fla; mem. nat. res. comt, Am. Counc. Better Broadcasts; Fla. Educ. TV Planning Comt, 53-55; South. Regional Educ. Bd. TV Comt, 53-59; bd. dir, United Community Fund, 58-61; assoc. mem. task force, Educ. TV Comn, 59, 61; proj. dir, South. Regional Sci. Sem, 61; Press & Bldg. Communities Sem, 64; consult. jour, Univ. Ala, spring 65; pres, Am. Asn. Sch. & Dept. Jour, 65-66; consult. jour, Cent. Fla. Jr. Col, 67. Citations of serv, Gov. Fla; outstanding serv. to state of Fla. citation, Gov. Fla, 62. Nat. Asn. Educ. Broadcasters; Broadcast Educ. Asn; Asn. Educ. in Jour. Add: 2042 N.W. Seventh Lane, Gainesville, FL 32603.

WEINBROT, HOWARD D, b. New York, N.Y, May 14, 36. ENGLISH. B.A, Antioch Col, 58; summer, Laval Univ, summer 58; M.A, Univ. Chicago, 59, Ph.D.(Eng. lit), 63. Instr. Eng. lit, Yale, 63-66; asst. prof, Univ. Calif, Riverside, 66-68, assoc. prof, 68-69; ENG, UNIV. WIS-MADISON, 69-73, PROF, 73- Morse jr. fac. fels, Yale, summers 64 & 65; Univ. Calif. summer fac. fel, 67. MLA; Am. Soc. 18th Century Stud; Johnson Soc. Cent. Region (secy-treas, 70-). Eighteenth century theory and practice of imitation and satire and 18th century attitudes towards classics; Pope; Johnson. Publ: The formal strain: studies in Augustan imitation and satire, Univ. Chicago, 69; ed, New aspects of lexicography: literary criticism, intellectual history and social change, South. Ill. Univ, 72; The reader, the general, and the particular: Johnson and Imlac in chapter 10 of Rasselas, Eighteenth-Century Stud, 71; The allusion to Horace: Rochester's imitative mode, Stud. Philol, 72; Samuel Johnson's Plan and preface to the Dictionary: the growth of a lexicographer's mind, In: New aspects of lexicography: literary criticism, intellectual history, and social change, South. Ill. Univ, 72; plus others. Add: Dept. of English, Helen White Hall, University of Wisconsin-Madison, 600 N. Park, Madison, WI 53706.

WEINER, ALBERT BYRON, b. Philadelphia, Pa, Mar. 13, 28; m. 51, 74; c. 3. THEATRE HISTORY, DIRECTING. B.A, Temple Univ, 54; Ph.D.(theatre hist), Yale, 58. Asst. prof. Eng, Rennselaer Polytech. Inst, 58-61; assoc. prof. theatre, Univ. New South Wales, 61-63; dir, Wis. Ctr. Theatre Res, Madison, 63-66; assoc. prof. THEATRE, Ohio Univ, 66-68; PROF, STATE UNIV. N.Y, ALBANY, 68- Am. Soc. Theatre Res; Am. Theatre Asn; AAUP. Shakespeare; Australian and English theatre history. Publ: Philippe de Mézières' description of the Festum Praesentationis Beatae Marie, Yale, 58; Hamlet: the first quarto, Barron's, 62; An age of kings, Nat. Educ. TV, 61; Elizabethan interior and aloft scenes, Theatre Surv, 61; Samuel Phelps' staging of Macbeth, Educ. Theatre J, 64; The Hibernian father: the mystery solved, Meanjin Quart, 66. Add: Dept. of Theatre, State University of New York at Albany, Albany, NY 12122.

WEINER, ANDREW DAVID, b. New York, N.Y, June 29, 43; m. 64, 74; c. 3. ENGLISH LITERATURE. A.B, City Col. New York, 66; NDEA fel. & Ph.D. (Eng), Princeton, 69. ASSOC. PROF. ENG, UNIV. WIS-MADISON, 69-, grad. sch. summer res. grants, 70, 72 & 73. Nat. Endowment for Humanities younger scholar, 73-74. MLA; Renaissance Soc. Am. Christian humanists, Elizabethan literature; history of ideas. Publ: Multiformitioe uniforme: A midsummer night's dream, ELH, 9/71; Moving and teaching: Sidney's Defence of Poesie as a Protestant poetic, J. Medieval & Renaissance Stud, fall 72; Fierce warres and faithfull loves: pattern as structure in Book I of The faerie queene, Huntington Libr. Quart, 11/73. Add: Dept. of English, University of Wisconsin-Madison, 600 N. Park St, Madison, WI 53706.

WEINGARTNER, CHARLES, b. New York, N.Y, May 30, 22; m. 46; c. 1. ENGLISH, EDUCATION. B.S, Syracuse Univ, 50, M.A, 51; Ed.D.(Eng, educ), Columbia Univ, 58. Chmn. Eng. dept, Daytona Beach Jr. Col, Fla, 58-59; prof. & chmn. dept, Jersey City State Col, 59-61; staff assoc. comt. instl. coop, Big Ten, 61-62; prof. Eng. & educ, State Univ. N.Y, 62-64; assoc. dir. ling, demonstration ctr, N.Y. Univ, 64-65; assoc. prof. EDUC, Queens Col. (N.Y), 65-70; PROF, UNIV. S.FLA, 70- Dir. state wide stud. need for commun. cols, N.J, 60-61; consult, NDEA Inst. Eng. for Disadvantaged, Pa. State Univ, summer 65 & Hunter Col, summer 66; chmn. sematics comt, NCTE, 66- U.S.A.A.F, 41-45. NCTE; Int. Soc. Gen. Semantics. Semantics; mass media. Publ: Education beyond high sch, N.J. State Educ. Dept, 62; co-auth, Linguistics: a revolution in teaching, 66 & Teaching as a subversive activity, 69, Dell; co-auth, Language in America, Pegasus, 69; co-auth, The school book, Delacorte, 73; auth, The student's viewpoint, In: High school 1980, Pitman, 70; Semantics: what and why?, In: Teaching English in secondary schools, Macmillan, 73; Some ruminations on the hazards of trying to view what lies ahead by squinting through a small posterior aperture, Media & Methods, 2/73; McNamara's band and the educational Edsel (tape cassette), NCTE; plus others. Add: College of Education, University of South Florida, Tampa, FL 33620.

WEINIG, MARY ANTHONY, S.H.C.J, b. New York, N.Y, May 19, 20. ENGLISH. B.A, Rosemont Col, 42; M.A, Fordham Univ, 51, Ph.D.(Eng), 57. Teacher, Sch. of the Holy Child, N.Y, 43-56; from instr. to PROF. ENG, ROSEMONT COL, 56- Am. Philos. Soc. res. grant, summer 65; Danforth assoc, 68; mem, Eng. Inst. MLA; NCTE. Victorian literature; T.S. Eliot. Publ: Concordance to T.S. Eliot's Four quartets, Univ. Microfilms, 62;

Fire in the well (poems) 66 & Rain in the chimney (poems), 72, South & West, Inc; Coventry Patmore, Twayne, (in prep); Verbal pattern in Burnt Norton I, Criticism, 60; Emily Dickinson's scriptural echoes, Mass. Rev, 61 & In: Emily Dickinson, Scott, 64; Some translations of Henri Coulette, West. Humanities Rev, 67. Add: Dept. of English, Rosemont College, Rosemont, PA 19010.

WEINKAUF, MARY STANLEY, b. Eau Claire, Wis, Sept. 22, 38; m. 61; c. 2. ENGLISH. B.A, Wis. State Univ, 61; M.A, Univ. Tenn, 62, Ph.D.(Eng), 66. Instr. ENG, Univ. Tenn, 65-66; asst. prof, Adrian Col, 66-69; PROF. & HEAD DEPT, DAKOTA WESLEYAN UNIV, 69- MLA; NCTE; Milton Soc. Am; Sci. Fiction Res. Asn; Am. Asn. Univ. Women. Renaissance courtesy and conduct literature; Utopian fiction; science fiction. Publ: Theme for science fiction: aesthetics and population, Extrapolation, 72; The escape from the garden, Tex. Quart, 73; Dalila: the worst of all possible wives, Stud. Eng. Lit, 73; plus others. Add: 914 University Blvd, Mitchell, SD 57301.

WEINMAN, GEOFFREY STEPHEN, b. Bronx, N.Y, Mar. 16, 43; m. 66; c. 1. AMERICAN LITERATURE. B.A, Hunter Col, 64; M.A, Johns Hopkins Univ, 65, Ph.D.(Eng), 68. ASST. PROF. ENG, FAIRLEIGH DICKINSON UNIV, 68-, COORD. AM. STUD, 73- Am. Stud. Asn; AAUP; MLA. Black American literature; 19th century American literature; American studies. Add: Dept. of English, Fairleigh Dickinson University, Madison Ave, Madison, NJ 07940.

WEINMAN, RICHARD JAY, b. New York, N.Y, Feb. 20, 33; m. 55; c. 6. BROADCAST MEDIA COMMUNICATION, SPEECH. A.B, Ind. Univ, 55, Ph.D.(theatre), 65; M.F.A, Columbia Univ, 56. Instr. speech & drama, Bucknell Univ, 56-57; asst. prof, Univ. Ga, 59-63; telecommun. arts, Iowa State Univ, 63-66, assoc. prof, 66-67; broadcast media commun, ORE. STATE UNIV, 67-72, PROF. SPEECH COMMUN, 72- Ind. Univ. grant, summer 64; Iowa State Univ. res. grant, 65-66. Speech Commun. Asn. Add: Dept. of Speech, Oregon State University, Corvallis, OR 97330.

WEINSTEIN, ARNOLD LOUIS, Comparative Literature, French Studies. See Volume III, Foreign Languages, Linguistics & Philology.

WEINSTEIN, MARK A, b. New York, N.Y, June 29, 37; m. 67; c. 1. ENGLISH. B.A, Cornell, 59; Woodrow Wilson fel, Yale, 59-61, M.A, 60, sr. Sterling fel, 61-62, Ph.D.(Eng), 62. Asst. prof. ENG, Brooklyn Col, 65-70; assoc. prof, UNIV. NEV, LAS VEGAS, 70-74, PROF, 74- U.S.A, 62-64, 1st Lt. MLA. Victorian fiction and poetry; Romantic poetry; novels of Sir Walter Scott. Publ: William Edmonstoune Aytoun and the spasmodic controversy, Yale, 68; Imagination and reality in Romantic fiction, Wordsworth Circle, 71; An echo of Mrs. Bennet in Waverley, Notes & Queries, 75. Add: 2933 Natalie, Las Vegas, NV 89121.

WEINSTEIN, PHILIP MEYER, b. Memphis, Tenn, July 8, 40; m. 63; c. 2. ENGLISH & AMERICAN LITERATURE. A.B, Princeton, 62; Univ. Paris, 62-63; M.A, Harvard, 66, Ph.D.(Eng), 68. Instr. ENG, Harvard, 68-69, asst. prof, 69-71; SWARTHMORE COL, 71-74, ASSOC. PROF, 74- AAUP; MLA. British fiction, Dickens through Joyce; American fiction, Hawthorne through Faulkner. Publ: Henry James and the requirements of the imagination, Harvard Univ, 71; Structure and collapse: a study of Bleak House, Dickens Stud, 68; The exploitative and protective imagination: unreliable narration in The Sacred fount, Harvard Eng. Stud, 70; An interpretation of pastoral in The winter's tale, Shakespeare Quart, 71. Add: Dept. of English Literature, Swarthmore College, Swarthmore, PA 19081.

WEINSTOCK, DONALD JAY, b. Chicago, Ill, Sept. 2, 34; m. 55. ENGLISH LITERATURE. A.B, Univ. Calif, Los Angeles, 56, M.A, 60, Ph.D.(Eng), 68. Acting asst. prof. ENG, Univ. Calif, Riverside, 65-68; lectr, Univ. Calif, Los Angeles, 68-69; ASST. PROF, CALIF. STATE UNIV, LONG BEACH, 69- U.S.A, 57-58, Res, 57-63. MLA (African Lit. Sect, Lit. Div, Bibliog. Comt, Int. Bibliog. Comt); Asn. Poetry Ther; Poetry Ther. Inst. Victorian literature; contemporary African writing in English; psychological applications of poetry. Publ: Review of Arthur Ravenscroft's Writers and their work pamphlet Chinua Achebe, fall 70, The two Boer wars and the Jameson Raid: a checklist of novels in Dutch and Afrikaans, spring 71 & The two Boer wars and the Jameson Raid: a checklist of novels in English, spring 72, Res. African Lit; plus six others. Add: Dept. of English, California State University, Long Beach, 6101 E. Seventh St, Long Beach, CA 90840.

WEINTRAUB, STANLEY, b. Philadelphia, Pa, Apr. 17, 29; m. 54; c. 3. ENGLISH LITERATURE. B.S, Pa. State Col, West Chester, 49; M.A, Temple Univ, 51; Ph.D.(Eng), Pa. State Univ, 56. From instr. to prof. ENG, PA. STATE UNIV, 53-70, RES. PROF. & DIR. INST. ARTS & HUMANISTIC STUD, 70- Ed, Shaw Rev, 56-; vis. prof, Univ. Calif, Los Angeles, summer 63; Guggenheim fel, 68-69; vis. prof. Eng, Univ. Hawaii, Manoa, summer 73. U.S.A, 51-53, 1st Lt. Auth. Guild. George Bernard Shaw; biographical writing; English literature since 1880. Publ: Ed, An unfinished novel by Bernard Shaw, Dodd & Constable, London, 58; auth, Private Shaw and public Shaw: a dual portrait of Lawrence of Arabia and G.B.S, Braziller & Jonathan Cape, 63; ed, C.P. Snow: a spectrum, Scribner, 63; ed, The yellow book: quintessence of the nineties, 64 & auth, The war in the wards, 64, Doubleday; co-auth, The art of William Golding, Harcourt, 65; auth, Reggie: a portrait of Reginald Turner, Braziller, 65, W.H. Allen, 66; ed, The Savoy: nineties experiment, 66, co-ed, Evolution of a revolt: early postwar writings of T.E. Lawrence, 68 & Directions in literary criticism, 73, Pa. State Univ; ed, The Court Theatre, Univ. Miami, 66 & Biography and truth, Bobbs, 67; auth, Beardsley: a biography, Braziller & W.H. Allen, 67; The last great cause: the intellectuals and the Spanish Civil War, Weybright & Talley & & W. H. Allen, 68; ed, The literary criticism of Oscar Wilde, Univ. Nebr, 68, Shaw: an autobiography, 1856-1898, 69 & Shaw: an autobiography 1898-1950, the playwright years, 70, Bodley Head & Weybright & Talley; auth, Journey to heartbreak: Bernard Shaw 1914-1918, Weybright & Talley, 71 & Routledge & Kegan Paul, 73; co-ed, Saint Joan: fifty years after 1923-24/1973-74, La. State Univ, 73; auth, Whistler, a biography, Collins, London, & Weybright & Talley, 74. Add: Institute for the Arts & Humanistic Studies, Pennsylvania State University, Ihlseng Cottage, University Park, PA 16802.

WEINTZ, CHRISTIAN, b. Cogelac, Romania, Sept. 10, 28; U.S. citizen; m. 51; c. 3. ENGLISH. Th.B, N. Am. Baptist Sem, 52; B.S, North. State Col, 55, M.S, 56; Ph.D.(Am. lit), Univ. Minn, 70. Teacher, high sch, Wyo, 56-57; from instr. to PROF. ENG, BETHEL COL.(MINN), 57-70, chmn. dept, 58-72, Bd. Educ. fel, 62-63, alumni grant, 65. NCTE. Poets of the 19th century American renaissance. Add: Dept. of English, Bethel College, 3900 Bethel Dr, St. Paul, MN 55112.

WEIR, MARY LORRAINE, b. Montreal, P.Q, May 20, 46. ANGLO-IRISH LITERATURE. B.A, McGill Univ, 67; M.A, Univ. Col, Dublin, 68, Ph.D.(Anglo-Irish stud), 71. ASST. PROF. ENG, UNIV. B.C, 70- James Joyce Found; Asn. Can. Univ. Teachers Eng. James Joyce's Finnegans Wake; theory of film and literature; surrealism. Publ: On his blindness: Joyce, myth and memory, Irish Univ. Rev, autumn 72. Add: Dept. of English, University of British Columbia, Vancouver 8, B.C, Can.

WEISENBORN, RAY EDWARD, b. Portland, Ore, July 10, 41; m. 66; c. 1. SPEECH COMMUNICATION. B.S, Portland State Univ, 63; M.A, East. N.Mex. Univ, 65; Ph.D.(speech), Mich. State Univ, 68. Instr. speech, Clark Col, 65-66; asst. instr, Mich. State Univ, 66-68; lectr, Europ. Div, Univ. Md, 68-71; ASST. PROF. SPEECH COMMUN, MONT. STATE UNIV, 71- Lectr. mass commun. U.S. Dept. Health, Educ. & Welfare, 71-72; Police Acad, Mont, 71-72; analyst, Dept. Agr, Mont, 72-; consult, Ten Dimensions Debate Assocs, 73- Speech Commun. Asn; Int. Commun. Asn. Communication media; interpersonal communication; deaf education. Publ: Introduction to speech communication, ArtCraft, 72; co-auth, A study of compressed deaf speech, 73, auth, Intercultural definition and communication design: propaganda and agitation, 74 & Rhetoric of discontent: the American Indian, 74, Eric. Add: Dept. of Speech Communication, Montana State University, Bozeman, MT 59715.

WEISER, JOHN C, b. St. Paul, Minn, Jan. 7, 22; m. 47; c. 3. SPEECH. B.A, State Univ. Iowa, 48, M.A, 49; Ph.D, West. Reserve Univ, 61. Instr. speech, KENT STATE UNIV, 49-53, asst. prof. speech & radio, 54-61, ASSOC. PROF. SPEECH, RADIO & TV, 62-, dir. radio oper, 56-72. Supply pastor, Lake Brady Community Church, 52-55. U.S.M.C, 42-45, Sgt. Speech Commun. Asn. Radio and television audience research; historical and critical studies in religion; religious leaders. Publ: Radio and television curricula belong in speech, 63 & Radio as a medium of direct instruction, 72, Ohio Speech J; co-auth, Radio and the 1948 presidential campaign in the west, West. States Speech J, 1/51. Add: School of Speech, Kent State University, Kent, OH 44242.

WEISGRAM, DIANNE HUNTER, b. Cleveland, Ohio, Oct. 4, 43; m. 68. LITERATURE, PSYCHOANALYSIS. B.A, Alfred Univ, 66; M.A, Purdue Univ, West Lafayette, 68; Ph.D.(Eng), State Univ. N.Y. Buffalo, 72. Teaching asst. Eng, Purdue Univ, West Lafayette, 66-68; State Univ. N.Y. Buffalo, 68-71, res. fel. psychoanal, 71-72; ASST. PROF. ENG, TRINITY COL.(CONN), 72- MLA; Asn. Appl. Psychoanal. Violence and the theatre; Elizabethan and Jacobean drama; psychoanalytic criticism. Publ: LeRoi Jones' Dutchman: interracial ritual of sexual violence, Am. Imago, fall 72. Add: Dept. of English, Trinity College, Hartford, CT 06106.

WEISINGER, HERBERT, b. Brooklyn, N.Y, May 19, 13; m. RENAISSANCE LITERATURE. A.B, Brooklyn Col, 34; A.M, Univ. Mich, 35, Ph.D, 41. Instr, Univ. Mich, 41-42; Mich. State Univ, 42-45, asst. prof, 45-48, assoc. prof. Eng. lit. & fine arts, 48-54, PROF, 54-66; ENG, STATE UNIV. N.Y. STONY BROOK, 67-, DEAN GRAD. SCH, 68-, chmn. dept. Eng, 67-68. Mem, Inst. Adv. Stud, 48-49; sr. res. fel, Warburg Inst. & Univ. London, 50-52; Howard fel, 55-56; ed, Centennial Rev; Berg prof. Eng, N.Y. Univ, 65-66; mem. bd. dirs, Grad. Rec. Exams, 71-; Grad. & Prof. Sch. Financial Aid Serv, 72- MLA; Mediaeval Acad. Am; Renaissance Soc. Am; Shakespeare Asn. Am. Renaissance literature; myth studies; Shakespeare. Publ: Tragedy and the paradox of the fortunate fall, 53, The agony and the triumph, 64 & co-auth, The crisis in comparative literature, 66, Mich. State Univ. Add: Graduate School, State University of New York at Stony Brook, Stony Brook, NY 11790.

WEISINGER, KENNETH DEAN, b. Blanco Co, Tex, Dec. 8, 42. GERMAN, COMPARATIVE LITERATURE. B.A, Stanford Univ, 64; Free Univ. Berlin, 64-65; M.A, Univ. Calif, Berkeley, 67, Ph.D.(comp. lit), 71; Univ. Tübingen, 69-70. ASST. PROF. GER. & COMP. LIT, UNIV. CALIF, BERKELEY, 71- MLA; Am. Philol. Asn. Greek and Latin literature; German literature. Publ: Irony and moderation in Juvenal XI, Calif. Stud. Class. Antiq, 72; Goethe's Phaethon, Deut. Vierteljahrsschrift, 73; The structure of Rilke's Seventh Duino elegy, Germanic Rev, 74; plus others. Add: Dept. of Comparative Literature, University of California, Berkeley, CA 94720.

WEISMILLER, EDWARD RONALD, b. Monticello, Wis, Aug. 3, 15; m. 41; c. 5. ENGLISH LITERATURE. A.B, Cornell Col, 38, D.Litt, 53; A.M, Harvard, 42; Rhodes scholar, Oxford, 38-39, 48-50, D.Phil, 50. Teaching fel. ENG, Harvard, 40-43; asst. prof, Pomona Col, 49-52, assoc. prof, 52-58, PROF, 58-68; GEORGE WASHINGTON UNIV, 68- Guggenheim fel, 46-47, 47-48; Ford Found. Fund Advan. Educ. fel, 53-54; Fulbright prof, Univ. Leyden, 57-58; Am. Counc. Learned Soc. grants-in-aid, 63, 66 & 69; Folger Shakespeare Libr. fel, 65, 72-73; Rockefeller Found. spec. grant, 65-66; Am. Philos. Soc. travel grant, 66 & 69; Ctr. Advan. Stud. sr. fel. lett, Wesleyan Univ, 67-68; mem. bd. eds. & contrib, A Variorum Commentary on the Poems of John Milton, Columbia Univ. & Routledge, Kegan Paul, 70-; Nat. Endowment for Humanities res. grant, 72-73. U.S.M.C, 43-46, Lt. MLA. Prosody and versification; poetry of the English Renaissance, especially Milton; contemporary British and American poetry. Publ: The deer come down, Yale, 36; The faultless shore, Houghton, 46; The serpent sleeping, Putnam, 62; Samson Agonistes: the 'dry' and 'rugged' verse, In: The lyric and dramatic Milton, Columbia Univ, 65; Materials dark and crude: a partial genealogy for Milton's Satan, Huntington Libr. Quart, 11/67; Studies of verse form in the minor English poems, In: Vol. 2, A variorum commentary on the poems of John Milton, Columbia Univ. & Routledge, Kegan Paul, 72; plus others. Add: Dept. of English, George Washington University, Washington, DC 20006.

WEISS, ADAM F, Marietta, Ohio, May 9, 33; m. 62; c. 1. THEATRE HISTORY. B.A, Univ. Pa, 61; M.A, Univ. Denver, 64, Ph.D.(dramatic criticism), 65. Asst. drama & scene design, Univ. Denver, 64-65; asst. prof. THEATRE HIST, CLARION STATE COL, 65-72, ASSOC. PROF, 72- Am. Theatre Asn. Study of the soical image in Germany from 1914-1917 found in the plays of Georg Kaiser, Hans Johst and Wolfgang Borchert; theatre history and criticism. Add: Dept. of Theatre History, Clarion State College, Clarion, PA 16214.

WEISS, DANIEL A, b. Philadelphia, Pa, Nov. 28, 17; m. 41; c. 3. ENGLISH LITERATURE. B.A, Northwest. Univ, 39, Ph.D, 55; M.A, Columbia Univ, 51. Instr. ENG, City Col. New York, 55-56; asst. prof, Univ. Wash, 56-62; from asst. prof. to ASSOC. PROF, SAN FRANCISCO STATE UNIV, 62- Fulbright exchange lectr, Norway, 63. U.S. Merchant Marine, 42-47. Philol. Asn. Pac. Coast; MLA. Psychoanalytic criticism, D.H. Lawrence, Stephen Crane, Franz Kafka. Publ: Oedipus in Nottingham: D.H. Lawrence, Univ. Wash, 63. Add: Dept. of English, San Francisco State University, San Francisco, CA 94132.

WEISS, DAVID WILLIAM, b. Milwaukee, Wis, Feb. 26, 28; m. 56; c. 2. DRAMA. B.A, Univ. Wis, 50, M.A, 51; Ph.D.(theatre), Ind. Univ, 61. Instr. DRAMA, Mont. State Univ, 51-53; asst. prof, UNIV. VA, 54-65, assoc. prof, 65-71, PROF, 71-, CHMN. DEPT, 73- Lectr, Ind. Univ, summer, 60. Am. Theatre Asn; U.S. Inst. Theatre Technol.(dir, 66-67); Speech Commun. Asn. Theatre architecture; history and theory of scene design. Publ: Low budget lighting, Wis. Idea Theatre, 52. Add: Dept. of Drama, University of Virginia, Culbreth Rd, Charlottesville, VA 22903.

WEISS, HAROLD, b. New York, N.Y, Oct. 18, 09. SPEECH. A.B, Univ. North Colo, 33, A.M, 37; Ph.D, Univ. Wis, 48. Dir. dept. speech & theater, Mary Washington Col, Univ. Va, 37-47; PROF. SPEECH & CHMN. DEPT. SPEECH & THEATRE, SOUTH. METHODIST UNIV, 47-, CHMN. DIV. COMMUN. ARTS, 67- Nat. Thespian Soc.(prize); Speech Commun. Asn. American phonetics. Publ: Co-auth, Technically speaking, McGraw, 63. Add: Division of Communication Arts, Southern Methodist University, Dallas, TX 75222.

WEISS, MORTON JERRY, b. Oxford, N.C, Apr. 16, 26; m. 50; c. 4. ENGLISH. B.A, Univ. N.C, 49; M.A, Columbia Univ, 51, Ed.D.(guidance), 52. Teacher high sch, Va, 49-50; Rhodes Sch, N.Y, 52-56; assoc. prof. Eng, Defiance Col, 56-58; asst. prof. sec. educ, Pa. State Univ, 58-61; prof. spec. educ. & reading, JERSEY CITY STATE COL, 61-68, DISTINGUISHED SERV. PROF. COMMUN, 68-, chmn. dept, 61-68. Mem. comn. mass media, Col. Reading Asn, 62-; mem. comt. jr. high sch. booklist, NCTE, 64-; consult. sch. syst, Clovis, Calif. & Midland Park, N.J, 68; consult. publ, Dell Publ. Co. & Odyssey Press, 68. Col. Reading Asn; NCTE; Int. Reading Asn. Visual-lingual reading materials; mass media, reading and English; reading problems. Publ: Guidance through drama, Whiteside, 54; ed, Reading in secondary schools, 60 & English teacher's reader, 61, Odyssey; Tales out of school, Dell, 67; co-auth, Visual-lingual program, Tweedy, 67; The unfinished journey, Webster Div, McGraw, 67; Effective reading series (text-film), McGraw, 68; Perspectives on man: kaleidoscope, 70 & Perspectives on man: man to himself, 71, Cummings; Teacher's guide to Warner Bros. Jungle habitat, 73; Change in behavior through reading, Reading Sec. Sch, 68. Add: Dept. of English, Jersey City State College, 2039 Kennedy Blvd, Jersey City, NJ 07305.

WEISS, ROBERT ORR, b. Kalamazoo, Mich, Apr. 8, 26; m. 51; c. 4. SPEECH. B.A, Albion Col, 48; M.A, Northwest. Univ, 49, Ph.D.(speech), 54. Instr. speech, Wayne Univ, 49-51; pub. speaking, Northwest. Univ, 54-55; asst. prof. SPEECH, DePAUW UNIV, 55-59, assoc. prof, 59-65, PROF, 65- Speech Commun. Asn; Int. Commun. Asn; Am. Forensic Asn.(secy-treas, 58-59). History of American public address; theory of argumentation; communication pedagogy. Publ: Co-ed, Current criticism, Delta Sigma Rho-Tau Kappa Alpha, 71. Add: Dept. of Speech, DePauw University, Greencastle, IN 46135.

WEISS, SAMUEL ABBA, b. Rochester, N.Y, Oct. 20, 22. ENGLISH. B.A, Brooklyn Col, 45; M.A, Columbia Univ, 46, Ph.D.(Eng), 53. Instr. Eng, Mohawk Col, 46-48; L.I. Univ, 49; assoc. prof. & chmn. dept, Knoxville Col, 55-57; asst. prof. ENG, UNIV. ILL, CHICAGO CIRCLE, 57-62, assoc. prof, 63-67, PROF, 67- Summer res. fel, Univ. Ill, 62. Silver Circle Award for excellence in teaching, 66 & 67. MLA; NCTE; AAUP. Restoration drama; modern drama; Shakespeare. Publ: Drama in the modern world, 64, 2nd ed, 74 & Drama in the Western world, 68, Heath; Solid, sullied and mutability, Shakespeare Quart, spring 59; Peter Weiss's Marat/Sade, Drama Survey, summer 66; The ordeal of Malcolm X, S.Atlantic Quart, winter 68. Add: Dept. of English, University of Illinois at Chicago Circle, Chicago, IL 60680.

WEISS, THEODORE RUSSELL, b. Reading, Pa, Dec. 16, 16; m. 41. ENGLISH. A.B, Muhlenberg Col, 38, Litt.D, 68; A.M, Columbia Univ, 40, 40-41; hon. Litt.D, Bard Col, 73. Instr. Eng, Univ. N.C, 41-43; Yale, 43-46; from asst. prof. to assoc. prof, Bard Col, 46-56, PROF, 56-68; ENG. & CREATIVE WRITING, PRINCETON, 68-, POET-IN-RESIDENCE, 66- Ford fel, 53-54; vis. prof. poetry, Mass. Inst. Tech, 61-62; ed, Quart. Rev. Lit; hon. fel, Ezra Stiles Col, Yale, 63-; judge, Bollingen Comt. for Poetry, 65; mem. Wesleyan Poetry Bd, 66-71; judge, Nat. Book Award for Poetry, 68; Nat. Found. Arts & Lett. grant, 67-68; Ingram Merrill Found. fel, 74-75. Stevens Award, 56. Shakespeare; modern poetry; Homer. Publ: The catch, Twayne, 51; Outlanders, 60, The medium, 65, The last day and the first, 68 & The world before us: poems, 1950-1970, 70, Macmillan; Gunsight, N.Y. Univ, 62; The poetry of Pasternak, Delos, 68; The breath of clowns and kings: Shakespeare's early comedies and histories, Chatto & Windus, London & Atheneum, 71. Add: 26 Haslet Ave, Princeton, NJ 08540.

WEISSBUCH, TED N, b. Chicago, Ill, May 28, 30; m. 54; c. 2. AMERICAN LITERATURE. A.B, Los Angeles State Col, 54, M.A, 55; Ph.D.(Eng), Univ. Iowa, 64. Instr. ENG, Univ. Nebr, 56-57; Univ. Iowa, 57-62; asst. prof. CALIF. STATE POLYTECH UNIV, POMONA, 62-65, assoc. prof, 65-69, PROF, 69- Heath lit. award, Am. Numis. Asn, 62, 68. U.S.A.R, 58, M/Sgt. NCTE. American literature and civilization; reconstruction era literature and history. Publ: Ishmael the ironist: the anti-salvation theme in Moby Dick, Emerson Soc. Quart, 63; A letter from Sweden: 1839, Whitman Numismatic J, 10/68; Nepotism backfires in U.S. Mint, Numismatic Scrapbook Mag, 2/70; plus others. Add: Dept. of English, Administration Bldg. 337, California State Polytechnic University, Pomona, CA 91768.

WEITZMAN, ARTHUR JOSHUA, b. Newark, N.J, Sept. 13, 33; m. 60; c. 2. ENGLISH. A.B, Univ. Chicago, 56, A.M, 57; Ph.D.(Eng), N.Y. Univ, 64. Lectr. ENG, Brooklyn Col, 60-63; instr, Temple Univ, 63-64; asst. prof, 64-69; assoc. prof, NORTHEAST. UNIV, 69-72, PROF, 72-, DIR. ENG. GRAD. PROG, 69- Co-ed. & founder, The Scriblerian, 68-; Nat. Endowment for Humanities,fel, 72-73. MLA. Am. Soc. 18th Century Stud. Neoclassical English literature; bibliography and literature; urban studies. Publ: Ed, The Turkish spy, Routledge & Kegan Paul, Columbia Univ. & Temple Univ, 70; A spider's poison: wit in Swift's Letter of advice to a young poet, Ariel, 73; Addendum to Teerink and Scouten: another edition of Swift's poems, Papers Bibliog. Soc. Am, 73; Eighteenth century London: urban paradise or fallen city?, J. Hist. Ideas, (in press); plus others. Add: Dept. of English, Northeastern University, Boston, MA 02115.

WELCH, JAMES DONALD, b. Philadelphia, Pa, Sept. 2, 43; m. 63; c. 3. ENGLISH. B.A, Wesleyan Univ, 65; M.A, Univ. Calif, Berkeley, 67, Ph.D. (Eng), 71. ASST. PROF. ENG, UNIV. HOUSTON, 70- MLA. Tennyson; stylistics; art and literature. Add: 4418 Kinglet, Houston, TX 77035.

WELCH, JOHN MORGAN, b. Searcy, Ark, May 19, 19; m. 42; c. 2. JOURNALISM. B.S, Northwest. Univ, 47, M.S, 48; M.A, Stetson Univ, 60. Asst. instr, Northwest. Univ, 47-48; managing ed, DeLAND SUN NEWS, 48-49, PUBL, 49-; ASST. PROF. JOUR. & POLIT. SCI, STETSON UNIV, 49- Trustee, Daytona Beach Jr. Col; mem. adv. counc, Fla. Technol. Univ. U.S.A, 40-45, 1st Lt. History of the United States propaganda program. Add: P.O. Box 1119, DeLand, FL 32720.

WELCH, LAURENCE C, b. Trenton, N.J, May 12, 05; m. 31. COMPARATIVE LITERATURE. A.B, Univ. Pa, 29; A.M, Univ. South. Calif, 36, Ph.D.(comp. lit), 59. Teacher Eng, Los Angeles City Schs, Calif, 37-49; assoc. prof. comp. lit. & philos, LOS ANGELES HARBOR COL, 49-67, PROF. HUMANITIES, 67- Mediaeval Acad. Am; Archaeol. Inst. Am; Am. Comp. Lit. Asn. Mythology. Add: 26700 Eastvale Rd, Rolling Hills, CA 90274.

WELCH, M. CHRISTINA, S.S.J, b. Penfield, N.Y, Feb. 22, 09. ENGLISH. B.A, Nazareth Col, 47; M.A, Univ. Rochester, 52. TEACHER, St. Patrick's Girls Home, 30-31; St. Bridget's Sch, 31-32; ENG, Nazareth Acad, 42-70, chmn. dept, 54-70; ST. AGNES HIGH SCH, 70- NCTE (awards judge, 62-74). High school writing; Robert Southwell and Elizabethan poets. Publ: A core writing program, Eng. Rec, winter 62; Training for research writing, Eng. J, 11/64; Research papers in high school English, NEA J, 11/65. Add: 300 E. River Rd, Rochester, NY 14623.

WELCHER, JEANNE K, b. Hartford, Conn, Mar. 14, 22. ENGLISH LITERATURE. B.A, Col. New Rochelle, 43; M.A, Fordham Univ, 46, Ph.D, 55. Asst, Fordham Univ, 43-44; from instr. to asst. prof. ENG. LIT, Rosemont Col, 47-54; asst. prof, St. John's Univ.(N.Y), 55-56, assoc. prof, 56-63, prof, 63-68, univ. fel, Brit. Mus, summer, 62; ASSOC. PROF, C.W. POST COL, LONG ISLAND UNIV, 68- Mem. Eng. Inst. MLA; NCTE. Eighteenth century English literature: fable, epic and letters; Chaucer. Publ: John Evelyn's diary, Thought Patterns, 61; Five joyful mysteries of Muriel Spark, Cath. Bk. Reporter, 11-12/61. Add: Dept. of English, C.W. Post College, Long Island University, Greenvale, NY 11548.

WELKE, JAMES WILLIAM, b. Peru, Ind, June 20, 36; m. 62; c. 2. BROADCASTING, COMMUNICATION RESEARCH. B.A, Ind. Univ, 62, M.A, 64, Ph.D.(mass commun), 67. Instr. commun. res, UNIV. WYO, 66-67, asst. prof. BROADCASTING, 67-72, ASSOC. PROF, 72-, CHMN. DEPT, 69-, acting chmn. dept, 68-69, grad. counc. res. grant, 67- Coord, Speech Commun. Module, Speech Commun. Asn. & Educ. Resources Inform. Ctr, 73-74. Speech Commun. Asn; West. Speech Commun. Asn; Broadcast Educ. Asn. (mem. course-curriculum comt, 69-, mem. bd. dirs, 73-75, mem. Harold E. Fellows scholar. comt, 74). Oral communication; broadcasting; cable television. Publ: Effects of intensional and extensional audiences on communicator anxiety, Cent. States Speech, 2/68; A harbinger of CATV?, TV Commun, 6/73. Add: Dept. of Communication & Theatre, University of Wyoming, Laramie, WY 82070.

WELKER, DAVID (HAROLD), b. La Rose, Ill, Mar. 25, 17; m. 37; c. 1. SPEECH. B.A, Univ. Ill, 39, M.A, 43; Ph.D.(Eng, speech), Univ. Minn, 56. Instr. speech, Univ. Minn, 48-55; lectr, Duluth Campus, Univ. Minn, 55-56; asst. prof. speech & dir. radio & TV, Wis. State Col, Eau Claire, 56-61; prof. speech & drama, chmn. speech dept. & dir. theater, Albion Col, 61-69; PROF. SPEECH COMMUN. & THEATER ARTS, WAKE FOREST UNIV, 69- Radio & TV adv, Gov. Freeman, Minn, 55; radio & TV consult, State Dept. Conserv, Minn, 55; Ed, N.C. J. Speech & Drama, 71-73. Nat. Col. Players; Speech Commun. Asn; Am. Theatre Asn. Theatre; broadcasting; communication. Publ: Theatrical set design: the basic techniques, 69 & Theatrical direction: the basic techniques, 71, Allyn & Bacon. Add: 1301 University Pkwy, Winston-Salem, NC 27106.

WELKER, ROBERT L, b. Clarksville, Tenn, June 26, 24. ENGLISH. B.A, George Peabody Col, 48; M.A, Vanderbilt Univ, 52, scholar, 54, fel, 55, Ph.D, 58; South. Univs. Fel, 57. Instr. ENG, Vanderbilt Univ, 54-57, asst. prof, 61-64; assoc. prof, UNIV. ALA, HUNTSVILLE, 64-67, PROF, 67-, CHMN. DEPT, 66- Asst. ed, POEM, 67, co-ed, 70-72, ed, 72- U.S.A, 43-46. S.Atlantic Mod. Lang. Asn; AAUP; MLA. Shakespeare; American novel, 1920-1940; contemporary Southern literature. Publ: Co-auth, Reality and myth, Vanderbilt, 64 & The sense of fiction, Prentice-Hall, 66. Add: 600 Franklin St, Huntsville, AL 35801.

WELLEK, RENÉ, English & Comparative Literature. See Volume III, Foreign Languages, Linguistics & Philology.

WELLINGTON, JAMES ELLIS, b. Arlington, Mass, July 9, 21; m. 52; c. 2. ENGLISH LITERATURE. A.B, Dartmouth Col, 48; A.M, Boston Univ, 50; Ph.D.(Eng), Fla. State Univ, 56. Instr. ENG, Univ. Nebr, 50-53; Fla. State Univ, 54-56; UNIV. MIAMI, 56-57, asst. prof, 57-63, assoc. prof, 63-70, PROF, 70-, univ. grant, summer 65. U.S.N, 41-46. MLA; S.Atlantic Mod. Lang. Asn; Southeast. Renaissance Conf; Renaissance Soc. Am; Malone Soc; Augustan Reprint Soc. Seventeenth and eighteenth century English literature. Publ: Pope's Epistles to several persons (moral essays), 63 & Pope's Eloisa to Abelard, with the Hughes letters, 65, Univ. Miami; Pope's Alas?

How chang'd, The Carrell, 12/66; Pope and charity, Philol. Quart, 4/67; The litany in Cranmer and Donne, Stud. Philol, 4/71. Add: Dept. of English, University of Miami, Coral Gables, FL 33124.

WELLS, ARVIN ROBERT, b. Chicago, Ill, Mar. 10, 27; m. 49; c. 1. ENGLISH LANGUAGE & LITERATURE. Parker fel, Univ. Mich, 51-52, 53-54, M.A, 52, Ph.D.(Eng), 59. Teaching fel. ENG, Univ. Mich, 52-55; instr, OHIO UNIV, 55-59, asst. prof, 59-63, assoc. prof, 63-67, PROF. & CHMN. DEPT, 67- Fulbright lectr. Am. lit, Germany, 60-61; Univ. Erlangen, 65-66. U.S.A, 45-46. MLA. James Branch Cabell Soc; Soc. Stud. South. Lit. Contemporary American and British fiction; 20th century criticism and stylistics; the teaching of literature. Publ: Jesting Moses, Univ. Fla, 62; co-auth, Insight I: Analyses of American literature, 62, Insight II: analyses of British literature, 63 & contrib, Insight IV: analyses of modern drama, 73, Hirshbraben, Frankfort; auth, The living and the dead in All my sons, Mod. Drama, 64; contrib, Das Amerikanische drama, Wissenschaftliche Buchgesellschaft, 72. Add: 40 Forest St, Athens, OH 45701.

WELLS, CELIA TOWNSEND, b. Florence, S.C, Feb. 10, 32; div; c. 1. MEDIEVAL LITERATURE, WOMEN IN LITERATURE. A.B, Meredith Col, 54; A.M, Fla. State Univ, 56; Ph.D.(Eng. & comp. lit), Columbia Univ, 70. Instr. ENG, Bradford Jr. Col, 56-59; Fairleigh Dickinson Univ, Teaneck Campus, 59-61; ASST. PROF, Conn. Col, 70-71; FAIRFIELD UNIV, 71- Lectr, S.S. France, French Line, N.Y.C, 74- MLA; Mediaeval Acad. Am; AAUP. Courtly love in Medieval literature; textual problems in Middle English manuscripts; misogyny in English and American literature. Publ: Ed, Prose and the essay, Houghton, 62 & James's The Bostonians, Apollo Bks, 74; auth, Line 21 of Middelerd for Mon Wes Mad, Eng. Lang. Notes, 73. Add: Dept. of English, Fairfield University, N. Benson Rd, Fairfield, CT 06430.

WELLS, CHARLES FLOYD, b. Lisbon, N.Dak, Oct. 19, 03; m. 35. AMERICAN RHETORIC. B.S, N.Dak. State Col, 25; A.M, Columbia Univ, 33, D.Ed, 39. Prin. jr. high sch, N.Dak, 25-27; dir. drama, Nat. Recreation Asn, N.Y, 27-35; instr, Teachers Col, Columbia Univ, 35-40; prof. Eng, State Univ. N.Y. Col, Oswego, 40-68, chmn. dept, 40-62, dir. div. arts & sci, 62-68; RETIRED. Vis. prof, Univ. Hawaii, 49. Col. Eng. Asn. Correction of foreign accent; materials and methods of teaching rhetoric; century of drama in Oswego County. Add: Edgewater Apts, 620 Edgewater Dr, Dunedin, FL 33528.

WELLS, DANIEL ARTHUR, b. Adams, Mass, Oct. 16, 43; m. 66; c. 2. ENGLISH & AMERICAN LITERATURE. A.B, Union Col.(N.Y), 65; M.A, Duke Univ, 68, Ph.D.(Eng), 72. ASST. PROF. ENG, UNIV. S.FLA, ST. PETERSBURG, 70- S.Atlantic Mod. Lang. Asn. Nineteenth century American literature; contemporary literature; poetry. Publ: Ed, Charles Fenno Hoffman's Greyslaer, Col. & Univ. Press, 75; auth, John Barth, In: Counter currents, Kendall/Hunt, 73. Add: Dept. of English, University of South Florida, St. Petersburg, FL 33701.

WELLS, DAVID MARSDEN, b. Wilmington, N.C, July 23, 32; m. 65. ENGLISH LITERATURE. B.A, Taylor Univ, 56; M.A, Univ. N.C, Chapel Hill, 60, Ph.D.(Eng), 69. Instr. ENG, Howard Col, 60-62; ASST. PROF, Wilmington, Col, 65-68; RANDOLPH-MACON COL, 70- Mediaeval Acad. Am. Old English poetry; history of the English language. Publ: More on the geography of Huckleberry Finn, S.Atlantic Bull, 73. Add: P.O. Box 3, Ashland, VA 23005.

WELLS, JAMES M, b. Charleston, W.Va, Nov. 4, 17. BIBLIOGRAPHY, ENGLISH LITERATURE. B.S, Northwest. Univ, 38; M.A, Columbia Univ, 39, Am. Counc. Learned Soc. fel, 41-42; Am. Counc. Learned Soc. traveling fel, London, 49-51. Instr. Eng, W.Va. Univ, 39-41; Columbia Univ, 46-49; CUR, WING FOUND. HIST. PRINTING, NEWBERRY LIBR, 51-, ASSOC. DIR. LIBR, 64- Ed, Newberry Libr. Bull, 62- Intel.C, U.S.N.R, 42-46, Lt. Bibliog. Soc, Eng; Bibliog. Soc. Am; MLA; Renaissance Eng. Text Soc.(secy-treas); Renaissance Soc. Am; Asn. Typographique Int. Printing history; calligraphy; history of learning. Publ: The scholar printers, Univ. Chicago, 64; The circle of knowledge, Newberry Libr, 68; Calligraphy, Typography & Printing history, In: Encycl. Britannica, 14th ed; Book typography in the U.S.A, In: Book typography in Europe and the U.S.A, Univ. Chicago, 66; Douglas McMurtrie, In: Dictionary American biography, Scribner, 73. Add: Newberry Library, 60 W. Walton St, Chicago, IL 60610.

WELLS, RICHARD ALBERT, b. Erie, Pa, July 17, 12; m. 45; c. 2. ENGLISH. A.B, Oberlin Col, 42; A.M, 45. Head counselor & dir. dormitories for freshman men, Oberlin Col, 42-45, emergency instr. ENG, 43-44; instr, CARNEGIE-MELLON UNIV, 45-48, asst. prof, 48-54, ASSOC. PROF, 54-, asst. dean freshmen, col. engineering & sci, 61-71. Carnegie intern, Univ. Chicago, 53-54. NCTE; Conf. Col. Compos. & Commun; Rhet. Soc. Am. Chaucer's rhetoric; the use of sentence in the Troilus and Criseide. Add: Dept. of English, Carnegie-Mellon University, Pittsburgh, PA 15213.

WELLS, ROSEMARY SIPLON, b. Charles City, Iowa, Dec. 12, 30; m. 50; c. 3. COMPOSITION & LEARNING DISABILITIES. B.A, Univ. North. Iowa, 51, M.A, 53; Univ. Iowa, summer 51; Northeast. Ill. Univ, summer 63; Art Inst. Chicago, summers 65-68; Ph.D.(Eng. educ), Northwest. Univ, Evanston, 73. Instr. Eng, Clear Lake Jr-Sr. High Sch, Iowa, 51-52; Roycemore Sch, Evanston, Ill, 63-65; instr. humanities, Kendall Col, 65-69; LECTR. ENG, NORTHWEST. DENT. SCH, 67-; dir. prog. develop, Hallmark Educ. Syst, 69-70. MLA; Int. Reading Asn; Counc. Except. Children; Col. Eng. Asn; NCTE; Conf. Col. Compos. & Commun; AAUP; NEA; Am. Asn. Univ. Women; Nat. Soc. Prog. Instr. Writing disorders. Publ: Co-auth, English writing patterns, Book 11, 68 & English writing patterns, Book 12, 68, Singer; Food—life, 71, Colorful meal planning, 71 & The exchange pantry, 71, Hallmark; Involved in mankind—some aspects of international dentistry, J. Am. Dent. Asn, 10/72. Add: 1219 Scott, Winnetka, IL 60093.

WELLS, WALTER, b. New York, N.Y, Dec. 13, 37; m. 61; c. 2. ENGLISH, AMERICAN STUDIES. B.S, N.Y. Univ, 60, M.A, 63; D.Phil.(Am. stud), Univ. Sussex, 71. Instr. lang. arts, Calif. State Polytech. Col, 63-66; asst. prof. ENG. & AM. STUD, CALIF. STATE COL, DOMINGUEZ HILLS, 67-72, ASSOC. PROF, 72-, CHMN. AM. STUD, 71- U.S.A, 60, Res, 60-66. Twentieth century America; literary regionalism; stylistics. Publ: Communications in business, Wadsworth, 68; Tycoons and locusts: a regional look at Hollywood fiction of the 1930's, South. Ill. Univ, 73. Add: Dept. of English, California State College, Dominguez Hills, 1000 E. Victoria St, Dominguez Hills, CA 90747.

WELLS, WILLIAM, b. Bethlehem, Pa, July 13, 08. ENGLISH RENAISSANCE. A.B, Univ. South. Calif, 29, A.M, 30; Ph.D, Stanford Univ, 35. Teaching asst. comp. lit, Univ. South. Calif, 29-30; teaching fel, Stanford Univ, 33-34, instr. Eng, 34-35; Univ. N.C, Chapel Hill, 35-37, asst. prof, 37-41, assoc. prof, 41-46, prof, 46-55, Kenan prof, 55-73, chmn. gen. faculty, 52-55, 58-60, chmn. div. humanities, 56-61, v.pres. acad. affairs, 66-71; RETIRED. Asst. ed, Stud. in Philol, 50-61, gen. ed, Annual Renaissance Bibliog, 54-66; adv. gen. col, Univ. N.C, 36-41, acad. coordinator Navy V-12 prog, 43-45, dean col. arts & sci, 46-51. MLA; Renaissance Soc. Am; S.Atlantic Mod. Lang. Asn. Add: Hampstead, NC 28443.

WELLWARTH, GEORGE E, b. Vienna, Austria, June 6, 32; U.S. citizen. DRAMATIC LITERATURE. B.A, N.Y. Univ, 53; M.A, Columbia Univ, 54; William Rainey Harper fel, Univ. Chicago, 54-55, Ph.D, 57. Instr. Eng, Chicago City Jr. Col, 56-58; City Col. New York, 59-60; asst. prof, Staten Island Community Col, 60-63, assoc. prof, 63-64; asst. prof, Pa. State Univ, 64-66, assoc. prof. Eng. & comp. lit, 66-70; PROF. THEATRE & COMP. LIT, STATE UNIV. N.Y. BINGHAMTON, 70- Co-ed, Mod. Int. Drama Mag, 70- MLA; Am. Comp. Lit. Asn. Contemporary avant-garde drama in France, Germany, Spain, England and United States; 19th century English and American drama; history of the theatre. Publ: The theatre of protest and paradox: developments in the avant-garde drama, 64, rev. ed, 71 & ed, The new wave Spanish drama, 70, N.Y. Univ; co-auth, Modern French theatre, 64, Post war German theatre, 67, Modern Spanish theatre, 68 & ed, German drama between the wars, 72, Dutton; Themes of drama, Crowell, 72; auth, Spanish underground drama, Pa. State Univ, 72; Hope deferred: the new American drama, Lit. Rev, 1/63; Drama as submission: the early nineteenth century Viennese folk drama, Theatre Annual, 67; From ritual to drama: the social backgroud of the early English theatre, J. Gen. Educ, 1/68. Add: Dept. of Theatre, State University of New York at Binghamton, Binghamton, NY 13901.

WELSBACHER, RICHARD C, b. Canton, Ohio, Jan. 9, 26; m. 46; c. 2. THEATRE, ENGLISH. A.B, Denison Univ, 48; M.A, Univ. Denver, 50; Ph.D. (theatre), Ohio State Univ, 64. Asst. prof. speech & drama, Kearney State Col, 53-57; from instr. Eng. to asst. prof, WICHITA STATE UNIV, 58-61, asst. prof. SPEECH & DRAMA, 61-64, assoc. prof, 64-68, PROF, 68-, DIR. THEATRE, 61- Am. Theatre Asn; Am. Community Theatre Asn. Theatre of the absurd; original adaptations; Greek tragedies; techniques of acting. Add: Division of Theatre, Wichita State University, Wichita, KS 67208.

WELSH, ALEXANDER, b. Albany, N.Y, Apr. 29, 33; m. 56; c. 3. ENGLISH. A.B, Harvard, 54, A.M, 57, Ph.D, 61. Teaching fel, Harvard, 57-59, mem. fac. arts & sci, 58-59; instr. ENG, Yale, 60-63, asst. prof, 63-66, assoc. prof, 66-67, PROF, Univ. Pittsburgh, 67-72; UNIV. CALIF, LOS ANGELES, 72- Morse fel, Yale, 64-65; Guggenheim fel, 69-70. U.S.A, 54-56. MLA. English novel; Victorian literature. Publ: The hero of the Waverley novels, Yale, 63; ed, Old Mortality, Houghton, 66 & Thackeray: a collection of critical essays, Prentice-Hall, 68; auth, The city of Dickens, Oxford Univ, 71; The allegory of truth in English fiction, Victorian Stud, 9/65; Contrast of styles in the Waverley novels, Novel, spring 73; plus others. Add: Dept. of English, University of California, Los Angeles, CA 90024.

WELSH, ANDREW, b. Pittsburgh, Pa, Nov. 20, 37; m. 71. ENGLISH LITERATURE. B.S, Univ. Pittsburgh, 59, Mellon Found. fel, 59-61, M.A, 61, Ph.D. (Eng), 70; Ford Found fel, Ind. Univ, 62-63; Scottish Comt. fel, Univ. Edinburgh, 66. ASST. PROF. ENG, RUTGERS UNIV, 71-, Res. Counc. grants, 72 & 73, Fac. Acad. Stud. Prog. res. grant, 73-74. AAUP. Critical theory; Medieval literature; folklore. Add: Dept. of English, Rutgers University, New Brunswick, NJ 08903.

WELSH, JOHN RUSHING, b. Monroe, N.C, May 19, 16; m. 41; c. 2. ENGLISH. A.B, Univ. of the South, 39; A.M, Syracuse Univ, 41; Ph.D, Vanderbilt Univ, 51. Instr. ENG. & head dept, Linsly Inst, 41-42; adj. prof, UNIV. S.C, 46-47, 49-51, assoc. prof, 51-60, PROF, 60-, DIR. EDUC. FOUND, 58-, HEAD DEPT. ENG, 73- Assoc. ed, S.Atlantic Bull, 69-; mem. ed. bd, Centennial Edition of the Writings of William Gilmore Simms, Univ. S.C. Press. Alumni Achievement Award, Wingate Col, 63. U.S.A, 43-46, Capt. MLA; S.Atlantic Mod. Lang. Asn; NCTE; Am. Stud. Asn; Soc. Stud. South. Lit. American literature; Southern literature; modern British and American literature. Publ: The mind of William Gilmore Simms: his social and political thought, Joint Univ. Libr, Nashville, Tenn, 51; Egdon Heath revisited—Glasgow's Barren ground in Reality and myth: essays in American literature, Vanderbilt, 63; An Anglo-American friendship: Allston and Coleridge, J. Am. Stud, 4/71; plus others. Add: Dept. of English, University of South Carolina, Columbia, SC 29208.

WELTON, JOHN LEE, b. Pampa, Tex, Dec. 23, 33; m. 56; c. 2. SPEECH, DRAMA. B.S, W.Tex. State Univ, 56, M.A, 60; Danforth grant, Univ. Bridgeport, 66; Ph.D.(speech), South. Ill. Univ, Carbondale, 74. Teacher Eng, speech & drama, Lefors High Sch, Tex, 56-59; from asst. prof. to ASSOC. PROF. SPEECH & DRAMA, Wayland Baptist Col, 59-60; CARSON-NEWMAN COL, 60- Artistic dir, Hancock County Drama Asn, 69-73; script writer, South. Ill. Univ. Develop. & Res, 71-72; dir, Smoky Mountain passion play, Tenn, 74. Oral interpretation; theatre. Add: Dept. of Speech & Drama, Carson-Newman College, Jefferson City, TN 37760.

WENBURG, JOHN RAYMOND, b. Cozad, Nebr, Jan. 27, 41; m. 62; c. 3. SPEECH COMMUNICATION. B.A, Kearney State Col, 62; M.A, Univ. S.Dak, 64; Ph.D.(speech), Mich. State Univ, 69. Teacher Eng. & speech, Cheyenne County High Sch, St. Francis, Kans, 62-63; asst. prof. speech, Morningside Col, 64-65; instr. speech & forensics, Univ. S.Dak, 65-67; assoc. prof. speech commun, Cent. Mich. Univ, 69-72; ASSOC. PROF. SPEECH COMMUN. & DIR. GRAD. STUD, UNIV. NEBR, LINCOLN, 72- Speech Commun. Asn; Cent. State Speech Asn; Int. Commun. Asn. Attitude change; interpersonal communication. Publ: Co-auth, The personal communication process, 73 & Communication involvement: personal perspectives, 74, Wiley; plus others. Add: Dept. of Speech and Dramatic Arts, Graduate Studies, University of Nebraska, Lincoln, NE 68501.

WENDELL, CHARLES WARNER, Comparative Literature. See Volume III, Foreign Languages, Linguistics & Philology.

WENDLING, RONALD CHARLES, b. Buffalo, N.Y, Mar. 31, 39; m. 66; c. 2. ENGLISH LITERATURE. B.A, Fordham Univ, 62, M.A, 65; U.S. Steel fel, Case West. Reserve Univ, 66-68, Ph.D.(Eng), 70. Instr. ENG, Canisius Col, 63-65; St. Joseph's Col.(Pa), 65-66; Hamilton Col, 69-70, ASST. PROF, 70-72, ST. JOSEPH'S COL.(PA), 72- MLA; AAUP. Nineteenth century English literature; romantic poetry; Coleridge. Publ: Coleridge and the consistency of The Eolian harp, Stud. Romanticism, autumn 68; Dramatic reconciliation in Coleridge's conversation poems, Papers Lang. & Lit, spring 73; The undergraduate curriculum: what did we do to it?, AAUP Bull, winter 73; plus others. Add: Dept. of English, St. Joseph's College, Philadelphia, PA 19131.

WENDT, ALLAN, b. Dubuque, Iowa, Mar. 30, 18; m. 44; c. 2. ENGLISH. B.A, Stanford Univ, 47, M.A, 49; Ph.D.(Eng), Ind. Univ, 56. Instr. ENG, Univ. Rochester, 49-54; asst. prof, MILLS COL, 56-61, assoc. prof, 61-66, PROF, 66- Stegner award, Stanford Univ, 49; Fulbright summer scholar, India, 62; Fulbright prof, France, 62-63; India, 67-68; dir, Nat. Endowment for Humanities Inst. in Eng. at the Community Col, 71-72. U.S.A.A.F, 41-44, 2nd Lt. Indian writing in English; creative writing; 18th century English literature. Publ: Ed, Johnson's journey to the Western Isles of Scotland and Boswell's journal of a tour to the Hebrides, Houghton, 63. Add: Box 9909 Mills College, Oakland, CA 94613.

WENNEKER, JEROME SIDNEY, b. St. Louis, Mo, June 29, 17; m. 50; c. 3. DRAMA, SPEECH. A.B, Univ. Mo, 39; M.F.A, Yale, 42, D.F.A, 61; summers, Northwest. Univ, 46, Wash. Univ, 47, 48; Univ. Wis, 54, Univ. Pittsburgh, 55-56. Asst. prof. DRAMA & SPEECH, CHATHAM COL, 46-67, ASSOC. PROF, 67- U.S.N.R, 42-45, Lt. Am. Theatre Asn; Am. Soc. Theatre Res. Direction; history of theatre; dramatic literature. Add: Dept. of Drama, Chatham College, Woodland Rd, Pittsburgh, PA 15232.

WENNER, EVELYN WINGATE, b. Wingate, Md, Apr. 30, 00; m. 36. ENGLISH. B.A, Blue Ridge Col, 20; M.A, Johns Hopkins Univ, 36; Ph.D.(Eng), George Washington Univ, 51. Teacher, high sch, Pa, 20-22; Md, 22-31, head dept. Eng, 28-31; instr. ENG, WEST. MD. COL, 31-36, asst. prof. 36-46, assoc. prof, 46-51, PROF, 51-, res. & writing grant, England, 67-69. MLA grant-in-aid, study in England, 58-59. MLA; Conf. Brit. Stud; Shakespeare Asn. Am. The life and works of George Steevens. Publ: George Steevens and the Boydell Shakespeare, George Washington Univ. Bull, 53. Add: 158 Pennsylvania Ave, Westminster, MD 21157.

WENSTRAND, THOMAS EDWARD, b. Chicago, Ill, May 31, 29. AESTHETICS, ENGLISH LANGUAGE. B.A, Univ. North. Iowa, 51; M.M, Northwest. Univ, 53; M.A, Univ. Chicago, 60; Ph.D.(stylistics), Columbia Univ, 67. Instr. music educ, Webster City Jr. Col, 56-58; ASSOC. PROF. SOC. STUD. & HUMANITIES, NORTH. ARIZ. UNIV, 60- U.S.A.F, 52-56, S/Sgt. NCTE; Conf. Col. Compos. & Commun. Aesthetics; stylistics; undergraduate honors programs. Publ: Co-auth, A role for aesthetics in the teaching process, J. Teacher Educ, winter 68. Add: Dept. of Humanities, Northern Arizona University, Flagstaff, AZ 86001.

WENTERSDORF, KARL PAUL, b. Windeck, Ger, Sept. 15, 15; U.S. citizen; m. 45; c. 1. ENGLISH LITERATURE. M.A, Xavier Univ, 57; Ph.D, Univ. Cincinnati, 60. Instr. ENG, XAVIER UNIV.(OHIO), 56-58, asst. prof, 58-62, assoc. prof, 62-66, PROF, 66- Fredin grant, summer 66. MLA; NCTE; Shakespeare Asn. Am. Shakespeare; history of the English language; Old and Middle English language and literature, especially Chaucer. Publ: Co-ed, Shakespeare studien: festschrift fuer Heinrich Mutschmann, Elwert Verlag, Marburg, 51; auth, Chaucer and the lost tale of Wade, J. Eng. & Ger. Philol, 5/66; Beowulf's withdrawal from Frisia: a reconsideration, Stud. Philol, 71; plus others. Add: 708 Sugarball Lane, Cincinnati, OH 45215.

WENZEL, JOSEPH WILFRED, b. Elkhart, Ind, Nov. 30, 33; m. 59; c. 2. SPEECH. B.S, Univ. Ill, 57, Ph.D.(speech), 63; M.A, Northwest. Univ, 58. Lectr. SPEECH, Hunter Col, City Univ. N.Y, 60-63; ASST. PROF, UNIV. ILL, URBANA, 63- U.S.A, 53-55. Speech Commun. Asn; Am. Forensic Asn. Argumentation, discussion and debate; modern rhetorical theory. Add: Dept. of Speech Communication, 244 Lincoln Hall, University of Illinois at Urbana, Urbana, IL 61801.

WENZEL, SIEGFRIED, b. Bernsdorf, Ger, Aug. 20, 28; U.S. citizen; m. 58; c. 4. ENGLISH, COMPARATIVE LITERATURE. B.A, Univ. Parana, 52; M.A, Ohio Univ, 56; Ph.D.(Eng), Ohio State Univ, 60. Instr. Eng, Ohio State Univ, 59-60; UNIV. N.C, CHAPEL HILL, 60-62, asst. prof, 62-65, assoc. prof, 65-70, PROF. ENG. & COMP. LIT, 70- Am. Counc. Learned Soc. fel, 64-65; Guggenheim fel, 68-69. MLA; Medieval Acad. Am.(mem. adv. bd, Speculum, 68-71, 71-74); S.Atlantic Mod. Lang. Asn; Ling. Soc. Am; Early Eng. Text Soc. Medieval literature. Publ: The sin of sloth, Univ. N.C, 67; Robert Grosseteste's Treatise on confession, Deus est, Franciscan Stud, 70; The source for the Remedia of the Parson's tale, Traditio, 71; The Pilgrimage of life as a late Medieval genre, Mediaeval Stud, 73; plus others. Add: Dept. of English, University of North Carolina, Chapel Hill, NC 27514.

WERGE, THOMAS, b. Weehawken, N.J, Oct. 25, 41; m. 63; c. 1. ENGLISH. B.A, Hope Col, 63; Woodrow Wilson fel, Cornell Univ, 63-64, M.A, 64, Ph.D.(Eng), 67. Asst. prof. ENG, UNIV. NOTRE DAME, 67-73, ASSOC. PROF, 73- Nat. Endowment for Humanities fel, summer 71. MLA; Conf. Christianity & Lit; Dante Soc. Early and 19th century American literature; history of ideas; religion and literature. Publ: Moby Dick and the Calvinist tradition, Stud. in Novel, winter 69; Mark Twain and the fall of Adam, Mark Twain J, summer 70; An apocalyptic voyage: God, Satan, and the American tradition in Norman Mailer's Of a fire on the moon, In: America in change: reflections on the 60's and 70's, Univ. Notre Dame, 72; plus several others. Add: Dept. of English, University of Notre Dame, Notre Dame, IN 46556.

WERMUTH, PAUL CHARLES, b. Philadelphia, Pa, Oct. 28, 25; m. 51; c. 4. ENGLISH. A.B. & M.A, Boston Univ, 51; Ph.D.(Eng), Pa. State Univ, 55. Instr. lib. stud, Clarkson Col, 51-52; part-time instr. ENG, Pa. State Univ, 52-55; asst. prof, Col. William & Mary, 55-57; Cent. Conn. State Col, 57-66, assoc. prof, 66-68; PROF. & CHMN. DEPT, NORTHEAST. UNIV, 68- Danforth Found. summer grant, 61; vis. assoc. prof. Am. lit, Middlebury Col, 63-64. U.S.A.A.F, 43-46. MLA; NCTE. Later 19th century American and English literature; the genteel tradition; Twain, James and Santayana. Publ: Modern essays on writing and style, 64 & Essays in English: Ascham to Baldwin, 67, Holt; Bayard Taylor, Twayne & G. Hall, 73; Can literature perish?, Lib. Educ, 12/62; Santayana and Huckleberry Finn, New Eng. Quart, 3/63. Add: Dept. of English, Northeastern University, Boston, MA 02115.

WERRY, RICHARD, b. Pittsburgh, Pa, Mar. 22, 16; m. 39; c. 3. CREATIVE WRITING. B.A. & M.A, Pittsburgh Univ, 39; Columbia Univ. Instr. ENG, Washington & Jefferson Col, 38-43; asst. prof, WAYNE STATE UNIV, 46-57, ASSOC. PROF, 57- Mem. staff. bk. reviewers, Detroit News, 65-, poetry ed, Other Sect, 69-70. U.S.N, 43-46. MLA; AAUP. Novel; poetry. Publ: Frozen tears and other poems, Dorrance, 46; Where town begins, Greenberg, 51, Signet Bks, 52; Hammer me home, Dodd, 55, Bantam, 56. Add: Dept. of English, Wayne State University, Detroit, MI 48202.

WERTHEIM, ALBERT, b. New York, N.Y, July 3, 40; m. 68; c. 2. ENGLISH. A.B, Columbia Univ, 61; M.A, Yale, 63, Ph.D.(Eng), 65. Instr. ENG, Princeton, 65-67, asst. prof, 67-69; vis. asst. prof, IND. UNIV, BLOOMINGTON, 69-70, asst. prof, 70-71, ASSOC. PROF, 71-, dir, overseas study prog, Hamburg, Ger, 74-75. Folger Shakespeare Libr. fel, 66; mem. selection comt, George Jean Nathan drama critic award, 66-68. Am. Soc. Theatre Res; MLA; Malone Soc; Renaissance Soc. Am. Seventeenth century drama; Shakespeare; modern drama. Publ: The treatment of Shylock and thematic integrity in The Merchant of Venice, Shakespeare Stud, 70; A new light on the dramatic works of Thomas Killigrew, Stud. Bibliog, 71; Courtship and games in James Shirley's Hyde Park, Anglia, 72; plus others. Add: Dept. of English, Indiana University, Bloomington, IN 47401.

WERTHEIM, STANLEY CLAUDE, b. Warburg, Ger, Nov. 11, 30; U.S. citizen; m. 63. ENGLISH. B.A, N.Y. Univ, 53, M.A, 54, Ph.D.(Eng), 63. Instr. ENG, N.Y. Univ, 55-61; Fairleigh Dickinson Univ, 62-63, asst. prof, 63-70; ASSOC. PROF, WILLIAM PATERSON COL, 70-, chmn. dept, 70-72. Assoc. ed, Lit. & Psychol, 68- American literature; Stephen Crane; Ernest Hemingway. Publ: Ed, Studies in Maggie and George's mother, Merrill, 70; co-auth, Hawthorne, Melville, Stephen Crane: a critical bibliography, Free Press, 71; ed, Stephen Crane: a photograph and a letter, Black Sun Bks, 73; plus three others. Add: Dept. of English, William Paterson College, Pompton Rd, Wayne, NJ 07470.

WERTIME, RICHARD ALLEN, b. Baltimore, Md, June 4, 42. ENGLISH RENAISSANCE, MODERN AMERICAN LITERATURE. B.A, Haverford Col, 64; M.A, Univ. Pa, 65, Ph.D.(Eng), 69. ASST. PROF. ENG. & AM. LIT, DOUGLASS COL, RUTGERS UNIV, 68- Lit. ed, Archaeology, 72- MLA; AAUP. Elizabethan and Jacobean drama; French literature. Publ: The theme and structure of the stanzaic Morte Arthur, PMLA, 10/72. Add: Dept. of English, Douglass College of Rutgers University, New Brunswick, NJ 08903.

WERTS, MATTIE, b. McPherson, Kans, Sept. 21, 05; m. 30; c. 1. ENGLISH. A.B. & B.S, McPherson Col, 26; summers, Northwest. Univ, 28; Univ. Idaho, 41; M.A, Kans. State Teachers Col, 57. Asst. prof. ENG, Friends Univ, 57-65, MODESTO JR. COL, 65-71, EMER, 71- AAUP. Twentieth century time concept in the works of William Faulkner. Add: 1601 Chapala Way, Modesto, CA 95355.

WESLEY, NORMAN, b. New York, N.Y, Mar. 29, 29. ENGLISH. A.B, Brooklyn Col, 51; fel, New York Univ, 58, M.A, 61. Instr, sch. commerce, accounts & finance, N.Y. Univ, 58-61; asst. prof. ENG, Dutchess Community Col, 61-62; STATE UNIV. N.Y. COL. ONEONTA, 62-66, ASSOC. PROF, 66- U.S.A, 51-53. MLA; NCTE. Seventeenth century English poetry; modern English grammar. Add: Dept. of English, State University of New York College at Oneonta, Oneonta, NY 13820.

WESOLOWSKI, JAMES WALTER, b. Milwaukee, Wis, Apr. 11, 37; m. 63; c. 2. COMMUNICATIONS. B.S, Univ. Wis, 60, M.A, 62, Ph.D.(commun. arts & jour), 71. Instr. speech, Univ. Wis-Milwaukee, 62-63; Villanova Univ, 63-64; asst. prof, Wis. State Univ-Stevens Point, 67-69; mass media, WEST. KY. UNIV, 69-70; MASS COMMUN, 70-71, ASSOC. PROF. & HEAD DEPT, 71- Fac. mem, Inst. Retail Appliance Mgt, Gen. Electric Co, 72-74. U.S.A, 61, Res, 62-68, Capt. Speech Commun. Asn; Am. Soc. Jour. Sch. Adminr. Mass communication regulation; journalism; popular culture. Publ: Obscene, indecent or profane broadcast language as construed by the Federal courts, J. Broadcasting, spring 69; Development of public libel in broadcast regulation, Radio-TV-Film Interest Group, Speech Asn. Am. Add: Dept. of Mass Communications, Western Kentucky University, Bowling Green, KY 42101.

WEST, FAIRINDA W, b. Elizabeth, N.J, Aug. 8, 43. ENGLISH DRAMA. A.B. Smith Col, 65; Fulbright fel. & Ph.D.(Eng), Univ. Leeds, 67. ASST. PROF. Eng. & humanities, Univ. Chicago, 67-72; COMMUN, OAKTON COMMUNITY COL, 72- Modern drama; 20th century Irish literature; English drama. Add: Communication, Oakton Community College, 7900 N. Nagle Ave, Morton Grove, IL 60053.

WEST, JAMES LEMUEL WILLS, III, b. Roanoke, Va, Nov. 15, 46; m. 66; c. 1. ENGLISH. B.A, Univ. S.C, 68, Reed Smith fel, 69-70, Reynolds fel, 70-71, Woodrow Wilson fel, 71, Ph.D.(Eng), 71. Instr. ENG, VA. POLYTECH. INST. & STATE UNIV, 71-72, ASST. PROF, 72- Ed, Costerus: Essays in Eng. & Am. Lang. & Lit, 72- MLA; Bibliog. Soc. Am; Conf. Ed. Learned Jour. Textual bibliography; 20th century American literature; Southern literature. Publ: Early backwoods humor in the Greenville Mountaineer, 1826-1840, Miss. Quart, winter 71; Notes on the text of F. Scott Fitzgerald's Early success, Resources Am. Lit. Stud, spring 73; The corrections lists for F. Scott Fitzgerald's This side of paradise, Stud. Bibliog, 73. Add: Dept. of English, Virginia Polytechnic Institute & State University, Blacksburg, VA 24061.

WEST, JOHN FOSTER, b. Champion, N.C, Dec. 10, 18; m. 44; c. 2. ENGLISH. A.B, Univ. N.C, 47, M.A, 49; summer, South. Fel. Fund, 56. Instr, Univ.

N.C, 49; from assoc. prof. to prof. ENG, Elon Col, 49-58; asst. prof, Old Dominion Col, 58-68, dir. jour. prog, 59-68; ASSOC. PROF. & WRITER-IN-RESIDENCE, APPALACHIAN STATE UNIV, 68- Chmn, N.C. Writers Conf, 70. U.S.A.A.F, 43-46. Auth. Guild. Modern literature and journalism; death in Hemingway; creative writing. Publ: Up egol; Time was, Random, 65; The ballad of Tom Dula, 70 & Appalachian dawn, 73, Moore; Anatomy of a novel, 8/65 & Dramatic conflict-fiction, 6/72, Writer; Dialect of the southern mountains, N.C. Folklore, 5/66. Add: Dept. of English, Appalachian State University, Boone, NC 28607.

WEST, JOHN OLIVER, b. El Paso, Tex, Jan. 1, 25; m. 70; c. 1. ENGLISH. B.A, Miss. Col, 48; teaching fel, Tex. Tech. Col, 50-51, 54-56, M.A, 51; Ph.D.(Am. lit. & folklore), Univ. Tex, 64. Teacher Eng. & jour, Cent. High Sch, Jackson, Miss, 48-50; hist. & jour, Gardiner High Sch, Laurel, 51-52; asst. prof. Eng. & jour. & publicity dir, Miss. Col, 52-53, assoc. prof, 53-54; asst. prof. Eng, W. Tex. State Col, 56-57; instr. Eng, Odessa Col, 57-59, 60-63, dir. pub. relat, 59-60; assoc. prof, Eng. & folklore, UNIV. TEX, EL PASO, 63-65, PROF. ENG, 65-, head dept, 65-71. Ed, Am. Folklore Newslett, 71- U.S.N.R, 43-44; U.S.A.R, 49-52, 2nd Lt. Am. Folklore Soc. American folklore; southwestern United States history and literature. Publ: Tom Lea: artist in two mediums, Steck, 67; Billy the Kid: hired gun or hero, Tex. Folklore Soc, 66; John Lomax and Jack Thorp: literary or oral transmission?, West. Folklore, 4/67; Tom Lea, realist, West. Rev, winter 67. Add: Dept. of English, University of Texas, El Paso, TX 79968.

WEST, MICHAEL DAVIDSON, b. Morristown, N.J, Apr. 13, 37; m. 61; c. 1. ENGLISH. A.B, Harvard, 59, Woodrow Wilson & John Harvard fels, 59; A.M, 61, Ph.D.(Eng), 65. Teaching fel. Eng. & humanities, Harvard, 61-64; instr. ENG, Wesleyan Univ, 64-65, asst. prof, 65-72, res. assoc, 72-73, ASSOC. PROF, UNIV. PITTSBURGH, 73- Sr. fel, Wesleyan Ctr. Humanities, 70. First Prize, Cornell Classical Transl. Contest, 71; cert. excellence in teaching, Asn. Depts. Eng. & MLA, 72. MLA; Northeast Mod. Lang. Asn.(chmn, Renaissance Eng. group, 71-72); Renaissance Soc. Am; Thoreau Soc. Renaissance English literature, especially Spenser, Shakespeare, and Dryden; comparative literature, especially influence of the classics on European heroic conventions; American literature, especially Thoreau and 19th century theories of language. Publ: Spenser and the Renaissance ideal of Christian heroism, 10/73 & Scatology and eschatology: the heroic dimensions of Thoreau's wordplay, 10/74, PMLA; Neglected continental analogues for Dryden's Mac Flecknoe, Stud. Eng. Lit, summer 73; plus others. Add: Dept. of English, Cathedral of Learning, University of Pittsburgh, Pittsburgh, PA 15213.

WEST, PAUL NODEN, b. Derbyshire, Eng, Feb. 23, 30; m. 60; c. 1. ENGLISH, COMPARATIVE LITERATURE. B.A, Univ. Birmingham, Eng, 50; A.E. Hills fel, Oxford, 50-52; Smith-Mundt scholar. & M.A, Columbia Univ, 53; Can. Counc. sr. fel, 59-60; Guggenheim fel, 61-62. Staff lectr. Eng. & world affairs, Royal Air Force Off. Cadet Training Unit, 54-57; from asst. prof. to assoc. prof. Eng, Mem. Univ. Nfld, 57-61; assoc. prof. ENG. & COMP. LIT, PA. STATE UNIV, 61-68, PROF, 68- Adv, Guggenheim Found, 62-; vis. prof, Univ. Wis, 65-66; adv, Rockefeller Found, 65-; Pratt lectr, Mem. Univ. Nfld, 70; Crawshaw prof. Eng, Colgate Univ, fall 72. R.A.F, 54-57, Res, 57-65, Flight Lt. PEN Club; Auth, Guild; Eng. Asn, Gt. Brit. Creative writing; 20th century European literature; science fiction. Publ: Byron and the spoiler's art, St. Martin's, 60; The snow leopard (poems), Harcourt, 65; Alley Jaggers (novel), 66, I'm expecting to live quite soon (novel), 70, Words for a deaf daughter (memoir), 70 & Bela Lugosi's White Christmas (novel), 72, Harper; The modern novel (2 vols), Hillary House, 67; Caliban's filibuster (novel), Doubleday, 71; Colonel Mint (novel), Dutton, 72; Adam's alembic or imagination versus mc^2, New Lit. Hist, spring 70; Doubt and Dylan Thomas, In: Pratt lectures: Memorial University of Newfoundland, Univ. Toronto, 70; Carlyle's Bravura prophetics, Costerus, 72; plus others. Add: 117 Burrowes Bldg, Pennsylvania State University, University Park, PA 16802.

WEST, PHILIP J, b. San Francisco, Calif, Dec. 21, 36; m. 67. MEDIEVAL ENGLISH LITERATURE, STYLISTICS. B.A, San Francisco State Col, 60; M.A, Rutgers Univ, 61, univ. fel, 66-67, Ph.D.(Eng), 67. Instr, Radio-TV dept, U.S. Army Inform. Sch, Ft. Slocum, N.Y, 61-64; lectr. ENG, Queens Col.(N.Y), 67-68, asst. prof, 68-69; ASSOC. PROF, SKIDMORE COL, 69- U.S.A, 61-64. MLA; NCTE; Mediaeval Acad. Am. Medieval Latin and English literature; stylistics. Publ: Liturgical style and structure in Bede's homily for the Easter Vigil, 1/72 & Liturgical style and structure in Bede's Christmas homilies, 12/72, Am. Benedictine Rev; Medieval style and the concerns of modern criticism, Col. Eng, 3/73. Add: Dept. of English, Skidmore College, Saratoga Springs, NY 12866.

WEST, RAY BENEDICT, JR, b. Logan, Utah, July 30, 08; m. 34; c. 2. ENGLISH. B.S, Utah State Col, 33; A.M, Univ. Utah, 35; Ph.D, State Univ. Iowa, 45. Chmn. Eng, speech & mod. lang, br. agr. col. Utah Agr. Col, 37-40; instr, Weber Col, 41-43; Mont. State Univ, 43-44; assoc. prof, Utah State Col, 45-46; assoc. prof. & dir. creative writing, Univ. Kans, 46-49, from assoc. prof. to prof. Eng, State Univ, Iowa, 49-59; PROF. ENG, SAN FRANCISCO STATE UNIV, 59-, chmn. dept. creative writing, 69-73. Vis. prof, Univ. Innsbruck, 51-52 & Ankara, Turkey, 56-58; mem. bd. dirs, Assoc. Writing Progs, 71- Ed, West. Rev, 37-59. MLA; PEN Club. American literature; Rocky Mountain stories, reader and cities. Publ: Kingdom of the saints; Short stories, 60, The art of writing fiction, 68 & Reading the short story, 68, Crowell; Katherine Anne Porter, Univ. Minn, 63; The writer in the room: selected essays, Mich. State Univ, 68. Add: Dept. of English, San Francisco State University, San Francisco, CA 94132.

WEST, ROBERT HUNTER, b. Nashville, Tenn, May 20, 07. ENGLISH. A.B, Vanderbilt Univ, 29, A.M, 30, Ph.D, 39. From asst. prof. to PROF. ENG, UNIV. GA, 36- U.S.A.A.F, 42-46, Capt. MLA; S.Atlantic Mod. Lang. Asn. (pres, 71-72); Milton Soc. Am.(v.pres, 74-75); Shakespeare Asn. Am; Renaissance Soc. Am. Supernatural in Shakespeare; 17th century occultism. Publ: Invisible world: a study of pneumatology in Elizabethan drama; Milton and the angels, Univ. Ga, 55; Shakespeare and the outer mystery, Univ. Ky, 68. Add: 133 West View Dr, Athens, GA 30601.

WEST, THEODORA LEE, b. Akron, Ohio, Dec. 17, 27; m. 60; c. 1. MODERN BRITISH LITERATURE. B.A, Univ. Akron, 50; M.A, Ohio State Univ, 51; Ph.D.(Eng), Univ. Pittsburgh, 60. Asst. prof. ENG, Duquesne Univ, 53-60; lectr, Ohio State Univ, 60-62; PROF, WEST CHESTER STATE COL, 63- Contemporary continental fiction; contemporary short story. Publ: The continental short story: an existential approach, Odyssey, 69. Add: Dept. of English, West Chester State College, West Chester, PA 19380.

WEST, WILLIAM F, JR, b. Ft. Smith, Ark, Dec. 18, 21; m. 51; c. 2. THEATRE ARTS. B.S.B.A, Univ. Ark, 43; M.A, Northwest. Univ, 49; Fulbright grant, London, 49-50; Ph.D.(speech), Univ. Mo, 64. Head dept. speech & drama, Henderson State Teachers Col, 47-48; Christian Col, 50-52; teacher, STEPHENS COL, 52-61, CHMN. DEPT, THEATRE ARTS, 61- Vis. prof, sch. drama, Univ. Wash, 66-67. U.S.A.A.F, 42-45. Am. Theatre Asn. Theatre history in mid-America and mid 1800's. Add: Dept. of Theatre Arts, Stephens College, Columbia, MO 65201.

WESTBROOK, MAX (ROGER), b. Malvern, Ark, Apr. 6, 27; m. 53; c. 3. ENGLISH. B.A, Baylor Univ, 49; M.A, Univ. Okla, 53; Univ. Wis, 54-55; Ph.D, Univ. Tex, 60. From instr. to asst. prof. AM. LIT, Univ. Ky, 60-62; asst. prof, UNIV. TEX, AUSTIN, 62-68, assoc. prof, 68-72, PROF, 72-, ASSOC. DEAN, COL. HUMANITIES, 73-, asst. dean, 71-73, summer fels, 58-59. U.S.N, 45-46; U.S.A, 50-51, Sgt. West. Lit. Asn.(pres, 73-74). American fiction and studies; Stephen Crane. Publ: Ed, The modern American novel: essays in criticism, Random, 66; auth, Walter van Tilburg Clark, Twayne, 69; Stephen Crane's social ethic, Am. Quart, 12/62; Conservative, liberal and western: three modes of American realism, S.Dak. Rev, summer 66; The stewardship of Ernest Hemingway, Tex. Quart, winter 66; plus others. Add: Dept. of English, University of Texas, Austin, TX 78712.

WESTBROOK, PERRY DICKIE, b. Brooklyn, N.Y, Jan. 23, 16; m. 40; c. 3. ENGLISH. A.B, Columbia Univ, 37, M.A, 38, Ph.D.(Eng), 51. Instr. ENG, Univ. Kans, 38-41; Ga. Inst. Tech, 41-42; Univ. Maine, 43-45; from instr. to PROF, STATE UNIV. N.Y. ALBANY, 45- Guggenheim fel, 53-54; Saxton fel, 55; Fulbright lectr, Univ. Kerala, 62-63. MLA; Am. Stud. Asn. New England culture and literature; American literature. Publ: Biography of an island, 58, Acres of Flint & Greatness of man: an essay on Dostoyevsky and Whitman, 61, Yoseloff; Mary Ellen Chase, 65 & Mary Wilkins Freeman, 67, Twayne; ed, Mary Wilkins Freeman's Pembroke, Col. & Univ, 71 & Seacoast and Upland: a New England anthology, A.S. Barnes, 72; Celia Thaxter: seeker of the unattainable, Colby Libr. Quart, 12/64; The short stories of R.K. Narayan, J. Commonwealth Lit, 7/68; John Burroughs and the transcendentalists, Emerson Soc. Quart, summer 69; plus others. Add: Dept. of English, State University of New York at Albany, 1400 Washington Ave, Albany, NY 12222.

WESTBURG, BARRY RICHARD, b. Des Moines, Iowa, Nov. 22, 38; m. 70. ENGLISH. B.A, Sacramento State Col, 62; M.A, Univ. Calif, Davis, 64; univ. fel, Cornell Univ, 65-66, Kent fel, 66-67, Ph.D.(Eng), 67. Mem. fac. lit, Bennington Col, 67-68; ASST. PROF. ENG, UNIV. ROCHESTER, 68- Nat. Endowment for Humanities younger humanist fel, 72-73. MLA; Am. Soc. Aesthet; Wordsworth Circle; Dickens Soc; Eng. Inst. English novel; linguistics and literary theory; 19th and 20th century literature. Publ: Forster's Fifth symphony, Mod. Fiction Stud, winter 64-65. Add: Dept. of English, University of Rochester, Rochester, NY 14627.

WESTERFIELD, HARGIS, b. Richmond, Ky, Nov. 1, 09; m. 50. ENGLISH & AMERICAN LITERATURE. A.B, Univ. Cincinnati, 31, M.A, 33; Univ. Ky, 38-40; Ph.D, Ind. Univ, 49. Assoc. prof. ENG, Parsons Col, 56-60; Mt. Union Col, 60-65; KEARNEY STATE COL, 65-69, PROF, 69- Res. historian, Forty-First Infantry Div. Asn, 57-, res. grant, 69-; contrib, Jungleer Quart, 57-; poetry consult, Iowa Poetry Soc, 58- Co-recipient, DeKalb Lit. Arts Prize, 71. A.U.S, 43-46. NCTE; AAUP. Military history; railroad history and poetry. Publ: Words into steel, Dutton, 49; Superstitions of freshmen, Col. Eng, 1/65; A reading of Jesse Stuart's Trees of heaven, Ball State Univ. Forum, 3/66; Advice to beginning instructors, Col. Compos. & Commun, 12/68; plus others. Add: Dept. of English, Kearney State College, Kearney, NE 68847.

WESTGATE, SAMUEL SHELTON, b. Grafton, N.Dak, Aug. 28, 44. SEVENTEENTH-CENTURY ENGLISH LITERATURE. A.B, Stanford Univ, 66; NDEA fel, Univ. Minn, 66-67; M.A, Univ. Calif, Berkeley, 68, Ph.D.(Eng), 72. Acting instr. ENG, Univ. Calif, Berkeley, 71-72; ASST. PROF, UNIV. ILL, CHICAGO CIRCLE, 72- MLA; Milton Soc. Am. Poetry of George Herbert; 17th century lyric; Samuel Beckett. Add: Dept. of English, University of Illinois at Chicago Circle, Chicago, IL 60680.

WESTMORELAND, REGINALD CONWAY, b. Navarro, Tex, Oct. 31, 26; m. 49; c. 3. JOURNALISM, ENGLISH. B.A, N.Tex. State Univ, 47, M.A, 56; Ph.D.(jour), Univ. Mo, 61. Sports makeup ed, Dallas Times Herald, 47-55; news dir. & assoc. prof. jour, Abilene Christian Col, 55-64; assoc. prof. & dir. news & publ, N.TEX. STATE UNIV, 64-67, assoc. prof. JOUR, 67-70, PROF, 70-, CHMN. DEPT, 74-, dir. jour. grad. stud, 71-74. U.S.A.R, 49-61, Capt. Asn. Educ. in Jour. Journalism history and literature; newspapers and current problems; public relations. Publ: How to write for newspapers, Car-Teach Inc, 67; A guide to church publicity, Sweet, 71; Campus Pacemaker changes to 6 cols, Ed. & Publ, 6/66; Words of rare wisdom from a great West Texan, 7/66 & co-auth, Study shows minorities needed on Texas daily newspapers, 11/72, Tex. Press Messenger. Add: Dept. of Journalism, North Texas State University, Denton, TX 76203.

WESTON, JOHN C, b. Los Angeles, Calif, Mar. 12, 24; m. 51; c. 2. ENGLISH LITERATURE. M.A, Univ. Chicago, 50; Ph.D, Univ. N.C, 56. Instr. ENG, Univ. Va, 56-59; ASSOC. PROF, UNIV. MASS, AMHERST, 59- Am. Philos. Soc. grants, 60-61. Sig.C, U.S.A.A.F, 43-46. MLA. Robert Burns; Scottish poetry; 18th century British popular culture. Publ: Ed, Robert Burns' The jolly beggars, Univ. Mass, 63, Hugh MacDiarmid, collected poems, Macmillan, 67, Robert Burns: selections, Bobbs, 67 & Hugh MacDiarmid's A drunk man looks at the thistle, Univ. Mass, 71; auth, The text of Burns' The jolly beggars, Stud. Bibliog, 60; The narrator of Tam O'Shanter, Stud. Eng. Lit, 68; Robert Burns' use of the Scots verse epistle, Philol. Quart, 71; plus others. Add: Dept. of English, University of Massachusetts, Amherst, MA 01002.

WESTON, JOHN HOWARD, b. New York, N.Y, Oct. 20, 45; m. 68; c. 1. ENGLISH & AMERICAN LITERATURE. A.B, Dartmouth Col, 67; M.A, Columbia Univ, 68, Ph.D.(Eng), 73. Teacher ENG, Wyandanch Jr-Sr. High Sch, N.Y, 68-69; lectr, Queens Col, 69-71; instr, UNIV. HAWAII, MANOA, 71-74, ASST. PROF, 74- MLA; AAUP; Am. Fed. Teachers. Joseph Conrad; Arthur Schopenhauer's influence on English thought; late Victorian and early modern British literature. Publ: Youth: Conrad's irony and time's darkness, Stud. Short Fiction (in press). Add: Dept. of English, University of Hawaii at Manoa, 1733 Donaghho Rd, Honolulu, HI 96822.

WETHERBEE, WINTHROP, III, b. Boston, Mass, July 10, 38; m. 62; c. 2. ENGLISH, COMPARATIVE LITERATURE. B.A, Harvard, 60; M.A, Univ. Leeds, 62; fel, Univ. Calif, Berkeley, 65-66, Danforth Found. Kent fel, 66-67, Ph.D.(Eng), 67. Asst. prof. ENG, CORNELL UNIV, 67-72, ASSOC. PROF, 72- Am. Counc. Learned Soc. fel, 70-71. Mediaeval Acad. Am. Medieval Latin literature. Publ: Platonism and poetry in the twelfth century, Princeton, 72; The cosmographia of Bernardus Silvestris, Columbia Univ, 73. Add: Dept. of English, Cornell University, College of Arts & Sciences, Ithaca, NY 14850.

WETHERBY, JOSEPH CABLE, b. Bellingham, Wash, May 2, 10; m. 36. SPEECH. A.B, Wayne Univ, 34, A.M, 36; summers, Univ. Wis, 40, Univ. Fla, 50-54. Asst. prof. speech, Okla. Agr. & Mech. Col, 36-46; instr. speech & dir. radio, Wayne Univ, 46-47; from asst. prof. to ASSOC. PROF. ENG. & SPEECH, DUKE UNIV, 47- U.S.N.R, 43, Lt. Comdr. Speech Commun. Asn; South. Speech Commun. Asn.(pres, 60-61); Am. Theatre Asn. Public address; broadcast media; speech pathology. Publ: In the realm of radio, 48 & Academic status seekers, 61, South. Speech; Debate—1984, Speaker, 63. Add: 2604 Sevier St, Durham, NC 27705.

WETMORE, THOMAS HALL, b. Kempner, Tex, July 30, 15; m. 41; c. 2. ENGLISH. A.B, Lincoln Mem. Univ, 34; M.A, Duke Univ, 40; Rackham fel, Univ. Mich, 51-52, Ph.D, 56. Prin, Rehobeth Sch, S.C, 34-37; teacher high sch, N.C, 37-40, prin, 40-43; instr. Eng, Ball State Univ, 46-48, asst. prof, 48-56, assoc. prof, 56-60, prof. & head dept, 60-72, ed, Ball State Forum, 60-61; PROF. ENG. & ASSOC. DEAN DIV. GRAD. STUD, WRIGHT STATE UNIV, 72- Ed, Midwest Eng. Rev, 59-60; lang. ed, Elem. Eng, 61; guest ed, Eng. J, 63. Dir-at-large, NCTE, 60-63, mem. comn. Eng. lang, 62-65, secy, 62-63. U.S.N, 43-46, Lt.(jg). NCTE; Col. Conf. Commun. & Compos; Col. Eng. Asn.(nat. dir, 67-70); MLA (chmn. sect. present-day Eng, 65-66); NEA; Ling. Soc. Am; Am. Dialect Soc; Can. Ling. Soc. American English; linguistics; Mediaeval Englishliterature. Publ: Low-back and low-central vowels in English, Am. Dialect Soc, 59; ed, Linguistics in the classroom, NCTE, 64; auth, New dimensions in English, McCormick-Mathers, 66; ed, Indiana sesquicentennial poets, Ball State Univ, 67; auth, New approaches to language and composition, Laidlaw, 68. Add: Div. of Graduate Studies, Wright State University, Dayton, OH 45431.

WHALING, ANNE, b. Houston, Tex, Mar. 30, 14. ENGLISH. B.A, South. Methodist Univ, 33, M.A, 34; fel, Yale, 37-38, Ph.D, 46. Cataloguing & ref. librn. for. lang. & music, South. Methodist Univ, 47-55; instr. ENG, UNIV. TEX, ARLINGTON, 55-57, asst. prof, 57-60, assoc. prof, 60-71, PROF, 71- Univ. Tex. res. grant, 62. MLA; S.Cent. Mod. Lang. Asn; Am. Stud. Asn; S.Cent. Renaissance Conf. English and American modern poetry; Shakespeare; Thoreau. Add: Dept. of English, University of Texas at Arlington, Arlington, TX 76010.

WHALLEY, (ARTHUR) GEORGE (CUTHBERT), b. Kingston, Ont, July 25, 15; m. 44; c. 3. ENGLISH. B.A, Bishop's Univ, Can, 35, M.A, 48; Rhodes scholar, Oxford, 36, B.A, 39, M.A, 45; Ph.D, Univ. London, 50. From lectr. to asst. prof, ENG, Bishop's Univ, Can, 45-48; from asst. prof. to assoc. prof, QUEEN'S UNIV.(ONT), 50-58, prof, 58-62, JAMES CAPPON PROF, 62-, head dept, 62-68. Nuffield & Can. Couns. awards, 54-59, 61, 62, 64; Nuffield fel, 56-57; vis. prof, Univ. Wis, 62; Guggenheim fel, 67-68; Killian award, 73-75. R.C.N, 40-45, Comdr. Fel. Royal Soc. Lit; fel. Royal Soc. Can; Bibliog. Soc. London; Asn; Can. Univ. Teachers Eng. Samuel Taylor Coleridge: criticism and aesthetics. Publ: Poetic process, Routledge & Kegan Paul, 53, Meridian Bks, 67; Coleridge and Sara Hutchinson, Routledge & Kegan Paul & Univ. Toronto, 55; The legend of John Hornby, John Murray, London, 62; ed. & co-auth, A place of liberty: essays on the government of Canadian universities, Irwin Clark, Toronto, 64; The mariner and the albatross, 47, Scholarship and criticism, 59 & Coleridge unlabyrinthed, 63, Univ. Toronto Quart; plus numerous essays and articles. Add: Dept. of English, Queen's University, Kingston, Ont. K7L 3N6, Can.

WHALLON, WILLIAM, Comparative Literature. See Volume III, Foreign Languages, Linguistics & Philology.

WHAN, EDGAR WILLIAM, b. Billings, Mont, Nov. 18, 20; m. 43; c. 3. ENGLISH. A.B, East. Mich. Univ, 42; M.A, Univ. Mich, 48, Ph.D, 53. Instr. Eng, Univ. Louisville, 48-49; supvr. adult educ, Univ. Mich, 53-55; asst. prof. Eng, OHIO UNIV, 55-58, assoc. prof, 58-67, chmn. dept, 63-67, PROF. ENG. & DIR. HONORS COL, 67- U.S.N, 43-46, Lt.(jg). Conf. Col. Compos. & Commun; MLA; NCTE. Tudor and Stuart prose and poetry; contemporary literature; theology. Publ: Co-auth, Literature: an introduction, McGraw, 60; Hamlet: enter critic, Appleton, 61; auth, Prose current, Heath, 62. Add: Dept. of English, Ohio University, Athens, OH 45701.

WHAN, FOREST LIVINGS, b. Marysville, Kans, Mar. 9, 05; m. 29; c. 2. SPEECH. B.S, Kans. State Col, 28; A.M, Univ. Ill, 31; Ph.D, State Univ. Iowa, 38. Mem. fac, high sch, Kans, 28-29; asst. speech, Univ. Ill, 29-30; instr, Iowa State Col, 30-32, asst. prof. speech & dir. forensics, 32-36, 37-38; asst. speech, State Univ. Iowa, 36-37; assoc. prof, Munic. Univ. Wichita, 38-40, prof. & head dept, 40-54; prof, Kans. State Univ, 53-66, head dept, 58-60, dir. summer sch. inst. res, 60-66; PARTNER & CONSULT, F.L. WHAN & ASSOCS, 41- Ed, Kans. Speech J, 40-41; assoc. ed, Quart. J. Speech, 46-48; consult, Fed. Commun. Comn, 45; Nat. Broadcasting Co, 46; Coleman Co, Inc, 46-48; Brit. Broadcasting Corp, 48; Can. Broadcasting Corp, 48-50; Australian Broadcasting Comn, 50; v.pres. & consult, Sta. KWFT, N.Tex. Radio, Inc, 57-; secy-treas, Sta. KCNY, Cent. Broadcasting Co, Inc, 57-; vis. prof. radio-TV training, Univ. Hawaii, 66-69. Radio audience; market and public opinion research. Publ: Co-auth, How to debate, H.W. Wilson Co, 5th ed, 73; Stephen A. Douglas, In: Vol. II, History and criticism of American public address, McGraw, 43. Add: F.L. Whan & Associates, 4100 Emerson, Wichita Falls, TX 76309.

WHARTON, ROBERT VERNER, b. Wilmington, Del, Oct. 4, 20; m. 50; c. 2. ENGLISH. B.A, Univ. Del, 42; M.A, Columbia Univ, 46, Ph.D, 54. Instr. ENG, L.I. Univ, 48-54, asst. prof, 54-56; EAST. ILL. UNIV, 56-59, assoc. prof, 59-62, PROF, 62- U.S.A, 42-45, Sgt. MLA; NCTE. Eighteenth century English drama. Publ: The divided sensibility of Samuel Foote, Educ. Theatre J, 3/65. Add: 818 Franklin St, Charleston, IL 61920.

WHEATCROFT, JOHN S, b. Philadelphia, Pa, July 24, 25; m. 50; c. 3. LITERATURE. A.B, Bucknell Univ, 49; M.A, Rutgers Univ, 50, Ph.D, 60. Instr. ENG, Univ. Kans, 50-52; BUCKNELL UNIV, 52-57, asst. prof, 57-62, assoc. prof, 62-66, PROF, 66-, ASSOC. ED, BUCKNELL REV, 63-, univ. res. grant, 61. Danforth Found. grant, 59; Lindback Award, 64; resident fel. writing, Yaddo, spring 72; MacDowell Colony, summer 73. MLA; AAUP. U.S.N, 43-46. Poetry of Emily Dickinson; contemporary American poetry; early English novel. Publ: Death of a clown, 64 & Prodigal son, 67, Yoseloff; Ofoti, A.S. Barnes, 70; Emily Dickinson's white robes, Criticism, spring 63; Hey, any work for poetry?, Col. Eng, 3/67; A poem takes shape, J. Creative Behavior, spring 70; plus others. Add: Dept. of English, Bucknell University, Lewisburg, PA 17837.

WHEATER, STANLEY BRIGHAM, b. Plainwell, Mich, Aug. 6, 13; m. 40; c. 2. SPEECH. A.B, West. Mich. Col, 36; M.A, Univ. Mich, 38; Ph.D, Univ. Wis, 55. Instr. speech, Univ. Colo, 48-52; PROF. SPEECH & DIR. FORENSICS, HANOVER COL, 54- Speech Commun. Asn; Am. Forensic Asn. Public address; debate; discussion. Add: Dept. of Speech, Hanover College, Hanover, IN 47243.

WHEATLEY, JAMES HOLBROOK, b. Evanston, Ill, Nov. 16, 29; m. 51; c. 3. ENGLISH. A.B, Dartmouth Col, 51; Ph.D, Harvard, 60. Instr. ENG, Univ. Ill, 60-63, asst. prof, 63-64; Wesleyan Univ, 64-68; ASSOC. PROF, TRINITY COL.(CONN), 68- Consult, Ga. State Dept. Educ, 69- U.S.N.R, 51-, Lt. MLA. Nineteenth century fiction. Publ: Patterns in Thackeray's fiction, M.I.T, 69; co-auth, The logic and rhetoric of exposition, Holt, 69. Add: Dept. of English, Trinity College, Hartford, CT 06106.

WHEATLEY, WILLIAM TOM, b. Buffalo, N.Y, Jan. 3, 32; m. 61; c. 2. DRAMATIC ART. B.A, Jacksonville State Univ, 53; M.F.A, Columbia Univ, 56; Ph.D.(drama), N.Y. Univ, 65. Instr. speech & Eng, Rutgers Univ, 65; oriental drama, N.Y. Univ, 66, directing, 67; ASST. PROF. world drama, Univ. B.C, 67-68; oriental drama & acting, Univ. Calif, Berkeley, 68-71; ENG, CALIF. STATE COL, DOMINGUEZ HILLS, 71- Fulbright scholar, Japan, 63-64, lectr, Colombia, S.Am, 66-67. U.S.A, 53-55. Acting in films and on Broadway. Publ: The performance, Univ. Calif, (in press); Kanzaburo Nakamura: Japan's Richard III, Japan Times, 2/64; The modern Sisyphus, Concord, City Univ. N.Y, 67; Colombia: land of theatre festivals, Drama Rev, (in press). Add: Dept. of English, California State College, Dominguez Hills, Dominguez Hills, CA 90247.

WHEELER, BURTON MAYNARD, b. Mullins, S.C, Mar. 12, 27; m. 50; c. 3. ENGLISH, RELIGION. A.B, Univ. S.C, 48, M.A, 51; South. Baptist Theol. Sem, 48-49; Ph.D.(Eng), Harvard, 61. Teaching fel. Eng, Harvard, 53-56; instr, WASH. UNIV, 56-61, asst. prof, 61-65, ASSOC. PROF. ENG. & DEAN COL. ARTS & SCI, 66- Interviewer, Danforth Found. fels, 60-; Eli Lilly fel, 65-66; mem. adv. counc, Kent Fel. Prog, 67-71. U.S.A, 45-46. MLA; Soc. Relig. Higher Educ. Novel of social protest; religious themes in contemporary literature. Publ: Research abstracts: religious themes in contemporary literature, 1/59, 1/64, 4/64 & Theology and the theatre, 7/60, J. Bible & Relig. Add: Dept. of English, Washington University, St. Louis, MO 63130.

WHEELER, CHARLES BENJAMIN, b. St. Louis, Mo, Jan. 12, 17. ENGLISH. A.B, Westminster Col.(Mo), 37; M.A, Cornell Univ, 39, Sampson fel, 51-52, Ph.D.(Eng), 54. Instr. ENG, Westminster Col.(Mo), 39-40; Wash. Univ, 46-49; OHIO STATE UNIV, 52-55, asst. prof, 55-64, assoc. prof, 64-69, PROF, 69- U.S.A, 42-45. MLA. Literary criticism and theory. Publ: The design of poetry, Norton, 66. Add: 134 W. Beechwold Blvd, Columbus, OH 43214.

WHEELER, CHARLES FRANCIS, b. Cincinnati, Ohio, May 19, 06; m. 50. ENGLISH. A.B, Xavier Univ.(Ohio), 28; A.M, Univ. Cincinnati, 29, Ph.D, 35. From instr. to prof. Eng. XAVIER UNIV.(OHIO), 29-70, chmn. dept. Eng, 39-65, dir. summer sessions, 53-62, dean summer sessions, 65-70, EMER. PROF. ENG, 70- Pres, N.Cent. Conf. Summer Schs, 59-60. NCTE; Col. Eng. Asn. Seventeenth century literature; Victorian poetry; teacher education. Add: 1836 Chase Ave, Cincinnati, OH 45223.

WHEELER, L. RAY, b. Kansas City, Mo, June 24, 40; m. 58; c. 2. CREATIVE WRITING, MODERN LITERATURE. B.A, Kans. State Col. Pittsburg, 63, M.A, 65; Ph.D.(Eng), Univ. N.Dak, 72. PROF. ENG, DICKINSON STATE COL, 65-, co-ed, Dickinson Rev, 66-73. Consult, N.Dak. Comt. for Humanities & Pub. Issues, 73- AAUP; NCTE; NEA. Contemporary fiction and poetry. Publ: A beer drinking soul: an interview with Miller Williams, Dickinson Rev, 73; Another postman dies, Miss. Rev, 73. Add: Dept. of English, Dickinson State College, Dickinson, ND 58601.

WHEELER, OTIS BULLARD, b. Mansfield, Ark, Feb. 1, 21; m. 43. ENGLISH. B.A, Univ. Okla, 42; M.A, Univ. Tex, 47; Ph.D.(Eng), Univ. Minn, 51. Instr. ENG, LA. STATE UNIV, 52-54, asst. prof, 54-60, assoc. prof, 60-65, PROF, 65-, CHMN. DEPT, 74-, asst. dean, grad. sch, 62-66, assoc. dean, 66-67. Lectr. Am. lit, Univ. Innsbruck, 68-69. U.S.A, 42-46, 51-52, Capt. MLA; Am. Stud. Asn. American and Victorian literature. Publ: The literary career of Maurice Thompson, La. State Univ, 65; Faulkner's wilderness, Am. Lit, 5/59; Four versions of The return of the native, 6/59 & Hawthorne and the fiction of sensibility, 9/64, Nineteenth Century Fiction. Add: 162 Clara Dr, Baton Rouge, LA 70808.

WHEELER, RICHARD PAUL, b. Newton, Iowa, Sept. 9, 43; m. 65; c. 3. ENGLISH LITERATURE. B.A, Cornell Col, 65; M.A, State Univ. N.Y. Buffalo, 67, Ph.D.(Eng. lit), 70. ASST. PROF. ENG. LIT, UNIV. ILL, URBANA, 69- MLA. Shakespeare; psychoanalytic criticism. Publ: History, character and conscience in Richard III, Comp. Drama, winter 70-71;

Poetry and fantasy in Shakespeare's Sonnets 88-96, Lit. & Psychol, 72; Marriage and manhood in All's well that ends well, Bucknell Rev, spring 73. Add: Dept. of English, University of Illinois at Urbana, Urbana, IL 61801.

WHEELER, ROBERT WALTER, b. Grand Rapids, Mich, July 4, 21; m. 51; c. 1. ENGLISH, EDUCATION. B.A, Wayne State Univ, 51; M.A, Univ. Mich, 60, Ph.D, 69. Teacher high sch, Mich, 56-66, chmn. dept. Eng, 64-66; INSTR. ENG, HENRY FORD COMMUNITY COL, 68- Mem. Col. Entrance Exam. Bd. Inst. Univ. Mich, summer 62. Hopwood awards, Univ. Mich, 58, 62. Sig.C, U.S.A, S/Sgt. NCTE. American and English literature; educational psychology; English methods. Publ: The cold turkey technique, 11-12/63 & Robert Wheeler reviews main issues in teaching of poetry, 5-6/68, Mich. Eng. Teacher; Spinoza, the click of a typewriter, a smell of cooking, In: The mermaids head and the dragon's tale, Kendall-Hunt, 72; plus one other. Add: Dept. of English, Henry Ford Community College, 5101 Evergreen, Dearborn, MI 48128.

WHEELER, THOMAS VAN HORN, b. Peekskill, N.Y, Sept. 14, 26; m. 51; c. 3. ENGLISH, COMPARATIVE LITERATURE. B.A, Maryville Col.(Tenn), 48; M.A, Univ. Tenn, 50; Ph.D.(Eng), Univ. N.C, 55. Instr. ENG, UNIV. TENN, KNOXVILLE, 55-60; asst. prof, 60-64; assoc. prof, 64-72, PROF, 72- Jr. fel, Southeast. Inst. Medieval & Renaissance Stud, summer 65, 67; fel, Folger Shakespeare Libr, summer 66. Renaissance Soc. Am. Milton; Italian-English cultural relations during the Renaissance. Publ: Paradise lost and the modern reader, Univ. Ga, 74; Milton's twenty-third sonnet, Stud. Philol, 7/61; Dante in the cinquecento, Renaissance Papers, 65. Add: Dept. of English, University of Tennessee, Knoxville, TN 37916.

WHEELESS, LAWRENCE RAY, b. Edna, Tex, Mar. 19, 41; m. 66; c. 2. SPEECH COMMUNICATION. B.A, Tex. Christian Univ, 64; Brite Divinity Sch, Ft. Worth, 64-65; M.A, Univ. Houston, 67; Ph.D.(commun), Wayne State Univ, 70. Instr. speech, Detroit Inst. Technol, 67-69; ASST. PROF. SPEECH COMMUN, Ill. State Univ, 69-72; W.VA. UNIV, 72- Int. Commun. Asn; Speech Commun. Asn; Am. Forensic Asn. Information acquisition; interpersonal communication; persuasion. Publ: Tournament debating: fundamentals for novices, Ill. State Univ, 70; The effects of comprehension loss on persuasion, Speech Monogr, 71; Some effects of time-compressed speech on persuasion, J. Broadcasting, 71; Two surveys of debate format preferences, J. Am. Forensic Asn, 72. Add: Dept. of Speech Communication, West Virginia University, Morgantown, WV 26506.

WHEELOCK, CHARLES WEBSTER, b. Wilmington, Del, July 2, 39; m. 65. ENGLISH. A.B, Princeton, 60, Ph.D.(Eng), 67; M.A, Columbia Univ, 63. Asst. prof. ENG, ST. LAWRENCE UNIV, 67-72, ASSOC. PROF, 72- MLA. 18th century American poetry; 19th century American novel. Publ: Benjamin Young Prime: poet-physician, Princeton Univ. Libr. Chronicle, winter 68; The poet Benjamin Prime (1733-1791), Am. Lit, 1/69. Add: Dept. of English, St. Lawrence University, Canton, NY 13617.

WHELAN, MARY deCHANTAL, b. St. Joseph, Ky. CONTEMPORARY BRITISH & AMERICAN LITERATURE. B.A, St. Louis Univ, 59, M.A, 65; grant from Ind. Univ, Brit. Mus, summers 68, 71; Ph.D.(lit), Ind. Univ, Bloomington, 72. Elem. teacher, parochial syst, Louisville, Ky, 40-56; teacher classics, pub. sch. syst, Marian Co, 56-59; instr. Eng, BRESCIA COL, 59-67, assoc. prof. HUMANITIES, 72-74, PROF, 74-, DIR. LEARNING RESOURCE CTR, 72- Brit. Drama League; MLA. British Edwardian drama; interdisciplinary study, humanities; film as an art form. Add: Dept. of Humanities, Brescia College, 120 W. Seventh St, Owensboro, KY 42301.

WHELAN, ROBERT EMMET, JR, b. Niagara Falls, N.Y, Apr. 13, 24; m. 64; c. 3. AMERICAN LITERATURE. B.A, Niagara Univ, 48, M.A, 56; Ph.D, Univ. Mich, 61. Assoc. prof. ENG, ST. JOHN'S UNIV.(N.Y), 61-73, PROF, 73- MLA. American literature. Publ: Hester Prynne's Little pearl: sacred and profane love, Am. Lit, 1/68; The Blithedale romance: the Holy War in Hawthorne's Mansoul, Tex. Stud. Lit. & Lang, spring 71; The marble faun: Rome as Hawthorne's Mansoul, Res. Stud, 9/72. Add: Dept. of English, St. John's University, Grand Central & Utopia Pkwy, Jamaica, NY 11439.

WHIDDEN, MARY BESS, b. San Angelo, Tex, Aug. 14, 36. ENGLISH. B.A, Univ. Tex, 57, univ. fel, 60-62, Ph.D.(Shakespeare), 65; Woodrow Wilson fel. & M.A, Univ. N.C, 59. Spec. instr. ENG, Univ. Tex, 62-63; asst. prof, UNIV. N.MEX, 63-70, ASSOC. PROF, 70- MLA. Elizabethan poetry. Add: Dept. of English, University of New Mexico, Albuquerque, NM 87106.

WHIPP, LESLIE THOMAS, b. Jacksonville, Fla, May 3, 31; m. 56; c. 3. ENGLISH. B.A, Univ. Minn, 53, M.A, 60; Nebr. Regents fel, Univ. Nebr, 65, Ph.D.(Eng), 67. Instr. ENG, Univ. Minn, 58-60; UNIV. NEBR-LINCOLN, 60-66, asst. prof, 66-70, ASSOC. PROF, 70- Consult, U.S. Gen. Accounting Off, Wash, D.C, 65-67. U.S.A, 53-55. MLA; NCTE. Renaissance literature; theory of language learning; descriptive rhetoric. Publ: Co-auth, A slide-rule composition course, Col. Eng, 63; auth, The language of rhetoric, Col. Compos. & Commun, 68. Add: Dept. of English, University of Nebraska-Lincoln, Lincoln, NE 68508.

WHIPPLE, WILLIAM, (JR), b. Chicago, Ill, Dec. 31, 16; m. 47; c. 4. ENGLISH. B.S, Nebr. State Teachers Col, 39; M.A, Northwest. Univ, 47, Ph.D.(Eng), 51. Teacher, high sch, Nebr, 39-40, supt, pub. schs, 40-42; coord. films & art, Nebr. Film & Arts Soc, 52-55; assoc. prof. Eng, Lamar State Col. Tech, 55-60; chmn. dept. Eng, Midwest. Univ, 60-62, dir, div. humanities & soc. sci. & prof. Eng, 62-72; CHMN. DIV. HUMANITIES & ARTS, SOUTHWEST MINN. STATE COL, 72- Adv, Minn. Counc. Humanities, 72- U.S.A, 42-45, 2nd Lt. MLA. Edgar Allan Poe; modern literature; film literature. Publ: Oregon Trail diary, Goosetree Press, 67; contrib. poems, Descant, Hawk & Whipporwill, Choice, Targets, Forum, Mustang Rev, Midwest. Quart, Penny Poems, Inland & Contemporary Poetry, 60-72; Rib that changed the world, Forum; plus others. Prod: If spring is here (triptych), 67. Add: Division of Humanities & Arts, Southwest Minnesota State College, E. College Dr, Marshall, MN 56258.

WHISNANT, DAVID EUGENE, b. Asheville, N.C, July 16, 38; m. 60; c. 1. ENGLISH. B.S, Ga. Inst. Technol, 61; Woodrow Wilson fel, Duke Univ, 61-62, Danforth fel, 61-65, A.M, 62, univ. fel, 63-64, Ph.D.(Eng), 65. Asst. prof. Eng, Univ. Ill, 65-73; RES. & WRITING, 73- Nat. Found. Arts & Humanities postdoctoral residency, 67-68; Danforth theological year, 69-70; mem. comt. res. & design of physical facilities, Nat. Med. Audiovisual Ctr, 73- Soc. Relig. Higher Educ; MLA; S.Atlantic Mod. Lang. Asn; Am. Stud. Asn; Southeast. Am. Stud. Asn; Am. Folklore Soc. American studies; Appalachian studies; American literature. Publ: James Boyd, Twayne, 73; The sacred and the profane in Walden, Centennial Rev, summer 70; Selling the Gospel news: or the strange career of Jimmy Brown the newsboy, J. Social Hist, spring 72; Ethnicity and the recovery of regional identity in Appalachia, Soundings, spring 73. Add: 1904 Sunset Ave, Durham, NC 27705.

WHISSEN, THOMAS REED, b. Akron, Ohio, Aug. 24, 29; m. 58. ENGLISH, COMPARATIVE LITERATURE. B.A, Kent State Univ, 55; M.A, Univ. Colo, Boulder, 63; Ph.D.(Eng. & comp. lit), Univ. Cincinnati, 69. Asst. prof. ENG, North. Ariz. Univ, 63-65; instr, WRIGHT STATE UNIV, 65-69, asst. prof, 69-71, ASSOC. PROF, 71-, dir. freshman Eng, 70-73. Intel.C, U.S.A, 51-53. Col. Eng. Asn; Midwest Mod. Lang. Asn. Composition; Isak Dinesen; decadent and cult literature. Publ: Isak Dinesen's aesthetics, Kennikat, 73; Components of composition, Allyn & Bacon, 74; Isak Dinesen's Portrait of the artist, Scand. Stud, 73; Governing principle: thesis statement, Ohio Educ. Asn. Bull, 73; Planned disorganization: CEA Forum, 73; plus one other. Add: Dept. of English, Wright State University, Col. Glenn Highway, Dayton, OH 45431.

WHITAKER, JOHN RALPH, b. Falls City, Nebr, Oct. 10, 06; m. 29; c. 1. JOURNALISM. B.J, Univ. Mo, 28; A.M, Univ. Tex, 38, res. fel, 46-47, Ph.D, 47. Ed. & staff writer, United Press, Chicago, Ill. & Denver, Colo, 28-29; reporter & asst. news ed, El Paso Herald & Times, Tex, 29-30; instr. jour, Univ. Mo, 30-32; High Schs, Tex, 34-42; dir. pub. relat, N.Mex. Highlands Univ, 42-44; assoc. prof. JOUR, Syracuse Univ, 47-48; prof, UNIV. OKLA, 48-71, EMER. PROF, 71- Vis. prof, Mich. State Univ, 55-56; Fulbright lectr, Cath. Univ, Peru, 61; Univ. San Simon, 64; dir, Univ. Okla. Jour. Field Study, Peru, 66. A.U.S, 44-45. Asn. Educ. Jour; Southwest. Jour. Congr.(pres, 63-64); Inter-Am. Press Asn. History of American journalism; influence of the west on evolution of personal journalism in the United States since the Civil War; press and journalism education in Latin America. Publ: The image of Latin America in U.S. magazines, Mag. Publ. Asn, 69. Add: 509 N. Sixth St, Alpine, TX 79830.

WHITAKER, THOMAS RUSSELL, b. Marquette, Mich, Aug. 7, 25; m. 50; c. 4. ENGLISH. A.B, Oberlin Col, 49; A.M, Yale, 50, Ph.D.(Eng), 53. Instr. Eng, Oberlin Col, 52-55, asst. prof, 55-59, assoc. prof, 59-63, prof, 63-64; teacher lit, Goddard Col, 64-66; PROF. ENG, UNIV. IOWA, 66- Haskell fel, Oberlin Col, 58-59; Am. Counc. Learned Soc. fel, 69-70. Harbison Award, Danforth Found, 72. A.U.S, 44-46, T/Sgt. MLA; AAUP. Twentieth century English and American literature; modern drama, continental, English and American. Publ: Swan and shadow: Yeats's dialogue with history, Univ. N.C, 64; William Carlos Williams, Twayne, 68; ed, Twentieth century interpretations of the playboy of the Western World, Prentice-Hall, 69; auth, Acting and witnessing in The ghost sonata, In: Papers in dramatic theory and criticism, Univ. Iowa, 68; On speaking humanly, In: The philosopher-critic, Univ. Tulsa, 70; Voices in the open: Wordsworth, Eliot and Stevens, Iowa Rev, 71. Add: Dept. of English, University of Iowa, Iowa City, IA 52242.

WHITAKER, VIRGIL KEEBLE, b. Spokane, Wash, Dec. 31, 08. ENGLISH LITERATURE. A.B, Stanford Univ, 29, A.M, 30, fel, 30-33, Ph.D, 33. Assoc. prof. Eng, Whitworth Col, 33-34; from instr. to asst. prof, Stanford Univ, 34-42; supt. educ, U.S. Indian Serv, 42-45; from assoc. prof. to prof. ENG, STANFORD UNIV, 45-63, Sadie Dernham Patek prof, 63-74, exec. head dept, 51-63, assoc. dean humanities & sci, 62-63, assoc. provost & dean grad. div, 64-69; EMER. PROF, 74- Fel, Henry E. Huntington Libr, 55-56; mem. ed. bd, Shakespeare Quart, 62-72; Phi Beta Kappa vis. scholar, 62-63; dir. Stanford Summer Festival of Arts, 64-69; Guggenheim fel, 69-70; mem. ed. bd, Eng. Lit. Renaissance, 70- MLA; Mediaeval Acad. Am; Int. Asn. Univ. Prof. Eng. Francis Bacon; Shakespeare; Spenser. Publ: Excidium Troiae, Mediaeval Acad. Am; Religious basis of Spenser's thought, Stanford Univ; Shakespeare's use of learning, 53 & The mirror up to nature: Shakespeare's tragic technique, 65, Huntington Libr; ed, Troilus and Cressida, Pelican Shakespeare, 58; Francis Bacon's intellectual milieu, Clark Libr, Univ. Calif, 62; Philosophy and romance in Shakespeare's problem comedies, In: The seventeenth century, Stanford Univ, 51; The theological structure of the Faerie Queene, book I, Eng. Lit. Hist, 52; In search of Shakespeare's journal, Stud. Eng. Lit, 65. Add: 793 Cedro Way, Stanford, CA 94305.

WHITBREAD, LESLIE GEORGE, b. Bromley, Eng, Dec. 15, 17; m. 63. ENGLISH, LINGUISTICS. B.A, Univ. London, 38, M.A, 52, Ph.D.(Eng), 57, D.Lit, 65. Assoc. prof. ENG. & HIST. LING, LA. STATE UNIV, NEW ORLEANS, 66-68, PROF, 68- Fel, Southeast. Inst. Medieval & Renaissance Stud, Duke Univ, summer 68; chmn. La. div, U.S. Placenames Surv, 72- Intel.C, Brit. Army, 40-45. MLA; Am. Name Soc. Old English literature; historical linguistics; place name studies. Publ: Fulgentius the mythographer, Ohio State Univ, 72; contrib, Westminster dictionary of church history, Westminster, 71; auth, Conrad of Hirsau as literary critic, Speculum, 72; The Liber Monstrorum and Beowulf, Mediaeval Stud, 74; plus others. Add: Dept. of English, Louisiana State University in New Orleans, New Orleans, LA 70122.

WHITBREAD, THOMAS BACON, b. Bronxville, N.Y, Aug. 22, 31. ENGLISH. A.B, Amherst Col, 52; A.M, Harvard, 53, Ph.D, 59. Instr. ENG, UNIV. TEX, AUSTIN, 59-62, asst. prof, 62-65, assoc. prof, 65-71, PROF, 71- Vis. assoc. prof, Rice Univ, 69-70. Poetry Award, Tex. Inst. Lett, 65; Nat. Endowment for Arts Award. MLA; AAUP. English and American poetry, especially 19th and 20th century. Publ: Four infinitives (poems), Harper, 64; The rememberer, In: Prize stories: the O. Henry awards, Doubleday, 62; The poet readers of Wallace Stevens, In: In defense of reading, Dutton, 62; introd, Seven contemporary authors: essays on Cozzens, Miller, West, Golding, Heller, Albee, and Powers, Univ. Tex, 66; plus others. Add: Dept. of English, University of Texas at Austin, Austin, TX 78712.

WHITE, BRADFORD, b. Rome, Ga, Nov, 3, 12; m. 48; c. 2. SPEECH, DRAMA. B.A, Univ. N.C, 34; Univ. Wis, 34-35; M.F.A, Yale, 39. Instr. drama, Univ. Tex, 39-42; Eng, Wake Forest Col, 45-46; assoc. prof, MEMPHIS STATE UNIV, 48, speech, 48-55, PROF. SPEECH & DRAMA, 55- Citation for contributions as dir. & producer, on the 10th anniversary of the Memphis Shakespeare Festival, 62. U.S.A, 42-45, S/Sgt. Play direction; history of theatre; history of dramatic literature. Add: Dept. of Speech & Drama, Memphis State University, Memphis, TN 38111.

WHITE, CHARLES A, b. Cambridge, Ohio, Sept. 11, 19; m. 46; c. 2. RHETORIC, PUBLIC ADDRESS PHILOSOPHY. B.A, Muskingum Col, 46, M.A, Northwest. Univ, 50; Ph.D.(speech), Univ. Wis, 57. Teacher high sch, Ohio, 46-48; head dept. SPEECH, Ripon Col, 50-54; PROF, ILL. STATE UNIV, 57-, ASSOC. DEAN GRAD. SCH, 72-, forensic dir, 57-59, chmn. dept. speech, 59-69, asst. to pres, 69-72, secy. of univ, 72-73, spec. prob. officer, 73. Resident scholar, Univ. Calif, Berkeley. Qm.C, U.S.A, 41-46, 1st Lt. Speech Commun. Asn. Add: Graduate School, Illinois State University, Normal, IL 61761.

WHITE, CHARLES WILLIAM, III, b. Boston, Mass, Aug. 27, 36; m. 64; c. 3. AMERICAN LITERATURE. B.A, Boston Univ, 58; M.A, Tufts Univ, 61; Ph.D.(Eng), Harvard, 67. Instr. ENG, Univ. Hawaii, 62-63; Mass. State Col. Lowell, 63-66; ASST. PROF, SOUTHEAST. MASS. UNIV, 66- MLA. Eighteenth century American studies. Add: Dept. of English, Southeastern Massachusetts University, North Dartmouth, MA 02747.

WHITE, DOUGLAS HOWARTH, b. Omaha, Nebr, Aug. 26, 29; m. 64. ENGLISH. B.A, Univ. Omaha, 51; M.A, Univ. Nebr, 54, Ph.D, Univ. Chicago, 63. Instr. ENG, Coe Col, 57-59; Ill. Inst. Technol, 60-63, asst. prof, 63-67; LOYOLA UNIV, CHICAGO, 67-70, ASSOC. PROF, 70- Nat. Endowment for Humanities fel, 67-68. U.S.A, 51-53. MLA. Eighteenth century literature; intellectual history of 18th century England. Publ: Pope and the context of controversy: the manipulation of ideas in an essay on man, Univ. Chicago, 70. Add: Dept. of English, Loyola University of Chicago, 6525 Sheridan Rd, Chicago, IL 60626.

WHITE, EDWARD MICHAEL, b. Brooklyn, N.Y, Aug. 16, 33; m. 56; c. 2. ENGLISH. B.A, N.Y. Univ, 55; M.A, Harvard, 56, fel, 58-60, Ph.D.(Eng), 60. Instr. Eng, Wellesley Col, 60-63, asst. prof, 63-65; assoc. prof, CALIF. STATE COL. SAN BERNARDINO, 65-69, PROF, 69-, CHMN. FRESHMAN COMPOS, 65-, CHMN. DEPT. ENG, 66- Huber Found. res. grant, summer 62; consult. Eng. testing, Educ. Testing Serv. & Col. Entrance Exam. Bd, 72-73; pres, Calif. State Univ. & Col. Eng. Counc, 73-75. MLA; NCTE; Soc. Relig. Higher Educ. Eighteenth and 19th century English fiction; freshman composition. Publ: The writer's control of tone, 70 & The pop culture tradition, 72, Norton; Equivalency testing in freshman English: a report and a proposal, Calif. State Univs. & Cols, 72; Thackeray's contributions to Fraser's Magazine, Stud. Bibliog, 66; A critical theory of Mansfield Park, Stud. Eng. Lit, fall 67; Equivalency testing in freshman English, Bull Asn. Dept. Eng, 3/73. Add: Dept. of English, California State College, San Bernardino, CA 92407.

WHITE, ELIZABETH S, R.S.C.J, b. New York, N.Y, July 12, 20. ENGLISH. B.A, Manhattanville Col, 41; M.A, Radcliffe Col, 42; Ph.D.(Eng), Cath. Univ. Am, 62. Teacher Eng. & Latin, Acad. Sacred Heart, Conn, 45-46; Pa, 46-48; instr. Eng, Newton Col. Sacred Heart, 48-50; teacher Eng, French & Latin, Acad. Sacred Heart, N.Y, 50-52; dir. stud. Eng. & Latin, Acad. Sacred Heart, Conn, 52-53; asst. prof. ENG, NEWTON COL. SACRED HEART, 53-56, assoc. prof, 60-65, PROF, 65- MLA; Eng. Inst; Col. Eng. Asn. Publ: English literature: 1600-1660, In: New Catholic encyclopedia, McGraw, 67. Add: Dept. of English, Newton College of the Sacred Heart, 885 Centre St, Newton, MA 02159.

WHITE, EUGENE EDMOND, b. Denver, Colo, Oct. 31, 19; m. 43; c. 1. SPEECH. B.S, Ore. State Univ, 42; A.M, La. State Univ, 44, Ph.D, 47. Instr, La. State Univ, 46-47; asst. prof, West. Reserve Univ, 47-49; assoc. prof. SPEECH, Univ. Miami, 49-55, prof, 55-60; assoc. prof, PA. STATE UNIV, 60-64, PROF, 64-, CHMN. AM. STUD. PROG, 73-, lib. arts res. scholar, 62-63, grad. coord. dept. speech, 68-73. Assoc. ed, Quart. J. Speech, 65-68, 75-78; Inst. Arts & Humanistic Stud. res. fel, 67; Am. Philos. Soc. fel, 71. James A. Winans Mem. Award, 67. Speech Commun. Asn. (Golden Anniversary award, 70); South. Speech Commun. Asn.(ed, Jour, 60-61); Speech Commun. Asn. East. States; AHA; Orgn. Am. Hist. History and criticism of American public address: colonial rhetoric; history and development of rhetorical theory. Publ: Practical speech fundamentals, 60 & Practical public speaking, 2nd ed, 64, Macmillan; co-auth, Selected speeches from American history, 66 & Speech preparation sourcebook, 66, Allyn & Bacon; auth, Puritan rhetoric: the issue of emotion in religion, South. Ill. Univ, 72; Solomon Stoddard's theories of persuasion, Speech Monogr, 11/62; Master Holdsworth and A knowledge very useful and necessary, Quart. J. Speech, 2/67; Puritan preaching and the authority of God, In: Preaching in American history, Abington, 69. Add: Dept. of Speech, 217 Sparks Bldg, Pennsylvania State University, University Park, PA 16802.

WHITE, F. EUGENE, b. Toledo, Ill, Mar. 2, 11; m. 52; c. 1. ENGLISH. B.S, Univ. Ill, 46, M.A, 47; Ph.D, 50. Teacher, pub. schs, Ill, 30-41; asst. Eng, Univ. Ill, 46-49, dir. writing clinic, 49-50; asst. prof. ENG. & HUMANITIES, OHIO WESLEYAN UNIV, 50-55, assoc. prof, 55-61, PROF, 61-, acting assoc. dean, 58-59, fac. res. fel, 61, chmn. dept. humanities, 60-63. Fulbright-Hays lectr, Univ. Jordan, 66-67. U.S.A, 41-43, U.S.A.F, 43-45, Res, 45-, Lt. Col. MLA; Johnson Soc. Great Lakes Region; NCTE; AAUP. Eighteenth century English literature, particularly novels of Fanny Burney, Laurence Sterne; American literature. Publ: Fanny Burney: novelist, Shoe String, 60; co-auth, Minor British novelists, South. Ill. Univ, 67; auth, Sterne's quiet journey of the heart, Enlightenment Essays, summer 71. Add: 184 W. Heffner St, Delaware, OH 43015.

WHITE, FREDERIC RANDOLPH, b. Pittsburgh, Pa, Apr. 13, 10; m. 35; c. 1. COMPARATIVE LITERATURE, CLASSICS. A.B, Oberlin Col, 31, A.M, 32; cert, Univ. Grenoble, France, 32; Univ. Paris, 33; univ. fel, Univ. Mich, 37-41, Ph.D, 42. Instr, Univ. Toledo, 35-36; asst. prof, Ill. Inst. Technol, 41-43; assoc. prof, Knox Col, 43-45; prof. Eng, Beloit Col, 45-60, chmn. dept, 54-60; PROF. COMP. LIT. & CLASSICS, ECKERD COL, 60- Ford fel, 55-56; Danforth fel, 55, 58, 61; U.S. Dept. State lectr. Am. lit, Nat. Univ. Iran, 56-57; fel, Asian Inst, Fla. State Univ, summer 65. MLA; Class. Asn. Comp. Lit. Soc. Arthurian literature; Euripides; classical mythology in Modern literature. Publ: The development of Homeric criticism; Edward Bellamy, Univ. Classics, Hendrick's House; Famous utopias of the Renaissance, Farrar, Straus. Add: Dept. of Comparative Literature, Eckerd College, St. Petersburg, FL 33733.

WHITE, GERTRUDE M, b. Pawtucket, R.I, Aug. 5, 15; m. 51; c. 2. ENGLISH LITERATURE. A.B, Mt. Holyoke Col, 36; A.M, Columbia Univ, 37; dept. fel, Univ. Chicago, 41-42, Encycl. Britannica fel, 45-46, Ph.D, 50. Instr. Eng, Col, Univ. Chicago, 42-43; lectr, Eng. lit, McGill Univ, 43-45; instr, Wayne State Univ, 46-50; instr. for U.S. Air Force, Univ. Md. Overseas Ruislip Air Base, Middlesex, Eng, 51-52; chmn. dept. hist, Kingswood Sch, Cranbrook, 57-59; asst. prof. ENG, OAKLAND UNIV, 59-62, assoc. prof, 62-66, PROF, 66- MLA. Nineteenth and 20th century English literature. Publ: You will die today, Dodd, 53; Wilfred Owen, Twayne, 70; co-ed, A moment's monument: the development of the sonnet, Scribner, 72; auth, Passage to India: analysis and re-evaluation, PMLA, 53. Add: Dept. of English, Oakland University, Rochester, MI 48063.

WHITE, HAROLD NORTON, b. Burwell, Nebr, Dec. 31, 06; m. 31; c. 3. ENGLISH. A.B, Univ. Nebr, 32, A.M, 41; Univ. Colo, 46; Univ. Tex, 46-49, Ph.D, 55. Supvr. sub-freshman Eng, Univ. Nebr, 40-42; instr, Univ. S.Dak, 42-43; asst. prof, Tex. Col. Arts & Indust, 43-46; instr, Univ. Tex, 46-49; asst. prof, Tex. Technol Col, 49-55, assoc. prof, 55-56; lang. & lit, West. N.Mex. Univ, 56-57, prof, 57-65, chmn. dept, 56-65; PROF. ENG, Pembroke State Col, 65-67; LIVINGSTON UNIV, 67- MLA; NCTE; Col. Eng. Asn; fel. Int. Inst. Arts & Lett. American literature; Willa Cather juvenilia. Add: Dept. of English, Livingston University, Livingston, AL 35470.

WHITE, HARVEY, b. New Haven, Conn, July 7, 28; m. 62; c. 2. SPEECH PATHOLOGY. B.S, N.Y. Univ, 50, Ph.D.(speech pathology), 63; M.S, State Univ, N.Y. Col. New Paltz, 57. Teacher of speech improvement, New York Bd. Ed, 54-60, teacher of the deaf, 60, teacher of aphasic child, 61-62; asst. prof. speech, St. John's Univ.(N.Y), 62-63; SPEECH PATHOLOGY, HOFSTRA UNIV, 63-72, ASSOC. PROF, 72- Speech consult, Nassau County Brain Injured Childrens Asn, 66-; Nat. Inst. Neurol. Diseases & Blindness fels. neurol, Mayo Clin, 67-69; consult. speech & hearing, Kings Park State Hosp, N.Y. U.S.A, 50-52. Am. Speech & Hearing Asn. Speech involvements of the neurologically impaired. Publ: Some techniques of teaching anatomy and physiology, Speech Teacher, 3/63; The Babinski sign, 9/65 & Some aspects of the neural integration involved in gait and posture, 4/67, J. Am. Podiatry Asn. Add: Dept. of Speech, Hofstra University, Hempstead, NY 11550.

WHITE, JACKSON ELLIOTT, b. Greenwood, Miss, June 7, 18; m. 42; c. 3. ENGLISH. B.A, Jackson Col, 58, M.A, 59. A.B, San Francisco State Col, 61; M.A, Ariz. State Univ, 64, Ph.D.(Eng), 67. Instr. ENG, Ariz. State Univ, 64-66; asst. prof, N.TEX. STATE UNIV, 67-71, ASSOC. PROF, 72-, CHMN. BASIC ENG. COURSES, 70- Inst. rep, Am. Asn. Cols. Teacher Educ, 70-; ed, Basic Courses Bull, N.Tex. State Univ, 73- Intel.C, U.S.A, 40-61, Maj. MLA; Conf. Col. Compos. & Commun. Modern literature, 19th and 20th century English; Humanities. Publ: Ed, Intelligence digest, Seventh U.S. Army, Europe, 50-52; contribr, Far East Digest, Cincpac, 58-60. Add: Dept. of English, North Texas State University, Denton, TX 76203.

WHITE, JAMES EDWARD, b. Meriden, Conn, Jan. 17, 26; m. 53; c. 5. NINETEENTH CENTURY AMERICAN LITERATURE, MODERN DRAMA. A.B, Wesleyan Univ, 51; A.M, Univ. Conn, 53; Univ. Kans, 52-54, 55-56; exchange scholar, Univ. Tübingen, 54-55; Ph.D.(Eng), Boston Univ, 64. Asst. prof. AM. LIT, R.I. COL, 56-64, assoc. prof, 64-68, PROF, 68-, chmn. dept, 66-70. U.S.A.A.F, 44-46, S/Sgt. Col. Eng. Asn; NCTE. American poetry; 19th and 20th centuries. Publ: Cummings' I, Explicator, 9/62; Hypocritic days: actors or deceivers?, Emerson Soc. Quart, winter 64; Emily Dickinson: metaphysician and miniaturist, CEA Critic, 3/67. Add: Dept. of English, Rhode Island College, Providence, RI 02908.

WHITE, JOHN WESLEY, JR, b. Nashville, Tenn, Oct. 20, 33; m. 56; c. 2. ENGLISH, HIGHER EDUCATION ADMINISTRATION. B.A, Vanderbilt Univ, 56, B.D, Divinity Sch, 59; M.A, George Peabody Col, 66, Ph.D.(Eng), 68. Dean admis, dir. stud. activities & instr. Eng, Martin Col, 60-65; asst. to v.pres, part-time, George Peabody Col, 65-67; asst. stud. dir, part-time, Tenn. Col. Asn, 67-68; ASSOC. PROF. ENG, OKLA. CITY UNIV, 68-, DEAN COL. ARTS & SCI, 70-, assoc. dean humanities, 68-70. Okla. City Univ. rep. int. intercult. study, Asn. Cols. & Univs, 71- MLA; Am. Asn. Higher Educ.(mem. regional counc, 72-). American literature, particularly the age of realism, and specifically Stephen Crane; administration in higher education, particularly academic administration. Publ: To teach or not to teach, Lib. Educ, 5/68. Add: College of Arts & Sciences, Oklahoma City University, N.W. 23rd at Blackwelder, Oklahoma City, OK 73106.

WHITE, JON MANCHIP, b. Cardiff, Wales, June 22, 24; m. 46; c. 2. ENGLISH, HISTORY. B.A, Cambridge, 47, M.A, 50. ASSOC. PROF. ENG. LIT, UNIV. TEX, EL PASO, 67- Distinguished Educator of Am, 72. R.N. & Welsh Guards, 42-46. Anthropology; archaeology, especially Egyptology; European history, especially 18th century. Publ: The rout of San Romano Hand & Flower, 51; Ancient Egypt, Wingate & Crowell, 52; Anthropology, Eng. Univs, 54; Marshal of France: the life and times of Maurice de Saxe, Hamilton & Rand McNally, 62; Everyday life in ancient Egypt, Batsford & Putnam, 65; novels, Mask of dust, Hodder & Morrow, 53; Build us a dam, 54, The girl from Indiana, 55 & No home but heaven, 56, Hodder; The mercenaries, 58 & Hour of the rat, 60, Hutchinson; The rose in the brandy glass, Eyre & Spottiswoode, 65; Nightclimber, Chatto & Windus & Morrow, 68; The land God made in anger, reflections on a journey through S.W. Africa, Unwin & MacNally, 65; Diego Velazquez, painter and courtier, Hamilton & MacNally, 65; Cortes and the downfall of the Aztec empire, Hamilton & St. Martin's, 71; The mountain lion and other poems, Chatto & Wesleyan, 72; The game of Troy (novel), Chatto & MacKay, 72; The garden game (novel), Chatto, 73. Add: Dept. of English, University of Texas at El Paso, El Paso, TX 79999.

WHITE, KENNETH STEELE, French. See Volume III, Foreign Languages, Linguistics & Philology.

WHITE, MARY FRANCES, b. Connersville, Ind, Nov. 13, 07. ENGLISH. B.S, Kans. State Col, 28, M.S, 30; Ph.D.(Eng), Univ. Denver, 55; State Univ. Iowa, Univ. Chicago. Teacher, high schs, Kans, 28-29, 30-34; Okla, 34-44; res. & pers. worker, U.S. War Dept. & U.S. Navy Dept, Wash, D.C, 44-47; asst. prof. ENG, KANS. STATE UNIV, 47-66, ASSOC. PROF, 66- NCTE. American literature; Kansas folklore. Add: Dept. of English, Kansas State University, Manhattan, KS 66502.

WHITE, MELVIN ROBERT, b. Chugwater, Wyo, Jan. 7, 11. SPEECH & THEATRE. B.A, State Univ. Iowa, 32, M.A, 33; Ph.D.(speech), Univ. Wis, 48. Prin, Andrew High Sch, Iowa, 33-34; dir. speech & drama, Galesburg High Sch, Ill, 34-38; radio prod. dir, State Col. Wash, 38-40; dir. radio broadcasting serv, Ind. Univ, 41-42; chmn. speech div, dept. Eng, Univ. Wyo, 46-47; asst. prof. speech, Univ. Md, 47-48; assoc. prof, Univ. Hawaii, 48-51; asst. prof. speech & theatre, Brooklyn Col, 52-65, assoc. prof, 65-69, dep. chmn. dept, 66-69; assoc. prof. speech & drama, Calif. State Col. Hayward, 68-71; dir. theatre, Univ. Hawaii, Hilo, 72-73; vis. prof. speech commun, Univ. Ariz, 73-74. Acting coord. radio & TV, Univ. Okla, summer 49; lectr. speech, Brooklyn Col, 49; summers vis. prof, Univ. Wis, 50; Wis. State Col, Eau Claire, 51; Wabash Col, 52; Southwest Mo. State Col, 52, 53; Danforth Found. grant, Univ. Tex, summer 60; vis. prof. speech, Univ. Hawaii, 62-63; Univ. Ark, summer 63; chmn. dept. speech, Banff Sch. Fine Arts, Univ. Alta, summers 65, 67 & 69; mem. theatre panel, Nat. Endowment for Arts, 65-66; consult. proj. change, NDEA Inst, South. Methodist Univ, 67; consult. fine arts, Tex. Res. Proj, 67; mem. adv. panel, Int. Theatre Inst, UNESCO, 67; lectr, Nihon Univ, Tokyo, spring 73; vis. prof. speech, Brooklyn Col, summers 73 & 74. Theatre Trophy, U.S. Army, 68; Surfside Theatre Gold Masque Award, 68. U.S.N.R, 42-45. Am. Theatre Asn.(managing ed. jour, 58-61, exec. secy-treas, 65-67); Speech Commun. Asn; West. Speech Commun. Asn; Pac. Speech Asn. Radio and television; oral interpretation. Publ: Beginning radio production, 50 & Beginning television production, 53, Burgess; co-auth, Studies in readers' theatre, 63 & auth, From the printed page, 65, S. & F. Press; co-auth, Playreaders repertory: anthology for an introduction to theatre, 70 & Readers theatre handbook: a dramatic approach to literature, rev. ed, 73, Scott; co-auth, Introduction to theatre courses, Today's Speech, 2/67; auth, Always another Hamlet, spring 72 & Fitch's Captain Jinks of the horse marines vs. Boucicault's Grimaldi, fall 73, Theatre J; plus others. Add: 583 Boulevard Way, Piedmont, CA 94610.

WHITE, ORVILLE FRANKLIN, b. Broom, Ark, Sept. 23, 11; m. 42; c. 3. ENGLISH. B.A, Ark. State Col, 37; M.A, Univ. Ark. 42; Ph.D, Univ. N.C, 52. Head dept, high sch, Ark, 39-40, prin, 40-41; head dept. Eng, Battle Ground Acad, Franklin, Tenn, 41-47; prof, Ark. State Teachers Col, 47-52; prof. Eng. & head dept. langs. & lit, Ark. State Col, 52-65; PROF. ENG. & HEAD DIV. LANG. & LIT, DELTA STATE COL, 65- MLA; Nat. Educ. Asn; NCTE (Miss. coord. achievement awards in writing progs, 74); Am. Econ. Asn; S-Cent. Mod. Lang. Asn. Byron. Publ: The three pointer, Miss. Educ. Advance, 1/66; The Negro American—a review, J. Miss. Hist, 8/67. Add: Dept. of English, Delta State College, Cleveland, MS 38732.

WHITE, PATRICK T, b. Birmingham, Ala, Feb. 9, 24; m. 56; c. 4. ENGLISH. B.S.S, Georgetown Univ, 48; M.A, George Washington Univ, 55; Ph.D.(Eng), Univ. Mich, 63. Asst. prof. ENG, Ala. Col, 58-61; Wis. State Univ, Oshkosh, 61-64; Ball State Univ, 64-67; EAST. MICH. UNIV, 67-68, ASSOC. PROF, 68- Eng. adv. col. educ, Nat. Teacher Educ. Ctr, Mogadiscio, Somali Repub, 68- U.S.A.F, 43-45, 49-53, Capt. Add: Dept. of English, Eastern Michigan University, Ypsilanti, MI 48197.

WHITE, RAY LEWIS, b. Aug. 11, 41; U.S. citizen. MODERN AMERICAN LITERATURE. B.A, Emory & Henry Col, 62; M.A, Univ. Ark, Fayetteville, 63, Ph.D.(Eng), 71. Instr. ENG, N.C. State Univ, 65-68, asst. prof, ILL. STATE UNIV, 68-70, assoc. prof, 70-73, PROF, 73- AAUP; MLA. Sherwood Anderson; Gertrude Stein; Gore Vidal. Publ: Ed, Achievement of Sherwood Anderson, 66, Return to Winesburg, 67, Sherwood Anderson's memoirs, 69 & Sherwood Anderson/Gertrude Stein, 72, Univ. N.C; auth, Gore Vidal, Twayne, 68; ed, A story teller's story, 68, Tar, 69 & Marching men, 72, Case West. Reserve Univ; ed, Checklist of Sherwood Anderson, 69 & Studies in Winesburg, Ohio, 71, C.E, Merrill. Add: Dept. of English, Illinois State University, Normal, IL 61761.

WHITE, ROBERT BENJAMIN, JR, b. Concord, N.C, May 1, 30; m. 51; c. 2. ENGLISH. B.A, Univ. N.C, Chapel Hill, 53, M.A, 55, Counc. South. Univs. fel, 58-60, Ph.D.(Eng), 66. Instr. ENG, N.C. State Col, 55-56 & 60-62; assoc. prof, N.C. STATE UNIV, 63-69, assoc. prof, 69-72, PROF, 72- Intel.C, U.S.A, 56-58. MLA; Am. Soc. 18th Century Stud. Medieval, 17th and 18th century English literature. Publ: A note on the Green Knight's red eyes, Eng. Lang. Notes, 6/65; The character of the Tatler, Philol. Quart, 4/66; Chaucer's Daun Piers and the rule of St. Benedict, J. Eng. & Germanic Philol, 1/72. Add: Dept. of English, North Carolina State University, Raleigh, NC 27607.

WHITE, ROBERT FINIS, JR, b. Moulton, Ala, Sept. 2, 21; m. 49; c. 2. ENGLISH. A.B, Univ. N.C, 46; M.A, Columbia Univ, 50; Ph.D, Univ. Pa, 59. Instr. ENG, Emory Univ, 46-47; Albright Col, 50; asst. instr, Univ. Pa, 51-56; instr, Cornell Univ, 56-59; asst. prof, EAST. ILL. UNIV, 60-64, assoc. prof, 64-67, PROF, 67-, HEAD DEPT, 66- U.S.A, 42-44. NCTE; Asn. Depts. Eng; AAUP; MLA. Modern fiction; modern comparative literature; English novel. Add: 2523 Fifth St, Charleston, IL 61920.

WHITE, ROBERT L, b. Louisville, Ky, May 3, 28; m. 58; c. 3. AMERICAN LITERATURE. B.A, Univ. Louisville, 50; M.A, Univ. Minn, 55, Carnegie fel, 57-58, Ph.D, 59; Fulbright fel, Italy, 55-56. Instr. Eng, Univ. Ky, 59-62, asst. prof, 62-67; ASSOC. PROF. ENG. & HUMANITIES, YORK UNIV. (ONT), 67- Fulbright lectr, Finland, 65-66, 72-73. C.Eng, 50-52, S/Sgt. Am. Stud. Asn. Relationships between literature and painting; influences of Italian culture in United States; literature of the 1930's. Publ: John Peale Bishop, Twayne, 66; Washington Allston: Banditti in Arcadia, Am. Quart, 61; Some unpublished poems by J.P. Bishop, Sewanee Rev, 63; Cultural ambivalence in Constance Fenimore Woolson's Italian tales, Tenn. Stud. Lit, 67; plus others. Add: Dept. of English, York University, Downsview, Ont. M3J 1P3, Can.

WHITE, SIDNEY HOWARD, b. Bangor, Maine, Aug. 29, 23; m. 50; c. 4. ENGLISH. B.S, Loyola Univ. Los Angeles, 50; A.M, Univ. South. Calif, 51, Ph.D, 62. Instr. Eng, Marymount Col.(Calif), 53-57, asst. prof, 57-61, assoc. prof, 61-66, chmn. dept, 57-66; PROF. ENG, UNIV. R.I. EXTEN, 66- Exten. lectr, Univ. Calif, Los Angeles, 63-66; vis. prof, Univ. Victoria, summer 65; Univ. R.I, summer 66; reviewer, Abstracts of Eng. U.S.A, 42-46; U.S.A.F, 50, 2nd Lt. MLA; Am. Stud. Asn; NCTE. Henry James; F. Scott Fitzgerald; dramatic literature. Publ: Hawthorne: The scarlet letter, 67 & Fitzgerald: The great Gatsby, 68, Barron's; Guide to Arthur Miller, C.E. Merrill, 70; Sidney Howard, Twayne, (in prep); What Freudian death-wish in the crown borrowing in 2 Henry IV? Forum, fall 64. Add: Dept. of English, University of Rhode Island Extension, Providence, RI 02908.

WHITE, WILLIAM, b. Paterson, N.J, Sept. 4, 10; m. 51; c. 2. JOURNALISM. A.B, Univ. Chattanooga, 33; A.M, Univ. South. Calif, 37; Univ. Calif, Los Angeles, 37; Univ. Dijon, France, 51; Ph.D.(Eng. lit), Univ. London, 53. Dir. publicity, Univ. Chattanooga, 31-33; asst, Univ. South. Calif, 35-40; instr. lib. arts, Pac. States, 38-41; Eng, Whitman Col, 41-42; asst. prof. jour. & dir. publicity, Mary Hardin-Baylor Col, 46-47; Ohio Wesleyan Univ, 47; from asst. prof. to assoc. prof. jour, Wayne State Univ, 47-60, prof, 60-74, acting chmn. dept. jour, 56-57, 65-66, dir. Am. stud. prog, 67-74; PROF. SPEECH COMMUN. & DIR. JOUR. PROG, OAKLAND UNIV, 74- Mem. Colby Libr. Assocs, 54-; fel, Found. Econ. Educ, 56; newspaper reporter & correspondent; ed, Walt Whitman Rev; co-ed, Collected Writings of Walt Whitman, N.Y. Univ, 61-; vis. prof, Univ. South. Calif, 62; Fulbright lectr, Chungang & Hankook Univs, Korea, 63-64; vis. prof, Soong Sil Col, Korea, 63-64; assoc. ed, Am. Bk. collector, 64-; Am. Philos. Soc. res. fel, summer 65; vis. prof, Univ. R.I, summer 66; mem. adv. comt, Am. Speech, Columbia Univ. Press, 66-67; assoc. ed, Mich. Sportscene, 67-68; gen. ed, Serif series: bibliographies and checklists, Kent State Univ, 67-; Nat. Endowment for Humanities res. fel, 67-68, 70, 72; vis. prof, Univ. Hawaii, summer 69 & Calif. State Col, Long Beach, summer 69; mem. adv. bd, Emily Dickinson Bull, 72-; book reviewer, Libr. J, Detroit News, Quill, Jour. Quarterly; copy ed, Los Angeles Times, summer 73. Citation Distinguished Serv, Baylor Sch, 71. MLA; Am. Asn. Hist. Med; Mod. Humanities Res. Asn, Gt. Brit; Bibliog. Soc. Am; Asn. Educ. in Jour; Am. Stud. Asn; Brit. Med. Asn; Med. Cong. Australia; Private Libr. Asn, Gt. Brit. American and English literature and history; bibliography. Publ: Henry David Thoreau bibliography, 1908-1937, 39 & John Donne since 1900, 42, Faxon; Sir William Osler: historian and literary essayist, 51, John Ciardi: a bibliography, 59, Karl Shapiro: a bibliography, 60, W.D. Snodgrass: a bibliography, 60, Walt Whitman's journalism: a bibliography, 69, ed, Walt Whitman in our time, 70 & co-ed, Walt Whitman in Europe today, 72, Wayne State Univ; auth, By-line: Ernest Hemingway, Scribner, 67 & Collins, London, 68; Wilfred Owen: a bibliography, 67 & Edwin Arlington Robinson: a supplementary bibliography, 71, Kent State Univ; ed, Studies in The sun also rises, 69, auth, Guide to Ernest Hemingway, 69 & Checklist of Ernest Hemingway, 70, Merrill; chaps. on Hemingway & Fitzgerald, In: American literary scholarship, Duke Univ, 67-70; plus others. Add: Dept. of Speech Communications, Oakland University, Rochester, MI 48063.

WHITE, WILLIAM BECKLER, b. Waynesboro, Va, Apr. 27, 19; m. 46. ENGLISH. B.A. & B.S, Hampden-Sydney Col, 40; M.A, Lehigh Univ, 42, Ph.D. (Eng), 55. Instr. ENG, Lehigh Univ, 48-55; asst. prof, SALEM COL.(N.C), 55-59, assoc. prof, 59-65, PROF. & HEAD DEPT, 65- U.S.N.R, 42-46, 50-52. Elizabethan travel and voyage literature. Add: Dept. of English, Salem College, Winston-Salem, NC 27108.

WHITE, WILLIAM LUTHER, Theology, English Literature. See Volume IV, Philosophy, Religion & Law.

WHITE, WILLIAM MONROE, b. Nashville, Tenn, Oct. 11, 26; m. 51; c. 3. AMERICAN LITERATURE. B.A, Vanderbilt Univ, 49, M.A, 50; Ph.D.(Eng), Univ. Fla, 53. Asst. prof. ENG, VA. POLYTECH. INST. & STATE UNIV, 53-57, assoc. prof, 57-66, PROF, 66- MLA; S.Atlantic Mod. Lang. Asn. Nineteenth century and modern American literature; creative writing. Publ: Hawthorne's eighteen year cycle: Ethan Brand and Reuben Bourne, Stud. Short Fiction, winter 69; The Crane-Hemingway code: a reevaluation, Forum, spring 69; The dynamics of Whitman's poetry, Sewanee Rev, 6/72. Add: Dept. of English, Virginia Polytechnic Institute & State University, Blacksburg, VA 24060.

WHITEHEAD, ALBERT E, b. Denver, Colo, Feb. 28, 07. SPEECH. A.B, Univ. Colo, 29; A.M, Univ. Wis, 30, Ph.D, 44. From assoc. prof. to prof. SPEECH & chmn. dept, UNIV. IDAHO, 45-72, EMER. PROF, 72- William Edgar Borah. Add: Dept. of Speech, University of Idaho, Moscow, ID 83843.

WHITEHEAD, JOAN GRENTHOT, b. New York, N.Y, m. 66; c. 3. ENGLISH LITERATURE. B.A, Wellesley Col, 51; M.A, Columbia Univ, 52; Woodrow Wilson fel, univ. fel. & Ph.D.(medieval Eng. lit.), Yale, 63. Asst. prof. ENG. LIT, Univ. Vt, 62-63, 64-65; lectr, Am. Col. Switz, 63-64; asst. prof, N.Y. Univ, 65-68; instr, Univ. Va, 68-70; ASSOC. PROF, BOSTON STATE COL, 71- Asst. prof. Eng. as for. lang. & Eng. lit, Yale, summers 61, 62, 63, 68, 69; Eng. lit, Conn. Wesleyan Univ, summers 65-67. MLA. Medieval, modern British and modern American literature. Publ: The Book of the Duchess, Now Circulating, 10/73. Add: 173 Woodland Rd, Auburndale, MA 02166.

WHITEHEAD, LEE MELVIN, b. Twin Falls, Idaho, Aug. 29, 32; m. 57; c. 2. ENGLISH. B.A, Univ. Wash, 57, M.A, 59; Ph.D.(Eng), Univ. Wis, 65. From asst. prof. to ASSOC. PROF. ENG, UNIV. B.S, 64- U.S.A, 53-55. MLA. Conrad; modern British and American literature; history of ideas. Publ: Tragic knowledge: the ethics of the imagination, Human Context, 11/71; The moment out of time: Golding's Pincher Martin, Contemporary Lit, winter 71; The shawl and the skull: Virginia Woolf's Magic mountain, Mod. Fiction Stud, autumn 72; plus several others. Add: Dept. of English, University of British Columbia, Vancouver 8, B.C, Can.

WHITESELL, JAMES EDWIN, b. Buchanan, Va, Nov. 21, 09; m. 36; c. 2. ENGLISH PHILOLOGY. A.B, Randolph-Macon Col, 30; A.M, Harvard, 31, Dexter scholar, 35, Ph.D, 35. Instr. Eng, Northwest. Univ, 35-39; asst. prof, Mary Washington Col, Univ. Va, 39-44; assoc. prof, Univ. S.C, 46-49, prof, 49-66; dean sch. arts & sci, VA. COMMONWEALTH UNIV, 66-72, PROF. ENG, 66- Co-founder & co-ed, The Explicator, 42-54, managing ed, 54- U.S.N.R, 44-46, Lt. MLA; Col. Eng. Asn; NCTE; Am. Dialect Soc; S.Atlantic Mod. Lang. Asn. Old English; Chaucer. Publ: Northumbrian dialect of Old English; co-auth, The explicator cyclopedia, Vol. 1, modern poetry, 66, Vol. 2, early poetry, 68 & Vol. 3, prose, 68, Quadrangle Bks; compiler, The explicator cumulative index, Explicator, Vols. I-XX, 62 & XXI-XXX, 73. Add: Dept. of English, Virginia Commonwealth University, Richmond, VA 23284.

WHITESIDE, DUNCAN, b. Austin, Tex, June 22, 10; m. 43. SPEECH, BROADCASTING. B.A, Southwest. Univ, 33; M.A, Univ. Tex, 48; Northwest. Univ, 50-53. Instr. theatre, Univ. Tex, 34-35; tech. dir. theatre prod, Chicago Fed. Theatre, 35-39; instr. drama, adult educ, Chicago Bd. Educ, 39-40; theatre, UNIV. MISS, 47-48, asst. prof. SPEECH, 48-71, ASSOC. PROF, 71-, DIR. DIVISION OF RADIO & TV, 53- Stage mgr, Oxford Players, 35; instr, Colo. Col, summer, 35; theatrical consult, U.S. Army, Natl. Theatre Conf, 41-42; state educ. TV consult, Miss, 52; ed, Miss. Broadcasters J, 59-61. A.U.S, 42-46, 1st Lt. Speech Commun. Asn. Teaching techniques in broadcast performance; the attention-span factor during audio-visual presentation of educational materials. Add: Room 323, Fine Arts Center, University of Mississippi, University, MS 38677.

WHITFIELD, GEORGE WILEY, b. Scottsboro, Ala, Nov. 18, 34; m. 58; c. 4. RHETORIC, PUBLIC ADDRESS. B.A, Univ. Ark, Pine Bluff, 58; South. Educ. Found. fels, Univ. Ark, Fayetteville, 61, 62-64, Woodrow Wilson fel, 61-62, M.A, 62, Ed.D.(speech pedagogy), 64. Instr. Eng. & Speech, Merrill High Sch, Pine Bluff, Ark, 58-61; asst. prof. SPEECH, SOUTH. UNIV, BATON ROUGE, 64-65, assoc. prof, 65-68, PROF, 68-, CHMN. DEPT. SPEECH & THEATRE, 72- U.S.A, 53-56, S/Sgt. Speech Commun. Asn; Am. Forensic Asn; AAUP; Am. Theatre Asn. Pedagogical methodology; assessment of the responses of minority students to aesthetic programs and events. Publ: Frederick Douglass: black abolitionist, Today's Speech, 2/73. Add: Dept. of Speech & Theatre, Southern University, Baton Rouge, LA 70813.

WHITFORD, KATHRYN, b. Malta, Mont, Oct. 13, 19; m. 47; c. 2. ENGLISH. B.E, North. Ill. State Teachers Col, 41; M.A, Univ. Ill, 42; Univ. Wis, 47-49. Teacher high sch, 44-47; instr. ENG, exten. div, Univ. Wis, 55-56; UNIV. WIS-MILWAUKEE, 56-63, asst. prof, 63-72, ASSOC. PROF, 72-, chmn. dept, 73-74. MLA; Am. Stud. Asn. Transcendentalists; Hamlin Garlin; Timothy Dwight. Publ: Co-auth, Thoreau—pioneer ecologist and conservationist, Sci. Monthly, 51; auth, Excursion into Romanticism: Timothy Dwight's travels, Publ. Lang. & Lit, summer 66; Miller of Boscobel: Hamlin Garland's labor play, Midcontinent Am. Stud. J, fall 67. Add: 319 Garland Hall, University of Wisconsin-Milwaukee, Milwaukee, WI 53211.

WHITING, BARTLETT JERE, b. East Northport, Maine, Sept. 17, 04; m. 28; c. 1. ENGLISH. A.B, Harvard, 25, A.M, 28, Ph.D, 32. Instr. Eng, HARVARD, 26-34, asst. prof, 34-38, assoc. prof, 38-46, prof, 46-67, GURNEY PROF. ENG. LIT, 67-, chmn. dept, 47-52, 63-65. Asst. ed, Speculum, 36-47; mem. bd. dir, Am. Counc. Learned Soc, 51-54; Guggenheim fel, 61. MLA.(mem. exec. counc, 62-65); fel. Mediaeval Acad. Am; Am. Dialect Soc; Am. Folklore Soc. Old and Middle English; folklore. Publ: Chaucer's use of proverbs, 34, Proverbs in the earlier English drama, 38, co-auth, Dictionary of American proverbs and proverbial phrases, 1820-1880 & auth, Proverbs, sentences and proverbial phrases from English writings mainly before 1500, 68, Harvard; Traditional British ballads, Appleton, 55; The early period, In: The college survey of English literature, Harcourt, 42. Add: 30 Walker St, Cambridge, MA 02138.

WHITING, FRANK M, b. Wallsburg, Utah, Dec. 6, 07; m. 31; c. 5. THEATRE ARTS. B.A, Brigham Young Univ, 30; M.A, Univ. Utah, 32; State Univ. Iowa, summer, 35; Ph.D.(speech & theatre), Univ. Minn, 41. Teacher, high sch, Idaho, 32-34; instr. & tech. dir. in theatre, Univ. Utah, 34-37; instr. SPEECH & tech. dir. in theatre, UNIV. MINN, MINNEAPOLIS, 37-43, from asst. prof. to assoc. prof, 43-51, prof, 51-72, dir. univ. theatre, 43-72, V.PROVOST, 72- Speech Commun. Asn; Nat. Theatre Conf; Am. Nat. Theatre & Acad; Am. Theatre Asn.(v.pres, 55; pres, 56). American theatre history. Publ: An introduction to the theatre, Harper & Bros, 54, rev. ed, 60, 69; Huckleberry Finn, (play), Children's Theatre Press, 68. Add: 2036 Seabury Ave, Minneapolis, MN 55406.

WHITLA, WILLIAM JOHN, b. Galt, Ont, May 1, 34; m. 65; c. 2. VICTORIAN LITERATURE. B.A, Univ. Toronto, 57, fel, 57-58, M.A, 61; S.T.B, Trinity Col.(Ont), 62; D.Phil.(Eng), Oxford, 68. Gen. secy, Stud. Christian Movement, Univ. N.B, 61-63; lectr. humanities, Glendon Col, YORK UNIV, 63-64, asst. prof. ENG. & HUMANITIES, 64-70, ASSOC. PROF, FOUNDERS COL, 70-, dir. grad. prog. Eng, 71-73. Kent fel, Danforth Found, 65-68, 68-; jr. chaplain, Merton Col, Oxford, 67-68. Fel. Soc. Relig. Higher Educ; MLA; NCTE; Asn. Can. Univ. Teachers Eng. Browning's poetry; Victorians and the Renaissance; medieval iconology. Publ: The central truth: the incarnation in Robert Browning's poetry, Univ. Toronto, 63; Sin and redemption in Whitehead and Teilhard de Chardin, Anglican Theol. Rev, 65; Robert Browning: six stray verses, Bibliog. Press, Oxford, 66; Browning and the Ashburton affair, Browning Soc. Notes, 72. Add: 311 Founders College, York University, 4700 Keele St, Downsview, Ont. M3J 1P3, Can.

WHITLATCH, ROBERT CALHOUN, b. Detroit, Mich, June 8, 35; m. 56; c. 1. SPEECH & THEATRE. B.A, Denison Univ, 57; M.A, Univ. Ill, 58, summer fel, 59, Ph.D.(speech & theatre), 62. Asst, Univ. Ill, 57-61, instr. verbal commun, 61-62; asst. prof. speech, Ill. State Univ, 62-64, assoc. prof, 64-66; asst. prof. theatre arts, KNOX COL.(ILL), 66-68, ASSOC. PROF. & CHMN. DEPT. THEATRE & COMMUN, 68- Speech Commun. Asn; Am. Theatre Asn; U.S. Inst. Theatre Technol. Theatre history and aesthetics. Add: Dept. of Theatre & Communications, Knox College, Galesburg, IL 61401.

WHITLEY, ALVIN, b. San Antonio, Tex, Nov. 4, 26. ENGLISH. B.A, Univ. Tex, 46; M.A, Columbia Univ, 47; M.A, Harvard, 48, Ph.D, 50. Instr. ENG, UNIV. WIS-MADISON, 50-53, asst. prof, 53-56, assoc. prof, 56-61, PROF, 61-, chmn. gen. hons. prog, Col. Let. & Sci, 60-63. Guggenheim fel, 57-58. English literature of the late 18th and 19th, and early 20th centuries. Publ: Co-auth, The comic in theory and practice, Appleton, 60 & English poetry of the mid and late eighteenth century, Knopf, 63. Add: Dept. of English, University of Wisconsin-Madison, Madison, WI 53706.

WHITLOCK, BAIRD WOODRUFF, b. New Brunswick, N.J, June 1, 24; m. 53; c. 4. ENGLISH LITERATURE. B.A, Rutgers Univ, 48; Ph.D.(Eng), Univ. Edinburgh, 53; D.Lit, Nasson Col, 73. Instr. Eng, Middlebury Col, 48-51; Univ. Vt, 53-54; asst. prof. humanities, Colby Col, 54-56; assoc. prof. music & humanities, Case Inst. Technol, 56-61; prof. Eng. & humanities, San Francisco State Col, 61-64: chmn. div. humanities, lang. & lit. & dept. Eng; prof. Eng. & chmn. dept, Univ. Wyo, 64-66; prof. Eng. & dir. lib. stud, Elmira Col, 66-72; PRES, SIMON'S ROCK COL, 72- Mem. bd. dir, Intercol. Music Counc. 59-62; vis. prof. Eng, Univ. Hawaii, 64. U.S.A.A.F, 43-45, 2nd Lt. MLA; Am. Guild Scholars. John Donne and John Hoskyns; Baroque art forms; general humanities. Publ: The counter-renaissance, Bibliotheque Humanisme et Renaissance, 58; Donne's University years, Eng. Stud, 62; From the counter-Renaissance to the Baroque, Bucknell Rev, 67. Add: Office of the President, Simon's Rock, Great Barrington, MA 01230.

WHITLOCK, DAVID COTTON, b. Jan. 24, 35; U.S. citizen; m. 56; c. 2. SPEECH COMMUNICATION. B.G.E, Univ. Nebr. at Omaha, 62; M.A, Univ. Colo, Boulder, 66, Ph.D.(commun, theatre), 70. U.S. Air Force, 52-, AV training off, N.Am. Air Defense Command, 63-67, instr. Eng. & speech, U.S. AIR FORCE ACAD, 67-69, asst. prof, 71-72, ASSOC. PROF, 72-73, SPEECH, 73- Instr, South. Colo. State Col, 63-65; Univ. Colo, Colorado Springs, 67-68; Univ. Colo, Denver, 70. U.S.A.F, 52-, Maj. Speech Commun. Asn; Am. Forensic Asn.(mem, educ. practices comt, 72-74). Coercive rhetoric; student unrest; communication in crises. Publ: Dimensions of oral communication: Hq. North American Air Defense Command, J. Colo-Wyo. Acad. Sci, 12/67; Shades of student iconoclasm: the dimensions of rhetorical power, Colo. J. Educ. Res, winter 72. Add: 1513 Lyle Dr, Colorado Springs, CO 80915.

WHITLOW, ROGER LEE, b. Galesburg, Ill, Jan. 13, 40; m. 60; c. 2. AMERICAN LITERATURE. B.S.Ed, Ill. State Univ, 62, M.S, 64; Univ. Iowa, 65-67. ASST. PROF. ENG, EAST. ILL. UNIV, 67- Am. Stud. Asn; Col. Lang. Asn; Midcontinent Am. Stud. Asn. Nineteenth and 20th century American literature; black American literature. Publ: Black American literature: a critical history, Nelson-Hall, 73; co-auth, The emerging university, Phillips, 74; contrib, The two hundred most important works of black American literature: a bibliography, Ill. Eng. Bull, 72, Why black literature?, East. Alumnus, 72 & Black American drama: a checklist of the most significant plays, anthologies, and criticism, Playbill, 73. Add: Dept. of English, Eastern Illinois University, Charleston, IL 61920.

WHITMAN, ROBERT FREEMAN, b. Boston, Mass, July 9, 25; m. 56. ENGLISH. A.B, Cornell Univ, 49, M.A, Harvard, 51, Ph.D.(Eng), 56. Teaching fel. gen. educ, Harvard, 53-55; instr. ENG, Princeton, 55-60, asst. prof, UNIV. PITTSBURGH, 60-65, assoc. prof, 65-67, PROF, 67-, chmn. dept, 67-72. Nat. Endowment for Humanities res. fel, 72-73. MLA; Malone Soc. English drama, especially Jacobean and Caroline; G.B. Shaw. Publ: The play-reader's handbook, Bobbs, 66; O'Neill's search for a language of the theatre, Quart. J. Speech, 4/60; Beyond melancholy: John Webster and the tragedy of darkness, In: Salzburg Studies in English literature, 73. Add: Dept. of English, University of Pittsburgh, Pittsburgh, PA 15260.

WHITNEY, BLAIR, b. Chicago, Ill, June 1, 42; m. 64; c. 2. ENGLISH & AMERICAN LITERATURE. B.A, Univ. Ill, 63, M.A, 65, Ph.D.(Eng), 67. ASST. PROF. Eng, Cent. Mo. State Col, 67-69; AM. THOUGHT & LANG, MICH. STATE UNIV, 69- MLA; AAUP; Soc. Stud. Midwest. Lit. American Indian literature; midwestern literature; modern drama. Publ: John G. Neihardt, Twayne, 74; Lincoln's life as dramatic art, J. Ill. State Hist. Soc, fall 68; Nat. Turner's mysticism, Barat Rev, spring-summer 71. Add: Dept. of American Thought and Language, Michigan State University, East Lansing, MI 48823.

WHITTEMORE, NENA THAMES, b. New Orleans, La, Apr. 17, 39; m. 63; c. 1. ENGLISH LITERATURE. B.A, Carleton Col, 61; M.A, Hunter Col, 63; Ph.D.(Eng), City Univ. New York, 68. Teaching fel. Eng, Hunter Col, 61-63, lectr, 63-69; instr, Rutgers Univ, Newark, 69-70; ASST. PROF, JOHN JAY COL. CRIMINAL JUSTICE, 70- Assoc. ed, Centerpoint: Interdisciplinary Jour. City Univ. New York, 72-74. Renaissance Soc. Am; MLA. English Renaissance; 17th century English literature; Renaissance Women's studies. Publ: The educated woman, Carleton, 71. Add: Dept. of English, John Jay College of Criminal Justice, 445 W. 59th St, New York, NY 10019.

WHITTEMORE, (EDWARD) REED, b. New Haven, Conn, Sept. 11, 19; m. 52; c. 2. ENGLISH. B.A, Yale, 41. From instr. to prof. Eng, Carleton Col, 47-66; sr. prog. assoc. urban affairs, Nat. Inst. Pub. Affairs, 66-68; PROF. ENG, UNIV. MD, COLLEGE PARK, 68- Ed, Furioso, 39-53; Carlton Miscellany, 60-64; consult. poetry, Libr. Congr, 64-65; mem. comn. lit, NCTE, 67-69; lit. ed, New Republic, 69-73. U.S.A.A.F, 41-45, Maj. MLA. Publ: An American takes a walk, Selfmade man, 59 & Fascination of the abomination, 63, Macmillan; Poems new and selected, 67 & 50 Poems 50, 70, Univ. Minn; From zero to the absolute, Crown, 67. Add: Dept. of English, University of Maryland, College Park, MD 20740.

WHITTEN, MARY EVELYN, b. Waskom, Tex, Aug. 23, 22. ENGLISH. B.A, E.Tex. State Teachers Col, 47; M.A, Univ. Tex, 49, Ph.D.(Eng), 57; Univ. Tenn, 51-53. Teacher high sch, Tex, 48-49; supvr. ENG, Cent. State Col, 49-51, asst. prof, 53-54; instr, Univ. Tenn, 52-53; Univ. Tex, 55-58; PROF, N.TEX. STATE UNIV, 58- MLA; NCTE. Skepticism in Victorian England; Victorian critics of Shakespeare. Publ: Co-auth, English grammar and composition: grade 9, 58, 63, 65, & Harbrace college handbook, 5th ed, 62, 6th ed, 67, 7th ed, 72, auth, Creative pattern practice, 66, co-auth, English workshop series: grade 9, 64, 73, College English: the first year, 4th ed, 64,

5th ed, 68, 6th ed, 73 & auth, Decisions, decisions: style in writing, 71, Harcourt. Add: P.O. Box 5354, North Texas Station, Denton, TX 76203.

WHITTIER, HENRY S, b. Boston, Mass, Jan. 20, 24; m. 68; c. 1. ENGLISH. B.S, U.S. Naval Acad, 45; M.A, Univ. N.H, 55; Ph.D.(Eng), Yale, 58. Instr. ENG, Middlebury Col, 58-60; asst. prof, C.W. Post Col, L.I. Univ. 60-61; DALHOUSIE UNIV, 61-65, ASSOC. PROF, 65- U.S.N, 45-53, Lt. Asn. Can. Univ. Teachers Eng. The novels of Joseph Conrad; the poems of Lord Byron and William Blake; American literature of the 19th century. Publ: Fisher's Valley of vision, Dalhousie Rev, spring 63; Byrm: poet of the human condition, Visva-Bharati Quart, 5-10/72. Add: Dept. of English, Dalhousie University, Halifax, N.S, Can.

WHITTINGTON, CURTIS CALVIN, JR, b. Greenwood, Miss, Sept. 6, 29; m. 50; c. 1. ENGLISH. B.A, Univ. Miss, 51; M.A, Vanderbilt Univ, 55, Ph.D, 72. Teaching fel, Vanderbilt Univ, 55-57; instr. ENG, Martin Br, Univ. Tenn, 57-59; asst. prof, McNeese State Col, 59-63; Mid. Tenn. State Univ, 63-70; ASSOC. PROF, McNEESE STATE UNIV, 70- MLA; NCTE; S.Cent. Mod. Lang. Asn. American literature; mythology. Publ: The burden of narration: democratic perspectives and first-person point of view, South. Humanities Rev, spring 68; The earned vision: Robert Penn Warren's The ballad of Billie Potts and Camus' Le malentendu, Four Quarters, 5/72; To one of the late deans of St. Paul's (poem), Vanderbilt Poetry Rev, fall 72; plus others. Add: Dept. of Languages, McNeese State University, Ryan St, Lake Charles, LA 70601.

WHITTLE, AMBERYS RAYVON, b. Burlington, N.C, Sept. 2, 35; m. 72. ENGLISH. A.B, Univ. N.C, Chapel Hill, 61, M.A, 65, Ph.D.(Eng), 68. Teacher, Baylor Sch, Tenn, 61-64; asst. prof. ENG, DRAKE UNIV, 68-73, ASSOC. PROF, 73- AAUP; Am. Lit. Group, MLA. Nineteenth century American literature; twentieth century British and American literature. Publ: Ed, The poems of Trumbull Stickney, Farrar, 72; auth, Trumbull Stickney, Bucknell Univ, 73; The dust of seasons: time in the poetry of Trumbull Stickney, Sewanee Rev, fall 66; Modern chivalry: the frontier as crucible, Early Am. Lit, 72. Add: Dept. of English, Drake University, Des Moines, IA 50311.

WHITWORTH, RICHARD G, b. Terre Haute, Ind, Jan. 2, 30. ENGLISH EDUCATION. B.S, Ind. State Univ, 51, M.S, 56; Ed.D.(sec. educ), Ind. Univ, 64. Teacher elem, jr. high & high schs, Ind, 56-65; asst. prof. ENG, BALL STATE UNIV, 65-68, assoc. prof, 68-73, PROF, 73- NDEA Inst. Lang. & Compos, summer 66. U.S.N, 51-55. NEA; NCTE. English education; preparation of secondary teachers of English. Publ: Improving reading tastes, Eng. J, 5/66; New slant on note-taking, Clearing House, 9/66; For a change of pace, J. Sec. Educ, 1/67. Add: Dept. of English, Ball State University, Muncie, IN 47306.

WIATT, WILLIAM HAUTE, b. Hampton, Va, Aug. 12, 23; m. 51; c. 4. ENGLISH. A.B, Univ. Mo, 49, M.A, 50; Ph.D.(Eng), Univ. N.C, 56. Instr. ENG, Univ. Mo, 50-51; Ohio Univ, 55-56; IND. UNIV, BLOOMINGTON, 56-58, asst. prof, 58-63, assoc. prof, 63-69, PROF, 69- U.S.A, 43-46. Life and works of Sir Thomas Wyatt; early English drama; English teacher preparation. Publ: The dramatic function of the Alexandro-Villuppo episode in the Spanish tragedy, Notes & Queries; On the date of Sir Thomas Wyatt's knighthood, J. Eng. & Ger. Philol; Sir Thomas Wyatt and Anne Boleyn, Eng. Lang. Notes, 12/68; plus one other. Add: Dept. of English, Indiana University, Bloomington, IN 47401.

WICHERT, ROBERT A, b. Utica, N.Y, Dec. 18, 16; m. 56; c. 1. ENGLISH LITERATURE. B.A, Cornell Univ, 38, M.A, 40, Ph.D.(Eng), 48; Oxford, 48. Instr. Eng, Univ. Conn, 46-50; asst. prof, N.MEX. STATE UNIV, 50-56, assoc. prof, 56-63, PROF. ENG. & ASST. DEAN, COL. ARTS & SCI, 63-, HEAD DEPT. ENG, 68- Lectr, Chautauqua Inst, 62-63. U.S.A, 42-46, Capt. NCTE; MLA. Romantic literature; the novel. Publ: The quality of Graham Greene's mercy, Col. Eng, 11/63. Add: Dept. of English, New Mexico State University, University Park, NM 88070.

WICK, ROBERT H, b. Mt. Union, Iowa, Jan. 23, 13; m. 42; c. 3. SPEECH & DRAMA. B.A, North. State Univ, 34; M.A, Univ. South. Calif, 40; Ph.D. (speech), State Univ, Iowa, 55. Prin. & teacher high sch, Andrew, Iowa, 34-36, teacher, Newton, Iowa, 36-42; teacher & chmn. dept. speech, ST. CLOUD STATE COL, 48-62, dean arts & sci, 62-65, pres, 65-72, DISTINGUISHED SERV. PROF. SPEECH, 72- U.S.A, 42-46, Capt. Am. Counc. Educ; Speech Commun. Asn; NEA. Discussion. Publ: Responsibility of colleges and universities, Vital Speeches, 2/1/67; College forum, Col. Mgt, 7/67. Add: St. Cloud State College, St. Cloud, MN 56301.

WICKERT, MAX ALBRECHT, b. Augsburg, Ger, May 26, 38; U.S. citizen; div; c. 1. ENGLISH & AMERICAN LITERATURE, MODERN POETRY. B.A, St. Bonaventure Univ, 58; M.A, Yale, 59, Ph.D.(Eng), 65. Instr. ENG, Nazareth Col. Rochester, 61-62, asst. prof, 62-66; STATE UNIV. N.Y. BUFFALO 66-70, ASSOC. PROF, 70- Dir, Outriders Poetry Prog, Buffalo, N.Y, 71- Spenser; Anglo-German literary relations; 19th century aesthetics. Publ: All the weight of the still midnight (poems), Outriders, 72; co-ed, 1001 ways to live without working, Eröffnungen, Vienna, 71; auth, Structure and ceremony in Spenser's Epithalamion, ELH, 6/68; auth, var. poems, Poetry, Choice, Works, Mich. Quart. Rev, 69-73; trans, var. poems by Georg Trakl, Chicago Rev, Choice, Extensions, Malahat Rev, 69- Add: Dept. of English, Annex B, State University of New York at Buffalo, Buffalo, NY 14214.

WICKES, GEORGE, b. Antwerp, Belgium, Jan. 6, 23; U.S. citizen; m. 51, 62; c. 5. ENGLISH. B.A, Univ. Toronto, 44; M.A, Columbia Univ, 49; Ph.D, Univ. Calif, 54. Asst. secy, Belgian-Am. Educ. Found, 47-49; exec. off, U.S. Educ. Found, Belgium, 52-54; instr. Eng, Duke Univ, 54-57; asst. prof, Harvey Mudd Col. & Claremont Grad. Sch, 57-60, assoc. prof, 60-66, PROF, 66-70; ENG. & COMP. LIT, UNIV. ORE, 70- Fulbright lectr, France, 62-63, summer 66; U.S. Inform. Serv. lectr, Europe, 69; vis. prof, Univ. Rouen, 70; Am. Philos. Soc. grant, 71; sr. fel, Ctr. Twentieth Century Stud, Univ. Wis-Milwaukee, 71; Am. Counc. Learned Soc. grant, 72; Nat. Endowment for Arts creative writing fel, 73. Off. Strategic Serv, 43-46. Renaissance poetry; modern literature; comparative literature. Publ: Ed, Durrell-Miller correspondence, Dutton, 63; Masters of modern British fiction, Macmillan, 63; Henry Miller and the critics, South. Ill. Univ, 63; Aldous Huxley at UCLA: a catalogue of the manuscripts in the Aldous Huxley collection, Univ. Calif. Libr, 64; Henry Miller, Univ. Minn, 66; Americans in Paris, Doubleday, 69. Add: Dept. of English, University of Oregon, Eugene, OR 97403.

WICKS, ROBERT GERALD, b. Streator, Ill, Feb. 9, 35. ENGLISH. B.A, Univ. Calif, Riverside, 56; M.A, Calif. State Col. Los Angeles, 58. INSTR. high sch, Calif, 59-64; ENG, FULLERTON COL, 64- Lectr. Eng, Calif. State Col. Los Angeles, 64-, staff mem, NDEA Eng. Inst, 66. U.S.A, 58-59, Sgt. NCTE. Publ: Co-auth, Scope reader 2, 66 & Language in your life, 66, Harper; co-auth, Society, systems, and man, Wiley, 72; auth, We talked of Frost, Col. Eng, 11/65. Add: 10159 Lower Azusa Rd, Temple City, CA 91780.

WICKS, ULRICH, b. Neumünster, Ger, July 8, 42; U.S. citizen; m. 64; c. 2. COMPARATIVE LITERATURE. B.A, North. Ill, Univ, 63; Ph.D.(comp. lit), Univ. Iowa, 70. Instr. ENG, UNIV. MAINE, ORONO, 69-70, ASST. PROF, 70- MLA. The novel; picaresque fiction; genre theory. Publ: Picaro, picaresque: the picaresque in literary scholarship, 6/72 & A picaresque bibliography, 6/72, Genre; The nature of picaresque narrative: a modal approach, PMLA, 3/74. Add: Dept. of English, University of Maine, Orono, ME 04473.

WICKSTROM, GORDON MINTON, b. Boulder, Colo, Apr. 26, 26; m. 48; c. 2. DRAMA, THEATRE. B.A, Univ. Colo, 50, M.A, 54; dipl, Brit. Drama League, 58; Ph.D.(dramatic lit, criticism), Stanford Univ, 68. Dir. drama & teacher drama & Eng, Powell High Sch, Wyo, 50-66; ASSOC. PROF. DRAMA, FRANKLIN & MARSHALL COL, 68- Guest dir, Colo. Shakespeare Festival, Univ. Colo, summers 62 & 73; ed. theatre in rev, Educ. Theatre J, 71- U.S.N, 44-46. Am. Theatre Asn; AAUP. Irish dramatic movement; Polish romantic drama; post-modern theatre modes. Publ: The theatre of the Congressional Record, Players, 68; The heroic dimension in Brendan Behan's The hostage, 70 & The un-divine comedy: drama of art and revolution, 72, Educ. Theatre J. Add: Dept. of Drama, Franklin & Marshall College, Lancaster, PA 17604.

WIDENER, RALPH WILLIAM, JR, b. Tulsa, Okla, Dec. 3, 22. SPEECH. B.S. Ed, East. Ill. Univ, 48; M.A, Univ. Okla, 50; Ph.D.(speech), South. Ill. Univ, 62. Instr. speech, Univ. Miss, 49-51; speech & soc. sci, High Park High Sch, Dallas, Tex, 51-52; Byrd High Sch, Shreveport, La, 52-54; asst. SPEECH, Fla. State Univ, 54-56; Univ. Ark, 57-60; South. Ill. Univ, 60-62; asst. prof, Univ. Houston, 62-67; assoc. prof. & head dept, Mary Hardin Baylor Col, 67-71; PROF. & CHMN. DEPT, ARK. STATE UNIV, 71- Training off, Ft. Chaffee, Ark, 58-59. U.S.A, 42-45, Sgt. Speech Commun. Asn. Charles Hillman Brough and his extant speeches. Publ: Everyday communication, Adams, 74; State speech requirements, Speech Teachers, 3/74; Biography of Charles Hillman Brough, Ark. Hist. Asn. J, spring 74. Add: Div. of Speech & Drama, Arkansas State University, P.O. Drawer Y, State University, AR 72467.

WIDMANN, R. L, b. Watertown, Wis, Nov. 16, 41; m. 67. ENGLISH, HUMANITIES. A.B, Univ. Wis, Madison, 63; A.M, Univ. Ill, Urbana, 64, Ph.D. (Eng), 67. ASST. PROF. ENG, UNIV. PA, 67- Vis. lectr. Eng, Univ. Md, 72-73. AAUP; Am. Soc. Inform. Sci.(secy-treas, spec. interest group-arts & humanities, 72-); Bibliog. Soc. Univ. Va; Shakespeare Asn. Am; MLA; Renaissance Soc. Am; Renaissance Eng. Text Soc. Bibliography; Renaissance literature; women in literature and psychology. Publ: Ed, the poems of Wentworth Dillon, Earl of Roscommon: a critical edition, Mouton, The Hague, 74; co-ed, South Carolina old-spelling Comedy of errors, Univ. S.C, 74; Murdoch's Under the net: theory and practice of fiction & An Iris Murdoch checklist, winter 67, Critique: Stud. Mod. Fiction; contrib, The computer in literary and linguistic research, Cambridge Univ, 71; Recent scholarship in literary and linguistic studies, Computers & the Humanities, 9/72. Add: Dept. of English, University of Pennsylvania, Philadelphia, PA 19174.

WIDMER, KINGSLEY, b. July 17, 25; U.S. citizen; m; c. 2. LITERATURE. B.A, Univ. Minn, 49; M.A, 51; Ph.D, Univ. Wash, 57. Teaching asst. gen. stud, Univ. Minn, 49-51; assoc, Univ. Wash, 52-55; Ford Found. intern. humanities, Reed Col, 55, instr, 55-56; asst. prof. ENG, SAN DIEGO STATE UNIV, 56-62, assoc. prof, 62-67, PROF, 67- Vis. asst. prof. Eng, Univ. Calif, Berkeley, 60-61; Fulbright sr. lectr. Am. lit, Tel Aviv Univ, 63-64; Mem. vis. prof. Eng. Simon Frazer Univ, 67; vis. prof, Univ. Nice, 70. Modern literature; cultural and social criticism. Publ: Co-ed, Literary censorship, 60, 69 & Freedom and culture, 70, Wadsworth; auth; The art of perversity: the shorter fictions of D.H. Lawrence, Univ. Wash, 62; Henry Miller, Twayne, 63; The literary rebel, South. Ill. Univ, 65; Ways of nihilism: Herman Melville, Ward-Ritchie, 70; Sensibility and society, San Diego State Univ, (in press); The experience of freedom: censorship and the teacher, Am. Fed. Teachers, 66; Feminism, Know, 71; plus articles in Nation, Village Voice and other literary and sociological journals. Add: School of Literature; San Diego State University, 5402 College Ave, San Diego, CA 92115.

WIEBE, DALLAS EUGENE, b. Newton, Kans, Jan. 9, 30; m. 51; c. 2. ENGLISH LITERATURE. A.B, Bethel Col.(Kans), 54; M.A, Univ. Mich, 55, Ph.D, 60. Instr. Eng. lit, Univ. Wis, 60-63; from asst. prof. to assoc. prof. ENG. & AM. LIT, UNIV. CINCINNATI, 63-72, PROF, 72- Major Hopwood Poetry Award, Univ. Mich, 57. U.S.A, 51-53. Contemporary British and American literature, especially poetry. Publ: Skyblue the badass, Doubleday, 69; Mr. Lowell and Mr. Edwards, Wis. Stud. Contemporary Lit, 62; Wyndham Lewis and the picaresque novel, S.Atlantic Quart, 63. Add: Dept. of English, University of Cincinnati, Cincinnati, OH 45221.

WIEBE, RUDY H, b. Fairholme, Sask, Oct. 4, 34; m. 58; c. 3. CREATIVE WRITING, CANADIAN LITERATURE. B.A, Univ. Alta, 56, M.A, 60; Univ. Tübingen, 57-58; Th.B, Mennonite Brethren Bible Col, Winnipeg, 61; State Univ, Iowa, 64. Lectr. Eng. lit, Univ. Alta, 58-59; ed. relig. weekly, Christian Press, Winnipeg, 61-63; asst. prof. Eng. lit, Goshen Col, 63-66, assoc. prof, 67; asst. prof. creative writing & Eng. lit, UNIV. ALTA, 67, ASSOC. PROF. CREATIVE WRITING & CAN. LIT, 71- Sr. arts fel, Can. Counc, 72-73. Canadian literature, including aboriginal folk songs and poetry; personal fiction research. Publ: Peace shall destroy many, McClelland & Stewart, 62 & Eerdmans, 64; First and vital candle, Eerdmans, 66; The blue mountains of China (novel), 70, The temptations of Big Bear (novel), 73 & Where is the voice coming from?, 74, McClelland & Stewart; ed, The storymakers, 71 & Stories from Western Canada, 73, Macmillan, Toronto; auth, Millstones for the sun's day, Tamarack Rev, summer 67; contrib, The narrative voice (short stories), McGraw-Ryerson, 72 & Conversations with Canadian novelists, Macmillan, 73; plus numerous short stories & articles. Add: Dept. of English, University of Alberta, Edmonton, Alta. T6G 2G2, Can.

WIEGAND, WILLIAM GEORGE, b. Detroit, Mich, June 11, 28. ENGLISH LITERATURE. A.B, Univ. Mich, 49, A.M, 50; Ph.D.(Eng), Stanford Univ, 60. Teaching fel. Eng, Univ. Mich, 54-55; writing fel, Stanford Univ, 55-56, teaching fel, 56-60, lectr, 63; Briggs-Copeland instr. ENG, Harvard, 60-62; asst. prof, SAN FRANCISCO STATE UNIV, 62-66, assoc. prof, 66-73, PROF, 73- Mary Roberts Rinehart Award, 50; Joseph Henry Jackson Award, 59. Contemporary American literature; creative writing. Publ: At last, Mr. Tolliver, Rinehart, 50; The treatment man, McGraw, 59; The school of soft knocks, Lippincott, 68; J.D. Salinger: 78 bananas, Chicago Rev, winter 58; Salinger and Kierkegaard, Minn. Rev, 5-6/65; The non-fiction novel, N.Mex. Quart, autumn 67. Add: Dept. of English, San Francisco State University, San Francisco, CA 94132.

WIEHE, ROGER EDWIN, b. Bronx, N.Y, May 27, 27; m. 60; c. 2. ENGLISH LANGUAGE & LITERATURE. B.A, Yale, 50; M.A, Univ. Ill, 51; Boston Univ, 63-64; Ph.D.(Eng, comp. lit), Columbia Univ, 64; Univ. London, 72-73. Instr. Eng, Wagner Col, 56-58, asst. prof, 58-60; instr. commun, Boston Univ, 60-64, asst. prof, 64-65; assoc. prof. LANG. & LIT, LOWELL TECHNOL. INST, 65-72, PROF, 72- U.S.A, 45-46. MLA. Seventeenth century British literature; philosophy of religion; philosophy of knowledge. Add: Dept. of Language & Literature, Lowell Technological Institute, Lowell, MA 01854.

WIELER, JOHN WILLIAM, b. Wheeling, W.Va, July 12, 07. ENGLISH. A.B, Dartmouth Col, 29; fel, Tufts Col, 29-30; M.A, Harvard, 31; Ph.D, Columbia Univ, 47. Instr. Eng, Eaglebrook Sch. for Boys, Mass, 31-38; asst. to head master, 36-38; tutor Eng, eve. session, Brooklyn Col, 39-40; LEHMAN COL, 40-48, instr, 48-51, asst. prof, 51-56, assoc. prof, 57-63, acting chmn. dept, 58-59, chmn. dept, 60-61, prof, 64-73, asst. dean fac, 61-65, asst. dir. instr, 65-66, asst. dean instr, 66-68, assoc. dean acad. standards & eval, 68-73, EMER. PROF. ENG, 73- Instr, exten. div, Columbia Univ, 40-42. A.U.S, 42-46, Capt. MLA; Renaissance Soc. Am; Mod. Humanities Res. Asn. English Renaissance. Publ: George Chapman: the influence of stoicism on his tragedies, 49, rev. ed, 68, King's Crown Press. Add: 19 Park Ave, White Plains, NY 10603.

WIENER, HAROLD SIMON LINCOLN, b. Newark, N.J, Feb. 12, 09. COMPARATIVE LITERATURE. A.B, Cornell Univ, 30; Ph.D, Yale, 38. Asst, Yale, 36-37; instr. Eng, Cornell Univ, 37-42; assoc. liaison off, Off. Lend Lease Admin, 42; mem. staff, U.S. Dept. State, 46-47; MEM. LIT. FAC, SARAH LAWRENCE COL, 47- Tew Prize, Yale, 34. U.S.N, 42-46, Lt. Comdr. Romanticism and the 19th century; the comic spirit in literature; Chaucer. Add: Dept. of Literature, Sarah Lawrence College, Bronxville, NY 10708.

WIENER, HARVEY SHELBY, b. Brooklyn, N.Y, Apr. 7, 40; m. 65; c. 1. ENGLISH & AMERICAN LITERATURE, COMPOSITION. B.S, Brooklyn Col, 61, M.A, 68; N.Y. State fel, Regents fel. & Ph.D.(Eng), Fordham Univ, 71. Asst, Fordham Univ, 70; instr. basic skills, Queensborough Community Col, CITY UNIV. NEW YORK, 70-71; ASST. PROF. ENG, LaGUARDIA COMMUNITY COL, 71- Adj. asst. prof, Brooklyn Col, 70-72; Nat. Endowment for Humanities fel, 72-73; vis. asst. prof, State Univ. N.Y. Stony Brook, 74- MLA; NCTE; Col. Eng. Asn; Conf. Col. Compos. & Commun. Seventeenth century non-dramatic literature; Shakespeare; 20th century American novel. Publ: Creating compositions, McGraw-Hill, 73; Bacon and poetry: a view of the New Atlantis, Anglia, (in press); Science or providence; towards knowledge in the New Atlantis, Enlightenment Essays, (in press). Add: 65 Narwood Rd, Massapequa, NY 11758.

WIERSMA, STANLEY M, b. Orange City, Iowa, July 15, 30; m. 55; c. 2. ENGLISH. A.B, Calvin Col, 51; M.Sc, Univ. Wis, 56, Ph.D, 61. Instr. Eng, West. Christian High Sch, Hull, Iowa, 51-52; CALVIN COL, 59-61, asst. prof, 61-63, assoc. prof, 63-67, PROF, 67- Lectr, Grand Rapids Jr. Col, 61-; part-time guest lectr, Grand Valley State Col, 64-67; guest lectr, Univ. Idaho, summer 68; Fulbright lectr, Free Univ, Amsterdam, 68-69; Kellogg Found. scholar, Eng, 73. U.S.A, 53-54. MLA; Conf. Christianity & Lit. Christopher Fry; English and continental poetry of the early 17th century; 20th century drama. Publ: Christopher Fry, Eerdmans, 70; Christopher Fry's A phoenix too frequent: a study in source and symbol, 12/65 & Spring and apocalypse, law and prophets: a reading of Fry's The lady's not for burning, 1/71, Mod. Drama; plus others. Add: Dept. of English, Calvin College, Grand Rapids, MI 49506.

WIESENFARTH, JOSEPH JOHN, b. Brooklyn, N.Y, Aug. 20, 33; m. 71. ENGLISH & AMERICAN LITERATURE. B.A, Cath. Univ. Am, 56, Ph.D.(Eng), 62; M.A, Univ. Detroit, 59. Asst. prof. ENG, La Salle Col, 62-64; Manhattan Col, 64-67, ASSOC. PROF, 67-70; UNIV. WIS-MADISON, 70- Vis. asst. prof. Eng, Manhattan Col, summer 62; Cath. Univ. Am, summer 63, vis. assoc. prof, summer 67; Finn Found. fel, summer 64; Nat. Endowment for Humanities fel, 67-68; Inst. Res. Humanities fel, 74-75. MLA; Eng. Inst. The English novel; Jane Austen; George Eliot and Henry James. Publ: Henry James and the dramatic analogy, 63 & The errand of form: an essay of Jane Austen's art, 67, Fordham Univ; Criticism and the semiosis of The good soldier, Mod. Fiction Stud, spring 63; Illusion and allusion: reflection in The cracked looking-glass, In: Katherine Anne Porter: a critical symposium, Univ. Ga, 69; Demythologizing Silas Marner, J. Eng. Lit. Hist, 6/70; plus others. Add: Dept. of English, Helen C. White Hall, University of Wisconsin-Madison, 600 N. Park St, Madison, WI 53706.

WIGGINS, EUGENE EDWARD, b. Bryson City, N.C, Sept. 18, 20; m. 50; c. 2. ENGLISH. B.A, Univ. Chattanooga, 42, M.A, Vanderbilt Univ, 47, Ph.D.(Eng), 54. Instr. ENG, Mid. Tenn. State Univ, 47-56; prof, Northeast Mo. State Teachers Col, 56-60; prof. & head dept, Cumberland Col, 60-69; PROF, N.GA. COL, 69- U.S.M.C, 42-46. MLA; NCTE; Col. Eng. Asn. Eighteenth century critical theory; Wordsworth; folklore. Add: Dept. of English, North Georgia College, Dahlonega, GA 30533.

WIGGINS, ROBERT ALONZO, b. Columbus, Ga, Feb. 8, 21; m. 44; c. 2. ENGLISH. A.B, Univ. Md, 42; M.A, Univ. Calif, 49, Ph.D, 53. Lectr. ENG, UNIV. CALIF, DAVIS, 50-52, instr, 52-54, asst. prof, 54-60, assoc. prof, 60-66, PROF, 66-, assoc. dean lett. & sci, 63-64, v.chancellor, 64-66, chmn. dept. Eng, 66-70, acad. senate, 71-72. U.S.A, 42-46, Capt. MLA; Am. Stud. Asn. American literature; fiction; criticism. Publ: Mark Twain: jackleg novelist, Univ. Wash, 64; Ambrose Bierce, Univ. Minn, 64; William Faulkner, In: American literary scholarship, 1965, 1966, Duke Univ, 66, 67. Add: Dept. of English, University of California, Davis, CA 95616.

WIGHT, MARJORIE, b. Cardston, Alta, June 12, 19. ENGLISH. A.B, Brigham Young Univ, 43; scholar & M.A, Univ. Calif, Los Angeles, 58; fel, Univ. South. Calif, 62-63, Ph.D.(Eng), 67. Asst. dir. visual aids dept, Brigham Young Univ, 43-45, exec. secy. for pres. univ, 53-56; exec. secy. counseling dept, col. arts & sci, Univ. South. Calif, 58-63; instr. ENG, BRIGHAM YOUNG UNIV, 63-67, ASST. PROF, 67- Rocky Mountain Mod. Lang. Asn; NCTE; Conf. Col. Compos. & Commun. Victorian period in English literature; Graham Greene, a comprehensive evaluation; science fiction, past, present and future. Add: Dept. of English, A280 JKB, Brigham Young University, Provo, UT 84601.

WIGHT, WILLIAM SAMUEL, b. Waynesboro, Ga, Oct. 16, 01. ENGLISH. Ph.B, Emory Univ, 22; A.M, Columbia Univ, 30; B.S. in L.S, George Peabody Col, 43. Teacher, Schs, N.C, 25-26; instr. Eng, S.Ga. Col, 26-28; teacher, high sch, Ga, 28-29; Peacock Sch, 32-35; Univ. Sch, 35-36; state ed, Fed. Writers' Proj, 36-39; asst. dir, State Writers' Proj, 39-41; reviser, libr. sch, George Peabody Col, 42-43; asst. ref. & circulation dept, libr, Univ. Mo, 43-46; asst. prof. Eng, UNIV. MIAMI, 46-51, assoc. prof, 51-63, ENG. & HUMANITIES, 63-68, dir. freshman Eng, 49-60, EMER. ASSOC. PROF, 68- Asst, Fourth Nat. Bank, Atlanta, Ga, 22-24. Inst. Gen. Semantics; Am. Libr. Asn; Am. Stud. Asn; Col. Eng. Asn; Conf. Col. Compos. & Commun; MLA; NCTE; Nat. Soc. Stud. Commun; S.Atlantic Mod. Lang. Asn; Speech Commun. Asn; Ling. Soc. Am. Teaching of English; language and linguistics. Publ: Co-auth, Practice in writing, Holt, 51; auth, The Post has word for it, monthly column in The Village Post, Miami, Fla, 64-69. Add: 7 Third Ave, SE, Cairo, GA 31728.

WIGOD, JACOB DAVID, b. Malden, Mass, May 12, 27; m. 48; c. 5. ENGLISH. A.B, N.Y. Univ, 49; A.M, Harvard, 50, Ph.D.(Eng), 55. Instr. ENG, Wayne Univ, 53-54; Univ. Mich, 55-59; asst. prof, UNIV. B.C, 59-66, ASSOC. PROF, 66- Fulbright vis. lectr. Eng. & Am. lit, Hiroshima Univ, Japan, 62-63. A.U.S, 45-46. MLA; Shakespeare Asn. Am; Philol. Asn. Pac. Coast; Renaissance Soc. Am. Shakespeare; poetry and drama; Romantic period. Publ: The darkening chamber: the growth of tragic consciousness in Keats, Univ. Salzburg, 72; The meaning of Endymion & Keats's ideal in the Ode on a Grecian urn, PMLA. Add: Dept. of English, University of British Columbia, Vancouver 8, B.C, Can.

WIKELUND, PHILIP RAYMOND, b. Chicago, Ill, Nov. 6, 13; m. 42; c. 1. ENGLISH LITERATURE. B.A, Univ. Calif, Los Angeles, 37, A.M, 39, William Andrews Clark Mem. Libr. fel, 46-47, Ph.D, 47; Johns Hopkins Univ, 39-42. Teaching asst, Univ. Calif, Los Angeles, 37-39; jr. instr, Johns Hopkins Univ, 39-42; instr, Univ. Mich, 47-50; assoc. prof. ENG. LIT, IND. UNIV, BLOOMINGTON, 50-69; PROF, 69-, chmn. compos, 50-60. Summer fels, Folger Shakespeare Libr, 54; Huntington Libr, 55; dir. postdoctoral fel. prog, William Andrews Clark Mem. Libr, Univ. Calif, Los Angeles, summer 71. U.S.N.R, 42-46, Lt. Comdr. MLA; Conf. Col. Compos. & Commun. Edition of Edmund Waller; 17th-century English literature and history; 20th-century English literature. Publ: Benedicite paraphrased by Rev. Mr. Merrick; a correction, ELH, 42; Thus I pass my time in this place: an unpublished letter of Thomas Hobbes, Eng. Lang. Notes, 6/69; Edmund Waller's fitt of versifying: deductions from a holograph fragment, Folger MS. X.d.309, Philol. Quart, 1/70; plus two others. Add: Dept. of English, Indiana University, Bloomington, IN 47401.

WIKSELL, MILTON JOEL, b. Marquette, Nebr, July 28, 10; m. 40; c. 2. COMMUNICATION. B.A, Wayne State Col, 35; M.A, La. State Univ, 38, Ph.D.(speech), 48. Asst. prof. speech, Univ. Md, 38-48; prof, Shepherd Col, 48-54; assoc. prof, Ind. Univ, 54-56; Mich. State Univ, 56-64; PROF. COMMUN, UNIV. WIS-MILWAUKEE, 64- Int. Commun. Asn.(2nd v.pres, 64-65); Speech Commun. Asn; Cent. States Speech Commun. Asn. Speech. Publ: Co-auth, Principles of speaking, Wadsworth, 62; auth, What employees expect from supervisors, Supervisory Mgt, 6/66; Talking it over is important, Personnel, 3/67; co-auth, Evaluating programs, Speech Teacher, 1/69; plus two others. Add: Dept. of Communication, University of Wisconsin-Milwaukee, Milwaukee, WI 53201.

WIKSELL, WESLEY, b. Kiron, Iowa, Jan. 7, 06; m. 34; c. 2. SPEECH, COMMUNICATION. A.B, State Univ. Iowa, 29, A.M, 31; Univ. Wis, 33; Ph.D, La. State Univ, 35; Univ. London, 39. Instr. speech, high sch, Nebr; prof, Stephens Col, 31-47, chmn. communs. staff, 36-47; PROF. SPEECH, LA. STATE UNIV, BATON ROUGE, 47- Dir, Little Theatre, Columbia, Mo, 34-35; spec. lectr. & consult, Esso Standard Oil Co, Baton Rouge, La, 49, 50; vis. prof, Univ. Hawaii, 54-55; lectr, Int. Consumers Credit Asn, 65- Nat. Soc. Stud. Commun.(v.pres, 50, pres, 60); Speech Commun. Asn.(ed, Quart. J. Speech, 50-). Controlled and uncontrolled types of breathing; individualizing speech training; library skills; programming in speech and parliamentary law. Publ: Do they understand you?, Macmillan, 60; How to conduct meetings, Harper, 66. Add: Dept. of Speech, Louisiana State University, Baton Rouge, LA 70803.

WILBUR, RICHARD PURDY, b. New York, N.Y, Mar. 1, 21; m. 42; c. 4. ENGLISH. B.A, Amherst Col, 42, hon. M.A, 52, Litt.D, 67; M.A, Harvard, 47; L.H.D, Lawrence Col, 60, Wash. Univ, 64. Asst. prof. ENG, Harvard, 50-54; assoc. prof, Wellesley Col, 55-57; PROF, WESLEYAN UNIV, 57- Guggenheim fels, 52-53, 63; Am. Acad. Arts & Lett. Prix de Rome fel, 54; Ford Found. fel, 60; chancellor, Acad. Am. Poets, 63- Pulitzer Prize in poetry, 57; Nat. Bk. Award in poetry, 57; Bollingen Prize in poetry, 71; Brandeis Creative Arts Award, 71; Shelley Mem. Prize, 73. U.S.A, 43-45. Am. Acad. Arts & Sci; Nat. Inst. Arts & Lett; Dramatists Guild; Am. Acad.

Arts & Lett. Publ: Poems, 1943-1956, Faber, London; transl, Moliere's Misanthrope, 55, auth, Things of this world, 56, Advice to a prophet, 61, transl, Tartuffe, 63, auth, The poems of Richard Wilbur, 63, Walking to sleep (poems), 69, School for wives, 71 & Opposites (verse for children), 73, Harcourt. Add: Dept. of English, Wesleyan University, Middletown, CT 06457.

WILCOX, EARL JUNIOR, b. Paragould, Ark, Aug. 9, 33; m. 53; c. 2. ENGLISH, AMERICAN LITERATURE. B.S, Ark. State Univ, 58; M.A, Univ. Tex, 59; Ph.D.(Eng), Vanderbilt Univ, 66. Asst. prof. Eng, Harding Col, 59-65, assoc. prof, 65-68; assoc. prof. Eng. & chmn. div. lit, lang. & philos, Ark. State Univ, 68-70; PROF. ENG, WINTHROP COL, 70- Consult, Educ. Testing Serv, N.J, 71-; mem. accreditation comt, South. Asn. Cols. & Schs, 73- U.S.A, 53-55. MLA. American literary naturalism; American realism; Robert Penn Warren's career. Publ: Co-auth, Fundamentals of fiction, Allyn & Bacon, 73; auth, Hemingway's use of Huck Finn, Fitzgerald/Hemingway Annual, 71; Emily Dickinson's Because I could not stop for death, Emily Dickinson Bull, 71; All the king's men in the classroom, Four Quarters, 72; plus others. Add: Dept. of English, Winthrop College, Rock Hill, SC 29730.

WILCOX, JOHN KENNETH, b. Denver, Colo, July 21, 09; m. 35. COMMUNICATION, EDUCATION. A.B, Univ. Denver, 42, M.A, 49, fel, 49-51, Ed.D, 51. Prin. pub. schs, Colo, 40-42, teacher high sch, 42-43, supt. schs, 46-48; teaching fel, UNIV. DENVER, 49-51, asst. prof. basic commun, 51-63, Eng. & reading, 63, EDUC, 63-66, ASSOC. PROF, 66- Consult. & educ. dir, Colo. Asn. Continuing Med. Lab. Educ, 73- U.S.A, 43-45. Nat. Soc. Stud. Commun. Communications skills of college freshmen and prospective teachers; reading improvement for adults; reading for teachers, elementary through adult. Publ: Co-auth, Speed reading, Developing modern reading techniques & Developing reading competence, Commun. Found, 61. Add: University of Denver, Denver, CO 80210.

WILCOX, RUTH ALICE, b. Chicago, Ill, June 6, 05. SPEECH & DRAMA. A.B, Dakota Wesleyan Univ, 27; Huron Col, 31; A.M, Northwest. Univ, 40; Columbia Univ, 49-50, dipl, 58. Instr, high sch, S.Dak, 27-31, jr. high sch, 31-32, sr. high sch, 32-43; asst. prof. speech & dean women, Dakota Wesleyan Univ, 43-46; asst. prof. speech, MARIETTA COL, 46-52, assoc. prof, 52-58, PROF. SPEECH & DRAMA, 58-, dean women, 46-70. Speech Commun. Asn; Am. Forensic Asn. Personnel administration in the secondary school and higher institutions. Publ: Co-auth, Teaching speech in high schools, Macmillan. Add: Marietta College, Marietta, OH 45750.

WILCOX, STEWART CONGER, b. Syracuse, N.Y, Nov. 11, 10. ENGLISH LITERATURE. A.B, Wesleyan Univ, 32; Ph.D, Johns Hopkins Univ, 38. Asst. Eng, Johns Hopkins Univ, 37-38; instr, Univ. Hawaii, 38-40, asst. prof, 40-42; Wesleyan Univ, 42-46; assoc. prof. ENG, UNIV. OKLA, 46-50, PROF, 50- MLA; S.Cent. Mod. Lang. Asn. Literature of the romantic period; William Hazlitt; Coleridge. Add: Dept. of English, University of Oklahoma, Norman, OK 73069.

WILCOX, THOMAS WILLIAM, b. New York, N.Y, Feb. 28, 21; m. 44; c. 2. ENGLISH. B.A, Amherst Col, 42, M.A, Harvard, 48. Faculty mem. ENG, Bennington Col, 49-60; PROF, UNIV. CONN, 60- Ed, Exercise Exchange, 51-68; Carnegie vis. prof, 59-60; dir, Nat. Surv. Undergrad. Prog. Eng, 65- U.S.N, 42-45, Lt.(jg). NCTE; MLA. Renaissance literature; teaching of English. Publ: The anatomy of college English, Jossey-Bass, 73; Composition where none is apparent, 5/65 & Non serviam: the reintegration of English, 10/67, Col. Compos. & Commun; The study of undergraduate programs, Col. Eng, 3/68. Add: Dept. of English, University of Connecticut, Storrs, CT 06268.

WILCOX, WALTER, b. Lewistown, Mont, May 2, 20; m. 41; c. 3. JOURNALISM. B.A, Univ. Nev, 41; M.A, State Univ. Iowa, 51, Ph.D.(mass commun), 58. Telegraph ed, Rev-Jour, Las Vegas, Nev, 45-46; manager & ed, Daily Times, Ely, Nev, 46-47; instr. jour. & mass commun, Univ. Wyo, 51-53; owner, Caribou County Sun, Soda Springs, Idaho, 53-55; instr. jour. & mass commun, Univ. Iowa, 56, instr. sch. jour, 57-58; assoc. prof, Tulane Univ, 58-60, dir. educ. TV programming, 59-60; assoc. prof. JOUR, UNIV. CALIF, LOS ANGELES, 60-63, PROF, 63-, CHMN. DEPT, 60-67, 71- Consult, univ. study, Univ. Ga, 57; staff researcher & consult, Inst. Higher Educ, Carnegie Corp-Teachers Col, Columbia Univ, 57-58; assoc. ed, Jour. Educator, 62-63. U.S.A, 42-46, Maj. Am. Soc. Jour. Sch. Adminr; Radio-TV News Dir. Asn; Asn. Educ. Jour. Mass communications. Publ: Liberal education and professional journalism education, State Univ. Iowa, 59; The press, the jury and the behavioral sciences, Jour. Monogr, 12/68. Add: Dept. of Journalism, University of California at Los Angeles, Los Angeles, CA 90024.

WILDE, ALAN, b. New York, N.Y, May, 26, 29. ENGLISH. B.A, N.Y. Univ, 50, M.A, 51; Fulbright fel, Sorbonne, 52-53; Ph.D, Harvard, 58. Instr. ENG, Williams Col, 58-61, asst. prof. 61-64; assoc. prof, TEMPLE, 64-67, PROF, 67- Scholar, N.Y. Univ, 50-51; Harvard, 51-52, teaching fel, 54-58. MLA; AAUP. Modern novel; stylistics; British literature between the wars. Publ: Art and order: a study of E.M. Forster, N.Y. Univ, 64; Christopher Isherwood, Twayne, 71; The aesthetic view of life, fall 61 & Irony and style, winter 70-71, Mod. Fiction Stud; The illusion of St. Mawr: technique and vision in D.H. Lawrence's novel, PMLA, 3/64. Add: Dept. of English, Temple University, Philadelphia, PA 19122.

WILDMAN, JOHN HAZARD, b. Mobile, Ala, Jan. 22, 11. ENGLISH LITERATURE. Ph.B, Brown Univ, 33, A.M, 34, Ph.D, 37. Instr. ENG, Brown Univ, 37-40; LA. STATE UNIV, BATON ROUGE, 40-46, asst. prof, 46-51, assoc. prof, 51-58, PROF, 58- U.S.A.A.F, 42-45, T/Sgt. MLA; S.Cent. Mod. Lang. Asn; Cath. Poetry Soc. Am. Victorian period; British novel; American novel. Publ: Fever, 53 & Sing no sad songs, 55, Exposition; Sun on the night, Sheed, 62; Forgotten land: another look, Dorrance, 66; contrib, Nine essays in modern literature, La. State Univ, 65; The do-it-yourself trap, fall 70 & Folly fighting death, winter 73, South. Rev. Add: Dept. of English, Louisiana State University, Baton Rouge, LA 70803.

WILDS, LILLIAN, b. Los Angeles, Calif. SHAKESPEARE. A.B, Univ. Calif, Los Angeles, 62, M.A, 64, Ph.D.(Shakespeare, Renaissance lit), 70. Asst. prof. ENG, CALIF. STATE POLYTECH. UNIV, POMONA, 68-70, ASSOC. PROF, 71- MLA; Int. Shakespeare Asn; Shakespeare Asn. Am; Col. Eng. Asn; Philol. Asn. Pac. Coast; Rocky Mt. Mod. Lang. Asn; Medieval Asn. Pac. Renaissance literature; drama and film. Add: Dept. of English, California State Polytechnic University, Pomona, CA 91768.

WILES, AMERICUS GEORGE DAVID, b. Lewistown, Md, Feb. 19, 06; m. 34. ENGLISH LITERATURE. A.B, Gettysburg Col, 29, LL.D, 64; univ. fel, Princeton, 31-32, Scribner fel, 32-33, Ph.D, 34; Litt.D, The Citadel, 60. Teacher, Hun Sch, N.J, 29-31, 33-36; prof. Eng. & head dept, The Citadel, 36-60; pres, NEWBERRY COL, 60-71, EMER. PRES, 71- MLA; S.Atlantic Mod. Lang. Asn; Southeast Renaissance Conf. Philip Sidney; Shakespeare; Milton. Publ: Co-auth, English for the Armed Forces, Harper; Parallel analyses of the two versions of Sidney's Arcadia, including major variations of the folio of 1593, Stud. Philol; What we face in the field of English, Col. Eng. Add: 112 Salisbury Dr, Summerville, SC 29483.

WILES, ROY McKEEN, b. Truro, N.S, Oct. 15, 03; m. 28; c. 2. ENGLISH LITERARY HISTORY. B.A, Dalhousie Univ, 27; univ. scholar, Harvard, 27-28, A.M, 28, Shattuck scholar, 31-32; Dexter scholar, 32, Townsend scholar, 32-33, Ph.D.(Eng. philol), 35; hon. LL.D, Mt. Allison Univ, 71. Instr. Latin, Colchester Co. Acad, 24-25; lectr. Eng, Univ. Alta, 28-31; asst. prof, McMaster Univ, 35-39, assoc. prof, 39-48, prof, 48-70, chmn. dept, 60-67, RETIRED. Can. Counc. sr. fel, 58-59; chmn, Humanities Res. Counc. Can, 60-62; visitor, Univs, N.Z, 7/66; vis. prof, Bowling Green State Univ, 67-68; vis. prof. Eng, Univ. Guelph, 70-71; chmn. comt. res. in progress, Humanities Res. Counc. Can, 71-72; vis. prof. Eng, McMaster Univ, 71-74. Mod. Humanities Res. Asn; Int. Asn. Univ. Prof. Eng.(ed, Bull, 73 & 74); fel. Royal Soc. Can.(hon. ed, 68-70); MLA; Am. Dialect Soc. Humanities Asn. Can.(secy-treas, 50, pres, 52); Johnson Soc. Great Lakes Region.(pres, 64-65); Asn. Can. Univ. Teachers Eng.(pres, 65-66); Am. Soc. 18th Century Stud.(1st v.pres, 72-73, pres, 73-74). English provincial newspapers to 1800; bibliography 1660-1800; provincial life in eighteenth century England. Publ: Serial publication in England before 1750, Cambridge, 57; Scholarly reporting in the humanities, 61 & The humanities in Canada: supplement to December 31, 1964, 66, Univ. Toronto; Freshest advices: early provincial newspapers in England, Ohio State Univ, 65; Early Georgian provincial magazines, Library, 64; contrib, New Cambridge bibliography of English literature, Cambridge, 71; auth, Samuel Johnson's response to beauty, Stud. Burke & His Time, winter 71-72; plus two others. Add: Dept. of English, McMaster University, Hamilton, Ont. L8S 4L9, Can.

WILEY, AUTREY NELL, b. St. Jo, Tex, May 27, 01. ENGLISH LITERATURE. A.B, Tex. Woman's Univ, 22; A.M, Columbia Univ, 24; summers, Univ. Colo, 26, Univ. Chicago, 27-29; Am. Asn. Univ. Women Maltby fel, Univ. Tex, 30-31; Ph.D, 31. Instr. Eng, Tex. Woman's Univ, 22-23, asst. prof, 24-31, assoc. prof, 31-39, prof, 39-71, dir. dept, 48-71, dean col. arts & sci, 60-71; RETIRED. Am. Counc. Learned Soc. fel, Eng. & Scotland, 32-33; pub. lectr, Univ. Tex, 42,45; chmn, NCTE Conf. Eng. Educ. Comt. in prep. & certification of Teachers Eng, 66-69. Piper Prof. Award, 63; Distinguished Alumna Award, 69. Mod. Humanities Res. Asn.(co-ed, Am. News Lett, 65-71); NCTE; Col. Eng. Asn; MLA; S.Cent. Mod. Lang. Asn.(assoc. ed, Bull, 47-58, v.pres, 51, secy-treas, 54-57, pres, 60-61). Restoration and 18th century literature; romanticism; 19th century American literature. Publ: Rare prologues and epilogues, 1642-1700, Allen & Unwin; Jonathan Swift, Univ. Tex; Preparation and certification of teachers of English: a bibliography 1950-1956, NCTE, annual suppl, 57-65. Add: 110 W. College Ave, Denton, TX 76201.

WILEY, BONNIE JEAN, b. Portland, Ore. JOURNALISM. B.A, Univ. Wash, 48; M.S, Columbia Univ, 57; Ph.D.(jour), South. Ill. Univ, Carbondale, 65. Lectr. jour, Ore. State Univ, 46; Univ. Wash, 47-48; managing ed, Yakima Morning Herald, Wash, 48-53; asst. prof. JOUR, Cent. Wash. State Col, 53-65; PROF, UNIV. HAWAII, MANOA, 65- Women in Commun; Asn. Educ. in Jour. Communications. Add: Dept. of English, University of Hawaii at Manoa, Honolulu, HI 96822.

WILEY, CHARLES GETCHELL, b. Santa Rosa, N.Mex, Feb. 14, 22; wid; c. 3. COMPARATIVE DRAMATIC LITERATURE, AMERICAN STUDIES & LITERATURE. B.A, Univ. N.Mex, 46, Ph.D.(Am. lit. & stud. & comp. dramatic lit), 57; M.A, Columbia Univ, 47. Instr. Eng, Univ. Ariz, 47-50; Colo. State Univ, 51-56; asst. prof. humanities, N.Mex. Inst. Technol, 56-59; chmn. div. humanities & head dept. Eng. & mod. lang, Ft. Lewis A&M Col, 59-62; dir. grad. & prof. stud, U.S. Naval Ord. Test Sta, China Lake, Calif, 62-64; assoc. prof. Eng. & Span, West. N.Mex. Univ, 64-66; prof. Eng. & chmn. dept, E.Carolina Univ, 66-68; vis. prof, Univ. N.Dak, 68-70; PROF. ENG. & ART & DEAN, COL. LIB. ARTS & SCI, EAST. N.MEX. UNIV, 70- Smith-Mundt lectr, 60-61; mem. ed. adv. bd, West. Am. Lit, 64-68. U.S.N.R, 41-45, Lt.(jg). MLA; Rocky Mt. Mod. Lang. Asn; S.Atlantic Mod. Lang. Asn; Melville Soc. Am; West. Lit. Asn; Mod. Humanities Res. Asn; Am. Stud. Asn; Col. Eng. Asn; NCTE; Am. Folklore Soc. Medicinal practices and uses of indigenous florae in rural New Mexico communities; libretti for song cycles; New Mexico rural arts. Add: Box 161, Santa Rosa, NM 88435.

WILEY, DAVID WATERMAN, b. Boston, Mass, Aug. 27, 28. SPEECH, DRAMA. B.L.I, Emerson Col, 50; M.Ed, Univ. Va, 55. Asst. prof. speech & drama, Longwood Col, 55-66; lectr. speech & theatre, Ind. Univ, 66-73; ASSOC. PROF. DRAMA, UNIV. HAWAII, HILO, 73- U.S.A, 51-53. Speech Commun. Asn; Am. Theatre Asn. Dramatics; arts. Publ: The image of a Southern orator: Wigfall's stand in the senate, In: Education in the South, Inst. South. Cult. Lect, Longwood Col, 59. Add: Dept. of Drama, University of Hawaii, Hilo College, 333 W. Lanikaula St, Hilo, HI 96720.

WILEY, MARGARET LEE, b. St. Jo, Tex, July 12, 05. ENGLISH LITERATURE. A.B, Tex. Woman's Univ, 23; univ. fel, Univ. Tex, 24, A.M, 24; summers, Univ. Chicago, 29, Columbia Univ, 31; du Pont fel, Univ. Va, 32-33, Ph.D, 36. Instr, Tex. Woman's Univ, 24-25; assoc. prof, W.Tex. State Col, 28-39; vis. asst. prof, Univ. Tex, 39-40; assoc. prof. Eng. & lib. arts counsel. woman, Univ. Southwest. La, 40-41; prof. ENG, E.Tex. State Col, 41-59; UNIV. TEX, ARLINGTON, 59-70, EMER. PROF, 70- Vis. asst. prof, Tex. Woman's Univ, 30-31; instr, Univ. Tex, 35-36; vis. prof, South. Methodist Univ, 44 & 48; Am. Asn. Univ. Women Tex. State Div. Centennial Fund Fels. Margaret Lee Wiley named endowment unit. Mod. Humanities Res.

Asn.(co-ed, Am. Newslett, 65-71); MLA; Col. Eng. Asn; Renaissance Soc. Am. Seventeenth and 18th century British literature; American literature; history of ideas. Publ: Ed, a treatise of the passions and faculties of the soule of man (1640) (facsimile reproduction with introduction), Scholars' Facsimiles, 71; Letters of Sidney Lanier to Colonel John G. James, 43 & Genius: a problem of definition, In: Studies in English, Univ. Tex; A Spence letter, In: Studies in honor of James Southall Wilson, Univ. Va. Bibliog. Soc. Add: 1330 S. Oak St, Arlington, TX 76010.

WILEY, MARGARET LENORE, b. Portland, Ore, Apr. 17, 08; m. 54. ENGLISH. A.B, Reed Col, 29, A.M, 31; Univ. Ore, 32-33; Am. Asn. Univ. Women fel, Radcliffe Col, 37-38, Ph.D, 40. Prof. Eng, Emerson Col, 38-43; stud. adv, New Sch. Soc. Res, 44-46; instr. ENG, BROOKLYN COL, 46-52, asst. prof, 52-60, assoc. prof, 60-66, prof, 66-70, EMER. PROF, 71- Fulbright res. fel, Univ. Calcutta, India, 57-58; Fulbright lectr. Am. lit, univs, India, 58-59. MLA. History of ideas; creative scepticism as a critical tool; parallels between thought movements in Orient and Occident. Publ: Subtle knot: creative scepticism in 17th century England, Allen & Unwin, London & Harvard Univ, 52; Creative sceptics, Allen & Unwin, 66; Creative scepticism in Emerson, Melville and Henry James, Univ. Panjab Res. Bull, 60. Add: Conant Rd, Lincoln, MA 01773.

WILEY, PAUL LUZON, b. Seattle, Wash, Sept. 9, 14; m. 39; c. 2. ENGLISH. A.B, Pomona Col, 34; grad. fel, Claremont Col, 34-35, M.A, 35; German-Am. exchange fel, Univ. Bonn, Ger, 35-36; Huntington Libr. res. fel, 40-41; Ph.D, Stanford Univ, 41. Instr. Eng, UNIV. WIS-MADISON, 42-44, asst. prof, 44-46, assoc. prof. ENG, LIB. STUD. & HUMANITIES, 46-52, PROF, 52- Lectr, Pomona Col, 51. MLA. English literature of the 16th and 17th centuries; 20th century English and American literature. Publ: Conrad's measure of man, Univ. Wis, 54; Novelist of three worlds, Ford M. Ford, Syracuse Univ, 62; co-auth, English poetry 1885-1920, Appleton, 69; auth, The British novel: Conrad to the present, AHM Publ, 73; George Cavendish, In: Encycl. Britannica, 60. Add: 2926 Gregory, Madison, WI 53711.

WILGUS, D. K. b. West Mansfield, Ohio, Dec. 1, 18; m. 40; c. 2. ENGLISH. B.A. & B.S, Ohio State Univ, 41, M.A, 47, Ph.D, 54. Educ. dir, Purdue Univ, 41-42; instr. Eng, Ohio State Univ, 46-50; assoc. prof, West. Ky. State Col, 50-60, prof. Eng. & folklore, 60-62; assoc. prof. ENG. & ANGLO-AM. FOLKSONG, UNIV. CALIF, LOS ANGELES, 62-66, PROF, 66-, HEAD, FOLKSONG PROG, CTR. STUD. COMP. FOLKLORE & MYTHOLOGY, 62-, DIR. FOLK FESTIVAL, 63-, CHMN. FOLKLORE & MYTHOLOGY GROUP, 63- Chicago folklore prize, 56; Guggenheim fel, 57-58; rec. rev. ed, J. Am. Folklore, 59-73; treas, John Edwards Mem. Found. 62-; Ford Found grant, 66-69; ed, West. Folklore, 70- U.S.A, 42-45. MLA; fel. Am. Folklore Soc.(1st v.pres, 63-71, pres, 71-72); Soc. Ethnomusicol; Int. Folk Music Counc; Folklore Soc, London; Soc. Folklife Stud; Folk Music Soc. Ireland. Anglo-American and Afro-American folk music and folklore. Publ: Anglo-American folksong scholarship since 1898, Rutgers Univ, 59; ed, Folklore International, Folklore Asn, 67 & Folk-songs of the Southern United States, Univ. Tex, 68; auth, Introduction to the study of hillbilly music, J. Am. Folklore, 65; Fiddler's farewell, Stud. Musicologia, 65; The oldest (?) text of Edward, West. Folklore, 66; plus others. Add: Folklore & Mythology Group, University of California, Los Angeles, CA 90024.

WILHELM, JAMES JEROME, b. Youngstown, Ohio, Feb. 2, 32. COMPARATIVE LITERATURE. B.A, Yale, 54, Ph.D.(comp. lit), 61; M.A, Columbia Univ, 58. From instr. to asst. prof. Eng, Queens Col, 61-65; ASSOC. PROF. COMP. LIT, RUTGERS UNIV, NEW BRUNSWICK, 65- MLA; Dante Soc; Mediaeval Acad. Am; Am. Comp. Lit. Asn. Publ: The cruelest month: spring, nature & love in classical & medieval lyrics, Yale, 65; Seven troubadours, Pa. State Univ, 70; Medieval song, Dutton, 71 & Allen & Unwin, 72. Add: 338 Lexington Ave, 3F, New York, NY 10016.

WILHELM, JOHN FERDINAND, b. Chicago, Ill, Aug. 30, 18; m. 44; c. 1. ENGLISH. B.S, Northwest. Univ, 43, M.A, 44; Ph.D.(Am. stud), Univ. Minn, 53. Instr. gen. stud, Univ. Minn, 48-53; asst. prof. ENG, CALIF. STATE UNIV, SACRAMENTO, 53-56, from assoc. prof. to PROF, 56- Calif. State Legis. distinguished teaching award, 65-66. U.S.N, 41-43, Ens. Col. Eng. Asn; Am. Stud. Asn. Nineteenth century American periodicals; Melville. Add: Dept. of English, California State University, Sacramento, Sacramento, CA 95819.

WILKENFELD, ROGER B, b. Brooklyn, N.Y, May 12, 38; m. 60. ENGLISH. B.A, Brooklyn Col, 59; Ph.D.(Eng), Univ. Rochester, 63. Instr. ENG, Univ. Rochester, 62-63; asst. prof, UNIV. CONN, 63-67, assoc. prof, 67-72, PROF, 72- Nat. Humanities Found. summer stipend, 68. MLA. Milton; Victorian literature; Ibsen. Publ: The seat at the center: an interpretation of Comus, ELH, 6/66; Theoretics or polemics: Milton criticism and the dramatic axiom, PMLA, 12/67; The kingdom of folly: Tennyson's Camelot, Univ. Toronto Quart, 4/68. Add: Dept. of English, University of Connecticut, Storrs, CT 06268.

WILKENS, KENNETH GERHARD, b. Red Lake Falls, Minn, Jan. 17, 21; m. 48; c. 3. PUBLIC SPEAKING. B.S.E, Minn. State Teachers Col, 42; A.M, Northwest. Univ, 47, Ph.D, 54. Instr, Minn. State Teachers Col, Moorhead, 46; asst. prof. SPEECH, St. Olaf Col, 47-56; Univ. Tex, 56-58; assoc. prof, ST. OLAF COL, 58-60, PROF, 60- U.S.A.A.F, 42-45. Speech Commun. Asn; Am. Forensic Asn; Cent. States Speech Asn. Public address and public speaking; forensics; speech education. Add: Dept. of Speech Communication & Theatre Arts, St. Olaf College, Northfield, MN 55057.

WILKERSON, ROBERT HAROLD, b. Norman, Okla, July 14, 21; m. 46; c. 2. JOURNALISM. B.A, Univ. Okla, 52, M.A, 54. Instr. jour, Ark. Agr. & Mech. Col, 54-55; East. Okla. Agr. & Mech. Col, 55-58; ASST. PROF, Hardin-Simmons Univ, 58-64; ENG, LAMAR UNIV, 64- U.S.N.R, 42-45. History of the press. Add: Dept. of Speech, Lamar University, Beaumont, TX 77710.

WILKIE, BRIAN, b. Brooklyn, N.Y, Mar. 30, 29; m. 57; c. 3. ENGLISH, COMPARATIVE LITERATURE. B.A, Columbia Univ, 51; M.A, Univ. Rochester, 52; Ph.D.(Eng), Univ. Wis, 59. Instr. ENG, Univ. Wis, 59; Dartmouth Col, 59-61, asst. prof, 61-63; UNIV. ILL, URBANA, 63-65, assoc. prof, 65-71, PROF, 71- Assoc, Univ. Ill. Ctr. Advan. Stud, 73-74. Univ. Ill. Teacher Excellence Award, 66. U.S.A, 52-54. MLA; NCTE. English romantic literature; the epic. Publ: Romantic poets and epic tradition, Univ. Wis, 65; Byron: artistry and style, In: Romantic and Victorian, Fairleigh Dickinson Univ, 71; Wordsworth and the tradition of the avant-garde, J. Eng. & Germanic Philol, 73; co-auth, On reading The four Zoas: inscape and analogy, In: Blake's Subline allegory, Univ. Wis, 73; plus others. Add: Dept. of English, University of Illinois, Urbana, IL 61801.

WILKINS, ARTHUR NORMAN, b. Kansas City, Mo, Sept. 24, 25. ENGLISH. M.A, Univ. Chicago, 50; univ. fel, Wash. Univ, 52-53, Ph.D.(Eng), 53. Instr. Eng, La. State Univ, 53-56; Jr. Col. Kans. City, 56-64, chmn. dept, 61-64; chmn. dept. Eng, Metropolitan Jr. Col, 64-68, CHMN. DIV. HUMANITIES, 68-69; chmn. dept. humanities, LONGVIEW COMMUNITY COL, 69-70, DEAN ACAD. AFFAIRS, 70- Educ. TV ser, The English language and you, KCSD-TV, 64. U.S.A, 43-46. MLA; NCTE; Johnson Soc. Midwest (cor. secy-treas, 62-66); Conf. Col. Compos. & Commun; Midwest Mod. Lang. Asn. English drama and light verse; 18th century English literature. Publ: Mortal taste, 65 & High seriousness, 71, Exposition; John Dennis' stolen thunder, 10/56, Robert Paltock and the Bishop of Chester, 12/58 & Pope and Appius, 8/60, Notes & Queries. Add: Longview Community College, 500 Longview Rd, Lee's Summit, MO 64063.

WILKINS, FREDERICK CHARLES, b. Lynn, Mass, May 23, 35. ENGLISH. A.B, Bowdoin Col, 57; M.A, Univ. Iowa, 58, Ph.D.(Eng), 65. Teaching asst. rhetoric & Eng, Univ. Iowa, 61-63; instr. rhetoric, Boston Univ, 63-65, asst. prof. rhetoric & Eng, 65-67; Fulbright prof. Am. lit, Univ. Lodz, 67-69; ASSOC. PROF. ENG, SUFFOLK UNIV, 70- MLA; Conf. Col. Compos. & Commun; NCTE; Am. Theatre Asn; Col. Eng. Asn; AAUP; Shakespeare Asn. Am. Contemporary theatre; world drama. Publ: Thomas Gray and the fortunate fall: a note on the twofold meaning of the Eton College ode, Explicator, 4/67. Add: Dept. of English, Suffolk University, 41 Temple St, Boston, MA 02114.

WILKINS, RUTH JONES, b. Allen, Md, May 1, 04; m. 25; c. 2. ENGLISH. A.B, Col. William & Mary, 44, M.Ed, 48; M.A, Univ. Richmond, 51. Teacher, high sch, 23-25, 43-45, jr. high sch, 45-49; Eng. & Am. lit, Richmond Prof. Inst, 49-53; assoc. prof. Eng, Madison Col.(Va), 53-74, dean women, 53-60; RETIRED. Col. Eng. Asn. Ellen Glasgow's novels. Add: Rte. 1, Box 211, Linville, VA 22843.

WILKINS, THURMAN, b. Malden, Mo, June 29, 15; m. 57; c. 2. ENGLISH. A.B, Univ. Calif, Los Angeles, 39, A.M, Berkeley, 47; Ph.D, Columbia Univ, 57. Lectr. ENG, Columbia Univ, 51-58, asst. prof, 58-64; assoc. prof, QUEENS COL.(N.Y), 64-72, PROF, 72- Guggenheim fel, 60-61. Adj. Gen. Dept, 42-46, Capt. Auth. Guild; Am. Mil. Inst.(secy. & assoc. ed, Mil. Affairs, 44-47); MLA; Am. Stud. Asn; Soc. Am. Hist. The American frontier in literature, art and history; the American Indian. Publ: Clarence King: a biography, 58 & Cherokee tragedy, 70, Macmillan; Thomas Moran: artist of the mountains, Univ. Okla, 66. Add: 211 W. 106th St, New York, NY 10025.

WILKINSON, CLYDE WINFIELD, b. Coleman, Tex, July 4, 10; m. 35. BUSINESS COMMUNICATION. B.S, Univ. Tex, 32, A.M, 34; Univ. Pa, 38, 40; Ph.D.(Eng), Univ. Ill, 47. From instr. to asst. prof. Eng, Agr. & Mech. Col. Tex, 35-40; Univ. Ill, 40-50; assoc. prof. jour. & prof. bus. admin, Mich. State Univ, 50-59; PROF. ENG, UNIV. FLA, 59- Consult, Citizen's Mutual Insurance Co, 54- Med. Dept, U.S.A, 42-46. Am. Bus. Commun. Asn.(asst. secy. & ed, 48-50, pres, 54). American literature; business and technical communication. Publ: Writing business letters, 55, 59 & Communicating through letters and reports, 63, 67, 72, Irwin; Life and literary career of M.E.M. Davis. Add: Dept. of English, University of Florida, Gainesville, FL 32601.

WILKINSON, ROBERT EDWIN, b. Meriden, Conn, Jan. 7, 26. AMERICAN LITERATURE. A.B, Stonehill Col, 52; M.A, Boston Univ, 56; Ph.D.(Am. lit), Univ. Pa, 65. Instr. Eng, Univ. Baltimore, 56-57; VILLANOVA UNIV, 57-61, asst. prof, 61-66, assoc. prof. AM. LIT, 66-71, PROF, 71-, CHMN. GRAD. COMT. ENG, 73-, chmn. dept. Eng, 68-73. U.S.N, 43-47, 52-54. Conf. Col. Compos. & Commun; Am. Stud. Asn; MLA. Theodore Dreiser. Add: 616 Hirst Ave, Havertown, PA 19083.

WILLARD, CHARLES BORROMEO, b. Dedham, Mass, Sept. 18, 11; m. 42; c. 5. AMERICAN LITERATURE. Ed.B, R.I. Col, 34; A.M, Brown Univ, 39, Ph.D.(Eng), 48. Stud. counselor, Providence Pub. Schs, R.I, 34-46; dir. Providence Ctr, Univ. R.I, 46-49; assoc. prof. Eng. educ, South. Ill. Univ, 49-57, prof, 57-58; prof. & dean prof. stud, R.I. COL, 58-59, dean, 59-73, PRES, 73-, acting pres, 66-68, v.pres. acad. affairs, 66-73. Consult. Eng. textbooks, U.S. Armed Forces Inst, 57- U.S.A.A.F, 42-46, Sgt. NCTE; NEA. Walt Whitman's literary reputation; techniques of teaching English; preparation of teachers of English. Publ: Whitman's American fame, Brown Univ, 50; co-auth, Teaching aids in the English language arts 57, rev. ed, 63 & Your reading, a book list for junior high schools, 60, rev. ed, 66, Nat. Counc. Teachers Eng. Add: Rhode Island College, Providence, RI 02908.

WILLAUER, GEORGE JACOB, JR, b. Philadelphia, Pa, Oct. 30, 35; m. 66; c. 2. ENGLISH. B.A, Wesleyan Univ, 57; M.A, Univ. Pa, 59, Ph.D.(Eng), 65. Asst. instr. ENG, Univ. Pa, 58-62, instr, CONN. COL, 62-66; asst. prof, 66-72, ASSOC. PROF. & CHMN. DEPT, 72- MLA; Am. Stud. Asn. Early American literature; Quaker history. Publ: Public Friends report to London yearly meeting on their missions to America, 69 & An Irish Friend and the Civil War: some letters of Frederic W. Pim to his father in Dublin, 72, J. Friends' Hist. Soc; Irish Friends report on their missions to America, Quaker Hist, 70. Add: Dept. of English, Connecticut College, New London, CT 06320.

WILLCOTT, PAUL JOSEPH, Applied Linguistics, English as a Foreign Language. See Volume III, Foreign Languages, Linguistics & Philology.

WILLCOXON, JOHN WEIR, III, b. Richmond, Va, Jan. 20, 31; m. 61; c. 1. THEATRE ARTS. B.A, Wash. & Lee Univ, 52, M.A, Univ. Minn, 57; Ph.D. 61. Asst. prof. theatre arts & dir. theatre, Kans. State Col. Pittsburgh, 61-65; assoc. prof. THEATRE ARTS, UNIV. NORTH. COLO, 65-68, PROF,

68-, CHMN. DEPT, 72-, DIR. LITTLE THEATRE OF THE ROCKIES, 65- Reviewer, Educ. Theatre J, 69-; mem. ed. bd, Speech Teacher, 73- Sig.C, U.S.A, 54-56. Am. Theatre Asn; Am. Nat. Theatre & Acad; Speech Commun. Asn. Classical theatre; dramatic and theatrical theory. Publ: A secular approach to tragedy, Midwest Quart, summer 64. Add: Dept. of Theatre Arts, University of Northern Colorado, Greeley, CO 80639.

WILLEN, GERALD, b. New York, N.Y, July 19, 18; m. 61; c. 2. ENGLISH. A.B, Johns Hopkins Univ, 38; M.A, Univ. Minn, 48, Ph.D.(Eng), 55. Instr. ENG, Univ. Minn, 49-56; Fairleigh Dickinson Univ, 56-57, asst. prof, 57-59, assoc. prof. & chmn. dept, 59-61; asst. prof, HUNTER COL, 61-69, assoc. prof, 69-73, PROF, 73- A.U.S, 43-45. MLA; NCTE. The English novel; American literature; the short story. Publ: Casebook on The turn of the screw, 60, co-ed, A casebook on Shakespeare's sonnets, 64, ed, Washington Square: a critical edition, 69 & ed, Henry James's The American: a critical edition, 72, Crowell; co-ed, Literature for writing, Wadsworth, 62; auth, The American voice, Weybright & Talley, 69; Dreiser's moral seriousness, Univ. Kans. City Rev. Add: 44 W. 22nd St, New York, NY 10010.

WILLER, WILLIAM H, b. Chicago, Ill, May 4, 09. ENGLISH. A.B, De Paul Univ, 31; A.M, Univ. Minn, 37, Ph.D, 44. Asst. prof, St. Mary's Col.(Minn), 36-46; assoc. prof. ENG, XAVIER UNIV, 46-57, PROF, 57- American literature; native themes and nationalism; poetic evolution of Gerard Manley Hopkins. Add: 4130 Sherel Lane, Cincinnati, OH 45209.

WILLETT, MAURITA. U.S. citizen. LITERATURE. B.A, Bradley Univ, 40; M.A, Univ. Chicago, 43; scholar. & fel, Brandeis Univ, 55-56, Ph.D, 59. Instr. Eng. compos, Univ. Chicago, 44; ENG. UNIV. ILL, CHICAGO CIRCLE, 47-59, asst. prof, 58-68, assoc. prof, 68-72, PROF, 72- MLA; Col. Eng. Asn.(mem. women's comt, 70-); Melville Soc; Eng. Inst. American literature; Thoreau, Melville, Hawthorne, James, Dostoevsky; Romanticism; Russian literature. Publ: Tolstoy's triunity: truth, simplicity, and love, Ball State Forum, spring 70; The silences of Herman Melville, Am. Transcendental Quart, summer 70; The ending of Crime and punishment, Orbis Litterarum, 9/70; plus others. Add: Dept. of English, University of Illinois at Chicago Circle, Box 4348, Chicago, IL 60680.

WILLEY, FREDERICK W, JR, b. Indiana, Pa, May 14, 26; m. 53; c. 2. ENGLISH. B.A, Bowdoin Col, 49; Ph.D, Harvard Univ, 62. Teaching fel. humanities, Harvard, 53-56; instr. ENG, Univ. Conn, 56-57; Vassar Col, 57-60; Boston Univ, 60-62, asst. prof, 62-66; UNIV. MASS, BOSTON, 66-68, ASSOC. PROF, 68- U.S.N, 44-46. MLA. Prose fiction; American-English novel; genre studies. Publ: The free spirit and the clever agent in Henry James, South. Rev, spring 66; The novel and the natural man, Mich. Quart. Rev, spring 68. Add: Dept. of English, University of Massachusetts, 100 Arlington St, Boston, MA 02116.

WILLIAMS, ALLEN, b. Greenwood, La, Nov. 18, 33; m. 60; c. 3. SPEECH, DRAMA. B.S, Grambling Col, 56; M.A.T, Ind. Univ, Bloomington, 62, Ford Found. grant, 70-71, Ph.D.(theatre, drama), 73. Asst. theatre, Ind. Univ, 56-57, 70-72; instr. speech & theatre, GRAMBLING COL, 59-68, PROF. SPEECH & DRAMA & CHMN. DEPT, 73-, acting head dept. speech, 68-70. U.S.A, 57-59, Res, 59-63. Nat. Asn. Dramatic & Speech Arts (v.pres, 67-69, pres, 69-71); U.S. Inst. Theatre Technol; Am. Theatre Asn; Speech Commun. Asn. Theatre. Publ: Teaching in an integrated school: awareness defined for the white literature teacher, Encore, 72; co-auth, Awareness: teaching black literature in the secondary school, J. Black Stud, 73. Add: Dept. of Speech & Drama, Grambling College, Grambling, LA 71245.

WILLIAMS, ARNOLD LEDGERWOOD, b. Englewood, Colo, Dec. 24, 07; m. 35; c. 2. ENGLISH LITERATURE. A.B, Univ. Notre Dame, 29; Ph.D, Univ. N.C, 35. Instr. ENG, Univ. N.C, 34-37; Mo. Sch. Mines, 37-39; MICH. STATE UNIV, 39-43, asst. prof, 43-48, assoc. prof, 48-54, prof, 54-73, EMER. PROF, 73- Spec. lectr, Calif. Inst. Technol, 43; fel, Huntington Libr, 43; Guggenheim fel, 49. MLA; Mediaeval Acad. Am. Cultural and literary history of the English 14th century; mediaeval drama; cultural history of the English Renaissance. Publ: The common expositor, Univ. N.C, 48; The characterization of Pilate, 50, Drama of Medieval England, 61 & Flower on a lowly stalk, 67, Mich. State Univ. Add: 243 Ridge Rd, East Lansing, MI 48823.

WILLIAMS, AUBREY LAKE, b. Jacksonville, Fla, Sept. 25, 22; m. 42; c. 6. ENGLISH. B.A, La. State Univ, 47; M.A, Yale, 48, Ph.D.(Eng), 52. Instr. ENG, Yale, 50-55, asst. prof, 55-58, assoc. prof, UNIV. FLA, 58-60, GRAD. RES. PROF, 61- Morse fel, 54-55; Fulbright & Guggenheim fels, 56-57; prof, Rice Univ, 60-61; vis. prof, N.Y. Univ, summer 68; Am. Counc. Learned Soc. fel, summer 71; Clark Mem. Libr. sr. fel, summer 72; dir, Nat. Endowment for Humanities grant & dir. summer sem, 73. U.S.A, 43-46. Works of William Congreve; 17th century drama. Publ: Pope's Dunciad, Methuen; co-auth, Works of Alexander Pope, Vol. 1, Twickenham, Methuen & Yale, 61; auth, Selected works of Alexander Pope, Houghton, 69. Add: 608 N.E. Fifth Ave, Gainesville, FL 32601.

WILLIAMS, BENJAMIN BUFORD, b. New York, N.Y, Apr. 28, 23; m. 53; c. 4. RENAISSANCE BRITISH LITERATURE. B.A, Univ. Ala, 48, M.A, 50; Ph.D. (Eng), Vanderbilt Univ, 71. Instr. ENG, Univ. Ala, Mobile, 50; teaching fel, Vanderbilt Univ, 50-52; asst. prof, Martin Col, 52-53; instr, Univ. Ala, Montgomery, 57-68; asst. prof, AUBURN UNIV, MONTGOMERY, 68-71, ASSOC. PROF, 71- U.S.A, 43-46, U.S.A.F.R, 47-, Col; Bronze Star Medal. MLA; NCTE. Literary history; 19th century Southern literature; literary biography. Publ: Ed, Sketches of Mobile 1868, Tipton, 71; auth, Alabama Civil War poets, Ala. Rev, 62; Thomas Cooper DeLeon: Alabama's first professional man-of-letters, Ala. Hist. Quart, 62; The trial of Mrs. Surratt and the Lincoln assassination trial, Ala. Lawyer, 64. Add: Dept. of English, Auburn University at Montgomery, Montgomery, AL 36109.

WILLIAMS, CLEM C, JR, b. Washington, D.C, Mar. 10, 21; m. 48; c. 2. ENGLISH. B.A, Yale, 42, M.A, 47, univ. fel, 47-48, Mitchell fel, 48-49, Ph.D. (Eng), 61. Instr. ENG, Yale, 49-51; Williams Col, 51-54; lectr, Hunter Col, 55-57; instr, N.Y. Univ, 57-58; asst. prof, DePAUW UNIV, 58-61, assoc. prof, 62-69, PROF, 69- Prog. off, Nat. Endowment for Humanities, 73. U.S.N.R, 42-46, Lt. MLA; Mediaeval Acad. Am: Soc. Relig. Higher Educ; AAUP. Mediaeval English and French literatures; history of critical thought. Add: 523 Anderson St, Greencastle, IN 46135.

WILLIAMS, CRATIS DEARL, b. Blaine, Ky, Apr. 5, 11; m. 49; c. 2. ENGLISH. A.B, Univ. Ky, 33, M.A, 37; Ph.D, N.Y. Univ, 61. Prin. & teacher, High Schs, Ky, 33-41; teacher, Apprentice Sch, Int. Nickel Co, 42; asst. prin. & critic, High Sch, N.C, 42-46; asst. prof. ENG, APPALACHIAN STATE UNIV, 46-49, PROF, 50-, DEAN GRAD. SCH, 58- Teaching fel, N.Y. Univ, 49-50; consult. grad. stud, Am. Asn. State Cols. & Univs, 68- MLA; Am. Folklore Soc. Appalachian studies; the Southern mountaineer in American history and literature; American fiction. Publ: Mountain speech, Mountain Life & Work, 60-67. Add: 101 Reynolds Rd, Boone, NC 28607.

WILLIAMS, DAVID, b. Boston, Mass, Feb. 12, 39; m. 66; c. 2. MEDIAEVAL ENGLISH LITERATURE. A.B, Boston Univ, 61; M.A, Univ. Toronto, 64, Ph.D.(Eng), 71. ASST. PROF. ENG, McGILL UNIV, 67-, ASSOC. CHMN. DEPT, 71-, prog. improv. grants, 69-70 & 72-73. MLA. Rhetoric; iconography; Mediaeval literature. Publ: Co-ed. & contrib, Guide to Medieval and Renaissance studies in Montreal, Stud. Mediaevalia, 72. Add: Dept. of English, McGill University, Montreal, P.Q, Can.

WILLIAMS, DAVID GARDNER, b. Platteville, Wis, Nov. 1, 07; m. 41; c. 3. ENGLISH LITERATURE. A.B, Univ. Wis, 30, Mus.B, 31, A.M, 32; A.M, Harvard, 39, Ph.D, 46. Asst. Eng, Univ. Wis, 31-32; master Eng. & music, Hotchkiss Sch, 32-37; teaching asst. & tutor, Harvard, 39-43; asst. prof, Amherst Col, 43-45; instr. HUMANITIES, UNIV. CHICAGO, 45-48, asst. prof, 48-51, assoc. prof, 51-56, PROF, 56- MLA; Keats-Shelley Asn. Am. English literature, 1790-1830. Add: 5427 S. Hyde Park Blvd, Chicago, IL 60615.

WILLIAMS, DONALD EDWARD, b. Odon, Ind, Aug. 17, 23; m. 49. SPEECH. B.A, Franklin Col, 48; M.S, Purdue Univ, 51; scholar, Northwest. Univ, 52-53, fel, 53-54, Ph.D, 58. Instr. SPEECH, Cornell Univ, 54-59, asst. prof, UNIV. FLA, 59-64, assoc. prof, 64-71, PROF, 71-, dir. div. rhetoric & pub. address, 62-74. Grad. Sch. Res. Counc. summer fels, 65, 67. Oral commun. consult, U.S. Naval Air Station, Jacksonville, Fla, 62-72. South. Speech Commun. Asn; Speech Commun. Asn; West. Speech Commun. Asn; AAUP. Rhetoric and public speaking; history and criticism of public address in the United States; interpersonal communication. Publ: Speech criticism on the British campus, winter 65 & The rhetorical critic: his raison d'etre, winter 70, South. Speech Commun. J; Protest under the cross: the Ku Klux Klan presents its case to the public, 1960, In: Rhetoric of our times, Appleton, 69; plus six others. Add: Dept. of Speech, University of Florida, Gainesville, FL 32611.

WILLIAMS, DONALD STEPHEN, b. West Pittston, Pa, Apr. 20, 20. SPEECH, EDUCATION. B.S, Pa. State Col, 42; A.M, Columbia Univ, 47; fel, N.Y. Univ, 50-51. Civilian instr, Air Depot, Rome, N.Y, 42-44; training dir, Naval Aviation Supply Depot, Phila, Pa, 44-46; asst. speech, Columbia Univ, 46; from asst. prof. to ASSOC. PROF. ENG. & EDUC, COLGATE UNIV, 46-, CHMN. DEPT. EDUC, 68- Speech Commun. Asn; NCTE. Public speaking; methods in English; communications. Publ: Help yourself to better communication. Add: 46 Broad St, Hamilton, NY 13346.

WILLIAMS, DUNCAN, b. Newcastle-Emlyn, Wales, Oct. 15, 27; m. 59; c. 3. ENGLISH, UNIVERSITY HONORS. B.A, Oxford, 51, M.A, 56. Mem. fac, Summer Fields, Oxford, 56-63; asst. prof. Eng, W.Va. Wesleyan Col, 63-66; vis. prof, MARSHALL UNIV, 66-67; assoc. prof. ENG, 67-69, PROF, 69-, dir. univ. honors, 67-70. Chief consult. & lectr. ESEA Inst, Shepherd Col, 66, 67, 68; lectr, Fine Arts Festival, Ft. Valley, Ga, 67; Benedum res. grant, 68; MLA deleg, Mod. Humanities Res. Asn. Jubilee Congr. Cambridge Eng, 68; chmn. dept. Eng, Alvescot Col, Eng, 70-72, dean, 71-72; dir. res, Farmington Educ. Res. Unit, Eng, 73- R.M, 45-46; Royal Welch Fusiliers, 46-47; Royal Army Educ.C, 47-48. MLA; Mod. Humanities Res. Asn; Nat. Col. Honors Counc. Eighteenth century English literature; English romantic period; Dylan Thomas. Publ: Trousered apes, Churchill, London, 71, Arlington House, N.Y, 72 & Rusconi, Milan, 73; Shelley's Demogorgon, Philol. Papers, W.Va. Univ, 70; contrib, Education: threatened standards, Churchill, London, 72; auth, Render unto Caesar, Aryan Path, 73. Add: Dept. of English, Marshall University, Huntington, WV 25701.

WILLIAMS, EDITH LOUISE (WHITEHURST), Old English, Language History. See Volume III, Foreign Languages, Linguistics, & Philology.

WILLIAMS, EDWIN WINSTON, b. Belzoni, Miss, June 22, 36; m. 65; c. 2. NINETEENTH CENTURY ENGLISH LITERATURE. B.A, Millsaps Col, 58; Univ. Edinburgh, 58-59; Rotary Found. fel, Univ. Hong Kong, 61-62; M.Div, Duke Univ, 62; Ph.D.(19th century Eng), Univ. N.C, Chapel Hill, 72. Clergyman, Hickory Ridge Methodist Church, 62-65; instr. Bibl. stud, Brevard Col, 65-67; ASST. PROF. ENG, E.TENN. STATE UNIV, 72- MLA; S.Atlantic Mod. Lang. Asn. Religion and literature. Publ: The religious theme of The glass menagerie as seen in its imagery, Tenn. Philol. Bull, 7/73. Add: Dept. of English, East Tennessee State University, Johnson City, TN 37601.

WILLIAMS, FRANKLIN BURLEIGH, JR, b. Cobleskill, N.Y, Nov. 21, 06; m. 47; c. 2. ENGLISH LITERATURE. A.B, Syracuse Univ, 31; A.M, Harvard, 32, Ph.D, 34. Sheldon traveling fel, Harvard, 34-35, instr. & tutor ENG, 35-39; asst. prof, GEORGETOWN UNIV, 39-49, assoc. prof, 49-60, prof, 60-74, chmn. dept, 59-66, EMER. PROF, 74- Guggenheim fel, 55-56. U.S.A.A.F, 42-46, Maj. MLA; Mod. Humanities Res. Asn, Gt. Brit; Bibliog. Soc, London (hon. treas. Am, 64-); Bibliog. Soc. Am; Renaissance Soc. Am; S.Atlantic Mod. Lang. Asn.(mem. counc, 70-72). Renaissance English literature; bibliography; patronage. Publ: Elizabethan England, Boston Mus. Fine Arts; Index of dedications in English books before 1641, Bibliog. Soc. London, 62; ed, Thomas Rogers' Leicester's ghost, Univ. Chicago, 72; plus numerous articles. Add: 724 N. Emerson St, Arlington, VA 22203.

WILLIAMS, FREDERICK DOWELL, b. Longview, Wash, Aug. 14, 33; m. 55; c. 2. COMMUNICATIONS. A.B, Univ. Idaho, 55; A.M, Univ. South. Calif, 60, fel. & Ph.D, 62. From asst. prof. to assoc. prof. speech & dir. speech exp. lab, Univ. Wis-Madison, 62-69; prof. commun, Univ. Tex, 69-73; PROF. COMMUN. & DEAN, ANNENBERG SCH. COMMUN, UNIV. SOUTH. CALIF, 73- U.S.N, 55-61, Res, 61-, Lt. Speech Commun. Asn; Int. Commun. Asn. Language and communication; socialization; communication policy studies. Publ: Reasoning with statistics, Holt, 68; ed, Language and poverty, Rand McNally, 70; auth, Language and speech, Prentice-Hall, 72; plus others. Add: Annenberg School of Communication, University of Southern California, Los Angeles, CA 90007.

WILLIAMS, GEORGE, b. Rogers, Tex, May 1, 02; m. 30; c. 2. ENGLISH. B.A, Rice Univ, 23, M.A, 25. Asst. ENG, N.Y. Univ, 27-28; from instr. to prof, RICE UNIV, 50-68, EMER. PROF, 68- McMurray Prize, 52. MLA; Am. Ornithol. Union. Chaucer; modern English poetry; ornithology. Publ: Creative writing & Readings for creative writers, Harper; The blind bull, Abelard; A new view of Chaucer, Duke Univ, 65; A guide to literary London, Batsford, London & Hastings, N.Y, 73. Add: Dept. of English, Rice University, Houston, TX 77001.

WILLIAMS, GEORGE WALTON, b. Charleston, S.C, Oct. 10, 22; m. 53; c. 3. ENGLISH LITERATURE. B.A, Yale Univ, 47; Adger & Dupont fels, Univ. Va, M.A, 49, Ph.D, 57. Asst. prof. ENG, DUKE UNIV, 57-62, assoc. prof, 62-67, PROF, 67- Mem, Episcopal Church Summer Sch, 58; grant-in-aid, Folger Libr, 60, mem. ed. bd, 69-73. U.S.A, 43-45, M/Sgt. MLA; Southeast. Renaissance Conf.(ed, 60-70, pres, 72-73); Renaissance Soc. Am; Soc. Archit. Hist.(asst. to ed, 54-57); S.Atlantic Mod. Lang. Asn; Renaissance Eng. Text Soc; Bibliog. Soc. Univ. Va; Malone Soc; Bibliog. Soc, Eng; Royal Soc. Arts. Seventeenth century literature; Shakespeare; textual criticism. Publ: St. Michael's Charleston, 1751-1951, 51, Image and symbol in the sacred poetry of Richard Crashaw, 63 & ed, Jacob Eckhard's choirmaster's book 1809, 70, Univ. S.C; co-auth, More traditional ballads of Virginia, Univ. N.C, 60; ed, Romeo and Juliet, Duke Univ, 64 & The changeling, Univ. Nebr, 65; co-ed, John Wesley's first hymn-book, Dalcho Soc, 64 & Henry VI, 2 & 3, Penguin, 66; ed, The woman hater, Cambridge, 66 & Poetry of Richard Crashaw, Doubleday-Anchor, 69; co-ed, Dering version of Shakespeare's Henry IV, Folger, 74. Add: Dept. of English, Duke University, Durham, NC 27706.

WILLIAMS, HARRY MARTIN, b. Muncie, Ind, Feb. 9, 05; m. 31. SPEECH. A.B, DePauw Univ, 27; A.M, 29; Ph.D, Univ. Mich, 47. Instr. SPEECH, MIAMI UNIV, 29-31, asst. prof, 31-40, assoc. prof, 40-47, PROF, 47-, chmn. dept, 47-71. Lectr. evening col, Univ. Cincinnati, 34-41. Speech Commun. Asn; Cent. States Speech Asn. American public address: David Swing; mid-19th century student speeches. Add: 212 N. Bishop St, Oxford, OH 45056.

WILLIAMS, HENRY BEATES, b. Philadelphia, Pa, Aug. 30, 07; m. 43. ENGLISH. Dipl, Pa. Mus. & Sch. Indust. Arts, 28; Adj.A, Harvard, 47; M.F.A, Yale, 48; M.A, Dartmouth Col, 50. Prof. ENG. & dir. exptl. theatre, DARTMOUTH COL, 31-73, EMER. PROF, 73- Dir, Wellesley Col. Summer Theatre & Sch, 49-51; exhibitor, Phila. Col. Art, Carpenter Galleries, Dartmouth Col, Univ. Ill, Chicago, St. Paul's Sch, N.H; comp. stud. grant, Dartmouth Col, summer 66; mem. cent. comt, Am. Col. Theatre Festival, 68- C.Eng, U.S.A, 42-46, Capt. Am. Soc. Theatre Res; New Eng. Theatre Conf; Am. Nat. Theatre & Acad; Am. Theatre Asn;(pres, 67); Gilbert & Sullivan Soc, London; Int. Fed. Theatre Res; U.S. Inst. Theatre Technol. History of the theatre; history of costume: Japanese theatre history. Publ: Adapting Box and Cox, 1/67 & Box and Cox and before, 5/67, Gilbert & Sullivan J: introd to The American theatre, a sum of its parts, French, 71; plus others. Add: Balch Hill, Hanover, NH 03755.

WILLIAMS, JIMMY LEE, b. Columbus, Miss, Dec. 15, 40; m. 62; c. 2. ENGLISH & AMERICAN LITERATURE. A.B, Clark Col, 62; M.A, Wash. Univ, 64; Piedmont Univ. Ctr. fel, 66; South. Fel. Fund fel, Ind. Univ. Bloomington, 67-69, Ford Found. fel, 69-70, Ph.D.(Eng), 71. Instr. Eng, N.C. A&T State Univ, 63-66; lectr. Afro-Am. lit, Ind. Univ, 70-71; assoc. prof. ENG, N.C. A&T STATE UNIV, 71-72, PROF. & CHMN. DEPT, 72- Vis. prof, Ind. Univ, summer 72. Col. Lang. Asn; MLA; NCTE. Shakespeare; black poetry; American humor. Add: Dept. of English, North Carolina A&T State University, Greensboro, NC 27411.

WILLIAMS, JOHN (EDWARD), b. Clarksville, Tex, Aug. 29, 22; m. 49; c. 3. ENGLISH. B.A, Univ. Denver, 49, M.A, 50; Ph.D.(Eng), Univ. Mo, 54. Instr. ENG, Univ. Mo, 50-54; asst. prof, UNIV. DENVER, 54-60, assoc. prof, 60-64, PROF, 64-, DIR. CREATIVE WRITING PROG, 54-, ED, THE DENVER QUARTERLY, 66- Writer-in-residence, Smith Col, 68; Fannie Hurst prof. writing, Brandeis Univ, 73-74. Rockefeller Fiction Award, 67; Nat. Endowment for Arts Award, 69; Nat. Book Award in Fiction, 73. U.S.A.A.F, 42-45. Sixteenth century lyric; contemporary literature; creative writing. Publ: The broken landscape, Swallow, 49; Butcher's crossing, Macmillan, 60; English Renaissance poetry, Anchor Bks, 63; The necessary lie (poems), Verb Publ, 65; Stoner (novel), 65 & Augustus (novel), 72, Viking; Henry Miller: the success of failure, Va. Quart. Rev, spring 68. Add: Dept. of English, University of Denver, Denver, CO 80210.

WILLIAMS, JOHN BRINDLEY, b. New York, N.Y, Aug. 4, 19; m. 51; c. 4. AMERICAN LITERATURE, STYLISTICS. B.A, Univ. South. Calif, 48, Ph.D. (Eng), 65; M.A, Univ. Calif, Los Angeles, 55. Suburban ed, San Pedro News-Pilot, Calif, 48-53, dir. res. & publ, Glendale Unified Sch. Dist, Calif, 56-58; instr. ENG, Glendale Col, 55-56 & 58-66; asst. prof, CALIF. STATE UNIV, LONG BEACH, 66-69, ASSOC. PROF, 69- U.S.A, 43-45. MLA; NCTE; Conf. Col. Compos. & Commun. American literature in the 19th century; novel. Publ: Style and grammar: a writer's handbook of transformations, Dodd, 73. Add: Dept. of English, California State University, Long Beach, 6101 E. Seventh St, Long Beach, CA 90840.

WILLIAMS, JOHN S, b. Villisca, Iowa, Mar. 6, 36; m. 56; c. 3. LITERATURE. B.A, Cornell Col, 58; Woodrow Wilson fel, Harvard, 58-59; Danforth fel, Univ. Chicago, 59-65, M.A, 61, M.A, 65, Ph.D.(theol. & lit), 68. Instr. Eng, Roosevelt Univ, 64-65; asst. prof. LIT, RAYMOND COL, UNIV. PAC, 65-68, ASSOC. PROF, 68- Soc. Relig. Higher Educ. Literature; religion; psychology. Publ: The final copper light of afternoon: Hightower's redemption, 20th Century Lit, 1/68; The dialectic of history: Sartre's Les séquestrés d'Altona, winter 70 & co-auth, The narrator of the Painted bird: a case study, summer 72, Renascence. Add: 1860 W. Euclid, Stockton, CA 95204.

WILLIAMS, JOSEPH M, b. Cleveland, Ohio, Aug. 18, 33; m. 60; c. 2. ENGLISH, LINGUISTICS. B.A, Miami Univ, 55, M.A, 60; Ph.D.(Eng), Univ. Wis, 66. Instr. ENG, Miami Univ, 59-60; UNIV. CHICAGO, 65-66, asst. prof, 66-72, ASSOC. PROF, 72- Consult. med. writing, Am. Med. Asn, 66. U.S.A, 55-58, Sgt. MLA; Lang. Soc. Am; Col. Eng. Asn. Stylistics; rhetoric; generative grammars. Publ: The source of Spenser's Labryde, Mod. Lang. Notes, 61; Caliban and Ariel meet Trager & Smith, Col. Eng, 62. Add: Dept. of English, University of Chicago, Chicago, IL 60637.

WILLIAMS, JUANITA H, English. See DUDLEY, JUANITA H. WILLIAMS.

WILLIAMS, KATHLEEN MARY, b. Briton Ferry, Gt. Brit. RENAISSANCE & EIGHTEENTH CENTURY ENGLISH. B.A, Oxford, 41, M.A, 45; D.Litt, Univ. Wales, 66. From lectr. to sr. lectr, ENG, Univ. Wales, 46-64; assoc. prof. Univ. Calif, Riverside, 64-66, PROF, Rice Univ, 66-67, UNIV. CALIF, RIVERSIDE, 67- Mem. ed. bd, PMLA & Stud. Eng. Lit, 72-; Guggenheim fel, 73-74. Renaissance Soc. Am; MLA; Mod. Humanities Res. Asn. Publ: Jonathan Swift and the age of compromise, Univ. Kans, 58, Constable, 59; Spenser's world of glass: the Faerie Queene, Univ. Calif. & Routledge & Kegan Paul, 66; Jonathan Swift, 68 & Swift: the critical heritage, 70, Routledge & Kegan Paul. Add: Dept. of English, University of California, Riverside, CA 92502.

WILLIAMS, KENNETH R, JR, b. Saxton, Pa, Feb. 14, 35; m. 60; c. 2. INTERPERSONAL COMMUNICATION. B.A, Pa. State Univ, 59, M.A, 61, Ph.D.(speech), 64. Instr. speech & humanities, Pa. State Univ, 61-64; asst. prof. speech, Univ. R.I, 64-66; Univ. Md, 66-67; ASSOC. PROF. INTERPERSONAL COMMUN, OHIO UNIV, 67- Mem, Creative Educ. Found; consult. orgn. develop. to bus, indust. & govt, 69- Int. Commun. Asn; Speech Commun. Asn; Cent. States Speech Asn; AAUP. Rhetorical and communication theory; organizational theory and development; interpersonal competence. Publ: But what can I do with a major in general speech?, West. Speech, spring 71; The omeletrician who wanted to be an egghead, Etc: Rev. Gen. Semantics, 12/71; Reflections on a human science of communication, J. Commun, 10/73; plus others. Add: School of Interpersonal Communication, College of Communication, Ohio University, Athens, OH 45701.

WILLIAMS, LOUISE LYLE GIVENS, Literature, Linguistics. See Volume III, Foreign Languages, Linguistics & Philology.

WILLIAMS, MARGARET ANNE, R.S.C.J, b. Manchester, Conn, July 15, 02. ENGLISH LITERATURE. A.B, Manhattanville Col, 23; B.A, Oxford, 35, M.A, 38. Prof. Eng, MANHATTANVILLE COL, 35-69, EMER. PROF. ENG. LIT, 69-; PROF. ENG. LIT, UNIV. SACRED HEART (JAPAN), 69- Mediaeval Acad. Am; MLA; Eng. Lit. Soc. Japan. Old and Middle English literature; oriental influences in mediaeval English literature; history of the Society of the Sacred Heart. Publ: Word-hoard, 39, Second sowing & Gleewood, 46 & The sacred heart in the life of the church, 57, Sheed; The Pearl-poet, 67 & auth, introd. & transl, Piers Plowman, 70, Random; auth, Saint Madeleine Sophie: her life and letters, Herder, 65; Oriental influences on T.S. Eliot, Tamkang Rev, 71. Add: Barat House, Hiroo 4, chome 3-1 Shibuya-ku, Tokyo 150, Japan.

WILLIAMS, MARILYN E, b. Trenton, N.J, June 4, 34; m. 60; c. 2. ENGLISH. B.A, Wilson Col, 55; Fulbright scholar, Queen's Univ.(Belfast), 55-56; M.A, N.Y. Univ, 62, Ph.D.(Eng), 67. Instr. Eng, State Univ. N.Y. Binghamton, 67-68, asst. prof, 68-70. Renaissance Soc. Am; MLA. English Renaissance drama. Publ: Moral perspective and dramatic action in Tudor interlude, Northeast Mod. Lang. Asn. Newslett, 70. Add: 714 N. Aurora St, Ithaca, NY 14850.

WILLIAMS, MARY CAMERON, b. Albany, N.Y, Sept. 16, 23; m. 45; c. 4. ENGLISH LITERATURE. B.A, Wellesley Col, 44; M.A, Univ. N.C, Chapel Hill, 60, Ph.D.(Eng), 70. From instr. to ASST. PROF. ENG, N.C. STATE UNIV, 62- MLA; Renaissance Soc; Southeast. Renaissance Conf. Ben Jonson; satire. Publ: Unity in Ben Jonson's early comedies, Salzburg Univ, 72. Add: Dept. of English, North Carolina State University, Raleigh, NC 27607.

WILLIAMS, MARY CLAY, b. Lancaster, Ky. ENGLISH. A.B, Randolph-Macon Women's Col, 18; M.A, Columbia Univ, 22; hon. D.Ed, Univ. Tulsa, 54. Teacher Eng. & hist, Pub. Schs, Tulsa, 22-31; nat. treas, Chi Omega Fraternity, 31-39; dean women, UNIV. TULSA, 39-62, prof. Eng, 62-72, Dir. personnel, 44-62, EMER. DEAN WOMEN, 72- Consult, Ark. Deans' State Conf, 59. Nat. Asn. Women Deans & Counselors. Student activities in selected colleges and universities in the North Central and Southern Associations; chapter house management; tests and testing programs. Add: Dept. of English, University of Tulsa, Tulsa, OK 74104.

WILLIAMS, MELVIN GILBERT, b. Collingswood, N.J, Nov. 7, 37; m. 58; c. 3. ENGLISH. A.B, Univ. Pa, 60, M.A, 61; Ph.D.(Eng), Univ. Mass, 73. Instr. ENG, AM. INT. COL, 61-63, asst. prof, 63-73, ASSOC. PROF, 73- MLA; Col. Eng. Asn; Conf. Christianity & Lit. Bible as literature; religion and literature; 18th century English literature. Publ: Martin Luther: portraits in prose, Christian Century, 10/67; Samuel Johnson and the concrete universal, CEA Critic, 3-4/72; In memoriam: a broad church poem, Costerus, summer 72. Add: Dept. of English, American International College, Springfield, MA 01109.

WILLIAMS, MILLER, b. Hoxie, Ark, Apr. 8, 30; m. 51; c. 3. ENGLISH, SPANISH TRANSLATIONS. B.S, Ark. State Col, 51; M.S, Univ. Ark, 52; Bread Loaf fel, 61; Amy Lowell travelling scholar, 63-64. Instr. ENG, La. State Univ, 62-65, asst. prof, 65-66; assoc. prof, Loyola Univ.(La), 66-70; UNIV. ARK, FAYETTEVILLE, 71-73, PROF, 73- U.S. deleg, Pan-Am. Conf. Univ. Artists & Writers, Concepcion, Chile, 4/64; lectr. poetry, Bread Loaf Writers Conf, 67-; Fulbright prof. U.S. stud, Nat. Univ. Mex, 70-71. Henry Bellaman Poetry Award, 57. MLA. Writing poetry and fiction; translation from the Spanish; criticism of contemporary poetry. Publ: A circle of stone (poems), 64, co-ed, Southern writing in the sixties: poetry, 66 & co-ed, Southern writing in the sixties: fiction, 66, La. State Univ; auth, Recital (poems), Oceano de Chile, 65; 19 poetas de hoy en los estados unidos, U.S. Inform. Serv, 66; ed. & major transl, The poems and antipoems of Nicanor Parra, 67 & transl, Emergency poems of Nicanor Parra, 72,

New Directions; Chile, a contemporary anthology, Kent State Univ, 68; auth, So long at the fair, (poems), 68, The only world there is (poems), 71 & Halfway from Hoxie (poems), 73, Dutton; The achievement of John Ciardi, Scott, 68; The poetry of John Crowe Ransom, Rutgers Univ, 71; ed, Contemporary poetry in America, Random, 72; auth, Yvor Winters, or how to measure the wings of a bumblebee, In: Nine essays in modern literature, La. State Univ, 65; Color as symbol and the 2-way metaphor in the poetry of John Crowe Ransom, Miss. Quart, winter 68-69. Add: Dept. of English, University of Arkansas, Fayetteville, AR 72701.

WILLIAMS, MIMA ANN, b. Brownwood, Tex, Jan. 18, 14. ENGLISH. A.B, Daniel Baker Col, 35, B.S, 36; A.M, Univ. Tex, 40, summers, 51-54, 55, 56; Univ. Colo, 48; Am. Asn. Univ. Women fel, Univ. London, summer, 55. Teacher high sch, Okla, 35-36; Star High Sch, Tex, 36-38, head dept. Eng, Eden High Sch, 38-43, 45-46, teacher, Austin High Sch, 46; asst. prof. ENG, ABILENE CHRISTIAN COL, 47-62, ASSOC. PROF, 62- Consult, Japanese teachers of English, Ibaraki Christian Col, Japan, summer 63; consult. & conductor in-serv. training course ling. for Abilene area teachers, sponsored by Tex. Educ. Agency under the NDEA, 65-66, conductor, 68; ling. workshop, Wayland Baptist Col, summer 67; hon. adv. summer sch, Univ. Edinburgh, Univ. London, Oxford & Univ. Birmingham, 72-; Am. Asn. Univ. Women honoree, 73. W.A.V.E.S, 43-45. NCTE (judge achievement award essays, 72-, mem. curriculum bull. comt, 73-); S.Cent. Mod. Lang. Asn; Col. Eng. Asn. A woman's military service; linguistics of American English. Publ: A median for teaching the English language, CEA Critic, 1/66; Those everlasting language changes, Horizons, summer 66; Updating language teaching, Delta Kappa Gamma Bull, spring 67. Add: Dept. of English, Abilene Christian College, Abilene, TX 79601.

WILLIAMS, MURIAL BRITTAIN, b. Tuscaloosa, Ala, May 19, 23; m. 46; c. 2. ENGLISH. A.B, Univ. Ala, 43, M.A, 44, Ph.D.(Eng), 63. Instr. Eng, Univ. Ala, 46-48; teacher high sch, Ala, 50-57; PROF. ENG, LA GRANGE COL, 63- S.Atlantic Mod. Lang. Asn. Eighteenth century English novel; Mark Twain. Add: Dept. of English, La Grange College, La Grange, GA 30240.

WILLIAMS, OTHO CLINTON, b. Ft. Worth, Tex, May 17, 08; m. 34; c. 1. ENGLISH LITERATURE. A.B, Univ. Calif, Los Angeles, 30; A.M, Univ. South. Calif, 35; Ph.D, Univ. Calif, 50. Teaching asst. Eng, Univ. Calif, 37-40; instr. lit. & hist, Placer Col. & high sch, 40-43; humanities, Reed Coll, 43-46; from assoc. prof. to PROF. ENG, SAN JOSE STATE UNIV, 46-, CHMN. DEPT. HUMANITIES, 73-, coord. humanities prog, 57-73. U.S.N, 43-46. MLA; Philol. Asn. Pac. Coast. American literature; 18th century English literature; contemporary poetry. Publ: The optick glass; A western sampler: nine contemporary poets, Talisman, 63. Add: Dept. of Humanities, San Jose State University, San Jose, CA 95192.

WILLIAMS, PAUL O, b. Chatham, N.J, Jan. 17, 35; m. 61; c. 1. ENGLISH. B.A, Principia Col, 56; M.A, Univ. Pa, 58, Ph.D, 62; Samuel Fels fel, 61-62. Instr. ENG, Duke Univ, 61-63, asst. prof, 63-64; PRINCIPIA COL, 64-70, ASSOC. PROF, 70- MLA; NCTE; Emerson Soc; Am. Stud. Asn; Thoreau Soc.(mem. exec. comt, 72-); Midwest Mod. Lang. Asn; Am. Asn. State & Local Hist. American transcendentalism, especially the poetry; local history, especially Jersey County, Illinois. Publ: Co-auth, Elsah: a historic guide, Hist. Elsah, 67; auth, The concept of inspiration in Thoreau's poetry, PMLA, 64; contrib, Later & minor transcendentalists, Transcendental Bks, 69. Add: Route 1, 4 Dogwood Lane, Elsah, IL 62028.

WILLIAMS, PORTER, JR, b. Charleston, S.C, Oct. 17, 22. ENGLISH. B.A, Univ. of the South, 47; M.A, Univ. Va, 49; B.A, Cambridge, 51, M.A, 55. Instr. ENG, Univ. of the South, 52-53; N.C. STATE UNIV, 53-57, asst. prof, 57-63, assoc. prof, 63-73, PROF, 73- Fulbright grant, Cambridge, 49-51. U.S.A, 42-45. MLA; Southeast. Renaissance Conf; S.Atlantic Mod. Lang. Asn. Seventeenth century; Shakespeare; romantic period. Publ: Mistakes in Twelfth night and their resolution, PMLA, 6/61; The brand of Cain in The secret sharer, Mod. Fiction Stud, spring 64; Story and frame in Conrad's The tale, Stud. Short Fiction, winter 68; plus others. Add: Dept. of English, North Carolina State University, Raleigh, NC 27607.

WILLIAMS, RALPH MEHLIN, b. Oberlin, Ohio, May 15, 11; m. 40; c. 2. ENGLISH. A.B, Amherst Col, 33; Ph.D, Yale, 38. Instr. Eng, Boston Univ, 38-42; compos, Wellesley Col, 42-46; asst. prof. ENG, TRINITY COL. (CONN), 46-57, assoc. prof, 57-62, prof, 62-73, EMER. PROF, 73- Ford Fund Advan. Educ. fel, 53-54; Fund for Advan. Econ. summer fel, 57; consult, Dept. Health, Educ. & Welfare Eng. proj, Westport Pub. Schs, Conn, 63. MLA; Mod. Humanities Res. Asn, Gt. Brit; New Eng. Asn. Teachers Eng.(secy-treas, 41-44); Ling. Soc. Am. Linguistics and the teaching of English and spelling; African linguistics. Publ: Poet, painter and parson: the life of John Dyer, Bookman Assocs, 56; Phonetic spelling for college students, Oxford, 60; sr. auth, From sound to spelling, Macmillan, 71; auth, An introduction to Oluluyia, Trinity Col, 73; co-auth, Private charity in England, 1747-1757, Yale, 38. Add: 32 Van Buren Ave, West Hartford, CT 06107.

WILLIAMS, ROBERT C, b. Detroit, Mich, Mar. 22, 38; m. 61; c. 1. SPEECH. B.A, Wayne State Univ, 59, Ph.D.(speech), 63; M.S, Syracuse Univ, 60. Instr. SPEECH, BROOKLYN COL, 61-66, asst. prof, 66-72, ASSOC. PROF, 72-, ACTING CHMN. DEPT. TV & RADIO, 73- Consult, RTV Int, Inc, 64-; Cath. Diocese Brooklyn, 65-66; Comt. All Channel Broadcasting, 67-; Am. Arbit. Asn, 68; Nat. Asn. Purchasing Mgt, Inc, 68; dist. 12, New York Bd. Educ, 68; broadcasting specialist, Agency Int. Develop, Repub. Zambia, 66-68. Broadcast Educ. Asn; Int. Broadcasters Soc; Nat. Asn. Educ. Broadcasters; Speech Commun. Asn. Television production variables; international broadcasting. Publ: On the value of varying TV shots, J. Broadcasting, winter 64-65; TV as an evaluation device for teacher promotion, Educ. TV Int, summer 67; Film shots and expressed interest levels, Speech Monogr, 6/68. Add: TV Center, Brooklyn College, Brooklyn, NY 11210.

WILLIAMS, ROBERT DICKSON, b. Cleveland, Ohio, Jan. 18, 01; m. 28; c. 3. ENGLISH. B.A, Kenyon Col, 22; M.A, Univ. Mich, 27, Ph.D.(Eng), 33; Riggs fel, Univ. Edinburgh, Scotland, 28-29. Teacher, high schs, Mich, 23-28; instr, Univ. Mich, 29-33; teacher Eng, Wis. State Univ, Superior, 33-34, 35-44, prof, 45-69; RETIRED. Teacher, Nebr. State Teachers Col, Chadron, 34-35; prof, Univ. Wis, 44-45. NCTE; Ling. Soc. Am. Elizabethan drama; criticism of the drama; English language. Publ: Antiquarian interest before Lamb, PMLA; Linguistics and grammar, Eng. J, 10/59; Structural grammar and usage, Wis. Eng. J, 4/62. Add: 242, 1231 Lawrence Expressway, Sunnyvale, CA 94086.

WILLIAMS, ROBERT VERNE, b. Paterson, N.J, Oct. 7, 21; m. 48. ENGLISH. B.A, Cornell Univ, 48; M.A, Stanford Univ, 50; Fulbright scholar, Univ. Rome, 51-52. Instr. ENG, Univ. Ariz, 55-57; asst. prof, CALIF. STATE UNIV, HAYWARD, 63-64, PROF, 65-, res. grant, 68. Lectr. creative writing, Univ. Iowa, 64-65. U.S.C.G, 42-45. Publ: The hard way, Putnam (novel), 52; Shake this town (novel, Fr. & Ital. transl), Viking, 60. Add: Dept. of English, California State University, Hayward, 25800 Hillary St, Hayward, CA 94542.

WILLIAMS, TREVOR LLOYD, b. Llangollen, Wales, Jan. 12, 42; Brit. & Can. citizen; m. 65, 74; c. 2. MODERN BRITISH LITERATURE & HISTORY. B.A, Univ. Manchester, 64, U.K. state studentship & M.A, 67; Can. Counc. fel. & Ph.D.(Eng), Univ. Wales, 70. Instr. ENG, UNIV. VICTORIA (B.C), 65-70, ASST. PROF, 70- Twentieth century British literature; interaction of literature, politics and modern history; public administration. Publ: Caradoc Evans, Univ. Wales, 70; Poetry of Wales, In: Mosaic, Univ. Man, 68; Three arts. on Anglo-Welsh writer Caradoc Evans, Anglo-Welsh Rev, 70-71. Add: Dept. of English, University of Victoria, Victoria, B.C, Can.

WILLIAMS, WALLACE EDWARD, b. Corona, Calif, July 18, 26. ENGLISH. A.B, Univ. Ala, 50; M.A, Univ. Calif, Berkeley, 55, Ph.D, 63. Lectr. ENG, IND. UNIV, BLOOMINGTON, 59-63, asst. prof, 63-66, assoc. prof, 66-70, PROF, 70- U.S.A.A.F, 45. MLA (mem. Am. Lit. Sect. & Early Am. Lit. Group); AAUP. Ralph Waldo Emerson; 19th century American Literature. Publ: Co-ed, The early lectures of Ralph Waldo Emerson, Vol. II, 64, Vol. III, 72, Harvard. Add: Dept. of English, Elisha Ballantine Hall, Indiana University, Bloomington, IN 47401.

WILLIAMS, WILLIAM PROCTOR, b. Glade, Kans, Sept. 1, 39; m. 62; c. 2. ENGLISH. B.A, Kans. State Univ, 61, M.A, 64, Ph.D.(Eng), 68; Oxford 62. Instr. freshman rhetoric, Kans. State Univ, 66-67; asst. prof. ENG, NORTH ILL. UNIV, 67-70, ASSOC. PROF, 70- Folger Libr. summer fel, 72; Am. Philos. Soc. fel, 72-73. MLA; Renaissance Soc. Am; Bibliog. Soc, Eng; Printing Hist. Soc; Midwest Mod. Lang. Asn.(chmn. bibliog. sect, 69, chmn, 70). Bibliography and textual studies; Renaissance English literature; Jeremy Taylor. Publ: Catalogue of 17th century religious literature, Kans. State Univ, 66; co-auth, Chapman and Marston bibliography (1939-1965), 68 & Beaumont and Fletcher, Massinger, Ford and Shirley bibliography (1939-1965), 68, Nether; co-auth, A bibliography of Jeremy Taylor, North. Ill. Univ, 71; auth, John Cleveland and the childrens threes, Am. Notes & Queries, 71; Other patterns of stoicism, Mod. Lang. Rev, 73; The first edition of Holy living, Library, 73. Add: Dept. of English, Northern Illinois University, De Kalb, IL 60115.

WILLIAMS, WIRT, b. Goodman, Miss, Aug. 21, 21; m. 54; c. 1. ENGLISH & COMPARATIVE LITERATURE. B.S, Delta Col, 40; M.A, La. State Univ, 41; Ph.D, State Univ. Iowa, 53. Instr. ENG, State Univ. Iowa, 52-53; PROF, CALIF. STATE UNIV, LOS ANGELES, 53- U.S.N, 42-46, Lt. Comdr. MLA; Col. Eng. Asn. Contemporary fiction and criticism. Publ: The enemy, Houghton; Love in a windy space, Reynal; Ada Dallas & A passage of hawks, McGraw; The Trojans, Little; The far side, Horizon. Add: Dept. of English, California State University, Los Angeles, CA 90032.

WILLIAMSON, ELSA WADE, b. Joplin, Mo, Sept. 19, 04; m. 29; c. 1. ENGLISH. B.A, Univ. Mo, 28, M.A, 31, summers 39, 61, 65; Univ. Mich, summer 36; hon. Litt.D, William Woods Col, 73. Instr. Eng, WILLIAM WOODS COL, 33-42, 47-51, 54-65, prof. ENG, 65-69, Beaumont prof, 69-73, chmn. dept. Eng, 47-51, 57-65, Eng. & jour, 65-73, EMER. PROF. ENG, 73- Instr, Culver-Stockton Col, summer 37; Univ. Mo, Columbia, summer 43. Delta Kappa Gamma Soc. award, 48. NCTE. Teaching of college English, especially composition and world literature; Chaucer; civil rights. Publ: Missouri's two state universities: a comparative study of educational offerings, 49 & Segregated schools in Missouri: a study of comparative costs in public schools, 53, Mo. Asn. Soc. Welfare; Employment (in Missouri), In: The 50 States, 1961 Report to the Fed. Comn. on Civil Rights, 61; plus others. Add: 707 Hollyhock Dr, Fulton, MO 65251.

WILLIAMSON, EUGENE LaCOSTE, JR, b. Gurley, Ala, Apr. 13, 30; m; c. 2. ENGLISH LITERATURE. B.A, Univ. Ala, 51; A.M, Univ. Mich, 55, Ph.D, 60; South. Fel. Fund Award, 58. Teaching fel, Univ. Mich, 55-57; instr. ENG, Univ. Ky, 57-59; asst. prof, UNIV. ALA, 59-63, assoc. prof, 63-68, PROF, 68-, dir. grad. stud, Dept. Eng, 71. U.S.N.R, 58-65, Lt. Comdr. MLA; NCTE; S.Atlantic Mod. Lang. Asn. Victorian literature, especially Arnold and Hopkins; literary criticism, especially modern; bibliography and methods. Publ: The liberalism of Thomas Arnold, Univ. Ala, 64; Significant points of comparison between the Biblical criticism of Thomas and Matthew Arnold, PMLA, 12/61; Words from Westminster Abbey: Matthew Arnold and Arthur Stanley, Stud. Eng. Lit, 1500-1900, 71; R.G. Moulton and modern criticism, J. Eng. & Ger. Philol, 71; plus others. Add: 53 Southmont Dr, Tuscaloosa, AL 35401.

WILLIAMSON, JANE LOUISE, b. St. Louis, Mo. ENGLISH LITERATURE. A.B, Wash. Univ, 58, M.A, Bryn Mawr Col, 60, univ. fel, 61-62, Fanny Bullock Workman traveling fel, 62-63, Ph.D.(Eng), 63. Instr. ENG, Univ. Wis, Madison, 63-64; asst. prof, Univ. Mo, St. Louis, 64-66; Univ. Calif, Santa Barbara, 66-67; UNIV. MO-ST. LOUIS, 67-69, ASSOC. PROF, 69-, CHMN. DEPT, 72- Univ. Mo. summer res. grant, 70. MLA; Am. Soc. Theatre Res; Soc. Theatre Res, Eng; Shakespeare Asn. Am; AAUP. Shakespeare and Elizabethan drama; theatre history. Publ: Charles Kemble, man of the theatre, Univ. Nebr, 70. Add: Dept. of English, University of Missouri-St. Louis, St. Louis, MO 63121.

WILLIAMSON, JERRY WAYNE, b. Dallas, Tex, Mar. 17, 44; m. 65. SEVENTEENTH CENTURY BRITISH LITERATURE & HISTORY. B.A, Wayland Col, 66; NDEA fel, Univ. Utah, 67, M.A, 70, Ph.D.(Eng), 70. ASST. PROF. ENG, APPALACHIAN STATE UNIV, 70- Ed, Appalachian J: A Regional Stud. Rev, 72- MLA; AAUP: Am. Civil Liberties Union; Am. Acad. Social

& Polit. Sci; Conf. Editors Learned Jour. Drama; Appalachian studies. Add: Dept. of English, Appalachian State University, Boone, NC 28608.

WILLIAMSON, JOHN STEWART, b. Bisbee, Ariz, Apr. 29, 08; m. 47; c. 2. ENGLISH LITERATURE. B.A. & M.A, East. N.Mex. Univ, 57; Ph.D, Univ. Colo, 64. Instr. ENG, N.Mex. Mil. Inst, 57-59; asst. prof, EAST. N.MEX. UNIV, 60-64, assoc. prof, 64-69, PROF, 69- U.S.A.A.F, 42-45, S/Sgt. MLA; NCTE; Teachers Eng. to Speakers Other Lang. Science fiction; H.G. Wells; linguistics. Publ: Darker than you think, Fantasy, 48; The humanoids, 50 & Dragon's Island, 51, Simon & Schuster; Bright new universe, Ace, 67; co-auth, Reefs of space, 63 & Rogue star, 69, Ballantine; auth, Trapped in space, Doubleday, 68; The Pandora effect, 69 & People machines, 71, Ace; The moon children, 72 & The power of blackness, (in press), Putnam; H.G. Wells: critic of progress, Mirage, 73; co-auth, Doomship, Ballantine, (in press). Add: Dept. of English, Eastern New Mexico University, Portales, NM 88130.

WILLIAMSON, MARILYN LAMMERT, b. Chicago, Ill, Sept. 6, 27; m. 50; c. 1. ENGLISH. B.A, Vassar Col, 49; M.A, Univ. Wis, 50; Ph.D.(Eng), Duke Univ, 56. Instr. ENG, Duke Univ, 55-56, 59; N.C. State Univ, 57-58, 61-62; asst. prof, Oakland Univ, 65-68, assoc. prof, 68-72; PROF, WAYNE STATE UNIV, 72-, ASSOC. DEAN COL. LIB. ARTS, 74-, chmn. dept. Eng, 72-74. Fel, Radcliffe Inst, Harvard, 69-70. MLA; Renaissance Soc. Am. Shakespeare; Renaissance drama and poetry. Publ: Co-ed, Essays in the Renaissance in honor of Allan H. Gilbert, S.Atlantic Quart, 72; auth, Infinite variety: Antony and Cleopatra in Renaissance drama and earlier tradition, L. Verry, 74; Patterns of development in Antony and Cleopatra, Tenn. Stud. Lit, 69; Did Shakespeare use Dio's Roman history?, Shakespeare Jahrbuch, 71; A reading of Milton's Twenty-third sonnet, Milton Stud, 72; plus others. Add: Dept. of English, Wayne State University, Detroit, MI 48202.

WILLIAMSON, MARY CELESTE, S.S.J, b. Rochester, N.Y, July 21, 10. ENGLISH. B.A, Nazareth Col.(N.Y), 32; M.A, Cath. Univ. Am, 46; Ph.D.(Eng), Fordham Univ, 66. Teacher, sec. schs, N.Y, 32-59; asst. ENG, Fordham Univ, 60-61; PROF, MATER DEI COL, 61-, CHMN. DEPT, 66- Instr, Sisters of St. Joseph Teacher Training Inst, Watertown, N.Y, 34-59. MLA; Cath. Renascence Soc. Eighteenth century literary history and criticism; the English epic and the epic tradition; Middle English language and literature. Publ: William Hayley's Essay on epic poetry, Univ. Microfilms, 66; ed, introd, William Hayley's Essay on epic poetry, Scholars' Facsimiles & Reprints, 68. Add: Dept. of English, Mater Dei College, Ogdensburg, NY 13669.

WILLIAMSON, MARY ELLEN, b. Kansas City, Mo. BROADCASTING, ADVERTISING. B.J, Univ. Mo-Columbia, 47, Ph.D.(jour), 73; M.A, Columbia Univ, 50. Asst. ed, NEA, 50-52; pub. affairs & prom. dir, Radio Sta. KXOK, St. Louis, Mo, 52-55; acct. exec, Jean Sullivan Advert, Omaha, Nebr, 55-68; ASST. PROF. SPEECH & BROADCASTING, UNIV. NEBR. AT OMAHA, 70- Lectr, Midland Col, 69-70; consult, Jean Sullivan Advert, 70-; lectr. jour, Univ. Nebr-Lincoln, 73-74. Int. Commun. Asn; Asn. Educ. in Jour. Mass communication. Add: 5217 Mason, Omaha, NE 68106.

WILLIAMSON, MERVYN WILTON, b. Appomattox, Va, Mar. 1, 21; m; c. 3. ENGLISH LITERATURE. B.A, Lynchburg Col, 48; M.A, Univ. Tex, 53. Instr. Eng, Lynchburg Col, 48-49, asst. prof, 49-55; instr, Univ. Tex, 56-57; from asst. prof. to assoc. prof, Culver-Stockton Col, 57-60, PROF. Eng. & philos, 60-68; ENG, LYNCHBURG COL, 68- Danforth grant, 55-56. U.S.A.A.F, 43-45. MLA; NCTE. T.S. Eliot. Add: Dept. of English, Lynchburg College, Lynchburg, VA 24505.

WILLIAMSON, RICHARD ARTHUR, b. San Francisco, Calif, Oct. 16, 30. ENGLISH, COMMUNICATION. A.B, San Francisco State Col, 53, M.A, 58. Teaching asst. lang. arts, San Francisco State Col, 57; instr, 57-58; ENG, Santa Barbara City Col, 58-63, chmn. dept, 61-63; INSTR, COL. SAN MATEO, 63-, ASST. CHMN. DIV, 69- Consult. col-level exam. prog, Col. Entrance Exam. Bd, 66-68; lectr. higher educ, San Francisco State Col, winter-spring 67; dir. & treas, Pac. Coast regional conf. Eng. two-year. col, Col. Conf. Compos. & Commun-NCTE, 67-; res. auditor, Am. Film Inst. Ctr. Advanced Film Stud, 71; coord. film & compos, Univ. Calif. Exten, summer 71, U.S.N.R, 51-57. NCTE; Col. Conf. Compos. & Commun.(chmn. Nat. jr. col. comt, 72-). Communication theory and linguistics; media and visual literacy. Publ: Co-auth, Anatomy of reading, McGraw, 65 & 70; Design for a composition, Harcourt, 66; The case for filmmaking as English Composition, Col. Compos. & Commun, 5/71. Add: Div. of English, College of San Mateo, 1700 W. Hillsdale Blvd, San Mateo, CA 94402.

WILLINGHAM, JOHN ROBERT, b. Quinlan, Tex, July 15, 19; m. 42; c. 2. ENGLISH. B.A, E.Tex. State Teachers Col, 40; B.S. in L.S, N.Tex. State Teachers Col, 40, M.A, 48; Ph.D.(Eng), Univ. Okla, 53. Asst. librn. & instr. lib. sci, E.Tex. State Teachers Col, 46-48; vis. asst. prof. Eng, Sam Houston State Teachers Col, 50-51; librn. & assoc. prof. lib. sci, Southeast. Okla. State Col, 53-54; prof. ENG, Centenary Col, 54-61; asst. prof, UNIV. KANS, 61-63, assoc. prof, 63-66, PROF, 66-, dir. freshman & sophomore Eng, 66-69. Vis. prof, Sam Houston State Col, summers, 55 & 56; Centenary Col. fac. summer grant, 60; Church Soc. for Col. Work fel, Episcopal Theol. Sch, Cambridge, Mass, 60; Kenyon Col, 64; acting ed, Midcontinent Am. Stud. J, 62; mem. advan. placement comt, Col. Entrance Exam. Bd, 66-70; vis. prof, Bowling Green State Univ, summer 67; Univ. Tex, Austin, summer 68; Am. Philos. Soc. grant, 68; Univ. Toledo, summer 69. U.S.A, 42-46, 1st Lt. MLA; NCTE; Col. Eng. Asn. Literary criticism; 19th century American literature; contemporary American poetry. Publ: Co-auth, A handbook of critical approaches to literature, 66 & co-auth, Mandala, 70, Harper; co-auth, Literary reflections, McGraw, 67, 2nd ed, 70; auth, Three songs of Hart Crane's The bridge, Am. Lit; Achievement of Waldo Frank, Lit. Rev, summer 59; co-auth, Class of '67: the gentle desperadoes, The Nation, 6/67; plus others. Add: 2511 Yale Rd, Lawrence, KS 66044.

WILLIS, EDGAR ERNEST, b. Calgary, Alta, July 12, 13; m. 38; c. 3. BROADCASTING, SPEECH COMMUNICATION; A.B, Wayne State Univ, 35, M.A, 36; Ph.D.(speech), Univ. Wis, 40. Radio producer, Detroit Pub. Schs, Mich, 35-38, 40-43; asst. prof. SPEECH, Wayne State Univ, 46; FROM ASSOC. PROF. TO PROF, San Jose State Col, 46-52; UNIV. MICH, ANN ARBOR, 52-, CHMN. DEPT, 69- Lectr, NBC Radio Inst, Stanford Univ, summers, 46 & 49-52; newsanalyst, WWJ-TV Detroit, 53-54; prod. assoc. Nat. Educ. TV, 58-59; Fulbright lectr, Univ. Durham & Univ. Hull, 63-64. U.S.N.R, 43-46, Lt.(jg). Speech Commun. Asn.(chmn. radio-TV div, 57-58). History of broadcasting; British broadcasting; writing for broadcasting. Publ: Foundations in broadcasting, Oxford, 51; Radio director's manual, Campus, 61; Writing television and radio programs, Holt, 67; co-auth, Television and radio, Appleton, 71; auth, Research in radio and television by graduate students in speech, 10/55 & Broadcasting and the British, 10/65, Quart. J. Speech. Add: 1112 Clair Circle, Ann Arbor, MI 48103.

WILLIS, HULON SIMS, b. Ala, July 11, 22; m. 50; c. 2. LITERATURE. A.B, Univ. Calif, Los Angeles, 46, M.A, 47, univ. fel, 53-54, Clark Libr. fel, 54-55, Ph.D.(Eng), 55. Instr. ENG, Univ. Idaho, 49-52; BAKERSFIELD COL, 55-57, CHMN. DEPT, 57- U.S.A, 42-44. MLA; NCTE; Conf. Col. Compos. & Commun. Eighteenth century; American literature. Publ: Structure, style, and usage, co-auth, Modern English practice, 58, Reading and writing, 62 & auth, Structural grammar and composition, 67, Holt; plus others. Add: Dept. of English, Bakersfield College, Bakersfield, CA 93305.

WILLIS, JOHN H, JR, b. Brooklyn, N.Y, Nov. 15, 29; m. 60; c. 2. ENGLISH. A.B, Univ. Va, 51; M.A, Columbia Univ, 59, Ph.D, 67. Instr. Eng, COL. WILLIAM & MARY, 59-64, asst. prof. & admin. asst. to pres, 62-65, assoc. dean col. & acting dean grad. stud, 67-68, ASSOC. PROF. ENG, 67-, asst. v.pres, 68-72. Alumni res. grant, Col. Summer Res. Prog, 67. U.S.N, 51-54, Res, 54-, Lt.(jg). MLA. The poetry of William Empson; the importance of the New Signatures (1932) anthology to contemporary British poetry. Add: Dept. of English, College of William and Mary, Williamsburg, VA 23185.

WILLIS, LEOTA GERALDINE SNIDER, b. Bakersfield, Calif, May 10, 02; div; c. 2. ENGLISH. A.B, Univ. Calif, 23; A.M, Univ. Pa, 30, Ph.D, 31; cert, Univ. Paris, 32. Instr. Eng, William Penn Sch, Bakersfield, Calif, 23-24; assoc, UNIV. WASH, 43-46, instr, 46-48, asst. prof, 48-72, fac. adv. dept, 45-72, lectr. lit, 54-72, asst. to dean col. arts & sci, 43-45, EMER. LECTR. LIT, 72- Vis. prof. Eng. lit, Silliman Univ, Philippines, 72-75. MLA; NCTE; Philol. Asn. Pac. Coast. Shakespeare; 17th century literature. Publ: Francis Lenton, queen poet. Add: Plaza A2A, Padelford Hall, University of Washington, Seattle, WA 98105.

WILLOUGHBY, JOHN WALLACE, b. Brumanna, Lebanon, July 30, 32; U.S. citizen; m. 59; c. 2. VICTORIAN LITERATURE. B.A, Yale, 52; B.A, Oxford, 54, hon. M.A, 58; Ph.D, Univ. Rochester, 59. Lectr, overseas prog, Univ. Md, 57-58; instr. Eng, Univ. N.Mex, 59-60; Univ. Chicago, 60-63; asst. prof. humanities, Southampton Col, L.I. Univ, 63-65, assoc. prof, 65-70, prof, 70-73, chmn. div. humanities, 63-70; V.PRES. ACAD. AFFAIRS, SOUTHWEST MINN. STATE COL, 73- Fel, Univ. Rochester, 69-70. MLA; Am. Asn. Rhodes Scholars. Browning; Sarah Orne Jewett and her circle; contemporary American poetry. Publ: Browning's familiarity with the Bible, Notes & Queries, 12/60; Browning's Johannes Agricola in meditation, Explicator, 9/62; Browning's Child Roland, Victorian Poetry, 10/63. Add: Office of the Vice President for Academic Affairs, Southwest Minnesota State College, Marshall, MN 56258.

WILLS, JACK CHARLES, b. Beaver, W.Va, Dec. 10, 36; m. 58; c. 1. ENGLISH. B.S.F, W.Va. Univ, 60; M.A, Univ. Del, 63, Ph.D.(Eng), 66. Asst. prof. ENG, Va. Polytech. Inst, 66-67; Westhampton Col, Univ. Richmond, 67-71; ASSOC. PROF, FAIRMONT STATE COL, 71- AAUP; Brontë Soc; MLA. Eighteenth and 19th century novel, especially Charlotte Brontë; romantic period, 18th century; Jane Austen and Samuel Richardson. Publ: The shrine of truth: an approach to the works of Charlotte Brontë, Brontë Soc. Trans, 70. Add: Div. of Language & Literature, Fairmont State College, Fairmont, WV 26554.

WILLS, JOHN W, b. Louisville, Miss, Jan. 17, 21; m. 46; c. 4. SPEECH. A.B, Miss. Col, 41; M.A, Univ. N.C, 48; Ph.D, Univ. South. Calif, 61. Asst. prof. SPEECH, Miss. South. Col, 48-51; assoc. prof, Miss. Col, 53-57; asst. prof, CALIF. STATE UNIV, LONG BEACH, 57-61, from assoc. prof. to PROF, 61- U.S.N.R, 42-46, Lt. Speech Commun. Asn. English; drama. Add: Dept. of Speech, California State University, Long Beach, Long Beach, CA 90801.

WILLSON, LAWRENCE, b. Lancaster, N.H, May 6, 11; m. 44; c. 2. ENGLISH. A.B, Wesleyan Univ, 34; Ph.D.(Eng), Yale, 44. Teaching fel. ENG, Wesleyan Univ, 34-35; instr, Univ. Del, 35-39; Yale, 40, 44; Univ. Tenn, 42-43; asst. prof, Univ. Conn, 44-47; assoc. prof, Colgate Univ, 47; from asst. prof. to assoc. prof, UNIV. CALIF, SANTA BARBARA, 47-62, PROF, 62- Vis. prof, Univ. Wash, summer, 59, 64, 68. Thoreau Soc. American literature of the 17th and 19th centuries, especially Thoreau. Publ: Assoc. ed, The writings of Thoreau, Princeton Univ, 64-73; auth, Thoreau's Canadian notebook, Huntington Libr. Quart, 5/59; Thoreau's medical vagaries, J. Hist. Med, 1/60; Another view of the pilgrims, New Eng. Quart, 6/61. Add: Dept. of English, University of California, Santa Barbara, CA 93106.

WILMETH, DON B, b. Houston, Tex, Dec. 15, 39; m. 63. ENGLISH, THEATRE HISTORY. B.A, Abilene Christian Col, 61; M.A, Univ. Ark, 62; Ph.D. (theatre), Univ. Ill, 64. Asst. prof. theatre, East. N.Mex. Univ, 64-65, head dept. drama, 65-67; asst. prof. Eng. & theatre hist, BROWN UNIV, 67-70, ASSOC. PROF. ENG. & THEATRE, 70-, grant to study in Europe, summer 68, res. grant, summer 71, acting chmn. theatre arts prog, 72-73. East. N.Mex. Univ. res. grants, 66-67, 67-68; consult, Asn. Col. & Res. Libr, 70- George Freedley Theatre Book Award, Theatre Libr. Asn, 71-72. Am. Theatre Asn; Am. Soc. Theatre Res; Int. Fed. Theatre Res; New Eng. Theatre Conf. American theatre of the 19th century; life and art of the 19th century actor, G.F. Cooke; history of the Margo Jones Theatre, 1947-1959. Publ: The Margo Jones Theatre, South. Speech J, spring 67; An index to: the life of George Frederick Cooke by William Dunlap, Theatre Documentation, fall-spring, 69-70; The posthumous career of George Frederick Cooke, Theatre Notebook, winter 69-70. Add: Theatre Arts Program, Box 1897, Brown University, Providence, RI 02912.

WILMOT, WILLIAM WALLACE, b. Vancouver, Wash, May 31, 43; m. 67; c. 2. INTERPERSONAL COMMUNICATION. B.A, Univ. Wyo, 65; M.A, Univ. Wash, 67, Ph.D.(speech), 70. ASST. PROF. INTERPERSONAL COM-

MUN, Cent. Mich. Univ, 70-72; UNIV. MONT, 72- Adv. consumerism & mkt, Northwest. Mutual Life Ins. Co, Missoula, Mont, 73- Distinguished Professionalism Award, Cent. Mich. Univ, 72. Speech Commun. Asn; Int. Commun. Asn. Persuasion. Publ: Co-auth, The personal communication process, 73 & co-ed, Communication involvement: personal perspectives, 74, Wiley; auth, A test of the construct and predictive validity of three measures of ego-involvement, Speech Monogr, 8/71; Ego-involvement: a confusing variable in speech communication research, Quart. J. Speech, 71. Add: Dept. of Interpersonal Communication, University of Montana, Missoula, MT 59801.

WILNER, HERBERT, b. Brooklyn, N.Y, Dec. 12, 25; m. 48; c. 3. ENGLISH. B.A, Brooklyn Col, 46; M.A, Columbia Univ, 48; Rockefeller grant, Univ. Iowa, 53, Ph.D.(Eng), 54. Instr. ENG, Univ. Kans, 48-50; asst, Univ. Iowa, 50-54; instr, South. Conn. State Col, 54-55; Yale, 55-57; asst. prof, SAN FRANCISCO STATE UNIV, 57-60, assoc. prof, 60-64, PROF, 64- Fulbright vis. prof, Univ. Innsbruck, 64-65; State Cols. Calif. res. grant, 67; writer-in-residence, Univ. Kans, 71. Fiction Gold Medal, Commonwealth Club Calif, 66. Auth. Guild. Novel; Keats. Publ: Co-auth, The seven years, Dutton, 57; auth, All the little heroes, 66 & Dovisch in the wilderness and other stories, 68, Bobbs-Merrill; co-auth, College days in earthquake country, Random, 72; auth, Aspects of American fiction, Americana-Austriaca, 66; San Francisco State College, Esquire, 67. Add: Dept. of English, San Francisco State University, San Francisco, CA 94132.

WILSON, ASHER (BOLDON), b. Long Beach, Calif, July 7, 20; m. 43; c. 4. THEATRE ARTS, DRAMATIC LITERATURE. B.A, Stanford Univ, 42, M.A, 52, Field-Hotalling fel, 54, Ph.D, 62. PROF. THEATRE ARTS, Col. Idaho, 50-53; Univ. Nevada, 56-59; PORTLAND STATE UNIV, 59-, HEAD DEPT, 63- U.S.N.R, 42-46. Am. Theatre Asn. John Galsworthy. Publ: John Galsworthy's letters to Leon Lion, Mouton, The Hague, 68; Oscar Wilde and loyalties, Educ. Theatre J. Add: 916 S.W. Davenport, Portland, OR 97201.

WILSON, BAXTER DOUGLAS, English Philology. See Volume III, Foreign Languages, Linguistics & Philology.

WILSON, DANIEL E, b. Lancaster, Pa, Mar. 4, 26; m. 54, 67; c. 3. ENGLISH. B.S, W.Chester State Col, 52; M.S, Kans. State Univ, 54; Univ. Pa, 56-57; Ph.D.(Eng), West. Reserve Univ, 66. Instr. ENG, Westminster Col, 56-57, asst. prof, 57-62; State Univ. N.Y. Col. Fredonia, 64-67; PROF, CALIFORNIA STATE COL.(PA), 67- Consult, Inst. Defense Anal, 66-67. U.S.A, 44-46, 50-51. MLA; Ling. Soc. Am; NCTE. Add: Dept. of English, California State College, California, PA 15419.

WILSON, DAVID SCOFIELD, b. Minneapolis, Minn, May 26, 31; m. 60; c. 2. AMERICAN STUDIES, ENGLISH. B.S, Univ. Minn, 53, M.A, 62, Ph.D.(Am. stud), 68. Teacher Eng, Morris High Sch, Minn, 57-60; Forest Lake High Sch, 60-62; instr, State Univ. N.Y. Col. Cortland, 64-66, ASST. PROF, 66-67; ENG. & AM. STUD, UNIV. CALIF, DAVIS, 68- Prog. coord. & lectr, Nat. Endowment for Humanities-Univ. Calif, Davis Exten, 71-72; consult, Nat. Am. Stud. Fac, 72-73; MLA summer stipend & textual ed, Irving's Tales of a traveller, Ctr. Eds. Am. Auth, 73. U.S.A, 55-57. Am. Stud. Asn; MLA; Am. Fed. Teachers. American culture studies; literature and art of early American ethnoscience; how-to books as cultural documents. Publ: The iconography of Mark Catesby, Eighteenth Century Stud, 71; co-ed, Science and literature issue (Festschrift for T. Hornberger), Early Am. Lit, 73; co-auth, American culture studies: the discipline and the curriculum, Am. Quart, 10/73; plus others. Add: 1109 Radcliffe Dr, Davis, CA 95616.

WILSON, DOUGLAS B, b. Denver, Colo, Aug. 19, 30; m. 56; c. 4. RENAISSANCE & ROMANTIC ENGLISH LITERATURE. B.A, Williams Col, 52; M.A, Oxford, 58; Ph.D.(Eng), Harvard, 67. Instr. ENG, Univ. Houston, 58-59; Williams Col, 64-65, asst. prof, 65-68; UNIV. DENVER, 68-71, ASSOC. PROF, 71- MLA. Samuel Taylor Coleridge; Romantic period; Shakespeare, especially Antony and Cleopatra. Publ: Coleridge: Dreams and poetry, Univ. Denver Quart, fall 68; Two modes of apprehending nature: a gloss on the Coleridgean symbol, PMLA, 1/72; Barfield on Coleridge: an exchange, Denver Quart, summer 72. Add: Dept. of English, University of Denver, University Park, Denver, CO 80210.

WILSON, DOUGLAS LAWSON, b. St. James, Minn, Nov. 10, 35; m. 57; c. 2. ENGLISH. A.B, Doane Col, 57; A.M, Univ. Pa, 59, Ph.D.(Eng), 64. Asst. instr. ENG, Univ. Pa, 59-61; instr, KNOX COL.(ILL), 61-64, asst. prof, 64-69, ASSOC. PROF, 69-, DIR. LIBR, 72- Agrarian tradition in America; history and literature of the Middle West. Publ: Ed, The genteel tradition: nine essays by George Santayana, Harvard, 67; auth, Santayana's Metanoia, N.Eng. Quart, 66. Add: College Library, Knox College, Galesburg, IL 61401.

WILSON, ELKIN CALHOUN, b. Valdosta, Ga, Nov. 13, 00; m. 37, 66. ENGLISH LITERATURE. Ph.B, Emory Univ, 22; A.M, Harvard, 27, Austin scholar, 32-33, Dexter traveling fel, 33, Ph.D, 34; Univ. Chicago, 30. Instr. Eng, Northwest. Univ, 27-31; asst. prof, Univ. Miss, 34-36, assoc. prof, 36; Folger Shakespeare Libr. res. fel, 36-37; instr. Eng, Cornell Univ, 37-42, asst. prof, 42-44; lectr, Queens Col.(N.Y), 45-46; asst. prof, N.Y. Univ, 46-47, assoc. prof, 47-50, prof, 50-67; RETIRED. MLA; Renaissance Soc. Am. English poetry of the Renaissance; Shakespeare. Publ: England's Eliza, Harvard, 39, Octagon, 66; Prince Henry and English literature, Cornell Univ, 46; ed, The lamentation of Troy for the death of Hector, Inst. Elizabethan Stud, 59; auth, Shakespeare, Santayana and the comic, Univ. Ala. & Allen & Unwin, 73. Add: 2537 Montevallo Dr, Birmingham, AL 35223.

WILSON, GARFF BELL, b. Ogden, Utah, Jan. 9, 09. DRAMATIC ART, RHETORIC. A.B, Univ. Calif, 31, A.M, 33; Ph.D, Cornell Univ, 40. Teaching fel. Eng, Univ. Calif, 31-33; dir. speech & drama, Humboldt State Col, Calif, 33-38, dean men, 35-38, 40-41; mem. direction staff, univ. theatre, Cornell Univ, 38-40; instr. pub. speaking, UNIV. CALIF, BERKELEY, 41-42, from asst. prof. to PROF. SPEECH, RHETORIC & DRAMATIC ART, 46-, SPEC. ASST. TO CHANCELLOR & PROTOCOL OFF, 52-, spec. asst. to pres, 46-66, dir. centennial celebration, 67-68. U.S.A, 42-46, Capt. Am. Theatre Asn.(assoc. ed, Educ. Theatre J, 63-65); Speech Commun. Asn. Drama; history of the American theatre; styles and theories of American acting. Publ: A history of American acting, Ind. Univ, 66; Three hundred years of American drama and theatre, Prentice-Hall, 73; plus numerous articles. Add: Dept. of Rhetoric, University of California, Berkeley, CA 94720.

WILSON, GENE ANDREW, b. Streator, Ill, June 27, 20; m. 49; c. 3. THEATRE, SPEECH. A.B, Denison Univ, 48; M.F.A, Yale, 51. Instr. THEATRE, Univ. Ala, 52-55, asst. prof, 55-65; ASSOC. PROF, UNIV. WIS-WHITEWATER, 65-, CHMN. THEATRE/DANCE, 71-, dir. drama, 68-70, acting chmn. theatre/dance, 70-71. U.S.A, 42-46, T/Sgt. U.S. Inst. Theatre Technol.(chmn, Midwest Sect, 72-73); Am. Theatre Asn; Speech Commun. Asn. Technical theatre; theatre architecture; stage design. Publ: New Alabama theatre designed to aid production, achieve audience intimacy, South. Theatre News, winter 57; Summer theatre auditions, South. Theatre, 64; contrib, Scenery for the theatre, Little, 71. Add: Dept. of Theatre/Dance, University of Wisconsin-Whitewater, 800 Main St, Whitewater, WI 53190.

WILSON, GEORGE PICKETT, JR, b. Nelson, Va, July 14, 18; m. 42; c. 7. SPEECH. B.A, Guilford Col, 39; M.A, Univ. N.C, 41; Ohio State Univ, summer 50; Ph.D.(speech), Columbia Univ, 58. Instr. radio, Univ. N.C, summer 41; drama, La. Polytech. Inst, 42-43, asst. prof. speech, 43-45; instr, Univ. Denver, 46; asst. prof, Univ. Va, 46-50; lectr. Eng, Columbia Univ, 50-52; assoc. prof. speech, Univ. Va, 52-62, chmn. dept. speech & drama, 58-61, dir. radio & TV, exten. div, 61-62; PROF. RADIO, TV & FILM, IOWA STATE UNIV, 62- Consult, U.S. Dept. Health, 68- Speech Commun. Asn; Univ. Film Asn; Broadcast Educ. Asn; Cent. States Speech Asn. Speech education; radio, television and film; drama. Add: 21 Exhibit Hall, Telecommunicative Arts, Iowa State University, Ames, IA 50010.

WILSON, GORDON DONLEY, b. Butler, Ohio, June 19, 05. ENGLISH. A.B, Miami Univ, 30, A.M, 32, hon. D.Lett, 73; Univ. Chicago, 37-39. Asst. prof. Eng, MIAMI UNIV, 32-48, assoc. prof, 48-59, prof, 60-72, asst. chmn. dept, 57-70, dir. grad. stud, 66-70, ARCHIVIST, & EMER. PROF. ENG, 72- NCTE; Conf. Col. Compos. & Commun. Eighteenth and 19th century English literature; composition. Publ: Co-auth, Chaucer: the Canterbury tales, Prentice-Hall, 47 & Selection: a reader for college writing, Dryden Press, 55. Add: Dept. of English, Miami University, Oxford, OH 45056.

WILSON, GRACE E, b. Waco, Tex, Feb. 14, 22. ENGLISH, EDUCATION. B.A, Baylor Univ, 40, M.A, 41; D.Ed.(Eng. supv. & reading), Univ. Va, 55. Secy. to prin. & teacher Eng, jr. high sch, Highland Park Independent Sch. Dist, Dallas, Tex, 42-43, sr. high sch, 43-44, teacher, 44-53, 54-56; counsel, Alex W. Spence Jr. High Sch, DALLAS INDEPENDENT SCH. DIST, 56-57, sec. Eng. consult, 57-71, coord. curriculum develop, 71-72, career educ, 72-73, COORD. SEC. READING, 73- Clin. asst, McGuffey Reading Clin, Univ. Va, 53-54; mem, Tex. State Textbk. Comt, 65. NCTE; NEA; Asn. Supv. & Curriculum Develop; Nat. Asn. Sec. Sch. Prin; Int. Reading Asn; Int. Platform Asn. Browning; teaching of reading in secondary school; modern scholarship related to the English language. Publ: Portraits, photographs, and other likenesses of Robert Browning, Baylor Univ, 43; co-auth, Composition situations, NCTE, 66 & Guided free reading versus other methods in high school English, 3/56 & auth, An experiment with accelerator training, 7/56, Peabody J. Add: Dallas Independent School District, 3700 Ross Ave, Dallas, TX 75204.

WILSON, GRAHAM CUNNINGHAM, b. Pittsburgh, Pa, Sept. 11, 15; m. 48. ENGLISH. A.B, Univ. Colo, 37, M.A, 40; Ph.D, Stanford Univ, 52. Instr. Eng, Univ. Colo, 40-42; asst. prof. naval sci, Stanford Univ, 45-46, instr. Eng, 46-50; lectr, Univ. Calif, Santa Barbara, 50-52, instr, 52-53; asst. prof, San Jose State Col, 53-56, assoc. prof, 56-59, prof, 59-67, mem. staff, Peace Corps training prog, summer 62, chmn. dept. Eng, 66-67; PROF. ENG, SAN FRANCISCO STATE UNIV, 67-, CHMN. DEPT, 73- Vis. prof, Ore. State Syst. Higher Educ, summer 60; Fulbright prof. Am. lit, Univ. Athens, 60-61; vis. lectr. appl. ling, Norway & Italy, 61; mem. lit. achievement exam. comt, Col. Entrance Exam. Bd, 64-70, chmn, 67-70; vis. lectr, Univ. Hawaii, Manoa, summers 68-71. Distinguished Teaching Award, San Jose State Col, 67. U.S.N.R, 42-46, Res, 46-, Comdr. MLA; Ling. Soc. Am. Applied linguistics; Renaissance and 17th century English literature. Publ: Auth. & ed, A linguistics reader, Harper, 67; co-auth, Usage in today's American English, Kairyudo, Tokyo, 72; auth, The structure of English, In: The structure of knowledge and the curriculum, Rand McNally, 64; A discipline for English, Calif. Eng. J, fall 66. Add: 2833 Vallejo St, San Francisco, CA 94123.

WILSON, HARRIS WARD, b. Frederick, Okla, Sept. 8, 19; m. 42; c. 2. ENGLISH. B.S. in Educ, Univ. Mo, 41; M.A, Univ. Chicago, 47; Ph.D.(Eng), Univ. Ill, 53. Instr. ENG, Ala. Polytech. Inst, 47-49; UNIV. ILL, URBANA, 53-55, asst. prof, 55-57, assoc. prof, 57-60, PROF, 60- Guggenheim fel, 61-62. U.S.A, 41-46, Capt. MLA; NCTE; Conf. Col. Compos. & Commun. Composition and rhetoric; 19th and 20th century novel. Publ: Co-auth, University handbook of English, Holt, 60; ed, Arnold Bennett and H.G. Wells: the record of a personal and literary friendship, Univ. Ill, 60; auth, James' What Maisie knew; ed, H.G. Wells' The wealth of Mr. Waddy, South. Ill. Univ, 69; auth, H.G. Wells' The death of Masterman, PMLA, 70. Add: 100 English Bldg, University of Illinois at Urbana, Urbana, IL 61801.

WILSON, HERMAN PLEDGER, b. Chattanooga, Tenn, Sept. 29, 24; div; c. 3. ENGLISH. B.A, Carson-Newman Col, 51; M.A, Univ. Tenn, 53, Ph.D.(Eng), 56; Ling. Inst, Univ. Tex, 61. Assoc. prof. ENG, Carson-Newman Col, 56-57; prof, William Jewell Col, 57-68, chmn. dept, 57-65, dir. libr, 65-68; assoc. prof, NORTHEAST MO. STATE UNIV, 68-73, PROF, 73- Ed, Mo. Eng. Bull, 70. A.U.S, 44-46, 50-52. MLA; NCTE; AAUP; Midwest Mod. Lang. Asn. Linguistics; Chaucer; 14th century English prose. Publ: Co-auth, Meeting censorship in the school: a series of case studies, NCTE, 67; Colleagues in composition, Mo. Eng. Bull. 70. Add: Division of Language and Literature, Northeast Missouri State University, Kirksville, MO 63501.

WILSON, HOWARD AARON, b. New Harmony, Ind, Nov. 18, 13. ENGLISH. A.B, DePauw Univ, 35; A.M, State Col. Wash, 37; Ph.D Univ. Wis, 41. Instr. ENG, Drake Univ, 41-42; Ind. Univ, 42-44; Cornell Univ, 44-45; asst. prof, Amherst Col, 45-46; assoc. prof, KNOX COL, 46-47, prof, 47-60, WILLIAM EDWARD SIMONDS PROF, 60-, chmn. dept, 47-72. MLA; NCTE. Chaucer; contemporary American literature; William Dean Howells. Publ: William

Dean Howells's unpublished letters about the Haymarket affair, J. Ill. State Hist. Soc, spring 63. Add: Dept. of English, Knox College, Galesburg, IL 61401.

WILSON, HUGH HAMILTON, b. Saranac Lake, N.Y, Aug. 14, 28. ENGLISH POETRY. B.A, Princeton, 51; M.S, Univ. Wis, 55, Ph.D.(Eng), 65. Instr. ENG, Univ. Wis, Green Bay, 60-62; Rutgers Univ, 62-65; N.Y. Univ, 65-66; asst. prof, 66-69; WAGNER COL, 69-70, ASSOC. PROF, 70- Vis. scholar, Norfolk div, Va. State Col, 66-67. U.S.N, 48. AAUP; NCTE. Poetry and life of Alfred Lord Tennyson; Victorian poetry; 19th century English and American literature. Publ: Tennyson: unscholarly Arthurian, Victorian Newslett, fall 67. Add: Dept. of English, Wagner College, Staten Island, NY 10301.

WILSON, JAMES DARRELL, b. Memphis, Tenn, July 27, 46; m. 70; c. 1. AMERICAN & COMPARATIVE LITERATURE. B.A, Baldwin-Wallace Col, 68; M.A, La. State Univ, Baton Rouge, 70, Ph.D.(Eng), 72; Univ. Manchester, 70-71. Spec. lectr. ENG, La. State Univ, 71-72; ASST. PROF, GA. STATE UNIV, 72- MLA; Int. Comp. Lit. Asn; Am. Stud. Asn; Popular Cult. Asn. Nineteenth century American literature; English, European and American romanticism; Southern literature. Publ: The role of slavery in agrarian myth, Recherches Anglaises Americaines, 71; Tirso, Moliere and Byron: the emergence of Don Juan as romantic hero, S.Cent. Bull, winter 72; Adventures of Huckleberry Finn: from abstraction to humanity, South. Rev, 1/74. Add: Dept. of English, Georgia State University, 33 Gilmer St, S.E, Atlanta, GA 30303.

WILSON, JAMES HARRISON, b. Baton Rouge, La, Apr. 22, 20; m. 52; c. 8. OLD & MIDDLE ENGLISH. B.A, Phillips Univ, 42; M.A, Tulane Univ, 53, Ph.D.(Eng), 65. Instr. ENG, Trinity Univ.(Tex), 56-58, asst. prof, 58-62, assoc. prof, 62-66; PROF. UNIV. SOUTHWEST. LA, 66- U.S.A.F, 43-45; Air Nat. Guard, 53-56; U.S.A.F.R, Maj. MLA; Mediaeval Acad. Am; Early Eng. Text Soc; S.Cent. Mod. Lang. Asn; Col. Eng. Asn; S.Cent. Col. Eng. Asn. (ed, Round Table, 70-75). Influence of Christian theology on Old English poetry; theology and myth in Middle English literature. Publ: Christian theology and Old English poetry, Vol. 71, Studies in English literature, Mouton, The Hague, 74; The Pardoner and the Second Nun: a defense of the Bradshaw order, Neuphilol. Mitt, LXXIV: 292-296. Add: University of Southwestern Louisiana, Box 1096, Lafayette, LA 70501.

WILSON, JAMES ROBERT, b. San Francisco, Calif, Feb. 11, 17; m. 61; c. 2. ENGLISH. A.B, Univ. of the Pac, 39, M.A, 40; Ed.D, Univ. Calif, Berkeley, 63, Instr. ENG, Stockton Col, 40-41, prof, 50-56; asst. prof, SAN FRANCISCO STATE UNIV, 57-61, assoc. prof, 61-66, PROF, 66-, acting chmn. dept, 66, dean sch. humanities, 66-70. MLA; NCTE. The response to literature; theory of lieterary form; rhetoric. Publ: Co-auth, Reading for rhetoric, Macmillan, 63. Add: Dept. of English, San Francisco State University, 1600 Holloway Ave, San Francisco, CA 94132.

WILSON, JAMES ROBERT, b. Caney, Kans, Oct. 6, 22; m. 43; c. 2. NEO-CLASSICISM, CRITICISM. B.A, Univ. Tulsa, 47, M.A, 49; Ph.D.(Eng), Univ. Okla, 53. Instr. ENG. LIT, Cent. Col.(Iowa), 48-50; assoc. prof, Hardin-Simmons Univ, 53-55; PROF. & HEAD DEPT, Univ. Tenn, Martin Campus, 55-61; Cent. Col.(Iowa), 61-67; UNIV. ALASKA, ANCHORAGE, 67- Mem. Int. comt. of one hundred, Shakespeare Birthplace Fund, Inc, 67. U.S.A, 42-46. NCTE; MLA. Swift; musical comedy in America; the Augustan age in English literature. Publ: Swift's Alazon, Stud. Neophilol, 10/58; Encountering vice with mirth, In: His firm estate, Univ. Tulsa Monogr, 67; Relentless self-scrutiny: the poetry of John Haines, Alaska Rev, 69. Add: Div. of Humanities, University of Alaska, 3211 Providence Ave, Anchorage, AK 99504.

WILSON, JOHN BYRON, b. Belleville, Ark, June 6, 09; m. 31; c. 1. ENGLISH LANGUAGE & LITERATURE. A.B, Ouachita Col, 30; Univ. Mo, 34; A.M, Univ. S.C, 36; Ph.D, Univ. N.C, 41. Teacher, High Sch, Ark, prin, 33-35; teacher, S.C, 36-37; from asst. prof. to prof. Eng, Ark. State Teachers Col, Conway, 41-48, dir. news bur, 44-45; prof. Eng, head dept. & dean, Centenary Col, 48-54, dir. news bur, 48-49; prof. Eng. & dean sch. arts & sci. La. Polytech. Inst, 54-64; dean grad. sch, W.Tex. State Univ, 64-67; PROF. ENG. & MEM. GRAD. FAC, LA. STATE UNIV, NEW ORLEANS, 67-, MEM. EXEC. GRAD. COUNC, UNIV. SYST, 67- Chmn. vis. comt, South. Asn. Cols. & Schs, 67. Superior Teacher Award, W.Tex. State Univ, 67. S.Cent. Mod. Lang. Asn. New England transcendentalism. Publ: Darwin and the transcendentalists, J. Hist. Ideas, 4/65; Horace Mann's aides: the New England transcendentalists, Educ. Forum, 5/67; Emerson and the Rochester rappings, New Eng. Quart, 6/68. Add: Dept. of English, Louisiana State University in New Orleans, New Orleans, LA 70122.

WILSON, JOHN FLETCHER, b.Keyser, W.Va, June 1, 23. SPEECH. B.A, Wayne Univ, 47, M.A, 48; Ph.D.(speech), Univ. Wis, 55. Instr. speech, Monmouth Col, 48-50; speech & drama, Cornell Univ, 53-57, asst. prof, 57-62, assoc. prof, 62-67; SPEECH & THEATRE, LEHMAN COL, 67-71, PROF, 71- Spec. instr, exten. div, col. indust. & labor relat, Cornell Univ, 55-56, consult. grad. sch. bus. & pub. admin, summers 65, 66, Bur. Employment Security, sch. indust. & labor relat, summer 67. U.S.A.A.F, 43-46, 50-51. Am. Forensic Asn; Speech Commun. Asn; Int. Commun. Asn. Rhetoric and public address; speech criticism; argumentation. Publ: An analysis of the criticism of selected speeches by Franklin D. Roosevelt; co-auth, Public speaking as a liberal art, Allyn & Bacon, 64, rev. eds, 68, 74; auth, Fifty years of rhetorical criticism by laymen, In: Reestablishing the speech profession: the first fifty years, Speech Asn. East. States, 59; Rhetorical echoes of a (Woodrow) Wilsonian idea, Quart. J. Speech, 12/57; Six rhetorics for perennial study, Today's Speech, winter 71. Add: Number 3k, 201 E. 21st St, New York, NY 10010.

WILSON, JOHN H, b. Binghamton, N.Y, June 20, 36. ENGLISH. A.B, Col. Holy Cross, 58; Woodrow Wilson fel, 58-59; M.A, Yale, 60, Ph.D.(Eng), 66. Instr. ENG, COL. HOLY CROSS, 61-67, asst. prof, 67-72, ASSOC. PROF, 72-, asst. dean, 68-72. Middle English literature; 18th century literature. Add: Box 122-A, College of the Holy Cross, Worcester, MA 01610.

WILSON, JOHN HAROLD, b. Springfield, Ohio, Feb. 11, 00. ENGLISH. A.B, Oberlin Col, 22; A.M, Syracuse Univ, 24; Ph.D, Ohio State Univ, 27. Instr. ENG, Syracuse Univ, 22-24; OHIO STATE UNIV, 24-29, asst. prof, 29-34; assoc. prof, 34-42, prof, 42-68, EMER. PROF, 68- Vis. prof, Univ. Tenn, 36, 38; Guggenheim fel, 50- MLA. The influence of Beaumont and Fletcher on restoration drama; court wits of the restoration; early 17th century plays. Publ: Nell Gwyn, royal mistress; A rake and his times; All the king's ladies, Chicago Univ, 58; Private life of Mr. Pepys, Farrar, Straus, 59; Mr. Goodman the player, Univ. Pittsburgh, 64; A preface to restoration drama, Houghton, 65; ed, Crowne's City politiques, Univ. Nebr, 67; auth, Mr. Pepys' clerk, Ohio State Univ, 72. Add: Dept. of English, Ohio State University, Columbus, OH 43210.

WILSON, JOHN ROBERT, b. Cambridge, Mass, Jan. 7, 36; m. 63; c. 4. ENGLISH & AMERICAN LITERATURE. A.B, Bates Col, 63; Ph.D.(Eng), Univ. Kans, 69. ASST. PROF. ENG, UNIV. MAINE, ORONO, 69- MLA. Victorian literature; the perennial philosophy; literature and religion. Publ: The writing-centered approach; or, neoclassicism revisited, Univ. Kans. Bull. Educ, 65; Signs of the times and The present age: essays of crisis, West. Humanities Rev, 72; Dickens and Christian mystery, S.Atlantic Quart, (in press). Add: Dept. of English, Stevens Hall, University of Maine, Orono, ME 04473.

WILSON, KEITH, b. Clovis, N.Mex, Dec. 26, 27; m. 59; c. 5. MODERN POETRY, SOUTHWESTERN LITERATURE. B.S, U.S. Naval Acad, 50; M.A, Univ. N.Mex, 56, fel, 58. Instr. Eng, Univ. Nev, 56-57; mem. staff, Sandia Corp, Albuquerquerque, 57-60; instr. Eng, Univ. Ariz, 60-65; ASSOC. PROF. ENG. & RESIDENT POET, N.MEX. STATE UNIV, 65- PEN-Am. Ctr. grant, 71; consult, Coord. Counc. Lit. Mag, 71-; D.H. Lawrence fel. creative writing, 72. Publ: Sketches for a New Mexico hill town, Wine Press, 66; Graves registry and other poems, Grove, 68; Homestead, Kayak, 68; The old man and others, N.Mex. State Univ, 71; Midwatch, Sumac, 72; auth, preface to Drummond Hadley's peoems, Cape Golliard; Notes toward a prosody, Their Place in the Heat, 71; Essay on poetry, Hiram Poetry Rev, 70; plus many others. Add: Box 3E, Dept. of English, New Mexico State University, Las Cruces, NM 88001.

WILSON, KENNETH GEORGE, b. Akron, Ohio, Apr. 21, 23; m. 46; c. 2. ENGLISH. A.B, Albion Col, 43; M.A, Univ. Mich, 48, Rackham fel, 50-51, Ph.D.(Eng), 51. Instr. ENG, UNIV. CONN, 51-55, asst. prof, 55-59, assoc. prof, 59-63, PROF, 63-, V.PRES. ACAD. PROG, 70-, head dept. Eng, 65-66, dean, Col. Lib. Arts & Sci, 66-70. Consult. lib. arts, Goodyear Tire & Rubber Co, 56-63. Sig.C, U.S.A, 43-46. MLA; Mediaeval Acad. Am; NCTE; Ling. Soc. Am; Conf. Col. Compos. & Commun. Mediaeval and comparative literature; linguistics. Publ: The complaint against hope, Univ. Mich, 57; co-auth, Essays on language and usage, 59, 63 & co-ed, The play of language, 71, Oxford; plus one other. Add: R.R. 1, Box 78, Separatist Rd, Storrs, CT 06268.

WILSON, LEWELLYN LEE, b. Bellingham, Wash, Sept. 25, 34; m. 56; c. 1. COMMUNICATIONS, SPEECH EDUCATION. B.A, Univ. Wash, 56; M.A, Northwest. Univ, 61, Ph.D.(speech educ), 67. Asst. prof. speech, Univ. Alta, 61-65, assoc. prof, 65-68, speech consult, 61-68; assoc. prof. & coord. speech educ, EAST. WASH. STATE COL, 68-72, PROF. SPEECH EDUC. & CHMN. DEPT. COMMUN. STUD, 72- Speech Commun. Asn.(v.pres. elect, 67-68, v.pres, 68-69); NCTE; Int. Commun. Asn; Can. Speech Asn.(U.S. rep, 68-). Speech education in Canada—curricula, personnel and facilities; speech pedagogy. Publ: Co-auth, Strategies for change in speech communication (monogr), Supt. Pub. Instr, Wash, 72; auth, A case for speech, Alta Teacher's Asn, Eng. Teacher, 6/65; The role of speech in the language arts, In: Proceedings of conference on elementary education, Holt, 66; co-auth, Speech education in Canadian higher education, Speech Teacher, 9/68. Add: Dept. of Communication Studies, Eastern Washington State College, Cheney, WA 99004.

WILSON, LOIS MAYFIELD, Linguistics. See Volume III, Foreign Languages, Linguistics & Philology.

WILSON, MARDIS GLEN, b. Roanoke, W.Va, Sept. 12, 23; m. 55; c. 1. THEATRE, ORAL INTERPRETATION OF LITERATURE. B.S, W.Va. Univ, 48, M.A, 49; Ph.D.(theatre), Ohio State Univ, 57. Instr. speech, Duke Univ, 49-50; speech & theatre, W.Va. Univ, 50-51; asst. prof, East. Ky. State Col, 53-56; West. Mich. Univ, 57-62; assoc. prof. theatre, Univ. Conn, 62-68; PROF. SPEECH & DRAMATIC ARTS, MACALESTER COL, 68- Ed, Ohio State Univ. Theatre Collection Bull, 56-57; Univ. Conn. Res. Found. res. grant, 66-68. U.S.A, 43-46. Speech Commun. Asn; Am. Theatre Asn; Am. Soc. Theatre Res; Soc. Theatre Res, Eng; Int. Fed. Theatre Res. Nineteenth century English; American and French theatre. Publ: The career of Charles Kean: a financial report, In: Nineteenth century British theatre, Methuen, 71; Charles Kean at the Princess's Theatre: a financial report, Educ, Theatre J, 3/71; Charles Kean: tragedian in transition, Quart. J. Speech, 2/74; plus others. Add: Dept. of Speech Communication & Dramatic Arts, Macalester College, St. Paul, MN 55101.

WILSON, MARYLAND W, b. Greenville, S.C. SPEECH. B.A, Winthrop Col, 36; M.A, Univ. Mich, 39, Trueblood fel. & Ph.D, 52. Teacher Eng. & jour. & dir. news serv, Sullins Col, 40-42; asst. prof. speech & dir. radio serv, Ala, Col, 44-48; teacher speech & Eng, U.S. Army Overseas Educ. Prog, Ger, 48-50; prof. speech & head dept, Pa. State Teachers Col, Bloomsburg, 52-53; Huntingdon Col, 53-62; prof. commun. & chmn. dept, Winthrop Col, 62-65; PROF. SPEECH, GA. SOUTH. COL, 65- Vis. prof, Furman Univ, summer 48; Brit. Readers Digest Scholar. combined summer session, Birmingham Univ. & Shakespeare Inst, Eng, 61. Speech Commun. Asn. History and broadcasting; communications; broadcasting by the newspaper owned stations in Detroit, 1920-1927. Publ: Ed, Alabama woman's page, 45, Alabama feature page, 47 & Alabama's cultural heritage, 48, Ala. Col. Add: Dept. of Speech, Georgia Southern College, Statesboro, GA 30458.

WILSON, MILTON THOMAS, b. Toronto, Can, Feb. 23, 23; m. 47; c. 6. ENGLISH. B.A, Univ. Toronto, 45, M.A, 46; Ph.D.(Eng), Columbia Univ, 57. Lectr. ENG, Univ. Syracuse, 48-49; TRINITY COL, UNIV. TORONTO, 49-55, asst. prof, 55-60, assoc. prof, 60-66, PROF, 66- R.C.N.V.R, 43-45, Lt. Romantic poetry; 16th century literature; Canadian literature. Publ: Shelley's later poetry, Columbia Univ, 59; Poetry of mid-century 64, Poets between the wars, 67 & E.J. Pratt, 69, McClelland & Stewart; co-auth, To every thing there is a season, Longmans, Can, 67; auth, Other Canadians and after, Tamarack Rev, autumn 58; Letters in Canada: poetry, Univ. Toronto Quart, annually, 7/61-65; Traveller's Venice: some images for Byron and Shelley, Univ. Toronto Quart, winter 74; plus others. Add: Dept. of English, Trinity College, University of Toronto, Toronto, Ont. M5S 1A1, Can.

WILSON, NOEL AVON, b. Weiser, Idaho, Feb. 10, 14; m. 65; c. 1. COMMUNICATIONS, POLITICAL SCIENCE. B.A, Univ. Idaho, 38; M.A, Univ. Mo, 60; Ph.D.(commun), Univ. Ill, 68. Managing ed, Cut Bank Pioneer Press, Mont, 46-52; free lance reporter, 53-56; instr. JOUR, Lincoln Univ.(Mo), 56-58; asst. prof. & head dept, Tex. South. Univ, 58-66; ASSOC. PROF, LINCOLN UNIV.(MO), 66- Mem. comt. standards, Am. Soc. Jour. Sch. Admin, 68-69. U.S.A, 41-45, Res, 38-66, Lt. Col. AAUP; Am. Acad. Advert; Asn. Educ. in Jour.(chmn. graphics div, 67-68). Urban studies, especially phenomena of civic bond; communications methodology; newspaper research. Publ: Co-auth, Missouri study number 8 of newspaper readership The Raytown News, Mo. Press Asn, 58; auth, The urbanization of man, 72 & Say it with pictures, 72, Wilson Mem. Publ. Fund; Politics has gone suburban, Grassroots Ed, 4/61; Changing pressures for graphic arts in journalism education, Jour. Quart, winter 68; The thrust of the mob and the media, J. Broadcasting, fall 70. Add: Dept. of Journalism, Lincoln University, 820 Chestnut, Jefferson City, MO 65101.

WILSON, OLLIE JAMES, b. Warbranch, Ky, Dec. 1, 09; m. 30; c. 5. ENGLISH, EDUCATION. B.S, Union Col, 35, hon. L.H.D, 63; M.A, Univ. Tenn, 48; M.S, Univ. Ky, 50, Ed.D.(Eng. & educ), 51; Univ. Chicago, 51; Ohio State Univ, 54, 57, 58. Teacher & prin, elem. sch, Leslie & Bell Counties, 28-34; sec. sch, Bell County, Ky, 35-40; instr. Eng. & speech, Univ. Tenn, 46-49; dir. Marietta Ctr, Univ. Ga, 51-53; prof. Eng. & jour. & chmn. div. humanities, Cent. State Univ, 53-54; prof. Eng. & speech & chmn. div. humanities, Morris Harvey Col, 54-58; from v.pres. & acting pres. to pres, Findlay Col, 58-63; prof. philos, West. Ky. State Col, 63-64; v.pres. develop. & educ, Appalachian Regional Hosp, 64; prof. educ, Chicago Teachers Col, South, 64-65; dean extended serv, Lake City Jr. Col, 65-66; PROF. SPEECH & THEATRE & DIR. INSTNL. RES, WEST. KY. UNIV, 66- U.S.A, 41-45, Col. NEA; Asn. Instnl. Res; Am. Asn. Higher Educ. Institutional evaluations; determination of institutional policy and status of various academic practices. Publ: Current trends in the teaching of college freshman English, Morris Harvey Col, 58; A report on the graduate program of Western Kentucky University, 67, Patent and copyright policies in forty-five colleges and universities, 67 & Evaluation of graduate instruction in 100 colleges and universities, 67, West. Ky. Univ; co-auth, chap. 23, In: Modern debate: its logic and strategy, McGraw, 60; auth, Status of institutional research in fifty-one colleges and universities, Col. Mgt, 3/67; Survey suggests guidelines for institutional patent policy, Col. & Univ. Bus, 4/68. Add: Western Kentucky University, Bowling Green, KY 42101.

WILSON, QUINTUS C, b. Fayette, Iowa, Dec. 31, 03. JOURNALISM. B.S, Univ. Minn, 36, M.A, 46, Ph.D, 53. City ed, Daily Free Press, Mankato, Minn, 24-25; farm ed, Cedar Rapids Daily Republican, Iowa, 25-27; copyreader, Des Moines Register, 27-28; Minneapolis Star, Minn, 28; copyreader, teletype, city, news & night ed, St. Paul Pioneer Press, 28-48; lectr, sch. jour, Univ. Minn, 42-43, instr, 43-45, asst. prof, 45-48; prof. jour. & head dept, Univ. Utah, 48-61; prof. jour. & dean sch. jour, W.Va. Univ, 61-69; PROF. JOUR, NORTH. ILL. UNIV, 69- Lectr, sch. jour, Univ. Tokyo, 54; Univ. Tehran, 57; adv, Govt. Press Dept, Afghanistan, summers 59, 60. Asn. Educ. in Jour; Jour. Educ. Asn. Newspaper censorship in the Civil War; impact of editorial direction of editor Joseph Wheelock and his St. Paul Pioneer Press on the history of the northwest, 1850-1906. Add: Dept. of Jouranlism, Northern Illinois University, De Kalb, IL 60115.

WILSON, ROBERT DAUDEN, b. Manila, Philippines, Dec. 14, 29; m. 54; c. 3. EDUCATION, LINGUISTICS. B.A, Ateneo de Manila Univ, 52, M.A, 59; Fulbright-Smith Mundt scholar, Univ. Calif, Los Angeles, 60-61; cert. teaching Eng. as second lang, 61, Philippine Ctr. Lang. Stud. & Phi Beta Kappa scholar, 61-62, Am. Counc. Learned Soc. fels, 62-64, univ. fel, 64, Ph.D. (ling), 65. High sch. teacher Eng, Ateneo de Manila Univ, 52-60, lectr, Grad. Sch, 59; res. asst, UNIV. CALIF, LOS ANGELES, 60-61, linguist-teacher, Peace Corps, 62, suprv, Teaching Eng. as Second Lang. Prog, 63, instr. Span. ling. & asst. dir. NDEA Eng. Inst, 64, acting asst. prof. ENG, 65-66, asst. prof. in residence, 66, asst. prof, 68-69, assoc. prof, 69-72, ADJ. PROF, 72-, PRES, CONSULT. IN TOTAL EDUC, INC, 70- Lectr. ling, NDEA Inst, Univ. Ariz, summer 65; asst. dir. res. & develop. H200 materials, Southwest Coop. Educ. Lab, N.Mex. & Educ. Serv. Ctr, Tex, 65-67; consult, Rough Rock Demonstration Sch, Ariz. State Univ, 66, 68, vis. lectr, 67; asst. prof. in residence, Ling. Soc. Am. Summer Inst. Ling, Univ. Calif, Los Angeles, summer 66, adv, NDEA Advan. Inst. Teaching Eng. as Second Lang, summer 66; consult, Bur. Indian Affairs, Window Rock, Ariz, 67-69. Int. Ling. Asn; Ling. Soc. Am; Philol. Asn. Pac. Coast; AAAS. Publ: English speech patterns for Filipinos, 60 & English sentence patterns for Filipinos, 60 & 63, Bookmark, Manila; Beginning fluency in English as a new language (filmstrip & record ser), Bowar Records, Inc, 69; Assumptions for bilingual instruction in the primary grades of Navajo schools, Consult. in Total Educ, Inc, 71; A schema in pedagogical insights, In: U.C.L.A. Work papers in TESL, 72; plus others. Add: Consultants in Total Education, Inc, 1081 Gayley Ave, Los Angeles, CA 90024.

WILSON, ROBERT H, b. Des Moines, Iowa, Jan. 21, 28; m. 63. AMERICAN LITERATURE. B.A, State Univ. Iowa, 48, M.A, 50. Instr. ENG, NORTH. ILL. UNIV, 54-57, asst. prof, 57-73, ASSOC. PROF, 73- Dir. grad. asst. in Eng. & exten. courses in Eng, North. Ill. Univ, 67; consult, Price-Waterhouse, 70. Mil.Intel, U.S.A, 51-53. Am. Stud. Asn; NCTE; MLA; Midwest Mod. Lang. Asn. Modern drama; American fiction; American drama since 1920. Add: Dept. of English, Northern Illinois University, De Kalb, IL 60115.

WILSON, ROBERT HENRY, b. Gary, Ind, Apr. 5, 09; m. 36; c. 1. ENGLISH LITERATURE. A.B, Stanford Univ, 28, A.M, 29; Ph.D.(Eng), Univ. Chicago, 32; Univ. Tex, 35-36. Asst. Latin, Stanford Univ, 28; prof. ENG, Carroll Col, 32-33; asst. prof, N.Mex. Norm. Univ, 34; instr, Univ. Tex, 34-36, 37-38; exchange asst. prof, N.Tex. State Teachers Col, 36-37; prof, Ark. Agr. & Mech. Col, 38-39; asst. prof, Howard Col, 39-42; assoc. prof, Southwest Tex. State Teachers Col, 42-43; Southwest Univ, 43-44; instr, La. State Univ, 44-47; asst. prof, UNIV. TEX, AUSTIN, 47-52, assoc. prof, 52-63, PROF, 63- MLA; Int. Arthurian Soc; Mod. Humanities Res. Asn. Mediaeval romances; Malory; Caxton. Publ: Co-auth, Manual of the writings in the Middle English, Vol. III, Conn. Acad. Arts & Sci, 72; How many books did Malory write?, Tex. Stud. Eng, 51; Addenda on Malory's minor characters, J. Eng. & Ger. Philol, 56. Add: Dept. of English, University of Texas at Austin, Austin, TX 78712.

WILSON, ROBIN SCOTT, b. Columbus, Ohio, Sept. 19, 28; m. 51; c. 4. ENGLISH. B.A, Ohio State Univ, 50; M.A, Univ. Ill, Urbana, 51, Ph.D.(Eng), 59. Asst. instr. Eng, Univ. Ill, Urbana, 57-59; intel. off, Cent. Intel. Agency, 59-67; prof. Eng, Clarion State Col, 67-70; ASSOC. DIR, COMT, INSTNL. COOP, 70- Vis. lectr, Tulane Univ, 71; Mich. State Univ, 72, 73. U.S.N, 53-57, Lt. Sci. Fiction Writers Am; MLA; Am. Asn. Higher Educ. Fiction writing. Publ: Ed, Clarion experiment, 71, Clarion II, 72, Clarion III, 73 & Those who can: a science fiction reader, 73, New Am. Libr; co-auth, To the sound of freedom, Charter Commun, 73; plus 25 short stories & novelettes. Add: Committee on Institutional Cooperation, 1603 Orrington Ave, Evanston, IL 60201.

WILSON, ROBLEY CONANT, JR, b. Brunswick, Maine, June 15, 30; m. 55; c. 2. ENGLISH, FOREIGN LANGUAGE. B.A, Bowdoin Col, 57; Ford fac. fel, Ind. Univ. Bloomington, 60; M.F.A, Univ. Iowa, 68. Instr. Eng. & Russian, Valparaiso Univ, 58-63; ENG, UNIV. NORTH. IOWA, 63-68, asst. prof, 68-70, ASSOC. PROF, 70- Ed, N.Am, Rev, 69- U.S.A.F, 51-55, S/Sgt. Contemporary fiction. Publ: All that lovemaking (poems), Country Press, 61; co-ed, Three stances of modern fiction, Winthrop, 72; plus numerous articles. Add: Dept. of English, University of Northern Iowa, Cedar Falls, IA 50613.

WILSON, STUART, b. Beaumont, Tex, Apr. 26, 32; m. 56; c. 3. ENGLISH LITERATURE. B.S, U.S. Merchant Marine Acad, 53; B.A, Lamar State Col, 58; fel, Rice Univ, 58-62, M.A, 60, Ph.D, 63. Asst. prof. Eng, State Univ. N.Y. Col. Fredonia, 62-64, assoc. prof, 64-69, prof. Eng. & dean arts & sci, 69-73; PROF. ENG. & V-CHANCELLOR ACAD. AFFAIRS, WEST. CAROLINA UNIV, 73- State Univ. N.Y. Res. Found. grants-in-aid, 62-64, 66-68 & fac. res. fel, 65; Nat. Endowment Humanities summer stipend, 67. MLA; NCTE. Restoration and 18th century English literature; the English novel. Publ: First dramatic version of Clarissa, Eng. Lang. Notes, 64; Bibliography of Restoration and 18th century theatre research, 1935-39, In: Restoration and 18th century theatre research, 66; Richardson's Pamela an interpretation, PMLA, 73. Add: Office of the Vice-Chancellor for Academic Affairs, Western Carolina University, Cullowhee, NC 28723.

WILSON, SUZANNE M, b. Los Angeles, Calif, Aug. 28, 28. ENGLISH LITERATURE. B.A, Stanford Univ, 50; M.A, San Francisco Col. Women, 53; Ph.D, Univ. South. Calif, 59. Instr. Fr. & Latin, Acad. Sacred Heart, 52-53; asst, Univ. South. Calif, 56-58; instr. ENG, CALIF. STATE UNIV, LONG BEACH, 58-59, asst. prof, 59-62, assoc. prof, 62-66, PROF, 66- Twentieth century English and American literature; the novel as a genre. Publ: Structural patterns in the poetry of Emily Dickinson, 3/63 & Emily Dickinson and twentieth-century poetry of sensibility, 11/64, Am. Lit. Add: Dept. of English, California State University, Long Beach, 6101 E. Seventh St, Long Beach, CA 90840.

WILSON, WILLIAM EDWARD, b. Evansville, Ind, Feb. 12, 06; m. 29; c. 3. ENGLISH. A.B, Harvard, 27, A.M, 30; Litt.D, Univ. Evansville, 62. Reporter, Evansville Press, Ind, 27-28; New Bedford Standard, 28-29; instr, Brown Univ, 30-33; head dept. Eng, R.I. Sch. Design, 33-42; assoc. ed, Baltimore Evening Sun, Md, 47-48; prof, Univ. Colo, 48-50; creative writing, IND. UNIV, BLOOMINGTON, 50-67, James A. Work prof. ENG, 67-73, EMER. JAMES A. WORK PROF, 73- Bell prize, Harvard, 30; Guggenheim fel, 46-47; Harvard Overseers Comt. to vis. Eng. Dept, 54-58; Fulbright prof, Univs. Aix-Marseille & Grenoble, France, 56-57; Am. Philos. Soc. res grant, 62-63; Fulbright travel grant, Eng, summer 63. Ind. Authors' Day Awards, 59, 65, 67; Southeast. Theatre Conf. Award, 62; Am. Asn. State & Local Hist. Award of Merit, 64. U.S.N.R, 42-46, Lt. Comdr. MLA. American history; creative writing. Publ: The Wabash, 40, Big Knife: the story of George Rogers Clark, 40 & Shooting Star: the story of Tecumseh, 42, Farrar & Rinehart; Yesterday's son, Farrar & Rinehart & Jarrolds, 41; Crescent City, Simon & Schuster, 47; Abe Lincoln of Pigeon Creek, McGraw, & Gollancz, 49; The strangers, McGraw, 52; The raiders, Rinehart & Hestia, 55; On the sunny side of a one-way street, Norton, 58; The angel and the serpent: the story of new harmony, 64 & Indiana: a history, 66, Ind. Univ; Every man is my father, Saturday Rev. Press, 73. Add: Dept. of English, Ballantine Hall, Indiana University, Bloomington, IN 47401.

WIMSATT, JAMES I, b. Detroit, Mich, Sept. 25, 27; m. 60; c. 2. ENGLISH. B.A, Univ. Mich, 50; M.A, Wayne State Univ, 59; Ph.D.(Eng), Duke Univ, 64. Instr. ENG, Univ. Tenn, 63-64; asst. prof, Tex. Christian Univ, 64-66; UNIV. N.C, GREENSBORO, 66-68, assoc. prof, 68-71, PROF, 71- Fels, Duke-Univ. N.C. Coop. Prog. in Humanities, 70-71; Huntington Libr, summer 73. MLA; S.Atlantic Mod. Lang. Asn; Mediaeval Acad. Am; Int. Arthurian Soc. Chaucer; Middle English literature; Old French literature. Publ: Chaucer and the French love poets, 68 & The Marguerite poetry of Guillaume de Machaut, 70, Univ. N.C; Allegory and mirror: tradition and structure in Middle English literature, Pegasus, 70; The apotheosis of Blanche in the Book of the duchess, J. Eng. & Ger. Philol, 1/67; The player king on friendship, Mod. Lang. Rev, 70; The Dit dou Bleu Chevalier: Froissart's imitation of Chaucer, Mediaeval Stud, 72. Add: Dept. of English, University of North Carolina at Greensboro, Greensboro, NC 27412.

WIMSATT, MARY ANN, b. Miami, Fla, Dec. 12, 34; m. 60; c. 2. ENGLISH & AMERICAN LITERATURE. A.B, Stetson Univ, 57; South. Fel. Fund fel, 57-60, M.A, Duke Univ, 58, Woodrow Wilson fel, summer 62, Ph.D.(Eng), 64. Instr. ENG, Tex. Christian Univ, 65-66; ASST. PROF, GREENSBORO COL, 69- Nat. Endowment for Humanities fel, 72-73. MLA; S.Atlantic Mod. Lang. Asn; Soc. Stud. South. Lit. American fiction; Southern literature; William Gilmore Simms. Publ: Simms and Irving, Miss. Quart, 67; Leonard Voltmeier's Invictus, 70 & Simms as novelist of manners: Katharine Walton, 72, South. Lit. J. Add: 3400 Kirby Dr, Greensboro, NC 27403.

WIMSATT, WILLIAM KURTZ, JR, b. Washington, D.C, Nov. 17, 07; m. 44; c. 2. ENGLISH LITERATURE. A.B, Georgetown Univ, 28, A.M, 29; Ph.D, Yale, 39; D.Litt, Villanova Univ, 62, Univ. Notre Dame, 63, LeMoyne Col. (N.Y), 65; LL.D, St. Louis Univ, 64; L.H.D, Kenyon Col, 70. Head dept. ENG, Portsmouth Priory Sch, R.I, 30-35; asst, Cath. Univ. Am, 35-36; from instr. to asst. prof, YALE, 39-49, assoc. prof, 49-55, PROF, 55-, fel, Silliman Col, 40. Yale Univ. sr. fac. fel, 60-61, Yale Rockefeller sr. res. grant, 65-66; mem, Eng. Inst. MLA; NCTE; Am. Acad. Arts & Sci; Cath. Comn. Intellectual & Cult. Affairs. Eighteenth century English literature; prose style, rhetoric and poetics; Alexander Pope. Publ: Prose style of Samuel Johnson, 41, The portraits of Alexander Pope, 65, Yale; The verbal icon, 54 & Hateful contraries, 65, Univ. Ky; co-auth, Literary criticism: a short history, Knopf, 57; ed, Samuel Johnson on Shakespeare, Hill & Wang, 60 & Explication as criticism, Columbia Univ, 63; ed, The idea of comedy, Prentice, 69; Versification, major language types, MLA & N.Y. Univ, 72. Add: Dept. of English, Yale University, 1882 Yale Sta, New Haven, CT 06520.

WINCHESTER, O. WILLIAM, b. Tulsa, Okla, May 23, 33; m. 53; c. 2. ENGLISH. B.A, Univ. Tulsa, 56, M.A, 57; Univ. Colo, 57; Ph.D.(speech, Eng), Univ. Okla, 62. Instr. speech, Univ. Wyo, 59-60; from asst. prof. to ASSOC. PROF. ENG, UNIV. TULSA, 61- Prose style; Victorian studies; pastoral tradition. Publ: Co-auth, The strategy of style, McGraw, 67, The prevalent forms of prose, Houghton, 68; auth, Copy and compose, 69 & co-auth, The attitudes of rhetoric, 70, Prenctice-Hall; auth, The sound of your voice, Allyn & Bacon, 72. Add: Dept. of English, University of Tulsa, Tulsa, OK 74104.

WINDES, RUSSEL R, b. Neosho, Mo, Nov. 11, 31. SOCIAL & BEHAVIORAL SCIENCES, COMMUNICATION. A.B, Drury Col, 51; M.A, Univ. Kans, 52; Ph.D, Northwest. Univ, 59; Harvard, 59-60. Asst. prof. pub. address, Northwest. Univ, 55-60; assoc. prof, San Francisco State Col, 60-64; PROF. COMMUN. & CHMN. DEPT, QUEENS COL.(N.Y), 64- Publ: Ed, Bobbs-Merrill series in speech communication (22 vols), 65- & Bobbs-Merrill series in communicative disorders (21 vols), 72-74, Bobbs; auth, Championship debating, 61, Vol. II, 69 & A guide to debate, 64, Walch; Argument and advocacy, 65 & ed, Random House series in speech (9 vols), 67-72, Random. Add: 412 E. 55th St, New York, NY 10022.

WINDT, THEODORE OTTO, b. Houston, Tex, Mar. 25, 36; m. 63; c. 1. SPEECH, RHETORIC. B.S, Tex. Lutheran Col, 58; M.A, Bowling Green State Univ, 59; Ph.D.(speech), Ohio State Univ, 65. Instr. speech & theatre, Temple Univ, 63-65; asst. prof. SPEECH, Univ. Tex, El Paso, 65-67, assoc. prof, 67-68; asst. prof, UNIV. PITTSBURGH, 68-70, ASSOC. PROF, 70- Vis. prof, Bowling Green State Univ, summer 65. Speech Commun. Asn. Rhetoric in the Soviet Union; rhetoric of Presidential campaign; rhetoric theory. Publ: The rhetoric of peaceful coexistence: Khrushchev in America, 1959, 2/71 & The diatribe: last resort for protest, 2/72, Quart. J. Speech; Everett Lee Hunt on rhetoric, Speech Teacher, 9/72; plus two others. Add: Dept. of Speech, University of Pittsburgh, Pittsburgh, PA 15213.

WINFREY, DAVID OUTCALT, b. Martinsburg, W.Va, Sept. 4, 24; m. 57; c. 2. ENGLISH, RELIGION. A.B, W.Va. Univ, 45; M.S, Univ. Md, 49, M.A, 57, Ph.D.(Eng), 66; B.D, Drew Univ, 53; M.Ed, Shippensburg State Col, 68. Engr, Philco Radio Corp, Phila, 45-46; instr. physics & math, Am. Univ, 49-50; math. & radio theory, Capitol Radio Eng. Inst, D.C, 53-54; minister, Poolesville Mem. Methodist Church, Md, 54-55; radiation physicist, Nat. Cancer Inst, 57-58; asst. prof. Eng, Bridgewater Col, 58-63, assoc. prof, 63-66, PROF, 66-67; ENG, PHILOS. & MATH, HAGERSTOWN JR. COL, 68- Theology and the philosophy and psychology of religion. Add: Smithsburg, MD 21783.

WINGATE, GIFFORD WENDELL, b. Valley Stream, N.Y, Nov. 29, 25; m. 49; c. 3. SPEECH, DRAMA. B.A, State Univ. N.Y. Albany, 49, M.A, 50; Ph.D, Cornell Univ, 54. Instr. speech, Ithaca Col, 53-54; asst. prof. SPEECH & DRAMA, Union Col.(N.Y), 54-58, assoc. prof, 58-64; PROF, UNIV. TEX, EL PASO, 64-, DIR. GRAD. PROG. DRAMA, 70-, head dept, 64-70. Danforth Found. vis. res. fel, Cornell Univ, 62-63. U.S.A, 43-46. Am. Theatre Asn; Speech Commun. Asn; Southwest Theatre Conf. Poetic drama; children's drama and theatre; playwriting. Publ: The lion who wouldn't (play), 69, The tiger in traction (play) & Family (play), 74, Samuel French. Add: Dept. of Drama, University of Texas at El Paso, El Paso, TX 79999.

WINKELMAN, DONALD MARVIN, b. Detroit, Mich, Aug. 27; 34; m. 54; c. 2. ENGLISH, FOLKLORE. B.A, Ohio State Univ, 57, M.A, 58; Ind. Univ, 60-62. Instr. Eng, Cottey Col, 58-60; Purdue Univ, 62-65; Bowling Green State Univ, 65-67, chmn, folklore prog, 66-67; assoc. higher educ, N.Y. State Educ. Dept, 67-69, supvr. higher educ, 69-70, coord. higher educ, 70-72; V.PRES, OSTROW, WINKELMAN & ASSOCS, 72- Lectr. radio ser, Folklore of Am. & Patterns in Folklore, Nat. Asn. Educ. Broadcasters, 65-67; secy, N.Y. State Col. Comt. on Educ. Opportunity, 67-72; ed, Educ. Opportunity Forum, 67-; J. Popular Cult, 68-; exec. secy, Nat. Coord. Counc. for Educ. Opportunity, 70-73. MLA (mem. folksong comt, comp. lit, II, 66-); Am. Folklore Soc.(ed, Abstr. Folklore Stud, 62-67); Int. Soc. Ethnol. & Folklore. Contemporary poetry; folklore and literature; Anglo-American folksong and balladry. Publ: Co-auth, New voices in American studies, Purdue Univ, 66; auth, Buckeyes and buckshot: folklore of Northwestern Ohio, Ohio Folklore Soc, 69; Making the college/career scene, 69 & ed, Minority group access to higher education (regents position paper), 72, N.Y. State Educ. Dept; ed, From out of the blue, Upward Bound Prog, Union Col.(N.Y), 73; Musicological techniques of ballad analysis, Midwest Folklore, winter 60-61; Three American authors as semi-folk artists, J. Am. Folklore, 4-6/65; Poetic/rhythmic stress in the Child ballads, Keystone Folklore Quart, summer 67. Add: Ostrow, Winkelman & Associates, 3511 Camino del Rio S, Suite 410, San Diego, CA 92108.

WINN, OTIS HOWARD, b. Poughkeepsie, N.Y, June 28, 25; m. 50; c. 4. ENGLISH. A.B, Vassar Col, 50; Newhouse scholar, Stanford Univ, 50-51, A.M, 53; N.Y. Univ, 60-63. Instr, pub. schs, Calif, 55-58; Eng, DUTCHESS COMMUNITY COL, 58-60, asst. prof, 60-62, assoc. prof. ENG, 62-65, PROF, 65-, HEAD DEPT, 62- Col. Eng. Asn; NCTE; MLA; Am. Fed. Teachers. Mass media; modern novel; contemporary poetry. Publ: Six short stories, Stanford, 53; plus poetry publ. in var. journals. Add: Dept. of English, Dutchess Community College, Pendell Rd, Poughkeepsie, NY 12601.

WINNER, ANTHONY, b. New York, N.Y, Aug. 17, 31; m. 64; c. 1. ENGLISH, COMPARATIVE LITERATURE. A.B, Harvard, 53, Ph.D, 62; M.A, Columbia Univ, 54; Fulbright fel, Facoltà di Magistero, Univ. Rome, 59-61. Instr. ENG, Univ. Pa, 61-63; Hunter Col, 63-65; asst. prof, UNIV. VA, 65-68, ASSOC. PROF, 68- MLA. Contemporary United States fiction; European realism; character in the novel. Publ: Ed, Great European short novels, Perennial Libr, Harper, 68; auth, Adjustment, tragic humanism, and Italy, Studi Americani, 61; co-transl, Ugo Foscolo, Last letters of Jacopo Ortis, In: Great European short novels, Perennial Libr, Harper, 68; auth, Richardson's Lovelace: character and prediction, Tex. Stud. Lit. & Lang, spring 72. Add: Dept. of English, University of Virginia, Charlottesville, VA 22903.

WINNER, VIOLA HOPKINS, b. Cleveland, Ohio, Mar. 13, 28; m. 64; c. 1. AMERICAN LITERATURE. B.A, Oberlin Col, 49; M.A, N.Y. Univ, 53, Ph.D. (Eng), 60. Instr. ENG, Adelphi Univ, 54-57; Hunter Col, 60-64; asst. prof, Univ. Va, 65-72; PROF, SWEET BRIAR COL, 73- Nat. Endowment for Humanities sr. fel, 72-73. Am. Stud. Asn; MLA. Henry James; American fiction; literature and the visual arts. Publ: Henry James and the visual arts, Univ. Va, 70; On Faulkner's The hamlet: a study in meaning and form, Accent, 55; Gloriani and the tides of taste, 19th Century Fiction, 63; Convention and prediction in Edith Wharton's Fast and loose, Am. Lit, 70; plus others. Add: 950 Locust Ave, Charlottesville, VA 22901.

WINSER, LEIGH, b. Brooklyn, N.Y, Jan. 18, 39; m. 69. ENGLISH LITERATURE. A.B, Colgate Univ, 60; Woodrow Wilson fel, Columbia Univ, 60-61, M.A, 62, Ph.D.(Eng, comp. lit), 69. Instr. ENG, SETON HALL UNIV, 65-69, asst. prof, 69-71, ASSOC. PROF, 71- MLA; Renaissance Soc. Am. Renaissance literature. Publ: Skelton's Magnyfycence, Renaissance Quart, spring 70. Add: Dept. of English, Seton Hall University, S. Orange Ave, South Orange, NJ 07079.

WINSHIP, GEORGE PARKER, JR, b. Providence, R.I, Mar. 17, 14; m. 44. ENGLISH LITERATURE. A.B, Harvard, 36; A.M, Lehigh Univ, 39; fel, Univ. N.C, 39-42, Ph.D, 48. Teaching fel, Lehigh Univ, 37-39; instr, Univ. N.C, 39-42; instr, Lehigh Univ, 46-48; PROF. ENG. & HEAD DEPT, KING COL, 48- Fund. Advan. Educ. fac. fel, Yale, 54-55; vis. prof. George Peabody Col, summer 68. MLA; NCTE. Modern grammar; novels of Charles Williams; 18th century essay journalism. Publ: Co-auth, Studies in the early English periodical, Univ. N.C, 57 & Shadows of imagination, South. Ill. Univ, 69. Add: Dept. of English, King College, Bristol, TN 37620.

WINSHIP, LOREN, b. Denver, Colo, May 30, 04; m. 29; c. 1. DRAMA EDUCATION. A.B, Nebr. Wesleyan Univ, 28, Litt.D, 66; A.M, Univ. Nebr, 30; Univ. Mich, summers 35-37; Ed.D, Univ. Tex, 53. Prin. high sch, Nebr, 29-31, Trenton, 31-34, Cent. City, 34-38; dir. drama & speech activities, exten. div, UNIV. TEX, AUSTIN, 38-42, from assoc. prof. to PROF. DRAMA, 42-, chmn. dept, 48-68. Nat. Award Merit, Theta Alpha Phi, 63; Founder's Award, Sec. Sch. Theatre Conf, 68; Award Merit, Am. Theatre Asn, 68. U.S.A.F, 42-46, 51-53, Lt. Col. Fel. Am. Theatre Asn.(managing ed, Jour, 49-54); Nat. Theatre Conf. Southwest Theatre Conf. Publ: Dramatics clubs; Drama in the secondary schools of Texas; co-auth, Speech teacher in competition, handbook for one act-play contest directors, judges and contest managers, 67. Add: Dept. of Drama, University of Texas at Austin, Austin, TX 78712.

WINSLOW, DAVID JOHN, b. Pittsfield, Mass, June 29, 31; m. 57; c. 2. FOLKLORE, ENGLISH. B.A, Goddard Col, 66; M.A, Univ. Pa, 67, Ph.D. (folklore), 72. ASSOC. PROF. ENG, STATE UNIV. N.Y. COL. OSWEGO, 68- Res. consult, Bishop's Mill Hist. Inst, 73- Am. Folklore Soc; Int. Soc. Ethnol. & Folklore; Soc. Folklife Stud. Folklore and literature; folk sculpture; Afro-American folklore. Publ: Children's derogatory epithets, J. Am. Folklore, 7-9/69; Hawthorne's folklore and the folklorist's Hawthorne: a re-examination, South. Folklore Quart, 3/70; Richard Harris Barham and his use of folklore, N.Y. Folklore Quart, 12/71. Add: Dept. of English, Sheldon Hall, State University of New York College at Oswego, Oswego, NY 13126.

WINSLOW, DONALD JAMES, b. Auburndale, Mass, Dec. 21, 11; div; c. 2. ENGLISH. B.S, Tufts Col, 34, A.M, 35; Ph.D, Boston Univ, 42. Teacher, Jr. High Sch, R.I, 35-36; teaching fel, ENG, BOSTON UNIV, 36-39; instr, 39-42, asst. prof, 46-49, assoc. prof, 49-52, PROF, 52-, chmn. dept, col. lib. arts & grad. sch, 52-62. Trustee, Lasell Jr. Col, 60- U.S.A.A.F, 42-46. MLA; Johnson Soc. London; Conf. Brit. Stud; Am. Soc. 18th Century Stud. Eighteenth century literature; the Bloomsbury group; Thomas Hardy. Add: 1109 Boylston St, Apt. 16, Boston, MA 02215.

WINSOR, WILLIAM T, b. Providence, R.I, Nov. 16, 30; m. 66; c. 4. ENGLISH. B.A, Brown Univ, 52; M.A, Columbia Univ, 57, Ph.D.(Eng. lit), 63. ASST. PROF. ENG. LIT, UNIV. BRIDGEPORT, 67- U.S.A, 52-54. AAUP; MLA. Irish literary renaissance; life and writings of W.H. Hudson and of Jack London. Publ: W.H. Hudson: England's neglected genius, Univ. Portland Rev, fall 72. Add: Dept. of English, University of Bridgeport, Bridgeport, CT 06602.

WINTER, JAMES PAUL, b. Moundsville, W.Va, Mar. 28, 08; m. 46. ENGLISH LITERATURE. A.B, Marshall Univ, 30; M.A, Columbia Univ, 32. Teacher Eng, high schs, Union, W.Va, 30-31, Charleston, 33-37; instr. speech, Defiance Col, 38-42; asst. prof. ENG, CLEMSON UNIV, 46-57, assoc. prof, 57-73, EMER. PROF, 73- Lectr, Far East Div, Univ. Md, 60-61. U.S.A.A.F, 42-45, M/Sgt. MLA; S.Atlantic Mod. Lang. Asn; Speech Commun. Asn; South. Speech Asn. Victorian poetry. Add: Dept. of English, Clemson University, Clemson, SC 29631.

WINTER, ROBERTA POWERS, b. Grenada, Miss, Aug. 15, 05. SPEECH, DRAMA. B.A, Agnes Scott Col, 27; Yale Sch. Drama, 29-31; M.A, N.Y. Univ, 39, Ed.D.(educ), 53. Instr. high schs, Tenn. & Conn, 27-39; SPEECH & DRAMA, AGNES SCOTT COL, 39-50, asst. prof, 51-54, assoc. prof, 54-67, prof, 67-72, ANNIE LOUISE HARRISON WATERMAN PROF, 72- Speech Commun. Asn; Am. Theatre Asn. Add: Dept. of Speech & Drama, Agnes Scott College, Decatur, GA 30030.

WINTER, WILLIAM E, b. Neosho, Mo, May 21, 17; m. 44; c. 4. JOURNALISM. B.J, Univ. Mo, 39, Ph.D.(jour), 55; M.A, Univ. Ark, 51. Asst. prof. jour, John Brown Univ, 40-41, prof, 49-51; instr, Univ. Mo, 51-53; polit. & legis. reporter, The State, S.C, 53-55; asst. prof. JOUR, Univ. Fla, 55-56; Univ. S.C, 57-59; assoc. prof, 59-63, prof, 63-66; PROF. & HEAD DEPT, UNIV. ALA, 66- Asst. to managing ed. & ed. writer, The State, S.C. 57-66. U.S.A.F.R, 41-45, Capt. Asn. Educ. in Jour; Am. Soc. Jour. Sch. Adminr. History of journalism; press law. Publ: New horizons for journalism at Alabama, South. Advertising & Publ, 7/67. Add: Dept. of Journalism, University of Alabama, Box 1448, University, AL 35486.

WINTEROWD, WALTER ROSS, b. Salt Lake City, Utah, Jan. 24, 30; m. 52; c. 2. ENGLISH, RHETORIC. B.S, Utah State Univ, 52; Univ. Vienna, 52-53; Kans. Univ, 56-57; Ph.D.(Eng), Univ. Utah, 65. Instr. ENG, Carbon Col, 55-56; Univ. Utah, 60-61; Univ. Mont, 62-65, asst. prof, 65-66; assoc. prof, UNIV. SOUTH. CALIF, 66-70, PROF, 70- Summers, consult, Ore. Curriculum Stud. Ctr, 64; vis. assoc. prof, Ohio State Univ, 66; Univ. Ore, 67; lectr, New Grammar Workshop, Calif. Polytech. Col, 67. U.S.A, 53-55. MLA; NCTE. History and theory of rhetoric; 18th century British literature. Publ: Rhetoric and writing, 65 & Co-auth, The relevance of rhetoric, 66, Allyn & Bacon; auth, Rhetoric: a synthesis, Holt, 68. Add: Dept. of English, University of Southern California, Los Angeles, CA 90007.

WINTERS, LEE EUGENE, JR, b. Detroit, Mich, June 28, 22; m. 59. ENGLISH, COMPARATIVE LITERATURE. B.A, Univ. Mich, 47; M.A, Univ. Calif, Berkeley, 52, Ph.D.(Eng), 56. Instr. Eng, Lingnan Univ, 47-50; lectr, Univ. Calif, Berkeley, 52-56; asst. prof. ENG, UNIV. HAWAII, MANOA, 56-63, assoc. prof, 63-71, PROF, 71- U.S.N.R, 43-46, Lt.(jg). MLA. Add: Dept. of English, University of Hawaii at Manoa, Honolulu, HI 96822.

WINTERS, ROBERT LOUIS, b. Columbus, Ohio, Nov. 11, 36. THEATER. B.A, Ohio State Univ, 58; M.A, Mich. State Univ, 62. Instr. THEATER, OHIO UNIV, 62-65, asst. prof, 65-71, ASSOC. PROF, 71- Designer-dir, Ohio Valley Summer Theater, 63-70, managing dir, 70- Speech Commun. Asn. Theater design, acting and directing; Appalachian folk-ethnic arts, music, dance, theater and crafts. Add: School of Theater, 097 RTV Bldg, Ohio University, College St, Athens, OH 45701.

WINTON, CALHOUN, b. Ft. Benning, Ga, Jan. 21, 27; m. 48; c. ENGLISH. B.A, Univ. of the South, 48; M.A, Vanderbilt Univ, 50; M.A, Princeton, 54, Ph.D.(Eng), 55. Ford Found. teaching fel, Dartmouth Col, 54-55, instr. Eng, 55-57; asst. prof, Univ. Va, 57-60; Winterthur asst. prof, Univ. Del, 60-64, assoc. prof, 64-67, coord. Winterthur Grad. Prog. Early Am. Cult, 61-67; PROF. ENG, UNIV. S.C, 67-, CHMN. DEPT, 70-, dir. grad. stud, 68-70. Am. Philos. Soc. grant, 60; Am. Counc. Learned Soc. grant, 63; deleg, Int. Congr. Enlightenment, Geneva, 63; Guggenheim fel, 65-66. U.S.N, 44-47, 50-52, Capt. MLA; Conf. Brit. Stud; Am. Stud. Asn; NCTE. Colonial American literature; 18th century literature. Publ: Captain Steele, 64 & Sir Richard Steele, M.P, 70, Johns Hopkins; ed, Richard Steele's The tender husband, Univ. Nebr, 67. Add: Dept. of English, University of South Carolina, Columbia, SC 29208.

WINZELER, CHARLOTTE MAE, b. Cambridge Springs, Pa, Oct. 26, 19; m. 41; c. 5. MODERN ENGLISH POETRY & DRAMA. B.S, Bowling Green State Univ, 60, M.A, 62. Grad. asst. ENG, Bowling Green State Univ, 61-62; instr, jr. col, Univ. Toledo, 64; Bowling Green State Univ, Bryan Br, 62-64; DEFIANCE COL, 65-71, ASST. PROF, 71- MLA; Midwest Mod. Lang. Asn; NCTE. John Millington Synge; Ben Jonson, especially Bartholomew Fair. Publ: The visual written image, CCCC J, 12/63; Curse upon a God: Classical and Elizabethan thought blended, Brigham Young Univ. Stud, winter 64; The 1910 Ghost edition of Synge's plays, Library, 6/73. Add: Dept. of English, Defiance College, Clinton St, Defiance, OH 43512.

WION, PHILIP KENNEDY, b. Bellefonte, Pa, Sept. 6, 41; m. 67; c. 2. ENGLISH LITERATURE. B.A, Swarthmore Col, 63; M.A, Yale, 64, Ph.D.(Eng), 67. Asst. prof. ENG, UNIV. PITTSBURGH, 67-72, ASSOC. PROF, 72- Woodrow Wilson fel, 63-64; mem. ed. bd, Milton Stud, 70- MLA; NCTE; AAUP. Sixteenth century English literature; Spenser; romance. Add: Dept. of English, University of Pittsburgh, Pittsburgh, PA 15260.

WIRKUS, THOMAS EDWARD, b. Marshfield, Wis, May 31, 33; m. 56; c. 4. SPEECH. B.S, Wis. State Univ, Stevens Point, 56, M.S, Univ. Wis, Madison, 59; Ph.D.(speech), Northwest. Univ, 66. Instr. high sch, Wis, 56-58; commun, UNIV. WIS-LA CROSSE, 59-61, from instr. to assoc. prof. SPEECH, 61-66, PROF, 66-, CHMN. DEPT, 70- Consult. speech educ, McCoy Job Corps, Wis, 66-67. Speech Commun. Asn; Cent. States Speech Asn. Status of speech education on secondary school level in Wisconsin and United States; history of speech education; utilization of instructional radio and television in secondary and university teaching. Publ: Co-auth, Communication and the technical man, Prentice-Hall, 72; auth, Speech education in the Catholic high schools of Wisconsin, Times-Rev, 8/59; A survey of speech education, Cath. Educr, 11/60. Add: Dept. of Speech & Theatre, University of Wisconsin-La Crosse, La Crosse, WI 54601.

WISE, JAMES NIAL, b. New Martinsville, W.Va, Apr. 6, 35; m. 59; c. 2. ENGLISH. B.S.J, W.Va. Univ, 57, M.A, 58; Ph.D.(Eng), Univ. Fla, 64. Instr. ENG, Georgetown Col, 58-59; interim instr, Univ. Fla, 59-62; ASSOC. PROF, West. Ky. Univ, 62-66; Ky. South. Col, 66-67; UNIV. MO-ROLLA, 67- Consult, Mo. Forum Humanities, 71 & Rolla Pub. Libr. grant, Nat. Endowment for Humanities, 71-72. MLA; AAUP. Sixteenth and 17th century English literature; archetypal myth in modern literature. Publ: Sir Thomas Browne's Religio medici and Two 17th century critics, Univ. Mo, 73; The floating world of Lambert Strether, Arlington Quart, winter 69; Emerson's Experience and Sons and lovers, Costerus Essays Eng. & Am. Lang. & Lit, 72; plus one other. Add: Dept. of Humanities, University of Missouri-Rolla, Rolla, MO 65401.

WISE, MATTHEW MONTGOMERY, b. Washington, D.C, Sept. 2, 21; m. 47, 63. ENGLISH LANGUAGE & LITERATURE. B.A, George Washington Univ, 44; M.A, Columbia Univ, 46, Ph.D, 55. Instr. ENG, Brown Univ, 47-51; ROANOKE COL, 53-55, assoc. prof, 55-58, PROF, 58-, CHMN. DEPT, 55- Col. Eng. Asn; MLA. Seventeenth century English literature. Publ: Introduction to evaluation, 59; co-auth, Introduction to argumentation, 60; Introduction to exposition, 65 & The Boston Family of Maryland, 67, privately publ. Add: Dept. of English, Roanoke College, Salem, VA 24153.

WISE, (ALFRED) SHELDON, (JR), b. Brooklyn, N.Y, Oct. 12, 23. LINGUISTICS. Ph.D.(ling), Yale, 53; Fulbright scholar, Paris, France. Linguist, Am. Counc. Learned Soc, 52-53; instr. Eng, Ford Found, Inst. Int. Educ, Indonesia, 53-55; assoc. prof. & dir. mil. Eng. prog, ROBERT COL, ISTANBUL, 56-58, PROF. ENG. & DIR. ENG. LANG. DIV, 58- Sig.Intel, U.S.A, 43-45. Ling. Soc. Am; Int. Ling. Asn; Teachers Eng. to Speakers Other Lang; Nat. Asn. For. Stud. Affairs. Structure of English; teaching of English to foreigners; Russian language. Publ: Common mistakes in English: as used in Indonesia, Pustaka Rakjat, Indonesia, 55; co-auth, Kurs Govornog Engleskog Jezika, Am. Counc. Learned Soc, 54; auth, Spoken English, Eng. Acad, Japan, Vol. IV, 62; co-auth. & chief ed, Spoken English for Turks, Robert Col, Istanbul, Vols. I-XVIII, 64-73. Add: English Language Division, Robert College, Arnavutköy, Istanbul, Turkey.

WISHMEYER, WILLIAM HOOD, b. New York, N.Y, Aug. 14, 18; m. 43, 61; c. 1. ENGLISH. A.B, Johns Hopkins Univ, 48, M.A, 49; Ph.D, Univ. Pa, 57. Instr. ENG, Johns Hopkins Univ, 49-50; Pa. State Univ, 49-50; Haverford Col, 50-54; asst. prof, Fenn Col, 54-57; DICKINSON COL, 57-60, assoc. prof, 60-70, PROF, 70- Med.C, 41-46, 1st Lt. MLA. Eighteenth and 19th century English literature. Add: Dept. of English, Dickinson College, Carlisle, PA 17013.

WITEMEYER, HUGH HAZEN, b. Flint, Mich, June 10, 39; m. 67; c. 1. ENGLISH & AMERICAN LITERATURE. B.A, Univ. Mich, Ann Arbor, 61; B.A, Oxford, 63, M.A, 68; Ph.D.(Eng), Princeton, 66. Asst. prof. ENG, Univ. Calif, Berkeley, 66-73; ASSOC. PROF, UNIV. N.MEX, 73- Am. Counc. Learned Soc. stud. fel, 71-72. MLA. Twentieth century British and American poetry; Victorian poetry; literature and visual arts. Publ: The poetry of Ezra Pound: forms and renewal, 1908-1920, Univ. Calif, 69; Line and round in Emerson's Uriel, 3/67 & Gaslight and magic lamp in Sister Carrie, 3/71, PMLA. Add: Dept. of English, University of New Mexico, Albuquerque, NM 87131.

WITHAM, BARRY BATES, b. Damariscotta, Maine, Dec. 11, 39; div; c. 2. MODERN DRAMA, AMERICAN THEATRE HISTORY. B.A, Tufts Univ, 61; M.A, Univ. Iowa, 64; Ph.D.(theatre), Ohio State Univ, 68. Asst. prof. THEATRE, MIAMI UNIV, 68-73, ASSOC. PROF, 73- Am. Soc. Theatre Res; Speech Commun Asn; Am. Theatre Asn; Theatre Libr. Asn. Nineteenth century American theatre history. Publ: America's forgotten playwright, Players Mag, 11/70; The play jury, Educ. Theatre J, 12/72; An index to mirror interviews, In: Performing arts resources, Theatre Libr. Asn, 73. Add: Dept. of Communication & Theatre, Miami University, Oxford, OH 45056.

WITHAM, WILLIAM TASKER, b. Worcester, Mass, May 20, 14; m. 40; c. 2. ENGLISH & AMERICAN LITERATURE. A.B, Drew Univ, 36; A.M, Columbia Univ, 40; Ph.D, Univ. Ill, 61. Teacher sch. boys, Newton, N.J, 36-38; activities secy, Bronx Union YMCA, New York, 40-42; head dept. Eng, Hiwassee Col, 42-43; asst. prof, Hartwick Col, 43-49, assoc. prof, 49-59, acting head dept, 43-48; asst. prof, IND. STATE UNIV, TERRE HAUTE, 59-63, assoc. prof. ENG. & AM. LIT, 63-67, PROF, 67- Danforth Found. grant, summer 61; Ind. State Univ. fac. res. grant, 61-62. Mod. Humanities Res. Asn; MLA; Col. Eng. Asn; NCTE; Conf. Col. Compos. & Commun. American colloquial speech; English and American literature. Publ: Americans as they speak and live, 45 & Adolescent in the American novel, 1920-1960, 64, Ungar; Panorama of American literature, 47 & Living American literature, 47, Stephen Daye. Add: Dept. of English, Indiana State University, Terre Haute, IN 47809.

WITHERS, SARA COOK, b. Birmingham, Ala, June 30, 24; div; m. 62; c. 1. LINGUISTICS. A.B, Ala. Col, 45; M.A, Univ. N.C, 47; Am. Univ, 53; Georgetown Univ. Inst. Lang. & Ling, 54; Univ. Buffalo, summer 56; Am. Counc. Learned Soc. grant, 56; Univ. Md, 66-68. Instr. Eng. for foreigners, Am. Lang. Ctr, Am. Univ, 52-56; ASSOC. PROF. ENG, GALLAUDET COL, 56- MLA; S.Atlantic Mod. Lang. Asn; Am. Instr. Deaf. Renaissance; 18th century; linguistics, especially as applied to teaching English to non-native speakers. Publ: Co-auth, Pronunciation drills for non-native speakers of English, 62, Eng. Lang. Serv; auth, A guide to improved English, Bobbs, 64; Stories of the American West, Prentice-Hall, 65; The United Nations in action: a structured reader, Crowell, 69; co-auth, A note on Browning's Statue and the bust, Browning Newslett, 72; plus three others. Add: Dept. of English, Gallaudet College, Kendall Green, Washington, DC 20002.

WITHEY, JOSEPH ANTHONY, b. New York, N.Y, Nov. 1, 18; m. 43; c. 2. ASIAN STUDIES, HUMANITIES. A.B, State Univ. N.Y. Albany, 41; M.A, Cornell Univ, 46, Ph.D.(drama), 53. Instr. drama, Kans. State Teachers Col, 47-49; Utica Col, 49-51; PROF. Eng, E.Carolina Col, 53-62; drama, HANOVER COL, 62-67, ASIAN STUD, 67- Fulbright res. scholar, Univ. Mandalay, 60-61; Ind. Univ. non-West. stud. proj. summer grant, 64 & 65; Inst. South. & Southeast Asia fel, Hamline Univ, summer 66; U.S. Dept. Health, Educ. & Welfare summer grant, E.Asia, 67; U.S. Off. Educ. South Asia Lang. & Area Stud. fel, 68-69. Sig.C, U.S.A, 43-46. Asia Soc.(mem, Burma counc, 64-); Am. Theatre Asn.(chmn, Afro-Asian theatre proj, 66-69 & film/tapes selection comt, 71-); Asn. Asian Stud. Asian theatre, literature and arts. Publ: Co-auth, The great Po Sein, Ind. Univ, 65; auth, Theater as a fine art, Brown, 65; Action in life and in drama, 58, Form and the dramatic text, 60 & Research in Asian theatre: an Indian model, 5/71, Educ. Theatre J. Add: Box 288, Hanover, IN 47243.

WITHINGTON, ELEANOR (MAY), b. Waterbury, Conn, June 13, 17. ENGLISH. B.A, Mt. Holyoke Col, 39; M.A, Radcliffe Col, 40, Ph.D.(Eng), 46. From instr. to asst. prof. ENG, Hollins Col, 43-48; asst. prof, Wells Col, 48-50; Champlain Col, 52; from instr. to ASSOC. PROF, QUEENS COL. (N.Y), 53- MLA; NCTE. Seventeenth century nondramatic poetry; English political satire. Publ: Co-auth, The poems of John Cleveland, Clarendon, 67. Add: Dept. of English, Queens College, Flushing, NY 11367.

WITMER, ANNE M, b. Essen, Ger, May 16, 01; nat; m. 32; c. 2. ENGLISH. M.A, Univ. Pa, 45, Ph.D, 59. Head dept. Ger, Wheaton Col, 26-36; asst. prof. Eng, Temple Univ, 56-67; assoc. prof. Ger. & Am. stud, EAST. COL.

(PA), 67-72, VIS. PROF. GER, 72- MLA; Am. Stud. Asn. American civilization; American-German relationships. Publ: The reception of the American novel in Germany, Cram, Ne Gruyter, Hamburg, 60; News from Virginia, Libr. Chronicle Univ. Pa, 2/68; plus others. Add: 281 Hathaway Lane, Wynnewood, PA 19096.

WITT, ROBERT WAYNE, b. Scottsville, Ky, Mar. 26, 37. SEVENTEENTH CENTURY LITERATURE. B.A, Georgetown Col, 59; M.A, Univ. Miss, 61, Ph.D.(Eng), 70. Instr. ENG, Univ. Miss, 65-70; ASST. PROF, EAST. KY. UNIV, 70- MLA. Dramatic literature and non-dramatic poetry of the 17th century. Publ: So we'll go no more a roving, 68 & Building a pillar of fame, 72, Univ. Miss. Stud. in Eng; Kipling as representative of the counter-aesthetes, Kipling J, 70. Add: 108 Sunset Ave, Richmond, KY 40475.

WITTIG, JOSEPH SYLVESTER, b. Pittsburgh, Pa, Aug. 18, 39; m. 69. ENGLISH, MEDIEVAL STUDIES. B.A, Wheeling Col, 63; M.A, Univ. Scranton, 65; Ph.D.(Eng, medieval stud), Cornell Univ, 69. ASST. PROF. ENG, UNIV. N.C, CHAPEL HILL, 69- Assoc. ed, Stud. Philol, 71- MLA; Mediaeval Acad. Am. Middle English literature; Old English literature; medieval studies. Publ: Homiletic fragment II and the Epistle to the Ephesians, 69 & Piers Plowman B, Passus IX-XII: elements in the design of the inward journey, 72, Traditio; The Aeneas-Dido allusion in Chretien's Erec et Enide, Comp. Lit, 70. Add: Dept. of English, University of North Carolina at Chapel Hill, Chapel Hill, NC 27514.

WITTIG, SUSAN W, b. Maywood, Ill, Jan. 2, 40; c. 4. MEDIEVAL LITERATURES, LITERARY THEORY. B.A, Univ. Ill, Urbana, 67; M.A, Univ. Calif, Berkeley, 69, Ph.D.(Eng), 72. ASST. PROF. ENG, UNIV. TEX, AUSTIN, 72- MLA; Soc. Relig. Higher Educ; Int. Asn. Semiotics. English education. Publ: Co-transl, Poetics of composition, Univ. Calif, 73; ed, Collected essays of Seymour Chatman, Mouton, (in press); co-auth, Notes on Grigori Permiakov's theory of the formulaic text, Paper Ctr. Int. Semiotica & Ling, Italy, 72; auth, Formulaic style in the middle English romances, Neuphilol. Mitt, (in press). Add: Dept. of English, University of Texas, Austin, TX 78712.

WITTREICH, JOSEPH ANTHONY, JR, b. Cleveland, Ohio, July 23, 39. ENGLISH LITERATURE. B.A, Univ. Louisville, 61, M.A, 62; Ph.D.(Eng), West. Reserve Univ, 66. Asst. prof. ENG, UNIV. WIS, MADISON, 66-70, assoc. prof, 71-73, PROF, 74- Am. Philos. Soc. summer fel, 68; Henry E. Huntington Libr. summer fel, 69; Folger Shakespeare Libr. short-term fel, 71 & 74; guest lectr, Calif. State Univ, Los Angeles, fall 72; adv. dir, Blake Found. Am, 72- Renaissance Soc. Am; MLA; Milton Soc. Am. Milton; Blake; epic tradition. Publ: Ed, The romantics on Milton, 70 & Calm of mind, 71, Case West. Reserve Univ; co-ed, Blake's sublime allegory, 73 & Literary monographs, 74 & auth, Angel of Apocalypse: Blake's idea of Milton, 74, Univ. Wis; auth, The crown of eloquence in achievements of the left hand, Univ. Mass, 73. Add: Dept. of English, 6145 White Hall, University of Wisconsin, Madison, WI 53706.

WITTROCK, VERNA D, b. St. Paul, Minn, Oct. 17, 14. ENGLISH. B.S.Ed, Univ. Ill, 42, A.M, 45, Ph.D.(Eng), 57. Teacher, High Sch, Ill, 42-44; asst. ENG, Univ. Ill, 45-55; instr, Univ. Nev, 55-57, asst. prof, 57-58; teacher, Oakland City Col, 58-60; asst. prof, West. Ill. Univ, 60-62; Purdue Univ, 62-64, ASSOC. PROF, 64-66; EAST. ILL. UNIV, 66- Danforth Found. grant, summer 61. MLA; Am. Name Soc. English novel; 19th century English literature. Publ: Henry Handel Richardson, Eng. Lit. in Transition, VII, No. 3; Henry Handel Richardson, In: Encyclopedia of world literature in the 20th century, Ungar. Add: Dept. of English, Eastern Illinois University, Charleston, IL 61920.

WOELLHAF, RICHARD, b. South Haven, Mich, Sept. 6, 05. SPEECH. A.B, Univ. Mich, 27, A.M, 30. Asst. prof. speech & drama, Denison Univ, 29-37; dean instr, Hollywood Motion Picture Inst, Calif, 37-40; asst. prof. speech & drama, Miami Univ, 41-45; SPEECH, UNIV. DENVER, 45-71, EMER. PROF, 71- Motion picture specialist, Nat. Park Serv, Washington, D.C, 63. Speech Commun. Asn. History of physical theatre; plays; motion picture scripts. Add: Apt. 58, 3695 S. Irving, Englewood, CO 80110.

WOERNER, ROBERT FREDERICK, b. Louisville, Ky, Feb. 1, 28; m. 56; c. 2. ENGLISH & COMPARATIVE LITERATURE. A.B, Univ. Louisville, 50; Swiss-Am. Soc. Cult. Relat. fel, Univ. Zurich & Eidgenössische Tech. Hochsch, Switz, 50-51; Ph.D, Ind. Univ, 62. Instr. ENG. & COMP. LIT. UNIV. IOWA, 57-61, asst. prof, 61-66, ASSOC. PROF, 66- Med.C, 46-47, S/Sgt. MLA. Nineteenth and 20th century English and comparative literature. Add: Dept. of English, University of Iowa, Iowa City, IA 52240.

WOHLGELERNTER, MAURICE, b. Serotsk, Poland, Feb. 13, 21; nat; m. 48; c. 3. ENGLISH. B.A, Yeshiva Univ, 41, ordained Rabbi, 44; M.A, Columbia Univ, 46, Ph.D, 60. Asst. prof. ENG, Yeshiva Univ, 55-72; ASSOC. PROF, BARUCH COL, 72- Vis. asst. prof, City Col. N.Y, summers 62-65; vis. prof, New Sch. Soc. Res, 66-68; Bar-Ilan Univ, Israel, summers 66, 68; vis. prof, Touro Col.(N.Y), 71- MLA; NCTE. Philosophy; Frank O'Connor; history of ideas. Publ: Israel Zangwill: a study, Columbia Univ, 64; Introd. to Israel Zangwill's King of Schnorrers, Dover, 65. Add: Dept. of English, Baruch College, 17 Lexington Ave, New York, NY 10010.

WOLCK, WOLFGANG, Linguistics. See Volume III, Foreign Languages, Linguistics & Philology.

WOLF, DONALD, b. Sandpoint, Idaho, Apr. 12, 24; m. 55; c. 1. ENGLISH. B.S, Lehigh Univ, 48, M.A, 52; Ph.D, Columbia Univ, 60. Instr. ENG, Lehigh Univ, 50-52; ADELPHI UNIV, 53-58, from asst. prof. to PROF, 58- U.S.A, 44-46. Romantic and Victorian English literature. Publ: Non-Euclidian geometry, 60 & A revolution that failed, 61, Adelphi Quart. Add: Dept. of English, Adelphi University, Garden City, NY 11530.

WOLF, EDWIN, II, American History. See Volume I, History.

WOLF, HOWARD R, b. New York, N.Y, Nov. 5, 36; div; c. 1. AMERICAN LITERATURE, PSYCHOLOGY. B.A, Amherst Col, 59; M.A, Columbia Univ, 60; Ph.D.(Eng), Univ. Mich, 67. Instr. ENG, East. Mich. Univ, 66-67; asst. prof, STATE UNIV. N.Y. BUFFALO, 67-72, ASSOC. PROF, 72- Education; American culture; literary journalism. Publ: Co-auth, The voice within: reading and writing autobiography, Knopf, 73; Classroom as microcosm, Col. Eng, 71; The drama of humanism, Symp. Humanities, 72; Quietude, apocalypse, and nostalgia, Am. Scholar, 73; plus others. Add: 155 Cleveland Ave, Buffalo, NY 14222.

WOLF, MELVIN HERBERT, b. Boston, Mass, May 24, 29; m. 52; c. 3. ENGLISH. B.A, Univ. Mass, 51; M.A, Univ. Mich, 57, Ph.D, 61. Instr. Eng, Univ. Mass, Amherst, 60-64, asst. prof, 64-68; ASSOC. PROF. HUMANITIES & ENG, PA. STATE UNIV, CAPITOL CAMPUS, 68- Fac. res. grants, Univ. Mass, Amherst, 62-63, 64, 66-67; U.S. Off. Educ. res. contract, 64-65. U.S.N, 52-55, Lt.(jg). Renaissance Eng. Text Soc; Malone Soc; NCTE. Interdisciplinary studies in the humanities; literature of the Renaissance in England; apolication of the digital computer to scholarship in the field of English language and literature. Publ: Ed, Faultes faults, and nothing else but faults (1606), Scholars' Facsimiles, 65; auth, Effect of writing frequency upon proficiency in a college freshmen English course, Univ. Mass, 66; The IBM 1620 as a tool for investigating principles of auto-abstracting, Lit. Data Processing Conf. Prod, 9/64; The unity of Samson Agonistes, Eng. Rec, 4/67; The lower-case 2-r in 16th century English black letter texts, Stud. Bibliog, 73. Add: Humanities Program, Pennsylvania State University, Capitol Campus, Middletown, PA 17057.

WOLF, MORRIS PHILIP, b. Brooklyn, N.Y, Apr. 28, 29. ENGLISH, SPEECH. B.A, N.Y. Univ, 49, M.A, 51; Ph.D.(Eng), Univ. Ga, 59. Instr. Eng. & speech, Columbus Ctr, Univ. Ga, 53-54, asst. prof, 54, univ. rep, Gainesville Ctr, 54-56, head dept. Eng. & speech & asst. dir. Gainesville Ctr, 56-58, dir. Augusta Ctr, 58; assoc. prof. Eng. & speech, asst. dean & dir. extended servs, Augusta Col, 59-60, prof. Eng. & speech & chmn. dept, 60-62; assoc. prof. BUS. COMMUN, COL. BUS. ADMIN, UNIV. HOUSTON, 62-67, PROF, 67-, chmn. dept. gen. bus. admin, 68-70. Consult. human commun, U.S. Army Educ. Ctr, Ft. Gordon, Ga, 59; lectr, personnel material sem, Southeast. Signal Sch. & Provost Marshal Gen. Sch, 61; lectr. & conf. leader seminars, Mgt. Develop. Ctr, 62-; commun. consult, Ctr. Res. Bus. & Econ, 62-; ed. consult, Bus. Rev, 62-; prof. actor, radio, TV & stage. Edith Hudson Poetry Prize, 53; Earplay Radio Drama Award. U.S.A, 51-54, Capt. MLA; NCTE; Am. Bus. Commun. Asn.(1st v.pres; pres, 71; dir-at-large); Int. Commun. Asn; Int. Soc. Gen. Semantics; South. Speech Commun. Asn. Radio and TV production; interpersonal, organizational, and mass-media communication. Publ: Co-auth, Effective communication in business, South-West Publ, 67 & 6th ed, 74; & Easy grammar, Kendall/Hunt Publ, 70; auth, Mirrors (radio drama), Univ. Wis, 73; University of Houston Business Communication Program: philosophy, scope, and materials, ABCA Bull, 69; plus three others. Add: Dept. of General Business Administration, College of Business Administration, University of Houston, Cullen Blvd, Houston, TX 77004.

WOLFARTH, DONALD LLOYD, b. Long Prairie, Minn, Oct. 27, 26; m. 50; c. 3. SPEECH. B.A, Hamline Univ, 50; M.A, Univ. Minn, 53, Danforth grant, 58-59, Ph.D.(speech), 59. Instr. SPEECH, Midland Lutheran Col, 53-56, asst. prof, 57-60, assoc. prof, 61-64, PROF, 65-67; UNIV. WIS-EAU CLAIRE, 67- U.S.A, 44-47, 51-52. Speech Commun. Asn; Am. Speech & Hearing Asn. Rhetoric; American public address; speech education. Publ: John F. Kennedy in the tradition of inaugural speeches, Quart. J. Speech, 61; contrib, Great American speeches, Appleton-Century-Crofts, 70. Add: Dept. of Speech, University of Wisconsin-Eau Claire, Eau Claire, WI 54701.

WOLFE, DON MARION, b. Parsons, W.Va, Oct. 24, 02; m. 31; c. 1. ENGLISH. B.S, Davis & Elkins Col, 23, D.Litt, 61; A.M, Univ. Pittsburgh, 27, Ph.D, 30. Assoc. prof. ENG, Geneva Col, 30-38; instr, N.Y. Univ, 42-45; assoc. prof, Am. Univ.(D.C), 45-46; from asst. to assoc. prof, Brooklyn Col, 46-56, PROF, 57-73; RETIRED. Gen. ed, Complete prose works of John Milton, Yale Univ. Press, 46-; Bollingen & Littauer Found. grants, 49, 53, 58, 62; Huntington Libr. fel, 56; mem, Inst. Advan. Stud, 57-58; Fulbright prof. Am. lit, Univ. Bordeaux, 59-60; Am. Philos. Soc. grant, summer, 61; citation, New Sch. Soc. Res, 62; Am. Counc. Learned Soc. fel, 63-64; Guggenheim fel, 71-72. MLA; Milton Soc. Am.(pres, 56-57). Milton; American literature; collections of new writing. Publ: Milton in the Puritan revolution, Nelson, 41, Humanities, 63; Leveller manifestoes, Nelson, 44; Image of man in America, South. Methodist Univ, 57, McGraw, 68 & Crowell, 70; ed, J. Hist. Stud, Vol I, No. 1, 67; auth, Milton and Cromwell: April, 1653, Eng. Stud. Today, Rome, 66; Historical introd, In: Complete prose works of John Milton, Vol. I, Yale, 53; plus others. Add: 42 Fackler Rd, R.D. 3, Princeton, NJ 08540.

WOLFE, GLENN JOSEPH, b. St. Francisville, Ill, Dec. 21, 33; m. 55; c. 4. MASS COMMUNICATION. B.S, East. Ill. Univ, 55; M.A, Univ. Iowa, 59, Ph.D.(speech & drama), 64. Instr. radio, TV & film, Univ. Md, 59-61; Univ. Iowa, 62-64; asst. prof, Univ. Md, 64-67; ASSOC. PROF. & DIR. RADIO, TV & FILM, UNIV. MO-COLUMBIA, 67- U.S.A, 55-57, Res, 57-59. Speech Commun. Asn; Broadcast Educ. Asn. Film theory; broadcast history. Publ: Vachel Lindsay: the poet as film theorist, Arno, 73; Setting up a TV facility, Bull. Nat. Asn. Sec. Sch. Prin, 66; Norman Baker and KTNT, 68 & Some reactions to the advent of campaigning by radio, 69, J. Broadcasting; plus one other. Add: Dept. of Radio, Television & Film, 200 Swallow Hall, University of Missouri-Columbia, Columbia, MO 65201.

WOLFE, PATRICIA MARY, Linguistics, English Literature. See Volume III, Foreign Languages, Linguistics & Philology.

WOLFE, PETER, b. New York, N.Y, Aug. 25, 33; c. 2. ENGLISH. B.A, City Col. New York, 55; M.A, Lehigh Univ, 57; Ph.D.(Eng), Univ. Wis, 65. Instr. ENG, Univ. Nebr, 64-65, asst. prof, 65-67; UNIV. MO-ST. LOUIS, 67-68, ASSOC. PROF, 68- Vis. prof. Eng, Univ. Windsor, summer 71; mem. bd. editors, Virginia Woolf Quart. Ord.C, U.S.A, 57-59. MLA (pres, mod. lit. sect, 72); Kipling Soc; James Joyce Soc; Arnold Bennett Soc; AAUP. Modern fiction; modern drama. Publ: The disciplined heart: Iris Murdoch and her novels, Univ. Mo, 66; Mary Renault, Twayne, 69; Rebecca West: artist and thinker, 71 & Graham Greene the entertainer, 72, 2nd ed, 73, South. Ill. Univ; Dreamers who live their dreams: the world of Ross MacDonald, Bowling Green Univ, 75; Image and meaning in Thus spake Zarathustra, Mod. Lang. Notes, 12/64; The social theater of Edward Albee,

Prairie Schooner, summer 65; The problems of Granny Wetherall, CLA Jour, 12/67. Add: Dept. of English, University of Missouri-St. Louis, 8001 Natural Bridge Rd, St. Louis, MO 63121.

WOLFE, RALPH HAVEN, b. Weston, Ohio, June 23, 31. ENGLISH. B.S, Bowling Green State Univ, 51, M.A, 56; Ph.D.(Eng), Ind. Univ, 60. Instr. ENG, Bowling Green State Univ, 60-61; asst. prof, Monmouth Col.(Ill), 61-62; assoc. prof, Ind. State Univ, Terre Haute, 62-69; PROF. & ASST. CHMN. DEPT, BOWLING GREEN STATE UNIV, 69- Vis. assoc. prof, Bowling Green State Univ, 67-69. C.Eng, U.S.A, 52-54, Sgt. MLA. English and American literature; drama. Publ: Co-auth, Beneath the dust of Dry September, Stud. Short Fiction, 64; auth, De Quincey and Wordsworth: some affinities, Forum, autumn 65; Two romantic birds: Shelley's Skylark and Keats' Nightingale, Teachers Col. J, spring 67; plus others. Add: Dept. of English, Bowling Green State University, Bowling Green, OH 43402.

WOLFF, CYNTHIA GRIFFIN, b. Sept. 20, 36; c. 2. EUROPEAN & AMERICAN LITERATURE. B.A, Radcliffe Col, 58; Harvard Med. Sch, 58-59; grad. fel, Radcliffe Col, 60, Alice Longfellow fel, 62, Am. Asn. Univ. Women fel, 63; Ph.D.(Eng), Harvard, 65. Instr. ENG, Boston Univ, 63-64; Queens Col.(N.Y), 65-68; asst. prof, Manhattanville Col, 68-71; ASSOC. PROF, UNIV. MASS, AMHERST, 71-, DIR. HONORS PROG, 72- MLA. Edith Wharton; psychology and literature; 18th century English novel. Publ: Samuel Richardson and the eighteenth century puritan character, Archon, 72; Other lives, Goodyear Publ, 73; Literary reflections of the puritan character, J. Hist. of Ideas, 68; A mirror for men: stereotypes of women in literature, Mass, Rev, 72; Thanatos and Eros: Kate Chopin's The awakening, Am. Quart, 73-74. Add: Honors Office, Machmer E-23, University of Massachusetts, Amherst, MA 01002.

WOLFF, JOSEPH J, b. Cleveland, Ohio, July 24, 21; m. 48; c. 1. ENGLISH LITERATURE. A.B, John Carroll Univ, 43; M.A, Univ. Chicago, 49, Ph.D. (Eng. lit), 58. From instr. to PROF. ENG. LIT, LOYOLA UNIV. CHICAGO, 48-, DIR. GRAD. PROG, 72- U.S.N.R, 43-46, Lt. MLA. Late Victorian literature; modern British and American literature. Add: Dept. of English, Loyola University of Chicago, Chicago, IL 60611.

WOLFF, MICHAEL, English History, Victorian Literature. See Volume I, History.

WOLFSON, LESTER MARVIN, b. Evansville, Ind, Sept. 13, 23; m. 49; c. 3. ENGLISH. A.B, Univ. Mich, 45, A.M, 46, univ. fel, 47-48, Rackham fel, 48-50, Ph.D.(Eng), 54. Teaching fel. Eng, Univ. Mich, 45-47; instr, Wayne State Univ, 50-53; asst. prof. Eng. & speech, Univ. Houston, 53-55; ENG, Ind. Univ, Gary, 55-61, assoc. prof, 61-64; IND. UNIV, SOUTH BEND, 64-67, PROF, 67-, CHANCELLOR, 69-, dir. & asst. dean, 64-66, dean, 66-69; acting chancellor, 68-69. Vis. asst. prof, Univ. Calif, Santa Barbara, 58-59. MLA; Col. Eng. Asn; NCTE. Literary criticism; romantic and Victorian periods. Add: Office of the Chancellor, Indiana University at South Bend, South Bend, IN 46615.

WOLK, ANTHONY, b. Pittsburgh, Pa, June 23, 35; m. 63; c. 2. ENGLISH. B.S.J, Northwest. Univ, 57, M.A, 59; Johnson fel, Univ. Nebr, 64-65, Ph.D. (Eng), 65. Instr. ENG, Univ. Nebr, 60-64; asst. prof, PORTLAND STATE UNIV, 65-70, ASSOC. PROF, 70- U.S.A, 57-58. Conf. Col. Compos. & Commun; NCTE; Shakespeare Asn. Am; Renaissance Soc. Am. Renaissance literature; descriptive rhetoric; science fiction. Publ: The relative importance of the final free modifier, Res. Teaching Eng, spring 70; Linguistic and social bias in the American heritage dictionary, Col. Eng, 5/72; The extra Jaques in As you like it, Shakespeare Quart, winter 72. Add: Dept. of English, Box 751, Portland State University, Portland, OR 97207.

WOLKENFELD, JACK, b. Berlin, Ger, May 26, 29; U.S. citizen; m. 52; c. 2. ENGLISH. B.A, Brooklyn Col, 52; M.A, Columbia Univ, 58, Ph.D.(Eng. & comp. lit), 66. Instr. ENG, Wayne State Univ, 58-62; Univ. Akron, 62-63; assoc. prof, KINGSBOROUGH COMMUNITY COL, 64-73, PROF, 73- State Univ. N.Y. res. fel, 68; res. dir, EPDA Inst. for Community Col. Fac, summers 71, 72. U.S.A, 52-54, 1st Lt. MLA; NCTE. Contemporary British literature; 18th century novel. Publ: Joyce Cary: the developing style, N.Y. Univ, 68; Isaac Bashevis Singer: the faith of his devils and fools, Criticism, 63; Three poems, Whereas, 69. Add: Dept. of English, Kingsborough Community College, Brooklyn, NY 11235.

WOLLESEN, CHARLES ALBERT, S.J, b. Pierre, S.Dak, Jan. 23, 22. ENGLISH LITERATURE. M.A, Gonzaga Univ, 46; S.T.L, Alma Col, 53; M.A, Fordham Univ, 56; Columbia Univ. Instr. ENG, Seattle Prep. Sch, 46-49; Jesuit High Sch, Portland, Ore, 58-60; asst. prof, SEATTLE UNIV, 60-72, ASSOC. PROF, 72- Dir. summer sch, 60-67, acting head dept, 62-63. English Renaissance literature. Publ: Co-auth, Better a day, 52; I lift my lamp, 53. Add: Dept. of English, Seattle University, Seattle, WA 98122.

WOLLOCK, ABE V, b. New York, N.Y, Sept. 7, 19; m. 61. THEATRE ARTS. B.A, Brooklyn Col, 47; M.A, Cornell Univ, 48; Ph.D, Univ. Ill, 62. Tech. dir. & designer, Cornell Univ, 47-48; instr. & asst. prof, Mont. State Univ, 48-56; prof. work motion pictures, N.Y, 56-60; PROF. THEATRE ARTS, UNIV. CALIF, LOS ANGELES, 60-, head div. TV-radio, dept. theatre arts, 66-68. Eng.C, 42-45, Sgt. Am. Theatre Asn; Nat. Acad. TV Arts & Sci. Early American theatre architecture and drama; theatre and television production; theatre history. Add: 3657 Cody Rd, Sherman Oaks, CA 91403.

WOLPER, ROY S, b. Pittsburgh, Pa, July 7, 31; m. 57; c. 2. ENGLISH. B.A, Univ. Pittsburgh, 52, M.A, 59, Ph.D.(Eng), 65. Instr. ENG. LIT, Carnegie Inst. Technol, 61-64; Univ. Pittsburgh, 64-65; asst. prof, Univ. Sask, 65-67; TEMPLE UNIV, 67-73, ASSOC. PROF, 73- Co-ed, The Scriblerian. Option Award, Doubleday & Co. Qm.C, U.S.A, 52-54, 1st Lt. MLA; Northeast. Mod. Lang. Asn. English and American drama; 18th century English literature. Publ: Johnson's neglected muse: the drama, Stud. in Eighteenth Century, 68; Candide, gull in the garden?, Eighteenth-Century Stud, 69; The rhetoric of gunpowder and the idea of progress, J. Hist. Ideas, 70; plus others. Add: Dept. of English, Temple University, Philadelphia, PA 19122.

WOLSCH, ROBERT ALLEN, b. New York, N.Y, Nov. 27, 25; m. 57; c. 3. SPEECH, EDUCATION. B.A, Wash. Sq. Col, 49; M.A, Columbia Univ, 54, dipl. speech path, 56, Ed.D, 69. Speech therapist, Mineola Pub. Schs, 55-62, lang. arts coord, 62-67; curriculum dir, Training Resources for Youth Inc, 67; asst. prof. speech, C.W. Post Col, 67-69; assoc. prof, WEST. CONN. STATE COL, 69-72, PROF. SPEECH & EDUC, 72- Sr. therapist, Speech & Hearing Ctr, Queens Col, 58-60, lectr. Col, 67-69; lectr, Adelphi Univ, 60-61 & C.W. Post Col, 62-67; curriculum consult, Y.M.C.A. Proj, 66-67; adj. asst. prof, L.I. Univ, 67; lang. arts consult, Yorktown Pub. Schs, 71-72; dir, Speech Commun. Assocs, 72-; workshop leader, Inserv. Educ, Inc, 73-; mem, Creative Educ. Found. Med.C, U.S.N, 44-46. Am. Speech & Hearing Asn; Speech Commun. Asn; NCTE; Asn. Childhood Educ. Int; NEA; Asn. Supv. & Curriculum Develop. Speech education and the interrelationships of the language arts; composition education; language development in children. Publ: Radio & Television projects in the classroom, Mineola Pub. Schs, 57; Handbook for life skills educators, Training Resources for Youth, 67; Poetic composition in the Elementary school, 69 & Poetic composition through the grades, 70, Columbia Univ; Emasculation of the public schools, Unitarian Church of Cent. Nassau, summer 63; co-auth, Low status blues, Express, 1/68. Add: Dept. of Speech & Theatre, Western Connecticut State College, Danbury, CT 06810.

WOLSELEY, ROLAND EDGAR, b. New York, N.Y, Mar. 9, 04; m. 28. JOURNALISM. B.S, Northwest. Univ, 28, M.S, 34; D.Litt, Albright Col, 55. Reporter, Herald-Telegram, News-Times & Tribune, Reading, Pa, 22-24; from reporter to managing ed, News-Index, Evanston, Ill, 27, 35-37; from ed. asst. to managing ed, Pa. R.R. News, Chicago, 28-32; lectr. jour, Mundelein Col, 32-33; from lectr. to asst. prof, Northwest. Univ, 35-46; assoc. prof, SYRACUSE UNIV, 46-47, prof. jour. & chmn. mag. dept, sch. jour, 47-72, EMER. PROF. JOUR, SCH. PUB. COMMUN, 72- Lectr, Roosevelt Col, 46; Fulbright lectr, Univ. Nagpur, 52-53; Willson lectr, Univ. Ctr, Nashville, Tenn, 64; mem. educ. comt, Mag. Publ. Asn; writer-in-residence, Aurora Col, 67. Asn. Educ. in Jour.(pres, 47-48). Magazines; journalism of the Afro-Americans; biography. Publ: Exploring journalism, 43, 49 & 57 & How to report and write the news, 61, Prentice-Hall; Journalist's bookshelf, 7th ed & Critical writing for the journalist, 59, Chilton; Journalism in modern India, 2nd ed, Taplinger, 64; Careers in religious journalism, Herald, rev. ed, 66; Understanding magazines, 66 & 69 & The black press, U.S.A, 71, Iowa State Univ; The Low Countries, Nelson, 69; co-auth, Gandhi: warrior of non-violence, Nat. Bk. Trust, India, 69; auth, The changing magazine, Hastings House, 73; contrib, The Asian newspapers' reluctant revolution, Iowa State Univ, 71; plus others. Add: 1307 Westmoreland Ave, Syracuse, NY 13210.

WOLVIN, ANDREW DAVIS, b. Columbus, Nebr, Sept. 9, 41; m. 64. SPEECH COMMUNICATION. B.S, Univ. Nebr, Lincoln, 62, M.A, 63; Ph.D.(speech commun), Purdue Univ, Lafayette, 68. Teacher speech & Eng, Omaha Pub. Schs, Nebr, 63-64; instr. speech, Doane Col, 64-65; asst. prof. speech educ, UNIV. MD, COLLEGE PARK, 68-71, ASSOC. PROF. & DIR. SPEECH COMMUN, 71- Commun. consult, NASA, 68-71 & Montgomery County Pub. Schs, Md, 72-; dir. commun. div, Transemantics, Inc, D.C, 72- Speech Commun. Asn. (v.chmn. instruct. develop. div, 73); East. Commun. Asn.(2nd v.pres, 73); Int. Commun. Asn; Rhetoric Soc. Am. Speech communication education; political communication; listening behavior. Publ: Co-auth, Small group induction, 11/71 & co-auth, Avoiding lockstep education, 11/72, Speech Teacher; co-auth, The speech communication curriculum in the community college, Today's Speech, fall 72. Add: Dept. of Speech & Dramatic Art, Speech Communication Division, University of Maryland, College Park, MD 20740.

WOMACK, MORRIS M, b. Daylight, Tenn, Dec. 12, 27; m. 48; c. 3. SPEECH, RELIGION. B.A, Butler Univ, 54, B.D, 58; Univ. Mich, 58-60; Ph.D. (speech), Wayne State Univ, 67. Minister, Church of Christ, Mich, 49-52, 58-60, 61-66, Ind, 52-58; instr. relig. & speech, Mich. Christian Jr. Col, 59-66; dir. institutional prog, Pepperdine Col, 67, registr. & assoc. prof. speech, 67-73, PROF. COMMUN, PEPPERDINE UNIV, MALIBU, 73- Pres, Prof. Develop. Progs, 73- Speech Commun. Asn; West. Speech Commun. Asn. Rhetoric; business and management leadership; church history. Publ: Miracles: fact or fantasy, Firm Found, 57; The church through the ages, Sweet, Vols. I & II, 62 & 63; co-auth, Pillars of faith, Baker Bk, 73. Add: Dept. of Speech, Pepperdine University, 24255 Pacific Coast Hwy, Malibu, CA 90265.

WONNBERGER, CARL GEORGE, b. Reading, Pa, Aug. 20, 01; m. 29; c. 2. ENGLISH LITERATURE & LANGUAGE. A.B, Univ. Pa, 22; Boston Univ, 27; M.A, Harvard, 29. Teacher Eng. & music, Moran Sch, Seattle, Wash, 22-23; Lake Placid Sch, Fla, 23-24; ENG, Storm King Sch, N.Y, 24-27; Montclair Acad, 27-28; head dept, Cranbrook Sch, 29-67; ASSOC. PROF, EAST. MICH. UNIV, 67- MLA; Col. Eng. Asn; NCTE. Shakespeare; English composition; drama in the schools. Publ: They can all learn to write & Writing a way of life, Eng. J. Add: Dept. of English, Eastern Michigan University, Ypsilanti, MI 48197.

WOOD, CHAUNCEY (DERBY), b. Englewood, N.J, June 16, 35; m. 61; c. 2. ENGLISH. A.B, Union Col, 57; M.A, Princeton, 60, Ph.D.(Eng), 63. Instr. ENG, Hollins Col, 60-63, asst. prof, 63-64; Univ. Cincinnati, 64-65; Univ. Wis, 65-68; assoc. prof, McMASTER UNIV, 68-72, PROF, 72- Nat. Endowment for Humanities summer res. grant, 67; Am. Counc. Learned Soc. stud. fel, 67-68. Mediaeval Acad. Am; MLA; Dante Soc. Am. Chaucer; Mediaeval literature. Publ: Chaucer and the country of the stars, Princeton, 70; Chaucer's astrology, In: A companion to Chaucer, Oxford, 68; The sources of Chaucer's Summoner's Garleek, oynons, and eek lekes, Chaucer Rev, 71; Chaucer and Sir Thopas: irony and concupiscence, Tex. Stud. in Lit. & Lang, 72; plus others. Add: Dept. of English, McMaster University, Hamilton, Ont. L8S 4L9, Can.

WOOD, DAVID CHARLES, b. Whitehall, Wis, Mar. 18, 36; m. 70. BRITISH LITERATURE, THEORY OF CRITICISM. B.S, Wis. State Col-Eau Claire, 58; M.A, Bowling Green State Univ, 59, Danforth fel, 62-63, Ph.D.(Eng), 69. Instr. ENG, Augustana Col.(Ill), 59-60; Ill. State Univ, 61-64; asst. prof, Wis. State Univ, 66-67; Ball State Univ, 67-68; ASSOC. PROF, AUGSBURG COL, 69- Columnist, Whitehall Times, Wis, 73- AAUP; MLA. Eighteenth century British literature; history of journalism. Add: Dept. of English, Div. of Humanities, Augsburg College, Minneapolis, MN 55404.

WOOD, GERALD CARL, b. Valparaiso, Ind, Mar. 22, 44; m. 67; c. 1. BRITISH LITERATURE. A.B, Wabash Col, 66; Ph.D.(Eng), Univ. Fla, 71. ASST. PROF. ENG, CARSON-NEWMAN COL, 71- MLA; S.Atlantic Mod. Lang. Asn. Writings of Lord Byron; satire; film studies. Publ: The wonder of art and the unity of Browning's My last duchess, Carson-Newman Fac. Stud, spring 72; Nature and narrative in Byron's Prisoner of Chillon, Keats-Shelley J, 73. Add: Dept. of English, Carson-Newman College, Jefferson City, TN 37760.

WOOD, GLENA DECKER, b. Taylor, Ariz, Apr. 12, 16; m. 37; c. 2. ENGLISH. B.A, Brigham Young Univ, 36; Univ. Ill, 39-40; M.A, Univ. Ky, 49, Ph.D.(Eng), 58. Head dept. Eng, Jr. High Sch, 36-37 & 41-42; asst. Eng, Univ. Ill, 39-40; instr, High Sch, 43-44; ENG, Ore. State Col, 45-46; part-time, Univ. Ky, 48-52; instr, BRIGHAM YOUNG UNIV, 52-58, asst. prof, 58-64, assoc. prof, 64-70, PROF, 70- Fulbright lectr, Pahlavi Univ, Iran, 59-60; vis. prof, Church Col. Hawaii, 66-67; vis. scholar, Univ. Ariz, 73-74. Am. Renaissance Soc; Rocky Mountain. Mod. Lang. Asn. Renaissance drama; middle and late 19th century American western. Publ: The jawbone of an ass, Vantage, 70; The tragi-comic dimensions of Lear's fool, Costerus, 72. Add: Dept. of English, Brigham Young University, Provo, UT 84602.

WOOD, GORDON REID, English Philology. See Volume III, Foreign Languages, Linguistics & Philology.

WOOD, GRETCHEN ANNE, b. Upland, Pa, Apr. 11, 44. ENGLISH. B.A, Oberlin Col, 66; M.A, Univ. Chicago, 67, Ph.D.(Eng), 70. ASST. PROF. ENG, UNIV. PA, 70-, fel, summer 71. MLA. Black humor; theory of the novel; 20th century British and American literature. Add: Dept. of English, 119 Bennett Hall, University of Pennsylvania, 34th & Walnut, Philadelphia, PA 19107.

WOOD, JAMES OSCAR, b. Glen Allen, Ala, Aug. 1, 99; m. 21; c. 1. ENGLISH LITERATURE. A.B, Univ. Okla, 22; A.M, Univ. Calif, 25; Stanford Univ, 26; Ph.D, Yale, 35. From instr. to asst. prof, E.Cent. Okla. State Col, 22-24; from assoc. prof. to prof. ENG. LIT, SAN JOSE STATE UNIV, 25-65, EMER. PROF, 65- Huntington Libr. res. grant, 54; Folger Shakespeare Libr. res. grant, 62; co-initiator, West. Shakespeare Sem, 64. Shakespeare Asn. Am; Renaissance Soc. Am; Int. Asn. Univ. Prof. Eng. Shakespeare; 17th century English literature. Publ: Thomas Fuller's thoughts and contemplations, Soc. Promoting Christian Knowledge, 64; Lady Macbeth's secret weapon, Notes & Queries, 3/65; The running image in Pericles, Shakespeare Stud. V, 69; Lost lore in Macbeth, Shakespeare Quart, spring 73; plus others. Add: 1056 Carolyn Ave, San Jose, CA 95125.

WOOD, MARGARET LOUISE, b. Denison, Iowa, Nov. 7, 09. SPEECH. B.A, Grinnell Col, 31; M.A, Univ. Iowa, 38, Ph.D.(speech), 50. Teacher speech & Eng, high sch, Iowa, 31-36; Minn, 36-42; Wis, 42-43; instr. skills, Stephens Col, 43-45; speech, Wellesley Col, 45-46; skills, Mich. State Univ, 46-47; asst. SPEECH, State Univ. Iowa, 47-49; asst. prof, NORTH. ILL. UNIV, 49-50, assoc. prof, 50-52, PROF, 52- Assoc. ed, J. Commun, 53-57. Speech Commun. Asn; Cent. State Speech Asn.(v.pres, 56); Int. Commun. Asn. Conf. Brit. Stud. British and American public address. Publ: Lord Macaulay, parliamentary speaker: his leading ideas, Quart J. Speech, 12/58; William Jennings Bryan, crusader for the common man, In: American public address: studies in honor of Albert Craig Baird, Univ. Mo, 61. Add: 351 Rolfe Rd, De Kalb, IL 60115.

WOOD, ROY V, b. Salida, Colo, Sept. 18, 39; m. 60; c. 1. SPEECH, COMMUNICATION. B.A, Univ. Denver, 61, M.A, 61, Ph.D.(speech), 65. Asst. prof. speech, Univ. Denver, 65-67; NORTHWEST. UNIV, EVANSTON, 67-68, asst. dean & coord. grad. stud. speech, 68-71, PROF. SPEECH & DEAN SCH. SPEECH, 71- Consult, U.S. Peace Corps, 64, 65, 67; Am. Med. Asn, 68; Evanston Pub. Schs, 68- Speech Commun. Asn. Small group research; communication theory. Publ: Strategic debate, Nat. Textbk, 68; co-auth, The effects of three styles of training on small group effectiveness, Speech Teacher, 9/68. Add: Dept. of Speech, Northwestern University, Evanston, IL 60201.

WOOD, WILLIAM R, b. Jacksonville, Ill, Feb. 3, 07; m. 44; c. 3. ENGLISH. A.B, Ill. Col, 27, LL.D, 60; M.A, Univ. Iowa, 36; Ph.D, Univ. Iowa, 39. Dir. & dep. supt, Evanston Community Col, 46; asst. supt, Evanston Township Schs, 47-50; spec, jr. cols. & lower div, U.S. Off. Educ, 50-53, prog. planning officer, 53-54; v.pres, Univ. Nev, 54-60; PRES. & PROF. ENG, UNIV. ALASKA, FAIRBANKS, 60-, head dept. Eng, 66-67. Mem. study training prog. in Europe, U.S. Dept. of Defense, 51; joint Libyan-Am. Reconstruction Comn, 55; Nev. Gov. Comt, President's Comt. Educ. Beyond High Sch, 57; Alaska mem, exec. comt, West. Interstate Comn. Higher Educ, 60; chmn, Alaska Comt. State Fulbright scholars, 60; mem. Army Civilian Adv. Comt, 60; hon. v.pres, Midnight Sun Area Boy Scout Counc, 60; exec. comt, Asn. Higher Educ, 61; mem. Rampart Dam Adv. Comt, 61; Northwest Asn. Sec. & Higher Schs; Gen. Medical Sci. Nat. Adv. Counc, 63; Regional Export Expansion Counc, 66-; Regional Health Adv. Comt, 68; Stud. Financing Private Insts. Asia, 68; Gov. Task Force Satellite Commun, 68. U.S.N, 43-46, Res, 46-69, Capt. Nat. Univ. Exten. Asn; AAAS; Arctic Inst. N.Am; Solar Energy Soc; Nat. Asn. State Univs. & Land Grant Cols. Keats; national systems of higher education in underdeveloped countries; people of the Far North. Publ: Short stories as you like them, 40; Fact and opinion, 45; Short, short stories, 51; plus others. Add: 305 El Dorado Estates, 665 Tenth Ave, Fairbanks, AK 99701.

WOODALL, GUY R, b. Hartselle, Ala, June 4, 26; m. 54; c. 1. ENGLISH. B.A, David Lipscomb Col, 51; M.A, George Peabody Col, 53; Ph.D.(Eng), Univ. Tenn, 66. Teacher ENG, Marion Inst, 51-60; assoc. prof, Lincoln Mem, Univ, 61-66; W.Ga.Col, 66-67; PROF. TENN. TECHNOL. UNIV, 67- U.S.N, 44-46. MLA; NCTE; S.Atlantic Mod. Lang. Asn; Col. Eng. Asn. American literary criticism and literary history. Publ: Robert Walsh and the Portfolio circle, Pa. Mag. Hist. & Biog, 4/68; Robert Walsh's role in the struggle against Byron and Byronism, Tenn. Technol. Univ. J, spring 68. Add: Dept. of English, Tennessee Technological University, Cookeville, TN 38501.

WOODALL, JAMES RAYMOND, b. Kuttawa, Ky, Dec. 20, 19; m. 48; c. 3. ENGLISH. B.S, Murray State Col, 41; fel. & M.A, Univ. Ky, 46; fel, Vanderbilt Univ, 49-51, Ph.D.(Eng), 51. Teacher, High Sch, Ky, 41-42; instr. ENG, Univ. Ky, 46-49, 51-52; asst. prof, AUBURN UNIV, 52-56, assoc. prof, 56-65, PROF, 65- Consult, Int. Paper Co. Prog. Schs, 61-63; consult, South. Union Jr. Col, Ala, 67- U.S.A, 42-45. MLA; NCTE; Col. Conf. Compos. & Commun. Television adaptation; John Ruskin. Publ: Co-auth, The writer and his reader, Educ. TV, rev. ed, 62. Add: Dept. of English, Auburn University, Auburn, AL 36830.

WOODARD, CHARLES ROBERT, b. Winchester, Tenn, Dec. 18, 22; m. 46; c. 1. ENGLISH. A.B, Univ. Tenn, 49, M.A, 50, Ph.D.(Eng), 53. Instr. ENG, Univ. Ky, 53-55; asst. prof, Univ. Chattanooga, 55-61, assoc. prof, 61-66; UNIV. ALA, HUNTSVILLE, 66-70, PROF, 70-, chmn. dept, 70-73. South. fel, Duke Univ. Libr, summer 57. U.S.A.A.F, 43-45. MLA; S.Atlantic Mod. Lang. Asn. Victorian poetry; modern poetry. Publ: The road to the dark tower, In: Studies in honor of John C. Hodges and Alwin Thaler, Univ. Tenn, 61; The archetype of the fall, Col. Eng, 5/67; poetry in Ga. Rev, South. Poetry Rev. Poem, Nimrod, Laurel Rev, Windsor Rev, Mainline and others. Add: 101 Roberta Rd, Huntsville, AL 35802.

WOODBURY, LAEL JAY, b. Fairview, Idaho, July 3, 27. SPEECH, DRAMATIC ARTS. B.S, Utah State Univ, 52; M.A, Brigham Young Univ, 53; fel, Univ. Ill, 53, Ph.D, 54. Asst. speech, Univ. Ill, 53; assoc. prof, Brigham Young Univ, 54-61; asst. prof. theatre arts, Bowling Green State Univ, 61-62; assoc. prof. speech & drama, Univ. Iowa, 62-65; PROF, BRIGHAM YOUNG UNIV, 65-72, DRAMATIC ARTS, 72-, DEAN, COL. FINE ARTS & COMMUN, 73-, chmn. dept. speech & drama, 65-70, assoc. dean, 70-73. U.S.N, 42-46; U.S.A.R, 51-53, 2nd Lt. Speech Commun. Asn; Am. Theatre Asn.(chmn, nat. comt. royalities, 72-); Rocky Mountain Theatre Conf.(pres, 59-60). History of speech and theatre, especially in 19th century America; non-verbal communication; multi-media dramatic production. Publ: Co-auth, Play production handbook, Mutual Improv. Asn, 59; co-ed, Mormon arts, Vol. I, Brigham Young Univ, 72; auth, Hold up from below, Instructor, 9/70; Mormonism and the commercial theatre, BYU Stud, winter 72; About values and facts, Improv. Era, 10/70; plus four others. Add: College of Fine Arts & Communications, Brigham Young University, Provo, UT 84601.

WOODEN, WARREN WALTER, b. Raleigh, N.C, Sept. 18, 41; m. 66; c. 3. RENAISSANCE LITERATURE, LITERARY CRITICISM. A.B, Univ. N.C, Chapel Hill, 63; M.A, Univ. Miss, 66; Ph.D.(Eng), Vanderbilt Univ, 71. Asst. prof. ENG, MARSHALL UNIV, 68-72, ASSOC. PROF, 72-, res. grant, summer 73. Claude Worthington Benedum Found. res. grants, summers 70, 72; Nat. Endowment for Humanities res. fel, summer 73. Renaissance Soc. Am; Southeast. Renaissance Conf; S.Atlantic Mod. Lang. Asn; AAUP. Elizabethan literature; 16th century humanism; 17th century poetry. Publ: More's Utopia: a problem of genre, fall 71 & Thomas More's Utopia and the pastoral tradition: the ramifications of a Renaissance mode, fall 73, Bull. W.Va. Asn. Col. Eng. Teachers; Thomas More and Lucian: a study of satiric influence and technique, Miss. Stud. Eng, 72. Add: Dept. of English, Marshall University, Huntington, WV 25701.

WOODFIELD, FLOYD J, b. North Ogden, Utah, June 4, 21; m. 51; c. 4. ENGLISH. B.A, Brigham Young Univ, 48, fel, 48-50, M.A, 50; Univ. Calif, Berkeley, 50-51; Ph.D.(Eng), Univ. Utah, 67. Teacher, High Sch, Calif, 51-55; from asst. prof. to assoc. prof. ENG, WEBER STATE COL, 55-65, PROF, 65-, ASST. DEAN. GEN. EDUC. & ACAD. ADVISEMENT, SCH. ARTS, LETT. & SCI, 67-, chmn. dept. Eng, 65-67. Thomas Hardy; Stephen Crane. Publ: We can improve English instruction, Utah Educ. Rev, 9/57. Add: Dept. of English, Weber State College, 3750 Harrison Blvd, Ogden, UT 84403.

WOODFIELD, JAMES, b. London, Eng, Sept. 10, 28; Can. citizen; m. 63; c. 3. ENGLISH LITERATURE. B.A, Univ. B.C, 65, Ph.D.(Eng), 71. Asst. prof. ENG, UNIV. N.B, 68-74, ASSOC. PROF, 74- Royal Artillery, 46-53, Capt. Humanities Asn. Can; Asn. Can. Univ. Teachers Eng; Can. Asn. Univ. Teachers. Modern drama. Add: Dept. of English, University of New Brunswick, Fredericton, N.B, Can.

WOODFORD, BRUCE POWERS, b. Astoria, Ore, Sept. 22, 19; m. 55. ENGLISH. B.A, Univ. Denver, 48, M.A, 49, fel, 49-51, Ph.D, 58. Asst. basic communs, Univ. Denver, 48-49, ed. asst, Univ. Denver Press, 51, 52, circulation librn, 53-55; instr. ENG, Univ. Idaho, 55-58; asst. prof, PURDUE UNIV, WEST LAFAYETTE, 58-65, ASSOC. PROF, 65- Instr, exten, Univ. Colo, 49-50, 53; poetry ed, Quartet. U.S.A, 41-43, Lt. MLA. Creative writing; philosophy, especially existentialism and Soren Kierkegaard; art history. Publ: Twenty one poems and a play, Swallow, 58; Love and other weathers (poems), Eastgate, 66; A suit of four (anthology of four poets), Purdue Univ, 73. Add: Dept. of English, Purdue University, West Lafayette, IN 47907.

WOODLAND, RONALD STANLEY, b. Braintree, Mass, Nov. 16, 40; m. 66; c. 1. DRAMATIC LITERATURE, STAGE DIRECTING. A.B, Harvard, 62; M.F.A, Tulane Univ, 64, Ph.D.(theatre), 72. Instr. drama, Syracuse Univ, 64-68; ASSOC. PROF. ENG, EDINBORO STATE COL, 68- AAUP; Am. Theatre Asn; Speech Commun. Asn; MLA. Modern European, Scottish and modern British drama. Publ: The danger of empathy in Mother Courage, Mod. Drama, 72. Add: Dept. of English, Edinboro State College, Edinboro, PA 16412.

WOODMAN, LEONORA, b. Chicago, Ill, Oct. 13, 25; m. 54; c. 2. AMERICAN LITERATURE, ENGLISH EDUCATION. B.E, Chicago Teachers Col, 46; M.A, Northwest. Univ, 59; Ph.D.(Eng), Univ. Mo, 70. Teacher Eng, Chicago Bd. Educ, 46-63; lab. sch. supvr. Eng, Univ. Mo, 63-67, instr, 67-69; ASST. PROF. Purdue Univ, Calumet Campus, 71-73; ENG, TEACHERS COL, COLUMBIA UNIV, 73- MLA; NCTE; Women's Caucus Mod. Lang.(secy-treas, 70-). Modern American poetry; stylistics. Publ: Teaching English thematically, 5/66 & A linguistic approach to prose style, 4/73, Eng. J; A giant on the horizon: Wallace Stevens and the Idea of man, Tex. Stud. Lit. & Lang, 74. Add: Dept. of Languages, Literature, Speech & Theatre, Teachers College, Columbia University, 525 W. 120th St, New York, NY 10027.

WOODRESS, JAMES, b. Webster Groves, Mo, July 7, 16; m. 40. AMERICAN LITERATURE. A.B, Amherst Col, 38; A.M, N.Y. Univ, 43; Ph.D, Duke Univ, 50. Asst. news ed, Sta. KWK, St. Louis, Mo, 38-40; radio writer, United Press Asn, N.Y.C, 40-43; asst, Duke Univ, 47-49, vis. lectr. & res. assoc, 54-55; instr. Eng, Grinnell Col, 49-50; asst. prof, Butler Univ, 50-53, assoc. prof, 53-58; San Fernando Valley State Col, 58-61, prof, 61-66, dean sch. lett. & sci, 63-65, chmn. dept, 58-63; PROF. ENG, UNIV. CALIF, DAVIS, 66-, chmn. dept, 70-74. Fund Advan. Educ. fel, 52-53; Guggenheim fel, 56-57; secy, Am. lit. group, MLA, 61-65; Fulbright lectr, France, 62-63, Italy, 65-66. U.S.A, 43-46, 2nd Lt. MLA; AAUP; Am. Stud. Asn. American civilization. Publ: Howells & Italy, 52, ed, American Literary Scholarship, 65-69, auth, Dissertations in American literature, 68 & ed, Essays mostly on periodical publishing in America, 73, Duke Univ; auth, Booth Tarkington: gentleman from Indiana, 55 & A yankee's odyssey: life of Joel Barlow, 58, Lippincott; ed, Voices from America's past, McGraw, 62; auth, Willa Cather: her life and art, Bobbs-Merrill, 70; ed, Eight American authors, Norton, 71. Add: Dept. of English, University of California, Davis, CA 95616.

WOODRING, CARL, b. Terrell, Tex, Aug. 29, 19; m. 42. ENGLISH LITERATURE. A.B, Rice Inst, 40, A.M, 42; A.M, Harvard, 47, Dexter traveling scholar, Gt. Brit, 48, Ph.D, 49. Asst, Rice Inst. & Harvard; instr. Eng. lit, Univ. Wis, 48-51, asst. prof, 51-54, assoc. prof, ENG, 54-58; PROF, 58-61; COLUMBIA UNIV, 61- Fels, Fund Advan. Educ. & Guggenheim Found, 55; Am. Counc. Learned Soc, 65. Mem. ed. bd, Stud. Eng. Lit, 61-; adv. bds, Wordsworth Circle, 70- & Essays in Lit, 73- Christian Gauss Prize, Nat. Phi Beta Kappa, 71. U.S.N.R, 42-45, Lt. MLA; Int. Asn. Univ. Prof. Eng; Grolier Club; Asn. Depts. Eng.(pres, 71); Keats-Shelley Asn. Am; Acad. Lit. Stud. Nineteenth century English literature. Publ: Victorian samplers: William and Mary Howitt, Univ. Kans, 52; Politics in the poetry of Coleridge, Univ. Wis, 61; Prose of the Romantic period, Houghton, 61; Wordsworth, Houghton, 65 & Harvard, 68; Virginia Woolf, Columbia Univ, 66; Politics in English romantic poetry, Harvard, 70. Add: Dept. of English & Comparative Literature, 615 Philosophy Hall, Columbia University, New York, NY 10027.

WOODRUFF, JOHN ROWLAND, b. Akron, Ohio, June 14, 09; m. 59; c. 4. DRAMA. A.B, Oberlin Col, 33; M.A, West. Reserve Univ, 37; Ph.D, Cornell Univ, 49. Assoc. prof. DRAMA, Tufts Univ, 40-57; PROF, CARLETON COL, 57- Mem. bd. dirs, Tyrone Guthrie Theater, Minneapolis, Minn, 70- Nat. Theatre Conf; U.S. Inst. Theatre Technol; Am. Theatre Asn. Arena theatre technique and design; educational theatre in the liberal arts; history of Boston, Massachusetts theater. Add: Carleton Arena Theater, Carleton College, Northfield, MN 55057.

WOODRUFF, NEAL, JR, b. Kans. City, Mo, Apr. 16, 25; m. 52; c. 2. ENGLISH. A.B, Univ. Kans, 46; M.A, Yale, 47, Ph.D.(Eng), 55. Instr. Eng, Univ. Kans, 47-48; instr. ENG, Carnegie-Mellon Univ, 52-54, asst. prof, 54-60, assoc. prof, 60-68, PROF. & CHMN. DEPT. COE COL, 68- MLA; NCTE; Asn. Depts. Eng.(pres, 73). Twentieth century literature, especially fiction; the English novel; the Augustan Age. Publ: The technique of All the king's men, 57 & The bear and Faulkner's moral vision, 61, Carnegie Ser. Eng; co-auth, Literature in the composition course, In: Teaching Freshman Composition, Oxford, 67. Add: Dept. of English, Coe College, Cedar Rapids, IA 52402.

WOODS, ALAN LAMBERT, b. Philadelphia, Pa, Nov. 23, 42; m. 67; c. 1. THEATRE HISTORY. A.B, Columbia Univ, 64; M.A, Univ. South. Calif, 69, Ph.D.(theatre), 72. Lectr. drama, Univ. South. Calif, 68-71; instr. THEATRE, Long Beach City Col, 71-72; ASST. PROF, OHIO STATE UNIV, 72- Lectr. theatre, Calif. State Univ, Los Angeles, 70; ed, Theatre Stud, 72-; coord. res. panel, Comt. Instnl. Coop, 73-; lectr, Am. Asn. Health, Phys. Educ. & Recreation, 74. U.S.A, 65-67; Bronze Star Medal. Speech Commun. Asn.(mem. ed. bd, 69-); Am. Theatre Asn; Am. Soc. Theatre Res. Ancient theatre; 19th century popular theatre; theatre historiography. Publ: Co-auth, A note on the symmetry of Delphi, Theatre Surv, 5/72; auth, Popular theatre in Los Angeles, Players, 5/73; A quanitification approach to popular American theatre, Res. in Educ, 1/74. Add: Theatre Research Institute, Ohio State University, 1858 Neil Ave, Columbus, OH 43210.

WOODS, SAMUEL HUBERT, JR. b. Ardmore, Okla, Mar. 10, 26; m. 62. ENGLISH & AMERICAN LITERATURE. A.B, Harvard, 47, M.A, 49; Ph.D, Yale, 56. Instr. ENG, Univ. Colo, 49-51; Duke Univ, 54-55; Rutgers Univ, 55-56; OKLA. STATE UNIV, 56-57, asst. prof, 57-61, assoc. prof, 61-65, PROF, 65- Consult. ed, Cimarron Rev, 69- MLA; NCTE; AAUP. Eighteenth century literature, especially Oliver Goldsmith; literary theory; John Crowe Ransom. Publ: Co-auth, Introduction to literature, 68 & Read- and writing about literature, 71, Random; Philomela: John Crowe Ransom's Ars poetica, Col. Eng, 2/66 & John Crowe Ransom's poetic revisions, PMLA, 3/68. Add: Dept. of English, Oklahoma State University, Stillwater, OK 74074.

WOODSON, THOMAS (MILLER), b. Hartford, Conn, Apr. 24, 31; m; c. 2. ENGLISH, AMERICAN LITERATURE. B.A, Yale, 53, M.A, 56, Ph.D.(Eng), 63. Instr. ENG, Williams Col, 59-62; asst. instr, Yale, 62-63; asst. prof, OHIO STATE UNIV, 63-69, assoc. prof, 69-74, PROF, 74- Fulbright lectr, Univ. Pau, France, 68-69; vis. assoc. prof. Eng. & Am. stud, Yale, 69-70. Intel.C, U.S.A, 53-55. MLA. American fiction and Renaissance; style and stylistics. Publ: Ed, 20th century interpretations of The fall of the House of Usher, Prentice-Hall, 69 & Thoreau's Walden, Hackett, 75; auth, Ahab's greatness: Prometheus as Narcissus, 9/66 & The two beginnings of Walden, 9/68, ELH; Thoreau on poverty and magnanimity, PMLA, 1/70. Add: Dept. of English, Ohio State University, Columbus, OH 43210.

WOODSON, WILLIAM CHARLES, b. Quincy, Ill, Oct. 22, 41; m. 63; c. 2. ENGLISH RENAISSANCE LITERATURE. B.A, Univ. Mich, 63, M.A, 65; Ph.D. (Eng), Univ. Pa, 68. Asst. prof. ENG, ILL. STATE UNIV, 68-72, ASSOC. PROF, 72- Fel, Folger Shakespeare Libr, summer 72. Shakespeare Asn. Am; Renaissance Soc. Am; MLA. Shakespeare; Renaissance drama. Publ: The new Variorum edition of Shakespeare, Shakespearean Res. & Opportunities, 70-71; John Bell's edition of Shakespeare, Libr. Chronicle, 72. Add: Dept. of English, Illinois State University, Normal, IL 61761.

WOODWARD, DANIEL HOLT, b. Ft. Worth, Tex, Oct. 17, 31; m. 54; c. 2. ENGLISH. B.A, Univ. Colo, 51, M.A, 55; Ph.D.(Eng), Yale, 58; M.S. in L.S, Cath. Univ. Am, 69. Asst. prof. Eng, Mary Wash. Col, Univ. Va, 57-61, assoc. prof, 61-68, prof, 68-72, col. librn, 69-72; LIBRN, ART GALLERY & BOT. GARDENS, HUNTINGTON LIBR, 72- U.S.A, 52-54. Grolier Club; Renaissance Soc. Am; Bibliog. Soc. Am. English Renaissance; bibliography. Publ: Ed, Poems and translations of Robert Fletcher, Univ. Fla, 70. Add: Huntington Library, 1151 Oxford Rd, San Marino, CA 91108.

WOODWARD, ROBERT HANSON, b. Lapel, Ind, Apr. 8, 25; m. 49; c. 2. AMERICAN LITERATURE. A.B, Ind. Univ, 51, M.A, 52, Ph.D, 57. Teaching assoc. ENG, Ind. Univ, 52-54; instr, SAN JOSE STATE UNIV, 54-56, asst. prof, 56-59, assoc. prof, 59-62, PROF, 62-, GRAD. COORD, DEPT. ENG, 70-, ASSOC. DEAN, SCH. HUMANITIES & ARTS, 72-, res. grants, 60, 62, 64, 68, 70 & 72, chmn. dept. Eng, 62-66. Am. Counc. Learned Soc. grant-in-aid, 63. U.S.A, 43-46. NCTE; MLA; West. Lit. Asn; John Steinbeck Soc. Am; Philol. Asn. Pac. Coast. Folklore in literature; Harold Frederic. Publ: The craft of prose, 63, 68 & 72 & co-auth, Success in America, 66, Wadsworth; co-auth, Hawthorne to Hemingway, Garrett, 65; co-ed, Perspectives on American literature, 68 & co-auth, The social rebel in American literature, 68, Odyssey; co-auth, Bibliography of Harold Frederic, Hall, 74; co-auth, Frederic's short fiction: a checklist, spring 68 & auth, A selection of Harold Frederic's early literary criticism, 1877-1881, winter 72, Am. Lit. Realism; auth, Steinbeck's The promise, Steinbeck Quart, winter 73; plus others. Add: Dept. of English, San Jose State University, 125 S. Seventh St, San Jose, CA 95192.

WOOLF, EUGENE T, b. Salt Lake City, Utah, Apr. 12, 23; m. 44; c. 4. ENGLISH, PHILOSOPHY. B.A, Univ. Utah, 47, M.A, 49, Ph.D.(Eng), 65; Stanford Univ, 49-50, 52. Asst. prof. Eng, SOUTH. UTAH STATE COL, 55-65, asst. to the pres, 66-67, PROF. ENG. & PHILOS. & DEAN SCH. ARTS & LETT. & CHMN. DEPT. ENG, 67- Consult. Eng. educ, NCTE. Nat. Guard, 39-, Lt. Col. MLA; NCTE. Seventeenth and eighteenth century English literature; nineteenth century American studies. Publ: Barriers in the novels of Henry James, Utah Acad. Sci. Arts & Lett. Proc, 68. Add: Dept. of English, Southern Utah State College, Cedar City, UT 84720.

WOOLF, JAMES DUDLEY, b. Rector, Ark, July 7, 14; m. 53; c. 3. ENGLISH. B.A, Col. of the Ozarks, 42; M.A, Univ. Mich, 49; Ph.D.(Eng), Vanderbilt Univ, 53. Instr. ENG, Univ. Ky, 48-49; Wayne Univ, 49-50; assoc. prof, Ark. State Col, 53-58, prof, 58-59; asst. prof, Memphis State Univ, 59-63, assoc. prof, 63-66; IND. UNIV, FT. WAYNE, 66-71, PROF, 71-, summer fac. fel, 68. U.S.N, 42-45, Lt.(jg). MLA. Nineteenth century English literature; Thomas Hardy. Publ: Sir Edmund Gosse: a biographical and interpretative study; Sir Edmund Gosse, Twayne, 72; Vers de Société and decadent poetry: descriptive comments on continuity, 64, Tragedy in Gosse's Father and son, 66 & Annotated bibliography of writings about Sir Edmund Gosse, 68, Eng. Lit. Transition. Add: 3810 Trier Rd, Ft. Wayne, IN 46805.

WOOLF, LEONARD, b. Baltimore, Md, Mar. 27, 16; m. 44; c. 1. ENGLISH. B.S, Johns Hopkins Univ, 52; M.Ed, Univ. Md, 51, D.Ed, 59. Chmn. dept. Eng, jr. high sch, Md, 50-54; teacher, Baltimore Polytech. Inst, 54-56; Eng. specialist, Baltimore City Pub. Schs, 56-63; supvr. Eng, Anne Arundel County Pub. Schs, 63-66; ASSOC. PROF. SEC. EDUC. & COORD. ENG. EDUC, UNIV. MD, COLLEGE PARK, 66- Consult, Eng. for foreign internes, Church Home & Hosp, 60-61; John Jay fel. humanities, Williams Col, summer 61; consult, U.S. Off. Educ, 65- Med.C, U.S.A, 42-46, 1st Lt. Secondary education; reading, especially literature for slow learner. Publ: Co-auth, Journeys in reading, Bk. I, 65 & Bk. II, 67, Globe Bk; Toward competence in reading, Baltimore Bull. Educ, 5-6/58; South of Eden, Clearing House, 10/64; Literature in a technological age, Eng. J, 12/71; plus others. Add: College of Education, University of Maryland, College Park, MD 20742.

WORK, JANE MAGRUDER, b. Owensboro, Ky, Mar. 30, 27; m. 60; c. 2. SPEECH, RADIO & TV. B.A, Furman Univ, 47; M.A, Univ. Wis, 48; Ph.D. (radio-TV), Ohio State Univ, 59. Instr. speech & radio, Univ. S.Miss, 48-51; copy writer, WBNS-TV, Columbus, Ohio, 52-53; pub. speaker, Columbia Gas of Ohio, Columbus, 53-61; from adj. assoc. prof. SPEECH to ADJ. PROF, PACE UNIV, WESTCHESTER CAMPUS, 62- Speaker & mgt. training sem. leader to var. groups. Speech Commun. Asn. Add: Dept. of Literature, Communication & Fine Arts, Pace University, Westchester Campus, 861 Bedford Rd, Pleasantville, NY 10570.

WORK, WILLIAM, b. Ithaca, N.Y, Aug. 10, 23; m. 60; c. 2. SPEECH & DRAMA. A.B, Cornell Univ, 46; M.A, Univ. Wis, 48, Ph.D, 54. Instr. speech & drama & assoc. dir. theater, Purdue Univ, 48-50; prof. speech & dir. theater, East. Mich. Univ, 51-63; EXEC. SECY, SPEECH COMMUN. ASN, 63- Vis. prof. theater, South. Ill. Univ, summer 59; mem. comn. Eng. curriculum, NCTE, 67-73; consult, U.S. Off. Educ, 67-; dir, Counc. Commun. Soc, 69-73; mem. adv. comt. Clearinghouse Reading & Commun. Skills, Educ. Resources Inform. Ctr, 72-; secy, Alliance Asns. Advan. Educ, 73- Alex Drier Award, 62. Cent. States Speech Asn.(v.pres, 62-63); Am. Theatre Asn; Speech Commun Asn. Theatre; television; speech education. Publ: Co-auth, Filmstrips for use in teaching drama and theatre, Am. Educ. Theatre Asn, 62; auth, Scholarship, professionalism, activism, Spectra, 2/70; Speculations, Acta Symbolica, fall 71; contrib, Encycl. Educ, Macmillan, 71; plus two others. Add: Speech Communication Association, Statler Hilton Hotel, New York, NY 10001.

WORKMAN, ARVIN LeROY, b. Pierson, Mich, Mar. 28, 31; m. 60; c. 4. SPEECH, MASS MEDIA. B.S, Ind. State, 54, M.S, 57; Ph.D, Mich. State, 65. Asst. radio, TV, film, Mich. State Univ, 57-60; writer, dir. & producer, Armed Forces Radio & TV Serv, Los Angeles, 61-64; asst. prof. speech, Kans. State Univ, 64-67; asst. prof. SPEECH & dir. instruct. TV, Cent. Mo. State Col, 67-69; ASSOC. PROF. & DIR. CLOSED CIRCUIT TV, IND. STATE UNIV, TERRE HAUTE, 69- U.S.N.R, 54-56, 61-64, Res. Comdr. Speech Commun. Asn. Rhetoric; educational television; television production techniques. Add: Dept. of Speech, 317 Parsons Hall, Indiana State University, Terre Haute, IN 47809.

WORKMAN, CHARLES THOMAS, b. Birmingham, Ala, June 21, 34; m. 64. ENGLISH. A.B, Samford Univ, 56; New Orleans Baptist Theol. Sem, 59-60; M.A, Univ. Ala, 62; Ph.D.(Eng), Tulane Univ, 68. Instr. ENG, Va. Polytech. Inst, 62-67; asst. prof, SAMFORD UNIV, 67-68, assoc. prof, 68-73, PROF, 73- Victorian period; contemporary British literature. Add: Dept. of English, Samford University, Birmingham, AL 35209.

WORKMAN, SAMUEL KLINGER, b. Gambier, Ohio, Aug. 28, 07; m. 31, 53; c. 2. ENGLISH LITERATURE. A.B, Kenyon Col, 26; A.M, Ohio State Univ, 27; Ph.D, Princeton, 35. Asst, Ohio State Univ, 26-27; instr. ENG, Univ. Ky, 27-29; Northwest. Univ, 35-40, asst. prof, 40-48; assoc. prof, Ill. Inst. Technol, 48-61; prof, NEWARK COL. ENGINEERING, 61-67, chmn. dept, 61-72, distinguished prof, 67-72, DISTINGUISHED EMER. PROF, 73- Ford fac. fel, 52-53. MLA; Eng. Inst; Am. Soc. Eng. Educ. English style; Jonathan Swift; William Faulkner. Publ: Fifteenth century translation as an influence on English prose. Add: R.D. 1, Riegelsville, PA 18077.

WORMHOUDT, ARTHUR LOUIS, English, Foreign Language. See Volume III, Foreign Languages, Linguistics & Philology.

WORRELL, ELIZABETH, b. Mexico, Mo, May 7, 05. LITERATURE. B.S, Univ. Mo, 26; M.A, Northwest. Univ, 31, Ph.D, 55; Univ. Wis, summer 40. Instr. SPEECH, Hardin Jr. Col, 27-30; Cent. Methodist Col, 32-42; William Woods Col, 45-47; prof, NORTHEAST MO. STATE UNIV, 47-70, EMER. PROF, 70- Vis. prof. speech, Univ. Mo-Columbia, 70-72 & Univ. Ariz, fall 72 & 73. U.S.W.M.C.R, 42-44, Res, 44-, 1st Lt. Speech Commun. Asn; MLA; Cent. States Speech Asn. Contemporary literature and oral interpretation. Publ: The unspoken word, In: Studies in interpretation, Rodopi NV, Amsterdam, 72. Add: Manor House 7H, 306 Hitt St, Columbia, MO 65201.

WORSTER, DONALD EUGENE, American History & Literature. See Volume I, History.

WORTH, GEORGE JOHN, b. Vienna, Austria, June 11, 29; nat; m. 51; c. 2. ENGLISH. A.B, Univ. Chicago, 48, A.M, 51; Fulbright fel, Univ. London, 53-54; Ph.D.(Eng), Univ. Ill, 54. Instr. ENG, Univ. Ill, 54-55; UNIV. KANS, 55-58, asst. prof, 58-62, assoc. prof, 62-65, PROF, 65-, CHMN. DEPT, 63-, asst. chmn. dept, 61-62, assoc. chmn. dept, 62-63. Am. Philos. Soc. grant, 62; mem. exec. comt, Asn. Depts. Eng, 66-69, chmn, future proj. comt, 67-68. Midwest Mod. Lang. Asn; MLA; Int. Asn. Univ. Prof. Eng; Dickens Fel; Dickens Soc. Victorian fiction. Publ: Co-ed, Six studies in 19th century English literature and thought, 62, auth, James Hannay, 64 & co-ed, The nineteenth century writer and his audience, 69, Univ. Kans; auth, William Harrison Ainsworth, Twayne, 72; plus others. Add: Dept. of English, University of Kansas, Lawrence, KS 66045.

WORTHAM, THOMAS RICHARD, b. Liberal, Kans, Dec. 5, 43. AMERICAN LITERATURE. A.B, Marquette Univ, 65; Ph.D.(Eng), Ind. Univ, Bloomington, 70. ASST. PROF. ENG, UNIV. CALIF, LOS ANGELES, 70-, ASST. ED, 19th CENTURY FICTION, 71- MLA (chmn. Pac. Coast region comt. manuscript holdings, Am. lit. sect, 71-). American literature and culture, 19th-20th centuries. Publ: Co-ed, Literary friends and acquaintance, Vol. 32, In: A selected edition of W.D. Howells, Ind. Univ, 68. Add: Dept. of English, University of California, 405 Hilgard Ave, Los Angeles, CA 90024.

WORTHINGTON, MABEL PARKER, b. Philadelphia, Pa, Nov. 8, 12. ENGLISH. A.B, Temple Univ, 32, M.A, 44; Ph.D, Columbia Univ, 53. Instr. ENG, Temple Univ, 44-46, 48-55; instr, Hunter Col. & lectr, Brooklyn Col, 46-47; asst. prof, TEMPLE UNIV, 55-58, assoc. prof, 58-63, prof, 63-72, EMER. PROF, 72- Am. Asn. Univ. Women stud. grant, Eng. & Ireland, 63. MLA; James Joyce Found. Nineteenth century; modern literature; James Joyce. Publ: Co-auth, Song in the works of James Joyce, Columbia Univ, 59; Irish songs in Joyce's Ulysses, PMLA; Nursery rhymes in Finnegans wake, J. Am. Folklore; plus others on Joyce and the Don Juan legend. Add: Grindleton Lane, Ambler, PA 19002.

WRAY, WILLIAM ROSE, b. Memphis, Tenn, Aug. 17, 18; m. 46; c. 2. ENGLISH. B.A, Yale, 41, M.A, 42, Ph.D.(Eng), 50. Instr. Eng, Univ. Rochester, 48-51; asst. prof, Okla. Baptist Univ, 51-55, assoc. prof, 55-56, chmn. dept, 51-56, chmn. div. lang. & lit, 56; prof. ENG, E.Cent. State Col, 57-66, chmn. dept, 65-66; ASSOC. PROF, OKLA. STATE UNIV, 66- Ford Found. fel, 54-55. U.S.A, 42-45. MLA. Shakespeare. Publ: Gulliver's travels, book I, chapter 1, Explicator, 9/67. Add: Dept. of English, Oklahoma State University, Stillwater, OK 74074.

WREN, ROBERT MERIWETHER, b. Washington, D.C, Feb. 21, 28. ENGLISH. B.A, Univ. Houston, 54; M.A, Princeton, 56, Ph.D.(Eng), 65. Instr. Eng, Douglass Col, Rutgers Univ, 56-60; drama, Harpur Col, State Univ. N.Y. Binghamton, 60-62; lectr. ENG, Knox Col.(Ill), 64-65; asst. prof, UNIV. HOUSTON, 65-68, ASSOC. PROF, 68- Univ. Houston res. grant, 66; vis. prof. Eng, Univ. Lagos, 72-75; Fulbright lectr, 73-75. Malone Soc; Soc. Theatre Res; Int. Fed. Theatre Res; African Stud. Asn; West. Asn. Africanists. English and Dutch Renaissance theatres; African literature. Publ: The five-entry stage at Blackfriars, Theatre Res, 67; Ben Jonson as producer, Educ. Theatre J, 70; Indigenization of English, Black Orpheus, 74; plus others. Add: Dept. of English, University of Houston, Houston, TX 77004.

WRENN, JOHN H, b. Norfolk, Va, Oct. 16, 20; m. 46; c. 4. ENGLISH. B.A, Univ. Mich, 48, fel, 48-49, M.A, 49; Ph.D, Univ. Pa, 58. Teacher, Punahou Sch, Hawaii, 51-53; instr. ENG, UNIV. COLO, BOULDER, 54-57, asst. prof, 57-61, assoc. prof, 61-66, PROF, 66-, fac. fels, 59-60, 63 & 74, dir. writer's conf, 65-72. Consult-reader, col. bd. exam, Educ. Testing Serv, N. J, 58-; ed, Abstr. Eng. Stud, 59-63; Eng. Lang. Notes, 63-; AAUP consult on prof. advising, Colo. Women's Col, 63- U.S.A.A.F, 42-45, 1st Lt; Air Medal & 5 Oak Leaves. NCTE; Am. Stud. Asn; AAUP. American literature; 20th century poetry. Publ: John Dos Passos, Twayne, 61; co-ed, Writers at work, Univ. Colo, 67- & American studies dissertations, Am. Quart, 63-72. Add: Dept. of English, University of Colorado, Boulder, CO 80302.

WRIGHT, ANDREW HOWELL, b. Columbus, Ohio, June 28, 23; m. 52; c. 2. ENGLISH. A.B, Harvard, 47; M.A, Ohio State Univ, 48, Ph.D, 51. Instr. ENG, Ohio State Univ, 52-54, asst. prof, 55-58, assoc. prof, 58-63; PROF, UNIV. CALIF, SAN DIEGO, 63-, CHMN. DEPT. LIT, 71- Fulbright fel, Univ. Col, Univ. London, 51-52, Fulbright sr. res. fel, 60-61; fel, Ohio State Univ, 54, res. grant, 58; Am. Philos. Soc. grant-in-aid, 56, 58; Am. Counc. Learned Soc. grant-in-aid, 61; Guggenheim fels, 61-62 & 70-71; adv. ed, Col. Eng, 63-66; mem. adv. bd, Nineteenth Century Fiction, 63-; adv. ed, Eighteenth Century Stud, 67- Sig.C, U.S.A, 43-46, 2nd Lt. MLA; Johnson Soc. Great Lakes Region (pres, 63); Jane Austen Soc; Mod. Humanities Res. Asn; PEN Club; fel. Royal Soc. Lit. U.K. Eighteenth century literature; the novel. Publ: Jane Austen's novels: a study in structure, Oxford, 53; Joyce Cary: a preface to his novels, Harper, 58; co-auth, Selective bibliography for the study of English and American literature, Macmillan, 60; Henry Fielding: mask and feast, Univ. Calif, 65; Blake's job: a commentary, Clarendon, 72. Add: 7227 Olivetas St, La Jolla, CA 92037.

WRIGHT, AUSTIN, b. Bedford, Pa, May 20, 04; m. 35; c. 1. ENGLISH LITERATURE. A.B, Haverford Col, 25; A.M, Harvard, 26, Ph.D, 31. Instr. Eng, Carnegie-Mellon Univ, 27-29, 30-31; Haverford Col, 31-32; CARNEGIE-MELLON UNIV, 32-33, asst. prof, 33-43, assoc. prof, 43-46, asst. to pres, 41-46, prof. ENG, 46-72, head dept, 46-68, EMER. PROF, 72- MLA; NCTE. Life and works of Joseph Spence: English 18th and 19th century literature; Shakespeare. Publ: Co-ed, College prose, an anthology, Heath 42, 2nd ed, 46; auth, Joseph Spence: critical biography, Univ. Chicago, 50; Handbook of English, Ronald, 56; Bibliographies of studies in Victorian literature, Univ. Ill, 56; Victorian literature, modern essays in criticism, Oxford, 61; The Warner administration at Carnegie Institute of Technology, 1950-1965, Carnegie Press, 73; plus other articles. Add: 118 E. Watson St, Bedford, PA 15522.

WRIGHT, AUSTIN McGIFFERT, b. Yonkers, N.Y, Sept. 6, 22; m. 50; c. 3. ENGLISH. A.B, Harvard, 43; M.A, Univ. Chicago, 48, Ph.D.(Eng), 59. Instr. ENG, Augustana Col.(Ill), 48-50; teacher, Wright Jr. Col, 55-60; asst. prof, Univ. Chicago, 60-62; UNIV. CINCINNATI, 62-66, assoc. prof, 66-69, PROF, 69- U.S.A, 43-46, 1st Lt. MLA. American short story and novel; writing of fiction; literary theory and criticism. Publ: The American short story in the twenties, Univ. Chicago, 61, Camden's eyes, Doubleday, 69; co-ed, The art of the short story: an introductory anthology, Allyn & Bacon, 69; auth, First persons, Harper, 73. Add: Dept. of English, University of Cincinnati, Cincinnati, OH 45221.

WRIGHT, BROOKS, b. Cambridge, Mass, Oct. 14, 22; m. 55. ENGLISH. A.B, Harvard Col, 43; M.A, Harvard, 47, Ph.D.(Eng), 51. Lectr. ENG, CITY COL. NEW YORK, 50-51, instr. 51-55, asst. prof, 55-68, assoc. prof, 68-71, PROF, 72- U.S.A.A.F, 42-45. MLA. Nineteenth century. Publ: Sir Edwin Arnold, Bookman Assoc; co-ed, Techniques of fiction, Liveright; co-auth, A student's guide to 50 European novels, Wash. Sq, 67. Add: 5 La Veta Place, Nyack, NY 10960.

WRIGHT, CARL C, b. Austin, Tex, Jan. 18, 10; m. 32; c. 2. ENGLISH. B.A, Southwest Tex. State Col, 40; M.A, Univ. Tex, 46. Prin, Pub. Sch, Tex, 35-42; supt. high sch, 42-45; tutor ENG, Univ. Tex, 45-46, instr, 46-51; ASSOC. PROF, PAN AM. UNIV, 51- Texas and the Southwest. Publ: Reading interests in Texas before the Civil War, Southwest. Hist. Quart, 1/51; The mesquite tree and the Southwest, Tech. Rev, 5/51. Add: Dept. of English, Pan American University, Edinburg, TX 78539.

WRIGHT, CELESTE TURNER, b. St. John, N.B, Mar. 17, 06; U.S. citizen; m. 33; c. 1. ENGLISH. A.B, Univ. Calif, Los Angeles, 25, A.M, 26, Ph.D, 28. From instr. to assoc. prof. ENG, UNIV. CALIF, DAVIS, 28-48, PROF, 48-, chmn. dept, 28-55, res. lectr, 63, writing fel, inst. creative arts, 66-67. MLA; Philol. Asn. Pac. Coast; Renaissance Soc. Am. Elizabethan literature; writing, especially poetry; 20th-century literature. Publ: Etruscan princess and other poems, A. Swallow, 64; A sense of place (poems), 73; Lazarus Pyott and other inventions of Anthony Mundy, Philol. Quart, 10/63; Elinor Wylie: the glass Chimaera and the Minotaur, Twentieth Century Lit, 4/66; plus others. Add: Dept. of English, University of California, Davis, CA 95616.

WRIGHT, CONSTANCE STOREY, b. Boston, Mass, Mar. 3, 28. ENGLISH, MEDIEVAL COMPARATIVE LITERATURE. B.A, Scripps Col, 50; M.A, Univ. Calif, Berkeley, 58, Ph.D.(Eng), 66. Instr. ENG, Grinnell Col, 62-65; asst. prof, UNIV. COLO, BOULDER, 65-73, ASSOC. PROF, 73-, fac. summer initiation fel, 65, fac. fel, 70-71. MLA; Mediaeval Acad. Am; Dante Soc. Am. Medieval scriptural exegesis; Medieval poetics; Chaucer. Publ: No art at all, Classical Philol, 7/73. Add: Dept. of English, University of Colorado, Boulder, CO 80302.

WRIGHT, DAVID ROLLAND, b. Springfield, Mo, Dec. 24, 35; m. 58; c. 2. SPEECH COMMUNICATION. A.A, Southwest Baptist Col, 55; B.J, Univ. Mo-Columbia, 61, M.A, 62; Ph.D.(interpersonal commun), Ohio Univ, 71. Minister, Simpson Baptist Church, La, 57-59; New Salem Baptist Church, Ashland, Mo, 60-66; asst. prof. SPEECH, Belmont Col, 66-68; instr, Ohio Univ, 68-71; PROF. & CHMN. DEPT. CLARION STATE COL, 71- Int. Commun. Asn; Speech Commun. Asn; Am. Bus. Commun. Asn; Nat. Counc. Family Relat. Interpersonal and organizational communication; public address. Add: Dept. of Speech Communication & Theatre, Clarion State College, Clarion, PA 16214.

WRIGHT, DONALD EDWARD, Comparative & General Linguistics. See Volume III, Foreign Languages, Linguistics & Philology.

WRIGHT, EDGAR, b. London, Eng, Sept. 1, 20; m. 50; c. 2. ENGLISH. B.A, Univ, London, 49, M.A, 55, Ph.D.(Eng), 64. Lectr. ENG, Univ. Col, Nairobi, Kenya, 56-59, sr. lectr, 59-66; PROF, LAURENTIAN UNIV, 66-, ASSOC. DEAN HUMANITIES, 70- R.A.S.C, 40-46, Capt. Asn. Commonwealth Lit. & Lang. Stud; fel. African Stud. Asn. Publ: Co-auth, On your own, Longman's, 63; auth, Mrs. Gaskell, Oxford, 65; The critical evaluation of African literature, Heinemanns, 73; Mrs. Gaskell and the world of Cranford, Rev. Eng. Stud, 1/65; African literature: problems in criticism, J. Commonwealth Lit, 12/66; Joseph Conrad and Bertrand Russell, Conradiana, Vol. 2, No. 1; plus one other. Add: Dept. of English, Laurentian University, Sudbury, Ont. P3E 2C6, Can.

WRIGHT, EDWARD A, b. Mt. Pleasant, Iowa, Jan. 25, 06; m. 40. THEATRE, DRAMA. B.A, State Univ. Iowa, 28, M.A, 30; hon. Dr. Fine Arts, Iowa Wesleyan Col, 61. Mem. fac. speech & theatre, Marshalltown Jr. Col, 30-37; prof. theatre & chmn. dept, Denison Univ, 37-67; prof. THEATRE, LONG BEACH STATE UNIVERSITY, 67-74, EMER. PROF, 74- U.S. Dept. Defense rep, clinics & theatre groups, Europe, 53; summers, mem. play companies, mil. installations, Europe & Far East, 54-58; Fulbright lectr, Aoyama Gakuin Univ. & Univ. Tokyo, Japan, 59-60; lectr, British Sch. Athens, summer, 67. Am. Nat. Theatre & Acad; Nat. Theatre Conf.(treas, 57-67); Am. Educ. Theatre Asn. Publ: Primer for playgoers, 57, co-auth, rev. ed, 69 & auth, Understanding today's theatre, 59 & 72, Prentice. Add: 530 S. Fuller Ave, Apt. 11-C, Los Angeles, CA 90036.

WRIGHT, ELIZABETH V, b. Northville, Mich, Oct. 13, 06; m. 29; c. 1. ENGLISH. A.B, Univ. Mich, 26; A.M, Univ. Chicago, 45; Ph.D.(Eng), Loyola Univ, (Ill), 54. Instr. ENG, UNIV. ILL, CHICAGO CIRCLE, 46-56, asst. prof, 56-60, assoc. prof, 60-66, prof, 66-72, EMER. PROF, 72- MLA; Am. Stud. Asn. Publ: Co-auth, Short fiction publication, Swallow, 58; auth, Index to fifty years of Poetry Magazine, AMS Press, 60; Bunyan's Pilgrim's progress (guide book), 64 & Faulkner's Sartoris (guide book), 65, Am. R.D.M; The tree in Pamela's garden, Explicator, 65; Short fiction bibliography, Stud. Short Fiction, summers 66, 67, 68. Add: Dept. of English, University of Illinois at Chicago Circle, Chicago, IL 60680.

WRIGHT, EVALINE UHL, b. Logansport, Ind, Apr. 1, 12. SPEECH. B.S, Northwest. Univ, 33; A.M, Univ. Mich, 41; Univ. Birmingham, Eng, summer 48. Mem. fac, Stephens Col, 33-37, mem. staff summer theatre, 35-37; asst. prof. speech & drama, MILLS COL, 37-41, assoc. prof, 41-63, PROF. DRAMATIC ARTS, 63-, mem. staff, Eng. lang. inst, 42-60, asst. dir, 60-61, dir, 61-63; dir. col. summer session, 54-57. Ford fel, sem. Southeast Asia, Univ. Mich, summer 64. Am. Theatre Asn; AAUP; Am. Asn. Univ. Women. Essentials of English for Latin Americans. Add: Dept. of Dramatic Arts, Mills College, Oakland, CA 94613.

WRIGHT, GEORGE THADDEUS, b. Staten Island, N.Y, Dec. 17, 25; m. 55. ENGLISH. A.B, Columbia Col, 46, M.A, Columbia Univ, 47; Benjamin P. Wall Mem. scholar, Univ. Calif, Berkeley, 55-56, Ph.D, 57. Lectr. ENG, Univ. Calif, Berkeley, 56-57; vis. asst. prof, N.Mex. Highlands Univ, summer 57; instr, Univ. Ky, 57-59, asst. prof, 59-60; San Francisco State Col, 60-61; assoc. prof, Univ. Tenn, 61-68; PROF, UNIV. MINN, MINNEAPOLIS, 68-, CHMN.DEPT, 74- Fulbright lectr. Am. lit, Univ. Aix-Marseille, 64-66; ed, Univ. Minn. Pamphlets on Am. Writers, 68- U.S.A, 44-46. MLA; AAUP; NCTE. Modern poetry and fiction; literary theory. Publ: The poet in the poem: the personae of Eliot, Yeats, and Pound, Univ. Calif, 60 & 62; W.H. Auden, Twayne, 69; ed, Seven American stylists from Poe to Mailer, Univ. Minn, 73. Add: Dept. of English, University of Minnesota, Minneapolis, MN 55455.

WRIGHT, GILBERT GEORGE, b. Oakland, Calif, Aug. 22, 26; m. 56; c. 5. ENGLISH LITERATURE. A.B, San Luis Rey Col, 52; M.A, Univ. Notre Dame, 58; fel, Univ. Wis, 62-63, Ph.D, 63. Instr. ENG, Canisius Col, 57-59, asst. prof, 59-60; Univ. Ill, Urbana, 63-72; PRES, NAT. ACAD. ARTS, 72- Chmn. bd. dir, Ill. Found. Dance, 70-; trustee, Ballet Theatre Found, 70-; mem. dance adv. panel, Ill. Arts Counc, 71-; mem. bd. dir, Asn. Am. Dance Companies, 71- U.S.A.A.F, 44-45. MLA; NCTE; Mediaeval Acad. Am. Mediaeval prose, especially Richard Rolle of Hampole; mediaeval poetry, especially Chaucer and the alliterative revival; mediaeval Latin literature. Add: National Academy of Arts, 303 E. John St, Champaign, IL 61820.

WRIGHT, GILSON, b. Paulding, Ohio, Aug. 25, 05. JOURNALISM. A.B, Ohio Wesleyan Univ, 30; Ohio State Univ, 41. Reporter, newspapers, Lima, Ohio, 23-26; Marion Star, 30-31; asst. dir. publicity, Ohio Wesleyan Univ, 31-33, dir, 33-40; asst. prof. Eng. & jour, MIAMI UNIV, 40-56, jour, 56-70, asst. dir. news bur, 40-43, dir, 43-46, EMER. PROF. ENG, 70- Correspondent, Newspapers, 23-; sports ed, Mansfield News, Ohio, 31. Add: 23 E. Collins, Oxford, OH 45056.

WRIGHT, H. BUNKER, b. Woodstock, Ill, Mar. 26, 07; m. 31; c. 1. ENGLISH LITERATURE. B.S, Northwest. Univ, 30, A.M, 31, Ph.D, 37; Univ. Chicago, 33. Asst. ENG, Northwest. Univ, 31-35, instr, 35-38; MIAMI UNIV, 38-39, asst. prof, 39-45, assoc. prof, 45-54, PROF, 54-, chmn. dept. Eng, 56-59, dean grad. sch, 59-69. Lectr, Univ. Cincinnati, 39-55; chmn, Midwest Conf. Grad. Stud. & Res, 65-66. MLA; Col. Eng. Asn; Midwest Mod. Lang. Asn; Eng. Inst; Am. Soc. 18th Century Stud. English literature and history of the 17th and 18th centuries. Publ: Contrib, Studies in the literature of the Augustan Age, 52; co-ed, Literary works of Matthew Prior, Oxford, 59 & 71; plus others. Add: 1033 Cedar Dr, Oxford, OH 45056.

WRIGHT, JOSEPH EDWARD, b. Memphis, Tenn, Jan. 22, 18; m. 43; c. 3. THEATRE. M.A, Northwest. Univ, 46; Carnegie award, summer 50; Ford fel, 53-54. Teacher, sch, Tenn, 38-42; PROF. SPEECH & DRAMA, VANDERBILT UNIV, 46, CHMN. DEPT, 55- U.S.A, 42-45. Am. Theatre Asn. Direction and production techniques and methods prior to 1900. Add: 2001 Linden Ave, Nashville, TN 37212.

WRIGHT, LEONARD N, b. Fulton, Mo, Oct. 26, 98; m. 21; c. 2. ENGLISH, PHILOSOPHY. A.B, Westminster Col.(Mo), 19; M.A, Univ. Mo, 25; Ph.D. (Eng), Univ. Tex, 39. Assoc. prof. Eng, Southwest Tex. State Col, 25-39, prof, 39-45, chmn. dept, 45-54; Defiance Col, 56-57; prof, Univ. Ark, Monticello, 57-71, chmn. div. lang. & lit, 67-71; RETIRED. MLA; Col. Eng. Asn; Int. Soc. Gen. Semantics. Seventeenth century—Milton; twentieth century fiction. Publ: Christian mortalism: a prospectus for the history of an idea, In: The great torch race, Univ. Tex, 61. Add: 203 Arlington Apts, 3106 Ben Wilson St, Victoria, TX 77901.

WRIGHT, LOUIS BOOKER, Renaissance Literature, American Colonial History & Culture. See Volume I, History.

WRIGHT, MARY ELIZABETH, b. Monte Vista, Colo. ENGLISH, GUIDANCE. A.B, Colo. State Col, 40; M.A, N.Y. Univ, 47; New Sch. Social Res, 48-52; Ed.D.(personnel admin. & guid), Columbia Univ, 57. Teacher high schs, Colo, 40-43; instr. Eng. & Psychol, Packard Jr. Col, N.Y, 46-54; counsel. high sch, N.Y, 55-66; assoc. prof. ENG, METROP. STATE COL, 66-72,

PROF, 72- W.A.V.E.S, 43-46, Lt. NCTE. Publ: Co-auth, Personality & human relations & Personality and human relations teachers manual, McGraw, 53, rev. ed, 61; co-auth, Planning for college, N.Y. Dept. Educ. Publ; plus others. Add: Dept. of English, Metropolitan State College, Denver, CO 80204.

WRIGHT, NATHALIA, b. Athens, Ga, Mar. 29, 13. AMERICAN LITERATURE. A.B, Maryville Col, 33; A.M, Yale, 38, Ph.D, 49. Instr, Maryville Col, 34-35, 41-47, asst. libr, 40-43, asst. librn, 43-48; asst. prof. ENG, UNIV. TENN, KNOXVILLE, 49-53, assoc. prof, 53-62, PROF, 62- Tew prize, Yale, 36 & Cook prize, 37; Am. Philos. Soc. grant, summer 52; Guggenheim fel, 53; Am. Asn. Univ. Women fel, 59; mem, Accad. Int. Siculo-Normanna, Catania, Sicily, 67- MLA; Melville Soc. Am. Melville; Italian background of American literature. Publ: The inner room (poems), Hawthorn House, 38; Melville's use of the Bible, Duke Univ, 49; ed, The travels, observations and experience of a Yankee stonecutter, 58, The life of Benjamin West, 59 & Lectures on art and poems and Monaldi, 67, Scholars Facsimiles; auth, Horatio Greenough, 63 & American novelists in Italy: the discoverers, 65, Univ. Pa. Add: Dept. of English, University of Tennessee, 1505 W. Cumberland Ave, Knoxville, TN 37916.

WRIGHT, PALMER, b. Toledo, Ohio, Apr. 16, 22; m. 50; c. 3. ENGLISH, AMERICAN STUDIES. B.S.E, Univ. Mich, 43, M.S.E, 47, Ph.D.(Am. stud), 66. Asst. prof. chem, Delta Col, 61-63; fel. ENG, Univ. Mich, 62; ASST. PROF, UNIV. TEX. AUSTIN, 66- Summer res. grant, Univ. Tex. Res. Inst, 67. MLA; Am. Stud. Asn. American studies; American literature. Add: Dept. of English, University of Texas, Austin, TX 78712.

WRIGHT, ROBERT C, b. Wayne, Nebr, Mar. 5, 21; m. 42; c. 2. ENGLISH. A.B, Wayne State Col, 41; M.A, Univ. Tex, 48; Ph.D, Univ. Nebr, 56; Univ. Wash, 60-61. Prin. sci. & math, Belden High Sch, Nebr, 41-42; instr. Eng, Univ. Tex, 46-48; Eng. & jour, Mankato State Col, 48-50; supvr. Eng, teachers col. high sch, Univ. Nebr, 50-51; asst. prof. Eng. & jour, MANKATO STATE COL, 51-56, assoc. prof, 52-62, PROF. ENG, 62-, CHMN. DEPT, 66- Gold Key Award, Columbia Scholastic Press Asn, 59. U.S.A.A.F, 42-46, Capt. NCTE; MLA. Creative writing; American literature of 20th century. Publ: What makes a leader?, Sch. Exec, 10/57; The universalizing technique of Eugene O'Neill, In: The iceman cometh, Mod. Drama, 64; Hardy's Heath and Cather's Prairie as naturalistic symbols, Mankato Stud. Eng, 66. Add: 224 Crocus Pl, Mankato, MN 56001.

WRIGHT, ROBERT LEE, b. Connersville, Ind, May 23, 20; m. 44; c. 1. ENGLISH, COMPARATIVE LITERATURE. A.B, Defiance Col, 43; A.M, Univ. Minn, 47; Harvard, summers 47-49; Ed.D, Columbia Univ, 55. Publicity dir, Ind. Union, 40; instr. writing, gen. col, Univ. Minn, 46-48; asst. prof. commun. skills, MICH. STATE UNIV, 48-51, 54-57, assoc. prof, 57-61, PROF. AM. THOUGHT & LANG, 61-, COMP. LIT, 62-, dir. writing clin, 49-51, 54-57. Ed, Naval Reserve Reservoir, 46-48; instr, Teachers Col, Columbia Univ, 53-54; Swed. govt. fel, Univ. Stockholm, 57-58; staff contrib, Abstr. Eng. Stud, 58-63; Fulbright res. scholar, 62-63; Am. Philos. Soc. grant, 66-67, 70-71, 74; Huntington Libr. fel, 69; Univ. Col. bk. award, 69. U.S.N, 43-46, 51-53, Lt. Comdr. Soc. Advan. Scand. Stud; Swed. Pioneer Hist. Soc; fel. Int. Inst. Arts & Lett; NCTE; Col. Conf. Compos. & Commun; MLA; Am. Folklore Soc. Comparative literature, particularly Scandinavian; ballad and folksong; American studies. Publ: Writing without rules; W.C. Brown, 51, rev. ed, 55; staff contrib, Bibliographies of research in the teaching of English; Swedish emigrant ballads, Univ. Nebr, 65; co-auth, Dark and tangled path, Houghton, 71; auth, Factors of readability in compositions written by students of low ability, J. Commun, spring 57; A study of rank in American higher education, Jr. Col. J, 11/56; A Swedish ballad of the American Civil War, Swed. Pioneer Hist. Quart, 10/60. Add: University College, Michigan State University, East Lansing, MI 48823.

WRIGHT, THOMAS EDWARD, b. Clarksburg, W.Va, July 8, 30; m. 58; c. 3. ENGLISH. A.B, Univ. Mo, 54; univ. scholar, Wash. Univ, 57, Henrietta Heermans fel, 57-58, M.A, 58, Woodrow Wilson fel, 59-60, Ph.D, 63. Asst. Wash. Univ, 58-59, instr, 60-61; ENG, CALIF. STATE UNIV, NORTHRIDGE, 61-63, asst. prof, 63-67, assoc. prof, 67-71, PROF, 71- San Fernando Valley State Col. Found. Fel. grant, 63-64, summer fel, 67; Huntington Libr. grant-in-aid, 66-67. U.S.A, 54-56. MLA; Renaissance Soc. Am. English Renaissance prose dialogues; Shakespeare; classical Chinese and Japanese poetry. Publ: Ed, Lodowick Bryskett's Discourse of civil life, Calif. State Univ, 70. Add: Dept. of English, California State University, Northridge, 18111 Nordhoff St, Northridge, CA 91324.

WRIGHT, THOMAS L, b. Hattiesburg, Miss, Dec. 19, 25. MEDIAEVAL LITERATURE. B.A, Tulane Univ, 49, M.A, 51, Carnegie grant, 55, Ph.D, 60; Fulbright grant Univ. Manchester, Eng, 56-57. Asst. prof. ENG, Auburn Univ, 60-62; ASSOC. PROF, Tex. Christian Univ, 62-64; AUBURN UNIV, 64- U.S.N, 44-46. Mediaeval Acad. Am; MLA; Int. Arthurian Soc. Arthurian romance. Publ: Co-auth, Malory's originality, Johns Hopkins Univ, 64; auth, Elegy: autumn 1961 (poem), 70, co-auth, Explication de texte: Ditsky-Wright, 72 & auth, From a wedding guest (poem), 73, South. Humanities Rev; plus one other. Add: Dept. of English, Auburn University, Auburn, AL 36830.

WRIGHT, WALTER FRANCIS, b. Ind, Jan. 5, 12; m. 36; c. 4. ENGLISH. B.S, Miami Univ, 30; Johns Hopkins Univ, 30-31; M.A, Univ. Ill, 32, Ph.D.(Eng), 35. Instr, N.Dak. State Col, 34-35; prof, Doane Col, 35-38; from instr. to asst. prof, Wash. State Col, 38-45; asst. prof, ENG, UNIV. NEBR, LINCOLN, 45-48, assoc. prof, 48-51, prof, 51-65, MARIE KOTOUC ROBERTS PROF, 65-, from asst. to assoc. dean, 54-65. MLA. Nineteenth and 20th centuries. Publ: Romance and tragedy in Joseph Conrad, 49, Art and substance in George Meredith, 53, The madness of art: a study of Henry James, 62, The shaping of the dynasts: a study in Thomas, 67 & Arnold Bennett: romantic realist, 71, Univ. Nebr. Add: 1021 Robert Rd, Lincoln, NE 68510.

WRIGHT, WARREN EARL, b. Springfield, Mass, June 2, 29; m. 51; c. 3. SPEECH, POLITICAL SCIENCE. A.B, Emerson Col, 51, M.A, 52; Ph.D. (speech & polit. sci), Univ. Ill, 60. Instr. SPEECH, Purdue Univ, 54-58; asst. prof, HAMILTON COL, 60-66, ASSOC. PROF, 66-, CHMN. DEPT, 72-, Huber grants, summers 64, 65, 68, Williams-Watrous-Couper grant, 68, fac. fel, 68. U.S.N.R, 48-54; A.U.S, 52-54, Sgt. Speech Commun. Asn. The rhetorical aspects of appellate judicial opinions; Presidential rhetoric; the rhetoric of John F. Kennedy. Publ: Public address, Hamilton Col, 64; Judicial rhetoric, Speech Monogr, 3/64; A myth that is rhetoric's adversary, Today's Speech, 2/65; The President vs. the preacher, Hamilton Alumni Rev, winter 73; plus others. Add: Five Chimneys, Chesterfield, MA 01012.

WRIGHT, WILLIAM CULVER, b. Baltimore, Md, Nov. 14, 29; m. 55; c. 4. ENGLISH & AMERICAN LITERATURE. B.A, Univ. Md, 58, M.A, 65, Ph.D. (Eng), 68. Linguist, Nat. Security Agency, 59-60; instr. Eng, Univ. Baltimore, 61-65; Univ. Md, 65-68; asst. prof, UNIV. HOUSTON, 68-72, ASSOC. PROF. ENG. & DIR. GRAD. STUD. IN ENG, 72- U.S.N, 47-50. MLA; Mod. Humanities Res. Asn; Col. Eng. Asn. Seventeenth century British and American literature; Restoration drama; Elizabethan drama. Publ: Contrib, Halkett and Laing dictionary of anonymous and pseudonymous literature (9 vols), Oliver & Boyd, rev. ed, 74; auth, Hazlitt, Ruskin and early nineteenth art criticism, J. Aesthetics & Art Criticism, 74; Pierre Desmaizeaux, John Toland, and a pirated publication of Shaftesbury's A letter concerning design, Notes & Queries, 74; plus others. Add: Dept. of English, University of Houston, Cullen Blvd, Houston, TX 77004.

WROBEL, ARTHUR, b. Jamaica, N.Y, July 14, 40; m. 63; c. 1. AMERICAN & ENGLISH LITERATURE. A.B, Queens Col.(N.Y), 62; M.A, Univ. N.C, 64, Ph.D.(Eng), 68. Grad. asst. freshman compos, Univ. N.C, 64-68; ASST. PROF. AM. LIT, UNIV. KY, 68- AAUP; Am. Lit. Group, MLA. Nineteenth century American poetry and fiction. Publ: Romantic realism: Nathaniel Beverly Tucker, Am. Lit, 10/70; Whitman's Divine body and sensuous soul, PMLA, 1/74. Add: Dept. of English, Patterson Office Tower 1215, University of Kentucky, Lexington, KY 40506.

WROTEN, HELEN, b. West Union, Iowa, Feb. 2, 18. ENGLISH. B.S, Kans. State Col, 39, M.S, 41; Univ. Chicago, 42-43; fel, Univ. Ill, 47-48, Ph.D, 50. Asst. instr. ENG, Univ. Kans, 43-44; asst, Univ. Ill, 44-49; asst. prof. Kans. State Univ, 49-65; assoc. prof, SOUTHWEST. COL.(KANS), 65-67, PROF, 67-, CHMN. DIV. LANG. & LIT, 65- NCTE; Int. Arthurian Soc; Conf. Col. Compos. & Commun; Mediaeval Acad. Am; Midwest Mod. Lang. Asn. Late Middle English; Arthurian romance; Malory. Add: Dept. of English, Southwestern College, Winfield, KS 67156.

WULBERN, JULIAN H, German, Comparative Literature. See Volume III, Foreign Languages, Linguistics & Philology.

WULLING, EMERSON G, b. Minneapolis, Minn, July 26, 03; m. 38; c. 3. BIBLIOGRAPHY. B.A, Univ. Minn, 23, Ph.D, 38; M.A, Harvard, 28; Univ. London, 30. Instr. Eng, Hamline Univ, 26-30; lectr. art & printing, Minneapolis Inst. & Sch. Art, 32-36; prof. ENG, UNIV. WIS-LA CROSSE, 38-73, chmn. dept, 57-60, EMER. PROF, 73- Bibliog. Soc, Eng; Bibliog. Soc. Am; Am. Inst. Graphic Arts; NCTE. Private press bibliography. Publ: Comp's-eye view of type, 47, Comp's-eye view of punctuation, 62 & Comp's-eye view of paper, 71, Sumac; plus one other. Add: 613 N. 22nd St, La Crosse, WI 54601.

WURTELE, DOUGLAS J, b. Montreal, Que, Feb. 5, 22; m. 65. ENGLISH. B.A, Univ. London, 56; M.A, McGill Univ, 63, Ph.D.(Eng), 68. Lectr. ENG, CARLETON UNIV, 60-62, 65, asst. prof, 66-69, ASSOC. PROF, 69- Chaucer studies. Add: Dept. of English, Carleton University, Ottawa, Ont. K1S 5B6, Can.

WYANT, JEROME LEE, b. Waterbury, Conn, July 21, 41; m. 68; c. 2. ENGLISH & AMERICAN LITERATURE. B.A, St. Francis Col.(Maine), 63; M.A, John Carroll Univ, 65; Vanderbilt Univ, 65-66; Ph.D.(Eng), Univ. Nebr-Lincoln, 72. Instr. ENG, Univ. Nebr, 66-71; ASST. PROF, COL. OF ST. JOSEPH THE PROVIDER, 71- MLA; Dickens Soc; AAUP. Nineteenth century British novel and poetry; 20th century British literature. Publ: The legal episodes in Browning's The ring and the book, Victorian Poetry, 68; Modern poetry, Prairie Schooner, 71. Add: Dept. of English, College of St. Joseph the Provider, Clement Rd, Rutland, VT 05701.

WYATT, BRYANT NELSON, b. Waverly, Va, Sept. 6, 37. AMERICAN LITERATURE, COMPOSITION. A.B, Va. State Col, 59; Woodrow Wilson fel, Boston Univ, 59-60, M.A, 60; Wemyss Found. fel, Univ. Del, summer 64; Ford Found advan. stud. grant, Univ. Va, 69-70, Ph.D.(Eng), 70. Instr. ENG, VA. STATE COL, 63-66, asst. prof, 66-70, ASSOC. PROF, 70- Teacher, Univ. Va, 68-69; Va. Commonwealth Univ, summer 70. Adj.Gen.C, U.S.A, 60-62, Res, 62-68, Capt. AAUP; MLA; Col. Lang. Asn. Southern literature; contemporary American novel; Afro-American literature. Publ: John Updike: the psychological novel in search of structure, 20th Century Lit, 7/67; The protest novels of John Steinbeck, Discourse, spring 69; Naturalism as expediency in the novels of Frank Norris, Markham Rev, 2/71. Add: Dept. of English, Virginia State College, Petersburg, VA 23803.

WYATT, ROBERT ODELL, II, b. Jackson, Tenn, Feb. 7, 46; m. 67. ENGLISH LITERATURE. B.A, Univ. of the South, 68; Seabury-West. Theol. Sem, Ill, 68-69; M.A, Northwest. Univ, 70, Ph.D.(Eng), 73. ASST. PROF. ENG, UNIV. TENN, NASHVILLE, 73- MLA. Renaissance literature: theology and literature; literary criticism. Publ: Co-auth, A bibliography of research on the Elizabethan stage since Chambers, In: Research opportunities in Renaissance drama, (in press). Add: Dept. of English, University of Tennessee at Nashville, 323 McLemore St, Nashville, TN 37203.

WYATT, SIBYL W, b. Hemphill, Tex, Nov. 12, 08; div; c. 1. ENGLISH LITERATURE. B.S, Stephen F. Austin State Col, 38, M.A, 48, B.A, 53; summers Univ. Colo, 47-52; fel. & Ph.D.(Eng), Rice Univ, 63. Teacher, High Schs, Tex, 28-47, 53-54; asst. prof. ENG, STEPHEN F. AUSTIN STATE UNIV, 55-58, assoc. prof, 58-67, PROF, 67- English Romantic poets. Publ: English Romantic novel, Exposition, 67. Add: Dept. of English, Stephen F. Austin State University, Nacogdoches, TX 75961.

WYKOFF, GEORGE STEWARD, b. New Columbia, Pa, June 28, 99; m. 35. COMPOSITION & LITERATURE. A.B, Pa. State Univ, 20; A.M, Columbia Univ, 22. Instr. ENG, PURDUE UNIV, WEST LAFAYETTE, 22-29, asst. prof, 29-40, assoc. prof, 40-45, prof, 45-67, EMER. PROF, 67- British literature, 18th century; composition; college teaching of English. Publ: Co-auth, Freshman prose annual, Vols. I, II, III, IV, Houghton, 40-45; & Handbook of college composition, Harper, 52, 57, 62, 69. Add: 1607 Ravinia Rd, West Lafayette, IN 47906.

WYLDER, DELBERT E, b. Jerseyville, Ill, Oct. 5, 23; m. 65; c. 2. ENGLISH. B.A, Univ. Iowa, 48, M.F.A, 50, Ph.D.(Eng), 68. Asst. prof. Eng, Bemidji State Col, 68-69; PROF. LIT, SOUTHWEST MINN. STATE COL, 69- MLA; AAUP. Ernest Hemingway; Western American literature; modern American literature. Publ: Hemingway's heroes, Univ. N.Mex, 69; Emerson Hough, Steck-Vaughn, 69; Emerson Hough's Heart's desire, West. Am. Lit, Vol. 1, No. 1; The novels of William Eastlake, N.Mex. Quart, Vol. 34, No. 2; contrib, chap, In: Hemingway in our time, Ore. State Univ, 73; plus one other. Add: Literature & American Language Dept, Southwest Minnesota State College, Marshall, MN 56258.

WYLDER, EDITH PERRY, b. Akron, Ohio, Feb. 15, 25; m. 65; c. 2. ENGLISH. B.A, Univ. Akron, 47; M.A, Univ. N.Mex, 49, Ph.D.(Eng), 67. Asst. prof. LIT, SOUTHWEST MINN. STATE COL, 69-71, assoc. prof, 71-73, PROF, 73- Mem. sem. lit. & cult. in Am. & Nat. Endowment Humanities grant, Univ. Calif, Berkeley, summer 73. MLA. Emily Dickinson. Publ: The last face: Emily Dickinson's manuscripts, Univ. N.Mex, 71; Emily Dickinson: poetry and punctuation, Saturday Rev, 3/30/63; The speaker of Emily Dickinson's My life had stood a loaded gun, Rocky Mt. Mod. Lang. Asn. Bull, 3/69. Add: Literature & American Language Dept, Southwest Minnesota State College, Marshall, MN 56258.

WYLDER, ROBERT CLAY, b. Malta, Mont, Jan. 10, 21; m. 44; c. 3. AMERICAN LITERATURE. B.A, Mont. State Univ, 47, M.A, 49; Ph.D, Univ. Wis, 55. Instr. ENG, CALIF. STATE UNIV, LONG BEACH, 53-55, asst. prof, 55-59, assoc. prof, 59-63, prof, 63- U.S.M.C.R. 43-46, Maj. NCTE; Col. Conf. Compos. & Commun. Composition. Publ: Co-auth, The narrative impulse, Odyssey, 63 & Functional English for writers, Scott, 64; co-auth, Rx: remedies for writing, 64 & Limits and latitudes, 65, Lippincott; co-auth, Writing practical English, 66 & auth, Writer to reader: fact and form, 68, Macmillan; co-auth, There is no away, Glencoe, 71. Add: 1817 Iroquois Ave, Long Beach, CA 90815.

WYLIE, DONALD GEORGE, b. Grand Rapids, Mich, May 29, 33; m. 68; c. 2. EDUCATION, SPEECH. A.B, Univ. Mich, 55; M.A, Mich. State Univ, 65, Ph.D.(educ), 67. Producer-dir. TV prod, Mich. State Univ, 59-60; asst. to pres, Fideler Co, 60-61; asst. dir. course develop, Midwest Prog. on Airborne TV Prod, 61-63; asst. prof. speech, SAN DIEGO STATE UNIV, 66-69, ASSOC. PROF. TELECOMMUNICATIONS & FILM, 69- Consult, San Diego Unified Sch. Dist, 66-71; Washington County Schs, Md, 66-69, state & local sch. syst. & univs; dir. Prog. for Afloat Col. Educ, 71-72. U.S.N, 55-58, Res, 58-, Lt. Comdr. NEA; Broadcast Educ. Asn; Asn. Educ. Commun. & Technol; West. Educ. Soc. Telecommunications (dir, 72-74). Instructional television effects especially the interaction of use of TV and learner variables. Publ: ITV rights: model policy statements, NAEB J, 5-6/66; Needed a new image for ITV, 5/71, Audiovisual Instr; An ITV Information office, Audiovisual Forum, 6/71; plus two others. Add: Dept. of Telecommunications & Film, San Diego State University, 5402 College Ave, San Diego, CA 92115.

WYMAN, LINDA LEE, b. Rockford, Ill, Apr. 1, 37. ENGLISH LITERATURE. A.B, South. Methodist Univ, 58; M.A, Univ. Mo-Columbia, 60; Ph.D.(Eng), George Peabody Col, 71. Instr. ENG, West. Ky. Univ, 60-65; ASSOC. PROF, MOTLOW STATE COMMUNITY COL, 71- Nat. Endowment for Humanities summer stipend, 73. Col. Eng. Asn; MLA; Midwest Mod. Lang. Asn; NCTE; AAUP. T.S. Eliot's plays; literary criticism; modern poetry. Publ: Concerning the relevance of Falconers (poems), 3/71 & Anthologizing (poem), 5/73, CEA Critic; Un-common mythology, CEA Forum, 74. Add: Dept. of English, Motlow State Community College, Tullahoma, TN 37388.

WYNN, DUDLEY, b. Cooper, Tex, Oct. 2, 04; m. 25; c. 1. ENGLISH LITERATURE, HUMANITIES. A.B, Univ. Tex, 25; A.M, N.Y. Univ, 29, Ph.D, 40. Instr. Eng, N.Y. Univ, 26-30, 31-33; Univ. N.Mex, 34-35, asst. prof, 35-39, assoc. prof, 39-44, prof, 44-47; prof. Eng. & chmn. staff gen. humanities course, Univ. Colo, 47-53; prof. Eng, UNIV. N.MEX, 53-71, dean col. arts & sci, 53-61, dir. gen. honors prog, 61-71, EMER. PROF. ENG. & EMER. DIR. GEN. HONORS PROG, 71- Ed, N.Mex. Quart. Rev, 40-47; Colo. Quart, 51-53; exec. secy, N.Mex. Humanities Counc, 72-73. Warshaw Essay Award. MLA; Nat. Col. Honors Counc.(v.pres, 67-68, pres, 68-69); Rocky Mountain Mod. Lang. Asn; AAUP. General humanities; Joseph Conrad; contemporary criticism. Publ: Integrity of T.S. Eliot, In: Writers of our years, Univ. Denver Stud. in Humanities, 50; Honors and the university, In: The superior student in American higher education, McGraw, 66; Honors programs and innovation, J. Higher Educ, 4/70; plus others. Add: 3807 Riverview Rd, NW, Albuquerque, NM 87105.

WYNN, EARL, b. Coal Valley, Ill, Nov. 25, 11; m. 52; c. 1. PERFORMING ARTS. A.B, Augustana Col, 32; M.S, Northwest. Univ, 34. Asst. prof. Eng. & speech & in charge div. speech, Tarkio Col, 34-36; from asst. to instr. speech, Northwest. Univ, 36-38; instr. dramatic art, UNIV. N.C, CHAPEL HILL, 38-40, asst. prof. dramatic art & in charge radio, 40-43, PROF. RADIO, TV & MOTION PICTURES, 47-, chmn. dept. & dir. commun. ctr, 47-62, dir. TV, 56-57, 58-59, producer & dir, Men in action, 41-42. TV consult, Fla. State Univ, 59; reader, Readers Theatre of N.C, spring 73 & Bi-centennial reader, 74. Writer & producer training films, Qm.C, Camp Lee, Va, 42-43; U.S.N.R, 42-46, Res, 46-52, Lt. Am. Theatre Asn; Nat. Asn. Educ. Broadcasters (chmn, prof. advan. comt, 50-54); Soc. Cinema Stud. Radio; television. Publ: Television: a new dimension in speech, In: The art of speaking, Ginn, 66; Performing, In: Radio broadcasting, Hastings, 67. Add: Dept. of Radio, Television & Motion Pictures, University of North Carolina at Chapel Hill, Chapel Hill, NC 27514.

WYNN, LAWRENCE, b. Pulaski, Tenn, Nov. 8, 15; m. 43. ENGLISH. A.B, Emory Univ, 36; M.A, Duke Univ, 40; univ. scholar & MacDonald fel, Princeton, M.A, 47, Ph.D.(Eng), 51. Teacher, High Sch, Ga, 36-41; lectr. ENG, Univ. Calif, Los Angeles, 48-50; asst. prof, MEMPHIS STATE UNIV, 50-56, assoc. prof, 56-61, PROF, 61- U.S.N.R, 42-45, Lt. Col. Eng. Asn; NCTE; MLA; S.Atlantic Mod. Lang. Asn; S.Cent. Mod. Lang. Asn; South.

Humanities Conf; AAUP; Tennyson Soc. Romantic period of English literature; Victorian literature; literary criticism. Add: 610 W. Clover Dr, Memphis, TN 38117.

WYRICK, GREEN D, b. Ash Grove, Mo, July 6, 20; m. 42; c. 3. ENGLISH. B.A, Univ. Mo, 47, M.A, 49; Ph.D.(Eng), Univ. Denver, 57. Instr. ENG, KANS. STATE TEACHERS COL, 49-52, asst. prof, 52-57, assoc. prof, 57-60, PROF, 60- U.S.A.F, 42-45, S/Sgt. NCTE; Midwest Mod. Lang.Asn. The modern American novel and poetry; teaching creative writing. Publ: The world of Ernest Hemingway, Kans. State Teachers Col, 53; Hemingway and Bergson, Mod. Fiction Stud, 56. Add: Dept. of English, Kansas State Teachers College, Emporia, KS 66801.

WYSONG, JOHN N, b. Portland, Ore, Jan. 8, 24; m. 48; c. 5. ENGLISH. B.A, Univ. Ore, 49; M.A, Univ. Calif, Berkeley, 51; Ph.D, Univ. Innsbruck, Austria, 58. Instr. ENG, Anderson Col.(Ind), 52-54; ASSOC. PROF, U.S. NAVAL ACAD, 54- U.S.A, 43-46. MLA. Late Victorian and Edwardian poetry; A.E. Housman. Publ: A.E. Housman's use of astronomy, Anglia, fall 63. Add: Dept. of English, U.S. Naval Academy, Annapolis, MD 21402.

WYVELL, MARY LUND, b. St. Paul, Minn, Oct. 31, 16; m. 35, 61; c. 4. WRITING, LITERATURE. B.A, Univ. Minn, 38, M.A, 41, Ph.D.(Eng), 53. Instr. LIT. & WRITING, UNIV. MINN, MINNEAPOLIS, 51-52, asst. prof, 57-66, assoc. prof, 67-73, PROF, 73- English and American novel; Indo-Anglian novel; non-Western contemporary literature in translation. Publ: American Haiku: a classroom experiment, Improving Col. & Univ. Teaching, spring 73. Add: 512 Westwood Village, Roseville, MN 55113.

Y

YABLONKY, BEN, b. Chicago, Ill, Aug. 26, 11; m. 41; c. 2. JOURNALISM, MASS COMMUNICATIONS. B.S, Northwest. Univ, Evanston, 34; M.A, Columbia Univ, 54; Nieman fel, Harvard, 45-46; Ford fel, Univ. Mich, Ann Arbor, 57-58; Fulbright fel, Osmania Univ, India, 65-66. Reporter & ed, Chicago Herald & Examiner, 36-40; asst. state supvr, Ill. WPA Writers Proj, 40-42; ed. & newscaster, WJWC Radio, Chicago, 42-43; nat. & labor ed, Newspaper PM, New York City, 43-48; assoc. prof. JOUR, N.Y. Univ, 48-59; PROF, UNIV. MICH, ANN ARBOR, 59-, DIR. NAT. ENDOWMENT FOR HUMANITIES FELS, 73- Writer & producer, CBS News, New York, N.Y, 55-66; ed, NBC News, Chicago, 61-62. Radio-TV News Dir. Asn; Asn. Educ. in Jour. Publ: Co-auth, Your newspaper—blueprint for better press, MacMillan, 47; auth, Newspaper writing, In: How to write for pleasure and profit, Lippincott, 50. Add: Dept. of Journalism, University of Michigan, Ann Arbor, MI 48104.

YACKSHAW, ROBERT R, b. Clinton, Iowa, Aug. 13, 25; m. 52; c. 12. ENGLISH LITERATURE. B.A, St. Ambrose Col, 46; M.A, State Univ. Iowa, 48, Ph.D, 54. Instr. ENG, JOHN CARROLL UNIV, 54-56, asst. prof, 56-61, assoc. prof, 61-68, PROF, 68- U.S.M.C, 43-45, 2nd Lt. MLA. British literature, 1880 to the present; Elizabethan drama; 17th century literature. Add: Dept. of English, John Carroll University, Cleveland, OH 44118.

YACOWAR, MAURICE, b. Prelate, Sask, Mar. 25, 42; m. 73. ENGLISH LITERATURE, FILM. B.A, Univ. Alta, Calgary, 62; M.A, Univ. Alta, Edmonton, 65; Ph.D.(Eng), Univ. Birmingham, 68. Lectr. Eng, Lethbridge Jr. Col, 64-66; Mt. Royal Jr. Col, 65; asst. prof, BROCK UNIV, 68-72, ASSOC. PROF. DRAMA & CHMN. DEPT, 72- Popular Cult. Asn; Asn. Can. Univ. Teachers Eng. Film; popular culture; pre-Shakespearean fiction. Publ: No use shutting the door, Fiddlehead, 71; Public and private visions, J. Popular Film, summer 72; Hitchcock's I confess, Film Heritage, VII:19-25. Add: Dept. of Drama, Brock University, St. Catharines, Ont, Can.

YANG, DANIEL SHIH P'ENG, b. Wuhsi, China, June 21, 35; m. 63; c. 2. DRAMA, THEATRE. B.A, Nat. Taiwan Univ, 59; fel, Univ. Hawaii, 61-63, M.F.A, 64; fel, Univ. Wis, 64-66, Ph.D.(speech), 68. Res. asst. speech, Univ. Wis, 66-67; asst. prof. speech & drama, UNIV. COLO, BOULDER, 67-70, ASSOC. PROF, THEATRE, 70- Vis. assoc. prof. drama & theatre, Univ. Hawaii, Manoa, 70-71; transl. & dir, Black dragon residence (a traditional Peking opera), Univ. Hawaii, spring 72 & Am. Col. Theatre Festival, Kennedy Ctr, 4/72; Univ. Colo, Boulder fac. fel, summer 69 & 73-74. Chinese Army, 60-61, 2nd Lt. Am. Theatre Asn.(v.chmn, Asian Theatre Proj, 69-71, chmn, Asian Theatre Prog, 71-73); Asn. Asian Stud. Theatre of China; stage directing; theatre history. Publ: An annotated bibliography of materials for the study of Peking theatre, Univ. Wis, 67; The Peking theatre under communism, Theatre Annual, 68; Peking drama with contemporary themes, Drama Rev, summer 69; Staging a traditional Peking opera with American actors and musicians, Educ. Theatre J, 10/71. Add: University Theatre, University of Colorado, Boulder, CO 80302.

YANG, WINSTON LIH-YEU, Chinese & Comparative Literature. See Volume III, Foreign Languages, Linguistics & Philology.

YANNELLA, PHILIP RICHARD, b. New York, N.Y, Jan. 22, 40; m. 65; c. 2. ENGLISH & AMERICAN LITERATURE. B.A, N.Y. Univ, 62, M.A, 65; Ph.D. (Eng), Univ. Wis-Milwaukee, 71. ASST. PROF. ENG, TEMPLE UNIV, 69- Rev. ed, J. Mod. Lit. MLA; AAUP. Modern American poetry; science and literature, particularly the relationships between theoretical physics and modern poetry. Publ: Toward apotheosis: Hart Crane's visionary lyrics, Criticism, 68; Problems of dislocation in Pale horse, pale rider, Stud. Short Fiction, 70; ed, Joyce, to The little review, J. Mod. Lit, 71. Add: Dept. of English, Temple University, Philadelphia, PA 19122.

YARBER, ROBERT EARL, b. East St. Louis, Ill, Sept. 28, 29; m. 52; c. 3. ENGLISH. B.A, McKendree Col, 51; M.A, St. Louis Univ, 53. Instr. & coord. ENG, East St. Louis Sr. High Sch, 53-63; PROF, SAN DIEGO MESA COL, 63- Eng. consult, J.B. Lippincott Publ, Inc, 67-, series ed; bk. ed, San Diego Times-Rev, 73- NCTE; Conf. Col. Compos. & Commun. Composition; linguistics; 17th century English literature. Publ: Co-auth, Reading, writing and rhetoric, 67 & 72, Phase blue: a systems approach to English, 70, 74 & Cycle 7, 73, Sci. Res. Assocs; co-auth, College reading and writing, Macmillan, 68; co-auth, Language: an introductory reader, Harper, 69; auth, Breakthrough, Cummings Publ, 69 & 73; co-auth, An introduction to poetry and criticism, 70, An introduction to drama and criticism, 71 & An introduction to short fiction and criticism, 71, Xerox; co-auth, The art of making sense, 3rd ed, Lippincott, 74. Add: 4125 Rochester Rd, San Diego, CA 92116.

YARBOROUGH, BETTY HATHAWAY, b. Portsmouth, Va, Apr. 17, 27; m. 49. ENGLISH, EDUCATION. A.B, Duke Univ, 48; M.A, Col. William & Mary, 55; Univ. Miami, 60; Richmond Prof. Inst, 63; Ed.D, Univ. Va, 64. Teacher, High Sch, Va, 48-56; supvr. lang. arts, Chesapeake Pub. Schs, Va, 56-57, High Sch, 57-66, dir. lang. arts, 66-72; PROF. EDUC, OLD DOM. UNIV, 72- Instr. Col. William & Mary, exten. classes, 57-67; vis. instr, Univ. Va, summers 59-62, instr, Hampton Roads Ctr, 65-, vis. instr, Mich. State Univ, summer 65, Old Dom. Univ, 67-72; Univ. Victoria (B.C), summer 68, educ. diagnostician, Psychiat. Assocs, Ltd, Portsmouth, Va, 71-; prin. investr. res. prof, Nat. Inst. Educ; Old Dom. Univ. Res. Found. grant. Ullin Leavell Award, Univ. Va, 67. Am. Educ. Res. Asn; Am. Psychol. Asn; NCTE; Conf. Res. Eng; Int. Reading Asn; Counc. Except. Children; Nat. Reading Conf; MLA; Nat. Counc. Measurement Educ; Col. Reading Asn. Initial screening and diagnostic procedures; vocabulary development of high school English students; the relationship of cerebral dominance to achievement in reading. Publ: Co-auth, Sound and sense in spelling (textbks. grades 1-8), Harcourt, 64, rev. ed, 68; auth, On wings of words, (reader & teacher's ed), Macmillan, 71; This is the way we go to school at Chesapeake Primary Demonstration School, 71; co-auth, A comparison of ten different beginning reading programs in first grade, Phi Delta Kappan, 6/65; auth, A systems approach to reading readiness, In: Yearbook, 1971-72, associated public school systems, Teachers Col, Columbia Univ, 71; entry on initial reading instruction, In: Encycl. Educ, Macmillan, 71. Add: School of Education, Old Dominion University, Norfolk, VA 23508.

YARINA, MARGARET ANNE, b. Yonkers, N.Y, May 27, 37. ENGLISH. B.A, Hartwick Col, 59; N.Y. State Regents fel. & M.A, Fordham Univ, 61; summers, State Univ. N.Y. Col. Oneonta, 62-64; Ph.D.(Am. lit), State Univ. N.Y. Binghamton, 73. Instr. ENG, MARYWOOD COL, 61-64, asst. prof, 64-74, ASSOC. PROF, 74-, asst. chmn. dept, 65-67, chmn. dept, 67-69. NCTE; AAUP; MLA. Henry James; 19th century American literature. Publ: The dualistic vision of Herman Melville's The encantadas, J. Narrative Tech, 5/73. Add: Dept. of English, Marywood College, Scranton, PA 18509.

YARRINGTON, H. ROGER, b. Des Moines, Iowa, Oct. 17, 31; m. 57; c. 3. JOURNALISM, AMERICAN STUDIES. B.S, Univ. Kans, 53; M.A, State Univ. Iowa, 56; Ph.D.(Am. stud), Univ. Md, College Park, 70. Managing ed, Herald House & ed, Saints Herald, Mo, 55-63; DIR. PUBL. & ED. JR. COL. J, AM. ASN. COMMUNITY & JR. COLS, 63-, V.PRES, 74-, moderator of the assembly, 72-74. Lectr. jour, Univ. Md, College Park, 72- Intel.C, U.S.A, 53-55, Sgt. Am. Stud. Asn; Asn. Educ. in Jour. History of the press. Publ: Auth, The auditorium, 62 & Restoration ethics today, 64, Herald, ed, Junior colleges: 50 states/50 years, 69, International development of the junior college idea, 70, An agenda for national action, 73 & Newstaff for new students, 74, Am. Asn. Community & Jr. Cols. Add: American Association of Community & Junior Colleges, One Dupont Circle, N.W, Washington, DC 20036.

YATES, NORRIS WILSON, b. Corvallis, Ore, Feb. 22, 23. ENGLISH, SPEECH. B.A, Univ. Ore, 46; M.A, Univ. Wis, 47; Ph.D, N.Y. Univ, 53. Instr. Eng, Univ. Ark, 47-49; Univ. S.Dak, 52-53; Eng. & speech, IOWA STATE UNIV, 53-54, asst. prof, 54-58, assoc. prof. ENG, 58-63, PROF, 63- Fulbright lectr. Am. lit, Univ. Hamburg, 64-65; Univ. Helsinki, 68-69. MLA; Am. Stud. Asn. American literature and folklore. Publ: William Trotter Porter and the spirit of the times, La. State Univ, 57; The American humorist: conscience of the twentieth century, Iowa State Univ, 63; Guenter Grass: a critical essay, Eerdmans, 67; Robert Benchley, Twayne, 68; The counter-conversation of Huckleberry Finn, Am. Lit, 60; What makes the modern American novel modern?, Jahrbuch Amerikastud, 66. Add: Dept. of English, Iowa State University, Ames, IA 50010.

YATRON, MICHAEL, b. Reading, Pa, July 20, 21; m. 54; c. 2. ENGLISH. B.S.Ed, Kutztown State Col, 42; Harvard, 42-43; Univ. Calif, Berkeley, 43-44, 45-46; M.A, Temple Univ, 50, Ph.D.(Eng), 57. Teaching asst. ENG, Temple Univ, 49-50; instr, Col. Agr, Univ. P.R, Mayaguez, 53-55; PROF, Del. State Col, 57-63; KUTZTOWN STATE COL, 63- U.S.A, 43-45. NCTE. American literature. Publ: American's literary revolt, Philos. Libr, 59. Add: Dept. of English, Kutztown State College, Kutztown, PA 19530.

YEAGER, RAYMOND, b. Smithsferry, Pa, Apr. 11, 20; m. 41; c. 2. SPEECH. B.S, Bowling Green State Univ, 49, M.A, 50; Ph.D, Ohio State Univ, 56, Instr. SPEECH, BOWLING GREEN STATE UNIV, 50-56, asst. prof, 56-60, assoc. prof, 60-64, PROF, 64-, DIR. FORENSICS, 73-, head pub. address: 61-72. Creative Educ. Found. fel, Univ. Buffalo, 59; consult, Ohio Bell Tel. Co, 60-; Standard Oil Col. Ohio, 67- Pi Kappa Delta Distinguished Alumnus Award, 63, Distinguished Serv. Award, 66; Outstanding Teacher Award, Bowling Green State Univ, 69. U.S.A.A.F, 42-45, U.S.A.F, 51-52, Capt. Speech Commun. Asn; Cent. States Speech Asn. Contemporary American political speaking; classical rhetoric and public address: discussion and debate. Publ: Co-auth, Speaker's guide to syllogistic reasoning, W.C. Brown, 67; auth, chap, In: Introduction to speech communication, W.C. Brown, 68. Add: 1034 Carol Rd, Bowling Green, OH 43402.

YEATON, KELLY, b. Portland, Maine, Apr. 21, 11; m. 55. THEATRE ARTS. B.S, Tufts Col, 32; A.M, Univ. Wash, 38. Instr. theatre acting & directing, Univ. Wash, 39-40; dir. community theatres, St. Louis, Mo, Lafayette, Ind. & Erie, Pa, 40-42; dean prof. stud, dramatic workshop, New Sch. Social Res, 46-47; from instr. to assoc. prof. THEATRE ARTS, PA. STATE UNIV, UNIVERSITY PARK, 47-70, PROF, 70- Guest dir, Stadium Theatre, Ohio State Univ, summer 61; managing dir, Arena Theatre, State Univ. N.Y. Albany, summer 64; guest dir, Stowe Repertory Theatre, summer 69. U.S.A.A.F, 42-45. Am. Theatre Asn; Am. Nat. Theatre & Acad.(dir, 63-65); U.S. Inst. Theater Technol. Arena theatre research; experimental theatre;

happenings and other performance structures. Publ: Co-auth, Creative process, Univ. Bookstore, Univ. Park, 62; auth, Arena production, In: Producing the play, Holt, 53; The great gaming house, Tulane Drama Rev, winter 65. Add: Dept. of Theatre Arts, Pennsylvania State University, University Park, PA 16802.

YEATS, ALVICE WHITEHURST, b. Snyder, Tex, Sept. 13, 10. ENGLISH LITERATURE. B.A, McMurry Col, 32; M.A, Univ. Tex, 40, fel, 50, Ph.D, 61. Teacher ENG, High Schs, Tex, 33-42; assoc. prof, Sam Houston State Col, 46-57; McMurry Col, 58-60; from assoc. prof. to PROF, LAMAR UNIV, 61- Kipling specialist to Dalhousie Univ, 56-57. U.S.N.R, 42-46, Lt.(jg). The writing and literary career of Rudyard Kipling; writings and career of Robert Browning; 19th century bibliography. Publ: Kipling collections: an appraisal, Printing Arts, Austin, Tex, 61; co-auth, Rudyard Kipling: a bibliographical catalogue, Univ. Toronto, 59. Add: Dept. of English, Lamar University, Beaumont, TX 77710.

YEATS, DONALD I, b. Kansas City, Mo, Oct. 22, 39; m. 59; c. 3. ENGLISH. B.A, Rockhurst Col, 61; M.A, Univ. Kans, 63, Ph.D.(Eng), 67. ASST. PROF. ENG, UNIV. MO-COLUMBIA, 66- MLA; Midwest Mod. Lang. Asn. Restoration, 18th century British literature; satire. Publ: Dryden's Cromwell: public hero and private villain, Clio, 73. Add: Dept. of English, 231 Arts & Science, University of Missouri-Columbia, Columbia, MO 65201.

YEAZELL, RUTH BERNARD, b. New York, N.Y, Apr. 4, 47; m. 69. ENGLISH & AMERICAN LITERATURE. B.A, Swarthmore Col, 67; Woodrow Wilson fel, Yale Univ, 67-68, M.Phil, 70, Ph.D.(Eng), 71. ASST. PROF. ENG, BOSTON UNIV, 71- MLA; Eng. Inst. Novel; modern literature; women in fiction. Publ: The new arithmetic of Henry James, Criticism, (in prep); More true than real: Jane Eyre's mysterious summons, 19th-Century Fiction, (in prep); Fictional heroines and the limits of the imagination, Novel, (in prep). Add: Dept. of English, Boston University, 236 Bay State Rd, Boston, MA 02215.

YEH, MAX WEI, b. Peking, China, Aug. 1, 37; U.S. citizen; m. 63. COMPARATIVE & ENGLISH LITERATURE. B.A, Amherst Col, 59; M.A, Columbia Univ, 61; univ. fel, Univ. Iowa, 65-66, Ph.D.(comp. lit), 70; Ford Found. fel, Warburg Inst, London, 66-68. Asst. prof. ENG. & COMP. LIT, Univ. Calif, Irvine, 68-74; ASSOC. PROF, HOBART & WILLIAM SMITH COLS, 74- Mem. Humanities Inst, Univ. Calif, Irvine, 72-73. Literary theory; interrelations between the arts; the 17th century. Publ: Poetry, art, and the structure of thought, Mouton, The Hague, 74. Add: Dept. of English, Hobart & William Smith Colleges, Geneva, NY 14456.

YELLEN, SAMUEL, b. Vilna, Russia, July 7, 06; U.S. citizen; m. 31, 66. ENGLISH. A.B, West. Reserve Univ, 26, A.M, Oberlin Col, 32. Instr. ENG, IND. UNIV, BLOOMINGTON, 29-41, asst. prof, 41-47, assoc. prof, 47-53, prof, 53-63, UNIV. PROF, 63- Consult, Army Inst, 43; Guggenheim fel, 63-64. Daroff Mem. Fiction Award, 62. PEN Club; MLA. Publ: American labor struggles, Harcourt, 36; In the house and out and other poems, 52, & New and selected poems, 64 & The convex mirror: collected poems, 71, Ind. Univ; Passionate shepherd: a book of stories, Knopf, 57; Wedding band, Atheneum, 61. Add: 922 E. University St, Bloomington, IN 47401.

YELLIN, DAVID GILMER, b. Philadelphia, Pa, Apr. 3, 16; m. 50; c. 4. BROADCASTING & FILM. A.B, Pa. State Col, 37; M.A, Columbia Univ, 63. Instr. commun, Voorhees Tech. Inst, 62-64; asst. prof. broadcasting, MEMPHIS STATE UNIV, 64-67, ASSOC. PROF. BROADCASTING & FILM, 67- Producer & moderator, Face to Face (TV prog), WMC-TV-AM-FM, 69-; dir, Multi-Media Sanitation Strike Proj, Nat. Endowment for Humanities, 71-74; U.S.A, 41-45. Broadcast Educ. Asn; Univ. Film Asn. Television documentaries; television dramatic productions. Publ: Special: Fred Freed and the television documentary, Macmillan, 73. Add: Dept. of Speech & Drama, Memphis State University, Memphis, TN 38152.

YELLIN, JEAN FAGAN, b. Lansing, Mich, Sept. 19, 30; m. 48; c. 3. AMERICAN LITERATURE & STUDIES. B.A, Roosevelt Univ, 51; M.A, Univ. Ill, Urbana, 63; Am. Asn. Univ. Women fel, 67-68, Ph.D.(Eng), 69. ASST. PROF, ENG, PACE UNIV, 68- Nat. Endowment for Humanities younger humanist fel, 74-75. Am. Stud. Asn; Asn. Stud. Afro-Am. Life & Hist; Col. Lang. Asn; Melville Soc; MLA; Northeast Mod. Lang. Asn; Women's Caucus Mod. Lang. American literature and culture; women's studies; radical literature. Publ: Auth, Introd, W.W. Brown's Clotel, Arno & N.Y. Times, 69; The intricate knot: black figures in American literature, 1776-1863, N.Y. Univ, 72; Black masks: Melville's Benito Cereno, Am. Quart, fall 70; An index of literary materials in The crisis, 1910-1934: articles, belles lettres, and book reviews, CLA J, 6 & 12/71; DuBois' Crisis and woman's suffrage, Mass. Rev, spring 73. Add: 38 Lakeside Dr, New Rochelle, NY 10801.

YEOMANS, GORDON ALLAN, b. Cherry Valley, Ohio, Sept. 30, 21; m. 49. SPEECH. B.A, Southwest. La. Inst, 51; M.A, La. State Univ, 52, Ph.D. (speech), 66; Danforth Found. grant, 56-57, summer 63. Instr. SPEECH, Univ. Miss, 52; assoc. prof. & head dept, Samford Univ, 52-66; assoc. prof, Univ. Southwest. La, 66-67; prof. & head dept, Miss. State Col. Women, 67-68; PROF, UNIV. TENN, KNOXVILLE, 68- Commun. consult, Union Carbide Corp, 69-72; Commun. lectr, Magnavox Corp. Leadership Conf, 72, Mgt. Analysts Inst, U.S. Dept. Labor, 72; Univ. Tenn. res. grant, summer 73. U.S.A, 40-45. Speech Commun. Asn; South. Speech Commun. Asn. American oratory; Southern oratory; theatre history. Publ: A handbook for speakers, Union Carbide Corp, 69; Southern oratory and the art of storytelling, South. Speech J, summer 67; co-auth, Telelectures, Speech Teacher, 1/69. Add: 805 Norgate Rd, Knoxville, TN 37919.

YERBURY, GRACE D, b. Danbury, Conn, July 8, 99; m. 22; wid. ENGLISH, MUSIC. B.A, Hunter Col, 20; B.Mus, N.Y. Univ, 31; M.A, Columbia Univ, 33; Ph.D, Ind. Univ, 53; Los Angeles Conserv. Workshop of Opera, summer 56. Instr. music, N.Y. Univ, 45-48; assoc. prof, Moravian Col, Women, 48-50; res. asst. psychol. warfare, George Washington Univ, 50-51; instr. music, Northeast La. State Col, 52-54; prof. music & Eng, Oakland City Col, 56-57; prof. Eng. & head dept, Campbellsville Col, 57-59; Mo. Valley Col, 60-69; RES. & WRITING, 69- Grad. asst, Ind. Univ, 50-52; Andrew Carnegie Auth. Fund res. grant, 56-57; ed, Rockford Rev, 71. Southwest Writer's Conf. Harrison Smith Essay Award, 56; Deep South Writers' Conf. Clara

Thompson Wilkinson Mem. Award, 65; Woman of Year & Hall of Fame, Mo. Valley Col, 73. NCTE; Int. Poetry Soc. Contemporary poetry and fiction; Shakespeare; Dylan Thomas. Publ: Refracted light, Pageant, 57; Reed song, Naylor, 65; Vistas unvisited (poetry), Prairie Press, 72; Delinquency vs. creative dramatics, Adult Leadership, 11/60; Of a city beside a river: Whitman, Eliot, Thomas, Miller, Walt Whitman Quart, 9/64; Calico cat, Int. Who's Who Poetry Anthology. Add: 518 E. Macomb, Belvidere, IL 61008.

YETMAN, MICHAEL G, b. New York, N.Y, Aug. 16, 39; m. 63; c. 3. ROMANTIC & VICTORIAN LITERATURE. B.S, St. Peter's Col.(N.J), 61; M.A, Univ. Notre Dame, 62, Ph.D.(Eng), 67. Instr. ENG, St. Mary's Col.(Ind), 65-68; asst. prof, PURDUE UNIV, WEST LAFAYETTE, 68-73, ASSOC. PROF, 73- MLA. Modern literature. Publ: Giuseppe Caponsacchi: a very reputable priest?, Baylor Browning Interest Stud, 70; Count Guido Franceschini: the villain as artist in The ring and the book, PMLA, 72; Emily Dickinson and the English romantic tradition, Tex. Stud. Lit. & Lang, 73. Add: Dept. of English, Purdue University, West Lafayette, IN 47907.

YOAKAM, RICHARD DAVID, b. Pittsburgh, Pa, Jan. 1, 24; m. 46; c. 3. JOURNALISM, RADIO-TELEVISION. B.A, Univ. Iowa, 46, M.A, 47. News ed, Radio Sta. WHO, Des Moines, Iowa, 47-50; news dir, Sta. KCRG, KCRG-TV, Cedar Rapids, 50-57; asst. prof. JOUR, IND. UNIV, BLOOMINGTON, 57-61, assoc. prof, 61-67, PROF, 67-; fac. res. grant, 61-63, Ford Found. fel, West. Europ. Area Stud. Prog, 66-67. News ed, Nat. Broadcasting Co, 61-62; Nat. Asn. Broadcasters res. grant, 68- Nat. Press Photographers Asn.(pres. medal, 66); Asn. Educ. in Jour; Radio-TV News Dir. Asn. International broadcasting; broadcast editorializing; media use in political campaigns. Publ: Co-auth, A production diary of the great debates & Predebate campaign interest and media use, In: The great debates, Ind. Univ, 62; Electronic media speed news coverage, The Rev, 67. Add: Dept. of Journalism, Indiana University, Bloomington, IN 47401.

YOCH, JAMES JOSEPH, JR, b. St. Louis, Mo, Sept. 11, 38; m. 68; c. 1. ENGLISH LITERATURE. B.A, Univ. Notre Dame, 60; Woodrow Wilson & Danforth fels, Princeton, 60, Ph.D, 66. Instr. ENG, UNIV. OKLA, 64-66, asst. prof, 66-69, ASSOC. PROF, 70- MLA; Shakespeare Asn; Royal Hort. Soc. Shakespeare; Italian and English Renaissance literature. Add: Dept. of English, 760 Van Fleet Oval, Room 113, University of Oklahoma, Norman, OK 73069.

YODER, JESS, b. Elverson, Pa, Nov. 16, 22; m. 57; c. 3. SPEECH. B.A, Goshen Col, 53, B.D, 56; univ. fel, Northwest. Univ, 53-54, 55-56, M.A, 54, Ph.D, 62. Asst. prof. speech, Goshen Col, 59-61, assoc. prof, 61-64; asst. prof, Case West. Reserve Univ, 64-67; CLEVELAND STATE UNIV, 67-68, assoc. prof, 68-73, PROF. COMMUN, 73- Mennonite Hist. Soc; Cent. States Speech Asn; Speech Commun. Asn; Int. Commun. Asn; Christian Preaching Conf; AAUP; Am. Civil Liberties Union. Rhetorical theory; interpersonal communication; the rhetoric of social movements. Publ: Co-ed, America in controversy, W.C. Brown, 73; The Frankenthal debates: an example of sixteenth century religous disputation, Quart. J. Speech, 10/67; Preaching on issues of war and peace during the twentieth century, In: Preaching in American history, Abington, 69; The rhetoric of the peace movement, In: America in controversy, W.C. Brown, 73. Add: Dept. of Communication, Cleveland State University, Cleveland, OH 44115.

YOGGERST, MARY HILARY, S.R.H, b. Garden Plain, Kans, Mar. 20, 13. ENGLISH LITERATURE. B.A, Mt. St. Scholastica Col, 45; M.A, Marquette Univ, 48; Ph.D.(Eng), Fordham Univ, 52. Head dept. Eng, Sacred Heart Col, 52-72, pres, 54-61; LECTR. ENG, ST. JOHN'S SEM. COL, 73- Lectr, Wichita State Univ, grad. sem, springs 65, 66; For. Lang. League lectr, London, Eng, summer 66; Reading, Eng, summer 67. MLA; NCTE; Cath. Renascence Soc; Milton Soc. Am. Seventeenth century English literature; especially Sir Tobie Matthew, recusant man of letters. Add: 28600 Palos Verdes Dr. East, Rolling Hills, CA 90274.

YOHANNAN, JOHN DAVID, b. Iran, May 10, 11; U.S. citizen; m. 43; c. 2. ENGLISH. A.B, City Col. New York, 35; A.M, Columbia Univ, 39; Blumenthal fel, N.Y. Univ, 41, Ph.D, 47. Tutor ENG, CITY COL. NEW YORK, 38-43, 46-47, instr, 47-50, asst. prof, 50-57, assoc. prof, 57-67, PROF, 67- Ford fel, 54-55; Fulbright fel, 58-60; Fulbright lectr, Tokyo, 63-64. Mil. Intel, U.S.A, 43-46. MLA; Am. Comp. Lit. Asn; Mid.E. Stud. Asn. Oriental influences and Persian poets in English and American literature. Publ: Treasury of Asian literature, Day; Joseph and Potiphar's wife in world literature, New Directions, 68; Emerson's translations of Persian poetry from German sources, Am. Lit; Persian poetry fad in England, 1770-1825, Comp. Lit; ed, Near East. lit. number of Lit. East & West, 6/67. Add: Dept. of English, City College of New York, New York, NY 10031.

YOKELSON, JOSEPH BERNARD, b. Brooklyn, N.Y, Nov. 20, 26; m. 52; c. 3. ENGLISH. B.A, Brooklyn Col, 48; M.A, Brown Univ, 51, univ. fel, 53-54, Ph.D, 60. Instr. ENG, Brown Univ, 55-56; Colby Col, 56-59, asst. prof, 59-64; from asst. prof. to assoc. prof, Bentley Col, 65-67; asst. prof, BRIDGEWATER STATE COL, 67-70, ASSOC. PROF, 70- U.S.A, 45-47. MLA. Contemporary literature, English and American; American literature. Publ: Ben Ames Williams: pastoral moralist, Colby Libr. Quart, 9/63. Add: Dept. of English, Bridgewater State College, Bridgewater, MA 02324.

YONCE, MARGARET JANIS, b. Aiken, S.C, Feb. 1, 42; m. 73. AMERICAN LITERATURE. B.A, Newberry Col, 64; M.A, Univ. Ga, 66; NDEA fel, Univ. S.C, Columbia, 67-70, Ph.D.(Eng), 71. Instr. ENG, Univ. S.C, Aiken, 66-67; ASST. PROF, AUGUSTA COL, 70- MLA. William Faulkner; Southern literature. Publ: The spiritual descent into the maelstrom: a debt to The rime of the ancient mariner, Poe Newslett, 4/69; Faulkner's Atthis and Attis: some sources of myth, Miss. Quart, summer 70; Soldiers' pay: a critical study of William Faulkner's first novel, Dissertation Abstracts Int, 71. Add: Dept. of English, Augusta College, Augusta, GA 30904.

YONICK, STEPHEN STANLEY, Ancient Near Eastern Literature & Religion. See Volume IV, Philosophy, Religion & Law.

YORDAN, EDWARD L, b. Ponce, P.R, Feb. 20, 03; U.S. citizen; m. 28. ENGLISH. B.Litt, Columbia Col, 25; fel, Harvard, 38-40; Ed.D, N.Y. Univ, 41.

Reporter & feature writer, New York Times, 25-36; res. analyst & writer, Miller McClintock, 36-43; Kudner Agency, New York, 44-50; adj. instr. ENG, FAIRLEIGH DICKINSON UNIV, 56-60, asst. prof, 60-68, EMER. PROF, 68- Adj. instr, Rutgers Univ, 47-63. MLA. Vocabulary building; pronunciation. Publ: Mark your words, 35 & If you are interested in effective speaking, 35, Contemporary Press; contrib, Encycl. Am, Grolier, 61. Add: Dept. of English, Fairleigh Dickinson University, Rutherford, NJ 07070.

YORK, ERNEST CHARLES, b. St. Louis, Mo, Jan. 11, 18; m. 66. ENGLISH. B.S, Univ. Houston, 44; M.A, Univ. Tex, Austin, 48; fel, Univ. Pa, 52-54, Ph.D.(Eng), 57. Instr. ENG, Tex. A&M Univ, 46-56, asst. prof, 56-58; UNIV. ALA, 58-63, assoc. prof, 63-69, PROF, 69-, res. comt. summer grants, 59-60, 63-66. Southeast. Inst. Medieval & Renaissance Stud. summer fel, 67. Renaissance Soc. Am; Col. Eng. Asn; MLA; Int. Arthurian Soc; Mod. Humanities Res. Asn; Mediaeval Acad. Am. Middle English; medieval Arthurian literature. Publ: The duel of chivalry in Malory's Book XIX, Philol. Quart, 4/69; An Anglo-Saxon custom in the Tristrams saga, Scand. Stud, 8/69; Isolt's ordeal; English legal customs in the medieval Tristan legend, Stud. Philol, 1/71; plus others. Add: Dept. of English, University of Alabama, Box 4393, University, AL 35486.

YORK, ZACK LEE, b. Portland, Mich, Mar. 13, 13; m. 52. SPEECH. A.B, West. Mich. Col, 37; Yale, 39; M.A, Univ. Wis, 49, Ph.D.(theater), 50. Teacher, WEST. MICH. UNIV, 46-48, PROF. SPEECH, 53-, head dept, 53-65. Designer & technician, Mich. State Univ, 52-53. U.S.A, 42-46, Maj. Speech Commun. Asn; Am. Theatre Asn; Cent. States Speech Commun. Asn; Add: Dept. of Communication Arts & Science, Western Michigan University, Kalamazoo, MI 49001.

YOSHA, LEE W, b. New Brunswick, N.J, Oct. 1, 26; m. 57; c. 1. AMERICAN LITERATURE. B.A, Wash. & Jefferson Col, 51; M.A, Univ. Conn, 53; Ph.D, Univ. Mich, 60. Teaching fel, Univ. Conn, 51-53; Univ. Mich, 53-57; instr. ENG, East. Mich. Univ, 57-59; asst. prof, Wash. & Jefferson Col, 59-60; Cooper Union, 60-61; from assoc. prof. to PROF. & CHMN. DEPT, UNIV. HARTFORD, 61- U.S.A.A.F, 44-46. MLA. The short story; Katherine Anne Porter; literary criticism. Add: Dept. of English, University of Hartford, Hartford, CT 06117.

YOST, GEORGE, JR, b. Trenton, N.J, Sept. 26, 10; m. 40; c. 2. ENGLISH LITERATURE. A.B, Princeton, 32, A.M, 33, Ph.D, 41. Asst. prof. Eng. & French & head dept, Scranton-Keystone Jr. Col, 35-39; instr. ENG, Univ. Pittsburgh, 39-44; prof. & head dept, Bloomfield Col. & Sem, 46-47; from assoc. prof. to PROF, FLA. STATE UNIV, 47- Vis. prof, Smith-Mundt grant, Univ. Damascus, 55-57, Fulbright prof, 64-66. U.S.N.R, 44-46, Lt. Comdr. MLA; Renaissance Soc. Am; Keats-Shelley Soc. Sir Thomas Browne; John Keats. Publ: Co-auth, Studies in Sir Thomas Browne, Univ. Ore, 65; auth, A source and interpretation of Keats's Minos, J. Eng. & Ger. Philol, 4/58; Keats's early religious phraseology, Stud. Philol, 7/62; plus others. Add: Dept. of English, Florida State University, Tallahassee, FL 32306.

YOTSUKURA, SAYO, Linguistics, Japanese. See Volume III, Foreign Languages, Linguistics & Philology.

YOUEL, DONALD BRUCE, b. Flandreau, S.Dak, Sept. 16, 07; m. 30; c. 3. ENGLISH. A.B, Wheaton Col, 29; M.A, Northwest. Univ, 33; fel, State Univ. Iowa, 43-44, Ph.D.(Eng), 44. Teacher high sch, Kans, 29-32, jr. col, 32-43; mem. fac. Eng, Mont. State Univ, 44-45; mem. fac. Eng. & chmn. dept. lang. & lit, Nebr. State Teachers Col, Chadron, 45-46; prof. Eng, Mankato State Col, 46-72, chmn. div. lang. & lit, 46-64, dir. libr. serv, 52-62; RETIRED. Ed, Sch. Progress, 46-68. Col. Eng. Asn; MLA. Literary theory and linguistic theory. Add: Rte. 4, Box 147, Mankato, MN 56001.

YOUNG, ARTHUR CLEMENTS, b. Detroit, Mich, Apr. 27, 23. ENGLISH. B.A, Wayne Univ, 48, M.A, 49; M A, Yale, 53, Ph.D.(Eng), 54. Instr. ENG, Wayne Univ, 49-50; Carnegie Inst. Technol, 53-54; Rutgers Univ, 54-67; PROF, RUSSELL SAGE COL, 67-, chmn. dept, Eng. & v.pres. acad. affairs, 68-72. Ed. J. Rutgers Univ. Libr, 58-67; vis. prof, Drew Univ, 66. U.S.A.F, 43-46, Sgt. MLA; East. Asn. Col. Deans & Advisors to Stud.(pres, 72). Modern British literature; Victorian novel; James Joyce. Publ: The letters of George Gissing to Eduard Bertz, Rutgers Univ, 61; George Gissing's friendship with Bertz, Nineteenth-Century Fiction, 58; Death of Gissing, Essays in Lit. Hist, 60; co-auth, A civil list pension for George Gissing, Victorian Newslett, fall 67. Add: Dept. of English, Russell Sage College, Troy, NY 12180.

YOUNG, ARTHUR PAUL, b. Washington, D.C, June 5, 43; m. 68; c. 1. ENGLISH & AMERICAN LITERATURE. B.A, Univ. Md, College Park, 66; M.A, Miami Univ, 68, univ. fel, 68-69, Ph.D.(Eng), 71. ASST. PROF. LIT. & PHILOS, MICH. TECHNOL. UNIV, 71-, ASST. HEAD DEPT. HUMANITIES, 73- AAUP; MLA; NCTE; Soc. Stud. Midwest. Lit. English Romantic literature; composition; mass media and society. Publ: Shelley and nonviolence, Mouton, (in press); Prisoners of war, mass media and human values, 6/72 & Mission impossible and America's bugged, drugged, and mugged syndrome, 4/73, Milwaukee J; Technical writing and freshman composition, Teachers Tech. Writing Newslett, 10/73. Add: Dept. of Humanities, Michigan Technological University, Houghton, MI 49931.

YOUNG, DAVID POLLOCK, b. Davenport, Iowa, Dec. 14, 36; m. 63; c. 2. ENGLISH. B.A, Carleton Col, 58; M.A, Yale, 59, Ph.D.(Eng), 65. Instr. ENG, OBERLIN COL, 61-65, asst. prof, 65-68, assoc. prof, 68-73, PROF, 73- Nat. Endowment for Humanities jr. fel, 67-68; ed, Field; Contemporary Poetry & Poetics, Oberlin Col, 69- U.S. Award, Int. Poetry Forum, 68. MLA. Shakespeare; contemporary poetry; poetics. Publ: Something of great constancy: the art of A midsummer night's dream, Yale, 66; Twentieth century interpretation of Henry IV, part two, Prentice-Hall, 68; Sweating out the winter, Univ. Pittsburgh, 69; The heart's forest: Shakespeare's pastoral plays, Yale Univ, 72; Boxcars (poems), Ecco, 73; A skeptical music: Wallace Stevens and George Santayana, Criticism, summer 65; contrib, The major young poets, World, 71 & Just what the country needs, another poetry anthology, Wadsworth, 71. Add: 220 Shipherd Circle, Oberlin, OH 44074.

YOUNG, DONALD LEROY, b. Portland, Maine, Nov. 23, 31; m. 55. ENGLISH. A.B, East. Nazarene Col, 53; A.M, Boston Univ, 54, fel, 55-58, Ph.D.(Eng), 60. Asst. prof. Eng, East. Nazarene Col, 58-60, assoc. prof. & chmn. dept, 60-63; assoc. prof. Eng. & chmn. div. lett, Pasadena Col, 63-66; DEAN, EAST. NAZARENE COL, 67- Scholar, Ctr. Stud. Higher Educ, Univ. Mich, 66-67. MLA; NCTE; Am. Conf. Acad. Deans. John Dryden; academic administration. Publ: Invest endowment in mutual funds, Col. & Univ. Bus, 11/67. Add: Eastern Nazarene College, Wollaston Park, Quincy, MA 02170.

YOUNG, HENRY ARCHIE, b. West Monroe, La, Apr. 15, 33; m. 57; c. 3. SPEECH, DRAMA. B.A, South. Univ, Baton Rouge, 55; M.A, La. State Univ, Baton Rouge, 63; Ph.D.(educ), Kans. State Univ, 73. Pub. sch. speech therapist, Iberville Parish Sch. Bd, La, 57-61; supv. teacher speech & Eng, SOUTH. UNIV, BATON ROUGE, 61-69, PROF. SPEECH, 69- Sig.C, U.S.A, 55-57, Res, 57-59, Sgt. Nat. Asn. Dramatic & Speech Arts. A history of the speech and drama rallies of the LIALO; an analysis of the impact on participants and consortia institutions of federally funded institutes in dramatic arts conducted from 1969-1971. Add: Dept. of Speech & Theatre, Southern University, Baton Rouge, LA 70813.

YOUNG, IONE D, b. Blum, Tex, May 28, 12. LITERATURE. B.A, Tex. Tech. Col, 33; M.A, Univ. Tex, 41, Ph.D, 55. Teacher Eng. & Spanish, Grandview High Sch, 35-40; Rosebud High Sch, 40-41; Spanish, Conroe High Sch, 41-42; Spanish & Eng, South Park High Sch, Beaumont, Tex, 42-43; Eng, Orange High Sch, 44; Edison Elem. Sch, Oakland, Calif, 45; instr. Eng, Univ. Tex, 46-51, 53-55, secy. romance lang, 52-53; asst. prof. Eng, Southwest Tex. State Univ, 55-60, assoc. prof, 60-69, prof, 69-73; RETIRED. Lectr, Univ. P.R, summers 57 & 58; Southwest Tex. State Univ. res. grant, 61-64, grant, 69-70. U.S.N, 43-44. MLA; S. Cent. Mod. Lang. Asn. Romantic, Victorian and modern English literature. Publ: A concordance to the poetry of Byron, (4 vols), Pemberton, 65. Add: 4107 Wildwood Rd, Austin, TX 78722.

YOUNG, JAMES DEAN, b. Los Angeles, Calif, Oct. 4, 25; m. 51; c. 1. ENGLISH. B.S, Calif. Inst. Technol, 49; M.A, Stanford Univ, 50; Ph.D, Rice Univ, 56. Instr. ENG, Rice Univ, 50-52, asst, 52-56; asst. prof, Ga. Inst. Technol, 56-58; instr, Tulane Univ, 58-60; asst. prof, 60-61; from assoc. prof. to PROF, GA. INST. TECHNOL, 61- Fulbright lectr. Am. lit, Univ. Vienna, 67-68; ed, Critique: Stud. Mod. Fiction, 70- U.S.A, 43-46, S/Sgt. MLA. American literature since 1830; prosody; modern literary criticism. Publ: The nine gams of the Pequod, Am. Lit, 54; Quentin's Maundy Thursday, Tulane Stud. Eng, 60; Bellow's View of the heart, Critique, 65. Add: Dept. of English, Georgia Institute of Technology, Atlanta, GA 30332.

YOUNG, JAMES DOUGLAS, b. Huntington, W.Va, May 30, 21; m. 43; c. 2. ENGLISH. B.S, Pepperdine Col, 43; M.A, Univ. South. Calif, 47, Ph.D. (speech), 51. Asst. prof. speech & drama, Pepperdine Col, 47-52, assoc. prof, 52-57; asst. prof. speech & Eng, Los Angeles State Col, 58-60; PROF. SPEECH & DRAMA, CHMN. DEPT. DRAMA & ASSOC. DEAN, SCH. LETT, ARTS & SCI, CALIF. STATE UNIV, FULLERTON, 60-, ASSOC. V.PRES. ACAD. PROG, 74- Consult, Mgt. Pac. Tel, 61-63; Bell Tel. Disneyland Exhibit, 61-63; South. Calif. Credit Union; dir. & actor, film, Search and research. U.S.N.R, 42-46, Lt. Speech Commun. Asn; West. Speech Commun. Asn; Am. Theatre Asn. Drama and speech; psychology; business communication. Publ: Co-auth, A teacher is many things, Ind. Univ, 68. Add: Dept. of Theatre, California State University, Fullerton, 800 N. College Blvd, Fullerton, CA 92634.

YOUNG, LORNA D, b. Ottawa, Ont. ENGLISH LANGUAGE & LITERATURE. B.A, Carleton Univ, 51; A.M, Univ. Rochester, 52; Ph.D, Trinity Col.(Dublin), 58. Instr. Eng. lang. & lit, Univ. Rochester, 54-55; librn, Can. Embassy, Dublin, 56-58; instr. ENG. LANG. & LIT, Smith Col, 58-61; asst. prof, CARLETON UNIV, 62-69, ASSOC. PROF, 69-, DIR, ARTS ACAD. ADV. SERV, 73-, arts medalist, 51. Fel. & scholar. Eng, Univ. Rochester, 51-52; consult. planning comt, Lady Eaton Col, Trent Univ, 65-68. Anglo-Irish literature; American literature. Add: Dept. of English, Carleton University, Colonel By Dr, Ottawa, Ont. K1S 5B6, Can.

YOUNG, LOUISE M, b. East Palestine, Ohio, Sept. 5, 03; m. 25; c. 3. HISTORY, ENGLISH LITERATURE. B.A, Ohio Wesleyan Univ, 25; M.A, Univ. Pa, 27, Pepper fel. & Ph.D, 39. Prof. lectr. Eng, AM. UNIV, 54-57, assoc. prof, 57-61, prof, 61-71, EMER. PROF. LIT, 71- Writer, 40-; trustee, Ohio Wesleyan Univ, 50-; consult, Radcliffe Women's Arch, 55-; vis. res. scholar, Radcliffe Inst. Independent Stud, 68; resident, Rockefeller Found. Bellagio Stud. & Conf. Ctr, Bellagio, Italy, fall 73. AHA; Am. Polit. Sci. Asn; Am. Stud. Asn; MLA. Emergence of women and its impact on political institutions; American studies; victorian studies, especially literature and society. Publ: Thomas Carlyle and the art of history; Understanding politics, a practical guide for women; American woman at mid-century: a bibliographic essay, Am. Rev, 12/61. Add: 2836 Chesapeake St, N.W, Washington, DC 20008.

YOUNG, MARK JAMES, b. Jackson, Mich, May 25, 26; m. 48; c. 2. DRAMA. A.B, Asbury Col, 48; M.A, Mich. State Univ, 53; Ph.D.(theatre), Univ. Mich, 61. Teacher high sch, Mich, 48-51; Ky, 51-53; instr. speech, Asbury Col, 53-54; asst. prof, 54-57; assoc. prof, Taylor Univ, 57-58, chmn. dept, 58-65; proj. assoc, Univ. Wis, Madison, 65-67; asst. prof, Univ. Mass, Amherst, 67-70, ASSOC PROF, THEATRE, 70-73; WHEATON COL, 73- Mem. relig. drama comt, Nat. Counc. Churches, 62-64. Am. Theatre Asn.(mem. publ. comt, 69-71); Speech Commun. Asn.(Golden Anniversary Award, 68); New Eng. Theatre Conf. Theater history; directing; medieval drama. Publ: The York pageant wagon, Speech Monogr, 3/67; Theatre and church: a belated reunion, Expression, fall 69; The unity of the English mystery cycles, Quart. J. Speech, 10/72; plus two others. Add: Dept. of Speech, Wheaton College, Wheaton, IL 60187.

YOUNG, PETER BAXTER, b. Pasadena, Calif, May 28, 38; m. 65; c. 1. DRAMA. A.B, Univ. Calif, Davis, 61; Ph.D.(drama), Stanford Univ, 68. Instr. DRAMA, KNOX COL.(ILL), 67-68, asst. prof, 68-73; ASSOC. PROF, UNIV. ARK, LITTLE ROCK, 73- Tech. dir, Ore. Shakespearean Festival Asn, 65-68. Am. Theatre Asn; U.S. Inst. Theatre Technol; AAUP. Restoration drama and theatre history; scene and lighting design. Add: Dept. of Theatre, University of Arkansas at Little Rock, 33rd & University, Little Rock, AR 72204.

YOUNG, PHILIP, b. Boston, Mass, May 26, 18; m. 44. ENGLISH. B.A, Amherst Col, 40; Ph.D.(Eng), State Univ. Iowa, 48; hon. D.H.L, Westminster Col.(Pa), 71. Instr. Eng, State Univ. Iowa, 46-48; N.Y. Univ, 48-51, asst. prof, 51-52; assoc. prof, Kans. State Univ, 52-54, 56-59; prof. Am. Lit, PA. STATE UNIV, UNIVERSITY PARK, 59-66, RES. PROF. ENG, 66- Am. Counc. Learned Soc. scholar, 50-51; vis. lectr, Univ. Minn, 55-56; Am. specialist to India, 57; Fulbright fel, Italy, 62-63. U.S.A, 42-46, Lt. MLA; PEN Club. Nineteenth and twentieth century American literature; myth in American culture. Publ: Ernest Hemingway, Holt, 52; Ernest Hemingway: a reconsideration, 67 & Three bags full: essays in American fiction, 72, Harcourt; The Hemingway manuscripts: an inventory, Pa. State Univ, 69; plus others. Add: Dept. of English, Pennsylvania State University, University Park, PA 16802.

YOUNG, RICHARD E, b. Owosso, Mich, July 12, 32; m. 53; c. 3. ENGLISH LITERATURE, RHETORIC. B.A, Univ. Mich, 54, Ph.D.(Eng. lit), 64; M.A, Univ. Conn, 56. Instr. Eng, COL. ENGINEERING, UNIV. MICH, ANN ARBOR, 58-64, asst. prof, 64-67, assoc. prof, 67-71, PROF. ENG. & CHMN. DEPT. HUMANITIES, 71- Mem. staff, Ctr. Res. Lang. & Lang. Behavior, 64-68; consult, NDEA Inst, 65-68; Educ. Prof. Develop. Act Inst, 68-70; Nat. Endowment for Humanities grant, 71-72. Distinguished Serv. Award, Col. Engineering, Univ. Mich, Ann Arbor, 68. NCTE; Conf. Col. Compos. & Commun; Speech Commun. Asn; Midwest Mod. Lang. Asn; Rhetoric Soc. Am. Rhetoric; literature; linguistics. Publ: Co-auth, Rhetoric: discovery and change, Harcourt, 70; Toward a modern theory of rhetoric: a tagmemic contribution, Harvard Educ. Rev, fall 65; The psychological reality of the paragraph, J. Verbal Learning & Verbal Behavior, 69. Add: Dept. of Humanities, College of Engineering, University of Michigan, Ann Arbor, MI 48104.

YOUNG, ROBERT F, b. Pittsburgh, Pa, Mar. 22, 05; m. 51; c. 2. RHETORIC, INTERPRETATION. A.B, Univ. Pittsburgh, 28; A.M, Cornell Univ, 33; Wash. Univ, 33-35; Harvard, 35-41. Instr. speech & Eng, Univ. Mo, 28-30; Wash. Univ, 30-35; Harvard, 35-41; asst. prof. speech, Williams Col, 41-45; Amherst Col, 45-49; BROOKLYN COL, 49-59, ASSOC. PROF. SPEECH & THEATRE, 67- Lect. ser, Harvard, 48, Columbia Univ, 54-60, Univ. N.C, summer 57 & St. John's Univ, summer 61; assoc. prof, Smith Col, 48-49; asst. prof, City Col. New York, 48-65. U.S.N, 42-45. Speech Commun. Asn; Speech Commun. Asn. East. States; New Eng. Speech Asn. Persuasion, especially motivation; argumentation, reasoning and evidence; discussion, dialectical method. Publ: Co-auth, Handbook of public speaking, Harvard, 40; auth, Career Opportunities, Brooklyn Col, 57. Add: Dept. of Speech & Theater, Brooklyn College, Bedford Ave. & Ave. H, Brooklyn, NY 11210.

YOUNG, STANLEY PRESTON, b. Greencastle, Ind, Feb. 3, 06; m. 40; c. 3. DRAMA, ENGLISH LITERATURE. Ph.D, Univ. Chicago, 29; cert. French lit, Univ. Grenoble, 29; cert. German lit, Univ. Munich, 30; M.A, Columbia Univ, 31. Instr. Eng, Williams Col, 31-34; managing dir, Bollingen Found, 42-47; Farrar, Straus & Young, 50-54; exec. dir, Am. Nat. Theatre & Acad, 63-66, exec. v.pres, 66-67; PROF. DRAMA. & ASST. TO PRES. FOR ARTS, HOFSTRA UNIV, 65- Rockefeller Found. fels, 36-38; mem. bd. dirs, Author's League Counc, 46-58; chmn. exec. comt, Nat. Counc. Arts, 64-66. John Golden Award, 38-39; Acad. Am. Poets & CBS Award, 58. U.S.A.A.F, 44-45, Capt, spec. war correspondent. European and American drama; the English novel; the American novel. Publ: Robin Landing (verse play), 37 & Sons without anger (novel), 37, Farrar & Rinehart; Mr. Pickwick (play), Random, 53; The sound of apples, Beacon, 58; The middle country (verse), Botteghe Oscure, 54; plus others. Add: Dept. of Drama, Hofstra University, Hempstead, NY 11550.

YOUNG, THOMAS DANIEL, b. Louisville, Miss, Oct. 22, 19; m. 41; c. 3. ENGLISH. B.S, Miss. South. Col, 41; M.A, Univ. Miss, 48; Ph.D, Vanderbilt Univ, 50. Instr. Eng, Univ. Miss, 46-48; asst. prof, Miss. South. Col, 50-51, prof. & chmn. dept, 51-57, acting dean Basic Col, 54-55; prof. & dean, Delta State Col, 57-61; lectr. Eng. & dean admis, Undergrad. Col, VANDERBILT UNIV, 61-67, prof. & chmn. dept. Eng, 67-73, VANDERBILT PROF. ENG, 73- Vis. prof. Am. lit, Univ. Leeds, 73-74. U.S.A.A.F, 42-45. Gen. Educ. Conf; S.Cent. Mod. Lang. Asn; Am. Stud. Asn; S.Atlantic Mod. Lang. Asn. Lower Miss.(pres, 55-57). Jack London; William Faulkner; modern Southern poetry. Publ: Co-auth, Donald Davidson: an essay & a bibliography, Vanderbilt Univ, 65; co-ed, The literature of the South, Scott, 67 & American literature: a critical survey, Am. Bk. Co, 68; auth, John Crowe Ransom: critical essays and a bibliography, La. State Univ, 68; John Crowe Ransom: a critical introduction, Steck, 68; co-auth, Donald Davidson, Twayne, 70; co-ed, The literary correspondence of Donald Davidson and Allen Tate, Univ. Ga, 73; auth, In his own country, South. Rev, 72; A slow fire, Sewanee Rev, 73; The master's in the garden again, Ga. Rev, 73. Add: Box 1509, Sta. B, Vanderbilt University, Nashville, TN 37235.

YOUNGBERG, KARIN LOUISE, b. Moline, Ill, Feb. 14, 36. ENGLISH LITERATURE. A.B, Augustana Col.(Ill), 58; M.A, Univ. Iowa, 60, Ph.D.(Eng), 67. Instr. ENG, Luther Col.(Iowa), 60-61; asst. prof, AUGUSTANA COL.(ILL), 67-72, ASSOC. PROF, 73- NCTE. Medieval Germanic literature; Shakespeare; fantasy literature. Add: Dept. of English, Augustana College, Rock Island, IL 61201.

YOUNGBLOOD, SARAH HELEN, b. Tyrone, Okla, Dec. 16, 28. ENGLISH. B.A, Univ. Okla, 50, M.A, 51, South. fel, 57-58, Ph.D, 58; Fulbright fel, Univ. Nottingham, Eng, 55-56. Grad. asst, Univ. Okla, 51-55; asst. prof. ENG, Univ. Minn, 58-64, assoc. prof, 64-68; MT. HOLYOKE COL, 68-69, PROF, 69- MLA. Modern poetry, especially Yeats. Publ: A reading of The tower, Twentieth Century Lit, 7/59; Structure and imagery in K.A. Porter's Pale horse, pale rider, Mod. Fiction Stud, 59-60; The structure of Yeats's long poems, Criticism, fall 63; plus others. Add: Dept. of English, Mt. Holyoke College, South Hadley, MA 01075.

YOUNGMAN, ROBERT CARL, b. Dayton, Ohio, July 4, 41. SPEECH, DRAMA. B.F.A, Ohio Univ, 63, M.A, 66, Ph.D.(higher educ. admin), 72. ASST. PROF. SPEECH & DRAMA, Univ. Dayton, 65-67; Edinboro State Col, 69-70; S.C. State Col, 70- Dir, Fed. Performing Arts Grant for Children's Theatre, 69-70; coord, Proj. Talent: Res, Inst. for Res, Palo Alto, Calif, 73-74. Am. Personnel & Guid. Asn; Am. Counr. Educr. Asn; Am. Theatre Asn; Int. Commun. Asn. Children's theatre; adolescent behavioral psychology and communication listening; programmed instruction in business and industry. Publ: Vocational development: a unique approach, Inst. for Res, 72; Communications: listening training, 72 & Programmed listening instruction in the counseling practicum, 73, S.C. State Col; Talk with your dog, Dog World, 73. Add: Star Rte, P.O. Box 193, Swansea, SC 29160.

YU, BEONGCHEON, b. Korea, Dec. 29, 25; m. 55; c. 3. LITERATURE. A.B, Seoul Nat. Univ, 49; A.M, Univ. Kans. City, 54; Ph.D, Brown Univ, 58. Instr. ENG, WAYNE STATE UNIV, 57-61, asst. prof, 61-64, assoc. prof, 64-68, PROF, 68- Korean transl, The cycle of American literature, Seoul, Korea, 59; assoc. ed, Criticism, 63-68, ed, 68-72; Fulbright lectr. Am. lit, Korea, 65-67; Fulbright inter-country lectr, India, 67. MLA; AAUP. American, Korean and Japanese literature; East-West literary relations. Publ: An ape of gods: the art and thought of Lafcadio Hearn, 64 & The wayfarer, (transl, Soseki, Kojin), 67 & Akutagawa: an introduction, 72, Wayne State Univ; Natsume Soseki, Twayne, 69; Ishmael's equal eye: the source of balance in Moby Dick, ELH, 65; The immortal twins: an aspect of Mark Twain, Eng. Lang. & Lit, 67; The still center of Hemingway's world, Phoenix, 68. Add: Dept. of English, Wayne State University, Detroit, MI 48202.

YUN, CHANG SIK, b. Korea. COMPARATIVE LITERATURE. B.A, Univ. Mich, Ann Arbor, 58, M.A, 63; Ph.D.(comp. lit), Princeton, 72. Instr. Japanese, Princeton, 68-69; ASST. PROF. comp. lit, Eisenhower Col, 69-71; JAPANESE & COMP. LIT, SAN DIEGO STATE UNIV, 72- Tragedy, East and West; Yeats; Japanese literature. Publ: The tragic metaphor in the Noh drama, Theatre Annual, 68. Add: Dept. of Classical & Oriental Languages & Literatures, San Diego State University, College Ave, San Diego, CA 92115.

YUNCK, JOHN A, b. Orange, N.J, July 8, 17; m. 43; c. 2. ENGLISH, COMPARATIVE LITERATURE. B.A, Mich. State Univ, 38, M.A, 40; Penfield fel, N.Y. Univ, 49-51, Ph.D, 53. Asst. ENG, MICH. STATE UNIV, 38-40, instr, 40-53, asst. prof, 53-59, assoc. prof, 59-63, PROF, 63, DIR. COMP. LIT. PROG, 67- U.S.A.F, 42-46, Res, 46-, Col. Mediaeval Acad. Am; Comp. Lit. Asn; Midwest Mod. Lang. Asn; Int. Arthurian Soc. Mediaeval literature, especially the themes, devices and techniques of mediaeval satire and mediaeval romance. Publ: The lineage of Lady Meed, Univ. Notre Dame, 63. Add: Dept. of English, Michigan State University, East Lansing, MI 48824.

Z

ZACHARIAS, DONALD WAYNE, b. Salem, Ind, Sept, 28, 35; m. 59; SPEECH DRAMA. B.A, Georgetown Col, 57; M.A, Ind. Univ, 59, Ph.D, 63. Dir. forensics, Georgetown Col, 58-59; instr. speech & theatre, Ind. Univ, Bloomington, 63-65, asst. prof, 65-69; assoc. prof. SPEECH COMMUN, UNIV. TEX, AUSTIN, 69-72, PROF, 73-, ASST. TO PRES, 74- Intel.C, U.S.A, 60-66. Speech Commun. Asn; Asn. Educ. Commun. & Technol; Int. Commun. Asn. Communication and social change; organizational communication; interpersonal communication. Publ: Ed, In pursuit of peace, Random, 70; co-auth, McElligott's American debater, J. Am. Forensic Asn, winter 67; auth, Oratory of the Know Nothing Party, In: Oratory of the Old South, La. State Univ, 70; On teaching speech criticism, In: Essays on teaching speech in the high school, Ind. Univ, 71; plus others. Add: Dept. of Speech Communication, University of Texas at Austin, Austin, TX 78712.

ZACHER, CHRISTIAN KEELER, b. St. Louis, Mo, Mar. 6, 41; m. 67; c. 1. ENGLISH LITERATURE, MEDIEVAL STUDIES. B.A, Col. of the Holy Cross, 63; M.A, Univ. Calif, Riverside, 65, Ph.D.(Eng), 69. Teaching asst. ENG, Univ. Calif, Riverside, 64-67; asst. prof, OHIO STATE UNIV, 68-74, ASSOC. PROF, 74- MLA; Mediaeval Acad. Am; Soc. Hist. Discoveries; AAUP. Medieval English and Latin literature; medieval and Renaissance travel literature. Publ: Co-ed, Critical studies of Sir Gawain and the Green Knight, Univ. Notre Dame, 68. Add: Dept. of English, Ohio State University, Columbus, OH 43210.

ZAHALKA, DONALD WILLIAM, b. Racine, Wis, Feb. 15, 25; m. 49; c. 4. JOURNALISM. B.S, Univ. Wis, 50, M.S, 54. City ed, Berlin Wis. Jour, 50-52; teaching asst, Univ. Wis, 52-54; ASST. PROF. JOUR, UNIV. WIS-OSHKOSH, 54-, DIR, ACAD. PUBL. & PRINTING, 70- U.S.A.A.F, 43-46. Informational broadcasting. Publ: Contrib. to Pub. Relat. J, 9/54. Add: Dept. of Journalism, University of Wisconsin-Oshkosh, Oshkosh, WI 54901.

ZAHN, LOUIS J, Romance Languages & Literatures. See Volume III, Foreign Languages, Linguistics & Philology.

ZAHORSKI, KENNETH, b. Cedarville, Ind, Oct. 23, 39; m. 62; c. 2. ENGLISH, SPEECH. B.S, Wis. State Univ, River Falls, 61; M.A, Ariz. State Univ, 63; Ph.D.(Eng), Univ. Wis, 67. Asst. prof. ENG, Univ. Wis-Eau Claire, 67-69; ST. NORBERT COL, 69-71, ASSOC. PROF, 71- Nat. Endowment for Humanities scholar, summer 70; consult, Choice, 72- MLA; NCTE; AAUP. Afro-American literature; speculative fiction; modern drama. Publ: A rap on race, 6/71 & Dynamite voices: black poets of the 1960's, 12/71, CLA Jour. Add: Dept. of English, St. Norbert College, De Pere, WI 54115.

ZAITZ, ANTHONY WILLIAM, b. Chelsea, Mass, May 22, 16; m. 44. SPEECH. B.S.O, Curry Col, 41; M.A, Boston Univ, 47; Nat. Asn. Educ. Broadcasters fel, Mich. State Univ, 54; Univ. Wis. Profess. musician, Boston, Mass, 34-41; instr. Eng, Univ. Mass, 47-48, Eng. & speech, 48-52; speech, Univ. Wis, 52-53; from instr. to asst. prof, Univ. Mass, 60; assoc. prof. speech, Univ. S.Fla, 60-66; chmn. div. lit. & lang, ST. LEO COL, 66-68, pres, 68-70, PROF. ENG. & SPEECH, 70- Asst. to pres, Nat. Asn. Educ. Broadcasters, 70-71. U.S.A.A.F, 42-45, Maj. Speech Commun. Asn; NEA. Broadcasters. Instructional uses of television; persuasion and the communications media; television and adult education. Add: Dept. of Speech, St. Leo College, St. Leo, FL 33574.

ZALE, ERIC M, b. Old Forge, Pa, July 6, 18; div; c. 2. ENGLISH LANGUAGE & LITERATURE. B.A, Univ. Mich, 44, M.A, 51, Ph.D, 61. Instr. Eng. & speech, East. Mich. Univ, 56-58, asst. prof, 58-63, assoc. prof. Eng, 63-65; assoc. dir. lang. & lang. behav, Univ. Mich, 65-67; PROF. ENG, WILBERFORCE UNIV, 67- Consult, Fifth Army Hq, U.S. Army, 59-64, Spec. Warfare Sch, Ft. Bragg, N.C, 64-67 & Am. Asn. Jr. Cols, 69- U.S.A, 43-46, Res, 40-43, 46-67, Maj; Bronze Star Medal. NCTE; Teachers Eng. to Speakers other Lang; Conf. Col. Compos. & Commun; Col. Eng. Asn; Int. Soc. Gen. Semantics. Black English; communications; Victorian literature. Publ: The defenses of John Henry Newman, Univ. Microfilms, 62; ed, Proceedings of conference on language & language behavior, Appleton, 68; auth, Jack Briley & The children of the damned, Mich. Quart. Rev, summer 65; Linguistics: an aid to teaching poetry, J. Mich. Counc. Teachers Eng, 66; Journalism and the English teacher, J. Eng. Teaching Techniques, 71; plus others. Add: Dept. of English, Wilberforce University, Wilberforce, OH 45384.

ZALL, PAUL MAXWELL, b. Lowell, Mass, Aug. 3, 22; m. 48; c. 3. ENGLISH LITERATURE. B.A, Swarthmore Col, 48; A.M, Harvard, 50, Ph.D, 51. Instr. Eng, Cornell Univ, 51-55, asst. to cur, Wordsworth Collection, 53-55; instr. Eng, Univ. Ore, 55-56; tech. res. ed, Boeing Co, Wash, 56-57; assoc. prof. ENG, CALIF. STATE UNIV, LOS ANGELES, 57-63, PROF, 63- Am. Philos. Soc. res. grants, 64-68; Huntington Libr. grant-in-aid, summer 65; John Carter Brown Libr. fel, 68. U.S.A.A.F, 42-45. MLA. Wordsworth and Coleridge; satire. Publ: A hundred merry tales and other jestbooks, 63 & Literary criticism of William Wordsworth, 66, Univ. Nebr; co-auth, Plain style, McGraw, 67; auth, Coleridge's sonnets from various authors, La Siesta, 68; Simple cobler of Aggawam, 69 & Nest of ninnies, 70, Univ. Nebr; Poems of Peter Pindar, Univ. S.Carolina, 72; contrib, Proverb to poem, McGraw-Hill, 70; auth, The cool world of Samuel Taylor Coleridge (ser), Wordsworth Circle, 70-74; plus others. Add: Dept. of English, California State University, Los Angeles, 5151 State University Dr, Los Angeles, CA 90032.

ZAMBRANO, ANA LAURA, b. Long Beach, Calif, Sept. 24, 46. LITERATURE, CINEMA. B.A, Calif. State Univ, Long Beach, 67, M.A, 68; Ph.D. (Eng), Univ. Calif, Los Angeles, 72. Teaching assoc, ENG, Univ. Calif, Los Angeles, 69-71; ASST. PROF, Mich. State Univ, 72-73; UNIV. SOUTH. CALIF, 73- MLA; AAUP. Charles Dickens; comparative literature. Publ: Women in love: counterpoint on film, Lit/Film Quart, 72; Great expectations: Dickens' style in terms of film, Hartford Stud. Lit, 72. Add: 4700 E. Fourth St, Long Beach, CA 90814.

ZAMONSKI, JOHN A, U.S. citizen. BRITISH LITERATURE, BRITISH & AMERICAN DRAMA. Ph.B, Univ. Detroit, 61, M.A, 66; Ph.D.(Eng), Ohio Univ, 70. ASST. PROF. ENG, WRIGHT STATE UNIV, 70- Intel.C, U.S.A, 61-64. AAUP; MLA. The plays of John Dryden; British neo-classical poetry; bibliography. Publ: Co-ed, The David McCandless McKell collection: a descriptive catalog of manuscripts, early printed books, and children's books, G.K. Hall, 73; auth, The spiritual nature of carnal love in Dryden's Assignation, Educational Theatre J, 5/73; Value-writing: an overview and practical model for elementary composition, Ohio Eng. Bull, 12/73. Add: Dept. of English, Wright State University, Dayton, OH 45431.

ZAVADIL, JOSEPH, b. St. Louis, Mo, Aug. 10, 28; m. 59; c. 6. ENGLISH LITERATURE. A.B, Loyola Univ.(Ill), 49, M.A, 54; Univ. Chicago, 53-54; fel, Stanford Univ, 54-55, 57-58, Ph.D.(Eng. & humanities), 62. Lectr, Loyola Univ.(Ill), 53-54; Univ. Md. Overseas Prog, Tokyo, Japan, 56-57; Acting instr. ENG, Stanford Univ, 59-61; asst. prof, UNIV. N.MEX, 61-67, assoc. prof, 67-70, PROF. & CHMN. DEPT, 70- U.S.A, 55-57, Sgt. MLA. Middle English literature; medieval literature of Europe. Add: Dept. of English, University of New Mexico, Albuquerque, NM 87131.

ZAVARZADEH, MAS'UD, b. Tehran, Iran, May 17, 38. MODERN AMERICAN LITERATURE. B.A, Tehran Univ, 63; dipl. Eng. stud, Univ. Nottingham, 64; dipl. ling, Cambridge, 64; M.A, Univ. Birmingham, 66; Ph.D.(Eng), Ind. Univ, Bloomington, 73. ASST. PROF. AM. LIT, UNIV. ORE, 71- MLA; NCTE. Theory of fiction; postwar American literature. Publ: The mythopoeic reality: the postwar American nonfiction novel, Univ. Ill, 75; The Persian short story, Muslim World, 68; Anti-intellectual intellectualism in postwar British fiction, Ball State Univ. Forum, 12/71; A typology of prose narrative, J. Lit. Semantics, 3/74. Add: Dept. of English, University of Oregon, Eugene, OR 97403.

ZEEVELD, WILLIAM GORDON, b. Rochester, N.Y, Feb. 20, 02; m. 37; c. 4. ENGLISH LITERATURE & HISTORY. A.B, Univ. Rochester, 24; A.M, Johns Hopkins Univ, 29, Ph.D, 36. Instr. ENG, Rice Inst, 29-32; Choate Sch, Conn, 34-35; Northwest. Univ, 36-37; asst. prof. UNIV. MD, COLLEGE PARK, 37-49, assoc. prof, 49-55, PROF, 55-, univ. gen. res. bd. grant, res. in Eng. & lectr, Oxford, 61, leave of absence res. Italy & Eng, 68. Moderator symp, Changing Interpretations of Shakespeare, 62; mem. panel scholar. awards, Pittsburgh Plate Glass Found, 63-; deleg, Int. Shakespeare Conf, Stratford-upon-Avon, Eng, Stratford, Conn. & Wash, D.C, 64; mem. nat. comt, Shakespeare Quatracentennial Celebration, 64; mem. Int. Shakespeare Conf, Stratford-upon-Avon, 64, lectr, 66; vis. prof. Eng, Univ. Wis, summer 65; prof Evening Col, Johns Hopkins Univ, 65- AHA; MLA; Renaissance Soc. Am; Conf. Brit. Stud; Amici Thomae Mori. Publ: Foundations of Tudor policy, Harvard, 48, Methuen, 69; The political and social order, In: Thought and culture of the English Renaissance, Cambridge, 56; plus others. Auth. & narrator, The three worlds of William Shakespeare, produced on WRC-NBC TV. Add: Dept. of English, University of Maryland, College Park, MD 20742.

ZEKOWSKI, ARLENE, b. New York, N.Y, May 13, 22; m. 52. ENGLISH. B.A, Brooklyn Col, 44; M.A, Duke Univ, 45; Lic. es Lett, Sorbonne, 48; fel, La. State Univ, 58-62. Asst. prof. ENG, EAST. N.MEX. UNIV, 63-67, ASSOC. PROF, 68-, res. grants, 66-73. Cult. affairs div. Dept. State & U.S. Embassy, Mexico City lect. tour, summer 65; guest lectr, Univ. of the Americas, 65; Univ. S.Dak, 68; Styrian Sch, Educ. Acad, Austria, 69. PEN Club; MLA. Contemporary novel and short story; aesthetics and criticism. Publ: Thursday's season, Parnasse, Paris, 50; co-auth, A first book of the neo-narrative, 54 & Cardinals and saints, 58, auth, Concretions, 62 & Abraxas, 64, Wittenborn; Seasons of the mind, Wittenborn, 68, Horizon, 73; The age of iron and other interludes (plays), Am. Can. Publ, Vol. I, 73; Breakthrough fictioneers, Something Else Press, 73. Add: Dept. of English, Eastern New Mexico University, Portales, NM 88130.

ZELLAR, LEONARD, b. DeKalb, Ill, Feb. 21, 28; m. 51; c. 5. ENGLISH. B.S, Purdue Univ, 53; M.A, Denver Univ, 53; Ph.D.(Eng), Univ. Ill, 58. Asst. prof. Eng, Franklin Col, 57-58, assoc. prof, 58-60, prof. Eng. & dir. lib. stud, 60-66, chmn. dept. Eng, 59-66; PROF. ENG, SAM HOUSTON STATE UNIV, 66-, dir. dept, 66-72. U.S.N, 46-48. MLA; NCTE; Nat. Asn. Gen. & Lib. Stud. Novels of Joseph Conrad; modern fiction; modern critical theory. Add: Dept. of English, Sam Houston State University, Huntsville, TX 77341.

ZELLERS, PARKER R, b. Worcester, Mass, Mar. 25, 27. SPEECH, DRAMATIC ARTS. B.A, Emerson Col, 50; M.A, Ind. Univ, 56; Ph.D.(speech, dramatic arts), Univ. Iowa, 64. Instr. speech & dramatic arts, Monmouth Col.(Ill), 56-59, asst. prof, 59-61; DRAMATIC ARTS, EAST. MICH. UNIV, 64-66, ASSOC. PROF, 66-70, PROF, 71- U.S.A, 45-47, Sgt. 1st class. Speech Commun Asn; Am. Theatre Asn. American theatre; American vaudeville. Publ: Tony Pastor: dean of the vaudeville stage, East. Mich. Univ, 71. Add: Dept. of Dramatic Arts, Eastern Michigan University, Ypsilanti, MI 48197.

ZESMER, DAVID MORDECAI, b. Dallas, Tex, Dec. 1, 24; m. 49; c. 2. ENGLISH. B.A, Columbia Univ, 47, M.A, 49, Ph.D, 61; summer, Kenyon Col, 48. Instr. ENG, Marietta Col, 49-51; lectr, Hunter Col, 53-54; instr, L.I. Univ, 59-61; assoc. prof, ILL. INST. TECHNOL, 62-67, PROF, 67- Ed. consult, 62-; coord. ed, Shakespeare Newslett, 66-70. U.S.A.A.F, 43-46, Sgt. MLA; Col. Eng. Asn. Medieval and Renaissance English; 17th century literary criticism; Shakespeare. Publ: Guide to English literature from Beowulf through Chaucer & medieval drama, Barnes & Noble, 61, ed, Poems, plays and essays of Dryden, Bantam, 67. Add: Dept. of English, Illinois Institute of Technology, Chicago, IL 60616.

ZETLER, ROBERT LEWIS, b. Summerville, Pa, July 30, 08; m. 58; c. 1. ENGLISH. A.B, Univ. Pittsburgh, 30, M.A, 42, Ph.D.(Eng), 45; Pa. State Univ, 37-38. Asst. Eng, Univ. Pittsburgh, 42-44, instr, 44-45; asst. prof, Chatham Col, 45-48, assoc. prof, 48-53, prof, 53-58; PROF. LANG. & LIT, UNIV. S.FLA, 60-, chmn. dept. Eng, 60-63, dir. div. lang. & lit, 62-66. Lectr, Univ. Pittsburgh, 45-60; consult, Atomic Energy Comn, 57-59; Pittsburgh Diagnostic Clinic, 60; Honeywell, Inc, 67-68. NCTE. English Romantic and Victorian literature; technical writing; effective reading. Publ: Co-auth, A guide to technical writing, 48, 54, 64 & Advanced writing, 51, Ronald; co-auth, Effective bank letters, Am. Inst. Banking, 52 & Successful communication in science and industry, McGraw, 61; auth, The inarticulate engineer, AAUP Bull, summer 46; What's base in a basic curriculum, J. Engineering Educ, 11/57; Humanities in general education at Chatham College, In: Humanities in general education, W.C. Brown, 60. Add: Division of Languages & Literature, University of South Florida, Tampa, FL 33620.

ZETTLER, HOWARD G, b. Yonkers, N.Y, Apr. 22, 26. ENGLISH. B.A, Univ. Colo, 50, M.A, 55; fel, Univ. Conn, 50-52; Univ. Mich, 56; Ph.D.(Eng. lang. & lit), Ohio Univ, 71. Master Eng, Va. Episcopal Sch, Lynchburg, 53-54; instr, Col. Engineering, Univ. Colo, 54-57; lib. stud, Clarkson Col, 57-58; asst. prof. Eng, Glassboro State Col, 61-64; assistantship, Ohio Univ, 64-65; asst. ed, Ohio Univ. Press, 66-67; ASST. PROF. ENG, CENT. CONN. STATE COL, 67- Am. Counc. Learned Soc. fel, 56; mem. & chmn. subcomt, Resource Group on Progs, Conn. Master Plan Higher Educ, 72-; consult, Conn. Educ. Sem, Trinity Col. & Ford Found, 73- U.S.A.A.F, 45-47, Sgt. NCTE; AAUP. English language; English syntax; Middle English literature. Publ: Linguistic convert in the classroom, Conn. Teacher Educ. Quart, 64. Add: Dept. of English, Central Connecticut State College, New Britain, CT 06050.

ZIEBARTH, E. WILLIAM, b. Columbus, Wis, Oct. 4, 10; m. 39; c. 1. SPEECH. B.S, Univ. Wis, 33, Ph.M, 34; Ph.D.(speech & educ. psychol), Univ. Minn, 48. Int. affairs analyst, World Health Assembly, Univ. Wis, 34; instr. speech, UNIV. MINN, MINNEAPOLIS, 36, dir. sch. of the air, 38-42, assoc. prof. SPEECH & chmn. dept, 48-49, PROF, 49-, DEAN, COL. LIB. ARTS, 63-, chmn. dept. speech & theatre arts, 49-63, dean summer session, 54-63. Consult. bds. educ. & pub. serv. & govt. groups, 44-; prod. mgr, WCCO, CBS, 45-46, news analyst, 45-, educ. dir, cent. div, 46-48; exec. consult, 48-54, roving int. affairs analyst, Middle East, 50, spec. assignment, Asiatic affairs, Tokyo, Japan & Far East, 52; spec. for. correspondent & int. affairs analyst, West. Europe, 49; consult. pub. serv. & educ, Midwest Radio TV, 54-, consult, Ministry of Educ, Fed. Repub. Ger, 66; mem, Nat. Comn. Arts & Sci, 66-, bd. gov, 67-; Hill Found. fel, Soviet Union & Southeast Asia, 68. Mem. bd. trustees, Macalester Col, KTCA Educ. TV Corp. & Midwest. Educ. TV Corp; bd. dirs, Respiratory Disease Asn. Hennepin County. Peabody Award, 48; Distinguished News Anal. Award, Radio Counc; News Interpretation Award, Nat. Inst. Radio & TV; Best Commentator Award, Am. Fed. TV & Radio Artists; Outstanding Achievement Award, Radio & TV Res. Counc; Peabody Award & Blakesee Award, Nat. Comn. Arts & Sci, 72. Speech Commun. Asn; Nat. Soc. Stud. Commun; Asn. Educ. Broadcasters. International communication; use of mass media in education; rhetoric of mass media. Publ: Co-auth, Six classic plays for radio, Burgess, 41; The Soviet airwaves, Holt, 62; Electronic media in the Soviet Union, Quart. J. Speech, 59. Add: 1596 Northrop St, St. Paul, MN 55108.

ZIEGELMUELLER, GEORGE WILLIAM, b. Indianapolis, Ind, July 28, 30. SPEECH. B.A, DePauw Univ, 52; fel, South. Ill. Univ, 52-54; M.A, 54; Ph.D, Northwest. Univ, 62. Asst, Northwest. Univ, 54-57; instr. SPEECH, WAYNE STATE UNIV, 57-58, asst. prof, 58-63, assoc. prof, 63-68, PROF, 68-, HEAD, AREA OF COMMUN, RHETORIC & PUB. ADDRESS, 70-, dir. forensics, 62-74. Speech Commun. Asn.(legis. assembly, 66-69); Am. Forensic Asn.(secy-treas, 61-63, v.pres, 63-65, pres, 65-68, ed. jour, 73-75); Cent. State Speech Asn.(consult. ed. jour, 71-73). Publ: Co-auth, Argumentation: inquiry and advocacy, Prentice-Hall, 74 & An audience debate tournament, Speech Teacher, 64; auth, The role of the coach & Forensic tournaments, In: Coaching debate and other forensic activities, Int. Textbk, 68. Add: 4401 N. Verona Circle, Royal Oak, MI 48072.

ZIETLOW, EDWARD R, b. Presho, S.Dak, Aug. 13, 32. ENGLISH. B.A, Dakota Wesleyan Univ, 54; M.A, Boston Univ, 59; Ph.D.(Negro lit), Univ. Wash, 67. ASST. PROF. ENG, UNIV. VICTORIA (B.C), 65- U.S.A, 54-57. MLA; Philol. Asn. Pac. Coast. American Negro literature; American Renaissance, especially Melville; Henry James. Publ: These same hills, Knopf, 60; A flaw in The American, CLA, 3/66; Saul Bellow: the theater of the soul, Ariel, 10/73; The burial of the bride, S.Dak. Rev, 5/74. Add: Dept. of English, University of Victoria, Victoria, B.C, Can.

ZIETLOW, PAUL NATHAN, b. Neenah, Wis, Feb. 14, 35; m. 57; c. 2. ENGLISH. B.A, Yale, 56; M.A, Univ. Mich, 57, Ph.D.(Eng), 65. Instr. ENG, Univ. Mich, 62-64; lectr, IND. UNIV, BLOOMINGTON, 64-65, asst. prof, 65-68, assoc. prof, 68-73, PROF, 73- Rev. ed, Victorian Stud, 65-69. MLA. English literature of the 19th and early 20th centuries. Publ: Moments of vision: the poetry of Thomas Hardy, Harvard Univ, 74; The meaning of Tilbury Town: Robinson as a regional poet, New Eng. Quart, 6/67; The tentative mode of Hardy's poems, Victorian Poetry, summer 67; Thomas Hardy and William Barnes: two dorset poets, PMLA, 3/69. Add: Dept. of English, Indiana University, Bloomington, IN 47401.

ZIFF, LARZER, b. Holyoke, Mass, Oct. 2, 27; m. 52; c. 4. AMERICAN LITERATURE. M.A, Univ. Chicago, 50, Asher fel, 53-54, Ph.D, 55. Test constructor Eng, Educ. Testing Serv, 51-52; lectr. humanities, Univ. Chicago, 52-53, dir. spec. prog, 53-56; asst. prof. ENG, UNIV. CALIF, BERKELEY, 56-60, assoc. prof, 60-65, PROF, 65- Huntington Libr. fel, 57; Univ. Calif, pres. fel, 58; Fulbright lectr, Univ. Copenhagen, 59-60; Ford Found. lectr, Univs. of Poland, 60; Am. Counc. Learned Soc. fel, 63-64; Fulbright lectr, Univ. Sussex, 64; Nat. Counc. Teachers Eng. distinguished lectr, 66-67; mem. comt. Am. stud, Int. Exchange Persons, 66-; ed. bd, Am. Quart, 66-; Nat. Endowment Humanities sr. fel, 67-68; univ. lectr. Am. lit. & fel. Exeter Col, Oxford, 73- Christian Gauss Award, 67. MLA; Am. Stud. Asn. Colonial American culture; modern American literature; 19th century culture. Publ: Ed, Selected writings of Benjamin Franklin, Holt, 60; auth, Career of John Cotton: Puritanism and the American experience, Princeton, 62; The American 1890's, 66 & Puritanism in America, 73, Viking; ed, The Genius & The Financier, Signet, 67; ed, John Cotton on the churches of New England, John Harvard Libr, Harvard, 68; plus others. Add: Exeter College, Oxford University, Oxford, 0X1 3DP, England.

ZIGERELL, JAMES, b. Monaca, Pa, June 12, 20; m. 49; c. 1. ENGLISH LITERATURE. A.B, Loyola Univ.(Ill), 40, A.M, 48; Ph.D, Univ. Chicago, 62. Prof. Eng, Wright Col, CITY COLS. CHICAGO, 47-70, dean TV instr, 65-70, EXEC. DEAN, LEARNING RESOURCES LAB. & TV COL, 70- Prof. rhetoric, NDEA Inst. High Sch. Eng. Teachers, Loyola Univ, summer 65; consult. uses TV in educ, Govt. Newf, 66; Univ. S.Dak, 67; mem. higher educ. comt, Ill. Telecommun. Comn, 68; mem. bd. dirs, Ill, Educ. TV Comn, 68. Sig.Intel, U.S.A, 42-45, S/Sgt. MLA; NCTE; Nat. Asn. Educ. Broadcasters (consult. uses TV in educ, 63-). Contemporary poetry and fiction; 18th century novel in England; 17th century English satire. Publ: Chicago's TV College, Am. Asn. Univ. Prof. Bull, spring 67; On the method of explication, J. Aesthetic Educ, 10/69; The community colleges in search of an identity, J. Higher Educ, 12/70; plus others. Add: TV College, City Colleges of Chicago, 5400 N. St. Louis, Chicago, IL 60625.

ZILLMAN, LAWRENCE JOHN, b. Shelton, Wash, Nov. 4, 02; m. 26. ENGLISH LITERATURE. A.B, Univ. Wash, 28, Ph.D, 36. Assoc. ENG, Univ. Wash, 30-31, 33-36; prof, Willamette Univ, 31-32; asst. prof, UNIV. WASH, 37-43, assoc. prof, 43-53, prof, 53-72, EMER. PROF, 72- MLA; Keats-Shelley Asn. Am. Romantic period; English verse; contemporary poetry. Publ: John Keats and the sonnet tradition, Caxton, 39; Shelley's Prometheus unbound, Univ. Wash, 59; Art and craft of poetry, Macmillan, 66; The complete known drafts of Shelley's Prometheus unbound: a literal transcription, Univ. Microfilms, 67; Shelley's Prometheus unbound: the text and the drafts—toward a modern definitive edition, Yale, 68. Add: 4553 52nd Ave. N.E, Seattle, WA 98105.

ZILLMER, H. LAWRENCE, b. Barronette, Wis, Oct. 22, 29; m. 49; c. 7. THEATRE. B.A, Ft. Hays Kans. State Col, 57; M.S, Kans. State Univ, 58; Ph.D.(speech, theatre), Univ. Wis, 65. Instr. theatre, Am. Univ, 58-60; speech, exten. div, Univ. Wis, 61-65; ASSOC. PROF. THEATRE, Presby. Col, 65-66; Univ. South. Miss, 66-69; STEPHEN F. AUSTIN STATE UNIV, 69- Consult, Arts Surv. Grant, 68. Am. Theatre Asn; AAAS. Paul Claudel, symbolic movement in theatre. Plays: Co-auth, The gay deceiver of Seville, produced 3/65; auth, Give us Barabbas, produced 5/67; co-auth, Proteè, produced 11/68; auth, Jefferson Davis: American patriot; co-auth, The bear and the moon, 73. Add: Dept. of Theater, Stephen F. Austin State University, Nacogdoches, TX 75961.

ZIMANSKY, CURT ARNO, b. San Francisco, Calif, Aug. 13, 13; m. 43; c. 4. ENGLISH LITERATURE. A.B, Stanford Univ, 33, A.M, 34; A.M, Princeton, 36, Ph.D, 37. From instr. to asst. prof. ENG, UNIV. IOWA, 37-49, assoc. prof, 49-60, PROF, 60-, chmn. lit. core course, 59-66. Summers, mem. fac, South. Ore. Col, 50, Univ. Colo, 55, West. Reserve Univ, 59, Univ. B.C, 63, Univ. Wash, 66; acad. adv, Ore. Shakespeare Festival, 50; assoc. ed, Philol. Quart, 53-62, managing ed, 62-64, ed, 64-; Fund. Advan. Educ. fel, 55-56; mem. adv. bd, Col. Eng, 64-65. U.S.A, 42-45, 51-52, Maj. MLA; Ling. Soc. Am; Mediaeval Acad. Am; Renaissance Soc. Am; Archaeol. Inst. Am. English neo-classicism; Shakespeare; medieval English literature. Publ: Ed, Critical works of Thomas Rymer, Yale, 56; co-ed, English literature 1660-1800: a bibliography of modern studies, Princeton, 62, Studies in English drama presented to Baldwin Maxwell, Univ. Iowa, 62 & The college teaching of English, Appleton, 65; plus others. Add: Dept. of English, University of Iowa, Iowa City, IA 52240.

ZIMBARDO, ROSE A, b. U.S, May 29, 32; m. 57; c. 1. ENGLISH. A.B, Brooklyn Col, 56; M.A, Yale, 57, fels, 57-60, Ph.D, 60. Instr. ENG, City Col. New York, 60-68, assoc. prof, 68-72, grant, 62; ASSOC. PROF, STATE UNIV. N.Y. STONY BROOK, 72- Eng. Inst; MLA. Restoration literature; Shakespeare; modern drama. Publ: Wycherley's drama, Yale, 65; co-auth, Tolkien and the critics, Notre Dame Univ, 68; auth, Form and disorder in The tempest, Shakespeare Quart, winter 63; Genet's Black mass, Mod. drama, 12/66; The formalism of Henry V, In: Casebook on Henry V, Macmillan, 68; plus others. Add: Dept. of English, State University of New York at Stony Brook, Stony Brook, NY 11790.

ZIMMER, GEORGE WILLIS, b. Detroit, Mich, Dec. 22, 24; m. 55; c. 4. ENGLISH. A.B, Univ. Detroit, 55, M.A, 60; Ph.D, Mich. State Univ, 68. Instr. Eng, Loyola Univ.(Ill), 64-68, asst. prof. Eng. & dir. freshman Eng, 68-69; INSTR. ENG, COL. OF LAKE COUNTY, 69- U.S.N.R, 42-43. MLA; NCTE; Midwest Mod. Lang. Asn. Add: 2303 Park Pl, Evanston, IL 60201.

ZIMMERMAN, EVERETT LEE, b. Lancaster, Pa, Dec. 9, 36; m. 63; c. 2. ENGLISH LITERATURE. B.A, Bob Jones Univ, 58; Pa. State Univ, 58-59; M.A, Temple Univ, 61, Ph.D.(Eng), 66. Instr. ENG, Temple Univ, 61-62; Rutgers Univ. Camden, 62-66, asst. prof, 66-69; UNIV. CALIF, SANTA BARBARA, 69-72, ASSOC. PROF, 72- MLA. Eighteenth century literature; satire; novel. Publ: Co-ed, Medea: myth and dramatic form, 67 & Oedipus: myth and dramatic form, 67, Houghton; auth, Defoe and the novel, Univ. Calif, 74; The function of parody in Northanger Abbey, Mod. Lang. Quart, 69; Defoe and Crusoe, Eng. Lit. Hist, 71; H.F.'s meditations: A journal of the plague year, PMLA, 72. Add: Dept. of English, University of California, Santa Barbara, CA 93106.

ZIMMERMAN, GORDON G, b. Flanagan, Ill, Mar. 8, 22; m. 46; c. 2. SPEECH. A.B, Sterling Col, 45; M.A, Bowling Green State Univ, 50; Ph.D. (speech), Univ. Mich, Ann Arbor, 61. Minister, Sterling Mennonite Church, Kans, 43-48; Evangelical Mennonite Church, Wauseon, Ohio, 48-57; prof. & dean of men, Univ. of the Pac, 57-65; dir. develop, Taylor Univ, 65-67, v.pres. acad. affairs, 67-73; PROF. SPEECH & CHMN. DEPT, GREENVILLE COL, 73- Coord, Comn. Liberal Arts Educ. N.Cent. Asn, 70-73. Speech Commun. Asn. Publ: Co-auth, Public speaking: philosophy and practice, Allyn & Bacon, 64. Add: Dept. of Speech, Greenville College, Greenville, IL 62246.

ZIMMERMAN, J. E, b. Lincoln, Nebr, Mar. 2, 01; m. 27; c. 1. ENGLISH. B.A, Baylor Univ, 29, M.A, 30, Litt.D, 71; hon. Litt.D, Grand Canyon Col, 71. Prof. ENG, ARIZ. STATE UNIV, 46-71, EMER. PROF, 72- Distinguished prof. Eng, Wayland Baptist Col, 71-72; prof, Baylor Univ, 72-73; Okla. Baptist Univ, 73-74. NCTE. Chaucer; Milton; classical mythology; 19th century, the Romantics and the Victorians. Publ: Dictionary of classical mythology, Harper, 64. Add: 304 E. 15th St, Tempe, AZ 85281.

ZIMMERMAN, LESTER FRED, b. Milwaukee, Wis, June 17, 09; m. 36; c. 1. ENGLISH. B.A. & M.A, Univ. Wis, 35, Ph.D, 49. Instr. ENG, Univ. Wis, 35-38, 41-42, 46; asst. prof, UNIV. TULSA, 46-49, assoc. prof, 49-57, PROF, 57- U.S.A.A.F, 42-46, 1st Lt. NCTE; S.Cent. Mod. Lang. Asn.(ed. Bull, 60-62); MLA. The reputation of Milton in America; 19th century American literature; literary criticism. Add: Dept. of English, University of Tulsa, Tulsa, OK 74104.

ZIMMERMAN, MELVIN, French, Comparative Literature. See Volume III, Foreign Languages, Linguistics & Philology.

ZIMMERMAN, MICHAEL, b. North Adams, Mass, July 29, 37; m. 61; c. 2. ENGLISH, AMERICAN LITERATURE. B.A, Columbia Univ, 59; M.A, 60, Ph.D.(Eng), 63. Lectr. ENG, Columbia Col, Columbia Univ, 61-62, preceptor, Sch. Gen. Stud, 62-63; acting instr, Univ. Calif, Berkeley, 63-64, instr, 64-65, asst. prof, 65-68; lectr, CALIF. STATE UNIV, SAN FRANCISCO, 68-69, ASSOC. PROF, 69- Univ. Calif, Berkeley summer fac. fel, 66; Fulbright lectr, Japan, 67-68. Philol. Asn. Pac. Coast. Nineteenth and 20th century American literature; James Joyce. Publ: Sociological criticism of the 1930's, Harper, 73; Literary revivalism in America, Am. Quart, spring 67; Thomas Hardy and the modern tradition in poetry & The American T.S. Eliot, Stud. Eng, Japan, 68-69. Add: 37 Plaza Dr, Berkeley, CA 94705.

ZINK, DAVID D, b. Kansas City, Mo, Sept. 17, 27; m. 48; c. 2. BRITISH & AMERICAN LITERATURE. B.Jour, Univ. Tex, 52; M.A, Univ. Colo, 57, Ph.D.(Eng), 62. Instr. ENG, U.S. Air Force Acad, 57-59, asst. prof, 61-64, assoc. prof, 64-65; LAMAR UNIV, 65-72, PROF, 72- U.S.A.F, 46-49, Res, 52-65, Maj. Mod. Humanities Res. Asn; Melville Soc. Am. Nineteenth-century American and British fiction set in Polynesia; Victorian rationalism; parapsychology. Publ: Leslie Stephen, Twayne, 72; contrib, Annual bibliog, Mod. Humanities Res. Asn, 65-68; auth, Who was Ann Parry's Jonah? Am. Neptune, 1/72; Structure and tone in graduate literature seminars, Asn. Dept. Eng. Bull, 5/73. Add: Dept. of English, Lamar University, Beaumont, TX 77710.

ZINK, JOSEPH PAUL, III, b. Pittsburgh, Pa, Sept. 10, 45; m. 66; c. 1. MEDIEVAL STUDIES, INSTRUCTIONAL TECHNOLOGY. B.A, Univ. Detroit, 68, M.A, 70, sr. fel, 72-73, Ph.D.(Eng), 73. Instr. ENG, Detroit Inst. Commerce, 67-68; Walsh Col, 68-70; Spring Hill Col, 70-72; ADJ. ASST. PROF, ALBION COL, 73- Consult, Mich. Dept. Social Serv, 73; Mich. Asn. Independent Cols. & Univs, 73; Walden Univ. for Advan. Stud. Higher Educ, 73-; ed. instruct. technol, Grad. Sch. Bus, Univ. Mich, 73- AAUP; MLA. Media-oriented autoinstructional programs; Chaucer scholarship; perspectives in the study of the English and American novel. Publ: Mark Perry, C.P.A. (film), Walsh Col, 69; Rihaku: twenty-one images, P-Q Press, 71; The world to our perceptions (film), Spring Hill Col, 72; Pronouncing Chaucer's language: the basic program, 73 & Pronouncing and understanding Chaucer's language: the advanced program, 73, Validated Instruct. Assocs. Add: Dept. of English, Albion College, Albion, MI 49224.

ZINK, KARL EDWIN, b. Jacksonville, Fla, Mar. 22, 17; m. 46; c. 3. ENGLISH LITERATURE. M.A, Univ. Fla, 40; Ohio State Univ, 40-41; Ph.D. (Eng), Univ. Wash, 52. Instr. ENG, Univ. Fla, 46-48; assoc, Univ. Wash, 48-51; prof. Ala. State Teachers Col, Florence, 52-54; asst. prof, Ind. Univ. Northwest, Gary, 54-61, assoc. prof, 61-68, asst. chmn. dept, 64-68; PROF, CENT. WASH. STATE COL, 68-, chmn. dept, 68-72. Fulbright lectr. Am. lit, Univ. Thessaloniki, 60-61; U.S. Dept. State lectr, Univ. Belgrade, 62-63. U.S.N.R, 41-46. MLA; Am. Stud. Asn. American literature; criticism of prose fiction; William Faulkner. Publ: Herman Melville and the forms, Accent; Flux and the frozen moment: imagery of Stasis in Faulkner's prose, PMLA; Faulkner's garden: woman and the immemorial earth, Mod. Fiction Stud. Add: Dept. of English, Central Washington State College, Ellensburg, WA 98926.

ZINNES, HARRIET F, b. Hyde Park, Mass; c. 2. ENGLISH. B.A, Hunter Col, 39; M.A, Brooklyn Col, 44; Ph.D, N.Y. Univ, 53. Ed, Publ. Div, Raritan Arsenal, N.J, 42-43; assoc. ed, Harper's Bazaar, 44-46; tutor ENG, Hunter Col, 46-49; QUEENS COL.(N.Y), 49-53, instr, 62-65, asst. prof, 65-71, ASSOC. PROF, 71- Vis. prof. Am. lit, Univ. Geneva, spring 70; art critic, Pictures on Exhibit, 71-; poetry coord, Great Neck Pub. Libr, 72-; MacDowell fel, MacDowell Colony, Peterborough, N.H, summers 72 & 73; mem, Acad. Am. Poets. MLA; PEN Club; Poetry Soc. Am. Ezra Pound; contemporary poetry; relationship between contemporary art and poetry. Publ: Waiting, Goosetree Press, 64; An eye for an I: poems, Folder Ed, 66; contrib, The fiction of Anais Nin, In: Casebook of Anais Nin, World, 73 & Entropisms (prose poems), In: New Directions 27, New Directions, 73; plus poetry and criticism in Nation, New Leader, New York Quart, Chelsea, Choice, Works, Voyages, Carleton Miscellany, Parnassus, South. Rev. & others. Add: Dept. of English, Queens College, Flushing, NY 11367.

ZIOLKOWSKI, THEODORE J, German. See Volume III, Foreign Languages, Linguistics & Philology.

ZIPES, JACK DAVID, German, Comparative Literature. See Volume III, Foreign Languages, Linguistics & Philology.

ZIRKER, MALVIN RALPH, JR, b. Oakland, Calif, Aug. 16, 32; m. 72. ENGLISH. A.B, Univ. Calif, Berkeley, 54, M.A, 56, Rosenthal fel, 57-58, Ph.D. (Eng), 62. Instr. ENG, Cornell Univ, 59-61; Univ. Calif, Berkeley, 61-63; asst. prof, IND. UNIV, BLOOMINGTON, 63-66, ASSOC. PROF, 66- Ind. Univ. summer res. grants, 64 & 67. MLA. English literature of the 18th century. Publ: Ed, An enquiry into the frequent execution at Tyburn, Augustan Reprint Soc, 64; auth, Fielding's social pamphlets, Univ. Calif, 66; co-ed. & contrib, The satirist's art, Ind. Univ, 72; auth, Richardson's correspondence: the personal letter as private experience, Familiar Lett. Eighteenth Century, 66; Fielding and reform in the 1750's, Stud. Eng. Lit, summer 67. Add: Dept. of English, Indiana University, Bloomington, IN 47401.

ZITNER, SHELDON P, b. New York, N.Y, Apr. 20, 23; m. 49; c. 1. ENGLISH. B.A, Brooklyn Col, 48, M.A, N.Y. Univ, 49; fel, Duke Univ, 50, Ph.D.(Eng), 55. Asst. prof. Eng, Hampton Inst, 50-56; Grinnell Col, 57-58, assoc. prof, 59-61, prof, 61-72, Carter-Adams prof. lit, 63-72, Roberts honor prof, 65-66; PROF. ENG, TRINITY COL, UNIV. TORONTO, 72- Roberts honor prof, 65-66. Lilly grant-in-aid; Newberry humanities fel, 66-67; Old Dominion fel, 67-68. Sig.C, U.S.A, 42-46. MLA; Renaissance Soc. Am. Shakespeare; Anglo-Italian literary relations; Spenser. Publ: Co-auth, Preface to literary criticism, 64 & ed, The practice of modern literary scholarship, 67, Scott; ed, Spenser's mutabilitie cantoes, Nelson, 68; auth, Gossen, ovid, and the Elizabethan audience, spring 58 & Anon, anon; or a mirror for a magistrate, winter 68; Shakespeare Quart; Spenser's diction and classical precedent, Philol. Quart, 4/67. Add: Dept. of English, Trinity College, University of Toronto, Toronto, Ont, Can.

ZIVLEY, SHERRY, b. Dallas, Tex, Oct. 1, 35; m. 57. ENGLISH. B.A, Univ. Tex, 57; M.A, N.Mex. State Univ, 60; Ph.D.(Eng), Tulane Univ, 73. Teacher high sch, Kans, 62-64; INSTR. ENG, UNIV. HOUSTON, 65- MLA; NCTE. Contemporary British and American literature; 19th century American literature. Publ: Sugar-coated point of view and tone—to be taken inductively, 9/64 & A cautious approach to student grading, 12/67, Eng. J; Imagery in John Donne's Satyres, Stud. Eng. Lit, winter 66. Add: Dept. of English, University of Houston, Houston, TX 77004.

ZLOTNICK, JOAN C, b. New York, N.Y, July 14, 42; m. 63; c. 2. AMERICAN LITERATURE. B.A, Brooklyn Col, 63; NDEA fel, Hunter Col, 63-64, M.A, 65; Ph.D.(Eng. lit), New York Univ, 69. Lectr. ENG, BROOKLYN COL, 65-69, instr, 69-71, ASST. PROF, 71- MLA; NCTE; AAUP. Jewish literature; women's literature. Publ: Abraham Cahan: a neglected realist, Am. Jewish Arch, 4/71; The medium is the message, or is it?: a study of Nathanael West's comic strip novel, J. Popular Cult, 8/71; The day of the locust, a night at the movies?: Nathanael West's Hollywood novel, Film Libr. Quart, winter 73; plus others. Add: Dept. of English, Brooklyn College, Brooklyn, NY 11210.

ZNEIMER, JOHN NICOLAS, b. Chicago, Ill, July 3, 25; m. 49; c. 4. ENGLISH. B.A, Ripon Col, 48; M.A, Columbia Univ, 50; Ph.D.(Eng), Univ. Wis, 66. Instr. ENG, Coe Col, 50-52; asst. prof, IND. UNIV. NORTHWEST, 64-70, ASSOC. PROF, 70-, asst. chmn. dept, 68-70. U.S.A.A.F, 43-45, 1st Lt. Contemporary literature. Publ: The literary vision of Liam O'Flaherty, Syracuse Univ, 70. Add: Dept. of English, Indiana University Northwest, 3400 Broadway, Gary, IN 46408.

ZOBEL, KONRAD, b. Kreuzburg, Silesia, June 7, 44; Austrian citizen; m. 64; c. 1. THEATRE HISTORY. Ph.D.(theatre), Univ. Vienna, 67. Lectr. Ger, Univ. Southampton, 68-70; ASST. PROF. theatre, Ohio State Univ, 70-72; DRAMATIC ART, UNIV. N.C, CHAPEL HILL, 72- Consult, Inst. Austrian Dramatic Technique, Vienna, 68; managing dir, Theatre Res. Inst, Ohio State Univ, 70-72, ed, Theatre Stud, 71-72. Speech Commun. Asn. Theatre sociology, historical and empirical; epistemology. Publ: Co-auth, The old Burgtheater: a structural history, Theatre Stud, 72-73; auth, Rollenspiel; theater der adaption, Sozialistische Erziehung, 73; Das Theater in den Vereinigten Staaten: eine oekonomische Analyse, Maske & Kothurn, 74; plus several others. Add: Dept. of Dramatic Art, Graham Memorial Bldg, University of North Carolina at Chapel Hill, Chapel Hill, NC 27514.

ZOCCA, LOUIS RALPH, b. Villa d'Ogna, Italy, May 20, 07. ENGLISH. Ph.B, Brown Univ, 29, A.M, 33, Ph.D, 39. Lectr. Romance lang, Brown Univ, 33, instr. Romance lang. & Eng, 34-39; free lance & radio writer, 39-41; assoc. prof. ENG, NEWARK COL, RUTGERS UNIV, 46-59, PROF, 59-, dir. div. humanities, 61-72. U.S.A, 42-46. MLA; Renaissance Soc. Am. European renaissance; Elizabethan period in England; Elizabethan narrative poetry. Add: Division of Humanities, Newark College, Rutgers University, Newark, NJ 07102.

ZOELLNER, ROBERT, b. Denver, Colo, June 22, 26; div; c. 5. LITERATURE, LANGUAGE. B.S, Marquette Univ, 53, M.A, 54; Ph.D, Univ. Wis, 61. Instr. ENG, Univ. N.Dak, 56-58; assoc. prof, COLO. STATE UNIV, 58-70, PROF, 70- Consult. sec. sch. pedag, Bantam Bks, Inc. & Holt, Rinehart & Winston, Inc, 69-; Nat. Endowment for Humanities grant, 71- U.S.N.R, 44-47. NCTE; MLA. American literature; behavioral theory; ordinary language. Publ: Co-auth, The strategy of composition, Ronald, 68; auth, The salt-sea mastodon: a reading of Moby-Dick, Univ. Calif, 73; contrib, Am. Lit; Am. Quart; Col. Eng. Add: Dept. of English, Liberal Arts 314, Colorado State University, Ft. Collins, CO 80521.

ZOLBROD, PAUL GEYER, b. Pittsburgh, Pa, Dec. 10, 32; m. 67; c. 2. LITERARY CRITICISM, LINGUISTICS. B.A, Univ. Pittsburgh, 58, Andrew Mellon fel, 60-62, M.A, 62, Ph.D.(Eng), 67; Fulbright fel, Univ. Caen, 58-59; univ. fel, Brown Univ, 59-60. Instr. ENG, Univ. Pittsburgh, Titusville, 63-64; ALLEGHENY COL, 64-66, asst. prof, 66-70, ASSOC. PROF, 70- Fel, Univ. N.Mex, 71-72. MLA; AAUP; NCTE. Renaissance literature; ethnopoetics; linguistics. Publ: Co-auth, Beyond Berkeley, World Publ, 66 & The rhetoric of revolution, Macmillan, 69; co-auth, Shakespeare's late plays, Ohio Univ, 74; auth, Coriolanus and Alceste: a study in misanthropy, Shakespeare Quart, 72; Past and future: searching for a new metaphor, Cithara, 72; Native American poetry; some possibilities for the linguist, Allegheny Col. J, 73; plus others. Add: Dept. of English, Allegheny College, Park Ave, Meadville, PA 16335.

ZOLLO, RICHARD PAUL, b. Danvers, Mass, Sept. 30, 26; m. 56; c. 1. ENGLISH, EDUCATION. A.B, Bowdoin Col, 47; M.Ed, Boston Univ, 57, fel, 66-67, D.Ed.(sec. Eng), 68. Teacher ENG, Danvers High Sch, Mass, 47-55, chmn. dept. Eng, 55-57; Masconomet Regional High Sch, Boxford, 57-65; asst. prof, SALEM STATE COL, 68-70, assoc. prof, 70-72, PROF, 72- NCTE; Col. Eng. Asn. Secondary school English; reading; American literature and history. Publ: Ed, Danvers historical collections, 61-67, auth, Whittier at Oak Knoll, 61 & Danvers Square: an informal history, 67, Danvers Hist. Soc; Danvers, In: Encycl. Americana, Grolier, 69. Add: Dept. of English, Salem State College, Salem, MA 01970.

ZORN, JOHN WILLIAM, b. Lawrence, Mass, May 11, 10; m. 38; c. 1. SPEECH. A.B, Emerson Col, 34, hon. M.A, 60; M.Ed, Boston Univ, 39; Harvard, 40-56. Teacher & head Eng. dept, High Sch, Mass; asst. prof. speech, EMERSON COL, 46-60, assoc. prof, 60-66, PROF. EDUC. & DIR. PLACEMENT, 66-, DIR. SUMMER SESSION, 50-, EVE. DIV, 57- Instr. Northeast. Univ, 48- U.S.A, 43-45. NEA; Speech Asn. East. States. Publ: One act plays, Ivan Bloom, 60; Witches sabbath, French, 63; Public speaking without tears, 63; Essential Delsarte, Scarecrow, 68; co-auth, Words in context, Holbrook, Allyn & Bacon, 68; plus others. Add: Dept. of Education, Emerson College, 130 Beacon St, Boston, MA 02116.

ZUCKER, DAVID HARD, b. Cleveland, Ohio, May 27, 38; m. 62; c. 2. ENGLISH & AMERICAN LITERATURE. B.A, Oberlin Col, 60; M.A, Syracuse Univ, 64, Ph.D.(Eng), 68. Asst. ed, Columbia Encycl, 60-62; asst. prof. ENG, Washington & Lee Univ, 68-71; QUINNIPIAC COL, 71-73, ASSOC. PROF, 73- U.S.A.R, 61-62, Res, 62-67. MLA. Elizabethan drama; Chaucer; 20th century poetry. Publ: Co-ed, Selected essays of Delmore Schwartz, Univ. Chicago, 70; auth, Stage and image in the plays of Christopher Marlowe, Univ. Salzburg, 72; The detached and judging narrator in Chaucer's House of fame, Thoth, 67; Shadow and light, 71 & An American elegist: the poetry of Horace Gregory, 73, Mod. Poetry Stud. Add: Dept. of English, Quinnipiac College, Hamden, CT 06518.

ZUCKER, JACK, b. Brooklyn, N.Y, Jan. 23, 35; m. 58; c. 2. ENGLISH. B.A, City Col. New York, 57; M.A, N.Y. Univ, 61, 61-65. Teacher, Garden Sch, 59-61; asst. instr. ENG, Ohio State Univ, 61-62; asst. prof, Newark State Col, 62-65; Babson Inst, 65-68; Marietta Col, 68-70; INSTR, PHILLIPS ACAD, 70- Fel, MacDowell Colony, summer 70. U.S.A.R, 58-64. Poetry Soc. Am. Creative writing; composition. Publ: Co-auth, Critical thinking: an anthology for composition, Macmillan, 69; auth, Searching through the sink (poem), Folio, 6/72; Beginnings (poem), South. Poetry Rev, 6/72 & Best Poems of '72, 5/73; Protest for my uncle, Lit. Rev, 9/73; plus others. Add: Dept. of English, Phillips Academy, Andover, MA 01810.

ZUCKER, LOUIS CLEMENT, b. Philadelphia, Pa, Apr. 10, 95; m. 20; c. 1. COMPARATIVE LITERATURE. A.B, Univ. Pa, 19, A.M, 20; Adams fel, Univ. Wis, 24-25, Ph.D, 28. Instr. ENG, Univ. Wis, 20-28, asst. prof, UNIV. UTAH, 28-37, assoc. prof, 37-44, prof, 44-63, EMER. PROF, 63-, LECTR. HEBREW, 65- MLA. Color distinction in older imaginative literature; process of English translation of Old Testament; the Jews in English and American literature. Publ: Joseph Smith as a student of Hebrew, Dialogue, summer 68; Utah & Idaho, In: Encyclopedia Judaica, 69. Add: 1138 E. 27th S, Salt Lake City, UT 84106.

ZULLI, FLOYD, Romance Languages. See Volume III, Foreign Languages, Linguistics & Philology.

ZUMWALT, EUGENE ELLSWORTH, b. Portland, Ore, Jan. 7, 24; m. 45; c. 4. ENGLISH. B.A, Univ. Ore, 48, M.A, 51; univ. fel, Univ. Calif, Berkeley, 52-54, Ph.D, 56. Teaching asst. ENG, Univ. Ore, 48-49, instr, 49-50; teaching asst, Univ. Calif, Berkeley, 50-52, lectr, 54-55; instr, Wash. State Univ, 55-58, asst. prof, 58-59; from asst. prof. to PROF, CALIF. STATE UNIV, FRESNO, 59- U.S.A.A.F, 42-45, 1st Lt. Medieval literature; English drama, especially pre-Shakespearean and Shakespearean. Publ: Irony in Towneley Shepherd's plays, 3/58 & The myth of the garden in Galsworthy's The apple tree, 9/59, Wash. State Univ. Res. Stud; Crabtree ducks, Univ. Kans. City Rev, spring 63. Add: Dept. of English, California State University, Fresno, Fresno, CA 93726.

ZUTHER, GERHARD HELMUT WALDEMAR, b. Berlin, Ger, Jan. 12, 30; U.S. citizen; m. 54; c. 2. COMPARATIVE LITERATURE. B.A, DePauw Univ, 53, M.A, 55; Ph.D, Ind. Univ, 59. Instr.ENG, UNIV. KANS, 58-61, asst. prof, 61-65, assoc. prof, 65-69, PROF, 69-, ASSOC. CHMN. DEPT, 63- Am. Philos. Soc. grant, 64-65; Alexander v. Humboldt Stiftung fel, Ger, 64-65. MLA; NCTE; Am. Comp. Lit. Asn; Int. Comp. Lit. Asn. Theory of modern translation; American-German literary relations; Shakespeare. Publ: Bibliographie der aufnahme Amerikanischer literatur in deutschen zeitschriften 1945-1960, Frank, Munich, 65; transl, Brecht: ovation for Shaw, Mod. Drama, 9/59; Theories of translation, Class. J, 10/62; List of translations, 66, 67 & 68, Yearbk. Gen. & Comp. Lit, 67, 68 & 69. Add: Dept. of English, University of Kansas, Lawrence, KS 66044.

ZWAHLEN, FRED CASPER, JR, b. Portland, Ore, Nov. 11, 24; m. 59; c. 2. JOURNALISM. B.A. Ore. State Univ, 49; A.M, Stanford Univ, 52. Instr. JOUR, ORE. STATE UNIV, 50-53, asst. prof, 53-62, assoc. prof, 62-67, PROF, 67-, CHMN. DEPT, 67-, acting head dept, 54-55. Assoc. Ore. State Univ, News Bur. & Dept. Inform, 50-69, ed, Staff Newslett, 61-69. Sigma Delta Chi Serv. Award, 62. Asn. Educ. Jour; Am. Soc. Jour. Sch. Adminr; Nat. Press Photographers Asn. Newswriting; feature writing; photojournalism. Add: Dept. of Journalism, Oregon State University, Corvallis, OR 97331.

ZWERDLING, ALEX, b. Breslau, Ger, June 21, 32; U.S. citizen. ENGLISH. B.A, Cornell Univ, 53; M.A, Princeton, 56, Ph.D.(Eng), 60; Fulbright fel, Univ. Munich, 53-54. Instr. ENG, Swarthmore Col, 57-61; asst. prof, UNIV. CALIF, BERKELEY, 61-67, assoc. prof, 67-73, PROF, 73- Am. Counc. Learned Soc. study fel, 64-65; Ctr. Advan. Stud. Behav. Sci. fel, 64-65; Nat. Endowment for Humanities fel, 73-74. MLA. Modern and Romantic poetry; literature and politics. Publ: Yeats and the heroic ideal, N.Y. Univ, 65; Orwell and the Left, Yale Univ, 74; On judging faculty, In: The contemporary university: USA, Houghton, 66; Orwell and the technique of didactic fantasy, In: Twentieth century interpretations of 1984, Prentice, 71; Esther Summerson rehabilitated, PMLA, 73; plus others. Add: Dept. of English, University of California, Berkeley, CA 94720.

ZWICKER, STEVEN NATHAN, b. San Diego, Calif, June 4, 43; m. 65; c. 2. SEVENTEENTH CENTURY LITERATURE. B.A, Univ. Calif, Los Angeles, 65; M.A, Brown Univ, 67, Woodrow Wilson dissertation fel, 68-69, Ph.D. (Eng), 69. ASST. PROF. ENG, WASH. UNIV, 69- Taft post-doctoral fel, Univ. Cincinnati, 70-71; Clark Libr. fel, summer 71; Wash. Univ. res. fel, summer 72. MLA. Seventeenth century political poetry; typology; Renaissance political history. Publ: Dryden's political poetry: the typology of king and nation, Brown Univ, 72; The king and Christ: figural imagery in Dryden's Restoration panegyrics, Philol. Quart, 71; Models of governance in Marvell's The first anniversary, Criticism, (in press). Add: Dept. of English, Washington University, St. Louis, MO 63130.

ZWICKY, LAURIE, b. Shawnee, Okla, Jan. 8, 31; m. 54. ENGLISH LITERATURE. B.A, Lindenwood Col, 52; Ph.D, Univ. Okla, 59. Instr. ENG, Wayne State Univ, 56-58; UNIV. HOUSTON, 58-59, asst. prof, 59-62, assoc. prof, 62-67, PROF, 67-, DIR, OPEN UNIV. PROG, 72-, dir. freshman Eng, 61-64. MLA; Milton Soc. Am; S.Cent. Mod. Lang. Asn; NCTE (mem. comt. affil. publ, 70-73); Conf. Col. Compos. & Commun. Milton; literature and science; non-traditional programs in education. Publ: Suggestions for teachers of Toward liberal education, 67 & Instructor's manual for Masterworks of English prose, 68, Holt; Relations of literature and science, Symposium, 55-67; Kairos in Paradise regained: the divine plan, ELH, 64; O.U. pilot schemes to continue, London Times Higher Educ. Suppl, 73. Add: Open University Program, University of Houston, Houston, TX 77004.

ZYROMSKI, ROBERT NICHOLAS, b. Detroit, Mich, May 27, 42; m. 66; c. 2. DRAMA, THEATRE. B.S, St. Louis Univ, 64; M.A, Univ. Va, 66; Ph.D. (theatre), Bowling Green State Univ, 69. ASST. PROF. THEATRE ARTS, VA. POLYTECH. INST. & STATE UNIV, 69- Am. Theatre Asn. World dramatic literature; acting; contemporary theatre. Publ: Putting the pieces together, Context, summer 70; co-auth, The reliability of judgments of directing technique, Empirical Res. in Theatre, spring 71. Add: Dept. of Performing Arts & Communications, Virginia Polytechnic Institute & State University, Blacksburg, VA 24061.

ZYTARUK, GEORGE J, b. Edwand, Alta, May 6, 27; m. 58; c. 2. ENGLISH. B.Ed, Univ. Alta, 49, B.A, 53, M.A, 58; Can. Counc. fel, Univ. Wash, 64-65, Ph.D.(Eng), 65. Asst. prof. Eng, Univ. Alta, 65-67; PROF. ENG. & PRIN, NIPISSING COL, 67-, PRES, 70- NCTE; MLA; Can. Counc. Teachers Eng. D.H. Lawrence; Russian literature in English. Publ: Ed, The quest for Rananim: D.H. Lawrence's letters to S.S. Koteliansky, McGill-Queen's Univ, Montreal & London, 70; auth, D.H. Lawrence's response to Russian literature, Mouton, The Hague & Paris, 71; D.H. Lawrence: letters to S.S, Koteliansky, Malahat Rev, 1/67; The phallic vision: D.H. Lawrence and V.V. Rozanov, CLS, 67; The last days of D.H. Lawrence, D.H. Lawrence Rev, spring 68. Add: Dept. of English, Nipissing College, Box 5002, North Bay, Ont. P1B 8L7, Can.

GEOGRAPHIC INDEX

ALABAMA

ATHENS
Laubenthal, Penne J, English Speech

AUBURN
Allen, Ward Sykes, English
Amacher, Richard Earl, American Literature
Benson, Carl, English
Bradley, Bert E, Jr, Speech
Breyer, Bernard R, English Literature
Brittin, Norman Aylsworth, English Literature
Current-Garcia, Eugene, American Literature
Davis, Frank Bell, Speech
Harrison, A. Cleveland, Theatre, Speech & Drama
Hudson, Sara Carruth, English Literature
Jones, Madison Percy, Jr, Fiction
Lawless, Donald Stewart, English
Littleton, Taylor Dowe, English Literature of Elizabethan Period
Nist, John Albert, English Language & Linguistics, Comparative Literature
Patrick, Walton Richard, American Literature
Phillips, Phyllis Purnell, Speech, English
Richardson, Don Ramon, Speech
Ritchey, R. David, Theatre, Speech
Rose, Charles S, Jr, English
Smith, William Stephen, Speech
Woodall, James Raymond, English
Wright, Thomas L, Medieval Literature

BIRMINGHAM
Abernethy, Cecil Emory, English
Atchison, Ray M, English
Conner, Frederick William, English
Creed, Howard Hall, English
Dobbins, Austin Charles, English
Haarbauer, Don Ward, Theatre History, Directing
Haddin, Theodore, American Literature
Harper, Hubert Hill, Jr, Classical Languages, English
Johnson, Gerald David, English Literature, Renaissance
McWilliams, Richebourg Gaillard, English
Mersmann, James F, English & American Literature
Ownbey, Egbert Sydnor, English Literature
Pool, John Paul, English
Powell, Arnold Francis, Drama
Ross, Joe Carl, British & American Literature
Wilson, Elkin Calhoun, English Literature
Workman, Charles Thomas, English

COTTONDALE
Russell, I. Willis, English Language & Literature

FLORENCE
Chandler, Patricia Richardson, English Literature
Foster, Charles William, American Literature, Dialect Geography
Johnston, Albert S, Jr, English

GADSDEN
Perkins, Marjorie Willene, English

GOSHEN
Dalton, William Theo, English, Teacher Education

HUNTSVILLE
Francis, Herbert Edward, Jr, Literature
Hutchens, Eleanor Newman, English
Kiser, John Edgar, English Literature
Martin, Carter Williams, English, American Literature
Welker, Robert L, English
Woodard, Charles Robert, English

JACKSONVILLE
Blanton, Raymond Eugene, Eighteenth Century English Literature
Calvert, William Jonathan, Jr, English
Johnson, Charles Everest, English
McMillan, Mary Evelyn, English

LIVINGSTON
Brandenburg, Alice Stayert, English Literature
Gilbert, Robert B, English
White, Harold Norton, English

MARION
Cunningham, Velma Teresa, English
Lewis, Elsie Brickett, English

MOBILE
Boyle, Charles J, English
Dendinger, Lloyd N, English
Deneau, Daniel Pierre, English
Hafner, John Henry, American & English Literature
Hamner, Eugenie Lambert, American Literature
Harvey, William Ronald, British Literature
Jackson, Richard Eugene, Theatre, Playwriting
Matlock, Charles Michael, Middle English Literature
Mele, Joseph Charles, Speech
Murray, John Franklin, S.J, English
Nolan, Barbara Schuler, American & Modern British Literature
Rountree, Thomas Jefferson, English
Stewart, John Craig, Creative Writing, American Literature
Todd, Carl E, English Education, Educational Administration
Trimble, John Clifton, Speech

MONTEVALLO
Chichester, William Taylor, Speech, Drama
Foley, Milton J, English
Harbour, Charles Clayton, Theatre History, Dramatic Criticism
Kunkel, Robert Raymond, Rhetoric, Public Address
Lott, John Bertrand, English
McMillan, Norman Robert, English Literature

MONTGOMERY
Bryson, Ralph Joseph, English Education
Chappell, Winn Ownbey, English
Ellison, Rhoda C, English
Figh, Margaret Gillis, Southern Literature & Folklore
Gay, William Teague, English, World Literature
Player, Raleigh Preston, English Language & Literature
Rankin, Martha Frazer, English, Dramatic Art
Williams, Benjamin Buford, Renaissance British Literature

NORMAL
Vinson, James, English

ST. BERNARD
Lott, Roger Richard Stanley, O.S.B, English

SYLACAUGA
Craddock, Patricia Bland, English

TROY
Pixton, William Hoover, English Romantic Literature, Composition
Roberts, Joseph Boxley, Jr, English

TUSCALOOSA
Brock, Elizabeth, English
Gallaway, Marian, Drama
Hobson, Fred Colby, Jr, American Literature
Johnson, Vernon E, American & Dramatic Literature
Salem, James Morris, English, Modern Drama
Scarritt, Charles Wesley, Journalism
Williamson, Eugene LaCoste, Jr, English Literature

TUSKEGEE INSTITUTE
Curran, Thomas M, S.J, English
Peters, Ada, English
Qualls, Youra T, English

UNIVERSITY
Arrendell, Odes Charles, Communication
Bales, Allen, Speech, Drama
Bell, (F) Kenneth, Journalism
Bowling, Lawrence Edward, English
Boyett, Woodrow Wilson, English
Deaver, Frank, Journalism, American Economic History
Eddins, Dwight, L, English
Emerson, O. B, American Literature
Foscue, Virginia Oden, English Linguistics
Hagood, Annabel Dunham, Speech
Halli, Robert William, Jr, English Literature
Johnson, Claudia Durst, American Literature
Kay, Carol McGinnis, English Literature
Kay, Wayne Donald, English Literature
Locke, Miriam (Austin), English
Loomis, Emerson Robert, English
Noble, Donald Rupert, American Literature
Smith, E. Marcel, English
Smith, Winston, English
Trawick, Buckner Beasley, English Literature
Watson, Charles Sullivan, English
Winter, William E, Journalism
York, Ernest Charles, English

ALASKA

ANCHORAGE
Byrd, Lemuel Brian, American & British Literature
Frost, Orcutt William Jr, English
McClure, Aretta Stevens, English
Wilson, James Robert, Neo-Classicism, Criticism

FAIRBANKS
Bedford, Jimmy Bertch, Journalism, Photography
Keim, Charles Joseph, English, Journalism
Salisbury, Lee Harvey, Drama, Cross Cultural Communication
Wood, William R, English

703

ARIZONA

FLAGSTAFF
Adams, Albert C, English
Bacon, Roger Lee, English, Cinema
Fitzmaurice, James Barry, English Renaissance Literature
Heiser, Merrill Francis, American & Comparative Literature, Amerindian Culture
Hunt, Timothy Earle, Integrated Humanities, English
James, Max Hubert, English, Linguistics
Larson, Harold C, Rhetoric & Public Address, Communicology
McGehee, Judson Dodds, English
Monsma, John William, Jr, Speech Education, Public Address
Newton, Ray, English, Journalism
Smallwood, Clyde George, Philosophy, Drama
Stevens, Robert Lowell, English
Wenstrand, Thomas Edward, Aesthetics, English Language
GREEN VALLEY
Abel, James Walden, Speech
Brewington, Arthur W, English Language & Literature
KINGMAN
Cox, John Francis, English Literature
PHOENIX
Bryan, Ralph Terry, English
Buzzard, Charles Eugene, Speech
Freeburg, Dorothy Dumble, English
Holmes, Frank Lincoln Duane, Speech
Livix, Mary Joanna (Fink), English
Lorenzini, August Peter, Speech, Communications
Sutherland, Robert Sherman, English Literature
PRESCOTT
Frogner, Ellen A, English, English Education
SCOTTSDALE
Moran, Dennis V, English, Humanities
Taylor, Louis, English
SUN CITY
Nutley, Grace Stuart, English
TEMPE
Archer, Jerome Walter, English
Arnold, William E, Communication, Speech
Baroody, Wilson George, Literature & Humanities
Brack, O. M, Jr, English
Colby, Arthur Leroy, English
D'Angelo, Frank Joseph, Rhetoric, Stylistics
Davis, Robert Edward, Rhetoric & Public Address
Dewey, Thomas Blanchard, English Literature
Doebler, Bettie Anne, English
Doebler, John Willard, English
Donelson, Kenneth L, English Education
Ellis, John C, English
Erno, Richard B, English
Evans, John X, English
Ferrell, Wilfred A, American Literature
Fisher, Marvin, American Studies
Gerber, Helmut E, English
Green, James Lee, English
Greene, Mildred Sarah, English, Comparative Literature
Haberman, Donald C, English Literature
Harris, Brice, English
Herman, George R, English Composition
Inglis, William Heard, Modern Drama, Arts Administration
Janssen, James George, American Literature
Johnson, Alan P, English
Kehl, Delmar George, American Literature
Levy, Leo B, English & American Literature
Lightfoot, Marjorie Jean, Contemporary English, American Literature
McSloy, Dean Franklin, Speech
Murray, Roger Nicholas, English
Myers, Louis McCorry, English, Linguistics
Nebeker, Helen Elizabeth, English, Contemporary American Literature
Ojala, William Truman, English Education
O'Malley, Glenn E, English
Perrill, Norman Kieth, Speech Communication
Portnoff, Collice Henry, English
Powers, Doris Cooper, English Literature
Randall, Virginia Frances, Comparative Literature
Richards, Gale Lee, Speech
Salerno, Nicholas Andrew, English Literature
Shafer, Robert Eugene, English
Stites, William Harrison, Speech
Travis, Mildred Klein, English, American Literature
Turner, Katharine Charlotte, English
Zimmerman, J.E, English

TUCSON
Burke, Alan Rucker, Victorian Literature
Clark, L.D, English
Davis, Ruth Brant, English
Deitz, Jonathan Eric, English Literature
Eisner, Sigmund, English
Fink, Zera S, English Literature
Fuller, Dorothy Van Arsdale, English
Gegenheimer, Albert Frank, English & American Literature
Gillmor, Frances, English
Granger, Byrd Howell, English, Folklore
Hamilton, Marie Padgett, English Language & Literature
Hosley, Richard, English
Ingalls, Mildred Dodge Jeremy, American, Chinese & Japanese Literature, Contemporary Poetry
Inman, Billie Jo (Andrew), English
Keppler, Carl Francis, English
Ketcham, Carl H, English Literature
King, Andrew Arthur, Rhetoric, Public Address
La Ban, Frank K, Speech, Phonetics
Lynn, Klonda, Speech, English
Marroney, Peter Ray, Drama
Mattingly, Alethea, Speech
Medine, Peter Ernest, Literature of the English Renaissance
Merren, John Jay, English
Mills, John Arvin, English
Muir, Arthur Laurence, Literature
Rafferty, Keen Alexander, Journalism
Ramsey, Robert W, Creative Writing
Robins, Harry Franklin, English
Robinson, Cecil, American Literature
St. Clair, Foster York, English Literature
Sigworth, Oliver Frederic, English
Sonnichsen, Charles Leland, English
Sparks, George Fray, Speech, Rhetoric
Trejo, Arnulfo Duenes, Library Science, Latin American Bibliography
Ulreich, John Charles, Jr, Sixteenth & Seventeenth Century English Literature

ARKANSAS

ARKADELPHIA
Crawford, John W, English
Ellis, Charles Merrill, English
Hobson, Stanley Preston, Education Administration, English
Hughes, Charles Willis, American Literature, Linguistics
McCommas, Betty Jo, English, Philosophy
Morris, Gilbert Leslie, English
Rowlette, Irene Wilson, English
Sumerlin, Claude Windell, Journalism
BELLA VISTA
Phillips, George H, Journalism, Printing Management
CLARKSVILLE
Kopp, Jane Baltzell, English
CONWAY
Behrens, Ralph, English
Busfield, Roger M, Jr, Speech
Crowder, Ashby Bland, Jr, English & American Literature
Moffatt, Walter Augustus, Jr, English Literature
Nolte, Eugene Arche, Jr, English
FAYETTEVILLE
Arias, Bogdanka, English, Spanish
Bennett, James Richard, English Literature, Humanities
Cowan, James Costello, English
Eaves, Thomas Cary Duncan, English
Faulkner, Claude Winston, English
Harrison, William Neal, Creative Writing, Contemporary Literature
Hart, Milton Blair, Speech, Dramatic Art
Kernodle, George Riley, Dramatics
Kimpel, Ben (Drew), English
Lindquist, Carol A, Renaissance & Restoration Literature
Montgomery, Lyna Lee, English Literature
Morris, Robert Lee, English & American Literature
Randolph, Vance, Folklore
Rogers, Jimmie Neal, Speech Communication
Rouse, Hubert Blair, English
Rudolph, Earle Leighton, English
Van Scyoc, Leo L, English
Watson, Harold Francis, English Literature
Williams, Miller, English, Spanish Translations
JONESBORO
James, Overton Philip, English
LITTLE ROCK
Arnold, Marc Hadley, English Literature
Eberly, Ralph Dunbar, English

Francis, Eleanor M, American Literature
Lyons, Eugene, English & American Literature
Mathews, Johnye Elizabeth, English, American Studies
Parins, James William, English Literature
Stratton, John David, English, Drama
Young, Peter Baxter, Drama
MAGNOLIA
Harton, Margaret Elizabeth, Speech
MONTICELLO
Coleman, Tom C, III, English
Frank, Edward John, Theatre, Dramatic Criticism
Viitanen, Wayne John, American Literature
NORTH LITTLE ROCK
Littlefield, Daniel Franklin, Jr, American Literature
PINE BLUFF
Coleman, Viralene Johnson, English Literature
Fuller, Edneil Elizabeth, English & American Literature
RUSSELLVILLE
Doss, Erma Sue Harrison, English
SEARCY
Elliott, Gary Douglas, English
Sears, Lloyd Cline, English Literature
Ulrey, Evan, Speech
Walker, Richard Waller, Speech Pathology
SILOAM SPRINGS
Panage, John H, English Literature
STATE UNIVERSITY
Dube, Anthony Zenon, American Literature, Modern Drama
Franson, John Karl, English Literature
Hagen, Lyman B, English
Harwell, Thomas Meade, Jr, English
Peek, George Sherman, Medieval English Literature, Drama
Widener, Ralph William, Jr, Speech
TEXARKANA
Montgomery, Margaret Barron, English

CALIFORNIA

ALTADENA
Turner, Rufus P, English
ANAHEIM
Berthelot, Joseph A, English
ANGWIN
Hawks, Paul Newton, Jr, Communications
Wehtje, Verne Virgil, English
APTOS
Grant, William A, English
ARCATA
Bivens, William Patterson, III, Stylistics, English Linguistics
Day, Richard C, English
McClary, Maclyn Howard, Journalism
McNelis, James Ignatius, English
Pauley, John Francis, Speech, Drama
Sinclair, Giles Merton, American Literature & Linguistics
Squires, Edgar Larry, English
BAKERSFIELD
Belkind, Allen J, English
Green, Donald Charles, English Linguistics
Spencer, David Gelvin, English
Spencer, Jeffry Burress, English Literature
Willis, Hulon Sims, Literature
BELMONT
Gavin, Rosemarie Julie, S.N.D, Education, English
BERKELEY
Adelman, Janet Ann, English Literature
Alpers, Paul Joel, English
Alter, Robert, English Literature
Anson, John S, English
Ault, Donald Duane, English Literature, Philosophy of Science
Barish, Jonas A, English
Beloof, Robert, Literature, Speech, Drama
Bentley, H. Wilder, English, Humanities
Bloom, Robert, English Literature
Bogard, Travis Miller, English
Breslin, James E, English
Bridgman, Richard, English
Bronson, Bertrand Harris, English Literature
Casteen, John, Old English Literature, History of the English Language
Chatman, Seymour B, English
Christ, Carol Tecla, English
Coolidge, John Stanhope, English & Comparative Literature
Crews, Frederick C, English & American Literature
Dundes, Alan, Folklore
Farnham, Willard, English Literature
Flanagan, Thomas James Bonner, English
Friedman, Donald M, English
Geiger, Don, Speech

Girdler, Lew, English
Goldsby, Robert W, Drama
Greenblatt, Stephen Jay, English
Griffin, Dustin Hadley, English Literature
Griffin, Robert Julian, English, American Literature
Hagopian, Richard, English
Hart, James David, American Literature
Hugo, Howard Eppens, English
Hutson, Arthur Eugene, English
Hutson, Richard Eugene
Jones, Charles Williams, English Literature
Jordan, John Emory, English Literature
Knoepflmacher, C, English Literature
Kratins, Ojars, English
McCullough, Constance, Education
McWilliams, John Probasco, Jr, English, American Literature
Manning, Peter J, English
Manning, Sylvia P, English
Merrill, Rodney Harpster, English Literature
Michaels, Leonard, English
Middleton, Anne Louise, English
Miles, Josephine, English Philology & Criticism
Miyoshi, Masao, English
Murray, Diane Johnson, Nineteenth Century Novel, Victorian Historical Background
Muscatine, Charles, English
Nathan, Edward Leonard, Rhetoric
Nelson, Alan H, English, Art History
Ogden, Dunbar Hunt, Dramatic Art
O Hehir, Brendan Peter, English
Oliver, Raymond Davies, English
Oliver, William I, Drama
Orgel, Stephen Kitay, English
Paley, Morton D, Romantic Poetry
Parkinson, Thomas Francis, English Language & Literature
Paterson, John, English
Pickerell, Albert George, Journalism
Porter, Carolyn Jane, American Literature
Rabkin, Norman Clifford, English
Rader, Ralph Wilson, English Literature
Raleigh, John Henry, English Literature
Renoir, Alain, English, Comparative Literature
Richardson, Janette, Rhetoric, Comparative Literature
Richardson, L. Janette, Comparative Literature, Rhetoric
Richmond, Hugh Macrae, English Literature
Rosenberg, Marvin, Dramatic Art
Schorer, Mark, English Literature
Scott, Peter Dale, English, Political Science
Shumaker, Wayne, English Literature
Sloan, Thomas O, Rhetoric
Smith, Henry Nash, American Literature
Starr, George A, English
Stout, Gardner Dominick, Jr, English
Taylor, Gordon Overton, English, American Literature
Tracy, Robert E, English
Traugott, John Lewis, English Literature
Tuveson, Ernest Lee, English Literature
Weisinger, Kenneth Dean, German, Comparative Literature
Wilson, Garff Bell, Dramatic Art, Rhetoric
Zimmerman, Michael, English, American Literature
Zwerdling, Alex, English

BURBANK
Sandelin, Clarence Kenneth, English
CARMEL
Dupee, Frederick Wilcox, English
Kerby-Miller, Sinclair, Communication
Sullens, Idelle, English, Humanities
CASTRO VALLEY
Barrett, Harold, Rhetoric
CHAPEL HILLS
Flora, Joseph Martin, English
CHICO
Adams, Charles Clinton, English
Adams, Harlen Martin, English, Speech, Drama
Crosland, George Nathaniel, English
Downes, David Anthony, English
Dyer, Armel, Speech, American Studies
Felver, Charles Stanley, English
Forbes, Allan Edward, Speech
Genthe, Charles V, American Studies, English
Glenn, Edgar Mungen, English
Jones, Lloyd S, Speech
Keithley, George Frederick, Modern Poetry & Creative Writing
Markland, Murray Faulds, English
Prince, Gilbert Parker, Jr, Restoration & Eighteenth Century Literature
Rawlins, Jack P, British Literature, History of the English Language
Souders, Robert Livingston, American Studies
Starmer, Garrett Ludlow, Speech Pathology

CHULA VISTA
Snyder, William Walter, English
CLAREMONT
Armour, Richard (Willard), English Literature
Barnes, Richard G, English
Bellman, Samuel Irving, English
Boyle, Harry Herbert, English, Neo-Latin Philology
Davenport, William Henry, English Literature
Dunbar, John Raine, American Literature
Elsbree, Langdon, English
Fogle, French R, English Literature
Fossum, Robert H, English & American Literature
Friedman, Albert Barron, English Philology
Fuller, Anne Elizabeth Havens, English
Germain, Edward Barnard, English Literature, Poetry
Holmes, Charles S, English
Hoskins, Herbert Wilson, Jr, English & Comparative Literature
Jackson, Agnes L. Moreland, English, American Literature
Jordan, Gretchen Graf Pahl, English Literature
Lohrli, Anne, English Language & Literature
Mulhauser, Frederick Ludwig, English Literature
O'Brien, Darcy G, English
Payne, (Clyde) Ladell, English
Pinney, Thomas, English
Quinones, Ricardo, Renaissance, Comparative Literature
Sanders, David Scott, American Literature
Sellery, J'Nan Morse, Modern British & American Literature
Siegel, Ben, Literary Criticism
Spengemann, William Charles, English
Strathmann, Ernest Albert, English Literature
Swan, Jesse R, Jr, Drama, Speech
Tilden, Lorraine F, Hispanic American Literature
Waingrow, Marshall, English

CLOVIS
Billings, Robert S, English
CORTE MADERA
Tillinghast, Richard Williford, English
COVINA
Chartier, Myron Raymond, Speech Communication, History

DAVIS
Berger, Sidney E, Medieval & Renaissance Literature
Campbell, Thomas Patterson, III, English Literature, Linguistics
Carr, Joan Christine, English Literature
Carter, Everett, English
Cohn, Ruby H, Literature
D'Harnoncourt, Everard, Dramatic Art
Gilbert, Elliot Lewis, Nineteenth Century English Literature
Hanzo, Thomas A, English Literature
Harsh, Wayne C, English, Linguistics
Hayden, John Olin, English
Hays, Peter L, English
Hoffman, Michael Jerome, English
Hopkins, Robert Hazen, English
McGuinness, Arthur Edward, English
Murphy, James Jerome, English & Speech
Needham, Gwendolyn Bridges, English, Fiction
Pomeroy, Ralph Stanley, Speech
Robertson, David Alan, Modern & Biblical Literature
Rossi, Alfred Anthony, Dramatic Art
Sarlos, Robert Karoly, Theatre History
Schleiner, Winfried, English
Shank, Theodore, Theatre, Drama
Shapiro, Karl Jay, English
Sharp, Harry W, Jr, Rhetoric, Communication
Silvia, Daniel (Shiver, Jr), Medieval & Renaissance English Literature
Stambusky, Alan Anthony, Dramatic Art
Weber, Brom, English
Wiggins, Robert Alonzo, English
Wilson, David Scofield, American Studies, English
Woodress, James, American Literature
Wright, Celeste Turner, English

DELMAR
Nyce, Benjamin M, English
DOMINGUEZ HILLS
Buckner, Claudia, American Literature & Studies
Geller, Lila Belle, English Literature
Laser, Marvin, English
Rankin, David B, English
Ravitz, Abe Carl, English

Riddell, James Allen, English Literature & Lexicography
Sando, Ephriam Gerald, English
Santas, Joan, American Literature
Vaughn, Jack Alfred, Theater Arts
Wells, Walter, English, American Studies
Wheatley, William Tom, Dramatic Art
EL CAJON
Danielson, Robert Walter, English
Theobald, John R, English, Theology
EL CERRITO
Anderson, Paul Bunyan, English, American Literature
Bond, Donald Frederic, English Literature
ENCINITAS
Hilty, Palmer A, English, Comparative Literature
FRESNO
Bluestein, Gene, American Studies, Folklore
Bochin, Hal William, Speech Communication
Duke, John Hamilton, Journalism
Everwine, Peter Paul, Poetry
Faderman, Lillian, English
Graham, Gaylord Owen, Theatre
Larrabee, Carlton H, English
Levine, Philip, Creative Writing
Logan, Barry L, English Literature
Lyon, Earl DeWitt, English
McDermott, John J, English
McKnight, Haven Ray, English
Poss, Stanley Horn, English
Randall, Charles Henry, Drama
Rosenthal, Judith Ann, English & American Literature
Satin, Joseph, Comparative Literature
Seib, Kenneth Allen, English & American Literature
Sheehan, Paul V, Journalism
Shepard, Bernard A, Journalism
Walker, Phillip N, Speech, Drama
Zumwalt, Eugene Ellsworth, English
FULLERTON
Andersen, Martin Perry, Speech
Cummings, Sherwood, English
Duerr, Edwin, Theatre
Enell, George O, Speech
Fessenden, Seth A, Speech
Granell, Lee E, Speech
Greenwood, Joan Voss, English
Hughes, Charlotte Bradford, English, Comparative Literature
Jones, Hazel James, English
Klammer, Thomas Paul, English Linguistics
Koon, William Henry, English, Folklore
McNelly, Willis Everett, English
Oaks, Priscilla (Shames), American Literature
Obler, Paul Charles, English Literature
Pollak, Paulina S, English
Ramsay, Orrington C, English
Rubinstein, William C, English
Schick, George Baldwin Powell, English Literature
Schreiner, Philip J, Organizational Communication, Business Administration
Sears, Donald Albert, Literature, Language
Seller, Howard Jay, English
Spangler, George Mervin, American Literature
Stupple, Alexander James, American Literature
Vogeler, Martha Salmon, English Literature
Wagner, M. John, English
Young, James Douglas, English
GROVER CITY
Kerr, John Fay, American Literature, Poetry
HAYWARD
Baird, John E, Speech
Bryant, Jerry H, English Literature
Clay, Edward Miller, English
Conner, Jack Edward, English
Costy, James Otto, Speech
Friedman, Martin Boris, English, Comparative Literature
Hall, Jeanne Lucille, Speech, Drama
Hammerback, John Clark, Speech
McMichael, George, American Literature
McVeigh, Terrence A, English
Markos, Donald W, American Literature
Martin, Robert Carl, Speech, Semantics
Peterson, Douglas L, English Literature
Ratner, Marc Leonard, English & American Literature
Rosenbaum, Morton, English
Stanford, Raney, Modern Literature, History of the Novel
Staniforth, Gwendolyn E, English
Williams, Robert Verne, English
HOLLYWOOD
Ubans, Maris Uldis, Theatre Arts, Drama
HUNTINGTON BEACH
Gorelik, Mordecai, Theatre

INDIO
  Furr, Leanora Reilly, English
IRVINE
  Adams, Hazard, English
  Babb, Howard Selden, English
  Calderwood, James Lee, English
  Flores, Ralph, Comparative Literature
  Gelley, Alexander, Comparative Literature
  Goetz, Walter L, English
  Hartman, Carl Frederick, English
  Heiney, Donald William, Comparative Literature
  Krieger, Murray, English Literature
  Lentricchia, Frank, English
  Martin, Jay H, English, American Studies
  Montgomery, Robert Langford, Jr, English
  Reed, Barbara Loraine, English & American Literature
  Schell, Edgar Thomas, English
  Tashjian, Dickran Levon, American Literature
  Toliver, Harold Earl, English & American Literature
KELSEYVILLE
  Dawson, Mildred Agnes, English Composition
KENSINGTON
  Littlejohn, David, English, Journalism
LAGUNA BEACH
  Newcomb, Stanley Spencer, Speech
  Peters, Robert Louis, English
LAGUNA NIGUEL
  Haaker, Ann, English, Drama
LA JOLLA
  Addison, Michael, C., Drama
  Desmond, Robert William, Journalism
  Dijkstra, Abraham J, American & Comparative Literature
  Elliott, Robert Carl, English Literature
  Fussell, Edwin, English & American Literature
  Pearce, Roy Harvey, English
  Stewart, John Lincoln, English
  Szanto, George H, Comparative Literature, Theatre
  Wagner, Arthur, Theatre
  Wright, Andrew Howell, English
LAKE SAN MARCOS
  Upton, Albert, English
LA MESA
  Gulick, Sidney Lewis, Jr, English Literature
  Phillips, George Lewis, English
LA VERNE
  Dupler, Dorothy, Speech
LOMA LINDA
  Stauffer, James Paul, English Literature
LONG BEACH
  Allen, Charles A, American Literature
  Ames, Kenneth John, English
  Applbaum, Ronald Lee, Speech Communication
  Aspiz, Harold, English, American Literature
  Avni, Abraham Albert, English, Comparative Literature
  Axelrad, Arthur Marvin, English Literature
  Bell, Alexander Robert Lundrigan, Old English Language & Literature
  Bonazza, Blaze Odell, English, Comparative Literature
  Briggs, Nancy Elaine, Speech Communication
  Brooks, Charles Benton, English
  Brophy, Robert Joseph, Modern American & British Literature
  Cain, Earl Richard, Speech
  Cooper, June Margaret, Speech Pathology
  Crane, George Francis, II, English
  Crawford, Walter Byron, English
  Davis, Jimmie D, Journalism
  Drum, Dale Douglas, Speech, Psychology
  Gilde, Helen Cheney, English
  Green, John Hurlbut, Drama
  Hauth, Luster E, Rhetoric, Public Address
  Hegarty, Mary Loyola, C.C.V.I, English Literature
  Hipkiss, Robert Arthur, English
  Hubble, Thomas N, Comparative Literature
  Kahan, Stanley, Theatre Arts, Dramatic Literature
  Locklin, Gerald Ivan, English
  Loganbill, G. Bruce, Speech
  Markman, Roberta Hoffman, English, Comparative Literature
  Martin, Howard S, Speech
  Masback, Frederic Joseph, English
  May, Charles Edward, English & American Literature
  Nielsen, Elizabeth E, English, Philology
  Purcell, Mary Joe, English Literature
  Rodabaugh, Delmer, English
  Rose, Stanley Charles, English & Children's Literature
  Schwab, Arnold T, English
  Skriletz, Dorothy June, Speech
  Stein, Meyer Lewis, Journalism, Mass Communications

Stephens, George Darwin, English
Stetler, Charles E, Modern American Literature
Stiver, Harry E, Jr, Theatre Arts, Speech
Weinstock, Donald Jay, English Literature
Williams, John Brindley, American Literature, Stylistics
Wills, John W, Speech
Wilson, Suzanne M, English Literature
Wylder, Robert Clay, American Literature
Zambrano, Ana Laura, Literature, Cinema
LOS ALTOS
  Leach, Elsie, English
  Meritt, Herbert Dean, English, Philology
  Nelson, Pauline W, Speech, Drama
  Philbrick, Norman (D), Dramatic Literature
  Richards, Marion Kazmann, English, Comparative Literature
  Stegner, Wallace Earle, English
LOS ANGELES
  Abood, Edward Francis, English & Comparative Literature
  Adams, Donald Knapp, English
  Adams, Robert Martin, English
  Albertson, Clinton Edward, S.J, English Literature
  Allen, Michael John B, Renaissance Literature & Philosophy
  Allen, Robert Randolph, English
  Anderson, Walter Eldon, English
  Arnold, Aerol, English
  Arpad, Joseph John, American Studies, Folklore
  Atchity, Kenneth John, Comparative Literature, English
  Barnelle, Virginia Marie, Theatre Arts, Educational Psychology
  Barth, Lewis M, Midrashic Literature
  Bassett, Sharon Marie, Nineteenth & Twentieth Century Literature
  Bates, Steven Latimer, English & American Literature
  Batten, Charles Linwood, Jr, Eighteenth Century English Literature
  Beckwith, Charles Emilio, English
  Berryman, Charles Beecher, English Literature
  Berst, Charles A, English
  Bird, Donald Arthur, English Language
  Braunmuller, Albert Richard, English Literature
  Brier, Peter A, English Literature
  Brown, James Anthony, S.J, Radio & Television Communications
  Brown, Robert Edward, Modern Literature, Literary Criticism
  Brown, William H, Jr, English, Linguistics
  Busacca, Basil, English
  Butler, James Harmon, Drama
  Calder, Daniel Gillmore, English & Medieval Literature
  Canfield, John Douglas, English & American Literature
  Carothers, Francis Barton, Jr, English
  Carroll, David Barry, English & American Literature
  Carter, Katherine Davis, Renaissance Literature, Rhetoric
  Christensen, Allan Conrad, English Literature
  Condren, Edward Ignatius, Medieval Literature
  Coonradt, Frederic Chapin, Journalism
  Cope, Jackson Irving, English
  Copperud, Roy Herman, Journalism
  Cronin, Morton John, English, Anthropology
  Cross, Richard Keith, English, Comparative Literature
  Cullen, Jack B, Speech
  Daly, Saralyn Ruth, English
  Davidson, C. Melvin, Jr, Theatre, English
  Dearing, Vinton Adams, English Literature
  Dent, Robert William, English
  Dickens, Milton (Clifford), Speech
  Digges, M. Laurentia, C.S.J, English
  Dilligan, Robert James, English Literature
  Durham, Philip, English
  Eisenstein, Sam A, English, Comparative Literature
  Engdahl, Bonnie Thoman, English
  Erlandson, Theodore R, English Literature
  Espey, John Jenkins, English
  Evans, Fallon, English
  Falk, Robert Paul, American Literature
  Fisher, Walter Ray, Speech, Drama
  Fong, David Douglas, English Literature
  Freeman, Ronald Edward, English
  Freestone, Norman W, Speech
  Friedman, Philip Allan, English Literature, American Philosophy
  Friedrich, Gerhard Gunter, English & Comparative Literature

Fruman, Norman, Romanticism, Aesthetic Theory
Georges, Robert A, Folklore, Linguistics
Gleason, John Haberman, Journalism, Administration
Goldberg, Gerald Jay, English
Goldstein, Harvey D, English, Aesthetics
Gordon, Marjorie Neeson, Medieval English Literature
Goyne, Grover Cleveland, English
Greene, Donald Johnson, English
Grose, Christopher Waldo, English
Guffey, George Robert, English
Gullans, Charles Bennett, English, Poetry
Guyer, Byron, English
Hahn, Elsie Stearns, Speech
Halperin, John William, English Literature
Hargis, Donald Erwin, Speech
Harris, Mark, Language Arts
Hendricks, Beverly Lusty, Speech Education
Hethmon, Robert H, Theatre, Theatre History
Hillbruner, Anthony, Speech
Holladay, Howard Preston, Rhetorical Theory
Howells, Anne Blackman
Hutter, Albert David, English, Comparative Literature
Jones, Everett L, English, American Studies
Jones, Warren Saunders, Speech
Jorgensen, Paul Alfred, English Literature
Kelly, Henry Ansgar, Medieval Renaissance Literature, Intellectual History
Kessler, Jascha Frederick, English Literature
Kinder, Marsha, English, Cinema
Kinsman, Robert Starr, English
Kipling, Gordon Lee, English Renaissance Literature
Kolb, Gwin Jackson, II, English Literature
Kruglak, Theodore Edward, Journalism, Political Science
Kubla, David Lawrence, English Literature
Kully, Robert Delmar, Speech
Kurtz, Kenneth, English & American Literature
Laird, David, English Literature
Lanham, Richard Alan, English
Leary, William G, English
Lecky, Eleazer, English Literature
Lehan, Richard D, American Literature
Lemay, Joseph Alberic Leo, English
Lincoln, Kenneth Robert, English & American Literature
Lomas, Charles Wyatt, Speech
Long, Emmett Thaddeus, Speech, Higher Education
Lowers, Virginia Belle, English
Luedtke, Luther Stephen, English & American Literature
McBath, James Harvey, Speech
McCoard, William Brinkerhoff, Speech
McLean, Alvin Hugh, English Literature
Magruder, Mildred (Anderson), English
Mahl, Mary R, English Literature
Malone, David Henry, Comparative Literature
Maniquis, Robert Manuel, Nineteenth Century English Literature, Comparative Literature
Marcus, Fred Harold, English
Marcus, Mitchell, English
Marshall, Donald Glenn, English
Matthews, William, English
Melnitz, William Wolf, Theatre Arts
Metzger, Charles Reid, English
Moore, Stephen C, English
Morrow, Patrick David, American Literature & Studies
Motley, Michael Tilden, Speech Communication, Linguistics
Murray, Thelma Taylor, English, Education
Nichol, John William, English
Nisbet, Ada Blanche, English
Novak, Maximillian, English Literature
Oberle, Marcella, Speech
Oliver, Kenneth Arthur, Comparative Literature & English
Owen, Lewis J, English Literature
Palmer, John A, English
Parker, Hershel, English
Paxson, Omar M, English Literature
Peterson, Joyce Elaine, English Literature
Phelps, Waldo Woodson, Speech Education
Phillips, James Emerson, Jr, English
Povey, John Frederick, English
Rees, Robert Alvin, American Literature
Richardson, Ralph, Speech
Riddel, Joseph Neill, English, American Literature
Ridley, Florence, English, Medieval Literature
Rolfe, Franklin Prescott, English Literature
Roper, Alan Henry, English
Rosenthal, Paul Irwin, Speech

Rousseau, George Sebastian, English Literature
Rowe, Karen Elizabeth, English & American Literature
Ryan, Harold Francis, S.J, English & American Literature
Ryf, Robert Stanley, English
Savage, George, Drama, Theatre Arts
Schell, George Aaron, Speech Communication
Schrader, Allen, Literary Criticism
Schulz, Max Frederick, English Literature
Sellin, Paul R, English
Sereno, Kenneth Keala, Speech Communication, Psychology
Sheats, Paul Douglas, English
Sherlock, Warren Curtis, Speech
Smith, Marjorie Marie, Theatre, Speech
Story, Patrick Lee, English & American Literature
Stuart, Gaby E, British Literature, Criticism
Sullivan, Frank, English
Sullivan, Majie Padberg, English
Swedenberg, Hugh Thomas, Jr, English Literature
Templeman, William Darby, English Language & Literature
Tennyson, Georg Bernhard, English
Thorslev, Peter L, Jr, English
Toscan, Richard Eric, Theatre History, Contemporary Dramatic Literature
Tufte, Virginia J, English
Welsh, Alexander, English
Wilcox, Walter, Journalism
Wilgus, D. K., English
Williams, Frederick Dowell, Communication
Williams, Wirt, English & Comparative Literature
Wilson, Robert Dauden, Education, Linguistics
Winterowd, Walter Ross, English, Rhetoric
Wortham, Thomas Richard, American Literature
Wright, Edward A, Theatre, Drama
Zall, Paul Maxwell, English Literature
MALIBU
Atteberry, James L, English Literature
Casmir, Fred L, Speech Communication
Levant, Howard, American Literature, Creative Writing
Smythe, James Erwin, English
Womack, Morris M, Speech, Religion
MANHATTAN BEACH
Eggenschwiler, David Lee, English
MENLO PARK
Fink, Jack E, English
MILL VALLEY
Jackson, Robin Carol, Theatre Arts
MILLBRAE
Miller, Clarence Adolph, Speech, Drama
MODESTO
Norton, Max C, Speech Pathology, Communications
Werts, Mattie, English
MONTECITO
Vanderlip, Eldad C, Comparative Literature, English
MONTEREY
Gabel, Barbara Bennett, American Literature
MONTEREY PARK
Shroyer, Frederick Benjamin, English
MORAGA
Bryant, Byron Ralph, English, Humanities
Springer, Mary Doyle, English
Springer, Norman, English
MOUNTAIN VIEW
Hastings, Arthur C, Speech
NEWHALL
King, Grace Hamilton, English
NEWPORT BEACH
Gross, Harvey, English, Comparative Literature
NORTHRIDGE
Abcarian, Richard, English
Anderson, William Davis, English
Bellman, Willard F, Drama
Brewer, Gwendolyn, Whitehead, Eighteenth Century English Literature, English Education
Brock, James W, Drama
Cameron, Donald J, Speech
Carlton, Charles Rogers, English, Linguistics
Cleary, James William, Communication, Comparative Literature
Clendenning, John, American Literature & Civilization
Devol, Kenneth Stowe, Journalism, Mass Communication
Dunn, Catherine Mary, English
Essick, Robert Newman, English Literature & Art

Evans, Oliver W, English
Falk, Heinrich Richard, Theatre History, Dramatic Literature & Criticism
Finestone, Harry, American Literature
Gaumer, Mahlon Conover, III, Medieval English Literature, English Linguistics
Graves, A. Wallace, Rhetoric
Gunkle, George, Speech & Drama
Halty-Dube, Adolfo, Art, Latin American Drama
Johnson, DeWayne Burton, Journalism
Kaplan, Charles, American Literature
Klinger, Mary Frances, English Literature
Klotz, Marvin, American Literature
Larson, Gale K, English
Lid, Richard W, English
McMahon, Fred Riley, Speech
Noreen, Robert Gerald, English Literature & Composition
Peterson, Annamarie W, English, American Literature
Plasberg, Elaine, English Literature
Schlosser, William Edwin, Theatre
Smith, James Steel, English, Popular Culture
Stafford, Arnold John, American Literature & History
Stanford, Ann, English
Stewart, Lawrence Delbert, English Romantic Literature, 20th Century American Literature
Stockwell, John Charles, Drama
Stone, Harry, English
Van Slooten, Henry, English
Vogler, Richard Allen, English Literature & Art
Wright, Thomas Edward, English
OAKLAND
Bridges, William Emery, English, American Civilization
Carlin, Claire Madeleine, S.N.J.M, English
Duff, Samuel E, English
Durst, Martin I, English & American Literature
Furay, Michael Mortimer, English, African Studies
Malpas, Edward Reginald Howard, English, Drama
Milowicki, Edward John, English
Pope, Elizabeth Marie, English Literature
Richmond, Velma E. Bourgeois, English
Walker, Imogene Bishop, English
Weber, Francesca Cabrini, S.N.J.M, English Literature
Wendt, Allan, English
Wright, Evaline Uhl, Speech
OJAI
Hubler, Richard G, English
ORANGE
Davis, John Lowell, English Literature
Watson, Melvin Ray, English
Watson, Richard Alan, English, Communications
ORINDA
Lyford, Joseph Philip, Journalism
PACIFIC GROVE
Bracher, Frederick (George), English Literature
Solve, Melvin Theodor, English Literature
PALO ALTO
Chase, Rowland Kimball, Speech, Theatre
Sensabaugh, George Frank, English Literature
PASADENA
Clark, Justus Kent, English
Cozart, William Reed, English
Ende, Stuart Alan, English Literature
Gregory-Panopoulos, John Fred, Communications, Telecommunications
Magill, Frank Northen, English & American Literature
Mandel, Oscar, English
Mayhew, George P, English
Pfister, Emil R, Speech
Smith, David Rodman, English & American Literature
Smith, Hallett Darius, English Literature
PIEDMONT
White, Melvin Robert, Speech & Theatre
PLACENTIA
Smythe, Ted Curtis, Mass Communication, History
POMONA
Adair, Virginia H, Literature
Elliott, Thomas Joseph, English Literature, Medieval Studies
Fulbeck, John F, Comparative Literature
Harmer, Ruth Mulvey, English
Morsberger, Robert E, English
Stodder, Joseph Henry, English & Comparative Literature
Weissbuch, Ted N, American Literature
Wilds, Lillian, Shakespeare
POWAY
Gaffney, Floyd, Drama, Dance

REDLANDS
Adams, Bess Porter, English
Baccus, Joseph Harold, Speech
Bromberger, Frederick S, English Literature
Childs, Barney, Music
Hone, Ralph E, English
Jelliffe, Rebecca Rio, English
Kanjo, Eugene Richard, American Literature
Main, William Wesley, English
Nelson, Lawrence Emerson, History of Civilization, Literature
Ouellette, Eugene G, Speech
Stuart, Robert Lee, American Literature
RIVERSIDE
Aproberts, Ruth, English Literature
Axelrod, Steven Gould, English & American Literature
Burton, Howard A, English Literature
Dana, Margaret Elizabeth, English Literature
Davis, Delmer Ivan, English
Dunn, Robert Paul, Renaissance English Literature
Eigner, Edwin Moss, English & American Literature
Gleckner, Robert Francis, English
Hanna, Ralph, III, English
Harris, William Oliver, English
Jones, Linda Bunnell, English Literature
Knox, George A, English
Lewis, Richard B, English
Lippman, Monroe, Theatre
Little, Helen, English
Mobley, Lawrence Eugene, English & American Literature
Moore, Roberta J, Journalism
Munson, William Frederick, English
Musacchio, George Louis, English Literature, Milton
Risso, Richard David, Drama
Stewart, Stanley N, English
Van Deusen, (L) Marshall, English
Vickery, John B, English
Williams, Kathleen Mary, Renaissance & Eighteenth Century English
ROHNERT PARK
Bullen, John Samuel, English
Dhesi, Nirmal Singh, English Literature
Haslam, Gerald William, American Literature, Linguistics
Hess, Judith Wright, American Literature, Film
Lee, Hector, American Folklore
Mountain, John Anthony, Comparative Literature
Sandy, Alan Francis, Jr, English & American Literature
Soules, Eugene H, English
ROLLING HILLS
Blatt, Muriel R, English, American Literature
Welch, Laurence C, Comparative Literature
Yoggerst, Mary Hilary, S.R.H, English Literature
ROSEMEAD
Christmas, Robert A, English
SACRAMENTO
Bankowsky, Richard James, Creative Writing
Bertonasco, Marc F, English
Biddle, Phillips R, Rhetoric, Psychology
Creel, George W, English Literature
Dickison, Roland Bishop, American Folklore, English Literature
Enroth, Clyde Adolph, English
Grybas, Algird A, Communication
Harris, Stephen LeRoy, English, Humanities
Hornback, Vernon T, Jr, English
Houghton, Donald Eugene, English
Huber, Paul, Speech, Religion
Hume, Charles Vernard, Speech, Drama
Kline, Herbert W, Speech, Theatre
McAlister, Floyd L, English Literature
McKee, Irving, English
Mackey, Mary Lou, Comparative Literature, Film
Marsh, Patrick Otis, Rhetoric & Public Address
Meindl, Robert James, English
Moore, Dwain Earl, Speech
Parkin, Rebecca P, Literature
Pattison, Joseph C, Literature
Pilant, Elizabeth H, English
Preus, Ove J. H, English
Redmond, Eugene Benjiman, English & Black American Literature
Sukkary, Shawky El, English, Arabic
Thornton, Hortense Eloise, Afro-American Literature
Wasser, Henry, English
Wilhelm, John Ferdinand, English
SAN ANSELMO
Ritter, Jesse Paul, Jr, English, Comparative Literature

SAN BERNARDINO
Barnes, Ronald Edgar, Dramatic Literature, Theatre History
Golden, Bruce, English & Comparative Literature
Hartung, Charles Vincent, English
Koon, Helen Wickham, English Literature, Drama
Rudisill, Amanda Sue, Theatre
White, Edward Michael, English
SAN BRUNO
Dell, George W, Rhetoric
SAN DIEGO
Adams, Elsie B, English
Adams, John R, English
Amble, Kjell, Drama
Arnold, Lois Virginia, English, Education
Baker, James Rupert, English
Bennett, Fordyce Judson, English
Bennett, Robert A, English, Education
Benson, Jackson J, Contemporary American Literature
Borkat, Roberta Friedman Sarfatt, English Literature
Brashers, Howard Charles, Creative Writing, American Literature
Brown, LeRoy, Speech, Education
Brown, Ruth Christiani, English Literature
Eulert, Donald Dean, English
Farber, Gerald Howard, Comparative Literature, English & American Literature
Foster, Edward E, English
Gervais, Ronald James, American Literature
Groff, Patrick J, English Education
Gross, George Clayburn, English Literature
Henig, Suzanne, English Poetry
Jackson, James Harvey, Public Address
Kehler, Harold F, English
Keller, Karl, English
King, Stephen William, Communication
McLeod, Susan Herminghaus, English & American Literature
Malmsheimer, Lonna Myers, American Literature & Studies
Moramarco, Fred Stephen, American Literature & Studies
Rogers, William Norris, II, English Literature
Rush, Richard Russell, English Literature
Sadler, Glenn Edward, English
Sanderlin, George William, English
Sandstrom, Glenn A, English
Santangelo, Gennaro, Literature
Savvas, Minas, Comparative Literature, Creative Writing
Scott, Arthur Lincoln, English
Sellman, Hunton Dade, Dramatic Art
Shouse, Claude F, English
Sterner, Alice, English
Stiehl, Harry Charles, Modern Literature & History
Thrane, James R, English
Tidwell, James Nathan, English
Tunberg, Jacqueline Duffie, English, Drama
Wall, Carey Gail, English & American Literature
Widmer, Kingsley, Literature
Winkelman, Donald Marvin, English, Folklore
Wylie, Donald George, Education, Speech
Yarber, Robert Earl, English
Yun, Chang Sik, Comparative Literature
SAN FRANCISCO
Bassan, Maurice, American Literature
Bertram, Jean De Sales, Theatre Arts, History
Biggs, Bernice Prince, English, Reading, Secondary Education
Bratset, Richard, English & World Literature
Cunningham, Dolora Gallagher, English
Dawson, Hugh Joseph, American Studies & Literature
Day, Dennis G, Speech
Derus, David Lee, English Literature
Dettering, Richard Whitson, Semantics, Education, Philosophy
Dickey, William, English
Dollard, Frank Drew, English
Dorius, Raymond Joel, English
Early, Raymond R, American Literature
Edwards, John, English
Evans, Matthew, Humanities, English
Feinstein, Herbert Charles Verschleisser, English, Mass Media of Communications
Feltham, Fredrik George, English
Flett, Alex S, Drama
Foff, Arthur (Raymond), English, Education
Gearhart, Sally Miller, Speech, Drama
Glyer, Richard T, Speech, Drama
Gregory, Hoosag, English
Gunn, Thomson William, English
Halperin, Irving, English
Hampton, Charles Christy, Jr, Drama
Hawkins, Gary J, Speech

House, Kay Seymour, English & American Literature
Josephson, Clifford A, English Language & Literature
Lee, Mark W, General Speech
Lowe, Irving, English
McGuckin, Henry E, Jr, Speech, Communication
Middlebrook, Diane W, English Literature
Middlebrook, Jonathan, English Literature
Nierenberg, Edwin H, English
Parker, Frank, Fine Arts, Drama
Patch, Gertrude Keiley, R.S.C.J, English Literature
Pearsall, Robert Brainard, Humanities
Smith, Patrick J, English, Film
Solomon, H Eric, English
Stackpoole, Edward Vincent, S.J, English Literature
Stannard, Una, English & American Literature
Stout, Douglas A, English
Waidelich, Richard Long, English
Weiss, Daniel A, English Literature
West, Ray Benedict, Jr, English
Wiegand, William George, English Literature
Wilner, Herbert, English
Wilson, Graham Cunningham, English
Wilson, James Robert, English
SAN GABRIEL
Bushman, John Conrad, English
SAN JOSE
Alden, Donald Hitt, English
Benedict, Ted W, Speech & Communication
Bezanker, Abraham, English
Birenbaum, Harvey, English Literature
Brown, Dennis Edward, Journalism, Mass Communication
Burbank, Rex James, English Language & Literature
Canario, John Wist, American Literature
Carr, Marie Bernice, Speech & Communication
Chaldecott, Dennis, English
Clark, James Jefferson, English
Cox, Martha Heasley, English
Craig, Herbert Rush, Speech, English
Crain, Harold, Speech, Dramatic Arts
Davee, Paul Wilson, Dramatic Arts
Durham, John, Education, Fiction Writing
Elliott, Jeanne Bate, English Literature
Flick, Clarence E, Speech, Drama
Gordon, Robert Coningsby, English Literature
Greb, Gordon Barry, Communication, History
Guth, Hans Paul, English
Hadley, Dorothy S, Oral Interpretation
Henderson, Lois Taylor, English & Comparative Literature
Kappen, Charles Vaughan, Journalism
Ludlum, Charles Daniel, English Philology
Mackay, LaMar S, Journalism, Mass Communication
Markham, David H, Speech, Behavioral Science
Meyer, Robert Holt, English
Mouat, Lawrence H, Rhetoric
Murray, Wallace R, Jr, Drama, Education
Okerlund, Arlene Naylor, English Literature
Ortego, Philip D, Literature, Linguistics
Pepper, Robert David, English, Humanities
Persky, Phillip, English
Pollock, John Joseph, Seventeenth Century Literature
Reed, Glenn Armstrong, American Literature
Regan, Arthur E, English
Rice, Scott Bradley, English Literature
Roche, Ruth Lavare, English, World Literature
Rogers, Franklin Robert, English
Rosenberg, Albert, English
Scofield, Alice G, English Education
Shephard, Esther, English
Tiedt, Sidney Willis, English Education
Todd, Hal J, Drama
Vanderbeets, Richard, English
Waters, Louis Addison, Jr, Comparative Literature
Williams, Otho Clinton, English Literature
Wood, James Oscar, English Literature
Woodward, Robert Hanson, American Literature
SAN LUIS OBISPO
Curzon, Gordon Anthony, English
Emmel, James Robert, Speech
Ericson, Jon Meyer, Rhetoric & Public Address
Jenkins, Starr, English, American Studies
Keetch, Brent Harris, American Literature
Luschei, Martin Louis, American Literature & Studies

Wahl, William Budd, English & American Literature
SAN MARINO
Simpson, Claude Mitchell, Jr, American Literature
Steadman, John Marcellus, III, English Literature
Thorpe, James, English Literature
Woodward, Daniel Holt, English
SAN MATEO
Pflug, Raymond J, American Literature
Pinney, Wilson Gifford, English, Education
Williamson, Richard Arthur, English, Communication
SAN PABLO
Liedlich, Raymond Dean, English
SAN RAFAEL
Barry, M. Martin, O.P, English
Conlan, Mary Samuel, O.P, English
Lust, Annette Bercut, French, Dramatic Art
Maltman, M. Nicholas, O.P, English
SANTA ANA
Talley, Charles Horton, Speech
SANTA BARBARA
Abbott, H. Porter, English Literature
Aitken, David, English
Allaback, Steven Lee, English
Blau, Sheridan D, English Literature & Education
Bowers, Edgar, English
Cooper, Charles William, Drama
Council, Norman Briggs, English Literature
Duffy, Edward Thomas, English & Comparative Literature
Elliott, John Richard, Jr, English
Erickson, Robert Allen, English
Foladare, Joseph, English
Frost, William, English
Gerber, Sanford Edwin, Speech, Linguistics
Glenn, Stanley Leonard, Speech, Theatre Arts
Gus, Donald Leroy, English Literature
Harrop, John Douglas, Drama, Theatre Aesthetics
Hay, Eloise Knapp, English
Helgerson, Richard, English Literature
Kernan, Anne, Medieval Literature
Levin, Lawrence Lee, Literature of the Renaissance
Loomis, Edward W, American Literature
McCarthy, Patrick Joseph, English
Marks, William S, III, English
Mathews, Joseph Chesley, English
Mills, Glen Earl, Rhetoric
Mudrick, Marvin, English
O'Connell, Michael William, English Literature, Renaissance Studies
Pearce, Donald R, English, Classics
Potter, Robert A, English, Drama
Preston, Raymond, English Literature
Reardon, William Robert, Speech, Drama
Ridland, John Murray, English & American Literature
Schneidau, Herbert N, English
Schneider, Elisabeth (Wintersteen), English Literature, Aesthetics
Schoel, Edwin Robert, Speech
Shoup-Hummel, June Eleanor, Speech Communication
Speirs, Logan Hastie, English
Steiner, Thomas Robert, English, Comparative Literature
Wachtel, Albert, Modern British & American Literature
Willson, Lawrence, English
Zimmerman, Everett Lee, English Literature
SANTA CLARA
Duggan, Francis Xavier, English
Gray, John H, S.J, English Literature
Long, Eleanor Ruth, Medieval Literature, Folklore
Macare, Helen Hanks, English & American Literature
Phipps, Charles Thomas, S.J, English
Sullwold, George John, Jr, Comparative Literature
Tiedt, Iris McClellan, English Education
SANTA CRUZ
Barber, Cesar Lombardi, English
Berger, Harry, Jr, English
Bierman, James Henry, Dramatic Arts, Humanities
Cowan, Michael Heath, English, American Studies
Hall, James B, English
Halverson, John, English
Hard, Frederick, English Literature
Hubach, Robert Rogers, English
Leicester, Henry Marshall, Jr, English Literature, Medieval Studies
Robinson, Forrest Glen, English & American Literature
Shaw, Priscilla Washburn, English
Stegner, Stuart Page, American Literature

SANTA ROSA
Stroven, Carl Gerhardt, American Literature
SARATOGA
Eaton, Mary Eleanor, S.N.D. de N, English
SAUSALITO
Ancker, Sidney Louis, English, Humanities
Shrodes, Caroline, English
SEAL BEACH
Uhlman, Thompson Potter, English
SHELL BEACH
Cleath, Robert Leroy, Speech Communication
SHERMAN OAKS
Nevius, Blake Reynolds, American Literature
Wollock, Abe V, Theatre Arts
SOUTH PASADENA
Rathbun, John W, English, American Studies
STANFORD
Bender, John Bryant, English Literature
Breitrose, Henry S, Film, Communication Research
Brown, Emerson, Jr, English Literature
Brown, George Hardin, Medieval English, Philology
Carnochan, Walter Bliss, English Literature
Chace, William Murdough, English & American Literature
Cole, Wendell, Theatre, Drama
Dekker, George Gilbert, English & American Literature
Dodds, John Wendell, English
Evans, John Martin, English Literature
Felstiner, John, English
Fields, Kenneth Wayne, English
Fifer, Charles N, English
Ford, Newell F, English
Foster, John Butt, Jr, Comparative Literature, English
Gelpi, Albert Joseph, English & American Literature
Guerard, Albert Joseph, English & Comparative Literature
Halliburton, David Garland, English, Comparative Literature
Kocher, Paul Harold, English
Lindenberger, Herbert (Samuel), Comparative Literature
Loftis, John, English Literature
Lyons, Charles R, Dramatic Literature & Criticism
Mellor, Anne Kostelanetz, English, Literature & Visual Arts
Momaday, Navarre Scott, English, American Studies
Moser, Thomas Colborn, English
Polhemus, Robert M, English
Prosser, Eleanor Alice, Dramatic Literature
Rebholz, Ronald Alexander, English
Ruotolo, Lucio Peter, English
Russell, Douglas A, Speech, Drama
Ryan, Lawrence Vincent, English
Scowcroft, Richard, English Literature
Stone, Wilfred Healey, English Literature
Watt, Ian Pierre, English
Weigle, Clifford Francis, Communication, Journalism
Whitaker, Virgil Keeble, English Literature
STOCKTON
Beighley, Kenneth Clare, Speech
Binkley, William O, English
Clerc, Charles, English
Cox, Robert Sturgeon, Jr, English, Linguistics
Faurot, Ruth Marie, English, Linguistics
Hansen, Arlen Jay, English & American Literature
Kahn, Sy M, English
Knighton, Robert Tolman, English & American Literature
Leiter, Louis H, English
Mueller, Roger C, English
Seaman, John Eugene, English
Talbot, Carl, Speech, Drama
Williams, John S, Literature
SUNNYVALE
Williams, Robert Dickson, English
TEMPLE CITY
Wicks, Robert Gerald, English
THOUSAND OAKS
Dudley, Barbara Hudson, Speech, Drama
Nelson, Armour Halstead, English
TURLOCK
Berkoben, Lawrence D, English Literature
Brewer, Joseph E, English, Linguistics
Jensen, James P, English
Johnson, Lola Vida, English & American Literature
McDermott, Douglas, Dramatic Art
Reuben, Paul Purushottam, English & American Literature
Ruechelle, Randall C, Speech, Rhetoric
Taylor, Douglas Hanson, American Literature & Ecclesiastical History

UPLAND
Taylor, Stanley H, Speech
VALENCIA
Benedetti, Robert Lawrence, Theatre
VAN NUYS
Graham, Roger John, Communication, Adult Education
Nimitz, Jack, English
Spingarn, Lawrence Perry, English Literature
WALNUT
Canavan, P. Joseph, English, World Literature
Harwood, Charles Edwin, English
WALNUT CREEK
Carpenter, Frederic Ives, English
WESTMINSTER
Burne, Kevin George, English, Linguistics
Thompson, Jesse Jackson, Speech Pathology, Psycholinguistics
WHITTIER
Forsberg, Roberta Jean, Comparative Literature
Geiger, William Andrew, Jr, English Language & Literature
McEwen, Gilbert D, English
Post, Mary Frances, English, Linguistics
Treser, Robert Morris, Drama, Speech
WILMINGTON
Bluefarb, Samuel, English
Garner, Dwight L, Speech, English
WOODSIDE
Trimpi, William Wesley, Jr, English
APO SAN FRANCISCO
Brown, Daniel Russell, American Literature

COLORADO

BOULDER
Anderson, Dorothy Iola, Speech
Baker, Donald C, English, Medieval Literature
Baskette, Floyd Kenneth, Journalism
Bowler, Ned W, Phonetics, Speech Pathology
Brockriede, Wayne Elmer, Communication
Carter, Paul Jefferson, English
Cobin, Martin Theodore, Speech, Drama
Crouch, Jack Herbert, English
Doty, Gladys, English, Speech
Fest, Thorrel Brooks, Speech
Folsom, James K, English, American Studies
Grillo, Virgil, Literature, Film
Hall, Louis Brewer, English Literature, Linguistics
Hunter, John Norman, English & American Literature
Irey, Eugene F, American Literature
Jones, Barbara Schindler, Speech & Communication
Kane, Harold Joseph, Medieval Language & Literature, Linguistics
Kelling, Harold Dunham, English Literature
Kinneavy, Gerald B, English
Knaub, Richard K, Speech & Drama
Lee, Robert Edson, English
Levitt, Paul M, English
McBride, Otis, English
Major, John McClelland, English
Mandel, Siegfried, English, Comparative Literature
Markward, William B, English
Mason, Ellsworth Goodwin, Modern Literature
Mercier, Vivian Herbert Samuel, English
Merkowitz, David Robert, American Studies & Literature
Michelson, Peter Fredrick, English
Moskovit, Leonard, English
Murphy, John Leo, English
Nolan, Edward P, English, Comparative Literature
Ogilvy, Jack David Angus, English
Pettit, Henry (Jewett, Jr), English Literature
Proudfit, Charles Louis, English
Rabinovitz, Rubin, English, Comparative Literature
Rhode, Robert Bartlett, Journalism
Robb, Mary Margaret, Speech
Robinson, Francis Carleton, English
Saner, Reginald Anthony, English, Italian
Sawin, Horace Lewis, English Literature
Squier, Charles La Barge, English
Thompson, Paul Vern, English Literature
Wrenn, John H, English
Wright, Constance Storey, English, Medieval Comparative Literature
Yang, Daniel Shih P'eng, Drama, Theatre
COLORADO SPRINGS
Knapp, Lewis Mansfield, English
Lentz, Sally Palmer, American Literature
Nethercot, Arthur Hobart, English Literature
Ormes, Robert Manly, English, Classics
Reinitz, Neale Robert, English
Ross, Thomas Wynne, English Literature

Scott, Evan James, Comparative Literature
Stanbrough, Jane, American Literature
Stavig, Mark Luther, English
Tynan, Daniel Joseph, American & English Literature
Whitlock, David Cotton, Speech Communication
DENVER
Akin, Johnnye, Speech
Bagley, Henry L, English, Journalism
Barbour, Alton Bradford, Interpersonal Communication
Blansett, Barbara Nieweg, American Literature
Boklund, K. Gunnar, English Literature
Burns, Rex Sehler, American Studies, English
Case, Keith Edmond, Speech, Communication
Chambers, Leland Hugh, Comparative Literature
Chapman, Gerald W, English
Dance, Frank Esburn Xavier, Speech Communication
Dillon, Richard Taylor, English & American Literature
Eldridge, Herbert G, English
Fasel, Ida Drapkin, English
Furness, Edna Lue, English & Spanish
Glorfeld, Louis Earl, Speech
Goldberg, Alvin, Speech
Grossman, Abraham, Drama, English
Horton, Rod William, American Literature, American Studies
Husinger, Paul, Speech
Keen, Joe J, English
Priest, Harold Martin, English Literature
Proudfit, Sharon Louise Wood, English
Rhine, Robley D, Communication
Richards, Robert F, English
Richardson, Robert Dale, Jr, American Literature
Salzberg, Joel, American Literature
Schiller, Philomene Clara, Education, English
Schwalbe, Doris J, English
Spradley, John O, English
Sullivan, Mary Rose, English & Comparative Literature
Teeling, John Paul, English
Thonssen, Lester, Speech
Tillson, Merl William, English
Todd, Donald, Drama
Weeks, Robert Lewis, English Literature
Wilcox, John Kenneth, Communication, Education
Williams, John (Edward), English
Wilson, Douglas B, Renaissance & Romantic English Literature
Wright, Mary Elizabeth, English, Guidance
DURANGO
Coburn, Mark David, American Literature & Civilization
Fox, Clyde Maynard, English
Periman, Kenneth Ivor, Literature
Peterson, Carroll V, English
ENGLEWOOD
Woellhaf, Richard, Speech
FORT COLLINS
Angell, Joseph Warner, Jr, Literature, History
Bates, Paul Allen, English
Bryant, Paul Thompson, English
Bucco, Martin, English
Clark, David Gillis, Journalism, Mass Communication
Garvey, James Joseph, English Language
Henry, William Claud, Literary Criticism
Henze, Richard Harold, English Literature
Hostettler, Gordon Floyd, Speech
Lakin, Barbara Holbeach, English Literature
Levine, L. Carl, English
Lipp, Frances Randall, English, Medieval Studies
Lowers, James K, English
McCann, Garth A, Criticism, Literature
Michaelson, Louis W, American Literature, Creative Writing
Nelson, Roy Conrad, Speech
Pratt, John Clark, English, American Studies
Schamberger, John Edward, American & English Literature
Smith, Charles Roger, English & Medieval Literature
Todd, Edgeley Woodman, English
Trimble, Martha Scott, English & American Literature
Zoellner, Robert, Literature, Language
GOLDEN
Merrin, James, English
Pegis, Anton George, English, Philosophy
GRAND JUNCTION
Showalter, Dan McGregor, English Literature

GREELEY
Boyle, Thomas E, English
Carriar, Shirley May, English Education
Frease, Cynthia Rice, English
Huff, Chester Clarence, Jr, English & American Literature
Jones, Dorothy Cameron, English Literature, Renaissance Humanism
Loftis, John Edgar, III, English Literature
Longwell, Robert Leroy, Speech Communication, English
Myers, Doris Evaline Thompson, Chaucer, Rhetoric
Starr, Wendell Reason, English, Education
Sturges, Christine Anne, Theatre
Willcoxon, John Weir, III, Theatre Arts
GUNNISON
Barnett, Lloyd, Jr, Creative Writing, Medieval English Literature
Gern, Jess W, Speech, Drama
O'Brien, Margaret Townsend, English Literature, Philosophy
Rouillard, Zelda Jeanne, English Composition, American Folklore
Spehar, Elizabeth Marie, English, Slavistics
INDIAN HILLS
Vardaman, George T, Speech, Communications
LITTLETON
Hill, Nancy Joan, English Literature
PUEBLO
Bassein, Beth Ann, English Literature
Griffin, John R, English, History
Humphrey, Charles Robert, English
Senatore, John J, English, Interpersonal Communications
U.S. AIR FORCE ACADEMY
Bayless, Ovid Lyndal, Speech Communication
Dwyer, William Guenther, English & American Literature
Gatlin, Jesse C, Jr, English
Grimshaw, James Albert, Jr, Bibliography & American Literature
Kiley, Frederick Thomas, English, Linguistics
Shuttleworth, Jack M, English & American Literature
Tuso, Joseph Frederick, English Literature, History of English Language

CONNECTICUT

BRIDGEPORT
Allen, Dick, English
Carrier, Warren Pendleton, English
Corrigan, Ralph L, Jr, English
Gouldin, Charles Benjamin, English Language & Literature
Haas, Gaylord Raymond, English Literature
Jacobs, Charles Juan Stephen Richard, English
Lewis, Allan, Contemporary Drama
Miles, Leland (Weber), English, History
Millhauser, Milton, English Literature
Scott, James Burton, Modern American Fiction & Drama
Swain, Victor Crowell, English
Walker, William Edward, English
Winsor, William T, English
BRIDGEWATER
Maloff, Saul, English, American Civilization
Schramm, Harold Bertram, English Literature, Literary Criticism
BRISTOL
Leeds, Barry Howard, English & American Literature
BROOKFIELD
Berger, Irwin, English, Semantics
BROOKFIELD CENTER
McGrory, M. Kathleen, Modern Irish & Comparative Medieval Literature
DANBURY
Cushman, Bigelow Paine, English, American Literature
Tufts, John Marshall, English
Wolsch, Robert Allen, Speech, Education
EAST GRANBY
Scanlon, Lawrence Eugene, English Literature
FAIRFIELD
McInerney, Thomas J, English
McIntyre, John Patrick, English Language & Literature
O'Connor, Leo Francis, English, American Studies
Rinaldi, Nicholas M, English
Van Den Berg, Sara Streich, English Literature
Wells, Celia Townsend, Medieval Literature, Women in Literature
FARMINGTON
Lewis, Wilmarth Sheldon, English, Social History
GLASTONBURY
Boucher, Wayne Irving, English, Philosophy

GREENWICH
Finch, Hardy Rundell, English & American Literature
Maizitis, Mara R, English
GUILFORD
Ellison, (Earl) Jerome, English
HAMDEN
Brown, Pearl LeBlanc, English
Brown, William Richard, English
Kent, Leonard J, English
Sylvester, Richard Standish, English
Zucker, David Hard, English & American Literature
HARTFORD
Benton, Richard Paul, English
Cameron, Kenneth Walter, American Literature
Dando, John, English
Kuyk, Dirk Adriaan, Jr, Nineteenth Century English Literature
Logan, Robert Alexander, III, English Literature
Manheim, Leonard Falk, English, Comparative Literature
Nichols, George Emory, III, Drama
Potter, James Lain, English
Rockas, Leo, English
Sherman, Roger, Speech
Smith, Paul, English
Thibeault, Mary Lou, English
Weisgram, Dianne Hunter, Literature, Psychoanalysis
Wheatley, James Holbrook, English
Yosha, Lee W, American Literature
HIGGANUM
Parsons, J.E, Intellectual History, American Literature
Reeve, Franklin (Dolier), Literature
KENT
Fuller, Edmund, English
MADISON
McClosky, Frank Howland, English Literature
MANCHESTER
Lowe, Frederick William, Jr, American Literature
Smith, Albert Scott, English, Speech
MIDDLETOWN
Cowie, Alexander, American Literature
Creeger, George Raymond, English
Franklin, H. Bruce, English & American Literature
Hawkins, Sherman Henry, English
Knight, William Nicholas, Medieval & Renaissance English
Murphy, Geraldine, English
Ohmann, Richard Malin, English
Reed, Joseph Wayne, Jr, English Literature
Rose, Phyllis Davidoff, English Literature
Rundle, James Urvin, English
Schwaber, Paul, English
Slotkin, Richard S, English, History
Snow, (Charles) Wilbert, English
Wilbur, Richard Purdy, English
MILFORD
Beal, Denton, English
NEW BRITAIN
Bailey, James W, English
Bassett, Clyde H, Theatre
Burney, William A, English
Ellis, Brobury Pearce, Speech, Drama
Fulghum, Walter Benjamin, Jr, English
Galvin, Brendan James, Modern Poetry
Glasheen, Francis James, English
Heitner, John A, American Literature
Hungerford, Edward Buell, English Literature
Schmutzler, Karl E, English
Zettler, Howard G, English
NEW HAVEN
Anisman, Martin Jay, Victorian Literature
Bloom, Harold, English & American Literature
Borroff, Marie, English Language & Literature
Branson, Virginia Marie, Speech Pathology
Brustein, Robert, English
Cole, Edward Cyrus, Drama
Culler, Arthur Dwight, English
Culler, Helen Simpson, English
Donaldson, Ethelbert Talbot, English Literature
Downey, Jean, English & American Literature
Fayen, George S, Jr, English
Feidelson, Charles, Jr, English & American Literature
Felperin, Howard Michael, English Literature
Florey, Kenneth, Anglo-Saxon & Medieval Studies
Foley, William Jay, Speech
Giamatti, Angelo Bartlett, English, Comparative Literature
Giskin, Henry, Speech Education
Greene, Richard Leighton, English

Griffin, Robert Arthur, Speech & History of Theatre
Hersey, John, American Literature
Howling, Robert Tunis, English Literature
Kaplan, Nathaniel, American & English Literature
Kendall, Robert E, Theatre Arts, Dramatic Literature
Knapp, Mary E, English Literature
Kuehn, Robert E, English
Lewars, Kenneth, English
Liebert, Herman Wardwell, English Literature
Long, Charles Howard, English
Lord, George deForest, English
Lustig, Irma S, English
McCabe, Bernard P, Jr, Rhetoric & Public Address
McIntosh, James Henry, English, American Studies
Mack, Maynard, English
Martz, Louis Lohr, English
Marx, Paul, English
Miller, Joseph Hillis, English Literature
Miskimin, Alice-Augusta Schwenk, Medieval Literature
Nagler, Alois, Theatre History
Nichols, Fred Joseph, English, Comparative Literature
O'Loughlin, Michael Jerome Kevin, English
Osborn, James Marshall, English Literature
Osborne, William Stewart, American Literature
Palmer, John James Ellis, English
Parks, Stephen Robert, English Literature
Pearson, Norman Holmes, American Studies, English
Pope, John Collins, English
Porter, Agnes Louise, Speech Psychology
Pottle, Frederick Albert, English Literature & Language
Price, Martin, English
Purdy, Richard Little, English Literature
Robinson, Fred Colson, English Philology, Medieval Literature
Sarason, Bertram Daniel, English
Seidel, Michael Alan, English Literature
Sewall, Richard Benson, English Literature
Smith, Warren Hunting, English
Sweetkind, Morris, English
Taylor, Charles Henry, Jr, English
Trachtenberg, Alan, English, American Studies
Waith, Eugene Mersereau, English Literature
Wimsatt, William Kurtz, Jr, English Literature
NEW LONDON
Baird, James Richard, American Literature
Evans, Robley Jo, English
Gezari, Janet K, English Literature
Hartman, Geoffrey H, English & Comparative Literature
Jarrell, Mackie Langham, English
Johnson, Alice E, English
Meredith, William, English
Noyes, Gertrude Elizabeth, English
Seng, Peter J, English Literature
Shain, Charles Edward, American & British Literature
Smyser, Hamilton Martin, English Philology
Smyser, Jane Worthington, English Literature
Taranow, Gerda, Theatre History
Willauer, George Jacob, Jr, English
NEW MILFORD
Adams, Leonie, English
NORTHFORD
Brooks, Cleanth, English
Hotson, Leslie, English Literature
SEYMOUR
Bakeless, John (Edwin), English
SIMSBURY
Minot, Stephen, Literature & Creative Writing
SOUTHBURY
Brooks, Richard Albert Edward, English Literature
STAMFORD
Frank, Yakira H, Linguistics
STORRS
Abbott, John L, English
Ballard, Frank Willard, Puppetry, Scene Design
Blanshard, Rufus Anderson, English
Booth, Marcella Joyce (Spann), American Literature
Brockman, Bennett Albert, English Medieval & Children's Literature
Butler, Francelia M, English, History of Medicine
Butterick, George F, American Literature, Modern Poetry
Carlson, Eric Walter, English
Curtin, William Martin, English
Davis, Jack M, English
Gatta, John Joseph, Jr, American Literature

Gibson, Donald Bernard, English
Goldstone, Herbert I, English
Hale, Margaret Randolph, Comparative Literature, English
Hankins, John David, English
Hemphill, George, English Literature
Jacobus, Lee Andre, English, Philosophy
Katter, Nafe Edmund, Dramatic Arts
Lamb, Jack Hall, Speech
Leeming, David Adams, English, Comparative Literature
McLaughlin, Charles Angus, English
McPeek, James Andrew Scarborough, English Literature
Medlicott, Alexander Guild, Jr, English, American Literature
Moynihan, William T, Literature
Owen, Chas. Abraham, Jr, English
Phillips, David C, Speech
Putzel, Max, English & American Literature
Rees, Compton, Jr, English Renaissance
Roberts, Thomas John, English
Rosen, William, English
Saul, George Brandon, English
Sheidley, William Edwards, English, Renaissance Literature
Stallman, Robert Wooster, English
Stern, Milton R, English
Weil, Herbert S, Jr, English, Comparative Literature
Wilcox, Thomas William, English
Wilkenfeld, Roger B, English
Wilson, Kenneth George, English
STRATFORD
Banks, William Stephen, Speech, Drama
TORRINGTON
Potter, Robert Russell, English
WATERFORD
Bethurum, (Frances) Dorothy, English Language & Literature
WATERTOWN
Embler, Weller Beardsley, English
WEST HARTFORD
Allen, Shirley Seifried, English Literature, Theatre History
Chiarenza, Frank John, English Literature
Doyle, Joseph, English
Finizio, Victor Lee, Theatre Research
Fowler, Mary Elizabeth, English
Goldstein, Melvin, English
Grant, Thomas Mark, Renaissance & Modern Drama
Hudnall, Clayton E, English
Kloten, Edgar L, Speech, Drama
Quirk, Eugene Francis, English & American Literature
Smith, Thomas Norris, English Literature
Vogel, Robert Maier, English
Williams, Ralph Mehlin, English
WEST HAVEN
Robillard, Douglas, English
Stevenson, Kay Gilliland, English Literature
WESTPORT
Koerner, James D, American Studies
Schnitzer, Robert C, Theatre
WILLIMANTIC
Lacey, James, American Studies
Philips, David Evan, English
Taylor, Alexander Douglas, Modern Poetry, Contemporary Danish Literature
WILTON
Richard, Margaret Cossé, Journalism, Mass Communications
WOODBRIDGE
Donaldson, Christine Hunter, English, World Literature
Haight, Gordon Sherman, English & American Literature
WOODBURY
Eaton, Charles Edward, English
Mabey, Marion K, Victorian English
WOODSTOCK
Bonin, Helen, D.H.S, English
Burda, Helen Elizabeth, D.H.S, English & American Literature

DELAWARE

DOVER
Del Tufo, Joseph P, English
Houpt, Gary L, English, Education
NEWARK
Anapol, Malthon M, Speech, Communication
Beasley, Jerry Carr, English Literature
Bennett, Robert Beale, Renaissance Drama
Bohner, Charles Henry, American Literature
Brock, Dewey Heyward, English & American Literature
Calhoun, Thomas O, English
Christensen, Merton Aubrey, English
Cox, Roger Lindsay, English & Comparative Literature

Cundiff, Paul A, English
Davison, Richard Allan, American Literature
DeArmond, Anna Janney, English & American Literature
Dunlap, Arthur Ray, English Philology
Finnie, W. Bruce, English
Gates, Barbara Timm, English Literature
Gordenstein, Arnold S, American Studies, Literature
Halio, Jay Leon, English
Hansen, Brian Kanne, Drama, Speech
Haslett, Betty Jeanne, Communications, Sociolinguistics
Henry, George H, English, Secondary Education
Henry, Mabel C. Wright, English, Theatre Arts
Hogan, Robert, English
Keesey, Ray Edward, Speech
Martin, Ronald Edward, English
Mell, Donald Charles, English Literature
Merrill, Thomas F, English
Moyne, Ernest John, American Literature
Pauly, Thomas Harry, American Literature
Rewa, Michael Peter, Jr, English
Robertson, Henry Alphonso, Jr, English
Robinson, Charles Edward, English
Rosenberry, Edward Hoffman, English
Safer, Elaine Berkman, English
Watson, Thomas Stoneman, Theatre
WILMINGTON
Crosby, Muriel, English

DISTRICT OF COLUMBIA

Anderson, Hurst Robins, Speech
Austin, Lettie Jane, English Education
Ayers, Robert Weaver, English Language & Literature
Berman, Ronald S, English Literature
Betz, Paul Fredrick, English Literature
Bischoff, Anthony D, S.J, English Literature
Blessing, James H, English
Bliss, Edward L, Broadcast Journalism
Brady, Leo, Drama
Broderick, John Caruthers, English
Brown, John L, Comparative Literature, French
Brown, Nancy Pollard, English
Brown, Theressa Wilson, English
Byington, Robert Harold, English
Cardaci, Paul Francis, Jr, Comparative Literature
Chinn, Harold Bruce, English Language & Literature
Claeyssens, Astere Evarist, Creative Writing
Clark, Charles Marston, English
Claydon, Margaret, S.N.D, English Language & Literature
Coberly, James Harold, English
Cole, Charles William, English
Cook, Mary Ann, S.N.D, English
Cooke, Paul P, English
Crane, Milton, English & American Literature
Croneberg, Carl Gustaf, English, Linguistics
Davis, Arthur Paul, English Literature
Davis, Bertram Hylton, English
Davis, Margaret, English
Dawson, Giles Edwin, Elizabethan Literature
Dunn, Ellen Catherine, English
Fenderson, Lewis H, English
Furniss, Warren Todd, English
Ganz, Robert Norton, Jr, English
Giovannini, Margaret (Cobb), English
Goldberg, Joseph Philip, English
Gosman, Michael Thomas, English & American Literature
Grant, Jason Clifton, Jr, English
Greenberg, Bernard L, English
Griest, Guinevere Lindley, English
Grumbach, Doris, Literature, Criticism
Han, Pierre, English, Comparative Literature
Hardison, Osborne Bennett, Jr, English
Harman, Roland Nelson, English
Hayworth, Donald, Speech
Hendrix, Jerry Allen, Speech
Herzbrun, Philip Ingram, English & Comparative Literature
Highfill, Philip Henry, Jr, English Literature
Hilliard, Robert L, Communications
Holton, Sylvia Wallace, Old & Middle English
Hudson, Theodore R, American & English Literature
Jackson, Margaret Young, English Composition & Literature
Kelly, Faye Lucius, English, Linguistics
Koob, C. Albert, English
Kraft, James, English
Linton, Calvin Darlington, English Literature
Lovell, John, Jr, Drama, American Literature
McCandlish, George Edward, American Literature & Civilization

MacIsaac, Warren Jordan, English
Marcuse, Michael Joseph, English Language & Literature
Marks, Barry Alan, English, American Civilization
Mondale, Clarence Cowan, American Studies
Morris, David Brown, Eighteenth Century English Literature
Mullaly, Columba, S.N.D, English, Educational Psychology
Niemeyer, Grover Charles, Film, Theatre
Norwood, Frank Wesley, Speech
Patton, Mary Miller, English, Speech
Pfordresher, John Charles, English Literature
Plotz, Judith Ann Abrams, English, Romanticism
Polisky, Jerome B, Speech
Quitslund, Jon Alrik, English
Radner, John Barnet, English
Reesing, John Palmer, Jr, English Literature
Reno, Raymond H, English
Roberts, Jeanne A, English
Rodin, Doris G, English, Cinema
Root, Vernon Metcalf, Philosophy
Rosenblatt, Jason Philip, English Literature
Sendry, Joseph M, English
Smith, Elden T, Speech, Drama
Stahr, William E, American Literature
Staroba, Frank Joseph, Drama
Sten, Christopher Willie, American Literature
Stevens, Edwin Lockwood, Speech
Taylor, Estelle Wormley, English & American Literature
Thompson, Wendel Lawrence, Speech, Psychology
Truss, Tom James, Jr, English
Tuttle, Donald Reuel, English & American Literature
Villarejo, Oscar Milton, Comparative Literature
Von Abele, Rudolph, European Literature, Literary Criticism
Wagner, Bernard Mathias, English Literature
Walker, Robert Harris, American Civilization
Ward, Kathryn Painter, English
Watkins, Charlotte Crawford, English
Weismiller, Edward Ronald, English Literature
Withers, Sara Cook, Linguistics
Yarrington, H. Roger, Journalism, American Studies
Young, Louise M, History, English Literature

FLORIDA

BOCA RATON
Coyle, William, American Literature
Greer, Allen Wilkinson, English
Nathan, Norman, English
Pearce, Howard D, American Literature
Smith, Voncile Marshall, Speech Communication, Communication Theory
Suberman, Jack, English
BRADENTOWN
Gilbreath, Allie Lou Felton, Education, English
CAPE CORAL
Hoerr, Willmer A, English
CLEARWATER
Cortright, Rupert L, Speech
Gordon, Kathryn I, English
COCONUT GROVE
Halstead, William Lewis, English
CORAL GABLES
Babula, William, English Literature
Baker, Roberta Hardy, Drama
Deam, William Luther, Speech, General Linguistics
Diers, Herman H, Drama
Emery, Clark Mixon, English Literature
Franklin, Phyllis, Early American Literature
Gilpin, George Heyburn, Eighteenth Century & Romantic English Literature
Goran, Sylvester L, English, Creative Writing
Helmick, Evelyn Thomas, English
Hively, Robert William, English & American Literature
Hochberger, Simon, Journalism
Hosmon, Robert Stahr, Victorian Literature & Art
McCollum, John Isaac, Jr, Renaissance English Literature
Newman, Ronald Bruce, English
Reynolds, Jack Adolphe, English
Rouse, John L, English
Skipp, Francis E, English
Smart, George K, American Cultural History
Smith, Helen Katherine, Reading
Solem, Delmar Everett, Drama
Wellington, James Ellis, English Literature
DAYTONA BEACH
Cabotaje, Arsenia Abellera, English, Education

GEORGIA

AMERICUS

Argo, Iris Stewart, Elizabethan Drama, American Romanticism
Davis, Keith Edwin, Education, Communications

ATHENS

Agee, Warren Kendall, Journalism
Agee, William Hugh, English, English Education
Alexander, James Wagner, Greek & Classical Civilization
Algeo, John Thomas, English
Appleby, Jane, English Language
Baine, Rodney Montgomery, English Literature
Ballew, Leighton Milton, Theatre
Beaumont, Charles Allen, English Literature
Buffington, Robert Ray, Modern American Literature
Bufkin, Ernest Claude, Jr, English
Camp, Paul Alfred, Drama
Carpenter, Nan Cooke, English, Music
Cherry, Kenneth Holland, American Literature
Colvert, James B, English
Drewry, John Eldridge, Journalism
Franklin, Rosemary Futrelle, American Literature
Free, William Joseph, English
Freshley, Dwight Lowell, Speech
Gruner, Charles Ralph, Communication, Speech
Harrison, Robert Ligon, Comparative Literature
Head, Faye Edwards, Speech & Drama
Irwin, Betty Jean, English, Linguistics
Kahan, Gerald, Drama, Theater
Kibler, James Everett, Jr, American Literature
Logue, Cal McLeod, Speech Communication
McDougald, (William) Worth, Journalism
McKenzie, Barbara, English Literature
McWhorter, H. Boyd, English
Marshall, George Octavius, Jr, English
Mitchell, Jerome, Middle English Literature
Montgomery, Marion, Modern Literature
Moore, Hamilton Frazier, Advertising, Mass Communications
Moore, Rayburn Sabatzky, English
O'Donnell, Roy C, English
Patterson, Charles (Ivey), Jr, English
Reeves, Walter Paschal, Jr, English
Stephens, John Calhoun, Jr, English Literature
Stephenson, Edward A, English
Stoddard, Richard Foster, History of Theatre
Tate, William, English
Tison, John Laurens, Jr, English
Torsey, Kathleen E, Speech
Vorpahl, Ben Merchant, English
Waller, Charles Thomas, Folklore, Eighteenth Century English Literature
West, Robert Hunter, English

ATLANTA

Adams, Henry Welch, American & English Literature
Aldridge, June McDonald, English & American Literature
Bain, Carl Edwin, English
Beaty, Jerome, English
Benton, Vera Louise, English Language & Literature
Bergamo, Ralph, English
Biles, Jack I, English
Blount, Paul Groves, Victorian Literature
Bryant, James Cecil, Jr, English
Bugge, John Michael, Medieval English Literature
Burch, James Charlie Horton, English
Burroughs, Baldwin Wesley, Drama
Chaikin, Milton, English
Colburn, William Elliot, English
Dillingham, William B, American Literature
Dowell, Peter Winthrop, English, American Studies
Edmondson, Elsie Fannie, English
Eidson, John Olin, American Literature
England, Kenneth Murchison, Southern Literature
English, Thomas Hopkins, English Literature
Evans, William Alfred, English
Fernandez, Thomas L, Speech and Drama
Foote, Irving Flint, Modern Literature, Folklore
Fusillo, Robert James, Theatre History, English Literature
Gibson, Richard Joseph, Renaissance English Literature
Gilmore, Thomas Barry, Jr, English
Gloster, Hugh Morris, English & American Literature
Grigsby, Lucy C, English Literature

Haich, George Donald, English & American Literature
Haman, James Blanding, English
Hesla, David H, Literature, Theology
Hollahan, Eugene, English & Continental Literature
Hunter, J. Paul, English Literature
Hunter, Kathryn Montgomery, English
Jacobs, Robert Durene, American Literature
Jarrett, Thomas Dunbar, English
Jenkins, Annibel, English
Johnson, Mary Lynn, English
Kramer, Victor Anthony, American Literature, Literary Criticism
Kropf, Carl R, Eighteenth Century English Literature
Long, Richard Alexander, English, Humanities
Luck, Edward Graham, Speech, Journalism
McHaney, Thomas Lafayette, American Literature
Manley, Frank, English
Metzger, Lore, English & Comparative Literature
Middleton, John Alexander, American Literature
Miller, Henry Prentice, American Literature
Molette, Carlton W, II, Afro-American Drama, Theatre Technology
Moore, Arthur Keister, English
Moore, Littleton, Hugh, English
Murphy, Karl Michael, English
Naugle, Helen Harrold, Eighteenth Century & English Literature
Nunan, Joseph Carlton, English
Passler, David Luther, English
Passler, Susan Miller, Eighteenth Century English Literature
Pickens, William Garfield, American Literature, Dialectology
Rogers, William Elford, Medieval English Literature
Rubin, Larry Jerome, Literature
Rusche, Harry Gordon, English
Schuchard, W. Ronald, Modern British Literature
Sessions, William Alfred, English
Sizemore, Christine Wick, English Renaissance & 20th Century Literature
Smith, Garland Garvey, Old & Middle English
Smith, James Penny, Modern English & American Literature
Spillman, Ralph R, English
Spivey, Ted Ray, English Literature
Stone, Albert Edward, English, American Studies
Sutherland, Raymond Carter, English
Suttles, William Maurrelle, Speech, Religion
Thomas, Mary Olive, English
Tillman, James Shannon, Jr, Seventeenth Century English Literature
Turner, Maxine Thompson, Eighteenth Century Studies
Utterback, Raymond Victor, English
Via, John Albert, English Literature
Waterman, Arthur E, American Literature
Watkins, Floyd C, English
Wilson, James Darrell, American & Comparative Literature
Young, James Dean, English

AUGUSTA

Evans, Walter Everett, III, English & American Literature
Yonce, Margaret Janis, American Literature

BLAKELY

Flanders, Bertram Holland, English

CAIRO

Wight, William Samuel, English

CARROLLTON

Bowdre, Paul H, Jr, English
Boyd, Ernest Lee, Speech, English
Chalfant, Fran Cernocky, English Literature, London History
Doxey, William Sanford, Jr, American & Continental Literature
Edwards, Corliss Hines, Jr, American & Southern Literature
Garmon, Gerald Meredith, English
Griffith, Benjamin Woodward Jr, English
Haltresht, Michael, English, Psychology
Mathews, James William, Literature
Meehan, Virginia M, English
Norrell, Lemuel Nathaniel, English

COCHRAN

McClary, Ben Harris, English

COLUMBUS

Brown, Jack A., English, Linguistics
Friedman, Lenemaja, English Literature

DAHLONEGA

Shott, Hugh I, II, English
Wiggins, Eugene Edward, English

DALTON

Bell, Wayne Edward, Literature, Religion

DECATUR

Green, Elvena Marion, Dramatic Art
Pepperdene, Margaret W, English
Perry, Marvin Banks, Jr, English
Pinka, Patricia Garland, Seventeenth Century English Literature
Taylor, Hubert V, Speech, Music
Trotter, Margret Guthrie, Comparative Literature, Modern Poetry
Winter, Roberta Powers, Speech, Drama

FORSYTH

Sullivan, Barbara W, English, Journalism

FORT VALLEY

Crew, Louie, English Literature, Rhetoric
Walker, Saunders E, English, Speech & Drama

GAINESVILLE

Isbell, Thomas, English

LA GRANGE

Freeman, Bernice, English Education
Williams, Murial Brittain, English

MACON

Cass, Michael McConnell, American Literature & History
Cousins, Paul Mercer, American Literature
Leitch, Vincent Barry, English Literature
Ruys, Constance, Theatre
Strong, Leah Audrey, American Studies, United States Literature
Taylor, Garland Forbes, English

MARIETTA

Hinton, Virginia Cooksey, English

MILLEDGEVILLE

Dawson, Edward Barker, American Literature

MOUNT BERRY

Cantrell, Dorothy Dean, English
Moran, William Charles, English

OXFORD

Gregory, John W, Humanities, American & English Literature
Guillebeau, Joseph Edwin, Jr, English, Humanities

ROME

Austin, Jessie Gardner, English
Noble, Paulina Buhl, English

SAVANNAH

Erickson, Marceline Louise, Speech
Fisher, James Randolph, English Language & Literature
Lunz, Elisabeth, English Literature
Milledge, Luetta C, Literature

STATESBORO

Cate, Hollis Lanier, American Literature
Gillis, Patricia Ingle, English
Huff, Lawrence, English
Humma, John Ballard, Nineteenth Century American Literature
Johnson, Richard Byron, Theatre, Dramatic Literature
Little, Edward Grant, Comparative Literature, Modern Languages
McCord, Clarence Wilton, Speech, Linguistics
Powell, Woodrow Wilson, English
Presley, Delma Eugene, American Literature
Quick, Nicholas Wilson, English
Rainwater, Frank Palmer, Literature
Sanders, Frederick Kirkland, English & American Literature
Scales, Luther Lee, Jr, English
Wilson, Maryland W, Speech

STONE MOUNTAIN

Davis, Joseph Kimbrell, American Literature, English

SWAINSBORO

Walker, George William, English

VALDOSTA

Cook, Raymond Allen, American Literature
Evans, Marvin Russell, English
Hiers, John Turner, American Literature
Marks, Sita Patricia, English & American Literature
Mayo, Marianne K, English
Stubbs, David C, English
Valencia, Willa Ferree, English

HAWAII

HILO

Allen, James Lovic, English
Nelson, Frank G, English
Pilecki, Gerard Anthony, English
Wiley, David Waterman, Speech, Drama

HONOLULU

Alm, Richard S, English Education, Reading
Anderson, George Lincoln, English, Comparative Literature
August, Eugene R, English
Backus, Joseph Moorhead, Literature
Bilsborrow, Eleanor J, Rhetoric, Public Address
Bouslog, Charles Scott, English Literature
Brandon, James R, Drama
Byers, Burton H, Speech

Carr, Elizabeth Ball, Speech
Carroll, William Dennis, Drama
Creed, Walter Gentry, English Literature
Crymes, Ruth Helen, English, Linguistics
Day, Arthur Grove, English
Dukore, Bernard F, Drama
Edel, (Joseph) Leon, English & American
 Comparative Literature
Edelstein, Arnold Stanley, English & American
 Literature
Ekroth, Lauren E, Speech, Communication
Ellingsworth, Huber W, Speech, Communication
Ellis, Dean S, Management, Communications,
 Psychology
Ernst, Earle, Drama, Theatre
Faires, Dena M. M, Speech
Foster, Richard Jackson, English
Friedson, Anthony M, English
Frierson, James Wright, English
Fujimura, Thomas H, English
Gordon, Morton, Speech
Huntsberry, William Emery, English
Kirtley, Bacil F, English, Folklore
Klopf, Donald William, Speech
Knapp, Terence Richard, Drama, Theatre
Langhans, Edward A, Drama, Theatre
Lefforge, Orland S, Speech
Leib, Amos Patten, English
Levy, Alfred J, English & American Litera-
 ture
McCutcheon, Elizabeth North, English
McHenry, Robert William, Jr, English Lit-
 erature
Maguire, Robert C, Speech, History
Maltby, Joseph, English Literature
Menikoff, Barry, English
Nam, Sunwoo, Journalism
Sanderson, Richard Arlo, Communication
Sanderson, Sarah E, Speech, Communication
Simson, George K, English, Biography
Sinclair, Marjorie Putnam, English
Solomon, Margaret Claire, English
Steinberg, Danny D, Psycholinguistics
Stempel, Daniel, English
Stillians, Bruce Moore, English
Summersgill, Travis L, English Literature
Teevan, Thomas Foster, English Literature
Thompson, Phyllis Hoge, English
Unterecker, John E, English Literature
Weston, John Howard, English & American
 Literature
Wiley, Bonnie Jean, Journalism
Winters, Lee Eugene, Jr, English, Compara-
 tive Literature
KANEOHE
 Shimer, Dorothy Blair, English, Asian Lit-
  erature
LAIE
 Jenson, Sidney LaMarr, English
 Mann, Kenneth Eugene, Speech Communication
 Shumway, Eric Brandon, English Literature,
  Polynesian Languages
 Thomas, Gordon Kent, English

IDAHO

BOISE
 Boren, Robert Reed, Communication
 Boyer, Dale Kenneth, English & American Lit-
  erature
 Chatterton, Roylance Wayne, English Literature
 Ericson, Robert Edward, Theatre History &
  Theory
 Hijiya, Yukihito, English & Modern Japanese
  Literature
 Lauterbach, Charles Everett, Drama
 Maguire, James Henry, American Literature
  & Studies
 Wallace, Eunice Ewer, English Education
CALDWELL
 Attebery, Louie Wayne, English & American
  Literature
 Sollers, John F, Drama
MOSCOW
 Barber, David Spear, English, American
  Studies
 Boone, Lalia Phipps, English Philology
 Chavez, Edmund Manuel, Dramatics
 Davis, Jack Laverne, American Literature
 Heningham, Eleanor Kellogg, English, Medi-
  eval Latin
 Knight, Joseph Elwood, English Literature
 McFarland, Ronald Earl, Seventeenth Century
  English Literature, Poetry
 Malek, James Stanley, English Literature
 Meldrum, Barbara Ruth, English
 Murphy, Robert Patrick, Drama, Irish Lit-
  erature
 Naples, Diane Clark, American Literature
 Sipahigil, Teoman, English & American Lit-
  erature
 Tung, Mason, English

Wallins, Roger Peyton, English & American
 Literature
Whitehead, Albert E, Speech
POCATELLO
 Bagley, Carol Lenore, American Literature
  & History
 Blomquist, Allen P, Theatre Arts
 Carlile, Clark Stites, Speech
 Corbin, William N, Public Address
 Donaghy, Henry J, English
 Gibson, William Arthur, English, Renaissance
  Architecture
 Kegel, Charles Herbert, English
 Kissane, Leedice, English Literature
 Lestrud, Vernon A. C, Drama, Speech
 Smith, Denzell Stewart, English

ILLINOIS

ALTON
 Joost, Nicholas Teynac, English
ASHMORE
 Norberg, Janet Louise, Speech, Dramatic Art
BARRINGTON
 Vitale, Philip Harold, English
BELVIDERE
 Yerbury, Grace D, English, Music
BLOOMINGTON
 Allen, Richard Eilers, English
 Beutner, Harvey Fremont, English Literature,
  Journalism
 Burda, Robert Warren, Modern Letters
 Clark, John L, English, Drama
 Ficca, John, Drama
 Hungerford, Harold Roe, Jr, Medieval Litera-
  ture, English Linguistics
 Meyers, Joseph Henry, Humanities
 Pearson, Justus Richard, Jr, English & Am-
  erican Literature
 Robinson, Marie J, Speech, Drama
BROCKPORT
 Marchant, Peter L, English
CARBONDALE
 Appleby, Bruce C, English, Education
 Atwood, Lynn Erwin, Journalism
 Baldwin, Thomas Whitfield, Elizabethan Lit-
  erature
 Benziger, James George, English Literature
 Boyle, Ted E, English
 Bradley, Earl Edsel, Speech
 Breniman, Lester, Speech
 Brown, James Montgomery, English
 Brown, William J, Renaissance & Medieval
  Literature
 Camp, George Carr, English
 Clayton, Charles Curtis, Journalism
 Cohn, Alan Martin, English, Library Science
 Donow, Herbert S, English
 Epstein, Edmund Lloyd, English, Linguistics
 Evans, William Howard, English, English Ed-
  ucation
 Fish, Robert Stevens, Speech, Oral Interpreta-
  tion
 Ford, James Lawrence Collier, Journalism
 Friend, Jewell Anne, English, Linguistics
 Goodin, George, English
 Griffin, Robert P, English
 Harrell, Robert Bruce, Victorian & Romantic
  Literature
 Harris, Jesse W, English
 Hatton, Thomas J, English
 Hibbs, Richard Paul, Speech, English
 Hillegas, Mark R, English
 Howell, John Michael, American Literature
 Hurley, Paul Joseph, American Literature,
  Drama
 Jennings, Russell Wayne, Interpersonal Com-
  munication
 Kleinau, Marvin Dale, Speech
 Lawson, Richard Alan, English
 Long, Howard Rusk, Journalism
 McLeod, Archibald, Drama
 Micken, Ralph Arlington, Speech
 Moe, Christian Hollis, Theatre
 Moss, Sidney Phil, English
 Olson, Thomas O, Mass Communications,
  Oral Interpretation
 Pace, Thomas Jennings, Jr, Speech
 Partlow, Robert B, Jr, English
 Potter, David, Speech
 Rainbow, Raymond Scott, Jr, English Lan-
  guage & Literature
 Raizis, Marios Byron, English & Comparative
  Literature
 Rucker, Bryce W(ilson), Journalism
 Rudnick, Hans H, Criticism, Aesthetics
 Schonhorn, Manuel, English
 Schultz, Howard, English
 Simeone, William E, English Literature
 Smith, William David, Speech, Communication
 Vieth, David Muench, English
 Webb, Howard William, Jr, English

CARLINVILLE
 Barnard, Ann W, English & American Litera-
  ture
CARROLL
 Hipple, Walter John, Jr, English, Philosophy
CARTERVILLE
 Moore, Harry T, Humanities
CHAMPAIGN
 Dussinger, John Andrew, English
 Puravs, Olgerts, English
 Scott, Joseph Wright, Theatre
 Stubbs, John C, English
 Wright, Gilbert George, English Literature
CHARLESTON
 Blair, Robert Lee, English
 Ekeberg, Gladys Winifred, English Language
  & Literature
 Gabbard, Earnest Glendon, Theatre Arts
 Garner, Donald, Speech, Drama
 Hadwiger, Ken E, Mass Communications,
  Communications Research
 Haught, Evelyn Hunt, English, English Educa-
  tion
 Hopkins, Jon James, Speech, Communication
 Kelleher, John J, English
 Kline, Judd William, English
 Lazenby, Walter Sylvester, Jr, English, Drama
 McClerren, Beryl F, Speech, Philosophy
 Moody, Peter Richard, English
 Rommel, George William, English
 Steinmetz, Marion Lee, English
 Stokes, Frank Christopher, English Literature
 Thurman, Wayne Laverne, Speech
 Wharton, Robert Verner, English
 White, Robert Finis, Jr, English
 Whitlow, Roger Lee, American Literature
 Wittrock, Verna D, English

CHICAGO
 Andresen, Oliver S, Reading Specialization
 Ashin, Mark, English
 Baldeshwiler, Eileen Mary, English
 Barry, James Donald, English
 Barter, Alice Knar, English Education
 Barushok, James William, Speech, Drama
 Bates, Allan, English
 Bellow, Saul, English
 Bergen, Mary Jeanelle, B.V.M, Theatre, Tele-
  vision
 Bevington, David M, English
 Blackwood, Robert James, English Drama
 Blair, Walter, English
 Bock, Darilyn Winifred, American & English
  Literature
 Bollinger, Evangeline Grace, English
 Booth, Wayne Clayson, English Literature
 Bowen, Merlin S, American Literature, Human-
  ities
 Brommel, Bernard J, Speech, History
 Brouse, Albert Joseph, English
 Byrd, Milton Bruce, English
 Byrd, Thomas L, Jr, English, Religion
 Campbell, Gladys, English, Philosophy
 Cawelti, John George, American Civilization
 Cirillo, Nancy Rockmore, Comparative Lit-
  erature, Modern Political History
 Clayes, Stanley Arnold, English Literature
 Conley, John Allan, English
 Coogan, Mary Philippa, B.V.M, English Lan-
  guage & Literature
 Corcoran, Mary Irma, B.V.M, English
 Creswell, Thomas James, English
 Cumings, Melinda Feldt, Modern Literature
 Cushman, Keith Maxwell, English Literature
 Danna, Sammy Richard, Speech
 Davis, William Virgil, English, Religion
 Donohue, Agnes McNeill, English & American
  Literature
 Egerer, Mary Teresa, Anglo-Irish & American
  Literature
 Engelhardt, George John, English
 Feeney, William Jackson, English
 Feldman, Reynold, English & Indonesian
  Studies`
 Fennell, Francis Leroy, Jr, English Literature,
  Writing
 Fields, Beverly, English
 Foster, John Lawrence, English
 Franklin, Ralph William, English, Bibliography
 Friedman, Arthur, English Literature
 Friedman, Muriel Sanderow, English Education,
  Bibliography
 Fromm, Gloria Glikin, English
 Gerrietts, John, English
 Gilman, Harvey, English, Colonial American
  Literature
 Goldhamer, Allen David, Medieval Literature,
  English Drama
 Gorman, Thomas Richard, American Studies,
  Literature
 Gossett, Suzanne S, English & American Lit-
  erature
 Griffin, Mary, English

Hansen, Chadwick (Clarke), American Literature & Studies
Hardy, John Edward, English & American Literature
Harnack, Robert Victor, Speech
Hayes, Albert McHarg, English, Humanities
Heiserman, Arthur R, English Literature
Hellenga, Robert Riner, English Literature
Hensley, Charles S., English
Hiebel, William Raymond, English
Hill, Hamlin, American Literature
Hine, Daryl, Comparative Literature
Hodges, Richard E, Elementary Education
Hudson, Randolph Hoyt, English Literature
Irving, Robert Francis Edward, English Literature
Jarrott, Catherine Anna Louise, English
Johnson, Raoul Fenton, Drama
Johnston, Robert A, Drama
Karanikas, Alexander, American Literature
Kelly, Ellin Margaret, English Literature
Kent, George E, English & American Literature
Kerr, Howard Hastings, American & English Literature
Kinahan, Francis Xavier, Modern Literature & Drama
Knepler, Henry William, English
Knopp, Josephine Zadovsky, American & European Literature
Kogan, Bernard Robert, English
Kolb, Gwin Jackson, English
Krump, Jacqueline, English
LaBranche, Anthony Spahr, English Literature
Lease, Benjamin, English
Leer, Norman Robert, English, Comparative Literature
Lenfest, David Stanley, English
Levine, Jay Arnold, English
Lieb, Michael J, English Literature
Liebman, Sheldon Wayne, English
Lindley, Daniel Allen, Jr, English
Loesch, Katharine Taylor, Speech
Long, Chester Clayton, Drama, Speech
Love, Willie Nell Stallings, English
Macauley, Robie Mayhew, English
McDavid, Virginia Glenn, English
McElroy, Bernard Patrick, Jr, English Literature
McFate, Patricia Ann, Modern Literature, Anglo-Irish Literature
McGann, Jerome John, English
McGaw, Charles James, Speech
McGugan, Ruth E, English Literature
Mackin, John H, English
Maclean, Norman Fitzroy, English
Maguire, John Bernard, English Literature
Maneikis, Walter, English & American Literature
Manion, Frederick Paul, S.J, English Literature
Marder, Louis, English
Markle, Joyce Bonners, Modern American Literature
Marsh, Robert Harrison, English Literature
Martia, Dominic Francis, English
Masi, Michael, English
Masterson, John Patrick, English, Humanities
Meltzer, Sharon B, English
Meredith, Robert Chidester, English
Messbarger, Paul Robert, American Literature
Miller, James Edwin, Jr, English
Mills, Ralph Joseph, Jr, English
Mueller, Janel M, English
Nabholtz, John R, English
Nemanic, Gerald Carl, American Literature
Neville, Margaret Mary, English
Novak, Jane Dailey, Modern English Literature
Ogle, Robert Bertram, Comparative Literature
Olson, Elder James, English
Page, William Douglas, English Education
Paine, Robert Nelson, English
Parrella, Gilda C, Interpretation of Literature, Communication Arts
Payne, Richard Champ, Old & Middle English Literature
Phillips, Gene Daniel, S.J, Modern Fiction, Film
Pinkerton, Jan, American Literature
Price, John Edward, English Literature
Puckett, Harry Thomas, English
Ringler, William Andrew, Jr, English Literature
Rocks, James Engel, English
Rosenheim, Edward Weil, Jr, English
Ruoff, A. LaVonne, English
Ruoff, Gene William, English & American Literature
Sacks, Sheldon, English
Sandke, Thomas John, English
Schejbal, Jaroslav, American Renaissance Literature
Shea, John Stephen, English

Sherman, Frank E, American Literature
Shipley, John B, English Literature
Silverstein, Theodore, English
Sinanoglou, Leah, English Literature
Snyder, Sherwood, III, Theatre, Speech
Sorensen, Gerald C, English
Stedman, Jane Winifred, English
Steinbrecher, George, Jr, English Language & Literature
Stenerson, Douglas C, American Studies, English
Stern, Frederick Curtis, Modern European & American Literature
Stern, Richard G, English
Stone, William B, English
Streeter, Robert Eugene, English
Sullivan, William Howard, English Literature
Suloway, Irwin J, English
Tave, Stuart Malcolm, English
Taylor, John Alfred, English
Tietze, Frederick I, English
Tinsley, James R, English
Van Doren, Charles Lincoln, English, Philosophy
Van Doren, John, English, History
Verbillion, June, English Language & Literature
Vest, Eugene Bartlett, English
Walker, Robert Jefferson, Speech Communication
Wallace, John Malcolm, English Literature
Ward, Ferdinand J, C.M, English
Weiss, Samuel Abba, English
Wells, James M, Bibliography, English Literature
Westgate, Samuel Shelton, Seventeenth-Century English Literature
White, Douglas Howarth, English
Willett, Maurita, Literature
Williams, David Gardner, English Literature
Williams, Joseph M, English, Linguistics
Wolff, Joseph J, English Literature
Wright, Elizabeth V, English
Zesmer, David Mordecai, English
Zigerell, James, English Literature

COLLINSVILLE
Kochman, Andrew J, Jr, Speech, Theatre

COUNTRY CLUB HILLS
Smith, Beverlee Ann, English

DECATUR
Bach, Bert Coates, English
Doubleday, Neal Frank, English
Gage, Elinor, English
Kreuger, William Edward, English
Mickel, Jere C, Speech
Mihm, Brian Lee, English Novel, American Literature
Onwuemene, Michael Chukwueloke, English

DEKALB
Abbott, Craig Stephens, American Literature
Armato, Philip Michele, Modern Drama, English Literature
Arnold, Richard Lee, Dramatic Art
Baker, S. Orville, English Drama
Burtness, Paul Sidney, Old & Middle English
Burwell, Rose Marie, Modern Fiction, Film
Carrington, George Cabell, Jr, English
Court, Franklin Edward, English Literature
Crawford, Paul K, Speech
Dallinger, Carl Arthur, Speech, Rhetoric
Durning, Russell Edward, Comparative Literature
Dust, Philip Clarence, English Renaissance Literature
Fox, Arnold Benjamin, English Literature
Garab, Arra M, English
Gardner, John B, English
Gray, Philip Alan, Speech Communication
Gulley, Halbert Edison, Speech
Hagelman, Charles William, Jr, English
Harris, Wendell V, English
Herbert, Edward Thomas, English & American Literature
James, Eugene Nelson, English Literature
Johannesen, Richard Lee, Speech Communication
Kallich, Martin, English
Kennedy, James Gettier, English
Mellard, James Milton, English, American Literature
Miller, James Ivan, Jr, English
Milosh, Joseph Edmund, Jr, Medieval English Literature
Mosher, Harold Frederick, Jr, English, Comparative Literature
Murray, Donald M, English
Peavler, James Martin, Medieval English Literature & Language
Pennel, Charles A, English
Polzin, Donald E, Drama
Potts, Norman Blaine, Theatre Arts, American Theatre History

Powell, Jon Tudor, Broadcasting, Educational-Television
Price, Granville, Journalism
Roscelli, William John, English, Classical Languages
Schaffer, Byron S, Jr, Theatre
Schriber, Mary Suzanne, Comparative Literature
Seat, William Robert, III, English Language & Literature
Shearer, William M, Speech
Van Cromphout, Gustaaf Victor, English & American Literature
Williams, William Proctor, English
Wilson, Quintus C, Journalism
Wilson, Robert H, American Literature
Wood, Margaret Louise, Speech

DOWNER'S GROVE
Oleson, Clinton Warren, English Literature
Sire, James Walter, English

EAST ALTON
Taylor, Marion Ansel, English, Fiction

EDWARDSVILLE
Ades, John I, English
Austin, James Clayton, English
Duncan, Robert W, English
Going, William Thornbury, English
Havens, Daniel F, English, Creative Writing
Hawkins, Robert Bentley, Speech
Revard, Stella Purce, English
Rider, John R, Broadcasting, Journalism
Stoppe, Richard Leon, Speech, Philosophy of Religion
Sullivan, Alvin D, Modern Literature

ELMHURST
Couchman, Gordon Ward, English
Gow, John E, Speech

ELSAH
Houpt, Charles Theodore, English Literature
Williams, Paul O, English

EUREKA
Bailey, Mabel Driscoll, English
Doran, Edwina Bean, English
Tookey, Mary D. Webber, English

EVANSTON
Appel, Alfred, Jr, English
Bacon, Wallace Alger, Speech
Baldwin, Benjamin Harrison, Journalism
Blum, Irving D, English
Brooks, Robert D, Communication
Brutus, Dennis (Vincent), English & African Literature
Cirillo, Albert Richard, English
Coakley, James Francis, Drama, English
Cole, Douglas, English
Dickinson, Hugh, Speech, Drama, Theatre
Dipple, Elizabeth Dorothea, English, Comparative Literature
Evans, Bergen Baldwin, English Literature
Evans, Lawrence Gove, English
Faverty, Frederic Everett, English Literature
Fuchs, Theodore, Dramatics
Gartley, John William, Radio & Television Production, Mass Communications
Gilliam, Harriet S, English & American Literature
Graff, Gerald Edward, English
Gray, Yohma, English, American Literature
Griffin, Leland Milburn, Speech
Hach, Clarence, English
Hagstrum, Jean Howard, English Literature
Hayford, Harrison (Mosher), English
Herbert, Christopher Clarke, English Literature
Heston, Lilla A, Interpretation
Hinderyckx, Leslie Alphonse, Drama, Communications
Hynes, Samuel L, English
Kaplan, Harold, English & American Literature
Lawler, Traugott, English
Lee, Charlotte Irene, Speech
McConnell, Frank DeMay, English
Margolis, John David, English
Mayo, Robert D, English
Mosse, Baskett, Journalism
Newman, Charles Hamilton, English
Regan, Catharine Ann, Old English & Medieval Literature
Rein, Irving Jacob, Speech
Roloff, Leland H, Speech
Samuels, Ernest, American Literature
Schneideman, Robert Ivan, Theatre
Schoenbaum, Samuel, English
Shanley, James Lyndon, English Literature
Silverman, Albert H, English, Drama
Torchiana, Donald T, English
Ward, Winifred, Speech, Drama
Wilson, Robin Scott, English
Wood, Roy V, Speech, Communication
Zimmer, George Willis, English

GALESBURG
  Brady, William E, English Literature
  Crowell, Michael Gardner, English Literature & Language
  Davenport, John Stewart, English
  Torrence, Donald L, Speech
  Whitlatch, Robert Calhoun, Speech & Theatre
  Wilson, Douglas Lawson, English
  Wilson, Howard Aaron, English
GLEN ELLYN
  Doster, William Clark, English
GLENVIEW
  Jordan, Moreen Elizabeth Crumley, English
GODFREY
  Pruitt, James Donald, English, Education
GRAYSLAKE
  Harnish, Frank James, Drama, Speech
GREENVILLE
  Dickerson, David, English
  McAllaster, Elva Arlene, English
  Zimmerman, Gordon G, Speech
HIGHLAND PARK
  Abrahamson, Irving, English Language & Literature
JACKSONVILLE
  Decker, Philip H, Speech & Drama
  Frank, Charles Edward, English Literature
  Lang, Phyllis Martin, English & American Literature
  Metcalf, Allan Albert, English, Linguistics
  Palmer, Richard E, Comparative European Literature
  Seybold, Ethel Louise, English, Linguistics
JOLIET
  Seraphim, M, O.S.F, English, Journalism
KANKAKEE
  McCombs, Athel Victor, Speech
  Phillips, Lottie Inez, Linguistics, English & American Literature
LAKE BLUFF
  Milne, William Gordon, English
LAKE FOREST
  Bennett, Kenneth Chisholm, Jr, English
  Cowler, Rosemary Elizabeth, English Literature
  Dunn, Margaret Mary, R.S.C.J, English & Norwegian Language & Literature
  Greenfield, Robert Morse, English
  Hentz, Ann Louise, English Literature, Renaissance
LA SALLE
  Weeg, Mary, English
LAWRENCEVILLE
  Dollahan, June Richey, English
LEBANON
  Rackham, Eric N, English Literature
LISLE
  Cohen, Richard, English
  Komechak, Michael, O.S.B, English & American Literature, Journalism
  Leeman, Richard Kendall, English, Comparative Literature
LOCKPORT
  French, Paul Douglas, F.S.C, English
  Stiker, Jeff M, English Literature
MACOMB
  Anderson, Norman Arthur, English Literature
  Balderson, Jay Russell, Early American Literature
  Banninga, Jerald Lyle, Speech
  Blackford, Paul Weldon, English
  Blackwelder, James Ray, American Literature
  Brown, Jared Allen, Drama, Speech
  Chandler, Arnold, English, Comparative Literature
  Faries, Clyde J, Rhetoric & Public Address
  Fite, Olive, English
  Garrison, Theodore Roosevelt, English
  Gee, Ronald Callaway, Speech, Drama
  Jacobs, Robert G, English
  Jessee, Jack W, English
  Lindsey, Alfred J, English Education
  McTeague, James H, Drama
  Mann, John Stuart, English & American Literature
  Preston, Dallas Dwain, English
  Reader, Dennis Joel, American Literature
  Robinson, Forrest Dean, American Literature, Creative Writing
  Shearer, Ned Alan, Speech
  Thornberry, Richard Thayer, English
  Ting, Nai-Tung, English
  Vanderburg, Ray Herschel, Journalism History
  Waldrep, Reef V, Jr, Journalism
MONMOUTH
  Boswell, Grace Hadaway, English
  De Young, James Lee, Theatre Arts
  Foxen, John Robert, Speech
  Kennedy, Adele, English
  Liedman, Jean Esther, Speech
  McNamara, Robert Jeremy, English

MORTON GROVE
  West, Fairinda W, English Drama
MURPHYSBORO
  Piper, Henry Dan, English & American Literature
NAPERVILLE
  Berry, Carolyn Fischer, English
  Cerovski, John, English
  Eastman, Richard Morse, English
  Reddick, Glenn Eugene, Speech
  Shanower, Donald, Speech & Drama
NORMAL
  Barber, George Bradford, Speech
  Bellas, Ralph A, English
  Bishop, Ferman, English
  Boaz, John Knox, Speech Communication
  Brake, Robert John, Speech, Dramatic Arts
  Brosnahan, Leger, English Literature & Linguistics
  Canning, George R, Jr, Victorian Literature
  Cox, Carrol Byron, Jr, English
  Crowell, Norton B, English
  Dammers, Richard Herman, English Literature
  Davidson, Keith Carlyle, Speech
  Easson, Kay Parkhurst, English Language & Literature
  Easson, Roger Ralph, English Language & Literature
  Ericksen, Donald Howard, Nineteenth Century English Literature
  Gimmestad, Victor Edward, English
  Harris, Charles Burt, American Literature
  Heissler, John M, Jr, English
  Henline, Ruth, English
  Hill, John Stanley, American Literature
  Hutton, Virgil Ralph, English
  Jochums, Milford Cyril, English
  Kagle, Steven Earl, English
  Kirk, John W, Speech, Theatre
  Lane, Ralph L, Speech, Drama
  Linneman, William Richard, English, Linguistics
  Newby, Richard Lee, English
  Pritner, Calvin Lee, Drama
  Ranta, Taimi Maria, English
  Rives, Stanley Gene, Speech
  Scharfenberg, Jean, Theatre
  Shanower, Donald, Speech & Drama
  Sharpham, John Raymond, Theatre Education
  Tarr, Rodger LeRoy, Nineteenth Century English Literature
  Vetter, Dale Benjamin, Literary History
  White, Charles A, Rhetoric, Public Address Philosophy
  White, Ray Lewis, Modern American Literature
  Woodson, William Charles, English Renaissance Literature
OAK PARK
  Clark, Earl John, English Literature
OAKLEY
  Buckingham, Minnie Susan, English
PALATINE
  Bartos, Michael William, English, Literature
PARK FOREST SOUTH
  Bernd, Daniel W, English, Drama
PEORIA
  Ballowe, James C, Literature
  Claussen, Ernest Neal, Speech Communication
  Clifford, John E, Theatre Arts
  Ferguson, George Burnham, English Literature
  Koperski, Ronald Joseph, Speech
  Norton, Laurence Eugene, Speech
  Paine, Stephen Curtiss, English
  Pearce, Josephine Anna, English
  Pichaske, David Richard, English
  Sawyer, Paul Simon, Literature, Theatre History
QUINCY
  Fitzgerald, Hugh D, Speech, Theatre, English
  Nevins, Thomas Frederick, Theatre
  Schweda, Donald Norman, American & English Literature
RIVER FOREST
  Davlin, Mary Clemente, O.P, English
  Finnegan, Mary Jeremy, O.P, Medieval Literature
  Grotelueschen, Paul G, Speech
  Heinitz, Kenneth, American Literature
  Hirsch, Leota, English
  Janzow, Frederick Samuel, English
  Lettermann, Henry, English
  McGinty, Carolyn, Literary Criticism, American Literature
  Radke, Merle Louis, American Literature
ROCK ISLAND
  Naeseth, Henriette Christiane Koren, American Literature
  Parkander, Dorothy J, English
  Youngberg, Karin Louise, English Literature

ROCKFORD
  Fowler, Knox, Theatre Arts
  Queenan, John Thomas, English
  Stanlis, Peter J, English Literature, History of Ideas
  Trafton, Dain Atwood, English, Comparative Literature
SKOKIE
  Smith, Elsdon Coles, Onomastics
SPRINGFIELD
  Camp, Dennis David, Literature
  Hagler, Margaret G, Comparative Literature, Folklore
  Hinton, Norman Dexter, English Literature
  Jackson, Jacqueline Dougan, Literature, Classics
  Jackson, Robert Sumner, English Literature
  Knoepfle, John Ignatius, English Renaissance
SYCAMORE
  Pflaumer, Elizabeth Mae, Speech Communication, Speech & Theatre Education
URBANA
  Adelman, Gary, English
  Aldridge, Alfred Owen, English
  Altenbernd, A. Lynn, American Literature
  Andersen, Kenneth Eldon, Public Address, Rhetoric
  Applebee, Roger Kenyon, English Literature
  Barksdale, Richard Kenneth, English
  Baym, Nina, English
  Behringer, Clara Marie, Theatre
  Bennett, Scott Boyce, English
  Brandabur, Edward, English
  Broadrick, King Woodard, Language Communication
  Campbell, Jackson Justice, English
  Carringer, Robert L, American Literature, Film Studies
  Clark, Roger G, English
  Cole, Howard Chandler, English Literature
  Danielson, Larry William, Folklore, American Civilization
  Davidson, Edward Hutchins, American Literature
  Davis, Nuel Pharr, English
  Douglas, George Halsey, American Literature & Studies
  Evertts, Eldonna L, Language Arts
  Fillion, Bryant Paul, Rhetorical Theory, English Education
  Flanagan, John T, American Literature
  Frayne, John (Patrick), English
  Friedman, John Block, Medieval English Literature
  Gettmann, Royal Alfred, English & American Literature
  Goldman, Marcus Selden, English & Comparative Literature
  Graham, Gene Swann, Journalism, Communications
  Halsband, Robert, English
  Hamilton, John Allen, English
  Hendrick, George, American Literature
  Hewitt, Barnard (Wolcott), Theatre, Drama
  Hogan, Donald J, English
  Hogan, Robert F, English Education
  Holaday, Allan Gibson, English Literature
  Hotch, Douglas Ripley, English Literature
  Hurt, James Riggins, English
  Ince, Robert Lee, Speech
  Jacobs, Paul Huland, Linguistics, Rhetoric
  Kaufman, Anthony David, English Literature
  Kaufman, U. Milo, English
  Kay, W. David, English Literature
  Kinnamon, Keneth, American Literature
  Kramer, Dale Vernon, English
  Lieberman, Laurence, English, Modern Poetry
  Maclay, Joanna Hawkins, Speech, Interpretation
  Mahood, Sharon Marie, Speech Communication
  Majdiak, Daniel, English
  Marder, Herbert, English
  Maxwell, John C, English Education
  Milligan, Burton Alviere, English
  Moake, Frank B, English
  Morisset, Gordon Rodney, English, English Education
  Mueller, Henry Lancaster, Speech
  Mullin, Michael, English Literature, Drama
  Murphy, Richard, Speech
  Nebergall, Roger Ellis, Speech Communication
  Nelson, Cary Robert, English & American Literature
  Nemanich, Donald Dean, English Language & Composition
  Nichols, Marie Hochmuth, Speech
  O'Donnell, Bernard, English, English Education
  Peterson, Theodore B, Mass Communications
  Prichard, Nancy Sawyer, English
  Purves, Alan Carroll, English

Rogers, Robert Wentworth, English Literature
Runyan, Michael Gracen, American Literature & History
Sanders, Charles, English
Schneider, Robert L, English Literature
Schooley, Frank Ellsworth, Journalism
Shapiro, Michael, English
Shattuck, Charles Harlen, English Literature
Smalley, Barbara Martin, Modern Novel
Smalley, Donald Arthur, English Literature
Stillinger, Jack, English
Swanson, John Wesley, Theatre
Thomas, Stafford H, Speech
Tibbetts, Arnold M, English
Trahern, Joseph Baxter, Jr, English
Vawter, Marvin L, English
Waldoff, Leon, English
Wenzel, Joseph Wilfred, Speech
Wheeler, Richard Paul, English Literature
Wilkie, Brian, English, Comparative Literature
Wilson, Harris Ward, English
WEST FRANKFORT
Claxton, Evelyn, Language & Literature
WHEATON
Hollatz, Edwin Arthur, Speech
Kilby, Clyde Samuel, English Literature
Lothers, William T, Speech
Paulson, Eleanor, Speech
Rudolph, Erwin P, English
Young, Mark James, Drama
WILMETTE
Bloom, Arthur William, Drama, Theatre History
Jacobi, Peter Paul, Journalism, Magazine & Arts Criticism
WINNETKA
Wells, Rosemary Siplon, Composition & Learning Disabilities

INDIANA

ANDERSON
Deubach, Vila Aprill, American Literature
Robertson, Thomas Luther, Jr, English
ANGOLA
Orlosky, Elizabeth Brown, Speech, English
BLOOMINGTON
Anderson, Judith Helena, English
Andrews, James Robertson, Speech
Appleman, Philip Dean, English
Auer, John Jeffery, Rhetoric, Public Address
Barnett, George Leonard, English Literature
Battenhouse, Roy Wesley, English Literature
Beaty, Frederick L, English
Bernhardt-Kabisch, Ernest, English
Bleich, David, English, Behavioral Science
Brewer, Fredric Aldwyn, Mass Communications
Bristow, Eugene Kerr, Theatre, Drama
Brockett, Oscar Gross, Speech & Drama
Burgan, Mary A, English
Burke, Richard C, Radio-Television, Speech
Callaway, James E, Journalism
Campbell, Mary Elizabeth, English Literature
Chenoweth, Eugene Clay, Speech
Cook, Don L, American Literature
Culbertson, James Edwin, Speech
Daghlian, Philip Bewer, English Literature
David, Alfred, English
Dickason, David Howard, American Literature
Eakin, Paul John, English
Edelen, Georges, English
Feddersen, Donley F, Radio-Television, Speech
Forker, Charles Rush, English Literature
Frenz, Horst, English, Comparative Literature
Gaiser, Gerhard Walter, Theatre
Gaither, Mary Elizabeth, English
Geduld, Harry Maurice, English
Gilbert, Sandra Mortola, Modern British & American Literature
Gottfried, Rudolf Brand, English Literature
Gray, Donald, English Literature
Gros Louis, Kenneth Richard Russell, English & Comparative Literature
Gross, Robert Eugene, English, American Literature
Gunderson, Robert Gray, Speech
Hawes, David Stewart, Theatre, Drama
Heffner, Hubert Crouse, Dramatic Literature
Holsinger, Ralph Lee, Journalism
Jenkinson, Edward B, English, Speech
Jensen, Harvey James, English Literature
Johnston, Kenneth R, English
Justus, James Huff, English
Kelly, Robert Glynn, English
Kinzer, William Edward, Theatre, Drama
Klotman, Phyllis Rauch, American Literature
Lawlis, Merritt Eugene, English
Lewis, Robert Enzer, English Language & Literature
Lohmann, Christoph Karl, English, American Studies

McEvoy, Poynter, Journalism
Martin, Terence John, English
Meserve, Walter J, Jr, Theatre
Miller, Lewis Holmes, Jr, English Literature
Mitchner, Robert Warren, English
Moody, Richard, Speech, Drama
Muller, Herbert Joseph, Literary Criticism
Nordloh, David Joseph, American Literature, Bibliography
Norvelle, Lee, Speech
Noyes, Russell, English Literature
Peet, Charles Donald, English
Piercy, Josephine Ketcham, English
Plotinsky, Melvin Lloyd, English
Richmond, Winthrop Edson, English Literature, Folklore
Robbins, John Albert, American Literature
Roberts, Warren Everett, English
Rosenfeld, Alvin Hirsch, English & American Literature
Scammon, Richard Lewis, Theatre Arts
Scrimgeour, Gary James, English, Drama
Seltz, Herbert Arnold, Radio, Television
Shipps, Anthony Wimberly, English, Library Science
Smiley, Sam Max, Drama
Smith, Raymond George, Speech
Sperry, Stuart M, English
Strickland, Ruth G, English Education
Strohm, Paul Holzworth, Jr, English
Thomas, Owen Paul, English
Wang, Joan Parsons, English, Comparative Literature
Wertheim, Albert, English
Wiatt, William Haute, English
Wikelund, Philip Raymond, English Literature
Williams, Wallace Edward, English
Wilson, William Edward, English
Yellen, Samuel, English
Yoakam, Richard David, Journalism, Radio-Television
Zietlow, Paul Nathan, English
Zirker, Malvin Ralph, Jr, English
CRAWFORDSVILLE
Baker, Donald Whitelaw, English Literature
Fertig, Walter L, American Literature
Harvey, Robert Sidney, English
Herring, Paul Donald, English
O'Rourke, Joseph, Speech
Powell, Victor Morgan, Speech
Seymour, Thaddeus, English
Stern, Herbert J, English
ELKHART
Roten, Paul, Speech, Library Science
EVANSVILLE
Clough, Galen Weare, English
Grabill, Virginia Lowell, English Literature
FORT WAYNE
Brennan, John Patrick, English
Cashman, Daniel Edward, Theatre, Interdisciplinary Studies
Conrad, Eunice J, English
Dillon, George Lewis, English, Linguistics
Essig, Erhardt Herbert, English
Fackler, Miriam Ernestine, English Literature & Language
Harms, Paul William Frederick, Speech, Drama
Headings, Philip R, Comparative Literature
McCants, David Arnold, Speech
Modic, John Leonard, English
Nault, Clifford Albert, Jr, Literature
Novak, Robert Lee, English
Pictor, James Matthew, English & American Literature
Posey, Horace Gadsden, Jr, English Literature
Rossow, Francis C, English Literature
Schramm, David Eugene, English Literature
Standley, Arline Elizabeth Reilein, English, Comparative Literature
Weimer, Mary E, English
Woolf, James Dudley, English
FRANKLIN
Graham, H. Richard, English
Jacobs, Elijah Lawrence, English
GARY
Austin, Allen Cletus, English
Barr, Alan Philip, English
Fromm, Harold, English, Humanities
Zneimer, John Nicolas, English
GOSHEN
Albrecht, Alfred J, Speech
Birky, Wilbur J, American & English Literature
Hartzler, Sara Kreider, Nineteenth Century British Literature
Umble, Roy Herman, Speech
GREENCASTLE
Bergmann, Fredrick Louis, English
Bittner, John Robert, Communication
Cavanaugh, William Charles, English
Garriott, Harold Milton, English

Gilmer, Frank Walker, Modern American Literature
Mizer, Raymond Everett, English
Opdahl, Keith Michael, English
Ross, Herold Truslow, Speech
Shumaker, Arthur Wesley, English & American Literature
Spicer, Harold, English
Weiss, Robert Orr, Speech
Williams, Clem C, Jr, English
HAMMOND
Carlisle, John Charles, American Studies, American Literature
Dixon, Maurice Edward, Theatre, Education
Geimer, Roger Anthony, English
Nichols, Robert E, Jr, English
Selig, Robert L, English
Tuckey, John Sutton, English
HANOVER
Baker, Frank Sheaffer, English Journalism
Bucks, Dorothy Sims, English
Clark, George Peirce, English & American Literature
Ferguson, James Lee, English, Comparative Literature
Fox, Charles Franklin, English
Wheater, Stanley Brigham, Speech
Withey, Joseph Anthony, Asian Studies, Humanities
INDIANAPOLIS
Amend, Victor Earl, English
Baetzhold, Howard George, English
Beyer, Werner William, English
Bisignano, Dominic J, English
Bowman, Sylvia E, English
Cassell, Richard Allan, English
Cripe, Nicholas M, Speech
Curtis, Richard K, Speech
Dauner, Louise, English, American Literature
French, Warren Graham, English
Gatto, Louis Constantine, English Medieval & Renaissance Literature
Jones, Alexander Elvin, English
Keller, Joseph R, Medieval Literature
Marz, Roy, English
Moore, Nancy, English
Peterson, Erling Winston, English Education
Phillippe, James R, Drama
Pitts, Rebecca E, English
Rea, Mary Louise, English
Rice, George Philip, Jr, English History
Richards, Jane Grills, Speech, Education
Schroeder, Rose Mary, O.S.F, English
Stewart, Allegra, English
Stewart, Paul Robert, English
Turner, Richard Charles, Restoration & Eighteenth Century English Literature
Waller, Martha Stifler, English
Walsh, William Patrick, Shakespeare, Elizabethan Drama
KOKOMO
Bosch, L. Alan, American Literature
Nelson, Nicolas Harding, English Literature
Rudy, John George, English & American Literature
LAFAYETTE
De Vitis, Angelo A, English
Fatout, Paul, English
Gibbens, Victor Ellison, English
Hayman, Allen, American Literature
Lazarus, Arnold Leslie, English
Mills, Barriss, English
Robb, Stephen, Speech
Staton, Walter F, Jr, English
MARION
Dodd, Mary Caroline, English Literature
Elder, Marjorie J, English
Emerson, Laura Salome, Humanities, Speech
MICHIGAN CITY
Webb, Chester James, Dramatic Art, Speech
MUNCIE
Adrian, Daryl B, English
Andrews, S. Gene, English Literature
Benson, James Allen, Speech
Clifton, Lucile, English
Conn, Earl Lewis, Journalism
Diedrich, Duane Norman, Public Address, Rhetoric
Eddy, Darlene M, Renaissance & Nineteenth Century American Studies
Evans, Robert Edward, Medieval English & Linguistics
Fifield, Merle, English, Linguistics
Foster, Edward Francis, English
Hayashi, Tetsumaro, Renaissance English Literature
Hoilman, Dennis Roland, English
Hozeski, Bruce William, English Literature, History of Language
Huckleberry, Alan Wright, Speech
Irving, George W, Speech, Theatre
Kearney, Flora McLaughlin, English Literature

Kirkham, Edwin Bruce, English, American Literature
Koontz, Thomas Wayne, American Literature & Folklore
Lindblad, William E, English Literature
Liston, William Thomas, English
Newcomb, Robert Howard, Literature
Nixon, Howard Kenneth, Jr, English
Poulakidas, Andreas K, English, Comparative Literature
Purifoy, Cecil Ernest, Jr, English, Religion
Renner, Dick Arnold, English Literature
Rippy, Frances Mayhew, English
Ross, Janet, Linguistics
Schulte, Emerita Schroer, English
Shepard, David W, Speech & English
Strother, Edward Spencer, Speech, Theater
Sutton, William Alfred, English, American Literature
Whitworth, Richard G, English Education
NEW ALBANY
Dunn, Millard Charles, Jr, English
Shusterman, David, English
NORTH MANCHESTER
Aungst, Ronald Lee, Speech
Garey, Doris Bates, English
Keller, Paul Watson, Speech
Martin, Jo Ann, English Literature
NOTRE DAME
Beichner, Paul Edward, C.S.C, English
Brennan, Joseph Xavier, English
Brzenk, Eugene Joseph, British Literature
Charles, Isabel, O.P, English, American Literature
Collins, Carvel, American Literature
Costello, Donald Paul, English
Davis, Walter Richardson, English
Dougherty, James P, English
Garvick, John Daniel, English & American Literature
Gutierrez, Donald, Modern British Literature, Novel
Huber, John Edward, English Literature
Jemielity, Thomas J, English
Kane, M. Franzita, C.S.C, English
Klene, Mary Jean, C.S.C, Renaissance Literature & Art
Lordi, Robert Joseph, English Literature
McDonald, John Joseph, American Literature, Theory of Criticism
Matthias, John Edward, English Literature
Nicholson, Lewis Edward, English
Noel, Elisabeth Ann, English
Rauh, Miriam Joseph, C.S.C, English
Robinson, James E, English
Sandeen, Ernest E, American Literature
Shuster, George N, German History
Slabey, Robert M, American Literature
Soens, Adolph Lewis, Jr, English
Soleta, Chester Anthony, C.S.C, English Literature
Walton, James Hackett, English
Werge, Thomas, English
RENSSELAER
Balice, Vincent Joseph, English Literature, Psychology
Cappuccilli, Ralph Michael, Speech & Drama
Druhman, Alvin William, English
Groppe, John Daniel, English
Gross, Raphael H, English Literature
RICHMOND
Atkinson, James Blakely, English & Comparative Literature
Blake, Lincoln Carlyle, English, American Studies
Holder, Glenn, English Education
Johnson, Everett Orville, Speech
Little, Arthur, Drama
Staebler, Warren, English
Thompson, Gordon W, English
ST. MARY-OF-THE-WOODS
Logan, Eugenia, S.P, English
Pomeroy, Mary Joseph, S.P, English Literature
Sullivan, Marie Denise, S.P, English Literature
ST. MEINRAD
Hettich, Blaise, O.S.B, English Literature
SOUTH BEND
Cassidy, John Albert, English
Clipper, Lawrence Jon, English Literature
Donovan, Mortimer John, English
Gering, William Marvin, Speech, Theatre
Hasley, Louis, American Literature
Kaufman, Gloria (Shapiro), English & American Literature
McLane, Paul Elliott, English
Smithberger, Andrew Thomas, English Literature
Vander Ven, Tom Robert, English
Vasta, Edward, English
Wolfson, Lester Marvin, English

TERRE HAUTE
Adkins, Gale Roy, Journalism, Speech & Drama
Aggertt, Otis J, Speech
Albaugh, Ralph M, English
Angell, Richard Churchill, English Literature
Backes, James Glenn, Rhetoric & Public Address
Baker, Ronald Lee, Folklore
Bash, James Richard, English
Boyd, John Allen, Journalism
Boyd, John Harvey, Jr, Journalism
Bracker, Jon, American Literature, Modern English
Brooks, Elmer Leroy, English
DeMarr, Mary Jean, English
Dougherty, Adelyn (O'Connell), English
Dowell, Richard Walker, English, American Literature
Etheridge, Eugene Wesley, English, Comparative Literature
Frushell, Richard Clayton, English
Fyfe, Albert John, English Literature
Haist, Gordon Keith, English
Hansell, Donald Wade, Speech & Drama
Hunt, Effie N, English Literature
Kleiner, Elaine Laura, English & Continental Literature
Lee, Berta Grattan, English, Linguistics
McGaughey, Florence Helen, English
Misenheimer, James Buford, Jr, English Literature
Mullen, Richard D, English
Mullican, James Stanley, Rhetoric, English
Pattison, Sheron J. Dailey, Speech Communication, Poetry
Reed, John Thomas, English
Reifsnyder, Henry Gillam, English
Richards, Bertrand Field, English
Saalbach, Robert P, American Literature
Schick, Joseph Schlueter, English
Shields, Donald J, Speech, Political Science
Smith, Laban C, English, Education
Smock, George Edward, English
Witham, William Tasker, English & American Literature
Workman, Arvin LeRoy, Speech, Mass Media
UPLAND
Carruth, Hazel E, English
Ewbank, Frances White, English
Greathouse, Gladys M, Drama, Speech
Lee, Herbert Grant, English
VALPARAISO
Friedrich, Walter George, English
Kussrow, Van Carl, Jr, Speech, Drama
Loucks, James Frederick, English
Phipps, Joel, English
Rubel, Warren G, English
Sitton, Fred, Theatre
Tobin, Terence A, English, Drama
Umbach, Herbert Herman, English & American Literature
VINCENNES
Klinker, Harriette Grayson, English
WAVELAND
Hook, Julius N, English
WEST LAFAYETTE
Abel, Darrel, English
Adler, Jacob Henry, English
Adler, Thomas Peter, English & American Literature
Braswell, William, American Literature
Brooks, William Dean, Speech Communication & Education
Burks, Don Marvin, Rhetoric & Communication
Church, Margaret, English
Cosper, Russell, English
Crowder, Richard, American Literature
Davis, Wendell Eugene, English Literature
Dudley, Juanita H. Williams, English
Eisinger, Chester Emanuel, English
Epstein, William Henry, English Literature
Ewbank, Henry Lee, Jr, Speech
Field, Leslie A, American & English Literature
Friedrich, Gustav William, Speech Communication
Gaston, Thomas Elmer, English Education
Griffin, Erville Glenn, Communication
Himelick, Raymond, English
Kildahl, Erling Eugene, Theatre, Oral Interpretation
Kottler, Barnet, English
Light, Martin, American Literature
Lowe, Robert Liddell, English
McKenzie, Alan Taber, English Literature
Marks, Samuel Milton, Speech
Miller, David Merlin, English Literature
Miller, Robert Alexander, English
Myers, Neil, English Literature
Reichard, Hugo Manley, English
Rudolph, Valerie Christine, English Literature, Drama

Ryan, Robert Edmund, English & American Literature
Scheele, Henry Zaegel, Speech, Communication
Schwienher, William Kaye, Speech
Shamo, George Wayne, Speech
Stafford, William Talmadge, English
Stallard, Owen M, Speech
Stefanile, Felix N, Modern Poetry
Stewart, Charles Joseph, Speech
Stuckey, William Joseph, English
Trachtman, Leon Emanuel, Science Communication
Van Gelder, Lizette O, English
Voorhees, Richard Joseph, English
Warner, John Riley, English Literature
Webb, Ralph, Jr, Speech
Woodford, Bruce Powers, English
Wykoff, George Steward, Composition & Literature
Yetman, Michael G, Romantic & Victorian Literature
WEST TERRE HAUTE
Rohrig, Gladys M, Speech, Theatre
WESTVILLE
Bostich, June Marie, English
Schlobin, Roger Clark, Medieval Language & Literature

IOWA

ALTA
Martz, Leonard John, Jr, English, Speech
AMES
Bataille, Robert Raymond, British Literature
Benson, Donald Robert, English
Davies, Phillips George, English Literature
Davies, Rosemary Reeves, English & American Literature
Dearin, Ray Dean, Speech
Drexler, Malcolm Burton, Speech, Drama
Feinberg, Leonard, English
Gustafson, Richard, Literature
Herrnstadt, Richard L, English
Hogrefe, Pearl, English Literature & Composition
Huntress, Keith Gibson, English
Hvistendahl, J.K, Journalism
Jones, Walter Paul, English
Jumper, Will Carragher, American Literature, Creative Writing
Lipa, Charles Buell, English & American Literature
Lowrie, James A, English
McCay, Dale, English Language & Literature
Nostwich, Theodore Daniel, American Literature, Bibliography
Schwartz, James Waldemar, Journalism
Underhill, William R, English, Speech
Walker, Albert Lyell, English Literature
Wilson, George Pickett, Jr, Speech
Yates, Norris Wilson, English, Speech
CEDAR FALLS
Cahill, Daniel Joseph, English & American Literature
Conklin, Royal Forrest, Speech
Cowley, John, English
Day, George Frederick, American Literature
De Hoff, Bernard C, English, Journalism
Goodman, Ralph Marvin, Linguistics, English Literature
Kalmar, Elaine Bush, English & Comparative Literature
Lash, Kenneth, English
McDavitt, Elaine E, Speech
McKean, Keith F, English & American Literature
Smith, M. B, Speech
Wagner, Lillian Rose, Speech
Ward, Robert Jackson, English
Wilson, Robley Conant, Jr, English, Foreign Language
CEDAR RAPIDS
Cannon, Charles Kendrick, English
Falk, Signi, English
Kern, Jean B, English
Roth, Mary Augustine, R.S.M, English
Woodruff, Neal, Jr, English
DAVENPORT
Bradley, Ritamary, S.F.C.C, English
Jordan, Raymond Joseph, English
Kelleher, James P, English Literature, Counseling
Kokjohn, Joseph Eugene, English
DECORAH
Jones, Dennis M, English
Mohr, Mary Hull, English Literature
Nelson, Harland S, English
Svanoe, Harold C, Speech
DES MOINES
Abel, Richard Owen, Comparative Literature, Cinema

Autrey, Max L, English
Barton, Mike Alan, Theatre History, Dramatic Literature
Bjornstad, William Bernard, English
Burns, Stuart LeRoy, American Literature
Coleman, William S. E, Drama, Speech
Daley, Arthur Stuart, English Renaissance Literature
Dunn, Thomas Franklin, English
Eckley, Grace Ester, Modern Literature, Mythology
Eckley, Wilton, English
Ericson, Jon Louis, Speech
Foster, David Earle, English & American Literature
Francois, William Edward, Mass Communications, Journalism
Jones, Hattie, Speech
LaBelle, Maurice Marc, Comparative Literature
Martin, Bruce Kirk, English & American Literature
Mayo, Edward Leslie, English
Noyes, Jeanice Williams, Speech, Drama
Page, Curtis Carling, English
Stroud, Theodore Albert, English
Whittle, Amberys Rayvon, English
DUBUQUE
Coens, Mary Xavier, B.V.M, Drama, English
Donohue, James John, English
Hart, Mary Adorita, B.V.M, Literature
Rogers, Daniel John, English
Roseliep, Raymond, English
FAIRFIELD
Sloca, Charles, English
FAYETTE
Paul, Aldrich K, Dramatic Arts
GRINNELL
Alden, (Howel) Henry, English
Cleaver, Charles Grinnell, English & American Studies
Hiser, Velma Bissell, Speech
Irving, Donald C, American Literature & Studies
Kissane, James, English
Leggett, Glenn, English
Moore, Edward Mumford, English
Prescott, Herbert, English, Journalism
Vanderpool, William S, Jr, Speech
INDIANOLA
Gruber, Loren Charles, Medieval Studies, English Literature
Koch, Donald Artenius, English
Lieber, Todd Michael, English, American Studies
IOWA CITY
Adams, Anthony Andrew, Electronic Mass Media
Anderson, Ruth Leila, English Literature
Armens, Sven Magnus, English
Baender, Paul, American Literature
Baird, Albert Craig, Speech, Rhetoric
Baker, Joseph Ellis, English Literature
Becker, Samuel Leo, Speech, Mass Media
Boos, Florence Saunders, English Literature, Women's Studies
Bowers, John Waite, Speech, Drama
Braddock, Richard Reed, English, Rhetoric
Brown, Merle Elliott, English
Brownstein, Oscar Lee, Theatre History, Playwriting
Bryant, Donald Cross, Speech, English
Carlsen, George Robert, English
Catalano, Cosmo A, Dramatic Art
Chamberlain, David S, English, Comparative Literature
Coolidge, Archibald Cary, Jr, English
Corrigan, Robert Anthony, American Civilization
Davis, Charles Twitchell, English
Deligiorgis, Stavros George, English & Comparative Literature
Drmola, Evzen, Theatre
Dunlap, Rhodes, English
Ehninger, Douglas, Speech
Engle, Paul Hamilton, Creative Writing
Gerber, John Christian, English
Gillespie, Patti Peete, Dramatic Literature, Theatre History
Gillette, Arnold Simpson, Drama
Goff, Lewin Alkire, Drama
Grant, John Ernest, English
Gronbeck, Bruce Elliott, Rhetoric, Speech Communication
Hardt, Hanno, Communication
Harshbarger, Henry Clay, Speech
Heffner, Ray Lorenzo, Jr, English
Hitchcock, Orville A, Speech
Huntley, John Faringdon, English Literature
Irwin, William Robert, English Literature
Justice, Donald Rodney, Writing
Kelley, Robert Emmett, English Literature

Kern, Alexander C, American Literature & Civilization
Klaus, Carl H, English
Kuhlmann, Susan, American Literature
Lagorio, Valerie M, Medieval English Literature
Lloyd-Jones, Richard, English
MacCann, Richard Dyer, Film History & Criticism
McDowell, Frederick Peter Woll, English
McGalliard, John Calvin, English
MacLean, Malcolm Shaw, Jr, Communication, Journalism
Moeller, Leslie George, Mass Communications
Ochs, Donovan Joseph, Speech
Paff, William J, English
Paul, Sherman, American Literature
Sayre, Robert Freeman, English
Schaal, David George, Theatre, Drama
Seabury, Hugh Francis, Speech Education
Spivak, Gayatri C, English, Comparative Literature
Thayer, David Lewis, Dramatic Art, Communications Research
Turner, Darwin Theodore Troy, English
Whitaker, Thomas Russell, English
Woerner, Robert Frederick, English & Comparative Literature
Zimansky, Curt Arno, English Literature
KEOKUK
Christin, Robert E, Jr, American Literature
LAMONI
Higdon, Barbara, English, Speech
Ruch, Velma Naomi, English
LE MARS
Dorweiler, Virgil Walter, Journalism, English Literature
Kruse, Alice Marie, English
MOUNT PLEASANT
Bensmiller, Mildred, English
Haselmayer, Louis A, English, Iowa History
Panzer, Vern Albert, English Linguistics, Literary Criticism
MOUNT VERNON
Dana, Robert Patrick, English
Isaacs, Emily Elizabeth, English Literature
Meers, Geneva (Mae), English
Schuman, Samuel, English Literature
Shackford, John Branner, English Literature
ORANGE CITY
England, Theora, Speech & Drama, English
Ericson, Edward Einar, Jr, English
Holland, E. Grady, English
PELLA
Huffman, Maxine Fish, English, English As Second Language
SIOUX CITY
Dessel, Mary Francis Joseph, O.S.F, Speech, Drama
Knepper, Bill Garton, English
McLaughlin, Carrol D, English
Nelson, Raymond Stanley, English
Phelps, C. Fred, Rhetoric & Public Address
WAUKON
Jacobson, Sibyl Chafer, English & American Literature
WAVERLY
Garland, Margaret Wolff, English, Journalism
Kildahl, Phillip Andrew, English, History
Moehl, Erna, English
WEST BRANCH
Murray, Willam Martin, English

KANSAS

ATCHISON
Brannan, Robert L, English
Carpinelli, Francis Paul, English
Doyle, Teresa Ann, O.S.B, English
Fry, Timothy Paul, O.S.B, English
Hansen, Regina, English & American Literature
Schuster, Mary Faith, O.S.B, English
Walsh, Mary Margaret, O.S.B, English Language & Literature
BALDWIN
Hatcher, Joe Branch, English
EMPORIA
Hill, Charles, Drama & Speech
Matheny, David Leon, Speech
Morgan, June J, English
Wyrick, Green D, English
HAYS
Coder, Ralph Vernon, English Literature
Doggett, John Rentz, English Literature, Composition
Garner, Naomi Roxie, English Literature
Gatschet, Paul A, English, Education
McFarland, Alice, English, Literature
Sackett, Samuel John, English
Thompson, William Ross, American Literature
Vogel, Nancy, English & American Literature

KANSAS CITY
Miller, Arthur Burton, Rhetoric
LAWRENCE
Albrecht, William Price, English
Atkins, George Douglas, English Literature
Berg, David Merlen, Speech, Communication
Biddle, Stephen Pierce, Contemporary Theatre
Blubaugh, Jon Alfred, Communication, Education
Boyd, Beverly, English
Brooking, Jack Thomas, Speech, Drama
Casagrande, Peter Joseph, English
Cherniss, Michael David, English
Cobb, Robert Paul, American Literature
Colyer, Richard Hall, Modern Literature, Film
Davis, Jed Horace, Jr, Speech, Theatre
Downs, Calvin W, Communication, Speech
Eversole, Richard Langley, English Literature
Farrell, John Philip, English
Findlay, Robert R, Theatre & Drama
Gagen, Jean Elizabeth, English
Giffin, Kim, Speech
Gold, Joel Jay, English
Gowen, James Anthony, American Literature & Linguistics
Gridley, Roy E, English
Grier, Edward Francis, American Literature & Civilization
Habegger, Alfred Carl, English
Hardin, Richard F, English
Haugh, Oscar M, English, Education
Hinman, Charlton, English Literature
Hinman, Myra Mahlow, English
Horowitz, Floyd R, English, Computer Application
Houck, Joseph Kemp, English
Hyder, Clyde Kenneth, English Literature
Johnson, Michael Lillard, English
Jones, John Bush, Dramatic Literature, Theatre History
Keltcher, Wesley, English
Kendall, Paul Murray, English Literature
Levine, Stuart George, American Studies
Linton, Bruce Allen, Speech, Journalism
Masinton, Charles G, English & American Literature
Orel, Harold, English Language & Literature
Oruch, Jack B, English
Paden, William Doremus, English Literature
Patton, Bobby Ray, Speech
Pickett, Calder M, Journalism, American Studies
Quinn, Dennis, English
Ruhe, Edward Lehman, English
Schultz, Elizabeth Avery, American Literature
Scott, William Osborne, English
Sedelow, Sally Yeates, Linguistics, Information Science
Springer, Haskell, Saul, English
Springer, Marlene Ann, Nineteenth Century British & American Literature
Sutton, Max Keith, English
Tsubaki, Andrew Takahisa, Speech & Drama
Waggoner, George Ruble, Elizabethan Drama, Comparative Education
Wedge, George Francis, English, Linguistics
Willingham, John Robert, English
Worth, George John, English
Zuther, Gerhard Helmut Waldemar, Comparative Literature
LEAVENWORTH
McGilley, Mary Janet, S.C.L, English
LINDSBORG
Homan, Delmar C, English
MCPHERSON
Green, Bob Rex, English Literature
Stump, Harley H, English, Education
MANHATTAN
Adams, Marjorie, English
Ansdell, (Ora) Joye, English
Carpenter, William E, Literature, Drama
Climenhaga, Joel Ray, Dramatic Literature, Creative Writing
Cunningham, Frank Robert, English, Drama
Dace, Wallace, Drama
Davis, Earle Rosco, English
Eitner, Walter Hugo, American Literature
Fedder, Norman Joseph, Playwriting, Dramatic Literature
Higginson, Fred Hall, English
Houser, David John, English Literature
Keiser, George Robert, English & American Literature
Koch, William Ernest, English
McCarthy, Paul Eugene, English
McGhee, Richard Dennis, English Literature
Moses, William Robert, English
Nichols, Harold James, Dramatic Literature, Theatre History
Noonan, John Patrick, English
Rees, John Owen, Jr, English, American Studies
Rogerson, Brewster, English

Shelton, Lewis Edward, Drama
Stewart, Donald Charles, English Literature
White, Mary Frances, English
NORTH NEWTON
Becker, Honora E, English
OTTAWA
McKenzie, Emory Jariel, English
Presley, Horton Edward, English
PITTSBURG
Blackmon, Jennings Mason, English
DeGruson, Eugene Henry, American Literature & Bibliography
Hemmens, Thomas J, English
Loy, Harold W, Speech Communication, Speech Education
Patterson, Rebecca, English
Reed, John Quincy, American Literature
Roberts, Mary Margaret, Speech
Shear, Walter L, English
Strawn, Robertson Irving, Speech, English
Teller, Stephen James, English
SALINA
Carlisle, Lilybelle Moutrie Lewin, Classical Literature
Fuson, Benjamin Willis, English
Schneider, Lucy, C.S.J, English, American Literature
TOPEKA
Bunge, Eldo Frederick, English
Lawson, Robert Nichol, English
Stein, Robert David, English
WICHITA
Besser, Milton, Journalism
Blake, Leslie M, Speech, Drama
Bolton, (Harold) Philip, English Literature
Craven, Dorothy Hadley, English Literature
Cutler, Bruce, Poetry
Erickson, James Paul, English
Goudie, Andrea Kay, American Literature
Grow, Lynn Merle, English Literature
Hammond, Geraldine, English
Hoag, Gerald Bryan, English
Kastor, Frank Sullivan, English & American Literature
Kidder, Rushworth Moulton, Twentieth Century English & American Literature
Merrill, Walter M, English
Merriman, James Douglas, English Literature
Meyers, Robert Rex, English
Mood, Robert Gibbs, English Literature
Stephens, Fran Carlock, Literature of the English Romantic Period
Throckmorton, Helen Jean, English
Walters, Dorothy Jeanne, English
Welsbacher, Richard C, Theatre, English
WINFIELD
Wroten, Helen, English

KENTUCKY

BARBOURVILLE
Merchant, Frank Eldredge, English Lingusitics
BEREA
Bolin, John Seelye, Dramatic Literature, Theatre History
Brown, Dorothy S, English
Faulkner, Rose Maureen, English
Gesner, Carol, English
Hughes, Jerome William, English
Kreider, Thomas McRoberts, English
Riffe, Nancy Lee, English
Schafer, William John, English
Sears, Richard Duane, English
BOWLING GREEN
Bowen, Hoyt Edwin, English
Capps, Randall, Speech
Clarke, Kenneth Wendell, Folklore
Clarke, Mary Washington, English, Folklore
Corts, Paul Richard, Speech, Theatre
Heldman, James M, English
Hilliard, Addie Suggs, English, Education
McCrory, Juliet (Key), Speech
Mitchell, Lee, Drama
Neal, Julia, English
O'Connor, John Regis, Speech, Communication Science
Ward, Robert Ernest, Eighteenth Century English Literature
Wesolowski, James Walter, Communications
Wilson, Ollie James, English, Education
CAMPBELLSVILLE
Hamilton, Lockard Mitchell, English, Classical Languages
Kennedy, L.D, English & American Literature
Meece, Shirley Baker, English
DANVILLE
Hazelrigg, Charles T, English & American Literature
FORT MITCHELL
Driscoll, Loretto Marie, C.D.P, English
FRANKFORT
Brooks, Alfred Russell, English Literature

Fletcher, Joseph Grant, English Literature
Fletcher, Winona Lee, Speech & Drama
GEORGETOWN
Curry, Ralph Leighton, English
May, Steven William, Renaissance English Literature
Snyder, Edwina Hunter, Speech, Oral Interpretation
Spears, Woodridge, English
HIGHLAND HEIGHTS
McNally, Terrence James, English Literature
Mullen, Robert William, Speech Communication
Price, Joseph E, Jr, English Language & Literature
Stallings, Frank Loyd, Jr, English
Wallace, Robert K, English & American Literature
HINDMAN
Still, James A, English
LEXINGTON
Adelstein, Michael E, English
Blues, Thomas, English
Blyton, Gifford, Speech
Bostrom, Robert N, Communication
Briggs, Wallace Neal, English, Speech
Bryant, Joseph Allen, Jr, English Literature
Campbell, William Royce, English
Crabb, Alfred Leland, Jr, English
Cutler, John Levi, English
Davenport, Guy Mattison, English
Donohew, Robert Lewis, Communication
Donovan, Josephine Campbell, Comparative Literature, Women's Studies
Elioseff, Lee Andrew, English
Epstein, Harry Sol, English
Evans, Robert Owen, English, Comparative Literature
Gardner, Joseph Hogue, English & American Literature
Gordon, William A, English
Haney, Roger Daniel, Communication
Harrison, John Francis, English and Comparative Literature
Hartwig, Helen Joan, English
Hatch, Maurice Addison, English
Hemenway, Robert E, English, American Studies
Herbert, Thomas Walter, Jr, American Literature
Holmes, Charles Mason, English
Jansen, William Hugh, Comparative Folklore
Jones, Winona Stevens, Romance Languages
Manning, Stephen, English, Medieval Literature
Meckier, Jerome Thomas, English Literature
Niles, John Jacob, Music
Patterson, J. W, Speech, Communication
Pearce, Walter Barnett, Interpersonal & Speech Communication
Ringe, Donald Arthur, English
Ripley, Joseph M, Speech
Robinson, Lolo, Drama, Speech
Semon, Kenneth Jeffrey, English Literature
Smith, Raymond Alfred, Drama, Theatre Arts
Stroup, Thomas Bradley, English Literature
Sugg, Richard Peter, American Literature, Film
Swingle, Larry J, English
Teeter, Dwight Leland, Jr, Communications Law & History
Ward, William Smith, English
Wrobel, Arthur, American & English Literature
LOUISVILLE
Axton, William F, English Literature
Badessa, Richard Paul, Medieval Literature, Linguistics
Bowden, James Henry, American Literature
Brittain, Joan Tucker, English
Burton, Mary Elizabeth, Literary History
Driskell, Leon Vinson, English, Humanities
Ekstrom, William Ferdinand, English
Freibert, Lucy Marie, American Literature
Grant, William Earl, American Literature & Studies
Hall, Wade H, English
Kain, Richard Morgan, English Literature
Lyons, Kathleen Virginia, English Literature
McGlon, Charles Addis, Speech
Mercer, Caroline G, American Literature
Miller, Robert Henry, English Literature, Bibliography
Morgan, Mary Louis, O.S.U, English Literature, Speech, Drama
Ohlmann, Gilbert Sylvester, English, Humanities
Richardson, Harold Edward, English
Rickey, Mary Ellen, English
Scherzer, Edwin J, English
Starling, Jeremiah Pelletier, English Language & Literature
Van, Thomas A, English, Linguistics
Webster, Harvey Curtis, Literature

MOREHEAD
Barnes, Wesley, Renaissance, Modern Novel
Charles, Robert Alan, English, Comparative Literature
Cunningham, Donald Hayward, English Literature
Dobler, George Ronald, English, Education
Pelfrey, Charles J, Literature
Thomas, Malayilmelathethil Koruthu, English, Education
Venettozzi, Victor A, English
Voigt, Frederick, Rhetoric, Communications
MURRAY
Adams, John Howard, American Literature
Battle, Guy Arthur, English
Cella, Charles Ronald, American Literature
Hatcher, Mildred, English, Folklore
Hayes, James Thomas, Composition & Literature
Hinton, Betty Jean, Speech
Johnson, Robert Eugene, Drama, Dramatic Literature
Lorrah, Jean, Medieval Literature, Linguistics
Mofield, William Ray, Speech, Journalism
Peterson, Clell T, English
Roulston, Charles Robert, English
Slow, John Ralph, English
Swan, Wallace John, English
Tracy, James Albert, Speech
Tucker, Kenneth Paul, English
OWENSBORO
Britton, Joe S, English & Dramatic Literature
Combs, John R, English
Denniston, Elliott Averett, English
Gehres, Mary Ruth, English
Lechner, Joan Marie, O.S.U, English
Whelan, Mary deChantal, Contemporary British & American Literature
RICHMOND
Alexander, Aimee H, English
Benson, Richard Lee, Drama, Speech
Browning, William Gordon, English
Buchanan, Pearl Leigh, English, Speech
Burkhart, Robert Edward, English
Carey, Glenn Owaroff, English
Culross, Jack Lewis, English
Davey, Francis Xavier, English, Comparative Literature
Hart, Dominick Joseph, English Literature
Hill, Ordelle Gerhard, Medieval English
Long, John M, English
Oldham, Janet Bock, English
Rhodes, Byno Ryvers, English Literature
Shearon, Forrest Bedford, British Literature, Humanities
Sporre, Robert A, Drama, Speech
Sutton, George W, English
Thurman, Kelly, English
Witt, Robert Wayne, Seventeenth Century Literature
STANVILLE
Roberts, Leonard Ward, English
WILLIAMSBURG
Fuson, Richard Elwyn, English
WILMORE
Fleser, Arthur F, English
Unthank, Luisa-Theresa Brown, English Literature

LOUISIANA

ALEXANDRIA
Kennedy, Verne Ray, Speech Communication
BATON ROUGE
Bates, Arthenia Jackson, American & English Literature, Composition
Borck, Jim Springer, English Literature
Braden, Waldo Warder, Speech
Bradford, Clinton William, Speech & Drama
Canaday, Nicholas, Jr, English
Crump, Rebecca W, English Literature
Doty, Gresdna Ann, Speech, Theatre
Evans, William W, English, Philology
Fischer, John Irwin, English
Gilbert, Jack G, English Literature
Goldsmith, Adolph Oliver, Journalism
Gudas, Fabian John, English
Hicks, Ronald Graydon, Mass Communications, Sociology
Hopkins, Mary Frances McKoy, Speech
Johnston, Wilma Montgomery, Speech
King, Montgomery Wordsworth, English
Kirby, Thomas (Austin), English
Lane, Pinkie Gordon, English
Lin, San-Su C, English, Education
McCormick, Annette M, English
Madden, Jerry David, English
Merritt, Francine, Speech
Mixon, Harold D, Speech
Moore, Don Dick, English Renaissance Drama

Nardin, James Thompson, American Drama
Olive, William John, English
Pennybacker, John Howard, Speech
Peterson, Owen M, Speech
Plasterer, Nicholas Nyle, Journalism
Price, Frank James, Journalism
Ragsdale, James Donald, Speech
Rowell, Charles Henry, English
Sasek, Lawrence Anton, English
Shaver, Claude L, Linguistics, Theatre
Simpson, Lewis Pearson, American History & Literature
Sklute, Larry Martin, English, Comparative Literature
Stanford, Donald Elwin, English
Van Der Poll, Jan, Theatre, Aesthetics
Watson, Thomas L, English
Wheeler, Otis Bullard, English
Whitfield, George Wiley, Rhetoric, Public Address
Wiksell, Wesley, Speech, Communication
Wildman, John Hazard, English Literature
Young, Henry Archie, Speech, Drama
GRAMBLING
Ennis, Dardanella Virginia, English, Speech
Perkins, Hattie Logan, English, Humanities
Sandle, Floyd Leslie, Speech, Drama
Williams, Allen, Speech, Drama
HAMMOND
Ballard, Lou Ellen, English
Fox, Dorothy Haynie, English, Education
Friman, Anne Elizabeth, English
Landry, Lowell, Modern Literature
McGill, Bruce Davidson, English
Orr, Guss, English
Speck, Paul Surgi, English & American Literature
Wade, Luther Irwin, III, Drama, Speech
LAFAYETTE
Barnes, Rey Leroy, Tele-Communications, Broadcasting
Broussard, Alton E, Journalism
Dichmann, Mary Ethel, English Literature
Fackler, Herbert Vern, Anglo-Irish & Modern Literature
Fields, Albert Whitehead, English
Fulmer, Oliver Bryan, English
Grossman, Rodney C, English
Kern, Ronald Chester, Speech & Drama
Meriwether, Frank T, English, American Literature
Murphy, Roy Dennis, Speech
Nolan, Paul Thomas, English
Poe, Harold Weller, Speech, Theatre
Reamer, Owen Jordan, English
Rickels, Milton Henry, English
Rickels, Patricia Kennedy, English
Webb, Bernice Larson, English
Wilson, James Harrison, Old & Middle English
LAKE CHARLES
Cash, Joe Lynn, English & Comparative Literature
Whittington, Curtis Calvin, Jr, English
MONROE
Adams, Martha Lou Latimer, English
Brian, George C, Speech, Drama
Brown, Eric Donald, English & American Literature
Fuller, Claude C, Speech
McLemore, John Anderson, English, History
Morgan, Frank, Jr, English
Parkerson, James Woodrow, Rhetoric, Public Address
NATCHITOCHES
Adams, Ezra John, Journalism, Modern History
Mosley, Walter Lynd, English Literature
Taylor, Irma Stockwell, Speech
Webber, Everett, English
NEW ORLEANS
Adams, Richard Perrill, English
Antippas, Andy Peter, English
Assad, Thomas Joseph, Literature
Banks, Landrum, English
Barranger, Milly Slater, Drama & Literature
Bergeron, David Moore, English
Bollier, Ernest Phillip, English
Bouise, Oscar Adonis, English
Boyette, Purvis Elton, English
Brady, Donald Vincent, Theatre, Speech
Branam, George Curtis, English
Byrne, Mary Enda Eileen, English
Christian, Mildred Gayler, English Literature
Cohen, Joseph, English
Cohen, Michael Martin, English Language & Literature
Corrington, John William, Modern English, American Literature
Eberle, Gerald Joseph, English
Edmonds, Dale Harlan, II, Twentieth Century British & American English

Finneran, Richard John, English & American Literature
Gaillard, Dawson Forman, English
Gallo, Louis Jacob, English
Gelderman, Carol Wettlaufer, Modern Drama & Literature
Harbert, Earl Norman, English, American Literature
Hendrickson, George Windsor, Drama
Henricksen, Bruce Conley, Renaissance Literature
Herndon, George Collins, English Literature
Hoadley, Frank M, English
Holditch, William Kenneth, American Literature
Husband, John Dillon, English
LaBrant, Lou, English, Language Growth
Mackin, Cooper Richerson, English Literature
McNeely, Samuel Sidney, Jr, English
Magaw, Malcolm, English, American Literature
Morillo, Marvin, English Literature
Mosier, John Friedel, English
Partridge, Edward Bellamy, English
Pizer, Donald, English
Reinecke, George F, English Literature
Reuss, Carol, S.P, Mass Communication, Journalism
Rogge, Edward, Speech
Roppolo, Joseph Patrick, English
Rush, Mary Minniece, English
Schueler, Donald G, English
Shaw, William Harlan, Theatre, Fine Arts
Simmons, Joseph Larry, English
Smith, Donald George, English
Snare, Gerald Howard, English Literature
Staub, August W, Drama, English
Stewart, Maaja Agur, English
Stibbs, John Henry, English Literature
Taplin, Gardner B, English Literature
Taylor, Aline Mackenzie, English Literary History
Torczon, Vernon James, English
Ussery, Huling Eakin, Jr, English, Medieval Studies
Varnado, Alban F, Speech, Drama
Warner, Frank Lawrence, Theatre Arts, Drama
Watson, Cresap Shaw, English
Whitbread, Leslie George, English, Linguistics
Wilson, John Byron, English Language & Literature
PINEVILLE
Amos, George, English
Hall, Ernest Eugene, Speech
RUSTON
Beasley, Mary Fowler, Speech, English Literature
Butler, A.Z, English
Evans, Winnie D, English
Fiehler, Rudolph, English
Fletcher, Mary Frances, English
Francis, Nelle Trew, English
Minchew, Elmer Reid, Speech
Pennington, Paul Jordan, Speech
Smith, Frellsen Fletcher, English
SHREVEPORT
Corey, Orlin Russell, Speech & Drama
Guerin, Wilfred Louis, English Literature
Labor, Earle G, American Literature
Miller, James Hull, Dramatic Art
Morgan, Lee, English
THIBODAUX
Delahaye, Alfred Newton, Journalism, English
Fletcher, Marie, English
Swetman, Glenn Robert, English, Languages

MAINE

ALFRED
Randel, William Peirce, English
BAR HARBOR
Carpenter, William Morton, English & Humanities
BIDDEFORD
Hennedy, Hugh L, English
Horn, Robert Lawrence, English
BRUNSWICK
Bonner, Willard Hallam, English & American Literature
Brown, Herbert Ross, American Literature
Coursen, Herbert R, Jr, English
Greason, Arthur LeRoy, Jr, English
Kaster, Barbara Jeanne, Communication, Film
Lauren, Barbara, English & American Literature
Quinby, George Hunnewell, English
Redwine, James Daniel, Jr, English
CAPE ELIZABETH
Jackson, George Stuyvesant, English & American Literature

DENMARK
Morris, Robert K, Contemporary British & American Literature
EAST VASSALBORO
Sutherland, John Hale, English
ELIOT
Fife, Hilda Mary, English
FARMINGTON
Bricker, Herschel Leonard, Theatre
Flint, Allen Denis, English, American Studies
GORHAM
Carper, Thomas Robson, English & American Literature
Miller, Newton Edd, Jr, Speech, Administration
Reuter, John Edward, English Literature
Rosen, Kenneth Frederic, Modern Literature
LEWISTON
Bamberg, Robert Douglas, English & American Literature
Deiman, Werner John, English & Comparative Literature
Hepburn, James Gordon, English
King, John Norman, English Literature
Nelson, David Arthur, English
Tagliabue, John, English
Turlish, Lewis Afton, American Literature & Studies
MONMOUTH
Peladeau, Marius Beaudoin, American Literature & History
NEW HARBOR
Griggs, Charles Irwin, English

ORONO
Bennett, Jacob, Medieval Literature, Linguistics
Brogunier, Joseph Edward, English & American Literature
Colbath, Arnold, Speech, Theatre
Edwards, Herbert Joseph, American Literature
Gardner, Wofford Gordon, Speech
Hartman, Maryann Doris, Speech
Hatlen, Burton Norval, English
Herbold, Anthony, English, Comparative Literature
Holmes, Edward Morris, American Literature
Hunting, Robert Stilwell, English
Ives, Edward Dawson, Folklore
Lemelin, Robert E, English, American Studies
Manlove, George Kendall, English
Rice, Harriet Epstein, Speech Communication
Scher, Saul N, Broadcasting, Film
Terrell, Carroll Franklin, English, Comparative Literature
Wicks, Ulrich, Comparative Literature
Wilson, John Robert, English & American Literature
ORR'S ISLAND
Hall, Lawrence Sargent, English
OXFORD
Hankins, John Erskine, English Literature
PORTLAND
Baier, Lee Stanley, English
Burke, (Lawrence) Morrill, Jr, American Literature
Hanna, John Greist, English Literature
Slavick, William Henry, English
PRESQUE ISLE
Bowman, George William, English
SOUTH PORTLAND
Jaques, John Frederick, American Literature
SPRINGVALE
Herberger, Charles Frederick, Jr, English
UNITY
Karstetter, Allan Boyd, Speech
WATERVILLE
Archibald, Douglas Nelson, English Literature
Bassett, Charles Walker, English, American Literature
Benbow, R. Mark, English Literature
Brancaccio, Patrick, English, American Studies
Cary, Richard, English
Chapman, Alfred King, English
Comparetti, Alice Pattee, English Literature
Curran, Eileen Mary, English Literature
Kenney, Edwin James, Jr, English
Marriner, Ernest Cummings, English Linguistics
Strider, Robert Edward Lee, II, English
Sweney, John Robert, English & American Literature
YORK
Sarton, May, English

MARYLAND

ANNAPOLIS
Adams, Henry Hitch, English Literature, Naval History
Arnold, James Alden, Literature, Naval History
Bell, Haney H, English
Crane, Charles Lacoste, Jr, English

Gibb, Carson, English
Heflin, Wilson L, English, American Literature
Mason, Robert L, American & Southern Literature
Pitt, Arthur Stuart, English
Smith, Charles William, English & American Literature
Wysong, John N, English
ARNOLD
Hall, Edwin Malburn, World Literature, Naval History
BALTIMORE
Arnquist, James, American History & Literature
Barth, John Simmons, English
Bettridge, William E, English
Butcher, Philip, English
Carey, Ruth Miriam, S.S.N.D, English
Cooper, Philip, Jr, English, Comparative Literature
Costello, Mary Cleophas, R.S.M, Literary Theory
Dowell, George Brendan, Speech & Drama
Eichner, Maura, S.S.N.D, English
Ferguson, Frances Cottrell, English Literature
Fish, Stanley E, Medieval & Renaissance English
Fleishman, Avrom, English
Flower, Annette Chappell, English Literature
Ford, Nick Aaron, English
Ford, Ola M, English
Fritz, Edward McDonel, English, History of Ideas
Geen, Elizabeth, English
Gillespie, C. Richard, Drama
Glick, Robert Alan, English & Comparative Literature
Gnerro, Mark Lawrence, English & Comparative Literature
Hands, Charles Bernard, English
Hatcher, Elizabeth Roberta, Medieval Literature, Folklore
Hawthorne, Lucia Shelia, Speech Communication, Theatre Arts
Hedges, Elaine Ryan, American Literature, Women's Studies
Hedges, William Leonard, American Literature
Holland, Laurence Bedwell, English
Howard, Donald Roy, English
Hughes, Nina Edwards, English, Speech
Irwin, John Thomas, American & English Medieval Literature
Kenner, (William) Hugh, English
Kinter, William L, Medieval Comparative Literature
Korenman, Joan Smolin, American Literature
Lamb, Arthur Clifton, Dramatics
Landon, Philip J, English Literature
Lewis, John Smith, American Literature
Mutch, George Ernest, III, Humanities, English
O'Daniel, Therman Benjamin, American Literature
Paulson, Ronald Howard, English Literature
Peirce, Brooke, English
Peirce, Carol Marshall, English
Shedd, Robert Gordon, English
Sheffey, Ruthe Garnetta, English
Shugg, Wallace, English
Siger, Leonard P, English
Small, Samuel Asa, English
Smith, Robert Alston, English
Stein, Arnold, English Literature
Tarcay, Eileen Schultz, English, American Studies
Thearle, Beatrice June, English Literature
Trueschler, Josephine, English & American Literature, Great Books
BETHESDA
Gunberg, Edwin W, English, Classical Studies
Neill, (James) Kerby, English Literature
BROOKLANDVILLE
Mueller, William Randolph, English, Theology
CHESTERTOWN
Tatum, Nancy R, English Literature & History
CHEVY CHASE
Greaney, Katherine B, English
Kuiper, John B, Speech, Mass Media
McManaway, James Gilmer, Shakespeare
COLLEGE PARK
Barry, Jackson Granville, English
Beauchamp, Virginia Walcott, English, Literature, Women's Studies
Birdsall, Esther Katherine, Literature
Bode, Carl, American Literature & Culture
Brown, Samuel Ernest, English
Bryer, Jackson Robert, English
Cate, George Allan, English Literature
Coleman, Leon Duncan, English, Afro-American Studies
Coogan, Robert M, English
Cooper, Sherod Monroe, Jr, English

Cothran, Kay Lorraine, Folklore & Sociolinguistics
Croft, Blanton, Speech, Drama
Dunn, N.E, English
Ehrensberger, Ray, Speech
Freedman, Morris, English & Comparative Literature
Gallick, Susan Lydia, Medieval Literature
Gravely, William Henry, Jr, English
Herman, Harold J, Middle English Literature & Language
Hiebert, Ray Eldon, Communications
Holton, William Milne, Modern & American Literature
Hovey, Richard Bennett, English
Hoyt, Richard Duane, Journalism, American Studies
Isaacs, Neil D, English Literature
Jamieson, Kathleen Mary, Speech
Jellema, Roderick Hartigh, English
Kenny, Shirley Strum, English
Kinnaird, John William, English
Lawson, Lewis Allen, English
Lutwack, Leonard, English
Meersman, Roger L, Drama, Speech
Mish, Charles Carroll, English Literature
Moore, Robert Henry, American Literature & History
Murphy, Charles Driscoll, English Literature
Myers, Robert Manson, English Literature
O'Leary, Ronald Thomas, Drama & Speech
Panichas, George Andrew, English Literature
Peterson, William Samuel, English
Pugliese, Rudolph E, Dramatic Arts
Russell, John D, English, Literatures
Rutherford, Charles Shepard, Medieval Literature
Schoeck, Richard J, English
Shoenberg, Robert Edward, English
Smith, Gayle S, English
Swigger, Ronald T, Comparative Literature
Whittemore, (Edward) Reed, English
Wolvin, Andrew Davis, Speech Communication
Woolf, Leonard, English
Zeeveld, William Gordon, English Literature & History
DAVIDSONVILLE
Vitzthum, Richard C, English
EMMITSBURG
Dillon, John Joseph, Jr, English
Good, Stephen Hanscom, English & American Literature
Kaliss, Bernard Stanley, English
Wasilifsky, Adolph M, English
FREDERICK
Briney, Martha M, English Literature
Cornwell, Ethel Frazier, English
Tremaine, Hadley Phillip, English
FROSTBURG
Fleischauer, Warren L, English
Press, David Robert, Speech, Drama
Smith, Don Noel, English
Vrieze, Jack W, Theatre, Speech
GREENBELT
Nutku, Emily Bohnett, English Language & Literature
HANCOCK
Jerome, Judson, English
HOLLYWOOD
Hoagland, Barbara M, English
HYATTSVILLE
Giovannini, Giovanni, English Literature
Hamelin, Marie, R.J.M, Medieval Devotional Prose
Lounsbury, Myron O, American Studies
Rodgers, Mary Columbro, English, Education
LANHAM
Elam, Julia Corene, English, American Literature
NEW WINDSOR
Phillips, Raymond Clarence, Jr, American Literature, American Studies
PRINCESS ANNE
Roache, Joel Hayden, III, English
ROCKVILLE
Lavin, Henry St. C, S.J, English Literature
ST. MICHAELS
Sixbey, George Lawton, English
SALISBURY
Nichols, Duane Cress, English
Vogelback, Arthur Lawrence, English
SILVER SPRING
Manning, Charles, English
SMITHSBURG
Winfrey, David Outcalt, English, Religion
TAKOMA PARK
Mauldin, Lloyd Wesley, English, Education
TIMONIUM
Cooley, Franklin Delany, English
TOWSON
Deford, Sara W, English
Robinson, Marion Parsons, Speech

Stone, Marlene Carole, Speech, Mass Communications
UPPER MARLBORO
Van Egmond, Peter, American Literature
UPPERCO
Marshall, Thomas Frederic, English
WESTMINSTER
Makosky, John Donald, English
Richwine, Keith Norton, English
Stevens, Harold Ray, English
Wenner, Evelyn Wingate, English

MASSACHUSETTS

AMHERST
Abramson, Doris E, Theatre
Aczel, Tamas, Creative Writing, History of Ideas
Aho, Gary L, English
Allen, Jeremiah M, Jr, English
Alspach, Russell King, Irish Literature
Ashton, Thomas L, English & American Literature
Barnard, Ellsworth, English
Barron, Leon Oser, English Literature
Bell, Bernard William, American & Afro-American Literature
Berlin, Normand, English
Berlind, Bruce, English
Bevilacqua, Vincent Michael, Speech
Brogan, Howard Oakley, English Literature
Brown, Kenneth Lee, Speech, Drama
Cameron, John, English
Campbell, Marie Alice, Folklore, English Literature
Canfield, Fayette Curtis, Drama
Carey, George Gibson, Folklore, English
Chametzky, Jules, English
Cheney, Donald Shepley, Jr, English
Chickering, Howell D, Jr, Medieval & Modern Literature
Clark, David Ridgley, English
Clayton, John J, Modern Literature, Humanities
Cody, Richard John, English
Collins, Dan Stead, English
Copeland, Thomas Wellsted, English Literature
Craig, George Armour, English Literature
Creed, Robert Payson, English
DeMott, Benjamin (Haile), English
Diamond, Arlyn, Medieval Literature
Donohue, Joseph Walter, Jr, English
Edwards, Lee R, English Literature
Emerson, Everett Harvey, English
Fetler, Andrew, English
Frank, Joseph, English
Freeman, Donald Cary, English, Linguistics
French, Roberts Walker, English
Gallo, Ernest A, English
Gibson, Walker, English
Golden, Morris, English
Gozzi, Raymond Dante, American Literature
Guttmann, Allen, English, American Civilization
Harrington, John Frederick, Jr, Film, English Literature
Haven, Richard, English Literature
Heath, William Webster, English
Helming, Vernon Parker, English
Hicks, John (Harland), English
Hofer, Ernest Harrison, English
Junkins, Donald A, American Literature, Creative Writing
Kaplan, Sidney, American Studies
Keefe, Robert, English
Kinney, Arthur Frederick, Jr, English Language & Literature
Koehler, G. Stanley, English
Langland, Joseph Thomas, English
Lowance, Mason Ira, Jr, American Literature & Studies
Lyon, Richard Colton, English, American Studies
McCarthy, Harold T, English
McGoun, Ralph Cleland, Dramatic Arts
Mariani, Paul Louis, Modern Poetry & Poetics
Marx, Leo, American Studies
Matlack, James Hendrickson, English American Studies
Matlon, Ronald John, Rhetoric, Public Address
Mitchell, John H, English
Noland, Richard Wells, English
O'Donnell, William Gregory, English & American Literature
Page, Alex, English
Plumstead, Arthur William, English & American Literature
Politella, Dario, English, Journalistic Studies
Porter, David Thomas, English & American Literature
Raymond, Meredith Bragg, English Literature

Reid, Ronald Forrest, Speech
Rudin, Seymour, English
Saagpakk, Paul Friidrih, English Philology, Contemporary British Literature
Savereid, Severt J, Rhetoric, Public Address
Schroeder, Henry Alfred, Jr, English, Comparative Literature
Shadoian, Jack, English & American Literature
Shelby, Maurice Earl, Speech
Sillars, Malcolm O, Speech
Sitter, John Edward, English
Sofield, David Robinson, English Literature
Spivack, Bernard, English
Spivack, Charlotte Kesler, English
Stewart, Gary L, Speech, Drama
Swaim, Kathleen Mackenzie, English
Townsend, Robert Campbell, English Literature
Tucker, Robert Garland, English
Turner, Frederick William III, English
Ulin, Richard O, English, Education
Varley, Henry Leland, English & American Literature
Volbach, Walther Richard, Drama
Wallace, Karl Richards, Rhetoric
Weston, John C, English Literature
Wolff, Cynthia Griffin, European & American Literature
ANDOVER
Zucker, Jack, English
ATTLEBORO
Gray, Ernest Weston, English
AUBURNDALE
Whitehead, Joan Grenthot, English Literature
BELMONT
Brace, Gerald Warner, English Literature
BOSTON
Allen, Samuel Washington, Literature
Alssid, Michael William, English Literature
Amato, Philip P, Education, Speech
Baird, Julian Thompson, Jr, English Literature
Beal, Richard S, English
Berman, Morton, English
Black, Sidney J, English Literature, Humanities
Blackman, Eugene J, Theatre Arts, English
Blair, Joel M, Jr, English
Blanch, Robert James, English
Bleeth, Kenneth Alan, Medieval Literature
Blessington, Francis Charles, English Literature, Classics
Broderick, James H, English Literature
Burton, Dolores Marie, English, Linguistics
Casey, Mary Elizabeth, English
Clark, Edward, English
Connors, Thomas Edward, English
Crosby, Harry Herbert, American Literature, Rhetoric
Cullen, Maurice Raymond, Jr, Journalism, Mass Communications
Curran, Mary Doyle, English
Dalgarno, Emily K, English, American Literature
Devine, Thomas G, English, Education
Doner, Dean Benton, English
Estey, George Fisher, English
Evans, Robert Rees, History of Ideas
Ferguson, Mary Anne Heyward, Old English
Ferrier, Stephen Wilfred, Literary Theory, Psychometrics
Fisher, James A, English Literature
Fitzgerald, Gerald Pierce, English & Comparative Literature
Foley, Joseph Jeremiah, English
Foy, Robert John, English
Freedman, Richard, Literature of Eighteenth & Nineteenth Centuries
Freeman, Arthur, English
Gill, Barbara, S.N.D, English & American Literature
Gilman, Albert, English, Drama
Gittleman, Edwin, American Literature
Green, Eugene, English Linguistics
Holmes, Doris, English
Holmes, William James, Jr, English
Howe, Ann R, English
Jurich, Joseph, English
Kaplan, Mort S, Drama
Katz, Seymour, English & American Studies
Kenney, William, English
Klein, Maxine Mae, Theatre
Knight, Charles Anthony, English
Kornfeld, Milton Herbert, American Literature
Langer, Lawrence L, Literature
Lanich, Lloyd J, Jr, Theatre Arts
Leisher, John F, English
Levine, Robert, English
L'Homme, Charles Edmund, English & Comparative Literature
Lindgren, Charlotte Holt, English

Littlefield, Walter A, Communications, Theatre
McKay, Ruth Capers, English Literature
Mansfield, Margaret A, Medieval Literature
Marks, Emerson Robert, English
Marvin, John R, Modern Literature
Mitchell, June Hamblin, Speech, Drama
Moyes, Norman B, Journalism
Mull, Dorothy Sipe, English Literature & Language
Nagel, James Edward, English & American Literature
Nelson, Duncan Morse, English
Nelson, Jane Armstrong, English & American Literature
Nitchie, George Wilson, English Literature
Norvish, Franklin, English Literature
Olmsted, Audrey Perryman, Public Address, Theatre History
Patterson, Frank Harmon, English
Perry, David Scott, English
Perry, John Douglas, Jr, American Literature
Perry, William, English
Petronella, Vincent F, English
Pettit, Norman, English, History
Read, Bill, English Literature
Riggs, William George, English Literature
Risse, Robert Gregory, English
Rosenthal, Sidney, English, Literature
Ryan, Alvan Sherman, English
Sears, John Franklin, English, American Civilization
Sharp, William Leslie, Drama, English
Simmons, James C, English Literature
Smith, Harris Gordon, Journalism
Starbuck, George Edwin, Poetry, English
Steele, Robert Scott, Cinema, Communication
Sterne, Richard Clark, English, American Studies
Stevenson, William Handforth, English
Stewart, Garrett Fitzgerald, English Literature
Stock, Irvin, English
Sussman, Herbert L, English
Sypher, Wylie, English Literature
Szittya, Penn Rodion, English Language & Literature, Medieval Studies
Vance, William Lynn, English
Vendler, Helen Hennessy, English
Vogel, Stanley Morton, American Literature
Watts, John Ransford, Theatre Arts
Weitzman, Arthur Joshua, English
Wermuth, Paul Charles, English
Wilkins, Frederick Charles, English
Willey, Frederick W, Jr, English
Winslow, Donald James, English
Yeazell, Ruth Bernard, English & American Literature
Zorn, John William, Speech
BRIDGEWATER
Anderson, Wallace Ludwig, English
DeRocco, Joseph, English
Warye, Richard Jonathan, Speech, Drama
Yokelson, Joseph Bernard, English
BROOKLINE
Baram, Robert, Journalism
Bluestone, George, American Literature, Film Aesthetics
Stone, Albert, Jr, English
Wager, Willis Joseph, English Literature, Music
CAMBRIDGE
Aaron, Daniel, American Studies
Alfred, William, English
Baker, Herschel, English Literature
Bate, Walter Jackson, English
Benson, Larry Dean, English
Berthoff, Warner Bement, English
Bloomfield, Morton Wilfred, English, History of Ideas
Brower, Reuben Arthur, English, Classics
Buckley, Jerome Hamilton, English Literature
Bullitt, John Marshall, English
Bush, Douglas, English Literature
Chapman, Robert Harris, Drama
Evans, Gwynne Blakemore, English
Fitzgerald, Robert Stuart, English
Garelick, Judith Spritzer, American & English Literature
Goldwyn, Merrill Harvey, English
Goodheart, Eugene, English, Comparative Literature
Heimert, Alan, American Civilization
Jones, Howard Mumford, English
Kaiser, Walter Jacob, English & Comparative Literature
Kampf, Louis, Comparative Literature, History
Kaplan, Justin, American Literature
Kiely, Robert J, English
La Driere, James Craig, Comparative Literature
Lamson, Roy, English
Levin, Harry, English, Comparative Literature
MacCaffrey, Isabel Gamble, English Literature

Merritt, Travis Rhodes, Literature
Morrison, Theodore, English
Nager, Rae Ann, English, Comparative Literature
Perkins, David Dodd, English Literature
Porte, Joel Miles, English & American Literature
Rathbone, Robert Reynolds, English, Technical Writing
Salamon, Linda Bradley, English Literature, Renaissance Intellectual History
Smith, Paul, English
Whiting, Bartlett Jere, English
CHARLEMONT
Calver, Edward Thomas, English
CHESTERFIELD
Temple, Ruth Zabriskie, Comparative Literature
Wright, Warren Earl, Speech, Political Science
CHESTNUT HILL
Appleyard, Joseph A, S.J, English
Casper, Leonard Ralph, American Literature, Asian Studies
Duhamel, Pierre Albert, English Literature
Ferry, Anne D, English
Hirsh, Edward L, English Literature
Hughes, Richard Edward, English
Longo, Joseph Anthony, English
Loofbourow, John W, English
McCarthy, John F, English
McCue, Daniel Lawrence, Jr, English, Comparative Literature
McDermott, Francis Joseph, English
MacGillivray, Arthur A, S.J, English
Randall, John Herman, III, English & American Literature
Regan, Charles Lionel, English
Siggins, Clara M, English
Sweeney, Francis, S.J, English
Tate, Cecil Foster, English & American Literature
Taylor, Edmund Dennis, English
CONWAY
McKeon, Newton Felch, English Literature
DENNISPORT
Noxon, Gerald Forbes, Film & Dramatic Writing
DUXBURY
Brinnin, John Malcolm, English
FAIRHAVEN
Dias, Earl Joseph, English, Drama
FITCHBURG
Berryman, Eric J, English Literature
Grabar, Terry Harris, English
Shepherd, Louis P, English
Siegel, Michael Alan, Speech Communication, Mass Communication
FRAMINGHAM
Allison, Luther William, English Literature & Education
Dodge, Evelyn C, English
Harter, Betsy Weller, English
Salenius, Elmer William, English
GREAT BARRINGTON
Whitlock, Baird Woodruff, English Literature
HADLEY
Brock, Marianne, English Literature
Mayer, Milton (Sanford), English
HARVARD
Finkelpearl, Philip J, English
Jones, E. Winston, Speech
HINGHAM
Brewer, Wilmon, Comparative Literature
HOUGHTON
Love, George John, English Language & Literature
JAMAICA PLAINS
Oliver, Leslie M, English Literature
LEXINGTON
McAleer, John Joseph, English
Mahoney, John L, English
Squire, James R, English, Education
LINCOLN
Marshall, Roderick, English & Comparative Literature
Wiley, Margaret Lenore, English
LONGMEADOW
Goldstein, Wallace L, English, Speech
LOWELL
Kramer, Mary Duhamel, English Literature
Miller, Virginia Rogers, Speech
Moore, Howard Kimball, English & American Literature
Riley, John James, English & American Literature
Wiehe, Roger Edwin, English Language & Literature
MARION
Ingraham, Vernon Leland, English
Reis, Richard H, English
MARSTONS MILLS
Hill, Rowland Merlin, English

MEDFORD
  Balch, Marston (Stevens), Dramatics, Biography
  Barnet, Sylvan, English
  Burnim, Kalman A, Drama & Theater, English
  Cavitch, David, English & American Literature
  Collins, Sherwood Clark, Drama
  Fixler, Michael, English Literature
  Flint, Paul Harry, English
  Kehoe, Constance DeMuzio, English
  McCabe, Bernard, English
  Perry, John Oliver, English
  Ritchie, Harry M, Dramatic Art
  Stange, George Robert, English Literature
MELROSE
  Crannell, Kenneth C, Oral Interpretation
MILTON
  Morse, Samuel French, English
NANTUCKET
  Claiborne, Jay Wood, Victorian Studies
NATICK
  Campbell, Charles Alexander, English
NEEDHAM
  Bosworth, Raymond Francis, English
  Travers, Linus, English Literature
NEWTON
  Dyroff, Jan Michael, Renaissance Studies, Creative Writing
  Gullette, David G, English
  Maguire, Catherine Elizabeth, English
  White, Elizabeth S, R.S.C.J, English
NEWTON HIGHLANDS
  Walen, Harry Leonard, English
NEWTONVILLE
  Rose, Ruth Ormsby, English
NORTH ADAMS
  Washburn, Donald Edward, Speech, English
NORTH ANDOVER
  Douglass, Kathryn Floyd, English
  Ground, Yvonne, English
  Murphy, John Joseph, English, Foreign Literature
NORTH DARTMOUTH
  Cass, Walter J, English, Education
  Macedo, Celestino D, English
  Marlow, James Elliott, English Literature
  Sandstrom, Yvonne Luttropp, English & Scandinavian Literature
  White, Charles William, III, American Literature
NORTH EASTON
  Huelsbeck, Charles J, English Literature
NORTH EGREMONT
  Le Comte, Edward Semple, English Literature
NORTHAMPTON
  Adams, Maurianne Schifreen, English Literature
  Bagg, Robert Ely, English
  Banerjee, (Ron) Dibyendu Kumar, English & Comparative Literature
  Berkman, Leonard, Theatre, Speech
  Chinoy, Helen Krich, English, Theatre
  Connelly, Kenneth Amor, Jr, English
  Dunn, Esther Cloudman, English
  Ellis, Frank Hale, English
  Flower, Dean Scott, English
  Harward, Vernon Judson, Jr, English
  Jaffe, Nora Crow, Eighteenth Century English Literature
  Lincoln, Eleanor Terry, English Literature
  Murphy, Francis, English & American Literature
  Paroissien, David Harry, Victorian Literature
  Petersson, Robert Torsten, English
  Pickrel, Paul, English
  Randall, Helen Whitcomb, English Literature
  Skarda, Patricia Lyn, 19th Century British Literature
  Skulsky, Harold Lawrence, English
  Van Voris, William H, English
  Von Klemperer, Elizabeth Gallaher, English
NORTON
  Aughtry, Charles Edward, English & American Melrose
  Briggs, Edwin Stuart, English
  Burton, Katherine, English Literature
  Coale, Samuel Chase, English, American Civilization
  Dahl, Curtis, English Literature
  Pearce, Richard A, American Literature
  Shirley, Frances Ann, English
PAXTON
  Chauvin, Clarice B, S.S.A, English
QUINCY
  Dygoski, Louise A, Speech
  Young, Donald Leroy, English
REHOBOTH
  Kirk, Elizabeth Doan, Middle English Literature
SALEM
  Antonakes, Michael, English
  Coon, Arthur Munson, English
  Devine, Mary Elizabeth, English Literature

Flibbert, Joseph Thomas, American Literature
  LaHood, Marvin John, English
  Mahaney, William Earle, English
  Zollo, Richard Paul, English, Education
SANDWICH
  Hutcheson, Harold Randolph, English Literature
SHERBORN
  Pitts, Willis Norman, Jr, Speech, History
SOMERVILLE
  Schreiber, Ronald P, Visionary Literature, Poetry
SOUTH HADLEY
  Bottkol, Joseph McGrath James, English Literature
  Collette, Carolyn Penney, Medieval English Literature
  Doyle, Anne Therese, English
  Ellis, James Delmont, English, Drama
  Farnham, Anthony Edward, English, Philology
  Green, Elizabeth Alden, Journalism, Contemporary Literature
  Horner, Joyce Mary, English
  Johnson, Richard August, English, American Studies
  Kaufman, Marjorie Ruth, English
  Olmsted, Charles H, English
  Potter, Adaline Pates, English
  Reid, Benjamin Lawrence, English
  Rountree, Mary Martin, English
  Saintonge, Constance, English
  Seelig, Sharon Cadman, English Literature
  Sudrann, Jean, English
  Viereck, Peter, Poetry, History
  Youngblood, Sarah Helen, English
SOUTH HINGHAM
  Kiely, James Joseph, English Language & Literature
SOUTH LANCASTER
  Kilgore, Rochelle Philmon, English
  Sauls, Richard Lynn, English & American Literature
  Stafford, Ottilie Frank, English Literature
SPRINGFIELD
  Birnbaum, Milton, English
  Child, Ruth Carpenter, English
  Hirsch, Lester Martin, American Literature
  Holt, Lee Elbert, English
  Resnick, Robert B, English Literature & Criticism
  Sims, Edward James, English
  Williams, Melvin Gilbert, English
SUNDERLAND
  Lenson, David Rollar, Comparative Literature
WALTHAM
  Cunningham, James Vincent, Renaissance Literature
  Deane, Paul C, American Studies
  Engelberg, Edward, Comparative Literature & English
  Grossman, Allen R, English
  Halpern, Martin, English, Drama
  Harris, Victor, English Literature
  Hindus, Milton, English
  Klein, Karen Wilk, Medieval Comparative Literature, English
  Lelchuk, Alan, Literature
  Matthews, John Floyd, Drama
  Onorato, Richard James, English & American Literature
  Preyer, Robert Otto, English
  Smith, John Hazel, English
  Sprich, Charles Robert, English Literature
  Swiggart, Peter, American Literature
  Vivian, Charles Horton, English Literature
  Ward, Aileen, English
WATERTOWN
  Bender, Coleman C, Speech, Education
WELLESLEY
  Balderston, Katharine Canby, English Literature
  Corsa, Helen Storm, English
  Ferry, David Russell, English Literature
  Garis, Robert, English
  Houghton, Walter Edwards, English Literature
  Layman, Beverly Joseph, English
  Lever, Katherine, English & Greek Literature
  Michael, Mary Ruth, English
  Pinsky, Robert, English & American Literature
  Post, Winifred L, English
  Spacks, Patricia Meyer, English Literature
  Stanton-Michaels, Elizabeth, English
WEST BARNSTABLE
  Heines, Donald Scott, English
WEST NEWTON
  Gurney, Albert Ramsdell, Jr, English Literature, Drama
  Wagenknecht, Edward, English & American Literature
WEST YARMOUTH
  Marnell, William H, English

WESTFIELD
  Delson, Abe, English & American Literature
  Powers, Edward Carroll, English, Theatre History
WESTON
  Bryan, Mary C, English Literature
  Covo, Jacqueline, English
  Higgins, Theresa, S.S.J, English
  Sexton, Anne, Poetry
WHITMAN
  Millett, Fred Benjamin, English Literature
WILLIAMSTOWN
  Allen, Robert Joseph, English Literature
  Barrada, Mohamed Amr, English, Linguistics
  Bell, Robert Huntley, English & American Literature
  Berek, Peter, English
  Bundtzen, Lynda Kathryn, English Literature
  Carr, Arthur Japheth, English
  Gifford, Don Creighton, English
  Graver, Lawrence, English Literature
  Hendrix, Richard George, English Literature, History
  Hunt, James Clay, English Literature
  Mansfield, Luther Stearns, American Literature
  Neel, Helen McDonnell, Composition, Literature
  Stocking, Fred Holly, English
  von Szeliski, John Jerome, Drama
WINCHESTER
  Arnott, Peter D, Foreign Languages, Dramatic Arts
WOLLASTON
  Cameron, Ruth Allen, English Language & Literature
  Dirks, Marvin J, Speech, Homiletics, Religion
  Munro, Bertha, English
WORCESTER
  Anderson, Karl Oscar Emanuel, English & American Literature
  Beard, James Franklin, English & American Literature
  Blinderman, Charles S, English
  Callahan, Edward F, English
  Carter, William Hoyt, Jr, English
  Di Pasquale, Pasquale, Jr, English
  Dorenkamp, John Henry Jr, English
  Farragher, Bernard Patrick, English
  Haweeli, Edward M, English
  Ilko, Donald Wilson, Theatre
  Kennedy, Arthur Afton, Jr, English
  Letendre, Donald Henry, English
  McCarthy, B. Eugene, English
  McGonigle, Paul F, English
  Packard, Theodore Hiram, English, Drama
  Reilly, John Edward, English & American Literature
  Rosenwald, John, English & American Literature
  Saunders, Carleton Earl, Speech, Literature
  Schroeder, Neil Rolf, History of the Theatre
  Sultan, Stanley, English
  Teichgraeber, Stephen E, English
  True, Michael D, English & American Literature
  Wall, Carolyn J, English
  Wilson, John H, English

MICHIGAN

ADRIAN
  Brown, Anne Marie, O.P, English
  Hoffman, Arnold R, American Literature
  Scully, Daniel William, Speech
  Simpson, Harold Burton, English
ALBION
  Bennett, Stephanie Mitchell, American Studies
  Cook, James Wyatt, English
  Crupi, Charles William, English
  Fennimore, Keith John, English
  Gildart, Robert Harr, English & Journalism
  Hart, John Edward, English
  Hosmer, Elizabeth Ruth, English
  Irwin, Joseph James, English Literature
  Loukides, Paul, American Literature, Film
  Miller, Eugene Ernest, English
  Zink, Joseph Paul, III, Medieval Studies, Instructional Technology
ALLENDALE
  Durocher, Aurele A, American Studies
  Kennedy, Dennis Edward, English Literature, Theatre
  Rus, Louis C, English Language
ALMA
  Cornelius, Samuel Robert, English
  Pattison, Eugene Hamilton, English, Religion
  Smith, Robert Wayne, Speech
  Wegner, Robert E, English, Creative Writing
ANN ARBOR
  Aldridge, John Watson, English
  Allison, Alexander W, English Literature
  Arthos, John, English Philology

Bader, Arno L, English
Bailey, Richard Weld, English
Baird, Claribel, Speech, Theatre
Baker, Sheridan (Warner, Jr), English Literature
Barrows, Herbert C, English
Bauland, Peter Max, English, Drama
Bender, Jack E, Drama
Billings, Alan Gailey, Theatre History & Design
Bishop, Robert Lee, Mass Communications
Blotner, Joseph Leo, English
Bonham, Hilda, I.H.M, English
Bornstein, George Jay, English & American Literature
Boros, Donald Michael, Theatre
Boys, Richard Charles, English
Britton, Webster Earl, English Literature
Carruth, Hayden Kenna, Sr, Speech
Chapin, Chester Fisher, English
Clark, Walter Houston, Jr, English, Philosophy of Education
Clarke, Peter, Communication Research, Journalism
Colburn, C. William, Speech
Coles, William Allan, English
Corrigan, Robert Willoughby, Drama
Creeth, Edmund Homer, English
Daugherty, Wilson, English, Comparative Literature
Davis, Joe Lee, English & American Literature
Dunning, Arthur Stephen, Jr, English
Eby, Cecil DeGrotte, American Literature
Edwards, Thomas C, English Literature
Elkins, Aubrey Christian, Jr, English
English, Hubert Morton, Jr, English Language & Literature
Fader, Daniel Nelson, English
Felheim, Marvin, English
Finney, Gretchen Ludke, English, Music
Franklin, Benjamin, V, American Literature
Fraser, Russell Alfred, English
Fulton, Albert Rondthaler, English
Garbaty, Thomas Jay, English
Gindin, James J, English Literature
Goldstein, Laurence Alan, Romanticism
Greenhut, Morris, English Literature
Halstead, William Perdue, Speech
Hatcher, Harlan Henthorne, Literature
Haugh, Robert Fulton, English
Hildebrandt, Herbert William, Speech, Comparative Literature
Hornback, Bert Gerald, English
Howes, Alan Barber, English
Huntley, Frank Livingstone, English, Literature
Ingram, William H, Renaissance Literature & Society
Jensen, Ejner Jacob, English
Khanna, Satendra, Seventeenth Century & Modern Indian Literature
Knott, John Ray, Jr, English
Konigsberg, Ira, English
Kuhn, Sherman McAllister, English
Lenaghan, Robert Thomas, English Literature
McDougal, Stuart Yeatman, English & Comparative Literature
McEwen, George Middleton, English
Marckwardt, Albert Henry, English Language
Martin, Howard Hastings, Speech
Mathes, John C, Comparative Literature
Meyer, Richard DeWitt, Drama, Theatre
Nelson, Norman Edward, English & Comparative Literature
Ogden, Henry Vining Seton, English
Ogden, Margaret Sinclair, English, Philology
Perkins, George B, Jr, American Literature
Powers, Lyall Harris, English
Rabkin, Eric S, English & American Literature
Raeburn, John Hay, American Literature & Studies
Reaske, Christopher Russell, English
Rice, Warner Grenelle, English Literature
Robertson, James Holman, English
Robinson, Jay Luke, English
Ross, Richard John, English Literature
Sands, Donald B, English
Sawyer, Thomas Mitchell, English, Speech
Schulze, Earl John, English, Romantics
Sharf, Donald J, Speech
Squires, Radcliffe, English
Stanton, Stephen Sadler, English
Stasheff, Edward, Speech
Steinhoff, William Richard, English
Stevenson, Dwight Ward, American Literature, Rhetoric
Styan, John Louis, English, Drama
Super, Robert Henry, English Literature
Thackrey, Donald Eugene, English Literature, Research Administration
Walcott, Fred George, English
Willis, Edgar Ernest, Broadcasting, Speech Communication

Yablonky, Ben, Journalism, Mass Communications
Young, Richard E, English Literature, Rhetoric
BERRIEN SPRINGS
Fattic, Grosvenor Russell, Medieval English Literature, Drama
Gibbs, Paul Thomas, English
Giddings, G. Elaine, Speech, Linguistics
Ogden, Merlene, American Literature
Penner, Jonathan G, Speech
Rochat, Joyce Hamilton, American Literature, Creative Writing
Stone, Edith O, English, Linguistics
Taylor, Harry Werbayne, English
Waller, John Oscar, English
BIG RAPIDS
Bond, Charles Alvin, English, Journalism
Carson, Herbert Lee, Drama
Hart, Andrew W, English, Chemistry
Kakonis, Thomas E, English
Milton, Dorothy, English
Sampson, William Robert, Speech Communication
BIRMINGHAM
Kell, Katharine Tolle, Modern American Literature, Folklore
DEARBORN
Arden, Eugene, English
Berkove, Lawrence Ivan, English Literature
Higgs, Elton Dale, English
Limbacher, James L, Drama, Film
Pebworth, Ted-Larry, English
Summers, Claude Joseph, English Literature
Sundstrom, Aileen L, Speech, English
Wheeler, Robert Walter, English, Education
DETROIT
Bahn, Eugene, Speech
Bassett, John Earl, American Literature
Bohman, George Vroom, Speech
Butler, Mary Marguerite, R.S.M, Speech, Drama
Cable, Chester Hubbard, English
Calarco, N. Joseph, Drama
Callow, James T, English
Fenner, Arthur Francis, Jr, English
Field, Bradford S, Jr, English
Fitzgibbons, Eleanor, I.H.M, English
Gay, Alva Angell, English
Gefvert, Constance Joanna, Colonial American Literature, American Sociolinguistics
Golden, Samuel Adler, English
Golemba, Henry Lawrence, Nineteenth Century American Literature
Goodman, Kenneth, Elementary English Education, Applied Linguistics
Gross, Seymour Lee, English
Hafner, Yates, English Literature
Hanawalt, Leslie Lyle, English
Hernlund, Patricia, English
Herreshoff, David, English
Hughes, Daniel John, English
Kearns, Robert John, S.J, English Literature
King, Terrance Joseph, American Literature
Kowalczyk, Richard L, English
Leone, Leonard, Speech, Drama
Leopold, Sara Ellen, English Literature
Levine, Bernard, English Literature
Loss, Archie Krug, Modern Literature, Art History
McCormick, James Patton, English Literature
MacDonald, Donald, English
McDonald, James L, English
McGlone, Edward Leon, Speech Communication
Marotti, Arthur Francis, English
Measell, James Scott, Speech, Philosophy
Montague, Gene Bryan, Literature
Nash, Ralph (Lee), English
Peckham, Robert Wilson, English
Porter, Thomas Emmet, S.J, English
Prescott, Joseph, English Language & Literature
Putzel, Rosamond, English
Raspa, Richard, Renaissance Literature
Reed, John Robert, English
Reilly, Robert James, English
Rule, Philip Charles, S.J, Nineteenth Century British Literature
Rumble, Thomas Clark, Medieval Literature
Schueller, Herbert Matthew, English
Schwarz, Alfred, English
Sharples, Edward, Jr, English
Shtogren, John Alexander, Jr, Modern Literature, Educational Technology
Smallenburg, Harry Russell, English Literature
Smitherman, Geneva, English Linguistics, Afro-American Language & Literature
Strozier, Robert Manning, II, Renaissance Literature
Tintera, James, Speech, Mass Communications
Traci, Philip J, Shakespeare, English Renaissance Drama
Wagner, Vern, English, American Literature
Wallace, Alva Dayle, English Literature

Warfield, Jack W, Mass Communications
Werry, Richard, Creative Writing
Williamson, Marilyn Lammert, English
Yu, Beongcheon, Literature

EAST LANSING
Anderson, David Daniel, American & South Asian Literature
Anderson, Howard Peter, English
Babb, Lawrence, English Literature
Babcock, Clarence Merton, American Thought
Baird, Reed M, English
Baskett, Sam S, American Literature
Benvenuto, Richard Ercole, English
Bergman, Herbert, English
Burhans, Clinton Searles, Jr, English
Carlisle, Ervin Frederick, English
Chamberlain, William Frederick, American Literature
Chapin, Richard Earl, Communications, Library Science
Cianciolo, Patricia Jean, English, Literature
Coelho, Richard Joseph, Speech, Communications
Crane, Maurice Aaron, English
Dietrich, John E, Speech & Drama
Drake, Albert Dee, Contemporary American Literature, Creative Writing
Engel, Bernard F, English, American Literature
Erickson, Mildred Brinkmeier, Literature, Higher Education
Ferres, John Howard, American & British Commonwealth Literature
Fox, Hugh Bernard, Jr, American Literature
Gardner, Mary A, Journalism, Political Science
Geist, Robert John, English, Linguistics
Gianakos, Perry Edgar, American Civilization
Gochberg, Donald S, English, Humanities
Greenberg, Herbert, English
Gross, Barry Edward, American Literature, Drama
Heist, William Watts, English
Hickok, Benjamin Blakely, Communication, American Literature
Hollingsworth, Alan M, English
Hoppe, Harry Reno, English
Huddleston, Eugene L, English
Hudson, Robert Vernon, History of Mass Communication
Hungiville, Maurice Neill, English & American Literature
Hunter, Armand Lee, Speech
Johnson, Lee Ann, American Literature
Jorgensen, Eling Sejr, Education, Instructional Media
Kennedy, Theodore R, Rhetoric
Landmark, Nora, English
Landrum, Larry N, English, Popular Culture
Lawrence, Elwood P, English & American Literature
McGuire, Philip Carroll, English
Mead, Carl David, English Literature
Meiners, Roger K, English
Meyers, Walter Cameron, Journalism
Mishra, Vishwa Mohan, Communication, Mass Communication
Myers, Joseph Wilson, English, American Studies
Nye, Russel B, English
Paananen, Victor Niles, English
Palmer, Osmond Ernest, English
Paris, Bernard Jay, English
Paul, Wilson Benton, Speech
Pickering, James H, English, American Literature
Price, George Rennie, English
Ralph, David Clinton, Speech
Richmond, Farley P, Theatre
Rohman, David Gordon, English
Rosenberg, Donald Maurice, English
Rusk, Elizabeth Hartley, English, Education
Rust, James Darius, English
Scott, Virgil Joseph, English
Sherbo, Arthur, English
Siebert, Fredrick Seaton, Journalism
Smith, Arthur James Marshall, English
Smith, Gordon Caldecott, Speech
Stalker, James Curtis, Applied English Linguistics, Modern Literature
Strandness, Theodore Benson, American Literature
Thomas, Gordon L, Speech
Thompson, Karl Frederick, English Literature
Thurman, Aurelius La Grant, Jr, Speech
Uphaus, Robert Walter, English & American Literature
Wagner, Linda Welshimer, English, Writing
Waite, John Allan, English
Waldmeir, Joseph J, English
Watkins, Evan Paul, English
Whitney, Blair, English & American Literature

Williams, Arnold Ledgerwood, English Literature
Wright, Robert Lee, English, Comparative Literature
Yunck, John A, English, Comparative Literature

ESCANABA
Butt, William Gibson, Communication Skills

FERNDALE
Morin, Edward A, English, Philosophy

FLINT
Brown, Helen E, Speech, Drama
Firebaugh, Joseph Jesse, English
Hamilton, Franklin W, English
Huffman, James Floyd, Speech, History
Rae, Wesley Dennis, English
Swift, Marvin Henry, Written Communication, Organizational Behavior
Tubbs, Stewart Leroy, Speech Communication, Social Psychology

FRANKLIN
Sivier, Evelyn M, Speech, Drama

GRAND RAPIDS
Berghuis, Melvin E, Speech
DeKoster, Lester Ronald, Speech
Harper, George Graham, Jr, English
Jefchak, Andrew Timothy, American Literature, Film Study
Kroese, Irvin B, English
Milhaupt, Jean, O.P, English Language & Literature
Noteboom, Ann M, Speech
Otten, Charlotte Fennema, English & American Literature
Ryan, Marybride, O.P, English Literature
Ten Harmsel, Henrietta, English Literature
Tiemersma, Richard Robert, English Language & Literature
Timmerman, John Johnson, English
Vande Guchte, Marten, Speech, Speech & Hearing Science
Van Der Weele, Steve John, English Language & Literature
Venderbush, Kenneth Ray, Speech
Walhout, Clarence P, English
Walker, Louise Jean, English
Wiersma, Stanley M, English

GROSSE POINTE
Canfield, Francis X, English
Maloney, Henry B, Education, Secondary English

GROSSE POINTE PARK
Ross, Woodburn Overstreet, English Language & Literature

HEMLOCK
Madden, Edgar Allen, English

HIGHLAND PARK
Merewether, John Armstrong, English

HILLSDALE
Collins, John D, English, Speech
Hale, George Hardin, Speech, Drama
King, James Boyd, English

HOLLAND
Fike, Francis George, Jr, English
Hollenbach, John William, American Literature
Hopkins, John Edward, Speech, Communication
Huttar, Charles Adolph, English
Mueller, Joan Eileen, English
Reynolds, William D, English & American Literature & Language

HOUGHTON
Andrews, Clarence Adelbert, English
Fryxell, Burton L, Literature
Mason, Richard G, English Language & Literature
Morgenstern, Barry Stephen, Modern British Literature
Powers, William Jennings, American Literature
Price, Sherwood Roy, English
Sachs, Harley Luther, Technical Communications, Creative Writing
Young, Arthur Paul, English & American Literature

KALAMAZOO
Adams, Phillip Duane, Comparative Arts, English
Brown, Charles Thomas, Speech
Buys, William E, Speech
Callan, Edward T, English Literature, African Studies
Carlson, Bernadine P, English Language & Literature
Carlson, Norman Eugene, English
Cooley, John Ryder, American Literature
Crane, Loren Danford, Interpersonal Communication, Public Address
Davidson, Clifford Oscar, English
Denenfeld, Philip S, English
Dieker, Richard J, Communication
Fisher, Stephanie Anne, Renaissance Literature
Galligan, Edward Lawrence, Literature

Gianakaris, Constantine John, English
Gingerich, Martin Ellsworth, Modern English & American Literature
Goldfarb, Clare R, English & American Literature
Goldfarb, Russell Marshal, English Literature
Harris, Harold Joel, English
Herman, Deldee M, Speech
Hilberry, Conrad Arthur, English Literature
Hinkel, Robert Craig, English
Holaday, Clayton Aldrich, American Literature
Limpus, Robert Moore, English
Macrorie, Kenneth, English
Malmstrom, Jean, English
Miller, Ralph Norman, American Literature
Nelson, Arnold Gerhard, English
Orr, John B, English & American Studies
Phillips, John R, English Literature
Ratliffe, Sharon Ann, Speech Communication
Rogers, Frederick John, English
Sadler, David Francis, American Studies
Smith, Charles Allen, English
Stallman, Robert Lester, English
Stavig, Richard Thorson, English
Syndergaard, Larry Edward, English Literature, Scandinavian Literature
Waring, Walter Weyler, English Literature
York, Zack Lee, Speech

LACHINE
Nicholson, Nancy Snider, English

LANSING
Angel, D. Duane, Communications, Political Science
Henson, Clyde Eugene, English
Pipes, William Harrison, Speech, English

LIVONIA
Brocki, Mary Damascene, C.S.S.F, English

MACKINAC ISLAND
McCabe, John Charles, III, Drama

MARQUETTE
Davis, Daryl Richard, English & American Literature, Medieval Studies
Foster, Leslie Donley, Literary Theory, Renaissance Literature
Hilton, Earl Raymond, English
Houston, Howard Rogers, English & American Literature
Jones, James H, English
Legler, Philip, English
Livingston, James L, Renaissance Literature
Pennell, Arthur Emmet, English Literature
Thundyil, Zacharias Pontian, English, Linguistics
Vinocur, Jacob, English

MARSHALL
Hampton, Charles Francis, English

MONROE
Mc Mahon, Mary Avila, I.H.M, Speech, English, Drama

MOUNT PLEASANT
Bowen, Elbert Russell, Speech & Drama
Bradshaw, James Stanford, Journalism, Modern History
Bronson, Larry Lawrence, Middle English Poetry
Cohen, Edwin, Interpretation, Drama
Dawson, Lawrence R, Jr, Literature
Emry, Hazel Thornburg, Comparative & American Literature
Fulton, Henry LeVan, English Literature
Hammack, James Alan, Speech, Drama
Hepler, John Chislett, English
McDermott, Frances McClellan, English
Maienknecht, Gilbert O, Journalism
Mayhew, Jean Binkley, Speech, Drama
Millar, Dan Pyle, Interpersonal & Nonverbal Communication
Molson, Francis Joseph, English
Moodie, Clara Lee Redwood, English, Education
Orlik, Peter Blythe, Radio & Television
Pfeiffer, John Richard, British & American Malmstrom
Primeau, Ronald R, English & American Literature, Rhetoric
Rydahl, Eugene E, Theatre
Smith, J. Harold, English
Weber, Daniel Barr, American Literature & Studies

NAZARETH
Smith, M. Dorothy, S.S.J, Renaissance

OLIVET
Hance, Kenneth Gordon, Speech

OWOSSO
Vliet, Rodney Meryl, Literature

OXFORD
Boswell, George Worley, Literature, English

PIERSON
Henkel, Julia S, English, Religious Education

ROCHESTER
Brown, Maurice F, Jr, American Literature
Cutts, John P, Literature & Drama
DeMent, Joseph Willis, English

Evarts, Peter G, English, Linguistics
Fitzsimmons, Thomas, English
Hirschfeld-Medalia, Adeline G, Communication, Theatre
Hoyle, James F, English Literature
Morse, Donald E, English
Schwab, William, English
White, Gertrude M, English Literature
White, William, Journalism

ROYAL OAK
Grewe, Eugene Francis, English
Piché, Priscilla M, English Literature, Literary Theory
Ziegelmueller, George William, Speech

ST. JAMES
Gladish, David, English

ST. JOSEPH
Webster, Mildred E, English

SAULT STE. MARIE
Matheson, John Morley, Journalism
Thomas, Peter D, English & African Studies
Ward, Louis Randolph, English

SOUTHFIELD
Angelescu, Victor, Eighteenth Century English Literature
Goldsmith, Arnold Louis, English

TIPTON
Jones, Mary Patricia, English

UNIVERSITY
Walton, Gerald Wayne, English
Webb, James Wilson, English

UNIVERSITY CENTER
Thomas, J. James, Literature, Humanities
Tyner, Raymond E, English Literature

WALLED LAKE
Brede, Alexander, English

WARREN
Gross, Alan Gerald, English, Education

YPSILANTI
Bensen, Alice Rhodus, English
Bowen, Harry W, Rhetoric
Brylowski, Walter Marion, English
Cross, Gilbert B, English Literature
Dume, Thomas Leslie, English
Foster, Milton P, Literature
Gohn, Ernest Salisbury, English
Gousseff, James W, Theatre
Harris, Arthur John, English
Hebert, Catherine Ackerman, English
Jernigan, E. Jay, English Language & Literature
Jordan, Hoover Harding, English Literature
Kornbluth, Martin Leonard, English
Koste, Virginia Glasgow, Theatre & Drama
Lawniczak, Donald Aloysius, English
McGlynn, Paul Dumon, English
Maddox, Notley Sinclair, English
Mohl, Ronald Alfred, English
Murray, Thomas James, Speech
Nelson, Alfred Lewis, Jr, Literature, Theatre
Potter, Edward Earle, English
Sattler, John William, Speech
Trowbridge, Ronald Lee, English Language & Literature
Virtue, John Bernard, English
Webb, Margaret Josephine, English
White, Patrick T, English
Wonnberger, Carl George, English Literature & Language
Zellers, Parker R, Speech, Dramatic Arts

MINNESOTA

BEMIDJI
Elliott, William Douglas, English
Field, Michael Jay, English Literature
Henriques, Kenneth Edmund, English, Theology
Mangelsdorf, Ruth Brune, English
Reynolds, Nydia Joan, Speech
Robinson, Forest Elmo, English
Russell, Leslie A, English
Sauer, Philip R, English Literature

COLLEGEVILLE
Blenkner, Louis, English
Deutsch, Alfred Henry, O.S.B, English
Humphrey, Stephen Benedict, English
Thimmesh, Hilary, O.S.B, English

DULUTH
Duncan, Joseph Ellis, English
Glick, Wendell, English
Hart, Robert Charles, English & American Literature
Katz, Albert M, Speech, Theatre
Owens, Robert Reiley, English
Schroeder, Fred Erich Harald, American Studies, English
Shea, Francis Xavier, S.J, English, Theology
Stensland, Anna Lee, English, English Education

Tezla, Albert, English & Hungarian Literature

MANKATO
Barber, Eddice Belle, English
Beckman, Vernon E, Speech
Brooks, Robert Scott, Speech
Dornberg, Curtis Leon, English
Foster, John Burt, English
Kelson, John Hofstad, English
Ladd, James Mathon, Speech
Lokensgard, Hjalmar O, English
Meyer, Roy Willard, English
Olauson, C. Ronald, Drama, Comparative Literature
Solensten, John Martin, English, American Studies
Wright, Robert C, English
Youel, Donald Bruce, English

MARSHALL
Rossillon, Joseph Pierre, Speech, Drama
Whipple, William, (Jr), English
Willoughby, John Wallace, Victorian Literature
Wylder, Delbert E, English
Wylder, Edith Perry, English

MINNEAPOLIS
Adey, Harvey Lee, Theatre
Alkon, Paul Kent, English Literature
Anderson, Chester Grant, English
Anderson, Raymond E, Speech
Bales, Kent R, English
Bormann, Ernest Gordon, Speech
Bowron, Bernard Roy, Jr, English
Browne, Donald R, Mass Communications
Bryan, Daniel Vance, Communication, Humanities
Burrows, Dorothy M, English
Cashman, Paul H, Speech Communication
Clark, John Williams, English
Clayton, Thomas, English
Cole, Ailene, Speech, Drama
D'Andrea, Paul, English
Davis, F. Mark, English
Downing, Edna C, English
Finnberg, F. Faith, French, English
Firchow, Peter Edgerly, English & Comparative Literature
Geizer, Ronald Stanley, Speech Communication
Graham, Kenneth L, Speech
Griffin, Edward M., English & American Literature
Haley, David Bruce, Renaissance English Literature
Hancher, Charles Michael, English
Howell, William Smiley, Speech
Hurrell, John Dennis, English
Jensen, J. Vernon, Speech
Kendall, Calvin B, English
Kwiat, Joseph J, American Literature & Studies, Humanities
Leyasmeyer, Archibald I, English
McNally, John, English
McNaron, Toni Ann Hurley, English
Madden, William Anthony, English
Meister, Celestia Anne, English
Miller, Harold A, Speech
Moore, Robert Etheridge, English Literature
Moulton, Robert Darrell, Theatre Arts
Nicholl, Grier, English, American Studies
Nichols, Ralph G, Rhetoric
O'Brien, Gordon Worth, English
Olson, Esther J, Speech
Paulu, Burton, Comparative World Broadcasting
Ramsland, Clement, Humanities
Reed, Peter J, English
Rosenman, John Brown, American Literature
Ross, Donald, Jr, English
Scoggins, James Lawrence, English
Scott, Robert Lee, Speech
Steinmann, Martin, Jr, English
Stekert, Ellen Jane, Folklore
Turpie, Mary Christine, American Literature & Civilization
Unger, Leonard Howard, English
Whiting, Frank M, Theatre Arts
Wood, David Charles, British Literature, Theory of Criticism
Wright, George Thaddeus, English

MOORHEAD
Anderson, Loren James, Speech Communication
Dille, Roland, English
Dovre, Paul J, Speech, Drama
Flood, Verle Dennis, English, History
Glasrud, Clarence A, English
Hanna, Allan Joseph, English
Hansen, Delmar J, Speech, Drama
Haugen, Clair O, Dramatic Art, Theatre History
Heringman, Bernard, English
Larson, George Stanley, Nineteenth Century English Literature
Lell, Virgil Gordon, English Literature
Meinke, Darrel M, English
Miller, Joseph Washburn, English
Monson, Allwin Douglas, Speech

Murray, Byron D, English
Prausnitz, Walther Gunther, English

MORRIS
Barber, Laird H, English Literature
Hart, Nathaniel Irwin, English

NORTH MANKATO
Fitterer, Harold Joseph, English, English Education

NORTHFIELD
Buckstead, Richard C, American Literature
Flamm, Dudley, English, Comparative Literature
Hove, Haldor Lauritz, English
Hove, Mary Rion, English, American Literature
Jenkins, Owen, English
Johnson, Lowell Edward, English
Larsen, Erling Lauritz, English
Lee, Ronald James, English, Humanities
Meyer, Marie Malmin, English
Morral, Frank R, English
Nelson, Theodore F, Speech
Nilsen, Frida R, English
Peterson, Richard Gustaf, English
Sheridan, Edward Philip, English Literature
Sheridan, Harriet W, English, Education
Soule, George, English Literature
Thorson, Gerald Howard, English & Comparative Literature
Tisdale, Robert George, English
Wee, David Luther, English
Wilkens, Kenneth Gerhard, Public Speaking
Woodruff, John Rowland, Drama

PEQUOT LAKES
Paulson, Clara J, English

ROSEVILLE
Wyvell, Mary Lund, Writing, Literature

ST. CLOUD
Cermele, Dominick Joseph, Theatre
Coard, Robert L, English
Falk, Armand E, English
Gottshall, James Kerwood, English
Hannah, Mary Emily, Speech, History
Lawson, Jonathan N, English Literature
Lundquist, James Carl, English
Melton, John Lester, English
Otto, Don Henry, English, Education
Sikkink, Donald Elwyn, Speech
Van Pelt, Elizabeth Stanfield, English
Wick, Robert H, Speech & Drama

ST. JOSEPH
Dufner, Mary Angeline, English
Gable, Mariella, O.S.B, Literature, Rhetoric
Reiten, Paula, O.S.B, English & American Literature

ST. PAUL
Bernstein, John Albert, English Literature
Brady, Mary William, C.S.J, English & American Literature
Brown, Carole Ann, English
Brown, James Isaac, Rhetoric
Ching, James Christopher, Speech, Drama
Greenberg, Alvin D, English
Grigg, Quay, Jr, English
Hagan, Michael Robert, Speech, Rhetoric
Hardman, Benedict Edward, Speech, English
Huber, Alberta, C.S.J, English
Kane, Patricia L, English
Kincaid, Gerald L, Language Arts, Social Science
Lincoln, Eleanor H, English
Mosvick, Roger K, Speech, Communication
Muellerleile, Mary Alice, English
Murray, Peter Bryant, English, Drama
Nobles, William Scott, Speech
Pearsall, Thomas E, English
Peck, Helen Margaret, C.S.J, English
Rathburn, Robert Charles, English
Rosendahl, William Armond, English
Savage, Edward Bernhard, Comparative Literature
Smith, Alice Gustava, C.S.J, English
Toman, George Edward, English, Philosophy
Toth, Susan Erickson Allen, English & American Literature
Vane, George Thomas, English Literature
Weintz, Christian, English
Wilson, Mardis Glen, Theatre, Oral Interpretation of Literature
Ziebarth, E. William, Speech

ST. PETER
Alexis, Gerhard T, American Literature
Buechmann, Claus-Peter, English
Freiert, William Kendall, Classics
Harrington, David Van, English
Owen, Lawrence S, English
Robertz, William George, Speech
Suderman, Elmer Francis, American Literature

SPICER
Olson, Enid Martell, English

WINONA
Boddy, Margaret Pearse, English

Erler, H. Raphael, F.S.C, English, American Literature
Magnus, Dorothy Barbara, Speech & Drama
Nelson, Augusta Charlotte, English, Comparative Literature
Nichols, James William, English
Roth, Emalou, Theatre History & Criticism

MISSISSIPPI

CLEVELAND
Butler, Maria Hogan, English
Jones, Andrew Melvin, Speech
White, Orville Franklin, English

CLINTON
Howell, Ralph Daniel, Linguistics, English
Rouse, Sarah A, English
Todd, Hollis Bailey, Speech, Bible
Todd, Julia McAmis, Speech
Voyles, Jimmy Ponder, English & American Literature

COLUMBUS
Allen, Lourie Strickland, Nineteenth Century English & American Literature
Blow, Suzanne Katherine, English
Bolen, Frances E, English & American Literature
Cone, Mary, English & Modern Drama
Craft, Harvey Milton, English
Cromwell, Harvey, Speech
Hitt, Ralph Eugene, English
Laurence, Frank Michael, American & English Literature
Loewen, Peter F, English

HATTIESBURG
Anderson, (William) Hilton, English
Bahr, Howard W, English Literature
Ernest, Joseph McDonald, Jr, English
Kay, Wallace Grant, Comparative Literature, Aesthetics
Lasater, Alice Elizabeth, Medieval English
Moorman, Charles, English
Orange, Linwood Elden, English
Quarnstrom, I. Blaine, Theatre, Oral Interpretation
Smith, Jack Alan, Old English Literature & Linguistics
Tharpe, Jac Lyndon, Comparative Literature
Weaver, Gordon Allison, English

HOLLY SPRINGS
Njoku, Benedict Chiaka, English
Stefanson, Donald Hal, Eighteenth Century English Literature
Stoll, John Edward, Victorian & Modern English

ITTA BENA
Howard, Zelma Inez Turner, English

JACKSON
Alexander, Margaret Abigail Walker, English
Boyd, George Wilson, English Language & Literature
Campbell, Joan Patrick, Modern Literature
Evans, Gloria Buchanan, Speech
Fry, Kenneth Richard, Humanities, Victorian Literature
Gregory, John Robert, Communications, Mass Media
Simmons, (Joseph) Edgar, English

LORMAN
Bangham, P. Jerald, Theatre
Haque, Abu Saeed Zahurul, Folklore, Comparative Literature

MISSISSIPPI STATE
Anderson, Robert Gene, Oral Interpretation of Literature
Dudley, Elford Samuel, Communication
Unger, Richard L, Comparative Literature, English

SCOOBA
Crickard, Annette Peek, English, Humanities

TOUGALOO
O'Mara, Philip Francis, Modern American & African Literature

UNIVERSITY
Bryant, William Alton, English
Cannon, Charles Dale, English
Dollarhide, Louis E, English
Harrington, Evans Burnham, English
McBryde, Donald M, Theatre, Speech
Nolen, Anne Daniel, Drama
Noyes, Charles Edward, English
Pilkington, John, English
Whiteside, Duncan, Speech, Broadcasting

MISSOURI

CAPE GIRARDEAU
Bierk, John Cashion, American Literature
Cordonnier, Max Edward, English
Goodwin, Fred Benton, Rhetoric & Public Address

Grisvard, Larry Eugene, Theatre
Hilty, Peter Daniel, English Literature
Monahan, Dean Wright, English
Stacy, Bill Wayne, Speech
CLAYTON
Bloom, Lynn Zimmerman, English Language &
Literature
COLUMBIA
Anderson, Donald K, Jr, English
Barth, John Robert, S.J, English
Bender, Robert Morton, English
Berry, Lloyd Eason, English Literature
Bray, William Albert, Journalism
Clark, Larry Dale, Dramatic Art
Cornwell, Clifton, Speech
Crowley, Joseph Donald, English, American
Literature
Daniel, Walter Clarence, English
Dickinson, Leon Townsend, English
Drummond, Donald Frazier, English
English, Earl F, Journalism, Psychology
Fisk, Norma Jean, English Literature, Renais-
sance Drama
Fulweiler, Howard W, English Literature
Garvey, Daniel Edward, Jr, Broadcast Journal-
ism, Communication Research
Gatch, Milton McCormick, Jr, English, Religion
Gelatt, Rod Gerald, Journalism
Gibson, James W, Speech & Drama
Griffith, Bartonil, Speech
Harris, Patricia Harn, English, English Lin-
guistics
Haverfield, Robert Walter, Journalism, Ad-
vertising
Hinnant, Charles Haskell, English
Hocks, Richard Allen, English
Holleran, James V, English
Holtz, William Victor, English
Hudson, Charles M, Jr, English Literature
Jones, William Mckendrey, English
Kline, John Alvin, Speech Communication
Lago, Mary McClelland, Modern English &
Bengali Literature
Lambert, Edward Charles, Journalism
Littleton, Betty J, English
McAfee, James Thomas, Creative Writing,
Modern Literature
McCurdy, Francis Lea, Speech & Drama
Materer, Timothy John, Modern & Comparative
Literature
Merrill, John Calhoun, Journalism, Philosophy
Miller, Edwin Shepard, English Literature
Nelms, Ben Frank, English, Education
Pace, George B, English
Parke, Catherine Neal, English
Patterson, Joye, Journalism
Peden, William, American Literary & Social
History
Porter, Marvin Gilbert, American & English
Literature
Reid, Loren Dudley, Speech
Rhynsburger, Donovan, Speech, Dramatics
Roberts, John Richard, English
Small, Edward Stuart, Film Communication
Theory
Stappenbeck, Herbert Louis, American Lit-
erature, Bibliography
Stoerker, Lewis Waldo, Speech, Dramatic Art
Taft, William Howard, Journalism
Votaw, Maurice Eldred, Journalism
Waal, Carla Rae, Drama, Theater
Weatherly, Edward Howell, English Literature
West, William F, Jr, Theatre Arts
Wolfe, Glenn Joseph, Mass Communication
Worrell, Elizabeth, Literature
Yeats, Donald I, English
COOTER
Hamlett, Mayme Lucille, English
FAYETTE
Baskett, Helen Wheeler, English
Eidson, Donald Ray, English
FULTON
Randolph, Esther Laursen, Literature
Randolph, John Wilson, English & American
Literature
Williamson, Elsa Wade, English
GROVES
Graham, Albert Edwin, English Literature
HANNIBAL
Groves, Florence, English
INDEPENDENCE
Newcomb, Mary Jane, English & Twentieth
Century American Literature
JEFFERSON CITY
Heermance, J. Noel, English
Pawley, Thomas Desire, Jr, Theatre & Dra-
matic Art
Pride, Armistead Scott, Journalism
Wilson, Noel Avon, Communications, Political
Science
JOPLIN
Harder, Henry Louis, English & American Lit-
erature

Headlee, Cleetis Juanita, English
Lambert, Joseph Patrick, English
Massa, Richard Wayne, English, Journalism
Preble, Harry Eldon, English
Rhodes, Dennis Harrison, Public Address,
Forensics
KANSAS CITY
Abbick, John F, S.J, English
Adelsberger, Jane, C.S.J, English
Aryanpur, Manoocher, English
Berets, Ralph Adolph, Modern Fiction, Film
Cappon, Alexander P, English Literature
Farnsworth, Robert M, English
Gazda, John M, English, English Education
Jaffe, Dan, English, History
Jones, William Clough, American Literature,
U.S. Social History
Knickerbocker, Maximilian Robert, Jr, English
Lakas, Robert Raymond, S.J, English Litera-
ture, Renaissance
Louis, William Joseph, Speech, Drama
McKinley, James Courtright, Twentieth Century
British & American Literature
McLeod, Frederick R, English
McMann, Mary A, English, Humanities
Oldani, Louis Joseph, American & English
Literature
Ray, David Eugene, English
Ryan, William Martin, Medieval Literature &
Linguistics
Spatz, Jonas, English
Spatz, Lois S, English, Classics
Tyler, Priscilla, English, Linguistics
Walker, Jones Morton, Theatre, History
Watson, Wallace Steadman, English, Humanities
KIRKSVILLE
Barnes, Jim Weaver, Comparative Literature,
Creative Writing
Carpenter, Edwin Cecil, Public Address
Clyde, Glenda Estelle, Speech
Huenemann, Calvin Victor, American Litera-
ture
Monroe, Howard Chandler, Speech, Drama
Severns, James (George), Drama
Wilson, Herman Pledger, English
LEE'S SUMMIT
Wilkins, Arthur Norman, English
LIBERTY
Bowman, Georgia B, Speech, Journalism
Dunham, Dana Dean, Jr, English Literature
& Composition
Harriman, Richard, English
MARYVILLE
Albertini, Virgil, English
Bohlken, Robert Leo, Speech Communication
& Theatre
Fry, Carrol Lee, English
Grube, Frank William, English
Jewett, Mike, English Literature
May, Leland Chandler, English Literature
& Education
Rivers, Charles Leo, English
Rowlette, Robert Oren, American Literature
PARKVILLE
Campbell, Elizabeth McClure, English
Sibley, Francis Martin, English
PERRYVILLE
Walz, Vincent (Phyllis Marie), D.C, English
POINT LOOKOUT
Smith, Patrick D, English
ROLLA
Brewer, John Motsinger, English, Speech
Patrick, Michael Davis, English
Pogue, Jim C, English Renaissance Literature
Wise, James Nial, English
ST. CHARLES
Barnett, Howard Albert, English
Sibley, Agnes, English Literature

ST. LOUIS
Bascom, Marion, R.S.C.J, English
Benoit, Raymond Paul, English
Carson, William Glasgow Bruce, English,
Drama
Chiasson, Elias Joseph, English
Cohen, Benjamin Bernard, English
Cowan, Gregory M, English
DiLorenzo, Ronald Eugene, English
Dougherty, Charles Thomas, English
Drummond, Edward Joseph, S.J, English
Friedman, Sidney Joseph, English, Drama
Gottfried, Leon Albert, English
Hamlin, William C, American Literature,
Modern Literature
Hartog, Curt Hardin, English Literature
Hazelton, Richard Marquard, Medieval English
Philology
Holloway, Marcella Marie, Literary Criticism
Jackson, Bernetta M, English
Knapp, Joseph George, S.J, English, History
Knipp, Thomas Richard, English
Lebowitz, Naomi Gordon, English, Comparative
Literature

Liles, Bruce Lynn, Linguistics, Medieval Lit-
erature
McAvoy, William Charles, English
McCoy, Donald Edward, English Language &
Literature
McNamee, Maurice Basil, S.J, English
McPherson, Elisabeth Allen, English
Madsen, William George, English Literature
Miller, Clarence Harvey, English Literature
Montesi, Albert Joseph, English
Morris, John Nelson, English
Murray, Eugene Bernard, English
Neeb, Martin J, Jr, Mass Communication
Nolan, Barbara, English
Ong, Walter Jackson, S.J, English
Onuska, John Thomas, Jr, English
Revard, Carter Curtis, English Literature &
Linguistics
Rogers, Joseph Aloysius, English Literature
Rogers, Winslow Smith, English & American
Literature
Ruland, Richard, English & American Litera-
ture
Sandford, William Phillips, Speech
Schmitz, Robert Morell, English Literature
Scott, James Frazier, English, Cinema
Shea, Daniel Bartholomew, Jr, American Lit-
erature
Skelly, Madge, Speech Pathology & Audiology,
Theatre
Stepsis, Robert Peter, English, Medieval Lit-
erature
Stueber, Stephanie, C.S.J, English
Thurston, Jarvis (Aydelotte), English
Tierney, James Edward, English Literature
Wheeler, Burton Maynard, English, Religion
Williamson, Jane Louise, English Literature
Wolfe, Peter, English
Zwicker, Steven Nathan, Seventeenth Century
Literature
SPRINGFIELD
Beckett, Robert D, English
Bedford, William Charles, English, American
Studies
Bicket, Zenas J, English
Blackwood, Byrne David, Speech, Drama
Bradley, Robert Harlow, Theatre
Coger, Leslie Irene, Speech
Gilmore, Robert K, Speech, Theatre
Gleason, George Donald, English
Hall, Wesley, Reading
Haswell, Richard Ellis, English Literature
Lederer, Katherine, English
Livingston, James T, Literature, Theology
Mears, Richard M, English
Pedersen, Glenn Malvern, English
Sweeney, Mary Rose, English, Educational
Psychology
Turner, Richard M, English
Warren, Bernice S, English
TARKIO
Davis, Robert Bernard, English
UNIVERSITY CITY
Elkin, Stanley Lawrence, American Literature
WARRENSBURG
Adams, Joseph Domenic, American Literature,
English As A Foreign Language
Coon, Gilbert Dennis, American Studies & Lit-
erature
Crump, Gail Bruce, Modern British & Ameri-
can Literature
Highlander, James L, Theatre
Jones, Robert Claude, English
Kindrick, Robert LeRoy, Medieval Literature,
Linguistics
McReynolds, Ronald Weldon, English Litera-
ture
Patterson, Frank Morgan, English
Pierce, Glenn Quimby, Drama
Ramsey, Allen Rodell, Literature of the En-
glish Renaissance
Sampson, Harold P, Speech
Schwartz, Robert George, Jr, Eighteenth Cen-
tury English Literature
Taylor, Velma Lotus (Adams), English, Educa-
tion
Tees, Arthur Thomas, Theatre
Titus, Catherine Fontelle, English
WEBSTER GROVES
Cargas, Harry James, World & American Lit-
erature
Pearson, Mary Deborah, English

MONTANA

BILLINGS
Moulton, Eugene R, Speech
Murphy, Margaret Sparling, English
Rodney, Robert Morris, English
BOZEMAN
Bryson, Kenneth D, Speech

Coffey, Jerome Edward, English Language & Linguistics
Coffin, Arthur Bonneau, American & Comparative Literature
Fitch, Joseph Clay, Theatre Arts
Folsom, John B, English
Goshorn, James William, American Literature
Isaacson, Carl Leonard, English, Communication
Jacobsen, Bruce C, Theatre Arts
Lawrence, Leslie Andrew, English
Roberts, Kathryn Healy, English, Speech
Sencer, Robert Abner, Communication Theory
Watson, Alan M, English Literature & Art History
Weisenborn, Ray Edward, Speech Communication

BUTTE
McGuire, John Francis, English, Science Education

HAVRE
Arends, Robert Lowell, English, Philosophy
Lisenby, William E, English, Speech

HELENA
Roesler, Miriam Clare, O.S.F, English & American Literature
Ward, Joseph Thomas, English

MISSOULA
Adler, Richard Raymond, English Education, Health & Physical Education
Bier, Jesse, English
Blumberg, Nathan Bernard, Journalism
Brenner, Gerry, Literature
Brier, Warren J, Journalism
Clubb, Merrel D, Jr, English
Cogswell, Andrew Colville, Journalism
Dugan, Edward Barnett, Journalism
Freer, Coburn, English
Gilbert, Vedder Morris, English Literature
Harrington, Henry R, English Literature & Theology
Hess, Philip Joseph, Radio-Television, Journalism
James, Richard H, Drama
King, Walter Neil, English
Landini, Richard George, English
McClintock, Michael William, Modern Literature, Literary Criticism
Merriam, Harold Guy, British Literature
Moore, John Eugene, American Literature
Wilmot, William Wallace, Interpersonal Communication

NEBRASKA

BLAIR
Bansen, Norman Clarence, American & Scandinavian Literature
Engelman, Herta, English
Nielsen, Luella Kaeding, English
Northwall, John Howard, Rhetoric, Philosophy

CHADRON
Brown, Douglas Mitchell, Humanities
Graves, R. Dorset, English

FREMONT
Gimmestad, Herman, English
Knudson, Keith Dean, English
Ritter, Darlene Mae, English Literature

HASTINGS
Gardner, Sara Jane, English, American Studies
Harwick, Robert (Duane), English
Langvardt, Arthur LeRoy, American Rural Fiction
Marsh, Dwight Chaney, English
Shiffler, Harrold C, Dramatic Arts

KEARNEY
Ahrendts, Harold L, Speech
Carroll, Joseph P, English
Clark, William Keith, Speech
Hoffman, Harland Lamont, English, Secondary Education
Hoffman, Harry Howard, English, Education
Westerfield, Hargis, English & American Literature

LINCOLN
Bailey, Dudley, English Language & Literature
Baldwin, Joseph Burkette, Speech, Dramatic Arts
Bestul, Thomas Howard, English
Bormann, Dennis Robert, Speech Communication, German
Bowers, Anthony Robin, English Literature
Clark, David Merriett, Theatre History
Cognard, Roger Allen, English
Copple, Robert Neale, Journalism
Cosgrave, Pearl-Joan, English, Languages
Crompton, Louis, English
Erlich, Bruce Sewell, Comparative Literature, History of Ideas
Gaffney, Wilbur Geoffrey, English
Gregory, Donald, English

Hall, Harold Ernest, English
Haller, Robert S, English Literature
Hardy, Gene Bennett, English Literature
Hedges, Ned S, English
Hilliard, Stephen Shortis, English
Hough, Robert Lee, American Literature
Kaye, Philip Albert, Speech
Knoll, Robert Edwin, English
Lemon, Lee Thomas, Literature, English
Lowdon, Jeannie Elizabeth, English Literature
Luke, Hugh Jay, English Literature
Lyon, Melvin Ernest, English
McShane, James Arthur, English
Marcus, Mordecai, English
Mignon, Charles William, English
Moler, Kenneth Lloyd, Jr, English
Morgan, Kenneth Scott, English
Morgan, William R, Speech, Theatre
Narveson, Robert D, English
Norland, Howard Bernett, English
Olson, Paul A, English
Petelle, John L, Speech, Dramatic Art
Poston, Lawrence S, III, English
Pulos, Christos Ernest, English
Rice, Frank Martin, English, Education
Robinson, John William, English
Seiler, William John, Speech Communication
Smith, Mary Daehler, Linguistics, Literature
Stock, Robert Douglas, English
Stubblefield, Charles, English
Wenburg, John Raymond, Speech Communication
Whipp, Leslie Thomas, English
Wright, Walter Francis, English

OMAHA
Aschenbrenner, Duane Leo, Forensics, Public Address
Brilhart, John K, Speech
Brown, Marion Marsh, English
Costello, Mary Angelica, R.S.M, English
Duncan, Harry A, Journalism
Fus, Dennis Anthony, Speech Communication
Harper, Robert Donald, English
Hubenka, Lloyd John, English
Kuhlman, Thomas A, English, American Civilization
Lane, Richard Lee, Medieval English Language & Literature
Magaret, Helene, English
Newkirk, Glen A, English Literature
Passon, Richard Henry, English
Stein, Charles Happy, English
Wardle, Ralph Martin, English
Waters, Leonard A, S.J, English Literature
Williamson, Mary Ellen, Broadcasting, Advertising

SEWARD
Baden, Robert C, English
Korinko, Stephen John, English, Linguistics

WAYNE
Johnson, Robert Garrett, Speech, Drama
Lewis, Katherine Ann, English Contemporary American Literature

NEVADA

DYER
Reid, Randall C, English & American Literature

LAS VEGAS
Adams, Charles L, English
Byrns, Richard Howard, English, Comparative Literature
Clark, Thomas Lloyd, Linguistics, Dialectology
Collier, Lewis Arlen, English & American Literature
Crawford, Jerry L, Drama
Dodge, Robert Kendall, English
Hazen, James, English
Irsfeld, John Henry, English & American Literature & Language
Stevens, A. Wilber, English
Weinstein, Mark A, English

RENO
Brown, Richard E, English Literature
Cole, Elmer Joseph, Jr, English
Conover, Theodore E, Journalism
Diamond, Robert E, English
Essa, Ahmed, Twentieth Century World Fiction, Third World Literature
Frohnen, Richard Gene, Journalism
Gabbard, Gregory Norman, English, Linguistics
Gilleland, LaRue Wesley, Journalism
Gorrell, Robert Mark, English
Griffin, Robert Stuart, Speech, Psychology
Harvey, Robert D, American Literature & History
Hettich, David William, English Literature
Howard, Anne Bail, American Literature, Composition
Hume, Robert Arthur, English
Miller, William Charles, Speech, Drama

Morrison, John Wilson, English
Ronald, Margaret Ann, English Literature
Walker, Franklin Trenaby, English

NEW HAMPSHIRE

CHESTERFIELD
Grayson, Janet, English

DOVER
Caldwell, S. Anthony, English

DURHAM
Batcheller, Joseph Donald, Speech
Bingham, Sylvester Hinckley, English
Carnicelli, Thomas Anthony, English
Dawson, Carl, English
DePorte, Michael Vital, English Literature
Goffe, Lewis C, American Literature, English Education
Hapgood, Robert (Derry), English
Hunter, William Bridges, Jr, English
Kolodny, Annette, American Literature, Women's Studies
Logan, Terence Patrick, Renaissance English Literature
Miller, Edmund Gillmore, English
Nicoloff, Philip Loveless, American Literature
Richardson, John Curtis, English
Rose, Harriet Ann, English & American Literature
Sabatelli, Philip Joseph, General Semantics, Interpersonal Communication
Smith, Julian, American Literature, Film
Smith, Mark Richard, Fiction
Webster, Robert Gordon, American Literature

ENFIELD
Quinlan, Maurice James, English

HANOVER
Adams, Ruth Marie, English
Alexander, Rodney Wilson, Drama
Baldwin, Marilyn Austin, English
Bien, Peter Adolph, English
Cornell, Louis Longacre, English
Cox, James Melville, American Literature
Eberhart, Richard, English
Epperson, James Allen, III, English
Finch, John, English
Gaylord, Alan Theodore, English Literature
Heffernan, James Anthony Walsh, English
Hill, Errol Gaston, Drama
Ives, Almon Bingham, Speech
Jensen, Arthur Eugene, English Literature
Loomis, Chauncey Chester, Jr, English
Mansell, Darrel Lee, Jr, English
Nash, John R, English & French Literature
Perrin, (Edwin) Noel, English Literature
Pickering, Samuel Francis, Jr, English
Saccio, Peter Churchill, English Literature
Siegel, Robert Harold, English Romantic Period
Terrie, Henry Larkin, Jr, English
Vance, Thomas Hume, English & American Literature
Vargish, Thomas, English
Walker, Samuel Jay, Jr, Victorian & Afro-American Literature
Williams, Henry Beates, English

HAVERHILL
Ross, Robert Henry, Jr, English

HENNIKER
Schuster, Richard, English

KEENE
Adams, Mildred Davis, Comparative Literature
Cunningham, Richard Earle, English
Lyle, Cornelius Railey, II, English, Journalism
Sullivan, William John, English, American Studies

NEW LONDON
Ewing, Wallace Kelley, English

PLYMOUTH
Duke, Charles Richard, American Literature & Writing
Vittum, Henry Earl, English, Education

RINDGE
Cervo, Nathan Anthony, English Language & Literature
Golffing, Francis Charles, English Literature

WALPOLE
Ackerman, Robert William, English

WASHINGTON
Hofford, James Loveday, Speech Communications

NEW JERSEY

ABSECON
Tilley, Wesley H, English Literature

ANDOVER
Burke, Kenneth, English

BLOOMFIELD
Leavitt, Charles Loyal, English

BOUND BROOK
O'Connor, John Joseph, English

BUTLER
    Reynolds, Terence J, O.F.M, English Language
        & Literature
CAMDEN
    Gordon, Walter Kelly, English Language & Lit-
        erature
CHATHAM
    Larsen, Francis Kevin, English & American
        Literature
CHERRY HILL
    Harbage, Alfred B, English Literature
CLOSTER
    Schmitter, Dean Morgan, English
CONVENT
    O'Connor, Mary Catharine, English
EAST ORANGE
    Cross, Donald Leroy, English
    Daniel, Carter Anderson, English
    Fullman, Christopher Edward, English, Phil-
        osophy
    Lovell, James Henry, Jr, English
FAIR HAVEN
    Stonesifer, Richard James, English
FORT LEE
    Ebel, Henry, English, Comparative Literature
    Ruoff, James E, English
GLASSBORO
    Carb, Nathan R. E, Jr, English
    Conrad, Lawrence H, Jr, English Language &
        Literature
    Fleisher, Siegel H, English, Comparative Lit-
        erature
    McKenzie, James Jeremiah, English
    Roch, John Henry, American Literature
    von Moltke, Henry, Speech
GLEN ROCK
    Jaarsma, Richard J, English
HACKETTSTOWN
    Schmidtberger, Loren F, English Literature
HADDONFIELD
    Gates, Norman Timmins, English & American
        Literature
    Sanderson, James Lee, English
HEWITT
    Mollenkott, Virginia Ramey, English Literature
HIGHLAND PARK
    Boyd, Elizabeth French, English
JERSEY CITY
    Belvedere, Joseph F, English Literature
    Deasy, Philip C, English
    Dexter, Erwin Brownell, English Language,
        Literature
    Gold, Robert S, English
    Goldman, Lloyd N, English & American Lit-
        erature
    Gordon, Nicholas Karl, English & American
        Literature
    Starke, Catherine Juanita, English
    Weiss, Morton Jerry, English
KINGSTON
    Fergusson, Francis, Comparative Literature,
        Drama
    Ives, Chauncey B, English
LAKEWOOD
    McDade, Mary Demetria, R.S.M, English Lit-
        erature
LAVALLETTE
    McGinn, Donald Joseph, English Literature
LAWRENCEVILLE
    Johnson, Thomas H, English
LITTLE FALLS
    Runden, John Paul, English
MADISON
    Bicknell, John W, English
    Brack, Harold Arthur, Speech
    Buchen, Irving H, English
    Cummins, Walter M, English
    Decavalles, Andonis George (Manganaris), En-
        glish, Comparative Literature
    Hewitt, Christian B, English
    Jones, Arthur E, Jr, English, Librarianship
    Keyishian, Harry, English Literature
    Mulder, John Rudolph, Comparative Literature
    Skaggs, Calvin Lee, English, Cinema
    Steiner, Joan Elizabeth, English & American
        Literature
    Thomas, Deborah Allen, English & American
        Literature
    Warner, John M, English Literature
    Weimer, Joan Myers, American Literature,
        Women's Studies
    Weinman, Geoffrey Stephen, American Litera-
        ture
MAHWAH
    Alaya, Flavia M, English & Comparative Lit-
        erature
MAYS LANDING
    Patton, John Joseph, English
METUCHEN
    Ciardi, John (Anthony), Poetry
MONTCLAIR
    Hanson, Frank Burton, English, Drama
    Pettegrove, James Parker, English

    Rich, Morton David, Modern American Litera-
        ture, English Education
MORRISTOWN
    Ross, Theodore John, Twentieth Century Lit-
        erature & Film
NEW BRUNSWICK
    Bazin, Nancy Topping, British Literature
    Bertram, Paul Benjamin, English Literature
    Bettenbender, John I, Theatre Arts
    Bezanson, Walter Everett, American Studies
    Bolton, Whitney French, English Language &
        Literature
    Burrows, David James, American Literature
    Cady, Joseph L, Jr, American Literature
    Charney, Maurice Myron, English
    Coad, Oral Sumner, English
    Comtois, Mary Elizabeth, Theater Arts
    Crozier, Alice Cooper, American Literature
    Edwards, Thomas Robert, Jr, English
    Fairweather, Clement Wilson, Jr, English Lit-
        erature
    Falk, Doris Virginia, English
    Guetti, James Lawrence, Jr, English & Ameri-
        can Literature
    Hamilton, Horace Ernst, English Literature
    Howard, Daniel F, English
    Kalstone, David Michael, English Literature
    Kellogg, Alfred Latimer, English
    Leondar, Barbara, Literary Criticism, Aes-
        thetics
    Mandel, Barrett John, English
    Meese, Elizabeth Ann, American Literature,
        Women's Studies
    Moynahan, Julian Lane, English
    Ostriker, Alicia, English
    Pack, Robert Frederick, English Literature
    Phillips, William, Literary Criticism & Theory
    Poirier, (William) Richard, American & En-
        glish Literature
    Quaintance, Richard Edgecombe, Jr, English
        Literature
    Rabkin, Gerald Edward, English, Dramatic Lit-
        erature
    Redden, Dorothy S, English & American Litera-
        ture
    Richetti, John J, English
    Ruben, Brent David, Communication
    Showalter, Elaine C, English Literature
    Sloane, David Edward Edison, American Litera-
        ture
    Smith, Carol Hertzig, English
    Smither, Nelle, American & English Literature
    Starkey, Penelope Schott, English Literature
    Wasson, Richard Howard, English
    Weimer, David Rhoads, American Literature
    Welsh, Andrew, English Literature
    Wertime, Richard Allen, English Renaissance,
        Modern American Literature
NEWARK
    Borchardt, Donald Arthur, Speech & Drama
    Camp, James E, English
    Christian, Henry Arthur, American Literature
        & Civilization
    Ehrlich, Heyward Bruce, American Studies
    Jaye, Michael C, English Literature
    Lee, Alfred Matthew, Poetry, Modern American
        Non-Fiction
    Lynch, Robert Edward, English & American
        Literature
    Lyngstad, Sverre, English
    Moore, Lester Lee, Speech, Dramatic Arts
    Pattinson, John Patrick, English
    Primer, Irwin, English
    Stallbaumer, Virgil R, English Literature
    Vantuono, William John, Middle English Litera-
        ture
    Watts, Ann Chalmers, English
    Zocca, Louis Ralph, English
NORTH PLAINFIELD
    Fry, Zella Jeanne, Speech, Drama
NUTLEY
    Alleman, Gellert Spencer, English
PISCATAWAY
    Lilien, David, English
PLAINFIELD
    Main, Charles Frederick, English
POMONA
    Enscoe, Gerald E, English
    Hollis, James R, English
    Klukoff, Philip J, English
    Tompkins, Kenneth D, English
PRINCETON
    Aarsleff, Hans, English
    Baker, Carlos, English & American Literature
    Bell, Michael Davitt, English & American Lit-
        erature
    Bentley, Gerald Eades, English
    Bronte, Diana Lydia, Comparative Literature
    Burt, Nathaniel, English, Music
    Danson, Lawrence Neil, English
    Diederich, Paul Bernard, English

    Dix, William Shepherd, English
    Drewry, Cecelia Hodges, Speech & Drama,
        English
    Fagles, Robert, Comparative Literature, En-
        glish
    Finch, Jeremiah Stanton, English Literature
    Fleming, John Vincent, English, French
    Freedman, Ralph (William Bernard), English
    Fussell, Paul, Jr, English
    Garrett, Peter Kornhauser, English Literature
    Howarth, William Louis, English & American
        Literature
    Howell, Wilbur Samuel, Rhetoric, Oratory
    Johnson, Edward Dudley Hume, English Litera-
        ture
    Keeley, Edmund LeRoy, English
    Kelley, Maurice, English
    Kernan, Alvin Bernard, English
    Kliewer, Warren, English, Theater Arts
    Landa, Louis A, English Literature
    Lewes, Ülle Erika, Medieval & Comparative
        Literature
    Lipking, Lawrence Irwin, English
    Litz, Arthur Walton, English
    Ludwig, Richard Milton, English
    Martin, Robert Bernard, English
    Miller, Henry Knight, English
    Miner, Earl Roy, English
    O'Donnell, Charles Patrick, Jr, English &
        American Literature
    Robertson, Durant Waite, Jr, English
    Roche, Thomas Patrick, Jr, English
    Rosenblatt, Louise Michelle, English,
        Comparative Literature
    Rudenstine, Neil Leon, English
    Schrader, Richard James, Medieval English
        Literature
    Seltzer, Daniel, English Literature
    Tuttle, Preston Heath, Theatre, Drama
    Weiss, Theodore Russell, English
    Wolfe, Don Marion, English
RIDGEWOOD
    McCullough, Bruce, English Literature
RINGWOOD
    McCarthy, James S, Speech
RUTHERFORD
    Mullany, Peter F, English Renaissance,
        Shakespeare
    Violi, Unicio Jack, English, Comparative Lit-
        erature
    Yordan, Edward L, English
SCOTCH PLAINS
    Estrin, Herman A, English
SHORT HILLS
    McGill, Frederick Thomas, Jr, American Lit-
        erature
SOMERVILLE
    Kolb, Alfred, English, German
SOUTH ORANGE
    Butrym, Alexander John, English Literature
    Byrnes, Edward T, Dramatic Literature, Lin-
        guistics
    Lucas, Thomas Edward, American Literature
    MacPhee, Laurence Edward, English
    O'Leary, Kenneth, English
    Petitpas, Harold M, English, Education
    Rogers, David M, English
    Scanlan, Mary Honora, English
    Winser, Leigh, English Literature
STOCKTON
    Knight, Douglas Maitland, English
TEANECK
    Becker, John Edward, American Literature
    Burress, Lee Allan, English
    Dick, Bernard Francis, Classical Philology
    Elliott, John Wesley, Jr, English Romantic Lit-
        erature
    Fleisher, David, English Literature
    Gordon, Lois G, English & American Literature
    Gross, Laila, Medieval Literature
    Kinoian, Vartkis, American & Comparative Con-
        temporary Literature
    Restaino, Katherine Marie, English
    Schrero, Elliot Mitchell, English Language &
        Literature
TRENTON
    Brazell, James Reid, English Literature
    Curry, Wade C, Speech, Drama
    Ford, Hugh D, English
    Guimond, James K, English & American Lit-
        erature
    Heap, Norman A, Speech
    Holman, Alfred P, English
    Hulsman, John Francis, English Literature
    Kiley, Frederick S, English
    Levin, Milton I, English & Drama
    Liddie, Alexander S, English
    McLeod, Alan L, English, Speech
    Oates, Mary I, English
    O'Brien, Audrey, Speech
    Rodnon, Stewart, American Literature
    Sherr, Paul Clinton, English
    Thomas, Jonathan, English

Turner, Frederick Hodson, Jr, Speech Communication
Ward, Herman M, English
UNION
Bauer, Walter John, Jr, English & American Literature
Huberman, Elizabeth Lyle, English & American Literature
Krueger, Sidney, English
Schlueter, Paul, Modern British & American Literature
UPPER MONTCLAIR
Cassady, Marshall Gary, Theatre
Dickson, David Watson Daly, English Literary History
Fox, Leslie Howard, Theatre
Healey, E. Claire, English, American Literature
McElroy, Clyde Wayne, Speech, Drama
Nash, James F, English Literature
Petty, George Raymond, Jr, Old & Middle English
Prosky, Murray, English
Thompson, Sharon Powers, English Literature & Language
VINELAND
Glickfield, Charlotte W, English Romantic Period
WAYNE
Davidow, Mary C, English
De Groot, Elizabeth Marie, English
Karp, Mark, English, Reading
Ludwig, Jay Ferris, Speech, Theater
Mahoney, John Francis, English, Classics
Wertheim, Stanley Claude, English
WEST LONG BRANCH
Andreach, Robert J, English
Brewer, Richard E, English, Comparative Religion
Coe, Charles Norton, English Literature
DeLoche, John Bruce, Jr, English
Gardner, Burdett H, English
Higgins, David James Monroe, English
Jaye, Barbara H, English Literature
Keith, Quentin G, English
WESTFIELD
Stock, Ely, English, American Studies

NEW MEXICO

ALBUQUERQUE
Arms, George (Warren), English Literature
Baughman, Ernest Warren, English, Folklore
Buchanan, Edith, English
Davis, Paul B, English Literature
Dick, Robert Christopher, Speech Communication
Dickey, Franklin Miller, English
Eaves, Morris Emery, Art & Literary Criticism
Eubank, Wayne C, Speech
Fleming, Robert Edward, American Literature, Old English
Frumkin, Gene, English
Garner, Wayne Lee, English
Guthrie, Shirley Law, English & Comparative Literature
Howard, Leon, English
Jacobs, Willis Dana, English & Comparative Literature
Johnson, David Marcus, English
Jones, Joel Mackey, American Literature & History
Kuntz, Joseph Marshall, English Literature
Latham-Pfeifer, Muriel, English
McPherson, David C, English
Martin, William John, Speech, Theatre
Owens, Cullen Bryant, Speech
Pearce, Thomas Matthews, Renaissance Studies
Pickett, Roy, American Literature
Remley, David A, English, American Literature
Simons, Katherine Gauss, English
Snapp, Robert Edwin, Dramatic Art
Spolsky, Ellen, English Literature
Stephenson, Muriel Lois, English Literature, Humanities
Thorson, James Llewellyn, English & American Literature
Trowbridge, Hoyt, English Literature
Whidden, Mary Bess, English
Witemeyer, Hugh Hazen, English & American Literature
Wynn, Dudley, English Literature, Humanities
Zavadil, Joseph, English Literature
CARLSBAD
Fooks, Jaquetta Beth, Theater History, Russian Theater
CERRILLOS
Tedlock, Ernest Warnock, Jr, English

LAS CRUCES
Dupree, John David, Communication, Foreign Languages
Erhard, Thomas A, English, Drama
Hardman, Marion Payzant, English
Hernández, Frances Baker, Comparative Literature, English
Owen, Gordon Richard, Public Speaking
Wilson, Keith, Modern Poetry, Southwestern Literature
LAS VEGAS
Mallory, Thomas Oliver, Jr, English Language & Literature
O'Connell, Richard Leo, Jr, Drama, English
PORTALES
Berne, Stanley, English
Hagan, Robert Lyle, Drama, Speech
Meister, Charles Walter, English & Humanities
Penrod, James, Folklore, American Literature
Robinson, Linda Jane, English & American Literature
Smith, E. Debs, English
Williamson, John Stewart, English Literature
Zekowski, Arlene, English
ROSWELL
Kemble, C. Robert, American Literature & History
Robbins, Gwen, English, Speech
SANTA FE
Bell, Charles Greenleaf, Humanities
Grabo, Norman S, English
King, Eleanor Campbell, Dance, Drama
Linck, Orville Francis, English
Schroder, William T, English Literature
Segura, Andrew Richard (Cyril), F.S.C, English
SANTA ROSA
Wiley, Charles Getchell, Comparative Dramatic Literature, American Studies & Literature
SILVER CITY
Peel, Donald Frank, English Literature
Richards, Lewis A, English
SOCORRO
McKee, John D, American Studies & English
UNIVERSITY PARK
Forsyth, Joseph H, English
Wichert, Robert A, English Literature

NEW YORK

ALBANY
Adams, Theodore S, English & American Literature
Bergmann, Johannes Dietrich, American Literature
Burian, Jarka Marsano, Dramatic Art
Colby, Frances L, English
Collins, Arthur Nethaway, English
Dearing, Bruce, English
Donna, Rose Bernard, C.S.J, English
Donovan, Robert Alan, English
Dorfman, Deborah, English Romantic Poetry
Dumbleton, William A, English
Eustace, Frances Regis, C.S.J, English Literature
Fleming, James T, English, Linguistics
Grenander, Mary Elizabeth, English
Hanley, Katherine, C.S.J, English
Hastings, George S, Jr, English Language & Literature
Hewitt, Ryland Hugh, Jr, Speech, Linguistics, Phonetics
Hoyle, Norman Eugene, English
Jennings, Edward Morton, III, English
Koban, Charles, English
Lennig, Arthur, Cinema, English
Littlefield, Thomson Hastings, English
McArthur, Herbert Christian, English
Maclean, Hugh Norman, English
Mahoney, Mary Berchmans, R.S.M, English
Mirabelli, Eugene, Jr, English & American Literature
Odell, Daniel W, English
Radley, Virginia L, English Literature
Redding, David Coleman, English
Reilly, John Marsden, American & Afro-American Literature
Rich, Townsend, English
Rotundo, Barbara R, English & American Literature
Sanford, Charles LeRoy, American Civilization
Schmidt, Dolores Barracano, English, American Studies
Schulz, Joan E, English
Sogliuzzo, A. Richard, Contemporary American & Italian Theatre
Staley, Harry C, English
Stauffer, Donald B, English
Symons, James Martin, Speech & Drama
Sypher, Francis Jacques, Jr, English Literature
Taylor, Myron Wilfred, English
Tritschler, Donald, English

Weiner, Albert Byron, Theatre History, Directing
Westbrook, Perry Dickie, English
ALBERTSON
Coleman, Arthur, English, American Civilization
ALFRED
Bernstein, Melvin Herbert, English
Brown, Ronald Martin, Speech, Drama
Dille, Ralph Guy, English, Education
Hassencahl, Frances Janet, Speech Communication, U.S. History
Ohara, David Mitsugi, English Literature
Phillips, Steven Ray, English Literature
Shilkett, Carol Lee, Medieval Literature
ANNANDALE-ON-HUDSON
Dewsnap, Terence F, English
ARMONK VILLAGE
Elson, Charles, Drama
AURORA
Clugston, George Alan, English Literature
Helmstadter, Thomas H, English
Nesselhof, John Morrison, English
BALLSTON LAKE
Weaver, Robert Bullard, English
BALLSTON SPA
Barba, Harry, English & Creative Writing
BAYSIDE
Rodeman, Norbert R, Speech, English
Scott, Aurelia Grether, English & Comparative Literature
BINGHAMTON
Bidney, Martin Paul, English & Comparative Literature
Bowen, Zack Rhollie, English
Brooks, Alfred Glenn, Theatre
Burns, Norman T, English Literature, Intellectual History
Carpenter, Charles Albert, Jr, English, Modern Drama
Clements, Arthur Leo, English
Colville, Derek, English
Corrigan, Matthew Anthony, English & American Literature
DiCesare, Mario Anthony, English & Comparative Literature
Freimarck, Vincent, English
Garber, Frederick Meyer, Comparative Literature, Romanticism
Grebstein, Sheldon Norman, Modern & American Literature
Hagan, John H, Jr, English Literature
Hagopian, John V, Literary Criticism
Huppe, Bernard Felix, English Literature
Jackson, Allan Stuart, Theater
Jones, Fred G, Jr, English Literature
Kessler, Milton, English
Kroetsch, Robert Paul, English
Levy, Bernard S, English
McLain, Richard Lee, English Literature
Macksoud, Saleem John, Rhetoric
Mattheisen, Paul Francis, English Literature
Rogers, Philip Edward, English
Schwartz, Elias, English
Smith, Richard Gordon, Drama
Spanos, William V, English, Existential Philosophy
Speckman, William Henry, Literature
Stein, Roger Breed, American Literature & Intellectual History
Stein, William Bysshe, English
Szarmach, Paul Edward, Old & Middle English Language & Literature
Tricomi, Albert Henry, English, Drama
Vasilew, Eugene, Speech
Vernon, John Edward, Modern Literature
Vos, Alvin Paul, English Literature
Walker, John David, English, Eighteenth Century Literature
Webster, Grant T, English & American Literature
Wellwarth, George E, Dramatic Literature
BLAUVELT
MacKellar, Walter, English Literature
Smith, Dorothy Anita, O.P, World & English Literature
BONAVENTURE
Jandoli, Russell Jerome, Journalism, English
BRIARCLIFF MANOR
Ludwigson, Kathryn, English, Theology
Ryther, Dwight Warren, English
BROCKPORT
Atherton, John William, English Literature
Blake, Robert William, English, Education
Bowman, Walter Parker, Comparative Literature
Burelbach, Frederick Michael, Jr, English
Burke, Armand F, English
Fitz Gerald, A. Gregory, English
Gemmett, Robert James, English
Grade, Arnold E, English
Hale, David George, English
Jenks, Joseph B, English

Kane, Peter E, Public Address
Lynch, James Joseph, English
Murray, Edward James, English
O'Donnell, Thomas Francis, English
Styza, Clarence J, German & Russian Literature

BRONX
Antush, John Vincent, English
Arzoomanian, Ralph Sarkis, Drama
Bady, David Michael, English & Dramatic Literature
Belson, Joel J, English
Beringause, Arthur F, English
Blehl, Vincent Ferrer, English Literature
Booth, Mark Warren, English Literature
Bowers, Francis R, F.S.C, English
Britton, John, English Literature
Bush, Robert B, English, American Literature
Carnicelli, Domenick D, English & American Literature
Casey, Floyd W, Victorian & Modern British & American Literature
Charyn, Jerome, English
Cortissoz, Paul, English
Cronin, Grover Jeremiah, Jr, English Literature
Dollard, William Anthony Stanislaus, English
Dubler, Walter, American Literature
Ehrsam, Theodore George, English
Einbond, Bernard Lionel, English
Fendelman, Earl Barry, British & American Modern Literature
Frank, Mortimer Henry, English, Musicology
Garavaglia, Abdon Lewis, F.S.C, World Literature
Geehern, Richard J, English & American Literature
Geissman, Erwin William, English
Giannone, Richard, English
Gilhooley, Leonard, English Language & Literature
Goodman, Oscar B, Comparative Drama
Gottesman, Lillian, English
Gottlieb, Marvin Ronald, Speech, Theatre
Grennan, Eamon, English Literature
Griffin, Alice, Literature
Hall, N. John, English Literature
Hissiger, Paul Frederick, Medieval Literature
Humpherys, Anne, English Literature
Isaacson, Norman, Speech Communication
Joseph, Gerhard Joseph, Victorian Literature
Kahn, Frank J, Mass Communications, Speech
Kearns, Francis Edward, American Literature
Kenney, William Patrick, English
King, Robert Gene, Communication, Rhetoric
Kligerman, Jack, English, Linguistics
Light, James Forest, English & American Literature
Loprete, Nicholas J, Jr, American Literature, Novel
O'Neill, Joseph Eugene, S.J, English
Pease, Marilyn Theresa, English
Perry, Merrill Ivan, English & American Literature
Proffitt, Edward L. F, English Literature, History of Ideas
Reed, Victor Brenner, English & Comparative Literature
Reedy, Gerard Charles, S.J, English Literature
Roberts, Edgar Verne, Jr, English
Schoen, Carol Bronston, American Literature
Schroth, Raymond A, S.J, Journalism, American Studies
Sexton, Richard J, English
Sicherman, Carol Marks, English Literature
Sies, Luther Frank, Speech Pathology, Semantics
Taylor, Mark, English Literature
Tichy, Henrietta, English Literature
Tyne, James Lawrence, S.J, Literature
Valgemae, Mardi, English

BRONXVILLE
Floan, Howard Russell, English & Comparative Literature
Krupat, Arnold, English
Mariani, John Francis, English, Film
Papaleo, Joseph Jr, Comparative Literature, Creative Writing
Park, William, English
Wiener, Harold Simon Lincoln, Comparative Literature

BROOKLINE
Kronenberger, Louis, English Drama

BROOKLYN
Anderson, Valborg, English Literature
Applbaum, Morris J, English
Ashley, Leonard R.N, English
Babey-Brooke, Anna (Mary), English, Medicine
Baumbach, Jonathan, English, Film Studies
Beckson, Karl, English
Berman, Albert Anatole, English, Classics
Boyum, Joy Gould, English
Breglio, Louis Anthony, English

Bruffee, Kenneth Allen, English
Buncombe, Marie Helen, English
Easton, Edward Raymond, English
Ebel, Julia Gracia, English
Edelman, Susanne Popper, English, Comparative Literature
Edwards, Christine, Speech, Theatre
Feigenbaum, Lawrence H, English, Education
Fjelde, Rolf Gerhard, Modern Drama
Fodaski-Black, Martha Haller, English, Comparative Literature
Fox, Robert Charles, English
Ganz, Margaret Leonore, English & Comparative Literature
Gelernt, Jules, English Literature
Goodman, Randolph, English, Drama
Hallmundsson, May Newman, English, Comparative Literature
Haring, Lee, Folklore
Harrington, Norman T, English
Hartman, Murray, English, Drama
Hartmann, Thomas Rae, English
Heffernan, Miriam Margaret, American Literature
Holloway, Emory, American Literature
Hyman, Lawrence W, English Literature
Jarrett, Hobart Sidney, English
Johnson, James Robert, Speech, Drama
Kaye, Julian B, English Literature
Kilcoyne, Francis P, British & American Literature
Kleinberg, Seymour, English Literature
Kramer, Maurice, English
Langley, Stephen G, Theatre, Speech
Lehr, Wilson, Philosophy, Drama
Leiter, Samuel Louis, Theatre
Lind, Sidney Edmund, English
Longtin, Ray Charles, English & American Literature
MacLennan, Donald Wallace, Broadcasting, Speech
McLeod, Stuart R, English, Comparative Literature
Manning, Robert Nickerson, Cinema, Communication
Merritt, James D, English
Murphy, Michael Anthony, Medieval English
Needleman, Morriss Hamilton, English, Education
New, George, Speech, Drama
Ortolani, Benito, Drama, Japanese
Ostrom, Alan B, English
Page, Cornelius Albert, Old English, Linguistics
Park, Bruce Robertson, English
Parkhurst, Charles Edward, Speech
Peck, George August, English Literature
Perkins, Lindsey Saunders, Speech
Perluck, Herbert Alan, English
Price, John R, English Literature
Quinn, Vincent, English
Reiter, Seymour, English Literature, Creative Writing
Reynolds, Beatrice Kay, Speech
Roach, Helen Pauline, Speech
Rogers, Katharine Munzer, English
Rupp, Richard Henry, American Literature
Salomon, Louis Bernard, English
Salzman, Eric, Music Theatre
Salzman, Jack, English
Schaeffer, Susan Fromberg, English & American Literature
Schlissel, Lillian Fischer, English, American Studies
Schreiber, Morris, English, Education
Scott, Kenneth W, Literature
Seiden, Morton Irving, English, Comparative Literature
Siegel, Paul N, English Literature
Silveira, Gerald E, English
Sleeth, Charles Robert, English
Spector, Robert Donald, English
Spielberg, Peter, English, Literature
Templeton, Joan, English
Toepfer, Raymond Grant, English
Tucker, Martin, English
Williams, Robert C, Speech
Wolkenfeld, Jack, English
Young, Robert F, Rhetoric, Interpretation
Zlotnick, Joan C, American Literature

BROOKLYN HEIGHTS
Loney, Glenn Meredith, Theatre & Speech

BUFFALO
Altieri, Charles F, English
Altieri, Joanne Smith, Renaissance Drama
Bernheimer, Charles Clarence, Comparative Literature
Carrithers, Gale H, Jr, English
Connolly, Thomas Edmund, English Language & Literature
Cook, Albert Spaulding, Jr, Comparative Literature
Courter, Eloise Norma, Education, English

Dauber, Kenneth Marc, American Literature
Dings, John Garetson, English
Doyno, Victor A, English
Dryden, Edgar A, American Literature
Duggan, Mary Kathleen, G.N.S.H, English Literature
Efron, Arthur, English
Feldman, Irving, English Literature
Fiedler, Leslie Aaron, English Literature
Fleischer, Martha Hester, Shakespeare, Renaissance Iconography
Fleischer, Stefan, English & Comparative Literature
Fletcher, Angus S, English Literature
Fradin, Joseph Irwin, English
Fried, Martin B, English
Gragg, Wilson B, English Literature
Hammond, Bruce Ray, Communication Theory, Mass Media
Hammond, Mac Sawyer, English Literature
Hochfield, George, English
Holland, Norman Norwood, Jr, English Literature
Jackson, Bruce, Folklore, Sociology
Jauch, Cleveland Edward, Jr, English
Jost, Edward Franklin, English
Klein, Marcus, American Literature
Lauerman, David Anthony, English Literature
Levine, George Richard, English
Lovering, Joseph Paul, English
Massey, Irving Joseph, Comparative Literature
Mazzaro, Jerome, Renaissance & Contemporary Literature
Michel, Laurence Anthony, Jr, English
Newman, Robert S, English & Literature
O'Donnell, Gerald R, English
Payne, Frances Anne, English, Medieval Studies
Piquette, Julia Camilla, Speech, Theatre
Popkin, Henry, English
Reedy, John Edward, English, Education
Riga, Frank P, English
Rosen, Aaron H, English
Sandman, Joseph Thomas, English
Shechner, Mark Ephraim, Modern Fiction
Silverman, Oscar Ansell, English
Slatin, Myles, English
Smith, Arthur L. (Asante), Communication
Smith, Dorothy Ann, R.S.M, English
Stavrou, Constantine Nicholas, English & American Literature
Sylvester, William Arthur, English
Tarbet, David William, English Literature
Thompson, Ernest Clifford, Jr, Speech
Thompson, Richard J, English Literature
Townsend, James Benjamin, English Literature, Humanities
Wickert, Max Albrecht, English & American Literature, Modern Poetry
Wolf, Howard R, American Literature, Psychology

CANTON
Angus, Douglas Ross, English
Bellamy, Joe David, Contemporary American Fiction & Poetry
Berger, Thomas Leland, English Literature
Blankman, Edward James, English, History
Delmage, Rutherford Earle, English & American Literature
Gillespie, Harold Reese, Jr, English
Jamieson, Paul Fletcher, English
Johnson, Donald Dodge, Jr, English
Makosky, Donald Robin, American Literature & Civilization
Matteson, Robert Steere, English
Wheelock, Charles Webster, English

CAZENOVIA
Bentley, Norma Elizabeth, English
Sharp, Lionel Richard, English

CLARKSON
Ryan, Pat M, English, Theatre History

CLINTON
Babbitt, Samuel Fisher, American Studies, American Literature
Bahlke, George Wilbon, English & American Literature
Barrett, Edwin Blois, English Literature
Briggs, Austin Eugene, Jr, English
Carson, Robert Rose, Public Speaking
Hoffa, William W, English
Lindley, Dwight N, English, Literature
Nesbitt, George Lyman, English Literature
O'Neill, John Higbee, English Literature
Rosenfeld, William, American Literature
Roth, Frederic Hull, Jr, Renaissance English Literature

CORTLAND
Beard, Raymond S, Speech
Bogard, Morris R, Speech, Theatre
Burd, Van Akin, English
Hnatko, Eugene, Literature
Kaminsky, Alice R, Literature
Malbone, Raymond Gates, English
Meyer, Gerald Dennis, English Literature

Shatzky, Joel Lawrence, Modern Drama
Talentino, Arnold V, English Literature
Toor, David, English
CRAGSMOOR
Weber, John Sherwood, English, Comparative
Literature
CRARYVILLE
Fitzhugh, Robert Tyson, Literature
DOUGLASTON
Blanchard, Elizabeth Sheila, English
McHugh, Ruth Nelson, English, Music
Parks, George Bruner, English Literature
ELBRIDGE
Speirs, Russell Freeman, English
ELMIRA
Hauser, David Roswell, English
Marsden, Malcolm Morse, American Literature
Murray, John Ralph, English, Administration
ELMSFORD
Rugoff, Milton, English, History
FLUSHING
Bornstein, Diane D, Medieval & Renaissance
Literature, Linguistics
Brewer, Helene Maxwell, American Literature
& Studies
Campbell, Paul Newell, Communication
Carlson, Harry Gilbert, Drama & Speech
Cathcart, Robert S, Rhetoric & Public Address
Colby, Robert Alan, English, Library Science
Colby, Vineta, English
Dahlberg, Charles, English
D'Avanzo, Mario L, English
Day, Robert Adams, English
DeVito, Joseph A, Speech
Dickstein, Morris, English & Comparative Lit-
erature
Dierlam, Robert Jackson, Speech
Donno, Daniel J, English & Comparative Litera-
ture
Dycke, Marjorie L, Theatre Education
Feder, Lillian, English, Classics
Fried, Harvey, English
Friedman, Norman, English
Gilman, Wilbur Elwyn, English, Rhetoric
Goldstein, Malcolm, English
Green, William, English & Drama
Greenberg, Robert Arthur, Literature
Gross, Beverly A, English
Grossman, Manuel Lester, Speech & Theater
Held, George, English & American Literature
Hill, Forbes I, Rhetoric, Public Speaking
Isler, Alan David, English Renaissance Litera-
ture, Shakespeare
Joseph, Bertram L, English, Drama
Kaplan, Fred, English
Kowal, Michael, English & Comparative Lit-
erature
Krummel, Regina Pomerenz, English, Education
Lindberg, Lucile, English, History
Linn, John Gaywood, English
Martin, Wendy, American Literature
Matlaw, Myron, English
Miller, Robert Parsons, English
Newman, John Benjamin, Speech
Phillips, Norma Anne, English
Ranald, Margaret Loftus, English Literature
Roever, James E, Speech
Silverstein, Norman, English
Starkman, Miriam Kosh, English Literature
Stepanchev, Stephen, American Literature
Stone, Donald David, English Literature
Timko, Michael, English Literature
Towers, Augustus Robert, Jr, English
Vande Kieft, Ruth Marguerite, English & Am-
erican Literature
Walcutt, Charles Child, American Fiction, En-
glish
Withington, Eleanor (May), English
Zinnes, Harriet F, English
FOREST HILLS
Bush, George Edward, English
Coleman, William Emmet, English Literature,
Medieval Languages & Literature
FORT PLAIN
Drake, Ormond John, Speech
FREDONIA
Cogdill, John L. Jack, Theatre, Speech
Courts, Patrick Lawrence, English Education,
American Literature
Deming, Robert Howard, English
Dunn, Albert Anthony, English & Comparative
Literature
Fries, Maureen Holmberg, English Literature
Golden, Daniel, American & English Literature
Huffman, James Richard, English, American
Studies
Kline, Richard Burton, English
Libby, Nancy Dorothea, English & American
Literature
Mix, Clarence Rex, Speech Communication
Nelson, Malcolm A, English
Neville, William A, English

Roberts, Ruth Eloise, English, Comparative
Literature
Rowland, J. Carter, English
Salerno, Henry Frank, English
Schweik, Robert Charles, English
Sebouhian, George, Literature
Shepard, Douglas H, English
Shokoff, James, English Literature, Film
Smith, Calvin Clifton, English
Steese, Peter B, English
Steinberg, Theodore Louis, Renaissance En-
glish, Modern Jewish Literature
Stinson, John Jerome, Modern British Litera-
ture
Symula, James Francis, English Education
Warner, Stephen Douglas, American Literature,
Novel
FREEPORT
Brodwin, Leonora Leet, English Literature
Fenyo, Jane K, English, Linguistics
GARDEN CITY
Blake, James Joseph, English & Irish Litera-
ture
Bodtke, Richard A, English Literature
Brostowin, Patrick Ronald, English
Clemo, Richard F, Speech & Dramatic Art
Greene, Philip L, American Literature
Himelstein, Morgan Yale, English
Hoffman, Russell, English
Koster, Donald Nelson, English
Lawn, Beverly Burghardt, American & En-
glish Literature
Marlor, Clark Strang, Speech
Rothman, Julius L, American Literature
Terris, Virginia Rinaldy, American Literature
Wolf, Donald, English
GENESEO
Berry, William Ray, Speech, Broadcasting
Gollin, Rita K, English Literature
Gottschalk, Hans W, English
Hoey, John B, English Literature
Klee, Bruce B, Theatre
Moss, Leonard Jerome, Comparative Litera-
ture
Shaw, Myron B, Speech, Broadcasting
Simpson, Herbert M, English, Dramatic Lit-
erature
Smith, Gerald Alfred, English Literature
Stelzig, Eugene Louis, English & American
Literature
Watt, Donald J, English
GENEVA
Atkinson, Benjamin Peter, Literature
Cummings, Peter March, English Literature
Griffith, Edward E, English & Drama
Lydenberg, John, English, American Studies
Yeh, Max Wei, Comparative & English Litera-
ture
GREAT NECK
Chupack, Henry, English, American Literature
Evans, Jack, English
Mammen, Edward William, Drama, Speech
Raben, Joseph, English
Ronsheim, Sally B, English
Rosenthal, Irving, English
Secord, Arthur, Speech
Waxman, Ruth, English & Comparative Lit-
erature
GREENLAWN
Corrigan, Francis Xavier, English
GREENVALE
Backman, Melvin Abraham, English
Dircks, Phyllis, English
Feinstein, Blossom, English
Gillis, Herbert Russell, English, Speech &
Drama
Greenberg, Martin, English Literature
Griffith, Richard Randolph, English
Kleinfield, Herbert L, English & American
Studies
Kruger, Arthur N, Speech, Philosophy
Lettis, Richard, English
Mates, Julian, Dramatic Literature
Reiner, Karol Sturm, Speech, English As A
Second Language
Rodax, Yvonne, English, Comparative Litera-
ture
Small, George A, Literature, Philology
Stetner, S.C.V, English & Comparative Lit-
erature
Welcher, Jeanne K, English Literature
GROVELAND
Harding, Walter, English
GUILDERLAND
McNally, James Richard, Speech
HAMILTON
Blackmore, Robert Long, English
Busch, Frederick Matthew, American & Mod-
ern Literature
Hitchcock, Ned, II, Theater, English
Hoben, John Burton, American Literature
Kinney, Stanley Newell, English, Speech

Kistler, Jonathan Hipperling, English & Am-
erican Literature
Lancaster, Robert Vaughan, English Literature,
Theology
Slater, Joseph, English
Sproul, Harold Atlee, Drama
Williams, Donald Stephen, Speech, Education
HARTSDALE
Smith, Loretta Wagner, Speech
HEMPSTEAD
Chalfant, Edward Allan, English
Dunbar, Georgia Sherwood, English Literature
Goldman, Hannah Stern, English
Gurko, Leo, English Literature
Hull, William Doyle, English
Keane, Robert Norwood, English Literature
McBrien, William Augustine, English
O'Donnell, Charles Robert, English
Reeves, John Drummond, English, Classics
Scott, Wilbur S, English & American Literature
Swinney, Donald Henry, Speech, Drama
Thune, Ensaf, English Literature, Drama
Tureen, Jack, Speech
Van Wart, James, Drama
Wagner, C. Roland, English, Philosophy
White, Harvey, Speech Pathology
Young, Stanley Preston, Drama, English Litera-
ture
HOUGHTON
Barcus, James E, English Literature
Davis, Abraham, Jr, Rhetoric & Public Address,
Speech Pathology & Therapy
HUDSON
Botkin, Benjamin Albert, Folklore
ITHACA
Abrams, Meyer Howard, English Literature
Adams, Barry Banfield, English
Albright, Harry Darkes, Theatre Arts
Baizer, Ashur, English
Bishop, Jonathan (Peale), English
Blackall, Jean Frantz, English Literature
Boyd, John Douglas, English
Brownell, Morris Ruggles, III, English Litera-
ture
Budick, Sanford, English Literature
Caputi, Anthony Francis, English
Carlson, Marvin A, Speech, Drama
Colacurcio, Michael Joseph, Jr, American Lit-
erature, Intellectual History
Cronkhite, George Ferris, English and Ameri-
can Literature
Eddy, Donald Davis, English Literature
Elias, Robert Henry, English, American Studies
Elledge, Scott Bowen, English Literature
Farrell, Robert Thomas, English
Fogel, Ephim Gregory, English
Gottschalk, Paul A, English
Harcourt, John Bertram, English
Hathaway, Baxter, English
Hill, Thomas Dana, English
Hume, Robert David, English Literature
Kaske, Carol Vonckx, English & Comparative
Literature
Kaske, Robert Earl, English, Comparative Lin-
guistics
Kaufman, Michael William, English
Kaye, Howard, English
Levy, Charles Samuel, English
McCall, Dan Elliott, English
McConkey, James R, English
McMillin, Harvey Scott, Jr, English Litera-
ture
Marcus, Phillip L, English
Mineka, Francis Edward, English Literature
Mizener, Arthur Moore, English Literature
Novarr, David, English Literature
Parker, William Henry, American Studies,
American Literature
Parrish, Stephen Maxfield, English
Redding, Jay Saunders, English
Rosenberg, Edgar, English & Comparative
Literature
Sale, William Merritt, Jr, English Literature
Schwarz, Daniel Roger, English
Slatoff, Walter Jacob, English
Stainton, Walter Hutchinson, Drama, Theatre
States, Bert O, Theatre Arts, English
Storrer, William Allin, Communications, Com-
parative Arts
Terwilliger, Ernest William, English
Ulloth, Dana Royal, Broadcasting, Film
Wetherbee, Winthrop, III, English, Comparative
Literature
Williams, Marilyn E, English
JAMAICA
Bachman, Ferdinand Francis, English
Belli, Angela, English, Comparative Literature
Broussard, Louis, English
Cevasco, George Anthony, English
Derrig, Patrick Austin, C.M, English & Ameri-
can Literature
Dircks, Richard J, English
Dorris, George Edward, English Literature

Galper, Pamela A, English & American Literature
Guereschi, Edward Fred, American & English Literature
Hafley, James Robert, English Language & Literature
Hallam, Virginia Ann, English
Hanley, Evelyn Alice, English
Hatvary, George Egon, English
Hux, Samuel H, English
Johnson, Edward Andrew, English, American Literature
Kunkel, Francis Leo, English
Lucow, Benjamin John, English
Luyben, Helen Louise, English
Marotta, Joseph Gerald, Medieval English Literature, History of Rhetoric
Mersand, Joseph, English
Nauss, George Murray, English & American Literature
Pineas, Rainer, English Literature
Ray, Paul Charles, English, Comparative Literature
Richmond, Lee John, English & American Literature
Whelan, Robert Emmet, Jr, American Literature
KENMORE
Brady, Charles Andrew, English
Drew, Fraser Bragg, English
Facos, Peter Christopher, English, Educational Administration
Vucinich, Mary Cochnower, English
KEUKA PARK
Wallis, Charles Langworthy, English
KEW GARDENS
Loughlin, Richard Lawrence, English, Speech
KINGS POINT
Fredman, Alice Green, English & Comparative Literature
Norton, Aloysius A, English, Literature as History
LACKAWANNA
Reimondo, Mary Sylvia, S.S.J, English, Drama
LAKE PLACID
Haponski, William Charles, English
LARCHMONT
Porter, Raymond James, English
LAWRENCE
Brownstone, Paul L, Speech, Education
LLOYD HARBOR
Mader, Thomas Francis, Speech
LOCUST VALLEY
Gondin, William Richard, Speech
LONDONVILLE
Hirten, William James, English
LONG ISLAND CITY
Groman, George L, American Literature & History
Shaftel, Oscar Hamilton, English Literature, Oriental Culture
LOUDONVILLE
Conlin, Matthew Thomas, O.F.M, English
Devlin, Vianney Martin, O.F.M, English
Fiore, Peter Amadeus, O.F.M, English
Jedynak, Stanley Louis, English
MAMARONECK
Krieghbaum, Hillier, Journalism, Current History
MANHASSET
Haney, John B, Communications, Instructional Technology
MANLIUS
Eaton, Winifred K, English, Asian Studies
MASSAPEQUA
Wiener, Harvey Shelby, English & American Literature, Composition
MILLBROOK
Hoyt, Charles Alva, English Literature
MONSEY
Artin, Thomas, English, Comparative Literature
Ochojski, Paul M, English
MORRISVILLE
Benson, Morris, English Literature
Hammond, Charles Montgomery, Journalism, English
Helmer, William Floyd, English, History
Mockovak, Paul William, English
MOUNT VERNON
Russell, Mariann B, English
NEW HARTFORD
Millett, Robert Walter, English
NEW PALTZ
Baisler, Perry, Speech
Bort, Barry Davis, English
Brown, Irving M, Theatre & Fine Arts
Cash, Arthur Hill, English Literature
Coffman, Stanley Knight, Jr, English
Fein, Richard J, English
Gillon, Adam, English & Comparative Literature
Hathaway, Richard Dean, American Literature

Irvine, Rose Abernethy, Speech
Irwin, Vera Rushforth, Drama
Kossmann, Rudolf R, English
Marks, Alfred Harding, English
Schwartz, Sheila Ruth, Language Arts, English
Thornton, Robert Donald, English Literature
NEW ROCHELLE
Bermel, Albert (Cyril), Theatre History
Brophy, Elizabeth Bergen, Eighteenth Century English Literature
Brophy, James David, Jr, English
Carson, Angela, O.S.U, English
Darretta, John Lawrence, American Literature, Communication Arts
Falls, Theresa C, O.S.U, English Literature
Hill, William Speed, Renaissance
Huguenin, Charles Arthur, English
Mahoney, Irene, O.S.U, English
Pecheux, Christopher, O.S.U, English Literature
Ruane, Darby T, English Literature
Solomon, Stanley J, English
Vergara, Allys Dwyer, English
Yellin, Jean Fagan, American Literature & Studies
NEW YORK CITY
Achtert, Walter Scott, English Literature
Adkins, Nelson Frederick, English
Albert, Leonard, English, Comparative Literature
Allen, Gay Wilson, English
Allentuck, Marcia Epstein, English
Amberg, George H, Art
Anderson, Quentin, English
Angoff, Charles, English, Journalism
Aptekar, Jane, English
Babinski, Hubert F, Comparative Literature
Bagster-Collins, Jeremy Felix, English
Baker, Elmer E, Jr, Speech
Baker, Richard T, Journalism
Barasch, Frances K, English
Bard, Isaiah S, Communications, Journalism
Barnouw, Erik, Dramatic Arts
Baron, Dennis E, English Literature, Linguistics
Barrett, Edward Ware, Journalism
Bazerman, Charles, English & American Literature
Beckerman, Bernard, Drama
Benardete, Jane, English & American Literature
Benson, Frederick R, Comparative Literature, English
Bentley, Eric, Drama, Comparative Literature
Bercovitch, Sacvan, English
Berggren, Paula S, English Renaissance Literature, English Poetry & Drama
Bernard, Kenneth, English
Bessinger, Jess Balsor, Jr, English
Black, Michael Lawrence, English
Bloomgarden, Ira Lewis, Medieval English, Comparative Literature
Bone, Robert A, English Literature
Bossone, Richard M, English Education
Bower, Warren, English
Bowman, Richard Stearns, Comparative Literature
Boxill, Roger, English
Boyd, John Dominic, S.J, English
Brady, Frank, English
Branman, Irving, Speech, English
Braudy, Leo, English
Brewster, Dorothy, Contemporary Literature
Brodtkorb, Paul, Jr, English & American Studies
Brody, Saul Nathaniel, English, Comparative Medieval Literature
Brown, Arthur Wayne, English
Browne, Michael, Communication & Theatre Arts
Buckler, William E, English
Byard, Margaret Mather, English
Byrnes, Joseph Alfred, English
Calder, Grace J, English
Callahan, Jennie Waugh, Communications
Cameron, Kenneth Neill, English Literature
Cash, Earl A, Twentieth Century American Literature
Cayer, Roger L, English, English Education
Chandler, Alice, English
Chandler, Daniel Ross, Speech Communication, Religion
Chester, Giraud, Speech
Clancy, Joseph P, English
Clees, James C, English
Clemons, Walter, (Jr), American History, English Literature
Clifford, James Lowry, English
Cohen, Morton Norton, English Literature
Colbourn, Frank E, Debate, Communications
Collins, Christopher, Modern Poetry, American Literature
Comito, Terry Allen, English

Cooley, E. Mason, English & Comparative Literature
Cooperman, Hasye, American & Comparative Literature
Cosman, Madeleine Pelner, English, Comparative Medieval Literature
Croman, Charlotte, Drama, Speech
Cullen, Patrick Colborn, English
Dace, Letitia Skinner, Dramatic Literature
Dalven, Rae, English, Foreign Language
Danzig, Allan (Peter), English Literature
Davis, Robert Gorham, English
Deakins, Roger Lee, English Literature
Dean, Leonard Fellows, English
Dean, Nancy, English, Medieval Literature
Deutsch, Babette, Poetry
Dodson, Daniel B, Comparative Literature
Donahue, Charles James, English, Celtic Philology
Donno, Elizabeth Story, English
Donovan, Richard A, English, Drama
Dooley, Roger Burke, English
Ebin, Lois A, English & Medieval Literature
Economou, George Demetrios, English, Comparative Literature
Elton, W.R, English
Emanuel, James A, Sr, American & English Literature
England, Martha Winburn, English
Fenaughty, Thomas J, English
Ferrante, Joan M, Comparative Medieval Literature
Ferrar, Harold, English, Comparative Literature
Fisher, William J, English
Fluharty, George Watson, Speech
Fone, Byrne Reginald Spencer, English
Fowler, Austin, English, Speech
Friedman, Alan, English
Friedman, Joel Joseph, Theatre, Playwrighting
Friend, Albert Charles, Literature
Ganz, Arthur Frederick, English
Gaubert, Helen A, Drama, Speech
Gilder, Rosamond, Drama
Gill, Richard, Modern British Literature
Glicksberg, Charles Irving, English
Golden, Arthur, English, American Literature
Goldman, Albert, English, Comparative Literature
Goldstone, Richard H, English, Dramatic Literature
Gordon, David J, English
Grace, Joan Carroll, English
Grace, Matthew, English
Grebanier, Bernard, English
Greene, David H, English Literature
Greene, James J, English, Drama
Greene, Maxine, English, Philosophy
Grennen, Joseph Edward, English Literature
Gross, Theodore L, English, American Civilization
Guilhamet, Leon Maurice, English
Hall, Robert Noel, Speech Communication
Hallett, Charles Arthur, (Jr), Shakespeare, Drama
Hamalian, Leo, English, Comparative Literature
Hanning, Robert William, Medieval & Renaissance Literature
Harrier, Richard Charles, English
Hartley, Robert Arnold, English Literature
Hartman, Joan Edna, English Literature
Harvey, J. Bailey, Speech
Hasch, Jack J, Speech
Hatch, James V, English, Theatre Arts
Hawkes, Carol, English
Hazen, Allen Tracy, English Literature
Healy, Timothy S, S.J, English Literature
Heffner, Richard D, Communications, History
Heilbrun, Carolyn G, English Literature
Hellinger, Benjamin, English Literature
Hendricks, Walter, English Literature
Herman, William, English, World Drama
Hohenberg, John, Journalism
Holder, Alan, English
Hollander, John, English
Hoopes, Ned Edward, British Novel, Teaching Secondary English
Hopper, Vincent Foster, Comparative Literature
Hornstein, Lillian Herlands, English Literature
Hovde, Carl F, English
Howe, Irving, English
Huss, Roy G, English, Film
Ives, Sumner (Albert), English Language
Jacoby, Gordon A, Speech, Drama
Jaffe, Harold, English
Janis, Jack Harold, Business Writing
Javitch, Daniel Gilbert, English, Comparative Literature
Jehlen, Myra, English, American Studies
Johnson, Edgar, English, Comparative Literature

Johnson, Samuel Frederick, English Literature
Johnson, Wendell Stacy, English
Jones, Dorothy Richardson, English
Kaplan, Milton A, English Education
Karl, Frederick R, English
Karp, Lila, Literature
Kauvar, Gerald Bluestone, English
Kavanagh, Peter, English
Kazin, Alfred, American Studies
Keener, Frederick M, English
Kelvin, Norman, English Literature
Kennedy, Sighle Aileen, Modern Literature
Kestner, Joseph, English Novel, Romanticism
Keyser, Barbara Yarbrough, Modern British
   & American Literature
King, Thomas James, English, Drama
Kivette, Ruth M, English Literature
Knouse, Margaret Livesay, English
Koch, Kenneth, English, Comparative Lit-
   erature
Kouwenhoven, John A, English
Kozelka, Edwin Paul, Speech
Kranidas, Thomas, English
Kriegel, Leonard, English
Kroeber, Karl, English
Kuehl, John Richard, American Literature,
   Creative Writing
Kuner, Mildred Christophe, English, Drama
Kunitz, Stanley, English
Kurrik, Maire Jaanus, English & German Lit-
   erature
Lachmann, Vera Regina, Greek Literature,
   Poetry
Lahey, Gerald, English Literature
Laurence, Dan H, English Literature
Leaska, Mitchell A, English Literary Criticism
Lederman-Birnbaum, Marie Jean, Contempo-
   rary Literature
Lehmann, Margaret Grennan, English
Levine, Norman, Tudor Literature
Levy, William Turner, English
Licklider, Patricia Minichino, Comparative
   Renaissance Literature
Lieb-Brilhart, Barbara, Speech, Education
Lifson, David S, Drama, English
Lind, Ilse Dusoir, English
Linn, Irving, English
Lippmann, Walter, Public Affairs
Lockridge, Laurence Shockley, English Lit-
   erature
Lovenheim, Barbara Irene, English Victorian
   Literature
Low, Anthony, English Literature
Luter, John, Journalism
Lyons, Nathan R, English
McAleer, Edward Cornelius, English Literature
McCaslin, Nellie, Drama & Theatre
McCoy, Kathleen, English
McDonald, Dennis K, Dramatic Literature
McFarland, Thomas (Alfred, Jr), English Lit-
   erature
McGlinchee, Claire, English
McNamara Brooks B, Drama
MacShane, Frank, Writing, English Litera-
   ture
Magalaner, Marvin, English
Malin, Irving, English
Malkoff, Karl, English
Mandelbaum, Bernard D, English, Comparative
   Literature
Marcett, Mildred Elizabeth, English
Marcus, Steven, English
Margolies, Alan, English & American Litera-
   ture
Margolies, Edward, American Civilization &
   Literature
Mazzeo, Joseph A, English, Comparative Lit-
   erature
Meisel, Martin, English
Mencher, Melvin, Journalism
Merton, Egon Stephen, English
Middendorf, John Harlan, English
Middlebrook, Leah Ruth, English
Middlebrook, Samuel Marvin, American Lit-
   erature
Miller, Edwin Haviland, English Literature
Mintz, Samuel Isaiah, English
Mirollo, James V, English
Mirsky, David, English
Moers, Ellen, English, Comparative Literature
Morris, Virginia Baumgartner, English & Irish
   Literature
Morrison, Jack, Theater
Mueller, Iris Wessel, English
Murphy, Daniel J, English
Murray, Michael H, English
Nelson, William, English
Newstead, Helaine, Medieval Literature
Nicolson, Marjorie Hope, English
Norman, Richard A, English, Speech
Norris, David, Modern Drama
Ogilvie, Mardel, Speech
Oman, William M, English

Oppenheimer, Paul, Medieval Literature,
   Writing
Owens, Curtis, English
Owens, William A, English
Palestrant, Stephen, Speech, Drama
Palmer, Winthrop, English
Parlakian, Nishan, Drama & Speech
Parsons, Coleman Oscar, English & American
   Literature
Patterson, Remington Perrigo, English
Payne, Robert O, English
Perry, Edward Samuel, Cinema Studies
Pfeffer, Arthur Saul, English
Pinckert, Robert C, English
Piscator, Maria Ley, French & Modern The-
   atre
Pollin, Burton Ralph, English
Pollock, Thomas Clark, American Literature
Potoker, Edward M, English & Comparative
   Literature
Potter, John Matthew, English Literature
Prescott, Anne Lake, English
Przybylska, Krystyna, Modern Theatre
Quinn, Edward, English
Quinn, Esther Casier, English
Ray, Gordon N, English
Raymo, Robert Rowland, English
Regueiro, Helen, Comparative Literature
Reiman, Donald Henry, English Literature
Resnick, Nathan, Art, American Literature
Reynolds, Ota Thomas, Rhetoric & Public Ad-
   dress
Ribman, Ronald Burt, English Literature
Ridenour, George Meyer, English
Ridgely, Joseph V, English
Roberts, Vera Mowry, English, Drama
Robertson, David Allan, Jr, English Literature
Robinson, Eleanor M, English
Rockwood, Jerome, Theatre, Speech
Rosenberg, Eleanor, English Literature
Rosenberg, John D, English Literature
Rosenfield, Lawrence William, Speech, Com-
   munications
Rosenthal, Macha Louis, English
Rovit, Earl Herbert, English
Rudman, Harry William, English Literature
Rukeyser, Muriel, Literature, Writing
Ryskamp, Charles Andrew, English
Said, Edward William, English
Samuel, Irene, English Literature
Saxon, Arthur Hartley, History of the Theatre
   Dramatic Literature
Schaefer, William David, English
Schechner, Richard, Theatre
Schendler, Sylvan, English
Schless, Howard Hugh, English
Schmidt, Carl Peter, Modern Japanese Lit-
   erature, English Education
Schreiber, Flora Rheta, Speech
Schulman, Grace, Modern Poetry
Scotto, Robert Michael, Modern Fiction
Seiger, Marvin, Speech & Drama
Seymour, Victor, Speech, Theatre

Shaw, Peter, English & American Literature
Shawcross, John Thomas, English
Sherwin, Oscar, English Literature
Shine, Muriel Gruber, English
Shoemaker, Francis, English, Humanities
Shugrue, Michael Francis, English Literature
Silverman, Kenneth Eugene, English, American
   Studies
Simonson, Solomon S, Rhetoric, Propaganda
Slattery, Mary Francis, S.C, English
Smith, Ralph Ruggles, Speech, American His-
   tory
Spiegler, Marlene, English & Comparative
   Literature
Spingarn, Edward, English
Sprague, Claire Sacks, Modern American &
   English Literature
Stade, George, English
Stark, Irwin, English
Starr, Nathan Comfort, English Literature
Stein, Jess, English, Linguistics
Steinberg, Abraham H, English
Stern, Bernard Herbert, English Literature
Stevenson, David Lloyd, English
Stimpson, Catharine R, Contemporary Lit-
   erature, Critical Theory
Stoddard, Donald Richard, American & En-
   glish Literature
Stone, George Winchester, Jr, English Lit-
   erature
Stone, Irving, Biography
Sullivan, Kevin, English
Sundwall, McKay, English & Comparative
   Literature
Swann, Brian S.F, English
Swortzell, Lowell Stanley, Educational Theatre,
   Speech & Drama
Syrkin, Marie, English
Tayler, Edward William, English Literature
Tayler, Irene, Literature, Art History

Tebbel, John William, Journalism
Thaddeus, Janice Farrar, English
Thiebaux, Marcelle, English, Comparative
   Literature
Thomas, (Frederick) Bryce, English
Tilton, Eleanor M, American Literature
Tindall, William York, English Literature
Todd, John Emerson, English
Todd, Waldemar Dwight, Comparative Lit-
   erature
Tomarken, Edward Lee, English
Traschen, Isadore, English
Trilling, Lionel, English Literature
Tuttleton, James Wesley, English
Ulanov, Barry, English
Valency, Maurice, English & Comparative
   Literature
Vogel, Dan, English
Waldhorn, Arthur, English
Waren, Stanley A, Speech, Theatre
Watson, Barbara Bellow, English
Weidhorn, Manfred, English
Whittemore. Nena Thames. English Literature
Wilhelm, James Jerome, Comparative Lit-
   erature
Wilkins, Thurman, English
Willen, Gerald, English
Williamson, Mary Celeste, S.S.J, English
Wilson, John Fletcher, Speech
Windes, Russel R, Social & Behavioral Sci-
   ences, Communication
Wohlgelernter, Maurice, English
Woodman, Leonora, American Literature, En-
   glish Education
Woodring, Carl, English Literature
Work, William, Speech & Drama
Yohannan, John David, English
NEWARK
Huberman, Edward, English
NEWBURGH
Cotter, James Finn, English Literature, Phi-
   losophy
NIAGARA
Burke, Edward J, C.M, English
McCrory, Thomas Edwin, English, Literary
   Criticism
Maloney, Leo James, English, Philosophy
NORWOOD
McFarland, George Foster, English Literature
NYACK
Wright, Brooks, English
OAKDALE
Kramer, Aaron, English
OCEANSIDE
Smithline, Arnold, English
OLCOTT
McGrath, Edward, French & English Literature
OLD WESTBURY
Collett, Jonathan H, English
Olander, James H, Speech & Drama, English
Salper, Roberta Linda, Latin American &
   Spanish Literature
ONEONTA
Baldwin, David, English, American Studies
Beattie, Thomas Charles, English Language &
   Literature
Carney, John Joseph, Jr, Speech
Casey, Daniel Joseph, Irish Literature, English
   Education
Davidson, Edith T. Aney, English, World Lit-
   erature
Hamblin, Junius N, Theatre
Harrison, Howard, English
Hutman, Norma Louise, Comparative Litera-
   ture, Humanities
Italia, Paul Gregory, English Romantic Poetry
Kelly, Edward Hanford, English
Knudson, Richard Lewis, English
Moynihan, Robert Duncan, English Literature
Perkus, Gerald H, Victorian & American Lit-
   erature
Rounds, Robert W, English
Rubin, Steven H, English
Rude, Leslie G, Speech
Sampson, Edward C, English
Schramm, Allan N, Communications
Test, George Austin, Literature
Warncke, Wayne Warren, English Literature
Wesley, Norman, English
ORIENT
De Maria, Robert, English
OSWEGO
Annunziata, Anthony W, English
Bishop, David Rand, Jr, Comparative Lit-
   erature, African Studies
Briand, Paul L, Jr, English
Chalifour, Clark Lester, English Literature
Drake, William D, English, Linguistics
McEvoy, J. Edward, Speech
Mincher, John W, Jr, Theatre, Speech
Palmer, Erwin, English
Rickert, Alfred E, English, Drama
Rogal, Samuel J, English

Sternlicht, Sanford, English
Sweetser, Wesley Duaine, English
Turco, Lewis, English
Winslow, David John, Folklore, English
OYSTER BAY
Gambone, Kenneth F, English, Humanities
PEEKSVILLE
Baptiste, Herman C, English
Corbin, Richard, English
PLATTSBURGH
Abbe, George, English
Clarkson, Philip B, Dramatic Literature & English
Donaho, Melvin Willard, Rhetoric & Public Address
Heuston, Edward F, English
Kline, H. Charles, Theatre
Pierce, Merle Scheffel, Speech
PLEASANT VALLEY
Farr, Judith Banzer, English & American Literature
PLEASANTVILLE
Dell, Robert Merritt, English, American Drama
Work, Jane Magruder, Speech, Radio & TV
PORT WASHINGTON
Ball, Robert Hamilton, English
Muller, Gilbert Henry, American Literature
POTSDAM
Broughton, Bradford Browne, English
Brunauer, Dalma H, English, Humanities
Cullen, William H, English, Education
Fairbanks, Rollin Jonathan, Jr, American & Commonwealth Literature
Fenner, Theodore Lincoln, English Romantic Writers
Harder, Kelsie Brown, English
Kaplan, Israel, English, Anglo-Irish Literature
Lowe, William John, Liberal Studies, English
Paige, Harry W, English, American Indian Studies
Stillman, Donald Gale, English
Vaid, Krishna Baldev, English & American Literature
POUGHKEEPSIE
Bartlett, Lynn Conant, English
Christie, John Aldrich, English & American Literature
Daniels, Elizabeth Adams, English
Darlington, Beth Mary, English Literature
Gifford, William W, English
Green, Howard Lewis, English
Hawkins, Harriett B, English
Mace, Dean Tolle, English
McGrew, Julia Helen, English
Parrott, Frederick James, English, Speech, Drama
Paul-Emile, Barbara Taylor, English Literature
Rothwell, William F, Jr, Drama
Sherwood, William Robert, English
Sommer, George J, Medieval Literature
Sprinchorn, Evert Manfred, Drama, Scandinavian Literature
Teichman, Milton, English
Tenenbaum, Elizabeth Brody, English & American Literature
Turner, Susan Jane, English, American Literature
Winn, Otis Howard, English
PURCHASE
Davies, Robert Morton, English
Eurich, Nell P, English
Houghton, Charles Norris, Drama
Isaac, Dan Bert, English, Drama
Levine, George, English Literature
Murtaugh, Daniel Maher, English
O'Clair, Robert M, English Literature
Piccolo, Anthony, English & American Literature
Wadsworth, Frank Whittemore, English
RENSSELAER
Cooper, Bernarr, Mass Communications, Speech
ROCHESTER
Bailey, Joe Allen, Communications, Adult Education
Collins, Rowland Lee, English
Collins, Sarah Huff, English Literature
Davis, Mary Ann Kelso, English Literature
Dorsey, Joseph B, C.S.B, English
Eder, Doris Leonora, Modern & Contemporary British & American Literature
Folkenflik, Robert, English
Ford, George Harry, English Literature
Gilman, William Henry, English
Golden, Robert Edward, English & American Literature
Gollin, Richard Myron, English
Graham, Susette Ryan, English & American Literature
Grella, George J, English
Hecht, Anthony Evan, Poetry
Hoctor, Thomas Marion, S.S.J, English

Horsford, Howard Clarke, English
Howard, Hubert Wendell, English Literature, Music
Hoy, Cyrus Henry, English, Renaissance Literature
Johnson, Bruce M, English
Johnson, James William, English Literature
Kelley, Margaret Teresa, S.S.J, English
Koller, Kathrine, English
McGrath, Juliet, Renaissance English Literature
McHugh, Richard W, English, Philosophy
McIntosh, Rustin Carey, English
Panara, Robert Frederic, English
Peck, Russell Albert, Middle English Literature
Perry, Margaret, Afro-American Literature, Library Science
Ramsey, Jarold William, English Literature
Rieger, James H, English
Rueckert, William Howe, English
Sherwin, Wilma, Literature
Shuffelton, Frank Charles, English & American Literature
Sullivan, Mary C, R.S.M, Literature, Religion
Summers, Joseph Holmes, English
Welch, M. Christina, S.S.J, English
Westburg, Barry Richard, English
ROCKVILLE CENTRE
Konigsberg, Evelyn, Speech & Drama, English
ROSLYN HEIGHTS
McLean, Robert Simpson, English
ST. BONAVENTURE
Farrow, Anthony, Modern British & Contemporary Literature
Litzinger, Boyd Anthony, Jr, English
Martine, James John, American Literature, English
Mulryan, John James, Renaissance Literature
Wehmeyer, William Anthony, English
SARATOGA SPRINGS
Benkovitz, Miriam, English Literature
Ciancio, Ralph Armando, American & English Literature
Foulke, Robert Dana, English Literature
Glasser, William Arnold, English
Keane, Patrick Joseph, English, American Literature
Kifer, Devra Rowland, English
Lewis, Thomas Spottswood Wellford, English & American Literature
Moseley, Edwin Maurice, English & Modern Literature
West, Philip J, Medieval English Literature, Stylistics
SAUGERTIES
Robbins, Rossell Hope, Middle English Literature
SCARSDALE
Danziger, Marlies Kallmann, English
SCHENECTADY
Blodgett, Harold William, American Literature
Freund, Hans Joachim, Comparative Literature
Gado, Frank, English
Murphy, William Michael, English Literature
Nelson, Hugh Alan, English
Niemeyer, Carl Anthony, English
Shinagel, Michael, English Literature
Stineback, David Ceburn, American Literature & Intellectual History
Ullmann, Samson Oettinger Altmayer, English
SETAUKET
Erdman, David Vorse, English Literature
Stauffer, Ruth M, English & Comparative Literature
Trowbridge, Clinton W, English
SNYDER
Sherwin, Joseph Stephen, English
SOUTHAMPTON
Peterson, William Moore, English, Drama
Sklare, Arnold Beryl, English
Thompson, William Irwin, English, Literary Anthropology
Weber, Richard Baker, American Studies & Literature
STAMFORD
Boynton, Robert Whitney, English
STATEN ISLAND
Battaglia, Francis Joseph, English, American Literature
Bogen, Nancy, English
Boies, Jack J, English & Drama
Fuchs, Daniel, English & American Literature
Grace, William Joseph, English Literature
Hinz, John Peter, English, American Studies
Houchin, Thomas D, Speech Pathology & Linguistics
Kendris, Thomas, English
Lamacchia, Grace A, English
Mast, Gerald J, English, Drama
Minerof, Arthur F, English
Rubinstein, Elliot L, English
Simms, Theodore F, English

Sullivan, Daniel Joseph, C.M, English
Suther, Marshall E, Jr, English & Comparative Literature
Volpe, Edmond Loris, English
Wilson, Hugh Hamilton, English Poetry
STONY BROOK
Bennett, Joseph Thomas, Victorian Literature
Bruehl, William J, English, Dramatic Arts
Dibble, Jerry Allen, English & Comparative Literature
Dolan, Paul J, English
Fiess, Edward, English
Fortuna, Diane De Turo, English
Fry, Donald Klein, English
Goldberg, Homer Beryl, English
Hackett, Laura L, English
Huffman, Clifford Chalmers, English Literature
Kott, Jan K, Drama, Comparative Literature
Levin, Richard Louis, English
Levine, Richard Allan, English
Lockerbie, Donald Bruce, English, American Civilization
Ludwig, Jack, English Literature
Maresca, Thomas Edward, English
Miller, Ruth, English, American Civilization
Neumeyer, Peter F, English
Newlin, Paul A, English
Rogers, Thomas, English Literature
Simpson, Louis A. M., English
Stampfer, Judah L, English
Stevens, Martin, English Language & Literature
Thompson, John Anderson, English
Weisinger, Herbert, Renaissance Literature
Zimbardo, Rose A, English
SUFFERN
Martin, Margaret R, Communications
Sauer, Frank, English
SYRACUSE
Booth, Philip, English
Boudreau, Gordon V, English
Brune, Randall, English
Cunningham, William F, Jr, English Literature
Curry, John Vincent, S.J, English
Diehl, John Dornfield, English
Dike, Donald Albyn, English
Elliott, George Paul, English Literature
Elson, James Hinsdale, English
Forrest, William Craig, English
Funk, Frank E, Speech
Golden, Joseph, Drama, Arts Planning & Administration
Halkett, John George, English
Haskell, George D, English Literature
Herber, Harold L, English, Reading
Hoffman, Arthur Wolf, English Literature
Krempel, Daniel Spartakus, Theatre
Lyttle, David Janes, English, American Literature
Marshall, Mary Hatch, English Literature
Marvin, Burton Wright, Journalism
Mortenson, Peter, English Literature
Noon, William Thomas, S.J, English
Owen, David H, English
Parsons, Thornton Harris, English & American Literature
Reidenbaugh, Gerald F, Drama
Ried, Paul Eugene, Speech
Rohrlich, Beulah F, Speech
Schulte, Henry F, Journalism
Smith, Charles Daniel, Rhetoric, Public Address
Snodgrass, William D, English, Speech
Sutton, Vivian R, English & American Literature, Writing
Sutton, Walter, American Literature, Literary Criticism
Theiner, Paul Frank, English
Thomas, Sidney, English Literature, Art History
Wasserstrom, William, English
Watson, Charles Nelles, Jr, American Literature
Weber, Sarah Appleton, English, Medieval Literature
Wolseley, Roland Edgar, Journalism
TROY
Cook, Thomas Edwin, English Literature
Flosdorf, James William, English Literature
Goode, Stephen H, English
Gould, Jay Reid, English Drama, Technical Writing
Hopkins, Vivian C, English & American Literature
Shields, Bruce Philbrook, English & Medieval Literature
Wasserman, George Russell, English Literature
Young, Arthur Clements, English
UTICA
Nassar, Eugene Paul, English, Criticism

Schmidt, Ralph Norman, (Sr), Speech, Education
VALLEY STREAM
  Morton, Leonard, English
VOORHEESVILLE
  Kendall, Kathleen Edgerton, Rhetoric & Communication
WEST ONEONTA
  Martin, Willard Edgar, Jr, English
WEST POINT
  Blair, Arthur Hadfield, English & American Literature
  Capps, Jack L, English
  Sutherland, Edwin Van Valkenburg, English & Comparative Literature
WHITE PLAINS
  Eisenberg, Ruth F, English, Speech
  Larson, Richard Leslie, English
  Wieler, John William, English
WILLISTON PARK
  Doyle, Paul A, English
WOODSTOCK
  Termine, Benjamin, Speech, Drama
YONKERS
  Lardas, Konstantinos, English, Modern Greek
  Tauber, Abraham, Speech

NORTH CAROLINA

BELMONT
  Brown, Louise Stephens, English
BOILING SPRINGS
  Brown, Joyce Compton, American Literature
  Cox, Betty Smith, Medieval English, Renaissance English
  Sandifer, Charley Lafayette, English Composition & Literature
BOONE
  Auston, John T, Speech, Research Methodology
  Dorgan, (Claude) Howard, Rhetoric and Public Address, Theatre
  Dunlap, Mary Montgomery, American & English Literature
  Eggers, Graydon Poe, English
  Frantz, Donald H, Jr, Humanities
  Heymann, Hans Gerhard, English, German
  Logan, Susan H, English
  Van Noppen, John James, III, English
  Ward, Wilber Henry, III, American Literature
  West, John Foster, English
  Williams, Cratis Dearl, English
  Williamson, Jerry Wayne, Seventeenth Century British Literature & History
BUIES CREEK
  Sinclair, Reid B, English
  Stewart, Dorothea Lou, Linguistics, American Literature
CHAPEL HILL
  Adams, Raymond, English
  Avery, Laurence Green, English
  Bailey, James Osler, English Literature
  Bain, Robert Addison, English
  Barnes, Samuel Gill, English
  Bond, Richmond Pugh, English
  Brandes, Paul Dickerson, Rhetoric
  Brookhouse, John Christopher, English
  Callaghan, Joseph Calvin, Speech
  Carmichael, Katherine Kennedy, English
  Cotten, Lyman Atkinson, English
  Cramer, Maurice Browning, English Literature
  Dessen, Alan Charles, English
  Devereux, James Ashton, S.J, English
  Donovan, Dennis George, English
  Eliason, Norman Ellsworth, English Literature & Linguistics
  Fogle, Richard Harter, English
  Gaskin, James Reuben, English
  Haig, Robert Louis, English
  Harper, Howard M, Jr, English
  Hinkle, Diane Leonard, Comparative Literature
  Hollis, Charles Carroll, English
  Holman, Clarence Hugh, American Literature
  Housman, Arthur Lloyd, Speech, Dramatic Art
  Jackson, Blyden, English
  King, James Kimball, English
  Leary, Lewis, American Literature
  Ludington, Charles T, Jr, English, American Studies
  Lyons, Clifford Pierson, English Literature
  McQueen, William Ashley, III, English Literature
  Moran, Ronald Wesson, English
  Parker, John William, Speech, Drama
  Patterson, Thomas McEvoy, Dramatic Art
  Pence, James Worth, Jr, Speech
  Phialas, Peter George, English Literature
  Read, Forrest, English
  Reed, Mark Lafayette, English Literature
  Royster, Vermont (Connecticut), Journalism, Political Science

Rubin, Louis D, Jr, English, American Literature
Russell, Harry Kitsun, English & American Literature
Rust, Richard Dilworth, English
Seelye, John Douglas, English & American Literature
Selden, Samuel, Theater Arts
Shapiro, Harold Israel, English
Spearman, Walter Smith, Journalism
Steele, (Henry) Maxwell, English
Strauss, Albrecht Benno, English
Talbert, Ernest William, English Literature
Thornton, Weldon E, English
Umberger, Wallace Randolph, Jr, Dramatic Literature & Criticism
Voitle, Robert (Brown), English
Wallace, Wesley Herndon, Radio, Television & Motion Pictures
Wenzel, Siegfried, English, Comparative Literature
Wittig, Joseph Sylvester, English, Medieval Studies
Wynn, Earl, Performing Arts
Zobel, Konrad, Theatre History
CHARLOTTE
  Atnally, Richard Francis, English
  Bryan, Margaret Bryan, English Renaissance Literature
  Burne, Glenn S, English, Comparative Literature
  Carver, Ann Cathey, English
  Ellis, Seth Howard, English Language & Literature
  Freeman, Sidney Lee, English & Speech
  Gatlin, Hallie Leon, III, British Victorian Literature
  Kelly, Charles M, Speech
  McCall, (Joseph) Darryl, Jr, English
  Mason, Julian Dewey, Jr, English
  Milner, Edward Willis, Theology, Literature
  Moose, Roy Clifton, English Literature
  Newman, Paul Baker, American Literature
CONCORD
  Goetzman, Robert Albert, English
CULLOWHEE
  Brown, Anthony Eugene, English Literature
  Crum, Mabel T, English Language & Literature
  Eberly, Ralph Stephens, Modern Novel
  Huguelet, Theodore Long, English
  Joyner, Nancy Carol, English
  Loeffler, Donald Lee, Theatre, Speech
  Nicholas, James Karl, English Language & Literature
  Nicholl, James Robert, English Literature
  Niggli, Josefina, Drama
  Paulk, William Eston, Jr, English
  Schroder, Charles Frederick, Music, Comparative Literature
  Wade, Philip Tyree, English
  Wilson, Stuart, English Literature
DAVIDSON
  Abbott, Anthony S, English
  Bliss, Frank Walker, Jr, English
  Cole, Richard Cargill, English
  Cumming, Elizabeth Chandler, English
  Cumming, William Patterson, English
DURHAM
  Anderson, Carl Lennart, English
  Bevington, Helen, English
  Bowman, Francis Ezra, English & American Literature
  Boyce, Benjamin, English, Literature
  Budd, Louis John, English
  Cady, Edwin Harrison, English & American Literature
  Clubbe, John Louis Edwin, English
  DeNeef, Arthur Leigh, English Literature
  Di Bona, Helene, English Literature
  Duffey, Bernard, Literature
  Farrison, William Edward, English Philology
  Ferguson, Oliver Watkins, English
  Gerber, Gerald E, English, Literary Criticism
  Gilbert, Allan H, English & Italian Literature
  Gohdes, Clarence, American Literature
  Harwell, George Corbin, English Literature
  Hassold, Ernest Christopher, Humanities
  Hubbell, Jay Broadus, American Literature
  Jackson, Wallace, English
  Lievsay, John Leon, English
  Mellown, Elgin Wendell, English Literature
  Monsman, Gerald Cornelius, English
  Nygard, Holger Olof, English, Folklore
  Randall, Dale Bertrand Jonas, English
  Reiss, Edmund, English & Comparative Literature
  Render, Sylvia Lyons, English
  Ryals, Clyde de L, English
  Sanders, Charles Richard, English Literature
  Schwerman, Esther Louise, English
  Shuman, R. Baird, English, Education
  Smith, Grover C, English

Strandberg, Victor Hugo, English
Turner, (Henry) Arlin, American Literature
Wetherby, Joseph Cable, Speech
Whisnant, David Eugene, English
Williams, George Walton, English Literature
ELIZABETH CITY
  Blackstock, Walter, English, American Literature
  Henderson, Anne Marie, English, Education
ELIZABETHTOWN
  Howell, James, English
ELON COLLEGE
  Blake, Robert Grady, English
  Priestley, Mary Ellen, English
FAYETTEVILLE
  Clark, Edward Depriest, English
GARNER
  Heaton, Cherrill Paul, English
GREENSBORO
  Batcheller, David R, Drama
  Beale, Walter Henry, English Language & Literature
  Bright, Jean Marie, American Literature, Afro-American Studies
  Buchert, Jean Ruth, English Literature
  Chappell, Fred Davis, English
  Charles, Amy Marie, English
  Darnell, Donald Gene, American Literature
  Dixon, Arthur Wilson, English
  Ellis, James Nelson, English
  Evans, James Edward, English Literature
  Griffith, Kelley Edward, Jr, American & 18th Century Literature
  Kelly, Robert Leroy, Medieval & Renaissance Literature
  Kirby-Smith, Henry Tompkins, Jr, English, Creative Writing
  Lane, William Guerrant, English
  Long, John Henderson, English
  Middleton, Herman David, Theatre
  Riley, Michael Howard, English Literature
  Sadler, Mary Lynn Veach, English Literature, Philology
  Spencer, Christopher, English
  Stephens, Robert Oren, English
  Tedford, Thomas Lee, Speech
  Thorne, Dorothy Gilbert, English
  Watson, Robert Winthrop, English
  Williams, Jimmy Lee, English & American Literature
  Wimsatt, James I, English
  Wimsatt, Mary Ann, English & American Literature
GREENVILLE
  Baker, Ira L, Journalism, English
  Bezanson, Warren B, English, American Studies
  Capwell, Richard Leonard, English
  Ebbs, John Dale, English Literature
  Herrin, Virginia (Townsend), English
  Hester, Waverly Erwin, English
  Kirkland, James Wilton, Nineteenth Century American Literature
  Lawler, Donald Lester, Victorian & Modern English Literature
  Loessin, Edgar Ray, Drama
  McMillan, Douglas Joseph, English
  Motley, Frank Wallace, English, Education
  Reilly, Bartholomew Michael, English, Theology
  Rives, Ralph Hardee, Dramatic Literature, English
  Sanders, Franklin David, English
  Sorensen, Frederick (Chester), English
  South, Malcolm Hudson, English Literature
  Steer, Helen Vane, Drama, Speech
  Stephenson, William Eaton, English
  Wang, Alfred Shih-Pu, English
  Wang, Veronica Chow, English
HAMPSTEAD
  Wells, William, English Renaissance
HICKORY
  Cosgrove, Mark Francis, O.S.B, English Literature, Theology
  Lyerly, Ralph Henry, English
  Mahan, Ronald Gair, English, American Civilization
  Mahan, Rose Selkis, English
  Setzler, Edwin (Lake), English Language
HIGH POINT
  DeLeeuw, William Lewis, Medieval Literature & Linguistics
  Mounts, Charles Eugene, English Literature
  Sullivan, Emily Bradsher, English
  Underwood, Sam Jesse, English
HOLLY RIDGE
  Wallace, Robert Marsden, Eighteenth Century English Literature
LAURINBURG
  Bayes, Ronald Homer, English
  Bennett, Carl Douglas, English, Christianity & Culture
  Carver, James Edward, English

MANTEO
Hruby, John Franklin, Drama
MARS HILL
Ihrig, Mary Alice, American & English Literature
PEMBROKE
Macleod, Norman Wicklund, English
RALEIGH
Baines, Barbara Joan Hurst, English Literature
Camp, Leon Raymond, Speech, Political Science
Champion, Larry Stephen, Literature
Clark, Joseph Deadrick, English
Dandridge, Edmund Pendleton, Jr, English
Davis, Philip Harvey, English
Durant, Jack Davis, English Literature
Elliott, Patrick Frank, Literature, Humanities
Franklin, William Glenwood, Speech Science, Oral Interpretation
Halperen, Max, Contemporary Literature
Hargrave, Harry A, English
Hartley, Lodwick, English Literature
Hester, Marvin Thomas, Renaissance Literature
Johnson, Mary Lynch, Old English
Kincheloe, Henderson Grady, American Literature
Knight, Ione Kemp, Middle English
Knowles, Albert Sidney, Jr, English
Koonce, Benjamin Granade, English
Meyers, Walter Earl, Medieval English Literature, English Linguistics
Moore, Frank Harper, English Literature
Munn, Harry Eugene, Jr, Speech Communication, Human Relations
Owen, Guy, English
Parker, Charles Alexander, Speech
Porter, Jack, Communication Arts
Shelley, Alfred Bernard Rowland, English Literature
Smoot, Jean Johannessen, English, Comparative Literature
Toole, William Bell, III, English
Walser, Richard, American Literature
Ward, Stanley Sidney, English Literature
White, Robert Benjamin, Jr, English
Williams, Mary Cameron, English Literature
Williams, Porter, Jr, English
RED SPRINGS
Pauli, Kenneth W, Speech, Drama
SALISBURY
Colson, Lilyan, American Literature
Dedmond, Francis Berneil, English
Honaker, Gerald Leon, English, Speech
Sinnott, Bethany Strong, English Literature
Stone, Martha Callicott, English
Turney, Charles, English
SKYLAND
Tedford, Barbara Wilkie, English
SWANNANOA
Churchill, Irving Lester, English & American Literature
TRYON
Gilkes, Lillian Barnard, American Literature
McBurney, James Howard, Speech
WADESBORO
Caraway, (Sarah) Hermine, English, Education
WILMINGTON
Powles, Marie Antoinette, Medieval & Renaissance Literature
Stokes, John Lemacks, III, English, Humanities
WILSON
Grimes, Terrence Layne, English
Hartsock, Mildred Edith, English
Hemby, James Benjamin, Jr, English
Johnston, Edna Long, English
WINSTON-SALEM
Aycock, Andrew Lewis, English
Carter, John Archer, Jr, English Literature
Fosso, Doyle Richard, English
Gossett, Thomas Frank, American Literature & Studies
Gray, Charles Farrell, English
Hayes, Merwyn Alfred, Speech, History
Jones, Henry Broadus, English
Milner, Joseph O'Beirne, English, Education
Phillips, Elizabeth, American Literature
Saad, Youssef S, English, Comparative Literature
Shirley, Franklin Ray, Speech
Shorter, Robert Newland, English
Welker, David (Harold), Speech
White, William Beckler, English

NORTH DAKOTA

BISMARCK
Mason, Mary Elizabeth, O.S.B, English, Neo-Latin
DICKINSON
Church, Harrison Leon, Journalism, Law
Wheeler, L. Ray, Creative Writing, Modern Literature

FARGO
Bonfield, June McKenna, Medieval Literature
Cater, A. Catherine, English & The Humanities
Cosgrove, William Emmett, American & Black Literature
Hove, John, Jr, American Studies
Lyons, Richard Eugene, English, American Studies
Schoff, Francis Gordon, English Literature
Walsh, Frederick George, Dramatic Arts, Speech
GRAND FORKS
Anderegg, Michael Alain, English Literature, Film History
Austin, Alvin E, Journalism, Communications
Caldwell, Mary Ellen, English & American Literature
Caldwell, Robert Atchison, English Philology
Christensen, Bonniejean McGuire, Rhetoric & Medieval Studies
Crawford, John Chapman, Linguistics
Engle, Ronald G, Theatre Arts
Fischer, Raymond Louis, Rhetoric & Public Address
Glassheim, Eliot Alan, American Literature
Hale, Richard Osborne, English, Languages
Hampsten, Richard Franklin, English & Comparative Literature
Heiman, Hazel Lucile, Speech Communication
Jacobson, Harvey Kenneth, Mass Communication
King, Robert Wendell, English, Creative Writing
Kinghorn, Norton Dean, American Literature, Rhetoric
Lewis, Robert William, Jr, English
Linkletter, Charles M, English Novel
McCaffrey, Donald W, Theatre, Cinema
O'Kelly, Bernard, English, Renaissance Studies
Pedersen, Myrtle Edith, English
Penn, John S, Speech
Robertson, Donald Jackson, English
MINOT
Abelseth, Muriel, English, Journalism
Gilbert, Edna, Speech

OHIO

ADA
Beck, Ronald James, English & American Literature
Dornbusch, Clyde Henry, American Literature
Price, Robert Paetzel, English
AKRON
Baer, Evelyn Esther, Communication Disorders
Brown, Harold Clifford, Jr, Eighteenth Century English Literature
Dial, Robert, English Language & Literature
Dunlap, James Francis, Speech, Theatre
Jones, David Llewellyn, English, Comparative Literature
Keister, Don Adam, English & American Literature
Levin, Gerald H, English
Lewis, Ruth B, Speech
Merrix, Robert Paul, English & Renaissance Drama
Pearson, D'Orsay White, Renaissance English
Phipps, Frank Thomas, English
Sandefur, Ray Harold, Speech
Sheehan, James Clement, English Literature
Slaughter, Howard K, Speech & Drama
Slocum, Sally Kennedy, Medieval English, Poetry
Spangehl, Stephen Douglas, Medieval Literature, Linguistics
Sterling, Wallace Stine, Drama, Speech
Sweeney, Gerard Michael, English & American Literature
Thackaberry, Robert Eugene, English
ALLIANCE
Chapman, Paul Hiram, English
Crist, Lyle Martin, English, Journalism
Vincent, James Edwin, Speech, Drama
ASHLAND
Janusko, Robert John, English
McGovern, Robert John, Seventeenth Century English Literature, Creative Writing
Miley, Wilbert Harley, Speech
Snyder, Richard Laurence, English
Stunz, Arthur Nesbitt, English
ATHENS
Baird, Russell Norman, Journalism
Boase, Paul Henshaw, Speech
Carlson, Charles Vernon, Interpersonal Communication
Click, John William, Journalism
Conover, James Harrington, Theater, Oral Interpretation
Culbert, Taylor, English Literature
Culbertson, Hugh McClellan, Communication Theory

Dodd, Wayne Donald, English
Dohn, Norman Harding, Journalism
Fieler, Frank Bernard, English
Fitch, Raymond E, Nineteenth Century Literature, Criticism
Flannagan, Roy C, English
Foster, Teddy Joe, Speech Communication
Harter, Carol Clancey, English & American Literature
Heidtmann, Peter, English
Hobbs, Robert Louis, Theatre
Hollow, John Walter, English & American Literature
Jones, John A, English & American Literature
Kantner, Claude Edgar, Communication
Kaufman, Alvin S, Drama, Theatre Arts
Keyes, Daniel, English
King, Roma Alvah, Jr, English & Comparative Literature
Kliesch, Ralph Ernest, Journalism
Knies, Earl Allen, English
McGraw, Rex T, Jr, Theatre
Mitchell, Edward B, English
Quattrocki, Edward A, English
Ramsey, Roy Vance, English
Schmidt, James Norman, Continental & American Literature, Creative Writing
Schneider, Duane Bernard, English
Stempel, Guido Hermann, III, Mass Communication
Stone, Edward, English
Summers, Hollis Spurgeon, English
Swardson, Harold Roland, English
Thayer, Calvin G, English Renaissance
Thompson, James Roy, English Literature
Timmis, John Henry, III, Communication, History
Weaver, Carl Harold, Interpersonal Communication
Wells, Arvin Robert, English Language & Literature
Whan, Edgar William, English
Williams, Kenneth R, Jr, Interpersonal Communication
Winters, Robert Louis, Theater
BEREA
Allman, William Arthur, Theatre Arts, Speech
Ashburn, William Alwyn, English
Hankins, (John) Richard, English Literature & Linguistics
Lappert, William Grayson, English Literature
Monahan, (Mary) Joan, Composition, English Education
Redinger, Ruby V, English, Linguistics
Rowe, Harrison Davis, English, Linguistics
Sturm, Albert, Theatre Arts, German
BLUFFTON
Templin, Lawrence Howard, English
BOWLING GREEN
Addington, David W, Speech, Drama
Baldanza, Frank, English
Blanchard, Carlene Bagnall, American Studies
Boughton, Charles R, Speech
Browne, Ray B, English
Carpenter, Richard Coles, English
Cheney, Lois A, Speech & Drama
Clark, Robert King, Speech
Del Porto, Joseph Antony, Journalism
Eckman, Frederick, English
Fricke, Donna Gillespie, Eighteenth Century Literature
Gross, Roger Dennis, Drama
Halpern, Sheldon, English
Harner, James Lowell, English Literature
Hilyard, Delmer Manford, Communication
Kepke, Allen Neal, Speech, Theatre
Kinney, Thomas L, English
Klein, Thomas Dicker, English, Education
Lee, Briant Hamor, Drama, History of Theatre
Leedy, Paul Francis, English Literature
Leland, Lowell Pond, English
Leland, Virginia Everett, English
McCord, Howard, English
Miesle, Frank L, Speech & Drama
Morton, Beatrice Kerr, English Education
Myers, Norman Jerald, Theatre, Speech
Obee, Harold Brehm, Speech, Theatre
O'Connor, Philip Francis, English, Creative Writing
Parnell, Paul E, English
Parrish, Beryl Margaret, English
Payne, Alma Jeanette, American Studies
Rickey, John Thomas, Speech
Salomon, Brownell, English
Steele, Harold Glendon, English
Tucker, Duane Emery, Speech
Tucker, Raymond Kenneth, Speech, Communications
Wolfe, Ralph Haven, English
Yeager, Raymond, Speech
BRATENAHL
Milic, Louis Tonko, English

BURTON
Ford, Margaret Patricia, English
CANTON
Cote, Andre, English
Lair, Robert Leland, English, Religion
CINCINNATI
Armstrong, Elizabeth P, English
Arner, Robert David, American Literature
Betz, Siegmund Alfred Eduard, English, Classics
Bryan, Martin, Speech
Chard, Leslie Frank, II, English
Comprone, Joseph John, English
Elder, Arlene Adams, Black & American Literature
Flynn, Lawrence Jerome, S.J, Speech
Fox, Stephen Douglas, Comparative Literature
Godshalk, William Leigh, English Literature
Golding, Sanford, English
Hamrick, William, English & Linguistics
Hursey, Richard C, English
Irvine, Peter L, English
Jisha, Henry Jerry, Speech, Theater Arts
Karns, Charles Franklin, Speech
Katt, Arthur F, Practical Ministry, Speech
Lashley, Warren L, Speech, Drama
LePage, Peter VanAtta, English
Lisle, Margery Lillian Cunningham Macoubrie, Comparative Literature, Drama
McCall, John Patrick, English
McDonald, Charles Osborne, English
Miller, Wayne Charles, American Literature & Studies
Morton, Lena Beatrice, English Literature
Porte, Michael Sheldon, Communication, Drama
Robinson, James Keith, English Literature
Rubenstein, Jill, English Literature
Savage, Thomas Gerard, S.J, English Language & Literature
Staples, Hugh B, English
Steible, Daniel Joseph, English Language & Literature
Stephens, Martha Thomas, English
Stewart, Keith, English
Tenoever, Donald Aloysius, English, History of Fine Arts
Verderber, Rudolph Francis, Speech
Wentersdorf, Karl Paul, English Literature
Wheeler, Charles Francis, English
Wiebe, Dallas Eugene, English Literature
Willer, William H, English
Wright, Austin McGiffert, English

CLEVELAND
Arntz, Mary Luke, S.N.D, English
Barbato, Louis Richard, English Literature
Berry, Margaret, English, South Asian Studies
Carruthers, Mary, English Literature & Language
Cherubini, William, English Literature
Chisholm, William Sherman, English Linguistics
Clancey, Richard W, English, Theology
Diekhoff, John Siemon, English Literature
Evans, Verda, Literature
Evett, David Hal, English
Ezekiel, Margaret Ulmer, Drama, Speech
Fredman, Raymond M, English, Drama
Freeley, Austin J, Speech
Gerlach, John Charles, Nineteenth Century American Literature
Giffin, Mary Elizabeth, English
Gilchrist, James A, English
Gorsky, Susan Rubinow, English & American Literature
Guthrie, Warren, Speech
Hastings, Elizabeth Thomson, English
Hazelrig, Matthew S, Jr, English
Kolker, Delphine, C.PP.S, English
Kraus, Sidney, Mass Media Communication
Kummer, George, English
Lang, Robert Alfred, Speech
Loewe, Ralph Elias, English
MacAndrew, Elizabeth, English Literature
McCollom, William G., English, Drama
MacEachen, Dougald Bernard, English
Magner, James Edmund, Jr, English
Marsh, Florence Gertrude, English
Olson, Glending, English Literature
Ornstein, Robert, English
Pecek, Louis G, American Literature
Randall, Randolph C, English
Rehor, Charles Frank, Journalism
Seltzer, Leon Francis, English
Smith, Francis J, S.J, Literary Criticism
Smith, Frederik Northrop, English & American Literature
Srail, George William, Speech, Dramatics
Taaffe, James G, English
Thomas, Mary Jean, Speech, Philosophy
Trace, Arther Storrey, Jr, English
Trawick, Leonard Moses, English
Turner, Alberta Tucker, Seventeenth Century & Contemporary Poetry

Wallace, Robert, English
Yackshaw, Robert R, English Literature
Yoder, Jess, Speech
CLEVELAND HEIGHTS
Adrian, Arthur Allen, English Literature
Coyle, Leo Perry, English
Richardson, Lyon Norman, American Literature
Tew, Arnold Gerard, American Literature
Watson, Sara Ruth, English
COLUMBUS
Altick, Richard Daniel, English Literature
Andrews, William David, American Literature & Cultural History
Auburn, Mark Stuart, English & American Literature, Drama
Baillie, William Mayan, English Literature
Barnes, Daniel Ramon, American Literature, Folklore
Battersby, James L, Eighteenth Century English Literature
Baxter, Mary Ruth, English
Beja, Morris, English
Berquist, Goodwin F, Jr, Speech
Boyer, Robert Downer, Theatre Studies, Dramatic Literature
Brooks, Keith, Communication, Oral Interpretation
Brown, Alan Kelsey, Medieval English
Burke, John Edward, Biomedical & Mass Communications
Burkman, Katherine H, Comparative Literature, Theatre
Canzoneri, Robert Wilburn, Creative Writing, Modern American Literature
Cegala, Donald Joseph, Speech Communication
Childs, Maryanna, O.P, English
Clarke, John J, Journalism, English Literature
Cooley, Thomas Winfield, American Literature, American Studies
Corbett, Edward Patrick Joseph, English
Cox, Lee Sheridan, English Literature
Crepeau, George Paul, Drama
Dathorne, Oscar Ronald, Modern British & World Black Literature
Edmondson, Harold S, Speech Correction
Estrich, Robert Mark, English Philology
Ewing, William Hollis, Speech, Communications
Fenton, Mary Arthur, O.P, English
Ferguson, Suzanne C, Modern English & American Literature
Frantz, David Oswin, Renaissance Literature
Gabel, John Butler, English
Gaumer, Frank Thomas, Journalism
Glancy, Donald Ray, Drama & Theatre
Golden, James L, Speech
Golding, Alfred Siemon, Theatre Performance & History
Good, Donald William, English Literature, Administration
Haber, Tom Burns, English
Haines, Robert Eugene Ned, English & American Literature
Hale, Frank Wilbur, Jr, Speech, Political Science
Hall, William Edward, Communications
Hughey, Ruth W, English Literature
Jones, Robert Charles, English
Kabealo, Thyra Bevier, Linguistics, Literature
Kahrl, Stanley Jadwin, Medieval English
Kincaid, James Russell, English Literature
Kuhn, Albert J, English
Langholz, Armin, Speech
Lawson, Harold Lewis, Speech, Communication
Lewis, George L, Speech, Education
Libby, Anthony Peter, English & American Literature
Lockridge, Ernest Hugh, English
Logan, James Venable, Jr, English Literature
Longenecker, Marlene Blaney, English & American Literature
MacDonald, James Campbell, Journalism
Markels, Julian, English
Marshall, Carl Leroy, American Literature
Martin, Richard Thomas, English Romantic Poetry
Maurer, A.E. Wallace, English
Mitchell, W.J. Thomas, Eighteenth & Nineteenth Century Literature
Monaghan, Robert R, Mass Communication, Humanistic Science
Montgomery, Allene Dorothy, Drama
Munday, Mildred Brand, Renaissance Drama
Muste, John M, American Literature
Neuman, Robert Michael, English Literature, Theatre
Nichols, Arthur Richard, Theatre
Owens, David Benton, English Literature
Rarick, Galen Ronald, Journalism
Riley, Donald W, Speech
Ritter, Charles Clifford, Theatre & Speech
Robbins, Edwin W, English

Scheps, Walter, English
Schoen, Kathryn T, Speech Education
Sena, John F, English Literature
Shapiro, Arnold, English
Smallwood, Osborn Tucker, Speech Communication, English
Snow, Royall Henderson, English
Soellner, Rolf, English
Summers, Harrison Boyd, Television, Radio
Sutton, Betty Smith, Eighteenth Century English Literature
Swetnam, Ford T, Jr, Literature
Weatherford, Richard Morris, American Literature
Wheeler, Charles Benjamin, English
Wilson, John Harold, English
Woods, Alan Lambert, Theatre History
Woodson, Thomas (Miller), English, American Literature
Zacher, Christian Keeler, English Literature, Medieval Studies
CUYAHOGA FALLS
Phillipson, John Samuel, English
DAYTON
Arons, Peter L, English
Baker, William DeGrove, American Literature, Composition
Bassett, Abraham Joseph, Theatre
Bedard, Bernard John, English
Blatt, Stephen Joseph, Communication
Bracher, Peter Scholl, English
Cochran, Bud T, American Literature
Correale, Robert M, English Literature
Dreher, Barbara Bender, Speech
Eakins, Rollin Gene, Speech
Harden, Elizabeth McWhorter, English
Henninger, Francis Joseph, English, American Studies
Hussman, Lawrence Eugene, Jr, English
Lees, Charles J, S.M, English
Marre, K. E. Deboo, Nineteenth & Twentieth Century Literature
Means, Michael H, English
Patrouch, Joseph Francis, Jr, English
Rudolph, Catherine, O.S.F, English, Children's Literature
Swanson, Donald Roland, English
Tortoriello, Thomas Ross, Rhetoric, Public Address
Trent, Judith Swanlund, Speech Communication
Wetmore, Thomas Hall, English
Whissen, Thomas Reed, English, Comparative Literature
Zamonski, John A, British Literature, British & American Drama
DEFIANCE
LeMaster, Jimmie R, English Language & Literature
Winzeler, Charlotte Mae, Modern English Poetry & Drama
DELAWARE
Eyssen, Donald C, Speech
Leathers, Lyman Lee, American Studies & Literature
Marshall, Robert Kossuth, English
Pratt, Samuel Maxon, English, Humanities
Reed, Libuse Lacina, English
Robinson, Edward Ray, Speech
Rollins, Ronald G, English, Modern Irish & American Literature
Spencer, Benjamin Townley, English & American Literature
White, F. Eugene, English
FINDLAY
Congleton, James Edmund, English
Gebhardt, Richard Coate, Modern Literature, Contemporary Fiction
GAMBIER
Crump, Galbraith M, English
Daniel, Robert Woodham, English Literature
Duff, Gerald Aldine, Nineteenth Century English Literature, Modern Poetry
Michael, James Elder, Dramatics
Roelofs, Gerrit Hubbard, English
GRANVILLE
Bennett, Paul Lewis, American Literature
Brasmer, William Otto, Jr, Theatre Arts
Consolo, Dominick Peter, English
Crocker, Lionel, Speech
Downs, Lenthiel Howell, Modern Drama, Comparative Literature
Dresser, William R, Speech
Kraft, Quentin Guild, English & American Literature
Lewis, Nancy Eloise, English
Markgraf, Bruce Richard, Speech Communication, Playwriting
Marshall, Kenneth B, English
Nichols, William Watson, English
Stoneburner, Charles Joseph (Tony), English, Religion
HAMILTON
Dunn, Thomas Peckham, Medieval Studies

Phelps, Bernard Fred, Speech
HANOVER
Bond, Harold Lewis, English Literature
HIRAM
Chatfield, Eugene Hale, English & American Literature
Shaw, John Burnham, English
Stranahan, Brainerd Payne, English
Vincent, Mary Louise, English
HOMEWORTH
Saffell, Helen Weaver, English
HOWARD
Kahrl, George Morrow, English Literature
HUDSON
Lodge, Evan Abel, English
HURON
Rudinger, Joel Douglas, Creative Writing, American Literature
KENT
Alfonso, Robert J, English, Education
Baird, Joseph Lee, English
Benstock, Bernard, English, Comparative Literature
Blair, Thomas Marshall Howe, English
Casale, Ottavio Mark, English
Collins, Harold, English
Cook, Richard Irving, English
Cooney, James Francis, English
Cowperthwaite, Lowery LeRoy, Speech
Davis, Thomas M, English
Erdmann, Louis O, Speech, Theater
Fisher, William Andrew, Journalism
Fried, Lewis Fredrick, American Literature
Gorden, William I, Speech
Gribben, John L, English
Hakutani, Yoshinobu, American Literature, Linguistics
Harkness, Bruce, English Literature
Hassler, Donald Mackey II, English
Heisey, David Ray, Speech Communication
Holm, James Noble, Speech
Jentoft, Clyde Willard, English Literature
Jerman, Bernard Robert, English
Kantrowitz, Joanne Spencer, English, Drama
Krause, Sydney Joseph, English & American Literature
Kvam, Wayne Eugene, American Literature
Landry, Hilton J, English
Larson, Orville K, Drama
Leed, Jacob R, English
McCormick, Edgar Lindsley, English
Macomber, Philip A, Television, Drama
Marovitz, Sanford E, English
Mills, Lloyd L, English
Noll, Dolores Louise, English
Nurmi, Martin Karl, English
Osborne, Wilbur J, Speech
Painter, Helen (Welch), English
Parr, Johnstone, English Literature
Perry, Murvin Henry, Journalism
Remly, Lynn Louise, English, Philology
Smith, Bobby Lee, English
Tener, Robert Lawrence, American & British Drama
Vincent, Howard P, English
Weiser, John C, Speech
KETTERING
Beaven, Winton H, Speech
MANSFIELD
Cobes, Jon P, Theatre, Music
MARIETTA
Buell, Arthur L, Speech
Dean, Harold Lester, English
Friederich, Willard Julius, Drama, Speech
Patterson, Merrill Reeves, English
Russi, Bernard A, Jr, Speech, Mass Communications
Wilcox, Ruth Alice, Speech & Drama
MIDDLETOWN
Keefer, Truman Frederick, English
MOUNT ST. JOSEPH
Seibert, Thomas L, English
NEW CANTON
Udell, Gerald R, English, Linguistics
NEW CONCORD
Chaffee, Alan Jewell, English Literature, Linguistics
Hill, Donald Phillip, Theatre
Johnson, Mary Elizabeth, Speech
King, Lauren Alfred, English
Nichols, James Richard, English Literature
Schultz, William J, American Literature
OBERLIN
Bongiorno, Andrew, English Literature
Buell, Lawrence I, English
Ganzel, Dewey Alvin, Jr, English Literature
Goulding, Daniel Joseph, Communication Studies
Hobbs, John Nelson, English & American Literature
Hoover, Andrew Graham, English
Koch, Christian Herbert, Communication Theory

Longsworth, Robert Morrow, English
Peterson, Carl Adrian, English
Pierce, Robert Bell, English
Roellinger, Francis Xavier, English
Shaver, Chester Linn, English Literature
Taylor, Warren, English Literature
Young, David Pollock, English
ORIENT
Koenig, Allen E, Speech
OXFORD
Abegglen, Homer N, Speech
Alderman, William Elijah, English Literature
Blitch, Alice Fox, Sixteenth & Seventeenth Century English
Bliss, Isabel St. John, English Literature
Branch, Edgar Marquess, American Literature
Clark, James Drummond, English
Cook, Marjorie Elizabeth, Literature, Composition
Daiker, Donald Arthur, American & English Literature
Donnell, Richard Stover, English
Duerksen, Roland A, English
Ellison, Curtis William, American Studies
Erlich, Richard Dee, English Language & Literature
Friedenberg, Robert Victor, American Public Address, Rhetorical Theory
Haley, Harold Leroy, Elizabethan Literature
Hardesty, William Howard, III, English & American Literature
Harwood, Britton James, Medieval Language & Literature
Hathaway, Stephen Conger, Communications, Speech
Havighurst, Walter, English
Houtchens, Carolyn Washburn, English
Houtchens, Lawrence (Huston), English Literature
Johnson, Robert Carl, English
Jordan, Frank, Jr, English
King, William W, English, Comparative Literature
Mann, David Douglas, English
Musgrave, Marian E, English
Peterson, Spiro, English
Pratt, William Crouch, Jr, English Literature
Raeth, Claire Joseph, English
Reardon, John D, English & American Literature
Reed, Kenneth Terrence, American & European Literature
Romano, John Rigoletto, English
Rosenberg, Jerome Howard, American & British Literature
Sosnoski, James Joseph, English
Trent, Jimmie Douglas, Speech
Wadsworth, Randolph Lincoln, Jr, English, Comparative Literature
Weigel, John Arthur, English
Williams, Harry Martin, Speech
Wilson, Gordon Donley, English
Witham, Barry Bates, Modern Drama, American Theatre History
Wright, Gilson, Journalism
Wright, H. Bunker, English Literature
PAINESVILLE
Hickerson, William Howard, English Literature
Hockey, Dorothy Corinne, English Literature
SALEM
Baker, William Calvin, American Literature
SHAKER HEIGHTS
Salomon, Roger Blaine, English
Taft, Frederick L, English
SOUTH EUCLID
Quinlivan, Frances Marie, English Literature
SPRINGFIELD
Balliet, Conrad A, English, American Literature
Brinkman, Elizabeth Abell, English
Call, Reginald, English
Cobau, William W, English
Damaser, Harvey G, English, American Drama
Henderlider, Clair R, Speech
Koppenhaver, Allen J, English
Miller, Paul William, English
Ostrom, John Ward, English
Otten, Terry Ralph, English
Parker, Robert Wesley, English
Rodgers, Paul Cochran, Jr, English
Veler, Richard Paul, English, American Literature
TIFFIN
Lemke, Frederick Daniel, English
TOLEDO
Boening, John, Comparative Literature
Bottorff, William Kenneth, English, American Studies
Chapman, Frederick Lamar, Theatre, Drama in Education
Cheney, David Raymond, English
Dandridge, Rita Bernice, English & American Literature

Daniels, Edgar F, English
Dessner, Lawrence Jay, English Literature
Fraiberg, Louis, English
Free, William Norris, English
Gregory, Elmer Richard, English, Comparative Literature
Hill, Joan Ann, English, Education
Kloucek, Jerome W, American Literature
Long, Jesse Raymond, Journalism
McDonald, William (Ulma), Jr, English
Manheim, Michael, English
Martin, Wallace Dean, English
Rose Margaret (Dostal), O.S.U, English
Rudolph, Robert Samuel, English
Scholten, Martin Edwin, English
Smith, David Quintin, English Literature
Southworth, James Granville, English Literature
Steele, Elizabeth, English
Stolzenbach, Norma Frizzelle, English, Theater
WAPAKONETA
Steahly, Vivian Eugenia Emrick, Foreign Languages, English
WESTERVILLE
Bailey, James Ross, American Literature, Victorian Fiction
Coulter, John Knox, Jr, English
Dodrill, Charles Ward, Theatre
Grissinger, James Adams, Speech
Hamilton, William Thornley, English & American Literature
Price, Robert, English
Ray, James Kendall, English Literature
WICKLIFFE
Mehok, Edward Eugene, English Literature & Scripture
WILBERFORCE
Fleissner, Robert Ferdinand, English
Howe, Clara, English
Zale, Eric M, English Language & Literature
WILMINGTON
Marcuson, Lewis R, Drama, English
Olmsted, Sterling Pitkin, English
WOOSTER
Clareson, Thomas Dean, English
Coolidge, Lowell William, English
Fick, Leonard J, English & American Literature
Havholm, Peter Leo, English, Speech
Herring, Henry Dunham, English & American Literature
Hilty, Deborah Pacini, English Language & Literature
Moldstad, David Franklyn, English Literature
Schutz, Walter Stanley, Theater, Speech
Stewart, Larry LeRoy, English & American Literature
YELLOW SPRINGS
Dallas, Meredith, Drama
Grauman, Lawrence, Jr, American Studies, English Literature
Treichler, Paul Felix, Drama
YOUNGSTOWN
Copeland, Thomas Arthur, English
Elser, Ralph Donald, Speech, Drama
Gay, Carol Jane, American Literature
Henke, James Thomas, English
Hwopek, Dorothy Ann, English Education
Kelty, Jean McClure, English Literature
McCracken, Hugh Thomas, English, Education
Miner, Thelma Smith, English
Miner, Ward Lester, English
Rosenthal, Lewis, English
Schultz, Werner William, English
Sniderman, Stephen Lee, Creative Writing
Solimine, Joseph, Jr, English
Trunk, Cecilia Mazurowski, English

OKLAHOMA

ADA
Disbrow, Jimmie Lynn, American Literature
Nabors, D.J, Jr, Speech
Payne, Robert Austin, Speech Communication, Mass Media
ALVA
Arthurs, Marie, English
Fredeman, Pat Hines, English & American Literature
BETHANY
Dobson, Willis Boring, Elizabethan Drama
Jennings, Lawrence Charles, English Literature, English Language
Laughbaum, Anna Belle, English
Murrow, Wayne Lee, Speech Communication, Small Group Communication
Rothwell, Helen Francis, English
CHICASHA
McCracken, Mildred Louise, English
COYLE
Flasch, Neva Joy, English

DURANT
Ball, Lee Hampton, Jr, American Literature
O'Riley, Margaret Catherine, English & Irish Literature
Slaughter, Eugene Edward, English
EDMOND
Altaffer, Clara Belle, English, Secondary Education
Ausmus, Martin Russey, English Literature
Dew, Arteola Brilbrey, Speech, Humanities
Dillingham, Faye Elizabeth, English
Finney, Frank, English
Hoig, Stanley W, Modern History
Rader, Katherine, English
Tassin, Raymond Jean, Journalism, American Literature
Warren, Clifton Lanier, Comparative Literature
ENID
Fortson, Frances Kay, English & American Literature
GOODWELL
Libbey, Edwin Bissell, English
Ryther, Mary Ruth, English Literature
LANGSTON
Breaux, Elwyn Ellison, English
LAWTON
Hicks, J.C, Speech, Drama
Snipes, Helen Joann, American Literature
Solstad, Kenneth deForest, Modern English
NORMAN
Bambas, Rudolph Charles, English
Barefield, Paul Acton, Speech
Cass, Carl Bartholomew, Drama, Speech
Clark, F. Donald, Fine Arts
Davis, Barbara Hillyer, English Literature, Human Relations
Davis, Gwenn, English Literature
Davis, Robert Murray, English
Eek, Nathaniel S, Drama
Evans, Betty Douglas, English
French, David Plunkett, English Literature
Granger, Bruce Ingham, English
Green, Charles Price, Speech
Gross, David Stuart, English, Comparative Literature
Holland, Cullen Joe, Journalism
Male, Roy Raymond, American Literature
Marshall, Geoffrey, English
Mooradian, Karlen, Journalism, Mass Communication
Pearcy, Roy James, English
Pritchard, John Paul, English
Ruggiers, Paul George, English
Sims, James Hylbert, English Literature
Wilcox, Stewart Conger, English Literature
Yoch, James Joseph, Jr, English Literature
OKLAHOMA CITY
Leverett, Ernestine, Education, English Spanish, Speech
Murphy, John M, English
North, Ross S, Speech, Religion
Thiessen, Valor Eugene, English, Journalism
Vaughn, Bill Edward, Speech Communication
White, John Wesley, Jr, English, Higher Education Administration
SHAWNEE
Craig, Opal Frazier, Speech, English
Jones, Shirley Jean, Old & Middle English
Mitchell, William R, Literature
STILLWATER
Berkeley, David Shelley, English Literature
Campbell, Harry Modean, English
Cox, Kenneth Dale (Jr), Theatre History
Douglas, Loyd, English Literature
Groom, Lemuel Downing, Journalism, Communications
Hughey, Jim Duff, Speech
Keeler, Clinton Clarence, English
Luecke, Jane Marie, O.S.B, English
Milburn, Daniel Judson, English
Milstead, John, English
Rohrberger, Mary H, English
Woods, Samuel Hubert, Jr, English & American Literature
Wray, William Rose, English
TAHLEQUAH
Arrington, Ruth Mozelle, Speech
Holland, Marjorie Dildy, English Education
Lombardi, Betty Ritch, British & American Literature
McQuitty, Robert Alan, English
Propst, Hattie Careen, English
Uzzell, Minter, English, Humanities
TULSA
Alworth, E. Paul, English & American Literature
Blechner, Michael Harry, Medieval & Renaissance English Literature
Bradshaw, Larry Lee, Speech Communication
Dumit, Edward S, Broadcasting, History of Film
Griffith, Philip Mahone, English

Hayden, Donald Eugene, English
Henneke, Ben Graf, Speech
Johnson, Ed H, Communications
Johnson, Manly, English
Jones, Horace Rodman, Speech, Theatre
McClendon, Paul I, Communications
Marder, Daniel, American Literature, Rhetoric
Millichap, Joseph Robert, English, American Literature
Norris, Margot Christa, English Literature
Staley, Thomas F, English & Comparative Literature
Weathers, Winston, English, Rhetoric
Williams, Mary Clay, English
Winchester, O. William, English
Zimmerman, Lester Fred, English
WEATHERFORD
Swanson, William Joseph, American Literature, Spanish
Thomas, Leroy, English

OREGON

ARCH CAPE
Stirling, Thomas Brents, English
ASHLAND
Anderson, John Richard, Rhetoric, Communication Studies
Bowen, James Keith, American Literature
Dean, James L, English
DeMordaunt, Walter Julius, Literary Criticism
Fitzpatrick, Edward Clement, Jr, Speech, Drama
Hungerford, Edward Arthur, English
Kaough, Richard James, Speech Communication
Kreisman, Arthur, English, Humanities
Merchant, Jerrold Jackson, Speech Communication
Moore, Donald Edwin, English, Education
Mulling, Leon Charles, Speech, Drama
Naiden, James Richard, Humanistic Studies
Stolp, Dorothy E, Theatre
CORVALLIS
Bennett, Cleon Vernon, Speech & Drama, Theatre History
Childs, Herbert Ellsworth, Literature
Finnigan, David Francis, English Literature
Foreman, Walter Cyril, English Language & Literature
Frank, Robert Joseph, English Literature
Garrison, Chester Arthur, English
Harris, Charles Newton, Speech
Hewitt, Ray Storla, English Literature
Keltner, John William, Speech Communication
Ligon, John Frank, Jr, English & American Literature
Lynch, James Joseph, English Renaissance Literature
Phillips, Robert Lee, Journalism
Robertson, William James, Speech & Drama
Schroeder, Elver August, English Literature
Valentine, Milton Albert, Speech, Communication
Weinman, Richard Jay, Broadcast Media Communication, Speech
Zwahlen, Fred Casper, Jr, Journalism
EUGENE
Albrecht, Robert Charles, American Literature
Aly, Bower, Rhetoric, Public Address
Aly, Lucile F, English
Bartel, Roland, English
Clark, Robert Donald, Rhetoric
Cutler, Jean Val Jean, Theatre Aesthetics & Production
Dahle, Thomas L, Adult Education, Communication
DeChaine, Faber, Theatre Arts
Duncan, Charles Thomas, Journalism
Friedman, Robert Phillip, Rhetoric & Public Address
Greenfield, Stanley Brian, English
Greenfield, Thelma Nelson, English
Griffith, Clark, English
Haislip, John Alpheus, English, Creative Writing
Handy, William J, English & American Literature
Horn, Robert Dewey, English
Hulteng, John Linne, Journalism
Hynes, Joseph Anthony, Jr, English Literature
Johnson, Gloria E, English
Kitzhaber, Albert Raymond, English
LaRusso, Dominic Anthony, Rhetoric
Love, Glen A, English
McNeir, Waldo Forest, English Literature
Malarkey, Stoddard, English, Education
Maveety, Stanley R, English Literature
Montgomery, Kirt Earl, Speech
Nelson, Roy Paul, Journalism, Graphic Arts
Robinson, Horace William, Drama

Salisbury, Ralph J, Creative Writing, Modern Literature
Sherriffs, Ronald Everett, Broadcast Communication
Sherwood, Irma Z, English
Sherwood, John Collingwood, English Literature
Starlin, Glenn, Speech
Stevenson, Richard Colton, English Novel, Victorian Literature
Taylor, Donald Stewart, English
Teich, Nathaniel, English & Comparative Literature
Toelken, John Barre, Medieval Literature
Weatherhead, Andrew Kingsley, English
Webb, Carl Curtis, Journalism
Wegelin, Christof, American & English Literature
Wickes, George, English
Zavarzadeh, Mas'ud, Modern American Literature
FOREST GROVE
Hingston, Albert Cardiff, Speech, Drama
Prince, William Stevens, English
Roberts, James Russell, American Literature
LA GRANDE
Bruecher, Werner, English & German
Fetz, Howard William, English & American Literature
Hiatt, Richard Gordon, Speech & Drama
Kaiser, Alvin Richard, Speech, Drama
Loso, Mary Jane, English Literature
LAKE OSWEGO
Burnam, Tom, American Literature, Creative Writing
MCMINNVILLE
Anderson, Colena Michael, English
Ericksen, Kenneth Jerrold, English
Filer, Charlotte Colleen, Journalism
Kimball, Arthur Gustaf, English
Singletary, Craig Everett, Speech
MONMOUTH
Baker, Robert Samuel, English
Clarke, Gordon Wilson, English, Linguistics
Rice, Leonard William, English
Soldati, Joseph Arthur, English & American Literature
Walking Bull, Montana Hopkins Rickars, English Education
NEWBERG
Martin, Cecilia Cutts, English, Language Arts
PORTLAND
Anderson, Freeman Burket, English
Ayo, Nicholas Richard, American Literature
Bierman, Judah, English, Humanities
Buell, Thomas C, English
Callahan, John Francis, American Literature
Cooper, John Rex, English Literature
Franchere, Hoyt C, English & American Literature & Language
Garner, (Lafayette) Ross, English
Hamar, Clifford E, Drama & Theatre
Harrison, Fred C, English
Jacobs, Morton Yale, English
Jenkins, William A, English Education
Johnson, Stanley Lewis, English
Knapp, Robert Stanley, English
Kosokoff, Stephen, Speech
Lucht, William Edward, English
Markgraf, Carl, English Literature, Theatre Arts
Millar, Branford Price, English
Nattinger, James Ralph, English Language, Linguistics
Oliver, Egbert Samuel, American Literature
Padrow, Ben, Speech
Reece, Shelley C, English
Scharbach, J. Alexander, English
Singleton, Ralph Herbert, English
Stafford, William Edgar, Literature & Composition
Sugarman, Alfred, Speech
Tuttle, Robert C, English, American Literature
Waller, Frederick O, English Literature
Ward, Jean M, Speech
Wilson, Asher (Boldon), Theatre Arts, Dramatic Literature
Wolk, Anthony, English
SALEM
Braden, Wilbur Sprong, English & American Literature
Putnam, Robert Morgan, Theatre, Drama
Runkel, Howard William, Speech
Trueblood, Paul Graham, English Literature

PENNSYLVANIA

ABINGTON
Kerner, David, English
ALLENTOWN
Chatfield, Minotte McIntosh, English
DeBellis, Jack Angelo, English

DeVinney, Russell N, English, Speech
Flautz, John Thomas, English
Graber, Ralph Schultz, English
Stenger, Harold LeRoy, Jr, English
Sulloway, Alison G, English
Thornburg, Robert Brenner, English
Vos, Nelvin LeRoy, English, Theology
ALTOONA
Sheridan, Margaret Gertrude, English, Music
AMBLER
Morse, Josiah Mitchell, English
Worthington, Mabel Parker, English
ANNVILLE
Struble, George Goodell, Literature
ARDMORE
Dunlap, George Arthur, American Literature
BALA-CYNWYD
Phillips, William John, English Literature
BEAVER FALLS
Carson, Norman Matthews, English Literature
Friesner, Donald Neil, English & American Literature
Morrill, Allen Conrad, English Literature
Paton, Florence Ann, English
Saxton, (Oliver) Kenneth, English
BEDFORD
Wright, Austin, English Literature
BERWYN
Black, Matthew Wilson, English Literature
BETHLEHEM
Allen, Margaret Vanderhaar, English & American Literature
Armstrong, Ray Livingstone, English
Barker, Thoburn Vail, Speech, Linguistics
Bross, Addison Clem, English & American Literature
Burcaw, Robert Theodore, Literature
Burkhart, Lloyd L, English
Criswell, Cloyd M, English
Davis, Harry Barrett, Speech
Dilworth, Ernest Nevin, English Literature
Gallagher, Edward Joseph, American Literature
Greene, David Mason, English Literature
Gregory, Thomas West, English Education, Linguistics
Hartung, Albert Edward, English Literature
Hook, Frank Scott, English
Severs, Jonathan Burke, English Literature
Strauch, Carl Ferdinand, English
Vickrey, John Frederick, English Linguistics & Philology
BLOOMSBURG
Eisenberg, William David, English & American Literature
Hopkins, Melville, Speech
McHale, Michael James, Theatre, Speech
Rice, Alva Wenonah, Communications
Seronsy, Cecil Cowden, English Language & Literature
Stamm, Janet, English
Thompson, Louis F, English
BRADFORD
Laing, Robert Cutter, English
BRYN ATHYN
Gladish, Robert Willis, English
Mitchell, John D, Speech
BRYN MAWR
Bernstein, Carol L, English
Burlin, Robert B, English
Hinton, Margaret Schofield, Middle English Literature
Kramer, Joseph Elliot, English Literature, British & American Drama
Lee, Henry Glenn, Theatre Arts, Speech
Mild, Warren Paul, English Literature
Stapleton, K. Laurence, English, Political Theory
BUTLER
Kopper, Edward Anthony, Jr, English
CALIFORNIA
Blayney, Glenn Hammond, English
Edwards, Ralph W, English
Flemings, Corinne Kranz, Speech Communication
Goodstein, Jack David, English
Kiralis, Karl, English
Langham, Norma, Speech, Drama
Limbacher, Karl, English, Linguistics
Major, Minor Wallace, English
Rockwood, Horace Seymour, III, English
Smith, Robert Wayne, Theater Arts
Watkins, John Pierce, English
Wilson, Daniel E, English
CARLISLE
Bowden, William Robert, English
Horlacher, Amos Benjamin, English Literature
Rosen, Kenneth Mark, American Literature
Schiffman, Joseph, English
Sloane, William, English Literature
Sweeney, Patricia Runk, English
Warlow, Francis Wayland, English

Wishmeyer, William Hood, English
CHAMBERSBURG
Applegate, James Earl, English
Evans, Willa McClung, English Literature
Gattiker, Godfrey Leonard, English
Havens, Paul Swain, English
McCrosson, Doris Ross, English Literature
Mattes, Eleanor Bustin, English, American Literature
CHESTER
Armold, Benjamin, English, Administration
LeStourgeon, Diana E, English
CHEYNEY
Johnstone, Coragreene, English
Lowe, Mervin R, English
Pollak, Vivian R, English & American Literature
CLARION
Arscott, John R, English
Barber, George S, English
Hardwick, Mary Ruth, Theatre, Speech Communication
Hufford, Roger A, Public Address
Marlin, Charles Lowell, Speech
Moses, Elbert Raymond, Jr, Phonetics
Neiman, Gilbert Howard, English, Romance Languages
Redfern, Richard K, English
Shumaker, Ronald Clair, English Language & Literature
Weiss, Adam F, Theatre History
Wright, David Rolland, Speech Communication
COLLEGEVILLE
Bozorth, Richard (Groth), English
DeCatur, Louis Aubrey, Renaissance Literature
Dolman, Geoffrey, English
Storey, George Gilbert, English Philology
CONSHOHOCKEN
Chester, Allan Griffith, English Literature
DIMOCK
Gray, Philip Hayward, English, Humanities
EAST STROUDSBURG
Gelber, Norman, English
Keller, Theodore Donald, English
Larson, Esther Elisabeth, American Literature & Civilization
Meyers, Ronald J, English
EASTON
Bradford, Robert Whitmore, English
Closs, Frederic Thomas, English
Duus, Louise, English, American Studies
Lusardi, James P, English
McCluskey, Donald, English Literature
Vitelli, James Robert, American Studies
Watt, William Whyte, English
EDINBORO
Carothers, Robert Lee, English
Edgerton, William L, English
Karrfalt, David Herbert, English
Marsh, John L, American Literature
Sturm, Ralph D, English Literature
Woodland, Ronald Stanley, Dramatic Literature, Stage Directing
ELIZABETHTOWN
Bomberger, Richard Watson, English
Maxfield, Malinda Ruth, Comparative & English Literature
Poe, M. Evelyn, English
Riley, Jobie E, Forensics
ELKINS PARK
Seltzer, Alvin Jay, English & American Literature
ERIE
Cavanaugh, M. Anne Francis, R.S.M, English, Anglo-Irish Literature
Dinn, Agnes Lucy, Sixteenth and Seventeenth Century English Poetry & Prose
Rouch, John Sears, English
Runzo, James Philip, Nineteenth Century English Literature
Vales, Robert L, English
FINLEYVILLE
Noble, Yvonne, English
GETTYSBURG
Baskerville, Edward J, English Language & Literature
Fredrickson, Robert Stewart, English & American Literature
Geyer, Richard Bennett, English
Lindeman, Ralph Donald, English
Pickering, James D, English & Comparative Literature
Schmidt, Emile O, Drama
Stewart, Mary Margaret, Literature
GLADWYNE
Earnest, Ernest, English Literature
GLENSHAW
Curtin, Frank Daniel, English Literature
GLENSIDE
Bracy, William, English
LeClair, Margaret Foster, English
Rossky, William, English

GREENSBURG
Schmidt, Mary Thecla, S.C, English
Toler, Colette, S.C, English
GREENVILLE
Heissenbuttel, Ernest Gerhardt, English
Morehead, Barbara, English
Pedicord, Harry William, English Literature
Wehner, Ralph S, English
GROVE CITY
Kauffmann, Roy C, American Literature
Kring, Hilda Adam, Folklore & Folklife, English
Paton, James, III, English
HARRISBURG
Faber, Anna Dunkle, English
O'Brien, Dominic Vincent, English
HAVERFORD
Ashmead, John, Jr, English Literature
Butman, Robert H, Drama, English
Lester, John Ashby, Jr, English Literature
Maimon, Elaine Plaskow, English & American Literature
Malard, Sandra Gene, English Literature
Pratt, Robert Armstrong, Medieval Literature
Rose, Edgar Smith, English Literature
Sargent, Ralph Millard, English & American Literature
Satterthwaite, Alfred Wanner, Comparative Literature
HAVERTOWN
Wilkinson, Robert Edwin, American Literature
HUNTINGDON
Church, Ralph Bruce, American Literature
Doyle, Esther M, English, Speech
IMMACULATA
Loretta Maria (Tenbusch), I.H.M, English, Philosophy
Monaghan, Mary Charles, I.H.M, English
INDIANA
Anderson, Edward L, English
Betts, William Wilson, Jr, English
Cook, David M, English
Craig, Harry E, American Literature, Linguistics
Day, Malcolm MacEwan, English
Ensley, Robert William, Speech, Drama
Force, William M, English, Drama
Freund, John Richard, English Literature
Gray, James L, English
Grubb, Daniel Studd, English Language & Literature
Heimer, Jackson W, English
Hull, Raymona E, English
Ianni, Lawrence Albert, English Linguistics, Literary Criticism
McClure, Donald Stuart, English & American Literature
McManmon, John Joseph, English, History of Ideas
Malkin, Michael Robert, Theater History, Dramatic Literature
Omrcanin, Margaret S, English
Rider, Maurice Lincoln, English
Roumm, Phyllis G, English & American Literature
Seinfelt, Frederick William, English
Smith, Helena M, English
Swigart, Ford Harris, Jr, English
Thomas, Raymond Lawrence, English
Truby, John David, Mass Communication
JERSEY SHORE
Stewart, Vincent (Astor, Jr), English, Linguistics
KITTANNING
Hayward, Ralph Malcolm, III, English Literature
Johnson, Robert Gordon, American Literature
KUTZTOWN
Dustan, W. Gordon, English Literature
Engelson, Henriette Rieger, Communication Disorders
Harris, Bennett, English
Kulseth, Leonard Irvin, English
Law, Richard Alexander, English Literature
Mazzaferri, E. Annette Monroe, Speech
Newman, Arnold Eugene, English
LANCASTER
Brubaker, Edward, English
Diller, William Franklin, English
Grushow, Ira, English
Pinsker, Sanford Sigmund, Modern Literature
Rollin, Roger Best, English Literature
Russell, Robert William, English
Schlosser, Ralph Wiest, English
Wickstrom, Gordon Minton, Drama, Theatre
LANDSDOWNE
Kuhn, John Gottlieb, Literature, Theater
Miller. Clarence William, English Literature
Nigro, August John, English
Richards, Emma S, English
Sinclair, Arthur Hayford, Theatre, Speech
Stickney, Ruth, English Literature
Yatron, Michael, English

LANSDALE
Lefevre, Carl Anthony, Sr, English, Linguistics
LA PLUME
Cogswell, Theodore R, English
LEWISBURG
Baumwoll, Dennis, English
Carens, James F, Literature
Gosse, Anthony Cabot, English
Holzberger, William George, English
Hooker, Kenneth Ward, English
McLaughlin, Elizabeth Taylor, Philology
Martin, Mildred Alice, English
Merritt, Frank Westley, English
Murphy, John Vincent, Nineteenth Century British Literature
Orbison, Theodore Tucker, English Drama, Renaissance Literature
Patten, Karl Watson, Jr, English
Payne, Michael, English
Rees, Ralph, English
Smith, Charles Willard, English
Smith, Richard Emmanuel, English Literature, Folklore
Tilton, John Wightman, English
Watts, Charles Henry, II, American Literature
Wheatcroft, John S, Literature
LOCK HAVEN
Becker, Isidore Herman, English & American Literature
Dayananda, James Yesupriya, American & English Literature
Konick, Marcus, English, Communications
Nielsen, Margaret Engel, Nineteenth Century British Literature
LORETTO
Fitzpatrick, Edward Timothy, English
Gergely, Emro J, English, Education
Hines, Bede Francis, T.O.R, English
MAINESBURG
Saveson, Marilyn Buehrer, English, French
MANSFIELD
Glimm, James York, English
Harrison, Stanley R, English
Saveson, John Edward, English
Tillinghast, John Kieth, Speech, Theatre
MEADVILLE
Carr, Virginia Mason, English Literature
Constantine, Aniko Vincze, English Novel
Frank, Frederick Stilson, English & American Literature
Juleus, Nels George, Speech
Katope, Christopher, English
Kern, Alfred, American Literature
Madtes, Richard Eastman, English
Seely, Frederick Franklin, English Literary History
Zolbrod, Paul Geyer, Literary Criticism, Linguistics
MEDIA
Burns, Landon Crawford, English
MELROSE PARK
Schuster, Edgar Howard, Modern Grammar, Modern Literature
MIDDLETOWN
Tischler, Nancy Marie, Literature
Wolf, Melvin Herbert, English
MILLERSVILLE
Kellner, Bruce, English
O'Donnell, John Francis, English
Sheaffer, Mary Patricia A, English
MONACA
Searles, Jo C, American Literature, Poetry
MOSCOW
Knedler, John Warren, Jr, English Philology
NEW WILMINGTON
Burbick, William George, Speech & Drama
Cook, Charles Henry, Jr, English
NEWTOWN
Stedman, Raymond W, Communication
NORRISTOWN
Kershner, Ammon George, Jr, English, Speech
OIL CITY
Clark, Frank M, Theatre History, Criticism
ORWIGSBURG
Fisher, Benjamin Franklin IV, Nineteenth & Twentieth Century Literature
PHILADELPHIA
Allison, Ralph Robert, Theatre
Baugh, Albert Croll, English Language & Literature
Baumgartner, Alex Miller, English
Beards, Richard Douglas, English Literature
Beckman, Richard, English Literature
Beebe, Maurice, English
Benjamin, Edwin Bonette, English Literature
Bentman, Raymond, English Literature
Blake, Howard E, English Education
Boll, Theophilus Ernest Martin, English Literature
Brater, Enoch, English & American Literature
Brown, Thomas Downing, English
Burch, Francis Floyd, S.J, Comparative Literature, Theology

Burke, Daniel, F.S.C, Literary Theory, English
Burkhart, Charles, English
Butler, James Albert, English & American Literature
Buttel, Robert William, English
Carter, Joseph Cleveland, Journalism
Chesebro, James William, Speech Communication
Clark, Richard, English
Cohen, Eileen Z, English Literature
Cohen, Mary B, Modern Literature, Women's Studies
Conarroe, Joel Osborne, English
Conn, Peter James, English & American Literature
Deaux, George Richard, Modern American Literature
DeLaura, David Joseph, English Literature
Dewees, Charles William, Jr, English Literature
Doran, Paul Richard, English Literature, Education
Dunn, Robert Francis, Literature
Ecroyd, Donald Howarth, Speech
Edenbaum, Robert I, English & American Literature
Egloff, Susan June, English & American Literature
Ellis, F. Patrick, F.S.C, English
Emery, John Pike, English
Feeney, Joseph John, S.J, American & Modern British Literature
Fielding, Raymond, Cinema
Freehafer, John Henry, English
Frye, Roland Mushat, English
Gaull, Marilyn, English
Goldberg, Jonathan S, Renaissance Literature
Graham, Don Ballew, American Literature, English
Green, Rose Basile, English, American Literature
Halfond, Murray Michael, Speech Pathology
Hallwachs, Robert Gordon, English Literature
Hazard, Patrick David, American Literature & Culture
Hoffman, Daniel, English
Hornberger, Theodore, American Literature
Irving, Edward Burroughs, Jr, English
Jackson, Gabriele Bernhard, English Literature
Jackson, Paul Russell, English
Jackson, Thomas H, English
Jenkins, Ralph Eugene, English Literature
Johnson, George W, English
Johnson, Maurice O, English Literature
Keenan, John Joseph, American Literature
Kelley, Alice van Buren, English Literature
Kennedy, Richard Sylvester, English
Knodt, Kenneth Simms, English & American Literature
Koch, Claude F, English
Korshin, Paul J, English
Lautz, Richard, English
Laws, George Malcolm, Jr, English
Lee, Charles, English
Lefevre, Helen E, English
Leonard, Neil, American Civilization
LeRoy, Gaylord Clarke, English Literature
Letzring, Monica, English & Comparative Literature
Levitt, Morton Paul, English
Llewellyn, Robert Hall, Medieval Literature & Language
Longaker, John Mark, English
Lucid, Robert Francis, English
Lumiansky, Robert Mayer, English
Luria, Maxwell Sidney, English, Medieval Studies
Lynch, William James, American Literature
McFadden, George, English
Magnuson, Paul Andrew, English Literature
Mangione, Jerre, English
Markus, Thomas Benjamin, Theatre
Marler, Robert Franklin, Jr, American & English Literature
Matonis, Ann, English
Mauskopf, Charles G, English
Mellen, Joan, Film, Literature
Mills, Moylan C, English, Drama
Mollenhauer, Emery C, F.S.C, English
Most, Ralph Christian, English
O'Connell, Richard James, English & American Literature, Creative Writing
Olley, Francis R, Drama
Omans, Glen A, English
Orvell, Miles David, English & American Literature
Paulits, Walter John, F.S.C, English Literature
Peck, Richard E, English
Perloff, Marjorie G, English Literature
Rackin, Donald, English
Rackin, Phyllis Rosalyn, English
Regan, Robert, English

Roberts, John Buckley, Communications, Radio & Television
Rodden, Daniel Joseph, Speech, Drama
Rose, Ernest D, Motion Pictures, Communications Esthetics
Ross, Robert N, Semiotics, Literary Theory
Scouten, Arthur Hawley, English Literature
Seydow, John Joseph, English
Shaaber, Matthias Adam, English Literature
Shankman, Florence V, Reading, Language Arts
Sharpless, Francis Parvin, English
Simons, Herbert W, Speech
Sims, Dwight Johnston, English Literature
Slepian, Barry, English
Smith, Gordon Ross, English
Snyder, Lee Lamar, English
Soler, William Gordan, English, English Education
Spiller, Robert Ernest, American Literature
Steene, Birgitta, Comparative Literature
Stevick, Philip T, English
Stokes, George Stewart, Literature
Stokes, Thomas Joseph, S.J, English Literature
Tasch, Peter Anthony, English
Thompson, Craig Ringwalt, English Literature & History
Tonkin, Humphrey Richard, English, Interlinguistics
Towne, Ralph L, Jr, Rhetoric, Public Address
Trautmann, Fredrick, Speech
Turner, Robert Y, English
Wallace, Emily Mitchell, English & American Literature
Weales, Gerald Clifford, English Literature
Webster, David Hume, English
Wendling, Ronald Charles, English Literature
Widmann, R.L, English, Humanities
Wilde, Alan, English
Wolper, Roy S, English
Wood, Gretchen Anne, English
Yannella, Philip Richard, English & American Literature
PITTSBURGH
Alexander, Robert Joseph, English Literature
Baim, Joseph, English
Bowman, Ned Alan, Theater Arts
Brignano, Russell Carl, English
Briscoe, Mary Louise, Medieval Literature, Literary Criticism
Carra, Lawrence, Drama, Theatre
Clair, John A, English, American Literature
Cohn, Jan Kadetsky, English & American Literature, American Studies
Cottrell, Beekman Waldron, English
Crow, Charles Rohrer, Jr, English
Culver, Montgomery Morton, English
Cummins, John W, English
Curran, Ronald Thomas, American Literature & Studies
David, Mary Elizabeth Meek, Old & Middle English Literature
Eastman, Arthur M, English
Elagin (Matveiev), Ivan, Russian Literature
Eldredge, Frances, English Literature & Arts
Elliott, Virginia Agnes, English
Emmett, Victor Jay, Jr, English Literature
Eskey, David Ellsworth, English, Linguistics
Evert, Walter H, English
Favorini, Attilio Anthony, History of Theatre, Theatre Criticism
Fowler, Lois Josephs, English
Gale, Robert Lee, English & American Literature
Gangewere, Robert Jay, English
Gister, Earle Robert, Drama
Grose, Lois Margaret, English
Hart, John Augustine, English Literature
Hayes, Ann Louise, English
Hazo, Samuel J, English & American Literature
Helfand, Michael S, Victorian & Modern English Literature
Hinman, Robert B, English
Hodges, Margaret Moore, Library Science
Hopkins, Thomas Aloysius, Speech
Huber, Joan R, English
Irwin, Eleanor Chima, Speech, Drama
Johnson, Clifford Ross, Jr, Eighteenth Century English Literature
Jones, Granville Hicks, English & American Literature
Jones, Nancy Carol, Journalism
Jones, Putnam Fennell, English Language & Literature
Katz, Leon, English, Drama
Kish, Dorothy, American Literature
Knapp, James Franklin, Modern Poetry, Myth
Knapp, Peggy Ann, English & American Literature
LaBarbera, Vincent James, English, Journalism
Labriola, Albert Christy, Renaissance & Seventeenth Century English Literature
Landy, Marcia, English

Laufe, Abe, English
Lauritis, Joseph A, C.S.Sp, English
Lee, Lawrence, Literature
Lewis, Robert John, English Renaissance Literature
Lillie, Vernell Audrey, English, Contemporary Black Drama
Longini, Peter Richard, Communication, Speech
McCoy, Dorothy Schuchman, Renaissance & Comparative Literature
McLean, Albert Forbes, American Studies
McTaggart, William Joseph, English Romantic Poetry
Mallinger, Anita Ellen, English, Creative Writing
Marrs, Edwin Wilson, Jr, English
Meli, Samuel Salvador, Speech Communication, Theatre
Miles, Thomas Hardy, Medieval Literature, History of Religion
Miller, John Hawkins, English Literature
Mitchell, Robert Earl, English & American Literature
Mooney, Harry John, Jr, English
Moore, Helen Jean, English, Library Science
Neeson, Jack (Mc) Henry, English
Newman, Robert Preston, Speech, Communications
Nossen, Robert Joseph, English
Papinchak, Robert Allen, Creative Writing, American Literature
Papousek, Marilyn Deweese, Literature, Drama
Parker, Wilford Oren, Scene Design, Theatre Architecture
Petit, Herbert Hanley, English Philology
Philbrick, Thomas Leslie, English
Provost, George Foster, Jr, English
Rinear, David Leslie, Dramatic Art, Theatre History
Rosenberg, James Leroy, Drama & English
Searle, William Miner, American & Modern Comparative Literature
Simmonds, James Dudley, English
Siporin, Rae Lee, Medieval English Literature, History & Structure of the English Language
Slack, Robert Charles, English
Smith, Philip Edward, II, English & American Literature
Snyder, Richard Clement, English Literature, Composition
Sochatoff, Albert Fred, Classical Paleography
Steinberg, Erwin Ray, English
Strauss, Mary Therese, American Literature
Swank, Earle Robert, English
Tacey, William Sanford, Speech
Tannacito, Dan John, Victorian Literature, Critical Theory
Taube, Myron, Creative Writing
Thorsen, Tor Henry, English
Tindall, Samuel Jones, Jr, English
Tobias, Richard Clark, English
Walter, Otis Monroe, Speech
Wells, Richard Albert, English
Wenneker, Jerome Sidney, Drama, Speech
West, Michael Davidson, English
Whitman, Robert Freeman, English
Windt, Theodore Otto, Speech, Rhetoric
Wion, Philip Kennedy, English Literature
READING
Brown, Benjamin Earl, English
Harding, Clyde Albert, English Literature
Reppert, James Donald, English
Trauger, Wilmer Kohl, English
RIEGELSVILLE
Workman, Samuel Klinger, English Literature
ROSEMONT
Bolger, Stephen Garrett, English
Weinig, Mary Anthony, S.H.C.J, English
ST. DAVIDS
Ruth, John L, English
SCRANTON
Casey, Ellen Miller, English Literature
Grady, Richard Francis, S.J, Psychology of Literature
Hertz, John Atlee, English, Medieval Literature
Hill, William B, S.J, English
Mitchell, Louis Duvalo, English Literature
Rakauskas, William Vincent, English
Ryan, Stephen P, English
Yarina, Margaret Anne, English
SELINSGROVE
Abler, Lawrence Anthony, English, Comparative Literature
McCune, Marjorie Wolfe, English
Rahter, Charles Augustus, English
SHIPPENSBURG
Frantz, Robert O, English
Gardner, Dorothea Breitwieser, English
Kalmey, Robert Pohl, English
Lindberg, John, English Literature
Steck, James Sperow, English

SLIPPERY ROCK
Bass, Eben E, English
Biswanger, Raymond Adam, Jr, English
Curry, Elizabeth Reichenbach, English
Curry, Stephen Jefferis, English
Hart, Alden Wadsworth, American Literature
Holtan, Orley Iver, Theatre
Kuhr, Manuel I, Speech
Laughner, Carl L, Speech
McIlvaine, Robert Morton, English & American Literature
McKay, James William, Education, Reading & Language Arts
O'Malley, Jerome Francis, English, History
Riggs, Joseph H, Speech
Schmittlein, Albert Edward, American Literature
Sharma, Mohan Lal, English & American Literature
Sledd, Hassell Brantley, English
Walsh, Edward John, English
SPRINGTOWN
Hunt, John Wesley, English
STATE COLLEGE
Arnold, Carroll Clyde, Speech
Bauer, Robert VanAkin, English & American Literature
Bayard, Samuel Preston, Music
Christy, (Frederick) Lynn, English Composition
Harrison, John M, Journalism, American Humor
Houp, Kenneth Wilton, English
Hungerford, E. Arthur, Speech, Broadcasting
Kelly, Louise Kline, English
Knapp, Edgar H, English, Education
Lewis, Arthur Orcutt, Jr, American Literature
Oliver, Robert Tarbell, Public Speaking
Reed, Robert Rentoul, Jr, English
Reifsnider, Robert Daniel, Theatre Arts
Rubinstein, Samuel Leonard, English
Schug, Clayton Horn, Speech
STROUDSBURG
Stoddard, Floyd Grady, English
SWARTHMORE
Blackburn, Thomas Harold, English Literature
Cohen, Hennig, American Studies, Literature
Coles, William Eliot, Jr, English
Cowden, David, English
Devin, Philip Lee, Drama
Gottsegen, Robert D, English
Haskell, Ann Sullivan, Medieval English Literature, History of the English Language
Hinchey, John Joseph, English & American Literature
James, Charles Lyman, American Literature
Pagliaro, Harold E, English Literature
Rosier, James Louis, English Literature & Philology
Smith, Barbara Herrnstein, English Literature
Snyder, Susan Brooke, English
Weinstein, Philip Meyer, English & American Literature
UNIVERSITY PARK
Arnold, Judd B, English
Begnal, Michael Henry, Modern English & Comparative Literature
Benson, Thomas W, Speech Communication
Buckalew, Ronald Eugene, English
Cohen, Herman, Speech
Condee, Ralph Waterbury, English Literature
Cook, Douglas Neilson, Drama
Crane, John Kenny, English
Damerst, William A, English
Dunham, Robert E, Speech
Ebbitt, Wilma Robb, English
Eckhardt, Caroline Davis, English & Comparative Literature
Euwema, Ben, English
Fiskin, Abram M. I, English
Fitzgerald, Robert Paul, English
Frandsen, Kenneth D, Communication
Frank, Robert Worth, Jr, English
Froke, Marlowe D, Journalism
Goodwin, Harry Eugene, Journalism
Goodwin, James Edward, English
Gregg, Richard Bevve, Speech
Haines, Raymond Michael, English Literature & Composition
Hauser, Gerard Alan, Rhetoric
Hill, William Henry, Jr, English
Holtzman, Paul D, Speech Communication
Hudspeth, Robert N., English
Kiernan, Michael Terence, English Literature
Lougy, Robert E, English
McAdams, James R, English
Manfull, Lowell L, Theatre
Mann, Charles William, English, Bibliography
Meserole, Harrison Talbot, English
Nelson, Harold Elroy, Speech
O'Brien, Harold James, Speech
O'Donnell, William Hugh, Twentieth Century British Literature, Anglo-Irish Literature

Paulson, Stanley Fay, Speech
Pfaff, Daniel Wayne, Journalism, Mass Communications
Phillips, Gerald M, Disturbed Communication
Preston, Lillian Elvira, Speech, TV & Radio
Price, Joseph Gerard, English Literature
Rambeau, James Morris, English
Rosenberg, Bruce, English, Folklore
Rubin, Joseph Jay, American Literature
Sams, Henry Whittington, English Literature
Schneeman, Peter Henry, English & American Literature, Creative Writing
Shedd, Gordon Michael, English
Smith, John Bristow, Modern British & American Literature, Computer Studies of Language
Smith, Warren S, Theatre, The Arts
Stewart, David H, English, Russian
Walden, Daniel, American Studies
Walters, Walter H, Theatre Arts
Weaver, Robert Glenn, English Composition
Weintraub, Stanley, English Literature
West, Paul Noden, English, Comparative Literature
White, Eugene Edmond, Speech
Yeaton, Kelly, Theatre Arts
Young, Philip, English
VERONA
Smith, Thomas Francis, English
VILLANOVA
Bernardin, Charles Wilhelm, American Literature
Brennan, Neil F, Modern British Literature
Cherry, Charles Lester, English & American Literature
Fischer, Jerome J, English Literature
Green, John M, English
Kantra, Robert Andrew, English
Kinney, Joseph Aloysius, Jr, English
Lansbury, Coral, English Literature, Modern History
Murphy, George Douglas, American Literature
WASHINGTON
Branton, Clarence Leroy, English
Gargano, James William, American & English Literature
Laun, Edward Carl, English
Taylor, John Alfred, English
WAYNESBURG
McEwen, Fred Bates, English
WEST CHESTER
Bailey, Dorothy Dee, English
Casagrande, Diane Oaks, Speech
Field, John Paul, English & American Literature
Hashimoto, Yoko, Occidental & Oriental Theatre
Haviland, J. Bernard, English Literature, Drama
Henry, William H, English
Morehouse, William Mantle, Speech Communication, Theatre
Newman, Franklin Baldwin, English Literature
Newman, Katharine D, English
Oldsey, Bernard Stanley, English
Page, W.E, Jr, English Linguistics
WILKES-BARRE
Fiester, Benjamin F, Jr, English
Groh, Alfred Stuart, English, Drama
Hammerbacher, George Henry, British Literature, Linguistics
Lord, Charlotte Virginia, English, Drama
Napieralski, Edmund Anthony, Dramatic Literature & Theory
Rader, Louis, English Literature
Sherrer, Charles David, English Literature
Valletta, Clement Lawrence, American Civilization
WILLIAMSPORT
Gustafson, Danny Davis, English, American Literature
Sawyer, David Elyot, English Literature
WILLOW GROVE
Smith, James Frederick, Jr, American Literature
WILMINGTON
Sells, Larry Francis, English Literature
WYNCOTE
Gordon, James D, English
WYNNEWOOD
Starr, Herbert Willmarth, English Literature
Witmer, Anne M, English
WYOMING
Warner, Edward Francis, English, Communication
YARDLEY
Cole, Robert Carlton, American Literature, Journalism
YORK
Barnard, Dean Stanton, Jr, English

RHODE ISLAND

BARRINGTON
Logan, Samuel Talbot, Jr, Literature, Theology
KINGSTON
Barker, Walter L, English
Doody, Agnes G, Speech
Gullason, Thomas Arthur, English
Hoffmann, Charles George, English
Jacobs, Dorothy Hieronymus, English Language & Literature
Joel, Helmuth Wulf, Jr, English Literature
Kunz, Don R, English Literature
MacLaine, Allan Hugh, English
Malina, Marilyn J, English
Marshall, James Morse, English & American Literature
Mathews, Francis X, English
Miller, Jordan Yale, Comparative Literature, Drama
Robinson, Erwin Arthur, English
Simmons, Walter (Lee), English Literature
Sorlien, Robert Parker, English & American Literature
Steeves, Edna L, English & Comparative Literature
PEACE DALE
Seigel, Jules Paul, English
PROVIDENCE
Anderson, George Kumler, English Literature
Barbour, Brian Michael, English & American Literature
Barnhill, James Orris, Theater, Speech
Blistein, Elmer Milton, English
Bloom, Edward Alan, English & American Literature
Bloom, Lillian Doris, English
Boulger, James Denis, English
Burrell, Edward William, English, Education
Cohn, Albert Marcus, Drama
Comery, Robert Whitfield, English
Crosman, Robert True, English & American Literature
Cubbage, Moyne L, Speech Communication
Curran, Sonia Terrie, Medieval English Literature
Delasanta, Rodney, English Literature
Devlin, Francis Patrick, English
Dillavou, George Jackson, Speech, Public Address
Ducey, Cathryn Annette, English, American Literature
Fortin, Rene E, English
Goldgar, Harry, English, Comparative Literature
Hawkes, John C.B, Jr, English
Hennedy, John Francis, English
Hirsch, David Harry, English & American Literature
Hoffman, C. Fenno, Jr, English, Humanities
Honig, Edwin, English
Jayne, Sears, English Literature
Kapstein, Israel James, English Literature
Krause, David, English
Latt, David Jay, English Literature
Lewalski, Barbara Kiefer, English Literature
Lowery, Thomas Vincent, English
McClelland, Benjamin Wright, English
Monteiro, George, English
Murphy, Richard Joseph, English
Robinson, William H, Jr, English & American Negro Literature
Rosenfield, Claire, English
St. Armand, Barton Levi, American Literature
Salzberg, Albert C, English Literature
Scheff, Edward Aaron, Speech Communication
Scholes, Robert, English
Shroeder, John William, English, Renaissance & American Literature
Spilka, Mark, English
Stevens, Earl Eugene, English
Thomson, Paul Van Kuykendall, English
Towers, Tom Hamilton, American Literature
Votoras, Taki Panajotis, English Literature
Waggoner, Hyatt Howe, American Literature
White, James Edward, Nineteenth Century American Literature, Modern Drama
White, Sidney Howard, English
Willard, Charles Borromeo, American Literature
Wilmeth, Don B, English, Theatre History
RUMFORD
Troendle, Dorothy, English, Linguistics
WAKEFIELD
Coffin, Tristram Potter, English
WEST BARRINGTON
Van Nostrand, Albert Douglass, English
WEST KINGSTON
Sullivan, Nancy, English

SOUTH CAROLINA

ANDERSON
Vandiver, Edward Pinckney, Jr, English Literature
BELTON
Cox, Luther Bigby, English
CHARLESTON
Achurch, Robert Waller, English
Anderson, Charles Roberts, American & English Literature
Doyle, John Robert, Jr, English & American Literature
Holbein, Woodrow Lee, English & American Literature
Morris, John Allen, English & American Literature
Redd, Tony Neil, English & American Literature
Rembert, James Aldrich Wyman, English
Rivers, James Clark Seabrook, English
CLEMSON
Bryant, Hallman B, English
Calhoun, Richard James, English
Cox, Headley Morris, Jr, English
Green, Claud Bethune, English
Gum, Coburn, English
Hill, Robert White, English & American Literature
Holman, Harriet R, English
Idol, John Lane, Jr, English & American Literature
Koon, George William, English Literature
Mandel, Jerome Herbert, English
Owings, Marvin Alpheus, English
Sawyer, Corinne Holt, English, Drama
Steadman, Mark Sidney, Jr, English
Usrey, Malcolm Orthell, English
Winter, James Paul, English Literature
CLINTON
Skinner, James Lister, III, English
COLUMBIA
Atkinson, Jennifer Elizabeth, Drama, American Literature
Barroll, John Leeds, III, English
Brauer, George C, Jr, English
Brown, Ashley, English & American Literature
Bruccoli, Matthew J, English
Carlisle, Carol Whitt Jones, Shakespeare, 19th Century Theatre
Castles, William Henry, Jr, English
Davis, Marianna W, English, Education
Dickey, James, English
Dillon, Bert, English
Dunlap, Benjamin Bernard, English & American Literature, Film Studies
Garrett, George P, English
Geckle, George Leo, English
Gibbs, Lloyd Graham, English
Green, Russell Earl, Drama
Greiner, Donald James, American Literature
Guilds, John Caldwell, Jr, English
Harrod, Ann Jennalie Cook, English Literature
Helterman, Jeffrey Alec, English, Medieval Studies
Howard-Hill, Trevor Howard, English Literature, Bibliography
Katz, Joseph, English & American Literature
Kim, Myung Whan, Comparative Literature
Kimmey, John Lansing, English
Lindemann, Erika Caroline, English Literature, Philology
Lindstrand, Gordon, English Literature
Matalene, Henry William, III, English, Comparative Literature
Meriwether, James Babcock, English, American Literature
Montgomery, Reid Hood, Journalism
Mott, Sara Louise, English
Myerson, Joel Arthur, American Literature
Neuffer, Claude Henry, English
Nolan, Edward Francis, English
Nolte, William Henry, English
Oakman, Robert Lee, III, Victorian Literature
Peckham, Morse, English Literature
Price, Henry Thomas, Journalism, Communication
Rees, Ennis, English
Rice, Thomas Jackson, English Literature
Rollinson, Philip Bruce, Renaissance Literature
Roy, George Ross, English, Comparative Literature
Seigler, Milledge Broadus, American Literature
Siebert, Donald Tate, Jr, English Literature
Sprague, Arthur Colby, English Literature
Starck, Kenneth, Communication Theory, Journalism
Sullivan, Harry Richards, English
Uray, Richard Martin, Broadcasting, Education
Welsh, John Rushing, English
Winton, Calhoun, English

GAFFNEY
McMillan, Montague, English
GREENVILLE
Bonner, Francis Wesley, English
Crabtree, John Henry, Jr, English
Hill, Philip George, Drama
Lowrey, Sara, Speech
Rasor, Charles Lewis, American Literature
Reid, Alfred Sandlin, English
Stewart, James Tate, English
GREENWOOD
Ellis, Herbert Alexander, Literature
LANDRUM
Sevier, Anne, English
MARION
Cusac, Marian Hollingsworth, English & American Literature
NEWBERRY
Irvin, Fredric Brinker, English Literature
Mullwee, Deloris Robinson, English
Spove, Steen Holst, English
ORANGEBURG
Abu-Shawareb, Hassan Muhammad, English
Mebane, Mary Elizabeth, American & Nineteenth Century British Literature
Parler, Nettie P, English Language
Trieber, Jacob Marshall, English, Humanities
ROCK HILL
Clark, Edward William, English, American Literature
Lane, Robert P, English Literature
Long, William Ivey, Drama
Murdy, Louise Baughan, English
Pettigrew, Bessie Joye, Black Literature & Language
Weaver, Jack Wayne, English Literature
Wilcox, Earl Junior, English, American Literature
SPARTANBURG
Ashmore, Charles DeLoach, English
Byars, John A, English
Chewning, Lawrence Harris, Jr, English
Coates, Kenneth Daniel, English
Covington, Philip Stanhope, English
Parker, James W, Drama
Stevenson, John Weamer, English
SUMMERVILLE
McCoy, Samuel Jesse, English
Wiles, Americus George David, English Literature
SWANSEA
Youngman, Robert Carl, Speech, Drama

SOUTH DAKOTA

ABERDEEN
Ahsan, Syed Mohammad, English Literature
Proctor, John William, English
BROOKINGS
Giddings, Joseph Addison, English Philology
Hoogestraat, Wayne E, Speech
Marken, Jack Walter, English
Markland, Ben Clifford, Speech, Journalism
Martin, Dexter, English
Stine, Lawrence, Speech, Drama
HURON
Meyer, Kenneth John, English, American Studies
MITCHELL
Weinkauf, Mary Stanley, English
RAPID CITY
Boyd, Leslie Emerson, English
SIOUX FALLS
Boe, Karen Elizabeth, English Language & Literature
Fryxell, Donald Raymond, English
Fryxell, Lucy Dickinson, English
Geyer, Charles William, American Literature
Hong, Theodore Norman, English Literature
Huseboe, Arthur R, English
Matthews, William R, Jr, English Literature
Seibel, Roy William, Speech
SPEARFISH
Phillips, Ron, Communications, Journalism
VERMILLION
Angotti, Vincent L, Theatre, Drama
Block, Raphael Herman, English Literature
Dill, Stephen Horton, English
Harrington, Elbert Willington, Speech
Knutson, Wayne Shafer, Theater
Lee, Warren Marion, Creative Playwriting
Milton, John Ronald, English
Selz, William Aaron, English
YANKTON
Ehrensperger, Edward Charles, English Language & Literature
Neville, Mary Eileen, O.S.B, English

TENNESSEE

ATHENS
Miller, Mary Ruth, English
BRISTOL
Landrum, Graham Gordon, English
Winship, George Parker, Jr, English Literature
CHATTANOOGA
Bryan, Enid Parker, English
Carter, Roland DeBuske, English
Connor, George C, English
Consacro, Dominic Peter, Medieval English
   Literature & Language
Herron, Arlie Edwards, English
Ramsey, Paul, English
Sanderlin, Robert Reed, English
Tinkler, John Douglas, English, Philology
Ward, Dorothy Hackett, Drama, Speech
CLARKSVILLE
Boercker, Marguerite Jeanne, Linguistics,
   Reading
Elliott, Leonard Reece, Communication Theory,
   Public Address
Irwin, Edward Eugene, English & American
   Literature
Lester, James D, Nineteenth Century Am-
   erican & British Literature
Lumpkin, Ben Gray, English
Tatham, Lewis Charles, Jr, English
Waters, Charles McManus, English
COLLEGEDALE
Bennett, Homer Douglas, Speech, Theology
Dick, Donald, Speech
Knittel, Frank Alvin, English
McClarty, Wilma King (Doering), English,
   English Education
COLUMBIA
Burkett, Eva Mae, American Literature
COOKEVILLE
Bode, Robert Francis, English Literature
Derryberry, William Everett, English Lan-
   guage & Literature
Henderson, Jerry E, Drama
Jenks, Mary Hathaway, English Literature
Kemp, Homer Dale, Early American Litera-
   ture & Culture
Mitchell, Eleanor Drake, Renaissance &
   Eighteenth Century English Literature
Warren, John W, English Literature
Woodall, Guy R, English
GREENVILLE
Cothran, Andrew Neilson, American Litera-
   ture & Intellectual History
Voss, Thomas Gorman, American & English
   Literature
HENDERSON
Fulkerson, Raymond Gerald, Rhetorical Crit-
   icism, American Public Address
Thomas, John David, Speech
JACKSON
Carter, Bernice Alleen, English
Clark, George E, English
JEFFERSON CITY
Bass, William Wilson, English
Welton, John Lee, Speech, Drama
Wood, Gerald Carl, British Literature

JOHNSON CITY
Dove, George Naff, English
Harris, William Styron, Jr, English Literature
Higgs, Robert Jackson, American Literature
Manning, Ambrose Nuel, English
Nilsen, George Howard, English Literature
Schneider, Valerie Lois, Speech & Communi-
   cation
Williams, Edwin Winston, Nineteenth Century
   English Literature

KNOXVILLE
Adams, Percy Guy, English
Allen, Ralph Gilmore, Theatre Arts
Bohringer, Kenneth Charles, English Literatur_
Broeker, Harriet Durkee, English
Burghardt, Lorraine Hall, Modern British &
   American Drama
Cade, Dozier Copeland, Journalism
Curry, Kenneth, English
Davis, Richard Beale, English
Drake, Robert (Young, Jr), English
Ensor, Allison Rash, English
Fisher, John Hurt, English
Gill, James Earl, English
Henshaw, Wandalie, Theatre
Jellicorse, John Lee, Communications, Public
   Communications History
Kelly, Richard Michael, English, Victorian
   Period
Knickerbocker, Kenneth Leslie, English Lit-
   erature
Leggett, B. J, Modern Literature
McMillan, Samuel H, Jr, Modern Drama &
   American Literature
Miller, Frederick DeWolfe, English
Penner, Allen R, English

Richards, Mary Juliet Proctor, English Lit-
   erature
Sanders, Norman Joseph, English
Soper, Paul Leon, Speech, Theatre
Stewart, Bain Tate, English Literature & Com-
   position
Thaler, Alwin, English Literature
Thornburg, Frank B, Journalism
Wheeler, Thomas Van Horn, English, Com-
   parative Literature
Wright, Nathalia, American Literature
Yeomans, Gordon Allan, Speech
MARTIN
Payne, Mildred Y., English, History
Roy, Emil L, English
MARYVILLE
Bushing, Arthur Story, English Literature
Fowler, Elizabeth Thomas, American & English
   Literature
MEMPHIS
Bannon, Peter Laurence, English
Bence, Eugene, Speech, Drama
Bensman, Marvin Robert, Mass Communica-
   tions, Speech & Drama
Carlson, Thomas Clark, American Literature
Clifton, Yerger Hunt, English
Cooper, Robert M, English
Dameron, John Lasley, English
Farris, Jack D, English
Howell, Elmo, English
Johnson, Albert Edward, English, Speech,
   Drama
Kennedy, James Keith, Theater
Long, Charles (E), (Jr), English, German
Lynch, Barbara Furber, English Renaissance
   Literature
McCray, William Edward, English, Drama,
   Speech
Malin, Stephen Durboraw, Theatre, Poetry
Osborn, Michael McDonald, Speech
Patterson, N. S, Journalism
Peyton, Henry Hall, III, Old & Middle English
Phillips, Elizabeth C, English
Queener, Lea Gibbs, Speech
Robinson, Clayton, English
Ross, Danforth Raynolds, English
Shaheen, Naseeb, Renaissance English Lit-
   erature
Sloan, John Herbert, Speech
Smith, Alfred Winn, Linguistics
Smith, Walter Rhea, British Literature
Stagg, Louis Charles, English
Tucker, Cynthia Grant, Comparative Litera-
   ture, English
White, Bradford, Speech, Drama
Wynn, Lawrence, English
Yellin, David Gilmer, Broadcasting & Film
MILLINGTON
Stewart, Mary E, English
MONTEAGLE
Lytle, Andrew (Nelson), English
MORRISTOWN
Ramsay, Ethel Davis, English, European His-
   tory
MURFREESBORO
Beasley, William Madison, English & Amer-
   ican Literature
Dunne, Michael Francis, American Literature
Gentry, William Larry, English & American
   Literature
Holland, William Holmes, Jr, English
Lowe, Larry Veazey, Speech, Drama
Walker, David Ellis, Jr, Speech Communica-
   tion

NASHVILLE
Aden, John M, English
Anderson, A. Edwin, Literature, Language
Archer, Leonard Courtney, English
Barrett, Alberta Gregg, English
Beach, Leonard B, American Literature
Bell, Vereen McNeill, English
Bennett, George Neil, American Literature
Booth, Willard Claude, Communications, Drama
   Education
Colley, John Scott, English Literature
Collins, Leslie Morgan, English & American
   Drama
Dilgard, Cynthia Corlew, Eighteenth Century
   English & Modern Literature
Duncan, Edgar Hill, English
Duncan, Ivar Lou Myhr, English
Eaton, Anthony Haskell, English, Humanities
Elledge, W. Paul, English
Ellis, Carroll Brooks, Speech, Religion
Fulmer, Constance Marie, English Literature
Gower, Herschel, English & American Lit-
   erature
Griffin, William James, English
Hassel, Rudolph Christopher, Jr, English, Re-
   naissance
Hudson, Robert J, English
Hunter, Robert Grams, English

Hutchison, Earl R, Sr, English, Mass Com-
   munications
Jahn, Jerald Duane, English Renaissance
Kilroy, James F, English
Lindsay, Crawford Bernard, English & Ameri-
   can Literature
Loyd, Allen Dennis, American Literature
Nathanson, Leonard, English Literature
Palmer, Rupert Elmer, Jr, English Language
   & Literature
Phy, Allene Stuart, English, Humanities
Poag, Thomas Edward, Speech, Drama
Purdy, Rob Roy, English
Purnell, Rosentene Bennett, English
Rhoads, Forrest Neil, Sr, English
Samuel, Dorothy Ione Johnson, English, French
Smith, Lewis, English
Stathis, James John, English
Sullivan, Walter L, English
Titus, Warren Irving, English, American
   Studies
Touster, Eva Beach, English
Walker, Fred Bynum, Speech, Bible
Weatherby, Harold L, Jr, English Literature
Wright, Joseph Edward, Theatre
Wyatt, Robert Odell, II, English Literature
Young, Thomas Daniel, English
SEWANEE
Core, George, British & American Literature
Harrison, Charles Trawick, English Literature
Marsh, Thad Norton, English
Rhys, Brinley John, English
Tate, Allen, Poetry
TULLAHOMA
Benson, LaVonn Marceil, English
Wyman, Linda Lee, English Literature

TEXAS

ABILENE
Barton, Fred Jackson, Speech
Blair, Caroline Couch, Speech & Drama
Bojarski, Edmund Antoni, English & American
   Literature
Bridges, Lloyd, English, American Literature
Canant, Ray Moschel, English
Emery, Emogene, Speech, Drama
Enzor, Edwin Harold, Jr, Communication
Ewing, George Wilmeth, English
Fulks, Lewis, Drama, Speech
Hamner, Robert Daniel, English & American
   Literature
Harper, Preston Frank, American Literature
Huff, Lloyd Dickason, English Language & Lit-
   erature
Odle, Zelma Ruth, English Literature
Perry, Lowell G, Speech, Communication
Reynolds, Jerry Dee, Speech Communication
Tanner, Jimmie Eugene, American Literature
Williams, Mima Ann, English
ALPINE
Boyd, Katharine, Drama & Speech
McCarty, Edward Clayton, Speech, Drama
McNeil, Norman L, American Literature
Miles, Elton Roger, American Literature
Whitaker, John Ralph, Journalism
AMARILLO
Erdman, Loula Grace, English
ARLINGTON
Beaudry, Harry Richard, English Literature
Eichelberger, Clayton L, English, American
   Literature
Estes, Emory Dolphous, English & American
   Literature
Fortenberry, George E, American Literature
Garner, Stanton Berry, English
Golladay, Gertrude LaDean, English
Kauffman, Corinne Elizabeth, English
Kendall, Lyle Harris, Jr, English
Lewis, John Samuel, English
Littlefield, Robert L, English
McDowell, Judith Hobson, English
O'Neal, Cothburn Madison, English
Polk, Noel Earl, American Fiction
Roemer, Kenneth Morrison, American Civi-
   lization
Sewell, Ernestine Porcher, English Literature,
   Linguistics
Whaling, Anne, English
Wiley, Margaret Lee, English Literature
AUSTIN
Abrahams, Roger David, Folklore
Ayres, James Bernard, English Literature,
   Shakespeare
Barnes, Warner J, English
Barton, Lucy (Adalade), Theatre Arts
Bennett, Alvin Lowell, English
Bowden, Edwin Turner, Jr, English
Brewer, June Harden, English
Brookes, Stella Brewer, English
Bump, Jerome Francis Anthony, English Lit-
   erature, Cultural Geography

Cable, Thomas Monroe, English Language & Linguistics
Cline, Clarence Lee, English
Conkle, Ellsworth Prouty, Drama
Cranfill, Thomas Mabry, English Literature
Crow, Martin Michael, Middle English
Currie, Eva Garcia, Speech
Cutting, Rose Marie, American Literature, Women's Studies
Donner, Stanley T, Communications
Farmer, David Robb, Twentieth Century English Literature
Farmer, Norman Kittrell, Jr, English
Flannery, Mary Catherine, Literature in English, History
Gordon, Ambrose, Jr, English Literature
Gray, Paul H, Speech
Hinkle, Olin Ethmer, Journalism
Hodge, Francis Richard, Drama
Horn, Thomas Darrough, English, Education
Hudson, Gertrude Reese, English
Hudson, Wilson Mathis, Jr, English
Hughes, Leo, English Literature
Hunter, Frederick James, Drama
Jeffrey, Robert Campbell, Speech
Jones, Joseph J., American & World English Literature
Kaufmann, Ralph James, English & Comparative Literature
Kaulbach, Ernest Norman, Medieval Studies & Philosophy
Keast, William Rea, English Literature
Kinneavy, James Louis, English, Education
Langford, Gerald, English
Lehmann, Ruth Preston, English, Celtic
Lovell, Ernest James, Jr, English Literature
Lyell, Frank Hallam, English Literature
McElroy, Maurine D, English, History
McKeithan, Daniel Morley, English & American Literature
Mahaffey, Kathleen, English
Malof, Joseph Fetler, English
Maurer, Oscar Edward, English Literature
Megaw, Robert Neill Ellison, English Literature
Mills, Gordon H, English
Moldenhauer, Joseph John, English
Mossner, Ernest Campbell, English Literature
Nance, William Leslie, American Literature
Paredes, Américo, Latin American Folklore & Cultural History
Pennybacker, Ruth, Literature, Creative Writing
Porter, Jenny Lind, English
Pratt, Willis Winslow, English
Ransom, Harry Huntt, English
Reddick, DeWitt Carter, Journalism
Roberts, Francis Warren, English
Rossman, Charles Raymond, English
Sackton, Alexander Hart, English Literature
Scheick, William Joseph, American Literature
Schenkkan, Robert, Drama
Scribner, Simon, C.S.C, English
Slate, Joseph Evans, English
Sledd, James Hinton, English Philology
Smalley, Webster Leroy C, Theatre
Steffan, (Truman) Guy, English Literature
Stephenson, William Curtis, English Romantic Poetry
Stewart, Powell, English
Stott, William Merrell, American Studies, English
Sutherland, William Owen Sheppard, English Literature
Taylor, Charles Bruce, Jr, Renaissance Literature
Taylor, Vi Marie, English
Todd, William Burton, English Literature
Twombly, Robert Gray, English
Varner, John Grier, English
Velz, John William, English
Villarreal, Jesse James, Speech
Walter, John Arnold, Technical Writing & Editing
Westbrook, Max (Roger), English
Whitbread, Thomas Bacon, English
Wilson, Robert Henry, English Literature
Winship, Loren, Drama Education
Wittig, Susan W, Medieval Literatures, Literary Theory
Wright, Palmer, English, American Studies
Young, Ione D, Literature
Zacharias, Donald Wayne, Speech, Drama
BEAUMONT
Barnes, Robert Jay, English
Berly, Charlsie Elizabeth, English
Brentlinger, W. Brock, Speech
de Schweinitz, George W, English
Emmons, Winfred S, Jr, English
Georgas, Marilyn Davis, English
Harrigan, William Patrick, III, Theatre
Harvill, Olga DeHart, English
Holland, DeWitte T, Speech, American History

Jones, Kirkland C, English Language & Literature
Olson, Robert C, English
Renfrow, Jack N, Renaissance English
Rule, Henry Burt, English, American Literature
Wilkerson, Robert Harold, Journalism
Yeats, Alvice Whitehurst, English Literature
Zink, David D, British & American Literature
BELLAIRE
Reeves, Ruth E, English
BELTON
Fussell, Iva Mildred, English
BROWNSVILLE
Schraer, Mimosa (Summers), English
BROWNWOOD
Ambrester, Marcus LaRoy, Oral Communication
Brooks, Roger L, English
Crider, Allen Billy, Contemporary American Fiction
Lowe, Alma Louise, English & American Literature
Reeve, Alexander, Speech, Drama
BRYAN
Peirce, James Franklin, Speech, English
CANYON
Cook, Larry Wayne, American Literature
Knott, A. Kirk, English
Mack, Mattie Swayne, English
Smith, John Warren, English & American Literature
SoRelle, Zell Rodgers, Speech
Sparling, Russell Paul, American & English Literature
Walker, Jack Harrison, Radio, Television
Watkins, Lloyd I, Speech
CLEAR LAKE CITY
Snyder, John Rudolph, English, American Studies
COLLEGE STATION
Abbott, John Paul, English, American Literature
Archer, Stanley Louis, English
Ballinger, Richard Henry, American Literature
Barzak, Robert William, English
Berthold, Dennis Alfred, American Literature
Burt, Forrest Dean, English
Costa, Richard Hauer, English
Elmquist, Karl Erik, English
Jernigan, Jesse Stewart, English
Kroitor, Harry Peter, English Literature
Laverty, Carroll Dee, English
Loving, Jerome MacNeill, American Literature
McAlexander, Hubert Horton, Jr, English & American Literature
Stokes, Elmore Ewing, Jr, English
Turner, William Henry, English
Van Domelen, John Emory, Renaissance Literature
Want, Elmer Cleveland, Jr, English Literature
West, Theodora Lee, Modern British Literature
COMFORT
Goforth, Lydia, English
COMMERCE
Buckley, Anthony J, Drama
Burke, John Emmett, English & Library Science
Farr, Cleburne L, Speech
Fulkerson, Richard Paul, British Literature
Grover, Dorys Crow, American Studies, British Literature
Hafner, Mamie, English
Jack, William Terry, American Literature & Drama
Lacy, James Maxwell, Classical & American Literature
Linck, Charles E, Jr, English
Lorimor, E. S, Mass Communications, Journalism
McNamee, Lawrence, English
Perry, Thomas Amherst, English, Comparative Literature
Pope, Curtis L, Speech, Drama
Stephens, Edna Buell, English
Sturcken, Johnye Cannon, English
Tuerk, Richard Carl, American Literature & English
CORPUS CHRISTI
Carroll, William Meredith, English
Creighton, Aileen Swafford, English, Renaissance
Kroeger, Frederick Paul, English
DALLAS
Carroll, Hazel Horn, Speech, Education
Covici, Pascal, Jr, English
Early, James, English
Herron, Ima Honaker, American Literature
Hicks, John, English Literature, Comparative Arts
Hobgood, Burnet McLean, Drama, Speech
Holahan, Michael Norris, English
Howard, C. Jeriel, English

McGrath, James B, Oral Communication
Matthews, Charles Eugene, English Literature
Nance, Gusta Barfield, Comparative Literature
Perrine, Laurence, English & American Literature
Powell, Walter Allen, English, American Literature
Reed, John William, Speech, Homiletics
Reese, Martin Sylvester, Journalism
Renshaw, Edyth May, Speech, Theatre
Robinson, Haddon W, Practical Theology, Speech
Shields, Kenneth Dale, English
Tucker, Edward Frederick John, English Literature
Weiss, Harold, Speech
Wilson, Grace E, English, Education
DENTON
Ballard, Emerald Garrett, English
Belcher, William Francis, Jr, English
Bishop, Jimmy Dean, English
Bogle, Edra Charlotte, Comparative Literature, Bibliography
Bruce, Charles Thomas, English
Chappell, Ben Arlen, Public Address
Clifton, Ernest Smith, English
Clogan, Julie Sydney, English & American Literature
Clogan, Paul Maurice, English, Comparative Literature
Culp, Ralph Borden, Speech & Drama
DeMougeot, William Robert, Speech, Drama
Dickey, Imogene Bentley, English
Ford, Howard Lee, English
Hendricks, George David, English
Holland, Reginald Valentine, Speech, Drama
James, Eleanor, English
Jeffrey, Lloyd Nicholas, English
Kesterson, David Bert, English
Key, Howard Cresap, English
Kirk, Gerald A, English Literature
Kobler, Jasper Fred, English, American Literature
Kobler, Turner Spencer, English
Kreps, Leslie R, Speech
Lee, James Ward, English
Linebarger, James M, English
Martin, Charles Basil, English Literature
Miller, Lee Wells, English, American Literature
Palmer, Joyce Cornette, English
Palmer, Leslie H, English
Parks, Lloyd C, English
Roach, Josh Philip, Speech
Rogers, James Lloyd, Jr, Journalism
Rulon, Curt Morris, English, Linguistics
Sale, Richard Barksdale, Jr, English
Sampley, Arthur McCullough, English Literature
Schulze, Ivan Leonard, English Literature
Shockley, Martin Staples, English
Shuford, Cecil Eugene, Journalism
Smith, F. Leslie, Mass Communication
Sutton, Carl, American & English Literature
Tanner, James Thomas Fontenot, English
Tramel, Agnes Catherine, English
Vann, Jerry Don, English
Warde, William Booth, Jr, English Literature
Westmoreland, Reginald Conway, Journalism, English
White, Jackson Elliott, English
Whitten, Mary Evelyn, English
Wiley, Autrey Nell, English Literature
EDINBURG
Evans, James Leroy, American Literature, Folklore
Grantz, Carl L, English Literature
Mitchell, Paul Lee, Nineteenth Century British Literature
Phillips, Phyllis (Josephine), Modern Language
Von Ende, Frederick Albert, Medieval & 17th Century English Literature
Wade, Seth, English
Wright, Carl C, English
EL PASO
Adkins, Patricia G, Speech Pathology, Linguistics
Boley, Tommy J, English
Braddy, Haldeen, English
Bratcher, James Terry, English
Burlingame, Robert Northcutt, English & American Literature
Coltharp, Lurline Hughes, English, Linguistics
Harding, Harold Friend, English Rhetorical Theory
Lacey, William Robert, English & American Literature
Leach, Joseph, American Literature
Leech, Robert Milton, Drama, Speech
Lewels, Francisco J, Mass Communication, Education
Past, Raymond Edgar, English
Small, Ray, English

Stafford, Tony Jason, English Literature
Standiford, Lester Alan, English & American Literature, Creative Writing
Taylor, Walter F, Jr, Modern Fiction, American Literature
West, John Oliver, English
White, Jon Manchip, English, History
Wingate, Gifford Wendell, Speech, Drama

FORT WORTH
Angell, Ruth Speer, English
Cecil, Levi Moffitt, English
Collier, Gaylan Jane, Speech & Drama
Colquitt, Betsy Feagan, English & American Literature
Corder, Jimmie Wayne, English
Erisman, Fred Raymond, American Studies & Literature
Gossman, Ann, English Literature
Gunn, Alan Murray, Medieval Literature
Hammack, Henry Edgar, Theatre Arts
Lewis, Marjorie Dunlavy, English
Major, Mabel, English & American Literature
Newcomer, James William, English
Odom, Keith Conrad, English
Rall, Eilene Muncie, English
Sorensen, George Wendell, American Theatre History
Tade, George Thomas, Speech
Tate, Gary Lee, English, Linguistics

GEORGETOWN
Clifford, Frederick Burr, Humanities
Springer, Angus, Drama, Speech

GOLDEN
Benthul, Herman Forrest, English Curriculum & Instruction

HAWKINS
Jones, John P, English

HOUSTON
Allen, Walter Powell, English
Anderson, John Quincy, American Literature
Apple, Max Isaac, Renaissance Literature, Creative Writing
Baker, James Volant, English
Baker, Stewart Addison, English
Battin, Tom C, Television
Berger, Sidney Louis, Theatre, Drama
Bernhard, Frank James, Jr, English Literature
Camden, Carroll, English
Daniels, Robertson Balfour, English
Day, Martin Steele, English
Dixon, Terrell Francis, English
Doggett, Joseph McSwain, English
Dorough, Charles Dwight, English
Doughtie, Edward Orth, English
Dowden, Wilfred Sellers, English
Eaker, Jay Gordon, English Literature
Ebaugh, Bessie Monroe, English, Classical Languages
Ford, Thomas Wellborn, American Literature
Giordano, Frank Ralph, Jr, English Literature
Grob, Alan, English Literature
Hartley, Jess (Dyson), Jr, English
Hawes, William, Communications
Heverin, Mary Rosina, C.C.V.I, English
Hiller, Charles Francis, English
Huckabay, Calvin, English, Milton
Huston, John Dennis, English Literature
Isle, Walter Whitfield, English
Judd, Larry R, Speech
Karchmer, Sylvan N, Creative Writing
Kelly, Thomas Daniel, English Literature
Linsley, William Allan, Speech
Lowe, Clarice Pierson, Speech, English
McCleary, Johnnie Marie, English, Linguistics
Madden, John F, English
Meixner, John A, English
Minter, David Lee, Modern & American Literature
Mitchell, Loyce Standlee, Drama, English
Nugent, Mary Louise, English, Classics
Parish, John Edward, English
Patten, Robert Lowry, English Literature, Graphic Arts
Peavy, Charles Druery, English, American Literature
Piper, William Bowman, English Literature
Pryor, William Lee, English & American Literature
Rosa, Jean, English
Southwell, Samuel Beall, English, Victorian Literature
Spears, Monroe Kirk, English Literature
Streeter, Donald Clint, Speech
Taylor, James Sheppard, Speech
Thomas, Joe David, English
Thompson, Wayne Noel, Speech, Rhetoric
Turner, Amy Lee, English, Architecture
Valdes, Helen Joyce Merrill, English Literature
Ward, Joseph Anthony, Jr, English
Welch, James Donald, English
Williams, George, English
Wolf, Morris Philip, English, Speech

Wren, Robert Meriwether, English
Wright, William Culver, English & American Literature
Zivley, Sherry, English
Zwicky, Laurie, English Literature

HUNTSVILLE
Allen, James Stewart, English Renaissance, Philosophy
Black, Laurence Norman, English
Jones, Alan Kent, English
Kimbrough, Joe Arthur, English
Koinm, Albert J, Jr, Medieval & Renaissance Literature
Murphey, Joseph Colin, Comparative Literature, English
Zellar, Leonard, English

IRVING
Bradford, Melvin Eustace Adonis, American Literature
Cowan, Louise Shillingburg, English & American Literature
Dupree, Robert Scott, English & Comparative Literature

JOHNSON CITY
Brand, Richard Clyde, Speech

KINGSVILLE
Buchanan, Randall John, Speech, Drama
Cook, George Allan, English
Dam, Hari Narayan, History, Mass Communication
Davis, Cynthia Ann, British & American Literature
Gallaway, Reuben Jackson, English
Rhode, Robert David, American Literature
Sawey, Orlan, American Literature
Underwood, Willard Alva, Speech, Drama

LAREDO
Briggs, F. Allen, English

LUBBOCK
Allen, James George, English Literature
Ashby, Clifford, Drama
Berry, J. Wilkes, English
Camp, Truman Wildes, English Literature
Carlock, Mary Sue, American Literature
Crider, John Richard, English
Culp, James William, English
Davis, Dale W, English Literature
Davis, Kenneth Waldron, English
Deethardt, John F, Jr, Speech Education
Eddleman, Floyd Eugene, World Literature
Gillis, Everett Alden, English, Folklore
Green, Lola Beth, English
Larson, Paul Merville, Speech
McDonald, Walter Robert, English
McGuire, Vernon R, Speech Education
Michael, Marion C, English
Mogan, Joseph J, Jr, English Literature
Nall, Kline Allen, English
Schulz, Ronald Edward, Drama
Strout, Alan Lang, English
Sullivan, Ernest Walter, II, Seventeenth Century Literature
Terrell, Dahlia Jewel, English
Wages, Jack Douglas, American Literature
Walker, Warren Stanley, English

MARSHALL
Daniel, Maggie Browne, English & American Literature

NACOGDOCHES
Abernathy, Francis Edward, English
Alexander, Stanley Gerald, English
Austin, Warren Barker, English
Bos, William Herman, Speech, English
Box, Terry Joe, English & American Literature
Butts, John Russell, Speech Communication, Religion
Cain, Roy Edward, English, Linguistics
Capel, Robert Bennett, Speech
Duncan, Kirby Luther, English
Ekfelt, Fred Emil, English
Gaston, Edwin W, Jr, English
Hays, John Q, English & American Literature
Houston, Neal Bryan, English
Kallsen, Theodore John, American Literature
Rodewald, Fred Arthur, American Literature
Schoenewolf, Carroll Robert, American Literature
Shivers, Alfred Samuel, English
Towns, James Edward, Speech Education, Public Address
Waters, Walter Kenneth, Jr, Theatre, Speech
Wyatt, Sibyl W, English Literature
Zillmer, H. Lawrence, Theatre

NEW BRAUNFELS
Krueger, Robert Charles, English

ODESSA
Colwell, James Lee, American Studies
Neufeldt, Leonard N, English
Sproule, James Michael, Speech Communication

PASADENA
Oglesbee, Rhea Simpson, English Literature

PRAIRIE VIEW
Campbell, Anne Lucille, English

SAN ANGELO
Brownlow, Paul C, Communication
Carpenter, Margaret Ann, English
Cowell, Catherine Rose, Speech Communication
Davis, Harold Edmund, English
Flores, Vetal, English, Speech
Gragg, Perry Earl, English
Hesser, Dale Cahill, English
Holcomb, Kathleen Anne (Duggan), Eighteenth Century English Literature
Holcomb, Phillip Anthony, English Literature
Lacy, Gerald Morris, English Literature
Reeves, Troy Dale, English Literature, Creative Writing
Skaggs, Peggy LaNell Dechert, American Literature
Watts, Billie Dean, Theatre

SAN ANTONIO
Baker, Paul, Drama
Benoist, Howard, III, English Literature
Brantley, John D, English
Britton, Robert Grubbs, Theatre History, Acting
Callahan, Mary Generosa, C.D.P, English, Religion
Corbin, Germaine, C.C.V.I, Theatre History
Craven, Alan Elliott, English
Eagan, M. Clement, C.C.V.I, English, Latin
Fleming, David Arnold, S.M, English
Frederick, Anthony Peter, S.M, English Literature
Gates, William Bryan, English & American Literature
Gibbons, Robert Ebbert, American Literature, Critical Theory
Goerdt, Arthur L, English
Griffith, Albert Joseph, Jr, English
Grissom, (Patsy) Coleen, English
Igo, John N, Jr, English
Keefe, Kathryn, C.D.P, Speech, Drama
Kersnowski, Frank Louis, English, Drama
McGavock, Ina Beth, English
McKinney, Eugene, Drama
Moe, Sigrid, English & Norwegian Literature
Myers, Gail Eldridge, Speech
Myler, Charles B, Drama, Speech
Novosal, Paul Peter, English, Library Science
O'Halloran, Bernard Christopher, English, Victorian Literature
Pearce, Bessie M, English
Pitcher, Seymour Maitland, English & Classical Philology
Power, Alacoque, C.C.V.I, English
Puckett, Walter, S.M, English Literature
Reile, Louis, S.M, English, Cinema
Schuster, Louis Anthony, S.M, English Literature
Semel, Ann, American Literature
Slattery, Margaret Patrice, C.C.V.I, English
Staggs, Kenneth Walton, American Literature, Creative Writing

SAN MARCOS
Abernathy, Elton, Speech
Baergen, John Darrel, Drama, Speech
Barton, James Gabriel, Theatre, Speech
Brasher, Thomas Lowber, English
Brunson, Martha Luan, Victorian & Eighteenth Century British Literature
Coulson, James Peter, Theatre, Drama
Gratz, Robert David, Speech Communication
Grayson, Nancy Jane, Comparative Literature
Hayes, Elizabeth Gentry, English, Linguistics
Houston, Ralph Hubert, English
Kirk, Clara Marburg, English, American Literature
Kirk, Rudolf, English & American Literature
Lynch, Vernon Eugene, English
Schilling, Lester Lorenzo, Jr, Speech, Drama
Stevens, David Ranald, English
Taylor, Alfred Heber, Journalism, English
Walts, Robert Warren, English
Ward, Doyle Glynn, Speech

SEABROOK
Everson, Ida Gertrude, English

SEGUIN
Bittrich, Louis Edward, Comparative Literature
Maroldo, William John, English, Philosophy

SHERMAN
Jernigan, Jack Julian, English
Moore, William Hamilton, English

STEPHENVILLE
Martin, William Bizzell, English Literature
Pilkington, William Thomas, English & American Literature

TEXARKANA
Carter, Betty, English, French

VICTORIA
Wright, Leonard N, English, Philosophy

WACO
Armstrong, Chloe, Speech

Capp, Glenn Richard, Speech
Caskey, Edna Payne, English
Collmer, Robert George, English
Fall, Christine, English
Herring, Jack W, English
Leavell, Frank Hartwell, English
Ray, Robert Henry, English
Stokes, George Mitchel, Speech
WICHITA FALLS
Brown, Harry Matthew, English
Campbell, Jefferson Holland, English
Darden, Frances K, English
Davis, Madge, American Literature
DeCamp, Jacqueline L, Speech
Hairston, Joe Beck, American Studies & Literature
Hindman, Jennie Louise, Drama, Speech
Hoggard, James Martin, English, Creative Writing
Kable, June Prentice, Rhetoric, Communication
McBroom, Robert Louis, Modern American & Comparative Literature
Taylor, Arvilla Kerns, Renaissance & English Literature
Whan, Forest Livings, Speech

UTAH

CEDAR CITY
Woolf, Eugene T, English, Philosophy
LOGAN
Anderson, Jarvis Lynn, Modern Drama, Theatre History
Booth, Thornton Young, English Literature
Culmsee, Carlton Fordis, Journalism
Hansen, Burrell Fenton, Speech
Hunsaker, Kenneth Burnice, American Literature
Kulkarni, Hanmant B, English, Philosophy
Nielsen, Veneta Leatham, English
Patrick, John Merton, English, History
Scherting, John Andrew, American Studies & Literature
Smith, Hubert Wayne, American Literature
Washington, Mary Aldridge, English Literature
OGDEN
Allred, Gordon Thatcher, Creative Writing, Modern Literature
Burton, Thomas R, English Literature
Cheney, Merlin Gene, Nineteenth Century British Literature, Linguistics
Ericson, Elmer Hodson, Renaissance English Literature
Monson, Leland Hans, English, Speech
Noid, Benjamin Maynard, Theatre, Speech
Peterson, Levi S, English
Rowley, T. Leonard, Theatre Arts, English
Seshachari, Candadai, American Literature, Ethics
Woodfield, Floyd J, English
OREM
Farnsworth, Dean Burton, English Literature
King, Arthur Henry, English Literature
Madsen, Harold Stanley, English
PROVO
Bateman, James LaVar, Speech
Blanch, Mae, English Literature
Britsch, Ralph A, English, Humanities
Cheney, Thomas E, Folklore
Clark, Bruce Budge, English
Clark, Marden J, English
Cracroft, Richard Holton, American Literature
Ellsworth, Richard Grant, American Civilization, English
Gassman, Byron W, English Literature
Geary, Edward Acord, English & American Literature
Gledhill, Preston Ray, Speech, Drama
Hart, Edward LeRoy, English Literature
Jacobs, Briant S, American Literature
Lambert, Neal Elwood, English
Larson, Clinton F, English
Mitchell, Olive Kimball B, English, Art
Oaks, Harold Rasmus, Theatre
Olson, Ernest Leroy, English
Peterson, Brent Dan, Speech & Organizational Communication
Pope, Karl T, Dramatic Arts & Theatre
Spears, Irene Osmond, English, French
Wight, Marjorie, English
Wood, Glena Decker, English
Woodbury, Lael Jay, Speech, Dramatic Arts
ST. GEORGE
Myers, Chester James, Speech
SALT LAKE CITY
Adix, Vern, Speech
Aggeler, Geoffrey Donovan, English
Bane. Clarence Laverne. Speech
Bentley, Harold Woodmansee, English, Spanish
Bindrup, Jewel Jacobsen, English, Speech
Brunvand, Jan Harold, Folklore
Catmull, Joseph F, Speech

Clarke, Lori Marie, English, English Education
Eble, Kenneth Eugene, English
Engar, Keith M, Speech
Faules, Don F, Behavioral Communication
Folland, Harold Freeze, English & American Literature
Garlington, Jack, English
Ghiselin, Brewster, English
Greaves, Halbert Spencer, Speech
Haley, Bruce Everts, English Literature
Hollstein, Milton Clifford, Mass Communications
Jabusch, David M, Speech
Jarvis, Joseph Boyer, Speech
Jones, David Edwards, English, Drama
Lueders, Edward George, American Studies
Major, Diana, English, Linguistics
Margetts, Ralph Elliot, Speech, Theatre
Mezey, Robert, American & European Poetry
Moore, Harold Eugene, English
Rieke, Richard Davis, Rhetorical & Communication Theory
Short, Clarice Evelyn, English
Snow, Dorothy, English Literature
Sobchack, Thomas J, English, Cinema
Steensma, Robert Charles, English Language & Literature
Sturges, Irene M, English
Thomas, Wanda Clayton, Speech, Theatre
Tiemens, Robert Kent, Speech
Voigt, Milton, English
Webb, Henry Jameson, English Literature
Zucker, Louis Clement, Comparative Literature

VERMONT

BELMONT
Harap, Louis, Library Science
BENNINGTON
Glazier, Lyle Edward, English
Sandy, Stephen Merrill, American Literature
BURLINGTON
Bandel, Betty, English
Bogorad, Samuel Nathaniel, English
Cochran, Robert Willard, English
Donoghue, John D, English
Eschholz, Paul Anderson, American Literature, Linguistics
Huber, Robert Bruce, Speech
Jones, Leonidas Monroe, English
London, Norman Theodore, Communication
Long, Littleton, English
Luse, Eleanor Merrifield, Speech
Manchel, Frank, English, Education
Orth, Ralph Harry, English
Poger, Sidney Boris, English
Pope, Willard Bissell, English Literature
Rosa, Alfred Felix, English
Rothwell, Kenneth Sprague, English
Shepherd, Allen Glass, III, English & American Literature
CASTLETON
Butterfield, Stephen Thomas, Literature
Steele, Theodore Manning, English Language & Literature, Philosophy
GRAFTON
Schemm, Mildred Walker, English Literature
JOHNSON
Duffy, John Joseph, English
Guttman, Selma, English
LINCOLN
Arrowsmith, William Ayres, Classics
MIDDLEBURY
Beck, Horace Palmer, English
Clagett, John Henry, American Studies
Cook, Reginald Lansing, American Literature
Cubeta, Paul Marsden, English
Littlefield, David J, English
Martin, Edward Alexander, English & American Literature
Munford, Howard McCoy, American Literature
MONTPELIER
Facos, James Francis, English
NORTHFIELD
Bruce, George Howard, English, Russian
Cutts, Richard, English
Hart, Loring Edward, English
Kloeckner, Alfred Joseph, English & American Literature
NORWICH
Bentley, Warner, Drama
PLAINFIELD
Gibson, Morgan, Poetry
PUTNEY
Emma, Ronald David, English, Philology
Fish, Charles Kelleway, Jr, English, American Studies
Hurwitz, Harold M, English
RUTLAND
Wyant, Jerome Lee, English & American Literature

TOWNSHEND
Cronin, James Emmet, English
WHITE RIVER JUNCTION
Smith, George William, Jr, English
WINDSOR
Brucker, Herbert, Journalism, Communication
WINOOSKI
Fairbanks, Henry George, Humanities
Henault, Marie Josephine, English
Murphy, Edward Francis, English

VIRGINIA

ALEXANDRIA
Henderson, Hanford Mead, Comparative Literature, History of Art
ARLINGTON
Boswell, Jackson Campbell, English Literature, American Studies
Gaebelein, Frank Ely, Bible, Christian Education
Lambeth, Edmund Barry, Journalism, Political Science
Martin-Trigona, Helen Vasiliou, Speech, English
Williams, Franklin Burleigh, Jr, English Literature
ASHLAND
Gray, William Shelton, English
Wells, David Marsden, English Literature
BIG STONE GAP
Rogers, Carolyn Sherrill White, Modern American & British Literature
BLACKSBURG
Broughton, Panthea Reid, Twentieth Century Literature, History of Ideas
Campbell, Hilbert Haynes, English Literature
Campbell, Michael Lee, English & American Literature
Cheney, Anne, English
Clausen, Christopher John, English Literature
Collins, Joseph Johnson, English Literature
Distler, Paul Antonie, Theatre Theory & Practice
Fordyce, Rachel Poole, English, Drama
Hancock, Edward Alexander, English Literature
Hoffman, Richard Lester, English
Johnston, George Burke, English Literature
McNeil, Robert Hooper, Journalism
Norstedt, Johann Albert, Anglo-Irish Literature
Phelps, Wayne Howe, English
Rollo, Duncan James, American Literature & Drama
Snipes, Wilson Currin, English
Squires, Michael George, English Literature
Tucker, Edward Llewellyn, English
Walker, Kenneth Ervin, English & American Literature
West, James Lemuel Wills, III, English
White, William Monroe, American Literature
Zyromski, Robert Nicholas, Drama, Theatre
BLUEFIELD
Hafer, Carol Braxton, English
BRIDGEWATER
May, Clarence Edward, English Literature
BURKE
Kelley, Michael Robert, English Literature, Linguistics
CHARLOTTESVILLE
Albright, Daniel, English, Linguistics
Baker, Houston A, Jr, Victorian & Black American Literature
Battestin, Martin Carey, English Literature
Beaurline, Lester Albert, English & American Literature
Berry, Edward I, English Literature
Bowers, Fredson, English Literature
Boyle, Eldridge Roger, Drama
Cauthen, Irby Bruce, Jr, English Literature
Clapper, Ronald (Earl), English, American Literature
Cohen, Ralph, English
Damrosch, Leopold, Jr, English Literature
Davis, Charles Roger, English
Day, Douglas Turner, III, English Literature
Ehrenpreis, Anne Henry, English
Ehrenpreis, Irvin, English
Elwood, William Allen, English Literature
Graham, John, Speech
Hench, Atcheson Laughlin, English Literature
Hirsch, E. Donald, Jr, English Literature
Howard, Alan (Blair), English
Kellogg, Robert Leland, English
Kirsch, Arthur Clifford, English
Kohler, Charlotte, English
Kolb, Harold Hutchinson, Jr, English, American Literature
Korte, Walter Francis, Jr, Film Aesthetics
Lang, Cecil Y, English Literature
Langbaum, Robert, English
Levenson, Jacob Clavner, English
Levin, David, English, American Studies

Lindberg, Gary H, English
Longley, John Lewis, Jr, Literary Criticism, Humanities
McLaughlin, Robert Guy, Drama
Meade, Richard A, English Education
Monk, Samuel Holt, English Literature & Criticism
Peterson, Richard Scot, English Literature & Music
Prosser, Michael H, Speech Communication
Shannon, Edgar Finley, Jr, English
Stovall, Floyd, Literature
Vandersee, Charles Andrew, American Literature
Vaughan, Joseph Lee, English
Waswo, Richard Arthur, English, Renaissance Studies
Weiss, David William, Drama
Winner, Anthony, English, Comparative Literature
Winner, Viola Hopkins, American Literature
EMORY
Blesi, Marius, English
Clinard, Turner Norman, English
Denham, Robert Dayton, English & American Literature
Goldsmith, Robert Hillis, English
FAIRFAX
Baxter, Ralph Clayton, English
Brown, Lorraine Anne, English, American Literature
Brown, Stephen Jeffry, English Literature
Garson, Helen Sylvia, English & American Novel
Jackson, James L, English Literature
Molin, S. Eric, Drama, English Literature
Sundell, Michael Gordon, English Literature, Art History
FALLS CHURCH
Moore, Robert Hamilton, English
FARMVILLE
Blackwell, Herbert R, English
Frank, William L, English, American Literature
Gresham, Foster Bagwell, English
Hooker, Charlotte Schrader, English, Children's Literature
Lockwood, Patton, Theatre, Speech
Sprague, Rosemary, English Literature, Creative Writing
FINCASTLE
Davis, James Paxton, Journalism, Writing
Waldrip, Louise Baker, English
FORK UNION
Jacobson, Richard Joseph, Nineteenth Century English Literature
FREDERICKSBURG
Brown, Nathaniel Hapgood, English Literature
Croushore, James Henry, American Literature
Fleming, Delmont Forrie, English
Glover, Donald Ellsworth, English
Griffith, William Wayne, American Literature
Kemp, James William, Jr, English Renaissance Literature, Film
Kenvin, Roger Lee, Drama
Mitchell, Nancy Heyroth, English
Mitchell, Sidney Hammond, English
Simpson, Grellet Collins, English
Singh, Raman Kumar, English & American Literature
HAMPDEN-SYDNEY
Simpson, Hassell Algernon, English & American Literature
HAMPTON
Brown, Jessie Lemon, English
McGhee, Nancy B, English, Humanities
HARRISONBURG
Adams, Francis Raymond, Jr, American Literature
Anderson, Patricia Davis, English
Bomberger, James Rohrer, English, Linguistics
Finney, Robert George, Communication
Funston, Jay Louis, English Literature & Composition
Kimball, Clark Douglas, Communication Theory
Leigh, Thomas Watkins, English
Locke, Louis Glenn, English Philology
McConkey, Donald LeMoyne, Rhetoric, Public Address
McMurray, William J, English
Mahler, Andrew John, English Literature
Pellman, Hubert R, English & American Literature
Poindexter, James Edward, English Literature
Ruff, James Lynn, Romantic Poets, Eighteenth Century Poetry
HOLLINS COLLEGE
Allen, John Alexander, English
Cunningham, John M, English Literature
Dillard, Richard Henry Wilde, English
Lee, Grace Farrell, English & American Literature

Moore, John Rees, English Literature
O'Brien, Frank Patrick, English, Irish Literature
Puzon, Bridget, O.S.U, English Literature
Randall, Julia Sawyer, English, Poetry
Smith, William Jay, English
LAWRENCEVILLE
Boyers, William Hayden, Romance Languages
LEXINGTON
Boatwright, James, III, English
Burgess, Chester Francis, English
Coulling, Sidney Mathias B, English Literature
Craun, Edwin David, English Poetry & Prose
Davidson, Lloyd Johnston, English Literature
Dillard, Herbert Nash, Jr, English
Duvall, Severn Parker Costin, American Literature
Gentry, Thomas Blythe, English Literature
Gordon, Albert C, Theatre, Humanities
Huntley, H. Robert, English
Keith, Philip Myron, American Literature, American Studies
Ray, George Washington III, English
Roth, George Leith, Jr, English
Ryan, Halford Ross, Speech, Public Speaking
Stuart, Dabney, Modern Fiction, Poetry
LINVILLE
Wilkins, Ruth Jones, English
LURAY
Foster, Charles Howell, English
LYNCHBURG
Ashe, Dora Jean, English
Cornelius, David K, English
Hailey, Robert Carter, Dramatic Arts
Hanenkrat, Frank Thomas, English, American Literature
Kirby, John Pendy, English
Turner, John Mills, Jr, American Literature
Williamson, Mervyn Wilton, English Literature
MCLEAN
Taylor, Henry Splawn, Creative Writing, Contemporary American Literature
NEWPORT NEWS
Rogers, Powell Burwell, English
Sancetta, Joyce Kellogg, English
NORFOLK
Andrews, Michael Cameron, English
Aycock, Roy E, English
Bowman, Wayne, English
Burgess, Charles Owen, English
Card, James Van Dyck, English
Carpenter, Margaret Haley, English
Festa, Conrad, Victorian & Romantic Poetry
Halladay, Jean Ruth, English
Hines, Samuel Philip, Jr, English
Knight, Karl Frederick, American Literature
McNally, James J, English, American Literature
Peterson, Leland D, English
Quinn, Mary Bernetta, O.S.F, English
Raisor, Philip Dean, English & American Literature
Reece, James Brady, English
Rhodes, Carolyn Hodgson, American Literature
Rhodes, Ernest Lloyd, English
Seward, William Ward, Jr, English Language & Literature
Shores, David Lee, English, Linguistics
Yarborough, Betty Hathaway, English, Education
ORLEAN
Kenney, Blair Gates, English Literature
PETERSBURG
Jenkins, Joseph Henry, Jr, English
Sato, Toshihiko, Comparative Literature
Wyatt, Bryant Nelson, American Literature, Composition
RADFORD
Dedmon, Donald Newton, Speech
Dyer, Henry Hopper, American Civilization, English
Gallagher, Mary Brigid, Theatre, Speech
Lanier, René Parks, Jr, English & American Literature
Stockton, Edwin L, Jr, American Literature
RICHMOND
Armour, Robert Alexander, American & English Literature
Ball, Lewis Franklin, English Literature
Beacham, Eugene Walton, Creative Writing, Criticism
Brown, E. Allan, Literature
Brown, Irby Bland, English Literature
Christopher, Georgia B, Renaissance English Literature
Coppedge, Walter Raleigh, English
Duke, Maurice, American Literature, Bibliography
Evans, Josephine, English Literature
Fultz, Mary Catherine, English, Religious Education
Gehring, Mary Louise, Speech
Henry, Nathaniel H, English

Inge, Milton Thomas, English & American Literature, American Studies
Longest, George Calvin, Nineteenth Century American Literature
Loxterman, Alan Searing, English
Lyles, Albert Marion, English
McDill, Joseph Moody, English Literature
Mangum, Anthony Bryant, American Literature
Newell, Kenneth Bernard, English
Pendleton, James Dudley, English
Penninger, Frieda Elaine, Medieval Language & Literature
Peple, Edward Cronin, English Philology
Priebe, Richard Karl, African Literature, English
Reynolds, Elizabeth Rogers, English
Roberts, Marguerite, English Literature & Philology
Sharp, Nicholas Andrew, English Renaissance Literature
Tarver, Jerry L, Speech
Taylor, Welford Dunaway, English
Whitesell, James Edwin, English Philology
RIVERTON
Link, S. Gordden, English
ROANOKE
Smith, Milton Shumway, English & American Literature
SALEM
Deegan, William John, English, Philology
Kendig, Perry Fridy, English
Wise, Matthew Montgomery, English Language & Literature
STAUNTON
Brice, Marshall Moore, English
Collins, Fletcher, Jr, Medieval Literature, Dramatic Arts
Garrison, Joseph M, Jr, English
Kelly, William Watkins, English
Smith, Ben H, Jr, English Literature
SWEET BRIAR
Piepho, Edward Lee, English Literature
Rowland, Richard (Creswell), English
VIRGINIA BEACH
Hadgopoulos, Saralyn Poole, English, Comparative Literature
Harkey, Joseph Harry, English & American Literature
Rubin, Gary Neil, Communication Theory, Classical Rhetoric
Schlegel, Dorothy Badders, Comparative Literature
WALLOPS ISLAND
Claudel, Alice Moser, English Literature
WAYNE
Ashbrook, William Sinclair, English, Humanities
WILLIAMSBURG
Ball, Donald Lewis, English
Bauer, Neil Stephen, English Literature
Catron, Louis E, Theatre, Playwriting
Davidson, Charles Edward, English
Davis, William F, Jr, English
Dolmetsch, Carl Richard, (Jr), English
Donaldson, Scott, American Literature & Studies
Elliott, Nathaniel Y, English
Evans, Frank Brooke, III, English Literature
Jenkins, David Clay, English
Jones, W. Melville, English Literature
Neiman, Fraser, English
Nettels, Elsa, English, American Literature
Scholnick, Robert James, American Literature
Smith, LeRoy Walter, English
Willis, John H, Jr, English
WISE
Peake, Richard Henry, English
WOODLAWN
Owen, John Isaac, English Literature

WASHINGTON

BELLINGHAM
Anderson, Jerry Maynard, Speech
Becker, George Joseph, English Literature
Brown, Robert D, English
Buckland, Roscoe Lawrence, English, American Civilization
Carlile, Sene R, Speech
Cederstrom, Moyle F, English
Clapp, Edwin Roosa, English Literature
Francis, Richard Lee, English, American Studies
Garber, Eugene K, English Literature
Hicks, Arthur Clark, English
Huff, Robert, English
Larner, Daniel, Dramatic Literature, History of Science
Larsen, Golden Lavon, English
Lavers, Norman Cecil, English Literature, Creative Writing
Lee, Lawrence Lynn, English

Lewis, Merrill Embert, Nineteenth Century
American Literature, American Studies
McDonnell, Robert Francis, English
Merrill, Reed Ballif, Comparative Literature
Miller, Gerson Frederic, Journalism, English
Richard, Jerry, English
Skinner, Knute R, English
Solomon, Arthur Lewis, Speech Pathology,
Human Relations

CENTRALIA
McElroy, Davis Dunbar, English Literature

CHENEY
Colton, Agnes Louise, English Literature
Halwas, Kenneth Arnold, English, Humanities
Lass, Robert N, English
McAuley, James John, Modern Poetry, Poetics
Nelson, Mary Ann, Children's Literature, En-
glish Education
Shuck, Emerson Clayton, American Literature
Steiner, Henry-York, English
Wall, Donald Clark, English Literature
Wilson, Lewellyn Lee, Communications, Speech
Education

COLLEGE PLACE
Dickinson, Loren, Speech
Evans, Helen Ward, English Literature
Moore, Nathan, English

ELLENSBURG
Anshutz, Herbert Leo, English
Benton, Robert Milton, English
Canedo, Anthony, English
Canzler, David George, English Renaissance
Drama
Cummings, Donald Wayne, English
Dunnington, Hazel Brain, Language Develop-
ment, Children's Drama
Lawrence, Larry Lee, English, Literature
Leinaweaver, Richard E, Theater
Lewis, Albert Luther, Speech Communication
Mathewson, Mary Elizabeth, English
Osborn, Lynn Robert, Speech, Education
Rinehart, Keith, English
Smith, Milo Le Roy, Theatre, Drama
Suits, Conrad B, English Literature
Teets, Bruce Earle, English
Vagenas, Peter Thomas, Theatre
Zink, Karl Edwin, English Literature

EVERETT
Branham, Mary Edith, English Composition &
Literature

KENT
Barchek, James R, English

KIRKLAND
Meador, Prentice Avery, Jr, Speech, Classical
Theory

LACEY
Jaynes, Bryson Lester, English

MEDICAL LAKE
Olafson, Robert B, English

OLYMPIA
Elbow, Peter Henry, English
Teske, Charles Bahn, English Literature

PULLMAN
Adams, John Festus, English Literature
Arntson, Herbert Edward, English
Blackburn, Charles Edwin, English
Cole, Charles Orr, Journalism
Ehrstine, John W, English, Linguistics & Phi-
lology
Ettlich, Ernest Earl, Speech
Fausti, Remo P, Speech
Gallagher, Kent G, Dramatic Literature
Haswell, Richard H, English
Hines, Donald Merrill, Folklore, American
Studies
Johnson, Robert Owen, English
Jones, Charles Asa, Speech
Kiessling, Nicolas Karl, Old and Middle En-
glish
Ligocki, Llewellyn, English Literature
Lord, John Bigelow, English
McLean, Robert Colin, English & American
Literature
Magill, Lewis Malcolm, English Literature
Meldrum, Ronald M, English
Ross, Donald H, Modern Literature, Creative
Writing
Shurr, William Howard, American Literature
Slonim, Ruth, English
Strother, David B, Speech
Taylor, John Chesley, English
Thompson, Gary Richard, English & American
Literature
Towne, Frank McConnell, English, Humanities
Wadleigh, Paul C, Drama
Wasson, John M, English Literature

RENTON
Kruegel, Eileen Helenanne, English, Philosophy

SEATTLE
Adams, Robert Pardee, English Literature &
Language
Alexander, Edward, English
Banta, Martha, English

Baskerville, Barnet, Speech
Benson, Merritt Elihu, Communications, Jour-
nalism
Blake, Kathleen Ann, English Literature
Bosmajian, Haig Aram, Speech
Bostetter, Edward Everett, English Literature
Burns, Wayne, English Literature
Carmody, Robert Joseph, S.J, English
Connors, James Victor, Speech, Drama
Conway, John Ashby, Drama
Dore, William John, Jr, Theatre, Fine Arts
Douglas, Donald G, English, Philosophy
Duckett, Margaret Ruth, American Literature
Dunn, Richard John, Nineteenth Century
English
Eby, Edwin Harold, American Literature
Erickson, Joyce Quiring, English & American
Literature
Falls, Gregory Alexander, Drama
Fowler, David Covington, English
Gerstenberger, Donna Lorine, American Lit-
erature
Gibson, Evan Keith, English Literature
Griffith, Malcolm A, English & American Lit-
erature
Guberlet, Muriel Lewin, English
Harrington, Donal Francis, Drama
Harris, Markham, Creative Writing, Medieval
Drama
Hatfield, Glenn Wilson, Jr, English
Heilman, Robert Bechtold, English Literature
Hilen, Andrew R, Jr, English & American Lit-
erature
Hostetler, Paul Smith, Speech
Irmscher, William F, English
Jones, Frank William, Comparative Literature
Kartiganer, Donald M, English
Kaufman, Paul, English Literature
Korg, Jacob, English
Lockwood, Thomas Frank, English Literature
Lorentzen, Arthur Andreas, English
McCracken, James David, English
McDonough, George E, English, Contemporary
Literature
McGuire, Allen Wayne, English
MacLean, Kenneth Duart, American Literature,
Writing
McNichols, Donald, English
Markert, Louise, English
Matchett, William Henry, English
Monda, Joseph B, English
Mortenson, Robert Lawrence, English
Oberg, Arthur K, English
Olson, Richard Dale, English
Phillips, William Louis, English
Pitt, Carl Allen, Communication, Public Ad-
dress
Post, Robert M, Speech
Powers, James G, S.J, English
Rahskopf, Horace G, Speech
Reinert, Otto, English
Rivenburgh, Viola K, English
Ross, Duncan, Drama
Rosser, Paul F, Speech
Sale, Roger H, English Literature
Siks, Geraldine Brain, Drama
Simonson, Harold Peter, English & American
Literature
Skeels, Dell R, Literature, Anthropology
Souther, James Walter, English
Stanton, Robert Bruce, English
Stevick, Robert David, English
Van Arsdel, Rosemary, English
Wagoner, David R, English
Warnke, Frank Joseph, English
Webb, Eugene, English, Comparative
Literature
Webber, Joan, English
Willis, Leota Geraldine Snider, English
Wollesen, Charles Albert, S.J, English Litera-
ture
Zillman, Lawrence John, English Literature

SPOKANE
Archer, Lewis Franklin, Theology & Literature
Conway, Margaret Mary, F.S.P.A, Speech &
Theatre Arts, English
Ebner, Ivan Dean, English
Gray, Alfred Orren, Journalism
Hazel, Harry Charles, Jr, Speech Communica-
tion
Herzog, Michael B, Comparative Literature
Keenan, Charles, S.J, English Language & Lit-
erature
Leigh, David Joseph, English
Safranek, William P, English & American Lit-
erature
Schneider, Franz, English & Comparative Lit-
erature
Simpson, Clarence J, Renaissance Literature
Sisk, John Paul, English
Stanton, Fred E, Speech
Wadden, Anthony Thomas, British & American
Literature

TACOMA
Blomquist, Grace Eleanor, Literature, Com-
position
Briody, David Mathew, Communication Theory
Clavadetscher, Carl Julius, Speech Communi-
cation
Frank, Charles Paul, English & American Lit-
erature
Hansen, Janis T, English
Johnson, Lucille Marguerite, English Lit-
erature Rhetoric
Karl, Theodore Oscar Henry, Speech
Klopsch, Raymond Albert, English
Nesvig, Milton Luther, English
Peterson, Gary Leonard, Speech & Public Ad-
dress
Ranson, Herbert (Robert), English Literature
Reigstad, Paul Matthew, English & American
Literature
Sandler, Florence Rosemary, English Lit-
erature
Van Tassel, Daniel Ellsworth, English Litera-
ture

WALLA WALLA
Broman, Walter Eric, English
Jackson, Paul Joseph, English
Maxfield, James F, English
Tyson, J. Patrick, English

WENATCHEE
Siemon, James Edward, English

WEST VIRGINIA

ATHENS
Bailey, Frederick, English
Hambrick, Thomas Gregory, English Literature
Stein, Frank, Speech, Drama

BETHANY
McGuffie, Helen Louise, English
Taylor, John Raymond, English Literature

BUCKHANNON
Baldwin, Arminta Tucker, English Literature
Presar, Charles Irvin, Dramatic Arts, Speech
Communication

CHARLESTON
Plumley, William C, Modern Poetry
Slattery, Kenneth Martin, Drama, Speech

ELKINS
Goddin, Margaret Ann Purdum, English
Kitch, John Ira, Jr, English
Shields, Ellis, Gale, English & Comparative
Literature

FAIRMONT
Boram, William, English
Cavanaugh, Jean C, English
Wills, Jack Charles, English

HUNTINGTON
Brown, Jack Richard, English & American Lit-
erature
Buell, Stephen David, Speech
Hart, Hymen H, English Literature
Novak, Elaine Adams, Speech, Theatre
Phillips, Bernice Maxine, English
Sullivan, William P, English
Thorn, Arline Roush, Comparative & English
Literature
Thorn, Eric P, English, Comparative Litera-
ture
Tyson, Archie Mervin, English Literature
Williams, Duncan, English, University Honors
Wooden, Warren Walter, Renaissance Litera-
ture, Literary Criticism

INSTITUTE
Gray, Virginia Pomroy, Theatre
Sheen, Edwin Drummond, English

KEYSER
Atwater, Elizabeth Amanda, Journalism, Speech

MONTGOMERY
Kuhn, Howard Frederick, English, American
Literature

MORGANTOWN
Atkins, Paul Alexander, Journalism
Blaydes, Sophia Boyatzies, English & American
Literature
Bond, Donovan Hiner, Journalism
Bordinat, Philip, English
Bramer, George Robert, English, Rhetoric
Brawner, James Paul, English & American Lit-
erature
Davis, Leonard M, Speech
Draper, John William, English Culture
Eaton, Richard Bozman, Jr, English
Foster, Ruel E, English
French, William Wirt, English Literature
Howard, Martha Cummins, English
Johnston, John H, English
McGraw, William R, Drama
Peterson, Virgil A, English
Racin, John, English
Stasny, John F, English, Humanities
Stewart, Guy Harry, Journalism
Stitzel, Judith Gold, English

Wheeless, Lawrence Ray, Speech Communication
SALEM
Kistler, Susan Woofter, Speech, Humanities
WEST LIBERTY
Cox, Mary Elizabeth, English
Gerhard, George B, English
Hughes, Raymond Grove, English
Kelly, Helen (Marie Térèse), Theatre, Oral Interpretation
Sykes, Robert Howard, English, American Studies
Thomas, Judith (Ann) Waugh, Speech Education

WISCONSIN

APPLETON
Beck, Warren, English
Bullis, Jerald Leroy, English & American Literature
Dale, Thomas Randall, English
Forter, Elizabeth Tusten, English
Fritzell, Peter Algren, English, Humanities
Goldgar, Bertrand Alvin, English Literature
Hart, Richard, O.F.M, Speech, English
Hopfensperger, Joseph Allen, Theatre, Drama
Schneider, Ben Ross, Jr, English
Schutte, William Metcalf, English Literature
Tjossem, Herbert Karl, English
BARABOO
Cole, David William, English Literature, Composition
BELOIT
Balson, Carl George, Speech
Barraclough, Elmer Davies, Theatre Arts
McBride, Thomas Eugene, English Literature
Mason, David Joseph, English, Journalism
Morrissey, Bernard Delbert, English Renaissance Drama & Poetry
Noll, Lou Barker (Bink), English
Perlis, Alan David, English & American Literature
Sanderson, David Roland, English & American Literature
Stocking, David Mackenzie, English
Stocking, Marion Kingston, English & American Literature
Walsh, Chad, English
DE PERE
Boyer, Robert Horace, English Literature, Humanities
Giovannini, John Daniel, Mass Communications
Rudolph, Leora Calkins, English
Zahorski, Kenneth, English, Speech
EAU CLAIRE
Alexander, Robert Ritchie, English
Browne, Thomas A, English
Christiani, Dounia Bunis, English, Drama
Haug, Frederick Ernest, Jr, Speech
Jackson, Alan S, English
Karward, Elwood C, Journalism, English
Lindquist, Wayne Paul, English
Morris, John William, English Language & Literature
Quayle, Calvin King, Drama
Spaulding, Kenneth Ansel, English
Walsh, Grace, Speech
Waters, D. Douglas, English
Wolfarth, Donald Lloyd, Speech
GREEN BAY
Londo, Richard Joseph, Literature, Linguistics
Nelson, Conny Edwin, English, Comparative Literature
KENOSHA
Bauer, Otto Frank, Speech, Semantics
Bedford, Emmett Gruner, English Literature
Canary, Robert Hughes, English
Carrington, Richard H, Speech, Theatre
Dean, Dennis Richard, English, History of Science
Dean, James Seay, English Literature
Foy, John Vail, English & American Literature
Gottesman, Ronald, English
Graffin, Walter Ray, Modern Literature, Popular Culture
Holland, T. Shandy, Jr, Dramatic Art, Speech
Kozicki, Henry, English
Kubly, Herbert Oswald, English, Speech
Kummings, Donald D, English & American Studies
McLean, Andrew Miller, English Renaissance Literature & History
Shucard, Alan Robert, American & English Literature
Tague, Wilma Long, English Literature, Creative Writing
Tolleson, Floyd Clyde, Jr, English
Vopat, Carole Gottlieb, Modern Literature
LA CROSSE
Geier, Norbert Joseph, English
Haas, Charles E, Speech

Hinck, Henry William, English
Hyde, William James, English
Judson, John I, Creative Writing, English
Parsons, Roger L, English Literature
Wirkus, Thomas Edward, Speech
Wulling, Emerson G, Bibliography
MADISON
Allen, Ronald Royce, Speech
Amor, Edward, Drama
Baker, Robert Samuel, English Literature
Balio, Agatino Thomas, Theatre, Drama
Bender, Todd K, English, Classical Languages
Bitzer, Lloyd Frank, Speech
Black, Edwin, Rhetoric & Public Address
Borchers, Gladys Louise, Speech
Brawer, Robert Allen, Medieval English Language & Literature
Brembeck, Winston Lamont, Speech
Brockhaus, Herman Henry, Speech
Bush, Sargent, Jr, English, American Literature
Carey, Mary Cecilia, O.P, Literature
Cassidy, Frederick Gomes, English & American Language
Chambers, Alexander B, English Literature
Curvin, Jonathan Wadhams, Speech, Drama
Dembo, Lawrence Sanford, English
Doane, Alger Nicolaus, English & Medieval European Literature
Doran, Madeleine, English
Doremus, Robert Barnard, English Literature
Eccles, Mark, English Literature
Elwood, William Robert, Theatre History, Continental Dramatic Literature
Feltskog, Elmer Nathaniel, English
Fosdick, James Albert, Mass Communications, Journalism
Friedman, Barton Robert, English
Gibson, William Merriam, English
Haberman, Frederick William, Speech
Hachten, William Andrews, Journalism, Mass Communication
Hall, Vernon, Jr, Comparative Literature
Harth, Phillip, English Literature
Hayman, David, English
Henning, Standish, English
Herring, Phillip F, English
Hinden, Michael Charles, English & American Literature
Jackson, Esther Merle, Drama
Kimbrough, Robert Alexander, III, English Literature
Knowles, Richard Alan John, English Renaissance
Lacy, Edgar Wilson, English Language & Literature
Lawson, Richard G, Speech, Mass Communication
Le Duc, Don Raymond, Mass Communication & International Communication Law
Lenehan, William Thurman, American Literature
Lichty, Lawrence Wilson, Mass Communications
Lyons, John O, English
McNeely, Jerry C, Speech
Nelson, James Graham, English Literature
Ness, Ordean Gerhard, Speech
Orsini, Gian Napoleone (Giordano), Comparative Literature
Paynter, Mary, O.P, English
Pondrom, Cyrena Norman, Comparative Literature
Presson, Robert King, English
Preston, Ivan L, Mass Communications
Quintana, Ricardo, English Literature
Ragsdale, Wilmott, Journalism
Ramsey, Lee C, English
Rehder, Robert M, English & Comparative Literature
Reuben, Elaine, English & American Literature
Rideout, Walter Bates, American Literature
Ringler, Richard N, English
Rodman, George Bush, English
Rothstein, Eric, English
Scheidel, Thomas Maynard, Speech
Schwartz, Richard Brenton, English Literature
Scott, A. C, Theatre, Drama
Sealts, Merton Miller, Jr, English
Searles, John Rexford, English Literature
Sherman, Charles Edwin, Communication Arts
Simley, Anne, Humanities
Skloot, Robert, Theatre, Drama
Smith, Donald Kliese, Speech
Stone, Vernon A, Broadcast Journalism, Mass Communication
Tanselle, George Thomas, English
Taylor, Jerome, English Language & Literature
Vowles, Richard Beckman, Comparative, English & Scandinavian Literature
Waddington, Raymond Bruce, English
Waterman, Margaret, English
Weinbrot, Howard D, English

Weiner, Andrew David, English Literature
Whitley, Alvin, English
Wiesenfarth, Joseph John, English & American Literature
Wiley, Paul Luzon, English
Wittreich, Joseph Anthony, Jr, English Literature
MANITOWOC
Karnis, Michael V, Speech, International Education
MENASHA
Johnson, Rue Corbett, Speech & Theatre, Comparative Literature
MENOMONIE
Byrns, Lois Elizabeth Ann, English
Cutnaw, Mary Frances, Speech, English
MIDDLETON
Stark, John Olsen, American Literature
MILTON
Kolin, Philip Charles, English Literature
MILWAUKEE
Aderman, Ralph Merl, English
Aldrich, Ruth Isabelle, British Literature, Drama
Allen, Judson Boyce, Medieval English & Latin
Baron, F. Xavier, Medieval & English Literature
Bishop, Conrad Joy, Theatre, Drama
Bovee, Warren Gilles, Journalism
Boyle, Robert Richard, S.J, English
Brown, Clarence Arthur, English, Education
Brundage, Gloria Swegman, Speech Communication, Journalism
Burke, Virginia M, English, English Education
Chang, Joseph S, M.J, English
Daeger, Giles Aloysius, English
De Falco, Joseph Michael, English
Dunleavy, Gareth Winthrop, English
Dunleavy, Janet Egleson, English & Irish Literature
Emerson, Donald Conger, English
Farrell, William Joseph, English, Rhetoric
Friedman, Melvin Jack, English, Comparative Literature
Greenbaum, Sidney, English Linguistics
Guerinot, Joseph Vincent, English Literature
Halloran, William F, English
Hamm, Agnes Curren, Speech
Hamm, Victor Michael, English Literature
Harrold, William Eugene, English Literature
Hassan, Ihab Habib, English
Helbert, Clifford L, Journalism
Hellman, Hugo E, Speech
Helton, Tinsley, English
Hill, Ruane Burton, Communication
Host, David Richard, Journalism
Jain, Nemi Chand, Speech & Intercultural Communication
Jones, Leo Monroe, Drama, Modern Theatre
Kennedy, Robert Martin, Voice Science
Kerr, Elizabeth Margaret, English
Larson, Barbara, Rhetoric & Public Address
Loacker, Georgine, O.S.F, English Literature & Language, Education
Lorenz, Alfred Lawrence, Jr, Journalism
McCanles, Michael F, English
MacDonald, Donald, Communication
McLaughlin, Ted John, Communication
Midura, Edmund Michael, Mass Communication, Journalism
Mitchell, Roger Sherman, English & American Literature
Parr, Roger Phillip, English
Partridge, Elinore Hughes, American Literature, Linguistics
Phillabaum, Corliss E, Drama
Pick, John, English Literature
Replogle, Justin M, English
Roby, Robert Curtis, English
Ross, Albion, Journalism
Sappenfield, James A, English
Schwartz, Joseph Michael, English
Siegchrist, Mark, Victorian Literature
Skelton, Susan, Comparative Literature
Sokolnicki, Alfred John, Speech Pathology, Phonetics
Staudacher, Joseph M, Speech Education
Stephens, James Willis, English Renaissance Literature
Stone, Robert K, English
Sullivan, M. Rosenda, O.S.F, Literary Criticism
Sullivan, Maureen, English
Sundell, Roger Henry, English Literature
Symonik, Emil F, English
Tatham, Campbell, Contemporary Literature
Turner, Robert Kean, Jr, English
Valentine, Mary Hester, S.S.N.D, English
Walzi, Florence Litchfield, English
Whitford, Kathryn, English
Wiksell, Milton Joel, Communication

OSHKOSH
Berner, Robert Leslie, Literature, American Studies
Bierly, Charles E, English
Brooks, John Bradbury, English
Bush, Jarvis E, English
Dodson, Charles Brooks, English
Eckstein, Neil T, English, American Studies
Fu, Sherwin S. S. (Shaw-Shien Fu), English, Comparative Literature
Gottschalk, Jane, English
Hartig, Hugo, English, Education
Herzing, Thomas Wayne, British Literature, Romantic Movement
Judson, Lyman Spicer Vincent, Speech, Voice Science
Leible, Arthur Bray, English
Liechti, Harris Nelson, Speech, Communications
Lippert, David James, Journalism
Mengeling, Marvin Edwin, American Literature
Nebel, Joyce Behm, English, Philosophy
Pyle, Everett Gustav, English
Rao, Kolar S. Narayana, English, Speech
Riley, Bryan M, English
Round, Harold Lapides, English, Religion
Sargent, Seymour Herbert, Contemporary Literature
Snyder, Robert L, Speech
Zahalka, Donald William, Journalism
PLATTEVILLE
Coffee, Bernice French, English
Edwards, Clifford Duane, English
Gauger, Paul William, Speech & Drama
Gober, Ruth Bell, English, Education, Speech
Hansen, Harold R, Speech, Theatre
Myrbo, Calvin L, English Education
POUND
Engels, Norbert Anthony, English
RACINE
Bruner, Marjorie Williamson, English, Comparative Literature
RIPON
Ashley, Robert Paul, Jr, English
Christ, Jack Morell, American & British Literature
Davis, Nelson V, English Romantics, Chaucer
Martz, William J, English
Northrop, Douglas Anthony, English
Pommer, Henry Francis, English
RIVER FALLS
Hagestad, William Thomson, English
Hawkins, Marion Elizabeth, English
Karolides, Nicholas J, English
Lewis, Earl E, English, American Studies
Odegard, Margaret, Twentieth Century English
Oostendorp, John Anthony, Speech, History
Paterek, Josephine Durkee, English, Speech & Drama
SHEBOYGAN
Hansell, William Harold, American Literature
Mersch, Arnold Roy Gordon, English & American Literature
Moss, Frederick Keith, English & American Literature
SHOREWOOD
Thale, Jerome, English
STEVENS POINT
Chapman, Abraham, English, American Studies
Dreyfus, Lee Sherman, Speech, Journalism
Ellery, John Blaise, Communication
Faulkner, Seldon, Drama
Faust, Alice L.P, Speech, Drama
Fortune, Michael J, English
Isaacson, Pauline, Speech History
Koskenlinna, Hazel M, English
Lehman, Alan D, English
Lewis, Leon E, English
Missey, James L, English
SUPERIOR
Adamany, Richard G, English Literature & Language
Adams, George Roy, English, Linguistics
Bennett, John, English & American Literature
Bishop, Allan Richard, English Literature
Bottman, Philip Nathaniel, English, Comparative Literature
Burrows, Robert Nelson, American Literature
Christensen, Norman F, English
Clark, Wilma Harmon, English Language, English & American Literature
Folsom, Gordon Raymond, English
Hemmer, Joseph John, Jr, Speech Communication
Hicklin, Fannie Ella Frazier, Speech Theatre
Jones, Sidney C., English Literature
Krouse, Agate Nesaule, Modern Literature, Women's Studies
Madson, Arthur L, English
Miller, Melvin Hull, Speech
Ostermeier, Terry Harlan, Speech Communication

Peters, Margot McCullough, Victorian Literature, Linguistics
Quinn, Robert Samuel, Speech, Drama
Sorber, Edna C, Speech
Taylor, Anne Robb, English
Townsend, Patricia Ann, Public Address
Utz, Kathryn E, English
Van Haitsma, Glenn A, English Language & Literature
Wilson, Gene Andrew, Theatre, Speech

WYOMING

LARAMIE
Biggs, Wallace Robert, Journalism
Clough, Wilson Ober, English & American Literature
Durer, Christopher, English, Comparative Literature
Eggers, Walter Frederick, Jr, English Literature
Fleck, Richard Francis, American Literature, Natural History
Funk, Alfred A, Speech, History
Harris, Duncan Seely, English & American Literature
Hillier, Richard Lionel, English
Linford, Ernest H, Journalism
Mathewson, Jeanne Thompson, English
Mathison, John Kelly, English Literature
Miller, Keith Allen, Communication Theory
Orth, Melvin Fay, English
Preston, Thomas Ronald, English
Reverand, Cedric Dwight, II, English Language & Literature
Reynolds, E. C., Theatre
Simpson, Arthur Lee, Jr, English & American Literature
Thomas, Glyn N, English Literature
Welke, James William, Broadcasting, Communication Research
MOOSE
Cardwell, Guy Adams, English

GUAM

AGANA
Shook, Andrew Woodson, Speech

PUERTO RICO

MAYAGÜEZ
Brown, Alan Willard, English & Comparative Literature, Intellectual History
Hunt, Joseph Anthony, English & American Literature
Marshall, Madeleine Forell, Comparative Literature
Squire, Donald Hovman D, Modern Languages & Literatures, Renaissance Studies
Todd, Janet M, English Literature, Women's Studies
RIO PIEDRAS
Bergquist, Barbara Edith, English
Bilder, John Raban, English

CANADA

ALBERTA

CALGARY
Adam, Ian William, English Literature
Alexander, Jean A, Comparative Literature
Baker, William Price, English
Black, James, English
Chorny, Merron, English Education
Courtney, Richard, Drama
Elliott, Craig Clifford, Acting, Creative Drama
Hornby, Richard, Drama
Kher, Inder Nath, English & American Literature
McLay, Catherine Margaret, English Literature
Magee, William Henry, English
Martin, John Sayre, English
Martin, John Stephen, English, American Studies
Mitchell, Victor Edward, Drama
Petti, Anthony Gaetano, English
Ray, Don Eldon, English Literature
Thorpe, Michael, English Literature
EDMONTON
Almon, Bert Lynn, English
Anderson, Roland Frank, English
Ayling, Ronald Frederick, English & American Literature

Baldwin, Robert George, English
Bilsland, John Winstanley, English
Buxton, Earl W, English, Education
Conolly, Leonard William, English Literature
Crowther, J. D. W, Middle English
Elder, Andrew Thomson, English
Engel, Bernard B, Drama
Forrest, James French, English
Giorgio, Benjamin David, English
Godfrey, Denis Rowley, English Literature
Gordon-Craig, Christopher, English
Grant, Raymond James Shepherd, Anglo-Saxon & English Language & Literature
Hargreaves, H.A, English
Hoffpauir, Richard, English Literature
Kreisel, Henry, English
Lauber, John, English
McCaughey, Gerald Sheldon, English Literature
MacIntyre, Jean Ann, English
McMaster, Juliet, English
McMaster, Rowland Douglas, English
Nelson, James Malcolm, English, Drama
Norman, Marion, I.B.V.M, English
Orrell, John Overton, English
Page, Norman, English Literature & Language
Peacock, Gordon Bruce, Drama
Peacocke, Charles Thomas, Drama
Qureshi, Ahmad Hasan, English Literature
Rose, Edward J, English, Interdisciplinary Criticism
Rose, Shirley, English Comparative Literature
Ross, Morton Lee, English, American Studies
Ryan, Aylmer Arther, English
Siemens, Reynold Gerrard, English, Music
Terfloth, John Hellmuth, Drama
Wiebe, Rudy H, Creative Writing, Canadian Literature
LETHBRIDGE
Mardon, Ernest George, English Literature, Canadian Studies

BRITISH COLUMBIA

BURNABY
Black, Stephen Ames, American Literature
Candelaria, Frederick Henry, English
Cooperman, Stanley R, English & American Literature
Curtis, Jared Ralph, English
Delany, Paul, English Literature
Elliott, Gordon R, English
Habenicht, Rudolph Everett, English Literature
Harden, Edgar Frederick, English
Maud, Ralph Noel, English
Maynard, Temple James, English Literature
Messenger, Ann P, English Literature, Drama
Mills, John, English
Page, Malcolm, English
Rudrum, Alan William, English
Steig, Michael, English Literature
VANCOUVER
Akrigg, George Philip Vernon, English
Andrew, Geoffrey Clement, English
Bankson, Douglas Henneck, Drama
Beach, D. M, English Literature
Bevis, Richard Wade, English Literature
Criegh, Geoffrey Creigh, English Literature
Daniells, Roy, English
Doheny, John Rodney, English
Durrant, Geoffrey H, English
Fredeman, William Evan, English
Globe, Alexander Victor, English, The Bible
Goldberg, Michael Kenneth, English Literature
Good, Graham, English & Comparative Literature
Gose, Elliott Bickley, Jr, English
Grenberg, Bruce L, English
Hart, James A, American Literature
Heninger, Simeon Kahn, Jr, English
Ingram, Reginald W, English
Johnson, Lee Milford, English Literature
Johnson, Ronald Conant, English
Jordan, Robert Maynard, English
Labrie, E. Ross, English
Lavin, Joseph Anthony, English
McConnell, Ruth E, English
Merivale, Patricia, English, Comparative Literature
Messenger, William Edmund, English
Miller, Craig William, English
Nadel, Ira Bruce, English & American Literature
Nemser, Ruby, English
New, William Herbert, English
Newby, Frank S, English
Parkin, Andrew Terence Leonard, English, Drama
Parshall, Raymond Edward, English
Piloto, Albert Edward, English
Pinkus, Philip, English
Powell, Grosvenor Edward, English & American Literature

Quartermain, Peter Allan, English
Revutsky, Valerian, Soviet Literature & Drama
Robbins, William, English
Ross, Ian Simpson, English
Seamon, Roger, English
Soule, Donald E, Theatre
Stanwood, Paul Grant, English Literature
Steinberg, Moses Wolfe, English
Stephens, Donald, Canadian, Modern British
Stevenson, Stanley Warren, English
Stewart, Jack F, English
Stockholder, Katherine S, Renaissance Literature, Shakespeare
Sylvester, Bickford, English & American Literature
Wasserman, Jerry Steven, English & Comparative Literature
Weir, Mary Lorraine, Anglo-Irish Literature
Whitehead, Lee Melvin, English
Wigod, Jacob David, English

VICTORIA
Adey, Lionel, English
Alford, Norman William, English
Benzie, William, English
Best, Michael R, English
Cleary, Thomas Raymond, English
Doyle, Charles Desmond, English, American Studies
England, Anthony Bertram, English Literature
Ewert, Leonore Helen, English
Faber, Melvyn D, Shakespeare, Drama
Gooch, Bryan Niel Shirley, English Literature, Music
Grant, J. Patrick, English
Jeffrey, David Lyle, English Literature, Art History
Jenkins, Anthony White, English
Johnson, Carol Virginia, Literature
Köster, Patricia, English
Kurth, Burton Oliver, English
Lawrence, Robert Gilford, English
Leslie, Roy Francis, English
Macey, Samuel L, English Literature
McCormond, G. Grant, English
Mayne, Frederick, English
Morgan, Gerald, English, Philosophy
Neufeldt, Victor Alfred, English & American Literature
Partridge, Colin J, English
Peter, John, English
Scargill, Matthew Harry, English, Linguistics
Schuler, Robert Michael, English Literature
Skelton, Robin, English
Smith, Herbert F, Literature
Smith, Nelson Charles, English
Sward, Robert S, English
Terry, Reginald Charles, English Literature
Thatcher, David S, English
Williams, Trevor Lloyd, Modern British Literature & History
Zietlow, Edward R, English

MANITOBA

BRANDON
Blanar, Michael, English Literature
King, Ralph F. B, English
Logan, Lillian M, English, Social Studies
Logan, Virgil Glenn, Speech
McNeely, James Trevor, English & American Literature
WINNIPEG
Adamson, Arthur H, English, French
Amabile, George N, Creative Writing, Contemporary Poetry
Bedford, Allen Gerald, English
Collins, Robert George, Modern English & Comparative Literature
Farag, Fahmy Fawzy, English Literature
Hamilton, Alice B, English
Hoople, Robin P, English, American Studies
Krüüner, Marta Regina, American & Comparative Literature
Lander, Clara, English, Ancient Greek
Ogden, John Terence, English Literature
Robinson, John Meredith, English
Saunders, Doris Boyce, English Literature
Siemens, Lloyd George, English
Sirluck, Ernest, English Literature
Swayze, Walter Eugene, English
Teunissen, John James, English
Wanamaker, Murray Gorham, English, Linguistics
Warhaft, Sidney, English

NEW BRUNSWICK

FREDERICTON
Bauer, William Alfred, English Literature
Cogswell, Frederick, English
Colson, Theodore, English

Gair, William Reavley, Renaissance Literature, Drama
Galloway, David Robertson, English Literature
Gibbs, Robert John, Canadian & Modern Literature
Kennedy, Judith Mary, English
Kennedy, Richard Frederick, English
Kinloch, A. Murray, English
Lane, Lauriat, Jr, English
Mullaly, Edward Joseph, American Literature, Theatre History
Pacey, Desmond, English Literature
Rowan, Donald Frederick, English
Taylor, Michael J. H, English
Thompson, Kent Elgin, English Literature, Creative Writing
Woodfield, James, English Literature
MONCTON
Campbell, Stephen Coady, English Literature
Mitcham, Elizabeth Allison, English & North American Literature
SACKVILLE
Burke, Herbert Caryl, English
Calkins, Roger Willard, English
Duchemin, Lloyd Allison, English

NEWFOUNDLAND

ST. JOHN'S
Francis, Cedric James, English
Kirwin, William James, English
Pitt, David George, English
Seary, Edgar Ronald, English
Story, George Morley, English

NOVA SCOTIA

ANTIGONISH
Currie, Sheldon, English
MacPherson, John A, English, Criticism
DARTMOUTH
Kennedy, Joyce Deveau, English & American Literature
HALIFAX
Bevan, Allan Rees, English
Dawson, Robert MacGregor, English Language & Literature
Fraser, John, English
Gray, James, English Language & Literature
Hafter, Ronald, English
Hartley, Allan John, English Literature
Lawrence, Lionel Houston, Theatre
Mendel, Sydney, English
Merritt, Robert G, Drama
Parks, Malcolm Gordon, English
Ross, Malcolm, English Literature
Smith, Rowland James, English Literature
Sproule, Hugh Douglas, English
Varma, Devendra P, English
Waller, Gary Fredric, English Literature
Whittier, Henry S, English
PORT MAITLAND
Tracy, Clarence (Rupert), English Literature
WOLFVILLE
Killam, Gordon Douglas, English & Commonwealth Literature
Kirkconnell, Watson, Comparative Literature
Sharma, Govind Narain, English

ONTARIO

BURLINGTON
Braswell, Laurel Anne, English, Comparative Medieval Literature
CLARKSON
De Luca, Vincent Arthur, English
DON MILLS
Rowland, Beryl, English Literature
Waddington, Miriam (Dworkin), Literature
DOWNSVIEW
Adolph, Robert, English
Cluett, Robert, English, Stylistics
Collie, Michael John, English & French Literature
Davey, Frank, Canadian & American Literature
Feltes, Norman Nicholas, English
Girling, Harry Knowles, English
Green, Joseph G, Theatre
Griffin, Ernest George, English
Koretsky, Allen C, English
Lewis, Janet Elizabeth, English Literature
Maxwell, Desmond E. S, English
Rehner, Michael John, American Literature, Rhetoric
Rinehart, Hollis, III, English
Rock, Virginia J, American Literature, American Studies

Stuckey, Johanna Heather, English, Comparative Literature
Thomas, Clara, English
White, Robert L, American Literature
Whitla, William John, Victorian Literature
GUELPH
Booth, Michael Richard, English, Drama
Graham, Kenneth Wayne, English Literature & Bibliography
Harrison, James Ernest, English Literature, History of Science
Hunter, Charles Stuart, English Literature
Korte, Donald MacCoull, English
MacKinnon, Malcolm Hugh Murdoch, English Literature
Matson, Marshall N, English, Drama
Mullin, Donald C, Drama
Ross, Alexander M, English
Rubio, Gerald John, English Literature
Smith, Joseph Percy, English
Waterston, Elizabeth, English & Canadian Literature
HAMILTON
Cain, Thomas Henry, English
Coldwell, Joan, English
Duncan, Douglas J. M, English Literature
Ferns, Henry John, English & Canadian Literature
Halsall, Maureen Patricia, English
Hammond, Antony Derek, Drama, English Literature
Juneja, Man Mohan Krishna, Drama, Theatre
King, James, English Literature
Lee, Alvin A, English Language & Literature
Morton, Richard (Everett), English
Owen, Warwick Jack Burgoyne, English
Ross, Michael Lawrence, Victorian & Modern English Literature
Shrive, Frank Norman, English
Sigman, Joseph Thomas, English Literature
Vichert, Gordon Stewart, English
Vince, Ronald Winston, English Literature, Drama
Wiles, Roy McKeen, English, Literary History
Wood, Chauncey (Derby), English
KING CITY
Smetana, Cyril L, O.S.A, English
KINGSTON
Beharriell, Stanley Ross, English
Clark, George Richard, English
Crawley, Derek French, English
Ferguson, William Craig, English
Greene, Elizabeth, Medieval & Modern English Literature
Hamilton, Albert Charles, Literature
MacKenzie, Norman Hugh, English
Matthews, John Pengwerne, English
Rogers, Phillip W, English
Sampson, Herbert Grant, English
Stedmond, John Mitchell, English
Thorne, William Barry, Renaissance Drama, Modern American & British Literature
Watters, Reginald Eyre, American & Canadian Literatures
Whalley, (Arthur) George (Cuthbert), English
LONDON
Bandeen, Betty Isobelle, English
Barker, Arthur Edward, English Literature
Bates, Ronald Gordon Nudell, English
Bolgan, Anne (Catherine), English
Collins, Thomas Joseph, English
Conron, Alfred Brandon, English
Dow, Marguerite Ruth, English, Drama
Fleck, Paul Duncan, English
Graham, John Whichello, English
Hair, Donald Sherman, English
Hensley, Don Harper, English
Hieatt, Allen Kent, English
Hieatt, Constance, English
Klinck, Carl Frederick, English
Poisson, Rodney, English
Rajan, Balachandra, English
Rans, Geoffrey, English
Reaney, James, English
Sharp, Corona, English, Foreign Languages
MISSISSAUGA
Skvorecky, Josef Vaclav, English, Film
NORTH BAY
Hewgill, Murray, Speech
Zytaruk, George J, English
OTTAWA
Beattie, Alexander Munro, English Literature
Campbell, Alphonsus Patrick, English Literature
Chari, V. K, English & American Literature
Clever, Glenn, Eighteenth Century & Canadian Literature
Edwards, Mary Jane, Canadian Literature
Eldredge, Laurence Milton, Middle English & Medieval Latin Literature
Gnarowski, Michael, English & Canadian Studies
Gunn, Maureen Mary, English Literature

Haines, Charles Murray Robert, English
Kesterton, Wilfred Harold, Journalism
Kramer, Jerome A, English
LaFrance, Marston, English & American Literature
MacDonald, Robert Hugh, English Literature
McDougall, Robert L, English, Cultural History
Mann, Lindsay Alfred, English
Marcotte, Paul, English
Middlebro, Thomas Galbraith, English Literature
Moseley, Virginia Douglas, English Literature
O'Donnell, Kathleen M, English
O'Neill, Michael Joseph, English
Pollard, Hazel M. (Batzer), English, Criticism
Pollard, Richard N, Comparative Literature, English Renaissance, Criticism
St. Jacques, Raymond Claude, English Literature
Steele, James A, English
Thistle, Melville William, General Semantics, History of Science
Thomson, George Henry, English
Wurtele, Douglas J, English
Young, Lorna D, English Language & Literature
PETERBOROUGH
Berkowitz, Morton Selig, American Literature, Milton
Chambers, Robert Douglas, English Literature
Gallagher, Sean Finbarr, English Literature
Kane, Sean, English Literature
McLachlan, William Ian, English, Comparative Literature
Rooke, Barbara E, English Literature
Roper, Gordon Herbert, American Literature
ST. CATHARINES
Smith, Marion B, English, Drama
Yacowar, Maurice, English Literature, Film
SCARBOROUGH
Thomas, Alan Cedric, Victorian Literature
SUDBURY
Lawry, Jon S, English Literature
Wright, Edgar, English
THUNDER BAY
Heath, William George, Jr, American Literature & Intellectual History
Ishak, Fayek, Modern & Seventeenth Century Literature
Merrill, George Jackson, English
Moser, Edwin, English
Rideout, John Granville, English Literature
TORONTO
Asals, Frederick John, English
Asals, Heather Ross, English Literature
Auster, Henry, English
Baird, John D, English Literature
Barker, Rosalind Allen, English
Bentley, Gerald Eades, Jr, English Literature
Beresford-Howe, Constance, English Literature
Birney, Earle, English
Blake, Caesar Robert, English Language & Literature
Blissett, William Frank, English Literature
Carroll, John J, English
Coburn, Kathleen, English Literature
Davies, Robertson, English
de Groot, Hans Bart, English Literature
Domville, Eric William, English
Dooley, David Joseph, English
Endicott, Norman Jamieson, English
Ewen, Douglas Richard, English Literature
Falle, George Gray, English
Fowke, Edith Margaret, English, Folklore
Fox, Denton, English
Frank, Roberta, Medieval English, Old Norse
Frye, (Herman) Northrop, English Literature
Graziani, Rene, English
Greene, Robert Allan, English
Grosskurth, Phyllis, English
Halewood, William H, Literature
Handscombe, Richard James, English
Harvey, Elisabeth Ruth, English Literature
Hayne, Barrie Stewart, English, American Literature
Heath, Jeffrey Morton, English Literature
Hepworth, Brian E, English
Herbert, Lucille Oaklander, English
Heyworth, Peter Lorriman, English, Medieval Studies
Hoeniger, F. David, English
Hosek, Chaviva Milada, English & American Literature
Howard, William James, English
Hughes, Peter A. M, English
Jackson, James Robert De Jager, English
Lancashire, Anne, English Literature, Drama
Lary, Nikita Michael, Comparative Literature
LeBel, Eugene Carlisle, English
Leech, Clifford, English
Leggatt, Alexander Maxwell, English
Lochhead, Douglas Grant, English

Lynen, John Fairbanks, English
MacCallum, Hugh R, English
McLuhan, Herbert Marshall, English Literature
MacLure, Millar, English
Macpherson, (Jean) Jay, English
Madden, Robert J, English
Madigan, Mary, EB.V.M, Medieval English
Mallon, Hugh Vincent, C.S.B, English
Margeson, John Malcolm Russell, English
Marinelli, Peter V, English
Marker, Frederick Joseph, English Literature, Comparative Drama
Marker, Lise-Lone, Theatrical History, Drama
Meagher, John Carney, English, Religion
Millgate, Jane, English
Millgate, Michael (Henry), English & American Literature
Morgan, Peter Frederick, English
Mueller, Martin, English & Comparative Literature
Namjoshi, Suniti Manohar, English Literature
Nims, Margaret Frances, English
O'Driscoll, Robert, English Literature
Parker, Dorothy, English
Parker, Reginald Brian, English, Drama
Patrick, Julian W. O, English
Priestley, Francis Ethelbert Louis, English
Pritchard, Allan, English
Reibetanz, John, English Literature
Robson, John M, English
Rosenbaum, Stanford Patrick, English & American Literature
Russell, Patricia H, English, Shakespeare
Rutledge, Donald G, English, Education
Saddlemyer, Ann, English
Schieder, Rupert Mohl, English
Shaw, W. David, English
Shook, Laurence Kennedy, English, Vernacular Literature
Sidnell, Michael John, English Literature
Smith, Donal Ian Brice, English
Thompson, M. Geraldine, C.S.J, English
Van Fossen, Richard Waight, English
Wilson, Milton Thomas, English
Zitner, Sheldon P, English
WATERLOO
Ballin, Michael Gerald, English Language & Literature
Boyd, Evelyn Mae, Medieval Literature
Campbell, Jane Lund, English
Dubinski, Roman Rudolph, English Literature
Dust, Alvin Irwin, English
Gold, Joseph, English
Gosselink, Robert Nicholas, English
Gray, Jack Cooper, English Literature
Haworth, Helen Ellis, English
Hibbard, George Richard, English Literature
Hinchcliffe, Peter Michael, English Literature
Hultin, Neil, English, Philology & Linguistics
Ledbetter, Kenneth Lee, American Literature
Levitsky, Ruth Mickelson, English
Lister, Rotraud, English, Drama
Logan, Harry Millard, Linguistics, Medieval Literature
McCormack, Eric Patrick, Renaissance English Literature
McDougall, Gordon, English
MacRae, Christopher Frederick, English
Martin, W. R, English
North, John Stanley, English Literature
Ober, Warren Upton, English
Roy, Flora, English
Shields, Ellen Frances, English
Slethaug, Gordon Emmett, English
Thomas, Walter Keith, English
WEST HILL
Martineau, Barbara Halpern, Cinema, Women's Studies
WINDSOR
Crowley, Cornelius Patrick Joseph, C.S.B, English
Ditsky, John Michael, English
Huang, Roderick, English Literature
MacKendrick, Louis King, English
McNamara, Eugene Joseph, English
Martin, Sue Gillespie, Speech & Early Childhood Education
Neilson, George Lockhart, Drama
Pappert, Edward Cecil, C.S.B, English
Smedick, Lois Katherine, Medieval Studies
Smith, Joyce Carol Oates, English
Stevens, Peter Stanley, Canadian Literature
Sullivan, John Francis, English
Watson, Edward Anthony, English Literature

PRINCE EDWARD ISLAND

CHARLOTTETOWN
Baker, Ronald James, English, Linguistics
Beum, Robert, English
Foley, Michael Myles, Middle English

Frazer, Frances Marilyn, English Literature
O'Grady, Brendan Anthony, English

QUEBEC

LENNOXVILLE
Gustafson, Ralph, English
Harper, Kathleen, English Literature
MONTREAL
Belkin, Roslyn K, English, Drama
Bouchard, Donald F, English Literature
Browne, Robert Michael, English
Buitenhuis, Peter Martinus, English, American Studies
Cecil, Curtis Drake, English
Dudek, Louis, English
Duer, Leslie Thrasher, English Literature
Foster, Malcolm Burton, Twentieth Century British & American English
Frith, May Beatrice, English
Frye, Dean Carson, English
Hemlow, Joyce, English Literature
Heuser, Alan, English Literature
Hoffman, Stanton, English Literature
Hooper, Alfred Gifford, English
Ketterer, David Anthony Theodor, English & American Literature
Kinsley, William Benton, English
Lucas, Alec, English
McKeen, David Bruce, English
McPherson, Hugo, North American Literature, Communications
Mahony, Patrick J, English Literature
Malloch, Archibald Edward, English
Mendelsohn, Leonard R, English
Morley, Patricia Ann, Canadian & Commonwealth Literature
O'Brien, John Egli, S.J, Communication, Social Sciences
Ohlin, Peter Hakan, English, Film
Pechter, Edward Lewis, English Literature
Piehler, Paul, English
Poteet, Lewis Jarrette, English
Puhvel, Martin, English
Ripley, John Daniel, English, Speech & Drama
Ronsley, Joseph, English
Simon, Marc, British & American Literature
Sommer, Richard J, English
Stratford, Philip C, English, Comparative Literature
Tembeck, Robert Edward, Theatre, Communication
Theall, Donald F, English, Communications
Wasserman, Rachael Chait, English Language & Literature
Wees, William Charles, English
Williams, David, Medieval English Literature
ST. JEAN
Tajuddin, Mohammad, English, Comparative Literature
ST. JOHNS
Bentley, John Albert, English Philology
ST. LAMBERT
Hacikyan, Agop Jack, English, Philology
SHERBROOKE
Jones, Douglas Gordon, Canadian & Modern Literature
Sutherland, Ronald, English, Comparative Literature
Veilleux, Juliette, English
TROIS-RIVIERES
Vitale, Geoffrey Edwards, Eighteenth Century English Literature
WESTMOUNT
Clarke, Douglass Burns, English, Fine Arts

SASKATCHEWAN

REGINA
Bergbusch, Martin Luther Theodore, English
Cosbey, Robert Culbertson, English
Costain, Keith Michael, English Literature
Cowasjee, Saros D, English
Crossman, Lester Gerald, English
Dillow, Harry C, English Literature
Murray, Donald Charles, English
Wagner, Frederick John, English Literature
Weber, Burton Jasper, English Literature
SASKATOON
Berry, Herbert, English
Calder, Robert Lorin, English Literature
Cherry, Douglas Raymond, English
Dean, Christopher, English
Gilliland, Marshall A, American Studies, American Literature
Hiatt, David, English
Horne, Lewis Benjamin, English
Johnstone, John Keith, English Literature
King, Carlyle Albert, English
Morrissey, Leroy J, English
Parsons, David Stewart, English

Robertson, Robert Telfer, English, Comparative
Literature
Scott, Robert Ian, English Literature, Linguistics
Slights, Camille, English
Thompson, Claud Adelbert, English Literature

OTHER COUNTRIES

AUSTRALIA

BEDFORD PARK
LeMire, Eugene D, English
NEDLANDS
Beston, John B, English

BRAZIL

SAO PAULO
Biderman, Sol, English & American Literature
Litto, Fredric Michael, Theatre History &
Bibliography

BRITISH WEST INDIES

JAMAICA
Taylor, Ivan Earle, English

ENGLAND

ALDERMASTON
Roche, Paul, English
ARUNDEL
Martin, Peter Edward, English
AYLESBURY
McLauchlan, Juliet, English & American Literature
BIRMINGHAM
Honan, Park, English Literature
CAMBRIDGE
Evans, Norma Carol, Bibliography
Walker, Ralph Spence, English
DURHAM
Bradley, John Lewis, English Literature
HESLINGTON
Patrides, Constantinos Apostolos, English
LONDON
Miller, Nolan, English

NORWICH
Hopkins, Hector Kenneth, English
NOTTINGHAM
Gray, James Martin, English
OXFORD
Ellmann, Richard David, English & American
Literature
Ziff, Larzer, American Literature
POOLE
Hamilton, Harlan Ware, English Literature

FRANCE

PARIS
Gunn, Drewey Wayne, American Literature

FEDERAL REPUBLIC OF GERMANY

COLOGNE
Bonheim, Helmut W, Literature
MUNSTER
Spevack, Marvin, English

HONG KONG

Chan, Jachin Yin-Man, English
Miller, Ward Searing, English

INDIA

NEW DELHI
Kale, Pramod Keshav, Speech & Drama, Mass
Communication

ISRAEL

BETHLEHEM
O'Connor, Antony Cyril, English
HAIFA
Knieger, Bernard (Martin), English
JERUSALEM
Kahn, Sholom J, English, Philosophy

ITALY

ROME
Martin, Harold C, English, Comparative Literature

JAPAN

KYOTO
Bedford, Richard Colbert, English
TOKYO
Williams, Margaret Anne, R.S.C.J, English
Literature

LEBANON

BEIRUT
Cook, Daniel, Linguistics, English

NEW GUINEA

PAPUA
Greicus, Michael S, Modern British Literature

NIGERIA

ILE-IFE
Taylor, Richard Dean, English

SOUTH AFRICA

GRAHAMSTOWN
Switzer, Lester Ernest, Communications,
African History

SPAIN

JAVEA
Pflaum, Melanie L, English, Creative Writing

SWITZERLAND

GENEVA
Blair, John George, English
LAUSANNE
Schroeter, James Marvin, English

TURKEY

ISTANBUL
Wise, (Alfred) Sheldon, (Jr), Linguistics